C000274745

Stanley Gibbons

STAMP CATALOGUE

PART 1

British Commonwealth 1999

101st edition

Including post-independence issues of Ireland

101st edition

VOLUME 1

Great Britain and Countries A to I

Stanley Gibbons Ltd
London and Ringwood

By Appointment to Her Majesty The Queen
Stanley Gibbons Ltd, London
Philatelists

Published by **Stanley Gibbons Ltd**
Editorial, Publications Sales Offices and Distribution Centre:
5 Parkside, Christchurch Road, Ringwood,
Hants BH24 3SH.

© **Stanley Gibbons Ltd 1998**

Copyright Notice

The contents of this Catalogue, including the
numbering system and illustrations, are fully
protected by copyright. No part of this publication
may be reproduced, stored in a retrieval system,
or transmitted in any form or by any means,
electronic, mechanical, photocopying, recording
or otherwise, without the prior permission of
Stanley Gibbons Limited. Requests for such
permission should be addressed to the Catalogue
Editor. This catalogue is sold on condition that it
is not, by way of trade or otherwise, lent, re-sold,
hired out, circulated or otherwise disposed of
other than in its complete, original and unaltered
form and without a similar condition including this
condition being imposed on the subsequent
purchaser.

ISBN: 0-85259-446-1

Item No. 2811 (99)

Text assembled by Black Bear Press Limited, Cambridge

Made and Printed in Great Britain by William Clowes Limited,
Beccles, Suffolk

Preface to the 1999 Edition

FLYING START

tamp collecting has never stood still. One of its nduring attractions has always been its ability to volve and add further facets to its already omplex structure.

If the great collectors from the last century ould return, it is an interesting speculation as to ow they would react to a hobby which is now pproaching the end of the next. Some would, I m sure, have heartily approved of postal history vith its emphasis on research into the use of ostage stamps, but I am not too sure as to their eaction to other aspects of the modern hobby. On the other hand, who is to say how we would ind stamp collecting at the end of the 21st entury!

As the hobby has changed the Stanley Gibbons atalogues have evolved with it. No stamp atalogue can afford to be complacent, and every rend in research, price and indeed production nethods must be evaluated.

It is generally agreed that the hobby is pproaching a watershed. Diverse influences, not he least of which must be the efforts of modern ost office marketing departments, are nfluencing the ordinary collector as never before vith unpredictable results.

At this critical point Stanley Gibbons has been icquired by Flying Flowers Ltd, the well-known pecialist mail-order company. The new owners iave announced their intention of re-asserting stanley Gibbons' position at the very centre of ihilately with a commitment to maintain and mprove stocks, products and, above all, the level of service provided to those most important ieople, our customers. Preparations have already commenced for the introduction of a new catalogue editing system with the intention that SG catalogues should lead the hobby into the new Millennium.

PRICES

There have been continued signs of consolidation in the stamp market during the last twelve months. Today's collectors are, however, becoming more selective in their interests with the result that some areas and periods have shown more movement than others.

As in previous years much of this activity has been concentrated in the period between the early 1880s and 1945. There have, however, been several changes of emphasis, with the result that a number of **British West Indies** colonies, **Bermuda**, **British Honduras (Belize)** and **British Guiana (Guyana)** for example, have seen a considerable spread of price rises. Changes for classic period stamps are less extensive, but in this edition both the first issue of **Fiji** and many early stamps from **British Guiana** show increases.

Other interesting repricing can be found in **New South Wales (Australian States)** where many issues from 1890 onwards are up, **Newfoundland (Canada)** where interest is clearly reviving and, more surprisingly, for **Cook Islands** including

Aitutaki and **Penhryn**, where the true scarcity of issues made under the New Zealand postal administration before 1965 has been recognised. Further increases have taken place amongst **Hong Kong** issues up to 1938 and also for some later definitives. Demand for **India**, in particular for the issues up to King George V, has been sustained.

The level of price changes for modern issues remains patchy. There are, however, only a few price reductions for those issues still recognised as being over-stocked, and thematic demand has initiated many increases in price for stamps appearing during the late 1980s and early 1990s.

Errors and varieties continue to be popular and there are also price rises for many pre-1945 stamp booklets, notably for **India** where all booklets up to 1937 have been increased.

The market for **Great Britain** stamps remains buoyant, with many rises over the last twelve months for issues stretching from the early Line Engraved to King George V, not forgetting the Official overprints where attention has also been paid to the used on cover prices. There are indications that interest is reviving in the pre-decimal stamps of the present reign. **Jersey** issues from the late 1980s up to 1993 are also up in price.

REVISIONS IN THIS EDITION

The listing of Commonwealth watermark varieties, started last year, has been expanded to cover issues between 1901 and 1936. This has involved considerable research as King Edward VII and King George V stamps are often found with watermark reversed, or watermark inverted and reversed in addition to watermark inverted. Watermark reversed varieties have been given "x" suffixes and those with watermark inverted and reversed "y" suffixes. Where possible prices have also been provided, but in a number of instances it is difficult to establish the true scarcity of the new listings. There are, no doubt, others to be discovered and these will be added to future editions. It is intended that similar coverage will eventually be provided for those Queen Victoria issues where the watermark position is not completely haphazard.

Adding the watermark varieties to this edition has involved not only the Colonial stamps produced by the Crown Agents, but also **Australia** and **India** where many inverted watermarks exist. The watermark positions of the **Dominica** 1908–21 Roseau definitives are so complex that this set has been completely rewritten.

Many Commonwealth printed on the gummed side errors are now listed for the first time and there have been improvements in the coverage of stamp booklets from **Fiji** (based on research by Ross Duberal), **Ghana** (a new discovery by Mike Orr) and **Guyana**.

Following the publication of Peter Fernbank's impressive new handbook on the King George V low value Key Plate stamps, the opportunity has

been taken to revise the catalogue listings of this fascinating series. There are a few number changes and some additions for this volume, but much of the work has involved the correcting of the dates provided for the listed shades.

Further King George VI flaws have been submitted by Richard Lockyer of the King George VI Collectors' Society, and examples can be found under **Bahamas, Canada (Newfoundland), Falkland Islands Dependencies** and **Fiji** in this volume.

Australia. The revision of the Australian States section has been continued. Separate listings and prices have been added for many of the **New South Wales** compound perforations, based on information from the Australian States Study Circle of Sydney. Parts of the **South Australia** listings between 1876 and 1899 have been rewritten to provide clearer coverage and there are also minor improvements in the 1955–57 definitives for **Australia** itself. Modern issues from this popular country continue to produce surprises and there are new varieties listed for the 1994 Kangaroos and Koalas stamps and for the ATM pane of the same year.

Norfolk Island. As an Australian External Territory **Norfolk Island** has been transferred from Volume 2 and now follows Australia.

Canada. The dies of the **Prince Edward Island** 1861 2d. are now listed.

Ghana. The two perforations of the **Gold Coast** 1937–44 King George VI definitives are now priced separately.

Gilbert & Ellice Islands. With the assistance of the Kiribati & Tuvalu Philatelic Society and the Pacific Study Circle, a project has been undertaken to identify which New Zealand stamps were used at the postal agencies established on Fanning Island between 1902 and 1939 and on Washington Island from 1921 until 1934. The result is a most comprehensive survey of these fascinating postal history items and I am grateful to the members of the two societies for their co-operation and to Michael Shaw who acted as co-ordinator for the project.

Hong Kong. Issues up to the handover to China on 30 June 1997 continue to appear in this volume. Subsequent issues appear in *Part 17 (China)*, a new edition of which was published in June.

India. A long standing anomaly has been corrected so that the catalogue entries for all issues in the anna currency now show the face values in the same form as they appear on the stamps. Further work has been undertaken on the overprint double one albino errors of the **Indian Convention States**.

As always it is impossible to individually thank all those collectors, dealers and postal professionals who have contributed to this edition. Without such assistance the task of compiling each *Part 1* would be virtually impossible.

David J. Aggersberg

Stanley Gibbons Holdings Plc Addresses

STANLEY GIBBONS LIMITED, STANLEY GIBBONS AUCTIONS
399 Strand, London WC2R 0LX
Auction Room and Specialist Stamp Departments. Open Monday–Friday 9.30 a.m. to 5 p.m.
Shop. Open Monday–Friday 8.30 a.m. to 6 p.m. and Saturday 10 a.m. to 4 p.m.
Telephone 0171 836 8444 and Fax 0171 836 7342 for all departments.

STANLEY GIBBONS PUBLICATIONS
5 Parkside, Christchurch Road, Ringwood, Hants BH24 3SH.
Telephone 01425 472363 (24 hour answer phone service), Fax 01425 470247 and E-mail info@stangib.demon.co.uk
Publications Showroom (at above address). Open Monday–Friday 9 a.m. to 3 p.m.
Publications Mail Order. FREEPHONE 0800 611622. Trade Desk. 01425 478776.
Both Monday–Friday 8.30 a.m. to 5 p.m.

URCH HARRIS & CO
(a division of Stanley Gibbons Ltd)
1 Denmark Avenue, Bristol, BS1 5HD.
UH New Issue Service
Telephone 0117 9349333 and Fax 0117 9273037
Monday–Friday 8.30 a.m. to 5 p.m.

FRASER'S
(a division of Stanley Gibbons Ltd)
399 Strand, London WC2R 0LX
Autographs, photographs, letters and documents.
Telephone 0171 836 8444 and Fax 0171 836 7342
Monday-Friday 9 a.m. to 5.30 p.m. and Saturday 10 a.m. to 4 p.m.

STANLEY GIBBONS PUBLICATIONS OVERSEAS REPRESENTATION

Stanley Gibbons Publications are represented overseas by the following sole distributors (*), distributors (**) or licensees (***).

Australia

Lighthouse Philatelic (Aust.) Pty Ltd*
PO Box 763
Strawberry Hills
New South Wales 2012
Australia

Stanley Gibbons (Australia) Pty Ltd***
Level 6, 36 Clarence Street
Sydney N.S.W. 2000
Australia

Belgium and Luxembourg**

Davo c/o Philac
Rue du Midi 48
Bruxelles 1000
Belgium

Canada*

Lighthouse Publications (Canada) Ltd
255 Duke Street
Montreal
Quebec
Canada H3C 2M2

Denmark**

Davo
c/o Lindner Falzlos
Gl Randersvej 28
8450 Hammel
Denmark

Finland**

Davo
c/o Suomen Postimerkkeily
Ludvingkatu 5
SF-00130 Helsinki
Finland

France*

Davo France (Casteilla)
10 Rue Leon Foucault
78184 St Quentin Yvelines Cesex
France

Germany and Austria*

Leuchtturm Albenverlag Gmbh u. Co.
Am Spakenberg 45
Postfach 1340
D21495 Geesthacht
Germany

Hong Kong**

Po-on Stamp Service
GPO Box 2498
Hong Kong

Israel**

Capital Stamps
PO Box 3769
Jerusalem 91036
Israel

Italy*

Secrian Srl
Via Pantelleria 2
1-20156 Milano
Italy

Japan**

Japan Philatelic Co Ltd
PO Box 2
Suginami-Minami
Tokyo
Japan

Netherlands*

Davo Publications
PO Box 411
7400 AK Deventer
Netherlands

New Zealand***

Stanley Gibbons (New Zealand) Ltd
PO Box 80
Wellington
New Zealand

Norway**

Davo Norge A/S
PO Box 738 Sentrum
N-01 05 Oslo
Norway

Singapore***

Stanley Gibbons (Singapore) Pte Ltd
Raffles City
PO Box 1689
Singapore 9117

South Africa**

Republic Coin and Stamp
    Accessories (Pty) Ltd
PO Box 11199
Johannesburg
RSA 2000

Sweden*

Chr Winther Sorensen AB
Box 43
S-310 Knaered
Sweden

Switzerland**

Phila Service
Burgstrasse 160
CH 4125 Riehen
Switzerland

West Indies/Caribbean**

Hugh Dunphy
PO Box 413
Kingston 10
Jamaica
West Indies

BY APPOINTMENT TO
HER MAJESTY THE QUEEN
STANLEY GIBBONS LTD
LONDON,
PHILATELISTS

First Class Stamp & Service
...from the world leaders in Philately

- Extensive stocks of specialised Great Britain and Commonwealth material
- Thousands of high quality items always available ● Detailed register of clients interests
- Specialist 'want list' service ● Regular lists and illustrated colour brochures
- Private viewing facilities and postal approval service ● Free advice from our knowledgeable team
- 0% interest free credit available on purchases over £1000

Free Membership Of Our Specialist Register

All discerning collectors are able to benefit from joining our specialist register and want list service. We maintain an up to date record of your specific collecting requirements and furnish you with regular lists containing only material that will interest you. We also provide a postal approval service for established clients.

New Luxury Colour Brochure

Published twice yearly our superbly illustrated brochure contains hundreds of carefully selected items recently added to our extensive GB and Commonwealth stocks. Copies can be obtained for a yearly subscription of just £10 and include a discount voucher for your next purchase.

Free Mail Order Stamp Listings
Choose from:
- Great Britain ● Australia & New Zealand
- Canada ● Falkland Islands ● Channel Islands & I.O.M.

Used by thousands of collectors worldwide our mail order service provides fast 48 hour order despatch, a 14 day money back guarantee and free telephone advice.
Packed full of popular material each of our comprehensive listings features colour illustrations, accurate descriptions, a useful checklist and pull out order form.

PRESTIGE
PAYMENT PLAN
0% INTEREST
FREE
CREDIT
ON PURCHASES
OVER £1000
All loans are subject to status. A written quotation is available on request.
TELEPHONE TODAY FOR AN
APPLICATION FORM

For membership of our specialist register and copies of our specialised and mail order listings.
Please contact our Commonwealth Department today.

STANLEY GIBBONS
Commonwealth

Stanley Gibbons Limited
399 Strand, London WC2R 0LX England. Tel: +44 (0)171 836 8444 Fax: +44 (0)171 836 7342
e.mail: stamps@stangiblondon.demon.co.uk

Stanley Gibbons Stamp Catalogue
Complete List of Parts

1 British Commonwealth
(Annual in two volumes)

2 Austria & Hungary (5th edition, 1994)
Austria, Bosnia & Herzegovina, U.N. (Vienna), Hungary

3 Balkans (4th edition, 1998)
Albania, Bosnia & Herzegovina, Bulgaria, Croatia, Greece & Islands, Macedonia, Rumania, Slovenia, Yugoslavia

4 Benelux (4th edition, 1993)
Belgium & Colonies, Netherlands & Colonies, Luxembourg

5 Czechoslovakia & Poland (5th edition, 1994)
Czechoslovakia, Bohemia & Moravia, Slovakia, Poland

6 France (4th edition, 1993)
France, Colonies, Post Offices, Andorra, Monaco

7 Germany (5th edition, 1996)
Germany, States, Colonies, Post.Offices

8 Italy & Switzerland (5th edition, 1997)
Italy & Colonies, Fiume, San Marino, Vatican City, Trieste, Liechtenstein, Switzerland, U.N. (Geneva)

9 Portugal & Spain (4th edition, 1996)
Andorra, Portugal & Colonies, Spain & Colonies

10 Russia (4th edition, 1991)
Russia, Baltic States, Mongolia, Tuva

11 Scandinavia (4th edition, 1994)
Aland Island, Denmark, Faroe Islands, Finland, Greenland, Iceland, Norway, Sweden

12 Africa since Independence A-E (2nd edition, 1983)
Algeria, Angola, Benin, Bophuthatswana, Burundi, Cameroun, Cape Verde, Central African Republic, Chad, Comoro Islands, Congo, Djibouti, Equatorial Guinea, Ethiopia

13 Africa since Independence F-M (1st edition, 1981)
Gabon, Guinea, Guinea-Bissau, Ivory Coast, Liberia, Libya Malagasy Republic, Mali, Mauritania, Morocco, Mozambique

14 Africa since Independence N-Z (1st edition, 1981)
Niger Republic, Rwanda, St. Thomas & Prince, Senegal Somalia, Sudan, Togo, Transkei, Tunisia, Upper Volta, Venda Zaire

15 Central America (2nd edition, 1984)
Costa Rica, Cuba, Dominican Republic, El Salvador, Guatemala, Haiti, Honduras, Mexico, Nicaragua, Panama

16 Central Asia (3rd edition, 1992)
Afghanistan, Iran, Turkey

17 China (6th edition, 1998)
China, Taiwan, Tibet, Foreign P.O.'s, Hong Kong, Macao

18 Japan & Korea (4th edition, 1997)
Japan, Ryukyus, Korean Empire, South Korea, North Korea

19 Middle East (5th edition, 1996)
Bahrain, Egypt, Iraq, Israel, Jordan, Kuwait, Lebanon, Oman Qatar, Saudi Arabia, Syria, U.A.E., Yemen A.R., Yemen P.D.R.

20 South America (3rd edition, 1989)
Argentina, Bolivia, Brazil, Chile, Colombia, Ecuador, Paraguay, Peru, Surinam, Uruguay, Venezuela

21 South-East Asia (3rd edition, 1995)
Bhutan, Burma, Indonesia, Kampuchea, Laos, Nepal, Philippines, Thailand, Vietnam

22 United States (4th edition, 1994)
U.S. & Possessions, Canal Zone, Marshall Islands, Micronesia, Palau, U.N. (New York, Geneva, Vienna)

GREAT BRITAIN SPECIALISED CATALOGUES

Volume 1 Queen Victoria (11th edition, 1997)
Volume 2 King Edward VII to King George VI (10th edition, 1996)
Volume 3 Queen Elizabeth II Pre-decimal Issues (10th edition, 1998)
Volume 4 Queen Elizabeth II Decimal Definitive Issues (8th edition, 1996)
Volume 5 Queen Elizabeth II Decimal Special Issues (3rd edition, 1998)

THEMATIC CATALOGUES

Collect Aircraft on Stamps (1st edition, 1994)
Collect Birds on Stamps (4th edition, 1996)
Collect Butterflies and Other Insects on Stamps (out of print)
Collect Chess on Stamps (out of print)
Collect Fish on Stamps (1st edition, 1998)
Collect Fungi on Stamps (2nd edition, 1997)
Collect Mammals on Stamps (out of print)
Collect Railways on Stamps (new edition late 1998)
Collect Shells on Stamps (1st edition, 1995)
Collect Ships on Stamps (out of print)

TREASURES *of the* BRITISH EMPIRE

PRE 1935 Stamps, Varieties and Postal History:
ADEN TO ZULULAND
WANTED TO BUY

We are <u>always</u> prepared to purchase both general and specialised collections. Rarities of the whole Empire are of <u>particular</u> interest.

For decades we have specialised in helping our international clientele in the building up of fine collections. <u>Your</u> want list will receive our prompt attention per quotation as on approval (references appreciated).

| MALAYSIA SG 10 | MAURITIUS SG 14 | CAPE OF GOOD HOPE SG 22 | NEW ZEALAND SG 2 | LEEWARD ISLANDS SG 16 |

| PAPUA NEW GUINEA SG 34 | UGANDA SG 43 | RHODESIA SG 93A | MADAGASCAR SG 8A |

These are only a sampling of 30 volumes of stock in all price ranges referenced by Stanley Gibbons and Scott numbers. We look forward to assisting you towards archiving your specific collecting needs and goals.

We hold several British Empire public auctions annually.
Subscription: £25

George W. Holschauer
COLONIAL STAMP CO.

5757 Wilshire Blvd., Penthouse 8
Los Angeles, CA 90036, U.S.A.
(213) 933-9435 — FAX (213) 939-9930

Members: IFSDA, PTS, ASDA, International Society of Appraisers

When enquiring or placing an order please quote that you have seen me in Stanley Gibbons British Commonwealth Catalogue

Numbers Added or Changed

STAMPS ADDED

Excluding new issues which have appeared in Gibbons *Stamp Monthly* Supplements, the following are the catalogue numbers of stamps listed in this edition for the first time. In addition watermark varieties have been added to Commonwealth countries between 1901 and 1936.

Great Britain. 87c, 696pd/9pd, 828c, 895e, 915b, 1658a, Y1692a, 1972a, 1978a, 1995a, 1996a, 2006a, 2015a, 2021ad

Abu Dhabi. 3a, 18b, 21a, 25a

Ascension. 338w, 410w

Australia—New South Wales. 208ba, 210ba, 214ba, 217ba, 221ba, 225ea, 226ba, 227ca, 228ab, 228ba, 230ba, 232ba, 232ca, 235ca, 235da, 236ca, 237ca, O3ba, O6ba, O12ba, O22c
Victoria. 356b, 359a, 385ca
Commonwealth of Australia. 1a, 545ad, 554ab, 586a, 591a, 602c, 653a, 1453c/ca, 1454c, 1455c, 1495ab, 1498a, 1502a, O80wa

Bahamas. 149b

Bermuda. 76a, 511aw

Botswana—Stellaland. 1b, 2b, 4b
Bechuanaland Protectorate. 86b, 95a
Botswana. SB35

British Occ of Italian Colonies. ED9w, TD9w.

British Virgin Islands. 78d, 79c, MS321a

Brunei. 379a, J10a, J17a

Burma. J58b.

Canada—Newfoundland. 264c, 269d, 270w, 287w
Prince Edward Island. 1d, 2a, 12c, 13a, 22a, 27a, 28a
Canada. 120a, 343b, 579b, 583ca, 693d, 698a, 786ab, 856a, 857a, 859a, 872ab, 873a, 874a, 884a, 895a, 1030b, 1055bb, 1088a, 1157cc, 1573b, D35a

Cayman Islands. 45*d*, 57a, 251w, 381w, 619w

Cook Islands. 128w, 141y

Dominica. 95i, 126a

Egypt. SB6a

Falkland Islands. 13c
Falkland Islands Dependencies. Z63*a*, G1c, G5c, G6c, G6dc, G7c, G8c

Fiji. 130ca, 244h, 253a, SB3a, SB4a

Ghana. 77d, 82c, 120A/31A, 382ga, 1246mh, 1643b, 1644b, 1645a

Gibraltar. 22a, 25a

Guyana. 151a, 864b, SB9b

Hong Kong. 155a, 332b
British Post Offices in China. Z31*a*, Z104/5, Z177, Z264, Z336*a*, Z509, Z565, Z584, Z633, Z745, Z795*a*, Z958, Z999, Z1076, Z1143
British Post Offices in Japan. Z30*a*

India. 333aw, 738b, 933cw, 934aw, 935bw, 1220w, 1556a, 1574a, MS1639a, 1650a, O166w, O172aw, O189ab, O260cw, O261w, O267w
Convention States—Chamba. 11a, 12a, 16c, 18a, 22a, 34a, 36a, 39a, 40a, 41a, 44a, 46a, O2e, O7c, O10a, O14d/e, O22a, O30a, O32b
Faridkot. 1c, 10b, 13a, 16a, O1d, O2b, O6a, O8c, O9a, O10c/d, O14a.
Gwalior. 4d, 5d, 9d, 16g, 17g, 24g, 25g, 27g, 34b, 38f, 39f, 40f, 41f, 45a, 49f, 57fa, 61a, 80a, O8a, O35a, O36ab, O48a, O58a
Jind. 10a, 14b, 15b, 18b, 20a, 22a, 26a, 29a, 30a, 40a, 41a, 46a, 47a, 49a, 51a, 55a, O7a, O10c, O11c/d, O12a, O13c, O15a/b, O16a, O17a, O20a, O21a/b, O25b, O26b, O29a, O35a, O43a
Nabha. 11a, 13a, 21a, 27a, 30b, 31a, 37b, 40ba, 43a, O6c, O12a, O15a, O18a/b, O25a, O29a, O35a, O36a
Patiala. 1b, 5c, 9c, 24a, 30b, 32b, O29a
Feudatory States—Bhopal. O335d
Bundi. O49a
Cochin. 51a, 124c, O99b
Kishangarh. 69a, O18a
Orchha. 8a, 10a, 11b/c, 15b, 16b, 17b/c, 19b, 20b, 23b
Rajasthan. 13b, 45a
Travancore. 48a.

Ireland. 2c, 104w, 107w, 112dw, 119bw, 123bw, 124cw, 125bw, 131w, 765a

CATALOGUE NUMBERS ALTERED

The table below is a cross-reference of those catalogue numbers which have been altered in this edition.

Old	New	Old	New
Great Britain— Jersey		265A	178
775/7	777/9	265B	180
778	781	266A	237
779	784	266B/7B	239/40
780	787	O44/54*a*	O43*g*/53
781	789	O55	O60
Antigua		O56/7	O54/5
2334/65	2345/76	O58	O71
Barbuda		O59/60	O61/*d*
1656	1657	O61	O72
MS1657	MS1656	O64	O73
Australia—New South Wales		O65/6	O64/5
122b	122ab	O67/8	O56/7
226f	226ca	O69	O66
235ca	235cb	O70	O74
South Australia		O71/2	O67/8
168/80	167*a*/72*a*	O73/4	O58/9
183/92	182*b*/6	O76	O69
193	*Deleted*	O77	O76
194	187	O78	O70
230/2a	229*b*/30*b*	O80a	O80b
233/5	231/2	O80b	O80a
236/7b	188/*c*	**Commonwealth of Australia**	
238/40a	173/4*b*	1a	1c
241/b	233/*b*	2c/*db*	2d/*eb*
242/4	189/90	5d/*da*	5e/*ea*
245/6	234/5	21g/*gc*	21h/*hc*
247/8	191/*a*	35b/*ca*	35c/*da*
249/50a	175/*b*	36a/*ab*	36*b*/*ba*
251/2	177/*a*	37c/*d*	37d/*e*
253	236	38c/*ca*	38d/*da*
254/6	192/3	40a/*b*	40b/*ba*
257/8	238/*a*	47d/*ea*	47e/*fa*
259/60	194/*a*	53*a*	53*b*
262	241/2	95a	95b
263A/4A*a*	176/*b*	100a	100b
263B/4B	179/*a*	282*a*	282*d*

Old	New
294/5	282*a*/c
1625/6	1622/3
1636/7	1631/2
O2a	O2d
O5d	O5e
O17c/d	O17d/e
O20d	O20e
O39a	O39h
O43c	O43d
O45c/d	O45d/e
O46c	O46d
O47a	O47b
O48a	O48b
O49*a*	O49*b*
O52ba	O52ab
O54d/e	O54d/f
O98a	O98b
O106a	O106b
Christmas Island	
416	417
417	419
Cocos (Keeling) Islands	
264/8	265/9
269	264
332/4	333/5
335/6	337/8
337	341
338	343
Bahamas	
149b/de	149c/ec
Barbados	
220*a*	220*b*
Belize	
116a	116*b*
Bermuda	
78b/c	78c/d
Botswana	
82*a*	82*b*
SB35	SB36

Old	New
British Post Offices in Crete	
1/5	B1/5
British Virgin Islands	
63/70	*Rewritten*
Burma	
8*a*	8*b*
Canada—Prince Edward Is.	
28a/b	28b/c
Canada	
81*b*	81*c*
81ba	81b
1055bb	1055bc
1716/20	1717/21
D35a	D35b
Cayman Islands	
45*d*	45*e*
546w	*Deleted*
Dominica	
37*a*	*Deleted*
47*a*	47*b*
48*a*	48*b*
49*a*	49*b*
50*a*	50*b*
51	51a
51a	51
53	53a
53a	53
2193/206	2201/14
Falkland Islands	
43*a*/b	43*b*/c
44a/*d*	44b/*e*
45*a*	45*b*
46*a*	46*b*
49*a*	49*b*
64*a*	64*b*
74*a*	74*b*
75a/*b*	75b/*c*
304w	*Deleted*
Falkland Is. Dependencies	
Z15*c*	Z15*d*

Old	New
Z16*a*	Z16*b*
Z17*a*	Z17*b*
Z26*a*/ab	Z26*b*/ba
G6c/cb	G6d/db
Fiji	
SB10	SB9a
Ghana	
77*a*/b	77*b*/c
77c	77e
80a	80b
82*c*/d	82*d*/e
MS2267/87	2267/95
Gibraltar	
57b	57c
Grenada	
MS3147/260	MS3156/269
Guyana	
261*a*	261*b*
SB9b/e	SB9c/f
Hong Kong	
124*a*	124*b*
155a	155b
British Post Offices in Chi	
Z999	Z998
India	
236*a*/b	236*b*/c
333*a*/b	333*b*/c
738b/cw	738c/dw
O260a	O260b
Convention States—Nabh	
37*b*	37*c*
O33a	O32a
Feudatory States—Bundi	
O49*a*	O49*b*
Orchha	
8a/ac	8b/bb
Ireland	
227w	*Deleted*
1031/5	1036/40

Contents

General Philatelic Information
and Guidelines to the Scope of the Part 1 (British Commonwealth) Catalogue

The notes which follow seek to reflect current practice in compiling the Part 1 (British Commonwealth) Catalogue.

It scarcely needs emphasising that the *Stanley Gibbons Stamp Catalogue* has a very long history and that the vast quantity of information it contains has been carefully built up by successive generations through the work of countless individuals. Philately itself is never static and the Catalogue has evolved and developed during this long time-span. Thus, while these notes are important for today's criteria, they may be less precise the further back in the listings one travels. They are not intended to inaugurate some unwanted series of piecemeal alterations in a widely respected work, but it does seem to us useful that Catalogue users know as exactly as possible the policies currently in operation.

PRICES

The prices quoted in this Catalogue are the estimated selling prices of Stanley Gibbons Ltd at the time of publication. They are, *unless it is specifically stated otherwise*, for examples in fine condition for the issue concerned. Superb examples are worth more; those of a lower quality considerably less.

All prices are subject to change without prior notice and Stanley Gibbons Ltd may from time to time offer stamps below catalogue price. Individual low value stamps sold at 399, Strand are liable to an additional handling charge. Purchasers of new issues are asked to note that the prices charged for them contain an element for the service rendered and so may exceed the prices shown when the stamps are subsequently catalogued. Postage and handling charges are extra.

No guarantee is given to supply all stamps priced, since it is not possible to keep every catalogued item in stock. Commemorative issues may, at times, only be available in complete sets and not as individual values.

Quotation of prices. The prices in the left-hand column are for unused stamps and those in the right-hand column are for used.

A dagger (†) denotes that the item listed does not exist in that condition and a blank, or dash, that it exists, or may exist, but no market price is known.

Prices are expressed in pounds and pence sterling. One pound comprises 100 pence (£1 = 100p).

The method of notation is as follows: pence in numerals (e.g. 10 denotes ten pence); pound and pence, up to £100, in numerals (e.g. 4·25 denotes four pounds and twenty-five pence); prices above £100 expressed in whole pounds with the "£" sign shown.

Unused stamps. Great Britain and Commonwealth: the prices for unused stamps of Queen Victoria to King George V are for lightly hinged examples. Unused prices for King Edward VIII to Queen Elizabeth II issues are for unmounted mint.

Some stamps from the King George VI period are often difficult to find in unmounted mint condition. In such instances we would expect that collectors would need to pay a high proportion of the price quoted to obtain mounted mint examples. Generally speaking lightly mounted mint stamps from this reign, issued before 1945, are in considerable demand.

Mounted mint stamps from the reign of Queen Elizabeth II are frequently available at lower prices than those quoted for the stamps unmounted.

Used stamps. The used prices are normally for stamps postally used but may be for stamps cancelled-to-order where this practice exists.

A pen-cancellation on early issues can sometimes correctly denote postal use. Instances are individually noted in the Catalogue in explanation of the used price given.

Prices quoted for bisects on cover or on large piece are for those dated during the period officially authorised.

Stamps not sold unused to the public (e.g. some official stamps) are priced used only.

The use of "unified" designs, that is stamps inscribed for both postal and fiscal purposes, results in a number of stamps of very high face value. In some instances these may not have been primarily intended for postal purposes, but if they are so inscribed we include them. We only price such items used, however, where there is evidence of normal postal usage.

Cover prices. To assist collectors, cover prices are quoted for issues up to 1945 at the beginning of each country.

The system gives a general guide in the form of a factor by which the corresponding used price of the loose stamp should be multiplied when found in fine average condition on cover.

Care is needed in applying the factors and they relate to a cover which bears a single of the denomination listed; strips and blocks would need individual valuation outside the scope. If more than one denomination is present the most highly priced attracts the multiplier and the remainder are priced at the simple figure for used singles in arriving at a total.

The cover should be of non-philatelic origin, bearing the correct postal rate for the period and distance involved and cancelled with the markings normal to the offices concerned. Purely philatelic items have a cover value only slightly greater than the catalogue value for the corresponding used stamps. This applies generally to those high-value stamps used philatelically rather than in the normal course of commerce. Low-value stamps, e.g. ½d. and ¼d., are desirable when used as a single rate on cover and merit an increase in "multiplier" value.

First-day covers in the period up to 1945 are not within the scope of the system and the multiplier should not be used. As a special category of philatelic usage, with wide variations in valuation according to scarcity, they require separate treatment.

Oversized covers, difficult to accommodate on an album page, should be reckoned as worth little more than the corresponding value of the used stamps. The condition of a cover affects its value. Except for "wreck covers", serious damage or soiling reduce the value where the postal markings and stamps are ordinary ones. Conversely, visual appeal adds to the value and this can include freshness of appearance, important addresses, old-fashioned but legible hand-writing, historic town-names, etc.

The multipliers are a base on which further value would be added to take account of the cover's postal historical importance in demonstrating such things as unusual, scarce or emergency cancels, interesting routes, significant postal markings, combination usage, the development of postal rates, and so on.

For *Great Britain*, rather than multiplication factors, the cover price is shown as a third column, following the prices for unused and used stamps. It will be extended beyond King Edward VII in subsequent editions.

Minimum price. The minimum catalogue price quoted is 10p. For individual stamps prices between 10p. and 30p. are provided as a guide for catalogue users. The lowest price *charged* for individual stamps purchased from Stanley Gibbons Ltd is 30p.

Set prices. Set prices are generally for one of each value, excluding shades and varieties, but including major colour changes. Where there are alternative shades, etc., the cheapest is usually included. The number of stamps in the set is always stated for clarity. The mint prices for sets

containing *se-tenant* pieces are based on the prices quoted for such combinations, and not on those for the individual stamps.

Varieties. Where plate or cylinder varieties are priced in a used condition the price quoted is for a fine used example with the cancellation well clear of the listed flaw.

Specimen stamps. The pricing of these items is explained under that heading.

Stamp booklets. Prices are for complete assembled booklets in fine condition with those issued before 1945 showing normal wear and tear. Incomplete booklets and those which have been "exploded" will, in general, be worth less than the figure quoted.

Repricing. Collectors will be aware that the market factors of supply and demand directly influence the prices quoted in this Catalogue. Whatever the scarcity of a particular stamp, if there is no one in the market who wishes to buy it it cannot be expected to achieve a high price. Conversely, the same item actively sought by numerous potential buyers may cause the price to rise.

All the prices in this Catalogue are examined during the preparation of each new edition by expert staff of Stanley Gibbons and repriced as necessary. They take many factors into account, including supply and demand, and are in close touch with the international stamp market and the auction world.

Commonwealth cover prices and advice on postal history material originally provided by Edward B. Proud.

GUARANTEE

All stamps are guaranteed genuine originals in the following terms:

If not as described, and returned by the purchaser, we undertake to refund the price paid to us in the original transaction. If any stamp is certified as genuine by the Expert Committee of the Royal Philatelic Society, London, or by B.P.A. Expertising Ltd, the purchaser shall not be entitled to make any claim against us for any error, omission or mistake in such certificate.

Consumers' statutory rights are not affected by the above guarantee.

The recognised Expert Committees in this country are those of the Royal Philatelic Society, 41 Devonshire Place, London W1N 1PE, and B.P.A. Expertising Ltd, P.O. Box 137, Leatherhead, Surrey KT22 0RG. They do not undertake valuations under any circumstances and fees are payable for their services.

THE CATALOGUE IN GENERAL

Contents. The Catalogue is confined to adhesive postage stamps, including miniature sheets. For particular categories the rules are:

(*a*) Revenue (fiscal) stamps or telegraph stamps are listed only where they have been expressly authorised for postal duty.

(*b*) Stamps issued only precancelled are included, but normally issued stamps available additionally with precancel have no separate precancel listing unless the face value is changed.

(*c*) Stamps prepared for use but not issued, hitherto accorded full listing, are nowadays footnoted with a price (where possible).

(*d*) Bisects (trisects, etc.) are only listed where such usage was officially authorised.

(*e*) Stamps issued only on first day covers or in presentation packs and not available separately are not listed but may be priced in a footnote.

(*f*) New printings are only included in this Catalogue where they show a major philatelic variety, such as a change in shade, watermark or paper. Stamps which exist with or without imprint dates are listed separately; changes in imprint dates are mentioned in footnotes.

(*g*) Official and unofficial reprints are dealt with by footnote.

(*h*) Stamps from imperforate printings of modern issues which also occur perforated are covered by footnotes, but are listed where widely available for postal use.

Exclusions. The following are excluded: (*a*) non-postal revenue or fiscal stamps; (*b*) postage stamps used fiscally; (*c*) local carriage labels and private local issues; (*d*) telegraph stamps; (*e*) bogus or phantom stamps; (*f*) railway or airline letter fee stamps, bus or road transport company labels; (*g*) cut-outs; (*h*) all types of non-postal labels and souvenirs; (*i*) documentary labels for the postal service, e.g. registration, recorded delivery, air-mail etiquettes, etc.; (*j*) privately applied embel-lishments to official issues and privately commis-sioned items generally; (*k*) stamps for training postal officers.

Full listing. "Full listing" confers our recognition and implies allotting a catalogue number and (wherever possible) a price quotation.

In judging status for inclusion in the catalogue broad considerations are applied to stamps. They must be issued by a legitimate postal authority, recognised by the government concerned, and must be adhesives valid for proper postal use in the class of service for which they are inscribed. Stamps, with the exception of such categories as postage dues and officials, must be available to the general public, at face value, in reasonable quanti-ties without any artificial restrictions being imposed on their distribution.

We record as abbreviated Appendix entries, without catalogue numbers or prices, stamps from countries which either persist in having far more issues than can be justified by postal need or have failed to maintain control over their distribution so that they have not been available to the public in reasonable quantities at face value. Miniature sheets and imperforate stamps are not mentioned in these entries.

The publishers of this catalogue have observed, with concern, the proliferation of "artificial" stamp-issuing territories. On several occasions this has resulted in separately inscribed issues for various component parts of otherwise united states or territories.

Stanley Gibbons Ltd have decided that where such circumstances occur, they will not, in the future, list these items in the SG catalogue without first satisfying themselves that the stamps represent a genuine political, historical or postal division within the country concerned. Any such issues which do not fulfil this stipulation will be recorded in the Catalogue Appendix only.

For errors and varieties the criterion is legitimate (albeit inadvertent) sale through a postal administration in the normal course of business. Details of provenance are always important; printers' waste and deliberately manufactured material are excluded.

Certificates. In assessing unlisted items due weight is given to Certificates from recognised Expert Committees and, where appropriate, we will usually ask to see them.

New issues. New issues are listed regularly in the Catalogue Supplement published in *Gibbons Stamp Monthly*, whence they are consolidated into the next available edition of the Catalogue.

Date of issue. Where local issue dates differ from dates of release by agencies, "date of issue" is the local date. Fortuitous stray usage before the officially intended date is disregarded in listing. For ease of reference, the Catalogue displays in the top corner the date of issue of the first set listed on each page.

Catalogue numbers. Stamps of each country are catalogued chronologically by date of issue. Sub-sidiary classes are placed at the end of the country, as separate lists, with a distinguishing letter prefix to the catalogue number, e.g. D for postage due, O for official and E for express delivery stamps.

The catalogue number appears in the extreme left column. The boldface Type numbers in the next column are merely cross-references to illus-

trations. Catalogue numbers in the *Gibbons Stamp Monthly* Supplement are provisional only and may need to be altered when the lists are consolidated. For the numbering of miniature sheets and sheet-lets *see* section below.

Once published in the Catalogue, numbers are changed as little as possible; really serious renum-bering is reserved for the occasions when a complete country or an entire issue is being rewritten. The edition first affected includes cross-reference tables of old and new numbers.

Our catalogue numbers are universally recog-nised in specifying stamps and as a hallmark of status.

Illustrations. Stamps are illustrated at three-quarters linear size. Stamps not illustrated are the same size and format as the value shown, unless otherwise indicated. Stamps issued only as minia-ture sheets have the stamp alone illustrated but sheet size is also quoted. Overprints, surcharges, watermarks and postmarks are normally actual size. Illustrations of varieties are often enlarged to show the detail. Stamp booklet covers are illustrated half-size, unless otherwise indicated.

Designers. Designers' names are quoted where known, though space precludes naming every individual concerned in the production of a set. In particular, photographers supplying material are usually named only where they also make an active contribution in the design stage; posed photo-graphs of reigning monarchs are, however, an exception to this rule.

CONTACTING THE CATALOGUE EDITOR

The editor is always interested in hearing from people who have new information which will improve or correct the Catalogue. As a general rule he must see and examine the actual stamps before they can be considered for listing; photo-graphs or photocopies are insufficient evidence.

Submissions should be made in writing to the Catalogue Editor, Stanley Gibbons Publications at the Ringwood office. The cost of return postage for items submitted is appreciated, and this should include the registration fee if required.

Where information is solicited purely for the benefit of the enquirer, the editor cannot under-take to reply if the answer is already contained in these published notes or if return postage is omitted. Written communications are greatly pre-ferred to enquiries by telephone and the editor regrets that he or his staff cannot see personal callers without a prior appointment being made. Correspondence may be subject to delay during the production period of each new edition.

The editor welcomes close contact with study circles and is interested, too, in finding reliable local correspondents who will verify and supple-ment official information in countries where this is deficient.

> We regret we do not give opinions as to the genuineness of stamps, nor do we identify stamps or number them by our Catalogue.

TECHNICAL MATTERS

The meanings of the technical terms used in the catalogue will be found in our *Philatelic Terms Illustrated* (3rd edition), (*price £7.50 plus postage and packing charge*).

References below to "more specialised" listings are to be taken to indicate, as appropriate, the Stanley Gibbons *Great Britain Specialised Catalogue* in 5 volumes or the *Great Britain Concise Catalogue*.

1. Printing

Printing errors. Errors in printing are of major interest to the Catalogue. Authenticated items meriting consideration would include: back-ground, centre or frame inverted or omitted; centre or subject transposed; error of colour; error

or omission of value; double prints and impres-sions; printed both sides; and so on. Designs *tête-bêche*, whether intentionally or by accident, are listable. *Se-tenant* arrangements of stamps are recognised in the listings or footnotes. Gutter pairs (a pair of stamps separated by blank margin) are not included in this volume. Colours only partially omitted are not listed. Stamps with embossing omitted and (for Commonwealth countries) stamps printed on the gummed side are reserved for our more specialised listings.

Printing varieties. Listing is accorded to major changes in the printing base which lead to comple-tely new types. In recess-printing this could be a design re-engraved; in photogravure or photolith-ography a screen altered in whole or in part. It can also encompass flat-bed and rotary printing if the results are readily distinguishable.

To be considered at all, varieties must be constant.

Early stamps, produced by primitive methods, were prone to numerous imperfections: the lists reflect this, recognising re-entries, retouches, broken frames, misshapen letters, and so on. Printing technology has, however, radically improved over the years, during which time photogravure and lithography have become pre-dominant. Varieties nowadays are more in the nature of flaws and these, being too specialised for this general catalogue, are almost always outside the scope. The development of our range of specialised catalogues allows us now to list those items which have philatelic significance in their appropriate volume.

In no catalogue, however, do we list such items as: dry prints, kiss prints, doctor-blade flaws, colour shifts or registration flaws (unless they lead to the complete omission of a colour from an individual stamp), lithographic ring flaws, and so on. Neither do we recognise fortuitous happenings like paper creases or confetti flaws.

Overprints (and surcharges). Overprints of different types qualify for separate listing. These include overprints in different colours; overprints from different printing processes such as litho and typo; overprints in totally different typefaces, etc. Major errors in machine-printed overprints are important and listable. They include: overprint inverted or omitted; overprint double (treble, etc.); overprint diagonal; overprint double, one inverted; pairs with one overprint omitted, e.g. from a radical shift to an adjoining stamp; error of colour; error of type fount; letters inverted or omitted, etc. If the overprint is handstamped, few of these would qualify and a distinction is drawn. We continue, however, to list pairs of stamps where one has a handstamped overprint and the other has not.

Varieties occurring in overprints will often take the form of broken letters, slight differences in spacing, rising spaces, etc. Only the most import-ant would be considered for footnote mention.

Sheet positions. If space permits we quote sheet positions of listed varieties and authenticated data is solicited for this purpose.

De La Rue plates. The Catalogue classifies the general plates used by De La Rue for printing British Colonial stamps as follows:

VICTORIAN KEY TYPE

Die I

1. The ball of decoration on the second point of the crown appears as a dark mass of lines.
2. Dark vertical shading separates the front hair from the bun.
3. The vertical line of colour outlining the front of the throat stops at the sixth line of shading on the neck.
4. The white space in the coil of the hair above the curl is roughly the shape of a pin's head.

Die II

1. There are very few lines of colour in the ball and it appears almost white.
2. A white vertical strand of hair appears in place of the dark shading.
3. The line stops at the eighth line of shading.
4. The white space is oblong, with a line of colour partially dividing it at the left end.

Plates numbered 1 and 2 are both Die I. Plates 3 and 4 are Die II.

GEORGIAN KEY TYPE

Die I

A. The second (thick) line below the name of the country is cut slanting, conforming roughly to the shape of the crown on each side.
B. The labels of solid colour bearing the words "POSTAGE" and "& REVENUE" are square at the inner top corners.
C. There is a projecting "bud" on the outer spiral of the ornament in each of the lower corners.

Die II

A. The second line is cut vertically on each side of the crown.
B. The labels curve inwards at the top.
C. There is no "bud" in this position.

Unless otherwise stated in the lists, all stamps with watermark Multiple Crown CA (w **8**) are Die I while those with watermark Multiple Crown Script CA (w **9**) are Die II. The Georgian Die II was introduced in April 1921 and was used for Plates 10 to 22 and 26 to 28. Plates 23 to 25 were made from Die I by mistake.

2. Paper

All stamps listed are deemed to be on "ordinary" paper of the wove type and white in colour; only departures from this are normally mentioned.

Types. Where classification so requires we distinguish such other types of paper as, for example, vertically and horizontally laid; wove and laid bâtonné; card(board); carton; cartridge; glazed; granite; native; pelure; porous; quadrillé; ribbed; rice; and silk thread.

Wove paper   Laid paper

Granite paper   Quadrillé paper

Burelé band

The various makeshifts for normal paper are listed as appropriate. The varieties of double paper and joined paper are recognised. The security device of a printed burelé band on the back of a stamp, as in early Queensland, qualifies for listing.

Descriptive terms. The fact that a paper is handmade (and thus probably of uneven thickness) is mentioned where necessary. Such descriptive terms as "hard" and "soft"; "smooth" and 'rough"; "thick", "medium" and "thin" are applied where there is philatelic merit in classifying papers. We do not, for example, even in more specialised listings, classify paper thicknesses in the Wilding and Machin definitives of Great Britain. Weight standards for the paper apply to complete reels only, so that differences on individual stamps are acceptable to the printer provided the reel conforms overall.

Coloured, very white and toned papers. A coloured paper is one that is coloured right through (front and back of the stamp). In the Catalogue the colour of the paper is given in *italics*, thus:
black/*rose* = black design on rose paper.
Papers have been made specially white in recent years by, for example, a very heavy coating of chalk. We do not classify shades of whiteness of paper as distinct varieties. There does exist, however, a type of paper from early days called toned. This is off-white, often brownish or buffish, but it cannot be assigned any definite colour. A toning effect brought on by climate, incorrect storage or gum staining is disregarded here, as this was not the state of the paper when issued.

Modern developments. Two modern developments also affect the listings: printing on self-adhesive paper and the use of metallic foils. For self-adhesive stamps *see* under "Gum", below. Care should be taken not to damage the embossing on stamps impressed on metallic foils, such as Sierra Leone 1965–67, by subjecting the album pages to undue pressure. The possibility of faked

"missing gold heads" is noted at the appropriate places in the listing of modern Great Britain.

"Ordinary" and "Chalk-surfaced" papers. The availability of many postage stamps for revenue purposes made necessary some safeguard against the illegitimate re-use of stamps with removable cancellations. This was at first secured by using fugitive inks and later by printing on chalk-surfaced paper, both of which made it difficult to remove any form of obliteration without also damaging the stamp design.

This catalogue lists these chalk-surfaced paper varieties from their introduction in 1905. Where no indication is given, the paper is "ordinary".

Our chalk-surfaced paper is specifically one which shows a black mark when touched with a silver wire. The paper used during the Second World War for high values, as in Bermuda, the Leeward Islands, etc., was thinly coated with some kind of surfacing which does not react to silver and is therefore regarded (and listed) as "ordinary". Stamps on chalk-surfaced paper can easily lose this coating through immersion in water.

Another paper introduced during the War as a substitute for chalk-surfaced is rather thick, very white and glossy and shows little or no watermark, nor does it show a black line when touched with silver. In the Bahamas high values this paper might be mistaken for the chalk-surfaced (which is thinner and poorer-looking) but for the silver test.

Some modern coated papers show little or no reaction to the silver test and, therefore, cannot be classed as chalk-surfaced.

Glazed paper. In 1969 the Crown Agents introduced a new general-purpose paper for use in conjunction with all current printing processes. It generally has a marked glossy surface but the degree varies according to the process used, being more marked in recess-printing stamps. As it does not respond to the silver test this presents a further test where previous printings were on chalky paper. A change of paper to the glazed variety merits separate listing.

Green and yellow papers. Issues of the First World War and immediate postwar period occur on green and yellow papers and these are given separate Catalogue listing. The original coloured papers (coloured throughout) gave way to surface-coloured papers, the stamps having "white backs"; other stamps show one colour on the front and a different one at the back. Because of the numerous variations a grouping of colours is adopted as follows:

YELLOW PAPERS
(1) The original *yellow* paper (throughout), usually bright in colour. The gum is often sparse, of harsh consistency and dull-looking. Used 1912–1920.

(2) The *white backs*. Used 1913–1914.

(3) A bright *lemon* paper. The colour must have a pronounced greenish tinge, different from the "yellow" in (1). As a rule, the gum on stamps using this lemon paper is plentiful, smooth and shiny, and the watermark shows distinctly. Care is needed with stamps printed in green on yellow paper (1) as it may appear that the paper is this lemon. Used 1914–1916.

(4) An experimental *orange-buff* paper. The colour must have a distinct brownish tinge. It is not to be confused with a muddy yellow (1) nor the misleading appearance (on the surface) of stamps printed in red on yellow paper where an engraved plate has been insufficiently wiped. Used 1918–1921.

(5) An experimental *buff* paper. This lacks the brownish tinge of (4) and the brightness of the yellow shades. The gum is shiny when compared with the matt type used on (4). Used 1919–1920.

(6) A *pale yellow* paper that has a creamy tone to the yellow. Used from 1920 onwards.

GREEN PAPERS
(7) The original "green" paper, varying considerably through shades of *blue-green* and *yellow-*

green, the front and back sometimes differing. Used 1912–1916.

(8) The *white backs*. Used 1913–1914.

(9) A paper blue-green on the surface with *pale olive* back. The back must be markedly paler than the front and this and the pronounced olive tinge to the back distinguish it from (7). Used 1916–1920.

(10) Paper with a vivid green surface, commonly called *emerald-green*; it has the olive back of (9). Used 1920.

(11) Paper with *emerald-green* both back and front. Used from 1920 onwards.

3. Perforation and Rouletting

Perforation gauge. The gauge of a perforation is the number of holes in a length of 2 cm. For correct classification the size of the holes (large or small) may need to be distinguished; in a few cases the actual number of holes on each edge of the stamp needs to be quoted.

Measurement. The Gibbons *Instanta* gauge is the standard for measuring perforations. The stamp is viewed against a dark background with the transparent gauge put on top of it. Though the gauge measures to decimal accuracy, perforations read from it are generally quoted in the Catalogue to the nearest half. For example:

Just over perf $12\frac{3}{4}$ to just under $13\frac{1}{4}$ = perf 13
Perf $13\frac{1}{4}$ exactly, rounded up = perf $13\frac{1}{2}$
Just over perf $13\frac{1}{4}$ to just under $13\frac{3}{4}$ = perf $13\frac{1}{2}$
Perf $13\frac{3}{4}$ exactly, rounded up = perf 14

However, where classification depends on it, actual quarter-perforations are quoted.

Notation. Where no perforation is quoted for an issue it is imperforate. Perforations are usually abbreviated (and spoken) as follows, though sometimes they may be spelled out for clarity. This notation for rectangular stamps (the majority) applies to diamond shapes if "top" is read as the edge to the top right.

P 14: perforated alike on all sides (read: "perf 14").

P 14 × 15: the first figure refers to top and bottom, the second to left and right sides (read: "perf 14 by 15"). This is a compound perforation. For an upright triangular stamp the first figure refers to the two sloping sides and second to the base. In inverted triangulars the base is first and the second figure refers to the sloping sides.

P 14–15: perforation measuring anything between 14 and 15: the holes are irregularly spaced, thus the gauge may vary along a single line or even along a single edge of the stamp (read: "perf 14 to 15").

P 14 *irregular*: perforated 14 from a worn perforator, giving badly aligned holes irregularly spaced (read: "irregular perf 14").

P comp(*ound*) 14 × 15: two gauges in use but not necessarily on opposite sides of the stamp. It could be one side in one gauge and three in the other; or two adjacent sides with the same gauge. (Read: "perf compound of 14 and 15".) For three gauges or more, abbreviated as "*P* 14, $14\frac{1}{2}$, 15 *or compound*" for example.

P 14, $14\frac{1}{2}$: perforated approximately $14\frac{1}{4}$ (read: "perf 14 or $14\frac{1}{2}$"). It does *not* mean two stamps, one perf 14 and the other perf $14\frac{1}{2}$. This obsolescent notation is gradually being replaced in the Catalogue.

Imperf: imperforate (not perforated).

Imperf × *P* 14: imperforate at top and bottom and perf 14 at sides.

Perf × imperf

P 14 × *imperf*: perf 14 at top and bottom and imperforate at sides.

Such headings as "*P* 13 × 14 (*vert*) and *P* 14 × 13 (*horiz*)" indicate which perforations apply to which stamp format—vertical or horizontal.

Some stamps are additionally perforated so that a label or tab is detachable; others have been perforated suitably for use as two halves. Listings are normally for whole stamps, unless stated otherwise.

Other terms. Perforation almost always gives circular holes; where other shapes have been used they are specified, e.g. square holes; lozenge perf. Interrupted perfs are brought about by the omission of pins at regular intervals. Perforations merely simulated by being printed as part of the design are of course ignored. With few exceptions, privately applied perforations are not listed.

In the nineteenth century perforations are often described as clean cut (clean, sharply incised holes), intermediate or rough (rough holes, imperfectly cut, often the result of blunt pins).

Perforation errors and varieties. Authenticated errors, where a stamp normally perforated is accidentally issued imperforate, are listed provided no traces of perforation (blind holes or indentations) remain. They must be provided as pairs, both stamps wholly imperforate, and are only priced in that form.

In Great Britain, numerous of these part-perforated stamps have arisen from the introduction of the Jumelle Press. This has a rotary perforator with rows of pins on one drum engaging with holes on another. Engagement is only gradual when the perforating unit is started up or stopped, giving rise to perforations "fading out", a variety mentioned above as not listed.

Stamps imperforate between stamp and sheet margin are not listed in this catalogue, but such errors on Great Britain stamps will be found in the *Great Britain Specialised Catalogue*.

Pairs described as "imperforate between" have the line of perforations between the two stamps omitted.

Imperf between (*horiz pair*): a horizontal pair of stamps with perfs all around the edges but none between the stamps.

Imperf between (*vert pair*): a vertical pair of stamps with perfs all around the edges but none between the stamps.

imperf
between
(vertical pair)

Imperf
horizontally
(vertical pair)

Where several of the rows have escaped perforation the resulting varieties are listable. Thus:

Imperf vert (*horiz pair*): a horizontal pair of stamps perforated top and bottom; all three vertical directions are imperf—the two outer edges and between the stamps.

Imperf horiz (*vert pair*): a vertical pair perforated at left and right edges; all three horizontal directions are imperf—the top, bottom and between the stamps.

Straight edges. Large sheets cut up before issue to post offices can cause stamps with straight edges,

i.e. imperf on one side or on two sides at right angles. They are not usually listable in this condition and are worth less than corresponding stamps properly perforated all round. This does not, however, apply to certain stamps, mainly from coils and booklets, where straight edges on various sides are the manufacturing norm affecting every stamp. The listings and notes make clear which sides are correctly imperf.

Malfunction. Varieties of double, misplaced or partial perforation caused by error or machine malfunction are not listable, neither are freaks, such as perforations placed diagonally from paper folds, nor missing holes caused by broken pins.

Centering. Well-centred stamps have designs surrounded by equal opposite margins. Where this condition affects the price the fact is stated.

Types of perforating. Where necessary for classification, perforation types are distinguished. These include:

Line perforation from one line of pins punching single rows of holes at a time.

Comb perforation from pins disposed across the sheet in comb formation, punching out holes at three sides of the stamp a row at a time.

Harrow perforation applied to a whole pane or sheet at one stroke.

Rotary perforation from toothed wheels operating across a sheet, then crosswise.

Sewing-machine perforation. The resultant condition, clean-cut or rough, is distinguished where required.

Pin-perforation is the commonly applied term for pin-roulette in which, instead of being punched out, round holes are pricked by sharp-pointed pins and no paper is removed.

Mixed perforation occurs when stamps with defective perforations are re-perforated in a different gauge.

Punctured stamps. Perforation holes can be punched into the face of the stamp. Patterns of small holes, often in the shape of initial letters, are privately applied devices against pilferage. These "perfins" are outside the scope except for Australia, Canada, Cape of Good Hope, Papua and Sudan where they were used as official stamps by the national administration. Identification devices, when officially inspired, are listed or noted; they can be shapes, or letters or words formed from holes, sometimes converting one class of stamp into another.

Rouletting. In rouletting the paper is cut, for ease of separation, but none is removed. The gauge is measured, when needed, as for perforations. Traditional French terms descriptive of the type of cut are often used and types include:

Arc roulette (*percé en arc*). Cuts are minute, spaced arcs, each roughly a semicircle.

Cross roulette (*percé en croix*). Cuts are tiny diagonal crosses.

Line roulette (*percé en ligne* or *en ligne droite*). Short straight cuts parallel to the frame of the stamp. The commonest basic roulette. Where not further described, "roulette" means this type.

Rouletted in colour or *coloured roulette* (*percé en lignes colorées* or *en lignes de couleur*). Cuts with coloured edges, arising from notched rule inked simultaneously with the printing plate.

Saw-tooth roulette (*percé en scie*). Cuts applied zigzag fashion to resemble the teeth of a saw.

Serpentine roulette (*percé en serpentin*). Cuts as sharply wavy lines.

Zigzag roulette (*percé en zigzags*). Short straight cuts at angles in alternate directions, producing sharp points on separation. U.S. usage favours "serrate(d) roulette" for this type.

Pin-roulette (originally *percé en points* and now *perforés trous d'epingle*) is commonly called pin-perforation in English.

4. Gum

All stamps listed are assumed to have gum of some kind; if they were issued without gum this is stated. Original gum (o.g.) means that which was present on the stamp as issued to the public. Deleterious climates and the presence of certain chemicals can cause gum to crack and, with early stamps, even make the paper deteriorate. Unscrupulous fakers are adept in removing it and regumming the stamp to meet the unreasoning demand often made for "full o.g." in cases where such a thing is virtually impossible.

The gum normally used on stamps has been gum arabic until the late 1960s when synthetic adhesives were introduced. Harrison and Sons Ltd for instance use *polyvinyl alcohol*, known to philatelists as PVA. This is almost invisible except for a slight yellowish tinge which was incorporated to make it possible to see that the stamps have been gummed. It has advantages in hot countries, as stamps do not curl and sheets are less likely to stick together. Gum arabic and PVA are not distinguished in the lists except that where a stamp exists with both forms this is indicated in footnotes. Our more specialised catalogues provide separate listing of gums for Great Britain.

Self-adhesive stamps are issued on backing paper, from which they are peeled before affixing to mail. Unused examples are priced as for backing paper intact, in which condition they are recommended to be kept. Used examples are best collected on cover or on piece.

5. Watermarks

Stamps are on unwatermarked paper except where the heading to the set says otherwise.

Detection. Watermarks are detected for Catalogue description by one of four methods: (1) holding stamps to the light; (2) laying stamps face down on a dark background; (3) adding a few drops of petroleum ether 40/60 to the stamp laid face down in a watermark tray; (4) by use of the Morley-Bright Detector, or other equipment, which work by revealing the thinning of the paper at the watermark (Note that petroleum ether is highly inflammable in use and can damage photogravure stamps.)

Listable types. Stamps occurring on both watermarked and unwatermarked papers are different types and both receive full listing.

Single watermarks (devices occurring once on every stamp) can be modified in size and shape as between different issues; the types are noted but not usually separately listed. Fortuitous absence of watermark from a single stamp or its gross displacement would not be listable.

To overcome registration difficulties the device may be repeated at close intervals (a *multiple watermark*), single stamps thus showing parts of several devices. Similarly, a large *sheet watermark* (or *all-over watermark*) covering numerous stamps can be used. We give informative notes and illustrations for them. The designs may be such that numbers of stamps in the sheet automatically lack watermark: this is not a listable variety. Multiple and all-over watermarks sometimes undergo modifications, but if the various types are difficult to distinguish from single stamps notes are given but not separate listings.

Papermakers' watermarks are noted where known but not listed separately, since most stamps in the sheet will lack them. Sheet watermarks which are nothing more than officially adopted papermakers' watermarks are, however, given normal listing.

Marginal watermarks, falling outside the pane of stamps, are ignored except where misplacement caused the adjoining row to be affected, in which case they are footnoted.

Watermark errors and varieties. Watermark errors are recognised as of major importance. They comprise stamps intended to be on unwatermarked paper but issued watermarked by mistake, or stamps printed on paper with the wrong watermark. Varieties showing letters omitted from the watermark are also included, but broken or deformed bits on the dandy roll are not.

Watermark positions. The diagram shows how watermark position is described in the Catalogue. Paper has a side intended for printing and watermarks are usually impressed so that they read normally when looked through from that printed side. However, since philatelists customarily detect watermarks by looking at the back of the stamp the watermark diagram also makes clear what is actually seen.

Illustrations in the Catalogue are of watermarks in normal positions (from the front of the stamps) and are actual size where possible.

Differences in watermark position are collectable as distinct varieties. This Catalogue now lists inverted, sideways inverted and reversed watermark varieties on Commonwealth stamps issued after 1900 *except* where the watermark position is completely haphazard. It is hoped to extend such listings to earlier issues in due course.

Great Britain inverted and sideways inverted watermarks can be found in the *Great Britain Specialised Catalogue* and the *Great Britain Concise Catalogue.*

Where a watermark comes indiscriminately in various positions our policy is to cover this by a general note: we do not give separate listings because the watermark position in these circumstances has no particular philatelic importance. There is a general note of this sort in modern Cyprus, for example. Issues printed since 1962 by Aspioti-Elka occur with the vertical stamps having the watermark normal or inverted, while horizontal stamps are likewise found with the watermark reading upwards or downwards.

AS DESCRIBED (Read through front of stamp)		AS SEEN DURING WATERMARK DETECTION (Stamp face down and back examined)
GvR	Normal	ꓤvꓱ
ꓤ∧ꓝ	Inverted	ꓱ∧ꓤ
ꓤvꓱ	Reversed	GvR
ꓱ∧ꓝ	Reversed and inverted	ꓤvꓱ
GvR (sideways)	Sideways	ꓤvꓱ (sideways)
GvR (sideways)	Sideways inverted	ꓤvꓱ (sideways)

Standard types of watermark. Some watermarks have been used generally for various British possessions rather than exclusively for a single colony. To avoid repetition the Catalogue classifies 17 general types, as under, with references in the headings throughout the listings being given either in words or in the form "W w 14" (meaning "watermark type w 14"). In those cases where watermark illustrations appear in the listings themselves, the respective reference reads,

for example, W 153, thus indicating that th watermark will be found in the normal sequence o illustrations as (type) **153**.

The general types are as follows, with a example of each quoted.

W	Description	Example
w 1	Large Star	St. Helena No. 1
w 2	Small Star	Turks Is. No. 4
w 3	Broad (pointed) Star	Grenada No. 24
w 4	Crown (over) CC, small stamp	Antigua No. 13
w 5	Crown (over) CC, large stamp	Antigua No. 31
w 6	Crown (over) CA, small stamp	Antigua No. 21
w 7	Crown CA (CA over Crown), large stamp	Sierra Leone No. 54
w 8	Multiple Crown CA	Antigua No. 41
w 9	Multiple Crown Script CA	Seychelles No. 158
w 9a	do. Error	Seychelles No. 158a
w 9b	do. Error	Seychelles No. 158b
w 10	V over Crown	N.S.W. No. 327
w 11	Crown over A	N.S.W. No. 347
w 12	Multiple St. Edward's Crown Block CA	Antigua No. 149
w 13	Multiple PTM	Johore No. 166
w 14	Multiple Crown CA Diagonal	Antigua No. 426
w 15	Multiple POST OFFICE	Kiribati No. 141
w 16	Multiple Crown Script CA Diagonal	Ascension No. 376
w 17	Multiple CARTOR	Brunei No. 357

CC in these watermarks is an abbreviation for "Crown Colonies" and CA for "Crown Agents". Watermarks w 1, w 2 and w 3 are on stamps printed by Perkins, Bacon; w 4 onwards on stamps from De La Rue and other printers.

w 1
Large Star

w 2
Small Star

w 3
Broad (pointed) Star

Watermark w 1, *Large Star,* measures 15 to 16 mm across the star from point to point and about 27 mm from centre to centre vertically between stars in the sheet. It was made for long stamps like Ceylon 1857 and St. Helena 1856.

Watermark w 2, *Small Star,* is of similar design but measures 12 to 13½ mm from point to point and 24 mm from centre to centre vertically. It was for use with ordinary-size stamps such as Grenada 1863–71.

When the Large Star watermark was used with the smaller stamps it only occasionally comes in the centre of the paper. It is frequently so misplaced as to show portions of two stars above and below and this eccentricity will very often help in determining the watermark.

Watermark w **3**, *Broad (pointed) Star*, resembles w **1** but the points are broader.

w **4**	w **5**
Crown (over) CC	Crown (over) CC

Two *Crown (over) CC* watermarks were used: w **4** was for stamps of ordinary size and w **5** for those of larger size.

w **6**	w **7**
Crown (over) CA	CA over Crown

Two watermarks of *Crown CA* type were used, w **6** being for stamps of ordinary size. The other, w **7**, is properly described as *CA over Crown*. It was specially made for paper on which it was intended to print long fiscal stamps: that some were used postally accounts for the appearance of w **7** in the Catalogue. The watermark occupies twice the space of the ordinary Crown CA watermark, w **6**. Stamps of normal size printed on paper with w **7** watermark show it *sideways*; it takes a horizontal pair of stamps to show the entire watermark.

w **8**	w **9**
Multiple Crown CA	Multiple Crown Script CA

Multiple watermarks began in 1904 with w **8**, *Multiple Crown CA*, changed from 1921 to w **9**, *Multiple Crown Script CA*. On stamps of ordinary size portions of two or three watermarks appear and on the large-sized stamps a greater number can be observed. The change to letters in script character with w **9** was accompanied by a Crown of distinctly different shape.

w **9a**: Error, Crown missing

w **9b**: Error, St. Edward's Crown

The *Multiple Crown Script CA* watermark, w **9**, is known with two errors recurring among the 1950–52 printings of several territories. In the first a crown has fallen away from the dandy-roll that impresses the watermark into the paper pulp. It gives w **9a**, *Crown missing*, but this omission has been found in both "Crown only" (*illustrated*) and "Crown CA" rows. The resulting faulty paper was used for Seychelles, Johore and the postage due stamps of nine colonies.

When the omission was noticed a second mishap occurred, which was to insert a wrong crown in the space, giving w **9b**, *St. Edward's Crown*. This produced varieties in Bahamas, St. Kitts-Nevis and Singapore and the incorrect crown likewise occurs in "Crown only" and "Crown CA" rows.

w **10**	w **11**
V over Crown	Crown over A

Resuming the general types, two watermarks found in issues of several Australian States are: w **10**, *V over Crown*, and w **11**, *Crown over A*.

w **12**
Multiple St. Edward's Crown Block CA

The *Multiple St. Edward's Crown Block CA* watermark, w **12**, was introduced in 1957 and besides the change in the Crown (from that used in *Multiple Crown Script CA,* w **9**) the letters reverted to block capitals. The new watermark began to appear sideways in 1966 and these stamps are generally listed as separate sets.

w **13**
Multiple PTM

The watermark w **13**, *Multiple PTM*, was introduced for new Malayan issues in November 1961.

w **14**
Multiple Crown CA Diagonal

By 1974 the two dandy-rolls (the "upright" and the "sideways") for w **12** were wearing out; the Crown Agents therefore discontinued using the sideways-watermark one and retained the other only as a stand-by. A new dandy-roll with the pattern of w **14**, *Multiple Crown CA Diagonal*, was introduced and first saw use with some Churchill Centenary issues.

The new watermark has the design arranged in gradually spiralling rows. It is improved in design to allow smooth passage over the paper (the gaps between letters and rows had caused jolts in previous dandy-rolls) and the sharp corners and angles, where fibres used to accumulate, have been eliminated by rounding.

This watermark has no "normal" sideways position amongst the different printers using it. To avoid confusion our more specialised listings do not rely on such terms as "sideways inverted" but describe the direction in which the watermark points.

w **15**
Multiple POST OFFICE

During 1981 w **15**, *Multiple POST OFFICE*, was introduced for certain issues prepared by Philatelists Ltd, acting for various countries in the Indian Ocean, Pacific and West Indies.

w **16**
Multiple Crown Script CA Diagonal

A new Crown Agents watermark was introduced during 1985, w **16**, *Multiple Crown Script CA Diagonal*. This was very similar to the previous w **14**, but showed "CA" in script rather than block letters. It was first used on the omnibus series of stamps commemorating the Life and Times of Queen Elizabeth the Queen Mother.

w 17
Multiple CARTOR

Watermark w 17, *Multiple CARTOR*, was used from 1985 for issues printed by this French firm for countries which did not normally use the Crown Agents watermark.

In recent years the use of watermarks has, to a small extent, been superseded by fluorescent security markings. These are often more visible from the reverse of the stamp (Cook Islands from 1970 onwards), but have occurred printed over the design (Hong Kong Nos. 415/30). In 1982 the Crown Agents introduced a new stock paper, without watermark, known as "C-Kurity" on which a fluorescent pattern of blue rosettes is visible on the reverse, beneath the gum. This paper was used for issues from Gambia and Norfolk Island.

6. Colours

Stamps in two or three colours have these named in order of appearance, from the centre moving outwards. Four colours or more are usually listed as multicoloured.

In compound colour names the second is the predominant one, thus:

orange-red = a red tending towards orange;
red-orange = an orange containing more red than usual.

Standard colours used. The 200 colours most used for stamp identification are given in the Stanley Gibbons Stamp Colour Key. The Catalogue has used the Stamp Colour Key as standard for describing new issues for some years. The names are also introduced as lists are rewritten, though exceptions are made for those early issues where traditional names have become universally established.

Determining colours. When comparing actual stamps with colour samples in the Stamp Colour Key, view in a good north daylight (or its best substitute: fluorescent "colour-matching" light). Sunshine is not recommended. Choose a solid portion of the stamp design; if available, marginal markings such as solid bars of colour or colour check dots are helpful. Shading lines in the design can be misleading as they appear lighter than solid colour. Postmarked portions of a stamp appear darker than normal. If more than one colour is present, mask off the extraneous ones as the eye tends to mix them.

Errors of colour. Major colour errors in stamps or overprints which qualify for listing are: wrong colours; one colour inverted in relation to the rest; albinos (colourless impressions), where these have Expert Committee certificates; colours completely omitted, but only on unused stamps (if found on used stamps the information is footnoted) and with good credentials, missing colours being frequently faked.

Colours only partially omitted are not recognised. Colour shifts, however spectacular, are not listed.

Shades. Shades in philately refer to variations in the intensity of a colour or the presence of differing amounts of other colours. They are particularly significant when they can be linked to specific printings. In general, shades need to be quite

marked to fall within the scope of this Catalogue; it does not favour nowadays listing the often numerous shades of a stamp, but chooses a single applicable colour name which will indicate particular groups of outstanding shades. Furthermore, the listings refer to colours as issued: they may deteriorate into something different through the passage of time.

Modern colour printing by lithography is prone to marked differences of shade, even within a single run, and variations can occur within the same sheet. Such shades are not listed.

Aniline colours. An aniline colour meant originally one derived from coal-tar; it now refers more widely to colour of a particular brightness suffused on the surface of a stamp and showing through clearly on the back.

Colours of overprints and surcharges. All overprints and surcharges are in black unless stated otherwise in the heading or after the description of the stamp.

7. Specimen Stamps

Originally, stamps overprinted SPECIMEN were circulated to postmasters or kept in official records, but after the establishment of the Universal Postal Union supplies were sent to Berne for distribution to the postal administrations of member countries.

During the period 1884 to 1928 most of the stamps of British Crown Colonies required for this purpose were overprinted SPECIMEN in various shapes and sizes by their printers from typeset formes. Some locally produced provisionals were handstamped locally, as were sets prepared for presentation. From 1928 stamps were punched with holes forming the word SPECIMEN, each firm of printers using a different machine or machines. From 1948 the stamps supplied for U.P.U. distribution were no longer punctured.

Stamps of some other Commonwealth territories were overprinted or handstamped locally, while stamps of Great Britain and those overprinted for use in overseas postal agencies (mostly of the higher denominations) bore SPECIMEN overprints and handstamps applied by the Inland Revenue or the Post Office.

De La Rue & Co. Ltd.

Bradbury, Wilkinson & Co. Ltd.

Waterlow & Sons Ltd.

Great Britain overprints

Some of the commoner types of overprints or punctures are illustrated here. Collectors are warned that dangerous forgeries of the punctured type exist.

The *Part 1 (British Commonwealth) Catalogue* records those Specimen overprints or perforations intended for distribution by the U.P.U. to member countries. In addition the Specimen overprints of Australia and its dependent territories, which were sold to collectors by the Post Office, are also included.

All other Specimens are outside the scope of this volume.

Specimens are not quoted in Great Britain as they are fully listed in the Stanley Gibbons *Great Britain Specialised Catalogue.*

In specifying type of specimen for individual high-value stamps, "H/S" means handstamped, "Optd" is overprinted and "Perf" is punctured. Some sets occur mixed, e.g. "Optd/Perf". If unspecified, the type is apparent from the date or it is the same as for the lower values quoted as a set.

Prices. Prices for stamps up to £1 are quoted in sets; higher values are priced singly after the colours, thus "(S. £20)". Where specimens exist in more than one type the price quoted is for the cheapest. Specimen stamps have rarely survived even as pairs; these and strips of three, four or five are worth considerably more than singles.

8. Luminescence

Machines which sort mail electronically have been introduced in recent years. In consequence some countries have issued stamps on fluorescent or phosphorescent papers, while others have marked their stamps with phosphor bands.

The various papers can only be distinguished by ultraviolet lamps emitting particular wavelengths. They are separately listed only when the stamps have some other means of distinguishing them, visible without the use of these lamps. Where this is not so, the papers are recorded in footnotes or headings.

For this Catalogue we do not consider it appropriate that collectors be compelled to have use of an ultraviolet lamp before being able to identify stamps by our listings. Some experience will also be found necessary in interpreting the results given by ultraviolet. Collectors using the lamps, nevertheless, should exercise great care in their use as exposure to their light is extremely dangerous to the eyes.

Phosphor bands are listable, since they are visible to the naked eye (by holding stamps at an angle to the light and looking along them, the bands appear dark). Stamps existing with and without phosphor bands or with differing numbers of bands are given separate listings. Varieties such as double bands, bands omitted, misplaced or printed on the back are not listed.

Detailed descriptions appear at appropriate places in the listings in explanation of luminescent papers; *see*, for example, Australia above No. 308, Canada above Nos. 472 and 611, Cook Is. above No. 249, etc.

For Great Britain, where since 1959 phosphors have played a prominent and intricate part in stamp issues, the main notes above Nos. 599, 723 and after the Decimal Machin issue (No. X841 onwards) should be studied, as well as the footnotes to individual listings where appropriate. In general the classification is as follows.

Stamps with *phosphor bands* are those where a separate cylinder applies the phosphor after the stamps are printed. Issues with "all-over" phosphor have the "band" covering the entire stamp. Parts of the stamp covered by phosphor bands, or the entire surface for "all-over" phosphor versions, appear matt. Stamps on *phosphorised paper* have the phosphor added to the paper coating before the stamps are printed. Issues on this paper have a completely shiny surface.

Further particularisation of phosphor—their methods of printing and the colours they exhibit under ultraviolet—is outside the scope. The more specialised listings should be consulted for this information.

9. Coil Stamps

Stamps issued only in coil form are given full listing. If stamps are issued in both sheets and coils the coil stamps are listed separately only where there is some feature (e.g. perforation or watermark sideways) by which singles can be distinguished. Coil strips containing different stamps *se-tenant* are also listed.

Coil join pairs are too random and too easily faked to permit of listing; similarly ignored are coil stamps which have accidentally suffered an extra row of perforations from the claw mechanism in a malfunctioning vending machine.

10. Stamp Booklets

Stamp booklets (with the exception of those from Great Britain, the Channel Islands and the Isle of Man, for which see the current editions of the *Great Britain Concise Catalogue* and *Collect Channel Islands and Isle of Man Stamps*) are now listed in this catalogue.

Single stamps from booklets are listed if they are distinguishable in some way (such as watermark or perforation) from similar sheet stamps.

Booklet panes are listed where they contain stamps of different denominations *se-tenant*, where stamp-size labels are included, or where such panes are otherwise identifiable. Booklet panes are placed in the listing under the lowest denomination present.

Particular perforations (straight edges) are covered by appropriate notes.

11. Miniature Sheets and Sheetlets

We distinguish between "miniature sheets" and "sheetlets" and this affects the catalogue numbering. An item in sheet form that is postally valid, containing a single stamp, pair, block or set of stamps, with wide, inscribed and/or decorative margins, is a *miniature sheet* if it is sold at post offices as an indivisible entity. As such the Catalogue allots a single **MS** number and describes what stamps make it up. (*See* Great Britain 1978 Historic Buildings, No. **MS**1058, as an example.) The *sheetlet* or *small sheet* differs in that the individual stamps are intended to be purchased separately for postal purposes. For sheetlets, all the component postage stamps are numbered individually and the composition explained in a footnote. (The 1978 Christmas Island Christmas sheetlet, Nos. 99/107, is an example.) Note that the definitions refer to post office sale—not how items may be subsequently offered by stamp dealers.

Production as sheetlets is a modern marketing development chosen by postal administrations to interest collectors in purchasing the item complete; if he has done so he should, as with all *se-tenant* arrangements, keep the sheetlet intact in his collection.

The Catalogue will in future no longer give full listing to designs, originally issued in normal sheets, which subsequently appear in sheetlets showing changes of colour, perforation, printing process or face value. Such stamps will be covered by footnotes.

12. Forgeries and Fakes

Forgeries. Where space permits, notes are considered if they can give a concise description that will permit unequivocal detection of a forgery. Generalised warnings, lacking detail, are not nowadays inserted, since their value to the collector is problematic.

Fakes. Unwitting fakes are numerous, particularly "new shades" which are colour changelings brought about by exposure to sunlight, soaking in water contaminated with dyes from adherent paper, contact with oil and dirt from a pocketbook, and so on. Fraudulent operators, in addition, can offer to arrange: removal of hinge marks; repairs of thins on white or coloured papers; replacement of missing margins or perforations; reperforating in true or false gauges; removal of fiscal cancellations; rejoining of severed pairs, strips and blocks; and (a major hazard) regumming. Collectors can only be urged to purchase from reputable sources and to insist upon Expert Committee certification where there is any kind of doubt.

The Catalogue can consider footnotes about fakes where these are specific enough to assist in detection.

1935 SILVER JUBILEE CROWN COLONY ISSUE

The Crown Colony Windsor Castle design by Harold Fleury is, surely, one of the most impressive produced in the 20th-century and its reproduction in the recess process by three of the leading stamp-printing firms of the era has provided a subject for philatelic research which has yet to be exhausted.

Each of the three, Bradbury, Wilkinson & Co. and Waterlow and Sons, who both produced fifteen issues, together with De La Rue & Co. who printed fourteen, used a series of vignette (centre) plates coupled with individual frame plates for each value. All were taken from dies made by Waterlow. Several worthwhile varieties exist on the frame plates, but most interest has been concentrated on the centre plates, each of which was used to print a considerable number of different stamps.

Sheets printed by Bradbury, Wilkinson were without printed plate numbers, but research has now identified eleven centre plates which were probably used in permanent pairings. A twelfth plate awaits confirmation. Stamps from some of these centre plates have revealed a number of prominent plate flaws, the most famous of which, the extra flagstaff, has been eagerly sought by collectors for many years.

Extra flagstaff
(Plate 1" R. 9/1)

Short extra flagstaff
(Plate "2" R. 2/1)

Lightning conductor
(Plate "3" R. 2/5)

Flagstaff on right-hand turret (Plate "5" R. 7/1)

Double flagstaff (Plate "6" R. 5/2)

De La Rue sheets were initially printed with plate numbers, but in many instances these were subsequently trimmed off. Surviving examples do, however, enable a positive identification of six centre plates, 2A, 2B, (2A), (2B), 4 and 4/ to be made. The evidence of sheet markings and plate flaws clearly demonstrates that there were two different pairs of plates numbered 2A 2B. The second pair is designated (2A) (2B) by specialist collectors to avoid further confusion. The number of major plate flaws is not so great as on the Bradbury, Wilkinson sheets, but four examples are included in the catalogue.

Diagonal line by turret
(Plate 2A R. 10/1 and
10/2)

Dot to left of chapel
(Plate 2B R. 8/3)

Dot by flagstaff (Plate 4
R. 8/4)

Dash by turret (Plate 4/
R. 3/6)

Much less is known concerning the Waterlow centre plate system as the sheets did not show plate numbers. Ten individual plates have, so far, been identified and it is believed that these were used in pairs. The two versions of the kite and log flaw from plate "2" show that this plate exists in two states.

Damaged turret
(Plate "1" R. 5/6)

Kite and vertical log
(Plate "2A" R. 10/6)

Kite and horizontal log
(Plate "2B" R. 10/6)

Bird by turret
(Plate "7" R. 1/5)

Abbreviations

Printers

A.B.N. Co	American Bank Note Co, New York.
A. & M.	Alden & Mowbray Ltd, Oxford.
Ashton-Potter	Ashton-Potter Ltd, Toronto.
Aspioti-Elka (Aspiotis)	Aspioti-Elka, Greece.
B.A.B.N.	British American Bank Note Co, Ottawa.
B.D.T.	B.D.T. International Security Printing Ltd, Dublin, Ireland.
B.W.	Bradbury Wilkinson & Co, Ltd.
Cartor	Cartor S.A., L'Aigle, France
C.B.N.	Canadian Bank Note Co, Ottawa.
Continental B.N. Co	Continental Bank Note Co.
Courvoisier	Imprimerie Courvoisier S.A., La-Chaux-de-Fonds, Switzerland.
D.L.R.	De La Rue & Co, Ltd, London, and (from 1961) Bogota, Colombia.
Edila	Editions de l'Aubetin, S.A.
Enschedé	Joh. Enschedé en Zonen, Haarlem, Netherlands.
Format	Format International Security Printers, Ltd, London.
Harrison	Harrison & Sons, Ltd, London
Heraclio Fournier	Heraclio Fournier S.A., Vitoria, Spain.
J.W.	John Waddington Security Print Ltd., Leeds
P.B.	Perkins Bacon Ltd, London.
Questa	Questa Colour Security Printers, Ltd., London
Ueberreuter	Ueberreuter (incorporating Bruder Rosenbaum), Korneuburg, Austria.
Walsall	Walsall Security Printers, Ltd.
Waterlow	Waterlow & Sons, Ltd, London.

General Abbreviations

Alph	Alphabet
Anniv	Anniversary
Comp	Compound (perforation)
Des	Designer; designed
Diag	Diagonal; diagonally
Eng	Engraver; engraved
F.C.	Fiscal Cancellation
H/S	Handstamped
Horiz	Horizontal; horizontally
Imp, Imperf	Imperforate
Inscr	Inscribed
L	Left
Litho	Lithographed
mm	Millimetres
MS	Miniature sheet
N.Y.	New York
Opt(d)	Overprint(ed)
P or P-c	Pen-cancelled
P, Pf or Perf	Perforated
Photo	Photogravure
Pl	Plate
Pr	Pair
Ptd	Printed
Ptg	Printing
R	Right
R.	Row
Recess	Recess-printed
Roto	Rotogravure
Roul	Rouletted

S	Specimen (overprint)
Surch	Surcharge(d)
T.C.	Telegraph Cancellation
T	Type
Typo	Typographed
Un	Unused
Us	Used
Vert	Vertical; vertically
W or wmk	Watermark
Wmk s	Watermark sideways

(†)=Does not exist.
(—) (or blank price column)=Exists, or may exist, but no market price is known.
/ between colours means "on" and the colour following is that of the paper on which the stamp is printed.

Colours of Stamps

Bl (blue); blk (black); brn (brown); car, carm (carmine); choc (chocolate); clar (claret); emer (emerald); grn (green); ind (indigo); mag (magenta); mar (maroon); mult (multicoloured); mve (mauve); ol (olive); orge (orange); pk (pink); pur (purple); scar (scarlet); sep (sepia); turq (turquoise); ultram (ultramarine); verm (vermilion); vio (violet); yell (yellow).

Colour of Overprints and Surcharges

(B.) = blue, (Blk.) = black, (Br.) = brown, (C.) = carmine, (G.) = green, (Mag.) = magenta, (Mve.) = mauve, (Ol.) = olive, (O.) = orange, (P.) = purple, (Pk.) = pink, (R.)=red, (Sil.) = silver, (V.) = violet, (Vm.) or (Verm.) = vermilion, (W.) = white, (Y.) = yellow.

Arabic Numerals

As in the case of European figures, the details of the Arabic numerals vary in different stamp designs, but they should be readily recognised with the aid of this illustration.

٠	١	٢	٣	٤	٥	٦	٧	٨	٩
0	1	2	3	4	5	6	7	8	9

International Philatelic Glossary

English	French	German	Spanish	Italian
Agate	Agate	Achat	Agata	Agata
Air stamp	Timbre de la poste aérienne	Flugpostmarke	Sello de correo aéreo	Francobollo per posta aerea
Apple Green	Vert-pomme	Apfelgrün	Verde manzana	Verde mela
Barred	Annulé par barres	Balkenentwertung	Anulado con barras	Sbarrato
Bisected	Timbre coupé	Halbiert	Partido en dos	Frazionato
Bistre	Bistre	Bister	Bistre	Bistro
Bistre-brown	Brun-bistre	Bisterbraun	Castaño bistre	Bruno-bistro
Black	Noir	Schwarz	Negro	Nero
Blackish Brown	Brun-noir	Schwärzlichbraun	Castaño negruzco	Bruno nerastro
Blackish Green	Vert foncé	Schwärzlichgrün	Verde negruzco	Verde nerastro
Blackish Olive	Olive foncé	Schwärzlicholiv	Oliva negruzco	Oliva nerastro
Block of four	Bloc de quatre	Viererblock	Bloque de cuatro	Bloco di quattro
Blue	Bleu	Blau	Azul	Azzurro
Blue-green	Vert-bleu	Blaugrün	Verde azul	Verde azzurro
Bluish Violet	Violet bleuâtre	Bläulichviolett	Violeta azulado	Violetto azzurrastro
Booklet	Carnet	Heft	Cuadernillo	Libretto
Bright Blue	Bleu vif	Lebhaftblau	Azul vivo	Azzurro vivo
Bright Green	Vert vif	Lebhaftgrün	Verde vivo	Verde vivo
Bright Purple	Mauve vif	Lebhaftpurpur	Púrpura vivo	Porpora vivo
Bronze Green	Vert-bronze	Bronzegrün	Verde bronce	Verde bronzo
Brown	Brun	Braun	Castaño	Bruno
Brown-lake	Carmin-brun	Braunlack	Laca castaño	Lacca bruno
Brown-purple	Pourpre-brun	Braunpurpur	Púrpura castaño	Porpora bruno
Brown-red	Rouge-brun	Braunrot	Rojo castaño	Rosso bruno
Buff	Chamois	Sämisch	Anteado	Camoscio
Cancellation	Oblitération	Entwertung	Cancelación	Annullamento
Cancelled	Annulé	Gestempelt	Cancelado	Annullato
Carmine	Carmin	Karmin	Carmín	Carminio
Carmine-red	Rouge-carmin	Karminrot	Rojo carmín	Rosso carminio
Centred	Centré	Zentriert	Centrado	Centrato
Cerise	Rouge-cerise	Kirschrot	Color de ceresa	Color Ciliegia
Chalk-surfaced paper	Papier couché	Kreidepapier	Papel estucado	Carta gessata
Chalky Blue	Bleu terne	Kreideblau	Azul turbio	Azzurro smorto
Charity stamp	Timbre de bienfaisance	Wohltätigkeitsmarke	Sello de beneficenza	Francobollo di beneficenza
Chestnut	Marron	Kastanienbraun	Castaño rojo	Marrone
Chocolate	Chocolat	Schokolade	Chocolate	Cioccolato
Cinnamon	Cannelle	Zimtbraun	Canela	Cannella
Claret	Grenat	Weinrot	Rojo vinoso	Vinaccia
Cobalt	Cobalt	Kobalt	Cobalto	Cobalto
Colour	Couleur	Farbe	Color	Colore
Comb-perforation	Dentelure en peigne	Kammzähnung, Reihenzähnung	Dentado de peine	Dentellatura e pettine
Commemorative stamp	Timbre commémoratif	Gedenkmarke	Sello conmemorativo	Francobollo commemorativo
Crimson	Cramoisi	Karmesin	Carmesí	Cremisi
Deep Blue	Bleu foncé	Dunkelblau	Azul oscuro	Azzurro scuro
Deep Bluish Green	Vert-bleu foncé	Dunkelbläulichgrün	Verde azulado oscuro	Verde azzurro scuro
Design	Dessin	Markenbild	Diseño	Disegno
Die	Matrice	Urstempel, Type, Platte	Cuño	Conio, Matrice
Double	Double	Doppelt	Doble	Doppio
Drab	Olive terne	Trüboliv	Oliva turbio	Oliva smorto
Dull Green	Vert terne	Trübgrün	Verde turbio	Verde smorto
Dull Purple	Mauve terne	Trübpurpur	Púrpura turbio	Porpora smorto
Embossing	Impression en relief	Prägedruck	Impresión en relieve	Impressione a relievo
Emerald	Vert-eméraude	Smaragdgrün	Esmeralda	Smeraldo
Engraved	Gravé	Graviert	Grabado	Inciso
Error	Erreur	Fehler, Fehldruck	Error	Errore
Essay	Essai	Probedruck	Ensayo	Saggio
Express letter stamp	Timbre pour lettres par exprès	Eilmarke	Sello de urgencia	Francobollo per espresso
Fiscal stamp	Timbre fiscal	Stempelmarke	Sello fiscal	Francobollo fiscale
Flesh	Chair	Fleischfarben	Carne	Carnicino
Forgery	Faux, Falsification	Fälschung	Falsificación	Falso, Falsificazione
Frame	Cadre	Rahmen	Marco	Cornice
Granite paper	Papier avec fragments de fils de soie	Faserpapier	Papel con filamentos	Carto con fili di seta
Green	Vert	Grün	Verde	Verde
Greenish Blue	Bleu verdâtre	Grünlichblau	Azul verdoso	Azzurro verdastro

International Philatelic Glossary

English	French	German	Spanish	Italian
Greenish Yellow	Jaune-vert	Grünlichgelb	Amarillo verdoso	Giallo verdastro
Grey	Gris	Grau	Gris	Grigio
Grey-blue	Bleu-gris	Graublau	Azul gris	Azzurro grigio
Grey-green	Vert gris	Graugrün	Verde gris	Verde grigio
Gum	Gomme	Gummi	Goma	Gomma
Gutter	Interpanneau	Zwischensteg	Espacio blanco entre dos grupos	Ponte
Imperforate	Non-dentelé	Geschnitten	Sin dentar	Non dentellato
Indigo	Indigo	Indigo	Azul indigo	Indaco
Inscription	Inscription	Inschrift	Inscripción	Dicitura
Inverted	Renversé	Kopfstehend	Invertido	Capovolto
Issue	Émission	Ausgabe	Emisión	Emissione
Laid	Vergé	Gestreift	Listado	Vergato
Lake	Lie de vin	Lackfarbe	Laca	Lacca
Lake-brown	Brun-carmin	Lackbraun	Castaño laca	Bruno lacca
Lavender	Bleu-lavande	Lavendel	Color de alhucema	Lavanda
Lemon	Jaune-citron	Zitrongelb	Limón	Limone
Light Blue	Bleu clair	Hellblau	Azul claro	Azzurro chiaro
Lilac	Lilas	Lila	Lila	Lilla
Line perforation	Dentelure en lignes	Linienzähnung	Dentado en linea	Dentellatura lineare
Lithography	Lithographie	Steindruck	Litografía	Litografia
Local	Timbre de poste locale	Lokalpostmarke	Emisión local	Emissione locale
Lozenge roulette	Percé en losanges	Rautenförmiger Durchstich	Picadura en rombos	Perforazione a losanghe
Magenta	Magenta	Magentarot	Magenta	Magenta
Margin	Marge	Rand	Borde	Margine
Maroon	Marron pourpré	Dunkelrotpurpur	Púrpura rojo oscuro	Marrone rossastro
Mauve	Mauve	Malvenfarbe	Malva	Malva
Multicoloured	Polychrome	Mehrfarbig	Multicolores	Policromo
Myrtle Green	Vert myrte	Myrtengrün	Verde mirto	Verde mirto
New Blue	Bleu ciel vif	Neublau	Azul nuevo	Azzurro nuovo
Newspaper stamp	Timbre pour journaux	Zeitungsmarke	Sello para periódicos	Francobollo per giornali
Obliteration	Oblitération	Abstempelung	Matasello	Annullamento
Obsolete	Hors (de) cours	Ausser Kurs	Fuera de curso	Fuori corso
Ochre	Ocre	Ocker	Ocre	Ocra
Official stamp	Timbre de service	Dienstmarke	Sello de servicio	Francobollo di servizio
Olive-brown	Brun-olive	Olivbraun	Castaño oliva	Bruno oliva
Olive-green	Vert-olive	Olivgrün	Verde oliva	Verde oliva
Olive-grey	Gris-olive	Olivgrau	Gris oliva	Grigio oliva
Olive-yellow	Jaune-olive	Olivgelb	Amarillo oliva	Giallo oliva
Orange	Orange	Orange	Naranja	Arancio
Orange-brown	Brun-orange	Orangebraun	Castaño naranja	Bruno arancio
Orange-red	Rouge-orange	Orangerot	Rojo naranja	Rosso arancio
Orange-yellow	Jaune-orange	Orangegelb	Amarillo naranja	Giallo arancio
Overprint	Surcharge	Aufdruck	Sobrecarga	Soprastampa
Pair	Paire	Paar	Pareja	Coppia
Pale	Pâle	Blass	Pálido	Pallido
Pane	Panneau	Gruppe	Grupo	Gruppo
Paper	Papier	Papier	Papel	Carta
Parcel post stamp	Timbre pour colis postaux	Paketmarke	Sello para paquete postal	Francobollo per pacchi postali
Pen-cancelled	Oblitéré à plume	Federzugentwertung	Cancelado a pluma	Annullato a penna
Percé en arc	Percé en arc	Bogenförmiger Durchstich	Picadura en forma de arco	Perforazione ad arco
Percé en scie	Percé en scie	Bogenförmiger Durchstich	Picado en sierra	Foratura a sega
Perforated	Dentelé	Gezähnt	Dentado	Dentellato
Perforation	Dentelure	Zähnung	Dentar	Dentellatura
Photogravure	Photogravure, Héliogravure	Rastertiefdruck	Fotograbado	Rotocalco
Pin perforation	Percé en points	In Punkten durchstochen	Horadado con alfileres	Perforato a punti
Plate	Planche	Platte	Plancha	Lastra, Tavola
Plum	Prune	Pflaumenfarbe	Color de ciruela	Prugna
Postage Due stamp	Timbre-taxe	Portomarke	Sello de tasa	Segnatasse
Postage stamp	Timbre-poste	Briefmarke, Frei-marke, Postmarke	Sello de correos	Francobollo postale
Postal fiscal stamp	Timbre fiscal-postal	Stempelmarke als Postmarke verwendet	Sello fiscal-postal	Fiscale postale
Postmark	Oblitération postale	Poststempel	Matasello	Bollo
Printing	Impression, Tirage	Druck	Impresión	Stampa, Tiratura
Proof	Épreuve	Druckprobe	Prueba de impresión	Prova
Provisionals	Timbres provisoires	Provisorische Mark-en, Provisorien	Provisionales	Provvisori

English	French	German	Spanish	Italian
Prussian Blue	Bleu de Prusse	Preussischblau	Azul de Prusia	Azzurro di Prussia
Purple	Pourpre	Purpur	Púrpura	Porpora
Purple-brown	Brun-pourpre	Purpurbraun	Castaño púrpura	Bruno porpora
Recess-printing	Impression en taille douce	Tiefdruck	Grabado	Incisione
Red	Rouge	Rot	Rojo	Rosso
Red-brown	Brun-rouge	Rotbraun	Castaño rojizo	Bruno rosso
Reddish Lilac	Lilas rougeâtre	Rötlichlila	Lila rojizo	Lilla rossastro
Reddish Purple	Pourpre-rouge	Rötlichpurpur	Púrpura rojizo	Porpora rossastro
Reddish Violet	Violet rougeâtre	Rötlichviolett	Violeta rojizo	Violetto rossastro
Red-orange	Orange rougeâtre	Rotorange	Naranja rojizo	Arancio rosso
Registration stamp	Timbre pour lettre chargée (recommandée)	Einschreibemarke	Sello de certificado	Francobollo per lettere raccomandate
Reprint	Réimpression	Neudruck	Reimpresión	Ristampa
Reversed	Retourné	Umgekehrt	Invertido	Rovesciato
Rose	Rose	Rosa	Rosa	Rosa
Rose-red	Rouge rosé	Rosarot	Rojo rosado	Rosso rosa
Rosine	Rose vif	Lebhaftrosa	Rosa vivo	Rosa vivo
Roulette	Percage	Durchstich	Picadura	Foratura
Rouletted	Percé	Durchstochen	Picado	Forato
Royal Blue	Bleu-roi	Königblau	Azul real	Azzurro reale
Sage Green	Vert-sauge	Salbeigrün	Verde salvia	Verde salvia
Salmon	Saumon	Lachs	Salmón	Salmone
Scarlet	Écarlate	Scharlach	Escarlata	Scarlatto
Sepia	Sépia	Sepia	Sepia	Seppia
Serpentine roulette	Percé en serpentin	Schlangenliniger Durchstich	Picado a serpentina	Perforazione a serpentina
Shade	Nuance	Tönung	Tono	Gradazione de colore
Sheet	Feuille	Bogen	Hoja	Foglio
Slate	Ardoise	Schiefer	Pizarra	Ardesia
Slate-blue	Bleu-ardoise	Schieferblau	Azul pizarra	Azzurro ardesia
Slate-green	Vert-ardoise	Schiefergrün	Verde pizarra	Verde ardesia
Slate-lilac	Lilas-gris	Schieferlila	Lila pizarra	Lilla ardesia
Slate-purple	Mauve-gris	Schieferpurpur	Púrpura pizarra	Porpora ardesia
Slate-violet	Violet-gris	Schieferviolett	Violeta pizarra	Violetto ardesia
Special delivery stamp	Timbre pour exprès	Eilmarke	Sello de urgencia	Francobollo per espressi
Specimen	Spécimen	Muster	Muestra	Saggio
Steel Blue	Bleu acier	Stahlblau	Azul acero	Azzurro acciaio
Strip	Bande	Streifen	Tira	Striscia
Surcharge	Surcharge	Aufdruck	Sobrecarga	Soprastampa
Tête-bêche	Tête-bêche	Kehrdruck	Tête-bêche	Tête-bêche
Tinted paper	Papier teinté	Getöntes Papier	Papel coloreado	Carta tinta
Too-late stamp	Timbre pour lettres en retard	Verspätungsmarke	Sello para cartas retardadas	Francobollo per le lettere in ritardo
Turquoise-blue	Bleu-turquoise	Türkisblau	Azul turquesa	Azzurro turchese
Turquoise-green	Vert-turquoise	Türkisgrün	Verde turquesa	Verde turchese
Typography	Typographie	Buchdruck	Tipografia	Tipografia
Ultramarine	Outremer	Ultramarin	Ultramar	Oltremare
Unused	Neuf	Ungebraucht	Nuevo	Nuovo
Used	Oblitéré, Usé	Gebraucht	Usado	Usato
Venetian Red	Rouge-brun terne	Venezianischrot	Rojo veneciano	Rosso veneziano
Vermilion	Vermillon	Zinnober	Cinabrio	Vermiglione
Violet	Violet	Violett	Violeta	Violetto
Violet-blue	Bleu-violet	Violettblau	Azul violeta	Azzurro violetto
Watermark	Filigrane	Wasserzeichen	Filigrana	Filigrana
Watermark sideways	Filigrane couché	Wasserzeichen liegend	Filigrana acostado	Filigrana coricata
Wove paper	Papier ordinaire, Papier uni	Einfaches Papier	Papel avitelado	Carta unita
Yellow	Jaune	Gelb	Amarillo	Giallo
Yellow-brown	Brun-jaune	Gelbbraun	Castaño amarillo	Bruno giallo
Yellow-green	Vert-jaune	Gelbgrün	Verde amarillo	Verde giallo
Yellow-olive	Olive jaunâtre	Gelboliv	Oliva amarillo	Oliva giallastro
Yellow-orange	Orange jaunâtre	Gelborange	Naranja amarillo	Arancio giallastro
Zig-zag roulette	Percé en zigzag	Sägezahnartiger Durchstich	Picado en zigzag	Perforazione a zigzag

GB & COMMONWEALTH
GEORGE VI & QUEEN ELIZABETH II 1937-1965
BUY OR SELL

HAVE YOU A COLLECTION OR ANY UNWANTED MATERIAL
FOR SALE OF THE ABOVE PERIOD
GVI - QEII

**POSTAL HISTORY ALSO REQUIRED ALL PERIODS A BROAD RANGE OF SPECIALIST
MATERIAL AVAILABLE
PLUS
LARGE STOCKS OF STANDARD MATERIAL TO SUIT ALL INTERESTS:
AIRMAILS, POSTAL HISTORY ETC**

**FOR INFORMATION OF AVAILABLE
STOCK PLEASE PHONE,
FAX OR WRITE**

ATTENTION: MIKE MERCER TO BE INCLUDED ON OUR FREE MAILING LIST

PARKSTONE PHILATELICS
PO Box No 72, Redcar, Cleveland TS11 8YY. Tel & Fax: 01642 470714
Email: 106556.3576@COMPUSERVE.COM

BRITISH COMMONWEALTH AND FOREIGN

BRITISH COMMONWEALTH, including GB and Regionals, 1840 to date. We have stocks of all periods, Mint and Used together with Booklets and Varieties, Aerogrammes and Postal Stationery. Anything unusual, we try to stock it. **ALL NEW ISSUES ARE HANDLED.**

REST OF THE WORLD, all countries throughout Europe, Asia, Africa and North and South America etc.

Stocks vary from country to country - some countries cover all periods, others are modern only. **ALL NEW ISSUES ARE HANDLED.**

THEMATICS - Any THEME available, covering the world. Send your wants lists to us. Special price list for Royal Events and Disney.

PRICE LISTS OF MANY COUNTRIES ARE AVAILABLE ON REQUEST.

JOIN OUR NEW ISSUE SERVICE NOW
Established in 1962 - Over 35 years of experience and expertise.

RECEIVE OUR MONTHLY NEW ISSUE LISTS
Write, Fax or Phone now or see us at the major UK and European Shows and other World Wide Internationals.

M. & N. Haworth
P. O. Box 20, Clitheroe, Lancs BB7 2JQ.   Telephone: 01200 423576 Fax: 01200 423576

Specialist Philatelic Societies

Requests for inclusion on this page should be sent to the Catalogue Editor.

British Decimal Stamps Study Circle
Secretary—Mr. S. van Kimmenade
32 Beaufort Heights, Beaufort Road,
St. George, Bristol BS5 8JX

Great Britain Philatelic Society
Membership Secretary—Mr. A. G. Lajer
The Old Post Office, Hurst,
Berks RG10 0TR

Great Britain Decimal Stamp Book Study
Circle
Membership Secretary—Mr. A. J. Wilkins
3 Buttermere Close, Brierley Hill, West
Midlands DY5 3SD

Channel Islands Specialists Society
Membership Secretary—Mr. T. Watkins
Holmcroft, Lewes Road, Ringmer, Lewes,
East Sussex, BN8 5ES

Ascension Study Circle
Secretary—Dr. R. C. F. Baker
Greys, Tower Road, Whitstable, Kent
CT5 2ER

Australian States Study Circle
Royal Sydney Philatelic Club
Honorary Secretary—Mr. B. Palmer
G.P.O. Box 1751, Sydney, N.S.W. 1043,
Australia

British Society of Australian Philately
Secretary—Mr. A. J. Griffiths
c/o The British Philatelic Centre,
107 Charterhouse Street,
London EC1M 6PT

Society of Australasian Specialists/Oceania
Secretary—Mr. S. Leven
P.O. Box 24764, San Jose, CA 95154-4764,
U.S.A.

Bechuanalands and Botswana Society
Membership Secretary—Mr. J. Catterall
Trevessa, Upper Castle Road, St. Mawes,
Truro, Cornwall TR2 5BZ

Bermuda Collectors Society
Secretary—Mr. T. J. McMahon
P.O. Box 1949, Stuart, FL 34995, U.S.A.

British Caribbean Philatelic Study Group
Overseas Director—Mr. D. N. Druett
Pennymead Auctions, 1 Brewerton Street,
Knaresborough, North Yorkshire HG5 8AZ

British West Indies Study Circle
Membership Secretary—Mr. S. A. Sharp
34 Lovelace Drive, Pyrford, Woking, Surrey
GU22 8QY

Burma Philatelic Study Circle
Secretary—Mr. A. Meech
7208-91 Avenue, Edmonton, Alberta,
Canada T6B 0R8

Ceylon Study Circle
Secretary—Mr. R.W.P. Frost
42 Lonsdale Road, Cannington, Bridgwater,
Somerset TA5 2JS

Cyprus Study Circle
Secretary—Mr. A. R. Everett
29 Diomed Drive, Great Barton,
Bury St. Edmunds, Suffolk IP31 2TN

East Africa Study Circle
Secretary—Mr. J. G. Harvey
22 High Street, Mepal, CB6 2AW

Falklands Islands Study Group
Membership Secretary—Mr. D. W. A.
Jeffery
38 Bradstock Road, Stoneleigh, Epsom,
Surrey KT17 2LH

Gibraltar Study Circle
Membership Secretary—Mr. D. A. Brook
80 Farm Road, Milton, Weston-super-Mare,
North Somerset, BS22 8BD

Great Britain Overprints Society
Membership Secretary—Mr. A. H. Bishop
The Coach House, Ridgemount Road,
Sunningdale, Berkshire SL5 9RL

Hong Kong Stamp Society
Secretary—Dr. An-Min Chung
P.O. Box 206, Glenside, PA 19038, U.S.A.

Hong Kong Study Circle
Membership Secretary—Mr. P. V. Ball
37 Hart Court, Newcastle-under-Lyme,
Staffordshire ST5 2AL

Indian Ocean Study Circle (Western
Islands)
Secretary—Mr. K. B. Fitton
50 Firlands, Weybridge, Surrey KT13 0HR

India Study Circle
Secretary—Dr. W. Fincham
10 Vallis Way, London W13 0DD

Irish Philatelic Circle
General Secretary—Mr. P. J. Wood
21 Loftus Road, London W12 7EH

King George V Silver Jubilee Study Circle
Secretary—Mr. N. Levinge
11 Broadway, Northampton NN1 4SF

King George VI Collectors Society
Secretary—Mr. F. R. Lockyer, OBE
98 Albany, Manor Road, Bournemouth,
Dorset BH1 3EW

Kiribati and Tuvalu Philatelic Society
Honorary Secretary—Mr. M. J. Shaw
88 Stoneleigh Avenue, Worcester Park,
Surrey KT4 8XY

Malaya Study Group
Secretary—Mr. J. Robertson
12 Lisa Court, Downsland Road,
Basingstoke, Hampshire RG21 8TU

Malta Study Circle
Membership Secretary—Mr. D. Ward
40 Kingsman Road, Stanford-le-Hope,
Essex SS17 0JW

New Zealand Society of Great Britain
General Secretary—Mr. K. C. Collins
13 Briton Crescent, Sanderstead,
Surrey CR2 0JN.

Orange Free State Study Circle
Secretary—Mr. J. R. Stroud
28 Oxford Street, Burnham-on-Sea,
Somerset TA8 1LQ

Pacific Islands Study Circle
Honorary Secretary—Mr. J. D. Ray
24 Woodvale Avenue, London SE25 4AE

Papuan Philatelic Society
Secretary—Mr. F. J. Prophet
5 Morcom Close, Menear Road, Boscoppa,
St. Austell, Cornwall PL25 3UF

Pitcairn Islands Study Group (U.K.)
Honorary Secretary—Mr. D. Sleep
6 Palace Gardens, 100 Court Road, Eltham,
London SE9 5NS

Rhodesian Study Circle
Secretary—Mr. A. Wilson
10 Alders Road, Reigate, Surrey RH2 0ED

St. Helena, Ascension and Tristan da Cunha
Philatelic Society
Secretary—Mr. J. Havill
205 N. Murray Blvd., #221, Colorado
Springs, CO 80916, U.S.A.

Sarawak Specialists Society (also Brunei,
North Borneo and Labuan)
Secretary—Dr. J. Higgins
31 Grimston Road, South Wootton,
Kings Lynn, Norfolk PE30 3NR

South African Collectors' Society
General Secretary—Mr. R. Ross
28 Duddon Drive, Barrow-in-Furness,
Cumbria LA14 3TW

Sudan Study Group
Secretary—Mr. N. D. Collier
34 Padleys Lane, Burton Joyce,
Nottingham NG14 5BZ

Tonga and Tin Can Mail Study Circle
Secretary/Treasurer—Mr. L. L. Benson
1832 Jean Avenue, Tallahassee
FL 32308-5227, U.S.A.

Transvaal Study Circle
Secretary—Mr. J. Woolgar
132 Dale Street, Chatham, Kent ME4 6QH

West Africa Study Circle
Secretary—Mr. J. Powell
23 Brook Street, Edlesborough, Dunstable,
Bedfordshire LU6 2JG

Aron R. Halberstam Philatelists, Ltd.

Specializing in

British Commonwealth

Pre-1960 only

Call or write to request a free price list detailing our comprehensive stock
of individual items and sets, organised by country, Scott and
Gibbons catalogue numbers, and condition
(Mounted, Unmounted, and Used)
Or send us your wants list.

We accept payment by Sterling cheque, or

P.O.B. 150168, Van Brunt Station,
Brooklyn, NY 11215-0168, U.S.A.,
Tel: +001 718 788 3978 Fax: +001 718 965 3099

Thinking of selling? We are eager buyers of collections and accumulations. Contact us with details of what you have to offer.

A Professional Auctioneering Service from the Most Famous Name in Philately

● A proven programme of specialised international sales ● 0% Vendor commission (on realisations over £5000)
● Free advice and expert valuations ● Fast guaranteed payment with cash advances available
● The industry's largest database of buyers ● High quality catalogues distributed worldwide
● Regular contact with major buyers ● Air conditioned venue and extensive viewing times

Post-Bid *Regular Postal Auctions*

● Obtain thousands of quality GB, Commonwealth and Foreign stamps at bargain prices
● Both simple and great fun to take part in, all from the comfort of your own home ● Established for over 15 years
● Regular bi-monthly catalogues contain illustrations, accurate descriptions and estimates
● At least 3,500 lots every sale from £5 to £3000 ● Fast and friendly service

Valuation Roadshows

Our team of philatelic experts are always on their travels in search of quality
collections and better individual items of stamps and postal history.
If you're thinking of selling and would like some free advice and an up to
date market valuation come along and meet us.

**For your free information pack, copy of our latest 'Postbid'
catalogue and further details on our forthcoming roadshows
telephone +44 (0) 171 836 8444**

Philatelic Auctioneers since 1901

Stanley Gibbons Auctions & Acquisitions,
399 Strand, London WC2R 0LX
Tel: +44 (0)171 836 8444 Fax: +44 (0)171 836 7342
e-mail auctions@stangiblondon.demon.co.uk.

Select Bibliography

The literature on British Commonwealth stamps is vast, but works are often difficult to obtain once they are out of print. The selection of books below has been made on the basis of authority together with availability to the general reader, either as new or secondhand. Very specialised studies, and those covering aspects of postal history to which there are no references in the catalogue, have been excluded.

The following abbreviations are used to denote publishers:
CRL–Christie's Robson Lowe; HH–Harry Hayes; PB–Proud Bailey Co. Ltd. and Postal History Publications Co.; PC–Philip Cockrill; RPSL–Royal Philatelic Society, London; SG–Stanley Gibbons Ltd.

Where no publisher is quoted, the book is published by its author.

GENERAL. *Encyclopaedia of British Empire Postage Stamps. Vols 1–6.* Edited Robson Lowe. (CRL, 1951–1991)
Specimen Stamps of the Crown Colonies 1857–1948. Marcus Samuel. (RPSL, 1976 and 1984 Supplement)
U.P.U. Specimen Stamps. J. Bendon. (1988)
King George V Key Plates of the Imperium Postage and Revenue Design. P. Fernbank. (West Africa Study Circle, 1997)
The Printings of King George VI Colonial Stamps. W.J.W. Potter & Lt-Col R.C.M. Shelton. (1952)
King George VI Large Key Type Stamps of Bermuda, Leeward Islands, Nyasaland. R.W. Dickgiesser and E.P. Yendall. (Triad Publications, 1985)
Madame Joseph Forged Postmarks. D. Worboys (RPSL, 1994)
G.B. Used Abroad: Cancellations and Postal Markings. J. Parmenter. (The Postal History Society, 1993)
GREAT BRITAIN. For extensive bibliographies see *G.B. Specialised Catalogues. Vols 1–5.*
ASCENSION. *Ascension. The Stamps and Postal History.* J.H. Attwood. (CRL, 1981)
BARBADOS. *The Stamps of Barbados.* E.A. Bayley. (1989)
BATUM. *British Occupation of Batum.* P.T. Ashford. (1989)
BERMUDA. *The King George V High-value Stamps of Bermuda, 1917–1938.* M. Glazer. (Calaby Publishers, 1994)
BRITISH EAST AFRICA. *British East Africa. The Stamps and Postal Stationery.* J. Minns. (RPSL, 1982 and 1990 Supplement)
BRITISH GUIANA. *The Postage Stamps and Postal History of British Guiana.* W.A. Townsend and F.G. Howe. (RPSL, 1970)
BRITISH OCCUPATION OF GERMAN COLONIES. *G.R.I.* R.M. Gibbs. (CRL, 1989)
BRITISH POSTAL AGENCIES IN EASTERN ARABIA. *The Postal Agencies in Eastern Arabia and the Gulf.* N. Donaldson (HH, 1975) and Supplement (Bridger & Kay Guernsey Ltd, 1994)
BURMA. *Burma Postal History.* G. Davis and D. Martin. (CRL, 1971 and 1987 Supplement)
CAMEROONS. *The Postal Arrangements of the Anglo-French Cameroons Expeditionary Force 1914–16.* R. J. Maddocks (1996)
CANADA. *Stamps of British North America.* F. Jarrett. (Quarterman Publications Inc, 1975)

The Edward VII Issue of Canada. G.C. Marler. (National Postal Museum, Canada, 1975)
The Admiral Issue of Canada. G.C. Marler. (American Philatelic Society, 1982)
CAYMAN ISLANDS. *The Postal History of the Cayman Islands.* T.E. Giraldi and P.P. McCann. (Triad Publications, 1989)
COOK ISLANDS. *The Early Cook Islands Post Office.* A.R. Burge. (Hawthorn Press, 1978)
CYPRUS. *Cyprus 1353–1986.* W. Castle. (CRL, 3rd edition, 1987)
DOMINICA. *Dominica Postal History, Stamps and Postal Stationery to 1935.* E.V. Toeg (B.W.I. Study Circle, 1994)
FALKLAND ISLANDS. *The De La Rue Definitives of the Falkland Islands 1901–29.* J.P. Bunt. (1986 and 1996 Supplement)
FIJI. *Fiji Philatelics.* D.W.F. Alford (Pacific Islands Study Circle, 1994)
The Postal History of Fiji 1911–1952. J.G. Rodger. (Pacific Islands Study Circle, 1991)
GAMBIA. *The Stamps and Postal History of the Gambia.* Edited J.O. Andrew. (CRL, 1985)
The Postal History of The Gambia. E.B. Proud (PB, 1994)
GIBRALTAR. *Posted in Gibraltar.* W. Hine-Haycock. (CRL, 1978)
Gibraltar. The Postal History and Postage Stamps. Vol 1 (to 1885). G. Osborn. (Gibraltar Study Circle, 1995)
GOLD COAST. *The Postal History of Gold Coast.* E.B. Proud (PB, 1995)
HONG KONG. *The Philatelic History of Hong Kong. Vol 1.* (Hong Kong Study Circle, 1984)
Hong Kong Postage Stamps of the Queen Victoria Period. R.N. Gurevitch (1993)
British Post Offices in the Far East. E.B. Proud. (PB, 1991)
Cancellations of the Treaty Ports of Hong Kong. H. Schoenfeld. (1988)
INDIA. *C.E.F. The China Expeditionary Force 1900–1923.* D.S. Virk, J.C. Hume, D. Lang, G. Sattin. (Philatelic Congress of India, 1992)
A Handbook on Gwalior Postal History and Stamps. V.K. Gupta. (1980)
IRAQ. *The Postal History of Iraq.* P.C. Pearson and E. B. Proud. (PB, 1996)
KENYA. *The Postal History of Kenya.* E.B. Proud. (PB, 1992)
KIRIBATI. *Kiribati Handbook.* Edited H. Bennet. (Kiribati and Tuvalu Phil Soc., 1997)
LABUAN. *A Concise Guide to the Queen Issues of Labuan.* R. Price. (Sarawak Specialists Society, 1991)
MALAYSIA. *The Postal History of British Malaya. Vols 1–3.* E.B.Proud. (PB, 1982–84)
The Postage Stamps of Federated Malay States. W.A. Reeves. (Malaya Study Group, 1978)
Kedah and Perlis. D.R.M. Holley. (Malaya Study Group, 1995)
Kelantan. Its Stamps and Postal History. W.A. Reeves and B.E. Dexter. (Malaya Study Group, 1992)
The Postal History of the Occupation of Malaya and British Borneo 1941–1945. E.B. Proud and M.D. Rowell. (PB, 1992)
MALTA. *Malta. The Postal History and Postage Stamps.* Edited R.E. Martin. (CRL, 1980 and 1985 Supplement)
MAURITIUS. *The Postal History and Stamps of Mauritius.* P. Ibbotson. (RPSL, 1991) revisions and additions supplement (Indian Ocean Study Circle, 1995)
NEW SOUTH WALES. *The Postal History of New South Wales 1788–1901.* Edited J.S. White. (Philatelic Assoc of New South Wales, 1988)

NEW ZEALAND. *The Postage Stamps of New Zealand. Vols I–VII.* (Royal Philatelic Society of New Zealand, 1939–88)
NIGERIA. *The Postal Services of the British Nigeria Region.* J. Ince and J. Sacher. (RPSL, 1992)
The Postal History of Nigeria. E.B. Proud. (P.B, 1995)
NORTH BORNEO. *The Stamps and Postal History of North Borneo. Parts 1–3.* L.H. Shipman and P.K. Cassells. (Sarawak Specialists Society, 1976–88)
ORANGE FREE STATE. *Stamps of the Orange Free State. Parts 1–3.* G.D. Buckley & W.B. Marriott. (O.F.S. Study Circle, 1967–80)
PAPUA. *The Postal History of British New Guinea and Papua 1885–1942.* R. Lee. (CRL, 1983)
RHODESIA. *Mashonaland. A Postal History 1890–96.* A. Drysdall and D. Collis (CRL, 1990)
ST. HELENA. *St. Helena, Postal History and Stamps.* E. Hibbert. (CRL, 1979)
ST. KITTS-NEVIS. *A Study of the King George VI Stamps of St. Kitts-Nevis.* P. L. Baldwin. (Murray Payne Ltd, 2nd edition 1997)
SAMOA. *A Postal History of the Samoan Islands (Parts 1 and II).* Edited R. Burge. (Royal Philatelic Society of New Zealand, 1987–89)
SARAWAK. *The Stamps and Postal History of Sarawak.* W.A. Forrester-Wood. (Sarawak Specialists Society, 1959 & 1970 Supplement)
Sarawak: The Issues of 1871 and 1875. W. Batty-Smith & W. Watterson.
SIERRA LEONE. *The Postal Service of Sierra Leone.* P.O. Beale. (RPSL, 1988)
The Postal History of Sierra Leone. E.B. Proud. (P.B, 1994)
SOUTH AUSTRALIA. *The Departmental Stamps of South Australia.* A.R. Butler. (RPSL, 1978)
SOUTH WEST AFRICA. *The Overprinted Stamps of South West Africa to 1930.* N. Becker. (Philatelic Holdings (Pty) Ltd, 1990)
SUDAN. *Sudan. The Stamps and Postal Stationery of 1867 to 1970.* E.C.W. Stagg. (HH, 1977)
TANGANYIKA. *The Postal History of Tanganyika. 1915–1961.* E.B. Proud. (PB, 1989)
TASMANIA. *Stamps and Postal History of Tasmania.* W.E. Tinsley. (RPSL, 1986)
The Pictorial Stamps of Tasmania 1899–1912. K.E. Lancaster. (Royal Philatelic Society of Victoria, 1986)
TOGO. *Togo—The Postal History of the Anglo-French Occupation 1914–22.* J. Martin and F. Walton. (West Africa S.C., 1995)
TRANSVAAL. *Transvaal Philately.* Edited I.B. Mathews. (Reijger Publishers (Pty) Ltd, 1986)
Transvaal. The Provisional Issues of the First British Occupation. Dr. A.R. Drysdall (Janes Bendon, 1994)
TRINIDAD AND TOBAGO. *The Postal History of Trinidad & Tobago.* J. C. Aleong and E. B. Proud. (PB, 1997)
TURKS AND CAICOS ISLANDS. *Turks Islands and Caicos Islands to 1950.* J.J. Challis. (Roses Caribbean Philatelic Society, 1983)
UGANDA. *The Postal History of Uganda and Zanzibar.* E.B. Proud (PB, 1993)
VICTORIA. *The Stamps of Victoria.* G. Kellow. (B. & K. Philatelic Publishing, 1990)
WESTERN AUSTRALIA. *Western Australia. The Stamps and Postal History.* Ed. M. Hamilton and B. Pope. (W. Australia Study Group, 1979)
Postage Stamps and Postal History of Western Australia. Vols 1–3. M. Juhl. (1981–83)

MARK BLOXHAM

88 Dacre Street, South Shields,
Tyne and Wear. NE33 5QB.
Phone/fax: (01670) 511180 Mobile: 0797 0123456
E-mail address:-m.bloxham@virgin.net.
Web site http://freespace.virgin.net/m.bloxham/

- WE STOCK FINE QUALITY QUEEN VICTORIA THROUGH TO MODERN DAY GB

- HUNDREDS OF HIGH QUALITY PENNY BLACKS ARE ALWAYS AVAILABLE

- LINE-ENGRAVED

- SURFACE PRINTED (ABNORMALS)

- PROOFS

- ESSAYS

- WE ALSO SPECIALISE IN BRITISH COMMONWEALTH AND WORLDWIDE

BUYING - TOP CASH PRICES PAID

•WE ARE ALWAYS INTERESTED IN BUYING EITHER SINGLE ITEMS OR COLLECTIONS.
•WE ALWAYS SETTLE WITH IMMEDIATE CASH PAYMENTS

Great Britain

Great Britain Postage Stamps, GB 1
Regional Issues—
  I. Northern Ireland, GB 74
  II. Scotland, GB 74
  III. Wales, GB 75
Postage Due Stamps, GB 75
Official Stamps, GB 76
Postal Fiscal Stamps, GB 77
Channel Islands General Issue, GB 78
Guernsey, GB 78
  Alderney, GB 89
Isle of Man, GB 91
Jersey, GB 103
British Post Offices Abroad, GB 115

STAMPS ON COVER. Prices are quoted, as a third price column, for those Victorian and Edwardian issues usually found used on cover. In general these prices refer to the cheapest version of each basic stamp with other shades, plates or varieties, together with unusual frankings and postmarks, being worth more.

UNITED KINGDOM OF GREAT BRITAIN AND IRELAND

QUEEN VICTORIA
20 June 1837—22 January 1901

MULREADY ENVELOPES AND LETTER SHEETS, so called from the name of the designer, William Mulready, were issued concurrently with the first British adhesive stamps.

1d. black

Envelopes: £140 *unused*; £210 *used*.
Letter Sheets: £125 *unused*; £190 *used*.

2d. blue

Envelopes: £200 *unused*; £600 *used*.
Letter Sheets: £175 *unused*; £575 *used*.

LINE-ENGRAVED ISSUES

GENERAL NOTES

Brief notes on some aspects of the line-engraved stamps follow, but for further information and a full specialist treatment of these issues collectors are recommended to consult Volume 1 of the Stanley Gibbons *Great Britain Specialised Catalogue*.

Alphabet I   Alphabet II

Alphabet III   Alphabet IV

Typical Corner Letters of the four Alphabets

Alphabets. Four different styles were used for the corner letters on stamps prior to the issue with letters in all four corners, these being known to collectors as:
Alphabet I. Used for all plates made from 1840 to the end of 1851. Letters small.
Alphabet II. Plates from 1852 to mid-1855. Letters larger, heavier and broader.
Alphabet III. Plates from mid-1855 to end of period. Letters tall and more slender.
Alphabet IV. 1861. 1d. Die II, Plates 50 and 51 only. Letters were hand-engraved instead of being punched on the plate. They are therefore inconsistent in shape and size but generally larger and outstanding.
While the general descriptions and the illustrations of typical letters given above may be of some assistance, only long experience and published aids can enable every stamp to be allocated to its particular Alphabet without hesitation, as certain letters in each are similar to those in one of the others.

Blue Paper. The blueing of the paper of the earlier issues is believed to be due to the presence of prussiate of potash in the printing ink, or in the paper, which, under certain conditions, tended to colour the paper when the sheets were damped for printing. An alternative term is bleuté paper.

Corner Letters. The corner letters on the early British stamps were intended as a safeguard against forgery, each stamp in the sheet having a different combination of letters. Taking the first 1d. stamp,

---

printed in 20 horizontal rows of 12, as an example, the lettering is as follows:

Row 1. A A, A B, A C, etc. to A L.

Row 2. B A, B B, B C, etc. to B L.

and so on to

Row 20. T A, T B, T C, etc. to T L.

On the stamps with four corner letters, those in the upper corners are in the reverse positions to those in the lower corners. Thus in a sheet of 240 (12 × 20) the sequence is:

Row 1.   AA BA CA etc. to LA
         AA AB AC   AL

Row 2.   AB BB CB etc. to LB
         BA BB BC   BL

and so on to

Row 20. AT BT CT etc. to LT
         TA TB TC   TL

Placing letters in all four corners was not only an added precaution against forgery but was meant to deter unmarked parts of used stamps being pieced together and passed off as an unused whole.

Dies. The first die of the 1d. was used for making the original die of the 2d., both the No Lines and White Lines issues. In 1855 the 1d. Die I was amended by retouching the head and deepening the lines on a transferred impression of the original. This later version, known to collectors as Die II, was used for making the dies for the 1d. and 2d. with letters in all four corners and also for the 1½d.

The two dies are illustrated above No. 17 in the catalogue.

Double letter   Guide line in corner

Guide line through value

Double Corner Letters. These are due to the workman placing his letter-punch in the wrong position at the first attempt, when lettering the plate, and then correcting the mistake; or to a slight shifting of the punch when struck. If a wrong letter was struck in the first instance, traces of a wrong letter may appear in a corner in addition to the correct one. A typical example is illustrated.

Guide Lines and Dots. When laying down the impressions of the design on the early plates, fine vertical and horizontal guide lines were marked on the plates to assist the operative. These were usually removed from the gutter margins, but could not be removed from the stamp impressions without damage to the plate, so that in such cases they appear on the printed stamps, sometimes in the corners, sometimes through "POSTAGE" or the value. Typical examples are illustrated.
Guide dots or cuts were similarly made to indicate the spacing of the guide lines. These too sometimes appear on the stamps.

Ivory Head

"Ivory Head." The so-called "ivory head" variety is one in which the Queen's Head shows white on the back of the stamp. It arises from the comparative absence of ink in the head portion of the design, with consequent absence of blueing. (*See* "Blued Paper" note above.)

Line-engraving. In this context "line-engraved" is synonymous with recess-printing, in which the engraver cuts recesses in a plate and printing (the coloured areas) is from these recesses. "Line-engraved" is the traditional philatelic description for these stamps; other equivalent terms found are "engraving in *taille-douce*" (French) or "in *intaglio*" (Italian).

Plates. Until the introduction of the stamps with letters in all four corners, the number of the plate was not indicated in the design of the stamp, but was printed on the sheet margin. By long study of identifiable blocks and the minor variations in the design, coupled with the position of the corner letters, philatelists are now able to allot many of these stamps to their respective plates. Specialist collectors often endeavour to obtain examples of a given stamp printed from its different plates and our catalogue accordingly reflects this depth of detail.

Maltese Cross   Type of Town postmark

Type of Penny Post cancellation

Example of 1844 type postmark

Postmarks. The so-called "Maltese Cross" design was the first employed for obliterating British postage stamps and was in use from 1840 to 1844. Being hand-cut, the obliterating stamps varied greatly in detail and some distinctive types can be allotted to particular towns or offices. Local types, such as those used at Manchester, Norwich, Leeds, etc., are keenly sought. A red ink was first employed, but was superseded by black, after some earlier experiments, in February 1841. Maltese Cross obliterations in other colours are rare.
Obliterations of this type, numbered 1 to 12 in the centre, were used at the London Chief Office in 1843 and 1844.
Some straight-line cancellations were in use in 1840 at the Penny Post receiving offices, normally applied on the envelope, the adhesives then being obliterated at the Head Office. They are nevertheless known, with or without Maltese Cross, on the early postage stamps.
In 1842 some offices in S.W. England used dated postmarks in place of the Maltese Cross, usually on the back of the letter since they were not originally intended as obliterators. These town postmarks have likewise been found on adhesives.
In 1844 the Maltese Cross design was superseded by numbered obliterators of varied type, one of which is illustrated. They are naturally comparatively scarce on the first 1d. and 2d. stamps. Like the Maltese Cross they are found in various colours, some of which are rare.

Re-entry

"Union Jack" re-entry

Re-entries. Re-entries on the plate show as a doubling of part of the design of the stamp generally at top or bottom. Many re-entries are very slight while others are most marked. A typical one is illustrated.
The "*Union Jack*" *re-entry,* so called owing to the effect of the re-entry on the appearance of the corner stars (*see* illustration) occurs on stamp L K of Plate 75 of the 1d. red, Die I.

THE ESSENTIAL GUIDE
TO THE LINE ENGRAVED 1840 TO 1864
1d & 2d STARS

We are pleased to announce that after more than 30 years of plating these issues and 11 years of concentrated research our consultant, DR. K. STATHAM, is preparing for publication the most comprehensive work ever written on this subject.

For each plate used, Dr Statham analyses it's HISTORY, ALIGNMENT, CHARACTERISTICS, CHECK LETTERS, DESCRIPTION, DATES, QUANTITIES, IMPRIMATURS and gives detailed listings of it's VARIETIES and an aid to PLANTING.

The impetus for this book came from the frustration in his early plating days and with the information then published. The availability and access to the new information, material and original documents has enabled previous date to be checked and amended where necessary. Many **THOUSANDS** of **NEW VARIEITIES** have been listed for the first time, following Dr. Stathams meticulous research and process of double checking. It is intended that virtually **EVERY VARIETY** is **ILLUSTRATED** - all drawn by Dr. Statham.

Dr. Statham hopes that his publication will enable other collectors, both specialist and beginners alike to derive the same pleasure that he has had over the years in collecting these issues.

As the scope of the book is so large, it is anticipated that it will be published in several parts. NOW AVIAILABLE

Volume 1 - Introduction

Volume 2 - THE ONE PENNY VALUE - DIE 1 PLATES.. 1-11

Volume 3 - THE ONE PENNY VALUE - DIE 1 PLATES.. 12-56

Volume 4 - Plating Summary covering all the red Plates from... 1-56

Volume 5 - THE ONE PENNY VALUE - DIE 1 PLATES.. 57-87

Volume 6 - Plating Summary covering Plates.. 57-87

Sets of Volumes 1&2, Volumes 3&4 and Volumes 5&6 each in an attractive Presentation Box available at £100 each plus postage and packing

WE SPECIALISE in the LINE ENGRAVED 1840 to 1864
1d & 2d SG1 TO SG42

We have good stocks of
IMPERFS, PERFS + PLATES both **UNPLATED** and **PLATED**
including
the **RARE PLATES 175, 176** and **177 IMPERF** with R.P.S. certificates
as well as
The **GARDINER HILL** collection of the First Perforated Issue
and
INVERTED WMKS from the whole range

LISTS

Reflecting our COMPREHENSIVE stocks of GB, Q.V. the KVI
They **include** our specialist areas mentioned above as well as:-

1) SG 43/44 **1d RED PLATES** with C.D.S. postmarks
2) Queen Victoria Surface Printed to KG VI C.D.S. & Mint.
3) **GB USED ABROAD**
4) **INDIVIDUALLY PLATED 1d RED IMPERFS & STARS**
5) **A RARE, UNUSUAL** and **DIFFICULT** to **FIND** section.

ALL STAMPS ARE ILLUSTRATED

Eric Paul Ltd.

Fax. No.	PO BOX 44, MARPLE	Tel. No.
0161 427 6386	CHESHIRE SK6 7EE	0161 427 2101

Members: **P.T.S.,**   **M.&D.P.T.A.,**   **G.B.P.S.**

T A (T L)   M A (M L)
Varieties of Large Crown Watermark

I   Two states of Large Crown Watermark   II

Watermarks. Two watermark varieties, as illustrated, consisting of crowns of entirely different shape, are found in sheets of the Large Crown paper and fall on stamps lettered M A and T A (or M L and T L when the paper is printed on the wrong side). Both varieties are found on the 1d. rose-red of 1857, while the M A (M L) variety comes also on some plates of the 1d. of 1864 (Nos. 43, 44) up to about Plate 96. On the 2d. the T A (T L) variety is known on plates 8 and 9, and the M A (M L) on later prints of plate 9. These varieties may exist inverted, or inverted reversed on stamps lettered A A and A L and H A and H L, and some are known.

In 1861 a minor alteration was made in the Large Crown watermark by the removal of the two vertical strokes, representing *fleurs-de-lis*, which projected upwards from the uppermost of the three horizontal curves at the base of the Crown. Hence two states are distinguishable, as illustrated.

CONDITION—IMPERFORATE LINE-ENGRAVED ISSUES

The prices quoted for the 1840 and 1841 imperforate Line-engraved issues are for "fine" examples. As condition is most important in assessing the value of a stamp, the following definitions will assist collectors in the evaluation of individual examples.

Four main factors are relevant when considering quality.

(a) **Impression.** This should be clean and the surface free of any rubbing or unnatural blurring which would detract from the appearance.

(b) **Margins.** This is perhaps the most difficult factor to evaluate. Stamps described as "fine", the standard adopted in this catalogue for pricing purposes, should have margins of the recognised width, defined as approximately one half of the distance between two adjoining unsevered stamps. Stamps described as "very fine" or "superb" should have margins which are proportionately larger than those of a "fine" stamp. Examples with close margins should not, generally, be classified as "fine".

(c) **Cancellation.** On a "fine" stamp this should be reasonably clear and not noticeably smudged. A stamp described as "superb" should have a neat cancellation, preferably centrally placed or to the right.

(d) **Appearance.** Stamps, at the prices quoted, should always be without any tears, creases, bends or thins and should not be toned on either the front or back. Stamps with such defects are worth only a proportion of the catalogue price.

Good   Fine

Very Fine   Superb

The above actual size illustrations of 1840 1d. blacks show the various grades of quality. When comparing these illustrations it should be assumed that they are all from the same plate and that they are free of any hidden defects.

STANLEY GIBBONS
STAMP COLLECTION SERIES

Introductory booklets on *How to Start, How to Identify Stamps* and *Collecting by Theme*. A series of well illustrated guides at a low price.
Write for details.

PRINTERS. Nos. 1/53a were recess-printed by Perkins, Bacon & Petch, known from 1852 as Perkins, Bacon & Co.

1   1a   2 Small Crown

(Eng Charles and Frederick Heath)

1840 (6–8 May).   *Letters in lower corners. Wmk Small Crown. W 2. Imperf.*

No.	Type		Un	Used	Used on cover
1	1	1d. intense black	£3500	£225	
2		1d. black	£3000	£160	£275
3		1d. grey-black (worn plate)	£3000	£225	
4	1a	2d. deep full blue (8.5.40)	£7000	£400	
5		2d. blue	£5500	£325	£750
6		2d. pale blue	£7000	£375	

The 1d. stamp in black was printed from Plates 1 to 11. Plate 1 exists in two states (known to collectors as 1a and 1b), the latter being the result of extensive repairs.

Repairs were also made to Plates 2, 5, 6, 8, 9, 10 and 11, and certain impressions exist in two or more states.

The so-called "Royal reprint" of the 1d. black was made in 1864, from Plate 66, Die II, on paper with Large Crown watermark, inverted. A printing was also made in carmine, on paper with the same watermark, normal.

For 1d. black with "VR" in upper corners *see* No. V1 under Official Stamps.

The 2d. stamps were printed from Plates 1 and 2.

Plates of 1d. black

Plate					Un	Used
1a	..	..	..	..	£4500	£180
1b	..	..	..	..	£3000	£160
2	..	..	..	..	£3000	£160
3	..	..	..	..	£3500	£190
4	..	..	..	..	£3000	£175
5	..	..	..	..	£3000	£175
6	..	..	..	..	£3000	£175
7	..	..	..	..	£3250	£200
8	..	..	..	..	£3500	£225
9	..	..	..	..	£4000	£275
10	..	..	..	..	£4500	£350
11	..	..	..	..	£4500	£1600

Varieties of 1d. black

				Un	Used
a.	On *bleuté* paper (Plates 1 to 8)	..	*from*	—	£250
b.	Double letter in corner	..	..	£3000	£200
bb.	Re-entry	..	..	£3250	£225
bc.	"PB" re-entry (Plate 5, 3rd state)	..		—	£4000
cc.	Large letters in each corner (E J, I L, J C and P A) (Plate 1b)	..	*from*	£3500	£350
c.	Guide line in corner	..	..	£3000	£200
d.	,, through value	..	..	£3000	£200
e.	Watermark inverted	..	..	£3750	£500
g.	Obliterated by Maltese Cross				
		In red		—	£175
		In black		—	£160
		In blue		—	£2000
		In magenta		—	£700
		In yellow		—	—
h.	Obliterated by Maltese Cross with number in centre		*from*		
		No. 1		—	£2750
		No. 2		—	£1750
		No. 3		—	£1750
		No. 4		—	£1750
		No. 5		—	£1750
		No. 6		—	£1750
		No. 7		—	£1750
		No. 8		—	£1750
		No. 9		—	£1750
		No. 10		—	£1750
		No. 11		—	—
		No. 12		—	£1750
i.	Obliterated "Penny Post" in black	*from*		—	£1300
j.	Obliterated by town postmark (without Maltese Cross)				
		In black	*from*	—	£1300
		In yellow	*from*	—	£6000
		In red	*from*	—	£1400
k.	Obliterated by 1844 type postmark in black		*from*	—	£500

Plates of 2d. blue

Plate				Un	Used
1	..	..	Shades from	£5500	£325
2	..	..	Shades from	£6500	£375

Varieties of 2d. blue

				Un	Used
a.	Double letter in corner	..	..	—	£450
aa.	Re-entry	..	..	—	£500
b.	Guide line in corner	..	..	—	£400
c.	,, ,, through value	..	..	—	£400
d.	Watermark inverted	..	..	£7000	£675
e.	Obliterated by Maltese Cross				
		In red		—	£350
		In black		—	£325
		In blue		—	£3000
		In magenta		—	£2500

---

f.	Obliterated by Maltese Cross with number in centre			*from*		
			No. 1		—	£2750
			No. 2		—	£2750
			No. 3		—	£2750
			No. 4		—	£2750
			No. 5		—	£2750
			No. 6		—	£3000
			No. 7		—	£2750
			No. 8		—	£2750
			No. 9		—	£3250
			No. 10		—	£3000
			No. 11		—	£3000
			No. 12		—	£2750
g.	Obliterated "Penny Post" in black	..	*from*		—	£1800
h.	Obliterated by town postmark (without Maltese Cross) in black	..	*from*		—	£1500
i.	Obliterated by 1844 type postmark					
			In black	*from*	—	£900
			In blue	*from*	—	£2500

1841 (10 Feb).   *Printed from "black" plates. Wmk W 2. Paper more or less blued. Imperf.*

No.	Type			Un	Used	Used on cover
7	1	1d. red-brown (*shades*)	..	£500	50·00	90·00
		a. "PB" re-entry (Plate 5, 3rd state)	..	—	£1200	

The first printings of the 1d. in red-brown were made from Plates 1b, 2, 5 and 8 to 11 used for the 1d. black.

1d. red-brown from "black" plates

Plate					Un	Used
1b	..	..	..	..	£3000	£150
2	..	..	..	..	£1750	£100
5	..	..	..	..	£700	60·00
8	..	..	..	..	£550	50·00
9	..	..	..	..	£500	50·00
10	..	..	..	..	£525	50·00
11	..	..	..	..	£550	50·00

1841 (late Feb).   *Plate 12 onwards. Wmk W 2. Paper more or less blued. Imperf.*

				Un	Used	Used on cover
8	1	1d. red-brown	..	£140	6·00	12·00
8a		1d. red-brown on very blue paper		£160	6·00	
9		1d. pale red-brown (worn plates)		£225	15·00	
10		1d. deep red-brown	..	£160	8·00	
11		1d. lake-red	..	£650	£250	
12		1d. orange-brown	..	£300	50·00	

Error. No letter "A" in right lower corner (*Stamp* B(A), *Plate 77*)

12a	1	1d. red-brown	..	..	—	£5000

The error "No letter A in right corner" was due to the omission to insert this letter on stamp B A of Plate 77. The error was discovered some months after the plate was registered and was then corrected.

There are innumerable variations in the colour and shade of the 1d. "red" and those given in the above list represent colour groups each covering a wide range.

Varieties of 1d. red-brown, etc.

				Un	Used
b.	Re-entry	..	*from*	—	25·00
c.	Double letter in corner	..	*from*	—	16·00
d.	Double Star (Plate 75) "Union Jack" re-entry	£6000		—	£600
e.	Guide line in corner	..	..	—	9·00
f.	,, ,, through value	..	..	—	15·00
g.	Thick outer frame to stamp	..	..	—	15·00
h.	Ivory head	..	..	..	£180	9·00
i.	Watermark inverted	..	..	£350	35·00
j.	Left corner letter "S" inverted (Plates 78, 105, 107)	..	*from*	—	50·00
k.	P converted to R (Plates 30, 33, 83, 86)	*from*		—	40·00
l.	Obliterated by Maltese Cross				
		In red		—	£1100
		In black		—	15·00
		In blue		—	£160
m.	Obliterated by Maltese Cross with number in centre				
		No. 1		—	38·00
		No. 2		—	38·00
		No. 3		—	55·00
		No. 4		—	£130
		No. 5		—	38·00
		No. 6		—	32·00
		No. 7		—	30·00
		No. 8		—	28·00
		No. 9		—	35·00
		No. 10		—	55·00
		No. 11		—	65·00
		No. 12		—	80·00
n.	Obliterated "Penny Post" in black	..	..	—	£225
o.	Obliterated by town postmark (without Maltese Cross)				
		In black	*from*	—	£150
		In blue	*from*	—	£275
		In green	*from*	—	£450
		In yellow	*from*	—	—
		In red	*from*	—	£2000
p.	Obliterated by 1844 type postmark				
		In blue	*from*	—	40·00
		In red	*from*	—	£950
		In green	*from*	—	£250
		In violet	*from*	—	£550
		In black	*from*	—	6·00

Stamps with thick outer frame to the design are from plates on which the frame-lines have been strengthened or recut, particularly Plates 76 and 90.

For "Union Jack" re-entry *see* General Notes to Line-engraved Issues.

In "P converted to R" the corner letter "R" is formed from the "P", the distinctive long tail having been hand-cut.

TL TL TL TL TL TL TL TL TL TL TL TL TL TL TL TL TL TL TL TL TL TL TL TL TL TL TL TL TL TL TL TL TL

 # FREE AUCTION CATALOGUES

For our next Public Auction are available on request. We hold our sales in Coventry every two months on a Saturday. Each sale comprises 1,000+ lots, with realistic estimates ranging from £10 to £1,000 or more, usually including 350-500 lots of G.B. If you have a collection for sale, we will be pleased to sell for you through one of our auctions or to make you an immediate offer, and suggest you telephone for our advice.

WRITE OR PHONE TODAY FOR YOUR FREE COPY OF OUR NEXT CATALOGUE

 TO: Tony Lester (Coventry Auctions)
29 Momus Boulevard, Binley Road,
Coventry, CV2 5NA

 on (01203) 454908
Fax: (01203) 650109

TL TL TL TL TL TL TL TL TL TL TL TL TL TL TL TL TL TL TL TL TL TL TL TL TL TL TL TL TL TL TL TL TL

Stanley Gibbons Limited
Great Britain Specialist Department
Catering For All Collectors

● The world's largest stocks of GB material from 1840 to date ● Over 3,000 specialised and rare items always available
● Detailed register of clients' interests ● Specialist 'wants list' service ● Regular mail order lists and luxury colour brochures
● Private viewing facilities and postal service for established clients ● Free advice from our knowledgeable team
● We cater for all niche markets with a wide range of material priced to condition

 STANLEY GIBBONS *Great Britain*

Stanley Gibbons GB Department
399 Strand, London WC2R 0LX
Tel: 0171 836 8444 Fax: 0171 836 7342
e.mail: shop@stangiblondon.demon.co.uk
(Nearest tube Charing Cross)

KEY TO LINE-ENGRAVED ISSUES

S.G. Nos.	Description	Date	Wmk	Perf	Die	Alphabet
	THE IMPERFORATE ISSUES					
1/3	1d. black	6.5.40	SC	Imp	I	I
4/6	2d. no lines	8.5.40	SC	Imp	I	I
	PAPER MORE OR LESS BLUED					
7	1d. red-brown	Feb 1841	SC	Imp	I	I
8/12	1d. red-brown	Feb 1841	SC	Imp	I	I
8/12	1d. red-brown	6.2.52	SC	Imp	I	II
13/15	2d. white lines	13.3.41	SC	Imp	I	I
	THE PERFORATED ISSUES					
	ONE PENNY VALUE					
16a	1d. red-brown	1848	SC	Roul	I	I
16b	1d. red-brown	1850	SC	16	I	I
16c	1d. red-brown	1853	SC	16	I	II
16d	1d. red-brown	1854	SC	14	I	I
17/18	1d. red-brown	Feb 1854	SC	16	I	II
22	1d. red-brown	Jan 1855	SC	14	I	II
24/5	1d. red-brown	28.2.55	SC	14	II	II
21	1d. red-brown	1.3.55	SC	16	II	II
26	1d. red-brown	15.5.55	LC	16	II	II
29/33	1d. red-brown	Aug 1855	LC	14	II	III
	NEW COLOURS ON WHITE PAPER					
37/41	1d. rose-red	Nov 1856	LC	14	II	III
36	1d. rose-red	26.12.57	LC	16	II	III
42	1d. rose-red	1861	LC	14	II	IV
	TWO PENCE VALUE					
19, 20	2d. blue	1.3.54	SC	16	I	I
23	2d. blue	22.2.55	SC	14	I	I
23a	2d. blue	5.7.55	SC	14	I	II
20a	2d. blue	18.8.55	SC	16	I	II
27	2d. blue	20.7.55	LC	14	I	II
34	2d. blue	20.7.55	LC	14	I	II
35	2d. blue	2.7.57	LC	14	I	III
36a	2d. blue	1.2.58	LC	16	I	III
	LETTERS IN ALL FOUR CORNERS					
48/9	½d. rose-red	1.10.70	W 9	14		—
43/4	1d. rose-red	1.4.64	LC	14		II
53a	1½d. rosy mauve	1860	LC	14		II
51/3	1½d. rose-red	1.10.70	LC	14		II
45	2d. blue	July 1858	LC	14		II
46/7	2d. thinner lines	7.7.69	LC	14		II

Watermarks: SC = Small Crown, T **2**.
 LC = Large Crown, T **4**.
Dies: See notes above No. 17 in the catalogue.
Alphabets: See General Notes to this section.

3 White lines added

1841 (13 Mar)–**51.** *White lines added. Wmk W* **2**. *Paper more or less blued. Imperf.*

			Un	*Used*	*Used on cover*
13	**3**	2d. pale blue	£1500	60·00	
14		2d. blue	£1200	50·00	£200
15		2d. deep full blue	£1600	65·00	
15aa		2d. violet-blue (1851)	£7500	£600	

The 2d. stamp with white lines was printed from Plates 3 and 4. No. 15aa came from Plate 4 and the price quoted is for examples on thicker, lavender tinted paper.

Plates of 2d. blue

Plate				*Un*	*Used*
3			*Shades from*	£1200	55·00
4			*Shades from*	£1400	50·00

Varieties of 2d. blue

		Un	*Used*
a.	Guide line in corner	—	50·00
b.	,, ,, through value	£1600	50·00
bb.	Double letter in corner	—	55·00
be.	Re-entry	£1900	70·00
c.	Ivory head	£1700	50·00
d.	Watermark inverted	£2250	£200
e.	Obliterated by Maltese Cross		
	In red	—	£5000
	In black	—	70·00
	In blue	—	£1200
f.	Obliterated by Maltese Cross with number in centre		
	No. 1	—	£200
	No. 2	—	£200
	No. 3	—	£200
	No. 4	—	£190
	No. 5	—	£275
	No. 6	—	£200
	No. 7	—	£375
	No. 8	—	£275
	No. 9	—	£375
	No. 10	—	£425
	No. 11	—	£275
	No. 12	—	£150
g.	Obliterated by town postmark (without Maltese Cross)		
	In black *from*	—	£450
	In blue *from*	—	£800

---

h.	Obliterated by 1844 type postmark			
	In black	*from*	—	50·00
	In blue	*from*	—	£375
	In red	*from*	—	£4500
	In green	*from*	—	£700

1841 (April). *Trial printing (unissued) on Dickinson silk-thread paper. No wmk. Imperf.*

16	**1**	1d. red-brown (Plate 11)	£2000	

Eight sheets were printed on this paper, six being gummed, two ungummed, but we have only seen examples without gum.

1848. *Wmk Small Crown, W* **2**. *Rouletted approx* 11½ *by Henry Archer.*

16a	**1**	1d. red-brown (Plates 70, 71)	£4000	

1850. *Wmk Small Crown, W* **2**. *P* 16 *by Henry Archer.*

16b	**1**	1d. red-brown (Alph 1) (from Plates 90–101)	£600	£200

Stamp on cover, dated prior to February 1854 (*price* £375); dated during or after February 1854 (*price* £275).

1853. *Government Trial Perforations. Wmk Small Crown, W* **2**.

16c	**1**	1d. red-brown (p 16) (Alph II) (on cover)	†	£5000
16d		1d. red-brown (p 14) (Alph I)		£4000

SEPARATION TRIALS. Although the various trials of machines for rouletting and perforating were unofficial, Archer had the consent of the authorities in making his experiments, and sheets so experimented upon were afterwards used by the Post Office.

As Archer ended his experiments in 1850 and plates with corner letters Alphabet II did not come into issue until 1852, perforated stamps with corner letters of Alphabet I may safely be assumed to be Archer productions, if genuine.

The Government trial perforations were done on Napier machines in 1853. As Alphabet II was by that time in use, the trials can only be distinguished from the perforated stamps listed below by being dated prior to 28 January 1854, the date when the perforated stamps were officially issued.

Die I   Die II   **4** Large Crown

Die I: The features of the portrait are lightly shaded and consequently lack emphasis.

Die II (Die I retouched): The lines of the features have been deepened and appear stronger.

The eye is deeply shaded and made more lifelike. The nostril and lips are more clearly defined, the latter appearing much thicker. A strong downward stroke of colour marks the corner of the mouth. There is a deep indentation of colour between lower lip and chin. The band running from the back of the ear to the chignon has a bolder horizontal line below it than in Die I.

The original die (Die I) was used to provide roller dies for the laying down of all the line-engraved stamps from 1840 to 1855. In that year a new master die was laid down (by means of a Die I roller die) and the impression was retouched by hand engraving by William Humphrys. This retouched die, always known to philatelists as Die II, was from that time used for preparing all new roller dies.

One Penny. The numbering of the 1d. plates recommenced at 1 on the introduction of Die II. Plates 1 to 21 were Alphabet II from which a scarce plum shade exists. Corner letters of Alphabet III appear on Plate 22 and onwards.

As an experiment, the corner letters were engraved by hand on Plates 50 and 51 in 1856, instead of being punched (Alphabet IV), but punching was again resorted to from Plate 52 onwards. Plates 50 and 51 were not put into use until 1861.

Two Pence. Unlike the 1d. the old sequence of plate numbers continued. Plates 3 and 4 of the 2d. had corner letters of Alphabet I, Plate 5 Alphabet II and Plate 6 Alphabet III. In Plate 6 the white lines are thinner than before.

1854–57. *Paper more or less blued.* (a) *Wmk Small Crown, W* **2**. *P* 16.

			Un	*Used*	★ *Used on cover*
17	**1**	1d. red-brown (Die I) (2.54)	£150	7·00	15·00
		a. Imperf three sides (horiz pair)	†		
18	**1**	1d. yellow-brown (Die I)	£240	18·00	
19	**3**	2d. deep blue (Plate 4) (1.3.54)	£1600	50·00	75·00
		a. Imperf three sides (horiz pair)	†		
20		2d. pale blue (Plate 4)	£1600	60·00	
20a		2d. blue (Plate 5) (18.8.55)	£2100	£160	£275
21	**1**	1d. red-brown (Die II) (22.2.55)	£225	25·00	40·00
		a. Imperf			
		(b) *Wmk Small Crown, W* **2**. *P* 14			
22	**1**	1d. red-brown (Die I) (1.55)	£350	30·00	50·00
23	**3**	2d. blue (Plate 4) (22.2.55)	£2100	£140	£200
23a		2d. blue (Plate 5) (5.7.55)	£2100	£140	£175
		b. Imperf (Plate 5)			
24	**1**	1d. red-brown (Die II) (27.2.55)	£290	25·00	35·00
24a		1d. deep red-brown (very blue paper) (Die II)	£340	28·00	
25		1d. orange-brown (Die II)	£750	55·00	
		(c) *Wmk Large Crown, W* **4**. *P* 16			
26	**1**	1d. red-brown (Die II) (15.5.55)	£600	45·00	70·00
		a. Imperf (Plate 7)			
27	**3**	2d. blue (Plate 5) (20.7.55)	£2600	£160	£275
		a. Imperf		— £2800	
		(d) *Wmk Large Crown, W* **4**. *P* 14			
29	**1**	1d. red-brown (Die II) (6.55)	£140	5·00	15·00
		a. Imperf (shades) (Plates 22, 24, 25, 32, 43)	£1100	£900	
30		1d. brick-red (Die II)	£225	20·00	

31	**1**	1d. plum (Die II) (2.56)	£1000	£325	
32		1d. brown-rose (Die II)	£225	22·00	
33		1d. orange-brown (Die II) (3.57)	£340	28·00	
34	**3**	2d. blue (Plate 5) (20.7.55)	£1300	40·00	£100
35		2d. blue (Plate 6) (2.7.57)	£1400	40·00	90·00
		a. Imperf	—	£3250	
		b. Imperf horiz (vert pair)	†	—	

★17/35a **For well-centred, lightly used** .. +125%

1856–58. *Paper no longer blued.* (a) *Wmk Large Crown, W* **4**. *P* 16.

36	**1**	1d. rose-red (Die II) (26.12.57)	£750	35·00	60·00
36a	**3**	2d. blue (Plate 6) (1.2.58)	£3750	£160	£250
		(b) (Die II) *Wmk Large Crown, W* **4**. *P* 14			
37	**1**	1d. red-brown (11.56)	£325	70·00	
38		1d. pale red (9.4.57)	40·00	5·00	
		a. Imperf	£600	£500	
39		1d. pale rose (3.57)	45·00	10·00	
40		1d. rose-red (9.57)	28·00	5·00	8·00
		a. Imperf	£650	£500	
41		1d. deep-rose-red (7.57)	50·00	6·00	

1861. *Letters engraved on plate instead of punched (Alphabet IV).*

42	**1**	1d. red-brown (Die II) (Plates 50 and 51)	£160	20·00	35·00
		a. Imperf	—	£2000	

★36/42a **For well-centred, lightly used** .. +125%

In both values, varieties may be found as described in the preceding issues—ivory heads, inverted watermarks, re-entries, and double letters in corners.

The change of perforation from 16 to 14 was decided upon late in 1854 since the closer holes of the former gauge tended to cause the sheets of stamps to break up when handled, but for a time both gauges were in concurrent use. Owing to faulty alignment of the impressions on the plates and to shrinkage of the paper when damped, badly perforated stamps are plentiful in the line-engraved issues.

5   6   Showing position of the plate number on the 1d. and 2d. values. (Plate 170 shown)

1858–79. *Letters in all four corners. Wmk Large Crown, W* **4**. *Die* II (1d. *and* 2d.). *P* 14.

			Un	*Used*	★ *Used on cover*
43	**5**	1d. rose-red (1.4.64)	5·00	1·50	4·00
44		1d. lake-red	5·00	1·50	
		a. Imperf *from*	£800	£625	

★43/4a **For well-centred, lightly used** .. +125%

Plate		*Un*	*Used*	Plate		*Un*	*Used*
71		15·00	2·25	133		50·00	·6·25
72		20·00	2·75	134		15·00	1·50
73		15·00	2·25	135		55·00	21·00
74		12·00	1·50	136		55·00	16·00
76		22·00	1·50	137		10·00	1·75
77		£100000	£80000	138		8·00	1·50
78		55·00	1·50	139		18·00	12·00
79		18·00	1·50	140		8·00	1·50
80		12·00	1·50	141		80·00	6·25
81		32·00	1·75	142		28·00	19·00
82		65·00	2·75	143		18·00	11·00
83		80·00	4·25	144		55·00	16·00
84		32·00	1·75	145		5·00	1·75
85		15·00	1·75	146		8·00	3·75
86		18·00	2·75	147		12·00	3·25
87		5·00	1·50	148		12·00	2·25
88		90·00	5·75	149		10·00	3·75
89		22·00	1·50	150		5·00	1·50
90		16·00	1·50	151		15·00	6·25
91		22·00	3·75	152		12·00	3·50
92		10·00	1·50	153		40·00	6·25
93		22·00	1·50	154		10·00	1·50
94		22·00	3·25	155		10·00	1·75
95		15·00	1·50	156		10·00	1·50
96		16·00	1·50	157		10·00	1·50
97		10·00	2·25	158		5·00	1·50
98		10·00	3·75	159		5·00	1·50
99		15·00	3·25	160		5·00	1·50
100		20·00	1·75	161		18·00	4·25
101		28·00	6·25	162		10·00	4·25
102		12·00	1·50	163		10·00	2·25
103		12·00	2·25	164		10·00	2·25
104		16·00	3·25	165		12·00	1·50
105		38·00	4·25	166		10·00	3·75
106		18·00	1·50	167		8·00	1·50
107		22·00	4·00	168		8·00	5·75
108		18·00	1·75	169		18·00	4·25
109		40·00	2·25	170		8·00	1·50
110		12·00	1·50	171		5·00	1·50
111		20·00	1·75	172		5·00	1·50
112		32·00	1·75	173		28·00	6·25
113		10·00	8·00	174		5·00	1·50
114		£190	8·50	175		20·00	2·25
115		55·00	1·75	176		15·00	1·75
116		40·00	6·25	177		8·00	1·50
117		10·00	1·50	178		10·00	2·25
118		15·00	1·50	179		10·00	1·75
119		10·00	1·50	180		10·00	1·50
120		5·00	1·50	181		10·00	1·50
121		55·00	4·25	182		55·00	3·25
122		5·00	1·50	183		15·00	2·25
123		8·00	1·50	184		5·00	1·75
124		8·00	1·50	185		10·00	2·25
125		8·00	1·75	186		18·00	1·75
127		20·00	1·75	187		8·00	1·50
129		8·00	5·25	188		12·00	7·50
130		Imperf		189		20·00	4·25
131		40·00	12·00	190		10·00	3·75
132		55·00	17·00	191		5·00	4·25

Plate	Un	Used	Plate	Un	Used
192	15·00	1·50	209	10·00	6·25
193	5·00	1·50	210	12·00	8·50
194	10·00	5·25	211	25·00	16·00
195	10·00	5·25	212	10·00	8·00
196	8·00	3·25	213	10·00	8·00
197	10·00	6·25	214	15·00	14·00
198	6·00	3·75	215	15·00	14·00
199	12·00	3·75	216	15·00	14·00
200	12·00	1·50	217	12·00	4·25
201	5·00	3·25	218	8·00	5·25
202	10·00	5·25	219	32·00	55·00
203	5·00	11·00	220	5·00	4·25
204	8·00	1·75	221	18·00	11·00
205	8·00	2·25	222	28·00	27·00
206	8·00	6·25	223	32·00	45·00
207	8·00	6·25	224	38·00	38·00
208	8·00	11·00	225	£1100	£375

Error. Imperf. Issued at Cardiff (Plate 116)

				Un	Used
44*b* **5**	1d. rose-red (18.1.70)			£2000	£1250

The following plate numbers are also known imperf and used (No. 44a); 72,79, 80, 81, 82, 83, 86, 87, 88, 90, 91, 92, 93, 96, 97, 100, 102, 103, 104, 105, 107, 108, 109, 112, 114, 117, 120, 121, 122, 136, 137, 142, 146, 148, 158, 162, 164, 166, 171, 174, 191 and 202.

The numbering of this series of 1d. red plates follows after that of the previous 1d. stamp, last printed from Plate 68.

Plates 69, 70, 75, 126 and 128 were prepared for this issue but rejected owing to defects, and stamps from these plates do not exist, so that specimens which appear to be from these plates (like many of those which optimistic collectors believe to be from Plate 77) bear other plate numbers. Owing to faulty engraving or printing it is not always easy to identify the plate number. Plate 77 was also rejected but some stamps printed from it were used. One specimen is in the Tapling Collection and six or seven others are known. Plates 226 to 228 were made but not used.

Specimens from most of the plates are known with inverted watermark. The variety of watermark described in the General Notes to this section occurs on stamp M A (or M L) on plates up to about 96 (*Prices from* £110 *used*).

Re-entries in this issue are few, the best being on stamps M K and T K of Plate 71 and on S L and T L, Plate 83.

				Un	Used	★ Used on cover
45 **6**	2d. blue (thick lines) (7.58)			£175	6·00	18·00
	a. Imperf (Plate 9)			—	£3250	
	Plate					
	7			£450	25·00	
	8			£475	20·00	
	9			£175	6·00	
	12			£800	55·00	
46	2d. blue (thin lines) (1.7.69)			£180	10·00	20·00
47	2d. deep blue (thin lines)			£175	10·00	
	a. Imperf (Plate 13)			£2250		
	Plate					
	13			£190	10·00	
	14			£225	12·00	
	15			£175	12·00	

★45/7 **For well-centred, lightly used** .. +125%

Plates 10 and 11 of the 2d. were prepared but rejected. Plates 13 to 15 were laid down from a new roller impression on which the white lines were thinner.

There are some marked re-entries and repairs, particularly on Plates 7, 8, 9 and 12.

Stamps with inverted watermark may be found and also the T A (T L) and M A (M L) watermark varieties (*see* General Notes to this section).

Though the paper is normally white, some printings showed blueing and stamps showing the "ivory head" may therefore be found.

7

Showing the plate number (9)

9

1870 (1 Oct). *Wmk* W **9**, *extending over three stamps.* P 14.

				Un	Used	★ Used on cover
48 **7**	½d. rose-red			55·00	10·00	30·00
49	½d. rose			55·00	10·00	
	a. Imperf (Plates 1, 4, 5, 6, 8, 14)	*from*		£1000	£650	
	Plate					
	1			£110	50·00	
	3			65·00	18·00	
	4			80·00	12·00	
	5			60·00	10·00	
	6			55·00	10·00	
	8			£100	55·00	
	9			£2250	£350	
	10			80·00	10·00	
	11			55·00	10·00	
	12			55·00	10·00	
	13			55·00	10·00	
	14			55·00	10·00	
	15			65·00	15·00	
	19			£100	28·00	
	20			£110	40·00	

★49/9a **For well-centred, lightly used** .. +200%

The ½d. was printed in sheets of 480 (24 × 20) so that the check letters run from
A A X T
to
A A T X

Plates 2, 7, 16, 17 and 18 were not completed while Plates 21 and 22, though made, were not used.

Owing to the method of perforating, the outer side of stamps in either the A or X row (ie the left or right side of the sheet) is imperf.

Stamps may be found with watermark inverted or reversed, or without watermark, the latter due to misplacement of the paper when printing.

8   Position of plate Number

1870 (1 Oct). *Wmk* W **4**. P 14.

					Un	Used	★ Used on cover
51 **8**	1½d. rose-red				£200	28·00	£175
52	1½d. lake-red				£200	28·00	
	a. Imperf (Plates 1 and 3)	*from*		£2000		†	
	Plate						
	(1)				£400	45·00	
	3				£200	28·00	

Error of lettering. OP-PC for CP-PC (*Plate* 1)

					Un	Used
53 **8**	1½d. rose-red				£4500	£675

★51/3 **For well-centred, lightly used** .. +125%

1860. *Prepared for use but not issued; blued paper.* Wmk W **4**. P 14.

				Un	Used
53*a* **8**	1½d. rosy mauve (Plate 1)			£2000	
	b. Error of lettering, OP-PC for CP-PC				

Owing to a proposed change in the postal rates, 1½d. stamps were first printed in 1860, in rosy mauve, No. 53*a*, but the change was not approved and the greater part of the stock was destroyed.

In 1870 a 1½d. stamp was required and was issued in rose-red.

Plate 1 did not have the plate number in the design of the stamps, but on stamps from Plate 3 the number will be found in the frame as shown above.

Plate 2 was defective and was not used.

The error of lettering OP-PC on Plate 1 was apparently not noticed by the printers, and therefore not corrected.

EMBOSSED ISSUES

Volume 1 of the Stanley Gibbons *Great Britain Specialised Catalogue* gives further detailed information on the embossed issues.

PRICES. The prices quoted are for cut-square stamps with average to fine embossing. Stamps with exceptionally clear embossing are worth more.

10   **11**

12   **13**

Position of die number

(Primary die engraved at the Royal Mint by William Wyon. Stamps printed at Somerset House)

1847–54. *Imperf.* (For paper and wmk see footnote.)

					Un	Used	★ Used on cover
54 **10**	1s. pale green (11.9.47)				£3250	£450	£550
55	1s. green				£3250	£500	
56	1s. deep green				£3750	£550	
	Die 1 (1847)				£3250	£450	
	Die 2 (1854)				£3750	£525	
57 **11**	10d. brown (6.11.48)				£2750	£675	£1100
	Die 1 (1848)				£3000	£725	
	Die 2 (1850)				£2750	£675	
	Die 3 (1853)				£2750	£675	
	Die 4 (1854)				£3000	£725	
	Die 5				£17000		
58 **12**	6d. mauve (1.3.54)				£3000	£525	
59	6d. dull lilac				£3000	£500	£600
60	6d. purple				£3000	£500	
61	6d. violet				£4250	£950	

The 1s. and 10d. are on "Dickinson" paper with "silk" threads (actually a pale blue twisted cotton yarn). The 6d. is on paper watermarked V R in single-lined letters, W **13**, which may be found in four ways—upright, inverted, upright reversed, and inverted reversed, upright being the most common.

The die numbers are indicated on the base of the bust. Only Die 1 (1 WW) of the 6d. was used for the adhesive stamps. The 10d. is from Die 1 (W.W.1 on stamps), and Dies 2 to 5 (2 W.W., 3 W.W., 4 W.W. and 5 W.W.) but the number and letters on stamps from Die 1 are seldom clear and many specimens are known without any trace of them. Because of this the stamp we previously listed as "No die number" has been deleted. That they are from Die 1 is proved by the existence of blocks showing stamps with and without the die number The 1s. is from Dies 1 and 2 (W.W.1, W.W.2).

The normal arrangement of the "silk" threads in the paper was in

---

pairs running down each vertical row of the sheet, the space betwee the threads of each pair being approximately 5 mm and betwee pairs of threads 20 mm. Varieties due to misplacement of the pape in printing show a single thread on the first stamp from the shee margin and two threads 20 mm apart on the other stamps of the row Faulty manufacture is the cause of stamps with a single thread in th middle.

Through bad spacing of the impressions, which were handstruck all values may be found with two impressions more or les overlapping. Owing to the small margin allowed for variation c spacing, specimens with good margins on all sides are not common.

Double impressions are known of all values.

Later printings of the 6d. had the gum tinted green to enable th printer to distinguish the gummed side of the paper.

SURFACE-PRINTED ISSUES

GENERAL NOTES

Volume 1 of the Stanley Gibbons *Great Britain Specialise Catalogue* gives further detailed information on the surface-printe issues.

"Abnormals". The majority of the great rarities in the surface printed group of issues are the so-called "abnormals", whos existence is due to the practice of printing six sheets from every plat as soon as made, one of which was kept for record purposes a Somerset House, while the others were perforated and usually issued If such plates were not used for general production or if, before the came into full use, a change of watermark or colour took place, th six sheets originally printed would differ from the main issue in plate colour or watermark and, if issued, would be extremely rare.

The abnormal stamps of this class listed in this Catalogue an distinguished, where not priced, by an asterisk (*), are:

No.		
78	3d. Plate 3 (with white dots)	
152	4d. vermilion, Plate 16	
153	4d. sage-green, Plate 17	
109	6d. mauve, Plate 10	
124/a	6d. chestnut and 6d. pale chestnut, Plate 12	
145	6d. pale buff, Plate 13	
88	9d. Plate 3 (hair lines)	
98	9d. Plate 5 (see footnote to No. 98)	
113	10d. Plate 2	
91	1s. Plate 3 ("Plate 2")	
148/50	1s. green, Plate 14	
120	2s. blue, Plate 3	

Those which may have been issued, but of which no specimens ar known, are 2½d. wmk Anchor, Plates 4 and 5; 3d. wmk Emblems Plate 5; 3d. wmk Spray, Plate 21; 6d. grey, wmk Spray, Plate 18; 8d orange, Plate 2; 1s. wmk Emblems, Plate 5. 5s. wmk Maltese Cross Plate 4.

The 10d. Plate 1, wmk Emblems (No. 99), is sometimes reckone among the abnormals, but was an error, due to the use of the wron paper.

Corner Letters. With the exception of the 4d., 6d. and 1s. of 1855 57, the ½d., 1½d., 2d. and 5d. of 1880, the 1s. lilac of 1881 and the £ (which had letters in lower corners only, and in the reverse order t the normal), all the surface-printed stamps issued prior to 1887 ha letters in all four corners, as in the later line-engraved stamps. Th arrangement is the same, the letters running in sequence right acros and down the sheets, whether these were divided into panes or no The corner letters existing naturally depend on the number of stamp in the sheet and their arrangement.

Imprimaturs and Imperforate Stamps. The Post Office retained i their records (now in the National Postal Museum) one imperforat sheet from each plate, known as the Imprimatur (or officiall approved) sheet. Some stamps were removed from time to time fo presentation purposes and have come on to the market, but thes imperforates are not listed as they were not issued. Full details ca. be found in Volume I of the *Great Britain Specialised Catalogue*.

However, other imperforate stamps are known to have been issue and these are listed where it has been possible to prove that they d not come from the Imprimatur sheets. It is therefore advisable t purchase these only when acccompanied by an Expert Committe certificate of genuineness.

Plate Numbers. All stamps from No. 75 to No. 163 bear in thei designs either the plate number or, in one or two earlier instances some other indication by which one plate can be distinguished fror another. With the aid of these and of the corner letters it is thu possible to "reconstruct" a sheet of stamps from any plate of an issue or denomination.

Surface-printing. In this context the traditional designatio "surface-printing" is synonymous with typo(graphy)—a philateli term—or letterpress—the printers' term—as meaning printing fror (the surface of) raised type. It is also called relief-printing, as th image is in relief (in French, *en épargne*), unwanted parts of th design having been cut away. Duplicate impressions can b electrotyped or stereotyped from an original die, the resulting *cliche* being locked together to form the printing plate.

Wing Margins. As the vertical gutters (spaces) between the panes into which sheets of stamps of most values were divided until th introduction of the Imperial Crown watermark, were perforate through the centre with a single row of holes, instead of each vertica row of stamps on the inner side of the panes having its own line c perforation as is now usual, a proportion of the stamps in each shee have what is called a "wing margin" about 5 mm wide on one c other side.

The stamps with "wing margins" are the watermark Emblems an Spray of Rose series (3d. 6d. 9d. 10d. 1s. and 2s.) with letters D, E, I or I in S.E. corner, and the watermark Garter series (4d. and 8d. with letters F or G in S.E. corner. Knowledge of this lettering wi enable collectors to guard against stamps with wing margin cut dow and re-perforated, but note that wing margin stamps of Nos. 62 to 7 are also to be found re-perforated.

PRINTERS. The issues of Queen Victoria, Nos. 62/214, were typo b Thomas De La Rue & Co.

PERFORATIONS. All the surface-printed issues of Queen Victori are Perf 14, with the exception of Nos. 126/9.

ALTERED CATALOGUE NUMBERS

Any Catalogue numbers altered from the las edition are shown as a list in the introductor pages.

KEY TO SURFACE-PRINTED ISSUES 1855–83

S.G. Nos.	Description	Watermark	Date of Issue
	NO CORNER LETTERS		
62	4d. carmine	Small Garter	31.7.55
63/5	4d. carmine	Medium Garter	25.2.56
66/a	4d. carmine	Large Garter	Jan 1857
69/70	6d. lilac	Emblems	21.10.56
71/3	1s. green	Emblems	1.11.56
	SMALL WHITE CORNER LETTERS		
75/7	3d. carmine	Emblems	1.5.62
78	3d. carmine (dots)	Emblems	Aug 1862
79/82	4d. red	Large Garter	15.1.62
83/5	6d. lilac	Emblems	1.12.62
86/8	9d. bistre	Emblems	15.1.62
89/91	1s. green	Emblems	1.12.62
	LARGE WHITE CORNER LETTERS		
92	3d. rose	Emblems	1.3.65
102/3	3d. rose	Spray	July 1867
93/5	4d. vermilion	Large Garter	4.7.65
96/7	6d. lilac	Emblems	7.3.65
104/7	6d. lilac	Spray	21.6.67
108/9	6d. lilac	Spray	8.3.69
122/4	6d. chestnut	Spray	12.4.72
125	6d. grey	Spray	24.4.73
98	9d. straw	Emblems	30.10.65
110/11	9d. straw	Spray	3.10.67
99	10d. brown	Emblems	11.11.67
112/14	10d. brown	Spray	1.7.67
101	1s. green	Emblems	19.1.65
115/17	1s. green	Spray	13.7.67
118/20b	2s. blue	Spray	1.7.67
121	2s. brown	Spray	27.2.80
126/7	5s. rose	Cross	1.7.67
128	10s. grey	Cross	26.9.78
129	£1 brown-lilac	Cross	26.9.78
130, 134	5s. rose	Anchor	25.11.82
131, 135	10s. grey-green	Anchor	Feb 1883
132, 136	£1 brown-lilac	Anchor	Dec 1882
133, 137	£5 orange	Anchor	21.3.82
	LARGE COLOURED CORNER LETTERS		
166	1d. Venetian red	Crown	1.1.80
138/9	2½d. rosy mauve	Anchor	1.7.75
141	2½d. rosy mauve	Orb	1.5.76
142	2½d. blue	Orb	5.2.80
157	2½d. blue	Crown	23.3.81
143/4	3d. rose	Spray	5.7.73
158	3d. rose	Crown	Jan 1881
159	3d. on 3d. lilac	Crown	1.1.83
152	4d. vermilion	Large Garter	1.3.76
153	4d. sage-green	Large Garter	12.3.77
154	4d. brown	Large Garter	15.8.80
160	4d. brown	Crown	9.12.80
145	6d. buff	Spray	15.3.73
146/7	6d. grey	Spray	20.3.74
161	6d. grey	Crown	1.1.81
162	6d. on 6d. lilac	Crown	1.1.83
156a	8d. purple-brown	Large Garter	July 1876
156	8d. orange	Large Garter	11.9.76
148/50	1s. green	Spray	1.9.73
151	1s. brown	Spray	14.10.80
163	1s. brown	Crown	24.5.81

Watermarks:		
	Anchor	W 40, 47
	Cross	W 39
	Crown	W 49
	Emblems	W 20
	Large Garter	W 17
	Medium Garter	W 16
	Orb	W 48
	Small Garter	W 15
	Spray	W 33

14

15 Small Garter

16 Medium Garter **17** Large Garter

1855–57. *No corner letters.*

(a) Wmk Small Garter, W **15.** *Highly glazed, deeply blued paper* (31 July 1855)

					Un	★ Used	Used on cover
62	**14**	4d. carmine (*shades*)			£2500	£250	£350
		a. Paper slightly blued			£2750	£250	
		b. White paper			£3250	£425	

(b) Wmk Medium Garter, W **16**

(i) Thick, blued highly glazed paper (25 February 1856)

63	**14**	4d. carmine (*shades*)	£3000	£250	£350
		a. White paper	£2750		

(ii) Ordinary thin white paper (September 1856)

64	**14**	4d. carmine	£2000	£225	£300
		a. Stamp printed double	†	—	

(iii) Ordinary white paper, specially prepared ink (1 November 1856)

65	**14**	4d. rose or deep rose	£2000	£225	£225

(c) Wmk Large Garter, W **17.** *Ordinary white paper* (January 1857)

66	**14**	4d. rose-carmine	£750	45·00	£110
		a. Rose	£650	45·00	
		b. Thick glazed paper	£1800	£150	

★62/6b For well-centred, lightly used   +125%

18   **19**   **20** Emblems wmk (normal)

20a Wmk error, three roses and shamrock   **20b** Wmk error, three roses and thistle

(d) Wmk Emblems, W **20**

					Un	★ Used	Used on cover
69	**18**	6d. deep lilac (21.10.56)			£625	75·00	
70		6d. pale lilac			£550	55·00	£100
		a. Azure paper			£2750	£425	
		b. Thick paper			£750	£160	
		c. Error. Wmk W **20a**					
71	**19**	1s. deep green (1.11.56)			£1400	£190	
72		1s. green			£700	£160	£190
73		1s. pale green			£700	£160	
		a. Azure paper			—	£575	
		b. Thick paper			—	£180	
		c. Imperf					

★69/73b For well-centred, lightly used   +125%

21   **22**

23   **24**   **25** Plate 2

A. White dots added

O SI

B. Hair lines

1862–64. *A small uncoloured letter in each corner, the 4d. wmk Large Garter, W* **17,** *the others Emblems, W* **20.**

					Un	★ Used	Used on cover
75	**21**	3d. deep carmine-rose (Plate 2) (1.5.62)			£1500	£160	
76		3d. bright carmine-rose			£800	£140	£300
77		3d. pale carmine-rose			£800	£150	
		b. Thick paper			—	£225	
78		3d. rose (with white dots, Type A, Plate 3) (8.62)			*	£2750	
		a. Imperf (Plate 3)			£2250		
79	**22**	4d. bright red (Plate 3) (15.1.62)			£850	65·00	
80		4d. pale red			£575	45·00	£110
81		4d. bright red (Hair lines, Type B, Plate 4) (16.10.63)			£750	50·00	
82		4d. pale red (Hair lines, Type B, Plate 4)			£650	40·00	£110
		a. Imperf (Plate 4)			£1750		
83	**23**	6d. deep lilac (Plate 3) (1.12.62)			£850	70·00	

					Un	★ Used	Used on cover
84	**23**	6d. lilac			£725	45·00	90·00
		a. Azure paper			—	£350	
		b. Thick paper			—	80·00	
		c. Error. Wmk W **20b** (stamp TF)					
85		6d. lilac (Hair lines, Plate 4) (20.4.64)			£850	90·00	£150
		a. Imperf			£1300		
		c. Thick paper			£1300	£100	
		d. Error. Wmk W **20b** (stamp TF)					
86	**24**	9d. bistre (Plate 2) (15.1.62)			£1500	£175	£300
87		9d. straw			£1500	£160	
		a. On azure paper					
		b. Thick paper			£2000	£275	
		c. Error. Watermark W **20b** (stamp TF)			†	—	
88		9d. bistre (Hair lines, Plate 3) (5.62)			£6500	£2250	
89	**25**	1s. deep green (Plate No. 1 = Plate 2) (1.12.62)			£1000	£140	
90		1s. green (Plate No. 1 = Plate 2)			£850	90·00	£175
		a. "K" in lower left corner in white circle (stamp KD)			£4500	£600	
		aa. "K" normal (stamp KD)			—	£850	
		b. On azure paper					
		c. Thick paper			—	£190	
		ca. Thick paper, "K" in circle as No. 90a			—	£1200	
91		1s. deep green (Plate No. 2 = Plate 3)			£12000		
		a. Imperf			£1750		

★75/91 For well-centred, lightly used   +125%

The 3d. as Type **21**, but with network background in the spandrels which is found overprinted SPECIMEN, was never issued.

The plates of this issue may be distinguished as follows:

3d. Plate 2. No white dots.
    Plate 3. White dots as Illustration A.
4d. Plate 3. No hair lines. Roman I next to lower corner letters.
    Plate 4. Hair lines in corners. (Illustration B). Roman II.
6d. Plate 3. No hair lines.
    Plate 4. Hair lines in corners.
9d. Plate 2. No hair lines.
    Plate 3. Hair lines in corners. Beware of faked lines.
1s. Plate 2. Numbered 1 on stamps.
    Plate 3. Numbered 2 on stamps and with hair lines.

The 9d. on azure paper (No. 87a) is very rare, only one confirmed example being known.

The variety "K" in circle, No. 90a, is believed to be due to a damaged letter having been cut out and replaced. It is probable that the punch was driven in too deeply, causing the flange to penetrate the surface, producing an indentation showing as an uncoloured circle.

The watermark variety "three roses and a shamrock" illustrated in W **20a** was evidently due to the substitution of an extra rose for the thistle in a faulty watermark bit. It is found on stamp TA of Plate 4 of the 3d., Plates 1 (No. 70c), 3, 5 and 6 of the 6d., Plate 4 of the 9d. and Plate 4 of the 1s.

A similar variety, W **20b**, but showing three roses and a thistle is found on stamp TF of the 6d. (Nos. 84/5) and 9d. (Nos. 87, 97/8).

26   **27**

28 (with hyphen)   **28a** (without hyphen)

29   **30**   **31**

1865–67. *Large uncoloured corner letters. Wmk Large Garter (4d.); others Emblems.*

					Un	★ Used	Used on cover
92	**26**	3d. rose (Plate 4) (1.3.65)			£500	55·00	£125
		a. Error. Wmk W **20a**			£1100	£325	
		b. Thick paper			£600	65·00	
93	**27**	4d. dull vermilion (4.7.65)			£275	30·00	70·00
94		4d. vermilion			£275	30·00	
		a. Imperf (Plates 11, 12)			£575		
95		4d. deep vermilion			£275	28·00	
		Plate					
		7 (1865)			£350	32·00	
		8 (1866)			£300	32·00	
		9 (1867)			£300	30·00	
		10 (1868)			£350	45·00	
		11 (1869)			£300	28·00	
		12 (1870)			£275	30·00	
		13 (1872)			£300	30·00	
		14 (1873)			£350	55·00	
96	**28**	6d. deep lilac (with hyphen) (7.3.65)			£475	60·00	
97		6d. lilac (with hyphen)			£400	45·00	90·00
		a. Thick paper			£500	70·00	
		b. Stamp doubly printed (Pl 6)			—	£5500	
		c. Error. Wmk W **20a** (Pl 5, 6)			from	—	£375
		d. Error. Wmk W **20b** (Plate 5)					
		Plate					
		5 (1865)			£400	45·00	
		6 (1867)			£1200	80·00	

Selling your Collection?

Highest Prices

Warwick & Warwick can obtain the highest prices through our private treaty service. Whether you have a specialised collection or general surplus material, from £100 to £100,000, you can realise its true potential through Warwick & Warwick.

All Material

We have clients keen to purchase world collections, better single items, covers, proof material, quality G.B., specialised single country studies, postal history - in fact anything and everything philatelic. Whatever you have, Warwick & Warwick can sell it.

Free Valuation

Warwick & Warwick provide written valuations free of charge and without obligation. If you decline our valuation you owe us nothing except return carriage costs. You will receive the full amount tendered in the valuation with no commission or service charge deducted.

Free Visits

Warwick & Warwick will completely free of charge and without obligation arrange to visit sellers of more valuable collections anywhere in the country within 48 hours. Visits abroad can also be arranged. Smaller collections are transported to our offices for valuation by insured security courier at no expense to the vendor.

Act Now *Telephone us today with details of your property. Write to us or fax us if you prefer. Ask for our service to Stamp Collectors Brochure. Alternatively visit us at Chalon House, with its large car park.*

Warwick & Warwick

Warwick & Warwick Limited, Chalon House, Scar Bank, Millers Road, Warwick, England. CV34 5DB.

Tel: 01926-499031. Fax: 01926-491906

Warwick & Warwick

			Un	Used	cover
8	29	9d. straw (Plate 4) (30.10.65)	£850	£275	£375
		a. Thick paper ..	£1200	£375	
		b. Error. Wmk W **20a**	—	£425	
		c. Error. Wmk W **20b** (stamp T F)			
9	30	10d. red-brown (Pl 1) (11.11.67)	†	£13000	
1	31	1s. green (Plate 4) (19.1.65)	£775	90·00	£140
		a. Error. Wmk W **20a**	—	£400	
		b. Thick paper ..	£900	£175	
		c. Imperf between (vert pair)	—	£4500	
★92/101c		**For well-centred, lightly used** ..	+100%		

From mid-1866 to about the end of 1871 4d. stamps of this issue ppeared generally with watermark inverted.

Unused examples of No. 98 from Plate 5 exist, but this was never ut to press and all evidence points to such stamps originating from portion of the Imprimatur sheet which was perforated by De La Rue in 1887 for insertion in albums to be presented to members of he Stamp Committee (*Price* £12000 *un*).

The 10d. stamps, No. 99, were printed in *error* on paper watermarked "Emblems" instead of on "Spray of Rose".

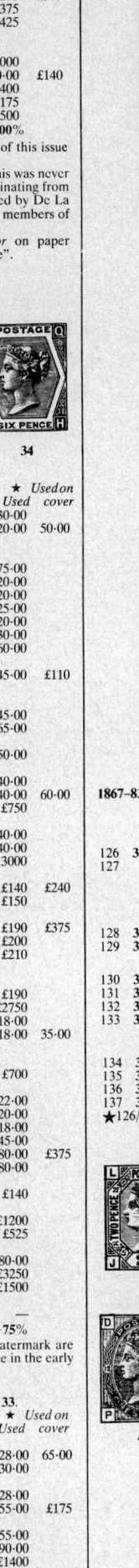

32 **33** Spray of Rose **34**

1867–80. *Wmk Spray of Rose, W* **33.**

			Un	★ Used	Used on cover
02	26	3d. deep rose (12.7.67)	£275	30·00	
03		3d. rose	£275	20·00	50·00
		a. Imperf (Plates 5, 6, 8) *from*	£775		
		Plate			
		4 (1867)	£350	75·00	
		5 (1868)	£250	20·00	
		6 (1870)	£275	20·00	
		7 (1871)	£350	20·00	
		8 (1872)	£300	20·00	
		9 (1872)	£300	30·00	
		10 (1873)	£350	60·00	
04	28	6d. lilac (with hyphen) (Plate 6) (21.6.67)	£625	45·00	£110
		a. Imperf			
05		6d. deep lilac (with hyphen) (Plate 6)	£625	45·00	
06		6d. purple (with hyphen) (Pl 6)	£625	65·00	
07		6d. bright violet (with hyphen) (Plate 6) (22.7.68)	£625	50·00	
08	28a	6d. dull violet (without hyphen) (Plate 8) (8.3.69)	£400	40·00	
09		6d. mauve (without hyphen)	£325	40·00	60·00
		a. Imperf (Plate Nos. 8 and 9)	£850	£750	
		Plate			
		8 (1869, mauve)	£325	40·00	
		9 (1870, mauve)	£325	40·00	
		10 (1869, mauve)	*	£13000	
10	29	9d. straw (Plate No. 4) (3.10.67)	£700	£140	£240
11		9d. pale straw (Plate No. 4)	£700	£150	
		a. Imperf (Plate 4) ..	£2100		
12	30	10d. red-brown (1.7.67)	£1100	£190	£375
13		10d. pale red-brown	£1100	£200	
14		10d. deep red-brown	£1300	£210	
		a. Imperf (Plate 1) ..	£2000		
		Plate			
		1 (1867)	£1100	£190	
		2 (1867)	£13000	£2750	
15	31	1s. deep green (13.7.67)	£475	18·00	
17		1s. green	£375	18·00	35·00
		a. Imperf between (horiz pair) (Plate 7)	£1200	£700	
		b. Imperf (Plate 4)	£375	22·00	
		Plate			
		4 (1867)	£375	22·00	
		5 (1871)	£425	20·00	
		6 (1871)	£600	18·00	
		7 (1873)	£600	45·00	
18	32	2s. dull blue (1.7.67)	£1100	80·00	£375
19		2s. deep blue	£1100	80·00	
		a. Imperf (Plate 1)	£2250		
20		2s. pale blue	£1700	£140	
		aa. Imperf (Plate 1)	£2000		
20a		2s. cobalt	£5500	£1200	
20b		2s. milky blue	£3500	£525	
		Plate			
		1 (1867)	£1100	80·00	
		3 (1868)	*	£3250	
21		2s. brown (Plate No. 1) (27.2.80)	£7500	£1500	
		a. Imperf	£4250		
		b. No watermark	†		
★102/21		**For well-centred, lightly used** ..	+75%		

Examples of the 1s. from Plates 5 and 6 *without* watermark re postal forgeries used at the Stock Exchange Post Office in the early 1870's.

1872–73. *Uncoloured letters in corners. Wmk Spray, W* **33.**

			Un	★ Used	Used on cover
22	34	6d. deep chestnut (Plate 11) (12.4.72)	£475	28·00	65·00
22a		6d. chestnut (Plate 11) (22.5.72)	£400	30·00	
22b		6d. pale chestnut (Plate 11) (1872)	£375	28·00	
23		6d. pale buff (19.10.72)	£400	55·00	£175
		Plate			
		11 (1872, pale buff)	£400	55·00	
		12 (1872, pale buff)	£850	90·00	
24		6d. chestnut (Plate 12) (1872)	*	£1400	
24a		6d. pale chestnut (Plate 12) (1872)	*	£1400	
25		6d. grey (Plate 12) (24.4.73)	£800	£140	£190
		a. Imperf	£1500		
★122/5		**For well-centred, lightly used** ..	+50%		

35 **36**

37

38

39 Maltese Cross **40** Large Anchor

1867–83. *Uncoloured letters in corners.*

(a) Wmk Maltese Cross, W **39.** P 15½ × 15

			Un	★ Used
126	35	5s. rose (1.7.67) ..	£3000	£350
127		5s. pale rose ..	£3250	£350
		a. Imperf (Plate 1)	£4750	
		Plate		
		1 (1867)	£3000	£350
		2 (1874)	£4000	£425
128	36	10s. greenish grey (Plate 1) (26.9.78)	£21000	£1100
129	37	£1 brown-lilac (Plate 1) (26.9.78)	£26000	£1600

(b) Wmk Anchor, W **40.** P 14. (i) *Blued paper*

130	35	5s. rose (Plate 4) (25.11.82)	£6000	£1200
131	36	10s. grey-green (Plate 1) (2.83)	£25000	£1750
132	37	£1 brown-lilac (Plate 1) (12.82)	£31000	£3000
133	38	£5 orange (Plate 1) (21.3.82)	£20000	£4500

(ii) *White paper*

134	35	5s. rose (Plate 4)	£6000	£1200
135	36	10s. greenish grey (Plate 1)	£25000	£1750
136	37	£1 brown-lilac (Plate 1)	£36000	£2600
137	38	£5 orange (Plate 1)	£5750	£1700
★126/37		**For well-centred, lightly used** ..	+75%	

41 **42** **43**

44 **45** **46**

47 Small Anchor **48** Orb

1873–80. *Large coloured letters in the corners.*

(a) Wmk Anchor, W **47**

			Un	★ Used	Used on cover
138	41	2½d. rosy mauve (*blued paper*) (1.7.75)	£450	60·00	
		a. Imperf			
139		2½d. rosy mauve (*white paper*) ..	£300	50·00	85·00
		Plate			
		1 (*blued paper*) (1875)	£450	60·00	
		1 (*white paper*) (1875)	£300	50·00	
		2 (*blued paper*) (1875)	£3250	£700	
		2 (*white paper*) (1875)	£300	50·00	
		3 (*white paper*) (1875)	£475	55·00	
		3 (*blued paper*) (1875)	—	£2500	

Error of Lettering L H—F L *for* L H—H L (*Plate* 2)

140	41	2½d. rosy mauve ..	£8000	£800

(b) Wmk Orb, W **48**

141	41	2½d. rosy mauve (1.5.76) ..	£275	25·00	55·00
		Plate			
		3 (1876) ..	£625	55·00	
		4 (1876) ..	£275	25·00	
		5 (1876) ..	£275	30·00	
		6 (1876) ..	£275	25·00	
		7 (1877) ..	£275	25·00	
		8 (1877) ..	£275	30·00	
		9 (1877) ..	£275	25·00	
		10 (1878) ..	£325	40·00	
		11 (1878) ..	£275	25·00	
		12 (1878) ..	£275	30·00	
		13 (1878) ..	£275	30·00	
		14 (1879) ..	£275	25·00	
		15 (1879) ..	£275	25·00	
		16 (1879) ..	£275	25·00	
		17 (1880) ..	£700	£140	
142		2½d. blue (5.2.80)	£240	20·00	30·00
		Plate			
		17 (1880) ..	£240	30·00	
		18 (1880) ..	£275	22·00	
		19 (1880) ..	£240	20·00	
		20 (1880) ..	£240	20·00	

(c) Wmk Spray, W **33**

143	42	3d. rose (5.7.73) ..	£240	20·00	40·00
144		3d. pale rose	£240	20·00	
		Plate			
		11 (1873) ..	£240	20·00	
		12 (1873) ..	£275	20·00	
		14 (1874) ..	£300	22·00	
		15 (1874) ..	£240	20·00	
		16 (1875) ..	£240	20·00	
		17 (1875) ..	£275	20·00	
		18 (1875) ..	£240	20·00	
		19 (1876) ..	£240	20·00	
		20 (1879) ..	£240	40·00	
145	43	6d. pale buff (Plate 13) (15.3.73)	*	£5000	
146		6d. deep grey (20.3.74)	£300	35·00	60·00
147		6d. grey ..	£275	28·00	
		Plate			
		13 (1874) ..	£275	30·00	
		14 (1875) ..	£275	30·00	
		15 (1876) ..	£275	28·00	
		16 (1878) ..	£275	28·00	
		17 (1880) ..	£375	55·00	
148	44	1s. deep green (1.9.73)	£400	55·00	
150		1s. pale green ..	£325	40·00	65·00
		Plate			
		8 (1873) ..	£400	55·00	
		9 (1874) ..	£400	55·00	
		10 (1874) ..	£375	55·00	
		11 (1875) ..	£375	55·00	
		12 (1875) ..	£325	40·00	
		13 (1876) ..	£325	40·00	
		14 (—) ..	*	£12000	
151		1s. orange-brown (Plate 13) (14.10.80) ..	£1400	£275	£400

(d) Wmk Large Garter, W **17**

152	45	4d. vermilion (1.3.76) ..	£800	£200	£350
		Plate			
		15 (1876) ..	£800	£200	
		16 (1877) ..	*	£12000	
153		4d. sage-green (12.3.77) ..	£500	£140	£225
		Plate			
		15 (1877) ..	£575	£160	
		16 (1877) ..	£500	£140	
		17 (1877) ..	*	£7000	
154		4d. grey-brown (Plate 17) (15.8.80) ..	£750	£225	£325
		a. Imperf	£2500		
156	46	8d. orange (Plate 1) (11.9.76) ..	£650	£175	£240
★138/56		**For well-centred, lightly used** ..	+100%		

1876 (July). *Prepared for use but not issued.*

156a	46	8d. purple-brown (Plate 1) ..	£3500

49 Imperial Crown **(50)**

1880–83. *Wmk Imperial Crown, W* **49.**

			Un	★ Used	Used on cover
157	41	2½d. blue (23.3.81) ..	£225	12·00	28·00
		Plate			
		21 (1881) ..	£275	18·00	
		22 (1881) ..	£225	18·00	
		23 (1881) ..	£225	12·00	
158	42	3d. rose (3.81) ..	£275	45·00	60·00
		Plate			
		20 (1881) ..	£325	60·00	
		21 (1881) ..	£275	45·00	

159	42	3d. on 3d. lilac (T **50**) (C.) (Plate 21) (1.1.83)	..	£275	90·00	£275
160	45	4d. grey-brown (8.12.80)	..	£225	35·00	90·00
		Plate				
		17 (1880)	..	£225	35·00	
		18 (1882)	..	£275	35·00	
161	43	6d. grey (1.1.81)	..	£210	38·00	65·00
		Plate				
		17 (1881)	..	£225	38·00	
		18 (1882)	..	£210	38·00	
162		6d. on 6d. lilac (as T **50**) (C.) (Plate 18) (1.1.83)	..	£240	90·00	£190
		a. Slanting dots (various) *from*		£290	95·00	
		b. Opt double ..	..	—	£5000	
163	44	1s. orange-brown (24.5.81)	..	£300	85·00	£160
		Plate				
		13 (1881)	..	£350	85·00	
		14 (1881)	..	£300	85·00	

★**157/63 For well-centred, lightly used** .. +75%

The 1s. Plate 14 (line perf 14) exists in purple, but was not issued in this shade (*Price £2750 unused*). Examples were included in a few of the Souvenir Albums prepared for members of the "Stamp Committee of 1884".

52	**53**

54	**55**	**56**

1880–81. *Wmk Imperial Crown, W* **49.**

				Un	★ Used	on cover
164	52	½d. deep green (14.10.80)	..	25·00	6·00	12·00
		a. Imperf		£700		
		b. No watermark		£3000		
165		½d. pale green	..	25·00	10·00	
166	53	1d. Venetian red (1.1.80)	..	10·00	6·00	10·00
		a. Imperf		£700		
167	54	1½d. Venetian red (14.10.80)	..	£110	25·00	90·00
168	55	2d. pale rose (8.12.80)	..	£125	55·00	90·00
168a		2d. deep rose	..	£125	55·00	
169	56	5d. indigo (15.3.81)	..	£400	70·00	£150
		a. Imperf		£1400	£1000	

★**164/9 For well-centred, lightly used** +75%

Die I	**57**	Die II

1881. *Wmk Imperial Crown, W* **49.** (*a*) 14 *dots in each corner, Die I* (12 July).

				Un	★ Used	on cover
170	57	1d. lilac	..	90·00	18·00	26·00
171		1d. pale lilac	..	90·00	18·00	

(*b*) 16 *dots in each corner, Die II* (13 December)

172	57	1d. lilac	..	1·50	1·00	2·00
172a		1d. bluish lilac	..	£200	60·00	
173		1d. deep purple	..	1·50	70	
		a. Printed both sides	..	£450	†	
		b. Frame broken at bottom	..	£525	£225	
		c. Printed on gummed side	..	£425	†	
		d. Imperf three sides (pair)	..	£2750	†	
		e. Printed both sides but impression on back inverted	..	£450	†	
		f. No watermark	..	£800	†	
		g. Blued paper	..	£1750		
174		1d. mauve	..	1·50	75	
		a. Imperf (pair)	..	£1000		

★**170/4 For well-centred, lightly used** +50%

1d. stamps with the words "PEARS SOAP" printed on back in *orange, blue* or *mauve price from £375, unused*.

The variety "frame broken at bottom" (No. 173b) shows a white space just inside the bottom frame-line from between the "N" and "E" of "ONE" to below the first "N" of "PENNY", breaking the pearls and cutting into the lower part of the oval below "PEN".

MINIMUM PRICE

The minimum price quote is 10p which represents a handling charge rather than a basis for valuing common stamps. For further notes about prices see introductory pages.

KEY TO SURFACE-PRINTED ISSUES 1880–1900

S.G. Nos.	Description	Date of Issue
164/5	½d. green	14.10.80
187	½d. slate-blue	1.4.84
197/e	½d. vermilion	1.1.87
213	½d. blue-green	17.4.1900
166	1d. Venetian red	1.1.80
170/1	1d. lilac, Die I	12.7.81
172/4	1d. lilac, Die II	12.12.81
167	1½d. Venetian red	14.10.80
188	1½d. lilac	1.4.84
198	1½d. purple and green	1.1.87
168/a	2d. rose	8.12.80
189	2d. lilac	1.4.84
199/200	2d. green and red	1.1.87
190	2½d. lilac	1.4.84
201	2½d. purple on blue paper	1.1.87
191	3d. lilac	1.4.84
202/4	3d. purple on yellow paper	1.1.87
192	4d. dull green	1.4.84
205/a	4d. green and brown	1.1.87
206	4½d. green and carmine	15.9.92
169	5d. indigo	15.3.81
193	5d. dull green	1.4.84
207	5d. purple and blue, Die I	1.1.87
207a	5d. purple and blue, Die II	1888
194	6d. dull green	1.4.84
208/a	6d. purple on rose-red paper	1.1.87
195	9d. dull green	1.8.83
209	9d. purple and blue	1.1.87
210/b	10d. purple and carmine	24.2.90
196	1s. dull green	1.4.84
211	1s. green	1.1.87
214	1s. green and carmine	11.7.1900
175	2s. 6d. lilac on blued paper	2.7.83
178/9	2s. 6d. lilac	1884
176	5s. rose on blued paper	1.4.84
180/1	5s. rose	1884
177/a	10s. ultramarine on blued paper	1.4.84
182/3a	10s. ultramarine	1884
185	£1 brown-lilac, wmk Crowns	1.4.84
186	£1 brown-lilac, wmk Orbs	2.88
212	£1 green	28.1.91

Note that the £5 value used with the above series is listed as Nos. 133 and 137.

58	**59**

60

1883–84. *Coloured letters in the corners. Wmk Anchor, W* **40.**

(*a*) *Blued paper*

				Un	★ Used
175	58	2s. 6d. lilac (2.7.83)	..	£2500	£650
176	59	5s. rose (1.4.84)	..	£4000	£1400
177	60	10s. ultramarine (1.4.84)	..	£13000	£3600
177a		10s. cobalt (5.84)	..	£15000	£5250

(*b*) *White paper*

178	58	2s. 6d. lilac	..	£275	80·00
179		2s. 6d. deep lilac	..	£275	80·00
		a. Error. On blued paper	..	£1750	£600
180	59	5s. rose	..	£475	£100
181		5s. crimson	..	£475	£100
182	60	10s. cobalt	..	£14000	£3600
183		10s. ultramarine	..	£900	£300
183a		10s. pale ultramarine	..	£900	£300

★**175/83a For well-centred, lightly used** +50%
For No. 180 perf 12 *see second note below No. 196.*

61

Broken frames, Plate 2

1884 (1 April). *Wmk Three Imperial Crowns, W* **49.**

				Un	★ Us...
185	61	£1 brown-lilac	..	£13000	£12...
		a. Frame broken	..	£19000	£17...

1888 (Feb). *Wmk Three Orbs. W* **48.**

| 186 | 61 | £1 brown-lilac | .. | £19000 | £17... |
| | | a. Frame broken | .. | £26000 | £27... |

★**185/6a For well-centred, lightly used** +50...
The broken-frame varieties, Nos. 185a and 186a, are on Plate stamps JC and TA, as illustrated. *See also* No. 212a.

62	**63**	**64**

65	**66**

1883 (1 Aug) (9*d*.) or **1884** (1 April) (*others*). *Wmk Imperial Crow...* *W* **49** (*sideways on horiz designs*).

				Un	★ Used o...	cove...
187	52	½d. slate-blue	..	15·00	5·00	10·...
		a. Imperf		£700		
188	62	1½d. lilac	..	75·00	28·00	80·...
		a. Imperf		£700		
189	63	2d. lilac	..	£110	55·00	90·...
		a. Imperf		£800		
190	64	2½d. lilac	..	60·00	10·00	20·...
		a. Imperf		£800		
191	65	3d. lilac	..	£140	75·00	£10...
		a. Imperf		£800		
192	66	4d. dull green	..	£350	£150	£20...
		a. Imperf		£850		
193	62	5d. dull green	..	£350	£150	£20...
		a. Imperf		£850		
194	63	6d. dull green	..	£375	£160	£21...
		a. Imperf		£850		
195	64	9d. dull green (1.8.83)	..	£700	£325	£77...
196	65	1s. dull green	..	£500	£175	£32...
		a. Imperf		£1750		

★**187/96 For well-centred, lightly used** +100%
The above prices are for stamps in the true dull green colour... Stamps which have been soaked, causing the colour to run, ar... virtually worthless.

Stamps of the above set and No. 180 are also found perf 12; thes... are official perforations, but were never issued. A second variety c... the 5d. is known with a line instead of a stop under the "d" in th... value; this was never issued and is therefore only known *unuse...* (*Price £5500*).

71	**72**	**73**

74	**75**	**76**

77	**78**	**79**

80	**81**	**82**

Die I   Die II

Die I: Square dots to right of "d".
Die II: Thin vertical lines to right of "d".

887 (1 Jan)–**1892.** *"Jubilee" issue. New types. The bicoloured stamps have the value tablets, or the frames including the value tablets, in the second colour. Wmk Imperial Crown, W* **49** *(Three Crowns on £1).*

			Un	Used	★ Used on cover
97	71	½d. vermilion	1·25	75	5·00
		a. Printed on gummed side	£1000	†	
		b. Printed both sides		†	
		c. Doubly printed	£5500		
		d. Imperf	£1250		
97e		½d. orange-vermilion	1·00	50	
98	72	1½d. dull purple and pale green	13·00	5·00	18·00
		a. Purple part of design double	—	£3750	
99	73	2d. green and scarlet	£300	£180	
00		2d. grey-green and carmine	20·00	9·00	20·00
01	74	2½d. purple/*blue*	13·00	2·00	5·00
		a. Printed on gummed side	£2500	†	
		b. Imperf three sides	£2250		
		c. Imperf	£2500		
02	75	3d. purple/*yellow*	18·00	2·50	20·00
		a. Imperf	£3500		
03		3d. deep purple/*yellow*	18·00	2·50	
04		3d. purple/*orange* (1890)	£400	£150	
05	76	4d. green and purple-brown	20·00	9·50	18·00
		a. Imperf	£3500		
05a		4d. green and deep brown	20·00	9·50	
06	77	4½d. green and carmine (15.9.92)	7·00	28·00	60·00
06a		4½d. green & deep brt carmine	£450	£300	
07	78	5d. dull purple and blue (Die I)	£450	45·00	90·00
07a		5d. dull pur & bl (Die II) (1888)	22·00	8·50	24·00
08	79	6d. purple/*rose-red*	20·00	8·50	15·00
08a		6d. deep purple/*rose-red*	20·00	8·50	
09	80	9d. dull purple and blue	48·00	30·00	55·00
10	81	10d. dull purple and carmine (shades) (24.2.90)	38·00	30·00	60·00
		aa. Imperf	£4000		
10a		10d. dull purple & dp dull carm	£350	£150	
10b		10d. dull purple and scarlet	50·00	38·00	
11	82	1s. dull green	£180	50·00	80·00
12	61	£1 green (28.1.91)	£2250	£400	
		a. Frame broken	£5000	£1000	

★197/212a **For well-centred, lightly used** .. +50%
The broken-frame varieties, No. 212a, are on Plate 2 stamps JC or JA, as illustrated above No. 185.
½d. stamps with "PEARS SOAP" printed on the back in *orange*, *blue* or *mauve*, price *from* £375 each.

900. *Colours changed. Wmk Imperial Crown, W* **49.**

			Un	Used	★ Used on cover
13	71	½d. blue-green (17.4)	1·25	1·00	5·00
		a. Printed on gummed side	—	†	
		b. Imperf	£1750		
14	82	1s. green and carmine (11.7)	45·00	£100	£250
97/214		Set of 14	£375	£225	

★213/14 **For well-centred, lightly used** .. +50%
The ½d., No. 213, in bright blue, is a colour changeling caused by a constituent of the ink used for some months in 1900.

KING EDWARD VII
22 January 1901–6 May 1910

PRINTINGS. Distinguishing De La Rue printings from the provisional printings of the same values made by Harrison & Sons Ltd. or at Somerset House may prove difficult in some cases. For very full guidance Volume 2 of the Stanley Gibbons *Great Britain Specialised Catalogue* should prove helpful.

Note that stamps perforated 15 × 14 must be Harrison; the 2½d., 3d. and 4d. in this perforation are useful reference material, their shades and appearance in most cases matching the Harrison perf 14 printings.

Except for the 6d. value, all stamps on chalk-surfaced paper were printed by De La Rue.

Of the stamps on ordinary paper, the De La Rue impressions are usually clearer and of a higher finish than those of the other printers. The shades are markedly different except in some printings of the 5d., 6d. and 7d. and in the 5s., 10s. and £1.

Used stamps in good, clean, unrubbed condition and with dated postmarks can form the basis of a useful reference collection, the dates often assisting in the assignment to the printers.

USED STAMPS. For well-centred, lightly used examples of King Edward VII stamps, add the following percentages to the used prices quoted below:

De La Rue printings (Nos. 215/66)—3d. values +35%, 4d. orange +100%, 6d. +75%, 7d. and 1s. +25%, all other values +50%.
Harrison printings (Nos. 267/86)—all values and perforations +75%.
Somerset House printings (Nos. 287/320)—1s. values +25%, all other values +50%.

83   84   85

86   87   88

89   90   91

92   93   94

95   96

97

(Des E. Fuchs)

1902 (1 Jan)–**10.** *Printed by De La Rue & Co. Wmk Imperial Crown (½d. to 1s.); Anchor (2s. 6d. to 10s.); Three Crowns (£1). Ordinary paper. P* 14.

			Un	Used	Used on cover
215	83	½d. dull blue-green (1.1.02)	1·00	75	1·00
216		½d. blue-green	1·00	75	
217		½d. pale yellowish grn (26.11.04)	1·00	75	1·00
218		½d. yellowish green	1·00	75	
		a. Booklet pane. Five stamps plus St. Andrew's Cross label (6.06)	£175		
		b. Doubly printed (bottom row on one pane) (Control H9)	£15000		
219		1d. scarlet (1.1.02)	1·00	75	1·00
220		1d. bright scarlet	1·00	75	
		a. Imperf (pair)	£8500		
221	84	1½d. dull purple & grn (21.3.02)	18·00	10·00	
222		1½d. slate-purple and green	20·00	9·00	15·00
223		1½d. pale dull pur & grn (chalk-surfaced paper) (8.05)	25·00	10·00	
224		1½d. slate-purple & bluish green (chalk-surfaced paper)	25·00	7·00	
225	85	2d. yellowish green & carmine-red (25.3.02)	25·00	10·00	18·00
226		2d. grey-grn & carm-red (1904)	25·00	10·00	
227		2d. pale grey-green & carm-red (chalk-surfaced paper) (4.06)	25·00	12·00	
228		2d. pale grey-grn & scar (chalk-surfaced paper) (1909)	22·00	12·00	
229		2d. dull blue-grn & carm (chalk-surfaced paper) (1907)	48·00	30·00	
230	86	2½d. ultramarine (1.1.02)	9·00	5·00	12·00
231		2½d. pale ultramarine	9·00	5·00	
232	87	3d. dull pur/orge-yell (20.3.02)	22·00	5·00	22·00
		a. Chalk-surfaced paper (3.06)	90·00	35·00	
232b		3d. deep purple/*orange-yellow*	22·00	6·00	
232c		3d. pale reddish pur/*orge-yell* (chalk-surfaced paper) (3.06)	85·00	25·00	
233		3d. dull reddish pur/*yell* (lemon back) (chalk-surfaced paper)	90·00	40·00	
233b		3d. pale purple/*lemon* (chalk-surfaced paper)	20·00	9·00	
234		3d. pur/*lemon* (chalk-surfaced paper)	20·00	9·00	
235	88	4d. green & grey-brn (27.3.02)	30·00	18·00	
236		4d. green and chocolate-brown	30·00	18·00	
		a. Chalk-surfaced paper (1.06)	22·00	10·00	30·00
238		4d. dp green & choc-brn (chalk-surfaced paper) (1.06)	22·00	10·00	
239		4d. brown-purple (1.11.09)	£100	90·00	
240		4d. pale orange (12.09)	12·00	10·00	28·00
241		4d. orange-red (12.09)	12·00	10·00	
242	89	5d. dull pur & ultram (14.5.02)	25·00	9·00	38·00
		a. Chalk-surfaced paper (5.06)	25·00	12·00	
244		5d. slate-pur & ultram (chalk-surfaced paper) (5.06)	25·00	12·00	

			Un	Used	Used on cover
245	83	6d. pale dull purple (1.1.02)	20·00	9·00	32·00
		a. Chalk-surfaced paper (1.06)	20·00	9·00	
246		6d. slate-purple	20·00	9·00	
248		6d. dull purple (chalk-surfaced paper) (1.06)	20·00	9·00	
249	90	7d. grey-black (4.5.10)	7·00	10·00	£140
249a		7d. deep grey-black	70·00	50·00	
250	91	9d. dull pur & ultram (7.4.02)	48·00	35·00	£140
		a. Chalk-surfaced paper (6.05)	48·00	38·00	
251		9d. slate-purple & ultramarine	48·00	35·00	
		a. Chalk-surfaced paper (6.05)	48·00	40·00	
254	92	10d. dull purple & carm (3.7.02)	48·00	40·00	£140
		a. No cross on crown	£200	£120	
		b. Chalk-surfaced paper (9.06)	48·00	30·00	
255		10d. slate-purple & carm (chalk-surfaced paper) (9.06)	48·00	38·00	
		a. No cross on crown	£175	£120	
256		10d. dull purple & scarlet (chalk-surfaced paper) (9.10)	45·00	48·00	
		a. No cross on crown	£160	£110	95·00
257	93	1s. dull green & carm (24.3.02)	42·00	15·00	
		a. Chalk-surfaced paper (9.05)	45·00	20·00	
259		1s. dull green & scarlet (chalk-surfaced paper) (9.10)	45·00	30·00	
260	94	2s. 6d. lilac (5.4.02)	£125	60·00	£550
261		2s. 6d. pale dull purple (chalk-surfaced paper) (7.10.05)	£120	£100	
262		2s. 6d. dull pur (chalk-surfaced paper)	£120	80·00	
263	95	5s. bright carmine (5.4.02)	£140	80·00	£600
264		5s. deep bright carmine	£140	80·00	
265	96	10s. ultramarine (5.4.02)	£375	£240	
266	97	£1 dull blue-green (16.6.02)	£900	£375	

97a

1910 (May). *Prepared for use by De La Rue but not issued. Wmk Imperial Crown, W* **49.** *P* 14.
266a **97a** 2d. Tyrian plum £13000
One example of this stamp is known used, but it was never issued to the public.

1911. *Printed by Harrison & Sons. Ordinary paper. Wmk Imperial Crown. (a) P* 14.

			Un	Used	Used on cover
267	83	½d. dull yellow-green (3.5.11)	2·00	1·00	3·00
268		½d. dull green	2·25	1·00	
269		½d. deep dull green	8·00	3·00	
270		½d. pale bluish green	30·00	28·00	
		a. Booklet pane. Five stamps plus St. Andrew's Cross label	£240		
		b. Wmk sideways	—	£12000	
		c. Imperf (pair)	£12000		
271		½d. brt green (fine impression) (6.11)	£190	£120	
272		1d. rose-red (3.5.11)	4·00	8·00	10·00
		a. No wmk	40·00	40·00	
273		1d. deep rose-red	4·00	7·00	
274		1d. rose-carmine	40·00	20·00	
275		1d. aniline pink (5.11)	£300	£140	
275a		1d. aniline rose	£100	90·00	
276	86	2½d. bright blue (10.7.11)	30·00	16·00	22·00
277	87	3d. purple/*lemon* (12.9.11)	48·00	£130	£400
277a		3d. grey/*lemon*	£2750		
278	88	4d. bright orange (12.7.11)	42·00	38·00	£110

(b) P 15 × 14

279	83	½d. dull green (30.10.11)	30·00	35·00	65·00
279a		½d. deep dull green	30·00	35·00	
280		1d. rose-red (4.10.11)	25·00	18·00	
281		1d. rose-carmine	10·00	9·00	18·00
282		1d. pale rose-carmine	15·00	8·00	
283	86	2½d. bright blue (14.10.11)	15·00	8·00	17·00
284		2½d. dull blue	15·00	8·00	
285	87	3d. purple/*lemon* (22.9.11)	25·00	8·00	20·00
285a		3d. grey/*lemon*	£2250		
286	88	4d. bright orange (11.11.11)	19·00	10·00	45·00
279/86		Set of 5	90·00	60·00	

1911–13. *Printed at Somerset House. Ordinary paper. Wmk as 1902–10. P* 14.

287	84	1½d. reddish purple and bright green (13.7.11)	30·00	22·00	
288		1½d. dull purple and green	15·00	15·00	32·00
289		1½d. slate-purple & grn (9.12)	18·00	16·00	
290	85	2d. dp dull grn & red (8.8.11)	16·00	10·00	32·00
291		2d. deep dull green & carmine	16·00	9·00	
292		2d. grey-green & bright carmine (carmine shows clearly on back) (11.3.12)	16·00	12·00	
293	89	5d. dull reddish purple and bright blue (7.8.11)	18·00	9·00	55·00
294		5d. deep dull reddish purple and bright blue	15·00	9·00	
295	83	6d. royal purple (31.10.11)	32·00	50·00	
296		6d. bright magenta (chalk-surfaced paper) (31.10.11)	£1900		
297		6d. dull purple	18·00	9·00	65·00
298		6d. reddish purple (11.11)	18·00	12·00	
		a. No cross on crown (various shades)	£225		
299		6d. very dp reddish pur (11.11)	30·00	26·00	
300		6d. dark purple (3.12)	20·00	20·00	
301		6d. dull purple ("Dickinson" coated paper) (3.13)	£110	95·00	
303		6d. deep plum (7.13)	15·00	50·00	
		a. No cross on crown	£250		
305	90	7d. slate-grey (1.8.12)	8·00	11·00	90·00
306	91	9d. reddish purple and light blue (24.7.11)	55·00	40·00	

306a	91	9d. deep dull reddish purple & deep bright blue (9.11)	55·00	40·00	
307		9d. dull reddish purple & blue (10.11)	38·00	30·00	£110
307a		9d. deep plum and blue (7.13)	38·00	40·00	
308		9d. slate-pur & cobalt-bl (3.12)	70·00	50·00	
309	92	10d. dull purple & scar (9.10.11)	55·00	40·00	
310		10d. dull reddish pur & aniline pink	£200	£140	
311		10d. dull reddish purple & carm (5.12)	45·00	30·00	£120
		a. No cross on crown	£500		
312	93	1s. dark green & scar (13.7.11)	65·00	35·00	
313		1s. dp green & scar (9.10.11)	45·00	20·00	
314		1s. green & carmine (15.4.12)	35·00	20·00	£100
315	94	2s. 6d. dull greyish purple (15.9.11)	£325	£180	
316		2s. 6d. dull reddish purple	£120	80·00	
317		2s. 6d. dark purple	£120	80·00	
318	95	5s. carmine (29.2.12)	£175	80·00	
319	96	10s. blue (14.1.12)	£425	£300	
320	97	£1 deep green (3.9.11)	£900	£400	

*No. 301 was on an experimental coated paper which does not respond to the silver test.

KING GEORGE V
6 May 1910–20 January 1936

Further detailed information on the issues of King George V will be found in Volume 2 of the Stanley Gibbons *Great Britain Specialised Catalogue.*

PRINTERS. Types **98** to **102** were typographed by Harrison & Sons Ltd, with the exception of certain preliminary printings made at Somerset House and distinguishable by the controls "A.11", "B.11" or "B.12" (the Harrison printings do not have a full stop after the letter). The booklet stamps, Nos. 334/7, and 344/5 were printed by Harrisons only.

WATERMARK VARIETIES. Many British stamps to 1967 exist without watermark owing to misplacement of the paper, and with either inverted, reversed, or inverted and reversed watermarks. A proportion of the low-value stamps issued in booklets have the watermark inverted in the normal course of printing.

Low values with *watermark sideways* are normally from stamp rolls used in machines with sideways delivery or, from June 1940, certain booklets.

STAMPS WITHOUT WATERMARK. Stamps found without watermark, due to misplacement of the sheet in relation to the dandy roll, are not listed here, but will be found in the *Great Britain Specialised Catalogue.*

The 1½d. and 5d. 1912–22, and 2d. and 2½d., 1924–26, listed here, are from *whole* sheets completely without watermark.

98   **99**

For type differences with T **101/2** *see* notes below the latter.

Die A   Die B

Dies of Halfpenny

Die A. The three upper scales on the body of the right hand dolphin form a triangle; the centre jewel of the cross inside the crown is suggested by a comma.

Die B. The three upper scales are incomplete; the centre jewel is suggested by a crescent.

Die A   Die B

Dies of One Penny

Die A. The second line of shading on the ribbon to the right of the crown extends right across the wreath; the line nearest to the crown on the right hand ribbon shows as a short line at the bottom of the ribbon.

Die B. The second line of shading is broken in the middle; the first line is little more than a dot.

(Des Bertram Mackennal and G. W. Eve. Head from photograph by W. & D. Downey. Die eng J. A. C. Harrison)

1911–12. *Wmk Imperial Crown, W* **49.** *P* 15 × 14.

				Un	Used
321	98	½d. pale green (Die A) (22.6.11)		4·00	1·50
322		½d. green (Die A) (22.6.11)		4·00	1·50
		a. Error. Perf 14 (8.11)		—	£300
323		½d. bluish green (Die A)		£260	£150
324		½d. yellow-green (Die B)		7·00	1·00
325		½d. bright green (Die B)		4·00	1·00
		a. Wmk sideways		—	£2500
326		½d. bluish green (Die B)		£150	90·00

327	99	1d. carmine-red (Die A) (22.6.11)		4·00	2·00
		c. Wmk sideways		†	—
328		1d. pale carmine (Die A) (22.6.11)		12·00	1·50
		a. No cross on crown		£300	£175
329		1d. carmine (Die B)		6·00	1·50
330		1d. pale carmine (Die B)		6·00	1·50
		a. No cross on crown		£400	£275
331		1d. rose-pink (Die B)		80·00	30·00
332		1d. scarlet (Die B) (6.12)		15·00	12·00
333		1d. aniline scarlet (Die B)		£110	70·00

For note on the aniline scarlet No. 333 see below No. 343.

100 Simple Cypher

1912 (Aug). *Booklet stamps. Wmk Royal Cypher* ("*Simple*"), *W* **100.** *P* 15 × 14.

334	98	½d. pale green (Die B)		28·00	30·00
335		½d. green (Die B)		28·00	30·00
336	99	1d. scarlet (Die B)		20·00	20·00
337		1d. bright scarlet (Die B)		20·00	20·00

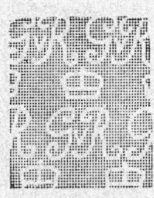

103 Multiple Cypher

Type differences

½d. In T **98** the ornament above "P" of "HALFPENNY" has two thin lines and the beard is well defined. In T **101** the ornament has one thick line and the beard is well defined.

1d. In T **99** the body of the lion is unshaded and in T **102** it is shaded.

101   **102**

1912 (1 Jan). *Wmk Imperial Crown, W* **49.** *P* 15 × 14.

338	101	½d. deep green		10·00	5·00
339		½d. green		5·00	1·00
340		½d. yellow-green		5·00	1·00
		a. No cross on crown		60·00	20·00
341	102	1d. bright scarlet		3·00	1·50
		a. No cross on crown		50·00	20·00
		b. Printed double, one albino		£110	
342		1d. scarlet		3·00	1·50
343		1d. aniline scarlet*		£120	70·00
		a. No cross on crown		£700	

* Our prices for the aniline scarlet 1d. stamps, Nos. 333 and 343, are for specimens in which the colour is suffused on the surface of the stamp and shows through clearly on the back. Specimens without these characteristics but which show "aniline" reactions under the quartz lamp are relatively common.

1912 (Aug). *Wmk Royal Cypher* ("*Simple*"), *W* **100.** *P* 15 × 14.

344	101	½d. green		5·00	1·00
		a. No cross on crown		70·00	20·00
345	102	1d. scarlet		6·00	1·50
		a. No cross on crown		70·00	20·00

1912 (Sept–Oct). *Wmk Royal Cypher* ("*Multiple*"), *W* **103.** *P* 15 × 14.

346	101	½d. green (Oct)		9·00	6·00
		a. No cross on crown		70·00	40·00
		b. Imperf		£100	
		c. Wmk sideways		†	£1200
		d. Printed on gummed side		—	†
347		½d. yellow-green		8·00	6·00
348		½d. pale green		8·00	6·00
349	102	1d. bright scarlet		8·00	6·00
350		1d. scarlet		8·00	6·00
		a. No cross on crown		80·00	22·00
		b. Imperf		80·00	
		c. Wmk sideways		80·00	80·00
		d. Wmk sideways. No cross on crown		£550	

104   **105**   **106**

No. 357a

No. 357ab

No. 357ac

107   **108**

Die I

Die II

Dies of 2d.

Die I.— Inner frame-line at top and sides close to solid of background. *Four* complete lines of shading between top of head and oval frame-line. These four lines do *not* extend to the oval itself. White line round "TWOPENCE" thin.

Die II.— Inner frame-line farther from solid of background. *Three* lines between top of head and extending to the oval. Whi[te] line round "TWOPENCE" thicker.

(Des Bertram Mackennal (heads) and G. W. Eve (frames). Coinag[e] head (½, 1½, 2, 3 and 4d.); large medal head (1d., 2½d.); intermedia[te] medal head (5d. to 1s.); small medal head used for fiscal stamp[s] Dies eng J. A. C. Harrison)

(Typo by Harrison & Sons Ltd., except the 6d. printed by th[e] Stamping Department of the Board of Inland Revenue, Somers[et] House. The latter also made printings of the following which c[an] only be distinguished by the controls: ½d. B.13; 1½d. A.12; 2[d.] C.13; 2½d. A.12; 3d. A.12, B.13, C.13; 4d. B.13; 5d. B.13; 7[d.] C.13; 8d. C.13; 9d. agate B.13; 10d. C.13; 1s. C.13)

1912–24. *Wmk Royal Cypher, W* **100.** *Chalk-surfaced paper* (6d.[...]) *P* 15 × 14.

351	105	½d. green (1.13)		75	5[...]
		a. Partial double print (half of bottom row from Control G15)		£15000	
		b. Gummed both sides			
352		½d. bright green		75	
353		½d. deep green		3·00	1·5[...]
354		½d. yellow-green		4·25	2·0[...]
355		½d. very yellow (Cyprus) green (1914)		£1750	
356		½d. blue-green		25·00	15·0[...]
357	104	1d. bright scarlet (8.10.12)		75	5[...]
		a. "Q" for "O" (R.1/4) (Control E14)		£150	90·0[...]
		ab. "Q" for "O" (R.4/11) (Control T22)		£300	£1[...]
		ac. Reversed "Q" for "O" (R.15/9) (Control T22)		£250	£1[...]
		ad. Inverted "Q" for "O" (R.20/3)		£325	£1[...]
		b. Tête-bêche (pair)		£50000	
358		1d. vermilion		2·25	1·5[...]
359		1d. pale rose-red		8·00	1·5[...]
360		1d. carmine-red		6·00	3·0[...]
361		1d. scarlet-vermilion		80·00	25·0[...]
		a. Printed on back†		£175	
362	105	1½d. red-brown (15.10.12)		1·75	5[...]
		a. "PENCF" (R.15/12)		£180	£12[...]
		b. Booklet pane. Four stamps plus two printed labels (2.24)		£300	
363		1½d. chocolate-brown		3·00	1·0[...]
		a. Without wmk		£120	90·0[...]
364		1½d. chestnut		3·00	5[...]
		a. "PENCF" (R.15/12)		£100	80·0[...]
365		1½d. yellow-brown		10·00	12·0[...]
366	106	2d. orange-yellow (Die I) (20.8.12)		5·00	2[...]
367		2d. reddish orange (Die I) (11.13)		2·00	1·0[...]
368		2d. orange (Die I)		2·00	1·0[...]
369		2d. bright orange (Die I)		2·50	1[...]
370		2d. orange (Die II) (9.21)		3·00	2·7[...]
371	104	2½d. cobalt-blue (18.10.12)		6·00	6·[...]
371a		2½d. bright blue (1914)		6·00	2·[...]
372		2½d. blue		6·00	2·0[...]
373		2½d. indigo-blue* (1920)		£850	£6[...]
373a		2½d. dull Prussian blue* (1921)		£475	£3[...]
374	106	3d. dull reddish violet (9.10.12)		7·00	1·5[...]
375		3d. violet		3·00	2·0[...]
376		3d. bluish violet (11.13)		4·00	1·5[...]
377		3d. pale violet		5·00	1·5[...]
378		4d. deep grey-green (15.1.13)		22·00	6·0[...]
379		4d. grey-green		6·00	1·5[...]
380		4d. pale grey-green		12·00	3·0[...]
381	107	5d. brown (30.6.13)		5·00	4·0[...]
382		5d. yellow-brown		6·00	4·0[...]
		a. Without wmk		£500	
383		5d. bistre-brown		75·00	30·0[...]
384		6d. dull purple (1.8.13)		15·00	6·0[...]
385		6d. reddish purple		8·00	3·[...]
		a. Perf 14 (10.20)		70·00	£1[...]
386		6d. deep reddish purple		15·00	3·0[...]
387		7d. olive (8.13)		10·00	5·0[...]
388		7d. bronze-green (1915)		45·00	18·0[...]
389		7d. sage-green (1917)		45·00	10·0[...]
390		8d. black/yellow (1.8.13)		22·00	9·0[...]
391		8d. black/yellow-buff (granite) (5.17)		25·00	12·0[...]
392	108	9d. agate (30.6.13)		12·00	4·0[...]
		a. Printed double, one albino			
393		9d. deep agate		14·00	4·0[...]
393a		9d. olive-green (9.22)		80·00	25·0[...]
393b		9d. pale olive-green		75·00	25·0[...]
394		10d. turquoise-blue (1.8.13)		12·00	15·0[...]
394a		10d. deep turquoise-blue		48·00	18·0[...]

5	108	1s. bistre (1.8.13)			12·00	2·00
6		1s. bistre-brown			22·00	7·00
1/95				Set of 15	£160	65·00

Imperf stamps of this issue exist but may be war-time colour trials.
† The impression of No. 361a is set sideways and is very pale.
* No. 373 comes from Control O 20 and also exists on toned paper.
‥ 373a comes from Control R 21 and also exists on toned paper, ‥t both are unlike the rare Prussian blue shade of the 1935 2½d. ‥bilee issue.
See also Nos. 418/29.
For the 2d., T 106 bisected, see note under Guernsey, War ‥ccupation Issues.

13 (Aug). *Wmk Royal Cypher* ("*Multiple*"). W 103. *P* 15×14.

‥7	105	½d. bright green			£150	£180
		a. Wmk sideways			†	£18000
‥8	104	1d. dull scarlet			£225	£225

Both these stamps were originally issued in rolls only. ‥bsequently sheets were found, so that horizontal pairs and blocks ‥ known but are of considerable rarity.

109

A

110 Single Cypher

Major Re-entries on 2s. 6d.

Nos. 400a and 408a

No. 415b

(Des Bertram Mackennal. Dies eng J. A. C. Harrison. Recess)

High values, so-called "Sea Horses" design: T **109**. *Background around portrait consists of horizontal lines, Type* A. *Wmk Single Cypher,* W **110**. *P* 11×12.

913 (30 June–Aug). *Printed by Waterlow Bros & Layton.*

‥99		2s. 6d. deep sepia-brown			£140	85·00
‥00		2s. 6d. sepia-brown			£130	75·00
		a. Re-entry (R.2/1)			£700	£450
‥01		5s. rose-carmine (4 July)			£225	£175
‥02		10s. indigo-blue (1 Aug)			£350	£275
‥03		£1 green (1 Aug)			£1200	725
‥04		£1 dull blue-green (1 Aug)			£1200	£775
★399/404 **For well-centred, lightly used**						+35%

915 (Nov–Dec). *Printed by De La Rue & Co.*

‥05		2s. 6d. deep yellow-brown			£150	80·00
‥06		2s. 6d. yellow-brown			£150	75·00
‥07		2s. 6d. pale brown (worn plate)			£140	75·00
‥08		2s. 6d. sepia (seal-brown)			£150	80·00
		a. Re-entry (R.2/1)			£600	£450
‥09		5s. bright carmine			£225	£160
‥10		5s. pale carmine (worn plate)			£300	£180
‥11		10s. deep blue (12.15)			£900	£450
‥12		10s. blue			£800	£400
‥13		10s. pale blue			£800	£400
★405/13 **For well-centred, lightly used**						+40%

918 (Dec)–19. *Printed by Bradbury, Wilkinson & Co, Ltd.*

‥13a		2s. 6d. olive-brown			65·00	35·00
‥14		2s. 6d. chocolate-brown			75·00	35·00
‥15		2s. 6d. reddish brown			80·00	35·00
‥15a		2s. 6d. pale brown			80·00	30·00
		b. Major re-entry (R.1/2)			£500	£275
‥16		5s. rose-red (1.19)			£170	50·00
‥17		10s. dull grey-blue (1.19)			£240	95·00
‥99/417				Set of 4	£1500	£800
★413a/17 **For well-centred, lightly used**						+35%

DISTINGUISHING PRINTINGS. Note that the £1 value was only printed by Waterlow.

Waterlow and De La Rue stamps measure exactly 22 mm vertically. In the De La Rue printings the gum is usually patchy and yellowish, and the colour of the stamp, particularly in the 5s. tends to show through the back. The holes of the perforation are smaller than those of the other two printers, but there is a thick perforation tooth at the top of each vertical side.

In the Bradbury Wilkinson printings the height of the stamp is 22¾ or 23 mm. On most of the 22¾ mm high stamps a minute coloured guide dot appears in the margin just above the middle of the upper frame-line.

For (1934) re-engraved Waterlow printings *see* Nos. 450/2.

UNITED KINGDOM OF GREAT BRITAIN AND NORTHERN IRELAND

111 Block Cypher **111a**

The watermark Type **111a**, as compared with Type **111**, differs as follows: Closer spacing of horizontal rows (12½ mm instead of 14½ mm). Letters shorter and rounder. Watermark thicker.

(Typo by Waterlow & Sons, Ltd (all values except 6d.) and later, 1934–35, by Harrison & Sons, Ltd (all values). Until 1934 the 6d. was printed at Somerset House where a printing of the 1½d. was also made in 1926 (identifiable only by control E.26). Printings by Harrisons in 1934–35 can be identified, when in mint condition, by the fact that the gum shows a streaky appearance vertically, the Waterlow gum being uniformly applied, but Harrisons also used up the balance of the Waterlow "smooth gum" paper)

1924 (Feb)–**26**. *Wmk Block Cypher,* W **111**. *P* 15×14.

418	105	½d. green			40	25
		a. Wmk sideways (5.24)			5·00	2·75
		b. Doubly printed			£7500	
419	104	1d. scarlet			40	25
		a. Wmk sideways			14·00	14·00
		b. Experimental paper, W **111a** (10.24)			22·00	
		c. Partial double print, one inverted				
		d. Inverted "Q" for "O" (R. 20/3)			£300	
420	105	1½d. red-brown			40	25
		a. *Tête-bêche* (pair)			£300	£525
		b. Wmk sideways (8.24)			6·00	3·00
		c. Printed on the gummed side			£325	†
		d. Booklet pane. Four stamps plus two printed labels (3.24)			90·00	
		e. Ditto. Wmk sideways			£3250	
		f. Experimental paper, W **111a** (10.24)			40·00	70·00
		g. Double impression			£8500	
421	106	2d. orange (Die II) (7.24)			1·50	1·25
		a. No wmk			£500	
		b. Wmk sideways (7.26)			60·00	70·00
		c. Partial double print			£13000	
422	104	2½d. blue (10.24)			3·25	1·50
		a. No wmk			£650	
		b. Wmk sideways			†	£3750
423	106	3d. violet (10.24)			5·50	1·50
424		4d. grey-green (11.24)			7·00	1·25
		a. Printed on the gummed side			£1600	†
425	107	5d. brown (11.24)			11·00	2·00
426		6d. reddish purple (*chalk-surfaced paper*) (9.24)			7·00	1·75
426a		6d. purple (6.26)			2·00	75
427	108	9d. olive-green (12.24)			7·00	2·50
428		10d. turquoise-blue (11.24)			22·00	22·00
429		1s. bistre-brown (10.24)			13·00	1·75
418/29				Set of 12	65·00	32·00

There are numerous shades in this issue.

The 6d. on both chalk-surfaced and ordinary papers was printed by both Somerset House and Harrisons. The Harrisons printings have streaky gum, differ slightly in shade, and that on chalk-surfaced paper is printed in a highly fugitive ink. The prices quoted are for the commonest (Harrison) printing in each case.

112

(Des H. Nelson. Eng J. A. C. Harrison. Recess Waterlow)

1924–25. *British Empire Exhibition.* W **111**. *P* 14.

(a) Dated "1924" (23.4.24)

| 430 | 112 | 1d. scarlet | | | 6·00 | 9·00 |
| 431 | | 1½d. brown | | | 9·00 | 13·00 |

(b) Dated "1925" (9.5.25)

| 432 | 112 | 1d. scarlet | | | 10·00 | 20·00 |
| 433 | | 1½d. brown | | | 30·00 | 55·00 |

113 **114** **115**

---

116 St. George and the Dragon

117

(Des J. Farleigh (T **113** and **115**), E. Linzell (T **114**) and H. Nelson (T **116**). Eng C. G. Lewis (T **113**), T. E. Storey (T **115**), both at the Royal Mint; J. A. C. Harrison, of Waterlow (T **114** and **116**). Typo by Waterlow from plates made at the Royal Mint, except T **116**, recess by Bradbury, Wilkinson from die and plate of their own manufacture)

1929 (10 May). *Ninth U.P.U. Congress, London.*

*(a) W **111**. P 15×14*

434	113	½d. green			2·00	2·00
		a. Wmk sideways			26·00	34·00
435	114	1d. scarlet			2·00	2·00
		a. Wmk sideways			45·00	48·00
436		1½d. purple-brown			1·75	1·50
		a. Wmk sideways			26·00	25·00
		b. Booklet pane. Four stamps plus two printed labels			£170	
437	115	2½d. blue			10·00	10·00

*(b) W **117**. P 12*

| 438 | 116 | £1 black | | | £650 | £450 |
| 434/7 | | | | Set of 4 (to 2½d.) | 14·00 | 14·00 |

PRINTERS. All subsequent issues to 1997 were printed in photogravure by Harrison and Sons Ltd, *except where otherwise stated.*

118 **119** **120**

121 **122**

1934–36. W **111**. *P* 15×14.

439	118	½d. green (19.11.34)			10	25
		a. Wmk sideways			7·00	3·50
		b. Imperf three sides			£1250	
440	119	1d. scarlet (24.9.34)			15	25
		a. Imperf (pair)			£950	
		b. Printed on the gummed side			£400	†
		c. Wmk sideways			11·00	4·75
		d. Double impression			†	£12500
		e. Imperf between (pair)			£1750	
		f. Imperf three sides (pair)			£1250	
441	118	1½d. red-brown (20.8.34)			10	25
		a. Imperf (pair)			£275	
		b. Imperf three sides (lower stamp in vert pair)			£700	
		c. Imperf between (horiz pair)				
		d. Wmk sideways			6·00	3·50
		e. Booklet pane. Four stamps plus two printed labels (1.35)			60·00	
442	120	2d. orange (21.1.35)			30	50
		a. Imperf (pair)			£1500	
		b. Wmk sideways			65·00	55·00
443	119	2½d. ultramarine (18.3.35)			1·25	1·00
444	120	3d. violet (18.3.35)			1·25	1·00
445		4d. deep grey-green (2.12.35)			1·75	1·00
446	121	5d. yellow-brown (17.2.36)			6·00	2·50
447	122	9d. deep olive-green (2.12.35)			12·00	2·00
448		10d. turquoise-blue (24.2.36)			15·00	10·00
449		1s. bistre-brown (24.2.36)			15·00	1·00
		a. Double impression				
439/49				Set of 11	48·00	18·00

Owing to the need for wider space for the perforations the size of the designs of the ½d. and 2d. were once, and the 1d. and 1½d. twice reduced from that of the first printings.

There are also numerous minor variations, due to the photographic element in the process.

The ½d. imperf three sides, No. 439b, is known in a block of four, from a sheet, in which the bottom pair is imperf at top and sides.

For No. 442 bisected, see Guernsey, War Occupation Issues.

B   123

(Eng J. A. C. Harrison. Recess Waterlow)

1934 (16 Oct). *T* **109** (*re-engraved*). *Background around portrait consists of horizontal and diagonal lines. Type B. W* **110**. *P* 11×12.

450	109	2s. 6d. chocolate-brown	..	55·00	25·00
451		5s. bright rose-red	..	*£110	70·00
452		10s. indigo	..	£275	60·00
450/2			*Set of 3*	£400	£140

There are numerous other minor differences in the design of this issue.

(Des B. Freedman)

1935 (7 May). *Silver Jubilee. W* **111**. *P* 15×14.

453	123	½d. green	.. ..	50	40
454		1d. scarlet	.. ..	1·25	1·50
455		1½d. red-brown	.. ..	50	40
456		2½d. blue	..	4·50	5·50
456a		2½d. Prussian blue	..	£3500	£3500
453/6			*Set of 4*	6·00	7·00

The 1½d. and 2½d. values differ from T **123** in the emblem in the panel at right.

Four sheets of No. 456a, printed in the wrong shade, were issued in error by the Post Office Stores Department on 25 June 1935. It is known that three of the sheets were sold from the sub-office at 134 Fore Street, Upper Edmonton, London, between that date and 4 July.

KING EDWARD VIII
20 January–10 December 1936

Further detailed information on the stamps of King Edward VIII will be found in Volume 2 of the Stanley Gibbons *Great Britain Specialised Catalogue*.

124   125

(Des H. Brown, adapted Harrison using a photo by Hugh Cecil)

1936. *W* **125**. *P* 15×14.

457	124	½d. green (1.9.36)	.. ..	20	20
		a. Double impression	.. ..		
458		1d. scarlet (14.9.36)	.. ..	50	25
459		1½d. red-brown (1.9.36)	..	25	20
		a. Booklet pane. Four stamps plus two printed labels (10.36)	..	50·00	
460		2½d. bright blue (1.9.36)	..	25	75
457/60			*Set of 4*	1·00	1·25

KING GEORGE VI
11 December 1936–6 February 1952

Further detailed information on the stamps of King George VI will be found in Volume 2 of the Stanley Gibbons *Great Britain Specialised Catalogue*.

126 King George VI and Queen Elizabeth

(Des E. Dulac)

1937 (13 May). *Coronation. W* **127**. *P* 15×14.

461	126	1½d. maroon	.. .. ..	50	40

127   128

129   130

King George VI and National Emblems

(Des T **128/9**, E. Dulac (head) and E. Gill (frames). T **130**, E. Dulac (whole stamp))

1937–47. *W* **127**. *P* 15×14.

462	128	½d. green (10.5.37)	.. ..	10	15
		a. Wmk sideways (1.38)	.. ..	25	25
		ab. Booklet pane of 4 (6.40)	..	25·00	
463		1d. scarlet (10.5.37)	.. ..	10	15
		a. Wmk sideways (2.38)	..	13·00	4·50
		ab. Booklet pane of 4 (6.40)	..	65·00	
464		1½d. red-brown (30.7.37)	..	20	15
		a. Wmk sideways (2.38)	..	80	1·00
		b. Booklet pane. Four stamps plus two printed labels (8.37)	..	45·00	
		c. Imperf three sides (pair)	..		
465		2d. orange (31.1.38)	..	75	50
		a. Wmk sideways (2.38)	..	65·00	28·00
		b. Bisected (on cover)	..	†	22·00
466		2½d. ultramarine (10.5.37)	..	25	15
		a. Wmk sideways (6.40)	..	50·00	16·00
		b. Tête-bêche (horiz pair)	..		
467		3d. violet (31.1.38)	..	3·25	90
468	129	4d. grey-green (21.11.38)	..	50	50
		a. Imperf (pair)	..	£2000	
		b. Imperf three sides (horiz pair)	..	£2500	
469		5d. brown (21.11.38)	..	2·00	60
		a. Imperf (pair)	..	£2500	
		b. Imperf three sides (horiz pair)	..	£2000	
470		6d. purple (30.1.39)	..	1·25	50
471	130	7d. emerald-green (27.2.39)	..	3·25	50
		a. Imperf three sides (horiz pair)	..	£2000	
472		8d. bright carmine (27.2.39)	..	3·50	60
473		9d. deep olive-green (1.5.39)	..	5·50	70
474		10d. turquoise-blue (1.5.39)	..	5·00	70
		aa. Imperf (pair)	..	£3500	
474a		11d. plum (29.12.47)	..	2·00	1·75
475		1s. bistre-brown (1.5.39)	..	5·75	60
462/75			*Set of 15*	30·00	7·50

For later printings of the lower values in apparently lighter shades and different colours, see Nos. 485/90 and 503/8.

No. 465b was authorised for use in Guernsey. See notes on War Occupation Issues.

Nos. 468b and 469b are perforated at foot only and each occurs in the same sheet as Nos. 468a and 469a.

No. 471a is also perforated at foot only, but occurs on the top row of a sheet.

131 King George VI   132 King George VI

133

(Des E. Dulac (T **131**) and Hon. G. R. Bellew (T **132**). Eng J. A. C. Harrison. Recess Waterlow)

1939–48. *W* **133**. *P* 14.

476	131	2s. 6d. brown (4.9.39)	..	38·00	6·50
476a		2s. 6d. yellow-green (9.3.42)	..	7·00	1·25
477		5s. red (21.8.39)	..	14·00	1·75
478	132	10s. dark blue (30.10.39)	..	£170	21·00
478a		10s. ultramarine (30.11.42)	..	35·00	5·50
478b		£1 brown (1.10.48)	..	10·00	23·00
476/8b			*Set of 6*	£250	55·00

134 Queen Victoria and King George VI.

(Des H. L. Palmer)

1940 (6 May). *Centenary of First Adhesive Postage Stamps. W* **127**. *P* 14½×14.

479	134	½d. green	.. ..	30	30
480		1d. scarlet	.. ..	1·00	50
481		1½d. red-brown	..	30	40
482		2d. orange	.. ..	50	50
		a. Bisected (on cover)	..	†	16·00
483		2½d. ultramarine	..	2·25	90
484		3d. violet	.. ..	3·00	3·25
479/84			*Set of 6*	6·50	5·25

No. 482a was authorised for use in Guernsey. See notes on War Occupation Issues.

1941–42. *Head as Nos. 462/7, but lighter background. W* **127**. *P* 15×14.

485	128	½d. pale green (1.9.41)	..	20	20
		a. Tête-bêche (horiz pair)	..	£3000	
		b. Imperf (pair)	..	£1750	
486		1d. pale scarlet (11.8.41)	..	20	20
		a. Wmk sideways (10.42)	..	3·50	5·00
		b. Imperf (pair)	..	£2500	
		c. Imperf three sides (horiz pair)	..	£2500	

487	128	1½d. pale red-brown (28.9.42)	..	85	55
488		2d. pale orange (6.10.41)	..	60	55
		a. Wmk sideways (6.42)	..	22·00	14·00
		b. Tête-bêche (horiz pair)	..	£2500	
		c. Imperf (pair)	..	£2000	
		d. Imperf pane*	..	£4500	
489		2½d. light ultramarine (21.7.41)	..	25	25
		a. Wmk sideways (8.42)	..	12·00	10·00
		b. Tête-bêche (horiz pair)	..	£2500	
		c. Imperf (pair)	..	£2250	
		d. Imperf pane*	..	£3500	
		e. Imperf three sides (horiz pair)	..	£3500	
490		3d. pale violet (3.11.41)	..	1·75	60
485/90			*Set of 6*	3·50	2·00

The *tête-bêche* varieties are from defectively made-up booklets.

Nos. 486c and 489e are perforated at foot only and occur in the same sheets as Nos. 486b and 489c.

*BOOKLET ERRORS. Those listed as "imperf panes" show one row of perforations either at the top or at the bottom of the pane of 6.

WATERMARK VARIETIES. Please note that *inverted watermarks* are outside the scope of this listing but are fully listed in the *Great Britain Specialised* and *Great Britain Concise* Catalogues. See also the notes about watermarks at the beginning of the King George V section.

135

136 Symbols of Peace and Reconstruction

(Des H. L. Palmer (T **135**) and R. Stone (T **136**))

1946 (11 June). *Victory. W* **127**. *P* 15×14.

491	135	2½d. ultramarine	.. ..	30	20
492	136	3d. violet	..	30	20

137   138 King George VI and Queen Elizabeth

(Des G. Knipe and Joan Hassall from photographs by Dorothy Wilding)

1948 (26 Apr). *Royal Silver Wedding. W* **127**. *P* 15×14 (2½d.) or 14×15 (£1).

493	137	2½d. ultramarine	..	30	20
494	138	£1 blue	..	38·00	35·00

1948 (10 May). Stamps of 1d. and 2½d. showing seaweed-gathering were on sale at eight Head Post Offices in Great Britain, but were primarily for use in the Channel Islands and are listed there (see after Great Britain Postal Fiscals).

139 Globe and Laurel Wreath

140 "Speed"

141 Olympic Symbol

142 Winged Victory

(Des P. Metcalfe (T **139**), A. Games (T **140**), S. D. Scott (T **141**) and E. Dulac (T **142**))

1948 (29 July). *Olympic Games.* W **127**. P 15 × 14.

95	**139**	2½d. ultramarine	..	..	10	10
96	**140**	3d. violet	..	..	30	30
97	**141**	6d. bright purple	..	..	60	30
98	**142**	1s. brown	..	..	1·25	1·50
95/8	..	..	..	*Set of* 4	2·00	2·00

143 Two Hemispheres

144 U.P.U. Monument, Berne

145 Goddess Concordia, Globe and Points of Compass

146 Posthorn and Globe

(Des Mary Adshead (T **143**), P. Metcalfe (T **144**), H. Fleury (T **145**) and Hon. G. R. Bellew (T **146**))

1949 (10 Oct). *75th Anniv of Universal Postal Union.* W **127**. P 15 × 14.

499	**143**	2½d. ultramarine	..	..	10	10
500	**144**	3d. violet	..	..	30	40
501	**145**	6d. bright purple	..	..	60	75
502	**146**	1s. brown	..	..	1·25	1·50
499/502	..	..	..	*Set of* 4	2·00	2·75

1950–52. 4d. *as Nos.* 468 *and others as Nos.* 485/9, *but colours changed.* W **127**. P 15 × 14.

503	**128**	½d. pale orange (3.5.51)	..		30	30
		a. Imperf (pair)	..	..		
		b. *Tête-bêche* (horiz pair)	..		£3000	
		c. Imperf pane*	..		£4000	
504		1d. light ultramarine (3.5.51)	..		30	30
		a. Wmk sideways (5.51)	..		50	60
		b. Imperf (pair)	..		£2000	
		c. Imperf three sides (horiz pair)		£1500	
		d. Booklet pane. Three stamps plus three printed labels (3.52)		15·00	
		e. Ditto. Partial *tête-bêche* pane		£2500	
505		1½d. pale green (3.5.51)	..		35	50
		a. Wmk sideways (9.51)	..		2·25	3·00
506		2d. pale red-brown (3.5.51)	..		35	30
		a. Wmk sideways (5.51)	..		1·25	1·40
		b. *Tête-bêche* (horiz pair)	..		£3000	
		c. Imperf three sides (horiz pair)		£1500	
507		2½d. pale scarlet (3.5.51)	..		35	30
		a. Wmk sideways (5.51)	..		1·25	1·25
		b. *Tête-bêche* (horiz pair)	..			
508	**129**	4d. light ultramarine (2.10.50)	..		2·25	1·50
		a. Double impression	..	†	£5000	
503/8	..	..	..	*Set of* 6	3·50	2·75

No. 504c is perforated at foot only and occurs in the same sheet as No. 504b.

No. 506c is also perforated at foot only.

*BOOKLET ERRORS. Those listed as "imperf panes" show one row of perforations either at the top or at the bottom of the pane of 6.

147 H.M.S. *Victory*

148 White Cliffs of Dover

149 St. George and the Dragon

150 Royal Coat of Arms

(Des Mary Adshead (T **147/8**), P. Metcalfe (T **149/50**). Recess Waterlow)

1951 (3 May). W **133**. P 11 × 12.

509	**147**	2s. 6d. yellow-green	..	..	6·00	75
510	**148**	5s. red	..	..	..	32·00	1·50
511	**149**	10s. ultramarine	..	..	21·00	8·00
512	**150**	£1 brown	..	..	32·00	18·00
509/12	..	..	..	*Set of* 4	80·00	24·00

151 "Commerce and Prosperity"

152 Festival Symbol

(Des E. Dulac (T **151**), A. Games (T **152**))

1951 (3 May). *Festival of Britain.* W **127**. P 15 × 14.

513	**151**	2½d. scarlet	..	..	25	20
514	**152**	4d. ultramarine	..	..	50	45

QUEEN ELIZABETH II
6 February 1952

Further detailed information on the stamps of Queen Elizabeth II will be found in volumes 3, 4 and 5 of the Stanley Gibbons *Great Britain Specialised Catalogue.*

USED PRICES. For Nos. 515 onwards the used prices quoted are for examples with circular dated postmarks.

153 Tudor Crown

154

155	156	157

158	159	160

Queen Elizabeth II and National Emblems

I II

Types of 2½d. Type I:—In the frontal cross of the diadem, the top line is only half the width of the cross.
Type II:—The top line extends to the full width of the cross and there are signs of strengthening in other parts of the diadem.

(Des Enid Marx (T **154**), M. Farrar-Bell (T **155/6**), G. Knipe (T **157**), Mary Adshead (T **158**), E. Dulac (T **159/60**). Portrait by Dorothy Wilding)

1952–54. W **153**. P 15 × 14.

515	**154**	½d. orange-red (31.8.53)	..	..	10	15
516		1d. ultramarine (31.8.53)	..	..	20	20
		a. Booklet pane. Three stamps plus three printed labels	..		22·00	
517		1½d. green (5.12.52)	..	..	10	15
		a. Wmk sideways (15.10.54)	..		50	70
		b. Imperf pane*	..			
518		2d. red-brown (31.8.53)	..	..	20	15
		a. Wmk sideways (8.10.54)	..		1·00	1·75
519	**155**	2½d. carmine-red (Type I) (5.12.52)		10	15
		a. Wmk sideways (15.11.54)	..		8·50	8·50
		b. Type II (Booklets) (5.53)	..		1·25	1·00
520		3d. deep lilac (18.1.54)	..		1·00	75
521	**156**	4d. ultramarine (2.11.53)	..		3·00	1·25
522	**157**	5d. brown (6.7.53)	..		90	2·75
523		6d. reddish purple (18.1.54)	..		3·00	90
		a. Imperf three sides (pair)	..			
524		7d. bright green (18.1.54)	..		9·00	5·00
525	**158**	8d. magenta (6.7.53)	..		1·00	1·00
526		9d. bronze-green (8.2.54)	..		22·00	3·75
527		10d. Prussian blue (8.2.54)	..		18·00	3·75
528		11d. brown-purple (8.2.54)	..		30·00	20·00
529	**159**	1s. bistre-brown (6.7.53)	..		1·25	60
530	**160**	1s. 3d. green (2.11.53)	..		4·50	3·00
531	**159**	1s. 6d. grey-blue (2.11.53)	..		11·00	3·50
515/31	..	..	..	*Set of* 17	95·00	42·00

*BOOKLET ERRORS—This pane of 6 stamps is completely imperf (see No. 540a, etc.).

See also Nos. 540/56, 561/6, 570/94 and 599/618a.

For stamps as Type **157** with face values in decimal currency see Nos. 2031/3.

161

162

163

164

(Des E. Fuller (2½d.), M. Goaman (4d.), E. Dulac (1s. 3d.), M. Farrar-Bell (1s. 6d.), Portrait (except 1s. 3d.) by Dorothy Wilding)

1953 (3 June). *Coronation.* W **153**. P 15 × 14.

532	**161**	2½d. carmine-red	..	..	10	50
533	**162**	4d. ultramarine	..	..	40	1·75
534	**163**	1s. 3d. deep yellow-green	..		3·50	2·75
535	**164**	1s. 6d. deep grey-blue	..		7·00	3·50
532/5	..	..	..	*Set of* 4	10·00	7·50

165 St. Edward's Crown   166 Carrickfergus Castle

167 Caernarvon Castle

168 Edinburgh Castle

169 Windsor Castle

(Des L. Lamb. Portrait by Dorothy Wilding. Recess Waterlow (until 31.12.57) and De La Rue (subsequently))

1955–58. W **165.** P 11 × 12.

536	166	2s. 6d. black-brown (23.9.55)	10·00	2·00
		a. De La Rue printing (17.7.58)	30·00	2·50
537	167	5s. rose-carmine (23.9.55)	30·00	3·50
		a. De La Rue printing (30.4.58)	75·00	10·00
538	168	10s. ultramarine (1.9.55)	80·00	12·00
		a. De La Rue printing. *Dull ultramarine* (25.4.58)	£170	20·00
539	169	£1 black (1.9.55)	£130	38·00
		a. De La Rue printing (28.4.58)	£300	60·00
536/9		*Set of 4*	£225	50·00
536a/9a		*Set of 4*	£525	85·00

See also Nos. 595/8a and 759/62.

On 1 January 1958, the contract for printing the high values, T **166** to **169** was transferred to De La Rue & Co, Ltd.

The work of the two printers is very similar, but the following notes will be helpful to those attempting to identify Waterlow and De La Rue stamps of the W **165** issue.

The De La Rue sheets are printed in pairs and have a ⊣ or ⊢ shaped guide-mark at the centre of one side-margin, opposite the middle row of perforations, indicating left- and right-hand sheets respectively.

The Waterlow sheets have a small circle (sometimes crossed) instead of a "⊢" and this is present in both side-margins opposite the 6th row of stamps, though one is sometimes trimmed off. Short dashes are also present in the perforation gutter between the marginal stamps marking the middle of the four sides and a cross is at the centre of the sheet. The four corners of the sheet have two lines forming a right-angle as trimming marks, but some are usually trimmed off. All these gutter marks and sheet-trimming marks are absent in the De La Rue printings.

De La Rue used the Waterlow die and no alterations were made to it, so that no difference exists in the design or its size, but the making of new plates at first resulted in slight but measurable variations in the width of the gutters between stamps, particularly the horizontal, as follows:

		W.	D.L.R.
Horiz gutters, mm		3.8 to 4.0	3.4 to 3.8

Later D.L.R. plates were however less distinguishable in this respect.

For a short time in 1959 the D.L.R. 2s. 6d. appeared with one dot in the bottom margin below the first stamp.

It is possible to sort singles with reasonable certainty by general characteristics. The individual lines of the D.L.R. impression are cleaner and devoid of the whiskers of colour of Waterlow's, and the whole impression lighter and softer.

Owing to the closer setting of the horizontal rows the strokes of the perforating comb are closer; this results in the topmost tooth on each side of the De La Rue stamps being narrower than the corresponding teeth in Waterlow's which were more than normally broad.

Shades also help. The 2s. 6d. D.L.R. is a warmer, more chocolate shade than the blackish brown of W.; the 5s. a lighter red with less carmine than W's; the 10s. more blue and less ultramarine; the £1 less intense black.

The paper of D.L.R. printings is uniformly white, identical with that of W. printings from February 1957 onwards, but earlier W. printings are on paper which is creamy by comparison.

In this and later issues of T **166/9** the dates given for changes of watermark or paper are those on which supplies were first sent by the Supplies Department to Postmasters.

1955–58. W **165.** P 15 × 14.

540	154	½d. orange-red (booklets 8.55, sheets 12.12.55)	10	15
		a. Part perf pane*	£1200	
541		1d. ultramarine (19.9.55)	25	15
		a. Booklet pane. Three stamps plus three printed labels	13·00	
		b. *Tête-bêche* (horiz pair)		
542		1½d. green (booklets 8.55, sheets 11.10.55)	25	25
		a. Wmk sideways (7.3.56)	25	75
		b. *Tête-bêche* (horiz pair)	£900	
543		2d. red-brown (6.9.55)	20	25
		aa. Imperf between (vert pair)	£1500	
		a. Wmk sideways (31.7.56)	20	60
		ab. Imperf between (horiz pair)	£1500	
543b		2d. light red-brown (17.10.56)	20	25
		ba. *Tête-bêche* (horiz pair)	£600	
		bb. Imperf pane*		
		bc. Part perf pane*	£1200	
		d. Wmk sideways (5.3.57)	9·00	5·50
544	155	2½d. carmine-red (Type I) (28.9.55)	20	25
		a. Wmk sideways (Type I) (23.3.56)	1·25	1·25
		b. Type II (booklets 9.55, sheets 1957)	25	50
		ba. *Tête-bêche* (horiz pair)	£750	
		bb. Imperf pane*	£900	
		bc. Part perf pane*		
545		3d. deep lilac (17.7.56)	20	25
		aa. *Tête-bêche* (horiz pair)	£750	
		a. Imperf three sides (pair)	£500	
		b. Wmk sideways (22.11.57)	14·00	12·50
546	156	4d. ultramarine (14.11.55)	1·40	50
547	157	5d. brown (21.9.55)	4·00	4·75
548		6d. reddish purple (20.12.55)	4·00	1·00
		aa. Imperf three sides (pair)	£400	
		a. *Deep claret* (8.5.58)	4·00	1·25
		ab. Imperf three sides (pair)	£400	
549		7d. bright green (23.4.56)	50·00	9·00

550	158	8d. magenta (21.12.55)	6·00	1·00
551		9d. bronze-green (15.12.55)	23·00	2·75
552		10d. Prussian blue (22.9.55)	19·00	2·75
553		11d. brown-purple (28.10.55)	50	1·50
554	159	1s. bistre-brown (3.11.55)	19·00	50
555	160	1s. 3d. green (27.3.56)	27·00	1·50
556	159	1s. 6d. grey-blue (27.3.56)	19·00	1·50
540/56		*Set of 18*	£150	23·00

The dates given for Nos. 540/556 are those on which they were first issued by the Supplies Dept to postmasters.

In December 1956 a completely imperforate sheet of No. 543b was noticed by clerks in a Kent post office, one of whom purchased it against P.O. regulations. In view of this irregularity we do not consider it properly issued.

Types of 2½d. In this issue, in 1957, Type II formerly only found in stamps from booklets, began to replace Type I on sheet stamps.

*BOOKLET ERRORS. Those listed as "imperf panes" show one row of perforations either at top or bottom of the booklet pane; those as "part perf panes" have one row of 3 stamps imperf on three sides.

170 Scout Badge and "Rolling Hitch"

171 "Scouts coming to Britain"

172 Globe within a Compass

(Des Mary Adshead (2½d.), P. Keely (4d.), W. H. Brown (1s. 3d.))

1957 (1 Aug). *World Scout Jubilee Jamboree.* W **165.** P 15 × 14.

557	170	2½d. carmine-red	15	25
558	171	4d. ultramarine	50	1·25
559	172	1s. 3d. green	5·00	4·75
557/9		*Set of 3*	5·00	5·50

173 ½d. to 1½d., 2½d., 3d.   2d.

Graphite-line arrangements
(Stamps viewed from back)

1957 (12 Sept). *46th Inter-Parliamentary Union Conference.* W **165.** P 15 × 14.

560	173	4d. ultramarine	1·00	1·25

GRAPHITE-LINED ISSUES. These were used in connection with automatic sorting machinery, first introduced experimentally at Southampton in December 1957.

The graphite lines were printed in black on the back, beneath the gum; two lines per stamp, except for the 2d.

In November 1959 phosphor bands were introduced (see notes after No. 598).

1957 (19 Nov). *Graphite-lined issue. Two graphite lines on the back, except 2d. value, which has one line.* W **165.** P 15 × 14.

561	154	½d. orange-red	20	30
562		1d. ultramarine	20	50
563		1½d. green	1·50	2·00
		a. Both lines at left	£800	£400
564		2d. light red-brown	2·50	2·75
		a. Line at left	£500	£175
565	155	2½d. carmine-red (Type II)	8·00	7·00
566		3d. deep lilac	30	70
561/6		*Set of 6*	10·50	11·50

No. 564a results from a misplacement of the line and horizontal pairs exist showing one stamp without line. No. 563a results from a similar misplacement.

See also Nos. 587/94.

176 Welsh Dragon

177 Flag and Games Emblem

178 Welsh Dragon

(Des R. Stone (3d.), W. H. Brown (6d.), P. Keely (1s. 3d.))

1958 (18 July). *Sixth British Empire and Commonwealth Games, Cardiff.* W **165.** P 15 × 14.

567	176	3d. deep lilac	15	
568	177	6d. reddish purple	25	
569	178	1s. 3d. green	2·75	2·
567/9		*Set of 3*	2·75	2·

179 Multiple Crowns

1958–65. W **179.** P 15 × 14.

570	154	½d. orange-red (25.11.58)	10	
		a. Wmk sideways (26.5.61)	10	
		c. Part perf pane*	£1000	
		k. Chalk-surfaced paper (15.7.63)	2·00	2·
		l. Booklet pane. No. 570a×4	3·00	
		m. Booklet pane. No. 570k×3 *se-tenant* with 574k	9·50	
		n. Booklet pane. No. 570a×2 *se-tenant* with 574l×2 (1.7.64)	2·00	
571		1d. ultramarine (booklets 11.58, sheets 24.3.59)	10	
		aa. Imperf (vert pair from coil)		
		a. Wmk sideways (26.5.61)	1·00	
		b. Part perf pane*	£1200	
		c. Imperf pane		
		l. Booklet pane. No. 571a×4	4·25	
		m. Booklet pane. No. 571a×2 *se-tenant* with 574a×2 (1d. values at left) (16.8.65)	9·00	
		ma. Ditto. 1d. values at right	10·00	
572		1½d. grn (booklets 12.58, sheets 30.8.60)	10	
		a. Imperf three sides (horiz strip of 3)		
		b. Wmk sideways (26.5.61)	8·00	4·
		l. Booklet pane. No. 572b×4	30·00	
573		2d. light red-brown (4.12.58)	10	
		a. Wmk sideways (3.4.59)	50	1·
574	155	2½d. carmine-red (Type I) (booklets 11.58, sheets 15.9.59)	10	
		a. Imperf strip of 3		
		b. *Tête-bêche* (horiz pair)		
		c. Imperf pane	£1200	
		d. Wmk sideways (Type I) (10.11.60)	20	
		da. Imperf strip of 6		
		e. Type I (wmk upright) (4.10.61)	15	
		k. Chalk-surfaced paper (Type II) (15.7.63)	20	4
		l. Wmk sideways (Type II) Ord paper (1.7.64)	75	1·2
575		3d. deep lilac (booklets 11.58, sheets 8.12.58)	10	2
		a. Wmk sideways (24.10.58)	15	2
		b. Imperf pane*	£850	
		c. Part perf pane*		
		d. Phantom "R" (Cyl 41 no dot)	£275	
		e. Phantom "R" (Cyl 37 no dot)	28·00	
		l. Booklet pane. No. 575a×4 (26.5.61)	2·50	
576	156	4d. ultramarine (29.10.58)	50	2
		a. *Deep ultramarine*†† (28.4.65)	15	2
		ab. Wmk sideways (31.5.65)	45	3
		ac. Imperf pane*	£1200	
		ad. Part perf pane*	£800	
		al. Booklet pane. No. 576ab×4 (16.8.65)	2·50	
577		4½d. chestnut (9.2.59)	10	2
578	157	5d. brown (10.11.58)	25	4
579		6d. deep claret (23.12.58)	40	3
		a. Imperf three sides (pair)	£450	
		b. Imperf (pair)	£550	
580		7d. bright green (26.11.58)	40	6
581	158	8d. magenta (24.2.60)	40	3
582		9d. bronze-green (24.3.59)	40	5
583		10d. Prussian blue (18.11.58)	1·00	5
584	159	1s. bistre-brown (30.10.58)	50	3
585	160	1s. 3d. green (17.6.59)	25	3
586	159	1s. 6d. grey-blue (16.12.58)	4·00	4
570/86		*Set of 17*	8·00	4·2

*BOOKLET ERRORS. See note after No. 556.

††This "shade" was brought about by making more deeply etched cylinders, resulting in apparent depth of colour in parts of the design. There is no difference in the colour of the ink.

Sideways watermark. The 2d., 2½d., 3d. and 4d. come from coils and the ½d., 1d., 1½d., 2½d., 3d. and 4d. come from booklets. In coil stamps the sideways watermark shows the top of the watermark to the left *as seen from the front of the stamp.* In the *booklet* stamps it comes equally to the left or right.

Nos. 570k and 574k only come from 2s. "Holiday Resort" Experimental undated booklets issued in 1963, in which one page contained 1 × 2½d. *se-tenant* with 3 × ½d. (See No. 570l).

No. 574l comes from coils, and the "Holiday Resort" Experimental booklets dated "1964" comprising four panes each containing two of these 2½d. stamps *se-tenant* vertically with two ½d. No. 570a (See No. 570m).

2½d. imperf No. 574a comes from a booklet with watermark upright. No. 574da is from a coil with sideways watermark.

No. 574e comes from *sheets* bearing cylinder number 42 and is also known on vertical delivery coils.

No. 575d and 615a occurred below the last stamp of the sheet from Cyl 41 (no dot), where an incomplete marginal rule revealed an "R". The cylinder was later twice retouched. The stamps listed show

...e original, unretouched "R". The rare variety, No. 575d, is best ...llected in a block of 4 or 6 with full margins in order to be sure that ... is not No. 615a with phosphor lines removed.

No. 575e is a similar variety but from Cyl. 37 (no dot). The ...arginal rule is much narrower and only a very small part of the "R" ... revealed. The cylinder was later retouched. The listed variety is for ...e original, unretouched state.

WHITER PAPER. On 18 May 1962 the Post Office announced that ... whiter paper was being used for the current issue (including Nos. ...95/8). This is beyond the scope of this catalogue, but the whiter ...apers are listed in Vol. 3 of the Stanley Gibbons *Great Britain* ...ecialised Catalogue.

...58 (24 Nov)–**61.** *Graphite-lined issue. Two graphite lines on the* ...back, except 2d. value, which has one line. W 179. P 15 × 14.

...87	154	½d. orange-red (15.6.59)†	6·00	7·50
...88		1d. ultramarine (18.12.58)	1·00	1·50
		a. Misplaced graphite lines (7.61)*	1·00	1·25
...89		1½d. green (4.8.59)†	40·00	40·00
...90		2d. light red-brown (24.11.58)	6·00	3·25
...91	155	2½d. carmine-red (Type II) (9.6.59)	8·00	10·00
...92		3d. deep lilac (24.11.58)	75	50
		a. Misplaced graphite lines (5.61)*	£375	£350
...93	156	4d. ultramarine (29.4.59)	3·50	4·50
		a. Misplaced graphite lines (1961)*	£1500	
...94		4½d. chestnut (3.6.59)	5·00	4·00
...87/94		*Set of 8*	60·00	60·00

Nos. 587/9 were only issued in booklets or coils (587/8).

*No. 588a (in coils), and Nos. 592a and 593a (both in sheets) result ...om the use of a residual stock of graphite-lined paper. As the use of ...raphite lines had ceased, the register of the lines in relation to the ...amps was of no importance and numerous misplacements oc-...urred—two lines close together, one line only, etc. No. 588a refers ... two lines at left or at right; No. 592a refers to stamps with two ...nes only at left and both clear of the perforations and No. 593a to ...amps with two lines at left (with left line down perforations) and ...aces of a third line down the opposite perforations.

†The prices quoted are for stamps with the watermark inverted. *Prices for upright watermark ½d. £7 un, £7 us; 1½d. £95 un, £60 us.*)

(Recess D.L.R. (until 31.12.62), then B.W.)

...959–68. W 179. P 11 × 12.

...95	166	2s. 6d. black-brown (22.7.59)	10·00	75
		a. B.W. printing (1.7.63)	50	30
		k. Chalk-surfaced paper (30.5.68)	50	1·25
...96	167	5s. scarlet-vermilion (15.6.59)	60·00	2·00
		a. B.W. ptg. *Red (shades)* (3.9.63)	1·00	60
		ab. Printed on the gummed side	£750	
...97	168	10s. blue (21.7.59)	38·00	5·00
		a. B.W. ptg. *Bright ultram* (16.10.63)	3·00	3·50
...98	169	£1 black (23.6.59)	90·00	12·00
		a. B.W. printing (14.11.63)	8·00	5·50
...95/8		*Set of 4*	£170	17·00
...95a/8a		*Set of 4*	11·00	9·00

The B.W. printings have a marginal Plate Number. They are ...enerally more deeply engraved than the D.L.R., showing more of ...e Diadem detail and heavier lines on Her Majesty's face. The ...ertical perf is 11.9 to 12 as against D.L.R. 11.8.

See also Nos. 759/62.

PHOSPHOR BAND ISSUES. These are printed on the front and ...re wider than graphite lines. They are not easy to see but show as ...road vertical bands at certain angles to the light.

Values representing the rate for printed papers (and when this was ...bolished in 1968 for second class mail) have one band and others ...wo, three or four bands as stated, according to the size and format.

In the small size stamps the bands are on each side with the single ...and at left (*except where otherwise stated*). In the large-size ...ommemorative stamps the single band may be at left, centre or ...ight, varying in different designs. The bands are vertical on both ...orizontal and vertical designs *except where otherwise stated*.

The phosphor was originally applied typographically but later ...sually by photogravure and sometimes using flexography, a ...ypographical process using rubber cylinders.

Three different types of phosphor have been used, distinguishable ...y the colour emitted under an ultra-violet lamp, the first being ...reen, then blue and now violet. Different sized bands are also ...nown. All these are fully listed in Vol. 3 of the Stanley Gibbons *Great Britain Specialised Catalogue.*

Varieties. Misplaced and missing phosphor bands are known but ...uch varieties are beyond the scope of this Catalogue.

...959 (18 Nov). *Phosphor-Graphite issue. Two phosphor bands on front* ...and two graphite lines on back, except 2d. value, which has one band ...on front and one line on back. P 15 × 14. (a) W 165.

...99	154	½d. orange-red	4·00	6·00
...00		1d. ultramarine	9·00	7·00
...01		1½d. green	2·00	6·00

(b) W 179

...05	154	2d. light red-brown (1 band)	4·50	4·00
		a. Error. W 165	£170	£170
...06	155	2½d. carmine-red (Type II)	20·00	13·00
...07		3d. deep lilac	9·00	8·00
...08	156	4d. ultramarine	12·00	25·00
...09		4½d. chestnut	35·00	15·00
...99/609		*Set of 8*	80·00	70·00

Examples of the 2½d., No. 606, exist showing watermark W 165 in ...error. It is believed that phosphor-graphite stamps of this value ...with this watermark were not used by the public for postal ...purposes.

...1960 (22 June)–**67.** *Phosphor issue. Two phosphor bands on front,* ...except where otherwise stated. W 179. P 15 × 14.

...610	154	½d. orange-red	10	15
		a. Wmk sideways (14.7.61)	10·00	10·00
		l. Booklet pane. No. 610a×4	35·00	
...611		1d. ultramarine	10	10
		a. Wmk sideways (14.7.61)	35	40
		l. Booklet pane. No. 611a×4	8·00	
		m. Booklet pane. No. 611a×2 *se-tenant* with 615d×2† (16.8.65)	12·50	
		n. Booklet pane. No. 611a×2 *se-tenant* with 615b×2†† (11.67)	7·00	
...612		1½d. green	10	20
		a. Wmk sideways (14.7.61)	10·00	10·00
		l. Booklet pane. No. 612a×4	40·00	
...613		2d. light red-brown (1 band)	22·00	19·00
...613a		2d. lt red-brown (two bands) (4.10.61)	10	10
		aa. Imperf three sides***	15	
		ab. Wmk sideways (6.4.67)	15	60

614	155	2½d. carmine-red (Type II) (2 bands)*	10	50
614a		2½d. carmine-red (Type II) (1 band) (4.10.61)	50	1·00
614b		2½d. carmine-red (Type I) (1 band) (4.10.61)	32·00	30·00
615		3d. deep lilac (2 bands)	60	75
		a. Phantom "R" (Cyl 41 no dot)	28·00	
		b. Wmk sideways (14.7.61)	1·75	1·50
		l. Booklet pane. No. 615b×4	4·00	
615c		3d. deep lilac (1 side band) (29.4.65)	50	75
		d. Wmk sideways (16.8.65)	5·00	4·00
		e. One centre band (8.12.66)	25	40
		ea. Wmk sideways (19.6.67)	40	75
616	156	4d. ultramarine	3·00	3·00
		a. Deep ultramarine (28.4.65)	30	30
		aa. Part perf pane		
		ab. Wmk sideways (16.8.65)	30	30
		al. Booklet pane. No. 616ab×4	2·50	
616b		4½d. chestnut (13.9.61)	30	30
616c	157	5d. brown (9.6.67)	50	30
617		6d. deep claret (27.6.60)	50	30
617a		7d. bright green (15.2.67)	60	30
617b	158	8d. magenta (28.6.67)	20	30
617c		9d. bronze-green (29.12.66)	60	30
617d		10d. Prussian blue (30.12.66)	80	35
617e	159	1s. bistre-brown (28.6.67)	40	40
618	160	1s. 3d. green	1·75	2·75
618a	159	1s. 6d. grey-blue (12.12.66)	2·00	1·25
610/18a		*Set of 17*	7·00	6·50

The automatic facing equipment was brought into use on 6 July 1960 but the phosphor stamps may have been released a few days earlier.

The stamps with watermark sideways are from booklets except Nos. 613ab and 615ea which are from coils. No. 616ab comes from both booklets and coils.

No. 615a. See footnote after No. 586.

*No. 614 with two bands on the creamy paper was originally from cylinder 50 dot and no dot. When the change in postal rates took place in 1965 it was reissued from cylinder 57 dot and no dot on the whiter paper. Some of these latter were also released in error in districts of S.E. London in September 1964. The shade of the reissue is slightly more carmine.

***This comes from the bottom row of a sheet which is imperf at bottom and both sides.

†Booklet pane No. 611m comes in two forms, with the 1d. stamps on the left or on the right. This was printed in this manner to provide for 3d. stamps with only one band.

††Booklet pane No. 611n comes from 2s. booklets of January and March 1968. The two bands on the 3d. stamp were intentional because of the technical difficulties in producing one band and two band stamps *se-tenant*.

Unlike previous one-banded phosphor stamps, No. 615c has a broad band extending over two stamps so that alternate stamps have the band at left or right (same prices either way).

180 Postboy of 1660	181 Posthorn of 1660

(Des R. Stone (3d.), Faith Jaques (1s. 3d.))

1960 (7 July). *Tercentenary of Establishment of General Letter Office.* W 179 (*sideways on 1s. 3d.*). P 15 × 14 (3d.) or 14 × 15 (1s. 3d.).

619	180	3d. deep lilac	10	10
620	181	1s. 3d. green	3·75	3·75

182 Conference Emblem

(Des R. Stone (emblem, P. Rahikainen))

1960 (19 Sept). *First Anniv of European Postal and Telecommunications Conference. Chalk-surfaced paper.* W 179. P 15 × 14.

621	182	6d. bronze-green and purple	40	60
622		1s. 6d. brown and blue	6·50	5·00

183 Thrift Plant	184 "Growth of Savings"

185 Thrift Plant

(Des P. Gauld (2½d.), M. Goaman (others))

1961 (28 Aug). *Centenary of Post Office Saving Bank. Chalk-surfaced paper.* W 179 (*sideways on 2½d.*) P 14 × 15 (2½d.) or 15 × 14 (others).
I. "TIMSON" Machine
II. "THRISSELL" Machine

			I		II	
623	183	2½d. black and red	20	20	2·25	2·25
		a. Black omitted	£6000	—	†	
624	184	3d. orange-brown & vio	20	20	25	25
		a. Orange-brn omitted	£110	—	£250	
		x. Perf through side sheet margin	35·00	35·00	†	
		xa. Orange-brn omitted	£400	—	†	
625	185	1s. 6d. red and blue	2·75	2·25	†	
623/5		*Set of 3*	2·75	2·25		

2½d. TIMSON. Cyls 1E–1F. Deeply shaded portrait (brownish black).
2½d. THRISSELL. Cyls 1D–1B or 1D (dot)–1B (dot). Lighter portrait (grey-black).
3d. TIMSON. Cyls 3D–3E. Clear, well-defined portrait with deep shadows and bright highlights.
3d. THRISSELL. Cyls 3C–3B or 3C (dot)–3B (dot). Dull portrait, lacking in contrast.

Sheet marginal examples *without* single extension perf hole on the short side of the stamp are always "Timson", as are those with large punch-hole *not* coincident with printed three-sided box guide mark.

The 3d. "Timson" perforated completely through the right-hand side margin comes from a relatively small part of the printing perforated on a sheet-fed machine.

Normally the "Timsons" were perforated in the reel, with three large punch-holes in both long margins and the perforations completely through both short margins. Only one punch-hole coincides with the guide-mark.

The "Thrissells" have one large punch-hole in one long margin, coinciding with guide-mark and one short margin imperf (except sometimes for encroachments).

186 C.E.P.T. Emblem

187 Doves and Emblem

188 Doves and Emblem

(Des M. Goaman (doves T. Kurpershoek))

1961 (18 Sept). *European Postal and Telecommunications (C.E.P.T.) Conference, Torquay. Chalk-surfaced paper.* W 179. P 15 × 14.

626	186	2d. orange, pink and brown	20	15
		a. Orange omitted	£10000	
627	187	4d. buff, mauve and ultramarine	20	15
628	188	10d. turquoise, pale green & Prussian bl	50	55
		a. Pale green omitted	£3500	
		b. Turquoise omitted	£1800	
626/8		*Set of 3*	75	75

189 Hammer Beam Roof, Westminster Hall	190 Palace of Westminster

(Des Faith Jaques)

1961 (25 Sept). *Seventh Commonwealth Parliamentary Conference. Chalk-surfaced paper.* W 179 (*sideways on 1s. 3d.*). P 15 × 14 (6d.) or 14 × 15 (1s. 3d.).

629	189	6d. purple and gold	25	25
		a. Gold omitted	£450	
630	190	1s. 3d. green and blue	2·75	2·50
		a. Blue (Queen's head) omitted	£4500	

191 "Units of Productivity"

192 "National Productivity"

193 "Unified Productivity"

(Des D. Gentleman)

1962 (14 Nov). *National Productivity Year. Chalk-surfaced paper.*
W **179** (*inverted on* 2½d. *and* 3d.). *P* 15 × 14.

631	191	2½d. myrtle-green & carm-red (*shades*)			20	10
		p. One phosphor band	..		1·00	50
632	192	3d. light blue and violet (*shades*)			25	10
		a. Light blue (Queen's head) omitted			£700	
		p. Three phosphor bands			1·00	50
633	193	1s. 3d. carmine, light blue & dp green			1·75	2·00
		a. Light blue (Queen's head) omitted			£3750	
		p. Three phosphor bands			32·00	22·00
631/3	..	..	..	*Set of* 3	2·00	2·00
631p/3p	..	..	..	*Set of* 3	32·00	22·00

194 Campaign Emblem and Family

195 Children of Three Races

(Des M. Goaman)

1963 (21 Mar). *Freedom from Hunger. Chalk-surfaced paper. W* **179**
(*inverted*). *P* 15 × 14.

634	194	2½d. crimson and pink	..	..	10	10
		p. One phosphor band			1·00	1·25
635	195	1s. 3d. bistre-brown and yellow	..		2·00	2·00
		p. Three phosphor bands	..		32·00	22·00

196 "Paris Conference"

(Des R. Stone)

1963 (7 May). *Paris Postal Conference Centenary. Chalk-surfaced*
paper. W **179** (*inverted*). *P* 15 × 14.

636	196	6d. green and mauve	..	..	50	50
		a. Green omitted			£1300	
		p. Three phosphor bands	..		6·50	6·50

197 Posy of Flowers

198 Woodland Life

(Des S. Scott (3d.), M. Goaman (4½d.))

1963 (16 May). *National Nature Week. Chalk-surfaced paper. W* **179**.
P 15 × 14.

637	197	3d. yellow, green, brown and black	..		25	20
		p. Three phosphor bands			50	60
638	198	4½d. black, blue, yellow, mag & brn-red			40	50
		p. Three phosphor bands	..		2·50	2·50

199 Rescue at Sea

200 19th-century Lifeboat

201 Lifeboatmen

(Des D. Gentleman)

1963 (31 May). *Ninth International Lifeboat Conference, Edinburgh.*
Chalk-surfaced paper. W **179**. *P* 15 × 14.

639	199	2½d. blue, black and red			10	10
		p. One phosphor band			40	50
640	200	4d. red, yellow, brown, black and blue			40	30
		p. Three phosphor bands			20	50
641	201	1s. 6d. sepia, yellow and grey-blue			2·50	2·75
		p. Three phosphor bands	..		48·00	30·00
639/41	..	..	..	*Set of* 3	2·75	2·75
639p/41p				*Set of* 3	48·00	30·00

202 Red Cross

203

204

(Des H. Bartram)

1963 (15 Aug). *Red Cross Centenary Congress. Chalk-surfaced paper.*
W **179**. *P* 15 × 14.

642	202	3d. red and deep lilac	..	..	10	10
		a. Red omitted		..	£2600	
		p. Three phosphor bands		..	60	60
		pa. Red omitted		..	£6000	
643	203	1s. 3d. red, blue and grey		..	3·25	2·75
		p. Three phosphor bands		..	40·00	38·00
644	204	1s. 6d. red, blue and bistre		..	3·00	2·75
		p. Three phosphor bands		..	35·00	30·00
642/4	..	..		*Set of* 3	6·00	5·00
642p/4p	..	..		*Set of* 3	70·00	60·00

205 Commonwealth Cable

(Des P. Gauld)

1963 (3 Dec). *Opening of COMPAC (Trans-Pacific Telephone Cable).*
Chalk-surfaced paper. W **179**. *P* 15 × 14.

645	205	1s. 6d. blue and black	..	..	2·25	2·25
		a. Black omitted	..	..	£2400	
		p. Three phosphor bands	..	..	18·00	18·00

206 Puck and Bottom
(*A Midsummer Night's Dream*)

208 Balcony Scene (*Romeo and Juliet*)

209 "Eve of Agincourt" (*Henry V*)

210 Hamlet contemplating Yorick's Skull
(*Hamlet*) and Queen Elizabeth II

(Des D. Gentleman. Photo Harrison & Sons (3d., 6d., 1s. 3d., 1s. 6d.)
Des C. and R. Ironside. Recess B.W. (2s. 6d.))

1964 (23 April). *Shakespeare Festival. Chalk-surfaced paper. W* **179**.
P 11 × 12 (2s. 6d.) *or* 15 × 14 (*others*).

646	206	3d. yell-bistre, blk & dp vio-bl (*shades*)			10	1
		p. Three phosphor bands			20	3
647	207	6d. yellow, orge, blk & yell-ol (*shades*)			20	3
		p. Three phosphor bands	..		60	9
648	208	1s. 3d. cerise, bl-grn, blk & sep (*shades*)			90	1·0
		p. Three phosphor bands			5·75	6·5
649	209	1s. 6d. violet, turq, blk & blue (*shades*)			1·25	1·0
		p. Three phosphor bands			11·00	6·7
650	210	2s. 6d. deep slate-purple (*shades*)			2·00	2·2
646/50				*Set of* 5	4·00	4·2
646p/9p	..			*Set of* 4	15·00	13·0

211 Flats near Richmond Park
("Urban Development")

212 Shipbuilding Yards, Belfast
("Industrial Activity")

213 Beddgelert Forest Park, Snowdonia
("Forestry")

214 Nuclear Reactor, Dounreay
("Technological Development")

(Des D. Bailey)

1964 (1 July). *20th International Geographical Congress, London.*
Chalk-surfaced paper. W **179**. *P* 15 × 14.

651	211	2½d. blk, olive-yellow, ol-grey & turq-bl			10	1
		p. One phosphor band			50	1
652	212	4d. orange-brn, red-brn, rose, blk & vio			25	2
		a. Violet omitted			£175	
		c. Violet and red-brown omitted			£175	
		p. Three phosphor bands			75	7
653	213	8d. yellow-brown, emerald, grn & blk			60	5
		a. Green (lawn) omitted	..		£5500	
		p. Three phosphor bands			1·75	1·5
654	214	1s. 6d. yellow-brn, pale pink, blk & brn			3·25	3·2
		p. Three phosphor bands			26·00	21·0
651/4				*Set of* 4	4·00	4·0
651p/4p	..			*Set of* 4	26·00	21·0

A used example of the 4d. is known with the red-brown omitted

215 Spring Gentian

216 Dog Rose

217 Honeysuckle

218 Fringed Water Lily

(Des M. and Sylvia Goaman)

1964 (5 Aug). *Tenth International Botanical Congress, Edinburgh. Chalk-surfaced paper. W* **179.** *P* 15 × 14.

655	215	3d. violet, blue and sage-green	10	10
		a. Blue omitted	£4000	
		b. Sage-green omitted	£4000	
		p. Three phosphor bands	20	30
656	216	6d. apple-green, rose, scarlet and green	20	20
		p. Three phosphor bands	2·00	1·50
657	217	9d. lemon, green, lake and rose-red	1·60	2·50
		a. Green (leaves) omitted	£4000	
		p. Three phosphor bands	4·50	3·00
658	218	1s. 3d. yellow, emerald, reddish violet and grey-green	2·50	1·90
		a. Yellow (flowers) omitted	£8000	
		p. Three phosphor bands	24·00	20·00
655/8		Set of 4	4·00	4·00
655p/8p		Set of 4	28·00	22·00

219 Forth Road Bridge

220 Forth Road and Railway Bridges

(Des A. Restall)

1964 (4 Sept). *Opening of Forth Road Bridge. Chalk-surfaced paper. W* **179.** *P* 15 × 14.

659	219	3d. black, blue and reddish violet	15	10
		p. Three phosphor bands	50	50
660	220	6d. black, light blue and carmine-red	45	40
		a. Light blue omitted	£1500	£1500
		p. Three phosphor bands	4·75	4·75

221 Sir Winston Churchill

(Des D. Gentleman and Rosalind Dease, from photograph by Karsh)

1965 (8 July). *Churchill Commemoration. Chalk-surfaced paper. W* **179.** *P* 15 × 14.

I. "REMBRANDT" Machine

661	221	4d. black and olive-brown	15	10
		p. Three phosphor bands	30	30

II. "TIMSON" Machine

661a	221	4d. black and olive-brown	50	50

III. "L. & M. 4" Machine

662	—	1s. 3d. black and grey	45	40
		p. Three phosphor bands	3·50	3·50

The 1s. 3d. shows a closer view of Churchill's head.

4d. REMBRANDT. Cyls 1A–1B dot and no dot. Lack of shading detail on Churchill's portrait. Queen's portrait appears dull and coarse. This is a rotary machine which is sheet-fed.

4d. TIMSON. Cyls 5A–6B no dot. More detail on Churchill's portrait—furrow on forehead, his left eyebrow fully drawn and more shading on cheek. Queen's portrait lighter and sharper. This is a reel-fed, two-colour 12-in. wide rotary machine and the differences in impression are due to the greater pressure applied by this machine.

1s. 3d. Cyls 1A–1B no dot. The "Linotype and Machinery No. 4" machine is an ordinary sheet-fed rotary press machine. Besides being used for printing the 1s. 3d. stamps it was also employed for overprinting the phosphor bands on both values.

Two examples of the 4d. value exist with the Queen's head omitted, one due to something adhering to the cylinder and the other due to a paper fold. The stamp also exists with Churchill's head omitted, also due to a paper fold.

222 Simon de Montfort's Seal

223 Parliament Buildings (after engraving by Hollar, 1647)

(Des S. Black (6d.), R. Guyatt (2s. 6d.))

1965 (19 July). *700th Anniv of Simon de Montfort's Parliament. Chalk-surfaced paper. W* **179.** *P* 15 × 14.

663	222	6d. olive-green	10	10
		p. Three phosphor bands	1·00	1·00
664	223	2s. 6d. black, grey and pale drab	1·25	1·25

224 Bandsmen and Banner

225 Three Salvationists

(Des M. Farrar-Bell (3d.), G. Trenaman (1s. 6d.))

1965 (9 Aug). *Salvation Army Centenary. Chalk-surfaced paper. W* **179.** *P* 15 × 14.

665	224	3d. indigo, grey-blue, cerise, yell & brn	10	10
		p. One phosphor band	50	40
666	225	1s. 6d. red, blue, yellow and brown	1·00	1·00
		p. Three phosphor bands	3·00	3·25

226 Lister's Carbolic Spray

227 Lister and Chemical Symbols

(Des P. Gauld (4d.), F. Ariss (1s.))

1965 (1 Sept). *Centenary of Joseph Lister's Discovery of Antiseptic Surgery. Chalk-surfaced paper. W* **179.** *P* 15 × 14.

667	226	4d. indigo, brown-red and grey-black	10	10
		a. Brown-red (tube) omitted	£160	
		b. Indigo omitted	£1750	
		p. Three phosphor bands	15	20
		pa. Brown-red (tube) omitted	£1500	
668	227	1s. black, purple and new blue	1·00	1·50
		p. Three phosphor bands	2·75	2·75

228 Trinidad Carnival Dancers

229 Canadian Folk-dancers

(Des D. Gentleman and Rosalind Dease)

1965 (1 Sept). *Commonwealth Arts Festival. Chalk-surfaced paper. W* **179.** *P* 15 × 14.

669	228	6d. black and orange	10	10
		p. Three phosphor bands	30	30
670	229	1s. 6d. black and light reddish violet	1·25	1·50
		p. Three phosphor bands	2·50	2·50

230 Flight of Supermarine Spitfires

231 Pilot in Hawker Hurricane Mk I

232 Wing-tips of Supermarine Spitfire and Messerschmitt Bf 109

233 Supermarine Spitfires attacking Heinkel HE-111H Bomber

234 Supermarine Spitfire attacking Junkers Ju 87B "Stuka" Dive-bomber

235 Hawker Hurricanes Mk I over Wreck of Dornier Do-17Z Bomber

236 Anti-aircraft Artillery in Action

237 Air-battle over St. Paul's Cathedral

(Des D. Gentleman and Rosalind Dease (4d. ×6 and 1s. 3d.), A. Restall (9d.))

1965 (13 Sept). *25th Anniv of Battle of Britain. Chalk-surfaced paper. W* **179.** *P* 15 × 14.

671	230	4d. yellow-olive and black	30	35
		a. Block of 6. Nos. 671/6	8·00	10·00
		p. Three phosphor bands	40	50
		pa. Block of 6. Nos. 671p/6p	12·00	15·00
672	231	4d. yellow-olive, olive-grey and black	30	35
		p. Three phosphor bands	40	50
673	232	4d. red, new blue, yell-ol, ol-grey & blk	30	35
		p. Three phosphor bands	40	50
674	233	4d. olive-grey, yellow-olive and black	30	35
		p. Three phosphor bands	40	50
675	234	4d. olive-grey, yellow-olive and black	30	35
		p. Three phosphor bands	40	50
676	235	4d. olive-grey, yell-olive, new blue & blk	30	35
		a. New blue omitted	†	£3500
		p. Three phosphor bands	40	50

677	236	9d. bluish violet, orange and slate-purple		1·25	1·25
		p. Three phosphor bands		1·25	80
678	237	1s. 3d. light grey, deep grey, black, light			
		blue and bright blue		1·25	1·25
		p. Three phosphor bands		1·25	80
671/8			Set of 8	9·50	4·25
671p/8p			Set of 8	14·00	4·25

Nos. 671/6 were issued together *se-tenant* in blocks of 6 (3×2) within the sheet.

No. 676a is only known commercially used on cover from Truro.

238 Tower and Georgian Buildings   **239** Tower and "Nash" Terrace, Regent's Park

(Des C. Abbott)

1965 (8 Oct). *Opening of Post Office Tower. Chalk-surfaced paper. W **179** (sideways on 3d.). P 14 × 15 (3d.) or 15 × 14 (1s. 3d.).*

679	238	3d. olive-yell, new blue & bronze-green		10	10
		a. Olive-yellow (Tower) omitted		£650	
		p. One phosphor band		10	10
680	239	1s. 3d. bronze-green, yellow-green & bl		65	85
		p. Three phosphor bands		50	60

The one phosphor band on No. 679p was produced by printing broad phosphor bands across alternate vertical perforations. Individual stamps show the band at right or left (same prices either way).

240 U.N. Emblem

241 I.C.Y. Emblem

(Des J. Matthews)

1965 (25 Oct). *20th Anniv of U.N.O. and International Co-operation Year. Chalk-surfaced paper. W **179**. P 15 × 14.*

681	240	3d. black, yellow-orange and light blue		15	20
		p. One phosphor band		25	50
682	241	1s. 6d. black, bright purple and lt blue		1·10	1·25
		p. Three phosphor bands		3·50	3·75

242 Telecommunications Network

243 Radio Waves and Switchboard

(Des A. Restall)

1965 (15 Nov). *I.T.U. Centenary. Chalk-surfaced paper. W **179**. P 15 × 14.*

683	242	9d. red, ultram, dp slate, vio, blk & pk		20	25
		p. Three phosphor bands		60	60
684	243	1s. 6d. red, greenish bl, ind, blk & lt pk		1·60	1·75
		a. Light pink omitted		£900	
		p. Three phosphor bands		5·25	5·50

Originally scheduled for issue on 17 May 1965, supplies from the Philatelic Bureau were sent in error to reach a dealer on that date and another dealer received his supply on 27 May.

244 Robert Burns (after Skirving chalk drawing)

245 Robert Burns (after Nasmyth portrait)

(Des G. Huntly)

1966 (25 Jan). *Burns Commemoration. Chalk-surfaced paper. W **179**. P 15 × 14.*

685	244	4d. black, deep violet-blue and new blue		15	15
		p. Three phosphor bands		25	40
686	245	1s. 3d. black, slate-blue & yellow-orge		70	85
		p. Three phosphor bands		2·25	2·50

246 Westminster Abbey

247 Fan Vaulting, Henry VII Chapel

(Des Sheila Robinson. Photo Harrison (3d.). Des and eng Bradbury, Wilkinson. Recess (2s. 6d.))

1966 (28 Feb). *900th Anniv of Westminster Abbey. Chalk-surfaced paper (3d.). W **179**. P 15 × 14 (3d.) or 11 × 12 (2s. 6d.).*

687	246	3d. black, red-brown and new blue		15	20
		p. One phosphor band		30	40
688	247	2s. 6d. black		85	1·25

248 View near Hassocks, Sussex

249 Antrim, Northern Ireland

250 Harlech Castle, Wales

251 Cairngorm Mountains, Scotland

(Des L. Rosoman. Queen's portrait, adapted by D. Gentleman from coinage)

1966 (2 May). *Landscapes. Chalk-surfaced paper. W **179**. P 15 × 14.*

689	248	4d. black, yellow-green and new blue		15	15
		p. Three phosphor bands		15	15
690	249	6d. black, emerald and new blue		15	15
		p. Three phosphor bands		25	25
691	250	1s. 3d. blk, greenish yell & greenish bl		35	45
		p. Three phosphor bands		35	45
692	251	1s. 6d. black, orange and Prussian blue		50	60
		p. Three phosphor bands		50	60
689/92			Set of 4	1·00	1·25
689p/92p			Set of 4	1·00	1·25

252 Players with Ball   **253** Goalmouth Mêlée

254 Goalkeeper saving Goal

(Des D. Gentleman (4d.), W. Kempster (6d.), D. Caplan (1s. 3d.) Queen's portrait adapted by D. Gentleman from coinage)

1996 (1 June). *World Cup Football Championship. Chalk-surfaced paper. W **179** (sideways on 4d.). P 14×15 (4d.) or 15×14 (others).*

693	252	4d. red, reddish pur, brt bl, flesh & blk		15	15
		p. Two phosphor bands		15	15
694	253	6d. black, sepia, red, apple-green & blue		20	35
		a. Black omitted		85·00	
		b. Apple-green omitted		£2000	
		c. Red omitted		£2250	
		p. Three phosphor bands		20	35
		pa. Black omitted		£500	
695	254	1s. 3d. black, blue, yell, red & lt yell-ol		75	90
		a. Blue omitted		£150	
		p. Three phosphor bands		75	90
693/5			Set of 3	1·00	1·25
693p/5p			Set of 3	1·00	1·25

255 Black-headed Gull

256 Blue Tit

257 European Robin

258 Blackbird

(Des J. Norris Wood)

1966 (8 Aug). *British Birds. Chalk-surfaced paper. W **179**. P 15 × 14.*

696	255	4d. grey, black, red, emerald-green, brt blue, greenish yellow and bistre		10	1
		a. Block of 4. Nos. 696/9		1·00	1·5
		ab. Black (value), etc. omitted* (block of four)		£4000	
		ac. Black only omitted*		£2500	
		p. Three phosphor bands		10	1
		pa. Block of 4. Nos. 696/9p		1·00	1·2
697	256	4d. black, greenish yellow, grey, emerald-green, bright blue and bistre		10	1
		p. Three phosphor bands		10	1
698	257	4d. red, greenish yellow, black, grey, bistre, reddish brown & emerald-grn		10	1
		p. Three phosphor bands		10	1
699	258	4d. black, reddish brown, greenish yellow, grey and bistre**		10	1
		p. Three phosphor bands		10	1
696/9			Set of 4	1·00	1
696p/9p			Set of 4	1·00	5

Nos. 696/9 were issued together *se-tenant* in blocks of four within the sheet.

* In No. 696ab the blue, bistre and reddish brown are also omitted but in No. 696ac only the black is omitted.

** On No. 699 the black was printed over the bistre.

Other colours omitted, and the stamps affected:

d.	Greenish yellow (Nos. 696/9)		£400
pd.	Greenish yellow (Nos. 696/9)		£400
e.	Red (Nos. 696 and 698)		£400
f.	Emerald-green (Nos. 696/8)		75·00
pf.	Emerald-green (Nos. 696/8p)		75·00
g.	Bright blue (Nos. 696/7)		£250
pg.	Bright blue (Nos. 696/7p)		£800
h.	Bistre (Nos. 696/9)		90·00
ph.	Bistre (Nos. 696/9p)		90·00
j.	Reddish brown (Nos. 698/9)		80·00
pj.	Reddish brown (Nos. 698/9p)		80·00

The prices quoted are for each stamp.

NEW INFORMATION

The editor is always interested to correspond with people who have new information that will improve or correct the Catalogue.

259 Cup Winners

1966 (18 Aug). *England's World Cup Football Victory. Chalk-surfaced paper. W* **179** (*sideways*). *P* 14 × 15.
700 **259** 4d. red, reddish pur, brt bl, flesh & blk   20   20
These stamps were only put on sale at post offices in England, the Channel Islands and the Isle of Man, and at the Philatelic Bureau in London and also, on 22 August, in Edinburgh on the occasion of the opening of the Edinburgh Festival as well as at Army post offices at home and abroad.

260 Jodrell Bank Radio Telescope

261 British Motor-cars

262 "SRN 6" Hovercraft

263 Windscale Reactor

(Des D. and A. Gillespie (4d., 6d.), A. Restall (others))

1966 (19 Sept). *British Technology. Chalk-surfaced paper. W* **179**. *P* 15 × 14.
701 **260** 4d. black and lemon   15   15
   p. Three phosphor bands   15   15
702 **261** 6d. red, deep blue and orange   15   20
   a. Red (Mini-cars) omitted   £4000
   b. Deep blue (Jaguar and inscr) omitted £2500
   p. Three phosphor bands   15   20
703 **262** 1s. 3d. black, orange-red, slate and light greenish blue   30   50
   p. Three phosphor bands   45   60
704 **263** 1s. 6d. black, yellow-green, bronze-green, lilac and deep blue   50   55
   p. Three phosphor bands   65   70
701/4   *Set of* 4   1·00   1·25
701p/4p   *Set of* 4   1·25   1·50

264

265

267

268

269

All the above show battle scenes and they were issued together *se-tenant* in horizontal strips of six within the sheet.

270 Norman Ship

271 Norman Horsemen attacking Harold's Troops

(All the above are scenes from the Bayeux Tapestry)

(Des D. Gentleman. Photo, Queen's head die-stamped (6d., 1s. 3d.))

1966 (14 Oct). *900th Anniv of Battle of Hastings. Chalk-surfaced paper. W* **179** (*sideways on* 1s. 3d.). *P* 15 × 14.
705 **264** 4d. black, olive-green, bistre, deep blue, orange, mag, grn, blue and grey   10   15
   a. Strip of 6. Nos. 705/10   2·50   5·00
   p. Three phosphor bands   10   25
   pa. Strip of 6. Nos. 705p/10p   2·50   5·00
706 **265** 4d. black, olive-green, bistre, deep blue, orange, mag, grn, blue and grey   10   15
   p. Three phosphor bands   10   25
707 **266** 4d. black, olive-green, bistre, deep blue, orange, mag, grn, blue and grey   10   15
   p. Three phosphor bands   10   25
708 **267** 4d. black, olive-green, bistre, deep blue, magenta, green, blue and grey   10   15
   p. Three phosphor bands   10   25
709 **268** 4d. black, olive-green, bistre, deep blue, orange, mag, grn, blue and grey   10   15
   p. Three phosphor bands   10   25
710 **269** 4d. black, olive-green, bistre, deep blue, orange, mag, grn, blue and grey   10   15
   p. Three phosphor bands   10   25
711 **270** 6d. black, olive-grn, vio, bl, grn & gold   10   10
   p. Three phosphor bands   10   10
712 **271** 1s. 3d. black, lilac, bronze-green, rosine, bistre-brown and gold   20   20
   a. Lilac omitted   £450
   p. Four phosphor bands   20   20
   pa. Lilac omitted   £650
705/12   *Set of* 8   2·75   1·50
705p/12p   *Set of* 8   2·75   1·90
Other colours omitted on the 4d. values and the stamps affected:
   b. Olive-green (Nos. 705/10)   30·00
   pb. Olive-green (Nos. 705p/10p)   30·00
   c. Bistre (Nos. 705/10)   30·00
   pc. Bistre (Nos. 705p/10p)   35·00
   d. Deep blue (Nos. 705/10)   40·00
   pd. Deep blue (Nos. 705p/10p)   40·00
   e. Orange (Nos. 705/7 and 709/10)   30·00
   pe. Orange (Nos. 705p/7p and 709p/10p)   25·00
   f. Magenta (Nos. 705/10)   35·00
   pf. Magenta (Nos. 705p/10p)   35·00
   g. Green (Nos. 705/10)   30·00
   pg. Green (Nos. 705p/10p)   30·00
   h. Blue (Nos. 705/10)   25·00
   ph. Blue (Nos. 705p/10p)   40·00
   j. Grey (Nos. 705/10)   25·00
   pj. Grey (Nos. 705p/10p)   25·00
   pk. Magenta and green (Nos. 705p/10p)
The prices quoted are for each stamp.
Nos. 705 and 709, with grey and blue omitted, have been seen commercially used, posted from Middleton-in-Teesdale.
Three examples of No. 712 in a right-hand top corner block of 10 (2 × 5) are known with the Queen's head omitted as a result of a double paper fold prior to die-stamping. The perforation is normal. Of the other seven stamps, four have the Queen's head misplaced and three are normal.

MISSING GOLD HEADS. The 6d and 1s. 3d. were also issued with the die-stamped gold head omitted but as these can also be removed by chemical means we are not prepared to list them unless a way is found of distinguishing the genuine stamps from the fakes which will satisfy the Expert Committees.
The same remarks apply to Nos. 713/14.

272 King of the Orient   **273** Snowman

(Des Tasveer Shemza (3d.), J. Berry (1s. 6d.) (winners of children's design competition). Photo, Queen's head die-stamped)

1966 (1 Dec). *Christmas. Chalk-surfaced paper. W* **179** (*sideways on* 3d.). *P* 14 × 15.
713 **272** 3d. black, blue, green, yell, red & gold   10   10
   a. Queen's head double   †
   b. Green omitted   —   £150
   p. One phosphor band   10   10
714 **273** 1s. 6d. blue, red, pink, black and gold   40   40
   a. Pink (hat) omitted   £750
   p. Two phosphor bands   40   40
See note below Nos. 679/80 which also applies to No. 713p.

274 Sea Freight

275 Air Freight

(Des C. Abbott)

1967 (20 Feb). *European Free Trade Association* (*EFTA*). *Chalk-surfaced paper. W* **179**. *P* 15 × 14.
715 **274** 9d. deep blue, red, lilac, green, brown, new blue, yellow and black   20   20
   a. Black (Queen's head, etc.), brown, new blue and yellow omitted   £650
   b. Lilac omitted   60·00
   c. Green omitted   40·00
   d. Brown omitted   45·00
   e. New blue omitted   42·00
   f. Yellow omitted   42·00
   p. Three phosphor bands   20   20
   pb. Lilac omitted   75·00
   pc. Green omitted   45·00
   pd. Brown omitted   45·00
   pe. New blue omitted   45·00
   pf. Yellow omitted   75·00
716 **275** 1s. 6d. violet, red, deep blue, brown, green, blue-grey, new bl, yell & blk   30   30
   a. Red omitted   ..
   b. Deep blue omitted   £250
   c. Brown omitted   45·00
   d. Blue-grey omitted   45·00
   e. New blue omitted   45·00
   f. Yellow omitted   45·00
   p. Three phosphor bands   30   30
   pa. Red omitted   ..
   pb. Deep blue omitted   £250
   pc. Brown omitted   45·00
   pd. Blue-grey omitted   45·00
   pf. New blue omitted   45·00

276 Hawthorn and Bramble

277 Larger Bindweed and Viper's Bugloss

278 Ox-eye Daisy, Coltsfoot and Buttercup

279 Bluebell, Red Campion and Wood Anemone

The above were issued together *se-tenant* in blocks of four within the sheet.

280 Dog Violet

281 Primroses

(Des Rev. W. Keble Martin (T **276/9**), Mary Grierson (others))

1967 (24 Apr). *British Wild Flowers. Chalk-surfaced paper.* W **179**. P 15 × 14.

717	276	4d. grey, lemon, myrtle-green, red, agate and slate-purple	15	10
		a. Block of 4. Nos. 717/20	1·40	2·75
		b. Grey double*		
		c. Red omitted	£2000	
		f. Slate-purple omitted		
		p. Three phosphor bands	10	10
		pa. Block of 4. Nos. 717p/20p	1·00	2·50
		pd. Agate omitted	£600	
		pf. Slate-purple omitted	£150	
718	277	4d. grey, lemon, myrtle-green, red, agate and violet	15	10
		b. Grey double*		
		p. Three phosphor bands	10	10
		pd. Agate omitted	£600	
		pe. Violet omitted	£2000	
719	278	4d. grey, lemon, myrtle-green, red and agate	15	10
		b. Grey double*		
		p. Three phosphor bands	10	10
		pd. Agate omitted	£600	
720	279	4d. grey, lemon, myrtle-green, reddish purple, agate and violet	15	10
		b. Grey double*		
		c. Reddish purple omitted	£950	
		p. Three phosphor bands	10	10
		pd. Agate omitted	£650	
		pe. Violet omitted	£2000	
721	280	9d. lavender-grey, green, reddish violet and orange-yellow	15	10
		p. Three phosphor bands	10	10
722	281	1s. 9d. lavender-grey, green, greenish yellow and orange	20	20
		p. Three phosphor bands	30	20
717/22		*Set of 6*	1·50	65
717p/22p		*Set of 6*	1·25	65

* The double impression of the grey printing affects the Queen's head, value and inscription.

PHOSPHOR BANDS. Issues from No. 723 are normally with phosphor bands only, except for the high values. However, most stamps have appeared with the phosphor bands omitted in error, but they are outside the scope of this catalogue. They are listed in Volumes 3, 4 and 5 of the Stanley Gibbons *Great Britain Specialised Catalogue* and in the *Great Britain Concise Catalogue*.

See also further notes after No. X1058.

PHOSPHORISED PAPER. Following the adoption of phosphor bands the Post Office started a series of experiments involving the addition of the phosphor to the paper coating before the stamps were printed. No. 743c was the first of these experiments to be issued for normal postal use. See also notes after No. X1058.

PVA GUM. Polyvinyl alcohol was introduced by Harrisons in place of gum Arabic in 1968. It is almost invisible except that a small amount of pale yellowish colouring matter was introduced to make it possible to see that the stamps had been gummed. Although this can be distinguished from gum arabic in unused stamps there is, of course, no means of detecting it in used examples. These varieties are outside the scope of this catalogue, but they are listed in the *Great Britain Concise Catalogue*. See further notes *re* gum after Nos. 744 and 762.

282   **282a**

I   II

Two types of the 2d.

I. Value spaced away from left side of stamp (cylinders 1 no dot and dot).

II. Value close to left side from new multipositive used for cylinders 5 no dot and dot onwards. The portrait appears in the centre, thus conforming to the other values.

(Des after plaster cast by Arnold Machin)

1967 (5 June)–**70**. *Chalk-surfaced paper. Two phosphor bands except where otherwise stated. No wmk. P* 15 × 14.

723	282	½d. orange-brown (5.2.68)	10	20
724		1d. lt olive (*shades*) (2 bands) (5.2.68)	10	10
		a. Imperf (coil strip)†	£1100	
		b. Part perf pane*		
		c. Imperf pane*	£3750	
		d. Uncoated paper**	65·00	
		l. Booklet pane. No. 724×2 *se-tenant* with 730×2 (6.4.68)	3·00	
		m. Booklet pane. No. 724×4 *se-tenant* with 734×2 (6.1.69)	3·50	
		n. Booklet pane. No. 724×6, 734×6 and 735×3 *se-tenant* (1.12.69)	8·50	
		na. Uncoated paper**	£900	
725		1d. yellowish olive (1 centre band) (16.9.68)	25	30
		l. Booklet pane. No. 725×4 *se-tenant* with 732×2	4·00	
		m. Coil strip. No. 728×2 *se-tenant* with 729, 725 and 733 (27.8.69)	1·25	
726		2d. lake-brown (Type I) (2 bands) (5.2.68)	10	15
727		2d. lake-brn (Type II) (2 bands) (1969)	15	15
728		2d. lake-brown (Type II) (1 centre band) (27.8.69)	50	75
729		3d. violet (*shades*) (1 centre band) (8.8.67)	10	10
		a. Imperf (pair)	£550	
730		3d. violet (2 bands) (6.4.68)	30	30
		a. Uncoated paper**	£2000	
731		4d. deep sepia (*shades*) (2 bands)	10	10
		b. Part perf pane*	£1000	
732		4d. dp olive-brown (*shades*) (1 centre band) (16.9.68)	10	10
		a. Part perf pane*	£1000	
		l. Booklet pane. Two stamps plus two printed labels	1·00	
733		4d. brt verm (1 centre band) (6.1.69)	10	10
		a. *Tête-bêche* (horiz pair)	£2500	
		b. Uncoated paper**	6·00	
		l. Booklet pane. Two stamps plus two printed labels (3.3.69)	1·00	
734		4d. brt vermilion (1 side band) (6.1.69)	1·75	1·50
		a. Uncoated paper**	£175	
735		5d. royal blue (*shades*) (1.7.68)	10	10
		a. Imperf pane*	£1200	
		b. Part perf pane*	£800	
		c. Imperf (pair)††	£200	
		d. Uncoated paper**	15·00	
736		6d. brt reddish pur (*shades*) (5.2.68)	20	20
737	282a	7d. bright emerald (1.7.68)	40	30
738		8d. bright vermilion (1.7.68)	15	30
739		8d. light turquoise-blue (6.1.69)	55	60
740		9d. myrtle-green (8.8.67)	50	30
741	282	10d. drab (1.7.68)	45	50
		a. Uncoated paper**	23·00	
742		1s. light bluish violet (*shades*)	40	30
743		1s. 6d. greenish blue and deep blue (*shades*) (8.8.67)	50	30
		a. Greenish blue omitted	80·00	
		c. Phosphorised paper. *Prussian blue and indigo* (10.12.69)	85	90
		ca. Prussian blue omitted	£400	
744		1s. 9d. dull orange and black (*shades*)	40	30
723/44		*Set of 16*	3·00	3·25

*BOOKLET ERRORS. See note after No. 556.

** Uncoated paper. This does not respond to the chalky test, and may be further distinguished from the normal chalk-surfaced paper by the fibres which clearly show on the surface, resulting in the printing impression being rougher, and by the screening dots which are not so evident. The 1d., 4d. and 5d. come from the £1 "Stamps for Cooks" Booklet (1970); and the 3d. and 10d. from sheets (1969). The 20p. and 50p. high values (Nos. 830/1) exist with similar errors.

† No. 724a occurs in a vertical strip of four, top stamp perforated on three sides, bottom stamp imperf three sides and the two middle stamps completely imperf.

†† No. 735c comes from the original state of cylinder 15 which is identifiable by the screening dots which extend through the gutters of the stamps and into the margins of the sheet. This must not be confused with imperforate stamps from cylinder 10, a large quantity of which was stolen from the printers early in 1970.

The 1d. with centre band (725) only came in the September 1968 booklets (PVA gum) and the coil strip (725m) (gum arabic); the 2d. with centre band (728) was only issued in the coil strip (725m); the 3d. (No. 730) appeared in booklets on 6.4.68, from coils during December 1968 and from sheets in January 1969; and the 4d. with one side band (734) only in 10s. (band at left) and £1 (band at left or right) booklets.

Gum. The 1d. (725), 3d. (729), 4d. (731 and 733), 9d., 1s., 1s. 6d. and 1s. 9d. exist with gum arabic as well as the PVA gum; the 2d. (728) and coil strip (725m) exist only with gum arabic; and the remainder exist with PVA gum only.

The 4d. (731) in shades of washed-out grey are colour changelings which we understand are caused by the concentrated solvents used in modern dry cleaning methods.

For decimal issue, see Nos. X841, etc.

283 "Master Lambton" (Sir Thomas Lawrence)

284 "Mares and Foals in a Landscape" (George Stubbs)

---

285 "Children Coming Out of School" (L. S. Lowry)

(Des S. Rose)

1967 (10 July). *British Paintings. Chalk-surfaced paper. Two phosphor bands. No wmk.* P 14 × 15 (4d.) *or* 15 × 14 (others).

748	283	4d. rose-red, lemon, brown, black, new blue and gold	10	10
		a. Gold (value and Queen's head) omitted	£200	
		b. New blue omitted	£2500	
749	284	9d. Venetian red, ochre, grey-black, new blue, greenish yellow and black	20	20
		a. Black (Queen's head and value) omitted	£400	
		b. Greenish yellow omitted	£1300	
750	285	1s. 6d. greenish yellow, grey, rose, new blue, grey-black and gold	45	40
		a. Gold (Queen's head) omitted	£750	
		b. New blue omitted	£160	
		c. Grey (clouds and shading) omitted	95·00	
748/50		*Set of 3*	60	60

286 *Gypsy Moth IV*

(Des M. and Sylvia Goaman)

1967 (24 July). *Sir Francis Chichester's World Voyage. Chalk-surfaced paper. Three phosphor bands. No wmk.* P 15 × 14.

751	286	1s. 9d. black, brown-red, lt emer & blue	25	25

287 Radar Screen

288 *Penicillium notatum*

289 Vickers VC-10 Jet Engines   **290** Television Equipment

(Des C. Abbott (4d., 1s.), Negus-Sharland team (others))

1967 (19 Sept). *British Discovery and Invention. Chalk-surfaced paper. Three phosphor bands* (4d.) *or two phosphor bands* (others). W **179** (*sideways on* 1s. 9d.). P 14 × 15 (1s. 9d.) *or* 15 × 14 (others).

752	287	4d. greenish yellow, black and vermilion	10	10
753	288	1s. blue-green, light greenish blue, slate-purple and bluish violet	10	10
754	289	1s. 6d. black, grey, royal blue, ochre and turquoise-blue	25	35
755	290	1s. 9d. black, grey-blue, pale olive-grey, violet and orange	40	40
		a. Grey-blue omitted		
752/5		*Set of 4*	70	80

WATERMARK. All issues from this date are on unwatermarked paper.

291 "The Adoration of the Shepherds" (School of Seville)

292 "Madonna and Child" (Murillo)

293 "The Adoration of the Shepherds"
(Louis le Nain)

(Des S. Rose)

1967. *Christmas. Chalk-surfaced paper. One phosphor band (3d.) or two phosphor bands (others). P 15 × 14 (1s. 6d.) or 14 × 15 (others).*

756	291	3d. ol-yell, rose, bl, blk & gold (27.11)		10	20
		a. Gold (value and Queen's head) omitted		75·00	
		b. Printed on the gummed side		£300	
		c. Rose omitted			
757	292	4d. bright purple, greenish yellow, new blue, grey-black and gold (18.10)		10	20
		a. Gold (value and Queen's head) omitted		60·00	
		b. Gold ("4D" only) omitted			
		c. Yellow (Child, robe and Madonna's face) omitted			
758	293	1s. 6d. brt purple, bistre, lemon, black, orange-red, ultram & gold (27.11)		45	50
		a. Gold (value and Queen's head) omitted		£3500	
		b. Ultramarine omitted		£350	
		c. Lemon omitted		£10000	
756/8			*Set of* 3	60	70

Distinct shades exist of the 3d. and 4d. values but are not listable as there are intermediate shades. For the 4d. stamps from one machine show a darker background and give the appearance of the yellow colour being omitted, but this is not so and these should not be confused with the true missing yellow No. 757c.

No. 757b comes from stamps in the first vertical row of a sheet.

(Recess Bradbury, Wilkinson)

1967–68. *No wmk. White paper. P 11 × 12.*

759	166	2s. 6d. black-brown (1.7.68)		40	50
760	167	5s. red (10.4.68)		1·00	1·00
761	168	10s. bright ultramarine (10.4.68)		5·50	7·00
762	169	£1 black (4.12.67)		4·50	6·00
759/62			*Set of* 4	10·00	13·00

PVA GUM. *All the following issues from this date have PVA gum except where footnotes state otherwise.*

294 Tarr Steps, Exmoor

295 Aberfeldy Bridge

296 Menai Bridge

297 M4 Viaduct

(Des A. Restall (9d.), L. Rosoman (1s. 6d.), J. Matthews (others))

1968 (29 Apr). *British Bridges. Chalk-surfaced paper. Two phosphor bands. P 15 × 14.*

763	294	4d. black, bluish violet, turq-blue & gold		10	10
		a. Printed on gummed side		25·00	
764	295	9d. red-brown, myrtle-green, ultramarine, olive-brown, black and gold		10	10
		a. Gold (Queen's head) omitted		£125	
		b. Ultramarine omitted		†	£3750
765	296	1s. 6d. olive-brown, red-orange, bright green, turquoise-green and gold		30	30
		a. Gold (Queen's head) omitted		£125	
		b. Red-orange (roof tops) omitted		£150	
766	297	1s. 9d. olive-brown, greenish yellow, dull green, deep ultramarine & gold		35	40
		a. Gold (Queen's head) omitted		£150	
763/6			*Set of* 4	70	80

No. 764b is only known on first day covers posted from Canterbury, Kent, or the Philatelic Bureau, Edinburgh.

298 "T U C" and Trades Unionists

299 Mrs. Emmeline Pankhurst (statue)

300 Sopwith Camel and English Electric Lightning Fighters

301 Captain Cook's *Endeavour* and Signature

(Des D. Gentleman (4d.), C. Abbott (others))

1968 (29 May). *British Anniversaries. Events described on stamps. Chalk-surfaced paper. Two phosphor bands. P 15 × 14.*

767	298	4d. emerald, olive, blue and black		10	10
768	299	9d. reddish violet, bluish grey and black		10	15
769	300	1s. olive-brown, bl, red, slate-bl & blk		25	30
770	301	1s. 9d. yellow-ochre and blackish brown		30	35
767/70			*Set of* 4	70	80

302 "Queen Elizabeth I"   **303** "Pinkie"
(unknown artist)   (Lawrence)

304 "Ruins of St. Mary   **305** "The Hay Wain"
Le Port" (Piper)   (Constable)

(Des S. Rose)

1968 (12 Aug). *British Paintings. Queen's head embossed. Chalk-surfaced paper. Two phosphor bands. P 15 × 14 (1s. 9d.) or 14 × 15 (others).*

771	302	4d. blk, verm, greenish yell, grey & gold		10	10
		a. Gold (value and Queen's head) omitted		£125	
		b. Vermilion omitted*		£225	
772	303	1s. mauve, new blue, greenish yellow, black, magenta and gold		15	15
		a. Gold (value and Queen's head) omitted		£200	
773	304	1s. 6d. slate, orange, black, mauve, greenish yellow, ultramarine & gold		20	30
		a. Gold (value and Queen's head) omitted		£100	
774	305	1s. 9d. greenish yellow, black, new blue, red and gold		35	35
		a. Gold (value and Queen's head) and embossing omitted		£500	
		b. Red omitted		£10000	
771/4			*Set of* 4	70	80

*The effect of this is to leave the face and hands white and there is more yellow and olive in the costume.

The 4d., 1s. and 1s. 9d. are known with the embossing only omitted. No. 774a is only known with the phosphor also omitted. No. 772a exists both with or without embossing or phosphor bands.

306 Boy and Girl with Rocking Horse

307 Girl with Doll's   **308** Boy with Train
House   Set

(Des Rosalind Dease. Head printed in gold and then embossed)

1968 (25 Nov). *Christmas. Chalk-surfaced paper. One centre phosphor band (4d.) or two phosphor bands (others). P 15 × 14 (4d.) or 14 × 15 (others).*

775	306	4d. black, orange, vermilion, ultramarine, bistre and gold		10	10
		a. Gold omitted		£2250	
		b. Vermilion omitted*		£275	
		c. Ultramarine omitted		£175	
776	307	9d. yellow-olive, black, brown, yellow, magenta, orange, turq-green & gold		15	25
		a. Yellow omitted		65·00	
		b. Turquoise-green (dress) omitted			
777	308	1s. 6d. ultramarine, yellow-orange, brt purple, blue-green, black and gold		35	35
775/7			*Set of* 3	50	60

*The effect of the missing vermilion is shown on the rocking horse, saddle and faces which appear orange instead of red.

A single used example of the 4d. exists with the bistre omitted. No. 775c is only known with the phosphor also omitted. All values exist with the embossing of Queen's head omitted.

309 *Queen Elizabeth 2*

310 Elizabethan Galleon

311 East Indiaman

312 *Cutty Sark*

313 *Great Britain*

314 *Mauretania I*

(Des D. Gentleman)

1969 (15 Jan). *British Ships. Chalk-surfaced paper. Two vertical phosphor bands at right* (1s.), *one horizontal phosphor band* (5d.) *or two phosphor bands* (9d.). *P* 15 × 14.

778	309	5d. black, grey, red and turquoise	..	10	10
		a. Black (Queen's head, value, hull and inscr) omitted		£700	
		b. Grey (decks, etc.) omitted	..	90·00	
		c. Red omitted	..	50·00	
779	310	9d. red, blue, ochre, brown, blk & grey	10	15
		a. Strip of 3. Nos. 779/81	..	1·75	3·00
		ab. Red and blue omitted	..	£1500	
		ac. Blue omitted	..	£1500	
780	311	9d. ochre, brown, black and grey	10	15
781	312	9d. ochre, brown, black and grey	10	15
782	313	1s. brown, blk, grey, grn & greenish yell	40	30
		a. Pair. Nos. 782/3	..	1·50	2·50
		ab. Greenish yellow omitted	..		
783	314	1s. red, black, brown, carmine and grey	40	30
		a. Carmine (hull overlay) omitted	..	£10000	
		b. Red (funnels) omitted	..	£10000	
		c. Carmine and red omitted	..		
778/83			*Set of* 6	2·50	1·00

The 9d. and 1s. values were arranged in horizontal strips of three and pairs respectively throughout the sheet.

No. 779ab is known only with the phosphor also omitted.

315 Concorde in Flight

316 Plan and Elevation Views

317 Concorde's Nose and Tail

(Des M. and Sylvia Goaman (4d.), D. Gentleman (9d., 1s. 6d.))

1969 (3 Mar). *First Flight of Concorde. Chalk-surfaced paper. Two phosphor bands. P* 15 × 14.

784	315	4d. yellow-orange, violet, greenish blue, blue-green and pale green ..		10	10
		a. Violet (value, etc.) omitted	..	£225	
		b. Yellow-orange omitted	..	£110	
785	316	9d. ultramarine, emerald, red & grey-bl	20	30
786	317	1s. 6d. deep blue, silver-grey & lt blue	40	40
		a. Silver-grey omitted	..	£275	
784/6	..	..	*Set of* 3	60	70

No. 786a affects the Queen's head which appears in the light blue colour.

318 Queen Elizabeth II. (See also Type 357)

(Des after plaster cast by Arnold Machin. Recess Bradbury, Wilkinson)

1969 (5 Mar). *P* 12.

787	318	2s. 6d. brown ..	..	50	30
788		5s. crimson-lake	..	2·25	60
789		10s. deep ultramarine ..	..	7·00	6·50
790		£1 bluish black	..	3·00	2·00
787/90	..	..	*Set of* 4	11·50	8·50

For decimal issue, see Nos. 829/31b and notes after No. 831b.

319 Page from *Daily Mail*, and Vickers FB-27 Vimy Aircraft

320 Europa and CEPT Emblems

321 ILO Emblem

322 Flags of NATO Countries

323 Vickers FB-27 Vimy Aircraft and Globe showing Flight

(Des P. Sharland (5d., 1s., 1s. 6d.), M. and Sylvia Goaman (9d., 1s. 9d.))

1969 (2 Apr). *Anniversaries. Events described on stamps. Chalk-surfaced paper. Two phosphor bands. P* 15 × 14.

791	319	5d. black, pale sage-grn, chest & new bl	10	10
792	320	9d. pale turq, dp bl, lt emer-green & blk	20	25
		a. Uncoated paper*	..	£1500	
793	321	1s. bright purple, deep blue and lilac	25	25
794	322	1s. 6d. red, royal blue, yellow-green, black, lemon and new blue	..	25	30
		e. Black omitted	..	60·00	
		f. Yellow-green omitted	..	48·00	
795	323	1s. 9d. yellow-olive, greenish yellow and pale turquoise-green	..	30	35
		a. Uncoated paper* ..	..	£200	
791/5	..	..	*Set of* 5	1·00	1·10

*Uncoated paper. The second note after No. 744 also applies here.

324 Durham Cathedral

325 York Minster

326 St. Giles' Cathedral, Edinburgh

327 Canterbury Cathedral

328 St. Paul's Cathedral

329 Liverpool Metropolitan Cathedral

(Des P. Gauld)

1969 (28 May). *British Architecture. Cathedrals. Chalk-surfaced paper. Two phosphor bands. P* 15 × 14.

796	324	5d. grey-blk, orge, pale bluish vio & blk	10	10
		a. Block of 4. Nos. 796/9		85	2·50
		ab. Block of 4. Uncoated paper**	..		
		b. Pale bluish violet omitted	..	£2500	

797	325	5d. grey-black, pale bluish violet, new blue and black		10	10
		b. Pale bluish violet omitted	..	£2500	
798	326	5d. grey-black, purple, green and black	10	10
		c. Green omitted*	..	40·00	
799	327	5d. grey-black, green, new blue & black	10	10
800	328	9d. grey-blk, ochre, pale drab, vio & blk	15	15
		a. Black (value) omitted	..	£100	
801	329	1s. 6d. grey-black, pale turquoise, pale reddish violet, pale yellow-ol & blk	15	15
		a. Black (value) omitted	..	£1600	
		b. Black (value) double	..		
796/801			*Set of* 6	1·00	55

The 5d. values were issued together *se-tenant* in blocks of four throughout the sheet.

*The missing green on the roof top is known on R. 2/5, R. 8/5 and R. 10/5, but all from different sheets, and it only occurred in part of the printing, being "probably caused by a batter on the impression cylinder". Examples are also known with the green partly omitted.

** Uncoated paper. The second note after No. 744 also applies here.

330 The King's Gate, Caernarvon Castle   331 The Eagle Tower, Caernarvon Castle

332 Queen Eleanor's Gate, Caernarvon Castle   333 Celtic Cross, Margam Abbey

334 H.R.H. The Prince of Wales (after photo by G. Argent)

(Des D. Gentleman)

1969 (1 July). *Investiture of H.R.H. The Prince of Wales. Chalk-surfaced paper. Two phosphor bands. P* 14 × 15.

802	330	5d. deep olive-grey, light olive-grey, deep grey, light grey, red, pale turquoise-green, black and silver ..		10	10
		a. Strip of 3. Nos. 802/4	..	70	1·50
		b. Black (value and inscr) omitted	..	£150	
		c. Red omitted*	..	£250	
		d. Deep grey omitted**	..	90·00	
		e. Pale turquoise-green omitted	..	£325	
803	331	5d. deep olive-grey, light olive-grey, deep grey, light grey, red, pale turquoise-green, black and silver ..		10	10
		b. Black (value and inscr) omitted	..	£150	
		c. Red omitted*	..	£250	
		d. Deep grey omitted**	..	90·00	
		e. Pale turquoise-green omitted	..	£325	
		f. Light grey (marks on walls, window frames, etc) omitted	..	†	£7500
804	332	5d. deep olive-grey, light olive-grey, deep grey, light grey, red, pale turquoise-green, black and silver ..		10	10
		b. Black (value and inscr) omitted	..	£150	
		c. Red omitted*	..	£250	
		d. Deep grey omitted**	..	90·00	
		e. Pale turquoise-green omitted	..	£325	
805	333	9d. deep grey, light grey, black and gold	20	10
806	334	1s. blackish yellow-olive and gold	20	10
802/6			*Set of* 5	1·00	45

The 5d. values were issued together, *se-tenant*, in strips of three throughout the sheet.

*The 5d. value is also known with the red misplaced downwards and where this occurs the red printing does not take very well on the silver background and in some cases is so faint that it could be mistaken for a missing red. However, the red can be seen under a magnifying glass and caution should therefore be exercised when purchasing copies of Nos. 802/4c.

**The deep grey affects the dark portions of the windows and doors.

No. 803f is only known commercially used on cover.

NEW INFORMATION

The editor is always interested to correspond with people who have new information that will improve or correct the Catalogue.

335 Mahatma Gandhi

(Des B. Mullick)

1969 (13 Aug). *Gandhi Centenary Year. Chalk-surfaced paper. Two phosphor bands. P 15 × 14.*

807	335	1s. 6d. black, green, red-orange & grey	30	30
		a. Printed on the gummed side ..	£300	

336 National Giro "G" Symbol

337 Telecommunications—International Subscriber Dialling

338 Telecommunications—Pulse Code Modulation

339 Postal Mechanisation— Automatic Sorting

(Des D. Gentleman. Litho De La Rue)

1969 (1 Oct). *Post Office Technology Commemoration. Chalk-surfaced paper. Two phosphor bands. P 13½ × 14.*

808	336	5d. new bl, greenish bl, lavender & blk	10	10
809	337	9d. emerald, violet-blue and black ..	15	20
810	338	1s. emerald, lavender and black	15	20
811	339	1s. 6d. brt purple, lt blue, grey-bl & blk	50	50
808/11		.. .. .. *Set of* 4	80	90

340 Herald Angel

341 The Three Shepherds

342 The Three Kings

(Des F. Wegner. Queen's head (and stars 4d., 5d. and scroll-work 1s. 6d.) printed in gold and then embossed)

1969 (26 Nov). *Christmas. Chalk-surfaced paper. Two phosphor bands (5d., 1s. 6d.) or one centre band (4d.). P 15 × 14.*

812	340	4d. vermilion, new blue, orange, bright purple, light green, bluish violet, blackish brown and gold	10	15
		a. Gold (Queen's head etc.) omitted ..	£2000	
813	341	5d. magenta, light blue, royal blue, olive-brown, green, greenish yellow, red and gold	10	15
		a. Light blue (sheep, etc) omitted ..	60·00	
		b. Red omitted*	£550	
		c. Gold (Queen's head) omitted ..	£450	
		d. Green omitted	£200	
		e. Olive-brown, red and gold omitted	£7000	

814	342	1s. 6d. greenish yellow, bright purple, bluish violet, deep slate, orange, green, new blue and gold ..	35	40
		a. Gold (Queen's head etc.) omitted ..	90·00	
		b. Deep slate (value) omitted ..	£250	
		c. Greenish yellow omitted	£150	
		d. Bluish violet omitted	£300	
		e. New blue omitted	60·00	
812/14		.. .. .. *Set of* 3	50	60

*The effect of the missing red is shown on the hat, leggings and purse which appear as dull orange.

The 5d. and 1s. 6d. values are known with the embossing omitted.

No. 813e was caused by a paper fold and also shows the phosphor omitted.

Used copies of the 5d. have been seen with the olive-brown or greenish yellow (tunic at left) omitted.

343 Fife Harling

344 Cotswold Limestone

345 Welsh Stucco

346 Ulster Thatch

(Des D. Gentleman (5d., 9d.), Sheila Robinson (1s., 1s. 6d.))

1970 (11 Feb). *British Rural Architecture. Chalk-surfaced paper. Two phosphor bands. P 15 × 14.*

815	343	5d. grey, grey-black, black, lemon, greenish bl, orge-brn, ultram & grn	10	15
		a. Lemon omitted	60·00	
		b. Grey (Queen's head and cottage shading) omitted	£4000	
816	344	9d. orange-brown, olive-yellow, bright green, black, grey-black and grey ..	25	25
817	345	1s. dp blue, reddish lilac, drab & new bl	25	25
		a. New blue omitted	55·00	
818	346	1s. 6d. greenish yell, blk, turq-bl & lilac	35	45
		a. Turquoise-blue omitted ..	£4000	
815/18		.. .. .. *Set of* 4	85	1·00

Used examples of the 5d. have been seen with the greenish blue colour omitted.

347 Signing the Declaration of Arbroath

348 Florence Nightingale attending Patients

349 Signing of International Co-operative Alliance

350 Pilgrims and *Mayflower*

351 Sir William Herschel, Francis Baily, Sir John Herschel and Telescope

(Des F. Wegner (5d., 9d., and 1s. 6d.), Marjorie Saynor (1s., 1s. 9d.). Queen's head printed in gold and then embossed)

1970 (1 Apr). *Anniversaries. Events described on stamps. Chalk-surfaced paper. Two phosphor bands. P 15 × 14.*

819	347	5d. blk, yell-olive, blue, emer, greenish yellow, rose-red, gold & orange-red	10	10
		a. Gold (Queen's head) omitted ..	£400	
		b. Emerald omitted	£100	
820	348	9d. ochre, deep blue, carmine, black, blue-green, yellow-olive, gold & bl	15	15
		a. Ochre omitted	£150	
821	349	1s. green, greenish yellow, brown black, cerise, gold and light blue ..	25	35
		a. Gold (Queen's head) omitted ..	50·00	
		c. Green omitted	75·00	
		d. Brown omitted	£100	
822	350	1s. 6d. greenish yellow, carmine, deep yellow-olive, emerald, black, blue gold and sage-green ..	30	40
		a. Gold (Queen's head) omitted ..	75·00	
		b. Emerald omitted	40·00	
823	351	1s. 9d. blk, slate, lemon, gold & brt pur	30	40
		a. Lemon (trousers and document) omitted	†	—
819/23		.. .. *Set of* 5	1·00	1·25

The 9d., 1s. and 1s. 6d. are known with the embossing omitted.

No. 821c also exists with embossing omitted.

No. 823a is only known used on first day cover postmarked London WC.

352 "Mr. Pickwick and Sam" (*Pickwick Papers*)

353 "Mr. and Mrs. Micawber" (*David Copperfield*)

354 "David Copperfield and Betsy Trotwood" (*David Copperfield*)

355 "Oliver asking for more" (*Oliver Twist*)

356 "Grasmere" (from engraving by J. Farrington, R.A.)

T **352/5** were issued together *se-tenant* in blocks of four throughout the sheet.

(Des Rosalind Dease. Queen's head printed in gold and then embossed)

1970 (3 June). *Literary Anniversaries. Death Centenary of Charles Dickens (novelist) (5d. × 4) and Birth Bicentenary of William Wordsworth (poet) (1s. 6d.). Chalk-surfaced paper. Two phosphor bands. P 14 × 15.*

824	352	5d. black, orange, silver, gold and mag	10	10
		a. Block of 4. Nos. 824/7 ..	1·00	2·00
		ab. Imperf (block of four)	£700	
		ac. Silver (inscr) omitted		
825	353	5d. black, magenta, silver, gold & orge	10	10
826	354	5d. black, light greenish blue, silver, gold and yellow-bistre ..	10	10
		b. Yellow-bistre (value) omitted ..	£1200	
827	355	5d. black, yellow-bistre, silver, gold and light greenish blue ..	10	10
		b. Yellow-bistre (background) omitted	£3000	
		c. Light greenish blue (value) omitted*	£400	
828	356	1s. 6d. light yellow-olive, black, silver, gold and bright blue ..	20	20
		a. Gold (Queen's head) omitted ..	£250	
		b. Silver ("Grasmere") omitted ..	70·00	
		c. Bright blue (face value) omitted ..		
824/8		.. .. .. *Set of* 5	1·00	55

*No 827c (unlike No. 827b) comes from a sheet on which the colour was only partially omitted so that, although No. 827 was completely without the light greenish blue colour, it was still partially present on No. 826.

The 1s. 6d. is known with embossing omitted.

Essays exist of Nos. 824/7 showing the Queen's head in silver and with different inscriptions.

357 (Value redrawn)

(Des after plaster cast by Arnold Machin. Recess B.W.)

1970 (17 June)–72. *Decimal Currency. Chalk-surfaced paper or phosphorised paper* (10p.). *P* 12.

829	357	10p. cerise	..	..	1·00	75
830		20p. olive-green	..	..	1·00	30
831		50p. deep ultramarine	..		2·00	50
831b		£1 bluish black (6.12.72)	..		4·00	80
829/31b	..	..	..	Set of 4	7·00	2·00

The 20p. and 50p. exist on thinner, uncoated paper and are listed in the *Great Britain Concise Catalogue.*

A whiter paper was introduced in 1973. The £1 appeared on 27 Sept. 1973, the 20p. on 30 Nov. 1973 and the 50p. on 20 Feb. 1974.

The 50p. was issued on 1 Feb. 1973 on phosphorised paper. This cannot be distinguished from No. 831 with the naked eye.

The £1, T **318**, was also issued, on 17 June 1970, in sheets of 100 (10 × 10) instead of panes of 40 (8 × 5) but it is not easy to distinguish from No. 790 in singles. It can be readily differentiated when in large strips or marginal pieces showing sheet markings or plate numbers.

358 Runners

359 Swimmers

360 Cyclists

(Des A. Restall. Litho D.L.R.)

1970 (15 July). *Ninth British Commonwealth Games. Chalk-surfaced paper. Two phosphor bands. P* 13½ × 14.

832	358	5d. pk, emer, greenish yell & dp yell-grn			10	10
		a. Greenish yellow omitted	..		£4500	
833	359	1s. 6d. light greenish blue, lilac, bistre-brown and Prussian blue		..	50	55
834	360	1s. 9d. yellow-orange, lilac, salmon and deep red-brown	..		50	55
832/4	..	..	..	Set of 3	1·00	1·10

361 1d. Black (1840)

362 1s. Green (1847)

363 4d. Carmine (1855)

(Des D. Gentleman)

1970 (18 Sept). *"Philympia 70" Stamp Exhibition. Chalk-surfaced paper. Two phosphor bands. P* 14 × 14½.

835	361	5d. grey-black, brownish bistre, black and dull purple			10	10
		a. Grey-black (Queen's head) omitted		£10000		
836	362	9d. light drab, bluish green, stone, black and dull purple			50	50
837	363	1s. 6d. carmine, lt drab, blk & dull pur			50	60
835/7			..	Set of 3	1·00	1·10

364 Shepherds and Apparition of the Angel

365 Mary, Joseph, and Christ in the Manger

366 The Wise Men bearing gifts

(Des Sally Stiff after De Lisle Psalter. Queen's head printed in gold and then embossed)

1970 (25 Nov). *Christmas. Chalk-surfaced paper. One centre phosphor band* (4d.) *or two phosphor bands* (others). *P* 14 × 15.

838	364	4d. brown-red, turquoise-green, pale chestnut, brn, grey-blk, gold & verm	10	10
839	365	5d. emerald, gold, blue, brown-red, ochre, grey-black and violet	10	10
		a. Gold (Queen's head) omitted	†	£2500
		b. Emerald omitted	60·00	
		c. Imperf (pair)	£250	
840	366	1s. 6d. gold, grey-black, pale turq-grn, salmon, ultram, ochre & yellow-grn	35	45
		a. Salmon omitted	80·00	
		b. Ochre omitted	50·00	
838/40		Set of 3	50	60

The 4d. and 5d. are known with embossing omitted, and the 1s. 6d. is known with embossing and phosphor omitted.

(New Currency. 100 new pence = £1)

"X" NUMBERS. The following definitive series has been allocated "X" prefixes to the catalogue numbers to avoid re-numbering all subsequent issues.

367

367a

NO VALUE INDICATED. Stamps as Types 367/a inscribed "2nd" or "1st" are listed as Nos. 1445/52, 1511/16, 1663a/6 and 1979.

ELLIPTICAL PERFORATIONS. These were introduced in 1993 and stamps showing them will be found listed as Nos. Y1667, etc.

PRINTING PROCESSES

Litho   Photo

(Illustrations enlarged ×6)

Litho. Clear outlines to value and frame of stamp.
Photo. Uneven lines to value and frame formed by edges of screen.

Two types of the 3p., 10p. and 26p. (Nos. X930/c, X886/b and X971/b).

I   II

I   II

Figures of face value as I (all ptgs of 3p. bright magenta except multi-value coil No. 930cl and sheets from 21.1.92 onwards, 10p. orange-brown except 1984 "Christian Heritage" £4 booklet and 26p. rosine except 1987 £1.04 "window" booklet).

Figures of face value narrower as in II (from coil No. X930cl and in sheets from 21.1.92 (3p.), 1984 "Christian Heritage" £4 booklet (10p.) or 1987 £1.04 "window" booklet (26p.)).

This catalogue includes changes of figure styles on those stamps where there is no other listable difference. Similar changes have also taken place on other values, but only in conjunction with listed colour, paper or perforation differences.

(Des from plaster cast by Arnold Machin)

1971 (15 Feb)–96. *Decimal Currency.* T **367**. *Chalk-surfaced paper.*

(a) Photo Harrison (except for some printings of Nos. X879 and X913 in sheets produced by Enschedé and issued on 12 Dec 1979 *(8p.) and* 19 Nov 1991 *(18p.)). With phosphor bands. P* 15×14.

X841	½p. turquoise-blue (2 bands) ..	10	10
	a. Imperf (pair)†	£900	
	l. Booklet pane. No. X841 × 2 se-tenant vert with X849 × 2	5·00	
	la. Ditto, se-tenant horiz (14.7.71)	80	
	m. Booklet pane. No. X841×5 plus label	3·50	
	n. Coil strip. No. X849, X841×2 and X844×2	35	
	o. Booklet pane. No. X841 × 3, X851 × 3 and X852 × 6 (24.5.72)	12·00	
	p. Booklet pane. No. X841 × 3, X842 and X852 × 2 (24.5.72)	75·00	
	q. Coil strip. No. X870, X849, X844 and X841 × 2 (3.12.75)	80	
	r. Booklet pane. No. X841 × 2, X844 × 3 and X870 (10.3.76)	70	
	s. Booklet pane. No. X841 × 2, X844 × 2, X873 × 2 and X881 × 4 (8½p. values at right) (26.1.77)	2·50	
	sa. Ditto. 8½p. values at left	2·50	
	t. Booklet pane. No. X841, X844, X894 × 3 and X902 (14p. value at right) (26.1.81)	2·00	
	ta. Ditto. 14p. value at left	2·00	
	u. Booklet pane. No. X841, X857 × 4 and X899 × 3 (12½p. values at left) (1.2.82)	2·50	
	ua. Ditto. 12½p. values at right	2·50	
X842	½p. turquoise-blue (1 side band) (24.5.72)	70·00	35·00
X843	½p. turquoise-bl (1 centre band) (14.12.77)	30	20
	l. Coil strip. No. X843 × 2, X875 and X845 × 2 (14.12.77)	55	
	m. Booklet pane. No. X843 × 2, X845 × 2 and X875 plus label (8.2.78)	75	
X844	1p. crimson (2 bands)	10	10
	a. Imperf (vert coil)		
	b. Pair, one imperf 3 sides (vert coil)		
	c. Imperf (pair)		
	l. Booklet pane. No. X844 × 2 se-tenant with X848 × 2	5·00	
	m. Ditto, se-tenant horiz (14.7.71)	80	
	n. Booklet pane. No. X844 × 2, X876 × 3 and X883 × 3 (9p. values at right) (13.6.77)	4·00	
	na. Ditto. 9p. values at left	2·50	
X845	1p. crimson (1 centre band) (14.12.77)	20	20
	l. Booklet pane. No. X879 and X845 × 2 plus label (17.10.79)	70	
	m. Coil strip. No. X879 and X845 × 2 plus 2 labels (16.1.80)	45	
	n. Booklet pane. No. X845 × 2, X860 and X898 each × 3 (5.4.83)	5·00	
	p. Booklet pane. No. X845 × 3, X863 × 2 and X900 × 3 (3.9.84)	4·00	
	q. Booklet pane. No. X845 × 2 and X896 × 4 (29.7.86)	8·00	
	s. Booklet pane. No. X845, X867 × 2 and X900 × 3 (20.10.86)	3·00	
	sa. Ditto, but with vert edges of pane imperf (29.9.87)	3·00	
X846	1p. crimson ("all-over") (10.10.79)	20	20
X847	1p. crimson (1 side band) (20.10.86)	1·00	1·25
	l. Booklet pane. X847, X901 and X912 ×2	3·00	
	m. Booklet pane. No. X847, X901×2, X912×5 and X918 with margins all round (3.3.87)	13·00	
X848	1½p. black (2 bands)	20	15
	a. Uncoated paper (1971)*	£110	
	b. Imperf (pair)		
	c. Imperf 3 sides (horiz pair)		
X849	2p. myrtle-green (face value as T 367) (2 bands)	20	10
	a. Imperf (horiz pair)		
	l. Booklet pane. No. X849×2, X880×2 and X886×3 plus label (10p. values at right) (28.8.79)	2·50	
	la. Ditto. 10p. values at left	2·00	
	m. Booklet pane. No. X849×3, X889×2 and X895×2 plus label (12p. values at right) (4.2.80)	2·00	
	ma. Ditto. 12p. values at left	2·00	
	n. Booklet pane. No. X849, X888×3, X889 and X895×4 with margins all round (16.4.80)	3·75	
	o. Booklet pane. No. X849×6 with margins all round (16.4.80)	80	
	p. Booklet pane. No. X849, X857, X898 and X899×6 with margins all round (19.5.82)	4·50	
X850	2p. myrtle-green (face value as T 367) ("all-over") (10.10.79)	20	15

X851	2½p. magenta (1 centre band)		15	10
	a. Imperf (pair)†		£250	
	l. Booklet pane. No. X851 × 5 plus label		2·75	
	m. Booklet pane. No. X851 × 4 plus two labels		4·00	
	n. Booklet pane. No. X851 × 3, X852 × 3 and X855 × 6 (24.5.72)		7·00	
X852	2½p. magenta (1 side band)		1·25	1·75
	l. Booklet pane. No. X852 × 2 and X855 × 4		5·00	
X853	2½p. magenta (2 bands) (21.5.75)		30	75
X854	2½p. rose-red (2 bands) (26.8.81)		50	75
	l. Booklet pane. No. X854 × 3, X862 × 2 and X894 × 3 (11½p. values at left)		5·00	
	la. Ditto. 11½p. values at right		6·50	
X855	3p. ultramarine (2 bands)		20	10
	a. Imperf (coil strip of 5)		£1000	
	b. Imperf (pair)†		£250	
	c. Uncoated paper (1972)*		40·00	
	l. Booklet pane. No. X855 × 5 plus label		2·00	
X856	3p. ultramarine (1 centre band) (10.9.73)		20	25
	a. Imperf (pair)†		£250	
	b. Imperf between (vert pair)†		£375	
	c. Imperf horiz (vert pair)†		£200	
X857	3p. bright magenta (Type I) (2 bands) (1.2.82)		40	40
X858	3½p. olive-grey (*shades*) (2 bands)		30	30
	a. Imperf (pair)		£350	
X859	3½p. olive-grey (1 centre band) (24.6.74)		30	15
X860	3½p. purple-brown (1 centre band) (5.4.83)		1·25	1·50
X861	3½p. ochre-brown (2 bands)		20	20
	a. Imperf (pair)†		£950	
X862	4p. greenish blue (2 bands) (26.8.81)		1·50	1·50
X863	4p. greenish blue (1 centre band) (3.9.84)		1·75	2·00
X864	4p. greenish blue (1 side band) (8.1.85)		1·75	2·00
	l. Booklet pane. No. X864×2, X901×4, X909×2 and X920 with margins all round		12·50	
X865	4½p. grey-blue (2 bands) (24.10.73)		20	25
	a. Imperf (pair)		£300	
X866	5p. pale violet (2 bands)		20	10
X867	5p. claret (1 centre band) (20.10.86)		1·75	1·75
X868	5½p. violet (2 bands) (24.10.73)		25	25
X869	5½p. violet (1 centre band) (17.3.75)		20	20
	a. Uncoated paper*		£375	
X870	6p. light emerald (2 bands)		30	15
	a. Uncoated paper*		17·00	
X871	6½p. greenish blue (2 bands) (4.9.74)		45	45
X872	6½p. greenish blue (1 centre band) (24.9.75)		30	15
	a. Imperf (vert pair)		£300	
	b. Uncoated paper*		£160	
X873	6½p. greenish blue (1 side band) (26.1.77)		70	75
X874	7p. purple-brown (2 bands) (15.1.75)		70	85
	a. Imperf (pair)		£250	
X875	7p. purple-brown (1 centre band) (13.6.77)		35	20
	a. Imperf (pair)		£100	
	l. Booklet pane. No. X875 × 10 and X883 × 10 (15.11.78)		4·50	
X876	7p. purple-brown (1 side band) (13.6.77)		60	75
X877	7½p. pale chestnut (2 bands)		30	25
X878	8p. rosine (2 bands) (24.10.73)		25	20
	a. Uncoated paper*		12·00	
X879	8p. rosine (1 centre band) (20.8.79)		25	15
	a. Uncoated paper*		£600	
	b. Imperf (pair)†		£600	
	l. Booklet pane. No. X879 and X886, each × 10 (14.11.79)		5·00	
X880	8p. rosine (1 side band) (28.8.79)		80	80
X881	8½p. light yellowish green (*shades*) (2 bands) (24.9.75)		35	20
	a. Imperf (pair)		£750	
X882	9p. yellow-orange and black (2 bands)		60	30
X883	9p. deep violet (2 bands) (25.2.76)		45	25
	a. Imperf (pair)		£200	
X884	9½p. purple (2 bands) (25.2.76)		45	30
X885	10p. orge-brown & chest (2 bands) (11.8.71)		40	30
	a. Orange-brown omitted		£150	
	b. Imperf (horiz pair)		£2000	
X886	10p. orange-brn (Type I) (2 bands) (25.2.76)		40	20
	a. Imperf (pair)		£250	
	b. Type II (4.9.84)		28·00	28·00
	bl. Booklet pane. No. X886b, X901 and X909 × 7, with margins all round		29·00	
X887	10p. orange-brown (Type I) ("all-over") (3.10.79)		30	45
X888	10p. orange-brown (Type I) (1 centre band) (4.2.80)		30	20
	a. Imperf (pair)		£275	
	l. Booklet pane. No. X888×9 with margins all round (16.4.80)		2·75	
	m. Booklet pane. No. X888 and X895, each × 10 (12.11.80)		6·00	
X889	10p. orange-brown (Type I) (1 side band) (4.2.80)		85	90
X890	10½p. yellow (2 bands) (25.2.76)		50	30
X891	10½p. deep dull blue (2 bands) (26.4.78)		70	45
X892	11p. brown-red (2 bands) (25.2.76)		60	25
	a. Imperf (pair)		£1750	
X893	11½p. drab (1 centre band) (14.1.81)		45	30
	a. Imperf (pair)		£225	
	l. Booklet pane. No. X893 and X902, each × 10 (11.11.81)		7·00	
X894	11½p. drab (1 side band) (26.1.81)		60	75
	l. Booklet pane. No. X894 × 4 and X902 × 6 (6.5.81)		4·00	
X895	12p. yellowish green (2 bands) (4.2.80)		60	40
	l. Booklet pane. No. X895 × 9 with margins all round (16.4.80)		3·00	
X896	12p. bright emerald (1 centre band) (29.10.85)		60	40
	a. Imperf (pair)			
	l. Booklet pane. No. X896 × 9 with margins all round (18.3.86)		3·00	
X897	12p. bright emerald (1 side band) (14.1.86)		90	90
	l. Booklet pane. No. X897×4 and X909×6 (12p. values at left)		6·00	
	la. Ditto. 12p. values at right		6·00	
	m. Booklet pane. No. X897×6, X909×2 and X919 with margins all round (18.3.86)		14·00	
X898	12½p. light emerald (1 centre band) (27.1.82)		45	25
	a. Imperf (pair)		£100	
	l. Booklet pane. No. X898 and X907, each × 10 (10.11.82)		9·00	

X899	12½p. light emerald (1 side band) (1.2.82)		60	60
	l. Booklet pane. No. X899 × 4 and X907 × 6 (1.2.82)		5·00	
	m. Booklet pane. No. X899 × 6 with margins all round (19.5.82)		2·50	
	n. Booklet pane. No. X899 × 4 and X908 × 6 (12½p. values at left) (5.4.83)		8·00	
	na. Ditto. 12½p. values at right		8·00	
X900	13p. pale chestnut (1 centre band) (28.8.84)		45	35
	a. Imperf (pair)		£500	
	l. Booklet pane. No. X900 × 9 with margins all round (8.1.85)		3·25	
	m. Booklet pane. No. X900 × 6 with margins all round (3.3.87)		2·50	
	n. Booklet pane. No. X900 × 4 with margins all round (4.8.87)		2·50	
	o. Booklet pane. No. X900 × 10 with margins all round (4.8.87)		5·00	
X901	13p. pale chestnut (1 side band) (3.9.84)		60	60
	l. Booklet pane. No. X901×4 and X909×6 (13p. values at left)		6·00	
	la. Ditto. 13p. values at right		6·00	
	m. Booklet pane. No. X901×6 with margins all round (4.9.84)		2·50	
	n. Booklet pane. No. X901 and X912×5 (20.10.86)		5·00	
	na. Ditto, but with vert edges of pane imperf (29.9.87)		5·00	
X902	14p. grey-blue (2 bands) (26.1.81)		1·00	45
X903	14p. deep blue (1 centre band) (23.8.88)		60	40
	a. Imperf (pair)		£275	
	l. Booklet pane. No. X903 × 4 with margins all round		4·50	
	m. Booklet pane. No. X903 × 10 with margins all round		8·00	
	n. Booklet pane. No. X903 × 4 with horiz edges of pane imperf (11.10.88)		7·00	
	p. Booklet pane. No. X903 × 10 with horiz edges of pane imperf (11.10.88)		9·00	
	q. Booklet pane. No. X903×4 with three edges of pane imperf (24.1.89)		20·00	
X904	14p. deep blue (1 side band) (5.9.88)		2·75	2·75
	l. Booklet pane. No. X904 and X914×2 plus label		4·50	
	m. Booklet pane. No. X904×2 and X914×4 with vert edges of pane imperf		7·50	
X905	15p. bright blue (1 centre band) (26.9.89)		60	40
	a. Imperf (pair)		£325	
X906	15p. bright blue (1 side band) (2.10.89)		2·50	2·25
	l. Booklet pane. No. X906×2 and X916 plus label		8·00	
	m. Booklet pane. No. X906, X916, X922, 1446, 1448, 1468, 1470 and 1472 plus label with margins all round (20.3.90)		18·00	
X907	15½p. pale violet (2 bands) (1.2.82)		60	60
	l. Booklet pane. No. X907×6 with margins all round (19.5.82)		3·00	
	m. Booklet pane. No. X907×9 with margins all round (19.5.82)		4·00	
X908	16p. olive-drab (2 bands) (5.4.83)		1·25	1·25
X909	17p. grey-blue (2 bands) (3.9.84)		75	75
	l. Booklet pane. No. X909×3 plus label (4.11.85)		3·00	
X910	17p. deep blue (1 centre band) (4.9.90)		1·00	1·00
	a. Imperf (pair)			
X911	17p. deep blue (1 side band) (4.9.90)		1·25	1·25
	l. Booklet pane. No. X911×3 plus label		3·00	
	m. Booklet pane. No. X911×2, X917×3 plus 3 labels with vert edges of pane imperf		4·00	
X912	18p. deep olive-grey (2 bands) (20.10.86)		75	75
X913	18p. bright green (1 centre band) (10.9.91)		60	40
	a. Imperf (pair)		£375	
X914	19p. bright orange-red (2 bands) (5.9.88)		1·25	1·25
X915	20p. dull purple (2 bands) (25.2.76)		1·00	50
X916	20p. brownish black (2 bands) (2.10.89)		1·50	1·75
X917	22p. bright orange-red (2 bands) (4.9.90)		1·25	1·25
X917a	25p. rose-red (2 bands) (6.2.96)		1·50	1·50
X918	26p. rosine (Type I) (2 bands) (3.3.87)		8·00	8·00
X919	31p. purple (2 bands) (18.3.86)		12·00	12·00
X920	34p. ochre-brown (2 bands) (8.1.85)		8·00	8·00
X921	50p. ochre-brown (2 bands) (2.2.77)		2·00	50
X922	50p. ochre (2 bands) (20.3.90)		4·25	4·25

(b) Photo Harrison. On phosphorised paper. P 15×14.

X924	½p. turquoise-blue (10.12.80)		10	10
	a. Imperf (pair)		£130	
	l. Coil strip. No. X924 and X932×3 (30.12.81)		75	
X925	1p. crimson (12.12.79)		10	10
	a. Imperf (pair)		£750	
	l. Coil strip. No. X925 and X932×3 (14.8.84)		80	
	m. Booklet pane. No. X925 and X969, each × 2 (10.9.91)		1·00	
X926	2p. myrtle-green (face value as T **367**) (12.12.79)		10	10
	a. Imperf (pair)		£900	
X927	2p. deep green (face value as T **367a**) (26.7.88)		10	10
	a. Imperf (pair)			
	l. Booklet pane. No. X927×2 and X969×4 plus 2 labels with vert edges of pane imperf (10.9.91)		1·50	
X928	2p. myrtle-green (face value as T **367a**) (5.9.88)		2·00	2·00
	l. Coil strip. No. X928 and X932×3		2·25	
X929	2½p. rose-red (14.1.81)		20	20
	l. Coil strip. No. X929 and X930×3 (6.81)		1·25	
X930	3p. bright magenta (Type I) (22.10.80)		20	20
	a. Imperf (horiz pair)		£1000	
	b. Booklet pane. No. X930, X931×2 and X949×6 with margins all round (14.9.83)		4·50	
	c. Type II (10.10.89)		1·00	50
	cl. Coil strip. No. X930c and X933×3		2·75	
X931	3½p. purple-brown (30.3.83)		45	45
X932	4p. greenish blue (30.12.81)		40	40

X933	4p. new blue (26.7.88)		20	20
	a. Imperf (pair)			
	l. Coil strip. No. X933×3 and X935 (27.11.90)		1·00	
	m. Coil strip. No. X933 and X935, each ×2 (1.10.91)		75	
	n. Coil strip. No. X933 and X935×3 (31.1.95)		30	
X934	5p. pale violet (10.10.79)		30	25
X935	5p. dull red-brown (26.7.88)		20	20
	a. Imperf (pair)			
X936	6p. yellow-olive (10.9.91)		25	25
X937	7p. brownish red (29.10.85)		1·75	1·75
X938	8½p. yellowish green (24.3.76)		40	55
X939	10p. orange-brown (Type I) (11.79)		40	20
X940	10p. dull orange (Type II) (4.9.90)		30	30
X941	11p. brown-red (27.8.80)		85	85
X942	11½p. ochre-brown (15.8.79)		50	45
X943	12p. yellowish green (30.1.80)		50	50
X944	13p. olive-grey (15.8.79)		60	45
X945	13½p. purple-brown (30.1.80)		65	60
X946	14p. grey-blue (14.1.81)		60	40
X947	15p. ultramarine (15.8.79)		60	40
X948	15½p. pale violet (14.1.81)		60	40
	a. Imperf (pair)		£200	
X949	16p. olive-drab (30.3.83)		60	30
	a. Imperf (pair)		£130	
	l. Booklet pane. No. X949×9 with margins all round (14.9.83)		3·75	
X950	16½p. pale chestnut (27.1.82)		85	75
X951	17p. light emerald (30.1.80)		70	40
X952	17p. grey-blue (30.3.83)		60	40
	a. Imperf (pair)		£275	
	l. Booklet pane. No. X952×6 with margins all round (4.9.84)		3·00	
	m. Booklet pane. No. X952×9 with margins all round (8.1.85)		4·50	
X953	17½p. pale chestnut (30.1.80)		80	80
X954	18p. deep violet (14.1.81)		80	75
X955	18p. deep olive-grey (28.8.84)		80	60
	a. Imperf (pair)		£130	
	l. Booklet pane. No. X955×9 with margins all round (3.3.87)		4·50	
	m. Booklet pane. No. X955×4 with margins all round (4.8.87)		3·00	
	n. Booklet pane. No. X955×10 with margins all round (4.8.87)		6·50	
X956	19p. bright orange-red (23.8.88)		70	50
	a. Imperf (pair)		£325	
	l. Booklet pane. No. X956×4 with margins all round		6·00	
	m. Booklet pane. No. X956×10 with margins all round		10·00	
	n. Booklet pane. No. X956×4 with horiz edges of pane imperf (11.10.88)		7·00	
	o. Booklet pane. No. X956×10 with horiz edges of pane imperf (11.10.88)		12·00	
	q. Booklet pane. No. X956×4 with three edges of pane imperf (24.1.89)		20·00	
X957	19½p. olive-grey (27.1.82)		1·50	1·50
X958	20p. dull purple (10.10.79)		90	30
X959	20p. turquoise-green (23.8.88)		90	60
X960	20p. brownish black (26.9.89)		90	40
	a. Imperf (pair)		£650	
	l. Booklet pane. No. X960×5 plus label with vert edges of pane imperf (2.10.89)		7·00	
X961	20½p. ultramarine (30.3.83)		1·25	1·10
	a. Imperf (pair)		£1100	
X962	22p. blue (22.10.80)		80	45
	a. Imperf (pair)		£200	
X963	22p. yellow-green (28.8.84)		80	55
	a. Imperf (horiz pair)		£900	
X964	22p. bright orange-red (4.9.90)		80	50
X965	23p. brown-red (30.3.83)		1·00	60
	a. Imperf (horiz pair)		£900	
X966	23p. bright green (23.8.88)		1·00	60
X967	24p. violet (28.8.84)		1·25	1·00
X968	24p. Indian red (26.9.89)		1·60	1·00
	a. Imperf (horiz pair)		£2250	
X969	24p. chestnut (10.9.91)		90	45
	a. Imperf (pair)		£200	
X970	25p. purple (14.1.81)		1·00	1·00
X971	26p. rosine (Type I) (27.1.82)		90	30
	a. Imperf (horiz pair)			
	b. Type II (4.8.87)		3·75	3·75
	bl. Booklet pane. No. X971b×4 with margins all round		14·00	
X972	26p. drab (4.9.90)		1·00	1·00
X973	27p. chestnut (23.8.88)		1·00	1·00
	l. Booklet pane. No. X973×4 with margins all round		7·00	
	m. Booklet pane. No. X973×4 with horiz edges of pane imperf (11.10.88)		25·00	
X974	27p. violet (4.9.90)		1·00	1·00
X975	28p. deep violet (30.3.83)		1·00	1·00
	a. Imperf (pair)		£1000	
X976	28p. ochre (23.8.88)		1·00	1·00
X977	28p. deep bluish grey (10.9.91)		1·00	1·00
	a. Imperf (pair)		£1500	
X978	29p. ochre-brown (27.1.82)		1·75	1·00
X979	29p. deep mauve (26.9.89)		1·75	1·00
X980	30p. deep olive-grey (26.9.89)		1·10	1·00
X981	31p. purple (30.3.83)		1·25	1·25
	a. Imperf (pair)		£1000	
X982	31p. ultramarine (4.9.90)		1·25	1·25
X983	32p. greenish blue (23.8.88)		1·25	1·25
	a. Imperf (pair)		£1000	
X984	33p. light emerald (4.9.90)		1·25	1·25
X985	34p. ochre-brown (28.8.84)		1·25	1·10
X986	34p. deep bluish grey (26.9.89)		1·50	1·25
X987	34p. deep mauve (10.9.91)		1·50	1·25
X988	35p. sepia (23.8.88)		1·50	1·25
	a. Imperf (pair)			
X989	35p. yellow (10.9.91)		1·25	1·00
X990	37p. rosine (26.9.89)		1·50	1·50
X991	39p. bright mauve (10.9.91)		1·25	1·25

(c) Photo Harrison. On ordinary paper. P 15×14

X992	50p. ochre-brown (21.5.80)		1·75	80
	a. Imperf (pair)		£600	
X993	75p. grey-black (face value as T **367a**) (26.7.88)		2·25	2·25

(d) Photo Harrison. On ordinary or phosphorised paper.
P 15×14

X994	50p. ochre (13.3.90)	1·50	60
	a. Imperf (pair)	£850	

(e) Litho J.W. P 14

X996	4p. greenish blue (2 phosphor bands) (30.1.80)	20	25
X997	4p. greenish blue (phosphorised paper) (11.81)	35	20
X998	20p. dull pur (2 phosphor bands) (21.5.80)	1·10	40
X999	20p. dull pur (phosphorised paper) (11.81)	1·40	40

(f) Litho Questa. P 14 (No. X1000, X1003/4 and X1023) or 15×14 (others)

X1000	2p. emerald-green (face value as T **367**) (phosphorised paper) (21.5.80)	20	20
	a. Perf 15×14 (10.7.84)	30	20
X1001	2p. bright green & dp green (face value as T **367a**) (phosphorised paper) (23.2.88)	1·00	60
X1002	4p. greenish blue (phosphorised paper) (13.5.86)	60	60
X1003	5p. lt violet (phosphorised paper) (21.5.80)	40	20
X1004	5p. claret (phosphorised paper) (27.1.82)	50	20
	a. Perf 15×14 (21.2.84)	60	40
X1005	13p. pale chestnut (1 centre band) (9.2.88)	70	70
	l. Booklet pane. No. X1005×6 with margins all round	3·50	
X1006	13p. pale chestnut (1 side band) (9.2.88)	1·00	1·00
	l. Booklet pane. No. X1006×6, X1010, X1015 and X1021 with margins all round	22·00	
X1007	14p. deep blue (1 centre band) (11.10.88)	1·75	1·75
X1008	17p. deep blue (1 centre band) (19.3.91)	75	75
	l. Booklet pane. No. X1008×6 with margins all round	3·50	
X1009	18p. deep olive-grey (phosphorised paper) (9.2.88)	75	75
	l. Booklet pane. No. X1009×9 with margins all round	4·50	
	m. Booklet pane. No. X1009×6 with margins all round	3·00	
X1010	18p. dp ol-grey (2 phosphor bands) (9.2.88)	5·00	5·00
X1011	18p. bright green (1 centre band) (27.10.92)	1·25	1·25
	l. Booklet pane. No. X1011×6 with margins all round	7·50	
X1012	18p. bright green (1 side band) (27.10.92)	1·50	1·50
	l. Booklet pane X1012×2, X1018×2, X1022×2, 1451a, 1514a and central label with margins all round	10·00	
	m. Booklet pane. Nos. X1012, X1020, X1022 and 1451a, each × 2, and central label with margins all round (10.8.93)	11·00	
X1013	19p. brt orange-red (phosphorised paper) (11.10.88)	1·75	1·75
X1014	20p. dull pur (phosphorised paper) (13.5.86)	1·25	1·25
X1015	22p. yellow-grn (2 phosphor bands) (9.2.88)	8·00	8·00
X1016	22p. bright orange-red (phosphorised paper) (19.3.91)	1·00	1·00
	l. Booklet pane. No. X1016×9 with margins all round	5·50	
	m. Booklet pane. No. X1016×6, X1019×2 and central label with margins all round	8·00	
X1017	24p. chestnut (phosphorised paper) (27.10.92)	1·00	80
	l. Booklet pane. No. X1017×6 with margins all round	6·00	
X1018	24p. chestnut (2 bands) (27.10.92)	1·25	1·25
X1019	33p. lt emer (phosphorised paper) (19.3.91)	1·75	1·75
X1020	33p. lt emer (2 phosphor bands) (25.2.92)	1·40	1·40
X1021	34p. ochre-brn (2 phosphor bands) (9.2.88)	7·00	7·00
X1022	39p. bright mauve (2 bands) (27.10.92)	2·00	2·00
X1023	75p. black (face value as T **367**) (ordinary paper) (30.1.80)	3·25	1·75
	a. Perf 15×14 (21.2.84)	3·75	3·50
X1024	75p. brownish grey and black (face value as T **367a**) (ordinary paper) (23.2.88)	10·00	9·00

(g) Litho Walsall. P 14

X1050	2p. dp green (phosphorised paper) (9.2.93)	1·00	1·00
	l. Booklet pane. No. X1050×2 and X1053×4 plus 2 labels with vert edges of the pane imperf	3·50	
X1051	14p. deep blue (1 side band) (25.4.89)	3·00	3·00
	l. Booklet pane. No. X1051×2 and X1052×4 with vert edges of pane imperf	10·00	
X1052	19p. bright orange-red (2 phosphor bands) (25.4.89)	1·50	1·75
X1053	24p. chestnut (phosphorised paper) (9.2.93)	1·25	1·25
X1054	29p. dp mauve (2 phosphor bands) (2.10.89)	5·50	5·50
	l. Booklet pane. No. X1054×4 with three edges of pane imperf	20·00	
X1055	29p. dp mve (phosphorised paper) (17.4.90)	6·50	6·50
	l. Booklet pane. No. X1055×4 with three edges of pane imperf	24·00	
X1056	31p. ultram (phosphorised paper) (17.9.90)	1·75	2·00
	l. Booklet pane. No. X1056×4 with horiz edges of pane imperf	7·00	
X1057	33p. lt emer (phosphorised paper) (16.9.91)	1·25	1·25
	l. Booklet pane. No. X1057×4 with horiz edges of pane imperf	5·00	
X1058	39p. brt mve (phosphorised paper) (16.9.91)	1·75	1·75
	l. Booklet pane. No. X1058×4 with horiz edges of pane imperf	7·00	

*See footnote after No. 744.
†These come from sheets with gum arabic.
Nos. X842, X847, X852, X854, X857, X860, X862/4, X867, X873, X876, X880, X886b, X889, X894/5, X897, X899, X901/2, X904, X906/9, X911/12, X914, X916/20, X922, X971b, X1005/13, X1015/22 and X1050/8 come from booklets; Nos. X843 and X845 come from booklets or coils. Nos. X917a, X928 and X932 come from coils: Nos. X852, X864, X873, X876, X880, X889, X894, X897, X899, X901, X911 and X1006 were each issued with the phosphor band at the right or left from the same stamp booklet, usually in equal quantities. Nos. X847, X906 and X1012 also exist with phosphor band at the left or right, but these come from different booklets.
In addition to booklet pane No. X1012m, No. X1020 also comes from the *se-tenant* pane on the Wales £6 booklet which is listed under No. W49a in the Wales Regional Section.
Nos. X844a/b come from a strip of eight of the vertical coil. It comprises two normals, one imperforate at sides and bottom, one completely imperforate, one imperforate at top, left and bottom

and partly perforated at right due to the bottom stamps being perforated twice. No. X844b is also known from another strip having one stamp imperforate at sides and bottom.

Nos. X848b/c come from the same sheet, the latter having perforations at the foot of the stamps only.

Multi-value coil strips Nos. X924l, X925l, X928l, X929l, X930cl and X933l/m were produced by the Post Office for a large direct mail marketing firm. Use of the first coil strip, No. X929l, is known from June 1981. From 2 September 1981 No. X929l was available from the Philatelic Bureau, Edinburgh and, subsequently, from a number of other Post Office counters.

Later coil stamps were sold at the Philatelic Bureau and Post Office philatelic counters.

PANES OF SIX FROM STITCHED BOOKLETS. Nos. X841m, X851l/m and X855l include one or two printed labels showing commercial advertisements. These were originally perforated on all four sides, but from the August 1971 editions of the 25p. and 30p. booklets and December 1971 edition of the 50p. the line of perforations between the label and the binding margin was omitted. Similar panes, with the line of perforations omitted, exist for the 3p., 3½p. and 4½p. values (Nos. X856, X858 and X865), but these are outside the scope of this listing as the labels are blank.

PART-PERFORATED SHEETS. Since the introduction of the "Jumelle" press in 1972 a number of part-perforated sheets, both definitive and commemoratives, have been discovered. It is believed that these occur when the operation of the press is interrupted. Such sheets invariably show a number of "blind" perforations, where the pins have failed to cut the paper. Our listings of imperforate errors from these sheets are for pairs showing no trace whatsoever of the perforations. Examples showing "blind" perforations are outside the scope of this catalogue.

In cases where perforation varieties affect *se-tenant* stamps fuller descriptions will be found in Vol. 4 of the *G.B. Specialised Catalogue*.

WHITE PAPER. From 1972 printings appeared on fluorescent white paper giving a stronger chalk reaction than the original ordinary cream paper.

GUM ARABIC. The following exist with gum arabic as well as PVA gum (with or without added dextrin): Nos. X841, X841n, X851, X855, X856, X861 and X870. See notes after No. 722.

DEXTRIN GUM. From 1973 printings in photogravure appeared with PVA gum to which dextrin had been added. As the resulting gum was virtually colourless bluish green colouring matter was added to distinguish it from the previous PVA. Questa printings in lithography from 1988 onwards used PVA gum with dextrin, but did not show the colouring agent.

"ALL-OVER" PHOSPHOR. To improve mechanised handling most commemoratives from the 1972 Royal Silver Wedding 3p. value to the 1979 Rowland Hill Death Centenary set had the phosphor applied by printing cylinder across the entire surface of the stamp, giving a matt effect. Printing of the 1, 2 and 10p. definitives, released in October 1979, also had "all-over" phosphor, but these were purely a temporary expedient pending the adoption of phosphorised paper. Nos. X883, X890 and X921 have been discovered with "all over" phosphor in addition to the normal phosphor bands. These error are outside the scope of this catalogue.

PHOSPHORISED PAPER. Following the experiments on Nos. 743c and 829 a printing of the 4½p. definitive was issued on 13 November 1974, which had, in addition to the normal phosphor bands, phosphor included in the paper coating. Because of dfficulties in identifying the phosphorised paper with the naked eye this printing is not listed separately in this catalogue.

No. X938 was the first value printed on phosphorised paper without phosphor bands and was a further experiment issue to test the efficacy of this system. From 15 August 1979 phosphorised paper was accepted for use generally, the paper replacing phosphor bands on values other than those required in the second-class rate.

Stamps on phosphorised paper show a shiny surface instead of the matt areas of those printed with phosphor bands.

VARNISH COATING. Nos. X841 and X883 exist with and without a varnish coating. This cannot easily be detected without the use of an ultra-violet lamp as it merely reduces the fluorescent paper reaction.

POSTAL FORGERIES. In mid-1993 a number of postal forgeries of the 24p. chestnut were detected in the London area. These forgeries, produced by lithography, can be identified by the lack of phosphor in the paper, screening dots across the face value and by the perforations which were applied by a line machine gauging 11.

UNDERPRINTS. From 1982 various values appeared with underprints, printed on the reverse, in blue, over the gum. These were usually from special stamp booklets, sold at a discount by the Post Office, but in 1985 surplus stocks of such underprinted paper were used for other purposes.

The following Decimal Machin stamps exist with underprints:

12p. bright emerald (1 centre band)—double-lined star underprint from sheet printing (also exists without).

12½p. light emerald (1 centre band)—star with central dot underprint from booklet pane X898l

12½p. light emerald (1 centre band)—double-lined star underprint from booklet pane of 20

13p. pale chestnut (1 centre band)—double-lined star underprint from booklet pane of 10 (also exists without)

15½p. pale violet (2 bands)—star with central dot underprint from booklet pane X898l

16p. olive-drab (phosphorised paper)—double-lined D underprint from booklet pane of 10 (also exists without)

17p. grey-blue (2 bands)—double-lined star underprint from booklet pane X909l

17p. grey-blue (phosphorised paper)—double-lined D underprint from booklet pane of 10 (also exists without)

Additional Information for GB Collectors

Stanley Gibbons

GREAT BRITAIN CONCISE STAMP CATALOGUE 1998 Edition

Based on the listings from the British Commonwealth 'Part 1' but containing a host of additional information on watermark varieties, errors, gutter pairs, first day covers, booklets, specimens and much more. This easy to understand value-for-money guide is out each Spring.

For our free colour brochure telephone 01425 472363 today.

STANLEY GIBBONS

• THE COLLECTOR'S CHOICE •

Stanley Gibbons Publications
5 Parkside, Christchurch Road,
Ringwood, Hants, BH24 3SH

368 "A Mountain Road" (T. P. Flanagan)

369 "Deer's Meadow" (Tom Carr)

370 "Slieve na brock" (Colin Middleton)

(Layout des Stuart Rose)

1971 (16 June). *"Ulster 1971" Paintings. Chalk-surfaced paper. Two phosphor bands. P* 15 × 14.

881	368	3p. yellow-buff, pale yellow, Venetian red, black, blue and drab ..		10	10
882	369	7½p. olive-brown, brownish grey, pale olive-grey, dp bl, cobalt & grey-bl		50	50
		a. Pale olive-grey omitted* ..	..	60·00	
883	370	9p. greenish yellow, orange, grey, lavender-grey, bistre, black, pale ochre-brown, and ochre-brown ..		50	50
		a. Orange omitted	..	1500	
881/3	..	.. .. ..	*Set of* 3	1·00	1·00

A used example of the 3p. has been seen with the Venetian red omitted.

371 John Keats (150th Death Anniv)

372 Thomas Gray (Death Bicentenary)

373 Sir Walter Scott (Birth Bicentenary)

(Des Rosalind Dease. Queen's head printed in gold and then embossed)

1971 (28 July). *Literary Anniversaries. Chalk-surfaced paper. Two phosphor bands. P* 15 × 14.

884	371	3p. black, gold and greyish blue	..	10	10
		a. Gold (Queen's head) omitted	..	90·00	
885	372	5p. black, gold and yellow-olive	..	50	50
		a. Gold (Queen's head) omitted	..	£160	
886	373	7½p. black, gold and yellow-brown	..	50	50
884/6		.. .. ..	*Set of* 3	1·00	1·00

The 7½p. exists with embossing omitted.

374 Servicemen and Nurse of 1921

375 Roman Centurion

376 Rugby Football, 1871

(Des F. Wegner)

1971 (25 Aug). *British Anniversaries. Events described on stamps. Chalk-surfaced paper. Two phosphor bands. P* 15 × 14.

887	374	3p. red-orange, grey, deep blue, olive-grn, olive-brn, blk, rosine & vio-bl		10	10
		a. Deep blue omitted* ..	..	£600	
		b. Red-orange (nurse's cloak) omitted		£275	
		c. Olive-brown (faces, etc.) omitted		£160	
		d. Black omitted ..	..	£10000	
888	375	7½p. grey, yellow-brown, vermilion, mauve, grey-black, black, silver, gold and ochre ..		50	50
		a. Grey omitted ..	..	75·00	
889	376	9p. new blue, myrtle-green, grey-blk, lemon, olive-brown, mag & yell-ol		50	50
		a. Olive-brown omitted	..	£110	
		b. New blue omitted	..	£2500	
		c. Myrtle-green omitted	..	£2250	
887/9		.. .. ..	*Set of* 3	1·00	1·00

*The effect of the missing deep blue is shown on the sailor's uniform, which appears as grey.

Used examples have been seen of the 3p. with grey omitted and of the 9p. with the lemon (jerseys) omitted.

377 Physical Sciences Building, University College of Wales, Aberystwyth

378 Faraday Building, Southampton University

379 Engineering Department, Leicester University

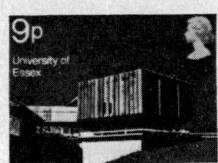

380 Hexagon Restaurant, Essex University

(Des N. Jenkins)

1971 (22 Sept). *British Architecture. Modern University Buildings. Chalk-surfaced paper. Two phosphor bands. P* 15 × 14.

890	377	3p. olive-brn, ochre, lem, blk & yell-ol		10	10
		a. Lemon omitted ..	..		
		b. Black (windows) omitted	..	£10000	
891	378	5p. rose, black, chestnut and lilac	..	20	20
892	379	7½p. ochre, black and purple-brown	..	50	50
893	380	9p. pale lilac, black, sepia-brn & dp bl		90	90
890/3		.. .. ..	*Set of* 4	1·50	1·50

Mint examples of the 5p. exist with a larger "P" following the face value.

381 "Dream of the Wise Men"

382 "Adoration of the Magi"

383 "Ride of the Magi"

(Des Clarke-Clements-Hughes design team, from stained-glass windows, Canterbury Cathedral. Queen's head printed in gold and then embossed)

1971 (13 Oct). *Christmas. Ordinary paper. One centre phosphor band (2½p.) or two phosphor bands (others). P* 15 × 14.

894	381	2½p. new blue, black, lemon, emerald, reddish violet, carmine-red, carmine-rose and gold ..		10	10
		a. Imperf (pair) ..	..	£400	
895	382	3p. black, reddish violet, lemon, new bl, carm-rose, emer, ultram & gold		10	10
		a. Gold (Queen's head) omitted	..	£500	
		b. Carmine-rose omitted	..	£1750	
		c. Lemon omitted ..	..	60·00	
		d. New blue omitted	..	†	£7000
		e. Reddish violet (tunics etc) omitted			
896	383	7½p. black, lilac, lemon, emerald, new blue, rose, green and gold ..		90	90
		a. Gold (Queen's head) omitted	..	80·00	
		b. Lilac omitted ..	..	£400	
		c. Emerald omitted ..	..	£200	
894/6		.. .. ..	*Set of* 3	1·00	1·00

All three values are known with the embossing omitted and the 7½p. with embossing double. Used examples of the 3p. have been seen with reddish violet and embossing omitted or with lemon and carmine-rose omitted. A used example of the 7½p. exists with the lemon omitted.

WHITE CHALK-SURFACED PAPER. From No. 897 all issues, with the exception of Nos. 904/8, were printed on fluorescent white paper, giving a stronger chalk reaction than the original cream paper.

384 Sir James Clark Ross   385 Sir Martin Frobisher

386 Henry Hudson   387 Capt. Scott

(Des Marjorie Saynor. Queen's head printed in gold and then embossed)

1972 (16 Feb). *British Polar Explorers. Two phosphor bands. P* 14 × 15.

897	384	3p. yellow-brown, indigo, slate-black, flesh, lemon, rose, brt blue & gold		10	10
		a. Gold (Queen's head) omitted	..	60·00	
		b. Slate-black (hair, etc.) omitted	..	£2250	
		c. Lemon omitted ..	..	£2000	
898	385	5p. salmon, flesh, purple-brown, ochre, black and gold ..		20	20
		a. Gold (Queen's head) omitted	..	90·00	
899	386	7½p. reddish violet, blue, deep slate, yellow-brown, buff, black and gold		50	50
		a. Gold (Queen's head) omitted	..	£200	

900 **387** 9p. dull blue, ultramarine, black, green-
    ish yell, pale pink, rose-red & gold 90 90
897/900 .. .. *Set of 4* .. 1·50 .. 1·50
The 3p. and 5p. are known with embossing omitted and the 3p. also
exists with gold and embossing omitted. An example of the 3p. is
known used on piece with the flesh colour omitted.

388 Statuette of Tutankhamun

389 19th-century Coastguard

390 Ralph Vaughan Williams and Score

(Des Rosalind Dease (3p.), F. Wegner (7½p.), C. Abbott (9p.).
Queen's head printed in gold and then embossed (7½p., 9p.))

1972 (26 Apr). *General Anniversaries. Events described on stamps.
Two phosphor bands. P 15 × 14.*
901 **388** 3p. black, grey, gold, dull bistre-brown,
        blackish brn, pale stone & lt brn 10 10
902 **389** 7½p. pale yellow, new blue, slate-blue,
        violet-blue, slate and gold 50 50
903 **390** 9p. bistre-brown, black, sage-green, dp
        slate, yellow-ochre, brown & gold 50 50
    a. Gold (Queen's head) omitted .. £1250
    b. Brown (facial features) omitted .. £750
    c. Deep slate omitted
901/3 .. .. *Set of 3* .. 1·00 .. 1·00
The 7½p. and 9p. exist with embossing omitted.

391 St. Andrew's,
Greensted-juxta-Ongar, Essex

392 All Saints, Earls Barton,
Northants

393 St. Andrew's,
Letheringsett, Norfolk

394 St. Andrew's,
Helpringham, Lincs

395 St. Mary the Virgin, Huish
Episcopi, Somerset

(Des R. Maddox. Queen's head printed in gold and then embossed)
1972 (21 June). *British Architecture. Village Churches. Ordinary
paper. Two phosphor bands. P 14 × 15.*
904 **391** 3p. violet-blue, black, lt yellow-olive,
        emerald-green, orange-verm & gold 10 10
    a. Gold (Queen's head) omitted .. 75·00
905 **392** 4p. deep yellow-olive, black, emerald,
        violet-blue, orge-vermilion & gold 20 20
    a. Gold (Queen's head) omitted .. £2500
    b. Violet-blue omitted £110
906 **393** 5p. deep emerald, black, royal blue, lt
        yellow-olive, orange-verm & gold 20 25
    a. Gold (Queen's head) omitted .. £150
907 **394** 7½p. orange-red, black, deep yellow-ol,
        royal blue, lt emerald & gold 70 80
908 **395** 9p. new blue, black, emerald-green, dp
        yellow-olive, orange-verm & gold 75 90
904/8 .. .. *Set of 5* .. 1·75 .. 2·00
The 3p., 4p., 5p. and 9p. exist with embossing omitted.
An example of the 3p. is known used on piece with the orange-
vermilion omitted.

396 Microphones, 1924–69

397 Horn Loudspeaker

398 T.V. Camera, 1972

399 Oscillator and Spark Transmitter, 1897

(Des D. Gentleman)

1972 (13 Sept). *Broadcasting Anniversaries. 75th Anniv of Marconi
and Kemp's Radio Experiments (9p.), and 50th Anniv of Daily
Broadcasting by the B.B.C. (others). Two phosphor bands. P 15 × 14.*
909 **396** 3p. pale brown, black, grey, greenish
        yellow and brownish slate 10 10
    a. Greenish yellow (terminals)
        omitted £2000
910 **397** 5p. brownish slate, lake-brown,
        salmon, lt brown, black & red-brn 15 20
911 **398** 7½p. light grey, slate, brownish slate,
        magenta and black 75 75
    a. Brownish slate (Queen's head)
        omitted .. .. † £2000
912 **399** 9p. lemon, brown, brownish slate, deep
        brownish slate, bluish slate & blk 75 75
    a. Brownish slate (Queen's head)
        omitted £1500
909/12 .. .. *Set of 4* .. 1·50 .. 1·50
No. 911a is only known on first day covers posted from the
Philatelic Bureau in Edinburgh.

400 Angel holding Trumpet

401 Angel playing Lute

---

402 Angel playing Harp

(Des Sally Stiff. Photo and embossed)
1972 (18 Oct). *Christmas. One centre phosphor band (2½p.) or two
phosphor bands (others). P 14 × 15.*
913 **400** 2½p. cerise, pale reddish brown, yellow-
        orange, orange-vermilion, lilac,
        gold, red-brown and deep grey .. .. 10 .. 15
    a. Gold omitted £250
    c. Deep grey omitted
914 **401** 3p. ultram, lavender, lt turq-blue, brt
        green, gold, red-brown & bluish vio .. 10 .. 15
    a. Red-brown omitted £500
    b. Bright green omitted .. .. 70·00
    c. Bluish violet omitted .. .. 75·00
915 **402** 7½p. deep brown, pale lilac, lt cinnamon,
        ochre, gold, red-brn & blackish vio .. 90 .. 80
    a. Ochre omitted .. .. .. 55·00
    b. Blackish violet (shadow) omitted
913/15 .. .. *Set of 3* .. 1·00 .. 1·00
All three values exist with embossing omitted.

403 Queen Elizabeth and   **404** "Europe"
Duke of Edinburgh

(Des J. Matthews from photo by N. Parkinson)

1972 (20 Nov). *Royal Silver Wedding. "All-over" phosphor (3p.) or
without phosphor (20p.). P 14 × 15.*

        I. "REMBRANDT" Machine
916 **403** 3p. brownish black, dp blue & silver .. 25 .. 25
    a. Silver omitted £300
917   20p. brownish blk, reddish pur & silver .. 1·00 .. 1·00

        II. "JUMELLE" Machine
918 **403** 3p. brownish black, deep blue & silver .. 20 .. 25
The 3p. "JUMELLE" has a lighter shade of the brownish black
than the 3p. "Rembrandt". It also has the brown cylinders less deeply
etched, which can be distinguished in the Duke's face which is
slightly lighter, and in the Queen's hair where the highlights are
sharper.

3p. "REMBRANDT". Cyls. 3A–1B–11C no dot. Sheets of 100 (10 × 10).
3p. "JUMELLE". Cyls. 1A–1B–3C dot and no dot. Sheets of 100
(two panes 5 × 10, separated by gutter margin).

(Des P. Murdoch)

1973 (3 Jan). *Britain's Entry into European Communities. Two
phosphor bands. P 14 × 15.*
919 **404** 3p. dull orange, bright rose-red, ultra-
        marine, light lilac and black .. .. 10 .. 10
920   5p. new blue, bright rose-red, ultramar-
        ine, cobalt-blue and black .. .. 25 .. 50
    a. Pair. Nos. 920/1 .. .. 1·25 .. 1·50
921   5p. light emerald-green, bright rose-red,
        ultramarine, cobalt-blue and black .. 25 .. 50
919/21 .. .. *Set of 3* .. 1·25 .. 1·00
Nos. 920/1 were printed horizontally *se-tenant* throughout the
sheet.

405 Oak Tree

(Des D. Gentleman)

1973 (28 Feb). *Tree Planting Year. British Trees (1st issue). Two
phosphor bands. P 15 × 14.*
922 **405** 9p. brownish black, apple-green, deep
        olive, sepia, blackish green and
        brownish grey .. .. 50 .. 50
    a. Brownish black (value and inscr)
        omitted £400
    b. Brownish grey (Queen's head)
        omitted £250
See also No. 949.

CHALK-SURFACED PAPER. The following issues are printed on chalk-surfaced paper but where "all-over" phosphor has been applied there is no chalk reaction except in the sheet margins outside the phosphor area.

406 David Livingstone   **407** H. M. Stanley

(T **406/7** were printed together, horizontally *se-tenant* within the sheet)

408 Sir Francis Drake   **409** Walter Raleigh

410 Charles Sturt

(Des Marjorie Saynor. Queen's head printed in gold and then embossed)

1973 (18 Apr). *British Explorers. "All-over" phosphor.* P 14×15.

923	406	3p. orange-yellow, lt orge-brown, grey-black, lt turq-blue, turq-blue & gold			25	20
		a. Pair. Nos. 923/4	..	..	1·00	1·25
		b. Gold (Queen's head) omitted	..	40·00		
		c. Turquoise-blue (background and inscr) omitted		..	£350	
		d. Light orange-brown omitted	..	£300		
924	407	3p. orange-yellow, lt orge-brown, grey-black, lt turq-blue, turq-blue & gold			25	20
		b. Gold (Queen's head) omitted	..	40·00		
		c. Turquoise-blue (background and inscr) omitted		..	£350	
		d. Light orange-brown omitted	..	£300		
925	408	5p. light flesh, chrome-yellow, orange-yellow, sepia, brownish grey-black, violet-blue and gold			20	30
		a. Gold (Queen's head) omitted	..	90·00		
		b. Grey-black omitted	..	..	£500	
		c. Sepia omitted	..	..	£450	
926	409	7½p. light flesh, reddish brown, sepia, ultram, grey-black, brt lilac & gold			20	30
		a. Gold (Queen's head) omitted	..	£1750		
		b. Ultramarine (eyes) omitted	..	£2500		
927	410	9p. flesh, pale stone, grey-blue, grey-black, brown-grey, Venetian red, brown-red and gold			25	40
		a. Gold (Queen's head) omitted	..	90·00		
		b. Brown-grey printing double .. *from*	£800			
		c. Grey-black omitted	..	..	£1000	
		d. Brown-red (rivers on map) omitted	£500			
923/7		..	..	*Set of 5*	1·50	1·25

Caution is needed when buying missing gold heads in this issue as they can be removed by using a hard eraser, etc., but this invariably affects the "all-over" phosphor. Genuine examples have the phosphor intact. Used examples off cover cannot be distinguished as much of the phosphor is lost in the course of floating.

In the 5p. value the missing grey-black affects the doublet, which appears as brownish grey, and the lace ruff, which is entirely missing. The missing sepia affects only Drake's hair, which appears much lighter.

The double printing of the brown-grey (cylinder 1F) on the 9p. is a most unusual type of error to occur in a multicoloured photogravure issue. Two sheets are known and it is believed that they stuck to the cylinder and went through a second time. This would result in the following two sheets missing the colour but at the time of going to press this error has not been reported. The second print is slightly askew and more prominent in the top half of the sheets. Examples from the upper part of the sheet showing a clear double impression of the facial features are worth a substantial premium over the price quoted.

The 3p values, the 5p. and the 9p. exist with embossing omitted.

411   **412**

413

(T **411/13** show sketches of W. G. Grace by Harry Furniss)

(Des E. Ripley. Queen's head printed in gold and then embossed)

1973 (16 May). *County Cricket 1873–1973. "All-over" phosphor.* P 14×15.

928	411	3p. black, ochre and gold	..	10	10
		a. Gold (Queen's head) omitted	£1800		
929	412	7½p. black, light sage-green and gold		80	70
930	413	9p. black, cobalt and gold	..	1·00	90
928/30		..	*Set of 3*	1·75	1·50

All three values exist with embossing omitted.

414 "Self-portrait"   **415** "Self-portrait"
(Reynolds)   (Raeburn)

416 "Nelly O'Brien"   **417** "Rev. R. Walker
(Reynolds)   (The Skater)" (Raeburn)

(Des S. Rose. Queen's head printed in gold and then embossed)

1973 (4 July). *British Paintings. 250th Birth Anniv of Sir Joshua Reynolds and 150th Death Anniv of Sir Henry Raeburn. "All-over" phosphor.* P 14×15.

931	414	3p. rose, new blue, magenta, greenish yellow, blk, ochre & gold		10	10
		a. Gold (Queen's head) omitted	60·00		
932	415	5p. cinnamon, greenish yellow, new bl, lt magenta, blk, yellow-olive & gold		20	25
		a. Gold (Queen's head) omitted	75·00		
		b. Greenish yellow omitted	..	£350	
933	416	7½p. greenish yellow, new blue, light magenta, black, cinnamon and gold		55	50
		a. Gold (Queen's head) omitted	75·00		
		b. Cinnamon omitted	..	£4000	
934	417	9p brownish rose, black, dull rose, pale yell, brownish grey, pale bl & gold		60	60
		b. Brownish rose omitted	..	30·00	
931/4		..	*Set of 4*	1·25	1·25

No. 931a is also known with the embossing also omitted or misplaced.

The 5p. and 7½p. are known with the embossing omitted.

The 9p. is known with the embossing and phosphor both omitted.

418 Court Masque Costumes

419 St. Paul's Church, Covent Garden

420 Prince's Lodging, Newmarket

421 Court Masque Stage Scene

T **418/19** and T **420/1** were printed horizontally *se-tenant* within the sheet

(Des Rosalind Dease. Litho and typo B.W.)

1973 (15 Aug). *400th Birth Anniv of Inigo Jones (architect and designer). "All-over" phosphor.* P 15×14.

935	418	3p. deep mauve, black and gold	..	10	15
		a. Pair. Nos. 935/6	..	35	40
936	419	3p. deep brown, black and gold	..	10	15
937	420	5p. blue, black and gold	..	40	45
		a. Pair. Nos. 937/8	..	1·50	1·50
938	421	5p. grey-olive, black and gold	..	40	45
935/8		..	*Set of 4*	1·60	1·10

422 Palace of Westminster   **423** Palace of Westminster
seen from Whitehall   seen from Millbank

(Des R. Downer. Recess and typo B.W.)

1973 (12 Sept). *19th Commonwealth Parliamentary Conference. "All-over" phosphor.* P 15×14.

939	422	8p. black, brownish grey and stone	..	50	60
940	423	10p. gold and black	..	50	40

424 Princess Anne and Capt. Mark Phillips.

(Des C. Clements and E. Hughes from photo by Lord Litchfield)

1973 (14 Nov). *Royal Wedding. "All-over" phosphor.* P 15×14.

941	424	3½p. dull violet and silver	..	10	10
		a. Imperf (horiz pair)	..	£1000	
942		20p. deep brown and silver	..	90	90
		a. Silver omitted	..	£1200	

425

426

427

428

429

T **425/9** depict the carol "Good King Wenceslas" and were printed horizontally *se-tenant* within the sheet.

430 "Good King Wenceslas, the Page and Peasant"

(Des D. Gentleman)

1973 (28 Nov). *Christmas. One centre phosphor band (3p.) or "all-over" phosphor (3½p.). P 15 × 14.*

943	425	3p. grey-black, blue, brownish grey, light brown, bright rose-red, turq-green, salmon-pink and gold		15	15
		a. Strip of 5. Nos. 943/7 ..		2·75	4·00
		b. Imperf (horiz strip of 5) ..		£1250	
944	426	3p. grey-black, violet-blue, slate, brown, rose-red, rosy mauve, turq-green, salmon-pink and gold		15	15
		a. Rosy mauve omitted ..		£625	
945	427	3p. grey-black, violet-blue, slate, brown, rose-red, rosy mauve, turq-green, salmon-pink and gold		15	15
		a. Rosy mauve omitted ..		£625	
946	428	3p. grey-black, violet-blue, slate, brown, rose-red, rosy mauve, turq-green, salmon-pink and gold		15	15
		a. Rosy mauve omitted ..		£625	
947	429	3p. grey-black, violet-blue, slate, brown, rose-red, rosy mauve, turq-green, salmon-pink and gold		15	15
		a. Rosy mauve omitted ..		£625	
948	430	3½p. salmon-pink, grey-black, red-brown, blue, turquoise-green, bright rose-red, rosy mauve, lavender-grey and gold ..		15	15
		a. Imperf (pair) ..		£400	
		b. Grey-black (value and inscr, etc) omitted		75·00	
		c. Salmon-pink omitted ..		70·00	
		d. Blue (leg, robes) omitted ..		£130	
		e. Rosy mauve (robe at right) omitted		80·00	
		f. Blue and rosy mauve omitted ..		£250	
		g. Bright rose-red (King's robe) omitted ..		75·00	
		h. Red-brown (logs, basket, etc) omitted			
		i. Turquoise-green (leg, robe, etc) omitted		£2000	
		j. Gold (background) omitted		†	£750
943/8		.. .. .. *Set of* 6		2·75	80

Examples of No. 948j are only known used on cover from Gloucester. The 3½p. has also been seen with the lavender-grey omitted used on piece.

The 3p. and 3½p. are normally with PVA gum with added dextrin, but the 3½p. also exists with normal PVA gum and 3p. with gum arabic.

431 Horse Chestnut

(Des D. Gentleman)

1974 (27 Feb). *British Trees (2nd issue). "All-over" phosphor. P 15 × 14.*

949	431	10p. light emerald, bright green, greenish yellow, brown-olive, black and brownish grey		50	50

432 First Motor Fire-engine, 1904

433 Prize-winning Fire-engine, 1863

434 First Steam Fire-engine, 1830

435 Fire-engine, 1766

(Des D. Gentleman)

1974 (24 Apr). *Bicentenary of the Fire Prevention (Metropolis) Act. "All-over" phosphor. P 15 × 14.*

950	432	3½p. grey-black, orange-yellow, greenish yellow, dull rose, ochre and grey		10	10
		a. Imperf (pair) ..		£800	
951	433	5½p. greenish yellow, deep rosy magenta, orange-yellow, light emerald, grey-black and grey ..		25	25
952	434	8p. greenish yellow, light blue-green, light greenish blue, light chestnut, grey-black and grey ..		35	35
953	435	10p. grey-black, pale reddish brown, lt brown, orange-yellow and grey ..		40	40
950/3		.. .. .. *Set of* 4		1·00	1·00

The 3½p. exists with ordinary PVA gum.

436 P & O Packet, *Peninsular*, 1888

437 Farman H.F.III Biplane, 1911

438 Airmail-blue Van and Postbox, 1930

439 Imperial Airways Short S.21 Flying Boat *Maia*, 1937

(Des Rosalind Dease)

1974 (12 June). *Centenary of Universal Postal Union. "All-over" phosphor. P 15 × 14.*

954	436	3½p. deep brownish grey, bright mauve, grey-black and gold		10	10
955	437	5½p. pale orge, lt emer, grey-blk & gold		20	25
956	438	8p. cobalt, brown, grey-black and gold		30	35
957	439	10p. deep brownish grey, orange, grey-black and gold		50	40
954/7		.. .. .. *Set of* 4		1·00	1·00

440 Robert the Bruce

441 Owain Glyndŵr

442 Henry the Fifth   **443** The Black Prince

(Des F. Wegner)

1974 (10 July). *Medieval Warriors. "All-over" phosphor. P 15 × 14.*

958	440	4½p. greenish yellow, vermilion, slate-blue, red-brown, reddish brown, lilac-grey and gold ..		10	10
959	441	5½p. lemon, vermilion, slate-blue red-brn, reddish brn, old-drab & gold		20	20
960	442	8p. deep grey, vermilion, greenish yellow, new blue, red-brown, deep cinnamon and gold ..		50	40
961	443	10p. vermilion, greenish yellow, new blue, red-brown, reddish brown, light blue and gold ..		55	40
958/61		.. .. .. *Set of* 4		1·25	1·00

444 Churchill in Royal Yacht Squadron Uniform

445 Prime Minister, 1940

446 Secretary for War and Air, 1919

447 War Correspondent, South Africa, 1899

(Des C. Clements and E. Hughes)

1974 (9 Oct). *Birth Centenary of Sir Winston Churchill. "All-over" phosphor. P 14 × 15.*

962	444	4½p. Prussian blue, pale turquoise-green and silver		15	15
963	445	5½p. sepia, brownish grey and silver ..		30	25
964	446	8p. crimson, light claret and silver ..		60	50
965	447	10p. light brown, stone and silver ..		65	50
962/5		.. .. .. *Set of* 4		1·50	1·50

448 "Adoration of the Magi" (York Minster, *circa* 1355)

449 "The Nativity" (St. Helen's Church, Norwich, *circa* 1480)

450 "Virgin and Child" (Ottery St. Mary Church, *circa* 1350)

451 "Virgin and Child" (Worcester Cathedral, *circa* 1224)

(Des Peter Hatch Partnership)

1974 (27 Nov).   *Christmas. Church Roof Bosses. One phosphor band (3½p.) or "all-over" phosphor (others). P 15 × 14.*
966	**448**	3½p. gold, light new blue, light brown, grey-black and light stone ..	10	10
		a. Light stone (background shading) omitted	£10000	
967	**449**	4½p. gold, yellow-orange, rose-red, light brown, grey-black, & lt new blue	10	10
968	**450**	8p. blue, gold, light brown, rose-red, dull green and grey-black ..	45	45
969	**451**	10p. gold, dull rose, grey-black, light new blue, pale cinnamon and light brown	50	50
966/9		.. .. .. *Set of* 4	1·00	1·00

The phosphor band on the 3½p. was first applied down the centre of the stamp but during the printing this was deliberately placed to the right between the roof boss and the value; however, intermediate positions, due to shifts, are known.

452 Invalid in Wheelchair

(Des P. Sharland)

1975 (22 Jan).   *Health and Handicap Funds. "All-over" phosphor. P 15 × 14.*
970	**452**	4½p. + 1½p. azure and grey-blue ..	25	25

453 "Peace—Burial at Sea"

454 "Snowstorm—Steamer off a Harbour's Mouth"

455 "The Arsenal, Venice"

456 "St. Laurent"

(Des S. Rose)

1975 (19 Feb).   *Birth Bicentenary of J. M. W. Turner (painter). "All-over" phosphor. P 15 × 14.*
971	**453**	4½p. grey-blk, salmon, stone, bl & grey	10	10
972	**454**	5½p. cobalt, greenish yellow, light yellow-brown, grey-black and rose	15	15
973	**455**	8p. pale yellow-orange, greenish yellow, rose, cobalt and grey-black	40	40
974	**456**	10p. deep blue, light yellow-ochre, light brown, deep cobalt and grey-black	45	45
971/4		.. .. *Set of* 4	1·00	1·00

457 Charlotte Square, Edinburgh

458 The Rows, Chester

T **457/8** were printed horizontally *se-tenant* within the sheet.

459 Royal Observatory, Greenwich

460 St. George's Chapel, Windsor

461 National Theatre, London

(Des P. Gauld)

1975 (23 Apr).   *European Architectural Heritage Year. "All-over" phosphor. P 15 × 14.*
975	**457**	7p. greenish yellow, bright orange, grey-black, red-brown, new blue, lavender and gold	30	30
		a. Pair. Nos. 975/6	80	90
976	**458**	7p. grey-black, greenish yellow, new blue, brt orange, red-brown & gold	30	30
977	**459**	8p. magenta, deep slate, pale magenta, lt yellow-olive, grey-black & gold	20	25
978	**460**	10p. bistre-brown, greenish yellow, deep slate, emer-green, grey-blk & gold	20	25
979	**461**	12p. grey-blk, new bl, pale mag & gold	20	35
975/9		.. .. *Set of* 5	1·25	1·25

462 Sailing Dinghies

463 Racing Keel Yachts

464 Cruising Yachts

465 Multihulls

(Des A. Restall. Recess and photo)

1975 (11 June).   *Sailing. "All-over" phosphor. P 15 × 14.*
980	**462**	7p. black, bluish violet, scarlet, orange-vermilion, orange and gold	20	20
981	**463**	8p. black, orge-verm, orange, lavender, brt mauve, brt bl, dp ultram & gold	35	30
		a. Black omitted	55·00	
982	**464**	10p. black, orange, bluish emerald, light olive-drab, chocolate and gold	40	30
983	**465**	12p. black, ultramarine, turquoise-blue, rose, grey, steel-blue and gold	45	35
980/3		.. .. *Set of* 4	1·25	1·00

On No. 981a the recess-printed black colour is completely omitted.

466 Stephenson's *Locomotion*, 1825

467 *Abbotsford*, 1876

468 *Caerphilly Castle*, 1923

469 High Speed Train, 1975

(Des B. Craker)

1975 (13 Aug).   *150th Anniv of Public Railways. "All-over" phosphor. P 15 × 14.*
984	**466**	7p. red-brown, grey-black, greenish yellow, grey and silver ..	20	20
985	**467**	8p. brown, orange-yellow, vermilion, grey-black, grey and silver ..	45	35
986	**468**	10p. emerald-green, grey-black, yellow-orange, vermilion, grey and silver	50	40
987	**469**	12p. grey-black, pale lemon, vermilion, blue, grey and silver	55	45
984/7		.. .. *Set of* 4	1·50	1·25

470 Palace of Westminster

(Des R. Downer)

1975 (3 Sept).   *62nd Inter-Parliamentary Union Conference. "All-over" phosphor. P 15 × 14.*
988	**470**	12p. light new blue, black, brownish grey and gold	50	50

471 Emma and Mr Woodhouse (*Emma*)

472 Catherine Morland (*Northanger Abbey*)

473 Mr. Darcy (*Pride and Prejudice*)

474 Mary and Henry Crawford (*Mansfield Park*)

(Des Barbara Brown)

1975 (22 Oct). *Birth Bicentenary of Jane Austen (novelist). "All-over" phosphor. P* 14 × 15.

989	471	8½p. blue, slate, rose-red, light yellow, dull green, grey-black and gold	20	20
990	472	10p. slate, bright magenta, grey, light yellow, grey-black and gold	25	25
991	473	11p. dull blue, pink, olive-sepia, slate, pale greenish yell, grey-blk & gold	30	30
992	474	13p. bright magenta, light new blue, slate, buff, dull blue-green, grey-black and gold	35	35
989/92		*Set of* 4	1·00	1·00

475 Angels with Harp and Lute

476 Angel with Mandolin

477 Angel with Horn

478 Angel with Trumpet

(Des R. Downer)

1975 (26 Nov). *Christmas. One phosphor band (6½p.), phosphor-inked background (8½p.), "all-over" phosphor (others). P* 15 × 14.

993	475	6½p. bluish violet, bright reddish violet, light lavender and gold	20	15
994	476	8½p. turquoise-green, bright emerald-green, slate, lt turq-green & gold	20	20
995	477	11p. vermilion, cerise, pink and gold	30	35
996	478	13p. drab, brn, brt orge, buff & gold	40	40
993/6		*Set of* 4	1·00	1·00

479 Housewife

480 Policeman

481 District Nurse

482 Industrialist

(Des P. Sharland)

1976 (10 Mar). *Telephone Centenary. "All-over" phosphor. P* 15 × 14.

997	479	8½p. greenish blue, dp rose, black & bl	20	20
		a. Deep rose (vase and picture frame) omitted	£2000	
998	480	10p. greenish blue, black & yellow-ol	25	25
999	481	11p. greenish bl, dp rose, blk & brt mve	30	30
1000	482	13p. olive-brn, dp rose, blk & orge-red	35	35
997/1000		*Set of* 4	1·00	1·00

483 Hewing Coal (Thomas Hepburn)

484 Machinery (Robert Owen)

485 Chimney Cleaning (Lord Shaftesbury)

486 Hands clutching Prison Bars (Elizabeth Fry)

(Des D. Gentleman)

1976 (28 Apr). *Social Reformers. "All-over" phosphor. P* 15 × 14.

1001	483	8½p. lavender-grey, grey-black, black and slate-grey	20	20
1002	484	10p. lavender-grey, grey-black, grey and slate-violet	25	25
1003	485	11p. black, slate-grey and drab	30	30
1004	486	13p. slate-grey, black & deep dull grn	35	35
1001/4		*Set of* 4	1·00	1·00

NEW INFORMATION

The editor is always interested to correspond with people who have new information that will improve or correct the Catalogue.

487 Benjamin Franklin (bust by Jean-Jacques Caffieri)

(Des P. Sharland)

1976 (2 June). *Bicentenary of American Revolution. "All-over" phosphor. P* 14 × 15.

1005	487	11p. pale bistre, slate-violet, pale blue-green, black and gold	50	50

488 "Elizabeth of Glamis"

489 "Grandpa Dickson"

490 "Rosa Mundi"

491 "Sweet Briar"

(Des Kristin Rosenberg)

1976 (30 June). *Centenary of Royal National Rose Society. "All-over" phosphor. P* 14 × 15.

1006	488	8½p. bright rose-red, greenish yellow, emerald, grey-black and gold	20	20
1007	489	10p. greenish yellow, bright green, reddish brown, grey-black and gold	30	30
1008	490	11p. bright magenta, greenish yellow, emerald, grey-blue, grey-black and gold	55	50
1009	491	13p. rose-pink, lake-brown, yellow-green, pale greenish yellow, grey-black and gold	60	40
		a. Value omitted*	£20000	
1006/9		*Set of* 4	1·50	1·25

*During repairs to the cylinder the face value on R. 1/9 was temporarily covered with copper. This covering was inadvertently left in place during printing, but the error was discovered before issue and most examples were removed from the sheets. Two mint and one used examples have so far been reported, but only one of the mint remains in private hands.

492 Archdruid

493 Morris Dancing

494 Scots Piper

495 Welsh Harpist

(Des Marjorie Saynor)

1976 (4 Aug). *British Cultural Traditions. "All-over" phosphor. P* 14 × 15.

1010	492	8½p. yellow, sepia, bright rose, dull ultramarine, black and gold	20	20
1011	493	10p. dull ultramarine, bright rose-red, sepia, greenish yellow, blk & gold	25	25
1012	494	11p. bluish green, yellow-brown, yell-orge, blk, brt rose-red & gold	30	30
1013	495	13p. dull violet-blue, yellow-orange, yell-brn, blk, bluish grn & gold	35	35
1010/13		*Set of* 4	1·00	1·00

The 8½p. and 13p. commemorate the 800th Anniv of the Royal National Eisteddfod.

496 Woodcut from *The Canterbury Tales*

497 Extract from *The Tretyse of Love*

498 Woodcut from *The Game and Play of Chesse*

499 Early Printing Press

(Des R. Gay. Queen's head printed in gold and then embossed)

1976 (29 Sept). *500th Anniv of British Printing.* "All-over" phosphor. P 14 × 15.

1014	496	8½p. black, light new blue and gold ..		20	20
1015	497	10p. black, olive-green and gold ..		25	25
1016	498	11p. black, brownish grey and gold ..		30	30
1017	499	13p. chocolate, pale ochre and gold ..		35	35
1014/17	..	.. .. *Set of 4*		1·00	1·00

500 Virgin and Child

501 Angel with Crown

502 Angel appearing to Shepherds

503 The Three Kings

(Des Enid Marx)

1976 (24 Nov). *Christmas. English Medieval Embroidery.* One phosphor band (6½p.), "all-over" phosphor (others). P 15 × 14.

1018	500	6½p. bl, bistre-yell, brn & brt orange	15	15
		a. Imperf (pair)	£400	
1019	501	8½p. sage-green, yellow, brown-ochre, chestnut and olive-black ..	20	20
1020	502	11p. deep magenta, brown-orange, new blue, black and cinnamon ..	35	35
		a. Uncoated paper*	60·00	30·00
1021	503	13p. bright purple, new blue, cinnamon, bronze-green and olive-grey	40	40
1018/21	..	.. .. *Set of 4*	1·00	1·00

* See footnote after No. 744.

504 Lawn Tennis

505 Table Tennis

506 Squash

507 Badminton

(Des A. Restall)

1977 (12 Jan). *Racket Sports.* Phosphorised paper. P 15 × 14.

1022	504	8½p. emer-grn, blk, grey & bluish grn	20	20
		a. Imperf (horiz pair)	£850	
1023	505	10p. myrtle-green, black, grey-black and deep blue-green	35	25
1024	506	11p. orange, pale yellow, black, slate-black and grey	40	30
1025	507	13p. brown, grey-black, grey and bright reddish violet	45	35
1022/5	..	.. .. .. *Set of 4*	1·25	1·00

508

(Des after plaster cast by Arnold Machin)

1977 (2 Feb)–87. P 14 × 15.

1026	508	£1 brt yellow-green & blackish olive	3·00	20
		a. Imperf (pair)	£650	
1026b		£1.30, pale drab and deep greenish blue (3.8.83)	5·50	5·00
1026c		£1.33, pale mve & grey-blk (28.8.84)	6·00	6·00
1026d		£1.41, pale drab and deep greenish blue (17.9.85)	7·00	6·00
1026e		£1.50, pale mauve & grey-blk (2.9.86)	5·50	4·00
1026f		£1.60 pale drab and deep greenish blue (15.9.87)	5·50	6·00
1027		£2 light emerald and purple-brown ..	5·50	75
1028		£5 salmon and chalky blue	13·00	2·00
		a. Imperf (vert pair)	£2750	
1026/8	..	.. .. .. *Set of 8*	45·00	27·00

509 Steroids—Conformational Analysis

510 Vitamin C—Synthesis

511 Starch—Chromatography

512 Salt—Crystallography

(Des J. Karo)

1977 (2 Mar). *Royal Institute of Chemistry Centenary.* "All-over" phosphor. P 15 × 14.

1029	509	8½p. rosine, new blue, olive-yellow, brt mauve, yellow-brown, blk & gold		20	20
		a. Imperf (horiz pair)		£850	
1030	510	10p. bright orange, rosine, new blue, bright blue, black and gold		30	30
1031	511	11p. rosine, greenish yellow, new blue, deep violet, black and gold		30	30
1032	512	13p. new blue, brt green, black & gold		30	30
1029/32	..	.. .. .. *Set of 4*		1·00	1·00

513

514

515

516

T 513/16 differ in the decorations of "ER".

(Des R. Guyatt)

1977 (11 May–15 June). *Silver Jubilee.* "All-over" phosphor. P 15 × 14.

1033	513	8½p. blackish green, black, silver, olive-grey and pale turquoise-green ..	20	20
		a. Imperf (pair)	£700	
1034		9p. maroon, black, silver, olive-grey and lavender (15 June)	25	25
1035	514	10p. blackish blue, black, silver, olive-grey and ochre	25	25
		a. Imperf (horiz pair)	£1300	
1036	515	11p. brown-purple, black, silver, olive-grey and rose-pink	30	30
		a. Imperf (horiz pair)	£1300	
1037	516	13p. sepia, black, silver, olive-grey and bistre-yellow	40	40
		a. Imperf (pair) .. .. *Set of 5*	£1000	
1033/7	..	.. .. .. *Set of 5*	1·25	1·25

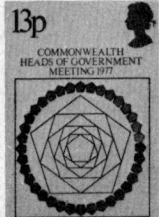

517 "Gathering of Nations"

(Des P. Murdoch. Recess and photo)

1977 (8 June). *Commonwealth Heads of Government Meeting, London.* "All-over" phosphor. P 14 × 15.

1038	517	13p. black, blackish green, rose-car and silver	50	50

518 Hedgehog   519 Brown Hare

520 Red Squirrel   521 Otter

522 Badger

T **518/22** were printed horizontally *se-tenant* within the sheet.

(Des P. Oxenham)

1977 (5 Oct). *British Wildlife. "All-over" phosphor. P* 14 × 15.
1039	518	9p. reddish brown, grey-black, pale lemon, brt turq-bl, brt mag & gold	25	20
		a. Horiz strip of 5. Nos. 1039/43	1·75	2·00
		b. Imperf (vert pair)	£600	
		c. Imperf (horiz pair, Nos. 1039/40)	£1000	
1040	519	9p. reddish brown, grey-black, pale lemon, brt turq-bl, brt mag & gold	25	20
1041	520	9p. reddish brown, grey-black, pale lemon, brt turq-bl, brt mag & gold	25	20
1042	521	9p. reddish brown, grey-black, pale lemon, brt turq-bl, brt mag & gold	25	20
1043	522	9p. grey-black, reddish brown, pale lemon, brt turq-bl, brt mag & gold	25	20
1039/43		*Set of* 5	1·75	1·00

523 "Three French Hens, Two Turtle Doves and a Partridge in a Pear Tree"

524 "Six Geese a-laying, Five Gold Rings, Four Colly Birds"

525 "Eight Maids a-milking, Seven Swans a-swimming"

526 "Ten Pipers piping, Nine Drummers drumming"

527 "Twelve Lords a-leaping, Eleven Ladies dancing"

T **523/7** depict the carol "The Twelve Days of Christmas" and were printed horizontally *se-tenant* within the sheet.

528 "A Partridge in a Pear Tree"

(Des D. Gentleman)

1977 (23 Nov). *Christmas. One centre phosphor band (7p.) or "all-over" phosphor (9p.). P* 15 × 14.
1044	523	7p. slate, grey, bright yellow-green, new blue, rose-red and gold	15	15
		a. Horiz strip of 5. Nos. 1044/8	1·00	1·50
		ab. Imperf (strip of 5, Nos. 1044/8)	£1100	
1045	524	7p. slate, brt yellow-grn, new bl & gold	15	15
1046	525	7p. slate, grey, bright yellow-green, new blue, rose-red and gold	15	15
1047	526	7p. slate, grey, bright yellow-green, new blue, rose-red and gold	15	15
1048	527	7p. slate, grey, bright yellow-green, new blue, rose-red and gold	15	15
1049	528	9p. pale brown, pale orange, brt emer, pale greenish yell, slate-blk & gold	20	20
		a. Imperf (pair)	£800	
1044/9		*Set of* 6	1·00	85

529 Oil—North Sea Production Platform   530 Coal—Modern Pithead

 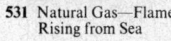

531 Natural Gas—Flame Rising from Sea   532 Electricity—Nuclear Power Station and Uranium Atom

(Des P. Murdoch)

1978 (25 Jan). *Energy Resources. "All-over" phosphor. P* 14 × 15.
1050	529	9p. deep brown, orange-vermilion, grey-black, greenish yellow, rose-pink, new blue and silver	25	20
1051	530	10½p. light emerald-green, grey-black, red-brown, slate-grey, pale apple-green and silver	25	30
1052	531	11p. greenish blue, bright violet, violet-blue, blackish brown, grey-black and silver	30	30
1053	532	13p. orange-vermilion, grey-black, deep brown, greenish yellow, light brown, light blue and silver	30	30
1050/3		*Set of* 4	1·00	1·00

533 The Tower of London

534 Holyroodhouse

535 Caernarvon Castle

536 Hampton Court Palace

(Des R. Maddox (stamps), J. Matthews (miniature sheet))

1978 (1 Mar). *British Architecture. Historic Buildings. "All-over" phosphor. P* 15 × 14.
1054	533	9p. black, olive-brown, new blue, brt green, lt yellow-olive & rose-red	25	20
1055	534	10½p. black, brown-olive, orange-yell, brt grn, lt yell-olive & vio-bl	25	30
1056	535	11p. black, brown-olive, violet-blue, brt green, lt yellow-olive & dull bl	30	30
1057	536	13p. black, orange-yellow, lake-brown, bright green and light yellow-olive	30	30
1054/7		*Set of* 4	1·00	1·00
MS1058		121×89 mm. Nos. 1054/7 (*sold at* 53½p.)	1·25	1·25
		a. Imperforate	£4250	
		b. Lt yellow-olive (Queen's head) omitted	£3500	
		c. Rose-red (Union Jack on 9p.) omitted	£2500	
		d. Orange-yellow omitted	£2500	
		e. New blue (Union Jack on 9p.) omitted	£10000	

The premium on No. MS1058 was used to support the London 1980 International Stamp Exhibition.

537 State Coach   538 St. Edward's Crown

539 The Sovereign's Orb   540 Imperial State Crown

(Des J. Matthews)

1978 (31 May). *25th Anniv of Coronation. "All-over" phosphor. P* 14 × 15.
1059	537	9p. gold and royal blue	20	20
1060	538	10½p. gold and brown-lake	25	30
1061	539	11p. gold and deep dull green	30	30
1062	540	13p. gold and reddish violet	35	30
1059/62		*Set of* 4	1·00	1·00

541 Shire Horse

542 Shetland Pony

543 Welsh Pony

544 Thoroughbred

(Des P. Oxenham)

1978 (5 July). *Horses. "All-over" phosphor. P* 15 × 14.

1063	541	9p. black, pale reddish brown, grey-black, greenish yellow, light blue, vermilion and gold	20	20
1064	542	10½p. pale chestnut, magenta, brownish grey, greenish yellow, greenish blue, grey-black and gold	35	25
1065	543	11p. reddish brown, black, light green, greenish yellow, bistre, grey-black and gold	40	30
1066	544	13p. reddish brown, pale reddish brown, emerald, greenish yellow, grey-black and gold	45	35
1063/6	..	.. .. *Set of* 4	1·25	1·00

545 "Penny-farthing" and 1884 Safety Bicycle

546 1920 Touring Bicycles

547 Modern Small-wheel Bicycles

548 1978 Road-racers

(Des F. Wegner)

1978 (2 Aug). *Centenaries of Cyclists Touring Club and British Cycling Federation. "All-over" phosphor. P* 15 × 14.

1067	545	9p. brown, deep dull blue, rose-pink, pale olive, grey-black and gold ..	20	20
		a. Imperf (pair)	£350	
1068	546	10½p. olive, pale yellow-orange, orange-vermilion, rose-red, light brown, grey-black and gold	25	25
1069	547	11p. orange-vermilion, greenish blue, light brown, pale greenish yellow, deep grey, grey-black and gold ..	30	30
1070	548	13p. new blue, orange-vermilion, light brn, olive-grey, grey-black & gold ..	35	35
		a. Imperf (pair)	£750	
1067/70	..	.. .. *Set of* 4	1·00	1·00

549 Singing Carols round the Christmas Tree

550 The Waits

551 18th-century Carol Singers

552 "The Boar's Head Carol"

(Des Faith Jaques)

1978 (22 Nov). *Christmas. One centre phosphor band* (7p.) *or "all-over" phosphor* (others). *P* 15 × 14.

1071	549	7p. bright green, greenish yellow, magenta, new blue, black and gold	20	20
		a. Imperf (vert pair)	£350	
1072	550	9p. magenta, greenish yellow, new blue, sage-green, black and gold	25	25
		a. Imperf (pair)	£750	
1073	551	11p. magenta, new blue, greenish yellow, yellow-brown, black & gold	30	30
		a. Imperf (horiz pair) ..	£750	
1074	552	13p. salmon-pink, new blue, greenish yellow, magenta, black and gold	35	35
1071/4	..	.. .. .. *Set of* 4	1·00	1·00

553 Old English Sheepdog

554 Welsh Springer Spaniel

555 West Highland Terrier

556 Irish Setter

(Des P. Barrett)

1979 (7 Feb). *Dogs. "All-over" phosphor. P* 15 × 14.

1075	553	9p. grey-black, sepia, turquoise-green, pale greenish yellow, pale greenish blue and grey	20	20
1076	554	10½p. grey-black, lake-brown, apple-green, pale greenish yellow, pale greenish blue and grey ..	40	30
1077	555	11p. grey-black, claret, yellowish grn, pale greenish yell, cobalt & grey	40	30
		a. Imperf (horiz pair) ..	£900	
1078	556	13p. grey-black, lake-brown, green, pale greenish yellow & dp turq-bl	40	30
1075/8	..	.. .. .. *Set of* 4	1·25	1·00

557 Primrose

559 Bluebell

558 Daffodil

560 Snowdrop

(Des P. Newcombe)

1979 (21 Mar). *Spring Wild Flowers. "All-over" phosphor. P* 14 × 15.

1079	557	9p. slate-black, deep brown, pale greenish yellow, deep olive, pale new blue and silver	20	20
		a. Imperf (pair)	£400	
1080	558	10½p. greenish yellow, grey-green, steel-blue, slate-blk, new blue & silver	40	30
		a. Imperf (vert pair) ..	£1500	
1081	559	11p. slate-black, deep brown, ultra-marine, light greenish blue, pale greenish yellow and silver ..	40	30
		a. Imperf (horiz pair) ..	£1200	
1082	560	13p. slate-black, indigo, grey-green, sepia, ochre and silver	40	30
		a. Imperf (horiz pair) ..	£750	
1079/82	..	.. .. .. *Set of* 4	1·25	1·00

561

562

563

564

T **561/4** show Hands placing National Flags in Ballot Boxes.

(Des S. Cliff)

1979 (9 May). *First Direct Elections to European Assembly. Phosphorised paper. P* 15 × 14.

1083	561	9p. grey-black, vermilion, cinnamon, pale greenish yellow, pale turq-green and dull ultramarine	..	20	20
1084	562	10½p. grey-black, vermilion, cinnamon, pale greenish yellow, dull ultramarine, pale turq-grn & chestnut		30	30
1085	563	11p. grey-black, vermilion, cinnamon, pale greenish yellow, dull ultramarine, pale turq-grn & grey-grn		30	30
1086	564	13p. grey-black, vermilion, cinnamon, pale greenish yellow, dull ultramarine, pale turq-grn & brown		30	30
1083/6	..		*Set of* 4	1·00	1·00

565 "Saddling 'Mahmoud' for the Derby, 1936" (Sir Alfred Munnings)

566 "The Liverpool Great National Steeple Chase, 1839" (aquatint by F. C. Turner)

567 "The First Spring Meeting, Newmarket, 1793" (J. N. Sartorius)

568 "Racing at Dorsett Ferry, Windsor, 1684" (Francis Barlow)

(Des S. Rose)

1979 (6 June). *Horseracing Paintings. Bicentenary of the Derby (9p.). "All-over" phosphor. P* 15 × 14.

1087	565	9p. light blue, red-brown, rose-pink, pale greenish yellow, grey-black and gold	..	25	25
1088	566	10½p. bistre-yellow, slate-blue, salmon-pink, lt blue, grey-black and gold		30	30
1089	567	11p. rose, vermilion, pale greenish yellow, new blue, grey-black and gold		30	30
1090	568	13p. bistre-yellow, rose, turquoise, grey-black and gold	..	30	30
1087/90	..	..	*Set of* 4	1·10	1·10

569 *The Tale of Peter Rabbit* (Beatrix Potter)   **570** *The Wind in the Willows* (Kenneth Grahame)

571 *Winnie-the-Pooh* (A. A. Milne)   **572** *Alice's Adventures in Wonderland* (Lewis Carroll)

(Des E. Hughes)

1979 (11 July). *International Year of the Child. Children's Book Illustrations. "All-over" phosphor. P* 14 × 15.

1091	569	9p. deep bluish green, grey-black, bistre-brown, bright rose, greenish yellow and silver		25	20
1092	570	10½p. dull ultramarine, grey-black, ol-brown, bright rose, yellow-orge, pale greenish yellow and silver	..	30	35
1093	571	11p. drab, grey-black, greenish yellow, new bl, yell-orge, agate & silver		35	40
1094	572	13p. pale greenish yellow, grey-black, bright rose, deep bluish green, olive-brown, new blue and silver		50	45
1091/4	..		*Set of* 4	1·25	1·25

573 Sir Rowland Hill   **574** Postman, *circa* 1839

575 London Postman, *circa* 1839   **576** Woman and Young Girl with Letters, 1840

(Des E. Stemp)

1979 (22 Aug–24 Oct). *Death Centenary of Sir Rowland Hill. "All-over" phosphor. P* 14 × 15.

1095	573	10p. grey-black, brown-ochre, myrtle-green, pale greenish yellow, rosine, bright blue and gold	..	25	25
		a. Imperf (horiz pair)	..		
1096	574	11½p. grey-black, brown-ochre, bright blue, rosine, bistre-brown, pale greenish yellow and gold	..	30	35
1097	575	13p. grey-black, brown-ochre, bright blue, rosine, bistre-brown, pale greenish yellow and gold	..	35	40
1098	576	15p. grey-black, brown-ochre, myrtle-green, bistre-brown, rosine, pale greenish yellow and gold	..	50	40
1095/8			*Set of* 4	1·25	1·25

MS1099 89×121 mm. Nos. 1095/8 (*sold at* 59½p.) (24 Oct)	..	1·25	1·25
a. Imperforate		£1000	
b. Brown-ochre (15p. background, etc) omitted		£750	
c. Gold (Queen's head) omitted ..		£175	
d. Brown-ochre, myrtle-green and gold omitted		£3000	
e. Bright blue (13p. background, etc) omitted		£900	
f. Myrtle-green (10p. (background), 15p.) omitted		£1200	
g. Pale greenish yellow omitted ..		£140	
h. Rosine omitted		£500	
i. Bistre-brown omitted		£650	
j. Grey-black and pale greenish yellow omitted		£10000	

The premium on No. **MS**1099 was used to support the London 1980 International Stamp Exhibition.

Examples of No. **MS**1099 showing face values on the stamps of 9p., 10½p., 11p. and 13p., with a sheet price of 53½p., were prepared, but not issued.

577 Policeman on the Beat

578 Policeman directing Traffic

---

579 Mounted Policewoman

580 River Patrol Boat

(Des B. Sanders)

1979 (26 Sept). *150th Anniv of Metropolitan Police. Phosphorised paper. P* 15 × 14.

1100	577	10p. grey-black, red-brown, emerald, greenish yellow, brt blue & mag	25	25
1101	578	11½p. grey-black, bright orange, purple-brown, ultramarine, greenish yellow and deep bluish green	30	35
1102	579	13p. grey-black, red-brown, magenta, ol-grn, greenish yell & dp dull bl	35	40
1103	580	15p. grey-black, magenta, brown, slate-bl, dp brown & greenish blk	50	40
1100/3	..	*Set of* 4	1·25	1·25

581 The Three Kings

582 Angel appearing to the Shepherds

583 The Nativity

584 Mary and Joseph travelling to Bethlehem

585 The Annunciation

(Des F. Wegner)

1979 (21 Nov). *Christmas. One centre phosphor band (8p.) or phosphorised paper (others). P* 15 × 14.

1104	581	8p. blue, grey-black, ochre, slate-violet and gold	20	20
		a. Imperf (pair)	£500	
1105	582	10p. bright rose-red, grey-black, chestnut, chrome-yell, dp vio & gold	25	25
		a. Imperf between (vert pair) ..	£450	
		b. Imperf (pair)	£600	
1106	583	11½p. orange-vermilion, steel-bl, drab, grey-black, deep blue-grn & gold	30	35
1107	584	13p. bright blue, orange-vermilion, bistre, grey-black and gold ..	40	40
1108	585	15p. orange-vermilion, blue, bistre, grey-black, green and gold ..	50	45
1104/8	..	*Set of* 5	1·50	1·50

586 Common Kingfisher

587 Dipper

588 Moorhen

589 Yellow Wagtails

(Des M. Warren)

1980 (16 Jan). *Centenary of Wild Bird Protection Act. Phosphorised paper. P 14 × 15.*

109	586	10p. bright blue, bright yellow-green, vermilion, pale greenish yellow, grey-black and gold	25	25
110	587	11½p. sepia, grey-black, dull ultramarine, vermilion, grey-green, pale greenish yellow and gold	40	35
111	588	13p. emerald-green, grey-black, bright bl, verm, pale greenish yell & gold	50	40
112	589	15p. greenish yellow, brown, light green, slate-bl, grey-blk & gold	55	45
109/12		*Set of 4*	1·50	1·25

590 "Rocket" approaching Moorish Arch, Liverpool

591 First and Second Class Carriages passing through Olive Mount cutting

592 Third Class Carriage and Cattle Truck crossing Chat Moss

593 Horsebox and Carriage Truck near Bridgewater Canal

594 Goods Truck and Mail-Coach at Manchester

T **590**/4 were printed together, *se-tenant*, in horizontal strips of 5 throughout the sheet.

(Des D. Gentleman)

1980 (12 Mar). *150th Anniv of Liverpool and Manchester Railway. Phosphorised paper. P 15 × 14.*

1113	590	12p. lemon, light brown, rose-red, pale blue and grey-black	25	25
		a. Strip of 5. Nos. 1113/17	1·50	1·60
		ab. Imperf (horiz strip of 5. Nos. 1113/17)	£1200	
		ac. Lemon omitted (horiz strip of 5. Nos. 1113/17)	£7500	
1114	591	12p. rose-red, light brown, lemon, pale blue and grey-black	25	25
1115	592	12p. pale blue, rose-red, lemon, light brown and grey-black	25	25
1116	593	12p. light brown, lemon, rose-red, pale blue and grey-black	25	25
1117	594	12p. light brown, rose-red, pale blue, lemon and grey-black	25	25
1113/17		*Set of 5*	1·50	1·10

595 Montage of London Buildings

(Des J. Matthews. Recess)

1980 (9 Apr–7 May). *"London 1980" International Stamp Exhibition. Phosphorised paper. P 14½ × 14.*

1118	595	50p. agate	1·50	1·25
MS1119		90 × 123 mm. No. 1118 *(sold at 75p.)* (7 May)	1·50	1·50
		a. Error. Imperf	£700	

596 Buckingham Palace   597 The Albert Memorial

598 Royal Opera House   599 Hampton Court

600 Kensington Palace

(Des Sir Hugh Casson)

1980 (7 May). *London Landmarks. Phosphorised paper. P 14 × 15.*

1120	596	10½p. grey, pale blue, rosine, pale greenish yell, yellowish green & silver	25	25
1121	597	12p. grey-black, bistre, rosine, yellowish green, pale greenish yellow and silver	30	30
		a. Imperf (vert pair)	£550	
1122	598	13½p. grey-black, pale salmon, pale olgreen, slate-blue and silver	35	35
		a. Imperf (pair)	£550	
1123	599	15p. grey-black, pale salmon, slateblue, dull yellowish green, oliveyellow and silver	40	40
1124	600	17½p. grey, slate-blue, red-brown, sepia, yellowish green, pale greenish yellow and silver	40	40
		a. Silver (Queen's head) omitted	£175	
1120/4		*Set of 5*	1·50	1·50

No. 1124a shows the Queen's head in pale greenish yellow, this colour being printed beneath the silver for technical reasons.

601 Charlotte Brontë (*Jane Eyre*)

602 George Eliot (*The Mill on the Floss*)

603 Emily Brontë (*Wuthering Heights*)

604 Mrs. Gaskell (*North and South*)

T **601**/4 show authoresses and scenes from their novels. T **601**/2 also include the "Europa" C.E.P.T. emblem.

(Des Barbara Brown)

1980 (9 July). *Famous Authoresses. Phosphorised paper. P 15 × 14.*

1125	601	12p. red-brown, bright rose, bright bl, greenish yellow, grey and gold	30	30
1126	602	13½p. red-brown, dull vermilion, pale bl, pale greenish yell, grey & gold	35	35
		a. Pale blue omitted	£1750	
1127	603	15p. red-brown, vermilion, blue, lemon, grey and gold	40	45
1128	604	17½p. dull vermilion, slate-blue, ultram, pale greenish yell, grey and gold	60	60
		a. Imperf and slate-blue omitted (pair)	£700	
1125/8		*Set of 4*	1·50	1·50

605 Queen Elizabeth the Queen Mother

(Des J. Matthews from photograph by N. Parkinson)

1980 (4 Aug). *80th Birthday of Queen Elizabeth the Queen Mother. Phosphorised paper. P 14 × 15.*

1129	605	12p. bright rose, greenish yellow, new blue, grey and silver	75	75
		a. Imperf (horiz pair)	£1200	

606 Sir Henry Wood

607 Sir Thomas Beecham

608 Sir Malcolm Sargent

609 Sir John Barbirolli

(Des P. Gauld)

1980 (10 Sept). *British Conductors. Phosphorised paper.* P 14 × 15.

1130	606	12p.	slate, rose-red, greenish yellow, bistre and gold	30	30
1131	607	13½p.	grey-black, vermilion, greenish yellow, pale carmine-rose and gold	35	40
1132	608	15p.	grey-black, bright rose-red, greenish yellow, turquoise-grn & gold	45	45
1133	609	17½p.	black, bright rose-red, greenish yellow, dull violet-blue and gold	55	50
1130/3			*Set of 4*	1·50	1·50

610 Running

611 Rugby

612 Boxing

613 Cricket

(Des R. Goldsmith. Litho Questa)

1980 (10 Oct). *Sport Centenaries. Phosphorised paper.* P 14 × 14½.

1134	610	12p.	pale new blue, greenish yellow, magenta, light brown, reddish purple and gold	30	30
		a.	Gold (Queen's head) omitted ..	£10000	
1135	611	13½p.	pale new blue, olive-yellow, bright purple, orange-vermilion, blackish lilac and gold	35	40
1136	612	15p.	pale new blue, greenish yellow, bright purple, chalky blue & gold	40	40
		a.	Gold (Queen's head) omitted ..	£10000	
1137	613	17½p.	pale new blue, greenish yellow, magenta, dp ol, grey-brn & gold	60	55
1134/7			*Set of 4*	1·50	1·50

Centenaries:—12p. Amateur Athletics Association; 13½p. Welsh Rugby Union; 15p. Amateur Boxing Association; 17½p. First England–Australia Test Match.

Nos. 1134a and 1136a were caused by paper folds.

614 Christmas Tree

615 Candles

616 Apples and Mistletoe

617 Crown, Chains and Bell

618 Holly

(Des J. Matthews)

1980 (19 Nov). *Christmas. One centre phosphor band* (10p.) *or phosphorised paper* (*others*). P 15 × 14.

1138	614	10p.	black, turquoise-green, greenish yellow, vermilion and blue	25	25
		a.	Imperf (horiz pair) ..	£950	
1139	615	12p.	grey, magenta, rose-red, greenish grey and pale orange	30	35
1140	616	13½p.	grey-black, dull yellow-green, brown, greenish yellow and pale olive-bistre	35	40
1141	617	15p.	grey-black, bistre-yellow, bright orange, magenta and new blue ..	40	40
1142	618	17½p.	black, vermilion, dull yellowish green and greenish yellow	50	40
1138/42			*Set of 5*	1·60	1·60

619 St. Valentine's Day

620 Morris Dancers

621 Lammastide

622 Medieval Mummers

T **619/20** also include the "Europa" C.E.P.T. emblem.

(Des F. Wegner)

1981 (6 Feb). *Folklore, Phosphorised paper.* P 15 × 14.

1143	619	14p.	cerise, green, yellow-orange, salmon-pink, black and gold	35	35
1144	620	18p.	dull ultramarine, lemon, lake-brown, brt green, black & gold	45	50
1145	621	22p.	chrome-yellow, rosine, brown, new blue, black and gold	60	60
1146	622	25p.	brt blue, red-brown, brt rose-red, greenish yellow, black and gold	75	70
1143/6			*Set of 4*	2·00	2·00

623 Blind Man with Guide Dog

624 Hands spelling "Deaf" in Sign Language

625 Disabled Man in Wheelchair

626 Disabled Artist painting with Foot

(Des J. Gibbs)

1981 (25 Mar). *International Year of the Disabled. Phosphorised paper.* P 15 × 14.

1147	623	14p.	drab, greenish yellow, bright rose-red, dull purple and silver ..	35	35
		a.	Imperf (pair) ..	£750	
1148	624	18p.	deep blue-green, brt orange, dull vermilion, grey-black and silver	45	50
1149	625	22p.	brown-ochre, rosine, purple-brn, greenish blue, black and silver	60	60
1150	626	25p.	vermilion, lemon, pale salmon, olive-brn, new blue, blk & silver	75	70
1147/50			*Set of 4*	2·00	2·00

All known examples of No. 1147a are creased.

627 *Aglais urticae*

628 *Maculinea arion*

629 *Inachis io*

630 *Carterocephalus palaemon*

(Des G. Beningfield)

1981 (13 May). *Butterflies. Phosphorised paper.* P 14 × 15.

1151	627	14p.	greenish yellow, yellow-green, brt rose, brt blue, emerald & gold ..	35	35
		a.	Imperf (pair) ..	£950	
1152	628	18p.	black, greenish yellow, dull yellowish green, bright mauve, bright blue, bright green and gold ..	60	50
1153	629	22p.	black, greenish yell, bronze-grn, rosine, ultramarine, lt grn & gold	70	65
1154	630	25p.	black, greenish yellow, bronze-green, bright rose-red, ultramarine, bright emerald and gold ..	80	75
1151/4			*Set of 4*	2·25	2·00

631 Glenfinnan, Scotland

632 Derwentwater, England

633 Stackpole Head, Wales

634 Giant's Causeway, Northern Ireland

635 St. Kilda, Scotland

(Des M. Fairclough)

1981 (24 June). *50th Anniv of National Trust for Scotland. British Landscapes. Phosphorised paper. P* 15 × 14.

1155	631	14p.	lilac, dull blue, reddish brown, bistre-yellow, black and gold	30	30
1156	632	18p.	bottle green, bright blue, brown, bistre-yellow, black and gold	40	40
1157	633	20p.	deep turq-blue, dull blue, greenish yellow, reddish brn, black & gold	50	50
1158	634	22p.	chrome-yellow, reddish brn, new blue, yellow-brown, black & gold	60	60
1159	635	25p.	ultramarine, new blue, olive-green, olive-grey and gold	70	70
1155/9			*Set of 5*	2·25	2·25

636 Prince Charles and Lady Diana Spencer

(Des J. Matthews from photograph by Lord Snowdon)

1981 (22 July). *Royal Wedding. Phosphorised paper. P* 14 × 15.

1160	636	14p.	grey-blk, greenish yellow, brt rose-red, ultram, pale bl, blue & silver	2·00	1·75
1161		25p.	drab, greenish yellow, bright rose-red, ultramarine, grey-brown, grey-black and silver	3·00	2·25

637 "Expeditions"

638 "Skills"

639 "Service"

640 "Recreation"

(Des P. Sharland. Litho J.W.)

1981 (12 Aug). *25th Anniv of Duke of Edinburgh Award Scheme. Phosphorised paper. P* 14.

1162	637	14p.	greenish yellow, magenta, pale new blue, black, emerald & silver	35	35
1163	638	18p.	greenish yellow, magenta, pale new blue, black, cobalt and gold	50	50
1164	639	22p.	greenish yellow, magenta, pale new blue, black, red-orge & gold	60	60
1165	640	25p.	bright orange, mauve, pale new blue, black, flesh and bronze	70	70
1162/5			*Set of 4*	2·00	2·00

641 Cockle-dredging from
Linsey II

642 Hauling in Trawl Net

643 Lobster Potting

644 Hoisting Seine Net

(Des B. Sanders)

1981 (23 Sept). *Fishing Industry. Phosphorised paper. P* 15 × 14.

1166	641	14p.	slate, greenish yellow, magenta, new blue, orange-brown, olive-grey and bronze-green	35	35
1167	642	18p.	slate, greenish yellow, brt crimson, ultramarine, blk & greenish slate	50	50
1168	643	22p.	grey, greenish yellow, bright rose, dull ultram, reddish lilac & black	60	60
1169	644	25p.	grey, greenish yellow, bright rose, cobalt and black	70	65
1166/9			*Set of 4*	2·00	2·00

Nos. 1166/9 were issued on the occasion of the centenary of the Royal National Mission to Deep Sea Fishermen.

645 Father Christmas

646 Jesus Christ

647 Flying Angel

648 Joseph and Mary arriving at Bethlehem

649 Three Kings approaching Bethlehem

(Des Samantha Brown (11½p.), Tracy Jenkins (14p.), Lucinda Blackmore (18p.), Stephen Moore (22p.), Sophie Sharp (25p.))

1981 (18 Nov). *Christmas. Children's Pictures. One phosphor band (11½p.) or phosphorised paper (others). P* 15 × 14.

1170	645	11½p.	ultramarine, black, red, olive-bistre, bright green and gold	30	30
1171	646	14p.	bistre-yellow, brt magenta, blue, greenish blue, brt grn, blk & gold	40	40
1172	647	18p.	pale blue-green, bistre-yellow, brt magenta, ultramarine, blk & gold	50	50
1173	648	22p.	deep turquoise-blue, lemon, magenta, black and gold	60	60
1174	649	25p.	royal blue, lemon, bright magenta, black and gold	70	70
1170/4			*Set of 5*	2·25	2·25

650 Charles Darwin and Giant Tortoises

651 Darwin and Marine Iguanas

652 Darwin, Cactus Ground Finch and Large Ground Finch

653 Darwin and Prehistoric Skulls

(Des D. Gentleman)

1982 (10 Feb). *Death Centenary of Charles Darwin. Phosphorised paper. P* 15 × 14.

1175	650	15½p.	dull purple, drab, bistre, black and grey-black	35	35
1176	651	19½p.	violet-grey, bistre-yellow, slate-black, red-brown, grey-blk & blk	60	60
1177	652	26p.	sage green, bistre-yellow, orange, chalky bl, grey-blk, red-brn & blk	70	70
1178	653	29p.	grey-brown, yellow-brn, brown-ochre, black and grey-black	75	75
1175/8			*Set of 4*	2·25	2·25

654 Boys' Brigade

655 Girls' Brigade

656 Boy Scout Movement   **657** Girl Guide Movement

(Des B. Sanders)

1982 (24 Mar). *Youth Organizations. Phosphorised paper. P* 15 × 14.
1179	**654**	15½p.	gold, greenish yellow, pale orange, mauve, dull blue and grey-black	35	35
1180	**655**	19½p.	gold, greenish yellow, pale orange, bright rose, deep ultramarine, olive-bistre and grey-black	60	50
1181	**656**	26p.	gold, greenish yellow, olive-sepia, rosine, deep blue, deep dull green and grey-black	85	75
1182	**657**	29p.	gold, yellow, dull orange, cerise, dull ultram, chestnut & grey-blk	1·00	90
1179/82			*Set of* 4	2·50	2·25

Nos. 1179/82 were issued on the occasion of the 75th anniversary of the Boy Scout Movement; the 125th birth anniversary of Lord Baden-Powell and the centenary of the Boys' Brigade (1983).

658 Ballerina   **659** Harlequin

660 Hamlet   **661** Opera Singer

(Des A. George)

1982 (28 Apr). *Europa. British Theatre. Phosphorised paper. P* 15 × 14.
1183	**658**	15½p.	carm-lake, greenish bl, greenish yell, grey-blk, bottle grn & silver	35	35
1184	**659**	19½p.	rosine, new blue, greenish yellow, black, ultramarine and silver	60	50
1185	**660**	26p.	carmine-red, bright rose-red, greenish yellow, black, dull ultramarine, lake-brown and silver	90	75
1186	**661**	29p.	rose-red, greenish yellow, bright blue, grey-black and silver	1·25	90
1183/6			*Set of* 4	2·75	2·25

662 Henry VIII and *Mary Rose*

663 Admiral Blake and *Triumph*

664 Lord Nelson and H.M.S. *Victory*

665 Lord Fisher and H.M.S. *Dreadnought*

666 Viscount Cunningham and
H.M.S *Warspite*

(Des Marjorie Saynor. Eng C. Slania. Recess and photo)

1982 (16 June). *Maritime Heritage. Phosphorised paper. P* 15 × 14.
1187	**662**	15½p.	black, lemon, bright rose, pale orange, ultramarine and grey	35	35
		a.	Imperf (pair)	£750	
1188	**663**	19½p.	black, greenish yellow, bright rose-red, pale orange, ultram and grey	60	60
1189	**664**	24p.	black, orange-yellow, bright rose-red, lake-brown, dp ultram & grey	70	70
1190	**665**	26p.	black, orange-yellow, bright rose, lemon, ultramarine and grey	80	80
		a.	Imperf (pair)		
1191	**666**	29p.	black, olive-yellow, bright rose, orange-yellow, ultram & grey	90	90
1187/91			*Set of* 5	3·00	3·00

Nos. 1187/91 were issued on the occasion of Maritime England Year, the Bicentenary of the Livery Grant by City of London to Worshipful Company of Shipwrights and the raising of *Mary Rose* from Portsmouth Harbour.

Several used examples of the 15½p. have been seen with the black recess (ship and waves) omitted.

667 "Strawberry Thief"   **668** Untitled
(William Morris)   (Steiner and Co)

669 "Cherry Orchard"   **670** "Chevron"
(Paul Nash)   (Andrew Foster)

(Des Peter Hatch Partnership)

1982 (23 July). *British Textiles. Phosphorised paper. P* 14 × 15.
1192	**667**	15½p.	blue, olive-yellow, rosine, deep blue-green, bistre & Prussian blue	35	35
		a.	Imperf (horiz pair)	£950	
1193	**668**	19½p.	olive-grey, greenish yellow, bright magenta, dull grn, yell-brn & blk	55	55
		a.	Imperf (vert pair)	£1500	
1194	**669**	26p.	bright scarlet, dull mauve, dull ultramarine and bright carmine	70	70
1195	**670**	29p.	bronze-green, orange-yellow, turq-green, stone, chestnut & sage-grn	90	90
1192/5			*Set of* 4	2·25	2·25

Nos. 1192/5 were issued on the occasion of the 250th birth anniversary of Sir Richard Arkwright (inventor of spinning machine).

671 Development of Communications

672 Modern Technological Aids

(Des Delaney and Ireland)

1982 (8 Sept). *Information Technology. Phosphorised paper. P* 14 × 15.
1196	**671**	15½p.	black, greenish yellow, bright rose-red, bistre-brn, new bl & lt ochre	45	50
		a.	Imperf (pair)	£200	
1197	**672**	26p.	black, greenish yellow, bright rose-red, ol-bistre, new bl & lt ol-grey	80	85
		a.	Imperf (pair)	£1300	

673 Austin "Seven" and "Metro"

674 Ford "Model T" and "Escort"

675 Jaguar "SS 1" and "XJ6"

676 Rolls-Royce "Silver Ghost"
and "Silver Spirit"

(Des S. Paine. Litho Questa)

1982 (13 Oct). *British Motor Cars. Phosphorised paper. P* 14½ × 14.
1198	**673**	15½p.	slate, orange-vermilion, bright orange, drab, yellow-green, olive-yellow, bluish grey and black	50	50
1199	**674**	19½p.	slate, brt orange, olive-grey, rose-red, dull vermilion, grey & black	70	70
1200	**675**	26p.	slate, red-brown, bright orange, turquoise-green, myrtle-green, dull blue-green, grey and olive	90	90
1201	**676**	29p.	slate, bright orange, carmine-red, reddish purple, grey and black	1·25	1·25
1198/201			*Set of* 4	3·00	3·00

677 "While Shepherds Watched"

678 "The Holly and the Ivy"

679 "I Saw Three Ships"

680 "We Three Kings"

681 "Good King Wenceslas"

(Des Barbara Brown)

982 (17 Nov). *Christmas. Carols. One phosphor band (12½p.) or phosphorised paper (others). P 15 × 14.*

202	677	12½p. black, greenish yellow, brt scar, steel blue, red-brown & gold	30	30
203	678	15½p. black, bistre-yellow, brt rose-red, bright blue, bright green & gold	40	40
		a. Imperf (pair)	£950	
204	679	19½p. black, bistre-yellow, brt rose-red, dull blue, deep brown & gold	70	70
		a. Imperf (pair)	£1300	
205	680	26p. black, bistre-yellow, brt magenta, brt blue, choc, gold & orange-red	80	80
206	681	29p. black, bistre-yellow, magenta, brt blue, chestnut, gold and brt mag	90	90
02/6		*Set of 5*	2·75	2·75

682 Atlantic Salmon

683 Northern Pike

684 Brown Trout

685 Eurasian Perch

(Des A. Jardine)

83 (26 Jan). *British River Fishes. Phosphorised paper. P 15 × 14.*

07	682	15½p. grey-black, bistre-yellow, bright purple, new blue and silver	35	35
		a. Imperf (pair)	£1300	
08	683	19½p. black, bistre-yellow, olive-bistre, dp claret, silver & dp bluish green	65	55
09	684	26p. grey-black, bistre-yell, chrome-yellow, magenta, silver & pale bl	80	70
		a. Imperf (pair)	£850	
10	685	29p. black, greenish yellow, bright carmine, new blue and silver	1·00	90
07/10		*Set of 4*	2·50	2·25

All known examples of No. 1209a are creased.

686 Tropical Island   687 Desert

688 Temperate Farmland   689 Mountain Range

(Des D. Fraser)

1983 (9 Mar). *Commonwealth Day. Geographical Regions. Phosphorised paper. P 14 × 15.*

1211	686	15½p. greenish blue, greenish yellow, bright rose, light brown, grey-black, deep claret and silver	35	35
1212	687	19½p. brt lilac, greenish yell, mag, dull blue, grey-blk, dp dull-bl & silver	55	55
1213	688	26p. lt blue, greenish yellow, brt mag, new blue, grey-blk, vio & silver	70	70
1214	689	29p. dull vio-bl, reddish vio, slate-lilac, new blue, myrtle-grn, blk & silver	90	90
1211/14		*Set of 4*	2·25	2·25

690 Humber Bridge

691 Thames Flood Barrier

692 *Iolair* (oilfield emergency support vessel)

(Des. M. Taylor)

1983 (25 May). *Europa. Engineering Achievements. Phosphorised paper. P 15 × 14.*

1215	690	16p. silver, orange-yellow, ultramarine, black and grey	45	45
1216	691	20½p. silver, greenish yellow, bright purple, blue, grey-black and grey	95	1·10
1217	692	28p. silver, lemon, brt rose-red, chestnut, dull ultramarine, blk & grey	1·10	1·25
1215/17		*Set of 3*	2·25	2·50

693 Musketeer and Pikeman, The Royal Scots (1633)   694 Fusilier and Ensign, The Royal Welch Fusiliers (mid-18th century)

695 Riflemen, 95th Rifles (The Royal Green Jackets) (1805)   696 Sergeant (khaki service uniform) and Guardsman (full dress), The Irish Guards (1900)

697 Paratroopers, The Parachute Regiment (1983)

(Des E. Stemp)

1983 (6 July). *British Army Uniforms. Phosphorised paper. P 14 × 15.*

1218	693	16p. black, buff, deep brown, slate-black, rose-red, gold & new blue	40	40
1219	694	20½p. black, buff, greenish yellow, slate-blk, brn-rose, gold & brt bl	70	70
1220	695	26p. black, buff, slate-purple, green, bistre and gold	85	85
		a. Imperf (pair)	£1300	
1221	696	28p. black, buff, light brown, grey, dull rose, gold and new blue	85	85
1222	697	31p. black, buff, olive-yellow, grey, deep magenta, gold and new blue	1·10	1·10
1218/22		*Set of 5*	3·50	3·50

Nos. 1218/22 were issued on the occasion of the 350th anniversary of the Royal Scots, the senior line regiment of the British Army.

698 20th-century Garden, Sissinghurst   699 19th-century Garden, Biddulph Grange

700 18th-century Garden, Blenheim   701 17th-century Garden, Pitmedden

(Des Liz Butler, Litho J.W.)

1983 (24 Aug). *British Gardens. Phosphorised paper. P 14.*

1223	698	16p. greenish yellow, brt purple, new blue, black, bright green & silver	40	40
1224	699	20½p. greenish yellow, brt purple, new blue, black, bright green & silver	50	50
1225	700	28p. greenish yellow, brt purple, new blue, black, bright green & silver	90	90
1226	701	31p. greenish yellow, brt purple, new blue, black, bright green & silver	1·00	1·00
1223/6		*Set of 4*	2·50	2·50

Nos. 1223/6 were issued on the occasion of the death bicentenary of "Capability" Brown (landscape gardener)

702 Merry-go-round

703 Big Wheel, Helter-skelter and Performing Animals

704 Side Shows

705 Early Produce Fair

(Des A. Restall)

1983 (5 Oct). *British Fairs. Phosphorised paper. P* 15 × 14.

1227	702	16p. grey-black, greenish yellow, orge-red, ochre & turquoise-blue	40	40
1228	703	20½p. grey-black, yellow-ochre, yellow-orange, brt magenta, violet & blk	65	65
1229	704	28p. grey-black, bistre-yellow, orange-red, violet and yellow-brown	85	85
1230	705	31p. grey-black, greenish yellow, red, dp turq-green, slate-violet & brn	90	90
1227/30		*Set of 4*	2·50	2·50

706 "Christmas Post"
(pillar-box)

707 "The Three Kings"
(chimney-pots)

708 "World at Peace"
(Dove and Blackbird)

709 "Light of Christmas"
(street lamp)

710 "Christmas Dove"
(hedge sculpture)

(Des T. Meeuwissen)

1983 (16 Nov). *Christmas. One phosphor band (12½p.) or phosphorised paper (others). P* 15 × 14.

1231	706	12½p. black, greenish yellow, bright rose-red, bright blue, gold and grey-black	30	30
		a. Imperf (horiz pair)	£750	
1232	707	16p. black, greenish yellow, bright rose, pale new blue, gold & brown-pur	35	35
		a. Imperf (pair)	£850	
1233	708	20½p. black, greenish yellow, bright rose, new blue, gold and blue	60	60
1234	709	28p. black, lemon, bright carmine, bluish violet, gold, deep turquoise-green and purple	70	80
1235	710	31p. black, greenish yellow, brt rose, new blue, gold, green & brn-olive	85	1·00
1231/5		*Set of 5*	2·50	2·75

711 Arms of the College
of Arms

712 Arms of King Richard III
(founder)

713 Arms of the Earl Marshal
of England

714 Arms of the City of London

(Des J. Matthews)

1984 (17 Jan). *500th Anniv of College of Arms. Phosphorised paper. P* 14½.

1236	711	16p. black, chrome-yellow, reddish brn, scar-verm, brt bl & grey-blk	40	40
1237	712	20½p. black, chrome-yellow, rosine, bright blue and grey-black	60	60
1238	713	28p. black, chrome-yellow, rosine, brt blue, dull green and grey-black	85	85
1239	714	31p. black, chrome-yellow, rosine, brt blue and grey-black	95	95
		a. Imperf (horiz pair)	£1800	
1236/9		*Set of 4*	2·50	2·50

715 Highland Cow

716 Chillingham Wild Bull

717 Hereford Bull

718 Welsh Black Bull

719 Irish Moiled Cow

(Des B. Driscoll)

1984 (6 Mar). *British Cattle. Phosphorised paper. P* 15 × 14.

1240	715	16p. grey-black, bistre-yellow, rosine, yellow-orge, new bl & pale drab	40	4
1241	716	20½p. grey-black, greenish yellow, magenta, bistre, dull blue-green, pale drab and light green	65	6
1242	717	26p. black, chrome-yellow, rosine, reddish brown, new blue & pale drab	70	7
1243	718	28p. black, greenish yellow, bright carmine, orange-brown, deep dull blue and pale drab	70	7
1244	719	31p. grey-black, bistre-yellow, rosine, red-brown, light blue & pale drab	90	9
1240/4		*Set of 5*	3·00	3·0

Nos. 1240/4 were issued on the occasion of the centenary of the Highland Cattle Society and the bicentenary of the Royal Highland and Agricultural Society of Scotland.

720 Liverpool Garden Festival Hall

721 Milburngate Centre, Durham

722 Bush House, Bristol

723 Commercial Street Development, Perth

(Des R. Maddox and Trickett and Webb Ltd)

1984 (10 Apr). *Urban Renewal. Phosphorised paper. P* 15 × 14.

1245	720	16p. bright emerald, greenish yellow, cerise, steel-bl, blk, silver & flesh	40	4
1246	721	20½p. bright orange, greenish yellow, deep dull blue, yellowish green, azure, black and silver	60	6
		a. Imperf (horiz pair)	£1000	
1247	722	28p. rosine, greenish yellow, Prussian blue, pale blue-green, blk & silver	90	9
1248	723	31p. blue, greenish yell, cerise, grey-blue, bright green, black & silver	90	9
		a. Imperf (pair)	£1000	
1245/8		*Set of 4*	2·50	2·50

Nos. 1245/8 were issued on the occasion of 150th anniversaries of the Royal Institute of British Architects and the Chartered Institute of Building, and to commemorate the first International Gardens Festival Liverpool.

ROYAL MAIL POSTAGE LABELS

These imperforate labels, printed in red on phosphorised paper with grey-green background design, were issued on 1 May 1984 as an experiment by the Post Office. Special microprocessor controlled machines were installed at post offices in Cambridge, London, Shirley (Southampton) and Windsor to provide an after-hours sales service to the public. The machines printed and dispensed the labels according to the coins inserted and the buttons operated by the customer. Values were initially available in ½p steps to 16p and in addition, the labels were sold at philatelic counters in two packs containing either 3 values (3½, 12½, 16p) or 32 values (½p to 16p).

From 28 August 1984 the machines were adjusted to provide values up to 17p. After 31 December 1984 labels including ½p values were withdrawn. The machines were withdrawn from service on 30 April 1985.

*24 C.E.P.T. 25th Aniversary Logo   725 Abduction of Europa

(Des J. Larrivière (T **724**), F. Wegner (T **725**)

1984 (15 May). *25th Anniv of C.E.P.T. ("Europa") (T **724**) and Second Elections to European Parliament (T **725**). Phosphorised paper. P 15 × 14.*

249	724	16p. greenish slate, deep blue and gold	90	90
		a. Horiz pair. Nos. 1249/50	1·75	1·75
		ab. Imperf (horiz pair)	£1300	
250	725	16p. greenish slate, deep blue, black and gold	90	90
251	724	20½p. Venetian red, dp magenta & gold	1·60	1·60
		a. Horiz pair. Nos. 1251/2	3·25	3·25
		ab. Imperf (horiz pair)		
252	725	20½p. Venetian red, deep magenta, black and gold	1·60	1·60
249/52		Set of 4	4·50	4·50

Nos. 1249/50 and 1251/2 were each printed together, *se-tenant*, in horizontal pairs throughout the sheets.

726 Lancaster House

(Des P. Hogarth)

1984 (5 June). *London Economic Summit Conference. Phosphorised paper. P 14 × 15.*

1253	726	31p. silver, bistre-yellow, brown-ochre, black, rosine, bright blue and reddish lilac	1·00	1·00

727 View of Earth from "Apollo 11"   728 Navigational Chart of English Channel

729 Greenwich Observatory   730 Sir George Airy's Transit Telescope

(Des. H. Waller. Litho Questa)

1984 (26 June). *Centenary of the Greenwich Meridian. Phosphorised paper. P 14 × 14½.*

1254	727	16p. new blue, greenish yellow, magenta, black, scar & blue-blk	40	40
1255	728	20½p. olive-sepia, light brown, pale buff, black and scarlet	65	65
1256	729	28p. new blue, greenish yellow, scarlet, black and bright purple	85	90
1257	730	31p. deep blue, cobalt, scarlet & black	90	1·10
1254/7		Set of 4	2·50	2·75

On Nos. 1254/7 the Meridian is represented by a scarlet line.

731 Bath Mail Coach, 1784

732 Attack on Exeter Mail, 1816

733 Norwich Mail in Thunderstorm, 1827

734 Holyhead and Liverpool Mails leaving London, 1828

735 Edinburgh Mail Snowbound, 1831

(Des K. Bassford and S. Paine. Eng C. Slania. Recess and photo)

1984 (31 July). *Bicentenary of First Mail Coach Run Bath and Bristol to London. Phosphorised paper. P 15 × 14.*

1258	731	16p. pale stone, black, grey-black and bright scarlet	60	40
		a. Horiz strip of 5 Nos. 1258/62	2·75	2·75
1259	732	16p. pale stone, black, grey-black and bright scarlet	60	40
1260	733	16p. pale stone, black, grey-black and bright scarlet	60	40
1261	734	16p. pale stone, black, grey-black and bright scarlet	60	40
1262	735	16p. pale stone, black, grey-black and bright scarlet	60	40
1258/62		Set of 5	2·75	1·75

Nos. 1258/62 were printed together, *se-tenant*, in horizontal strips of 5 throughout the sheet.

736 Nigerian Clinic

737 Violinist and Acropolis, Athens

738 Building Project, Sri Lanka

739 British Council Library, Middle East

(Des F. Newell and J. Sorrell)

1984 (25 Sept). *50th Anniv of the British Council. Phosphorised paper. P 15 × 14.*

1263	736	17p. grey-green, greenish yellow, bright purple, dull blue, black, pale green and yellow-green	50	50
1264	737	22p. crimson, greenish yellow, bright rose-red, dull green, black, pale drab and slate-purple	65	65
1265	738	31p. sepia, olive-bistre, red, black, pale stone and olive-brown	90	90
1266	739	34p. steel blue, yellow, rose-red, new blue, black, azure and pale blue	1·00	1·00
1263/6		Set of 4	2·75	2·75

740 The Holy Family

741 Arrival in Bethlehem

742 Shepherd and Lamb

743 Virgin and Child

744 Offering of Frankincense

(Des Yvonne Gilbert)

1984 (20 Nov). *Christmas. One phosphor band (13p.) or phosphorised paper (others). P 15 × 14.*

1267	740	13p. pale cream, grey-black, bistre-yellow, mag, red-brn & lake-brn	30	30
1268	741	17p. pale cream, grey-black, yellow, magenta, dull blue & dp dull bl	50	50
		a. Imperf (pair)		
1269	742	22p. pale cream, grey-black, olive-yellow, bright magenta, bright blue and brownish grey	60	60
1270	743	31p. pale cream, grey-black, bistre-yellow, magenta, dull bl & lt brn	95	95
1271	744	34p. pale cream, olive-grey, bistre-yellow, magenta, turquoise-green and brown-olive	1·00	1·00
1267/71		Set of 5	3·00	3·00

Examples of No. 1267 from the Christmas £2.30 discount stamp booklet show a blue underprint of a double-lined star printed on the reverse over the gum.

745 "The Flying Scotsman"

746 "The Golden Arrow"

747 "The Cheltenham Flyer"

748 "The Royal Scot"

749 "The Cornish Riviera"

(Des T. Cuneo)

1985 (22 Jan). *Famous Trains. Phosphorised paper. P* 15 × 14.

1272	**745**	17p. black, lemon, magenta, dull glue, grey-black and gold	50	50
		a. Imperf (pair)	£1800	
1273	**746**	22p. black, greenish yellow, bright rose, dp dull blue, grey-blk & gold	85	70
1274	**747**	29p. black, greenish yellow, magenta, blue, grey-black and gold ..	1·00	90
1275	**748**	31p. black, bistre-yellow, bright magenta, new blue slate-black & gold	1·25	1·00
1276	**749**	34p. black, greenish yellow, bright rose, blue, slate-black and gold ..	1·40	1·10
1272/6		.. .. .. *Set of* 5	4·50	4·00

Nos. 1272/6 were issued on the occasion of the 150th anniversary of the Great Western Railway Company.

750 *Bombus terrestris* (bee)

751 *Coccinella septempunctata* (ladybird)

752 *Decticus verrucivorus* (bush-cricket)

753 *Lucanus cervus* (stag beetle)

754 *Anax imperator* (dragonfly)

(Des G. Beningfield)

1985 (12 Mar). *Insects. Phosphorised paper. P* 14 × 15.

1277	**750**	17p. black, greenish yellow, magenta, blue, azure, gold and slate-black	40	40
1278	**751**	22p. black, greenish yellow, bright rose-red, dull blue-green, slate-black and gold	60	60
1279	**752**	29p. black, greenish yellow, bright rose, greenish blue, grey-black, gold and bistre-yellow..	80	80
1280	**753**	31p. black, greenish yellow, rose, pale new blue and gold	90	90
1281	**754**	34p. black, greenish yellow, magenta, greenish blue, grey-black and gold	90	90
1277/81		.. .. .. *Set of* 5	3·25	3·25

Nos. 1277/81 were issued on the occasion of the centenaries of the Royal Entomological Society of London's Royal Charter, and of the Selborne Society.

755 "Water Music" (George Frideric Handel)

756 "The Planets" Suite (Gustav Holst)

757 "The First Cuckoo" (Frederick Delius)

758 "Sea Pictures" (Edward Elgar)

(Des W. McLean)

1985 (14 May). *Europa. European Music Year. British Composers. Phosphorised paper. P* 14 × 14½.

1282	**755**	17p. black, brt yellow-grn, dp magenta, new blue, grey-black & gold ..	65	65
		a. Imperf (vert pair) ..		
1283	**756**	22p. black, greenish yellow, brt mag, new blue, grey-black and gold	90	90
		a. Imperf (pair)	£1300	
1284	**757**	31p. black, greenish yellow, magenta, greenish blue, grey-black and gold	1·40	1·40
1285	**758**	34p. black, olive-yellow, bistre, turq-blue, slate and gold	1·50	1·50
1282/5		.. .. *Set of* 4	4·00	4·00

Nos. 1282/5 were issued on the occasion of the 300th birth anniversary of Handel.

759 R.N.L.I. Lifeboat and Signal Flags

760 Beachy Head Lighthouse and Chart

761 "Marecs A" Communications Satellite and Dish Aerials

762 Buoys

(Des F. Newell and J. Sorrel. Litho J.W.)

1985 (18 June). *Safety at Sea. Phosphorised paper. P* 14.

1286	**759**	17p. black, azure, emerald, ultramarine, orange-yellow, vermilion, bright blue, and chrome-yellow	50	50
1287	**760**	22p. black, azure, emerald, ultramarine, orange-yellow, vermilion, bright blue and chrome-yellow ..	65	65
1288	**761**	31p. black, azure, emerald, ultramarine, orange-yellow, vermilion, and bright blue	1·10	1·10
1289	**762**	34p. black, azure, emerald, ultramarine, orange-yellow, vermilion, bright blue and chrome-yellow ..	1·10	1·10
1286/9		.. .. .. *Set of* 4	3·00	3·00

Nos. 1286/9 were issued on the occasion of the Bicentenary of the unimmersible lifeboat and the 50th anniversary of radar.

763 Datapost Motorcyclist, City of London

764 Rural Postbus

765 Parcel Delivery in Winter

766 Town Letter Delivery

(Des P. Hogarth)

1985 (30 July). *350 Years of Royal Mail Public Postal Service. Phosphorised paper. P* 14 × 15.

1290	**763**	17p. black, greenish yellow, bright carmine, greenish blue, yellow-brown, grey-black and silver ..	50	50
		a. Imperf on 3 sides (vert pair)	£1300	
1291	**764**	22p. black, greenish yellow, cerise, steel bl, lt grn, grey-blk & silver	65	65
1292	**765**	31p. black, greenish yellow, brt carm, dull blue, drab, grey-blk & silver	1·10	1·10
		a. Imperf (vert pair)	£1300	
1293	**766**	34p. black, greenish yellow, cerise, ultram, lt brn, grey-blk & silver	1·10	1·10
		a. Imperf between (vert pair)		
1290/3		.. .. *Set of* 4	3·00	3·00

Examples of No. 1290 from the commemorative £1.53 discount stamp booklet show a blue underprint of a double-lined D printed on the reverse over the gum.

No. 1290a shows perforation indentations at right, but is imperforate at top, bottom and on the left-hand side.

767 King Arthur and Merlin

768 Lady of the Lake

769 Queen Guinevere and Sir Lancelot

770 Sir Galahad

(Des Yvonne Gilbert)

1985 (3 Sept). *Arthurian Legends. Phosphorised paper. P 15 × 14.*
1294 767 17p. grey-black, lemon, brown-lilac,
            ultramarine, grey-black and silver   50   50
       a. Imperf (pair) £1800
1295 768 22p. black, lemon, brown-lilac, pale
            blue, grey-black, silver & grey-blk   65   75
1296 769 31p. black, lemon, magenta, turquoise-
            blue, grey-black, silver & grey-blk   1·10 1·10
1297 770 34p. grey, lemon, magenta, new blue,
            grey-black, silver and grey-black. .   1·10 1·25
1294/7 .. .. *Set of* 4   3·00 3·25
Nos. 1294/7 were issued on the occasion of the 500th anniversary
of the printing of Sir Thomas Malory's *Morte d'Arthur*.

771 Peter Sellers (from   **772** David Niven (from
photo by Bill Brandt)   photo by Cornell Lucas)

773 Charlie Chaplin   **774** Vivien Leigh (from
(from photo by Lord   photo by Angus
Snowdon)   McBean)

775 Alfred Hitchcock
(from photo by Howard
Coster)

(Des K. Bassford)

1985 (8 Oct). *British Film Year. Phosphorised paper. P 14½.*
1298 771 17p. grey-black, ol-grey, gold & silver   50   50
1299 772 22p. black, brown, gold and silver ..   75   75
1300 773 29p. black, lavender, gold and silver .. 1·10 1·10
1301 774 31p. black, pink, gold and silver ..   1·25 1·25
1302 775 34p. black, greenish blue, gold & silver 1·40 1·40
1298/302 .. .. *Set of* 5   4·50 4·50

776 Principal Boy

777 Genie

778 Dame

779 Good Fairy

780 Pantomime Cat

(Des A. George)

1985 (19 Nov). *Christmas. Pantomine Characters. One phosphor
band* (12p.) *or phosphorised paper* (others). *P 15 × 14.*
1303 776 12p. new blue, greenish yellow, bright
            rose, gold, grey-black and silver   35   30
       a. Imperf (pair) £1300
1304 777 17p. emerald, greenish yellow, bright
            rose, new blue, blk, gold & silver   45   40
       a. Imperf (pair) £1800
1305 778 22p. bright carmine, greenish yellow,
            pale new blue, grey, gold & silver   70   80
1306 779 31p. bright orange, lemon, rose, slate-
            purple, silver and gold ..   95   1·00
1307 780 34p. brt reddish violet, brt blue, brt
            rose, blk, grey-brn, gold & silver   1·00 1·10
1303/7 .. .. *Set of* 5   3·00 3·25
Examples of No. 1303 from the Christmas £2.40 stamp booklet
show a blue underprint of a double-lined star printed on the reverse
over the gum.

17 PENCE · INDUSTRY YEAR 1986

781 Light Bulb and North Sea
Oil Drilling Rig (Energy)

22 PENCE · INDUSTRY YEAR 1986

782 Thermometer and Pharmaceutical
Laboratory (Health)

31 PENCE · INDUSTRY YEAR 1986

783 Garden Hoe and
Steelworks (Steel)

34 PENCE · INDUSTRY YEAR 1986

784 Loaf of Bread and
Cornfield (Agriculture)

(Des K. Bassford. Litho Questa)

1986 (14 Jan). *Industry Year. Phosphorised paper. P 14½ × 14.*
1308 781 17p. gold, black, magenta, greenish
            yellow and new blue ..   45   45
1309 782 22p. gold, pale turquoise-green, black,
            magenta, greenish yellow and blue   60   60
1310 783 31p. gold, black, magenta, greenish
            yellow and new blue ..   90   90
1311 784 34p. gold, black, magenta, greenish
            yellow and new blue ..   1·10 1·10
1308/11 .. .. *Set of* 4   2·75 2·75

785 Dr. Edmond Halley as
Comet

786 *Giotto* Spacecraft
approaching Comet

787 "Twice in a Lifetime"

788 Comet orbiting Sun and
Planets

(Des R. Steadman)

1986 (18 Feb). *Appearance of Halley's Comet. Phosphorised
paper. P 15 × 14.*
1312 785 17p. black, bistre, rosine, blue, grey-
            black, gold and deep brown   45   45
1313 786 22p. orange-vermilion, greenish yel-
            low, brt purple, new bl, blk & gold   70   70
1314 787 31p. black, greenish yellow, brt purple
            dp turquoise-blue, grey-blk & gold   1·10 1·10
1315 788 34p. blue, greenish yellow, magenta,
            deep turquoise-blue, black & gold   1·10 1·10
1312/15 .. .. *Set of* 4   3·00 3·00

HER MAJESTY THE QUEEN
Sixtieth Birthday   17p

789 Queen Elizabeth II in
1928, 1942 and 1952

HER MAJESTY THE QUEEN
Sixtieth Birthday   17p

790 Queen Elizabeth II in
1958, 1973 and 1982

(Des J. Matthews)

1986 (21 Apr). *60th Birthday of Queen Elizabeth II. Phosphorised
paper. P 15 × 14.*
1316 789 17p. grey-black, turquoise-green,
            bright green, green and dull blue. .   70   40
       a. Horiz pair. Nos. 1316/17. .   1·40 1·40
1317 790 17p. grey-black, dull blue, greenish
            blue and indigo ..   70   40
1318 789 34p. grey-black, deep dull purple,
            yellow-orange and red ..   1·50 1·50
       a. Horiz pair. Nos. 1318/19. .   3·00 3·00
1319 790 34p. grey-black, olive-brown, yellow-
            brown, olive-grey and red ..   1·50 1·50
1316/19 .. .. *Set of* 4   4·00 4·00
Nos. 1316/17 and 1318/19 were printed together, *se-tenant*, in
horizontal pairs throughout the sheets.

NEW INFORMATION

The editor is always interested to correspond with
people who have new information that will
improve or correct the Catalogue.

791 Barn Owl   792 Pine Marten

793 Wild Cat   794 Natterjack Toad

(Des K. Lilly)

1986 (20 May). *Europa. Nature Conservation. Endangered Species. Phosphorised paper. P 14½ × 14.*

1320	791	17p. gold, greenish yellow, rose, yellow-brown, olive-grey, new blue & blk	50	50
1321	792	22p. gold, greenish yellow, reddish brn, ol-yell, turq-bl, grey-blk & blk	90	75
1322	793	31p. gold, brt yellow-green, magenta, lt brown, ultramarine, ol-brn & blk	1·25	1·10
1323	794	34p. gold, greenish yellow, bright rose-red, brt green, grey-black & black	1·50	1·25
1320/3		Set of 4	3·75	3·25

795 Peasants working in Fields

796 Freemen working at Town Trades

797 Knight and Retainers

798 Lord at Banquet

(Des Tayburn Design Consultancy)

1986 (17 June). *900th Anniv of Domesday Book. Phosphorised paper. P 15 × 14.*

1324	795	17p. yell-brn, verm, lemon, brt emer, orge-brn, grey & brownish grey	50	50
1325	796	22p. yellow-ochre, red, greenish blue, chestnut, grey-blk & brownish grey	75	75
1326	797	31p. yellow-brown, verm, grn, Indian red, grey-blk & brownish grey	1·10	1·10
1327	798	34p. yellow-ochre, brt scar, grey-brn, new bl, lake-brn, grey-blk & grey	1·25	1·25
1324/7		Set of 4	3·25	3·25

MINIMUM PRICE

The minimum price quote is 10p which represents a handling charge rather than a basis for valuing common stamps. For further notes about prices see introductory pages.

799 Athletics

800 Rowing

801 Weightlifting

802 Rifle Shooting

803 Hockey

(Des N. Cudworth)

1986 (15 July). *Thirteenth Commonwealth Games, Edinburgh and World Hockey Cup for Men, London (34p.). Phosphorised paper. P 15 × 14.*

1328	799	17p. black, greenish yellow, orange-vermilion, ultram, chestnut & emer	50	50
1329	800	22p. black, lemon, scarlet, new blue, royal blue, chestnut & dp ultram	70	70
1330	801	29p. grey-black, greenish yellow, scarlet, new blue, brown-ochre, brown-rose and pale chestnut	90	90
1331	802	31p. black, greenish yellow, rose, blue, dull yell-grn, chestnut & yell-grn	1·10	1·10
1332	803	34p. black, lemon, scarlet, brt blue, brt emerald, red-brown & vermilion	1·25	1·25
		a. Imperf (pair)	£1300	
1328/32		Set of 5	4·00	4·00

No. 1332 also commemorates the Centenary of the Hockey Association.

804   805

Prince Andrew and Miss Sarah Ferguson (from photo by Gene Nocon)

(Des J. Matthews)

1986 (22 July). *Royal Wedding. One phosphor band (12p.) or phosphorised paper (17p.). P 14 × 15.*

1333	804	12p. lake, greenish yellow, cerise, ultramarine, black and silver	60	60
1334	805	17p. steel blue, greenish yellow, cerise, ultramarine, black and gold	90	90
		a. Imperf (pair)	£850	

806 Stylised Cross on Ballot Paper

(Des J. Gibbs. Litho Questa)

1986 (19 Aug). *32nd Commonwealth Parliamentary Association Conference. Phosphorised paper. P 14 × 14½.*

1335	806	34p. pale grey-lilac, black, vermilion, yellow and ultramarine	1·25	1·25

807 Lord Dowding and Hawker Hurricane Mk I   808 Lord Tedder and Hawker Typhoon 1B

809 Lord Trenchard and De Havilland D.H.9A   810 Sir Arthur Harris and Avro Type 683 Lancaster

811 Lord Portal and De Havilland D.H.98 Mosquito

(Des B. Sanders)

1986 (16 Sept). *History of the Royal Air Force. Phosphorised paper. P 14½.*

1336	807	17p. pale blue, greenish yellow, bright rose, blue, black and grey-black	50	40
		a. Imperf (pair)	£950	
1337	808	22p. pale turquoise-green, greenish yell, mag, new bl, blk & grey-blk	75	85
		a. Face value omitted*	£400	
		b. Queen's head omitted*	£400	
1338	809	29p. pale drab, olive-yellow, magenta, blue, grey-black and black	1·00	1·00
1339	810	31p. pale flesh, greenish yellow, magenta, ultram, blk & grey-blk	1·25	1·10
1340	811	34p. buff, greenish yellow, magenta, blue, grey-black and black	1·50	1·25
1336/40		Set of 5	4·50	4·25

*Nos. 1337a/b come from three consecutive sheets on which the stamps in the first vertical row are without the face value and those in the second vertical row the Queen's head.

Nos. 1336/40 were issued to celebrate the 50th anniversary of the first R.A.F. Commands.

812 The Glastonbury Thorn

813 The Tanad Valley Plygain

814 The Hebrides Tribute

815 The Dewsbury Church Knell

816 The Hereford Boy Bishop

(Des Lynda Gray)

1986 (18 Nov–2 Dec). *Christmas. Folk Customs. One phosphor band* (12p., 13p.) *or phosphorised paper* (others). *P* 15×14.

1341	812	12p. gold, greenish yellow, vermilion, dp brown, emerald & dp bl (2.12)		50	50
		a. Imperf (pair)		£900	
1342		13p. deep blue, greenish yellow, verm, deep brown, emerald and gold		30	30
1343	813	18p. myrtle-green, yellow, vermilion, dp blue, black, reddish brn & gold		45	45
1344	814	22p. vermilion, olive-bistre, dull blue, deep brown, deep green and gold		65	65
1345	815	31p. deep brown, yellow, vermilion, violet, dp dull green, black & gold		80	80
1346	816	34p. violet, lemon, vermilion, deep dull blue, reddish brown and gold		90	90
1341/6		.. .. *Set of 6*		3·25	3·25

No. 1341 represented a discount of 1p., available between 2 and 24 December 1986, on the current second class postage rate.

Examples of the 13p. value from special folders, containing 36 stamps and sold for £4.30, show a blue underprint of double-lined stars printed on the reverse over the gum.

817 North American Blanket Flower   **818** Globe Thistle

819 *Echeveria*   **820** Autumn Crocus

(Adapted J. Matthews)

1987 (20 Jan). *Flower Photographs by Alfred Lammer. Phosphorised paper. P* 14½×14.

1347	817	18p. silver, greenish yellow, rosine, deep green and black		50	50
1348	818	22p. silver, greenish yellow, new blue, greenish blue and black		80	70
1349	819	31p. silver, greenish yellow, scarlet, blue-green, deep green and black		1·25	1·10
		a. Imperf (pair)		£1600	
1350	820	34p. silver, greenish yellow, magenta, dull blue, deep green and black		1·40	1·25
1347/50		.. .. *Set of 4*		3·50	3·25

OMNIBUS ISSUES

Details, together with prices for complete sets, of the various Omnibus issues from the 1935 Silver Jubilee series to date are included in a special section following Zimbabwe at the end of Volume 2.

821 *The Principia Mathematica*   **822** *Motion of Bodies in Ellipses*

823 *Optick Treatise*   **824** *The System of the World*

(Des Sarah Godwin)

1987 (24 Mar). *300th Anniv of* The Principia Mathematica *by Sir Isaac Newton. Phosphorised paper. P* 14×15.

1351	821	18p. black, greenish yellow, cerise, blue-green, grey-black and silver		50	50
1352	822	22p. black, greenish yellow, brt orange, blue, brt emer, silver & bluish vio		70	70
1353	823	31p. black, greenish yellow, scar, new bl, bronze-grn, silver & slate-grn		1·10	1·10
1354	824	34p. black, greenish yellow, red, bright blue, grey-black and silver		1·25	1·25
1351/4		.. .. *Set of 4*		3·25	3·25

825 Willis Faber & Dumas Building, Ipswich

826 Pompidou Centre, Paris

827 Staatsgalerie, Stuttgart

828 European Investment Bank, Luxembourg

(Des Brian Tattersfield)

1987 (12 May). *Europa. British Architects in Europe. Phosphorised paper. P* 15×14.

1355	825	18p. black, bistre-yellow, cerise, bright blue, deep grey and grey-black		50	50
1356	826	22p. black, greenish yellow, carmine, bright blue, dp grey & grey-black		70	70
1357	827	31p. grey-black, bistre-yellow, cerise, brt blue, brt green, black & dull vio		1·10	1·10
		a. Imperf (horiz pair)		£1000	
1358	828	34p. black, greenish yellow, cerise, bright blue, grey-black & deep grey		1·25	1·25
1355/8		.. .. *Set of 4*		3·25	3·25

829 Brigade Members with Ashford Litter, 1887   **830** Bandaging Blitz Victim, 1940

831 Volunteer with fainting Girl, 1965   **832** Transport of Transplant Organ by Air Wing, 1987

(Des Debbie Cook. Litho Questa)

1987 (16 June). *Centenary of St. John Ambulance Brigade. Phosphorised paper. P* 14×14½.

1359	829	18p. new blue, greenish yellow, magenta, black, silver and pink		50	50
1360	830	22p. new blue, greenish yellow, magenta, black, silver and cobalt		65	65
1361	831	31p. new blue, greenish yellow, magenta, black, silver & bistre-brn		1·10	1·10
1362	832	34p. new blue, greenish yellow, mag. blk, silver & greenish grey		1·10	1·10
1359/62		.. .. *Set of 4*		3·00	3·00

833 Arms of the Lord Lyon King of Arms   **834** Scottish Heraldic Banner of Prince Charles

835 Arms of Royal Scottish Academy of Painting, Sculpture and Architecture   **836** Arms of Royal Society of Edinburgh

(Des J. Matthews)

1987 (21 July). *300th Anniv of Revival of Order of the Thistle. Phosphorised paper. P* 14½.

1363	833	18p. black, lemon, scarlet, blue, deep green, slate and brown		50	50
1364	834	22p. black, greenish yellow, carmine, new blue, dp grn, grey & lake-brn		65	65
1365	835	31p. black, greenish yellow, scarlet, new blue, dull grn, grey & grey-blk		1·10	1·10
1366	836	34p. black, greenish yellow, scarlet, dp ultram, dull grn, grey & yell-brn		1·10	1·10
1363/6		.. .. *Set of 4*		3·00	3·00

837 Crystal Palace, "Monarch of the Glen" (Landseer) and Grace Darling

838 *Great Eastern, Beeton's Book of Household Management* and Prince Albert

839 Albert Memorial, Ballot Box and Disraeli

840 Diamond Jubilee Emblem, Newspaper Placard for Relief of Mafeking and Morse Key

(Des M. Dempsey. Eng C. Slania. Recess and photo)

1987 (8 Sept). *150th Anniv of Queen Victoria's Accession. Phosphorised paper. P 15 × 14.*

1367	837	18p. pale stone, dp blue, lemon, rose, greenish bl, brn-ochre & grey-blk	50	50
1368	838	22p. pale stone, deep brown, lemon, rose, grey-black and brown-ochre	75	75
1369	839	31p. pale stone, dp lilac, lemon, cerise, brn-ochre, greenish bl & grey-blk	1·10	1·10
1370	840	34p. pale stone, myrtle-green, yellow-ochre, reddish brown & brn-ochre	1·25	1·25
1367/70		Set of 4	3·25	3·25

841 Pot by Bernard Leach

842 Pot by Elizabeth Fritsch

843 Pot by Lucie Rie

844 Pot by Hans Coper

(Des T. Evans)

1987 (13 Oct). *Studio Pottery. Phosphorised paper. P 14½ × 14.*

1371	841	18p. gold, lemon, light red-brown, chestnut, light grey and black	50	50
1372	842	26p. blue over silver, yellow-orange, bright purple, lavender, bluish violet, grey-brown and black	70	70
1373	843	31p. rose-lilac over silver, greenish yellow, cerise, new bl, grey-lilac & blk	1·10	1·10
1374	844	34p. copper, yellow-brown, reddish brown, grey-lilac and black	1·25	1·25
1371/4		Set of 4	3·25	3·25

845 Decorating the Christmas Tree

846 Waiting for Father Christmas

847 Sleeping Child and Father Christmas in Sleigh

848 Child reading

849 Child playing Recorder and Snowman

(Des M. Foreman)

1987 (17 Nov). *Christmas. One phosphor band (13p.) or phosphorised paper (others). P 15 × 14.*

1375	845	13p. gold, greenish yellow, rose, greenish blue and black	30	30
1376	846	18p. gold, greenish yellow, bright purple, greenish blue, brt blue & blk	50	50
1377	847	26p. gold, greenish yellow, bright purple, new blue, bright blue and black	75	75
1378	848	31p. gold, greenish yellow, scarlet, brt mag, dull rose, greenish bl & blk	95	1·10
1379	849	34p. gold, greenish yellow, dull rose, greenish blue, bright blue & black	1·10	1·25
1375/9		Set of 5	3·25	3·50

Examples of the 13p. value from special folders, containing 36 stamps and sold for £4.60, show a blue underprint of double-lined stars printed on the reverse over the gum.

850 Short-spined Seascorpion ("Bull-rout") (Jonathan Couch)

851 Yellow Waterlily (Major Joshua Swatkin)

852 Whistling ("Bewick's") Swan (Edward Lear)

853 *Morchella esculenta* (James Sowerby)

(Des E. Hughes)

1988 (19 Jan). *Bicentenary of Linnean Society. Archive Illustrations. Phosphorised paper. P 15 × 14.*

1380	850	18p. grey-black, stone, orange-yellow, bright purple, olive-bistre & gold	60	45
1381	851	26p. black, stone, bistre-yellow, dull orange, greenish bl, gold & pale bis	80	70
1382	852	31p black, stone, greenish yellow, rose-red, dp blue, gold & olive-bis	1·25	1·10
		a. Imperf (horiz pair)	£1300	
1383	853	34p. black, stone, yellow, pale bistre, olive-grey, gold and olive-bistre	1·25	1·10
1380/3		Set of 4	3·50	3·00

854 Revd William Morgan (Bible translator, 1588)

855 William Salesbury (New Testament translator, 1567)

856 Bishop Richard Davies (New Testament translator, 1567)

857 Bishop Richard Parry (editor of Revised Welsh Bible, 1620)

(Des K. Bowen)

1988 (1 Mar). *400th Anniv of Welsh Bible. Phosphorised paper. P 14½ × 14.*

1384	854	18p. grey-black, greenish yellow, cerise, blue, black and emerald	45	
		a. Imperf (pair)	£1300	
1385	855	26p. grey-black, yellow, bright rose-red, turquoise-blue, black & orge	70	7
1386	856	31p. black, chrome-yellow, carmine, new blue, grey-black and blue	1·10	1·1
1387	857	34p. grey-black, greenish yellow, cerise, turquoise-grn, blk & brt vio	1·10	1·1
1384/7		Set of 4	3·00	3·0

858 Gymnastics (Centenary of British Amateur Gymnastics Association)

859 Downhill Skiing (Ski Club of Great Britain)

860 Tennis (Centenary of Lawn Tennis Association)

861 Football (Centenary of Football League)

(Des J. Sutton)

1988 (22 Mar). *Sports Organizations. Phosphorised paper. P 14½*

1388	858	18p. violet-blue, greenish yellow, rosine, brt rose, new blue & silver	45	45
1389	859	26p. violet-blue, greenish yellow, vermilion, carmine, yell-orge & silver	70	70
1390	860	31p. violet-bl, greenish yell, rose, bl, pale greenish bl, silver & brt orge	1·10	1·10
1391	861	34p. violet-blue, greenish yellow, vermilion, bl, brt emer, silver & pink	1·10	1·10
1388/91		Set of 4	3·00	3·00

862 *Mallard* and Mailbags on Pick-up Arms

863 Loading Transatlantic Mail on Liner *Queen Elizabeth*

864 Glasgow Tram No. 1173
and Pillar Box

865 Imperial Airways Handley
Page H.P.45 *Horatius* and
Airmail Van

(Des M. Dempsey)

1988 (10 May). *Europa. Transport and Mail Services in 1930s. Phosphorised paper.* P 15×14.

1392	862	18p. brown, yellow, rose-red, dull blue, dp brown, reddish vio & blk	50	50
1393	863	26p. brown, yellow, orange-vermilion, dull blue, violet-bl, brt emer & blk	80	80
1394	864	31p. brown, yellow-orange, carmine, dull purple, vio-bl, brt grn & blk	1·10	1·10
1395	865	34p. brown, orange-yellow, carmine-rose, bluish vio, brt bl, sepia & blk	1·25	1·25
1392/5		*Set of 4*	3·25	3·25

866 Early Settler and
Sailing Clipper

867 Queen Elizabeth II with
British and Australian
Parliament Buildings

868 W. G. Grace (cricketer)
and Tennis Racquet

869 Shakespeare, John Lennon
(entertainer) and Sydney
Landmarks

(Des G. Emery. Litho Questa)

1988 (21 June). *Bicentenary of Australian Settlement. Phosphorised paper.* P 14½.

1396	866	18p. deep ultramarine, orange-yellow, scarlet, black, bluish grey & emerald	60	60
		a. Horiz pair. Nos. 1396/7	1·25	1·25
1397	867	18p. deep ultramarine, orange-yellow, black, bluish grey and emerald	60	60
1398	868	34p. deep ultramarine, orange-yellow, scarlet, black, bluish grey & emerald	1·10	1·10
		a. Horiz pair. Nos. 1398/9	2·40	2·40
1399	869	34p. deep ultramarine, orange-yellow, black, bluish grey and emerald	1·10	1·10
1396/9		*Set of 4*	3·25	3·25

Nos. 1396/7 and 1398/9 were printed together, *se-tenant*, in horizontal pairs throughout the sheets, each pair showing a background design of the Australian flag.

Stamps in similar designs were also issued by Australia.

870 Spanish Galeasse off The Lizard

871 English Fleet leaving Plymouth

872 Engagement off Isle of Wight

873 Attack of English Fire-ships, Calais

874 Armada in Storm, North Sea

(Des G. Everndon)

1988 (19 July). *400th Anniv of Spanish Armada. Phosphorised paper.* P 15×14.

1400	870	18p. slate-black, yellow-orange, bright carm, brt bl, turq-bl, yell-grn & gold	65	65
		a. Horiz strip of 5. Nos. 1400/4	2·75	2·75
1401	871	18p. slate-black, yellow-orange, bright carm, brt bl, turq-bl, yell-grn & gold	65	65
1402	872	18p. slate-black, yellow-orange, bright carm, brt bl, turq-bl, yell-grn & gold	65	65
1403	873	18p. slate-black, yellow-orange, bright carm, brt bl, turq-bl, yell-grn & gold	65	65
1404	874	18p. slate-black, yellow-orange, bright carm, brt bl, turq-bl, yell-grn & gold	65	65
1400/4		*Set of 5*	2·75	2·75

Nos. 1400/4 were printed together, *se-tenant*, in horizontal strips of 5 throughout the sheet, forming a composite design.

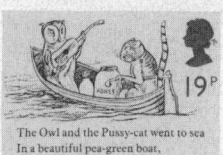

875 "The Owl and the
Pussy-cat"

876 "Edward Lear as a Bird"
(self-portrait)

877 "Cat" (from alphabet
book)

878 "There was a Young Lady
whose Bonnet .." (limerick)

(Des M. Swatridge and S. Dew)

1988 (6–27 Sept). *Death Centenary of Edward Lear (artist and author). Phosphorised paper.* P 15 × 14.

1405	875	19p. black, pale cream and carmine	50	50
1406	876	27p. black, pale cream and yellow	65	80
1407	877	32p. black, pale cream and emerald	1·10	1·10
1408	878	35p. black, pale cream and blue	1·10	1·25
1405/8		*Set of 4*	3·00	3·25

MS1409 122 × 90 mm. Nos. 1405/8 (*sold at £1.35*)
(27 Sept) .. .. .. 8·00 7·00

The premium on No. **MS**1409 was used to support the "Stamp World London 90" International Stamp Exhibition.

879 Carrickfergus Castle

880 Caernarfon Castle

881 Edinburgh Castle

882 Windsor Castle

(Des from photos by Prince Andrew, Duke of York. Eng C. Matthews. Recess Harrison)

1988 (18 Oct). *Ordinary paper.* P 15 × 14.

1410	879	£1 deep green	3·00	50
1411	880	£1.50, maroon	4·50	1·25
1412	881	£2 indigo	6·50	1·75
1413	882	£5 deep brown	15·00	3·50
1410/13		*Set of 4*	26·00	6·25

For similar designs, but with silhouette Queen's head see Nos. 1611/14 and 1993/6.

883 Journey to Bethlehem

884 Shepherds and Star

885 Three Wise Men

886 Nativity

887 The Annunciation

(Des L. Trickett)

1988 (15 Nov). *Christmas. Christmas Cards. One phosphor band (14p.) or phosphorised paper (others). P* 15 × 14.
1414 **883** 14p. gold, orange-yellow, bright mauve, bluish violet, brt blue & grey-black .. 35 35
    a. Error. "13p." instead of "14p." .. £5500
    b. Imperf (pair) £750
1415 **884** 19p. gold, yell-orange, brt violet, ultram, rose-red, grey-black & bright blue 40 45
    a. Imperf (pair) £600
1416 **885** 27p. gold, red, deep lavender, deep lilac, emerald, grey-black and bright blue 70 70
1417 **886** 32p. gold, orange-yellow, bright rose, dp mauve, violet, grey-black & brt blue 90 1·00
1418 **887** 35p. gold, green, reddish violet, bright blue, bright purple and grey-black .. 1·00 1·10
1414/18 .. .. *Set of* 5 3·00 3·25
Examples of No. 1414a were found in some 1988 Post Office Yearbooks.

888 Atlantic Puffin   889 Avocet

890 Oystercatcher   891 Northern Gannet

(Des D. Cordery)

1989 (17 Jan). *Centenary of Royal Society for the Protection of Birds. Phosphorised paper. P* 14 × 15.
1419 **888** 19p. grey, orange-yellow, orange-red, dull ultramarine, grey-black and silver .. 45 45
1420 **889** 27p. grey, bistre, rose, steel-blue, lavender, silver and grey-black .. 1·25 1·10
1421 **890** 32p. grey, bistre, scarlet, orange-red, lavender, silver and black .. 1·25 1·10
1422 **891** 35p. grey, lemon, rose-carmine, green, new blue, silver and black .. 1·50 1·25
1419/22 .. .. *Set of* 4 4·00 3·50

892 Rose   893 Cupid

894 Yachts   895 Fruit

896 Teddy Bear

(Des P. Sutton)

1989 (31 Jan). *Greetings Stamps. Phosphorised paper. P* 15 × 14.
1423 **892** 19p. black, greenish yellow, bright rose, red, new blue, light green and gold .. 6·25 4·50
    a. Booklet pane. Nos. 1423/7 × 2 plus 12 half stamp-size labels .. 55·00
1424 **893** 19p. black, greenish yellow, bright rose, red, new blue, light green and gold .. 6·25 4·50
1425 **894** 19p. black, greenish yellow, bright rose, red, new blue, light green and gold .. 6·25 4·50
1426 **895** 19p. black, greenish yellow, bright rose, red, new blue, light green and gold .. 6·25 4·50
1427 **896** 19p. black, greenish yellow, bright rose, red, new blue, light green and gold .. 6·25 4·50
1423/7 .. .. *Set of* 5 28·00 20·00
Nos. 1423/7 were only issued in £1.90 booklets.

897 Fruit and Vegetables   898 Meat Products

899 Dairy Produce   900 Cereal Products

(Des Sedley Place Ltd)

1989 (7 Mar). *Food and Farming Year. Phosphorised paper. P* 14 × 14½.
1428 **897** 19p. brownish grey, greenish yellow, rose, new blue, black, pale grey & emerald 50 50
1429 **898** 27p. brownish grey, greenish yellow, bright carmine, new blue, black, pale grey and bright orange .. 80 80
1430 **899** 32p. brownish grey, greenish yellow, rose-red, new blue, black, pale grey and bistre-yellow .. .. 1·10 1·10
1431 **900** 35p. brownish grey, greenish yellow, bright carmine, new blue, black, pale grey and brown-red .. 1·25 1·25
1428/31 .. .. *Set of* 4 3·25 3·25

901 Mortar Board (150th Anniv of Public Education in England)   902 Cross on Ballot Paper (3rd Direct Elections to European Parliament)

903 Posthorn (26th Postal, Telegraph and Telephone International Congress, Brighton)   904 Globe(Inter-Parliamentary Union Centenary Conference, London)

(Des Lewis Moberly from firework set-pieces. Litho Questa)

1989 (11 Apr). *Anniversaries. Phosphorised paper. P* 14 × 14½.
1432 **901** 19p. new blue, greenish yellow, mag & blk 1·25 1·25
    a. Horiz pair. Nos. 1432/3 .. 2·50 2·50
1433 **902** 19p. new blue, greenish yellow, mag & blk 1·25 1·25
1434 **903** 35p. new blue, greenish yellow, mag & blk 1·75 1·75
    a. Horiz pair. Nos. 1434/5 .. 3·50 3·50
1435 **904** 35p. new blue, greenish yellow, mag & blk 1·75 1·75
1432/5 .. .. *Set of* 4 5·50 5·50
Nos. 1432/3 and 1434/5 were each printed together, *se-tenant,* in horizontal pairs throughout the sheets.
Stamps as No. 1435, but inscribed "ONE HUNDREDTH CONFERENCE" were prepared, but not issued.

---

905 Toy Train and Airplane   906 Building Bricks

907 Dice and Board Games   908 Toy Robot, Boat and Doll's House

(Des D. Fern)

1989 (16 May). *Europa. Games and Toys. Phosphorised paper. P* 14 × 15.
1436 **905** 19p. black, greenish yellow, vermilion, blue-green, blue, gold and pale ochre 50 50
1437 **906** 27p. black, greenish yellow, reddish orange, blue-green, blue and gold .. 90 90
1438 **907** 32p. black, greenish yellow, orange-red, blue-green, blue, gold and pale ochre 1·25 1·25
1439 **908** 35p. black, greenish yellow, reddish orange, blue-green, bl, gold & stone 1·40 1·40
1436/9 .. .. *Set of* 4 3·50 3·50

909 Ironbridge, Shropshire   910 Tin Mine, St. Agnes Head, Cornwall

911 Cotton Mills, New Lanark, Strathclyde   912 Pontcysyllte Aqueduct, Clwyd

(Des R. Maddox)

1989 (4–25 July). *Industrial Archaeology. Phosphorised paper. P* 14×15.
1440 **909** 19p. black, bistre-yellow, rose-red, apple-green, lt blue, grey-black & emerald 50 50
1441 **910** 27p. black, bistre-yellow, rose-red, apple-green, lt blue, grey-black & dull blue 80 80
1442 **911** 32p. black, yellow-orange, apple-green, yellow, dull blue, grey-black and deep reddish violet .. 1·00 1·00
1443 **912** 35p. black, yellow, bright rose, apple-green, dull blue, grey-black & verm 1·10 1·10
1440/3 .. .. *Set of* 4 3·00 3·00
MS1444 122×90 mm. 19p., 27p., 32p., 35p. each black, olive-yellow, bright rose-red, dull blue, apple-green, grey-black and vermilion. P 15×14 (*sold at* £1.40) (25 July) .. 6·50 5·50
The stamps in No. MS1444 are horizontal versions of Nos. 1440/3 with each design continuing onto the sheet margins.
The premium on No. MS1444 was used to support "Stamp World London 90" International Stamp Exhibition.

913   914

1989 (22 Aug)–93. *Booklet Stamps.*

(a) Photo Harrison. P 15×14

1445	913	(2nd) bright blue (1 centre band)	1·00	35
		a. Booklet pane. No. 1445×10 with horiz edges of pane imperf	6·00	
		b. Booklet pane. No. 1445×4 with three edges of pane imperf (28.11.89)	24·00	
1446		(2nd) bright blue (1 side band) (20.3.90)	2·50	2·50
1447	914	(1st) brownish black (phosphorised paper)	1·25	60
		a. Booklet pane. No. 1447×10 with horiz edges of pane imperf	8·00	
		b. Booklet pane. No. 1447×4 with three edges of pane imperf (5.12.89)	24·00	
1448		(1st) brownish black (2 bands) (20.3.90)	2·50	2·50

(b) Litho Walsall. P 14

1449	913	(2nd) bright blue (1 centre band)	1·00	1·00
		a. Imperf between (vert pair)		
		b. Booklet pane. No. 1449×4 with three edges of pane imperf	3·50	
		c. Booklet pane. No. 1449×4 with horiz edges of pane imperf (6.8.91)	3·00	
		d. Booklet pane. No. 1449×10 with horiz edges of pane imperf (6.8.91)	6·00	
1450	914	(1st) blackish brown (2 bands)	2·50	2·00
		a. Booklet pane. No. 1450×4 with three edges of pane imperf	9·00	

(c) Litho Questa. P 15×14

1451	913	(2nd) brt blue (1 centre band) (19.9.89)	1·00	1·00
1451a		(2nd) brt blue (1 side band) (25.2.92)	2·00	2·00
		a1. Booklet pane. Nos. 1451a and 1514a, each × 3, with margins all round (10.8.93)	6·00	
1452	914	(1st) brownish black (phosphorised paper) (19.9.89)	1·50	1·50

Nos. 1445, 1447, 1449/51 and 1452 were initially sold at 14p. (2nd) and 19p. (1st), but these prices were later increased to reflect new postage rates.

Nos. 1446 and 1448 come from the *se-tenant* pane in the 1990 London Life £5 booklet: This pane is listed as No. X906m.

No. 1449a occurred on a miscut example of pane No. 1449d which showed an additional vertical pair beneath the last stamp in the bottom row.

No. 1451a with phosphor band at right comes from the *se-tenant* panes in the Wales and Tolkien £6 booklets. These panes are listed under Nos. X1012l and W49a (Wales Regionals). The version with band at left which appears in No. 1451al comes from the £6 Beatrix Potter booklet. No. 1446 only comes with band at right.

Nos. 1445, 1447 and 1449/50 do not exist perforated on all four sides, but come with either one or two adjacent sides imperforate.

For illustrations showing the difference between photogravure and lithography see beneath Type 367.

For similar designs, but in changed colours see Nos. 1511/16, for those with elliptical perforations Nos. 1663a/6 and 1979 and for self-adhesive versions Nos. 2039/40.

915 Snowflake (×10)

916 *Calliphora erythrocephala* (×5) (fly)

917 Blood Cells (×500)

918 Microchip (×600)

(Des K. Bassford. Litho Questa)

1989 (5 Sept). *150th Anniv of Royal Microscopical Society. Phosphorised paper.* P 14½×14.

1453	915	19p. gold, lemon, pale blue, grey, black and grey-black	50	50
1454	916	27p. gold, lemon, drab, black & grey-blk	85	85
1455	917	32p. gold, lemon, orange-vermilion, flesh, black and grey-black	1·25	1·25
1456	918	35p. gold, lemon, blk, brt grn & grey-blk	1·40	1·40
1453/6			*Set of 4*	3·50	3·50

919 Royal Mail Coach

920 Escort of Blues and Royals

921 Lord Mayor's Coach

922 Coach Team passing St Paul's

923 Blues and Royals Drum Horse

(Des P. Cox)

1989 (17 Oct). *Lord Mayor's Show, London. Phosphorised paper.* P 14×15.

1457	919	20p. gold, lemon, rose, orge, pale bl & blk	75	80
		a. Horiz strip of 5. Nos. 1457/61	3·25	3·50
		ab. Imperf (horiz strip of 5. Nos. 1457/61)	£5000	
		ac. Imperf (horiz strip of 4. Nos. 1457/60)	£2000	
		ad. Imperf (horiz strip of 3. Nos. 1457/9)	£950	
1458	920	20p. gold, lemon, rose, orge, pale bl & blk	75	80
1459	921	20p. gold, lemon, rose, orge, pale bl & blk	75	80
1460	922	20p. gold, lemon, rose, orge, pale bl & blk	75	80
1461	923	20p. gold, lemon, rose, orge, pale bl & blk	75	80
1457/61			*Set of 5*	3·25	3·50

This issue commemorates the 800th anniversary of the installation of the first Lord Mayor of London.

Nos. 1457/61 were printed together, *se-tenant*, in horizontal strips of 5 throughout the sheet.

Nos. 1457ab/ad come from a sheet partly imperforate at left.

924 14th-century Peasants from Stained-glass Window

925 Arches and Roundels, West Front

926 Octagon Tower

927 Arcade from West Transept

928 Triple Arch from West Front

(Des D. Gentleman)

1989 (14 Nov). *Christmas. 800th Anniversary of Ely Cathedral. One phosphor band* (15p., 15p.+1p.) *or phosphorised paper* (*others*). P 15×14.

1462	924	15p. gold, silver and blue	35	35
1463	925	15p. + 1p. gold, silver and blue	50	40
		a. Imperf (pair)	£1300	
1464	926	20p. + 1p. gold, silver and rosine	60	50
		a. Imperf (pair)	£1300	
1465	927	34p. + 1p. gold, silver and emerald	1·25	1·40
1466	928	37p. + 1p. gold, silver and yellow-olive	1·25	1·40
1462/6			*Set of 5*	3·50	3·50

929 Queen Victoria and Queen Elizabeth II

(Des J. Matthews (from plaster casts by Wyon and Machin))

1990 (10 Jan–12 June). *150th Anniv of the Penny Black.*

(a) Photo Harrison. P 15×14

1467	929	15p. bright blue (1 centre band)	50	50
		a. Imperf (pair)	£1250	
		l. Booklet pane. No. 1467×10 with horiz edges of pane imperf (30.1.90)	7·50	
1468		15p. bright blue (1 side band) (30.1.90)	2·50	2·50
		l. Booklet pane. No. 1468×2 and 1470 plus label	5·00	
1469		20p. brownish black and cream (phosphorised paper)	75	75
		a. Imperf (pair)	£900	
		l. Booklet pane. No. 1469×5 plus label with vert sides of pane imperf (30.1.90)	7·00	
		m. Booklet pane. No. 1469×10 with horiz edges of pane imperf (30.1.90)	9·00	
		n. Booklet pane. No. 1469×6 with margins all round (20.3.90)	2·50	
		r. Booklet pane. No. 1469×4 with three edges of pane imperf (17.4.90)	6·00	
1470		20p. brownish black and cream (2 bands) (30.1.90)	1·75	1·50
1471		29p. deep mauve (phosphorised paper)	1·25	1·25
1472		29p. deep mauve (2 bands) (20.3.90)	8·00	8·00
1473		34p. dp bluish grey (phosphorised paper)	1·50	1·25
1474		37p. rosine (phosphorised paper)	1·50	1·50

(b) Litho Walsall. P 14

1475	929	15p. bright blue (1 centre band) (30.1.90)	1·00	70
		l. Booklet pane. No. 1475×4 with three edges of pane imperf	7·50	
		m. Booklet pane. No. 1475×10 with three edges of pane imperf (12.6.90)	8·00	
1476		20p. brownish black and cream (phosphorised paper) (30.1.90)	1·25	80
		l. Booklet pane. No. 1476×5 plus label with vertical edges of pane imperf	7·00	
		m. Booklet pane. No. 1476×4 with three edges of pane imperf	7·50	
		n. Booklet pane. No. 1476×10 with three edges of pane imperf (12.6.90)	10·00	

(c) Litho Questa. P 15×14

1477	929	15p. bright blue (1 centre band) (17.4.90)	1·50	1·50
1478		20p. brownish black (phosphorised paper) (17.4.90)	1·50	1·50

Nos. 1475/6 do not exist perforated on all four sides, but come with either one or two adjacent sides imperforate.

Nos. 1468, 1470, 1472 and 1475/8 were only issued in stamp booklets. No. 1468 exists with the phosphor band at left or right. Nos. 1468 (band at right), 1470 and 1472 occur in the *se-tenant* pane from the 1990 London Life £5 booklet. This pane is listed as No. X906m.

For illustrations showing the difference between photogravure and lithography see beneath Type 367.

For No. 1469 in miniature sheet see No. MS1501.

930 Kitten

931 Rabbit

932 Duckling

933 Puppy

(Des T. Evans. Litho Questa)

1990 (23 Jan). *150th Anniv of Royal Society for Prevention of Cruelty to Animals. Phosphorised paper. P* 14×14½.

1479	**930**	20p. new blue, greenish yellow, bright magenta, black and silver	65	70
		a. Silver (Queen's head and face value) omitted ..	£175	
1480	**931**	29p. new blue, greenish yellow, bright magenta, black and silver ..	1·25	1·10
		a. Imperf (horiz pair) ..	£2500	
1481	**932**	34p. new blue, greenish yellow, bright magenta, black and silver ..	1·50	1·25
		a. Silver (Queen's head and face value) omitted ..	£350	
1482	**933**	37p. new blue, greenish yellow, bright magenta, black and silver	1·60	1·40
1479/82	..	.. .. .. *Set of* 4	4·50	4·00

934 Teddy Bear

935 Dennis the Menace

936 Punch

937 Cheshire Cat

938 The Man in the Moon

939 The Laughing Policeman

940 Clown

941 Mona Lisa

942 Queen of Hearts

943 Stan Laurel (comedian)

(Des Michael Peters and Partners Ltd)

1990 (6 Feb). *Greetings Stamps. "Smiles". Two phosphor bands. P* 15×14.

1483	**934**	20p. gold, greenish yellow, bright rose-red, new blue and grey-black	3·25	2·50
		a. Booklet pane. Nos. 1483/92 with margins all round	28·00	
1484	**935**	20p. gold, greenish yellow, brt rose-red, new blue, deep blue and grey-black	3·25	2·50
1485	**936**	20p. gold, greenish yellow, brt rose-red, new blue, deep blue and grey-black	3·25	2·50
1486	**937**	20p. gold, greenish yellow, brt rose-red, new blue and grey-black	3·25	2·50
1487	**938**	20p. gold, greenish yellow, brt rose-red, new blue and grey-black	3·25	2·50
1488	**939**	20p. gold, greenish yellow, brt rose-red, new blue and grey-black	3·25	2·50
1489	**940**	20p. gold, greenish yellow, brt rose-red, new blue and grey-black	3·25	2·50
1490	**941**	20p. gold, greenish yellow, bright rose-red, and grey-black	3·25	2·50
1491	**942**	20p. gold, greenish yellow, bright rose-red, new blue and grey-black	3·25	2·50
1492	**943**	20p. gold and grey-black	3·25	2·50
1483/92		*Set of* 10	28·00	22·00

Nos. 1483/92 were only issued in £2 booklets. The designs of Nos. 1483, 1485/7, 1489 and 1492 extend onto the pane margin.

For these designs with the face value expressed as "1st" see Nos. 1550/9.

944 Alexandra Palace ("Stamp World London 90" Exhibition)

945 Glasgow School of Art

946 British Philatelic Bureau, Edinburgh

947 Templeton Carpet Factory, Glasgow

(Des P. Hogarth)

1990 (6–20 Mar). *Europa (Nos.* 1493 *and* 1495) *and "Glasgow* 1990 *European City of Culture" (Nos.* 1494 *and* 1496). *Phosphorised paper. P* 14×15.

1493	**944**	20p. silver, lemon, flesh, grey-brown, blue, grey-black and black	50	50
		a. Booklet pane. No. 1493×4 with margins all round (20 March)	2·00	
1494	**945**	20p. silver, greenish yellow, dull orange, blue, grey-black and black	50	50
1495	**946**	29p. silver, stone, orange, olive-sepia, grey-blue, grey-black and black	1·10	1·10
1496	**947**	37p. silver, greenish yellow, brt emerald, salmon, olive-sepia, brt blue & black	1·25	1·25
1493/6	..	.. .. *Set of* 4	3·00	3·00

948 Export Achievement Award

949 Technological Achievement Award

(Des S. Broom. Litho Questa)

1990 (10 Apr). *25th Anniv of Queen's Awards for Export and Technology. Phosphorised paper. P* 14×14½.

1497	**948**	20p. new blue, greenish yellow, magenta, black and silver	75	75
		a. Horiz pair. Nos. 1497/8 ..	1·50	1·50
1498	**949**	20p. new blue, greenish yellow, magenta, black and silver	75	75
1499	**948**	37p. new blue, greenish yellow, magenta, black and silver	1·40	1·40
		a. Horiz pair. Nos. 1499/500 ..	2·75	2·75
1500	**949**	37p. new blue, greenish yellow, magenta, black and silver	1·40	1·40
1497/500		*Set of* 4	3·75	3·75

Nos. 1497/8 and 1499/500 were each printed together, *se-tenant,* in horizontal pairs throughout the sheets.

(Des J. Matthews and Sedley Place Design Ltd. Eng C. Matthews. Recess and photo)

1990 (3 May). *"Stamp World London 90" International Stamp Exhibition, London. Sheet,* 122×90 *mm., containing No.* 1469. *Phosphorised paper. P* 15×14.

MS1501	**929**	20p. brownish blk & cream (*sold at* £1)	4·25	4·25
		a. Error. Imperf	£6500	
		b. Black (recess printing) omitted	£7500	
		c. Black (recess printing) inverted	£7500	

The premium on No. **MS1501** was used to support the "Stamp World London 90" International Stamp Exhibition.

On examples of No. **MS1501b** the 1d. black and seahorse background are omitted due to a printer's sheet becoming attached to the underside before the recess part of the design was printed. There is an albino impression visible on the reverse.

No. **MS1501c** shows the recess part of the design inverted in relation to the photogravure printing of Type **929**.

950 Cycad and Sir Joseph Banks Building

951 Stone Pine and Princess of Wales Conservatory

952 Willow Tree and Palm House

953 Cedar Tree and Pagoda

(Des P. Leith)

1990 (5 June). *150th Anniv of Kew Gardens. Phosphorised paper. P* 14×15.

1502	**950**	20p. black, brt emerald, pale turquoise-green, light brown and lavender	50	50
1503	**951**	29p. black, brt emerald, turquoise-green, reddish orange and grey-black	80	80
1504	**952**	34p. Venetian red, brt green, cobalt, dull purple, turquoise-grn & yellow-green	1·10	1·25
1505	**953**	37p. pale violet-blue, bright emerald, red-brown, steel-blue and brown-rose ..	1·25	1·40
1502/5		.. .. *Set of* 4	3·25	3·50

954 Thomas Hardy and Clyffe Clump, Dorset

(Des J. Gibbs)

1990 (10 July). *150th Birth Anniv of Thomas Hardy (author).*
Phosphorised paper. P 14×15.
1506 **954** 20p. vermilion, greenish yellow, pale
lake-brown, deep brown, light
red-brown and black 75 75
  a. Imperf (pair) £950

955 Queen Elizabeth   **956** Queen Elizabeth
the Queen Mother

957 Elizabeth, Duchess   **958** Lady Elizabeth
of York   Bowes-Lyon

(Des J. Gorham from photographs by N. Parkinson (20p.),
Dorothy Wilding (29p.), B. Park (34p.), Rita Martin (37p.))

1990 (2 Aug). *90th Birthday of Queen Elizabeth the Queen
Mother. Phosphorised paper.* P 14×15.
1507 **955** 20p. silver, greenish yellow, magenta,
turquoise-blue and grey-black .. 70 70
1508 **956** 29p. silver, indigo and grey-blue .. 1·00 1·00
1509 **957** 34p. silver, lemon, red, new blue and
grey-black .. .. .. 1·50 1·50
1510 **958** 37p. silver, sepia and stone .. .. 1·75 1·75
1507/10 .. .. *Set of 4* 4·50 4·50

1990 (7 Aug)–**92**. *Booklet Stamps. As T* **913/14**, *but colours
changed.*

    (*a*) *Photo Harrison.* P 15×14
1511 **913** (2nd) deep blue (1 centre band) .. 90 90
  a. Booklet pane. No. 1511×10 with
horiz edges of pane imperf 7·00
1512 **914** (1st) brt orge-red (phosphorised paper) 80 80
  a. Booklet pane. No. 1512×10 with
horiz edges of pane imperf 5·25
    (*b*) *Litho Questa.* P 15×14
1513 **913** (2nd) deep blue (1 centre band) .. 1·60 1·60
1514 **914** (1st) brt orge-red (phosphorised paper) 75 75
1514*a* (1st) brt orange-red (2 bands) (25.2.92) 2·00 2·00
    (*c*) *Litho Walsall.* P 14
1515 **913** (2nd) deep blue (1 centre band) .. 80 80
  a. Booklet pane. No. 1515×4 with
horiz edges of pane imperf 3·00
  b. Booklet pane. No. 1515×10 with
horiz edges of pane imperf 6·00
1516 **914** (1st) brt orge-red (phosphorised paper) 80 80
  a. Booklet pane. No. 1516×4 with
horiz edges of pane imperf 2·50
  b. Booklet pane. No. 1516×10 with
horiz edges of pane imperf 5·25
  c. Perf 13 .. .. 2·25 2·25
  ca. Booklet pane. No. 1516c×4 with
horiz edges of pane imperf .. 10·00

Nos. 1511/14 and 1515/16 were initially sold at 15p. (2nd) and
20p. (1st), but these prices were later increased to reflect new
postage rates.
Nos. 1511/12 and 1515/16 do not exist perforated on all four
sides, but come with either the top or the bottom edge imperforate.
No. 1514*a* comes from the *se-tenant* panes in the £6 Wales, £6
Tolkien and £5.64 Beatrix Potter booklets. These panes are listed
under Nos. X1012l, 1451al and W49a (Wales Regionals).
No. 1516c was caused by the use of an incorrect perforation
comb.
For similar stamps with elliptical perforations see Nos. 1663a/6.
For illustrations showing the difference between photogravure
and lithography see beneath Type 367.

959 Victoria Cross   **960** George Cross

961 Distinguished Service
Cross and Distinguished Service
Medal

962 Military Cross and Military
Medal

963 Distinguished Flying Cross
and Distinguished Flying Medal

(Des J. Gibbs and J. Harwood)

1990 (11 Sept). *Gallantry Awards. Phosphorised paper.* P 14×15
(*vert*) *or* 15×14 (*horiz*).
1517 **959** 20p. grey-black, pale stone, stone,
bistre-brown and bright carmine .. 80 80
1518 **960** 20p. grey-black, pale stone, flesh, grey
and ultramarine 80 80
1519 **961** 20p. grey-black, pale stone, flesh, pale
blue and ultramarine 80 80
  a. Imperf (pair) .. .. ..
1520 **962** 20p. grey-black, pale stone, ochre, pale
blue, ultramarine, scarlet and violet 80 80
1521 **963** 20p. grey-black, pale stone, yellow-
brown, bluish grey and purple .. 80 80
1517/21 .. .. *Set of 5* 3·50 3·50

964 Armagh Observatory,   **965** Newton's Moon and
Jodrell Bank Radio   Tides Diagram with Early
Telescope and La Palma   Telescopes
Telescope

966 Greenwich Old   **967** Stonehenge, Gyroscope
Observatory and Early   and Navigating by Stars
Astronomical Equipment

(Des J. Fisher. Litho Questa)

1990 (16 Oct). *Astronomy. Phosphorised paper.* P 14×14½.
1522 **964** 22p. cream, grey, dull blue-grn, slate-bl,
blue-grn, orange-red, gold & black 50 40
  a. Gold (Queen's head) omitted .. £350
1523 **965** 26p. black, yellow, dull purple, pale
cream, brown-rose, new blue,
greenish yellow, vermilion & gold 80 90
1524 **966** 31p. black, cream, pale cream, yellow-
orge, salmon, lemon, verm & gold 1·00 1·00
1525 **967** 37p. black, pale buff, olive-bistre, pale
cream, pale flesh, flesh, grey,
rose-red and gold 1·10 1·10
1522/5 .. .. *Set of 4* 3·00 3·00
Nos. 1522/5 commemorate the Centenary of the British
Astronomical Association and the Bicentenary of the Armagh
Observatory.

968 Building a Snowman

969 Fetching the Christmas
Tree

970 Carol Singing

971 Tobogganing

972 Ice-skating

(Des J. Gorham and A. Davidson)

1990 (13 Nov). *Christmas. One phosphor band* (17p) *or
phosphorised paper* (*others*). P 15×14.
1526 **968** 17p. gold, greenish yellow, rose, new
blue and grey-black 45 35
  a. Booklet pane of 20 .. .. 9·00
1527 **969** 22p. gold, greenish yellow, magenta, new
blue and black 55 65
  a. Imperf (horiz pair) £450
1528 **970** 26p. gold, olive-yellow, pale magenta,
agate, new blue, dull violet-bl & blk 80 80
1529 **971** 31p. gold, greenish yellow, bright
rose-red, dull mauve, new blue,
turquoise-blue and grey-black .. 1·00 1·00
1530 **972** 37p. gold, greenish yellow, rose, new
blue and slate-green .. .. 1·10 1·10
1526/30 .. .. *Set of 5* 3·50 3·50
Booklet pane No. 1526a comes from a special £3.40 Christmas
booklet and has the horizontal edges of the pane imperforate.

973 "King Charles Spaniel"   **974** "A Pointer"

975 "Two Hounds in a   **976** "A Rough Dog"
Landscape"

977 "Fino and Tiny"

(Des Carroll, Dempsey & Thirkell Ltd)

1991 (8 Jan). *Dogs. Paintings by George Stubbs. Phosphorised paper.* P 14×14½.

1531	**973**	22p. gold, greenish yellow, magenta, new blue black and drab		75	75
		a. Imperf (pair)		£400	
1532	**974**	26p. gold, greenish yellow, magenta, new blue, black and drab		90	80
1533	**975**	31p. gold, greenish yellow, magenta, new blue, black and drab		1·00	85
		a. Imperf (pair)		£950	
1534	**976**	33p. gold, greenish yellow, magenta, new blue, black and drab		1·10	95
1535	**977**	37p. gold, greenish yellow, magenta, new blue, black and drab		1·25	1·10
1531/5			Set of 5	4·50	4·00

978 Thrush's Nest

979 Shooting Star and Rainbow

980 Magpies and Charm Bracelet

981 Black Cat

982 Common Kingfisher with Key

983 Mallard and Frog

984 Four-leaf Clover in Boot and Match Box

985 Pot of Gold at End of Rainbow

986 Heart-shaped Butterflies

987 Wishing Well and Sixpence

(Des T. Meeuwissen)

1991 (5 Feb). *Greetings Stamps. "Good Luck". Two phosphor bands.* P 15×14.

1536	**978**	(1st) silver, greenish yellow, magenta new blue, olive-brown and black	1·40	1·40
		a. Booklet pane. Nos. 1536/45 plus 12 half stamp-size labels with margins on 3 sides	12·50	
1537	**979**	(1st) silver, greenish yellow, magenta new blue, olive-brown and black	1·40	1·40
1538	**980**	(1st) silver, greenish yellow, magenta new blue, olive-brown and black	1·40	1·40
1539	**981**	(1st) silver, greenish yellow, magenta new blue, olive-brown and black	1·40	1·40
1540	**982**	(1st) silver, greenish yellow, magenta new blue, olive-brown and black	1·40	1·40
1541	**983**	(1st) silver, greenish yellow, magenta new blue, olive-brown and black	1·40	1·40
1542	**984**	(1st) silver, greenish yellow, magenta new blue, olive-brown and black	1·40	1·40
1543	**985**	(1st) silver, greenish yellow, magenta new blue, olive-brown and black	1·40	1·40
1544	**986**	(1st) silver, greenish yellow, magenta new blue, olive-brown and black	1·40	1·40
1545	**987**	(1st) silver, greenish yellow, magenta new blue, olive-brown and black	1·40	1·40
1536/45			Set of 10 12·50	12·50

Nos. 1536/45 were initially sold at 22p. each and were only issued in £2.20 booklets. It is intended that the price will be increased to reflect future alterations in postage rates. The backgrounds of the stamps form a composite design.

988 Michael Faraday (inventor of electric motor) (Birth Bicentenary)

989 Charles Babbage (computer science pioneer) (Birth Bicentenary)

990 Radar Sweep of East Anglia (50th anniv of operational radar network)

991 Gloster Whittle E28/39 Aircraft over East Anglia (50th anniv of first flight of Sir Frank Whittle's jet engine)

(Des P. Till (Nos. 1546/7), J. Harwood (Nos. 1548/9))

1991 (5 Mar). *Scientific Achievements. Phosphorised paper.* P 14×15.

1546	**988**	22p. silver, olive-brown greenish yellow, magenta, slate-blue, grey and black	65	65
		a. Imperf (pair)	£325	

1547	**989**	22p. silver, chrome yellow, red, grey-black, brownish grey and sepia	65	65
1548	**990**	31p. silver, deep turquoise-green, violet-blue, steel blue and deep dull blue	95	95
1549	**991**	37p. silver, olive-bistre, rose-red, turq-blue, new blue and grey-black	1·10	1·10
1546/9			Set of 4 3·00	3·00

992 Teddy Bear

1991 (26 Mar). *Greetings Stamps. "Smiles". As Nos. 1483/92, but inscr "1st" as in T* **992**. *Two phosphor bands.* P 15×14.

1550	**992**	(1st) gold, greenish yellow, bright rose-red, new blue and grey-black	90	90
		a. Booklet pane. Nos. 1550/9 plus 12 half stamp-size labels with margins on 3 sides	8·00	
1551	**935**	(1st) gold, greenish yellow, brt rose-red, new blue, deep blue & grey-black	90	90
1552	**936**	(1st) gold, greenish yellow, brt rose-red, new blue, deep blue & grey-black	90	90
1553	**937**	(1st) gold, greenish yellow, bright rose-red, new blue and grey-black	90	90
1554	**938**	(1st) gold, greenish yellow, bright rose-red, new blue and grey-black	90	90
1555	**939**	(1st) gold, greenish yellow, bright rose-red, new blue and grey-black	90	90
1556	**940**	(1st) gold, greenish yellow, bright rose-red, new blue and grey-black	90	90
1557	**941**	(1st) gold, greenish yellow, bright rose-red and grey-black	90	90
1558	**942**	(1st) gold, greenish yellow, bright rose-red, new blue and grey-black	90	90
1559	**943**	(1st) gold and grey-black	90	90
1550/9			Set of 10 8·00	8·00

Nos. 1550/9 were only issued in £2.20 booklets (sold at £2.40 from 16 September 1991 and at £2.50 from 1 November 1993). The designs of Nos. 1550, 1552/4, 1556 and 1559 extend onto the pane margin.

993 Man looking at Space **994**

995 Space looking at Man **996**

(Des J.-M. Folon)

1991 (23 Apr). *Europa. Europe in Space. Phosphorised paper.* P 14×15.

1560	**993**	22p. silver-mauve, greenish yellow, scar, violet-blue, brt blue, brt green & blk	55	55
		a. Horiz pair. Nos. 1560/1	1·10	1·10
1561	**994**	22p. silver-mauve, greenish yellow, scar, violet-blue, bright blue and black	55	55
1562	**995**	37p. silver-mauve, bistre-yellow, dull vermilion, blue and black	1·10	1·10
		a. Horiz pair. Nos. 1562/3	2·25	2·25
1563	**996**	37p. silver-mauve, bistre-yellow, dull vermilion, blue and black	1·10	1·10
1560/3			Set of 4 3·00	3·00

Nos. 1560/1 and 1562/3 were each printed together, *se-tenant*, in horizontal pairs throughout the sheets, each pair forming a composite design.

997 Fencing   **998** Hurdling

999 Diving   **1000** Rugby

(Des Huntley Muir)

1991 (11 June). *World Student Games, Sheffield (Nos. 1564/6) and World Cup Rugby Championship (No. 1567). Phosphorised paper. P 14½×14.*

1564	**997**	22p. black, greenish yellow, vermilion, bright orange, ultramarine and grey	50	50
1565	**998**	26p. pale blue, greenish yellow, red, bright blue and black	80	80
1566	**999**	31p. bright blue, bistre-yellow, rose, vermilion, new blue and black	95	95
1567	**1000**	37p. yellow-orange, greenish yellow, rose, bright blue, emerald & black	1·10	1·10
1564/7		*Set of 4*	3·00	3·00

1001 "Silver Jubilee"   **1002** "Mme Alfred Carrière"

1003 *Rosa moyesii*   **1004** "Harvest Fayre"

1005 "Mutabilis"

(Des Yvonne Skargon. Litho Questa)

1991 (16 July). *9th World Congress of Roses, Belfast. Phosphorised paper. P 14½×14.*

1568	**1001**	22p. new blue, greenish yellow, magenta, black and silver	75	50
		a. Silver (Queen's head) omitted	£750	
1569	**1002**	26p. new blue, greenish yellow, magenta, black and silver	90	80
1570	**1003**	31p. new blue, greenish yellow, magenta, black and silver	1·00	85
1571	**1004**	33p. new blue, greenish yellow, magenta, black and silver	1·10	95
1572	**1005**	37p. new blue, greenish yellow, magenta, black and silver	1·25	1·25
1568/72		*Set of 5*	4·50	4·00

1006 Iguanodon   **1007** Stegosaurus

1008 Tyrannosaurus   **1009** Protoceratops

1010 Triceratops

(Des B. Kneale)

1991 (20 Aug). *150th Anniv of Dinosaurs' Identification by Owen. Phosphorised paper. P 14½×14.*

1573	**1006**	22p. grey, pale blue, magenta, bright blue, dull violet and grey-black	75	50
		a. Imperf (pair)	£1000	
1574	**1007**	26p. grey, greenish yellow, pale emerald, bright blue-green, pale bright blue, grey-black and black	90	1·00
1575	**1008**	31p. grey, light blue, magenta, brt blue, pale blue, brown and grey-black	1·10	1·10
1576	**1009**	33p. grey, dull rose, pale brt bl, brt rose-red, yellow-orge, grey-blk & blk	1·40	1·10
1577	**1010**	37p. grey, greenish yellow, turquoise-blue, dull violet, yellow-brn & blk	1·50	1·25
1573/7		*Set of 5*	5·00	4·50

1011 Map of 1816   **1012** Map of 1906

1013 Map of 1959   **1014** Map of 1991

(Des H. Brown. Recess and litho Harrison (24p.), Litho Harrison (28p.), Questa (33p., 39p.))

1991 (17 Sept). *Bicentenary of Ordnance Survey. Maps of Hamstreet, Kent. Phosphorised paper. P 14½×14.*

1578	**1011**	24p. black, magenta, and cream	50	50
1579	**1012**	28p. blk, brt yellow-grn, new bl, reddish orge, magenta, olive-sepia & cream	80	85
1580	**1013**	33p. dull blue-green, orange-brown, magenta, olive-grey, greenish yellow, verm, greenish grey, pale bl, bl, dull orge, apple grn & blk	95	1·00
1581	**1014**	39p. black, mag, greenish yell & new bl	1·10	1·25
1578/81		*Set of 4*	3·00	3·25

Mint examples of Type **1012** exist with a face value of 26p.

1015 Adoration of the Magi

1016 Mary and Baby Jesus in the Stable

1017 The Holy Family and Angel

1018 The Annunciation

1019 The Flight into Egypt

(Des D. Driver)

1991 (12 Nov). *Christmas. Illuminated Letters from "Acts of Mary and Jesus" Manuscript in Bodleian Library. Oxford. One phosphor band (18p.) or phosphorised paper (others). P 15×14.*

1582	**1015**	18p. steel-blue, greenish yellow, rose-red, orange-red, black & gold	70	40
		a. Imperf (pair)	£1750	
		b. Booklet pane of 20	8·25	
1583	**1016**	24p. bright rose-red, greenish yellow, vermilion, slate-blue, yellow-green, grey-black and gold	80	50
1584	**1017**	28p. reddish brn, bistre-yellow, orange-vermilion, orange-red, deep dull blue, grey-black and gold	85	1·00
1585	**1018**	33p. green, greenish yell, red, orange-red, blue, grey and gold	95	1·10
1586	**1019**	39p. orange-red, greenish yell, orange-vermilion, deep dull blue, olive-sepia, black and gold	1·10	1·40
1582/6		*Set of 5*	4·00	4·00

Booklet pane No. 1582b comes from special £3.60 Christmas booklet and has margins at left, top and bottom.

1020 Fallow Deer in Scottish Forest

1021 Hare on North Yorkshire Moors

1022 Fox in the Fens

1023 Redwing and Home Counties Village

1024 Welsh Mountain Sheep in Snowdonia

GB 57

(Des J. Gorham and K. Bowen)
1992 (14 Jan–25 Feb). *The Four Seasons. Wintertime. One phosphor band* (18*p.*) *or phosphorised paper* (*others*). P 15×14.

1587	1020	18p. silver, greenish yellow, grey, dull rose, new blue and black ..	45	50
1588	1021	24p. silver, lemon, rose, blue & grey-blk	60	65
		a. Imperf (pair)	£300	
1589	1022	28p. silver, greenish yellow, bright rose, steel-blue and grey black ..	80	75
1590	1023	33p. silver, greenish yellow, brt orange, brt purple, greenish blue & grey	95	90
1591	1024	39p. silver, yellow, yellow-orange, grey, vermilion, new blue and black ..	1·10	1·10
		a. Booklet pane. No. 1591×4 with margins all round (25 Feb)	3·25	
1587/91	..	.. .. .. Set of 5	3·50	3·50

Booklet pane No. 1591a comes from the £6 "Cymru-Wales" booklet.

1025 Flower Spray

1026 Double Locket

1027 Key

1028 Model Car and Cigarette Cards

1029 Compass and Map

1030 Pocket Watch

1031 1854 1d. Red Stamp and Pen

1032 Pearl Necklace

1033 Marbles

1034 Bucket, Spade and Starfish

(Des Trickett and Webb Ltd)
1992 (28 Jan). *Greetings Stamps. "Memories". Two phosphor bands.* P 15×14.

1592	1025	(1st) gold, greenish yellow, magenta, ochre, light blue and grey-black ..	80	80
		a. Booklet pane. Nos. 1592/1601 plus 12 half stamp-size labels with margins on 3 sides	7·00	
1593	1026	(1st) gold, greenish yellow, magenta, ochre, light blue and grey-black ..	80	80
1594	1027	(1st) gold, greenish yellow, magenta, ochre, light blue and grey-black ..	80	80
1595	1028	(1st) gold, greenish yellow, magenta, ochre, light blue and grey-black ..	80	80
1596	1029	(1st) gold, greenish yellow, magenta, ochre, light blue and grey-black ..	80	80
1597	1030	(1st) gold, greenish yellow, magenta, ochre, light blue and grey-black ..	80	80
1598	1031	(1st) gold, greenish yellow, magenta, ochre, light blue and grey-black ..	80	80
1599	1032	(1st) gold, greenish yellow, magenta, ochre, light blue and grey-black ..	80	80
1600	1033	(1st) gold, greenish yellow, magenta, ochre, light blue and grey-black ..	80	80
1601	1034	(1st) gold, greenish yellow, magenta, ochre, light blue and grey-black ..	80	80
1592/1601		.. Set of 10	7·00	7·00

Nos. 1592/1601 were only issued in £2.40 booklets (sold at £2.50 from 1 November 1993 and at £2.60 from 8 July 1996). The backgrounds of the stamps form a composite design.

1035 Queen Elizabeth in Coronation Robes and Parliamentary Emblem

1036 Queen Elizabeth in Garter Robes and Archiepiscopal Arms

1037 Queen Elizabeth with Baby Prince Andrew and Royal Arms

1038 Queen Elizabeth at Trooping the Colour and Service Emblems

1039 Queen Elizabeth and Commonwealth Emblem

(Des Why Not Associates. Litho Questa)
1992 (6 Feb). *40th Anniv of Accession. Two phosphor bands.* P 14½×14.

1602	1035	24p. new blue, greenish yellow, magenta, black, silver and gold ..	1·40	1·40
		a. Horiz strip of 5. Nos. 1602/6	6·00	6·00
1603	1036	24p. new blue, greenish yellow, magenta, black, silver and gold ..	1·40	1·40
1604	1037	24p. new blue, greenish yellow, magenta, black and silver ..	1·40	1·40
1605	1038	24p. new blue, greenish yellow, magenta, black, silver and gold ..	1·40	1·40
1606	1039	24p. new blue, greenish yellow, magenta, black, silver and gold ..	1·40	1·40
1602/6		.. Set of 5	6·00	6·00

Nos. 1602/6 were printed together, *se-tenant*, in horizontal strips of five throughout the sheet.

1040 Tennyson in 1888 and "The Beguiling of Merlin" (Sir Edward Burne-Jones)

1041 Tennyson in 1856 and "April Love" (Arthur Hughes)

1042 Tennyson in 1864 and "I am Sick of the Shadows" (John Waterhouse)

1043 Tennyson as a Young Man and "Mariana" (Dante Gabriel Rossetti)

(Des Irene von Treskow)
1992 (10 Mar). *Death Centenary of Alfred, Lord Tennyson* (*poet*). *Phosphorised paper.* P 14½×14.

1607	1040	24p. gold, greenish yellow, magenta, new blue and black ..	50	50
1608	1041	28p. gold, greenish yellow, magenta, new blue and black ..	65	65
1609	1042	33p. gold, greenish yellow, magenta, new blue and black ..	1·10	1·10
1610	1043	39p. gold, greenish yellow, magenta, new blue, bistre and black ..	1·10	1·10
1607/10		.. .. Set of 4	3·00	3·00

1044 Carrickfergus Castle

Elliptical hole in vertical perforations

GH CASTLE
Harrison Plates (Nos. 1611/14)

GH CASTLE
Enschedé Plates (Nos. 1993/6)

(Des from photos by Prince Andrew, Duke of York. Eng C. Matthews. Recess Harrison)
1992 (24 Mar)–**95**. *Designs as Nos. 1410/13, but showing Queen's head in silhouette as T 1044.* P 15×14 (*with one elliptical hole on each vertical side*).

1611	1044	£1 bottle green and gold† ..	4·50	1·50
1612	880	£1.50, maroon and gold† ..	3·25	2·25
1613	881	£2 indigo and gold† ..	4·50	3·00

1613*a*	**1044**	£3 reddish violet and gold† (22.8.95)	6·50	4·50
1614	**882**	£5 deep brown and gold†	11·00	7·50
		a. Gold (Queen's head) omitted	£275	
1611/14		Set of 5	27·00	18·00

† The Queen's head on these stamps is printed in optically variable ink which changes colour from gold to green when viewed from different angles.

The £1.50 (5 March 1996), £2 (2 May 1996) and £5 (17 September 1996) subsequently appeared on PVA (white gum) instead of the tinted PVAD previously used.

See also Nos. 1993/6.

1045 British Olympic Association Logo (Olympic Games, Barcelona)   **1046** British Paralympic Association Symbol (Paralympics '92, Barcelona)

1047 *Santa Maria* (500th Anniv of Discovery of America by Columbus)   **1048** *Kaisei* (Japanese cadet brigantine) (Grand Regatta Columbus, 1992)

1049 British Pavilion, "Expo '92", Seville

(Des K. Bassford (Nos. 1615/16, 1619), K. Bassford and S. Paine, Eng. C. Matthews (Nos. 1617/18). Litho Questa (Nos. 1615/16, 1619) or recess and litho Harrison (Nos. 1617/18))

1992 (7 Apr). *Europa. International Events. Phosphorised paper.* P 14×14½.

1615	**1045**	24p. new blue, lemon, magenta & black	65	65
		a. Horiz pair. Nos. 1615/16	1·25	1·25
1616	**1046**	24p. new blue, lemon, magenta & black	65	65
1617	**1047**	24p. black, grey, carmine, cream & gold	65	65
1618	**1048**	39p. black, grey, carmine, cream & gold	1·10	1·10
1619	**1049**	39p. new blue, lemon, magenta & black	1·10	1·10
1615/19		Set of 5	3·75	3·75

Nos. 1615/16 were printed together, *se-tenant*, throughout the sheet.

No. 1617 is known with the cream omitted used from Cornwall in September 1992.

1050 Pikeman   **1051** Drummer

1052 Musketeer   **1053** Standard Bearer

(Des J. Sancha)

1992 (16 June). *350th Anniv of the Civil War. Phosphorised paper.* P 14½×14.

1620	**1050**	24p., black, stone, bistre, scarlet, indigo, grey-green and yellow-ochre	55	55
		a. Imperf (pair)		
1621	**1051**	28p. black, yellow-ochre, ochre, rose-pink, bl, dull yell-grn & slate-lilac	70	70
1622	**1052**	33p. black, ochre, pale orange, lemon, reddish orange, new bl & olive-grn	1·00	1·00
1623	**1053**	39p. black, yellow-ochre, yell, greenish yellow, vermilion, ind & orge-brn	1·10	1·10
1620/3		Set of 4	3·00	3·00

1054 *The Yeomen of the Guard*   **1055** *The Gondoliers*

1056 *The Mikado*   **1057** *The Pirates of Penzance*

1058 *Iolanthe*

(Des Lynda Gray)

1992 (21 July). *150th Birth Anniv of Sir Arthur Sullivan (composer). Gilbert and Sullivan Operas.* One phosphor band (18p.) or phosphorised paper (others). P 14½×14.

1624	**1054**	18p. bluish violet, bistre-yellow, scarlet, stone, blue and grey-black	40	45
1625	**1055**	24p. purple-brown, lemon, scarlet, stone, blue, olive-bistre and black	55	55
		a. Imperf (pair)	£250	
1626	**1056**	28p. rose-red, lemon, stone, new blue, bluish violet, brt emerald & black	70	70
1627	**1057**	33p. blue-green, orange-yellow, scarlet, olive-bistre, blue, brown-pur & blk	1·10	1·10
1628	**1058**	39p. deep blue, lemon, scarlet, stone, lavender, olive-bistre & lake-brown	1·25	1·25
1624/8		Set of 5	3·50	3·50

1059 "Acid Rain Kills"   **1060** "Ozone Layer"

1061 "Greenhouse Effect"   **1062** "Bird of Hope"

(Des Christopher Hall (24p.), Lewis Fowler (28p.), Sarah Warren (33p.), Alice Newton-Mold (39p.). Adapted Trickett and Webb Ltd)

1992 (15 Sept). *Protection of the Environment. Children's Paintings. Phosphorised paper.* P 14×14½.

1629	**1059**	24p. emerald, greenish yellow, pale olive-yellow, brt carmine & black	60	45
1630	**1060**	28p. vermilion, lemon, bright blue, new blue, brt green, ultramarine & blk	85	90
1631	**1061**	33p. greenish blue, greenish yellow, brt rose-red, brt green, emer, bl & blk	90	1·00
1632	**1062**	39p. emerald, greenish yellow, bright magenta, brt orange, brt blue & blk	1·00	1·00
1629/32		Set of 4	3·00	3·00

1063 European Star

(Des D. Hockney)

1992 (13 Oct). *Single European Market. Phosphorised paper.* P 15×14.

1633	**1063**	24p. gold, greenish yellow, bright magenta, dull ultramarine & black	75	75

1064 "Angel Gabriel", St. James's, Pangbourne

1065 "Madonna and Child", St. Mary's, Bibury

1066 "King with Gold", Our Lady and St. Peter, Leatherhead

1067 "Shepherds", All Saints, Porthcawl

1068 "Kings with Frankincense and Myrrh", Our Lady and St. Peter, Leatherhead

(Des Carroll, Dempsey and Thirkell Ltd from windows by Karl Parsons (18, 24, 33p.) and Paul Woodroffe (28, 39p.))

1992 (10 Nov). *Christmas. Stained Glass Windows.* One centre band (18p.) or phosphorised paper (others). P 15×14.

1634	**1064**	18p. black, greenish yellow, mauve, ultramarine, bright emerald & gold	40	40
		a. Booklet pane of 20	7·50	
1635	**1065**	24p. blk, greenish yell, brt pur, ultram, new blue, brt greenish yell & gold	65	65
1636	**1066**	28p. black, lemon, rosine, ultramarine, reddish lilac, red-orange and gold	80	80
1637	**1067**	33p. bright ultramarine, greenish yell, rosine, brn, yellow-orge, blk & gold	95	95
1638	**1068**	39p. black, lemon, rosine, bright blue, deep violet, yellow-orange and gold	1·10	1·10
1634/8		Set of 5	3·50	3·50

Booklet pane No. 1634a comes from a special £3.60 Christmas booklet and has margins at left, top and bottom.

1069 Mute Swan Cob and St. Catherine's Chapel, Abbotsbury   **1070** Cygnet and Decoy

1071 Swans and Cygnet

1072 Eggs in Nest and Tithe Barn, Abbotsbury

1073 Young Swan and the Fleet

(Des D. Gentleman)

1993 (19 Jan). *600th Anniv of Abbotsbury Swannery. One phosphor band (18p) or phosphorised paper (others). P* 14×15.

1639	1069	18p. gold, greenish yellow, bistre, green, vermilion and black	..	1·50	60
1640	1070	24p. gold, cream, bright green, grey-brown, dull blue and grey-black	..	1·00	1·00
1641	1071	28p. gold, greenish grey, yellow-brown, myrtle-green, brown, verm & blk		1·25	1·40
1642	1072	33p. gold, ochre, apple-green, olive-brown, bright orange & grey-black		1·50	1·75
1643	1073	39p. gold, cream, bright green, cobalt, light brown and black	..	2·00	2·00
1639/43	..	.. .. ..	*Set of 5*	6·50	6·00

1074 Long John Silver and Parrot (*Treasure Island*)

1075 Tweedledum and Tweedledee (*Alice Through the Looking-Glass*)

1076 William (*William* books)

1077 Mole and Toad (*The Wind in the Willows*)

1078 Teacher and Wilfrid ("The Bash Street Kids")

1079 Peter Rabbit and Mrs. Rabbit (*The Tale of Peter Rabbit*)

1080 Snowman (*The Snowman*) and Father Christmas (*Father Christmas*)

1081 The Big Friendly Giant and Sophie (*The BFG*)

1082 Bill Badger and Rupert Bear

1083 Aladdin and the Genie

(Des Newell and Sorell)

1993 (2 Feb–10 Aug). *Greetings Stamps. "Gift Giving". Two phosphor bands. P* 15×14 (*with one elliptical hole on each vertical side*).

1644	1074	(1st) gold, greenish yellow, magenta, pale brown, light blue and black		95	85
		a. Booklet pane. Nos. 1644/53		8·50	
1645	1075	(1st) gold, cream and black	..	95	85
1646	1076	(1st) gold, greenish yellow, magenta, cream, new blue and black	..	95	85
1647	1077	(1st) gold, greenish yellow, magenta, cream, new blue and black		95	85
1648	1078	(1st) gold, greenish yellow, magenta, cream, new blue and black		95	85
1649	1079	(1st) gold, greenish yellow, magenta, cream, new blue and black		95	85
		a. Booklet pane. No. 1649×4 with margins all round (10 Aug)		4·00	
1650	1080	(1st) gold, greenish yellow, magenta, cream, new blue and black		95	85
1651	1081	(1st) gold, greenish yellow, magenta, cream, new blue and black	..	95	85
1652	1082	(1st) gold, greenish yellow, magenta, cream, new blue and black	..	95	85
1653	1083	(1st) gold, greenish yellow, magenta, cream, new blue and black	..	95	85
1644/53	..	.. ..	*Set of 10*	8·50	7·50

Nos. 1644/53 were only issued in £2.40 booklets (sold at £2.50 from 1 November 1993).

Booklet pane No. 1649a comes from the £6 (£5.64) Beatrix Potter booklet.

1084 Decorated Enamel Dial

1085 Escapement, Remontoire and Fusee

1086 Balance, Spring and Temperature Compensator

1087 Back of Movement

(Des H. Brown and D. Penny. Litho Questa)

1993 (16 Feb). *300th Birth Anniv of John Harrison (inventor of the marine chronometer). Details of "H4" Clock. Phosphorised paper. P* 14½×14.

1654	1084	24p. new blue, greenish yellow, mag, black, grey-black and pale cream..	50	50
1655	1085	28p. new blue, greenish yellow, mag, black, grey-black and pale cream..	80	80
1656	1086	33p. new blue, greenish yellow, mag, black, grey-black and pale cream..	95	95
1657	1087	39p. new mag, greenish yellow, black, grey-black and pale cream..	1·10	1·10
1654/7	..	.. .. *Set of 4*	3·00	3·00

1088 Britannia

(Des B. Craddock, adapted Roundel Design Group. Litho (silver die-stamped, Braille symbol for "10" embossed) Questa)

1993 (2 Mar). *Granite paper. P* 14×14½ (*with two elliptical holes on each horizontal side*).

1658	1088	£10 greenish grey, rosine, yellow, new blue, reddish violet, vermilion, violet, bright green and silver ..	15·00	6·00
		a. Silver omitted		

The paper used for No. 1658 contains fluorescent coloured fibres which, together with the ink on the shield, react under U.V. light.

1089 *Dendrobium hellwigianum*

1090 *Paphiopedilum* Maudiae "Magnificum"

1091 *Cymbidium lowianum*

1092 *Vanda* Rothschildiana

1093 *Dendrobium vexillarius* var *albiviride*

(Des Pandora Sellars)

1993 (16 Mar). *14th World Orchid Conference, Glasgow. One phosphor band (18p.) or phosphorised paper (others). P* 15×14.

1659	1089	18p. green, greenish yellow, magenta, pale blue, apple-green and slate	40	40
		a. Imperf (pair)	£900	
1660	1090	24p. green, greenish yellow, bright green and grey-black	65	65
1661	1091	28p. green, greenish yellow, red, bright turquoise-blue and drab	90	90
1662	1092	33p. green, greenish yellow, pale mag, bright violet, bright green and grey	1·10	1·00
1663	1093	39p. green, greenish yellow, red, pale olive-yell, brt grn, vio & grey-blk	1·40	1·25
1659/63		Set of 5	4·00	3·50

FLUORESCENT PHOSPHOR BANDS. Following the introduction of new automatic sorting machinery in 1991 it was found necessary to substantially increase the signal emitted by the phosphor bands. This was achieved by adding a fluorescent element to the phosphor which appears yellow under U.V. light. This combination was first used on an experimental sheet printing of the 18p., No. X913, produced by Enschedé in 1991. All values with phosphor bands from the elliptical perforations issue, including the No Value Indicated design, originally showed this yellow fluor.

From mid-1995 printings of current sheet and booklet stamps began to appear with the colour of the fluorescent element changed to blue. As such differences in fluor colour can only be identified by use of a U.V. lamp they are outside the scope of this catalogue, but full details will be found in the *Great Britain Specialised Catalogue Volume 4.*

The first commemorative/special stamp issue to show the change to blue fluor was the Centenary of Rugby League set, Nos. 1891/5.

COMPUTER-ENGRAVED CYLINDERS. In 1991 Enschedé introduced a new method of preparing photogravure cylinders for Great Britain stamps. This new method utilised computer-engraving instead of the traditional acid-etching and produced cylinders without the minor flaws which had long been a feature of the photogravure process. Such cylinders were first used on Great Britain stamps for the printing of the 18p. released on 19 November 1991 (see No. X913).

Harrison and Sons continued to use the acid-etching method until mid-1996 after which most Machin values, including N.V.I.'s, were produced from computer-engraved cylinders using a very similar process to that of Enschedé. Some values exist in versions from both cylinder production methods and can often be identified by minor differences. Such stamps are, however, outside the scope of this listing, but full details can be found in the current edition of the *Great Britain Specialised Catalogue Volume 4.*

For commemorative stamps the first Harrison issue to use computer-engraved cylinders was the Centenary of Cinema set (Nos. 1920/4).

When Walsall introduced photogravure printing in 1997 their cylinders were produced using a similar computer-engraved process.

1993 (6 Apr)–97. *Booklet stamps. As T 913/14, but P* 15×14 (*with one elliptical hole on each vertical side*).

(*a*) *Photo Harrison (No. 1664), Harrison or Walsall (others)*

1663a	913	(2nd) brt blue (1 centre band) (7.9.93)	30	35
1664	914	(1st) brt orge-red (phosphorised paper)	60	55
1664a		(1st) bright orange-red (2 phosphor bands) (4.4.95)	40	45

(*b*) *Litho Questa, Walsall or Enschedé (No. 1666ma)*

1665	913	(2nd) bright blue (1 centre band)	30	35
1666	914	(1st) brt orange-red (2 phosphor bands)	40	45
		l. Booklet pane. No. 1666×4 plus commemorative label at left (27.7.94)	5·00	
		la. Ditto, but with commemorative label at right (16.5.95)	1·50	
		m. Pane. No. 1666 with margins all round (roul 8 across top corners of pane) (17.8.94)	40	
		ma. Ditto, but roul 10 across top corners of pane (20.2.97)	40	

Nos. 1663a/6, were issued in booklet panes showing perforations on all four edges.

On 6 September 1993 Nos. 1665/6 printed in lithography by Questa were made available in sheets from post offices in Birmingham, Coventry, Falkirk and Milton Keynes. These sheet stamps became available nationally on 5 October 1993. On 29 April 1997 No. 1663a printed in photogravure by Walsall became available in sheets. On the same date Nos. 1663a and 1664a were issued in coils printed by Harrison.

No. 1666l includes a commemorative label for the 300th anniversary of the Bank of England and No. 1666la exists with labels for the birth centenary of R. J. Mitchell, 70th birthday of Queen Elizabeth II, "Hong Kong '97" International Stamp Exhibition or Commonwealth Heads of Government Meeting, Edinburgh.

No. 1666m, printed by Questa, was provided by the Royal Mail for inclusion in single pre-packed greetings cards. The pane shows large margins at top and sides with lines of roulette gauging 8 stretching from the bottom corners to the mid point of the top edge. Examples included with greetings cards show the top two corners of the pane folded over. The scheme was originally limited to Boots and their logo appeared on the pane margin. Other card retailers subsequently participated and later supplies omitted the logo. Unfolded examples were available from the British Philatelic Bureau and from other Post Office philatelic outlets. A further printing by Enschedé in 1997 showed the roulettes gauging 10 (No. 1666ma). Blank pieces of gummed paper have been found showing the perforation and rouletting of No. 1666ma, but no printing.

In mid-1994 a number of postal forgeries of the 2nd bright blue printed in lithography were detected, after having been rejected by the sorting equipment. These show the Queen's head in bright greenish blue, have a fluorescent, rather than a phosphor, band and show matt, colourless gum on the reverse. These forgeries come from booklets of ten which also have forged covers.

For 1st in gold see No. 1979.

1993 (27 Apr)–97. *As Nos. X841, etc, but P* 15×14 (*with one elliptical hole on each vertical side*).

(*a*) *Photo*

Enschedé:—20p. (Y1674), 29p., 35p. (Y1682), 36p., 38p., 41p. (Y1688), 43p. (Y1690)
Harrison:—19p., 20p. (Y1675/b), 25p. (Y1676), 26p., 35p., (Y1683), 41p. (Y1689), 43p (Y1691)
Enschedé or Harrison:—1p., 2p., 4p., 5p., 6p., 10p., 25p. (Y1677), 30p., 31p., 37p., 39p., 50p., 63p., £1
Enschedé, Harrison or Walsall:—37p., 63p.

Y1667	367	1p. crimson (2 bands) (8.6.93)	10	10
Y1668		2p. deep green (2 bands) (11.4.95)	10	10
Y1669		4p. new blue (2 bands) (1993)	10	10
Y1670		5p. dull red-brown (2 bands) (8.6.93)	10	10
Y1671		6p. yellow-olive (2 bands)	10	15
Y1672		10p. dull orange (2 bands) (8.6.93)	15	20
Y1673		19p. bistre (1 centre band) (26.10.93)	30	35
		a. Imperf (pair)	£350	
Y1674		20p. turquoise-grn (2 bands) (14.12.93)	50	50
Y1675		20p. brt green (1 centre band) (25.6.96)	30	35
		a. Imperf (horiz pair)		
Y1675b		20p. bright green (1 side band) (23.9.97)	1·00	1·00
		bl. Booklet pane Nos. Y1675b and Y1678, each × 3 with margins all round	4·00	
Y1676		25p. rose-red (phosphorised paper) (26.10.93)	70	70
		a. Imperf (pair)		
		l. Booklet pane. No. Y1676×2 plus 2 labels (1.11.93)	1·25	
Y1677		25p. rose-red (2 bands) (20.12.94)	60	60
		l. Booklet pane. No. Y1677×2 plus 2 labels (6.6.95)	80	
Y1678		26p. red-brown (2 bands) (25.6.96)	40	45
Y1679		29p. grey (2 bands) (26.10.93)	70	70
Y1680		30p. deep olive-grey (2 bands) (27.7.93)	45	50
Y1681		31p. deep mauve (2 bands) (25.6.96)	50	55
Y1682		35p. yellow (2 bands) (17.8.93)	80	80
Y1683		35p. yell (phosphorised paper) (1.11.93)	80	80
Y1684		36p. bright ultramarine (26.10.93)	80	80
Y1685		37p. bright mauve (2 bands) (25.6.96)	60	65
Y1686		38p. rosine (2 bands) (26.10.93)	80	80
		a. Imperf (pair)	£200	
Y1687		39p. bright magenta (2 bands) (25.6.96)	60	65
Y1688		41p. grey-brown (2 bands) (26.10.93)	90	90
Y1689		41p. drab (phosphorised paper) (1.11.93)	90	90
Y1690		43p. dp olive-brown (2 bands) (25.6.96)	65	70
Y1691		43p. sepia (2 bands) (8.7.96)	65	70
Y1692		50p. ochre (2 bands) (14.12.93)	75	80
		a. Imperf (pair)		
Y1693		63p. light emerald (2 bands) (25.6.96)	95	1·00
Y1694		£1 bluish violet (2 bands) (22.8.95)	1·50	1·60

(*b*) *Litho Walsall* (37p., 60p., 63p.), *Questa or Walsall* (25p., 35p., 41p.), *Questa* (others)

Y1743	367	1p. lake (2 bands) (8.7.96)	10	10
		l. Booklet pane. Nos. Y1743×2, Y1751 and Y1753×3 plus 2 labels	1·50	
Y1748		6p. yellow-olive (2 bands) (26.7.94)	6·50	6·50
		l. Booklet pane. Nos. Y1748, Y1750 and Y1752×4 with margins all round	9·00	
		la. 6p. value misplaced		
Y1749		10p. dull orange (2 bands) (25.4.95)	3·00	3·00
		l. Booklet pane. Nos. Y1749, Y1750 ×2, Y1752×2, Y1754/5, Y1757 and centre label with margins all round	10·00	
Y1750		19p. bistre (1 side band) (26.7.94)	1·00	1·00
		l. Booklet pane. No. Y1750×6 with margins all round (25.4.95)	6·00	
Y1751		20p. brt yell-grn (1 centre band) (8.7.96)	30	35
		l. Booklet pane. Nos. Y1751 and Y1753×7	3·00	
Y1752		25p. red (2 bands) (1.11.93)	60	60
		l. Booklet pane. Nos. Y1752, NI72, S84 and W73, each × 2 with centre label and margins all round (14.5.96)	3·00	
Y1753		26p. chestnut (2 bands) (8.7.96)	40	45
Y1754		30p. olive-grey (2 bands) (25.4.95)	2·00	2·00
Y1755		35p. yellow (2 bands) (1.11.93)	80	80
Y1756		37p. bright mauve (2 bands) (8.7.96)	60	65
Y1757		41p. drab (shades) (2 bands) (1.11.93)	65	70
Y1758		60p. dull blue-grey (2 bands) (9.8.94)	90	95
Y1759		63p. light emerald (2 bands) (8.7.96)	95	1·00

No. Y1694 is printed in Iriodin ink which gives a shiny effect to the solid part of the background behind the Queen's head.

Nos. Y1683 and Y1689 were only issued in coils and Nos. Y1748/50, Y1752, Y1754/5 and Y1757/8 only in booklets.

No. Y1748la shows the 6p. value 22 mm to the left so that its position in the booklet pane is completely blank except for the phosphor bands. Other more minor misplacements exist.

No. Y1675b shows the phosphor band at right and No. Y1750 at left or right.

For 26p. in gold see No. 1978.

Stanley Gibbons
'ONE COUNTRY'
Albums

THE ONLY ALBUMS FEATURING SG CATALOGUE NUMBERS

Available for:

- Great Britain ● Guernsey
- Jersey ● Isle of Man
- Australia ● New Zealand
- Canada

- Easy to use 2 and 3 volume sets.
- Padded leather finish maroon PVC binders.
- Secure 4 and 22 ring locking mechanism.
- High quality leaves with illustrations.
- Includes self-adhesive album title sheet.

Available from our showroom at 399 Strand, London and by Mail Order

PHONE 0800 611622
FOR YOUR FREE COLOUR BROCHURE.

STANLEY GIBBONS

• THE COLLECTOR'S CHOICE •

STANLEY GIBBONS PUBLICATIONS
5 Parkside, Christchurch Road, Ringwood, Hants
BH24 3SH England
Tel: 01425 472363 Fax: 01425 470247

BCI/96

1094 "Family Group" (bronze sculpture) (Henry Moore)

1095 "Kew Gardens" (lithograph) (Edward Bawden)

1096 "St. Francis and the Birds" (Stanley Spencer)

1097 "Still Life: Odyssey I" (Ben Nicholson)

(Des A. Dastor)

1993 (11 May). *Europa. Contemporary Art. Phosphorised paper.* P 14×14½.

1767	**1094**	24p. brownish grey, lemon, magenta, turquoise-blue, and grey-black ..	50	50
1768	**1095**	28p. brownish grey, buff, lt grn, yellow-brown, brt orge, new bl & grey-blk	80	80
1769	**1096**	33p. brownish grey, cream, greenish yellow, magenta, new bl & grey-blk	95	95
1770	**1097**	39p. brownish grey, cream, yell-ochre, rose-lilac, red, light blue & grey-blk	1·10	1·10
1767/70		.. .. *Set of* 4	3·00	3·00

1098 Emperor Claudius (from gold coin)

1099 Emperor Hadrian (bronze head)

1100 Goddess Roma (from gemstone)

1101 Christ (Hinton St. Mary mosaic)

(Des J. Gibbs)

1993 (15 June). *Roman Britain. Phosphorised paper with two phosphor bands.* P 14×14½.

1771	**1098**	24p. blk, pale orange, lt brown & silver	50	50
1772	**1099**	28p. black, greenish yellow, bright rose-red, silver, brt blue & grey-black	80	80
1773	**1100**	33p. black, greenish yellow, bright rose-red, silver and grey	95	95
1774	**1101**	39p. black, greenish yellow, rosine, silver, pale violet and grey	1·10	1·10
1771/4		.. .. *Set of* 4	3·00	3·00

1102 *Midland Maid* and other Narrow Boats, Grand Junction Canal

1103 *Yorkshire Lass* and other Humber Keels, Stainforth and Keadby Canal

1104 *Valley Princess* and other Horse-drawn Barges, Brecknock and Abergavenny Canal

1105 Steam Barges, including *Pride of Scotland*, and Fishing Boats, Crinan Canal

(Des T. Lewery. Litho Questa)

1993 (20 July). *Inland Waterways. Two phosphor bands.* P 14½×14.

1775	**1102**	24p. new bl, greenish yell, brt mag, blk, bl, verm, brownish grey & sage-grn	50	50
1776	**1103**	28p. new bl, greenish yell, brt mag, blk, blue, bluish grey, verm & sage-grn	80	80
1777	**1104**	33p. new bl, greenish yell, brt mag, blk, bl, verm, greenish grey & sage-grn	95	95
1778	**1105**	39p. new blue, greenish yellow, brt mag, blk, bl, verm, sage-grn & dull mve	1·10	1·10
1775/8		.. .. *Set of* 4	3·00	3·00

Nos. 1775/8 commemorate the bicentenary of the Acts of Parliament authorising the canals depicted.

1106 Horse Chestnut

1107 Blackberry

1108 Hazel

1109 Rowan

1110 Pear

(Des Charlotte Knox)

1993 (14 Sept). *The Four Seasons. Autumn. Fruits and Leaves. One phosphor band* (18p.) *or phosphorised paper* (others). P 15×14.

1779	**1106**	18p. black, greenish yellow, cerise, bright green, gold and chestnut ..	40	40
1780	**1107**	24p. black, lemon, cerise, myrtle-green, gold, bright green and brown ..	65	65
1781	**1108**	28p. grey, lemon, emer, lake-brn & gold	90	80
1782	**1109**	33p. grey-black, greenish yellow, rosine, light green and brown ..	1·10	95
1783	**1110**	39p. myrtle-green, greenish yellow, rosine, olive-sepia, gold, apple-green and deep myrtle-green	1·40	1·10
1779/83		.. .. *Set of* 5	4·00	3·50

SHERLOCK HOLMES & DR WATSON "THE REIGATE SQUIRE"

SHERLOCK HOLMES & SIR HENRY "THE HOUND OF THE BASKERVILLES"

1111 *The Reigate Squire*

1112 *The Hound of the Baskervilles*

SHERLOCK HOLMES & LESTRADE "THE SIX NAPOLEONS"

SHERLOCK HOLMES & MYCROFT "THE GREEK INTERPRETER"

1113 *The Six Napoleons*

1114 *The Greek Interpreter*

SHERLOCK HOLMES & MORIARTY "THE FINAL PROBLEM"

1115 *The Final Problem*

(Des A. Davidson. Litho Questa)

1993 (12 Oct). *Sherlock Holmes. Centenary of the Publication of The Final Problem. Phosphorised paper.* P 14×14½.

1784	**1111**	24p. new blue, greenish yellow, mag, black and gold	90	90
		a. Horiz strip. Nos. 1784/8	4·00	4·00
1785	**1112**	24p. new blue, greenish yellow, mag, black and gold ..	90	90
1786	**1113**	24p. new blue, greenish yellow, mag, black and gold ..	90	90
1787	**1114**	24p. new blue, greenish yellow, mag, black and gold ..	90	90
1788	**1115**	24p. new blue, greenish yellow, mag, black and gold ..	90	90
1784/8		.. .. *Set of* 5	4·00	4·00

Nos. 1785/8 were printed together, *se-tenant*, in horizontal strips of 5 throughout the sheet.

1116

(Des J. Matthews. Litho Walsall)

1993 (19 Oct). *Self-adhesive Booklet Stamp. Two phosphor bands. Die-cut* P 14×15 *(with one elliptical hole on each vertical side).*

1789	**1116**	(1st) orange-red	1·00	1·00
		a. Booklet pane. No. 1789×20 ..	15·00	

No. 1789 was initially sold at 24p., which was increased to 25p. from 1 November 1993. It was only issued in booklets containing 20 stamps, each surrounded by die-cut perforations .

For similar 2nd and 1st designs printed in photogravure by Enschedé see Nos. 1976/7.

1117 Bob Cratchit and Tiny Tim

1118 Mr. and Mrs. Fezziwig

1119 Scrooge

1120 The Prize Turkey

1121 Mr. Scrooge's Nephew

(Des Q. Blake)

1993 (9 Nov). *Christmas. 150th Anniv of Publication of* A Christmas Carol *by Charles Dickens. One phosphor band* (19p.) *or phosphorised paper* (*others*). *P* 15×14.

1790	1117	19p. new blue, yellow, magenta, salmon, bright emerald & grey-blk	40	40
		a. Imperf (pair)		
1791	1118	25p. yellow-orange, brn-lilac, steel-bl, lake-brown, lt grn, grey-blk & blk	65	65
1792	1119	30p. cerise, bistre-yellow, dull blue, brn-rose, pale green, grey-black & blk	80	80
1793	1120	35p. dp turquoise-green, lemon, verm, dull ultramarine, Indian red, bluish grey and black	95	95
1794	1121	41p. reddish purple, lemon, purple, light blue, salmon, bright green & black	1·10	1·10
1790/4		*Set of 5*	3·50	3·50

1122 Class "5" No. 44957 and Class "B1" No. 61342 on West Highland Line

1123 Class "A1" No. 60149 *Amadis* at Kings Cross

1124 Class "4" No. 43000 on Turntable at Blyth North

1125 Class "4" No. 42455 near Wigan Central

1126 Class "Castle" No. 7002 *Devizes Castle* on Bridge crossing Worcester and Birmingham Canal

(Des B. Delaney)

1994 (18 Jan). *The Age of Steam. Railway Photographs by Colin Gifford. One phosphor band* (19p.) *or phosphorised paper with two bands* (*others*). *P* 14½.

1795	1122	19p. dp blue-green, grey-black & black	45	40
1796	1123	25p. slate-lilac, grey-black and black	75	65
1797	1124	30p. lake-brown, grey-black and black	90	80
1798	1125	35p. deep claret, grey-black and black	1·10	95
1799	1126	41p. indigo, grey-black and black	1·25	1·10
1795/9		*Set of 5*	4·00	3·50

Nos. 1796/9 are on phosphorised paper and also show two phosphor bands.

MINIMUM PRICE

The minimum price quote is 10p which represents a handling charge rather than a basis for valuing common stamps. For further notes about prices see introductory pages.

1127 Dan Dare and the Mekon

1128 The Three Bears

1129 Rupert Bear

1130 Alice (*Alice in Wonderland*)

1131 Noggin and the Ice Dragon

1132 Peter Rabbit posting Letter

1133 Red Riding Hood and Wolf

1134 Orlando the Marmalade Cat

1135 Biggles

1136 Paddington Bear on Station

(Des Newell and Sorrell)

1994 (1 Feb). *Greetings Stamps. "Messages". Two phosphor bands. P* 15×14 (*with one elliptical hole on each vertical side*).

1800	1127	(1st) gold, greenish yellow, brt purple, bistre-yellow, new blue and black	80	65
		a. Booklet pane. Nos. 1800/9	7·25	
1801	1128	(1st) gold, greenish yellow, brt purple, bistre-yellow, new blue and black	80	65
1802	1129	(1st) gold, greenish yellow, brt purple, bistre-yellow, new blue and black	80	65
1803	1130	(1st) gold, bistre-yellow and black	80	65
1804	1131	(1st) gold, greenish yellow, brt purple, bistre-yellow, new blue and black	80	65
1805	1132	(1st) gold, greenish yellow, brt purple, bistre-yellow, new blue and black	80	65
1806	1133	(1st) gold, greenish yellow, brt purple, bistre-yellow, new blue and black	80	65
1807	1134	(1st) gold, greenish yellow, brt purple, bistre-yellow, new blue and black	80	65
1808	1135	(1st) gold, greenish yellow, brt purple, bistre-yellow, new blue and black	80	65
1809	1136	(1st) gold, greenish yellow, brt purple, bistre-yellow, new blue and black	80	65
1800/9		*Set of 10*	7·25	6·00

Nos. 1800/9 were only issued in £2.50 stamp booklets (sold at £2.60 from 8 July 1996).

Castell Y Waun / Chirk Castle, Clwyd, Cymru / Wales

1137 Castell Y Waun (Chirk Castle), Clwyd, Wales

Ben Arkle, Sutherland, Scotland

1138 Ben Arkle, Sutherland, Scotland

Mourne Mountains, County Down, Northern Ireland

1139 Mourne Mountains, County Down, Northern Ireland

Dersingham, Norfolk, England

1140 Dersingham, Norfolk, England

Dolwyddelan, Gwynedd, Cymru / Wales

1141 Dolwyddelan, Gwynedd, Wales

1994 (1 Mar–26 July). *25th Anniv of Investiture of the Prince of Wales. Paintings by Prince Charles. One phosphor band* (19p.) *or phosphorised paper* (*others*). *P* 15×14.

1810	1137	19p. grey-black, greenish yellow, magenta, new blue, black and silver	40	40
1811	1138	25p. grey-black, orange-yellow, bright magenta, new blue, silver and black	75	75

1812 **1139** 30p. grey-black, greenish yellow,
magenta, new blue, silver and black   1·00   1·00
  a. Booklet pane. No. 1812×4 with
margins all round (26 July)   3·50
1813 **1140** 35p. grey-black, greenish yellow,
magenta, new blue, silver and black   1·10   1·10
1814 **1141** 41p. grey-black, lemon, magenta, new
blue, silver and black   1·25   1·25
1810/14   ..   ..   *Set of 5*   4·00   4·00
   Booklet pane No. 1812a comes from the £6.04 "Northern
Ireland" booklet.

1142 Bather at   **1143** "Where's my
Blackpool   Little Lad?"

1144 "Wish You were   **1145** Punch and Judy
Here!"   Show

1146 "The Tower
Crane" Machine

(Des M. Dempsey and B. Dare. Litho Questa)

1994 (12 Apr). *Centenary of Picture Postcards. One side band
(19p.) or two phosphor bands (others). P* 14×14½.
1815 **1142** 19p. new blue, greenish yell, mag & blk   40   40
1816 **1143** 25p. new blue, greenish yell, mag & blk   65   65
1817 **1144** 30p. new blue, greenish yell, mag & blk   80   80
1818 **1145** 35p. new blue, greenish yell, mag & blk   95   95
1819 **1146** 41p. new blue, greenish yell, mag & blk   1·10   1·10
1815/19   ..   ..   *Set of 5*   3·50   3·50

1147 British Lion and French Cockerel
over Tunnel

1148 Symbolic Hands over Train

(Des G. Hardie (T **1147**), J.-P. Cousin (T **1148**))

1994 (3 May). *Opening of Channel Tunnel. Phosphorised paper.
P* 14×14½.
1820 **1147** 25p. ultram, brt orange, scar, new blue,
emerald, turquoise-blue & silver   ..   60   60
  a. Horiz pair. Nos. 1820/1   ..   1·25   1·25
1821 **1148** 25p. ultram, scar, new bl, emer & silver   60   60

1822 **1147** 41p. new blue, brt orge, scar, turquoise-
blue, emerald, ultramarine & silver   1·40   1·40
  a. Horiz pair. Nos. 1822/3   ..   2·75   2·75
  ab. Imperf (horiz pair)   ..   £700
1823 **1148** 41p. ultram, scar, new bl, emer & silver   1·40   1·40
1820/3   ..   ..   *Set of 4*   3·50   3·50
   Nos. 1820/1 and 1822/3 were printed together, *se-tenant*, in
horizontal pairs throughout the sheets.
   Stamps in similar designs were also issued by France.

 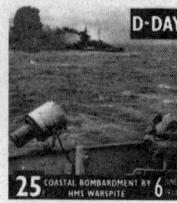

1149 Groundcrew replacing   **1150** H.M.S. *Warspite*
Smoke Canisters on   (battleship) shelling
Douglas Boston of 88 Sqn   Enemy Positions

 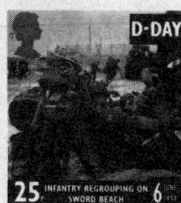

1151 Commandos landing   **1152** Infantry regrouping
on Gold Beach   on Sword Beach

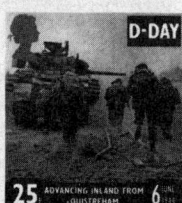

1153 Tank and Infantry
advancing, Ouistreham

(Des K. Bassford from contemporary photographs. Litho Questa)

1994 (6 June). *50th Anniv of D-Day. Two phosphor bands.
P* 14½×14.
1824 **1149** 25p. pink, greenish yell, blackish lilac,
slate-black, brt scarlet & silver-grey   80   80
  a. Horiz strip of 5. Nos. 1824/8   ..   3·50   3·50
1825 **1150** 25p. pink, greenish yell, blackish lilac,
slate-black, brt scarlet & silver-grey   80   80
1826 **1151** 25p. pink, greenish yell, blackish lilac,
slate-black, brt scarlet & silver-grey   80   80
1827 **1152** 25p. pink, greenish yell, blackish lilac,
slate-black, brt scarlet & silver-grey   80   80
1828 **1153** 25p. pink, greenish yell, blackish lilac,
slate-black, brt scarlet & silver-grey   80   80
1824/8   ..   ..   *Set of 5*   3·50   3·50
   Nos. 1824/8 were printed together, *se-tenant*, in horizontal strips
of 5 throughout the sheet.

1154 The Old Course, St.   **1155** The 18th Hole,
Andrews   Muirfield

1156 The 15th Hole   **1157** The 8th Hole ("The
("Luckyslap"), Carnoustie   Postage Stamp"), Royal
                    Troon

1158 The 9th Hole,
Turnberry

(Des P. Hogarth)

1994 (5 July). *Scottish Golf Courses. One phosphor band (19p.) or
phosphorised paper (others). P* 14½×14.
1829 **1154** 19p. yellow-green, olive-grey, orange-
verm, apple-green, blue & grey-blk   55   55
1830 **1155** 25p. yellow-green, lemon, brt orange,
apple-green, blue, mag & grey-blk   80   80
1831 **1156** 30p. yellow-green, yellow, rosine, emer,
blue-green, new blue & grey-black   1·00   1·00
1832 **1157** 35p. yellow-green, yellow, rosine, apple-
green, new blue, dull bl & grey-blk   1·25   1·25
1833 **1158** 41p. yellow-grn, lemon, magenta, apple-
green, dull blue, new bl & grey-blk   1·40   1·40
1829/33   ..   ..   *Set of 5*   4·75   4·75
   Nos. 1829/33 commemorate the 250th anniversary of golf's first
set of rules produced by the Honourable Company of Edinburgh
Golfers.

1159 Royal Welsh Show,
Llanelwedd

1160 All England Tennis
Championships, Wimbledon

1161 Cowes Week

1162 Test Match, Lord's

1163 Braemar Gathering

(Des M. Cook)

1994 (2 Aug). *The Four Seasons. Summertime. One phosphor
band (19p.) or phosphorised paper (others). P* 15×14.
1834 **1159** 19p. black, greenish yell, brt magenta,
brown, yellow-brown & new blue   50   50
1835 **1160** 25p. black, greenish yellow, magenta,
reddish violet, yellow-grn, myrtle-
green and new blue   70   70
1836 **1161** 30p. black, greenish yellow, bright
magenta, yellow-ochre, deep
slate-blue, blue-green and blue   ..   90   80

1837 **1162** 35p. black, greenish yellow, magenta, slate-lilac, yellow-green, deep bluish green and bright blue .. 1·00 90
1838 **1163** 41p. black, greenish yellow, bright magenta, deep claret, light brown, myrtle-green and bright blue 1·10 1·00
1834/8 .. .. *Set of* 5 3·75 3·50

1164 Ultrasonic Imaging

1165 Scanning Electron Microscopy

1166 Magnetic Resonance Imaging

1167 Computed Tomography

(Des P. Vermier and J-P. Tibbles. Photo Enschedé)

1994 (27 Sept). *Europa. Medical Discoveries. Phosphorised paper.* P 14×14½.
1839 **1164** 25p. greenish yellow, bright magenta, new blue, black and silver .. 65 65
a. Imperf (vert pair) .. ..
1840 **1165** 30p. greenish yellow, bright magenta, new blue, black and silver .. 85 85
1841 **1166** 35p. greenish yellow, bright magenta, new blue, black and silver .. 90 90
1842 **1167** 41p. greenish yellow, bright magenta, new blue, black and silver .. 1·00 1·00
1839/42 .. .. *Set of* 4 3·00 3·00

1168 Mary and Joseph

1169 Three Wise Men

1170 Mary with Doll

1171 Shepherds

1172 Angels

(Des Yvonne Gilbert)

1994 (1 Nov). *Christmas. Children's Nativity Plays. One phosphor band (19p) or phosphorised paper (others).* P 15×14.
1843 **1168** 19p. turquoise-green, greenish yell, brt magenta, new bl, dull bl & grey-blk 50 50
a. Imperf (pair) £200
1844 **1169** 25p. orange-brown, greenish yellow, brt mag, new bl, lt bl, bistre & grey-blk 70 70
1845 **1170** 30p. lt brown, greenish yellow, brt mag, bl, turq-bl, new bl & brownish grey 80 80
1846 **1171** 35p. dp grey-brn, greenish yell, brt mag, turq-bl, dull violet-bl, ochre & brn 90 90
1847 **1172** 41p. blue, greenish yellow, brt magenta, turquoise-blue, light blue & dp grey 1·00 1·00
1843/7 .. .. .. *Set of* 5 3·50 3·50

1173 Sophie (black cat)

1174 Puskas (Siamese) and Tigger (tabby)

1175 Chloe (ginger cat)

1176 Kikko (tortoiseshell) and Rosie (Abyssinian)

1177 Fred (black and white cat)

(Des Elizabeth Blackadder. Litho Questa)

1995 (17 Jan). *Cats. One phosphor band (19p.) or two phosphor bands (others).* P 14½×14.
1848 **1173** 19p. new blue, greenish yellow, magenta, black and brown-red .. 60 60
1849 **1174** 25p. new blue, greenish yellow, mag, black and dull yellow-green 75 75

1850 **1175** 30p. new blue, greenish yellow, mag, black and yellow-brown .. 1·00 1·00
1851 **1176** 35p. new blue, greenish yellow, magenta, black and yellow .. 1·10 1·10
1852 **1177** 41p. new blue, greenish yellow, mag, black and reddish orange 1·25 1·25
1848/52 .. .. .. *Set of* 5 4·25 4·25

1178 Dandelions

1179 Sweet Chestnut Leaves

1180 Garlic Leaves

1181 Hazel Leaves

1182 Spring Grass

1995 (14 Mar). *The Four Seasons. Springtime. Plant Sculptures by Andy Goldsworthy. One phosphor band (19p.) or two phosphor bands (others).* P 15×14.
1853 **1178** 19p. silver, greenish yellow, magenta, green and grey-black 55 55
1854 **1179** 25p. silver, greenish yellow, magenta, new blue, and black 65 65
1855 **1180** 30p. silver, greenish yellow, magenta, new blue, and black 90 90
1856 **1181** 35p. silver, greenish yellow, magenta, new blue, and black .. .. 1·00 1·00
1857 **1182** 41p. silver, greenish yellow, magenta, new blue, blue-green and black .. 1·10 1·10
1853/7 .. .. .. *Set of* 5 3·75 3·75

1183 "La Danse a la Campagne" (Renoir)

1184 "Troilus and Criseyde" (Peter Brookes)

1185 "The Kiss" (Rodin)

1186 "Girls on the Town" (Beryl Cook)

1187 "Jazz" (Andrew Mockett)

1188 "Girls performing a Kathal Dance" (Aurangzeb period)

1189 "Alice Keppel with her Daughter" (Alice Hughes)

1190 "Children Playing" (L. S. Lowry)

1191 "Circus Clowns" (Emily Firmin and Justin Mitchell)

1192 Decoration from "All the Love Poems of Shakespeare" (Eric Gill)

(Des Newell and Sorrell. Litho Walsall)

1995 (21 Mar). *Greetings Stamps. "Greetings in Art". Two phosphor bands. P 14½×14 (with one elliptical hole on each vertical side).*

1858	1183	(1st) greenish yellow, new blue, magenta, black and silver	..	40	45
		a. Booklet pane. Nos. 1858/67		4·00	
		ab. Silver (Queen's head and "1ST") omitted		£5500	
1859	1184	(1st) greenish yellow, new blue, magenta, black and silver		40	45

1860	1185	(1st) greenish yellow, new blue, magenta, black and silver		40	45
1861	1186	(1st) greenish yellow, new blue, magenta, black and silver		40	45
1862	1187	(1st) greenish yellow, new blue, magenta, black and silver		40	45
1863	1188	(1st) greenish yellow, new blue, magenta, black and silver		40	45
1864	1189	(1st) purple-brown and silver		40	45
1865	1190	(1st) greenish yellow, new blue, magenta, black and silver		40	45
1866	1191	(1st) greenish yellow, new blue, magenta, black and silver		40	45
1867	1192	(1st) black, greenish yellow and silver		40	45
1858/67		*Set of* 10		4·00	4·25

Nos. 1858/67 were only available in £2.50 stamp booklets (sold at £2.60 from 8 July 1996).
No. 1858ab also shows the phosphor bands omitted.

1193 Fireplace Decoration, Attingham Park, Shropshire

1194 Oak Seedling

1195 Carved Table Leg, Attingham Park

1196 St. David's Head, Dyfed, Wales

1197 Elizabethan Window, Little Moreton Hall, Cheshire

(Des T. Evans)

1995 (11–25 Apr). *Centenary of The National Trust. One phosphor band (19p.), two phosphor bands (25p., 35p.) or phosphorised paper (30p., 41p.). P 14×15.*

1868	1193	19p. grey-green, stone, grey-brown, grey-black and gold	..	55	55
1869	1194	25p. grey-green, greenish yellow, mag, new blue, gold and black	..	65	65
		a. Booklet pane. No. 1869×6 with margins all round (25 April)		3·50	
1870	1195	30p. grey-green, greenish yellow, mag, new blue, gold, black & slate-black		80	80
1871	1196	35p. grey-green, greenish yellow, magenta, blue, gold and black		90	90
1872	1197	41p. grey-green, greenish yell, brt green, slate-grn, gold, blackish brn & blk	1·10	1·10
1868/72		*Set of* 5		3·50	3·50

Booklet pane No. 1869a comes from the £6 "National Trust" booklet.

1198 British Troops and French Civilians celebrating

1199 Symbolic Hands and Red Cross

1200 St. Paul's Cathedral and Searchlights

1201 Symbolic Hand releasing Peace Dove

1202 Symbolic Hands

(Des J. Gorham (Nos. 1873, 1875), J-M. Folon (others))

1995 (2 May). *Europa. Peace and Freedom. One phosphor band (Nos. 1873/4) or two phosphor bands (others). P 14½×14.*

1873	1198	19p. silver, bistre-brown and grey-black	60	50
1874	1199	19p. silver, bistre-yellow, brt rose-red, vermilion, bright blue & slate-blue	60	50
1875	1200	25p. silver, blue and grey-black	..	85	65
1876	1201	25p. silver, verm, brt blue & grey-black	85	65
		a. Imperf (vert pair)		
1877	1202	30p. silver, bistre-yellow, brt magenta, pale greenish blue, grey-blk & flesh	1·00	75
1873/7		*Set of* 5	3·50	2·75

Nos. 1873 and 1875 commemorate the 50th anniversary of the end of the Second World War, No. 1874 the 125th anniversary of the British Red Cross Society and Nos. 1876/7 the 50th anniversary of the United Nations
Nos. 1876/7 include the "EUROPA" emblem.

1203 *The Time Machine*

1204 *The First Men in the Moon*

1205 *The War of the Worlds*

1206 *The Shape of Things to Come*

(Des Siobhan Keaney. Litho Questa)

1995 (6 June). *Science Fiction. Novels by H. G. Wells. Two phosphor bands. P 14½×14.*

1878	1203	25p. new blue, greenish yellow, magenta, black and rosine	..	65	65
1879	1204	30p. new blue, greenish yellow, black, rosine and violet	..	85	85
1880	1205	35p. rosine, greenish yellow, violet, black and bright blue-green	90	90
1881	1206	41p. new blue, greenish yellow, magenta, black and rosine	1·00	1·00
1878/81		*Set of* 4	3·00	3·00

Nos. 1878/81 commemorate the centenary of publication of Wells's *The Time Machine.*

1207 The Swan, 1595

1208 The Rose, 1592

1209 The Globe, 1599   **1210** The Hope, 1613

1211 The Globe, 1614

(Des C. Hodges. Litho Walsall)

1995 (8 Aug). *Reconstruction of Shakespeare's Globe Theatre. Two phosphor bands.* P 14½.

1882	**1207**	25p.	brownish grey, black, magenta, new blue and greenish yellow	65	65
		a.	Horiz strip of 5. Nos. 1882/6	3·00	3·00
1883	**1208**	25p.	brownish grey, black, magenta, new blue and greenish yellow	65	65
1884	**1209**	25p.	brownish grey, black, magenta, new blue and greenish yellow	65	65
1885	**1210**	25p.	brownish grey, black, magenta, new blue and greenish yellow	65	65
1886	**1211**	25p.	brownish grey, black, magenta, new blue and greenish yellow	65	65
1882/6			*Set of* 5	3·00	3·00

Nos. 1882/6 were printed together, *se-tenant*, in horizontal strips of 5 throughout the sheet with the backgrounds forming a composite design.

1212 Sir Rowland Hill and Uniform Penny Postage Petition   **1213** Hill and Penny Black

1214 Guglielmo Marconi and Early Wireless   **1215** Marconi and Sinking of *Titanic* (liner)

(Des The Four Hundred, Eng C. Slania. Recess and litho Harrison)

1995 (5 Sept). *Pioneers of Communications. One phosphor band (19p.) or phosphorised paper (others).* P 14½×14.

1887	**1212**	19p.	silver, red and black	55	55
1888	**1213**	25p.	silver, brown and black	80	80
		a.	Silver (Queen's head and face value) omitted	£200	
1889	**1214**	41p.	silver, grey-green and black	1·10	1·10
1890	**1215**	60p.	silver, deep ultramarine and black	1·50	1·50
1887/90			*Set of* 4	3·50	3·50

Nos. 1887/8 mark the birth bicentenary of Sir Rowland Hill and Nos. 1889/90 the centenary of the first radio transmissions.

1216 Harold Wagstaff   **1217** Gus Risman

1218 Jim Sullivan   **1219** Billy Batten

1220 Brian Bevan

(Des C. Birmingham)

1995 (3 Oct). *Centenary of Rugby League. One phosphor band (19p.) or two phosphor bands (others).* P 14×14½.

1891	**1216**	19p.	blue, greenish yellow, magenta, new blue, grey-black and black	45	45
1892	**1217**	25p.	slate-purple, greenish yellow, mag, new blue, grey-black & black	60	60
1893	**1218**	30p.	slate-green, greenish yellow, bright purple, new blue, grey-black & blk	70	70
1894	**1219**	35p.	slate-black, greenish yellow, mag, new blue and black	95	95
1895	**1220**	41p.	bluish grey, orange-yellow, mag, new blue, grey-black and black	1·25	1·25
1891/5			*Set of* 5	3·50	3·50

1221 European Robin in Mouth of Pillar Box

1222 European Robin on Railings and Holly

1223 European Robin on Snow-covered Milk Bottles

1224 European Robin on Road Sign

1225 European Robin on Door Knob and Christmas Wreath

(Des K. Lilly)

1995 (30 Oct). *Christmas. Christmas Robins. One phosphor band (19p.) or two phosphor bands (others).* P 15×14.

1896	**1221**	19p.	silver, greenish yellow, vermilion, orange-vermilion, bistre and black	45	45
1897	**1222**	25p.	silver, greenish yellow, scarlet, pale blue, ochre and black	60	60
1898	**1223**	30p.	silver, greenish yellow, rose-carmine, lt green, olive-brn & grey	80	80
1899	**1224**	41p.	silver, greenish yellow, rose-red, dull blue, bistre and black	1·10	1·10
1900	**1225**	60p.	silver, orange-yellow, red-orange, bistre and black	1·50	1·50
1896/1900			*Set of* 5	4·00	4·00

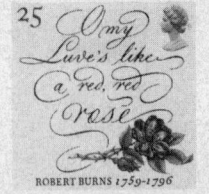

1226 Opening Lines of "To a Mouse" and Fieldmouse   **1227** "O my Luve's like a red, red rose" and Wild Rose

1228 "Scots, wha hae wi Wallace bled" and Sir William Wallace   **1229** "Auld Lang Syne" and Highland Dancers

(Des Tayburn Design Consultancy. Litho Questa)

1996 (25 Jan). *Death Bicentenary of Robert Burns (Scottish poet). One phosphor band (19p.) or 2 phosphor bands (others).* P 14½.

1901	**1226**	19p.	cream, bistre-brown and black	55	55
1902	**1227**	25p.	cream, bistre-brown, black, mag, bistre-yellow and new blue	80	80
1903	**1228**	41p.	cream, bistre-brown, black, mag, bistre-yellow and new blue	1·10	1·10
1904	**1229**	60p.	cream, bistre-brown, black, mag, bistre-yellow and new blue	1·50	1·50
1901/4			*Set of* 4	3·50	3·50

1230 "MORE! LOVE" (Mel Calman)

1231 "Sincerely" (Charles Barsotti)

1232 "Do you have something for the HUMAN CONDITION?" (Mel Calman)

1233 "MENTAL FLOSS" (Leo Cullum)

1234 "4.55 P.M." (Charles Barsotti)

1235 "Dear lottery prize winner" (Larry)

1236 "I'm writing to you because...." (Mel Calman)

1237 "FETCH THIS, FETCH THAT" (Charles Barsotti)

1238 "My day starts before I'm ready for it" (Mel Calman)

1239 "THE CHEQUE IN THE POST" (Jack Ziegler)

(Des M. Wolff. Litho Walsall)

1996 (26 Feb–11 Nov). *Greeting Stamps. Cartoons. "All-over" phosphor.* P 14½×14 (with one elliptical hole on each vertical side).

1905	**1230**	(1st) black and bright mauve	..	40	45
		a. Booklet pane. Nos. 1905/14		4·00	
		p. Two phosphor bands (11 Nov)		40	45
		pa. Booklet pane. Nos. 1905p/14p		4·00	
1906	**1231**	(1st) black and blue-green	..	40	45
		p. Two phosphor bands (11 Nov)		40	45
1907	**1232**	(1st) black and new blue	..	40	45
		p. Two phosphor bands (11 Nov)		40	45
1908	**1233**	(1st) black and bright violet	..	40	45
		p. Two phosphor bands (11 Nov)		40	45
1909	**1234**	(1st) black and vermilion	..	40	45
		p. Two phosphor bands (11 Nov)		40	45
1910	**1235**	(1st) black and new blue	..	40	45
		p. Two phosphor bands (11 Nov)		40	45
1911	**1236**	(1st) black and vermilion	..	40	45
		p. Two phosphor bands (11 Nov)		40	45
1912	**1237**	(1st) black and bright violet	..	40	45
		p. Two phosphor bands (11 Nov)		40	45
1913	**1238**	(1st) black and blue-green	..	40	45
		p. Two phosphor bands (11 Nov)		40	45
1914	**1239**	(1st) black and bright mauve	..	40	45
		p. Two phosphor bands (11 Nov)		40	45
1905/14		..	Set of 10	4·00	4·50
1905p/14p		..	Set of 10	4·00	4·50

Nos. 1905/14 were issued in £2·50 stamp booklets (sold at £2·60 from 8 July 1996), together with a pane of twenty half stamp-sized labels. The stamps and labels were attached to the booklet cover by a common gutter margin.

1240 "Muscovy Duck"   **1241** "Lapwing"

1242 "White-fronted Goose"   **1243** "Bittern"

1244 "Whooper Swan"

(Des Moseley Webb)

1996 (12 Mar). *50th Anniv of the Wildfowl and Wetlands Trust. Bird paintings by C. F. Tunnicliffe. One phosphor band (19p.) or phosphorised paper (others).* P 14½×14½.

1915	**1240**	19p. sepia, orange-yellow, brown, pale buff, grey and gold	40	40
1916	**1241**	25p. bistre-brown, greenish yell, mag, new blue, pale buff, gold & black	60	60
1917	**1242**	30p. bistre-brown, greenish yell, mag, new bl, pale buff, gold & grey-blk	70	70
1918	**1243**	35p. sepia, pale orange, lake-brn, brn-olive, pale buff, gold & grey-black	95	95
1919	**1244**	41p. sepia, greenish yellow, magenta, new bl, pale buff, gold & grey-blk	1·25	1·25
1915/19		.. .. Set of 5	3·50	3·50

1245 The Odeon, Harrogate

1246 Laurence Olivier and Vivien Leigh in *Lady Hamilton* (film)

1247 Old Cinema Ticket

1248 Pathé News Still

1249 Cinema Sign, The Odeon, Manchester

(Des The Chase)

1996 (16 Apr). *Centenary of Cinema. One phosphor band (19p.) or two phosphor bands (others).* P 14×14½.

1920	**1245**	19p. black, greenish yellow, silver, bright magenta and new blue ..	40	40
1921	**1246**	25p. black, greenish yellow, silver, bright magenta and new blue ..	60	60
1922	**1247**	30p. black, greenish yellow, silver, bright magenta and new blue ..	70	70
1923	**1248**	35p. black, red and silver	95	95
1924	**1249**	41p. black, greenish yellow, silver, bright magenta and new blue ..	1·25	1·25
1920/4		.. .. Set of 5	3·50	3·50

1250 Dixie Dean

1251 Bobby Moore

1252 Duncan Edwards

1253 Billy Wright

1254 Danny Blanchflower

(Des H. Brown. Litho Questa)

1996 (14 May). *European Football Championship. One phosphor band (19p.) or two phosphor bands (others).* P 14½×14.

1925	**1250**	19p. vermilion, black, pale grey and grey	40	40
		a. Booklet pane. No. 1925×4 with margins all round ..	1·50	
1926	**1251**	25p. brt emerald, blk, pale grey & grey	60	60
		a. Booklet pane. No. 1926×4 with margins all round ..	2·25	
1927	**1252**	35p. orge-yellow, blk, pale grey & grey	1·10	1·10
		a. Booklet pane. No. 1927/9, each × 2, with margins all round ..	6·50	
1928	**1253**	41p. new blue, black, pale grey and grey	1·10	1·10
1929	**1254**	60p. brt orange, black, pale grey & grey	1·50	1·50
1925/9		.. .. .. Set of 5	4·25	4·25

1255 Athlete on Starting Blocks

1256 Throwing the Javelin

1257 Basketball

1258 Swimming

1259 Athlete celebrating and
Olympic Rings

(Des N. Knight. Litho Questa)

1996 (9 July). *Olympic and Paralympic Games, Atlanta. Two
phosphor bands.* P 14½×14.

1930	**1255**	26p. greenish grey, silver, rosine, black, magenta, bistre-yellow & new blue	65	65
		a. Horiz strip of 5. Nos. 1930/4	3·00	3·00
1931	**1256**	26p. greenish grey, silver, rosine, black, magenta, bistre-yellow & new blue	65	65
1932	**1257**	26p. greenish grey, silver, rosine, black, magenta, bistre-yellow & new blue	65	65
1933	**1258**	26p. greenish grey, silver, rosine, black, magenta, bistre-yellow & new blue	65	65
1934	**1259**	26p. greenish grey, silver, rosine, black, magenta, bistre-yellow & new blue	65	65
1930/4		*Set of* 5	3·00	3·00

Nos. 1930/4 were printed together, *se-tenant*, in horizontal strips
of 5 throughout the sheet.

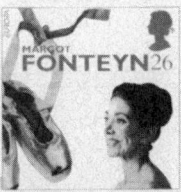

1260 Prof. Dorothy
Hodgkin (scientist)

1261 Dame Margot
Fonteyn (ballerina)

1262 Dame Elisabeth
Frink (sculptress)

1263 Dame Daphne du
Maurier (novelist)

1264 Dame Marea Hartman
(sports administrator)

(Des Stephanie Nash)

1996 (6 Aug). *Europa. Famous Women. One phosphor band*
(20*p.*) *or two phosphor bands* (*others*). P 14½.

1935	**1260**	20p. dull blue-grn, brownish grey & blk	50	50
1936	**1261**	26p. dull mauve, brownish grey & black	70	70
		a. Imperf (horiz pair)		
1937	**1262**	31p. bronze, brownish grey and black	90	90
1938	**1263**	37p. silver, brownish grey and black	1·10	1·10
1939	**1264**	43p. gold, brownish grey and black	1·25	1·25
1935/9		*Set of* 5	4·00	4·00

Nos. 1936/7 include the "EUROPA" emblem.

1265 *Muffin the Mule*

1266 *Sooty*

1267 *Stingray*

1268 *The Clangers*

1269 *Dangermouse*

(Des Tutssells. Photo Enschedé)

1996 (3 Sept)–97. *50th Anniv of Children's Television. One
phosphor band* (20*p.*) *or two phosphor bands* (*others*).
P 14½×14.

1940	**1265**	20p. deep claret, black, magenta, rosine and greenish yellow	50	50
		a. Perf 15×14 (23.9.97)	1·00	1·00
		ab. Booklet pane. No. 1940a×4 with margins all round	4·00	
1941	**1266**	26p. bright blue, black, deep grey-blue, magenta and greenish yellow	70	70
1942	**1267**	31p. greenish blue, black, new blue, magenta and greenish yellow	90	90
1943	**1268**	37p. dull violet-blue, black, new blue, magenta and greenish yellow	1·10	1·10
1944	**1269**	43p. bright purple, black, new blue, magenta and greenish yellow	1·25	1·25
1940/4		*Set of* 5	4·00	4·00

No. 1940a comes from stamp booklets and was printed by
Harrison & Sons Ltd.

1270 Triumph TR3

1271 MG TD

1272 Austin-Healey 100

1273 Jaguar XK120

1274 Morgan Plus 4

(Des S. Clay)

1996 (1 Oct). *Classic Sports Cars. One phosphor band* (20*p.*) *or
two phosphor bands* (*others*). P 14½.

1945	**1270**	20p. silver, greenish yellow, bright scarlet, vermilion, new blue & blk	40	40
1946	**1271**	26p. silver, greenish yellow, magenta, greenish blue and black	55	55
		a. Imperf (pair)		
1947	**1272**	37p. silver, greenish yellow, brt mag, deep turq-blue, new blue & black	75	75
		a. Imperf (pair)		
1948	**1273**	43p. silver, greenish yellow, magenta, greenish blue and black	90	90
		a. Imperf (horiz pair)		
1949	**1274**	63p. silver, greenish yellow, magenta, greenish blue, stone and black	1·25	1·25
1945/9		*Set of* 5	3·50	3·50

On Nos. 1946/9 the left-hand phosphor band on each stamp is
three times the width of that on the right.

1275 The Three Kings

1276 The Annunciation

1277 The Journey to Bethlehem

1278 The Nativity

1279 The Shepherds

(Des Laura Stoddart)

1996 (28 Oct). *Christmas. One phosphor band (2nd class) or two phosphor bands (others).* P 15×14.

1950	**1275**	(2nd) gold, greenish yellow, magenta, blue, black and light brown ..	40	40
1951	**1276**	(1st) gold, yellow, cerise, new blue, black and light brown ..	55	55
1952	**1277**	31p. gold, orange-yellow, cerise, blue, black and light brown ..	65	65
1953	**1278**	43p. gold, greenish yellow, magenta, new blue, grey-black & lt brown	90	90
1954	**1279**	63p. gold, greenish yellow, magenta, new blue, black and light brown	1·25	1·25
1950/4	..	.. .. .. Set of 5	3·25	3·25

1280 *Gentiana acaulis* (Georg Ehret)

1281 *Magnolia grandiflora* (Ehret)

1282 *Camellia japonica* (Alfred Chandler)

1283 *Tulipa* (Ehret)

1284 *Fuchsia* "Princess of Wales" (Augusta Withers)

1285 *Tulipa gesneriana* (Ehret)

1286 *Guzmania splendens* (Charlotte Sowerby)

1287 *Iris latifolia* (Ehret)

1288 *Hippeastrum rutilum* (Pierre-Joseph Redoute)

1289 *Passiflora coerulea* (Ehret)

(Des Tutssels. Litho Walsall)

1997 (6 Jan). *Greeting Stamps. 19th-century Flower Paintings. Two phosphor bands.* P 14½×14 (with one elliptical hole on each vertical side).

1955	**1280**	(1st) greenish yellow, new blue, magenta, black, blue-green & gold	40	45
		a. Booklet pane. Nos. 1955/64 ..	4·00	
		ab. Gold, blue-green and phosphor omitted		
1956	**1281**	(1st) greenish yellow, new blue, magenta, black, blue-green & gold	40	45
1957	**1282**	(1st) greenish yellow, new blue, magenta, black, blue-green & gold	40	45
1958	**1283**	(1st) greenish yellow, new blue, magenta, black, blue-green & gold	40	45
1959	**1284**	(1st) greenish yellow, new blue, magenta, black, blue-green & gold	40	45
1960	**1285**	(1st) greenish yellow, new blue, magenta, black, blue-green & gold	40	45
1961	**1286**	(1st) greenish yellow, new blue, magenta, black, blue-green & gold	40	45
1962	**1287**	(1st) greenish yellow, new blue, magenta, black, blue-green & gold	40	45
1963	**1288**	(1st) greenish yellow, new blue, magenta, black, blue-green & gold	40	45
1964	**1289**	(1st) greenish yellow, new blue, magenta, black, blue-green & gold	40	45
1955/64	..	.. .. .. Set of 10	4·00	4·50

Nos. 1955/64 were issued in £2.60 stamp booklets together with a pane of twenty half-sized labels. The stamp and labels were attached to the booklet cover by a common gutter margin.

1290 "King Henry VIII"

1291 "Catherine of Aragon"

1292 "Anne Boleyn"

1293 "Jane Seymour"

1294 "Anne of Cleves"

1295 "Catherine Howard"

1296 "Catherine Parr"

(Des Kate Stephens from contemporary paintings. Photo Harrison)

1997 (21 Jan). *450th Death Anniv of King Henry VIII. Two phosphor bands.* P 15 (No. 1965) *or* 14×15 (others).

1965	**1290**	26p. gold, greenish yellow, bright purple, new blue and black ..	60	60
		a. Imperf (pair)		
1966	**1291**	26p. gold, greenish yellow, bright carmine, new blue and black ..	65	65
		a. Horiz strip of 6. Nos. 1966/71 ..	3·75	3·75
1967	**1292**	26p. gold, greenish yellow, bright carmine, new blue and black ..	65	65
1968	**1293**	26p. gold, greenish yellow, bright carmine, new blue and black ..	65	65
1969	**1294**	26p. gold, greenish yellow, bright carmine, new blue and black ..	65	65
1970	**1295**	26p. gold, greenish yellow, bright carmine, new blue and black ..	65	65
1971	**1296**	26p. gold, greenish yellow, bright carmine, new blue and black ..	65	65
1965/71	..	.. .. .. Set of 7	4·00	4·00

Nos. 1966/71 were printed together, *se-tenant*, in horizontal strips of six throughout the sheet.

1297 St. Columba in Boat

1298 St. Columba on Iona

1299 St. Augustine with King Ethelbert

1300 St. Augustine with Model of Cathedral

(Des Claire Melinsky. Litho Enschedé)

1997 (11 Mar). *Religious Anniversaries. Two phosphor bands.* P 14½.

1972	**1297**	26p. greenish yellow, magenta, new blue, grey-black and gold ..	55	55
		a. Imperf (pair)		
1973	**1298**	37p. greenish yellow, magenta, new blue, grey-black and gold ..	75	75
1974	**1299**	43p. greenish yellow, magenta, new blue, grey-black and gold ..	90	90
1975	**1300**	63p. greenish yellow, magenta, new blue, grey-black and gold ..	1·25	1·25
1972/5	..	.. .. .. Set of 4	3·00	3·00

Nos. 1972/3 commemorate the 1400th death anniversary of St. Columba and Nos. 1974/5 the 1400th anniversary of the arrival of St. Augustine of Canterbury in Kent.

1301

1302

(Des J. Matthews. Photo Enschedé)

1997 (18 Mar). *Self-adhesive Coil Stamps. One centre phosphor band (2nd) or two phosphor bands (1st). P 14×15 die-cut (with one elliptical hole on each vertical side).*

1976	1301	(2nd) bright blue	30	35
1977	1302	(1st) bright orange-red	40	45

Nos. 1976/7, which were initially priced at 20p. and 26p, were each sold in rolls of 100 with the stamps separate on the backing paper.

(Photo Harrison (No. 1978), Harrison (booklets) or Walsall (sheets and booklets) (No. 1979))

1997 (21 Apr–23 Sept). *Royal Golden Wedding (1st issue). Designs as T 367 and 914 but colours changed. Two phosphor bands. P 15×14 (with one elliptical hole on each vertical side).*

1978	367	26p. gold	40	45
		a. Imperf (horiz pair)		
		1. Booklet pane Nos. 1978/9, each × 4, and centre label with margins all round (23 Sept)	3·50	
1979	914	(1st) gold	40	45

See also Nos. 2011/14.

1303 *Dracula*   1304 *Frankenstein*

1305 *Dr. Jekyll and Mr. Hyde*   1306 *The Hound of the Baskervilles*

(Des I. Pollock. Photo Walsall)

1997 (13 May). *Europa. Tales and Legends. Horror Stories. Two phosphor bands. P 15×14.*

1980	1303	26p. grey-black, black, new blue, magenta and greenish yellow	55	55
1981	1304	31p. grey-black, black, new blue, magenta and greenish yellow	65	65
1982	1305	37p. grey-black, black, new blue, magenta and greenish yellow	75	75
1983	1306	43p. grey-black, black, new blue, magenta and greenish yellow	85	85
1980/3		Set of 4	2·50	2·50

Nos. 1980/3 commemorate the birth bicentenary of Mary Shelley (creator of Frankenstein) with the 26p. and 31p. values incorporating the "EUROPA" emblem.

Each value has features printed in fluorescent ink which are visible under ultra-violet light.

1307 Reginald Mitchell and Supermarine Spitfire MkIIA

1308 Roy Chadwick and Avro Lancaster MkI

1309 Ronald Bishop and De Havilland Mosquito B MkXVI

1310 George Carter and Gloster Meteor T Mk 7

1311 Sir Sidney Camm and Hawker Hunter FGA Mk9

(Des Turner Duckworth. Photo Harrison)

1997 (10 June). *British Aircraft Designers. One phosphor band (20p.) or two phosphor bands (others). P 15×14.*

1984	1307	20p. silver, greenish yellow, magenta, new blue, black and grey	40	40
1985	1308	26p. silver, greenish yellow, magenta, new blue, black and grey	55	55
1986	1309	37p. silver, greenish yellow, magenta, new blue, black and grey	75	75
1987	1310	43p. silver, greenish yellow, magenta, new blue, black and grey	85	85
1988	1311	63p. silver, greenish yellow, magenta, new blue, black and grey	1·25	1·25
1984/8		Set of 5	3·50	3·50

1312 Carriage Horse and Coachman   1313 Lifeguards Horse and Trooper

1314 Blues and Royals Drum Horse and Drummer   1315 Duke of Edinburgh's Horse and Groom

(Des J.-L. Benard. Litho Walsall)

1997 (8 July). *"All the Queen's Horses". 50th Anniv of the British Horse Society. One phosphor band (20p.) or two phosphor bands (others). P 14½.*

1989	1312	20p. scarlet-vermilion, black, magenta, new blue and greenish yellow	40	40
1990	1313	26p. scarlet-vermilion, black, magenta, new blue and greenish yellow	55	55
1991	1314	43p. scarlet-vermilion, black, magenta, new blue and greenish yellow	85	85
1992	1315	63p. scarlet-vermilion, black, magenta, new blue and greenish yellow	1·25	1·25
1989/92		Set of 4	2·75	2·75

GH CASTLE

Harrison Nos. 1611/14

GH CASTLE

Enschedé Nos. 1993/6

Differences between Harrison and Enschedé:
Harrison – "C" has top serif and tail of letter points to right. "A" has flat top. "S" has top and bottom serifs.
Enschedé – "C" has no top serif and tail of letter points upwards. "A" has pointed top. "S" has no serifs.

(Des from photos by Prince Andrew, Duke of York. Eng Inge Madle. Recess (Queens head by silk screen process) Enschedé)

1997 (29 July). *Designs as Nos. 1612/14 with Queen's head in silhouette as T 1044, but re-engraved with differences in inscription as shown above. P 15×14 (with one elliptical hole on each vertical side).*

1993	880	£1.50, deep claret and gold †	2·25	2·40
1994	881	£2 indigo and gold †	3·00	3·25
1995	1044	£3 violet and gold †	4·50	4·75
		a. Gold (Queen's head) omitted		
1996	882	£5 deep brown and gold †	7·50	7·75
		a. Gold (Queen's head) omitted		
1993/6		Set of 4	17·00	18·00

†The Queen's head on these stamps is printed in optically variable ink which changes colour from gold to green when viewed from different angles.

No. 1996a occurs on R. 5/8 and R. 6/8 from some sheets.

1316 Haroldswick, Shetland   1317 Painswick, Gloucestershire

1318 Beddgelert, Gwynedd   1319 Ballyroney, County Down

(Des T. Millington. Photo Enschedé)

1997 (12 Aug). *Sub-Post Offices. One phosphor band (20p.) or two phosphor bands (others). P 14½.*

1997	1316	20p. greenish yellow, brt magenta, new blue, grey-black, rosine & bl-grn	30	35
1998	1317	26p. greenish yellow, brt magenta, new blue, grey-black, rosine & bl-grn	40	45
1999	1318	43p. greenish yellow, brt magenta, new blue, grey-black, rosine & bl-grn	65	70
2000	1319	63p. greenish yellow, brt magenta, new blue, grey-black, rosine & bl-grn	95	1·00
1997/2000		Set of 4	2·25	2·50

Nos. 1997/2000 were issued on the occasion of the Centenary of the National Federation of Sub-Postmasters.

PRINTERS. Harrison and Sons Ltd became De La Rue Security Print on 8 September 1997. This was not reflected in the sheet imprints until mid-1998.

1320 *Noddy*   1321 *Famous Five*

1322 *Secret Seven*   1323 *Faraway Tree*

1324 *Malory Towers*

(Des C. Birmingham. Photo Enschedé)

1997 (9 Sept). *Birth Centenary of Enid Blyton (children's author).*
One phosphor band (20p) or two phosphor bands (others).
P 14×14½.

2001	**1320**	20p. greenish yellow, magenta, new blue, grey-black & deep grey-blue	30	35
2002	**1321**	26p. greenish yellow, magenta, new blue, grey-black & deep grey-blue	40	45
2003	**1322**	37p. greenish yellow, magenta, new blue, grey-black & deep grey-blue	60	65
2004	**1323**	43p. greenish yellow, magenta, new blue, grey-black & deep grey-blue	65	70
2005	**1324**	63p. greenish yellow, magenta, new blue, grey-black & deep grey-blue	95	1·00
2001/5	..	.. *Set of* 5	3·00	3·25

1325 Children and Father Christmas pulling Cracker

1326 Father Christmas with Traditional Cracker

1327 Father Christmas riding Cracker

1328 Father Christmas on Snowball

1329 Father Christmas and Chimney

(Des J. Gorham and M. Thomas (1st), J. Gorham (others). Photo Harrison)

1997 (27 Oct). *Christmas. 150th Anniv of the Christmas Cracker.*
One phosphor band (2nd) or two phosphor bands (others).
P 15×14.

2006	**1325**	(2nd) gold, greenish yellow, bright magenta, new blue & grey-black	30	35
		a. Imperf (pair)	£1100	
2007	**1326**	(1st) gold, greenish yellow, bright magenta, new blue & grey-black	40	45
2008	**1327**	31p. gold, greenish yellow, brt mag, new blue, brt black & grey-black	50	55
2009	**1328**	43p. gold, greenish yellow, brt mag, pale new blue & grey-black	65	70
2010	**1329**	63p. gold, greenish yellow, bright magenta, new blue & grey-black	95	1·00
2006/10	.. .. *Set of* 5		2·75	3·00

1330 Wedding Photograph, 1947

1331 Queen Elizabeth II and Prince Philip, 1997

(Des D. Driver (20p., 43p.), Lord Snowdon (26p., 63p.). Photo Harrison)

1997 (13 Nov). *Royal Golden Wedding (2nd issue). One phosphor band (20p.) or two phosphor bands (others). P* 15.

2011	**1330**	20p. gold, yellow-brown and grey-black	30	35
2012	**1331**	26p. gold, bistre-yellow, magenta, new blue, grey-black and greenish grey	40	45
2013	**1330**	43p. gold, bluish green and grey-black	65	70
2014	**1331**	63p. gold, bistre-yellow, magenta, new blue, grey-black & lavender-grey	95	1·00
2011/14	.. .. .. *Set of* 4		2·25	2·50

1332 Common Dormouse

1333 Lady's Slipper Orchid

1334 Song Thrush

1335 Shining Ram's-horn Snail

1336 Mole Cricket

1337 Devil's Bolete

(Des R. Maude. Litho Questa)

1998 (20 Jan). *Endangered Species. One side phosphor band (20p.) or two phosphor bands (others). P* 14×14½.

2015	**1332**	20p. black, new blue, mag, greenish yellow, dp bl & pale lavender-grey	30	35
		a. Imperf (pair)		
2016	**1333**	26p. black, new blue, mag, greenish yellow, dp blue & pale yell-olive	40	45
2017	**1334**	31p. black, new blue, mag, greenish yellow, dp blue & pale bluish grey	50	55
2018	**1335**	37p. black, new blue, mag, greenish yellow, dp bl & pale greenish grey	60	65
2019	**1336**	43p. black, new blue, mag, greenish yellow, dp blue & pale dull mauve	65	70
2020	**1337**	63p. black, new blue, mag, greenish yellow, dp blue & pale grey-brown	95	1·00
2015/20	.. .. .. *Set of* 6		3·50	3·75

1338 Diana, Princess of Wales (photo by Lord Snowdon)

1339 At British Lung Foundation Function, April 1997 (photo by John Stillwell)

1340 Wearing Tiara, 1991 (photo by Lord Snowdon)

1341 On Visit to Birmingham, October 1995 (photo by Tim Graham)

1342 In Evening Dress, 1987 (photo by Terence Donovan)

(Des B. Robinson. Photo Harrison)

1998 (3 Feb). *Diana, Princess of Wales Commemoration. Two phosphor bands. P* 14×15.

2021	**1338**	26p. purple, greenish yellow, magenta, new blue and black	40	45
		a. Horiz strip of 5. Nos. 2021/5	2·00	2·25
		ad. Imperf (horiz strip of 3. Nos. 2021/3)		
2022	**1339**	26p. purple, greenish yellow, magenta, new blue and black	40	45
2023	**1340**	26p. purple, greenish yellow, magenta, new blue and black	40	45
2024	**1341**	26p. purple, greenish yellow, magenta, new blue and black	40	45
2025	**1342**	26p. purple, greenish yellow, magenta, new blue and black	40	45
2021/5	.. .. .. *Set of* 5		2·00	2·25

Nos. 2021/5 were printed together, *se-tenant*, in horizontal strips of five throughout the sheet.

1343 Lion of England and Griffin of Edward III

1344 Falcon of Plantagenet and Bull of Clarence

1345 Lion of Mortimer and Yale of Beaufort

1346 Greyhound of Richmond and Dragon of Wales

1347 Unicorn of Scotland and Horse of Hanover

(Des J. Matthews. Recess and litho Harrison)

1998 (24 Feb). *650th Anniv of the Order of the Garter. The Queen's Beasts. Two phosphor bands.* P 15×14.

2026	**1343**	26p. silver, green, brt blue, carmine-red, verm, lemon, grey-blk & blk		40	45
		a. Horiz strip of 5. Nos. 2026/30		2·00	2·25
2027	**1344**	26p. silver, green, brt blue, carm-red, verm, lemon, grey, grey-blk & blk		40	45
2028	**1345**	26p. silver, green, brt blue, carm-red, verm, lemon, grey, grey-blk & blk		40	45
2029	**1346**	26p. silver, green, brt blue, carm-red, verm, lemon, grey, grey-blk & blk		40	45
2030	**1347**	26p. silver, green, brt blue, vermilion, lemon, grey, grey-black & black		40	45
2026/30			Set of 5	2·00	2·25

Nos. 2026/30 were printed together, *se-tenant*, in horizontal strips of five throughout the sheet.

The phosphor bands on Nos. 2026/30 are only half the height of the stamps and do not cover the silver parts of the designs.

1348

(Des G. Knipe, adapted Dew Gibbons Design Group. Photo Walsall)

1998 (10 Mar). *As T 157 (Wilding definitive of 1952–54) but with face values in decimal currency as T 1348. One side phosphor band* (20p.) *or two phosphor bands* (others). P 14 (with one elliptical hole on each vertical side).

2031	**1348**	20p. light green		60	60
		b. Booklet pane. No. 2031×6 with margins all round		3·50	
		c. Booklet pane. Nos. 2031×4 and 2032/3, each × 2 and central label with margins all round		5·50	
2032		26p. red-brown		60	60
		a. Booklet pane. No. 2032×9		5·25	
		b. Booklet pane. Nos. 2032/3, each × 3		5·00	
2033		37p. light purple		1·10	1·10
2031/3			Set of 3	2·25	2·25

Nos. 2031/3 were issued in £7.49 stamp booklets. No. 2031 exists with the phosphor band at left or right

1349 St. John's Point Lighthouse, County Down

1350 Smalls Lighthouse, Pembrokeshire

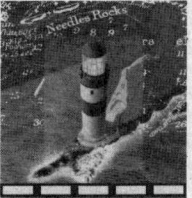

1351 Needles Rock Lighthouse, Isle of Wight, c 1900

1352 Bell Rock Lighthouse, Arbroath, mid-19th-century

1353 Eddystone Lighthouse, Plymouth, 1698

(Des D. Davis and J. Boon. Litho Questa)

1998 (24 Mar). *Lighthouses. One side phosphor band* (20p.) *or two phosphor bands* (others). P 14½×14.

2034	**1349**	20p. gold, greenish yellow, magenta, new blue and black		30	35
2035	**1350**	26p. gold, greenish yellow, magenta, new blue and black		40	45
2036	**1351**	37p. gold, greenish yellow, magenta, new blue and black		60	65
2037	**1352**	43p. gold, greenish yellow, magenta, new blue and black		65	70
2038	**1353**	63p. gold, greenish yellow, magenta, new blue and black		95	1·00
2034/8			Set of 5	3·00	3·25

Nos. 2034/8 commemorate the 300th anniversary of the first Eddystone Lighthouse and the final year of manned lighthouses.

(Photo Enschedé)

1998 (6 Apr). *Self-adhesive Coil Stamps. Designs as T 913/14. One centre phosphor band* (2nd), *or two phosphor bands* (1st). P 15×14 die-cut (with one elliptical hole on each vertical side).

2039	(2nd) bright blue		30	35
2040	(1st) bright orange-red		40	45

Nos. 2039/40 were initially sold for 20p. and 26p., and were issued in rolls of 200 with the surplus self-adhesive paper removed.

1354 Tommy Cooper

1355 Eric Morecambe

1356 Joyce Grenfell

1357 Les Dawson

1358 Peter Cook

(Des G. Scarfe. Litho Walsall)

1998 (23 Apr). *Comedians. One side phosphor band* (20p.) *or two phosphor bands* (others). P 14½×14.

2041	**1354**	20p. vermilion, black, rose-pink, new blue and greenish-yellow		30	35
2042	**1355**	26p. verm, black, rose-pink & new blue		40	45
2043	**1356**	37p. vermilion, black, rose-pink, new blue and greenish-yellow		60	65
2044	**1357**	43p. vermilion, black, rose-pink, new blue and pale orange		65	70
2045	**1358**	63p. vermilion, black, deep rose-pink, new blue and greenish-yellow		95	1·00
2041/5			Set of 5	3·00	3·25

MINIMUM PRICE

The minimum price quote is 10p which represents a handling charge rather than a basis for valuing common stamps. For further notes about prices see introductory pages.

1359 Hands forming Heart

1360 Adult and Child holding Hands

1361 Hands forming Cradle

1362 Hand taking Pulse

(Des V. Frost from photos by A. Wilson. Litho Questa)

1998 (23 June). *50th Anniv of the National Health Service. One side phosphor band* (20p.) *or two phosphor bands* (others). P 14×14½.

2046	**1359**	20p. deep claret, black, grey-brown, pale cream and cream		30	35
2047	**1360**	26p. deep grey-green, black, grey-brown, pale cream and cream		40	45
2048	**1361**	43p. deep lilac, black, grey-brown, pale cream and cream		65	70
2049	**1362**	63p. deep dull blue, black, grey-brown, pale cream and cream		95	1·00
2046/9			Set of 4	2·25	2·50

REGIONAL ISSUES

For Regional Issues of Guernsey, Jersey and the Isle of Man, *see* after Great Britain Postal Fiscals.
Printers (£ s. d. stamps of all regions):—Photo Harrison & Sons. Portrait by Dorothy Wilding Ltd.

DATES OF ISSUE. Conflicting dates of issue have been announced for some of the regional issues, partly explained by the stamps being released on different dates by the Philatelic Bureau in Edinburgh or the Philatelic Counter in London and in the regions. We have adopted the practice of giving the earliest known dates, since once released the stamps could have been used anywhere in the U.K.

I. NORTHERN IRELAND

| N 1 | N 2 | N 3 |

(Des W. Hollywood (3d., 4d., 5d.), L. Pilton (6d., 9d.), T. Collins (1s. 3d., 1s. 6d.))

1958–67. *W* 179. *P* 15 × 14.
NI1	N 1	3d. deep lilac (18.8.58)		20	10
		p. One centre phosphor band (9.6.67)		20	15
NI2		4d. ultramarine (7.2.66)		20	15
		p. Two phosphor bands (10.67)		20	15
NI3	N 2	6d. deep claret (29.9.58)		30	70
NI4		9d. bronze-green (2 phosphor bands) (1.3.67)		30	70
NI5	N 3	1s. 3d. green (29.9.58)		30	70
NI6		1s. 6d. grey-blue (2 phosphor bands) (1.3.67)		30	70

1968–69. *No wmk. Chalk-surfaced paper. One centre phosphor band* (*Nos.* NI8/9) *or two phosphor bands* (*others*). *P* 15 × 14.
NI 7	N 1	4d. deep bright blue (27.6.68)		20	15
NI 8		4d. olive-sepia (4.9.68)		20	15
NI 9		4d. bright vermilion (26.2.69)		20	20
NI10		5d. royal blue (4.9.68)		20	20
NI11	N 3	1s. 6d. grey-blue (20.5.69)		2·50	3·25

No. NI7 was only issued in Northern Ireland with gum arabic. After it had been withdrawn from Northern Ireland but whilst still on sale at the philatelic counters elsewhere, about fifty sheets with PVA gum were sold over the London Philatelic counter on 23 October 1968, and some were also on sale at the British Philatelic Exhibition Post Office in October, without any prior announcement. The other values exist with PVA gum only.

N 4

(Des J. Mathews after plaster cast by Arnold Machin)

1971 (7 July)–**93.** *Decimal Currency. Chalk-surfaced paper. Type* N 4. (*a*) *Photo Harrison. With phosphor bands. P* 15 × 14.
NI12		2½p. bright magenta (1 centre band)		80	25
NI13		3p. ultramarine (2 bands)		40	15
NI14		3p. ultramarine (1 centre band) (23.1.74)		20	15
NI15		3½p. olive-grey (2 bands) (23.1.74)		20	20
NI16		3½p. olive-grey (1 centre band) (6.11.74)		20	25
NI17		4½p. grey-blue (2 bands) (6.11.74)		25	25
NI18		5p. reddish violet (2 bands)		1·50	1·50
NI19		5½p. violet (2 bands) (23.1.74)		20	20
NI20		5½p. violet (1 centre band) (21.5.75)		20	20
NI21		6½p. greenish blue (1 centre band) (14.1.76)		20	20
NI22		7p. purple-brown (1 centre band) (18.1.78)		35	25
NI23		7½p. chestnut (2 bands)		2·25	2·25
NI24		8p. rosine (2 bands) (23.1.74)		30	30
NI25		8½p. yellow-green (2 bands) (14.1.76)		30	30
NI26		9p. deep violet (2 bands) (18.1.78)		30	30
NI27		10p. orange-brown (2 bands) (20.10.76)		35	35
NI28		10p. orange-brown (1 centre band) (23.7.80)		35	35
NI29		10½p. steel-blue (2 bands) (18.1.78)		50	50
NI30		11p. scarlet (2 bands) (20.10.76)		50	50

(*b*) *Photo Harrison. On phosphorised paper. P* 15 × 14.
NI31		12p. yellowish green (23.7.80)		50	50
NI32		13½p. purple-brown (23.7.80)		70	80
NI33		15p. ultramarine (23.7.80)		70	70

(*c*) *Litho Questa. P* 14 (11½p., 12½p., 14p. (*No.* NI38), 15½p., 16p., 18p. (*No.* NI45), 19½p., 20½p., 22p. (*No.* NI53), 26p. (*No.* NI60), 28p. (*No.* NI62) *or* 15 × 14 (*others*)
NI34		11½p. drab (1 side band) (8.4.81)		70	70
NI35		12p. bright emerald (1 side band) (7.1.86)		70	70
NI36		12½p. light emerald (1 side band) (24.2.82)		60	60
		a. Perf 15 × 14 (28.2.84)		4·25	4·25
NI37		13p. pale chestnut (1 side band) (23.10.84)		1·25	70
NI38		14p. grey-bl (phosphorised paper) (8.4.81)		70	60
NI39		14p. deep blue (1 centre band) (8.11.88)		70	60
NI40		15p. bright blue (1 centre band) (28.11.89)		70	60
NI41		15½p. pale violet (phosphorised paper) (24.2.82)		80	65
NI42		16p. drab (phosphorised paper) (27.4.83)		1·00	1·00
		a. Perf 15 × 14 (28.2.84)		9·50	8·00
NI43		17p. grey-blue (phosphorised paper) (23.10.84)		1·00	80
NI44		17p. deep blue (1 centre band) (4.12.90)		70	70
NI45		18p. dp vio (phosphorised paper) (8.4.81)		90	90
NI46		18p. deep olive-grey (phosphorised paper) (6.1.87)		80	80
NI47		18p. bright green (1 centre band) (3.12.91)		70	70
		a. Perf 14 (31.12.92*)		1·25	1·25
NI48		18p. bright green (1 side band) (10.8.93)		2·50	2·50
		l. Booklet pane. Nos. NI48, NI59, S61, S71, W49 and W60 with margins all round		6·00	

NI49		19p. bright orange-red (phosphorised paper) (8.11.88)		80	70
NI50		19½p. olive-grey (phosphorised paper) (24.2.82)		1·75	2·25
NI51		20p. brownish black (phosphorised paper) (28.11.89)		80	70
NI52		20½p. ultram (phosphorised paper) (27.4.83)		4·00	4·00
NI53		22p. blue (phosphorised paper) (8.4.81)		1·00	1·10
NI54		22p. yellow-green (phosphorised paper) (23.10.84)		1·00	1·10
NI55		22p. bright orange-red (phosphorised paper) (4.12.90)		1·00	85
NI56		23p. bright green (phosphorised paper) (8.11.88)		1·00	1·10
NI57		24p. Indian red (phosphorised paper) (28.11.89)		1·00	1·10
NI58		24p. chestnut (phosphorised paper) (3.12.91)		90	75
NI59		24p. chestnut (2 bands) (10.8.93)		2·00	2·00
NI60		26p. rosine (phosphorised paper) (24.2.82)		1·10	1·40
		a. Perf 15 × 14 (27.1.87)		3·50	3·50
NI61		26p. drab (phosphorised paper) (4.12.90)		1·00	1·00
NI62		28p. deep violet-blue (phosphorised paper) (27.4.83)		1·10	1·10
		a. Perf 15 × 14 (27.1.87)		1·10	1·10
NI63		28p. deep bluish grey (phosphorised paper) (3.12.91)		1·10	1·10
NI64		31p. bright purple (phosphorised paper) (23.10.84)		1·40	1·40
NI65		32p. greenish blue (phosphorised paper) (8.11.88)		1·25	1·25
NI66		34p. deep bluish grey (phosphorised paper) (28.11.89)		1·40	1·40
NI67		37p. rosine (phosphorised paper) (4.12.90)		1·40	1·40
NI68		39p. bright mauve (phosphorised paper) (3.12.91)		1·40	1·40

*Earliest known date of use.
No. NI47a was caused by the use of a reserve perforating machine for some printings in the second half of 1992.
Nos. NI48 and NI59 only come from booklets.
From 1972 printings were made on fluorescent white paper and from 1973 printings had dextrin added to the PVA gum (see notes after the 1971 Decimal Machin issue).

(Des J. Matthews after plaster cast by Arnold Machin)

1993 (7 Dec)–**97.** *Chalk-surfaced paper. One phosphor band* (19p., 20p.) *or two phosphor bands* (*others*). *P* 15 × 14 (*with one elliptical hole on each vertical side*). (*a*) *Litho Questa.*
NI69	N 4	19p. bistre (1 centre band)		40	40
NI70		19p. bistre (1 side band) (26.7.94)		2·25	2·25
		a. Booklet pane. Nos. NI70×2, NI72×4, NI74, NI76 and centre label with margins all round		6·50	
		b. Booklet pane. Nos. NI70, NI72, NI74 and NI76 with margins all round		3·50	
		d. Booklet pane. Nos. NI70, NI72, S82, S84 and W71 and W73 (25.4.95)		7·00	
		da. Part perf pane*			
NI71		20p. brt green (1 centre band) (23.7.96)		30	35
NI72		25p. red		50	50
NI73		26p. red-brown (23.7.96)		40	45
NI74		30p. deep olive-grey		60	60
NI75		37p. bright mauve (23.7.96)		60	65
NI76		41p. grey-brown		90	90
NI77		63p. light emerald (23.7.96)		95	1·00

(*b*) *Photo Walsall* (20p., 63p.), *Harrison or Walsall* (26p., 37p))
NI78	N 4	20p. bright green (1 centre band) (1.7.97)		30	35
NI79		26p. chestnut (2 bands) (1.7.97)		40	45
		l. Booklet pane. Nos. NI79/80, S91/2 and W80/1 with margins all round (23.9.97)		2·75	
NI80		37p. bright mauve (2 bands) (1.7.97)		60	65
NI81		63p. light emerald (2 bands) (1.7.97)		95	1·00

No. NI70 comes from various booklets and exists with phosphor band at left or right.
*No. NI70da, which comes from the 1995 National Trust £6 booklet, shows the top two values in the pane of 6 (Nos. S82, S84) completely imperforate and the two Wales values below partly imperforate.
No. NI79l, which was printed by Harrison, comes from the 1997 B.B.C. £6.15 booklet.

II. SCOTLAND

| S 1 | S 2 | S 3 |

(Des G. Huntly (3d., 4d., 5d), J. Fleming (6d., 9d.), A. Imrie (1s. 3d., 1s. 6d.))

1958–67. *W* 179. *P* 15 × 14.
S1	S 1	3d. deep lilac (18.8.58)		20	15
		p. Two phosphor bands (29.1.63)		13·00	1·25
		pa. One side phosphor band (30.4.65)		20	25
		pb. One centre phosphor band (9.11.67)		20	15
S2		4d. ultramarine (7.2.66)		20	10
		p. Two phosphor bands		20	20
S3	S 2	6d. deep claret (29.9.58)		20	20
		p. Two phosphor bands (29.1.63)		20	25
S4		9d. bronze-green (2 phosphor bands) (1.3.67)		30	30
S5	S 3	1s. 3d. green (29.9.58)		30	30
		p. Two phosphor bands (29.1.63)		30	30
S6		1s. 6d. grey-blue (2 phosphor bands) (1.3.67)		35	30

The one phosphor band on No. S1pa was produced by printing broad phosphor bands across alternate vertical perforations. Individual stamps show the band at right or left (same prices either way).

S 4

(Des J. Matthews after plaster cast by Arnold Machin)

1971 (7 July)–**93.** *Decimal Currency. Chalk-surfaced paper. Type* S 4.
(*a*) *Photo Harrison. With phosphor bands. P* 15 × 14
S14		2½p. bright magenta (1 centre band)		25	15
S15		3p. ultramarine (2 bands)		30	15
		a. Imperf (pair)†		£400	
S16		3p. ultramarine (1 centre band) (23.1.74)		15	15
S17		3½p. olive-grey (2 bands) (23.1.74)		20	20
S18		3½p. olive-grey (1 centre band) (6.11.74)		20	20
S19		4½p. grey-blue (2 bands) (6.11.74)		25	20
S20		5p. reddish violet (2 bands)		1·00	1·00
S21		5½p. violet (2 bands) (23.1.74)		20	20
S22		5½p. violet (1 centre band) (21.5.75)		20	20
		a. Imperf (pair)		£350	
S23		6½p. greenish blue (1 centre band) (14.1.76)		20	20
S24		7p. purple-brown (1 centre band) (18.1.78)		25	25
S25		7½p. chestnut (2 bands)		1·25	1·25
S26		8p. rosine (23.1.74)		30	40
S27		8½p. yellow-green (2 bands) (14.1.76)		30	30
S28		9p. deep violet (2 bands) (18.1.78)		30	30
S29		10p. orange-brown (2 bands) (20.10.76)		35	30
S30		10p. orange-brown (1 centre band) (23.7.80)		35	35
S31		10½p. steel-blue (2 bands) (18.1.78)		50	50
S32		11p. scarlet (2 bands)		50	35

(*b*) *Photo Harrison. On phosphorised paper. P* 15 × 14
S33		12p. yellowish green (23.7.80)		50	30
S34		13½p. purple-brown (23.7.80)		70	65
S35		15p. ultramarine (23.7.80)		60	45

(*c*) *Litho J.W. One side phosphor band* (11½p., 12p., 12½p., 13p.) *or phosphorised paper* (*others*). *P* 14
S36		11½p. drab (8.4.81)		80	60
S37		12p. bright emerald (7.1.86)		1·75	1·50
S38		12½p. light emerald (24.2.82)		60	50
S39		13p. pale chestnut (23.10.84)		70	50
S40		14p. grey-blue (8.4.81)		60	50
S41		15½p. pale violet (24.2.82)		70	65
S42		16p. drab (27.4.83)		70	55
S43		17p. grey-blue (23.10.84)		3·50	2·25
S44		18p. deep violet (8.4.81)		80	80
S45		19½p. olive-grey (24.2.82)		1·75	1·75
S46		20½p. ultramarine (27.4.83)		4·00	4·00
S47		22p. blue (8.4.81)		90	1·25
S48		22p. yellow-green (23.10.84)		2·25	2·00
S49		26p. rosine (24.2.82)		1·10	1·25
S50		28p. deep violet-blue (27.4.83)		1·10	1·10
S51		31p. bright purple (23.10.84)		2·00	1·75

(*d*) *Litho Questa. P* 15 × 14
S52		12p. bright emerald (1 side band) (29.4.86)		2·00	1·75
S53		13p. pale chestnut (1 side band) (4.11.86)		70	50
S54		14p. deep blue (1 centre band) (8.11.88)		50	50
		l. Booklet pane. No. S54×6 with margins all round (21.3.89)		2·75	
S55		14p. deep blue (1 side band) (21.3.89)		80	1·00
		l. Booklet pane. No. S55×5, S63×2, S68 and centre label with margins all round		16·00	
		la. Error. Booklet pane imperf			
S56		15p. bright blue (1 centre band) (28.11.89)		70	55
		a. Imperf three sides (block of 4)		£275	
S57		17p. grey-bl (phosphorised paper) (29.4.86)		4·25	2·25
S58		17p. deep blue (1 centre band) (4.12.90)		60	60
S59		18p. ol-grey (phosphorised paper) (6.1.87)		80	80
S60		18p. bright green (1 centre band) (3.12.91)		70	70
		a. Perf 14 (26.9.92*)		1·00	75
S61		18p. brt green (1 side band) (10.8.93)		2·00	1·00
S62		19p. bright orange-red (phosphorised paper) (8.11.88)		80	65
		l. Booklet pane. No. S62×9 with margins all round (21.3.89)		5·50	
		m. Booklet pane. No S62×6 with margins all round (21.3.89)		3·50	
S63		19p. bright orange-red (2 bands) (21.3.89)		1·50	1·50
S64		20p. brownish black (phosphorised paper) (28.11.89)		80	60
S65		22p. yell-grn (phosphorised paper) (27.1.87)		90	90
S66		22p. bright orange-red (phosphorised paper) (4.12.90)		1·00	75
S67		23p. brt grn (phosphorised paper) (8.11.88)		1·00	1·10
S68		23p. bright green (2 bands) (21.3.89)		12·00	11·00
S69		24p. Indian red (phosphorised paper) (28.11.89)		1·00	1·00
S70		24p. chestnut (phosphorised paper) (3.12.91)		75	75
		a. Perf 14 (10.92*)		2·50	2·50
S71		24p. chestnut (2 bands) (10.8.93)		2·00	2·00
S72		26p. rosine (phosphorised paper) (27.1.87)		2·50	2·50
S73		26p. drab (phosphorised paper) (4.12.90)		1·00	1·00
S74		28p. deep violet-blue (phosphorised paper) (27.1.87)		1·10	1·10
S75		28p. deep bluish grey (phosphorised paper) (3.12.91)		1·10	1·10
		a. Perf 14 (18.2.93*)		3·25	3·25
S76		31p. brt pur (phosphorised paper) (29.4.86)		1·75	1·75
S77		32p. greenish blue (phosphorised paper) (8.11.88)		1·25	1·25

1967–70. *No wmk. Chalk-surfaced paper. One centre phosphor band* (S7, S9/10) *or two phosphor bands* (*others*). *P* 15 × 14.
S 7	S 1	3d. deep lilac (16.5.68)		10	15
S 8		4d. deep bright blue (28.11.67)		10	15
S 9		4d. olive-sepia (4.9.68)		10	15
S10		4d. bright vermilion (26.2.69)		10	10
S11		5d. royal blue (4.9.68)		20	10
S12	S 2	9d. bronze-green (28.9.70)		5·00	6·50
S13	S 3	1s. 6d. grey-blue (12.12.68)		1·40	1·00

Nos. S7/8 exist with both gum arabic and PVA gum; others with PVA gum only.

S78	34p. deep bluish grey (phosphorised paper) (28.11.89)	1·40	1·40
S79	37p. rosine (phosphorised paper) (4.12.90)	1·40	1·40
S80	39p. brt mve (phosphorised paper) (3.12.91)	1·40	1·40
	a. Perf 14 (11.92)	2·25	2·25

*Earliest known date of use.
†Exists only with gum arabic.
Nos. S55, S61, S63, S68 and S71 only come from booklets.
No. S56a occurred in the second vertical row on two sheets. The error is best collected as a block of four to include the left-hand vertical pair imperforate on three sides.
Nos. S60a, S70a, S75a and S80a were caused by the use of a reserve perforating machine for some printings in late 1992.
From 1972 printings were on fluorescent white paper. Nos. S14/15 exist with PVA and gum arabic and the remainder with PVA only. From 1973 printings had extra dextrin added (see notes after the 1971 Decimal Machin issue).

(Des J. Matthews after plaster cast by Arnold Machin)

1993 (7 Dec)–97. *Chalk-surfaced paper. One phosphor band (19p., 20p.) or two phosphor bands (others). P 15×14 (with one elliptical hole on each vertical side). (a) Litho Questa.*

S81	S 4	19p. bistre (1 centre band)	40	40
S82		19p. bistre (1 side band) (25.4.95)	2·25	2·25
S83		20p. bright green (1 centre band) (23.7.96)	30	35
S84		25p. red	50	50
S85		26p. red-brown (23.7.96)	40	45
S86		30p. deep olive-grey	60	60
S87		37p. bright mauve (23.7.96)	60	65
S88		41p. grey-brown	90	90
S89		63p. light emerald (23.7.96)	95	1·00

(b) Photo Walsall (20p., 63p.), Harrison or Walsall (26p., 37p.))

S90	S 4	20p. bright green (1 centre band) (1.7.97)	30	35
S91		26p. chestnut (2 bands) (1.7.97)	40	45
S92		37p. bright mauve (2 bands) (1.7.97)	60	65
S93		63p. light emerald (2 bands) (1.7.97)	95	1·00

No. S82 only comes from booklets.
The Harrison printings of the Nos. S91/2 are from booklet pane No. N1791.

III. WALES

From the inception of the Regional stamps, the Welsh versions were tendered to members of the public at all Post Offices within the former County of Monmouthshire but the national alternatives were available on request. Offices with a Monmouthshire postal address but situated outside the County, namely Beachley, Brockweir, Redbrook, Sedbury, Tutshill, Welsh Newton and Woodcroft, were not supplied with the Welsh Regional stamps.
With the re-formation of Counties, Monmouthshire became known as Gwent and was also declared to be part of Wales. From July 1974, therefore, except for the offices mentioned above, only Welsh Regional stamps were available at the offices under the jurisdiction of Newport, Gwent.

W 1   W 2   W 3

(Des R. Stone)

1958–67. *W 179. P 15 × 14.*

W1	W 1	3d. deep lilac (18.8.58)	20	10
		p. One centre phosphor band (16.5.67)	20	15
W2		4d. ultramarine (7.2.66)	20	15
		p. Two phosphor bands (10.67)	20	15
W3	W 2	6d. deep claret (29.9.58)	40	20
W4		9d. bronze-green (2 phosphor bands) (1.3.67)	40	40
W5	W 3	1s. 3d. green (29.9.58)	30	30
W6		1s. 6d. grey-blue (2 phosphor bands) (1.3.67)	35	40

1967–69. *No wmk. Chalk-surfaced paper. One centre phosphor band (W7, W9/10) or two phosphor bands (others). P 15 × 14.*

W 7	W 1	3d. deep lilac (6.12.67)	20	10
W 8		4d. ultramarine (21.6.68)	20	10
W 9		4d. olive-sepia (4.9.68)	20	10
W10		4d. bright vermilion (26.2.69)	20	20
W11		5d. royal blue (4.9.68)	20	10
W12	W 2	1s. 6d. grey-blue (1.8.69)	3·00	3·75

The 3d. exists with gum arabic only; the remainder with PVA gum only.

W 4 With "p"   W 5 Without "p"

(Des J. Matthews after plaster cast by Arnold Machin)

1971 (7 July)–93. *Decimal Currency. Chalk-surfaced paper. Type W 4. (a) Photo Harrison. With phosphor bands. P 15×14*

W13	W 4	2½p. bright magenta (1 centre band)	20	15
		a. Imperf (pair)†	£350	
W14		3p. ultramarine (2 bands)	25	15
W15		3p. ultramarine (1 centre band) (23.1.74)	20	20
W16		3½p. olive-grey (2 bands) (23.1.74)	20	25
W17		3½p. olive-grey (1 centre band) (6.11.74)	20	25
W18		4½p. grey-blue (2 bands) (6.11.74)	25	20
W19		5p. reddish violet (2 bands)	1·00	1·00
W20		5½p. violet (2 bands) (23.1.74)	20	20
W21		5½p. violet (1 centre band) (21.5.75)	20	25
		a. Imperf (pair)	£400	

W22	6½p. greenish blue (1 centre band) (14.1.76)	20	20
W23	7p. purple-brn (1 centre band) (18.1.78)	25	25
W24	7½p. chestnut (2 bands)	1·25	1·50
W25	8p. rosine (2 bands) (23.1.74)	30	30
W26	8½p. yellow-green (2 bands) (14.1.76)	30	30
W27	9p. deep violet (2 bands) (18.1.78)	30	30
W28	10p. orange-brown (2 bands) (20.10.76)	35	30
W29	10p. orange-brn (1 centre band) (23.7.80)	35	30
W30	10½p. steel-blue (2 bands) (18.1.78)	50	50
W31	11p. scarlet (2 bands) (20.10.76)	50	50

(b) Photo Harrison. On phosphorised paper. P 15 × 14

W32	12p. yellow-green (23.7.80)	50	45
W33	13½p. purple-brown (23.7.80)	60	70
W34	15p. ultramarine (23.7.80)	60	50

(c) Litho Questa. P 14 (11½p., 12½p., 14p. (No. W39), 15½p., 16p., 18p. (No. W46), 19½p., 20½p., 22p., 26p. (No. W61), 28p. (No. W63)) or 15×14 (others).

W35	11½p. drab (1 side band) (8.4.81)	85	60
W36	12p. bright emerald (1 side band) (7.1.86)	1·25	1·10
W37	12½p. light emerald (1 side band) (24.2.82)	80	60
	a. Perf 15×14 (10.1.84)	6·00	6·00
W38	13p. pale chestnut (1 side band) (23.10.84)	50	35
W39	14p. grey-bl (phosphorised paper) (8.4.81)	65	50
W40	14p. deep blue (1 centre band) (8.11.88)	55	50
W41	15p. bright blue (1 centre band) (28.11.89)	50	50
W42	15½p. pale violet (phosphorised paper) (24.2.82)	80	65
W43	16p. drab (phosphorised paper (27.4.83)	1·75	1·25
	a. Perf 15×14 (10.1.84)	1·75	1·50
W44	17p. grey-blue (phosphorised paper) (23.10.84)	90	70
W45	17p. deep blue (1 centre band) (4.12.90)	70	55
W46	18p. deep violet (8.4.81)	80	75
W47	18p. deep olive-grey (phosphorised paper) (6.1.87)	80	70
W48	18p. bright green (1 centre band) (3.12.91)	55	55
	a. Booklet pane. No. W48×6 with margins all round (25.2.92)	2·75	
	b. Perf 14 (12.1.93*)	2·25	2·25
W49	18p. bright green (1 side band) (25.2.92)	2·00	2·00
	a. Booklet pane. No. X1020×2, 1451a, 1514a, W49×2, W60×2 and centre label with margins all round	10·00	
W50	19p. bright orange-red (phosphorised paper) (8.11.88)	85	60
W51	19½p. olive-grey (phosphorised paper) (24.2.82)	2·00	2·00
W52	20p. brownish black (phosphorised paper) (28.11.89)	80	80
W53	20½p. ultram (phosphorised paper) (27.4.83)	4·00	4·00
W54	22p. blue (phosphorised paper) (8.4.81)	1·10	1·10
W55	22p. yellow-green (phosphorised paper) (23.10.84)	90	1·25
W56	22p. bright orange-red (phosphorised paper) (4.12.90)	80	70
W57	23p. brt grn (phosphorised paper) (8.11.88)	90	1·25
W58	24p. Indian red (phosphorised paper) (28.11.89)	1·00	1·25
W59	24p. chestnut (phosphorised paper) (3.12.91)	90	90
	a. Booklet pane. No. W59×6 with margins all round (25.2.92)	4·75	
	b. Perf 14 (14.9.92*)	2·75	2·75
W60	24p. chestnut (2 bands) (25.2.92)	1·25	1·25
W61	26p. rosine (phosphorised paper) (24.2.82)	1·10	1·40
	a. Perf 15×14 (27.1.87)	4·75	5·00
W62	26p. drab (phosphorised paper) (4.12.90)	1·00	1·00
W63	28p. deep violet-blue (phosphorised paper) (27.4.83)	1·10	1·25
	a. Perf 15×14 (27.1.87)	1·10	1·10
W64	28p. deep bluish grey (phosphorised paper) (3.12.91)	1·10	1·10
W65	31p. bright purple (phosphorised paper) (23.10.84)	1·25	1·25
W66	32p. greenish blue (phosphorised paper) (8.11.88)	1·25	1·25
W67	34p. deep bluish grey (phosphorised paper) (28.11.89)	1·50	1·40
W68	37p. rosine (phosphorised paper) (4.12.90)	1·50	1·40
W69	39p. bright mauve (phosphorised paper) (3.12.91)	1·50	1·40

*Earliest known date of use.
†Exists with gum arabic.
Nos. W48b and W59b were caused by the use of a reserve perforating machine for some printings in late 1992.
Nos. W49 and W60 only come from booklets. No. W49 exists with phosphor band at left or right from different booklets.
From 1972 printings were on fluorescent white paper. Nos. W13/14 exist with PVA and gum arabic and the remainder with PVA only. From 1973 printings had extra dextrin added (see notes after the 1971 Decimal Machin issue).

(Des J. Matthews after plaster cast by Arnold Machin. Litho Questa)

1993 (7 Dec)–96. *Chalk-surfaced paper. One phosphor band (19p., 20p.) or two phosphor bands (others). P 15×14 (with one elliptical hole on each vertical side).*

W70	W 4	19p. bistre (1 centre band)	40	40
W71		19p. bistre (1 side band) (25.4.95)	2·25	2·25
W72		20p. brt green (1 centre band) (23.7.96)	40	40
W73		25p. red	50	50
W74		26p. red-brown (23.7.96)	50	50
W75		30p. deep olive-grey	60	60
W76		37p. bright mauve (23.7.96)	75	75
W77		41p. grey-brown	90	90
W78		63p. light emerald (23.7.96)	1·40	1·40

No. W71 only comes from booklets.

(Photo Walsall (20p., 63p), Harrison or Walsall (26p., 37p.))

1997 (1 July). *Chalk-surfaced paper. One centre phosphor band (20p.) or two phosphor bands (others). P 15×14 (with one elliptical hole on each vertical side).*

W79	W 5	20p. bright green	30	35
W80		26p. chestnut	40	45
W81		37p. bright mauve	60	65
W82		63p. light emerald	95	1·00

The Harrison printings of Nos. W80/1 come from booklet pane No. N1791.

STAMP BOOKLETS

For a full listing of Great Britain stamp booklets see the *Great Britain Concise Catalogue* published each Spring.

POSTAGE DUE STAMPS

PERFORATIONS. All postage due stamps to No. D101 are perf 14×15.

D 1   D 2

(Des G. Eve. Typo Somerset House (early trial printings of ½d., 1d., 2d., and 5d.; all printings of 1s.) or Harrison (later printings of all values except 1s.)).

1914 (20 Apr)–22. *W 100 (Simple Cypher) sideways.*

D1	D 1	½d. emerald	50	50
D2		1d. carmine	50	50
		a. Pale carmine	75	75
D3		1½d. chestnut (1922)*	40·00	12·00
D4		2d. agate	50	70
D5		3d. violet (1918)	2·50	1·00
		a. Bluish violet	3·50	3·50
D6		4d. dull grey-green (12.20)*	10·00	15·00
D7		5d. brownish cinnamon	5·00	3·25
D8		1s. bright blue (1915)*	20·00	20·00
		a. Deep bright blue	40·00	5·00
D1/8		Set of 8	90·00	28·00

*Prices quoted are for cheapest watermark position.
The 1d. is known bisected and used to make up a 1½d. rate on understamped letters from Ceylon (1921) or Tasmania (1922, Palmers Green) and the 2d. bisected and used as 1d. at Christchurch, Malvern, Streatham and West Kensington in 1921.

1924. *As 1914–22, but on thick chalk-surfaced paper.*

D9	D 1	1d. carmine	2·25	3·50

(Typo Waterlow and (from 1934) Harrison)

1924–31. *W 111 (Block Cypher) sideways.*

D10	D 1	½d. emerald (6.25)	90	75
D11		1d. carmine (4.25)	60	60
D12		1½d. chestnut (10.24)	40·00	18·00
D13		2d. agate (7.24)	1·00	40
D14		3d. dull violet (10.24)	1·50	40
		a. Printed on gummed side	60·00	†
		b. Experimental paper W 111a	35·00	30·00
D15		4d. dull grey-green (10.24)	13·00	3·00
D16		5d. brownish cinnamon (1.31)	29·00	22·00
D17		1s. deep blue (9.24)	8·50	75
D18	D 2	2s. 6d. purple/yellow (5.24)	40·00	2·00
D10/18		Set of 9	£120	45·00

The 2d. is known bisected to make up the 2½d. rate at Perranwell Station, Cornwall, in 1932.

1936–37. *W 125 (E 8 R) sideways.*

D19	D 1	½d. emerald (6.37)	7·50	7·00
D20		1d. carmine (5.37)	1·50	1·50
D21		2d. agate (5.37)	7·00	9·00
D22		3d. dull violet (3.37)	1·50	1·60
D23		4d. dull grey-green (12.36)	23·00	23·00
D24		5d. brownish cinnamon (11.36)	44·00	22·00
		a. Yellow-brown (1937)	16·00	21·00
D25		1s. deep blue (12.36)	11·00	7·00
D26	D 2	2s. 6d. purple/yellow (5.37)	£250	8·00
D19/26		Set of 8 (cheapest)	£300	70·00

The 1d. is known bisected (Solihull, 3 July 1937).

1937–38. *W 127 (G VI R) sideways.*

D27	D 1	½d. emerald (5.38)	8·00	4·50
D28		1d. carmine (5.38)	2·50	50
D29		2d. agate (5.38)	2·50	50
D30		3d. violet (12.37)	12·00	90
D31		4d. dull grey-green (9.37)	65·00	10·00
D32		5d. yellow-brown (11.38)	12·00	1·50
D33		1s. deep blue (10.37)	60·00	1·50
D34	D 2	2s. 6d. purple/yellow (9.38)	60·00	2·50
D27/34		Set of 8	£200	19·00

The 2d. is known bisected in June 1951 (Boreham Wood, Harpenden and St. Albans) and on 30 October 1954 (Harpenden).

DATES OF ISSUE. The dates for Nos. D35/68 are those on which stamps were first issued by the Supplies Department to postmasters.

1951–52. *Colours changed and new value (1½d.). W 127 (G VI R) sideways.*

D35	D 1	½d. orange (18.9.51)	1·00	2·50
D36		1d. violet-blue (6.6.51)	1·50	1·25
D37		1½d. green (11.2.52)	1·75	2·50
D38		4d. blue (14.8.51)	30·00	11·00
D39		1s. ochre (6.12.51)	35·00	13·00
D35/9		Set of 5	60·00	22·00

The 1d. is known bisected (Dorking, 1952, and Camberley, 6 April 1954).

1954–55. *W 153 (Mult Tudor Crown and E 2 R) sideways.*

D40	D 1	½d. orange (8.6.55)	6·00	4·50
D41		2d. agate (28.7.55)	4·00	4·00
D42		3d. violet (4.5.55)	50·00	32·00
D43		4d. blue (14.7.55)	18·00	19·00
		a. Imperf (pair)	£225	
D44		5d. yellow-brown (19.5.55)	25·00	9·00
D45	D 2	2s. 6d. purple/yellow (11.54)	£100	3·00
D40/5		Set of 6	£190	65·00

1955–57. *W 165 (Mult St. Edward's Crown and E 2 R) sideways.*

D46	D 1	½d. orange (16.7.56)	1·25	2·25
D47		1d. violet-blue (7.6.56)	5·50	1·50
D48		1½d. green (13.2.56)	5·50	5·00
D49		2d. agate (22.5.56)	40·00	3·25
D50		3d. violet (5.3.56)	6·00	1·25
D51		4d. blue (24.4.56)	21·00	3·75
D52		5d. brown-ochre (23.3.56)	32·00	2·00
D53		1s. ochre (22.11.55)	70·00	2·00

D54	D 2	2s. 6d. purple/*yellow* (28.6.57)	..	£140	8·00
D55		5s. scarlet/*yellow* (25.11.55)	..	80·00	25·00
D46/55			*Set of 10*	£350	48·00

The 1d. is known bisected in June 1957 (London S.E.D.O.), the 2d. in June 1956, the 3d. in April/May 1957 (London S.E.D.O.) and the 4d. in April 1957 (Poplar).

1959–63. *W 179 (Mult St Edward's Crown) sideways.*

D56	D 1	½d. orange (18.10.61)	..	10	1·00
D57		1d. violet-blue (9.5.60)	..	10	50
D58		1½d. green (5.10.60)	..	90	2·75
D59		2d. agate (14.9.59)	..	1·25	50
D60		3d. violet (24.3.59)	..	40	30
D61		4d. blue (17.12.59)	..	40	30
D62		5d. yellow-brown (6.11.61)	..	45	75
D63		6d. purple (29.3.62)	..	60	30
D64		1s. ochre (11.4.60)	..	1·40	30
D65	D 2	2s. 6d. purple/*yellow* (11.5.61)	..	4·25	45
D66		5s. scarlet/*yellow* (8.5.61)	..	8·00	1·00
D67		10s. blue/*yellow* (2.9.63)	..	10·00	5·00
D68		£1 black/*yellow* (2.9.63)	..	45·00	8·00
D56/68	..		*Set of 13*	65·00	19·00

Whiter paper. The note after No. 586 also applies to Postage Due stamps.

The 1d. is known bisected (Newbury, December 1962 and March 1963).

1968–69. *Typo. No wmk. Chalk-surfaced paper.*

D69	D 1	2d. agate (11.4.68)	..	20	60
D70		3d. violet (9.9.68)	..	25	60
D71		4d. blue (6.5.68)	..	25	60
D72		5d. orange-brown (3.1.69)	..	5·00	6·00
D73		6d. purple (9.9.68)	..	60	90
D74		1s. ochre (19.11.68)	..	2·00	1·40
D69/74			*Set of 6*	7·50	9·00

The 2d. and 4d. exist with gum arabic and PVA gum; remainder with PVA gum only.

1968–69. *Photo. No wmk. Chalk-surfaced paper. PVA gum.*

D75	D 1	4d. blue (12.6.69)	..	5·00	5·00
D76		8d. red (3.10.68)	..	1·00	1·00

Nos. D75/6 are smaller, 21½×17½ mm.

D 3   D 4

(Des J. Matthews. Photo Harrison)

1970 (17 June)–75. *Decimal Currency. Chalk-surfaced paper.*

D77	D 3	½p. turquoise-blue (15.2.71)	..	10	20
D78		1p. deep reddish purple (15.2.71)	..	10	15
D79		2p. myrtle-green (15.2.71)	..	10	15
D80		3p. ultramarine (15.2.71)	..	15	15
D81		4p. yellow-brown (15.2.71)	..	15	15
D82		5p. violet (15.2.71)	..	20	20
D83		7p. red-brown (21.8.74)	..	35	45
D84	D 4	10p. carmine	..	30	20
D85		11p. slate-green (18.6.75)	..	60	60
D86		20p. olive-brown	..	60	50
D87		50p. ultramarine	..	1·50	50
D88		£1 black	..	3·50	75
D89		£5 orange-yellow and black (2.4.73)	..	35·00	2·00
D77/89	..		*Set of 13*	38·00	5·00

Later printings were on fluorescent white paper, some with dextrin added to the PVA gum (see notes after X1058 of Great Britain).

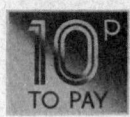

D 5   D 6

(Des Sedley Place Design Ltd. Photo Harrison)

1982 (9 June). *Chalk-surfaced paper.*

D 90	D 5	1p. lake	..	10	10
D 91		2p. bright blue	..	20	10
D 92		3p. deep mauve	..	10	15
D 93		4p. deep blue	..	10	20
D 94		5p. sepia	..	20	20
D 95	D 6	10p. light brown	..	20	25
D 96		20p. olive-green	..	40	30
D 97		25p. deep greenish blue	..	50	70
D 98		50p. grey-black	..	1·00	75
D 99		£1 red	..	2·00	50
D 100		£2 turquoise-blue	..	4·50	50
D 101		£5 dull orange	..	12·00	50
D90/101			*Set of 12*	19·00	3·75

D 7

(Des Sedley Place Design Ltd. Litho Questa)

1994 (15 Feb). *P* 15×14 (*with one elliptical hole on each vertical side*).

D102	D 7	1p. red, yellow and black	..	10	10
D103		2p. magenta, purple and black	..	10	10
D104		5p. yellow, red-brown and black	..	10	20
D105		10p. yellow, emerald and black	..	15	20
D106		20p. blue-green, violet and black	..	30	35
D107		25p. cerise, rosine and black	..	40	45
D108		£1 violet, magenta and black	..	1·50	1·60
D109		£1.20, greenish blue, blue-green & black	..	1·75	1·90
D110		£5 greenish black, blue-green and black	..	7·50	7·75
D102/10			*Set of 9*	11·50	12·50

Following changes in the method of collecting money due on unpaid or underpaid mail the use of postage due stamps was restricted from April 1995 to mail addressed to business customers and to Customs/V.A.T. charges levied by the Royal Mail on behalf of the Customs and Excise.

OFFICIAL STAMPS

In 1840 the 1d. black (Type **1**), with "V R" in the upper corners, was prepared for official use, but never issued for postal purposes. Obliterated specimens are those which were used for experimental trials of obliterating inks, or those that passed through the post by oversight.

V 1

1840. *Prepared for use but not issued;* "V" "R" *in upper corners. Imperf.*

				Un	Used	Used on cover
V1	V 1	1d. black	..	..	£6000	£6000

The following Official stamps would be more correctly termed Departmental stamps as they were exclusively for the use of certain government departments. Until 1882 official mail used ordinary postage stamps purchased at post offices, the cash being refunded once a quarter. Later the government departments obtained Official stamps by requisition.

Official stamps were on sale to the public for a short time at Somerset House but they were not sold from post offices. The system of only supplying the Government departments was open to abuse so that all Official stamps were withdrawn on 13 May 1904.

OVERPRINTS, PERFORATIONS, WATERMARKS. All Official stamps were overprinted by Thomas De La Rue & Co. and are perf 14. They are on Crown watermarked paper unless otherwise stated.

INLAND REVENUE

These stamps were used by revenue officials in the provinces, mail to and from Head Office passing without a stamp. The London Office used these stamps only for foreign mail.

I.R.   **I. R.**

OFFICIAL   **OFFICIAL**

(O 1)   (O 2)

Optd with Types O 1 (½*d. to 1s.*) *or* O 2 (*others*)

1882–1901. *Stamps of Queen Victoria. (a) Issues of 1880–81.*

				Un	Used	★ Used on cover
O 1	½d. deep green (1.11.82)	..	..	15·00	5·00	50·00
O 2	½d. pale green	..	..	15·00	5·00	
O 3	1d. lilac (Die II) (1.10.82)	..	..	2·00	1·00	15·00
	a. Optd in blue-black	..	..	70·00	40·00	
	b. "OFFICIAL" omitted	..	..	—	£2500	
O 4	6d. grey (Plate 18) (3.11.82)	..	..	80·00	25·00	

No. O3 with the lines of the overprint transposed is an essay.

(b) Issues of 1884–88

O 5	½d. slate-blue (8.5.85)	..	..	30·00	20·00	85·00
O 6	2½d. lilac (12.3.85)	..	..	£140	50·00	£650
O 7	1s. dull green (12.3.85)	..	..	£2600	£500	
O 8	5s. rose (*blued paper*) (wmk Anchor) (12.3.85)	..		£2900	£525	
O 9	5s. rose (wmk Anchor) (3.90)	..		£1500	£450	
	a. Raised stop after "R"	..		£1750	£450	
	b. Optd in blue-black	..		£2250	£500	
O 9c	10s. cobalt (*blued paper*) (wmk Anchor) (12.3.85)	..		£5500	£900	
O 9d	10s. ultramarine (*blued paper*) (wmk Anchor) (12.3.85)	..		£5500	£1750	
O10	10s. ultram (wmk Anchor) (3.90)	..		£2750	£600	
	a. Raised stop after "R"	..		£3500	£625	
	b. Optd in blue-black	..		£3750	£800	
O11	£1 brown-lilac (wmk Crowns) (12.3.85)	..		£20000		
	a. Frame broken	..		£25000		
O12	£1 brown-lilac (wmk Orbs) (3.90)	..		£27500		
	a. Frame broken	..		£30000		

(c) Issues of 1887–92

O13	½d. vermilion (15.5.88)	..	..	2·00	1·00	25·00
	a. Without "I.R."	..	..	£2000		
	b. Imperf	..	..	£1250		
	c. Opt double (imperf)	..	..	£1500		
O14	2½d. purple/*blue* (2.92)	..	..	60·00	5·00	£200
O15	1s. dull green (9.89)	..	..	£225	25·00	£1200
O16	£1 green (6.92)	..	..	£3750	£500	
	a. No stop after "R"	..	..	—	£850	
	b. Frame broken	..	..	£6000	£1000	

Nos. O3, O13, O15 and O16 may be found with two varieties of overprint, namely, 1882 printings, *thin* letters, and 1894 printings, *thicker* letters.

(d) Issues of 1887 and 1900

O17	½d. blue-green (4.01)	..	..	5·00	4·00	£100
O18	6d. purple/*rose-red* (1.7.01)	..	..	£125	25·00	
O19	1s. green and carmine (12.01)	..	..	£800	£175	
★O1/19 For well-centred, lightly used			..	+35%		

1902–04. *Stamps of King Edward VII. Ordinary paper.*

O20	½d. blue-green (4.2.02)	..	..	20·00	2·00	£100
O21	1d. scarlet (4.2.02)	..	..	12·00	1·00	60·00
O22	2½d. ultramarine (19.2.02)	..	..	£450	90·00	
O23	6d. pale dull purple (14.3.04)	..		£85000	£65000	
O24	1s. dull green & carmine (29.4.02)	..		£550	95·00	
O25	5s. bright carmine (29.4.02)	..		£4500	£1500	
	a. Raised stop after "R"	..		£5000	£1600	

O26	10s. ultramarine (29.4.02)	..	£16000	£9500	
	a. Raised stop after "R"	..	£19000	£12000	
O27	£1 dull blue-green (29.4.02)	..	£13000	£7000	

OFFICE OF WORKS

These were issued to Head and Branch (local) offices in London and to Branch (local) offices at Birmingham, Bristol, Edinburgh, Glasgow, Leeds, Liverpool, Manchester and Southampton. The overprints on stamps of value 2d. and upwards were created later in 1902, the 2d. for registration fees and the rest for overseas mail.

O. W.

OFFICIAL

(O 3)

Optd with Type O 3

1896 (24 Mar)–02. *Stamps of Queen Victoria.*

O31	½d. vermilion	..	..	£100	50·00	£250
O32	½d. blue-green (2.02)	..	..	£175	85·00	
O33	1d. lilac (Die II)	..	..	£175	50·00	£275
O34	5d. dull purple and blue (II) (29.4.02)	..	£850	£190	
O35	10d. dull purple and carmine (28.5.02)	..	£1400	£275	

1902 (11 Feb)–03. *Stamps of King Edward VII. Ordinary paper.*

O36	½d. blue-green (8.02)	..	..	£400	£100	£950
O37	1d. scarlet	..	..	£400	£100	£200
O38	2d. yellowish green and carmine-red (29.4.02)	..	£700	£100	£1200
O39	2½d. ultramarine (29.4.02)	..	£800	£275	
O40	10d. dull purple & carmine (28.5.03)	..	£5250	£1750	
★O31/40 For well-centred, lightly used		..		+25%		

ARMY

Letters to and from the War Office in London passed without postage. The overprinted stamps were distributed to District and Station Paymasters nationwide, including Cox and Co., the Army Agents, who were paymasters to the Household Division.

ARMY   **ARMY**   **ARMY**

OFFICIAL   **OFFICIAL**   **OFFICIAL**

(O 4)   (O 5)   (O 6)

1896 (1 Sept)–01. *Stamps of Queen Victoria optd with Type* O 4 (½*d. 1d.*) *or* O 5 (2½*d., 6d.*).

O41	½d. vermilion	..	..	2·00	1·00	25·00
	a. "OFFICIAI" (R. 13/7)	..	..	40·00	20·00	
	b. Lines of opt transposed	..	..	£1100		
O42	½d. blue-green (6.00)	..	..	2·00	4·00	
O43	1d. lilac (Die II)	..	..	2·00	1·00	40·00
	a. "OFFICIAI" (R. 13/7)	..	..	40·00	20·00	
O44	2½d. purple/*blue*	..	..	5·00	3·00	£300
O45	6d. purple/*rose-red* (20.9.01)	..	17·00	10·00	£300

Nos. O41a and O43a occur on sheets overprinted by Forme 1.

1902–03. *Stamps of King Edward VII optd with Type* O 4 (*Nos.* O48/50) *or Type* O 6 (*No.* O52). *Ordinary paper.*

O48	½d. blue-green (11.2.02)	..	..	2·50	1·00	70·00
O49	1d. scarlet (11.2.02)	..	..	2·00	1·00	70·00
	a. "ARMY" omitted	..	..	†	—	
O50	6d. pale dull purple (23.8.02)	..	£75·00	35·00	
O52	6d. pale dull purple (12.03)	..	£900	£325	

GOVERNMENT PARCELS

These stamps were issued to all departments, including the Head Office, for use on parcels weighing over 3 lb. Below this weight government parcels were sent by letter post to avoid the 55% of the postage paid from accruing to the railway companies, as laid down by parcel-post regulations. Most government parcels stamps suffered heavy postmarks in use.

GOVᵗ

PARCELS

(O 7)

Optd as Type O 7

1883 (1 Aug)–86. *Stamps of Queen Victoria.*

				Un	★ Used
O61	1½d. lilac (1.5.86)	..	..	£125	30·00
	a. No dot under "T"	..	..	£150	32·00
	b. Dot to left of "T"	..	..	£125	32·00
O62	6d. dull green (1.5.86)	..	..	£825	£300
O63	9d. dull green	..	..	£675	£190
O64	1s. orange-brown (wmk Crown, Pl 13)	..	£450	80·00
	a. No dot under "T"	..	..	£500	90·00
	b. Dot to left of "T"	..	..	£500	90·00
O64c	1s. orange-brown (Pl 14)	..	..	£775	£125
	ca. No dot under "T"	..	..	£850	£110
	cb. Dot to left of "T"	..	..		

1887–90. *Stamps of Queen Victoria.*

O65	1½d. dull purple and pale green (29.10.87)	..	15·00	3·00
	a. No dot under "T"	..	..	20·00	7·00
	b. Dot to right of "T"	..	..	18·00	6·00
	c. Dot to left of "T"	..	..	18·00	6·00
O66	6d. purple/*rose-red* (19.12.87)	..	30·00	12·00
	a. No dot under "T"	..	..	35·00	14·00
	b. Dot to right of "T"	..	..	35·00	14·00
	c. Dot to left of "T"	..	..	35·00	12·00
O67	9d. dull purple and blue (21.8.88)	..	60·00	16·00

O68	1s. dull green (25.3.90)		.. ..	£140	80·00
	a. No dot under "T"		..	£160	85·00
	b. Dot to right of "T"		..	£160	85·00
	c. Dot to left of "T"		..	£180	90·00
	d. Optd in blue-black		..		

1891–1900. *Stamps of Queen Victoria.*

O69	1d. lilac (Die II) (18.6.97)	.. ..	30·00	9·00
	a. No dot under "T"	..	32·00	21·00
	b. Dot to left of "T"	..	32·00	21·00
	c. Opt inverted	..	£1000	£850
	d. Ditto. Dot to left of "T"		£1000	£550
O70	2d. grey-green and carmine (24.10.91)		50·00	8·00
	a. No dot under "T"	..	60·00	10·00
	b. Dot to left of "T"	..	60·00	10·00
O71	4½d. green and carmine (29.9.92)		£125	80·00
	b. Dot to right of "T"			
O72	1s. green and carmine (11.00)		£175	55·00
	a. Opt inverted		†	£4000

★O61/72 **For well-centred lightly used** .. .. **+100%**

The "no dot under T" variety occurred on R.12/3 and 20/2. The "dot to left of T" comes four times in the sheet on R.2/7, 6/7, 7/9 and 12/9. The best example of the "dot to right of T" is on R.20/1. All three varieties were corrected around 1897.

1902. *Stamps of King Edward VII. Ordinary paper.*

O74	1d. scarlet (30.10.02)	17·00	6·00
O75	2d. yellowish green & carmine-red (29.4.02)	70·00	18·00
O76	6d. pale dull purple (19.2.02) ..	£110	18·00
	a. Opt double, one albino ..	£4500	
O77	9d. dull purple and ultramarine (28.8.02)	£240	60·00
O78	1s. dull green and carmine (17.12.02) ..	£375	90·00

BOARD OF EDUCATION

BOARD OF EDUCATION

(O 8)

Optd with Type O 8

1902 (19 Feb). *Stamps of Queen Victoria.*

			Un Used	Used on Cover
O81	5d. dull purple and blue (II)	..	£575 £120	
O82	1s. green and carmine	..	£1000 £400	

1902 (19 Feb)–**04.** *Stamps of King Edward VII. Ordinary paper.*

O83	½d. blue-green	.. ..	20·00 8·00	£275
O84	1d. scarlet	.. ..	20·00 7·00	£300
O85	2½d. ultramarine	..	£550 60·00	
O86	5d. dull purple & ultram (6.2.04)		£2250 £1000	
O87	1s. dull green & carmine (23.12.02)		£40000 £30000	

ROYAL HOUSEHOLD

R.H.

OFFICIAL

(O 9)

1902. *Stamps of King Edward VII optd with Type O 9. Ordinary paper.*

O91	½d. blue-green (29.4.02)	..	..	£160 £100	£600
O92	1d. scarlet (19.2.02)		..	£140 90·00	£400

ADMIRALTY

ADMIRALTY   ADMIRALTY

OFFICIAL   **OFFICIAL**

(O 10)   (O 11)

(with different "M")

1903 (1 Apr). *Stamps of King Edward VII optd with Type O 10. Ordinary paper.*

O101	½d. blue-green	.. ..	11·00 5·00	
O102	1d. scarlet	..	6·00 3·00	£200
O103	1½d. dull purple and green	..	65·00 50·00	
O104	2d. yellowish green & carmine-red	..	£125 60·00	
O105	2½d. ultramarine	..	£140 50·00	
O106	3d. purple/yellow	..	£125 50·00	

1903–04. *Stamps of King Edward VII optd with Type O 11. Ordinary paper.*

O107	½d. blue-green (9.03)	..	10·00 6·00	£300
O108	1d. scarlet (12.03)	..	9·00 5·00	60·00
O109	1½d. dull purple and green (2.04)		£220 85·00	
O110	2d. yellowish green and carmine-red (3.04)		£425	£110
O111	2½d. ultramarine (3.04)		£550	£300
O112	3d. dull purple/orange-yell (12.03)		£375 95·00	

Stamps of various issues perforated with a Crown and initials ("H.M.O.W.", "O.W.", "B.T." or "S.O.") or with initials only ("H.M.S.O." or "D.S.I.R.") have also been used for official purposes, but these are outside the scope of the catalogue.

POSTAL FISCAL STAMPS

PRICES. Prices in the used column are for stamps with genuine postal cancellations dated from the time when they were authorised for use as postage stamps. Beware of stamps with fiscal cancellations removed and fraudulent postmarks applied.

VALIDITY. The 1d. Surface-printed stamps were authorised for postal use from 1 June 1881 and at the same time the 1d. postage issue, No. 166, was declared valid for fiscal purposes. The 3d. and 6d. values, together with the Embossed issues were declared valid for postal purposes by another Act effective from 1 January 1883.

SURFACE-PRINTED ISSUES

(Typo Thomas De La Rue & Co)

F 1 F 2

Rectangular Buckle

F 3 F 4

Octagonal Buckle

F 5 F 6
Double-lined Anchor Single-lined Anchor

1853–57. *P* 15½ × 15. (*a*) *Wmk* F 5 (*inverted*) (1853–55).

				Un	Used	Used on cover
F1	F 1	1d. light blue (10.10.53)	..	15·00	18·00	80·00
F2	F 2	1d. ochre (10.53)	..	60·00	40·00	£175
		a. *Tête-bêche* (in block of four)		£8000		
F3	F 3	1d. pale turquoise-blue (12.53)		20·00	18·00	£140
F4		1d. light blue/*blue* (12.53)	..	40·00	25·00	£160
F5	F 4	1d. reddish lilac/*blue* glazed paper (25.3.55)	..	60·00	14·00	£110

Only one example is known of No. F2a outside the National Postal Museum and the Royal Collection.

(*b*) *Wmk* F 6 (1856–57)

F6	F 4	1d. reddish lilac (*shades*)	..	5·50	4·00	80·00
F7		1d. reddish lilac/*bluish* (*shades*) (1857)	..	5·50	4·00	80·00

INLAND REVENUE

(F 7)

1860 (3 Apr). *No. F7 optd with Type* F 7, *in red.*

F8	F 4	1d. dull reddish lilac/*blue*	£400	£325	£550

BLUE PAPER. In the following issues we no longer distinguish between bluish and white paper. There is a range of papers from white or greyish to bluish.

F 8 F 9

F 10

1860–67. *Bluish to white paper. P* 15½ × 15. (*a*) *Wmk* F 6 (1860).

F 9	F 8	1d. reddish lilac (May)	..	6·00	6·00	80·00
F10	F 9	3d. reddish lilac (June)	..	£250	90·00	£175
F11	F 10	6d. reddish lilac (Oct)	..	£100	75·00	£200

(*b*) W 40. (*Anchor 16 mm high*) (1864)

F12	F 8	1d. pale reddish lilac (Nov)	4·75	4·75	65·00
F13	F 9	3d. pale reddish lilac	90·00	70·00	£160
F14	F 10	6d. pale reddish lilac	90·00	70·00	£160

(*c*) W 40 (*Anchor 18 mm high*) (1867)

F15	F 8	1d. reddish lilac	13·00	6·00	£130
F16	F 9	3d. reddish lilac	70·00	65·00	£175
F17	F 10	6d. reddish lilac	80·00	45·00	£170

For stamps perf 14, see Nos. F24/7.

F 11 F 12

Four Dies of Type F 12

Die 1. Corner ornaments small and either joined or broken; heavy shading under chin

Die 2. Ornaments small and always broken; clear line of shading under chin

Die 3. Ornaments larger and joined; line of shading under chin extended half way down neck

Die 4. Ornaments much larger; straight line of shading continued to bottom of neck

1867–81. *White to bluish paper. P* 14. (*a*) *W* 47 (*Small Anchor*).

F18	F 11	1d. purple (1.9.67)	..	8·00	5·00	60·00
F19	F 12	1d. purple (Die 1) (6.68)	..	1·75	1·50	40·00
F20		1d. purple (Die 2) (6.76)	..	10·00	10·00	£180
F21		1d. purple (Die 3) (3.77)	..	4·00	4·00	75·00
F22		1d. purple (Die 4) (7.78)	..	3·00	2·50	65·00

(*b*) *W* 48 (*Orb*)

F23	F 12	1d. purple (Die 4) (1.81)	..	2·00	1·50	40·00

1881. *White to bluish paper. P* 14.

(*a*) *W* 40 (*Anchor 18 mm high*) (Jan)

F24	F 9	3d. reddish lilac	..	£350	£225	£350
F25	F 10	6d. reddish lilac	..	£190	75·00	£175

(*b*) *W* 40 (*Anchor 20 mm high*) (May)

F26	F 9	3d. reddish lilac	..	£275	70·00	£175
F27	F 10	6d. reddish lilac	..	£150	90·00	£275

ISSUES EMBOSSED IN COLOUR

(Made at Somerset House)

The embossed stamps were struck from dies not appropriated to any special purpose on paper which had the words "INLAND REVENUE" previously printed, and thus became available for payment of any duties for which no special stamps had been provided.

The die letters are included in the embossed designs and holes were drilled for the insertion of plugs showing figures indicating dates of striking.

F 13

F 14

INLAND REVENUE

(F 15)

INLAND REVENUE

(F 16)

1860 (3 Apr)–**71.** *Types F **13/14** and similar types embossed on bluish paper. Underprint Type F **15**. No wmk. Imperf.*

				Un	Used
F28	2d. pink (Die A) (1.1.71)	..	..	£140	£140
F29	3d. pink (Die C)	..	..	£100	95·00
	a. *Tête-bêche* (vert pair)	..	..	£1200	
F30	3d. pink (Die D)	..		£350	
F31	6d. pink (Die T)	..	..	£700	
F32	6d. pink (Die U)	..	..	£100	90·00
	a. *Tête-bêche* (vert pair)	..		£1400	
F33	9d. pink (Die C) (1.1.71)	..	..	£250	
F34	1s. pink (Die E) (28.6.61)	..	..	£350	£150
F35	1s. pink (Die F) (28.6.61)	..	..	£125	£100
	a. *Tête-bêche* (vert pair)	..	..	£600	
F36	2s. pink (Die K) (6.8.61)	..	..	£275	£175
F37	2s. 6d. pink (Die N) (28.6.61)	..		£850	
F38	2s. 6d. pink (Die O) (28.6.61)	..		85·00	85·00

1861–71. *As last but perf 12½.*

F39	2d. pink (Die A) (8.71)	..	..	£250	£130
F40	3d. pink (Die C)	..	..		
F41	3d. pink (Die D)	..	..		
F42	9d. pink (Die C) (8.71)	..	..	£275	£140
F43	1s. pink (Die E) (8.71)	..	..	£200	£130
F44	1s. pink (Die F) (8.71)	..	..	£180	£100
F45	2s. 6d. pink (Die O) (8.71)	..	..	£120	65·00

1874 (Nov). *Types as before embossed on white paper. Underprint Type F **16**, in green. W **47** (Small Anchor). P 12½.*

F46	2d. pink (Die A)	..	..	—	£175
F47	9d. pink (Die C)	..	..		
F48	1s. pink (Die F)	..	..	£190	£100
F49	2s. 6d. pink (Die O)	..	..	—	£150

1875 (Nov)–**80.** *As last but colour changed and on white or bluish paper.*

F50	2d. vermilion (Die A) (1880)	..	..	£275	£100
F51	9d. vermilion (Die C) (1876)	..	..	£275	£150
F52	1s. vermilion (Die E)	..	..	£175	75·00
F53	1s. vermilion (Die F)	..	..	£175	75·00
F54	2s. 6d. vermilion (Die O) (1878)	..	..	£225	£100

1882 (Oct). *As last but W **48** (Orbs).*

F55	2d. vermilion (Die A)	..	..		
F56	9d. vermilion (Die C)	..	..		
F57	1s. vermilion (Die E)	..	..		
F58	2s. 6d. vermilion (Die O)	..	..	£500	£250

The sale of Inland Revenue stamps up to the 2s. value ceased from 30 December 1882 and stocks were called in and destroyed. The 2s. 6d. value remained on sale until 2 July 1883 when it was replaced by the 2s. 6d. "Postage & Revenue" stamp. Inland Revenue stamps still in the hands of the public continued to be accepted for revenue and postal purposes.

CONTROLS. Since the 1967 edition of the Part 1 Catalogue the priced lists of stamps with control letters have been transferred to Volumes 1 and 2 of the Stanley Gibbons *Great Britain Specialised Catalogue.*

TELEGRAPH STAMPS. A priced listing of the Post Office telegraph stamps appears in Volume 1 of the Stanley Gibbons *Great Britain Specialised Catalogue.* The last listing for the private telegraph companies in the Part 1 Catalogue was in the 1940 edition and for military telegraphs the 1941 edition.

ISLAND ISSUES

Several islands off the coast of Great Britain have issued local stamps (usually termed British Private Local Issues or Local Carriage Labels) ostensibly to cover the cost of ferrying mail to the nearest mainland post office. No official post offices operate on most of these islands. As these stamps are not recognised as valid for national or international mail they are not listed here. The following islands are known to have issued stamps from the dates shown:

Bardsey, Gwynedd (from 1979); *Bernera,* Hebrides (from 1977); *Brecqhou,* Channel Is. (1969); *Caldey,* Dyfed (from 1973); *Calf of Man,* Isle of Man (1962–73); *Calve,* Hebrides (from 1984); *Canna,* Hebrides (from 1958); *Carn Iar,* Hebrides (1961–62); *Davaar,* Argyllshire (from 1964); *Drake's Island,* Devon (1973–82); *Easdale,* Argyllshire (from 1988); *Eynhallow,* Orkney (from 1973); *Gairsay,* Orkney (from 1980); *Grunay,* Shetland (from 1981); *Gugh,* Isles of Scilly (1972–80 and from 1995); *Herm,* Channel Is. (1949–69); *Heston,* Wigtownshire (1960s); *Hilbre,* Cheshire (1960s); *Hildasay,* Shetland (from 1997); *Jethou,* Channel Is. (1960–69); *Lihou,* Channel Is. (1966–69); *Lundy,* Devon (from 1929; *Pabay,* Skye (1962–70, 1972–81 and from 1982); *St. Kilda,* Hebrides (1968–71); *St. Martin's* and *St. Mary's,* Isles of Scilly (from 1995); *Sanda,* Argyllshire (from 1962); *Shuna,* Hebrides (from 1949); *Soay,* Skye (1965–67); *Staffa,* Hebrides (from 1969); *Steep Holm,* Avon (1980–87); *Stroma,* Caithness (1962–70 and from 1988) and *Summer Isles,* Hebrides (1970–88 and from 1992). Those issued for Soay have been declared bogus by a committee of the Philatelic Traders Society.

Issues of the *Commodore Shipping Co* (1950–69), the *Alderney Shipping Co* (1969–75) and the *Isle of Sark Shipping Co* (from 1969) were/are for use on parcels carried by ship between Guernsey and Alderney and Sark. They are not valid for the carriage of letters and postcards.

Issues inscribed Alderney (1975–83 and from 1990) are issued in conjunction with an internal parcel delivery service. They are not valid for use on letters or postcards.

CHANNEL ISLANDS

GENERAL ISSUE

C 1 Gathering Vraic

C 2 Islanders gathering Vraic

(Des J. R. R. Stobie (1d.) or from drawing by E. Blampied (2½d.). Photo Harrison)

1948 (10 May). *Third Anniv of Liberation. W **127** of Great Britain. P 15 × 14.*

C1	C **1**	1d. scarlet	..	..	20	20
C2	C **2**	2½d. ultramarine	..	..	30	30

GUERNSEY

Further detailed information on the stamps of Guernsey will be found in the Stanley Gibbons *Channel Islands Specialised Catalogue.*

WAR OCCUPATION ISSUES

Stamps issued under British authority during the German Occupation

BISECTS. On 24 December 1940 authority was given, by Post Office notice, that prepayment of penny postage could be effected by using half a British 2d. stamp, diagonally bisected. Such stamps were first used on 27 December 1940.

The 2d. stamps generally available were those of the Postal Centenary issue, 1940 (S.G. 482) and the first colour of the King George VI issue (S.G. 465). These are listed under Nos. 482a and 465b. A number of the 2d. King George V, 1912–22, and of the King George V photogravure stamp (S.G. 442) which were in the hands of philatelists, were also bisected and used.

1

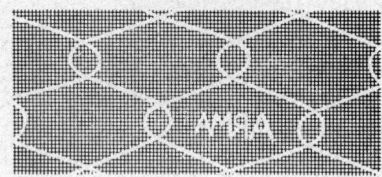

1a Loops (half actual size)

(Des E. W. Vaudin. Typo Guernsey Press Co Ltd)

1941–44. *Rouletted. (a) White paper. No wmk.*

1	1	½d. light green (7.4.41)	..	..	2·75	2·00
		a. *Emerald-green* (6.41)	..	..	3·75	2·25
		b. *Bluish green* (11.41)	..	..	40·00	16·00
		c. *Bright green* (2.42)	..	..	24·00	10·00
		d. *Dull green* (9.42)	..	..	3·75	2·75
		e. *Olive-green* (2.43)	..	..	29·00	18·00
		f. *Pale yellowish green* (7.43 and later) (shades)	..	..	2·50	2·25
		g. Imperf (pair)	..	..	£150	
		h. Imperf between (horiz pair)	..		£600	
		i. Imperf between (vert pair)	..		£700	
2		1d. scarlet (18.2.41)	..	..	2·00	1·00
		a. *Pale vermilion* (7.43) (etc.)	..	..	2·25	1·50
		b. *Carmine* (1943)	..	..	2·50	2·75
		c. Imperf (pair)	..	..	£150	75·00
		d. Imperf between (horiz pair)	..		£600	
		da. Imperf vert (centre stamp of horiz strip of 3)	..		£700	
		e. Imperf between (vert pair)	..		£700	
		f. Printed double (scarlet shade)	..		75·00	
3		2½d. ultramarine (12.4.44)	..	..	4·00	4·00
		a. *Pale ultramarine* (7.44)	..	..	4·00	4·00
		b. Imperf (pair)	..	..	£350	
		c. Imperf between (horiz pair)	..		£800	

*(b) Bluish French bank-note paper. W **1a** (sideways).*

4	1	½d. bright green (11.3.42)	..	..	18·00	19·00
5		1d. scarlet (9.4.42)	..	..	9·00	21·00

The dates given for the shades of Nos. 1/3 are the months in which they were printed as indicated in the printer's imprints. Others are issue dates.

REGIONAL ISSUES

DATES OF ISSUE. Conflicting dates of issue have been announced for some of the regional issues, partly explained by the stamps being released on different dates by the Philatelic Bureau in Edinburgh or the Philatelic Counter in London and in the regions. We have adopted the practice of giving the earliest known dates, since once released the stamps could have been used anywhere in the U.K.

2

3

(Des E. A. Piprell. Portrait by Dorothy Wilding Ltd. Photo Harrison & Sons)

1958 (18 Aug)–**67.** *W **179** of Great Britain. P 15 × 14.*

6	**2**	2½d. rose-red (8.6.64)	..	35	40
7	**3**	3d. deep lilac	..	35	30
		p. One centre phosphor band (24.5.67)		20	20
8		4d. ultramarine (7.2.66)	..	25	30
		p. Two phosphor bands (24.10.67)		20	20
6/8p.			Set of 3	70	75

1968–69. *No wmk. Chalk-surfaced paper. PVA gum*. One centre phosphor band (Nos. 10/11) or two phosphor bands (others). P 15 × 14.*

9	**3**	4d. pale ultramarine (16.4.68)	..	10	25
10		4d. olive-sepia (4.9.68)	..	15	20
11		4d. bright vermilion (26.2.69)	..	15	30
12		5d. royal blue (4.9.68)	..	15	30
9/12			Set of 4	40	95

No. 9 was not issued in Guernsey until 22 April.

* PVA Gum. See note after No. 722 of Great Britain.

INDEPENDENT POSTAL ADMINISTRATION

4 Castle Cornet and Edward the Confessor

5 View of Sark

Two Types of 1d. and 1s. 6d.:

I. Latitude inscr "40° 30′ N".
II. Corrected to "49° 30′ N".

(Des R. Granger Barrett. Photo Harrison (½d. to 2s. 6d.); Delrieu (others))

1969 (1 Oct)–**70.** *Designs as T **4/5**. P 14 (½d. to 2s. 6d.) or 12½ (others).*

13	½d. deep magenta and black	..		10	10
14	1d. bright blue and black (I)	..		10	10
14b	1d. bright blue and black (II) (12.12.69)		30	30
	c. Booklet stamp with blank margins		40	40
15	1½d. yellow-brown and black	..		10	10
16	2d. gold, bright red, deep blue and black		10	10
17	3d. gold, pale greenish yellow, orge-red & blk		15	15
	a. Error. Wmk w **12**	..	..	£1100	
18	4d. multicoloured	..		25	25
	a. Booklet stamp with blank margins (12.12.69)		40	45
	ab. Yellow omitted	..	..	£225	
	ac. Emerald (stem) omitted	..		£100	
19	5d. gold, brt vermilion, bluish violet & black		25	15
	a. Booklet stamp with blank margins (12.12.69)		50	50
	b. Gold (inscr etc.) omitted (booklets)		£450	
20	6d. gold, pale greenish yellow, light bronze-green and black		30	30
21	9d. gold, bright red, crimson and black	..	40	30
22	1s. gold, bright vermilion, bistre and black		30	30
23	1s. 6d. turquoise-green and black (I)		30	30
23b	1s. 6d. turquoise-green and black (II) (4.2.70)		2·25	1·75
24	1s. 9d. multicoloured	..		1·25	1·50
	a. Emerald (stem) omitted	..		£300	
25	2s. 6d. bright reddish violet and black		5·00	4·25
26	5s. multicoloured	..		3·25	3·25
27	10s. multicoloured	..		26·00	22·00
	a. Perf 13½×13 (4.3.70)	..		48·00	40·00
28	£1 multicoloured	..		2·00	1·75
	a. Perf 13½×13 (4.3.70)	..		2·00	2·00
13/28		Set of 16	35·00	30·00

Designs: *Horiz as T **4**—1d. (both), 1s. 6d. (both),* Map and William I; 1½d. Martello Tower and Henry II; 2d. Arms of Sark and King John; 3d. Arms of Alderney and Edward III; 4d. Guernsey Lily and Henry V; 5d. Arms of Guernsey and Elizabeth I; 6d. Arms of Alderney and Charles II; 9d. Arms of Sark and George III; 1s. Arms of Guernsey and Queen Victoria; 1s. 9d. Guernsey Lily and Elizabeth I; 2s. 6d. Martello Tower and King John. *Horiz as T **5**—10s.* View of Alderney; £1, View of Guernsey.

The booklet panes consist of single perforated stamps with wide margins all round intended to fit automatic machines designed for the Great Britain 2s. booklets. They are therefore found with three margins when detached from booklets or four margins when complete.

There was no postal need for the ½d. and 1½d. values as the ½d. coin had been withdrawn prior to their issue in anticipation of decimalisation. These values were only on sale at the Philatelic Bureau and the Crown Agents as well as in the U.S.A.

Nos. 14b and 23b are known only on thin paper and Nos. 13, 14, 16, 17, 20, 21, 22, 23, 24 and 25 also exist on thin paper.

| 19 | Isaac Brock as Colonel | 23 | H.M.S. *L103* (landing craft) entering St. Peter's Harbour |

(Litho Format)

1969 (1 Dec). *Birth Bicentenary of Sir Isaac Brock. T 19 and similar multicoloured designs. P 13½ × 14 (2s. 6d.) or 14 × 13½ (others).*

29	4d.	Type 19					20	20
30	5d.	Sir Isaac Brock as Major-General				20	20
31	1s. 9d.	Isaac Brock as Ensign		..	..	1·40	1·25
32	2s. 6d.	Arms and flags (*horiz*)		..	..	1·40	1·25
29/32					Set of 4	2·75	2·50

(Des and photo Courvoisier)

1970 (9 May). *25th Anniv of Liberation. T 23 and similar designs. Granite paper. P 11½.*

33	4d.	blue and pale blue ..		..	..	40	40
34	5d.	brown-lake and pale grey		..	..	40	40
35	1s. 6d.	bistre-brown and buff ..			..	3·25	2·50
33/5					Set of 3	3·50	3·00

Designs: *Horiz*—5d. British ships entering St. Peter's Port. *Vert*—1s. 6d. Brigadier Snow reading Proclamation.

| 26 | Guernsey "Toms" | 32 | St. Peter Church, Sark |

(Des and photo Courvoisier)

1970 (12 Aug). *Agriculture and Horticulture. T 26 and similar horiz designs. Multicoloured. Granite paper. P 11½.*

36	4d.	Type 26		..	..	80	20
37	5d.	Guernsey Cow	..		..	90	20
38	9d.	Guernsey Bull		..	..	5·00	2·75
39	1s. 6d.	Freesias	..	..	..	6·00	3·00
36/9					Set of 4	12·00	5·50

(Des and photo Courvoisier)

1970 (11 Nov). *Christmas. Guernsey Churches (1st series). T 32 and similar multicoloured designs. Granite paper. P 11½.*

40	4d.	St. Anne's Church, Alderney (*horiz*)	..	35	20
41	5d.	St. Peter's Church (*horiz*)		..	45	25
42	9d.	Type 32		..	..	1·75	1·10
43	1s. 6d.	St. Tugual Chapel, Herm		..	2·00	1·50
40/3					Set of 4	4·00	2·75

See also Nos. 63/6.

INVALIDATION. The regional issues for Guernsey were invalidated for use in Guernsey and Jersey on 1 November 1969 but remained valid for use in the rest of the United Kingdom. Nos. 13/43 (except Nos. 28/a) and Nos. D1/7 were invalidated on 14 February 1972.

34 Martello Tower and King John

(Photo Harrison (½p. to 10p.), Delrieu (others))

1971 (6 Jan)–**73**. *Decimal Currency. Designs as Nos. 13/27, but values inscr in decimal currency as in T 34. Chalk-surfaced paper. P 14 (½p. to 10p.) or 13½×13 (20p., 50p.).*

44	½p.	deep magenta and black (15.2.71)		10	15
	a.	Booklet stamp with margins (*glazed, ordinary paper*) ..		..	15	20
	ab.	Ditto. Chalk-surfaced paper (2.4.73)	..	15	20
45	1p.	bright blue and black (II) (15.2.71)		10	10
46	1½p.	yellow-brown and black (15.2.71)	..	15	15
47	2p.	multicoloured (15.2.71)	..	..	15	15
	a.	Booklet stamp with margins (*glazed, ordinary paper*) ..		..	20	20
	ab.	Ditto. Chalk-surfaced paper (2.4.73)	..	20	20
	ac.	Emerald (stem) omitted	..	..	£1100	
	b.	Glazed, ordinary paper (15.2.71)	..	20	20
48	2½p.	gold, brt verm, bluish vio & blk (15.2.71)	15	10
	a.	Bright vermilion omitted	..	..	£450	
	b.	Booklet stamp with margins (*glazed, ordinary paper*) ..		..	20	20
	ba.	Ditto. Chalk-surfaced paper (2.4.73)	..	20	20
49	3p.	gold, pale greenish yellow, orange-red and black (15.2.71)	..	20	20
50	3½p.	mult (*glazed, ordinary paper*) (15.2.71)	25	25
51	4p.	multicoloured (15.2.71)	..	35	15

52	5p.	turquoise-green and black (II) (15.2.71)	30	25
53	6p.	gold, pale greenish yellow, light bronze-green and black (15.2.71)		30	35
54	7½p.	gold, brt verm, bistre & black (15.2.71)	40	45
55	9p.	gold, brt red, crimson & black (15.2.71)	50	75
56	10p.	bright reddish violet and black ..	2·25	1·75
	a.	Ordinary paper. *Bright reddish violet and deep black* (1.9.72)		1·75	1·75
57	20p.	multicoloured (*glazed, ordinary paper*) ..	1·00	1·00
	a.	*Shade** (25.1.73)		1·00	1·00
58	50p.	multicoloured (*glazed, ordinary paper*) ..	2·00	2·00
44/58			Set of 15	7·00	7·00

*No. 57 has the sky in a pale turquoise-blue; on No. 57a it is pale turquoise-green.

Thomas De La Rue
THE GUERNSEY PRINTER 1793 - 1866

35 Hong Kong 2 c. of 1862

(Des and recess D.L.R.)

1971 (2 June). *Thomas De La Rue Commemoration. T 35 and similar horiz designs. P 14 × 13½.*

59	2p.	dull purple to brown-purple*	..	50	30
60	2½p.	carmine-red		..	50	30
61	4p.	deep bluish green		..	3·00	2·25
62	7½p.	deep blue	..	..	3·25	2·25
59/62				Set of 4	6·50	4·50

Designs: (each incorporating portraits of Queen Elizabeth II and Thomas De La Rue as in T 35)—2½p. Great Britain 4d. of 1855–7; 4p. Italy 5 c. of 1862; 7½p. Confederate States 5 c. of 1862.

* These colours represent the extreme range of shades of this value. The majority of the printing, however, is in an intermediate shade.

36 Ebenezer Church, St. Peter Port

(Des and photo Courvoisier)

1971 (27 Oct). *Christmas. Guernsey Churches (2nd series). T 36 and similar multicoloured designs. Granite paper. P 11½.*

63	2p.	Type 36	..	..	25	25
64	2½p.	Church of St. Pierre du Bois	..	25	25
65	5p.	St. Joseph's Church, St. Peter Port (*vert*)	2·50	2·00
66	7½d.	Church of St. Philippe de Torteval (*vert*)	2·75	2·00
63/6				Set of 4	5·25	4·00

37 Earl of Chesterfield (1794)

(Des and photo Courvoisier)

1972 (10 Feb). *Mail Packet Boats (1st series). T 37 and similar horiz designs. Multicoloured. Granite paper. P 11½.*

67	2p.	Type 37	..	..	..	15	15
68	2½p.	Dasher (1827)	..	..	20	20
69	7½p.	Ibex (1891)	..	..	90	1·00
70	9p.	Alberta (1900)	..	..	1·50	1·40
67/70				Set of 4	2·50	2·50

See also Nos. 80/3.

38 Guernsey Bull

(Photo Courvoisier)

1972 (22 May). *World Conference of Guernsey Breeders, Guernsey. Granite paper. P 11½.*

| 71 | 38 | 5p. | multicoloured | .. | .. | 75 | 60 |

| 39 | Bermuda Buttercup | 40 | Angels adoring Christ |

(Des and photo Courvoisier)

1972 (24 May). *Wild Flowers. T 39 and similar multicoloured designs. Granite paper. P 11½.*

72	2p.	Type 39			..	15	20
73	2½p.	Heath Spotted Orchid (*vert*)	..	15	20
74	7½p.	Kaffir Fig		..	..	90	90
75	9p.	Scarlet Pimpernel (*vert*)	..	1·25	1·25
72/5				Set of 4	2·25	2·25

(Des and photo Courvoisier)

1972 (20 Nov). *Royal Silver Wedding and Christmas. T 40 and similar vert designs showing stained-glass windows from Guernsey Churches. Multicoloured. Granite paper. P 11½.*

76	2p.	Type 40		..	..	10	10
77	2½p.	The Epiphany		..	..	15	15
78	7½p.	The Virgin Mary ..		..	60	55
79	9p.	Christ	..	..	..	75	60
76/9				Set of 4	1·50	1·25

See also Nos. 89/92.

(Des and photo Courvoisier)

1973 (9 Mar). *Mail Packet Boats (2nd series). Multicoloured designs as T 37. Granite paper. P 11½.*

80	2½p.	St. Julien (1925)	..	..	10	10
81	3p.	Isle of Guernsey (1930)	..	30	20
82	7½p.	St. Patrick (1947)	..	..	90	60
83	9p.	Sarnia (1961)	..	..	1·00	75
80/3				Set of 4	2·00	1·50

| 41 | Supermarine Sea Eagle | 42 | "The Good Shepherd" |

(Des and photo Courvoisier)

1973 (4 July). *50th Anniv of Air Service. T 41 and similar horiz designs. Multicoloured. Granite paper. P 11½.*

84	2½p.	Type 41		..	..	10	10
85	3p.	Westland Wessex trimotor	..	15	15
86	5p.	De Havilland D.H.89 Dragon Rapide	30	25
87	7½p.	Douglas DC-3	..	..	80	50
88	9p.	Vickers Viscount 800 *Anne Marie*	85	55
84/8				Set of 5	2·00	1·40

(Des and photo Courvoisier)

1973 (24 Oct). *Christmas. T 42 and similar vert designs showing stained-glass windows from Guernsey Churches. Multicoloured. Granite paper. P 11½.*

89	2½p.	Type 42		..	..	10	10
90	3p.	Christ at the well of Samaria	..	10	10
91	7½p.	St. Dominic	..	..	30	30
92	20p.	Mary and the Child Jesus	..	60	60
89/92				Set of 4	1·00	1·00

43 Princess Anne and Capt. Mark Phillips

(Des G. Anderson. Photo Courvoisier)

1973 (14 Nov). *Royal Wedding. Granite paper. P 11½.*

| 93 | 43 | 25p. | multicoloured | .. | .. | 1·00 | 75 |

44 John Lockett, 1875

(Des and photo Courvoisier)

1974 (15 Jan). *150th Anniv of Royal National Lifeboat Institution. T 44 and similar horiz designs. Multicoloured. Granite paper. P 11½.*

94	2½p.	Type 44		..	..	10	10
95	3p.	Arthur Lionel, 1912	..	..	10	10
96	8p.	Euphrosyne Kendal, 1954	..	45	45
97	10p.	Arun, 1972	..	..	45	45
94/7				Set of 4	1·00	1·00

MINIMUM PRICE

The minimum price quote is 10p which represents a handling charge rather than a basis for valuing common stamps. For further notes about prices see introductory pages.

45 Private, East Regt,
1815

46 Driver, Field Battery,
Royal Guernsey Artillery,
1848

(Photo Courvoisier (½ to 10p.) or Delrieu (others))

1974 (2 Apr)–78. *Designs as T* **45**/**6**. *Multicoloured.*

(a) *Vert designs as T* **45**. *Granite paper. P* 11½

98	½p. Type **45**	.. ..	10	10
	a. Booklet strip of 8 (98 × 5 and 102 × 3)†		30	
	b. Booklet pane of 16 (98 × 4, 102 × 6 and 103 × 6)†		65	
99	1p. Officer, 2nd North Regt, 1825 ..		10	10
	a. Booklet strip of 8 (99 × 4, 103, 105 × 2 and 105a) (8.2.77)†		80	
	b. Booklet strip of 4 (99, 101 × 2 and 105a) (7.2.78)†		50	
100	1½p. Gunner, Guernsey Artillery, 1787 ..		10	10
101	2p. Gunner, Guernsey Artillery, 1815 ..		10	10
102	2½p. Corporal, Royal Guernsey Artillery, 1868		10	10
103	3p. Field Officer, Royal Guernsey Artillery, 1895		10	10
104	3½p. Sergeant, 3rd Regt, 1867 ..		10	10
105	4p. Officer, East Regt, 1822 ..		15	15
105a	5p. Field Officer, Royal Guernsey Artillery, 1895 (29.5.76)		15	15
106	5½p. Colour-Sergeant of Grenadiers, East Regt, 1833		20	25
107	6p. Officer, North Regt, 1832 ..		20	25
107a	7p. Officer, East Regt, 1822 (29.5.76)		25	25
108	8p. Field Officer, Rifle Company, 1868 ..		25	30
109	9p. Private, 4th West Regt, 1785 ..		30	30
110	10p. Field Officer, 4th West Regt, 1824 ..		30	30

(b) *Size as T* **46**. *P* 13 × 13½ (20, 50p.) *or* 13½ × 13 (£1)

111	20p. Type **46** (1.4.75) ..	..	55	40
112	50p. Officer, Field Battery, Royal Guernsey Artillery, 1868 (1.4.75) ..		1·50	1·25
113	£1 Cavalry Trooper, Light Dragoons, 1814 (*horiz*) (1.4.75) ..		3·25	2·50
98/113	.. .. ..	*Set of 18*	7·00	6·00

The ½p. and 2½p. with the red colour omitted are chemically produced fakes.

† Nos. 98a/b come from special booklet sheets of 88 (8 × 11), and Nos. 99a/b from separate booklet sheets of 80 (2 panes 8 × 5). These sheets were put on sale in addition to the normal sheets. The strips and panes have the left-hand selvedge stuck into booklet covers, except for No. 99b which was loose, and then folded and supplied in plastic wallets.

47 Badge of Guernsey and U.P.U. Emblem

(Photo Courvoisier)

1974 (7 June). *U.P.U. Centenary. T* **47** *and similar horiz designs. Multicoloured. Granite paper. P* 11½.

114	2½p. Type **47**		10	10
115	3p. Map of Guernsey ..		10	10
116	8p. U.P.U. Building, Berne, and Guernsey flag		45	45
117	10p. "Salle des Etats" ..		45	45
114/17	..	*Set of 4*	1·00	1·00

48 "Cradle Rock"

49 Guernsey Spleenwort

(Des and photo Delrieu)

1974 (21 Sept). *Renoir Paintings. T* **48** *and similar multicoloured designs. P* 13.

118	3p. Type **48**		10	10
119	5½p. "Moulin Huet Bay" ..		15	15
120	8p. "Au Bord de la Mer" (*vert*)		40	40
121	10p. Self-portrait (*vert*) ..		45	45
118/21		*Set of 4*	1·00	1·00

(Des and photo Courvoisier)

1975 (7 Jan). *Guernsey Ferns. T* **49** *and similar vert designs. Multicoloured. Granite paper. P* 11½.

122	3½p. Type **49**		15	10
123	4p. Sand Quillwort ..		15	10
124	8p. Guernsey Quillwort ..		40	40
125	10p. Least Adder's Tongue ..		60	50
122/5		*Set of 4*	1·25	1·00

50 Victor Hugo House

51 Globe and Seal of Bailiwick

(Des and photo Courvoisier)

1975 (6 June). *Victor Hugo's Exile in Guernsey. T* **50** *and similar multicoloured designs. Granite paper. P* 11½.

126	3½p. Type **50**		10	10
127	4p. Candie Gardens (*vert*) ..		20	10
128	8p. United Europe Oak, Hauteville (*vert*)		40	40
129	10p. Tapestry Room, Hauteville ..		50	50
126/9		*Set of 4*	1·10	1·00
MS130	114 × 143 mm. Nos. 126/9 ..		1·10	1·00

(Des and photo Delrieu)

1975 (7 Oct). *Christmas. Multicoloured designs each showing Globe as T* **51**. *P* 13.

131	4p. Type **51**		10	10
132	6p. Guernsey flag ..		15	15
133	10p. Guernsey flag and Alderney shield (*horiz*)		45	35
134	12p. Guernsey flag and Sark shield (*horiz*) ..		50	50
131/4	.. ..	*Set of 4*	1·10	1·00

52 Les Hanois

(Des and photo Courvoisier)

1976 (10 Feb). *Lighthouses. T* **52** *and similar horiz designs. Multicoloured. Granite paper. P* 11½.

135	4p. Type **52**		10	10
136	6p. Les Casquets ..		20	25
137	11p. Quesnard ..		50	45
138	13p. Point Robert ..		55	60
135/8		*Set of 4*	1·25	1·25

53 Milk Can

(Des and photo Courvoisier)

1976 (29 May). *Europa. T* **53** *and similar horiz design. Granite paper. P* 11½.

139	10p. chestnut and greenish black ..		40	40
140	25p. slate and deep dull blue ..		85	85

Design:—25p. Christening Cup.

54 Pine Forest, Guernsey

(Des and photo Courvoisier)

1976 (3 Aug). *Bailiwick Views. T* **54** *and similar multicoloured designs. Granite paper. P* 11½.

141	5p. Type **54**		15	10
142	7p. Herm and Jethou ..		15	20
143	11p. Grand Greve Bay, Sark (*vert*) ..		55	45
144	13p. Trois Vaux Bay, Alderney (*vert*) ..		55	65
141/4		*Set of 4*	1·25	1·25

55 Royal Court House, Guernsey

56 Queen Elizabeth II

(Des and photo Courvoisier)

1976 (14 Oct). *Christmas. Buildings. T* **55** *and similar horiz designs Multicoloured. Granite paper. P* 11½.

145	5p. Type **55**		15	10
146	7p. Elizabeth College, Guernsey ..		15	10
147	11p. La Seigneurie, Sark ..		55	50
148	13p. Island Hall, Alderney ..		55	65
145/8		*Set of 4*	1·25	1·25

(Des R. Granger Barrett. Photo Courvoisier)

1977 (8 Feb). *Silver Jubilee. T* **56** *and similar vert design. Multicoloured. Granite paper. P* 11½.

149	7p. Type **56**		25	25
150	35p. Queen Elizabeth (half-length portrait)		1·00	1·00

57 Woodland, Talbot's Valley

58 Statue-menhir, Castel

(Des and photo Courvoisier)

1977 (17 May). *Europa. T* **57** *and similar horiz design. Multicoloured. Granite paper. P* 11½.

151	7p. Type **57**		35	35
152	25p. Pastureland, Talbot's Valley ..		90	90

(Des and photo Courvoisier)

1977 (2 Aug). *Prehistoric Monuments. T* **58** *and similar multicoloured designs. Granite paper. P* 11½.

153	5p. Type **58**		10	10
154	7p. Megalithic tomb, St. Saviour (*horiz*)		15	15
155	11p. Cist, Tourgis (*horiz*) ..		55	55
156	13p. Statue-menhir, St. Martin ..		60	60
153/6		*Set of 4*	1·25	1·25

59 Mobile First Aid Unit

(Des P. Slade and M. Horder. Photo Courvoisier)

1977 (25 Oct). *Christmas and St. John Ambulance Centenary. T* **59** *and similar multicoloured designs. Granite paper. P* 11½.

157	5p. Type **59**		10	10
158	7p. Mobile radar unit ..		15	15
159	11p. Marine Ambulance *Flying Christine II* (*vert*)		55	55
160	13p. Cliff rescue (*vert*) ..		60	60
157/60	..	*Set of 4*	1·25	1·25

60 View from Clifton, *circa* 1830

(Des, recess and litho D.L.R.)

1978 (7 Feb). *Old Guernsey Prints* (1st series). *T* **60** *and similar horiz designs. P* 14 × 13½.

161	5p. black and pale apple-green ..		10	10
162	7p. black and stone ..		15	15
163	11p. black and light pink ..		55	55
164	13p. black and light azure ..		60	60
161/4		*Set of 4*	1·25	1·25

Designs:—7p. Market Square, St. Peter Port, *circa* 1838; 11p. Petit-Bo Bay, *circa* 1839; 13p. The Quay, St. Peter Port, *circa* 1830.
See also Nos. 249/52.

61 *Prosperity* Memorial

62 Queen Elizabeth II

(Des R. Granger Barrett. Litho Questa)

1978 (2 May). *Europa. T* 61 *and similar vert design. Multicoloured. P* 14½.
65	5p. Type 61	.. .. ..	35	35
66	7p. Victoria Monument	.. .. ..	40	40

Des R. Granger Barrett from bust by Arnold Machin. Photo Courvoisier)

1978 (2 May). *25th Anniv of Coronation. Granite paper. P* 11½.
67	62	20p. black, grey and bright blue	75	75

1978 (28 June). *Royal Visit. Design as No.* 167 *but inscr.* "VISIT OF H.M. THE QUEEN AND H.R.H. THE DUKE OF EDINBURGH JUNE 28–29, 1978 TO THE BAILIWICK OF GUERNSEY".
68	62	7p. black, grey and bright green	..	50	50

63 Northern Gannet

(Des J.W. Photo Courvoisier)

1978 (29 Aug). *Birds. T* 63 *and similar horiz designs. Multicoloured. Granite paper. P* 11½.
169	5p. Type 63	.. ..	15	15
170	7p. Firecrest	.. .. ..	25	25
171	11p. Dartford Warbler	.. ..	45	45
172	13p. Spotted Redshank	..	55	55
169/72	..	*Set of* 4	1·25	1·25

64 Solanum

(Des and photo Courvoisier)

1978 (31 Oct). *Christmas. T* 64 *and similar designs. Granite paper. P* 11½.
173	5p. multicoloured	.. .. ..	10	10
174	7p. multicoloured	.. .. ..	20	20
175	11p. multicoloured	.. .. ..	40	40
176	13p. dp blue-green, grey & greenish yellow	50	50
173/6	..	*Set of* 4	1·10	1·10

Designs: *Horiz*—7p. Christmas Rose. *Vert*—11p. Holly; 13p. Mistletoe.

65 One Double Coin, 1830

66 Ten Shillings William I Commemorative Coin, 1966

66a Seal of the Bailiwick

(Des R. Reed and Courvoisier (£5). Photo Courvoisier)

1979 (13 Feb)–83. *Designs as T* 65/6a. *Granite paper. P* 11½.
177	½p. multicoloured	.. ..	10	10
	a. Booklet pane of 10. Nos. 177×2, 178×3, 179×2, 181, 183 and 187 (6.5.80)	1·00		
	b. Booklet pane of 10. Nos. 177×2, 178, 179×2, 183×2 and 187×3 (6.5.80) ..	1·25		
178	1p. multicoloured	.. ..	10	10
	a. Booklet strip of 4. Nos. 178×2, 179 and 182	60		
179	2p. multicoloured	.. ..	10	10
	a. Booklet strip of 5. Nos. 179, 182×2 and 184×2	1·25		

180 4p. multicoloured 10 10
  a. Booklet pane of 10. Nos. 180 and 184, each × 5 (24.2.81) .. 1·75
  b. Booklet pane of 15. Nos. 180, 184 and 190, each × 5 (24.2.81) 2·75
  c. Booklet pane of 10. Nos. 180×2, 185×3 and 191×5 (14.3.83) 3·00
  d. Booklet pane of 15. Nos. 180, 185 and 191, each × 5 (14.3.83) 3·75
181 5p. grey-black, silver and chestnut (*shades*) 15 10
  b. Booklet pane. Nos. 181×5, 184×4 and 191 (2.2.82) 2·25
  c. Booklet pane. Nos. 181, 184 and 191, each × 5 (2.2.82) 3·75
182 6p. grey-black, silver and brown-red .. 15 15
183 7p. grey-black, silver and green .. 15 20
184 8p. grey-black, silver and brown .. 20 20
185 9p. multicoloured 25 20
186 10p. multicoloured (green background) .. 50 50
187 10p. mult (orange background) (5.2.80) .. 35 30
188 11p. multicoloured 25 30
189 11½p. multicoloured (5.2.80) 25 30
190 12p. multicoloured 30 30
191 13p. multicoloured 30 30
192 14p. grey-black, silver and dull blue .. 30 30
193 15p. grey-black, silver and bistre .. 35 35
194 20p. grey-black, silver and dull brown .. 50 45
195 50p. grey-black, orange-red & silver (5.2.80) 1·00 75
196 £1 grey-blk, yellowish grn & silver (5.2.80) 2·00 1·50
197 £2 grey-black, new blue and silver (5.2.80) 4·00 2·50
198 £5 multicoloured (22.5.81) .. .. 10·00 7·50
177/98 .. *Set of* 22 19·00 14·50

Coins: *Vert as T* 65—1p. Two doubles, 1899; 2p. Four doubles, 1902; 4p. Eight doubles 1959; 5p. Three pence, 1956; 6p. Five new pence, 1968; 7p. Fifty new pence, 1969; 8p. Ten new pence, 1970; 9p. Half new penny, 1971; 10p. (*both*), One new penny, 1971; 11p. Two new pence, 1971; 11½p. Half penny, 1979; 12p. One penny, 1977; 13p. Two pence, 1977; 14p. Five pence, 1977; 15p. Ten pence, 1977; 20p. Twenty-five pence, 1972. *Horiz as T* 66—£1 Silver Jubilee commemorative crown, 1977; £2 Royal Silver Wedding crown, 1972.

Nos. 177a/b, 178a, 179a, 180a/d and 181b/c come from special booklet sheets of 40 (8 × 5) (Nos. 177a and 178a); 30 (6 × 5) (Nos. 177b, 180a/b, 180d and 181 b/c), 25 (5 × 5) (No. 179a) or 20 (4 × 5) No. 180c). These were put on sale in addition to the normal sheets, being first separated into strips, then folded and either affixed by the selvedge to booklet covers or supplied loose in plastic wallets.

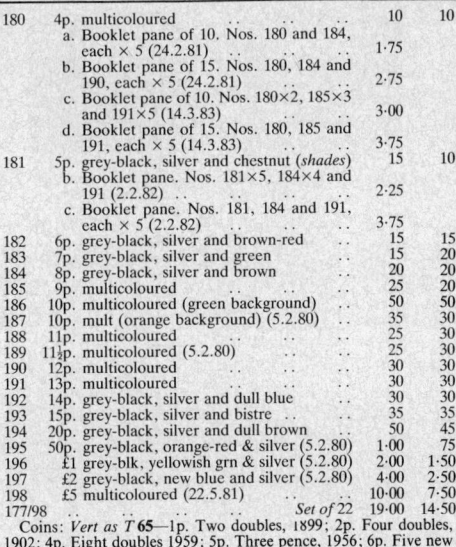

67 Pillar-box and Postmark, 1853, Mail Van and Postmark, 1979
68 Steam Tram, 1879

(Des R. Granger Barrett. Photo Courvoisier)

1979 (8 May). *Europa. Communications. T* 67 *and similar vert design. Multicoloured. Granite paper. P* 11½.
201	6p. Type 67	.. ..	30	30
202	8p. Telephone, 1897 and telex machine, 1979	30	30	

(Photo Courvoisier)

1979 (7 Aug). *History of Public Transport. T* 68 *and similar horiz designs. Multicoloured. Granite paper. P* 11½.
203	6p. Type 68	.. ..	15	15
204	8p. Electric tram, 1896	.. ..	20	20
205	11p. Motor bus, 1911	.. ..	55	55
206	13p. Motor bus, 1979	.. ..	60	60
203/6	..	*Set of* 4	1·25	1·25

69 Bureau and Postal Headquarters
70 Major-General Le Marchant

(Des R. Granger Barrett. Photo Courvoisier)

1979 (1 Oct). *Christmas and 10th Anniv of Guernsey Postal Administration. T* 69 *and similar horiz designs. Multicoloured. Granite paper. P* 11½.
207	6p. Type 69	.. ..	15	15
208	8p. "Mails and telegrams"	.. ..	25	15
209	13p. "Parcels"	.. ..	50	55
210	15p. "Philately"	.. ..	60	60
207/10	..	*Set of* 4	1·25	1·25
MS211	120 × 80 mm. Nos. 207/10	..	1·00	70

One copy of a pre-release sample as No. 210, but with a face value of 11p., is known. Such stamps were not sold for postal purposes.

(Des and photo Courvoisier)

1980 (6 May). *Europa. Personalities. T* 70 *and similar vert design. Multicoloured. Granite paper. P* 11½.
212	10p. Type 70	.. ..	45	45
213	13½p. Admiral Lord De Saumarez	..	55	50

71 Policewoman with Lost Child

(Litho J.W.)

1980 (6 May). *60th Anniv of Guernsey Police Force. T* 71 *and similar horiz designs. Multicoloured. P* 13½ × 14.
214	7p. Type 71	.. ..	20	20
215	15p. Police motorcyclist escorting lorry	..	55	55
216	17½p. Police dog-handler	..	65	65
214/16	..	*Set of* 3	1·25	1·25

72 Golden Guernsey Goat

(Des P. Lambert. Photo Delrieu)

1980 (5 Aug). *Golden Guernsey Goats. T* 72 *and similar horiz designs showing goats. P* 13.
217	7p. multicoloured	.. ..	20	20
218	10p. multicoloured	.. ..	30	35
219	15p. multicoloured	.. ..	55	45
220	17½p. multicoloured	.. ..	65	60
217/20	..	*Set of* 4	1·50	1·40

73 "Sark Cottage"

(Photo Courvoisier)

1980 (15 Nov). *Christmas. Peter le Lievre Paintings. T* 73 *and similar multicoloured designs. Granite paper. P* 11½.
221	7p. Type 73	.. ..	25	20
222	10p. "Moulin Huet"	.. ..	35	25
223	13½p. "Boats at Sea"	.. ..	40	35
224	15p. "Cow Lane" (*vert*)	.. ..	50	40
225	17½p. "Peter le Lievre" (*vert*)	..	65	50
221/5	..	*Set of* 5	2·00	1·50

74 *Polyommatus icarus*
75 Sailors paying respect to "Le Petit Bonhomme Andriou" (rock resembling head of a man)

(Photo Harrison)

1981 (24 Feb). *Butterflies. T* 74 *and similar horiz designs. Multicoloured. P* 14.
226	8p. Type 74	.. ..	25	25
227	12p. *Vanessa atalanta*	.. ..	40	40
228	25p. *Aglais urticae*	.. ..	75	70
229	25p. *Lasiommata megera*	..	85	90
226/9	..	*Set of* 4	2·00	2·00

(Des C. Abbott. Litho Questa)

1981 (22 May). *Europa. Folklore. T* 75 *and similar vert design. P* 14½.
230	12p. gold, red-brown and cinnamon	..	45	45
231	18p. gold, indigo and azure	..	55	55

Design:—18p. Fairies and Guernsey Lily.

76 Prince Charles
77 Sark Launch

(Des C. Abbott. Litho Questa)

1981 (29 July). *Royal Wedding. T* 76 *and similar multicoloured designs. P* 14½.
232	8p. Type 76	.. ..	50	50
	a. Horiz strip of 3. Nos. 232/4	1·50	1·50	
233	8p. Prince Charles and Lady Diana Spencer	50	50	
234	8p. Lady Diana	.. ..	50	50

235	12p.	Type **76**		90	90
	a.	Horiz strip of 3. Nos. 235/7		2·75	2·75
236	12p.	As No. 233		90	90
237	12p.	As No. 234		90	90
238	25p.	Royal family (49 × 32 *mm*)		1·50	1·50
232/8			Set of 7	5·00	5·00
MS239	104 × 127 mm. Nos. 232/8. P 14			6·50	6·50

The 8 and 12p. values were each printed together, *se-tenant*, in
horizontal strips of 3 throughout the sheets.

(Des and photo Courvoisier)

1981 (25 Aug). *Inter-island Transport. T* **77** *and similar horiz designs.*
Multicoloured. Granite paper. P 11½.

240	8p.	Type **77**		20	20
241	12p.	Britten Norman "Short nose" Trislander airplane		40	40
242	18p.	Hydrofoil		60	50
243	22p.	Herm catamaran		75	65
244	25p.	*Sea Trent* (coaster)		90	75
240/4			Set of 5	2·50	2·25

78 Rifle Shooting   79 Sir Edgar MacCulloch
(founder-president) and
Guille-Allès Library, St. Peter Port

(Des P. le Vasseur. Litho Questa)

1981 (17 Nov). *International Year for Disabled Persons. T* **78** *and*
similar horiz designs. Multicoloured. P 14½.

245	8p.	Type **78**		20	20
246	12p.	Riding		35	35
247	22p.	Swimming		65	55
248	25p.	"Work"		75	60
245/8			Set of 4	1·75	1·50

(Des, recess and litho D.L.R.)

1982 (2 Feb). *Old Guernsey Prints (2nd series). Prints from sketches*
by T. Compton. Horiz designs as T **60**. *P* 14 × 13½.

249	8p.	black and pale blue		20	20
250	12p.	black and pale turquoise-green		35	35
251	22p.	black and pale yellow-brown		65	65
252	25p.	black and pale rose-lilac		75	75
249/52			Set of 4	1·75	1·75

Designs:—8p. Jethou; 12p. Fermain Bay; 22p. The Terres; 25p.
St. Peter Port.

(Des G. Drummond. Photo Courvoisier)

1982 (28 Apr). *Centenary of La Société Guernesiaise. T* **79** *and similar*
horiz designs. Multicoloured. Granite paper. P 11½.

253	8p.	Type **79**		20	20
254	13p.	French invasion fleet crossing English Channel, 1066 ("History")		35	35
255	20p.	H.M.S. *Crescent*, 1793 ("History")		45	45
256	24p.	Dragonfly ("Entomology")		70	70
257	26p.	Common Snipe caught for ringing ("Ornithology")		80	80
258	29p.	Samian Bowl, 160–200 A.D. ("Archaeology")		85	85
253/8			Set of 6	3·00	3·00

The 13 and 20p. values also include the Europa C.E.P.T. emblem
in the designs.

80 "Sea Scouts"   81 Midnight Mass

(Des W.L.G. Creative Services Ltd. Litho Questa)

1982 (13 July). *75th Anniv of Boy Scout Movement. T* **80** *and similar*
vert designs. Multicoloured. P 14½ × 14.

259	8p.	Type **80**		20	25
260	13p.	"Scouts"		50	50
261	26p.	"Cub Scouts"		70	70
262	29p.	"Air Scouts"		85	80
259/62			Set of 4	2·25	2·25

(Des Lynette Hemmant. Photo Harrison)

1982 (12 Oct). *Christmas. T* **81** *and similar horiz designs. Multi-*
coloured. P 14½.

263	8p.	Type **81**		20	20
	a.	Black (Queen's head, value and inscr) omitted			
264	13p.	Exchanging gifts		30	30
265	24p.	Christmas meal		75	75
266	26p.	Exchanging cards		75	75
267	29p.	Queen's Christmas message		80	80
263/7			Set of 5	2·50	2·50

NEW INFORMATION

The editor is always interested to correspond with
people who have new information that will
improve or correct the Catalogue.

82 Flute Player and Boats   83 Building Albert Pier
Extension, 1850s

(Des Sally Stiff. Photo Harrison)

1983 (18 Jan). *Centenary of Boys' Brigade. T* **82** *and similar horiz*
designs. Multicoloured. P 14.

268	8p.	Type **82**		25	25
269	13p.	Cymbal player and tug 'o' war		40	40
270	24p.	Trumpet player and bible class		85	85
271	26p.	Drummer and cadets marching		90	90
272	26p.	Boys' Brigade band		95	95
268/72			Set of 5	3·00	3·00

(Des C. Abbott. Photo Courvoisier)

1983 (14 Mar). *Europa. Development of St. Peter Port Harbour. T* **83**
and similar horiz designs. Multicoloured. Granite paper. P 11½.

273	13p.	Type **83**		35	35
	a.	Horiz pair. Nos. 273/4		70	70
274	13p.	St. Peter Port Harbour, 1983		35	35
275	20p.	St. Peter Port, 1680		75	75
	a.	Horiz pair. Nos. 275/6		1·50	1·50
276	20p.	Artist's impression of future development scheme		75	75
273/6			Set of 4	2·00	2·00

The two designs of each value were issued together, *se-tenant*, in
horizontal pairs throughout the sheets.

84 "View at Guernsey"
(Renoir)

(Des and photo Courvoisier)

1983 (6 Sept). *Centenary of Renoir's Visit to Guernsey. T* **84** *and*
similar multicoloured designs, showing paintings. Granite paper.
P 11 × 11½ (13p.) *or* 11½ (*others*).

277	9p.	Type **84**		25	25
278	13p.	"Children on the Seashore" (25 × 39 *mm*)		45	45
279	26p.	"Marine, Guernsey"		80	80
280	28p.	"La Baie du Moulin Huet à travers les Arbres"		1·10	1·10
281	31p.	"Brouillard à Guernesey"		1·25	1·25
277/81			Set of 5	3·50	3·50

85 Launching *Star of the West*, 1869,
and Capt. J. Lenfestey

(Des R. Granger Barrett. Litho Questa)

1983 (15 Nov). *Guernsey Shipping (1st series). "Star of the West"*
(brigantine). T **85** *and similar horiz designs. Multicoloured. P* 14.

282	9p.	Type **85**		25	25
283	13p.	Leaving St. Peter Port		40	40
284	26p.	Off Rio Grande Bar		80	80
285	28p.	Off St. Lucia		1·10	1·10
286	31p.	Map of 1879–80 voyage		1·25	1·25
282/6			Set of 5	3·50	3·50

See also Nos. 415/19.

86 Dame of Sark as Young Woman

(Des Jennifer Toombs. Litho Questa)

1984 (7 Feb). *Birth Centenary of Sibyl Hathaway, Dame of Sark.*
T **86** *and similar horiz designs. Multicoloured. P* 14½.

287	9p.	Type **86**		25	25
288	13p.	German occupation, 1940–45		40	45
289	26p.	Royal Visit, 1957		90	90
290	28p.	Chief Pleas		95	95
291	31p.	The Dame of Sark rose		1·10	1·10
287/91			Set of 5	3·25	3·25

87 C.E.P.T. 25th Anniversary Logo

(Des J. Larrivière and C. Abbott. Litho Questa)

1984 (10 Apr). *Europa. P* 15 × 14½.

292	87	13p.	cobalt, dull ultramarine and black	65	65
293		20½p.	emerald, deep dull green and black	85	85

88 The Royal Court and St. George's Flag   89 St. Apolline Chape

(Des C. Abbott. Litho Questa)

1984 (10 Apr). *Links with the Commonwealth. T* **88** *and similar horiz*
design. Multicoloured. P 14 × 14½.

294	9p.	Type **88**		40	40
295	31p.	Castle Cornet and Union flag		1·10	1·10

(Des C. Abbott. Litho Questa)

1984 (18 Sept)–**91**. *Views. T* **89** *and similar multicoloured designs.*
Chalk-surfaced paper. P 14½.

296	1p.	Little Chapel (23.7.85)		20	10
297	2p.	Fort Grey (*horiz*) (23.7.85)		20	10
	a.	Booklet pane. Nos. 297×2, 299×4, 300×2 and 305×2 (2.12.85)		2·75	
298	3p.	Type **89**		20	10
	a.	Booklet pane. Nos. 298, 299×2, 306×4 and 309×3 (30.3.87)		4·25	
299	4p.	Petit Port (*horiz*)		20	10
	a.	Booklet pane. Nos. 299×2, 304×3 and 307×5		4·00	
	b.	Booklet pane. Nos. 299, 304 and 307, each × 5		4·75	
	c.	Booklet pane. Nos. 299×4, 306b×3 and 309c×3 (28.3.88)		4·00	
	d.	Booklet pane. Nos. 299, 301, 306b×3 and 309d×3 (28.2.89)		4·50	
300	5p.	Little Russel (*horiz*) (23.7.85)		20	10
	a.	Booklet pane. Nos. 300×2, 301×2, 309×3 and 310b×3 (2.4.91)		4·00	
301	6p.	The Harbour, Herm (*horiz*) (23.7.85)		20	15
	a.	Booklet pane. Nos. 301×4, 308×4 and 310×2 (27.12.89)		4·25	
	b.	Uncoated paper			
302	7p.	Saints (*horiz*) (23.7.85)		20	20
303	8p.	St. Saviour (23.7.85)		20	20
304	9p.	New jetty (inscr "Cambridge Berth") (*horiz*)		20	25
	a.	Booklet pane. Nos. 304×4 and 308×6 (19.3.85)		4·75	
	b.	Booklet pane. Nos. 304×2 and 308×8 (19.3.85)		4·50	
305	10p.	Belvoir, Herm (*horiz*)		25	25
	a.	Booklet pane. Nos. 305 and 308, each × 5 (1.4.86)		4·50	
306	11p.	La Seigneurie, Sark (*horiz*) (23.7.85)		25	25
	a.	Booklet pane. Nos. 306 and 309, each × 5 (30.3.87)		4·50	
306b	12p.	Petit Bot (28.3.88)		40	30
	ba.	Booklet pane. Nos. 306b and 309c, each × 5		4·25	
	bb.	Booklet pane. Nos. 306b and 309d, each × 4 (28.2.89)		4·75	
307	13p.	St. Saviours reservoir (*horiz*)		30	30
308	14p.	St. Peter Port		30	35
	a.	Booklet pane. Nos. 308 and 310, each × 5 (27.12.89)		4·75	
	b.	Uncoated paper			
309	15p.	Havelet (23.7.85)		30	35
	a.	Booklet pane. Nos. 309 and 310b, each × 5 (2.4.91)		5·25	
	b.	Imperf at sides and foot (horiz pair)			
309c	16p.	Hostel of St. John (*horiz*) (28.3.88)		35	35
309d	18p.	Le Variouf (28.2.89)		35	40
310	20p.	La Coupee, Sark (*horiz*)		50	45
	a.	Uncoated paper			
310b	21p.	King's Mills (*horiz*) (2.4.91)		50	45
310c	26p.	Town Church (2.4.91)		70	55
	ca.	Imperf at sides and foot (horiz pair)		£800	
311	30p.	Grandes Rocques (*horiz*) (23.7.85)		60	65
312	40p.	Torteval church		80	85
313	50p.	Bordeaux (*horiz*)		1·00	1·10
314	£1	Albecq (*horiz*)		2·00	2·10
315	£2	L'Ancresse (*horiz*) (23.7.85)		4·25	4·25
296/315			Set of 25	12·50	12·50

Booklet panes Nos. 297a, 298a, 299a/c, 304a/b, 305a, 306a and
306ba have margins all round and were issued, folded and loose
within the booklet covers.

Booklet panes Nos. 299d, 300a, 301a, 306bb, 308a and 309a have
the outer edges imperforate on three sides and were also issued
loose within the booklet covers.

The uncoated errors, Nos. 301b, 308b and 310a, come from
examples of booklet panes Nos. 301a and 308a.

For 11p., 12p., 15p. and 16p. stamps in a smaller size see Nos.
398/9a.

90 "A Partridge in a Pear Tree'

91 Sir John Doyle and Coat of Arms

(Des R. Downer. Litho Questa)

1984 (20 Nov). *Christmas. "The Twelve Days of Christmas". T* **90** *and similar vert designs. Multicoloured. P* 14½.

316	5p. Type **90**	..	..	20	20
	a. Sheetlet of 12. Nos. 316/27			2·50	
317	5p. "Two turtle doves"	..	..	20	20
318	5p. "Three French hens"	..	..	20	20
319	5p. "Four colly birds''	..	..	20	20
320	5p. "Five gold rings"	..	..	20	20
321	5p. "Six geese a-laying"	..	..	20	20
322	5p. "Seven swans a-swimming"		..	20	20
323	5p. "Eight maids a-milking"	..	..	20	20
324	5p. "Nine drummers drumming"	..	..	20	20
325	5p. "Ten pipers piping"	..	..	20	20
326	5p. "Eleven ladies dancing"	..	..	20	20
327	5p. "Twelve lords a-leaping"	..	..	20	20
316/27	..	*Set of* 12		2·50	2·50

Nos. 316/27 were printed, *se-tenant*, in sheetlets of 12.

(Des E. Stemp. Photo Courvoisier)

1984 (20 Nov). *150th Death Anniv of Lieut-General Sir John Doyle. T* **91** *and similar multicoloured designs. Granite paper. P* 11½.

328	13p. Type **91**	..	..	40	40
329	29p. Battle of Germantown, 1777 (*horiz*)		1·00	1·00
330	31p. Reclamation of Braye du Valle, 1806 (*horiz*)	1·25	1·25
331	34p. Mail for Alderney, 1812 (*horiz*)		1·25	1·25
328/31	..	..	*Set of* 4	3·50	3·00

92 Cuckoo Wrasse

93 Dove

(Des P. Barrett. Photo Courvoisier)

1985 (22 Jan). *Fishes. T* **92** *and similar horiz designs. Multicoloured. Granite paper. P* 11½.

332	9p. Type **92**	..	..	40	40
333	13p. Red Gurnard	..	..	60	60
334	29p. Red Mullet	..	..	1·50	1·10
335	31p. Mackerel	..	..	1·50	1·10
336	34p. Oceanic Sunfish	..	..	1·60	1·25
332/6	..	..	*Set of* 5	5·00	4·00

(Des C. Abbott. Litho Questa)

1985 (9 May). *40th Anniv of Peace in Europe. P* 14 × 14½.

337	**93** 22p. multicoloured	..	..	1·10	1·10

94 I.Y.Y. Emblem and Young People of Different Races

95 Stave of Music enclosing Flags

(Des Suzanne Brehaut (9p.), Mary Harrison (31p.). Litho Questa)

1985 (14 May). *International Youth Year. T* **94** *and similar square design. Multicoloured. P* 14.

338	9p. Type **94**	..	..	40	40
339	31p. Girl Guides cooking over campfire	..	1·00	1·00

(Des Fiona Sloan (14p.), Katie Lillington (22p.). Litho Questa)

1985 (14 May). *Europa. European Music Year. T* **95** *and similar horiz designs. Multicoloured. P* 14 × 14½.

340	14p. Type **95**	..	..	45	40
341	22p. Stave of music and musical instruments	..	..	95	1·00

96 Guide Leader, Girl Guide and Brownie

97 Santa Claus

(Des Karon Mahy. Litho Questa)

1985 (14 May). *75th Anniv of Girl Guide Movement. P* 14.

342	**96** 34p. multicoloured	..	..	1·50	1·50

(Des C. Abbott. Photo Courvoisier)

1985 (19 Nov). *Christmas. Gift-bearers. T* **97** *and similar vert designs. Multicoloured. Granite paper. P* 12½.

343	5p. Type **97**	..	..	25	25
	a. Sheetlet of 12. Nos. 343/54			4·25	
344	5p. Lussibruden (Sweden)	..	..	25	25
345	5p. King Balthazar	..	..	25	25
346	5p. Saint Nicholas (Netherlands)	..	25	25
347	5p. La Befana (Italy)	..	..	25	25
348	5p. Julenisse (Denmark)	..	..	25	25
349	5p. Christkind (Germany)	..	..	25	25
350	5p. King Wenceslas (Czechoslovakia)	..	25	25
351	5p. Shepherd of Les Baux (France)	..	25	25
352	5p. King Caspar	..	..	25	25
353	5p. Baboushka (Russia)	..	..	25	25
354	5p. King Melchior	..	..	25	25
343/54	..	*Set of* 12		4·25	4·00

Nos. 343/54 were printed, *se-tenant*, in sheetlets of 12.

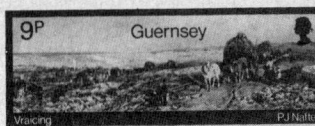

98 "Vraicing"

(Des and photo Harrison)

1985 (19 Nov). *Paintings by Paul Jacob Naftel. T* **98** *and similar horiz designs. Multicoloured. P* 15 × 14.

355	9p. Type **98**	..	..	30	30
356	14p. "Castle Cornet"	..	..	40	40
357	22p. "Rocquaine Bay"	..	..	90	90
358	31p. "Little Russel"	..	..	1·40	1·40
359	34p. "Seaweed gatherers"	..	..	1·50	1·50
355/9	..	..	*Set of* 5	4·00	4·00

99 Squadron off Nargue Island, 1809

100 Profile of Queen Elizabeth II (after R. Maklouf)

(Des T. Thompson. Photo Courvoisier)

1986 (4 Feb). *150th Death Anniv of Admiral Lord De Saumarez. T* **99** *and similar horiz designs. Multicoloured. Granite paper. P* 11½.

360	9p. Type **99**	..	..	40	40
361	14p. Battle of the Nile, 1798	..	50	50
362	29p. Battle of St. Vincent, 1797	..	1·25	1·25
363	31p. H.M.S. *Crescent* off Cherbourg, 1793	1·40	1·40
364	34p. Battle of the Saints, 1782	..	1·40	1·40
360/4	..	..	*Set of* 5	4·50	4·00

(Des C. Abbott. Litho Questa)

1986 (21 Apr). *60th Birthday of Queen Elizabeth II. P* 14.

365	**100** 60p. multicoloured	..	..	2·50	2·50

101 Northern Gannet and Nylon Net ("Operation Gannet")

102 Prince Andrew and Miss Sarah Ferguson

(Des P. Newcombe. Photo Courvoisier)

1986 (22 May). *Europa. Nature and Environmental Protection. T* **101** *and similar vert designs. Multicoloured. Granite paper. P* 11½.

366	10p. Type **101**	..	..	45	45
367	14p. Loose-flowered Orchid	..	..	75	75
368	22p. Guernsey Elm	..	..	1·00	1·00
366/8	..	..	*Set of* 3	2·00	2·00

(Des C. Abbott. Litho Questa)

1986 (23 July). *Royal Wedding. T* **102** *and similar multicoloured design. P* 14 (14p.) *or* 13½ × 14 (34p.).

369	14p. Type **102**	..	..	75	75
370	34p. Prince Andrew and Miss Sarah Ferguson (*different*) (47 × 30 *mm*)	..	..	1·50	1·50

---

103 Bowls

104 Guernsey Museum and Art Gallery, Candie Gardens

(Des R. Goldsmith. Litho Questa)

1986 (24 July). *Sport in Guernsey. T* **103** *and similar multicoloured designs. P* 14½.

371	10p. Type **103**	..	..	30	30
372	14p. Cricket	..	..	50	50
373	22p. Squash	..	..	75	75
374	29p. Hockey	..	..	1·25	1·25
375	31p. Swimming (*horiz*)	..	..	1·40	1·40
376	34p. Rifle-shooting (*horiz*)	..	..	1·50	1·50
371/6	..	..	*Set of* 6	5·00	5·00

(Des Sir Hugh Casson. Litho Questa)

1986 (18 Nov). *Centenary of Guernsey Museums. T* **104** *and similar horiz designs. Multicoloured. P* 14½.

377	14p. Type **104**	..	..	60	60
378	29p. Fort Grey Maritime Museum	..	1·10	1·10
379	31p. Castle Cornet	..	..	1·10	1·10
380	34p. National Trust of Guernsey Folk Museum	..	..	1·40	1·40
377/80	..	..	*Set of* 4	3·75	3·75

105 "While Shepherds Watched their Flocks by Night"

(Des Wendy Bramall. Photo Courvoisier)

1986 (18 Nov). *Christmas. Carols. T* **105** *and similar vert designs. Multicoloured. Granite paper. P* 12½.

381	6p. Type **105**	..	..	40	40
	a. Sheetlet of 12. Nos. 381/92			4·00	
382	6p. "In The Bleak Mid-Winter"	..	40	40
383	6p. "O Little Town of Bethlehem"	..	40	40
384	6p. "The Holly and the Ivy"	..	40	40
385	6p. "O Little Christmas Tree"	..	40	40
386	6p. "Away in a Manger"	..	..	40	40
387	6p. "Good King Wenceslas"	..	..	40	40
388	6p. "We Three Kings of Orient Are"	..	40	40
389	6p. "Hark the Herald Angels Sing"	..	40	40
390	6p. "I Saw Three Ships"	..	..	40	40
391	6p. "Little Donkey"	..	..	40	40
392	6p. "Jingle Bells"	..	..	40	40
381/92	..	*Set of* 12		4·00	4·00

Nos. 381/92 were printed, *se-tenant*, in sheetlets of 12.

106 Duke of Richmond and Portion of Map

(Des J. Cooter. Litho Questa)

1987 (10 Feb). *Bicentenary of Duke of Richmond's Survey of Guernsey. Sheet* 134 × 103 *mm containing T* **106** *and similar horiz designs showing sections of map. Multicoloured. P* 14½ × 14.

MS393	14p. Type **106**; 29p. North-east; 31p. South-west; 34p. South-east	..	4·00	4·00

The stamps within No. MS393 show a composite design of the Duke of Richmond's map of Guernsey.

107 Post Office Headquarters

108 Sir Edmund Andros and La Plaiderie, Guernsey

(Des R. Reed. Litho Cartor)

1987 (5 May). *Europa. Modern Architecture.* T **107** *and similar vert designs. Multicoloured.* P 13×13½.

394	15p.	Type **107**			55	55
	a.	Horiz pair. Nos. 394/5			1·10	1·10
395	15p.	Architect's elevation of Post Office Headquarters			55	55
396	22p.	Guernsey Grammar School			80	80
	a.	Horiz pair. Nos. 396/7			1·75	1·75
397	22p.	Architect's elevation of Grammar School			80	80
394/7				*Set of 4*	2·50	2·50

Nos. 394/5 and 396/7 were each printed together, *se-tenant*, in horizontal pairs throughout the sheets.

(Photo Harrison)

1987 (15 May)–**88.** *Coil Stamps. Designs as Nos. 306, 306b, 309 and 309c, but smaller.* P 14×14½ (11p., 16p.) *or* 14½×14 (12p., 15p.).

398	11p.	La Seigneurie, Sark (22×18 *mm*)			30	40
398a	12p.	Petit Bôt (18×22 *mm*) (28.3.88)			25	25
399	15p.	Havelet (18×22 *mm*)			45	55
399a	16p.	Hospital of St. John (22×18 *mm*) (28.3.88)			35	35
398/9a				*Set of 4*	1·40	1·25

(Des B. Sanders. Photo Courvoisier)

1987 (7 July). *350th Birth Anniv of Sir Edmund Andros (colonial administrator).* T **108** *and similar horiz designs, each showing portrait. Multicoloured. Granite paper.* P 12.

400	15p.	Type **108**			45	45
401	29p.	Governor's Palace, Virginia			1·00	1·00
402	31p.	Governor Andros in Boston			1·10	1·10
403	34p.	Map of New Amsterdam (New York), 1661			1·40	1·40
400/3				*Set of 4*	3·50	3·50

109 The Jester's Warning to Young William

110 John Wesley preaching on the Quay, Alderney

(Des P. le Vasseur. Litho Cartor)

1987 (9 Sept). *900th Death Anniv of William the Conqueror.* T **109** *and similar vert designs. Multicoloured.* P 13½×14.

404	11p.	Type **109**			45	35
405	15p.	Hastings battlefield			50	50
	a.	Horiz pair. Nos. 405/6			1·00	1·00
406	15p.	Norman soldier with pennant			50	50
407	22p.	William the Conqueror			80	75
	a.	Horiz pair. Nos. 407/8			1·60	1·50
408	22p.	Queen Matilda and Abbaye aux Dames, Caen			80	80
409	34p.	William's Coronation regalia and Halley's Comet			1·25	1·25
404/9				*Set of 6*	4·00	3·75

Nos. 405/6 and 407/8 were each printed together, *se-tenant*, in horizontal pairs throughout the sheets.

(Des R. Geary. Litho Questa)

1987 (17 Nov). *Bicentenary of John Wesley's Visit to Guernsey.* T **110** *and similar horiz designs. Multicoloured.* P 14½.

410	7p.	Type **110**			30	30
411	15p.	Wesley preaching at Mon Plaisir, St. Peter Port			45	45
412	29p.	Preaching at Assembly Rooms			1·25	1·25
413	31p.	Wesley and La Ville Baudu (early Methodist meeting place)			1·25	1·25
414	34p.	Wesley and first Methodist Chapel, St. Peter Port			1·25	1·25
410/14				*Set of 5*	4·00	4·00

111 *Golden Spur* off St. Sampson Harbour

(Des R. Granger Barrett. Litho B.D.T.)

1988 (9 Feb). *Guernsey Shipping (2nd series). "Golden Spur" (full-rigged ship).* T **111** *and similar horiz designs. Multicoloured.* P 13½.

415	11p.	Type **111**			35	35
416	15p.	*Golden Spur* entering Hong Kong harbour			50	50
417	29p.	Anchored off Macao			1·25	1·25
418	31p.	In China Tea Race			1·25	1·25
419	34p.	*Golden Spur* and map showing voyage of 1872–74			1·25	1·25
415/19				*Set of 5*	4·00	4·00

112 Rowing Boat and Bedford "Rascal" Mail Van

113 Frederick Corbin Lukis and Lukis House, St. Peter Port

(Des C. Abbott. Litho Questa)

1988 (10 May). *Europa. Transport and Communications.* T **112** *and similar horiz designs. Multicoloured.* P 14½.

420	16p.	Type **112**			60	60
	a.	Horiz pair. Nos. 420/1			1·25	1·25
421	16p.	Rowing boat and Vickers Viscount 800 mail plane			60	60
422	22p.	Postman on bicycle and horse-drawn carriages, Sark			95	95
	a.	Horiz pair. Nos. 422/3			1·90	1·90
423	22p.	Postmen on bicycles and carriage			95	95
420/3				*Set of 4*	2·75	2·75

Nos. 420/1 and 422/3 were each printed together, *se-tenant*, in horizontal pairs throughout the sheets, the two stamps of each value forming a composite design.

(Des Wendy Bramall. Photo Courvoisier)

1988 (12 July). *Birth Bicentenary of Frederick Corbin Lukis (archaeologist).* T **113** *and similar horiz designs. Multicoloured. Granite paper.* P 12½.

424	12p.	Type **113**			40	40
425	16p.	Natural history books and reconstructed pot			50	50
426	29p.	Lukis directing excavation of Le Creux ès Faies and prehistoric beaker			1·10	1·10
427	31p.	Lukis House Observatory and garden			1·25	1·25
428	35p.	Prehistoric artifacts			1·25	1·25
424/8				*Set of 5*	4·00	4·00

114 Powerboats and Westland Wessex Rescue Helicopter off Jethou

115 Joshua Gosselin and Herbarium

(Des and photo Courvoisier)

1988 (6 Sept). *World Offshore Powerboat Championships.* T **114** *and similar multicoloured designs. Granite paper.* P 12.

429	16p.	Type **114**			60	60
430	30p.	Powerboats in Gouliot Passage			1·10	1·10
431	32p.	Start of race at St. Peter Port (*vert*)			1·25	1·25
432	35p.	Admiralty chart showing course (*vert*)			1·50	1·50
429/32				*Set of 4*	4·00	4·00

(Des M. Oxenham. Litho Cartor)

1988 (15 Nov). *Bicentenary of Joshua Gosselin's Flora Sarniensis.* T **115** *and similar vert designs. Multicoloured.* P 13½×14.

433	12p.	Type **115**			40	40
434	16p.	Hares-tail Grass			55	55
	a.	Horiz pair. Nos. 434/5			1·10	1·10
435	16p.	Dried Hares-tail Grass			55	55
436	23p.	Variegated Catchfly			80	80
	a.	Horiz pair. Nos. 436/7			1·60	1·60
437	23p.	Dried Variegated Catchfly			80	80
438	35p.	Rock Sea Lavender			1·40	1·40
433/8				*Set of 6*	4·00	4·00

Nos. 434/5 and 436/7 were each printed together, *se-tenant*, in horizontal pairs throughout the sheets.

116 Coutances Cathedral, France

117 Lé Cat (Tip Cat)

(Des R. Downer. Litho Questa)

1988 (15 Nov). *Christmas. Ecclesiastical Links.* T **116** *and similar vert designs. Multicoloured.* P 14½.

439	8p.	Type **116**			25	25
	a.	Sheetlet of 12. Nos. 439/50			3·50	
440	8p.	Interior of Notre Dame du Rosaire Church, Guernsey			25	25
441	8p.	Stained glass, St. Sampson's Church, Guernsey			25	25
442	8p.	Dol-de-Bretagne Cathedral, France			25	25
443	8p.	Bishop's throne, Town Church, Guernsey			25	25
444	8p.	Winchester Cathedral			25	25
445	8p.	St. John's Cathedral, Portsmouth			25	25
446	8p.	High altar, St. Joseph's Church, Guernsey			25	25
447	8p.	Mont Saint-Michel, France			25	25
448	8p.	Chancel, Vale Church, Guernsey			25	25
449	8p.	Lychgate, Forest Church, Guernsey			25	25
450	8p.	Marmoutier Abbey, France			25	25
439/50				*Set of 12*	3·50	3·50

Nos. 439/50 were printed, *se-tenant*, in sheetlets of 12.

(Des P. le Vasseur. Litho Cartor)

1989 (28 Feb). *Europa. Children's Toys and Games.* T **117** *and similar horiz designs. Multicoloured.* P 13½.

451	12p.	Type **117**			40	40
452	16p.	Girl with Cobo Alice doll			60	60
453	23p.	Lé Colimachaön (hopscotch)			1·25	1·25
451/3				*Set of 3*	2·00	2·00

118 Outline Map of Guernsey

119 Guernsey Airways De Havilland D.H.86 Dragon Express and Mail Van

(Photo Harrison)

1989 (3 Apr–27 Dec). *Coil Stamps. No value expressed.* P 14½×14.

454	**118**	(–) ultramarine (27.12.89)			40	40
455		(–) emerald			60	60

No. 454 is inscribed "MINIMUM BAILIWICK POSTAGE PAID" and No. 455 "MINIMUM FIRST CLASS POSTAGE TO UK PAID". They were initially sold at 14p. and 18p., but this was changed in line with postage rate rises.

In these coils every fifth stamp is numbered on the reverse.

(Des N. Foggo. Litho B.D.T.)

1989 (5 May). *50th Anniv of Guernsey Airport (Nos. 456, 458, and 460) and 201 Squadron's Affiliation with Guernsey (Nos. 457, 459 and 461).* T **119** *and similar horiz designs. Multicoloured.* P 13½.

456	12p.	Type **119**			50	40
	a.	Booklet pane. No. 456×6			2·00	
457	12p.	Supermarine Southampton II flying boat at mooring			50	40
458	18p.	B.E.A. De Havilland D.H.89 Dragon Rapide			75	75
	a.	Booklet pane. No. 458×6			3·00	
459	18p.	Short S.25 Sunderland Mk V flying boat taking off			75	75
460	35p.	Air U.K. British Aerospace BAe 146			1·25	1·25
	a.	Booklet pane. No. 460×6			6·00	
461	35p.	Avro Shackleton M.R.3			1·25	1·25
456/61				*Set of 6*	4·50	4·50

Each booklet pane has margins all round with text printed at the foot.

120 "Queen Elizabeth II" (June Mendoza)

121 *Ibex* at G.W.R. Terminal, St. Peter Port

(Des A. Theobald. Litho B.D.T.)

1989 (23 May). *Royal Visit.* P 15 × 14.

462	**120**	30p. multicoloured			1·25	1·25

(Des C. Jaques. Litho B.D.T.)

1989 (5 Sept). *Centenary of Great Western Railway Steamer Service to Channel Islands.* T **121** *and similar horiz designs. Multicoloured.* P 13½.

463	12p.	Type **121**			30	30
464	18p.	*Great Western* (paddle-steamer) in Little Russel			65	65
465	29p.	*St. Julien* passing Casquets Light			90	90
466	34p.	*Roebuck* off Portland			1·25	1·25
467	37p.	*Antelope* and boat train at Weymouth quay			1·40	1·40
463/7				*Set of 5*	4·00	4·00
MS468		115×117 mm. Nos. 463/7			4·00	4·00

122 Two-toed Sloth

123 Star

(Des Anne Farncombe. Litho Cartor)

1989 (17 Nov). *10th Anniv of Guernsey Zoological Trust. Animals of the Rainforest.* T **122** *and similar vert designs. Multicoloured.* P 13½×14.
469	18p. Type **122**	..	..	1·00	90
	a. Horiz strip of 5. Nos. 469/73			4·50	
470	29p. Capuchin Monkey	..	..	1·00	90
471	32p. White-lipped Tamarin		..	1·00	90
472	34p. Common Squirrel-Monkey	..	..	1·00	90
473	37p. Common Gibbon	..	..	1·00	90
469/73		..	*Set of 5*	4·50	4·00

Nos. 469/73 were printed together, *se-tenant*, in horizontal strips of five throughout the sheet.

(Des Wendy Bramall. Litho B.D.T.)

1989 (17 Nov). *Christmas. Christmas Tree Decorations.* T **123** *and similar square designs. Multicoloured.* P 13.
474	10p. Type **123**	..	..	30	30
	a. Sheetlet. Nos. 474/85		..	4·00	
475	10p. Fairy	..	..	30	30
476	10p. Candles	..	..	30	30
477	10p. Bird	..	..	30	30
478	10p. Present	..	..	30	30
479	10p. Carol-singer	..	..	30	30
480	10p. Christmas cracker	..	..	30	30
481	10p. Bauble	..	..	30	30
482	10p. Christmas stocking	..	..	30	30
483	10p. Bell	..	..	30	30
484	10p. Fawn	..	..	30	30
485	10p. Church	..	..	30	30
474/85		..	*Set of 12*	4·00	4·00

Nos. 474/85 were printed, *se-tenant*, in sheetlets of 12.

124 Sark Post Office, *c.* 1890

(Des C. Abbott. Litho Enschedé)

1990 (27 Feb). *Europa. Post Office Buildings.* T **124** *and similar horiz designs.* P 13½×14.
486	20p. blackish brown, sepia and pale cinnamon		60	60
487	20p. multicoloured	..	..	60	60
488	24p. blackish brown, sepia and pale cinnamon		75	75
489	24p. multicoloured	..	..	75	75
486/9		..	*Set of 4*	2·50	2·50

Designs:—No. 487, Sark Post Office, 1990; 488, Arcade Post Office counter, St. Peter Port, *c.* 1840; 489, Arcade Post Office counter, St. Peter Port, 1990.

125 Penny Black and Mail
Steamer off St. Peter Port, 1840

(Des Jennifer Toombs. Litho Questa)

1990 (3 May). *150th Anniv of the Penny Black.* T **125** *and similar horiz designs. Multicoloured.* P 14.
490	14p. Type **125**	..	..	45	45
491	20p. Penny Red, 1841, and pillar box of 1853		60	60
492	32p. Bisected 2d., 1940, and German Army band		1·00	90
493	34p. Regional 3d., 1958, and Guernsey emblems		1·10	95
494	37p. Independent postal administration 1½d., 1969, and queue outside Main Post Office	1·10	1·00
490/4		..	*Set of 5*	3·75	3·50
MS495	151×116 mm. Nos. 490/4		4·00	3·75

No. **MS**495 also commemorates "Stamp World London 90" International Stamp Exhibition. It was reissued on 24 August 1990 overprinted for "NEW ZEALAND 1980" and sold at this international stamp exhibition in Auckland.

126 Lt. Philip Saumarez writing
Log Book

(Des R. Granger Barrett. Litho Enschedé)

1990 (26 July). *250th Anniv of Anson's Circumnavigation.* T **126** *and similar horiz designs. Multicoloured.* P 13½×14.
496	14p. Type **126**	..	..	45	45
497	20p. Anson's squadron leaving Portsmouth, 1740		60	60
498	29p. Ships at St. Catherine's Island, Brazil	..	1·00	90
499	34p. H.M.S. *Tryal* (sloop) dismasted, Cape Horn, 1741		1·10	95
500	37p. Crew of H.M.S. *Centurion* on Juan Fernandez		1·10	1·00
496/500		..	*Set of 5*	3·75	3·50

127 Grey Seal and Pup   **128** Blue Tit and
Great Tit

(Des Jennifer Toombs. Litho Questa)

1990 (16 Oct). *Marine Life.* T **127** *and similar horiz designs. Multicoloured.* P 14½.
501	20p Type **127**	..	..	60	60
502	26p. Bottle-nosed Dolphin	..	..	1·10	1·10
503	31p. Basking Shark	..	..	1·10	1·10
504	37p. Common Porpoise	..	..	1·40	1·40
501/4		..	*Set of 4*	3·75	3·75

(Des Wendy Bramall. Litho B.D.T.)

1990 (16 Oct). *Christmas. Winter Birds.* T **128** *and similar square designs. Multicoloured.* P 13.
505	10p. Type **128**	..	..	25	25
	a. Sheetlet of 12. Nos. 505/16			4·00	
506	10p. Snow Bunting	..	..	25	25
507	10p. Common Kestrel	..	..	25	25
508	10p. Common Starling	..	..	25	25
509	10p. Greenfinch	..	..	25	25
510	10p. European Robin	..	..	25	25
511	10p. Winter Wren	..	..	25	25
512	10p. Barn Owl	..	..	25	25
513	10p. Mistle Thrush	..	..	25	25
514	10p. Grey Heron	..	..	25	25
515	10p. Chaffinch	..	..	25	25
516	10p. Common Kingfisher	..	..	25	25
505/16		..	*Set of 12*	4·00	4·00

Nos. 505/16 were printed, *se-tenant*, in sheetlets of 12.

129 Air Raid and 1941 ½d.
Stamp

(Des C. Abbott. Litho B.D.T.)

1991 (18 Feb). *50th Anniv of First Guernsey Stamps.* T **129** *and similar square designs. Multicoloured.* P 13½.
517	37p. Type **129**	..	..	1·25	1·25
	a. Booklet pane. Nos. 517/19	..		4·00	
518	53p. 1941 1d. stamp	..	..	1·60	1·60
519	57p. 1944 2½d. stamp	..	..	1·60	1·60
517/19		..	*Set of 3*	4·00	4·00

Booklet pane No. 517a exists in three versions which differ in the order of the stamps from left to right and in the information printed on the pane margins.

130 Visit of Queen Victoria to
Guernsey, and Discovery of
Neptune, 1846

(Des Jennifer Toombs. Litho Enschedé)

1991 (30 Apr). *Europa. Europe in Space.* T **130** *and similar horiz designs. Multicoloured.* P 13½×14.
520	21p. Type **130**	..	..	65	65
521	21p. Visit of Queen Elizabeth II and Prince Philip to Sark, and "Sputnik" (first artificial satellite), 1957		65	65
522	26p. Maiden voyage of *Sarnia* (ferry), and "Vostok 1" (first manned space flight), 1961		90	75
523	26p. Cancelling Guernsey stamps, and first manned landing on Moon, 1969		90	75
520/3		..	*Set of 4*	2·75	2·50

131 Children in   **132** Pair of Oystercatchers
Guernsey Sailing Trust
"GP14" Dinghy

(Des C. Abbott. Litho B.D.T.)

1991 (2 July). *Centenary of Guernsey Yacht Club.* T **131** *and similar vert designs. Multicoloured.* P 14.
524	15p. Type **131**	..	..	50	50
525	21p. Guernsey Regatta	..	..	80	80
526	26p. Lombard Channel Islands Challenge race		90	90
527	31p. Rolex Swan Regatta	..	..	1·00	1·00
528	37p. Old Gaffers' Association gaff-rigged yacht		1·25	1·25
524/8		..	*Set of 5*	4·00	4·00
MS529	163×75 mm. As Nos. 524/8, but "GUERNSEY" and face values in yellow		4·00	4·00

(Des Wendy Bramall. Litho Questa)

1991 (15 Oct). *Nature Conservation. L'Eree Shingle Bank Reserve.* T **132** *and similar horiz designs. Multicoloured.* P 14½.
530	15p. Type **132**	..	..	40	40
	a. Horiz strip of 5. Nos 530/4			3·00	
531	15p. Three Turnstones	..	..	40	40
532	15p. Dunlins and Turnstones	..	..	40	40
533	15p. Curlew and Turnstones	..	..	40	40
534	15p. Ringed Plover with chicks	..	..	40	40
535	21p. Gull, Sea Campion and Sea Radish	..	50	50
	a. Horiz strip of 5. Nos. 535/9			3·00	
536	21p. Yellow Horned Poppy	..	..	50	50
537	21p. Pair of Stonechats, Hare's Foot Clover and Fennel		50	50
538	21p. Hare's Foot Clover, Fennel and Slender Oat		50	50
539	21p. Sea Kale on shore	..	..	50	50
530/9		..	*Set of 10*	5·50	4·00

Nos. 530/4 and 535/9 were each printed together, *se-tenant*, in horizontal strips of 5, throughout sheets of 20, with the backgrounds forming composite designs which continue onto the sheet margins.

133 "Rudolph the   **134** Queen
Red-nosed   Elizabeth II in 1952
Reindeer"
(Melanie Sharpe)

(Litho B.D.T.)

1991 (15 Oct). *Christmas. Children's Paintings.* T **133** *and similar square designs. Multicoloured.* P 13½×13.
540	12p. Type **133**	..	..	35	35
	a. Sheetlet of 12. Nos. 540/51		..	4·00	
541	12p. "Christmas Pudding" (James Quinn)		35	35
542	12p. "Snowman" (Lisa Guille)	..	..	35	35
543	12p. "Snowman in Top Hat" (Jessica Ede-Golightly)		35	35
544	12p. "Robins and Christmas Tree" (Sharon Le Page)		35	35
545	12p. "Shepherds and Angels" (Anna Coquelin)		35	35
546	12p. "Nativity" (Claudine Lihou)	..	..	35	35
547	12p. "Three Wise Men" (Jonathan Le Noury)		35	35
548	12p. "Star of Bethlehem and Angels" (Marcia Mahy)		35	35
549	12p. "Christmas Tree" (Laurel Garfield)	..	35	35
550	12p. "Santa Claus" (Rebecca Driscoll)	..	35	35
551	12p. "Snowman and Star" (Ian Lowe)	..	35	35
540/51		..	*Set of 12*	4·00	4·00

Nos. 540/51 were printed, *se-tenant*, in sheetlets of 12.

(Des C. Abbott. Litho Questa)

1992 (6 Feb). *40th Anniv of Accession.* T **134** *and similar vert designs. Multicoloured.* P 14.
552	23p. Type **134**	..	..	70	70
553	28p. Queen Elizabeth in 1977	..	..	75	75
554	33p. Queen Elizabeth in 1986	..	..	85	85
555	39p. Queen Elizabeth in 1991	..	..	1·10	1·10
552/5		..	*Set of 4*	3·00	3·00

135 Christopher Columbus

(Des R. Ollington. Litho Walsall)

1992 (6 Feb). *Europa. 500th Anniv of Discovery of America by Columbus.* T **135** *and similar horiz designs. Multicoloured.* P 13½×14.
556	23p. Type **135**	..	..	60	60
557	23p. Examples of Columbus's signature	..	60	60
558	28p. *Santa Maria*	..	..	1·10	1·10
559	28p. Map of first voyage	..	..	1·10	1·10
556/9		..	*Set of 4*	3·00	3·00
MS560	157×77 mm. Nos. 556/9		3·00	3·00

No. **MS**560 was reissued on 22 May 1992 overprinted for "WORLD COLUMBIAN STAMP EXPO 92" and sold at this international stamp exhibition in Chicago.

136 Guernsey Calves   **137** Stock

(Des R. Goldsmith. Litho Questa)

1992 (22 May). *150th Anniv of Royal Guernsey Agricultural and Horticultural Society. Sheet, 93×71 mm, containing T* **136**. *P* 14.
MS561 **136** 75p. multicoloured .. .. .. 2·00 2·00

(Des R. Gorringe, Litho Walsall (Nos. 572a, 572ba, 574a, 575a, 576ba, 577a), Questa (No. 576a), Cartor (No. 582a) or B.D.T. (others))

1992 (22 May)–**97**. *Horticultural Exports. T* **137** *and similar multicoloured designs. P* 14 (£1, £2) *or* 13 (*others*).

562	1p. *Stephanotis floribunda* (2.3.93)	10	10
563	2p. Potted Hydrangea (2.3.93)	10	10
564	3p. Type **137**	10	10
565	4p. Anemones	10	10
566	5p. Gladiolus	10	15
567	6p. *Asparagus plumosus* and *Gypsophila paniculata* (2.3.93)	10	15
568	7p. Guernsey Lily (2.3.93)	15	20
569	8p. Enchantment Lily (2.3.93)	15	20
570	9p. Clematis "Freckles" (2.3.93)	20	25
571	10p. Alstroemeria	20	25
572	16p. Standard Carnation (*horiz*)	30	35
	a. Perf 14	50	50
	ac. Booklet pane. Nos. 572a×5 and 574a×3	4·00	
	ad. Booklet pane of 8 (2.3.93)	3·00	
572b	18p. Standard Rose (2.1.97)	35	40
	ba. Perf 14	35	40
	bb. Booklet pane of 8	3·00	
573	20p. Spray Rose	40	45
574	23p. Mixed Freesia (*horiz*)	45	50
	a. Perf 14	60	60
	ac. Booklet pane of 8	4·50	
575	24p. Standard Rose (*horiz*) (2.3.93)	50	55
	a. Perf 14	50	55
	ab. Booklet pane of 8	4·00	
576	25p. Iris "Ideal" (*horiz*) (18.2.94)	50	55
	a. Perf 14½×15	50	55
	ab. Booklet pane of 4	2·00	
576b	26p. Freesia "Pink Glow" (*horiz*) (2.1.97)	55	60
	ba. Perf 14	55	60
	bb. Booklet pane of 4	2·10	
577	28p. Lisianthus (*horiz*) (2.3.93)	55	60
	a. Perf 14	55	60
	ab. Booklet pane of 4	2·25	
578	30p. Spray Chrysanthemum (*horiz*) (2.3.93)	60	65
579	40p. Spray Carnation	80	85
580	50p. Single Freesia (*horiz*)	1·00	1·10
581	£1 Floral arrangement (35×26½ *mm*)	2·00	2·10
582	£2 Chelsea Flower Show exhibit (35×26½ *mm*) (2.3.93)	4·00	4·25
582a	£3 "Floral Fantasia" (exhibit) (35×28 *mm*) (24.1.96)	6·00	6·25
562/82a	*Set of* 24	18·50	20·00

Imprint dates: "1992", Nos. 564/6, 571/2ac, 573/4ac, 579/81; "1993", Nos. 562/3, 567/70, 572ad, 575/ac, 577/ab, 578, 582; "1994", Nos. 576/ab; "1996", No. 582a; "1997", Nos. 572b/ba, 576b/ba.

Nos. 572a, 572ba, 574a, 575a, 576a, 576ba and 577a were only issued in booklets with the upper and lower edges of the panes imperforate.

For No. 581 in miniature sheets see Nos. **MS644** and **MS681**.

138 Building the Ship

(Des Studio Legrain. Litho Cartor)

1992 (18 Sept). *"Operation Asterix" (excavation of Roman ship). T* **138** *and similar horiz designs showing Asterix cartoon characters. Multicoloured. P* 13.

583	16p. Type **138**	45	45
	a. Booklet pane. Nos. 583/7 plus label with margins all round	3·50	
584	23p. Loading the cargo	60	60
585	28p. Ship at sea	80	80
586	33p. Ship under attack	95	95
587	39p. Crew swimming ashore	1·10	1·10
583/7	*Set of* 5	3·50	3·50

Booklet pane No. 583a exists with marginal inscriptions in English, French, Italian or German.

139 Tram No. 10 decorated for Battle of Flowers   **140** Man in Party Hat

(Des A. Peck. Litho Enschedé)

1992 (17 Nov). *Guernsey Trams. T* **139** *and similar horiz designs. Multicoloured. P* 13½.

588	16p. Type **139**	45	45
589	23p. Tram No.10 passing Hougue a la Perre	60	60
590	28p. Tram No. 1 at St. Sampsons	80	80
591	33p. First steam tram at St. Peter Port, 1879	95	95
592	39p. Last electric tram, 1934	1·10	1·10
588/92	*Set of* 5	3·50	3·50

(Des Wendy Bramall. Litho B.D.T.)

1992 (17 Nov). *Christmas. Seasonal Fayre. T* **140** *and similar square designs. Multicoloured. P* 13.

593	13p. Type **140**	35	35
	a. Sheetlet of 12. Nos. 593/604	4·00	
594	13p. Girl and Christmas tree	35	35
595	13p. Woman and balloons	35	35
596	13p. Mince pies and champagne	35	35
597	13p. Roast turkey	35	35
598	13p. Christmas pudding	35	35
599	13p. Christmas cake	35	35
600	13p. Fancy cakes	35	35
601	13p. Cheese	35	35
602	13p. Nuts	35	35
603	13p. Ham	35	35
604	13p. Chocolate log	35	35
593/604	*Set of* 12	4·00	4·00

Nos. 593/604 were printed together, *se-tenant*, in sheetlets of 12 forming a composite design.

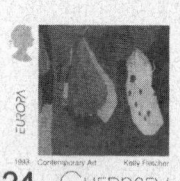

141 Rupert Bear, Bingo and Dog   **142** Tapestry by Kelly Fletcher

(Des J. Harrold. Litho Walsall)

1993 (2 Feb). *Rupert Bear and Friends (cartoon characters created by Mary and Herbert Tourtel). T* **141** *and similar vert designs. Multicoloured. P* 13½×13.

605	24p. Type **141**	1·00	1·00
MS606	116×97 mm. 16p. Airplane and castle; 16p. Professor's servant and Autumn Elf; 16p. Algy Pug; 16p. Baby Badger on sledge; 24p. Bill Badger, Willie Mouse, Reggie Rabbit and Podgy playing in snow; 24p. Type **141**; 24p. The Balloonist avoiding Gregory on toboggan; 24p. Tiger Lily and Edward Trunk	5·00	5·00

The 24p. values in No. MS606 are as Type **141**; the 16p. designs are smaller, each 25½×26 mm.

(Des B. Bell. Litho Enschedé)

1993 (7 May). *Europa. Contemporary Art. T* **142** *and similar multicoloured designs. P* 13½×14.

607	24p. Type **142**	80	80
608	24p. "Le Marchi a Paissaon" (etching and aquatint, Sally Reed) (48×33½ *mm*)	80	80
609	28p. "Red Abstract" (painting, Molly Harris)	90	90
610	28p. "Dress Shop, King's Road" (painting, Damon Bell) (48×33½ *mm*)	90	90
607/10	*Set of* 4	3·00	3·00

143 Arrest of Guernsey Parliamentarians, Fermain Bay

(Des C. Abbott. Litho Questa)

1993 (7 May). *350th Anniv of Siege of Castle Cornet. T* **143** *and similar horiz designs. Multicoloured. P* 14½×14.

611	16p. Type **143**	40	40
612	24p. Parliamentary ships attacking Castle Cornet	65	65
613	28p. Parliamentary captives escaping	85	85
614	33p. Castle cannon firing at St. Peter Port	95	95
615	39p. Surrender of Castle Cornet, 19 December 1651	1·10	1·10
611/15	*Set of* 5	3·50	3·50
MS616	203×75 mm. Nos. 611/15	3·50	3·50

OMNIBUS ISSUES

Details, together with prices for complete sets, of the various Omnibus issues from the 1935 Silver Jubilee series to date are included in a special section following Zimbabwe at the end of Volume 2.

144 Playing Cards   **145** "The Twelve Pearls"

(Des J. Stephenson. Litho (16, 24, 28p.) or recess (33, 39p.) Enschedé)

1993 (27 July). *Birth Bicentenary of Thomas de la Rue (printer). T* **144** *and similar vert designs. P* 13½.

617	16p. multicoloured	40	40
	a. Booklet pane of 4 with margins all round	1·25	
618	24p. multicoloured	65	65
	a. Booklet pane of 4 with margins all round	1·90	
619	28p. multicoloured	80	80
	a. Booklet pane of 4 with margins all round	2·25	
620	33p. carmine-lake	95	95
	a. Booklet pane of 4 with margins all round	2·75	
621	39p. blackish green	1·10	1·10
	a. Booklet pane of 4 with margins all round	3·00	
617/21	*Set of* 5	3·50	3·50

Designs:—24p. Fountain pens; 28p. Envelope-folding machine; 33p. Great Britain 1855 4d. stamp; 39p. Thomas de la Rue and Mauritius £1 banknote.

(Des Jennifer Toombs. Litho B.D.T.)

1993 (2 Nov). *Christmas. Stained Glass Windows by Mary-Eily de Putron from the Chapel of Christ the Healer. T* **145** *and similar square designs. Multicoloured. P* 13.

622	13p. Type **145**	45	45
	a. Sheetlet. Nos. 622/33	4·00	
623	13p. "Healing rays"	45	45
624	13p. "Hand of God over the Holy City"	45	45
625	13p. "Wing and Seabirds" (facing left)	45	45
626	13p. "Christ the Healer"	45	45
627	13p. "Wing and Seabirds" (facing right)	45	45
628	13p. "The Young Jesus in the Temple"	45	45
629	13p. "The Raising of Jairus' Daughter"	45	45
630	13p. "Suffer little Children to come unto Me"	45	45
631	13p. "Pilgrim's Progress"	45	45
632	13p. "The Light of the World"	45	45
633	13p. "Raphael, the Archangel of Healing, with Tobias"	45	45
622/33	*Set of* 12	4·00	4·00

Nos. 622/33 were printed together, *se-tenant*, in sheetlets of 12.

146 Les Fouaillages (ancient burial ground)

(Des Miranda Schofield. Litho Cartor)

1994 (18 Feb). *Europa. Archaeological Discoveries. T* **146** *and similar horiz designs. Multicoloured. P* 13¼.

634	24p. Type **146**	60	60
635	24p. Mounted Celtic warrior	60	60
636	30p. Jars, arrow heads and stone axe from Les Fouaillages	80	80
637	30p. Sword, spear head and torque from King's Road burial	80	80
634/7	*Set of* 4	2·50	2·50

Nos. 634/7 were each issued in small sheets of 10 (2×5) with a large inscribed margin at left. Some sheets of No. 635 were overprinted with the "Hong Kong '94" emblem on the left margin for sale at this philatelic exhibition.

147 Canadian Supermarine Spitfires Mk V over Normandy Beaches   **148** Peugeot "Type 3", 1894

(Des N. Trudgian. Litho B.D.T.)

1994 (6 June). *50th Anniv of D-Day. Sheet* 93×71 *mm. P* 14.
MS638 **147** £2 multicoloured .. .. 4·50 4·50

(Des R. Ollington. Litho B.D.T.)

1994 (19 July). *Centenary of First Car in Guernsey. T* **148** *and similar horiz designs. Multicoloured. P* 14½×14.

639	16p. Type **148**	45	45
	a. Booklet pane. No. 639×4 with margins all round	1·75	

40	24p.	Mercedes "Simplex", 1903	70	70
	a.	Booklet pane. No. 640×4 with margins all round	2·75	
41	35p.	Humber tourer, 1906	1·00	1·00
	a.	Booklet pane. No. 641×4 with margins all round	4·00	
42	41p.	Bentley sports tourer, 1936	1·10	1·10
	a.	Booklet pane. No. 642×4 with margins all round	4·25	
43	60p.	MG TC Midget, 1948	1·75	1·75
	a.	Booklet pane. No. 643×4 with margins all round	7·00	
39/43		*Set of 5*	4·50	4·50

(Des R. Gorringe and M. Whyte. Litho Cartor)

1994 (16 Aug). *"Philakorea '94" International Stamp Exhibition, Seoul. Sheet 110×90 mm containing stamp as No. 581 with changed imprint date. P 13.*

MS644	£1 multicoloured		2·50	2·50

149 *Trident* (Herm ferry)   **150** Dolls' House

(Des A. Copp. Litho Questa)

1994 (1 Oct). *25th Anniv of Guernsey Postal Administration. T 149 and similar horiz designs. Multicoloured. P 14.*

645	16p.	Type **149**	35	35
646	24p.	Handley Page HPR-7 Super Dart Herald of Channel Express	55	55
647	35p.	Britten Norman Trislander G-JOEY of Aurigny Air Services	75	75
648	41p.	*Bon Marin de Serk* (Sark ferry)	85	85
649	60p.	Map of Bailiwick	1·40	1·40
645/9		*Set of 5*	3·75	3·75
MS650	150×100 mm. Nos. 645/9		3·75	3·75

(Des A. Peck. Litho B.D.T.)

1994 (1 Oct). *Christmas. Bygone Toys. T 150 and similar square designs. Multicoloured. P 13.*

651	13p.	Type **150**	40	40
	a.	Sheetlet. Nos. 651/6	2·00	
652	13p.	Doll	40	40
653	13p.	Teddy in bassinette	40	40
654	13p.	Sweets in pillar box and playing cards	40	40
655	13p.	Spinning top	40	40
656	13p.	Building blocks	40	40
657	24p.	Rocking horse	75	75
	a.	Sheetlet. Nos. 657/62	3·50	
658	24p.	Teddy bear	75	75
659	24p.	Tricycle	75	75
660	24p.	Wooden duck	75	75
661	24p.	Hornby toy locomotive	75	75
662	24p.	Ludo game	75	75
651/62		*Set of 12*	5·00	5·00

Nos. 651/6 and 657/62 were each printed together, *se-tenant*, in sheetlets of 6, each sheetlet forming a composite design.

151 Seafood "Face"   **152** Winston Churchill and Wireless

(Des R. Ollington. Litho Questa)

1995 (28 Feb). *Greetings Stamps. "The Welcoming Face of Guernsey". T 151 and similar vert designs. Multicoloured. P 14.*

663	24p.	Type **151**	65	65
664	24p.	Buckets and spade "face"	65	65
665	24p.	Flowers "face"	65	65
666	24p.	Fruit and vegetables "face"	65	65
667	24p.	Sea shells and seaweed "face"	65	65
668	24p.	Anchor and life belts "face"	65	65
669	24p.	Glasses, cork and cutlery "face"	65	65
670	24p.	Butterflies and caterpillars "face"	65	65
663/70		*Set of 8*	4·50	4·50
MS671	137×109 mm. Nos. 663/70		4·50	4·50

(Des M. Whyte. Litho Enschedé)

1995 (9 May). *50th Anniv of Liberation. T 152 and similar horiz designs. Multicoloured. P 13½×14.*

672	16p.	Type **152**	50	50
673	24p.	Union Jack and Royal Navy ships off St. Peter Port	75	75
674	35p.	Royal Arms and military band	1·00	1·00
675	41p.	*Vega* (Red Cross supply ship)	1·00	1·00
676	60p.	Rejoicing crowd	1·75	1·75
672/6		*Set of 5*	4·50	4·50
MS677	189×75 mm. Nos. 672/6		4·50	4·50

153 Silhouette of Doves on Ground

(Des K. Bassford. Litho Walsall)

1995 (9 May). *Europa. Peace and Freedom. T 153 and similar horiz design. Multicoloured. P 14.*

678	25p.	Type **153**	65	65
679	30p.	Silhouette of doves in flight	85	85

The designs of Nos. 678/9 each provide a stereogram or hidden three-dimensional image of a single dove designed by D. Burder.

154 Prince Charles, Castle Cornet and Bailiwick Arms

(Des C. Abbott. Litho Questa)

1995 (9 May). *Royal Visit. P 14.*

680	154	£1.50, multicoloured	4·00	4·00

(Des R. Corringe and M. Whyte. Litho Cartor)

1995 (1 Sept). *"Singapore '95" International Stamp Exhibition. Sheet 110×90 mm containing stamp as No. 581 with changed imprint date. P 13.*

MS681	£1 multicoloured		2·50	2·50

155 Part of United Nations Emblem (face value at top left)   **156** "Christmas Trees for Sale in Bern" (Cornelia Nussbrum-Weibel)

(Des K. Bassford. Litho and embossed Enschedé)

1995 (24 Oct). *50th Anniv of United Nations. T 155 and similar horiz designs showing different segments of the United Nations emblem. Each pale new blue and gold. P 14×13½.*

682	50p.	Type **155**	1·25	1·25
	a.	Block of 4. Nos. 682/5	5·00	
683	50p.	Face value at top right	1·25	1·25
684	50p.	Face value at bottom left	1·25	1·25
685	50p.	Face value at bottom right	1·25	1·25
682/5		*Set of 4*	5·00	5·00

Nos. 682/5 were printed together, *se-tenant*, throughout the sheet with each block of 4 showing the complete emblem.

(Adapted M. Whyte from U.N.I.C.E.F. Christmas Cards. Litho B.D.T.)

1995 (16 Nov). *Christmas. 50th Anniv of U.N.I.C.E.F. T 156 and similar vert designs. Multicoloured. P 13.*

686	13p.	Type **156** (face value at left)	40	40
	a.	Horiz pair. Nos. 686/7	80	80
687	13p.	"Christmas Trees for Sale in Bern" (face value at right)	40	40
688	13p. + 1p.	"Evening Snowfall" (Katerina Mertikas) (face value at left)	40	40
	a.	Horiz pair. Nos. 688/9	80	80
689	13p. + 1p.	"Evening Snowfall" (face value at right)	40	40
690	24p.	"It came upon a Midnight Clear" (Georgia Guback) (face value at left)	70	70
	a.	Horiz pair. Nos. 690/1	1·40	1·40
691	24p.	"It came upon a Midnight Clear" (Georgia Guback) (face value at right)	70	70
692	24p. + 2p.	"Children of the World" (face value at left)	70	70
	a.	Horiz pair. Nos. 692/3	1·40	1·40
693	24p. + 2p.	"Children of the World" (face value at right)	70	70
686/93		*Set of 8*	4·00	4·00

Nos. 686/7, 688/9, 690/1 and 692/3 were printed together, *se-tenant*, as horizontal pairs in sheets of 12, each pair forming a composite design.

ALTERED CATALOGUE NUMBERS

Any Catalogue numbers altered from the last edition are shown as a list in the introductory pages.

157 Princess Anne (President, Save the Children Fund) and Children

(Des D. Miller. Litho B.D.T.)

1996 (21 Apr). *Europa. Famous Women. T 157 and similar horiz design. Multicoloured. P 14.*

694	25p.	Type **157**	65	65
695	30p.	Queen Elizabeth II and people of the Commonwealth	85	85

The background designs of Nos. 694/5 continue on to the vertical sheet margins.

158 England v. U.S.S.R., 1968 (value at right)   **159** Maj-Gen. Brock meeting Tecumseh (Indian chief)

(Des M. Whyte. Litho Questa)

1996 (25 Apr). *European Football Championship. T 158 and similar horiz designs. Multicoloured. P 14½×14.*

696	16p.	Type **158**	55	55
	a.	Horiz pair. Nos. 696/7	1·10	1·10
697	16p.	England v. U.S.S.R., 1968 (value at left)	55	55
698	24p.	Italy v. Belgium, 1972 (value at right)	75	75
	a.	Horiz pair. Nos. 698/9	1·50	1·50
699	24p.	Italy v. Belgium, 1972 (value at left)	75	75
700	35p.	Ireland v. Netherlands, 1988 (value at right)	80	80
	a.	Horiz pair. Nos. 700/1	1·60	1·60
701	35p.	Ireland v. Netherlands, 1988 (value at left)	80	80
702	41p.	Denmark v. Germany, 1992 final (value at right)	95	95
	a.	Horiz pair. Nos. 702/3	1·90	1·90
703	41p.	Denmark v. Germany, 1992 final (value at left)	95	95
696/703		*Set of 8*	5·50	5·50

Nos. 696/7, 698/9, 700/1 and 702/3 were printed together, *se-tenant*, in horizontal pairs throughout the sheets of 8 which had illustrated margins.

(Des A. Peck. Litho Enschedé)

1996 (8 June). *"CAPEX '96" International Stamp Exhibition, Toronto. Sheet 110×90 mm containing T 159 and similar horiz design. P 13½.*

MS704	24p. Type **159**; £1 Major-General Sir Isaac Brock on horseback, 1812		2·50	2·75

160 Ancient Greek Runner   **161** Humphrey Bogart as Philip Marlowe

(Des K. Bassford. Litho Questa)

1996 (19 July). *Centenary of Modern Olympic Games. T 160 and similar designs, each black, orange-yellow and orange, showing ancient Greek athletes. P 14.*

705	16p.	Type **160**	50	50
706	24p.	Throwing the javelin	95	95
707	41p.	Throwing the discus	1·10	1·10
708	55p.	Wrestling (53×31 mm)	1·40	1·40
709	60p.	Jumping	1·60	1·60
705/9		*Set of 5*	5·00	5·00
MS710	192×75 mm. Nos. 705/9		5·00	5·00

No. 708 also includes the "OLYMPHILEX '96" International Stamp Exhibition, Atlanta, logo.

(Des R. Ollington. Litho Enschedé)

1996 (6 Nov). *Centenary of Cinema. Screen Detectives. T 161 and similar horiz designs. Multicoloured. P 15×14.*

711	16p.	Type **161**	30	35
	a.	Booklet pane. No. 711×3 with margins all round	90	
	b.	Booklet pane. No. 711/15 with margins all round	3·50	
712	24p.	Peter Sellers as Inspector Clouseau	50	55
	a.	Booklet pane. No. 712×3 with margins all round	1·50	
713	35p.	Basil Rathbone as Sherlock Holmes	70	75
	a.	Booklet pane. No. 713×3 with margins all round	2·10	
714	41p.	Margaret Rutherford as Miss Marple	80	85
	a.	Booklet pane. No. 714×3 with margins all round	2·40	
715	60p.	Warner Oland as Charlie Chan	1·25	1·40
	a.	Booklet pane. No. 715×3 with margins all round	3·75	
711/15		*Set of 5*	3·50	4·00

162 The
Annunciation

163 Holly Blue (*Celastrina
argiolus*)

(Des P. le Vasseur. Litho B.D.T)

1996 (6 Nov). *Christmas. T 162 and similar multicoloured designs.*
P 13.

716	13p.	Type 162		25	30
	a.	Sheetlet of 12. Nos. 716/29		3·00	
717	13p.	Journey to Bethlehem		25	30
718	13p.	Arrival at the inn		25	30
719	13p.	Angel and shepherds		25	30
720	13p.	Mary, Joseph and Jesus in stable		25	30
721	13p.	Shepherds worshipping Jesus		25	30
722	13p.	Three Kings following star		25	30
723	13p.	Three Kings with gifts		25	30
724	13p.	The Presentation in the Temple		25	30
725	13p.	Mary and Jesus		25	30
726	13p.	Joseph warned by angel		25	30
727	13p.	The Flight into Egypt		25	30
728	24p.	Mary cradling Jesus (*horiz*)		50	55
729	25p.	The Nativity (*horiz*)		50	55
716/29			Set of 14	4·00	4·75

Nos. 716/27 were printed together, *se-tenant*, in sheetlets of 12.

(Des A. Peck. Litho B.D.T.)

1997 (12 Feb). *Endangered Species. Butterflies and Moths. T 163
and similar horiz designs. Multicoloured.* P 14.

730	18p.	Type 163		35	40
731	25p.	Hummingbird Hawk-moth (*Macroglossum stellatarum*)		50	55
732	26p.	Emperor Moth (*Saturnia pavonia*)		55	60
733	37p.	Brimstone (*Gonepteryx rhamni*)		75	80
730/3			Set of 4	2·10	2·25
MS734		92×68 mm. £1 Painted Lady (*Cynthia cardui*). P 13½		2·00	2·10

No. MS734 includes the "HONG KONG '97" International
Stamp Exhibition logo on the sheet margin.

164 Gilliatt fighting Octopus

165 Shell Beach, Herm

(Des M. Wilkinson. Litho Cartor)

1997 (24 Apr). *Europa. Tales and Legends. Scenes from* Les
Travailleurs de la Mer *by Victor Hugo. T 164 and similar horiz
design. Multicoloured.* P 13½.

735	26p.	Type 164		55	60
736	31p.	Gilliatt grieving on rock		60	65

Nos. 735/6 were each isued in small sheets of 10 (2×5) with an
enlarged inscribed margin at left.

(Litho B.D.T.)

1997 (24 Apr). *Guernsey Scenes (1st series). T 165 and similar
multicoloured designs. Self-adhesive.* P 9½.

737	18p.	Type 165		40	45
	a.	Booklet pane of 8		3·00	
738	25p.	La Seigneurie, Sark (*vert*)		55	60
	a.	Booklet pane of 8		4·25	
739	26p.	Castle Cornet, Guernsey		55	60
	a.	Booklet pane of 4		2·10	
737/9			Set of 3	1·50	1·60

Nos. 737/9 were issued as stamp booklets or as rolls of 100 (18p.
and 25p.).

See also Nos. 737/9.

166 19th-century Shipyard,
St. Peter's Port

(Des C. Abbott. Litho Questa)

1997 (29 May). *"Pacific '97" World Philatelic Exhibition, San
Francisco. Sheet 110×90 mm containing T 166 and similar horiz
design.* P 14.

MS740 30p. brown-olive and gold; £1 multicoloured
(*Costa Rica Packet* (coffee clipper)) .. .. 2·50 2·75

NEW INFORMATION

The editor is always interested to correspond with
people who have new information that will
improve or correct the Catalogue.

167 Transistor Radio, Microphone
and Radio Logos

(Des Miranda Schofield. Litho Cartor)

1997 (21 Aug). *Methods of Communication. T 167 and similar
horiz designs. Multicoloured.* P 13½×13.

741	18p.	Type 167		40	45
742	25p.	Television, video camera and satellite dish		55	60
743	26p.	Fax machine, telephones and mobile phone		55	60
744	37p.	Printing press, newspaper and type		75	80
745	43p.	Stamp, coding machine and postbox		85	90
746	63p.	C.D., computer and disk		1·25	1·40
741/6			Set of 6	4·25	4·75

168 Teddy Bear making
Cake

169 Visiting Guernsey,
1957

(Des Sally Diamond. Litho Walsall)

1997 (6 Nov). *Christmas. Teddy Bears. T 168 and similar vert
designs. Multicoloured.* P 14½×14.

747	15p.	Type 168		30	35
748	25p.	Teddy bears decorating Christmas tree		50	55
749	26p.	Two teddy bears in armchair		50	55
750	37p.	Teddy bear as Father Christmas		75	80
751	43p.	Teddy bears unwrapping presents		85	90
752	63p.	Teddy bears eating Christmas dinner		1·25	1·40
747/52			Set of 6	4·00	4·50
MS753		123×107 mm. Nos. 747/52		4·00	4·50

(Des M. Whyte. Litho Questa)

1997 (20 Nov). *Golden Wedding of Queen Elizabeth and Prince
Philip. T 169 and similar square designs. Multicoloured.* P 14½.

754	18p.	Type 169		35	40
	a.	Booklet pane. Nos. 754/5, each × 3 with margins all round		2·50	
	b.	Booklet pane. Nos. 754/9 with margins all round		50	55
755	25p.	Coronation Day, 1953		50	55
756	26p.	Royal family, 1957		50	55
	a.	Booklet pane. Nos. 756/7, each × 3 with margins all round		3·75	
757	37p.	On royal yacht, 1972		75	80
758	43p.	Queen Elizabeth and Prince Philip at Trooping the Colour, 1987		85	90
	a.	Booklet pane. Nos. 758/9, each × 3 with margins all round		6·25	
759	63p.	Queen Elizabeth and Prince Philip, 1997		1·25	1·40
754/9			Set of 6	4·25	4·50

No. 755 is inscribed "1947" in error.

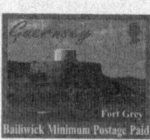

170 Tapestry of
11th-century
Guernsey (St.
Martin)

171 Fort Grey

(Des Sally Diamond. Litho Questa)

1998 (10 Feb). *The Millennium Tapestries Project. T 170 and
similar vert designs each showing a different century contributed
by individual parishes. Multicoloured.* P 15×14½.

760	25p.	Type 170		50	55
	a.	Horiz strip of 10 or two strips of 5. Nos. 760/9		5·00	
	b.	Booklet pane. Nos. 760/1, each × 2, and 762/3 with margins all round		3·00	
	c.	Booklet pane. Nos. 760/1, and 768/9 each × 2 with margins all round		3·00	
761	25p.	12th-century (St. Saviour)		50	55
762	25p.	13th-century (Vale)		50	55
	a.	Booklet pane. Nos. 762/3, each × 2, and 764/5 with margins all round		3·00	
763	25p.	14th-century (St. Sampson)		50	55
764	25p.	15th-century (Torteval)		50	55
	b.	Booklet pane. Nos. 764/5, each × 2, and 766/7 with margins all round		3·00	
765	25p.	16th-century (Castel)		50	55

766	25p.	17th-century (St. Andrew)		50	5
	a.	Booklet pane. Nos. 766/7, each × 2, and 768/9 with margins all round		3·00	
767	25p.	18th-century (Forest)		50	55
768	25p.	19th-century (St. Pierre du Bois)		50	55
769	25p.	20th-century (St. Peter Port)		50	55
760/9			Set of 10	5·00	5·5

Nos. 760/9 were printed together, *se-tenant*, in horizontal strips o
10 throughout the sheet. These stamps were often supplied by the
Guernsey Philatelic Bureau as two horizontal strips of 5.

(Des Joanna Brehaut. Litho B.D.T.)

1998 (25 Mar). *Guernsey Scenes (2nd series). T 171 and simila
horiz designs. Multicoloured. Self-adhesive.* P 9½.

770	(20p.)	Type 171		40	45
	a.	Horiz pair. Nos. 770/1		80	
	b.	Booklet pane. Nos. 770/1, each × 4 with margins all round		3·25	
771	(20p.)	Grand Havre		40	45
772	(25p.)	Little Chapel		50	55
	a.	Horiz pair. Nos. 772/3		90	
	b.	Booklet pane. Nos. 772/3, each × 4 with margins all round		4·00	
773	(25p.)	Guernsey Cow		50	55
770/3			Set of 4	1·75	2·00

Nos. 770/1 are inscribed "Bailiwick Minimum Postage Paid" and
were initially sold at 20p. Nos. 772/3 are inscribed "UK Minimum
Postage Paid" and were initially sold at 25p.

Nos. 770/3 were issued in stamp booklets or as rolls of 100, each
roll containing two designs.

172 Fairey IIIC, Balloon,
Sopwith Camel and Avro 504

(Des C. Abbott. Litho Cartor)

1998 (7 May). *80th Anniv of the Royal Air Force. T 172 and
similar horiz designs. Multicoloured.* P 13½×13.

774	20p.	Type 172		40	45
775	25p.	Fairey Swordfish, Tiger Moth, Supermarine Walrus and Gloster Gladiator		50	55
776	30p.	Hawker Hurricane, Supermarine Spitfire, Vickers Wellington, Short Sunderland (flying boat), Westland Lysander and Bristol Blenheim		60	65
777	37p.	De Havilland Mosquito, Avro Lancaster, Auster III, Gloster Meteor and Horsa glider		75	80
778	43p.	Canberra, Hawker Sea Fury, Bristol Sycamore, Hawker Hunter, Handley Page Victor and BAe Lightning		85	90
779	63p.	Panavia Tornado GRI, BAe Hawk, BAe Sea Harrier, Westland Lynx (helicopter) and Hawker Siddeley Nimrod		1·25	1·40
774/9			Set of 6	4·25	4·75

173 Jules Rimet (first
President of F.I.F.A.)

(Des A. Peck. Litho Enschedé)

1998 (7 May). *150th Anniv of the Cambridge Rules for Football.
Sheet 110×90 mm containing T 173 and similar horiz design.*
P 13½×14.

MS780 30p. Type 173; £1.75, Bobby Moore and
Queen Elizabeth II, 1966 .. .. .. 4·00 4·25

STAMP BOOKLETS

For a full listing of Guernsey stamp booklets see *Collect Channel Islands and Isle of Man Stamps* published each January.

POSTAGE DUE STAMPS

D 1 Castle Cornet   D 2 St. Peter Port

(Des R. Granger Barrett. Photo Delrieu)

1969 (1 Oct). *Value in black ; background colour given. No wmk. P 12½ × 12.*

D1	D 1	1d. plum	2·25	1·25
D2		2d. bright green	2·25	1·25
D3		3d. vermilion	3·75	4·00
D4		4d. ultramarine	5·00	5·00
D5		5d. yellow-ochre	5·50	5·50
D6		6d. turquoise-blue	6·50	6·00
D7		1s. lake-brown	17·00	17·00
D1/7		Set of 7	35·00	35·00

1971 (15 Feb)–**76.** *As Type D 1 but values in decimal currency.*

D 8	D 1	½p. plum	10	10
D 9		1p. bright green	10	10
D10		2p. vermilion	10	10
D11		3p. ultramarine	10	15
D12		4p. yellow-ochre	10	15
D13		5p. turquoise-blue	10	15
D14		6p. violet (10.2.76)	15	20
D15		8p. light yellow-orange (7.10.75)	25	20
D16		10p. lake-brown	30	30
D17		15p. grey (10.2.76)	40	40
D8/17		Set of 10	1·50	1·60

(Photo Delrieu)

1977 (2 Aug)–**80.** *Face value in black ; background colour given. P 13.*

D18	D 2	½p. lake-brown	10	10
D19		1p. bright purple	10	10
D20		2p. bright orange	10	10
D21		3p. vermilion	10	10
D22		4p. turquoise-blue	15	15
D23		5p. yellow-green	15	15
D24		6p. turquoise-green	20	20
D25		8p. brown-ochre	25	25
D26		10p. ultramarine	30	30
D27		14p. green (5.2.80)	35	35
D28		15p. bright violet	35	35
D29		16p. rose-red (5.2.80)	45	45
D18/29		Set of 12	2·10	2·10

D 3 Milking Cow

(Litho Questa)

1982 (13 July). *Guernsey Scenes, circa 1900. Horiz designs as Type D 3. P 14½.*

D30	1p. indigo, blue-black and bright green			10	10
D31	2p. sepia, yellow-brown and azure		10	10
D32	3p. blackish green, black and lilac		10	10
D33	4p. bottle-green, black and dull orange		10	10
D34	5p. dp violet-blue, blue-black & turq-grn		10	10
D35	10p. deep grey-blue, deep blue and cobalt		30	35
D36	18p. steel-blue, indigo and apple-green		35	40
D37	20p. brown-olive, agate and pale blue		40	45
D38	25p. Prussian blue, blue-black and rose-pink		50	55
D39	30p. dp bluish grn, blackish ol & bistre-yell		60	65
D40	50p. olive-brown, sepia and dull violet-blue		1·00	1·10
D41	£1 light brown, brown and pale brown		2·00	2·10
D30/41	Set of 12		5·25	5·75

Designs:—2p. Vale Mill; 3p. Sark cottage; 4p. Quay-side, St. Peter Port; 5p. Well, Water Lane, Moulin Huet; 16p. Seaweed gathering; 18p. Upper Walk, White Rock; 20p. Cobo Bay; 25p. Saint's Bay; 30p. La Coupee, Sark; 50p. Old Harbour, St. Peter Port; £1 Greenhouses, Doyle Road, St. Peter Port.

ALDERNEY

The following issues are provided by the Guernsey Post Office for use on Alderney. They are also valid for postal purposes throughout the rest of the Bailiwick of Guernsey.

A 1 Island Map

(Des G. Drummond. Litho B.D.T. (20p. to 28p.). Photo Courvoisier (others))

1983 (14 June)–**93.** *Island Scenes. Type A 1 and similar horiz designs. Multicoloured. Granite paper (Nos. A1/12). P 15×14 (20p. to 28p.) or 11½ (others).*

A 1	1p. Type A 1		10	10
A 2	4p. Hanging Rock		10	10
A 3	9p. States' Building, St. Anne		20	25
A 4	10p. St. Anne's Church		25	25

A 5	11p. Yachts in Braye Bay	25	25
A 6	12p. Victoria St.. St. Anne	25	30
A 7	13p. Map of Channel	25	30
A 8	14p. Fort Clonque	30	35
A 9	15p. Corblets Bay and Fort	30	35
A10	16p. Old Tower, St. Anne	30	35
A11	17p. Golf course and Essex Castle	35	40
A12	18p. Old Harbour	35	40
A12a	20p. Quesnard Lighthouse (27.12.89)	80	80
A12b	21p. Braye Harbour (2.4.91)	80	80
A12c	23p. Island Hall (6.2.92)	70	70
A12d	24p. J. T. Daly (steam locomotive) (2.3.93)	1·75	1·75
A12e	28p. *Louis Marchesi of Round Table* (lifeboat) (2.3.93)	2·00	2·00
A1/12e	Set of 17	8·00	8·00

Nos. A12*a/e* are larger, 38×27 mm.

A 2 Oystercatcher

(Des and photo Harrison)

1984 (12 June). *Birds. Type A 2 and similar horiz designs. Multicoloured. P 14½.*

A13	9p. Type A 2	1·50	1·50
A14	13p. Turnstone	1·50	2·00
A15	26p. Ringed Plover	5·00	4·00
A16	28p. Dunlin	5·00	4·00
A17	31p. Curlew	5·00	4·00
A13/17	Set of 5	16·00	14·00

A 3 Westland Wessex HU   A 4 Royal
Mk 5 Helicopter of the   Engineers, 1890
Queen's Flight

(Des A. Theobald. Photo Courvoisier)

1985 (19 Mar). *50th Anniv of Alderney Airport. Type A 3 and similar horiz designs. Multicoloured. Granite paper. P 11½.*

A18	9p. Type A 3	2·50	2·25
A19	13p. Britten Norman "long nose" Trislander	2·50	3·00
A20	29p. De Havilland D.H.114 Heron 1B	6·00	5·00
A21	31p. De Havilland D.H.89A Dragon Rapide *Sir Henry Lawrence*	6·50	5·50
A22	34p. Saro A.21 Windhover flying boat *City of Portsmouth*	7·00	5·50
A18/22	Set of 5	22·00	19·00

(Des E. Stemp. Litho Harrison)

1985 (24 Sept). *Regiments of the Alderney Garrison. Type A 4 and similar vert designs. Multicoloured. P 14½.*

A23	9p. Type A 4	45	45
A24	14p. Duke of Albany's Own Highlanders (72nd Highland Regt), 1856	1·00	1·00
A25	29p. Royal Artillery, 1855	1·50	1·50
A26	31p. South Hampshire Regiment, 1810	1·75	1·75
A27	34p. Royal Irish Regiment, 1782	2·00	2·00
A23/7	Set of 5	6·00	6·00

No. A24 shows the tartan and insignia of the 78th Highland Regiment in error.

A 5 Fort Grosnez   A 6 *Liverpool* (full-rigged ship) 1902

(Des R. Reed. Litho Cartor)

1986 (23 Sept). *Alderney Forts. Type A 5 and similar vert designs. Multicoloured. P 13×13½.*

A28	10p. Type A 5	1·10	1·10
A29	14p. Fort Tourgis	1·75	1·75
A30	31p. Fort Clonque	4·00	4·00
A31	34p. Fort Albert	4·25	4·25
A28/31	Set of 4	10·00	10·00

(Des C. Jaques. Litho Questa)

1987 (5 May). *Alderney Shipwrecks. Type A 6 and similar horiz designs. Multicoloured. P 14×14½.*

A32	11p. Type A 6	2·00	1·50
A33	15p. *Petit Raymond* (schooner), 1906	2·25	2·00
A34	29p. *Maina* (yacht), 1910	5·50	5·00
A35	31p. *Burton* (steamer), 1911	6·00	5·50
A36	34p. *Point Law* (oil tanker), 1975	6·50	6·00
A32/6	Set of 5	20·00	18·00

A 7 Moll's Map of 1724

(Des J. Cooter. Litho Enschedé)

1989 (7 July). *250th Anniv of Bastide's Survey of Alderney. Type A 7 and similar horiz designs. P 13½×14.*

A37	12p. multicoloured	40	40
A38	18p. black, greenish blue and orange-brown	60	60
A39	27p. black, greenish blue & dull yellow-green	1·10	1·10
A40	32p. black, greenish blue and bright rose-red	1·25	1·25
A41	35p. multicoloured	1·40	1·40
A37/41	Set of 5	4·25	4·25

Designs:—18p. Bastide's survey of 1739; 27p. Goodwin's map of 1831; 32p. General Staff map of 1943; 35p. Ordnance Survey map, 1988.

A 8 H.M.S. *Alderney* (bomb ketch), 1738

(Des A. Theobald. Litho B.D.T.)

1990 (3 May). *Royal Navy Ships named after Alderney. Type A 8 and similar horiz designs. P 13½.*

A42	14p. black and olive-bistre	45	45
A43	20p. black and orange-brown	60	60
A44	29p. black and cinnamon	1·10	1·10
A45	34p. black and pale turquoise-blue	1·10	1·10
A46	37p. black and cobalt	1·25	1·25
A42/6	Set of 5	4·00	4·00

Designs:—20p. H.M.S. *Alderney* (frigate), 1742; 29p. H.M.S. *Alderney* (sloop), 1755; 34p H.M.S. *Alderney* (submarine), 1945; 37p. H.M.S. *Alderney* (patrol vessel), 1979.

A 9 Wreck of H.M.S. *Victory*,   A 10 Two French
1744   Warships on Fire

(Des A. Theobald. Litho Cartor)

1991 (30 Apr). *Automation of The Casquets Lighthouse. Type A 9 and similar horiz designs. Multicoloured. P 14×13½.*

A47	21p. Type A 9	1·60	2·00
A48	26p. Lighthouse keeper's daughter rowing back to the Casquets	2·00	2·25
A49	31p. MBB-Bolkow Bo 105D helicopter leaving pad on St. Thomas Tower	2·50	2·75
A50	37p. Migrating birds over lighthouse	3·50	3·75
A51	50p. Trinity House vessel *Patricia* and arms	6·00	5·00
A47/51	Set of 5	14·00	14·00

(Des C. Abbott. Litho B.D.T.)

1992 (18 Sept). *300th Anniv of the Battle of La Hogue. Type A 10 and similar multicoloured designs. P 14×15 (50p.) or 13½ (others).*

A52	23p. Type A 10	1·50	1·50
A53	28p. Crews leaving burning ships	2·25	2·25
A54	33p. French warship sinking	2·50	2·50
A55	50p. "The Battle of La Hogue" (47×32 mm)	3·75	3·75
A52/5	Set of 4	9·00	9·00

Nos. A52/4 show details of the painting on the 50p. value.

A 11 Spiny Lobster   A 12 Blue-tailed Damselfly, Dark Hair Water Crowfoot and Branched Bur-reed

(Des A. Peck. Litho Questa)

1993 (2 Nov). *Endangered Species. Marine Life. Type* A **11** *and similar horiz designs. Multicoloured.* P 14½.
A56	24p. Type A **11**		90	90
	a. Horiz strip of 4. Nos. A56/9		4·25	
A57	28p. Plumose Anemone		1·00	1·00
A58	33p. Starfish		1·25	1·25
A59	39p. Sea Urchin		1·60	1·60
A56/9		*Set of* 4	4·25	4·25

Nos. A56/9 were printed together, *se-tenant*, in horizontal strips of 4, throughout the sheet, the backgrounds of each strip forming a composite design.

(Des Wendy Bramall. Litho Questa)

1994 (5 May)–**97**. *Flora and Fauna. Type* A **12** *and similar multicoloured designs.* P 14½.
A60	1p. Type A **12**		10	10
A61	2p. White-toothed Shrew and Flax-leaved St. John's Wort		10	10
A62	3p. Fulmar and Kaffir Fig		10	10
A63	4p. Clouded Yellow (butterfly) and Red Clover		10	10
A64	5p. Bumble Bee, Prostrate Broom and Giant Broomrape		10	10
A65	6p. Dartford Warbler and Lesser Dodder		15	20
A66	7p. Peacock (butterfly) and Stemless Thistle		15	20
A67	8p. Mole and Bluebell		15	20
A68	9p. Great Green Grasshopper and Common Gorse		20	25
A69	10p. Six-spot Burnet (moth) and Viper's Bugloss		20	25
A70	16p. Common Blue (butterfly) and Pyramidal Orchid		30	35
	a. Perf 14×15		30	35
	ab. Booklet pane of 8		2·50	
A70b	18p. Small Tortoiseshell (butterfly) and Buddleia (2.1.97)		35	40
	ba. Perf 14×15		35	40
	bb. Booklet pane of 8		3·00	
A71	20p. Common Rabbit and Creeping Buttercup		40	45
A72	24p. Great Black-backed Gull and Sand Crocus		50	55
	a. Perf 14×15		50	55
	ab. Booklet pane of 8		3·75	
A72b	25p. Rock Pipit and Sea Stock (2.1.97)		50	55
	ba. Perf 14×15		50	55
	bb. Booklet pane of 8		4·00	
A72c	26p. Sand Digger Wasp and Sea Bindweed (*horiz*) (2.1.97)		50	55
A73	30p. Atlantic Puffin and English Stonecrop		60	65
A74	40p. Emperor (moth) and Bramble		80	85
A75	50p. Pale-spined Hedgehog and Pink Oxalis		1·00	1·10
A76	£1 Common Tern and Bermuda Grass (*horiz*)		2·00	2·10
A77	£2 Northern Gannet and *Fucus vesiculosus* (seaweed) (*horiz*) (28.2.95)		4·00	4·25
A60/77		*Set of* 21	11·50	12·50

Nos. A70a, A70ba, A72a, and A72ba were only issued in booklets with the upper and lower edges of the panes imperforate.

A **13** Royal Aircraft Factory SE5A

(Des C. Abbott. Litho B.D.T.)

1995 (1 Sept). *Birth Centenary of Tommy Rose (aviator). Type* A **13** *and similar horiz designs. Multicoloured.* P 14×15.
A78	35p. Type A **13**		85	85
	a. Horiz strip of 3. Nos. A78/80		2·50	
A79	35p. Miles Master II and other Miles aircraft		85	85
A80	35p. Miles Aerovan and Miles Monitor		85	85
A81	41p. Miles Falcon Six winning King's Cup air race, 1935		1·00	1·00
	a. Horiz strip of 3. Nos. A81/3		3·00	
A82	41p. Miles Hawk Speed Six winning Manx Air Derby, 1947		1·00	1·00
A83	41p. Miles Falcon Six breaking U.K.–Cape record, 1936		1·00	1·00
A78/83		*Set of* 6	5·50	5·50

Nos. A78/80 and A81/3 were printed together, *se-tenant*, as horizontal strips of 3 in sheets of 12 (2 panes 3×2).

A **14** Returning Islanders

(Des C. Abbott. Litho B.D.T.)

1995 (16 Nov). *50th Anniv of Return of Islanders to Alderney. Sheet 93×70 mm.* P 13½.
MSA84	A **14** £1.65, multicoloured		4·00	4·00

A **15** Signallers training on Alderney A **16** Cat with Butterfly

(Des A. Theobald. Litho Walsall)

1996 (24 Jan). *25th Anniv of Adoption of 30th Signal Regiment by Alderney. Type* A **15** *and similar horiz designs. Multicoloured.* P 14.
A85	24p. Type A **15**		65	65
	a. Horiz strip of 4. Nos. A85/8		5·00	
A86	41p. Communications station, Falkland Islands		1·10	1·10
A87	60p. Dish aerial and Land Rover, Gulf War		1·50	1·50
A88	75p. Service with United Nations		1·75	1·75
A85/8		*Set of* 4	5·00	5·00

Nos. A85/8 were printed together, *se-tenant*, in horizontal strips of 4 throughout the sheet, each strip forming a composite design.

(Des P. le Vasseur. Litho B.D.T.)

1996 (19 July). *Cats. Type* A **16** *and similar square designs. Multicoloured.* P 13½.
A89	16p. Type A **16**		45	45
A90	24p. Blue and White on table		65	65
A91	25p. Tabby kitten grooming Blue and White Persian kitten		65	65
A92	35p. Red Persian under table		95	95
A93	41p. White cat with Tortoiseshell and White in toy cart		1·10	1·10
A94	60p. Siamese playing with wool		1·75	1·75
A89/94		*Set of* 6	5·00	5·00
MSA95	144×97 mm. Nos. A89/94		5·00	5·00

A **17** Harold Larwood   A **18** Railway under Construction

(Des R. Ollington. Litho Walsall)

1997 (21 Aug). *150th Anniv of Cricket on Alderney. Type* A **17** *and similar vert designs. Multicoloured.* P 13½.
A 96	18p. Type A **17**		40	45
A 97	25p. John Arlott		55	60
A 98	37p. Pelham J. Warner		75	80
A 99	43p. W. G. Grace		85	90
A100	63p. John Wisden		1·25	1·40
A96/100		*Set of* 5	3·75	4·00
MSA101	190×75 mm. Nos. A96/100 and label		3·75	4·00

(Des R. Carter. Litho Questa)

1997 (20 Nov). *Garrison Island (1st series). 150th Anniv of Harbour. Type* A **18** *and similar horiz designs. Multicoloured.* P 14½×14.
A102	18p. Type A **18**		35	40
	a. Horiz pair. Nos. A102/3		70	80
A103	18p. *Ariadne* (paddle steamer) at anchor		35	40
A104	25p. Quarrying stone		50	55
	a. Horiz pair. Nos. A104/5		1·00	1·10
A105	25p. Quarry railway		50	55
A106	26p. Queen Victoria and Prince Albert on Alderney		50	55
	a. Horiz pair. Nos. A106/7		1·00	1·10
A107	26p. Royal Yacht *Victoria and Albert* and guard of honour		50	55
A108	31p. Railway workers greet Queen Victoria		60	65
	a. Horiz pair. Nos. A108/9		1·10	1·25
A109	31p. Royal party in railway wagons		60	65
A102/9		*Set of* 8	3·75	4·25

Nos. A102/3, A104/5, A106/7 and A108/9 were each printed together, *se-tenant*, as horizontal pairs throughout sheetlets of 10.

A **19** Modern Superlite Helmet and Wreck of *Point Law* (oil tanker)

(Des Victoria Kinnersly. Litho B.D.T.)

1998 (10 Feb). *21st Anniv of Alderney Diving Club. Type* A **19** *and similar vert designs. Multicoloured.* P 13.
A110	20p. Type A **19**		40	45
A111	30p. Cousteau-Gagnan Demand Valve and wreck of *Stella* (steamer)		60	65
A112	37p. Heinke Closed Helmet and *Liverpool* (full-rigged ship)		75	80
A113	43p. Siebe Closed Helmet		85	90
A114	63p. Deane Open Helmet		1·25	1·40
A110/14		*Set of* 5	3·75	4·25
MSA115	190×75 mm. Nos. A110/14 and label		3·75	4·25

The Philatelic Register

LOOKING FOR A COMPLETE, CLASSIFIED, BUYERS GUIDE?

YOU'LL FIND OUR PHILATELIC REGISTER IN THE YELLOW SECTION AT THE BACK OF VOLUME ONE OF THIS CATALOGUE

CLASSIFIED TRADE DIRECTORY EASY TO USE

ISLE OF MAN
REGIONAL ISSUES

Although specifically issued for use in the Isle of Man, these issues were also valid for use throughout Great Britain.

DATES OF ISSUE: The note at the beginning of Guernsey also applies here.

Nos. 8/11 and current stamps of Great Britain were withdrawn from sale on the island from 5 July 1973 when the independent postal administration was established but remained valid for use there until 5 August 1973. They also remained on sale at the Philatelic Sales counters in the United Kingdom until 4 July 1974.

    1   **2**   **3**

(Des J. Nicholson. Portrait by Dorothy Wilding Ltd. Photo Harrison)

1958 (18 Aug)–**68.** *W* 179. *P* 15 × 14.

1	1	2½d. carmine-red (8.6.64)	..	45	80
2	2	3d. deep lilac	..	20	10
		a. Chalk-surfaced paper (17.5.63)		10·00	8·50
		p. One centre phosphor band (27.6.68)		20	40
3		4d. ultramarine (7.2.66)	..	1·50	1·10
		p. Two phosphor bands (5.7.67)		20	25
1/3p			*Set of 3*	75	1·00

No. 2a was released in London sometime after 17 May 1963, this being the date of issue in Douglas.

1968–69. *No wmk. Chalk-surfaced paper. PVA gum. One centre phosphor band (Nos. 5/6) or two phosphor bands (others). P* 15 × 14.

4	2	4d. blue (24.6.68)	..	20	25
5		4d. olive-sepia (4.9.68)	..	20	30
6		4d. bright vermilion (26.2.69)	..	45	60
7		5d. royal blue (4.9.68)	..	45	60
4/7			*Set of 4*	1·00	1·60

(Des J. Matthews. Portrait after plaster cast by Arnold Machin. Photo Harrison)

1971 (7 July). *Decimal Currency. Chalk-surfaced paper. One centre phosphor band (2½p.) or two phosphor bands (others). P* 15 × 14.

8	3	2½p. bright magenta	..	20	15
9		3p. ultramarine	..	20	15
10		5p. reddish violet	..	40	50
11		7½p. chestnut	..	40	65
8/11			*Set of 4*	1·10	1·25

All values exist with PVA gum on ordinary cream paper and the 2½p. and 3p. also on fluorescent white paper.

INDEPENDENT POSTAL ADMINISTRATION

  4 Castletown   **5** Manx Cat

(Des J. Nicholson. Photo Courvoisier)

1973 (5 July)–**75.** *Horiz designs as T* **4** *(½p. to 9p., 11p. and 13p.) or vert designs as T* **5** *(others). Multicoloured. Granite paper. P* 11½.

12	½p. Type 4	..	..	10	10
13	1p. Port Erin	..	..	10	10
14	1½p. Snaefell	..	..	10	10
15	2p. Laxey	..	..	10	10
16	2½p. Tynwald Hill	..	..	10	10
17	3p. Douglas Promenade (sage-green border)		10	10
	a. Error. Olive-bistre border†		£150	£100
18	3½p. Port St. Mary (olive-brown border)		15	15
	a. Error. Grey-brown border†		£150	£100
19	4p. Fairy Bridge	..	..	15	15
20	4½p. As 2½p. (8.1.75)	..	20	20
21	5p. Peel	..	..	20	20
22	5½p. As 3p. (28.5.75)	..	25	25
23	6p. Cregneish	..	..	25	25
24	7p. As 2p. (28.5.75)	..	30	30
25	7½p. Ramsey Bay	..	..	25	25
26	8p. As 7½p. (8.1.75)	..	35	35
27	9p. Douglas Bay	..	..	30	35
28	10p. Type 5	..	..	40	35
29	11p. Monk's Bridge, Ballasalla (29.10.75)		30	30
30	13p. Derbyhaven (29.10.75)	..	40	40
31	20p. Manx Loaghtyn Ram	..	50	50
32	50p. Manx Shearwater	..	1·25	1·25
33	£1 Viking longship	..	2·50	2·50
12/33			*Set of 22*	7·50	7·50

† These errors occur on printings in 1974. That on the 3p. resembles the border colour of the ½p. and that on the 3½p. the 2p. Some printings from late 1973 have invisible gum.

ALTERED CATALOGUE NUMBERS

Any Catalogue numbers altered from the last edition are shown as a list in the introductory pages.

---

  6 Viking landing on Man,   **7** *Sutherland*
      A.D. 938

(Des J. Nicholson. Photo Harrison)

1973 (5 July). *Inauguration of Postal Independence. P* 14.

34	6	15p. multicoloured	..	60	60

(Des J. Nicholson. Photo Harrison)

1973 (4 Aug). *Steam Railway Centenary. T* **7** *and similar horiz designs showing steam locomotives. Multicoloured. P* 15 × 14.

35	2½p. Type 7	..	..	20	20
36	3p. *Caledonia*	..	..	20	20
37	7½p. *Kissack*	..	..	70	90
38	9p. *Pender*	..	..	85	90
35/8			*Set of 4*	1·75	2·00

8 Leonard Randles, First Winner, 1923

(Des J. Nicholson. Litho J.W.)

1973 (4 Sept). *Golden Jubilee of the Manx Grand Prix. T* **8** *and similar horiz design. Multicoloured. P* 14.

39	3p. Type 8	..	..	30	20
40	3½p. Alan Holmes, Double Winner, 1957		30	20

9 Princess Anne and Capt. Mark Phillips

(Des A. Larkins. Recess and litho D.L.R.)

1973 (14 Nov). *Royal Wedding. P* 13½.

41	9	25p. multicoloured	..	1·00	1·00

10 Badge, Citation and Sir William
     Hillary (Founder)

(Des J. Nicholson. Photo Courvoisier)

1974 (4 Mar). *150th Anniv of Royal National Lifeboat Institution. T* **10** *and similar horiz designs. Multicoloured. Granite paper. P* 11½.

42	3p. Type 10	..	..	10	10
43	3½p. Wreck of *St. George*, 1830		15	15
44	8p. R.N.L.B. *Manchester & Salford*, 1868–87		40	40
45	10p. R.N.L.B. *Osman Gabriel*		45	45
42/5			*Set of 4*	1·00	1·00

11 Stanley Woods, 1935

(Des J. Nicholson. Litho D.L.R.)

1974 (29 May). *Tourist Trophy Motor-cycle Races (1st issue). T* **11** *and similar horiz designs. Multicoloured. P* 13 × 13½.

46	3p. Type 11	..	..	10	10
47	3½p. Freddy Frith, 1937	..	10	10
48	8p. Max Deubel and Emil Horner, 1961		45	45
49	10p. Mike Hailwood, 1961		60	45
46/9			*Set of 4*	1·10	1·00

See also Nos. 63/6.

---

12 Rushen Abbey and Arms

(Des J. Nicholson from ideas by G. Kneale. Litho Questa (3½p., 10p.) or J.W. (others))

1974 (18 Sept). *Historical Anniversaries. T* **12** *and similar horiz designs. Multicoloured. P* 14.

50	3½p. Type 12	..	..	10	10
51	4½p. Magnus Haraldson rows King Edgar on the Dee		10	10
52	8p. King Magnus and Norse fleet	..	40	40
53	10p. Bridge at Avignon and bishop's mitre		50	50
50/3			*Set of 4*	1·00	1·00

Nos. 50 and 53 mark the 600th Death Anniv of William Russell, Bishop of Sodor and Man, and Nos. 51/2 the 1000th Anniv of the rule of King Magnus Haraldson.

13 Churchill and Bugler Dunne at Colenso, 1899

(Des G. Kneale. Photo Courvoisier)

1974 (22 Nov). *Birth Centenary of Sir Winston Churchill. T* **13** *and similar horiz designs. Multicoloured. Granite paper. P* 11½.

54	3½p. Type 13	..	..	10	10
55	4½p. Churchill and Government Buildings, Douglas		10	10
56	8p. Churchill and Manx ack-ack crew		25	35
57	20p. Churchill as Freeman of Douglas		75	55
54/7			*Set of 4*	1·10	1·00
MS58	121 × 91 mm. Nos. 54/7			1·10	1·00

No. MS58 is inscribed "30th Nov. 1974".

14 Cabin School and Names of Pioneers

(Des J. Nicholson. Photo Courvoisier)

1975 (14 Mar). *Manx Pioneers in Cleveland, Ohio. T* **14** *and similar horiz designs. Multicoloured. Granite paper. P* 11½.

59	4½p. Type 14	..	..	10	10
60	5½p. Terminal Tower Building, J. Gill and R. Carran		15	10
61	8p. Clague House Museum, and Robert and Margaret Clague		35	40
62	10p. S.S. *William T. Graves* and Thomas Quayle		50	50
59/62			*Set of 4*	1·00	1·00

15 Tom Sheard, 1923

(Des J. Nicholson. Litho J.W.)

1975 (28 May). *Tourist Trophy Motor-cycle Races (2nd issue). T* **15** *and similar horiz designs. Multicoloured. P* 13½.

63	5½p. Type 15	..	..	10	15
64	7p. Walter Handley, 1925	..	20	20
65	8p. Geoff Duke, 1955	..	40	30
66	12p. Peter Williams, 1973	..	40	40
63/6			*Set of 4*	1·00	1·00

16 Sir George Goldie   **17** Title Page of Manx Bible
  and Birthplace

(Des G. Kneale. Photo Courvoisier)

1975 (9 Sept). *50th Death Anniv of Sir George Goldie. T* **16** *and similar multicoloured designs. Granite paper. P* 11½.

67	5½p. Type 16	..	..	10	15
68	7p. Goldie and map of Africa (*vert*)		20	20
69	10p. Goldie as President of Geographical Society (*vert*)		40	30
70	12p. River scene on the Niger		40	45
67/70			*Set of 4*	1·00	1·00

(Des J. Nicholson. Litho Questa)

1975 (29 Oct). *Christmas and Bicentenary of Manx Bible.* T **17** *and similar horiz designs. Multicoloured.* P 14.

71	5½p. Type **17**	15	15
72	7p. Rev. Philip Moore and Ballaugh Old Church	20	20
73	11p. Bishop Hildesley and Bishops Court	35	35
74	13p. John Kelly saving Bible manuscript	40	40
71/4	*Set of 4*	1·00	1·00

18 William Christian listening to Patrick Henry   **19** First Horse Tram, 1876

(Des and litho J.W.)

1976 (12 Mar). *Bicentenary of American Revolution.* T **18** *and similar vert designs. Multicoloured.* P 13½.

75	5½p. Type **18**	15	15
76	7p. Conveying the Fincastle Resolutions	20	20
77	13p. Patrick Henry and William Christian	35	35
78	20p. Christian as an Indian fighter	50	50
75/8	*Set of 4*	1·10	1·10
MS79	153 × 89 mm. Nos. 75/8. P 14	1·50	1·60

(Des J. Nicholson. Photo Courvoisier)

1976 (26 May). *Douglas Horse Trams Centenary.* T **19** *and similar horiz designs. Multicoloured. Granite paper.* P 11½.

80	5½p. Type **19**	10	15
81	7p. "Toast-rack" tram, 1890	15	15
82	11p. Horse-bus, 1895	45	35
83	13p. Royal tram, 1972	50	45
80/3	*Set of 4*	1·10	1·00

20 Barroose Beaker   **21** Diocesan Banner

(Des J. Nicholson. Photo Courvoisier)

1976 (28 July). *Europa. Ceramic Art.* T **20** *and similar multicoloured designs. Granite paper.* P 11½.

84	5p. Type **20**	25	20
	a. Strip of 3. Nos. 84/6	70	60
85	5p. Souvenir teapot	25	20
86	5p. Laxey jug	25	20
87	10p. Cronk Aust food vessel (*horiz*)	40	35
	a. Strip of 3. Nos. 87/9	1·25	1·10
88	10p. Sansbury bowl (*horiz*)	40	35
89	10p. Knox urn (*horiz*)	40	35
84/9	*Set of 6*	1·75	1·50

Nos. 84/6 and 87/9 were each printed in sheets of 9 (3 × 3) the three designs being horizontally and vertically *se-tenant*.

(Des G. Kneale. Litho Questa)

1976 (14 Oct). *Christmas and Centenary of Mothers' Union.* T **21** *and similar vert designs. Multicoloured.* P 14½.

90	6p. Type **21**	15	15
91	7p. Onchan banner	15	15
92	11p. Castletown banner	40	35
93	13p. Ramsey banner	40	45
90/3	*Set of 4*	1·00	1·00

22 Queen Elizabeth II

(Des A. Larkins. Litho and recess D.L.R.)

1977 (1 Mar). *Silver Jubilee.* T **22** *and similar multicoloured designs.* P 14 × 13 (7p.) *or* 13 × 14 (*others*).

94	6p. Type **22**	20	20
95	7p. Queen Elizabeth and Prince Philip (*vert*)	20	20
96	25p. Queen Elizabeth	80	70
94/6	*Set of 3*	1·10	1·00

The 25p. is similar to T **22** but has the portrait on the right.

23 Carrick Bay from "Tom-the-Dipper"

(Des J. Nicholson. Litho Questa)

1977 (26 May). *Europa. Landscapes.* T **23** *and similar horiz design. Multicoloured.* P 13½ × 14.

97	6p. Type **23**	20	20
98	10p. View from Ramsey	30	30

24 F. A. Applebee, 1912

(Des J. Nicholson. Litho J.W.)

1977 (26 May). *Linked Anniversaries.* T **24** *and similar horiz designs. Multicoloured.* P 13½.

99	6p. Type **24**	15	15
100	7p. St. John Ambulance Brigade at Governor's Bridge, *c.* 1938	15	20
101	11p. Scouts working scoreboard	40	40
102	13p. John Williams, 1976	40	40
99/102	*Set of 4*	1·00	1·00

The events commemorated are: 70th Anniv of Manx TT; 70th Anniv of Boy Scouts; Centenary of St John Ambulance Brigade.

25 Old Summer House, Mount Morrison, Peel

(Des and photo Courvoisier)

1977 (19 Oct). *Bicentenary of the First Visit of John Wesley.* T **25** *and similar horiz designs. Multicoloured. Granite paper.* P 11½.

103	6p. Type **25**	15	15
104	7p. Wesley preaching in Castletown Square, 1915	20	20
105	11p. Wesley preaching outside Braddan Church	35	35
106	13p. New Methodist Church, Douglas	40	40
103/6	*Set of 4*	1·00	1·00

Nos. 104/5 are larger, 38 × 26 mm.

26 H.M.S. *Ben-My-Chree* and Short Type 184 Seaplane, 1915

(Des A. Theobald. Litho J.W.)

1978 (28 Feb). *R.A.F. Diamond Jubilee.* T **26** *and similar horiz designs. Multicoloured.* P 13½ × 14.

107	6p. Type **26**	15	15
108	7p. H.M.S. *Vindex* and Bristol Scout C, 1915	20	20
109	11p. Boulton Paul Defiant over Douglas Bay, 1941	35	35
110	13p. Sepecat Jaguar over Ramsey, 1977	40	40
107/10	*Set of 4*	1·10	1·00

27 Watch Tower, Langness   **27a** Queen Elizabeth II

(Des J. Nicholson (½p. to £1), G. Kneale (£2). Litho Questa (½p. to 16p.). Photo Courvoisier (20p. to £2))

1978 (28 Feb)–**81**. *Various multicoloured designs.*

(a) As T **27**. A. P 14. B. P 14½.

			A		B	
111	½p. Type **27**		10	10	20	10
112	1p. Jurby Church		10	10	20	10
113	6p. Government Buildings		30	30	†	
114	7p. Tynwald Hill		35	35	8·00	6·50
115	8p. Milner's Tower		25	25	35	35
116	9p. Laxey Wheel		35	35	35	35
117	10p. Castle Rushen		40	40	35	35
118	11p. St. Ninian's Church		40	40	40	40
119	12p. Tower of Refuge		50	50	50	40
120	13p. St. German's Cathedral		60	60	40	40
121	14½p. Point of Ayre Lighthouse		45	45	40	40
122	15p. Corrin's Tower		60	60	40	40
123	16p. Douglas Head Lighthouse		80	80	25·00	21·00

(b) As T **27** but size 25 × 31 mm. Granite paper. P 11½ (18.10.78)

124	20p. Fuchsia	40	40
125	25p. Manx cat	50	50
126	50p. Chough	1·00	1·00
127	£1 Viking warrior	2·00	2·00

(c) T **27a**. P 11½ (29.9.81)

128	£2 multicoloured	4·25	4·25
111/28	*Set of 18*	11·50	11·50

The 1p., 7p., 10p., 12p. to 16p are horiz designs.

Although both perforations of Nos. 111/23 were printed at the same time some did not appear in use until some time after 28 February 1978. Earliest dates for these are as follows: 1p. (112B) 8.79, 7p. (114B) 8.78, 8p. (115B) 6.80, 10p. (117B) 8.79, 12p. (119A) 9.80.

28 Queen Elizabeth in Coronation Regalia   **29** Wheel-headed Cross-slab

(Des G. Kneale. Litho Questa)

1978 (24 May). *25th Anniv of Coronation.* P 14½ × 14.

132	**28** 25p. multicoloured	75	75

(Des J. Nicholson. Photo Courvoisier)

1978 (24 May). *Europa. Sculpture.* T **29** *and similar vert designs showing Celtic and Norse Crosses. Multicoloured. Granite paper.* P 11½.

133	6p. Type **29**	20	15
	a. Strip of 3. Nos. 133/5	60	50
134	6p. Celtic wheel-cross	20	15
135	6p. Keeil Chiggyrt Stone	20	15
136	11p. Olaf Liotulfson Cross	35	30
	a. Strip of 3. Nos. 136/8	1·10	90
137	11p. Odd's and Thorleif's Crosses	35	30
138	11p. Thor Cross	35	30
133/8	*Set of 6*	1·50	1·25

Nos. 133/5 and 136/8 were each printed together, *se-tenant*, in horizontal and vertical strips of 3 throughout the sheet.

30 J. K. Ward and Ward Library, Peel   **31** Hunt the Wren

(Des J.W. (7p.), G. Kneale (11p.), J. Nicholson (others). Litho J.W.)

1978 (10 June). *Anniversaries and Events.* T **30** *and similar horiz designs. Multicoloured. Invisible gum.* P 13½.

139	6p. Type **30**	15	15
140	7p. Swimmer, cyclist and walker (42 × 26 mm)	20	20
141	11p. American Bald Eagle, Manx arms and maple leaf (42 × 26 mm)	35	35
142	13p. Lumber camp at Three Rivers, Quebec	40	40
139/42	*Set of 4*	1·00	1·00

Commemorations:—6, 13p. James Kewley Ward (Manx pioneer in Canada); 7p. Commonwealth Games, Edmonton; 11p. 50th anniversary of North American Manx Association.

(Des J. Nicholson. Litho J.W.)

1978 (18 Oct). *Christmas.* P 13.

143	**31** 5p. multicoloured	50	50

32 P. M. C. Kermode (founder) and *Nassa kermodei*   **33** Postman, 1859

(Des J. Nicholson. Litho Questa)

1979 (27 Feb). *Centenary of Natural History and Antiquarian Society.* T **32** *and similar horiz designs. Multicoloured.* P 14.

144	6p. Type **32**	15	15
145	7p. Peregrine Falcon	20	20
146	11p. Fulmar	35	35
147	13p. *Epiriptus cowini* (fly)	40	40
144/7	*Set of 4*	1·00	1·00

(Des A. Theobald. Litho Questa)

979 (16 May). *Europa. Communications. T 33 and similar vert design. Multicoloured. P 14½.*

48	6p. Type 33	..	25	25
49	11p. Postman, 1979	..	50	50

34 Viking Longship Emblem

35 Viking Raid at Garwick

wo types of No. 150:

Type I. Wrongly inscribed "INSULAREM". "1979" imprint date.

Type II. Inscription corrected to "INSULARUM". "1980" imprint date.

(Des J. Nicholson. Litho Harrison (3, 4p.), J.W. (others))

1979 (16 May)–80. *Millenium of Tynwald. Multicoloured.*

(a) Vert designs as T 34. P 14½ × 14

150	3p. Type 34 (Type I) ..	..	15	15
	a. Booklet pane. Nos. 150 × 4, 151 × 2 (4p. stamps at top)	..	80	
	ab. Ditto (4p. stamps in centre) ..		1·00	
	b. Type II (29.9.80) ..	..	10	10
	ba. Booklet pane. Nos. 150b × 4, 151 × 2 (4p. stamps at bottom) ..		75	
151	4p. "Three Legs of Man" emblem ..		15	15

(b) Horiz designs as T 35. P 13

152	6p. Type 35 ..	..	15	15
153	7p. 10th-century meeting of Tynwald	..	20	20
154	11p. Tynwald Hill and St. John's Church	..	30	30
155	13p. Procession to Tynwald Hill	..	45	35
150/5	..	*Set of 6*	1·25	1·10

See also Nos. 188/9.

The 3 and 4p. values were printed in sheets containing ten blocks of 6 and five blocks of 4 separated by blank margins. The blocks of 6 contained four 3p. values and two 4p., *se-tenant*, with the 4p. in either the top or centre rows. The blocks of 4 contain the 4p. value only.

No. 151 exists with different dates below the design.

For details of No. 150ba see after No. 189.

36 Queen and Court on Tynwald Hill

(Des G. Kneale. Litho Questa)

1979 (5 July). *Royal Visit. T 36 and similar horiz design. Multicoloured. P 14½.*

156	7p. Type 36 ..	..	35	35
157	13p. Queen and procession from St. John's Church to Tynwald Hill	..	50	50

37 Odin's Raven

(Des J. Nicholson. Litho Questa)

1979 (19 Oct). *Voyage of "Odin's Raven". P 14 × 14½.*

158	37	15p. multicoloured	..	70	70

38 John Quilliam seized by the Press Gang

39 Young Girl with Teddybear and Cat

(Des A. Theobald. Litho Questa)

1979 (19 Oct). *150th Death Anniv of Captain John Quilliam. T 38 and similar horiz designs. Multicoloured. P 14.*

159	6p. Type 38	..	15	15
160	8p. Steering H.M.S. *Victory*, Battle of Trafalgar		20	20
161	13p. Capt. John Quilliam and H.M.S. *Spencer*		35	35
162	15p. Capt. John Quilliam (member of the House of Keys)		40	40
159/62	..	*Set of 4*	1·00	1·00

(Des Mrs E. Moore. Litho J.W.)

1979 (19 Oct). *Christmas. International Year of the Child. T 39 and similar vert design. Multicoloured. P 13.*

163	5p. Type 39	..	25	25
164	7p. Father Christmas with young children		35	35

40 Conglomerate Arch, Langness

(Des J. Nicholson. Litho Questa)

1980 (5 Feb). *150th Anniv of Royal Geographical Society. T 40 and similar horiz designs. Multicoloured. P 14½.*

165	7p. Type 40	..	20	20
166	8p. Braaid Circle	..	20	20
167	12p. Cashtal-yn-Ard	..	25	25
168	13p. Volcanic Rocks at Scarlett	..	35	35
169	15p. Sugar-loaf Rock	..	40	40
165/9	..	*Set of 5*	1·25	1·25

41 Mona's Isle I

(Des J. Nicholson. Photo Courvoisier)

1980 (6 May). *150th Anniv of Isle of Man Steam Packet Company. T 41 and similar horiz designs. Multicoloured. Granite paper. P 11½.*

170	7p. Type 41	..	20	20
171	8p. *Douglas I*	..	20	20
172	11½p. H.M.S. *Mona's Queen II* sinking U-boat		30	30
173	12p. H.M.S. *King Orry III* at surrender of German fleet		30	30
174	13p. *Ben-My-Chree IV*	..	40	35
175	15p. *Lady of Mann II*	..	50	40
170/5	..	*Set of 6*	1·75	1·60
MS176	180×125 mm. Nos. 170/5	..	1·75	1·75

No. MS176 was issued to commemorate the "London 1980" International Stamp Exhibition.

42 Stained Glass Window, T. E. Brown Room, Manx Museum

(Des G. Kneale. Photo Courvoisier)

1980 (6 May). *Europa. Personalities. Thomas Edward Brown (poet and scholar) Commemoration. T 42 and similar horiz design. Multicoloured. Granite paper. P 11½.*

177	7p. Type 42	..	20	20
178	13½p. Clifton College, Bristol	..	40	40

43 King Olav V and *Norge* (Norwegian royal yacht)

(Des J. Nicholson. Litho Questa)

1980 (13 June). *Visit of King Olav of Norway, August 1979. P 14×14½.*

179	43 12p. multicoloured	..	50	50
MS180	125×157 mm. Nos. 158 and 179		1·00	1·00

No. MS180 also commemorates the "NORWEX 80" Stamp Exhibition, Oslo.

44 Winter Wren and View of Calf of Man

(Des J. Nicholson. Litho J.W.)

1980 (29 Sept). *Christmas and Wildlife Conservation Year. T 44 and similar horiz design. Multicoloured. P 13½ × 14.*

181	6p. Type 44	..	20	20
182	8p. European Robin and view of Port Erin Marine Biological Station		30	30

45 William Kermode and Brig *Robert Quayle*, 1819

46 Peregrine Falcon

(Des A. Theobald. Litho Questa)

1980 (29 Sept). *Kermode Family in Tasmania Commemoration. T 45 and similar horiz designs. Multicoloured. P 14½.*

183	7p. Type 45	..	20	20
184	9p. "Mona Vale", Van Diemen's Land, 1834		25	25
185	13½p. Ross Bridge, Tasmania	..	40	35
186	15p. "Mona Vale", Tasmania (completed 1868)		45	40
187	17½p. Robert Q. Kermode and Parliament Buildings, Tasmania	..	50	45
183/7	..	*Set of 5*	1·60	1·50

(Des J. Nicholson. Litho Harrison)

1980 (29 Sept). *Booklet stamps. Vert designs as T 46. Multicoloured. P 14½ × 14.*

188	1p. Type 46	..	40	40
	a. Booklet pane. Nos. 151, 188 and 189 each × 2	..	75	
189	5p. Loaghtyn Ram	..	40	40

In addition to 40p. and 80p. booklets Nos. 188/9 also come from special booklet sheets of 60. These sheets contained No. 150ba and 188a, each × 5.

47 Luggers passing Red Pier, Douglas

(Des J. Nicholson. Litho Questa)

1981 (24 Feb). *Centenary of Royal National Mission to Deep Sea Fishermen. T 47 and similar horiz designs. Multicoloured. P 14.*

190	8p. Type 47	..	25	25
191	9p. Peel Lugger *Wanderer* rescuing survivors from the *Lusitania*		30	30
192	18p. Nickeys leaving Port St. Mary Harbour		45	45
193	20p. Nobby entering Ramsey Harbour		50	50
194	22p. Nickeys *Sunbeam* and *Zebra* at Port Erin		50	50
190/4	..	*Set of 5*	1·75	1·75

48 "Crosh Cuirn" Superstition

(Des J. Nicholson. Litho Questa)

1981 (22 May). *Europa. Folklore. T 48 and similar horiz design. Multicoloured. P 14½.*

195	8p. Type 48	..	25	25
196	18p. "Bollan Cross" superstition	..	75	75

49 Lt. Mark Wilks (Royal Manx Fencibles) and Peel Castle

(Des A. Theobald. Litho Questa)

1981 (22 May). *150th Death Anniv of Colonel Mark Wilks. T* **49** *and similar horiz designs. Multicoloured. P* 14.

197		8p.	Type **49**	25	25
198		20p.	Ensign Mark Wilks and Fort St. George, Madras	50	50
199		22p.	Governor Mark Wilks and Napoleon, St. Helena	70	55
200		25p.	Col. Mark Wilks (Speaker of the House of Keys) and estate, Kirby	80	80
197/200	..	..	..	.. *Set of 4*	2·00	1·90

50 Miss Emmeline Goulden (Mrs. Pankhurst) and Mrs. Sophia Jane Goulden

(Des A. Theobald. Litho Questa)

1981 (22 May). *Centenary of Manx Women's Suffrage. P* 14.

201	**50**	9p.	black, olive-grey and stone ..	50	50

51 Prince Charles and Lady Diana Spencer

(Des G. Kneale. Litho Harrison)

1981 (29 July). *Royal Wedding. P* 14.

202	**51**	9p.	black, bright blue and pale blue	50	50
203		25p.	black, bright blue and pink ..	1·50	1·50
MS204		130 × 183 mm. Nos. 202/3 × 2 ..		4·50	4·50

52 Douglas War Memorial, Poppies and Commemorative Inscription

(Des A. Theobald. Photo Courvoisier)

1981 (29 Sept). *60th Anniv of The Royal British Legion. T* **52** *and similar horiz designs. Multicoloured. Granite paper. P* 11½.

205		8p.	Type **52**	25	25
206		10p.	Major Robert Cain (war hero) ..	30	35
207		18p.	Festival of Remembrance, Royal Albert Hall	65	65
208		20p.	T.S.S. *Tynwald* at Dunkirk, May 1940	75	75
205/8	..	..	.. .. *Set of 4*	1·75	1·75

53 Nativity Scene (stained-glass window, St. George's Church)

(Des J.W. (7p.), G. Kneale (9p.). Litho J.W.)

1981 (29 Sept). *Christmas. T* **53** *and similar multicoloured design. P* 14.

209		7p.	Type **53**	25	25
210		9p.	Children from Special School performing nativity play (48 × 30 mm)	35	35

The 7p. value also commemorates the bicentenary of St. George's Church, Douglas and the 9p. the International Year for Disabled Persons.

54 Joseph and William Cunningham (founders of Isle of Man Boy Scout Movement) and Cunningham House Headquarters

(Des G. Kneale. Litho Questa)

1982 (23 Feb). *75th Anniv of Boy Scout Movement and 125th Birth Anniv of Lord Baden-Powell. T* **54** *and similar multicoloured designs. P* 14 × 14½ (19½p.) *or* 13½ × 14 (*others*).

211		9p.	Type **54**	30	30
212		10p.	Baden-Powell visiting Isle of Man, 1911	30	30
213		19½p.	Baden-Powell and Scout emblem (40 × 31 mm)	60	60
214		24p.	Scouts and Baden-Powell's last message	70	70
215		29p.	Scout salute, handshake, emblem and globe	90	90
211/15	..	..	.. .. *Set of 5*	2·50	2·50

55 The Principals and Duties of Christianity (Bishop T. Wilson) (first book printed in Manx, 1707)

(Des A. Theobald. Photo Courvoisier)

1982 (1 June). *Europa. Historic Events. T* **55** *and similar horiz design. Multicoloured. Granite paper. P* 12 × 12½.

216		9p.	Type **55**	25	25
217		19½p.	Landing at Derbyhaven (visit of Thomas, 2nd Earl of Derby, 1507)	50	50

56 Charlie Collier (first TT race (single cylinder) winner) and Tourist Trophy Race, 1907

(Des J. Nicholson. Litho Questa)

1982 (1 June). *75th Anniv of Tourist Trophy Motorcycle Racing. T* **56** *and similar horiz designs. Multicoloured. P* 14.

218		9p.	Type **56** ..	20	20
219		10p.	Freddie Dixon (Sidecar and Junior TT winner) and Junior TT race, 1927	25	25
220		24p.	Jimmie Simpson (TT winner and first to lap at 60, 70 and 80 mph) and Senior TT, 1932	70	70
221		26p.	Mike Hailwood (winner of fourteen TT's) and Senior TT, 1961	75	75
222		29p.	Jock Taylor (Sidecar TT winner, 1978, 1980 and 1981) and Sidecar TT (with Benga Johansson), 1980	90	90
218/22	..	..	.. .. *Set of 5*	2·50	2·50

57 *Mona I*

(Des J. Nicholson. Litho Questa)

1982 (5 Oct). *150th Anniv of Isle of Man Steam Packet Company Mail Contract. T* **57** *and similar horiz design. Multicoloured. P* 13½ × 14.

223		12p.	Type **57** ..	50	50
224		19½p.	*Manx Maid II* ..	75	75

58 Three Wise Men bearing Gifts **59** Princess Diana with Prince William

(Des and litho J.W.)

1982 (5 Oct). *Christmas. T* **58** *and similar multicoloured design. P* 13 × 13½ (8p.) *or* 13½ × 13 (11p.).

225		8p.	Type **58**	50	50
226		11p.	Christmas snow scene (*vert*)	50	50

(Des G. Kneale. Litho Questa)

1982 (12 Oct). *21st Birthday of Princess of Wales and Birth of Prince William. Sheet* 100 × 83 *mm. P* 14½ × 14.

MS227	**59**	50p. multicoloured		3·00	3·00

60 Opening of Salvation Army Citadel, and T.H. Cannell, J.P.

(Des A. Theobald. Photo Courvoisier)

1983 (15 Feb). *Centenary of Salvation Army in Isle of Man. T* **60** *and similar horiz designs. Multicoloured. Granite paper. P* 11½.

228		10p.	Type **60**	30	30
229		12p.	Early meeting place and Gen. William Booth	40	40
230		19½p.	Salvation Army band	60	60
231		26p.	Treating lepers and Lt.-Col. Thomas Bridson ..	90	90
228/31	..	..	.. .. *Set of 4*	2·00	2·00

61 Atlantic Puffins   **61***a* "Queen Elizabeth II" (Ricardo Macarron)

(Des Colleen Corlett (£5), J. Nicholson (others). Litho Questa)

1983 (15 Feb)–**85**. *Horiz designs as T* **61**, *showing sea birds, and T* **61***a. Multicoloured. P* 14 (20*p.* to £1), 14 × 13½ (£5) *or* 14½ (*others*).

232		1p.	Type **61** ..	30	30
233		2p.	Northern Gannets	30	30
234		5p.	Lesser Black-backed Gulls	60	40
235		8p.	Common Cormorants	60	40
236		10p.	Kittiwakes	60	35
237		11p.	Shags	60	35
238		12p.	Grey Herons	70	40
239		13p.	Herring Gulls	70	40
240		14p.	Razorbills	70	40
241		15p.	Great Black-backed Gulls	80	50
242		16p.	Common Shelducks	80	50
243		18p.	Oystercatchers	80	60
244		20p.	Arctic Terns (14.9.83)	90	1·00
245		25p.	Common Guillemots (14.9.83)	1·00	1·00
246		50p.	Redshanks (14.9.83)	1·75	1·75
247		£1	Mute Swans (14.9.83)	3·25	3·00
248		£5	Type **61***a* (31.1.85)	10·00	10·00
232/48	..	..	.. .. *Set of 17*	21·00	19·00

Nos. 244/7 are larger, 39×26 mm.

62 Design Drawings by Robert Casement for the Great Laxey Wheel

(Des J. Nicholson. Litho Questa)

1983 (18 May). *Europa. The Great Laxey Wheel. T* **62** *and similar horiz design. P* 14.

249		10p.	black, azure and buff ..	40	35
250		20½p.	multicoloured ..	60	70

Design:—20½p. Robert Casement and the Great Laxey Wheel.

63 Nick Keig (international yachtsman) and Trimaran *Three Legs of Man III*   **64** New Post Office Headquarters, Douglas

(Des J. Nicholson (10p., 31p.), Colleen Corlett (12p., 28p.). Photo Courvoisier)

1983 (18 May). *150th Anniv of King William's College. T* **63** *and similar horiz designs. Multicoloured. Granite paper. P* 11½.

251		10p.	Type **63**	20	20
252		12p.	King William's College, Castletown	30	30
253		28p.	Sir William Bragg (winner of Nobel Prize for Physics) and spectrometer	80	80
254		31p.	General Sir George White V.C. and action at Charasiah	1·00	1·00
251/4	..	..	.. .. *Set of 4*	2·00	2·00

(Des Colleen Corlett (10p.), J. Nicholson (15p.). Litho Questa)

1983 (5 July).   *World Communications Year and 10th Anniv of Isle of Man Post Office Authority. T* **64** *and similar vert design. Multicoloured. P* 14½.

255	10p.	Type **64**	..	40	40
256	15p.	As Type **6**, but inscr "POST OFFICE DECENNIUM 1983"		60	60

65 Shepherds

(Des Colleen Corlett. Litho J.W.)

1983 (14 Sept).   *Christmas. T* **65** *and similar horiz design. Multicoloured. P* 13.

257	9p.	Type **65**	..	50	50
258	12p.	Three Kings	..	50	50

66 *Manx King*
(full-rigged ship)

67 C.E.P.T. 25th
Anniversary Logo

(Des J. Nicholson (10p. to 31p.); Colleen Corlett, J. Nicholson and J. Smith (miniature sheet). Litho Questa)

1984 (14 Feb).   *The Karran Fleet. T* **66** *and similar horiz designs. Multicoloured. P* 14.

259	10p.	Type **66**	..	40	40
260	13p.	*Hope* (barque)	..	55	55
261	20½p.	*Rio Grande* (brig)	..	85	85
262	28p.	*Lady Elizabeth* (barque)	..	1·00	1·00
263	31p.	*Sumatra* (barque)	..	1·10	1·10
259/63			*Set of 5*	3·50	3·50

MS264   103 × 94 mm. 28p. As No. 262, 31p. *Lady Elizabeth* (as shown on Falkland Islands No. 417) (*sold at* 60p.) .. .. 3·00 3·00
No. **MS**264 was issued to commemorate links between the Isle of Man and Falkland Islands.

(Des J. Larrivière, adapted Colleen Corlett. Photo Courvoisier)

1984 (27 Apr).   *Europa. Granite paper. P* 12 × 11½.

265	**67**	10p.	dull orange, deep reddish brown and pale orange		35	35
266		20½p.	light blue, deep blue and pale blue		70	70

68 Railway Air Services De
Havilland D.H.84 Dragon Mk 2

69 Window from Glencrutchery
House, Douglas

(Des A. Theobald, Litho Questa)

1984 (27 Apr).   *50th Anniv of First Official Airmail to the Isle of Man and 40th Anniv of International Civil Aviation Organization. T* **68** *and similar horiz designs. Multicoloured. P* 14.

267	11p.	Type **68**	..	45	45
268	13p.	West Coast Air Services De Havilland D.H.86A Dragon Express *Ronaldsway*		55	55
269	26p.	B.E.A. Douglas DC-3	..	95	95
270	28p.	B.E.A. Vickers Viscount 800	..	1·00	1·00
271	31p.	Telair Britten Norman Islander	..	1·25	1·25
267/71			*Set of 5*	3·75	3·75

(Des D. Swinton. Litho J.W.)

1984 (21 Sept).   *Christmas. Stained-glass Windows. T* **69** *and similar vert design. Multicoloured. P* 14.

272	10p.	Type **69**	..	50	50
273	13p.	Window from Lonan Old Church..	..	50	50

70 William Cain's Birthplace,
Ballasalla

(Des J. Nicholson. Litho Questa)

1984 (21 Sept).   *William Cain (civic leader, Victoria) Commemoration. T* **70** *and similar horiz designs. Multicoloured. P* 14½ × 14.

274	11p.	Type **70**	..	35	35
275	22p.	The *Anna* leaving Liverpool, 1852	..	75	75
276	28p.	Early Australian railway	..	1·00	1·00
277	30p.	William Cain as Mayor of Melbourne, and Town Hall	..	1·10	1·10
278	33p.	Royal Exhibition Building, Melbourne	..	1·25	1·25
274/8		.. ..	*Set of 5*	4·00	4·00

71 Queen Elizabeth II and Commonwealth
Parliamentary Association Badge

(Des and litho J.W.)

1984 (21 Sept).   *Links with the Commonwealth. 30th Commonwealth Parliamentary Association Conference. T* **71** *and similar horiz design. Multicoloured. P* 14.

279	14p.	Type **71**	..	50	50
280	33p.	Queen Elizabeth II and Manx emblem	..	1·10	1·10

72 Cunningham House Headquarters, and Mrs. Willie Cunningham
and Mrs. Joseph Cunningham (former Commissioners)

(Des Colleen Corlett. Photo Courvoisier)

1985 (31 Jan).   *75th Anniv of Girl Guide Movement. T* **72** *and similar horiz designs. Multicoloured. Granite paper. P* 11½.

281	11p.	Type **72**	..	45	45
282	14p.	Princess Margaret, Isle of Man standard and guides	..	75	75
283	29p.	Lady Olave Baden-Powell opening Guide Headquarters, 1955	..	1·10	1·10
284	31p.	Guide uniforms from 1910 to 1985	..	1·40	1·40
285	34p.	Guide handclasp, salute and early badge ..		1·60	1·60
281/5			*Set of 5*	4·75	4·75

73 Score of Manx National
Anthem

(Des D. Swinton. Photo Courvoisier)

1985 (24 Apr).   *Europa. European Music Year. T* **73** *and similar horiz designs. Granite paper. P* 11½.

286	12p.	black, orange-brown and chestnut	..	50	45
	a.	Horiz pair. Nos. 286/7	..	1·00	90
287	12p.	black, orange-brown and chestnut	..	50	45
288	22p.	black, bright new blue and new blue	..	1·00	95
	a.	Horiz pair. Nos. 288/9	..	2·10	1·90
289	22p.	black, bright new blue and new blue	..	1·00	95
286/9			*Set of 4*	2·75	2·50

Designs:—No. 287, William H. Gill (lyricist); 288, Score of hymn "Crofton"; 289, Dr. John Clague (composer).
Nos. 286/7 and 288/9 were printed together, *se-tenant,* in horizontal pairs throughout the sheets.

74 Charles Rolls in 20 h.p. Rolls-Royce
(1906 Tourist Trophy Race)

(Des A. Theobald. Litho Questa)

1985 (25 May).   *Century of Motoring. T* **74** *and similar horiz designs. Multicoloured. P* 14.

290	12p.	Type **74**	..	40	40
	a.	Horiz pair. Nos. 290/1	..	85	85
291	12p.	W. Bentley in 3 litre Bentley (1922 Tourist Trophy Race)	..	40	40
292	14p.	F. Gerrard in E.R.A. (1950 British Empire Trophy Race)	..	55	55
	a.	Horiz pair. Nos. 292/3	..	1·10	1·10
293	14p.	Brian Lewis in Alfa Romeo (1934 Mannin Moar Race)	..	55	55
294	31p.	Jaguar "XJ-SC" ("Roads Open" car, 1984 Motor Cycle T.T. Races) ..		1·40	1·25
	a.	Horiz pair. Nos. 294/5	..	2·75	2·50
295	31p.	Tony Pond and Mike Nicholson in Vauxhall "Chevette" (1981 Rothmans International Rally)		1·40	1·25
290/5			*Set of 6*	4·25	4·00

Nos. 290/1, 292/3 and 294/5 were printed together, *se-tenant,* in horizontal pairs throughout the sheets.

75 Queen Alexandra and Victorian
Sergeant with Wife

(Des Colleen Corlett. Litho Questa)

1985 (4 Sept).   *Centenary of the Soldiers', Sailors' and Airmen's Families Association. T* **75** *and similar horiz designs showing Association Presidents. Multicoloured. P* 14.

296	12p.	Type **75**	..	40	40
297	15p.	Queen Mary and Royal Air Force family		55	55
298	29p.	Earl Mountbatten and Royal Navy family		1·10	1·10
299	34p.	Prince Michael of Kent and Royal Marine with parents, 1982	..	1·25	1·25
296/9			*Set of 4*	3·00	3·00

76 Kirk Maughold (Birthplace)

(Des A. Theobald. Litho Questa)

1985 (2 Oct).   *Birth Bicentenary of Lieutenant-General Sir Mark Cubbon (Indian administrator). T* **76** *and similar multicoloured designs. P* 14.

300	12p.	Type **76**	..	45	45
301	22p.	Lieutenant-General Sir Mark Cubbon (vert)	..	1·10	1·10
302	45p.	Memorial Statue, Bangalore, India (vert)		1·90	1·90
300/2		.. ..	*Set of 3*	3·00	3·00

77 St. Peter's Church, Onchan

(Des A. Theobald. Litho J.W.)

1985 (2 Oct).   *Christmas. Manx Churches. T* **77** *and similar horiz designs. Multicoloured. P* 13 × 13½.

303	11p.	Type **77**	..	45	45
304	14p.	Royal Chapel of St. John, Tynwald		55	55
305	31p.	Bride Parish Church	..	1·25	1·25
303/5		..	*Set of 3*	2·00	2·00

78 Swimming

(Des C. Abbott. Litho Questa)

1986 (5 Feb).   *Commonwealth Games, Edinburgh. T* **78** *and similar horiz designs. Multicoloured. P* 14.

306	12p.	Type **78**	..	40	40
307	15p.	Race walking	..	50	50
308	31p.	Rifle-shooting	..	1·50	1·50
309	34p.	Cycling	..	1·50	1·50
306/9			*Set of 4*	3·50	3·50

No. 309 also commemorates the 50th anniversary of Manx International Cycling Week.

79 Viking Necklace and Peel Castle   **80** Viking Longship

(Des J. Nicholson. Litho Questa)

1986 (5 Feb).   *Centenary of the Manx Museum. T* **79** *and similar multicoloured designs. P* 14.

310	12p.	Type **79**	..	35	35
311	15p.	Meayll Circle, Rushen	..	45	45
312	22p.	Skeleton of Great Deer and Manx Museum (vert)	..	85	85
313	26p.	Viking longship model (vert)	..	1·00	1·00
314	29p.	Open Air Museum, Cregneash	..	1·25	1·25
310/14			*Set of 5*	3·50	3·50

(Des Colleen Corlett. Litho Harrison)

1986 (10 Apr). *Manx Heritage Year. Booklet stamps. T* **80** *and similar vert design.* P 14½ × 14.

315	2p. multicoloured	20	20
	a. Booklet pane. Nos. 315×2 and 316×4	2·50	
316	10p. black, apple green and brownish grey	55	55
	a. Booklet pane. No. 316×3 and 3 stamp-size labels	2·50	

Design:—10p. Celtic cross logo.
In addition to 50p. and £1.14 booklets Nos. 315/16 also come from special booklet sheets of 60 containing five each of Nos. 315a and 316a.

81 *Usnea articulata* (lichen) and *Neotinea intacta* (orchid), The Ayres

82 Ellanbane (home of Myles Standish)

(Des J. Nicholson and Nancy Corkish. Photo Courvoisier)

1986 (10 Apr). *Europa. Protection of Nature and the Environment. T* **81** *and similar horiz designs. Multicoloured. Granite paper.* P 11½.

317	12p. Type **81**	60	60
	a. Horiz pair. Nos. 317/18	1·25	1·25
318	12p. Hen Harrier, Calf of Man	60	60
319	22p. Manx Stoat, Eary Cushlin	95	95
	a. Horiz pair. Nos. 319/20	1·90	1·90
320	22p. *Stenobothus stigmaticus* (grasshopper), St. Michael's Isle	95	95
317/20		*Set of 4*	2·75	2·75

The two designs of each value were printed together, *se-tenant*, in horizontal pairs throughout the sheets.

(Des C. Abbott. Litho Cartor)

1986 (22 May). *"Ameripex '86" International Stamp Exhibition, Chicago. Captain Myles Standish of the "Mayflower". T* **82** *and similar vert designs. Multicoloured.* P 13½.

321	12p. Type **82**	35	35
322	15p. *Mayflower* crossing the Atlantic, 1620	55	55
323	31p. Pilgrim Fathers landing at Plymouth, 1620	1·40	1·40
324	34p. Captain Myles Standish	1·60	1·60
321/4		*Set of 4*	3·50	3·50
MS325	100×75 mm. Nos. 323/4. P 12½	2·75	2·75

No. **MS325** also commemorates the 75th anniversary of the World Manx Association.

83 Prince Andrew in Naval Uniform and Miss Sarah Ferguson

84 Prince Philip (from photo by Karsh)

(Des Colleen Corlett. Litho B.D.T.)

1986 (23 July). *Royal Wedding. T* **83** *and similar horiz design. Multicoloured.* P 15 × 14.

326	15p. Type **83**	75	75
327	40p. Engagement photograph	1·50	1·50

(Des Colleen Corlett. Photo Courvoisier)

1986 (28 Aug). *Royal Birthdays. T* **84** *and similar multicoloured designs. Granite paper.* P 11½.

328	15p. Type **84**	80	80
	a. Horiz pair. Nos. 328/9	1·60	1·60
329	15p. Queen Elizabeth II (from photo by Karsh)	80	80
330	34p. Queen Elizabeth and Prince Philip (from photo by Karsh) (48 × 35 *mm*)	1·75	1·75
328/30		*Set of 3*	3·00	3·00

Nos. 328/9 were printed together, *se-tenant*, in horizontal pairs throughout the sheet.
Nos. 328/30 also commemorate "Stockholmia '86" International Stamp Exhibition, Sweden and the 350th anniversary of the Swedish Post Office and are so inscribed on the margins of the sheet of twelve (Nos. 328/9) and six (No. 330).

85 European Robins on Globe and "Peace and Goodwill" in Braille

86 North Quay

(Des Colleen Corlett. Litho Questa)

1986 (25 Sept). *Christmas. International Peace Year. T* **85** *and similar vert designs. Multicoloured.* P 14.

331	11p. Type **85**	50	50
332	14p. Hands releasing peace dove	55	55
333	31p. Clasped hands and "Peace" in sign language	1·25	1·25
331/3		*Set of 3*	2·00	2·00

(Des A. Theobald. Litho Questa)

1987 (21 Jan–26 Mar). *Victorian Douglas. T* **86** *and similar horiz designs. Multicoloured.* P 14 × 14½.

334	2p. Type **86**	10	10
	a. Booklet pane. Nos. 334×2, 335×2 and 336×4 (2p. stamps at top) (26.3)	3·25	
	ab. Ditto, but 2p. stamps at bottom (26.3)	3·25	
	b. Booklet pane. Nos. 334/7, each ×2 (26.3)	3·00	
335	3p. Old Fishmarket	10	10
336	10p. The Breakwater	35	35
337	15p. Jubilee Clock	50	50
338	31p. Loch Promenade	1·50	1·50
339	34p. Beach	1·75	1·75
334/9		*Set of 6*	3·75	3·75

87 "The Old Fishmarket and Harbour, Douglas"

(Des A. Theobald. Litho Cartor)

1987 (18 Feb). *Paintings by John Miller Nicholson. T* **87** *and similar horiz designs. Multicoloured.* P 13½.

340	12p. Type **87**	35	35
341	26p. "Red Sails at Douglas"	90	90
342	29p. "The Double Corner, Peel"	1·40	1·40
343	34p. "Peel Harbour"	1·60	1·60
340/3		*Set of 4*	3·75	3·75

88 Sea Terminal, Douglas

(Des R. Maddox. Litho B.D.T.)

1987 (29 Apr). *Europa. Architecture. T* **88** *and similar horiz designs. Multicoloured.* P 13½.

344	12p. Type **88**	60	60
	a. Horiz pair. Nos. 344/5	1·25	1·25
345	12p. Tower of Refuge, Douglas	60	60
346	22p. Gaiety Theatre, Douglas	1·10	1·10
	a. Horiz pair. Nos. 346/7	2·10	2·10
347	22p. Villa Marina, Douglas	1·10	1·10
344/7		*Set of 4*	3·00	3·00

Nos. 344/5 and 346/7 were each printed, *se-tenant*, in horizontal pairs throughout the sheets.

89 Supercharged BMW 500cc Motor Cycle, 1939

(Des B. Dix. Litho Cartor)

1987 (27 May). *80th Anniv of Tourist Trophy Motor Cycle Races. T* **89** *and similar horiz designs. Multicoloured.* P 13½×13.

348	12p. Type **89**	40	40
349	15p. Manx "Kneeler" Norton 350cc, 1953	60	60
350	29p. MV Agusta 500cc 4, 1956	1·00	1·00
351	31p. Guzzi 500cc V8, 1957	1·10	1·10
352	34p. Honda 250cc 6, 1967	1·40	1·40
348/52		*Set of 5*	4·00	4·00
MS353	150 × 140 mm. Nos. 348/52. P 14 × 13½	4·75	4·75

Nos. 348/53 also commemorate the Centenary of the St. John Ambulance Brigade and the miniature sheet also carries the logo of "Capex '87" International Stamp Exhibition, Toronto, on its margin.

90 Fuchsia and Wild Roses

91 Stirring the Christmas Pudding

(Des Nancy Corkish. Litho Enschedé)

1987 (9 Sept). *Wild Flowers. T* **90** *and similar vert designs. Multicoloured.* P 14½×13.

354	16p. Type **90**	60	60
355	29p. Field Scabious and Ragwort	1·10	1·10
356	31p. Wood Anemone and Celandine	1·25	1·25
357	34p. Violets and Primroses	1·50	1·50
354/7		*Set of 4*	4·00	4·00

(Des Colleen Corlett. Litho Questa)

1987 (16 Oct). *Christmas. Victorian Scenes. T* **91** *and similar vert designs. Multicoloured.* P 14.

358	12p. Type **91**	50	50
359	15p. Bringing home the Christmas tree	75	75
360	31p. Decorating the Christmas tree	1·25	1·25
358/60		*Set of 3*	2·25	2·25

92 Russell Brookes in Vauxhall Opel (Manx Rally winner, 1985)

(Des C. Abbott. Litho Enschedé)

1988 (10 Feb). *Motor Sport. T* **92** *and similar horiz designs. Multicoloured.* P 13½×14½.

361	13p. Type **92**	75	70
362	26p. Ari Vatanen in Ford "Escort" (Manx Rally winner, 1976)	1·25	1·10
363	31p. Terry Smith in Repco "March 761" (Hill Climb winner, 1980)	1·40	1·25
364	34p. Nigel Mansell in Williams/Honda (British Grand Prix winner, 1986 and 1987)	1·60	1·40
361/4		*Set of 4*	4·50	4·00

93 Horse Tram Terminus, Douglas Bay Tramway

93a Queen Elizabeth II taking Salute at Trooping the Colour

(Des Colleen Corlett (£2). A. Theobald (others). Litho B.D.T. (up. to 19p., 21p., 23p), Questa (20p. and 25p. to £2))

1988 (10 Feb)–92. *Manx Railways and Tramways. Horiz designs as T* **93**, *and T* **93a**. *Multicoloured.* P 13 (1p. to 19p., 21p., 23p.), 14½×15 (20p., 25p. to £1) or 14½ (£2).

365	1p. Type **93**	10	10
366	2p. Snaefell Mountain Railway	10	10
367	3p. Marine Drive Tramway	10	10
	a. Booklet pane. Nos. 367×2, 370 and 373×2 (16.3.88)	2·50	
	b. Booklet pane. Nos. 367×2, 371×2 and 374 (16.10.89)	2·25	
367c	4p. Douglas Cable Tramway (9.1.91)	10	10
	ca. Booklet pane. Nos. 367c×3, 374 and 377a	2·50	
	cb. Booklet pane. Nos. 367c×3, 374×4 and 377a	3·75	
368	5p. Douglas Head Incline Railway	10	10
369	10p. Manx Electric Railway train at Maughold Head	20	25
370	13p. As 4p.	40	30
	a. Booklet pane. Nos. 370×4 and 373×6 (16.3.88)	5·00	
371	14p. Manx Northern Railway No. 4, *Caledonia*, at Gob-y-Deigan	30	35
	a. Booklet pane. Nos. 371×4 and 374×6 (16.10.89)	4·00	
372	15p. Laxey Mine Railway Lewin locomotive *Ant*	30	35
	a. Booklet pane. Nos. 372 and 376×2 (14.2.90)	2·25	
	b. Booklet pane. Nos. 372×4 and 376×6 (14.2.90)	5·00	
373	16p. Port Erin Breakwater Tramway locomotive *Henry B. Loch*	40	35
374	17p. Ramsey Harbour Tramway	40	40
375	18p. Locomotive No. 7, *Tynwald*, on Foxdale line	50	40
375a	18p. T.P.O. Special leaving Douglas, 3 July 1991 (8.1.92)	50	40
	ab. Booklet pane. Nos. 375a×3 and 377b×2	2·50	
	ac. Booklet pane. Nos. 375a×6 and 377b×4	4·75	
376	19p. Baldwin Reservoir Tramway steam locomotive *Injebreck*	50	45
377	20p. I.M.R. No. 13, *Kissack*, near St. Johns (21.9.88)	50	45
377a	21p. As 14p. (9.1.91)	50	45
377b	23p. Double-decker horse tram, Douglas (8.1.92)	50	50
378	25p. I.M.R. No. 12, *Hutchinson*, leaving Douglas (21.9.88)	60	55
379	50p. Groudle Glen Railway locomotive *Polar Bear* (21.9.88)	1·50	1·10
380	£1 I.M.R. No. 11, *Maitland*, pulling Royal Train, 1963 (21.9.88)	3·00	2·10

380a £2 Type 93a (14.2.90) .. .. ..   5·00 4·25
365/80a   *Set of 21* 14·00 11·50

In addition to stamp booklets Nos. 367a/b, 370a, 371a, 372a/b and 375ab/ac also come from special booklet sheets of 50 containing either ten examples of the strips of five or five examples of the strips of ten.

Nos. 367c and 377a show the Queen's head in white. The 4p. value was only issued in 50p and £1 stamp booklets or in special booklet sheets of 50 containing five vertical strips of No. 367cb and five extra examples of both Nos. 367c and 377a. The 17p. from these booklets shows a 1991 imprint date.

Nos. 379/80 were reissued on 16 November 1992 with the imprint date changed to "1992".

For miniature sheet containing Nos. 367c and 377a see No. MS484.

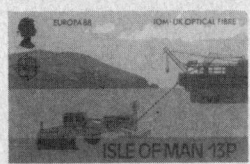

94 Laying Isle of Man—U.K. Submarine Cable

(Des C. Abbott. Litho Cartor)

1988 (14 Apr). *Europa. Transport and Communications. T* **94** *and similar horiz designs. Multicoloured. P* 14×13½.
381 13p. Type **94**   50   50
     a. Horiz pair. Nos. 381/2 ..   1·00 1·00
382 13p. *Flex Service 3* (cable ship) ..   50   50
383 22p. Earth station, Braddan   90   90
     a. Horiz pair. Nos. 383/4 ..   1·75 1·75
384 22p. "INTELSAT 5" satellite ..   90   90
381/4   *Set of 4* 2·50 2·50
Nos. 381/2 and 383/4 were each printed together, *se-tenant*, in horizontal pairs throughout the sheets. Nos. 381/2 form a composite design.

95 *Euterpe* (full-rigged ship) off   **96** "*Magellanica*"
    Ramsey, 1863

(Des J. Nicholson. Litho Questa)

1988 (11 May). *Manx Sailing Ships. T* **95** *and similar horiz designs. Multicoloured. P* 14.
385 16p. Type **95**   50   50
386 29p. *Vixen* (topsail schooner) leaving Peel for
    Australia, 1853 .. .. ..   1·00 1·00
387 31p. *Ramsey* (full-rigged ship) off Brisbane,
    1870 .. ..   1·25 1·25
388 34p. *Star of India* (formerly *Euterpe*) (barque)
    off San Diego, 1976 .. ..   1·40 1·40
385/8   *Set of 4* 3·75 3·75
MS389 110 × 85 mm. Nos. 385 and 388 ..   2·50 2·50
Nos. 386/7 also commemorate the Bicentenary of Australian Settlement.

(Des Colleen Corlett. Litho Enschedé)

1988 (21 Sept). *50th Anniv of British Fuchsia Society. T* **96** *and similar vert designs. Multicoloured. P* 13½ × 14.
390 13p. Type **96**   50   50
391 16p. "Pink Cloud"   60   60
392 22p. "Leonora"   80   70
393 29p. "Satellite" .. .. ..   1·00 1·00
394 31p. "Preston Guild" .. ..   1·25 1·25
395 34p. "Thalia" .. .. ..   1·40 1·40
390/5   *Set of 6* 5·00 5·00

97 Long-eared Owl

(Des Audrey North. Litho Questa)

1988 (12 Oct). *Christmas. Manx Birds. T* **97** *and similar horiz designs. Multicoloured. P* 14.
396 12p. Type **97**   55   55
397 15p. European Robin   85   85
398 31p. Grey Partridge .. ..   1·40 1·40
396/8   *Set of 3* 2·50 2·50

STANLEY GIBBONS STAMP COLLECTING SERIES

Introductory booklets on *How to Start, How to Identify Stamps* and *Collecting by Theme*. A series of well illustrated guides at a low price.
Write for details.

---

98 Ginger Cat   **99** Tudric Pewter
                      Clock, *c.* 1903

(Des P. Layton. Litho Questa)

1989 (8 Feb). *Manx Cats. T* **98** *and similar horiz designs. Multicoloured. P* 14.
399 16p. Type **98**   50   50
400 27p. Black and white cat ..   1·00 1·00
401 30p. Tortoiseshell and white cat   1·40 1·40
402 40p. Tortoiseshell cat .. ..   1·60 1·60
399/402   *Set of 4* 4·00 4·00

(Des Colleen Corlett. Litho Cartor)

1989 (8 Feb). *125th Birth Anniv of Archibald Knox* (*artist and designer*). *T* **99** *and similar multicoloured designs. P* 13.
403 13p. Type **99**   35   35
404 16p. "Celtic Cross" watercolour ..   45   45
405 23p. Silver cup and cover, 1902-03   75   75
406 32p. Gold and silver brooches from Liberty's
    Cymric range (*horiz*) ..   1·40 1·40
407 35p. Silver jewel box, 1900 (*horiz*)   1·50 1·50
403/7   *Set of 5* 4·00 4·00

100 William Bligh and Old
    Church, Onchan

(Des C. Abbott. Litho B.D.T.)

1989 (28 Apr). *Bicentenary of the Mutiny on the Bounty. T* **100** *and similar horiz designs. Multicoloured. P* 14.
408 13p. Type **100**   25   30
     a. Booklet pane. Nos. 408/10 and 412/14 ..   3·00
     b. Booklet pane. Nos. 408/9 and 411/14 ..   3·00
409 16p. Bligh and loyal crew cast adrift ..   30   35
410 23p. Pitcairn Islands 1989 Settlement
    Bicentenary 90 c., No. 345 ..   1·10 1·10
     a. Booklet pane. Nos. 410/11, each × 3 ..   3·00
411 27p. Norfolk Island 1989 Bicentenary 39 c., No.
    461 .. ..   1·10 1·10
412 30p. Midshipman Peter Heywood and Tahiti   70   70
413 32p. H.M.S. *Bounty* anchored off Pitcairn
    Island   75   75
414 35p. Fletcher Christian and Pitcairn Island ..   80   80
408/14   *Set of 7* 4·50 4·50
MS415 110×85 mm. Nos. 410/11 and 414   5·00 4·75
Nos. 410/11 were only issued in £5.30 booklets and as part of No. MS415.

Booklet panes Nos. 408a/b and 410a each contain two vertical rows of three stamps, separated by a central gutter.

101 Skipping and Hopscotch   **102** Atlantic Puffin

(Des Colleen Corlett. Litho Enschedé)

1989 (17 May). *Europa. Children's Games. T* **101** *and similar horiz designs. Multicoloured. P* 13½.
416 13p. Type **101**   60   60
     a. Horiz pair. Nos. 416/17 ..   1·25 1·25
417 13p. Wheelbarrow, leapfrog and piggyback ..   60   60
418 23p. Completing model house and blowing
    bubbles   95   95
     a. Horiz pair. Nos. 418/19 ..   1·90 1·90
419 23p. Girl with doll and doll's house ..   95   95
416/19   *Set of 4* 2·75 2·75
Nos. 416/17 and 418/19 were printed together, *se-tenant* as composite designs, in horizontal pairs throughout the sheets.

(Des W. Oliver. Litho Questa)

1989 (20 Sept). *Sea Birds. T* **102** *and similar vert designs. Multicoloured. P* 14.
420 13p. Type **102**   80   80
     a. Strip of 4. Nos. 420/3 ..   3·00
421 13p. Black Guillemot   80   80
422 13p. Common Cormorant ..   80   80
423 13p. Kittiwake   80   80
420/3   *Set of 4* 3·00 3·00
Nos. 420/3 were printed together, *se-tenant*, in horizontal and vertical strips of 4 throughout the sheet. The sheet exists with or without perforations across the side margins.

Examples of Nos. 420/3 sold at "World Stamp Expo '89", held at Washington D.C. between 17 November and 8 December 1989, carried a commemorative inscription on the bottom sheet margin.

---

103 Red Cross Cadets learning   **104** Mother with
    Resuscitation   Baby, Jane
                                    Crookall
                                    Maternity Home

(Des A. Theobald. Litho Questa)

1989 (16 Oct). *125th Anniversary of International Red Cross and Centenary of Noble's Hospital, Isle of Man. T* **103** *and similar horiz designs. P* 14.
424 14p. multicoloured   40   40
425 17p. grey and orange-vermilion ..   65   65
426 23p. multicoloured   90   90
427 30p. multicoloured .. ..   1·25 1·25
428 35p. multicoloured .. ..   1·50 1·50
424/8   *Set of 5* 4·25 4·25
Designs:—17p. Anniversary logo; 23p. Signing Geneva Convention, 1864; 30p. Red Cross ambulance; 35p. Henri Dunant (founder).

(Des Colleen Corlett. Litho Questa)

1989 (16 Oct). *Christmas. 50th Anniversary of Jane Crookall Maternity Home and 75th Anniversary of St. Ninian's Church, Douglas. T* **104** *and similar vert designs. Multicoloured. P* 14½.
429 13p. Type **104**   45   45
430 16p. Mother with child   55   55
431 34p. Madonna and Child ..   1·10 1·10
432 37p. Baptism, St. Ninian's Church ..   1·25 1·25
429/32   *Set of 4* 3·00 3·00

105 "The Isle of Man Express   **106** Modern
    going up a Gradient"   Postman

(Des D. Swinton. Litho B.D.T.)

1990 (14 Feb). *Isle of Man Edwardian Postcards. T* **105** *and similar horiz designs. Multicoloured. P* 14.
433 15p. Type **105**   30   30
434 19p. "A way we have in the Isle of Man" ..   55   55
435 32p. "Douglas–waiting for the male boat" ..   1·00 1·00
436 34p. "The last toast rack home, Douglas
    Parade" .. .. ..   1·40 1·40
437 37p. "The last Isle of Man boat" ..   1·50 1·50
433/7   *Set of 5* 4·25 4·25

(Des A. Kellett. Litho Cartor)

1990 (18 Apr). *Europa. Post Office Buildings. T* **106** *and similar multicoloured designs. P* 13½.
438 15p. Type **106**   55   55
     a. Horiz pair. Nos. 438/9 ..   1·10 1·10
439 15p. Ramsey Post Office, 1990 (40×26 *mm*)   55   55
440 24p. Postman, 1890   95   95
     a. Horiz pair. Nos. 440/1 ..   1·90 1·90
441 24p. Douglas Post Office, 1890 (40×26 *mm*)   95   95
438/41   *Set of 4* 2·75 2·75
Nos. 438/9 and 440/1 were each printed together, *se-tenant*, in horizontal pairs throughout the sheets.

107 Penny Black   **108** Queen
                                    Elizabeth the
                                    Queen Mother

(Des Colleen Corlett. Eng Inge Madle (No. MS447). Recess and litho (No. MS447) or litho (others) Enschedé)

1990 (3 May). *150th Anniv of the Penny Black. T* **107** *and similar vert designs. P* 14×13½.
442 1p. black, buff and gold   10   10
     a. Sheetlet. Horiz strip of 5. Nos. 442/6 ..   4·50
     b. Sheetlet. No. 442×25 ..   2·50
     c. Booklet pane. No. 442×8 with margins all
     round   50
443 19p. gold, black and buff   65   65
     a. Booklet pane. Nos. 443/6×2 with margins
     all round .. .. ..   6·50
444 32p. multicoloured .. ..   1·25 1·25
445 34p. multicoloured .. ..   1·25 1·25
446 37p. multicoloured .. ..   1·50 1·50
442/6   *Set of 5* 4·00 4·00
MS447 100×71 mm. £1 black, gold and buff (50×60
mm) .. ..   3·75 3·75
Designs:—19p. Wyon Medal, 1837; 32p. Wyon's stamp essay; 34p. Perkins Bacon engine-turned essay, 1839; 37p. Twopence Blue, 1840; £1 Block of four Penny Black stamps lettered IM–JN.

Sheetlet No. 442a was reissued on 24 August 1990 overprinted "From STAMP WORLD LONDON '90 to NEW ZEALAND 1990" for sale at the New Zealand exhibition.

The Penny Black stamps shown on Nos. 442b/c each have different corner letters at foot. The sheetlet of 25 was issued in conjunction with a special postal concession which allowed hand-addressed personal mail for the island to be posted for 1p. between 10 am. and 12 noon on 6 May 1990.

No. MS447 also commemorates "Stamp World London 90" International Stamp Exhibition, London.

(Des Colleen Corlett. Litho B.D.T.)

1990 (4 Aug). *90th Birthday of Queen Elizabeth the Queen Mother. P* 13×13½.
448 **108** 90p. multicoloured .. .. 3·00 3·00
No. 448 was printed in sheets of ten stamps and ten *se-tenant* inscribed labels.

109 Hawker Hurricane Mk 1, Bristol Type 142 Blenheim Mk 1 and Home Defence

(Des A. Theobald. Litho Questa)

1990 (5 Sept). *50th Anniv of Battle of Britain. T* **109** *and similar horiz designs. Multicoloured. P* 14.
449 15p. Type **109** 40 40
  a. Horiz pair. Nos. 449/50 .. .. 80 80
450 15p. Supermarine Spitfire with Westland Lysander Mk I rescue aircraft and launch 40 40
451 24p. Rearming Hawker Hurricane Mk I fighters 90 90
  a. Horiz pair. Nos. 451/2 .. 1·75 1·75
452 24p. Ops room and scramble 90 90
453 29p. Civil Defence personnel 95 95
  a. Horiz pair. Nos. 453/4 .. 1·90 1·90
454 29p. Anti-aircraft battery 95 95
449/54 .. .. .. *Set of* 6 4·00 4·00
The two designs of each value were printed together, *se-tenant*, in horizontal pairs throughout the sheets of 8.

110 Churchill with Freedom of Douglas Casket

111 Boy on Toboggan and Girl posting Letter

(Des C. Abbott. Litho Cartor)

1990 (5 Sept). *25th Death Anniv of Sir Winston Churchill. T* **110** *and similar horiz designs. Multicoloured. P* 13¼.
455 19p. Type **110** 60 60
456 32p. Churchill and London blitz .. 1·10 1·10
457 34p. Churchill and searchlights over Westminster .. .. 1·40 1·40
458 37p. Churchill with R.A.F. Hawker Hurricane Mk I fighters .. .. .. 1·40 1·40
455/8 .. .. .. *Set of* 4 4·25 4·25

(Des C. Abbott. Litho B.D.T.)

1990 (10 Oct). *Christmas. T* **111** *and similar vert designs. Multicoloured. P* 13×13½.
459 14p. Type **111** 40 40
460 18p. Girl on toboggan and skaters .. 60 60
461 34p. Boy with snowman .. .. 1·25 1·25
462 37p. Children throwing snowballs .. 1·40 1·40
459/62 .. .. .. *Set of* 4 3·50 3·50
MS463 123×55 mm. As Nos. 459/62, but face values in black .. .. .. 3·50 3·50
  a. Blue (inscriptions) omitted .. £600

112 Henry Bloom Noble and Orphans (Marshall Wane)

113 Lifeboat *Sir William Hillary*, Douglas

(Des Colleen Corlett. Litho Walsall)

1991 (9 Jan). *Manx Photography. T* **112** *and similar horiz designs. P* 14.
464 17p. blackish brown, pale brownish grey & blk 45 45
465 21p. deep brown and ochre 60 60
466 26p. blackish brown, stone and brownish black 90 90
467 31p. agate, pale grey-brown and black 1·25 1·25
468 40p. multicoloured .. .. .. 1·50 1·50
464/8 .. .. .. *Set of* 5 4·25 4·25
Designs:—21p. Douglas (Frederick Frith); 26p. Studio portrait of three children (Hilda Newby); 31p. Cashtal yn Ard (Christopher Killip); 40p. Peel Castle (Colleen Corlett).

(Des A. Peck. Litho Questa)

1991 (13 Feb). *Manx Lifeboats. T* **113** *and similar horiz designs. Multicoloured. P* 14.
469 17p. Type **113** 45 45
470 21p. *Osman Gabriel*, Port Erin .. 60 60
471 26p. *Ann and James Ritchie*, Ramsey 90 90
472 31p. *The Gough Ritchie*, Port St. Mary .. 1·25 1·25
473 37p. *John Batstone*, Peel .. .. 1·50 1·50
469/73 .. .. .. *Set of* 5 4·25 4·25
No. 469 is inscribed "HILARY" and No. 471 "JAMES & ANN RITCHIE", both in error.

114 "Intelsat" Communications Satellite

115 Oliver Godfrey with Indian 500cc at Start, 1911

(Des D. Miller. Litho B.D.T.)

1991 (24 Apr). *Europa. Europe in Space. T* **114** *and similar vert designs. Multicoloured. P* 14.
474 17p. Type **114** 70 70
  a. Vert pair. Nos. 474/5 .. .. 1·40 1·40
475 17p. "Ariane" rocket launch and fishing boats in Douglas harbour 70 70
476 26p. Weather satellite and space station 1·00 1·00
  a. Vert pair. Nos. 476/7 .. .. 2·00 2·00
477 26p. Ronaldsway Airport, Manx Radio transmitter and Space shuttle launch 1·00 1·00
474/7 .. .. .. *Set of* 4 3·00 3·00
Nos. 474/5 and 476/7 were each printed together, *se-tenant*, in vertical pairs throughout the sheets, each pair forming a composite design.

(Des A. Theobald. Litho Enschedé)

1991 (30 May). *80th Anniv of Tourist Trophy Mountain Course. T* **115** *and similar horiz designs. Multicoloured. P* 14½×13.
478 17p. Type **115** 40 40
479 21p. Freddie Dixon on Douglas "banking" sidecar, 1923 .. .. .. 60 60
480 26p. Bill Ivy on Yamaha 125cc, 1968 .. 85 85
481 31p. Giacomo Agostini on MV Agusta 500cc, 1972 .. .. 1·25 1·25
482 37p. Joey Dunlop on RVF Honda 750cc, 1985 1·40 1·40
478/82 .. .. .. *Set of* 5 4·00 4·00
MS483 149×144 mm. Nos. 478/82 .. 4·25 4·25
No. MS483 was reissued on 16 November 1991 overprinted for the Phila Nippon Exhibition, Japan.

(Des Colleen Corlett. Litho B.D.T.)

1991 (1 July). *9th Conference of Commonwealth Postal Administrations, Douglas. Sheet* 119×77 *mm containing Nos.* 367c *and* 377a, *each* × 2. *Multicoloured. P* 13.
MS484 Nos. 367c and 377a, each × 2 .. 1·50 1·50

116 Laxey Hand-cart, 1920

117 Mute Swans, Douglas Harbour

(Des C. Abbott. Litho Questa)

1991 (18 Sept). *Fire Engines. T* **116** *and similar square designs. Multicoloured. P* 14½.
485 17p. Type **116** 40 40
486 21p. Horse-drawn steamer, Douglas, 1909 .. 60 60
487 30p. Merryweather "Hatfield" pump, 1936 .. 85 85
488 33p. Dennis "F8" pumping appliance, Peel, 1953 .. .. 1·25 1·25
489 37p. Volvo turntable ladder, Douglas, 1989 .. 1·40 1·40
485/9 .. .. .. *Set of* 5 4·00 4·00

(Des Colleen Corlett. Litho Cartor)

1991 (18 Sept). *Swans. T* **117** *and similar horiz designs. Multicoloured. P* 13.
490 17p. Type **117** 55 55
  a. Horiz pair. Nos. 490/1 .. .. 1·10 1·10
491 17p. Black Swans, Curraghs Wildlife Park 55 55
492 26p. Whooper Swans, Bishop's Dub, Ballaugh 1·10 1·10
  a. Horiz pair. Nos. 492/3 .. .. 2·25 2·25
493 26p. Whistling ("Bewick's") Swans, Eairy Dam, Foxdale .. .. .. 1·10 1·10
494 37p. Coscoroba Swans, Curraghs Wildlife Park 1·40 1·40
  a. Horiz pair. Nos. 494/5 .. .. 2·75 2·75
495 37p. Whooper ("Trumpeter") Swans, Curraghs Wildlife Park .. .. 1·40 1·40
490/5 .. .. .. *Set of* 6 5·50 5·50
The two designs of each value were printed together, *se-tenant*, in horizontal pairs throughout the sheets with the backgrounds forming composite designs.

118 The Three Kings

119 North African and Italian Campaigns, 1942–43

(Des D. Swinton. Litho Walsall)

1991 (14 Oct). *Christmas. Paper Sculptures. T* **118** *and similar square designs. Multicoloured.* (a) *Sheet stamps. P* 14×14½.
496 16p. Type **118** 50 40
497 20p. Mary with manger 65 70
498 26p. Shepherds with sheep 80 85
499 37p. Choir of angels .. .. .. 1·10 1·10
496/9 .. .. .. *Set of* 4 2·75 2·75
  (b) *Booklet stamps. Self-adhesive. Stamps die-cut*
500 16p. Type **118** 75 75
  a. Booklet pane. Nos. 500×8 and 501×4 10·00
501 20p. As No. 497 .. .. .. 1·00 1·00

(Des A. Theobald. Litho Questa)

1992 (6 Feb). *50th Anniv of Parachute Regiment. T* **119** *and similar horiz designs. Multicoloured. P* 14.
502 23p. Type **119** 60 60
  a. Horiz pair. Nos. 502/3 .. .. 1·25 1·25
503 23p. D-Day, 1944 .. .. .. 60 60
504 28p. Arnhem, 1944 .. .. .. 70 70
  a. Horiz pair. Nos. 504/5 .. .. 1·40 1·40
505 28p. Rhine crossing, 1945 .. .. 70 70
506 39p. Operations in Near, Middle and Far East, 1945–68 .. .. .. 1·00 1·00
  a. Horiz pair. Nos. 506/7 .. .. 2·00 2·00
507 39p. Liberation of Falkland Islands, 1982 1·00 1·00
502/7 .. .. .. *Set of* 6 4·00 4·00
The two designs of each value were printed together, *se-tenant*, in horizontal pairs throughout the sheets of 8.

120 Queen Elizabeth II at Coronation, 1953

121 Brittle-stars

(Des D. Miller. Litho B.D.T.)

1992 (6 Feb). *40th Anniv of Accession. T* **120** *and similar vert designs. Multicoloured. P* 14.
508 18p. Type **120** 50 50
509 23p. Queen visiting Isle of Man, 1979 .. 60 60
510 28p. Queen in evening dress 70 70
511 33p. Queen visiting Isle of Man, 1989 .. 1·10 1·10
512 39p. Queen arriving for film premiere, 1990 1·25 1·25
508/12 .. .. .. *Set of* 5 3·75 3·75

(Des Jennifer Toombs. Litho Questa)

1992 (16 Apr). *Centenary of Port Erin Marine Laboratory. T* **121** *and similar horiz designs. Multicoloured. P* 14×14½.
513 18p. Type **121** 50 50
514 23p. Phytoplankton 60 60
515 28p. Atlantic Herring 70 70
516 33p. Great Scallop .. .. .. 1·10 1·10
517 39p. Dahlia Anemone and Delesseria .. 1·25 1·25
513/17 .. .. .. *Set of* 5 3·75 3·75

122 The Pilgrim Fathers embarking at Delfshaven

123 Central Pacific Locomotive *Jupiter*, 1869

(Des C. Abbott. Litho Enschedé)

1992 (16 Apr). *Europa. 500th Anniv of Discovery of America by Columbus. T* **122** *and similar square designs. Multicoloured. P* 14×13½.
518 18p. Type **122** 60 60
  a. Horiz pair. Nos. 518/19 .. .. 1·25 1·25
519 18p. *Speedwell* leaving Delfshaven .. 60 60
520 28p. *Mayflower* setting sail for America .. 1·00 1·00
  a. Horiz pair. Nos. 520/1 .. .. 2·00 2·00
521 28p. *Speedwell* anchored at Dartmouth 1·00 1·00
518/21 .. .. .. *Set of* 4 2·75 2·75
Nos. 518/19 and 520/1 were each printed together, *se-tenant*, in separate sheets, each horizontal pair forming a composite design. The designs of Nos. 520/1 are after the painting by L. Wilcox.

(Des A. Peck. Litho Enschedé)

92 (22 May). *Construction of the Union Pacific Railroad,
1866–69. T 123 and similar horiz designs.* P 13½×14.

2	33p. Type **123**		95	95
	a. Horiz pair. Nos. 522/3 plus label		1·90	1·90
	b. Booklet pane. Nos. 522/5×2 and **MS526**		9·25	
3	33p. Union Pacific locomotive No. 119, 1869		95	95
4	39p. Union Pacific locomotive No. 844, 1992		1·10	1·10
	a. Horiz pair. Nos. 524/5 plus label		2·25	2·25
5	39p. Union Pacific locomotive No. 3985, 1992		1·10	1·10
2/5		*Set of 4*	3·75	3·75
MS526	105×78 mm. £1.50, Golden Spike			
	ceremony, 10 May 1869 (60×50 mm)		5·25	5·25

The two designs for each value were printed in small sheets of 10
(×5) with each horizontal pair separated by a half stamp-size label
owing Union Pacific emblem or portraits of Dan and Jack
asement (railroad contractors).
Booklet pane No. 522b contains two blocks of four of Nos. 522/5
ith No. **MS526** between them. Miniature sheets from the booklet
ow a white margin and line of roulettes at left and right. In the
locks of four each horizontal pair is separated by a half stamp-size
bel.

124 *King Orry V* in Douglas Harbour

(Des Colleen Corlett. Litho Walsall)

1992 (18 Sept). *Manx Harbours. T 124 and similar horiz designs.
Multicoloured.* P 14½×14.

527	18p. Type **124**			50	50
528	23p. Castletown			60	60
529	37p. Port St. Mary			1·25	1·25
530	40p. Ramsey			1·25	1·25
527/30			*Set of 4*	3·25	3·25

125 *Saint Eloi* in 1972   126 Stained Glass
Window, St.
German's
Cathedral, Peel

(Des Colleen Corlett. Litho Walsall)

1992 (18 Sept). *"Genova '92" International Thematic Stamp
Exhibition. Sheet 111×68 mm containing T 125 and similar horiz
design. Multicoloured.* P 14½×14.

MS531	18p. *King Orry V* in 1992 (as in Type **124**);		
	£1 Type **125**	3·50	3·50

(Des Colleen Corlett. Litho Questa)

1992 (13 Oct). *Christmas. Manx Churches. T 126 and similar vert
designs. Multicoloured.* P 14½.

532	17p. Type **126**		50	50
533	22p. Reredos, St. Matthew the Apostle			
	Church, Douglas		70	70
534	28p. Stained glass window, St. George's			
	Church, Douglas		85	85
535	37p. Reredos, St. Mary of the Isle Catholic			
	Church, Douglas		1·00	1·00
536	40p. Stained glass window, Trinity Methodist			
	Church, Douglas		1·10	1·10
532/6		*Set of 5*	3·75	3·75

127 Mansell on Lap of
Honour, British Grand Prix,
1992

(Des A. Theobald. Litho Walsall)

1992 (8 Nov). *Nigel Mansell's Victory in Formula 1 World Motor
Racing Championship. T 127 and similar horiz design.
Multicoloured.* P 13½.

537	20p. Type **127**		50	50
538	24p. Mansell in French Grand Prix, 1992		75	75

128 H.M.S. *Amazon*
(frigate)

128*a* Manx Red Ensign   128*b* Queen Elizabeth
II (hologram)

(Des A. Theobald (1p. to 27p.), J. Nicholson (30p. and 40p. to £1),
Colleen Corlett (£2, £5). Litho Enschedé (1p. to £1), Questa (£2)
or Walsall (£5) (hologram by Applied Holographics))

1993 (4 Jan)–97. *Ships. Horiz designs as T 128 and 128a/b.
Multicoloured.* P 13½×13 (1p. to £1), 14½ (£2) or 14½×14 (£5).

539	1p. Type **128**		10	10
540	2p. *Fingal* (lighthouse tender)		10	10
541	4p. *Sir Winston Churchill* (cadet schooner)		10	10
	a. Booklet pane. Nos. 541, 544 and 548, each			
	× 2 (14.5.97)		2·00	
542	5p. *Dar Mlodziezy* (full-rigged cadet ship)		10	10
543	20p. *Tynwald I* (paddle-steamer), 1846		40	45
	a. Booklet pane. Nos. 543×2 and 547×3		2·50	
	b. Booklet pane. Nos. 543×4 and 547×6		4·75	
544	21p. *Ben Veg* (freighter)		40	45
545	22p. *Waverley* (paddle-steamer)		45	50
546	23p. Royal Yacht *Britannia*		45	50
547	24p. *Francis Drake* (ketch)		50	55
548	25p. *Royal Viking Sky* (liner)		50	55
549	26p. *Lord Nelson* (cadet barque)		55	60
550	27p. *Europa* (liner)		55	60
551	30p. *Snaefell V* (ferry) leaving Ardrossan			
	(15.9.93)		60	65
552	35p. *Seacat* (catamaran ferry) (11.1.96)		70	75
553	40p. *Lady of Mann I* (ferry) off Ramsey			
	(15.9.93)		80	85
554	50p. *Mona's Queen II* (paddle ferry) leaving			
	Fleetwood (15.9.93)		1·00	1·10
555	£1 *Queen Elizabeth 2* (liner) and *Mona's*			
	Queen V (ferry) off Liverpool (15.9.93)		2·00	2·10
556	£2 Type **128***a* (12.1.94)		4·00	4·25
557	£5 Type **128***b* (5.7.94)		10·00	10·50
539/57		*Set of 19*	23·00	24·00

In addition to stamp booklets Nos. 543a/b also come from a
special booklet sheet of 50 (5×10) which provides either 5 examples
of No. 543b or 10 of No. 543a. No. 541a comes from a special
booklet sheet of 30 (5×6).
Imprint dates: "1993", Nos. 539/51, 553/5; "1994", Nos. 556/7;
"1995", Nos. 543 and 547; "1996", No. 552; "1997", Nos. 541, 544,
548 and 555.
For 4p. 20p. and 24p. in similar designs, but smaller, see Nos.
687/93.
For miniature sheet containing the 23p. see No. **MS760**.

129 No. 1 Motor Car and No. 13 Trailer at
Groudle Glen Hotel

(Des A. Theobald. Litho B.D.T.)

1993 (3 Feb). *Centenary of Manx Electric Railway. T 129 and
similar horiz designs. Multicoloured.* P 14.

559	20p. Type **129**		50	50
	a. Booklet pane. Nos. 559/62		2·50	
560	24p. No. 9 Tunnel Car and No. 19 Trailer at			
	Douglas Bay Hotel		65	65
561	28p. No. 19 Motor Car and No. 59 Royal			
	Trailer Special at Douglas Bay		70	70
562	39p. No. 33 Motor Car, No. 45 Trailer and No.			
	13 Van at Derby Castle		1·00	1·00
559/62		*Set of 4*	2·50	2·50

Booklet pane. No. 559a exists in four versions, which differ in the
order of the stamps within the block of four and in the information
printed on the pane margins.

130 "Sir Hall Caine"
(statue) (Bryan Kneale)

(Des Colleen Corlett. Litho B.D.T.)

1993 (14 Apr). *Europa. Contemporary Art. Works by Bryan
Kneale. T 130 and similar square designs. Multicoloured.* P 14.

563	20p. Type **130**		55	55
	a. Horiz pair. Nos. 563/4		1·10	1·10
564	20p. "The Brass Bedstead" (painting)		55	55
565	28p. Abstract bronze sculpture		90	90
	a. Horiz pair. Nos. 565/6		1·75	1·75
566	28p. "Polar Bear Skeleton" (drawing)		90	90
563/6		*Set of 4*	2·50	2·50

Nos. 563/4 and 565/6 were each printed together, *se-tenant*, in
horizontal pairs throughout the sheets.

131 Graham Oates and Bill Marshall
(1933 International Six Day Trial)
on Ariel Square Four

(Des C. Abbott. Litho Walsall)

1993 (3 June). *Manx Motor Cycling Events. T 131 and similar
horiz designs. Multicoloured.* P 13½×14.

567	20p. Type **131**		45	45
568	24p. Sergeant Geoff Duke (1947 Royal Signals			
	Display Team) on Triumph 3T Twin		60	60
569	28p. Denis Parkinson (1953 Senior Manx			
	Grand Prix) on Manx Norton		80	80
570	33p. Richard Swallow (1991 Junior Classic			
	MGP) on Aermacchi		1·10	1·10
571	39p. Steve Colley (1992 Scottish Six Day Trial)			
	on Beta Zero		1·25	1·25
567/71		*Set of 5*	3·75	3·75
MS572	165×120 mm. Nos. 567/71		4·00	4·00

132 *Inachis io* (Peacock)   133 Children
decorating
Christmas Tree

(Des Colleen Corlett. Litho Questa)

1993 (15 Sept). *Butterflies. T 132 and similar square designs.
Multicoloured.* P 14½.

573	24p. Type **132**		75	75
	a. Horiz strip of 5. Nos. 573/7		3·25	
574	24p. *Argynnis aglaja* (Dark Green Fritillary)		75	75
575	24p. *Cynthia cardui* (Painted Lady)		75	75
576	24p. *Celastrina argiolus* (Holly Blue)		75	75
577	24p. *Vanessa atalanta* (Red Admiral)		75	75
573/7		*Set of 5*	3·25	3·25

Nos. 573/7 were printed together, *se-tenant*, both horizontally
and vertically within the sheet of 20 (5×4).
Examples of Nos. 573/7 sold at "Philakorea '94" and "Singpex
'94" come with commemorative cachets on the bottom margin.

(Des Christine Haworth. Litho Questa)

1993 (12 Oct). *Christmas. T 133 and similar vert designs.
Multicoloured.* P 14.

578	19p. Type **133**		55	55
579	23p. Girl with snowman		65	65
580	28p. Boy opening presents		80	80
581	30p. Girl with teddy bear		1·10	1·10
582	40p. Children with toboggan		1·10	1·10
578/82		*Set of 5*	3·75	3·75

134 White-throated Robin

(Des Colleen Corlett. Litho B.D.T.)

1994 (18 Feb). *Calf of Man Bird Observatory. T 134 and similar
multicoloured designs.* P 14.

583	20p. Type **134**		60	60
	a. Pair. Nos. 583/4		1·25	1·25
584	20p. Black-eared Wheatear		60	60
585	24p. Goldcrest		90	90
	a. Pair. Nos. 585/6		1·75	1·75
586	24p. Northern Oriole		90	90
587	30p. Common Kingfisher		1·00	1·00
	a. Pair. Nos. 587/8		2·00	2·00
588	30p. Hoopoe		1·00	1·00
583/8		*Set of 6*	4·25	4·25
MS589	100×71 mm. £1 Magpie (51½×61 mm).			
	P 13½×13		3·00	3·00

Nos. 583/4, 585/6 and 587/8 were printed together, *se-tenant*, in
horizontal and vertical pairs throughout the sheets of 10.
No. **MS589** also commemorates the "Hong Kong '94" philatelic
exhibition.

135 Gaiety Theatre, Douglas

(Des Colleen Corlett. Litho Cartor)

1994 (18 Feb). *Booklet Stamps. Manx Tourism Centenary.* T **135** *and similar horiz designs. Multicoloured.* P 13½.
590	24p.	Type **135**		60	60
	a.	Booklet pane. Nos. 590/9 with margins all			
		round		5·50	
591	24p.	Sports		60	60
592	24p.	Artist at work and yachts racing		60	60
593	24p.	TT Races and British Aerospace Hawk			
		T.1's of Red Arrows display team		60	60
594	24p.	Musical instruments		60	60
595	24p.	Laxey Wheel and Manx cat		60	60
596	24p.	Tower of Refuge, Douglas, with bucket			
		and spade		60	60
597	24p.	Cyclist		60	60
598	24p.	Tynwald Day and classic car		60	60
599	24p.	Santa Mince Pie train, Groudle Glen		60	60
590/9			*Set of 10*	5·50	5·50

Nos. 590/9 were only issued in £2.40 stamp booklets.

136 *Eubranchus tricolor* (sea slug)

(Des Jennifer Toombs. Litho Enschedé)

1994 (5 May). *Europa. Discoveries of Edward Forbes (marine biologist).* T **136** *and similar horiz designs. Multicoloured.* P 13×14½.
600	20p.	Type **136**		50	50
	a.	Horiz strip of 3. Nos. 600/2		1·50	
601	20p.	*Loligo forbesii* (Common Squid)		50	50
602	20p.	Edward Forbes and signature		50	50
603	30p.	*Solaster moretonis* (fossil starfish)		90	90
	a.	Horiz strip of 3. Nos. 603/5		2·75	
604	30p.	*Adamsia carciniopados* (anemone) on			
		Hermit Crab		90	90
605	30p.	*Solaster endeca* (starfish)		90	90
600/5			*Set of 6*	3·75	3·75

Nos. 600/2 and 603/5 were printed together, *se-tenant*, in horizontal strips of 3 throughout the sheets of 15.

137 Maj-Gen. Bedell Smith and Naval Landing Force including *Ben-My-Chree IV* (ferry)

(Des A. Theobald. Litho Questa)

1994 (6 June). *50th Anniv of D-Day.* T **137** *and similar horiz designs. Multicoloured.* P 14.
606	4p.	Type **137**		15	15
	a.	Horiz pair. Nos. 606/7		30	30
607	4p.	Admiral Ramsay and naval ships including			
		Victoria and *Lady of Mann* (ferries)		15	15
608	20p.	Gen. Montgomery and British landings		70	70
	a.	Horiz pair. Nos. 608/9		1·40	1·40
609	20p.	Lt-Gen. Dempsey and 2nd Army landings		70	70
610	30p.	Air Chief Marshal Leigh-Mallory and U.S.			
		paratroops and aircraft		80	80
	a.	Horiz pair. Nos. 610/11		1·50	1·50
611	30p.	Air Chief Marshal Tedder and British			
		paratroops and aircraft		80	80
612	41p.	Lt-Gen. Bradley and U.S. 1st Army			
		landings		1·00	1·00
	a.	Horiz pair. Nos. 612/13		2·00	2·00
613	41p.	Gen. Eisenhower and American landings		1·00	1·00
606/13			*Set of 8*	4·75	4·75

The two designs for each value were printed together, *se-tenant*, in horizontal pairs throughout the sheets of 8.

138 Postman Pat visits the Isle of Man, Jess and Ffinlo at Sea Terminal, Douglas

139 Cycling

(Des Colleen Corlett. Litho B.D.T.)

1994 (14 Sept). *Postman Pat visits the Isle of Man.* T **138** *and similar multicoloured designs.* P 15×14.
614	1p.	Type **138**		10	10
	a.	Booklet pane. No. 614×2 with margins all			
		round		20	
615	20p.	Laxey Wheel		60	60
	a.	Booklet pane. No. 615×2 with margins all			
		round		1·00	
616	24p.	Cregneash		70	70
	a.	Booklet pane. No. 616×2 with margins all			
		round		1·25	
617	30p.	Manx Electric Railway trains		80	80
	a.	Booklet pane. No. 617×2 with margins all			
		round		1·50	

618	36p.	Peel Harbour		90	90
	a.	Booklet pane. No. 618×2 with margins all			
		round		1·75	
619	41p.	Douglas Promenade		1·10	1·10
	a.	Booklet pane. No. 619×2 with margins all			
		round		2·00	
614/19			*Set of 6*	3·75	3·75
MS620		110×85 mm. £1 Postman Pat (25×39 *mm*)			
		P 13		2·50	2·50

Examples of No. MS620 from stamp booklets show a line of roulettes at left.

(Des D. Miller. Litho Walsall)

1994 (11 Oct). *Centenary of International Olympic Committee.* T **139** *and similar square designs. Multicoloured.* P 14×14½.
621	10p.	Type **139**		30	30
622	20p.	Downhill skiing		55	55
623	24p.	Swimming		70	70
624	35p.	Hurdling		95	95
625	48p.	Centenary logo		1·40	1·40
621/5			*Set of 5*	3·50	3·50

140 Santa Train to Santon

141 Foden Steam Wagon, Highway Board Depot, Douglas

(Des Colleen Corlett. Litho Cartor)

1994 (11 Oct). *Christmas. Father Christmas in the Isle of Man.* T **140** *and similar multicoloured designs.* P 13½×14 (23p.) or 14×13½ (others).
626	19p.	Type **140**		50	50
627	23p.	Father Christmas and Postman Pat on mini			
		tractor, Douglas (*vert*)		70	70
628	60p.	Father Christmas and majorettes in sleigh,			
		Port St. Mary		1·60	1·60
626/8			*Set of 3*	2·50	2·50

(Des A. Peck. Litho Enschedé)

1995 (8 Feb). *Steam Traction Engines.* T **141** *and similar horiz designs. Multicoloured.* P 13½×13.
629	20p.	Type **141**		60	60
630	24p.	Clayton & Shuttleworth and Fowler			
		engines pulling dead whale		70	70
631	30p.	Wallis and Steevens engine at Ramsey			
		Harbour		85	85
632	35p.	Marshall engine with threshing machine,			
		Ballarhenny		95	95
633	41p.	Marshall convertible steam roller		1·10	1·10
629/33			*Set of 5*	3·75	3·75

142 Car No. 2 and First Train, 1895

(Des A. Theobald. Litho B.D.T.)

1995 (8 Feb). *Centenary of Snaefell Mountain Railway.* T **142** *and similar horiz designs. Multicoloured.* P 14.
634	20p.	Type **142**		60	60
	a.	Booklet pane. Nos. 634/7 with margins all			
		round		3·00	
635	24p.	Car No. 4 in green livery and Car No. 3 in			
		Laxey Valley		70	70
636	35p.	Car No. 6 and Car No. 5 in 1971		95	95
637	42p.	Goods Car No. 7 and *Caledonia* steam			
		locomotive pulling construction train		1·10	1·10
634/7			*Set of 4*	3·00	3·00
MS638		110×87 mm. £1 Passenger car and Argus			
		char-a-banc at Bungalow Hotel (60×37 *mm*)		2·50	2·50
	a.	Booklet pane. As No. MS638 with			
		additional margins all round showing			
		further inscriptions at right and left		2·50	

Booklet pane No. 634a exists in three versions, which differ in the order of the stamps within the block of four.

No. MS638a from stamp booklets shows a white margin, description of the design and line of roulettes at left and an additional inscription, "1895. CENTENARY SNAEFELL MOUNTAIN RAILWAY. 1995", vertically in the margin at right.

143 Peace Doves forming Wave and Tower of Refuge, Douglas Bay

144 Spitfire, Tank and Medals

(Des Colleen Corlett and M. Magleby (20p.), Colleen Corlett (30p.). Litho Enschedé)

1995 (28 Apr). *Europa. Peace and Freedom.* T **143** *and similar vert design. Multicoloured.* P 14×13½.
639	20p.	Type **143**		50	50
640	30p.	Peace dove breaking barbed wire		75	75

(Des A. Theobald. Litho B.D.T.)

1995 (8 May). *50th Anniv of End of Second World War.* T **144** *and similar horiz designs. Multicoloured.* P 14.
641	10p.	Type **144**		30	30
	a.	Horiz pair. Nos. 641/2		60	
642	10p.	Typhoon, anti-aircraft gun and medals		30	30
643	20p.	Lancaster, escort carrier and medals		55	55
	a.	Horiz pair. Nos. 643/4		1·10	1·10
644	20p.	U.S. Navy aircraft, jungle patrol and			
		medals		55	55
645	24p.	Celebrations in Parliament Square		70	70
	a.	Horiz pair. Nos. 645/6		1·40	1·40
646	24p.	V.E. Day bonfire		70	70
647	40p.	Street party		1·10	1·10
	a.	Horiz pair. Nos. 647/8		2·25	2·25
648	40p.	King George VI and Queen Elizabeth on			
		Isle of Man in July 1945		1·10	1·10
641/8			*Set of 8*	4·75	4·75

The two designs for each value were printed together, *se-tenant*, in horizontal pairs throughout sheets of 8.

145 Reg Parnell in Maserati "4 CLT", 1951

(Des N. Sykes. Litho Questa)

1995 (8 May). *90th Anniv of Motor Racing on Isle of Man.* T **145** *and similar multicoloured designs.* P 14.
649	20p.	Type **145**		60	60
650	24p.	Stirling Moss in Frazer Nash, 1951		75	75
651	30p.	Richard Seaman in Delage, 1936		85	85
652	36p.	Prince Bira in ERA R2B "Romulus",			
		1937		1·00	1·00
653	41p.	Kenelm Guinness in Sunbeam 1, 1914		1·10	1·10
654	42p.	Freddie Dixon in Riley, 1934		1·10	1·10
649/54			*Set of 6*	4·75	4·75
MS655		103×73 mm. £1 John Napier in Arrol			
		Johnston, 1905 (47×58 *mm*)		2·50	2·50

146 Thomas the Tank Engine and Bertie Bus being Unloaded

147 *Amanita muscaria*

(Des O. Bell. Litho B.D.T.)

1995 (15 Aug). *50th Anniv of Thomas the Tank Engine Stories by Revd. Awdry.* "Thomas the Tank Engine's Dream". T **146** *and similar horiz designs. Multicoloured.* P 14.
656	20p.	Type **146**		60	60
	a.	Booklet pane. Nos. 656/7 with margins all			
		round		1·25	
	b.	Booklet pane. Nos. 656 and 661 with			
		margins all round		1·75	
657	24p.	Mail train		75	75
	a.	Booklet pane. Nos. 657/8 with margins all			
		round		1·50	
658	30p.	Bertie and engines at Ballasalla		85	85
	a.	Booklet pane. Nos. 658/9 with margins all			
		round		1·75	
659	36p.	Viking the Diesel Engine, Port Erin		1·00	1·00
	a.	Booklet pane. Nos. 659/60 with margins all			
		round		2·00	
660	41p.	Thomas and railcar at Snaefell summit		1·10	1·10
	a.	Booklet pane. Nos. 660/1 with margins all			
		round		2·25	
661	45p.	Engines racing past Laxey Wheel		1·25	1·25
656/61			*Set of 6*	5·00	5·00

(Des Colleen Corlett. Litho Enschedé)

1995 (1 Sept). *Fungi.* T **147** *and similar multicoloured designs.* P 13½.
662	20p.	Type **147**		50	50
663	24p.	*Boletus edulis*		65	65
664	30p.	*Coprinus disseminatus*		85	85
665	35p.	*Pleurotus ostreatus*		95	95
666	42p.	*Geastrum triplex*		1·25	1·25
662/6			*Set of 5*	3·75	3·75
MS667		100×71 mm. £1 Shaggy Ink Cap and Bee			
		Orchid (50×59 *mm*)		2·50	2·50

No. MS667 is inscribed "Singapore World Stamp Exhibition 1st–10th September 1995" on the sheet margin.

MINIMUM PRICE

The minimum price quote is 10p which represents a handling charge rather than a basis for valuing common stamps. For further notes about prices see introductory pages.

148 St. Catherine's
Church, Port Erin

149 Langness
Lighthouse

(Des Colleen Corlett. Litho B.D.T.)

1995 (10 Oct). *Christmas. T* **148** *and similar square designs. Multicoloured. P* 14.

668	19p. Type **148**	50	50
669	23p. European Robin on Holly branch	60	60
670	42p. St. Peter's Church and wild flowers	1·10	1·10
671	50p. Hedgehog hibernating under farm machinery	1·40	1·40
668/71	*Set of* 4	3·25	3·25

(Des D. Swinton. Litho Questa)

1996 (24 Jan). *Lighthouses. T* **149** *and similar multicoloured designs. P* 14.

672	20p. Type **149**	55	55
	a. Booklet pane. No. 672×4 with margins all round	1·60	
673	24p. Point of Ayre lighthouse (*horiz*)	65	65
	a. Booklet pane. No. 673×4 with margins all round	2·00	
674	30p. Chicken Rock lighthouse	85	85
	a. Booklet pane. Nos. 674 and 676 each × 2 with margins all round	2·75	
675	36p. Calf of Man lighthouse (*horiz*)	1·00	1·00
	a. Booklet pane. Nos. 675 and 677 each × 2 with margins all round	3·25	
676	41p. Douglas Head lighthouse	1·10	1·10
677	42p. Maughold Head lighthouse (*horiz*)	1·10	1·10
672/7	*Set of* 6	4·75	4·75

150 White Manx Cat and Celtic
Interlaced Ribbons

151 Douglas
Borough Arms

(Des Nancy Corkish. Litho B.D.T.)

1996 (14 Mar). *Manx Cats. T* **150** *and similar multicoloured designs. P* 14.

678	20p. Type **150**	60	60
679	24p. Cat and Union Jack ribbons	75	75
680	36p. Cat on rug in German colours, mouse and Brandenburg Gate	1·00	1·00
681	42p. Cat, U.S.A. flag and Statue of Liberty	1·10	1·10
682	48p. Cat, map of Australia and kangaroo	1·25	1·25
678/82	*Set of* 5	4·25	4·25
MS683	100×71 mm. £1.50, Cat with kittens (51×61 mm). P 13½×13	3·50	3·50

For No. MS683 with "CAPEX '96" logo see No. MS712.

(Des Colleen Corlett. Litho B.D.T.)

1996 (14 Mar). *Centenary of Douglas Borough. Self-adhesive. Die-cut perf* 9×10.

684	151 (20p.) multicoloured	40	45

No. 684 was printed in sheets of 40, each stamp surrounded by white backing paper divided by roulettes. The actual stamps were separated from the backing paper by die-cut perforations. It was initially sold for 20p. and was only valid for postage within the Isle of Man.

(Des A. Theobald. Litho Walsall)

1996 (21 Apr). *Ships. As Nos.* 541, 543 *and* 547, *but smaller,* 21×18 *mm. Multicoloured. P* 14.

687	4p. Sir Winston Churchill (cadet schooner)	10	10
	a. Booklet pane. Nos. 687, 689 and 693, each × 2	1·90	
689	20p. Tynwald I (paddle-steamer), 1846	40	45
693	24p. Francis Drake (ketch)	50	55
687/93	*Set of* 3	1·00	1·10

The 20p. and 24p. show the positions of the face value and Queen's head reversed.

152 Princess Anne (President,
Save the Children Fund) and
Children

(Des D. Miller. Litho B.D.T.)

1996 (21 Apr). *Europa. Famous Women. T* **152** *and similar horiz design. Multicoloured. P* 14.

701	24p. Type **152**	60	60
702	30p. Queen Elizabeth II and people of the Commonwealth	80	80

The background designs of Nos. 701/2 continue onto the vertical sheet margins.

153 Alec Bennett

154 National Poppy
Appeal Trophy

(Des J. Dunne. Litho Questa)

1996 (30 May). *Tourist Trophy Motorcycle Races. Irish Winners. T* **153** *and similar multicoloured designs. P* 14.

703	20p. Type **153**	65	65
704	24p. Stanley Woods	70	70
705	45p. Artie Bell	1·25	1·25
706	60p. Joey and Robert Dunlop	1·50	1·50
703/6	*Set of* 4	3·75	3·75
MS707	100×70 mm. £1 R.A.F. Red Arrows display team (*vert*)	2·50	2·50

(Des C. Abbott. Litho B.D.T.)

1996 (8 June). *75th Anniv of Royal British Legion. T* **154** *and similar square designs. Multicoloured. P* 14.

708	20p. Type **154**	60	60
709	24p. Manx War Memorial, Braddan	65	65
710	42p. Poppy appeal collection box	1·10	1·10
711	75p. Royal British Legion badge	2·10	2·10
708/11	*Set of* 4	4·00	4·00

1996 (8 June). *"CAPEX '96" International Stamp Exhibition, Toronto. No.* **MS**683 *additionally inscribed with "CAPEX '96" exhibition logo on sheet margin.*

MS712	100×71 mm. £1.50 Cat with kittens (51×61 mm)	3·50	3·50

155 U.N.I.C.E.F. Projects in
Mexico

156 Labrador

(Des C. Abbott. Litho Enschedé)

1996 (18 Sept). *50th Anniv of U.N.I.C.E.F. T* **155** *and similar horiz designs. Multicoloured. P* 13½×14.

713	24p. Type **155**	50	55
	a. Horiz pair. Nos. 713/14	1·00	1·10
714	24p. Projects in Sri Lanka	50	55
715	30p. Projects in Colombia	60	65
	a. Horiz pair. Nos. 715/16	1·25	1·25
716	30p. Projects in Zambia	60	65
717	42p. Projects in Afghanistan	85	90
	a. Horiz pair. Nos. 717/18	1·75	1·75
718	42p. Projects in Vietnam	85	90
713/18	*Set of* 6	3·50	4·25

Nos. 713/14, 715/16 and 717/18 were each printed together, *se-tenant*, in horizontal pairs throughout the sheets.

(Des Colleen Corlett. Litho Questa)

1996 (18 Sept). *Dogs. T* **156** *and similar multicoloured designs. P* 14½.

719	20p. Type **156**	45	45
	a. Booklet pane. No. 719×4 with margins all round	1·60	
720	24p. Border Collie	55	55
	a. Booklet pane. No. 720×4 with margins all round	2·00	
721	31p. Dalmatian	65	65
	a. Booklet pane. Nos. 721/4 with margins all round	3·50	
722	38p. Mongrel	80	80
723	43p. English Setter	90	90
724	63p. Alsatian	1·40	1·40
719/24	*Set of* 6	4·75	4·75
MS725	100×71 mm. £1.20, Labrador guide dog and working Border Collie (38×50 mm). P 13½×14	2·75	2·75
	a. Booklet pane. As No. MS725, but with additional white margins all round separated by roulette	2·75	

The new-issue supplement to this Catalogue
appears each month in

GIBBONS
STAMP MONTHLY

—from your newsagent or by postal subscription—
sample copy and details on request.

---

157 "Snowman and
Pine Trees" (David
Bennett)

158 Primroses and
Cashtyl ny Ard

(Adapted Colleen Corlett. Litho Walsall)

1996 (2 Nov). *Christmas. Children's Paintings. T* **157** *and similar square designs. Multicoloured. P* 14×14½.

726	19p. Type **157**	40	45
727	23p. "Three-legged Father Christmas" (Louis White)	45	50
728	50p. "Family around Christmas Tree" (Robyn Whelan)	1·00	1·10
729	75p. "Father Christmas in Sleigh" (Claire Bradley)	1·50	1·60
726/9	*Set of* 4	3·25	3·50

(Des Colleen Corlett. Litho B.D.T.)

1997 (12 Feb). *Spring in Man. T* **158** *and similar square designs. Multicoloured. P* 14.

730	20p. Type **158**	40	45
731	24p. Lochtan sheep and lambs	50	55
732	43p. Daffodils, duck and ducklings	85	90
733	63p. Dabchick with young and frog on lily pad	1·25	1·40
730/3	*Set of* 4	3·00	3·25

159 Barn Owl

160 Moddey Dhoo, Peel Castle

(Des J. Paul. Litho B.D.T.)

1997 (12 Feb). *Owls. T* **159** *and similar vert designs. Multicoloured. P* 14.

734	20p. Type **159**	40	45
	a. Booklet pane. No. 734×4 with margins all round	1·60	
735	24p. Short-eared Owl	50	55
	a. Booklet pane. No. 735×4 with margins all round	2·00	
736	31p. Long-eared Owl	60	65
	a. Booklet pane. Nos. 736/9 with margins all round	3·50	
737	36p. Little Owl	75	80
738	43p. Snowy Owl	85	90
739	56p. Tawny Owl	1·10	1·25
734/9	*Set of* 6	4·00	4·50
MS740	100×71 mm. £1.20, Long-eared Owl (*different*) (51×60 mm). P 13	2·40	2·50
	a. Booklet pane. As No. MS740 but with additional white margins all round and with line of roulettes at left	2·40	

No. MS740 includes the "HONG KONG '97" International Stamp Exhibition Logo on the sheet margin.

(Des Colleen Corlett. Litho Enschedé)

1997 (24 Apr). *Europa. Tales and Legends. T* **160** *and similar horiz designs. Multicoloured. P* 13½×14.

741	21p. Type **160**	40	45
742	25p. Fairies in tree and cottage	50	55
743	31p. Fairies at Fairy bridge	60	65
744	36p. Giant Finn MacCooil and Calf of Man	70	75
745	37p. The Buggane of St. Trinian's	75	80
746	43p. Fynoderee and farm	85	90
741/6	*Set of* 6	3·75	4·00

161 Sopwith Tabloid

(Des R. Carter. Litho Questa)

1997 (24 Apr). *Manx Aircraft. T* **161** *and similar horiz designs. Multicoloured. P* 14.

747	21p. Type **161**	40	45
	a. Horiz pair. Nos. 747/8	80	90
748	21p. Grumman Tiger (winner of 1996 Schneider Trophy)	40	45
749	25p. BAe ATP (15th anniv of Manx Airlines)	50	55
	a. Horiz pair. Nos. 749/50	1·00	1·10
750	25p. BAe 146-200 (15th anniv of Manx Airlines)	50	55
751	31p. Boeing 757 200 (largest aircraft to land on Isle of Man)	60	65
	a. Horiz pair. Nos. 751/2	1·10	1·25

752	31p. Earman Biplane (1st Manx flight, 1911)		60	65
753	36p. Spitfire		70	75
	a. Horiz pair. Nos. 753/4		1·40	1·50
754	36p. Hawker Hurricane		70	75
747/54		*Set of 8*	4·25	4·75

Nos. 747/8, 749/50, 751/2 and 753/4 were each printed together, *se-tenant*, in horizontal pairs, the backgrounds forming composite designs.

162 14th Hole, Ramsey Golf Club

(Des D. Swinton. Litho Questa)

1997 (29 May). *Golf. T* **162** *and similar multicoloured designs. P* 14.

755	21p. Type **162**		40	45
	a. Booklet pane. No. 755×3 with margins all round		1·25	
756	25p. 15th Hole, King Edward Bay Golf and Country Club		50	55
	a. Booklet pane. No. 756×3 with margins all round		1·50	
757	43p. 17th Hole, Rowany Golf Club		85	90
	a. Booklet pane. Nos. 757/8 each × 2 with margins all round		3·75	
758	50p. 8th Hole, Castletown Golf Links		1·00	1·10
755/8		*Set of 4*	2·75	3·00
MS759	100×71 mm. £1.30, Golf ball (*circular, diameter* 39 *mm*)		2·50	2·75
	a. Booklet pane. As No. MS759, but with additional white margins all round		2·50	

No. MS759 includes the "Pacific 97" International Stamp Exhibition logo on the sheet margin.

(Litho Walsall)

1997 (20 June). *Return of Hong Kong to China. Sheet* 130×90 *mm, containing design as No. 546 with changed imprint date. Multicoloured. W w* 14. *P* 13×13½.

MS760	23p. Royal Yacht *Britannia*		45	50

163 Steve Colley   164 Angel and Shepherd

(Des R. Organ. Litho Cartor)

1997 (17 Sept). *F.I.M. "Trial des Nations" Motorcycle Team Trials. T* **163** *and similar multicoloured design. P* 13½.

761	21p. Type **163**		40	45
762	25p. Steve Saunders (*vert*)		50	55
763	37p. Sammy Miller (*vert*)		75	80
764	44p. Don Smith		90	95
761/4		*Set of 4*	2·50	2·75

(Des Jennifer Toombs. Litho B.D.T.)

1997 (3 Nov). *Christmas. T* **164** *and similar multicoloured designs. P* 14.

765	20p. Type **164**		40	45
766	24p. Angel and King		50	55
767	63p. The Nativity (54×39 *mm*)		1·25	1·40
765/7		*Set of 3*	2·00	2·40

165 Engagement of Princess Elizabeth and Lieut. Philip Mountbatten, 1947   166 Shamrock

(Des Colleen Corlett. Litho and die-stamped Questa)

1997 (3 Nov). *Golden Wedding of Queen Elizabeth and Prince Philip. T* **165** *and similar vert designs. Multicoloured (except No. 768). P* 14×14½.

768	50p. Type **165** (sepia and gold)		1·00	1·10
	a. Strip of 4. Nos. 768/71		4·00	
769	50p. Wedding photograph, 1947		1·00	1·10
770	50p. At Ascot, 1952		1·00	1·10

771	50p. Golden Wedding photograph, 1997		1·00	1·10
768/71		*Set of 4*	4·00	4·50
MS772	100×72 mm. £1 Queen Elizabeth and Prince Philip at Peel, 1989 (47×58 *mm*). P 14		2·00	2·10

Nos. 768/71 were printed together, *se-tenant*, as horizontal or vertical strips of 4 throughout the sheet of 16.

(Des Colleen Corlett. Litho Walsall)

1998 (12 Feb). *Flowers. T* **166** *and similar vert designs. Multicoloured. P* 13×13½.

773	4p. Type **166**		10	10
	a. Booklet pane. Nos. 773/5 each × 2		2·00	
774	21p. Cushag		40	45
775	25p. Princess of Wales Rose		50	55
776	50p. Daffodil		1·00	1·10
777	£1 Spear Thistle		2·00	2·10
773/7		*Set of 5*	4·00	4·25

 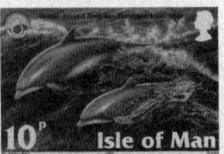

167 Viking Figurehead   168 Bottle-nosed Dolphins

(Des A. Bell. Litho B.D.T.)

1998 (14 Feb). *Viking Longships. T* **167** *and similar vert designs. Multicoloured. P* 14.

793	21p. Type **167**		40	45
794	25p. Viking longship at sea		50	55
795	31p. Viking longship on beach		60	65
796	75p. Stern of ship		1·50	1·60
793/6		*Set of 4*	3·00	3·25
MS797	100×71 mm. £1 Viking ship at Peel Castle		2·00	2·10

(Des J. Paul. Litho Questa)

1998 (16 Mar). *U.N.E.S.C.O. International Year of the Ocean. T* **168** *and similar horiz designs. Multicoloured. P* 14.

798	10p. Type **168**		20	25
	a. Booklet pane. Nos. 798/9, each × 3 and 3 labels with margins all round		1·75	
	b. Booklet pane. Nos. 798/99, 800/2 each × 2 and 1 central label with margins all round		3·50	
799	21p. Basking Shark		40	45
800	25p. Front view of Basking Shark		50	55
801	31p. Minke Whale		60	65
802	63p. Killer Whale and calf		60	65
798/802		*Set of 5*	3·00	3·25

STAMP BOOKLETS

For a full listing of Isle of Man stamp booklets see *Collect Channel Islands and Isle of Man Stamps* published each January.

POSTAGE DUE STAMPS

D 1   D 2   D 3

(Litho Questa)

1973 (5 July). *P* 13½×14.

D1	D 1	½p. red, black and bistre-yellow		1·75	1·50
D2		1p. red, black and cinnamon		65	65
D3		2p. red, black and light apple-green		15	20
D4		3p. red, black and grey		25	25
D5		4p. red, black and carmine-rose		35	35
D6		5p. red, black and cobalt		40	40
D7		10p. red, black and light lavender		50	50
D8		20p. red, black and pale turquoise-green		90	90
D1/8			*Set of 8*	4·50	4·25

A second printing of all values was put on sale by the Philatelic Bureau from 1 September 1973, although examples are known used from mid-August onwards. These can be distinguished by the addition of a small "A" after the date "1973" in the bottom left margin of the stamps. Spurious examples of the second printing exist with the "A" removed.

Prices quoted above are for the second printing. *Prices for set of 8 original printing £30 mint; £30 used.*

(Des and litho Questa)

1975 (8 Jan). *Arms and inscriptions in black and red; background colour given. P* 14×13½.

D 9	D 2	½p. greenish yellow		10	10
D10		1p. flesh		10	10
D11		4p. rose-lilac		10	10
D12		7p. light greenish blue		20	20
D13		9p. brownish grey		25	25
D14		10p. bright mauve		30	30
D15		50p. orange-yellow		1·10	1·10
D16		£1 turquoise-green		2·00	2·00
D9/16			*Set of 8*	3·75	3·75

(Litho B.D.T.)

1982 (5 Oct). *P* 15×14.

D17	D 3	1p. multicoloured		10	10
D18		2p. multicoloured		10	10
D19		5p. multicoloured		10	10
D20		10p. multicoloured		20	25
D21		20p. multicoloured		40	45
D22		50p. multicoloured		1·00	1·10
D23		£1 multicoloured		2·00	2·10
D24		£2 multicoloured		4·00	4·25
D17/24			*Set of 8*	7·75	8·25

D 4

(Des Colleen Corlett. Litho B.D.T.)

1992 (18 Sept). *P* 13×13½.

D25	D 4	£5 multicoloured		10·00	10·50

— **URCH HARRIS** —

ALL WORLD

NEW ISSUE SERVICE

- Over thirty year's experience.
- 260 countries and 100 plus themes.
- Service tailored to your requirements.
- Regular distributions every 6 weeks.
- Free magazine with every distribution.
- Customer advice helpline.
- Free gifts and regular special offers.

Telephone 0117 9349333 for a Free Welcome Pack.

Urch Harris & Co
1 Denmark Avenue
Bristol BS1 5HD
A Division of Stanley Gibbons Ltd

JERSEY

Further detailed information on the stamps of Jersey will be found in the Stanley Gibbons *Channel Islands Specialised Catalogue*.

WAR OCCUPATION ISSUES

Stamps issued under British authority during the German Occupation

1

(Des Major N. V. L. Rybot. Typo *Jersey Evening Post*, St. Helier)

1941–43. *White paper (thin to thick). No wmk.* P 11.

1	1	½d. bright green (29.1.42)	..	3·75	3·00
		a. Imperf between (vert pair)	..	£700	
		b. Imperf between (horiz pair)	..	£600	
		c. Imperf (pair) ..	..	£200	
		d. On greyish paper (1.43)	..	5·00	5·75
2		1d. scarlet (1.4.41)	..	4·00	3·00
		a. Imperf between (vert pair)	..	£700	
		b. Imperf between (horiz pair)	..	£600	
		c. Imperf (pair) ..	..	£225	
		d. On chalk-surfaced paper	..	40·00	38·00
		e. On greyish paper (1.43)	..	5·00	5·75

2 Old Jersey Farm   3 Portelet Bay

4 Corbière Lighthouse   5 Elizabeth Castle

6 Mont Orgueil Castle   7 Gathering Vraic (seaweed)

(Des E. Blampied. Eng H. Cortot. Typo French Govt Works, Paris)

1943–44. *No wmk.* P 13½.

3	2	½d. green (1 June)	..	7·00	5·50
		a. Rough, grey paper (6.10.43)	..	8·50	8·50
4	3	1d. scarlet (1 June)	..	1·50	75
		a. On newsprint (28.2.44)	..	2·50	2·00
5	4	1½d. brown (8 June)	..	3·00	3·00
6	5	2d. orange-yellow (8 June)	..	4·00	3·00
7	6	2½d. blue (29 June)	..	2·00	1·75
		a. On newsprint (25.2.44)	..	1·00	1·50
		ba. Thin paper*	..	£200	
8	7	3d. violet (29 June)	..	1·00	2·75
3/8		.. .. .. Set of 6		15·00	16·00

*On No. 7ba the design shows clearly through the back of the stamp.

REGIONAL ISSUES

DATES OF ISSUE. The note at the beginning of the Guernsey Regional Issues also applies here.

8   9

(Des E. Blampied (T **8**), W. Gardner (T **9**). Portrait by Dorothy Wilding Ltd. Photo Harrison & Sons.)

1958 (18 Aug)–**67.** *W 179 of Great Britain.* P 15 × 14.

9	8	2½d. carmine-red (8.6.64)	..	35	60
		a. Imperf three sides (pair)	..	£2000	
10	9	3d. deep lilac	..	35	30
		p. One centre phosphor band (9.6.67)	20	20
11		4d. ultramarine (7.2.66)	..	25	30
		p. Two phosphor bands (5.9.67)	20	25
9/11p		.. .. Set of 3		60	1·00

1968–69. *No wmk. Chalk-surfaced paper. PVA gum*. One centre phosphor band (4d. values) or two phosphor bands (5d.).* P 15 × 14.

12	9	4d. olive-sepia (4.9.68)	..	20	25
13		4d. bright vermilion (26.2.69)	..	20	35
14		5d. royal blue (4.9.68)	..	20	50
12/14		.. .. Set of 3		50	1·00

*PVA Gum. See note after No. 722 of Great Britain.

INDEPENDENT POSTAL ADMINISTRATION

10 Elizabeth Castle

11 Queen Elizabeth II (after Cecil Beaton)   13 Queen Elizabeth II (after Cecil Beaton)

12 Jersey Airport

(Des V. Whiteley. Photo Harrison (½d. to 1s. 9d.); Courvoisier (others))

1969 (1 Oct). *T* **10**/**13** *and similar horiz designs as T* **10** (½d. to 1s. 6d.) or *T* **12** (5s., 10s., £1). Multicoloured. Granite paper (2s. 6d. to £1). P 14 (½d. to 1s. 9d.) or 12 (others).

15		½d. Type **10**	..	10	70
16		1d. La Hougue Bie (prehistoric tomb) (*shades*)	15	20
		a. Booklet stamp with blank margins	75	
17		2d. Portelet Bay	..	10	15
18		3d. La Corbière Lighthouse	..	20	15
		b. Orange omitted ..	..	£110	
19		4d. Mont Orgueil Castle by night	15	10
		a. Booklet stamp with blank margins	40	
20		5d. Arms and Royal Mace	..	15	10
21		6d. Jersey Cow	..	25	30
22		9d. Chart of English Channel	..	40	75
23		1s. Mont Orgueil Castle by day	..	75	75
24		1s. 6d. As 9d. ..	..	1·25	1·25
25		1s. 9d. Type **11**	..	1·25	1·25
26		2s. 6d. Type **12**	..	2·00	1·75
27		5s. Legislative Chamber	..	11·00	7·00
28		10s. The Royal Court	..	26·00	17·00
		a. Error. Green border*	..	£4500	
29		£1 Type **13** (*shades*) ..	..	2·00	1·50
15/29		.. .. Set of 15		40·00	27·00

*During the final printing of the 10s. a sheet was printed in the colours of the 50p., No. 56, i.e. green border instead of slate.

The 3d. is known with the orange omitted.

There was no postal need for the ½d. value as the ½d. coin had been withdrawn prior to its issue in anticipation of decimalisation.

Nos. 16a and 19a come from 2s. booklets for the automatic machines formerly used for the Great Britain 2s. booklets (see also note after Guernsey No. 28).

Various papers were used by Harrisons. The ½d. and 1d. exist on much thicker paper from 2s. booklets and the 2d. to 1s. 9d. exist on thinner paper having white instead of creamy gum.

24 First Day Cover   25 Lord Coutanche, former Bailiff of Jersey

(Des R. Sellar. Photo Harrison)

1969 (1 Oct). *Inauguration of Post Office.* P 14.

30	24	4d. multicoloured	..	25	20
31		5d. multicoloured	..	30	30
32		1s. 6d. multicoloured	..	1·25	1·60
33		1s. 9d. multicoloured	..	1·25	1·60
30/3		.. .. Set of 4		2·75	3·25

(Des Rosalind Dease. Photo Courvoisier)

1970 (9 May). *25th Anniv of Liberation. T* **25** *and similar multicoloured designs. Granite paper* P 11½.

34	25	4d. Type **25**	..	25	25
35		5d. Sir Winston Churchill	..	25	25
36		1s. 6d. "Liberation" (Edmund Blampied) (*horiz*)	1·75	1·75
37		1s. 9d. S.S. *Vega* (*horiz*)	..	1·75	1·75
34/7		.. .. Set of 4		3·50	3·50

---

29 "A Tribute to Enid Blyton"

(Des Jennifer Toombs. Photo Courvoisier)

1970 (28 July). *"Battle of Flowers" Parade. T* **29** *and similar horiz designs. Multicoloured. Granite paper.* P 11½.

38		4d. Type **29**	..	25	25
39		5d. "Rags to Riches" (Cinderella and pumpkin) ..	..	40	40
40		1s. 6d. "Gourmet's Delight" (lobster and cornucopia)	..	7·00	2·50
41		1s. 9d. "We're the Greatest" (ostriches)	..	7·25	2·50
38/41		.. Set of 4		13·00	5·00

INVALIDATION. The regional issues for Jersey were invalidated for use in Jersey and Guernsey on 1 November 1969 but remained valid for use in the rest of the United Kingdom. Nos. 15/41 (except No. 29) and Nos. D1/6 were invalidated on 14 February 1972.

33 Jersey Airport

(Des V. Whiteley. Photo Harrison (½ to 9p.), Courvoisier (others))

1970 (1 Oct)–**74.** *Decimal Currency. Designs as Nos. 15/28, but with values inscr in decimal currency as in T* **33**, *and new horiz design as T* **10** (6p.). Chalk-surfaced paper (4½, 5½, 8p.), granite paper (10, 20, 50p.).

42		½p. Type **10** (15.2.71)	..	10	10
		a. Booklet stamp with blank margins	40	
43		1p. La Corbière Lighthouse (*shades*) (15.2.71)	10	10
		a. Orange omitted	..	£350	
44		1½p. Jersey Cow (15.2.71)	..	10	10
45		2p. Mont Orgueil Castle by night (15.2.71)	10	10
		a. Booklet stamp with blank margins	1·25	
46		2½p. Arms and Royal Mace (15.2.71)	10	10
		a. Booklet stamp with blank margins	40	
		ab. Gold (Mace) omitted ..	..	£350	
		ac. Gold (Mace) printed double	..	£275	
47		3p. La Hougue Bie (prehistoric tomb) (15.2.71)	..	10	10
		a. Booklet stamp with blank margins (1.12.72)	50	
48		3½p. Portelet Bay (15.2.71)	..	15	15
		a. Booklet stamp with blank margins (1.7.74)	50	
49		4p. Chart of English Channel (15.2.71)	..	15	15
49a		4½p. Arms and Royal Mace (1.11.74)	20	20
		ab. Uncoated paper ..	..	£350	
50		5p. Mont Orgueil Castle by day (15.2.71)	10	15
50a		5½p. Jersey Cow (1.11.74)	..	40	25
51		6p. Martello Tower, Archirondel (15.2.71)	25	30
52		7½p. Chart of English Channel (15.2.71)	30	40
52a		8p. Mont Orgueil Castle by night (1.11.74)	25	25
53		9p. Type **11** (15.2.71)	..	50	30
54		10p. Type **33**	..	50	55
55		20p. Legislative Chamber	..	75	75
56		50p. The Royal Court	..	1·75	1·75
42/56		.. Set of 18		5·00	5·00

Original printings of the ½p. to 4p., 5p. and 6p. to 9p. were with PVA gum; printings from 1974 (including original printings of the 4½p. and 5½p.) have dextrin added (see notes after 1971 Great Britain Decimal Machin issue). The 10p. to 50p. have gum arabic.

The border of No. 56 has been changed from turquoise-blue to dull green.

34 White Eared-Pheasant

(Des Jennifer Toombs. Photo Courvoisier)

1971 (12 Mar). *Wildlife Preservation Trust (1st series). T* **34** *and similar multicoloured designs. Granite paper.* P 11½.

57		2p. Type **34**	..	75	25
58		2½p. Thick-billed Parrot (*vert*)	..	75	25
59		7½p. Western Black and White Colobus Monkey (*vert*)	..	7·75	3·75
60		9p. Ring-tailed Lemur	..	8·00	3·75
57/60		.. .. Set of 4		15·50	7·25

See also Nos. 73/6, 217/21, 324/9, 447/51 and 818/23.

35 Poppy Emblem and Field   36 "Tante Elizabeth" (E. Blampied)

(Des G. Drummond. Litho Questa)

1971 (15 June). *50th Anniv of Royal British Legion. T* **35** *and similar horiz designs. Multicoloured. P* 14.

61	2p.	Royal British Legion Badge	50	50
62	2½p.	Type **35**	50	50
63	7½p.	Jack Counter, V.C., and Victoria Cross	2·40	2·40
64	9p.	Crossed Tricolour and Union Jack	2·40	2·40
61/4		*Set of* 4	5·00	5·00

(Des and photo Courvoisier)

1971 (5 Oct). *Paintings. T* **36** *and similar multicoloured designs. Granite paper. P* 11½.

65	2p.	Type **36**	15	15
66	2½p.	"English Fleet in the Channel" (P. Monamy) (*horiz*)	25	20
67	7½p.	"The Boyhood of Raleigh" (Millais) (*horiz*)	3·00	2·50
68	9p.	"The Blind Beggar" (W. W. Ouless)	3·25	2·75
65/8		*Set of* 4	6·00	5·00

See also Nos. 115/18 and 213/16.

37 Jersey Fern   38 Artillery Shako

(Des G. Drummond. Photo Courvoisier)

1972 (18 Jan). *Wild Flowers of Jersey. T* **37** *and similar vert designs. Multicoloured. Granite paper. P* 11½.

69	3p.	Type **37**	25	15
70	5p.	Jersey Thrift	60	45
71	7½p.	Jersey Orchid	2·25	2·25
72	9p.	Jersey Viper's Bugloss	2·50	2·25
69/72		*Set of* 4	5·00	4·50

(Des Jennifer Toombs. Photo Courvoisier)

1972 (17 Mar). *Wildlife Preservation Trust (2nd series). Multicoloured designs similar to T* **34**. *Granite paper. P* 11½.

73	2½p.	Cheetah	65	20
74	3p.	Rothschild's Mynah (*vert*)	40	35
75	7½p.	Spectacled Bear	1·40	1·50
76	9p.	Tuatara	1·75	1·75
73/6		*Set of* 4	3·75	3·25

(Des and photo Courvoisier)

1972 (27 June). *Royal Jersey Militia. T* **38** *and similar vert designs. Multicoloured. Granite paper. P* 11½.

77	2½p.	Type **38**	15	15
78	3p.	Shako (2nd North Regt)	20	20
79	7½p.	Shako (5th South-West Regt)	70	50
80	9p.	Helmet (3rd Jersey Light Infantry)	90	60
77/80		*Set of* 4	1·75	1·25

39 Princess Anne   40 Armorican Bronze Coins

(Des G. Drummond from photographs by D. Groves. Photo Courvoisier)

1972 (1 Nov). *Royal Silver Wedding. T* **39** *and similar multicoloured designs. Granite paper. P* 11½.

81	2½p.	Type **39**	10	10
82	3p.	Queen Elizabeth and Prince Philip (*horiz*)	10	10
83	7½p.	Prince Charles	40	40
84	20p.	The Royal Family (*horiz*)	60	50
81/4		*Set of* 4	1·10	1·00

(Des G. Drummond. Photo Courvoisier)

1973 (23 Jan). *Centenary of La Société Jersiaise. T* **40** *and similar multicoloured designs. Granite paper. P* 11½.

85	2½p.	Silver cups	10	10
86	3p.	Gold torque (*vert*)	10	10
87	7½p.	Royal Seal of Charles II (*vert*)	40	40
88	9p.	Type **40**	50	50
85/8		*Set of* 4	1·00	1·00

41 Balloon *L'Armee de la Loire* and Letter, Paris, 1870   42 *North Western*

(Des and photo Courvoisier)

1973 (16 May). *Jersey Aviation History. T* **41** *and similar horiz designs. Multicoloured. Granite paper. P* 11½.

89	3p.	Type **41**	10	10
90	5p.	Astra seaplane, 1912	15	15
91	7½p.	Supermarine Sea Eagle	50	40
92	9p.	De Havilland D.H.86 Dragon Express *Giffard Bay*	65	50
89/92		*Set of* 4	1·25	1·00

(Des G. Drummond. Photo Courvoisier)

1973 (6 Aug). *Centenary of Jersey Eastern Railway. T* **42** *and similar designs showing early locomotives. Multicoloured. Granite paper. P* 11½.

93	2½p.	Type **42**	10	10
94	3p.	Calvados	10	10
95	7½p.	Carteret	50	40
96	9p.	Caesarea	65	50
93/6		*Set of* 4	1·25	1·00

43 Princess Anne and Capt. Mark Phillips

(Des and photo Courvoisier)

1973 (14 Nov). *Royal Wedding. Granite paper. P* 11½.

97	**43**	3p. multicoloured	10	10
98		20p. multicoloured	90	90

44 Spider Crab   45 Freesias

(Des Jennifer Toombs. Photo Courvoisier)

1973 (15 Nov). *Marine Life. T* **44** *and similar horiz designs. Multicoloured. Granite paper. P* 11½.

99	2½p.	Type **44**	10	10
100	3p.	Conger Eel	10	10
101	7½p.	Lobster	45	35
102	20p.	Tuberculate Ormer	70	55
99/102		*Set of* 4	1·25	1·00

(Des G. Drummond. Photo Courvoisier)

1974 (13 Feb). *Spring Flowers. T* **45** *and similar vert designs. Multicoloured. Granite paper. P* 11½.

103	3p.	Type **45**	10	10
104	5½p.	Anemones	20	10
105	8p.	Carnations and Gladioli	50	40
106	10p.	Daffodils and Iris	60	50
103/6		*Set of* 4	1·25	1·00

46 First Letter-Box and Contemporary Cover   47 John Wesley

(Des G. Drummond. Photo Courvoisier)

1974 (7 June). *U.P.U. Centenary. T* **46** *and similar horiz designs. Multicoloured. Granite paper. P* 11½.

107	2½p.	Type **46**	10	10
108	3p.	Postmen, 1862 and 1969	10	10
109	5½p.	Letter-box and letter, 1974	35	30
110	20p.	R.M.S. *Aquila* (1874) and B.A.C. One Eleven 200 (1974)	85	60
107/10		*Set of* 4	1·25	1·00

(Des, recess and litho D.L.R.)

1974 (31 July). *Anniversaries. T* **47** *and similar vert designs. P* 13 × 14.

111	3p.	agate and light cinnamon	10	10
112	3½p.	blackish violet and light azure	10	10
113	8p.	blue-black and pale rose-lilac	30	35
114	20p.	black and pale buff	70	65
		a. Pale buff (background) omitted		
111/14		*Set of* 4	1·00	1·00

Portraits and events:—3p. Type **47** (Bicentenary of Methodism in Jersey); 3½p. Sir William Hillary, founder (150th Anniv of R.N.L.I.); 8p. Cannon Wace, poet and historian (800th Death Anniv); 20p. Sir Winston Churchill (Birth Centenary).

48 *Catherine* and *Mary* (Royal yachts)   49 Potato Digger

(Des and photo Courvoisier)

1974 (22 Nov). *Marine Paintings by Peter Monamy. T* **48** *and similar multicoloured designs. Granite paper. P* 11½.

115	3½p.	Type **48**	10	10
116	5½p.	French two-decker	20	15
117	8p.	Dutch vessel (*horiz*)	30	30
118	25p.	Battle of Cap La Hague, 1692 (55 × 27 mm)	80	60
115/18		*Set of* 4	1·25	1·00

(Des G. Drummond. Photo Courvoisier)

1975 (25 Feb). *19th-Century Farming. T* **49** *and similar horiz designs. Multicoloured. Granite paper. P* 11½.

119	3p.	Type **49**	10	10
120	3½p.	Cider crusher	10	15
121	8p.	Six-horse plough	35	35
122	10p.	Hay cart	55	50
119/22		*Set of* 4	1·00	1·00

50 H.M. Queen Elizabeth, the Queen Mother (photograph by Cecil Beaton)   51 Nautilus Shell

(Des and photo Courvoisier)

1975 (30 May). *Royal Visit. Granite paper. P* 11½.

123	**50**	20p. multicoloured	75	75

(Des A. Games. Photo Courvoisier)

1975 (6 June). *Jersey Tourism. T* **51** *and similar vert designs based on holiday posters. Multicoloured. Granite paper. P* 11½.

124	5p.	Type **51**	10	10
125	8p.	Parasol	15	15
126	10p.	Deckchair	35	35
127	12p.	Sandcastle with flags of Jersey and the U.K.	50	50
124/7		*Set of* 4	1·00	1·00
MS128	146 × 68 mm. Nos. 124/7		1·00	1·10

52 Common Tern   53 Armstrong Whitworth Siskin IIIA

(Des Jennifer Toombs. Photo Courvoisier)

1975 (28 July). *Sea Birds. T* **52** *and similar vert designs. Multicoloured. Granite paper. P* 11½.

129	4p.	Type **52**	15	15
130	5p.	British Storm Petrel	15	15
131	8p.	Brent Geese	40	35
132	25p.	Shag	70	45
129/32		*Set of* 4	1·25	1·00

(Des A. Theobald. Photo Courvoisier)

1975 (30 Oct). *50th Anniv of Royal Air Forces Association, Jersey Branch. T* **53** *and similar horiz designs. Multicoloured. Granite paper. P* 11½.

133	4p.	Type **53**	10	10
134	5p.	Supermarine Southampton I flying boat	15	15
135	10p.	Supermarine Spitfire Mk I	40	30
136	25p.	Folland Fo.141 Gnat T.1	75	60
133/6		*Set of* 4	1·25	1·00

54 Map of Jersey Parishes

55 Parish Arms and Island Scene

(Des Courvoisier (£2). G. Drummond (others). Litho Questa (½ to 15p.). Photo Courvoisier (others))

1976–80. *Various multicoloured designs as T* **54/5.**

(a) *Parish Arms and Views as T* **54**. *P* 14½. (29 Jan)

137	½p.	Type **54**		10	10
138	1p.	Zoological Park		10	10
	a.	Booklet pane of 2 plus 2 *se-tenant* labels (5.4.76)		1·00	
	b.	Booklet pane of 4 (5.4.76)		1·00	
139	5p.	St. Mary's Church		15	15
	a.	Booklet pane of 4 (5.4.76)		50	
140	6p.	Seymour Tower		15	15
	a.	Booklet pane of 4 (28.2.78)		60	
141	7p.	La Corbière Lighthouse		20	20
	a.	Booklet pane of 4 (5.4.76)		60	
142	8p.	St. Saviour's Church		20	20
	a.	Booklet pane of 4 (28.2.78)		80	
143	9p.	Elizabeth Castle		25	25
	a.	Booklet pane of 4 (6.5.80)		1·00	
144	10p.	Gorey Harbour		25	25
145	11p.	Jersey Airport		30	25
146	12p.	Grosnez Castle		30	30
147	13p.	Bonne Nuit Harbour		35	35
148	14p.	Le Hocq Tower		35	40
149	15p.	Morel Farm		40	45

(b) *Emblems as T* **55**. *Granite paper. P* 12 (20 Aug 1976–16 Nov 1977)

150	20p.	Type **55**		50	50
151	30p.	Flag and map		75	75
152	40p.	Postal H.Q. and badge		1·00	1·00
153	50p.	Parliament, Royal Court and arms		1·25	1·00
154	£1	Lieutenant-Governor's flag and Government House		2·50	2·25
155	£2	Queen Elizabeth II (photograph by Alex Wilson) (*vert*) (16.11.77)		4·50	4·25
137/55			*Set of 19*	12·00	11·50

Nos. 156/9 are vacant.

56 Sir Walter Ralegh and Map of Virginia

(Des M. Orbell. Photo Courvoisier)

1976 (29 May). *"Links with America". T* **56** *and similar horiz designs. Multicoloured. Granite paper. P* 11½.

160	5p.	Type **56**		10	10
161	7p.	Sir George Carteret and map of New Jersey		15	15
162	11p.	Philippe Dauvergne and Long Island Landing		40	35
163	13p.	John Copley and sketch		45	50
160/3			*Set of 4*	1·00	1·00

57 Dr. Grandin and Map of China

58 Coronation, 1953 (photographed by Cecil Beaton)

(Des Jennifer Toombs. Photo Courvoisier)

1976 (25 Nov). *Birth Centenary of Dr. Lilian Grandin (medical missionary). T* **57** *and similar horiz designs. Granite paper. P* 11½.

164	5p.	multicoloured		10	10
165	7p.	light yellow, yellow-brown and black		15	15
166	11p.	multicoloured		50	35
167	13p.	multicoloured		50	50
164/7			*Set of 4*	1·10	1·00

Designs:—7p. Sampan on the Yangtze; 11p. Overland trek; 13p. Dr. Grandin at work.

(Des G. Drummond. Photo Courvoisier)

1977 (7 Feb). *Silver Jubilee. T* **58** *and similar vert designs. Multicoloured. Granite paper. P* 11½.

168	5p.	Type **58**		25	15
169	7p.	Visit to Jersey, 1957		30	20
170	25p.	Queen Elizabeth II (photo by Peter Grugeon)		90	80
168/70			*Set of 3*	1·25	1·00

59 Coins of 1871 and 1877

(Des D. Henley. Litho Questa)

1977 (25 Mar). *Centenary of Currency Reform. T* **59** *and similar horiz designs. Multicoloured. P* 14.

171	5p.	Type **59**		10	10
172	7p.	One-twelfth shilling, 1949		15	15
173	11p.	Silver Crown, 1966		40	35
174	13p.	£2 piece, 1972		45	50
171/4			*Set of 4*	1·00	1·00

60 Sir William Weston and *Santa Anna*, 1530

(Des A. Theobald. Litho Questa)

1977 (24 June). *St. John Ambulance Centenary. T* **60** *and similar horiz designs each showing a Grand Prior of the Order. Multicoloured. P* 14 × 13½.

175	5p.	Type **60**		10	10
176	7p.	Sir William Drogo and ambulance, 1877		15	15
177	11p.	Duke of Connaught and ambulance, 1917		40	35
178	13p.	Duke of Gloucester and stretcher-team, 1977		45	50
175/8			*Set of 4*	1·00	1·00

61 Arrival of Queen Victoria, 1846

(Des R. Granger Barrett. Litho Questa)

1977 (29 Sept). *125th Anniv of Victoria College. T* **61** *and similar multicoloured designs. P* 14½.

179	7p.	Type **61**		20	20
180	10½p.	Victoria College, 1852		25	20
181	11p.	Sir Galahad statue, 1924 (*vert*)		30	35
182	13p.	College Hall (*vert*)		35	35
179/82			*Set of 4*	1·00	1·00

62 Harry Vardon Statuette and Map of Royal Jersey Course

(Des Jennifer Toombs. Litho Questa)

1978 (28 Feb). *Centenary of Royal Jersey Golf Club. T* **62** *and similar horiz designs. Multicoloured. P* 14.

183	6p.	Type **62**		15	15
184	8p.	Harry Vardon's grip and swing		20	20
185	11p.	Harry Vardon's putt		50	35
186	13p.	Golf trophies and book by Harry Vardon		50	40
183/6			*Set of 4*	1·25	1·00

63 Mont Orgueil Castle

64 "Gaspé Basin" (P. J. Ouless)

(Des from paintings by Thomas Phillips. Photo Courvoisier)

1978 (1 May). *Europa. Castles. T* **63** *and similar horiz designs. Multicoloured. Granite paper. P* 11½.

187	6p.	Type **63**		20	20
188	8p.	St. Aubin's Fort		40	40
189	10½p.	Elizabeth Castle		50	50
187/9			*Set of 3*	1·00	1·00

(Des R. Granger Barrett. Litho Questa)

1978 (9 June). *Links with Canada. T* **64** *and similar horiz designs. Multicoloured. P* 14½.

190	6p.	Type **64**		15	15
191	8p.	Map of Gaspé Peninsula		20	20
192	10½p.	*Century* (brigantine)		25	25
193	11p.	Early map of Jersey		40	30
194	13p.	St. Aubin's Bay, town and harbour		45	35
190/4			*Set of 5*	1·25	1·10

65 Queen Elizabeth and Prince Philip

66 Mail Cutter, 1778–1827

(Des and photo Courvoisier)

1978 (26 June). *25th Anniv of Coronation. T* **65** *and similar vert design. Granite paper. P* 11½.

195	8p.	silver, black and cerise		30	30
196	25p.	silver, black and new blue		70	70

Design:—25p. Hallmarks of 1953 and 1977.

(Des Jersey P.O. Litho Harrison)

1978 (18 Oct). *Bicentenary of England-Jersey Government Mail Packet Service. T* **66** *and similar horiz designs. P* 14½ × 14.

197	6p.	black, yellow-brown and greenish yellow		15	15
198	8p.	black, dull yellowish grn & pale yell-grn		20	20
199	10½p.	black, ultramarine and cobalt		40	30
200	11p.	black, purple and pale rose-lilac		45	35
201	13p.	black, Venetian red and pink		50	45
197/201			*Set of 5*	1·50	1·25

Designs:—8p. *Flamer*, 1831–37; 10½p. *Diana*, 1877–90; 11p. *Ibex*, 1891–1925; 13p. *Caesarea*, 1960–75.

67 Jersey Calf

68 Jersey Pillar Box, circa 1860

(Des Jersey P.O. and Questa. Litho Questa)

1979 (1 Mar). *9th World Jersey Cattle Bureau Conference. T* **67** *and similar horiz design. Multicoloured. P* 13½.

202	6p.	Type **67**		20	20
203	25p.	"Ansom Designette" (cow presented to the Queen, 27 June 1978) (46 × 29 *mm*)		80	80

(Des Jennifer Toombs. Litho Questa)

1979 (1 Mar). *Europa. T* **68** *and similar vert designs. Multicoloured. A. P* 14. B. *P* 14½.

			A		B	
204	8p.	Type **68**	25	25	25	25
	a.	Horiz pair. Nos. 204/5	50	50	50	50
205	8p.	Clearing a modern Jersey post box	25	25	25	25
206	10½p.	Telephone switchboard, circa 1900	30	30	30	30
	a.	Horiz pair, Nos. 206/7	60	65	60	65
207	10½p.	Modern S.P.C. telephone system	30	30	30	30
204/7		*Set of 4*	1·00	1·00	1·00	1·00

Nos. 204/5 and 206/7 were each printed together, *se-tenant*, in horizontal pairs throughout the sheets.

Although both perforations were supplied to Jersey at the same time the 8p perforated 14½ is not known used before early April.

69 Percival Mew Gull *Golden City*

70 "My First Sermon"

(Des A. Theobald. Photo Courvoisier)

1979 (24 Apr). *25th Anniv of International Air Rally. T* **69** *and similar horiz designs. Multicoloured. Granite paper. P* 11½.

208	6p.	Type **69**		15	15
209	8p.	De Havilland D.H.C.1 Chipmunk		20	20
210	10½p.	Druine D.31 Turbulent		40	20
211	11p.	De Havilland D.H.82A Tiger Moth		45	25
212	13p.	North American AT-6 Harvard		50	30
208/12			*Set of 5*	1·50	1·00

(Des Jersey P.O. and Courvoisier. Photo Courvoisier)

1979 (13 Aug). *International Year of the Child and 150th Birth Anniv of Millais. Paintings. T* **70** *and similar multicoloured designs. Granite paper. P* 12 × 12½ (25p.) *or* 12 × 11½ (others).

213	8p.	Type **70**		25	15
214	10½p.	"Orphans"		30	25
215	11p.	"The Princes in the Tower"		30	25
216	25p.	"Christ in the House of His Parents" (50 × 32 *mm*)		55	45
213/16			*Set of 4*	1·25	1·00

(Des Jennifer Toombs. Photo Courvoisier)

1979 (8 Nov). *Wildlife Preservation Trust (3rd series). Multicoloured designs as T* **34**. *Granite paper. P* 11½.

217	6p.	Pink Pigeon (*vert*)		15	15
218	8p.	Orang-Utan (*vert*)		20	20
219	11½p.	Waldrapp		50	25
220	13p.	Lowland Gorilla (*vert*)		55	25
221	15p.	Rodriguez Flying Fox (*vert*)		60	30
217/21			Set of 5	1·75	1·00

71 Plan of Mont Orgueil

(Litho Enschedé)

1980 (5 Feb). *Fortresses. T* **71** *and similar multicoloured designs showing drawings by Thomas Phillips. P* 13 × 13½ (25p.) *or* 13½ × 13 (*others*).

222	8p.	Type **71**		30	25
223	11½p.	Plan of La Tour de St. Aubin		35	30
224	13p.	Plan of Elizabeth Castle		55	45
225	25p.	Map of Jersey showing fortresses (38 × 27 mm)		80	70
222/5			Set of 4	1·75	1·50

72 Sir Walter Raleigh and Paul Ivy (engineer) discussing Elizabeth Castle

(Des Jersey Post Office and Questa. Litho Questa)

1980 (6 May). *Europa. Personalities. Links with Britain. T* **72** *and similar vert design. Multicoloured. P* 14.

226	9p.⎫	Type **72**		20	20
227	9p.⎭			20	20
	a.	Horiz. pair. Nos. 226/7		50	50
228	13½p.⎫	Sir George Carteret receiving rights to Smith's Island, Virginia from King		40	35
229	13½p.⎭	Charles II		40	35
	a.	Horiz. pair. Nos. 228/9		80	70
226/9			Set of 4	1·25	1·10

Nos. 226/7 and 228/9 were each printed together, *se-tenant*, in horizontal pair throughout the sheet, forming composite designs.

73 Planting　　　**74** Three Lap Event

(Des R. Granger Barrett. Litho Questa)

1980 (6 May). *Centenary of Jersey Royal Potato. T* **73** *and similar vert designs. Multicoloured. P* 14.

230	7p.	Type **73**		15	15
231	15p.	Digging		35	35
232	17½p.	Weighbridge		60	60
230/2			Set of 3	1·00	1·00

(Des A. Theobald. Photo Courvoisier)

1980 (24 July). *60th Anniv of Jersey Motor-cycle and Light Car Club. T* **74** *and similar horiz designs. Multicoloured. Granite paper. P* 11½.

233	7p.	Type **74**		25	25
234	9p.	Jersey International Road Race		25	25
235	13½p.	Scrambling		45	45
236	15p.	Sand racing (saloon cars)		50	50
237	17½p.	National Hill Climb		55	55
233/7			Set of 5	1·75	1·75

75 *Eye of the Wind*　　**76** Detail of "The Death of Major Peirson"

(Des G. Drummond. Litho Questa)

1980 (1 Oct). *"Operation Drake" Round the World Expedition and 150th Anniv of Royal Geographical Society* (14p.). *P* 14.

238	7p.	Type **75**		20	20
239	9p.	Diving from inflatable dinghy		25	25
240	13½p.	Exploration of Papua New Guinea		35	35
241	14p.	Captain Scott's *Discovery*		45	35
242	15p.	Using aerial walkways, Conservation Project, Sulawesi		45	35
243	17½p.	*Eye of the Wind* and Goodyear Aerospace airship *Europa*		55	45
238/43			Set of 6	2·00	1·75

(Photo Courvoisier)

1981 (6 Jan). *Bicentenary of Battle of Jersey. Painting "The Death of Major Peirson" by J. S. Copley. T* **76** *and similar vert designs showing details of the work. Granite paper. P* 12½ × 12.

244	7p.	multicoloured		25	25
245	10p.	multicoloured		30	30
246	15p.	multicoloured		60	60
247	17½p.	multicoloured		80	80
244/7			Set of 4	1·75	1·75
MS248	144 × 97 mm. Nos. 244/7			2·00	2·00

Stamps from No. MS248 are without white margins.

77 De Bagot　　**78** Jersey Crest and Map of Channel

78a "Queen Elizabeth II" (Norman Hepple)

(Des and photo Courvoisier (£5). Des G. Drummond. Litho Questa (*others*))

1981 (24 Feb)–**88**. *Arms of Jersey Families. T* **77** *and similar designs in black, silver and turquoise-green* (½p.), *black, silver and mauve* (4p.), *black, silver and lemon* (20p.), *black and dull blue* (25p.), *black, silver and carmine* (26p.) *or multicoloured* (*others*) *with T* **78**/a. *Granite paper* (£5). *P* 12½×12 (£5), 15×14 (16p., 17p., 18p., 19p., 26p., 75p.) *or* 14 (*others*).

249	½p.	Type **77**		20	20
250	1p.	De Carteret		10	10
	a.	Booklet pane of 6		20	
	b.	Perf 15×14 (12.1.88)		25	25
251	2p.	La Cloche		10	10
	a.	Booklet pane of 6 (1.12.81)		70	
	b.	Perf 15×14 (15.11.84)		20	20
	ba.	Booklet pane of 6 (1.4.86)		20	
252	3p.	Dumaresq		20	30
	a.	Booklet pane of 6		60	
	b.	Perf 15×14 (27.4.84)		10	10
	ba.	Booklet pane of 6		85	
253	4p.	Payn		25	15
	a.	Perf 15×14 (4.3.86)		20	25
	ab.	Booklet pane of 6 (6.4.87)		70	
254	5p.	Janvrin		15	15
	a.	Perf 15×14 (4.3.86)		35	35
255	6p.	Poingdestre		20	20
	a.	Perf 15×14 (4.3.86)		50	20
256	7p.	Pipon		20	20
	a.	Booklet pane of 6		90	
257	8p.	Marett		25	25
	a.	Booklet pane of 6 (19.4.83)		1·50	
258	9p.	Le Breton		30	30
	a.	Perf 15×14 (27.4.84)		35	35
	ab.	Booklet pane of 6		2·25	
259	10p.	Le Maistre		30	30
	a.	Booklet pane of 6		1·50	
	b.	Perf 15×14 (1.4.86)		35	35
	ba.	Booklet pane of 6		1·60	
260	11p.	Bisson (28.7.81)		35	35
	a.	Booklet pane of 6 (19.4.83)		1·75	
	b.	Perf 15×14 (6.4.87)		40	45
	ba.	Booklet pane of 6		1·75	
261	12p.	Robin (28.7.81)		50	40
	a.	Perf 15×14 (27.4.84)		40	25
	ab.	Booklet pane of 6		1·75	
262	13p.	Herault (28.7.81)		40	40
	a.	Perf 15×14 (15.11.84)		60	60
263	14p.	Messervy (28.7.81)		45	45
	a.	Perf 15×14 (15.11.84)		50	50
	ab.	Booklet pane of 6 (1.4.86)		1·75	
264	15p.	Fiott (28.7.81)		45	45
	a.	Perf 15×14 (6.4.87)		45	45
	ab.	Booklet pane of 6		1·75	
265	16p.	Malet (25.10.85)		45	45
	a.	Booklet pane of 6 (17.5.88)		2·25	
266	17p.	Mabon (25.10.85)		50	50
266a	18p.	De St. Martin (26.4.88)		75	75
266b	19p.	Hamptonne (26.4.88)		80	80
267	20p.	Badier (28.7.81)		60	60
	a.	Perf 15×14 (4.3.86)		90	90
268	25p.	L'Arbalestier (23.2.82)		60	60
268a	26p.	Type **77** (26.4.88)		60	60

269	30p.	Journeaux (23.2.82)		90	90
	a.	Perf 15×14 (4.3.86)		1·10	1·10
270	40p.	Lempriere (23.2.82)		1·25	1·25
	a.	Perf 15×14 (6.4.87)		1·25	1·25
271	50p.	Auvergne (23.2.82)		1·50	1·50
	a.	Perf 15×14 (6.4.87)		1·60	1·60
272	75p.	Remon (23.4.87)		2·25	1·75
273	£1	Type **78** (23.2.82)		3·25	3·00
274	£5	Type **78**/a (17.11.83)		11·00	10·50
249/74			Set of 29	25·00	23·00

No. 258a only occurs in the £2.16 stamp booklet issued 27 April 1984, No. 259b from the £3.12 booklet of 1 April 1986, No. 260b from the £3.60 booklet of 6 April 1987 and No. 261a from the £2.16 booklet of 27 April 1984 and the £3.84 booklet of 17 May 1988.

79 Knight of Hambye slaying Dragon

(Des Jennifer Toombs. Litho Questa)

1981 (7 Apr). *Europa. Folklore. T* **79** *and similar horiz designs. Multicoloured. P* 14.

275	10p.	Type **79**		25	25
	a.	Horiz. pair. Nos. 275/6		55	55
276	10p.	Servant slaying Knight of Hambye, and awaiting execution		25	25
277	18p.	St. Brelade celebrating Easter on island		50	50
	a.	Horiz. pair. Nos. 277/8		1·10	1·10
278	18p.	Island revealing itself as a huge fish		50	50
275/8			Set of 4	1·50	1·40

Legends:—10p. (*both*), Slaying of the Dragon of Lawrence by the Knight of Hambye; 18p. (*both*), Voyages of St. Brelade.

Nos. 275/6 and 277/8 were each printed together, *se-tenant*, in horizontal pairs throughout the sheet.

80 The Harbour by Gaslight　　**81** Prince Charles and Lady Diana Spencer

(Des R. Granger Barrett. Photo Courvoisier)

1981 (22 May). *150th Anniv of Gas Lighting in Jersey. T* **80** *and similar horiz designs showing Jersey by gaslight. Multicoloured. Granite paper. P* 11½.

279	7p.	Type **80**		25	25
280	10p.	The Quay		30	30
281	18p.	Royal Square		45	45
282	22p.	Halkett Place		55	55
283	25p.	Central Market		65	65
279/83			Set of 5	2·00	2·00

(Des Jersey P.O. and Courvoisier. Photo Courvoisier)

1981 (28 July). *Royal Wedding. Granite paper. P* 11½.

284	**81**	10p.	multicoloured	75	75
285		25p.	multicoloured	1·75	1·75

82 Christmas Tree in Royal Square　　**83** Jersey, 16,000 B.C.

(Des A. Copp. Litho Questa)

1981 (29 Sept). *Christmas. T* **82** *and similar vert designs. Multicoloured. P* 14½.

286	7p.	Type **82**		25	25
287	10p.	East window, Parish Church, St. Helier		40	40
288	18p.	Boxing Day meet of Jersey Drag Hunt		50	50
286/8			Set of 3	1·00	1·00

(Des A. Copp. Litho Questa)

1982 (20 Apr). *Europa. Historic Events. Formation of Jersey. T* **83** *and similar multicoloured designs. P* 14½.

289	11p.	Type **83**		30	30
290	11p.	Jersey, 10,000 B.C. (*vert*)		30	30
291	19½p.	7,000 B.C. (*vert*)		70	60
292	19½p.	4,000 B.C.		70	60
289/92			Set of 4	1·75	1·60

84 Duke Rollo of Normandy, William the Conqueror and "Clameur de Haro" (traditional procedure for obtaining justice)

(Des R. Granger Barrett. Litho Questa)

1982 (11 June–7 Sept). *Links with France. T* **84** *and similar horiz designs. Multicoloured. P* 14.
293	8p. Type **84**	..	25	25
	a. Horiz pair. Nos. 293/4	..	50	50
	b. Booklet pane. Nos. 293 and 294 each × 2 (7 Sept)		1·00	
294	8p. John of England, Philippe Auguste of France and Siege of Rouen		25	25
295	11p. Jean Martell (brandy merchant), early still and view of Cognac		35	35
	a. Horiz pair. Nos. 295/6	..	70	70
	b. Booklet pane. Nos. 295 and 296 each × 2 (7 Sept)		1·40	
296	11p. Victor Hugo, "Le Rocher des Proscrits" (rock where he used to meditate) and Marine Terrace		35	35
297	19½p. Pierre Teilhard de Chardin (philosopher) and "Maison Saint Louis" (science institute)		60	60
	a. Horiz pair. Nos. 297/8	..	1·25	1·25
	b. Booklet pane. Nos. 297 and 298 each × 2 (7 Sept)		2·50	
298	19½p. Père Charles Rey (scientist), anemotachymeter and The Observatory, St. Louis		60	60
293/8		*Set of* 6	2·25	2·25

The two designs of each value were printed together, *se-tenant*, in horizontal pairs throughout the sheet.

Each booklet pane has margins all round and text, in English or French, printed on the binding selvedge.

85 Sir William Smith, Founder of Boys' Brigade | 86 H.M.S. *Tamar* with H.M.S. *Dolphin* at Port Egmont

(Des A. Theobald. Photo Courvoisier)

1982 (18 Nov). *75th Anniv of Boy Scout Movement (Nos. 301/3) and Centenary of Boys' Brigade (Nos. 299/301). T* **85** *and similar multicoloured designs. Granite paper. P* 11½.
299	8p. Type **85**	..	25	25
300	11p. Boys' Brigade "Old Boys" band, Liberation Parade, 1945 (*vert*)		30	30
301	24p. William Smith and Lord Baden-Powell at Royal Albert Hall, 1903		60	60
302	26p. Lord and Lady Baden-Powell in St. Helier, 1924 (*vert*)		75	75
303	29p. Scouts at "Westward Ho" campsite, St. Ouen's Bay		90	90
299/303..		*Set of* 5	2·50	2·50

(Des R. Granger Barrett. Litho Questa)

1983 (15 Feb). *Jersey Adventurers (1st series). 250th Birth Anniv of Philippe de Carteret. T* **86** *and similar horiz designs. Multicoloured. P* 14 × 14½.
304	8p. Type **86**	..	25	25
305	11p. H.M.S. *Dolphin* and H.M.S. *Swallow* off Magellan Strait		30	30
306	19½p. Discovering Pitcairn Island		50	50
307	24p. Carteret taking possession of English Cove, New Ireland	..	70	70
308	26p. H.M.S. *Swallow* sinking a pirate, Macassar Strait		85	75
309	29p. H.M.S. *Endymion* leading convoy from West Indies		1·00	85
304/9		*Set of* 6	3·25	3·00

See also Nos. 417/21 and 573/8.

87 1969 5s. Legislative Chamber Definitive

(Des G. Drummond. Litho Questa)

1983 (19 Apr). *Europa. T* **87** *and similar multicoloured designs. P* 14½.
310	11p. Type **87**	..	50	50
	a. Horiz pair. Nos. 310/11	..	1·00	1·00
311	11p. Royal Mace (23 × 32 *mm*)		50	50
312	19½p. 1969 10s. Royal Court definitive showing green border error		75	75
	a. Horiz pair. Nos. 312/13	..	1·50	1·50
313	19½p. Bailiff's Seal (23 × 32 *mm*)		75	75
310/13		*Set of* 4	2·25	2·25

The two designs of each value were issued together, *se-tenant*, in horizontal pairs throughout the sheets.

88 Charles Le Geyt and Battle of Minden (1759)

(Des A. Copp. Litho Questa)

1983 (21 June). *World Communications Year and 250th Birth Anniv of Charles Le Geyt (first Jersey postmaster). T* **88** *and similar horiz designs. Multicoloured. P* 14.
314	8p. Type **88**	..	25	25
315	11p. London to Weymouth mail coach		35	35
316	24p. P.O. Mail Packet *Chesterfield* attacked by French privateer		75	75
317	26p. Mary Godfray and the Hue Street Post Office		90	90
318	29p. Mail steamer leaving St. Helier harbour		1·10	1·10
314/18 ..		*Set of* 5	3·00	3·00

89 Assembly Emblem | 90 "Cardinal Newman"

(Des A. Copp. Litho Questa)

1983 (21 June). *13th General Assembly of the A.I.P.L.F. (Association Internationale des Parlementaires de Langue Francaise), Jersey. P* 14½.
319	**89**	19½p. multicoloured	75	75

(Des and photo Courvoisier)

1983 (20 Sept). *50th Death Anniv of Walter Ouless (artist). T* **90** *and similar multicoloured designs, showing paintings. Granite paper. P* 11½.
320	8p. Type **90**	..	25	25
321	11p. "Incident in the French Revolution"		45	45
322	19½p. "Thomas Hardy"	..	85	85
323	31p. "David with the head of Goliath" (38 × 32 *mm*)		1·25	1·25
320/3		*Set of* 4	2·50	2·50

91 Golden Lion Tamarin | 92 C.E.P.T. 25th Anniversary Logo

(Des W. Oliver. Litho Questa)

1984 (17 Jan). *Wildlife Preservation Trust (4th series). T* **91** *and similar vert designs. Multicoloured. P* 13½ × 14.
324	9p. Type **91**	..	30	30
325	12p. Snow Leopard	..	40	40
326	20½p. Jamaican Boa	..	60	60
327	26p. Round Island Gecko	..	95	75
328	28p. Coscoroba Swan	..	1·10	90
329	31p. St. Lucia Amazon	..	1·10	90
324/9		*Set of* 6	4·00	3·50

(Des J. Larrivière. Litho Questa)

1984 (12 Mar). *Europa. P* 14½ × 15.
330	**92**	9p. cobalt, dull ultramarine and black	30	30
331		12p. light green, green and black	40	40
332		20½p. rose-lilac, deep magenta and black	70	70
330/2		*Set of* 3	1·25	1·25

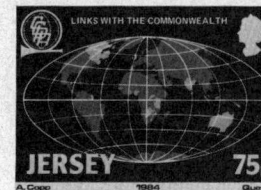

93 Map showing Commonwealth

(Des A. Copp. Litho Questa)

1984 (12 Mar). *Links with the Commonwealth. Sheet* 108 × 74 *mm. P* 15 × 14½.
MS333	**93**	75p. multicoloured	2·50	2·50

94 *Sarah Bloomshoft* at Demie de Pas Light, 1906

(Des G. Palmer. Litho Questa)

1984 (1 June). *Centenary of the Jersey R.N.L.I. Lifeboat Station T* **94** *and similar horiz designs showing famous rescues. Multicoloured. P* 14½.
334	9p. Type **94**	..	40	40
335	9p. *Hearts of Oak* and *Maurice Georges*, 1949		40	40
336	12p. *Elizabeth Rippon* and *Hanna*, 1949	..	50	50
337	12p. *Elizabeth Rippon* and *Santa Maria*, 1951		50	50
338	20½p. *Elizabeth Rippon* and *Bacchus*, 1973	..	90	75
339	20½p. *Thomas James King* and *Cythara*, 1983	..	90	75
334/9		*Set of* 6	3·25	3·00

95 Bristol Type 170 Freighter Mk 32

(Des G. Drummond. Litho Questa)

1984 (24 July). *40th Anniversary of International Civil Aviation Organization. T* **95** *and similar horiz designs. Multicoloured. P* 14.
340	9p. Type **95**	..	30	30
341	12p. Airspeed A.S.57 Ambassador 2	..	40	40
342	26p. De Havilland D.H. 114 Heron 1B	..	1·00	90
343	31p. De Havilland D.H.89A Dragon Rapide	1·25	1·10
340/3		*Set of* 4	2·75	2·50

96 "Robinson Crusoe leaves the Wreck" | 97 "B.L.C. St Helier" Orchid

(Des R. Granger Barrett. Photo Courvoisier)

1984 (21 Sept). *Links with Australia. Paintings by John Alexander Gilfillan. T* **96** *and similar horiz designs. Multicoloured. Granite paper. P* 11½ × 12.
344	9p. Type **96**	..	30	30
345	12p. "Edinburgh Castle"	..	40	40
346	20½p. "Maori Village"	..	75	75
347	26p. "Australian Landscape"	..	95	95
348	28p. "Waterhouse's Corner, Adelaide"	..	1·00	1·00
349	31p. "Captain Cook at Botany Bay"	..	1·10	1·10
344/9		*Set of* 6	4·00	4·00

(Photo Courvoisier)

1984 (15 Nov). *Christmas. Jersey Orchids (1st series). T* **97** *and similar vert design. Multicoloured. Granite paper. P* 12 × 11½.
350	9p. Type **97**	..	50	45
351	12p. "Oda Mt Bingham"	..	75	65

See also Nos. 433/7 and 613/17.

98 "*Hebe* off Corbiere, 1874"

(Photo Harrison)

1985 (26 Feb). *Death Centenary of Philip John Ouless (artist). T* **98** *and similar horiz designs. Multicoloured. P* 14 × 15.
352	9p. Type **98**	..	30	30
353	12p. "The *Gaspe* engaging the *Diomede*"	..	40	40
354	22p. "The Paddle-steamer *London* entering Naples, 1856"		80	80
355	31p. "The *Rambler* entering Cape Town, 1840"		1·25	1·10
356	34p. "St. Aubin's Bay from Mount Bingham, 1872"		1·40	1·25
352/6		*Set of* 5	3·75	3·50

99 John Ireland (composer) and Faldouet Dolmen | 100 Girls' Brigade

(Des Jennifer Toombs. Litho Questa)

1985 (23 Apr). *Europa. European Music Year. T* **99** *and similar horiz designs. Multicoloured. P* 14.
357	10p. Type **99**	..	40	40
358	13p. Ivy St. Helier (actress) and His Majesty's Theatre, London		55	55
359	22p. Claude Debussy (composer) and Elizabeth Castle		1·00	90
357/9		*Set of* 3	1·75	1·60

(Des A. Theobald. Litho Questa)

1985 (30 May). *International Youth Year. T* **100** *and similar vert designs. Multicoloured. P* 14½ × 14.

360	10p. Type **100**		30	30
361	13p. Girl Guides (75th anniversary)		50	50
362	29p. Prince Charles and Jersey Youth Service Activities Base		1·00	1·00
363	31p. Sea Cadet Corps		1·10	1·00
364	34p. Air Training Corps		1·25	1·10
360/4		*Set of* 5	3·75	3·50

101 *Duke of Normandy* at Cheapside

(Des G. Palmer. Photo Courvoisier)

1985 (16 July). *The Jersey Western Railway. T* **101** *and similar horiz designs. Multicoloured. Granite paper. P* 11½.

365	10p. Type **101**		55	55
366	13p. Saddletank at First Tower		70	70
367	22p. *La Moye* at Millbrook		1·10	1·10
368	29p. *St. Heliers* at St. Aubin		1·25	1·25
369	34p. *St. Aubyns* at Corbière		1·40	1·40
365/9		*Set of* 5	4·50	4·50

102 Memorial Window to Revd. James Hemery (former Dean) and St. Helier Parish Church

(Des R. Granger Barrett. Litho Questa)

1985 (10 Sept). *300th Anniv of Huguenot Immigration. T* **102** *and similar horiz designs. Multicoloured. P* 14.

370	10p. Type **102**		30	30
	a. Booklet pane of 4		1·25	
371	10p. Judge Francis Jeune, Baron St. Helier, and Houses of Parliament		30	30
	a. Booklet pane of 4		1·25	
372	13p. Silverware by Pierre Amiraux		45	45
	a. Booklet pane of 4		1·75	
373	13p. Francis Voisin (merchant) and Russian port		45	45
	a. Booklet pane of 4		1·75	
374	22p. Robert Brohier, Schweppes carbonation plant and bottles		75	75
	a. Booklet pane of 4		2·50	
375	22p. George Ingouville, V.C., R.N., and attack on Viborg		75	75
	a. Booklet pane of 4		2·50	
370/5		*Set of* 6	2·75	2·75

Each booklet pane has margins all round and text printed on the binding selvedge.

103 Howard Davis Hall, Victoria College

(Des A. Copp. Litho Cartor)

1985 (25 Oct). *Thomas Benjamin Davis (philanthropist) Commemoration. T* **103** *and similar horiz designs. Multicoloured. P* 13½.

376	10p. Type **103**		40	40
377	13p. Racing schooner *Westward*		60	60
378	31p. Howard Davis Park, St. Helier		1·10	1·10
379	34p. Howard Davis Experimental Farm, Trinity		1·25	1·25
376/9		*Set of* 4	3·00	3·00

104 *"Amaryllis belladonna"* (Pandora Sellars)

105 King Harold, William of Normandy and Halley's Comet, 1066 (from Bayeux Tapestry)

(Des C. Abbott. Litho Questa)

1986 (28 Jan). *Jersey Lilies. T* **104** *and similar multicoloured design. P* 15 × 14½.

380	13p. Type **104**		75	75
381	34p. "A Jersey Lily" (Lily Langtry) (Sir John Millais) (30 × 48 *mm*)		1·50	1·50
MS382	140 × 96 mm. Nos. 380 × 4 and 381		4·25	4·25

(Des Jennifer Toombs. Litho Cartor)

1986 (4 Mar). *Appearance of Halley's Comet. T* **105** *and similar horiz designs. Multicoloured. P* 13½ × 13.

383	10p. Type **105**		40	40
384	22p. Lady Carteret, Edmond Halley, map and Comet		85	85
385	31p. Aspects of communications in 1910 and 1986 on TV screen		1·25	1·25
383/5		*Set of* 3	2·25	2·25

106 Dwarf Pansy

107 Queen Elizabeth II (from photo by Karsh)

(Des Pandora Sellars. Litho Questa)

1986 (21 Apr). *Europa. Environmental Conservation. T* **106** *and similar vert designs. Multicoloured. P* 14½ × 14.

386	10p. Type **106**		35	35
387	14p. Sea Stock		65	65
388	22p. Sand Crocus		95	95
386/8		*Set of* 3	1·75	1·75

(Photo Courvoisier)

1986 (21 Apr). *60th Birthday of Queen Elizabeth II. Granite paper. P* 11½.

389	**107** £1 multicoloured		3·25	3·25

No. 389 was retained in use as part of the current definitive series until replaced by No. 500.
For a £2 value in this design see No. 491b.

108 Le Rât Cottage

109 Prince Andrew and Miss Sarah Ferguson

(Des A. Copp. Litho Cartor)

1986 (17 June). *50th Anniv of National Trust for Jersey. T* **108** *and similar horiz designs. Multicoloured. P* 13½ × 13.

390	10p. Type **108**		30	30
391	14p. The Elms (Trust headquarters)		45	45
392	22p. Morel Farm		80	80
393	29p. Quétivel Mill		90	90
394	31p. La Vallette		95	95
390/4		*Set of* 5	3·00	3·00

(Des A. Copp. Litho Cartor)

1986 (23 July). *Royal Wedding. P* 13½.

395	**109** 14p. multicoloured		50	50
396	40p. multicoloured		1·50	1·50

110 "Gathering Vraic"

111 Island Map on Jersey Lily, and Dove holding Olive Branch

(Des A. Copp. Litho Questa)

1986 (28 Aug). *Birth Centenary of Edmund Blampied (artist). T* **110** *and similar vert designs. P* 14.

397	10p. multicoloured		40	40
398	14p. black, light blue and brownish grey		70	70
399	29p. multicoloured		1·00	1·00
400	31p. black, pale orange and brownish grey		1·25	1·25
401	34p. multicoloured		1·40	1·40
397/401		*Set of* 5	4·25	4·25

Designs:—14p. "Driving Home in the Rain"; 29p. "The Miller"; 31p. "The Joy Ride"; 34p. "Tante Elizabeth".

(Des G. Taylor. Litho Questa)

1986 (4 Nov). *Christmas. International Peace Year. T* **111** *and similar vert designs. Multicoloured. P* 14½.

402	10p. Type **111**		40	40
403	14p. Mistletoe wreath encircling European Robin and dove		60	60
404	34p. Christmas cracker releasing dove		1·25	1·25
402/4		*Set of* 3	2·00	2·00

---

112 *Westward* under Full Sail

(Des A. Copp. Litho Cartor)

1987 (15 Jan). *Racing Schooner "Westward". T* **112** *and similar horiz designs. Multicoloured. P* 13½.

405	10p. Type **112**		40	40
406	14p. T. B. Davis at the helm		60	60
407	31p. *Westward* overhauling *Britannia*		1·25	1·10
408	34p. *Westward* fitting-out at St. Helier		1·40	1·25
405/8		*Set of* 4	3·25	3·00

113 De Havilland D.H.86 Dragon Express *Belcroute Bay*

(Des G. Palmer. Litho Questa)

1987 (3 Mar). *50th Anniv of Jersey Airport. T* **113** *and similar horiz designs. Multicoloured. P* 14.

409	10p. Type **113**		30	30
410	14p. Boeing 757 and Douglas DC-9-15		50	50
411	22p. Britten Norman "long nose" Trislander and Islander aircraft		70	70
412	29p. Short 330 and Vickers Viscount 800		1·10	1·10
413	31p. B.A.C. One Eleven 500 and Handley Page H.P.R.7 Dart Herald		1·25	1·25
409/13		*Set of* 5	3·50	3·50

114 St. Mary and St. Peter's Roman Catholic Church

(Des A. Copp. Litho Questa)

1987 (23 Apr). *Europa. Modern Architecture. T* **114** *and similar horiz designs. Multicoloured. P* 15 × 14.

414	15p. Type **114**		45	45
415	15p. Villa Devereux, St. Brelade		65	65
416	22p. Fort Regent Leisure Centre, St. Helier (57 × 29 *mm*)		90	90
414/16		*Set of* 3	1·75	1·75

115 H.M.S. *Racehorse* and H.M.S. *Carcass* (bomb-ketches) trapped in Arctic

(Des R. Granger Barrett. Litho Questa)

1987 (9 July). *Jersey Adventurers (2nd series). Philippe D'Auvergne. T* **115** *and similar horiz designs. Multicoloured. P* 14.

417	11p. Type **115**		40	40
418	15p. H.M.S. *Alarm* on fire, Rhode Island		50	50
419	29p. H.M.S. *Arethusa* wrecked off Ushant		90	80
420	31p. H.M.S. *Rattlesnake* stranded on Isle de Trinidad		1·00	90
421	34p. Mont Orgueil Castle and fishing boats		1·10	1·00
417/21		*Set of* 5	3·50	3·25

See also Nos. 501/6 and 539/44.

116 Grant of Lands to Normandy, 911 and 933

(Des Jennifer Toombs. Litho Cartor)

1987 (9 Sept–16 Oct). *900th Death Anniv of William the Conqueror. T* **116** *and similar horiz designs. Multicoloured. P* 13½.

422	11p. Type **116**		40	40
	a. Booklet pane of 4 (16 Oct)		2·00	
423	15p. Edward the Confessor and Duke Robert I of Normandy landing on Jersey, 1030		45	45
	a. Booklet pane of 4 (16 Oct)		2·25	

424	22p.	King William's coronation, 1066, and fatal fall, 1087		80	80
	a.	Booklet pane of 4 (16 Oct)		3·50	
425	29p.	Death of William Rufus, 1100, and Battle of Tinchebrai, 1106		95	95
	a.	Booklet pane of 4 (16 Oct)		4·50	
426	31p.	Civil war between Matilda and Stephen, 1135–41		1·10	1·10
	a.	Booklet pane of 4 (16 Oct)		5·00	
427	34p.	Henry inherits Normandy, 1151; John asserts ducal rights in Jersey, 1213		1·25	1·25
	a.	Booklet pane of 4 (16 Oct)		5·50	
422/7			Set of 6	4·50	4·50

Each booklet pane has margins all round and text printed on the binding selvedge.

117 "Grosnez Castle"

(Photo Courvoisier)

1987 (3 Nov). *Christmas. Paintings by John Le Capelain. T 117 and similar horiz designs. Multicoloured. Granite paper. P 11½.*

428	11p.	Type 117		40	40
429	15p.	"St. Aubin's Bay"		60	60
430	22p.	"Mont Orgueil Castle"		80	80
431	31p.	"Town Fort and Harbour, St. Helier"		1·10	1·10
432	34p.	"The Hermitage"		1·25	1·25
428/32			Set of 5	3·75	3·75

118 Cymbidium pontac

(Litho Questa)

1988 (12 Jan). *Jersey Orchids (2nd series). T 118 and similar multicoloured designs. P 14.*

433	11p.	Type 118		50	50
434	15p.	Odontioda Eric Young (vert)		60	60
435	29p.	Lycaste auburn "Seaford" and "Ditchling"		1·00	1·00
436	31p.	Odontoglossum St. Brelade (vert)		1·10	1·10
437	34p.	Cymbidium mavourneen "Jester"		1·25	1·25
433/7			Set of 5	4·00	4·00

119 Labrador Retriever

(Des P. Layton. Litho Questa)

1988 (2 Mar). *Centenary of Jersey Dog Club. T 119 and similar horiz designs. Multicoloured. P 14.*

438	11p.	Type 119		50	50
439	15p.	Wire-haired Dachshund		75	75
440	22p.	Pekingese		1·10	1·10
441	31p.	Cavalier King Charles Spaniel		1·10	1·10
442	34p.	Dalmatian		1·25	1·25
438/42			Set of 5	4·25	4·25

120 De Havilland D.H.C.7 Dash Seven Aircraft, London Landmarks and Jersey Control Tower **121 Rodriguez Fody**

(Des A. Copp. Litho Cartor)

1988 (26 Apr). *Europa. Transport and Communications. T 120 and similar multicoloured designs. P 14×13½ (horiz) or 13½×14 (vert).*

443	16p.	Type 120		50	50
444	16p.	Weather radar and Jersey airport landing system (vert)		50	50
445	22p.	Hydrofoil, St. Malo and Elizabeth Castle, St. Helier		90	90
446	22p.	Port control tower and Jersey Radio maritime communication centre, La Moye (vert)		90	90
443/6			Set of 4	2·50	2·50

(Des W. Oliver. Litho Cartor)

1988 (6 July). *Wildlife Preservation Trust (5th series). T 121 and similar multicoloured designs. P 13½×14 (vert) or 14×13½ (horiz).*

447	12p.	Type 121		55	55
448	16p.	Volcano Rabbit (horiz)		70	70
449	29p.	White-faced Marmoset		1·10	1·10
450	31p.	Ploughshare Tortoise (horiz)		1·25	1·25
451	34p.	Mauritius Kestrel		1·40	1·40
447/51			Set of 5	4·50	4·50

122 Rain Forest Leaf Frog, Costa Rica **123 St. Clement Parish Church**

(Des V. Ambrus. Photo Courvoisier)

1988 (27 Sept). *Operation Raleigh. T 122 and similar horiz designs. Multicoloured. Granite paper. P 12.*

452	12p.	Type 122		45	45
453	16p.	Archaeological survey, Peru		55	55
454	22p.	Climbing glacier, Chile		80	80
455	29p.	Red Cross Centre, Solomon Islands		1·00	1·00
456	31p.	Underwater exploration, Australia		1·10	1·10
457	34p.	Zebu (brigantine) returning to St. Helier		1·25	1·25
452/7			Set of 6	4·50	4·50

(Des P. Layton. Litho B.D.T.)

1988 (15 Nov). *Christmas. Jersey Parish Churches (1st series). T 123 and similar horiz designs. Multicoloured. P 13½.*

458	12p.	Type 123		35	35
459	16p.	St. Ouen		60	60
460	31p.	St. Brelade		90	90
461	34p.	St. Lawrence		95	95
458/61			Set of 4	2·50	2·50

See also Nos. 535/8 and 597/600.

124 Talbot "Type 4 CT Tourer", 1912

(Des A. Copp. Litho Questa)

1989 (31 Jan). *Vintage Cars (1st series). T 124 and similar horiz designs. P 14.*

462	12p.	Type 124		40	40
463	16p.	De Dion "Bouton Type 1-D", 1920		60	60
464	23p.	Austin 7 "Chummy", 1926		75	75
465	30p.	Ford "Model T", 1926		90	90
466	32p.	Bentley 8 litre, 1930		1·10	1·10
467	35p.	Cadillac "452A -V16 Fleetwood Sports Phaeton", 1931		1·25	1·25
462/7			Set of 6	4·50	4·50

See also Nos. 591/6.

125 Belcroute Bay **125a Arms of King George VI**

(Des G. Drummond (1p. to 75p.). Photo Courvoisier (£2), Litho Questa (£4), B.D.T. (others))

1989 (21 Mar)–95. *Jersey Scenes. T 125 and similar horiz designs, Queen's portrait as T 107 and T 125a. Multicoloured. P 11½×12 (£2), 15×14 (£4) or 13×13½ (others).*

468	1p.	Type 125		10	10
469	2p.	High Street, St. Aubin		10	10
470	4p.	Royal Jersey Golf Course		10	10
	a.	Booklet pane of 6 with margins all round (3.5.90)		60	
471	5p.	Portelet Bay		10	10
	a.	Booklet pane of 6 with margins all round (12.2.91)		75	
472	10p.	Les Charrières D'Anneport		20	25
473	13p.	St. Helier Marina		25	30
474	14p.	Sand yacht racing, St. Ouen's Bay		30	35
	a.	Booklet pane of 6 with margins all round (3.5.90)		2·00	
	b.	Booklet pane of 8 with margins all round (22.5.92)		2·75	
475	15p.	Rozel Harbour		30	35
	a.	Booklet pane of 6 with margins all round (12.2.91)		2·00	
476	16p.	St. Aubin's Harbour		30	35
	a.	Booklet pane of 8 with margins all round (22.5.92)		3·50	
477	17p.	Jersey Airport		35	40

478	18p.	Corbière Lighthouse		35	40
	a.	Booklet pane of 6 with margins all round (3.5.90)		2·50	
479	19p.	Val de la Mare		40	45
480	20p.	Elizabeth Castle		40	45
	a.	Booklet pane of 6 with margins all round (12.2.91)		3·00	
481	21p.	Greve de Lecq (16.1.90)		40	45
482	22p.	Samarès Manor (16.1.90)		45	50
	a.	Booklet pane of 8 with margins all round (22.5.92)		4·25	
483	23p.	Bonne Nuit Harbour (16.1.90)		45	50
484	24p.	Grosnez Castle (16.1.90)		50	55
485	25p.	Augrès Manor (16.1.90)		50	55
486	26p.	Central Market (16.1.90)		50	55
487	27p.	St. Brelade's Bay (16.1.90)		55	60
488	30p.	St. Ouen's Manor (13.3.90)		60	65
489	40p.	La Hougue Bie (13.3.90)		80	85
490	50p.	Mont Orgueil Castle (13.3.90)		1·00	1·10
491	75p.	Royal Square, St Helier (13.3.90)		1·50	1·60
491b	£2	Type 107 (19.3.91)		4·00	4·25
491c	£4	Type 125a (24.1.95)		8·00	8·25
468/91c			Set of 26	22·00	23·00

126 Agile Frog **127 Toddlers' Toys**

(Des W. Oliver. Litho Cartor)

1989 (25 Apr). *Endangered Jersey Fauna. T 126 and similar multicoloured designs. P 13½×13 (Nos. 492 and 495), 13×13½ (No. 493) or 13½×14 (No. 494).*

492	13p.	Type 126		1·00	1·00
493	13p.	Heteropterus morpheus (butterfly) (vert)		1·00	1·00
494	17p.	Barn Owl (vert)		1·10	1·10
495	17p.	Green Lizard		1·10	1·10
492/5			Set of 4	3·25	3·25

(Des Clare Luke. Litho Questa)

1989 (25 Apr). *Europa. Children's Toys and Games. T 127 and similar square designs showing clay plaques. Multicoloured. P 14.*

496	17p.	Type 127		50	50
497	17p.	Playground games		50	50
498	23p.	Party games		90	90
499	23p.	Teenage sports		90	90
496/9			Set of 4	2·50	2·50

128 Queen Elizabeth II and Royal Yacht *Britannia* in Elizabeth Harbour

(Des A. Copp. Litho Questa)

1989 (24 May). *Royal Visit. P 14½.*

| 500 | 128 | £1 multicoloured | | 3·00 | 3·00 |

No. 500 was retained in use as part of the current definitive series until replaced by No. 634.

129 Philippe D'Auvergne presented to Louis XVI, 1786

(Des V. Ambrus. Litho Cartor)

1989 (7 July). *Bicentenary of the French Revolution. Philippe D'Auvergne. T 129 and similar horiz designs. Multicoloured. P 13½.*

501	13p.	Type 129		45	45
	a.	Booklet pane of 4		1·25	
502	17p.	Storming the Bastille, 1789		60	60
	a.	Booklet pane of 4		2·00	
503	23p.	Marie de Bouillon and revolutionaries, 1790		80	80
	a.	Booklet pane of 4		2·50	
504	30p.	Auvergne's headquarters at Mont Orgueil, 1795		1·10	1·10
	a.	Booklet pane of 4		4·25	
505	32p.	Landing arms for Chouan rebels, 1796		1·10	1·10
	a.	Booklet pane of 4		4·25	
506	35p.	The last Chouan revolt, 1799		1·25	1·25
	a.	Booklet pane of 4		4·75	
501/6			Set of 6	4·75	4·75

Each booklet pane has margins all round and text printed on the binding selvedge.

See also Nos. 539/44.

130 *St. Helier* off Elizabeth Castle

(Des G. Palmer. Litho Questa)

1989 (5 Sept). *Centenary of Great Western Railway Steamer Service to Channel Islands.* T **130** *and similar horiz designs. Multicoloured. P* 13½×14.

507	13p. Type **130**	..	40	40
508	17p. *Caesarea II* off Corbière Lighthouse	..	50	50
509	27p. *Reindeer* in St. Helier harbour	..	1·00	1·00
510	32p. *Ibex* racing *Frederica* off Portelet	..	1·25	1·25
511	35p. *Lynx* off Noirmont	..	1·40	1·40
507/11		*Set of* 5	4·00	4·00

131 "Gorey Harbour" **132** Head Post Office, Broad Street, 1969

(Litho Enschedé)

1989 (24 Oct). *150th Birth Anniv of Sarah Louisa Kilpack (artist).* T **131** *and similar horiz designs. Multicoloured. P* 13×12½.

512	13p. Type **131**	..	40	40
513	17p. "La Corbière"	..	50	50
514	23p. "Grève de Lecq"	..	1·00	1·00
515	32p. "Bouley Bay"	..	1·25	1·25
516	35p. "Mont Orgueil"	..	1·40	1·40
512/16		*Set of* 5	4·00	4·00

(Des P. Layton. Litho Cartor, France)

1990 (13 Mar). *Europa. Post Office Buildings.* T **132** *and similar multicoloured designs. P* 13½×14 (*vert*) *or* 14×13½ (*horiz*).

517	18p. Type **132**	..	50	50
518	18p. Postal Headquarters, Mont Millais, 1990	..	50	50
519	24p. Hue Street Post Office, 1815 (*horiz*)	..	90	90
520	24p. Head Post Office, Halkett Place, 1890 (*horiz*)	..	90	90
517/20		*Set of* 4	2·50	2·50

133 "Battle of Flowers" Parade **134** Early Printing Press and Jersey Newspaper Mastheads

(Des A. Copp. Litho Enschedé)

1990 (3 May). *Festival of Tourism.* T **133** *and similar vert designs. Multicoloured. P* 14×13½.

521	18p. Type **133**	..	60	60
522	24p. Sports	..	75	75
523	29p. Mont Orgueil Castle and German Underground Hospital Museum	..	95	95
524	32p. Salon Culinaire	..	1·00	1·00
521/4		*Set of* 4	3·00	3·00
MS525	151×100 mm. Nos. 521/4	..	3·00	3·00

(Des A. Copp. Litho Cartor)

1990 (26 June). *International Literacy Year. Jersey News Media.* T **134** *and similar horiz designs. Multicoloured. P* 13½.

526	14p. Type **134**	..	55	55
527	18p. Modern press, and offices of *Jersey Evening Post* in 1890 and 1990	..	60	60
528	34p. Radio Jersey broadcaster	..	1·10	1·10
529	37p. Channel Television studio cameraman	..	1·10	1·10
526/9		*Set of* 4	3·00	3·00

PRICES OF SETS

Set prices are given for many issues, generally those containing three stamps or more. Definitive sets include one of each value or major colour change, but do not cover different perforations, die types or minor shades. Where a choice is possible the set prices are based on the cheapest versions of the stamps included in the listings.

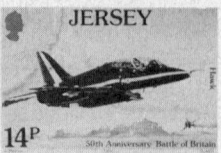

135 British Aerospace Hawk T.1

136 "Landsat 5" and Thematic Mapper Image over Jersey

(Des G. Palmer. Litho Questa)

1990 (4 Sept). *50th Anniv of Battle of Britain.* T **135** *and similar horiz designs. Multicoloured. P* 14.

530	14p. Type **135**	..	45	45
531	18p. Supermarine Spitfire	..	50	50
532	24p. Hawker Hurricane Mk I	..	75	75
533	34p. Vickers-Armstrong Wellington	..	1·40	1·40
534	37p. Avro Type 683 Lancaster	..	1·40	1·40
530/4		*Set of* 5	4·00	4·00

(Des P. Layton. Litho B.D.T.)

1990 (13 Nov). *Christmas. Jersey Parish Churches (2nd series). Horiz designs as* T **123**. *Multicoloured. P* 13½.

535	14p. St. Helier	..	40	40
536	18p. Grouville	..	60	60
537	34p. St. Saviour	..	1·10	1·10
538	37p. St. John	..	1·25	1·25
535/8		*Set of* 4	3·00	3·00

(Des V. Ambrus. Litho Cartor)

1991 (22 Jan). *175th Death Anniv of Philippe d'Auvergne. Horiz designs as* T **129**. *Multicoloured. P* 13½.

539	15p. Prince's Tower, La Hougue Bie	..	50	50
540	20p. Auvergne's arrest in Paris	..	60	60
541	26p. Auvergne plotting against Napoleon	..	80	80
542	31p. Execution of George Cadoudal	..	1·00	1·00
543	37p. H.M.S. *Surly* (cutter) attacking French convoy	..	1·25	1·25
544	44p. Auvergne's last days in London	..	1·40	1·40
539/44		*Set of* 6	5·00	5·00

(Des A. Copp. Litho Enschedé)

1991 (19 Mar). *Europa. Europe in Space.* T **136** *and similar vert designs. Multicoloured. P* 14½×13.

545	20p. Type **136**	..	55	55
546	20p. "ERS-1" earth resources remote sensing satellite	..	55	55
547	26p. "Meteosat" weather satellite	..	85	85
548	26p. "Olympus" direct broadcasting satellite	..	85	85
545/8		*Set of* 4	2·50	2·50

137 1941 1d. Stamp (50th anniv of first Jersey postage stamp) **138** *Melitaea cinxia*

(Des A. Copp. Litho Cartor)

1991 (16 May). *Anniversaries.* T **137** *and similar vert designs. Multicoloured. P* 13½.

549	15p. Type **137**	..	40	40
550	20p. Steam train (centenary of Jersey Eastern Railway extension to Gorey Pier)	..	60	60
551	26p. Jersey cow and Herd Book (125th anniv of Jersey Herd Book)	..	80	80
552	31p. Stone-laying ceremony (from painting by P. J. Ouless) (150th anniv of Victoria Harbour)	..	90	90
553	53p. Marie Bartlett and hospital (250th anniv of Marie Bartlett's hospital bequest)	..	1·75	1·75
549/53		*Set of* 5	4·00	4·00

(Des W. Oliver. Litho Enschedé)

1991 (9 July). *Butterflies and Moths.* T **138** *and similar horiz designs. Multicoloured. P* 13×12½.

554	15p. Type **138**	..	40	40
555	20p. *Euplagia quadripunctaria*	..	50	50
556	37p. *Deilephila porcellus*	..	1·60	1·60
557	57p. *Inachis io*	..	2·00	2·00
554/7		*Set of* 4	4·00	4·00

139 Drilling for Water, Ethiopia **140** "This is the Place for Me"

(Des A. Theobald. Litho B.D.T.)

1991 (3 Sept). *Overseas Aid.* T **139** *and similar horiz designs. Multicoloured. P* 13½×14.

558	15p. Type **139**	..	50	40
559	20p. Building construction, Rwanda	..	60	65
560	26p. Village polytechnic, Kenya	..	80	80
561	31p. Treating leprosy, Tanzania	..	1·00	1·00
562	37p. Ploughing, Zambia	..	1·25	1·25
563	44p. Immunisation clinic, Lesotho	..	1·40	1·40
558/63		*Set of* 6	5·00	5·00

(Litho Questa)

1991 (5 Nov). *Christmas. Illustrations by Edmund Blampied for J.M. Barrie's* Peter Pan. T **140** *and similar vert designs. Multicoloured. P* 14.

564	15p. Type **140**	..	40	40
565	20p. "The Island Come True"	..	65	65
566	37p. "The Never Bird"	..	1·25	1·25
567	53p. "The Great White Father"	..	1·60	1·60
564/7		*Set of* 4	3·50	3·50

141 Pied Wagtail **142** Shipping at Shanghai, 1860

(Des W. Oliver. Litho Cartor)

1992 (7 Jan). *Winter Birds.* T **141** *and similar vert designs. Multicoloured. P* 13½×14.

568	16p. Type **141**	..	50	45
569	20p. Firecrest	..	70	60
570	28p. Common Snipe	..	80	70
571	39p. Lapwing	..	1·25	1·00
572	57p. Fieldfare	..	1·75	1·50
568/72		*Set of* 5	4·50	4·25

See also Nos. 635/9.

(Des V. Ambrus. Litho Cartor)

1992 (25 Feb). *Jersey Adventurers (3rd series). 150th Birth Anniv of William Mesny.* T **142** *and similar horiz designs. Multicoloured. P* 13½.

573	16p. Type **142**	..	50	50
	b. Booklet pane of 4	..	1·25	
574	16p. Mesny's junk running Taiping blockade, 1862	..	50	50
	a. Booklet pane of 4	..	1·25	
575	22p. General Mesny outside river gate, 1874	..	75	75
	a. Booklet pane of 4	..	1·75	
576	22p. Mesny in Burma, 1877	..	75	75
	a. Booklet pane of 4	..	1·75	
577	33p. Mesny and Governor Chang, 1882	..	1·00	1·00
	a. Booklet pane of 4	..	2·50	
578	33p. Mesny in mandarin's sedan chair, 1886	..	1·00	1·00
	a. Booklet pane of 4	..	2·50	
573/8		*Set of* 6	4·00	4·00

Each booklet pane has margins all round and text printed on the binding selvedge.

143 *Tickler* (brigantine)

(Des A. Copp. Litho Questa)

1992 (14 Apr). *Jersey Shipbuilding.* T **143** *and similar horiz designs. Multicoloured. P* 14.

579	16p. Type **143**	..	50	50
580	22p. *Hebe* (brig)	..	80	70
581	50p. *Gemini* (barque)	..	1·60	1·50
582	57p. *Percy Douglas* (full-rigged ship)	..	1·90	1·75
579/82		*Set of* 4	4·25	4·00
MS583	148×98 mm. Nos. 579/82	..	4·25	4·00

144 John Bertram (ship owner) and Columbus

'145 "Snow Leopards" (Allison Griffiths)

(Des V. Ambrus. Litho Questa)

1992 (14 Apr). *Europa. 500th Anniv of Discovery of America by Columbus. T* **144** *and similar horiz designs. P* 14×14½.
584	22p. Type **144**		70	70
585	28p. Sir George Carteret (founder of New Jersey)		85	85
586	39p. Sir Walter Ralegh (founder of Virginia)		1·25	1·25
584/6		Set of 3	2·50	2·50

(Litho Questa)

1992 (23 June). *Batik Designs. T* **145** *and similar vert designs. Multicoloured. P* 14½.
587	16p. Type **145**		50	50
588	22p. "Three Elements" (Nataly Miorin)		70	70
589	39p. "Three Men in a Tub" (Amanda Crocker)		1·25	1·25
590	57p. "Cockatoos" (Michelle Millard)		1·75	1·75
587/90		Set of 4	3·75	3·75

(Des A. Copp. Litho Enschedé)

1992 (8 Sept). *Vintage Cars (2nd series). Horiz designs as T* **124**. *Multicoloured. P* 13×12½.
591	16p. Morris Cowley "Bullnose", 1925		35	35
592	22p. Rolls Royce "20/25", 1932		50	50
593	28p. Chenard and Walcker "T5", 1924		80	80
594	33p. Packard 900 series "Light Eight", 1932		90	90
595	39p. Lanchester "21", 1927		1·10	1·10
596	50p. Buick "30 Roadster", 1913		1·50	1·50
591/6		Set of 6	4·50	4·50

(Des P. Layton. Litho B.D.T.)

1992 (3 Nov). *Christmas. Jersey Parish Churches (3rd series). Horiz designs as T* **123**. *Multicoloured. P* 13½.
597	16p. Trinity		40	35
598	22p. St. Mary		55	60
599	39p. St. Martin		1·00	1·00
600	57p. St. Peter		1·40	1·40
597/600		Set of 4	3·00	3·00

146 Farmhouse

147 *Phragmipedium* Eric Young "Jersey"

(Des A. Copp. Litho B.D.T.)

1993 (11 Jan). *Booklet Stamps. T* **146** *and similar horiz designs. Multicoloured. P* 13.
601	(–) Type **146**		40	45
	a. Booklet pane. Nos. 601/4, each × 2, with margins all round		3·25	
602	(–) Trinity Church		40	45
603	(–) Daffodils and cows		40	45
604	(–) Jersey cows		40	45
605	(–) Sunbathing		50	55
	a. Booklet pane. Nos. 605/8, each × 2, with margins all round		4·00	
606	(–) Windsurfing		50	55
607	(–) Crab (Queen's head at left)		50	55
608	(–) Crab (Queen's head at right)		50	55
609	(–) "Singin' in the Rain" float		60	65
	a. Booklet pane. Nos. 609/12, each × 2, with margins all round		5·00	
610	(–) "Dragon Dance" float		60	65
611	(–) "Bali, Morning of the World" float		60	65
612	(–) "Zulu Fantasy" float		60	65
601/12		Set of 12	5·75	6·25

The above do not show face values, but are inscribed "BAILIWICK POSTAGE PAID" (Nos. 601/4), "U.K. MINIMUM POSTAGE PAID" (Nos. 605/8) or "EUROPE POSTAGE PAID" (Nos. 609/12). They were initially sold at 17p., 23p, or 28p, but Nos. 601/4 and 609/12 were increased to 18p. and 30p. on 10 January 1994 and Nos. 601/4 to 19p. on 4 July 1995. On 10 March 1997 Nos. 601/4 were increased to 20p., Nos. 605/8 to 24p. and Nos. 609/12 to 31p.

(Litho Enschedé)

1993 (26 Jan). *Jersey Orchids (3rd series). T* **147** *and similar vert designs. Multicoloured. P* 14×13.
613	17p. Type **147**		50	35
614	23p. *Odontoglossum* Augres "Trinity"		75	45
615	28p. *Militonia* St. Helier "Colomberie"		90	65
616	39p. *Phragmipedium pearcei*		1·25	1·25
617	57p. *Calanthe* Grouville "Grey"		1·75	1·75
613/17		Set of 5	4·50	4·00

148 Douglas DC-3 Dakota

149 "Jersey's Opera House" (Ian Rolls)

(Des A. Theobald. Litho Questa)

1993 (1 Apr). *75th Anniv of Royal Air Force. T* **148** *and similar horiz designs. Multicoloured. P* 14.
618	17p. Type **148**		50	50
619	23p. Wight seaplane		70	70
620	28p. Avro Shackleton A.E.W.2		80	80
621	33p. Gloster Meteor Mk III and De Havilland D.H.100 Vampire FB.5		90	90
622	39p. Hawker Siddeley Harrier GR.1A		1·10	1·10
623	57p. Panavia Tornado F Mk 3		1·60	1·60
618/23		Set of 6	5·00	5·00
MS624	147×98 mm. Nos. 619 and 623		3·50	3·50

Nos. 618/24 also commemorate the 50th anniversary of the Royal Air Force Association and the 40th anniversary of the first air display on Jersey.

(Litho Cartor)

1993 (1 Apr). *Europa. Contemporary Art. T* **149** *and similar vert designs. Multicoloured. P* 13½×14.
625	23p. Type **149**		70	70
626	28p. "The Ham and Tomato Bap" (Jonathan Hubbard)		85	85
627	39p. "Vase of Flowers" (Neil MacKenzie)		1·25	1·25
625/7		Set of 3	2·50	2·50

150 1943 ½d. Occcupation Stamp

151 Queen Elizabeth II (from painting by Marca McGregor)

(Des G. Drummond. Litho Cartor)

1993 (2 June). *50th Anniv of Edmund Blampied's Occupation Stamps. T* **150** *and similar horiz designs showing stamps from the 1943 issue. P* 13½.
628	17p. myrtle-green, pale green and black		40	45
629	23p. vermilion, salmon-pink and black		55	55
630	28p. chocolate, cinnamon and black		75	75
631	33p. reddish orange, salmon and black		90	90
632	39p. royal blue, cobalt and black		1·25	1·25
633	50p. bright magenta, pale mauve and black		1·40	1·40
628/33		Set of 6	4·75	4·75

Designs:—23p. 1d. value; 28p. 1½d. value; 33p. 2d. value; 39p. 2½d. value; 50p. 3d. value.

(Litho Questa)

1993 (2 June). *40th Anniv of Coronation. P* 14½.
634	**151** £1 multicoloured		2·00	2·10

No. 634 will be retained in use as part of the current definitive series.

152 Short-toed Treecreeper

153 Two Angels holding "Hark the Herald Angels Sing" Banner

(Des W. Oliver. Litho Cartor)

1993 (7 Sept). *Summer Birds. T* **152** *and similar vert designs. Multicoloured. P* 13½×14.
635	17p. Type **152**		50	50
636	23p. Dartford Warbler		75	75
637	28p. Common Wheatear		85	85
638	39p. Cirl Bunting		1·25	1·25
639	57p. Jay		1·75	1·75
635/9		Set of 5	4·50	4·50

(Des N. MacKenzie. Litho Enschedé)

1993 (2 Nov). *Christmas. Stained Glass Windows by Henry Bosdet from St. Aubin on the Hill Church. T* **153** *and similar vert designs. Multicoloured. P* 14×13.
640	17p. Type **153**		45	45
641	23p. Two angels playing harps		65	65
642	39p. Two angels playing violins		1·25	1·25
643	57p. Two angels holding "Once in Royal David's City" banner		1·90	1·90
640/3		Set of 4	3·75	3·75

154 *Coprinus comatus*

(Des W. Oliver. Litho Questa)

1994 (11 Jan). *Fungi. T* **154** *and similar vert designs. Multicoloured. P* 14½.
644	18p. Type **154**		45	45
645	23p. *Amanita muscaria*		70	70
646	30p. *Cantharellus cibarius*		90	90
647	41p. *Macrolepiota procera*		1·25	1·25
648	60p. *Clathrus ruber*		1·75	1·75
644/8		Set of 5	4·50	4·50

155 Pekingese

(Des P. Layton, adapted A. Copp. Litho Questa)

1994 (18 Feb). *"Hong Kong '94" International Stamp Exhibition. "Chinese Year of the Dog". Sheet* 110×75 mm. *P* 15×14½.
MS649	**155** £1 multicoloured		3·00	3·00

156 Maine Coon

157 Mammoth Hunt, La Cotte de St. Brelade

(Des P. Layton. Litho B.D.T.)

1994 (5 Apr). *21st Anniv of Jersey Cat Club. T* **156** *and similar multicoloured designs. P* 14.
650	18p. Type **156**		45	45
651	23p. British Shorthair (*horiz*)		70	60
652	35p. Persian		90	80
653	41p. Siamese (*horiz*)		1·25	1·10
654	60p. Non-pedigree		1·75	1·75
650/4		Set of 5	4·50	4·25

(Des A. Copp. Litho Enschedé)

1994 (5 Apr). *Europa. Archaeological Discoveries. T* **157** *and similar horiz designs. Multicoloured. P* 13½×14.
655	23p. Type **157**		50	50
	a. Horiz pair. Nos. 655/6		1·00	1·00
656	23p. Stone Age hunters pulling mammoth into cave		50	50
657	30p. Chambered passage, La Hougue Bie		75	75
	a. Horiz pair. Nos. 657/8		1·50	1·50
658	30p. Transporting stones		75	75
655/8		Set of 4	2·25	2·25

Nos. 655/6 and 657/8 were printed together, *se-tenant*, in horizontal pairs throughout the sheets.

158 Gliders and Towing Aircraft approaching France

(Des A. Theobald. Litho B.D.T.)

1994 (6 June). *50th Anniv of D-Day. T* **158** *and similar horiz designs. Multicoloured.* P 13½×14.
659	18p. Type **158**		60	50
	a. Booklet pane. Nos. 659/60, each × 3, with margins all round		2·75	
	b. Booklet pane. Nos. 659/64, with margins all round		6·00	
660	18p. Landing craft approaching beaches		60	50
661	23p. Disembarking from landing craft on Gold Beach		80	70
	a. Booklet pane. Nos. 661/2, each × 3, with margins all round		5·50	
662	23p. British troops on Sword Beach		80	70
663	30p. Spitfires over beaches		90	80
	a. Booklet pane. Nos. 663/4, each × 3, with margins all round		6·00	
664	30p. Invasion map		90	80
659/64		*Set of 6*	4·00	3·50

No. 659b was also available as a loose pane from the Philatelic Bureau.

159 Sailing

(Des A. Theobald. Litho Questa)

1994 (6 June). *Centenary of International Olympic Committee. T* **159** *and similar horiz designs. Multicoloured.* P 14.
665	18p. Type **159**		45	45
666	23p. Rifle shooting		60	60
667	30p. Hurdling		85	85
668	41p. Swimming		1·10	1·10
669	60p. Hockey		1·50	1·50
665/9		*Set of 5*	4·00	4·00

160 Strawberry Anemone

(Des W. Oliver. Litho Cartor)

1994 (2 Aug). *Marine Life. T* **160** *and similar horiz designs. Multicoloured.* P 13½.
670	18p. Type **160**		45	45
671	23p. Hermit Crab and parasitic anemone		60	60
672	41p. Velvet Swimming Crab		1·25	1·25
673	60p. Common Jellyfish		1·60	1·60
670/3		*Set of 4*	3·50	3·50

161 Condor 10 Wavepiercer Catamaran

(Des A. Copp. Litho Questa)

1994 (1 Oct). *25th Anniv of Jersey Postal Administration. T* **161** *and similar horiz designs. Multicoloured.* P 14.
674	18p. Type **161**		45	45
675	23p. Map of Jersey and pillar box		60	60
676	35p. Vickers Type 953 Vanguard of B.E.A.		85	75
677	41p. Shorts 360 of Aurigny Air Services		1·10	1·00
678	60p. *Caesarea* (Sealink ferry)		1·50	1·40
674/8		*Set of 5*	4·00	3·75
MS679	150×100 mm. Nos. 674/8		3·75	3·75

162 "Away in a Manger" **163** Dog and "GOOD LUCK"

(Des A. Copp. Litho Questa)

1994 (8 Nov). *Christmas. Carols. T* **162** *and similar horiz designs. Multicoloured.* P 14.
680	18p. Type **162**		45	45
681	23p. "Hark! the Herald Angels Sing"		60	60
682	41p. "While Shepherds watched"		1·25	1·25
683	60p. "We Three Kings of Orient Are"		1·60	1·60
680/3		*Set of 4*	3·50	3·50

(Des A. Copp. Litho B.D.T.)

1995 (24 Jan). *Greetings Stamps. T* **163** *and similar vert designs. Multicoloured.* P 13.
684	18p. Type **163**		35	40
	a. Horiz strip of 4. Nos. 684/7		1·40	
	b. Booklet pane of 9. Nos. 684/92		4·50	
685	18p. Rose and "WITH LOVE"		35	40
686	18p. Chick and "CONGRATULATIONS"		35	40
687	18p. Bouquet of flowers and "THANK YOU"		35	40
688	23p. Dove with letter and "WITH LOVE"		45	50
	a. Horiz strip of 4. Nos. 688/91		1·75	
689	23p. Cat and "GOOD LUCK"		45	50
690	23p. Carnations and "THANK YOU"		45	50
691	23p. Parrot and "CONGRATULATIONS"		45	50
692	60p. Pig and "HAPPY NEW YEAR" (25×63 mm)		1·25	1·40
684/92		*Set of 8*	4·00	4·50

Nos. 684/7 and 688/91 were printed together, *se-tenant*, in horizontal strips of 4 throughout sheets of 20 (4×5).

No. 692 commemorates the Chinese New Year of the Pig and was also printed in sheets of 10 (5×2).

164 Camellia "Captain Rawes" **165** "Liberation" (sculpture, Philip Jackson)

(Des and litho Questa)

1995 (21 Mar). *Camellias. T* **164** *and similar horiz designs. Multicoloured.* P 14½.
693	18p. Type **164**		55	50
694	23p. "Brigadoon"		70	70
695	30p. "Elsie Jury"		80	80
696	35p. "Augusto L'Gouveia Pinto"		85	85
697	41p. "Bella Romana"		1·00	1·00
693/7		*Set of 5*	3·50	3·50

(Des A. Theobald. Litho Cartor)

1995 (9 May). *Europa. Peace and Freedom.* P 13½.
698	**165** 23p. black and dull violet-blue		55	55
699	30p. black and rose-pink		70	75

166 Bailiff and Crown Officers in Launch **167** Bell Heather

(Des A. Theobald. Litho B.D.T.)

1995 (9 May). *50th Anniv of Liberation. T* **166** *and similar horiz designs. Multicoloured.* P 15×14.
700	18p. Type **166**		40	40
	a. Booklet pane. Nos. 700/1, each × 3, with margins all round		2·00	
701	18p. *Vega* (Red Cross supply ship)		40	40
702	23p. H.M.S. *Beagle* (destroyer)		60	60
	a. Booklet pane. Nos. 702/3, each × 3, with margins all round		2·75	
703	23p. British troops in Ordnance Yard, St. Helier		60	60
704	60p. King George VI and Queen Elizabeth in Jersey		1·50	1·50
	a. Booklet pane. Nos. 704/5, each × 3, with margins all round		7·50	
705	60p. Unloading supplies from landing craft, St. Aubin's		1·50	1·50
700/5		*Set of 6*	4·50	4·50
MS706	110×75 mm. £1 Royal Family with Winston Churchill on Buckingham Palace balcony, V.E. Day (80×39 mm)		2·50	2·50
	a. Booklet pane. As No. MS706 with additional margins all round showing arms, mace and inscriptions		2·50	

(Des N. Parlett. Litho B.D.T.)

1995 (4 July). *European Nature Conservation Year. Wild Flowers. T* **167** *and similar vert designs. Multicoloured.* P 13.
707	19p. Type **167**		45	45
	a. Horiz strip of 5. Nos. 707/11		2·25	
708	19p. Sea Campion		45	45
709	19p. Spotted Rock-rose		45	45
710	19p. Thrift		45	45
711	19p. Sheep's-bit Scabious		45	45
712	23p. Field Bind-weed		50	50
	a. Horiz strip of 5. Nos. 712/16		2·50	
713	23p. Common Bird's-foot-trefoil		50	50
714	23p. Sea-holly		50	50
715	23p. Common Centaury		50	50
716	23p. Dwarf Pansy		50	50
707/16		*Set of 10*	4·75	4·75

Nos. 707/11 and 712/16 were printed together, *se-tenant*, in horizontal strips of 5 throughout sheets of 20, the backgrounds forming composite designs.

168 *Precis almana*

(Des W. Oliver. Litho Questa)

1995 (1 Sept). *Butterflies. T* **168** *and similar horiz. designs. Multicoloured.* P 14.
717	19p. Type **168**		45	45
718	23p. *Papilio palinurus*		60	60
719	30p. *Catopsilia scylla*		75	75
720	41p. *Papilio rumanzovia*		1·00	1·00
721	60p. *Troides helena*		1·60	1·60
717/21		*Set of 5*	4·00	4·00
MS722	150×100 mm. Nos. 720/1		2·50	2·50
	a. 41p. value imperforate			

No. MS722 includes the "Singapore '95" International Stamp Exhibition logo on the sheet margin and shows the two stamp designs without frames.

169 Peace Doves and United Nations Anniversary Emblem

(Des A. Copp. Litho Enschedé)

1995 (24 Oct). *50th Anniv of United Nations. T* **169** *and similar horiz design.* P 13×14½.
723	**169** 19p. cobalt and royal blue		45	45
724	– 23p. turquoise-green and deep blue-green		50	50
725	– 41p. deep blue-green and turquoise-green		85	85
726	**169** 60p. royal blue and cobalt		1·40	1·40
723/6		*Set of 4*	3·00	3·00

Design:—23p., 41p. Symbolic wheat and anniversary emblem.

170 "Puss in Boots"

(Des V. Ambrus. Litho Cartor)

1995 (24 Oct). *Christmas. Pantomimes. T* **170** *and similar horiz designs. Multicoloured.* P 13½.
727	19p. Type **170**		45	45
728	23p. "Cinderella"		50	50
729	41p. "Sleeping Beauty"		85	85
730	60p. "Aladdin"		1·40	1·40
727/30		*Set of 4*	3·25	3·25

171 Rat with Top Hat

(Des V. Ambrus. Litho Questa)

1996 (19 Feb). *Chinese New Year ("Year of the Rat"). Sheet* 110×75 mm. P 13½×14.
MS731	**171** £1 multicoloured		2·50	2·50

172 African Child and Map

(Des A. Copp. Litho Questa)

1996 (19 Feb). *50th Anniv of U.N.I.C.E.F. T* **172** *and similar horiz designs. Multicoloured.* P 14½.
732	19p. Type **172**		50	50
733	23p. Children and Globe		60	60
734	30p. European child and map		80	80
735	35p. South American child and map		95	95
736	41p. Asian child and map		1·10	1·10
737	60p. South Pacific child and map		1·60	1·60
732/7		*Set of 6*	5·00	5·00

173 Queen Elizabeth II (from photo by T. O'Neill)

(Litho Questa)

1996 (21 Apr). *70th Birthday of Queen Elizabeth II.* P 14×15.
738　173　£5 multicoloured　.. .. 10·00 10·50
　No. 738 will be retained in use as part of the current definitive series.

174 Elizabeth Garrett (first British woman doctor)　**175** Player shooting at Goal

(Des Jennifer Toombs. Litho B.D.T.)

1996 (25 Apr). *Europa. Famous Women.* T **174** and similar horiz design. Multicoloured. P 13½×14.
739　23p. Type **174** 60 60
740　30p. Emmeline Pankhurst (suffragette) .. 80 80

(Des A. Theobald. Litho B.D.T.)

1996 (25 Apr). *European Football Championship, England.* T **175** and similar horiz designs. Multicoloured. P 13½×14.
741　19p. Type **175** 50 50
742　23p. Two players chasing ball .. 70 70
743　35p. Player avoiding tackle .. 95 95
744　41p. Two players competing for ball .. 1·10 1·10
745　60p. Players heading ball .. 1·75 1·75
741/5 .. .. *Set of 5* 4·50 4·50

176 Rowing

(Des A. Theobald. Litho Questa)

1996 (8 June). *Sporting Anniversaries.* T **176** and similar horiz designs. Multicoloured. P 14.
746　19p. Type **176** 50 50
747　23p. Judo 70 70
748　35p. Fencing 95 95
749　41p. Boxing .. .. 1·10 1·10
750　60p. Basketball .. .. 1·75 1·75
746/50 .. .. *Set of 5* 4·50 4·50
MS751　150×100 mm. £1 Olympic torch (50×37 mm). P 13½ .. .. 2·50 2·50
Anniversaries:—Nos. 746/8, 750/1, Centenary of Modern Olympic Games; No. 749, 50th anniv of International Amateur Boxing Association.
　No. **MS**751 also includes the "CAPEX '96" International Stamp Exhibition logo.

177 Bay on North Coast

(Des A. Copp. Litho B.D.T.)

1996 (8 June). *Tourism. Beaches.* T **177** and similar horiz designs. Multicoloured. P 14.
752　19p. Type **177** 50 50
　a. Booklet pane. Nos. 752/3, each × 3, with margins all round .. 2·50
　b. Booklet pane. Nos. 752/7, with margins all round .. 4·25
753　23p. Portelet Bay 60 60
754　30p. Greve de Lecq Bay .. 80 80
　a. Booklet pane. Nos. 754/5, each × 3, with margins all round .. 4·00
755　35p. Beauport Beach 95 95
756　41p. Plemont Bay .. .. 1·10 1·10
　a. Booklet pane. Nos. 756/7, each × 3, with margins all round .. 6·00
757　60p. St. Brelade's Bay .. .. 1·60 1·60
752/7 .. .. *Set of 6* 5·00 5·00

178 Drag Hunt　**179** The Journey to Bethlehem

(Des P. Layton. Litho Enschedé)

1996 (13 Sept). *Horses.* T **178** and similar horiz designs. Multicoloured. P 13½×14.
758　19p. Type **178** 40 45
759　23p. Pony and trap 45 50
760　30p. Training racehorses on beach .. 60 65
761　35p. Show jumping 70 75
762　41p. Pony Club event 80 85
763　60p. Shire mare and foal .. 1·25 1·40
758/63 .. .. *Set of 6* 3·75 4·25

(Des V. Ambrus. Litho Cartor)

1996 (12 Nov). *Christmas.* T **179** and similar horiz designs. Multicoloured. P 13×13½.
764　19p. Type **179** 40 45
765　23p. The Shepherds 45 50
766　30p. The Nativity 60 65
767　60p. The Three Kings .. .. 1·40 1·40
764/7 .. .. *Set of 4* 2·50 3·00

180 Jersey Cow wearing Scarf

(Des V. Ambrus. Litho Questa)

1997 (7 Feb). *Chinese New Year ("Year of the Ox"). Sheet* 110×74 mm. P 14×13½.
MS768　180　£1 multicoloured .. .. 2·00 2·10

1997 (7 Feb). *"HONG KONG '97" International Stamp Exhibition. No.* **MS**768 *optd with exhibition emblem in black and "JERSEY AT HONG KONG '97" in red, both on sheet margin.*
MS769　180　£1 multicoloured .. .. 2·00 2·10

181 Lillie the Cow on the Beach　**182** Red-breasted Merganser

(Des A. Copp. Litho B.D.T.)

1997 (12 Feb). *Tourism. "Lillie the Cow".* T **181** and similar horiz designs. Multicoloured. Self-adhesive. P 9½.
770　(23p.) Type **181** 45 50
771　(23p.) Lillie taking photograph .. 45 50
772　(23p.) Carrying bucket and spade .. 45 50
773　(23p.) Eating meal at Mont Orgueil .. 45 50
770/3 .. .. *Set of 4* 1·75 2·00
　Nos. 770/3, which are inscribed "UK MINIMUM POSTAGE PAID", come, *se-tenant*, in strips of 4 or rolls of 100 with the surplus self-adhesive paper around each stamp removed.

(Des N. Parlett. Litho Questa)

1997 (12 Feb)–98. *Seabirds and Waders.* T **182** and similar horiz designs. Multicoloured. P 14½.
774　1p. Type **182** 10 10
775　2p. Sanderling (28.1.98) 10 10
776　5p. Great Crested Grebe (28.1.98) .. 10 15
777　10p. Common Tern 20 25
778　15p. Black-headed Gull 30 35
779　20p. Dunlin 40 45
780　21p. Sandwich Tern (28.1.98) .. 40 45
781　24p. Puffin 45 50
782　25p. Brent Goose (28.1.98) .. 50 55
783　30p. Fulmar (28.1.98) 60 65
784　37p. Oystercatcher 75 80
785　40p. Turnstone (28.1.98) 80 85
786　60p. Avocet (28.1.98) .. .. 1·25 1·40
787　£1 Redshank .. .. 1·50 1·60
788　£1 Razorbill (28.1.98) .. .. 2·00 2·10
789　£2 Shag .. .. 4·00 4·25
774/89 .. .. *Set of 16* 13·00 14·00
MS790　Two sheets, each 136×130 mm. (a) Nos. 774, 777/9, 781, 784, 787 and 789. (b) Nos. 775/6, 780, 782/3, 785/6 and 788 (28.1.98) .. *Set of 2 sheets* 13·00 14·00

183 De Havilland D.H.95 Flamingo

(Des A. Theobald. Litho Enschedé)

1997 (10 Mar). *60th Anniv of Jersey Airport.* T **183** and similar horiz designs. Multicoloured. P 13½×14.
801　20p. Type **183** 40 45
802　24p. Handley Page H.P.R. Marathon .. 50 55
803　31p. De Havilland D.H.114 Heron .. 60 65
804　37p. Boeing 737-236 .. .. 75 80
805　43p. Britten Norman Trislander .. 85 90
806　63p. BAe 146-200 .. .. 1·25 1·40
801/6 .. .. *Set of 6* 4·25 4·75

184 The Bull of St. Clement　**185** Cycling

(Des Jennifer Toombs. Litho B.D.T.)

1997 (15 Apr). *Europa. Tales and Legends.* T **184** and similar horiz designs. Multicoloured. P 15×14.
807　20p. Type **184** 40 45
808　24p. The Black Horse of St. Ouen .. 50 55
809　31p. The Black Dog of Bouley Bay .. 60 65
810　63p. Les Fontaines des Mittes .. 1·25 1·40
807/10 .. .. *Set of 4* 2·75 3·00
　Nos. 808/9 include the "EUROPA" emblem.

1997 (29 May). *"Pacific 97" International Stamp Exhibition, San Francisco. No.* **MS**790a *optd with exhibition emblem on sheet margin.*
MS811　136×130 mm. Nos. 774, 777/9, 781, 784, 787 and 789 .. .. 7·50 8·00

(Des A. Theobald. Litho B.D.T.)

1997 (28 June). *7th Island Games, Jersey.* T **185** and similar horiz designs. Multicoloured. P 13½.
812　20p. Type **185** 40 45
　a. Booklet pane. Nos. 812/13, each × 3, with margins all round .. 2·50
　b. Booklet pane. Nos. 812/17, with margins all round .. 4·25
813　24p. Archery 50 55
814　31p. Windsurfing 60 65
　a. Booklet pane. Nos. 814/15, each × 3, with margins all round .. 4·00
815　37p. Gymnastics 75 80
816　43p. Volleyball 85 90
　a. Booklet pane. Nos. 816/17, each × 3, with margins all round .. 6·25
817　63p. Running .. .. 1·25 1·40
812/17 .. .. *Set of 6* 4·25 4·75

186 Mallorcan Midwife Toad　**187** Ash

(Des W. Oliver. Litho Cartor)

1997 (2 Sept). *Wildlife Preservation Trust (6th series).* T **186** and similar horiz designs. Multicoloured. P 13.
818　20p. Type **186** 40 45
819　24p. Aye-Aye 50 55
820　31p. Echo Parakeet 60 65
821　37p. Pigmy Hog 75 80
822　43p. St. Lucia Whip-tail 85 90
823　63p. Madagascar Teal .. .. 1·25 1·40
818/23 .. .. *Set of 6* 4·25 4·75

(Des Norah Bryan. Litho Questa)

1997 (2 Sept). *Trees.* T **187** and similar vert designs. Multicoloured. P 14½.
824　20p. Type **187** 40 45
825　24p. Elder 50 55
826　31p. Beech 60 65
827　37p. Sweet Chestnut 75 80
828　43p. Hawthorn 85 90
829　63p. Common Oak .. .. 1·25 1·40
824/9 .. .. *Set of 6* 4·25 4·75

188 Father Christmas and
Reindeer outside Jersey Airport

(Des Colleen Corlett. Litho B.D.T.)

1997 (11 Nov). *Christmas. T* **188** *and similar horiz designs. Multicoloured. P* 14.
830	20p. Type **188**	40	45
831	24p. Father Christmas with presents, St. Aubin's Harbour	50	55
832	31p. Father Christmas in sleigh, Mont Orgueil Castle	60	65
833	63p. Father Christmas with children, Royal Square, St. Helier	1·25	1·40
830/3	*Set of* 4	2·75	3·00

189 Wedding Photograph, 1947

(Des G. Drummond. Litho Questa)

1997 (20 Nov). *Golden Wedding of Queen Elizabeth and Prince Philip. T* **189** *and similar multicoloured designs. P* 14½.
834	50p. Type **189**	1·00	1·10
	a. Horiz pair. Nos. 834/5		
835	50p. Queen Elizabeth and Prince Philip, 1997	1·00	1·10
MS836	150×100 mm. £1.50, Full-length Wedding photograph, 1947 (38×50 *mm*). P 13½	3·00	3·25

Nos. 834/5 were printed together, *se-tenant*, in horizontal pairs throughout the sheet.

190 Tiger wearing Scarf

(Des V. Ambrus. Litho Questa)

1998 (28 Jan). *Chinese New Year ("Year of the Tiger"). Sheet* 110×75 *mm. P* 14×13½.
MS837	**190** £1 multicoloured	2·00	2·10

191 Hobie Cat and
Duke of Normandy
(launch)

(Des A. Theobald. Litho Cartor)

1998 (15 May). *Opening of Elizabeth Marina, St. Helier. T* **191** *and similar vert designs. Multicoloured. P* 13.
838	20p. Type **191**	40	45
	a. Horiz strip of 5. Nos. 838/42	2·00	
839	20p. Hobie Cat with white, yellow, red and green sails	40	45
840	20p. Hobie Cats with pink, purple and orange sails	40	45
841	20p. Bow of Hobie Cat with yellow, blue and purple sail	40	45
842	20p. Hobie Cat heeling	40	45
843	24p. Yacht with red, white and blue spinnaker	40	45
	a. Horiz strip of 5. Nos. 843/47	2·00	
844	24p. Yacht with pink spinnaker	40	45
845	24p. Yacht with two white sails	40	45
846	24p. Trimaran	40	45
847	24p. Yacht with blue, white and yellow spinnaker in foreground	40	45
838/47	*Set of* 10	4·00	4·50

Nos. 838/42 and 843/7 were each printed together, *se-tenant*, in horizontal strips of five throughout the sheet and form composite designs of yacht races.

STAMP BOOKLETS

For a full listing of Jersey stamp booklets see *Collect Channel Islands and Isle of Man Stamps* published each January.

POSTAGE DUE STAMPS

D 1   D 2 Map

(Des F. Guénier. Litho Bradbury, Wilkinson)

1969 (1 Oct). P 14×13½.
D1	D 1	1d. bluish violet	1·50	1·50
D2		2d. sepia	2·25	2·00
D3		3d. magenta	3·00	2·75
D4	D 2	1s. bright emerald	9·00	7·50
D5		2s. 6d. olive-grey	21·00	16·00
D6		5s. vermilion	30·00	27·00
D1/6		*Set of* 6	60·00	50·00

1971 (15 Feb)–75. *As Type* D 2 *but values in decimal currency.*
D 7	½p. black	10	10
D 8	1p. violet-blue	10	10
D 9	2p. olive-grey	10	10
D10	3p. reddish purple	10	10
D11	4p. pale red	10	10
D12	5p. bright emerald	15	15
D13	6p. yellow-orange (12.8.74)	15	15
D14	7p. bistre-yellow (12.8.74)	15	15
D15	8p. light greenish blue (1.5.75)	25	25
D16	10p. pale olive-grey	35	35
D17	11p. ochre (1.5.75)	35	40
D18	14p. violet	40	45
D19	25p. myrtle-green (12.8.74)	80	90
D20	50p. dull purple (1.5.75)	1·40	1·50
D7/20	*Set of* 14	4·00	4·25

D 3 Arms of St. Clement and   D 4 St. Brelade
Dovecote at Samares

(Des G. Drummond. Litho Questa)

1978 (17 Jan). *Type* D 3 *and similar horiz designs showing the Parish Arms given. P* 14.
D21	1p. blue-green and black	10	10
D22	2p. orange-yellow and black (St. Lawrence)	10	10
D23	3p. lake-brown and black (St. John)	10	10
D24	4p. orange-vermilion and black (St. Ouen)	10	10
D25	5p. ultramarine and black (St. Peter)	10	10
D26	10p. brown-olive and black (St. Martin)	20	20
D27	12p. greenish blue and black (St. Helier)	25	25
D28	14p. red-orange and black (St. Saviour)	25	30
D29	15p. bright magenta and black (St. Brelade)	25	30
D30	20p. yellow-green and black (Grouville)	35	40
D31	50p. deep brown and black (St. Mary)	90	1·10
D32	£1 chalky blue and black (Trinity)	2·00	2·25
D21/32	*Set of* 12	4·25	4·75

Parish Views shown:—2p. Handois Reservoir; 3p. Sorel Point; 4p. Pinnacle Rock; 5p. Quetivel Mill; 10p. St. Catherine's Breakwater; 12p. St. Helier Harbour; 14p. Highlands College; 15p. Beauport Bay; 20p. La Hougue Bie; 50p. Perry Farm; £1 Bouley Bay.

(Des G. Drummond. Litho Questa)

1982 (7 Sept). *Type* D **4** *and similar vert designs depicting Jersey Harbours. P* 14.
D33	1p. bright turquoise-green and black	10	10
D34	2p. chrome-yellow and black	10	10
D35	3p. lake-brown and black	10	10
D36	4p. red and black	10	10
D37	5p. bright blue and black	10	10
D38	6p. yellow-olive and black	10	15
D39	7p. bright reddish mauve and black	15	20
D40	8p. bright orange-red and black	15	20
D41	9p. bright green and black	20	25
D42	10p. turquoise-blue and black	20	25
D43	20p. apple-green and black	40	45
D44	30p. bright purple and black	60	65
D45	40p. dull orange and black	80	85
D46	£1 bright reddish violet and black	2·00	2·10
D33/46	*Set of* 14	4·50	5·00

Designs:—2p. St. Aubin; 3p. Rozel; 4p. Greve de Lecq; 5p. Bouley Bay; 6p. St. Catherine; 7p. Gorey; 8p. Bonne Nuit; 9p. La Roque; 10p. St. Helier; 20p. Ronez; 30p. La Collette; 40p. Elizabeth Castle; £1 Upper Harbour Marina.

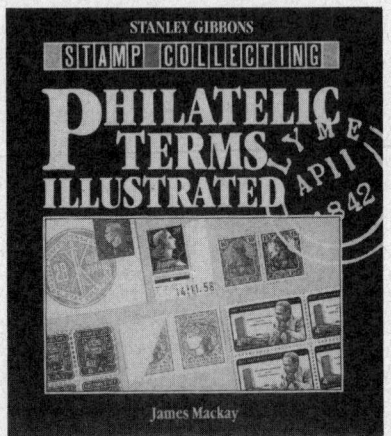

HELP!

Even the most knowledgeable collector can be faced by philatelic terms of which he does not know the meaning – if this has ever been your problem then you need:

PHILATELIC TERMS ILLUSTRATED

Now completely revised and updated in a bright new format as part of the popular Stanley Gibbons 'Stamp Collecting' series.

The new edition of this useful book not only includes all the terms which have come into use since publication of the second edition in 1978 but also provides much new information on postal markings and services.

Noted philatelic author and journalist, James Mackay, has carefully updated and augmented the original text of Russell Bennett and James Watson to produce a work of great assistance to the postal historian and an indispensable aid to stamp identification.

Fully illustrated in colour or black and white, its encyclopedic style and helpful system of cross-referencing makes Philatelic Terms Illustrated extremely easy to use and provides a helpful work of reference for all collectors from the youngest beginner to the most advanced specialist.

Available direct from:

Stanley Gibbons Publications, Parkside, Christchurch Road, Ringwood, Hampshire BH24 3SH Telephone: 01425 472363

British Post Offices Abroad

The origins of the network of Post Offices, Postal Agencies and Packet Agents can be recognised from the 18th century, but the system did not become established until the expansion of trade, following the end of the Napoleonic Wars in 1815.

Many offices were provided in newly acquired dependent territories, and were then, eventually, transferred from the control of the British Post Office to the evolving local administrations.

Those in foreign countries, nearly always based on existing British Consular appointments, were mostly connected to the network of British Packet lines which had been re-established in 1814. They tended to survive in the country in which they were situated established its own efficient postal service or joined the U.P.U. The term "Post Office Agent" was employed by the British G.P.O. and "Packet Agent" by the shipping lines to describe similar functions.

Listed in this section are the Crowned-circle handstamps and G.B. stamps used in the Post Offices and Agencies situated in foreign countries. Those for the territories within the scope of this catalogue will be found under the following headings:

Prices. Catalogue prices quoted in this section, and throughout the volume, covering Crowned-circle handstamps and stamps of Great Britain used abroad are for fine used examples with the cancellation or handstamp clearly legible. Poor impressions of the cancellations and handstamps are worth much less than the prices quoted.

CROWNED-CIRCLE HANDSTAMPS

Following the introduction, in 1840, of adhesive stamps in Great Britain there was considerable pressure from a number of the dependent territories for the British Post Office to provide something similar for their use.

Such suggestions were resisted, however, because of supposed operational problems, but the decision was taken, in connection with an expansion of the Packet Service, to issue a uniform series of handstamps and date stamps to the offices abroad, both in the dependent territories and in foreign countries.

Under the regulations circulated in December 1841, letters and packets forwarded through these offices to the United Kingdom or any of its territories were to be sent unpaid, the postage being collected on delivery. Where this was not possible, for example from a British colony to a foreign country or between two foreign ports, then a *crowned-circle handstamp* was to be applied with the postage, paid in advance, noted alongside in manuscript.

Examples of these handstamps were supplied over twenty years from 1842, but many continued to fulfil other functions long after the introduction of adhesive stamps in the colony concerned.

Our listings cover the use of these handstamps for their initial purpose and the prices quoted are for examples used on cover during the pre-adhesive period.

In most instances the dates quoted are those on which the handstamp appears in the G.P.O. Record Books, but it seems to have been normal for the handstamp to be sent to the office concerned immediately following this registration.

Many of the handstamps were individually cut by hand, so that each has its own characteristics, but for the purposes of the listing they have been grouped into nine Types as shown in the adjacent column. No attempt has been made to identify them by anything but the most major differences, so that minor differences in size and in the type of the crown have been ignored.

DOUBLE CIRCLE

CC 1   CC 1a

Curved "PAID"

CC 1b   CC 1c

Curved "PAID"

CC 2

Straight "PAID"

SINGLE CIRCLE

CC 3   CC 4

Straight "PAID"

CC 5

Curved "PAID"

CC 6   CC 7

Straight "PAID"   Curved "PAID"

GREAT BRITAIN STAMPS USED ABROAD

Prices quoted are for single stamps not on cover unless otherwise stated. Stamps on cover are worth considerably more in most cases.

In many instances obliterators allocated to post offices abroad were, at a later date re-allocated to offices at home. Postmarks on issues later than those included in our lists can therefore safely be regarded as *not* having been "used abroad".

INDEX

ALTERED CATALOGUE NUMBERS

Any Catalogue numbers altered from the last edition are shown as a list in the introductory pages.

TYPES OF OBLITERATOR FOR GREAT BRITAIN STAMPS USED ABROAD

HORIZONTAL OVAL

(1)

(2)

(3)

(4)

(5)

(6)

(7)

VERTICAL OVAL

(8)

(9)

(10)

(11)

(12)

(13)

(14)

(15)

CIRCULAR DATE STAMPS

(16)

(17)

(18)

(19)

(20)

ARGENTINE REPUBLIC
BUENOS AYRES

The first regular monthly British mail packet service was introduced in 1824, replacing a private arrangement which had previously existed for some years.

Great Britain stamps were used from 1860 until the office closed at the end of June 1873. Until 1878 the British Consul continued to sell stamps which were used in combination with an Argentine value prepaying the internal rate. The British stamps on such covers were cancelled on arrival in England.

CROWNED-CIRCLE HANDSTAMPS

CC1 CC 7 BUENOS AYRES (Black or R.) (5.1.1851)
Price on cover £700

Stamps of GREAT BRITAIN cancelled "B 32" as in Types **2, 12** *or* **13.**

1860 to 1873.

Z 1	1d. rose-red (1857)			
Z 2	1d. rose-red (1864)		*From*	14·00
	Plate Nos. 71, 72, 73, 74, 76, 78, 79, 80, 81, 82, 85, 87, 89, 90, 91, 92, 93, 94, 95, 96, 97, 99, 101, 103, 104, 107, 108, 110, 112, 113, 114, 117, 118, 119, 120, 121, 123, 125, 127, 129, 130, 131, 135, 136, 138, 139, 140, 142, 143, 145, 147, 149, 150, 151, 155, 159, 163, 164, 166, 169, 172.			
Z 3	2d. blue (1858–69)		*From*	22·00
	Plate Nos. 8, 9, 12, 13, 14.			
Z 4	3d. carmine-rose (1862)			£160
Z 5	3d. rose (1865) (Plate No. 4)			70·00
Z 6	3d. rose (1867–73)		*From*	32·00
	Plate Nos. 4, 5, 6, 7, 8, 9, 10.			
Z 7	4d. rose (1857)			55·00
Z 8	4d. red (1862) (Plate Nos. 3, 4)			60·00
Z 9	4d. vermilion (1865–73)		*From*	32·00
	Plate Nos. 7, 8, 9, 10, 11, 12, 13.			
Z10	6d. lilac (1856)			65·00
Z11	6d. lilac (1862) (Plate Nos. 3, 4)			
Z12	6d. lilac (1865–67) (Plate Nos. 5, 6)		*From*	48·00
Z13	6d. lilac (1867) (Plate No. 6)			80·00
Z14	6d. violet (1867–70) (Plate Nos. 6, 8, 9)		*From*	45·00
Z15	6d. buff (1872) (Plate No. 11)			75·00
Z16	6d. chestnut (1872) (Plate No. 11)			38·00
Z17	9d. bistre (1862)			£275
Z18	9d. straw (1862)			£225
Z19	9d. straw (1865)			£400
Z20	9d. straw (1867)			£250
Z21	10d. red-brown (1867)			£275
Z22	1s. green (1856)			£175
Z23	1s. green (1862)			£140
Z24	1s. green (1865) (Plate No. 4)			95·00
Z25	1s. green (1867–73) (Plate Nos. 4, 5, 6, 7)		*From*	22·00
Z26	1s. green (1873–77) (Plate No. 8)			£120
Z27	2s. blue (1867)			£350
Z28	5s. rose (1867) (Plate No. 1)			

A "B 32" obliteration was later used by Mauritius on its own stamps.

AZORES
ST. MICHAELS (SAN MIGUEL)

A British Postal Agency existed at Ponta Delgada, the chief port of the island, to operate with the services of the Royal Mail Steam Packet Company.

CROWNED-CIRCLE HANDSTAMPS

CC1 CC 1b ST. MICHAELS (27.5.1842)

BOLIVIA
COBIJA

It is believed that the British Postal Agency opened in 1862. The stamps of Great Britain were used between 1865 and 1878. They can be found used in combination with Bolivia adhesive stamps paying the local postage. The Agency closed in 1881, the town having been occupied by Chile in 1879.

CROWNED-CIRCLE HANDSTAMPS

CC1 CC 4 COBIJA (29.3.1862) .. *Price on cover* £4500

Stamps of GREAT BRITAIN cancelled "C 39" as Types **4, 8** *or* **12.**

1865 to 1878.

Z 1	1d. rose-red (Plate Nos. 93, 95)			
Z 2	2d. blue (1858–69) (Plate No. 14)			
Z 3	3d. rose (1867–73) (Plate No. 6)			
Z 4	3d. rose (1873–76) (Plate Nos. 16, 19)			
Z 5	4d. sage-green (1877) (Plate No. 15)			
Z 6	6d. violet (1867–70) (Plate No. 9)			£350
Z 7	6d. buff (1872) (Plate No. 11)			
Z 8	6d. grey (1874–76) (Plate Nos. 13, 14, 15, 16)			£275
Z 9	1s. green (1867–73) (Plate Nos. 4, 5)			
Z10	1s. green (1873–77) (Plate Nos. 10, 11, 12, 13)			£275
Z11	2s. blue (1867)			£450
Z12	5s. rose (1867–74) (Plate No. 2)			

BRAZIL

The first packets ran to Brazil in 1808 when the Portuguese royal family went into exile at Rio de Janeiro. The Agencies at Bahia and Pernambuco did not open until 1851. All three agencies used the stamps of Great Britain from 1866 and these can be found used in combination with Brazil adhesive stamps paying the local postage. The agencies closed on 30 June 1874.

BAHIA
CROWNED-CIRCLE HANDSTAMPS

CC1 CC 7 BAHIA (Black, G. or R.) (6.1.1851)
Price on cover £1700

Stamps of GREAT BRITAIN cancelled "C 81" as Type **12.**

1866 to 1874.

Z 1	1d. rose-red (1864–79)		*From*	30·00
	Plate Nos. 90, 93, 96, 108, 113, 117, 135, 140, 147, 155.			
Z 2	2d. blue (1870–74) (Plate No. 3)			75·00
Z 3	2d. blue (1858–69) (Plate Nos. 9, 12, 13, 14)			55·00
Z 4	3d. rose (1865) (Plate No. 4)			
Z 5	3d. rose (1867–73) (Plate Nos. 4, 6, 8, 9, 10)			50·00
Z 6	3d. rose (1873–79) (Plate No. 11)			

Z 7	4d. vermilion (1865–73)		*From*	32·00
	Plate Nos. 8, 9, 10, 11, 12, 13.			
Z 8	6d. lilac (1865–67) (Plate No. 5)			
Z 9	6d. lilac (1867) (Plate No. 6)			75·00
Z10	6d. violet (1867–70) (Plate Nos. 6, 8, 9)		*From*	50·00
Z11	6d. buff (1872–73) (Plate Nos. 11, 12)		*From*	90·00
Z12	6d. chestnut (1872) (Plate No. 11)			
Z13	6d. grey (1873) (Plate No. 12)			
Z14	6d. grey (1874–76) (Plate No. 13)			
Z15	9d. straw (1865)			£350
Z16	9d. straw (1867)			£200
Z17	1s. green (1865) (Plate No. 4)			90·00
Z18	1s. green (1867–73) (Plate Nos. 4, 5, 6, 7)		*From*	35·00
Z19	1s. green (1873–77) (Plate Nos. 8, 9)		*From*	60·00
Z20	2s. blue (1867)			£200
Z21	5s. rose (1867) (Plate No. 1)			£400

PERNAMBUCO
CROWNED-CIRCLE HANDSTAMPS

CC2 CC 7 PERNAMBUCO (Black or R.) (6.1.1851)
Price on cover £1700

Stamps of GREAT BRITAIN cancelled "C 82" as Type **12.**

1866 to 1874.

Z22	1d. rose-red (1864–79)		*From*	30·00
	Plate Nos. 85, 108, 111, 130, 131, 132, 149, 157, 159, 160, 187.			
Z23	2d. blue (1858–69) (Plate Nos. 9, 12, 13, 14)		*From*	40·00
Z23a	3d. rose (1865) (Plate No. 4)			70·00
Z24	3d. rose (1867–73) (Plate Nos. 4, 5, 6, 7, 10)			40·00
Z25	3d. rose (1873–77) (Plate No. 11)			
Z26	4d. vermilion (1865–73)		*From*	30·00
	Plate Nos. 9, 10, 11, 12, 13, 14.			
Z27	6d. lilac (1865–67) (Plate Nos. 5, 6)			
Z28	6d. lilac (1867) (Plate No. 6)			60·00
Z29	6d. violet (1867–70) (Plate Nos. 8, 9)		*From*	35·00
Z30	6d. buff (1872–73) (Plate Nos. 11, 12)			50·00
Z31	6d. chestnut (1872) (Plate No. 11)			38·00
Z32	6d. grey (1873) (Plate No. 12)			
Z33	9d. straw (1865)			£350
Z34	9d. straw (1867)			£140
Z35	10d. red-brown (1867)			£200
Z36	1s. green (1865) (Plate No. 4)			80·00
Z37	1s. green (1867–73) (Plate Nos. 4, 5, 6, 7)			30·00
Z38	2s. blue (1867)			£225
Z39	5s. rose (1867–74) (Plate Nos. 1, 2)			£425

RIO DE JANEIRO
CROWNED-CIRCLE HANDSTAMPS

CC3 CC 7 RIO DE JANEIRO (Black, B., G. or R.)
(6.1.1851) .. *Price on cover* £450

Stamps of GREAT BRITAIN cancelled "C 83" as Type **12.**

1866 to 1874.

Z40	1d. rose-red (1857)			38·00
Z41	1d. rose-red (1864–79)		*From*	20·00
	Plate Nos. 71, 76, 80, 82, 86, 94, 103, 113, 117, 119, 123, 130, 132, 134, 135, 146, 148, 159, 161, 166, 185, 200, 204.			
Z42	2d. blue (1858–69) (Plate Nos. 9, 12, 13, 14)		*From*	22·00
Z43	3d. rose (1867–73) (Plate Nos. 4, 5, 6, 7, 8)		*From*	30·00
Z44	3d. rose (1873–77) (Plate No. 11)			
Z45	4d. vermilion (1865–73)		*From*	30·00
	Plate Nos. 8, 9, 10, 11, 12, 13, 14.			
Z46	6d. lilac (1865–67) (Plate No. 5)			
Z47	6d. lilac (1867) (Plate No. 6)			60·00
Z48	6d. violet (1867–70) (Plate Nos. 6, 8, 9)		*From*	30·00
Z49	6d. buff (1872) (Plate No. 11)			65·00
Z50	6d. chestnut (1872) (Plate No. 11)			35·00
Z51	6d. grey (1873) (Plate No. 12)			
Z52	9d. straw (1865)			£250
Z53	9d. straw (1867)			£120
Z54	10d. red-brown (1867)			£150
Z55	1s. green (1865) (Plate No. 4)			80·00
Z56	1s. green (1867–73) (Plate Nos. 4, 5, 6, 7)		*From*	18·00
Z57	1s. green (1873–77) (Plate Nos. 8, 9)			50·00
Z58	2s. blue (1867)			95·00
Z59	5s. rose (1867–74) (Plate Nos. 1, 2)		*From*	£300

CAPE VERDE ISLANDS

The British Packet Agency at St. Vincent opened in 1851 as part of the revised service to South America. The agency was closed by 1860.

CROWNED-CIRCLE HANDSTAMPS

CC1 CC 6 ST. VINCENT C.DE.V. (6.1.1851)
Price on cover £4250

CHILE

The British Postal Agency at Valparaiso opened on 7 May 1846, to be followed by further offices at Caldera (1858) and Coquimbo (1863). The stamps of Great Britain were introduced in 1865 and can be found used in combination with Chile adhesives paying the local postage. All three offices closed on 31 March 1881 when Chile joined the U.P.U.

CALDERA

Stamps of GREAT BRITAIN cancelled "C 37" as in Type **4.**

1865 to 1881.

Z 1	1d. rose-red (1864–79)		*From*	25·00
	Plate Nos. 71, 72, 88, 90, 95, 160, 195.			
Z 2	1½d. lake-red (1870–74) (Plate No. 3)			
Z 3	2d. blue (1858–69) (Plate No. 9)			35·00
Z 4	3d. rose (1865) (Plate No. 4)			80·00
Z 5	3d. rose (1867–73) (Plate Nos. 5, 7)			
Z 6	3d. rose (1873–76)		*From*	28·00
	Plate Nos. 11, 12, 16, 17, 18, 19.			
Z 7	4d. red (1862) (Plate No. 4)			
Z 8	4d. vermilion (1865–73)		*From*	42·00
	Plate Nos. 8, 11, 12, 13, 14.			
Z 9	4d. sage-green (1877) (Plate No. 16)			
Z10	6d. lilac (1862) (Plate No. 4)			80·00
Z11	6d. lilac (1865–67) (Plate Nos. 5, 6)			
Z12	6d. violet (1867–70) (Plate Nos. 6, 8, 9)		*From*	40·00
Z13	6d. buff (1872) (Plate No. 11)			
Z14	6d. chestnut (1872) (Plate No. 11)			
Z15	6d. grey (1873) (Plate No. 12)			

Z16	6d. grey (1874–80)		*From*	30·00
	Plate Nos. 13, 14, 15, 16, 17.			
Z17	8d. orange (1876)			£275
Z18	9d. straw (1867)			£160
Z19	10d. red-brown (1867)			£225
Z20	1s. green (1865) (Plate No. 4)			
Z21	1s. green (1867–73) (Plate Nos. 4, 5, 6)		*From*	24·00
Z22	1s. green (1873–77)		*From*	45·00
	Plate Nos. 8, 10, 11, 12, 13.			
Z23	2s. blue (1867)			£200
Z23a	2s. cobalt (1867)			
Z24	2s. brown (1880)			£1600
Z25	5s. rose (1867–74) (Plate No. 2)			£425

COQUIMBO

Stamps of GREAT BRITAIN cancelled "C 40" as in Type **4.**

1865 to 1881.

Z26	½d. rose-red (1870–79) (Plate No. 14)			
Z27	1d. rose-red (1857)			
Z28	1d. rose-red (1864–79) (Plate Nos. 85, 204)			
Z29	2d. blue (1858–69) (Plate Nos. 9, 14)			
Z30	3d. rose (1865)			
Z31	3d. rose (1872) (Plate No. 8)			
Z32	3d. rose (1873–76) (Plate Nos. 18, 19)		*From*	28·00
Z33	4d. red (1863) (Plate No. 4)			50·00
Z34	4d. vermilion (1865–73) (Plate Nos. 12, 14)			
Z35	4d. sage-green (1877) (Plate Nos. 15, 16)			£150
Z36	6d. lilac (1862) (Plate Nos. 3, 4)			65·00
Z37	6d. lilac (1865–67) (Plate No. 5)			
Z38	6d. lilac (1867) (Plate No. 6)			60·00
Z39	6d. violet (1867–70) (Plate Nos. 6, 8, 9)		*From*	35·00
Z40	6d. buff (1872–73) (Plate Nos. 11, 12)		*From*	60·00
Z41	6d. chestnut (1872) (Plate No. 11)			
Z42	6d. grey (1873) (Plate No. 12)			£120
Z43	6d. grey (1874–76) (Plate Nos. 13, 14, 15, 16)		*From*	25·00
Z44	8d. orange (1876)			
Z45	9d. straw (1862)			£225
Z46	9d. straw (1867)			£150
Z47	10d. red-brown (1867)			
Z48	1s. green (1865) (Plate No. 4)			80·00
Z49	1s. green (1867–73) (Plate Nos. 4, 5, 6)			25·00
Z50	1s. green (1873–77)		*From*	40·00
	Plate Nos. 8, 10, 11, 12, 13.			
Z51	2s. blue (1867)			£130
Z51a	2s. cobalt (1867)			
Z52	2s. brown (1880)			£1700
Z53	5s. rose (1867–74) (Plate Nos. 1, 2)			£375

VALPARAISO
CROWNED-CIRCLE HANDSTAMPS

CC1 CC 2 VALPARAISO (R.) (13.1.1846) *Price on cover* £350
CC2 CC 1 VALPARAISO. (R.) (16.7.1846) *Price on cover* £400

Stamps of GREAT BRITAIN cancelled "C 30", as in Types **12** *and* **14** *or circular date stamp as Type* **16.**

1865 to 1881.

Z54	½d. rose-red (1870–79)		*From*	55·00
	Plate Nos. 6, 11, 12, 13, 14.			
Z55	1d. rose-red (1864–79)		*From*	16·00
	Plate Nos. 80, 84, 85, 89, 91, 101, 106, 113, 116, 122, 123, 138, 140, 141, 146, 148, 149, 152, 157, 158, 162, 167, 175, 178, 181, 185, 186, 187, 189, 190, 195, 197, 198, 199, 200, 201, 207, 209, 210, 211, 212, 213, 214, 215, 217.			
Z56	1½d. lake-red (1870–74) (Plate Nos. 1, 3)		*From*	55·00
Z57	2d. blue (1858–69) (Plate Nos. 9, 13, 14, 15)			35·00
Z58	2½d. rosy mauve (1875), white paper (Plate No. 2)			65·00
Z59	2½d. rosy mauve (1876) (Plate Nos. 4, 8)			50·00
Z60	3d. carmine-rose (1862)			
Z61	3d. rose (1865) (Plate No. 4)			
Z62	3d. rose (1867–73)		*From*	24·00
	Plate Nos. 5, 6, 7, 8, 9, 10.			
Z63	3d. rose (1873–76)		*From*	24·00
	Plate Nos. 11, 12, 14, 16, 17, 18, 19.			
Z63a	4d. red (1862) (Plate No. 4)			
Z63b	4d. red (1863) (Plate No. 4) (Hair lines)			
Z64	4d. vermilion (1865–73)		*From*	28·00
	Plate Nos. 9, 10, 11, 12, 13, 14.			
Z65	4d. vermilion (1876) (Plate No. 15)			£150
Z66	4d. sage-green (1877) (Plate Nos. 15, 16)			£125
Z67	4d. grey-brown (1880) wmk Large Garter			
	Plate No. 17.			
Z68	6d. lilac (1862) (Plate Nos. 3, 4)		*From*	55·00
Z69	6d. lilac (1865) (Plate Nos. 5, 6)			
Z70	6d. lilac (1867) (Plate No. 6)			
Z71	6d. violet (1867–70) (Plate Nos. 6, 8, 9)		*From*	32·00
Z72	6d. buff (1872–73) (Plate Nos. 11, 12)		*From*	45·00
Z73	6d. chestnut (1872) (Plate Nos. 11, 12)			28·00
Z74	6d. grey (1873) (Plate No. 12)			£120
Z75	6d. grey (1874–80)		*From*	24·00
	Plate Nos. 13, 14, 15, 16, 17.			
Z76	6d. grey (1881) (Plate No. 17)			£180
Z77	8d. orange (1876)			
Z78	9d. straw (1862)			
Z79	9d. straw (1865)			
Z80	9d. straw (1867)			£160
Z81	10d. red-brown (1867)			£160
Z82	1s. green (1865) (Plate No. 4)			
Z83	1s. green (1867–73) (Plate Nos. 4, 5, 6, 7)		*From*	20·00
Z84	1s. green (1873–77)		*From*	40·00
	Plate Nos. 8, 9, 10, 11, 12, 13.			
Z85	1s. orange-brown (1880) (Plate No. 13)			£220
Z86	2s. blue (1867)			80·00
Z86a	2s. cobalt (1867)			£1000
Z87	2s. brown (1880)			£1400
Z88	5s. rose (1867–74) (Plate Nos. 1, 2)		*From*	£300
Z89	10s. grey-green (1878) (wmk Cross)			£1500
Z90	£1 brown-lilac (1878) (wmk Cross)			£2500

1880.

Z91	1d. Venetian red	
Z92	1½d. Venetian red	

COLOMBIA

The system of British Postal Agencies in the area was inaugurated by the opening of the Carthagena office in 1825. In 1842 agencies at Chagres, Panama and Santa Martha were added to the system. A further office opened at Colon in 1852, this port also being known as Aspinwall. During 1872 the system was further enlarged by an office at Savanilla, although this agency was later, 1878, transferred to Barranquilla.

Stamps of Great Britain were supplied to Carthagena, Panama and Santa Martha in 1865, Colon in 1870 and Savanilla in 1872. Combination covers with Colombia stamps paying the local postage are known from Santa Martha and Savanilla as are similar covers from Panama showing Costa Rica and El Salvador stamps.

All offices, except Chagres which had ceased to operate in 1855, closed for public business on 30 June 1881. Colon and Panama continued to exist as transit offices to deal with the mail across the isthmus. Both finally closed on 31 March 1921.

CARTHAGENA
CROWNED-CIRCLE HANDSTAMPS
CC1 CC 1b CARTHAGENA (R.) (15.1.1841) *Price on cover* £800
CC2 CC 1   CARTHAGENA (1.7.1846) .. *Price on cover* £700

Stamps of GREAT BRITAIN *cancelled* "C 56" *as in Type* 4.

1865 to 1881.
Z 1	½d. rose-red (1870–79) (Plate No. 10)		
Z 2	1d. rose-red (1864–79) .. .. *From*	34·00
	Plate Nos. 78, 87, 100, 111, 113, 117, 119, 125, 172, 189, 217.	
Z 3	2d. blue (1858–69) (Plate Nos. 9, 14) .. *From*	30·00
Z 4	3d. rose (1865) (Plate No. 4)	
Z 5	3d. rose (1865–68) (Plate Nos. 4, 5) ..	
Z 6	3d. rose (1873–79) (Plate Nos. 12, 17, 18) *From*	40·00
Z 7	4d. vermilion (1865–73) .. .. *From*	30·00
	Plate Nos. 7, 8, 9, 10, 11, 12, 13, 14.	
Z 8	4d. vermilion (1876) (Plate No. 15) ..	£180
Z 9	4d. sage-green (1877) (Plate Nos. 15, 16) *From*	£160
Z10	6d. lilac (1865–67) (Plate Nos. 5, 6) ..	
Z11	6d. violet (1867–70) (Plate Nos. 6, 8) *From*	48·00
Z12	6d. grey (1873) (Plate No. 12)	£130
Z13	6d. grey (1874–76) (Plate Nos. 13, 14, 15, 16) *From*	34·00
Z14	8d. orange (1876)	£200
Z15	9d. straw (1865)	
Z16	1s. green (1865)	
Z17	1s. green (1867–73) (Plate Nos. 4, 5, 7)	36·00
Z18	1s. green (1873–77) (Plate Nos. 8, 9, 10, 11, 12, 13)	40·00
Z19	1s. orange-brown (1880)	
Z20	2s. blue (1867)	£200
Z21	5s. rose (1867) (Plate No. 1) ..	£400

Cancelled "C 65" *(incorrect handstamp, supplied in error) as* T 12.

1866 to 1881.
Z22	½d. rose-red (1870–79) (Plate No. 10)	
Z23	1d. rose-red (1864–79) (Plate Nos. 100, 106, 111, 123) .. .. *From*	42·00
Z23a	1½d. lake-red (1870) (Plate No. 3)	
Z24	2d. blue (1858–69) (Plate No. 9) ..	40·00
Z25	2d. rose (1880)	
Z26	2½d. rose (1880) (Plate No. 19)	
Z27	3d. rose (1867–73) (Plate No. 9)	
Z28	3d. rose (1873–79) (Plate Nos. 14, 17, 19, 20)	
Z29	4d. vermilion (1865–73) .. *From*	40·00
	Plate Nos. 7, 8, 9, 11, 12, 13, 14.	
Z30	4d. vermilion (1876) (Plate No. 15)	£200
Z31	4d. sage-green (1877) (Plate Nos. 15, 16) *From*	£175
Z32	6d. violet (1867–70) (Plate Nos. 6, 8)	80·00
Z33	6d. pale buff (1872) (Plate No. 11) ..	£120
Z34	6d. grey (1873) (Plate No. 12)	40·00
Z35	6d. grey (1874–80) (Plate Nos. 13, 15, 16, 17)	£275
Z36	8d. orange (1876)	£275
Z37	9d. straw (1865)	85·00
Z38	1s. green (1865) (Plate No. 4)	30·00
Z39	1s. green (1867) (Plate Nos. 4, 5, 6, 7)	38·00
Z40	1s. green (1873–77) (Plate Nos. 8, 11, 12, 13) *From*	
Z41	1s. orange-brown (1880)	£350
Z42	2s. blue (1867)	£2000
Z43	2s. brown (1880)	£425
Z44	5s. rose (1867) (Plate Nos. 1, 2)	

CHAGRES
CROWNED-CIRCLE HANDSTAMPS
CC3 CC 1 CHAGRES (16.9.1846) .. .. ..

COLON
CROWNED-CIRCLE HANDSTAMPS
CC4 CC 5 COLON (R.) (21.6.1854) .. *Price on cover* £3500

Stamps of GREAT BRITAIN *cancelled* "E 88" *as in Type* 12.

1870 to 1881.
Z45	1d. rose-red (1864–79) .. .. *From*	25·00
	Plate Nos. 107, 121, 122, 123, 125, 127, 130, 131, 133, 136, 138, 142, 150, 151, 152, 153, 155, 156, 157, 158, 160, 169, 170, 171, 174, 176, 178, 179, 184, 187, 188, 194, 195, 201, 209, 213, 214, 217.	
Z46	1d. Venetian red (1880)	
Z47	1½d. lake-red (1870–74) (Plate No. 3) ..	90·00
Z48	2d. blue (1858–69) (Plate Nos. 14, 15) ..	28·00
Z49	2d. pale rose (1880)	
Z50	3d. rose (1867–73) (Plate Nos. 6, 9)	
Z51	3d. rose (1873–76)	35·00
	Plate Nos. 11, 12, 16, 18, 19, 20.	
Z52	4d. vermilion (1865–73) .. *From*	32·00
	Plate Nos. 10, 11, 12, 13, 14.	
Z53	4d. vermilion (1876) (Plate No. 15)	
Z54	4d. sage-green (1877) (Plate Nos. 15, 16)	£150
Z55	4d. grey-brown (1880) *wmk Large Garter* ..	£200
	Plate No. 17.	
Z56	4d. grey-brown (1880) *wmk Crown* (Plate No. 17)	
Z57	6d. violet (1867–70) (Plate Nos. 6, 8, 9)	
Z58	6d. buff (1872) (Plate No. 11)	
Z59	6d. chestnut (1872) (Plate No. 11) ..	50·00
Z60	6d. grey (1873) (Plate No. 12)	
Z61	6d. grey (1874–80) .. .. *From*	28·00
	Plate Nos. 13, 14, 15, 16, 17.	
Z62	8d. orange (1876)	
Z63	9d. straw (1867)	£150
Z63a	10d. red-brown (1867)	
Z64	1s. green (1867–73) (Plate Nos. 4, 5, 6, 7) ..	28·00
Z65	1s. green (1873–77) .. .. *From*	35·00
	Plate Nos. 8, 9, 10, 11, 12, 13.	
Z66	1s. orange-brown (1880) (Plate 13)	£250
Z67	1s. orange-brown (1881) (Plate 13) ..	60·00
Z68	2s. blue (1867)	£120

Z69	2s. brown (1880)	£1700
Z70	5s. rose (1867) (Plate Nos. 1, 2)	£400

PANAMA
CROWNED-CIRCLE HANDSTAMPS
CC5 CC 1 PANAMA (R.) (24.8.1846) ..*Price on cover* £1200

Stamps of GREAT BRITAIN *cancelled* "C 35" *as in Types* 4, 11 *or* 14.

1865 to 1881.
Z 71	½d. rose-red (1870–79) .. .. *From*	27·00
	Plate Nos. 10, 11, 12, 13, 14, 15, 19	
Z 72	1d. rose-red (1864–79) .. .. *From*	18·00
	Plate Nos. 71, 72, 76, 81, 85, 87, 88, 89, 93, 95, 96, 101, 104, 114, 122, 124, 130, 138, 139, 142, 159, 168, 171, 172, 174, 177, 179, 180, 184, 185, 187, 189, 191, 192, 193, 196, 197, 200, 203, 204, 205, 207, 208, 209, 210, 211, 213, 214, 215, 218, 224	
Z 73	1½d. lake-red (1870–74) (Plate No. 3) ..	50·00
Z 74	2d. blue (1858–69) .. .. *From*	24·00
	Plate Nos. 9, 12, 13, 14, 15.	
Z 75	2½d. rosy mauve (1875) (Plate No. 1) ..	
Z 76	2½d. rosy mauve (1876–80) (Plate Nos. 4, 12, 16)	
Z 77	2½d. blue (1880) (Plate No. 19)	
Z 78	2½d. blue (1881) (Plate Nos. 22, 23)	
Z 79	3d. carmine-red (1862)	£120
Z 80	3d. rose (1865) (Plate No. 4)	
Z 81	3d. rose (1867–73) .. .. *From*	24·00
	Plate Nos. 4, 5, 6, 7, 8, 9.	
Z 82	3d. rose (1873–76) .. .. *From*	24·00
	Plate Nos. 12, 14, 15, 16, 17, 18, 19, 20.	
Z 83	3d. rose (1881) (Plate Nos. 20, 21)	
Z 84	4d. red (1863) (Plate No. 4)	65·00
Z 85	4d. vermilion (1865–73) .. *From*	28·00
	Plate Nos. 7, 8, 9, 10, 11, 12, 13, 14.	
Z 86	4d. vermilion (1876) (Plate No. 15) ..	£175
Z 87	4d. sage-green (1877) (Plate Nos. 15, 16)	£130
Z 88	4d. grey-brown (1880) *wmk Crown* *From*	45·00
	Plate No. 17.	
Z 89	6d. lilac (1862) (Plate Nos. 3, 4) *From*	55·00
Z 90	6d. lilac (1865–67) (Plate Nos. 5, 6) *From*	35·00
Z 91	6d. lilac (1867) (Plate No. 6)	
Z 92	6d. violet (1867–70) (Plate Nos. 6, 8, 9)	28·00
Z 93	6d. buff (1872–73) (Plate Nos. 11, 12) *From*	45·00
Z 94	6d. chestnut (1872) (Plate No. 11)	28·00
Z 95	6d. grey (1873) (Plate No. 12)	£120
Z 96	6d. grey (1874–80) .. .. *From*	28·00
	Plate Nos. 13, 14, 15, 16, 17.	
Z 97	6d. grey (1881) (Plate No. 17)	65·00
Z 98	8d. orange (1876)	£175
Z 99	9d. straw (1862)	£200
Z100	9d. straw (1867)	£225
Z101	10d. red-brown (1867)	£190
Z102	1s. green (1865) (Plate No. 4)	80·00
Z103	1s. green (1867–73) (Plate Nos. 4, 5, 6, 7) *From*	20·00
Z104	1s. green (1873–77) .. .. *From*	35·00
	Plate Nos. 8, 9, 10, 11, 12, 13.	
Z105	1s. orange-brown (1880) (Plate No. 13)	£250
Z106	1s. orange-brown (1881) (Plate No. 13)	55·00
Z107	2s. blue (1867)	80·00
Z108	2s. brown (1880)	£1500
Z109	5s. rose (1867–74) (Plate Nos. 1, 2) *From*	£300

1880.
Z110	1d. Venetian red	16·00
Z111	2d. rose	45·00
Z112	5d. indigo	80·00

Later stamps cancelled "C 35" are believed to originate from sailors' letters or other forms of maritime mail.

SANTA MARTHA
CROWNED-CIRCLE HANDSTAMPS
CC6 CC 1b SANTA MARTHA (R.) (15.12.1841)
Price on cover £1200

Stamps of GREAT BRITAIN *cancelled* "C 62" *as in Type* 4.

1865 to 1881.
Z113	½d. rose-red (1870–79) (Plate No. 6) ..	70·00
Z114	1d. rose-red (1864–79) (Plate No. 106) ..	50·00
Z115	2d. blue (1858–69) (Plate Nos. 9, 13) ..	70·00
Z116	4d. vermilion (1865–73) .. *From*	32·00
	Plate Nos. 7, 8, 9, 11, 12, 13, 14.	
Z117	4d. sage-green (1877) (Plate No. 15) ..	£140
Z118	4d. grey-brown (1880) *wmk Large Garter* ..	£200
	Plate No. 17.	
Z119	4d. grey-brown (1880) *wmk Crown* (Plate No. 17)	55·00
Z120	6d. lilac (1865–67) (Plate No. 5) ..	55·00
Z121	6d. grey (1873) (Plate No. 12)	
Z122	6d. grey (1874–76) (Plate No. 14)	
Z123	8d. orange (1876)	£225
Z123a	9d. bistre (1862)	
Z124	1s. green (1865) (Plate No. 4)	90·00
Z125	1s. green (1867–73) (Plate Nos. 5, 7)	50·00
Z126	1s. green (1873–77) (Plate No. 8)	
Z127	2s. blue (1867)	£275
Z128	5s. rose (1867) (Plate No. 2)	£425

SAVANILLA (BARRANQUILLA)
Stamps of GREAT BRITAIN *cancelled* "F 69" *as in Type* 12.

1872 to 1881.
Z129	½d. rose-red (1870–79) (Plate No. 6) ..	55·00
Z130	1d. rose-red (1864–79) (Plate Nos. 122, 171)	50·00
Z131	1½d. lake-red (1870–74) (Plate No. 3) ..	90·00
Z132	3d. rose (1867–73) (Plate No. 7)	
Z133	3d. rose (1873–76) (Plate No. 20) ..	85·00
Z134	3d. rose (1881) (Plate No. 20)	85·00
Z135	4d. vermilion (1865–73) (Plate Nos. 12, 13, 14)	32·00
Z136	4d. vermilion (1876) (Plate No. 15) ..	£175
Z137	4d. sage-green (1877) (Plate Nos. 15, 16)	£140
Z138	4d. grey-brown (1880) *wmk Large Garter* ..	£200
	Plate No. 17.	
Z139	4d. grey-brown (1880) *wmk Crown* (Plate No. 17)	50·00
Z140	6d. buff (1872) (Plate No. 11)	
Z141	6d. grey (1878) (Plate Nos. 16, 17) *From*	60·00
Z142	8d. orange (1876)	£225
Z143	1s. green (1867–73) (Plate Nos. 5, 7)	40·00
Z144	1s. green (1873–77) (Plate Nos. 8, 11, 12, 13)	50·00
Z145	1s. orange-brown (1880)	£250
Z146	2s. blue (1867)	£170
Z147	5s. rose (1867–74) (Plate No. 2)	£425

CUBA
The British Postal Agency at Havana opened in 1762, the island then being part of the Spanish Empire. A further office, at St. Jago de Cuba, was added in 1841.

Great Britain stamps were supplied to Havana in 1865 and to St. Jago de Cuba in 1866. They continued in use until the offices closed on 30 May 1877.

HAVANA
CROWNED-CIRCLE HANDSTAMPS
CC1 CC 1b HAVANA (13.11.1841).. .. *Price on cover* £800
CC2 CC 1c HAVANA (1848) .. .. *Price on cover* £800
CC3 CC 2   HAVANA (14.7.1848) .. .. *Price on cover* £675

Stamps of GREAT BRITAIN *cancelled* "C 58" *as in Types* 4, 12 *or* 14.

1865 to 1877.
Z 1	½d. rose-red (1870) (Plate Nos. 6, 12)	50·00
Z 2	1d. rose-red (1864–79)	30·00
	Plate Nos. 86, 90, 93, 115, 120, 123, 144, 146, 171, 174, 208.	
Z 3	2d. blue (1858–69) (Plate Nos. 9, 14, 15)	35·00
Z 4	3d. rose (1867–73) (Plate No. 4)	80·00
Z 5	3d. rose (1873–76) (Plate Nos. 18, 19)	
Z 6	4d. vermilion (1865–73) .. *From*	32·00
	Plate Nos. 7, 8, 10, 11, 12, 13, 14.	
Z 7	4d. vermilion (1876) (Plate No. 15)	
Z 8	6d. lilac (1865) (with hyphen) (Plate No. 5)	
Z 9	6d. grey (1874–76) (Plate No. 15)	
Z10	8d. orange (1876)	
Z11	9d. straw (1867)	£200
Z12	10d. red-brown (1867)	£250
Z13	1s. green (1865) (Plate No. 4)	85·00
Z14	1s. green (1867–73) (Plate Nos. 4, 5, 7) *From*	35·00
Z15	1s. green (1873–77) (Plate Nos. 10, 12, 13) *From*	50·00
Z16	2s. blue (1867)	£160
Z17	5s. rose (1867–74) (Plate Nos. 1, 2)	£425

ST. JAGO DE CUBA
CROWNED-CIRCLE HANDSTAMPS
CC4 CC 1b ST. JAGO-DE-CUBA (R.) (15.12.1841)
Price on cover £4750

Stamps of GREAT BRITAIN *cancelled* "C 88" *as Type* 12.

1866 to 1877.
Z18	½d. rose-red (1870–79) (Plate Nos. 4, 6, 14)	
Z19	1d. rose-red (1864–79) .. .. *From*	75·00
	Plate Nos. 100, 105, 106, 109, 111, 120, 123, 138, 144, 146, 147, 148, 171, 208.	
Z20	1½d. lake-red (1870–74) (Plate No. 3) ..	
Z21	2d. blue (1858–69) (Plate Nos. 9, 12, 13, 14)	
Z22	3d. rose (1867) (Plate No. 5)	
Z23	4d. vermilion (1865–73) .. .. *From*	75·00
	Plate Nos. 9, 10, 11, 12, 13, 14.	
Z24	4d. vermilion (1876) (Plate No. 15)	£225
Z25	6d. violet (1867–70) (Plate Nos. 6, 8, 9) *From*	£225
Z26	6d. buff (Plate No. 11)	
Z27	9d. straw (1865)	
Z27a	9d. straw (1867)	
Z28	10d. red-brown (1867)	£350
Z29	1s. green (1867–73) (Plate Nos. 4, 5, 6) *From*	£225
Z30	1s. green (1873–77) (Plate Nos. 9, 10, 12, 13)	
Z31	2s. blue (1867)	
Z32	5s. rose (1867) (Plate 1)	

DANISH WEST INDIES
ST. THOMAS
The British Postal Agency at St. Thomas opened in January 1809 and by 1825 was the office around which many of the packet routes were organised.

Great Britain stamps were introduced on 3 July 1865 and can be found used in combination with Danish West Indies adhesives paying the local postage.

Following a hurricane in October 1867 the main British packet office was moved to Colon in Colombia.

The British Post Office at St. Thomas opened to the public on 1 September 1877, but continued to operate as a transit office for a further two years.

CROWNED-CIRCLE HANDSTAMPS
CC1 CC 1 ST. THOMAS (R.) (20.2.49) *Price on cover* £450
CC2 CC 6 ST. THOMAS (R.) (1.5.1855) *Price on cover* £850

Stamps of GREAT BRITAIN *cancelled* "C 51" *as in Types* 4, 12 *or* 14.

1865 to 1879.
Z 1	½d. rose-red (1870–79)	32·00
	Plate Nos. 5, 6, 8, 10, 11, 12.	
Z 2	1d. rose-red (1857)	
Z 3	1d. rose-red (1864–79) .. .. *From*	20·00
	Plate Nos. 71, 72, 79, 81, 84, 85, 86, 87, 88, 89, 90, 93, 94, 95, 96, 97, 98, 99, 100, 101, 102, 105, 106, 107, 108, 109, 110, 111, 112, 113, 114, 116, 117, 118, 119, 120, 121, 122, 123, 124, 125, 127, 129, 130, 131, 133, 134, 136, 137, 138, 139, 140, 141, 142, 144, 145, 146, 147, 148, 149, 150, 151, 152, 154, 155, 156, 157, 158, 159, 160, 161, 162, 163, 164, 165, 166, 167, 169, 170, 171, 172, 173, 174, 175, 176, 177, 178, 179, 180, 181, 182, 184, 185, 186, 187, 189, 190, 197.	
Z 4	1½d. lake-red (1870–74) (Plate Nos. 1, 3) ..	50·00
Z 5	2d. blue (1858–69) .. .. *From*	26·00
	Plate Nos. 9, 12, 13, 14, 15.	
Z 6	3d. rose (1865) (Plate No. 4)	65·00
Z 7	3d. rose (1867–73)	28·00
	Plate Nos. 4, 5, 6, 7, 8, 9, 10.	
Z 8	3d. rose (1873–76) .. .. *From*	28·00
	Plate Nos. 11, 12, 14, 15, 16, 17, 18, 19.	
Z 9	4d. red (1862) (Plate Nos. 3, 4)	45·00
Z10	4d. vermilion (1865–73) .. *From*	30·00
	Plate Nos. 7, 8, 9, 10, 11, 12, 13, 14.	
Z11	4d. vermilion (1876) (Plate No. 15) ..	£175
Z12	4d. sage-green (1877) (Plate Nos. 15, 16) *From*	£140

Z14	6d. lilac (1864) (Plate No. 4)	£100
Z15	6d. lilac (1865–67) (Plate Nos. 5, 6) *From*	40·00
Z16	6d. lilac (1867) (Plate No. 6)	60·00
Z17	6d. violet (1867–70) (Plate Nos. 6, 8, 9) *From*	30·00
Z18	6d. buff (1872–73) (Plate Nos. 11, 12) *From*	65·00
Z19	6d. chestnut (1872) (Plate No. 11)	28·00
Z20	6d. grey (1873) (Plate No. 12)	£120
Z21	6d. grey (1874–76) (Plate Nos. 13, 14, 15, 16)	30·00
Z22	8d. orange (1876)	£175
Z23	9d. straw (1862)	£175
Z24	9d. bistre (1862)	£250
Z25	9d. straw (1865)	£150
Z26	9d. straw (1867)	£175
Z27	10d. red-brown (1867)	90·00
Z28	1s. green (1865) (Plate No. 4)	90·00
Z29	1s. green (1867–73) (Plate Nos. 4, 5, 6, 7) *From*	22·00
Z30	1s. green (1873–77) *From*	55·00
	Plate Nos. 8, 9, 10, 11, 12, 13.	
Z31	2s. blue (1867)	£120
Z32	5s. rose (1867–74) (Plate Nos. 1, 2) *From*	£300

DOMINICAN REPUBLIC

British Postal Agencies may have existed in the area before 1867, but it is only from that year that details can be found concerning offices at Porto Plata and St. Domingo. Both were closed in 1871, but re-opened in 1876.

Although postmarks were supplied in 1866 it seems likely that Great Britain stamps were not sent until the offices re-opened in 1876.

Covers exist showing Great Britain stamps used in combination with those of Dominican Republic with the latter paying the local postage. Both agencies finally closed in 1881.

PORTO PLATA

Stamps of GREAT BRITAIN *cancelled* "C 86" *or circular date stamp as in Types* **8** *or* **17.**

1876 *to* **1881**

Z 1	½d. rose-red (1870–79) (Plate Nos. 10, 12, 14) *From*	60·00
Z 2	1d. rose-red (1864–79) *From*	32·00
	Plate Nos. 123, 130, 136, 146, 151, 178, 199, 200, 205, 217.	
Z 3	1½d. lake-red (1870–74) (Plate No. 3)	£100
Z 4	2d. blue (1858–69) (Plate Nos. 14, 15)	40·00
Z 5	2½d. rosy mauve (1876–79) (Plate Nos. 13, 14) *From*	£140
Z 6	3d. rose (1873–76) (Plate No. 18)	80·00
Z 7	4d. vermilion (1873) (Plate No. 14)	80·00
Z 8	4d. vermilion (1876) (Plate No. 15)	£200
Z 9	4d. sage-green (1877) (Plate No. 15)	£160
Z10	6d. violet (1867–70) (Plate No. 8)	60·00
Z11	6d. grey (1874–76) (Plate No. 15)	£275
Z12	8d. orange (1876)	£275
Z13	1s. green (1867–73) (Plate Nos. 4, 7) *From*	40·00
Z14	1s. green (1873–77) (Plate Nos. 11, 12, 13) *From*	42·00
Z15	2s. blue (1867)	£200
Z15a	5s. rose (1867–83) (Plate No. 2)	

ST. DOMINGO

Stamps of GREAT BRITAIN *cancelled* "C 87" *or circular date stamp as in Types* **12** *or* **16.**

1876 *to* **1881**

Z16	½d. rose-red (1870–79) *From*	60·00
	Plate Nos. 5, 6, 8, 10, 11, 13.	
Z17	1d. rose-red (1864–79) *From*	40·00
	Plate Nos. 146, 154, 171, 173, 174, 176, 178, 186, 190, 197, 220.	
Z18	1½d. lake-red (1870–74) (Plate No. 3)	£100
Z19	2d. blue (1858–69) (Plate Nos. 13, 14)	70·00
Z20	3d. rose (1873–76) (Plate No. 18)	
Z21	4d. vermilion (1865–73) *From*	48·00
	Plate Nos. 11, 12, 14.	
Z22	4d. vermilion (1876) (Plate No. 15)	£225
Z23	4d. sage-green (1877) (Plate No. 15)	£160
Z24	6d. grey (1874–76) (Plate No. 15)	
Z25	9d. straw (1867)	
Z26	1s. green (1867) (Plate No. 4)	
Z27	1s. green (1873–77) *From*	70·00
	Plate Nos. 10, 11, 12, 13.	
Z28	2s. blue (1867)	

ECUADOR

GUAYAQUIL

The first British Postal Agent in Guayaquil was appointed in 1848.

Great Britain stamps were supplied in 1865 and continued to be used until the agency closed on 30 June 1880. They can be found used in combination with stamps of Ecuador with the latter paying the local postage.

Stamps of GREAT BRITAIN *cancelled* "C 41" *as Type* **4.**

1865 *to* **1880.**

Z 1	½d. rose-red (1870–79) (Plate Nos. 5, 6)	55·00
Z 2	1d. rose-red (1857)	
Z 3	1d. rose-red (1864–79) *From*	27·00
	Plate Nos. 74, 78, 85, 92, 94, 105, 110, 115, 133, 140, 145, 166, 174, 180, 216.	
Z 4	1½d. lake-red (1870–74) (Plate No. 3)	75·00
Z 5	2d. blue (1858–69) (Plate Nos. 9, 13, 14) *From*	30·00
Z 6	3d. carmine-rose (1862)	£175
Z 7	3d. rose (1865) (Plate No. 4)	60·00
Z 8	3d. rose (1867–73) (Plate Nos. 6, 7, 9, 10) *From*	28·00
Z 9	3d. rose (1873–76) *From*	28·00
	Plate Nos. 11, 12, 15, 16, 17, 18, 19, 20.	
Z10	4d. red (1862) (Plate Nos. 3, 4) *From*	70·00
Z11	4d. vermilion (1865–73) *From*	28·00
	Plate Nos. 7, 8, 9, 10, 11, 12, 13, 14.	
Z12	4d. vermilion (1876) (Plate No. 15)	£175
Z13	4d. sage-green (1877) (Plate Nos. 15, 16)	£150
Z14	6d. lilac (1864) (Plate No. 4)	70·00
Z15	6d. lilac (1865–67) (Plate Nos. 5, 6)	40·00
Z16	6d. lilac (1867) (Plate No. 6)	
Z17	6d. violet (1867–70) (Plate Nos. 6, 8, 9) *From*	32·00
Z18	6d. buff (1872–73) (Plate Nos. 11, 12)	75·00

Z19	6d. chestnut (1872)	
Z20	6d. grey (1873) (Plate No. 12)	
Z21	6d. grey (1874–76) (Plate Nos. 13, 14, 15, 16) *From*	30·00
Z22	8d. orange (1876)	£200
Z23	9d. straw (1862)	£200
Z24	9d. straw (1867)	£150
Z25	10d. red-brown (1867)	£160
Z26	1s. green (1865) (Plate No. 4)	90·00
Z27	1s. green (1867–73) (Plate Nos. 4, 5, 6, 7) *From*	25·00
Z28	1s. green (1873–77) *From*	48·00
	Plate Nos. 8, 9, 10, 11, 12, 13.	
Z29	2s. blue (1867)	£125
Z30	2s. brown (1880)	£1600
Z31	5s. rose (1867–74) (Plate Nos. 1, 2) *From*	£400

FERNANDO PO

The British government leased naval facilities on this Spanish island from 1827 until 1834. A British Consul was appointed in 1849 and a postal agency was opened on 1 April 1858.

The use of Great Britain stamps was authorised in 1858, but a cancellation was not supplied until 1874. The office remained open until 1877.

CROWNED-CIRCLE HANDSTAMPS

CC1 CC **4** FERNANDO-PO (R.) (19.2.1859)
Price on cover £3750

Stamps of GREAT BRITAIN *cancelled* "247" *as Type* **9.**

1874 *to* **1877.**

Z1	4d. vermilion (1865–72) (Plate Nos. 13, 14)	£700
Z2	4d. vermilion (1876) (Plate No. 15)	
Z3	6d. grey (1874–76) (Plate Nos. 13, 14, 15, 16)	£600

GUADELOUPE

A British Packet Agency was established on Guadeloupe on 1 October 1848 and continued to function until 1874.

No. CC1 is often found used in conjunction with French Colonies (General Issues) adhesive stamps.

A similar packet agency existed on Martinique from 1 October 1848 until 1879, but no crowned-circle handstamp was issued for it.

CROWNED-CIRCLE HANDSTAMPS

CC1 CC **1** GUADELOUPE (R., B. or Black) (9.3.1849)
Price on cover £1800

HAITI

The original British Postal Agencies in Haiti date from 1830 when it is known a Packet Agency was established at Jacmel. An office at Port-au-Prince followed in 1842, both these agencies remaining in operation until 30 June 1881.

During this period short-lived agencies also operated in the following Haitian towns: Aux Cayes (1848 to 1863), Cap Haitien (1842 to 1863), Gonaives (1849 to 1857) and St. Marc (1854 to 1861). A further agency may have operated at Le Mole around the year 1841.

Great Britain stamps were supplied to Jacmel in 1865 and to Port-au-Prince in 1869.

CAP HAITIEN

CROWNED-CIRCLE HANDSTAMPS

CC1 CC **1b** CAPE-HAITIEN (R.) (31.12.1841)
Price on cover £3000

JACMEL

CROWNED-CIRCLE HANDSTAMPS

CC2 CC **1b** JACMEL (R.) (29.6.1843) . . *Price on cover* £1000

Stamps of GREAT BRITAIN *cancelled* "C 59" *as Type* **4.**

1865 *to* **1881.**

Z 1	½d. rose-red (1870–79) *From*	40·00
	Plate Nos. 4, 5, 6, 10, 11, 12, 14, 15.	
Z 2	1d. rose-red (1864–79) *From*	30·00
	Plate Nos. 74, 81, 84, 87, 95, 106, 107, 109, 122, 136, 137, 139, 148, 150, 151, 152, 156, 157, 159, 160, 162, 164, 166, 167, 170, 171, 179, 181, 183, 184, 186, 187, 189, 192, 194, 198, 200, 204, 206, 215, 219.	
Z 3	1½d. lake-red (1870–74) (Plate No. 3)	60·00
Z 4	2d. blue (1858–69) (Plate Nos. 9, 13, 14, 15)	40·00
Z 5	2½d. rosy mauve (1876) (Plate No. 4)	
Z 6	3d. rose (1867–73) (Plate Nos. 5, 6, 7, 8, 9, 10) *From*	38·00
Z 7	3d. rose (1873–76)	38·00
	Plate Nos. 11, 12, 14, 16, 17, 18, 19.	
Z 8	4d. red (1863) (Plate No. 4) (*Hair lines*)	80·00
Z 9	4d. vermilion (1865–73) *From*	38·00
	Plate Nos. 7, 8, 9, 10, 11, 12, 13, 14.	
Z10	4d. vermilion (1876) (Plate No. 15)	£200
Z11	4d. sage-green (1877) (Plate Nos. 15, 16)	£150
Z12	4d. grey-brown (1880) *wmk* Large Garter	£250
	Plate No. 17.	
Z13	4d. grey-brown (1880) *wmk* Crown (Plate No. 17)	35·00
Z14	6d. lilac (1867) (Plate Nos. 5, 6)	42·00
Z15	6d. violet (1867–70) (Plate Nos. 8, 9)	35·00
Z16	6d. buff (1872–73) (Plate Nos. 11, 12) *From*	60·00
Z17	6d. chestnut (1872) (Plate No. 11)	
Z18	6d. grey (1873) (Plate No. 12)	
Z19	6d. grey (1874–76) *From*	35·00
	Plate Nos. 13, 14, 15, 16, 17.	
Z20	8d. orange (1876)	£250
Z21	9d. straw (1862)	£200
Z22	9d. straw (1867)	£175
Z23	10d. red-brown (1867)	£160
Z24	1s. green (1865) (Plate No. 4)	£100
Z25	1s. green (1867–73) (Plate Nos. 4, 5, 6, 7) *From*	30·00
Z26	1s. green (1873–77) *From*	48·00
	Plate Nos. 8, 9, 10, 11, 12, 13.	
Z27	1s. orange-brown (1880) (Plate No. 13)	£300
Z28	2s. blue (1867)	£100
Z29	2s. brown (1880)	£2000
Z30	5s. rose (1867–74) (Plate Nos. 1, 2) *From*	£300

1880.		
Z31	½d. green (1880)	28·00
Z32	1d. Venetian red	24·00
Z33	1½d. Venetian red	40·00
Z34	2d. rose	65·00

PORT-AU-PRINCE

CROWNED-CIRCLE HANDSTAMPS

CC3 CC **1b** PORT-AU-PRINCE (R.) (29.6.1843)
Price on cover £1500

Stamps of GREAT BRITAIN *cancelled* "E 53" *as in Types* **8** *or* **12.**

1869 *to* **1881.**

Z35	½d. rose-red (1870–79) *From*	42·00
	Plate Nos. 5, 6, 10, 11, 12, 13, 14.	
Z36	1d. rose-red (1864–79) *From*	28·00
	Plate Nos. 87, 134, 154, 167, 171, 173, 174, 183, 187, 189, 193, 199, 200, 201, 202, 206, 209, 210, 218, 219.	
Z37	1½d. lake-red (1870–74) (Plate No. 3)	70·00
Z38	2d. blue (1858–69) (Plate Nos. 9, 14, 15)	38·00
Z40	2½d. rosy mauve (1876–79) (Plate Nos. 3, 9)	80·00
Z41	3d. rose (1867–73) (Plate Nos. 6, 7)	
Z42	3d. rose (1873–79) (Plate Nos. 17, 18, 20)	30·00
Z43	4d. vermilion (1865–73) *From*	38·00
	Plate Nos. 11, 12, 13, 14.	
Z44	4d. vermilion (1876) (Plate No. 15)	£200
Z45	4d. sage-green (1877) (Plate Nos. 15, 16) *From*	£130
Z46	4d. grey-brown (1880) *wmk* Large Garter	£250
	Plate No. 17.	
Z47	4d. grey-brown (1880) *wmk* Crown (Plate No. 17)	32·00
Z48	6d. grey (1874–76) (Plate Nos. 15, 16)	£190
Z49	8d. orange (1876)	
Z50	1s. green (1867–73) (Plate Nos. 4, 5, 6, 7) *From*	30·00
Z51	1s. green (1873–77) *From*	45·00
	Plate Nos. 8, 9, 10, 11, 12, 13.	
Z52	1s. orange-brown (1880) (Plate No. 13)	£300
Z53	1s. orange-brown (1881) (Plate No. 13)	70·00
Z54	2s. blue (1867)	£100
Z55	2s. brown (1880)	£2000
Z56	5s. rose (1867–74) (Plate Nos. 1, 2)	£375
Z57	10s. greenish grey (1878)	£2500

1880.		
Z58	½d. green	40·00
Z59	1d. Venetian red	30·00
Z60	1½d. Venetian red	40·00
Z61	2d. rose	

MACAO

A British Consular Post Office opened in 1841. It had been preceded by the Macao Boat Office, possibly a private venture, which operated in the 1830s. The office closed when the consulate closed on 30 September 1845, but was back in operation by 1854.

The Agency continued to function, in conjunction with the Hong Kong Post Office, until 28 February 1884 when Portugal joined the U.P.U.

CROWNED-CIRCLE HANDSTAMPS

Z 2

CC1 – PAID AT MACAO (crowned-oval 20 mm wide) (R.) (1844) . . *Price on cover* £14000
CC2 Z **2** Crown and Macao (1881)

No. CC2 with the Crown removed was used by the Portuguese post office in Macao as a cancellation until 1890.

A locally-cut mark, as Type CC **2**, inscribed "PAGO EM MACAO" is known on covers between 1870 and 1877. It was probably used by the Portuguese postmaster to send letters via the British Post Office (*Price* £10000).

MADEIRA

The British Packet Agency on this Portuguese island was opened in 1767 and was of increased importance from 1808 following the exile of the Portuguese royal family to Brazil. The South American packets ceased to call in 1858. It appears to have closed sometime around 1860.

CROWN-CIRCLE HANDSTAMPS

CC1 CC **1b** MADEIRA (R.) (28.2.1842) . *Price on cover* £12000

MEXICO

The British Postal Agency at Vera Cruz opened in 1825, following the introduction of the Mexican Packet service. No handstamps were supplied, however, until 1842, when a similar agency at Tampico was set up.

Great Britain stamps were used at Tampico from 1867 but, apparently, were never sent to the Vera Cruz office. Combination covers exist showing the local postage paid by Mexican adhesives. The Agency at Vera Cruz closed in 1874 and that at Tampico in 1876.

TAMPICO
CROWNED-CIRCLE HANDSTAMPS

CC1　CC **1b**　TAMPICO (R.) (13.11.1841). . *Price on cover* £1400

No. CC1 may be found on cover, used in conjunction with Mexico adhesive stamps.

Stamps of GREAT BRITAIN *cancelled* "C 63" *as Type* **4**.

1867 *to* **1876**.
Z 1	1d. rose-red (1864–79)	..	*From*	80·00
	Plate Nos. 81, 89, 103, 117, 139, 147.			
Z 2	2d. blue (1858–69) (Plate Nos. 9, 14)	..		£100
Z 3	4d. vermilion (1865–73)	..	*From*	55·00
	Plate Nos. 7, 8, 10, 11, 12, 13, 14.			
Z 4	1s. green (1867–73) (Plate Nos. 4, 5, 7, 8)	..		70·00
Z 5	2s. blue (1867)			£350

VERA CRUZ
CROWNED-CIRCLE HANDSTAMPS

CC2　CC **1b**　VERA CRUZ (R.) (13.11.1841) *Price on cover* £1600
CC3　　　　　VERA CRUZ (Black) (*circa* 1845)
　　　　　　　　　　　　　Price on cover　£800
No. CC3 can also be found used in conjunction with Mexico adhesive stamps.

NICARAGUA
GREYTOWN

British involvement on the Mosquito Coast of Nicaragua dates from 1655 when contacts were first made with the indigenous Misquito Indians. A formal alliance was signed in 1740 and the area was considered as a British dependency until the Spanish authorities negotiated a withdrawal in 1786.

The Misquitos remained under British protection, however, and, following the revolutionary period in the Spanish dominions, this eventually led to the appropriation, by the Misquitos with British backing, of the town of San Juan del Norte, later renamed Greytown.

The port was included in the Royal West Indian Mail Steam Packet Company's mail network from January 1842, forming part of the Jamaica District. This arrangement only lasted until September of that year, however, although packets were once again calling at Greytown by November 1844. Following the discovery of gold in California the office increased in importance, owing to the overland traffic, although the first distinctive postmark is not recorded in use until February 1856.

A subsidiary agency, without its own postmark, operated at Bluefields from 1857 to 1863.

The British Protectorate over the Misquitos ended in 1860, but the British Post Office at Greytown continued to operate, being supplied with Great Britain stamps in 1865. These are occasionally found used in combination with Nicaragua issues, which had only internal validity.

The British Post Office at Greytown closed on 1 May 1882 when the Republic of Nicaragua joined the U.P.U.

CROWNED-CIRCLE HANDSTAMPS

Z 1

CC1　Z **1**　GREYTOWN (R.) (14.4.1859)　　. .

Z 2　　　　　　　　　　Z 4

Z 3

Stamps of GREAT BRITAIN *cancelled* "C 57" *as in Types* Z **2** (*issued* 1865), Z **3** (*issued* 1875), *or with circular postmark as Type* Z **4** (*issued* 1864).

1865 *to* **1882**.
Z 1	1d. rose-red (1870–79) (Plate Nos. 5, 10, 11)	..	50·00
Z 2	1d. rose-red (1864–79) (Plate Nos. 180, 197, 210)	..	30·00
Z 3	1½d. lake-red (1870) (Plate No. 3)	..	60·00
Z 4	2d. blue (1858–69) (Plate Nos. 9, 14, 15)	..	
Z 5	3d. rose (1873–76) (Plate Nos. 17, 18, 19, 20)	..	40·00

Z 6	3d. rose (1881) (Plate No. 20)		
Z 7	4d. vermilion (1865–73)	*From*	35·00
	Plate Nos. 8, 10, 11, 12, 13, 14.		
Z 8	4d. vermilion (1876) (Plate No. 15)	..	£200
Z 9	4d. sage-green (1877) (Plate Nos. 15, 16)	..	£140
Z10	4d. grey-brown (1880) *wmk* Large Garter ..		£250
	Plate No. 17.		
Z11	4d. grey-brown (1880) *wmk* Crown (Plate No. 17)		85·00
Z12	6d. grey (1874–76) (Plate Nos. 14, 15, 16)	..	50·00
Z13	8d. orange (1876)		
Z14	1s. green (1865) (Plate No. 4)		
Z15	1s. green (1867–73) (Plate Nos. 6, 7)		
Z16	1s. green (1873–77) (Plate Nos. 8, 10, 12, 13)	..	45·00
Z17	1s. orange-brown (1880) (Plate No. 13)	..	£250
Z18	1s. orange-brown (1881) (Plate No. 13)	..	70·00
Z19	2s. blue (1867)	..	£150
Z20	2s. brown (1880)	..	£150
Z21	5s. rose (1867–74) (Plate Nos. 1, 2)	..	£2000
Z22	5s. rose (1882) (Plate No. 4), blue *paper*	..	£300
Z23	10s. greenish grey (1878)	..	£1100
			£1800

1880.
Z24	1d. Venetian red	..	
Z25	1½d. Venetian red	..	45·00

PERU

British Agencies in Peru date from 1846 when offices were established at Arica and Callao. The network was later expanded to include agencies at Paita (1848), Pisco (1868) and Iquique and Islay (both 1869). This last office was transferred to Mollendo in 1877.

It is believed that a further agency existed at Pisagua, but no details exist.

Great Britain stamps were supplied from 1865 and can be found used in combination with Peru adhesives paying the local postage. The Postal Agency at Pisco closed in 1870 and the remainder in 1879, the towns of Arica, Iquique and Pisagua passing to Chile by treaty in 1883.

ARICA
CROWNED-CIRCLE HANDSTAMPS

CC1　CC **1**　ARICA (Black or R.) (5.11.1850)
　　　　　　　　　　　　　Price on cover £2750

Stamps of GREAT BRITAIN *cancelled* "C 36" *as in Types* **4**, **12** *or* **14**.

1865 *to* **1879**.
Z 1	½d. rose-red (1870–79)		*From*	50·00
	Plate Nos. 5, 6, 10, 11, 13.			
Z 2	1d. rose-red (1864–79)		*From*	40·00
	Plate Nos. 102, 139, 140, 163, 167.			
Z 3	1½d. lake-red (1870–74) (Plate No. 3)			
Z 4	2d. blue (1858–69) (Plate No. 14)			70·00
Z 5	3d. rose (1867–73) (Plate Nos. 5, 9)			
Z 6	3d. rose (1873–76)		*From*	30·00
	Plate Nos. 11, 12, 17, 18, 19.			
Z 7	4d. vermilion (1865–73)	..	*From*	32·00
	Plate Nos. 10, 11, 12, 13, 14.			
Z 8	4d. vermilion (1876) (Plate No. 15)			
Z 9	4d. sage-green (1877) (Plate Nos. 15, 16)			£140
Z10	6d. lilac (1862) (Plate Nos. 3, 4)			
Z11	6d. lilac (1865–67) (Plate No. 5)			
Z12	6d. violet (1867–70) (Plate Nos. 6, 8, 9)			35·00
Z13	6d. buff (1873) (Plate No. 11)			80·00
Z14	6d. chestnut (1872) (Plate No. 11)			
Z15	6d. grey (1873) (Plate No. 12)			£120
Z16	6d. grey (1874–76) (Plate Nos. 13, 14, 15, 16)	*From*		28·00
Z17	8d. orange (1876)	..	..	
Z18	9d. straw (1862)	..	..	
Z19	9d. straw (1865)	..	..	
Z20	9d. straw (1867)	..	..	£150
Z21	10d. red-brown (1867)	..	..	
Z22	1s. green (1862)	..	..	
Z23	1s. green (1865)	..	..	
Z24	1s. green (1867–73) (Plate Nos. 4, 5, 6, 7)	*From*		26·00
Z25	1s. green (1873–77)		*From*	50·00
	Plate Nos. 8, 9, 10, 11, 12, 13.			
Z26	2s. blue (1867)	..		£150
Z27	5s. rose (1867–74) (Plate Nos. 1, 2)	..		£350

CALLAO
CROWNED-CIRCLE HANDSTAMPS

CC2　CC **2**　CALLAO (R.) (13.1.1846)　. . *Price on cover* £1000
CC3　CC **1**　CALLAO (R.) (16.7.1846)　. . *Price on cover* £550
Nos. CC2/3 can be found used on covers from 1865 showing the local postage paid by a Peru adhesive.

Stamps of GREAT BRITAIN *cancelled* "C 38" *as in Types* **4**, **12** *or with circular date stamp as Type* **5**.

1865 *to* **1879**.
Z28	½d. rose-red (1870–79)	..	*From*	35·00
	Plate Nos. 5, 6, 10, 11, 12, 13, 14.			
Z29	1d. rose-red (1864–79)	..	*From*	14·00
	Plate Nos. 74, 88, 89, 93, 94, 97, 108, 123,			
	127, 128, 130, 134, 137, 139, 140, 141, 143,			
	144, 145, 146, 148, 149, 156, 157, 160, 163,			
	167, 171, 172, 173, 175, 176, 180, 181, 182,			
	183, 185, 187, 190, 193, 195, 198, 199, 200,			
	201, 204, 206, 209, 210, 212, 213, 215.			
Z30	1½d. lake-red (1870–74) (Plate No. 3)	..		
Z31	2d. blue (1858–69)		*From*	18·00
	Plate Nos. 9, 12, 13, 14, 15.			
Z32	3d. carmine-rose (1862)	..		
Z33	3d. rose (1865) (Plate No. 4)			55·00
Z34	3d. rose (1867–73)		*From*	24·00
	Plate Nos. 5, 6, 7, 8, 9, 10.			
Z35	3d. rose (1873–76)		*From*	30·00
	Plate Nos. 11, 12, 14, 15, 16, 17, 18, 19.			
Z36	4d. red (1862) (Plate Nos. 3, 4)			
Z37	4d. vermilion (1865–73)	..	*From*	28·00
	Plate Nos. 8, 10, 11, 12, 13, 14.			
Z38	4d. vermilion (1876) (Plate No. 15)			£175
Z39	4d. sage-green (1877) (Plate Nos. 15, 16)			£140
Z40	6d. lilac (1862) (Plate Nos. 3, 4)			
Z40a	6d. lilac (1865) (Plate No. 5)			
Z41	6d. lilac (1867)			

Z42	6d. violet (1867–70) (Plate Nos. 6, 8, 9)		*From*	38·00
Z43	6d. buff (1872–73) (Plate Nos. 11, 12)		*From*	55·00
Z44	6d. chestnut (1872) (Plate No. 11)			30·00
Z45	6d. grey (1873) (Plate No. 12)			£120
Z46	6d. grey (1874–80) (Plate Nos. 13, 14, 15, 16)	*From*		28·00
Z47	8d. orange (1876)			£175
Z48	9d. straw (1862)			
Z49	9d. straw (1865)			£275
Z50	9d. straw (1867)			£160
Z51	10d. red-brown (1867)			£200
Z52	1s. green (1865)			
Z53	1s. green (1867–73) (Plate Nos. 4, 5, 6, 7)	*From*		22·00
Z54	1s. green (1873–77)		*From*	38·00
	Plate Nos. 8, 9, 10, 11, 12, 13.			
Z55	2s. blue (1867)			£110
Z56	5s. rose (1867–74) (Plate Nos. 1, 2)	..	*From*	£300

IQUIQUE

Stamps of GREAT BRITAIN *cancelled* "D 87" *as Type* **12**.

1865 *to* **1879**.
Z57	½d. rose-red (1870–79) (Plate Nos. 5, 6, 13, 14)	..		70·00
Z58	1d. rose-red (1864–79) (Plate Nos. 76, 179, 185, 205)		42·00
Z59	2d. blue (1858–69) (Plate Nos. 9, 12, 13, 14)		
Z60	3d. rose (1867–73) (Plate Nos. 5, 6, 7, 8, 9)	*From*		40·00
Z61	3d. rose (1873–76) (Plate Nos. 12, 18, 19)			60·00
Z62	4d. vermilion (1865–73) (Plate Nos. 12, 13, 14)			42·00
Z63	4d. vermilion (1876) (Plate No. 15)			£200
Z64	4d. sage-green (1877) (Plate Nos. 15, 16)	*From*		£150
Z65	6d. mauve (1869) (Plate Nos. 8, 9)	..		
Z66	6d. buff (1872–73) (Plate Nos. 11, 12)	*From*		85·00
Z67	6d. chestnut (1872) (Plate No. 11)			
Z68	6d. grey (1873) (Plate No. 12)			£120
Z69	6d. grey (1874–76) (Plate Nos. 13, 14, 15, 16)			
Z70	8d. orange (1876)	..	..	£275
Z71	9d. straw (1867)	..	..	£175
Z72	10d. red-brown (1867)	..		
Z73	1s. green (1867–73) (Plate Nos. 4, 6, 7)	*From*		38·00
Z74	1s. green (1873–77)		*From*	48·00
	Plate Nos. 8, 9, 10, 11, 12, 13.			
Z75	2s. blue (1867)			

ISLAY (*later* MOLLENDO)
CROWNED-CIRCLE HANDSTAMPS

CC4　CC **1**　ISLAY (Black or R.) (23.10.1850)

Stamps of GREAT BRITAIN *cancelled* "C 42" *as Types* **4** *or* **12**.

1865 *to* **1879**.
Z76	1d. rose-red (1864–79)	..	*From*	38·00
	Plate Nos. 78, 84, 87, 88, 96, 103, 125, 134.			
Z77	1½d. lake-red (1870–74) (Plate No. 3)			
Z78	2d. blue (1858–69) (Plate Nos. 9, 13, 15)			30·00
Z79	3d. carmine-rose (1862)			
Z80	3d. rose (1865)			75·00
Z81	3d. rose (1867–73) (Plate Nos. 4, 5, 6, 10)			40·00
Z82	4d. red (1862) (Plate Nos. 3, 4)			80·00
Z83	4d. vermilion (1867–73)		*From*	40·00
	Plate Nos. 9, 10, 11, 12, 13.			
Z84	4d. vermilion (1876) (Plate No. 15)			
Z85	4d. sage-green (1877) (Plate Nos. 15, 16)			£150
Z86	6d. lilac (1862) (Plate Nos. 3, 4)			80·00
Z87	6d. lilac (1865) (Plate No. 5)			60·00
Z88	6d. violet (1867–70) (Plate Nos. 6, 8, 9)	*From*		45·00
Z89	6d. buff (1873) (Plate No. 11)			
Z90	6d. grey (1873) (Plate No. 12)			
Z91	6d. grey (1874–76) (Plate Nos. 13, 14, 15, 16)	*From*		38·00
Z92	9d. straw (1865)			£275
Z93	9d. straw (1867)			£160
Z94	10d. red-brown (1867)			£180
Z95	1s. green (1865) (Plate No. 4)			
Z96	1s. green (1867–73) (Plate Nos. 4, 5, 6, 7)	*From*		32·00
Z97	1s. green (1873–77) (Plate Nos. 8, 10, 12, 13)	*From*		44·00
Z98	2s. blue (1867)			
Z99	5s. rose (1867) (Plate No. 1)			

PAITA
CROWNED-CIRCLE HANDSTAMPS

CC5　CC **1**　PAITA (Black *or* R.) (5.11.1850)
　　　　　　　　　　　　　Price on cover £3750

Stamps of GREAT BRITAIN *cancelled* "C 43" *as Type* **4**.

1865 *to* **1879**.
Z100	1d. rose-red (1864–79) (Plate Nos. 127, 147)	..		
Z101	2d. blue (1858–69) (Plate Nos. 9, 14)	..		
Z102	3d. rose (1867–73) (Plate Nos. 5, 6)	..		40·00
Z103	3d. rose (1876) (Plate Nos. 17, 18, 19)	..		40·00
Z104	4d. vermilion (1865–73)	..	*From*	40·00
	Plate Nos. 10, 11, 12, 13, 14.			
Z105	4d. sage-green (1877) (Plate No. 15)			
Z106	6d. lilac (1862) (Plate No. 3)			85·00
Z107	6d. lilac (1865–67) (Plate Nos. 5, 6)			50·00
Z108	6d. violet (1867–70) (Plate Nos. 6, 8, 9)			42·00
Z109	6d. buff (1872–73) (Plate Nos. 11, 12)	*From*		70·00
Z110	6d. chestnut (Plate No. 11)			42·00
Z111	6d. grey (1873)			
Z112	6d. grey (1874–76) (Plate Nos. 13, 14, 15)	..		
Z113	9d. straw (1862)	..		
Z114	10d. red-brown (1867)	..		£275
Z115	1s. green (1865) (Plate No. 4)	..		
Z116	1s. green (1867–73) (Plate No. 4)	..		40·00
Z117	1s. green (1873–77) (Plate Nos. 8, 9, 10, 13)	..		42·00
Z118	2s. blue (1867)	..		£175
Z119	5s. rose (1867) (Plate No. 1)	..		£450

PISAGUA(?)

Stamp of GREAT BRITAIN *cancelled* "D 65" *as Type* **12**.

Z120	2s. blue (1867)		

PISCO AND CHINCHA ISLANDS

Stamps of GREAT BRITAIN *cancelled* "D 74" *as Type* **12**.

1865 *to* **1870**.
Z121	2d. blue (1858–69) (Plate No. 9)		
Z122	4d. vermilion (1865–73) (Plate Nos. 10, 12)		£200
Z123	6d. violet (1868) (Plate No. 6)		£800
Z124	1s. green (1867) (Plate No. 4)		
Z125	2s. blue (1867)		£700

PORTO RICO

A British Postal Agency operated at San Juan from 1844. On 24 October 1872 further offices were opened at Aguadilla, Arroyo, Mayaguez and Ponce, with Naguabo added three years later.

Great Britain stamps were used during 1865–66 and from 1873 to 1877. All the British Agencies closed on 1 May 1877.

AGUADILLA

Stamps of GREAT BRITAIN *cancelled* "F 84" *as Type* **8**.

1873 to 1877.

Z 1	½d. rose-red (1870) (Plate No. 6)	..	..	..	80·00
Z 2	1d. rose-red (1864–79)	..	..	..	42·00
	Plate Nos. 119, 122, 139, 149, 156, 160.				
Z 3	2d. blue (1858–69) (Plate No. 14)	..	..	
Z 4	3d. rose (1867–73) (Plate Nos. 7, 8, 9)	..	
Z 5	3d. rose (1873–76) (Plate No. 12)	..	..	
Z 6	4d. vermilion (1865–73) (Plate Nos. 12, 13, 14)	..	50·00
Z 7	4d. vermilion (1876) (Plate No. 15)	..	£175
Z 7a	6d. pale buff (1872–73) (Plate No. 11)	..	
Z 8	6d. grey (1874–76) (Plate Nos. 13, 14)	..	
Z 9	9d. straw (1867)	..	..	..	£300
Z10	10d. red-brown (1867)	..	..	..	£200
Z11	1s. green (1867–73) (Plate Nos. 4, 5, 6, 7)	.. *From*	40·00
Z12	1s. green (1873–77)	..	..	..	55·00
	Plate Nos. 8, 9, 10, 11, 12.				
Z13	2s. blue (1867)	..	..	..	£225

ARROYO

Stamps of GREAT BRITAIN *cancelled* "F 83" *as Type* **8**.

1873 to 1877.

Z14	½d. rose-red (1870) (Plate No. 5)	..	..	55·00
Z15	1d. rose-red (1864–79)	..	..	..	45·00
	Plate Nos. 149, 150, 151, 156, 164, 174, 175.				
Z16	1½d. lake-red (1870) (Plate Nos. 1, 3)	..	
Z17	2d. blue (1858–69) (Plate No. 14)	..	
Z18	3d. rose (1867–73) (Plate Nos. 5, 7, 10)	..	40·00
Z19	3d. rose (1873–76) (Plate Nos. 11, 12, 14, 16, 18)	..	45·00
Z20	4d. vermilion (1865–73) (Plate Nos. 12, 13, 14)	..	40·00
Z21	4d. vermilion (1876) (Plate No. 15)	..	£175
Z22	6d. chestnut (1872) (Plate No. 11)	..	55·00
Z23	6d. pale-buff (1872) (Plate No. 11)	..	60·00
Z23a	6d. grey (1873) (Plate No. 12)	..	
Z24	6d. grey (1874–76) (Plate Nos. 13, 14, 15)	..	50·00
Z25	9d. straw (1867)	..	..	..	£225
Z26	10d. red-brown (1867)	..	..	£175
Z27	1s. green (1865) (Plate No. 4)	..	
Z28	1s. green (1867–73) (Plate Nos. 4, 5, 6, 7)	..	40·00
Z29	1s. green (1873–77)	..	..	..	50·00
	Plate Nos. 8, 9, 10, 11, 12, 13.				
Z30	2s. blue (1867)	..	..	..	£180
Z31	5s. rose (1867–74) (Plate No. 2)	..	

MAYAGUEZ

Stamps of GREAT BRITAIN *cancelled* "F 85" *as Type* **8**.

1873 to 1877.

Z32	½d. rose-red (1870)	..	..	*From*	45·00
	Plate Nos. 4, 5, 6, 8, 10, 11.				
Z33	1d. rose-red (1864–79)	..	*From*	24·00
	Plate Nos. 76, 120, 121, 122, 124, 134, 137, 140, 146, 149, 150, 151, 154, 155, 156, 157, 160, 167, 170, 171, 174, 175, 176, 178, 180, 182, 185, 186, 189.				
Z34	1½d. lake-red (1870–74) (Plate Nos. 1, 3)	..	40·00
Z35	2d. blue (1858–69) (Plate Nos. 13, 14)	..	38·00
Z36	3d. rose (1867–73) (Plate Nos. 7, 8, 9, 10)	..	30·00
Z37	3d. rose (1873–76)	..	..	..	30·00
	Plate Nos. 11, 12, 14, 15, 16, 17, 18, 19.				
Z38	4d. vermilion (1865–73) (Plate Nos. 11, 12, 13, 14)	..	32·00
Z39	4d. vermilion (1876) (Plate No. 15)	..	£160
Z40	4d. sage-green (1877) (Plate No. 15)	..	
Z41	6d. mauve (1870) (Plate No. 9)	..	
Z42	6d. buff (1872) (Plate No. 11)	..	75·00
Z43	6d. chestnut (1872) (Plate No. 11)	..	65·00
Z44	6d. grey (1873) (Plate No. 12)	..	
Z45	6d. grey (1874–80) (Plate Nos. 13, 14, 15, 16)	..	38·00
Z46	8d. orange (1876)	..	..	..	£175
Z47	9d. straw (1867)	..	..	..	£140
Z48	10d. red-brown (1867)	..	..	£175
Z49	1s. green (1867–73) (Plate Nos. 4, 5, 6, 7)	..	25·00
Z50	1s. green (1873–77)	..	..	*From*	45·00
	Plate Nos. 8, 9, 10, 11, 12.				
Z51	2s. blue (1867)	..	..	..	£160
Z52	5s. rose (1867–74) (Plate Nos. 1, 2)	..	

NAGUABO

Stamps of GREAT BRITAIN *cancelled* "582" *as Type* **9**.

1875 to 1877.

Z53	½d. rose-red (1870–79) (Plate Nos. 5, 12, 14)	..	
Z54	1d. rose-red (1864–79) (Plate Nos. 159, 165)	..	
Z55	3d. rose (1873–76) (Plate Nos. 17, 18)	..	£400
Z56	4d. vermilion (1872–73) (Plate Nos. 13, 14)	*From*	£375
Z57	4d. vermilion (1876) (Plate No. 15)	..	
Z58	6d. grey (1874–76) (Plate Nos. 14, 15)	..	
Z59	9d. straw (1867)	..	..	
Z60	10d. red-brown (1867)	..	..	£800
Z61	1s. green (1873–77) (Plate Nos. 11, 12)	..	
Z62	2s. dull blue (1867) (Plate No. 1)	..	£600

PONCE

Stamps of GREAT BRITAIN *cancelled* "F 88" *as Type* **8**.

1873 to 1877.

Z63	½d. rose-red (1870) (Plate Nos. 5, 10, 12)	..	50·00
Z64	1d. rose-red (1864–79)	..	*From*	30·00
	Plate Nos. 120, 121, 122, 123, 124, 146, 148, 154, 156, 157, 158, 160, 167, 171, 174, 175, 179, 186, 187.				
Z65	1½d. lake-red (1870–74) (Plate No. 3)	..	£100
Z66	2d. blue (1858–69) (Plate Nos. 13, 14)	..	40·00
Z67	3d. rose (1867–73) (Plate Nos. 7, 8, 9)	..	
Z68	3d. rose (1873–76) (Plate Nos. 12, 16, 17, 18, 19)	..	35·00
Z69	4d. vermilion (1865–73)	..	*From*	35·00
	Plate Nos. 8, 9, 12, 13, 14.				
Z70	4d. vermilion (1876) (Plate No. 15)	..	£175
Z71	4d. sage-green (1877) (Plate Nos. 15, 16)	..	£140
Z72	6d. buff (1872–73) (Plate Nos. 11, 12)	..	70·00
Z73	6d. chestnut (1872) (Plate No. 11)	..	50·00

Z74	6d. grey (1873) (Plate No. 12)	..	
Z75	6d. grey (1874–76) (Plate Nos. 13, 14, 15)	.. *From*	35·00
Z76	9d. straw (1867)	..	..	..	£200
Z77	10d. red-brown (1867)	..	..	£150
Z78	1s. green (1867–73) (Plate Nos. 4, 6, 7)	..	30·00
Z79	1s. green (1873–77)	..	..	*From*	45·00
	Plate Nos. 8, 9, 10, 11, 12, 13.				
Z80	2s. blue (1867)	..	..	
Z81	5s. rose (1867–74) (Plate Nos. 1, 2)	*From*	£350

SAN JUAN

CROWNED-CIRCLE HANDSTAMPS

CC1	CC **1**	SAN JUAN PORTO RICO (R. *or* Black)			
		(25.5.1844)	..	*Price on cover*	£800

No. CC1 may be found on cover, used in conjunction with Spanish colonial adhesive stamps paying the local postage.

Stamps of GREAT BRITAIN *cancelled* "C 61" *as in Types* **4**, **8** *or* **14**.

1865 to 1866 *and* **1873 to 1877.**

Z 82	½d. rose-red (1870) (Plate Nos. 5, 10, 15)	.. *From*	30·00
Z 83	1d. rose-red (1857)	..	
Z 84	1d. rose-red (1864–79)	..	*From*	20·00
	Plate Nos. 73, 74, 81, 84, 90, 94, 100, 101, 102, 107, 117, 122, 124, 125, 127, 130, 137, 138, 139, 140, 145, 146, 149, 153, 156, 159, 160, 162, 163, 169, 171, 172, 173, 174, 175, 179, 180, 182, 186.				
Z 85	1½d. lake-red (1870–74) (Plate Nos. 1, 3)	.. *From*	60·00
Z 86	2d. blue (1858–69) (Plate Nos. 9, 13, 14)	*From*	25·00
Z 87	3d. rose (1865) (Plate No. 4)	..	55·00
Z 88	3d. rose (1867–73)	..	*From*	25·00
	Plate Nos. 5, 6, 7, 8, 9, 10.				
Z 89	3d. rose (1873–76)	..	*From*	25·00
	Plate Nos. 11, 12, 14, 15, 16, 17, 18.				
Z 90	4d. vermilion (1865–73)	..	*From*	30·00
	Plate Nos. 7, 8, 9, 10, 11, 12, 13, 14.				
Z 91	4d. vermilion (1876) (Plate No. 15)	..	£175
Z 92	6d. lilac (1865–67) (Plate Nos. 5, 6)	..	35·00
Z 93	6d. lilac (1867) (Plate No. 6)	..	40·00
Z 94	6d. violet (1867–70) (Plate Nos. 6, 8, 9)	*From*	30·00
Z 95	6d. buff (1872–73) (Plate Nos. 11, 12)	..	60·00
Z 96	6d. chestnut (1872) (Plate No. 11)	..	40·00
Z 97	6d. grey (1873) (Plate No. 12)	..	
Z 98	6d. grey (1874–76) (Plate Nos. 13, 14, 15)	*From*	24·00
Z 99	9d. straw (1862)	..	..	£175
Z100	9d. straw (1865)	..	..	£275
Z101	9d. straw (1867)	..	..	£150
Z102	10d. red-brown (1867)	..	..	£200
Z103	1s. green (1865) (Plate No. 4)	..	90·00
Z104	1s. green (1867–73) (Plate Nos. 4, 5, 6, 7)	*From*	24·00
Z105	1s. green (1873–77)	..	*From*	40·00
	Plate Nos. 8, 9, 10, 11, 12, 13.				
Z106	2s. blue (1867)	..	..	£110
Z107	5s. rose (1867) (Plate Nos. 1, 2)	.. *From*	£300

RUSSIA

ARMY FIELD OFFICES IN THE CRIMEA

1854 *to* **1857.**

Crown between Stars

Z 1	1d. red-brown (1841), *imperf*	..	..	£450
Z 2	1d. red-brown (1854), Die I, *wmk Small Crown, perf* 16			
Z 3	1d. red-brown (1855), Die II, *wmk Small Crown, perf* 16			£140
Z 4	1d. red-brown, Die I, *wmk Small Crown, perf* 14		
Z 5	1d. red-brown (1855), Die II, Small Crown, *perf* 14		
Z 6	2d. blue (1841)	..	..	..	£900
Z 7	2d. blue, Small Crown (1854), *perf* 16 (Plate No. 4)			
Z 8	1s. green (1847), *embossed*	..	..	£1200

Star between Cyphers

Z 9	1d. red-brown (1841), *imperf*	..	
Z10	1d. red-brown (1854), Die I, *wmk Small Crown, perf* 16			70·00
Z11	1d. red-brown (1855), Die II, *wmk Small Crown, perf* 16			70·00
Z12	1d. red-brown (1855), Die I, *wmk Small Crown, perf* 14			70·00
Z13	1d. red-brown (1855), Die II, *wmk Small Crown, perf* 14			70·00
Z14	1d. red-brown (1855), Die I, *wmk Large Crown, perf* 16			90·00
Z15	1d. red-brown (1855), Die II, *wmk Large Crown, perf* 14			42·00
Z16	2d. blue (1841), *imperf*	..	..	£1000
Z17	2d. blue (1854) *wmk Small Crown, perf* 16	*From*	£130
	Plate Nos. 4, 5.				
Z18	2d. blue (1855) *wmk Small Crown, perf* 14	..	£175
	Plate No. 4.				
Z19	2d. blue (1855), *wmk Large Crown, perf* 16	..	£200
	Plate No. 5.				
Z20	2d. blue (1855), *wmk Large Crown, perf* 14	..	£120
	Plate No. 5.				
Z21	4d. rose (1857)	..	..	..	£800
Z22	6d. violet (1854), *embossed*	..	..	£1100
Z23	1s. green (1847), *embossed*	..	..	£1100

SPAIN

Little is known about the operation of British Packet Agencies in Spain, other than the dates recorded for the various postal markings in the G.P.O. Proof Books. The Agency at Corunna is said to date from the late 17th century when the Spanish packets for South America were based there. The Spanish port of call was changed to Vigo in 1846 and the office at Corunna was then closed. Teneriffe became a port-of-call for the South American packets in 1817 and this arrangement continued until 1858.

CORUNNA

CROWNED-CIRCLE HANDSTAMPS

CC1	CC **1b**	CORUNNA (28.2.1842)	..	..	

Although recorded in the G.P.O. Proof Books no example of No. CC1 on cover is known.

TENERIFFE (CANARY ISLANDS)

CROWNED-CIRCLE HANDSTAMPS

CC2	CC **7**	TENERIFFE (6.1.1851)	..	*Price on cover* £3000
CC3	CC **4**	TENERIFFE (23.10.1857)	..	*Price on cover* £3000

No. CC2/3 can be found used on covers from Spain to South America with the rate from Spain to Teneriffe paid in Spanish adhesive stamps.

UNITED STATES OF AMERICA

The network of British Packet Agencies, to operate the trans-Atlantic Packet system, was re-established in 1814 after the War of 1812.

The New York Agency opened in that year to be followed by further offices at Boston, Charleston (South Carolina), New Orleans, Savannah (Georgia) (all in 1842), Mobile (Alabama) (1848) and San Francisco (1860). Of these agencies Charleston and Savannah closed the same year (1842) as did New Orleans, although the latter was re-activated from 1848 to 1850. Mobile closed 1850, Boston in 1865, New York in 1882 and San Francisco, for which no postal markings have been recorded, in 1883.

Although recorded in the G.P.O. Proof Books no actual examples of the Crowned-circle handstamps for Charleston, Mobile, New Orleans and Savannah are known on cover.

The G.P.O. proof books record, in error, a Crowned-circle handstamp for St. Michaels, Maryland. This handstamp was intended for the agency on San Miguel in the Azores.

CHARLESTON

CROWNED-CIRCLE HANDSTAMPS

CC1	CC **1b**	CHARLESTON (15.12.1841)	..	

MOBILE

CROWNED-CIRCLE HANDSTAMPS

CC2	CC **1b**	MOBILE (15.12.1841)	..	

NEW ORLEANS

CROWNED-CIRCLE HANDSTAMPS

CC3	CC **1b**	NEW ORLEANS (15.12.1841)	..	
CC4	CC **1**	NEW ORLEANS (27.4.1848)	..	

NEW YORK

CROWNED-CIRCLE HANDSTAMPS

CC5	CC **1b**	NEW YORK (R.) (15.12.1841)	..	

SAVANNAH

CROWNED-CIRCLE HANDSTAMPS

CC6	CC **1b**	SAVANNAH (15.12.1841)		

URUGUAY

MONTEVIDEO

British packets commenced calling at Montevideo in 1824 on passage to and from Buenos Aires.

Great Britain stamps were in use from 1864. Combination covers exist with the local postage paid by Uruguay adhesive stamps. The agency was closed on 31 July 1873.

CROWNED-CIRCLE HANDSTAMPS

CC1	CC **5**	MONTEVIDEO (Black *or* R.) (6.1.1851)		
			Price on cover £750

Stamps of GREAT BRITAIN *cancelled* "C 28" *as in Types* **4** *or* **12**.

1864 to 1873.

Z 1	1d. rose-red (1864)	..	..	..	45·00
	Plate Nos. 73, 92, 93, 94, 119, 148, 154, 157, 171.				
Z 2	2d. blue (1858–69) (Plate Nos. 9, 13)	..	38·00
Z 3	3d. rose (1865) (Plate No. 4)	..	
Z 4	3d. rose (1867–71) (Plate Nos. 4, 5, 7)	..	38·00
Z 6	4d. rose (1857)	..	
Z 7	4d. red (1862) (Plate No. 4)	..	
Z 8	4d. vermilion (1865–70)	..	*From*	35·00
	Plate Nos. 7, 8, 9, 10, 11, 12.				
Z 9	6d. lilac (1856)	..	
Z10	6d. lilac (1862) (Plate No. 4)	..	
Z11	6d. lilac (1865–67) (Plate Nos. 5, 6)	..	48·00
Z12	6d. lilac (1867) (Plate No. 6)	..	
Z13	6d. violet (1870) (Plate Nos. 8, 9)	*From*	38·00
Z14	6d. buff (1872)	..	
Z15	6d. chestnut (1872)	..	
Z16	9d. straw (1862)	..	
Z17	9d. straw (1865)	..	
Z18	9d. straw (1867)	..	..	£160
Z19	10d. red-brown (1867)	..	..	£150
Z20	1s. green (1862)	..	..	£150
Z21	1s. green (1865) (Plate No. 4)	..	90·00
Z22	1s. green (1867–73) (Plate Nos. 4, 5)	..	30·00
Z23	2s. blue (1867)	..	..	95·00
Z24	5s. rose (1867) (Plate No. 1)	..	£300

VENEZUELA

British Postal Agencies were initially opened at La Guayra and Porto Cabello on 1 January 1842. Further offices were added at Maracaibo in 1842 and Ciudad Bolivar during January 1868. Porto Cabello closed in 1858 and Maracaibo was also short-lived. The remaining offices closed at the end of 1879 when Venezuela joined the U.P.U.

Great Britain stamps were used at La Guayra from 1865 and at Ciudad Bolivar from its establishment in 1868. They can be found used in combination with Venezuela adhesives paying the local postage.

CIUDAD BOLIVAR

Stamps of GREAT BRITAIN *cancelled* "D 22" *as Type* **12**, *or circular date stamp as Type* **17**.

1868 *to* **1879**.

Z 1	1d. rose-red (1864–79) (Plate No. 133)	..	..	75·00
Z 2	2d. blue (1858–69) (Plate No. 13)	..	..	
Z 3	3d. rose (1867–73) (Plate No. 5)	..	..	
Z 4	3d. rose (1873–79) (Plate No. 11)	..	..	£130
Z 5	4d. vermilion (1865–73) (Plate Nos. 9, 11, 12, 14)			45·00
Z 6	4d. sage-green (1877) (Plate Nos. 15, 16)		*From*	£140
Z 7	4d. grey-brown (1880) *wmk* Crown (Plate No. 17)			
Z 8	9d. straw (1867)	..	..	
Z 9	10d. red-brown (1867)	..	..	
Z10	1s. green (1867–73) (Plate Nos. 4, 5, 7)		*From*	95·00
Z11	1s. green (1873–77) (Plate Nos. 10, 12, 13)			70·00
Z12	2s. blue (1867)	..	..	£300
Z13	5s. rose (1867–74) (Plate Nos. 1, 2)			£450

LA GUAYRA
CROWNED-CIRCLE HANDSTAMPS

CC1 CC **1b** LA GUAYRA (R.) (15.12.1841) *Price on cover* £850

Stamps of GREAT BRITAIN *cancelled* "C 60" *as Type* **4**, *circular date stamp as Type* **16** *or with No.* CC1.

1865 *to* **1880**.

Z14	½d. rose-red (1870) (Plate No. 6)	..	..	
Z15	1d. rose-red (1864–79)	..	*From*	40·00
	Plate Nos. 81, 92, 96, 98, 111, 113, 115, 131, 138, 144, 145, 154, 177, 178, 180, 196.			
Z16	1½d. lake-red (1870–74) (Plate No. 3)	..		
Z17	2d. blue (1858–69) (Plate Nos. 13, 14)	..	..	42·00
Z18	3d. rose (1873–76)	..	*From*	50·00
	Plate Nos. 14, 15, 17, 18, 19.			
Z19	4d. vermilion (1865–73)	..	*From*	40·00
	Plate Nos. 7, 9, 11, 12, 13, 14.			
Z20	4d. vermilion (1876) (Plate No. 15)	..		£175
Z21	4d. sage-green (1877) (Plate Nos. 15, 16)			£140
Z22	6d. lilac (1865) (Plate No. 5)	..		
Z23	6d. violet (1867–70) (Plate Nos. 6, 8)			
Z24	6d. buff (1872–73) (Plate Nos. 11, 12)	*From*	90·00
Z25	6d. grey (1873) (Plate No. 12)	..		£120
Z26	6d. grey (1874–76) (Plate Nos. 13, 14, 15, 16)		42·00
Z27	8d. orange (1876)	..	..	£250
Z28	9d. straw (1862)	..	..	
Z29	9d. straw (1867)	..	..	
Z30	10d. red-brown (1867)	..	..	
Z31	1s. green (1865) (Plate No. 4)	..		90·00
Z32	1s. green (1867–73) (Plate Nos. 4, 7)			
Z33	1s. green (1873–77)	..	*From*	34·00
	Plate Nos. 8, 9, 10, 11, 12, 13.			
Z34	2s. blue (1867)	..	..	£200
Z35	5s. rose (1867–74) (Plate Nos. 1, 2)	*From*	£400

MARACAIBO
CROWNED-CIRCLE HANDSTAMPS

CC2 CC **1b** MARACAIBO (31.12.1841)
No examples of No. CC2 on cover have been recorded.

PORTO CABELLO
CROWNED-CIRCLE HANDSTAMPS

CC3 CC **1b** PORTO-CABELLO (R.) (15.12.1841)
Price on cover £1500

MAIL BOAT OBLITERATIONS

The following cancellations were supplied to G.P.O. sorters operating on ships holding mail contracts from the British Post Office. They were for use on mail posted on board, but most examples occur on letters from soldiers and sailors serving overseas which were forwarded to the mailboats without postmarks.

P. & O. MEDITERRANEAN AND FAR EAST MAILBOATS

The first such cancellation, "A 17" as Type **2**, was issued to the Southampton–Alexandria packet in April 1858, but no examples have been recorded.

The G.P.O. Proof Book also records "B 16", in Type **2**, as being issued for marine sorting in November 1859, but this postmark was subsequently used by the Plymouth and Bristol Sorting Carriage.

Sorting on board P. & O. packets ceased in June 1870 and many of the cancellation numbers were subsequently reallocated using Types **9**, **11** or **12**.

Stamps of GREAT BRITAIN *cancelled* "A 80" *as Type* **2**.

1859 (Mar) *to* **1870**.

Z1 1d. rose-red (1857), Die II, *wmk* Large Crown, *perf* 14
Z2 6d. lilac (1856)

Stamps of GREAT BRITAIN *cancelled* "A 81" *as Type* **2**.

1859 (Mar) *to* **1870**.

Z 3 1d. rose-red (1857), Die II, *wmk* Large Crown, *perf* 14
Z 4 1d. rose-red (1864–79)
      Plate Nos. 84, 85, 86, 91, 97.
Z 5 2d. blue (1858–69) (Plate No. 9)
Z 6 4d. red (1862) (Plate No. 4)

Z 7 4d. vermilion (1865–73) (Plate No. 8)
Z 8 6d. lilac (1856)
Z 9 6d. lilac (1862) (Plate No. 3)
Z10 6d. lilac (1865–67)
       Plate Nos. 5, 6.
Z11 6d. lilac (1867) (Plate No. 6)
Z12 6d. violet (1867–70)
       Plate Nos. 6, 8.
Z13 10d. red-brown (1867)
Z14 1s. green (1856)

Stamps of GREAT BRITAIN *cancelled* "A 82" *as Type* **2**.

1859 (Mar) *to* **1870**.

Z15 1d. rose-red (1857), Die II, *wmk* Large Crown, *perf* 14
Z16 2d. blue (1858) (Plate No. 7)
Z17 4d. rose (1856)
Z18 6d. lilac (1856)
Z19 6d. lilac (1865–67)
       Plate Nos. 5, 6.
Z20 6d. lilac (1867) (Plate No. 6)

Stamps of GREAT BRITAIN *cancelled* "A 83" *as Type* **2**.

1859 (Apr) *to* **1870**.

Z21 1d. rose-red (1857), Die II, *wmk* Large Crown, *perf* 14
Z22 1d. rose-red (1864–79)
       Plate Nos. 73, 74, 84, 91, 109.
Z23 3d. carmine-rose (1862)
Z24 4d. rose (1857)
Z25 4d. red (1862)
Z26 4d. vermilion (1865–73)
       Plate Nos. 9, 10.
Z27 6d. lilac (1856)
Z28 6d. lilac (1862)
Z29 6d. lilac (1865–67)
       Plate Nos. 5, 6.
Z30 6d. violet (1867–70)
       Plate Nos. 6, 8.
Z31 10d. red-brown (1867)
Z32 1s. green (1862)

Stamps of GREAT BRITAIN *cancelled* "A 84" *as Type* **2**.

1859 (Apr) *to* **1870**.

Z33 1d. rose-red (1857). Die II, *wmk* Large Crown, *perf* 14

Stamps of GREAT BRITAIN *cancelled* "A 85" *as Type* **2**.

1859 (Apr) *to* **1870**.

Z34 1d. rose-red (1857), Die II, *wmk* Large Crown, *perf* 14
Z35 1d. rose-red (1864–79)
       Plate Nos. 79, 97, 103.
Z36 3d. carmine-rose (1862)
Z37 4d. red (1862)
Z38 6d. lilac (1856)
Z39 6d. lilac (1862)
       Plate Nos. 3, 4.
Z40 6d. lilac (1865–67) (Plate No. 5)
Z41 6d. lilac (1867) (Plate No. 6)
Z42 1s. green (1862)

Stamps of GREAT BRITAIN *cancelled* "A 86" *as Type* **2**.

1859 (Apr) *to* **1870**.

Z43 1d. rose-red (1857), Die II, *wmk* Large Crown, *perf* 14
Z44 1d. rose-red (1864–79)
       Plate Nos. 73, 84, 94, 97, 114, 118.
Z45 3d. rose (1865)
Z46 3d. rose (1867–73)
       Plate Nos. 4, 5.
Z47 4d. rose (1857)
Z48 4d. red (1862) (Plate No. 4)
Z49 4d. vermilion (1865–73) (Plate No. 10)
Z50 6d. lilac (1856)
Z51 6d. lilac (1862)
       Plate Nos. 3, 4.
Z52 6d. lilac (1865–67)
       Plate Nos. 5, 6.
Z53 6d. lilac (1867)
       Plate Nos. 6, 8.
Z54 10d. red-brown (1867)
Z55 1s. green (1862)

Stamps of GREAT BRITAIN *cancelled* "A 87" *as Type* **2**.

1859 (Apr) *to* **1870**.

Z56 1d. rose-red (1857), Die II, *wmk* Large Crown, *perf* 14
Z57 4d. rose (1856)
Z58 6d. lilac (1867) (Plate No. 6)

Stamps of GREAT BRITAIN *cancelled* "A 88" *as Type* **2**.

1859 (Apr) *to* **1870**.

Z59 1d. rose-red (1857), Die II, *wmk* Large Crown, *perf* 14
Z60 1d. rose-red (1864–79)
       Plate Nos. 74, 80, 85.
Z61 4d. rose (1857)
Z62 4d. red (1862)
Z63 4d. vermilion (1865–73) (Plate No. 8)
Z64 6d. lilac (1856)
Z65 6d. lilac (1862) (Plate No. 4)
Z66 6d. lilac (1865–67) (Plate No. 5)
Z67 6d. lilac (1867) (Plate No. 6)
Z68 6d. violet (1867–70) (Plate No. 8)
Z69 10d. red-brown (1867)
Z70 1s. green (1856)

Stamps of GREAT BRITAIN *cancelled* "A 89" *as Type* **2**.

1859 (Apr) *to* **1870**.

Z71 1d. rose-red (1857), Die II, *wmk* Large Crown, *perf* 14
Z72 6d. lilac (1856)

Stamps of GREAT BRITAIN *cancelled* "A 90" *as Type* **2**.

1859 (June) *to* **1870**.

Z73 1d. rose-red (1857), Die II, *wmk* Large Crown, *perf* 14
Z74 4d. rose (1856)
Z75 6d. lilac (1856)
Z76 6d. lilac (1865–67)
       Plate Nos. 5, 6.
Z77 9d. straw (1867)

Stamps of GREAT BRITAIN *cancelled* "A 99" *as Type* **2**.

1859 (June) *to* **1870**.

Z78 1d. rose-red (1857), Die II, *wmk* Large Crown, *perf* 14
Z79 1d. rose-red (1864–79)
       Plate Nos. 93, 97, 99, 118.
Z80 4d. rose (1857)
Z81 4d. red (1862)
Z82 4d. vermilion (1865–73) (Plate No. 11)
Z83 6d. lilac (1856)
Z84 6d. lilac (1862)
Z85 6d. lilac (1865–67)
       Plate Nos. 5, 6.
Z86 10d. red-brown (1867)

Stamps of GREAT BRITAIN *cancelled* "B 03" *as Type* **2**.

1859 (Aug) *to* **1870**.

Z87 1d. rose-red (1857), Die II, *wmk* Large Crown, *perf* 14
Z88 1d. rose-red (1864–79)
       Plate Nos. 109, 116.
Z89 3d. rose (1865) (Plate No. 4)
Z90 6d. lilac (1856)
Z91 6d. lilac (1867) (Plate No. 6)
Z92 6d. violet (1867–70)
       Plate Nos. 6, 8.
Z93 10d. red-brown (1867)

Stamps of GREAT BRITAIN *cancelled* "B 12" *as Type* **2**.

1859 (Oct) *to* **1870**.

Z 94 1d. rose-red (1857), Die II, *wmk* Large Crown, *perf* 14
Z 95 1d. rose-red (1864–79) (Plate No. 94)
Z 96 3d. rose (1865) (Plate No. 4)
Z 97 4d. red (1862)
Z 98 4d. vermilion (1865–73) (Plate No. 8)
Z 99 6d. lilac (1856)
Z100 6d. lilac (1862)
Z101 6d. lilac (1865–67)
       Plate Nos. 5, 6.
Z102 6d. violet (1867–70) (Plate No. 8)

Stamps of GREAT BRITAIN *cancelled* "B 56" *as Type* **2**.

1861 (July) *to* **1870**.

Z103 1d. rose-red (1864–70) (Plate No. 84)
Z104 2d. blue (1858–69) (Plate No. 9)
Z105 4d. red (1862) (Plate No. 4)
Z106 4d. vermilion (1865–73)
       Plate Nos. 7, 8.
Z107 6d. lilac (1862)
       Plate Nos. 3, 4.
Z108 6d. lilac (1865–67)
       Plate Nos. 5, 6.
Z109 6d. violet (1867–70)
       Plate Nos. 6, 8.

Stamps of GREAT BRITAIN *cancelled* "B 57" *as Type* **2**.

1861 (July) *to* **1870**.

Z110 1d. rose-red (1857). Die II. *wmk* Large Crown, *perf* 14
Z111 1d. rose-red (1864–79) (Plate No. 81)
Z112 2d. blue (1858–69) (Plate No. 9)
Z113 4d. red (1862)
Z114 4d. vermilion (1865–73)
       Plate Nos. 7, 8.
Z115 6d. lilac (1865–67)
       Plate Nos. 5, 6.

Stamps of GREAT BRITAIN *cancelled* "C 79" *as Type* **12**.

1866 (June) *to* **1870**.

Z116 6d. violet (1867–70)
       Plate Nos. 6, 8.
Z117 10d. red-brown (1867)

CUNARD LINE ATLANTIC MAILBOATS

These were all issued in June 1859. No examples are known used after August 1868. "B 61" is recorded as being issued in March 1862, but no examples are known. Cancellation numbers were subsequently reallocated to offices in Great Britain or, in the case of "A 91", the British Virgin Islands.

Stamps of GREAT BRITAIN *cancelled* "A 91" *as Type* **2**.

1859 (June) *to* **1868**.

Z130 1d. rose-red (1857), Die II, *wmk* Large Crown, *perf* 14
Z131 1d. rose-red (1864–79) (Plate No. 121)
Z132 2d. blue (1855), *wmk* Small Crown, *perf* 14

Z133 2d. blue (1858–69)
      Plate Nos. 8, 9.
Z134 4d. rose (1857)
Z135 4d. red (1862)
Z136 6d. lilac (1856)
Z137 6d. lilac (1862)
Z138 6d. lilac (1865–67)
Z139 9d. straw (1862)
Z140 1s. green (1856)

Stamps of GREAT BRITAIN *cancelled* "A 92" *as Type* **2**.

1859 (June) *to* **1868**.
Z141 1d. rose-red (1857), Die II, *wmk* Large Crown, *perf* 14
Z142 1d. rose-red (1864–79)
      Plate Nos. 93, 97.
Z143 6d. lilac (1856)
Z144 6d. lilac (1862) (Plate No. 3)
Z145 6d. lilac (1865–67)
      Plate Nos. 5, 6.

Stamps of GREAT BRITAIN *cancelled* "A 93" *as Type* **2**.

1859 (June) *to* **1868**.
Z146 1d. rose-red (1857), Die II, *wmk* Large Crown, *perf* 14
Z147 1d. rose-red (1864–79) (Plate No. 85)
Z148 6d. lilac (1856)
Z149 6d. lilac (1865–67) (Plate No. 6)
Z150 10d. red-brown (1867)

Stamps of GREAT BRITAIN *cancelled* "A 94" *as Type* **2**.

1859 (June) *to* **1868**.
Z151 1d. rose-red (1857), Die II, *wmk* Large Crown, *perf* 14

Z152 1d. rose-red (1864–79)
      Plate Nos. 74, 97.
Z153 4d. vermilion (1865–73) (Plate No. 7)
Z154 6d. lilac (1856)
Z155 6d. lilac (1862)
Z156 6d. lilac (1865–67)
      Plate Nos. 5, 6.

Stamps of GREAT BRITAIN *cancelled* "A 95" *as Type* **2**.

1859 (June) *to* **1868**.
Z157 1d. rose-red (1857), Die II, *wmk* Large Crown, *perf* 14
Z158 1d. rose-red (1864–79)
      Plate Nos. 72, 89, 97.
Z159 3d. rose (1867–73) (Plate No. 5)
Z160 4d. red (1862)
Z161 4d. vermilion (1865–73) (Plate No. 8)
Z162 6d. lilac (1862)
Z163 6d. lilac (1865–67) (Plate No. 5)
Z164 6d. lilac (1867) (Plate No. 6)
Z165 1s. green (1856)

Stamps of GREAT BRITAIN *cancelled* "A 96" *as Type* **2**.

1859 (June) *to* **1868**.
Z166 1d. rose-red (1857), Die II, *wmk* Large Crown, *perf* 14
Z167 4d. vermilion (1865–73) (Plate No. 7)
Z168 6d. lilac (1856)
Z169 1s. green (1856)

Stamps of GREAT BRITAIN *cancelled* "A 97" *as Type* **2**.

1859 (June) *to* **1868**.
Z170 1d. rose-red (1857), Die II, *wmk* Large Crown, *perf* 14

Z171 1d. rose-red (1864–79) (Plate No. 71)
Z172 4d. red (1862) (Plate No. 3)

Stamps of GREAT BRITAIN *cancelled* "A 98" *as Type* **2**.

1859 (June) *to* **1868**.
Z173 1d. rose-red (1857), Die II, *wmk* Large Crown, *perf* 14
Z174 4d. red (1862)
Z175 6d. lilac (1856)
Z176 6d. lilac (1862) (Plate No. 4)
Z177 6d. lilac (1865–67)
      Plate Nos. 5, 6.

ALLAN LINE ATLANTIC MAILBOATS

British G.P.O. sorters worked on these Canadian ships between November 1859 and April 1860. Cancellations as Type **2** numbered "B 17", "B 18", "B 27", "B 28", "B 29" and "B 30" were issued to them, but have not been reported used during this period. All were subsequently reallocated to British post offices.

SPANISH WEST INDIES MAILBOATS

"D 26" was supplied for use by British mail clerks employed on ships of the Herrara Line operating between St. Thomas (Danish West Indies), Cuba, Dominican Republic and Porto Rico.

1868 *to* **1871**.
Z190 1d. rose-red (1864–79)
      Plate Nos. 98, 125.
Z191 4d. vermilion (1865–73)   £600
      Plate Nos. 9, 10, 11.
Z192 6d. violet (1867–70) (Plate No. 8)
Z193 1s. green (1867) (Plate No. 4)

Stanley Gibbons, 399 Strand, London

Visit The World's Biggest Stamp Shop

Located in London's Strand, our showroom has been serving visitors to the world's stamp capital for over 100 years. Within the prestigious air conditioned surroundings lies a team of dedicated staff, probably the finest selection of stamps, postal history and literature ever assembled and the world's most comprehensive range of stamp catalogues, albums and accessories - all under one roof.

Over 1000 Giant Stockbooks of Stamps

Take a seat at our stamp counter and our staff will guide you through over 1000 giant stockbooks packed full of some of the latest and greatest GB, European, Commonwealth, Foreign and Thematic stamps.

Plus Stamp Pages, Packets, Kiloware & Specialised Stock

We've also a great selection of stamp pages, packets and kiloware always available plus over 5,000 rare and specialised items which can be examined in one of our private viewing rooms.

Valuations & Advice

Advice on the sale of collections is available free of charge from our team of expert valuers. We are always interested in buying and will pay top prices for quality collections and individual items.

The Collector's Bookshelf

We have on our shelves one of the largest selections of philatelic literature ever seen, including numerous rare and unusual titles - many collectibles in their own right, plus the latest handbooks, magazines and catalogues from publishers all over the world.

Albums, Accessories and Much More

We stock not just Stanley Gibbons albums and accessories but also those from a number of other manufacturers including Davo, Lighthouse, Prinz, Safe, Uvitec, Showguard and Kabe plus a wide choice of giftware and souvenirs for visitors of all ages.

STANLEY GIBBONS

399 Strand, London WC2R 0LX
Tel: 0171 836 8444 Fax: 0171 836 7342
e.mail: shop@stangiblondon.demon.co.uk
(Nearest tubes Charing Cross or Covent Garden)

≈ 399 ≈
S T R A N D
• A Collector's Paradise •

Open 6 days a week • Mon-Fri 8.30 'til 6.00 Sat 9.30 'til 5.30

Abu Dhabi

Stamps of the BRITISH POSTAL AGENCIES IN EASTERN ARABIA were used from the oil installation on Das Island from December 1960 onwards, being postmarked at Bahrain. A British postal agency, using the same issues, postmarked "ABU DHABI" or "DAS ISLAND", operated in the shaikdom from 30 March 1963 until the introduction of Abu Dhabi issues in 1964.

An independent Arab Shaikhdom (one of the Trucial States), with a British postal administration until 31 December 1966.

(Currency. 100 naye paise = 1 rupee)

1 Shaikh Shakhbut   3 Ruler's Palace
bin Sultan

(Des M. Farrar Bell. Photo Harrison (5 n.p. to 75 n.p.). Des C. T. Kavanagh (1, 2 r.), Miss P. M. Goth (5, 10 r.). Recess B.W.)

1964 (30 Mar). *T* 1, 3 *and similar designs. P* 14½ (5 to 75 n.p.) or 13 × 13½ (others).

1	1	5 n.p. green		1·50	1·50
2		15 n.p. red-brown		2·00	1·00
3		20 n.p. ultramarine		2·00	75
		a. Perf 13×13½		£200	
4		30 n.p. red-orange		3·00	1·50
5	—	40 n.p. reddish violet		3·25	50
6	—	50 n.p. bistre		3·50	1·50
7	—	75 n.p. black		3·50	2·50
8	3	1 r. emerald		4·00	1·25
9		2 r. black		7·50	3·25
10	—	5 r. carmine-red		16·00	8·00
11	—	10 r. deep ultramarine		23·00	14·00
1/11			*Set of* 11	60·00	32·00

Designs: As Type 1—40, 50, 75 n.p. Mountain Gazelle. As Type 3—5, 10 r. Oil rig and camels.

5   6   7
Saker Falcon

(Des V. Whiteley. Photo Harrison)

1965 (30 Mar). *Falconry. P* 14½.

12	5	20 n.p. light brown and grey-blue		9·50	1·50
13	6	40 n.p. light brown and blue		12·00	2·50
14	7	2 r. sepia and turquoise-green		21·00	12·00
12/14			*Set of* 3	38·00	14·50

(New Currency. 1,000 fils = 1 dinar)

═══

Fils فلس
(8)

1966 (1 Oct). *Nos.* 1/11 *such as T* 8 ("FILS" *only on* 40 f. *to* 70 f.) *with new value expressed on remainder), by Arabian Printing and Publishing House, Bahrain. P* 13 × 13½ (20 f.), *others as before.*

15	1	5 f. on 5 n.p. green		7·50	5·50
16		15 f. on 15 n.p. red-brown		7·50	4·00
17		20 f. on 20 n.p. ultramarine		8·50	6·00
		b. Perf 14½		£100	
		ba. Surch inverted		£200	£350
18		30 f. on 30 n.p. red-orange		9·00	12·00
		a. Arabic "2" for "3" in surch		£1700	
		b. Surch double, one albino		£150	
19	—	40 f. on 40 n.p. reddish violet		13·00	85
20	—	50 f. on 50 n.p. bistre		20·00	19·00
21	—	75 f. on 75 n.p. black		20·00	17·00
		a. Surch double, one albino		£150	
22	3	100 f. on 1 r. emerald		16·00	3·50
23		200 f. on 2 r. black		18·00	12·00
24	—	500 f. on 5 r. carmine-red		30·00	38·00
25	—	1 d. on 10 r. deep ultramarine		40·00	65·00
		a. Short extra bar below portrait (R. 7/3)		£250	
15/25			*Set of* 11	£170	£160

The Abu Dhabi Post Department took over the postal services on 1 January 1967. Later stamp issues will be found in Part 19 (*Middle East*) of this Catalogue.

Aden
see South Arabian Federation

Anguilla

St. Christopher, Nevis and Anguilla were granted Associated Statehood on 27 February 1967, but, following a referendum, Anguilla declared her independence on 30 May 1967 and the St. Christopher authorities withdrew. The following stamps were issued by the governing Council and have been accepted for international mail. On 7 July 1969 the Anguilla post office was officially recognised by the Government of St. Christopher, Nevis and Anguilla and normal postal communications via St. Christopher were resumed. By the Anguilla Act of 27 July 1971, Anguilla was restored to direct British control.

A degree of internal self-government with an Executive Council was introduced on 10 February 1976 and the links with St. Kitts-Nevis were officially severed on 18 December 1980.

(Currency. 100 cents = 1 Eastern Caribbean dollar)

Independent Anguilla
(1)

2 Mahogany Tree, The Quarter

1967 (4 Sept). *Nos.* 129/44 *of St. Kitts-Nevis optd as T* 1, *by Island Press Inc, St. Thomas, U.S. Virgin Islands.*

1		½ c New lighthouse, Sombrero		26·00	20·00
2		1 c. Loading sugar cane, St. Kitts		27·00	6·50
3		2 c. Pall Mall Square, Basseterre		28·00	1·25
4		3 c. Gateway, Brimstone Hill Fort, St. Kitts		28·00	4·50
		w. Wmk inverted		—	32·00
5		4 c. Nelson's Spring, Nevis		28·00	5·50
6		5 c. Grammar School, St. Kitts		£100	18·00
7		6 c. Crater, Mt Misery, St. Kitts		50·00	9·00
8		10 c. Hibiscus		28·00	6·50
9		15 c. Sea Island cotton, Nevis		60·00	11·00
10		20 c. Boat building, Anguilla		95·00	12·00
11		25 c. White-crowned Pigeon		85·00	20·00
		w. Wmk inverted		£110	35·00
12		50 c. St. George's Church Tower, Basseterre		£1800	£450
13		60 c. Alexander Hamilton		£2000	£850
14		$1 Map of St. Kitts–Nevis		£1600	£400
15		$2.50, Map of Anguilla		£1500	£300
16		$5 Arms of St. Christopher, Nevis and Anguilla		£1500	£300
1/16			*Set of* 16	£8000	£2250

Owing to the limited stocks available for overprinting, the sale of the above stamps was personally controlled by the Postmaster and no orders from the trade were accepted.

(Des John Lister Ltd. Litho A. & M.)

1967 (27 Nov)—**68.** *T* 2 *and similar horiz designs. P* 12½ × 13.

17		1 c. dull green, bistre-brown and pale orange		10	20
18		2 c. bluish green and black (21.3.68)		10	20
19		3 c. black and light emerald (10.2.68)		10	10
20		4 c. cobalt-blue and black (10.2.68)		10	10
21		5 c. multicoloured		10	10
22		6 c. light vermilion and black (21.3.68)		10	10
23		10 c. multicoloured		15	10
24		15 c. multicoloured (10.2.68)		60	20
25		20 c. multicoloured		60	40
26		25 c. multicoloured		60	20
27		40 c. apple green, light greenish blue and black		80	25
28		60 c. multicoloured (10.2.68)		3·00	2·25
29		$1 multicoloured (10.2.68)		1·75	2·75
30		$2.50, multicoloured (21.3.68)		2·00	3·00
31		$5 multicoloured (10.2.68)		3·00	4·25
17/31			*Set of* 15	11·50	12·50

Designs:—2 c. Sombrero Lighthouse; 3 c. St. Mary's Church; 4 c. Valley Police Station; 5 c. Old Plantation House, Mt Fortune; 6 c. Valley Post Office; 10 c. Methodist Church, West End; 15 c. Wall-Blake Airport; 20 c. Beech A90 King Air aircraft over Sandy Ground; 25 c. Island Harbour; 40 c. Map of Anguilla; 60 c. Hermit Crab and Starfish; $1 Hibiscus; $2.50, Local scene; $5, Spiny Lobster.

On 9 January 1969 Anguilla reaffirmed her independence from St. Kitts and issued Nos. 17/31 overprinted in black "INDEPENDENCE JANUARY 1969" in two lines. These are outside the scope of this catalogue.

17 Yachts in Lagoon   18 Purple-throated Carib

(Des John Lister Ltd. Litho A. & M.)

1968 (11 May). *Anguillan Ships. T* 17 *and similar horiz designs. Multicoloured. P* 14.

32		10 c. Type 17		30	10
33		15 c. Boat on beach		35	10
34		25 c. *Warspite* (schooner)		50	15
35		40 c. *Atlantic Star* (schooner)		60	20
32/5			*Set of* 4	1·60	40

(Des John Lister Ltd. Litho A. & M.)

1968 (8 July). *Anguillan Birds. T* 18 *and similar multicoloured designs. P* 14.

36		10 c. Type 18		75	15
37		15 c. Bananaquit		95	20
38		25 c. Black-necked Stilt (*horiz*)		1·25	20
39		40 c. Royal Tern (*horiz*)		1·50	30
36/9			*Set of* 4	4·00	75

19 Guides' Badge and Anniversary Years

(Des John Lister Ltd. Litho A. & M.)

1968 (14 Oct). *35th Anniv of Anguillan Girl Guides. T* 19 *and similar multicoloured designs. P* 13 × 13½ (10, 25 c.) or 13½ × 13 (others).

40		10 c. Type 19		10	10
41		15 c. Badge and silhouettes of Guides (*vert*)		15	10
42		25 c. Guides' badge and Headquarters		20	15
43		40 c. Association and Proficiency badges (*vert*)		25	15
40/3			*Set of* 4	65	35

20 The Three Kings

(Des John Lister Ltd. Litho A. & M.)

1968 (18 Nov). *Christmas. T* 20 *and similar designs. P* 13.

44		1 c. black and cerise		10	10
45		10 c. black and light greenish blue		10	10
46		15 c. black and chestnut		15	10
47		40 c. black and blue		15	10
48		50 c. black and dull green		20	15
44/8			*Set of* 5	55	30

Designs: Vert—10 c. The Wise Men; 15 c. Holy Family and manger. Horiz—40 c. The Shepherds; 50 c. Holy Family and donkey.

21 Bagging Salt   22 "The Crucifixion" (Studio of Massys)

(Des John Lister Ltd. Litho A. & M.)

1969 (4 Jan). *Anguillan Salt Industry. T* 21 *and similar horiz designs. Multicoloured. P* 13.

49		10 c. Type 21		25	10
50		15 c. Packing salt		30	10
51		40 c. Salt pond		35	10
52		50 c. Loading salt		35	10
49/52			*Set of* 4	1·10	30

(Des John Lister Ltd. Litho Format)

1969 (31 Mar). *Easter Commemoration. T* 22 *and similar vert design. P* 13½.

53		25 c. multicoloured		25	15
54		40 c. multicoloured		35	15

Design:—40 c. "The Last Supper" (ascribed to Roberti).

23 Amaryllis

(Des John Lister Ltd. Litho Format)

1969 (10 June). *Flowers of the Caribbean. T* **23** *and similar horiz designs. Multicoloured. P* 14.

55	10 c. Type **23**	..	20	15
56	15 c. Bougainvillea	..	25	15
57	40 c. Hibiscus	..	50	30
58	50 c. *Cattleya* orchid	..	1·50	90
55/8	..	Set of 4	2·25	1·40

24 Superb Gaza, Channelled Turban, Chestnut Turban and Carved Star Shell

(Des John Lister Ltd. Litho A. & M.)

1969 (22 Sept). *Sea Shells. T* **24** *and similar horiz designs. Multicoloured. P* 14.

59	10 c. Type **24**	..	20	10
60	15 c. American Thorny Oyster	..	20	10
61	40 c. Scotch, Royal and Smooth Scotch Bonnets	..	30	15
62	50 c. Atlantic Trumpet Triton	..	40	20
59/62	..	Set of 4	1·00	45

(25)

(26)

(27)

(28)

(29)

1969 (Oct). *Christmas. Nos.* 17, 25/8 *optd with T* **25/29**.

63	1 c. dull green, bistre-brown & light orange	..	10	10
64	20 c. multicoloured	..	20	10
65	25 c. multicoloured	..	20	10
66	40 c. apple-green, light greenish blue & black	..	25	15
67	60 c. multicoloured	..	40	20
63/7	..	Set of 5	1·00	45

30 Spotted Goatfish

31 "Morning Glory"

(Des John Lister Ltd. Litho A. & M.)

1969 (1 Dec). *Fishes. T* **30** *and similar horiz designs. Multicoloured. P* 14.

68	10 c. Type **30**	..	30	15
69	15 c. Blue-striped Grunt	..	45	15
70	40 c. Nassau Grouper	..	55	20
71	50 c. Banded Butterflyfish	..	65	20
68/71	..	Set of 4	1·75	65

(Des John Lister Ltd. Litho A. & M.)

1970 (23 Feb). *Flowers. T* **31** *and similar vert designs. Multicoloured, P* 14.

72	10 c. Type **31**	..	30	10
73	15 c. Blue Petrea	..	45	10
74	40 c. Hibiscus	..	70	20
75	50 c. "Flame Tree"	..	80	25
72/5	..	Set of 4	2·00	55

32 "The Crucifixion" (Masaccio)

33 Scout Badge and Map

(Des John Lister Ltd. Litho Format)

1970 (26 Mar). *Easter. T* **32** *and similar multicoloured designs. P* 13½.

76	10 c. "The Ascent to Calvary" (Tiepolo) (*horiz*)		15	10
77	20 c. Type **32**		20	10
78	40 c. "Deposition" (Rosso Fiorentino)		25	15
79	60 c. "The Ascent to Calvary" (Murillo) (*horiz*)		25	15
76/9	Set of 4		75	40

(Des John Lister Ltd. Litho A. & M.)

1970 (10 Aug). *40th Anniv of Scouting in Anguilla. T* **33** *and similar horiz designs. Multicoloured. P* 13.

80	10 c. Type **33**		15	10
81	15 c. Scout camp and cubs practising first-aid		20	10
82	40 c. Monkey Bridge		25	15
83	50 c. Scout H.Q. Building and Lord Baden-Powell		35	15
80/3	..	Set of 4	85	45

34 Boatbuilding

(Des John Lister Ltd. Litho Format)

1970 (23 Nov). *Various horiz designs as T* **34**. *Multicoloured. P* 14.

84	1 c. Type **34**	..	30	30
85	2 c. Road Construction	..	30	30
86	3 c. Quay, Blowing Point	..	30	20
87	4 c. Broadcaster, Radio Anguilla	..	30	40
88	5 c. Cottage Hospital Extension	..	40	40
89	6 c. Valley Secondary School	..	30	40
90	10 c. Hotel Extension	..	30	30
91	15 c. Sandy Ground	..	30	30
92	20 c. Supermarket and Cinema	..	55	30
93	25 c. Bananas and Mangoes	..	35	80
94	40 c. Wall Blake Airport	..	2·00	2·00
95	60 c. Sandy Ground Jetty	..	65	2·00
96	$1 Administration Buildings	..	1·25	1·40
97	$2.50, Livestock	..	1·50	3·75
98	$5 Sandy Hill Bay	..	2·75	3·75
84/98	..	Set of 15	10·50	15·00

35 "The Adoration of the Shepherds" (Reni)

36 "Ecce Homo" (detail, Correggio)

(Des John Lister Ltd. Litho Questa)

1970 (11 Dec). *Christmas. T* **35** *and similar vert designs. Multicoloured. P* 13½.

99	1 c. Type **35**	..	10	10
100	20 c. "The Virgin and Child" (Gozzoli)	..	30	20
101	25 c. "Mystic Nativity" (detail, Botticelli)	..	30	20
102	40 c. "The Santa Margherita Madonna" (detail, Mazzola)	..	40	25
103	50 c. "The Adoration of the Magi" (detail, Tiepolo)	..	40	25
99/103	..	Set of 5	1·25	85

(Des John Lister Ltd. Litho Format)

1971 (29 Mar). *Easter. T* **36** *and similar designs. P* 13½.

104	10 c. multicoloured	..	15	10
105	15 c. multicoloured	..	25	10
106	40 c. multicoloured	..	30	10
107	50 c. multicoloured	..	30	15
104/7	..	Set of 4	90	30

Designs: *Vert*—15 c. "Christ appearing to St. Peter" (detail, Carracci). *Horiz*—40 c. "Angels weeping over the Dead Christ" (detail, Guercino); 50 c. "The Supper at Emmaus" (detail, Caravaggio).

37 *Hypolimnas misippus*

38 *Magnanime* and *Aimable* in Battle

(Des John Lister Ltd. Litho Questa)

1971 (21 June). *Butterflies. T* **37** *and similar horiz designs. Multicoloured. P* 14 × 14½.

108	10 c. Type **37**	..	1·00	7
109	15 c. *Junonia evarete*	..	1·10	8
110	40 c. *Agraulis vanillae*	..	1·75	1·2
111	50 c. *Danaus plexippus*	..	1·90	1·5
108/11	..	Set of 4	5·25	3·7

(Des John Lister Ltd. Litho Format)

1971 (30 Aug). *Sea-battles of the West Indies. T* **38** *and similar ver designs. Multicoloured. P* 14.

112	10 c. Type **38**	..	85	9
	a. Horiz strip of 5. Nos. 112/16	..	6·00	
113	15 c. H.M.S. *Duke*, *Glorieux* and H.M.S. *Agamemnon*		1·00	1·1
114	25 c. H.M.S. *Formidable* and H.M.S. *Namur* against *Ville de Paris*		1·40	1·5
115	40 c. H.M.S. *Canada*		1·50	1·6
116	50 c. H.M.S. *St. Albans* and wreck of *Hector*		1·75	1·9
112/16	..	Set of 5	6·00	6·5

Nos. 112/16 were issued in horizontal *se-tenant* strips within the sheet, to form a composite design in the order listed.

ADMINISTRATION BY BRITISH COMMISSION

39 "The Ansidei Madonna" (detail, Raphael)

40 Map of Anguilla and St. Martins by Thomas Jefferys (1775)

(Des John Lister Ltd. Litho Questa)

1971 (29 Nov). *Christmas. T* **39** *and similar vert designs. P* 13½.

117	20 c. multicoloured	..	20	2
118	25 c. multicoloured	..	20	2
119	40 c. multicoloured	..	30	3
120	50 c. multicoloured	..	35	4
117/20	..	Set of 4	95	1·1

Designs:—25 c. "Mystic Nativity" (detail, Botticelli); 40 c. "Adoration of the Shepherds" (detail; ascr to Murillo); 50 c. "The Madonna of the Iris" (detail; ascr to Dürer).

(Litho Format)

1972 (24 Jan). *Maps. T* **40** *and similar multicoloured designs showing maps by the cartographers given. P* 14.

121	10 c. Type **40**	..	25	1
122	15 c. Samuel Fahlberg (1814)	..	35	1
123	40 c. Thomas Jefferys (1775) (*horiz*)	..	50	2
124	50 c. Capt. E. Barnett (1847) (*horiz*)	..	60	2
121/4	..	Set of 4	1·50	6

41 "Jesus Buffeted"

42 Loblolly Tree

(Des John Lister Ltd. Litho Format)

1972 (14 Mar). *Easter. Stained Glass Windows from Church of St. Michael, Bray, Berkshire. T* **41** *and similar vert designs. Multicoloured. P* 14 × 13½.

125	10 c. Type **41**	..	25	25
	a. Horiz strip of 5. Nos. 125/9	..	1·40	
126	15 c. "The Way of Sorrows"	..	30	30
127	25 c. "The Crucifixion"	..	30	30
128	40 c. "Descent from the Cross"	..	35	35
129	50 c. "The Burial"	..	40	40
125/9	..	Set of 5	1·40	1·40

Nos. 125/9 were printed horizontally *se-tenant* within the sheet

(Litho Questa ($10), Format (others))

1972 (30 Oct)–**75**. *T* **42** *and similar multicoloured designs (horiz, except* 2, 4 *and* 6 *c.). P* 13½.

130	1 c. Spear fishing	..	10	40
131	2 c. Type **42**	..	10	40
132	3 c. Sandy Ground	..	10	40
133	4 c. Ferry at Blowing Point	..	75	20
134	5 c. Agriculture	..	15	40
135	6 c. St. Mary's Church	..	25	20
136	10 c. St. Gerard's Church	..	25	40
137	15 c. Cottage Hospital extension	..	25	30
138	20 c. Public library	..	30	35

139 25 c. Sunset at Blowing Point .. .. 40 1·00
140 40 c. Boat building .. .. .. 3·25 1·50
141 60 c. Hibiscus .. .. .. 4·00 3·50
142 $1 Magnificent Frigate Bird .. 8·50 6·00
143 $2.50, Frangipani .. .. 6·00 7·00
144 $5 Brown Pelican .. .. 14·00 13·00
144a $10 Green-back turtle (20.5.75) 15·00 18·00
130/44a .. .. .. Set of 16 48·00 48·00

43 *Malcolm Miller* (schooner) and Common Dolphin

(Des (from photograph by D. Groves) and photo Harrison)
1972 (20 Nov). *Royal Silver Wedding. Multicoloured; background colour given.* W w **12**. P 14 × 14½.
145 **43** 25 c. yellow-olive (*shades*) .. 55 75
146 40 c. chocolate 55 75
   w. Wmk inverted .. 1·75

44 Flight into Egypt   **45** "The Betrayal of Christ"

(Des John Lister Ltd. Litho Questa)
1972 (4 Dec). *Christmas. T* **44** *and similar vert designs. Multicoloured.* P 13½.
147 1 c. Type **44** .. 10 10
148 20 c. Star of Bethlehem .. 20 20
   a. Vert strip of 4. Nos. 148/51 .. 75
149 25 c. Holy Family .. 20 20
150 40 c. Arrival of the Magi .. 20 25
151 50 c. Adoration of the Magi .. 25 25
147/51 Set of 5 75 85
Nos. 148/51 were printed vertically *se-tenant* within a sheet of 20 stamps.

(Des John Lister Ltd. Litho Questa)
1973 (26 Mar). *Easter. T* **45** *and similar vert designs. Multicoloured; bottom panel in gold and black.* P 13½.
152 1 c. Type **45** .. 10 10
153 10 c. "The Man of Sorrows" .. 10 10
   a. Vert strip of 5. Nos. 153/7 .. 55
154 20 c. "Christ bearing the Cross" .. 10 15
155 25 c. "The Crucifixion" .. 15 15
156 40 c. "The Descent from the Cross" .. 15 15
157 50 c. "The Resurrection" .. 15 20
152/7 Set of 6 55 70
MS158 140 × 141 mm. Nos. 152/7. Bottom panel in gold and mauve .. 70 80
Nos. 153/7 were printed within one sheet, vertically *se-tenant*.

46 *Santa Maria*   **47** Princess Anne and Captain Mark Phillips

(Des John Lister Ltd. Litho Questa)
1973 (10 Sept). *Columbus Discovers the West Indies. T* **46** *and similar horiz designs. Multicoloured.* P 13½.
159 1 c. Type **46** .. 10 10
160 20 c. Early map .. 1·25 75
   a. Horiz strip of 4. Nos. 160/3 .. 6·00
161 40 c. Map of voyages .. 1·40 90
162 70 c. Sighting land .. 1·75 1·50
163 $1.20, Landing of Columbus .. 2·25 2·25
159/63 Set of 5 6·00 5·00
MS164 193 × 93 mm. Nos. 159/63 .. 6·00 7·00
Nos. 160/3 were printed horizontally *se-tenant* within the sheet.

(Des PAD Studio. Litho Questa)
1973 (14 Nov). *Royal Wedding. Centre multicoloured.* W w **12** (*sideways*). P 13½.
165 **47** 60 c. turquoise-green .. 20 15
166 $1.20, deep mauve .. 30 15

48 "The Adoration of the Shepherds" (Reni)   **49** "The Crucifixion" (Raphael)

(Des John Lister Ltd. Litho Questa)
1973 (2 Dec). *Christmas. T* **48** *and similar horiz designs. Multicoloured.* P 13½.
167 1 c. Type **48** .. 10 10
168 10 c. "The Madonna and Child with Saints Jerome and Dominic" (Lippi) .. 10 10
   a. Horiz strip of 5. Nos. 168/72 .. 75
169 20 c. "The Nativity" (Master of Brunswick) .. 15 15
170 25 c. "Madonna of the Meadow" (Bellini) .. 15 15
171 40 c. "Virgin and Child" (Cima) .. 20 20
172 50 c. "Adoration of the Kings" (Geertgen) .. 20 20
167/72 Set of 6 75 75
MS173 148 × 149 mm. Nos. 167/72 .. 80 1·60
Nos. 168/72 were printed within the sheet, horizontally *se-tenant*.

(Des John Lister Ltd. Litho Questa)
1974 (30 Mar). *Easter. T* **49** *and similar vert designs showing various details of Raphael's "Crucifixion".* P 13½.
174 1 c. multicoloured .. 10 10
175 15 c. multicoloured .. 10 10
   a. Vert strip of 5. Nos. 175/9 .. 70
176 20 c. multicoloured .. 15 15
177 25 c. multicoloured .. 15 15
178 40 c. multicoloured .. 15 15
179 $1 multicoloured .. 20 25
174/9 Set of 6 70 70
MS180 123 × 141 mm. Nos. 174/9 .. 95 1·25
Nos. 175/9 were printed vertically *se-tenant* within one sheet.

50 Churchill making "Victory" Sign

(Des John Lister Ltd. Litho Questa)
1974 (24 June). *Birth Centenary of Sir Winston Churchill. T* **50** *and similar horiz designs. Multicoloured.* P 13½.
181 1 c. Type **50** .. 10 10
182 20 c. Churchill with Roosevelt .. 20 20
   a. Horiz strip of 5. Nos. 182/6 .. 1·50
183 25 c. Wartime broadcast .. 20 20
184 40 c. Birthplace, Blenheim Palace .. 30 30
185 60 c. Churchill's statue .. 40 35
186 $1.20, Country residence, Chartwell .. 60 55
181/6 Set of 6 1·50 1·50
MS187 195 × 96 mm. Nos. 181/6 .. 1·75 2·25
Nos. 182/6 were printed horizontally *se-tenant* within the sheet.

51 U.P.U. Emblem

(Des John Lister Ltd. Litho Questa)
1974 (27 Aug). *Centenary of Universal Postal Union.* P 13½*.
188 **51** 1 c. black and bright blue .. 10 10
189 20 c. black and pale orange .. 15 15
   a. Horiz strip of 5. Nos. 189/93 .. 1·10
190 25 c. black and light yellow .. 15 15
191 40 c. black and bright mauve .. 20 25
192 60 c. black and light emerald .. 30 40
193 $1.20, black and light blue .. 50 60
188/93 Set of 6 1·10 1·40
MS194 195 × 96 mm. Nos. 188/93 .. 1·25 2·00
Nos. 189/93 were printed horizontally *se-tenant* within the sheet.
*In No. MS194 the lower row of three stamps, 40 c., 60 c. and $1.20 values, are line-perforated 15 at foot, the remaining 3 stamps being comb-perforated 13½.

52 Anguillan pointing to Star   **53** "Mary, John and Mary Magdalene" (Matthias Grünewald)

(Litho Questa)
1974 (16 Dec). *Christmas. T* **52** *and similar horiz designs. Multicoloured.* P 14.
195 1 c. Type **52** 10 10
196 20 c. Child in Manger 10 15
   a. Horiz strip of 5. Nos. 196/200 .. 70
197 25 c. King's offering 10 15
198 40 c. Star over Map of Anguilla .. 15 15
199 60 c. Family looking at star .. 15 20
200 $1.20, Angels of Peace .. 20 30
195/200 Set of 6 70 95
MS201 177 × 85 mm. Nos. 195/200 .. 1·40 1·75
Nos. 196/200 were printed horizontally *se-tenant* within the sheet.

(Litho Questa)
1975 (25 Mar). *Easter. T* **53** *and similar multicoloured designs showing details of the Isenheim altarpiece.* P 14.
202 1 c. Type **53** 10 10
203 10 c. "The Crucifixion" 15 15
   a. Horiz strip of 5. Nos. 203/7 .. 1·00
204 15 c. "St. John the Baptist" .. 15 15
205 20 c. "St. Sebastian and Angels" .. 20 20
206 $1 "The Entombment" .. 25 35
207 $1.50, "St. Anthony the Hermit" .. 35 45
202/7 Set of 6 1·00 1·25
MS208 134 × 127 mm. Nos. 202/7. Imperf. .. 1·00 1·75
Nos. 203/7 were printed horizontally *se-tenant* within the sheet.

54 Statue of Liberty   **55** "Madonna, Child and the Infant John the Baptist" (Raphael)

(Des John Lister Ltd. Litho Questa)
1975 (10 Nov). *Bicentenary of American Revolution. T* **54** *and similar horiz designs. Multicoloured.* P 13½*.
209 1 c. Type **54** .. 10 10
210 10 c. The Capitol .. 20 10
   a. Horiz strip of 5. Nos. 210/14 .. 1·60
211 15 c. "Congress voting for Independence" (Pine and Savage) .. 30 15
212 20 c. Washington and map .. 30 15
213 $1 Boston Tea Party .. 45 40
214 $1.50, Bicentenary logo .. 50 60
209/14 Set of 6 1·60 1·25
MS215 198 × 97 mm. Nos. 209/14 .. 1·60 2·50
Nos. 210/14 were printed horizontally *se-tenant* within the sheet.
*In No. MS215 the lower row of three stamps, 20 c., $1 and $1.50 values, are line-perforated 15 at foot, the remaining 3 stamps being comb-perforated 13½.

(Des John Lister Ltd. Litho Questa)
1975 (8 Dec). *Christmas. T* **55** *and similar vert designs showing the "Madonna and Child". Multicoloured.* P 13½.
216 1 c. Type **55** 10 10
217 10 c. Cima 15 10
   a. Horiz strip of 5. Nos. 217/21 .. 1·25
218 15 c. Dolci 20 15
219 20 c. Dürer 20 15
220 $1 Bellini 35 25
221 $1.50, Botticelli 45 35
216/21 Set of 6 1·25 90
MS222 130 × 145 mm. Nos. 216/21 .. 2·00 2·25
Nos. 217/21 were printed horizontally *se-tenant* within the sheet.

PRICES OF SETS

Set prices are given for many issues, generally those containing three stamps or more. Definitive sets include one of each value or major colour change, but do not cover different perforations, die types or minor shades. Where a choice is possible the set prices are based on the cheapest versions of the stamps included in the listings.

EXECUTIVE COUNCIL

NEW
CONSTITUTION
1976

(56)   57 Almond

 TION

Italic second "O" in "CONSTITUTION". Occurs on Row 2/2 (Nos. 226, 228, 232, 235, 239), Row 3/2 (Nos. 230/1, 233/4, 236/8), Row 4/5 (Nos. 223/4, 240) or Row 5/2 (Nos. 225, 227, 229).

1976 (10 Feb–1 July). *New Constitution. Nos. 130 etc. optd with T 56 or surch also.*

223	1 c. Spear fishing		30	40
	a. Italic "O"		1·50	
224	2 c. on 1 c. Spear fishing		30	40
	a. Italic "O"		1·50	
225	2 c. Type 42 (1.7.76)		4·00	1·40
	a. Italic "O"		11·00	
226	3 c. on 40 c. Boat building		75	70
	a. "3 c" omitted		£300	
	b. Typo. "3 c"*		6·00	7·00
	c. Italic "O"		3·00	
227	4 c. Ferry at Blowing Point		1·00	1·00
	a. Italic "O"		4·00	
228	5 c. on 40 c. Boat building		30	50
	a. Italic "O"		1·75	
229	6 c. St. Mary's Church		30	50
	a. Italic "O"		2·00	
230	10 c. on 20 c. Public Library		30	50
	a. Italic "O"		2·25	
231	10 c. St. Gerard's Church (1.7.76)		4·00	3·00
	a. Italic "O"		11·00	
232	15 c. Cottage Hospital extension		30	90
	a. Italic "O"		2·25	
233	20 c. Public Library		30	50
	a. Italic "O"		2·25	
234	25 c. Sunset at Blowing Point		30	50
	a. Italic "O"		2·75	
235	40 c. Boat building		1·00	70
	a. Italic "O"		4·00	
236	60 c. Hibiscus		70	70
	a. Italic "O"		3·50	
237	$1 Magnificent Frigate Bird		5·00	2·25
	a. Italic "O"		13·00	
238	$2.50, Frangipani		2·25	2·25
	a. Italic "O"		8·00	
239	$5 Brown Pelican		6·50	6·50
	a. Italic "O"		17·00	
240	$10 Green-back turtle		4·00	6·00
	a. Italic "O"		15·00	
223/40		*Set of 18*	28·00	26·00

*No. 226a/b occur on R. 5/2, the "3 c" having been omitted during the normal litho surcharging.

(Des John Lister Ltd. Litho Questa)

1976 (16 Feb). *Flowering Trees. T 57 and similar horiz designs. Multicoloured. P 13½.*

241	1 c. Type 57		10	10
242	10 c. Autograph		20	10
	a. Horiz strip of 5. Nos. 242/6		1·25	
243	15 c. Calabash		20	15
244	20 c. Cordia		20	15
245	$1 Papaya		30	45
246	$1.50, Flamboyant		35	55
241/6		*Set of 6*	1·25	1·25
MS247	194 × 99 mm. Nos. 241/6		1·50	2·00

Nos. 242/6 were printed horizontally *se-tenant* within the sheet.

58 The Three Marys   59 French Ships approaching
                                               Anguilla

(Litho Questa)

1976 (5 Apr). *Easter. T 58 and similar multicoloured designs showing portions of the Altar Frontal Tapestry, Rheinau. P 13½.*

248	1 c. Type 58		10	10
249	10 c. The Crucifixion		10	10
	a. Horiz strip of 5. Nos. 249/53		1·75	
250	15 c. Two Soldiers		15	15
251	20 c. The Annunciation		15	15
252	$1 The complete tapestry (*horiz*)		65	65
253	$1.50, The Risen Christ		80	80
248/53		*Set of 6*	1·75	1·75
MS254	138 × 130 mm. Nos. 248/53. Imperf		1·75	2·10

Nos. 249/53 were printed horizontally *se-tenant* within the sheet.

(Des John Lister Ltd. Litho Questa)

1976 (8 Nov). *Battle for Anguilla, 1796. T 59 and similar horiz designs. Multicoloured. P 13½.*

255	1 c. Type 59		10	10
256	3 c. *Margaret* (sloop) leaving Anguilla		90	35
	a. Horiz strip of 5. Nos. 256/60		7·00	
257	15 c. Capture of *Le Desius*		1·25	55
258	25 c. *La Vaillante* forced aground		1·50	80
259	$1 H.M.S. *Lapwing*		2·00	1·25
260	$1.50, *Le Desius* burning		2·25	1·75
255/60		*Set of 6*	7·00	4·25
MS261	205×103 mm. Nos. 255/60		7·00	6·00

Nos. 256/60 were printed horizontally *se-tenant* within the sheet.

60 "Christmas Carnival" (A. Richardson)

(Litho Questa)

1976 (22 Nov). *Christmas. T 60 and similar horiz designs showing children's paintings. Multicoloured. P 13½.*

262	1 c. Type 60		10	10
263	3 c. "Dreams of Christmas Gifts" (J. Connor)		10	10
	a. Horiz strip of 5, Nos. 263/7		1·00	
264	15 c. "Carolling" (P. Richardson)		15	15
265	25 c. "Candle-light Procession" (A. Mussington)		20	20
266	$1 "Going to Church" (B. Franklin)		30	30
267	$1.50, "Coming Home for Christmas" (E. Gumbs)		40	40
262/7		*Set of 6*	1·00	1·10
MS268	232 × 147 mm. Nos. 262/7		1·50	1·75

Nos. 263/7 were printed horizontally *se-tenant* within the sheet.

61 Prince Charles and H.M.S. *Minerva* (frigate)

(Des John Lister Ltd. Litho Questa)

1977 (9 Feb). *Silver Jubilee. T 61 and similar horiz designs. Multicoloured. P 13½.*

269	25 c. Type 61		15	10
270	40 c. Prince Philip landing at Road Bay, 1964		15	10
271	$1.20, Coronation scene		20	20
272	$2.50, Coronation regalia and map of Anguilla		25	30
269/72		*Set of 4*	65	55
MS273	145 × 96 mm. Nos. 269/72		65	90

63 "The Crucifixion" (Massys)

(Des John Lister Ltd. Litho Questa)

1977 (25 Apr). *Easter. T 63 and similar horiz designs showing paintings by Castagno ($1.50) or Ugolino (others). Multicoloured. P 13½.*

291	1 c. Type 63		10	10
292	3 c. "The Betrayal"		10	10
	a. Horiz strip of 5. Nos. 292/6		1·60	
293	22 c. "The Way to Calvary"		20	20
294	30 c. "The Deposition"		25	25
295	$1 "The Resurrection"		50	50
296	$1.50, "The Crucifixion"		65	65
291/6		*Set of 6*	1·60	1·60
MS297	192 × 126 mm. Nos. 291/6		1·60	1·75

Nos. 292/6 were printed horizontally *se-tenant* within the sheet.

ROYAL VISIT
TO WEST INDIES

(64)   65 "Le Chapeau de Paille"

1977 (26 Oct). *Royal Visit. Nos. 269/MS273 optd with T 64.*

298	25 c. Type 61		10	10
299	40 c. Prince Philip landing at Road Bay, 1964		10	20
300	$1.20, Coronation scene		20	30
301	$2.50, Coronation regalia and map of Anguilla		25	50
298/301		*Set of 4*	60	1·00
MS302	145 × 96 mm. Nos. 298/301		80	90

(Des John Lister Ltd. Litho Questa)

1977 (1 Nov). *400th Birth Anniv of Rubens. T 65 and similar vert designs. Multicoloured. P 13½.*

303	25 c. Type 65		15	15
304	40 c. "Helène Fourment and her Two Children"		20	25
305	$1.20, "Rubens and his Wife"		60	65
306	$2.50, "Marchesa Brigida Spinola-Doria"		75	95
303/6		*Set of 4*	1·50	1·75
MS307	93 × 145 mm. Nos. 303/6		1·75	2·10

Each value was issued in sheets of 5 stamps and 1 label.

 5c

EASTER 1978

(66)   (67)

1977 (14 Nov). *Christmas. Nos. 262/8 with old date blocked out and additionally inscr "1977", some surch also as T 66.*

308	1 c. Type 60		10	10
309	5 c. on 3 c. "Dreams of Christmas Gifts"		10	10
	a. Horiz strip of 5. Nos. 309/13		1·75	
310	12 c. on 15 c. "Carolling"		15	15
311	18 c. on 25 c. "Candle-light Procession"		20	20
312	$1 "Going to Church"		45	45
313	$2.50 on $1.50, "Coming Home for Christmas"		90	90
308/13		*Set of 6*	1·75	1·75
MS314	232 × 147 mm. Nos. 308/13		2·50	2·50

1978 (6 Mar). *Easter. Nos. 303/7 optd with T 67, in gold.*

315	25 c. Type 65		15	20
316	40 c. "Helène Fourment and her Two Children"		15	20
317	$1.20, "Rubens and his Wife"		30	40
318	$2.50, "Marchesa Brigida Spinola-Doria"		40	60
315/18		*Set of 4*	90	1·25
MS319	93 × 145 mm. Nos. 315/18		1·25	1·50

Yellow-crowned Night Heron and other section:

62 Yellow-crowned Night Heron

(Des John Lister Ltd. Litho Questa)

1977 (18 Apr)–78. *T 62 and similar horiz designs. Multicoloured. P 13½.*

274	1 c. Type 62		30	70
275	2 c. Great Barracuda		30	1·10
276	3 c. Queen or Pink Conch		90	1·50
277	4 c. Spanish Bayonet		40	30
278	5 c. Honeycomb Trunkfish		1·50	30
279	6 c. Cable and Wireless Building		30	30
280	10 c. American Kestrel (20.2.78)		3·25	1·75
281	15 c. Ground Orchid (20.2.78)		2·75	1·75
282	20 c. Stop-light Parrotfish (20.2.78)		2·00	75
283	22 c. Lobster fishing boat (20.2.78)		45	60
284	35 c. Boat race (20.2.78)		1·40	70
285	50 c. Sea Bean (20.2.78)		90	45
286	$1 Sandy Island (20.2.78)		60	45
287	$2.50 Manchineel (20.2.78)		1·00	1·00
288	$5 Ground Lizard (20.2.78)		2·00	1·75
289	$10 Red-billed Tropic Bird		8·50	4·25
274/89		*Set of 16*	24·00	16·00

STANLEY GIBBONS
STAMP COLLECTING SERIES

Introductory booklets on *How to Start, How to Identify Stamps* and *Collecting by Theme*. A series of well illustrated guides at a low price.
Write for details.

68 Coronation Coach at   (69)   (70)
   Admiralty Arch

(Des John Lister Ltd. Litho Questa)

1978 (6 Apr). *25th Anniv of Coronation. T* **68** *and similar horiz designs. Multicoloured. P* 14.

320	22 c. Buckingham Palace	..	..	10	10
321	50 c. Type **68**	..	..	10	10
322	$1.50, Balcony scene	..	..	15	15
323	$2.50, Royal coat of arms	..	..	25	25
320/3			*Set of 4*	50	50
MS324	138 × 92 mm. Nos. 320/3	..		60	60

1978 (14 Aug). *Anniversaries. Nos. 283/8 optd as T* **69** *or surch as T* **70**.

325	22 c. Lobster fishing boat	..	..	20	15
	a. Opt double	..	..	£130	
	b. "C" omitted from "SECONDARY"		..	3·50	
326	35 c. Boat race	..	..	30	20
	a. "C" omitted from "SECONDARY"		..	3·75	
327	50 c. Sea Bean	..	..	30	30
	a. "I" omitted from "METHODIST"		..	3·75	
328	$1 Sandy Island	..	..	40	40
	a. "I" omitted from "METHODIST"		..	4·00	
329	$1.20 on $5 Ground Lizard	..	..	45	45
	a. "I" omitted from "METHODIST"		..	5·00	
330	$1.50 on $2.50, Manchineel	..	..	60	55
	a. "C" omitted from "SECONDARY"		..	6·00	
325/30			*Set of 6*	2·00	1·75

The 22, 35 c. and $1.50 values commemorate the 25th anniversary of Valley Secondary School; the other values commemorate the Centenary of Road Methodist Church.

Nos. 325b, 326a and 330a occur on R. 4/1 and Nos. 327a, 328a and 329a on R. 2/4.

71 Mother and Child

(Des and litho Questa)

1978 (11 Dec). *Christmas. Children's Paintings. T* **71** *and similar horiz designs. Multicoloured. P* 13½.

331	5 c. Type **71**	..	..	10	10
332	12 c. Christmas masquerade	..	..	10	10
333	18 c. Christmas dinner	..	..	10	10
334	22 c. Serenading	..	..	10	10
335	$1 Child in manger	..	..	45	20
336	$2.50, Family going to church	..		90	40
331/6			*Set of 6*	1·40	70
MS337	191 × 101 mm. Nos. 331/6	..		1·60	1·75

1979 (15 Jan). *International Year of the Child. As Nos. 331/7 but additionally inscr with emblem and "1979 INTERNATIONAL YEAR OF THE CHILD". Borders in different colours.*

338	5 c. Type **71**	..	..	10	10
339	12 c. Christmas masquerade	..	..	10	10
340	18 c. Christmas dinner	..	..	10	10
341	22 c. Serenading	..	..	10	10
342	$1 Child in manger	..	..	30	30
343	$2.50, Family going to church	..		50	50
338/43			*Set of 6*	90	90
MS344	205 × 112 mm. Nos. 338/43	..		2·25	2·50

(72) 73 Valley Methodist Church

1979 (12 Feb). *Nos. 274/7 and 279/80 surch as T* **72**.

345	12 c. on 2 c. Great Barracuda	..	..	50	50
346	14 c. on 4 c. Spanish Bayonet	..	..	40	50
	a. Surch inverted	..	..	32·00	
347	18 c. on 3 c. Queen or Pink Conch	..		80	55
348	25 c. on 6 c. Cable and Wireless Building	..	55	50
349	38 c. on 10 c. American Kestrel	..	..	1·60	70
350	40 c. on 1 c. Type **62**	..	..	1·75	70
345/50			*Set of 6*	5·00	3·00

(Des John Lister Ltd. Litho Questa)

1979 (30 Mar). *Easter. Church Interiors. T* **73** *and similar horiz designs. Multicoloured. P* 14.

351	5 c. Type **73**	..	..	10	10
	a. Horiz strip of 6. Nos. 351/6	..		1·60	
352	12 c. St. Mary's Anglican Church, The Valley		10	10
353	18 c. St. Gerard's Roman Catholic Church, The Valley	..	..	15	15
354	22 c. Road Methodist Church	..	..	15	15
355	$1.50, St. Augustine's Anglican Church, East End	..	..	60	60
356	$2.50, West End Methodist Church	..		75	75
351/6			*Set of 6*	1·60	1·60
MS357	190 × 105 mm. Nos. 351/6	..		1·75	2·25

Nos. 351/6 were printed together horizontally *se-tenant*, within the sheet.

74 Cape of Good Hope 1d. "Woodblock" of 1881

(Des Stanley Gibbons Ltd. Litho Questa)

1979 (23 Apr). *Death Centenary of Sir Rowland Hill. T* **74** *and similar horiz designs showing stamps. Multicoloured. P* 14.

358	1 c. Type **74**	..	..	10	10
359	1 c. U.S.A. "inverted Jenny" of 1918	..		10	10
360	22 c. Penny Black ("V.R. Official")	..		15	15
361	35 c. Germany 2 m. *Graf Zeppelin* of 1928	..	20	20
362	$1.50, U.S.A. $5 Columbus of 1893	..		45	60
363	$2.50, Great Britain £5 orange of 1882	..		75	95
358/63			*Set of 6*	1·50	1·75
MS364	187 × 123 mm. Nos. 358/63	..		1·50	2·10

75 Wright *Flyer I* (1st powered flight, 1903)

(Des John Lister Ltd. Litho Questa)

1979 (21 May). *History of Powered Flight. T* **75** *and similar horiz designs. Multicoloured. P* 14.

365	5 c. Type **75**			15	10
366	12 c. Louis Blériot at Dover after Channel crossing, 1909		20	10
367	18 c. Vickers FB-27 Vimy (1st non-stop crossing of Atlantic, 1919)		25	15
368	22 c. Ryan NYP Special *Spirit of St. Louis* (1st solo Atlantic flight by Charles Lindbergh, 1927)		25	20
369	$1.50, Airship LZ-127 *Graf Zeppelin*, 1928		60	60
370	$2.50, Concorde, 1979	..	..	1·75	90
365/70			*Set of 6*	2·75	1·75
MS371	200×113 mm. Nos. 365/70	..		2·75	2·50

76 Sombrero Island

(Des John Lister Ltd. Litho Questa)

1979 (20 Aug). *Outer Islands. T* **76** *and similar horiz designs. Multicoloured. P* 14.

372	5 c. Type **76**	..	..	10	10
373	12 c. Anguillita Island	..	..	10	10
374	18 c. Sandy Island	..	..	15	15
375	25 c. Prickly Pear Cays	..	..	15	15
376	$1 Dog Island	..	..	30	40
377	$2.50, Scrub Island	..	..	50	70
372/7			*Set of 6*	1·10	1·40
MS378	180×91 mm. Nos. 372/7	..		2·25	2·25

77 Red Poinsettia

(Des John Lister Ltd. Litho Format)

1979 (22 Oct). *Christmas. Flowers. T* **77** *and similar diamond-shaped designs. Multicoloured. P* 14½.

379	22 c. Type **77**	..	..	15	20
380	35 c. Kalanchoe	..	..	20	30
381	$1.50, Cream Poinsettia	..	..	40	50
382	$2.50, White Poinsettia	..	..	60	70
379/82			*Set of 4*	1·25	1·50
MS383	146 × 164 mm. Nos. 379/82	..		1·75	2·25

78 Exhibition Scene

(Des R. Granger Barrett. Litho Format)

1979 (10 Dec). *"London 1980" International Stamp Exhibition (1st issue). T* **78** *and similar horiz designs. Multicoloured. A. P* 13 *(from sheets of 20). B. P* 14½ *(from booklets except* **MS**388B*)*

				A		B	
384	35 c. Type **78**	..	15	20	15	20
385	50 c. Earls Court Exhibition Centre	..	15	25	20	25

386	$1.50, Penny Black and Two-penny Blue stamps	..	25	60	30	60
387	$2.50, Exhibition logo	..	45	95	50	95
384/7			*Set of 4*	90	1·75	1·00	1·75
MS388	150×94 mm. Nos. 384/7	..	1·40	2·00	1·40	2·00

Nos. 384B/7B also exist from uncut booklet sheets of 10.
See also Nos. 407/10.

79 Games Site

(Des John Lister Ltd. Litho Format)

1980 (14 Jan). *Winter Olympic Games, Lake Placid, U.S.A. T* **79** *and similar horiz designs. Multicoloured. P* 13.

389	5 c. Type **79**	..	..	10	10
390	18 c. Ice-hockey	..	..	10	10
391	35 c. Ice-skating	..	..	15	20
392	50 c. Bobsleighing	..	..	15	20
393	$1 Skiing	..	..	20	35
394	$2.50, Luge-tobogganing	..	..	40	80
389/94			*Set of 6*	80	1·50
MS395	136 × 128 mm. Nos. 389/94	..		1·25	2·00

Nos. 389/94 also exist perforated 14½ (*Price for set of 6 £1.60 mint, £1.90 used*) from additional sheetlets of 10. Stamps perforated 13 are from normal sheets of 40.

80 Salt ready for Reaping	50th Anniversary Scouting 1980 (81)	75th Anniversary Rotary 1980 (82)

(Des John Lister Ltd. Litho Questa)

1980 (14 Apr). *Salt Industry. T* **80** *and similar horiz designs. Multicoloured. P* 14.

396	5 c. Type **80**	..	..	10	10
397	12 c. Tallying salt	..	..	10	10
398	18 c. Unloading salt flats	..	..	15	15
399	22 c. Salt storage heap	..	..	15	15
400	$1 Salt for bagging and grinding	..	..	30	40
401	$2.50, Loading salt for export	..	..	50	70
396/401			*Set of 6*	1·10	1·40
MS402	180 × 92 mm. Nos. 396/401	..		1·10	1·75

Nos. 396/7, 398/9 and 400/1 were each printed in the same sheet, but with the values in separate panes.

1980 (16 Apr). *Anniversaries. Nos. 280, 282 and 287/8 optd with T* **81** *(10 c., $2.50) or* **82** *(others).*

403	10 c. American Kestrel	..	..	70	15
404	20 c. Stop-light Parrotfish	..	..	70	20
405	$2.50, Manchineel	..	..	1·50	1·25
406	$5 Ground Lizard	..	..	2·25	1·90
403/6			*Set of 4*	4·75	3·25

Commemorations:—10 c., $2.50, 50th anniversary of Anguilla Scout Movement; others, 75th anniversary of Rotary International.

83 Palace of Westminster and Great Britain 1970 9d. "Philympia" Commemorative	84 Queen Elizabeth the Queen Mother

(Des Stamp Magazine. Litho Rosenbaum Bros, Vienna)

1980 (6 May). *"London 1980" International Stamp Exhibition (2nd issue). T* **83** *and similar horiz designs showing famous landmarks and various international stamp exhibition commemorative stamps. Multicoloured. P* 13½.

407	50 c. Type **83**	..	..	55	65
408	$1.50, City Hall, Toronto and Canada 1978 $1.50, "CAPEX"	..	..	85	1·00
409	$2.50, Statue of Liberty and U.S.A. 1976 13 c. "Interphil"	..	..	1·10	1·40
407/9			*Set of 3*	2·25	2·75
MS410	157 × 130 mm. Nos. 407/9	..		2·25	2·75

(Des R. Granger Barrett from photograph by N. Parkinson. Litho Rosenbaum Bros, Vienna)

1980 (4 Aug). *80th Birthday of Queen Elizabeth the Queen Mother. P* 13½.

411	**84**	35 c. multicoloured	..	..	30	25
412		50 c. multicoloured	..	..	45	35
413		$1.50, multicoloured	..	..	90	85
414		$3 multicoloured	..	..	2·25	1·75
411/14				*Set of 4*	3·50	2·75
MS415		160×110 mm. Nos. 411/14	..		4·75	3·50

85 Brown Pelicans   (86)

SEPARATION 1980

(Des John Lister Ltd. Litho Questa)

1980 (13 Nov). *Christmas. Birds. T 85 and similar vert designs. Multicoloured. P 13½.*

416	5 c. Type 85	30	10
417	22 c. Great Blue Heron	75	20
418	$1.50, Barn Swallow	1·75	60
419	$3 Ruby-throated Hummingbird	2·25	1·40
416/19	*Set of 4*	4·50	2·10
MS420	126 × 160 mm. Nos. 416/19	8·00	6·50

1980 (18 Dec). *Separation of Anguilla from St. Kitts-Nevis. Nos. 274, 277, 279/89, 341 and 418/19 optd as T 86 or surch also.*

421	1 c. Type 62	10	40
422	2 c. on 4 c. Spanish Bayonet	10	40
423	5 c. on 15 c. Ground orchid	15	45
424	5 c. on $1.50, Barn Swallow	15	45
425	5 c. on $3 Ruby-throated Hummingbird	15	45
426	10 c. American Kestrel	20	60
427	12 c. on $1 Sandy Island	20	60
428	14 c. on $2.50, Manchineel	20	60
429	15 c. Ground orchid	25	60
430	18 c. on $5 Ground Lizard	25	60
431	20 c. Stop-light Parrotfish	25	60
432	22 c. Lobster fishing boat	25	60
433	25 c. on 15 c. Ground orchid	30	65
434	35 c. Boat race	30	65
435	38 c. on 22 c. Serenading	30	65
436	40 c. on 1 c. Type 62	30	65
437	50 c. Sea Bean	35	75
438	$1 Sandy Island	50	10
439	$2.50, Manchineel	1·00	2·25
440	$5 Ground Lizard	2·25	3·75
441	$10 Red-billed Tropic Bird	5·00	6·00
442	$10 on 6 c. Cable and Wireless Building	5·00	6·00
421/42	*Set of 22*	16·00	26·00

87 First Petition for Separation,
1825

(Des John Lister Ltd. Litho Format)

1980 (18 Dec). *Separation of Anguilla from St. Kitts-Nevis. T 87 and similar horiz designs. Multicoloured. P 14.*

443	18 c. Type 87	10	10
444	22 c. Referendum ballot paper, 1967	15	10
445	35 c. Airport blockade, 1967	15	15
446	50 c. Anguilla flag	20	20
447	$1 Separation celebrations, 1980	30	35
443/7	*Set of 5*	80	85
MS448	178 × 92 mm. Nos. 443/7	80	1·25

Nos. 443/4 and 445/6 were each printed in the same sheet with the two values in separate panes.

88 "Nelson's Dockyard"   89 Minnie Mouse
(R. Granger Barrett)   being chased by Bees

(Litho Rosenbaum Bros, Vienna)

1981 (2 Mar). *175th Death Anniv of Lord Nelson. Paintings. T 88 and similar horiz designs. Multicoloured. P 14.*

449	22 c. Type 88	1·00	30
450	35 c. "Ships in which Nelson served" (Nicholas Pocock)	1·25	50
451	50 c. "H.M.S. *Victory*" (Monamy Swaine)	1·50	65
452	$3 "Battle of Trafalgar" (Clarkson Stanfield)	2·00	2·25
449/52	*Set of 4*	5·25	3·25
MS453	82 × 63 mm. $5 "Horatio Nelson" (L. F. Abbott) and coat of arms	3·00	3·25

(Litho Questa)

1981 (30 Mar). *Easter. Walt Disney Cartoon Characters. T 89 and similar vert designs. Multicoloured. P 13½ × 14.*

454	1 c. Type 89	10	10
455	2 c. Pluto laughing at Mickey Mouse	10	10
456	3 c. Minnie Mouse tying ribbon round Pluto's neck	10	10
457	5 c. Minnie Mouse confronted by love-struck bird who fancies her bonnet	10	10
458	7 c. Dewey and Huey admiring themselves in mirror	10	10
459	9 c. Horace Horsecollar and Clarabelle Cow out for a stroll	10	10
460	10 c. Daisy Duck with hat full of Easter eggs	10	10
461	$2 Goofy unwrapping Easter hat	1·40	1·40
462	$3 Donald Duck in his Easter finery	1·60	1·60
454/62	*Set of 9*	2·75	3·00
MS463	134 × 108 mm. $5 Chip and Dale making off with hat	3·50	3·50

90 Prince Charles, Lady Diana Spencer and St. Paul's Cathedral

Extra flagstaff at right of Windsor
Castle (R. 1/5 of each pane)

(Des R. Granger Barrett. Litho Rosenbaum Bros, Vienna)

1981 (15 June). *Royal Wedding. T 90 and similar horiz designs showing Prince Charles, Lady Diana Spencer and buildings. Multicoloured. P 14.* (a) *No wmk.*

464	50 c. Type 90	15	20
465	$2.50, Althorp	30	50
466	$3 Windsor Castle	35	60
	a. Extra flagstaff	8·50	
464/6	*Set of 3*	70	1·25
MS467	90 x 72 mm. $5 Buckingham Palace	1·25	1·50

(b) *Booklet stamps. W w 15 (sideways*)*

468	50 c. Type 90	25	45
	a. Booklet pane of 4	75	
	ab. Black printed twice	7·00	
	w. Wmk reading upwards	25	
	wa. Booklet pane of 4	75	
469	$3 As No. 466	40	85
	a. Booklet pane of 4	1·40	
	ab. Black printed twice	7·00	
	w. Wmk reading upwards	40	
	wa. Booklet pane of 4	1·40	

*On Nos. 468/9 the normal sideways watermark reads downwards.

Nos. 464/6 also exist from additional sheetlets of two stamps and one label with changed background colours (*Price for set of 3 80p mint or used*).

Nos. 468/9 come from $14 stamp booklets.

Nos. 468ab and 469ab show the black features of the portraits strengthened by a further printing applied by typography. This is particularly visible on the Prince's suit and on the couple's hair.

91 Children playing in Tree

(Des Susan Csomer. Litho Rosenbaum Bros, Vienna)

1981 (31 July–30 Sept). *35th Anniv of U.N.I.C.E.F. T 91 and similar horiz designs. Multicoloured. P 14.*

470	5 c. Type 91	20	30
471	10 c. Children playing by pool	20	30
472	15 c. Children playing musical instruments	20	30
473	$3 Children playing with pets (30 Sept)	2·50	3·00
470/3	*Set of 4*	2·75	3·50
MS474	78 × 106 mm. $4 Children playing football (vert) (30 Sept)	3·50	4·50

(Litho Questa)

1981 (2 Nov). *Christmas. Horiz designs as T 89 showing scenes from Walt Disney's cartoon film "The Night before Christmas". P 13½.*

475	1 c. multicoloured	10	10
476	2 c. multicoloured	10	10
477	3 c. multicoloured	10	10
478	5 c. multicoloured	10	10
479	7 c. multicoloured	10	10
480	10 c. multicoloured	10	10
481	12 c. multicoloured	10	10
482	$2 multicoloured	2·75	1·40
483	$3 multicoloured	2·75	1·60
475/83	*Set of 9*	5·00	2·75
MS484	130 × 105 mm. $5 multicoloured	5·00	3·50

---

92 Red Grouper   (93)

(Des R. Granger Barrett. Litho Questa)

1982 (1 Jan). *Horiz designs as T 92. Multicoloured. P 13½×14.*

485	1 c. Type 92	15	50
486	5 c. Ferry service, Blowing Point	30	50
487	10 c. Island dinghies	20	50
488	15 c. Majorettes	20	50
489	20 c. Launching boat, Sandy Hill	40	50
490	25 c. Corals	90	50
491	30 c. Little Bay cliffs	30	60
492	35 c. Fountain Cave interior	1·25	70
493	40 c. Sunset over Sandy Island	30	60
494	45 c. Landing at Sombrero	50	65
495	60 c. Seine fishing	2·50	1·75
496	75 c. Boat race at sunset, Sandy Ground	80	1·40
497	$1 Bagging lobster at Island Harbour	2·00	1·50
498	$5 Brown Pelicans	13·00	8·50
499	$7.50, Hibiscus	10·00	9·00
500	$10 Queen Triggerfish	13·00	11·00
485/500	*Set of 16*	42·00	35·00

1982 (22 Mar). *No. 494 surch with T 93.*

501	50 c. on 45 c. Landing at Sombrero	50	35

94 Anthurium and   95 Lady Diana Spencer
Heliconius   in 1961
charithonia

(Des R. Granger Barrett. Litho Questa)

1982 (5 Apr). *Easter. Flowers and Butterflies. T 94 and similar vert designs. Multicoloured. P 14.*

502	10 c. Type 94	45	15
503	35 c. Bird of Paradise and *Junonia evarete*	80	40
504	75 c. Allamanda and *Danaus plexippus*	1·25	70
505	$3 Orchid Tree and *Biblis hyperia*	2·00	2·25
502/5	*Set of 4*	4·00	3·25
MS506	65×79 mm. $5 Amaryllis and *Dryas julia*	2·75	3·50

(Des R. Granger Barrett. Litho Ueberreuter)

1982 (17 May–30 Aug). *21st Birthday of Princess of Wales. T 95 and similar vert designs. Multicoloured. P 14.*

507	10 c. Type 95	10	10
	a. Booklet pane of 4 (30 Aug)	40	
508	30 c. Lady Diana Spencer in 1968	20	20
	a. Booklet pane of 4 (30 Aug)	1·00	
509	40 c. Lady Diana in 1970	25	25
	a. Booklet pane of 4 (30 Aug)	1·40	
510	60 c. Lady Diana in 1974	35	35
	a. Booklet pane of 4 (30 Aug)	1·40	
511	$2 Lady Diana in 1981	80	1·10
	a. Booklet pane of 4 (30 Aug)	3·00	
512	$3 Lady Diana in 1981 (*different*)	1·10	1·40
507/12	*Set of 6*	2·50	3·00
MS513	72 × 90 mm. $5 Princess of Wales	3·50	3·00
MS514	125 × 125 mm. As Nos. 507/12, but with buff borders	4·00	4·25

96 Pitching Tent

(Litho Ueberreuter)

1982 (5 July). *75th Anniv of Boy Scout Movement. T 96 and similar horiz designs. Multicoloured. P 14.*

515	10 c. Type 96	45	20
516	35 c. Scout band	85	50
517	75 c. Yachting	1·25	90
518	$3 On parade	3·00	2·75
515/18	*Set of 4*	5·00	4·00
MS519	90 × 72 mm. $5 Cooking	4·50	4·00

(Litho Format)

1982 (3 Aug). *World Cup Football Championship, Spain. Horiz designs as T 89 showing scenes from Walt Disney's cartoon film "Bedknobs and Broomsticks". P 11.*

520	1 c. multicoloured	10	10
521	2 c. multicoloured	10	10
522	4 c. multicoloured	10	10
523	5 c. multicoloured	10	10
524	7 c. multicoloured	10	10
525	9 c. multicoloured	10	10
526	10 c. multicoloured	10	10
527	$2.50 multicoloured	2·00	1·75
528	$3 multicoloured	2·00	2·00
520/8	*Set of 9*	4·00	3·75
MS529	126×101 mm. $5 mult. P 14×13½	5·00	5·50

COMMONWEALTH GAMES 1982

(97)

1982 (18 Oct). *Commonwealth Games, Brisbane. Nos. 487, 495/6 and 498 optd with T* 97.

30	10 c. Island dinghies	..	15	25
	a. "S" omitted from "GAMES"	..	1·75	
31	60 c. Seine fishing ..	..	45	60
	a. "S" omitted from "GAMES"	..	2·75	
32	75 c. Boat race at sunset, Sandy Ground		60	80
	a. "S" omitted from "GAMES"	..	3·25	
33	$5 Brown Pelicans	..	3·25	3·75
	a. "S" omitted from "GAMES"	..	9·00	
30/3		*Set of* 4	4·00	4·75

The "S" omitted variety occurs on R.2/2 of the right-hand pane for all values.

(Litho Questa)

1982 (29 Nov). *Birth Centenary of A. A. Milne (author). Horiz designs as T* 89 *showing scenes from various "Winnie the Pooh" stories. P* 14 × 13½.

34	1 c. multicoloured	..	10	10
35	2 c. multicoloured	..	10	10
36	3 c. multicoloured	..	15	10
37	5 c. multicoloured	..	20	10
38	7 c. multicoloured	..	20	15
39	10 c. multicoloured	..	20	15
40	12 c. multicoloured	..	30	15
41	20 c. multicoloured	..	40	20
42	$5 multicoloured	..	5·00	5·50
34/42		*Set of* 9	6·00	5·75
MS543	120 × 93 mm. $5 multicoloured	..	5·50	6·00

98 Culture

99 "I am the Lord Thy God"

(Des R. Granger Barrett. Litho Ueberreuter)

1983 (28 Feb). *Commonwealth Day. T* 98 *and similar horiz designs. Multicoloured. P* 14.

544	10 c. Type 98	..	10	15
545	35 c. Anguilla and British flags	..	30	30
546	75 c. Economic co-operation	..	60	80
547	$2.50, Salt industry (salt pond)	..	3·75	4·25
544/7		*Set of* 4	4·25	5·00
MS548	76 × 61 mm. $5 World map showing position of Commonwealth countries	..	3·00	2·50

(Litho Questa)

1983 (31 Mar). *Easter. The Ten Commandments. T* 99 *and similar vert designs. Multicoloured. P* 14.

549	1 c. Type 99	..	10	10
550	2 c. "Thou shalt not make any graven image"	10	10
551	3 c. "Thou shalt not take My Name in vain"	10	10
552	10 c. "Remember the Sabbath Day"	20	10
553	35 c. "Honour thy father and mother"	45	20
554	60 c. "Thou shalt not kill"	80	40
555	75 c. "Thou shalt not commit adultery"	90	50
556	$2 "Thou shalt not steal"	2·25	1·50
557	$2.50, "Thou shalt not bear false witness"	2·50	1·50
558	$5 "Thou shalt not covet"	3·75	2·75
549/58		*Set of* 10	10·00	6·50
MS559	126 × 102 mm. $5 "Moses receiving the Tablets" (16th-century woodcut)	..	2·50	3·00

100 Leatherback Turtle

101 Montgolfier Hot Air Balloon, 1783

(Des R. Granger Barrett. Litho Questa)

1983 (10 Aug). *Turtles. T* 100 *and similar horiz designs. Multicoloured. A. P* 13½. *B. P* 12.

		A		B	
560	10 c. Type 100	1·00	30	1·50	40
561	35 c. Hawksbill Turtle	2·00	75	2·75	1·50
562	75 c. Green Turtle	2·75	1·60	3·50	2·75
563	$1 Loggerhead Turtle	3·25	3·00	4·00	3·75
560/3	*Set of* 4	8·00	5·00	10·50	7·75
MS564	93 × 72 mm. $5 Leatherback Turtle (*different*)	4·50	3·00		†

(Des R. Granger Barrett. Litho Questa)

1983 (22 Aug). *Bicentenary of Manned Flight. T* 101 *and similar vert designs. Multicoloured. P* 13½.

565	10 c. Type 101		30	20
566	60 c. Blanchard and Jeffries crossing English Channel by balloon, 1785		85	45
567	$1 Henri Giffard's steam-powered dirigible airship, 1852		1·25	65
568	$2.50, Otto Lilienthal and biplane glider, 1890–96		2·00	1·50
565/8		*Set of* 4	4·00	2·50
MS569	72×90 mm. $5 Wilbur Wright flying round Statue of Liberty, 1909	..	2·50	3·25

102 Boys' Brigade Band and Flag

(Des R. Granger Barrett. Litho Questa)

1983 (12 Sept). *Centenary of Boys' Brigade. T* 102 *and similar horiz design. Multicoloured. P* 13½.

570	10 c. Type 102	..	25	15
571	$5 Brigade members marching	..	3·00	2·75
MS572	96 × 115 mm. Nos. 570/1	..	3·25	3·75

150TH ANNIVERSARY ABOLITION OF SLAVERY ACT

(103)

1983 (24 Oct). *150th Anniv of the Abolition of Slavery* (1st issue). *Nos. 487, 493 and 497/8 optd with T* 103.

573	10 c. Island dinghies	..	10	10
	a. Opt inverted	..	35·00	
574	40 c. Sunset over Sandy Island	..	25	25
575	$1 Bagging lobster at Island Harbour	60	50
576	$5 Brown Pelicans	..	4·00	2·75
573/6		*Set of* 4	4·50	3·25

See also Nos. 616/24.

104 Jiminy on Clock (*Cricket on the Hearth*)

(Litho Format)

1983 (14 Nov). *Christmas. Walt Disney Cartoon Characters. T* 104 *and similar vert designs depicting scenes from Dickens' Christmas stories. Multicoloured. P* 13½.

577	1 c. Type 104	..	10	10
578	2 c. Jiminy with fiddle (*Cricket on the Hearth*)	10	10
579	3 c. Jiminy among toys (*Cricket on the Hearth*)	10	10
580	4 c. Mickey as Bob Cratchit (*A Christmas Carol*)	10	10
581	5 c. Donald Duck as Scrooge (*A Christmas Carol*)	10	10
582	6 c. Mini and Goofy in *The Chimes*	10	10
583	10 c. Goofy sees an imp appearing from bells (*The Chimes*)	10	10
584	$2 Donald Duck as Mr. Pickwick (*The Pickwick Papers*)	2·75	2·00
585	$3 Disney characters as Pickwickians (*The Pickwick Papers*)	3·00	2·25
577/85		*Set of* 9	5·75	4·25
MS586	130 × 104 mm. $5 Donald Duck as Mr. Pickwick with gifts (*The Pickwick Papers*)	6·00	8·00

105 100 Metres Race

(Litho Questa)

1984 (20 Feb–24 Apr). *Olympic Games, Los Angeles. T* 105 *and similar horiz designs showing Mickey Mouse in Decathlon events. Multicoloured. A. Inscr.* "1984 Los Angeles". *P* 14 × 13½. *B. Inscr.* "1984 Olympics Los Angeles" *and Olympic emblem. P* 14 × 13½ (*MS*596B) *or* 12 (*others*) (24 April).

		A		B	
587	1 c. Type 105	10	10	10	10
588	2 c. Long jumping	10	10	10	10
589	3 c. Shot-putting	10	10	10	10
590	4 c. High jumping	10	10	10	10
591	5 c. 400 metres race	10	10	10	10
592	6 c. Hurdling	10	10	10	10
593	10 c. Discus-throwing	10	10	10	10
594	$1 Pole-vaulting	2·50	1·25	3·00	2·25
595	$4 Javelin-throwing	5·00	3·50	6·50	6·00
587/95	*Set of* 9	7·00	4·75	9·00	8·00
MS596	117 × 93 mm. $5 1500 metres race	6·00	4·00	6·00	4·00

Nos. 587B/95B were each printed in small sheets of 6 stamps including one *se-tenant* stamp-size label in position 2.

106 "Justice" (107)

(Des and litho Questa)

1984 (19 Apr). *Easter. T* 106 *and similar vert designs showing details from "La Stanza della Segnatura" by Raphael. Multicoloured. P* 13½ × 14.

597	10 c. Type 106	..	15	10
598	25 c. "Poetry"	..	20	20
599	35 c. "Philosophy"	..	30	30
600	40 c. "Theology"	..	30	30
601	$1 "Abraham and Paul"	..	85	95
602	$2 "Moses and Matthew"	..	1·60	1·75
603	$3 "John and David"	..	2·25	2·50
604	$4 "Peter and Adam"	..	2·50	2·75
597/604		*Set of* 8	7·25	8·00
MS605	83 × 110 mm. $5 "Astronomy"	..	3·50	3·00

1984 (24 Apr–17 May). *Nos. 485, 491 and 498/500 surch as T* 107.

606	10 c. on $7.50, Hibiscus (17 May)	..	45	35
607	35 c. on 30 c. Little Bay cliffs	..	50	40
608	60 c. on 1 c. Type 92	..	55	45
609	$2.50 on $5 Brown Pelicans	..	2·25	1·50
	a. Surch at left with decimal point*	18·00	
610	$2.50 on $10 Queen Triggerfish	..	1·75	1·50
	a. Surch at right without decimal point*	18·00	
606/10		*Set of* 5	5·00	3·75

*The surcharge on No. 609 shows the figures at right of the design and without a decimal point. On No. 610 they are to the left and include a decimal point. No 609a shows, in error, the surcharge for No. 610 and No. 610a that intended for No. 609.

108 Australia 1913 1d. Kangaroo Stamp

(Des K. Cato. Litho Leigh-Mardon Ltd, Melbourne)

1984 (16 July). *"Ausipex 84" International Stamp Exhibition, Melbourne. T* 108 *and similar horiz designs showing Australian stamps. Multicoloured. P* 13½ × 14.

611	10 c. Type 108	..	30	20
612	75 c. 1914 6d. Laughing Kookaburra	..	1·00	85
613	$1 1932 2d. Sydney Harbour Bridge	..	1·50	1·25
614	$2.50, 1938 10s. King George VI	..	2·25	2·00
611/14		*Set of* 4	4·50	4·00
MS615	95 × 86 mm. $5 £1 Bass and £2 Admiral King	4·50	5·50

109 Thomas Fowell Buxton

(Des R. Granger Barrett. Litho Questa)

1984 (1 Aug). *150th Anniv of Abolition of Slavery* (2nd issue). *T* 109 *and similar horiz designs. Multicoloured. P* 14.

616	10 c. Type 109	..	10	10
617	25 c. Abraham Lincoln	..	25	25
618	35 c. Henri Christophe	..	35	35
619	60 c. Thomas Clarkson	..	50	50
620	75 c. William Wilberforce	..	60	60
621	$1 Olaudah Equiano	..	70	70
622	$2.50, General Charles Gordon	..	1·60	1·60
623	$5 Granville Sharp	..	2·25	2·25
616/23		*Set of* 8	6·50	6·50
MS624	150 × 121 mm. Nos. 616/23. P 12	..	6·50	8·00

U.P.U. CONGRESS HAMBURG 1984

PRINCE HENRY BIRTH 15.9.84

(110)　　　　(111)

1984 (13 Aug). *Universal Postal Union Congress, Hamburg. Nos. 486/7 and 498 optd as T 110 or surch also (No. 626).*

625	5 c. Ferry services, Blowing Point	20	10
626	20 c. on 10 c. Island dinghies ..	30	15
627	$5 Brown Pelicans	4·50	3·50
625/7	*Set of 3*	4·50	3·50

1984 (31 Oct). *Birth of Prince Henry. Nos. 507/14 optd as T 111.*

628	10 c. Type **95**	10	10
	a. Booklet pane of 4	60	
629	30 c. Lady Diana Spencer in 1968 ..	20	25
630	40 c. Lady Diana in 1970 ..	25	30
	a. Booklet pane of 4	1·00	
631	60 c. Lady Diana in 1974 ..	40	45
	a. Booklet pane of 4	1·60	
632	$2 Lady Diana in 1981 ..	1·00	1·25
	a. Booklet pane of 4	4·00	
633	$3 Lady Diana in 1981 (*different*)	1·10	1·75
628/33	*Set of 6*	2·75	3·75
MS634	72×90 mm. $5 Princess of Wales	2·00	3·00
MS635	125×125 mm. As Nos. 628/33, but with buff borders	2·50	4·00

On No. MS634 the lines of overprint are larger, being placed vertically each side of the portrait.

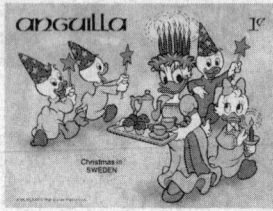

112 Christmas in Sweden

(Litho Questa)

1984 (12 Nov). *Christmas. Walt Disney Cartoon Characters. T 112 and similar horiz designs showing national scenes. Multicoloured. P 12 ($2) or 14×13½ (others).*

636	1 c. Type **112**	10	10
637	2 c. Italy	10	10
638	3 c. Holland	10	10
639	4 c. Mexico	10	10
640	5 c. Spain	10	10
641	10 c. Disneyland, U.S.A. ..	10	10
642	$1 Japan	2·50	2·00
643	$2 Anguilla	3·25	3·50
644	$4 Germany	4·75	5·50
636/44	*Set of 9*	9·50	10·00
MS645	126×102 mm. $5 England ..	7·00	5·00

No. 643 was printed in sheetlets of 8 stamps.

113 Icarus in Flight

114 Barn Swallow

(Des H. Herni (60 c.), S. Diouf (75 c.), adapted R. Granger Barrett. Litho Ueberreuter)

1984 (3 Dec). *40th Anniv of International Civil Aviation Organization. T 113 and similar multicoloured designs. P 14.*

646	60 c. Type **113**	60	75
647	75 c. "Solar Princess" (abstract) ..	80	90
648	$2.50, I.C.A.O. emblem (*vert*) ..	2·25	3·00
646/8	*Set of 3*	3·25	4·25
MS649	65×49 mm. $5 Map of air routes serving Anguilla	3·00	4·25

(Litho Questa)

1985 (29 Apr). *Birth Bicentenary of John J. Audubon (ornithologist). T 114 and similar multicoloured designs. P 14.*

650	10 c. Type **114**	60	30
651	60 c. American Wood Stork ..	1·00	60
652	75 c. Roseate Tern	1·00	70
653	$5 Osprey	4·00	3·50
650/3	*Set of 4*	6·00	4·50
MS654	Two sheets, each 73 × 103 mm. (a) $4 Western Tanager (*horiz*); (b) $4 Solitary Vireo (*horiz*) .. .. *Set of 2 sheets*	6·50	5·00

Nos. 650/3 were each issued in sheetlets of five stamps and one stamp-size label, which appears in the centre of the bottom row.

115 The Queen Mother visiting King's College Hospital, London

116 White-tailed Tropic Bird

(Des J.W. Litho Questa)

1985 (2 July). *Life and Times of Queen Elizabeth the Queen Mother. T 115 and similar vert designs. Multicoloured. P 14.*

655	10 c. Type **115**	10	10
656	$2 The Queen Mother inspecting Royal Marine Volunteer Cadets, Deal	80	1·25
657	$3 The Queen Mother outside Clarence House	1·10	1·50
655/7	*Set of 3*	1·75	2·50
MS658	56 × 85 mm. $5 At Ascot, 1979 ..	1·75	2·50

Nos. 655/7 also exist perforated 12×12½ from additional sheetlets of five stamps and one label (*Price for set of 3 £1.75 mint, £2.50 used*).

(Des R. Granger Barrett. Litho Questa)

1985 (22 July)-**86**. *Birds. T 116 and similar horiz designs. Multicoloured. P 13½×14.*

659	5 c. Brown Pelican (11.11.85) ..	80	1·00
660	10 c. Mourning Dove (11.11.85) ..	80	1·00
661	15 c. Magnificent Frigate Bird (inscr "Man-o-War") (11.11.85) ..	90	1·00
662	20 c. Antillean Crested Hummingbird (11.11.85) ..	90	1·00
663	25 c. Type **116**. ..	90	1·00
664	30 c. Caribbean Elaenia (11.11.85) ..	90	1·00
665	35 c. Black-whiskered Vireo (11.11.85) ..	4·75	4·50
665a	35 c. Lesser Antillean Bullfinch (10.3.86)	90	1·00
666	40 c. Yellow-crowned Night Heron (11.11.85)	90	1·00
667	45 c. Pearly-eyed Thrasher (30.9.85) ..	90	1·00
668	50 c. Laughing Gull (30.9.85) ..	90	1·00
669	65 c. Brown Booby ..	90	1·00
670	80 c. Grey Kingbird (30.9.85) ..	1·50	2·25
671	$1 Audubon's Shearwater (30.9.85)	1·75	2·50
672	$1.35, Roseate Tern ..	1·50	2·50
673	$2.50, Bananaquit (11.11.85) ..	3·75	5·00
674	$5 Belted Kingfisher ..	3·75	6·00
675	$10 Green Heron (30.9.85) ..	6·50	8·50
659/75	*Set of 18*	30·00	38·00

GIRL GUIDES 75TH ANNIVERSARY 1910–1985

(117)

1985 (14 Oct). *75th Anniv of Girl Guide Movement. Nos. 486, 491, 496 and 498 optd with T 117.*

676	5 c. Ferry service, Blowing Point ..	20	10
677	30 c. Little Bay cliffs	40	50
678	75 c. Boat race at sunset, Sandy Ground	60	70
679	$5 Brown Pelicans	4·75	3·50
	a. Opt double	85·00	
676/9	*Set of 4*	5·50	4·00

118 Goofy as Huckleberry Finn Fishing

(Des Walt Disney Productions. Litho Questa)

1985 (11 Nov). *150th Birth Anniv of Mark Twain (author). T 118 and similar horiz designs showing Walt Disney cartoon characters in scenes from "Huckleberry Finn". Multicoloured. P 12 ($1) or 14×13½ (others).*

680	10 c. Type **118**. ..	20	15
681	60 c. Pete as Pap surprising Huck ..	85	75
682	$1 "Multiplication tables" ..	1·40	1·25
683	$3 The Duke reciting Shakespeare ..	3·00	3·00
680/3	*Set of 4*	4·75	4·75
MS684	127×102 mm. $5 "In school but out"	6·00	6·00

No. 682 was printed in sheetlets of 8 stamps.

119 Hansel and Gretel (Mickey and Minnie Mouse) awakening in Forest

(Des Walt Disney Productions. Litho Questa)

1985 (11 Nov). *Birth Bicentenaries of Grimm Brothers (folklorists). T 119 and similar horiz designs showing Walt Disney cartoon characters in scenes from "Hansel and Gretel". Multicoloured. P 12 (90 c.) or 14×13½ (others).*

685	5 c. Type **119**. ..	10	10
686	50 c. Hansel and Gretel find the gingerbread house	55	40
687	90 c. Hansel and Gretel meeting the Witch ..	90	75
688	$4 Hansel and Gretel captured by the Witch	3·00	3·00
685/8	*Set of 4*	4·00	3·75
MS689	126×101 mm. $5 Hansel and Gretel riding on swan ..	6·00	6·50

No. 687 was printed in sheetlets of 8 stamps.

---

120 Statue of Liberty and *Danmark* (Denmark)

(Litho Format)

1985 (14 Nov). *Centenary of the Statue of Liberty (1986). T 120 and similar multicoloured designs showing the Statue of Liberty and cadet ships. P 15.*

690	10 c. Type **120**.	50	50
691	20 c. *Eagle* (U.S.A.)	70	70
692	60 c. *Amerigo Vespucci* (Italy) ..	1·25	1·50
693	75 c. *Sir Winston Churchill* (Great Britain)..	1·25	1·75
694	$2 *Nippon Maru* (Japan) ..	1·75	2·50
695	$2.50, *Gorch Fock* (West Germany) ..	2·00	2·50
690/5	*Set of 6*	6·50	8·50
MS696	96×69 mm. $5 Statue of Liberty (*vert*) ..	6·50	4·50

80TH ANNIVERSARY ROTARY 1985

(121)

INTERNATIONAL YOUTH YEAR

(122)

1985 (18 Nov). *80th Anniv of Rotary (10, 35 c.) and International Youth Year (others). Nos. 487, 491 and 497 surch or optd as T 121 (10 c., 35 c.) or 122 (others).*

697	10 c. Island dinghies	10	10
698	35 c. on 30 c. Little Bay cliffs ..	25	25
699	$1 Bagging lobster at Island Harbour	70	70
700	$5 on 30 c. Little Bay cliffs ..	3·50	3·50
697/700	*Set of 4*	4·00	4·00

123 Johannes Hevelius (astronomer) and Mayan Temple Observatory

124 The Crucifixion

(Des W. Hanson. Litho Questa)

1986 (17 Mar). *Appearance of Halley's Comet. T 123 and similar horiz designs. Multicoloured. P 14.*

701	5 c. Type **123**.	25	25
702	10 c. "Viking Lander" space vehicle on Mars, 1976 ..	25	25
703	60 c. Comet in 1664 (from *Theatri Cosmicum*, 1668) ..	85	85
704	$4 Comet over Mississippi riverboat, 1835 (150th birth anniv of Mark Twain)	3·50	3·50
701/4	*Set of 4*	4·25	4·25
MS705	101×70 mm. $5 Halley's Comet over Anguilla	4·50	5·50

(Des R. Granger Barrett. Litho Questa)

1986 (27 Mar). *Easter. T 124 and similar designs showing stained glass windows from Chartres Cathedral. P 14×13½.*

706	10 c. multicoloured ..	20	20
707	25 c. multicoloured ..	35	35
708	45 c. multicoloured ..	65	65
709	$4 multicoloured ..	3·25	3·75
706/9	*Set of 4*	4·00	4·50
MS710	93×75 mm. $5 multicoloured (*horiz*). P 13½×14	4·75	6·00

125 Princess Elizabeth inspecting Guards, 1946

AMERIPEX 1986

(126)

(Litho Questa)

1986 (21 Apr). *60th Birthday of Queen Elizabeth II. T* **125** *and similar vert designs. P* 14.

711	20 c. black and yellow	..	15	15
712	$2 multicoloured	..	1·25	1·25
713	$3 multicoloured	..	1·75	1·75
711/13		Set of 3	2·75	2·75
MS714	120 × 85 mm. $5 black and grey-brown . .		2·75	3·50

Designs:—$2 Queen at Garter Ceremony; $3 At Trooping the Colour; $5 Duke and Duchess of York with baby Princess Elizabeth, 1926.

1986 (22 May). *"Ameripex" International Stamp Exhibition, Chicago. Nos. 659, 667, 671, 673 and 675 optd with T* **126**.

715	5 c. Brown Pelican ..	..	30	30
716	45 c. Pearly-eyed Thrasher ..	..	50	35
717	$1 Audubon's Shearwater ..	..	85	75
718	$2.50, Bananaquit ..	..	2·00	2·00
719	$10 Green Heron ..	..	6·00	7·00
715/19		Set of 5	8·75	9·25

INTERNATIONAL
YEAR OF
PEACE

127 Prince Andrew and Miss Sarah Ferguson   (**128**)

(Des and litho Questa)

1986 (23 July). *Royal Wedding. T* **127** *and similar vert designs. Multicoloured. A. P* 14. *B. P* 12.

		A		B	
720	10 c. Type **127**	15	15	15	15
721	35 c. Prince Andrew	35	35	35	35
722	$2 Miss Sarah Ferguson ..	1·25	1·25	1·60	1·60
723	$3 Prince Andrew and Miss Sarah Ferguson (different)	1·75	1·75	2·00	2·00
720/3	Set of 4	3·25	3·25	3·75	3·75
MS724	119 × 90 mm. $6 Westminster Abbey	5·50	6·50	5·50	6·50

1986 (29 Sept). *International Peace Year. Nos. 616/24 optd with T* **128**.

725	10 c. Type **109**	..	15	15
726	25 c. Abraham Lincoln ..	..	25	25
727	35 c. Henri Christophe ..	..	35	35
728	60 c. Thomas Clarkson ..	..	55	55
729	75 c. William Wilberforce ..	..	70	70
730	$1 Olaudah Equiano ..	..	80	80
731	$2.50, General Gordon ..	..	1·75	1·75
732	$5 Granville Sharp . .	..	3·00	3·00
725/32		Set of 8	6·75	6·75
MS733	150 × 121 mnm. Nos. 725/32 ..	..	10·00	12·00

129 Trading Sloop

130 Christopher Columbus with Astrolabe

(Des R. Granger Barrett. Litho Questa)

1986 (25 Nov). *Christmas. Ships. T* **129** *and similar multicoloured designs. P* 14.

734	10 c. Type **129**. . ..	..	70	50
735	45 c. Lady Rodney (cargo liner) ..	..	1·60	1·10
736	80 c. West Derby (19th-century sailing ship)		2·25	2·25
737	$3 Warspite (local sloop) ..	..	4·25	5·00
734/7		Set of 4	8·00	8·00
MS738	130 × 100 mm. $6 Boat race day (vert) ..		11·00	13·00

(Des Mary Walters. Litho Questa)

1986 (22 Dec). *500th Anniv of Discovery of America (1992) (1st issue). T* **130** *and similar multicoloured designs. P* 14.

739	5 c. Type **130**. . ..	..	20	20
740	10 c. Columbus on board ship ..	..	30	30
741	35 c. Santa Maria ..	..	90	85
742	80 c. King Ferdinand and Queen Isabella of Spain (horiz) ..	..	1·25	1·40
743	$4 Caribbean Indians smoking tobacco (horiz)	..	3·25	4·00
739/43		Set of 5	5·50	6·00
MS744	Two sheets, each 96 × 66 mm. (a) $5 Caribbean Manatee (horiz). (b) $5 Dragon Tree	Set of 2 sheets	11·00	13·00

See also Nos. 902/6.

NEW INFORMATION

The editor is always interested to correspond with people who have new information that will improve or correct the Catalogue.

---

131 *Danaus plexippus*

(Des R. Vigurs. Litho Questa)

1987 (14 Apr). *Easter. Butterflies. T* **131** *and similar horiz designs. Multicoloured. P* 14.

745	10 c. Type **131** ..	..	65	40
746	80 c. Anartia jatrophae ..	..	2·00	2·00
747	$1 Heliconius charithonia ..	..	2·25	2·25
748	$2 Junonia evarete ..	..	3·50	4·00
745/8		Set of 4	7·50	7·75
MS749	90 × 69 mm. $6 Dryas julia ..		8·50	10·00

132 Old Goose Iron and Modern Electric Iron   (**133**)

(Des R. Vigurs. Litho Questa)

1987 (25 May). *20th Anniv of Separation from St. Kitts–Nevis. T* **132** *and similar horiz designs. Multicoloured. P* 14.

750	10 c. Type **132**. .	..	15	20
751	35 c. Old East End School and Albena Lake-Hodge Comprehensive College ..		20	20
752	45 c. Past and present markets ..		25	25
753	80 c. Previous sailing ferry and new motor ferry, Blowing Point ..		45	55
754	$1 Original mobile office and new telephone exchange ..		55	75
755	$2 Open-air meeting, Burrowes Park, and House of Assembly in session ..		1·10	1·75
750/5		Set of 6	2·40	3·25
MS756	159 × 127 mm. Nos. 750/5 ..		4·50	6·00

1987 (13 June). *"Capex '87" International Stamp Exhibition, Toronto. Nos. 665a, 667, 670 and 675 optd with T* **133** *in red.*

757	35 c. Lesser Antillean Bullfinch ..	..	50	50
758	45 c. Pearly-eyed Thrasher ..	..	60	60
759	80 c. Grey Kingbird ..	..	1·00	1·00
760	$10 Green Heron ..	..	6·25	7·25
757/60		Set of 4	7·50	8·50

20 YEARS OF PROGRESS

1967 – 1987

(**134**)

1987 (4 Sept). *20th Anniv of Independence. Nos. 659, 661/4 and 665a/75 optd as T* **134** *in red or surch additionally in black (No. 762).*

761	5 c. Brown Pelican ..	..	70	70
762	10 c. on 15 c. Magnificent Frigate Bird ..		70	70
763	15 c. Magnificent Frigate Bird ..		75	75
764	20 c. Antillean Crested Hummingbird ..		80	80
765	25 c. Type **116**. .	..	80	80
766	30 c. Caribbean Elaenia ..	..	85	90
767	35 c. Lesser Antillean Bullfinch ..		90	90
768	40 c. Yellow-crowned Night Heron ..		90	1·00
769	45 c. Pearly-eyed Thrasher ..	..	1·00	1·10
	a. Opt double, one albino ..	..	42·00	
770	50 c. Laughing Gull ..	..	1·00	1·10
771	65 c. Brown Booby ..	..	1·00	1·25
772	80 c. Grey Kingbird ..	..	1·25	1·50
773	$1 Audubon's Shearwater ..	..	1·25	1·50
774	$1.35, Roseate Tern ..	..	1·50	2·00
775	$2.50, Bananaquit ..	..	2·00	3·00
776	$5 Belted Kingfisher ..	..	3·00	4·50
777	$10 Green Heron ..	..	6·00	8·50
761/77		Set of 17	22·00	28·00

135 Wicket Keeper and Game in Progress

(Des R. Granger Barrett. Litho Questa)

1987 (5 Oct). *Cricket World Cup. T* **135** *and similar horiz designs. Multicoloured. P* 13½ × 14.

778	10 c. Type **135**. .	..	55	40
779	35 c. Batsman and local Anguilla team ..		85	55
780	45 c. Batsman and game in progress ..		1·00	70
781	$2.50, Bowler and game in progress ..		2·50	3·50
778/81		Set of 4	4·50	4·75
MS782	100 × 75 mm. $6 Batsman and game in progress (different) ..		8·50	10·00

---

136 West Indian Top Shell

(Des R. Granger Barrett. Litho Questa)

1987 (2 Nov). *Christmas. Sea Shells and Crabs. T* **136** *and similar horiz designs. Multicoloured. P* 13½ × 14.

783	10 c. Type **136**. .	..	50	30
784	35 c. Ghost Crab ..	..	75	55
785	50 c. Spiny Caribbean Vase ..	..	1·25	1·25
786	$2 Great Land Crab ..	..	2·50	3·50
783/6 ..		Set of 4	4·50	5·00
MS787	101 × 75 mm. $6 Queen or Pink Conch		6·00	8·00

40TH WEDDING ANNIVERSARY

H.M. QUEEN ELIZABETH II

H.R.H. THE DUKE OF EDINBURGH

(**137**)

1987 (16 Dec). *Royal Ruby Wedding. Nos. 665a, 671/2 and 675 optd with T* **137** *in carmine.*

788	35 c. Lesser Antillean Bullfinch ..		15	20
789	$1 Audubon's Shearwater ..	..	45	55
790	$1.35, Roseate Tern ..	..	60	70
791	$10 Green Heron ..	..	4·50	5·25
788/91		Set of 4	5·00	6·00

138 *Crinum erubescens*

139 Relay Racing

(Des R. Vigurs. Litho Questa)

1988 (28 Mar). *Easter. Lilies. T* **138** *and similar vert designs. Multicoloured. P* 14 × 13½.

792	30 c. Type **138** ..	..	20	15
793	45 c. Spider Lily ..	..	30	25
794	$1 Crinum macowanii ..	..	75	60
795	$2.50, Day Lily ..	..	1·25	2·00
792/5		Set of 4	2·25	2·75
MS796	100 × 75 mm. $6 Easter Lily ..		2·75	3·75

(Des R. Vigurs. Litho Questa)

1988 (25 July). *Olympic Games, Seoul. T* **139** *and similar vert designs. Multicoloured. P* 14 × 13½.

797	30 c. Type **139** ..	..	40	30
798	45 c. Windsurfing ..	..	55	45
799	50 c. Tennis ..	..	1·25	1·00
800	80 c. Basketball ..	..	2·00	2·25
797/800		Set of 4	3·75	3·50
MS801	104 × 78 mm. $6 Athletics ..		3·00	4·00

140 Common Sea Fan

(Des R. Vigurs. Litho Questa)

1988 (28 Nov). *Christmas. Marine Life. T* **140** *and similar horiz designs. Multicoloured. P* 13½ × 14.

802	35 c. Type **140** ..	..	30	30
803	80 c. Coral Crab ..	..	70	70
804	$1 Grooved Brain Coral ..	..	85	85
805	$1.60, Queen Triggerfish ..	..	1·40	2·00
802/5		Set of 4	3·00	3·50
MS806	103 x 78 mm. $6 West Indies Spiny Lobster. ..		2·50	3·50

H.R.H. PRINCESS

ALEXANDRA'S

VISIT NOVEMBER 1988

(**141**)

1988 (14 Dec). *Visit of Princess Alexandra. Nos. 665a, 670/1 and 673 optd with T* **141**.

807	35 c. Lesser Antillean Bullfinch ..		70	60
808	80 c. Grey Kingbird ..	..	1·10	1·25
809	$1 Audubon's Shearwater ..	..	1·25	1·50
810	$2.50, Bananaquit ..	..	2·50	3·25
807/10		Set of 4	5·00	6·00

142 Wood Slave   143 "Christ Crowned with Thorns" (detail) (Bosch)

(Des R. Vigurs. Litho Questa)

1989 (20 Feb). *Lizards. T* **142** *and similar horiz designs. Multicoloured. P* 13½ × 14.

811	45 c. Type **142**	45	35
812	80 c. Slippery Back	70	70
813	$2.50, *Iguana delicatissima*	2·00	2·50
811/13	Set of 3	2·75	3·25
MS814	101 × 75 mm. $6 Tree Lizard	2·75	3·50

(Des R. Vigurs. Litho Questa)

1989 (23 Mar). *Easter. Religious Paintings. T* **143** *and similar vert designs. Multicoloured. P* 14 × 13½.

815	35 c. Type **143**	20	20
816	80 c. "Christ bearing the Cross" (detail) (Gerard David)	45	55
817	$1 "The Deposition" (detail) (Gerard David)	50	60
818	$1.60, "Pietà" (detail) (Rogier van der Weyden)	85	1·40
815/18	Set of 4	1·75	2·50
MS819	103 × 77 mm. $6 "Crucified Christ with the Virgin Mary and Saints" (detail) (Raphael)	2·75	3·50

144 University Arms   (145)

20th ANNIVERSARY MOON LANDING

(Des R. Vigurs. Litho Questa)

1989 (24 Apr). *40th Anniv of University of the West Indies. P* 14 × 13½.

820	144 $5 multicoloured	2·40	3·00

1989 (31 July). *20th Anniv of First Manned Landing on Moon. Nos.* 670/2 *and* 674 *optd with T* **145**.

821	80 c. Grey Kingbird	60	60
822	$1 Audubon's Shearwater	70	70
823	$1.35, Roseate Tern	90	1·10
824	$5 Belted Kingfisher	2·75	3·50
821/4	Set of 4	4·50	5·50

146 Lone Star House, 1930

(Des J. Vigurs. Litho Questa)

1989 (11 Dec). *Christmas. Historic Houses. T* **146** *and similar horiz designs. Multicoloured. P* 13½×14.

825	5 c. Type **146**	10	10
826	35 c. Whitehouse, 1906	25	25
827	45 c. Hodges House	30	35
828	80 c. Warden's Place	60	85
825/8	Set of 4	1·10	1·40
MS829	102×77 mm. $6 Wallblake House, 1787	2·75	3·50

147 Bigeye ("Blear Eye")   148 The Last Supper

(Des J. Vigurs. Litho Questa)

1990 (2 Apr)–**92**. *Fishes. T* **147** *and similar horiz designs. Multicoloured. P* 13½×14. A. *Wihout imprint date at foot.* B. *With imprint date* (10.6.92).

			A		B	
830	5 c. Type **147**		45	45	30	30
831	10 c. Long-spined Squirrelfish ("Redman")		45	45	30	30
832	15 c. Stop-light Parrotfish ("Speckletail")		30	30	†	
833	25 c. Blue-striped Grunt		40	40	†	
834	30 c. Yellow Jack		50	50	†	
835	35 c. Red Hind		60	60	40	40
836	40 c. Spotted Goatfish		40	40	†	
837	45 c. Queen Triggerfish ("Old Wife")		40	40	†	
838	50 c. Coney ("Butter Fish")		40	40	†	
839	65 c. Smooth Trunkfish ("Shell Fish")		45	45	†	
840	80 c. Yellow-tailed Snapper		50	55	†	
841	$1 Banded Butterflyfish ("Katy")		55	60	†	
842	$1.35, Nassau Grouper		70	80	†	
843	$2.50, Blue Tang ("Doctor Fish")		1·10	1·25	†	
844	$5 Queen Angelfish		2·25	2·40	†	
845	$10 Great Barracuda		4·50	4·75	†	
830A/45A	Set of 16		12·50	13·00		
830B/5B	Set of 3				90	90

(Des M. Pollard. Litho Questa)

1990 (2 Apr). *Easter. T* **148** *and similar vert designs. Multicoloured. P* 14×13½.

846	35 c. Type **148**	45	20
847	45 c. The Trial	45	25
848	$1.35, The Crucifixion	1·25	90
849	$2.50, The Empty Tomb	1·75	2·25
846/9	Set of 4	3·50	3·75
MS850	114×84 mm. $6 The Resurrection	4·50	5·50

149 G.B. 1840 Penny Black   (150)

WORLD CUP FOOTBALL CHAMPIONSHIPS 1990

(Litho Questa)

1990 (30 Apr). *"Stamp World London 90" International Stamp Exhibition. T* **149** *and similar multicoloured designs showing stamps. P* 14.

851	25 c. Type **149**	30	25
852	50 c. G.B. 1840 Twopenny Blue	50	40
853	$1.50, Cape of Good Hope 1861 1d. "woodblock" (*horiz*)	1·25	1·50
854	$2.50, G.B. 1882 £5 (*horiz*)	1·75	2·25
851/4	Set of 4	3·50	4·00
MS855	86×71 mm. $6 Penny Black and Twopence Blue (*horiz*)	5·00	6·00

1990 (24 Sept). *Anniversaries and Events. Nos.* 841A/4A *optd as T* **150**.

856	$1 Banded Butterflyfish (optd "EXPO '90")	85	95
857	$1.35, Nassau Grouper (optd "1990 INTERNATIONAL LITERACY YEAR")	1·00	1·25
858	$2.50, Blue Tang (optd with T **150**)	2·25	2·75
859	$5 Queen Angelfish (optd "90TH BIRTHDAY H.M. THE QUEEN MOTHER")	3·50	4·00
856/9	Set of 4	7·00	8·00

151 Mermaid Flag

(Des R. Vigurs. Litho Questa)

1990 (5 Nov). *Island Flags. T* **151** *and similar horiz designs. Multicoloured. P* 13½×14.

860	50 c. Type **151**	50	40
861	80 c. New Anguilla official flag	75	75
862	$1 Three Dolphins flag	85	85
863	$5 Governor's official flag	3·25	4·00
860/3	Set of 4	4·75	5·50

152 Laughing Gulls   (153)

1991

(Des R. Vigurs. Litho Questa)

1990 (26 Nov). *Christmas. Sea Birds. T* **152** *and similar horiz designs. Multicoloured. P* 13½×14.

864	10 c. Type **152**	25	25
865	35 c. Brown Booby	40	40
866	$1.50, Bridled Tern	1·00	1·25
867	$3.50, Brown Pelican	2·00	2·50
864/7	Set of 4	3·25	4·00
MS868	101×76 mm. $6 Little Tern	6·00	8·00

1991 (30 Apr). *Easter. Nos.* 846/50 *optd with T* **153**.

869	35 c. Type **148**	45	45
870	45 c. The Trial	55	45
871	$1.35, The Crucifixion	1·25	1·50
872	$2.50, The Empty Tomb	2·00	2·50
869/72	Set of 4	3·75	4·25
MS873	114 × 84 mm. $6 The Resurrection	4·50	5·50

On No. **MS873** the "1990" inscription on the sheet margin has also been obliterated.

154 Angel   155 Angels with Palm Branches outside St. Gerard's Church

(Des Michele Lavalette. Litho Questa)

1991 (16 Dec). *Christmas. T* **154** *and similar designs. P* 14×13½ (5 c., 35 c.) *or* 13½×14 (*others*).

874	5 c. dull violet, chestnut and black	15	15
875	35 c. multicoloured	55	45
876	80 c. multicoloured	1·10	1·10
877	$1 multicoloured	1·25	1·25
874/7	Set of 4	2·75	2·75
MS878	131×97 mm. $5 mult. P 13½×14	3·50	4·00

Designs: *Vert*—35 c. Father Christmas. *Horiz*—80 c. Church and house; $1 Palm trees at night; $5 Anguilla village.

(Des Lucia Butler. Litho Questa)

1992 (21 Apr). *Easter. T* **155** *and similar multicoloured designs. P* 13½×14 (80 c., $5) *or* 14×13½ (*others*).

879	35 c. Type **155**	25	25
880	45 c. Angels singing outside Methodist Church	35	35
881	80 c. Village (*horiz*)	60	70
882	$1 Congregation going to St. Mary's Church	75	85
883	$5 Dinghy regatta (*horiz*)	3·25	4·00
879/83	Set of 5	4·75	5·50

$1.60

(156)   157 Anguillan Flags

1992 (10 June). *As No.* 834, *but with imprint date, surch with T* **156**.

884	$1.60 on 30 c. Yellow Jack	90	1·00

(Litho Questa)

1992 (10 Aug). *25th Anniv of Separation from St. Kitts-Nevis. T* **157** *and similar square designs. Multicoloured. P* 14.

885	80 c. Type **157**	70	70
886	$1 Present official seal	85	85
887	$1.60, Anguillan flags at airport	1·50	1·50
888	$2 Royal Commissioner's official seal	1·60	1·75
885/8	Set of 4	4·25	4·50
MS889	116×117 mm. $10 "Independent Anguilla" overprinted stamps of 1967 (85×85 mm)	5·00	6·00

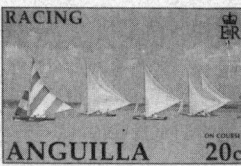

158 Dinghy Race

(Des Michele Lavalette. Litho Questa)

1992 (12 Oct). *Sailing Dinghy Racing. T* **158** *and similar designs. P* 13½×14 (*horiz*) *or* 14×13½ (*vert*).

890	20 c. multicoloured	40	30
891	35 c. multicoloured	50	40
892	45 c. multicoloured	55	45
893	80 c. multicoloured	1·00	1·50
	a. Vert pair. Nos. 893/4	2·00	3·00

'94   80 c. black and pale azure   ..   ..   ..   1·00   1·50
95    $1 multicoloured   ..   ..   1·00   1·50
90/5   ..   ..   *Set of 6*   4·00   5·00
MS896   129×30 mm. $6 multicoloured ..   ..   ..   3·25   4·00
Designs: *Vert*—35 c. Stylized poster; 80 c. (No. 893) *Blue Bird*
n race; 80 c. (No. 894) Construction drawings of *Blue Bird* by
ouglas Pyle; $1 Stylized poster (*different*). *Horiz* (as *T* **158**)—
5 c. Dinghies on beach. (97×32 *mm*)—$6 Composite design as
0 and 45 c. values.
No. 893/4 were printed together, *se-tenant*, in vertical pairs
hroughout the sheet.

159 Mucka Jumbie on Stilts

(Litho Questa)

1992 (7 Dec). *Christmas. Local Traditions. T* **159** *and similar
horiz designs. Multicoloured. P* 14.
897   20 c. Type **159**   15   15
898   70 c. Masqueraders   45   50
899    $1.05, Baking in old style oven   65   80
900    $2.40, Collecting presents from Christmas
tree   ..   ..   1·25   1·90
897/900   ..   ..   *Set of 4*   2·25   3·00
MS901   128×101 $5 As No. 900   ..   ..   3·50   4·50
No. MS901 also contains labels in designs as Nos. 897/9, but
without face values.

160 Columbus landing in   **161** "Kite Flying"
New World   (Kyle Brooks)

(Des Michele Lavalette. Litho Questa)

1992 (15 Dec). *500th Anniv of Discovery of America by
Columbus* (2nd issue). *T* **160** *and similar designs. P* 14.
902   80 c. multicoloured   85   85
903    $1 brownish black and yellow-brown   ..   95   95
904    $2 multicoloured   ..   ..   ..   1·75   2·25
905    $3 multicoloured   ..   ..   ..   2·00   2·50
902/5   ..   ..   *Set of 4*   5·00   6·00
MS906   78×54 mm. $6 multicoloured   ..   ..   5·50   6·50
Designs: *Vert*—$1 Christopher Columbus; $6 Columbus and
map of West Indies. *Horiz*—$2 Fleet of Columbus; $3 *Pinta*.

(Litho Questa)

1993 (29 Mar). *Easter. Children's Paintings. T* **161** *and similar
vert designs. Multicoloured. P* 14.
907   20 c. Type **161**   40   30
908   45 c. "Clifftop Village Service" (Kara
Connor)   60   45
909   80 c. "Morning Devotion on Sombrero"
(Junior Carty)   ..   ..   ..   1·10   1·25
910    $1.50, "Hill Top Church Service" (Leana
Harris)   ..   ..   1·50   2·25
907/10   ..   ..   *Set of 4*   3·25   3·75
MS911   90×110 mm. $5 "Good Friday Kites"
(Marvin Hazel and Kyle Brooks) (39×53 *mm*)   4·00   5·00

162 Salt Picking   **163** Lord Great
Chamberlain
presenting Spurs
of Chivalry to
Queen

(Des Penny Slinger. Litho Questa)

1993 (23 June). *Traditional Industries. T* **162** *and similar
horiz designs. Multicoloured. P* 14.
912   20 c. Type **162**   60   35
913   80 c. Tobacco growing   80   80
914    $1 Cotton picking   90   90
915    $2 Harvesting sugar cane   ..   ..   1·50   2·00
912/15   ..   ..   *Set of 4*   3·50   3·50
MS916   111×85 mm. $6 Fishing   ..   ..   6·00   7·00

(Des John Lister Ltd. Litho Questa)

1993 (16 Aug). *40th Anniv of Coronation. T* **163** *and similar
vert designs. Multicoloured. P* 14.
917   80 c. Type **163**   40   45
918    $1 The Benediction   50   55
919    $2 Queen Elizabeth II in Coronation robes   95   1·25
920    $3 St. Edward's Crown   ..   ..   1·40   1·75
917/20   ..   ..   *Set of 4*   3·00   3·50
MS921   114×95 mm. $6 The Queen and Prince
Philip in Coronation coach   ..   ..   5·00   6·00

164 Carnival Pan Player   **165** Mucka Jumbies
Carnival Characters

(Des Penny Slinger. Litho Questa)

1993 (23 Aug). *Anguilla Carnival. T* **164** *and similar horiz
designs. Multicoloured. P* 13½×14.
922   20 c. Type **164**   20   15
923   45 c. Revellers dressed as pirates   40   30
924   80 c. Revellers dressed as stars   65   65
925    $1 Mas dancing   75   75
926    $2 Masked couple   ..   ..   ..   1·50   1·75
927    $3 Revellers dressed as commandos   ..   2·00   2·25
922/7   ..   ..   *Set of 6*   5·00   5·25
MS928   123×94 mm. $5 Revellers in fantasy
costumes   ..   ..   4·25   4·75

(Litho Questa)

1993 (7 Dec). *Christmas. T* **165** *and similar multicoloured
designs. P* 14×13½.
929   20 c. Type **165**   15   20
930   35 c. Local carol singers   25   25
931   45 c. Christmas home baking   35   35
932    $3 Decorating Christmas tree   ..   ..   1·90   2·50
929/32   ..   ..   *Set of 4*   2·40   3·00
MS933   123×118 mm. $4 Mucka Jumbies and
carol singers (58½×47 *mm*). P 14   ..   ..   2·75   3·50

166 Travelling Branch Mail   **167** Princess
Van at Sandy Ground   Alexandra, 1988

(Litho Questa)

1994 (11 Feb). *Delivering the Mail. T* **166** *and similar
multicoloured designs. P* 14.
934   20 c. Type **166**   40   30
935   45 c. *Betsy R* (mail schooner) at The Forest
(*vert*)   65   45
936   80 c. Mail van at old Post Office   ..   1·00   1·00
937    $1 Jeep on beach, Island Harbour (*vert*)   1·10   1·10
938    $4 New Post Office   ..   ..   ..   3·50   4·00
934/8   ..   ..   *Set of 5*   6·00   6·25

(Litho Questa)

1994 (18 Feb). *Royal Visitors. T* **167** *and similar vert designs.
Multicoloured. P* 14.
939   45 c. Type **167**   45   35
940   50 c. Princess Alice, 1960   50   45
941   80 c. Prince Philip, 1993   75   75
942    $1 Prince Charles, 1973   85   85
943    $2 Queen Elizabeth II, 1994   ..   ..   1·50   2·00
939/43   ..   ..   *Set of 5*   3·50   4·00
MS944   162×90 mm. Nos. 939/43   ..   ..   4·50   5·00

168 "The   **169** Cameroun Player and
Crucifixion"   Pontiac Silverdome, Detroit

(Litho Questa)

1994 (6 Apr). *Easter. Stained-glass Windows. T* **168** *and
similar vert designs. Multicoloured. P* 14×15.
945   20 c. Type **168**   30   30
946   45 c. "The Empty Tomb"   45   45
947   80 c. "The Resurrection"   80   90
948    $3 "Risen Christ with Disciples"   ..   2·75   3·25
945/8   ..   ..   *Set of 4*   3·75   4·50

(Des R. Vigurs. Litho Questa)

1994 (3 Oct). *World Cup Football Championship, U.S.A. T* **169**
and similar horiz designs. Multicoloured. P 14.
949   20 c. Type **169**   20   20
950   70 c. Argentine player and Foxboro
Stadium, Boston   55   65
951    $1.80, Italian player and RFK Memorial
Stadium, Washington   ..   ..   1·40   1·60
952    $2.40, German player and Soldier Field,
Chicago   ..   ..   ..   1·90   2·25
949/52   ..   ..   *Set of 4*   3·50   4·25
MS953   112×85 mm. $6 American and
Colombian players   ..   ..   ..   4·25   4·75

170 "The Nativity"   **171** Pair of Zenaida Doves
(Gustave Doré)

(Des R. Vigurs. Litho Questa)

1994 (22 Nov). *Christmas. Religious Paintings. T* **170** *and
similar vert designs. Multicoloured. P* 14.
954   20 c. Type **170**   20   20
955   30 c. "The Wise Men guided by the Star"
(Doré)   30   30
956   35 c. "The Annunciation" (Doré)   ..   35   35
957   45 c. "Adoration of the Shepherds" (detail)
(Poussin)   40   45
958    $2.40, "The Flight into Egypt" (Doré)   1·50   2·00
954/8   ..   ..   *Set of 5*   2·50   3·00

(Des R. Vigurs. Litho Questa)

1995 (10 Apr). *Easter. Zenaida Doves. T* **171** *and similar horiz
designs. Multicoloured. P* 13½×14.
959   20 c. Type **171**   20   20
960   45 c. Dove on branch   40   40
961   50 c. Guarding nest   45   45
962    $5 With chicks   ..   ..   ..   4·25   5·00
959/62   ..   ..   *Set of 4*   4·75   5·50

172 Trygve Lie (first Secretary-
General) and General Assembly

(Des R. Vigurs. Litho Questa)

1995 (26 June). *50th Anniv of United Nations. T* **172** *and
similar multicoloured designs. P* 14×13½ (*vert*) *or* 13½×14
(*others*).
963   20 c. Type **172**   20   20
964   80 c. Flag and building showing "50"   ..   60   60
965    $1 Dag Hammarskjöld and U. Thant
(former Secretary-Generals) and U.N.
Charter   70   70
966    $5 U.N. Building (*vert*)   ..   ..   4·00   4·50
963/6   ..   ..   *Set of 4*   5·00   5·50

173 Anniversary Emblem and
Map of Anguilla

(Des R. Vigurs. Litho Questa)

1995 (15 Aug). *25th Anniv of Caribbean Development Bank.
T* **173** *and similar horiz design. Multicoloured. P* 13½×14.
967   45 c. Type **173**   ..   ..   ..   1·00   1·25
a. Horiz pair. Nos. 967/8   ..   ..   4·50   5·00
968    $5 Bank building and launches   ..   3·50   3·75
Nos. 967/8 were printed together, *se-tenant*, in horizontal
pairs throughout sheets of 10.

174 Blue Whale

(Litho Questa)

1995 (24 Nov). *Endangered Species. Whales. T* **174** *and similar multicoloured designs. P* 14×13½ (45 c.) *or* 13½×14 *(others).*

969	20 c. Type 174 ..	35	25
970	45 c. Right Whale (*vert*) ..	55	35
971	$1 Sperm Whale ..	1·00	1·00
972	$5 Humpback Whale ..	4·75	5·50
969/72	.. .. .. *Set of* 4	6·00	6·50

175 Palm Tree

176 Deep Water Gorgonia

(Litho Questa)

1995 (12 Dec). *Christmas. T* **175** *and similar square designs. Multicoloured. P* 14½.

973	10 c. Type 175	15	15
974	25 c. Balloons and fishes	25	20
975	45 c. Shells	35	25
976	$5 Fishes in shape of Christmas Tree ..	4·50	5·00
973/6	.. .. .. *Set of* 4	4·75	5·00

(Des Michele Lavalette. Litho Cot Printery Ltd, Barbados)

1996 (21 June). *Corals. T* **176** *and similar horiz designs. Multicoloured. P* 14×14½.

977	20 c. Type 176	30	30
978	80 c. Common Sea Fan	60	60
979	$5 Venus Sea Fern	3·00	3·50
977/9	.. .. .. *Set of* 3	3·50	4·00

177 Running

178 Siege of Sandy Hill Fort

(Des Iris Lewis. Litho Cot Printery Ltd, Barbados)

1996 (12 Dec). *Olympic Games, Atlanta. T* **177** *and similar vert designs. Multicoloured. P* 14.

980	20 c. Type 177	20	20
981	80 c. Javelin throwing and wheelchair basketball	70	70
982	$1 High jumping and hurdles	85	85
983	$3.50, Olympic rings and torch with Greek and American flags	2·75	3·00
980/3	.. .. .. *Set of* 4	4·00	4·25

(Des Iris Lewis. Litho Cot Printery Ltd, Barbados)

1996 (12 Dec). *Bicentenary of the Battle for Anguilla. T* **178** *and similar multicoloured designs. P* 14.

984	60 c. Type 178	60	60
985	75 c. French troops destroying church (*horiz*)	70	70
986	$1.50, Naval battle (*horiz*)	1·40	1·50
987	$4 French troops landing at Rendezvous Bay	2·75	3·00
984/7	.. .. .. *Set of* 4	5·00	5·25

179 Gooseberry

(Des Michele Lavalette. Litho Questa)

1997 (30 Apr). *Fruit. T* **179** *and similar horiz designs. Multicoloured. P* 14.

988	10 c. Type 179	10	10
989	20 c. West Indian Cherry	10	10
990	40 c. Tamarind	20	25
991	50 c. Pomme-surette	25	30
992	60 c. Sea Almond	25	30
993	75 c. Sea Grape	35	40
994	80 c. Banana	35	40
995	$1 Genip	45	50
996	$1.10, Coco Plum	50	55
997	$1.25, Pope	55	60
998	$1.50, Pawpaw	70	75
999	$2 Sugar Apple	90	95

1000	$3 Soursop		1·40	1·50
1001	$4 Pomegranate		1·90	2·00
1002	$5 Cashew		2·25	2·40
1003	$10 Mango		4·50	4·75
998/1003	.. .. .. *Set of* 16		15·00	16·00

STAMP BOOKLETS

1977 (9 Feb). *Silver Jubilee. Multicoloured cover showing Crown and map of Anguilla. Stapled.*

SB1 $8.70, booklet containing 25 c., 40 c., $1.20 and $2.50 (Nos. 269/72), each in pair .. .. 2·25
   a. Stamps with margin at right .. .. 4·00
No. SB1 was produced from normal sheets and can be found stapled at the left or the right. A further printing was later produced from specially prepared sheets, so that stamps from Booklet No. SB1a occur with small vertical margins at the right of each pair, in addition to the binding margin at left.

1978. *25th Anniv of Coronation. Multicoloured cover, 105×38 mm, showing Royal coat-of-arms and map of Anguilla. Stapled.*

SB2 $9.44, booklet containing 22 c., 50 c., $1.50 and $2.50 (Nos. 320/3), each in pair .. .. 1·75
   a. Stamps with margin at right .. .. 2·00
No. SB2 exists with three different scenes on the back cover. A second printing of No. SB2 exists with a sheet arrangement as described for No. SB1a.

1979. *Death Centenary of Sir Rowland Hill. Multicoloured cover, 104×39 mm, showing design from "Mulready" envelope on the front and coral beaches on the back. Stapled.*

SB3 $9.18, booklet containing 1 c. ×2, 22 c., 35 c., $1.50 and $2.50 (Nos. 358/63), each in pair .. 3·00
No. SB3 exists with three different scenes on the back cover.

1980. *"London 1980" International Stamp Exhibition. Three multicoloured covers, each 109×39 mm, showing designs from Anguilla stamps, either No. 384, 385 or 387, on front and different views of Anguilla on back. Stapled.*

SB4 $9.70, booklet (*any cover*) containing 35 c., 50 c., $1.50 and $2.50 (Nos. 384B/7B), each in pair .. 2·50
   Set of 3 *different cover designs* .. 7·00

1981 (15 June). *Royal Wedding. Multicoloured covers, each 105×65 mm, showing Prince of Wales emblem on front and local scene on back. Stapled.*

SB5 $14 booklet containing two panes of 4 (either Nos. 468a, 469a or Nos. 468wa, 469wa) .. .. 2·00
No. SB5 exists with three different scenes on the back cover.

1982 (30 Aug). *21st Birthday of Princess of Wales. Multicoloured cover, 105×65 mm, showing Prince of Wales emblem on front and coral beach on back. Stapled.*

SB6 $12.40, booklet containing four panes of 4 (Nos. 507a, 509a, 510a, 511a) .. .. .. 5·25

1984 (31 Oct). *Birth of Prince Henry. Booklet No.* SB6 *optd* "PRINCE HENRY BIRTH 15.9.84" *on cover.*

SB7 $12.40, booklet containing four panes of 4 (Nos. 628a, 630a, 631a, 632a) .. .. .. 7·00

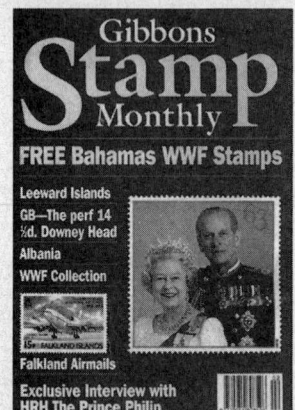

Keep This Catalogue up to Date With

Gibbons Stamp Monthly

FREE Bahamas WWF Stamps

Leeward Islands
GB—The perf 14 ½d. Downey Head
Albania
WWF Collection
Falkland Airmails
Exclusive Interview with HRH The Prince Philip

The Magazine with the Stanley Gibbons Catalogue Supplement

Plus
- More editorial than other magazines.
- Regular features for all collectors from beginners to specialists.
- Authoritatively written.
- Regular special offers, competitions and free gifts.

Get Gibbons Stamp Monthly delivered direct to your door!

For a free sample copy and subscription details phone
01425 472363
or write to:

Hugh Jefferies
Gibbons Stamp Monthly
5 Parkside, Christchurch Road, Ringwood, Hants BH24 3SH

Antigua

The first mention of a local postmaster for Antigua is in 1760, but the earliest straight-line mark, inscribed "ANTE/GOA", is known on a letter of 1757. Mail services before 1850 were somewhat haphazard, until St. John's was made a branch office of the British G.P.O. in 1850. A second office, at English Harbour, opened in 1857.

The stamps of Great Britain were used between May 1858 and the end of April 1860, when the island postal service became the responsibility of the local colonial authorities. In the interim period, between the take-over and the appearance of Antiguan stamps, the crowned-circle handstamps were again utilised and No. CC1 can be found used as late as 1869.

For illustrations of the handstamp and postmark types see BRITISH POST OFFICES ABROAD notes, following GREAT BRITAIN.

ST. JOHN'S

CROWNED-CIRCLE HANDSTAMPS

CC1 CC 1 ANTIGUA (St. John's) (22.3.1850) (R.)
Price on cover £550

Stamps of GREAT BRITAIN cancelled "A 02" as Type 2.

1858 to 1860.

Z1	1d. rose-red (1857), *perf* 14	..	£475
Z2	2d. blue (1855), *perf* 14 (Plate No. 6)		£900
Z3	2d. blue (1858) (Plate Nos. 7, 8, 9)		£600
Z4	4d. rose (1857)		£450
Z5	6d. lilac (1856)		£160
Z6	1s. green (1856)		£1500

ENGLISH HARBOUR

CROWNED-CIRCLE HANDSTAMPS

CC2 CC 3 ENGLISH HARBOUR (10.12.1857)
Price on cover £4250

Stamps of GREAT BRITAIN cancelled "A 18" as Type 2.

1858 to 1860.

Z7	2d. blue (1858) (Plate No. 7)	..	£5000
Z8	4d. rose (1857)		£5000
Z9	6d. lilac (1856)		£2000
Z10	1s. green (1856)		£2000

PRICES FOR STAMPS ON COVER TO 1945

No. 1	*from* × 6
Nos. 2/4	†
Nos. 5/10	*from* × 15
Nos 13/14	*from* × 20
No. 15	*from* × 50
Nos. 16/18	*from* × 30
Nos. 19/23	*from* × 12
No. 24	*from* × 40
Nos. 25/30	*from* × 10
Nos. 31/51	*from* × 4
No. 52/4	*from* × 10
Nos. 55/61	*from* × 4
Nos. 62/80	*from* × 3
Nos. 81/90	*from* × 4
Nos. 91/4	*from* × 5
Nos. 95/7	*from* × 4
Nos. 98/109	*from* × 3

CROWN COLONY

1
ANTIGUA ONE PENNY

3 (Die I)
ANTIGUA FOUR PENCE

(Eng C. Jeens after drawing by Edward Corbould. Recess P.B.)

1862 (Aug). *No wmk.* (a) *Rough perf* 14 *to* 16.
1	1	6d. blue-green	£800	500

(b) P 11 to 12½
1	6d. blue-green	..	£4000

(c) P 14 to 16 × 11 to 12½
1	6d. blue-green		£2750

(d) P 14 to 16 compound with 11 to 12½
1	6d. blue-green	£3000

Nos. 2/4 may be trial perforations. They are not known used.

1863 (Jan)–**67.** *Wmk Small Star.* W **2** (*sideways on* 6d.). *Rough perf* 14 *to* 16.
5	1	1d. rosy mauve	..	£110 42·00
6		1d. dull rose (1864)		90·00 35·00
		a. Imperf between (vert pair)		£14000
7		1d. vermilion (1867)		£140 22·00
		a. Imperf between (horiz pair)		£14000
		b. Wmk sideways		£180 38·00
8		6d. green (shades)		£375 22·00
		a. Wmk upright		
9		6d. dark green		£400 22·00
10		6d. yellow-green		£2500 70·00

Caution is needed in buying No. 10 as some of the shades of No. 8 verge on yellow-green.

The 1d. rosy mauve exists showing trial perforations of 11 to 12½ and 14 to 16.

(Recess D.L.R. from P.B. plates)

1872. *Wmk Crown CC.* P 12½.
13	1	1d. lake		95·00 15·00
14		1d. scarlet		£130 16·00
15		6d. blue-green		£500 6·00

1876. *Wmk Crown CC.* P 14.
16	1	1d. lake		£100 9·00
		a. Bisected (½d.) (1883) (on cover)		† £2500
17		1d. lake-rose		£100 9·00
18		6d. blue-green		£300 11·00

(Recess (T 1); typo (T 3) De La Rue & Co)

1879. *Wmk Crown CC.* P 14.
19	3	2½d. red-brown		£600 £160
		a. Large "2" in "2½" with slanting foot		£7500 £2250
20		4d. blue		£250 14·00

Top left triangle detached
(Pl 2 R. 3/3 of right pane)

1882. *Wmk Crown CA.* P 14.
21	3	½d. dull green		1·90 10·00
		a. Top left triangle detached		£110
22		2½d. red-brown		£130 50·00
		a. Large "2" in "2½" with slanting foot		£2500 £1100
23		4d. blue		£275 15·00

1884. *Wmk Crown CA.* P 12.
24	1	1d. carmine-red		50·00 15·00

The 1d. scarlet is a colour changeling.

1884–86. *Wmk Crown CA.* P 14.
25	1	1d. carmine-red		1·25 2·50
26		1d. rose		55·00 12·00
27	3	2½d. ultramarine (1886)		6·00 11·00
		a. Large "2" in "2½" with slanting foot		£160 £250
		b. Top left triangle detached		£250
28		4d. chestnut (1886)		1·50 2·00
		a. Top left triangle detached		£100
29	1	6d. deep green		55·00 £120
30	3	1s. mauve (1886)		£160 £120
		a. Top left triangle detached		£750
27/28, 30 Optd "Specimen"			Set of 3	£150

Nos. 25 and 26 postmarked "A 12" in place of "A 02" were used in St. Christopher.

2½ 2½ 2½
A   B   C

The variety "Large '2' in '2½' with slanting foot" occurs on the first stamp of the seventh row in both left (A) and right (B) panes (in which positions the "NN" of "PENNY" have three vertical strokes shortened) and on the first stamp of the third row of the right-hand pane (C). The "2" varies slightly in each position.

From 31 October 1890 until July 1903 Leeward Islands general issues were used. Subsequently both general issues and the following separate issues were in concurrent use until July 1956, when the general Leewards Island stamps were withdrawn.

4
ANTIGUA ONE PENNY

5
ANTIGUA 5 FIVE SHILLINGS

(Typo D.L.R.)

1903 (July)–**09.** *Wmk Crown CC. Ordinary paper.* P 14.
31	4	½d. grey-black and grey-green		3·00 4·75
32		1d. grey-black and rose-red		4·75 70
		a. Bluish paper (1909)		90·00 90·00
33		2d. dull purple and brown		6·00 24·00
34		2½d. grey-black and blue		8·00 13·00
		a. Chalk-surfaced paper (1907)		15·00 32·00
35		3d. grey-green and orange-brown		9·50 30·00
36		6d. purple and black		28·00 48·00
		w. Wmk inverted		
37		1s. blue and dull purple		35·00 48·00
		a. Chalk-surfaced paper (1907)		38·00 75·00
38		2s. grey-green and pale violet		60·00 80·00
39		2s. 6d. grey-black and purple		17·00 48·00
40	5	5s. grey-green and violet		70·00 90·00
		a. Chalk-surfaced paper (1907)		70·00 90·00
31/40			Set of 10	£190 £325
31/40 Optd "Specimen"			Set of 10	£150

1908–17. *Wmk Mult Crown CA. Chalk-surfaced paper* (2d., 3d. to 2s.). P 14.
41	4	½d. green		2·25 3·50
		w. Wmk inverted		
42		½d. blue-green (1917)		2·75 4·75
43		1d. red (1909)		4·00 1·75
44		1d. scarlet (5.8.15)		4·25 2·75
45		2d. dull purple and brown (1912)		3·75 24·00
46		2½d. ultramarine		9·00 15·00
		a. Blue		14·00 20·00
47		3d. grey-green and orange-brown (1912)		6·50 17·00
48		6d. purple and black (1911)		7·50 32·00

49	4	1s. blue and dull purple		15·00 65·00
50		2s. grey-green and violet (1912)		60·00 75·00
41/50			Set of 8	95·00 £200
41, 43, 46 Optd "Specimen"		Set of 3	65·00	

1913. *As T* 5, *but portrait of King George V. Wmk Mult Crown CA. Chalk-surfaced paper.* P 14.
51		5s. grey-green and violet (Optd S. £60)		70·00 £100

WAR STAMP
(7)   8

1916 (Sept)–**17.** *No. 41 optd in London with T* 7.
52	4	½d. green (Bk.)		50 1·25
53		½d. green (R.) (1.10.17)		80 1·25

1918 (July). *Optd with T* 7. *Wmk Mult Crown CA.* P 14.
54	4	1½d. orange		50 70
52/4 Optd "Specimen"			Set of 3	70·00

(Typo D.L.R.)

1921–29. P 14. (a) *Wmk Mult Crown CA. Chalk-surfaced paper.*
55	8	3d. purple/*pale yellow*		3·50 11·00
56		4d. grey-black and red/*pale yellow* (1922)		1·50 5·00
57		1s. black/*emerald*		3·75 7·00
		y. Wmk inverted and reversed		
58		2s. purple and blue/*blue*		10·00 19·00
59		2s. 6d. black and red/*blue*		13·00 42·00
60		5s. green and red/*pale yellow* (1922)		8·00 38·00
61		£1 purple and black/*red* (1922)		£170 £250
55/61			Set of 7	£190 £325
55/61 Optd "Specimen"			Set of 7	£170

(b) *Wmk Mult Script CA. Chalk-surfaced paper* (3d. *to* 4s.).
62	8	½d. dull green		1·00 20
63		1d. carmine-red		85 20
64		1d. bright violet (1923)		2·00 1·50
		a. Mauve		8·00 6·50
65		1d. bright scarlet (1929)		10·00 2·50
67		1½d. dull orange (1922)		1·75 7·00
68		1½d. carmine-red (1926)		3·00 1·75
69		1½d. pale red-brown (1929)		1·75 60
70		2d. grey (1922)		1·25 75
		a. Wmk sideways		
71		2½d. bright blue (1922)		6·00 15·00
72		2½d. orange-yellow (1923)		1·25 17·00
73		2½d. ultramarine (1927)		3·25 5·50
74		3d. purple/*pale yellow* (1925)		4·00 8·50
75		6d. dull and bright purple (1922)		2·75 6·00
76		1s. black/*emerald* (1929)		6·00 8·00
77		2s. purple and blue/*blue* (1927)		10·00 48·00
78		2s. 6d. black and red/*blue* (1927)		17·00 23·00
79		3s. green and violet (1922)		24·00 70·00
80		4s. grey-black and red (1922)		48·00 55·00
62/80			Set of 16	£110 £225
62/80 Optd/Perf "Specimen"			Set of 18	£325

9 Old Dockyard, English Harbour   10 Government House, St. John's

(Des Mrs. J. Goodwin (5s.), Waterlow (others). Recess Waterlow)

1932 (27 Jan). *Tercentenary. T* **9/10** *and similar designs. Wmk Mult Script CA.* P 12½.
81	9	½d. green		1·75 5·00
82		1d. scarlet		2·50 3·75
83		1½d. brown		3·00 4·25
84	10	2d. grey		3·75 15·00
85		2½d. deep blue		3·75 8·50
86		3d. orange		3·75 12·00
87		6d. violet		11·00 12·00
88		1s. olive-green		18·00 25·00
89		2s. 6d. claret		38·00 48·00
90		5s. black and chocolate		75·00 £110
81/90			Set of 10	£140 £200
81/90 Perf "Specimen"			Set of 10	£200

Designs: *Horiz*—6d., 1s., 2s. 6d. Nelson's *Victory. Vert*—5s. Sir Thomas Warner's *Concepcion.*

Examples of all values are known showing a forged St. Johns postmark dated "MY 18 1932".

13 Windsor Castle

(Des H. Fleury. Recess D.L.R.)

1935 (6 May). *Silver Jubilee. Wmk Mult Script CA.* P 13½ × 14.
91	13	1d. deep blue and carmine		2·00 1·75
		f. Diagonal line by turret		45·00
92		1½d. ultramarine and grey		2·75 45
93		2½d. brown and deep blue		5·50 1·00
		g. Dot to left of chapel		£120
94		1s. slate and purple		8·50 12·00
		h. Dot by flagstaff		£160
91/4			Set of 4	17·00 13·50
91/4 Perf "Specimen"			Set of 4	70·00

For illustrations of plate varieties see Catalogue Introduction.

14 King George VI and Queen Elizabeth

(Des D.L.R.. Recess B.W.)

1937 (12 May). *Coronation. Wmk Mult Script CA. P* 11×11½.
95	14	1d. carmine			50	70
96		1½d. yellow-brown			60	80
97		2½d. blue			1·25	1·40
95/7			*Set of* 3		2·10	2·50
95/7	Perf "Specimen"		*Set of* 3		50·00	

15 English Harbour   **16** Nelson's Dockyard

(Recess Waterlow)

1938 (15 Nov)–51. *T* **15, 16** *and similar designs. Wmk Mult Script CA. P* 12½.
98	15	½d. green			30	70
99	16	1d. scarlet			2·75	1·50
		a. Red (8.42 and 11.47)			3·00	1·50
100		1½d. chocolate-brown			4·75	50
		a. Dull reddish brown (12.43)			2·25	1·25
		b. Lake-brown (7.49)			25·00	13·00
101	15	2d. grey			50	50
		a. Slate-grey (6.51)			6·00	4·50
102	16	2½d. deep ultramarine			70	80
103	–	3d. orange			60	70
104	–	6d. violet			1·40	70
105	15	1s. black and brown			3·00	85
		a. Black and red-brown (7.49)			30·00	9·50
		ab. Frame ptd double, once albino			£2500	
106	–	2s. 6d. brown-purple			40·00	7·50
		a. Maroon (8.42)			22·00	7·50
107	–	5s. olive-green			14·00	7·00
108	16	10s. magenta (1.4.48)			16·00	25·00
109	–	£1 slate-green (1.4.48)			25·00	32·00
98/109			*Set of* 12		75·00	65·00
98/109	Perf "Specimen"		*Set of* 12		£180	

Designs: *Horiz*—3d., 2s. 6d., £1 Fort James. *Vert*—6d., 1s., 5s. St. John's Harbour.

17 Houses of Parliament, London

(Des and recess D.L.R.)

1946 (1 Nov). *Victory. Wmk Mult Script CA. P* 13½×14.
110	17	1½d. brown			15	10
111		3d. red-orange			15	30
110/111	Perf "Specimen"		*Set of* 2		50·00	

18   **19**
King George VI and Queen Elizabeth

(Des and photo Waterlow (T **18**). Design recess; name typo B.W. (T **19**))

1949 (3 Jan). *Royal Silver Wedding. Wmk Mult Script CA.*
112	18	2½d. ultramarine (p 14×15)			40	1·00
113	19	5s. grey-olive (p 11½×11)			8·00	5·50

20 Hermes, Globe and Forms of Transport   **21** Hemispheres, Jet-powered Vickers Viking Airliner and Steamer

14

---

22 Hermes and Globe   **23** U.P.U. Monument

(Recess Waterlow (T **20, 23**). Designs recess, name typo B.W. (T 21/2))

1949 (10 Oct). *75th Anniv of Universal Postal Union. Wmk Mult Script CA.*
114	20	2½d. ultramarine (*p* 13½–14)		40	50
115	21	3d. orange (*p* 11 × 11½)		1·25	1·40
116	22	6d. purple (*p* 11 × 11½)		60	1·25
117	23	1s. red-brown (*p* 13½–14)		60	75
114/17			*Set of* 4		2·50	3·50

(New Currency. 100 cents = 1 West Indian, later Eastern Caribbean, dollar)

24 Arms of University   **25** Princess Alice

(Recess Waterlow)

1951 (16 Feb). *Inauguration of B.W.I. University College. Wmk Mult Script CA. P* 14×14½.
118	24	3 c. black and brown			45	40
119	25	12 c. black and violet			45	70

26 Queen Elizabeth II   **27** Martello Tower

(Des and eng B.W. Recess D.L.R.)

1953 (2 June). *Coronation. Wmk Mult Script CA. P* 13½×13.
120	26	2 c. black and deep yellow-green		30	60

(Recess Waterlow until 1961, then D.L.R.)

1953 (2 Nov)–**62**. *Designs previously used for King George VI issue, but with portrait of Queen Elizabeth II as in T* **27**. *Wmk Mult Script CA. P* 13×13½ *(horiz) or* 13½×13 *(vert).*
120a	–	½ c. brown (3.7.56)			20	30
121	–	1 c. slate-grey			30	70
		a. Slate (7.11.61)			1·50	1·00
122	–	2 c. green			30	10
123	–	3 c. black and orange-yellow		40	20
		a. Black and yellow-orange (5.12.61)		1·75	1·75
124	–	4 c. scarlet			1·25	10
		a. Brown-red (11.12.62)			1·25	30
125	–	5 c. black and slate-lilac			2·50	40
126	–	6 c. yellow-ochre			2·00	10
		a. Dull yellow-ochre (5.12.61)			4·00	90
127	27	8 c. deep blue			2·25	10
128	–	12 c. violet			2·25	10
129	–	24 c. black and chocolate			2·50	15
130	27	48 c. purple and deep blue			7·00	2·50
131	–	60 c. maroon			7·50	80
132	–	$1.20, olive-green			2·25	70
		a. Yellowish olive (10.8.55)			2·25	70
133	–	$2.40, bright reddish purple		10·00	12·00
134	–	$4.80, slate-blue			15·00	20·00
120a/134			*Set of* 15		48·00	35·00

Designs: *Horiz*—½ c., 6 c., 60 c., $4.80, Fort James; 2 c., 3 c., 5 c., $2.40, Nelson's Dockyard. *Vert*—1 c., 4 c., English Harbour; 12 c., 24 c., $1.20, St. John's Harbour.
See also Nos. 149/58.

28 Federation Map   (29)

COMMEMORATION
ANTIGUA
CONSTITUTION
1960

(Recess B.W.)

1958 (22 Apr). *Inauguration of British Caribbean Federation. W* w **12**. *P* 11½ × 11.
135	28	3 c. deep green			1·00	30
136		6 c. blue			1·40	2·00
137		12 c. scarlet			1·60	70
135/7			*Set of* 3		3·50	2·75

MINISTERIAL GOVERNMENT

1960 (1 Jan). *New Constitution. Nos.* 123 *and* 128 *optd with T* 29.
138		3 c. black and orange-yellow (R.)			15	15
139		12 c. violet			15	15

30 Nelson's Dockyard and Admiral Nelson   **31** Stamp of 1862 and R.M.S.P. *Solent I* at English Harbour

(Recess B.W.)

1961 (14 Nov). *Restoration of Nelson's Dockyard. W* w **12**. *P* 11½ × 11.
140	30	20 c. purple and brown			90	80
141		30 c. green and blue			1·10	90

(Des A. W. Morley. Recess B.W.)

1962 (1 Aug). *Stamp Centenary. W* w **12**. *P* 13½.
142	31	3 c. purple and deep green			50	10
143		10 c. blue and deep green			60	10
144		12 c. deep sepia and deep green			70	10
145		50 c. orange-brown and deep green		1·50	1·25
142/5			*Set of* 4		3·00	1·25

32 Protein Foods   **33** Red Cross Emblem

(Des M. Goaman. Photo Harrison)

1963 (4 June). *Freedom from Hunger. W* w **12**. *P* 14×14½.
146	32	12 c. bluish green			15	15

(Des V. Whiteley. Litho B.W.)

1963 (2 Sept). *Red Cross Centenary. W* w **12**. *P* 13½.
147	33	3 c. red and black			30	50
148		12 c. red and blue			50	1·00

(Recess D.L.R.)

1963 (16 Sept)–**65**. *As* 1953—61 *but wmk w* **12**.
149	–	½ c. brown (13.4.65)			1·25	90
150	–	1 c. slate (13.4.65)			80	1·00
151	–	2 c. green			50	20
152	–	3 c. black and yellow-orange			45	20
153	–	4 c. brown-red			30	20
154	–	5 c. black and slate-lilac			20	10
		a. Black and reddish violet (15.1.65)		20	10
155	–	6 c. yellow-ochre			60	30
156	27	8 c. deep blue			30	20
157	–	12 c. violet			40	20
158	–	24 c. black and deep chocolate		3·00	90
		a. Black and chocolate-brown (28.4.65)		4·25	2·25
149/158			*Set of* 10		7·00	3·50

34 Shakespeare and Memorial Theatre, Stratford-upon-Avon   (35)

(Des R. Granger Barrett. Photo Harrison)

1964 (23 April). *400th Birth Anniv of William Shakespeare. W* w **12**. *P* 14 × 14½.
164	34	12 c. orange-brown			15	10
		w. Wmk inverted			48·00	

1965 (1 April). *No.* 157 *surch with T* **35**.
165	15	15 c. on 12 c. violet			10	10

36 I.T.U. Emblem

(Des M. Goaman. Litho Enschedé)

1965 (17 May). *I.T.U. Centenary. W* w **12**. *P* 11 × 11½.
166	36	2 c. light blue and light red			20	80
167		50 c. orange-yellow and ultramarine		90	80

37 I.C.Y. Emblem

(Des V. Whiteley. Litho Harrison)

1965 (25 Oct). *International Co-operation Year.* W w **12.** *P* 14½.
168 **37** 4 c. reddish purple and turquoise-green 15 10
169 15 c. deep bluish green and lavender .. 25 20

38 Sir Winston Churchill, and St. Paul's Cathedral in Wartime

(Des Jennifer Toombs. Photo Harrison)

1966 (24 Jan). *Churchill Commemoration. Printed in black, cerise and gold and with background in colours stated.* W w **12.** *P* 14.
170 **38** ½ c. new blue .. .. .. 10 1·25
  a. Value omitted £275
171 4 c. deep green 30 10
172 25 c. brown 75 45
173 35 c. bluish violet 85 55
170/3 *Set of 4* 1·75 2·00
No. 170a was caused by misplacement of the gold and also shows "ANTIGUA" moved to the right.

39 Queen Elizabeth II and Duke of Edinburgh

(Des H. Baxter. Litho B.W.)

1966 (4 Feb). *Royal Visit.* W w **12.** *P* 11 × 12.
174 **39** 6 c. black and ultramarine .. 1·75 1·10
175 15 c. black and magenta .. .. 1·75 1·40

40 Footballer's Legs, Ball and Jules Rimet Cup

(Des V. Whiteley. Litho Harrison)

1966 (1 July). *World Football Cup Championships.* W w **12** *(sideways). P* 14.
176 **40** 6 c. violet, yellow-green, lake & yell-brn 15 15
177 35 c. chocolate, blue-grn, lake & yell-brn 50 25

41 W.H.O. Building

(Des M. Goaman. Litho Harrison)

1966 (20 Sept). *Inauguration of W.H.O. Headquarters, Geneva.* W w **12** *(sideways). P* 14.
178 **41** 2 c. black, yellow-green and light blue 15 15
179 15 c. black, light purple and yellow-brown 70 25

42 Nelson's Dockyard

(Des, eng and recess B.W.)

1966 (1 Nov)–**68.** *Horiz designs as T* **42.** W w **12.** *P* 11½×11.
180 ½ c. green and turquoise-blue .. 10 40
181 1 c. purple and cerise .. 10 30
182 2 c. slate-blue and yellow-orange .. 10 20
183 3 c. rose-red and black .. 10 30
184 4 c. slate-violet and brown .. 30 10
185 5 c. ultramarine and yellow-olive .. 10 10
186 6 c. salmon and purple .. 15 10
187 10 c. emerald and rose-red .. 15 10
188 15 c. brown and new blue .. 85 10
189 25 c. slate-blue and sepia .. 35 20

190 35 c. cerise and blackish brown .. 1·50 55
191 50 c. dull green and black .. 1·50 2·50
192 75 c. greenish blue and ultramarine 1·50 2·50
193 $1 cerise and yellow-olive .. 4·00 2·50
  a. *Carmine and yellow-olive* (14.5.68) 15·00 12·00
194 $2.50, black and cerise .. 3·50 5·50
195 $5 olive-green and slate-violet .. 5·50 6·50
180/195 *Set of 16* 17·00 19·00
Designs:—1 c. Old Post Office, St. John's; 2 c. Health Centre; 3 c. Teachers' Training College; 4 c. Martello Tower, Barbuda; 5 c. Ruins of Officers' Quarters, Shirley Heights; 6 c. Government House, Barbuda; 10 c. Princess Margaret School; 15 c. Air Terminal building; 25 c. General Post Office; 35 c. Clarence House; 50 c. Government House, St. John's; 75 c. Administration Building; $1, Courthouse, St. John's; $2.50, Magistrates' Court; $5, St. John's Cathedral.
See also Nos. 234/48.

54 "Education"

55 "Science"

56 "Culture"

(Des Jennifer Toombs. Litho Harrison)

1966 (1 Dec). *20th Anniv of U.N.E.S.C.O.* W w **12** *(sideways). P* 14.
196 **54** 4 c. slate-violet, red, yellow and orange 15 10
197 **55** 25 c. orange-yellow, violet and deep olive 35 10
198 **56** $1 black, bright purple and orange 1·10 2·25
196/8 .. .. *Set of 3* 1·40 2·25

ASSOCIATED STATEHOOD

57 State Flag and Maps

(Des W. D. Cribbs. Photo Harrison)

1967 (27 Feb). *Statehood. T* **57** *and similar horiz designs. Multicoloured.* W w **12** *(sideways*). *P* 14.
199 4 c. Type **57** 10 10
200 15 c. State Flag 10 20
  w. Wmk Crown to right of CA .. 1·75
201 25 c. Premier's Office and State Flag 10 25
202 35 c. As 15 c. 15 25
199/202 .. *Set of 4* 30 65
*The normal sideways watermark shows Crown to left of CA, as seen from the back of the stamp.

60 Gilbert Memorial Church

(Des G. Drummond (from sketches by W. D. Cribbs). Photo Harrison)

1967 (18 May). *Attainment of Autonomy by the Methodist Church. T* **60** *and similar horiz designs.* W w **12.** *P* 14½ × 13½.
203 4 c. black and orange-red .. 10 10
204 25 c. black and bright green .. 15 15
205 35 c. black and bright blue .. 15 15
203/5 .. .. *Set of 3* 30 30
Designs:—25 c. Nathaniel Gilbert's House; 35 c. Caribbean and Central American map.

NEW INFORMATION

The editor is always interested to correspond with people who have new information that will improve or correct the Catalogue.

63 Coat of Arms

64 Susan Constant (settlers' ship)

(Des V. Whiteley (from sketches by W. D. Cribbs). Photo Harrison)

1967 (21 July). *300th Anniv of Treaty of Breda and Grant of New Arms.* W w **12** *(sideways*). *P* 14½×14.
206 **63** 15 c. multicoloured .. 15 10
  w. Wmk Crown to right of CA .. 10·00 10·00
207 35 c. multicoloured .. 15 10
*The normal sideways watermark shows Crown to left of CA, as seen from the back of the stamp.

(Des and recess B.W.)

1967 (14 Dec). *300th Anniv of Barbuda Settlement. T* **64** *and similar horiz design.* W w **12.** *P* 11½ × 11.
208 **64** 4 c. deep ultramarine .. 25 10
209 – 6 c. purple 25 60
210 **64** 25 c. emerald 30 20
211 – 35 c. black 30 25
208/11 *Set of 4* 1·00 1·00
Design:—6, 35 c. Blaeu's map of 1665.

66 Tracking Station   **70 Limbo-dancing**

(Des G. Vasarhelyi. Photo Harrison)

1968 (29 Mar). *N.A.S.A. Apollo Project. Inauguration of Dow Hill Tracking Station. T* **66** *and similar vert designs in deep blue, orange-yellow and black.* W w **12** *(sideways). P* 14½ × 14.
212 4 c. Type **66** 10 10
213 15 c. Antenna and spacecraft taking off 20 10
214 25 c. Spacecraft approaching Moon .. 20 10
215 50 c. Re-entry of space capsule .. 30 30
212/15 .. .. *Set of 4* 70 40

(Des and photo Harrison)

1968 (1 July). *Tourism. T* **70** *and similar horiz designs. Multicoloured.* W w **12.** *P* 14½ × 14.
216 ½ c. Type **70** 10 10
217 15 c. Water-skiing and bathers .. 25 10
218 25 c. Yachts and beach .. 30 10
219 35 c. Underwater swimming .. 30 10
220 50 c. Type **70** 50 65
216/20 .. *Set of 5* 1·25 80

74 Old Harbour in 1768

(Des R. Granger Barrett. Recess B.W.)

1968 (31 Oct). *Opening of St. John's Deep Water Harbour. T* **74** *and similar horiz designs.* W w **12.** *P* 13.
221 2 c. light blue and carmine .. 10 20
222 15 c. light yellow-green and sepia .. 35 10
223 25 c. olive-yellow and blue .. 40 10
224 35 c. salmon and emerald .. 50 10
225 $1 black .. .. 90 1·50
221/5 .. .. *Set of 5* 2·00 1·60
Designs:—15 c. Old Harbour in 1829; 25 c. Freighter and chart of New Harbour; 35 c. New Harbour, 1968; $1, Type **74.**

78 Parliament Buildings

(Des R. Granger Barrett. Photo Harrison)

1969 (3 Feb). *Tercentenary of Parliament. T* **78** *and similar square designs. Multicoloured.* W w **12** *(sideways). P* 12½.
226 4 c. Type **78** 10 10
227 15 c. Antigua Mace and bearer .. 20 10
228 25 c. House of Representatives' Room 20 10
229 50 c. Coat of arms and Seal of Antigua 30 80
226/9 .. .. *Set of 4* 70 95

82 Freight Transport

(Des Jennifer Toombs. Litho D.L.R.)

1969 (14 Apr). *1st Anniv of CARIFTA (Caribbean Free Trade Area). T* **82** *and similar design. W* w **12** *(sideways on 4 c., 15 c).* P 13.

230	4 c. black and reddish purple	..	10	10
231	15 c. black and turquoise-blue		20	25
232	25 c. chocolate, black and yellow-ochre		25	25
233	35 c. chocolate, black and yellow-brown		25	25
230/3		*Set of 4*	65	70

Designs: Horiz—4, 15 c. Type 82. Vert—25, 35 c. Crate of cargo.

1969–70. *As Nos. 180/91 and 193/5 but perf 13½.*
   A. *Ordinary paper (24.6.69).*
   B. *Glazed paper (30.9.69 or 6.4.70 (4 c.))*

			A		B	
234	½ c. green and turquoise-blue	..	10	80		†
235	1 c. purple and cerise ..		10	50	60	15
236	2 c. slate-blue & yellow-orange		10	30	70	10
237	3 c. rose-red and black		15	15		†
238	4 c. slate-violet and brown		15	15	16·00	9·00
239	5 c. ultramarine & yellow-olive		15	10	40	10
240	6 c. salmon and purple		15	50		†
241	10 c. emerald and rose-red		15	15	2·50	10
242	15 c. brown and new blue			†	55	10
243	25 c. slate-blue and sepia			†	45	10
244	35 c. cerise & blackish brown			†	60	1·00
245	50 c. dull green and black			†	70	2·25
246	$1 cerise and yellow-olive			†	1·25	4·50
247	$2.50, black and cerise			†	1·50	8·00
248	$5 olive-green & slate-violet ..			†	12·00	24·00
234/41A		*Set of 8*	90	2·25		†
235/48B		*Set of 12*		†	32·00	45·00

84 Island of Redonda (Chart)

(Des R. Granger Barrett. Photo Enschedé)

1969 (1 Aug). *Centenary of Redonda Phosphate Industry. T* **84** *and similar horiz design. W* w **12** *(sideways).* P 13 × 13½.

249	15 c. Type 84	..	..	20	10
250	25 c. Redonda from the sea	..		20	10
251	50 c. Type 84	..	..	45	75
249/51			*Set of 3*	75	80

86 "The Adoration of the Magi" (Marcillat)   (88)

(Des adapted by V. Whiteley. Litho Enschedé)

1969 (15 Oct). *Christmas. Stained-glass Windows. T* **86** *and similar vert design. Multicoloured. W* w **12** *(sideways*).* P 13×14.

252	6 c. Type 86	..	10	10
253	10 c. "The Nativity" (unknown German artist, 15th-century) ..		10	10
254	35 c. Type 86		25	10
255	50 c. As 10 c.		50	40
	w. Wmk Crown to right of CA	..	12·00	
252/5		*Set of 4*	80	55

*The normal sideways watermark shows Crown to left of CA, as seen from the back of the stamp.

1970 (2 Jan). *No. 189 surch with T* **88**.
256	20 c. on 25 c. slate-blue and sepia		10	10

89 Coat of Arms   90 Sikorsky S-38 Flying Boat

(Des and photo Harrison)

1970–73. *Coil Stamps. W* w **12**. P 14½ × 14.
   A. *Chalk-surfaced paper. Wmk upright (30.1.70).*
   B. *Glazed paper. Wmk sideways (8.3.73).*

				A		B	
257	89	5 c. blue	..	10	10	1·00	1·25
258		10 c. emerald	..	10	15	1·10	1·25
259		25 c. crimson	..	20	25	1·75	2·00
257/9			*Set of 3*	35	45	3·50	4·00

For these stamps with watermark W w **14**, see Nos. 541a/c.

(Des R. Granger Barrett. Litho J.W.)

1970 (16 Feb). *40th Anniv of Antiguan Air Services. T* **90** *and similar designs. Multicoloured. W* w **12** *(sideways).* P 14½.

260	5 c. Type 90	..	40	10
261	20 c. Dornier Do-X flying boat	..	1·00	10
262	35 c. Hawker Siddeley H.S. 748	..	1·25	10
263	50 c. Douglas C-124C Globemaster II		1·40	1·50
264	75 c. Vickers Super VC-10	..	1·50	2·00
260/4		*Set of 5*	5·00	3·50

91 Dickens and Scene from *Nicholas Nickleby*

(Des Jennifer Toombs. Litho Walsall)

1970 (19 May). *Death Centenary of Charles Dickens. T* **91** *and similar horiz designs. W* w **12** *(sideways).* P 14.

265	5 c. bistre, sepia and black	..	10	10
266	20 c. light turquoise-blue, sepia and black		20	10
267	35 c. violet-blue, sepia and black		30	10
268	$1 rosine, sepia and black	..	75	50
265/8		*Set of 4*	1·25	60

Designs:—20 c. Dickens and Scene from *Pickwick Papers*; 35 c. Dickens and Scene from *Oliver Twist*; $1 Dickens and Scene from *David Copperfield*.

92 Carib Indian and War Canoe   93 "The Small Passion" (detail) (Dürer)

(Des J.W. Litho Questa)

1970 (19 Aug)–75. *Horiz designs as T* **92**. *Multicoloured. Toned paper. W* w **12** *(sideways*).* P 14.

269	½ c. Type 92		10	40
270	1 c. Columbus and *Nina* ..		30	60
271	2 c. Sir Thomas Warner's emblem and *Concepcion* ..		40	1·00
	a. Whiter paper (20.10.75)	..	1·50	3·25
272	3 c. Viscount Hood and H.M.S. *Barfleur*	..	40	75
	w. Wmk Crown to right of CA	..	2·75	2·75
273	4 c. Sir George Rodney and H.M.S. *Formidable*	..	40	1·00
274	5 c. Nelson and H.M.S. *Boreas*		50	40
275	6 c. William IV and H.M.S. *Pegasus*		50	1·25
276	10 c. "Blackbeard" and pirate ketch		65	20
277	15 c. Captain Collingwood and H.M.S. *Pelican*		3·25	1·00
278	20 c. Nelson and H.M.S. *Victory*		1·25	40
279	25 c. *Solent I* (paddle-steamer)		1·25	40
280	35 c. George V (when Prince George) and H.M.S. *Canada* (screw corvette)		1·75	80
281	50 c. H.M.S. *Renown* (battle cruiser)		5·00	3·25
282	75 c. *Federal Maple* (freighter)	..	7·00	5·50
283	$1 *Sol Quest* (yacht) and class emblem		7·00	2·00
284	$2.50, H.M.S. *London* (destroyer)		7·00	7·50
285	$5 *Pathfinder* (tug)	..	7·00	7·50
269/85		*Set of 17*	38·00	30·00

*The normal sideways watermark shows Crown to left of CA as seen from the back of the stamp.

See also Nos. 323/34 and 426

(Des G. Drummond. Recess and litho D.L.R.)

1970 (28 Oct). *Christmas. T* **93** *and similar vert design. W* w **12**. P 13½ × 14.

286	93	3 c. black and turquoise-blue	..	10	10
287	—	10 c. dull purple and pink		10	10
288	93	35 c. black and rose-red		30	10
289	—	50 c. black and lilac		45	50
286/9			*Set of 4*	80	60

Design:—10 c., 50 c. "Adoration of the Magi" (detail) (Dürer).

OMNIBUS ISSUES

Details, together with prices for complete sets, of the various Omnibus issues from the 1935 Silver Jubilee series to date are included in a special section following Zimbabwe at the end of Volume 2.

---

94 4th King's Own Regt, 1759   95 Market Woman casting Vote

(Des P. W. Kingsland. Litho Questa)

1970 (14 Dec). *Military Uniforms (1st series). T* **94** *and similar vert designs. Multicoloured. W* w **12**. P 14 × 13½.

290	½ c. Type 94		10	10
291	10 c. 4th West India Regiment, 1804	..	50	10
292	20 c. 60th Regiment, The Royal American, 1809		1·00	10
293	35 c. 93rd Regiment, Sutherland Highlanders, 1826–34		1·40	10
294	75 c. 3rd West India Regiment, 1851 ..		2·25	2·50
290/4 ..		*Set of 5*	4·75	2·50
MS295	128 × 146 mm. Nos. 290/4.		7·50	11·00

See also Nos. 303/8, 313/18, 353/8 and 380/5.

(Des Sylvia Goaman. Photo Harrison)

1971 (1 Feb). *20th Anniversary of Adult Suffrage. T* **95** *and similar vert designs. W* w **12** *(sideways).* P 14½ × 14.

296	5 c. brown		10	10
297	20 c. deep olive		10	10
298	35 c. reddish purple		10	10
299	50 c. ultramarine		15	30
296/9		*Set of 4*	30	40

People voting:—20 c. Executive; 35 c. Housewife; 50 c. Artisan.

96 "The Last Supper"   97 "Madonna and Child" (detail, Veronese)

(Des Jennifer Toombs. Litho Questa)

1971 (7 Apr). *Easter. Works by Dürer. T* **96** *and similar vert designs. W* w **12**. P 14 × 13½.

300	5 c. black, grey and scarlet	..	10	10
301	35 c. black, grey and bluish violet	..	10	10
302	75 c. black, grey and gold	..	20	30
300/2		*Set of 3*	30	35

Designs:—35 c. The Crucifixion; 75 c. The Resurrection.

(Des J. W. Litho Questa)

1971 (12 July). *Military Uniforms (2nd series). Multicoloured designs as T* **94**. *W* w **12**. P 13½.

303	½ c. Private, 12th Regiment, The Suffolk (1704)		10	10
	w. Wmk inverted	..	45·00	
304	10 c. Grenadier, 38th Regiment, South Staffs (1751) ..		35	15
305	20 c. Light Company, 5th Regiment, Royal Northumberland Fusiliers (1778)	..	65	20
306	35 c. Private, 48th Regiment, The Northamptonshire (1793)	..	1·10	25
307	75 c. Private, 15th Regiment, East Yorks (1805)	..	2·25	3·75
	w. Wmk inverted	..	3·25	
303/7		*Set of 5*	4·00	4·00
MS308	127×144 mm. Nos. 303/7	..	5·50	6·50

(Des Jennifer Toombs. Litho Questa)

1971 (4 Oct). *Christmas. T* **97** *and similar vert design. Multicoloured. W* w **12**. P 13½.

309	3 c. Type 97	..	10	10
310	5 c. "Adoration of the Shepherds" (detail, Veronese)		10	10
311	35 c. Type 97		25	10
312	50 c. As 5 c.		40	30
309/12		*Set of 4*	70	40

(Des J.W. Litho Questa)

1972 (1 July). *Military Uniforms (3rd series). Multicoloured designs as T* **94**. *W* w **12**. P 13½.

313	½ c. Battalion Company Officer, 25th Foot, 1815		10	10
314	10 c. Sergeant, 14th Foot, 1837	..	75	10
315	20 c. Private, 67th Foot, 1853..	..	1·40	15
316	35 c. Officer, Royal Artillery, 1854	..	1·90	20
317	75 c. Private, 29th Foot, 1870..	..	2·25	3·25
313/17		*Set of 5*	5·50	3·25
MS318	125 × 141 mm. Nos. 313/17	..	7·00	8·50

---

98 Reticulated Cowrie-Helmet

(Des J.W. Litho Questa)

1972 (1 Aug). *Shells. T 98 and similar horiz designs. Multicoloured. W w 12 (sideways). P 14½.*
319	3 c. Type 98		40	10
320	5 c. Measled Cowrie		40	10
321	35 c. West Indian Fighting Conch		1·25	15
322	50 c. Hawk-wing Conch		1·40	2·50
319/22		Set of 4	3·00	2·50

1972–74. *As No. 269 etc., but W w 12 (upright) and whiter paper.*
323	½ c. Type 92		20	40
324	1 c. Columbus and *Nina*		30	70
325	3 c. Viscount Hood and H.M.S. *Barfleur*		35	50
326	4 c. Sir George Rodney and H.M.S. *Formidable*		35	1·25
327	5 c. Nelson and H.M.S. *Boreas*		50	40
328	6 c. William IV and H.M.S. *Pegasus*		50	2·00
329	10 c. "Blackbeard" and pirate ketch		55	60
330	15 c. Collingwood and H.M.S. *Pelican*		7·50	90
	w. Wmk inverted		60·00	
331	75 c. *Federal Maple* (freighter)		7·50	3·00
332	$1 *Sol Quest* (yacht) and class emblem		3·00	1·75
333	$2.50 H.M.S. *London* (destroyer)		2·75	6·50
334	$5 *Pathfinder* (tug)		4·00	11·00
323/34		Set of 12	25·00	26·00

Dates of issue:—2.11.72, ½ c., 15 c., 75 c., $1, $5; 2.1.74, 1 to 10 c.; 25.2.74, $2.50.
See also No. 426.

99 St. John's Cathedral, Side View

(Des J.W. Litho Format)

1972 (6 Nov). *Christmas and 125th Anniversary of St. John's Cathedral. T 99 and similar horiz designs. Multicoloured. W w 12. P 14.*
335	35 c. Type 99		20	10
336	50 c. Cathedral interior		25	25
337	75 c. St. John's Cathedral		30	60
335/7		Set of 3	65	80
MS338	165 × 102 mm. Nos. 335/7. P 15		65	1·00

100 Floral Pattern

(Des (from photograph by D. Groves) and photo Harrison)

1972 (20 Nov). *Royal Silver Wedding. Multicoloured; background colour given. W w 12. P 14 × 14½.*
339	100	20 c. bright blue	15	15
340		35 c. turquoise-blue	15	15
		w. Wmk inverted	13·00	

101 Batsman and Map

(Des G. Vasarhelyi. Litho Questa)

1972 (15 Dec). *50th Anniv of Rising Sun Cricket Club. T 101 and similar horiz designs. Multicoloured. W w 12. P 13½.*
341	5 c. Type 101		55	15
	w. Wmk inverted		3·50	
342	35 c. Batsman and wicket-keeper		1·25	65
343	$1 Club badge		2·25	3·50
341/3		Set of 3	3·50	3·75
MS344	88 × 130 mm. Nos. 341/3		4·50	7·50
	w. Wmk inverted		55·00	

NEW INFORMATION

The editor is always interested to correspond with people who have new information that will improve or correct the Catalogue.

102 Yacht and Map   103 "Episcopal Coat of Arms"

(Des M. and G. Shamir. Litho Format)

1972 (29 Dec). *Sailing Week and Inauguration of Tourist Office, New York. T 102 and similar square designs. Multicoloured. W w 12. P 14½.*
345	35 c. Type 102		15	10
346	50 c. Yachts		20	15
347	75 c. St. John's G.P.O.		25	25
348	$1 Statue of Liberty		25	25
345/8		Set of 4	75	65
MS349	100 × 94 mm. Nos. 346, 348		75	1·25

(Des PAD Studio. Litho Format)

1973 (16 Apr). *Easter. T 103 and similar vert designs showing stained-glass windows from St. John's Cathedral. Multicoloured. W w 12 (sideways*). P 13½.*
350	5 c. Type 103		10	10
351	35 c. "The Crucifixion"		15	10
352	75 c. "Arms of 1st Bishop of Antigua"		25	30
	w. Wmk Crown to right of CA		11·00	
350/2		Set of 3	40	35

*The normal sideways watermark shows Crown to left of CA on the 75 c., and to right of CA on the others, *as seen from the back of the stamp.*

(Des J.W. Litho Questa)

1973 (1 July). *Military Uniforms (4th series). Multicoloured designs as T 94. W w 12 (sideways*). P 13½.*
353	½ c. Private, Zacharia Tiffin's Regiment of Foot, 1701		10	10
354	10 c. Private, 63rd Regiment of Foot, 1759		30	10
355	20 c. Light Company Officer, 35th Regiment of Foot, 1828		45	15
	w. Wmk Crown to right of CA		7·00	
356	35 c. Private, 2nd West India Regiment, 1853		75	15
357	75 c. Sergeant, 49th Regiment, 1858		1·50	1·00
353/7		Set of 5	2·75	1·25
MS358	127 × 145 mm. Nos. 353/7		3·50	3·25

*The normal sideways watermark shows Crown to right of CA on the 35 and 75 c., and to left of CA on the others, *as seen from the back of the stamp.*

104 Butterfly Costumes

(Des G. Vasarhelyi. Litho Format)

1973 (30 July). *Carnival. T 104 and similar horiz designs. Multicoloured. P 13½.*
359	5 c. Type 104		10	10
360	20 c. Carnival street scene		15	10
361	35 c. Carnival troupe		20	10
362	75 c. Carnival Queen		30	30
359/62		Set of 4	65	35
MS363	134 × 95 mm. Nos. 359/62		65	1·00

105 "Virgin of the Milk Porridge" (Gerard David)   106 Princess Anne and Captain Mark Phillips

(Des G. Vasarhelyi. Litho Format)

1973 (15 Oct). *Christmas. T 105 and similar vert designs. Multicoloured. P 14½.*
364	3 c. Type 105		10	10
365	5 c. "Adoration of the Magi" (Stomer)		10	10
366	20 c. "The Granducal Madonna" (Raphael)		15	10
367	35 c. "Nativity with God the Father and Holy Ghost" (Battista)		20	10
368	$1 "Madonna and Child" (Murillo)		40	60
364/8		Set of 5	75	70
MS369	130 × 128 mm. Nos. 364/8		1·10	1·75

(Des G. Drummond. Litho Format)

1973 (14 Nov). *Royal Wedding. T 106 and similar horiz design. P 13½.*
370	106	35 c. multicoloured	10	10
371	–	$2 multicoloured	25	25
MS372	78 × 100 mm. Nos. 370/1		50	40

The $2 is as T 106 but has a different border.
Nos. 370/1 were each issued in small sheets of five stamps and one stamp-size label.

HONEYMOON VISIT   DECEMBER 16th 1973

(107)

1973 (15 Dec). *Honeymoon Visit of Princess Anne and Captain Phillips. Nos. 370/MS372 optd with T 107 by lithography.**
373	106	35 c. multicoloured	15	10
		a. Typo opt	95	95
374	–	$2 multicoloured	30	30
		a. Typo opt	2·75	2·75
MS375	78 × 100 mm. Nos. 373/4		55	55
		a. Typo opt	8·50	12·00

*The litho overprints can be distinguished from the typo by the latter being less clear, less intense, and showing through on the reverse.

108 Coats of Arms of Antigua and University

(Des PAD Studio. Litho D.L.R.)

1974 (18 Feb). *25th Anniv of University of West Indies. T 108 and similar horiz designs. Multicoloured. W w 12. P 13.*
376	5 c. Type 108		10	10
377	20 c. Extra-mural art		10	10
378	35 c. Antigua campus		15	10
379	75 c. Antigua chancellor		25	25
376/9		Set of 4	40	30

(Des J.W. Litho Questa)

1974 (1 May). *Military Uniforms (5th series). Multicoloured designs as T 94. W w 12 (sideways*). P 13½.*
380	½ c. Officer, 59th Foot, 1797		10	10
381	10 c. Gunner, Royal Artillery, 1800		45	10
	a. Error. Wmk T 55 of Malawi		70·00	
382	20 c. Private, 1st West India Regiment, 1830		70	10
383	35 c. Officer, 92nd Foot, 1843		85	10
384	75 c. Private, 23rd Foot, 1846		1·25	1·60
380/4		Set of 5	3·00	1·75
MS385	127 × 145 mm. Nos. 380/4		3·00	2·50

*The normal sideways watermark shows Crown to right of CA on the 20 c., and to left of CA on the others, *as seen from the back of the stamp.*

109 English Postman, Mailcoach and Westland Dragonfly Helicopter   110 Traditional Player

(Des G. Vasarhelyi. Litho Format)

1974 (15 July). *Centenary of Universal Postal Union. T 109 and similar horiz designs. Multicoloured. P 14½.*
386	½ c. Type 109		10	10
387	1 c. Bellman, mail steamer *Orinoco* and satellite		10	10
388	2 c. Train guard, post-bus and hydrofoil		10	10
389	5 c. Swiss messenger, Wells Fargo coach and Concorde		30	10
390	20 c. Postilion, Japanese postmen and carrier pigeon		35	10
391	35 c. Antiguan postman, Sikorsky S-88 flying boat and tracking station		45	15
392	$1 Medieval courier, American express train and Boeing 747-100		1·75	1·40
386/92		Set of 7	2·75	1·50
MS393	141 × 164 mm. Nos. 386/92 plus label. P 13		2·75	2·50

On the ½ c. "English" is spelt "Enlish", and on the 2 c. "Postal" is spelt "Fostal".

(Des C. Abbott. Litho Questa)

1974 (1 Aug). *Antiguan Steel Bands. T 110 and similar designs. W w 12 (sideways on 5 c., 75 c. and MS398). P 13.*
394	5 c. rose-red, carmine and black		10	10
395	20 c. brown-ochre, chestnut and black		10	10
396	35 c. light sage-green, blue-green and black		10	10
397	75 c. dull blue, dull ultramarine and black		20	30
394/7		Set of 4	30	40
MS398	115 × 108 mm. Nos. 394/7		35	65

Designs: *Horiz*—20 c. Traditional band; 35 c. Modern band. *Vert*—75 c. Modern player.

EARTHQUAKE RELIEF

111 Footballers   (112)

(Des G. Vasarhelyi. Litho Format)

1974 (23 Sept). *World Cup Football Championships. T* 111 *and similar vert designs showing footballers. P* 14½.
399	111	5 c. multicoloured	10	10
400	–	35 c. multicoloured	10	10
401	–	75 c. multicoloured	25	30
402	–	$1 multicoloured	30	40
399/402		Set of 4	55	70

MS403 135 × 130 mm. Nos. 399/402 plus two labels. P 13 75 90
Nos. 399/402 were each issued in small sheets of five stamps and one stamp-size label.

1974 (16 Oct). *Earthquake Relief Fund. Nos.* 400/2 *and* 397 *optd with T* 112, *No.* 397 *surch also.*
404	35 c. multicoloured	20	10
405	75 c. multicoloured	30	25
406	$1 multicoloured	40	30
407	$5 on 75 c. dull blue, dull ultram & black	1·25	2·00
404/7		Set of 4	2·00	2·40

113 Churchill as Schoolboy and School College Building, Harrow
114 "Madonna of the Trees" (Bellini)

(Des V. Whiteley. Litho Format)

1974 (20 Oct). *Birth Centenary of Sir Winston Churchill. T* 113 *and similar horiz designs. Multicoloured. P* 14½.
408	5 c. Type 113	10	10
409	35 c. Churchill and St. Paul's Cathedral	15	10
410	75 c. Coat of arms and catafalque	20	45
411	$1 Churchill, "reward" notice and South African escape route	30	75
408/11		Set of 4	65	1·25

MS412 107×82 mm. Nos. 408/11. P 13 65 1·25

(Des M. Shamir. Litho Format)

1974 (18 Nov). *Christmas. T* 114 *and similar vert designs showing "Madonna and Child" by the artists given. Multicoloured. P* 14½.
413	½ c. Type 114	10	10
414	1 c. Raphael	10	10
415	2 c. Van der Weyden	10	10
416	3 c. Giorgione	10	10
417	5 c. Mantegna	10	10
418	20 c. Vivarini	20	10
419	35 c. Montagna	30	10
420	75 c. Lorenzo Costa	55	60
413/20		Set of 8	1·25	90

MS421 139 × 126 mm. Nos. 417/20. P 13 95 1·40

$10

(115)   116 Carib War Canoe, English Harbour, 1300

1975 (14 Jan). *Nos.* 331 *and* 390/2 *surch as T* 115.
422	50 c. on 20 c. multicoloured	1·25	1·75
423	$2.50, on 35 c. multicoloured	3·00	5·00
424	$5 on $1 multicoloured	4·50	7·00
425	$10 on 75 c. multicoloured	4·50	7·50
422/5		Set of 4	12·00	19·00

1975 (21 Jan). *As No.* 334, *but W w* 14 (*sideways*).
426 $5 *Pathfinder* (tug) 3·75 10·00

(Des G. Drummond. Litho Format)

1975 (17 Mar). *Nelson's Dockyard. T* 116 *and similar horiz designs. Multicoloured. P* 14½.
427	5 c. Type 116	15	10
428	15 c. Ship of the line, English Harbour, 1770	60	10
429	35 c. H.M.S. *Boreas* at anchor, and Lord Nelson, 1787	1·00	15
430	50 c. Yachts during "Sailing Week", 1974	1·25	1·00
431	$1 Yacht Anchorage, Old Dockyard, 1970	1·50	1·75
427/31		Set of 5	4·00	2·75

MS432 130 × 134 mm. As Nos. 427/31, but in larger format, 43 × 28 mm. P 13½ 3·25 2·00

---

117 Lady of the Valley Church

(Des R. Vigurs. Litho Format)

1975 (19 May). *Antiguan Churches. T* 117 *and similar horiz designs. Multicoloured. P* 14½.
433	5 c. Type 117	10	10
434	20 c. Gilbert Memorial	10	10
435	35 c. Grace Hill Moravian	15	10
436	50 c. St. Phillips	20	20
437	$1 Ebenezer Methodist	35	50
433/7		Set of 5	65	75

MS438 91 × 101 mm. Nos. 435/7. P 13 65 1·25

118 Map of 1721 and Sextant of 1640

(Des PAD Studio. Litho Questa)

1975 (21 July). *Maps of Antigua. T* 118 *and similar horiz designs. Multicoloured. W w* 14 (*sideways*). *P* 14.
439	5 c. Type 118	20	10
440	20 c. Map of 1775 and galleon	45	10
441	35 c. Maps of 1775 and 1955	55	15
442	$1 1973 maps of Antigua and English Harbour	1·40	1·75
439/42		Set of 4	2·40	1·90

MS443 130 × 89 mm. Nos. 439/42 2·75 2·00

119 Scout Bugler

(Des G. Vasarhelyi. Litho Questa)

1975 (26 Aug). *World Scout Jamboree, Norway. T* 119 *and similar horiz designs. Multicoloured. P* 14.
444	15 c. Type 119	25	15
445	20 c. Scouts in camp	30	15
446	35 c. "Lord Baden-Powell" (D. Jagger)	50	20
447	$2 Scout dancers from Dahomey	1·50	1·75
444/7		Set of 4	2·25	2·00

MS448 145 × 107 mm. Nos. 444/7 3·25 3·50

120 *Eurema elathea*
121 "Madonna and Child" (Correggio)

(Des. G. Vasarhelyi. Litho Questa)

1975 (30 Oct). *Butterflies. T* 120 *and similar horiz designs. Multicoloured. P* 14.
449	½ c. Type 120	10	10
450	1 c. *Danaus plexippus*	10	10
451	2 c. *Phoebis philea*	10	10
452	5 c. *Hypolimnas misippus*	15	10
453	20 c. *Eurema proterpia*	60	60
454	35 c. *Battus polydamas*	90	90
455	$2 *Cynthia cardui*	4·00	7·00
449/55		Set of 7	5·50	8·00

MS456 147×94 mm. Nos 452/5 6·00 9·50
No. 452 is incorrectly captioned "Marpesia petreus thetys".

(Des G. Vasarhelyi. Litho Questa)

1975 (17 Nov). *Christmas. T* 121 *and similar vert designs showing "Madonna and Child". Multicoloured. P* 14.
457	½ c. Type 121	10	10
458	1 c. El Greco	10	10
459	2 c. Dürer	10	10
460	3 c. Antonello	10	10
461	5 c. Bellini	10	10
462	10 c. Dürer (*different*)	10	10
463	35 c. Bellini (*different*)	40	10
464	$2 Dürer (*different*)	1·00	70
457/64		Set of 8	1·50	85

MS465 138 × 119 mm. Nos. 461/4 1·50 1·60

---

122 Vivian Richards
123 Antillean Crested Hummingbird

(Des G. Vasarhelyi. Litho Format)

1975 (15 Dec). *World Cup Cricket Winners. T* 122 *and similar multicoloured designs. P* 13½.
466	5 c. Type 122	1·25	20
467	35 c. Andy Roberts	2·25	60
468	$2 West Indies team (*horiz*)	4·25	8·00
466/8		Set of 3	7·00	8·00

(Des G. Vasarhelyi. Litho Format)

1976 (19 Jan)–**78**. *Various multicoloured designs as T* 123. *Without imprint* (19.1.76). B. *With imprint date at foot* (1978).

(a) Size as T 123. *P* 14½.
			A	B
469	½ c. Type 123	20	35	70
470	1 c. Imperial Amazon	30	50	90	70
471	2 c. Zenaida Dove	30	50	90	70
472	3 c. Loggerhead Kingbird	30	60	90	70
473	4 c. Red-necked Pigeon	30	60	90	70
474	5 c. Rufous-throated Solitaire	90	10	1·25	45
475	6 c. Orchid Tree	30	60	30	70
476	10 c. Bougainvillea	30	10	30	30
477	15 c. Geiger Tree	35	10	30	30
478	20 c. Flamboyant	35	35	30	65
479	25 c. Hibiscus	40	15	35	50
480	35 c. Flame of the Wood	40	40	35	50
481	50 c. Cannon at Fort James	55	50	50	70
482	75 c. Premier's Office	60	75	55	80
483	$1 Potworks Dam	75	90	75	90

(b) Size 44 × 28 mm. P 13½
484	$2.50, Irrigation Scheme, Diamond Estate	1·50	3·50	3·00	6·00
485	$5 Government House	3·50	5·50	2·50	6·50
486	$10 Coolidge Airport	3·50	6·50	8·00	9·50
469/86		Set of 18	13·00	20·00	20·00	28·00

Nos. 469A, 472B, 473A, 474B, 475A/B, 476A/B, 477A, 478B, 479A/B, 480B, 481A/B, 482A/B, 483A, 484A/B, 485A/B and 486A/B exist imperforate from stock dispersed by the liquidator of Format International Security Printers Ltd.

124 Privates, Clark's Illinois Regt
125 High Jump

(Des J.W. Litho Format)

1976 (17 Mar). *Bicentenary of American Revolution. T* 124 *and similar vert designs. Multicoloured. P* 14½.
487	½ c. Type 124	10	10
488	1 c. Riflemen, Pennsylvania Militia	10	10
489	2 c. Powder horn	10	10
	a. Imperf (pair)	£160	
490	5 c. Water bottle	10	10
491	35 c. American flags	50	10
492	$1 *Montgomery* (American brig)	1·75	40
493	$5 *Ranger* (privateer sloop)	3·00	2·75
487/93		Set of 7	5·00	3·00

MS494 71×84 mm. $2.50 Congress flag. P 13 1·25 1·75

(Des J.W. Litho Format)

1976 (17 July). *Olympic Games, Montreal. T* 125 *and similar horiz designs. P* 14½.
495	½ c. orange-brown, bistre-yellow and black	10	10
496	1 c. light reddish violet, bright blue & black	10	10
497	2 c. light green and black	10	10
498	15 c. bright blue and black	15	10
499	30 c. olive-brown, yellow-ochre and black	20	15
500	$1 red-orange, Venetian red and black	40	40
501	$2 rosine and black	60	80
495/501		Set of 7	1·25	1·40

MS502 88 ×138 mm. Nos. 498/501. P 13½ 1·75 2·25
Designs:—1 c. Boxing; 2 c. Pole vault; 15 c. Swimming; 30 c. Running; $1 Cycling; $2 Shot put.

126 Water Skiing

(Des J.W. Litho Questa)

1976 (26 Aug). *Water Sports. T* **126** *and similar horiz designs. Multicoloured. P* 14.

503	½ c. Type **126** ..		..	..	10	10
504	1 c. Sailing	..	..	..	10	10
505	2 c. Snorkeling		..	..	10	10
506	20 c. Deep sea fishing	..	..	..	15	10
507	50 c. Scuba diving	..	..	..	35	35
508	$2 Swimming	..	..	..	1·00	1·25
503/8				*Set of* 6	1·40	1·60
MS509	89 × 114 mm. Nos. 506/8 ..		..	..	1·40	1·75

127 French Angelfish   **128** The Annunciation

(Des G. Drummond. Litho Questa)

1976 (4 Oct). *Fishes. T* **127** *and similar horiz designs. Multicoloured. W w* 14 (*sideways*). *P* 13½.

510	15 c. Type **127**	..	..	..	50	15
511	30 c. Yellow-finned Grouper	..	..	75	30
512	50 c. Yellow-tailed Snapper	..	..	95	50
513	90 c. Shy Hamlet ..	..	..	..	1·25	80
510/13				*Set of* 4	3·00	1·60

(Des J.W. Litho Walsall)

1976 (15 Nov). *Christmas. T* **128** *and similar vert designs. Multicoloured. P* 13½.

514	8 c. Type **128** ..	..	..	..	10	10
515	10 c. The Holy Family..	..	..	10	10
516	15 c. The Magi ..	..	..	..	10	10
517	50 c. The Shepherds	..	..	..	20	25
518	$1 Epiphany scene	..	..	..	30	50
514/18				*Set of* 5	60	75

129 Mercury and U.P.U. Emblem   **130** Royal Family

(Des BG Studio. Litho Questa)

1976 (28 Dec). *Special Events, 1976. T* **129** *and similar horiz designs. Multicoloured. P* 14.

519	½ c. Type **129** ..	..	..	..	10	10
520	1 c. Alfred Nobel	..	..	..	10	10
521	10 c. Space satellite	..	..	..	20	10
522	50 c. Viv Richards and Andy Roberts..		3·00	1·75
523	$1 Bell and telephones	..	..	1·00	2·00
524	$2 Yacht *Freelance*	..	..	..	2·25	4·00
519/24				*Set of* 6	6·00	7·00
MS525	127 × 101 mm. Nos. 521/4 ..		..	7·50	11·00

Events:—½ c. 25th Anniv of U.N. Postal Administration; 1 c. 75th Anniv of Nobel Prize; 10 c. "Viking" Space Mission; 50 c. Cricketing achievements; $1 Telephone Centenary; $2 "Operation Sail", U.S. Bicentennial.

(Des J. W. Litho Questa (Nos. 526/31); Manufactured by Walsall (Nos. 532/3))

1977 (7 Feb–26 Sept). *Silver Jubilee. T* **130** *and similar vert designs. Multicoloured.* (*a*) *Sheet stamps. P* 14 (7 Feb).

526	10 c. Type **130**..	..	..	..	10	10
527	30 c. Royal Visit, 1966	..	..	10	10
528	50 c. The Queen enthroned	..	..	15	15
529	90 c. The Queen after Coronation	..	15	25
530	$2.50, Queen and Prince Charles..	..	30	55
526/30				*Set of* 5	60	95
MS531	116×78 mm. $5 Queen and Prince Philip	65	85
	a. Error. Imperf	..	..	..	£350	

(*b*) *Booklet stamps. Roul* 5 × *imperf* (50 c.) *or imperf* ($5).* *Self-adhesive* (26 Sept)

532	50 c. Design as No. 529 (24 × 42 *mm*)	35	60
	a. Booklet pane of 6..				1·75	
533	$5 Design as stamp from No. **MS531**		
	(24 × 42 *mm*)			..	2·00	3·50
	a. Booklet pane of 1..				2·00	

*No. 532 was separated by various combinations of rotary knife (giving a straight edge) and roulette. No. 533 exists only with straight edges.

Stamps as Nos. 526/30 but perforated 11½ × 12, come from sheets of 5 stamps and 1 label. These were not placed on sale by the Antigua Post Office.

131 Making Camp   **132** Carnival Costume

(Des J.W. Litho Questa)

1977 (23 May). *Caribbean Scout Jamboree, Jamaica. T* **131** *and similar horiz designs. Multicoloured. P* 14.

534	½ c. Type **131** ..	..	..	..	10	10
535	1 c. Hiking	..	..	..	10	10
536	2 c. Rock-climbing	..	..	..	10	10
537	10 c. Cutting logs	..	..	..	15	10
538	30 c. Map and sign reading	..	..	40	10
539	50 c. First aid	..	..	..	65	25
540	$2 Rafting	..	..	..	1·75	2·25
534/40				*Set of* 7	2·75	2·50
MS541	127 × 114 mm. Nos. 538/40 ..	..	3·75	3·75

1977. *Coil Stamps. As Nos.* 257/9, *but W w* 14 (*inverted on* 10 c.). *P* 14½×14.

541a	89	5 c. blue	..	..	5·00	
541b		10 c. emerald	..	..	—	50
541c		25 c. crimson ..	..	..	9·00	

(Des C. Abbott. Litho Walsall)

1977 (18 July). *21st Anniv of Carnival. T* **132** *and similar vert designs. Multicoloured. P* 14.

542	10 c. Type **132** ..	..	..	..	10	10
543	30 c. Carnival Queen	..	..	..	20	10
544	50 c. Butterfly costume	..	..	25	15
545	90 c. Queen of the band	..	..	35	25
546	$1 Calypso King and Queen	..	35	30
542/6				*Set of* 5	1·10	95
MS547	140 × 120 mm. Nos. 542/6	..	1·10	1·60

ROYAL VISIT
28th OCTOBER 1977

(**133**)   **134** "Virgin and Child Enthroned" (Tura)

1977 (17 Oct). *Royal Visit. Nos.* 526/531 *optd with T* **133**. *P* 14.

548	10 c. Type **130**..	..	..	..	10	10
549	30 c. Royal Visit, 1966	..	..	10	10
550	50 c. The Queen enthroned	..	..	15	10
551	90 c. The Queen after Coronation	..	25	20
552	$2.50, Queen and Prince Charles..	..	45	35
548/52				*Set of* 5	80	65
MS553	116 × 78 mm. $5 Queen and Prince Philip	80	1·00
	a. Opt double	..	..	..	50·00	

Nos. 548/52 also exist perf 11½×12 (*Price for set of 5 80p mint or used*) from additional sheetlets of five stamps and one label.

(Des M. Shamir. Litho Questa)

1977 (21 Nov). *Christmas. T* **134** *and similar vert designs showing "Virgin and Child" by the artists given. Multicoloured. P* 14.

554	½ c. Type **134** ..	..	..	..	10	10
555	1 c. Crivelli	..	..	..	10	10
556	2 c. Lotto	..	..	..	10	10
557	8 c. Pontormo..	..	..	..	15	10
558	10 c. Tura (*different*)	..	..	15	10
559	25 c. Lotto (*different*)	..	..	30	10
560	$2 Crivelli (*different*)	..	..	85	60
554/60				*Set of* 7	1·50	75
MS561	144 × 118 mm. Nos. 557/60 ..	..	1·50	2·25

135 Pineapple

(Des and litho J.W.)

1977 (29 Dec). *Tenth Anniv of Statehood. T* **135** *and similar horiz designs. Multicoloured. P* 13.

562	10 c. Type **135** ..	..	..	..	10	10
563	15 c. State flag ..	..	..	..	10	10
564	50 c. Police band	..	..	..	2·00	80
565	90 c. Premier V. C. Bird	..	..	55	80
566	$2 State Coat of Arms	..	..	90	1·40
562/6				*Set of* 5	3·25	2·75
MS567	126 × 99 mm. Nos. 563/6. P 14 ..	..	3·25	2·75

136 Wright Glider III, 1902

(Des PAD Studio. Litho Questa)

1978 (23 Mar). *75th Anniv of Powered Flight. T* **136** *and similar multicoloured designs. P* 14.

568	½ c. Type **136** ..	..	..	..	10	10
569	1 c. Wright Flyer I, 1903 ..	..	..	10	10
570	2 c. Launch system and engine	..	10	10
571	10 c. Orville Wright (*vert*)	..	..	10	10
572	50 c. Wright Flyer III, 1905	..	..	40	15
573	90 c. Wilbur Wright (*vert*)	..	..	60	30
574	$2 Wright Type B, 1910	..	..	80	80
568/74				*Set of* 7	1·75	1·25
MS575	90×75 mm. $2.50, Wright Flyer I on launch system ..	..	..	..	1·25	2·50

137 Sunfish Regatta

(Des G. Drummond. Litho Format)

1978 (27 Apr). *Sailing Week. T* **137** *and similar horiz designs. Multicoloured. P* 15.

576	10 c. Type **137** ..	..	..	..	20	10
577	50 c. Fishing and work boat race	..	35	20
578	90 c. Curtain Bluff race	..	..	60	35
579	$2 Power boat rally	..	..	1·10	1·25
576/9				*Set of* 4	2·00	1·75
MS580	110 × 77 mm. $2.50, Guadeloupe–Antigua race	..	..	..	..	1·50	1·75

Nos. 576/9 exist imperforate from stock dispersed by the liquidator of Format International Security Printers Ltd.

138 Queen Elizabeth and Prince Philip   **139** Glass Coach

(Des J.W. Litho Questa (Nos. 581/6); Manufactured by Walsall (Nos. 587/9))

1978 (2 June). *25th Anniv of Coronation. Multicoloured.* (*a*) *Sheet stamps. Vert designs as T* **138**. *P* 14.

581	10 c. Type **138** ..	..	..	..	10	10
582	30 c. Crowning	..	..	..	10	10
583	50 c. Coronation procession	..	..	15	10
584	90 c. Queen seated in St. Edward's Chair	20	15
585	$2.50, Queen wearing Imperial State Crown	40	40
581/5				*Set of* 5	65	65
MS586	114 × 104 mm. $5 Queen and Prince Philip	80	80

(*b*) *Booklet stamps. Horiz design as T* **139** *showing State Coaches. Imperf* ($5) *or roul* 5 × *imperf*.* *Self-adhesive.*

587	25 c. Type **139** ..	..	..	..	15	30
	a. Booklet pane. Nos. 587/8 × 3	..	1·25	
588	50 c. Irish State Coach	..	..	25	50
589	$5 Coronation Coach	..	..	1·75	3·00
	a. Booklet pane of 1..				1·75	
587/9				*Set of* 3	2·00	3·50

Nos. 587/9 also exist perf 12 (*Price for set of 5 65p mint or used*) from additional sheetlets of three stamps and one label. These stamps have changed background colours.

*Nos. 587/8 were separated by various combinations of rotary-knife (giving a straight edge) and roulette. No. 589 exists only with straight edges.

140 Player running with Ball   **141** Petrea

(Des BG Studio. Litho Format)

1978 (17 Aug). *World Cup Football Championship, Argentina. T* **140** *and similar vert designs. Multicoloured.* P 14½.
590 10 c. Type **140** 15 10
591 15 c. Players in front of goal 15 10
592 $3 Referee and player .. .. 2·00 1·75
590/2 *Set of 3* 2·00 1·75
MS593 126 × 88 mm. 25 c. Player crouching with ball; 30 c. Players heading ball; 50 c. Players running with ball; $2 Goalkeeper diving. (*All horiz*) .. .. 3·00 2·50
Nos. 590/2 were each printed in small sheets of 6 including 1 *se-tenant* stamp-size label.
Nos. 590/2 exist imperforate from stock dispersed by the liquidator of Format International Security Printers Ltd.

(Des G. Drummond. Litho Questa)

1978 (5 Oct). *Flowers. T* **141** *and similar vert designs. Multicoloured.* P 14.
594 25 c. Type **141** 25 10
595 50 c. Sunflower 35 20
596 90 c. Frangipani 60 30
597 $2 Passion Flower .. .. 1·25 1·10
594/7 *Set of 4* 2·25 1·40
MS598 118 × 85 mm. $2.50, Hibiscus .. 1·40 1·60

142 "St Ildefonso receiving the Chasuble from the Virgin" (Rubens) 143 1d. Stamp of 1863

(Des BG Studio. Litho Questa)

1978 (30 Oct). *Christmas Paintings. T* **142** *and similar horiz designs. Multicoloured.* P 14.
599 8 c. Type **142** 10 10
600 25 c. "The Flight of St. Barbara" (Rubens) .. 20 10
601 $2 "Madonna and Child, with St. Joseph, John the Baptist and Donor" (Sebastiano del Piombo*) 65 55
599/601 *Set of 3* 80 60
MS602 170 × 113 mm. $4 "The Annunciation" (Rubens) .. .. .. 2·00 2·25
*The work is incorrectly attributed to Rubens on the stamp.

(Des G. Vasarhelyi. Litho Questa)

1979 (12 Feb). *Death Centenary of Sir Rowland Hill. T* **143** *and similar vert designs. Multicoloured.* P 14.
603 25 c. Type **143** 10 10
604 50 c. Penny Black 20 15
605 $1 Stage-coach and woman posting letter, *circa* 1840 .. .. .. 30 20
606 $2 Modern mail transport .. .. 1·10 60
603/6 *Set of 4* 1·50 85
MS607 108 × 82 mm. $2.50, Sir Rowland Hill 80 90
Nos. 603/6 also exist perf 12 (*Price for set of 4 £1.75 mint or used*) from additional sheetlets of five stamps and one label.

144 "The Deposition from the Cross" (painting) 145 Toy Yacht and Child's Hand

(Des BG Studio. Litho Questa)

1979 (15 Mar). *Easter. Works by Dürer. T* **144** *and similar vert designs.* P 14.
608 10 c. multicoloured 10 10
609 50 c. multicoloured 35 20
610 $4 black, magenta and greenish yellow 1·25 90
608/10 *Set of 3* 1·50 1·00
MS611 114 × 99 mm. $2.50, multicoloured .. 80 80
Designs:—50 c.; $2.50, "Christ on the Cross—The Passion" (wood engravings) (*both different*); $4 "Man of Sorrows with Hands Raised" (wood engraving).

(Des M. Rubin. Litho Questa)

1979 (9 Apr). *International Year of the Child. T* **145** *and similar vert designs showing toys and hands of children of different races. Multicoloured.* P 14.
612 25 c. Type **145** 10 10
613 50 c. Rocket 25 15
614 90 c. Car 40 25
615 $2 Train .. .. 1·00 90
612/15 *Set of 4* 1·60 1·25
MS616 80 × 112 mm. $5 Aeroplane .. 1·50 1·50

146 Yellow Jack 147 Cook's Birthplace, Marton

(Des P. Powell. Litho Questa)

1979 (14 May). *Fishes. T* **146** *and similar horiz designs. Multicoloured.* P 14½ × 14.
617 30 c. Type **146** 40 15
618 50 c. Blue-finned Tuna 50 25
619 90 c. Sailfish 75 40
620 $3 Wahoo .. .. .. 2·25 1·75
617/20 *Set of 4* 3·50 2·25
MS621 122×75 mm. $2.50, Great Barracuda .. 1·50 1·40

(Des J.W. Litho Questa)

1979 (2 July). *Death Bicentenary of Captain Cook. T* **147** *and similar vert designs. Multicoloured.* P 14.
622 25 c. Type **147** 55 25
623 50 c. H.M.S. *Endeavour* 75 60
624 90 c. Marine chronometer 75 80
625 $3 Landing at Botany Bay .. 1·60 2·75
622/5 *Set of 4* 3·25 4·00
MS626 110 × 85 mm. $2.50, H.M.S. *Resolution* .. 2·25 2·00

148 The Holy Family 149 Javelin Throwing

1979 (1 Oct). *Christmas. T* **148** *and similar vert designs. Multicoloured.* P 14.
627 8 c. Type **148** 10 10
628 25 c. Virgin and Child on Ass.. .. 15 10
629 50 c. Shepherd and star 30 35
630 $4 Wise Men with gifts .. 1·10 2·25
627/30 *Set of 4* 1·50 2·50
MS631 113 × 94 mm. $3 Angel with trumpet. P 12 1·00 1·50

(Des Design Images Inc. Litho Questa)

1980 (18 Feb). *Olympic Games, Moscow. T* **149** *and similar multicoloured designs.* P 14.
632 10 c. Type **149** 15 10
633 25 c. Running 20 10
634 $1 Pole vaulting 50 50
635 $2 Hurdling .. .. .. 80 1·25
632/5 *Set of 4* 1·50 1·75
MS636 127 × 96 mm. $3 Boxing (*horiz*) .. 65 90

150 Mickey Mouse and Aeroplane (151)

(Litho Format)

1980 (24 Mar). *International Year of the Child* (1979). *Walt Disney Cartoon Characters. T* **150** *and similar multicoloured designs showing characters and transport.* P 11.
637 ½ c. Type **150** 10 10
638 1 c. Donald Duck driving car .. 10 10
639 2 c. Goofy driving taxi 10 10
640 3 c. Mickey Mouse on motorcycle with Minnie Mouse in sidecar 10 10
641 4 c. Huey, Dewey and Louie riding cycle .. 10 10
642 5 c. Grandma Duck, chickens and pickup truck 10 10
643 10 c. Mickey Mouse driving jeep (*vert*) .. 10 10
644 $1 Chip and Dale in sailing boat .. 1·75 1·90
645 $4 Donald Duck riding toy train (*vert*) 3·75 5·50
637/45 *Set of 9* 5·50 7·00
MS646 101 × 127 mm. $2.50, Goofy flying biplane. P 14 × 13½ .. 4·50 3·25
See also Nos. 671/80.

1980 (6 May). *"London 1980" International Stamp Exhibition.* Nos. 603/6 optd with *T* **151**. P 12.
647 25 c. Type **143** 20 15
648 50 c. Penny Black 30 35
649 $1 Stage-coach and woman posting letter, *circa* 1840 .. .. 55 60
650 $2 Modern mail transport .. 2·50 2·75
647/50 *Set of 4* 3·25 3·50

152 "David" (statue, Donatello) 153 Rotary International 75th Anniversary Emblem and Headquarters, U.S.A.

(Des J.W. Litho Questa)

1980 (23 June). *Famous Works of Art. T* **152** *and similar multi coloured designs.* P 13½.
651 10 c. Type **152** 10 10
652 30 c. "The Birth of Venus" (painting, Sandro Botticelli) (*horiz*) 30 15
653 50 c. "Reclining Couple" (sarcophagus), Cerveteri (*horiz*) 45 40
654 90 c. "The Garden of Earthly Delights" (painting, Hieronymus Bosch) (*horiz*) 65 65
655 $1 "Portinari Altarpiece" (painting, Hugo van der Goes) (*horiz*) .. 75 75
656 $4 "Eleanora of Toledo and her Son Giovanni de'Medici" (painting, Agnolo Bronzino) .. 2·25 3·00
651/6 *Set of 6* 4·00 4·50
MS657 99 × 124 mm. $5 "The Holy Family" (painting, Rembrandt) .. .. 2·50 2·25

(Des G. Vasarhelyi. Litho Questa)

1980 (21 July). *75th Anniv of Rotary International. T* **153** *and similar horiz designs. Multicoloured.* P 14.
658 30 c. Type **153** 30 30
659 50 c. Rotary anniversary emblem and Antigua Rotary Club banner 40 50
660 90 c. Map of Antigua and Rotary emblem 60 70
661 $3 Paul P. Harris (founder) and Rotary emblem .. .. .. 2·00 3·25
658/61 *Set of 4* 3·00 4·25
MS662 102 × 78 mm. $5 Antiguan flags and Rotary emblems .. .. .. 1·25 2·00

154 Queen Elizabeth the Queen Mother 155 Ringed Kingfisher

(Des G. Vasarhelyi. Litho Questa)

1980 (4 Aug). *80th Birthday of Queen Elizabeth the Queen Mother.* P 14.
663 **154** 10 c. multicoloured 20 10
664 $2.50, multicoloured .. .. 1·10 1·75
MS665 68 × 90 mm. **154** $3 multicoloured. P 12 1·25 2·00

(Des Jennifer Toombs. Litho Questa)

1980 (3 Nov). *Birds. T* **155** *and similar vert designs. Multicoloured.* P 14.
666 10 c. Type **155** 50 25
667 30 c. Plain Pigeon 75 40
668 $1 Green-throated Carib .. 1·50 1·50
669 $2 Black-necked Stilt .. .. 2·00 2·75
666/9 *Set of 4* 4·25 4·50
MS670 73 × 73 mm. $2.50, Roseate Tern .. 4·75 4·50

(Litho Format)

1980 (23 Dec). *Christmas. Scenes from Walt Disney's Cartoon Film "Sleeping Beauty". Horiz designs as T* **150**. P 11.
671 ½ c. multicoloured 10 10
672 1 c. multicoloured 10 10
673 2 c. multicoloured 10 10
674 4 c. multicoloured 10 10
675 8 c. multicoloured 10 10
676 10 c. multicoloured 15 10
677 25 c. multicoloured 20 20
678 $2 multicoloured .. .. 2·25 2·25
679 $2.50, multicoloured .. .. 2·50 2·50
671/9 *Set of 9* 4·75 4·50
MS680 126 × 101 mm. $4 multicoloured (*vert*) P 13½ × 14 .. .. 5·00 3·25

156 Diesel Locomotive No. 15

(Des G. Drummond. Litho Questa)

1981 (12 Jan). *Sugar Cane Railway Locomotives. T* **156** *and similar horiz designs. Multicoloured. P* 14.
681	25 c. Type **156**		15	15
682	50 c. Narrow-gauge steam locomotive		30	30
683	90 c. Diesel locomotives Nos. 1 and 10		55	60
684	$3 Steam locomotive hauling sugar cane		2·00	2·25
681/4		*Set of 4*	2·75	3·00
MS685	82 × 111 mm. $2.50, Antigua sugar factory, railway yard and sheds		1·75	1·75

"INDEPENDENCE 1981"
(157)   158 "Pipes of Pan"

1981 (31 Mar). *Independence. Optd with T* **157**. A. *On Nos.* 475A, 478A, 480A *and* 484A/6A. B. *On Nos.* 475B/6B *and* 478B/86B.
		A		B	
686	6 c. Orchid Tree	60	60	10	10
687	10 c. Bougainvillea	†		10	10
688	20 c. Flamboyant	60	60	10	10
689	25 c. Hibiscus	15	15	15	15
690	35 c. Flame of the Wood	1·25	1·25	20	20
691	50 c. Cannon at Fort James	†		35	35
692	75 c. Premier's Office	†		40	40
693	$1 Potworks Dam	†		55	55
694	$2.50, Irrigation Scheme, Diamond Estate	3·00	4·00	1·25	1·25
695	$5 Government House	5·00	7·50	2·50	2·50
696	$10 Coolidge Airport	7·50	11·00	3·50	5·00
686A/96A	*Set of 6*	15·00	22·00	†	
686B/96B	*Set of 11*	†		8·00	9·50

(Des J.W. Litho Questa)

1981 (5 May). *Birth Centenary of Picasso. T* **158** *and similar vert designs. Multicoloured. P* 14.
697	10 c. Type **158**		10	10
698	50 c. "Seated Harlequin"		30	30
699	90 c. "Paulo as Harlequin"		55	55
700	$4 "Mother and Child"		2·50	2·50
697/700		*Set of 4*	3·00	3·00
MS701	115 × 140 mm. $5 "Three Musicians" (detail)		2·75	2·75

159 Prince Charles and Lady Diana Spencer   160 Prince of Wales at Investiture, 1969

(Des J.W. Litho Questa)

1981 (23 June). *Royal Wedding. T* **159** *and similar vert designs. Multicoloured. P* 14.
702	25 c. Type **159**		10	10
703	50 c. Glamis Castle		10	10
704	$4 Prince Charles skiing		80	80
702/4		*Set of 3*	80	80
MS705	96 × 82 mm. $5 Glass Coach		80	80

Nos. 702/4 also exist perforated 12 (*Price for set of 3 80p mint or used*) from additional sheetlets of five stamps and one label. These stamps have changed background colours.

(Manufactured by Walsall)

1981 (23 June). *Royal Wedding. Booklet stamps. T* **160** *and similar vert designs. Multicoloured* ($5) *or black and flesh* (*others*). *Roul* 5 × *imperf*. *Self-adhesive.*
706	25 c. Type **160**		15	25
	a. Booklet pane. Nos. 706/11		1·50	
707	25 c. Prince Charles as baby, 1948		15	25
708	$1 Prince Charles at R.A.F. College, Cranwell, 1971		25	50
709	$1 Prince Charles attending Hill House School, 1956		25	50
710	$2 Prince Charles and Lady Diana Spencer		50	75
711	$2 Prince Charles at Trinity College, 1967		50	75
712	$5 Prince Charles and Lady Diana (*different*)		1·00	1·50
	a. Booklet pane of 1.		1·00	
706/12		*Set of 7*	2·50	4·00

*The 25 c. to $2 values were each separated by various combinations of rotary knife (giving a straight edge) and roulette. The $5 value exists only with straight edges.

161 Irene Joshua (founder)   162 Antigua and Barbuda Coat of Arms

(Des M. Diamond. Litho Format)

1981 (28 Oct). *50th Anniv of Antigua Girl Guide Movement. T* **161** *and similar horiz designs. Multicoloured. P* 14½.
713	10 c. Type **161**		15	10
714	50 c. Campfire sing-song		45	35
715	90 c. Sailing		75	65
716	$2.50, Animal tending		1·75	2·00
713/16		*Set of 4*	2·75	2·75
MS717	110 × 85 mm. $5 Raising the flag		5·50	3·50

INDEPENDENT

Nos. 718/22 and 733 onwards are inscribed "ANTIGUA & BARBUDA".

(Des E. Henry. Litho Format)

1981 (1 Nov). *Independence. T* **162** *and similar multicoloured designs. P* 14½.
718	10 c. Type **162**		15	10
719	50 c. Pineapple, Antigua flag and map		35	20
720	90 c. Prime Minister Vere Bird		55	55
721	$2.50, St. John's Cathedral (38×25 mm)		1·25	2·25
718/21		*Set of 4*	2·10	2·75
MS722	105×79 mm. $5 Map of Antigua and Barbuda (42×42 mm)		3·75	2·75

163 "Holy Night" (Jacques Stella)   164 Swimming

(Des Clover Mill. Litho Format)

1981 (16 Nov). *Christmas. Paintings. T* **163** *and similar vert designs. Multicoloured. P* 14½.
723	8 c. Type **163**		15	10
724	30 c. "Mary with Child" (Julius Schnorr von Carolfeld)		40	15
725	$1 "Virgin and Child" (Alonso Cano)		1·00	90
726	$3 "Virgin and Child" (Lorenzo di Credi)		1·75	3·75
723/6		*Set of 4*	3·00	4·25
MS727	77 × 111 mm. $5 "Holy Family" (Pieter von Avon)		3·00	5·50

(Des M. Diamond. Litho Format)

1981 (1 Dec). *International Year for Disabled Persons. Sport for the Disabled. T* **164** *and similar horiz designs. Multicoloured. P* 15.
728	10 c. Type **164**		10	10
729	50 c. Discus throwing		20	30
730	90 c. Archery		40	50
731	$2 Baseball		1·25	1·40
728/31		*Set of 4*	1·75	2·10
MS732	108 × 84 mm. $4 Basketball		5·00	2·75

165 Scene from Football Match   166 Airbus Industrie A300

(Des Clover Mill. Litho Questa)

1982 (15 Apr). *World Cup Football Championship, Spain. T* **165** *and similar horiz designs showing scenes from different matches. P* 14.
733	10 c. multicoloured		20	10
734	50 c. multicoloured		50	35
735	90 c. multicoloured		80	70
736	$4 multicoloured		3·50	3·50
733/6		*Set of 4*	4·50	4·25
MS737	75 × 92 mm. $5 multicoloured		7·00	8·00

Nos. 733/6 also exist perforated 12 (*Price for set of 4, £4.50 mint or used*) from additional sheetlets of five stamps and one label. These stamps have changed inscription colours.

(Des Clover Mill. Litho Format)

1982 (17 June). *Coolidge International Airport. T* **166** *and similar multicoloured designs. P* 14½.
738	10 c. Type **166**		10	10
739	50 c. Hawker Siddeley H.S. 748		30	30
740	90 c. De Havilland D.H.C.6 Twin Otter		60	60
741	$2.50, Britten Norman Islander		1·75	1·75
738/41		*Set of 4*	2·50	2·50
MS742	99×73 mm. $5 Boeing 747-100 (*horiz*)		3·25	3·75

167 Cordia

(Des G. Drummond. Litho Questa)

1982 (28 June). *Death Centenary of Charles Darwin. Fauna and Flora. T* **167** *and similar multicoloured designs. P* 15.
743	10 c. Type **167**.		15	10
744	50 c. Small Indian Mongoose (*horiz*)		45	40
745	90 c. Corallita		75	75
746	$3 Mexican Bulldog Bat (*horiz*)		2·00	3·25
743/6		*Set of 4*	3·00	4·00
MS747	107×85 mm. $5 Caribbean Monk Seal		6·50	8·00

168 Queen's House, Greenwich   169 Princess of Wales

(Des PAD Studio. Litho Questa)

1982 (1 July). *21st Birthday of Princess of Wales. T* **168/9** *and similar vert design. Multicoloured. P* 14½ × 14.
748	90 c. Type **168**		45	45
749	$1 Prince and Princess of Wales		50	50
750	$4 Princess Diana (*different*)		2·00	2·00
748/50		*Set of 3*	2·75	2·75
MS751	102 × 75 mm. $5 Type **169**		2·40	2·50

Nos. 748/50 also exist in sheetlets of 5 stamps and 1 label.

170 Boy Scouts decorating Streets for Independence Parade   ROYAL BABY 21.6.82 (171)

(Des J.W. Litho Questa)

1982 (15 July). *75th Anniv of Boy Scout Movement. T* **170** *and similar horiz designs. Multicoloured. P* 14.
752	10 c. Type **170**		20	10
753	50 c. Boy Scout giving helping hand during street parade		50	40
754	90 c. Boy Scouts attending Princess Margaret at Independence Ceremony		85	75
755	$2.20, Cub Scout giving directions to tourists		1·75	2·75
752/5		*Set of 4*	3·00	3·50
MS756	102 × 72 mm. $5 Lord Baden-Powell		7·50	7·00

1982 (30 Aug). *Birth of Prince William of Wales. Nos.* 748/51 *optd with T* **171**.
757	90 c. Type **168**		45	45
758	$1 Prince and Princess of Wales		50	50
759	$4 Princess Diana (*different*)		2·00	2·00
757/9		*Set of 3*	2·75	2·75
MS760	102 × 75 mm. $5 Type **169**		2·40	2·50

Nos. 757/9 also exist in sheetlets of 5 stamps and 1 label.

172 Roosevelt in 1940

(Des PAD Studio. Litho Format)

1982 (20 Sept). *Birth Centenary of Franklin D. Roosevelt (Nos. 761, 763, 765/6 and MS767) and 250th Birth Anniv of George Washington (others). T 172 and similar multicoloured designs. P 15.*

761	10 c. Type 172				20	10
762	25 c. Washington as blacksmith				45	15
763	45 c. Churchill, Roosevelt and Stalin at Yalta Conference				1·00	40
764	60 c. Washington crossing the Delaware (*vert*)				1·00	40
765	$1 "Roosevelt Special" train (*vert*)				1·25	90
766	$3 Portrait of Roosevelt (*vert*)				1·40	2·40
761/6				*Set of 6*	4·75	3·75
MS767	92 × 87 mm. $4 Roosevelt and Wife				2·50	2·25
MS768	92 × 87 mm. $4 Portrait of Washington (*vert*)				2·50	2·25

173 "Annunciation"

(Des Design Images. Litho Questa)

1982 (Nov). *Christmas. Religious Paintings by Raphael. T 173 and similar horiz designs. Multicoloured. P 14 × 13½.*

769	10 c. Type 173				10	10
770	30 c. "Adoration of the Magi"				15	15
771	$1 "Presentation at the Temple"				50	50
772	$4 "Coronation of the Virgin"				2·10	2·25
769/72				*Set of 4*	2·50	2·75
MS773	95 × 124 mm. $5 "Marriage of the Virgin"				2·75	2·50

174 Tritons and Dolphins   175 Pineapple Produce

(Des Design Images. Litho Format)

1983 (28 Jan). *500th Birth Anniv of Raphael. Details from "Galatea" Fresco. T 174 and similar multicoloured designs. P 14½.*

774	45 c. Type 174				20	25
775	50 c. Sea Nymph carried off by Triton				25	30
776	60 c. Winged angel steering Dolphins (*horiz*)				30	35
777	$4 Cupids shooting arrows (*horiz*)				1·90	2·00
774/7				*Set of 4*	2·40	2·50
MS778	101 × 125 mm. $5 Galatea pulled along by Dolphins				2·50	2·75

(Des Artists International. Litho Questa)

1983 (14 Mar). *Commonwealth Day. T 175 and similar horiz designs. Multicoloured. P 14.*

779	25 c. Type 175				15	15
780	45 c. Carnival				20	25
781	60 c. Tourism				30	35
782	$3 Airport				1·00	1·50
779/82				*Set of 4*	1·50	2·00

176 T.V. Satellite Coverage of Royal Wedding

(Des PAD Studio. Litho Questa)

1983 (5 Apr). *World Communications Year. T 176 and similar horiz designs. Multicoloured. P 14.*

783	15 c. Type 176				40	20
784	50 c. Police communications				2·25	1·50
785	60 c. House-to-train telephone call				2·25	1·50
786	$3 Satellite earth station with planets Jupiter and Saturn				4·75	5·00
783/6				*Set of 4*	8·50	7·50
MS787	100 × 90 mm. $5 "Comsat" satellite over West Indies				3·25	3·75

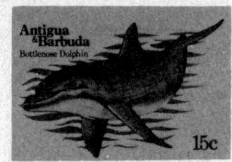

177 Bottle-nosed Dolphin

(Des D. Miller. Litho Format)

1983 (9 May). *Whales. T 177 and similar horiz designs. Multicoloured. P 14½.*

788	15 c. Type 177				85	20
789	50 c. Fin Whale				1·75	1·25
790	60 c. Bowhead Whale				2·00	1·25
791	$3 Spectacled Porpoise				3·75	4·25
788/91				*Set of 4*	7·50	6·25
MS792	122 × 101 mm. $5 Narwhal				8·50	6·00

Nos. 788/92 exist imperforate from stock dispersed by the liquidator of Format International Security Printers Ltd.

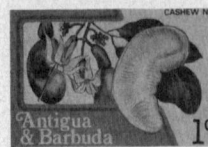

178 Cashew Nut

(Des J.W. Litho Questa)

1983 (11 July)–85. *Fruits and Flowers. T 178 and similar horiz designs. Multicoloured. A. P 14. B. P 12.*

			A		B	
793	1 c. Type 178		15	50	20	50
794	2 c. Passion Fruit		15	50	20	50
795	3 c. Mango		15	50	20	50
796	5 c. Grapefruit		20	30	30	30
797	10 c. Pawpaw		40	20	30	20
798	15 c. Breadfruit		50	20	50	20
799	20 c. Coconut		50	20	60	20
800	25 c. Oleander		55	30	60	20
801	30 c. Banana		60	40	75	30
802	40 c. Pineapple		70	40	75	30
803	45 c. Cordia		80	55	85	40
804	50 c. Cassia		90	60	1·25	50
805	60 c. Poui		1·50	1·00	1·25	1·10
806	$1 Frangipani		2·25	1·75	2·25	1·25
807	$2 Flamboyant		3·75	3·75	3·25	3·75
808	$2.50, Lemon		4·50	5·50	3·75	4·50
809	$5 Lignum Vitae		7·00	10·00	6·00	10·00
810	$10 National flag and coat of arms		11·00	15·00	9·50	15·00
793A/810A		*Set of 18*	32·00	38·00		
793B/810B		*Set of 18*			29·00	35·00

Dates of issue: 11.7.83, Nos. 793A/810A; 3.85, Nos. 793B/806B, 810B; 12.85, 807B/9B.

179 Dornier Do X Flying Boat

(Des W. Wright. Litho Format)

1983 (15 Aug). *Bicentenary of Manned Flight. T 179 and similar horiz designs. Multicoloured. P 14½.*

811	30 c. Type 179				75	30
812	50 c. Supermarine S6B seaplane				90	60
813	60 c. Curtiss F-9C Sparrowhawk biplane and airship U.S.S. Akron				1·00	85
814	$4 Hot-air balloon *Pro Juventute*				3·00	5·00
811/14				*Set of 4*	5·00	6·00
MS815	80×105 mm. $5 Airship LZ-127 *Graf Zeppelin*				2·50	3·25

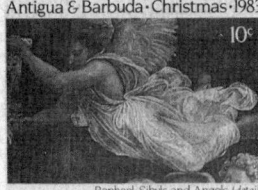

Antigua & Barbuda · Christmas · 1983

180 "Sibyls and Angels" (detail) (Raphael)

(Des W. Wright. Litho Format)

1983 (4 Oct). *Christmas. 500th Birth Anniv of Raphael. T 180 and similar designs. P 13½.*

816	10 c. multicoloured				30	20
817	30 c. multicoloured				65	35
818	$1 multicoloured				1·50	1·25
819	$4 multicoloured				4·00	5·00
816/19				*Set of 4*	5·75	6·25
MS820	101 × 131 mm. $5 multicoloured				1·50	2·25

Designs: *Horiz*—10 c. to $4 Different details from "Sibyls and Angels". *Vert*—$5 "The Vision of Ezekiel".

181 John Wesley (founder)   182 Discus

(Des M. Diamond. Litho Questa)

1983 (7 Nov). *Bicentenary of Methodist Church (1984). T 181 and similar vert designs. Multicoloured. P 14.*

821	15 c. Type 181				25	15
822	50 c. Nathaniel Gilbert (founder in Antigua)				70	50
823	60 c. St. John Methodist Church steeple				75	65
824	$3 Ebenezer Methodist Church, St. John's				2·50	4·00
821/4				*Set of 4*	3·75	4·75

(Des Artists International. Litho Format)

1984 (9 Jan). *Olympic Games, Los Angeles. T 182 and similar vert designs. Multicoloured. P 14½.*

825	25 c. Type 182				20	15
826	50 c. Gymnastics				35	40
827	90 c. Hurdling				65	70
828	$3 Cycling				2·25	3·50
825/8				*Set of 4*	3·00	4·25
MS829	82 × 67 mm. $5 Volleyball				2·75	3·00

183 *Booker Vanguard*   184 Chenille
(freighter)

(Des Artists International. Litho Format)

1984 (14 June). *Ships. T 183 and similar multicoloured designs. P 15.*

830	45 c. Type 183				1·25	55
831	50 c. S.S. *Canberra* (liner)				1·50	80
832	60 c. Sailing boats				1·75	1·00
833	$4 *Fairwind* (cargo liner)				4·00	7·00
830/3				*Set of 4*	7·50	8·50
MS834	107×80 mm. $5 Eighteenth-century British man-of-war (*vert*)				1·75	3·50

Nos. 830/3 exist imperforate from stock dispersed by the liquidator of Format International Security Printers Ltd.

(Des J.W. Litho Format)

1984 (19 June). *Universal Postal Union Congress, Hamburg. T 184 and similar vert designs showing flowers. Multicoloured. P 15.*

835	15 c. Type 184				40	15
836	50 c. Shell Flower				1·00	70
837	60 c. Anthurium				1·10	1·10
838	$3 Angels Trumpet				4·00	6·50
835/8				*Set of 4*	6·00	7·50
MS839	100 × 75 mm. $5 Crown of Thorns				1·50	3·25

Nos. 835/9 exist imperforate from stock dispersed by the liquidator of Format International Security Printers Ltd.

$2

(185)   (186)

1984 (25 June). (*a*) *Nos. 702/5 surch with T 185*

840	$2 on 25 c. Type 159				3·00	3·00
841	$2 on 50 c. Glamis Castle				3·00	3·00
842	$2 on $4 Prince Charles skiing				3·00	3·00
840/2				*Set of 3*	8·00	8·00
MS843	96 × 82 mm. $2 on $5 Glass Coach				4·00	4·00

(*b*) *Nos. 748/51 surch with T 186*

844	$2 on 90 c. Type 168 (Gold)*				2·40	2·25
845	$2 on $1 Prince and Princess of Wales (Gold)*				2·40	2·25
846	$2 on $4 Princess Diana (*different*) (Gold)*				2·40	2·25
844/6				*Set of 3*	6·50	6·00
MS847	102 × 75 mm. $2 on $5 Type 169 (Gold)				4·00	4·00

(*c*) *Nos. 757/60 surch with T 186*

848	$2 on 90 c. Type 168 (Gold)*				2·40	2·25
849	$2 on $1 Prince and Princess of Wales (Gold)*				2·40	2·25
850	$2 on $4 Princess Diana (*different*) (Gold)*				2·40	2·25
848/50				*Set of 3*	6·50	6·00
MS851	102 × 75 mm. $2 on $5 Type 169 (Gold)				4·00	4·00

(*d*) *Nos. 779/82 surch as T 185*

852	$2 on 25 c. Type 175				1·75	1·25
853	$2 on 45 c. Carnival				1·75	1·25
854	$2 on 60 c. Tourism				1·75	1·25
855	$2 on $3 Airport				1·75	1·25
852/5				*Set of 4*	4·50	4·50

*Nos. 844/6 and 848/50 also exist with similar surcharges in gold or silver on the sheetlets of five stamps and 1 label (*price for set of 3 as Nos. 844/6, £6 mint or used*) (*price for set of 3 as Nos. 848/50, £6 mint or used*).

187 Abraham Lincoln

188 View of Moravian Mission

(Des Liane Fried. Litho Questa)

1984 (18 July). *Presidents of the United States of America. T 187 and similar vert designs. Multicoloured. P 14.*

856	10 c. Type **187**	..	..	15	10
857	20 c. Harry Truman	..	..	20	15
858	30 c. Dwight Eisenhower	..	..	30	25
859	40 c. Ronald Reagan	..	..	50	30
860	90 c. Gettysburg Address, 1863	..		90	75
861	$1.10, Formation of N.A.T.O., 1949	..	1·25	1·10
862	$1.50, Eisenhower during Second World War	1·60	1·40
863	$2 Reagan and Caribbean Basin Initiative	1·75	1·75
856/63	..	..	*Set of 8*	6·00	5·00

(Des and litho Questa)

1984 (1 Aug). *150th Anniv of Abolition of Slavery. T 188 and similar horiz designs. Multicoloured. P 14.*

864	40 c. Type **188**	..	..	80	50
865	50 c. Antigua Courthouse, 1823	..	90	65
866	60 c. Planting sugar-cane, Monks Hill	..	95	75
867	$3 Boiling house, Delaps' estate	..	4·00	4·75
864/7	..	..	*Set of 4*	6·00	6·00
MS868	95 × 70 mm. $5 Loading sugar, Willoughby Bay			6·50	4·75

189 Rufous-sided Towhee

190 Grass-skiing

(Des Jennifer Toombs. Litho Format)

1984 (15 Aug). *Songbirds. T 189 and similar vert designs. Multicoloured. P 15.*

869	40 c. Type **189**	..	..	1·25	85
870	50 c. Parula Warbler	..	..	1·40	1·10
871	60 c. House Wren	..	..	1·50	1·50
872	$2 Ruby-crowned Kinglet	..	..	2·00	3·75
873	$3 Common Flicker	..	..	2·75	5·00
869/73	..	..	*Set of 5*	8·00	11·00
MS874	76 × 76 mm. $5 Yellow-breasted Chat		3·00	6·00

(Des Bonny Redecker. Litho Questa)

1984 (21 Sept). *"Ausipex" International Stamp Exhibition, Melbourne. Australian Sports. T 190 and similar vert designs. Multicoloured. P 14½.*

875	$1 Type **190**	..	..	1·50	1·50
876	$5 Australian Football	..	..	4·25	5·50
MS877	108 × 78 mm. $5 Boomerang-throwing	..	3·00	4·00

191 "The Virgin and Infant with Angels and Cherubs" (Correggio)

192 "The Blue Dancers" (Degas)

(Litho Format)

1984 (4 Oct). *450th Death Anniv of Correggio (painter). T 191 and similar vert designs. Multicoloured. P 15.*

878	25 c. Type **191**	..	..	40	20
879	60 c. "The Four Saints"	..	..	80	50
880	90 c. "St. Catherine"	..	..	1·10	90
881	$3 "The Campori Madonna"	..	..	2·75	3·75
878/81	..	..	*Set of 4*	4·50	4·75
MS882	90 × 60 mm. $5 "St. John the Baptist"		2·00	2·50

(Litho Format)

1984 (4 Oct). *150th Birth Anniv of Edgar Degas (painter). T 192 and similar multicoloured designs. P 15.*

883	15 c. Type **192**	..	..	35	15
884	50 c. "The Pink Dancers"	..	..	80	60
885	70 c. "Two Dancers"	..	..	1·10	95
886	$4 "Dancers at the Bar"	..	..	3·00	4·75
883/6	..	..	*Set of 4*	4·75	5·75
MS887	90 × 60 mm. $5 "The Folk Dancers" (40 × 27 mm)		2·00	2·50

193 Sir Winston Churchill

194 Donald Duck fishing

(Des J. Iskowitz. Litho Format)

1984 (19 Nov). *Famous People. T 193 and similar multicoloured designs. P 15.*

888	60 c. Type **193**.	..	..	1·10	1·50
889	60 c. Mahatma Gandhi	..	..	1·10	1·50
890	60 c. John F. Kennedy	..	..	1·10	1·50
891	60 c. Mao Tse-tung	..	..	1·10	1·50
892	$1 Churchill with General De Gaulle, Paris, 1944 (*horiz*)		1·25	1·75
893	$1 Gandhi leaving London by train, 1931 (*horiz*)		1·25	1·75
894	$1 Kennedy with Chancellor Adenauer and Mayor Brandt, Berlin, 1963 (*horiz*)		1·25	1·75
895	$1 Mao Tse-tung with Lin Piao, Peking, 1969 (*horiz*)		1·25	1·75
888/95	..	..	*Set of 8*	8·50	11·50
MS896	114 × 80 mm. $5 Flags of Great Britain, India, the United States and China		9·00	4·50

Nos. 890 and 893 exist imperforate from stock dispersed by the liquidator of Format International Security Printers Ltd.

(Litho Format)

1984 (26 Nov). *Christmas. 50th Birthday of Donald Duck. T 194 and similar multicoloured designs showing Walt Disney cartoon characters. P 11.*

897	1 c. Type **194**.	..	..	10	10
898	2 c. Donald Duck lying on beach	..	10	10
899	3 c. Donald Duck and nephews with fishing rods and fishes		10	10
900	4 c. Donald Duck and nephews in boat	..	10	10
901	5 c. Wearing diving masks	..	..	10	10
902	10 c. In deckchairs reading books	..	10	10
903	$1 With toy shark's fin	..	..	2·00	1·25
904	$2 In sailing boat	..	..	3·00	3·00
905	$5 Attempting to propel boat	..	5·00	6·00
897/905	..	..	*Set of 9*	9·50	9·50
MS906	Two sheets, each 125 × 100 mm. (a) $5 Nephews with crayon and paintbrushes (*horiz*). P 14 × 13½. (b) $5 Donald Duck in deckchair. P 13½ × 14	*Set of 2 sheets*	9·00	12·00

No. 904 was printed in sheetlets of 8 stamps.
Nos. 899/900 and 904 exist imperforate from stock dispersed by the liquidator of Format International Security Printers Ltd.

195 Torch from Statue in Madison Square Park, 1885

(Des J. Iskowitz. Litho Format)

1985 (7 Jan). *Centenary of the Statue of Liberty (1986) (1st issue). T 195 and similar multicoloured designs. P 15.*

907	25 c. Type **195**.	..	..	20	20
908	30 c. Statue of Liberty and scaffolding ("Restoration and Renewal") (*vert*)		20	20
909	50 c. Frederic Bartholdi (sculptor) supervising construction, 1876	..	30	30
910	90 c. Close-up of Statue	..	..	55	55
911	$1 Statue and cadet ship ("Operation Sail", 1976) (*vert*)		90	90
912	$3 Dedication ceremony, 1886	..	1·75	2·00
907/12	..	..	*Set of 6*	3·50	3·75
MS913	110 × 80 mm. $5 Port of New York	3·75	3·75

See also Nos. 1110/19.

196 Arawak Pot Sherd and Indians making Clay Utensils

(Des N. Waldman. Litho Format)

1985 (21 Jan). *Native American Artefacts. T 196 and similar designs. Multicoloured. P 15.*

914	15 c. Type **196**.	..	..	15	10
915	50 c. Arawak body design and Arawak Indians tattooing		30	40
916	60 c. Head of the god "Yocahu" and Indians harvesting manioc		40	50
917	$3 Carib war club and Carib Indians going into battle		1·75	2·50
914/17	..	..	*Set of 4*	2·40	3·25
MS918	97 × 68 mm. $5 Taino Indians worshipping stone idol		2·00	2·50

197 Triumph 2hp "Jap", 1903

(Des BG Studio. Litho Questa)

1985 (7 Mar). *Centenary of the Motorcycle. T 197 and similar horiz designs. Multicoloured. P 14.*

919	10 c. Type **197**.	..	..	65	15
920	30 c. Indian "Arrow", 1949	..	1·10	40
921	60 c. BMW "R100RS", 1976	..	1·60	1·25
922	$4 Harley-Davidson "Model II", 1916	5·50	6·00
919/22	..	..	*Set of 4*	8·00	7·00
MS923	90 × 93 mm. $5 Laverda "Jota", 1975	..	5·00	5·50

198 Slavonian Grebe

(Litho Questa)

1985 (25 Mar). *Birth Bicentenary of John J. Audubon (ornithologist) (1st issue). T 198 and similar multicoloured designs showing original paintings. P 14.*

924	90 c. Type **198**.	..	..	1·75	1·25
925	$1 British Storm Petrel	..	..	2·00	1·25
926	$1.50, Great Blue Heron	..	..	2·50	3·00
927	$3 Double-crested Cormorant	..	3·75	5·00
924/7	..	..	*Set of 4*	9·00	9·50
MS928	103 × 72 mm. $5 White-tailed Tropic Bird (*vert*)		7·00	4·75

Nos. 924/7 were each issued in sheetlets of five stamps and one stamp-size label, which appears in the centre of the bottom row. See also Nos. 990/4.

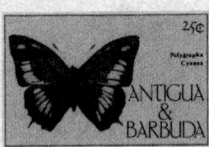

199 *Anaea cyanea*

(Des R. Sauber. Litho Questa)

1985 (16 Apr). *Butterflies. T 199 and similar horiz designs. Multicoloured. P 14.*

929	25 c. Type **199**	..	..	1·00	30
930	60 c. *Leodonta dysoni*	..	..	2·25	1·25
931	90 c. *Junea doraete*	..	..	2·75	1·50
932	$4 *Prepona pylene*	..	..	7·50	9·00
929/32	..	..	*Set of 4*	12·00	11·00
MS933	132 × 105 mm. $5 *Caerois gerdtrudtus*	..	4·50	6·00

200 Cessna 172D Skyhawk

201 Maimonides

(Des A. DiLorenzo. Litho Questa)

1985 (30 Apr). *40th Anniv of International Civil Aviation Organization. T 200 and similar horiz designs. Multicoloured. P 14.*

934	30 c. Type **200**	..	..	1·25	30
935	90 c. Fokker D.VII	..	..	2·75	1·25
936	$1.50, SPAD VII	..	..	3·75	2·50
937	$3 Boeing 747-100	..	..	5·50	6·50
934/7	..	..	*Set of 4*	12·00	9·50
MS938	97 × 83 mm. $5 De Havilland D.H.C.6 Twin Otter		4·50	5·50

(Des and litho Questa)

1985 (17 June). *850th Birth Anniv of Maimonides (physician, philosopher and scholar). P 14.*

939	**201** $2 bright green	..	..	4·00	3·25
MS940	70 × 84 mm. **201** $5 reddish brown	..	7·00	4·50

No. 939 was printed in sheetlets of 6 stamps.

ALTERED CATALOGUE NUMBERS

Any Catalogue numbers altered from the last edition are shown as a list in the introductory pages.

202 Young Farmers with Produce   203 The Queen Mother attending Church

(Des Susan David. Litho Questa)

1985 (1 July). *International Youth Year. T* **202** *and similar horiz designs. Multicoloured. P* 14.

941	25 c. Type **202**	20	20
942	50 c. Hotel management trainees	30	35
943	60 c. Girls with goat and boys with football ("Environment")	40	55
944	$3 Windsurfing ("Leisure")	1·75	2·50
941/4	*Set of* 4	2·40	3·25
MS945	102×72 mm. $5 Young people with Antiguan flags	2·75	3·00

(Des J.W. Litho Questa)

1985 (10 July). *Life and Times of Queen Elizabeth the Queen Mother. T* **203** *and similar vert designs. Multicoloured. P* 14.

946	$1 Type **203**	45	60
947	$1.50, Watching children playing in London garden	60	85
948	$2.50, The Queen Mother in 1979	90	1·40
946/8	*Set of* 3	1·75	2·50
MS949	56×85 mm. $5 With Prince Edward at Royal Wedding, 1981	3·00	3·00

Stamps as Nos. 946/8, but with face values of 90 c., $1 and $3, exist from additional sheetlets of 5 plus a label issued 13 January 1986. These also have changed background colours and are perforated 12×12½ (*price for set of 3 stamps £2 mint*).

204 Magnificent Frigate Bird   205 Girl Guides Nursing

(Des Mary Walters. Litho Questa)

1985 (1 Aug). *Marine Life. T* **204** *and similar vert designs. Multicoloured. P* 14.

950	15 c. Type **204**	1·00	30
951	45 c. Brain Coral	2·00	95
952	60 c. Cushion Star	2·25	1·75
953	$3 Spotted Moray	7·00	9·00
950/3	*Set of* 4	11·00	11·00
MS954	110×80 mm. $5 Elkhorn Coral	7·00	7·00

(Des Y. Berry. Litho Questa)

1985 (22 Aug). *75th Anniv of Girl Guide Movement. T* **205** *and similar horiz designs. Multicoloured. P* 14.

955	15 c. Type **205**	75	20
956	45 c. Open-air Girl Guide meeting	1·40	60
957	60 c. Lord and Lady Baden-Powell	1·75	90
958	$3 Girl Guides gathering flowers	4·25	4·50
955/8	*Set of* 4	7·50	5·75
MS959	67× 96 mm. $5 Barn Swallow (Nature study)	6·00	7·00

206 Bass Trombone   207 Flags of Great Britain and Antigua

(Des Susan David. Litho Questa)

1985 (26 Aug). *300th Birth Anniv of Johann Sebastian Bach (composer). T* **206** *and similar vert designs. P* 14.

960	25 c. multicoloured	1·40	55
961	50 c. multicoloured	1·75	1·10
962	$1 multicoloured	3·25	1·75
963	$3 multicoloured	6·00	7·00
960/3	*Set of* 4	11·00	9·50
MS964	104×73 mm. $5 black and brownish grey	4·50	4·75

Designs:—50 c. English horn; $1 Violino piccolo; $3 Bass rackett; $5 Johann Sebastian Bach.

(Des Mary Walters. Litho Format)

1985 (24 Oct). *Royal Visit. T* **207** *and similar multicoloured designs. P* 14½.

965	60 c. Type **207**	1·00	65
966	$1 Queen Elizabeth II (*vert*)	1·50	1·25
967	$4 Royal Yacht *Britannia*	3·25	5·00
965/7	*Set of* 3	5·25	6·25
MS968	110×83 mm. $5 Map of Antigua	3·00	3·25

(Des Walt Disney Productions. Litho Questa)

1985 (4 Nov). *150th Birth Anniv of Mark Twain (author). Horiz designs as T* **118** *of Anguilla showing Walt Disney cartoon characters in scenes from "Roughing It". Multicoloured. P* 14×13½.

969	25 c. Donald Duck and Mickey Mouse meeting Indians	50	20
970	50 c. Mickey Mouse, Donald Duck and Goofy canoeing	75	55
971	$1.10, Goofy as Pony Express rider	1·25	1·50
972	$1.50, Donald Duck and Goofy hunting buffalo	1·75	2·25
973	$2 Mickey Mouse and silver mine	2·50	3·00
969/73	*Set of* 5	6·00	6·75
MS974	127×101 mm. $5 Mickey Mouse driving stagecoach	7·50	7·50

(Des Walt Disney Productions. Litho Questa)

1985 (11 Nov). *Birth Bicentenaries of Grimm Brothers (folklorists). Horiz designs as T* **119** *of Anguilla showing Walt Disney cartoon characters in scenes from "Spindle, Shuttle and Needle". Multicoloured. P* 14×13½.

975	30 c. The Prince (Mickey Mouse) searches for a bride	80	40
	a. Error. Wmk w **16**	95·00	
976	60 c. The Prince finds the Orphan Girl (Minnie Mouse)	1·10	80
977	70 c. The Spindle finds the Prince	1·40	90
978	$1 The Needle tidies the Girl's House	1·90	1·75
979	$3 The Prince proposes	4·00	4·50
975/9	*Set of* 5	8·50	7·50
MS980	125×101 mm. $5 The Orphan Girl and spinning wheel on Prince's horse	7·50	7·50

208 Benjamin Franklin and U.N. (New York) 1953 U.P.U. 5 c. Stamp   209 "Madonna and Child" (De Landi)

(Litho Walsall)

1985 (18 Nov). *40th Anniv of United Nations Organization. T* **208** *and similar multicoloured designs showing United Nations (New York) stamps. P* 13½×14.

981	40 c. Type **208**	1·00	70
982	$1 George Washington Carver (agricultural chemist) and 1982 Nature Conservation 28 c. stamp	2·00	2·00
983	$3 Charles Lindbergh (aviator) and 1978 I.C.A.O. 25 c. stamp	4·25	5·50
981/3	*Set of* 3	6·50	7·50
MS984	101×77 mm. $5 Marc Chagall (artist) (*vert*). P 14×13½	6·00	4·75

(Des Mary Walters. Litho Format)

1985 (30 Dec). *Christmas. Religious Paintings. T* **209** *and similar vert designs. Multicoloured. P* 15.

985	10 c. Type **209**	20	15
986	25 c. "Madonna and Child" (Berlinghiero)	40	25
987	60 c. "The Nativity" (Fra Angelico)	50	60
988	$4 "Presentation in the Temple" (Giovanni di Paolo)	1·75	4·25
985/8	*Set of* 4	2·50	4·75
MS989	113×81 mm. $5 "The Nativity" (Antoniazzo Romano)	3·00	3·75

No. **MS989** exists imperforate from stock dispersed by the liquidator of Format International Security Printers Ltd.

(Litho Questa)

1986 (6 Jan). *Birth Bicentenary of John J. Audubon (ornithologist) (2nd issue). Horiz designs as T* **198** *showing original paintings. Multicoloured. P* 12.

990	60 c. Mallard	2·00	1·25
991	90 c. North American Black Duck	2·50	1·75
992	$1.50, Pintail	3·25	4·25
993	$3 American Wigeon	4·50	6·00
990/3	*Set of* 4	11·00	12·00
MS994	102×73 mm. $5 American Eider. P 14	7·00	5·50

Nos. 990/3 were issued in sheetlets of 5 as Nos. 924/7.

210 Football, Boots and Trophy   211 Tug

(Des M. Donk. Litho Questa)

1986 (17 Mar). *World Cup Football Championship, Mexico T* **210** *and similar multicoloured designs. P* 14.

995	30 c. Type **210**	85	4
996	60 c. Goalkeeper (*vert*)	1·25	
997	$1 Referee blowing whistle (*vert*)	1·75	1·6
998	$4 Ball in net	5·50	7·5
995/8	*Set of* 4	8·50	9·2
MS999	87×76 mm. $5 Two players competing for ball	8·50	7·5

(Des W. Hanson. Litho Questa)

1986 (24 Mar). *Appearance of Halley's Comet (1st issue). Horiz designs as T* **123** *of Anguilla. Multicoloured. P* 14.

1000	5 c. Edmond Halley and Old Greenwich Observatory	20	1
1001	10 c. Messerschmitt Me 163B Komet (fighter aircraft), 1944	20	1
1002	60 c. Montezuma (Aztec Emperor) and Comet in 1517 (from "Historias de las Indias de Neuva Espana")	1·25	7
1003	$4 Pocahontas saving Capt. John Smith and Comet in 1607	4·50	5·0
1000/3	*Set of* 4	5·50	5·5
MS1004	101×70 mm. $5 Halley's Comet over English Harbour, Antigua	3·50	3·7

See also Nos. 1047/51.

(Litho Questa)

1986 (21 Apr). *60th Birthday of Queen Elizabeth II. Vertical designs as T* **125** *of Anguilla. P* 14.

1005	60 c. black and yellow	30	3
1006	$1 multicoloured	50	5
1007	$4 multicoloured	1·40	1·9
1005/7	*Set of* 3	2·00	2·5
MS1008	120×85 mm. $5 black and grey-brown.	2·00	3·0

Designs:—60 c. Wedding photograph, 1947; $1 Queen at Trooping the Colour; $4 In Scotland; $5 Queen Mary and Princess Elizabeth, 1927.

(Des A. DiLorenzo. Litho Questa)

1986 (15 May). *Local Boats. T* **211** *and similar vert designs. Multicoloured. P* 14.

1009	30 c. Type **211**	25	2
1010	60 c. Game fishing boat	45	3
1011	$1 Yacht	75	6
1012	$4 Lugger with auxiliary sail	2·50	3·2
1009/12	*Set of* 4	3·50	4·0
MS1013	108×78 mm. $5 Boats under construction	3·00	4·0

212 "Hiawatha Express"   213 Prince Andrew and Miss Sarah Ferguson

(Des W. Wright. Litho Format)

1986 (22 May). *"Ameripex '86" International Stamp Exhibition, Chicago. Famous American Trains. T* **212** *and similar horiz designs. Multicoloured. P* 15.

1014	25 c. Type **212**	1·00	4
1015	50 c. "Grand Canyon Express"	1·25	7
1016	$1 "Powhattan Arrow Express"	1·50	1·7
1017	$3 "Empire State Express"	3·00	6·0
1014/17	*Set of* 4	6·00	8·0
MS1018	116×87 mm. $5 "Daylight Express"	4·50	5·0

Nos. 1015/16 exist imperforate from stock dispersed by the liquidator of Format International Security Printers Ltd.

(Des and litho Questa)

1986 (1 July). *Royal Wedding. T* **213** *and similar vert designs. Multicoloured. P* 14.

1019	45 c. Type **213**	35	3
1020	60 c. Prince Andrew	40	4
1021	$4 Prince Andrew with Prince Philip	2·00	3·0
1019/21	*Set of* 3	2·50	3·5
MS1022	88×88 mm. $5 Prince Andrew and Miss Sarah Ferguson (*different*)	4·00	4·5

214 Fly-specked Cerith   215 *Nymphaea ampla* (Water Lily)

(Des L. Birmingham. Litho Format)

1986 (6 Aug). *Sea Shells. T* **214** *and similar multicoloured designs. P* 15.

1023	15 c. Type **214**	75	4
1024	45 c. Smooth Scotch Bonnet	1·75	1·2
1025	60 c. West Indian Crown Conch	2·00	2·0
1026	$3 Ciboney Murex	6·50	9·0
1023/6	*Set of* 4	10·00	11·5
MS1027	109×75 mm. $5 Colourful Atlantic Moon (*horiz*)	7·50	8·5

(Des Mary Walters. Litho Format)

1986 (25 Aug). *Flowers. T* **215** *and similar horiz designs. Multicoloured. P* 15.
1028	10 c. Type 215	..	15	15
1029	15 c. Queen of the Night	..	20	15
1030	50 c. Cup of Gold	..	55	55
1031	60 c. Beach Morning Glory..	..	70	70
1032	70 c. Golden Trumpet	..	80	80
1033	$1 Air Plant	..	1·10	1·10
1034	$3 Purple Wreath..	..	2·50	3·00
1035	$4 Zephyr Lily	..	3·00	3·75
1028/35		*Set of* 8	8·00	9·00

MS1036 Two sheets, each 102×72 mm. (a) $4 Dozakie. (b) $5 Four O'Clock Flower
	Set of 2 *sheets*	5·00	7·50

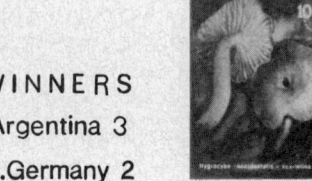

WINNERS

Argentina 3

W.Germany 2

(216)

217 *Hygrocybe occidentalis* var. *scarletina*

1986 (15 Sept). *World Cup Football Championship Winners, Mexico. Nos.* 995/9 *optd as T* **216** *in gold.*
1037	30 c. Type 210	..	50	40
1038	60 c. Goalkeeper (*vert*)	..	80	75
1039	$1 Referee blowing whistle (*vert*)	..	1·10	1·10
1040	$4 Ball in net	..	4·25	4·50
1037/40		*Set of* 4	6·00	6·00

MS1041 87×76 mm. $5 Two players competing for ball .. .. .. 3·50 4·00
The overprint on the horizontal designs is in two lines.

(Litho Format)

1986 (15 Sept). *Mushrooms. T* **217** *and similar vert designs. Multicoloured. P* 15.
1042	10 c. Type 217	..	30	20
1043	50 c. *Trogia buccinalis*	..	70	55
1044	$1 *Collybia subpruinosa*	..	1·25	1·00
1045	$4 *Leucocoprinus brebissonii*	..	3·00	4·00
1042/5		*Set of* 4	4·75	5·25

MS1046 102×82 mm $5 *Pyrrhoglossum pyrrhum* 12·00 11·00
An unissued 3$ and examples of No. 1045 with the face value shown as "4$" exist from stock dispersed by the liquidator of Format International Security Printers Ltd.

(218)

219 Auburn "Speedster" (1933)

1986 (15 Oct). *Appearance of Halley's Comet (2nd issue). Nos.* 1000/4 *optd with T* **218** *(in silver on $5).*
1047	5 c. Edmond Halley and Old Greenwich Observatory	..	15	10
1048	10 c. Messerschmitt Me 163B Komet (fighter aircraft), 1944	..	20	10
1049	60 c. Montezuma (Aztec Emperor) and Comet in 1517 (from "Historias de las Indias de Neuva Espana")	..	1·00	65
1050	$4 Pocahontas saving Capt. John Smith and Comet in 1607	..	4·50	4·00
1047/50		*Set of* 4	5·25	4·25

MS1051 101×70 mm. $5 Halley's Comet over English Harbour, Antigua .. .. 5·50 6·50

(Des J. Martin. Litho Questa)

1986 (20 Oct). *Centenary of First Benz Motor Car. T* **219** *and similar horiz designs. Multicoloured. P* 14.
1052	10 c. Type 219	..	15	10
1053	15 c. Mercury "Sable" (1986)	..	20	10
1054	50 c. Cadillac (1959)	..	55	30
1055	60 c. Studebaker (1950)	..	70	45
1056	70 c. Lagonda "V-12" (1939)	..	80	55
1057	$1 Adler "Standard" (1930)	..	1·10	75
1058	$3 DKW (1956)	..	2·50	2·50
1059	$4 Mercedes "500K" (1936)	..	3·00	3·00
1052/9		*Set of* 8	8·00	7·00

MS1060 Two sheets, each 99×70 mm. (a) $5 Daimler (1896). (b) $5 Mercedes "Knight" (1921)
	Set of 2 *sheets*	6·00	6·50

220 Young Mickey Mouse playing Santa Claus

221 Arms of Antigua

(Des Walt Disney Co. Litho Format)

1986 (4 Nov). *Christmas. T* **220** *and similar horiz designs showing Walt Disney cartoon characters as babies. Multicoloured. P* 11.
1061	25 c. Type 220	..	45	35
1062	30 c. Mickey and Minnie Mouse building snowman	..	50	40
1063	40 c. Aunt Matilda and Goofy baking	..	55	45
1064	60 c. Goofy and Pluto	..	80	85
1065	70 c. Pluto, Donald and Daisy Duck carol singing	..	95	1·00
1066	$1.50, Donald Duck, Mickey Mouse and Pluto stringing popcorn		1·60	2·00
1067	$3 Grandma Duck and Minnie Mouse	..	3·00	4·25
1068	$4 Donald Duck and Pete	..	3·25	4·25
1061/8		*Set of* 8	10·00	12·00

MS1069 Two sheets, each 127×102 mm. P 14 × 13½. (a) $5 Goofy, Donald Duck and Minnie Mouse playing reindeer. (b) $5 Mickey Mouse, Donald and Daisy Duck playing with toys.
	Set of 2 *sheets*	11·00	12·00

1986 (25 Nov). *Coil stamps. T* **221** *and similar vert design. Litho. P* 14.
1070	10 c. new blue	..	50	50
1071	25 c. orange-vermilion	..	75	75

Design:—25 c. Flag of Antigua.

222 *Canada I* (1981)

223 Bridled Burrfish

(Des J. Iskowitz. Litho Format)

1987 (5 Feb). *America's Cup Yachting Championship. T* **222** *and similar multicoloured designs. P* 15.
1072	30 c. Type 222	..	30	20
1073	60 c. *Gretel II* (1970)	..	45	50
1074	$1 *Sceptre* (1958)	..	85	1·00
1075	$3 *Vigilant* (1893)	..	2·25	3·00
1072/5		*Set of* 4	3·50	4·25

MS1076 113×84 mm. $5 *Australia II* defeating *Liberty* (1983) (*horiz*) .. .. 4·00 5·00

(Des G. Drummond. Litho Questa)

1987 (23 Feb). *Marine Life. T* **223** *and similar horiz designs. Multicoloured. P* 14.
1077	15 c. Type 223	..	1·25	30
1078	30 c. Common Noddy	..	2·50	60
1079	40 c. Nassau Grouper	..	1·75	70
1080	50 c. Laughing Gull..	..	3·50	1·50
1081	60 c. French Angelfish	..	2·50	1·50
1082	$1 Porkfish	..	2·50	1·75
1083	$2 Royal Tern	..	5·00	5·00
1084	$3 Sooty Tern	..	5·50	6·00
1077/84		*Set of* 8	22·00	15·00

MS1085 Two sheets, each 120×94 mm. (a) $5 Banded Butterflyfish. (b) $5 Brown Booby
	Set of 2 *sheets*	14·00	14·00

Nos. 1078, 1080 and 1083/5 are without the World Wildlife Fund logo shown on Type **223**.

224 Handball

225 "The Profile"

(Litho Questa)

1987 (23 Mar). *Olympic Games, Seoul (1988) (1st issue). T* **224** *and similar horiz designs. Multicoloured. P* 14.
1086	10 c. Type 224	..	30	10
1087	60 c. Fencing	..	45	35
1088	$1 Gymnastics	..	60	75
1089	$3 Football	..	1·75	2·00
1086/9		*Set of* 4	2·75	3·50

MS1090 100×72 mm. $5 Boxing gloves.. .. 3·50 4·25
See also Nos. 1222/6.

(Litho Questa)

1987 (30 Mar). *Birth Centenary of Marc Chagall (artist). T* **225** *and similar multicoloured designs. P* 13½×14.
1091	10 c. Type 225	..	20	15
1092	30 c. "Portrait of the Artist's Sister"		35	30
1093	40 c. "Bride with Fan"	..	40	40
1094	60 c. "David in Profile"	..	45	45
1095	90 c. "Fiancee with Bouquet"	..	60	60
1096	$1 "Self Portrait with Brushes"	..	65	65
1097	$3 "The Walk"	..	1·75	2·00
1098	$4 "Three Candles"	..	2·00	2·25
1091/8		*Set of* 8	5·75	6·00

MS1099 Two sheets, each 110×95 mm. (a) $5 "Fall of Icarus" (104×89 *mm*). (b) $5 "Myth of Orpheus" (104×89 *mm*). Imperf *Set of* 2 *sheets* 6·00 6·00

---

226 *Spirit of Australia* (fastest powerboat), 1978

227 Lee Iacocca at Unveiling of Restored Statue

(Des W. Wright. Litho Format)

1987 (9 Apr). *Milestones of Transportation. T* **226** *and similar horiz designs. Multicoloured. P* 15.
1100	10 c. Type 226	..	40	30
1101	15 c. Siemen's electric locomotive, 1879	..	60	40
1102	30 c. U.S.S. *Triton* (first submerged circumnavigation), 1960	..	60	45
1103	50 c. Trevithick's steam carriage (first passenger-carrying vehicle), 1801	..	70	60
1104	60 c. U.S.S. *New Jersey* (battleship), 1942	..	80	70
1105	70 c. Draisaine bicycle, 1818	..	80	80
1106	90 c. *United States* (liner) (holder of Blue Riband), 1952	..	1·00	1·00
1107	$1.50, Cierva C.4 (first autogyro), 1923	..	1·40	2·00
1108	$2 Curtiss NC-4 (first flying boat (first transatlantic flight), 1919	..	1·50	2·25
1109	$3 *Queen Elizabeth 2* (liner), 1969	..	2·50	3·00
1100/9		*Set of* 10	9·00	10·50

(Litho Questa)

1987 (23 Apr). *Centenary of Statue of Liberty (1986) (2nd issue). T* **227** *and similar multicoloured designs. P* 14.
1110	15 c. Type 227	..	15	15
1111	30 c. Statue at sunset (side view)	..	20	20
1112	45 c. Aerial view of head	..	30	30
1113	50 c. Lee Iacocca and torch..	..	35	35
1114	60 c. Workmen inside head of Statue (*horiz*)	..	35	35
1115	90 c. Restoration work (*horiz*)	..	50	50
1116	$1 Head of Statue..	..	55	55
1117	$2 Statue at sunset (front view)..	..	1·00	1·25
1118	$3 Inspecting restoration work (*horiz*)	..	1·60	1·75
1119	$5 Statue at night	..	2·50	3·00
1110/19		*Set of* 10	6·75	7·50

228 Grace Kelly

229 Scouts around Camp Fire and Red Kangaroo

(Des Lynda Bruscheni. Litho Questa)

1987 (11 May). *Entertainers. T* **228** *and similar vert designs. Multicoloured. P* 14.
1120	15 c. Type 228	..	90	40
1121	30 c. Marilyn Monroe	..	1·25	65
1122	45 c. Orson Welles	..	90	60
1123	50 c. Judy Garland	..	90	65
1124	60 c. John Lennon	..	1·75	1·10
1125	$1 Rock Hudson	..	1·40	1·10
1126	$2 John Wayne	..	2·25	2·00
1127	$3 Elvis Presley	..	5·50	3·50
1120/7		*Set of* 8	13·50	9·00

(Litho Format)

1987 (25 May). *16th World Scout Jamboree, Australia. T* **229** *and similar horiz designs. Multicoloured. P* 15.
1128	10 c. Type 229	..	35	15
1129	60 c. Scouts canoeing and Blue-winged Kookaburra	..	90	70
1130	$1 Scouts on assault course and Ring-tailed Rock Wallaby	..	1·00	85
1131	$3 Field kitchen and Koala	..	3·50	3·50
1128/31		*Set of* 4	3·75	4·75

MS1132 103×78 mm. $5 Flags of Antigua, Australia and Scout Movement .. .. 2·75 3·25

230 Whistling Frog

(231)

(Des B. Bundock. Litho Questa)

1987 (15 June). *"Capex '87" International Stamp Exhibition, Toronto. Reptiles and Amphibians. T* **230** *and similar horiz designs. Multicoloured. P* 14.
1133	30 c. Type 230	..	25	20
1134	60 c. Croaking Lizard	..	35	40
1135	$1 Antiguan Anole	..	55	60
1136	$3 Red-footed Tortoise	..	1·50	2·25
1133/6		*Set of* 4	2·40	3·00

MS1137 106×76 mm. $5 Ground Lizard .. 2·25 2·75

1987 (9 Sept). *10th Death Anniv of Elvis Presley (entertainer).* No. 1127 optd with T **231.**
1138 $3 Elvis Presley   ..   ..   ..   4·75   3·50

232 House of Burgesses,   **233** "Madonna and
Virginia ("Freedom of Speech")   Child" (Bernardo Daddi)

(Des and litho Questa)

1987 (16 Nov). *Bicentenary of U.S. Constitution.* T **232** and similar multicoloured designs. P 14.
1139   15 c. Type **232**   10   10
1140   45 c. State Seal, Connecticut   ..   20   25
1141   60 c. State Seal, Delaware   ..   25   35
1142 $4 Gouverneur Morris (Pennsylvania delegate) (vert)..   ..   1·75   2·25
1139/42   ..   ..   *Set of 4*   2·10   2·75
MS1143   105×75 mm. $5 Roger Sherman (Connecticut delegate) (vert)   ..   2·25   2·75
Nos. 1139/42 were each issued in sheetlets of five stamps and one stamp-size label, which appears in the centre of the bottom row.

(Litho Questa)

1987 (1 Dec). *Christmas. Religious Paintings.* T **233** and similar vert designs. Multicoloured. P 14.
1144   45 c. Type **233**   30   15
1145   60 c. "St. Joseph" (detail, "The Nativity" (Sano di Pietro))   ..   40   30
1146 $1 "Virgin Mary" (detail, "The Nativity" (Sano di Pietro))   ..   60   55
1147 $4 "Music-making Angel" (Melozzo da Forli)   ..   2·00   2·75
1144/7   ..   ..   *Set of 4*   3·00   3·25
MS1148   99×70 mm. $5 "The Flight into Egypt" (Sano di Pietro)   ..   2·25   2·75

234 Wedding Photograph, 1947   **235** Great Blue Heron

(Des and litho Questa)

1988 (8 Feb). *Royal Ruby Wedding.* T **234** and similar vert designs. P 14.
1149   25 c. deep brown, black and bright new blue   15   15
1150   60 c. multicoloured   30   40
1151 $2 deep brown, black and light green   ..   90   1·10
1152 $3 multicoloured   ..   ..   1·40   1·60
1149/52   ..   ..   *Set of 4*   2·50   3·00
MS1153   102×77 mm. $5 multicoloured.   ..   2·25   2·75
Designs:—60 c. Queen Elizabeth II; $2 Princess Elizabeth and Prince Philip with Prince Charles at his christening, 1948; $3 Queen Elizabeth (from photo by Tim Graham), 1980; $5 Royal Family, 1952.

(Des W. Wright. Litho Questa)

1988 (1 Mar). *Birds of Antigua.* T **235** and similar multicoloured designs. P 14.
1154   10 c. Type **235**   25   20
1155   15 c. Ringed Kingfisher (horiz)   ..   25   20
1156   50 c. Bananaquit (horiz)   ..   50   40
1157   60 c. Purple Gallinule (horiz)   ..   50   50
1158   70 c. Blue-hooded Euphonia (horiz)   ..   60   55
1159 $1 Brown-throated Conure ("Caribbean Parakeet")   ..   80   65
1160 $3 Troupial (horiz)   ..   ..   2·25   2·75
1161 $4 Purple-throated Carib (horiz)   ..   2·50   3·00
1154/61   ..   ..   *Set of 8*   7·00   7·50
MS1162   Two sheets, each 115×86 mm. (a) $5 Greater Flamingo. (b) $5 Brown Pelican
    Set of 2 sheets   4·50   5·50

236 First Aid at Daycare Centre, Antigua

(Des G. Vasarhelyi. Litho Format)

1988 (10 Mar). *Salvation Army's Community Service.* T **236** and similar horiz designs. Multicoloured. P 14×13½.
1163   25 c. Type **236**   65   55
1164   30 c. Giving penicillin injection, Indonesia   65   55
1165   40 c. Children at daycare centre, Bolivia   75   65
1166   45 c. Rehabilitation of the handicapped, India   ..   75   65
1167   50 c. Training blind man, Kenya   ..   90   1·00
1168   60 c. Weighing baby, Ghana   ..   90   1·00
1169 $1 Training typist, Zambia   ..   1·40   1·75
1170 $2 Emergency food kitchen, Sri Lanka   2·00   3·25
1163/70   ..   ..   *Set of 8*   7·00   8·50
MS1171   152×83 mm. $5 General Eva Burrows   3·75   4·50

237 Columbus' Second Fleet,   **238** "Bust of Christ"
1493

(Des I. MacLaury. Litho Questa)

1988 (16 Mar–16 May). *500th Anniv of Discovery of America by Columbus (1992) (1st issue).* T **237** and similar horiz designs. Multicoloured. P 14.
1172   10 c. Type **237**   40   30
1173   30 c. Painos Indian village and fleet (16.5)   50   35
1174   45 c. Santa Mariagalante (flagship) and Painos village (16.5)   ..   60   35
1175   60 c. Painos Indians offering Columbus fruit and vegetables (16.5)   60   50
1176   90 c. Painos Indian and Columbus with Scarlet Macaw   ..   80   80
1177 $1 Columbus landing on island..   80   80
1178 $3 Spanish soldier and fleet   ..   1·60   2·25
1179 $4 Fleet under sail (16.5)   ..   2·50   2·00
1172/9   ..   ..   *Set of 8*   6·50   7·00
MS1180   Two sheets, each 110×80 mm. (a) $5 Queen Isabella's cross. (b) $5 Gold coin of Ferdinand and Isabella (16.5)
    Set of 2 sheets   6·00   6·50
See also Nos. 1267/71, 1360/8, 1503/11, 1654/60 and 1670/1.

(Litho Questa)

1988 (11 Apr). *500th Birth Anniv of Titian.* T **238** and similar vert designs showing paintings. Multicoloured. P 13½×14.
1181   30 c. Type **238**   25   20
1182   40 c. "Scourging of Christ"   ..   30   25
1183   45 c. "Madonna in Glory with Saints"   30   25
1184   50 c. "The Averoldi Polyptych" (detail)   35   35
1185 $1 "Christ Crowned with Thorns"   ..   55   55
1186 $2 "Christ Mocked"   ..   90   1·25
1187 $3 "Christ and Simon of Cyrene"   ..   1·50   1·75
1188 $4 "Crucifixion with Virgin and Saints"   1·75   2·25
1181/8   ..   ..   *Set of 8*   5·50   6·25
MS1189   Two sheets, each 110×95 mm. (a) $5 "Ecce Homo" (detail). (b) $5 "Noli me Tangere" (detail)   ..   *Set of 2 sheets*   6·00   7·00

239 Two Yachts rounding Buoy

(Des G. Drummond. Litho Format)

1988 (18 Apr). *Sailing Week.* T **239** and similar horiz designs. Multicoloured. P 15.
1190   30 c. Type **239**   20   20
1191   60 c. Three yachts   35   40
1192 $1 British yacht under way   ..   50   55
1193 $3 Three yachts (different)   ..   1·10   2·25
1190/3   ..   ..   *Set of 4*   2·00   3·00
MS1194   103×92 mm. $5 Two yachts   ..   1·75   3·25

240 Mickey Mouse and Diver with   (241)
Porpoise

(Des Walt Disney Co. Litho Questa)

1988 (3 May). *Disney EPCOT Centre, Orlando, Florida.* T **240** and similar multicoloured designs showing cartoon characters and exhibits. P 14×13½ (horiz) or 13½×14 (vert).
1195   1 c. Type **240**   10   10
1196   2 c. Goofy and Mickey Mouse with futuristic car (vert)   ..   10   10
1197   3 c. Mickey Mouse and Goofy as Atlas (vert)   ..   10   10
1198   4 c. Mickey Mouse and Edaphosaurus (prehistoric reptile)   ..   10   10
1199   5 c. Mickey Mouse at Journey into Imagination exhibit   ..   10   10
1200   10 c. Mickey Mouse collecting vegetables (vert)   ..   10   10
1201   25 c. Type **240**   25   25
1202   30 c. As 2 c.   25   25
1203   40 c. As 3 c.   30   30
1204   60 c. As 4 c.   50   50
1205   70 c. As 5 c.   60   60
1206 $1.50, As 10 c.   ..   ..   1·25   1·25
1207 $3 Goofy and Mickey Mouse with robot (vert)   ..   2·00   2·00
1208 $4 Mickey Mouse and Clarabelle at Horizons exhibit   ..   2·25   2·25
1195/1208   ..   *Set of 14*   7·00   7·00
MS1209   Two sheets, each 125×99 mm. (a) $5 Mickey Mouse and monorail (vert). (b) $5 Mickey Mouse flying over EPCOT Centre
    Set of 2 sheets   6·00   6·50

1988 (9 May). *Stamp Exhibitions.* Nos. 1083/5 optd as T **241** showing various emblems.
1210 $2 Royal Tern (optd T **241**, Prague)   1·25   1·25
1211 $3 Sooty Tern (optd "INDEPENDENCE 40", Israel)   ..   1·75   1·75
MS1212   Two sheets, each 120×94 mm. (a) $5 Banded Butterflyfish (optd "OLYMPHILEX '88", Seoul). (b) $5 Brown Booby (optd "FINLANDIA 88", Helsinki)
    Set of 2 sheets   5·50   6·00

242 Jacaranda   **243** Gymnastics

(Des Mary Walters. Litho Questa)

1988 (16 May). *Flowering Trees.* T **242** and similar vert designs. Multicoloured. P 14.
1213   10 c. Type **242**   20   15
1214   30 c. Cordia   25   20
1215   50 c. Orchid Tree   40   40
1216   90 c. Flamboyant   50   50
1217 $1 African Tulip Tree   55   55
1218 $2 Potato Tree   ..   ..   1·10   1·25
1219 $3 Crepe Myrtle   ..   ..   1·40   1·75
1220 $4 Pitch Apple   ..   ..   1·75   2·50
1213/20   ..   ..   *Set of 8*   5·50   6·50
MS1221   Two sheets, each 106×76 mm. (a) $5 Cassia. (b) $5 Chinaberry   *Set of 2 sheets*   5·00   6·00

(Des J. Martin. Litho Questa)

1988 (10 June). *Olympic Games, Seoul (2nd issue).* T **243** and similar multicoloured designs. P 14.
1222   40 c. Type **243**   20   25
1223   60 c. Weightlifting   25   30
1224 $1 Water polo (horiz)   45   50
1225 $3 Boxing (horiz)   ..   ..   1·40   2·00
1222/5   ..   ..   *Set of 4*   2·10   2·75
MS1226   114×80 mm. $5 Runner with Olympic torch   ..   ..   2·00   3·00

244 Danaus plexippus

(Des S. Heimann. Litho Questa)

1988 (29 Aug)–90. *Caribbean Butterflies.* T **244** and similar horiz designs. Multicoloured. P 14.
1227   1 c. Type **144**   20   20
1228   2 c. Greta diaphanus   30   30
1229   3 c. Calisto archebates   30   30
1230   5 c. Hamadryas feronia   40   40
1231   10 c. Mestra dorcas   50   30
1232   15 c. Hypolimnas misippus   ..   60   30
1233   20 c. Dione juno   70   30
1234   25 c. Heliconius charithonia   ..   70   30
1235   30 c. Eurema pyro   70   30
1236   40 c. Papilio androgeus   75   30
1237   45 c. Anteos maerula   75   30
1238   50 c. Aphrissa orbis   90   45
1239   60 c. Astraptes xagua   ..   ..   1·00   60
1240 $1 Heliopetes arsalte   ..   ..   1·50   1·00
1241 $2 Polites baracoa   ..   ..   2·50   2·50
1242 $2.50, Phocides pigmalion   ..   3·00   3·75
1243 $5 Prepona amphitoe   ..   ..   4·50   5·50
1244 $10 Oarisma nanus   ..   ..   7·00   8·00
1244a $20 Parides lycimenes (19.2.90)   13·00   15·00
1227/44a   ..   *Set of 19*   35·00   35·00

245 President Kennedy and Family   **246** Minnie Mouse carol singing

(Des J. Iskowitz. Litho Questa)

1988 (23 Nov). *25th Death Anniv of John F. Kennedy (American statesman). T* **245** *and similar horiz designs, each showing different inset portrait. Multicoloured. P* 14.

1245	1 c. Type **245**		10	10
1246	2 c. Kennedy commanding *PT109*		10	10
1247	3 c. Funeral cortege		10	10
1248	4 c. In motorcade, Mexico City		10	10
1249	30 c. As 1 c.		15	15
1250	60 c. As 4 c.		25	30
1251	$1 As 3 c.		45	50
1252	$4 As 2 c.		1·60	2·25
1245/52		*Set of 8*	2·40	3·00

MS1253 105 × 75 mm. $5 Kennedy taking presidential oath of office .. .. 2·50 3·25

(Des Walt Disney Co. Litho Questa)

1988 (1 Dec). *Christmas. "Mickey's Christmas Chorale". T* **246** *and similar multicoloured designs showing Walt Disney cartoon characters. P* 13½ × 14.

1254	10 c. Type **246**		30	30
1255	25 c. Pluto		45	45
1256	30 c. Mickey Mouse playing ukelele		45	45
1257	70 c. Donald Duck and nephew		80	80
1258	$1 Mordie and Ferdie carol singing		80	80
	a. Sheetlet. Nos. 1258/65		5·75	
1259	$1 Goofy carol singing		80	80
1260	$1 Chip n'Dale sliding off roof		80	80
1261	$1 Two of Donald Duck's nephews at window		80	80
1262	$1 As 10 c.		80	80
1263	$1 As 25 c.		80	80
1264	$1 As 30 c.		80	80
1265	$1 As 70 c.		80	80
1254/65		*Set of 12*	7·50	7·50

MS1266 Two sheets, each 127 × 102 mm. (a) $7 Donald Duck playing trumpet and Mickey and Minnie Mouse in carriage. P 13½ × 14. (b) $7 Mickey Mouse and friends singing carols on roller skates (*horiz*). P 14 × 13½ *Set of 2 sheets* 8·50 8·50
Nos. 1258/65 were printed together, *se-tenant* as a composite design, in sheetlets of eight.

247 Arawak Warriors   **248** De Havilland Comet 4 Airliner

(Des D. Miller. Litho Questa)

1989 (16 May). *500th Anniv of Discovery of America by Columbus* (1992) *(2nd issue). Pre-Columbian Arawak Society. T* **247** *and similar vert designs. Multicoloured. P* 14.

1267	$1.50, Type **247**		1·00	1·25
	a. Horiz strip of 4. Nos. 1267/70		3·50	
1268	$1.50, Whip dancers		1·00	1·25
1269	$1.50, Whip dancers and chief with pineapple		1·00	1·25
1270	$1.50, Family and camp fire		1·00	1·25
1267/70		*Set of 4*	3·50	4·50

MS1271 71 × 84 mm. $6 Arawak chief .. .. 2·50 3·00
Nos. 1267/70 were printed together, *se-tenant*, in horizontal strips of 4 throughout the sheet, each strip forming a composite design.

(Des W. Wright. Litho Questa)

1989 (29 May). *50th Anniv of First Jet Flight. T* **248** *and similar horiz designs. Multicoloured. P* 14.

1272	10 c. Type **248**		25	25
1273	30 c. Messerschmitt Me 262 fighter		40	40
1274	40 c. Boeing 707 airliner		45	45
1275	60 c. Canadair CL-13 Sabre ("F-86 Sabre") fighter		55	55
1276	$1 Lockheed F-104 Starfighter		80	80
1277	$2 Douglas DC-10 airliner		1·60	1·60
1278	$3 Boeing 747-300/400 airliner		2·00	2·00
1279	$4 McDonnell Douglas F-4 Phantom II fighter		2·25	2·25
1272/9		*Set of 8*	7·50	7·50

MS1280 Two sheets, each 114×83 mm. (a) $7 Grumman F-14A Tomcat fighter. (b) $7 Concorde airliner .. .. *Set of 2 sheets* 7·00 8·00

249 *Festivale*

(Des W. Wright. Litho Questa)

1989 (20 June). *Caribbean Cruise Ships. T* **249** *and similar horiz designs. Multicoloured. P* 14.

1281	25 c. Type **249**		45	30
1282	45 c. *Southward*		70	30
1283	50 c. *Sagafjord*		70	30
1284	60 c. *Daphne*		70	50
1285	75 c. *Cunard Countess*		80	70
1286	90 c. *Song of America*		90	90
1287	$3 *Island Princess*		2·25	3·00
1288	$4 *Galileo*		2·25	3·00
1281/8		*Set of 8*	8·00	8·00

MS1289 (a) 113 × 87 mm. $6 *Norway*. (b) 111 × 82 mm. $6 *Oceanic*   *Set of 2 sheets* 6·50 8·00

250 "Fish swimming by Duck half-submerged in Stream"

(Litho Questa)

1989 (1 July). *Japanese Art. Paintings by Hiroshige. T* **250** *and similar horiz designs. Multicoloured. P* 14 × 13½.

1290	25 c. Type **250**		30	30
1291	45 c. "Crane and Wave"		40	40
1292	50 c. "Sparrows and Morning Glories"		40	40
1293	60 c. "Crested Blackbird and Flowering Cherry"		50	50
1294	$1 "Great Knot sitting among Water Grass"		70	70
1295	$2 "Goose on a Bank of Water"		1·50	1·50
1296	$3 "Black Paradise Flycatcher and Blossoms"		2·00	2·00
1297	$4 "Sleepy Owl perched on a Pine Branch"		2·50	2·50
1290/7		*Set of 8*	7·50	7·50

MS1298 Two sheets, each 102 × 75 mm. (a) $5 "Bullfinch flying near a Clematis Branch". (b) $5 "Titmouse on a Cherry Branch" *Set of 2 sheets* 6·50 7·00
Nos. 1290/7 are each printed in sheetlets of 10 containing two horizontal strips of 5 stamps separated by printed labels commemorating Emperor Hirohito.

251 Mickey and Minnie Mouse in Helicopter over River Seine

(Des Walt Disney Company. Litho Questa)

1989 (7 July). *"Philexfrance 89" International Stamp Exhibition, Paris. T* **251** *and similar multicoloured designs showing Walt Disney cartoon characters in Paris. P* 14 × 13½.

1299	1 c. Type **251**		10	10
1300	2 c. Goofy and Mickey Mouse passing Arc de Triomphe		10	10
1301	3 c. Mickey Mouse painting picture of Notre Dame		10	10
1302	4 c. Mickey and Minnie Mouse with Pluto leaving Metro station		10	10
1303	5 c. Minnie Mouse as model in fashion show		10	10
1304	10 c. Daisy Duck, Minnie Mouse and Clarabelle as Folies Bergere dancers		10	10
1305	$5 Mickey and Minnie Mouse shopping in street market		4·75	5·50
1306	$6 Mickey and Minnie Mouse, Jose Carioca and Donald Duck at pavement cafe		4·75	5·50
1299/1306		*Set of 8*	9·00	10·00

MS1307 Two sheets, each 127 × 101 mm. (a) $5 Mickey and Minnie Mouse in hot air balloon. P 14 × 13½. (b) $5 Mickey Mouse at Pompidou Centre cafe (*vert*). P 13½ × 14   *Set of 2 sheets* 9·00 10·00

MINIMUM PRICE

The minimum price quote is 10p which represents a handling charge rather than a basis for valuing common stamps. For further notes about prices see introductory pages.

252 Goalkeeper   **253** *Mycena pura*

(Des D. Bruckner. Litho B.D.T.)

1989 (21 Aug). *World Cup Football Championship, Italy* (1990). *T* **252** *and similar multicoloured designs. P* 14.

1308	15 c. Type **252**		50	15
1309	25 c. Goalkeeper moving towards ball		55	15
1310	$1 Goalkeeper reaching for ball		1·25	1·25
1311	$4 Goalkeeper saving goal		2·75	3·75
1308/11		*Set of 4*	4·50	4·75

MS1312 Two sheets, each 75 × 105 mm. (a) $5 Three players competing for ball (*horiz*). (b) $5 Ball and players' legs (*horiz*) *Set of 2 sheets* 6·00 6·50

(Litho Questa)

1989 (12 Oct). *Fungi. T* **253** *and similar multicoloured designs. P* 14.

1313	10 c. Type **253**		30	30
1314	25 c. *Psathyrella tuberculata* (*vert*)		50	30
1315	50 c. *Psilocybe cubensis*		70	50
1316	60 c. *Leptonia caeruleocapitata* (*vert*)		70	70
1317	75 c. *Xeromphalina tenuipes* (*vert*)		80	80
1318	$1 *Chlorophyllum molybdites* (*vert*)		95	95
1319	$3 *Marasmius haematocephalus*		2·50	2·75
1320	$4 *Cantharellus cinnabarinus*		2·75	3·00
1313/20		*Set of 8*	8·50	8·50

MS1321 Two sheets, each 88×62 mm. (a) $6 *Leucopaxillus gracillimus* (*vert*). (b) $6 *Volvariella volvacea* .. *Set of 2 sheets* 11·00 11·00

254 Desmarest's Hutia   **255** Goofy and Old Printing Press

(Des J. Barbaris. Litho B.D.T.)

1989 (19 Oct). *Local Fauna. T* **254** *and similar multicoloured designs. P* 14.

1322	25 c. Type **254**		50	30
1323	45 c. Caribbean Monk Seal		1·00	70
1324	60 c. Mustache Bat (*vert*)		1·00	85
1325	$4 American Manatee (*vert*)		3·00	4·25
1322/5		*Set of 4*	5·00	5·50

MS1326 113×87 mm. $5 West Indies Giant Rice Rat .. .. 5·00 6·00

(Des Walt Disney Co. Litho Questa)

1989 (2 Nov). *"American Philately". T* **255** *and similar multicoloured designs, each showing Walt Disney cartoon characters with stamps and the logo of the American Philatelic Society. P* 14½×14.

1327	1 c. Type **255**		10	10
1328	2 c. Donald Duck cancelling first day cover for Mickey Mouse		10	10
1329	3 c. Donald Duck's nephews reading recruiting poster for Pony Express riders		10	10
1330	4 c. Morty and Ferdie as early radio broadcasters		10	10
1331	5 c. Donald Duck and water buffalo watching television		10	10
1332	10 c. Donald Duck with stamp album		10	10
1333	$4 Daisy Duck with computer system		3·25	3·50
1334	$6 Donald's nephews with stereo radio, trumpet and guitar		4·00	4·50
1327/34		*Set of 8*	7·00	7·50

MS1335 Two sheets, each 127×102 mm. (a) $5 Donald's nephews donating stamps to charity. P 13½×14. (b) $5 Minnie Mouse flying mailplane upside down (*horiz*). P 14×13½   *Set of 2 sheets* 9·00 9·00

256 Mickey Mouse and Donald Duck with Locomotive *John Bull*, 1831

(Des Walt Disney Co. Litho Questa)

1989 (17 Nov). *"World Stamp Expo '89" International Stamp Exhibition, Washington* (1st issue). *T 256 and similar multicoloured designs showing Walt Disney cartoon characters and locomotives. P 14×13½.*

1336	25 c.	Type 256	40	40
1337	45 c.	Mickey Mouse and friends with *Atlantic,* 1832	50	50
1338	50 c.	Mickey Mouse and Goofy with *William Crooks,* 1861	50	50
1339	60 c.	Mickey Mouse and Goofy with *Minnetonka,* 1869	60	65
1340	$1	Chip n'Dale with *Thatcher Perkins,* 1863	65	70
1341	$2	Mickey and Minnie Mouse with *Pioneer,* 1848	1·25	1·50
1342	$3	Mickey Mouse and Donald Duck with cog railway locomotive *Peppersass,* 1869	1·50	1·75
1343	$4	Mickey Mouse with Huey, Dewey and Louie aboard N.Y. World's Fair *Gimbels Flyer,* 1939	2·00	2·25
1336/43		*Set of 8*	6·50	7·50

MS1344 Two sheets, each 127×101 mm. (a) $6 Mickey Mouse and Thomas Jefferson, 1835 (*vert*). P 13½×14. (b) $6 Mickey Mouse and friends at "Golden Spike" ceremony, 1869. P 14×13½ .. .. *Set of 2 sheets* 7·50 8·50

257 Smithsonian Institution, Washington   **258** Launch of "Apollo 11"

(Des Design Element. Litho Questa)

1989 (17 Nov). *"World Stamp Expo '89" International Stamp Exhibition, Washington* (2nd issue). *Sheet 78×61 mm. P 14.*

MS1345 **257** $4 multicoloured .. .. 1·75 2·25

(Des J. Iskowitz. Litho B.D.T.)

1989 (24 Nov). *20th Anniv of First Manned Landing on Moon. T 258 and similar multicoloured designs. P 14.*

1346	10 c.	Type 258	20	15
1347	45 c.	Aldrin on Moon	50	30
1348	$1	Module *Eagle* over Moon (*horiz*)	90	85
1349	$4	Recovery of "Apollo 11" crew after splashdown (*horiz*)	2·75	3·50
1346/9		*Set of 4*	4·00	4·25

MS1350 107×77 mm. $5 Astronaut Neil Armstrong .. .. .. 3·00 3·50

259 "The Small Cowper Madonna" (Raphael)   **260** Star-eyed Hermit Crab

(Litho Questa)

1989 (11 Dec). *Christmas. Paintings by Raphael and Giotto. T 259 and similar vert designs. Multicoloured. P 14.*

1351	10 c.	Type 259	10	10
1352	25 c.	"Madonna of the Goldfinch" (Raphael)	20	15
1353	30 c.	"The Alba Madonna" (Raphael)	20	15
1354	50 c.	Saint (detail, "Bologna Altarpiece") (Giotto)	40	30
1355	60 c.	Angel (detail, "Bologna Altarpiece") (Giotto)	45	35
1356	70 c.	Angel slaying serpent (detail, "Bologna Altarpiece") (Giotto)	50	40
1357	$4	Evangelist (detail, "Bologna Altarpiece") (Giotto)	2·50	3·00
1358	$5	"Madonna of Foligno" (detail) (Raphael)	3·00	3·75
1351/8		*Set of 8*	6·50	7·50

MS1359 Two sheets, each 71×96 mm. (a) $5 "The Marriage of the Virgin" (detail) (Raphael). (b) $5 Madonna and Child (detail, "Bologna Altarpiece") (Giotto) .. *Set of 2 sheets* 7·00 8·50

(Des Mary Walters. Litho Questa)

1990 (26 Mar). *500th Anniv of Discovery of America by Columbus* (1992) (3rd issue). *New World Natural History – Marine Life. T 260 and similar vert designs. Multicoloured. P 14.*

1360	10 c.	Type 260	15	15
1361	20 c.	Spiny Lobster	20	20
1362	25 c.	Magnificent Banded Fanworm	25	25
1363	45 c.	Cannonball Jellyfish	40	40
1364	60 c.	Red-spiny Sea Star	60	60
1365	$2	Peppermint Shrimp	1·50	1·75
1366	$3	Coral Crab	1·75	2·00
1367	$4	Branching Fire Coral	2·25	2·50
1360/7		*Set of 8*	6·25	7·00

MS1368 Two sheets, each 100×69 mm. (a) $5 Common Sea Fan. (b) $5 Portuguese Man-of-war *Set of 2 sheets* 7·00 8·00

261 Vanilla mexicana

262 Queen Victoria and Queen Elizabeth II

(Des Mary Walters. Litho Questa)

1990 (17 Apr). *"EXPO 90" International Garden and Greenery Exhibition, Osaka. Orchids. T 261 and similar vert designs. Multicoloured. P 14.*

1369	15 c.	Type 261	40	30
1370	45 c.	*Epidendrum ibaguense*	50	40
1371	50 c.	*Epidendrum secundum*	55	45
1372	60 c.	*Maxillaria conferta*	65	50
1373	$1	*Oncidium altissimum*	85	75
1374	$2	*Spiranthes lanceolata*	1·50	1·75
1375	$3	*Tonopsis utricularioides*	2·00	2·50
1376	$5	*Epidendrum nocturnum*	3·00	3·50
1369/76		*Set of 8*	8·50	9·00

MS1377 Two sheets, each 102×70 mm. (a) $5 *Octomeria graminifolia.* (b) $5 *Rodriguezia lanceolata* .. .. *Set of 2 sheets* 5·50 7·00

(Des M. Pollard. Litho B.D.T.)

1990 (3 May). *150th Anniv of the Penny Black. T 262 and similar horiz designs. P 14½×14.*

1378	**262** 45 c.	blue-green	50	30
1379	– 60 c.	magenta	60	55
1380	– $5	ultramarine	3·00	4·25
1378/80		*Set of 3*	3·75	4·50

MS1381 102×80 mm. **262** $6 blackish purple 3·75 4·50

Designs:—60 c., $5 As Type **262**, but with different backgrounds.

263 Britannia (mail paddle-steamer), 1840

(Des M. Pollard. Litho B.D.T.)

1990 (3 May). *"Stamp World London 90" International Stamp Exhibition. T 263 and similar horiz designs. P 13½.*

1382	50 c.	deep grey-green and scarlet-vermilion	55	35
1383	75 c.	purple-brown and scarlet-vermilion	75	70
1384	$4	deep ultramarine & scarlet-vermilion	3·00	4·00
1382/4		*Set of 3*	3·75	4·50

MS1385 104×81 mm. $6 brownish black and scarlet-vermilion .. .. 3·25 4·00

Designs:—75 c. Railway sorting carriage, 1892; $4 Short S.23 Empire "C" Class flying boat *Centaurus,* 1938; $6 Post Office underground railway, London, 1927.

264 Flamefish   **265** "Voyager 2" passing Saturn

(Des G. Drummond. Litho Questa)

1990 (21 May). *Reef Fishes. T 264 and similar horiz designs. Multicoloured. P 14.*

1386	10 c.	Type 264	35	35
1387	15 c.	Coney	45	35
1388	50 c.	Long-spined Squirrelfish	70	50
1389	60 c.	Sergeant Major	70	50
1390	$1	Yellow-tailed Snapper	90	75
1391	$2	Rock Beauty	1·75	2·00
1392	$3	Spanish Hogfish	2·25	2·50
1393	$4	Striped Parrotfish	2·50	2·75
1386/93		*Set of 8*	8·50	8·75

MS1394 Two sheets, each 99×70 mm. (a) $5 Black-barred Soldierfish. (b) $5 Four-eyed Butterflyfish .. .. *Set of 2 sheets* 7·00 8·00

(Des K. Gromell. Litho B.D.T)

1990 (11 June). *Achievements in Space. T 265 and similar square designs. Multicoloured. P 14.*

1395	45 c.	Type 265	40	40
		a. Sheetlet. Nos. 1395/1414	7·00	
1396	45 c.	"Pioneer 11" photographing Saturn	40	40
1397	45 c.	Astronaut in transporter	40	40
1398	45 c.	Space shuttle *Columbia*	40	40
1399	45 c.	"Apollo 10" command module on parachutes	40	40
1400	45 c.	"Skylab" space station	40	40
1401	45 c.	Astronaut Edward White in space	40	40
1402	45 c.	"Apollo" spacecraft on joint mission	40	40
1403	45 c.	"Soyuz" spacecraft on joint mission	40	40
1404	45 c.	"Mariner 1" passing Venus	40	40
1405	45 c.	"Gemini 4" capsule	40	40
1406	45 c.	"Sputnik 1"	40	40
1407	45 c.	Hubble space telescope	40	40

1408	45 c.	North American X-15	40	40
1409	45 c.	Bell XS-1 airplane	40	40
1410	45 c.	"Apollo 17" astronaut and lunar rock formation	40	40
1411	45 c.	Lunar Rover	40	40
1412	45 c.	"Apollo 14" lunar module	40	40
1413	45 c.	Astronaut Buzz Aldrin on Moon	40	40
1414	45 c.	Soviet "Lunokhod" lunar vehicle	40	40
1395/1414		*Set of 20*	7·00	7·00

Nos. 1395/1414 were printed together, *se-tenant*, in sheetlets of 20 forming a composite design.

266 Queen Mother in Evening Dress   **267** Mickey Mouse as Animator

(Des D. Miller. Litho Questa)

1990 (27 Aug). *90th Birthday of Queen Elizabeth the Queen Mother. T 266 and similar vert designs showing recent photographs of the Queen Mother. P 14.*

1415	15 c.	multicoloured	20	15
1416	35 c.	multicoloured	30	25
1417	75 c.	multicoloured	60	60
1418	$3	multicoloured	2·00	2·50
1415/18		*Set of 4*	2·75	3·25

MS1419 67×98 mm. $6 multicoloured .. 3·75 4·50

(Des Walt Disney Co. Litho Questa)

1990 (3 Sept). *Mickey Mouse in Hollywood. T 267 and similar horiz designs showing Walt Disney cartoon characters. Multicoloured. P 14×13½.*

1420	25 c.	Type 267	25	25
1421	45 c.	Minnie Mouse learning lines while being dressed	35	25
1422	50 c.	Mickey Mouse with clapper board	45	30
1423	60 c.	Daisy Duck making-up Mickey Mouse	50	35
1424	$1	Clarabelle Cow as Cleopatra	75	60
1425	$2	Mickey Mouse directing Goofy and Donald Duck	1·40	1·60
1426	$3	Mickey Mouse directing Goofy as birdman	1·75	2·00
1427	$4	Donald Duck and Mickey Mouse editing film	2·00	2·50
1420/7		*Set of 8*	6·50	7·00

MS1428 Two sheets, each 132×95 mm. (a) $5 Minnie Mouse, Daisy Duck and Clarabelle as musical stars. (b) $5 Mickey Mouse on set as director .. .. *Set of 2 sheets* 6·00 7·00

268 Men's 20 Kilometres Walk   **269** Huey and Dewey asleep (*Christmas Stories*)

(Des B. Grout. Litho Questa)

1990 (1 Oct). *Olympic Games, Barcelona* (1992) (1st issue). *T 268 and similar vert designs. Multicoloured. P 14.*

1429	50 c.	Type 268	45	30
1430	75 c.	Triple jump	60	55
1431	$1	Men's 10,000 metres	80	80
1432	$5	Javelin	2·75	3·75
1429/32		*Set of 4*	4·25	4·75

MS1433 100×70 mm. $6 Athlete lighting Olympic flame at Los Angeles Olympics 3·75 5·00 See also Nos. 1553/61 and 1609/17.

(Des Walt Disney Co. Litho Questa)

1990 (15 Oct). *International Literacy Year. T 269 and similar vert designs showing Walt Disney cartoon characters illustrating works by Charles Dickens. Multicoloured. P 13½×14.*

1434	15 c.	Type 269	25	25
1435	45 c.	Donald Duck as Poor Jo looking at grave (*Bleak House*)	45	45
1436	50 c.	Dewey as Oliver asking for more (*Oliver Twist*)	50	50
1437	60 c.	Daisy Duck as The Marchioness (*Old Curiosity Shop*)	55	55
1438	$1	Little Nell giving nosegay to her grandfather (*Little Nell*)	85	85
1439	$2	Scrooge McDuck as Mr. Pickwick (*Pickwick Papers*)	1·50	1·50
1440	$3	Minnie Mouse as Florence and Mickey Mouse as Paul (*Dombey and Son*)	2·00	2·00
1441	$5	Minnie Mouse as Jenny Wren (*Our Mutual Friend*)	2·75	2·75
1434/41		*Set of 8*	8·00	8·00

MS1442 Two sheets, each 126×102 mm. (a) $6 Artful Dodger picking pocket (*Oliver Twist*). (b) $6 Unexpected arrivals at Mr. Peggoty's (*David Copperfield*) .. *Set of 2 sheets* 7·00 8·00

Winners
West Germany 1
Argentina 0

(270)

271 Pearly-eyed Thrasher

1990 (11 Nov). *World Cup Football Championship Winners, Italy. Nos.* 1308/12 *optd as T* **270** *by Questa.*

1443 15 c. Type **252** 45 20
1444 25 c. Goalkeeper moving towards ball .. 45 20
1445 $1 Goalkeeper reaching for ball .. 1·10 1·10
1446 $4 Goalkeeper saving goal .. .. 3·00 4·00
1443/6 .. .. *Set of* 4 4·50 5·00
MS1447 Two sheets, each 75×105 mm. (a) $5 Three players competing for ball (*horiz*). (b) $5 Ball and players' legs (*horiz*) .. *Set of 2 sheets* 7·00 8·50

The overprint on No. **MS**1447 is larger and thicker, 31×13 mm.

(Des Jennifer Toombs. Litho B.D.T.)

1990 (19 Nov). *Birds. T* **271** *and similar horiz designs. Multicoloured. P* 14.

1448 10 c. Type **271** 15 15
1449 25 c. Purple-throated Carib 20 20
1450 50 c. Yellowthroat 35 35
1451 60 c. American Kestrel 45 45
1452 $1 Yellow-bellied Sapsucker 70 70
1453 $2 Purple Gallinule .. .. .. 1·25 1·25
1454 $3 Yellow-crowned Night Heron .. 1·75 1·75
1455 $4 Blue-hooded Euphonia .. .. 2·10 2·10
1448/55 .. .. *Set of* 8 6·25 6·25
MS1456 Two sheets, each 76×60 mm. (a) $6 Brown Pelican. (b) $6 Magnificent Frigate Bird *Set of 2 sheets* 11·00 12·00

272 "Madonna and Child with Saints" (detail, Sebastiano del Piombo)

(Litho Questa)

1990 (10 Dec). *Christmas. Paintings by Renaissance Masters. T* **272** *and similar multicoloured designs. P* 14×13½ (*horiz*) *or* 13½×14 (*vert*).

1457 25 c. Type **272** 25 20
1458 30 c. "Virgin and Child with Angels" (detail, Grünewald) (*vert*) 30 20
1459 40 c. "The Holy Family and a Shepherd" (detail, Titian) 40 25
1460 60 c. "Virgin and Child" (detail, Lippi) (*vert*) 50 35
1461 $1 "Jesus, St. John and Two Angels" (Rubens) 70 60
1462 $2 "Adoration of the Shepherds" (detail, Vincenzo Catena) .. .. .. 1·40 1·60
1463 $4 "Adoration of the Magi" (detail, Giorgione) .. .. 2·50 3·00
1464 $5 "Virgin and Child adored by Warrior" (detail, Vincenzo Catena) .. .. 2·50 3·00
1457/64 .. .. *Set of* 8 7·75 8·25
MS1465 Two sheets, each 71×101 mm. (a) $6 "Allegory of the Blessings of Jacob" (detail, Rubens) (*vert*). (b) $6 "Adoration of the Magi" (detail, Fra Angelico) (*vert*) .. *Set of 2 sheets* 3·00 4·00

273 "Rape of the Daughters of Leucippus" (detail)

(Litho Questa)

1991 (21 Jan). *350th Death Anniv of Rubens. T* **273** *and similar horiz designs. Multicoloured. P* 14×13½.

1466 25 c. Type **273** 45 30
1467 45 c. "Bacchanal" (detail) 65 45
1468 50 c. "Rape of the Sabine Women" (detail) 70 50
1469 60 c. "Battle of the Amazons" (detail) .. 75 65
1470 $1 "Rape of the Sabine Women" (different detail) .. .. 1·00 1·00
1471 $2 "Bacchanal" (different detail) .. 1·50 1·75
1472 $3 "Rape of the Sabine Women" (different detail) .. .. 2·00 2·50
1473 $4 "Bacchanal" (different detail) .. 2·50 2·75
1466/73 .. .. *Set of* 8 8·50 9·00
MS1474 Two sheets, each 101×71 mm. (a) $6 "Rape of Hippodameia" (detail). (b) $6 "Battle of the Amazons" (different detail) .. *Set of 2 sheets* 6·50 7·50

274 U.S. Troops cross into Germany, 1944

(Des W. Wright. Litho B.D.T.)

1991 (11 Mar). *50th Anniv of Second World War. T* **274** *and similar horiz designs. Multicoloured. P* 14.

1475 10 c. Type **274** 10 10
1476 15 c. Axis surrender in North Africa, 1943 10 10
1477 25 c. U.S. tanks invade Kwalajalein, 1944 10 10
1478 45 c. Roosevelt and Churchill meet at Casablanca, 1943 .. .. .. 20 25
1479 50 c. Marshal Badoglio, Prime Minister of Italian anti-fascist government, 1943 25 30
1480 $1 Lord Mountbatten, Supreme Allied Commander South-east Asia, 1943 .. 45 50
1481 $2 Greek victory at Koritza, 1940 .. 90 95
1482 $4 Anglo-Soviet mutual assistance pact, 1941 .. .. 1·90 2·00
1483 $5 Operation Torch landings, 1942 .. 2·25 2·40
1475/83 .. .. *Set of* 9 6·00 6·50
MS1484 Two sheets, each 108×80 mm. (a) $6 Japanese attack Pearl Harbor, 1941. (b) $6 U.S.A.A.F. daylight raid on Schweinfurt, 1943 *Set of 2 sheets* 5·50 6·50

275 Locomotive *Prince Regent*, Middleton Colliery, 1812

(Des W. Hanson Studio. Litho Walsall)

1991 (18 Mar). *Cog Railways. T* **275** *and similar multicoloured designs. P* 14.

1485 25 c. Type **275** 50 30
1486 30 c. Snowdon Mountain Railway 50 35
1487 40 c. First railcar at Hell Gate, Manitou & Pike's Peak Railway, U.S.A. .. 55 45
1488 60 c. Pnka rack railway, Amberawa, Java 75 65
1489 $1 Green Mountain Railway, Maine, 1883 .. .. 1·00 1·00
1490 $2 Cog locomotive *Pike's Peak*, 1891 .. 1·75 2·00
1491 $4 Vitznau-Rigi Railway, Switzerland, and Mt Rigi hotel local post stamp .. 3·00 3·25
1492 $5 Leopoldina Railway, Brazil .. .. 3·00 3·25
1485/92 .. .. *Set of* 8 10·00 10·00
MS1493 Two sheets, each 100×70 mm. (a) $6 Electric donkey locomotives, Panama Canal. (b) $6 Gornergrat Railway, Switzerland (*vert*) *Set of 2 sheets* 9·50 10·00

276 *Heliconius charithonia*

(Des T. Pedersen. Litho B.D.T.)

1991 (15 Apr). *Butterflies. T* **276** *and similar multicoloured designs. P* 14.

1494 10 c. Type **276** 30 30
1495 35 c. *Marpesia petreus* 50 50
1496 50 c. *Anartia amathea* 60 60
1497 75 c. *Siproeta stelenes* 85 85
1498 $1 *Battus polydamas* 95 95
1499 $2 *Historis odius* .. .. .. 1·75 1·75
1500 $4 *Hypolimnas misippus* .. .. 3·00 3·00
1501 $5 *Hamadryas feronia* .. .. .. 3·00 3·00
1494/1501 .. .. .. *Set of* 8 10·00 10·00
MS1502 Two sheets. (a) 73×100 mm. $6 *Vanessa cardui* caterpillar (*vert*). (b) 100×73 mm. $6 *Danaus plexippus* caterpillar (*vert*) *Set of 2 sheets* 11·00 12·00

(Des T. Agans. Litho Questa)

1991 (22 Apr). *500th Anniv of Discovery of America by Columbus* (1992) (*4th issue*). *History of Exploration. T* **277** *and similar designs. P* 14.

1503 10 c. multicoloured 15 15
1504 15 c. multicoloured 20 20
1505 45 c. multicoloured 45 45
1506 60 c. multicoloured 55 55
1507 $1 multicoloured 75 75
1508 $2 multicoloured .. .. .. 1·50 1·50
1509 $4 multicoloured .. .. .. 2·50 2·50
1510 $5 multicoloured .. .. .. 2·75 2·75
1503/10 .. .. *Set of* 8 8·00 8·00
MS1511 Two sheets, each 106×76 mm. (a) $6 black and Indian red. (b) $6 black and Indian red *Set of 2 sheets* 5·75 6·50

Designs: *Horiz*—15 c. Pytheas the Greek, 325 B.C.; 45 c. Erik the Red discovering Greenland, 985 A.D.; 60 c. Leif Eriksson reaching Vinland, 1000 A.D.; $1 Scylax the Greek in the Indian Ocean, 518 A.D.; $2 Marco Polo sailing to the Orient, 1259 A.D.; $4 Ship of Queen Hatshepsut of Egypt, 1493 B.C.; $5 St. Brendan's coracle, 500 A.D. *Vert*—$6 (No. **MS**1511a) Engraving of Columbus as Admiral; $6 (No. **MS**1511b) Engraving of Columbus bare-headed

(Litho Walsall)

1991 (13 May). *Death Centenary of Vincent van Gogh* (*artist*) (1990). *T* **278** *and similar multicoloured designs. P* 13½.

1512 5 c. Type **278** 10 10
1513 10 c. "Armand Roulin" 10 10
1514 15 c. "Young Peasant Woman with Straw Hat sitting in the Wheat" 15 15
1515 25 c. "Adeline Ravoux" 20 20
1516 30 c. "The Schoolboy" 25 25
1517 40 c. "Doctor Gachet" 30 30
1518 50 c. "Portrait of a Man" 40 40
1519 75 c. "Two Children" 55 55
1520 $2 "The Postman Joseph Roulin" .. 1·40 1·40
1521 $3 "The Seated Zouave" .. .. 1·75 1·75
1522 $4 "L'Arlésienne" .. .. .. 2·50 2·50
1523 $5 "Self-Portrait, November/December 1888" .. .. 2·75 2·75
1512/23 .. .. *Set of* 12 9·00 9·00
MS1524 Three sheets, each 102×76 mm. (a) $5 "Farmhouse in Provence" (*horiz*). (b) $5 "Flowering Garden" (*horiz*). (c) $6 "The Bridge at Trinquetaille" (*horiz*). Imperf .. *Set of 3 sheets* 10·00 11·00

279 Mickey Mouse as Champion Sumo Wrestler

(Des Walt Disney Co. Litho Questa)

1991 (20 June). *"Phila Nippon '91" International Stamp Exhibition, Tokyo. T* **279** *and similar multicoloured designs showing Walt Disney cartoon characters participating in martial arts. P* 13½×14 (*vert*) *or* 14×13½ (*horiz*).

1525 10 c. Type **279** 30 20
1526 15 c. Goofy using the tonfa (*horiz*) .. 40 25
1527 45 c. Donald Duck as a Ninja (*horiz*) .. 70 50
1528 60 c. Mickey armed for Kung fu 85 65
1529 $1 Goofy with Kendo sword .. .. 1·25 1·25
1530 $2 Mickey and Donald demonstrating Aikido (*horiz*) .. .. .. 1·75 2·00
1531 $4 Mickey and Donald in Judo bout (*horiz*) .. .. 2·75 3·00
1532 $5 Mickey performing Yabusame (mounted archery) .. .. .. 3·00 3·25
1525/32 .. .. *Set of* 8 10·00 10·00
MS1533 Two sheets, each 127×102 mm. (a) $6 Mickey delivering Karate kick (*horiz*). (b) $6 Mickey demonstrating Tamashiwara *Set of 2 sheets* 9·00 10·00

277 Hanno the Phoenician, 450 B.C.

278 "Camille Roulin" (Van Gogh)

280 Queen Elizabeth and Prince Philip in 1976

281 Daisy Duck teeing-off

(Des D. Miller. Litho Walsall)

1991 (8 July). *65th Birthday of Queen Elizabeth II. T 280 and similar horiz designs. Multicoloured.* P 14.

1534	15 c. Type **280**	15	10
1535	20 c. The Queen and Prince Philip in Portugal, 1985	15	10
1536	$2 Queen Elizabeth II	1·25	1·50
1537	$4 The Queen and Prince Philip at Ascot, 1986	2·50	2·75
1534/7		Set of 4	3·50 4·00
MS1538	68×90 mm. $4 The Queen at National Theatre, 1986, and Prince Philip	3·00	4·00

(Des D. Miller. Litho Walsall)

1991 (8 July). *10th Wedding Anniv of Prince and Princess of Wales. Horiz designs as T 280. Multicoloured.* P 14.

1539	10 c. Prince and Princess of Wales at party, 1986	15	10
1540	40 c. Separate portraits of Prince, Princess and sons	30	25
1541	$1 Prince Henry and Prince William	70	70
1542	$5 Princess Diana in Australia and Prince Charles in Hungary	3·00	3·50
1539/42		Set of 4	3·75 4·00
MS1543	68×90 mm. $4 Prince Charles in Hackney and Princess and sons in Majorca, 1987	3·25	4·25

(Des Walt Disney Co. Litho Questa)

1991 (7 Aug). *Golf. T 281 and similar multicoloured designs showing Walt Disney cartoon characters.* P 13½×14.

1544	10 c. Type **281**	30	30
1545	15 c. Goofy playing ball from under trees	40	30
1546	45 c. Mickey Mouse playing deflected shot	70	50
1547	60 c. Mickey hacking divot out of fairway	80	65
1548	$1 Donald Duck playing ball out of pond	1·00	1·00
1549	$2 Minnie Mouse hitting ball over pond	2·00	2·25
1550	$4 Donald in a bunker	2·75	3·00
1551	$5 Goofy trying snooker shot into hole	3·00	3·25
1544/51		Set of 8	10·00 10·00
MS1552	Two sheets, each 127×102 mm. (a) $6 Grandma Duck in senior tournament. P 13½×14. (b) $6 Mickey and Minnie Mouse on course (*horiz*). P 14×13½	Set of 2 sheets	8·00 10·00

282 Moose receiving Gold Medal

283 Presidents De Gaulle and Kennedy, 1961

(Des Archie Comic Publications Inc. Litho Questa)

1991 (19 Aug). *50th Anniv of Archie Comics, and Olympic Games, Barcelona (1992) (2nd issue). T 282 and similar multicoloured designs.* P 14×13½ (*vert*) or 13½×14 (*horiz*).

1553	10 c. Type **282**	30	30
1554	25 c. Archie playing polo on a motorcycle (*horiz*)	40	30
1555	40 c. Archie and Betty at fencing class	70	45
1556	60 c. Archie joining girls' volleyball team	80	65
1557	$1 Archie with tennis ball in his mouth	1·00	1·00
1558	$2 Archie running marathon	2·00	2·25
1559	$4 Archie judging women's gymnastics (*horiz*)	3·50	3·75
1560	$5 Archie watching the cheer-leaders	3·50	3·75
1553/60		Set of 8	11·00 11·00
MS1561	Two sheets, each 128×102 mm. (a) $6 Archie heading football. (b) $6 Archie catching baseball (*horiz*)	Set of 2 sheets	9·00 10·00

(Des J. Iskowitz. Litho Questa)

1991 (11 Sept). *Birth Centenary of Charles de Gaulle (French statesman). T 283 and similar multicoloured designs.* P 14.

1562	10 c. Type **283**	40	40
1563	15 c. General De Gaulle with Pres. Roosevelt, 1945 (*vert*)	40	30
1564	45 c. Pres. De Gaulle with Chancellor Adenauer, 1962 (*vert*)	70	40
1565	60 c. De Gaulle at Arc de Triomphe, Liberation of Paris, 1944 (*vert*)	80	65
1566	$1 General De Gaulle crossing the Rhine, 1945	1·00	1·00
1567	$2 General De Gaulle in Algiers, 1944	1·75	2·00
1568	$4 Presidents De Gaulle and Eisenhower, 1960	2·75	3·00
1569	$5 De Gaulle returning from Germany, 1968 (*vert*)	3·00	3·25
1562/9		Set of 8	9·75 9·75
MS1570	Two sheets. (a) 76×106 mm. $6 De Gaulle with crowd. (b) 106×76 mm. $6 De Gaulle and Churchill at Casablanca, 1943	Set of 2 sheets	8·00 9·00

284 Parliament Building and Map

(Litho Questa)

1991 (28 Oct). *10th Anniv of Independence. T 284 and similar horiz design.* P 14.

1571	284 10 c. multicoloured	40	40
MS1572	87×97 mm. $6 Old Post Office, St. Johns, and stamps of 1862 and 1981 (50×37 mm)	4·25	4·75

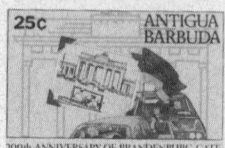

285 Germans celebrating Reunification

(Des L. Fried (Nos. 1573, 1576, 1580, MS1583a), W. Hanson Studio (Nos. 1574, 1577, 1581, MS1583b), J. Iskowitz (Nos. 1575, 1582) or W. Wright (others). Litho Questa)

1991 (9 Dec). *Anniversaries and Events. T 285 and similar multicoloured designs.* P 14.

1573	25 c. Type **285**	30	30
1574	75 c. Cubs erecting tent	50	50
1575	$1.50, Don Giovanni and Mozart	1·50	1·50
1576	$2 Chariot driver and Gate at night	1·10	1·10
1577	$2 Lord Baden-Powell and members of 3rd Antigua Methodist cub pack (*vert*)	1·25	1·25
1578	$2 Lilienthal's signature and glider Flugzeug Nr. 5	2·00	2·00
1579	$2.50, Driver in modern locomotive (*vert*)	2·00	2·00
1580	$3 Statues from podium	1·75	1·75
1581	$3.50, Cubs and camp fire	1·90	1·90
1582	$4 St. Peter's Cathedral, Salzburg	2·75	2·75
1573/82		Set of 10	13·50 13·50
MS1583	Two sheets. (a) 100×72 mm. $4 Detail of chariot and helmet, (b) 89×117 mm. $5 Antiguan flag and Jamboree emblem (*vert*)	Set of 2 sheets	6·00 7·00

Anniversaries and Events:—Nos. 1573, 1576, 1580, MS1583a, Bicentenary of Brandenburg Gate, Germany; Nos. 1574, 1577, 1581, MS1583b, 17th World Scout Jamboree, Korea; Nos. 1575, 1582, Death bicentenary of Mozart; No. 1578, Centenary of Otto Lilienthal's gliding experiments; No. 1579, Centenary of Trans–Siberian Railway.

286 *Nimitz* Class Carrier and *Ticonderoga* Class Cruiser

287 "The Annunciation" (Fra Angelico)

(Des L. Birmingham. Litho Questa)

1991 (9 Dec). *50th Anniv of Japanese Attack on Pearl Harbor. T 286 and similar horiz designs. Multicoloured,* P 14½.

1585	$1 Type **286**	80	80
	a. Sheetlet. Nos. 1585/94	7·00	
1586	$1 Tourist launch	80	80
1587	$1 U.S.S. *Arizona* memorial	80	80
1588	$1 Wreaths on water and aircraft	80	80
1589	$1 White Tern	80	80
1590	$1 Mitsubishi A6M Zero-Sen fighters over Pearl City	80	80
1591	$1 Mitsubishi A6M Zero-Sen fighters attacking	80	80
1592	$1 Battleship Row in flames	80	80
1593	$1 U.S.S. *Nevada* (battleship) underway	80	80
1594	$1 Mitsubishi A6M Zero-Sen fighters returning to carriers	80	80
1585/94		Set of 10	7·00 7·00

Nos. 1585/94 were printed together, *se-tenant*, in sheetlets of 10 with the stamps arranged in two horizontal strips of 5 separated by a gutter showing the wreck of U.S.S. *Arizona*.

(Litho Walsall)

1991 (12 Dec). *Christmas. Religious Paintings by Fra Angelico. T 287 and similar vert designs. Multicoloured.* P 12.

1595	10 c. Type **287**	20	20
1596	30 c. "Nativity"	35	25
1597	40 c. "Adoration of the Magi"	40	30
1598	60 c. "Presentation in the Temple"	55	45
1599	$1 "Circumcision"	75	65
1600	$3 "Flight into Egypt"	2·25	2·75
1601	$4 "Massacre of the Innocents"	2·50	3·00
1602	$5 "Christ teaching in the Temple"	2·50	3·00
1595/1602		Set of 8	8·50 9·50
MS1603	Two sheets, each 102×127 mm. (a) $6 "Adoration of the Magi" (Cook Tondo). (b) $6 "Adoration of the Magi" (*different*). P 14	Set of 2 sheets	8·50 10·00

ALTERED CATALOGUE NUMBERS

Any Catalogue numbers altered from the last edition are shown as a list in the introductory pages.

---

288 Queen Elizabeth II and Bird Sanctuary

289 Mickey Mouse awarding Swimming Gold Medal to Mermaid

(Des D. Miller. Litho Questa)

1992 (27 Feb). *40th Anniv of Queen Elizabeth II's Accession. T 288 and similar horiz designs. Multicoloured.* P 14.

1604	10 c. Type **288**	30	30
1605	30 c. Nelson's Dockyard	40	30
1606	$1 Ruins on Shirley Heights	70	70
1607	$5 Beach and palm trees	2·50	3·25
1604/7		Set of 4	3·50 4·00
MS1608	Two sheets, each 75×98 mm. (a) $6 Beach. (b) $6 Hillside foliage	Set of 2 sheets	6·50 7·00

(Des Walt Disney Co. Litho B.D.T.)

1992 (16 Mar). *Olympic Games, Barcelona (3rd issue). T 289 and similar multicoloured designs showing Walt Disney cartoon characters.* P 13.

1609	10 c. Type **289**	20	20
1610	15 c. Huey, Dewey and Louie with kayak	25	25
1611	30 c. Donald Duck and Uncle Scrooge in yacht	35	35
1612	50 c. Donald and horse playing water polo	50	50
1613	$1 Big Pete weightlifting	80	80
1614	$2 Donald and Goofy fencing	1·40	1·40
1615	$4 Mickey and Donald playing volleyball	2·50	2·50
1616	$5 Goofy vaulting	2·50	2·50
1609/16		Set of 8	7·75 7·75
MS1617	Four sheets, each 123×98 mm. (a) $6 Mickey playing football. (b) $6 Mickey playing basketball (*horiz*). (c) $6 Minnie Mouse on uneven parallel bars (*horiz*). (d) $6 Mickey, Goofy and Donald judging gymnastics (*horiz*)	Set of 4 sheets	13·00 14·00

290 Pteranodon

291 "Supper at Emmaus" (Caravaggio)

(Des R. Frank. Litho Walsall)

1992 (6 Apr). *Prehistoric Animals. T 290 and similar multicoloured designs.* P 14.

1618	10 c. Type **290**	40	30
1619	15 c. Brachiosaurus	45	30
1620	30 c. Tyrannosaurus Rex	55	35
1621	50 c. Parasaurolophus	65	50
1622	$1 Deinonychus (*horiz*)	1·00	1·00
1623	$2 Triceratops (*horiz*)	1·75	1·75
1624	$4 Protoceratops hatching (*horiz*)	2·25	2·50
1625	$5 Stegosaurus (*horiz*)	2·25	2·50
1618/25		Set of 8	8·50 8·25
MS1626	Two sheets, each 100×70 mm. (a) $6 Apatosaurus (*horiz*). (b) $6 Allosaurus (*horiz*)	Set of 2 sheets	7·50 8·50

(Litho Questa)

1992 (15 Apr). *Easter. Religious Paintings. T 291 and similar multicoloured designs.* P 14×13½.

1627	10 c. Type **291**	25	25
1628	15 c. "The Vision of St. Peter" (Zurbarán)	35	25
1629	30 c. "Christ driving the Money-changers from the Temple" (Tiepolo)	55	40
1630	40 c. "Martyrdom of St. Bartholomew" (detail) (Ribera)	65	50
1631	$1 "Christ driving the Money-changers from the Temple" (detail) (Tiepolo)	1·00	1·00
1632	$2 "Crucifixion" (detail) (Altdorfer)	2·00	2·25
1633	$4 "The Deposition" (detail) (Fra Angelico)	3·00	3·25
1634	$5 "The Deposition" (different detail) (Fra Angelico)	3·00	3·25
1627/34		Set of 8	9·75 10·00
MS1635	Two sheets. (a) 102×71 mm. $6 "The Last Supper" (detail) (Masip). P 14×13½. (b) 71×102 mm. $6 "Crucifixion" (detail) (*vert*) (Altdorfer). P 13½×14	Set of 2 sheets	8·50 10·00

292 "The Miracle at the Well" (Alonso Cano)

293 *Amanita caesarea*

(Litho B.D.T.)

1992 (11 May). *"Granada '92" International Stamp Exhibition, Spain. Spanish Paintings. T 292 and similar multicoloured designs. P 13×13½ (vert) or 13½×13 (horiz).*

1636	10 c. Type 292	30	30
1637	15 c. "The Poet Luis de Goingora y Argote" (Velázquez)	40	30
1638	30 c. "The Painter Francisco Goya" (Vincente López Portana)	55	40
1639	40 c. "María de las Nieves Michaela Fourdinier" (Luis Paret y Alcázar)	65	50
1640	$1 "Carlos III eating before his Court" (Alcázar) (*horiz*)	1·00	1·00
1641	$2 "Rain Shower in Granada" (Antonio Munoz Degrain) (*horiz*)	1·50	1·75
1642	$4 "Sarah Bernhardt" (Santiago Rusinol i Prats)	2·50	2·75
1643	$5 "The Hermitage Garden" (Joaquim Mir Trinxet)	2·75	3·00
1636/43	*Set of 8*	8·75	9·00

MS1644 Two sheets, each 120×95 mm. (a) $6 "The Ascent of Monsieur Boucié's Montgolfier Balloon in the Gardens of Aranjuez" (Antonio Carnicero) (112×87 *mm*). (b) $6 "Olympus: Battle with the Giants" (Francisco Bayeu y Subías) (112×87 *mm*). Imperf . *Set of 2 sheets* 9·00 10·00

(Litho Walsall)

1992 (18 May). *Fungi. T 293 and similar vert designs. Multicoloured. P 14.*

1645	10 c. Type 293	40	30
1646	15 c. *Collybia fusipes*	45	30
1647	30 c. *Boletus aereus*	60	40
1648	40 c. *Laccaria amethystina*	70	50
1649	$1 *Russula virescens*	1·25	1·25
1650	$2 *Tricholoma equestre* ("*Tricholoma auratum*")	2·00	2·25
1651	$4 *Calocybe gambosa*	3·00	3·25
1652	$5 *Lentinus tigrinus* ("*Panus tigrinus*")	3·25	3·50
1645/52	*Set of 8*	10·50	10·50

MS1653 Two sheets, each 100×70 mm. (a) $6 *Clavariadelphus truncatus*. (b) $6 *Auricularia auricula-judae* . *Set of 2 sheets* 9·50 10·50

294 Memorial Cross and Huts, San Salvador

(Des R. Jung. Litho Questa)

1992 (25 May). *500th Anniv of Discovery of America by Columbus (5th issue). World Columbian Stamp "Expo '92", Chicago. T 294 and similar horiz designs. Multicoloured. P 14.*

1654	15 c. Type 294	20	20
1655	30 c. Martin Pinzon with telescope	35	25
1656	40 c. Christopher Columbus	45	35
1657	$1 *Pinta*	1·00	1·00
1658	$2 *Nina*	1·60	1·75
1659	$4 *Santa Maria*	2·50	2·75
1654/9	*Set of 6*	5·50	5·75

MS1660 Two sheets, each 108×76 mm. (a) $6 Ship and map of West Indies. (b) $6 Sea monster . *Set of 2 sheets* 7·50 8·50

295 Antillean Crested Hummingbird and Wild Plantain

296 Columbus meeting Amerindians

(Des J. Papeo. Litho Walsall)

1992 (10 Aug). *"Genova '92" International Thematic Stamp Exhibition. Hummingbirds and Plants. T 295 and similar horiz designs. Multicoloured. P 14.*

1661	10 c. Type 295	20	20
1662	25 c. Green Mango and Parrot's Plantain	30	30
1663	45 c. Purple-throated Carib and Lobster Claws	45	45

1664	60 c. Antillean Mango and Coral Plant	55	55
1665	$1 Vervain Hummingbird and Cardinal's Guard	85	85
1666	$2 Rufous-breasted Hermit and Heliconia	1·50	1·50
1667	$4 Blue-headed Hummingbird and Red Ginger	2·75	2·75
1668	$5 Green-throated Carib and Ornamental Banana	3·00	3·00
1661/8	*Set of 8*	8·50	8·50

MS1669 Two sheets, each 100×70 mm. (a) $6 Bee Hummingbird and Jungle Flame. (b) $6 Western Streamertail and Bignonia . *Set of 2 sheets* 8·50 9·00

(Des F. Paul ($1), J. Esquino ($2). Litho Questa)

1992 (24 Aug). *500th Anniv of Discovery of America by Columbus (6th issue). Organization of East Caribbean States. T 296 and similar vert design. Multicoloured. P 14½.*

1670	$1 Type 296	65	65
1671	$2 Ships approaching island	1·25	1·25

297 Ts'ai Lun and Paper

(Des L. Fried. Litho Questa)

1992 (19 Oct). *Inventors and Inventions. T 297 and similar horiz designs. Multicoloured. P 14.*

1672	10 c. Type 297	15	15
1673	25 c. Igor Sikorsky and *Bolshoi Baltiskii* (first four-engined airplane)	30	30
1674	30 c. Alexander Graham Bell and early telephone	30	30
1675	40 c. Johannes Gutenberg and early printing press	35	35
1676	60 c. James Watt and stationary steam engine	70	70
1677	$1 Anton van Leeuwenhoek and early microscope	85	85
1678	$4 Louis Braille and hands reading braille	2·75	2·75
1679	$5 Galileo and telescope	3·00	3·00
1672/9	*Set of 8*	7·50	7·50

MS1680 Two sheets, each 100×73 mm. (a) $6 Edison and Latimer's phonograph. (b) $6 Fulton's steamboat . *Set of 2 sheets* 8·50 9·00

298 Elvis looking Pensive

(Des J. Iskowitz. Litho Questa)

1992 (26 Oct). *15th Death Anniv of Elvis Presley. T 298 and similar vert designs. Multicoloured. P 14.*

1681	$1 Type 298	80	80
	a. Sheetlet. Nos. 1681/9	6·50	
1682	$1 Wearing black and yellow striped shirt	80	80
1683	$1 Singing into microphone	80	80
1684	$1 Wearing wide-brimmed hat	80	80
1685	$1 With microphone in right hand	80	80
1686	$1 In Army uniform	80	80
1687	$1 Wearing pink shirt	80	80
1688	$1 In yellow shirt	80	80
1689	$1 In jacket and bow tie	80	80
1681/9	*Set of 9*	6·50	6·50

Nos. 1681/9 were printed together, *se-tenant*, in sheetlets of 9.

299 Madison Square Gardens

(Des Kerri Schiff. Litho Questa)

1992 (28 Oct). *Postage Stamp Mega Event, New York. Sheet 100×70 mm. P 14.*

MS1690 **299** $6 multicoloured . 4·25 5·00

NEW INFORMATION

The editor is always interested to correspond with people who have new information that will improve or correct the Catalogue.

300 "Virgin and Child with Angels" (detail) (School of Piero della Francesca)

301 Russian Cosmonauts

(Litho Questa)

1992 (16 Nov). *Christmas. T 300 and similar vert designs showing details of the Holy Child from various paintings. Multicoloured. P 13½.*

1691	10 c. Type 300	15	15
1692	25 c. "Madonna degli Alberelli" (Giovanni Bellini)	20	15
1693	30 c. "Madonna and Child with St. Anthony Abbot and St. Sigismund" (Neroccio)	30	20
1694	40 c. "Madonna and the Grand Duke" (Raphael)	40	30
1695	60 c. "The Nativity" (Georges de la Tour)	60	60
1696	$1 "Holy Family" (Jacob Jordaens)	85	85
1697	$4 "Madonna and Child Enthroned" (Magaritone)	3·00	3·25
1698	$5 "Madonna and Child on a Curved Throne" (Byzantine school)	3·25	3·50
1691/8	*Set of 8*	8·00	8·00

MS1699 Two sheets, each 76×102 mm. (a) $6 "Madonna and Child" (Domeno Ghirlando). (b) $6 "The Holy Family" (Pontormo) *Set of 2 sheets* 8·50 9·00

(Des W. Wright and L. Fried (Nos. 1700, 1711, **MS**1714a), W. Wright and W. Hanson (Nos. 1701, 1713, **MS**1714b), W. Wright (others). Litho Questa)

1992 (14 Dec). *Anniversaries and Events. T 301 and similar multicoloured designs. P 14.*

1700	10 c. Type 301	40	40
1701	40 c. Airship LZ-127 *Graf Zeppelin*, 1929	70	55
1702	45 c. Bishop Daniel Davis	50	40
1703	75 c. Konrad Adenauer making speech	65	65
1704	$1 Bus Mosbacher and *Weatherly* (yacht)	1·00	1·00
1705	$1.50, Rain forest	1·10	1·10
1706	$2 Tiger	3·00	3·00
1707	$2 National flag, plant and emblem (*horiz*)	1·75	1·75
1708	$2 Members of Community Players company (*horiz*)	1·75	1·75
1709	$2.25, Women carrying pots	1·75	1·75
1710	$3 Lions Club emblem	2·00	2·00
1711	$4 Chinese rocket on launch tower	2·00	2·00
1712	$4 West German and N.A.T.O. flags	2·00	2·00
1713	$6 Hugo Eckener (airship pioneer)	3·00	3·00
1700/13	*Set of 14*	19·00	19·00

MS1714 Four sheets, each 100×71 mm. (a) $6 Projected European space station. (b) $6 Airship LZ-129 *Hindenburg*, 1936. (c) $6 Brandenburg Gate on German flag. (d) $6 *Danaus plexippus* (butterfly) . *Set of 4 sheets* 17·00 18·00

Anniversaries and Events:—Nos. 1700, 1711, **MS**1714a, International Space Year; Nos. 1701, 1713, **MS**1714b, 75th death anniv of Count Ferdinand von Zeppelin; No. 1702, 150th anniv of Anglican Diocese of North-eastern Caribbean and Aruba; Nos. 1703, 1712, **MS**1714c, 25th death anniv of Konrad Adenauer (German statesman); No. 1704, Americas Cup Yachting Championship; Nos. 1705/6, **MS**1714d, Earth Summit '92, Rio; No. 1707, 50th anniv of Inter-American Institute for Agricultural Co-operation; No. 1708, 40th anniv of Cultural Development; No. 1709, United Nations World Health Organization Projects; No. 1710, 75th anniv of International Association of Lions Clubs.

302 Boy Hiker resting

303 Goofy playing Golf

(Litho Questa)

1993 (6 Jan). *Hummel Figurines. T 302 and similar vert designs. Multicoloured. P 14.*

1715	15 c. Type 302	15	15
1716	30 c. Girl sitting on fence	25	25
1717	40 c. Boy hunter	35	35
1718	50 c. Boy with umbrella	45	45
1719	$1 Hikers at signpost	75	75
1720	$2 Boy hiker with pack and stick	1·40	1·40
1721	$4 Girl with young child and goat	2·50	2·50
1722	$5 Boy whistling	2·75	2·75
1715/22	*Set of 8*	7·50	7·50

MS1723 Two sheets, each 97×122 mm. (a) $1.50 ×4, As Nos. 1715/18. (b) $1.50×4, As Nos. 1719/22 . *Set of 2 sheets* 11·00 12·00

(Des Euro-Disney, Paris. Litho Questa)

1993 (22 Feb). *Opening of Euro-Disney Resort, Paris. T* **303** *and similar multicoloured designs. P* 14×13½.

1724	10 c. Type **303**	30	30
1725	25 c. Chip and Dale at Davy Crockett's Campground	40	30
1726	30 c. Donald Duck at the Cheyenne Hotel	40	35
1727	40 c. Goofy at the Santa Fe Hotel	45	35
1728	$1 Mickey and Minnie Mouse at the New York Hotel	80	80
1729	$2 Mickey, Minnie and Goofy in car	1·40	1·40
1730	$4 Goofy at Pirates of the Caribbean	2·50	2·50
1731	$5 Donald at Adventureland	2·50	2·50
1724/31	*Set of 8*	8·00	7·75

MS1732 Four sheets, each 127×102 mm. (a) $6 Mickey in bellboy outfit. P 14×13½. (b) $6 Mickey on star (*vert*). P 13½×14. (c) $6 Mickey on opening poster (*vert*). P 13½×14. (d) $6 Mickey and balloons on opening poster (*vert*). P 13½×14 .. .. *Set of 4 sheets* 13·00 14·00

304 Cardinal's Guard

305 "The Destiny of Marie de' Medici" (upper detail) (Rubens)

(Des Dot Barlowe. Litho Questa)

1993 (15 Mar). *Flowers. T* **304** *and similar vert designs. Multicoloured. P* 14.

1733	15 c. Type **304**	35	30
1734	25 c. Giant Granadilla	40	30
1735	30 c. Spider Flower	40	35
1736	40 c. Gold Vine	45	35
1737	$1 Frangipani	80	80
1738	$2 Bougainvillea	1·40	1·40
1739	$4 Yellow Oleander	2·50	2·50
1740	$5 Spicy Jatropha	2·50	2·50
1733/40	*Set of 8*	8·00	7·75

MS1741 Two sheets, each 100×70 mm. (a) $6 Bird Lime Tree. (b) $6 Fairy Lily *Set of 2 sheets* 7·00 8·00

(Litho Walsall)

1993 (22 Mar). *Bicentenary of the Louvre, Paris. Paintings by Peter Paul Rubens. T* **305** *and similar vert designs. Multicoloured. P* 12.

1742	$1 Type **305**	60	60
	a. Sheetlet. Nos. 1742/9	4·25	
1743	$1 "The Birth of Marie de' Medici"	60	60
1744	$1 "The Education of Marie de' Medici"	60	60
1745	$1 "The Destiny of Marie de' Medici" (lower detail)	60	60
1746	$1 "Henry VI receiving the Portrait of Marie"	60	60
1747	$1 "The Meeting of the King and Marie at Lyons"	60	60
1748	$1 "The Marriage by Proxy"	60	60
1749	$1 "The Birth of Louis XIII"	60	60
1750	$1 "The Capture of Juliers"	60	60
	a. Sheetlet. Nos. 1750/7	4·25	
1751	$1 "The Exchange of the Princesses"	60	60
1752	$1 "The Regency"	60	60
1753	$1 "The Majority of Louis XIII"	60	60
1754	$1 "The Flight from Blois"	60	60
1755	$1 "The Treaty of Angouléme"	60	60
1756	$1 "The Peace of Angers"	60	60
1757	$1 "The Reconciliation of Louis and Marie de' Medici"	60	60
1742/57	*Set of 16*	8·50	8·50

MS1758 70×100 mm. $6 "Helene Fourment with a Coach" (52×85 *mm*). P 14½ .. .. 3·25 3·50

Nos. 1742/9 and 1750/7 depict details from "The Story of Marie de' Medici" and were each printed together, *se-tenant*, in sheetlets of 8 stamps and one centre label.

306 St. Lucia Amazon

(Des D. Burkhardt. Litho Questa)

1993 (5 Apr). *Endangered Species. T* **306** *and similar horiz designs. Multicoloured. P* 14.

1759	$1 Type **306**	60	60
	a. Sheetlet. Nos. 1759/70	6·50	
1760	$1 Cahow	60	60
1761	$1 Swallow-tailed Kite	60	60
1762	$1 Everglade Kite	60	60
1763	$1 Imperial Amazon	60	60
1764	$1 Humpback Whale	60	60
1765	$1 Plain Pigeon	60	60
1766	$1 St. Vincent Amazon	60	60
1767	$1 Puerto Rican Amazon	60	60
1768	$1 Leatherback Turtle	60	60

1769	$1 American Crocodile	60	60
1770	$1 Hawksbill Turtle	60	60
1759/70	*Set of 12*	6·50	6·50

MS1771 Two sheets, each 100×70 mm. (a) $6 As No. 1764. (b) $6 West Indian manatee *Set of 2 sheets* 7·00 8·00

Nos.1759/70 were printed together, *se-tenant*, in sheetlets of 12 with the background forming a composite design.

Coronation Anniversary 1953-1993

H.M. Queen Elizabeth II Coronation Anniversary 1953-1993

307 Queen Elizabeth II at Coronation (photograph by Cecil Beaton)

308 Princess Margaret and Antony Armstrong-Jones

(Des Kerri Schiff. Litho Questa)

1993 (2 June). *40th Anniv of Coronation* (1st issue). *T* **307** *and similar vert designs. P* 13½×14.

1772	30 c. multicoloured	50	50
	a. Sheetlet. Nos. 1772/5×2	8·00	
1773	40 c. multicoloured	60	60
1774	$2 indigo and black	1·50	1·75
1775	$4 multicoloured	1·90	2·00
1772/5	*Set of 4*	4·00	4·25

MS1776 70×100 mm. $6 multicoloured. P 14 3·75 4·00

Designs:—40 c. Queen Elizabeth the Queen Mother's Crown, 1937; $2 Procession of heralds; $4 Queen Elizabeth II and Prince Edward. (28½×42½ *mm*)—$6 "Queen Elizabeth II" (detail) (Dennis Fildes).

Nos. 1772/5 were printed together in sheetlets of 8, containing two *se-tenant* blocks of 4.

(Litho Questa)

1993 (2 June). *40th Anniv of Coronation* (2nd issue). *T* **308** *and similar vert designs. P* 13½×14.

1777/1808 $1×32 either grey and black or mult 18·00 20·00
Nos. 1777/1808 were printed in four *se-tenant* sheetlets of 9 (3×3) containing eight stamps and one bottom centre label, each sheetlet showing views from a decade of the reign.

WORLD CUP '94

309 Edward Stanley Gibbons and Catalogue of 1865

310 Paul Gascoigne

(Des Kerri Schiff (Nos. 1809/14), D. Keren (No. **MS**1815). Litho Questa)

1993 (14 June). *Famous Professional Philatelists* (1st series). *T* **309** *and similar horiz designs. P* 14.

1809	$1.50, agate, black and green	1·00	1·10
1810	$1.50, multicoloured	1·00	1·10
1811	$1.50, multicoloured	1·00	1·10
1812	$1.50, multicoloured	1·00	1·10
1813	$1.50, multicoloured	1·00	1·10
1814	$1.50, multicoloured	1·00	1·10
1809/14	*Set of 6*	5·50	6·00

MS1815 98×69 mm. $3 black; $3 black .. 4·00 4·25

Designs:—No. 1810, Theodore Champion and France 1849 1 f. stamp; No. 1811, J. Walter Scott and U.S.A. 1918 24 c. "Inverted Jenny" error; No. 1812, Hugo Michel and Bavaria 1849 1 k. stamp; No. 1813, Giulio and Giulio Bolaffi with Sardinia 1851 5 c. stamp; No. 1814, Richard Borek and Brunswick 1865 1 gr. stamp; No. **MS**1815, Front pages of *Mekeel's Weekly Stamp News* in 1891 (misdated 1890) and 1993.

See also No. 1957.

(Des Rosemary DeFiglio. Litho Questa)

1993 (30 July). *World Cup Football Championship, U.S.A.* (1st issue). *T* **310** *and similar vert designs showing English players. Multicoloured. P* 14.

1816	$2 Type **310**	1·25	1·40
1817	$2 David Platt	1·25	1·40
1818	$2 Martin Peters	1·25	1·40
1819	$2 John Barnes	1·25	1·40
1820	$2 Gary Lineker	1·25	1·40
1821	$2 Geoff Hurst	1·25	1·40
1822	$2 Bobby Charlton	1·25	1·40
1823	$2 Bryan Robson	1·25	1·40
1824	$2 Bobby Moore	1·25	1·40
1825	$2 Nobby Stiles	1·25	1·40
1826	$2 Gordon Banks	1·25	1·40
1827	$2 Peter Shilton	1·25	1·40
1816/27	*Set of 12*	13·50	15·00

MS1828 Two sheets, each 135×109 mm. (a) $6 Bobby Moore holding World Cup. (b) $6 Gary Lineker and Bobby Robson .. *Set of 2 sheets* 8·00 8·50

See also Nos. 2039/45.

311 Grand Inspector W. Heath

312 Hugo Eckener and Dr. W. Beckers with Airship LZ-127 *Graf Zeppelin* over Lake George, New York

(Des Kerri Schiff (Nos. 1830, 1837, 1840, 1844, **MS**1847b and **MS**1847e). Litho Questa)

1993 (16 Aug). *Anniversaries and Events. T* **311** *and similar designs. Deep blue-green and black (No.* **MS**1847c) *or multicoloured (others). P* 14.

1829	10 c. Type **311**	30	30
1830	15 c. Rodnina and Oulanov (U.S.S.R.) (pairs figure skating) (*horiz*)	30	30
1831	30 c. Present Masonic Hall, St. John's (*horiz*)	50	50
1832	30 c. Willy Brandt with Helmut Schmidt and George Leber (*horiz*)	30	30
1833	30 c. "Cat and Bird" (Picasso) (*horiz*)	40	40
1834	40 c. Previous Masonic Hall, St. John's (*horiz*)	50	50
1835	40 c. "Fish on a Newspaper" (Picasso) (*horiz*)	40	40
1836	40 c. Early astronomical equipment	40	40
1837	40 c. Prince Naruhito and engagement photographs (*horiz*)	40	40
1838	60 c. Grand Inspector J. Jeffery	60	60
1839	$1 "Woman Combing her Hair" (W. Slewinski) (*horiz*)	70	70
1840	$3 Masako Owada and engagement photographs (*horiz*)	1·75	1·75
1841	$3 "Artist's Wife with Cat" (Konrad Kryzanowski) (*horiz*)	1·75	1·75
1842	$4 Willy Brandt and protest march (*horiz*)	2·25	2·40
1843	$4 Galaxy	2·25	2·40
1844	$5 Alberto Tomba (Italy) (giant slalom) (*horiz*)	2·25	2·40
1845	$5 "Dying Bull" (Picasso) (*horiz*)	2·25	2·40
1846	$5 Pres. Clinton and family (*horiz*)	2·25	2·40
1829/46	*Set of 18*	18·00	18·00

MS1847 Seven sheets. (a) 106×75 mm. $5 Copernicus. (b) 106×75 mm. $6 Womens' 1500 metre speed skating medallists (*horiz*). (c) 106×75 mm. $6 Willy Brandt at Warsaw Ghetto Memorial (*horiz*). (d) 106×75 mm. $6 "Woman with a Dog" (detail) (Picasso) (*horiz*). (e) 106×75 mm. $6 Masako Owada. (f) 70×100 mm. $6 "General Confusion" (S. I. Witkiewicz). (g) 106×75 mm. $6 Pres. Clinton taking the Oath (42½×57 *mm*) .. .. *Set of 7 sheets* 22·00 23·00

Anniversaries and Events:—Nos. 1829, 1831, 1834, 1838, 150th anniv of St. John's Masonic Lodge No. 492; Nos. 1830, 1844, **MS**1847b, Winter Olympic Games '94, Lillehammer; Nos. 1832, 1842, **MS**1847c, 80th birth anniv of Willy Brandt (German politician); Nos. 1833, 1835, 1845, **MS**1847d, 20th death anniv of Picasso (artist); Nos.1836, 1843, **MS**1847a, 450th death anniv of Copernicus (astronomer); Nos. 1837, 1840, **MS**1847e, Marriage of Crown Prince Naruhito of Japan; Nos. 1839, 1841, **MS**1847f, "Polska '93" International Stamp Exhibition, Poznań; Nos. 1846, **MS**1847g, Inauguration of U.S. President William Clinton.

(Des W. Hanson. Litho Questa)

1993 (16 Aug–11 Oct). *Aviation Anniversaries. T* **312** *and similar multicoloured designs. P* 14.

1848	30 c. Type **312**	45	45
1849	40 c. Chicago World's Fair from *Graf Zeppelin*	50	50
1850	40 c. Gloster Whittle E28/39, 1941 (11 Oct)	50	50
1851	40 c. George Washington writing balloon mail letter (*vert*) (11 Oct)	50	50
1852	$4 Pres. Wilson and Curtiss JN-4 "Jenny" (11 Oct)	2·75	2·75
1853	$5 Airship LZ-129 *Hindenburg* over Ebbets Field baseball stadium, 1937	2·75	2·75
1854	$5 Gloster Meteor in dogfight (11 Oct)	2·75	2·75
1848/54	*Set of 7*	9·00	9·00

MS1855 Three sheets. (a) 86×105 mm. $6 Hugo Eckener (*vert*). (b) 105×86 mm. $6 Consolidated PBY-5 Catalina flying boat (57×42½ *mm*). (c) 105×86 mm. $6 Alexander Hamilton, Washington and John Jay watching Blanchard's balloon, 1793 (*horiz*) .. *Set of 3 sheets* 10·00 11·00

Anniversaries:—Nos. 1848/9, 1853, **MS**1855a, 125th birth anniv of Hugo Eckener (airship commander); Nos. 1850, 1854, **MS**1855b, 75th anniv of Royal Air Force; Nos. 1851/2, **MS**1855c, Bicent of First Airmail Flight.

313 Lincoln Continental

(Des W. Hanson. Litho Questa)

1993 (11 Oct). *Centenaries of Henry Ford's First Petrol Engine (Nos. 1856, 1858, **MS**1860a) and Karl Benz's First Four-wheeled Car (others). T **313** and similar horiz designs. Multicoloured. P 14.*

1856	30 c. Type **313**		40	40
1857	40 c. Mercedes racing car, 1914		45	45
1858	$4 Ford "GT40", 1966		2·50	2·50
1859	$5 Mercedes Benz "gull-wing" coupe, 1954		2·50	2·50
1856/9		*Set of 4*	5·25	5·25

MS1860 Two sheets. (a) 114×87 mm. $6 Ford's Mustang emblem. (b) 87×114 mm. $6 Germany 1936 12 pf. Benz and U.S.A. 1968 12 c. Ford stamps .. .. .. *Set of 2 sheets* 7·50 8·00

314 *The Musical Farmer, 1932*

(Des Rosemary DeFiglio. Litho Questa)

1993 (25 Oct). *Mickey Mouse Film Posters. T **314** and similar vert designs. Multicoloured. P 13½×14.*

1861	10 c. Type **314**		30	30
1862	15 c. *Little Whirlwind, 1941*		35	35
1863	30 c. *Pluto's Dream House, 1940*		40	40
1864	40 c. *Gulliver Mickey, 1934*		40	40
1865	50 c. *Alpine Climbers, 1936*		45	45
1866	$1 *Mr. Mouse Takes a Trip, 1940*		70	70
1867	$2 *The Nifty Nineties, 1941*		1·25	1·25
1868	$4 *Mickey Down Under, 1948*		2·25	2·50
1869	$5 *The Pointer, 1939*		2·25	2·50
1861/9		*Set of 9*	7·50	8·00

MS1870 Two sheets, each 125×105 mm. (a) $6 *The Simple Things,* 1953. (b) $6 *The Prince and the Pauper, 1990* .. .. *Set of 2 sheets* 7·50 8·00

315 Marie and Fritz with Christmas Tree

(Des Alvin White Studio. Litho Questa)

1993 (8 Nov). *Christmas. Mickey's Nutcracker. T **315** and similar multicoloured designs showing Walt Disney cartoon characters in scenes from The Nutcracker. P 14×13½.*

1871	10 c. Type **315**		30	30
1872	15 c. Marie receives Nutcracker from Godfather Drosselmeir		30	30
1873	20 c. Fritz breaks Nutcracker		35	30
1874	30 c. Nutcracker with sword		40	30
1875	40 c. Nutcracker and Marie in the snow		45	30
1876	50 c. Marie and the Prince meet Sugar Plum Fairy		50	40
1877	60 c. Marie and Prince in Crystal Hall		50	50
1878	$3 Huey, Dewey and Louie as Cossack dancers		1·75	2·00
1879	$6 Mother Ginger and her puppets		3·00	3·50
1871/9		*Set of 9*	6·75	7·25

MS1880 Two sheets, each 127×102 mm. (a) $6 Marie and Prince in sleigh. P 14×13½. (b) $6 The Prince in sword fight (*vert*). P 13½×14 .. .. .. *Set of 2 sheets* 7·50 8·00

316 "Hannah and Samuel" (Rembrandt)

(Des Kerri Schiff. Litho Questa)

1993 (22 Nov). *Famous Paintings by Rembrandt and Matisse. T **316** and similar vert designs. Multicoloured. P 13½×14.*

1881	15 c. Type **316**		30	30
1882	15 c. "Guitarist" (Matisse)		30	30
1883	30 c. "The Jewish Bride" (Rembrandt)		40	30
1884	40 c. "Jacob wrestling with the Angel" (Rembrandt)		40	30
1885	60 c. "Interior with a Goldfish Bowl" (Matisse)		50	50
1886	$1 "Mlle Yvonne Landsberg" (Matisse)		80	80
1887	$4 "The Toboggan" (Matisse)		2·50	2·75
1888	$5 "Moses with the Tablets of the Law" (Rembrandt)		2·50	2·75
1881/8		*Set of 8*	7·00	7·25

MS1889 Two sheets. (a) 124×99 mm. $6 "The Blinding of Samson by the Philistines" (detail) (Rembrandt). (b) 99×124 mm. $6 "The Three Sisters" (detail) (Matisse) .. *Set of 2 sheets* 7·50 8·00

317 Hong Kong 1981 $1 Golden Threadfin Bream Stamp and Fishing Boats, Shau Kei Wan

(Des W. Hanson. Litho Questa)

1994 (18 Feb). *"Hong Kong '94" International Stamp Exhibition (1st issue). T **317** and similar horiz design. Multicoloured. P 14.*

1890	40 c. Type **317**		20	25
	a. Horiz pair. Nos. 1890/1		40	50
1891	40 c. Antigua 1990 $2 Rock Beauty stamp and fishing boats, Shau Kei Wan		20	25

Nos. 1890/1 were printed together, *se-tenant*, in horizontal pairs throughout the sheet with the centre part of each pair forming a composite design.

Antigua & Barbuda 40¢

318 Terracotta Warriors

(Des Kerri Schiff. Litho Questa)

1994 (18 Feb). *"Hong Kong '94" International Stamp Exhibition (2nd issue). Qin Dynasty Terracotta Figures. T **318** and similar horiz designs. Multicoloured. P 14.*

1892	40 c. Type **318**		20	25
	a. Sheetlet. Nos. 1892/7		1·10	
1893	40 c. Cavalryman and horse		20	25
1894	40 c. Warriors in armour		20	25
1895	40 c. Painted bronze chariot and team		20	25
1896	40 c. Pekingese dog		20	25
1897	40 c. Warriors with horses		20	25
1892/7		*Set of 6*	1·10	1·50

Nos. 1892/7 were printed together, *se-tenant*, in sheetlets of 6.

319 Mickey Mouse in Junk

320 Sumatran Rhinoceros lying down

(Litho Questa)

1994 (18 Feb). *"Hong Kong '94" International Stamp Exhibition (3rd issue). T **319** and similar multicoloured designs showing Walt Disney cartoon characters. P 13½×14.*

1898	10 c. Type **319**		10	10
1899	15 c. Minnie Mouse as mandarin		10	10
1900	30 c. Donald and Daisy Duck on house boat		15	20
1901	50 c. Mickey holding bird in cage		25	30
1902	$1 Pluto and ornamental dog		45	50
1903	$2 Minnie and Daisy celebrating Bun Festival		90	95
1904	$4 Goofy making noodles		1·90	2·00
1905	$5 Goofy pulling Mickey in rickshaw		2·25	2·40
1898/1905		*Set of 8*	6·00	6·50

MS1906 Two sheets, each 133×109 mm. (a) $5 Mickey and Donald on harbour ferry (*horiz*). (b) $5 Mickey in traditional dragon dance (*horiz*). P 14×13½. .. .. *Set of 2 sheets* 4·50 4·75

(Litho Questa)

1994 (1 Mar). *Centenary of Sierra Club (environmental protection society) (1992). Endangered Species. T **320** and similar multicoloured designs. P 14.*

1907	$1.50, Type **320**		70	75
	a. Sheetlet. Nos. 1907/14		4·75	
1908	$1.50, Sumatran Rhinoceros feeding		70	75
1909	$1.50, Ring-tailed Lemur on ground		70	75
1910	$1.50, Ring-tailed Lemur on branch		70	75
1911	$1.50, Red-fronted Brown Lemur on branch		70	75
1912	$1.50, Head of Red-fronted Brown Lemur		70	75
1913	$1.50, Head of Red-fronted Brown Lemur in front of trunk		70	75
1914	$1.50, Sierra Club Centennial emblem (black, buff and deep blue-green)		70	75
	a. Sheetlet. Nos. 1914/21		4·75	
1915	$1.50, Head of Bactrian Camel		70	75
1916	$1.50, Bactrian Camel		70	75
1917	$1.50, African Elephant drinking		70	75
1918	$1.50, Head of African Elephant		70	75
1919	$1.50, Leopard sitting upright		70	75
1920	$1.50, Leopard in grass (emblem at right)		70	75
1921	$1.50, Leopard in grass (emblem at left)		70	75
1907/21		*Set of 15*	10·50	11·00

MS1922 Four sheets. (a) 100×70 mm. $1.50, Sumatran Rhinoceros (*horiz*). (b) 70×100 mm. $1.50, Ring-tailed Lemur (*horiz*). (c) 70×100 mm. $1.50, Bactrian Camel (*horiz*). (d) 100×70 mm. $1.50, African Elephant (*horiz*) .. .. *Set of 4 sheets* 2·75 3·00

Nos. 1907/14 and 1914/21 were printed together, *se-tenant*, in sheetlets of 8 with each sheetlet containing No. 1914 at bottom right.

321 West Highland White Terrier

322 *Spiranthes lanceolata*

(Des Jennifer Toombs. Litho Questa)

1994 (5 Apr). *Dogs of the World. Chinese New Year ("Year of the Dog"). T **321** and similar horiz designs. Multicoloured. P 14×14½.*

1923	50 c. Type **321**		25	30
	a. Sheetlet. Nos. 1923/34		3·00	
1924	50 c. Beagle		25	30
1925	50 c. Scottish Terrier		25	30
1926	50 c. Pekingese		25	30
1927	50 c. Dachshund		25	30
1928	50 c. Yorkshire Terrier		25	30
1929	50 c. Pomeranian		25	30
1930	50 c. Poodle		25	30
1931	50 c. Shetland Sheepdog		25	30
1932	50 c. Pug		25	30
1933	50 c. Shih Tzu		25	30
1934	50 c. Chihuahua		25	30
1935	75 c. Mastiff		35	40
	a. Sheetlet. Nos. 1935/46		4·00	
1936	75 c. Border Collie		35	40
1937	75 c. Samoyed		35	40
1938	75 c. Airedale Terrier		35	40
1939	75 c. English Setter		35	40
1940	75 c. Rough Collie		35	40
1941	75 c. Newfoundland		35	40
1942	75 c. Weimarana		35	40
1943	75 c. English Springer Spaniel		35	40
1944	75 c. Dalmatian		35	40
1945	75 c. Boxer		35	40
1946	75 c. Old English Sheepdog		35	40
1923/46		*Set of 24*	7·00	8·50

MS1947 Two sheets, each 93×58 mm. (a) $6 Welsh Corgi. (b) $6 Labrador Retriever .. .. *Set of 2 sheets* 5·50 5·75

Nos. 1923/34 and 1935/46 were printed together, *se-tenant*, in sheetlets of 12.

(Litho Questa)

1994 (11 Apr). *Orchids. T **322** and similar vert designs. Multicoloured. P 14.*

1948	10 c. Type **322**		10	10
1949	20 c. *Ionopsis utricularioides*		10	10
1950	30 c. *Tetramicra canaliculata*		15	20
1951	50 c. *Oncidium picturatum*		25	30
1952	$1 *Epidendrum difforme*		45	50
1953	$2 *Epidendrum ciliare*		90	95
1954	$4 *Epidendrum ibaguense*		1·90	2·00
1955	$5 *Epidendrum nocturnum*		2·25	2·40
1948/55		*Set of 8*	6·00	6·50

MS1956 Two sheets, each 100×73 mm. (a) $6 *Rodriguezia lanceolata.* (b) $6 *Encyclia cochleata* .. .. *Set of 2 sheets* 5·50 5·75

The new-issue supplement to this Catalogue appears each month in

GIBBONS STAMP MONTHLY

—from your newsagent or by postal subscription— sample copy and details on request.

323 Hermann E. Sieger, Germany 1931 1 m. Zeppelin Stamp and Airship LZ-127 *Graf Zeppelin*

324 *Danaus plezippus*

(Litho Questa)

1994 (6 June). *Famous Professional Philatelists (2nd series).* P 14.
1957 323 $1.50, multicoloured 70 75

(Des B. Hargreaves. Litho Questa)

1994 (27 June). *Butterflies. T 324 and similar vert designs. Multicoloured.* P 14.
1958 10 c. Type **324** 10 10
1959 15 c. *Appias drusilla* 10 10
1960 30 c. *Eurema lisa*.. .. .. 15 20
1961 40 c. *Anaea troglodyta* 20 25
1962 $1 *Urbanus proteus* 45 50
1963 $2 *Junonia evarete* 90 95
1964 $4 *Battus polydamas* .. .. 1·90 2·00
1965 $5 *Heliconius charitonia* .. 2·25 2·40
1958/65 .. .. .. *Set of 8* 6·00 6·50
MS1966 Two sheets, each 102×72 mm. (a) $6 *Phoebis sennae*. (b) $6 *Hemiargus hanno*
.. .. .. *Set of 2 sheets* 5·50 5·75
No. 1959 is inscribed "Appisa drusilla" and No. 1965 "Heliconius charitonius", both in error.

325 Bottlenose Dolphin

326 Edwin Aldrin (astronaut)

(Des J. Genzo. Litho Questa)

1994 (21 July). *Marine Life. T 325 and similar multicoloured designs.* P 14.
1967 50 c. Type **325** 25 30
a. Sheetlet. Nos. 1967/75 .. .. 2·25
1968 50 c. Killer Whale 25 30
1969 50 c. Spinner Dolphin 25 30
1970 50 c. Oceanic Sunfish 25 30
1971 50 c. Caribbean Reef Shark and Short Fin Pilot Whale 25 30
1972 50 c. Copper-banded Butterflyfish .. 25 30
1973 50 c. Mosaic Moray 25 30
1974 50 c. Clown Triggerfish 25 30
1975 50 c. Red Lobster 25 30
1967/75 .. .. .. *Set of 9* 2·25 2·50
MS1976 Two sheets, each 106×76 mm. (a) $6 Seahorse. (b) $6 Swordfish ("Blue Marlin") *(horiz)* .. .. *Set of 2 sheets* 5·50 5·75
Nos. 1967/75 were printed together, *se-tenant*, in sheetlets of 9.

(Des W. Hanson. Litho Questa)

1994 (4 Aug). *25th Anniv of First Moon Landing. T 326 and similar horiz designs. Multicoloured.* P 14.
1977 $1.50, Type **326** 70 75
a. Sheetlet. Nos. 1977/82 .. 4·25
1978 $1.50, First lunar footprint .. 70 75
1979 $1.50, Neil Armstrong (astronaut) .. 70 75
1980 $1.50, Aldrin stepping onto Moon .. 70 75
1981 $1.50, Aldrin and equipment .. 70 75
1982 $1.50, Aldrin and U.S.A. flag .. 70 75
1983 $1.50, Aldrin at Tranquility Base .. 70 75
a. Sheetlet. Nos. 1983/8 .. 4·25
1984 $1.50, Moon plaque 70 75
1985 $1.50, *Eagle* leaving Moon .. 70 75
1986 $1.50, Command module in lunar orbit .. 70 75
1987 $1.50, First Man on Moon stamp .. First day cover of U.S.A. 1969 10 c. .. 70 75
1988 $1.50, Pres. Nixon and astronauts .. 70 75
1977/88 .. .. .. *Set of 12* 8·25 9·00
MS1989 72×102 mm. $6 Armstrong and Aldrin with postal official .. .. 2·75 3·00
Nos. 1977/82 and 1983/8 were printed together, *se-tenant*, in sheetlets of 6.

327 Edwin Moses (U.S.A.) (400 metres hurdles), 1984

(Des Kerri Schiff. Litho Questa)

1994 (4 Aug). *Centenary of International Olympic Committee. Gold Medal Winners. T 327 and similar horiz designs. Multicoloured.* P 14.
1990 50 c. Type **327** 25 30
1991 $1.50, Steffi Graf (Germany) (tennis), 1988 .. .. 70 75
MS1992 79×110 mm. $6 Johann Olav Koss (Norway) (500, 1500 and 10,000 metre speed skating), 1994 .. .. 2·75 3·00

328 Antiguan Family

(Litho Questa)

1994 (4 Aug). *International Year of the Family.* P 14.
1993 328 90 c. multicoloured 40 45

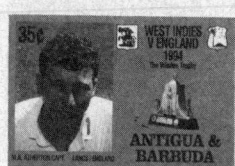

329 Mike Atherton (England) and Wisden Trophy

(Des A. Melville-Brown. Litho Questa)

1994 (4 Aug). *Centenary of First English Cricket Tour to the West Indies (1995). T 329 and similar multicoloured designs.* P 14.
1994 35 c. Type **329** 15 20
1995 75 c. Viv Richards (West Indies) *(vert)* .. 35 40
1996 $1.20, Richie Richardson (West Indies) and Wisden Trophy .. 55 60
1994/6 .. .. .. *Set of 3* 1·00 1·10
MS1997 80×100 mm. $3 English team, 1895 (black and grey-brown) .. 1·40 1·50

330 Entrance Bridge, Songgwangsa Temple

(Des Kerri Schiff. Litho Questa (Nos. 1998, 2007/9), B.D.T. (Nos. 1999/2006))

1994 (4 Aug). *"Philakorea '94" International Stamp Exhibition, Seoul. T 330 and similar multicoloured designs.* P 13½ (Nos. 1999/2006) or 14 (*others*).
1998 40 c. Type **330** 20 25
1999 75 c. Long-necked bottle .. 35 40
a. Sheetlet. Nos. 1999/2006 .. 2·75
2000 75 c. Punch'ong ware jar with floral decoration 35 40
2001 75 c. Punch'ong ware jar with blue dragon pattern 35 40
2002 75 c. Ewer in shape of bamboo shoot .. 35 40
2003 75 c. Punch'ong ware green jar .. 35 40
2004 75 c. Pear-shaped bottle .. 35 40
2005 75 c. Porcelain jar with brown dragon pattern 35 40
2006 75 c. Porcelain jar with floral pattern .. 35 40
2007 90 c. Song-op Folk Village, Cheju .. 40 45
2008 $3 Port Sogwipo .. .. 1·40 1·50
1998/2008 .. .. .. *Set of 11* 4·75 5·25
MS2009 104×71 mm. $4 Ox herder playing flute *(vert)* .. .. 1·90 2·00
Nos. 1999/2006, each 24×47 mm, were printed together, *se-tenant*, in sheetlets of 8.

331 Short S.25 Sunderland Flying Boat

332 Travis Tritt

(Des J. Batchelor. Litho Questa)

1994 (4 Aug). *50th Anniv of D-Day. T 331 and similar horiz designs. Multicoloured.* P 14.
2010 40 c. Type **331** 20 25
2011 $2 Lockheed P-38 Lightning fighters attacking train 90 95
2012 $3 Martin B-26 Marauder bombers .. 1·40 1·50
2010/12 .. .. .. *Set of 3* 2·50 2·75
MS2013 108×78 mm. $6 Hawker Typhoon fighter bomber .. .. 2·75 3·00

(Des J. Iskowitz. Litho Questa)

1994 (18 Aug). *Stars of Country and Western Music. T 332 and similar multicoloured designs.* P 14.
2014 75 c. Type **332** 35 40
a. Sheetlet. Nos. 2014/21 .. 2·75
2015 75 c. Dwight Yoakam 35 40
2016 75 c. Billy Ray Cyrus 35 40
2017 75 c. Alan Jackson 35 40
2018 75 c. Garth Brooks 35 40
2019 75 c. Vince Gill 35 40
2020 75 c. Clint Black 35 40
2021 75 c. Eddie Rabbit 35 40
2022 75 c. Patsy Cline 35 40
a. Sheetlet. Nos. 2022/9 .. 2·75
2023 75 c. Tanya Tucker 35 40
2024 75 c. Dolly Parton 35 40
2025 75 c. Anne Murray 35 40
2026 75 c. Tammy Wynette 35 40
2027 75 c. Loretta Lynn 35 40
2028 75 c. Reba McEntire 35 40
2029 75 c. Skeeter Davis 35 40
2030 75 c. Hank Snow 35 40
a. Sheetlet. Nos. 2030/7 .. 2·75
2031 75 c. Gene Autry 35 40
2032 75 c. Jimmie Rodgers 35 40
2033 75 c. Ernest Tubb 35 40
2034 75 c. Eddy Arnold 35 40
2035 75 c. Willie Nelson 35 40
2036 75 c. Johnny Cash 35 40
2037 75 c. George Jones 35 40
2014/37 .. .. .. *Set of 24* 8·25 9·50
MS2038 Three sheets. (a) 100×70 mm. $6 Hank Williams Jr. (b) 100×70 mm. $6 Hank Williams Sr. (c) 70×100 mm. $6 Kitty Wells *(horiz)* .. .. *Set of 3 sheets* 8·25 8·50
Nos. 2014/21, 2022/9 and 2030/7 were printed together *se-tenant*, in sheetlets of 8.

333 Hugo Sanchez (Mexico)

(Litho B.D.T.)

1994 (19 Sept). *World Cup Football Championship, U.S.A. (2nd issue). T 333 and similar multicoloured designs.* P 14.
2039 15 c. Type **333** 10 10
2040 35 c. Jürgen Klinsmann (Germany) .. 15 20
2041 65 c. Antiguan player 30 35
2042 $1.20, Cobi Jones (U.S.A.) .. 55 60
2043 $4 Roberto Baggio (Italy) .. 1·90 2·00
2044 $5 Bwalya Kalusha (Zambia) .. 2·25 2·40
2039/44 .. .. .. *Set of 6* 5·25 5·50
MS2045 Two sheets. (a) 72×105 mm. $6 Maldive Islands player *(vert)*. (b) 107×78 mm. $6 World Cup trophy *(vert)* .. *Set of 2 sheets* 5·50 5·75
No. 2040 is inscribed "Klinsman" in error.

334 Sir Shridath Ramphal

(Litho Questa)

1994 (26 Sept). *First Recipients of Order of the Caribbean Community. T 334 and similar horiz designs. Multicoloured.* P 14.
2046 65 c. Type **334** 30 35
2047 90 c. William Demas 40 45
2048 $1.20, Derek Walcott 55 60
2046/8 .. .. .. *Set of 3* 1·25 1·40

335 Pair of Magnificent Frigate Birds

336 "Virgin and Child by the Fireside" (Robert Campin)

(Des Tracy Pedersen. Litho Questa)

1994 (12 Dec). *Birds. T 335 and similar multicoloured designs. P 14.*

2049	10 c. Type 335	10	10
2050	15 c. Bridled Quail Dove ..	10	10
2051	30 c. Magnificent Frigate Bird chick hatching	15	20
2052	40 c. Purple-throated Carib (*vert*)	20	25
2053	$1 Male Magnificent Frigate Bird in courtship display (*vert*)	45	50
2054	$1 Broad-winged Hawk (*vert*)	45	50
2055	$3 Young Magnificent Frigate Bird	1·40	1·50
2056	$4 Yellow Warbler	1·90	2·00
2049/56	*Set of 8*	4·75	5·00

MS2057 Two sheets. (a) 70×100 mm. $6 Female Magnificent Frigate Bird (*vert*). (b) 100×70 mm. $6 Black-billed Whistling Duck ducklings
Set of 2 sheets 5·50 5·75
Nos. 2049, 2051, 2053 and 2055 also show the W.W.F. Panda emblem.

(Litho Questa)

1994 (12 Dec). *Christmas. Religious Paintings. T 336 and similar vert designs. Multicoloured. P 13½×14.*

2058	15 c. Type 336	10	10
2059	35 c. "The Reading Madonna" (Giorgione)	15	20
2060	40 c. "Madonna and Child" (Giovanni Bellini)	20	25
2061	45 c. "The Litta Madonna" (Da Vinci)	20	25
2062	65 c. "The Virgin and Child under the Apple Tree" (Lucas Cranach the Elder)	30	35
2063	75 c. "Madonna and Child" (Master of the Female Half-lengths)	35	40
2064	$1.20, "An Allegory of the Church" (Alessandro Allori)	55	60
2065	$5 "Madonna and Child wreathed with Flowers" (Jacob Jordaens)	2·25	2·40
2058/65	*Set of 8*	4·00	4·50

MS2066 Two sheets. (a) 123×88 mm. $6 "Madonna and Child with Commissioners" (detail) "Palma Vecchio". (b) 88×123 mm. $6 "The Virgin Enthroned with Child" (detail) (Bohemian master) .. *Set of 2 sheets* 5·50 5·75

337 Magnificent
Frigate Bird

338 Head of
Pachycephalosaurus

(Des W. Wright. Litho China Security Ptg Ltd, Hong Kong)

1995 (6 Feb). *Birds. T 337 and similar vert designs. Multicoloured. P 15×14.*

2067	15 c. Type 337	10	10
2068	25 c. Blue-hooded Euphonia	10	10
2069	35 c. Eastern Meadowlark	15	20
2070	40 c. Red-billed Tropic Bird	20	25
2071	45 c. Greater Flamingo	20	25
2072	60 c. Yellow-faced Grassquit	25	30
2073	65 c. Yellow-billed Cuckoo	30	35
2074	70 c. Purple-throated Carib	30	35
2075	75 c. Bananaquit ..	35	40
2076	90 c. Painted Bunting	40	45
2077	$1.20, Red-legged Honeycreeper	55	60
2078	$2 Northern Jacana	90	95
2079	$5 Greater Antillean Bullfinch	2·25	2·40
2080	$10 Caribbean Elaenia ..	4·50	4·75
2081	$20 Brown Trembler	9·25	9·50
2067/81	*Set of 15*	20·00	21·00

(Des B. Regal. Litho Questa)

1995 (15 May). *Prehistoric Animals. T 338 and similar multicoloured designs. P 14.*

2082	15 c. Type 338	10	10
2083	20 c. Head of Afrovenator	10	10
2084	65 c. Centrosaurus	30	35
2085	75 c. Kronosaurus (*horiz*)	35	40
	a. Sheetlet. Nos. 2085/96	4·25	
2086	75 c. Ichthyosaurus (*horiz*)	35	40
2087	75 c. Plesiosaurus (*horiz*)	35	40
2088	75 c. Archelon (*horiz*)	35	40
2089	75 c. Pair of Tyrannosaurus (*horiz*)	35	40
2090	75 c. Tyrannosaurus (*horiz*)	35	40
2091	75 c. Parasaurolophus (*horiz*)	35	40
2092	75 c. Pair of Parasaurolophus (*horiz*)	35	40
2093	75 c. Oviraptor (*horiz*)	35	40
2094	75 c. Protoceratops with eggs (*horiz*)	35	40
2095	75 c. Pteranodon and Protoceratops (*horiz*)	35	40
2096	75 c. Pair of Protoceratops (*horiz*)	35	40
2097	90 c. Pentaceratops drinking	40	45
2098	$1.20, Head of Tarbosaurus	55	60
2099	$5 Head of Styracosaurus	2·25	2·40
2082/99	*Set of 18*	8·00	8·75

MS2100 Two sheets, each 101×70 mm. (a) $6 Head of Corythosaurus (*horiz*). (b) $6 Head of Carnotaurus (*horiz*) .. *Set of 2 sheets* 5·50 5·75
Nos. 2085/96 were printed together, *se-tenant*, in sheetlets of 12.

339 Al Oerter (U.S.A.) (discus
– 1956, 1960, 1964, 1968)

(Des R. Sauber. Litho B.D.T.)

1995 (6 June). *Olympic Games, Atlanta (1996). Previous Gold Medal Winners (1st issue). T 339 and similar multicoloured designs. P 14.*

2101	15 c. Type 339	10	10
2102	20 c. Greg Louganis (U.S.A.) (diving – 1984, 1988)	10	10
2103	65 c. Naim Suleymanoglu (Turkey) (weightlifting – 1988)	30	35
2104	90 c. Louise Ritter (U.S.A.) (high jump – 1988)	40	45
2105	$1.20, Nadia Comaneci (Rumania) (gymnastics – 1976)	55	60
2106	$5 Olga Bondarenko (Russia) (10,000 metres – 1988)	2·25	2·40
2101/6	*Set of 6*	3·75	4·00

MS2107 Two sheets, each 106×76 mm. (a) $6 United States crew (eight-oared shell — 1964). (b) $6 Lutz Hessilch (Germany) (cycling — 1988) (*vert*) .. *Set of 2 sheets* 5·50 5·75
No. 2106 is inscribed "BOLDARENKO" in error.
See also Nos. 2302/23.

340 Map of Berlin showing
Russian Advance

341 Signatures
and Earl of Halifax

(Des W. Wright. Litho Questa)

1995 (20 July). *50th Anniv of End of Second World War in Europe. T 340 and similar multicoloured designs. P 14.*

2108	$1.20, Type 340	55	60
	a. Sheetlet. Nos. 2108/15	4·50	
2109	$1.20, Russian tank and infantry	55	60
2110	$1.20, Street fighting in Berlin	55	60
2111	$1.20, German tank exploding	55	60
2112	$1.20, Russian air raid ..	55	60
2113	$1.20, German troops surrendering	55	60
2114	$1.20, Hoisting the Soviet flag on the Reichstag	55	60
2115	$1.20, Captured German standards	55	60
2108/15	*Set of 8*	4·50	4·75

MS2116 104×74 mm. $6 Gen. Konev (*vert*) 2·75 3·00
Nos. 2108/15 were printed together, *se-tenant*, in sheetlets of 8 with the stamps arranged in two horizontal strips of 4 separated by a gutter showing a German soldier in the ruins of Berlin.

(Des L. Fried. Litho Questa)

1995 (20 July). *50th Anniv of United Nations. T 341 and similar vert designs. Multicoloured. P 14.*

2117	75 c. Type 341	35	40
	a. Horiz strip of 3. Nos. 2117/19	1·25	
2118	90 c. Virginia Gildersleeve	40	45
2119	$1.20, Harold Stassen ..	55	60
2117/19	*Set of 3*	1·25	1·40

MS2120 100×70 mm. $6 Pres. Franklin D. Roosevelt .. .. 2·75 3·00
Nos. 2117/19 were printed together in sheets of 9 (3×3) containing three *se-tenant* horizontal strips, each forming a composite design.

342 Woman
buying Produce
from Market

343 Beach and
Rotary Emblem

(Des L. Fried. Litho Questa)

1995 (20 July). *50th Anniv of Food and Agriculture Organization. T 342 and similar vert designs. Multicoloured. P 14.*

2121	75 c. Type 342	35	40
	a. Horiz strip of 3. Nos. 2121/3	1·25	
2122	90 c. Women shopping	40	45
2123	$1.20, Women talking	55	60
2121/3	*Set of 3*	1·25	1·40

MS2124 100×70 mm. $6 Tractor 2·75 3·00
Nos. 2121/3 were printed together in sheets of 9 (3×3) containing three *se-tenant* horizontal strips, each forming a composite design.

(Litho Questa)

1995 (20 July). *90th Anniv of Rotary International. T 343 and similar multicoloured designs. P 14.*

2125	$5 Type 343	2·25	2·40

MS2126 74×104 mm. $6 National flag and emblem .. .. 2·75 3·00

344 Queen Elizabeth the
Queen Mother

(Litho Questa)

1995 (20 July). *95th Birthday of Queen Elizabeth the Queen Mother. T 344 and similar vert designs. P 13½×14.*

2127	$1.50, orange-brown, pale brown and black	70	75
	a. Sheetlet. Nos. 2127/30×2	5·50	
2128	$1.50, multicoloured	70	75
2129	$1.50, multicoloured	70	75
2130	$1.50, multicoloured	70	75
2127/30	*Set of 4*	2·75	3·00

MS2131 102×127 mm. $6 multicoloured .. 2·75 3·00
Designs:—No. 2127, Queen Elizabeth the Queen Mother (pastel drawing); No. 2128, Type 344; No. 2129, At desk (oil painting); No. 2130, Wearing green dress; No. MS2131, Wearing blue dress
Nos. 2128/30 were printed together in sheetlets of 8, containing two *se-tenant* horizontal strips of 4.

(Des J. Batchelor. Litho Questa)

1995 (20 July). *50th Anniv of End of Second World War in the Pacific. Horiz designs as T 340. Multicoloured. P 14.*

2132	$1.20, Gen. Chiang Kai-shek and Chinese guerrillas	55	60
	a. Sheetlet. Nos. 2132/7	3·25	
2133	$1.20, Gen. Douglas MacArthur and beach landing	55	60
2134	$1.20, Gen. Claire Chennault and U.S. fighter aircraft	55	60
2135	$1.20, Brig. Orde Wingate and supply drop	55	60
2136	$1.20, Gen. Joseph Stilwell and U.S. supply plane ..	55	60
2137	$1.20, Field-Marshal Bill Slim and loading cow into plane	55	60
2132/7	*Set of 6*	3·25	3·50

MS2138 108×76 mm. $3 Admiral Nimitz and aircraft carrier .. 1·40 1·50
Nos. 2132/7 were printed together, *se-tenant*, in sheetlets of 6 with the stamps arranged in two horizontal strips of 3 separated by a gutter showing Japanese soldiers surrendering.

345 Family ("Caring")

346 Purple-throated
Carib

1995 (31 July). *Tourism. Sheet 95×72 mm, containing T 345 and similar horiz designs. Multicoloured. Litho. P 14.*

MS2139 $2 Type 345; $2 Market trader ("Marketing"); $2 Workers and housewife ("Working"); $2 Leisure pursuits ("Enjoying Life") .. .. 3·50 3·75

(Des Tracy Pedersen. Litho Questa)

1995 (31 Aug). *Birds. T 346 and similar vert designs. Multicoloured. P 14.*

2140	75 c. Type 346	35	40
	a. Sheetlet. Nos. 2140/51	4·25	
2141	75 c. Antillean Crested Hummingbird	35	40
2142	75 c. Bananaquit	35	40
2143	75 c. Mangrove Cuckoo	35	40
2144	75 c. Troupial	35	40
2145	75 c. Green-throated Carib	35	40
2146	75 c. Yellow Warbler	35	40
2147	75 c. Blue-hooded Euphonia	35	40
2148	75 c. Scaly-breasted Thrasher	35	40
2149	75 c. Burrowing Owl	35	40
2150	75 c. Carib Grackle	35	40
2151	75 c. Adelaide's Warbler	35	40
2152	75 c. Ring-necked Duck	35	40
	a. Sheetlet. Nos. 2152/63	4·25	
2153	75 c. Ruddy Duck	35	40
2154	75 c. Green-winged Teal	35	40
2155	75 c. Wood Duck	35	40
2156	75 c. Hooded Merganser	35	40
2157	75 c. Lesser Scaup	35	40

2158	75 c.	Black-billed Whistling Duck ("West Indian Tree Duck")	35	40
2159	75 c.	Fulvous Whistling Duck	35	40
2160	75 c.	Bahama Pintail	35	40
2161	75 c.	Shoveler	35	40
2162	75 c.	Masked Duck	35	40
2163	75 c.	American Wigeon	35	40
2140/63		Set of 24	8·50	9·50

MS2164 Two sheets, each 104×74 mm. (a) $6 Head of Purple Gallinule. (b) $6 Heads of Blue-winged Teals .. *Set of 2 sheets* 5·50 5·75

Nos. 2140/51 and 2152/63 were printed together, *se-tenant*, in sheetlets of 12 with the background forming a composite design.

347 Original Church, 1845   348 Mining Bees

(Litho Questa)

1995 (4 Sept). *150th Anniv of Greenbay Moravian Church. T* 347 *and similar vert designs. Multicoloured. P* 14.

2165	20 c.	Type 347	10	10
2166	60 c.	Church in 1967	25	30
2167	75 c.	Present church	35	40
2168	90 c.	Revd. John Buckley (first minister of African descent)	40	45
2169	$1.20,	Bishop John Ephraim Knight (longest-serving minister)	55	60
2170	$2	As 75 c.	90	95
2165/70		Set of 6	2·50	2·75

MS2171 110×81 mm. $6 Front of present church 2·75 3·00

(Des Y. Lee. Litho Questa)

1995 (7 Sept). *Bees. T* 348 *and similar horiz designs. Multicoloured. P* 14.

2172	90 c.	Type 348	40	45
2173	$1.20,	Solitary Bee	55	60
2174	$1.65,	Leaf-cutter Bee	75	80
2175	$1.75,	Honey Bees	80	85
2172/5		Set of 4	2·50	2·75

MS2176 110×80 mm. $6 Solitary Mining Bee 2·75 3·00

349 Narcissus   350 Somali

(Des Y. Lee. Litho Questa)

1995 (7 Sept). *Flowers. T* 349 *and similar vert designs. Multicoloured. P* 14.

2177	75 c.	Type 349	35	40
		a. Sheetlet. Nos. 2177/88	4·25	
2178	75 c.	Camellia	35	40
2179	75 c.	Iris	35	40
2180	75 c.	Tulip	35	40
2181	75 c.	Poppy	35	40
2182	75 c.	Peony	35	40
2183	75 c.	Magnolia	35	40
2184	75 c.	Oriental Lily	35	40
2185	75 c.	Rose	35	40
2186	75 c.	Pansy	35	40
2187	75 c.	Hydrangea	35	40
2188	75 c.	Azaleas	35	40
2177/88		Set of 12	4·25	4·75

MS2189 80×110 mm. $6 Calla Lily .. 2·75 3·00

Nos. 2177/88 were printed together, *se-tenant*, in sheetlets of 12.

No. 2186 is inscribed "Pansie" in error.

(Des Y. Lee. Litho Questa)

1995 (7 Sept). *Cats. T* 350 *and similar multicoloured designs. P* 14.

2190	45 c.	Type 350	20	25
		a. Sheetlet. Nos. 2190/201	2·40	
2191	45 c.	Persian and butterflies	20	25
2192	45 c.	Devon Rex	20	25
2193	45 c.	Turkish Angora	20	25
2194	45 c.	Himalayan	20	25
2195	45 c.	Maine Coon	20	25
2196	45 c.	Ginger non-pedigree	20	25
2197	45 c.	American Wirehair	20	25
2198	45 c.	British Shorthair	20	25
2199	45 c.	American Curl	20	25
2200	45 c.	Black non-pedigree and butterfly	20	25
2201	45 c.	Birman	20	25
2190/2201		Set of 12	2·40	3·00

MS2202 104×74 mm. $6 Siberian kitten (*vert*) 2·75 3·00

Nos. 2190/2201 were printed together, *se-tenant*, in sheetlets of 12, with the backgrounds forming a composite design.

351 The Explorer Tent

1995 (5 Oct). *18th World Scout Jamboree, Netherlands. Tents. T* 351 *and similar multicoloured designs. Litho. P* 14.

2203	$1.20,	Type 351	55	60
		a. Horiz strip of 3. Nos. 2203/5	1·60	
2204	$1.20,	Camper tent	55	60
2205	$1.20,	Wall tent	55	60
2206	$1.20,	Trail tarp	55	60
		a. Horiz strip of 3. Nos. 2206/8	1·60	
2207	$1.20,	Miner's tent	55	60
2208	$1.20,	Voyager tent	55	60
2203/8		Set of 6	3·25	3·50

MS2209 Two sheets, each 76×106 mm. (a) $6 Scout and camp fire. (b) $6 Scout with back pack (*vert*) .. .. *Set of 2 sheets* 5·50 5·75

Nos. 2203/5 and 2206/8 were printed together, *se-tenant*, as horizontal strips of 3 in sheets of 9.

352 Trans-Gabon Diesel Train

(Des B. Regal. Litho Questa)

1995 (23 Oct). *Trains of the World. T* 352 *and similar multicoloured designs. P* 14.

2210	35 c.	Type 352	15	20
2211	65 c.	Canadian Pacific diesel locomotive	30	35
2212	75 c.	Santa Fe Railway diesel locomotive, U.S.A.	35	40
2213	90 c.	High Speed Train, Great Britain	40	45
2214	$1.20,	"TGV" train, France	55	60
2215	$1.20,	Diesel locomotive, Australia	55	60
		a. Sheetlet. Nos. 2215/23	5·00	
2216	$1.20,	"ETR 450" electric train, Italy	55	60
2217	$1.20,	Diesel locomotive, Thailand	55	60
2218	$1.20,	Pennsylvania Railroad stream-lined steam locomotive, U.S.A.	55	60
2219	$1.20,	Steam locomotive, South Africa	55	60
2220	$1.20,	Steam locomotive, Natal	55	60
2221	$1.20,	Rail gun, American Civil War	55	60
2222	$1.20,	Early steam locomotive (red livery), Great Britain	55	60
2223	$1.20,	Early steam locomotive (green livery), Great Britain	55	60
2224	$6	Amtrak diesel locomotive, U.S.A.	2·75	3·00
2210/24		Set of 15	9·50	10·50

MS2225 Two sheets, each 110×80 mm. (a) $6 Chinese steam locomotive (*vert*). (b) $6 "Indian-Pacific" diesel locomotive, Australia (*vert*) .. .. *Set of 2 sheets* 5·50 5·75

Nos. 2215/23 were printed together, *se-tenant*, in sheetlets of 9.

353 Dag Hammarskjöld (1961 Peace)

(Des B. Regal. Litho Walsall)

1995 (8 Nov). *Centenary of Nobel Prize Trust Fund. T* 353 *and similar multicoloured designs. P* 14.

2226	$1	Type 353	45	50
		a. Sheetlet. Nos. 2226/34	4·00	
2227	$1	Georg Wittig (1979 Chemistry)	45	50
2228	$1	Wilhelm Ostwald (1909 Chemistry)	45	50
2229	$1	Robert Koch (1905 Medicine)	45	50
2230	$1	Karl Ziegler (1963 Chemistry)	45	50
2231	$1	Alexander Fleming (1945 Medicine)	45	50
2232	$1	Hermann Staudinger (1953 Chemistry)	45	50
2233	$1	Manfred Eigen (1967 Chemistry)	45	50
2234	$1	Arno Penzias (1978 Physics)	45	50
2235	$1	Shmuel Agnon (1966 Literature)	45	50
		a. Sheetlet. Nos. 2235/43	4·00	
2236	$1	Rudyard Kipling (1907 Literature)	45	50
2237	$1	Aleksandr Solzhenitsyn (1970 Literature)	45	50
2238	$1	Jack Steinberger (1988 Physics)	45	50
2239	$1	Andrei Sakharov (1975 Peace)	45	50
2240	$1	Otto Stern (1943 Physics)	45	50
2241	$1	John Steinbeck (1962 Literature)	45	50
2242	$1	Nadine Gordimer (1991 Literature)	45	50
2243	$1	William Faulkner (1949 Literature)	45	50
2226/43		Set of 18	8·00	9·00

MS2244 Two sheets, each 100×70 mm. (a) $6 Elie Wiesel (1986 Peace) (*vert*). (b) $6 The Dalai Lama (1989 Peace) (*vert*) .. *Set of 2 sheets* 5·50 5·75

Nos. 2226/34 and 2235/43 were printed together, *se-tenant*, in sheetlets of 9.

354 Elvis Presley   355 John Lennon and Signature

1995 (8 Dec). *60th Birth Anniv of Elvis Presley. T* 354 *and similar vert designs. Multicoloured. Litho. P* 13½×14.

2245	$1	Type 354	45	50
		a. Sheetlet. Nos. 2245/53	4·00	
2246	$1	Holding microphone in right hand	45	50
2247	$1	In blue shirt and with neck of guitar	45	50
2248	$1	Wearing blue shirt and smiling	45	50
2249	$1	On wedding day	45	50
2250	$1	In army uniform	45	50
2251	$1	Wearing red shirt	45	50
2252	$1	Wearing white shirt	45	50
2253	$1	In white shirt with microphone	45	50
2245/53		Set of 9	4·00	4·50

MS2254 101×71 mm. $6 "Ghost" image of Elvis amongst the stars .. .. 2·75 3·00

Nos. 2245/54 were printed together, *se-tenant*, in sheetlets of 9.

(Litho Questa)

1995 (8 Dec). *15th Death Anniv of John Lennon (entertainer). T* 355 *and similar vert designs. Multicoloured. P* 14.

2255	45 c.	Type 355	50	40
2256	50 c.	In beard and spectacles	50	50
2257	65 c.	Wearing sunglasses	55	55
2258	75 c.	In cap with heart badge	65	65
2255/8		Set of 4	2·00	1·90

MS2259 103×73 mm. $6 As 75 c. .. 4·75 5·00

Nos. 2255/8 were each issued in numbered sheets of 16 which have enlarged illustrated left-hand margins.

"Hurricane Relief"   (356)   357 "Rest on the Flight into Egypt" (Paolo Veronese)

1995 (14 Dec). *Hurricane Relief. Nos.* 2203/9 optd as *T* 356.

2260	$1.20,	Type 351	55	60
		a. Horiz strip of 3. Nos. 2260/2	1·60	
2261	$1.20,	Camper tent	55	60
2262	$1.20,	Wall tent	55	60
2263	$1.20,	Trail tarp	55	60
		a. Horiz strip of 3. Nos. 2263/5	1·60	
2264	$1.20,	Miner's tent	55	60
2265	$1.20,	Voyager tent	55	60
2260/5		Set of 6	3·25	3·50

MS2266 Two sheets, each 76×106 mm. (a) $6 Scout and camp fire. (b) $6 Scout with back pack (*vert*) .. .. *Set of 2 sheets* 5·50 5·75

The overprints on No. **MS**2266 are larger, 12½×5 mm or 5×12½ mm on the vertical design.

(Litho Questa)

1995 (18 Dec). *Christmas. Religious Paintings. T* 357 *and similar vert designs. Multicoloured. P* 13½×14.

2267	15 c.	Type 357	10	15
2268	35 c.	"Madonna and Child" (Van Dyck)	15	20
2269	65 c.	"Sacred Conversation Piece" (Veronese)	30	35
2270	75 c.	"Vision of St. Anthony" (Van Dyck)	35	40
2271	90 c.	"Virgin and Child" (Van Eyck)	40	45
2272	$6	"The Immaculate Conception" (Giovanni Tiepolo)	2·75	3·00
2267/72		Set of 6	4·00	4·50

MS2273 Two sheets. (a) 101×127 mm. $5 "Christ appearing to his Mother" (detail) (Van der Weyden). (b) 127×101 mm. $6 "The Infant Jesus and the Young St. John" (Murillo) *Set of 2 sheets* 5·00 5·25

STANLEY GIBBONS STAMP COLLECTING SERIES

Introductory booklets on *How to Start, How to Identify Stamps* and *Collecting by Theme.* A series of well illustrated guides at a low price.

Write for details.

358 Hygrophoropsis
aurantiaca

359 H.M.S. *Resolution* (Cook)

(Des D. Burkhart. Litho Questa)

1996 (22 Apr). *Fungi.* T **358** *and similar vert designs.*
Multicoloured. P 14.
2274	75 c. Type **358**		35	40
	a. Horiz strip of 4. Nos. 2274/7		1·40	
2275	75 c. *Hygrophorus bakerensis*		35	40
2276	75 c. *Hygrophorus conicus*		35	40
2277	75 c. *Hygrophorus miniatus* (*Hygrocybe miniata*)		35	40
2278	75 c. *Suillus brevipes*		35	40
	a. Horiz strip of 4. Nos. 2278/81		1·40	
2279	75 c. *Suillus luteus*		35	40
2280	75 c. *Suillus granulatus*		35	40
2281	75 c. *Suillus caerulescens*		35	40
2274/81		*Set of 8*	2·75	3·00

MS2282 Two sheets, each 105×75 mm. (a) $6
Conocybe filaris. (b) $6 *Hygrocybe flavescens*
Set of 2 sheets 5·50 5·75
Nos. 2274/7 and 2278/81 were each printed together in
sheetlets of 12 containing three horizontal *se-tenant* strips.

(Litho B.D.T.)

1996 (25 Apr). *Sailing Ships.* T **359** *and similar horiz designs.*
Multicoloured. P 14.
2283	15 c. Type **359**		10	10
2284	25 c. *Mayflower* (Pilgrim Fathers)		10	15
2285	45 c. *Santa Maria* (Columbus)		20	25
2286	75 c. *Aemilia* (Dutch galleon)		35	40
2287	75 c. *Sovereign of the Seas* (English galleon)		35	40
2288	90 c. *H.M.S. Victory* (ship of the line, 1765)		40	45
2289	$1.20, As No. 2286		55	60
	a. Sheetlet. Nos. 2289/94		3·25	
2290	$1.20, As No. 2287		55	60
2291	$1.20, *Royal Louis* (French galleon)		55	60
2292	$1.20, H.M.S. *Royal George* (ship of the line)		55	60
2293	$1.20, *Le Protecteur* (French frigate)		55	60
2294	$1.20, As No. 2288		55	60
2295	$1.50, As No. 2285		70	75
	a. Sheetlet. Nos. 2295/2300		4·25	
2296	$1.50, *Vitoria* (Magellan)		70	75
2297	$1.50, *Golden Hind* (Drake)		70	75
2298	$1.50, As No. 2284		70	75
2299	$1.50, *Griffin* (La Salle)		70	75
2300	$1.50, Type **359**		70	75
2283/2300		*Set of 18*	9·00	9·75

MS2301 (a) 102×72 mm. $6 U.S.S. *Constitution*
(frigate); (b) 98×67 mm. $6 *Grande Hermine*
(Cartier) *Set of 2 sheets* 5·50 5·75
Nos. 2289/94 and 2295/2300 were each printed together,
se-tenant, in sheetlets of 6.

360 Florence Griffith
Joyner (U.S.A.) (Gold
– track, 1988)

361 Black Skimmer

(Des R. Martin. Litho Questa)

1996 (6 May). *Olympic Games, Atlanta. Previous Medal
Winners (2nd issue).* T **360** *and similar multicoloured designs.*
P 14.
2302	65 c. Type **360**		30	35
2303	75 c. Olympic Stadium, Seoul (1988) (*horiz*)		35	40
2304	90 c. Allison Jolly and Lynne Jewell (U.S.A.) (Gold – yachting, 1988) (*horiz*)		40	45
2305	90 c. Wolfgang Nordwig (Germany) (Gold – pole vaulting, 1972)		40	45
	a. Sheetlet. Nos. 2305/13		3·50	
2306	90 c. Shirley Strong (Great Britain) (Silver – 100 metres hurdles, 1984)		40	45
2307	90 c. Sergei Bubka (Russia) (Gold – pole vault, 1988)		40	45
2308	90 c. Filbert Bayi (Tanzania) (Silver – 3000 metres steeplechase, 1980)		40	45
2309	90 c. Victor Saneyev (Russia) (Gold – triple jump, 1968, 1972, 1976)		40	45
2310	90 c. Silke Renk (Germany) (Gold – javelin, 1992)		40	45
2311	90 c. Daley Thompson (Great Britain) (Gold – decathlon, 1980, 1984)		40	45
2312	90 c. Robert Richards (U.S.A.) (Gold – pole vault, 1952, 1956)		40	45
2313	90 c. Parry O'Brien (U.S.A.) (Gold – shot put, 1952, 1956)		40	45

2314	90 c. Ingrid Kramer (Germany) (Gold – Women's platform diving, 1960)		40	45
	a. Sheetlet. Nos. 2314/22		3·50	
2315	90 c. Kelly McCormick (U.S.A.) (Silver – Women's springboard diving, 1984)		40	45
2316	90 c. Gary Tobian (U.S.A.) (Gold – Men's springboard diving, 1960)		40	45
2317	90 c. Greg Louganis (U.S.A.) (Gold – Men's diving, 1984 and 1988)		40	45
2318	90 c. Michelle Mitchell (U.S.A.) (Silver – Women's platform diving, 1984 and 1988)		40	45
2319	90 c. Zhou Jihong (China) (Gold – Women's platform diving, 1984)		40	45
2320	90 c. Wendy Wyland (U.S.A.) (Bronze –Women's platform diving, 1984)		40	45
2321	90 c. Xu Yanmei (China) (Gold – Women's platform diving, 1988)		40	45
2322	90 c. Fu Mingxia (China) (Gold – Women's platform diving, 1992)		40	45
2323	$1.20, 2000 metre tandem cycle race (*horiz*)		55	60
2302/23		*Set of 21*	8·50	9·50

MS2324 Two sheets, each 106×76 mm. (a) $5
Bill Toomey (U.S.A.) (Gold – decathlon, 1968)
(*horiz*). (b) $6 Mark Lenzi (U.S.A.) (Gold – Men's
springboard diving, 1992) . . *Set of 2 sheets* 5·00 5·25
Nos. 2305/13 and 2314/22 were each printed together,
se-tenant, in sheetlets of 9, with the backgrounds forming
composite designs.

1996 (13 May). *Sea Birds.* T **361** *and similar horiz designs.*
Multicoloured. Litho. P 14.
2325	75 c. Type **361**		35	40
	a. Vert strip of 4. Nos. 2325/8		1·40	
2326	75 c. Black-capped Petrel		35	40
2327	75 c. Sooty Tern		35	40
2328	75 c. Royal Tern		35	40
2329	75 c. Pomarine Skua ("Pomarine Jaegger")		35	40
	a. Vert strip of 4. Nos. 2329/32		1·40	
2330	75 c. White-tailed Tropic Bird		35	40
2331	75 c. Northern Gannet		35	40
2332	75 c. Laughing Gull		35	40
2325/32		*Set of 8*	2·75	3·25

MS2333 Two sheets, each 105×75 mm. (a) $5
Great Frigate Bird. (b) $6 Brown Pelican
Set of 2 sheets 5·00 5·25
Nos. 2325/8 and 2329/32 were each printed together,
se-tenant, in vertical strips of 4 throughout sheets of 12.

362 Mickey and Goofy on Elephant
(*Around the World in Eighty Days*)

(Litho Questa)

1996 (6 June). *Novels of Jules Verne.* T **362** *and similar horiz
designs showing Walt Disney cartoon characters in scenes
from the books. Multicoloured.* P 14×13½.
2334	1 c. Type **362**		10	10
2335	2 c. Mickey, Donald and Goofy entering cave (*A Journey to the Centre of the Earth*)		10	10
2336	5 c. Mickey and Minnie driving postcart (*Michel Strogoff*)		10	10
2337	10 c. Mickey, Donald and Goofy in space rocket (*From the Earth to the Moon*)		10	10
2338	15 c. Mickey and Goofy in balloon (*Five Weeks in a Balloon*)		10	10
2339	20 c. Mickey and Goofy in China (*Around the World in Eighty Days*)		10	10
2340	$1 Mickey, Goofy and Pluto on island (*The Mysterious Island*)		45	50
2341	$2 Mickey, Pluto, Goofy and Donald on Moon (*From the Earth to the Moon*)		90	95
2342	$3 Mickey being lifted by bird (*Captain Grant's Children*)		1·40	1·50
2343	$5 Mickey with seal and squid (*Twenty Thousand Leagues Under the Sea*)		2·25	2·40
2334/43		*Set of 10*	5·25	5·50

MS2344 Two sheets, each 124×99 mm. (a) $6
Mickey on *Nautilus* (*Twenty Thousand Leagues
Under the Sea*). (b) $6 Mickey and Donald on raft
(*A Journey to the Centre of the Earth*)
Set of 2 sheets 5·50 5·75

363 Bruce Lee

364 Queen Elizabeth II

1996 (13 June). "CHINA '96" *9th Asian International Stamp
Exhibition, Peking. Bruce Lee (actor).* T **363** *and similar vert
designs. Multicoloured. Litho* P 14.
2345	75 c. Type **363**		35	40
	a. Sheetlet. Nos. 2345/53		3·00	
2346	75 c. Bruce Lee in white shirt and red tie		35	40
2347	75 c. In plaid jacket and tie		35	40
2348	75 c. In mask and uniform		35	40
2349	75 c. Bare-chested		35	40
2350	75 c. In mandarin jacket		35	40
2351	75 c. In brown jumper		35	40
2352	75 c. In fawn shirt		35	40
2353	75 c. Shouting		35	40
2345/53		*Set of 9*	3·00	3·50

MS2354 76×106 mm. $5 Bruce Lee 2·25 2·40
Nos 2345/53 were printed together, *se-tenant*, in numbered
sheetlets of 9 with enlarged illustrated left-hand margin.

(Litho Questa)

1996 (17 July). *70th Birthday of Queen Elizabeth II.* T **364** *and
similar multicoloured designs.* P 13½×14.
2355	$2 Type **364**		90	95
	a. Strip of 3. Nos. 2355/7		2·00	
2356	$2 With bouquet		90	95
2357	$2 In garter robes		90	95
2355/7		*Set of 3*	2·00	2·75

MS2358 96×111 mm. $6 Wearing white dress 2·75 3·00
Nos. 2355/7 were printed together, *se-tenant*, in horizontal
and vertical strips of 3 throughout sheets of 9.

365 Ancient Egyptian
Cavalryman

366 Girl in Red Sari

1996 (24 July). *Cavalry through the Ages.* T **365** *and similar
multicoloured designs. Litho.* P 14.
2359	60 c. Type **365**		25	30
	a. Block of 4. Nos. 2359/62		1·00	
2360	60 c. 13th-century English knight		25	30
2361	60 c. 16th-century Spanish lancer		25	30
2362	60 c. 18th-century Chinese cavalryman		25	30
2359/62		*Set of 4*	1·00	1·25

MS2363 100×70 mm. $6 19th-century French
cuirassier (*vert*) 2·75 3·00
Nos. 2359/62 were printed together, *se-tenant*, in blocks of
four within sheets of 16.

(Litho Questa)

1996 (30 July). *50th Anniv of U.N.I.C.E.F.* T **366** *and similar
vert designs. Multicoloured.* P 14.
2364	75 c. Type **366**		35	40
2365	90 c. South American mother and child		40	45
2366	$1.20, Nurse with child		55	60
2364/6		*Set of 3*	1·25	1·40

MS2367 114×74 mm. $6 Chinese child 2·75 3·00

367 Tomb of Zachariah
and *Verbascum
sinuatum*

368 Kate Smith

(Des Jennifer Toombs. Litho Questa)

1996 (30 July). *3000th Anniv of Jerusalem.* T **367** *and similar
vert designs. Multicoloured.* P 14½.
2368	75 c. Type **367**		35	40
2369	90 c. Pool of Siloam and *Hyacinthus orientalis*		40	45
2370	$1.20, Hurva Synagogue and *Ranunculus asiaticus*		55	60
2368/70		*Set of 3*	1·25	1·40

MS2371 66×80 mm. $6 Model of Herod's Temple
and *Cercis siliquastrum* 2·75 3·00

(Des J. Iskowitz. Litho Questa)

1996 (30 July). *Centenary of Radio. Entertainers.* T **368** *and
similar vert designs.* P 13½.
2372	65 c. Type **368**		30	35
2373	75 c. Dinah Shore		35	40
2374	90 c. Rudy Vallee		40	45
2375	$1.20 Bing Crosby		55	60
2372/5		*Set of 4*	1·60	1·75

MS2376 72×104 mm. $6 Jo Stafford (28×42
mm). P 14 2·75 3·00

369 "Madonna Enthroned" **370** Robert Preston (*The Music Man*)

(Litho Questa)

1996 (25 Nov). *Christmas. Religious Paintings by Filippo Lippi. T* **369** *and similar vert designs. Multicoloured. P* 13½×14.

2377	60 c. Type **369**	25	30
2378	90 c. "Adoration of the Child and Saints"	40	45
2379	$1 "The Annunciation"	45	50
2380	$1.20 "Birth of the Virgin"	55	60
2381	$1.60, "Adoration of the Child"	75	80
2382	$1.75, "Madonna and Child"	80	85
2377/82	*Set of 6*	3·00	3·50

MS2383 Two sheets, each 76×106 mm. (a) $6 "Madonna and Child" (*different*). (b) $6 "The Circumcision" .. .. *Set of 2 sheets* 5·50 5·75

(Des J. Iskowitz. Litho Questa)

1997 (17 Feb). *Broadway Musical Stars. T* **370** *and similar vert designs. Multicoloured. P* 13½×14.

2384	$1 Type **370**	45	50
	a. Sheetlet. Nos. 2384/92	4·00	
2385	$1 Michael Crawford (*Phantom of the Opera*)	45	50
2386	$1 Zero Mostel (*Fiddler on the Roof*)	45	50
2387	$1 Patti Lupone (*Evita*)	45	50
2388	$1 Raul Julia (*Threepenny Opera*)	45	50
2389	$1 Mary Martin (*South Pacific*)	45	50
2390	$1 Carol Channing (*Hello Dolly*)	45	50
2391	$1 Yul Brynner (*The King and I*)	45	50
2392	$1 Julie Andrews (*My Fair Lady*)	45	50
2384/92	*Set of 9*	4·00	4·50

MS2393 106×76 mm. $6 Mickey Rooney (*Sugar Babies*).. .. .. .. 2·75 3·00

Nos. 2384/92 were printed together, *se-tenant*, in sheetlets of 9 with the backgrounds forming a composite design.

371 Charlie Chaplin as Young Man **372** *Charaxes porthos*

(Des J. Iskowitz. Litho Questa)

1997 (24 Feb). *20th Death Anniv of Charlie Chaplin (film star). T* **371** *and similar vert designs. Multicoloured. P* 13½×14.

2394	$1 Type **371**	45	50
	a. Sheetlet. Nos. 2394/402	4·25	
2395	$1 Pulling face	45	50
2396	$1 Looking over shoulder	45	50
2397	$1 In cap	45	50
2398	$1 In front of star	45	50
2399	$1 In *The Great Dictator*	45	50
2400	$1 With movie camera and megaphone	45	50
2401	$1 Standing in front of camera lens	45	50
2402	$1 Putting on make-up	45	50
2394/402	*Set of 9*	4·25	4·50

MS2403 76×106 mm. $6 Charlie Chaplin .. 2·75 3·00

Nos. 2394/402 were printed together, *se-tenant*, in sheetlets of 9 with the backgrounds forming a composite design.

(Des T. Wood. Litho Questa)

1997 (10 Mar). *Butterflies. T* **372** *and similar multicoloured designs. P* 14.

2404	90 c. Type **372**	40	45
2405	$1.10, *Charaxes protoclea protoclea*	50	55
	a. Sheetlet. Nos. 2405/13	4·50	
2406	$1.10, *Byblia ilithyia*	50	55
2407	$1.10, Black-headed Bush Shrike ("Tchagra") (bird)	50	55
2408	$1.10, *Charaxes nobilis*	50	55
2409	$1.10, *Pseudacraea boisduvali trimeni*	50	55
2410	$1.10, *Charaxes smaragdalis*	50	55
2411	$1.10, *Charaxes lasti*	50	55
2412	$1.10, *Pseudacrea poggei*	50	55
2413	$1.10, *Graphium colonna*	50	55
2414	$1.10, Carmine Bee Eater (bird)	50	55
	a. Sheetlet. Nos. 2414/22	50	55
2415	$1.10, *Pseudacraea eurytus*	50	55
2416	$1.10, *Hypolimnas monteironis*	50	55
2417	$1.10, *Charaxes anticlea*	50	55
2418	$1.10, *Graphium leonidas*	50	55
2419	$1.10, *Graphium illyris*	50	55
2420	$1.10, *Nephronia argia*	50	55

2421	$1.10, *Graphium policenes*	50	55
2422	$1.10, *Papilio dardanus*	50	55
2423	$1.20, *Aethiopana honorius*	55	60
2424	$1.60, *Charaxes hadrianus*	75	80
2425	$1.75, *Precis westermanni*	80	85
2404/25	*Set of 22*	11·50	12·50

MS2426 Three sheets, each 106×76 mm. (a) $6 *Charaxes lactitinctus* (*horiz*). (b) $6 *Eupheadra neophron.* (c) $6 *Euxanthe tiberius* (*horiz*) *Set of 3 sheets* 8·25 8·50

Nos. 2405/13 and 2414/22 were each printed together, *se-tenant*, in sheetlets of 9 with the backgrounds forming composite designs.

No. 2420 is inscribed "Nepheronia argia" in error.

373 Convent of The Companions of Jesus, Morelia, Mexico

(Des M. Freedman and Dena Rubin. Litho Questa)

1997 (10 Apr). *50th Anniv of U.N.E.S.C.O. T* **373** *and similar multicoloured designs. P* 14×13½ (*horiz*) *or* 13½×14 (*vert*).

2427	60 c. Type **373**	25	30
2428	90 c. Fortress at San Lorenzo, Panama (*vert*)	40	45
2429	$1 Canaima National Park, Venezuela (*vert*)	45	50
2430	$1.10, Aerial view of church with tower, Guanajuato, Mexico (*vert*)	50	55
	a. Sheetlet. Nos. 2430/7 and central label	4·00	
2431	$1.10, Church facade, Guanajuato, Mexico (*vert*)	50	55
2432	$1.10, Aerial view of churches with domes, Guanajuato, Mexico (*vert*)	50	55
2433	$1.10, Jesuit Missions of the Chiquitos, Bolivia (*vert*)	50	55
2434	$1.10, Huascaran National Park, Peru (*vert*)	50	55
2435	$1.10, Jesuit Missions of La Santisima, Paraguay (*vert*)	50	55
2436	$1.10, Cartagena, Colombia (*vert*)	50	55
2437	$1.10, Fortification, Havana, Cuba (*vert*)	50	55
2438	$1.20, As No. 2434 (*vert*)	55	60
2439	$1.60, Church of San Fransisco, Guatemala (*vert*)	75	80
2440	$1.65, Tikal National Park, Guatemala	75	80
	a. Sheetlet. Nos. 2440/4 and label	3·75	
2441	$1.65, Rio Platano Reserve, Honduras	75	80
2442	$1.65, Ruins of Copan, Honduras	75	80
2443	$1.65, Antigua ruins, Guatemala	75	80
2444	$1.65, Teotihuacan, Mexico	75	80
2445	$1.75, Santo Domingo, Dominican Republic (*vert*)	80	85
2427/45	*Set of 19*	11·00	12·00

MS2446 Two sheets, each 127×102 mm. (a) $6 Tikal National Park, Guatemala. (b) $6 Teotihuacan pyramid, Mexico .. *Set of 2 sheets* 5·50 5·75

Nos. 2430/7 and 2440/4 were each printed, *se-tenant*, in sheetlets of 8 and 5 with a label.

No. 2436 is inscribed "Columbia" in error.

374 Red Bishop **375** Child's Face and U.N.E.S.C.O. Emblem

(Des J. Iskowitz. Litho Questa)

1997 (24 Apr). *Endangered Species. T* **374** *and similar vert designs. Multicoloured. Litho. P* 14.

2447	$1.20, Type **374**	55	60
	a. Sheetlet. Nos. 2447/52	3·25	
2448	$1.20, Yellow Baboon	55	60
2449	$1.20, Superb Starling	55	60
2450	$1.20, Ratel	55	60
2451	$1.20, Hunting Dog	55	60
2452	$1.20, Serval	55	60
2453	$1.65, Okapi	75	80
	a. Sheetlet. Nos. 2453/8	4·50	
2454	$1.65, Giant Forest Squirrel	75	80
2455	$1.65, Lesser Masked Weaver	75	80
2456	$1.65, Small-spotted Genet	75	80
2457	$1.65, Yellow-billed Stork	75	80
2458	$1.65, Red-headed Agama	75	80
2447/58	*Set of 12*	7·75	8·50

MS2459 Three sheets, each 106×76 mm. (a) $6 South African Crowned Crane. (b) $6 Bat-eared Fox. (c) $6 Malachite Kingfisher *Set of 3 sheets* 8·25 8·50

Nos. 2447/52 and 2453/8 were each printed together, *se-tenant*, in sheetlets of 6 with the backgrounds forming composite designs.

(Litho Questa)

1997 (12 June). *10th Anniv of Chernobyl Nuclear Disaster. T* **375** *and similar vert design. Multicoloured. P* 13½.

2460	$1.65, Type **375**	75	80
2461	$2 As Type **375**, but inscribed "CHABAD'S CHILDREN OF CHERNOBYL" at foot	90	95

376 Paul Harris and James Grant

(Des J. Iskowitz. Litho Questa)

1997 (12 June). *50th Death Anniv of Paul Harris (founder of Rotary International). T* **376** *and similar horiz design. Multicoloured. P* 14.

2462	$1.75, Type **376**	80	85

MS2463 78×107 mm. $6 Group study exchange, New Zealand .. .. .. 2·75 3·00

377 Queen Elizabeth II

(Litho Questa)

1997 (12 June). *Golden Wedding of Queen Elizabeth and Prince Philip. T* **377** *and similar horiz designs. Multicoloured. P* 14.

2464	$1 Type **377**	45	50
	a. Sheetlet. Nos. 2464/9	2·75	
2465	$1 Royal coat of arms	45	50
2466	$1 Queen Elizabeth and Prince Philip at reception	45	50
2467	$1 Queen Elizabeth and Prince Philip in landau	45	50
2468	$1 Balmoral	45	50
2469	$1 Prince Philip	45	50
2464/9	*Set of 6*	2·75	3·00

MS2470 100×71 mm. $6 Queen Elizabeth with Prince Philip in naval uniform .. 2·75 3·00

Nos. 2464/9 were printed together, *se-tenant*, in sheetlets of 6.

378 Kaiser Wilhelm I and Heinrich von Stephan **379** The Ugly Sisters and their Mother

(Des J. Iskowitz. Litho Questa)

1997 (12 June). *"Pacific '97" International Stamp Exhibition, San Francisco. Death Centenary of Heinrich von Stephan (founder of the U.P.U.). T* **378** *and similar horiz designs. P* 14.

2471	$1.75, dull blue	80	85
2472	$1.75, chestnut	80	85
2473	$1.75, deep magenta	80	85
2471/3	*Set of 3*	2·40	2·50

MS2474 82×119 mm. $6 black and violet .. 2·75 3·00

Designs:—No. 2471, Type **378**; No. 2472, Von Stephan and Mercury; No. 2473, Carrier pigeon and loft; No. MS2474, Von Stephan and 15th-century Basle messenger.

Nos. 2471/3 were printed together, *se-tenant*, in sheetlets of 3 with enlarged right-hand margin.

(Des R. Sauber. Litho Questa)

1997 (12 June). *175th Anniv of Brothers Grimm's Third Collection of Fairy Tales. Cinderella. T* **379** *and similar vert designs. Multicoloured. P* 13½×14.

2475	$1.75, Type **379**	80	85
	a. Sheetlet. Nos. 2475/7	2·40	
2476	$1.75, Cinderella and her Fairy Godmother	80	85
2477	$1.75, Cinderella and the Prince	80	85
2475/7	*Set of 3*	2·40	2·50

MS2478 124×96 mm. $6 Cinderella trying on slipper .. .. .. 2·75 3·00

Nos. 2475/7 were printed together, *se-tenant*, in sheetlets of 3 with illustrated margins.

380 *Marasmius rotula*   381 *Odontoglossum cervantesii*

(Des D. Burkhart. Litho Questa)

1997 (12 Aug). *Fungi. T* **380** *and similar horiz designs. Multicoloured. P* 14.
2479	45 c. Type **380**	20	25
2480	65 c. *Cantharellus cibarius*	30	35
2481	70 c. *Lepiota cristata*	30	35
2482	90 c. *Auricularia mesenterica*	40	45
2483	$1 *Pholiota alnicola*	45	50
2484	$1.65, *Leccinum aurantiacum*	75	80
2485	$1.75, *Entoloma serrulatum*	80	85
	a. Sheetlet. Nos. 2485/90	4·75	
2486	$1.75, *Panaeolus sphinctrinus*	80	85
2487	$1.75, *Volvariella bombycina*	80	85
2488	$1.75, *Conocybe percincta*	80	85
2489	$1.75, *Pluteus cervinus*	80	85
2490	$1.75, *Russula foetens*	80	85
2479/90	*Set of 12*	7·25	7·50

MS2491 Two sheets, each 106×76 mm. (a) $6 *Amanita cothurnata*. (b) $6 *Panellus serotinus*
	Set of 2 sheets	5·50 5·75

Nos. 2485/90 were printed together, *se-tenant*, in sheetlets of 6.

(Des T. Wood. Litho Questa)

1997 (19 Aug). *Orchids of the World. T* **381** *and similar vert designs. Multicoloured. P* 14.
2492	45 c. Type **381**	20	25
2493	65 c. *Phalaenopsis* Medford Star	30	35
2494	75 c. *Vanda* Motes Resplendent	35	40
2495	90 c. *Odontonia* Debutante	40	45
2496	$1 *Iwanagaara* Apple Blossom	45	50
2497	$1.65, *Cattleya* Sophia Martin	75	80
	a. Sheetlet. Nos. 2497/504	6·00	
2498	$1.65, Dogface Butterfly	75	80
2499	$1.65, *Laeliocattleya* Mini Purple	75	80
2500	$1.65, *Cymbidium* Showgirl	75	80
2501	$1.65, *Brassolaeliocattleya* Dorothy Bertsch	75	80
2502	$1.65, *Disa blackii*	75	80
2503	$1.65, *Paphiopedilum leeanum*	75	80
2504	$1.65, *Paphiopedilum macranthum*	75	80
2505	$1.65, *Brassocattleya* Angel Lace	75	80
	a. Sheetlet. Nos. 2505/12	6·00	
2506	$1.65, *Saphrolae liocattleya* Precious Stones	75	80
2507	$1.65, Orange Theope Butterfly	75	80
2508	$1.65, *Promenaea xanthina*	75	80
2509	$1.65, *Lycaste macrobulbon*	75	80
2510	$1.65, *Amestella philippinensis*	75	80
2511	$1.65, *Masdevallia* Machu Picchu	75	80
2512	$1.65, *Phalaenopsis* Zuma Urchin	75	80
2513	$2 *Dendrobium victoria-reginae*	90	95
2492/513	*Set of 22*	14·50	15·50

MS2514 Two sheets, each 76×106 mm. (a) $6 *Miltonia* Seine. (b) $6 *Paphiopedilum gratrixianum*
	Set of 2 sheets	5·50 5·75

Nos. 2497/504 and 2505/12 were each printed together, *se-tenant*, in sheetlets of 8 with the backgrounds forming composite designs.

382 Maradonna holding World Cup Trophy, 1986

(Litho Questa)

1997 (16 Oct). *World Cup Football Championship, France* (1998). *T* **382** *and multicoloured designs. P* 14×13¹⁄₂.
2515	60 c. multicoloured	25	30
2516	75 c. agate	35	40
2517	90 c. multicoloured	40	45
2518	$1 agate	45	50
	a. Sheetlet. Nos. 2518/25 and central label	3·50	
2519	$1 agate	45	50
2520	$1 agate	45	50
2521	$1 grey-black	45	50
2522	$1 agate	45	50
2523	$1 agate	45	50
2524	$1 agate	45	50
2525	$1 agate	45	50
2526	$1.20, multicoloured	55	60
2527	$1.65, multicoloured	75	80
2528	$1.75, multicoloured	80	85
2515/28	*Set of 14*	6·50	7·50

MS2529 Two sheets each, 102×127 mm. $6 multicoloured. P 13¹⁄₂×14. (b) $6 multicoloured. P 14×13¹⁄₂
	Set of 2 sheets	5·50 5·75

Designs: *Horiz*—No. 2516, Fritzwalter, West Germany, 1954;

No. 2517, Zoff, Italy, 1982; No. 2526, Moore, England, 1966; No. 2527, Alberto, Brazil, 1970; No. 2528, Matthaus, West Germany, 1990; No. **MS**2529(b), West German players celebrating, 1990. *Vert*—No. 2518, Ademir, Brazil, 1950; No. 2519, Eusebio, Portugal, 1966; No. 2520, Fontaine, France, 1958; No. 2521, Schillaci, Italy, 1990; No. 2522, Leonidas, Brazil, 1938; No. 2523, Stabile, Argentina, 1930; No. 2524, Nejedly, Czechoslovakia, 1934; No. 2525, Muller, West Germany, 1970; No. **MS**2529(a), Bebto, Brazil.
Nos. 2518/25 were printed together, *se-tenant*, in sheetlets of 8 stamps and a central label.

383 Original Drawing by Trevithick, 1804

1997 (10 Nov). *Railway Locomotives of the World. T* **383** *and similar horiz designs. Each blackish brown. Litho. P* 14.
2530	$1.65, Type **383**	75	80
	a. Sheetlet. Nos. 2530/5	4·00	
2531	$1.65, William Hedley's *Puffing Billy*, c. 1860	75	80
2532	$1.65, Crampton Locomotive of French Northern Railway, 1858	75	80
2533	$1.65, Lawrence Machine Shop locomotive, 1860s	75	80
2534	$1.65, *Mississippi*, 1837	75	80
2535	$1.65, "Coppernob" locomotive by Edward Berry, Furness Railway	75	80
2536	$1.65, David Joy's *Jenny Lind*	75	80
	a. Sheetlet. Nos. 2536/41	4·50	
2537	$1.65, "Atlantic" type locomotive, 1899	75	80
2538	$1.65, Kitsons' tank engine, Japan, 1881	75	80
2539	$1.65, Pennsylvania Railroad express freight	75	80
2540	$1.65, Golsdorf's 4 cylinder locomotive, Austria	75	80
2541	$1.65, Lugansk Works "E" Series locomotive, Russia, 1930	75	80
2530/41	*Set of 12*	9·00	9·50

MS2542 Two sheets, each 72×100 mm. (a) $6 George Stephenson locomotive, 1843. (b) $6 Brunel's trestle bridge over Lynher River
	Set of 2 sheets	5·50 5·75

Nos. 2530/5 and 2536/41 were each printed together, *se-tenant*, in sheetlets of 6.

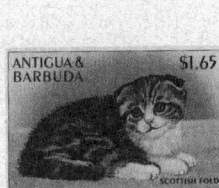

384 Scottish Fold Kitten   385 "The Angel leaving Tobias and his Family" (Rembrandt)

(Des R. Martin. Litho Questa)

1997 (27 Oct). *Cats and Dogs. T* **384** *and similar multicoloured designs. P* 14.
2543	$1.65, Type **384**	75	80
	a. Sheetlet. Nos. 2543/8	4·50	
2544	$1.65, Japanese Bobtail	75	80
2545	$1.65, Tabby Manx	75	80
2546	$1.65, Bicolor American Shorthair	75	80
2547	$1.65, Sorrel Abyssinian	75	80
2548	$1.65, Himalayan Blue Point	75	80
2549	$1.65, Dachshund	75	80
	a. Sheetlet. Nos. 2549/54	4·50	
2550	$1.65, Staffordshire Terrier	75	80
2551	$1.65, Shar-pei	75	80
2552	$1.65, Beagle	75	80
2553	$1.65, Norfolk Terrier	75	80
2554	$1.65, Golden Retriever	75	80
2543/54	*Set of 12*	9·00	9·50

MS2555 Two sheets, each 107×77 mm. (a) $6 Red Tabby (*vert*). (b) $6 Siberian Husky (*vert*)
	Set of 2 sheets	5·50 5·75

Nos. 2543/8 and 2549/54 were each printed together, *se-tenant*, in sheetlets of 6.

(Litho B.D.T.)

1997 (2 Dec). *Christmas. Religious Paintings. T* **385** *and similar multicoloured designs. P* 14.
2556	15 c. Type **385**	10	10
2557	25 c. "The Resurrection" (Martin Knoller)	10	15
2558	60 c. "Astronomy" (Raphael)	25	30
2559	75 c. "Music-making Angel" (Melozzo da Forli)	35	40
2560	90 c. "Amor" (Parmigianino)	40	45
2561	$1.20, "Madonna and Child with Saints" (Rosso Fiorentino)	55	60
2556/61	*Set of 6*	1·75	2·25

MS2562 Two sheets, each 105×96 mm. (a) $6 "The Wedding of Tobias" (Gianantonio and Francesco Guardi) (*horiz*). (b) $6 "The Portinari Altarpiece" (Hugo van der Goes) (*horiz*)
	Set of 2 sheets	5·50 5·75

STAMP BOOKLETS

1968 (2 Oct). *Blue cover. Stitched.*
SB1 $1.20, booklet containing 5 c., 10 c. and 15 c. (Nos. 185, 187, 188) in blocks of 4 .. .. 7·50

1977 (26 Sept). *Silver Jubilee. Blue, silver and sepia cover, 165×82 mm, showing the Royal Family. Stitched.*
SB2 $8 booklet containing pane of 6 (No. 532a) and pane of 1 (No. 533a) .. .. 3·25

1978 (2 June). *25th Anniv of Coronation. Multicoloured cover, 165×92 mm, showing Coronation Coach. Stitched.*
SB3 $7.25, booklet containing pane of 6 (No. 587a) and pane of 1 (No. 589a) .. .. .. 2·75

1981 (23 June). *Royal Wedding. Multicoloured cover, 165×92 mm, showing Prince Charles and Lady Diana Spencer on front and Prince Charles on back. Stitched.*
SB4 $11.50, booklet containing pane of 6 (No. 706a) and pane of 1 (No. 712a) .. .. .. 2·50

BARBUDA

DEPENDENCY OF ANTIGUA

> **PRICES FOR STAMPS ON COVER TO 1945**
> Nos. 1/11 *from* × 4

BARBUDA

(1)

1922 (13 July). *Stamps of Leeward Islands optd with T* **1**. *All Die II. Chalk-surfaced paper* (3d. *to* 5s.).

(a) Wmk Mult Script CA

1	11	½d. deep green	..	..	1·00	7·50
2		1d. bright scarlet	..	..	1·00	7·50
		x. Wmk reversed	..	..	£450	
3	10	2d. slate-grey	..	..	1·00	7·00
		x. Wmk reversed	..	..	50·00	
4	11	2½d. bright blue	..	..	1·00	7·50
		w. Wmk inverted	..	..	25·00	
5		6d. dull and bright purple	..	1·75	16·00	
6	10	2s. purple and blue/*blue*	..	12·00	48·00	
7		3s. bright green and violet	..	30·00	75·00	
8		4s. black and red (R.)..	..	40·00	75·00	

(b) Wmk Mult Crown CA

9	10	3d. purple/*pale yellow*..	..		1·00	8·50
10	12	1s. black/*emerald* (R.)	..		1·50	8·00
11		5s. green and red/*pale yellow*	..	65·00	£130	
1/11				*Set of* 11	£130	£325
1/11 Optd "Specimen"				*Set of* 11	£225	

Examples of all values are known showing a forged Barbuda postmark of "JU 1 23".

Stocks of the overprinted stamps were exhausted by October 1925 and issues of Antigua were then used in Barbuda until 1968.

The following issues of Barbuda were also valid for use in Antigua.

(New Currency. 100 cents = 1 Eastern Caribbean dollar)

2 Map of Barbuda

3 Greater Amberjack

(Des R. Granger Barrett. Litho Format)

1968 (19 Nov)–**70**. *Designs as T* **2/3**. *P* 14.

12		½ c. brown, black and pink	..	..	20	30
13		1 c. orange, black and flesh	..		30	10
14		2 c. blackish brown, rose-red and rose		30	10	
15		3 c. blackish brown, orange-yellow and lemon		30	10	
16		4 c. black, bright green and apple-green		30	10	
17		5 c. blue-green, black and pale blue-green		30	10	
18		6 c. black, bright purple and pale lilac		40	10	
19		10 c. black, ultramarine and cobalt	..	30	10	
20		15 c. black, blue-green and turquoise-green	..	30	55	
20a		20 c. multicoloured (22.7.70)	..	..	1·50	2·00
21		25 c. multicoloured (5.2.69)	..	..	60	25
22		35 c. multicoloured (5.2.69)	..	..	60	25
23		50 c. multicoloured (5.2.69)	..	..	60	55
24		75 c. multicoloured (5.2.69)	..	..	70	80
25		$1 multicoloured (6.3.69)	..	..	85	2·00
26		$2.50, multicoloured (6.3.69)	..	..	1·50	5·00
27		$5 multicoloured (6.3.69)	..	..	3·75	7·50
12/27				*Set of* 17	11·50	17·00

Designs:—½ to 15 c. Type **2**. *Horiz as T* **3**—20 c. Great Barracuda; 35 c. French Angelfish; 50 c. Porkfish; 75 c. Princess Parrotfish; $1, Long-spined Squirrelfish; $2.50, Bigeye; $5, Blue Chromis.

10 Sprinting and Aztec Sun-stone

14 "The Ascension" (Orcagna)

(Des R. Granger Barrett. Litho Format)

1968 (20 Dec). *Olympic Games, Mexico. T* **10** *and similar horiz designs. Multicoloured. P* 14.

28		25 c. Type **10**	..	..	25	25
29		35 c. High-jumping and Aztec statue ..	..	30	25	
30		75 c. Yachting and Aztec lion mask	..	45	45	
28/30				*Set of* 3	90	85
MS31		85 × 76 mm. $1 Football and engraved plate	1·40	3·25		

(Des R. Granger Barret. Litho Format)

1969 (24 Mar). *Easter Commemoration. P* 14.

32	14	25 c. black and light blue		15	45	
33		35 c. black and deep carmine	..	15	50	
34		75 c. black and bluish lilac	..	15	55	
32/4				*Set of* 3	40	1·40

15 Scout Enrolment Ceremony

18 "Sistine Madonna" (Raphael)

(Des R. Granger Barrett. Litho Format)

1969 (7 Aug). *3rd Caribbean Scout Jamboree. T* **15** *and similar horiz designs. Multicoloured. P* 14.

35		25 c. Type **15**			45	55
36		35 c. Scouts around camp fire ..		60	65	
37		75 c. Sea Scouts rowing boat	..	75	85	
35/7				*Set of* 3	1·60	1·90

(Des R. Granger Barrett. Litho Format)

1969 (20 Oct). *Christmas. P* 14.

38	18	½ c. multicoloured		10	10	
39		25 c. multicoloured		10	15	
40		35 c. multicoloured		10	20	
41		75 c. multicoloured		20	35	
38/41				*Set of* 4	30	60

19 William I (1066–87)   **(20)**

20c

(Des R. Granger Barrett. Litho Format (Nos. 42/9) or Questa (others))

1970–71. *English Monarchs. T* **19** *and similar vert designs. Multicoloured. P* 14½ × 14.

42		35 c. Type **19** (16.2.70)..			30	15
43		35 c. William II (2.3.70)	..	..	10	15
44		35 c. Henry I (16.3.70)..	..	..	10	15
45		35 c. Stephen (1.4.70)	..	..	10	15
46		35 c. Henry II (15.4.70)	..	..	10	15
47		35 c. Richard I (1.5.70)	..	..	10	15
48		35 c. John (15.5.70)	..	..	10	15
49		35 c. Henry III (1.6.70)	..	..	10	15
50		35 c. Edward I (15.6.70)	..	..	10	15
51		35 c. Edward II (1.7.70)	..	..	10	15
52		35 c. Edward III (15.7.70)	..	..	10	15
53		35 c. Richard II (1.8.70)	..	..	10	15
54		35 c. Henry IV (15.8.70)	..	..	10	15
55		35 c. Henry V (1.9.70) ..	..	..	10	15
56		35 c. Henry VI (15.9.70)	..	..	10	15
57		35 c. Edward IV (1.10.70)	..	..	10	15
58		35 c. Edward V (15.10.70)	..	..	10	15
59		35 c. Richard III (2.11.70)	..	..	10	15
60		35 c. Henry VII (16.11.70)	..	..	10	15
61		35 c. Henry VIII (1.12.70)	..	..	10	15
62		35 c. Edward VI (15.12.70)	..	..	10	15
63		35 c. Lady Jane Grey (2.1.71)..	..	10	15	
64		35 c. Mary I (15.1.71)	..	..	10	15
65		35 c. Elizabeth I (1.2.71)	..	..	10	15
66		35 c. James I (15.2.71)	..	..	10	15
67		35 c. Charles I (1.3.71)..	..	..	10	15
68		35 c. Charles II (15.3.71)	..	..	10	15
69		35 c. James II (1.4.71) ..	..	..	10	15
70		35 c. William III (15.4.71)	..	..	10	15
71		35 c. Mary II (1.5.71)	..	..	10	15
72		35 c. Anne (15.5.71)	..	..	15	15
73		35 c. George I (1.6.71)	..	..	15	15
74		35 c. George II (15.6.71)	..	..	15	15
75		35 c. George III (1.7.71)	..	..	15	15
76		35 c. George IV (15.7.71)	..	..	15	15
77		35 c. William IV (2.8.71)	..	..	15	40
78		35 c. Victoria (16.8.71)	..	..	15	40
42/78				*Set of* 37	3·75	5·50

See also Nos. 710/15.

1970 (26 Feb). *No. 12 surch with T* **20**.

79	2	20 c. on ½ c. brown, black and pink	..	10	20	
		a. Surch inverted	..	..	50·00	
		b. Surch double ..	..	..	50·00	

21 "The Way to Calvary" (Ugolino)

22 Oliver is introduced to Fagin (*Oliver Twist*)

(Des R. Granger Barrett. Litho Questa)

1970 (16 Mar). *Easter Paintings. T* **21** *and similar vert designs. Multicoloured P* 14.

80		25 c. Type **21**	..	..	15	30
		a. Horiz strip of 3. Nos. 80/2		40		
81		35 c. "The Deposition from the Cross" (Ugolino)	15	30		
82		75 c. Crucifix (The Master of St. Francis)	15	35		
80/2				*Set of* 3	40	85

Nos. 80/2 were printed together, *se-tenant*, in horizontal strips of 3 throughout the sheet.

(Des R. Granger Barrett. Litho Questa)

1970 (10 July). *Death Centenary of Charles Dickens. T* **22** *and similar horiz design. Multicoloured. P* 14.

83		20 c. Type **22**			10	15
84		75 c. Dickens and Scene from *The Old Curiosity Shop*		20	40	

23 "Madonna of the Meadow" (Bellini)   24 Nurse with Patient in Wheelchair

(Des R. Granger Barrett. Litho Questa)

1970 (15 Oct). *Christmas. T* **23** *and similar horiz designs. Multicoloured. P* 14.

85		20 c. Type **23**			10	25
86		50 c. "Madonna, Child and Angels" (from Wilton diptych)		15	30	
87		75 c. "The Nativity" (della Francesca)		15	35	
85/7				*Set of* 3	30	80

(Des R. Granger Barrett. Litho Questa)

1970 (21 Dec). *Centenary of British Red Cross. T* **24** *and similar multicoloured designs. P* 14.

88		20 c. Type **24**			15	30
89		35 c. Nurse giving patient magazines (*horiz*)		20	40	
90		75 c. Nurse and mother weighing baby (*horiz*)		25	70	
88/90				*Set of* 3	55	1·25

25 Angel with Vases   26 Martello Tower

(Des R. Granger Barrett. Litho Questa)

1971 (7 Apr). *Easter. Details of the "Mond" Crucifixion by Raphael. T* **25** *and similar vert designs. Multicoloured. P* 14.

91		35 c. Type **25**			15	75
		a. Horiz strip of 3. Nos. 91/3		40		
92		50 c. Christ crucified		15	85	
93		75 c. Angel with vase		15	90	
91/3				*Set of* 3	40	2·25

Nos. 91/3 were issued horizontally *se-tenant* within the sheet.

(Des R. Granger Barrett. Litho Questa)

1971 (10 May). *Tourism. T* **26** *and similar horiz designs. Multicoloured. P* 14.

				10	25
94	20 c. Type **26**	..	..	20	30
95	35 c. Sailing boats	..	..	20	35
96	50 c. Hotel bungalows..	..	..	25	40
97	75 c. Government House and Mystery Stone	60	1·10		
94/7			*Set of* 4		

27 "The Granducal Madonna" (Raphael)   (28)

(Des R. Granger Barrett. Litho Questa)

1971 (4 Oct). *Christmas. T* **27** *and similar vert designs. Multicoloured. P* 14.

98		½ c. Type **27**			10	10
99		35 c. "The Ansidei Madonna" (Raphael)		10	20	
100		50 c. "The Madonna and Child" (Botticelli)		15	25	
101		75 c. "The Madonna of the Trees" (Bellini) ..		15	30	
98/101				*Set of* 4	35	65

The contract with the agency for the distribution of Barbuda stamps was cancelled by the Antiguan Government on 15 August 1971 but the above issue was duly authorised. Four stamps (20, 35, 50 and 70 c.) were prepared to commemorate the 500th anniversary of the birth of Albrecht Dürer but their issue was not authorised.

Barbuda ceased to have separate stamps issues in 1972 but again had stamps of her own on 14 November 1973 with the following issue.

1973 (14 Nov). *Royal Wedding. Nos. 370/1 of Antigua optd with T* **28**.
102	35 c. multicoloured	..	5·00	3·25
	a. Opt inverted	..	£100	
103	$2 multicoloured	..	2·00	1·75
	a. Opt inverted	..	£120	

No. MS372 of Antigua also exists with this overprint, but was not placed on sale at post offices. Examples of this sheet are known with "Specimen" overprint (*Price* £120).

B A R B U D A (29) B A R B U D A (30) B A R B U D A (30a) B A R B U D A (31)

BARBUDA (29)

1973 (26 Nov)–74. *T* **92** *etc. of Antigua optd with T* **29**.

(a) On Nos. 270 etc. W w **12** (*sideways*)
104	1 c. Columbus and *Nina*	..	15	30
105	2 c. Sir Thomas Warner's emblem and *Concepcion*	..	25	30
106	4 c. Sir George Rodney and H.M.S. *Formidable*	..	30	30
107	5 c. Nelson and H.M.S. *Boreas*	..	40	40
108	6 c. William IV and H.M.S. *Pegasus*	..	40	40
109	10 c. "Blackbeard" and pirate ketch	..	45	45
110	20 c. Nelson and H.M.S. *Victory*	..	55	60
111	25 c. *Solent I* (paddle-steamer)	..	55	60
112	35 c. George V (when Prince George) and H.M.S. *Canada* (screw corvette)	..	55	70
113	50 c. H.M.S. *Renown* (battle cruiser)	..	55	70
114	75 c. *Federal Maple* (freighter)	..	55	70
115	$2.50, H.M.S. *London* (destroyer) (18.2.74)	1·25	1·50

(b) On Nos. 323 etc. W w **12** (*upright*). *White paper*
116	½ c. Type **92** (11.12.73)	..	15	20
117	3 c. Viscount Hood and H.M.S. *Barfleur* (11.12.73)	25	25
	w. Wmk inverted	..	35·00	
118	15 c. Captain Collingwood and H.M.S. *Pelican* (11.12.73)	45	50
119	$1 *Sol Quest* (yacht) and class emblem (11.12.73)	55	70
120	$2.50, H.M.S. *London* (destroyer) (18.2.74)	8·50	12·00
121	$5 *Pathfinder* (tug) (26.11.73)	..	1·40	2·50
104/21		*Set of 18*	15·00	20·00

1973 (26 Nov). *Commemorative stamps of Antigua optd.*

(a) Nos. 353, 355 and 357/8 optd with T **30**
122	½ c. Private, Zacharia Tiffin's Regt of Foot, 1701	10	10
123	20 c. Light Company Officer, 35th Regt of Foot, 1828	15	10
	aw. Wmk Crown to right of CA	7·00	
	b. Optd with T **30a**	60	70
	bw. Wmk Crown to right of CA	6·00	
124	75 c. Sergeant, 49th Regt, 1858	40	15
122/4		*Set of 3*	55	25
MS125	127×145 mm. Nos. 353/7 of Antigua	2·00	3·50

(b) Nos 360/3 optd with T **31**, *in red*
126	20 c. Carnival street scene	..	10	10
127	35 c. Carnival troupe	..	10	10
	a. Opt inverted	..	30·00	
128	75 c. Carnival Queen	..	20	25
126/8		*Set of 3*	30	40
MS129	134×95 mm. Nos. 359/62 of Antigua	1·25	2·25
	a. Albino opt	..	£275	
	a. Opt double	..		

Type **30a** is a local overprint, applied by typography.

B A R B U D A (32) B A R B U D A (33) BARBUDA (34) B A R B U D A (35)

1973 (11 Dec). *Christmas. Nos. 364/9 of Antigua optd with T* **32**.
130	3 c. Type **105** (Sil.)	..	10	10
	a. Opt inverted	..	24·00	
	b. "BABRUDA" (R.4/2)	..	5·50	5·50
131	5 c. "Adoration of the Magi" (Stomer) (Sil.)	10	10
	a. "BABRUDA" (R.4/2)	..	7·00	7·00
132	20 c. "Granducal Madonna" (Raphael) (Sil.)	10	10
	a. "BABRUDA" (R.4/2)	..	9·00	9·00
133	35 c. "Nativity with God the Father and Holy Ghost" (Battista) (R.)	15	15
134	$1 "Madonna and Child" (Murillo) (R.)	30	30
	a. Opt inverted	..	45·00	
130/4		*Set of 5*	60	60
MS135	130 × 128 mm. Nos. 130/4 (Sil.)	..	3·25	10·00

1973 (15 Dec). *Honeymoon Visit of Princess Anne and Capt. Phillips. Nos. 373/5 of Antigua further optd with T* **33**.
136	35 c. multicoloured	..	30	20
	a. Type 33 double, one albino	..	65·00	
	b. Optd on Antigua No. 373a	..		

137	$2 multicoloured	..	70	60
	a. Type 33 double, one albino	..	†	—
	b. Optd on Antigua No. 374a	..		
MS138	78×100 mm. Nos. 136/7	..	5·00	7·50

1974 (18 Feb). *25th Anniv of University of West Indies. Nos. 376/9 of Antigua optd with T* **34**.
139	5 c. Coat of arms	..	10	10
	a. Opt double, one albino	..	†	—
140	20 c. Extra-mural art	..	10	10
141	35 c. Antigua campus	..	15	15
	a. Opt double	..		
142	75 c. Antigua Chancellor	..	15	15
139/42		*Set of 4*	30	30

No. 139a has only been seen used on first day cover. It shows the "normal" impression misplaced and very faint

1974 (1 May). *Military Uniforms. Nos. 380/4 of Antigua optd with T* **35**.
143	½ c. Officer, 59th Foot, 1797	..	10	10
144	10 c. Gunner, Royal Artillery, 1800	..	10	10
	a. Horiz pair, left-hand stamp without opt	£120	
145	20 c. Private, 1st West India Regt, 1830	20	10
	a. Horiz pair, left-hand stamp without opt	£120	
146	35 c. Officer, 92nd Foot, 1843	..	25	10
	a. Opt inverted	..	50·00	
147	75 c. Private, 23rd Foot, 1846	..	45	25
	a. Horiz pair, left-hand stamp without opt		
143/7		*Set of 5*	90	45

Nos. 144a, 145a and 147a come from sheets on which the overprint was so misplaced as to miss the first vertical row completely. Other stamps in these sheets show the overprint at left instead of right.

No. MS385 of Antigua also exists with this overprint, but was not placed on sale at post offices.

BARBUDA 13 JULY 1922 (36) BARBUDA 15 SEPT. 1874 G.P.U. (37) "General Postal Union") BARBUDA (38)

1974 (15 July). *Centenary of Universal Postal Union (1st issue). Nos. 386/92 of Antigua optd with T* **36** (*Nos. 148, 150, 152, 154, 156, 158 and 160*) *or T* **37** (*others*), *in red.*
148	½ c. English postman, mailcoach and Westland Dragonfly helicopter	10	10
149	½ c. English postman, mailcoach and Westland Dragonfly helicopter	10	10
150	1 c. Bellman, mail steamer *Orinoco* and satellite	10	10
151	1 c. Bellman, mail steamer *Orinoco* and satellite	10	10
152	2 c. Train guard, post-bus and hydrofoil	15	15
153	2 c. Train guard, post-bus and hydrofoil	15	15
154	5 c. Swiss messenger, Wells Fargo coach and Concorde	15	15
155	5 c. Swiss messenger, Wells Fargo coach and Concorde	15	15
156	20 c. Postilion, Japanese postmen and carrier pigeon	40	70
157	20 c. Postilion, Japanese postmen and carrier pigeon	40	70
158	35 c. Antiguan postman, Sikorsky S-38 flying boat and tracking station	80	1·50
159	35 c. Antiguan postman, Sikorsky S-38 flying boat and tracking station	80	1·50
160	$1 Medieval courier, American express train and Boeing 747-100	2·25	4·00
161	$1 Medieval courier, American express train and Boeing 747-100	2·25	4·00
148/61		*Set of 14*	7·00	12·00
MS162	141×164 mm. No. MS393 of Antigua overprinted with T **38**, in red	3·00	6·00
	a. Albino opt	..		

Nos. 148/9, 150/1, 152/3, 154/5, 156/7, 158/9 and 160/1 were each printed together, *se-tenant*, in horizontal pairs throughout the sheet.

See also Nos. 177/80.

1974 (14 Aug). *Antiguan Steel Bands. Nos. 394/8 of Antigua optd with T* **38**.
163	5 c. rose-red, carmine and black	..	10	10
164	20 c. brown-ochre, chestnut and black	..	10	10
165	35 c. light sage-green, blue-green and black	..	10	10
166	75 c. dull blue, dull ultramarine and black	..	20	20
163/6		*Set of 4*	35	35
MS167	115 × 108 mm. Nos. 163/6	..	65	80

B A R B U D A

39 Footballers (40)

(Des G. Drummond. Litho Format)

1974 (2 Sept). *World Cup Football Championships (1st issue). Various horiz designs as T* **39** *each showing footballers in action. P* 14.
168	**39**	35 c. multicoloured	..	10	10
169		$1.20, multicoloured	..	25	35
170		$2.50, multicoloured	..	30	35
168/70			*Set of 3*	60	75
MS171	70 × 128 mm. Nos. 168/70	..	85	90

Nos. 168/71 exist imperforate from stock dispersed by the liquidator of Format International Security Printers Ltd.

1974 (23 Sept). *World Cup Football Championships (2nd issue). Nos. 399/403 of Antigua optd with T* **40**.
172	5 c. multicoloured	..	10	10
173	35 c. multicoloured	..	10	10
174	75 c. multicoloured	..	15	15
175	$1 multicoloured	..	20	25
172/5		*Set of 4*	35	45
MS176	135 × 130 mm. Nos. 172/5	..	75	1·25

---

41 Ship Letter of 1833 42 Greater Amberjack

(Des G. Drummond. Litho Format)

1974 (30 Sept). *Centenary of Universal Postal Union (2nd issue). T* **41** *and similar vert designs. Multicoloured. P* 13½.
177	35 c. Type **41**	..	10	10
178	$1.20, Stamps and postmark of 1922	30	50
179	$2.50, Britten Norman Islander mailplane over map of Barbuda	55	75
177/9		*Set of 3*	75	1·25
MS180	128×97 mm. Nos. 177/9	..	1·00	2·00

Nos. 177/80 exist imperforate from stock dispersed by the liquidator of Format International Security Printers Ltd.

(Des G. Drummond. Litho Format)

1974 (15 Oct)–75. *Multicoloured designs as T* **42**. *P* 14×14½ (½c. *to* 3 c., 25 c.), 14½×14 (4 c. *to* 20 c., 35 c.), 14 (50 c. *to* $1) *or* 13½ (*others*).
181	½ c. Oleander, Rose Bay (6.1.75)	10	40
182	1 c. Blue Petrea (6.1.75)	15	40
183	2 c. Poinsettia (6.1.75)	15	40
184	3 c. Cassia tree (6.1.75)	15	40
185	4 c. Type **42**	..	1·40	40
186	5 c. Holy Trinity School	15	15
187	6 c. Snorkelling	..	15	30
188	10 c. Pilgrim Holiness Church	15	20
189	15 c. New Cottage Hospital	15	20
190	20 c. Post Office and Treasury	15	20
191	25 c. Island jetty and boats	30	30
192	35 c. Martello Tower	30	30
193	50 c. Warden's House (6.1.75)	30	30
194	75 c. Britten Norman Islander aircraft	75	1·00
195	$1 Tortoise (6.1.75)	70	80
196	$2.50, Spiny lobster (6.1.75)	80	1·75
197	$5 Magnificent Frigate Bird (6.1.75)	5·00	3·00
	a. Perf 14×14½ (24.7.75)*	12·00	22·00
197b	$10 Hibiscus (19.9.75)	12·00	22·00
181/97b		*Set of 18*	12·00	14·00

*See footnote below Nos. 227/8.

The 50 c. to $1 are larger, 39 × 25 mm; the $2.50 and $5 are 45 × 29 mm; the $10 is 34 × 48 mm and the ½ c. to 3c. 25 c. and $10 are vert designs.

1974 (15 Oct). *Birth Centenary of Sir Winston Churchill (1st issue). Nos. 408/12 of Antigua optd with T* **38** *in red.*
198	5 c. Churchill as schoolboy, and school college building, Harrow	10	10
	a. Opt inverted	..	60·00	
199	35 c. Churchill and St. Paul's Cathedral	20	15
200	75 c. Coat of arms and catafalque	35	45
201	$1 Churchill, "reward" notice and South African escape route	55	70
	a. Opt inverted	..	60·00	
198/201		*Set of 4*	1·10	1·25
MS202	107 × 82 mm. Nos. 198/201	..	6·00	13·00

BARBUDA 5c

43 Churchill making Broadcast BARBUDA (44)

(Des G. Drummond. Litho Questa)

1974 (20 Nov). *Birth Centenary of Sir Winston Churchill (2nd issue). T* **43** *and similar horiz designs. Multicoloured. P* 13½ × 14.
203	5 c. Type **43**	..	10	10
204	35 c. Churchill and Chartwell	10	10
205	75 c. Churchill painting	20	20
206	$1 Churchill making "V" sign	25	30
203/6		*Set of 4*	55	60
MS207	146×95 mm. Nos. 203/6	..	75	2·50

1974 (25 Nov). *Christmas. Nos. 413/21 of Antigua optd with T* **33**.
208	½ c. Bellini	..	10	10
	a. Opt inverted	..	45·00	
209	1 c. Raphael	..	10	10
210	2 c. Van der Weyden	..	10	10
211	3 c. Giorgione	..	10	10
212	5 c. Mantegna	..	10	10
213	20 c. Vivarini	..	10	10
214	35 c. Montagna	..	15	15
215	75 c. Lorenzo Costa	..	30	30
208/15		*Set of 8*	60	60
MS216	139 × 126 mm. Nos. 208/15	..	80	1·40

1975 (17 Mar). *Nelson's Dockyard. Nos. 427/32 of Antigua optd with T* **44**.
217	5 c. Carib war canoe, English Harbour, 1300	20	15
218	15 c. Ship of the line, English Harbour, 1770	40	25
219	35 c. H.M.S. *Boreas* at anchor, and Lord Nelson, 1787	55	35
220	50 c. Yachts during "Sailing Week", 1974	70	50
221	$1 Yacht Anchorage, Old Dockyard, 1970	90	80
217/21		*Set of 5*	2·50	1·75
MS222	130 × 134 mm. As Nos. 217/21, but in larger format; 43 × 28 mm	2·25	2·75

45 Battle of the Saints, 1782

(Des G. Vasarhelyi. Litho Format)

1975 (30 May). *Sea Battles. T 45 and similar horiz designs showing scenes from the Battle of the Saints, 1782. Multicoloured. P 13½.*

223	35 c. Type 45	..	..	75	65
224	50 c. H.M.S. *Ramillies*	..	..	75	75
225	75 c. Ships firing broadsides	..	..	90	90
226	95 c. Sailors fleeing burning ship	..	1·00	1·25
223/6		..	*Set of 4*	3·00	3·25

(46)

1975 (24 July). *"Apollo-Soyuz" Space Project. No. 197a optd with T 46 and similar ("Soyuz") opt.*

227	$5 Magnificent Frigate Bird ("Apollo")	..	4·00	7·50
	a. *Se-tenant* strip of 3. Nos. 227/8 and 197a	18·00	
228	$5 Magnificent Frigate Bird ("Soyuz")	..	4·00	7·50

Nos. 227/8 were issued together *se-tenant* in sheets of 25 (5 × 5), with the "Apollo" opts in the first and third vertical rows and the "Soyuz" opts in the second and fourth vertical rows, the fifth vertical row comprising five unoverprinted stamps (No. 197a).

47 Officer, 65th Foot, 1763

30TH ANNIVERSARY UNITED NATIONS 1945 — 1975 (48)

(Des G. Drummond. Litho Questa)

1975 (17 Sept). *Military Uniforms. T 47 and similar vert designs. Multicoloured. P 13½.*

229	35 c. Type 47	..	..	75	75
230	50 c. Grenadier, 27th Foot, 1701–10	..	90	90
231	75 c. Officer, 21st Foot, 1793–6	..	1·00	1·00
232	95 c. Officer, Royal Regt of Artillery, 1800	1·25	1·25
229/32		..	*Set of 4*	3·50	3·50

1975 (24 Oct). *30th Anniv of United Nations. Nos. 203/6 optd with T 48.*

233	5 c. Churchill making broadcast	..	10	10
234	35 c. Churchill and Chartwell	..	10	15
235	75 c. Churchill painting	..	15	20
236	$1 Churchill making "V" sign	..	20	30
233/6	..	..	*Set of 4*	40	60

BARBUDA (49)   **BARBUDA** (50)

1975 (17 Nov). *Christmas. Nos. 457/65 of Antigua optd with T 49.*

237	½ c. Correggio	..	..	10	10
238	1 c. El Greco	..	..	10	10
239	2 c. Dürer	..	..	10	10
240	3 c. Antonello	..	..	10	10
241	5 c. Bellini	..	..	10	10
242	10 c. Dürer	..	..	10	10
243	25 c. Bellini	..	..	15	20
244	$2 Dürer	..	..	60	1·00
237/44		..	*Set of 8*	95	1·50
MS245	138 × 119 mm. Nos. 241/4	..	1·10	2·25

1975 (15 Dec). *World Cup Cricket Winners. Nos. 466/8 of Antigua optd with T 50.*

246	5 c. Vivian Richards	..	..	90	1·00
247	35 c. Andy Roberts	..	..	1·75	2·00
248	$2 West Indies team	..	..	3·25	4·25
246/8	..	..	*Set of 3*	5·50	6·50

51 "Surrender of Cornwallis at Yorktown" (Trumbull)

(Des G. Vasarhelyi. Litho Format)

1976 (8 Mar). *Bicentenary of American Revolution. T 51 and similar horiz designs. Multicoloured. P 13½ × 13.*

249	15 c.		10	15
250	15 c. } Type 51		10	15
251	15 c.		10	15
252	35 c.		10	15
253	35 c. } "The Battle of Princeton"		10	15
254	35 c.		10	15
255	$1	"Surrender of General Burgoyne	15	25
256	$1	at Saratoga" (W. Mercer)	15	25
257	$1		15	25
258	$2	"The Declaration of	25	40
259	$2 } Independence" (Trumbull)		25	40
260	$2		25	40
249/60		*Set of 12*	1·50	2·50
MS261	140 × 70 mm. Nos. 249/54 and 255/60 (*two sheets*)		2·75	9·00

The three designs of each value were printed horizontally *se-tenant* within the sheet to form the composite designs listed. Type 51 shows the left-hand stamp of the 15 c. design.

52 Bananaquits

(Des G. Drummond. Litho Format)

1976 (30 June). *Birds. T 52 and similar horiz designs. Multicoloured. P 13½.*

262	35 c. Type 52	..	..	1·00	50
263	50 c. Blue-hooded Euphonia	..	1·25	60
264	75 c. Royal Tern	..	..	1·25	80
265	95 c. Killdeer	..	..	1·75	85
266	$1.25, Common Cowbird	..	1·75	1·00
267	$2 Purple Gallinule	..	..	2·00	1·25
262/7		..	*Set of 6*	8·00	4·50

1976 (12 Aug). *Royal Visit to the U.S.A. As Nos. 249/60 but redrawn and inscr at top "H.M. QUEEN ELIZABETH ROYAL VISIT 6TH JULY 1976 H.R.H. DUKE OF EDINBURGH".*

268	15 c.		10	15
269	15 c. } As Type 51		10	15
270	15 c.		10	15
271	35 c.		10	20
272	35 c. } As Nos. 252/4		10	20
273	35 c.		10	20
274	$1		20	50
275	$1 } As Nos. 255/7		20	50
276	$1		20	50
277	$2		30	70
278	$2 } As Nos. 258/60		30	70
279	$2		30	70
268/79		*Set of 12*	1·75	4·25
MS280	143 × 81 mm. Nos. 268/73 and 274/9 (*two sheets*)		3·00	9·00

The three designs of each value were printed horizontally *se-tenant*, imperf between.

BARBUDA (53)   **BARBUDA** (54)

1976 (2 Dec). *Christmas. Nos. 514/18 of Antigua optd with T 53.*

281	8 c. The Annunciation	..	10	10
282	10 c. The Holy Family	..	10	10
283	15 c. The Magi	..	..	10	10
284	50 c. The Shepherds	..	15	15
285	$1 Epiphany scene	..	25	30
281/5	..	..	*Set of 5*	45	55

1976 (28 Dec). *Olympic Games, Montreal. Nos. 495/502 of Antigua optd with T 54.*

286	½ c. High-jump	..	..	10	10
287	1 c. Boxing	..	..	10	10
288	2 c. Pole-vault	..	..	10	10
289	15 c. Swimming	..	..	10	10
290	30 c. Running	..	..	10	10
291	$1 Cycling	..	..	20	20
292	$2 Shot put	..	..	35	35
286/92		..	*Set of 7*	60	60
MS293	88 × 138 mm. Nos. 289/92	..	1·50	2·40

55 Post Office Tower, Telephones and Alexander Graham Bell

(Des G. Vasarhelyi. Litho Format)

1977 (31 Jan). *Telephone Centenary (1976). T 55 and similar horiz designs. Multicoloured. P 13½.*

294	75 c. Type 55	..	15	35
295	$1.25, Dish aerial and television	20	55
296	$2 Globe and satellites	..	30	75
294/6		..	*Set of 3*	60	1·50
MS297	96 × 144 mm. Nos. 294/6. P 15	70	2·00

56 St. Margaret's Church, Westminster

1977 (7 Feb). *Silver Jubilee (1st issue). T 56 and similar horiz designs. Multicoloured. Litho. P 13½ × 13.*

298	75 c. Type 56	..	..	10	15
299	75 c. Entrance, Westminster Abbey	..	10	15
300	75 c. Westminster Abbey	..	10	15
301	$1.25, Household Cavalry	..	15	20
302	$1.25, Coronation Coach	..	15	20
303	$1.25, Team of Horses	..	15	20
298/303		..	*Set of 6*	65	90
MS304	148×83 mm. As Nos. 298/303, but with silver borders. P 15		75	1·50

Nos. 298/300 and 301/3 were printed horizontally *se-tenant*, forming composite designs.
See also Nos. 323/30 and 375/8.

1977 (4 Apr). *Nos. 469A/86A of Antigua optd with T 54.*

305	½ c. Antillean Crested Hummingbird	..	20	20
306	1 c. Imperial Amazon	..	..	30	20
307	2 c. Zenaida Dove	..	..	30	20
308	3 c. Loggerhead Kingbird	..	30	20
309	4 c. Red-necked Pigeon	..	30	20
310	5 c. Rufous-throated Solitaire	..	30	20
311	6 c. Orchid Tree	..	..	30	20
312	10 c. Bougainvillea	..	..	30	20
313	15 c. Geiger Tree	..	..	30	25
314	20 c. Flamboyant	..	..	30	25
315	25 c. Hibiscus	..	..	30	25
316	35 c. Flame of the Wood	..	35	30
317	50 c. Cannon at Fort James	..	40	40
318	75 c. Premier's Office	..	40	40
319	$1 Potworks Dam	..	..	50	60
320	$2.50, Irrigation scheme	..	1·25	1·60
321	$5 Government House	..	2·25	3·25
322	$10 Coolidge Airport	..	4·00	7·50
305/22		..	*Set of 18*	11·00	15·00

B A R B U D A (57)   **B A R B U D A** (58)   **BARBUDA** (59)

1977 (4 Apr–20 Dec). *Silver Jubilee (2nd issue).*

(a) Sheet stamps. Nos. 526/31 of Antigua optd with T 57

323	10 c. Royal Family	..	..	15	15
	a. Opt double	..	..	45·00	
324	30 c. Royal Visit, 1966	..	15	20
325	50 c. Queen enthroned	..	20	30
326	90 c. Queen after Coronation	..	25	40
327	$2.50, Queen and Prince Charles	75	1·25
323/7		..	*Set of 5*	1·25	2·10
MS328	116×78 mm. $5 Queen Elizabeth and Prince Philip		1·10	1·75
	a. Error. Imperf	..	..	£600	
	b. Opt albino	..	..	25·00	
	c. Opt double				

(b) Booklet stamps. Nos. 532/3 of Antigua optd with T 58 in silver (50 c.) or T 59 in gold ($5) (20 Dec)

329	50 c. Queen after Coronation	..	40	70
	a. Booklet pane of 6.	..	2·25	
330	$5 The Queen and Prince Philip	..	5·50	13·00
	a. Booklet pane of 1.	..	5·50	

BARBUDA (60)   **61** Royal Yacht *Britannia*

1977 (13 June). *Caribbean Scout Jamboree, Jamaica. Nos. 534/41 of Antigua optd with T 60.*

331	½ c. Making camp	..	..	10	10
332	1 c. Hiking	..	..	10	10
333	2 c. Rock-climbing	..	..	10	10
334	10 c. Cutting logs	..	..	10	10
335	30 c. Map and sign reading	..	40	40
336	50 c. First aid	..	..	55	65
337	$2 Rafting	..	..	2·00	2·25
331/37		..	*Set of 7*	2·75	3·00
MS338	127 × 114 mm. Nos. 335/7	..	3·25	4·00

1977 (12 Aug). *21st Anniv of Carnival. Nos. 542/7 of Antigua optd with T 60.*

339	10 c. Carnival costume	..	10	10
340	30 c. Carnival Queen	..	10	10
341	50 c. Butterfly costume	..	15	20
342	90 c. Queen of the band	..	20	30
343	$1 Calypso King and Queen	..	25	40
339/43		..	*Set of 5*	65	90
MS344	140 × 120 mm. Nos. 339/43	..	1·00	1·75

(Des G. Drummond. Litho Format)

1977 (27 Oct). *Royal Visit (1st issue). T 61 and similar horiz designs. Multicoloured. P 14½.*

345	50 c. Type 61	..	..	10	15
346	$1.50, Jubilee emblem	..	25	35
347	$2.50, Union Jack and flag of Antigua	35	55
345/7		..	*Set of 3*	60	95
MS348	77 × 124 mm. Nos. 345/7	..	85	2·25

BARBUDA   BARBUDA

(62)   (63)   64 Airship LZ-1

1977 (28 Nov–20 Dec).   *Royal Visit (2nd issue)*. Nos. 548/**MS**553 *of Antigua optd*. A. *With T* 57. P 14 (28 Nov). B. *With T* 62. P 11½ × 12 (20 Dec).

			A		B	
349	10 c. Royal Family	..	10	10	10	10
	a. Blue opt	..		†	35	35
350	30 c. Royal Visit, 1966 ..		15	20	15	15
	a. Blue opt	..		†	90	95
351	50 c. Queen enthroned ..		20	30	20	20
	a. Blue opt	..		†	2·75	1·90
352	90 c. Queen after Coronation	..	30	50	30	30
	a. Blue opt	..		†	5·00	3·50
353	$2.50, Queen and Prince Charles	..	75	1·75	60	80
	a. Blue opt	..		†	11·00	9·50
349/53	*Set of* 5		1·25	2·50	1·10	1·40
MS354	116 × 78 mm. $5 Queen and Prince Philip	..	1·75	4·00	†	

Nos. 349B/53B were each printed in small sheets of 6 including one *se-tenant* stamp-size label.

1977 (28 Nov).   *Christmas*. Nos. 554/61 *of Antigua optd with T* 63. *"Virgin and Child" paintings by the artists given*.

355	½ c. Tura	..	..	10	10
356	1 c. Crivelli	..		10	10
357	2 c. Lotto	..		10	10
358	8 c. Pontormo..			10	10
359	10 c. Tura	..		10	10
360	25 c. Lotto	..		15	10
361	$2 Crivelli	..		45	45
355/61			*Set of* 7	70	65
MS362	144 × 118 mm. Nos. 358/61	..		1·00	1·75

(Des I. Oliver. Litho Format)

1977 (29 Dec).   *Special Events, 1977. T* 64 *and similar horiz designs. Multicoloured*. P 14.

363	75 c. Type 64		..	30	30
	a. Nos. 363/6 in *se-tenant* block		1·10	
364	75 c. German battleship and naval airship L-31	..		30	30
365	75 c. Airship LZ-127 *Graf Zeppelin* in hangar		..	30	30
366	75 c. Gondola of military airship	..		30	30
367	95 c. "Sputnik 1"	..		35	35
	a. Nos. 367/70 in *se-tenant* block		1·25	
368	95 c. "Vostok"	..		35	35
369	95 c. "Voskhod"	..		35	35
370	95 c. Space walk	..		35	35
371	$1.25, Fuelling for flight	..		40	45
	a. Nos. 371/4 in *se-tenant* block		1·40	
372	$1.25, Leaving New York	..		40	45
373	$1.25, Ryan NYP Special *Spirit of St. Louis* ..	..		40	45
374	$1.25, Welcome in France	..		40	45
375	$2 Lion of England ..	..		50	70
	a. Nos. 375/8 in *se-tenant* block	..	1·75	
376	$2 Unicorn of Scotland	..		50	70
377	$2 Yale of Beaufort	..		50	70
378	$2 Falcon of Plantagenets	..		50	70
379	$5 ⎫			50	1·25
380	$5 ⎪ "Daniel in the Lion's Den"		50	1·25
381	$5 ⎬ (Rubens)			50	1·25
382	$5 ⎭			50	1·25
	a. Nos. 379/82 in *se-tenant* block		1·75	
363/82			*Set of* 20	6·00	11·00
MS383	132 × 156 mm. Nos. 363/82	..		6·00	17·00

Events:—75 c. 75th Anniv of Navigable Airships; 95 c. 20th Anniv of U.S.S.R. Space Programme; $1.25, 50th Anniv of Lindbergh's Transatlantic Flight; $2 Silver Jubilee of Queen Elizabeth II; $5 400th Birth Anniv of Rubens.

Nos. 363/66, 367/70, 371/74, 375/78 and 379/82 were printed in *se-tenant* blocks of four within the sheet.

Nos. 363/83 exist imperforate from stock dispersed by the liquidator of Format International Security Printers Ltd.

BARBUDA

(65)   66 "Pieta" (sculpture) (detail)

1978 (15 Feb).   *Tenth Anniv of Statehood*. Nos. 562/7 *of Antigua optd with T* 65.

384	10 c. Pineapple	..	..	..	10	10
385	15 c. State flag..	..			15	10
386	50 c. Police band	..			1·25	60
387	90 c. Premier V. C. Bird	..		20	30
388	$2 State Coat of Arms	..		40	60
384/8	..		*Set of* 5	1·75	1·50
MS389	126 × 99 mm. Nos. 385/88. P 14	..		5·50	3·50

(Des G. Vasarhelyi. Litho Format)

1978 (23 Mar).   *Easter. Works by Michelangelo. T* 66 *and similar horiz designs. Multicoloured*. P 13½ × 14.

390	75 c. Type 66	..		15	15
391	95 c. "The Holy Family" (painting)	..	20	20
392	$1.25, "Libyan Sibyl" from Sistine Chapel Rome	..		25	25
393	$2 "The Flood" from Sistine Chapel	30	35
390/3	..		*Set of* 4	75	85
MS394	117 × 85 mm. No. 390/3	..		1·60	2·00

Nos. 390/4 exist imperforate from stock dispersed by the liquidator of Format International Security Printers Ltd.

BARBUDA

(67)   68 St. Edward's Crown

1978 (28 Mar).   *75th Anniv of Powered Flight*. Nos. 568/75 *of Antigua optd with T* 67.

395	½ c. Wright Glider III, 1902	..	..	10	10
396	1 c. Wright Flyer I, 1903	..		10	10
397	2 c. Launch system and engine	..		10	10
398	10 c. Orville Wright	..		10	10
399	50 c. Wright Flyer III, 1905	..		25	15
400	90 c. Wilbur Wright	..		35	15
401	$2 Wright Type B, 1910	..		60	45
395/401			*Set of* 7	1·25	75
MS402	90×75 mm. $2.50, Wright Flyer I on launch system	..		1·50	2·25

1978 (22 May).   *Sailing Week*. Nos. 576/80 *of Antigua optd with T* 67.

403	10 c. Sunfish regatta	..		20	10
404	50 c. Fishing and work boat race	..		40	25
405	90 c. Curtain Bluff race	..		55	35
406	$2 Power boat rally	..		85	75
403/6 ..			*Set of* 4	1·75	1·25
MS407	110 × 77 mm. $2.50, Guadeloupe–Antigua race	..		1·25	1·60
	a. Albino opt	..		†	—

(Des J. Cooter. Litho Format)

1978 (2 June).   *25th Anniv of Coronation (1st issue). T* 68 *and similar vert designs. Multicoloured*. P 15.

408	75 c. Type 68	..		15	15
409	75 c. Imperial State Crown	..		15	15
410	$1.50, Queen Mary's Crown ..			20	25
411	$1.50, Queen Mother's Crown	..		20	25
412	$2.50, Queen Consort's Crown	..		35	45
413	$2.50, Queen Victoria's Crown	..		35	45
408/413			*Set of* 6	1·10	1·50
MS414	123 × 117 mm. Nos. 408/13. P 14½	..		1·10	1·75

The two designs for each value were issued as two *se-tenant* pairs, together with 2 labels, in small sheets of 6.

Examples of the 75 c. and $2.50 values exist in separate miniature sheets of four from stock dispersed by the liquidator of Format International Security Printers Ltd, as do imperforate examples of No. **MS**414.

1978 (2 June–12 Oct).   *25th Anniv of Coronation (2nd issue)*.

(a) Sheet stamps. Nos. 581/6 of Antigua optd with T 67. P 14 (2.6)

415	10 c. Queen Elizabeth and Prince Philip	..	10	10
416	30 c. Crowning	..		10	10
417	50 c. Coronation procession	..		10	15
418	90 c. Queen seated in St. Edward's Chair	..	15	20
	a. Opt triple	..		.85·00	
419	$2.50, Queen wearing Imperial State Crown	30	60
415/19	..		*Set of* 5	60	1·00
MS420	114 × 103 mm. $5 Queen and Prince Philip (17.7)	..	..	1·00	1·50
	a. Albino opt	..	..	.£250	

(b) Booklet stamps. Horiz designs as Nos. 587/9 of Antigua but additionally inscr "BARBUDA". Multicoloured. Roul 5 × imperf*. Self-adhesive (12.10)

421	25 c. Glass Coach	..		30	70
	a. Booklet pane. Nos. 421/2 × 3	..	1·60	
422	50 c. Irish State Coach	..		30	70
423	$5 Coronation Coach	..		1·00	2·25
	a. Booklet pane of 1.	..		1·00	
421/3 ..			*Set of* 3	1·75	3·25

*The 25 and 50 c. values were separated by various combinations of rotary knife (giving a straight edge) and roulette. The $5 value exists only with straight edges.

Nos. 415/19 also exist perf 12 (*Price for set of* 5 55p *mint or used*) from additional sheetlets of three stamps and one label, issued 12 October 1978. These stamps have different background colours from Nos. 415/19.

1978 (12 Sept).   *World Cup Football Championship, Argentina*. Nos. 590/3 *of Antigua optd with T* 67.

424	10 c. Player running with ball	..		10	10
425	15 c. Players in front of goal	..		10	10
426	$3 Referee and player	..		1·00	1·25
424/6 ..			*Set of* 3	1·00	1·25
MS427	126 × 88 mm. 15 c. Player crouching with ball; 30 c. Players heading ball; 50 c. Players running with ball; $2 Goalkeeper diving..	..	80	90

BARBUDA

(69)   70 Black-barred Soldierfish

1978 (20 Nov).   *Flowers*. Nos. 594/8 *of Antigua optd with T* 69.

428	25 c. Petrea	..		20	30
429	50 c. Sunflower	..		50	60
430	90 c. Frangipani	..		50	60
431	$2 Passion Flower	..		75	1·25
428/31			*Set of* 4	1·60	2·40
MS432	118 × 85 mm. $2.50, Hibiscus	..		1·50	2·00

1978 (20 Nov).   *Christmas. Paintings*. Nos. 599/602 optd with *T* 69 *in silver*.

433	8 c. "St. Ildefonso receiving the Chasuble from the Virgin"	..		10	10
434	25 c. "The Flight of St. Barbara"	..		15	15
435	$2 "Madonna and Child, with St. Joseph, John the Baptist and Donor"	..	60	1·25
433/5 ..			*Set of* 3	75	1·25
MS436	170 × 113 mm. $4 "The Annunciation"	..	1·75	2·25

(Litho Format)

1978 (20 Nov).   *Flora and Fauna. T* 70 *and similar horiz designs. Multicoloured*. P 14½.

437	25 c. Type 70	..		1·50	1·50
438	50 c. *Cynthia cardui* (butterfly)	..	2·25	2·25
439	75 c. Dwarf Poinciana	..		1·75	2·25
440	95 c. *Heliconius charithonia* (butterfly)	..	2·50	3·00
441	$1.25, Bougainvillea	..		2·00	3·00
437/41			*Set of* 5	9·00	11·00

71 Footballers and World Cup   72 Sir Rowland Hill

(Des J. Cooter. Litho Format)

1978 (29 Dec).   *Anniversaries and Events. T* 71 *and similar multicoloured designs*. P 14.

442	75 c. Type 71	..		30	40
443	95 c. Wright brothers and Flyer I (*horiz*)	..	40	50
444	$1.25, Balloon *Double Eagle II* and map of Atlantic (*horiz*)	..		50	60
445	$2 Prince Philip paying homage to the newly crowned Queen	..		60	90
442/5			*Set of* 4	1·60	2·25
MS446	122×90 mm. Nos. 442/5. Imperf	..	5·00	6·00

Events:—75 c. Argentina—Winners of World Cup Football Championship; 95 c. 75th anniversary of powered flight; $1.25 1st Atlantic crossing by balloon; $2 25th anniversary of Coronation.

(Des J. Cooter. Litho Format)

1979 (4 Apr).   *Death Centenary of Sir Rowland Hill (1st issue). T* 72 *and similar multicoloured designs*. P 14.

447	75 c. Type 72	..		25	45
448	95 c. Mail coach, 1840 (*horiz*) ..		25	50
449	$1.25, London's first pillar box, 1855 (*horiz*)	30	60
450	$2 Mail leaving St. Martin's Le Grand Post Office, London	..		45	85
447/50			*Set of* 4	1·10	2·25
MS451	129 × 104 mm. Nos. 447/50 Imperf	..	1·75	2·25

Nos. 447/50 were each printed in small sheets of 4 including one *se-tenant* stamp-size label.

BARBUDA

(73)   74 Passengers alighting from Boeing 747-200

1979 (4 Apr).   *Death Centenary of Sir Rowland Hill (2nd issue)*. Nos. 603/7 *of Antigua optd with T* 73 *in black (No.* **MS**456) *or blue (others)*. P 14.

452	25 c. Antigua 1863 1d. stamp	..		15	15
453	50 c. Penny Black stamp	..		20	20
454	$1 Stage-coach and woman posting letter, circa 1840	..		35	30
455	$2 Modern mail transport	..		80	60
452/5 ..			*Set of* 4	1·40	1·10
MS456	108 × 82 mm. $2.50, Sir Rowland Hill	..	75	80

Nos. 452/5 also exist perf 12 (*Price for set of* 4 £1.75 *mint or used*) from additional sheetlets of four stamps and one label, issued 28 December 1979.

1979 (12 Apr).   *Easter. Works by Dürer*. Nos. 608/11 *of Antigua optd with T* 67.

457	10 c. multicoloured	..		10	10
458	50 c. multicoloured	..		20	20
459	$4 black, magenta and greenish yellow	..	90	1·10
457/9 ..			*Set of* 3	1·00	1·25
MS460	114 × 99 mm. $2.50, multicoloured	..	55	75

(Litho Format)

1979 (24 May).   *35th Anniv of International Civil Aviation Organisation. T* 74 *and similar horiz designs. Multicoloured*. P 13½×14.

461	75 c. Type 74	..		25	50
	a. Block of 4. Nos. 461/3 plus label	65	
462	95 c. Air traffic control	..		25	50
463	$1.25, Ground crew-man directing Douglas DC-8 on runway	..		25	50
461/3			*Set of* 3	65	1·40

Nos. 461/3 were either printed in separate sheets, or together with a stamp-size label, *se-tenant*, in blocks of 4, each block divided in the sheet by margins.

1979 (24 May).   *International Year of the Child (1st issue)*. Nos. 612/16 *of Antigua optd with T* 67.

464	25 c. Yacht	..		20	15
465	50 c. Rocket	..		30	25
466	90 c. Car	..		40	35
467	$2 Train	..		80	60
464/7 ..			*Set of* 4	1·50	1·25
MS468	80 × 112 mm. $5 Aeroplane	..		1·10	1·10

BARBUDA (75) BARBUDA (76)

1979 (1 Aug). *Fishes. Nos. 617/21 of Antigua optd with T 75.*
469	30 c. Yellow Jack		20	15
470	50 c. Blue-finned Tuna		30	20
471	90 c. Sailfish		40	30
472	$3 Wahoo		1·10	1·10
469/72		Set of 4	1·75	1·60
MS473	122×75 mm. $2.50, Great Barracuda (overprinted with T 73)		1·00	1·25
	a. Albino opt			

1979 (1 Aug). *Death Bicentenary of Captain Cook. Nos. 622/6 of Antigua optd with T 76.*
474	25 c. Cook's Birthplace, Marton		30	30
475	50 c. H.M.S. *Endeavour*		85	45
476	90 c. Marine chronometer		90	60
477	$3 Landing at Botany Bay		1·75	1·50
474/7		Set of 4	3·50	2·50
MS478	110 × 85 mm. $2.50, H.M.S. *Resolution* (overprinted with T 82)		1·25	1·50
	a. Albino opt			

77 "Virgin with the Pear"   BARBUDA (78)

(Des G. Vasarhelyi. Litho Format)

1979 (24 Sept). *International Year of the Child (2nd issue). Details of Paintings by Dürer, showing the infant Jesus. T 77 and similar vert designs. Multicoloured. P 14 × 13½.*
479	25 c. Type 77		15	15
480	50 c. "Virgin with the Pink"		25	25
481	75 c. "Virgin with the Pear" (different)		30	30
482	$1.25, "Nativity"		40	40
479/82		Set of 4	1·00	1·00
MS483	86 × 118 mm. Nos. 479/82		1·00	1·75

1979 (21 Nov). *Christmas. Nos. 627/31 of Antigua optd with T 78.*
484	8 c. The Holy Family		10	10
485	25 c. Virgin and Child on Ass		15	10
486	50 c. Shepherd and star		25	15
487	$4 Wise Men with gifts		85	80
484/7		Set of 4	1·10	1·00
MS488	113 × 94 mm. $3 Angel with trumpet		80	1·10

1980 (18 Mar). *Olympic Games, Moscow. Nos. 632/6 of Antigua optd with T 67.*
489	10 c. Javelin throwing		10	10
490	25 c. Running		10	10
491	$1 Pole vaulting		30	20
492	$2 Hurdling		55	40
489/92		Set of 4	90	65
MS493	127 × 96 mm. $3 Boxing		70	1·10

LONDON 1980 (79)   80 "Apollo 11" Crew Badge

1980 (6 May). *"London 1980" International Stamp Exhibition. As Nos. 452/5 optd with T 79 in blue. P 12.*
494	25 c. Antigua 1863 1d. stamp		35	20
495	50 c. Penny Black stamp		45	40
496	$1 Mail coach and woman posting letter, circa 1840		85	65
497	$2 Modern mail transport		2·75	1·50
494/7		Set of 4	4·00	2·50

(Litho Format)

1980 (21 May). *10th Anniv of Moon Landing. T 80 and similar horiz designs. Multicoloured. P 13½ × 14.*
498	75 c. Type 80		30	25
499	95 c. Plaque left on Moon		35	30
500	$1.25, Rejoining mother ship		45	50
501	$2 Lunar Module		70	75
498/501		Set of 4	1·60	1·60
MS502	118 × 84 mm. Nos. 498/501		1·75	2·50

81 American Wigeon

(Litho Questa)

1980 (16 June). *Birds. Multicoloured designs as T 81. P 14.*
503	1 c. Type 81		70	70
504	2 c. Snowy Plover		70	70
505	4 c. Rose-breasted Grosbeak		75	70
506	6 c. Mangrove Cuckoo		75	70
507	10 c. Adelaide's Warbler		75	70
508	15 c. Scaly-breasted Thrasher		80	70
509	20 c. Yellow-crowned Night Heron		80	70
510	25 c. Bridled Quail Dove		80	70
511	35 c. Carib Grackle		85	70
512	50 c. Pintail		90	55
513	75 c. Black-whiskered Vireo		1·00	55
514	$1 Blue-winged Teal		1·25	80
515	$1.50, Green-throated Carib (vert)		1·50	80
516	$2 Red-necked Pigeon (vert)		2·25	1·25
517	$2.50, Wied's Crested Flycatcher (vert)		2·75	1·50
518	$5 Yellow-bellied Sapsucker (vert)		3·50	2·50
519	$7.50, Caribbean Elaenia (vert)		4·50	5·00
520	$10 Great Egret (vert)		5·00	5·00
503/20		Set of 18	26·00	22·00

1980 (29 July). *Famous Works of Art. Nos. 651/7 of Antigua optd with T 67.*
521	10 c. "David" (statue, Donatello)		10	10
522	30 c. "The Birth of Venus" (painting, Sandro Botticelli)		15	15
523	50 c. "Reclining Couple" (sarcophagus), Cerveteri		20	20
524	90 c. "The Garden of Earthly Delights" (painting, Hieronymus Bosch)		25	25
525	$1 "Portinari Altarpiece" (painting, Hugo van der Goes)		25	25
526	$4 "Eleanora of Toledo and her Son Giovanni de' Medici" (painting, Agnolo Bronzino)		80	80
521/6		Set of 6	1·50	1·50
MS527	99 × 124 mm. $5 "The Holy Family" (painting, Rembrandt)		1·50	1·75

1980 (8 Sept). *75th Anniv of Rotary International. Nos. 658/62 of Antigua optd with T 67.*
528	30 c. Rotary anniversary emblem and head-quarters, U.S.A.		15	15
529	50 c. Rotary anniversary emblem and Antigua Rotary Club banner		20	20
530	90 c. Map of Antigua and Rotary emblem		25	25
531	$3 Paul P. Harris (founder) and Rotary emblem		65	65
528/31		Set of 4	1·10	1·10
MS532	102 × 77 mm. $5 Antigua flags and Rotary emblems		1·50	2·25

BARBUDA (82)   BARBUDA (83)

1980 (6 Oct). *80th Birthday of Queen Elizabeth the Queen Mother. Nos. 663/5 of Antigua optd with T 82.*
533	10 c. multicoloured		50	15
	a. Opt inverted		38·00	
	b. Opt double		30·00	
534	$2.50, multicoloured		1·50	1·50
MS535	68 × 88 mm. $3 multicoloured		2·00	1·75

1980 (8 Dec). *Birds. Nos. 666/70 of Antigua optd with T 83.*
536	10 c. Ringed Kingfisher		1·25	60
537	30 c. Plain Pigeon		1·75	90
538	$1 Green-throated Carib		3·00	2·00
539	$2 Black-necked Stilt		3·50	4·00
536/9		Set of 4	8·50	6·75
MS540	73 × 73 mm. $2.50, Roseate Tern		3·50	2·75

1981 (26 Jan). *Sugar Cane Railway Locomotives. Nos. 681/5 of Antigua optd with T 67.*
541	25 c. Diesel Locomotive No. 15		1·00	25
542	50 c. Narrow-gauge steam locomotive		1·25	35
543	90 c. Diesel locomotives Nos. 1 and 10		1·75	45
544	$3 Steam locomotive hauling sugar cane		3·25	1·40
541/4		Set of 4	6·50	2·25
MS545	82 × 111 mm. $2.50, Antigua sugar factory, railway yard and sheds		1·50	1·75

84 Florence Nightingale   85 Goofy in Motor-boat

(Litho Format)

1981 (9 Mar). *Famous Women. T 84 and similar vert designs. P 14 × 13½.*
546	50 c. multicoloured		15	30
547	90 c. multicoloured		40	55
548	$1 multicoloured		35	60
549	$4 black, yellow-brown and rose-lilac		50	1·75
546/9		Set of 4	1·25	2·75

Designs:—90 c. Marie Curie; $1 Amy Johnson; $4 Eleanor Roosevelt.
Nos. 546/9 exist imperforate from stock dispersed by the liquidator of Format International Security Printers Ltd.

(Litho Format)

1981 (15 May). *Walt Disney Cartoon Characters. T 85 and similar vert designs showing characters afloat. Multicoloured. P 13½.*
550	10 c. Type 85		55	15
551	20 c. Donald Duck reversing car into sea		65	20
552	25 c. Mickey Mouse asking tug-boat to take on more than it can handle		80	30

553	30 c. Porpoise turning the tables on Goofy		80	35
554	35 c. Goofy in sailing boat		80	35
555	40 c. Mickey Mouse and boat being lifted out of water by fish		90	40
556	75 c. Donald Duck fishing for flying-fish with butterfly net		1·00	60
557	$1 Minnie Mouse in brightly decorated sailing boat		1·10	80
558	$2 Chip and Dale on floating ship-in-bottle		1·75	1·40
550/8		Set of 9	7·50	4·00
MS559	127 × 101 mm. $2.50, Donald Duck		4·00	3·00

BARBUDA (86)

1981 (9 June). *Birth Centenary of Picasso. Nos. 697/701 of Antigua optd with T 86.*
560	10 c. "Pipes of Pan"		10	10
561	50 c. "Seated Harlequin"		25	25
562	90 c. "Paulo as Harlequin"		45	45
563	$4 "Mother and Child"		1·60	1·60
560/3		Set of 4	2·10	2·10
MS564	115 × 140 mm. $5 "Three Musicians" (detail)		2·75	2·25

87 Buckingham Palace 88

(Des G. Drummond. Litho Format)

1981 (27 July). *Royal Wedding (1st issue). Buildings. T 87/8 and similar horiz designs. Each bicoloured*. P 11 × 11½.*
565	$1 Type 87		35	55
566	$1 Type 88		35	55
	a. Sheetlet. Nos. 565/70		2·75	
	b. Booklet pane. Nos. 565/6 × 2 in imperf between horiz pairs		2·00	
567	$1.50 \ Caernarvon Castle		40	60
568	$1.50 /		40	60
	b. Booklet pane. Nos. 567/8 × 2 in imperf between horiz pairs		2·25	
569	$4 \ Highgrove House		70	1·25
570	$4 /		70	1·25
	b. Booklet pane. Nos. 569/70 × 2 in imperf between horiz pairs		3·50	
565/70		Set of 6	2·75	4·25
MS571	75 × 90 mm. $5 black and olive-yellow (St. Paul's Cathedral—26 × 32 mm). P 11½ × 11		80	1·25

*Nos. 565/70 each exist printed in black with three different background colours, rose-pink, turquoise-green and lavender.
No. 566b was printed only in black and rose-pink. No. 568b black and turquoise-green and No. 570b black and lavender.
Nos. 565/70 were printed together, *se-tenant*, in sheetlets of 6, the two versions of each value forming a composite design.
Nos. 565/70 exist imperforate from stock dispersed by the liquidator of Format International Security Printers Ltd.

1981 (14 Aug). *Royal Wedding (2nd issue). Nos. 702/5 of Antigua optd with T 86.*
572	25 c. Prince Charles and Lady Diana Spencer		15	15
573	50 c. Glamis Castle		25	25
	a. Opt double		25·00	
574	$4 Prince Charles skiing		75	1·00
	a. Error. Optd on unissued Uganda 20s. showing Prince Charles at Balmoral		60·00	
	ab. Opt double			
572/4		Set of 3	1·10	1·25
MS575	95×85 mm. $5 Glass Coach		90	90

Nos. 572/4 exist perforated 12 (*Price for set of 3 £1.10 mint or used*) from additional sheetlets of five stamps and one label. These stamps have changed background colours. One sheetlet of the 25 c. is known with the overprint inverted.

89 "Integration and Travel"

(Litho Format)

1981 (14 Sept). *International Year for Disabled Persons (1st issue). T 89 and similar horiz designs. P 14.*
576	50 c. multicoloured		30	25
577	90 c. black, red-orange and blue-green		35	40
578	$1 black, light blue and bright green		40	45
579	$4 black, yellow-ochre and orange-brown		60	1·75
576/9		Set of 4	1·50	2·50

Designs:—90 c. Braille and sign language; $1 "Helping hands"; $4 "Mobility aids for disabled".
No. 576 exists imperforate from stock dispersed by the liquidator of Format International Security Printers Ltd.
See also Nos. 603/7.

BARBUDA (90)

1981 (12 Oct). *Royal Wedding (3rd issue). Booklet stamps. Nos. 706/12 of Antigua optd with T 90 in silver.*
580	25 c. Prince of Wales at Investiture, 1969		35	45
	a. Booklet pane. Nos. 580/5		2·50	
581	25 c. Prince Charles as baby, 1948		35	45
582	$1 Prince Charles at R.A.F. College, Cranwell, 1971		40	50
583	$1 Prince Charles attending Hill House School, 1956		40	50

,84	$2 Prince Charles and Lady Diana Spencer		65	80
,85	$2 Prince Charles at Trinity College, 1967		65	80
,86	$5 Prince Charles and Lady Diana..		2·50	3·00
	a. Booklet pane of 1..		2·50	
,80/6	*Set of 7*	5·00	6·00

1981 (1 Nov). *Independence. Nos. 686B/96B of Antigua additionally optd with T 86.*

687	6 c. Orchid Tree		50	15
688	10 c. Bougainvillea		55	15
689	20 c. Flamboyant		70	20
690	25 c. Hibiscus		80	25
691	35 c. Flame of the Wood		90	30
692	50 c. Cannon at Fort James		1·10	45
693	75 c. Premier's Office		1·25	75
694	$1 Potworks Dam		1·50	80
695	$2.50, Irrigation scheme, Diamond Estate		2·50	2·75
696	$5 Government House		2·75	3·75
697	$10 Coolidge International Airport..		4·50	6·00
687/97	*Set of 11*	15·00	14·00

BARBUDA   BARBUDA
(91)   (92)

1981 (14 Dec). *50th Anniv of Antigua Girl Guide Movement. Nos. 713/17 of Antigua optd with T 83 (No. MS602) or T 91 (others).*

598	10 c. Irene Joshua (founder)		55	10
599	50 c. Campfire sing-song		1·25	30
600	90 c. Sailing		1·75	45
601	$2.50, Animal tending		3·00	1·40
598/601	*Set of 4*	6·00	2·00
MS602	110 × 85 mm. $5 Raising the flag..		3·50	3·50

1981 (14 Dec). *International Year for Disabled Persons (2nd issue). Nos. 728/32 of Antigua optd with T 83 (No. MS607) or T 91 (others).*

603	10 c. Swimming		20	15
604	50 c. Discus throwing		35	35
605	90 c. Archery		90	70
606	$2 Baseball		2·25	1·75
603/6	*Set of 4*	3·25	2·75
MS607	108 × 84 mm. $4 Basketball		2·75	2·25

1981 (22 Dec). *Christmas. Paintings. Nos. 723/7 of Antigua optd with T 92.*

608	8 c. "Holy Night" (Jacques Stella)		10	10
609	30 c. "Mary with Child" (Julius Schnorr von Carolfeld)		20	20
610	$1 "Virgin and Child" (Alonso Cano) (S.)		40	40
611	$3 "Virgin and Child" (Lorenzo di Credi)		1·10	1·10
608/11	*Set of 4*	1·60	1·60
MS612	77 × 111 mm. $5 "Holy Family" (Pieter von Avon)		1·75	2·25

BARBUDA $1
93 Princess of Wales

S. Atlantic Fund + 50c.
(94)

(Des G. Drummond. Litho Format)

1982 (21 June). *Birth of Prince William of Wales (1st issue). T 93 and similar vert portraits. W w 15. P 14.*

613	$1 multicoloured		50	50
	w. Wmk inverted		60	
614	$2.50, multicoloured		90	1·10
	a. Reddish violet (top inscr) omitted		£180	
	w. Wmk inverted		1·10	
615	$5 multicoloured		2·00	2·25
	w. Wmk inverted		2·40	
613/15	*Set of 3*	3·00	3·50
MS616	88×108 mm. $4 multicoloured. No wmk		2·00	2·10

Nos. 613/15 were issued in sheets of 10 stamps with 2 undenominated black prints, in positions 9 and 13, and 9 blank labels. These sheets exist in two different formats, with all stamps upright or with 6 stamps and one black print inverted.

1982 (28 June). *South Atlantic Fund. Booklet stamps. Nos. 580/6 surch as T 94.*

617	25 c. +50 c. Prince of Wales at Investiture, 1969		20	20
	a. Booklet pane. Nos. 617/22		2·50	
	b. Surch double		20·00	
618	25 c. +50 c. Prince Charles as baby, 1948		20	20
	b. Surch double		20·00	
619	$1 +50 c. Prince Charles at R.A.F. College, Cranwell, 1971		45	45
	b. Surch double		20·00	
620	$1 +50 c. Prince Charles attending Hill House School, 1956		45	45
	b. Surch double		20·00	
621	$2 +50 c. Prince Charles and Lady Diana Spencer		75	75
	b. Surch double		20·00	
622	$2 +50 c. Prince Charles at Trinity College, 1967		75	75
	b. Surch double		20·00	
623	$5 +50 c. Prince Charles and Lady Diana		2·00	2·00
	a. Booklet pane of 1..		2·00	
	b. Surch double		£150	
617/23	*Set of 7*	4·00	4·00

97 Vincenzo Lunardi's Balloon
Flight, London, 1785

(98)

(Des G. Drummond. Litho Format)

1982 (1 July). *21st Birthday of Princess of Wales (1st issue). As Nos. 613/16 but inscribed "Twenty First Birthday Greetings to H.R.H. The Princess of Wales". W w 15. P 14.*

624	$1 multicoloured		55	45
	w. Wmk inverted		60	
625	$2.50, multicoloured		1·00	1·25
	w. Wmk inverted		1·25	
626	$5 multicoloured		2·25	2·40
	w. Wmk inverted		2·50	
624/6	*Set of 3*	3·50	3·75
MS627	88×108 mm. $4 multicoloured. No wmk		2·50	2·25

See note beneath Nos. 613/16.

BARBUDA
MAIL   BARBUDA MAIL
(95)   (96)

1982 (30 Aug). *21st Birthday of Princess of Wales (2nd issue). Nos. 748/51 of Antigua optd as T 95, in silver (No. 629) or black (others).*

628	90 c. Queen's House, Greenwich		65	45
629	$1 Prince and Princess of Wales		75	50
630	$4 Princess of Wales		1·60	1·50
628/30	*Set of 3*	2·75	2·25
MS631	102 × 75 mm. $5 Princess of Wales (different)		1·75	2·00

The overprint on No. MS631 measures 18 × 6 mm.
Nos. 628/30 also exist from additional sheetlets of 5 stamps and 1 label overprinted with a larger overprint, 18 × 6 mm long (price for set of 3 £3 mint or used). On the $1 and $4 values the second line of overprint aligns to left.

1982 (12 Oct). *Birth of Prince William of Wales (2nd issue). Nos. 757/60 of Antigua further optd with T 95, in silver ($1, $4) or black (others).*

632	90 c. Queen's House, Greenwich		55	45
633	$1 Prince and Princess of Wales		60	50
634	$4 Princess of Wales		2·25	2·00
632/4	*Set of 3*	3·00	2·75
MS635	102 × 75 mm. $5 Princess of Wales (different)		2·40	2·50

The overprint on No. MS635 measures 18 × 6 mm.

1982 (6 Dec). *Birth Centenary of Franklin D. Roosevelt (Nos. 636, 638, 640/2) and 250th Birth Anniv of George Washington (others). Nos. 761/2 of Antigua optd as T 95 (second line ranged left on No. MS642).*

636	10 c. Roosevelt in 1940		10	10
637	25 c. Washington as blacksmith		15	15
638	45 c. Churchill, Roosevelt and Stalin at Yalta conference		35	25
639	60 c. Washington crossing the Delaware		25	30
640	$1 "Roosevelt Special" train		65	55
641	$3 Portrait of Roosevelt		80	1·25
636/41	*Set of 6*	2·00	2·25
MS642	92 × 87 mm. $4 Roosevelt and wife		1·00	1·75
MS643	92 × 87 mm. $4 Portrait of Washington		1·00	1·75

1982 (6 Dec). *Christmas. Religious Paintings by Raphael. Nos. 769/73 of Antigua optd with T 96.*

644	10 c. "Annunciation"		10	10
645	30 c. "Adoration of the Magi"		15	15
646	$1 "Presentation at the Temple"		40	40
647	$4 "Coronation of the Virgin"		1·25	1·25
644/7	*Set of 4*	1·75	1·75
MS648	95 × 124 mm. $5 "Marriage of the Virgin"		2·00	3·00

1983 (14 Mar). *500th Birth Anniv of Raphael. Details from "Galatea" Fresco. Nos. 774/8 of Antigua optd as T 95 (45, 50 c. and larger (18 × 6 mm) on MS653) or T 96 (others).*

649	45 c. Tritons and Dolphins		20	20
650	50 c. Sea Nymph carried off by Triton		25	25
651	60 c. Winged angel steering Dolphins (horiz)		30	30
652	$4 Cupids shooting arrows (horiz)		1·60	1·60
649/52	*Set of 4*	2·10	2·10
MS653	101 × 126 mm. $5 Galatea pulled along by Dolphins		2·00	2·75

1983 (14 Mar). *Commonwealth Day. Nos. 779/82 of Antigua optd as T 96.*

654	25 c. Pineapple produce		55	70
655	45 c. Carnival		80	90
656	60 c. Tourism		1·25	1·60
657	$3 Airport		2·75	4·00
654/7	*Set of 4*	4·75	6·50

1983 (12 Apr). *World Communications Year. Nos. 783/7 of Antigua optd as T 96 (Nos. 658/61) or as T 95 with second line ranged left (No. MS662).*

658	15 c. T.V. satellite coverage of Royal Wedding		55	25
659	50 c. Police communications		1·75	90
660	60 c. House-to-train telephone call		1·75	90
661	$3 Satellite earth station with planets Jupiter and Saturn		3·50	2·50
658/61	*Set of 4*	6·75	4·00
MS662	100×90 mm. $5 "Comsat" satellite over West Indies		2·75	3·00
	a. Albino opt		30·00	

(Des G. Drummond. Litho)

1983 (13 June). *Bicentenary of Manned Flight (1st issue). T 97 and similar vert designs. Multicoloured. P 14.*

663	$1 Type 97		25	35
664	$1.50, Montgolfier brothers' balloon flight, Paris, 1783		40	55
665	$2.50, Blanchard and Jeffries' Cross-Channel balloon flight, 1785		60	90
663/5	*Set of 3*	1·10	1·60
MS666	111×111 mm. $5 Maiden flight of Airship LZ-127 Graf Zeppelin, 1928		2·00	2·75

See also Nos. 672/6.

1983 (4 July). *Whales. Nos. 788/92 of Antigua optd as T 95 (Nos. 667/70) or larger, 17 × 5½ mm (No. MS671), each with the second line ranged left.*

667	15 c. Bottle-nosed Dolphin		1·25	40
668	50 c. Fin Whale		4·00	1·60
669	60 c. Bowhead Whale..		4·50	1·75
670	$3 Spectacled Porpoise		5·50	4·25
667/70	*Set of 4*	14·00	7·25
MS671	122×101 mm. $5 Narwhal		3·75	4·50

1983 (12 Sept). *Bicentenary of Manned Flight (2nd issue). Nos. 811/15 of Antigua optd as T 96.*

672	30 c. Dornier Do-X flying boat		85	35
673	50 c. Supermarine S6B seaplane		1·10	60
674	60 c. Curtiss F-9C Sparrowhawk biplane and airship U.S.S. Akron		1·25	70
675	$4 Hot-air balloon Pro Juventute		4·50	4·00
672/5	*Set of 4*	7·00	5·00
MS676	80×105 mm. $5 Airship LZ-127 Graf Zeppelin		3·75	4·25

1983 (21 Oct). *Nos. 565/70 surch as T 98. A. P 11 × 11½. B. P 14½.*

			A		B	
677	45 c. on $1 Type 87		50	65	1·75	2·50
	a. Sheetlet. Nos. 677/82	2·75		9·50		
	b. Error. 50 c. on $1		†	4·50	—	
	c. Surch omitted		†	35·00	—	
678	45 c. on $1 Type 88		50	65	1·75	2·50
	b. Error. 50 c. on $1		†	4·50	—	
	c. Surch omitted		†	35·00	—	
679	50 c. on $1.50, Caernarvon Castle (left)		50	70	1·75	2·50
	b. Error. 45 c. on $1.50		†	4·50	—	
	c. Surch omitted		†	35·00	—	
680	50 c. on $1.50, Caernarvon Castle (right)		50	70	1·75	2·50
	b. Error. 45 c. on $1.50		†	4·50	—	
	c. Surch omitted		†	35·00	—	
681	60 c. on $4 Highgrove House (left)		50	80	1·75	2·50
	c. Surch omitted		†	35·00	—	
682	60 c. on $4 Highgrove House (right)		50	80	1·75	2·50
	c. Surch omitted		†	35·00	—	
677/82	*Set of 6*		2·75	4·00	9·50	13·50

Nos. 677b, 678b, 679b and 680b occur on the 14½ perforated sheetlets with rose-pink background.
Examples of No. 677a, and also of the errors, imperforate exist from stock dispersed by the liquidator of Format International Security Printers Ltd.

1983 (28 Oct). *Nos. 793A/810A of Antigua optd with T 96.*

683	1 c. Cashew Nut		10	10
684	2 c. Passion Fruit		15	10
685	3 c. Mango		15	10
686	5 c. Grapefruit		15	10
687	10 c. Pawpaw		20	10
688	15 c. Breadfruit		40	10
689	20 c. Coconut		50	10
690	25 c. Oleander		50	15
691	30 c. Banana		55	20
692	40 c. Pineapple		65	25
693	45 c. Cordia		70	30
694	50 c. Cassia		80	30
695	60 c. Poui		80	30
696	$1 Frangipani		1·10	50
697	$2 Flamboyant		2·00	1·25
698	$2.50, Lemon		2·25	1·75
699	$5 Lignum Vitae		3·50	2·75
700	$10 National flag and coat of arms		5·50	5·50
683/700	*Set of 18*	18·00	12·00

BARBUDA MAIL
(99)   **100** Edward VII

1983 (28 Oct). *Christmas. 500th Birth Anniv of Raphael. Nos. 816/20 of Antigua optd with T 99 or slightly smaller (29 × 4 mm) (MS705).*

701	10 c. multicoloured		10	10
702	30 c. multicoloured		15	20
703	$1 multicoloured		40	50
704	$4 multicoloured		1·25	1·75
701/4	*Set of 4*	1·60	2·25
MS705	101 × 131 mm. $5 multicoloured		2·25	2·75

1983 (14 Dec). *Bicentenary of Methodist Church (1984). Nos. 821/4 of Antigua optd as T 95 (in silver on 15 c. and 50 c.).*

706	15 c. John Wesley (founder)		25	15
707	50 c. Nathaniel Gilbert (founder in Antigua)		50	30
708	60 c. St. John Methodist Church steeple		55	35
709	$3 Ebenezer Methodist Church, St. John's		1·25	1·75
706/9	*Set of 4*	2·25	2·25

(Des G. Drummond. Litho Format)

1984 (14 Feb). *Members of British Royal Family.* T **100** and *similar vert portraits. Multicoloured.* P 14½.

710	$1 Type **100**	..	..	50	1·10
711	$1 George V	..	..	50	1·10
712	$1 George VI	..	..	50	1·10
713	$1 Elizabeth II	..	..	50	1·10
714	$1 Charles, Prince of Wales	..	..	50	1·10
715	$1 Prince William	..	..	50	1·10
710/15	..	..	*Set of* 6	2·75	6·00

1984 (26 Apr). *Olympic Games, Los Angeles* (1st issue). *Nos. 825/9 of Antigua optd as* T **99** (23 × 3 mm in size on Nos. 716/19).

716	25 c. Discus	..	..	15	20
717	50 c. Gymnastics	..	..	35	40
718	90 c. Hurdling	..	..	50	60
719	$3 Cycling	..	..	1·25	1·50
716/19	..	..	*Set of* 4	2·00	2·40
MS720	82 × 67 mm. $5 Volleyball	..	..	2·75	3·25

1984 (12 July). *Ships. Nos. 830/4 of Antigua optd with* T **95** (MS725) *or* T **99** (*others*).

721	45 c. *Booker Vanguard* (freighter)	..	..	1·50	45
722	50 c. *Canberra* (liner)	..	..	1·50	50
723	60 c. Sailing boats	..	..	1·75	60
724	$4 *Fairwind* (cargo liner)	..	..	4·25	2·75
721/4	..	..	*Set of* 4	8·00	3·75
MS725	107×80 mm. $5 Eighteen-century British man-of-war (vert)	..	..	4·50	4·25

1984 (12 July). *Universal Postal Union Congress, Hamburg. Nos. 835/9 of Antigua optd with* T **95**.

726	15 c. Chenille	..	..	30	15
727	50 c. Shell Flower	..	..	50	40
728	60 c. Anthurium	..	..	60	50
729	$3 Angels Trumpet	..	..	1·25	1·50
726/9	..	..	*Set of* 4	2·40	2·25
MS730	100 × 75 mm. $5 Crown of Thorns	..	..	2·50	3·00

101 Olympic Stadium, Athens, 1896   (**102**)

(Litho Format)

1984 (27 July). *Olympic Games, Los Angeles* (2nd issue). T **101** *and similar horiz designs. Multicoloured.* P 13½.

731	$1.50, Type **101**	..	..	80	1·10
732	$2.50, Olympic stadium, Los Angeles, 1984	..	1·25	1·50
733	$5 Athlete carrying Olympic torch	..	2·25	2·75
731/3	..	..	*Set of* 3	3·75	5·00
MS734	121 × 95 mm. No. 733. P 15	..	1·75	3·00

1984 (1 Oct). *Presidents of the United States of America. Nos. 856/63 of Antigua optd with* T **95** (in silver on 10, 90 c., $1.10 and $1.50).

735	10 c. Abraham Lincoln	..	..	10	10
736	20 c. Harry Truman	..	..	15	15
737	30 c. Dwight Eisenhower	..	..	20	25
738	40 c. Ronald Reagan	..	..	25	30
739	90 c. Gettysburg Address, 1863	..	50	55
740	$1.10, Formation of N.A.T.O., 1949.	..	60	65
741	$1.50, Eisenhower during Second World War	80	85
742	$2 Reagan and Caribbean Basin Initiative	1·00	1·25
735/42	..	..	*Set of* 8	3·25	3·75

1984 (1 Oct). *150th Anniv of Abolition of Slavery. Nos. 864/8 of Antigua optd with* T **96** (Nos. 743/6) *or as* T **95**, *but* 18 × 6½ mm (No. MS747).

743	40 c. View of Moravian Mission	..	30	30
744	50 c. Antigua Courthouse, 1823	..	40	40
745	60 c. Planting sugar-cane, Monks Hill	..	45	45
746	$3 Boiling house, Delaps' Estate	..	1·90	1·90
743/6	..	..	*Set of* 4	2·75	2·75
MS747	95 × 70 mm. $5 Loading sugar, Willoughby Bay	..	..	3·00	3·50

1984 (21 Nov). *Songbirds. Nos. 869/74 of Antigua optd with* T **95** *or larger* (18 × 7 mm) (No. MS753).

748	40 c. Rufous-sided Towhee	..	..	1·00	45
749	50 c. Parula Warbler	..	..	1·10	50
750	60 c. House Wren	..	..	1·25	55
751	$2 Ruby-crowned Kinglet	..	..	2·50	1·50
752	$3 Common Flicker	..	..	3·00	2·25
748/52	..	..	*Set of* 5	8·00	4·75
MS753	76 × 76 mm. $5 Yellow-breasted Chat	..	4·00	4·50

1984 (21 Nov). *450th Death Anniv of Correggio (painter). Nos. 878/82 of Antigua optd with* T **95** *or larger* (18 × 7 mm) No. MS758), *all in silver.*

754	25 c. "The Virgin and Infant with Angels and Cherubs"	..	..	15	20
755	60 c. "The Four Saints"	..	..	40	45
756	90 c. "St. Catherine"	..	..	60	65
757	$3 "The Campori Madonna"	..	..	1·75	2·25
754/7	..	..	*Set of* 4	2·50	3·25
MS758	90 × 60 mm. $5 "St. John the Baptist"	..	2·75	3·75

1984 (30 Nov). *"Ausipex" International Stamp Exhibition, Melbourne. Australian Sports. Nos. 875/7 of Antigua optd with* T **95** *or larger* (18 × 7 mm) (No. MS761).

759	15 c. Grass-skiing	..	..	70	75
760	$5 Australian Football	..	..	3·00	3·75
MS761	108 × 78 mm. $5 Boomerang-throwing	3·00	3·75

1984 (30 Nov). *150th Birth Anniv of Edgar Degas (painter). Nos. 883/7 of Antigua optd with* T **95** (Nos. 762/5) *or* T **99** (No. MS766), *all in silver.*

762	15 c. "The Blue Dancers"	..	..	10	10
763	50 c. "The Pink Dancers"	..	..	30	40
764	70 c. "Two Dancers"	..	..	45	55
765	$4 "Dancers at the Bar"	..	..	2·40	3·50
762/5	..	..	*Set of* 4	3·00	4·00
MS766	90 × 60 mm. $5 "The Folk Dancers" (40 × 27 mm)	..	..	2·75	3·25

1985 (18 Feb). *Famous People. Nos. 888/96 of Antigua optd with* T **102** (*horizontally on Nos. 771/5*).

767	60 c. Winston Churchill	..	..	1·75	80
768	60 c. Mahatma Gandhi	..	..	1·75	80
769	60 c. John F. Kennedy	..	..	1·75	80
770	60 c. Mao Tse-tung	..	..	1·75	80
771	$1 Churchill with General De Gaulle, Paris, 1944 (*horiz*)	..	2·00	1·00
772	$1 Gandhi leaving London by train, 1931 (*horiz*)	..	2·00	1·00
773	$1 Kennedy with Chancellor Adenauer and Mayor Brandt, Berlin, 1963 (*horiz*)	2·00	1·00
774	$1 Mao Tse-tung with Lin Piao, Peking, 1969 (*horiz*)	..	2·00	1·00
767/74	..	..	*Set of* 8	13·50	6·50
MS775	114×80 mm. $5 Flags of Great Britain, India, the United States and China	..	3·50	3·75

103 Lady Elizabeth Bowes-Lyon, 1907, and Camellias   **104** Roseate Tern

(Des G. Drummond. Litho Format)

1985 (26 Feb). *Life and Times of Queen Elizabeth the Queen Mother* (1st issue). T **103** *and similar vert designs. Multicoloured.* P 14 × 14½.

776	15 c. Type **103**	..	..	10	10
777	45 c. Duchess of York, 1926, and "Elizabeth of Glamis" roses	..	20	25
778	50 c. The Queen Mother after the Coronation, 1937	..	20	25
779	60 c. In Garter robes, 1971, and Dog Roses ..	20	30
780	90 c. Attending Royal Variety show, 1967, and red Hibiscus	..	30	45
781	$2 The Queen Mother in 1982, and blue Plumbago	..	60	1·10
782	$3 Receiving 82nd birthday gifts from children, and Morning Glory	..	90	1·60
776/82	..	..	*Set of* 7	2·25	3·50

See also Nos. 826/9.

(Des G. Drummond. Litho Format)

1985 (4 Apr). *Birth Bicentenary of John J. Audubon (ornithologist)* (1st issue). T **104** *and similar vert designs showing original paintings. Multicoloured.* P 14.

783	45 c. Type **104**.	..	..	25	30
784	50 c. Mangrove Cuckoo	..	..	25	30
785	60 c. Yellow-crowned Night Heron	..	30	40
786	$5 Brown Pelican	..	..	2·25	3·50
783/6	..	..	*Set of* 4	2·75	4·00

See also Nos. 794/8 and 914/17.

1985 (10 May). *Centenary of the Statue of Liberty* (1986) (1st issue). *Nos. 907/13 of Antigua optd horizontally with* T **102**.

787	25 c. Torch from Statue in Madison Square Park, 1885	..	..	20	20
788	30 c. Statue of Liberty and scaffolding ("Restoration and Renewal") (*vert*)	..	20	20
789	50 c. Frederic Bartholdi (sculptor) supervising construction, 1876	..	30	30
790	90 c. Close-up of Statue	..	..	55	55
791	$1 Statue and sailing ship ("Operation Sail", 1976) (*vert*)	..	60	60
792	$3 Dedication ceremony, 1886 (*vert*)	1·75	1·75
787/92	..	..	*Set of* 6	3·00	3·00
MS793	110×80 mm. $5 Port of New York	..	2·75	3·00

See also Nos. 987/96.

BARBUDA MAIL   BARBUDA MAIL   4TH AUG 1900-1985

(**105**)   (**106**)   (**107**)

1985 (18 July). *Birth Bicentenary of John J. Audubon (ornithologist)* (2nd issue). *Nos. 924/8 of Antigua optd with* T **105**.

794	90 c. Slavonian Grebe	..	..	3·50	3·50
795	$1 British Storm Petrel	..	..	3·75	3·50
796	$1.50, Great Blue Heron	..	..	4·25	4·00
797	$3 Double-crested Cormorant	..	6·50	6·00
794/7	..	..	*Set of* 4	16·00	15·00
MS798	103×72 mm. $5 White-tailed Tropic Bird (vert)	..	..	13·00	8·50

1985 (18 July). *Butterflies. Nos. 929/33 of Antigua optd with* T **106**.

799	25 c. *Anaea cyanea*..	..	..	2·00	1·00
800	60 c. *Leodonta dysoni*	..	..	3·50	1·75
801	90 c. *Junea doraete*	..	..	4·00	2·25
802	$4 *Prepona pylene*	..	..	8·50	9·00
799/802	..	..	*Set of* 4	16·00	12·50
MS803	132×105 mm. $5 *Caerois gerdtrudtus* ..	13·00	13·00

1985 (2 Aug). *Centenary of the Motorcycle. Nos. 919/23 of Antigua optd with* T **106**.

804	10 c. Triumph 2hp "Jap", 1903	..	40	10
805	30 c. Indian "Arrow", 1949	..	70	20
806	60 c. BMW "R100RS", 1976	..	1·10	40
807	$4 Harley-Davidson "Model II", 1916	3·50	2·75
804/7	..	..	*Set of* 4	5·25	3·00
MS808	90 × 93 mm. $5 Laverda "Jota", 1975 ..	4·00	4·00

1985 (2 Aug). *85th Birthday of Queen Elizabeth the Queen Mother. Nos. 776/8 optd with* T **107**.

809	15 c. Type **103**.	..	..	45	30
	a. Red (frame, flowers, etc) omitted	32·00	
810	45 c. Duchess of York, 1926, and "Elizabeth of Glamis" roses	..	75	50
811	50 c. The Queen Mother after the Coronation, 1937	..	75	50
812	60 c. In Garter robes, 1971, and Dog Roses..	85	80
813	90 c. Attending Royal Variety show, 1967, and red Hibiscus	..	90	1·10
814	$2 The Queen Mother in 1982, and blue Plumbago	..	1·25	2·50
815	$3 Receiving 82nd birthday gifts from children, and Morning Glory	1·40	2·75
809/15	..	..	*Set of* 7	5·50	7·50

The 45 c. exists with the yellow omitted from stock dispersed by the liquidator of Format International Security Printers Ltd.

1985 (30 Aug). *Native American Artefacts. Nos. 914/18 of Antigua optd horizontally with* T **102**.

816	15 c. Arawak pot sherd and Indians making clay utensils	..	15	10
817	50 c. Arawak body design and Arawak Indians tattooing	..	30	30
818	60 c. Head of the god "Yocahu" and Indians harvesting manioc	..	40	40
819	$3 Carib war club and Carib Indians going into battle	..	1·60	1·75
816/19	..	..	*Set of* 4	2·25	2·25
MS820	97×68 mm. $5 Taino Indians worshipping stone idol	..	..	2·50	3·50

1985 (30 Aug). *40th Anniv of International Civil Aviation Organization. Nos. 934/8 of Antigua optd with* T **106**.

821	30 c. Cessna 172D Skyhawk	..	65	50
822	90 c. Fokker D.VII	..	..	1·25	1·00
823	$1.50, SPAD VII	..	..	2·00	2·50
824	$3 Boeing 747	..	..	3·00	3·75
821/4	..	..	*Set of* 4	6·25	7·00
MS825	97×83 mm. De Havilland D.H.C.6 Twin Otter	..	..	3·25	3·50

1985 (8 Nov). *Life and Times of Queen Elizabeth the Queen Mother* (2nd issue). *Nos. 946/9 of Antigua optd with* T **95** (in silver on Nos. 826/7 and MS829).

826	$1 The Queen Mother attending church	2·25	2·00
827	$1.50, Watching children playing in London garden	..	..	2·50	2·25
828	$2.50, The Queen Mother in 1979	..	3·00	3·00
826/8	..	..	*Set of* 3	7·00	6·50
MS829	56×85 mm. $5 With Prince Edward at Royal Wedding, 1981	..	..	6·00	6·50

Nos. 826/7 also exist with black and No. 828 with silver overprints (*Price for set of 3 £50 mint*).

The stamps from the sheetlets mentioned beneath Antigua No. MS949 also exist overprinted with Type **95**.

1985 (25 Nov). *850th Birth Anniv of Maimonides (physician, philosopher and scholar). Nos. 939/40 of Antigua optd with* T **95**.

830	$2 bright green	..	..	4·50	3·75
MS831	70 × 84 mm. $5 reddish brown	..	4·25	4·25

1985 (25 Nov). *Marine Life. Nos. 950/4 of Antigua optd with* T **95** (in silver on 15 c. and $3).

832	15 c. Magnificent Frigate Bird	..	2·50	60
833	45 c. Brain Coral	..	..	2·75	70
834	60 c. Cushion Star	..	..	2·75	90
835	$3 Spotted Moray	..	..	5·50	4·00
832/5	..	..	*Set of* 4	12·00	5·50
MS836	110×80 mm. $5 Elkhorn Coral	..	6·50	5·00

1986 (17 Feb). *International Youth Year. Nos. 941/5 of Antigua optd with* T **95**.

837	25 c. Young farmers with produce	..	15	15
838	50 c. Hotel management trainees	..	25	30
839	60 c. Girls with goat and boys with football ("Environment")	..	30	35
840	$3 Windsurfing ("Leisure")	..	1·50	1·60
837/40	..	..	*Set of* 4	2·00	2·10
MS841	102 × 72 mm. $5 Young people with Antiguan flags	..	..	2·75	3·25

1986 (17 Feb). *Royal Visit. Nos. 965/8 of Antigua optd with* T **106**.

842	60 c. Flags of Great Britain and Antigua	1·10	35
843	$1 Queen Elizabeth II (*vert*)	..	1·25	55
844	$4 Royal Yacht *Britannia* ..	..	3·25	2·10
842/4	..	..	*Set of* 3	5·00	2·50
MS845	110×83 mm. $5 Map of Antigua	..	3·50	3·50

1986 (10 Mar). *75th Anniv of Girl Guide Movement. Nos. 955/9 of Antigua optd with T 95.*

956	15 c. Girl Guides nursing	1·00	70
957	45 c. Open-air Girl Guide meeting	2·25	1·75
958	60 c. Lord and Lady Baden-Powell	2·50	2·50
959	$3 Girl Guides gathering flowers	5·25	7·00
956/9	*Set of 4*	10·00	11·00
MS850	67×96 mm. $5 Barn Swallow (Nature study)	15·00	15·00

1986 (10 Mar). *300th Birth Anniv of Johann Sebastian Bach (composer). Nos. 960/4 of Antigua optd with T 95.*

951	25 c. multicoloured	1·50	70
952	50 c. multicoloured	2·00	1·40
953	$1 multicoloured	2·75	2·00
954	$3 multiciloured	5·50	7·00
951/4	*Set of 4*	10·50	10·00
MS855	104×73 mm. $5 black and brownish grey	14·00	12·00

1986 (4 Apr). *Christmas. Religious Paintings. Nos. 985/9 of Antigua optd with T 106.*

856	10 c. "Madonna and Child" (De Landi)	40	20
857	25 c. "Madonna and Child" (Berlinghiero)	80	50
858	60 c. "The Nativity" (Fra Angelico)	1·50	1·00
859	$4 "Presentation in the Temple" (Giovanni di Paolo)	4·00	6·00
856/9	*Set of 4*	6·00	7·00
MS860	113×81 mm. $5 "The Nativity" (Antoniazzo Romano)	4·25	5·50

108 Queen Elizabeth II meeting
Members of Legislature

(Litho Format)

1986 (21 Apr). *60th Birthday of Queen Elizabeth II (1st issue). T 108 and similar horiz designs. Multicoloured. P 15.*

861	$1 Type 108	50	1·00
862	$2 Queen with Headmistress of Liberta School	60	1·10
863	$2.50, Queen greeted by Governor-General of Antigua	60	1·25
861/3	*Set of 3*	1·50	3·00
MS864	95×75 mm. $5 Queen Elizabeth in 1928 and 1986 (33×27 mm). P 13½×14	5·00	7·00

See also Nos. 872/5.

109 Halley's Comet over
Barbuda Beach

(Des and litho Format)

1986 (10 July). *Appearance of Halley's Comet (1st issue). T 109 and similar multicoloured designs. P 15.*

865	$1 Type 109	80	1·00
866	$2.50, Early telescope and dish aerial (vert)	1·50	2·00
867	$5 Comet and World map	2·50	3·50
865/7	*Set of 3*	4·25	6·00

See also Nos. 886/90.

1986 (12 Aug). *40th Anniv of United Nations Organization. Nos. 981/4 of Antigua optd with T 96 (Nos. 868/70) or T 95 (No. MS871).*

868	40 c. Benjamin Franklin and U.N. (New York) 1953 U.P.U. 5 c. stamp	1·50	1·00
869	$1 George Washington Carver (agricultural chemist) and 1982 Nature Conservation 28 c. stamp	2·25	2·25
870	$3 Charles Lindbergh (aviator) and 1978 I.C.A.O. 25 c. stamp	4·00	4·50
868/70	*Set of 3*	7·00	7·00
MS871	101×77 mm. $5 Marc Chagall (artist) (vert)	9·00	9·50

1986 (12 Aug). *60th Birthday of Queen Elizabeth II (2nd issue). Nos. 1005/8 of Antigua optd with T 95 in black (No. MS875) or silver (others).*

872	60 c. black and yellow	1·25	1·25
873	$1 multicoloured	1·75	1·75
874	$4 multicoloured	3·50	4·00
872/4	*Set of 3*	6·00	6·25
MS875	120×85 mm. $5 black and grey-brown	6·00	7·00

1986 (28 Aug). *World Cup Football Championship, Mexico. Nos. 995/9 of Antigua optd with T 96 (30 c., $4) or T 95 (others).*

876	30 c. Football, boots and trophy	1·75	1·00
877	60 c. Goalkeeper (vert)	2·75	2·00
878	$1 Referee blowing whistle (vert)	3·00	2·25
879	$4 Ball in net	7·00	7·00
876/9	*Set of 4*	13·00	11·00
MS880	87×76 mm. $5 Two players competing for ball	15·00	12·00

1986 (28 Aug). *"Ameripex '86" International Stamp Exhibition, Chicago. Famous American Trains. Nos. 1014/18 of Antigua optd with T 106.*

881	25 c. "Hiawatha Express"	2·00	1·50
882	50 c. "Grand Canyon Express"	2·75	2·25
883	$1 "Powhattan Arrow Express"	3·50	3·00
884	$3 "Empire State Express"	6·00	6·50
881/4	*Set of 4*	13·00	12·00
MS885	116×87 mm. $5 "Daylight Express"	7·00	8·50

1986 (22 Sept). *Appearance of Halley's Comet (2nd issue). Nos. 1000/4 of Antigua optd with T 96 (Nos. 886/9) or T 95 (MS890).*

886	5 c. Edmond Halley and Old Greenwich Observatory	75	55
887	10 c. Messerschmitt Me 163B Komet (fighter aircraft), 1944	75	55
888	60 c. Montezuma (Aztec Emperor) and Comet in 1517 (from "Historias de las Indias de Neuva Espana")	2·50	2·00
889	$4 Pocahontas saving Capt. John Smith and Comet in 1607	7·50	7·00
886/9	*Set of 4*	10·50	9·00
MS890	101×70 mm. $5 Halley's Comet over English Harbour, Antigua	4·25	4·75

1986 (22 Sept). *Royal Wedding. Nos. 1019/22 of Antigua optd with T 95 in silver.*

891	45 c. Prince Andrew and Miss Sarah Ferguson	75	50
892	60 c. Prince Andrew	90	65
893	$4 Prince Andrew with Prince Philip	3·50	4·00
891/3	*Set of 3*	4·75	4·75
MS894	88×88 mm. $5 Prince Andrew and Miss Sarah Ferguson (different)	6·00	7·00

1986 (10 Nov). *Sea Shells. Nos. 1023/7 of Antigua optd with T 106 (in silver on 15 c. to $3).*

895	15 c. Fly-specked Cerith	2·50	1·75
896	45 c. Smooth Scotch Bonnet	2·75	2·25
897	60 c. West Indian Crown Conch	3·50	2·75
898	$3 Ciboney Murex	8·00	9·50
895/8	*Set of 4*	15·00	14·50
MS899	109×75 mm. $5 Colourful Atlantic Moon (horiz)	16·00	16·00

1986 (10 Nov). *Flowers. Nos. 1028/36 of Antigua optd with T 106.*

900	10 c. Nymphaea ampla (water lily)	20	20
901	15 c. Queen of the Night	30	30
902	50 c. Cup of Gold	50	65
903	60 c. Beach Morning Glory	55	70
904	70 c. Golden Trumpet	70	85
905	$1 Air Plant	85	90
906	$3 Purple Wreath	2·25	2·75
907	$4 Zephyr Lily	2·75	3·25
900/7	*Set of 8*	7·50	8·75
MS908	Two sheets, each 102×72 mm. (a) $4 Dozakie. (b) $5 Four O'Clock Flower		
	Set of 2 sheets	16·00	17·00

1986 (28 Nov). *Mushrooms. Nos. 1042/6 of Antigua optd with T 106.*

909	10 c. Hygrocybe occidentalis var. scarletina	90	50
910	50 c. Trogia buccinalis	3·25	1·75
911	$1 Collybia subpruinosa	4·75	5·00
912	$4 Leucocoprinus brebissonii	9·50	8·00
909/12	*Set of 4*	16·00	11·50
MS913	102×82 mm. $5 Pyrrhoglossum pyrrhum	17·00	13·00

1986 (Dec). *Birth Bicentenary of John J. Audubon (ornithologist) (3rd issue). Nos. 990/3 of Antigua optd with T 96 (in silver on 60, 90 c.).*

914	60 c. Mallard	2·50	1·75
915	90 c. North American Black Duck	3·25	2·25
916	$1.50, Pintail	4·25	4·00
917	$3 American Wigeon	5·50	6·00
914/17	*Set of 4*	14·00	12·50

1987 (12 Jan). *Local Boats. Nos. 1009/13 of Antigua optd with T 95.*

918	30 c. Tugboat	50	50
919	60 c. Game fishing boat	70	70
920	$1 Yacht	1·10	1·10
921	$4 Lugger with auxiliary sail	3·00	3·50
918/21	*Set of 4*	4·75	5·25
MS922	108×78 mm. $5 Boats under construction	12·00	12·00

1987 (12 Jan). *Centenary of First Benz Motor Car. Nos. 1052/60 of Antigua optd with T 95 (No. MS931) or T 96 (others).*

923	10 c. Auburn "Speedster" (1933)	35	25
924	15 c. Mercury "Sable" (1986)	45	30
925	50 c. Cadillac (1959)	90	60
926	60 c. Studebaker (1950)	90	70
927	70 c. Lagonda "V-12" (1939)	1·00	90
928	$1 Adler "Standard" (1930)	1·25	1·00
929	$3 DKW (1956)	2·50	2·50
930	$4 Mercedes "500K" (1936)	2·50	2·50
923/30	*Set of 8*	8·75	8·00
MS931	Two sheets, each 99×70 mm. (a) $5 Daimler (1896). (b) $5 Mercedes "Knight" (1921)		
	Set of 2 sheets	9·50	10·00

1987 (10 Mar). *World Cup Football Championship Winners, Mexico. Nos. 1037/40 of Antigua optd with T 95 (60 c., $1) or T 96 (30 c., $4).*

932	30 c. Football, boots and trophy	85	60
933	60 c. Goalkeeper (vert)	1·25	85
934	$1 Referee blowing whistle (vert)	1·75	1·50
935	$4 Ball in net	4·00	4·50
932/5	*Set of 4*	7·00	6·75

1987 (23 Apr). *America's Cup Yachting Championship. Nos. 1072/6 of Antigua optd horizontally as T 102.*

936	30 c. Canada I (1981)	20	30
937	60 c. Gretel II (1970)	35	50
938	$1 Sceptre (1958)	60	80
939	$3 Vigilant (1893)	1·75	2·50
936/9	*Set of 4*	2·75	3·75
MS940	113×84 mm. $5 Australia II defeating Liberty (1983) (horiz)	3·50	4·00

1987 (1 July). *Marine Life. Nos. 1077/85 of Antigua optd with T 95 (No. MS949) or T 96 (others).*

941	15 c. Bridled Burrfish	2·75	70
942	30 c. Common Noddy	3·00	85
943	40 c. Nassau Grouper	3·00	90
944	50 c. Laughing Gull	4·50	1·50
945	60 c. French Angelfish	4·50	1·50
946	$1 Porkfish	4·50	1·75
947	$2 Royal Tern	10·00	5·00
948	$3 Sooty Tern	10·00	6·00
941/8	*Set of 8*	38·00	16·00
MS949	Two sheets, each 120×94 mm. (a) $5 Banded Butterflyfish. (b) $5 Brown Booby		
	Set of 2 sheets	11·00	12·00

1987 (28 July). *Milestones of Transportation. Nos. 1100/9 of Antigua optd with T 106.*

950	10 c. Spirit of Australia (fastest powerboat), 1978	80	40
951	15 c. Siemen's electric locomotive, 1879	1·25	70
952	30 c. U.S.S. Triton (first submerged circumnavigation), 1960	1·50	80
953	50 c. Trevithick's steam carriage (first passenger-carrying vehicle), 1801	1·75	1·00
954	60 c. U.S.S. New Jersey (battleship), 1942	2·00	1·00
955	70 c. Draisine bicycle, 1818	2·00	1·25
956	90 c. United States (liner) (holder of Blue Riband), 1952	2·00	1·25
957	$1.50, Cierva C.4 (first autogyro), 1923	2·25	2·25
958	$2 Curtiss NC-4 (first transatlantic flight), 1919	3·00	3·25
959	$3 Queen Elizabeth 2 (liner), 1969	3·75	3·25
950/9	*Set of 10*	18·00	14·00

110 Shore Crab

(Litho Format)

1987 (15 Sept). *Marine Life. T 110 and similar multicoloured designs. P 15.*

960	5 c. Type 110	10	20
961	10 c. Sea Cucumber	15	20
962	15 c. Stop-light Parrotfish	15	20
963	25 c. Banded Coral Shrimp	15	20
964	35 c. Spotted Drum	15	20
965	60 c. Thorny Starfish	25	40
966	75 c. Atlantic Trumpet Triton	35	60
967	90 c. Feather Star and Yellow Beaker Sponge	40	65
968	$1 Blue Gorgonian	45	65
969	$1.25, Slender Filefish (vert)	55	85
970	$5 Barred Hamlet (vert)	1·75	4·00
971	$7.50 Royal Gramma ("Fairy Basslet") (vert)	2·50	5·50
972	$10 Fire Coral and Banded Butterflyfish (vert)	3·00	6·50
960/72	*Set of 13*	9·00	18·00

1987 (12 Oct). *Olympic Games, Seoul (1988). Nos. 1086/90 of Antigua optd with T 95 (No. MS977) or T 96 in silver (others).*

973	10 c. Handball	50	35
974	60 c. Fencing	75	60
975	$1 Gymnastics	1·00	1·00
976	$3 Football	2·25	3·00
973/6	*Set of 4*	4·00	4·50
MS977	100×72 mm. $5 Boxing gloves	3·75	4·25

1987 (12 Oct). *Birth Centenary of Marc Chagall (artist). Nos. 1091/9 of Antigua optd as T 95 (in silver on Nos. 983, MS986b).*

978	10 c. "The Profile"	10	10
979	30 c. "Portrait of the Artist's Sister"	15	15
980	40 c. "Bride with Fan"	20	25
981	60 c. "David in Profile"	25	30
982	90 c. "Fiancee with Bouquet"	40	50
983	$1 "Self Portrait with Brushes"	45	55
984	$3 "The Walk"	1·40	1·60
985	$4 "Three Candles"	1·75	2·00
978/85	*Set of 8*	4·25	5·00
MS986	Two sheets, each 110×95 mm. (a) $5 "Fall of Icarus" (104×89 mm). (b) $5 "Myth of Orpheus" (104×89 mm)		
	Set of 2 sheets	4·50	5·50

1987 (5 Nov). *Centenary of Statue of Liberty (1986) (2nd issue). Nos 1110/19 of Antigua optd with T 95 (15, 30, 45, 50 c., $1, $2, $5) or T 96 (60, 90 c., $3), in black (50 c., $3) or silver (others).*

987	15 c. Lee Iacocca at unveiling of restored Statue	10	10
988	30 c. Statue at sunset (side view)	15	15
989	45 c. Aerial view of head	20	25
990	50 c. Lee Iacocca and torch	25	30
991	60 c. Workmen inside head of Statue (horiz)	25	40
992	90 c. Restoration work (horiz)	40	50
993	$1 Head of Statue	45	55
994	$2 Statue at Sunset (front view)	90	1·40
995	$3 Inspecting restoration work (horiz)	1·40	2·00
996	$5 Statue at night (horiz)	2·25	4·00
987/96	*Set of 10*	5·75	7·75

1987 (5 Nov). *Entertainers. Nos. 1120/7 of Antigua optd with T **95** (in silver on $3).*

997	15 c. Grace Kelly	..	80	50
998	30 c. Marilyn Monroe	..	1·25	90
999	45 c. Orson Welles	..	90	75
1000	50 c. Judy Garland	..	95	85
1001	60 c. John Lennon	..	2·00	1·40
1002	$1 Rock Hudson	..	1·75	1·50
1003	$2 John Wayne	..	2·75	2·75
1004	$3 Elvis Presley	..	4·75	4·75
997/1004		*Set of 8*	13·50	12·00

1987 (5 Nov). *"Capex '87" International Stamp Exhibition, Toronto. Reptiles and Amphibians. Nos. 1133/7 of Antigua optd with T **95** (No. MS1009) or T **96** (others).*

1005	30 c. Whistling Frog	..	1·25	75
1006	60 c. Croaking Lizard	..	1·75	1·10
1007	$1 Antiguan Anole	..	2·00	1·40
1008	$3 Red-footed Tortoise	..	4·50	5·00
1005/8		*Set of 4*	8·50	7·25
MS1009	106×76 mm. $5 Ground Lizard		8·50	7·50

1988 (12 Jan). *Christmas. Religious Paintings. Nos. 1144/8 of Antigua optd with T **95**.*

1010	45 c. "Madonna and Child" (Bernardo Daddi)		40	25
1011	60 c. "St. Joseph" (detail, "The Nativity" (Sano di Pietro))		55	45
1012	$1 "Virgin Mary" (detail, "The Nativity" (Sano di Pietro))		75	70
1013	$4 "Music-making Angel" (Melozzo da Forli)	..	2·25	3·25
1010/13		*Set of 4*	3·50	4·25
MS1014	99×70 mm. $5 "The Flight into Egypt" (Sano di Pietro)	..	3·75	3·75

1988 (25 Mar). *Salvation Army's Community Service. Nos. 1163/71 of Antigua optd with T **106**.*

1015	25 c. First aid at daycare centre, Antigua	..	80	80
1016	30 c. Giving penicillin injection, Indonesia		80	80
1017	40 c. Children at daycare centre, Bolivia		85	85
1018	45 c. Rehabilitation of the handicapped, India		85	85
1019	50 c. Training blind man, Kenya	..	1·25	1·25
1020	60 c. Weighing baby, Ghana	..	1·25	1·25
1021	$1 Training typist, Zambia	..	1·75	1·75
1022	$2 Emergency food kitchen, Sri Lanka	..	2·25	2·75
1015/22		*Set of 8*	8·75	9·25
MS1023	152×83 mm. $5 General Eva Burrows		11·00	13·00

1988 (6 May). *Bicentenary of U.S. Constitution. Nos. 1139/43 of Antigua optd with T **95** ($4, $5) or T **96** (others), all in silver.*

1024	15 c. House of Burgesses, Virginia ("Freedom of Speech")		10	10
1025	45 c. State Seal, Connecticut	..	20	25
1026	60 c. State Seal, Delaware	..	25	35
1027	$4 Gouverneur Morris (Pennsylvania delegate) (*vert*)	..	1·75	3·00
1024/7		*Set of 4*	2·10	3·25
MS1028	105×75 mm. $5 Roger Sherman (Connecticut delegate) (*vert*)	..	2·75	3·25

1988 (4 July). *Royal Ruby Wedding. Nos. 1149/53 of Antigua optd with T **95**.*

1029	25 c. deep brown, black and bright new blue	45	30
1030	60 c. multicoloured	..	80	65
1031	$2 deep brown, black and light green	..	1·75	2·00
1032	$3 multicoloured	..	2·00	2·50
	a. Opt triple	..	†	
1029/32		*Set of 4*	4·50	5·00
MS1033	102×77 mm. $5 multicoloured	..	5·00	5·00

The only known example of No. 1032a is used, uncancelled, on cover from the Philatelic Bureau.

1988 (4 July). *Birds of Antigua. Nos. 1154/62 of Antigua optd with T **95** (10 c., $1, $5) or T **96** (others).*

1034	10 c. Great Blue Heron	..	1·10	60
1035	15 c. Ringed Kingfisher (*horiz*)	..	1·40	60
1036	50 c. Bananaquit (*horiz*)	..	2·00	1·25
1037	60 c. Purple Gallinule (*horiz*)	..	2·00	1·25
1038	70 c. Blue-hooded Euphonia (*horiz*)	..	2·25	1·75
1039	$1 Brown-throated Conure ("Caribbean Parakeet")	..	2·50	1·75
1040	$3 Troupial (*horiz*)	..	3·75	4·25
1041	$4 Purple-throated Carib (*horiz*)	..	3·75	4·50
1034/41		*Set of 8*	17·00	14·00
MS1042	Two sheets, each 115×86 mm. (a) $5 Greater Flamingo. (b) $5 Brown Pelican		
		Set of 2 sheets	10·00	8·50

1988 (25 July–8 Dec). *500th Anniv of Discovery of America by Columbus (1992) (1st issue). Nos. 1172/80 of Antigua optd with T **96** (Nos. 1043/50 or 70 No. MS1051).*

1043	10 c. Columbus' second fleet, 1493	..	50	50
1044	30 c. Painos Indian village and fleet	..	75	75
1045	45 c. Santa Mariagalante (flagship) and Painos village		90	75
1046	60 c. Painos Indians offering Columbus fruit and vegetables		90	75
1047	90 c. Painos Indian and Columbus with Scarlet Macaw		1·50	1·10
1048	$1 Columbus landing on island	..	1·50	1·10
1049	$3 Spanish soldier and fleet	..	2·25	2·50
1050	$4 Fleet under sail	..	2·50	3·00
1043/50		*Set of 8*	9·75	9·50
MS1051	Two sheets, each 110×80 nn. (a) $5 Queen Isabella's cross. (b) $5 Gold coin of Ferdinand and Isabella (8 Dec) *Set of 2 sheets*	6·00	7·00

See also Nos. 1112/16, 1177/85, 1285/93, 1374/80 and 1381/2.

1988 (25 July). *500th Birth Anniv of Titian. Nos. 1181/9 of Antigua optd with T **96** (Nos. 1052/9) or T **95** (No. MS1060), all in silver.*

1052	30 c. "Bust of Christ"	..	15	15
1053	40 c. "Scourging of Christ"	..	20	25
1054	45 c. "Madonna in Glory with Saints"	..	20	25
1055	50 c. "The Averoldi Polyptych" (detail)		25	30
1056	$1 "Christ Crowned with Thorns"	..	45	50
1057	$2 "Christ Mocked"	..	90	1·10
1058	$3 "Christ and Simon of Cyrene"	..	1·40	1·75
1059	$4 "Crucifixion with Virgin and Saints"		1·75	2·25
1052/9		*Set of 8*	4·75	6·00
MS1060	Two sheets, each 110×95 mm. (a) $5 "Ecce Homo" (detail). (b) $5 "Noli me Tangere" (detail)	
		Set of 2 sheets	4·50	5·50

1988 (25 Aug). *16th World Scout Jamboree, Australia. Nos. 1128/32 of Antigua optd with T **95** (No. MS1064) or T **96** (others).*

1061	10 c. Scouts around camp fire and Red Kangaroo		60	50
1062	60 c. Scouts canoeing and Blue-winged Kookaburra	..	1·50	85
1063	$1 Scouts on assault course and Ring-tailed Rock Wallaby	..	1·50	1·25
1064	$3 Field kitchen and Koala	..	3·00	4·00
1061/4		*Set of 4*	6·00	6·00
MS1065	103 × 78 mm. $5 Flags of Antigua, Australia and Scout Movement		2·50	3·25

1988 (25 Aug–8 Dec). *Sailing Week. Nos. 1190/4 of Antigua optd with T **95** (No. MS1070) or T **96** (others).*

1066	30 c. Two yachts rounding buoy	..	20	20
1067	60 c. Three yachts	..	45	55
1068	$1 British yacht under way	..	70	85
1069	$3 Three yachts (*different*)	..	1·60	2·25
1066/9		*Set of 4*	2·75	3·50
MS1070	103 × 92 mm. $5 Two yachts (8 Dec)	2·50	3·25

1988 (16 Sept). *Flowering Trees. Nos. 1213/21 of Antigua optd with T **95**.*

1071	10 c. Jacaranda	..	10	10
1072	30 c. Cordia	..	15	15
1073	50 c. Orchid Tree	..	20	25
1074	90 c. Flamboyant	..	40	45
1075	$1 African Tulip Tree	..	45	50
1076	$2 Potato Tree	..	80	1·25
1077	$3 Crepe Myrtle	..	1·25	1·75
1078	$4 Pitch Apple	..	1·60	2·25
1071/8		*Set of 8*	4·50	6·00
MS1079	Two sheets, each 106 × 76 mm. (a) $5 Cassia. (b) $5 Chinaberry	*Set of 2 sheets*	4·25	5·00

1988 (16 Sept). *Olympic Games, Seoul. Nos. 1222/6 of Antigua optd with T **95** (Nos. 1080/1, MS1084) or T **96** (Nos. 1082/3).*

1080	40 c. Gymnastics	..	20	30
1081	60 c. Weightlifting	..	25	30
1082	$1 Water polo (*horiz*)	..	45	60
1083	$3 Boxing (*horiz*)	..	1·25	1·60
1080/3		*Set of 4*	1·90	2·50
MS1084	114 × 80 mm. $5 Runner with Olympic torch	..	2·10	2·40

BARBUDA MAIL

(111)

1988 (8 Dec)–**90**. *Caribbean Butterflies. Nos. 1227/44a of Antigua optd with T **96** (Nos. 1085/1102) or T **111** (No. 1102a).*

1085	1 c. Danaus plexippus	..	20	40
1086	2 c. Greta diaphanus	..	20	40
1087	3 c. Calisto archebates	..	30	40
1088	5 c. Hamadryas feronia	..	30	40
1089	10 c. Mestra dorcas	..	40	30
1090	15 c. Hypolimnas misippus	..	50	30
1091	20 c. Dione juno	..	55	40
1092	25 c. Heliconius charithonia	..	55	40
1093	30 c. Eurema pyro	..	60	40
1094	40 c. Papilio androgeus	..	65	40
1095	45 c. Anteos maerula	..	65	40
1096	50 c. Aphrissa orbis	..	75	60
1097	60 c. Astraptes xagua	..	75	50
1098	$1 Heliopetes arsalte	..	1·00	80
1099	$2 Polites baracoa	..	2·00	2·50
1100	$2.50 Phocides pigmalion	..	2·25	3·00
1101	$5 Prepona amphitoe	..	4·25	4·50
1102	$10 Oarisma nanus	..	7·00	8·00
1102a	$20 Parides lycimenes (4.5.90)	..	11·00	12·00
1085/102a		*Set of 19*	30·00	32·00

BARBUDA MAIL

(112)

BARBUDA MAIL

(113)

1989 (28 Apr). *25th Death Anniv of John F. Kennedy (American statesman). Nos. 1245/53 of Antigua optd with T **96** (Nos. 1103/10) or T **112** (No. MS1111).*

1103	1 c. President Kennedy and family	..	10	10
1104	2 c. Kennedy commanding PT109	..	10	10
1105	3 c. Funeral cortege	..	10	10
1106	4 c. In motorcade, Mexico City	..	10	10
1107	30 c. As 1 c.	..	50	30
1108	60 c. As 4 c.	..	70	55
1109	$1 As 3 c.	..	85	80
1110	$4 As 2 c.	..	2·75	3·75
1103/10		*Set of 8*	4·50	5·00
MS1111	105 × 74 mm. $5 Kennedy taking presidential oath of office	..	2·40	3·50

1989 (24 May). *500th Anniv of Discovery of America by Columbus (1992) (2nd issue). Pre-Columbian Arawak Society. Nos. 1267/71 of Antigua optd with T **113**.*

1112	$1.50, Arawak warriors	..	1·10	1·4
	a. Horiz strip of 4. Nos. 1112/15	4·00	
1113	$1.50, Whip dancers	..	1·10	1·4
1114	$1.50, Whip dancers and chief with pineapple	..	1·10	1·4
1115	$1.50, Family and camp fire	..	1·10	1·4
1112/15		*Set of 4*	4·00	5·0
MS1116	71 × 84 mm. $6 Arawak chief	..	2·75	3·5

1989 (29 June). *50th Anniv of First Jet Flight. Nos. 1272/80 of Antigua optd with T **111**.*

1117	10 c. Hawker Siddeley Comet 4 airliner	..	75	6
1118	30 c. Messerschmitt Me 262 fighter	..	1·10	7
1119	40 c. Boeing 707 airliner	..	1·25	7
1120	60 c. Canadair CL-13 Sabre ("F-86 Sabre") fighter	..	1·40	8
1121	$1 Lockheed F-104 Starfighter	..	1·60	1·1
1122	$2 Douglas DC-10 airliner	..	2·75	3·0
1123	$3 Boeing 747-300/400 airliner	..	3·25	3·5
1124	$4 McDonnell Douglas F-4 Phantom II fighter	..	3·25	3·5
1117/24		*Set of 8*	14·00	12·5
MS1125	Two sheets, each 114×83 mm. (a) $7 Grumman F-14 Tomcat fighter. (b) $7 Concorde airliner	..	*Set of 2 sheets*	16·00	15·0

BARBUDA MAIL

(114)

BARBUDA MAIL

(115)

1989 (18 Sept). *Caribbean Cruise Ships. Nos. 1281/9 of Antigua optd as T **114**, but with lines spaced (No. MS1134b) or with T **111** (others).*

1126	25 c. Festivale	..	60	5
1127	45 c. Southward	..	80	6
1128	50 c. Sagafjord	..	90	7
1129	60 c. Daphne	..	1·00	8
1130	75 c. Cunard Countess	..	1·10	1·2
1131	90 c. Song of America	..	1·25	1·2
1132	$3 Island Princess	..	3·25	3·7
1133	$4 Galileo	..	3·25	3·7
1126/33		*Set of 8*	11·00	11·5
MS1134	(a) 113×87 mm. $6 Norway. (b) 111×82 mm. $6 Oceanic	..	*Set of 2 sheets*	17·00	18·0

1989 (14 Dec). *Japanese Art. Paintings by Hiroshige. Nos 1290/8 of Antigua optd with T **114**.*

1135	25 c. "Fish swimming by Duck half-submerged in Stream"		45	4
1136	45 c. "Crane and Wave"	..	70	5
1137	50 c. "Sparrows and Morning Glories"	..	75	6
1138	60 c. "Crested Blackbird and Flowering Cherry"	..	90	7
1139	$1 "Great Knot sitting among Water Grass"	..	1·25	1·2
1140	$2 "Goose on a Bank of Water"	..	2·00	2·2
1141	$3 "Black Paradise Flycatcher and Blossoms"	..	2·25	2·50
1142	$4 "Sleepy Owl perched on a Pine Branch"	..	2·50	2·7
1135/42		*Set of 8*	9·75	10·00
MS1143	Two sheets, each 102×75 mm. (a) $5 "Bullfinch flying near a Clematis Branch". (b) $5 "Titmouse on a Cherry Branch"	*Set of 2 sheets*	14·00	15·0

1989 (20 Dec). *World Cup Football Championship, Italy (1990). Nos. 1308/12 of Antigua optd with T **115**.*

1144	15 c. Goalkeeper	..	40	3
1145	25 c. Goalkeeper moving towards ball	..	50	3
1146	$1 Goalkeeper reaching for ball	..	1·00	1·0
1147	$4 Goalkeeper saving goal	..	2·75	3·50
1144/7		*Set of 4*	4·25	4·5
MS1148	Two sheets, each 75×105 mm. (a) $5 Three players competing for ball (*horiz*). (b) $5 Ball and players' legs (*horiz*)	*Set of 2 sheets*	13·00	14·00

1989 (20 Dec). *Christmas. Paintings by Raphael and Giotto. Nos. 1351/9 of Antigua optd with T **114**.*

1149	10 c. "The Small Cowper Madonna" (Raphael)		10	10
1150	25 c. "Madonna of the Goldfinch" (Raphael)		10	1
1151	30 c. "The Alba Madonna" (Raphael)		15	1
1152	50 c. Saint (detail, "Bologna Altarpiece") (Giotto)		25	3
1153	60 c. Angel (detail, "Bologna Altarpiece") (Giotto)		30	4
1154	70 c. Angel slaying serpent (detail, "Bologna Altarpiece") (Giotto)		35	5
1155	$4 Evangelist (detail, "Bologna Altarpiece") (Giotto)		1·90	2·5
1156	$5 "Madonna of Foligno" (Raphael)		2·40	2·6
1149/56		*Set of 8*	5·00	6·5
MS1157	Two sheets, each 71×96 mm. (a) $5 "The Marriage of the Virgin" (detail) (Raphael). (b) $5 Madonna and Child (detail, "Bologna Altarpiece") (Giotto)		10·00	11·00

1990 (21 Feb). *Fungi. Nos. 1313/21 of Antigua optd with T **111**.*

1158	10 c. Mycena pura	..	75	55
1159	25 c. Psathyrella tuberculata (*vert*)	..	1·00	55
1160	50 c. Psilocybe cubensis	..	1·50	90
1161	60 c. Leptonia caeruleocapitata (*vert*)	..	1·90	1·40
1162	75 c. Xeromphalina tenuipes (*vert*)	..	1·90	1·40
1163	$1 Chlorophyllum molybdites (*vert*)	..	2·00	1·40
1164	$3 Marasmius haematocephalus	..	4·00	4·25
1165	$4 Cantharellus cinnabarinus	..	4·00	4·50
1158/65		*Set of 8*	15·00	13·00
MS1166	Two sheets, each 88×62 mm. (a) $6 Leucopaxillus gracillimus (*vert*). (b) $6 Volvariella volvacea	*Set of 2 sheets*	20·00	18·00

BARBUDA MAIL

(116)

1990 (30 Mar). *Local Fauna. Nos. 1322/6 of Antigua optd with T 116 (vertically on 60 c., $4).*

167	25 c. Desmarest's Hutia	40	35
168	45 c. Caribbean Monk Seal	85	70
169	60 c. Mustache Bat (*vert*)	90	80
170	$4 American Manatee (*vert*)	2·75	3·50
167/70	*Set of 4*	4·50	4·75
MS1171	113×87 mm. $5 West Indies Giant Rice Rat	7·00	8·50

1990 (30 Mar). *20th Anniv of First Manned Landing on Moon. Nos. 1346/50 of Antigua optd with T 116 (vertically on 10, 45 c. and $5).*

1172	10 c. Launch of "Apollo 11"	60	45
1173	45 c. Aldrin on Moon	1·25	70
1174	$1 Module *Eagle* over Moon (*horiz*)	2·00	1·50
1175	$4 Recovery of "Apollo 11" crew after splashdown (*horiz*)	4·50	6·00
1172/5	*Set of 4*	7·50	7·75
MS1176	107×77 mm. $5 Astronaut Neil Armstrong	7·50	8·50

1990 (6 June). *500th Anniv of Discovery of America by Columbus (1992) (3rd issue). New World Natural History – Marine Life. Nos. 1360/8 of Antigua optd as T 114, but with lines spaced.*

1177	10 c. Star-eyed Hermit Crab	45	40
1178	20 c. Spiny Lobster	60	50
1179	25 c. Magnificent Banded Fanworm	60	50
1180	45 c. Cannonball Jellyfish	80	60
1181	60 c. Red-spiny Sea Star	90	75
1182	$2 Peppermint Shrimp	1·75	2·00
1183	$3 Coral Crab	2·00	2·25
1184	$4 Branching Fire Coral	2·00	2·25
1177/84	*Set of 8*	8·00	8·25
MS1185	Two sheets, each 101×69 mm. (a) $5 Common Sea Fan. (b) $5 Portuguese Man-of-war *Set of 2 sheets*	10·50	11·50

1990 (12 July). *"EXPO 90" International Garden and Greenery Exhibition, Osaka. Orchids. Nos. 1369/77 of Antigua optd as T 114, but with lines spaced.*

1186	15 c. Vanilla mexicana	85	50
1187	45 c. Epidendrum ibaguense	1·50	70
1188	50 c. Epidendrum secundum	1·50	80
1189	60 c. Maxillaria conferta	1·75	1·10
1190	$1 Onicidium altissimum	2·00	1·75
1191	$2 Spiranthes lanceolata	3·25	3·50
1192	$3 Tonopsis utricularioides	4·00	4·25
1193	$5 Epidendrum nocturnum	5·00	5·50
1186/93	*Set of 8*	18·00	16·00
MS1194	Two sheets, each 101×69 mm. (a) $6 Octomeria graminifolia. (b) $6 Rodriguezia lanceolata *Set of 2 sheets*	11·00	11·00

1990 (14 Aug). *Reef Fishes. Nos. 1386/94 of Antigua optd with T 111.*

1195	10 c. Flamefish	50	40
1196	15 c. Coney	65	45
1197	50 c. Long-spined Squirrelfish	1·00	85
1198	60 c. Sergeant Major	1·25	1·00
1199	$1 Yellow-tailed Snapper	1·75	1·75
1200	$2 Rock Beauty	2·75	2·75
1201	$3 Spanish Hogfish	3·00	3·00
1202	$4 Striped Parrotfish	3·00	3·00
1195/1202	*Set of 8*	12·50	12·00
MS1203	Two sheets, each 99×70 mm. (a) $5 Black-barred Soldierfish. (b) $5 Four-eyed Butterflyfish *Set of 2 sheets*	16·00	15·00

$5.00

**1st Anniversary
Hurricane Hugo
16th September, 1989-1990**

═══

(117)

1990 (17 Sept). *First Anniv of Hurricane Hugo. Nos. 971/2 surch as T 117.*

1204	$5 on $7.50, Fairy Basslet (*vert*)	4·00	4·50
1205	$7.50 on $10 Fire Coral and Butterfly Fish (*vert*)	4·50	5·00

1990 (12 Oct). *90th Birthday of Queen Elizabeth the Queen Mother. Nos. 1415/19 of Antigua optd as T 114, but with lines spaced.*

1206	15 c. multicoloured	60	45
1207	35 c. multicoloured	1·00	65
1208	75 c. multicoloured	1·75	1·25
1209	$3 multicoloured	3·50	3·75
1206/9	*Set of 4*	6·25	5·50
MS1210	67×98 mm $6 multicoloured	8·00	9·00

NEW INFORMATION

The editor is always interested to correspond with people who have new information that will improve or correct the Catalogue.

BARBUDA MAIL

(118)

119 Troupial

1990 (14 Dec). *Achievements in Space. Nos. 1395/1414 of Antigua optd with T 118 in silver.*

1211	45 c. "Voyager 2" passing Saturn	70	70
	a. Sheetlet. Nos. 1211/30	12·50	
1212	45 c. "Pioneer 11" photographing Saturn	70	70
1213	45 c. Astronaut in transporter	70	70
1214	45 c. Space shuttle *Columbia*	70	70
1215	45 c. "Apollo 10" command module on parachutes	70	70
1216	45 c. "Skylab" space station	70	70
1217	45 c. Astronaut Edward White in space	70	70
1218	45 c. "Apollo" spacecraft on joint mission	70	70
1219	45 c. "Soyuz" spacecraft on joint mission	70	70
1220	45 c. "Mariner 1" passing Venus	70	70
1221	45 c. "Gemini 4" capsule	70	70
1222	45 c. "Sputnik 1"	70	70
1223	45 c. Hubble space telescope	70	70
1224	45 c. North American X-15	70	70
1225	45 c. Bell XS-1 airplane	70	70
1226	45 c. "Apollo 17" astronaut and lunar rock formation	70	70
1227	45 c. Lunar Rover	70	70
1228	45 c. "Apollo 14" lunar module	70	70
1229	45 c. Astronaut Buzz Aldrin on Moon	70	70
1230	45 c. Soviet "Lunokhod" lunar vehicle	70	70
1211/30	*Set of 20*	12·50	12·50

1990 (14 Dec). *Christmas. Paintings by Renaissance Masters. Nos. 1457/65 of Antigua optd with T 111.*

1231	25 c. "Madonna and Child with Saints" (detail, Sebastiano del Piombo)	45	25
1232	30 c. "Virgin and Child with Angels" (detail, Grünewald) (*vert*)	50	30
1233	40 c. "The Holy Family and a Shepherd" (detail, Titian)	60	30
1234	60 c. "Virgin and Child" (detail, Lippi) (*vert*)	85	50
1235	$1 "Jesus, St. John and Two Angels" (Rubens)	1·00	80
1236	$2 "Adoration of the Shepherds" (detail, Vincenzo Catena)	1·75	2·25
1237	$4 "Adoration of the Magi" (detail, Giorgione)	2·50	3·25
1238	$5 "Virgin and Child adored by Warrior" (detail, Vincenzo Catena)	2·50	3·25
1231/8	*Set of 8*	9·00	9·75
MS1239	Two sheets, each 71×101 mm. (a) $6 "Allegory of the Blessings of Jacob" (detail, Rubens) (*vert*). (b) $6 "Adoration of the Magi" (detail, Fra Angelico) (*vert*) *Set of 2 sheets*	9·50	10·50

1991 (4 Feb). *150th Anniv of the Penny Black. Nos. 1378/81 of Antigua optd with T 116.*

1240	45 c. blue-green	1·00	60
1241	60 c. magenta	1·10	75
1242	$5 ultramarine	4·50	5·50
1240/2	*Set of 3*	6·00	6·25
MS1243	102×80 mm. $6 blackish purple	6·00	6·50

1991 (4 Feb). *"Stamp World London 90" International Stamp Exhibition. Nos. 1382/5 of Antigua optd with T 116.*

1244	50 c. deep grey-green and scarlet-vermilion	1·00	65
1245	75 c. purple-brown and scarlet-vermilion	1·25	85
1246	$4 deep ultramarine & scarlet-vermilion	4·25	4·75
1244/6	*Set of 3*	6·00	5·75
MS1247	104×81 mm. $6 brownish black and scarlet-vermilion	6·00	6·50

(Des G. Drummond. Litho Questa)

1991 (25 Mar). *Wild Birds. T 119 and similar vert designs. Multicoloured. P 14.*

1248	60 c. Type 119	40	40
1249	$2 Adelaide's Warbler ("Christmas Bird")	1·25	1·50
1250	$4 Rose-breasted Grosbeak	2·50	3·00
1251	$7 Wied's Crested Flycatcher	4·25	4·75
1248/51	*Set of 4*	7·50	8·75

1991 (23 Apr). *Olympic Games, Barcelona (1992). Nos. 1429/33 of Antigua optd as T 114, but with lines spaced.*

1252	50 c. Men's 20 kilometres walk	60	60
1253	75 c. Triple jump	75	75
1254	$1 Men's 10,000 metres	1·00	1·00
1255	$5 Javelin	3·75	4·50
1252/5	*Set of 4*	5·50	6·25
MS1256	100 × 70 mm. $6 Athlete lighting Olympic flame at Los Angeles Olympics	4·75	6·00

1991 (23 Apr). *Birds. Nos. 1448/56 of Antigua optd with T 116 diagonally.*

1257	10 c. Pearly-eyed Thrasher	65	65
1258	25 c. Purple-throated Carib	90	65
1259	50 c. Yellowthroat	1·40	90
1260	60 c. American Kestrel	1·50	1·10
1261	$1 Yellow-bellied Sapsucker	2·00	1·50
1262	$2 Purple Gallinule	2·75	3·00
1263	$3 Yellow-crowned Night Heron	3·00	3·50
1264	$4 Blue-hooded Euphonia	3·25	3·75
1257/64	*Set of 8*	14·00	13·50
MS1265	Two sheets, each 76×60 mm. (a) $6 Brown Pelican. (b) $6 Magnificent Frigate Bird *Set of 2 sheets*	14·00	14·00

1991 (21 June). *350th Death Anniv of Rubens. Nos. 1466/74 of Antigua optd with T 111.*

1266	25 c. "Rape of the Daughters of Leucippus" (detail)	45	45
1267	45 c. "Bacchanal" (detail)	60	60
1268	50 c. "Rape of the Sabine Women" (detail)	75	75
1269	60 c. "Battle of the Amazons" (detail)	85	85
1270	$1 "Rape of the Sabine Women" (different detail)	1·25	1·25
1271	$2 "Bacchanal" (different detail)	1·90	1·90
1272	$3 "Rape of the Sabine Women" (different detail)	2·25	2·25
1273	$4 "Bacchanal" (different detail)	2·50	2·50
1266/73	*Set of 8*	9·50	9·50
MS1274	Two sheets, each 101 × 71 mm. (a) $6 "Rape of Hippodameia" (detail). (b) $6 "Battle of the Amazons" (different detail) *Set of 2 sheets*	8·50	9·50

1991 (25 July). *50th Anniv of Second World War. Nos. 1475/84 of Antigua optd diagonally with T 116.*

1275	10 c. U.S. troops cross into Germany, 1944	65	60
1276	15 c. Axis surrender in North Africa, 1943	85	70
1277	20 c. U.S. tanks invade Kwalajalein, 1944	1·00	85
1278	45 c. Roosevelt and Churchill meet at Casablanca, 1943	1·50	1·25
1279	50 c. Marshall Badoglio, Prime Minister of Italian anti-fascist government, 1943	1·25	1·25
1280	$1 Lord Mountbatten, Supreme Allied Commander South-east Asia, 1943	2·25	2·25
1281	$2 Greek victory at Koritza, 1940	3·25	3·25
1282	$4 Anglo-Soviet mutual assistance pact, 1941	4·00	4·00
1283	$5 Operation Torch landings, 1942	4·00	4·00
1275/83	*Set of 9*	17·00	16·00
MS1284	Two sheets, each 108×80 mm. (a) $6 Japanese attack on Pearl Harbor, 1941. (b) $6 U.S.A.A.F. daylight raid on Schweinfurt, 1943 *Set of 2 sheets*	17·00	16·00

1991 (26 Aug). *500th Anniv of Discovery of America by Columbus (1992) (4th issue). History of Exploration. Nos. 1503/11 of Antigua optd with T 111.*

1285	10 c. multicoloured	55	50
1286	15 c. multicoloured	70	60
1287	45 c. multicoloured	85	70
1288	60 c. multicoloured	1·00	1·00
1289	$1 multicoloured	1·40	1·40
1290	$2 multicoloured	2·25	2·25
1291	$4 multicoloured	3·50	3·50
1292	$5 multicoloured	3·75	3·75
1285/92	*Set of 8*	12·50	12·50
MS1293	Two sheets, each 106×76 mm. (a) $6 black and Indian red. (b) $6 black and Indian red *Set of 2 sheets*	12·50	12·50

1991 (18 Oct). *Butterflies. Nos. 1494/502 of Antigua optd with T 116 diagonally.*

1294	10 c. Heliconius charithonia	70	70
1295	35 c. Marpesia petreus	1·10	1·10
1296	50 c. Anartia amathea	1·40	1·40
1297	75 c. Siproeta stelenes	1·60	1·60
1298	$1 Battus polydamas	1·75	1·75
1299	$2 Historis odius	2·50	2·50
1300	$4 Hypolimnas misippus	4·00	4·00
1301	$5 Hamadryas feronia	4·00	4·00
1294/1301	*Set of 8*	15·00	15·00
MS1302	Two sheets. (a) 73×100 mm. $6 Vanessa cardui caterpillar (*vert*). (b) 100×73 mm. $6 Danaus plexippus caterpillar (*vert*) *Set of 2 sheets*	15·00	15·00

BARBUDA MAIL

(120)

1991 (18 Nov). *65th Birthday of Queen Elizabeth II. Nos. 1534/8 of Antigua optd with T 120.*

1303	15 c. Queen Elizabeth and Prince Philip in 1976	50	40
1304	20 c. The Queen and Prince Philip in Portugal, 1985	50	40
1305	$2 Queen Elizabeth II	1·50	1·75
1306	$4 The Queen and Prince Philip at Ascot, 1986	2·50	2·75
1303/6	*Set of 4*	4·50	4·75
MS1307	68×90 mm. $4 The Queen at National Theatre, 1986, and Prince Philip	4·00	4·50

1991 (18 Nov). *10th Wedding Anniv of Prince and Princess of Wales. Nos. 1539/43 of Antigua optd with T 120.*

1308	10 c. Prince and Princess of Wales at party, 1986	40	35
1309	40 c. Separate portraits of Prince, Princess and sons	60	50
1310	$1 Prince Henry and Prince William	95	95
1311	$5 Princess Diana in Australia and Prince Charles in Hungary	3·00	3·50
1308/11	*Set of 4*	4·50	4·75
MS1312	68×90 mm. $4 Prince Charles in Hackney and Princess and sons in Majorca, 1987	4·00	4·50

1991 (24 Dec). *Christmas. Religious Paintings by Fra Angelico. Nos. 1595/602 of Antigua optd with T 120.*

1313	10 c. "The Annunciation"	30	30
1314	30 c. "Nativity"	45	35
1315	40 c. "Adoration of the Magi"	45	35
1316	60 c. "Presentation in the Temple"	60	45
1317	$1 "Circumcision"	1·00	80
1318	$3 "Flight into Egypt"	2·50	2·75
1319	$4 "Massacre of the Innocents"	2·75	3·25
1320	$5 "Christ teaching in the Temple"	3·00	3·75
1313/20	*Set of 8*	10·00	11·00

1992 (20 Feb). *Death Centenary of Vincent van Gogh (artist)* (1990). Nos. 1512/24 of Antigua optd with **T 120**.
1321	5 c. "Camille Roulin"		25	25
1322	10 c. "Armand Roulin"		30	30
1323	15 c. "Young Peasant Woman with Straw Hat sitting in the Wheat"		35	35
1324	25 c. "Adeline Ravoux"		45	45
1325	30 c. "The Schoolboy"		45	45
1326	40 c. "Doctor Gachet"		50	50
1327	50 c. "Portrait of a Man"		55	55
1328	75 c. "Two Children"		85	85
1329	$2 "The Postman Joseph Roulin"		2·00	2·00
1330	$3 "The Seated Zouave"		2·25	2·25
1331	$4 "L'Arlésienne"		2·50	2·50
1332	$5 "Self-Portrait, November/December 1888"		3·00	3·00
1321/32		Set of 12	12·00	12·00

MS1333 Three sheets, each 102×76 mm. (a) $5 "Farmhouse in Provence" (horiz). (b) $5 "Flowering Garden" (horiz). (c) $6 "The Bridge at Trinquetaille" (horiz). Imperf .. Set of 3 sheets 12·00 12·00

1992 (7 Apr). *Birth Centenary of Charles de Gaulle (French statesman)*. Nos. 1562/70 of Antigua optd with **T 111** (10 c., $1, $2, $4, $6) or **T 114** (others).
1334	10 c. Presidents De Gaulle and Kennedy, 1961		50	45
1335	15 c. General De Gaulle with Pres. Roosevelt, 1945 (vert)		65	50
1336	45 c. Pres. De Gaulle with Chancellor Adenauer, 1962 (vert)		90	75
1337	60 c. De Gaulle at Arc de Triomphe, Liberation of Paris, 1944 (vert)		1·10	1·00
1338	$1 General De Gaulle crossing the Rhine, 1945		1·50	1·50
1339	$2 General De Gaulle in Algiers, 1944		2·25	2·50
1340	$4 Presidents De Gaulle and Eisenhower, 1960		3·00	3·25
1341	$5 De Gaulle returning from Germany, 1968 (vert)		3·25	3·50
1334/41		Set of 8	12·00	12·00

MS1342 Two sheets, (a) 76×106 mm. $6 De Gaulle with crowd. (b) 106×76 mm. $6 De Gaulle and Churchill at Casablanca, 1943
Set of 2 sheets 12·00 12·00

1992 (16 Apr). *Easter. Religious Paintings*. Nos. 1627/35 of Antigua optd with **T 111**.
1343	10 c. "Supper at Emmaus" (Caravaggio) ..		30	30
1344	15 c. "The Vision of St. Peter" (Zurbarán)		45	30
1345	30 c. "Christ driving the Money-changers from the Temple" (Tiepolo)		60	45
1346	40 c. "Martyrdom of St. Bartholomew" (detail) (Ribera)		70	50
1347	$1 "Christ driving the Money-changers from the Temple" (detail) (Tiepolo) ..		1·25	1·00
1348	$2 "Crucifixion" (detail) (Altdorfer)		2·00	2·50
1349	$4 "The Deposition" (detail) (Fra Angelico)		3·00	3·50
1350	$5 "The Deposition" (different detail) (Fra Angelico)		3·00	3·50
1343/50		Set of 8	10·00	11·00

MS1351 Two sheets. (a) 102×71 mm. $6 "The Last Supper" (detail) (Masip). (b) 71×102 mm. $6 "Crucifixion" (detail) (vert) (Altdorfer)
Set of 2 sheets 10·00 11·00

1992 (19 June). *Anniversaries and Events*. Nos. 1573/83 of Antigua optd as **T 114**, but with lines spaced (Nos. 1358 and MS1362b) or with **T 111** (others).
1352	25 c. Germans celebrating Reunification ..		40	40
1353	75 c. Cubs erecting tent		1·00	1·00
1354	$1.50, Don Giovanni and Mozart		2·00	2·00
1355	$2 Chariot driver and Gate at night		2·00	2·00
1356	$2 Lord Baden-Powell and members of the 3rd Antigua Methodist cub pack (vert)		2·00	2·00
1357	$2 Lilienthal's signature and glider Flugzeug Nr. 5		2·00	2·00
1358	$2.50, Driver in modern locomotive (vert)		2·25	2·25
1359	$3 Statues from podium		2·25	2·25
1360	$3.50, Cubs and camp fire		2·75	2·75
1361	$4 St. Peter's Cathedral, Salzburg ..		2·75	2·75
1352/61		Set of 10	17·00	17·00

MS1362 Two sheets. (a) 100×72 mm. $4 Detail of chariot and helmet. (b) 89×117 mm. $5 Antiguan flag and Jamboree emblem (vert)
Set of 2 sheets 7·50 9·00

1992 (12 Aug). *50th Anniv of Japanese Attack on Pearl Harbor*. Nos. 1585/94 of Antigua optd as **T 114**, but with lines spaced.
1364	$1 Nimitz class carrier and Ticonderoga class cruiser		1·40	1·40
	a. Sheetlet. Nos. 1364/73		12·50	
1365	$1 Tourist launch		1·40	1·40
1366	$1 U.S.S. Arizona memorial		1·40	1·40
1367	$1 Wreaths on water and aircraft		1·40	1·40
1368	$1 White Tern		1·40	1·40
1369	$1 Mitsubishi A6M Zero-Sen fighters over Pearl City		1·40	1·40
1370	$1 Mitsubishi A6M Zero-Sen fighters attacking		1·40	1·40
1371	$1 Battleship Row in flames		1·40	1·40
1372	$1 U.S.S. Nevada (battleship) underway		1·40	1·40
1373	$1 Mitsubishi A6M Zero-Sen fighters returning to carriers		1·40	1·40
1364/73		Set of 10	12·50	12·50

1992 (12 Oct). *500th Anniv of Discovery of America by Columbus (5th issue). World Columbian Stamp "Expo '92", Chicago.* Nos. 1654/60 of Antigua optd with **T 111**.
1374	15 c. Memorial cross and huts, San Salvador		40	40
1375	30 c. Martin Pinzon with telescope		50	50
1376	40 c. Christopher Columbus		50	50
1377	$1 Pinta		1·75	1·75
1378	$2 Nina		2·25	2·25
1379	$4 Santa Maria		2·75	2·75
1374/9		Set of 6	7·25	7·25

MS1380 Two sheets, each 108×76 mm. (a) $6 Ship and map of West Indies. (b) $6 Sea monster
Set of 2 sheets 10·00 11·00

1992 (12 Oct). *500th Anniv of Discovery of America by Columbus (6th issue). Organization of East Caribbean States.* Nos. 1670/1 of Antigua optd with **T 111**.
1381	$1 Columbus meeting Amerindians ..	1·50	1·50
1382	$2 Ships approaching island	2·00	2·25

1992 (29 Oct). *Postage Stamp Mega Event, New York*. No. MS1690 of Antigua optd with **T 111**.
MS1383 $6 multicoloured .. .. .. 4·50 5·50

1992 (3 Nov). *40th Anniv of Queen Elizabeth II's Accession*. Nos. 1604/8 of Antigua optd with **T 111**.
1384	10 c. Queen Elizabeth II and bird sanctuary	60	50
1385	30 c. Nelson's Dockyard ..	1·25	80
1386	$1 Ruins on Shirley Heights	1·75	1·75
1387	$5 Beach and palm trees	4·75	5·50
1384/7		Set of 4	7·50	7·75

MS1388 Two sheets, each 75×98 mm. (a) $6 Beach. (b) $6 Hillside foliage .. Set of 2 sheets 12·00 13·00

1992 (8 Dec). *Prehistoric Animals*. Nos. 1618/26 of Antigua optd with **T 120** (sideways on Nos. 1391/2 and MS1397).
1389	10 c. Pteranodon		60	60
1390	15 c. Brachiosaurus		80	80
1391	30 c. Tyrannosaurus Rex ..		1·00	1·00
1392	50 c. Parasaurolophus		1·25	1·25
1393	$1 Deinonychus (horiz)		1·75	1·75
1394	$2 Triceratops (horiz) ..		2·50	2·50
1395	$4 Protoceratops hatching (horiz)		3·50	3·50
1396	$5 Stegosaurus (horiz)		3·50	3·50
1389/96		Set of 8	13·50	13·50

MS1397 Two sheets, each 100×70 mm. (a) $6 Apatosaurus (horiz). (b) $6 Allosaurus (horiz)
Set of 2 sheets 13·00 13·00

1992 (8 Dec). *Christmas*. Nos. 1691/9 of Antigua optd with **T 111**.
1398	10 c. "Virgin and Child with Angels" (School of Piero della Francesca)		40	40
1399	25 c. "Madonna Degli Alberelli" (Giovanni Bellini)		60	40
1400	30 c. "Madonna and Child with St. Anthony Abbot and St. Sigismund" (Neroccio)		65	45
1401	40 c. "Madonna and the Grand Duke" (Raphael)		70	50
1402	60 c. "The Nativity" (George de la Tour) ..		90	70
1403	$1 "Holy Family" (Jacob Jordaens)		1·40	1·25
1404	$4 "Madonna and Child Enthroned" (Magaritone)		4·00	4·50
1405	$5 "Madonna and Child on a Curved Throne" (Byzantine school) ..		4·00	4·50
1398/405		Set of 8	11·50	11·50

MS1406 Two sheets, each 76×102 mm. (a) $6 "Madonna and Child" (Domenco Ghirlando). (b) $6 "The Holy Family" (Pontormo)
Set of 2 sheets 11·50 12·50

1993 (25 Jan). *Fungi*. Nos. 1645/53 of Antigua optd with **T 120**.
1407	10 c. Amanita caesarea		60	60
1408	15 c. Collybia fusipes		75	75
1409	30 c. Boletus aereus		1·00	1·00
1410	40 c. Laccaria amethystina		1·00	1·00
1411	$1 Russula virescens		1·50	1·50
1412	$2 Tricholoma equestre ("Tricholoma auratum")		2·25	2·25
1413	$4 Calocybe gambosa		3·00	3·00
1414	$5 Lentinus tigrinus ("Panus tigrinus")		3·00	3·00
1407/14		Set of 8	12·00	12·00

MS1415 Two sheets, each 100×70 mm. (a) $6 Clavariadelphus truncatus. (b) $6 Auricularia auricula-judae .. .. Set of 2 sheets 12·00 12·00

1993 (22 Mar). *"Granada '92" International Stamp Exhibition, Spain. Spanish Paintings*. Nos. 1636/44 of Antigua optd diagonally with **T 116**.
1416	10 c. "The Miracle at the Well" (Alonzo Cano)		45	45
1417	15 c. "The Poet Luis de Goingora y Argote" (Velázquez)		55	55
1418	30 c. "The Painter Francisco Goya" (Vincente López Portana)		75	75
1419	40 c. "Maria de las Nieves Michaela Fourdinier" (Luis Paret y Alcázar) ..		85	85
1420	$1 "Carlos III eating before his Court" (Alcázar) (horiz)		1·50	1·50
1421	$2 "Rain Shower in Granada" (Antonio Munoz Degrain) (horiz)		2·25	2·25
1422	$4 "Sarah Bernhardt" (Santiago Ruisnol i Prats)		3·25	3·25
1423	$5 "The Hermitage Garden" (Joaquim Mir Trinxet)		3·25	3·25
1416/23		Set of 8	11·50	11·50

MS1424 Two sheets, each 120×95 mm. (a) $6 "The Ascent of Monsieur Boucle's Montgolfier Balloon in the Gardens of Aranjuez" (Antonio Carnicero) (112×87 mm). (b) $6 "Olympus: Battle with the Giants" (Francisco Bayeu y Subias) (112×87 mm). Imperf .. Set of 2 sheets 11·50 12·00

1993 (10 May). *"Genova '92" International Thematic Stamp Exhibition. Hummingbirds and Plants*. Nos. 1661/9 of Antigua optd with **T 120**.
1425	10 c. Antillean Crested Hummingbird and Wild Plantain		55	55
1426	25 c. Green Mango and Parrot's Plantain		70	70
1427	45 c. Purple-throated Carib and Lobster Claws		90	90
1428	60 c. Antillean Mango and Coral Plant		1·00	1·00
1429	$1 Vervain Hummingbird and Cardinal's Guard		1·50	1·50
1430	$2 Rufous-breasted Hermit and Heliconia		2·00	2·00
1431	$4 Blue-headed Hummingbird and Red Ginger		2·75	2·75
1432	$5 Green-throated Carib and Orna-mental Banana		2·75	2·75
1425/32		Set of 8	11·00	11·00

MS1433 Two sheets, each 100×70 mm. (a) $6 Bee Hummingbird and Jungle Flame. (b) $6 Western Streamertail and Bignonia
Set of 2 sheets 10·00 12·00

1993 (29 June). *Inventors and Inventions*. Nos. 1672/80 of Antigua optd with **T 111**.
1434	10 c. Ts'ai Lun and paper		15	1.
1435	25 c. Igor Sikorsky and Bolshoi Baltiskii (first four-engined airplane)		35	3.
1436	30 c. Alexander Graham Bell and early telephone		40	4.
1437	40 c. Johannes Gutenberg and early printing press		40	4.
1438	60 c. James Watt and stationary steam engine		90	9.
1439	$1 Anton van Leeuwenhoek and early microscope		1·10	1·1.
1440	$4 Louis Braille and hands reading braille		3·00	3·0.
1441	$5 Galileo and telescope		3·00	3·0.
1434/41		Set of 8	8·50	8·5.

MS1442 Two sheets, each 100×71 mm. (a) $6 Edison and Latimer's phonograph. (b) $6 Fulton's steamboat .. Set of 2 sheets 8·50 10·00

1993 (16 Aug). *Anniversaries and Events*. Nos. 1700/14 of Antigua optd with **T 111** (Nos. 1450/1) or as **T 114**, but with lines spaced (others).
1443	10 c. Russian cosmonauts		40	4.
1444	40 c. Airship LZ-127 Graf Zeppelin, 1929		75	75
1445	45 c. Bishop Daniel Davis		50	5.
1446	75 c. Konrad Adenauer making speech		70	7.
1447	$1 Bus Mosbacher and Weatherly (yacht)		1·00	1·0.
1448	$1.50, Rain Forest		1·25	1·2.
1449	$2 Tiger		3·00	3·0.
1450	$2 National flag, plant and emblem (horiz)		1·50	1·50
1451	$2 Members of Community Players company (horiz)		1·50	1·50
1452	$2.25, Women carrying pots		1·50	1·50
1453	$3 Lions Club emblem		2·50	2·50
1454	$4 Chinese rocket on launch tower		2·75	2·75
1455	$4 West German and N.A.T.O. flags		2·75	2·75
1456	$6 Hugo Eckener (airship pioneer)		4·00	4·00
1443/56		Set of 14	22·00	22·0.

MS1457 Four sheets, each 100×71 mm. (a) $6 Projected European space station. (b) $6 Airship LZ-129 Hindenburg, 1936. (c) $6 Brandenburg Gate on German flag. (d) $6 Danaus plexippus (butterfly) .. .. Set of 4 sheets 18·00 19·00

1993 (21 Sept). *Flowers*. Nos. 1733/41 of Antigua optd with **T 114**, but with lines spaced (Nos. 1458/65) or **T 111** (No. MS1466).
1458	15 c. Cardinal's Guard		65	65
1459	25 c. Giant Granadilla		80	80
1460	30 c. Spider Flower		90	90
1461	40 c. Gold Vine		1·00	1·00
1462	$1 Frangipani		1·75	1·75
1463	$2 Bougainvillea		2·50	2·50
1464	$4 Yellow Oleander		3·50	3·50
1465	$5 Spicy Jatropha		3·50	3·50
1458/65		Set of 8	13·00	13·00

MS1466 Two sheets, each 100×70 mm. (a) $6 Bird Lime Tree. (b) $6 Fairy Lily Set of 2 sheets 13·00 13·00

WORLD BIRDWATCH
9-10 OCTOBER 1993

(121)

1993 (9 Oct). *World Bird Watch*. Nos. 1248/51 optd as **T 121** (horiz opt on $2, $4).
1467	60 c. Type 119		1·75	1·75
1468	$2 Adelaide's Warbler		3·00	3·00
1469	$4 Rose-breasted Grosbeak		4·25	4·50
1470	$7 Wied's Crested Flycatcher		5·50	6·50
1467/70		Set of 4	13·00	14·00

1993 (11 Nov). *Endangered Species*. Nos. 1759/71 of Antigua optd with **T 111**.
1471	$1 St. Lucia Amazon		1·25	1·25
	a. Sheetlet. Nos. 1471/82		13·50	
1472	$1 Cahow		1·25	1·25
1473	$1 Swallow-tailed Kite		1·25	1·25
1474	$1 Everglade Kite		1·25	1·25
1475	$1 Imperial Amazon		1·25	1·25
1476	$1 Humpback Whale		1·25	1·25
1477	$1 Plain Pigeon		1·25	1·25
1478	$1 St. Vincent Amazon		1·25	1·25
1479	$1 Puerto Rican Amazon		1·25	1·25
1480	$1 Leatherback Turtle		1·25	1·25
1481	$1 American Crocodile		1·25	1·25
1482	$1 Hawksbill Turtle		1·25	1·25
1471/82		Set of 12	13·50	13·50

MS1483 Two sheets, each 100×70 mm. (a) $6 As No. 1476. (b) $6 West Indian Manatee
Set of 2 sheets 13·00 13·00

1994 (6 Jan). *Bicentenary of the Louvre, Paris. Paintings by Peter Paul Rubens*. Nos. 1742/9 and MS1758 of Antigua optd with **T 120**.
1484	$1 "The Destiny of Marie de Medici" (upper detail)		1·10	1·10
	a. Sheetlet. Nos. 1484/91		8·00	
1485	$1 "The Birth of Marie de Medici"		1·10	1·10
1486	$1 "The Education of Marie de Medici"		1·10	1·10
1487	$1 "The Destiny of Marie de Medici" (lower detail)		1·10	1·10
1488	$1 "Henry VI receiving the Portrait of Marie"		1·10	1·10
1489	$1 "The Meeting of the King and Marie de Medici"		1·10	1·10
1490	$1 "The Marriage by Proxy"		1·10	1·10
1491	$1 "The Birth of Louis XIII"		1·10	1·10
1484/91		Set of 8	8·00	8·00

MS1492 70×100 mm. $6 "Helene Fourment with a Coach" (52×85 mm) .. .. .. 7·00 7·00

1994 (3 Mar). *World Cup Football Championship 1994, U.S.A. (1st issue). Nos. 1816/28 of Antigua optd with T* **114**, *but with lines spaced (Nos. 1493/1504) or T* **111** *(No. MS1505).*
1493	$2 Paul Gascoigne			2·00 2·00
1494	$2 David Platt			2·00 2·00
1495	$2 Martin Peters			2·00 2·00
1496	$2 John Barnes			2·00 2·00
1497	$2 Gary Lineker			2·00 2·00
1498	$2 Geoff Hurst			2·00 2·00
1499	$2 Bobby Charlton			2·00 2·00
1500	$2 Bryan Robson			2·00 2·00
1501	$2 Bobby Moore			2·00 2·00
1502	$2 Nobby Stiles			2·00 2·00
1503	$2 Gordon Banks			2·00 2·00
1504	$2 Peter Shilton			2·00 2·00
1493/1504			*Set of 12*	22·00 22·00

MS1505 Two sheets, each 135×109 mm. (a) $6 Bobby Moore holding World Cup. (b) $6 Gary Lineker and Bobby Robson .. *Set of 2 sheets* 11·50 11·50
See also Nos. 1573/9.

1994 (21 Apr). *Anniversaries and Events. Nos. 1829/38, 1840 and 1842/7 of Antigua optd with T* **111**.
1506	10 c. Grand Inspector W. Heath		45 45
1507	15 c. Rodnina and Oulanov (U.S.S.R.) (pairs figure skating) (*horiz*)		50 50
1508	30 c. Present Masonic Hall, St. John's (*horiz*)		70 70
1509	30 c. Willy Brandt with Helmut Schmidt and George Leber (*horiz*)		70 70
1510	30 c. "Cat and Bird" (Picasso) (*horiz*)		70 70
1511	40 c. Previous Masonic Hall, St. John's (*horiz*)		70 70
1512	40 c. "Fish on a Newspaper" (Picasso) (*horiz*)		70 70
1513	40 c. Early astronomical equipment		70 70
1514	40 c. Prince Naruhito and engagement photographs (*horiz*)		70 70
1515	60 c. Grand Inspector J. Jeffery		75 75
1516	$3 Masako Owada and engagement photographs (*horiz*)		2·00 2·00
1517	$4 Willy Brandt and protest march (*horiz*)		2·75 2·75
1518	$4 Galaxy		2·75 2·75
1519	$5 Alberto Tomba (Italy) (giant slalom) (*horiz*)		2·75 2·75
1520	$5 "Dying Bull" (Picasso) (*horiz*)		2·75 2·75
1521	$5 Pres. Clinton and family (*horiz*)		2·75 2·75
1506/21		*Set of 16*	20·00 20·00

MS1522 Six sheets. (a) 106×75 mm. $5 Copernicus. (b) 106×75 mm. $6 Womens' 1500 metre speed skating medallists (*horiz*). (c) 106×75 mm. $6 Willy Brandt at Warsaw Ghetto Memorial (*horiz*). (d) 106×75 mm. $6 "Woman with a Dog" (detail) (Picasso). (e) 106×75 mm. $6 Masako Owada. (f) 106×75 mm. $6 Pres. Clinton taking the Oath (42½×57 *mm*)
.. *Set of 6 sheets* 22·00 23·00

1994 (15 June). *Aviation Anniversaries. Nos. 1848/55 of Antigua optd with T* **111** *(vertically reading down on No. 1526).*
1523	30 c. Hugo Eckener and Dr. W. Beckers with Airship LZ-127 *Graf Zeppelin* over Lake George, New York		70 70
1524	40 c. Chicago World's Fair from *Graf Zeppelin*		70 70
1525	40 c. Gloster Whittle E28/39, 1941		70 70
1526	40 c. George Washington writing balloon mail letter (*vert*)		70 70
1527	$4 Pres. Wilson and Curtiss JN-4 "Jenny"		3·25 3·25
1528	$5 Airship LZ-129 *Hindenburg* over Ebbets Field baseball stadium, 1937		3·25 3·25
1529	$5 Gloster Meteor in dogfight		3·25 3·25
1523/9		*Set of 7*	11·50 11·50

MS1530 Three sheets. (a) 86×105 mm. $6 Hugo Eckener (*vert*). (b) 105×86 mm. $6 Consolidated Catalina PBY-5 flying boat (57×42½ *mm*). (c) 105×86 mm. $6 Alexander Hamilton, Washington and John Jay watching Blanchard's balloon, 1793 (*horiz*) .. *Set of 3 sheets* 14·00 15·00

1994 (15 June). *Centenaries of Henry Ford's First Petrol Engine (Nos. 1531, 1533,* **MS**1535a) *and Karl Benz's First Four-wheeled Car (others). Nos. 1856/60 of Antigua optd with T* **111**.
1531	30 c. Lincoln Continental		65 65
1532	40 c. Mercedes racing car, 1914		70 70
1533	$4 Ford "GT40", 1966		3·50 3·50
1534	$5 Mercedes Benz "gull-wing" coupe, 1954		3·50 3·50
1531/4		*Set of 4*	7·50 7·50

MS1535 Two sheets. (a) 114×87 mm. $6 Ford's Mustang emblem. (b) 87×114 mm. $6 Germany 1936 12pf. Benz and U.S.A. 1968 12 c. Ford stamps .. *Set of 2 sheets* 9·00 10·00

1994 (18 Aug). *Famous Paintings by Rembrandt and Matisse. Nos. 1881/9 of Antigua optd with T* **111**.
1536	15 c. "Hannah and Samuel" (Rembrandt)		40 40
1537	15 c. "Guitarist" (Matisse)		40 40
1538	30 c. "The Jewish Bride" (Rembrandt)		60 60
1539	40 c. "Jacob wrestling with the Angel" (Rembrandt)		65 65
1540	60 c. "Interior with a Goldfish Bowl" (Matisse)		80 80
1541	$1 "Mlle. Yvonne Landsberg" (Matisse)		1·00 1·00
1542	$4 "The Toboggan" (Matisse)		3·00 3·00
1543	$5 "Moses with the Tablets of the Law" (Rembrandt)		3·00 3·00
1536/43		*Set of 8*	9·00 9·00

MS1544 Two sheets. (a) 124×99 mm. $6 "The Blinding of Samson by the Philistines" (detail) (Rembrandt). (b) 99×124 mm. $6 "The Three Sisters" (detail) (Matisse) .. *Set of 2 sheets* 9·00 9·50

1994 (21 Sept). *"Polska '93" International Stamp Exhibition, Poznań. Nos. 1839, 1841 and* **MS**1847f *of Antigua optd with T* **114**, *but with lines spaced (sideways on $1, $3).*
1545	$1 "Woman Combing her Hair" (W. Slewinski) (*horiz*)		1·50 1·50
1546	$3 "Artist's Wife with Cat" (Konrad Kryzanowski) (*horiz*)		3·00 3·00
MS1547	70×100 mm. $6 "General Confusion" (S. I. Witkiewicz)		5·00 5·50

1994 (21 Sept). *Orchids. Nos. 1948/56 of Antigua optd with T* **114**, *but with lines spaced (Nos. 1548/55) or T* **111** *(No.* **MS**1556).
1548	10 c. *Spiranthes lanceolata*		50 50
1549	20 c. *Ionopsis utriculariodies*		70 70
1550	30 c. *Tetramica canaliculata*		80 80
1551	50 c. *Oncidium picturatum*		1·10 1·10
1552	$1 *Epidendrum difforme*		1·60 1·60
1553	$2 *Epidendrum ciliare*		2·50 2·50
1554	$4 *Epidendrum ibaguense*		4·00 4·00
1555	$5 *Epidendrum nocturnum*		4·00 4·00
1548/55		*Set of 8*	13·50 13·50

MS1556 Two sheets, each 100×73 mm. (a) $6 *Rodriguezia lanceolata*. (b) $6 *Encyclia cochleata* .. *Set of 2 sheets* 13·00 13·00

1994 (3 Nov). *Centenary of Sierra Club (environmental protection society) (1992). Endangered Species. Nos. 1907/22 of Antigua optd with T* **114**, *but lines spaced (Nos. 1557/71) or T* **111** *(No.* **MS**1572).
1557	$1.50, Sumatran Rhinoceros lying down		2·00 2·00
	a. Sheetlet. Nos. 1557/64		13·50
1558	$1.50, Sumatran Rhinoceros feeding		2·00 2·00
1559	$1.50, Ring-tailed Lemur on ground		2·00 2·00
1560	$1.50, Ring-tailed Lemur on branch		2·00 2·00
1561	$1.50, Red-fronted Brown Lemur on branch		2·00 2·00
1562	$1.50, Head of Red-fronted Brown Lemur		2·00 2·00
1563	$1.50, Head of Red-fronted Brown Lemur in front of trunk		2·00 2·00
1564	$1.50, Sierra Club Centennial emblem		1·25 1·25
	a. Sheetlet. Nos. 1564/71		13·50
1565	$1.50, Head of Bactrian Camel		2·00 2·00
1566	$1.50, Bactrian Camel		2·00 2·00
1567	$1.50, African Elephant drinking		2·00 2·00
1568	$1.50, Head of African Elephant		2·00 2·00
1569	$1.50, Leopard sitting upright		2·00 2·00
1570	$1.50, Leopard in grass (emblem at right)		2·00 2·00
1571	$1.50, Leopard in grass (emblem at left)		2·00 2·00
1557/71		*Set of 15*	27·00 27·00

MS1572 Four sheets. (a) 100×70 mm. $1.50, Sumatran Rhinoceros (*horiz*). (b) 70×100 mm. $1.50, Ring-tailed Lemur (*horiz*). (c) 70×100 mm. $1.50, Bactrian Camel (*horiz*). (d) 100×70 mm. $1.50, African Elephant (*horiz*) .. *Set of 4 sheets* 4·50 5·50

1995 (12 Jan). *World Cup Football Championship, U.S.A. (2nd issue). Nos. 2039/45 of Antigua optd with T* **116** *diagonally in silver.*
1573	15 c. Hugo Sanchez (Mexico)		45 45
1574	35 c. Jürgen Klinsmann (Germany)		70 70
1575	65 c. Antiguan player		1·00 1·00
1576	$1.20, Cobi Jones (U.S.A.)		1·40 1·40
1577	$4 Roberto Baggio (Italy)		3·00 3·00
1578	$5 Bwalya Kalusha (Zambia)		3·00 3·00
1573/8		*Set of 6*	8·50 8·50

MS1579 Two sheets. (a) 72×105 mm. $6 Maldive Islands player (*vert*). (b) 107×78 mm. $6 World Cup trophy (*vert*) .. *Set of 2 sheets* 8·50 9·50

1995 (12 Jan). *Christmas. Religious Paintings. Nos. 2058/66 of Antigua optd with T* **111**.
1580	15 c. "Virgin and Child by the Fireside" (Robert Campin)		40 25
1581	35 c. "The Reading Madonna" (Giorgione)		55 40
1582	40 c. "Madonna and Child" (Giovanni Bellini)		55 40
1583	45 c. "The Litta Madonna" (Da Vinci)		55 45
1584	65 c. "The Virgin and Child under the Apple Tree" (Lucas Cranach the Elder)		80 80
1585	75 c. "Madonna and Child" (Master of the Female Half-lengths)		90 90
1586	$1.20, "An Allegory of the Church" (Alessandro Allori)		1·40 1·75
1587	$5 "Madonna and Child wreathed with Flowers" (Jacob Jordaens)		3·75 4·25
1580/7		*Set of 8*	8·00 8·25

MS1588 Two sheets. (a) 123×88 mm. $6 "Madonna and Child with Commissioners" (detail) (Palma Vecchio). (b) 88×123 mm. $6 "The Virgin Enthroned with Child" (detail) (Bohemian master) .. *Set of 2 sheets* 8·50 9·50

1995 (24 Feb). *"Hong Kong '94" International Stamp Exhibition (1st issue). Nos. 1890/1 of Antigua optd with T* **111**.
1589	40 c. Hong Kong 1981 $1 Fish stamp and fishing boats, Shau Kei Wan		70 70
	a. Horiz pair. Nos. 1589/90		1·40 1·40
1590	40 c. Antigua 1990 $2 Reef Fish stamp and fishing boats, Shau Kei Wan		70 70

1995 (24 Feb). *"Hong Kong '94" International Stamp Exhibition (2nd issue). Nos. 1892/7 of Antigua optd with T* **111**.
1591	40 c. Terracotta warriors		30 30
	a. Sheetlet. Nos. 1591/6		1·60
1592	40 c. Cavalryman and horse		30 30
1593	40 c. Warriors in armour		30 30
1594	40 c. Painted bronze chariot and team		30 30
1595	40 c. Pekingese dog		30 30
1596	40 c. Warriors with horses		30 30
1591/6		*Set of 6*	1·60 1·60

1995 (24 Feb). *Centenary of International Olympic Committee. Nos. 1990/2 of Antigua optd with T* **114**, *but with lines spaced.*
1597	50 c. Edwin Moses (U.S.A.) (400 metres hurdles), 1984		65 65
1598	$1.50, Steffi Graf (Germany) (tennis), 1988		2·25 2·25
MS1599	79×110 mm. $6 Johann Olav Koss (Norway) (500, 1500 and 10,000 metre speed skating), 1994		4·00 4·50

1995 (4 Apr). *Dogs of the World. Chinese New Year ("Year of the Dog"). Nos. 1923/47 of Antigua optd with T* **111**.
1600	50 c. West Highland White Terrier		50 50
	a. Sheetlet. Nos. 1600/11		5·50
1601	50 c. Beagle		50 50
1602	50 c. Scottish Terrier		50 50
1603	50 c. Pekingese		50 50
1604	50 c. Dachshund		50 50
1605	50 c. Yorkshire Terrier		50 50
1606	50 c. Pomeranian		50 50
1607	50 c. Poodle		50 50
1608	50 c. Shetland Sheepdog		50 50
1609	50 c. Pug		50 50
1610	50 c. Shih Tzu		50 50
1611	50 c. Chihuahua		50 50
1612	50 c. Mastiff		50 50
	a. Sheetlet. Nos. 1612/23		5·50
1613	50 c. Border Collie		50 50
1614	50 c. Samoyed		50 50
1615	50 c. Airedale Terrier		50 50
1616	50 c. English Setter		50 50
1617	50 c. Rough Collie		50 50
1618	50 c. Newfoundland		50 50
1619	50 c. Weimarana		50 50
1620	50 c. English Springer Spaniel		50 50
1621	50 c. Dalmatian		50 50
1622	50 c. Boxer		50 50
1623	50 c. Old English Sheepdog		50 50
1600/23		*Set of 24*	11·00 11·00

MS1624 Two sheets, each 93×58 mm. (a) $6 Welsh Corgi. (b) $6 Labrador Retriever
.. *Set of 2 sheets* 9·00 9·00

1995 (18 May). *Centenary of First English Cricket Tour to the West Indies (1995). Nos. 1994/7 of Antigua optd with T* **114**, *but with lines spaced.*
1625	35 c. Mike Atherton (England) and Wisden Trophy		35 35
1626	75 c. Viv Richards (West Indies) (*vert*)		70 70
1627	$1.20, Richie Richardson (West Indies) and Wisden Trophy		90 90
1625/7		*Set of 3*	1·75 1·75

MS1628 80×100 mm. $3 English team, 1895 (black and grey-brown) .. 2·25 2·50

1995 (18 May–12 July). *"Philakorea '94" International Stamp Exhibition (1st issue). Nos. 1998/2009 of Antigua optd with T* **114**, *but with lines spaced (Nos. 1629 and 1638/40) or T* **111** *(others).*
1629	40 c. Entrance bridge, Songgwangsa Temple (12 July)		40 40
1630	75 c. Long-necked Bottle		60 60
	a. Sheetlet. Nos. 1630/7		5·00
1631	75 c. Punch'ong ware jar with floral decoration		60 60
1632	75 c. Punch'ong ware jar with blue dragon pattern		60 60
1633	75 c. Ewer in shape of bamboo shoot		60 60
1634	75 c. Punch'ong ware green jar		60 60
1635	75 c. Pear-shaped bottle		60 60
1636	75 c. Porcelain jar with brown dragon pattern		60 60
1637	75 c. Porcelain jar with floral pattern		60 60
1638	90 c. Song-op Folk Village, Cheju (12 July)		60 60
1639	$3 Port Sogwipo (12 July)		2·00 2·00
1629/39		*Set of 11*	6·50 6·50

MS1640 104×71 mm. $4 Ox herder playing flute (*vert*) .. 2·50 3·00

1995 (18 May). *First Recipients of Order of the Caribbean Community. Nos. 2046/8 of Antigua optd with T* **111**.
1641	65 c. Sir Shridath Ramphal		45 50
1642	90 c. William Demas		55 60
1643	$1.20, Derek Walcott		75 85
1641/3		*Set of 3*	1·60 1·75

1995 (12 July–29 Sept). *25th Anniv of First Moon Landing. Nos. 1977/89 of Antigua optd with T* **114**, *but with lines spaced (vertically reading upward on Nos. 1644/55).*
1644	$1.50, Edwin Aldrin (astronaut)		1·25 1·25
	a. Sheetlet. Nos. 1644/49		6·75
1645	$1.50, First lunar footprint		1·25 1·25
1646	$1.50, Neil Armstrong (astronaut)		1·25 1·25
1647	$1.50, Aldrin stepping onto Moon		1·25 1·25
1648	$1.50, Aldrin and equipment		1·25 1·25
1649	$1.50, Aldrin and U.S.A. flag		1·25 1·25
1650	$1.50, Aldrin at Tranquillity Base		1·25 1·25
	a. Sheetlet. Nos. 1650/55		6·75
1651	$1.50, Moon plaque		1·25 1·25
1652	$1.50, *Eagle* leaving Moon		1·25 1·25
1653	$1.50, Command module in lunar orbit		1·25 1·25
1654	$1.50, First day cover of U.S.A. 1969 10 c. First Man on Moon stamp		1·25 1·25
1655	$1.50, Pres. Nixon and astronauts		1·25 1·25
1644/55		*Set of 12*	13·50 13·50

MS1656 72×102 mm. $6 Armstrong and Aldrin with postal official (29 Sept) .. 4·50 5·00

1995 (12 July). *International Year of the Family. No. 1993 of Antigua optd with T* **114**, *but with lines spaced.*
1657	90 c. Antiguan family		80 80

1995 (29 Sept). *50th Anniv of D-Day. Nos. 2010/13 of Antigua optd as T 113, but with lines spaced.*
1658 40 c. Short S.25 Sunderland flying boat .. 65 65
1659 $2 Lockheed P-38 Lightning fighters
attacking train .. 2·25 2·25
1660 $3 Martin B-26 Marauder bombers .. 2·50 2·50
1658/60 .. *Set of 3* 4·75 4·75
MS1661 108×78 mm. $6 Hawker Typhoon
fighter bomber .. .. 5·50 6·50

122 Queen Elizabeth the Queen
Mother (90th birthday)

(Des G. Vasarhelyi. Litho B.D.T.)

1995 (13–27 Nov). *Anniversaries. T 122 and similar multicoloured designs. P 13.*
1662 $7.50, Type 122 (20 Nov) .. 5·00 5·00
1663 $8 German bombers over St. Paul's
Cathedral, London (*horiz*) (50th anniv
of end of Second World War) .. 6·00 6·00
1664 $8 New York skyline with U.N. and
national flags (*horiz*) (50th anniv of
United Nations) (27 Nov) .. 5·00 5·00
1662/4 .. .. *Set of 3* 14·50 14·50

HURRICANE RELIEF
+ $1
(123)

BARBUDA
MAIL
(124)

1995 (13–27 Nov). *Hurricane Relief. Nos. 1662/4 surch with T 123 in silver.*
1665 $7.50 + $1 Type 122 (90th birthday)
(20 Nov) .. .. 5·00 5·50
1666 $8 + $1 German bombers over St. Paul's
Cathedral, London (*horiz*) (50th anniv
of end of Second World War) .. 5·00 5·50
1667 $8 + $1 New York skyline with U.N. and
national flags (*horiz*) (50th anniv of
United Nations) (27 Nov) .. 5·00 5·50
1665/7 .. .. *Set of 3* 13·50 15·00

1996 (22 Jan). *Marine Life. Nos. 1967/76 of Antigua optd as T 114, but with lines spaced.*
1668 50 c. Bottlenose Dolphin 50 50
a. Sheetlet. Nos. 1668/76 .. 4·00
1669 50 c. Killer Whale 50 50
1670 50 c. Spinner Dolphin 50 50
1671 50 c. Oceanic Sunfish 50 50
1672 50 c. Caribbean Reef Shark and Short Fin
Pilot Whale 50 50
1673 50 c. Copper-banded Butterflyfish .. 50 50
1674 50 c. Mosaic Moray 50 50
1675 50 c. Clown Triggerfish 50 50
1676 50 c. Red Lobster 50 50
1668/76 .. .. *Set of 9* 4·00 4·00
MS1677 Two sheets, each 106×76 mm. (a) $6
Seahorse. (b) $6 Swordfish ("Blue Marlin")
(*horiz*) .. .. *Set of 2 sheets* 8·50 9·00

1996 (22 Jan). *Christmas. Religious Paintings. Nos. 2267/73 of Antigua optd with T 111.*
1678 15 c. "Rest on the Flight into Egypt" (Paolo
Veronese) 20 20
1679 35 c. "Madonna and Child" (Van Dyck) .. 30 30
1680 65 c. "Sacred Conversation Piece"
(Veronese) 45 45
1681 75 c. "Vision of St. Anthony" (Van Dyck) .. 50 50
1682 90 c. "Virgin and Child" (Van Eyck) .. 60 70
1683 $6 "The Immaculate Conception"
(Giovanni Tiepolo) .. .. 3·25 4·00
1678/83 .. .. *Set of 5* 4·75 5·50
MS1684 Two sheets. (a) 101×127 mm. $5 "Christ
appearing to his Mother" (detail) (Van der
Weyden). (b) 127×101 mm. $6 "The Infant Jesus
and the Young St. John" (Murillo) *Set of 2 sheets* 8·00 9·00

1996 (14 Feb). *Stars of Country and Western Music. Nos. 2014/38 of Antigua optd with T 114, but with lines spaced.*
1685 75 c. Travis Tritt 50 50
a. Sheetlet. Nos. 1685/92 .. 3·50
1686 75 c. Dwight Yoakam 50 50
1687 75 c. Billy Ray Cyrus 50 50
1688 75 c. Alan Jackson 50 50
1689 75 c. Garth Brooks 50 50
1690 75 c. Vince Gill 50 50
1691 75 c. Clint Black 50 50
1692 75 c. Eddie Rabbit 50 50
1693 75 c. Patsy Cline 50 50
a. Sheetlet. Nos. 1693/1700 .. 3·50
1694 75 c. Tanya Tucker 50 50
1695 75 c. Dolly Parton 50 50
1696 75 c. Anne Murray 50 50
1697 75 c. Tammy Wynette 50 50
1698 75 c. Loretta Lynn 50 50

1699 75 c. Reba McEntire 50 50
1700 75 c. Skeeter Davis 50 50
1701 75 c. Hank Snow 50 50
a. Sheetlet. Nos. 1701/8 .. 3·50
1702 75 c. Gene Autry 50 50
1703 75 c. Jimmie Rodgers 50 50
1704 75 c. Ernest Tubb 50 50
1705 75 c. Eddy Arnold 50 50
1706 75 c. Willie Nelson 50 50
1707 75 c. Johnny Cash 50 50
1708 75 c. George Jones 50 50
1685/1708 .. .. *Set of 24* 11·00 11·00
MS1709 Three sheets. (a) 100×70 mm. $6 Hank
Williams Jr. (b) 100×70 mm. $6 Hank Williams
Sr. (c) 70×100 mm. $6 Kitty Wells (*horiz*)
Set of 3 sheets 11·00 11·00

1996 (14 Feb). *Birds. Nos. 2067/81 of Antigua optd with T 124.*
1710 15 c. Magnificent Frigate Bird .. 10 10
1711 25 c. Blue-hooded Euphonia .. 10 10
1712 35 c. Eastern Meadowlark .. 15 20
1713 40 c. Red-billed Tropic Bird .. 20 25
1714 45 c. Greater Flamingo .. 20 25
1715 60 c. Yellow-faced Grassquit .. 25 30
1716 65 c. Yellow-billed Cuckoo .. 30 35
1717 70 c. Purple-throated Carib .. 30 35
1718 75 c. Bananaquit 35 40
1719 90 c. Painted Bunting 40 45
1720 $1.20, Red-legged Honeycreeper .. 55 60
1721 $2 Northern Jacana 90 95
1722 $5 Greater Antillean Bullfinch .. 2·25 2·40
1723 $10 Caribbean Elaenia .. .. 4·50 4·75
1724 $20 Brown Trembler .. .. 9·25 9·50
1710/24 .. .. *Set of 15* 19·00 20·00

1996 (2 Apr). *Birds. Nos. 2050, 2052, 2054 and 2056/7 of Antigua optd with T 111.*
1725 15 c. Bridled Quail Dove 40 30
1726 40 c. Purple-throated Carib (*vert*) .. 60 40
1727 $1 Broad-winged Hawk (*vert*) .. 1·25 1·00
1728 $4 Yellow Warbler .. .. 2·50 3·00
1725/8 .. .. *Set of 4* 4·25 4·25
MS1729 Two sheets. (a) 70×100 mm. $6 Female
Magnificent Frigate Bird (*vert*). (b) 100×70 mm.
$6 Black-billed Whistling Duck ducklings
Set of 2 sheets 8·50 8·50

1996 (13 June). *Prehistoric Animals. Nos. 2082/100 of Antigua optd with T 114, but with lines spaced (Nos. 1730/2 and 1745/7) or T 111 (others).*
1730 15 c. Head of Pachycephalosaurus .. 30 30
1731 20 c. Head of Afrovenator .. 30 30
1732 65 c. Centrosaurus 45 45
1733 75 c. Kronosaurus (*horiz*) .. 50 50
a. Sheetlet. Nos. 1733/44 .. 5·50
1734 75 c. Ichthyosaurus (*horiz*) .. 50 50
1735 75 c. Plesiosaurus (*horiz*) .. 50 50
1736 75 c. Archelon (*horiz*) .. 50 50
1737 75 c. Pair of Tyrannosaurus (*horiz*) .. 50 50
1738 75 c. Tyrannosaurus (*horiz*) .. 50 50
1739 75 c. Parasaurolophus (*horiz*) .. 50 50
1740 75 c. Pair of Parasaurolophus (*horiz*) .. 50 50
1741 75 c. Oviraptor (*horiz*) .. 50 50
1742 75 c. Protoceratops with eggs (*horiz*) .. 50 50
1743 75 c. Pteranodon and Protoceratops (*horiz*) 50 50
1744 75 c. Pair of Protoceratops (*horiz*) .. 50 50
1745 90 c. Pentaceratops drinking .. 60 60
1746 $1.20, Head of Tarbosaurus .. 75 75
1747 $5 Head of Styracosaurus .. 2·75 2·75
1730/47 .. .. *Set of 18* 10·00 10·00
MS1748 Two sheets, each 101×70 mm. (a) $6
Head of Corythosaurus (*horiz*) (b) $6 Head of
Carnotaurus (*horiz*) .. *Set of 2 sheets* 8·50 9·00

1996 (16 July). *Olympic Games, Atlanta. Previous Gold Medal Winners. Nos. 2101/7 of Antigua optd diagonally with T 116.*
1749 15 c. Al Oerter (U.S.A.) (discus – 1956,
1960, 1964, 1968) .. 25 25
1750 20 c. Greg Louganis (U.S.A.) (diving –
1984, 1988) 25 25
1751 65 c. Naim Suleymanoglu (Turkey)
(weightlifting – 1988) .. 55 55
1752 90 c. Louise Ritter (U.S.A.) (high jump –
1988) 70 70
1753 $1.20, Nadia Comaneci (Rumania)
(gymnastics – 1976) .. 85 85
1754 $5 Olga Boldarenko (Russia) (10,000
metres – 1988) .. .. 2·50 3·00
1749/54 .. .. *Set of 6* 4·50 5·00
MS1755 Two sheets, 106×76 mm. (a) $6 United
States crew (eight-oared shell – 1964). (b) $6
Lutz Hessilch (Germany) (cycling – 1988) (*vert*).
Set of 2 sheets 7·50 8·00

1996 (10 Sept). *18th World Scout Jamboree, Netherlands. Tents. Nos. 2203/9 of Antigua optd with T 116 diagonally.*
1756 $1.20, The Explorer Tent .. 1·00 1·00
a. Horiz strip of 3. Nos. 1756/8 .. 2·75
1757 $1.20, Camper tent .. .. 1·00 1·00
1758 $1.20, Wall tent .. .. 1·00 1·00
1759 $1.20, Trail tent .. .. 1·00 1·00
a. Horiz strip of 3. Nos. 1759/61 .. 2·75
1760 $1.20, Miner's tent .. .. 1·00 1·00
1761 $1.20, Voyager tent .. .. 1·00 1·00
1756/61 .. .. *Set of 6* 5·50 5·50
MS1762 Two sheets, each 76×106 mm. (a) $6
Scout and camp fire. (b) $6 Scout with back pack
(*vert*) .. .. *Set of 2 sheets* 7·50 8·00

1996 (25 Oct). *Centenary of Nobel Prize Trust Fund. Nos. 2226/44 of Antigua optd with T 120.*
1763 $1 Dag Hammarskjold (1961 Peace) .. 60 60
a. Sheetlet. Nos. 1763/71 .. 4·75
1764 $1 Georg Wittig (1979 Chemistry) .. 60 60
1765 $1 Wilhelm Ostwald (1909 Chemistry) .. 60 60

1766 $1 Robert Koch (1905 Medicine) .. 60 60
1767 $1 Karl Ziegler (1963 Chemistry) .. 60 60
1768 $1 Alexander Fleming (1945 Medicine) .. 60 60
1769 $1 Hermann Staudinger (1953 Chemistry) .. 60 60
1770 $1 Manfred Eigen (1967 Chemistry) .. 60 60
1771 $1 Arno Penzias (1978 Physics) .. 60 60
1772 $1 Shumal Agnon (1966 Literature) .. 60 60
a. Sheetlet. Nos. 1772/80 .. 4·75
1773 $1 Rudyard Kipling (1907 Literature) .. 60 60
1774 $1 Aleksandr Solzhenitsyn (1970
Literature) 60 60
1775 $1 Jack Steinburger (1988 Physics) .. 60 60
1776 $1 Andrei Sakharov (1975 Peace) .. 60 60
1777 $1 Otto Stern (1943 Physics) .. 60 60
1778 $1 John Steinbeck (1962 Literature) .. 60 60
1779 $1 Nadine Gordimer (1991 Literature) .. 60 60
1780 $1 William Faulkner (1949 Literature) .. 60 60
1763/80 .. .. *Set of 18* 9·50 9·50
MS1781 Two sheets, each 100×70 mm. (a) $6
Elie Wiesel (1986 Peace) (*vert*). (b) $6 Dalai
Lama (1989 Peace) (*vert*) .. *Set of 2 sheets* 8·00 8·50

1996 (14 Nov). *70th Birthday of Queen Elizabeth II. Nos. 2355/8 of Antigua optd with T 111.*
1782 $2 Queen Elizabeth II in blue dress .. 1·10 1·10
a. Strip of 3. Nos. 1782/4 .. 3·00
1783 $2 With bouquet .. .. 1·10 1·10
1784 $2 In Garter robes .. .. 1·10 1·10
1782/4 .. .. *Set of 3* 3·00 3·00
MS1785 96×111 mm. $6 Wearing white dress .. 3·50 3·75

1997 (28 Jan). *Christmas. Religious Paintings by Filippo Lippi. Nos. 2377/83 of Antigua optd with T 111.*
1786 60 c. "Madonna Enthroned" .. 35 35
1787 90 c. "Adoration of the Child and Saints" .. 55 55
1788 $1 "The Annunciation" .. 60 60
1789 $1.20, "Birth of the Virgin" .. 75 75
1790 $1.60, "Adoration of the Child" .. 90 90
1791 $1.75, "Madonna and Child" .. 1·00 1·00
1786/91 .. .. *Set of 6* 3·75 3·75
MS1792 Two sheets, each 76×106 mm. (a) $6
"Madonna and Child" (*different*). (b) $6 "The
Circumcision" .. *Set of 2 sheets* 5·50 5·75

1997 (24 Feb). *50th Anniv of Food and Agriculture Organization. Nos. 2121/4 of Antigua optd with T 114, but with lines spaced.*
1793 75 c. Woman buying produce from market .. 50 50
a. Horiz strip of 3. Nos. 1793/5 .. 1·60
1794 90 c. Women shopping 60 60
1795 $1.20, Women talking 70 70
1793/5 .. .. *Set of 3* 1·75 1·90
MS1796 100×70 mm. $6 Tractor .. 3·25 3·50

1997 (24 Feb). *90th Anniv of Rotary International (1995). Nos. 2125/6 of Antigua optd with T 114, but with lines spaced.*
1797 $5 Beach and rotary emblem .. 2·75 3·00
MS1798 74×104 mm. $6 National flag and
emblem .. .. 3·25 3·50

1997 (4 Apr). *50th Anniv of End of Second World War in Europe and the Pacific. Nos. 2108/16 and 2132/8 of Antigua optd with T 114 but with lines spaced (No. MS1813b) or with T 111 (others).*
1799 $1.20, Map of Berlin showing Russian
advance 55 60
a. Sheetlet. Nos. 1799/1806 .. 4·25
1800 $1.20, Russian tank and infantry .. 55 60
1801 $1.20, Street fighting in Berlin .. 55 60
1802 $1.20, German tank exploding .. 55 60
1803 $1.20, Russian air raid .. 55 60
1804 $1.20, German troops surrendering .. 55 60
1805 $1.20, Hoisting the Soviet flag on the
Reichstag 55 60
1806 $1.20, Captured German standards .. 55 60
1807 $1.20, Gen. Chiang Kai-shek and Chinese
guerrillas 55 60
a. Sheetlet. Nos. 1807/12 .. 4·25
1808 $1.20, Gen. Douglas MacArthur and beach
landing 55 60
1809 $1.20, Gen. Claire Chennault and U.S.
fighter aircraft .. 55 60
1810 $1.20, Brig. Orde Wingate and supply drop .. 55 60
1811 $1.20, Gen. Joseph Stilwell and U.S.
supply plane 55 60
1812 $1.20, Field-Marshal Bill Slim and loading
cow onto plane 55 60
1799/1812 .. .. *Set of 14* 8·50 8·75
MS1813 Two sheets, each 100×70 mm. (a) $3
Admiral Nimitz and aircraft carrier. (b) $6 Gen.
Konev (*vert*) .. .. *Set of 2 sheets* 4·25 4·50

1997 (25 Apr). *95th Birthday of Queen Elizabeth the Queen Mother. Nos. 2127/31 of Antigua optd with T 111.*
1814 $1.50, orange-brown, pale brown and black .. 70 75
a. Sheetlet. Nos. 1814/17×2 .. 5·50
1815 $1.50, multicoloured 70 75
1816 $1.50, multicoloured 70 75
1817 $1.50, multicoloured 70 75
1814/17 .. .. *Set of 4* 2·75 3·00
MS1818 102×27 mm. $6 multicoloured .. 2·75 3·00

1997 (25 Apr). *50th Anniv of United Nations. Nos. 2117/20 optd with T 114 but with lines spaced.*
1819 75 c. Signatures and Earl of Halifax .. 35 40
a. Horiz strip of 3. Nos. 1819/21 .. 1·25
1820 90 c. Virginia Gildersleeve .. 40 45
1821 $1.20, Harold Stassen 55 60
1819/21 .. .. *Set of 3* 1·25 1·40
MS1822 100×70 mm. $6 Pres. Franklin D.
Roosevelt .. .. 3·25 3·50

1997 (30 May). *Trains of the World.* Nos. 2210/25 of Antigua optd with *T* **114***, but with lines spaced (No.* **MS1838**) or with *T* **111** (others).

1823	35 c.	Trans-Gabon diesel train	15	20
1824	65 c.	Canadian Pacific diesel locomotive	30	35
1825	75 c.	Santa Fe Railway diesel locomotive, U.S.A.	35	40
1826	90 c.	High Speed Train, Great Britain	40	45
1827	$1.20,	"TGV" train, France	55	60
1828	$1.20,	Diesel locomotive, Australia	55	60
	a.	Sheetlet. Nos. 1828/36	5.00	
1829	$1.20,	"ETR 450" electric train, Italy	55	60
1830	$1.20,	Diesel locomotive, Thailand	55	60
1831	$1.20,	Pennsylvania Railroad stream-lined steam locomotive, U.S.A.	55	60
1832	$1.20,	Steam locomotive, South Africa	55	60
1833	$1.20,	Steam locomotive, Natal	55	60
1834	$1.20,	Rail gun, American Civil War	55	60
1835	$1.20,	Early steam locomotive (red livery), Great Britain	55	60
1836	$1.20,	Early steam locomotive (green livery), Great Britain	55	60
1837	$6	Amtrak diesel locomotive, U.S.A.	2.75	3.00
1823/37		*Set of 15*	9.50	10.50

MS1838 Two sheets, each 110×80 mm. (a) $6 Chinese steam locomotive (*vert*). (b) $6 "Indian-Pacific" diesel locomotive, Australia (*vert*)

	Set of 2 sheets	5.50	5.75

1997 (25 July). *Golden Wedding of Queen Elizabeth II and Prince Philip.* Nos. 1662/3 optd with "Golden Wedding of H.M. Queen Elizabeth II and H.R.H. Prince Philip 1947–1997" in gold.

1839	$7.50,	Type **122**	3.50	3.75
1840	$8	German bombers over St. Paul's Cathedral, London (*horiz*)	3.75	4.00

1997 (16 Sept). *Fungi.* Nos. 2274/82 of Antigua optd with *T* **114***, but with lines spaced.*

1841	75 c.	Hygrophoropsis aurantiaca	35	40
	a.	Horiz strip of 4. Nos. 1841/4	1.40	
1842	75 c.	Hygrophorus bakerensis	35	40
1843	75 c.	Hygrophorus conicus	35	40
1844	75 c.	Hygrophorus miniatus (Hygrocybe miniata)	35	40
1845	75 c.	Suillus brevipes	35	40
	a.	Horiz strip of 4. Nos. 1845/8	1.40	
1846	75 c.	Suillus luteus	35	40
1847	75 c.	Suillus granulatus	35	40
1848	75 c.	Suillus caerulescens	35	40
1841/8		*Set of 8*	2.75	3.25

MS1849 Two sheets, each 106×76 mm. (a) $6 Conocybe filaris. (b) $6 Hygrocybe flavescens

	Set of 2 sheets	5.50	5.75

1997 (16 Sept). *Birds.* Nos. 2140/64 of Antigua optd with *T* **114** with lines spaced (Nos. 1850/73) or *T* **111** (No. **MS1874**).

1850	75 c.	Purple-throated Carib	35	40
	a.	Sheetlet. Nos. 1850/61	4.25	
1851	75 c.	Antillean Crested Hummingbird	35	40
1852	75 c.	Bananaquit	35	40
1853	75 c.	Mangrove Cuckoo	35	40
1854	75 c.	Troupial	35	40
1855	75 c.	Green-throated Carib	35	40
1856	75 c.	Yellow Warbler	35	40
1857	75 c.	Blue-hooded Euphonia	35	40
1858	75 c.	Scaly-breasted Thrasher	35	40
1859	75 c.	Burrowing Owl	35	40
1860	75 c.	Carib Grackle	35	40
1861	75 c.	Adelaide's Warbler	35	40
1862	75 c.	Ring-necked Duck	35	40
	a.	Sheetlet. Nos. 1862/73	4.25	
1863	75 c.	Ruddy Duck	35	40
1864	75 c.	Green-winged Teal	35	40
1865	75 c.	Wood Duck	35	40
1866	75 c.	Hooded Merganser	35	40
1867	75 c.	Lesser Scaup	35	40
1868	75 c.	Black-billed Whistling Duck	35	40
1869	75 c.	Fulvous Whistling Duck	35	40
1870	75 c.	Bahama Pintail	35	40
1871	75 c.	Shoveler	35	40
1872	75 c.	Masked Duck	35	40
1873	75 c.	American Wigeon	35	40
1850/73		*Set of 24*	8.50	9.50

MS1874 Two sheets, each 104×74 mm. (a) $6 Head of Purple Gallinule. (b) $6 Heads of Blue-winged Teals

	Set of 2 sheets	5.50	5.75

1997 (3 Nov). *Sailing Ships.* Nos. 2283/301 of Antigua optd with *T* **116** diagonally.

1875	15 c.	H.M.S. *Resolution* (Cook)	10	10
1876	25 c.	*Mayflower* (Pilgrim Fathers)	10	15
1877	45 c.	*Santa Maria* (Columbus)	20	25
1878	75 c.	*Aemilia* (Dutch galleon)	35	40
1879	75 c.	*Soverign of the Seas* (English galleon)	35	40
1880	90 c.	H.M.S. *Victory* (ship of the line, 1765)	40	45
1881	$1.20,	As No. 1878	55	60
	a.	Sheetlet. Nos. 1881/6	3.25	
1882	$1.20,	As No. 1879	55	60
1883	$1.20,	*Royal Louis* (French galleon)	55	60
1884	$1.20,	H.M.S. *Royal George* (ship of the line)	55	60
1885	$1.20,	*Le Protecteur* (French frigate)	55	60
1886	$1.20,	As No. 1880	55	60
1887	$1.50,	As No. 1877	70	75
	a.	Sheetlet. Nos. 1887/92	4.25	
1888	$1.50,	*Vitoria* (Magellan)	70	75
1889	$1.50,	*Golden Hind* (Drake)	70	75
1890	$1.50,	As No. 1876	70	75
1891	$1.50,	*Griffin* (La Salle)	70	75
1892	$1.50,	As No. 1875	70	75
1875/92		*Set of 18*	9.00	9.25

MS1893 (a) 102×72 mm. $6 U.S.S. *Constitution* (frigate). (b) 98×67 mm. $6 Grande Hermine (Cartier)

	Set of 2 sheets	5.50	5.75

1997 (3 Nov). *Golden Wedding of Queen Elizabeth and Prince Philip.* Nos. 2464/70 of Antigua optd with *T* **111**.

1894	$1	Queen Elizabeth II	45	50
	a.	Sheetlet. Nos. 1894/9	2.75	
1895	$1	Royal coat of arms	45	50
1896	$1	Queen Elizabeth and Prince Philip at reception	45	50
1897	$1	Queen Elizabeth and Prince Philip in landau	45	50
1898	$1	Balmoral	45	50
1899	$1	Prince Philip	45	50
1894/9		*Set of 6*	2.75	3.00

MS1900 100×71 mm. $6 Queen Elizabeth with Prince Philip in naval uniform

	2.75	3.00

STAMP BOOKLETS

1977 (20 Dec). *Silver Jubilee.* No. SB2 of Antigua with cover optd "BARBUDA".

SB1	$8 booklet containing pane of 6 (No. 329a) and pane of 1 (No. 330a)		7.00

1978 (12 Oct). *25th Anniv of Coronation.* No. SB3 of Antigua with cover optd "BARBUDA".

SB2	$7.25, booklet containing pane of 6 (No. 421a) and pane of 1 (No. 423a)		2.50

1981 (27 July). *Royal Wedding* (1st issue). *Cover printed in grey,* 98×63 *mm, showing crown, bells and inscription. Stitched.*

SB3	$26 booklet containing panes of four (Nos. 566b, 568b, 570b)		7.00

The panes in this booklet each consist of two imperforate-between horizontal pairs.

1981 (12 Oct). *Royal Wedding* (3rd issue). No. SB4 of Antigua with cover optd "BARBUDA" in silver.

SB4	$11.50, booklet containing pane of 6 (No. 580a) and pane of 1 (No. 586a)		5.00

1982 (28 June). *South Atlantic Fund.* No. SB4 with contents surcharged.

SB5	$15 booklet containing pane of 6 (No. 617a) and pane of 1 (No. 623a)		4.75

REDONDA

DEPENDENCY OF ANTIGUA

Appendix

The following stamps were issued in anticipation of commercial and tourist development, philatelic mail being handled by a bureau in Antigua. Since at the present time the island is uninhabited, we do not list or stock these items. It is understood that the stamps are valid for the prepayment of postage in Antigua. Miniature sheets, imperforate stamps etc., are excluded from this section.

1979

Antigua 1976 *definitive issue optd* "REDONDA". 3, 5, 10, 25, 35, 50, 75 c., $1, $2.50, $5, $10.
Antigua Coronation Anniversary issue optd "REDONDA". 10, 30, 50, 90 c., $2.50.
Antigua World Cup Football Championship issue optd "REDONDA". 10, 15 c., $3.
Death Centenary of Sir Rowland Hill. 50, 90 c., $2.50, $3.
International Year of the Child. 25, 50 c., $1, $2.
Christmas. Paintings. 8, 50, 90 c., $3.

1980

Marine Life. 8, 25, 50 c., $4.
75th Anniv of Rotary International. 25, 50 c., $1, $2.
Birds of Redonda. 8, 10, 15, 25, 30, 50 c., $1, $2, $5.
Olympic Medal Winners, Lake Placid and Moscow. 8, 25, 50 c., $3.
80th Birthday of Queen Elizabeth the Queen Mother. 10 c., $2.50.
Christmas. Paintings. 8, 25, 50 c., $4.

1981

Royal Wedding. 25, 55 c., $4.
Christmas. Walt Disney Cartoon Characters. ½, 1, 2, 3, 4, 5, 10 c., $2.50, $3.
World Cup Football Championship, Spain (1982). 30 c. × 2, 50 c. × 2, $1 × 2, $2 × 2.

1982

Boy Scout Anniversaries. 8, 25, 50 c., $3, $5.
Butterflies. 8, 30, 50 c., $2.
21st Birthday of Princess of Wales. $2, $4.
Birth of Prince William of Wales. Optd on 21st Birthday of Princess of Wales issue. $2, $4.
Christmas. Walt Disney's "One Hundred and One Dalmatians". ½, 1, 2, 3, 4, 5, 10 c., $2.50, $3.

1983

Easter. 500th Birth Anniv of Raphael. 10, 50, 90 c., $4.
Bicentenary of Manned Flight. 10, 50, 90 c., $2.50.
Christmas. Walt Disney Cartoon Characters. "Deck the Halls". ½, 1, 2, 3, 4, 5, 10 c., $2.50, $3.

1984

Easter. Walt Disney Cartoon Characters. ½, 1, 2, 3, 4, 5, 10 c., $2, $4.
Olympic Games, Los Angeles. 10, 50, 90 c., $2.50.
Christmas. 50th Birthday of Donald Duck. 45, 60, 90 c., $2, $4.

1985

Birth Bicentenary of John J. Audubon (ornithologist) (1st issue). 60, 90 c., $1, $3.
Life and Times of Queen Elizabeth the Queen Mother. $1, $1.50, $2.50.
Royal Visit. 45 c., $1, $4.
150th Birth Anniv of Mark Twain (author). 25, 50 c., $1.50, $3.
Birth Bicentenaries of Grimm Brothers (folklorists). *Walt Disney Cartoon Characters.* 30, 60, 70 c., $4.

1986

Birth Bicentenary of John J. Audubon (ornithologist) (2nd issue). 90 c., $1, $1.50, $3.
Appearance of Halley's Comet. 5, 15, 55 c., $4.
Centenary of Statue of Liberty (1st issue). 20, 25, 30 c., $4.
60th Birthday of Queen Elizabeth II. 50, 60 c., $4.
Royal Wedding. 60 c., $1, $4.
Christmas (1st issue). *Disney characters in Hans Andersen Stories.* 30, 60, 70 c., $4.
Christmas (2nd issue). "Wind in the Willows" (Kenneth Grahame). 25, 50 c., $1.50, $3.

1987

"Capex '87" International Stamp Exhibition, Toronto. *Disney characters illustrating Art of Animation.* 25, 30, 50, 60, 70 c., $1.50, $3, $4.
Birth Centenary of Marc Chagall (artist). 10, 30, 40, 60, 90 c., $1, $3, $4.
Centenary of Statue of Liberty (2nd issue). 10, 15, 25, 30, 40, 60, 70, 90 c., $1, $2, $3, $4.
250th Death Anniv of Sir Isaac Newton (scientist). 20 c., $2.50.
750th Anniv of Berlin. $1, $4.
Bicentenary of U.S. Constitution. 30 c., $3.
16th World Scout Jamboree, Australia. 10 c., $4.

1988

500th Anniv of Discovery of America by Columbus (1992) (1st issue). 15, 30, 45, 60, 90 c., $1, $2, $3.
"Finlandia '88" International Stamp Exhibition, Helsinki. *Disney characters in Finnish scenes.* 1, 2, 3, 4, 5, 6 c., $5, $6.
Olympic Games, Seoul. 25, 60 c., $1.25, $3.
500th Birth Anniv of Titian. 10, 25, 40, 70, 90 c., $2, $3, $4.

1989

20th Anniv of First Manned Landing on Moon. Disney characters on Moon. ½, 1, 2, 3, 4, 5 c., $5, $6.
500th Anniv of Discovery of America by Columbus (1992) (2nd issue). *Pre-Columbian Societies.* 15, 45, 45, 50 c., $2, $2, $3, $3.
Christmas. Disney characters and Cars of 1950's. 25, 35, 45, 60 c., $1, $2, $3, $4.

1990

Christmas. Disney characters and Hollywood Cars. 25, 35, 40, 60 c., $1, $2, $4, $5.

1991

Nobel Prize Winners. 5, 15, 25, 40, 50 c., $1, $2, $4.

Ascension
DEPENDENCY OF ST. HELENA

Ascension, first occupied in 1815, was retained as a Royal Navy establishment from 1816 until 20 October 1922 when it became a dependency of St. Helena by Letters Patent.

Under Post Office regulations of 1850 (ratings) and 1854 (officers) mail from men of the Royal Navy serving abroad had the postage prepaid in Great Britain stamps, supplies of which were issued to each ship. Great Britain stamps used on Ascension before 1860 may have been provided by the naval officer in charge of the postal service.

The British G.P.O. assumed responsibility for such matters in 1860, but failed to send any stamps to the island until January 1867.

Until about 1880 naval mail, which made up most early correspondence, did not have the stamps cancelled until arrival in England. The prices quoted for Nos. Z1/3 and Z6 are for examples on cover or large piece showing the Great Britain stamps cancelled on arrival and an Ascension postmark struck elsewhere on the front of the envelope.

The use of British stamps ceased in December 1922.

The following postmarks were used on Great Britain stamps from Ascension:

Z 1   Z 2

Z 3   Z 4

Z 5

Postmark Type	Approx Period of Use	Diameter	Index Letter
Z 1	1862	20 mm	A
Z 2	1864–1872	20 mm	A
	1872–1878	21½ mm	A
	1879–1889	19½ mm	A
	1891–1894	21½ mm	C
	1894–1902	22 mm	A
	1903–1907	20½ mm	A
	1908–1920	21 mm	A or none
	1909–1920	23 mm	C sideways (1909), none (1910–11), B (1911–20)
Z 3	1920–1922	24 mm	none
Z 4	1897–1903 Registered	24 mm	none
Z 5	1900–1902 Registered	28 mm	C
	1903–1904 Registered	29 mm	A

Postmark Type Z 1 appears in the G.P.O. proof book for 1858, but the first recorded use is 3 November 1862.

Forged postmarks exist. Those found most frequently are genuine postmarks of the post-1922 period with earlier date slugs fraudulently inserted, namely a 20 mm postmark as Type Z 2 (because of the shape of the "O" in "ASCENSION" this is often known as the Square O postmark) and a 24 mm postmark as Type Z 3 but with the index letter A.

Stamps of GREAT BRITAIN *cancelled with Types Z 2/5. Prices quoted for Nos. Z 1/6 are for complete covers.*

Line-engraved issues.

Z 1	1d. red-brown (1855)	£2750
Z 2	1d. rose-red (1864–79)	From £1300

Plate Nos. 71, 74, 76, 78, 83, 85, 96, 100, 102, 103, 104, 122, 134, 168, 154, 155, 157, 160, 168, 178.

Surface-printed issues (1856–1883).

Z 2a	6d. lilac (1856)	
Z 3	6d. lilac (1865) (Plate No. 5)	£2750
Z 4	1s. green (1865) (Plate No. 4)	
Z 5	1s. green (1867) (Plate No. 7)	
Z 6	6d. grey (1874) (Plate Nos. 15, 16)	£2000
Z 6a	6d. on 6d. lilac (1883)	
Z 7	1d. lilac (1881) (16 dots)	28·00

1887–92.

Z 8	½d. vermilion	42·00
Z 9	1½d. purple and green	£170
Z 10	2d. green and carmine	90·00
Z 11	2½d. purple/blue	40·00
Z 12	3d. purple/yellow	£160
Z 13	4d. green and brown	£130
Z 14	4½d. green and carmine	£350
Z 15	5d. dull purple and blue	£130
Z 16	6d. purple/rose-red	£110
Z 17	9d. purple and blue	£300
Z 17a	10d. dull purple and carmine	£375
Z 18	1s. green	£300

1900.

Z 19	½d. blue-green	42·00
Z 20	1s. green and carmine	£325

King Edward VII issues (1902–1911).

Z 21	½d. green	27·00
Z 22	1d. red	16·00
Z 23	1½d. purple and green	90·00
Z 24	2d. green and carmine	65·00
Z 25	2½d. blue	60·00
Z 26	3d. purple/yellow	90·00
Z 27	4d. green and brown	£275
Z 28	4d. orange (1909)	£110
Z 29	5d. purple and ultramarine	£110
Z 30	6d. purple	£100
Z 31	7d. grey-black (1910)	£225
Z 32	9d. purple and ultramarine (1910)	£170
Z 32a	10d. dull purple and scarlet	£200
Z 33	1s. green and carmine	65·00
Z 33a	2s. 6d. dull reddish purple (1911)	£500
Z 34	5s. carmine	£750
Z 35	10s. ultramarine	£1100
Z 35a	£1 green	£2250

1911–12. T 98/9 of Great Britain.

Z 36	½d. green (Die A)	60·00
Z 37	½d. yellow-green (Die B)	27·00
Z 38	1d. scarlet (Die B)	45·00

1912. T 101/2 of Great Britain.

Z 38a	½d. green	45·00
Z 38b	1d. scarlet	45·00

1912–22.

Z 39	½d. green (1913)	25·00
Z 40	1d. scarlet (1913)	16·00
Z 41	1½d. red-brown (1913)	35·00
Z 42	2d. orange (Die I)	30·00
Z 42a	2d. orange (Die II) (1921)	£225
Z 43	2½d. blue	38·00
Z 44	3d. violet	50·00
Z 45	4d. grey-green (1913)	70·00
Z 46	5d. brown (1913)	70·00
Z 47	6d. purple (1913)	60·00
Z 47a	7d. green (1913)	£250
Z 47b	8d. black/yellow (1913)	£275
Z 48	9d. agate (1913)	£190
Z 49	9d. olive-green (1922)	£475
Z 50	10d. turquoise-blue (1913)	£190
Z 51	1s. bistre (1913)	£100
Z 52	2s. 6d. brown (1918)	£700
Z 53	5s. rose-red (1919)	

Supplies of some values do not appear to have been sent to the island and known examples originate from maritime or, in the case of high values, philatelic mail.

```
PRICES FOR STAMPS ON COVER TO 1945
    Nos. 1/34    from × 5
    Nos. 35/7    from × 10
    Nos. 38/47   from × 6
```

ASCENSION

(1)   Line through "P" of "POSTAGE" (R. 3/6)

1922 (2 Nov). *Stamps of St. Helena, showing Government House or the Wharf, optd with T 1 by D.L.R.*

(a) Wmk Mult Script CA

1	½d. black and green	3·25	11·00
	w. Wmk reversed	£300	
2	1d. green	3·75	11·00
3	1½d. rose-scarlet	14·00	45·00
4	2d. black and grey	13·00	12·00
	a. Line through "P" of "POSTAGE"	£160	£160
5	3d. bright blue	12·00	15·00
6	8d. black and dull purple	24·00	42·00
7	2s. black and blue/blue	80·00	£110
8	3s. black and violet	£120	£150

(b) Wmk Mult Crown CA

9	1s. black/green (R.)	26·00	42·00
1/9		Set of 9	£250 £375
1/9 Optd "Specimen"		Set of 9	£600

Nos. 1, 4 and 6/8 are on special printings which were not issued without overprint.

Examples of all values are known showing a forged Ascension postmark dated "MY 24 23".

PLATE FLAWS ON THE 1924–33 ISSUE. Many constant plate varieties exist on both the vignette and duty plates of this issue.

The three major varieties are illustrated and listed below with prices for mint examples. Fine used stamps showing these flaws are worth a considerable premium over the mint prices quoted.

This issue utilised the same vignette plate as the St. Helena 1922–36 set so that these flaws occur there also.

2 Badge of St. Helena

Broken mainmast. Occurs on R.2/1 of all values.

Torn flag. Occurs on R.4/6 of all values except the 5d. Retouched on sheets of ½d. and 1d. printed after 1927.

Cleft rock. Occurs on R.5/1 of all values.

Broken scroll. Occurs on R. 1/4 of 1½d. only

(Typo D.L.R.)

1924 (20 Aug)–**33.** *Wmk Mult Script CA. Chalk-surfaced paper. P 14.*

10	2	½d. grey-black and black	3·00	11·00
		a. Broken mainmast	48·00	
		b. Torn flag	60·00	
		c. Cleft rock	42·00	
11		1d. grey-black and deep blue-green	4·75	6·50
		a. Broken mainmast	55·00	
		b. Torn flag	65·00	
		c. Cleft rock	48·00	
11d		1d. grey-black & brt blue-green (1933)	75·00	£300
		da. Broken mainmast	£275	
		dc. Cleft rock	£250	
12		1½d. rose-red	6·00	24·00
		a. Broken mainmast	65·00	
		b. Torn flag	65·00	
		c. Cleft rock	60·00	
		d. Broken scroll	70·00	
13		2d. grey-black and grey	9·00	5·50
		a. Broken mainmast	70·00	
		b. Torn flag	70·00	
		c. Cleft rock	65·00	
14		3d. blue	6·00	11·00
		a. Broken mainmast	65·00	
		b. Torn flag	65·00	
		c. Cleft rock	60·00	
15		4d. grey-black and black/yellow	45·00	75·00
		a. Broken mainmast	£170	
		b. Torn flag	£170	
		c. Cleft rock	£150	
15d		5d. purple and olive-green (8.27)	10·00	20·00
		da. Broken mainmast	£100	
		dc. Cleft rock	90·00	
16		6d. grey-black and bright purple	45·00	80·00
		a. Broken mainmast	£225	
		b. Torn flag	£225	
		c. Cleft rock	£190	

```
17   2   8d. grey-black and bright violet      .. 12·00 40·00
           a. Broken mainmast     ..    ..    £110
           b. Torn flag           ..    ..    £110
           c. Cleft rock          ..    ..    90·00
18       1s. black and brown      ..    ..    18·00 45·00
           a. Broken mainmast     ..    ..    £130
           b. Torn flag           ..    ..    £130
           c. Cleft rock          ..    ..    £110
19       2s. grey-black and blue/blue   ..     55·00 85·00
           a. Broken mainmast     ..    ..    £225
           b. Torn flag           ..    ..    £225
           c. Cleft rock          ..    ..    £190
20       3s. grey-black and black/blue  ..     80·00 85·00
           a. Broken mainmast     ..    ..    £325
           b. Torn flag           ..    ..    £325
           c. Cleft rock          ..    ..    £300
10/20    ..    ..    Set of 12    £250  £425
10/20 Optd "Specimen"    ..    Set of 12   £500
```

3 Georgetown   4 Ascension Island

(Des and recess D.L.R.)

1934 (2 July). *T* **3/4** *and similar designs. Wmk Mult Script CA. P* 14.

```
21   3   ½d. black and violet     ..    ..    90    80
22   4   1d. black and emerald    ..    ..    1·75  1·25
23       1½d. black and scarlet   ..    ..    1·75  2·25
24   4   2d. black and orange     ..    ..    1·75  2·50
25       3d. black and ultramarine      ..    1·75  1·50
26       5d. black and blue       ..    ..    2·25  3·25
27   4   8d. black and sepia      ..    ..    4·25  4·75
28       1s. black and carmine    ..    ..    18·00 6·50
29   4   2s. 6d. black and bright purple ..   35·00 32·00
30       5s. black and brown      ..    ..    45·00 55·00
21/30    ..    ..    Set of 10    95·00 £100
21/30 Perf "Specimen"   ..    Set of 10   £250
```
Designs: *Horiz*—1½d. The Pier; 3d. Long Beach; 5d. Three Sisters; 1s. Sooty Tern and Wideawake Fair; 5s. Green Mountain.

1935 (6 May). *Silver Jubilee. As Nos. 91/4 of Antigua, but ptd by Waterlow. P* 11 × 12.

```
31   1½d. deep blue and scarlet ..    ..    3·50  5·50
       l. Kite and horizontal log   ..    85·00
32   2d. ultramarine and grey   ..    ..    11·00 22·00
       l. Kite and horizontal log   ..    £160
33   5d. green and indigo       ..    ..    16·00 23·00
       k. Kite and vertical log     ..    £200
       l. Kite and horizontal log   ..    £250
34   1s. slate and purple       ..    ..    22·00 27·00
       l. Kite and horizontal log   ..    £275
31/4   ..    ..    Set of 4    48·00 70·00
31/4 Perf "Specimen"   ..    Set of 4   £160
```
For illustrations of plate varieties see Catalogue Introduction.

1937 (19 May). *Coronation. As Nos. 95/7 of Antigua, but printed by D.L.R. P* 14.

```
35   1d. green       ..    ..    50    50
36   2d. orange      ..    ..    1·50  40
37   3d. bright blue ..    ..    1·50  50
35/7   ..    ..    Set of 3    3·25  1·25
35/7 Perf "Specimen"   ..    Set of 3   £130
```

10 The Pier

Long centre bar to "E" in "GEORGETOWN" (R. 2/3)

"Davit" flaw (R. 5/1) (all ptgs of 1½d. and 2s. 6d.)

(Recess D.L.R.)

1938 (12 May)-53. *Horiz designs as King George V issue, but modified and with portrait of King George VI as in T* **10.** *Wmk Mult Script CA. P* 13½.

```
38   3   ½d. black and violet            ..    ..    3·00  1·00
           a. Long centre bar to E       ..    70·00
           b. Perf 13. Black and bluish violet (17.5.44) ..   70  1·50
           ba. Long centre bar to E      ..    32·00
39   –   1d. black and green             ..    ..    40·00 7·50
39a  –   1d. black and yellow-orange (8.7.40) ..  14·00 9·00
           b. Perf 13 (5.42)             ..    45    60
           c. Perf 14 (17.2.49)          ..    70   16·00
39d  –   1d. black and green, p 13 (1.6.49)   ..    30    30
40  10   1½d. black and vermilion        ..    3·00  1·40
           a. Davit flaw                 ..    £120
           b. Perf 13 (17.5.44)          ..    85    80
           ba. Davit flaw                ..    65·00
           c. Perf 14 (17.2.49)          ..    2·75 13·00
           ca. Davit flaw                ..    £120
40d  –   1½d. black and rose-carmine, p 14 (1.6.49)  55  80
           da. Davit flaw                ..    60·00
           db. Black and carmine ..    6·50  5·00
           dba. Davit flaw               ..    £170
           e. Perf 13 (25.2.53)          ..    45    5·50
           ea. Davit flaw                ..    55·00
41   –   2d. black and red-orange        ..    3·50  1·00
           a. Perf 13 (17.5.44)          ..    80    40
           b. Perf 14 (17.2.49)          ..    2·75 35·00
41c  –   2d. black and scarlet, p 14 (1.6.49)   ..    50    75
42   –   3d. black and ultramarine       ..    £100 26·00
42a  –   3d. black and grey (8.7.40)      ..    15·00 90
           b. Perf 13 (17.5.44)          ..    70    80
42c  –   4d. black and ultramarine (8.7.40)  ..  11·00 3·25
           d. Perf 13 (17.5.44)          ..    4·50  3·00
43   –   6d. black and blue              ..    ..    9·00  90
           a. Perf 13 (17.5.44)          ..    9·00  4·25
44   3   1s. black and sepia             ..    ..    12·00 1·50
           a. Perf 13 (17.5.44)          ..    4·75  2·00
45  10   2s. 6d. black and deep carmine   ..    40·00 7·50
           a. Frame printed double, once albino £2250
           b. Perf 13 (17.5.44)          ..    £475  £225
           c. Perf 13 (17.5.44)          ..    35·00 32·00
           ca. Davit flaw                ..    £425
46   –   5s. black and yellow-brown      ..    £110  7·50
           a. Perf 13 (17.5.44)          ..    48·00 26·00
47   –   10s. black and bright purple    ..    £110 42·00
           a. Perf 13 (17.5.44)          ..    65·00 55·00
38/47a   ..    ..    Set of 16    £275 90·00
38/47 Perf "Specimen"   ..    Set of 13   £450
```
Designs: *Horiz*—1d. (Nos. 39/c), 2d., 4d. Green Mountain; 1d. (No. 39d), 6d., 10s. Three Sisters; 3d., 5s. Long Beach.

1946 (21 Oct). *Victory. As Nos. 110/11 of Antigua.*

```
48   2d. red-orange    ..    ..    40    40
49   4d. blue          ..    ..    40    30
48/9 Perf "Specimen"   ..    Set of 2   £140
```

1948 (20 Oct). *Royal Silver Wedding. As Nos. 112/13 of Antigua.*

```
50   3d. black          ..    ..    50    30
51   10s. bright purple ..    ..    45·00 38·00
```

1949 (10 Oct). *75th Anniv of Universal Postal Union. As Nos. 114/17 of Antigua.*

```
52   3d. carmine        ..    ..    1·40  1·00
53   4d. deep blue      ..    ..    3·50  1·10
54   6d. olive          ..    ..    3·75  2·50
55   1s. blue-black     ..    ..    3·75  1·50
52/5   ..    ..    Set of 4    11·00 5·50
```

1953 (2 June). *Coronation. As No. 120 of Antigua.*

```
56   3d. black and grey-black   ..    ..    1·00  1·50
```

15 Water Catchment

(Recess B.W.)

1956 (19 Nov). *T* **15** *and similar horiz designs. Wmk Mult Script CA. P* 13.

```
57   ½d. black and brown ..    ..    10    30
58   1d. black and magenta     ..    ..    1·50  60
59   1½d. black and orange..    ..    30    60
60   2d. black and carmine-red  ..    1·25  50
61   2½d. black and orange-brown ..    85    80
62   3d. black and blue        ..    ..    2·25  60
63   4d. black and deep turquoise-green ..  1·25 1·40
64   6d. black and indigo      ..    ..    1·25  90
65   7d. black and deep olive  ..    1·00  1·00
66   1s. black and vermilion   ..    1·00  90
67   2s. 6d. black and deep dull purple ..  27·00 6·50
68   5s. black and blue-green  ..    35·00 17·00
69   10s. black and purple..    ..    48·00 35·00
57/69   ..    ..    Set of 13    £110 60·00
```
Designs:—1d. Map of Ascension; 1½d. View of Georgetown; 2d. Map showing cable network; 2½d. Mountain road; 3d. White-tailed Tropic Bird; 4d. Yellow-finned Tuna; 6d. Rollers on the seashore; 7d. Young turtles; 1s. Land Crab; 2s. 6d. Sooty Tern; 5s. Perfect Crater; 10s. View of Ascension from North-west.

STANLEY GIBBONS STAMP COLLECTING SERIES

Introductory booklets on *How to Start, How to Identify Stamps* and *Collecting by Theme.* A series of well illustrated guides at a low price. Write for details.

28 Brown Booby   42 Satellite Station

(Des after photos by N. P. Ashmole. Photo Harrison)

1963 (23 May). *T* **28** *and similar horiz designs. W w* **12.** *P* 14×14½.

```
70   1d. black, lemon and new blue   ..    70    30
71   1½d. black, cobalt and ochre    ..    1·00  50
       a. Cobalt omitted             ..    75·00
72   2d. black, grey and bright blue ..    1·00  30
73   3d. black, magenta and turquoise-blue ..   1·00  30
74   4½d. black, bistre-brown and new blue ..   1·00  30
       w. Wmk inverted               ..    £180
75   6d. bistre, black and yellow-green ..   1·00  30
76   7d. black, brown and reddish violet    1·00  30
77   10d. black, greenish yellow and blue-green  1·00  30
78   1s. multicoloured ..    ..    1·00  30
79   1s. 6d. multicoloured  ..    4·00  1·75
80   2s. 6d. multicoloured  ..    5·50  6·00
81   5s. multicoloured  ..    7·00  5·50
82   10s. multicoloured  ..    13·00 6·50
83   £1 multicoloured  ..    20·00 8·00
70/83   ..    ..    Set of 14    55·00 27·00
```
Designs:—1½d. White-capped Noddy; 2d. White Tern; 3d. Red-billed Tropic Bird; 4½d. Common Noddy; 6d. Sooty Tern; 7d. Ascension Frigate Bird; 10d. Blue-faced Booby; 1s. White-tailed Tropic Bird; 1s. 6d. Red-billed Tropic Bird; 2s. 6d. Madeiran Storm Petrel; 5s. Red-footed Booby (brown phase); 10s. Ascension Frigate Birds; £1 Red-footed Booby (white phase).

1963 (4 June). *Freedom from Hunger. As No. 146 of Antigua.*

```
84   1s. 6d. carmine    ..    ..    ..    1·40  40
```

1963 (2 Sept). *Red Cross Centenary. As Nos. 147/8 of Antigua.*

```
85   3d. red and black  ..    ..    3·50  75
86   1s. 6d. red and blue ..    ..    7·50  2·00
```

1965 (17 May). *I.T.U. Centenary. As Nos. 166/7 of Antigua.*

```
87   3d. magenta and bluish violet  ..    1·00  35
88   6d. turquoise-blue and light chestnut  1·25  35
```

1965 (25 Oct). *International Co-operation Year. As Nos. 168/9 of Antigua.*

```
89   1d. reddish purple and turquoise-green ..   50    30
90   6d. deep bluish green and lavender ..   1·00  50
```

1966 (24 Jan). *Churchill Commemoration. As Nos. 170/3 of Antigua.*

```
91   1d. new blue       ..    ..    50    50
92   3d. deep green     ..    ..    2·75  1·10
93   6d. brown          ..    ..    3·50  1·25
94   1s. 6d. bluish violet  ..    4·50  1·75
91/4   ..    ..    Set of 4    10·00 4·25
```

1966 (1 July). *World Cup Football Championships. As Nos. 176/7 of Antigua.*

```
95   3d. violet, yellow-green, lake and yell-brn  1·25  30
96   6d. chocolate, blue-green, lake & yellow-brn  1·50  40
```

1966 (20 Sept). *Inauguration of W.H.O. Headquarters, Geneva. As Nos. 178/9 of Antigua.*

```
97   3d. black, yellow-green and light blue  1·75  55
98   1s. 6d. black, light purple and yellow-brown  4·25  1·25
```

(Des V. Whiteley. Photo Harrison)

1966 (7 Nov). *Opening of Apollo Communications Satellite Earth Station. W w* **12.** *(sideways.) P* 14 × 14½.

```
99  42   4d. black and reddish violet  ..    15    15
100      8d. black and deep bluish green ..   15    20
101      1s. 3d. black and olive-brown  ..    20    25
102      2s. 6d. black and turquoise-blue..   25    35
99/102   ..    ..    Set of 4    65    85
```

43 B.B.C. Emblem   44 Human Rights Emblem and Chain Links

(Des B.B.C. staff. Photo, Queen's head and emblem die-stamped, Harrison)

1966 (1 Dec). *Opening of B.B.C. Relay Station. W w* **12.** *P* 14½.

```
103 43   1d. gold and ultramarine  ..    ..    10    15
104      3d. gold and myrtle-green  ..    15    20
         w. Wmk inverted            ..    75    1·25
105      6d. gold and reddish violet  ..    15    20
106      1s. 6d. gold and red      ..    ..    15    25
103/6   ..    ..    Set of 4    50    70
```

1967 (1 Jan). *20th Anniv of U.N.E.S.C.O. As Nos. 196/8 of Antigua.*

107	3d. slate-violet, red, yellow and orange		2·25	90
108	6d. orange-yellow, violet and deep olive		3·50	1·25
109	1s. 6d. black, bright purple and orange		5·50	1·60
107/9		*Set of 3*	10·00	3·25

(Des and litho Harrison)

1968 (8 July). *Human Rights Year.* W w **12** (*sideways**). P 14½×14.

110	**44** 6d. light orange, red and black		20	15
111	1s. 6d. light grey-blue, red and black		30	20
112	2s. 6d. light green, red and black		35	20
	w. Wmk Crown to right of CA		£200	
110/12		*Set of 3*	75	50

*The normal sideways watermark shows Crown to left of CA, as seen from the back of the stamp.

45 Black Durgon ("Ascension   46 H.M.S. *Rattlesnake*
Black-Fish")

(Des M. Farrar Bell. Litho D.L.R.)

1968 (23 Oct). *Fishes* (1st series). T **45** and similar horiz designs. W w **12** (*sideways**). P 13.

113	4d. black, slate and turquoise-blue		40	30
114	8d. multicoloured		50	55
	w. Wmk Crown to right of CA		£180	
115	1s. 9d. multicoloured		60	60
116	2s. 3d. multicoloured		70	60
113/16		*Set of 4*	2·00	1·25

Designs:—8d. Scribbled Filefish ("Leather-jacket"); 1s. 9d. Yellow-finned Tuna; 2s. 3d. Short-finned Mako.
*The normal sideways watermark shows Crown to left of CA, as seen from the back of the stamp.
See also Nos. 117/20 and 126/9.

(Des M. Farrar Bell. Litho D.L.R.)

1969 (3 Mar). *Fishes* (2nd series). Horiz designs as T **45**. Multicoloured. W w **12** (*sideways**). P 13.

117	4d. Sailfish		1·00	80
118	6d. White Seabream ("Old Wife")		1·25	1·00
119	1s. 6d. Yellowtail		2·00	2·00
120	2s. 11d. Rock Hind ("Jack")		3·00	2·25
117/20		*Set of 4*	6·50	5·50

(Des L. Curtis. Photo Harrison)

1969 (1 Oct). *Royal Naval Crests* (1st series). T **46** and similar vert designs. W w **12** (*sideways**). P 14×14½.

121	4d. multicoloured		60	15
122	9d. multicoloured		80	15
123	1s. 9d. deep blue, pale blue and gold		1·40	25
124	2s. 3d. multicoloured		1·60	30
121/4		*Set of 4*	4·00	75
MS125	165×105 mm. Nos. 121/4. P 14½		7·50	9·50
	w. Wmk Crown to right of CA		£450	

Designs:—9d. H.M.S. *Weston*; 1s. 9d. H.M.S. *Undaunted*; 2s. 3d. H.M.S. *Eagle.*
*The normal sideways watermark shows Crown to left of CA, as seen from the back of the stamp.
See also Nos. 130/4, 149/53, 154/8 and 166/70.

(Des M. Farrar Bell. Litho D.L.R.)

1970 (6 Apr). *Fishes* (3rd series). Horiz designs as T **45**. Multicoloured. W w **12** (*sideways**). P 14.

126	4d. Wahoo		4·00	2·00
127	9d. Ascension Jack ("Coalfish")		4·00	2·00
	w. Wmk Crown to right of CA		4·00	1·75
128	1s. 9d. Pompano Dolphin		5·00	2·75
129	2s. 6d. Squirrelfish ("Soldier")		5·00	2·75
	w. Wmk Crown to right of CA		5·00	2·50
126/9		*Set of 4*	16·00	8·50

*The normal sideways watermark shows Crown to left of CA, as seen from the back of the stamp.

(Des L. Curtis. Photo D.L.R.)

1970 (7 Sept). *Royal Naval Crests* (2nd series). Designs as T **46**. Multicoloured. W w **12**. P 12½.

130	4d. H.M.S. *Penelope*		1·50	65
131	9d. H.M.S. *Carlisle*		2·00	90
132	1s. 6d. H.M.S. *Amphion*		2·50	1·25
133	2s. 6d. H.M.S. *Magpie*		2·75	1·50
130/3		*Set of 4*	8·00	3·75
MS134	153 × 96 mm. Nos. 130/3.		14·00	11·00

50 Early Chinese Rocket   51 Course of the *Quest*

(Des V. Whiteley. Litho Format)

1971 (15 Feb). *Decimal Currency. The Evolution of Space Travel.* T **50** and similar multicoloured designs. W w **12** (*sideways on horiz designs*). P 14.

135	½p. Type 50		15	20
136	1p. Medieval Arab Astronomers		20	20
137	1½p. Tycho Brahe's Observatory, Quadrant and Supernova		30	30
138	2p. Galileo, Moon and Telescope		40	30
139	2½p. Isaac Newton, Instruments and Apple		1·00	70
140	3½p. Harrison's Chronometer and Ship		1·50	70
141	4½p. Space Rocket taking-off		1·25	60
142	7½p. World's largest Telescope, Palomar		1·00	60
143	7½p. World's largest Radio Telescope, Jodrell Bank		4·00	1·40
144	10p. Mariner VII and Mars		3·50	1·75
145	12½p. Sputnik II and Space Dog, Laika		6·00	2·00
146	25p. Walking in Space		7·00	2·25
147	50p. Apollo XI Crew on Moon		5·00	2·50
148	£1 Future Space Research Station		5·00	2·50
135/48		*Set of 14*	32·00	16·00

The ½p, 1p, 4½p. and 25p. are vertical, and the remainder are horizontal.

(Des L. Curtis. Photo D.L.R.)

1971 (15 Nov). *Royal Naval Crests* (3rd series). Designs as T **46**. Multicoloured. W w **12**. P 13.

149	2p. H.M.S. *Phoenix*		1·50	30
150	4p. H.M.S. *Milford*		1·75	55
151	9p. H.M.S. *Pelican*		2·25	80
152	15p. H.M.S. *Oberon*		5·00	1·00
149/52		*Set of 4*	7·00	2·40
MS153	151×104 mm. Nos. 149/52		8·00	15·00

(Des L. Curtis. Litho Questa)

1972 (29 May). *Royal Naval Crests* (4th series). Multicoloured designs as T **46**. W w **12** (*sideways**). P 14.

154	1½p. H.M.S. *Lowestoft*		60	50
155	3p. H.M.S. *Auckland*		65	75
156	6p. H.M.S. *Nigeria*		70	1·25
157	17½p. H.M.S. *Bermuda*		1·50	2·50
154/7		*Set of 4*	3·00	4·50
MS158	157×93 mm. Nos. 154/7.		3·00	7·50
	w. Wmk Crown to right of CA		£200	

*The normal sideways watermark shows Crown to left of CA, as seen from the back of the stamp.

(Des J. Cooter. Litho Questa)

1972 (2 Aug). *50th Anniv of Shackleton's Death.* T **51** and similar multicoloured designs. W w **12** (*sideways on 4 and 7½p.*). P 14.

159	2½p. Type 51		55	60
160	4p. Shackleton and *Quest* (horiz)		60	70
161	7½p. Shackleton's cabin and *Quest* (horiz)		65	75
162	11p. Shackleton's statue and memorial		75	1·00
159/62		*Set of 4*	2·25	2·75
MS163	139 × 114 mm. Nos. 159/62 (wmk sideways)	2·25	6·00

52 Land Crab and Short-finned
Mako

(Des (from photograph by D. Groves) and photo Harrison)

1972 (20 Nov). *Royal Silver Wedding. Multicoloured; background colour given.* W w **12**. P 14 × 14½.

164	**52** 2p. bright bluish violet.		15	10
165	16p. rose-carmine		35	30

(Des L. Curtis. Litho J.W.)

1973 (28 May). *Royal Naval Crests* (5th series). Multicoloured designs as T **46**. W w **12** (*sideways**). P 14.

166	2p. H.M.S. *Birmingham*		2·50	1·00
167	4p. H.M.S. *Cardiff*		3·00	1·00
168	9p. H.M.S. *Penzance*		4·00	1·25
169	13p. H.M.S. *Rochester*		4·50	1·50
	w. Wmk Crown to right of CA		7·00	
166/9		*Set of 4*	12·50	4·25
MS170	109×152 mm. Nos. 166/9.		28·00	10·00

*The normal sideways watermark shows Crown to left of CA on 2, 4, 13p. and MS170, or Crown to right of CA on 9p., as seen from the back of the stamp.

53 Green Turtle

(Des V. Whiteley Studio. Litho Enschedé)

1973 (28 Aug). *Turtles.* T **53** and similar triangular designs. Multicoloured. W w **12**. P 13½.

171	4p. Type 53		3·75	1·25
172	9p. Loggerhead turtle		4·00	1·50
173	12p. Hawksbill turtle		4·25	1·75
171/3		*Set of 3*	11·00	4·00

54 Sergeant, R.M. Light   55 Letter and H.Q., Berne
Infantry, 1900

(Des G. Drummond from paintings by C. Stadden. Litho Walsall)

1973 (31 Oct). *50th Anniv of Departure of Royal Marines from Ascension.* T **54** and similar vert designs. Multicoloured. W w **12** (*sideways**). P 14.

174	2p. Type 54		2·00	2·00
175	6p. R.M. Private, 1816		3·00	1·75
176	12p. R.M. Light Infantry Officer, 1880		3·50	2·25
	w. Wmk Crown to right of CA		24·00	
177	20p. R.M. Artillery Colour Sergeant, 1910		4·00	2·50
174/7		*Set of 4*	11·00	7·00

*The normal sideways watermark shows Crown to left of CA, as seen from the back of the stamp.

1973 (14 Nov). *Royal Wedding. As Nos. 165/6 of Anguilla. Centre multicoloured.* W w **12** (*sideways*). P 13½.

178	2p. ochre		15	10
179	18p. dull blue-green		25	15

(Des PAD Studio. Litho Questa)

1974 (27 Mar). *Centenary of U.P.U.* T **55** and similar horiz design. Multicoloured. W w **12**. P 14½ × 14.

180	2p. Type 55		25	30
181	9p. Hermes and U.P.U. monument		40	45

56 Churchill as a Boy, and Birthplace, Blenheim Palace

(Des J.W. Litho Questa)

1974 (30 Nov). *Birth Centenary of Sir Winston Churchill.* T **56** and similar horiz design. Multicoloured. No wmk. P 14.

182	5p. Type 56		25	35
183	25p. Churchill as statesman, and U.N. Building		40	75
MS184	93 × 87 mm. Nos. 182/3.		1·25	2·50

57 "Skylab 3" and Photograph of Ascension

(Des PAD Studio. Litho Questa)

1975 (20 Mar). *Space Satellites.* T **57** and similar horiz design. Multicoloured. W w **12** (*sideways*). P 14.

185	2p. Type 57		30	30
186	18p. "Skylab 4" command module and photograph		35	40

The date "11.1.73" given on the 2p. is incorrect, "Skylab 3" was launched in July 1973 and returned to Earth in September 1973.
The date on the 18p. is also incorrect. The photograph was taken on 6 January 1974, three days later than the date given in the caption.

APOLLO-SOYUZ
LINK
1975

58 U.S.A.F. Lockheed C-141A   (59)
Starlifter

(Des R. Granger Barrett. Litho Questa)

1975 (19 June). *Wideawake Airfield.* T **58** and similar horiz designs. Multicoloured. W w **12** (*sideways**). P 13½.

187	2p. Type 58		1·75	65
188	5p. R.A.F. Lockheed C-130 Hercules		2·00	85
189	7p. Vickers Super VC-10		2·25	1·40
190	24p. U.S.A.F. Lockheed C-5A Galaxy		4·00	3·00
	w. Wmk Crown to right of CA			
187/90		*Set of 4*	9·00	5·50
MS191	144×99 mm. Nos 187/90		17·00	21·00

*The normal sideways watermark shows Crown to left of CA, as seen from the back of the stamp.

1975 (18 Aug). *"Apollo–Soyuz" Space Link. Nos. 141 and 145/6 optd with T 59.*
192	4½p. Space rocket taking-off	15	15
193	12½p. Sputnik II and Space Dog, Laika	20	20
194	25p. Walking in Space	30	35
192/4	*Set of 3*	60	65

60 Arrival of Royal Navy, 1815

(Des J.W. from paintings by Isobel McManus. Litho Walsall)

1975 (22 Oct). *160th Anniv of Occupation. T 60 and similar horiz designs. Multicoloured. W w 14 (sideways*). P 14.*
195	2p. Type 60	30	25
	w. Wmk Crown to right of CA	95·00	
196	5p. Water Supply, Dampiers Drip	40	40
197	9p. First landing, 1815	45	60
198	15p. The garden on Green Mountain	60	85
195/8	*Set of 4*	1·60	1·90

*The normal sideways watermark shows Crown to left of CA, as seen from the back of the stamp.

61 Yellow Canary

62 Boatswain Bird Island Sanctuary

(Des J.W. Litho Questa)

1976 (26 Apr). *Birds. Multicoloured designs as T 61 and T 62. W w 14 (sideways on horiz designs*). P 13½ (£2) or 14 (others).*
199	1p. Type 61	40	90
200	2p. White Tern (vert)	45	1·00
	w. Wmk inverted	£160	
201	3p. Common Waxbill	45	1·00
202	4p. White-capped Noddy (vert)	50	1·00
203	5p. Common Noddy	70	1·25
204	6p. Common Mynah	70	1·25
205	7p. Madeiran Storm Petrel (vert)	70	1·50
206	8p. Sooty Tern	70	1·50
	w. Wmk Crown to right of CA	£130	
207	9p. Blue-faced Booby (vert)	70	1·50
208	10p. Red-footed Booby	70	1·50
209	15p. Bare-throated Francolin (vert)	1·25	1·75
210	18p. Brown Booby (vert)	1·25	1·75
211	25p. Red-billed Tropic Bird	1·40	1·75
212	50p. White-tailed Tropic Bird	2·25	2·50
213	£1 Ascension Frigate Bird (vert)	2·75	3·25
214	£2 Type 62	5·50	7·50
199/214	*Set of 16*	18·00	27·00

*The normal sideways watermark shows Crown to left of CA, as seen from the back of the stamp.

63 G.B. Penny Red with Ascension Postmark

(Des C. Abbott. Litho J.W.)

1976 (4 May). *Festival of Stamps, London. T 63 and similar designs. W w 14 (sideways on 5 and 25p). P 13½.*
215	5p. rose-red, black and cinnamon	20	15
216	9p. green, black and greenish stone	30	20
217	25p. multicoloured	50	45
215/17	*Set of 3*	90	70

MS218 133×121 mm. No. 217 with St. Helena 318 and Tristan da Cunha 206 (wmk sideways*).
P 13		1·50	2·00
	w. Wmk Crown to left of CA	£325	

Designs: *Vert*—9p. ½d. stamp of 1922. *Horiz*—25p. Southampton Castle (liner).
*The normal sideways watermark shows Crown to right of CA, as seen from the back of the stamp.
No. MS218 was postally valid on each island to the value of 25p.

64 U.S. Base, Ascension   65 Visit of Prince Philip, 1957

(Des V. Whiteley Studio. Litho J.W.)

1976 (4 July). *Bicentenary of American Revolution. T 64 and similar horiz designs. Multicoloured. W w 14 (sideways). P 13.*
219	8p. Type 64	1·00	40
220	9p. NASA Station at Devils Ashpit	1·00	45
221	25p. "Viking" landing on Mars	1·50	80
219/21	*Set of 3*	3·25	1·50

(Des J. Cooter. Litho Walsall)

1977 (7 Feb). *Silver Jubilee. T 65 and similar horiz designs. Multicoloured. W w 14 (sideways on 12 and 25p). P 13½.*
222	8p. Type 65	15	15
	w. Wmk inverted	£120	
223	12p. Coronation Coach leaving Buckingham Palace	20	20
224	25p. Coronation Coach	35	40
222/4	*Set of 3*	60	65

66 Tunnel carrying Water Pipe   67 Mars Bay Location, 1877

(Des G. Drummond. Litho Harrison)

1977 (27 June). *Water Supplies. T 66 and similar multicoloured designs. W w 14 (sideways on 12 and 25p). P 14.*
225	3p. Type 66	15	15
226	5p. Breakneck Valley wells	20	20
227	12p. Break tank (horiz)	35	35
228	25p. Water catchment (horiz)	55	65
225/8	*Set of 4*	1·10	1·25

(Des J.W. Litho Questa)

1977 (3 Oct). *Centenary of Visit of Professor Gill (astronomer). T 67 and similar horiz designs. Multicoloured. W w 14 (sideways). P 13½.*
229	3p. Type 67	15	20
230	8p. Instrument sites, Mars Bay	20	25
231	12p. Sir David and Lady Gill	30	40
232	25p. Maps of Ascension	60	70
229/32	*Set of 4*	1·10	1·40

68 Lion of England   69 Queen Elizabeth II

(Des C. Abbott. Litho Questa)

1978 (2 June). *25th Anniv of Coronation. T 68/9 and similar vert design. P 15.*
233	68	25p. yellow, sepia and silver	35	50
		a. Sheetlet. Nos. 233/5 × 2	1·75	
234	69	25p. multicoloured	35	50
235	—	25p. yellow, sepia and silver	35	50
233/5		*Set of 3*	95	1·40

Design:—No. 235, Green Turtle.
Nos. 233/5 were printed together in small sheets of 6, containing two se-tenant strips of 3 with horizontal gutter margin between.

PRICES OF SETS

Set prices are given for many issues, generally those containing three stamps or more. Definitive sets include one of each value or major colour change, but do not cover different perforations, die types or minor shades. Where a choice is possible the set prices are based on the cheapest versions of the stamps included in the listings.

70 Flank of Sisters, Sisters' Red Hill and East Crater   71 "The Resolution" (H. Roberts)

(Des J.W. Litho Questa)

1978 (4 Sept). *Volcanic Rock Formations of Ascension. T 70 and similar horiz designs. Multicoloured. W w 14. P 14½.*
236	3p. Type 70	15	20
	a. Horiz strip of 5. Nos. 236/40	1·10	
237	5p. Holland's Crater (Hollow Tooth)	20	30
238	12p. Street Crater, Lower Valley Crater and Bear's Back	25	40
239	15p. Butt Crater, Weather Post and Green Mountain	30	45
240	25p. Flank of Sisters, Thistle Hill and Two Boats Village	35	50
236/40	*Set of 5*	1·10	1·60
MS241	185 × 100 mm. Nos. 236/40, each × 2	2·00	5·00
	a. Blue ("Ascension Island") omitted	£3750	

Nos. 236/40 were printed together, se-tenant, in horizontal strips of 5 throughout the sheet forming a composite design.

(Des and litho (25p. also embossed) Walsall)

1979 (19 Feb*). *Bicentenary of Captain Cook's Voyages, 1768–79. T 71 and similar vert designs. Multicoloured. P 11.*
242	3p. Type 71	40	25
243	8p. Chronometer	40	40
244	12p. Green Turtle	45	50
245	25p. Flaxman/Wedgwood medallion of Captain Cook	55	70
242/5	*Set of 4*	1·60	1·75

*This is the local date of issue; the stamps were released in London on 8 January.

72 St. Mary's Church, Georgetown   73 Landing Cable, Comfortless Cove

(Des Walsall. Litho Format)

1979 (24 May). *Ascension Day. T 72 and similar vert designs. Multicoloured. W w 14. P 14.*
246	8p. Type 72	15	20
247	12p. Map of Ascension	20	30
248	50p. "The Ascension" (painting by Rembrandt)	55	90
246/8	*Set of 3*	80	1·25

(Des G. Vasarhelyi. Litho Walsall)

1979 (15 Sept). *80th Anniv of Eastern Telegraph Company's Arrival on Ascension. T 73 and similar designs. W w 14 (inverted on 12p. or sideways on others*). P 14.*
249	3p. black and carmine	15	10
250	8p. black and yellowish green	20	20
251	12p. black and yellow	25	25
252	15p. black and bright violet	25	35
	w. Wmk Crown to right of CA	35·00	
253	25p. black and orange-brown	35	50
249/53	*Set of 5*	1·10	1·25

Designs: *Horiz*—8p. C.S. *Anglia*; 15p. C.S. *Seine*; 25p Cable and Wireless earth station. *Vert*—12p. Map of Atlantic cable network.
*The normal sideways watermark shows Crown to left of CA, as seen from the back of the stamp.

74 1938 6d. Stamp

(Des BG Studio. Litho Questa)

1979 (12 Dec). *Death Centenary of Sir Rowland Hill. T 74 and similar designs. W w 14 (sideways on 3 and 8p). P 14.*
254	3p. black, new blue & deep turquoise-blue	15	10
255	8p. black, blue-green and light green	15	20
256	12p. black, bright blue and turquoise-blue	20	25
	w. Wmk inverted	70·00	
257	50p. black, brownish grey and red	60	90
254/7	*Set of 4*	1·00	1·25

Designs: *Horiz*—8p. 1956 5s. definitive stamp. *Vert*—12p. 1924 3s. stamp; 50p. Sir Rowland Hill.

75 *Anogramma ascensionis* **76** 17th-century Bottle Post

(Des J. Cooter. Litho Format)

1980 (18 Feb). *Ferns and Grasses. T* **75** *and similar multicoloured designs. W* w **14** *(sideways on 12 to 24p.). P* 14½ × 14 (3 to 8p.) or 14 × 14½ (12 to 24p.).

258	3p. Type 75				10	10
259	6p. *Xiphopteris ascensionense*				15	15
260	8p. *Sporobolus caespitosus*				15	15
261	12p. *Sporobolus durus* (*vert*)				15	25
262	18p. *Dryopteris ascensionis* (*vert*)				20	30
	a. Brown (thorns) omitted				£110	
263	24p. *Marattia purpurascens* (*vert*)				30	50
258/63				*Set of* 6	90	1·25

(Des L. Curtis. Litho Format)

1980 (1 May). *"London 1980" International Stamp Exhibition. T* **76** *and similar horiz designs. Multicoloured. W* w **14** *(sideways). P* 13½.

264	8p. Type 76				15	20
265	12p. 19th-century chance calling ship				20	25
266	15p. *Garth Castle* (regular mail service from 1863)				20	30
267	50p. *St. Helena* (mail services, 1980)				60	90
264/7				*Set of* 4	1·00	1·50
MS268	102×154 mm. Nos. 264/7				1·00	2·40

77 Queen Elizabeth the Queen Mother **78** Lubbock's Yellowtail

(Des Harrison. Litho Questa)

1980 (11 Aug)*. *80th Birthday of Queen Elizabeth the Queen Mother. W* w **14** *(sideways). P* 14.

269	77	15p. multicoloured			40	40

*This was the local release date. The Crown Agents placed stocks on sale in London on 4 August.

(Des G. Drummond. Litho Enschedé)

1980 (15 Sept). *Fishes. T* **78** *and similar horiz designs. Multicoloured. W* w **14** *(sideways*). P* 13×13½.

270	3p. Type 78				30	15
271	10p. Resplendent Angelfish				45	25
272	25p. Bicoloured Butterflyfish				75	50
	w. Wmk Crown to right of CA				1·00	
273	40p. Marmalade Razorfish				1·00	65
	w. Wmk Crown to right of CA				1·50	
270/3				*Set of* 4	2·25	1·40

*The normal sideways watermark shows Crown to left of CA, as seen from the back of the stamp.

79 H.M.S. *Tortoise*

(Des D. Bowen. Litho Rosenbaum Bros, Vienna)

1980 (17 Nov). *150th Anniv of Royal Geographical Society. T* **79** *and similar multicoloured designs. W* w **14** *(sideways*). P* 14 (60p.) or 13½ (others).

274	10p. Type 79				35	40
	w. Wmk Crown to left of CA				75	
275	15p. "Wideawake Fair"				45	45
	w. Wmk Crown to left of CA				1·00	
276	60p. Mid-Atlantic Ridge (38×48 *mm*)				80	1·25
	w. Wmk Crown to left of CA				2·50	
274/6				*Set of* 3	1·40	2·00

*The normal sideways watermark shows Crown to right of CA, as seen from the back of the stamp.

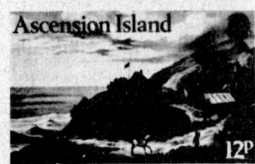

80 Green Mountain Farm, 1881

(Des C. Abbott. Litho Format)

1981 (15 Feb). *Green Mountain Farm. T* **80** *and similar horiz designs. Multicoloured. W* w **14** *(sideways). P* 13½ × 14.

277	12p. Type 80				15	35
278	15p. Two Boats, 1881				20	40
279	20p. Green Mountain and Two Boats, 1981				25	50
280	30p. Green Mountain Farm, 1981				35	70
277/80				*Set of* 4	85	1·75

---

81 Cable and Wireless Earth Station

(Des G. Vasarhelyi and Walsall. Litho Walsall)

1981 (27 Apr). *"Space Shuttle" Mission and Opening of 2nd Earth Station. W* w **14** *(sideways). P* 14.

281	81	15p. black, bright blue and pale blue			30	35

82 Poinsettia

83 Solanum

(Des J. Cooter. Litho J.W.)

1981 (11 May)–82. *Flowers. Designs as T* **82** (1 *to* 40p.) *or vert as T* **83** (50p. *to* £2). *Multicoloured. W* w **14** *(sideways* on* 1, 2, 4, 5, 8, 15, 20, 40, 50p., £1 and £2). P* 13½. A. *Without imprint date.* B. *With imprint date ("1982") (27.8.82).*

		A		B	
282	1p. Type 82	70	70		†
283	2p. Clustered Wax Flower	80	75	50	75
284	3p. Kolanchoe (*vert*)	80	75	50	75
285	4p. Yellow Pops	80	75		†
286	5p. Camels Foot Creeper	80	75		†
287	8p. White Oleander	80	80		†
288	10p. Ascension Lily (*vert*)	1·40	1·25	45	75
289	12p. Coral Plant (*vert*)	1·50	85		†
290	15p. Yellow Allamanda	1·25	85	50	75
291	20p. Ascension Euphorbia	1·25	1·00	1·00	75
	w. Wmk Crown to left of CA	2·00	—		†
292	30p. Flame of the Forest (*vert*)	1·25	1·25		†
293	40p. Bougainvillea "King Leopold"	1·25	2·00		†
294	50p. Type 83	1·25	2·50		†
295	£1 Ladies Petticoat	2·00	4·00	2·00	2·75
	w. Wmk Crown to left of CA	†	12·00		—
296	£2 Red Hibiscus	3·75	5·50		†
282A/96A		*Set of* 15	17·00	21·00	
283B/95B		*Set of* 6	†	4·50	6·00

*The normal sideways watermark shows Crown to right of CA, as seen from the back of the stamp.

Nos. 283B/95B had the imprint dates printed on the stamps by typography.

84 Map by Maxwell, 1793

(Des L. Curtis. Litho Walsall)

1981 (22 May). *Early Maps of Ascension. T* **84** *and similar horiz designs. W* w **14** *(sideways). P* 14 × 14½.

297	10p. black, gold and pale blue				25	35
298	12p. black, gold and apple-green				25	35
299	15p. black, gold and stone				25	35
300	40p. black, gold and pale greenish yellow				55	70
297/300				*Set of* 4	1·10	1·60
MS301	79 × 64 mm. 5p. × 4, multicoloured				60	75

Designs:—12p. Maxwell, 1793 (*different*); 15p. Ekeberg and Chapman, 1811; 40p. Campbell, 1819; miniature sheet, Linschoten, 1599.

Stamps from No. MS301 form a composite design.

MINIMUM PRICE

The minimum price quote is 10p which represents a handling charge rather than a basis for valuing common stamps. For further notes about prices see introductory pages.

---

85 Wedding Bouquet from Ascension **86** Prince Charles and Lady Diana Spencer

(Des J.W. Litho Questa)

1981 (22 July). *Royal Wedding. T* **85/6** *and similar vert design. Multicoloured. W* w **14**. *P* 14.

302	10p. Type 85				15	15
303	15p. Prince Charles in Fleet Air Arm flying kit				25	25
304	50p. Type 86				65	75
302/4				*Set of* 3	95	1·00

87 "Interest" **88** Scout crossing Rope Bridge

(Des BG Studio. Litho Questa)

1981 (14 Sept). *25th Anniv of Duke of Edinburgh Award Scheme. T* **87** *and similar vert designs. Multicoloured. W* w **14**. *P* 14.

305	5p. Type 87				15	15
306	10p. "Physical activities"				15	15
307	15p. "Service"				20	20
308	40p. Duke of Edinburgh				45	45
	w. Wmk inverted				24·00	
305/8				*Set of* 4	85	85

(Des A. Theobald. Litho Format)

1982 (22 Feb). *75th Anniv of Boy Scout Movement. T* **88** *and similar designs. W* w **14** *(sideways). P* 14.

309	10p. black, bright blue and azure				15	35
310	15p. black, orange-brown and greenish yellow				20	50
311	25p. black, bright mauve and pale mauve				30	60
312	40p. black, rosine and pale orange				50	85
309/12				*Set of* 4	1·00	2·00
MS313	121 × 121 mm. 10p., 15p., 25p., 40p. As Nos. 309/12 (*each diamond*, 40 × 40 *mm*). *P* 14½				1·25	2·50

Designs:—15p. 1st Ascension Scout Group flag; 25p. Scouts learning to use radio; 40p. Lord Baden-Powell.

Stamps from No. MS313 have an overall design showing a flag printed on the reverse beneath the gum.

89 Charles Darwin

(Des L. Curtis. Litho Questa)

1982 (19 Apr). *150th Anniv of Charles Darwin's Voyage. T* **89** *and similar horiz designs. Multicoloured. W* w **14** *(sideways). P* 14.

314	10p. Type 89				25	40
315	12p. Darwin's pistols				30	50
316	15p. Rock Crab				35	55
317	40p. H.M.S. *Beagle*				75	95
314/17				*Set of* 4	1·50	2·25

90 Fairey Swordfish Torpedo Bomber

(Des A. Theobald. Litho Walsall)

1982 (15 June). *40th Anniv of Wideawake Airfield. T* **90** *and similar horiz designs. Multicoloured. W* w **14** *(sideways). P* 14.

318	5p. Type 90				80	35
319	10p. North American B-25C Mitchell				1·00	40
320	15p. Boeing EC-135N Aria				1·25	55
321	50p. Lockheed C-130 Hercules				2·00	1·10
318/21				*Set of* 4	4·50	2·25

91 Ascension Coat of Arms   **92** Formal Portrait

(Des Jennifer Toombs. Litho Questa)

1982 (1 July). *21st Birthday of Princess of Wales. T* **91/2** *and similar vert designs. Multicoloured.* W w 14. P 14 × 14½.

322	12p. Type **91**		25	25
323	15p. Lady Diana Spencer in Music Room, Buckingham Palace		25	25
324	25p. Bride and Earl Spencer leaving Clarence House		40	40
325	50p. Type **92**		75	75
322/5	..	*Set of 4*	1·50	1·50

1st PARTICIPATION COMMONWEALTH GAMES 1982
(93)   **94** Bush House, London

1982 (29 Oct). *Commonwealth Games, Brisbane. Nos.* 290B/1B *optd with T* **93**.

326	15p. Yellow Allamanda		30	40
327	20p. Ascension Euphorbia		40	45

(Des A. Theobald. Litho Questa)

1982 (1 Dec). *Christmas. 50th Anniv of B.B.C. External Broadcasting. T* **94** *and similar horiz designs. Multicoloured.* W w 14 *(sideways***).* P 14.

328	5p. Type **94**		15	20
329	10p. Atlantic relay station		20	30
330	25p. Lord Reith, first director-general		40	60
	w. Wmk Crown to right of CA		4·50	
331	40p. King George V making his first Christmas broadcast, 1932		60	75
328/31	..	*Set of 4*	1·25	1·60

**The normal sideways watermark shows Crown to left of CA, as seen from the back of the stamp.*

95 *Marasmius thwaitesii* ("*Marasmius echinosphaerus*")   **96** Aerial View of Georgetown

(Des Harrison. Litho Questa)

1983 (1 Mar). *Fungi. T* **95** *and similar vert designs. Multicoloured.* W w 14. P 14.

332	7p. Type **95**		55	30
333	12p. *Chlorophyllum molybdites*		75	45
334	15p. *Leucocoprinus cepaestripes*		90	50
335	20p. *Lycoperdon marginatum*		1·10	65
336	50p. *Marasmiellus distantifolius*		1·75	1·25
332/6	..	*Set of 5*	4·50	2·75

(Des Jennifer Toombs. Litho Format)

1983 (12 May). *Island Views (1st series). T* **96** *and similar horiz designs. Multicoloured.* W w 14 *(sideways***).* P 14 × 13½.

337	12p. Type **96**		20	25
338	15p. Green Mountain farm		20	25
	w. Wmk Crown to right of CA			
339	20p. Boatswain Bird Island		35	40
340	60p. Telemetry Hill by night		70	80
337/40	..	*Set of 4*	1·25	1·50

**The normal sideways watermark shows Crown to left of CA, as seen from the back of the stamp.*
See also Nos. 367/70.

97 Westland Wessex 5 Helicopter of No. 845 Naval Air Squadron

(Des D. Hartley-Marjoram. Litho Questa)

1983 (1 Aug). *Bicentenary of Manned Flight. British Military Aircraft. T* **97** *and similar horiz designs. Multicoloured.* W w 14 *(sideways).* P 13½.

341	12p. Type **97**		85	65
342	15p. Avro Vulcan B.2 of No. 44 Squadron		95	75
343	20p. Hawker Siddeley H.S.801 Nimrod M.R. 2P of No. 120 Squadron		1·10	85
344	60p. Handley Page H.P.80 Victor K2 of No. 55 Squadron		2·00	2·00
341/4	..	*Set of 4*	4·50	3·75

98 Iguanid

(Des D. Nockles. Litho Questa)

1983 (20 Sept). *Introduced Species. T* **98** *and similar horiz designs. Multicoloured.* W w 14 *(sideways).* P 14.

345	12p. Type **98**		30	30
346	15p. Rabbit		35	35
347	20p. Cat		45	45
348	60p. Donkey		1·40	1·40
345/8	..	*Set of 4*	2·25	2·25

99 Speckled Tellin (*Tellina listeri*)   **100** 1922 1½d. Stamp

(Des G. Wilby. Litho Format)

1983 (28 Nov). *Sea Shells. T* **99** *and similar horiz designs. Multicoloured.* W w 14 *(sideways).* P 14½ × 14.

349	7p. Type **99**		20	20
350	12p. Lion's Paw Scallop (*Lyropecten nodosa*)		30	30
351	15p. Lurid Cowrie (*Cypraea lurida oceanica*)		35	35
352	20p. Ascension Nerite (*Nerita ascensionis*)		45	45
353	50p. Miniature Melo (*Micromelo undatus*)		1·10	1·10
349/53	..	*Set of 5*	2·25	2·25

(Des C. Abbott. Litho Questa)

1984 (3 Jan). *150th Anniv of St. Helena as a British Colony. T* **100** *and similar vert designs showing stamps of the 1922 issue overprinted on St. Helena. Multicoloured.* W w 14. P 14.

354	12p. Type **100**		40	45
355	15p. 1922 2d. stamp		45	50
356	20p. 1922 8d. stamp		50	55
357	60p. 1922 1s. stamp		1·00	1·40
354/7	..	*Set of 4*	2·10	2·50

101 Prince Andrew   **102** Naval Semaphore

(Des L. Curtis. Litho Questa)

1984 (10 Apr). *Visit of Prince Andrew. Sheet,* 124 × 90 *mm, containing vert designs as T* **101**. W w 14. P 14½ × 14.
MS358 12p. Type **101**; 70p. Prince Andrew in naval uniform .. .. 1·40 1·60

(Des D. Hartley-Marjoram. Litho Questa)

1984 (28 May). *250th Anniv of "Lloyd's List" (newspaper). T* **102** *and similar vert designs. Multicoloured.* W w 14. P 14½ × 14.

359	12p. Type **102**		40	30
360	15p. *Southampton Castle* (liner)		45	35
361	20p. Pier Head		55	45
362	70p. *Dane* (screw steamer)		1·60	1·50
359/62	..	*Set of 4*	2·75	2·40

NEW INFORMATION

The editor is always interested to correspond with people who have new information that will improve or correct the Catalogue.

103 Penny Coin and Yellow-finned Tuna   **104** Bermuda Cypress

(Des G. Drummond. Litho Questa)

1984 (26 July). *New Coinage. T* **103** *and similar horiz designs. Multicoloured.* W w 14 *(sideways).* P 14.

363	12p. Type **103**		50	35
364	15p. Twopenny coin and donkey		60	40
365	20p. Fifty pence coin and Green Turtle		75	50
366	70p. Pound coin and Sooty Tern		2·00	1·75
363/6	..	*Set of 4*	3·50	2·75

(Des Jennifer Toombs. Litho B.D.T.)

1984 (26 Oct). *Island Views (2nd series). Horiz designs as T* **96**. *Multicoloured.* W w 14 *(sideways).* P 13½.

367	12p. The Devil's Riding-school		30	30
368	15p. St. Mary's Church		35	35
369	20p. Two Boats Village		45	45
370	70p. Ascension from the sea		1·50	1·50
367/70	..	*Set of 4*	2·40	2·40

(Des N. Shewring. Litho Questa)

1985 (8 Mar). *Trees. T* **104** *and similar vert designs. Multicoloured.* W w 14. P 14½.

371	7p. Type **104**		55	20
372	12p. Norfolk Island Pine		65	30
373	15p. Screwpine		75	35
374	20p. Eucalyptus		90	45
375	65p. Spore Tree		2·25	1·40
371/5	..	*Set of 5*	4·50	2·40

105 The Queen Mother with Prince Andrew at Silver Jubilee Service   **106** 32 Pdr. Smooth Bore Muzzle-loader, c 1820, and Royal Marine Artillery Hat Plate, c 1816

(Des A. Theobald (75p.), C. Abbott (others). Litho Questa)

1985 (7 June). *Life and Times of Queen Elizabeth the Queen Mother. T* **105** *and similar vert designs. Multicoloured.* W w 16. P 14½ × 14.

376	12p. With the Duke of York at Balmoral, 1924		25	35
	w. Wmk inverted		15·00	
377	15p. Type **105**		25	40
	w. Wmk inverted		1·50	
378	20p. The Queen Mother at Ascot		30	55
	w. Wmk inverted		24·00	
379	70p. With Prince Henry at his christening (from photo by Lord Snowdon)		80	1·75
376/9	..	*Set of 4*	1·40	2·75
MS380	91×73 mm. 75p. Visiting the *Queen Elizabeth 2* at Southampton, 1968. Wmk sideways		1·10	1·60

(Des W. Fenton. Litho Walsall)

1985 (19 July). *Guns on Ascension Island. T* **106** *and similar horiz designs. Multicoloured.* W w 14 *(sideways).* P 14 × 14½.

381	12p. Type **106**		70	90
382	15p. 7 inch rifled muzzle-loader, c 1866, and Royal Cypher on barrel		80	1·00
383	20p. 7 pdr. rifled muzzle-loader, c 1877, and Royal Artillery badge		90	1·25
384	70p. 5·5 inch gun, 1941, and crest from H.M.S. *Hood*		2·50	3·50
381/4	..	*Set of 4*	4·50	6·00

107 Guide Flag   **108** *Clerodendrum fragrans*

(Des N. Shewring. Litho Questa)

1985 (4 Oct). *75th Anniv of Girl Guide Movement and International Youth Year. T* **107** *and similar vert designs. Multicoloured.* W w 14. P 14½ × 14.

385	12p. Type **107**		75	60
	w. Wmk inverted		5·00	
386	15p. Practising first aid		85	75
	w. Wmk inverted		5·00	
387	20p. Camping		95	85
388	70p. Lady Baden-Powell		2·75	2·00
385/8	..	*Set of 4*	4·75	3·75

(Des Josephine Martin. Litho Questa)

1985 (6 Dec). *Wild Flowers. T* **108** *and similar vert designs. Multicoloured. W* w **16**. *P* 14.

389	12p. Type **108**	..	45	65
390	15p. Shell Ginger	..	55	80
391	20p. Cape Daisy	..	65	90
392	70p. Ginger Lily	..	2·00	2·25
389/92		*Set of 4*	3·25	4·00

109 Newton's Reflector Telescope

110 Princess Elizabeth in 1926

(Des D. Hartley. Litho B.D.T.)

1986 (7 Mar). *Appearance of Halley's Comet. T* **109** *and similar vert designs. Multicoloured. W* w **16**. *P* 14.

393	12p. Type **109**	..	75	95
394	15p. Edmond Halley and Old Greenwich Observatory	..	85	1·10
395	20p. Short's Gregorian telescope and comet, 1759	..	95	1·25
396	70p. Ascension satellite tracking station and ICE spacecraft	..	2·75	3·00
393/6		*Set of 4*	4·50	5·50

(Des A. Theobald. Litho Format)

1986 (21 Apr). *60th Birthday of Queen Elizabeth II. T* **110** *and similar vert designs. Multicoloured. W* w **16**. *P* 14×14½.

397	7p. Type **110**	..	15	25
398	15p. Queen making Christmas broadcast, 1952	..	20	40
399	20p. At Garter ceremony, Windsor Castle, 1983	..	25	50
400	35p. In Auckland, New Zealand, 1981	..	35	80
401	£1 At Crown Agents' Head Office, London, 1983	..	1·00	2·25
397/401		*Set of 5*	1·75	3·75

111 1975 Space Satellites 2p. Stamp

112 Prince Andrew and Miss Sarah Ferguson

(Des L. Curtis. Litho Walsall)

1986 (22 May). *"Ameripex '86" International Stamp Exhibition, Chicago. T* **111** *and similar horiz designs showing previous Ascension stamps. Multicoloured. W* w **16** *(sideways*). P* 14×14½.

402	15p. Type **111**	..	40	60
403	15p. 1980 "London 1980" International Stamp Exhibition 50p.	..	45	70
404	20p. 1976 Bicentenary of American Revolution 8p.	..	55	90
	w. Wmk Crown to right of CA	..	45·00	
405	70p. 1982 40th Anniv of Wideawake Airfield 10p.	..	1·25	2·00
402/5		*Set of 4*	2·40	3·75
MS406	60×75 mm. 75p. Statue of Liberty	..	2·00	2·75

*The normal sideways watermark shows Crown to left of CA, as seen from the back of the stamp.

(Des D. Miller. Litho Questa)

1986 (23 July). *Royal Wedding. T* **112** *and similar square design. Multicoloured. W* w **16**. *P* 14.

407	15p. Type **112**	..	25	35
408	35p. Prince Andrew aboard H.M.S. *Brazen*	..	50	75

113 H.M.S. *Ganymede* (c 1811)

(Des E. Nisbet. Litho Questa)

1986 (14 Oct). *Ships of the Royal Navy. T* **113** *and similar horiz designs. Multicoloured. W* w **16** *(sideways*). P* 14½.

409	1p. Type **113**	..	55	80
410	2p. H.M.S. *Kangaroo* (c 1811)	..	60	90
	w. Wmk Crown to right of CA			
411	4p. H.M.S. *Trinculo* (c 1811)	..	60	90
412	5p. H.M.S. *Daring* (c 1811)	..	60	90
413	9p. H.M.S. *Thais* (c 1811)	..	70	1·00
414	10p. H.M.S. *Pheasant* (1819)	..	70	1·00
415	15p. H.M.S. *Myrmidon* (1819)	..	80	1·10

416	18p. H.M.S. *Atholl* (1825)	..	90	1·25
417	20p. H.M.S. *Medina* (1830)	..	90	1·25
418	25p. H.M.S. *Saracen* (1840)	..	1·00	1·50
419	30p. H.M.S. *Hydra* (c 1845)	..	1·00	1·50
420	50p. H.M.S. *Sealark* (1849)	..	1·25	2·00
421	70p. H.M.S. *Rattlesnake* (1868)	..	1·75	2·50
422	£1 H.M.S. *Penelope* (1889)	..	2·40	3·25
423	£2 H.M.S. *Monarch* (1897)	..	5·00	6·50
409/23		*Set of 15*	17·00	24·00

*The normal sideways watermark shows Crown to left of CA, as seen from the back of the stamp.

114 Cape Gooseberry

115 Ignition of Rocket Motors

(Des R. Gorringe. Litho Walsall)

1987 (29 Jan). *Edible Bush Fruits. T* **114** *and similar horiz designs. Multicoloured. W* w **16** *(sideways). P* 14.

424	12p. Type **114**	..	65	80
425	15p. Prickly Pear	..	75	90
426	20p. Guava	..	85	1·00
427	70p. Loquat	..	2·00	2·50
424/7		*Set of 4*	3·75	4·75

(Des D. Hartley. Litho Questa)

1987 (30 Mar). *25th Anniv of First American Manned Earth Orbit. T* **115** *and similar vert designs. Multicoloured. W* w **16**. *P* 14.

428	15p. Type **115**	..	55	65
429	18p. Lift-off	..	60	70
430	25p. Re-entry	..	75	85
431	£1 Splashdown	..	2·50	2·75
428/31		*Set of 4*	4·00	4·50
MS432	92×78 mm. 70p. "Friendship 7" capsule		1·75	2·00

116 Captains in Full Dress raising Red Ensign

117 *Cynthia cardui*

(Des C. Collins. Litho Format)

1987 (29 June). *19th-century Uniforms (1st series). Royal Navy, 1815–20. T* **116** *and similar vert designs. Multicoloured. W* w **16**. *P* 14.

433	25p. Type **116**	..	60	60
	a. Horiz strip of 5. Nos. 433/7	..	2·75	
434	25p. Surgeon and seamen	..	60	60
435	25p. Seaman with water-carrying donkey	..	60	60
436	25p. Midshipman and gun	..	60	60
437	25p. Commander in undress uniform surveying	..	60	60
433/7		*Set of 5*	2·75	2·75

Nos. 433/7 were printed together, *se-tenant*, in horizontal strips of five throughout the sheet.

See also Nos. 478/82.

(Des I. Loe. Litho Questa)

1987 (10 Aug). *Insects (1st series). Butterflies. T* **117** *and similar horiz designs. Multicoloured. W* w **16** *(sideways). P* 14×14½.

438	15p. Type **117**	..	55	65
439	18p. *Danaus chrysippus*	..	60	75
440	25p. *Hypolimnas misippus*	..	75	85
441	£1 *Lampides boeticus*	..	2·25	2·50
438/41		*Set of 4*	3·75	4·25

See also Nos. 452/5 and 483/6.

118 Male Ascension Frigate Birds

(119) 40TH WEDDING ANNIVERSARY

(Des N. Arlott. Litho B.D.T.)

1987 (8 Oct). *Sea Birds (1st series). T* **118** *and similar vert designs. Multicoloured. W* w **16**. *P* 14.

442	25p. Type **118**	..	1·10	1·40
	a. Horiz strip of 5. Nos. 442/6	..	5·00	
443	25p. Juvenile Ascension Frigate Bird, Brown Booby and Blue-faced Boobies		1·10	1·40
444	25p. Male Ascension Frigate Bird and Blue-faced Boobies		1·10	1·40

445	25p. Female Ascension Frigate Bird	..	1·10	1·40
446	25p. Adult male feeding juvenile Ascension Frigate Bird	..	1·10	1·40
442/6		*Set of 5*	5·00	6·00

Nos. 442/6 were printed together, *se-tenant*, in horizontal strips of five throughout the sheet, forming a composite design. See also Nos. 469/73.

1987 (9 Dec). *Royal Ruby Wedding. Nos. 397/401 optd with T* **119** *in silver.*

447	7p. Type **110**	..	15	15
448	15p. Queen making Christmas broadcast, 1952	..	25	30
449	20p. At Garter ceremony, Windsor Castle, 1983	..	30	40
	a. Opt double	..	75·00	
450	35p. In Auckland, New Zealand, 1981	..	50	60
451	£1 At Crown Agents' Head Office, London, 1983	..	1·25	1·40
447/51		*Set of 5*	2·25	2·50

(Des I. Loe. Litho Questa)

1988 (18 Jan). *Insects (2nd series). Horiz designs as T* **117**. *Multicoloured. W* w **16** *(sideways). P* 14×14½.

452	15p. *Gryllus bimaculatus* (field cricket)	..	50	50
453	18p. *Ruspolia differeus* (bush cricket)	..	55	55
454	25p. *Chilomenus lunata* (ladybird)	..	70	70
455	£1 *Diachrysia orichalcea* (moth)	..	2·25	2·25
452/5		*Set of 4*	3·50	3·50

120 Bate's Memorial, St. Mary's Church

(Des S. Noon. Litho Questa)

1988 (14 Apr). *150th Death Anniv of Captain William Bate (garrison commander, 1828–38). T* **120** *and similar horiz designs. Multicoloured. W* w **16** *(sideways). P* 14.

456	9p. Type **120**	..	35	35
457	15p. Commodore's Cottage	..	45	45
458	18p. North East Cottage	..	50	50
459	25p. Map of Ascension	..	70	70
460	70p. Captain Bate and marines	..	1·75	1·75
456/60		*Set of 5*	3·25	3·25

121 H.M.S. *Resolution* (ship of the line), 1667

(Des E. Nisbet. Litho Questa)

1988 (23 June). *Bicentenary of Australian Settlement. Ships of the Royal Navy. T* **121** *and similar diamond-shaped designs. Multicoloured. W* w **16** *(sideways*). P* 14.

461	9p. Type **121**	..	65	35
	w. Wmk Crown to left of CA	..	45·00	
462	18p. H.M.S. *Resolution* (Captain Cook), 1772	..	90	55
	w. Wmk Crown to left of CA	..	45·00	
463	25p. H.M.S. *Resolution* (battleship), 1892		1·25	75
464	65p. H.M.S. *Resolution* (battleship), 1916		2·25	1·50
461/4		*Set of 4*	4·50	2·75

*The normal sideways watermark shows Crown to right of CA, as seen from the back of the stamp positioned with the Royal cypher in the top left corner.

(122) SYDPEX 88 · 30.7.88 – 7.8.88

123 Lloyd's Coffee House, London, 1688

1988 (30 July). *"Sydpex '88" National Stamp Exhibition, Sydney. Nos. 461/4 optd with T* **122**.

465	9p. Type **121**	..	40	25
466	18p. H.M.S. *Resolution* (Captain Cook), 1772	..	60	40
467	25p. H.M.S. *Resolution* (battleship), 1892		75	55
468	65p. H.M.S. *Resolution* (battleship), 1916		1·60	1·40
465/8		*Set of 4*	3·00	2·50

(Des N. Arlott. Litho Questa)

1988 (15 Aug). *Sea Birds (2nd series). Sooty Tern. Vert designs as T* **118**. *Multicoloured.* W w **16**. P 14.

469	25p.	Pair displaying		1·00	1·00
	a.	Horiz strip of 5. Nos. 469/73		4·50	
470	25p.	Turning egg		1·00	1·00
471	25p.	Incubating egg		1·00	1·00
472	25p.	Feeding chick		1·00	1·00
473	25p.	Immature Sooty Tern		1·00	1·00
469/73			*Set of 5*	4·50	4·50

Nos. 469/73 were printed together, *se-tenant*, in horizontal strips of five throughout the sheet, forming a composite design of a nesting colony.

(Des E. Nisbet and D. Miller (8p., 25p.), D. Miller (others). Litho Questa)

1988 (17 Oct). *300th Anniv of Lloyd's of London. T* **123** *and similar multicoloured designs.* W w **14** (sideways on 18, 25p.). P 14.

474	8p.	Type **123**		25	30
475	18p.	*Alert IV* (cable ship) (horiz)		50	60
476	25p.	Satellite recovery in space (horiz)		70	80
477	65p.	*Good Hope Castle* (cargo liner) on fire off Ascension, 1973		1·50	1·75
474/7			*Set of 4*	2·75	3·00

(Des C. Collins. Litho B.D.T.)

1988 (21 Nov). *19th-century Uniforms (2nd series). Royal Marines, 1821–34. Vert designs as T* **116**. *Multicoloured.* W w **14**. P 14.

478	25p.	Marines landing on Ascension, 1821		1·10	1·50
	a.	Horiz strip of 5. Nos. 478/82		5·00	
479	25p.	Officer and Marine at semaphore station, 1829		1·10	1·50
480	25p.	Sergeant and Marine at Octagonal Tank, 1831		1·10	1·50
481	25p.	Officers at water pipe tunnel, 1833		1·10	1·50
482	25p.	Officer supervising construction of barracks, 1834		1·10	1·50
478/82			*Set of 5*	5·00	6·50

Nos. 478/82 were printed together, *se-tenant*, in horizontal strips of five throughout the sheet.

(Des I. Loe. Litho Questa)

1989 (16 Jan). *Insects (3rd series). Horiz designs as T* **117**. *Multicoloured.* W w **16** (sideways). P 14×14½.

483	15p.	*Trichoptilus wahlbergi* (moth)		65	40
484	18p.	*Lucilia sericata* (fly)		70	45
485	25p.	*Alceis ornatus* (weevil)		90	60
486	£1	*Polistes fuscatus* (wasp)		2·75	2·40
483/6			*Set of 4*	4·50	3·50

124 Two Land Crabs

125 1949 75th Anniversary of U. P. U. 1s. Stamp

(Des Doreen McGuiness. Litho Questa)

1989 (17 Apr). *Ascension Land Crabs (Gecarcinus lagostoma). T* **124** *and similar vert designs. Multicoloured.* W w **16**. P 14.

487	15p.	Type **124**		40	45
488	18p.	Crab with claws raised		45	50
489	25p.	Crab on rock		60	70
490	£1	Crab in surf		2·25	2·50
487/90			*Set of 4*	3·25	3·75
MS491	98 × 101 mm. Nos. 487/90			3·50	3·75

(Des D. Miller. Litho Walsall)

1989 (7 July). *"Philexfrance '89" International Stamp Exhibition, Paris, and "World Stamp Expo '89", Washington* (1st issue). Sheet 104×86 mm. W w **16**. P 14×13½.

MS492	**125** 75p. multicoloured		1·50	1·75

See also Nos. 498/503.

126 "Apollo 7" Tracking Station, Ascension

127 *Queen Elizabeth 2* (liner) and U.S.S. *John F. Kennedy* (aircraft carrier) in New York Harbour

(Des A. Theobald (£1), D. Miller (others). Litho Questa)

1989 (20 July). *20th Anniv of First Manned Landing on Moon. T* **126** *and similar multicoloured designs.* W w **16** (sideways on 18, 25p.). P 14 × 13½ (15, 70p.) or 14 (others).

493	15p.	Type **126**		65	45
494	18p.	Launch of "Apollo 7" (30 × 30 mm)		70	50
495	25p.	"Apollo 7" emblem (30 × 30 mm)		90	70
496	70p.	"Apollo 7" jettisoning expended Saturn rocket		1·75	1·75
493/6			*Set of 4*	3·50	3·00
MS497	101 × 83 mm. £1 Diagram of "Apollo 11" mission. P 14 × 13½.			2·00	2·10

(Des D. Miller. Litho Walsall)

1989 (21 Aug). *"Philexfrance 89" International Stamp Exhibition, Paris, and "World Stamp Expo '89", Washington* (2nd issue). T **127** *and similar vert designs showing Statue of Liberty and Centenary celebrations. Multicoloured.* W w **14**. P 14×13½.

498	15p.	Type **127**		35	35
	a.	Sheetlet. Nos. 498/503		1·90	
499	15p.	Cleaning Statue		35	35
500	15p.	Statue of Liberty		35	35
501	15p.	Crown of Statue		35	35
502	15p.	Warships and New York skyline		35	35
503	15p.	*Jean de Vienne* (French destroyer) and skyscrapers		35	35
498/503			*Set of 6*	1·90	1·90

Nos. 498/503 were printed, *se-tenant*, in sheetlets of 6.

128 Devil's Ashpit Tracking Station

(Des D. Miller. Litho Questa)

1989 (30 Sept). *Closure of Devil's Ashpit Tracking Station, Ascension. T* **128** *and similar horiz design. Multicoloured.* W w **16** (sideways). P 14.

504	18p.	Type **128**		80	50
	a.	Sheetlet. Nos. 504/5, each × 5		7·00	
505	25p.	Launch of shuttle *Atlantis*		80	55

Nos. 504/5 were issued in sheetlets of ten containing vertical strips of five of each design, separated by a central inscribed gutter.

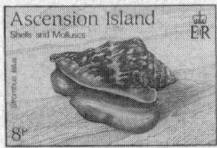

129 Bubonian Conch (*Strombus latus*)

130 Donkeys

(Des I. Loe. Litho Questa)

1989 (2 Nov). *Sea Shells. T* **129** *and similar horiz designs. Multicoloured.* W w **16** (sideways). P 14.

506	8p.	Type **129**		25	20
507	18p.	Giant Tun (*Tonna galea*)		45	40
508	25p.	Doris Harp (*Harpa doris*)		60	55
509	£1	Atlantic Trumpet Triton (*Charonia variegata*)		2·25	2·25
506/9			*Set of 4*	3·25	3·00

(Des G. Drummond, adapted N. Harvey. Litho Walsall)

1989 (17 Nov). *Booklet stamps. T* **130** *and similar vert design. Multicoloured.* W w **16** (sideways). P 14.

510	18p.	Type **130**		35	40
	a.	Booklet pane. No. 510×6		2·10	
511	25p.	Green Turtle		50	55
	a.	Booklet pane. No. 511×4		2·00	

Nos. 510/11 come with either the left or right-hand side imperforate.

131 Seaman's Pistol, Hat and Cutlass

132 Pair of Ascension Frigate Birds with Young

(Des C. Collins. Litho Questa)

1990 (12 Feb). *Royal Navy Equipment, 1815-20. T* **131** *and similar vert designs. Multicoloured.* W w **16**. P 14.

512	25p.	Type **131**		65	65
	a.	Horiz strip of 5. Nos. 512/16		3·00	
513	25p.	Midshipman's belt plate, button, sword and hat		65	65
514	25p.	Surgeon's hat, sword and instrument chest		65	65
515	25p.	Captain's hat, telescope and sword		65	65
516	25p.	Admiral's epaulette, megaphone, hat and pocket		65	65
512/16			*Set of 5*	3·00	3·00

Nos. 512/16 were printed together, *se-tenant*, in horizontal strips of 5 throughout the sheet.
See also Nos. 541/5.

(Des W. Oliver. Litho Questa)

1990 (5 Mar). *Ascension Frigate Bird. T* **132** *and similar vert designs. Multicoloured.* W w **14**. P 14½×14.

517	9p.	Type **132**		1·00	70
518	10p.	Fledgeling		1·10	80
519	11p.	Adult male in flight		1·10	80
520	15p.	Female and immature birds in flight		1·25	90
517/20			*Set of 4*	4·00	2·75

133 Penny Black and Twopence Blue

(Des D. Miller. Litho Walsall)

1990 (3 May). *"Stamp World London 90" International Stamp Exhibition, London. T* **133** *and similar horiz designs. Multicoloured.* W w **14** (sideways). P 14.

521	9p.	Type **133**		50	30
522	18p.	Ascension postmarks used on G.B. stamps		70	50
523	25p.	Unloading mail at Wideawake Airfield		95	75
524	£1	Mail van and Main Post Office		2·25	2·25
521/4			*Set of 4*	4·00	3·50

134 "Queen Elizabeth, 1940" (Sir Gerald Kelly)

135 King George VI and Queen Elizabeth with Bren-gun Carrier

(Des D. Miller. Litho Questa)

1990 (4 Aug). *90th Birthday of Queen Elizabeth the Queen Mother.* W w **16**. P 14×15 (25p.) or 14½ (£1).

525	**134** 25p. multicoloured			75	75
526	**135** £1 black and deep lilac			2·25	2·25

136 "Madonna and Child" (sculpture, Dino Felici)

137 *Garth Castle* (mail steamer), 1910

(Des D. Miller. Litho B.D.T.)

1990 (24 Oct). *Christmas. Works of Art. T* **136** *and similar vert designs. Multicoloured.* W w **14**. P 13½.

527	8p.	Type **136**		70	60
528	18p.	"Madonna and Child" (anon)		1·25	1·10
529	25p.	"Madonna and Child with St. John" (Johann Gebhard)		1·75	1·50
530	65p.	"Madonna and Child" (Giacomo Gritti)		3·00	3·00
527/30			*Set of 4*	6·00	5·50

(Des L. Curtis. Litho Walsall)

1990 (27 Nov). *Maiden Voyage of St. Helena II. T* **137** *and similar horiz designs. Multicoloured.* W w **14** (sideways). P 14×14½.

531	9p.	Type **137**		90	60
532	18p.	*St. Helena I* during Falkland Islands campaign, 1982		1·25	1·10
533	25p.	Launch of *St. Helena II*		1·75	1·50
534	70p.	Duke of York launching *St. Helena II*		3·00	3·00
531/4			*Set of 4*	6·25	5·50
MS535	100×100 mm. £1 *St. Helena II* and outline map of Ascension			3·50	5·00

No. MS535 also contains two imperforate designs of similar stamps from St. Helena and Tristan da Cunha without face values.

BRITISH FOR 175 YEARS

(138)　　　139 Queen Elizabeth
II at Trooping the
Colour

1991 (5 Feb). *175th Anniv of Occupation. Nos. 418, 420 and
422 optd with T* **138** *in silver by Cartor.*

536	25p.	H.M.S. *Saracen* (1840)	..	1·50	1·50
537	50p.	H.M.S. *Sealark* (1849)	..	2·00	2·00
538	£1	H.M.S. *Penelope* (1889)	..	3·00	3·00
536/8			*Set of 3*	6·00	6·00

(Des D. Miller. Litho Questa)

1991 (18 June). *65th Birthday of Queen Elizabeth II and 70th
Birthday of Prince Philip. T* **139** *and similar vert design.
Multicoloured. W w* **16** *(sideways). P* 14½ × 14.

539	25p.	Type **139**	..	75	1·00
	a.	Horiz pair. Nos. 539/40 separated by label		1·50	2·00
540	25p.	Prince Philip in naval uniform	..	75	1·00

Nos. 539/40 were printed together, *se-tenant*, in sheetlets of 10
(2 × 5) with designs alternating and the vertical rows separated
by inscribed labels.

(Des C. Collins. Litho Questa)

1991 (1 Aug). *Royal Marines Equipment, 1821–44. Vert
designs as T* **131**. *Multicoloured. W w* **14**. *P* 14.

541	25p.	Officer's shako, epaulettes, belt plate and button	1·10	1·10
	a.	Horiz strip of 5. Nos. 541/5 ..	5·00	
542	25p.	Officer's cap, sword, epaulettes and belt plate	1·10	1·10
543	25p.	Drum major's shako and staff	1·10	1·10
544	25p.	Sergeant's shako, chevrons, belt plate and canteen	1·10	1·10
545	25p.	Drummer's shako and side-drum ..	1·10	1·10
541/5		*Set of 5*	5·00	5·00

Nos. 541/5 were printed together, *se-tenant*, in horizontal
strips of 5 throughout the sheet.

140 B.B.C. World Service Relay
Station

(Des D. Miller. Litho Questa)

1991 (17 Sept). *25th Anniv of B.B.C. Atlantic Relay Station.
T* **140** *and similar multicoloured designs. W w* **16** *(sideways
on* 15, 18p.*). P* 14½.

546	15p.	Type **140**	..	90	80
547	18p.	Transmitters at English Bay	..	1·00	90
548	25p.	Satellite receiving station (*vert*)	..	1·25	1·25
549	70p.	Antenna support tower (*vert*)	..	2·50	2·75
546/9			*Set of 4*	5·00	5·25

141 St. Mary's Church

(Des D. Miller. Litho Questa)

1991 (1 Oct). *Christmas. Ascension Churches. T* **141** *and
similar horiz designs. Multicoloured. W w* **16** *(sideways). P* 14.

550	8p.	Type **141**	..	55	45
551	18p.	Interior of St. Mary's Church	..	1·00	90
552	25p.	Our Lady of Ascension Grotto	..	1·25	1·10
553	65p.	Interior of Our Lady of Ascension Grotto	..	2·75	3·25
550/3			*Set of 4*	5·00	5·25

142 Black Durgon
("Blackfish")

(Des G. Drummond. Litho Walsall)

1991 (10 Dec). *Fishes. T* **142** *and similar horiz designs.
Multicoloured. W w* **14** *(sideways). P* 14.

554	1p.	Type **142**	..	10	10
555	2p.	Sergeant Major ("Five Finger")	..	15	15
556	4p.	Resplendent Angelfish	..	20	20
557	5p.	Derbio ("Silver Fish")	..	20	20

558	9p.	Spotted Scorpionfish ("Gurnard")	..	35	35
559	10p.	St Helena Parrotfish ("Blue Dad")	..	35	35
560	15p.	St. Helena Butterflyfish ("Cunning Fish")		50	50
561	15p.	Rock Hind ("Grouper")	..	55	55
562	20p.	Spotted Moray	..	60	60
563	25p.	Squirrelfish ("Hardback Soldierfish")		70	70
564	30p.	Blue Marlin	..	80	80
565	50p.	Wahoo	..	1·40	1·50
566	70p.	Yellow-finned Tuna	..	2·00	2·25
567	£1	Blue Shark	..	2·75	3·00
568	£2.50,	Bottlenose Dolphin	..	6·00	6·50
554/68			*Set of 15*	15·00	16·00

143 Holland's Crater

(Des D. Miller. Litho Questa (70p.), Walsall (others))

1992 (6 Feb). *40th Anniv of Queen Elizabeth II's Accession.
T* **143** *and similar horiz designs. W w* **14** *(sideways). P* 14.

569	9p.	Type **143**	..	30	30
570	15p.	Green Mountain	..	50	50
571	18p.	Boatswain Bird Island	..	60	60
572	25p.	Three portraits of Queen Elizabeth	..	80	80
573	70p.	Queen Elizabeth II	..	2·00	2·00
569/73			*Set of 5*	3·75	3·75

The portraits shown on the 25p. are repeated from the three
lower values of the set.

144 Compass Rose and *Eye of
the Wind* (cadet brig)　　145 Control Tower,
Wideawake Airfield

(Des R. Watton. Litho Walsall)

1992 (18 Feb). *500th Anniv of Discovery of America by
Columbus and Re-enactment Voyages. T* **144** *and similar
horiz designs. Multicoloured. W w* **14** *(sideways). P* 13½×14.

574	9p.	Type **144**	..	75	70
575	18p.	Map of re-enactment voyages and *Soren Larsen* (cadet brigantine)		1·25	1·00
576	25p.	*Santa Maria, Pinta* and *Nina*	..	1·50	1·25
577	70p.	Columbus and *Santa Maria*	..	2·75	2·75
574/7			*Set of 4*	5·75	5·25

(Des N. Shewring. Litho Questa)

1992 (5 May). *50th Anniv of Wideawake Airfield. T* **145** *and
similar square designs. Multicoloured. W w* **14** *(sideways).
P* 14.

578	15p.	Type **145**	..	55	55
579	18p.	Nose hangar	..	60	60
580	25p.	Site preparation by U.S. Army engineers		80	80
581	70p.	Laying fuel pipeline	..	2·25	2·25
578/81			*Set of 4*	3·75	3·75

 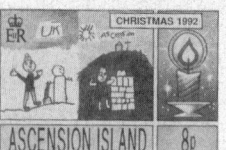

146 Hawker Siddeley　　147 "Christmas in Great
H.S.801 Nimrod　　　　Britain and Ascension"

(Des N. Shewring. Litho Questa)

1992 (12 June). *10th Anniv of Liberation of Falkland Islands.
Aircraft. T* **146** *and similar square designs. Multicoloured.
W w* **14** *(sideways). P* 14.

582	15p.	Type **146**	..	85	75
583	18p.	Vickers VC-10 landing at Ascension		95	85
584	25p.	Westland Wessex HU Mk 5 helicopter lifting supplies		1·10	1·00
585	65p.	Avro Vulcan B.2 over Ascension	..	2·50	2·50
582/5			*Set of 4*	4·75	4·50
MS586		116×116 mm. 15p. + 3p. Type **146**; 18p. + 4p. As No. 583; 25p. +5p. As No. 584; 65p. + 13p. As No. 585		4·25	5·50

The premiums on No. **MS**586 were for the S.S.A.F.A.

(Adapted G. Vasarhelyi. Litho Walsall)

1992 (13 Oct). *Christmas. Children's Paintings. T* **147** *and
similar horiz designs. Multicoloured. W w* **16** *(sideways). P* 14.

587	8p.	Type **147**	..	45	35
588	18p.	"Santa Claus riding turtle"	..	80	70
589	25p.	"Nativity"	..	1·10	1·00
590	65p.	"Nativity with rabbit"	..	2·50	2·50
587/90			*Set of 4*	4·25	4·00

148 Male Canary　　149 Sopwith Snipe
singing

(Des N. Arlott. Litho Questa)

1993 (12 Jan). *Yellow Canary. T* **148** *and similar vert designs.
Multicoloured. W w* **14**. *P* 14½×14.

591	15p.	Type **148**	..	60	50
592	18p.	Adult male and female	..	70	60
593	25p.	Young birds calling for food	..	85	75
594	70p.	Adults and young birds on the wing	..	2·25	2·25
591/4			*Set of 4*	4·00	3·75

(Des A. Theobald. Litho Questa)

1993 (1 Apr). *75th Anniv of Royal Air Force. T* **149** *and similar
horiz designs. Multicoloured. W w* **14** *(sideways). P* 14.

595	20p.	Type **149**	..	80	60
596	25p.	Supermarine Southampton	..	85	65
597	30p.	Avro Type 652 Anson	..	95	75
598	70p.	Vickers-Armstrong Wellington	..	2·00	2·00
595/8			*Set of 4*	4·25	3·50
MS599		110×77 mm. 25p. Westland Lysander; 25p. Armstrong-Whitworth Meteor ("Gloster Meteor"); 25p. De Havilland D.H.106 Comet; 25p. Hawker Siddeley H.S.801 Nimrod		2·40	3·25

150 Map of South Atlantic　　151 Lanatana Camara
Cable

(Des D. Miller. Litho Questa)

1993 (8 June). *25th Anniv of South Atlantic Cable Company.
T* **150** *and similar horiz designs. Multicoloured. W w* **16**
(sideways). P 14½.

600	20p.	Type **150**	..	70	80
601	25p.	*Vercors* laying cable	..	80	80
602	30p.	Map of Ascension	..	90	1·00
603	70p.	*Vercors* (cable ship) off Ascension	..	2·00	2·50
600/3			*Set of 4*	4·00	4·50

(Des N. Shewring. Litho Questa)

1993 (3 Aug). *Local Flowers. T* **151** *and similar horiz designs.
Multicoloured. W w* **16** *(sideways). P* 14×14½.

604	20p.	Type **151**	..	60	60
605	25p.	Moonflower	..	65	65
606	30p.	Hibiscus	..	75	75
607	70p.	Frangipani	..	1·75	1·75
604/7			*Set of 4*	3·25	3·25

 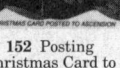

152 Posting　　　153 Ichthyosaurus
Christmas Card to
Ascension

(Des N. Shewring. Litho Walsall)

1993 (19 Oct). *Christmas. T* **152** *and similar vert designs.
Multicoloured. W w* **14**. *P* 14½×14.

608	12p.	Type **152**	..	45	35
609	20p.	Loading mail onto R.A.F. Lockheed L-1011 TriStar at Brize Norton		75	55
610	25p.	Tristar over South Atlantic	..	85	65
611	30p.	Unloading mail at Wideawake Airfield		1·10	75
612	65p.	Receiving card and Georgetown Post Office		1·60	1·60
608/12			*Set of 5*	4·25	3·50
MS613		161×76 mm. Nos. 608/12		5·00	4·50

(Des N. Shewring. Litho B.D.T.)

1994 (25 Jan). *Prehistoric Aquatic Reptiles. T* **153** *and similar
vert designs. Multicoloured. W w* **14**. *P* 14.

614	12p.	Type **153**	..	55	45
615	20p.	Metriorhynchus	..	75	65
616	25p.	Mosasaurus	..	80	70
617	30p.	Elasmosaurus	..	90	85
618	65p.	Plesiosaurus	..	1·75	1·75
614/18			*Set of 5*	4·25	4·00

NEW INFORMATION

The editor is always interested to correspond with
people who have new information that will
improve or correct the Catalogue.

(154)   155 Young Green Turtles
heading towards Sea

1994 (18 Feb). *"Hong Kong '94" International Stamp Exhibition. Nos. 614/18 optd with T* **154**.
619	12p. Type 153	..	..	65	55
620	20p. Metriorhynchus	..	..	85	75
621	25p. Mosasaurus	..	..	90	80
622	30p. Elasmosaurus	..	..	1·00	90
623	65p. Plesiosaurus	..	..	1·90	2·00
619/23			*Set of 5*	4·75	4·50

(Des A. Robinson. Litho Questa)

1994 (22 Mar). *Green Turtles. T* **155** *and similar horiz designs. Multicoloured. W w* **14** *(sideways). P* 14.
624	20p. Type 155	..	..	90	65
625	25p. Turtle digging nest	..	..	95	70
626	30p. Turtle leaving sea	..	..	1·10	85
627	65p. Turtle swimming	..	..	2·00	1·75
624/7			*Set of 4*	4·50	3·50

MS628 116×90 mm. 30p. Turtle leaving sea (*different*); 30p. Turtle digging nest (*different*); 30p. Young turtles heading towards sea (*different*); 30p. Young turtle leaving nest .. 5·00 5·50

156 *Yorkshireman* (tug)

(Des R. Watton. Litho Walsall)

1994 (14 June). *Civilian Ships used in Liberation of Falkland Islands, 1982. T* **156** *and similar horiz designs. Multicoloured. P* 14.
629	20p. Type 156	..	..	80	65
630	25p. *St. Helena I* (minesweeper support ship)	..	..	85	70
631	30p. *British Esk* (tanker)	..	..	95	80
632	65p. *Uganda* (hospital ship)	..	..	1·75	1·75
629/32			*Set of 4*	4·00	3·50

157 Sooty Tern Chick

(Des N. Arlott. Litho Walsall)

1994 (16 Aug). *Sooty Tern. T* **157** *and similar horiz designs. Multicoloured. W w* **14** *(sideways). P* 14½.
633	20p. Type 157	..	..	70	80
634	25p. Juvenile bird	..		75	85
635	30p. Brooding adult	..	..	85	95
636	65p. Adult male performing courting display			1·60	1·90
633/6			*Set of 4*	3·50	4·00

MS637 77×58 mm. £1 Flock of Sooty Terns .. 2·50 3·25

158 Donkey Mare with   159 *Leonurus*
Foal   *japonicus*

(Des Josephine Martin. Litho Questa)

1994 (11 Oct). *Christmas. Donkeys. T* **158** *and similar horiz designs. Multicoloured. W w* **16** *(sideways). P* 14½.
638	12p. Type 158	..	..	55	50
639	20p. Juvenile	..	..	75	70
640	25p. Foal	..	..	80	75
641	30p. Adult and Cattle Egrets	..	..	95	90
642	65p. Adult	..	..	1·90	1·90
638/42			*Set of 5*	4·50	4·25

(Des Jennifer Toombs. Litho Walsall)

1995 (10 Jan). *Flowers. T* **159** *and similar multicoloured designs. W w* **16** *(sideways on horiz designs). P* 14.
643	20p. Type 159	..	..	80	70
644	25p. *Catharanthus roseus* (horiz)	..		90	80
645	30p. *Mirabilis jalapa*	..	..	1·00	90
646	65p. *Asclepias curassavica* (horiz)			2·00	1·75
643/6			*Set of 4*	4·25	3·75

160 Two Boats and Green
Mountain

(Des S. Noon. Litho Questa)

1995 (7 Mar). *Late 19th-century Scenes. T* **160** *and similar horiz designs, each in cinnamon and reddish brown. W w* **16** *(sideways). P* 14×14½.
647	12p. Type 160	..	..	50	50
648	20p. Island Stewards' Store	..	..	70	70
649	25p. Navy headquarters and barracks		80	80
650	30p. Police office	..	..	1·50	1·00
651	65p. Pierhead	..	..	1·75	1·75
647/51			*Set of 5*	4·75	4·25

161 5.5-inch Coastal Battery   162 Male and Female
Lampides boeticus

(Des R. Watton. Litho Questa)

1995 (8 May). *50th Anniv of End of Second World War. T* **161** *and similar multicoloured designs. W w* **16** *(sideways). P* 14.
652	20p. Type 161	..	..	65	65
653	25p. Fairey Swordfish aircraft	..		80	75
654	30p. H.M.S. *Dorsetshire* (cruiser)	..		90	85
655	65p. H.M.S. *Devonshire* (cruiser)	..		1·90	1·60
652/5			*Set of 4*	3·75	3·75

MS656 75×85 mm. £1 Reverse of 1939–45 War Medal (*vert*). *W w* **14** .. .. 2·50 3·25

(Des K. McGee. Litho B.D.T.)

1995 (1 Sept). *Butterflies. T* **162** *and similar vert designs. Multicoloured. W w* **16**. *P* 14.
657	20p. Type 162	..	..	70	65
658	25p. *Vanessa cardui*	..	..	80	75
659	30p. Male *Hypolimnas misippus*	..		95	85
660	65p. *Danaus chrysippus*	..	..	1·90	1·90
657/60			*Set of 4*	4·00	3·75

MS661 114×85 mm. £1 *Vanessa atalanta* .. 3·00 3·00
No. **MS661** includes the "Singapore '95" International Stamp Exhibition logo on the sheet margin.

163 "Santa Claus on Boat"
(Phillip Stephens)

(Des B. Dare. Litho Walsall)

1995 (10 Oct). *Christmas. Children's Drawings. T* **163** *and similar horiz designs. Multicoloured. W w* **14** *(sideways). P* 14.
662	12p. Type 163	..	..	40	45
663	20p. "Santa sitting on Wall" (Kelly Lemon)	65	75
664	25p. "Santa in Chimney" (Mario Anthony)	70	80
665	30p. "Santa riding Dolphin" (Verena Benjamin)			80	90
666	65p. "Santa in Sleigh over Ascension" (Tom Butler)			1·75	2·00
662/6			*Set of 5*	3·75	4·50

164 *Cyprаea lurida oceanica*   165 Queen Elizabeth
II and St. Mary's
Church

(Des I. Loe. Litho B.D.T.)

1996 (10 Jan). *Molluscs. T* **164** *and similar horiz designs. Multicoloured. W w* **16** *(sideways). P* 14.
667	12p. Type 164	..	..	30	30
	a. Horiz strip of 4. Nos. 667/70	..	3·00	
668	25p. *Cypraea spurca sanctaehelenae*	..	55	55
669	30p. *Harpa doris*	..	..	65	65
670	65p. *Umbraculum umbraculum*	..		1·40	1·40
667/70			*Set of 4*	3·00	3·00

Nos. 667/70 were printed together, *se-tenant*, in horizontal strips of 4 throughout the sheet with the backgrounds forming a composite design.

(Des D. Miller. Litho B.D.T.)

1996 (22 Apr). *70th Birthday of Queen Elizabeth II. T* **165** *and similar vert designs. W w* **16**. *P* 13½.
671	20p. Type 165	..	..	55	55
672	25p. The Residency	..	..	60	60
673	30p. The Roman Catholic Grotto	..		70	70
674	65p. The Exiles' Club	..	..	1·75	1·75
671/4			*Set of 4*	3·25	3·25

166 American Army Jeep   167 Madeiran
Storm Petrel

(Des B. Dare. Litho Walsall)

1996 (8 June). *"CAPEX '96" International Stamp Exhibition, Toronto. Island Transport. T* **166** *and similar horiz designs. Multicoloured. W w* **16** *(sideways). P* 14.
675	20p. Type 166	..	..	55	55
676	25p. Citroen 7.5hp two-seater car, 1924	..	60	60
677	30p. Austin ten tourer car, 1930	..		70	70
678	65p. Series 1 Land Rover	..	..	1·75	1·75
675/8			*Set of 4*	3·25	3·25

(Des N. Arlott. Litho Walsall)

1996 (12 Aug). *Birds and their Young. T* **167** *and similar vert designs. Multicoloured. W w* **14**. *P* 13½×13.
679	1p. Type 167	..	..	10	10
680	2p. Red-billed Tropic Bird	..		10	10
681	4p. Common Mynah	..	..	10	10
682	5p. House Sparrow	..	..	10	15
683	7p. Common Waxbill	..	..	15	20
684	10p. White Tern	..	..	20	25
685	12p. Bare-throated Francolin	..		25	30
686	15p. Common Noddy	..	..	30	35
687	20p. Yellow Canary	..	..	40	45
688	25p. Lesser Noddy	..	..	50	55
689	30p. Red-footed Booby	..	..	60	65
690	40p. White-tailed Tropic Bird	..		80	85
691	65p. Brown Booby	..	..	1·25	1·40
692	£1 Blue-faced Booby	..	..	2·00	2·10
693	£2 Sooty Tern	..	..	4·00	4·25
694	£3 Ascension Frigate Bird	..	..	6·00	6·25
679/94			*Set of 16*	16·00	17·00

For 65p. and £1 (with "1997" imprint date) used in miniature sheets see Nos. MS708 and MS718.
For 15p. and 35p. in designs of 7p and 20p, but 20×24 mm from booklets see Nos. 726/7.

168 Pylons   169 Santa Claus on Dish
Aerial

(Des D. Miller. Litho Walsall)

1996 (9 Sept). *30th Anniv of B.B.C. Atlantic Relay Station. T* **168** *and similar horiz designs. Multicoloured. W w* **16** *(sideways). P* 14×14½.
695	20p. Type 168	..	..	55	55
696	25p. Pylons (*different*)	..	..	60	60
697	30p. Pylons and station buildings	..		70	70
698	65p. Dish aerial, pylon and beach	..		1·75	1·75
695/8			*Set of 4*	3·25	3·25

(Des B. Dare. Litho Questa)

1996 (23 Sept). *Christmas. T* **169** *and similar horiz designs showing Santa Claus. Multicoloured. W w* **14** *(sideways). P* 14×14½.
699	12p. Type 169	..	..	35	35
700	20p. Playing golf	..	..	60	65
701	25p. In deck chair	..	..	60	65
702	30p. On top of aircraft	..	..	70	75
703	65p. On funnel of *St. Helena II* (mail ship)	1·60	2·00
699/703			*Set of 5*	3·50	4·00

170 Date Palm

171 Red Ensign and *Maersk Ascension* (tanker)

(Des R. Watton. Litho Walsall)

1997 (7 Jan). *"HONG KONG '97" International Stamp Exhibition. Trees. T* **170** *and similar vert designs. Multicoloured. W* w 14. *P* 14½×14.

704	20p. Type **170**	..	..	45	55
705	25p. Mauritius Hemp	..	..	55	65
706	30p. Norfolk Island Pine	..	..	65	75
707	65p. Dwarf Palm	..	..	1·50	1·60
704/7			*Set of* 4	2·75	3·25

(Des D. Miller. Litho Questa)

1997 (3 Feb). *"HONG KONG '97" International Stamp Exhibition. Sheet 130×90 mm containing design as No. 691. Multicoloured. W* w 14. *P* 14.

MS708	65p. Brown Booby	..	..	1·50	1·50

(Des A. Theobald. Litho Walsall)

1997 (1 Apr). *Flags. T* **171** *and similar vert designs. Multicoloured. W* w 14. *P* 14½.

709	12p. Type **171**	..	..	35	40
710	25p. R.A.F. flag and Tristar airliner		65	70
711	30p. N.A.S.A. emblem amd Space Shuttle *Atlantis* landing		75	80
712	65p. White Ensign and H.M.S. *Northumberland* (frigate)		1·40	1·60
709/12			*Set of* 4	2·75	3·25

172 *Solanum sodomaeum*

173 Queen Elizabeth II

(Des I. Loe. Litho Questa)

1997 (2 June). *Wild Herbs. T* **172** *and similar horiz designs. Multicoloured. W* w 14 (*sideways*). *P* 14½.

713	30p. Type **172**	..	..	90	1·00
	a. Horiz strip of 5. Nos. 713/17	..	4·00	
714	30p. *Ageratum conyzoides*	..	..	90	1·00
715	30p. *Leonurus sibiricus*	..	..	90	1·00
716	30p. *Cerastium vulgatum*	..	..	90	1·00
717	30p. *Commelina diffusa*	..	..	90	1·00
713/17			*Set of* 5	4·00	4·50

Nos. 713/17 were printed together, *se-tenant*, in horizontal strips of 5 with the backgrounds forming a composite design.

(Des D. Miller. Litho Questa)

1997 (20 June). *Return of Hong Kong to China. Sheet 130×90 mm containing design as No. 692, but with "1997" imprint date. W* w 14 (*inverted*). *P* 13½×13.

MS718	£1 Blue-faced Booby	..	..	2·00	2·10

(Des N. Shewring (No. MS725), D. Miller (others). Litho Questa (No. MS725), B.D.T. (others))

1997 (10 July). *Golden Wedding of Queen Elizabeth and Prince Philip. T* **173** *and similar vert designs. Multicoloured. W* w 16. *P* 13½.

719	20p. Type **173**	..	..	50	50
	a. Horiz pair. Nos. 719/20	..	1·00	1·00
720	20p. Prince Philip on horseback	..	50	50
721	25p. Queen Elizabeth with polo pony		65	65
	a. Horiz pair. Nos. 721/2	..	1·25	1·25
722	25p. Prince Philip in Montserrat	..	65	65
723	30p. Queen Elizabeth and Prince Philip		80	80
	a. Horiz pair. Nos. 723/4	..	1·60	1·60
724	30p. Prince William and Prince Harry on horseback	..	..	80	80
719/24			*Set of* 6	3·50	3·50
MS725	110×70 mm. $1.50, Queen Elizabeth and Prince Philip in landau (*horiz*). W w 14 (*sideways*). P 14×14½			3·50	3·50

Nos. 719/20, 721/2 and 723/4 were each printed together, *se-tenant*, in horizontal pairs throughout the sheets with the backgrounds forming composite designs.

(Des N. Arlott. Litho Walsall)

1997 (1 Sept). *Booklet Stamps. Birds and their Young. Designs as Nos. 683 and 687, but smaller, size 20×24 mm. W* w 14 (*sideways*). *P* 14.

726	15p. Common Waxbill	..	..	30	35
	a. Booklet pane. Nos. 726/7, each ×2		2·00	
727	35p. Yellow Canary	..	..	70	75

No. 726a has the vertical edges of the booklet pane imperforate so that Nos. 726/7 exist imperforate at left or right.

174 Black Marlin

175 Interior of St. Mary's Church

(Des R. Watton. Litho Walsall)

1997 (3 Sept). *Gamefish. T* **174** *and similar horiz designs. Multicoloured. W* w 16 (*sideways*). *P* 14×14½.

728	12p. Type **174**	..	..	40	40
729	20p. Atlantic Sailfish	..	..	65	65
730	25p. Swordfish	..	..	75	75
731	30p. Wahoo	..	..	85	85
732	£1 Yellowfin Tuna	..	..	2·25	2·25
728/32			*Set of* 5	4·50	4·50

(Des G. Vasarhelyi. Litho Walsall)

1997 (1 Oct). *Christmas. T* **175** *and similar vert designs. W* w 16. *P* 14.

733	15p. Type **175**	..	..	30	35
734	35p. Falklands memorial window showing Virgin and Child		70	75
735	40p. Falklands memorial window showing Archangel		80	85
736	50p. Pair of stained glass windows	..	1·00	1·10
733/6			*Set of* 4	2·75	3·00

STAMP BOOKLETS

1963 (23 May). *Buff cover. Stitched.*

SB1	10s.6d. booklet containing 1d., 1½d., 2d., 3d., 6d. and 1s. 6d. (Nos. 70/3, 75, 79), each in block of 4 70·00

1971 (15 Feb). *White cover. Stitched.*

SB2	44p. booklet containing ½p., 1p., 1½p., 2p., 2½p. and 3½p. (Nos 135/40), each in block of 4 ... 17·00
	a. "5/71" imprint on back cover .. .. 30·00

1981 (9 Nov)–**84**. *Printed cover, 104×58 mm, showing Ascension landscape. A. Black and pink cover. Stapled at left. B. Black and lemon cover. Stapled at right. (4.84).*

		A	B
SB3	£1.20, booklet containing 2p., 3p., 10p. and 15p. (Nos. 283A/4A, 288A, 290A), each in block of 4	12·00	10·00

1982 (15 June). *Blue, red and brown cover, 101×60 mm, showing World War II aircraft. A. Cover stapled at left and inscriptions printed in brown. B. Cover stapled at right and inscriptions printed in blue.*

		A	B
SB4	60p. booklet containing 5p. and 10p. (Nos. 318/19), each in block of 4 ..	6·00	6·00

1989 (17 Nov). *Blackish olive and deep brown cover, 54×41 mm, showing turtle and outline map of Ascension. Panes attached by selvedge.*

SB5	£1 booklet containing pane of 6 (No. 510a)	..	2·25
SB6	£1 booklet containing pane of 4 (No. 511a)	..	2·25

1989 (17 Nov). *As Nos. SB5/6, but with "Expo 89" logo printed on cover in black.*

SB7	£1 booklet containing pane of 6 (No. 510a)	..	4·25
SB8	£1 booklet containing pane of 4 (No. 511a)	..	4·25

1997 (1 Sept). *Cover as Nos. SB5/6. Pane attached by selvedge.*

SB9	£1 booklet containing pane of 4 (No. 726a)	..	2·00

POSTAGE DUE STAMPS

D 1 Outline Map of Ascension

(Des L. Curtis. Litho Questa)

1986 (9 June). *W* w 16. *P* 14½×14.

D1	D 1	1p. deep brown and cinnamon	..	10	10
D2		2p. deep brown and bright orange	..	10	10
D3		5p. deep brown and orange-vermilion	..	10	10
D4		7p. black and bright reddish violet	..	15	20
D5		10p. black and violet-blue	..	20	25
D6		25p. black and pale emerald	..	50	55
D1/6	..	..	*Set of* 6	1·10	1·25

HELP!

Even the most knowledgeable collector can be faced by philatelic terms of which he does not know the meaning – if this has ever been your problem then you need:

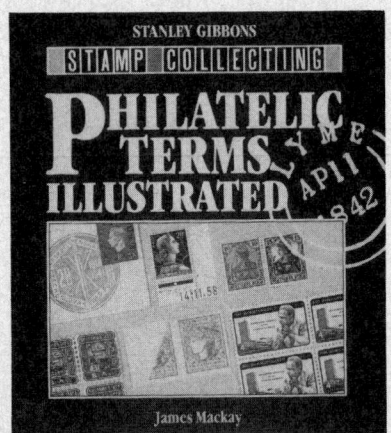

STANLEY GIBBONS
STAMP COLLECTING
PHILATELIC TERMS ILLUSTRATED

James Mackay

PHILATELIC TERMS ILLUSTRATED

Now completely revised and updated in a bright new format as part of the popular Stanley Gibbons 'Stamp Collecting' series.

The new edition of this useful book not only includes all the terms which have come into use since publication of the second edition in 1978 but also provides much new information on postal markings and services.

Noted philatelic author and journalist, James Mackay, has carefully updated and augmented the original text of Russell Bennett and James Watson to produce a work of great assistance to the postal historian and an indispensable aid to stamp identification.

Fully illustrated in colour or black and white, its encyclopedic style and helpful system of cross-referencing makes Philatelic Terms Illustrated extremely easy to use and provides a helpful work of reference for all collectors from the youngest beginner to the most advanced specialist.

Available direct from:

Stanley Gibbons Publications, Parkside, Christchurch Road, Ringwood, Hampshire BH24 3SH Telephone: 01425 472363

Australia

The Australian colonies of New South Wales, Queensland, South Australia, Tasmania, Victoria and Western Australia produced their own issues before federation in 1901. Stamps inscribed for the individual states continued in use after federation until the end of December 1912.

NEW SOUTH WALES

PRICES FOR STAMPS ON COVER

Nos. 1/83	*from* ×2
Nos. 84/110	*from* ×3
No. 110*b*	*from* ×10
Nos. 111/13	*from* × 2
No. 114	—
Nos. 115/24	*from* × 2
Nos. 125/6	—
Nos. 127/53	*from* × 2
Nos. 154/70	*from* × 3
Nos. 171/2	—
No. 173	*from* × 2
Nos. 174/81	—
Nos. 186/202	*from* × 2
Nos. 203/6	*from* × 10
Nos. 207/21	*from* × 5
Nos. 222/39	*from* × 6
Nos. 240/1	*from* × 2
Nos. 241*a*/3	*from* × 10
Nos. 244/52	—
Nos. 253/73	*from* × 10
Nos. 274/80	—
Nos. 281/4	*from* × 15
Nos. 285/7	*from* × 10
Nos. 287*c*/*d*	*from* × 2
Nos. 288/97	*from* × 12
Nos. 298/312	*from* × 10
Nos. 313/28	*from* × 10
No. 329	—
Nos. 330/45	*from* × 12
No. 346	—
Nos. 347/60	*from* × 12
No. O1	—
Nos. O2/12	*from* × 4
Nos. O13/18	—
Nos. O19/34	*from* × 20
Nos. O35/8	—
Nos. O39/47	*from* × 40
Nos. O48/53	—
Nos. O54/8	*from* × 20
No. O59	—
Nos. D1/7	*from* × 50
Nos. D8/10	—
Nos. D11/15	*from* × 50

NEW SOUTH WALES USED IN NEW CALEDONIA. From October 1859 mail for Europe from New Caledonia was routed via Sydney and franked with New South Wales stamps in combination with local issues. Such N.S.W. stamps were cancelled on arrival in Sydney.

PRINTERS. The early issues of New South Wales were printed on a press supervised by the Inspector of Stamps. On 1 January 1857 this responsibility passed to the Government printer who produced all subsequent issues, *unless otherwise stated.*

SPECIMEN OVERPRINTS. Those listed are from U.P.U. distributions between 1892 and 1903. Further "Specimen" overprints exist, but these were used for other purposes. From 1891 examples of some of these Specimens, together with cancelled stamps, were sold to collectors by the N.S.W. Post Office.

1   2

(Eng Robert Clayton, Sydney)

1850 (1 Jan). *T* **1**. *Plate I. No clouds.* (a) *Soft yellowish paper.*
1	1d. crimson-lake		£4250	£450
2	1d. carmine		£4000	£400
3	1d. reddish rose		£3750	£375
4	1d. brownish red		£4000	£400

(b) *Hard bluish paper*
5	1d. pale red		£3750	£375
6	1d. dull lake		£4000	£400

1850 (Aug). *T* **2**. *Plate I, re-engraved by H. C. Jervis, commonly termed Plate II. With clouds.* (a) *Hard toned white to yellowish paper.*
7	1d. vermilion		£2500	£300
8	1d. dull carmine		£2500	£300
	a. No trees on hill (R.2/2)		£4500	£475
	b. Hill unshaded (R.2/3)		£4500	£475
	c. Without clouds (R.3/5)		£4500	£475

(b) *Hard greyish or bluish paper*
9	1d. crimson-lake		£2500	£300
10	1d. gooseberry-red		£3000	£450
11	1d. dull carmine		£2250	£275
12	1d. brownish red		£2250	£275
	a. No trees on hill (R.2/2)		£4500	£475
	b. Hill unshaded (R.2/3)		£4500	£475
	c. Without clouds (R.3/5)		£4500	£475

(c) *Laid paper*
13	1d. carmine		£4000	£475
14	1d. vermilion		£4500	£450
	a. No trees on hill (R.2/2)		—	£800
	b. Hill unshaded (R.2/3)		—	£800
	c. Without clouds (R.3/5)		—	£800

The varieties quoted with the letters "a", "b", "c" of course exist in each shade; the prices quoted are for the commonest shade, and the same applies to the following portions of this list.
Nos. 1/14 were printed in sheets of 25 (5×5).

LAID PAPER. Nos. 13/14, 34/5, 38 and 43*d*/*e* can be found showing parts of the papermaker's watermark (T. H. SAUNDERS 1847 in double-lined capitals and the figure of Britannia seated in an oval beneath a crown).

3   4   A (Pl I)

Illustrations A, B, C, and D are sketches of the lower part of the inner circular frame, showing the characteristic variations of each plate.

(Eng John Carmichael)

1850 (1 Jan). *Plate I. Vertical-lined background. T* **3**.

(a) *Early impressions, full details of clouds, etc.*
15	2d. greyish blue		£4500	£375
16	2d. deep blue		—	£425
	a. Double lines on bale (R.2/7)		—	£650

(b) *Intermediate impressions*
16*b*	2d. greyish blue		£3000	£275
16*c*	2d. deep blue		£3250	£325

(c) *Later impressions, clouds, etc., mostly gone, T* **4**
17	2d. blue		£2250	£150
18	2d. dull blue		£1800	£140

(d) *Stamps in the lower row partially retouched (end Jan)*
19	2d. blue		£3000	£275
20	2d. greyish blue		£2750	£225

5   B (Pl II)   C (Pl III)

(Plate entirely re-engraved by H. C. Jervis)

1850 (Apr). *T* **5**. *Plate II. Horizontal-lined background. Bale on left side supporting the seated figure, dated. Dot in centre of the star in each corner.* (a) *Early impressions.*
21	2d. indigo		£3500	£275
22	2d. lilac-blue		—	£1000
23	2d. grey-blue		£3500	£225
24	2d. bright blue		£3500	£225
	a. Fan as in Pl III, but with shading outside (R.1/1)		—	£375
	b. Fan as in Pl III, but without shading, and inner circle intersects the fan (R.1/2)		—	£375
	c. Pick and shovel omitted (R.1/10)		—	£375
	d. "CREVIT" omitted (R.2/1)		—	£600
	e. No whip (R.1/4, 1/8, 2/8)		—	£300

(b) *Worn impressions*
25	2d. dull blue		£1800	£130
26	2d. Prussian blue		£1900	£170
	a. Fan as in Pl III, but with shading outside (R.1/1)		—	£300
	b. Fan as in Pl III, but without shading, and inner circle intersects the fan (R.1/2)		—	£300
	c. Pick and shovel omitted (R.1/10)		—	£300
	d. "CREVIT" omitted (R.2/1)		—	£400
	e. No whip (R.1/4, 1/8, 2/8)		£2500	£225

(c) *Bottom row retouched with dots and dashes in lower spandrels (Aug)*
27	2d. Prussian blue		£2750	£225
28	2d. dull blue		£2500	£150
	a. No whip (R.2/8)		—	£250
	b. "CREVIT" omitted (R.2/1)		—	£375

(Plate re-engraved a second time by H.C. Jervis)

1850 (Sept). *Plate III. Bale not dated and single-lined, except on No. 30c which is doubled-lined. No dots in stars.*
29	2d. ultramarine		£2250	£160
30	2d. deep blue		£2250	£160
	a. No whip (R.2/3, 2/7)		—	£250
	b. Fan with 6 segments (R.2/8)		—	£375
	c. Double lines on bale (R. 1/7, 1/10, 1/12)		—	£225

(Plate re-engraved a third time by H. C. Jervis)

1851 (Jan). *Plate IV. Double-lined bale, and circle in centre of each star.* (a) *Hard bluish grey wove paper.*
31	2d. ultramarine		£2750	£160
32	2d. Prussian blue		£2250	£130
33	2d. bright blue		£2500	£150
	a. Hill not shaded (R.1/12)		—	£225
	b. Fan with 6 segments (R.2/8)		—	£225
	c. No clouds (R.2/10)		—	£225
	d. Retouch (R.2/1)		—	£300
	e. No waves (R.1/9, 2/5)		—	£190

(b) *Stout yellowish vertically laid paper*
34	2d. ultramarine		£2750	£170

35	2d. Prussian blue		£3000	£180
	a. Hill not shaded (R.1/12)		—	£250
	b. Fan with 6 segments (R.2/8)		—	£250
	c. No clouds (R.2/10)		—	£250
	d. Retouch (R.2/1)		—	£325
	e. No waves (R.1/9, 2/5)		—	£200
	f. "PENOE" (R.1/10, 2/12)		—	£250

The retouch, Nos. 33d and 35d., occurs outside the left margin line on R.2/1.

6   D (Pl V)   7

(Plate re-engraved a fourth time by H. C. Jervis)

1851 (Apr). *T* **6**. *Plate V. Pearl in fan.* (a) *Hard greyish wove paper.*
36	2d. ultramarine		£2500	£140
37	2d. dull blue		£2500	£140
	a. Pick and shovel omitted (R.2/5)		—	£250
	b. Fan with 6 segments (R.2/8)		—	£250

(b) *Stout yellowish vertically laid paper*
38	2d. dull ultramarine		£3750	£300
	a. Pick and shovel omitted (R.2/5)		—	£425
	b. Fan with 6 segments (R.2/8)		—	£425

Nos. 15/38 were printed in sheets of 24 (12×2), although the existence of an inter-panneau *tête-bêche* pair from Plate II indicates that the printer applied two impressions of the plate to each sheet of paper. The two panes were normally separated before issue. The original plate I was re-cut four times to form Plates II to V. An interesting variety occurs on R.1/9-11 and 2/7 in all five plates. It consists of ten loops of the engine-turning on each side of the design instead of the normal nine loops.

(Eng H. C. Jervis)

1850. *T* **7**. (a) *Soft yellowish wove paper.*
39	3d. yellow-green		£3000	£250
40	3d. myrtle-green		£10000	£1000
41	3d. emerald-green		£3500	£275
	a. No whip (R.4/3–4)		—	£375
	b. "SIGIIIUM" for "SIGILLUM" (R.5/3)		—	£450

(b) *Bluish to grey wove paper*
42	3d. yellow-green		£2500	£225
43	3d. emerald-green		£3000	£225
	b. No whip (R.4/3–4)		—	£300
	c. "SIGIIIUM" for "SIGILLUM" (R.5/3)		—	£375

(c) *Yellowish to bluish laid paper*
43*d*	3d. bright green		£5500	£500
43*e*	3d. yellowish green		£5000	£450
	f. No whip (R.4/3–4)		—	£650
	g. "SIGIIIUM" for "SIGILLUM" (R.5/3)		—	£750

Nos. 39/43*e* were printed in sheets of 25 (5×5).
A used example of No. 42 is known printed double, one albino.

8   9

(Des A. W. Manning from sketch by W. T. Levine; eng on steel by John Carmichael, Sydney)

1851 (18 Dec)–**52**. *Imperf.* (a) *Thick yellowish wove paper*
44	8	1d. carmine	£1800	£190
	a. No leaves right of "SOUTH" (R.1/7, 3/1)		—	£375
	b. Two leaves right of "SOUTH" (R.2/5)		—	£450
	c. "WALE" (R.1/9)		—	£450

(b) *Bluish medium wove paper* (1852)
45	8	1d. carmine	£1000	£120
46		1d. scarlet	£1000	£120
47		1d. vermilion	£900	£100
48		1d. brick-red	£900	£100
	a. No leaves right of "SOUTH" (R.1/7, 3/1)		—	£225
	b. Two leaves right of "SOUTH" (R.2/5)		—	£300
	c. "WALE" (R.1/9)		—	£300

(c) *Thick vertically laid bluish paper* (1852?)
49	8	1d. orange-brown	£3000	£350
50		1d. claret	£3000	£375
	a. No leaves right of "SOUTH" (R.1/7, 3/1)		—	£550
	b. Two leaves right of "SOUTH" ((R.2/5)		—	£650
	c. "WALE" (R.1/9)		—	£650

Nos. 44/50 were printed in sheets of 50 (10×5).

(Eng on steel by John Carmichael)

1851 (21 July). *Plate I. Imperf.* (a) *Thick yellowish wove paper*
51	8	2d. ultramarine	£800	80·00

(b) *Fine impressions, blue to greyish medium paper*
52	8	2d. ultramarine	£750	30·00
53		2d. chalky blue	£650	30·00
54		2d. dark blue	£650	30·00
55		2d. greyish blue	£650	30·00

(c) *Worn plate, blue to greyish medium paper*
56	8	2d. ultramarine	£450	30·00
57		2d. Prussian blue	£450	30·00

(d) *Worn plate, blue wove medium paper*
58	8	2d. ultramarine	£350	30·00
59		2d. Prussian blue	£325	30·00

Nos. 51/9 were printed in sheets of 50 (10×5).

(Plate II eng H. C. Jervis)

1853 (Oct). *Plate II. Stars in corners. Imperf.*

(a) *Bluish medium to thick wove paper*
60	9	2d. deep ultramarine	£1000	£110
61		2d. indigo	£1100	80·00
	a. "WAEES" (R.3/3)		—	£375

(b) *Worn plate, hard blue wove paper*

62	9	2d. deep Prussian blue	..	£1000	£100
		a. "WAEES" (R.3/3)	..	—	£375

Nos. 60/2 were printed in sheets of 50 (10×5).

1855 (Sept). *Plate III, being Plate I (T 8) re-engraved by H. C. Jervis. Background of crossed lines. Imperf.*

(a) *Medium bluish wove paper*

63		2d. Prussian blue	..	£475	55·00
		a. "WALES" partly covered with wavy lines (R.1/3)	..	—	£190

(b) *Stout white wove paper*

64		2d. Prussian blue	..	£475	55·00
		a. "WALES" partly covered with wavy lines (R.1/3)	..	—	£190

Nos. 63/4 were printed in sheets of 50 (10×5).

(Eng John Carmichael)

1852 (3 Dec). *Imperf. (a) Medium greyish blue wove paper*

65	8	3d. deep green	..	£1600	£200
66		3d. green	..	£1300	£140
67		3d. dull yellow-green	..	£1200	£100
		a. "WAEES" with centre bar of first "E" missing (R.4/7)	..	—	£350

(b) *Thick blue wove paper*

69	8	3d. emerald-green	..	£1600	£200
71		3d. blue-green	..	£1600	£200
		a. "WAEES" with centre bar of first "E" missing (R.4/7)	..	—	£550

Nos. 65/71 were printed in sheets of 50 (10×5).

1852 (Apr). *Fine background. Imperf.*

(a) *Medium white wove paper*

72	8	6d. vandyke-brown	..	—	£900
		a. "WALLS" (R.2/3)	..	—	£1500

(b) *Medium bluish grey wove paper*

73	8	6d. vandyke-brown	..	£1700	£250
74		6d. yellow-brown	..	£1800	£275
75		6d. chocolate-brown	..	£1700	£250
76		6d. grey-brown	..	£1600	£250
		a. "WALLS" (R.2/3)	..	—	£500

Examples of the 6d. in vandyke-brown on thick yellowish paper are proofs.

1853 (June). *Plate I re-engraved by H. C. Jervis. Coarse background. Imperf.*

77		6d. brown	..	£1800	£300
78		6d. grey-brown	..	£1700	£300

Nos. 72/6 and 77/8 were printed in sheets of 25 (5×5).

(Eng H. C. Jervis)

1853 (May). *Medium bluish paper. Imperf.*

79		8d. dull yellow	..	£3500	£600
80		8d. orange-yellow	..	£3500	£600
81		8d. orange	..	£3750	£650
		a. No bow at back of head (R.1/9)	..	—	£1300
		b. No leaves right of "SOUTH" (R.3/1)	..	—	£1300
		c. No lines in spandrel (R.2/3, 3/2, 4/2)	..	—	£800

Nos. 79/81 were issued in sheets of 50 (10×5).

10	13	14

NOTE. All watermarked stamps from No. 82 to No. 172 have double-lined figures, as T **10**.

1854 (Feb). *Wmk "1", T 10. Yellowish wove paper. Imperf.*

82	8	1d. red-orange	..	£170	16·00
83		1d. orange-vermilion	..	£170	16·00
		a. No leaves right of "SOUTH" (R.1/7, 3/1)	..	£350	85·00
		b. Two leaves right of "SOUTH" (R.2/5)	..	£475	£120
		c. "WALE" (R.1/9)	..	£475	£120

Nos. 82/3 were printed in sheets of 50 (10×5).

1854 (Jan). *Plate III. Wmk "2". Imperf.*

84		2d. ultramarine	..	£110	10·00
85		2d. Prussian blue	..	£110	10·00
86		2d. chalky blue	..	£110	8·00
		a. "WALES" partly covered by wavy lines (R.1/3)	..	£425	50·00

Nos. 84/6 were printed in sheets of 50 (10×5).

1854 (Mar). *Wmk "3". Imperf.*

87	8	3d. yellow-green	..	£200	27·00
		a. "WAEES" with centre bar of first "E" missing (R. 4/7)	..	—	£120
		b. Error. Wmk "2"	..	£3000	£1500

No. 87 was printed in sheets of 50 (10×5).

(Eng John Carmichael)

1856 (1 Jan). *For Registered Letters. T 13. No wmk. Imperf. Soft medium yellowish paper.*

88		(6d.) vermilion and Prussian blue	..	£700	£150
		a. Frame printed on back	..	£2500	£2000
89		(6d.) salmon and indigo	..	£700	£170
90		(6d.) orange and Prussian blue	..	£700	£200
91		(6d.) orange and indigo	..	£700	£180

1859 (Apr)—**60.** *Hard medium bluish wove paper, with manufacturer's wmk in sans-serif, double-lined capitals across sheet and only showing portions of letters on a few stamps in a sheet.*

(a) *Imperf.*

92		(6d.) orange and Prussian blue	..	£700	£130

(b) *P 12 (2.60)*

93		(6d.) orange and Prussian blue	..	£350	40·00
94		(6d.) orange and indigo	..	£325	40·00

1860 (Feb)—**62.** *Coarse yellowish wove paper having the manufacturer's wmk in Roman capitals. (a) P 12.*

95		(6d.) rose-red and Prussian blue	..	£250	35·00
96		(6d.) rose-red and indigo	..	£325	80·00
97		(6d.) salmon and indigo	..		

(b) *P 13 (1862)*

98		(6d.) rose-red and Prussian blue	..	£225	50·00

1863 (May). *Yellowish wove paper. Wmk "6". P 13.*

99		(6d.) rose-red and Prussian blue	..	90·00	15·00
100		(6d.) rose-red and indigo	..	£140	17·00
101		(6d.) rose-red and pale blue	..	70·00	15·00
		a. Double impression of frame	..	—	£500

(T **14/21** and **24** printed by the New South Wales Govt Ptg Dept from plates engraved by Perkins, Bacon & Co)

Two plates of the 2d. and 6d. were used. On Plate II of the 2d. the stamps are wider apart and more regularly spaced than on Plate I.

1856 (6 Apr). *Wmk "1". Imperf.*

102	14	1d. orange-vermilion	..	£150	22·00
		a. Error. Wmk "2"			
103		1d. carmine-vermilion	..	£150	22·00
104		1d. orange-red	..	£150	22·00
		a. Printed on both sides	..	£1400	£1400

1856 (7 Jan)—**58.** *Plate I. Wmk "2". Imperf.*

105	14	2d. deep turquoise-blue	..	£140	8·00
106		2d. ultramarine	..	£130	8·00
107		2d. blue	..	£130	8·00
		a. Major retouch (1858)	..	£1800	£450
		b. Error. Wmk "1"	..	—	£4000
		c. Wmk "5" (3.57)	..	£450	60·00
		d. Error. Wmk "8"			
108		2d. pale blue	..	£130	8·00

The 2d. Plate I was retouched, on a total of ten positions, several times.

No. 107c comes from a printing made when supplies of the "2" paper were unavailable.

1859 (3 Aug). *Lithographic transfer of Plate I.*

110	14	2d. pale blue	..	—	£750
		a. Retouched	..	—	£2500

1860 (Jan). *Plate II. Recess. Stamps printed wider apart and with a white patch between the "A" of "WALES" and the back of the Queen's head.*

110b	14	2d. blue	..	£500	50·00

No. 110b was principally issued to post offices in Queensland.

1856 (10 Oct). *Wmk "3". Imperf.*

111	14	3d. yellow-green	..	£800	80·00
112		3d. bluish green	..	£850	80·00
113		3d. dull green	..	£850	80·00
		a. Error. Wmk "2"	..	—	£3000

In the 3d. the value is in block letters on a white ground.

15	17
19	21

(6d. and 1s. des E. H. Corbould after sketches by T. W. Levinge)

1855 (1 Dec). *Wmk "5". Imperf.*

114	15	5d. dull green	..	£1000	£550

1854 (1 Feb)—**59.** *Wmk "6". Imperf.*

115	17	6d. deep slate	..	£500	32·00
		a. Wmk sideways	..	†	£750
116		6d. greenish grey	..	£400	32·00
117		6d. slate-green	..	£400	32·00
		a. Printed both sides			
118		6d. bluish grey	..	£450	55·00
119		6d. fawn	..	£500	95·00
		a. Wmk "8" (15.8.59)	..	£1600	£110
120		6d. grey	..	£450	55·00
121		6d. olive-grey	..	£450	32·00
122		6d. greyish brown	..	£450	32·00
		a. Wmk "8" (15.8.59)	..	£1600	£110
		ab. Wmk sideways	..	—	£350

Nos. 119a and 122a come from a printing made when supplies of the "6" paper were unavailable.

1855 (1 Dec). *Wmk "8". Imperf.*

125	19	8d. golden yellow	..	£4000	£850
126		8d. dull yellow-orange	..	£3500	£800

1854 (Feb)—**57.** *Wmk "12". Imperf.*

127	21	1s. rosy vermilion	..	£750	65·00
		a. Wmk "8" (20.6.57)	..	£2000	£180
128		1s. pale red	..	£750	65·00
129		1s. brownish red	..	£800	75·00

No. 127a comes from a printing made when supplies of the "12" paper were unavailable.

1860 (14 Feb)—**63.** *Wmk double-lined figure of value. P 12.*

131	14	1d. orange-red	..	£170	16·00
		a. Imperf between (pair)			
		b. Double impression			
132		1d. scarlet	..	£100	16·00
133		2d. pale blue (Pl I)	..	£500	£140
		a. Retouched	..	—	£1300
134		2d. greenish blue (Pl II)	..	90·00	10·00

136	14	2d. Prussian blue (Pl II)	..	90·00	10·00
		a. Error. Wmk "1"	..	—	£2750
		b. Retouched (shades)	..	—	£400
137		2d. Prussian blue (Pl I) (3.61)	..	£110	11·00
138		2d. dull blue (Pl I)	..	£100	10·00
139		3d. yellow-green (1860)	..	£1000	55·00
140		3d. blue-green	..	£550	42·00
141	15	5d. dull green (1863)	..	£100	35·00
142		5d. yellowish green (1863)	..	£100	35·00
143	17	6d. grey-brown	..	£275	45·00
144		6d. olive-brown	..	£275	55·00
145		6d. greenish grey	..	£350	45·00
146		6d. fawn	..	£325	65·00
147		6d. mauve	..	£300	35·00
148		6d. violet	..	£275	16·00
		a. Imperf between (pair)	..	—	£1400
149	19	8d. lemon-yellow	..	£275	45·00
150		8d. orange	..	£2250	£650
151		8d. red-orange	..	£2250	£650
152	21	1s. brownish red	..	£450	48·00
153		1s. rose-carmine	..	£450	48·00
		a. Imperf between (pair)			

No. 133 was made by perforating a small remaining stock of No. 108. Nos. 137/8 were printed from the original plate after its return from London, where it had been repaired.

1862–72. *Wmk double-lined figure of value. (a) P 13.*

154	14	1d. scarlet (1862)	..	55·00	8·00
155		1d. dull red	..	55·00	8·00
156		3d. blue-green (12.62)	..	45·00	11·00
157		3d. yellow-green	..	50·00	8·50
		a. Wmk "6" (7.72)	..	£100	12·00
158		3d. dull green	..	50·00	8·00
		a. Wmk "6" (7.72)	..	£100	15·00
160	15	5d. bluish green (12.63)	..	38·00	15·00
161		5d. bright yellow-green (8.65)	..	60·00	28·00
162		5d. sea-green (1866)	..	42·00	17·00
162a		5d. dark bluish green (11.70)	..	30·00	17·00
163	17	6d. reddish purple (Pl I) (7.62)	..	80·00	5·50
164		6d. mauve	..	80·00	5·50
165		6d. purple (Pl II) (1864)	..	55·00	4·50
		a. Wmk "5" (7.66)	..	£350	25·00
		b. Wmk "12" (12.66 and 1868)	..	£275	20·00
166		6d. violet	..	55·00	6·00
167		6d. aniline mauve	..	£900	£120
167a	19	8d. red-orange	..	£140	55·00
167b		8d. yellow-orange	..	£150	40·00
167c		8d. bright yellow	..	£140	40·00
168	21	1s. rose-carmine	..	70·00	7·50
169		1s. carmine	..	70·00	8·00
170		1s. crimson-lake	..	70·00	8·00

(b) *Perf compound 12×13*

171	14	1d. scarlet	..	—	£1700
172		2d. dull blue (1.62)	..	£2000	£180

Nos. 157a, 158a and 165a/b come from printings made when supplies of paper with the correct face value were unavailable.

23

1864 (June). *W 23. P 13.*

173	14	1d. pale red	..	38·00	13·00

24	25

(Des E. H. Corbould, R.I.)

1861–88. *W 25. Various perfs.*

174	24	5s. dull violet, p. 12 (1861)	..	£1000	£325
		a. Perf 13 (1861)	..	£160	28·00
175		5s. royal purple, p 13 (1872)	..	£275	45·00
176		5s. deep rose-lilac, p 13 (1875)	..	95·00	28·00
177		5s. deep purple, p 13 (1880)	..	£150	40·00
		a. Perf 10 (1882)	..	£150	45·00
178		5s. rose-lilac, p 10 (1883)	..	£110	40·00
179		5s. purple, p 12 (1885)	..	—	45·00
		a. Perf 10 × 12 (1885)	..	—	£120
180		5s. reddish purple, p 10 (1886)	..	£110	40·00
		a. Perf 12 × 10 (1887)	..	£225	45·00
181		5s. rose-lilac, p 11 (1888)	..	—	£120

This value was replaced by Nos. 261, etc. in 1888 but reissued in 1897, see Nos. 297c/e.

26	28	29

(Printed by De La Rue & Co, Ltd, London and perf at Somerset House, London)

1862–65. *Surfaced paper.* P 14. (i) W **23**.
186 **26** 1d. dull red .. .. 80·00 28·00

(ii) *No wmk*

187 **26** 1d. dull red (Pl II) (1.65) .. .. 60·00 28·00
188 **28** 2d. pale blue (3.62) .. .. .. 60·00 28·00

(Printed from the De La Rue plates in the Colony)

1862 (12 Apr). *Wmk double-lined* "**2**". P 13.
189 **28** 2d. blue .. .. 45·00 7·00
  a. Perf 12 .. .. £120 30·00
  b. Perf 12 × 13 .. .. .. £400

1864–65. W **23**. P 13.
190 **26** 1d. dark red-brown (Pl I) .. .. 70·00 14·00
191   1d. brownish red (Pl II) .. 18·00 1·50
  a. Imperf between (horiz pair) .. † £500
192   1d. brick-red (Pl II) .. .. 18·00 1·50
  a. Highly surfaced paper (1865) .. £180
194 **28** 2d. pale blue .. .. .. £110 3·50
Plates I and II were made from the same die; they can only be distinguished by the colour or by the marginal inscription.

1865–66. *Thin wove paper. No wmk.* P 13.
195 **26** 1d. brick-red .. .. .. 90·00 15·00
196   1d. brownish red .. .. 90·00 15·00
197 **28** 2d. pale blue .. .. .. 40·00 3·00

1863–69. W **29**. P 13.
198 **26** 1d. pale red (3.69) .. .. 70·00 11·00
199 **28** 2d. pale blue .. .. .. 8·50 50
  a. Perf 12
200   2d. cobalt-blue .. .. .. 8·50 50
201   2d. Prussian blue .. .. 21·00 3·50

1862 (Sept). *Wmk double-lined* "**5**". P 13.
202 **28** 2d. dull blue .. .. .. 60·00 8·50

32   34

33   35

1867 (Sept)–93. W **33** *and* **35**.
203 **32** 4d. red-brown, *p* 13 .. .. 35·00 3·00
204   4d. pale red-brown, *p* 13 .. 35·00 3·00
205 **34** 10d. lilac, *p* 13 (Optd S. £25) .. 12·00 3·00
  a. Imperf between (pair) .. £450
206   10d. lilac, *p* 11 (1893) .. 13·00 3·00
  a. Perf 10 .. .. .. 15·00 3·00
  b. Perf 10 and 11, compound .. 20·00 7·50
  c. Perf 12 × 11 .. .. £110 15·00

36   37   38

NINEPENCE
(**39**)

From 1871 to 1903 the 9d. is formed from the 10d. by a *black* surch. (T **39**), 15 mm long on Nos. 219 to 220h, and 13½ mm long on subsequent issues.

1871–85. W **36**.
207 **26** 1d. dull red, *p* 13 (8.71) .. 5·00 20
  a. Imperf vert (horiz pair) ..
208   1d. salmon, *p* 13 .. .. 5·00 20
  a. Perf 10 .. .. .. £250 30·00
  b. Perf 10×13 .. .. 50·00 5·00
  ba. Perf 13×10 .. .. 16·00 20
  c. *Scarlet.* Perf 10 .. — £180
209 **28** 2d. Prussian-blue, *p* 13 (11.71) .. 7·00 20
  a. Perf 11×12, comb .. £250 40·00
  b. Imperf vert (horiz pair) .. £500
210   2d. pale blue, *p* 13 .. .. 7·00 20
  aa. "TWO PENCE" double impression at right .. .. — 30·00
  a. Perf 10 .. .. .. £250 22·00
  b. Perf 10×13 .. .. £100 15·00
  ba. Perf 13×10 .. .. 7·00 20
  c. Surfaced paper. Perf 13
211 **14** 3d. yellow-green (3.74), *p* 13 .. 18·00 2·40
  a. Perf 10 .. .. .. 65·00 5·50
  b. Perf 11 .. .. .. £150 £100
  c. Perf 12 .. .. .. £150
  d. Perf 10×12 .. .. £150 32·00
  e. Perf 11×12 .. .. £120 32·00
212   3d. bright green, *p* 10 .. £120 11·00
  a. Perf 13×10 .. .. £110 15·00
  b. Perf 13
213 **32** 4d. pale red-brown (8.77), *p* 13 .. 50·00 6·00
214   4d. red-brown, *p* 13 .. .. 50·00 6·00
  a. Perf 10 .. .. .. £180 50·00
  b. Perf 10×13 .. .. £100 20·00
  ba. Perf 13×10 .. .. 75·00 3·50

215 **15** 5d. bluish green (8.84), *p* 10 .. 15·00 8·00
  a. Perf 12 (5.85) £250 £100
  b. Perf 10×13
  c. Perf 10×12 .. .. £120 40·00
216 **37** 6d. bright mauve (1.72), *p* 13 .. 35·00 1·00
  a. Imperf between (horiz pair) .. — £500
217   6d. pale lilac, *p* 13 .. .. 38·00 1·00
  a. Perf 10 .. .. .. £180 12·00
  b. Perf 10×13 .. .. 80·00 15·00
  ba Perf 13×10 .. .. 55·00 1·00
  c. Imperf between (horiz pair). Perf 13×10 .. .. — £500
218 **19** 8d. yellow (3.77), *p* 13 .. £100 17·00
  a. Perf 10 .. .. .. £250 24·00
  b. Perf 13×10 .. .. £170 22·00
219 **34** 9d. on 10d. pale red-brown (8.71), *p* 13 .. 20·00 4·50
220   9d. on 10d. red-brown, *p* 13 (optd S. £25) .. 20·00 6·00
  a. Perf 10 .. .. .. 12·00 4·50
  b. Perf 12 .. .. .. 12·00 4·50
  c. Perf 11 .. .. .. 26·00 7·00
  d. Perf 12×10 .. .. £250 £160
  e. Perf 10×11 or 11×10 .. 42·00 9·00
  f. Perf 12×11 .. .. 14·00 5·00
  g. Perf 12×11, comb .. 14·00 5·50
  h. In black and blue. Perf 11 .. £110
221 **38** 1s. black (4.76), *p* 13 .. .. 80·00 2·50
  a. Perf 10 .. .. .. £200 12·00
  b. Perf 10×13 .. .. £240 15·00
  ba. Perf 13×10 .. .. £170 4·50
  c. Perf 11
  d. Imperf between (horiz pair) .. — £750

Collectors should note that the classification of perforations is that adopted by the Royal Philatelic Society, London. "Perf 12" denotes the perforation formerly called "11½, 12" and "perf 13" that formerly called "12½, 13".

40   41

1882–97. W **40**.
222 **26** 1d. salmon, *p* 10 .. .. 9·50 20
  a. Perf 13
  b. Perf 13×10 .. .. 28·00 1·50
223   1d. orange *to* scarlet, *p* 13 .. £800 £400
  a. Perf 10 .. .. .. 8·00 20
  ab. Imperf between (horiz pair)
  b. Perf 10×13 .. .. £120 6·00
  c. Perf 10×12 .. .. £250 65·00
  d. Perf 10×11 .. .. £450 £120
  e. Perf 12×11 .. .. — £120
  f. Perf 11×12, comb .. 5·50 25
  h. Perf 11 .. .. .. — £130
224 **28** 2d. pale blue, *p* 13 .. .. £450 90·00
  a. Perf 10 .. .. .. 11·00 25
  b. Perf 10×13 or 13×10 .. 65·00 2·00
225   2d. Prussian blue, *p* 10 .. 20·00 25
  a. Perf 10×13 .. .. £100 30·00
  b. Perf 12 .. .. .. — £225
  c. Perf 11 .. .. .. — £100
  d. Perf 12×11 .. .. £400 £100
  e. Perf 10×12 .. .. £225 65·00
  ea. Perf 12×10 .. .. £400 £100
  f. Perf 10×11 or 11×10 .. £450 £150
  g. Perf 11×12, comb .. 12·00 15
226 **14** 3d. yellow-green (1886), *p* 10 .. 5·00 80
  a. Wmk sideways
  b. Perf 10×12 .. .. £160 30·00
  ba. Perf 12×10 .. .. £120 15·00
  c. Perf 11 .. .. .. 5·00 80
  ca. Imperf between (horiz pair) .. £150
  d. Perf 11×12 or 12×11 .. 5·00 80
  e. Perf 12 .. .. .. 9·00 1·00
  g. Imperf (pair) £120
227   3d. bluish green, *p* 10 .. 5·00 80
  a. Wmk sideways .. .. 50·00 10·00
  b. Perf 11 .. .. .. 5·00 80
  c. Perf 10×11 .. .. 15·00 1·50
  ca. Perf 11×10 .. .. £100 30·00
  d. Perf 12×11 .. .. 5·00 1·00
  e. Perf 10×12 or 12×10 .. 30·00 3·00
228   3d. emerald-green, *p* 10 (1893) .. 55·00 7·50
  a. Perf 11×10 .. .. 55·00 3·00
  ab. Perf 11×10 .. .. £120 35·00
  b. Perf 10×12 .. .. 50·00 5·00
  ba. Perf 12×10 .. .. 75·00 5·00
  c. Perf 12×11
229 **32** 4d. red-brown, *p* 10 .. .. 35·00 3·00
  a. Perf 10×12 .. .. — £130
  b. Perf 11×12, comb .. 42·00 1·25
230   4d. dark brown, *p* 10 .. 35·00 3·00
  a. Perf 12 .. .. .. £250 £100
  b. Perf 10×12 .. .. £200 60·00
  ba. Perf 12×10 .. .. £300 £150
  c. Perf 11×12, comb .. 25·00 1·00
231 **15** 5d. dull grn, *p* 10 (1890) (Optd S. £25) 12·00 90
  a. Perf 12×10 (4.85) .. 80·00 3·50
232   5d. bright green, *p* 10 (4.82) .. 32·00 4·50
  a. Perf 10×11 (12.85) .. 38·00 4·50
  ba. Perf 11×10 .. .. 45·00 6·00
  c. Perf 10×12 (4.85) .. £150 30·00
  ca. Perf 12×10 .. .. £100 70·00
233   5d. bluish-green, *p* 10 (4.82) .. 8·50 90
  a. Perf 12 (4.85) .. .. 11·00 90
  ab. Wmk sideways .. 50·00
  b. Perf 11 (12.85) .. 8·50 90
  c. Perf 10×11 (12.85) .. 24·00 1·60
  d. Perf 11×12 or 12×11 .. 6·50 55
  da. Wmk sideways (*p* 11×12) .. — 20·00
  e. Imperf (pair) £200

234 **37** 6d. pale lilac, *p* 10 .. .. 35·00 1·00
  a. Perf 10×13 or 13×10 .. — £300
  b. Perf 10×12 or 12×10 .. 38·00 1·50
235   6d. mauve, *p* 10 .. .. 35·00 1·00
  a. Perf 12 .. .. .. 80·00 10·00
  b. Perf 11 .. .. .. 80·00 8·00
  c. Perf 10×12 .. .. 50·00 8·00
  ca. Perf 12×10 .. .. 35·00 2·00
  cb. Imperf between (horiz pair) .. — £650
  d. Perf 11×12 .. .. 80·00 12·00
  da. Perf 12×11 .. .. 35·00 1·40
  e. Perf 11×10 .. .. 55·00 2·00
236 **19** 8d. yellow, *p* 10 (1883) .. £100 15·00
  a. Perf 12 .. .. .. £150 24·00
  b. Perf 11 .. .. .. £100 17·00
  c. Perf 10×12 .. .. £130 25·00
  ca. Perf 12×10 .. .. £100 22·00
236d **34** 9d. on 10d. red-brown, *p* 11×12 (1897) (Optd S. £25) .. 8·00 3·75
  da. Perf 12 .. .. .. 11·00 5·00
  db. Perf 11 .. .. .. 11·00 5·50
  dc. Surch double, *p* 11 .. £140 £120
236e   10d. vio, *p* 11×12 (1897) (Optd S. £25) 12·00 3·25
  ea. Perf 12×11½ .. .. 12·00 3·25
  eb. Perf 12 .. .. .. 15·00 4·00
  ec. Perf 11 .. .. .. 20·00 5·00
237 **38** 1s. black, *p* 10 .. .. 65·00 2·00
  a. Perf 11 .. .. .. £200 9·00
  b. Perf 10×12
  c. Perf 10×13
  ca. Perf 13×10 .. .. £200 20·00
  d. Perf 11×12, comb .. 65·00 2·00

1886–87. W **41**.
238 **26** 1d. scarlet, *p* 10 .. .. 11·00 3·75
  a. Perf 11 × 12, comb .. 3·75 90
239 **28** 2d. deep blue, *p* 10 .. .. 32·00 5·00
  a. Perf 11 × 12, comb .. 12·00 95
  b. Imperf

1891 (July). *Wmk* "**10**" *as* W **35**. P 10.
240 **14** 3d. green (Optd S. £25) .. 12·00 80·00
241   3d. dark green .. .. 5·00 17·00

42   43

NOTE. The spacing between the Crown and "NSW" is 1 mm in T **42**, as against 2 mm in T **40**.

1903–8. W **42**.
241a **14** 3d. yellow-green, *p* 11 .. 6·00 90
  b. Perf 12 .. .. .. 5·00 90
  c. Perf 11×12 or 12×11 .. 5·00 90
242   3d. dull green, *p* 12 .. 19·00 1·75
  a. Perf 11×12 or 12×11 .. 7·00 1·00
  b. Perf 11
243 **15** 5d. dark blue-green, *p* 11×12 .. 5·50 90
  a. Wmk sideways .. 15·00 5·00
  b. Perf 11 .. .. .. 12·00 90
  ba. Wmk sideways
  c. Perf 12 .. .. .. 19·00 3·50
  ca. Wmk sideways .. 30·00 10·00
  d. Imperf (pair) £130

1885–86. W **41** (*sideways*). (i). *Optd* "POSTAGE", *in black.*
244 **43** 5s. green and lilac, *p* 13
  a. Perf 10
  b. Perf 12 × 10 .. .. £325 80·00
245   10s. claret and lilac, *p* 13
  a. Perf 12 .. .. .. £450 £140
246   £1 claret and lilac, *p* 13 (1886) .. — £2250
  a. Perf 12 .. .. .. £2250

(ii) *Overprinted in blue*
247 **43** 10s. claret and mauve, *p* 10 (Optd S. £60) £550 £160
  a. Perf 12 .. .. .. £160 50·00
  b. Perf 12 × 11
248   £1 claret and rose-lilac, *p* 12 × 10 .. £2500 £1100

44

1894. *Optd* "POSTAGE" *in blue.* W **44** (*sideways*).
249 **43** 10s. claret and mauve, *p* 10 .. £275 £100
249a   10s. claret and violet, *p* 12 .. £160 40·00
  b. Perf 11 .. .. .. £250 75·00
  c. Perf 12 × 11 .. .. £180 50·00
250   10s. aniline crimson & violet, *p* 12 × 11 £160 45·00
  a. Perf 12 .. .. .. £250 75·00
250b   £1 claret and violet, *p* 12 × 11

1903–04. *Optd* "POSTAGE" *in blue. Chalk-surfaced paper.* W **44** (*sideways*).
250c **43** 10s. aniline crimson & violet, *p* 12 × 11
251   10s. rosine and violet, *p* 12 (1904) .. £140 70·00
  a. Perf 11 .. .. .. £200 85·00
  b. Perf 12 × 11 .. .. £140 45·00
252   10s. claret and violet, *p* 12 × 11 (1904) .. £225 85·00

45 View of Sydney **46** Emu **47** Captain Cook

48 Queen Victoria and Arms of Colony **49** Superb Lyrebird **50** Eastern Grey Kangaroo

51 Map of Australia **52** Capt. Arthur Phillip, first Governor and Lord Carrington, Governor in 1888

(Des M. Tannenberg (1d., 6d.), Miss Devine (2d., 8d.), H. Barraclough (4d.), Govt Ptg Office (1s.), C. Turner (5s.), Mrs. F. Stoddard (20s.). Eng W. Bell).

1888 (1 May)–**89.** *Centenary of New South Wales.* (a) W **40.** P 11 × 12.

253	45	1d. lilac (9.7.88)			3·75	10
		a. Perf 12 × 11½			17·00	90
		b. Perf 12			5·00	10
		c. Imperf (pair)				
		d. *Mauve*			3·75	10
		da. Imperf between (pair)				
		db. Perf 12×11½			6·00	25
		dc. Perf 12			5·50	25
254	46	2d. Prussian blue (1.9.88)			4·25	10
		a. Imperf (pair)			£100	
		b. Imperf between (pair)			£375	
		c. Perf 12 × 11½			8·00	10
		d. Perf 12			6·00	10
		e. *Chalky blue*			4·25	10
		ea. Perf 12×11½				
		eb. Perf 12			5·50	25
255	47	4d. purple-brown (8.10.88)			10·00	3·00
		a. Perf 12 × 11½			28·00	7·50
		b. Perf 12			24·00	3·25
		c. Perf 11			£300	90·00
		d. *Red-brown*			10·00	3·00
		da. Perf 12×11½			13·00	2·75
		db. Perf 12			13·00	2·75
		e. *Orange-brown, p 12 × 11½*			13·00	2·75
		f. *Yellow-brown, p 12 × 11½*			11·00	3·00
256	48	6d. carmine (26.11.88)			20·00	2·50
		a. Perf 12 × 11½			25·00	3·00
		b. Perf 12			21·00	2·50
257	49	8d. lilac-rose (17.1.89)			14·00	1·75
		a. Perf 12 × 11½			35·00	10·00
		b. Perf 12			14·00	2·00
		c. *Magenta*			75·00	9·00
		ca. Perf 12 × 11½			14·00	2·00
		cb. Perf 12			14·00	2·50
258	50	1s. maroon (21.2.89)			15·00	90
		a. Perf 12 × 11½			17·00	90
		b. Perf 12			20·00	90
		c. *Violet-brown*			15·00	90
		ca. Imperf (pair)			£550	
		cb. Perf 12 × 11½			38·00	1·25
		cc. Perf 12			38·00	90

(b) W **41.** P 11 × 12

259	45	1d. lilac (1888)			14·00	
		a. *Mauve*			12·00	85
260	46	2d. Prussian blue (1888)			40·00	3·00

(c) W **25.** P 10

261	51	5s. deep purple (13.3.89)		£180	45·00
		a. *Deep violet*		£180	45·00
262	52	20s. cobalt-blue		£225	£110
253/8 Optd "Specimen"			Set of 6	£150

Nos. 255c and 261/2 are line perforated, the remainder are comb.

A postal forgery exists of the 2d. on unwatermarked paper and perforated 11.

53 **54**

1890. W **53** (5s.) *or* **54** (20s.). P 10.

263	51	5s. lilac		£120	27·00
		a. Perf 11		£160	38·00
		ab. Imperf between (horiz pair)			
		b. Perf 12		£225	42·00
		c. Perf 10×11 or 11×10		£160	27·00
		d. *Mauve*		£160	27·00
		da. Perf 11		£160	38·00

264	52	20s. cobalt-blue		£300	£130
		a. Perf 11		£225	75·00
		b. Perf 11 × 10			
		c. *Ultramarine. p 11*		£180	75·00
		ca. Perf 12		£225	£130
		cb. Perf 11×12 or 12×11		£160	75·00
263/4 Optd "Specimen"			Set of 2	£180

55 Allegorical figure of Australia

SEVEN-PENCE

Halfpenny **HALFPENNY**

(56) (57)

1890 (22 Dec). W **40.**

281	55	2½d. ultramarine, p 11 × 12 *comb* (Optd S. £25)	2·50	40
		a. Perf 12 × 11½, comb	45·00	40
		b. Perf 12, comb	7·00	40

1891 (5 Jan). *Surch as T* **56** *and* **57.** W **40.**

282	26	½d. on 1d. grey, p 11×12 *comb*	2·75	2·75
		a. Surch omitted		
		b. Surch double	£200	
283	37	7½d. on 6d. brown, p 10	5·50	2·50
		a. Perf 11	5·00	2·50
		b. Perf 12	6·00	3·00
		c. Perf 11×12 or 12×11	5·50	3·00
		d. Perf 10×12	6·00	3·00
284	38	12½d. on 1s. red, p 10	12·00	6·50
		a. "HALFPENCE" omitted		
		b. Perf 11	13·00	6·50
		c. Perf 11×12, comb	12·00	6·00
		d. Perf 12×11½, comb	10·00	6·00
		e. Perf 12, comb	15·00	6·00
282/4 Optd "Specimen"		Set of 3	70·00	

58 Type I. Narrow "H" in "HALF"

1892 (21 Mar)–**99.** *Type I.* W **40.**

285	58	½d. grey, p 10	15·00	45
		a. Perf 11	60·00	5·00
		b. Perf 10×12	55·00	7·50
		c. Perf 11×12 (Optd S. £20)	1·50	10
		d. Perf 12	1·75	10
286		½d. slate, p 11×12 (1897)	1·50	10
		a. Perf 12×11½	1·50	10
		b. Perf 12	1·50	10
		c. Imperf between (horiz pair). Perf 11×12	£400	
287		½d. bluish green, p 11×12 (1899)	2·00	10
		a. Perf 12×11½	1·25	10
		b. Perf 12	1·25	10

The perforations 11×12, 12×11½, 12, are from comb machines.

The die for Type **58** was constructed from an electro taken from the die of the De La Rue 1d., Type **26**, with "ONE" replaced by "HALF" and two "½" plugs added to the bottom corners. These alterations proved to be less hard-wearing than the remainder of the die and defects were visible by the 1905 plate of No. 330. It seems likely that repairs were undertaken before printing from the next plate in late 1907 which produced stamps as Type II.

58a

58b

(Des C. Turner. Litho Govt Printing Office, Sydney)

1897. *Diamond Jubilee and Hospital Charity. T* **58a** *and* **58b.** W **40.** P 12×11 (1d.) or 11 (2½d.).

287c	58a	1d. (1s.) green and brown (22.6)	40·00	40·00
287d	58b	2½d. (2s. 6d.), gold, carmine & bl (28.6)	£150	£150
287c/d Optd "Specimen"		Set of 2	£200	

These stamps, sold at 1s. and 2s. 6d respectively, paid postage of 1d. and 2½d. only, the difference being given to a Consumptives' Home.

59 **60** **61**

Dies of the 1d.

Die I Die II

1d. Die I. The first pearl on the crown on the left side is merged into the arch, the shading under the fleur-de-lis is indistinct, the "S" of "WALES" is open.
Die II. The first pearl is circular, the vertical shading under the fleur-de-lis clear, the "S" of "WALES" not so open.

Dies of the 2½d.

Die I Die II

2½d. Die I. There are 12 radiating lines in the star on the Queen's breast.
Die II. There are 16 radiating lines in the star and the eye is nearly full of colour.

Des D. Souter (2d., 2½d.). Eng W. Amor)

1897 (22 June)–**99.** W **40** (*sideways on* 2½d.). P 12×11 (2½d.) or 11×12 (others).

288	59	1d. carmine (Die I)			1·75	10
		a. Perf 12×11½			2·00	10
289		1d. scarlet (Die I)			1·75	10
		a. Perf 12×11½			4·50	40
		b. Perf 12			4·50	50
		ba. Imperf horiz (vert pair)				
290		1d. rose-carmine (Die II) (11.97)			1·75	10
		a. Perf 12×11½			1·50	10
		b. Perf 12			1·50	10
		c. Imperf between (pair)			£400	
291		1d. salmon-red (Die II) (p 12×11½)			1·75	10
		a. Perf 12			3·25	30
292	60	2d. deep dull blue			2·00	10
		a. Perf 12×11½			2·00	10
		b. Perf 12			4·50	10
293		2d. cobalt-blue			3·00	10
		a. Perf 12×11½			2·50	10
		b. Perf 12			3·00	10
294		2d. ultramarine (1.12.97)			2·50	10
		a. Perf 12×11½			2·00	10
		b. Perf 12			2·00	10
		c. Imperf between (pair)				
295	61	2½d. purple (Die I)			5·00	1·25
		a. Perf 11½×12			6·00	80
		b. Perf 11			6·00	1·75
296		2½d. deep violet (Die II) (11.97)			3·50	80
		a. Perf 11½×12			6·00	1·25
		b. Perf 12			3·25	1·25
297		2½d. Prussian blue (17.1.99)			6·00	1·25
		a. Perf 11½×12			4·00	1·00
		b. Perf 12			3·25	1·00
288, 292, 294/5 Optd "Specimen"			Set of 4	60·00	

The perforations 11 × 12, 12 × 11½ and 12 are from comb machines, the perforation 11 is from a single-line machine.

1897. *Reissue of T* **24.** W **25.** P 11.

297c		5s. reddish purple (*shades*)	32·00	12·00
		ca. Imperf between (horiz pair)	£2750	
		d. Perf 12	42·00	20·00
		e. Perf 11×12 or 12×11	35·00	19·00

1898–99. W **40.** P 11×12.

297f	48	6d. emerald-green (Optd S. £20)			30·00	8·00
		fa. Perf 12×11½			22·00	7·00
		fb. Perf 12			22·00	7·00
297g		6d. orange-yellow (1899)			14·00	3·25
		ga. Perf 12×11½			13·00	2·75
		gb. Perf 12			23·00	4·50
		gc. *Yellow, p 12×11½*			14·00	1·50

1899 (Oct). *Chalk-surfaced paper.* W **40** (*sideways on* 2½d.). P 12×11½ or 11½×12 (2½d.), comb.

298	58	½d. blue-green (Type I)		90	10
		a. Imperf (pair)		65·00	10
299	59	1d. carmine (Die II)		1·50	10
		a. Imperf horiz (vert pair)		£200	
300		1d. scarlet (Die II)		1·00	10
301		1d. salmon-red (Die II)		1·50	10
		a. Imperf (pair)		65·00	75·00
302	60	2d. cobalt-blue		1·75	10
		a. Imperf (pair)		65·00	

303	61	2½d. Prussian blue (Die II)		2·75	70
		a. Imperf (pair)		80·00	
303b	47	4d. red-brown		9·50	3·00
		c. Imperf (pair)		£200	
304		4d. orange-brown		9·50	3·00
305	48	6d. deep orange		11·00	90
		a. Imperf (pair)		£150	
306		6d. orange-yellow		11·00	90
307		6d. emerald-green		75·00	20·00
		a. Imperf (pair)		£190	
308	49	8d. magenta		15·00	3·00
309	34	9d. on 10d. dull brown		8·00	4·00
		a. Surcharge double		90·00	90·00
		b. Without surcharge		80·00	
310		10d. violet		12·00	3·00
311	50	1s. maroon		17·00	80
312		1s. purple-brown		17·00	1·25
		a. Imperf (pair)		£180	

62 Superb Lyrebird   63

1902–03. *Chalk-surfaced paper. W 42 (sideways on 2½d.). P 12×11½ or 11½×12 (2½d.), comb.*

313	58	½d. blue-green (Type I)		3·25	10
		a. Perf 12×11		3·25	
314	59	1d. carmine (Die II)		1·50	10
315	60	2d. cobalt-blue		2·25	10
316	61	2½d. dark blue (Die II)		4·25	10
317	47	4d. orange-brown		24·00	3·50
318	48	6d. yellow-orange		18·00	90
319		6d. orange		17·00	90
320		6d. orange-buff		17·00	90
321	49	8d. magenta		14·00	2·25
322	34	9d. on 10d. brownish orange		8·00	3·50
323		10d. violet		18·00	3·00
324	50	1s. maroon		17·00	80
325		1s. purple-brown		18·00	80
326	62	2s. 6d. green (1903) (Optd S. £35)		42·00	16·00

(Typo Victoria Govt Printer, Melbourne)

1903 (18 July). *Wmk double-lined V over Crown. W w 10.*

327	63	9d. brown & ultram, p 12¼ × 12½, comb (Optd S. £27)		8·00	1·75
328		9d. brown & dp blue, p 12¼ × 12½, comb		8·00	1·75
329		9d. brown and blue, p 11		£450	£275

Type II. Broad   66
"H" in "HALF"

1905 (Oct)–10. *Chalk-surfaced paper. W 66 (sideways on 2½d.). P 12×11½ or 11½×12 (2½d.) comb, unless otherwise stated.*

330	58	½d. blue-green (Type I)		1·75	10
		a. Perf 11½×11		1·25	10
		b. Type II (1908)		1·75	
		ba. Perf 11½×11		1·75	
332	59	1d. rose-carmine (Die II)		1·25	10
		a. Double impression		£225	
		b. Perf 11½×11		1·75	
333	60	2d. deep ultramarine		1·75	10
		a. Perf 11½×11		2·00	
333d		2d. milky blue (1910)		1·75	90
		da. Perf 11		45·00	
		db. Perf 11½×11			
334	61	2½d. Prussian blue (Die II)		2·75	80
335	47	4d. orange-brown		9·50	3·00
336		4d. red-brown		11·00	3·00
337	48	6d. dull yellow		13·00	1·00
		a. Perf 11½×11		21·00	
338		6d. orange-yellow		13·00	90
		a. Perf 11×11½		27·00	
339		6d. deep orange		11·00	90
		a. Perf 11		£160	
339b		6d. orange-buff		11·00	90
		c. Perf 11½×11		17·00	2·75
340	49	8d. magenta		16·00	2·50
341		8d. lilac-rose		16·00	2·75
342	34	10d. violet		14·00	3·00
		a. Perf 11½×11		13·00	2·75
		b. Perf 11		13·00	2·75
343	50	1s. maroon		15·00	85
344		1s. purple-brown (1908)		18·00	85
345	62	2s. 6d. blue-green		42·00	15·00
		a. Perf 11½×11		27·00	13·00
		b. Perf 11		30·00	16·00

67

1905 (Dec). *Chalk-surfaced paper. W 67. P 11.*

346	52	20s. cobalt-blue		£150	65·00
		a. Perf 12		£160	70·00
		b. Perf 11 × 12 or 12 × 11		£140	60·00

(Typo Victoria Govt Printer, Melbourne)

1906 (Sept). *Wmk double-lined "A" and Crown, W w 11. P 12×12½, comb.*

347	63	9d. brown and ultramarine		6·00	1·10
		a. Perf 11		42·00	35·00
348		9d. yellow-brown and ultramarine		6·00	90

1907 (July). *W w 11 (sideways on 2½d.). P 12×11½ or 11½×12 (2½d.), comb, unless otherwise stated.*

349	58	½d. blue-green (Type I)		3·00	10
351	59	1d. dull rose (Die II)		2·75	10
352	60	2d. cobalt-blue		3·00	10
353	61	2½d. Prussian blue (Die II)		42·00	
354	47	4d. orange-brown		10·00	3·50
355	48	6d. orange-buff		26·00	4·00
356		6d. dull yellow		24·00	4·00
357	49	8d. magenta		16·00	3·50
358	34	10d. violet, p 11		18·00	
359	50	1s. purple-brown		22·00	3·00
		a. Perf 11			
360	62	2s. 6d. blue-green		45·00	25·00

STAMP BOOKLETS

There are very few surviving examples of Nos. SB1/4. Listings are provided for those believed to have been issued with prices quoted for those known to still exist.

1904 (May)–09. *Black on red cover with map of Australia on front and picture of one of six different State G.P.O's on back. Stapled.*

SB1   £1 booklet containing two hundred and forty 1d. in four blocks of 30 and two blocks of 60
    a. Red on pink cover (1909)
    b. Blue on pink cover

1904 (May). *Black on grey cover as No. SB1. Stapled.*
SB2   £1 booklet containing one hundred and twenty 2d. in four blocks of 30

1910 (May). *Black on cream cover inscribed "COMMON-WEALTH OF AUSTRALIA/POSTMASTER-GENERAL'S DEPARTMENT". Stapled.*
SB3   2s. booklet containing eleven ½d. (No. 331), either in block of 6 plus block of 5 or block of 11, and eighteen 1d. (No. 332), either in three blocks of 6 or block of 6 plus 1 block of 12   £2000
Unsold stock of No. SB3 was uprated with one additional ½d. in May 1911.

1911 (Aug). *Red on pink cover as No. SB3. Stapled.*
SB4   2s. booklet containing twelve ½d. (No. 331), either in two blocks of 6 or block of 12, and eighteen 1d. (No. 332) either in three blocks of 6 or 1 block of 6 plus block of 12   £1500

OFFICIAL STAMPS

O S   O S   O S
(O 1)   (O 2)   (O 3)

The space between the letters is normally 7 mm as illustrated, except on the 5d. and 8d. (11–11½ mm), 5s. (12 mm) and 20s. (14 mm). Later printings of the 3d., W 40, are 5½ mm, and these are listed. Varieties in the settings are known on the 1d. (8 and 8½ mm), 2d. (8½ mm) and 3d. (9 mm).
Varieties of Type O 1 exist with "O" sideways.

Nos. O1/35 overprinted with Type O 1

1879. *Wmk double-lined "6". P 13.*

O1	14	3d. dull green		—	£400

1879 (Oct)–85. *W 36. P 13.*

O 2	26	1d. salmon		10·00	2·00
		a. Perf 10 (5.81)		£180	30·00
		a. Perf 13×10 (1881)		20·00	3·50
O 3	28	2d. blue		14·00	1·25
		a. Perf 10 (7.81)		£225	32·00
		b. Perf 10×13 (1881)		40·00	20·00
		ba. Perf 13×10		22·00	2·50
		d. Perf 11×12 (11.84?)		—	£225
O 4	14	3d. dull green (R.) (12.79)		£400	£250
O 5		3d. dull green (3.80)		£250	45·00
		a. Perf 10 (1881)		£140	40·00
		b. Yellow-green. Perf 10 (10.81)		£140	25·00
		c. Ditto. Perf 13×10 (1881)		£140	25·00
		d. Ditto. Perf 12 (4.85)		£200	50·00
		e. Ditto. Perf 12×10 (4.85)		£200	50·00
O 6	32	4d. red-brown		£160	7·50
		a. Perf 10 (1881)		—	£190
		b. Perf 10×13 (1881)		£200	90·00
		ba. Perf 13×10		£150	11·00
O 7	15	5d. green, p 10 (8.84)		18·00	12·00
O 8	37	6d. pale lilac		£225	6·00
		a. Perf 10 (1881)		£350	40·00
		b. Perf 13×10 (1881)		£160	40·00
O 9	19	8d. yellow (R.) (12.79)		—	£160
O10		8d. yellow (1880)		—	15·00
		a. Perf 10 (1881)		£275	75·00
O11	34	9d. on 10d. brown, p 10 (30.5.80) (Optd S. £60)		£350	
O12	38	1s. black (R.)		£225	7·50
		a. Perf 10 (1881)		—	16·00
		b. Perf 10×13 (1881)		—	25·00
		ba. Perf 13×10		—	10·00

Other stamps are known with red overprint but their status is in doubt.

1880–88. *Wmk "5/-", W 25. (a) P 13.*

O13	24	5s. deep purple (15.2.80)		£425	90·00
		a. Royal purple		—	£300
		b. Deep rose-lilac		£425	90·00

		(b) P 10			
O14	24	5s. deep purple (9.82)		£425	£160
		a. Opt double			†£1500
		b. Rose-lilac (1883)		£300	£100
		(c) P 10 × 12			
O15	24	5s. purple (10.86)			
		(d) P 12 × 10			
O16	24	5s. reddish purple (1886)		£425	£100
		(e) P 12			
O17	24	5s. purple		†	£500
		(f) P 11			
O18	24	5s. rose-lilac (1888)		£170	80·00

1880 (31 May). *Wmk "10". W 35. P 13.*

O18a	34	10d. lilac (Optd S. £60)		£130	80·00
		ab. Perf 10 and 11, compound		£200	£180
		ac. Perf 10		£200	
		ad. Opt double, one albino (p 10)			

1882–85. *W 40. P 10.*

O19	26	1d. salmon		8·50	2·00
		a. Perf 13×10		—	£130
O20		1d. orange to scarlet		7·00	1·50
		a. Perf 10×13		—	£130
		b. Perf 11×12, comb (1.84)		5·00	1·40
		c. Perf 10×12 or 12×10 (4.85)		—	£110
		d. Perf 12×11 (12.85)			
O21	28	2d. blue		6·00	1·00
		a. Perf 10×13 or 13×10		£190	75·00
		c. Perf 11×12, comb (1.84)		5·50	1·00
		d. Ditto. Opt double		—	£150
		e. Perf 12×11 (12.85)			
O22	14	3d. yellow-green (7 mm)		7·00	3·50
		a. Perf 12 (4.85)		£120	80·00
		b. Perf 12×10 (4.85)			
		c. Perf 12×11			
O23		3d. bluish green (7 mm)		7·00	3·50
		a. Perf 12 (4.85)		£120	80·00
		b. Perf 12×10 (4.85)			
		c. Perf 10×11 (12.85)			
O24		3d. yellow-green (5½ mm)		7·00	3·50
		a. Wmk sideways		—	20·00
		b. Perf 10×12 or 12×10 (4.85)		6·00	3·50
		c. Perf 10×11 or 11×10 (12.85)			
O25		3d. bluish green (5½ mm) (Optd S. £35)		7·00	3·50
		a. Perf 10×12 or 12×10 (4.85)		6·00	3·50
		c. Perf 10×11 or 11×10 (12.85)		5·00	3·50
O26	32	4d. red-brown		30·00	4·00
		a. Perf 11×12, comb (1.84)		12·00	3·00
		b. Perf 10×12 (4.85)		—	70·00
O27		4d. dark brown		15·00	3·00
		a. Perf 11×12, comb (1.84)		12·00	3·00
		b. Perf 12 (4.85)		£200	£150
		c. Perf 10×12 (4.85)		£200	90·00
O28	15	5d. dull green (Optd S. £35)		12·00	10·00
		a. Perf 12×10 (4.85)			
O29		5d. blue-green		13·00	11·00
		a. Perf 12 (4.85)		£100	
		b. Perf 10×11		13·00	11·00
O30	37	6d. pale lilac		18·00	4·00
		a. Perf 11 (12.85)		19·00	3·50
O31		6d. mauve		18·00	4·00
		a. Perf 12 (4.85)		—	45·00
		b. Perf 10×12 or 12×10 (4.85)		20·00	3·50
		d. Perf 11×10 (12.85)		18·00	4·00
		e. Perf 12×11 (12.85)		55·00	15·00
O32	19	8d. yellow		20·00	10·00
		a. Perf 12 (4.85)		£130	38·00
		b. Perf 10×12 or 12×10 (4.85)		20·00	9·00
		d. Perf 11 (12.85)		22·00	10·00
		da. Opt double			
		db. Opt treble		†	—
O33	38	1s. black (R.)		25·00	5·50
		a. Perf 10×13		—	55·00
		b. Perf 11×12, comb (1.84)		25·00	5·50
		c. Ditto. Opt double		—	£200

1886–87. *W 41. P 10.*

O34	26	1d. scarlet		20·00	3·00
O35	28	2d. deep blue			
		a. Perf 11 × 12			

1887–89. *Nos. 247/8 overprinted in black. (a) With Type O 1.*

O36	43	10s. claret and mauve, p 12		—	£800

(b) With Type O 2 (April 1889)

O37	43	10s. claret and mauve, p 12 (Optd S. £75)		£1200	£600
		a. Perf 10		£2250	£1300

(c) With Type O 3 (Jan 1887)

O38	43	£1 claret and rose-lilac, p 12 × 10		£4000	£3000

Only nine examples of No. O38 are recorded, three of which are mint. One of the used stamps, in the Royal Collection, shows overprint Type O 3 double.

1888 (17 July)–90. *Optd as Type O 1. (a) W 40. P 11 × 12.*

O39	45	1d. lilac		2·00	15
		a. Perf 12		2·00	15
		b. Mauve		2·00	15
		a. Perf 12		2·00	15
O40	46	2d. Prussian blue (15.10.88)		3·25	15
		a. Perf 12		3·25	15
O41	47	4d. purple-brown (10.10.89)		9·00	2·00
		a. Perf 12		12·00	2·25
		b. Perf 11			
		c. Red-brown		9·00	2·00
		ca. Opt double		†	
		cb. Perf 12		12·00	2·25
O42	48	6d. carmine (16.1.89)		8·50	3·00
		a. Perf 12		11·00	3·00
O43	49	8d. lilac-rose (1890)		16·00	7·50
		a. Perf 12		20·00	10·00
O44	50	1s. maroon (9.1.90)		15·00	3·00
		a. Perf 12		15·00	3·00
		b. Purple-brown		15·00	3·00
		ba. Opt double			
		bb. Perf 12		15·00	3·00

(b) W 41. P 11 × 12 (1889)

O45	45	1d. mauve			
O46	46	2d. blue			

(c) W 25. P 10

O47	51	5s. deep purple (R.) (9.1.90)		..	£600	£500
O48	52	20s. cobalt-blue (10.3.90)		..	£1600	£800
O39/44		Optd "Specimen" ..		*Set of 6*	£200	

1890 (Feb)–**91.** *Optd as Type O 1. W 53 (5s.) or 54 (20s.) P 10.*

O49	51	5s. lilac	..	..	£300	£120
		a. *Mauve*	..	..	£160	70·00
		b. *Dull lilac, p 12*		..	£450	£130
O50	52	20s. cobalt-blue (3.91)	..	..	£1600	£600
O49/50		Optd "Specimen" ..		*Set of 2*	£200	

1891 (Jan). *Optd as Type O 1. W 40.*

(a) On No. 281. P 11×12

O54	55	2½d. ultramarine	..	..	7·00	3·00

(b) On Nos. 282/4

O55	26	½d. on 1d. grey, p 11×12		..	50·00	40·00
O56	37	7½d. on 6d. brown, p 10		..	35·00	27·00
O57	38	12½d. on 1s. red, p 11×12		..	60·00	50·00

1892 (May). *No. 285 optd as Type O 1. P 10.*

O58	58	½d. grey	..	..	8·00	11·00
		a. Perf 11×12	..	..	6·00	7·00
		b. Perf 12	..	..	7·50	8·00
		c. Perf 12×11½	..	..	11·00	
O54/8		Optd "Specimen" ..		*Set of 5*	£160	

Official stamps were withdrawn from the government departments on 31 December 1894.

POSTAGE DUE STAMPS

D 1

(Dies eng by A. Collingridge. Typo Govt Printing Office, Sydney)

1891 (1 Jan)–**92.** *W 40. P 10.*

D 1	D 1	½d. green (21.1.92)		..	3·00	2·00
D 2		1d. green	..	..	4·00	90
		a. Perf 11	..	..	4·25	90
		b. Perf 12	..	..	13·00	2·50
		c. Perf 12 × 10	..	..	16·00	1·75
		d. Perf 10 × 11	..	..	7·00	1·25
		e. Perf 11 × 12 or 12 × 11		..	4·50	90
D 3		2d. green	..	..	6·00	80
		a. Perf 11	..	..	6·00	80
		b. Perf 12	..	..	—	8·00
		c. Perf 12×10	..	..	15·00	3·00
		d. Perf 10×11	..	..	7·50	1·50
		e. Perf 11×12 or 12×11		..	6·00	80
		f. Wmk sideways	..	..	12·00	5·00
D 4		3d. green	..	..	10·00	2·75
		a. Perf 10 × 11	..	..	10·00	2·75
D 5		4d. green	..	..	8·00	80
		a. Perf 11	..	..	9·00	80
		b. Perf 10 × 11	..	..	8·00	80
D 6		6d. green	..	..	15·00	2·00
D 7		8d. green	..	..	60·00	9·00
D 8		5s. green	..	..	£120	30·00
		a. Perf 11	..	..	£200	75·00
		b. Perf 11 × 12	..	..	—	£250
D 9		10s. green (early 1891)		..	£225	45·00
		a. Perf 11 × 12	..	..	£180	80·00
D10		20s. green (early 1891)		..	£300	80·00
		a. Perf 12	..	..	£300	
		b. Perf 12 × 10	..	..	£225	£100
D1/10		Optd "Specimen"	..	*Set of 10*	£180	

1900. *Chalk-surfaced paper. W 40. P 11.*

D11	D 1	½d. emerald-green		..		
D12		1d. emerald-green	..	..	3·75	2·00
		a. Perf 12	..	..	10·00	3·50
		b. Perf 11 × 12 or 12 × 11		..	3·75	1·25
D13		2d. emerald-green	..	..	7·00	2·75
		a. Perf 12	..	..	—	12·00
		b. Perf 11 × 12 or 12 × 11		..	6·00	2·50
D14		3d. emerald-green, p 11 × 12 or 12 × 11	13·00	4·00		
D15		4d. emerald-green	..	..	8·00	2·75

New South Wales became part of the Commonwealth of Australia on 1 January 1901.

QUEENSLAND

The area which later became Queensland was previously part of New South Wales known as the Moreton Bay District. The first post office, at Brisbane, was opened in 1834 and the use of New South Wales stamps from the District became compulsory from 1 May 1854.

Queensland was proclaimed a separate colony on 10 December 1859, but continued to use New South Wales issues until 1 November 1860.

Post Offices opened in the Moreton Bay District before 10 December 1859, and using New South Wales stamps, were

Office	Opened	Numeral Cancellation
Brisbane	1834	95
Burnett's Inn (*became* Goodes Inn)	1850	108
Callandoon	1850	74
Condamine	1856	151
Dalby	1854	133
Drayton	1846	85
Gayndah	1850	86
Gladstone	1854	131
Goode's Inn	1858	108
Ipswich	1846	87
Maryborough	1849	96
Rockhampton	1858	201
Surat	1852	110
Taroom	1856	152
Toowoomba	1858	214
Warwick	1848	81

PRICES FOR STAMPS ON COVER

Nos. 1/3	*from* × 2
Nos. 4/56	*from* × 3
Nos. 57/8	
Nos. 59/73	*from* × 4
Nos. 74/82	*from* × 2
Nos. 83/109	*from* × 3
Nos. 110/13	*from* × 4
Nos. 116/17	*from* × 3
Nos. 118/27	
Nos. 128/50	*from* × 4
Nos. 151/65	
Nos. 166/78	*from* × 10
Nos. 179/83	*from* × 4
Nos. 184/206	*from* × 15
No. 207	
Nos. 208/54	*from* × 15
Nos. 256/62c	*from* × 10
Nos. 264a/b	*from* × 2
Nos. 265/6	*from* × 20
Nos. 270/4	
Nos. 281/5	*from* × 10
Nos. 286/308	*from* × 12
Nos. 309/13	—
Nos. F1/37	

1   **2 Large Star**   **3 Small Star**

(Dies eng W. Humphrys. Recess P.B.)

1860 (1 Nov). *W 2. Imperf.*

1	1	1d. carmine-rose	..	£2750	£800
2		2d. blue	..	£5500	£1500
3		6d. green	..	£4000	£800

1860 (Nov). *W 2. Clean-cut perf 14–15½.*

4	1	1d. carmine-rose (1.11)	..	£1200	£250
5		2d. blue (1.11)	..	£500	£100
		a. Imperf between (pair)		—	
6		6d. green (15.11)	..	£550	60·00

1860–61. *W 3. Clean-cut perf 14–15½.*

7	1	2d. blue	..	£500	£100
		a. Imperf between (horiz pair)	..	—	£900
8		3d. brown (15.4.61)	..	£275	55·00
		a. Re-entry	..	—	£200
		b. Retouch (R. 2/8)	..	—	£200
9		6d. green	..	£550	60·00
10		1s. violet (15.11.60)	..	£500	70·00
11		"REGISTERED" (6d.) olive-yellow (1.61)	£350	70·00	
		a. Imperf between (pair)		—	£2750

The perforation of the 3d. is that known as "intermediate between clean-cut and rough".

The 3d. re-entry which occurs on one stamp in the second row, shows doubling of the left-hand arabesque and the retouch has redrawn spandrel dots under "EN" of "PENCE", a single dot in the centre of the circle under "E" and the bottom outer frame liner closer to the spandrel's frame line.

1861 (July (?)). *W 3. Clean-cut perf 14.*

12	1	1d. carmine-rose	..	£100	40·00
13		2d. blue	..	£275	50·00

1861 (Sept). *W 3. Rough perf 14–15½.*

14	1	1d. carmine-rose ..	..	75·00	28·00
15		2d. blue	..	90·00	28·00
		a. Imperf between (horiz pair)	..	£1800	
16		3d. brown	..	50·00	30·00
		a. Imperf vert (horiz pair)	..	£1800	
		b. Re-entry	..	£200	£110
		c. Retouch (R. 2/8)	..	—	£110
17		6d. deep green	..	£100	27·00
18		6d. yellow-green ..	..	£200	27·00
19		1s. violet ..	..	£350	80·00
20		"REGISTERED" (6d.) orange-yellow	..	50·00	35·00

(Printed and perforated in Brisbane)

1862–67. *Thick toned paper. No wmk. (a) P 13 (1862–63).*

21	1	1d. Indian red (16.12.62) ..	..	£250	60·00
22		1d. orange-vermilion (2.63)	..	60·00	12·00
		a. Imperf (pair)	..	—	£550
		b. Imperf between (pair)			
23		2d. pale blue (16.12.62)	..	80·00	27·00
24		2d. blue	..	40·00	9·00
		a. Imperf (pair)	..	—	£550
		b. Imperf between (horiz pair)	..	—	£900
		c. Imperf between (vert pair)	..	£1200	
25		3d. brown ..	..	55·00	30·00
		a. Re-entry	..	—	£110
		b. Retouch (R. 2/8)	..	—	£110
26		4d. apple-green (17.4.63)	..	90·00	15·00
27		6d. yellow-green	..	80·00	12·00
		a. Imperf between (horiz pair)	..	—	£1000
28		6d. pale bluish green	..	£130	27·00
		a. Imperf (pair)	..	—	£550
29		1s. grey (14.7.63) (H/S S. £40)	..	£130	22·00
		a. Imperf between (horiz pair)	..	—	£1100
		b. Imperf between (vert pair)	..		

The top or bottom row of perforation was sometimes omitted from the sheet, resulting in stamps perforated on three sides only.

(b) P 12½×13 (1863–67)

30	1	1d. orange-vermilion	..	60·00	27·00
31		2d. blue	..	50·00	20·00
32		3d. brown	..	65·00	25·00
		a. Re-entry	..	—	95·00
		b. Retouch (R. 2/8)	..	—	95·00
33		6d. apple-green	..	85·00	27·00
34		6d. yellow-green	..	85·00	27·00
34a		6d. pale bluish green			
35		1s. grey	..	£170	32·00
		a. Imperf between (horiz pair)			

The previously listed stamps perforated 13 round holes come from the same perforating machine as Nos. 21/9 after the pins had been replaced. The holes vary from rough to clean-cut.

1864–65. *W 3. (a) P 13.*

44	1	1d. orange-vermilion (1.65)	..	65·00	20·00
		a. Imperf between (horiz pair) ..		—	£450
45		2d. pale blue (1.65)	..	50·00	16·00
46		2d. deep blue	..	50·00	16·00
		a. Imperf between (vert pair)	..	—	£900
		b. Bisected (on cover)	..	†	£1900
47		6d. yellow-green (1.65)	..	£120	22·00
48		6d. deep green	..	£140	22·00
49		"REGISTERED" (6d.) orge-yell (21.6.64)	70·00	30·00	
		a. Double printed	..	—	£750
		b. Imperf			

(b) P 12½ × 13

50	1	1d. orange-vermilion	..	95·00	40·00
50a		2d. deep blue			

1866 (24 Jan). *Wmk "QUEENSLAND/POSTAGE—POSTAGE/ STAMPS—STAMPS" in three lines in script capitals with double wavy lines above and below the wmk and single wavy lines with projecting sprays between each line of words. There are ornaments ("fleurons") between "POSTAGE" "POSTAGE" and between "STAMPS" "STAMPS". Single stamps only show a portion of one or two letters of this wmk. (a) P 13.*

51	1	1d. orange-vermilion	..	£130	27·00
52		2d. blue	..	50·00	17·00

(b) P 12½ × 13

52a	1	1d. orange-vermilion	..		
52b		2d. blue	..		

1866 (24 Sept). *Lithographed on thick paper. No wmk. P 13.*

53	1	4d. slate (H/S S. £40)	..	£150	20·00
		a. Re-entry	..	—	85·00
		b. Retouch (R. 2/8)	..	—	85·00
55		4d. lilac	..	95·00	16·00
		a. Re-entry	..	—	75·00
		b. Retouch (R. 2/8)	..	—	75·00
56		4d. reddish lilac	..	95·00	16·00
		a. Re-entry	..	—	75·00
		b. Retouch (R. 2/8)	..	—	75·00
57		5s. bright rose (H/S S. £45)	..	£275	80·00
58		5s. pale rose	..	£200	55·00
		a. Imperf between (vert pair)	..	—	£750

The 4d. is from a transfer taken from the 3d. plate and the 5s. was taken from the 1s. plate, the final "s" being added. The alteration in the values was made by hand on the stone, and there are many varieties, such as tall and short letters in "FOUR PENCE", some of the letters of "FOUR" smudged out, and differences in the position of the two words.

4

1868–74. *Wmk small truncated Star, W 4 on each stamp, and the word "QUEENSLAND" in single-lined Roman capitals four times in each sheet. (a) P 13.*

59	1	1d. orange-vermilion (18.1.71) ..		45·00	4·50
60		2d. pale blue	..	45·00	4·50
61		2d. blue (3.4.68) ..	..	40·00	2·75
62		2d. bright blue	..	50·00	2·75
63		2d. greenish blue	..	85·00	2·50
64		2d. dark blue	..	45·00	2·50
		a. Imperf	..		
65		3d. olive-green (27.2.71)	..	80·00	5·00
		a. Re-entry	..	—	30·00
		b. Retouch (R. 2/8)	..	—	30·00
66		3d. greenish grey	..	95·00	5·50
		a. Re-entry	..	—	32·00
		b. Retouch (R. 2/8)	..	—	32·00
67		3d. brown	..	80·00	5·50
		a. Re-entry	..	—	32·00
		b. Retouch (R. 2/8)	..	—	32·00
68		6d. yellow-green (10.11.71)	..	£140	7·00
69		6d. green	..	£130	10·00
70		6d. deep green	..	£170	17·00
71		1s. greenish grey (13.11.72)	..	£350	32·00
72		1s. brownish grey	..	£350	32·00
73		1s. mauve (19.2.74)	..	£225	22·00
59, 61, 65, 69, 73, H/S "Specimen"			*Set of 5*	£180	

(b) P 12 (about Feb 1874)

74	1	1d. orange-vermilion	..	£275	24·00
75		2d. blue	..	£600	35·00
76		3d. greenish grey	..	—	£140
		a. Re-entry	..		
		b. Retouch (R. 2.8)			
77		3d. brown	..	£300	£140
		a. Re-entry	..		
		b. Retouch (R. 2/8)			
78		6d. green	..	£850	40·00
79		1s. mauve	..	£375	40·00

(c) P 13 × 12

80	1	1d. orange-vermilion	..	—	£170
81		2d. blue	..	£850	40·00
82		3d. greenish grey			

Reprints were made in 1895 of all five values on the paper of the regular issue, and perforated 13; the colours are:—1d. orange and orange-brown, 2d. dull blue and bright blue, 3d. deep brown, 6d. yellow-green, 1s. red-violet and dull violet. The "Registered" was also reprinted with these on the same paper, but perforated 12. One sheet of the 2d. reprint is known to have had the perforations missing between the fourth and fifth vertical rows.

| 5 | 6 |

(4d., litho. Other values recess)

1868–78. *Wmk Crown and Q, W* 5. *(a) P* 13 (1868–75).
83	1	1d. orange-vermilion (10.11.68)	..	..	50·00	4·50
		a. Imperf (pair)	..	..	£160	
84		1d. pale rose-red (4.11.74)	..	..	48·00	8·50
85		1d. deep rose-red	..	..	95·00	9·00
86		2d. pale blue (4.11.74)	..	..	48·00	1·75
87		2d. deep blue (20.11.68)	..	..	38·00	4·50
		a. Imperf (pair)	..	..	£300	
		b. Imperf between (vert pair)				
88		3d. brown (11.6.75)	..	..	70·00	12·00
		a. Re-entry	..	..	—	55·00
		b. Retouch (R. 2/8)	..	..	—	55·00
89		4d. yellow (1.1.75) (H/S S. £60)	..	£750	42·00
90		6d. deep green (9.4.69)	..	..	£120	9·00
91		6d. yellow-green	..	..	£100	6·50
92		6d. pale apple-green (1.1.75)	..	£130	9·00
		a. Imperf (pair)	..	..	£300	
93		1s. mauve	..	..	£140	29·00

(b) P 12 (1876–78)
94	1	1d. deep orange-vermilion	..	38·00	5·00
95		1d. pale orange-vermilion	..	40·00	5·00
		a. Imperf between (vert pair)	..		
96		1d. rose-red	..	..	45·00	10·00
97		1d. flesh	..	..	60·00	10·00
98		2d. pale blue	..	..	80·00	15·00
99		2d. bright blue	..	..	22·00	1·00
100		2d. deep blue	..	..	25·00	1·50
101		3d. brown	..	..	60·00	9·00
		a. Re-entry	..	..	—	45·00
		b. Retouch (R. 2/8)	..	—	45·00
102		4d. yellow	..	..	£600	25·00
103		4d. buff	..	..	£600	20·00
104		6d. deep green	..	..	£140	7·00
105		6d. green	..	..	£130	4·25
106		6d. yellow-green	..	..	£140	4·50
107		6d. apple-green	..	..	£140	7·00
108		1s. mauve	..	..	40·00	9·00
109		1s. purple	..	..	£140	5·00
		a. Imperf between (pair)	..		

(c) P 13 × 12 *or* 12 × 13
110	1	1d. orange-vermilion	..	..	—	£150
110a		1d. rose-red	..	..		
111		2d. deep blue	..	..	£1100	£250
112		4d. yellow	..	..	—	£300
113		6d. deep green	..	..	—	£300

(d) P 12½ × 13
114	1	1d. orange-vermilion	..	..	—	£350
115		2d. deep blue	..	..	—	£350
115a		6d. yellow-green	..	..		

(e) P 12½
| 115b | 1 | 2d. deep blue | .. | .. | | |

Reprints exist from 1895 of the 1d., 2d., 3d., 6d. and 1s. on thicker paper, Wmk *W* 6, and in different shades from the originals.

1879. *No wmk. P* 12.
116	1	6d. pale emerald-green	..	..	£150	25·00
		a. Imperf between (horiz pair)	..	—	£600
117		1s. mauve (*fiscal-cancel £5*)	..	95·00	48·00

No. 117 has a very indistinct lilac *burelé* band at back.
Nos. 116/17 can be found showing portions of a papermaker's watermark, either T. H. Saunders & Co or A. Pirie & Sons.

1881. *Lithographed from transfers from the 1s. die. Wmk Crown and Q, W* 6. *P* 12.
118	1	2s. pale blue (6 Apr)	..	..	60·00	22·00
119		2s. blue (*fiscal-cancel £3*)	..	60·00	22·00
		a. Imperf vert (horiz pair)	..		
120		2s. deep blue (*fiscal-cancel £3*)	..	75·00	22·00
121		2s. 6d. dull scarlet (28 Aug)	..	£110	42·00
122		2s. 6d. bright scarlet (*fiscal-cancel £3*)	..	£130	42·00
123		5s. pale yellow-ochre (28 Aug)	..	£150	60·00
124		5s. yellow-ochre (*fiscal-cancel £4*)	..	£150	60·00
125		10s. reddish brown (Mar)	..	£350	£110
		a. Imperf	..	..	£375	
126		10s. bistre-brown	..	..	£350	£110
127		20s. rose (*fiscal-cancel £6*)	..	£700	£130

Of the 2s. and 20s. stamps there are five types of each, and of the other values ten types of each.
Beware of fiscally used copies that have been cleaned and provided with forged postmarks.

7

Die I Die II

Dies I and II often occur in the same sheet.
Die I. The white horizontal inner line of the triangle in the upper right-hand corner merges into the outer white line of the oval above the "L".
Die II. The same line is short and does not touch the inner oval.

1879–80. *Typo. P* 12. *(a) Wmk Crown and Q, W* 5.
128	7	1d. reddish brown (Die I)	..	65·00	15·00
		a. Die II	..	..	£100	15·00
		ab. "QOEENSLAND"	..	£850	£150
129		1d. orange-brown (Die I)	..	£100	15·00
130		2d. blue (Die I)	..	..	55·00	10·00
		a. "PENGE" (R. 12/6)	..	£650	£110
		b. "QUEENSbAND" (R. 5/6)	..	—	£110
		c. "QU" joined	..	..	—	£110
131		4d. orange-yellow	..	..	£300	35·00

(b) No wmk, with lilac burelé band on back
132	7	1d. reddish brown (Die I)	..	£275	35·00
		a. Die II	..	..	£300	65·00
		ab. "QOEENSLAND"	..	—	£1400
133		2d. blue (Die I)	..	..	£350	17·00
		a. "PENGE" (R. 12/6)	..	£3250	£600
		b. "QUEENSbAND" (R. 5/6)	..		

(c) Wmk Crown and Q, W 6
134	7	1d. reddish brown (Die I)	..	32·00	5·00
		a. Imperf between (pair)	..	—	£300
		b. Die II	..	..	40·00	5·00
		ba. "QOEENSLAND"	..	£200	40·00
		bb. Imperf between (pair)	..	—	£300
135		1d. dull orange (Die I)	..	15·00	3·00
		a. Die II	..	..	18·00	3·00
		ab. "QOEENSLAND"	..	55·00	20·00
136		1d. scarlet (Die I)	..	12·00	1·75
		a. Die II	..	..	14·00	2·25
		ab. "QOEENSLAND"	..	80·00	24·00
137		2d. blue (Die I)	..	..	25·00	1·00
		a. "PENGE"	..	..	£120	40·00
		b. "QUEENSbAND"	..	£120	40·00
		c. Die II	..	..	27·00	3·00
138		2d. grey-blue (Die I)	..	25·00	1·00
		a. "PENGE"	..	..	£120	40·00
		b. "QUEENSbAND"	..	£120	40·00
		c. Die II	..	..	27·00	3·00
139		2d. bright blue (Die I)	..	28·00	1·00
		a. "PENGE"	..	..	£130	40·00
		b. "QUEENSbAND"	..	£130	40·00
		c. Imperf between (pair)	..	£450	
		d. Die II	..	..	30·00	3·00
140		2d. deep blue (Die I)	..	30·00	1·00
		a. "PENGE"	..	..	£140	40·00
		b. "QUEENSbAND"	..	£140	40·00
		c. Die II	..	..	24·00	3·00
141		4d. orange-yellow	..	..	£100	10·00
		a. Imperf between (pair)	..		
142		6d. deep green	..	..	55·00	4·50
		a. Imperf between (pair)	..		
143		6d. yellow-green	..	..	60·00	4·50
144		1s. deep violet	..	..	50·00	4·50
145		1s. pale lilac	..	..	45·00	5·50

The variety "QO" is No. 48 in the first arrangement, and No. 44 in a later arrangement on the sheets.
All these values have been seen imperf and unused, but we have no evidence that any of them were used in this condition.
The above were printed in sheets of 120, from plates made up of 30 groups of four electrotypes. There are four different types in each group, and two such groups of four are known of the 1d. and 2d., thus giving eight varieties of these two values. There was some resetting of the first plate of the 1d., and there are several plates of the 2d.; the value in the first plate of the latter value is in thinner letters, and in the last plate three types in each group of four have the "TW" of "TWO" joined, the letters of "PENCE" are larger and therefore much closer together, and in one type the "O" of "TWO" is oval, that letter being circular in the other types.

Half-penny

(8) 9 10

1880 (21 Feb). *Surch with T* 8.
151	7	½d. on 1d. (No. 134) (Die I)	..	£160	90·00
		a. Die II	..	..	£425	£350
		ab. "QOEENSLAND"	..	£850	£700

Examples with "Half-penny" reading downwards are forged surcharges.

(Eng H. Bourne. Recess Govt Printing Office, Brisbane from plates made by B.W.)

1882 (13 Apr)–95. *P* 12. *(a) W* 5 (*twice sideways*). *Thin paper*
152	9	2s. bright blue (14.4.82)	..	60·00	17·00
153		2s. 6d. vermilion (12.7.82)	..	50·00	20·00
154		5s. rose	..	..	45·00	22·00
155		10s. brown (12.7.82)	..	95·00	40·00
156		£1 deep green (30.5.83)	..	£225	£120
		a. Re-entry (R.1/2)	..	—	£180
		b. Retouch (R.6/4)	..	—	£180
152, 154/6 H/S "Specimen"			*Set of* 4	£150

(b) W 10. *Thick paper* (10.11.86)
157	9	2s. bright blue	..	..	60·00	28·00
158		2s. 6d. vermilion	..	..	38·00	20·00
159		5s. rose	..	..	35·00	28·00

160	9	10s. brown	..	..	95·00	40·00
161		£1 deep green	..	..	£170	60·00
		a. Re-entry (R.1/2)	..	—	£100
		b. Retouch (R.6/4)	..	—	£100

(c) W 6 (*twice sideways*). *Thin paper* (1895)
162	9	2s. 6d. vermilion	..	..	40·00	30·00
163		5s. rose	..	..	45·00	20·00
164		10s. brown	..	..	£180	50·00
165		£1 deep green	..	..	£180	60·00
		a. Re-entry (R.1/2)	..	—	£100
		b. Retouch (R.6/4)	..	—	£100

The re-entry on the £1 shows as a double bottom frame line and the retouch occurs alongside the bottom right numeral.
See also Nos. 270/1, 272/4 and 309/12.

| 11 | 12 |

In T **12** the shading lines do not extend entirely across, as in T **11**, thus leaving a white line down the front of the throat and point of the bust.

1882–83. *W* 6. *(a) P* 12.
166	11	1d. pale vermilion-red	..	..	3·00	30
		a. Double impression	..		
167		1d. deep vermilion-red	..	..	3·00	30
168		2d. blue	..	..	4·25	30
		a. Imperf between (horiz pair)	..		
169		4d. pale yellow	..	..	12·00	1·40
		a. "PENGE" for "PENCE" (R.8/1)	..	£120	40·00
		b. "EN" joined in "PENCE" (R.4/6)	..	90·00	30·00
		c. Imperf	..		
170		6d. green	..	..	9·00	70
171		1s. violet	..	..	18·00	2·00
172		1s. lilac	..	..	11·00	1·75
173		1s. deep mauve	..	..	11·00	1·40
174		1s. pale mauve	..	..	12·00	1·40
		a. Imperf	..	..	†	—

(b) P 9½ × 12
176	11	1d. pale red	..	..	60·00	22·00
177		2d. blue	..	..	£200	35·00
178		1s. mauve	..	..	£100	26·00

The above were printed from plates made up of four electrotypes as previously. In the 1d. the words of value are followed by a full stop. There are four types of the 4d., 6d., and 1s., eight types of the 1d., and twelve types of the 2d.
No. 169c is from a sheet used at Roma post office and comes cancelled with the "46" numeral postmark.

1887–89. *W* 6. *(a) P* 12.
179	12	1d. vermilion-red	..	..	2·75	30
180		2d. blue	..	..	5·00	30
		a. Oval white flaw on Queen's head behind diadem (R. 12/5)	..	25·00	7·50
181		2s. deep brown	..	..	55·00	23·00
182		2s. pale brown	..	..	50·00	20·00

(b) P 9½ × 12
183	12	2d. blue	..	..	£180	30·00

These are from new plates; four types of each value grouped as before. The 1d. is without stop. In all values No. 2 in each group of four has the "L" and "A" of "QUEENSLAND" joined at the foot, and No. 3 of the 2d. has "P" of word "PENCE" with a long downstroke.
The 2d. is known bisected and used as a 1d. value.

| 13 | 14 |

1890–94. *W* 6 (*sideways on* ½d.). *P* 12½, 13 (*comb machine*).
184	13	½d. pale green	..	..	3·00	50
185		½d. deep green	..	..	3·00	50
186		½d. deep blue-green	..	3·25	50
187	12	1d. vermilion-red	..	..	2·00	15
		a. Imperf	..	..	26·00	26·00
		b. Oval broken by tip of bust (R.10/3)	..	20·00	5·00
		c. Double impression	..	†	£190
188		2d. blue (old plate)	..	..	4·00	15
189		2d. pale blue (old plate)	..	3·75	15
190		2d. pale blue (retouched plate)	..	3·50	30
		a. "FWO" for "TWO" (R.8/7)	..	—	20·00
191	14	2½d. carmine	..	..	10·00	50
192	12	3d. brown	..	..	8·50	1·60
193	11	4d. yellow	..	..	13·00	1·25
		a. "PENGE" for "PENCE" (R.8/1)	..	60·00	22·00
		b. "EN" joined in "PENCE" (R.4/6)	..	45·00	16·00
194		4d. orange	..	..	16·00	1·25
		a. "PENGE" for "PENCE" (R.8/1)	..	70·00	22·00
		b. "EN" joined in "PENCE" (R.4/6)	..	50·00	16·00
195		4d. lemon	..	..	20·00	1·50
		a. "PENGE" for "PENCE" (R.8/1)	..	80·00	28·00
		b. "EN" joined in "PENCE" (R.4/6)	..	60·00	20·00
196		6d. green	..	..	10·00	1·25
197	12	2s. red-brown	..	..	38·00	8·00
198		2s. pale brown	..	..	42·00	9·50

This issue is perforated by a new vertical comb machine, gauging about 12¾ × 12¾. The 3d. is from a plate similar to those of the last issue, No. 2 in each group of four types having "L" and "A" joined at the foot. The ½d. and 2½d. are likewise in groups of four types, but the differences are very minute. In the retouched plate of the 2d. the letters "L" and "A" no longer touch in No. 2 of each group and the "P" in No. 3 is normal.

1894–95. *A. Thick paper.* W **10.** (*a*) P 12½, 13.
202	12	1d. vermilion-red		2·50	15
		a. Oval broken by tip of bust (R. 10/3)		25·00	5·00
203		1d. red-orange		2·50	15
		a. Oval broken by tip of bust (R. 10/3)		25·00	5·00
204		2d. blue (retouched plate)		3·00	20
		a. "FWO" for "TWO" (R. 8/7)		—	20·00
205	11	1s. mauve		12·00	2·75

B. Unwmkd paper; with blue burelé band at back. P 12½, 13
206	12	1d. vermilion-red		2·00	15
		a. Oval broken by tip of bust (R. 10/3)		20·00	5·00
		b. "PE" of "PENNY" omitted (R. 1/2)		£110	75·00
206c		1d. red-orange			

C. Thin paper. Crown and Q faintly impressed. P 12½, 13
207	12	2d. blue (retouched plate)		9·00
		a. "FWO" for "TWO" (R. 8/7)		80·00

15

16

17

18

1895–96. *A.* W **6** (*sideways on ½d.*). (*a*) P 12½, 13.
208	15	½d. green		1·00	45
		a. Double impression			
209		½d. deep green		1·00	45
		a. Printed both sides		75·00	
210	16	1d. orange-red		2·25	20
211		1d. pale red		2·00	20
212		2d. blue		4·00	35
213	17	2½d. carmine		10·00	3·00
214		2½d. rose		11·00	3·00
215	18	5d. purple-brown		13·00	2·75

(*b*) P 12
217	16	1d. red		25·00	8·50
218		2d. blue		25·00	12·00

B. Thick paper. W **10** (*sideways*) (*part only on each stamp*).
(*a*) P 12½, 13
219	15	½d. green		1·50	45
220		½d. deep green		1·50	45

(*b*) P 12
221	15	½d. green		12·00
222		½d. deep green		12·00

C. No wmk; with blue burelé band at back. (*a*) P 12½, 13
223	15	½d. green		1·50	50
		a. Without *burelé* band		40·00	
224		½d. deep green		1·50	

(*b*) P 12
225	15	½d. green		15·00
		a. Without *burelé* band		50·00

Nos. 223a and 225a are from the margins of the sheet.

D. Thin paper, with Crown and Q faintly impressed. P 12½, 13
227	15	½d. green		1·40	50
228	16	1d. orange-red		3·00	30

19

1896. W **6.** P 12½, 13.
229	19	1d. vermilion		8·50	40

Used examples of a 6d. green as Type **19** (figures in lower corners only) are known, mostly with readable 1902 postmark dates. It is believed that this 6d. was prepared, but not officially issued (*Price £1700 used*).

20

21

22

23

24

25

Die I

Die II

Two Dies of 4d.:

Die I. Serif of horizontal bar on lower right 4d. is clear of vertical frame line.
Die II. Serif joins vertical frame line.

1897–1907. *Figures in all corners.* W **6** (*sideways on ½d*). P 12½, 13.
231	20	½d. deep green			3·50	3·00
		a. Perf 12			—	90·00
232	21	1d. orange-vermilion			1·50	15
233		1d. vermilion			1·50	15
		a. Perf 12 (1903)			2·50	70
234		2d. blue			1·50	15
		a. Cracked plate			55·00	20·00
		b. Perf 12 (1903)			—	5·00
235		2d. deep blue			1·50	15
		a. Cracked plate			55·00	20·00
236	22	2½d. rose			16·00	10·00
237		2½d. purple/*blue* (1899)			8·50	85
238		2½d. brown-purple/*blue*			8·50	85
239		2½d. slate/*blue*			11·00	2·75
240	21	3d. brown			10·00	1·00
241		3d. deep brown			8·00	80
242		3d. reddish brown (1906)			8·00	80
243		3d. grey-brown (1907)			9·50	80
244		4d. yellow (Die I)			8·00	80
		a. Die II			18·00	1·75
245		4d. yellow-buff (Die I)			8·00	80
		a. Die II			18·00	1·75
246	23	5d. purple-brown			7·50	80
247		5d. dull brown (1906)			8·50	1·50
248		5d. black-brown (1907)			9·50	1·75
249	21	6d. green			7·00	1·25
250		6d. yellow-green			6·00	1·25
251	24	1s. pale mauve			13·00	1·00
252		1s. dull mauve			13·00	1·00
253		1s. bright mauve			15·00	2·00
254	25	2s. turquoise-green			30·00	8·00

The 1d. perf 12×9½ was not an authorised issue.
The cracked plate variety on the 2d. developed during 1901 and shows as a white break on the Queen's head and neck. The electro was later replaced.

1897–8. W **6** (*a*) *Zigzag roulette in black.* (*b*) *The same but plain.* (*c*) *Roulette* (*a*) *and also* (*b*). (*d*) *Roulette* (*b*) *and perf* 12½, 13. (*e*) *Roulette* (*a*) *and perf* 12½, 13. (*f*) *Compound of* (*a*), (*b*), *and perf* 12½, 13.
256	21	1d. vermilion (*a*)			7·00	5·50
257		1d. vermilion (*b*)			3·00	2·50
258		1d. vermilion (*c*)			7·00	9·00
259		1d. vermilion (*d*)			4·50	3·75
260		1d. vermilion (*e*)			65·00	80·00
261		1d. vermilion (*f*)			80·00	80·00

26

27

(Des M. Kellar)

1899–1906. W **6.** P 12½, 13.
262	26	½d. deep green			1·50	30
		a. Grey-green			1·50	30
		b. Green (p 12) (1903)			2·00	40
		c. Pale green (1906)			1·50	30

Stamps of T **26** without wmk, are proofs.

(Des F. Elliott)

1900 (19 June). *Charity.* T **27** *and horiz design showing Queen Victoria in medallion inscr* "PATRIOTIC FUND 1900". W **6.** P 12.
264a		1d. (6d.) claret		£100	£100
264b		2d. (1s.) violet		£250	£250

These stamps, sold at 6d. and 1s. respectively, paid postage of 1d. and 2d. only, the difference being contributed to a Patriotic Fund.

28

QUEENSLAND QUEENSLAND
A B

TWO TYPES OF "QUEENSLAND". Three different duty plates, each 120 (12×10), were produced for Type **28.** The first contained country inscriptions as Type A and was only used for Nos. 265/6. The second duty plate used for Nos. 265/6 and 282/5 contained 117 examples as Type A and 3 as Type B occurring on R. 1/6, R. 2/6 and R. 3/6. The third plate, also used for Nos. 265/6 and 282/5, had all inscriptions as Type B.

(Typo Victoria Govt Printer, Melbourne)

1903 (4 July)–05. W w **10.** P 12½.
265	28	9d. brown and ultramarine (A)		11·00	1·75
266		9d. brown and ultramarine (B) (1905)		11·00	1·75

1903 (Oct). *As Nos.* 162 *and* 165. W **6** (*twice sideways*). P 12½, 13 (*irregular line*).
270	9	2s. 6d. vermilion		60·00	32·00
271		£1 deep green		£900	£500
		a. Re-entry (R.1/2)		—	£750
		b. Retouch (R.6/4)		—	£750

(Litho Govt Ptg Office, Brisbane, from transfers of the recess plates)

1905 (Nov)–06. W **6** (*twice sideways*).
(*a*) P 12½, 13 (*irregular line*)
272	9	£1 deep green		£350	£100
		a. Re-entry (R.1/2)		—	£160
		b. Retouch (R.6/4)		—	£160

(*b*) P 12
273	9	5s. rose (7.06)		65·00	65·00
274		£1 deep green (7.06)		£250	90·00
		a. Re-entry (R.1/2)		£375	£150
		b. Retouch (R.6/4)		£375	£150

30

32

Redrawn types of T **21**

T **30.** The head is redrawn, the top of the crown is higher and touches the frame, as do also the back of the chignon and the point of the bust. The forehead is filled in with lines of shading, and the figures in the corners appear to have been redrawn also.

T **32.** The forehead is plain (white instead of shaded), and though the top of the crown is made higher, it does not touch the frame; but the point of the bust and the chignon still touch. The figure in the right lower corner does not touch the line below, and has not the battered appearance of that in the first redrawn type. The stamps are very clearly printed, the lines of shading being distinct.

1906 (Sept). W **6.** P 12½, 13 (*comb*).
281	30	2d. dull blue (*shades*)		6·00	2·25

(Typo Victoria Govt Printer, Melbourne)

1906 (Sept)–10. *Wmk Crown and double-lined A,* W w **11.**
(*a*) P 12 × 12½.
282	28	9d. brown and ultramarine (A)		24·00	2·50
283		9d. brown and ultramarine (B)		12·00	2·00
283a		9d. pale brown and blue (A)			
284		9d. pale brown and blue (B)		12·00	2·25

(*b*) P 11 (1910)
285	28	9d. brown and blue (B)		—	£200

33

1907–09. W **33.** (*a*) P 12½, 13 (*comb*).
286	26	½d. deep green		1·50	20
287		½d. deep blue-green		1·50	20
288	21	1d. vermilion		1·75	15
		a. Imperf (pair)		£160	
289	30	2d. dull blue		2·25	15
289a		2d. bright blue (3.08)		9·00	2·50
290	32	2d. bright blue (4.08)		2·25	15
291	21	3d. pale brown (8.08)		10·00	70
292		3d. bistre-brown		10·00	80
293		4d. yellow (Die I)		10·00	1·25
		a. Die II		22·00	2·75
294		4d. grey-black (Die I) (4.09)		12·00	1·50
		a. Die II		27·00	3·50
295	23	5d. dull brown		7·50	1·50
295a		5d. sepia (12.09)		12·00	2·25
296	21	6d. yellow-green		8·50	1·25
297		6d. bright green		10·00	1·50
298	24	1s. violet (1908)		11·00	1·60
299		1s. bright mauve		12·00	1·50
300	25	2s. turquoise-green (8.08)		30·00	7·00

Stamps of this issue also exist with the irregular line perforation 12½, 13. This was used when the comb perforation was under repair.

(*b*) P 13 × 11 *to* 12½
301	26	½d. deep green		5·00	1·00
302	21	1d. vermilion		5·00	80
303	32	2d. blue		6·50	80
304	21	3d. bistre-brown		13·00	4·00
305		4d. grey-black		28·00	9·00
306	23	5d. dull brown		18·00	9·00
307	21	6d. yellow-green		18·00	9·00
308	23	1s. violet		35·00	12·00

The perforation (*b*) is from a machine introduced to help cope with the demands caused by the introduction of penny postage. The three rows at top (or bottom) of the sheet show varieties gauging 13 × 11½, 13 × 11, and 13 × 12 respectively, these are obtainable in strips of three showing the three variations.

(Litho Govt Ptg Office, Brisbane)

1907 (Oct)–12. *W 33 (twice sideways). P 12½, 13 (irregular line).*

309	9	2s. 6d. vermilion	..	..	..	40·00	26·00
		a. *Dull orange* (1910)	..	..		55·00	42·00
		b. *Reddish orange* (1912)	..	..		£150	£180
310		5s. rose (12.07)	..	..	..	45·00	28·00
		a. *Deep rose* (1910)	..	..		55·00	38·00
		b. *Carmine-red* (1912)	..	..		£150	£225
311		10s. blackish brown	..	..		£100	35·00
		a. *Sepia* (1912)	..			£300	
312		£1 bluish green	..	..		£170	80·00
		a. Re-entry (R. 1/2)	..	..		—	£130
		b. Retouch (R. 6/4)	..	..		—	£130
		c. *Deep bluish green* (1910)	..			£375	£250
		ca. Re-entry (R. 1/2)	..	..		—	£350
		cb. Retouch (R. 6/4)	..	..		—	£350
		d. *Yellow-green* (1912)	..	..		£700	
		da. Re-entry (R. 1/2)	..	..			
		db. Retouch (R. 6/4)	..	..			

The 1912 printings are on thinner, whiter paper.
The lithographic stone used for Nos. 272/4 and 309/12 took the full sheet of 30 so the varieties on the £1 recess-printed version also appear on the stamps printed by lithography.

1911. *W 33. Perf irregular compound, 10½ to 12½.*

313	21	1d. vermilion	..	..	..	£350	£190

This was from another converted machine, formerly used for perforating Railway stamps. The perforation was very unsatisfactory and only one or two sheets were sold.

STAMP BOOKLETS

There are very few surviving examples of Nos. SB1/4. Listings are provided for those believed to have been issued with prices quoted for those known to still exist.

1904 (1 Jan)–09. *Black on red cover as No. SB1 of New South Wales. Stapled.*

SB1	£1 booklet containing two hundred and forty 1d. in four blocks of 30 and two blocks of 60	..	
	a. Red on pink cover (1909)	..	..	
	b. Blue on pink cover	..	..	£6000

1904 (1 Jan). *Black on grey cover as No. SB1. Stapled.*

SB2 £1 booklet containing one hundred and twenty 2d. in four blocks of 30 .. .. ..

1910 (May). *Black on cream cover as No. SB3 of New South Wales. Stapled.*

SB3 2s. booklet containing eleven ½d. (No. 301), either in block of 6 plus block of 5 or block of 11, and eighteen 1d. (No. 302), either in three blocks of 6 or block of 6 plus block of 12
Unsold stock of No. SB3 was uprated with one additional ½d. in May 1911.

1911 (Aug). *Red on pink cover as No. SB3. Stapled.*

SB4	2s. booklet containing twelve ½d. (No. 301), either in two blocks of 6 or block of 12, and eighteen 1d. (No. 302), either in three blocks of 6 or block of 6 plus block of 12	..	..	£1500
	a. Red on white	..	..	..	£1500

POSTAL FISCALS

Authorised for use from 1 January 1880 until 1 July 1892

CANCELLATIONS. Beware of stamps which have had pen-cancellations cleaned off and then had faked postmarks applied. Used prices quoted are for postally used examples between the above dates.

F 1   F 2

1866–68. A. *No wmk. P 13.*

F 1	F 1	1d. blue	..	..	..	25·00	7·00
F 2		6d. deep violet	..	..	..	25·00	30·00
F 3		1s. blue-green	..	..	..	30·00	9·00
F 4		2s. brown	..	..	..	85·00	42·00
F 5		2s. 6d. dull red	..	..	..	85·00	30·00
F 6		5s. yellow	..	..	..	£200	60·00
F 6a		6s. light brown	..				
F 7		10s. green	..	..	..	£350	£100
F 8		20s. rose	..	..	..	£425	£150

B. *Wmk F 2. P 13*

F 9	F 1	1d. blue	..	..	..	15·00	20·00
F10		6d. deep violet	..	..	..	25·00	30·00
F11		6d. blue	..	..	..	25·00	14·00
F12		1s. blue-green	..	..	..	30·00	14·00
F13		2s. brown	..	..	..	85·00	30·00
F13a		5s. yellow	..	..	..	£200	65·00
F14		10s. green	..	..	..	£350	£100
F15		20s. rose	..	..	..	£425	£150

COVER PRICES

Cover factors are quoted at the beginning of each country for most issues to 1945. An explanation of the system can be found on page x. The factors quoted do not, however, apply to philatelic covers.

F 3   F 3a

1871–2. *P 12 or 13. A. Wmk Large Crown and Q, Wmk F 3a.*

F16	F 3	1d. mauve	..	..	..	10·00	5·00
F17		6d. red-brown	..	..	..	20·00	10·00
F18		1s. green	..	..	..	30·00	12·00
F19		2s. blue	..	..	..	40·00	10·00
F20		2s. 6d. brick-red	..	..		60·00	25·00
F21		5s. orange-brown	..	..		£100	25·00
F22		10s. brown	..	..	..	£200	75·00
F23		20s. rose	..	..	..	£350	£120

B. *No wmk. Blue burelé band at back*

F24	F 3	1d. mauve	..	..	..	14·00	6·50
F25		6d. red-brown	..	..	..	20·00	10·00
F26		6d. mauve	..	..	..	60·00	30·00
F27		1s. green	..	..	..	30·00	12·00
F28		2s. blue	..	..	..	45·00	50·00
F29		2s. 6d. vermilion	..	..		85·00	35·00
F30		5s. yellow-brown	..	..		£120	40·00
F31		10s. brown	..	..	..	£225	90·00
F32		20s. rose	..	..	..	£350	£110

F 4   F 5

1878–9. A. *No wmk. Lilac burelé band at back. P 12.*

F33	F 4	1d. violet	..	..	..	40·00	12·00

B. *Wmk Crown and Q, W 5. P 12*

F34	F 4	1d. violet	..	..	..	15·00	8·00

Stamps as Type F 5 were not issued until 1 July 1892. The existence of postal cancellations on such issues was unauthorised.

Queensland became part of the Commonwealth of Australia on 1 January 1901.

SOUTH AUSTRALIA

PRICES FOR STAMPS ON COVER

Nos. 1/3	*from* × 3
No. 4	†
Nos. 5/12	*from* × 2
Nos. 13/18	*from* × 3
Nos. 19/43	*from* × 4
Nos. 44/9b	—
Nos. 50/110	*from* × 3
No. 111	—
Nos. 112/34	*from* × 6
Nos. 135/45	*from* × 3
Nos. 146/66	*from* × 5
Nos. 167/70a	*from* × 10
Nos. 171/2a	—
Nos. 173/94a	*from* × 12
Nos. 195/208	—
Nos. 229/31	*from* × 12
No. 232	—
Nos. 233/42	*from* × 12
Nos. 268/75	*from* × 30
Nos. 276/9	—
Nos. 280/8	*from* × 30
Nos. 289/92	—
Nos. 293/304	*from* × 15
No. 305	—
Nos. O1/13	—
Nos. O14/36	*from* × 20
Nos. O37/42	*from* × 5
Nos. O43/4	*from* × 50
Nos. O45/7	—
Nos. O48/52	*from* × 30
No. O53	—
Nos. O54/85	*from* × 50
Nos. O86/7	—

SPECIMEN OVERPRINTS. Those listed are from U.P.U. distributions between 1889 and 1895. Further "Specimen" overprints exist, but these were used for other purposes.

---

1   2 Large Star

(Eng Wm Humphrys. Recess P.B.)

1855. *Printed in London. W 2. Imperf.*

1	1	1d. dark green (26.10.55)	..	£2500	£350
2		2d. rose-carmine (*shades*) (1.1.55)	..	£550	80·00
3		6d. deep blue (26.10.55)	..	£2000	£150

Prepared and sent to the Colony, but not issued

4	1	1s. violet	..	..	..	£4750	

A printing of 500,000 of these 1s. stamps was made and delivered, but as the colour was liable to be confused with that of the 6d. stamp, the stock was destroyed on 5 June 1857.

NOTE. Proofs of the 1d. and 6d. without wmk exist, and these are found with forged star watermarks added, and are sometimes offered as originals.
For reprints of the above and later issues, see note after No. 194.

1856–58. *Printed by Govt Ptr, Adelaide, from Perkins, Bacon plates. W 2. Imperf.*

5	1	1d. deep yellow-green (15.6.58)	..	£5000	£400
6		1d. yellow-green (11.10.58)	..	—	£475
7		2d. orange-red (23.4.56)	..	—	75·00
8		2d. blood-red (14.11.56)	..	£1200	60·00
		a. Printed on both sides	..		
9		2d. red (*shades*) (29.10.57)	..	£650	40·00
		a. Printed on both sides	..	—	£600
10		6d. slate-blue (7.57)	..	£2000	£150
11		1s. red-orange (8.7.57)	..	—	£400
12		1s. orange (11.6.58)	..	£3750	£325

1858–59. *W 2. Rouletted. (This first rouletted issue has the same colours as the local imperf issue).*

13	1	1d. yellow-green (8.1.59)	..	£475	45·00
14		1d. light yellow-green (18.3.59)	..	£475	50·00
		a. Imperf between (pair)	..		
15		2d. red (17.2.59)	..	£110	18·00
		a. Printed on both sides			
17		6d. slate-blue (12.12.58)	..	£375	25·00
18		1s. orange (18.3.59)	..	£800	35·00
		a. Printed on both sides	..	—	£1000

3   4   (5)

1860–69. *Second rouletted issue, printed (with the exception of No. 24) in colours only found rouletted or perforated. Surch with T 5 (Nos. 35/7). W 2.*

19	1	1d. bright yellow-green (22.4.61)	..	45·00	25·00
20		1d. dull blue-green (17.12.63)	..	42·00	23·00
21		1d. sage-green	..	50·00	27·00
22		1d. pale sage-green (27.5.65)	..	42·00	
23		1d. deep green (1864)	..	£225	65·00
24		1d. deep yellow-green (1869)	..	90·00	
24a		2d. pale red	..	65·00	4·00
		b. Printed on both sides	..	—	£375
25		2d. pale vermilion (3.2.63)	..	50·00	4·00
26		2d. bright vermilion (19.8.64)	..	42·00	2·75
		a. Imperf between (horiz pair)	..	£700	£300
27	3	4d. dull violet (24.1.67)	..	55·00	17·00
28	1	6d. violet-blue (19.3.60)	..	£140	6·00
29		6d. greenish blue (11.2.63)	..	70·00	4·00
30		6d. dull ultramarine (25.4.64)	..	65·00	4·00
		a. Imperf between (horiz pair)	..	—	£300
31		6d. violet-ultramarine (11.4.68)	..	£150	6·00
32		6d. dull blue (26.8.65)	..	£100	6·50
		a. Imperf between (pair)	..	—	£600
33		6d. Prussian blue (7.9.69)	..	£550	50·00
33a		6d. indigo	..	—	55·00
34	4	9d. grey-lilac (24.12.60)	..	55·00	9·00
		a. Imperf between (horiz pair)	..		
35		10d. on 9d. orange-red (B.) (20.7.66)	..	£130	24·00
36		10d. on 9d. yellow (B.) (29.7.67)	..	£160	20·00
37		10d. on 9d. yellow (Blk.) (14.8.69)	..	£1200	30·00
		a. Surch inverted at the top	..	—	£2500
		b. Printed on both sides	..	—	£800
		c. Roul × perf 10	..	†	
38	1	1s. yellow (25.10.61)	..	£450	28·00
		a. Imperf between (vert pair)	..	—	£1200
39		1s. grey-brown (10.4.63)	..	£150	16·00
40		1s. dark grey-brown (26.5.63)	..	£130	16·00
41		1s. chestnut (25.8.63)	..	£150	11·00
42		1s. lake-brown (27.3.65)	..	£110	12·00
		a. Imperf between (horiz pair)	..	—	£400
43	3	2s. rose-carmine (24.1.67)	..	£160	25·00
		a. Imperf between (vert pair)	..	—	£750

1868–71. *Remainders of old stock subsequently perforated by the 11½–12½ machine.*

(a) Imperf stamps. P 11½–12½

44	1	2d. pale vermilion (Feb 1868)	..	—	£900
45		2d. vermilion (18.3.68)	..	—	£1000

(b) Rouletted stamps. P 11½–12½

46	1	1d. bright green (9.11.69)		—	£450
47		2d. pale vermilion (15.8.68)		—	£400
48		6d. Prussian blue (8.11.69)		—	£200
		aa. Horiz pair perf all round, roul between			
48a		6d. indigo		—	£300
49	4	9d. grey-lilac (29.3.71)		£1500	£160
		a. Perf × roulette		—	£150
49b	1	1s. lake-brown (23.5.70)			

1867–70. *W* **2.** *P* 11½–12½ × *roulette.*

50	1	1d. pale bright green (2.11.67)		£150	18·00
51		1d. bright green (1868)		£130	18·00
52		1d. grey-green (26.1.70)		£150	20·00
		a. Imperf between (horiz pair)			
53		1d. blue-green (29.11.67)		£190	30·00
54	3	4d. dull violet (July 1868)		£1400	£130
55		4d. dull purple (1869)		—	90·00
56	1	6d. bright pale blue (29.5.67)		£450	19·00
57		6d. Prussian blue (7.67)		£400	19·00
		a. Printed on both sides			
58		6d. indigo (1.8.69)		£500	24·00
59	4	10d. dull yellow (B.) (2.2.69)		£600	30·00
		a. Printed on both sides		—	£550
60	1	1s. chestnut (April 1868)		£250	15·00
61		1s. lake-brown (3.3.69)		£250	15·00

NOTE. The stamps perf 11½, 12½, or compound of the two, are here combined in one list, as both perforations are on the one machine, and all the varieties *may* be found in each sheet of stamps. This method of classifying the perforations by the machines is by far the most simple and convenient.

3-PENCE

(6)   7 (=Victoria *W* 19)

1868–79. *Surch with T* **6** (*Nos.* 66/8). *W* **2.** *P* 11½–12½.

62	1	1d. pale bright green (8.2.68)		£150	18·00
63		1d. grey-green (18.2.68)		£120	40·00
64		1d. dark green (20.3.68)		55·00	17·00
		a. Printed on both sides			
65		1d. deep yellow-green (28.6.72)		50·00	18·00
		a. Imperf between (horiz pair)		†	£500
66	3	3d. on 4d. Prussian blue (Blk.) (7.2.71)		—	£700
67		3d. on 4d. sky-blue (Blk.) (12.8.70)		£275	10·00
		a. Imperf		—	£500
		b. Rouletted		—	£500
68		3d. on 4d. deep ultramarine (Blk.) (9.72)		70·00	8·00
		a. Surch double (10.9.74)		—	£3250
		b. Additional surch on back		—	£2500
		c. Surch omitted (26.4.74)		£14000	£8000
70		4d. dull purple (1.2.68)		60·00	15·00
		a. Imperf between (horiz pair)			
71		4d. dull violet (1868)		55·00	8·00
72	1	6d. bright pale blue (23.2.68)		£300	11·00
73		6d. Prussian blue (29.9.69)		90·00	6·00
		a. Perf 11½×imperf (horiz pair)		†	£500
74		6d. indigo (1869)		£120	17·00
75	4	9d. claret (7.72)		£100	8·00
76		9d. bright mauve (1.11.72)		£100	8·00
		a. Printed on both sides		—	£300
77		9d. red-purple (15.1.74)		65·00	8·00
78		10d. on 9d. yellow (B.) (15.8.68)		£1000	24·00
		a. Wmk Crown and S A (*W* **10**) (1868)		—	£750
79		10d. on 9d. yellow (Blk.) (13.9.69)		£200	27·00
80	1	1s. lake-brown (9.68)		£150	11·00
81		1s. chestnut (8.10.72)		£110	16·00
82		1s. dark red-brown		90·00	11·00
83		1s. red-brown (6.1.69)		£100	11·00
84	3	2s. pale rose-pink (10.10.69)		£950	£150
85		2s. deep rose-pink (8.69)		—	£100
86		2s. crimson-carmine (16.10.69)		80·00	18·00
87		2s. carmine (1868)		70·00	10·00
		a. Printed on both sides		—	£300

No. 78a was a trial printing made to test the perforating machine on the new D.L.R. paper.

1870–71. *W* **2.** *P* 10.

88	1	1d. grey-green (6.70)		£120	15·00
89		1d. pale bright green (9.8.70)		£120	15·00
90		1d. bright green (1871)		£100	15·00
91	3	3d. on 4d. dull ultramarine (R.) (6.8.70)		£325	60·00
92		3d. on 4d. ultram (Blk.) (14.2.71)		£250	14·00
93		3d. on 4d. ultramarine (Blk.) (14.8.71)		£100	17·00
93a		3d. on 4d. Prussian blue (Blk.) (16.12.71)			
94		4d. dull lilac (1870)		£110	10·00
95		4d. dull purple (1871)		£100	10·00
96	1	6d. bright blue (19.6.70)..		£180	17·00
97		6d. indigo (11.10.71)		£225	16·00
98		1s. chestnut (4.1.71)		£150	19·00

1870–73. *W* **2.** *P* 10 × 11½–12½, 11½–12½ × 10, *or compound.*

99	1	1d. pale bright green (11.10.70)		£140	14·00
		a. Printed on both sides			
100		1d. grey-green		£130	15·00
101		1d. deep green (19.6.71)		75·00	10·00
102	3	3d. on 4d. pale ultram (Blk.) (9.11.70)		£180	30·00
103		4d. dull lilac (1871)		—	18·00
104		4d. slate-lilac (5.3.73)		£120	18·00
105	1	6d. Prussian blue (2.3.70)		£140	8·00
106		6d. bright Prussian blue (26.10.70)		£150	10·00
107	4	10d. on 9d. yellow (Blk.) (1.70)		£110	17·00
108	1	1s. chestnut (17.6.71)		£200	32·00
109	3	2s. rose-pink (24.4.71)		—	£170
110		2s. carmine (2.3.72)		£130	25·00

1871 (17 July). *W* **7.** *P* 10.

111	3	4d. dull lilac		£1500	£200
		a. Printed on both sides			

8 Broad Star

8 PENCE

(9)

1876–1900. *W* **8.** *Surch with T* **9** (*Nos.* 118/21). (*a*) *P* 11½–12½.

112	3	3d. on 4d. ultramarine (1.6.79)		55·00	15·00
		a. Surch double		—	£1000
113		4d. violet-slate (15.3.79)		90·00	11·00
114		4d. plum (16.4.80)		45·00	6·00
115		4d. deep mauve (8.6.82)		45·00	5·00
116	1	6d. indigo (2.12.76)		90·00	4·50
		a. Imperf between (horiz pair)			
117		6d. Prussian blue (7.78)		60·00	4·00
118	4	8d. on 9d. brown-orange (7.76)		55·00	5·00
119		8d. on 9d. burnt umber (1880)		60·00	5·00
120		8d. on 9d. brown (9.3.80)		60·00	5·00
		a. Imperf between (vert pair)		£375	
121		8d. on 9d. grey-brown (10.5.81)		55·00	6·50
		a. Surch double		—	£350
122		9d. purple (9.3.80)		40·00	7·00
		a. Printed on both sides		—	£200
123		9d. rose-lilac (21.8.80)		15·00	3·00
124		9d. rose-lilac (*large holes*) (26.5.00)		10·00	3·25
125	1	1s. red-brown (3.11.77)		45·00	2·75
		a. Imperf between (horiz pair)		—	£250
126		1s. reddish lake-brown (1880)		42·00	3·00
127		1s. lake-brown (1.9.83)		48·00	2·75
128		1s. Vandyke brown (1891)		55·00	8·00
129		1s. dull brown (1891)		38·00	2·75
130		1s. chocolate (*large holes*) (6.5.97)		24·00	3·00
		a. Imperf vert (horiz pair)		£200	
131		1s. sepia (*large holes*) (22.5.00)		24·00	3·00
		a. Imperf between (vert pair)		£150	
132	3	2s. carmine (15.2.77)		32·00	4·50
		a. Imperf between (horiz pair)		—	£425
		b. Imperf (pair)			
133		2s. rose-carmine (1885)		38·00	6·50
134		2s. rose-carmine (*large holes*) (6.12.98)		30·00	6·00

The perforation with larger, clean-cut holes resulted from the fitting of new pins to the machine.

(b) P 10

135	1	6d. Prussian blue (11.11.79)		80·00	12·00
136		6d. bright blue (1879)		£100	11·00
136a		1s. reddish lake-brown..		£225	

(c) P 10 × 11½–12½, 11½–12½ × 10, *or compound*

137	3	4d. violet-slate (21.5.79)		£100	10·00
138		4d. dull purple (4.10.79)		38·00	2·00
139	1	6d. Prussian blue (29.12.77)		50·00	2·50
140		6d. bright blue		70·00	5·50
141		6d. bright ultramarine ..		38·00	1·75
142		1s. reddish lake-brown (9.2.85)		75·00	9·00
143		1s. dull brown (29.6.86)		90·00	10·00
144	3	2s. carmine (27.12.77)		55·00	5·50
145		2s. rose-carmine (1887)		50·00	5·00
		a. Imperf between (horiz pair)		—	£400

10   11   12

1901–2. *Wmk Crown SA* (*wide*), *W* **10.** *P* 11½–12½ (*large holes*).

146	4	9d. claret (1.2.02)		15·00	13·00
147	1	1s. dark brown (12.6.01)		20·00	10·00
148		1s. dark reddish brown (1902)..		22·00	11·00
		a. Imperf between (vert pair) ..			
149		1s. red-brown (aniline) (18.7.02)		20·00	12·00
150	3	2s. crimson (29.8.01)		28·00	13·00
151		2s. carmine		22·00	9·00

(Plates and electrotypes by D.L.R. Printed in Adelaide)

1868–76. *W* **10.** (*a*) *Rouletted.*

152	12	2d. deep brick-red (8.68)		45·00	3·25
153		2d. pale orange-red (5.10.68)		42·00	2·75
		a. Printed on both sides		—	£225
		b. Imperf between (horiz pair)		—	£275

(b) P 11½–12½

154	11	1d. blue-green (10.1.75)		65·00	11·00
155	12	2d. pale orange-red (5.5.69)		£850	£190

(c) P 11½–12½ × *roulette*

156	12	2d. pale orange-red (20.8.69)		—	£120

(d) P 10 × *roulette*

157	12	2d. pale orange-red (7.5.70)		£200	20·00

(e) P 10

158	11	1d. blue-green (4.75)		22·00	3·75
159	12	2d. brick-red (4.70)		10·00	35
160		2d. orange-red (1.7.70)		8·50	30
		a. Printed on both sides		—	£170

(f) P 10 × 11½–12½, 11½–12½ × 10, *or compound*

161	11	1d. blue-green (27.8.75)		42·00	12·00
162	12	2d. brick-red (19.1.71)		£400	6·00
163		2d. orange-red (3.2.71)		£100	8·50
		a. Imperf (8.76)		£750	

1869. *Wmk Large Star, W* **2.** (*a*) *Rouletted.*

164	12	2d. orange-red (13.3.69)		45·00	11·00

(b) P 11½–12½ × *roulette*

165	12	2d. orange-red (1.8.69)		—	90·00

(c) P 11½–12½

165a	12	2d. orange-red (7.69)		—	£800

1871 (15 July). *Wmk V and Crown, W* **7.** *P* 10.

166	12	2d. brick-red		42·00	13·00

HALF-

PENNY

13   (14)

1876–1904. *Wmk Crown SA* (*close*), *W* **13.** (*a*) *P* 10 (1876–85)

167	11	1d. blue-green (9.2.76)		6·00	20
		a. Yellowish green (11.78)		7·00	20
		b. Deep green (11.79)		7·00	20
		ba. Imperf between (horiz pair)			
		bb. Printed double		†	—
168	12	2d. orange-red (8.76)		6·00	10
		a. Dull brick-red (21.5.77)		6·00	10
		b. Blood-red (31.10.79)		£200	3·00
		c. Pale red (4.85)		6·00	10

(b) P 10 × 11½–12½, 11½–12½ × 10 *or compound* (1877–80)

169	11	1d. deep green (11.2.80)		18·00	1·50
		a. Blue-green (2.3.80)		8·50	1·90
170	12	2d. orange-red (4.9.77)		£120	3·00
		a. Dull brick-red (6.80)		£120	3·00

(c) P 11½–12½ (1877–84)

171	11	1d. blue-green (2.84)		—	£110
172	12	2d. orange-red (14.9.77)		—	£110
		a. Blood-red (1.4.80)		—	£110

(d) P 15 (1893)

173	11	1d. green (8.5.93)		4·00	20
174	12	2d. pale orange (9.2.93)		7·50	10
		a. Orange-red		7·00	10
		b. Imperf between (vert pair)		£170	

(e) P 13 (1895–1903)

175	11	1d. pale green (11.1.95)		4·00	20
		a. Green		4·00	20
		b. Imperf between (vert pair)			
176		1d. rosine (8.8.99)		2·25	10
		a. Scarlet (23.12.03)		2·75	10
		b. Deep red		2·50	10
177	12	2d. pale orange (19.1.95)		3·75	10
		a. Orange-red (9.5.95)		2·75	10
178		2d. bright violet (10.10.99)		2·00	10

(f) P 12×11½ (*comb*) (1904)

179	11	1d. rosine (2.2.04)		5·50	10
		a. Scarlet (25.7.04)		4·00	10
180	12	2d. bright violet (11.10.04)		3·00	10

Examples of the 1d. pale green with thicker lettering come from a worn plate.

1882 (1 Jan). *No.* 167 *surch with T* **14.**

181	11	½d. on 1d. blue-green ..		11·00	3·25

15   16

17   18

1883–99. *W* **13** (*sideways on* ½d.). (*a*) *P* 10 (1883–95)

182	15	½d. chocolate (1.3.83)		2·75	50
		a. Imperf between (horiz pair)			
		b. Red-brown (4.4.89)		2·50	4
		c. Brown (1895)		2·50	4
183	16	3d. sage-green (12.86) (Optd S. £25)		8·00	1·1
		a. Olive-green (6.6.90)		8·00	1·5
		b. Deep green (12.4.93)		5·50	7
184	17	4d. pale violet (3.90) (Optd S. £30)		7·00	1·2
		a. Aniline violet (3.1.93)		9·00	1·5
185	18	6d. pale blue (4.87) (Optd S. £25)		7·00	1·4
		a. Blue (5.5.87)		8·50	6

(b) P 10×11½–12½, 11½–12½×10 *or compound* (1891)

186	15	½d. red-brown (25.9.91)		4·25	1·2
		a. Imperf between (horiz pair)		£80·00	

(c) P 11½–12½ (1890)

187	15	½d. red-brown (12.10.90)		6·50	1·0

(d) P 15 (1893–94)

188	15	½d. pale brown (1.93)		2·50	4
		a. Deep brown		2·50	4
		b. Imperf between (pair)		80·00	
		c. Perf 12½ between (pair)		£120	28·0
189	17	4d. purple (1.1.94)		12·00	2·0
		a. Slate-violet		12·00	1·7

190	18	6d. blue (20.11.93)	..	..	22·00	3·50

(e) P 13 (1895–99)

191	15	½d. pale brown (9.95) ..	..	2·50	30
		a. Deep brown (19.3.97)	..	2·50	30
192	16	3d. pale olive-green (26.7.97)	..	6·00	75
		a. Deep olive-green (27.11.99)	..	5·00	70
193	17	4d. violet (21.1.96)	..	..	6·00	40
194	18	6d. pale blue (3.96)	..	..	7·00	65
		a. Blue	..	..	7·00	65

REPRINTS. In 1884, and in later years, reprints on paper wmkd Crown SA, W **10**, were made of Nos. 1, 2, 3, 4, 12, 13, 14, 15, 19, 24, 27, 28, 32, 33, 34, 35, 36, 37, 38, 40, 43, 44, 49*a*, 53, 65, 67, 67 with surcharge in red, 70, 71, 72, 73, 78, 79, 81, 83, 86, 90, 118, 119, 120, 121, 122, 155, 158, 159, 164, 181, 182. They are overprinted "REPRINT".

In 1889 examples of the reprints for Nos. 1/3, 12, 15, 19, 27, 32/8, 44, 67, 67 surcharged in red, 70/1, 73, 83, 86, 118, 121/2, 158/9, 164 and 181/2, together with No. 141 overprinted "Specimen", were supplied to the U.P.U. for distribution.

19	(20)	(21)

(Plates and electrotypes by D.L.R. Printed in Adelaide)

1886–96. *T* **19** (*inscr* "POSTAGE & REVENUE"). W **13**. *Parts of two or more wmks, on each stamp, sometimes sideways.* A. *Perf* 10. B. *Perf* 11½–12½ *(small or large holes).*

				A	B
195		2s. 6d. mauve ..	..	27·00	8·00	†
		a. Dull violet	..	†	24·00	6·00
		b. Bright aniline violet	..	†	25·00	7·00
196		5s. rose-pink ..	..	45·00	12·00	32·00	12·00
		a. Rose-carmine	..	†	35·00	14·00
197		10s. green ..	..	£110	35·00	80·00	35·00
198		15s. brownish yellow	..	£275	—	£300	£120
199		£1 blue	..	£200	90·00	£150	80·00
200		£2 Venetian red	..	£475	£200	£475	£200
201		50s. dull pink	..	£700	£250	£700	—
202		£3 sage green	..	£750	£250	£750	£250
203		£4 lemon	..	£950	—	£850	—
204		£5 grey	..	£1600	—	£1700	—
205		£5 brown (1896)	..	†	£1700	£600
206		£10 bronze	..	£2500	£700	£1800	£700
207		£15 silver	..	£4500	—	£4500	—
208		£20 claret	..	£5000	—	£5000	—
195/208 *(all perf 10 ex No. 205)*					
	Optd "Specimen" *Set of 14*	£400			

Variations exist in the length of the words and shape of the letters of the value inscription.

The 2s. 6d. dull violet, 5s. rose-pink, 10s., £1 and £5 brown exist perf 11½–12½ with either large or small holes; the 2s. 6d. aniline, 5s. rose-carmine, 15s., £2 and 50s. with large holes only and the remainder only with small holes.

Stamps perforated 11½–12½ small holes, are, generally speaking, rather rarer than those with the 1895 (large holes) gauge.

Stamps perf 10 were issued on 20 Dec 1886. Stamps perf 11½–12½ (small holes) are known with earliest dates covering the period from June 1890 to Feb 1896. Earliest dates of stamps with large holes range from July 1896 to May 1902.

1891 (1 Jan)–**93.** *T* **17/18** *surch with T* **20/1**. W **13**. *(a) P* 10

229	17	2½d. on 4d. pale grn (Br.) (Optd S. £25)	7·50	2·50
		a. Fraction bar omitted	..	90·00	75·00
		b. Deep green	..	8·00	1·75
		ba. Fraction bar omitted			
		bb. "2" and "½" closer together	..	20·00	18·00
		bc. Imperf between (horiz pair)			
		bd. Imperf between (vert pair)	..	—	£400
230	18	5d. on 6d. pale brn (C.) (Optd S. £25)	16·00	4·00
		a. Deep brown	..	16·00	3·75
		b. No stop after "5D"	..	£150	

(b) P 10×11½–12½ *or* 11½–12½×10

231	17	2½d. on 4d. pale green (Br.)	..	14·00	3·00
		a. Deep green	..	14·00	3·00

(c) P 11½–12½

232	17	2½d. on 4d. deep green	..	27·00	42·00

(d) P 15

233	17	2½d. on 4d. green (14.10.93)	..	11·00	2·50
		a. Fraction bar omitted			
		b. "2" and "½." closer together	..	40·00	22·00

22 Red Kangaroo	23	24 G.P.O., Adelaide

(Des M. Tannenberg, plates by D.L.R.)

1894 (1 Mar)–**1906.** W **13**. *(a) P* 15

234	22	2½d. violet-blue	..	12·00	2·00
235	23	5d. brown-purple	..	12·00	1·75
234/5	Optd "Specimen"	*Set of 2*	50·00	

(b) P 13

236	22	2½d. violet-blue (11.2.95)	..	10·00	70
237		2½d. indigo (25.3.98)	..	4·50	30
238	23	5d. brown-purple (1.96)	..	6·50	50
		a. Purple	..	6·50	45

(c) P 12×11½ *(comb)*

239	22	2½d. indigo (4.7.06)	..	6·50	30
240	23	5d. dull purple (1.05)	..	7·50	85

(Typo D.L.R.)

1899 (27 Dec)–**1905.** W **13**. *(a) P* 13

241	24	½d. yellow-green	..	1·50	50

(b) P 12×11½ *(comb)*

242	24	½d. yellow-green (7.05)	..	1·50	40

25

The measurements given indicate the length of the value inscription in the bottom label. The dates are those of the earliest known postmarks.

1902–4. *As T* **19**, *but top tablet as T* **25** (thin "POSTAGE"). W **13**.

(a) P 11½–12½

268		3d. olive-green (18½ mm) (1.8.02)	..	3·50	80
269		4d. red-orange (17 mm) (29.11.02)	..	5·00	1·25
270		6d. blue-green (16–16½ mm) (29.11.02)..	6·00	1·25
271		8d. ultramarine (19 mm) (25.4.02)	..	7·50	3·00
272		8d. ultramarine (16½ mm) (22.3.04)	..	7·50	3·00
		a. "EIGNT"	..	£800	£1100
273		9d. rosy lake (19.9.02)	..	8·00	1·75
		a. Imperf between (vert pair)	..	£275	
		b. Imperf between (horiz pair)	..		
274		10d. dull yellow (29.11.02)	..	11·00	4·00
275		1s. brown (18.8.02)	..	11·00	2·25
		a. Imperf between (horiz pair)			
		b. Imperf between (vert pair)	..	£450	
		c. "POSTAGE" and value in red-brown	45·00	20·00
276		2s. 6d. pale violet (19.9.02)	..	28·00	10·00
		a. Bright violet (2.2.03)	..	22·00	7·00
277		5s. rose (17.10.02)	..	55·00	40·00
278		10s. green (1.11.02)	..	£100	60·00
279		£1 blue (1.11.02)	..	£225	£120

(b) P 12

280		3d. olive-green (20 mm) (15.4.04)	..	5·00	1·25
		a. "POSTAGE" omitted; value below "AUSTRALIA"	..	£350	
281		4d. orange-red (17½–18 mm) (18.2.03)	..	6·50	1·25
282		6d. blue-green (15 mm) (14.11.03)	..	16·00	2·75
283		9d. rosy lake (2.12.03)	..	26·00	3·50

PRINTER. Stamp printing in Adelaide ceased in 1909 when the printer, J. B. Cooke, was appointed head of the Commonwealth Stamp Printing Branch in Melbourne. From 9 March 1909 further printings of current South Australia stamps were made in Melbourne.

26

TWO SHILLINGS AND SIX PENCE	TWO SHILLINGS AND SIX PENCE
V	X

In Type X the letters in the bottom line are slightly larger than in Type V, especially the "A", "S" and "P".

FIVE SHILLINGS	FIVE SHILLINGS
Y	Z

In Type Z the letters "S" and "G" are more open than in Type Y. Nos. 196/*a* and 277 are similar to Type Y with all letters thick and regular and the last "S" has the top curve rounded instead of being slightly flattened.

1904–11. *As T* **19**, *but top tablet as T* **26** (thick "POSTAGE"). W **13**. *P* 12.

284		6d. blue-green (27.4.04)	..	6·50	1·25
		a. Imperf between (vert pair)			
285		8d. bright ultramarine (4.7.05)	..	7·00	3·00
		a. Value closer (15¼ mm)	..	16·00	
		b. Dull ultramarine (2.4.08)	..	9·00	2·75
		ba. Ditto. Value closer (15¼ mm)	..	23·00	
286		9d. rosy lake (17–17¼ mm) (18.7.04)	..	8·00	1·75
		a. Value 16½–16¾ mm (2.06)	..	17·00	3·50
		b. Brown-lake. Perf 12½ small holes (6.6.11)	30·00	
287		10d. dull yellow (8.07) ..	..	14·00	6·00
		a. Imperf between (horiz pair)	..	£325	£250
		b. Imperf between (vert pair)	..	£300	
288		1s. brown (12.4.04)	..	12·00	1·75
		a. Imperf between (vert pair)	..	£200	
		b. Imperf between (horiz pair)	..	£275	
289		2s. 6d. bright violet (V.) (14.7.05)	..	38·00	7·50
		a. Dull violet (X) (8.06)	..	38·00	7·50
290		5s. rose-scarlet (Y) (8.04)	..	40·00	23·00
		a. Scarlet (Z) (8.06)	..	40·00	23·00
		b. Pale rose. Perf 12½ (small holes) (Z) (7.10)	55·00	26·00
291		10s. green (26.8.08)	..	£100	£130
292		£1 blue (29.12.04)	..	£150	£100
		a. Perf 12½ (small holes) (7.10)	..	£130	80·00

The "value closer" variety on the 8d. occurs six times in the sheet of 60. The value normally measures 16½ mm but in the variety it is 15¼ mm.

The 9d., 5s. and £1, perf 12½ (small holes), are late printings made in 1910–11 to use up the Crown SA paper.

No. 286*b* has the value as Type C of the 9d. on Crown over A paper.

27

1905–11. W **27**. *P* 12 × 11½ *(new comb machine).*

293	24	½d. pale green (4.07)	..	2·75	50
		a. Yellow-green	..	2·75	50
294	11	1d. rosine (2.12.05)	..	2·75	10
		a. Scarlet (4.11)	..	2·50	20
295	12	2d. bright violet (2.2.06)	..	4·00	10
		aa. Imperf three sides (horiz pair)			
		a. Mauve (4.08)	..	3·00	10
296	22	2½d. indigo-blue (14.9.10)	..	8·00	1·75
297	23	5d. brown-purple (11.3.08)	..	8·50	1·75
No. 295aa is perforated at foot.					

Three types of the 9d., perf 12½, distinguishable by the distance between "NINE" and "PENCE". A. Distance 1¾ mm. B. Distance 2¼ mm. C. Distance 2½ mm.

1906–12. *T* **19** ("POSTAGE" thick as *T* **26**). W **27**. *P* 12 or 12½ *(small holes).*

298		3d. sage-green (19 mm) (26.6.06)	..	4·75	1·25
		a. Imperf between (horiz pair)	..	†	£550
		b. Sage-green (17 mm) (9.12.09)	..	4·75	1·00
		c. Perf 12½. Deep olive (20 mm) (7.10)	..	22·00	4·00
		d. Perf 12½. Yellow-olive (14 mm) (16.12.11)	9·00	3·00
		da. Perf 12½. Bright olive-green (19–19¾ mm) (5.12)	..	8·50	3·50
		e. Perf 11 (17 mm) (10.7.11)	..	£200	£180
299		4d. orange-red (10.9.06)	..	7·50	1·25
		a. Orange	..	8·00	1·10
		b. Perf 12½. Orange (27.10.09)	..	6·50	1·60
300		6d. blue-green (1.9.06)	..	8·00	1·25
		a. Perf 12½ (21.4.10)	..	6·50	1·50
		ab. Perf 12½. Imperf between (vert pair)	£325	£300
301		8d. bright ultramarine (p 12½) (8.09)	10·00	4·50
		a. Value closer (8.09)	..	32·00	24·00
302		9d. brown-lake (3.2.06)	..	10·00	1·50
		a. Imperf between (vert pair)	..	£275	
		aa. Imperf between (horiz pair)	..	£275	
		b. Deep lake (9.5.08)	..	10·00	3·50
		c. Perf 12½. Lake (A) (5.9.09)	..	11·00	3·00
		d. Perf 12½. Lake (B) (7.09)	..	13·00	3·00
		e. Perf 12½. Brown-lake (C)	..	17·00	5·00
		ea. Perf 12½. Deep lake. Thin paper (C)	15·00	3·00
		f. Perf 11 (1909)	..	—	£250
303		1s. brown (30.5.06)	..	12·00	2·50
		a. Imperf between (horiz pair)	..	£275	
		b. Perf 12½ (10.3.10)	..	10·00	2·00
304		2s. 6d. bright violet (X) (10.6.09)	..	35·00	6·00
		a. Perf 12½. Pale violet (X) (6.10)	..	35·00	7·50
		ab. Perf 12½. Deep purple (X) (5.11.12)	38·00	13·00
305		5s. bright rose (p 12½) (Z) (24.4.11)..	55·00	

The "value closer" variety of the 8d. occurred 11 times in the sheet of 60 in the later printing only. On No. 301 the value measures 16½ mm while on No. 301a it is 15¼ mm.

The 1s. brown, perf compound of 11½ and 12½, formerly listed is now omitted, as it must have been perforated by the 12 machine, which in places varied from 11½ to 13. The 4d. has also been reported with a similar perforation.

STAMP BOOKLETS

There are very few surviving examples of Nos. SB1/4. Listings are provided for those believed to have been issued with prices quoted for those known to still exist.

1904 (1 Jan)–**09.** *Black on red cover as No.* SB1 *of New South Wales. Stapled.*
SB1 £1 booklet containing two hundred and forty 1d. in four blocks of 30 and two blocks of 60 ..
a. Red on pink cover (1909)
b. Blue on pink cover £6000

1904 (1 Jan). *Black on grey cover as No.* SB1. *Stapled.*
SB2 £1 booklet containing one hundred and twenty 2d. in four blocks of 30

1910 (May). *Black on cream cover as No.* SB3 *of New South Wales. Stapled.*
SB3 2s. booklet containing eleven ½d. (No. 262A), either in block of 6 plus block of 5 or block of 11, and eighteen 1d. (No. 264A), either in three blocks of 6 or block of 6 plus block of 12
Unsold stock of No. SB3 was uprated with one additional ½d. in May 1911.

1911 (Aug). *Red on pink cover as No.* SB3. *Stapled.*
SB4 2s. booklet containing twelve ½d. (No. 262A), either in two blocks of 6 or block of 12, and eighteen 1d. (No. 264A), either in three blocks of 6 or block of 6 plus block of 12 .. .. £1500

OFFICIAL STAMPS

A. Departmentals

Following suspected abuses involving stamps supplied for official use it was decided by the South Australian authorities that such supplies were to be overprinted with a letter, or letters, indicating to which the department of the administration to which the stamps had been invoiced.

The system was introduced on 1 April 1868 using overprints struck in red. Later in the same year the colour of the overprints was amended to blue, and, during the latter months of 1869, to black.

In 1874 the Postmaster-General recommended that this somewhat cumbersome system be replaced by a general series of "O.S." overprints with the result that the separate accounting for the Departmentals ceased on 30 June of that year. Existing stocks continued to be used, however, and it is believed that much of the residue was passed to the Government Printer to pay postage on copies of the *Government Gazette*.

We are now able to provide a check list of these most interesting issues based on the definitive work, *The Departmental Stamps of South Australia* by A. R. Butler, FRPSL, RDP, published by the Royal Philatelic Society, London in 1978.

No attempt has been made to assign the various overprints to the catalogue numbers of the basic stamps, but each is clearly identified by both watermark and perforation. The colours are similar to those of the contemporary postage stamps, but there can be shade variations. Errors of overprint are recorded in footnotes, but not errors occurring on the basic stamps used.

Most departmental overprints are considered to be scarce to rare in used condition, with unused examples, used multiples and covers being regarded as considerable rarities.

Forgeries of a few items do exist, but most can be readily identified by comparison with genuine examples. A number of forged overprints on stamps not used for the genuine issues also occur.

A. (Architect)

Optd in red with stop. W 2. 2d. (*roul*), 4d. (*p* 11½–12½), 6d. (*roul*), 1s. (*roul*)
Optd in red without stop. W 2. *Roul*. 1d., 6d., 1s.
Optd in black. (*a*) W 2. 4d. (*p* 11½–12½), 4d. (*p* 10), 4d. (*p* 10 × 11½–12½), 6d. (*p* 10), 2s. (*roul*)
  (*b*) W 10. 2d. D.L.R. (*roul*), 2d. D.L.R. (*p* 10)

A.G. (Attorney–General)

Optd in red. W 2. *Roul*. 1d., 2d., 6d., 1s.
Optd in blue. (*a*) W 2. *Roul*. 6d.
  (*b*) W 10. *Roul*. 2d. D.L.R.
Optd in black. (*a*) W 2. 1d. (*p* 11½–12½ × *roul*), 4d. (*p* 11½–12½), 4d. (*p* 10), 6d. (*p* 11½–12½ × *roul*), 6d. (*p* 11½–12½), 1s. (*p* 11½–12½ × *roul*), 1s. (*p* 10)
  (*b*) W 10. 2d. D.L.R. (*roul*), 2d. D.L.R. (*p* 10)

A.O. (Audit Office)

Optd in red. W 2. 2d. (*roul*), 4d. (*p* 11½–12½), 6d. (*roul*)
Optd in blue. (*a*) W 2. *P* 11½–12½. 1d., 6d.
  (*b*) W 10. *Roul*. 2d. D.L.R.
Optd in black. (*a*) W 2. 1d. (*p* 11½–12½), 1d. (*p* 10), 1d. (*p* 10 × 11½–12), 2d. D.L.R. (*roul*), 4d. (*p* 11½–12½), 4d. (*p* 10), 4d. (*p* 10 × 11½–12½), 6d. (*roul*), 6d. (*p* 11½–12½ × *roul*)
  (*b*) W 7. *P* 10. 4d.
  (*c*) W 10. 2d. D.L.R. (*roul*), 2d. D.L.R. (*p* 10)

B.D. (Barracks Department)

Optd in red. W 2. *Roul*. 2d., 6d., 1s.

B.G. (Botanic Garden)

Optd in black. (*a*) W 2. 1d. (*p* 11½–12½ × *roul*), 1d. (*p* 10), 1d. (*p* 10 × 11½–12½), 2d. D.L.R. (*roul*), 6d. (*roul*), 6d. (*p* 11½–12½ × *roul*), 6d. (*p* 11½–12½), 6d. (*p* 10), 1s. (*p* 11½–12½ × *roul*), 1s. (*p* 11½–12½), 1s. (*p* 10 × 11½–12½)
  (*b*) W 7. *P* 10. 2d. D.L.R.
  (*c*) W 10. 2d. D.L.R. (*roul*), 2d. D.L.R. (*p* 10)

B.M. (Bench of Magistrates)

Optd in red. W 2. *Roul*. 2d.
Optd in black. W 10. *Roul*. 2d. D.L.R.

C. (Customs)

Optd in red. W 2. 1d. (*roul*), 2d. (*roul*), 4d. (*p* 11½–12½), 6d. (*roul*), 1s. (*roul*)
Optd in blue. (*a*) W 2. *Roul*. 1d., 4d., 6d., 1s., 2s.
  (*b*) W 10. *Roul*. 2d. D.L.R.
Optd in black. (*a*) W 2. 1d. (*roul*), 1d. (*p* 10), 1d. (*p* 10 × 11½–12½), 2d. D.L.R. (*p* 10 × 11½–12½), 2d. D.L.R. (*roul*), 4d. (*p* 11½–12½), 4d. (*p* 10), 4d. (*p* 10 × 11½–12½), 6d. (*roul*), 6d. (*p* 11½–12½), 6d. (*p* 10), 1s. (*p* 11½–12½ × *roul*), 1s. (*p* 11½–12½), 2s. (*roul*)
  (*b*) W 7. *P* 10. 2d. D.L.R.
  (*c*) W 10. 2d. D.L.R. (*roul*), 2d. D.L.R. (*p* 10 × *roul*), 2d. D.L.R. (*p* 10), 2d. D.L.R. (*p* 10 × 11½–12½)
The 2d. (W 10. *Roul*) with black overprint is known showing the error "G" for "C".

C.D. (Convict Department)

Optd in red. W 2. 2d. (*roul*), 4d. (*p* 11½–12½), 6d. (*roul*), 1s. (*roul*)
Optd in black. (*a*) W 2. 1d. (*p* 11½–12½ × *roul*), 2d. D.L.R. (*roul*), 2d. D.L.R. (*p* 11½–12½), 2d. D.L.R. (*p* 11½–12½ × *roul*), 4d. (*p* 11½–12½), 6d. (*p* 11½–12½ × *roul*), 1s. (*p* 11½–12½ × *roul*)
  (*b*) W 10. *Roul*. 2d. D.L.R.

C.L. (Crown Lands)

Optd in red. W 2. 2d. (*roul*), 4d. (*p* 11½–12½), 6d. (*roul*), 1s. (*roul*)
Optd in blue. (*a*) W 2. *Roul*. 4d., 6d.
  (*b*) W 10. *Roul*. 2d. D.L.R.
Optd in black. (*a*) W 2. 2d. D.L.R. (*roul*), 4d. (*p* 11½–12½), 4d. (*p* 10), 4d. (*p* 10 × 11½–12½), 6d. (*roul*), 6d. (*p* 11½–12½), 1s. (*p* 11½–12½ × *roul*), 1s. (*p* 11½–12½), 2s. (*roul*), 2s. (*p* 11½–12½ × *roul*)
  (*b*) W 7. *P* 10. 2d. D.L.R., 4d.
  (*c*) W 10. 2d. D.L.R. (*roul*), 2d. D.L.R. (*p* 10 × 11½–12½)
The 2s. (W 10. *P* 11½–12½) with black overprint is known showing the stop omitted after "L".

C.O. (Commissariat Office)

Optd in red. W 2. 2d. (*roul*), 4d. (*roul*), 6d. (*roul*), 1s. (*roul*)
Optd in black. (*a*) W 2. 4d. (*p* 11½–12½), 4d. (*p* 10), 4d. (*p* 10 × 11½–12½), 6d. (*p* 11½–12½), 1s. (*p* 11½–12½), 2s. (*p* 11½–12½)
  (*b*) W 10. 2d. D.L.R. (*roul*), 2d. D.L.R. (*p* 10)
The 2s. (W 2. *P* 11½–12½) with black overprint is known showing the stop omitted after "O".

C.P. (Commissioner of Police)

Optd in red. W 2. 2d. (*roul*), 4d. (*p* 11½–12½), 6d. (*roul*)

C.S. (Chief Secretary)

Optd in red. W 2. 2d. (*roul*), 4d. (*p* 11½–12½), 6d. (*roul*), 1s. (*roul*)
Optd in blue. (*a*) W 2. *Roul*. 4d., 6d.
  (*b*) W 10. *Roul*. 2d. D.L.R.
Optd in black. (*a*) W 2. 2d. D.L.R. (*roul*), 4d. (*roul*), 4d. (*p* 11½–12½ × *roul*), 4d. (*p* 11½–12½), 4d. (*p* 10), 4d. (*p* 10 × 11½–12½), 6d. (*p* 11½–12½ × *roul*), 6d. (*p* 11½–12½), 6d. (*p* 10), 6d. (*p* 10 × 11½–12½), 1s. (*p* 11½–12½ × *roul*), 1s. (*p* 11½–12½), 1s. (*p* 10), 1s. (*p* 10 × 11½–12½), 2s. (*p* 10 × 11½–12½)
  (*b*) W 7. *P* 10. 4d.
  (*c*) W 10. 2d. D.L.R. (*roul*), 2d. D.L.R. (*p* 10)

C.Sgn. (Colonial Surgeon)

Optd in red. W 2. 2d. (*roul*), 4d. (*p* 11½–12½), 6d. (*roul*)
Optd in black. (*a*) W 2. 2d. D.L.R. (*roul*), 4d. (*p* 11½–12½), 4d. (*p* 10), 4d. (*p* 10 × 11½–12½), 6d. (*p* 11½–12½), 6d. (*p* 11½–12½ × *roul*), 1s. (*p* 11½–12½ × *roul*)
  (*b*) W 10. 2d. D.L.R. (*roul*), 2d. D.L.R. (*p* 11½–12½ × *roul*), 2d. D.L.R. (*p* 10)
Two types of overprint exist on the 2d. D.L.R. (W 10. *Roul*), the second type having block capitals instead of the serifed type used for the other values.

D.B. (Destitute Board)

Optd in red. W 2. 1d. (*roul*), 2d. (*roul*), 4d. (*p* 11½–12½), 6d. (*roul*), 1s. (*roul*)
Optd in blue. (*a*) W 2. *Roul*. 2d. D.L.R., 6d.
  (*b*) W 10. *Roul*. 2d. D.L.R.
Optd in black. (*a*) W 2. 1d. (*p* 11½–12½), 4d. (*p* 11½–12½), 4d. (*p* 10), 6d. (*p* 10 × 11½–12½), 1s. (*p* 10)
  (*b*) W 10. 2d. D.L.R. (*roul*), 2d. D.L.R. (*p* 10), 2d. D.L.R. (*p* 10 × 11½–12½)
The 2d. D.L.R. (W 10. *P* 10) with black overprint is known showing the stop omitted after "D".

D.R. (Deeds Registration)

Optd in red. W 2. *Roul*. 2d., 6d.

E. (Engineer)

Optd in red. W 2. 2d. (*roul*), 4d. (*p* 11½–12½), 6d. (*roul*), 1s. (*roul*)
Optd in blue. (*a*) W 2. *Roul*. 1s.
  (*b*) W 10. *Roul*. 2d. D.L.R.
Optd in black. (*a*) W 2. 4d. (*p* 11½–12½ × *roul*), 4d. (*p* 11½–12½), 4d. (*p* 10), 4d. (*p* 10 × 11½–12½), 6d. (*p* 11½–12½), 6d. (*p* 10 × 11½–12½), 1s. (*p* 11½–12½ × *roul*), 1s. (*p* 11½–12½), 1s. (*p* 10 × 11½–12½), 2s. (*p* 10 × 11½–12½)
  (*b*) W 7. *P* 10. 4d.
  (*c*) W 10. 2d. D.L.R. (*roul*), 2d. D.L.R. (*p* 10)

E.B. (Education Board)

Optd in red. W 2. 2d. (*roul*), 4d. (*p* 11½–12½), 6d. (*roul*)
Optd in blue. (*a*) W 2. *Roul*. 4d., 6d.
  (*b*) W 10. *Roul*. 2d. D.L.R.
Optd in black. (*a*) W 2. 2d. D.L.R. (*roul*), 4d. (*roul*), 4d. (*p* 11½–12½), 4d. (*p* 10), 4d. (*p* 10 × 11½–12½), 6d. (*p* 11½–12½ × *roul*), 6d. (*p* 11½–12½)
  (*b*) W 7. *P* 10. 2d. D.L.R.
  (*c*) W 10. 2d. D.L.R. (*roul*), 2d. D.L.R. (*p* 10), 2d. D.L.R. (*p* 10 × 11½–12½)

G.F. (Gold Fields)

Optd in black. (*a*) W 2. *Roul*. 6d.
  (*b*) W 10. 2d. D.L.R. (*p* 10 × *roul*), 2d. D.L.R. (*p* 10)

G.P. (Government Printer)

Optd in red. W 2. *Roul*. 1d., 2d., 6d., 1s.
Optd in blue. (*a*) W 2. *Roul*. 1d., 6d., 1s., 2s.
  (*b*) W 10. *Roul*. 2d. D.L.R.
Optd in black. (*a*) W 2. 1d. (*roul*), 1d. (*p* 11½–12½ × *roul*), 1d. (*p* 11½–12½), 1d. (*p* 10), 1d. (*p* 10 × 11½–12½), 6d. (*p* 11½–12½ × *roul*), 1s. (*p* 10), 1s. (*p* 10 × 11½–12½), 2s. (*roul*), 2s. (*p* 11½–12½), 2s. (*p* 10 × 11½–12½)
  (*b*) W 10. 2d. D.L.R. (*roul*), 2d. D.L.R. (*p* 10)
The 1d. (W 2. *Roul*) with red overprint is known showing "C.P." instead of "G.P.".

G.S. (Government Storekeeper)

Optd in red. W 2. *Roul*. 2d., 6d., 1s.

G.T. (Goolwa Tramway)

Optd in red. W 2. 1d. (*roul*), 2d. (*roul*), 4d. (*p* 11½–12½), 6d. (*roul*), 1s. (*roul*)
Optd in black. (*a*) W 2. 2d. D.L.R. (*roul*), 4d. (*p* 11½–12½)
  (*b*) W 10. 2d. D.L.R. (*roul*), 2d. D.L.R. (*p* 10)
The 2d. and 6d. (both W 2. *Roul*) with red overprint are known showing the stop omitted after "T". The 1s. (W 2. *Roul*) with red overprint is known showing "C.T." instead of "G.T.".

H. (Hospitals)

Optd in black. (*a*) W 7. *P* 10. 2d. D.L.R.
  (*b*) W 10. 2d. D.L.R. (*p* 10), 2d. D.L.R. (*p* 10 × 11½–12½)

H.A. (House of Assembly)

Optd in red. W 2. 1d. (*roul*), 2d. (*roul*), 4d. (*p* 11½–12½), 6d. (*roul*), 1s. (*roul*)
Optd in black. (*a*) W 2. 1d. (*p* 11½–12½), 1d. (*p* 10), 1d. (*p* 10 × 11½–12½), 4d. (*p* 11½–12½), 4d. (*p* 10), 6d. (*roul*), 6d. (*p* 11½–12½), 1s. (*p* 11½–12½ × *roul*), 1s. (*p* 11½–12½)
  (*b*) W 10. 2d. D.L.R. (*roul*), 2d. D.L.R. (*p* 10)

I.A. (Immigration Agent)

Optd in red. W 2. 1d. (*roul*), 2d. (*roul*), 4d. (*p* 11½–12½), 6d. (*roul*)

I.E. (Intestate Estates)

Optd in black. W 10. *P* 10. 2d. D.L.R.

I.S. (Inspector of Sheep)

Optd in red. W 2. *Roul*. 2d., 6d.
Optd in blue. W 2. *P* 11½–12½. 6d.
Optd in black. (*a*) W 2. 2d. D.L.R. (*roul*), 6d. (*p* 11½–12½ × *roul*)
  (*b*) W 10. 2d. D.L.R. (*roul*), 2d. D.L.R. (*p* 10)

L.A. (Lunatic Asylum)

Optd in red. W 2. 1d. (*roul*), 2d. (*roul*), 4d. (*p* 11½–12½), 6d. (*roul*), 1s. (*roul*)
Optd in black. (*a*) W 2. 4d. (*p* 11½–12½), 4d. (*p* 10), 4d. (*p* 10 × 11½–12½), 6d. (*p* 11½–12½ × *roul*), 6d. (*p* 11½–12½), 1s. (*p* 11½–12½), 2s. (*roul*)
  (*b*) W 10. 2d. D.L.R. (*roul*), 2d. D.L.R. (*p* 10)

L.C. (Legislative Council)

Optd in red. W 2. *Roul*. 2d., 6d.
Optd in black. (*a*) W 2. *Roul*. 2d. D.L.R.
  (*b*) W 10. 2d. D.L.R. (*roul*), 2d. D.L.R. (*p* 10 × *roul*)
The 2d. and 6d. (both W 2. *Roul*) with red overprint are known showing the stop omitted after "C".

L.L. (Legislative Librarian)

Optd in red. W 2. 2d. (*roul*), 4d. (*p* 11½–12½), 6d. (*roul*)
Optd in black. (*a*) W 2. *P* 11½–12½. 6d.
  (*b*) W 10. *P* 10. 2d. D.L.R.
The 2d. and 6d. (both W 2. *Roul*) with red overprint are known showing the stop omitted from between the two letters.

L.T. (Land Titles)

Optd in red. W 2. 2d. (*roul*), 4d. (*p* 11½–12½), 6d. (*roul*), 1s. (*roul*)
Optd in blue. W 10. *Roul*. 2d. D.L.R.
Optd in black. (*a*) W 2. 4d. (*p* 11½–12½), 4d. (*p* 10), 4d. (*p* 10 × 11½–12½ × *roul*), 6d. (*p* 11½–12½), 6d. (*p* 10), 6d. (*p* 10 × 11½–12½)
  (*b*) W 7. *P* 10. 2d. D.L.R.
  (*c*) W 10. 2d. D.L.R. (*roul*), 2d. D.L.R. (*p* 10)
The 2d. and 6d. (both W 2. *Roul*) with red overprint are known showing the stop omitted after "T".

M. (Military)

Optd in red. W 2. *Roul*. 2d., 6d., 1s.
Optd in black. W 2. 6d. (*p* 11½–12½ × *roul*), 1s. (*p* 11½–12½ × *roul*), 2s. (*roul*)

M.B. (Marine Board)

Optd in red. W 2. 1d. (*roul*), 2d. (*roul*), 4d. (*roul*), 4d. (*p* 11½–12½), 6d. (*roul*), 1s. (*roul*)
Optd in black. (*a*) W 2. 1d. (*roul*), 1d. (*p* 11½–12½ × *roul*), 2d. D.L.R. (*roul*), 4d. (*p* 11½–12½ × *roul*), 4d. (*p* 11½–12½), 4d. (*p* 10), 4d. (*p* 10 × 11½–12½), 6d. (*roul*), 6d. (*p* 11½–12½), 6d. (*p* 10), 6d. (*p* 10 × 11½–12½), 1s. (*p* 11½–12½ × *roul*), 1s. (*p* 10), 1s. (*p* 10 × 11½–12½)
  (*b*) W 7. *P* 10. 2d. D.L.R., 4d.
  (*c*) W 10. 2d. D.L.R. (*roul*), 2d. D.L.R. (*p* 10)

M.R. (Manager of Railways)

Optd in red. W 2. *Roul*. 2d., 6d.
Optd in black. (*a*) W 2. 1d. (*p* 11½–12½), 1d. (*p* 10), 2d. D.L.R. (*roul*), 4d. (*roul*), 4d. (*p* 11½–12½), 6d. (*roul*), 6d. (*p* 11½–12½ × *roul*), 6d. 10d. on 9d. (*roul*), 1s. (*p* 11½–12½ × *roul*), 2s. (*p* 11½–12½), 2s. (*p* 10 × 11½–12½)
  (*b*) W 10. 2d. D.L.R. (*roul*), 2d. D.L.R. (*p* 10), 2d. D.L.R. (*p* 10 × 11½–12½)

M.R.G. (Main Roads Gambierton)

Optd in red without stops. W 2. *Roul*. 2d., 6d.
Optd in blue without stops. W 10. *Roul*. 2d. D.L.R.
Optd in black without stops. W 10. 2d. D.L.R. (*roul*), 2d. D.L.R. (*p* 10)
Optd in black with stops. W 10. 2d. D.L.R. (*roul*), 2d. D.L.R. (*p* 10)
The 2d. D.L.R. (W 10. *P* 10) with black overprint is known showing the stops omitted after "M" and "R".

N.T. (Northern Territory)

Optd in black. (*a*) W 2. *P* 11½–12½. 1d., 3d. on 4d., 4d., 6d., 1s.
  (*b*) W 10. 2d. D.L.R. (*roul*), 2d. D.L.R. (*p* 10)

O.A. (Official Assignee)

Optd in red. W 2. 2d. (*roul*), 4d. (*p* 11½–12½)
Optd in blue. W 10. *Roul*. 2d. D.L.R.
Optd in black. (*a*) W 2. 4d. (*p* 11½–12½), 4d. (*p* 10)
  (*b*) W 7. *P* 10. 2d. D.L.R.
  (*c*) W 10. 2d. D.L.R. (*roul*), 2d. D.L.R. (*p* 10 × *roul*), 2d. D.L.R. (*p* 10)

P. (Police)

Optd in blue. (*a*) W 2. *Roul*. 6d.
  (*b*) W 10. *Roul*. 2d. D.L.R.
Optd in black. (*a*) W 2. 6d. (*p* 11½–12½ × *roul*), 6d. (*p* 11½–12½), 6d. (*p* 10)
  (*b*) W 7. *P* 10. 2d. D.L.R.
  (*c*) W 10. 2d. D.L.R. (*roul*), 2d. D.L.R. (*p* 11½–12½ × *roul*), 2d. D.L.R. (*p* 10 × *roul*), 2d. D.L.R. (*p* 10), 2d. D.L.R. (*p* 10 × 11½–12½)

P.A. (Protector of Aborigines)

Optd in red. W 2. *Roul*. 2d., 6d.
Optd in black. (*a*) W 2. *Roul*. 2d. D.L.R., 6d.
  (*b*) W 10. 2d. D.L.R. (*roul*), 2d. D.L.R. (*p* 10)

P.O. (Post Office)

Optd in red. W 2. *Roul*. 1d., 2d., 6d., 1s.
Optd in blue. W 2. *Roul*. 2d., 2d. D.L.R.
Optd in black. (*a*) W 2. 1d. (*p* 10 × 11½–12½), 2d. D.L.R. (*roul*), 4d. (*p* 11½–12½), 2d. D.L.R. (*p* 10), 4d. (*p* 11½–12½ × *roul*), 1s. (*p* 11½–12½), 1s. (*p* 10), 1s. (*p* 10 × 11½–12½)
  (*b*) W 10. 2d. D.L.R. (*roul*), 2d. D.L.R. (*p* 10 × *roul*), 2d. D.L.R. (*p* 10)
The 6d. (W 2. *Roul*) with red overprint is known showing the stop omitted after "O", but with two stops after "P".

P.S. (Private Secretary)

Optd in red. *W* **2.** 1d. (*roul*), 2d. (*roul*), 4d. (*p* 11½–12½), 6d. (*roul*), 1s. (*roul*)

Optd in black. (*a*) *W* **2.** 1d. (*p* 11½–12½ × *roul*), 1d. (*p* 11½–12½), 1d. (*p* 10), 3d. (*in black*) on 4d. (*p* 11½–12½), 3d. (*in red*) on 4d. (*p* 10), 3d. (*in black*) on 4d. (*p* 10), 4d. (*p* 11½–12½), 4d. (*p* 10 × 11½–12½), 6d. 6d. (*p* 11½–12½ × *roul*), 6d. (*p* 11½–12½ × *roul*), 6d. (*p* 11½–12½), 6d. (*p* 10), 9d. (*roul*), 9d. (*p* 11½–12½), 10d. on 9d. (*p* 10 × 11½–12½), 1s. (*p* 11½–12½ × *roul*), 2s. (*p* 11½–12½)

(*b*) *W* **7.** *P* 10. 2d. D.L.R.

(*c*) *W* **10.** 2d. D.L.R. (*roul*), 2d. D.L.R. (*p* 10)

P.W. (Public Works)

Optd in red without stop after "W". *W* **2.** *Roul.* 2d., 6d., 1s.

Optd in black. (*a*) *W* **2.** 2d. D.L.R. (*roul*), 4d. (*p* 10), 6d. (*roul*), 6d. (*p* 11½–12½), 1s. (*p* 11½–12½ × *roul*)

(*b*) *W* **10.** 2d. D.L.R. (*roul*), 2d. D.L.R. (*p* 10)

R.B. (Road Board)

Optd in red. *W* **2.** 1d. (*roul*), 2d. (*roul*), 4d. (*p* 11½–12½), 6d. (*roul*), 1s. (*roul*)

Optd in blue without stops. *W* **10.** *Roul.* 2d. D.L.R.

Optd in black. (*a*) *W* **2.** 1d. (*p* 11½–12½ × *roul*), 1d. (*p* 10), 4d. (*p* 10), 2s. (*roul*)

(*b*) *W* **7.** *P* 10. 2d. D.L.R.

(*c*) *W* **10.** 2d. D.L.R. (*roul*), 2d. D.L.R. (*p* 10)

The 6d. (*W* **2.** *Roul.*) with red overprint is known showing the top omitted after "B".

R.G. (Registrar-General)

Optd in red. *W* **2.** *Roul.* 2d., 6d., 1s.

Optd in blue. (*a*) *W* **2.** *P* 11½–12½ × *roul.* 6d.

(*b*) *W* **10.** 2d. D.L.R. (*roul*), 2d. D.L.R. (*p* 11½–12½ × *roul*)

Optd in black. (*a*) *W* **2.** 2d. D.L.R. (*roul*), 6d. (*p* 10), 6d. (*p* 10 × 11½–12½), 1s. (*p* 11½–12½ × *roul*), 1s. (*p* 10)

(*b*) *W* **7.** *P* 10. 2d. D.L.R.

(*c*) *W* **10.** 2d. D.L.R. (*roul*), 2d. D.L.R. (*p* 10 × 11½–12½), (*p* 10), 2d. D.L.R. (*p* 10 × 11½–12½)

S. (Sheriff)

Optd in red. *W* **2.** *Roul.* 2d., 6d.

Optd in black. (*a*) *W* **2.** *P* 11½–12½ × *roul.* 6d.

(*b*) *W* **10.** *Roul.* 2d. D.L.R.

Optd in black. (*a*) *W* **2.** 4d. (*p* 11½–12½), 4d. (*p* 10), 6d. (*roul*), 6d. (*p* 11½–12½), 6d. (*p* 10)

(*b*) *W* **10.** 2d. D.L.R. (*roul*), 2d. D.L.R. (*p* 10 × *roul*), 2d. D.L.R. (*p* 10 × 11½–12½)

S.C. (Supreme Court)

Optd in red. *W* **2.** *Roul.* 2d., 6d.

Optd in black. *W* **10.** *P* 10. 2d. D.L.R.

S.G. (Surveyor-General)

Optd in red. *W* **2.** 2d. (*roul*), 4d. (*p* 11½–12½), 6d. (*roul*)

Optd in blue. (*a*) *W* **2.** *Roul.* 4d.

(*b*) *W* **10.** *Roul.* 2d. D.L.R.

Optd in black. (*a*) *W* **2.** 2d. D.L.R. (*roul*), 4d. (*p* 11½–12½), 4d. (*p* 10), 4d. (*p* 10 × 11½–12½), 6d. (*p* 11½–12½ × *roul*), 6d. (*p* 11½–12½), 6d. (*p* 10), 6d. (*p* 10 × 11½–12½)

(*b*) *W* **7.** *P* 10. 2d. D.L.R.

(*c*) *W* **10.** 2d. D.L.R. (*roul*), 2d. D.L.R. (*p* 10 × *roul*), 2d. D.L.R. (*p* 10)

S.M. (Stipendiary Magistrate)

Optd in red. *W* **2.** 1d. (*roul*), 2d. (*roul*), 4d. (*roul*), 4d. (*p* 11½–12½), 6d. (*roul*), 1s. (*roul*)

Optd in blue. (*a*) *W* **2.** *Roul.* 2d., 4d., 6d.

(*b*) *W* **10.** *Roul.* 2d. D.L.R.

Optd in black. (*a*) *W* **2.** 1d. (*p* 11½–12½), 1d. (*p* 10), 2d. D.L.R. (*roul*), 4d. (*roul*), 4d. (*p* 11½–12½ × *roul*), 4d. (*p* 11½–12½), 4d. (*p* 10), 4d. (*p* 10 × 11½–12½), 6d. (*p* 11½–12½ × *roul*), 6d. (*p* 11½–12½), 6d. (*p* 10), 6d. (*p* 10 × 11½–12½), 1s. (*p* 11½–12½ × *roul*)

(*b*) *W* **7.** *P* 10. 2d. D.L.R.

(*c*) *W* **10.** 2d. D.L.R. (*roul*), 2d. D.L.R. (*p* 10 × *roul*), 2d. D.L.R. (*p* 10), 2d. D.L.R. (*p* 10 × 11½–12½)

The 2d. and 4d. (both *W* **2.** *Roul.*) with red overprint are known showing the stop omitted after "M".

S.T. (Superintendent of Telegraphs)

Optd in red. *W* **2.** *Roul.* 2d., 6d.

Optd in blue. *W* **10.** 2d. D.L.R. (*roul*), 2d. D.L.R. (*p* 11½–12½)

Optd in black. (*a*) *W* **2.** *Roul.* 2d. D.L.R., 6d.

(*b*) *W* **7.** *P* 10. 2d. D.L.R.

(*c*) *W* **10.** 2d. D.L.R. (*roul*), 2d. D.L.R. (*p* 10 × *roul*), 2d. D.L.R. (*p* 10)

The 2d. and 6d. (both *W* **2.** *Roul.*) with red overprint (2d., 6d.) or black overprint (6d.) are known showing the stop omitted after "T".

T. (Treasury)

Optd in red. *W* **2.** 1d. (*roul*), 2d. (*roul*), 4d. (*p* 11½–12½ × *roul*), 6d. (*roul*), 1s. (*roul*)

Optd in black. (*a*) *W* **2.** *Roul.* 1d., 4d., 6d., 2s.

(*b*) *W* **10.** *Roul.* 2d. D.L.R.

Optd in black. (*a*) *W* **2.** 1d. (*p* 10), 2d. D.L.R. (*roul*), 4d. (*roul*), 4d. (*p* 11½–12½), 6d. (*roul*), 6d. (*p* 11½–12½ × *roul*), 1s. (*p* 11½–12½ × *roul*), 1s. (*p* 10 × 11½–12½), 2s. (*roul*), 2s. (*p* 10 × 11½–12½)

(*b*) *W* **7.** *P* 10. 2d. D.L.R.

(*c*) *W* **10.** 2d. D.L.R. (*roul*), 2d. D.L.R. (*p* 10)

T.R. (Titles Registration)

Optd in black. (*a*) *W* **2.** 4d. (*p* 10 × 11½–12½), 4d. (*p* 10 × 11½–12½), 6d. (*p* 11½–12½), 4d. (*p* 11½–12½), 1s. (*p* 11½–12½)

(*b*) *W* **10.** *P* 10. 2d. D.L.R.

V. (Volunteers)

Optd in red. *W* **2.** *Roul.* 2d., 6d., 1s.

Optd in black. (*a*) *W* **2.** *Roul.* 6d.

(*b*) *W* **7.** *P* 10. 2d. D.L.R.

(*c*) *W* **10.** 2d. D.L.R. (*roul*), 2d. D.L.R. (*p* 10)

The 2d. (*W* **10.** *P* 10 × *roul*) overprinted in black is only known howing the stop omitted after "V".

VA. (Valuator of Runs)

Optd in black without stop after "V". (*a*) *W* **2.** *P* 10. 4d.

(*b*) *W* **10.** *P* 10. 2d. D.L.R.

VN. (Vaccination)

Optd in black without stop after "V". *W* **2.** *P* 10. 4d.

W. (Waterworks)

Optd in red. *W* **2.** *Roul.* 2d.

Optd in black. (*a*) *W* **2.** *P* 11½–12½. 6d., 2s.

(*b*) *W* **10.** 2d. D.L.R. (*roul*), 2d. D.L.R. (*p* 10)

The 2d. (*W* **2.** *Roul*) with red overprint is known showing the stop omitted after "W".

B. General

O.S.   O.S.
(O 1)   (O 2)

1874–77. *Optd with Type O* **1.** *W* **2.** (*a*) *P* 10.

O 1	3	4d. dull purple (18.2.74)	£1000	£275

(*b*) *P* 11½–12½ × 10.

O 2	1	1d. green (2.1.74)	—	£100
O 3	3	4d. dull violet (12.2.75)	55·00	5·00
O 4	1	6d. Prussian blue (20.10.75)	65·00	8·00
O 4a	3	2s. rose-pink	—	
O 5		2s. carmine (3.12.76)	—	90·00

(*c*) *P* 11½–12½

O 6	1	1d. deep yellow-green (30.1.74)	£1000	16·00
		a. Printed on both sides	—	£400
O 7	3	3d. on 4d. ultramarine (26.6.77)	£1200	£475
		a. No stop after "S"	—	£800
O 8		4d. dull violet (13.7.74)	40·00	6·00
		a. No stop after "S"	—	30·00
O 9	3	6d. bright blue (31.8.75)	70·00	11·00
		a. "O.S." double	—	65·00
O10		6d. Prussian blue (27.3.74)	60·00	6·00
		a. No stop after "S"	—	35·00
O11	4	9d. red-purple (22.3.76)	£600	£250
		a. No stop after "S"	£1000	£450
O12	1	1s. red-brown (5.8.74)	55·00	6·00
		a. "O.S." double	—	70·00
		b. No stop after "S"	£120	35·00
O13	3	2s. crimson-carmine (13.7.75)	95·00	13·00
		a. No stop after "S"	—	60·00
		b. No stops	—	75·00
		c. Stops at top of letters		

1876–85. *Optd with Type O* **1.** *W* **8.** (*a*) *P* 10.

O14	1	6d. bright blue (1879)	65·00	9·00

(*b*) *P* 10 × 11½–12½, 11½–12½ × 10, *or compound*

O15	3	4d. violet-slate (24.1.78)	65·00	6·50
O16		4d. plum (29.11.81)	38·00	2·75
O17		4d. deep mauve	25·00	2·50
		a. No stop after "S"	£100	24·00
		b. No stop after "O"		
		c. "O.S." double		
		d. "O.S." inverted	—	£100
O18	1	6d. bright blue (1877)	42·00	4·25
		a. "O.S." inverted		
		b. No stop after "O"		
O19		6d. bright ultramarine (27.3.85)	38·00	4·00
		a. "O.S." inverted		
		b. "O.S." double		
		c. "O.S." double, one inverted	—	£225
		d. No stop after "S"	—	35·00
		e. No stops after "O" & "S"		
O20		1s. red-brown (27.3.83)	38·00	5·50
		a. "O.S." inverted		
		b. No stop after "O"		
		c. No stop after "S"	—	35·00
O21	3	2s. carmine (16.3.81)	75·00	7·50
		a. "O.S." inverted	—	£130
		b. No stop after "S"	—	50·00

(*c*) *P* 11½–12½

O22	3	3d. on 4d. ultramarine	£1200	
O23		4d. violet-slate (14.3.76)	£120	6·50
O24		4d. deep mauve (19.8.79)	40·00	2·75
		a. "O.S." inverted		
		b. "O.S." double, one inverted		
		c. No stop after "S"	—	25·00
O25	1	6d. Prussian blue (6.77)	45·00	5·00
		a. "O.S." double	—	55·00
		b. "O.S." inverted		
O26	4	8d. on 9d. brown (9.11.76)	£900	£375
		a. "O.S." double	£1400	
		b. "O" only	—	£600
O26c		9d. purple	£2250	
O27	1	1s. red-brown (12.2.78)	30·00	8·50
		a. "O.S." inverted	£190	90·00
		b. No stop after "S"	£160	38·00
O28		1s. lake-brown (8.11.83)	27·00	3·50
O29	3	2s. rose-carmine (12.8.85)	75·00	6·00
		a. "O.S." double	—	80·00
		b. "O.S." inverted	—	85·00
		c. No stop after "S"	—	35·00

1891–1903. *Optd with Type O* **2.** (*a*) *W* **8.** *P* 11½–12½.

O30	1	1s. lake-brown (18.4.91)	28·00	9·00
O31		1s. Vandyke brown	35·00	6·00
O32		1s. dull brown (2.7.96)	26·00	4·50
		a. No stop after "S"	—	50·00
O33		1s. sepia (*large holes*) (4.1.02)	25·00	4·00
		a. No stop after "S"		
		b. No stop after "S"		
O34	3	2s. carmine (26.6.00)	75·00	10·00
		a. No stop after "S"		

(*b*) *W* **8.** *P* 10 × 11½–12½

O35	3	2s. rose-carmine (9.11.95)	60·00	8·00
		a. No stop after "S"	£110	
		b. "O.S." double		

(*c*) *W* **10.** *P* 11½–12½

O36	1	1s. dull brown (1902)	30·00	4·50

1874–76. *Optd with Type O* **1.** *W* **10.** (*a*) *P* 10.

O37	11	1d. blue-green (30.9.75)	60·00	15·00
		a. "O.S." inverted		
		b. No stop after "S"		
O38	12	2d. orange-red (18.2.74)	11·00	50
		a. No stop after "S"	—	20·00
		b. "O.S." double		

(*b*) *P* 10 × 11½–12½, 11½–12½ × 10, *or compound*

O39	11	1d. blue-green (16.9.75)		
		a. No stop after "S"		
O40	12	2d. orange-red (27.9.76)	—	4·25

(*c*) *P* 11½–12½

O41	11	1d. blue-green (13.8.75)	—	13·00
		a. "O.S." inverted		
		b. No stop after "S"		
O42	12	2d. orange-red (20.5.74)	—	80·00

1876–80. *Optd with Type O* **1.** *W* **13.** (*a*) *P* 10

O43	11	1d. blue-green (2.10.76)	8·50	40
		a. "O.S." inverted	—	35·00
		b. "O.S." double	45·00	30·00
		c. "O.S." double, one inverted		
		d. No stops	—	20·00
		e. No stop after "O"		
		f. No stop after "S"	—	10·00
		g. *Deep green*	9·50	40
		ga. "O.S." double	—	32·00
O44	12	2d. orange-red (21.9.77)	7·50	40
		a. "O.S." inverted	—	18·00
		b. "O.S." double	55·00	27·00
		c. "O.S." double, one inverted		
		d. "O.S." double, both inverted	—	85·00
		e. No stops	—	40·00
		f. No stop after "O"	—	14·00
		g. No stop after "S"		
		h. *Dull brick-red*	24·00	65

(*b*) *P* 10 × 11½–12½, 11½–12½ × 10 *or compound*

O45	11	1d. deep green (14.8.80)	—	18·00
		a. "O.S." double		
O46	12	2d. orange-red (6.4.78)	42·00	6·00
		a. "O.S." inverted	—	85·00
		b. No stop after "S"	—	40·00

(*c*) *P* 11½–12½

O47	12	2d. orange-red (15.7.80)	—	60·00

1882 (20 Feb). *No. 181 optd with Type O* **1.**

O48	11	½d. on 1d. blue-green	55·00	14·00
		a. "O.S." inverted		

1888 (15 Nov)–**91.** *Nos.* 184 *and* 185a *optd with Type O* **1.** *P* 10.

O49	17	4d. pale violet (24.1.91)	45·00	3·50
O50	18	6d. blue	15·00	1·25
		a. "O.S." double		
		b. No stop after "S"		

1891. *Nos.* 229b *and* 231a/2 *optd with Type O* **1.** (*a*) *P* 10

O51	17	2½d. on 4d. deep green (Br.) (1 Aug)	40·00	6·50
		a. "2" and "½" closer together	—	42·00
		b. "O.S." inverted		
		c. "O.S." double		
		d. "O.S." omitted (in vert pair with normal)		
		e. No stop after "S"		

(*b*) *P* 10 × 11½–12½ *or* 11½–12½ × 10

O52	17	2½d. on 4d. deep green (Br.) (1 Oct)	45·00	9·50

(*c*) *P* 11½–12½

O53	17	2½d. on 4d. deep green (Br.) (1 June)	£100	50·00

1891–96. *Optd with Type O* **2.** *W* **13.** (*a*) *P* 10

O54	11	1d. deep green (22.4.91)	9·00	1·40
		a. "O.S." double	45·00	27·00
		b. "O.S." double, one inverted		
		c. No stop after "S"	32·00	8·00
		d. Blackish blue opt	£200	40·00
O55	12	2d. orange-red (22.4.91)	9·00	30
		a. "O.S." double, both inverted		
		c. No stop after "S"	—	9·00

(*b*) *P* 15

O56	11	1d. green (8.9.94)	7·00	40
		a. "O.S." double		
		b. No stop after "S"		
O57	12	2d. orange-red (16.6.94)	7·00	25
		a. "O.S." double	—	21·00
		b. "O.S." inverted	—	15·00

(*c*) *P* 13

O58	11	1d. green (20.5.95)	12·00	40
		a. No stop after "S"	48·00	8·00
O59	12	2d. orange-red (11.2.96)	10·00	30
		a. "O.S." double	75·00	
		b. No stop after "S"	45·00	8·00

1891–99. *Optd with Type O* **2.** *W* **13** (*sideways on* ½d.). (*a*) *P* 10

O60	15	½d. brown (2.5.94)	7·50	3·50
		a. No stop after "S"	32·00	20·00
O61	17	4d. pale violet (13.2.91)	45·00	2·75
		b. "S." omitted	—	48·00
		c. No stop after "S"		
		d. *Aniline violet* (31.8.93)	48·00	2·50
		da. No stop after "S"		
		dc. No stop after "S"		
O62	18	6d. blue (4.4.93)	15·00	1·75
		a. No stop after "S"		
		b. Blackish blue opt		

(*b*) *P* 10 × 11½–12½

O63	15	½d. brown (26.3.95)	8·50	3·50

(*c*) *P* 11½–12½

O64	15	½d. red-brown (13.6.91)	20·00	4·25

(d) P 15

O65	15	½d. pale brown (8.6.95)		12·00	3·50
O66	17	4d. slate-violet (4.4.95)		45·00	2·75
		a. "O.S." double		£150	27·00
O67	18	6d. blue (20.9.93)		14·00	1·25

(e) P 13

O68	15	½d. deep brown (17.5.98)		8·50	3·50
		a. Opt triple, twice sideways		£150	
O69	17	4d. violet (12.96)		45·00	2·25
		a. "O.S." double		£120	28·00
		b. No stop after "S"		£120	20·00
O70	18	6d. blue (13.9.99)		18·00	1·50
		a. No stop after "S"		70·00	50·00

1891–95. *Nos. 229b, 230a and 231a optd with Type* O 2. *(a)* P 10

O71	17	2½d. on 4d. deep green (Br.) (18.8.94)	32·00	4·50
		a. Fraction bar omitted			
		b. "2" and "½" closer together	75·00	20·00
		c. "O.S." inverted	£130	
		d. No stop after "S"	—	30·00
O72	18	5d. on 6d. deep brown (C.) (2.12.91)	38·00	11·00
		a. No stop after "5D"	£170	
		b. No stop after "S"	95·00	32·00

(b) P 10×11½–12½

O73	17	2½d. on 4d. deep green (Br.) (17.9.95)	—	38·00
		a. "O.S." double		

1897–1901. *Nos. 235/6 and 238a optd with Type* O 2. *(a)* P 15

O74	23	5d. brown-purple (29.3.01)	50·00	6·00

(b) P 13

O75	22	2½d. violet-blue (5.7.97)	42·00	3·75
		a. No stop after "S"	—	25·00
O76	23	5d. purple (29.9.01)	50·00	7·50
		a. No stop after "S"		

O. S.

(O 3)

1899–1901. *Optd with Type* O 3. W 13. P 13.

O80	24	¼d. yellow-green (12.2.00)		8·00	3·75
		a. "O.S." inverted		48·00	
		b. No stop after "S"		32·00	
O81	11	1d. rosine (22.9.99)		9·00	60
		a. "O.S." inverted		42·00	30·00
		b. "O.S." double			
		c. No stop after "S"		38·00	14·00
O82	12	2d. bright violet (1.6.00)		9·00	50
		a. "O.S." inverted		38·00	20·00
		b. "O.S." double			
		c. No stop after "S"		27·00	
O83	22	2½d. indigo (2.10.01)		50·00	12·00
		a. "O.S." inverted		—	55·00
		b. No stop after "S"		£140	
O84	17	4d. violet (18.11.00)		42·00	2·00
		a. "O.S." inverted		£160	
		b. No stop after "S"		£120	
O85	18	6d. blue (8.10.00)		15·00	1·60
		a. No stop after "S"		50·00	

1891 (May). *Optd as Type* O 3 *but wider.* W 13. P 10.

O86	19	2s. 6d. plate violet	£2000	£1600
O87		5s. pale rose	£2000	£1600

Only one sheet (60) of each of these stamps was printed.

The use of stamps overprinted "O S" was made invalid by the Posts and Telegraph Act of 1 November 1902.

South Australia became part of the Commonwealth of Australia on 1 January 1901.

TASMANIA

PRICES FOR STAMPS ON COVER

SPECIMEN OVERPRINTS. Those listed are from U.P.U. distributions between 1892 and 1904. Further "Specimen" overprints exist, but these were used for other purposes.

1	2	3

(Eng C. W. Coard. Recess H. and C. Best at the *Courier* newspaper, Hobart)

1853 (1 Nov). *No wmk. Imperf. Twenty-four varieties in four rows of six each.*

(a) Medium soft yellowish paper with all lines clear and distinct

1	1	1d. pale blue		£3250	£750
2		1d. blue		£3250	£750

(b) Thin hard white paper with lines of the engraving blurred and worn

3	1	1d. pale blue		£3000	£650
4		1d. blue		£3000	£650

1853–55. *No wmk. Imperf. In each plate there are twenty-four varieties in four rows of six each.*

(a) Plate I. Finely engraved. All lines in network and background thin, clear, and well defined.

(i) First state of the plate, brilliant colours

5	2	4d. bright red-orange		£2250	£600
		a. Double impression			
6		4d. bright brownish orange		—	£750

(ii) Second state of plate, with blurred lines and worn condition of the central background

7	2	4d. red-orange		£2000	£375
8		4d. orange		£1800	£350
9		4d. pale orange		—	£350

(b) Plate II. Coarse engraving, lines in network and background thicker and blurred (1855)

10	2	4d. orange		£2000	£375
		a. Double print, one albino			
11		4d. dull orange		£2000	£325
12		4d. yellowish orange		£2000	£325

In the 4d. Plate I, the outer frame-line is thin all round. In Plate II it is, by comparison with other parts, thicker in the lower left angle.

The 4d. is known on vertically laid paper from proof sheets. Examples from Plate I have the lines close together and those from Plate II wide apart (*Price* £5000 *unused*).

In 1879 reprints were made of the 1d. in blue and the 4d., Plate I, in brownish yellow, on thin, tough, white wove paper, and perforated 11½. In 1887, a reprint from the other plate of the 4d. was made in reddish brown and in black, and in 1889 of the 1d. in blue and in black, and of the 4d. (both plates) in yellow and in black on white card, imperforate. As these three plates were defaced after the stamps had been superseded, all these reprints show two, or three thick strokes across the Queen's head.

All three plates were destroyed in July 1950.

(Eng. W. Humphrys, after water-colour sketch by E. Corbould. Recess P.B.)

1855 (17 Aug–16 Sept). *Wmk Large Star,* W w 1. *Imperf.*

14	3	1d. carmine (16.9)		£4000	£700
15		2d. deep green (16.9)		£1800	£500
16		2d. green (16.9)		£1800	£450
17		4d. deep blue		£1200	85·00
18		4d. blue		£1200	95·00

Proofs of the 1d. and 4d. on thick paper, *without watermark*, are sometimes offered as the issued stamps.

(Recess H. and C. Best, Hobart, from P.B. plates)

1856 (Apr)–57. *No wmk. Imperf.* (a) *Thin white paper.*

19	3	1d. pale brick-red (4.56)		£4000	£550
20		2d. dull emerald-green (1.57)		£5000	£700
21		4d. deep blue (5.57)		£600	85·00
22		4d. blue (5.57)		£500	85·00
23		4d. pale blue (5.57)		—	£120

(b) Pelure paper

24	3	1d. deep red-brown (11.56)		£3000	£600

4	7	8

(Recess H. Best (August 1857–May 1859), J. Davies (August 1859–March 1862), J. Birchall (March 1863), M. Hood (October 1863–April 1864), Govt Printer (from July 1864), all from P.B. plates)

1857 (Aug)–69. *Wmk double-lined numerals "1", "2" or "4" as* W 4 *on appropriate value. Imperf.*

25	3	1d. deep red-brown		£400	21·00
26		1d. pale red-brown		£275	16·00
27		1d. brick-red (1863)		£140	15·00
28		1d. dull vermilion (1865)		80·00	15·00
29		1d. carmine (1867)		80·00	15·00
		a. Double print		—	£120
		b. Error. Wmkd "2" (1869)			
30		2d. dull emerald-green		—	60·00
31		2d. green		—	27·00
		a. Double print		—	£150
32		2d. yellow-green		£200	55·00
33		2d. deep green (1858)		£170	30·00
34		2d. slate-green (1860)		£120	45·00
35		4d. deep blue		—	70·00
		a. Double print		—	£150
36		4d. pale blue		£100	11·00

37	3	4d. blue		£100	15·00
		a. Double print		—	£150
38		4d. bright blue		£100	15·00
		a. Printed on both sides		—	†
		b. Double print		—	£120
39		4d. cobalt-blue		—	55·00

Printings before July 1864 were all carried out at the *Courier* printing works which changed hands several times during this period.

CANCELLATIONS. Beware of early Tasmanian stamps with pen-cancellations cleaned off and faked postmarks applied.

(Recess P.B.)

1858 (Jan). *Wmk double-lined numerals "6" or "12" as* W 5. *Imperf.*

40	7	6d. dull lilac		£600	65·00
41	8	1s. vermilion (*shades*)		£500	55·00

Examples of the 6d. lilac on paper watermarked Large Star exist from a proof sheet. These are always creased (*Price* £650 *unused*).

(Recess J. Davies (March 1860), J. Birchall (April 1863), Govt Printer (from February 1865), all from P.B. plates)

1860 (Mar)–67. *Wmk double-lined "6" as* W 4. *Imperf.*

44	7	6d. dull slate-grey		£225	50·00
45		6d. grey		—	55·00
46		6d. grey-violet (4.63)		£130	50·00
		a. Double print		—	£200
47		6d. dull cobalt (2.65)		£350	75·00
48		6d. slate-violet (2.65)		£250	45·00
49		6d. reddish mauve (4.67)		£550	£150

In 1871 reprints were made of the 6d. (in mauve) on thin, white wove paper, and perforated 11½. They are found with or without "REPRINT". In 1889 they were again reprinted on white card, imperforate. These later impressions are also found overprinted "REPRINT" and perforated 11½.

PERFORATED ISSUES. From 1 October 1857 the Tasmanian Post Office only supplied purchasers requiring five or more complete sheets of stamps. The public obtained their requirements, at face value, from licensed stamp vendors, who obtained their stocks at a discount from the Post Office.

From 1863 onwards a number of the stamp vendors applied their own roulettes or perforations. The Hobart firm of J. Walch & Sons achieved this so successfully that they were given an official contract in July 1869 to perforate sheets for the Post Office. The Government did not obtain a perforating machine until late in 1871.

1863–71. *Double-lined numeral watermarks. Various unofficial roulettes and perforations.*

(a) By J. Walch & Sons, Hobart

(i) Roulette about 8, often imperf × roul (1863–68)

50	3	1d. brick-red		—	£150
51		1d. carmine		£300	£100
52		2d. yellow-green		—	£400
53		2d. slate-green			
54		4d. pale blue		—	£140
55	7	6d. dull lilac		—	£170
56	8	1s. vermilion		—	£500

(ii) P 10 (1864–69)

57	3	1d. brick-red		45·00	18·00
58		1d. dull vermilion		45·00	18·00
		a. Double print		—	†
59		1d. carmine		42·00	18·00
60		2d. yellow-green		£225	70·00
61		2d. slate-green		£275	£120
62		4d. pale blue		90·00	9·50
63		4d. blue		90·00	9·50
		a. Double print		—	£110
64	7	6d. grey-violet		£150	13·00
65		6d. dull cobalt		£200	50·00
66		6d. slate-violet		—	18·00
67		6d. reddish mauve		£300	60·00
68	8	1s. vermilion		90·00	19·00
		a. Imperf vert (horiz pair)			

(iii) P 12 (1865–71—from July 1869 under contract to the Post Office)

69	3	1d. dull vermilion		45·00	
		a. Double print		—	†
70		1d. carmine		35·00	6·50
		a. Error. Wmkd "2" (*pen cancel* £75)	—	£100
71		2d. yellow-green		£110	38·00
72		4d. deep blue		70·00	11·00
73		4d. blue		70·00	13·00
74		4d. cobalt-blue		—	28·00
75	7	6d. slate-violet		£120	18·00
		a. Imperf between (vert pair)			
76		6d. reddish mauve		70·00	32·00
		a. Imperf between (vert or horiz pair)			
77	8	1s. vermilion		95·00	28·00
		a. Double print		—	£150
		b. Imperf between (horiz pair)			

(iv) Perf compound 10 × 12 (1865–69)

78	3	1d. carmine		£1300
79		4d. blue		£900

(b) P 12½ by R. Harris, Launceston (1864–68)

80	3	1d. brick-red		45·00	23·00
81		1d. dull vermilion		42·00	17·00
82		1d. carmine		25·00	6·50
83		2d. yellow-green		£225	80·00
84		2d. slate-green		£200	£100
85		4d. blue		£130	35·00
86		4d. bright blue		£130	35·00
87	7	6d. dull cobalt		£250	70·00
88		6d. slate-violet		£170	40·00
89		6d. reddish mauve		£350	90·00
90	8	1s. vermilion		£180	65·00

(c) Imperf × oblique roulette 11½ at Oatlands (1866)

91	3	4d. blue		—	£375

(d) Oblique roulette 10–10½, possibly at Deloraine (1867)

92	3	1d. brick-red	..	..	..	—	£325
93		1d. carmine	..	..	..	£900	£275
94		2d. yellow-green	..	..	..	—	£425
95		4d. bright blue	..	..	..	—	£375
96	7	6d. grey-violet	..	..	..	—	£600

(e) Oblique roulette 14–15, probably at Cleveland (1867–69)

97	3	1d. brick-red	..	..	..	—	£375
98		1d. dull vermilion	..	..	..	—	£375
99		1d. carmine	..	..	..	—	£375
100		2d. yellow-green	..	..	..	—	£425
101		4d. pale blue	..	..	..	—	£325
102	7	6d. grey-violet	..	..	..	—	£600
103	8	1s. vermilion	..	..	..	—	£750

(f) Pin-perf 5½ to 9½ at Longford (1867)

104	3	1d. carmine	..	..	..	£300	70·00
105		2d. yellow-green	..	..	..	—	£200
106		4d. bright blue	..	..	..	—	£160
107	7	6d. grey-violet	..	..	..	—	£150
108		6d. reddish mauve	..	..	..	—	£425
109	8	1s. vermilion	..	..	..		

(g) Pin-perf 12 at Oatlands (1867)

110	3	4d. blue	..	..	..		

(h) Pin-perf 13½ to 14½ (1867)

111	3	1d. brick-red	..	..	..	—	£190
112		1d. dull vermilion	..	..	..	—	£190
113		1d. carmine	..	..	..		
114		2d. yellow-green	..	..	..	—	£275
115		4d. pale blue	..	..	..	—	£160
116	7	6d. grey-violet	..	..	..	—	£375
117	8	1s. vermilion	..	..	..		

(j) Serrated perf 19 at Hobart (1868–69)

118	3	1d. carmine (pen-cancel £9)	..	..	£225	£100
119		2d. yellow-green	..	..	..	—	£200
120		4d. deep blue	..	..	..	£550	95·00
121		4d. cobalt-blue	..	..	..	—	95·00
122	7	6d. slate-violet	..	..	..	—	£375
123	8	1s. vermilion	..	..	..		

(k) Roul 4½, possibly at Macquarie River (1868)

124	3	4d. blue	..	..	..		
125	7	6d. reddish mauve	..	..	..		
126	8	1s. vermilion	..	..	..		

An example of the 1d. carmine is known perforated 10 on three sides and serrated 19 on the fourth.

For stamps perforated 11½ or 12 by the Post Office see Nos. 134a/43.

11   12

13   14

(Typo Govt Printer, Hobart, from plates made by D.L.R.)

1870 (1 Nov)–**71.** *Wmk single-lined numerals* W **12** (2d.), **13** (1d., 4d.) or **14** (1d., 10d.). (a) *P* 12 *by J. Walch & Sons.*

127	11	1d. rose-red (wmk "10")	..	..	27·00	8·50
		a. Imperf (pair)	..	..	£275	£275
		b. Deep rose-red	..	..	45·00	6·50
128		1d. rose-red (wmk "4") (3.71)	..	40·00	8·50
		a. Imperf (pair)	..	..	—	£225
129		2d. yellow-green	..	..	42·00	4·50
		a. Imperf (pair)	..	..		
		b. Blue-green	..	..	45·00	4·50
130		4d. blue	..	..	..	£700	£400
131		10d. black	..	..	..	23·00	17·00
		a. Imperf (pair)	..	..	£160	

(b) P 11½ by the Post Office (1871)

132	11	1d. rose-red (wmk "10")	..	..	£900	
133		2d. yellow-green	..	..	80·00	6·50
		a. Blue-green	..	..	38·00	3·25
		ab. Double print	..	..		
134		10d. black	..	..	..	26·00	17·00

The above were printed on paper obtained from New South Wales.

See also Nos. 144/55, 156/8, 159/66, 170/4, 226/7, 242 and 255/6.

(Recess P.B.)

1871. *Wmk double-lined numeral "6". P* 11½ *by the Post Office.*

134a	7	1s. vermilion	..	..		

(Recess Govt Printer, Hobart)

1871–91. *Double-lined numeral watermarks as* W **4**. *Perforated by the Post Office.* (a) *P* 11½.

135	7	6d. dull lilac	..	..	70·00	19·00
136		6d. lilac	..	..	..	65·00	19·00
		a. Imperf between (pair)	..	—	£475	
137		6d. deep slate-lilac (3.75)	..	65·00	19·00
		a. Imperf (pair)	..	..	—	£450
138		6d. bright violet (5.78)	..	65·00	28·00
		a. Double print	..	..	—	£110
		b. Imperf between (horiz pair)	..	£750	
139		6d. dull reddish lilac (10.79)	..	70·00	38·00

140	8	1s. brown-red (1.73)	..	..	80·00	38·00
		a. Imperf between (horiz pair)	..		
141		1s. orange-red (3.75)	..	..	70·00	38·00
141a		1s. orange (5.78)	..	..		

(b) P 12

142	7	6d. reddish purple (1884)	..	..	80·00	18·00
		a. Imperf between (horiz pair)	..	£425	
143		6d. dull claret (7.91)	..	..	24·00	12·00

The perforation machine used on Nos. 142/3 was previously owned by J. Walch and Sons and passed to the ownership of the Government in 1884. It may have been used to perforate left-over sheets of previous printings.

15   16

(Typo Govt Printer, Hobart, from plates made by D.L.R.)

1871 (25 Mar)–**78.** W **15.** (a) *P* 11½.

144	11	1d. rose (5.71)	..	..	3·50	50
		a. Imperf (pair) (pen cancel £30)		
		b. Bright rose	..	..	3·50	50
		c. Carmine	..	..	5·00	50
		d. Pink	..	..	..	5·00	1·50
		e. Vermilion (4.75)	..	..	£200	65·00
145		2d. deep green (11.72)	..	..	14·00	50
		a. Blue-green	..	..	22·00	50
		b. Yellow-green (12.75)	..	£110	1·50
146		3d. pale red-brown	..	..	35·00	3·25
		a. Imperf (pair)	..	..	£160	
		b. Deep red-brown	..	..	35·00	3·75
		ba. Imperf between (pair)	..		
		c. Purple-brown (1.78)	..	35·00	3·25
		ca. Imperf (pair)	..	..	—	£375
		d. Brownish purple	..	..	35·00	3·25
147		4d. pale yellow (8.8.76)	..	35·00	12·00
		a. Ochre (7.78)	..	..	45·00	9·00
		b. Buff	..	..	..	40·00	9·50
148		9d. blue (2.10.71)	..	..	16·00	5·00
		a. Imperf (pair)	..	..	£160	
		b. Double print	..	..		
149		5s. purple (pen cancel £3.75)	..	£140	38·00
		a. Imperf (pair)	..	..		
		b. Mauve	..	..	£120	38·00

(b) P 12

150	11	1d. rose	..	..	..	60·00	5·50
		a. Carmine	..	..	65·00	7·00
151		2d. green	..	..	..	£400	95·00
		a. Imperf (pair)	..	..	—	£250
152		3d. red-brown	..	..	60·00	14·00
		a. Deep red-brown	..	..	60·00	14·00
153		4d. buff	..	..	..	£225	15·00
154		9d. pale blue	..	..	28·00	
155		5s. purple	..	..	..	£250	
		a. Mauve	..	..	£160	

(Typo D.L.R.)

1878 (28 Oct). W **16.** *P* 14.

156	11	1d. carmine	..	..	2·75	40
		a. Rose-carmine	..	..	2·75	40
		b. Scarlet	..	..	2·75	40
157		2d. pale green	..	..	3·00	40
		a. Green	..	..	..	3·00	40
158		8d. dull purple-brown	..	..	14·00	3·50

(Typo Govt Printer, Hobart (some printings of 1d. in 1891 by *Mercury* Press) from plates made by Victoria Govt Printer, Melbourne (½d.) or D.L.R. (others))

1880 (Apr)–**91.** W **16** (*sideways on* 1d.). (a) *P* 11½.

159	11	1d. orange (8.3.89)	..	..	1·90	1·40
		a. Deep orange	..	..	1·90	1·40
160		1d. dull red (14.2.89)	..	..	3·50	1·10
		a. Vermilion-red	..	..	2·75	1·10
161		3d. red-brown	..	..	10·00	2·50
		a. Imperf (pair)	..	..	£120	
162		4d. deep yellow (1.83)	..	..	27·00	10·00
		a. Chrome-yellow	..	..	27·00	11·00
		b. Olive-yellow	..	..	95·00	20·00
		c. Buff	..	..	..	28·00	8·50

(b) P 12

163	11	1d. orange	..	..	2·00	2·50
		a. Deep orange	..	..	1·90	2·50
		ab. Wmk sideways	..	..		
164		1d. pink (1891)	..	..	14·00	2·75
		a. Imperf (pair)	..	..	£130	£150
		b. Rosine	..	..	6·00	1·50
		c. Dull rosine	..	..	8·00	3·00
		ca. Imperf (pair)	..	..	£100	
165		3d. red-brown	..	..	8·00	2·50
		a. Imperf between (pair)	..	£500	
166		4d. deep yellow	..	..	50·00	12·00
		a. Chrome-yellow	..	..	70·00	12·00
		ab. Printed both sides	..	£250	

SPECIMEN AND PRESENTATION REPRINTS OF TYPE 11. In 1871 the 1d., 2d., 3d., 4d. blue, 9d., 10d. and 5s. were reprinted on soft white wove paper to be followed, in 1879, by the 4d. yellow and 8d. on rough white wove. Both these reprintings were perforated 11½. In 1886 it was decided to overprint remaining stocks with the word "REPRINT".

In 1889 Tasmania commenced sending sample stamps to the U.P.U. in Berne and a further printing of the 4d. blue was made, imperforate, on white card. This, together with the 5s. known in mauve on white card, both perforated 11½ and overprinted "RE-PRINT", were included in presentation sets supplied to members of the states' legislatures in 1901.

---

d. d.

Halfpenny	2½	2½
(17)	(18) (2¼ mm between "d", and "2")	(19) (3½ mm between "d" and "2")

1889 (1 Jan). *No.* 156b *surch locally with* T **17**.

167	11	½d. on 1d. scarlet	..	..	8·00	9·00
		a. "al" in "Half" printed sideways (R. 1/2)	..	£700	£475

No. 167a occurred in a second printing and was later corrected.

A reprint on white card, perforated 11½ or imperforate, overprinted "REPRINT" was produced in 1901.

1891 (1 Jan–June). *Surch locally.* W **16.** (a) *With* T **18**. *P* 11½.

168	11	2½d. on 9d. pale blue	..	..	6·50	2·75
		a. Surch double, one inverted	..	£250	£275
		b. Deep blue (May)	..	..	7·00	3·25

(b) With T 19. P 12

169	11	2½d. on 9d. pale blue (June)	..	5·00	2·50
		a. Blue surch.	..	..		

A reprint, using a third setting, perforated 11½ and overprinted "REPRINT" was produced in 1901.

(Typo Govt Printer, Hobart)

1891 (Apr–Aug). W **15.** (a) *P* 11½.

170	11	½d. orange	..	..	18·00	6·50
		a. Brown-orange	..	..	14·00	6·00
171		1d. rosine	..	..	11·00	4·00

(b) P 12

172	11	½d. orange	..	..	15·00	9·00
		a. Imperf (pair)	..	..	85·00	
173		1d. dull rosine	..	..	17·00	8·00
		a. Rosine	..	..	28·00	11·00
174		4d. bistre (Aug)	..	..	14·00	6·00

20   21   21a

1892 (12 Feb)–**99.** W **16.** *P* 14.

216	20	½d. orange and mauve (11.92)	..	1·25	50
217	21	2½d. purple	..	..	2·50	1·00
218	20	5d. pale blue and brown	..	4·50	1·40
219		6d. violet and black (11.92)	..	5·50	1·75
220	21a	10d. purple-lake & deep green (30.1.99)	9·00	6·50
221	20	1s. rose and green (11.92)	..	6·00	1·75
222		2s. 6d. brown and blue (11.92)	..	22·00	9·00
223		5s. lilac and red (3.2.97)	..	38·00	18·00
224		10s. mauve and brown (11.92)	..	75·00	50·00
225		£1 green and yellow (2.97)	..	£225	£150
216/25		..	..	..	Set of 10	£350	£200
216/25	Optd "Specimen"	..	Set of 10	£250

See also Nos. 243 and 257/8.

(Typo Govt Printer, Hobart)

1896. W **16.** *P* 12.

226	11	4d. pale bistre	..	..	12·00	5·50
227		9d. pale blue	..	..	8·00	2·25
		a. Blue	..	..	..	8·50	3·25

22 Lake Marion   23 Mount Wellington

24 Hobart   25 Tasman's Arch

26 Spring River, Port Davey   27 Russell Falls

28 Mount Gould, Lake   29 Dilston Falls
St. Clair

30

(Eng. L. Phillips. Recess D.L.R.)

1899 (Dec)–**1900.** *W* **30.** *P* 14.

229	22	½d. deep green (31.3.00)	..	6·00	2·75
230	23	1d. bright lake (13.12.99)*		4·50	65
231	24	2d. deep violet (15.12.99)*		8·00	65
232	25	2½d. indigo (1900)	..	10·00	3·75
233	26	3d. sepia (1900)	..	7·50	2·50
234	27	4d. deep orange-buff (1900)	..	14·00	2·50
235	28	5d. bright blue (31.3.00)	..	14·00	6·50
236	29	6d. lake (31.3.00)	..	18·00	9·00
229/36			*Set of* 8	70·00	25·00
229/36		Optd "Specimen"	*Set of* 8	£225	

*Earliest known postmark dates.
See also Nos. 237/9, 240/1, 245/8, 249/54, 259 and 261/2.

DIFFERENCES BETWEEN LITHOGRAPHED AND TYPOGRAPHED PRINTINGS OF TYPES 22/9

Lithographed	Typographed
General appearance fine.	*Comparatively crude and coarse appearance.*
½d. All "V over Crown" wmk.	All "Crown over A" wmk.
1d. The shading on the path on the right bank of the river consists of very fine dots. In printings from worn stones the dots hardly show.	The shading on the path is coarser, consisting of large dots and small patches of colour.
The shading on the white mountain is fine (or almost absent in many stamps).	The shading on the mountain is coarse, and clearly defined.
2d. Three rows of windows in large building on shore, at extreme left, against inner frame.	Two rows of windows.
3d. Clouds very white.	Clouds dark.
Stars in corner ornaments have long points.	Stars have short points.
Shading of corner ornaments is defined by a coloured outer line.	Shading of ornaments terminates against white background.
4d. Lithographed only.	
6d. No coloured dots at base of waterfall.	Coloured dots at base of waterfall.
Outer frame of value tablets is formed by outer line of design.	Thick line of colour between value tablets and outer line. Small break in inner frame below second "A" of "TASMANIA".

(Litho, using transfers from D.L.R. plates, Victoria Government Printing Office, Melbourne)

1902 (Jan)–**04.** *Wmk V over Crown, W w* **10** (*sideways on* ½d., 2d.). *P* 12½.

237	22	½d. green (2.03)	..	1·25	75
		a. Wmk upright	..		
		b. Perf 11	..	3·25	2·25
		c. Perf comp of 12½ and 11	..	50·00	35·00
		d. Perf comp of 12½ and 12	..		
238	23	1d. carmine-red	..	5·00	70
239	24	2d. deep reddish violet	..	3·50	30
		a. Perf 11	..	3·50	1·75
		b. Perf comp of 12½ and 11	..	55·00	35·00
		c. Wmk upright (2.04)	..		
		d. *Deep rose-lilac* (4.05)	..	6·00	10
		da. Perf 11	..	5·00	75
		db. Perf comp of 12½ and 11	..		
237 and 239		Optd "Specimen"	*Set of* 2	85·00	

As the V and Crown paper was originally prepared for stamps of smaller size, portions of two or more watermarks appear on each stamp.

We only list the main groups of shades in this and the following issues. There are variations of shade in all values, particularly in the 2d. where there is a wide range, also in the 1d. in some issues.

(Typo, using electrotyped plates, Victoria Govt Ptg Office, Melbourne)

1902 (Oct)–**04.** *Wmk V over Crown, W w* **10.** *P* 12½.

240	23	1d. pale red (*wmk sideways*)	..	7·00	80
		a. Perf 11	..	22·00	90
		b. Perf comp of 12½ and 11	..	£150	35·00
		c. Wmk upright (1.03)	..	22·00	6·00
		ca. Perf 11	..	27·00	
		d. *Rose-red* (*wmk upright*) (4.03) (Optd S. £40)	..	3·50	60
		da. Perf 11	..	15·00	60
		db. Perf comp of 12½ and 11	..	£150	35·00

241	23	1d. scarlet (*wmk upright*) (9.03)	..	2·50	25
		a. Perf 11		3·75	40
		b. Perf comp of 12½ and 11	..		
		c. *Rose-scarlet* (1904)		2·00	30
		ca. Perf 11		2·50	40
		cb. Perf comp of 12½ and 11	..	50·00	15·00

The 1d. scarlet of September 1903 was from new electrotyped plates which show less intense shading.

(Typo Victoria Govt Ptg Office, Melbourne)

1903–05. *Wmk V over Crown, W w* **10.** *P* 12½.

242	11	9d. blue (1905)	..	8·00	2·50
		a. Perf 11		8·00	3·75
		b. Perf comp of 12½ and 11	..	—	£375
		c. Wmk sideways	..	50·00	15·00
		d. *Pale blue*	..	9·50	3·50
		e. *Bright blue*	..	9·50	4·00
		f. *Ultramarine*	..	£350	
		g. *Indigo*	..	£130	
243	20	1s. rose and green	..	11·00	3·00
		a. Perf 11	..	28·00	
242/3		Optd "Specimen"	*Set of* 2	£100	

1½d. ONE PENNY

(31)   (32)

1904 (29 Dec). No. 218 *surch with T* **31.**

244	20	1½d. on 5d. pale blue & brn (Optd S. £28)	1·25	60	

Stamps with inverted surcharge or without surcharge *se-tenant* with stamps with normal surcharge were obtained irregularly and were not issued for postal use.

PRINTER. The Victoria Govt Ptg Office became the Commonwealth Stamp Printing Branch in March 1909.

(Litho, using transfers from D.L.R. plates, Victoria Govt Ptg Office, Melbourne)

1905 (Sept)–**12.** *Wmk Crown over A, W w* **11** (*sideways on horiz stamps*). *P* 12½.

245	24	2d. deep purple	..	3·75	15
		a. Perf 11	..	9·50	20
		b. Perf comp of 12½ and 11	..	17·00	3·00
		c. Perf comp of 12½ and 12	..	—	45·00
		d. Perf comp of 11 and 12	..	90·00	
		e. *Slate-lilac* (1906)	..	4·00	
		ea. Perf 11	..	17·00	25
		eb. Perf comp of 12½ and 11	..		
		ed. Perf comp of 11 and 12	..		
		f. *Reddish lilac* (1907)	..	9·50	75
		fa. Perf 11	..		
		fb. Perf comp of 12½ and 11	..		
246	26	3d. brown (5.06)	..	8·50	2·00
		a. Perf 11	..	12·00	4·00
		b. Perf comp of 12½ and 11	..	60·00	
247	27	4d. pale yellow-brown (3.07)	..	12·00	2·75
		a. Perf 11	..	15·00	3·25
		b. *Orange-buff* (5.09)	..	12·00	2·75
		ba. Perf 11	..	15·00	3·00
		bb. Perf comp of 12½ and 11	..	£160	
		c. *Brown-ochre* (*wmk sideways*). Perf 11 (6.11)	..	24·00	25·00
		d. *Orange-yellow* (3.12)	..	15·00	11·00
		da. Perf 11	..	25·00	15·00
		db. Perf comp of 12½ and 11	..		
248	29	6d. lake (7.08)	..	35·00	4·25
		a. Perf 11	..	42·00	4·50
		b. Perf comp of 12½ and 11	..	£130	

Stamps with perf compound of 12½ and 12 or 11 and 12 are found on sheets which were sent from Melbourne incompletely perforated along the outside edge of the pane or sheet. The missing perforations were applied in Hobart using a line machine measuring 12 (11.8 is the exact gauge). This perforation can only occur on one side of a stamp.

(Typo, using electrotyped plates, Victoria Govt Ptg Office, Melbourne)

1905 (Aug)–**11.** *Wmk Crown over A, W w* **11** (*sideways on horiz designs*). *P* 12½.

249	22	½d. yellow-green (10.12.08)	..	1·25	20
		a. Perf 11	..	1·25	20
		b. Perf comp of 12½ and 11	..	25·00	5·00
		c. Perf comp of 11 and 12	..	65·00	
		d. Wmk upright (1909)	..	5·50	1·75
		da. Perf 11	..		
250	23	1d. rose-red	..	1·50	10
		a. Perf 11	..	2·50	10
		b. Perf comp of 12½ and 11	..	3·75	1·25
		c. Perf comp of 12½ and 12	..	40·00	5·50
		d. Perf comp of 11 and 12	..	45·00	20·00
		e. Wmk sideways (1908)	..	5·00	75
		ea. Perf 11	..		
		f. *Imperf* (*pair*)	..	£140	
250g		1d. carmine-red (3.10)	..	3·00	30
		ga. Perf 11	..	4·75	35
		gb. Perf comp of 12½ and 11	..	8·00	4·00
		gc. Perf comp of 12½ and 12	..	40·00	
		gd. Perf comp of 11 and 12	..	45·00	
		ge. *Imperf* (*pair*)	..	£140	
		h. *Carmine-vermilion* (1911)	..	8·00	2·00
		ha. Perf 11	..	9·00	2·00
		hb. Perf comp of 12½ and 11	..		
		hc. Perf comp of 12½ and 12	..		
		hd. Perf comp of 11 and 12	..		
251	24	2d. plum (8.07)	..	3·75	10
		a. Wmk upright	..	7·50	80
		b. Perf 11	..	2·50	10
		ba. Wmk upright (12.07)	..	7·50	80
		c. Perf comp of 12½ and 11	..	20·00	6·00
		d. Perf comp of 12½ and 12	..	£110	45·00
		e. Perf comp of 11 and 12	..	70·00	38·00
		f. *Bright reddish violet* (1910)	..	3·00	70
		fa. Perf 11	..	3·25	40
		fb. Perf comp of 12½ and 11	..		

253	26	3d. brown (3.09)	..	6·50	2·00
		a. Wmk upright	..		
		b. Perf 11	..	11·00	2·50
		c. Perf comp of 12½ and 11	..	£130	
254	29	6d. carmine-lake (12.10)	..	16·00	14·00
		a. Perf 11	..	20·00	17·00
		b. Perf comp of 12½ and 11	..	£180	
		c. *Dull carmine-red* (3.11)	..	22·00	17·00
		ca. Wmk upright	..	27·00	
		cb. Perf 11	..	23·00	17·00
		cc. Perf comp of 12½ and 11	..	£150	

The note after No. 248 *re* perfs compound with perf 12 also applies here.
Nos. 250/f were printed from the same plates as Nos. 241/cb. Nos. 250g/hd are from a further pair of new plates and the images are sharper.

(Typo Victoria Govt Printing Office, Melbourne)

1906–13. *Wmk Crown over A, W w* **11.** *P* 12½.

255	11	8d. purple-brown (1907)	..	17·00	4·50
		a. Perf 11	..	15·00	3·50
256		9d. blue (1907)	..	7·00	2·75
		a. Perf 11	..	7·00	2·75
		b. Perf comp of 12½ and 11 (1909)	..	55·00	
		c. Perf comp of 12½ and 12 (1909)	..	£110	
		d. Perf comp of 11 and 12	..	£190	
257	20	1s. rose and green (1907)	..	12·00	2·50
		a. Perf 11 (1907)	..	16·00	7·50
		b. Perf comp of 12½ and 11	..	22·00	
		c. Perf comp of 12½ and 12	..	65·00	
258		10s. mauve and brown (1906)	..	£110	90·00
		a. Perf 11	..	£170	
		b. Perf comp of 12½ and 11	..	£170	

The note after No. 248 *re* perfs compound with perf 12, also applies here.

(Typo, using stereotyped plates, Commonwealth Stamp Ptg Branch, Melbourne)

1911 (Jan). *Wmk Crown over A, W w* **11** (*sideways*). *P* 12½.

259	24	2d. bright violet	..	4·00	30
		a. Wmk upright	..	14·00	2·00
		b. Perf 11	..	4·25	1·00
		c. Perf comp of 12½ and 11	..	50·00	15·00
		d. Perf comp of 12½ and 12	..	£150	

Stamps from this stereotyped plate differ from No. 251 in the width of the design (33 to 33¾ mm, against just over 32 mm), in the taller, bolder letters of "TASMANIA", in the slope of the mountain in the left background, which is clearly outlined in white, and in the outer vertical frame-line at left, which appears "wavy". Compare Nos. 260, etc, which are always from this plate.

1912 (Oct). No. 259 *surch with T* **32.** *P* 12½.

260	24	1d. on 2d. bright violet (R.)	..	90	30
		a. Perf 11	..	1·50	40
		b. Perf comp of 12½ and 11	..	85·00	85·00

(Typo, using electrotyped plates, Commonwealth Stamp Ptg Branch, Melbourne)

1912 (Dec). *Thin paper, white gum* (*as Victoria,* 1912). *W w* **11** (*sideways on* 3d.). *P* 12½.

261	23	1d. carmine-vermilion	..	15·00	4·25
		a. Perf 11	..	15·00	4·25
		b. Perf comp of 12½ and 11	..		
262	26	3d. brown	..	38·00	42·00

STAMP BOOKLETS

There are very few surviving examples of Nos. SB1/4. Listings are provided for those believed to have been issued with prices quoted for those known to still exist.

1904 (1 Jan)–**09.** *Black on red cover as No.* SB1 *of New South Wales. Stapled.*

SB1	£1 booklet containing two hundred and forty 1d. in twelve blocks of 20 (5×4)	..		
	a. Red on pink cover (1909)	..		
	b. Blue on pink cover	..		

1904 (1 Jan). *Black on grey cover as No.* SB1. *Stapled.*

SB2	£1 booklet containing one hundred and twenty 2d. in four blocks of 30	..		

1910 (May). *Black on white cover as No.* SB3 *of New South Wales. Stapled.*

SB3	2s. booklet containing eleven ½d. (No. 249), either in block of 6 plus block of 5 or block of 11, and eighteen 1d. (No. 250), either in three blocks of 6 or block of 6 plus block of 12	£200

Unsold stock No. SB3 was uprated with one additional ½d. in May 1911.

1911 (Aug). *Red on pink cover as No.* SB3. *Stapled.*

SB4	2s. booklet containing twelve ½d. (No. 249), either in two blocks of 6 or block of 12, and eighteen 1d. (No. 250), either in three blocks of 6 or block of 6 plus block of 12	£150

POSTAL FISCAL STAMPS

VALIDITY. Nos. F1/29 were authorised for postal purposes on November 1882.

CLEANED STAMPS. Beware of postal fiscal stamps with pe cancellations removed.

F 1

F 2

F 3

F 4

(Recess Alfred Bock, Hobart)

1863–80. *Wmk double-lined "1", W 4. (a) Imperf.*
F 1	F 1	3d. green (1.65)	..	..	60·00	40·00
F 2	F 2	2s. 6d. carmine (11.63)		..	65·00	40·00
F 3		2s. 6d. lake (5.80)	..	..		
F 4	F 3	5s. brown (1.64)	..	..	£160	£130
F 5		5s. sage-green (1880)	..	..	65·00	48·00
F 6	F 4	10s. orange (1.64)	..	..	£225	£130
F 7		10s. salmon (5.80)	..	..	£160	£130

(b) P 10
F 8	F 1	3d. green	..	..	38·00 20·00
F 9	F 2	2s. 6d. carmine	..	..	40·00
F10	F 3	5s. brown..	..	..	60·00
F11	F 4	10s. orange	..	..	40·00

(c) P 12
F12	F 1	3d. green	..	..	40·00 24·00
F13	F 2	2s. 6d. carmine	..	..	40·00 32·00
F14	F 3	5s. brown..	..	..	70·00
F15		5s. sage-green	..	..	29·00 24·00
F16	F 4	10s. orange	..	..	40·00 32·00
F17		10s. salmon	..	..	30·00 24·00

(d) P 12½
F18	F 1	3d. green	..	..	70·00
F19	F 2	2s. 6d. carmine	..	..	70·00
F20	F 3	5s. brown..	..	..	90·00
F21	F 4	10s. orange-brown	..	..	60·00

(e) P 11½
F22	F 1	3d. green	..	..	
F23	F 2	2s. 6d. lake	..	..	38·00 30·00
F24	F 3	5s. sage-green	..	..	30·00 20·00
F25	F 4	10s. salmon	..	..	50·00 38·00

See also No. F30.

In 1879, the 3d., 2s. 6d., 5s. (brown), and 10s. (orange) were reprinted on thin, tough, white paper, and are found with or without "REPRINT". In 1889 another reprint was made on white card, imperforate and perforated 12. These are also found with or without "REPRINT".

F 5 Duck-billed Platypus   (F 6)

REVENUE

(Typo D.L.R.)

1880 (19 Apr). *W* 16 *(sideways). P* 14.
F26	F 5	1d. slate	..	..	9·00 3·50
F27		3d. chestnut	..	..	9·00 2·75
F28		6d. mauve	..	..	60·00 2·00
F29		1s. rose-pink	..	..	70·00 5·00
		a. Perf comp of 14 and 11	..		

All values are known imperf, but not used.

Reprints are known of the 1d. in *deep blue* and the 6d. in lilac. The former is on yellowish white, the latter on white card. Both values also exist on wove paper, perf 12, with the word "REPRINT".

1888 (Aug). *W* 16. *P* 12
F30	F 2	2s. 6d. lake	..	..	15·00 11·00
		a. Imperf between (horiz pair)	..		£450

1900 (15 Nov). *Optd with Type F* 6. *(a) On Types F* 2 *and F* 4.
F31	F 2	2s. 6d. carmine (No. F13)	..	
		a. "REVFNUE"	..	
F32		2s. 6d. lake (No. F30)	..	£160
		a. "REVFNUE"	..	£250
		b. Opt inverted	..	£350
		c. Imperf	..	£170
F33	F 4	10s. salmon (No. F17)	..	
		a. "REVFNUE"	..	

*(b) On Nos. F*27 *and F*29
F34	F 5	3d. chestnut	..	15·00 15·00
		a. Double opt, one vertical	..	75·00 £100
F35		1s. rose-pink	..	

*(c) On stamps as Nos. F*26/9, *but typo locally. W* 16. *P* 12
F36	F 5	1d. blue	..	18·00
		a. Imperf between (horiz pair)	..	£300
		b. "REVENUE" inverted	..	£100
		c. "REVENUE" double	..	£160
		d. Pale blue	..	18·00
F37		6d. mauve	..	50·00
		a. Double print	..	£200
F38		1s. pink	..	75·00

(d) On No. 225
F39	20	£1 green and yellow	..	£150 £130
		a. Opt double, one vertical	..	£275 £275

It was not intended that stamps overprinted with Type F 6 should be used for postal purposes, but an ambiguity in

regulations permitted such usage until all postal fiscal stamps were invalidated on 30 November 1900.

Printings of some of the above with different watermarks, together with a 2d. as Nos. F36/8, did not appear until after the stamps had become invalid for postal purposes.

Tasmania became part of the Commonwealth of Australia on 1 January 1901.

VICTORIA

<table>
<tr><td colspan="2" align="center">**PRICES FOR STAMPS ON COVER**</td></tr>
<tr><td>Nos. 1/17</td><td>*from* × 2</td></tr>
<tr><td>Nos. 18/22</td><td>*from* × 4</td></tr>
<tr><td>Nos. 23/4</td><td>*from* × 2</td></tr>
<tr><td>No. 25</td><td>*from* × 3</td></tr>
<tr><td>Nos. 26/32</td><td>*from* × 2</td></tr>
<tr><td>No. 33</td><td>*from* × 6</td></tr>
<tr><td>No. 34</td><td>*from* × 8</td></tr>
<tr><td>Nos. 35/9</td><td>*from* × 4</td></tr>
<tr><td>No. 40</td><td>*from* × 3</td></tr>
<tr><td>Nos. 41/53</td><td>*from* × 2</td></tr>
<tr><td>No. 54</td><td>*from* × 3</td></tr>
<tr><td>No. 55</td><td></td></tr>
<tr><td>No. 56</td><td>*from* × 4</td></tr>
<tr><td>Nos. 57/72</td><td>*from* × 2</td></tr>
<tr><td>No. 73</td><td>*from* × 3</td></tr>
<tr><td>Nos. 74/80</td><td>*from* × 2</td></tr>
<tr><td>No. 81</td><td>*from* × 3</td></tr>
<tr><td>Nos. 82/7</td><td>*from* × 4</td></tr>
<tr><td>Nos. 88/200</td><td>*from* × 3</td></tr>
<tr><td>Nos. 201/6</td><td>*from* × 5</td></tr>
<tr><td>Nos. 207/8</td><td>*from* × 10</td></tr>
<tr><td>Nos. 209/14</td><td>*from* × 5</td></tr>
<tr><td>Nos. 215/19</td><td>*from* —</td></tr>
<tr><td>Nos. 220/6</td><td>*from* × 20</td></tr>
<tr><td>Nos. 227/33</td><td>*from* × 20</td></tr>
<tr><td>Nos. 234/7</td><td>*from* × 20</td></tr>
<tr><td>Nos. 238/52</td><td>—</td></tr>
<tr><td>Nos. 253/6</td><td>*from* × 20</td></tr>
<tr><td>No. 257</td><td>*from* × 10</td></tr>
<tr><td>No. 258</td><td>*from* × 20</td></tr>
<tr><td>No. 259</td><td>*from* × 10</td></tr>
<tr><td>Nos. 260/4</td><td>—</td></tr>
<tr><td>Nos. 265/6</td><td>*from* × 20</td></tr>
<tr><td>Nos. 267/73</td><td>*from* × 10</td></tr>
<tr><td>Nos. 274/91</td><td>—</td></tr>
<tr><td>Nos. 292/304</td><td>*from* × 10</td></tr>
<tr><td>Nos. 305/9</td><td>*from* × 5</td></tr>
<tr><td>Nos. 310/23</td><td>*from* × 10</td></tr>
<tr><td>Nos. 324/8</td><td>—</td></tr>
<tr><td>No. 329</td><td>*from* × 12</td></tr>
<tr><td>Nos. 330/50</td><td>*from* × 8</td></tr>
<tr><td>Nos. 351/2</td><td>—</td></tr>
<tr><td>Nos. 353/4</td><td>*from* × 4</td></tr>
<tr><td>No. 355</td><td>*from* × 10</td></tr>
<tr><td>Nos. 356/73</td><td>*from* × 15</td></tr>
<tr><td>Nos. 374/5</td><td>*from* × 3</td></tr>
<tr><td>Nos. 376/98</td><td>*from* × 10</td></tr>
<tr><td>Nos. 399/400</td><td>—</td></tr>
<tr><td>Nos. 401/6</td><td>*from* × 10</td></tr>
<tr><td>Nos. 407/15</td><td>—</td></tr>
<tr><td>Nos. 416/30</td><td>*from* × 10</td></tr>
<tr><td>Nos. 431/2</td><td>—</td></tr>
<tr><td>Nos. 433/43</td><td>*from* × 4</td></tr>
<tr><td>Nos. 444/53</td><td>—</td></tr>
<tr><td>Nos. 454/5</td><td>*from* × 10</td></tr>
<tr><td>Nos. 456/63</td><td>*from* × 6</td></tr>
<tr><td>No. 464</td><td></td></tr>
<tr><td>Nos. D1/8</td><td>*from* × 30</td></tr>
<tr><td>Nos. D9/10</td><td></td></tr>
<tr><td>Nos. D11/37</td><td>*from* × 30</td></tr>
</table>

SPECIMEN OVERPRINTS. Those listed are from U.P.U. distributions in 1892 and 1897. Further "Specimen" overprints exist, but these were used for other purposes.

During the expansion of the Australian settlements in the fourth decade of the nineteenth century the growing population of the Port Phillip District in the south of New South Wales led to a movement for its creation as a separate colony. This aspiration received the approval of the British Government in 1849, but the colony of Victoria, as it was to be called, was not to be created until 1 July 1851.

In the meantime the New South Wales Legislative Council voted for the introduction of postal reforms, including the use of postage stamps, from 1 January 1850, and this act was also to apply to the Port Phillip District where stamps inscribed "VICTORIA" would predate the creation of that colony by eighteen months.

Until the end of 1859 the stamps of Victoria, with the exception of Nos. 40 and 73, were produced by local contractors working under the supervision of the colonial administration.

HAM PRINTINGS. The first contractor was Thomas Ham of Melbourne. He was responsible for the initial printings of the "Half-Length" 1d., 2d. and 3d., together with the replacement "Queen on Throne" 2d. The first printings were produced from small sheets of 30 (5×6) laid down directly from the engraved die which showed a single example of each value. Subsequent printings, of which No. 4a was the first, were in sheets of 120 (two panes of 60) laid down using intermediate stones of various sizes. Impressions from the first printings were fine and clear, but the quality deteriorated when intermediate stones were used.

1 Queen Victoria ("Half Length")

(Lithographed by Thomas Ham, Melbourne)

1850 (3 Jan)–53. *Imperf.*

1d. Thin line at top

2d. Fine border and background

3d. White area to left of orb

(a) Original state of dies: 1d. *(tops of letters of "VICTORIA" reach to top of stamp);* 2d. *(fine border and background);* 3d. *(thicker white outline around left of orb, central band of orb does not protrude at left). No frame-lines on dies.*
1	1	1d. orange-vermilion	..	£7500	£1500
		a. Orange-brown	..	†	£750
		b. Dull chocolate-brown (shades)	..	£3500	£850
2		2d. lilac-mauve (shades) (Stone A)	..	£2250	£400
3		2d. brown-lilac (shades) (Stone B)	..	£2250	£250
		a. Grey-lilac	..	—	£250
4		3d. bright blue (shades)	..	£1800	£300
		a. Blue (shades)	..	£1800	£170
		ab. Retouched (between Queen's head and right border) (No. 11 in transfer-group) (8 varieties)	..	—	£275
		ac. Retouched (under "V") (No. 10 in transfer group)	..	—	£275

With the exception of No. 4a the above were printed from small stones of 30 (5×6) laid down directly from the engraved die which showed a single example of each value. There were two stones of the 2d. and one for each of the other values. No. 4a is the second printing of the 3d. for which the sheet size was increased to 120, the printing stone being constructed from an intermediate stone of 15 (5×3).

1d. Thick line at top

2d. Coarse background

3d. White area small and band protruding to left of orb

(b) Second state of dies: 1d. *(more colour over top of letters of "VICTORIA");* 2d. *(fine border as (a) but with coarse background);* 3d. *(thinner white outline around left of orb, central band of orb protrudes at left).*
5	1	1d. red-brown (shades) (2.50)	..	£2750	£300
		a. Pale dull red-brown	..	£2000	£300
6		2d. grey-lilac (shades) (1.50)	..	£1100	£100
		a. Dull grey	..	£1100	£110
7		3d. blue (shades) (6.51)	..	£1000	£110
		a. Retouched (22 varieties)	*from*	£1600	£225

Printed in sheets of 120 (10×12) with the printing stones constructed from intermediate stones of 30 (5×6) for the 1d. and 2d. or 10 (5×2) for the 3d. It is believed that the use of the smaller intermediate stone for the latter resulted in the many retouches.

Frame-lines added

(c) *Third state of dies: As in (b) but with frame-lines added, very close up, on all four sides.*

8	1	1d. dull orange-vermilion (11.50)			£1300	£400
		a. Dull red (*shades*)			£1000	£120
9		1d. deep red-brown (5.51)			—	£450
		a. Brownish red (*shades*)			£650	£110
		b. Dull rose (*shades*)			£650	£110
10		2d. grey (*shades*) (8.50)			£850	£130
		a. Olive-grey (*shades*)			£1000	£130
11		3d. blue (*shades*) (12.52)			£400	£50·00
		a. Deep blue (*shades*)			£500	£50·00
		b. Pale greenish blue (*shades*)			£650	£100

Printed in sheets of 120 (12×10) produced from intermediate stones of 30 (6×5) for No. 8 and 12 (6×2) for the others.

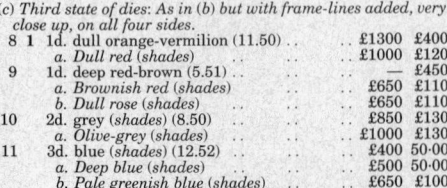

White veil

(d) *As (c) but altered to give, for the 1d. and 3d., the so-called "white veils", and for the 2d., the effect of vertical drapes to the veil.*

12	1	1d. reddish brown (6.51)			£700	£100
		a. Bright pinky red (*shades*)			£450	£100
13		2d. drab (1.51)			£1000	£110
		a. Grey-drab			£1000	£110
		b. Lilac-drab			—	£110
		c. Red-lilac			—	£500
		d. Void lower left corner				£1800
14		3d. blue (*shades*) (1.53)			£400	45·00
		a. Deep blue (*shades*)			£400	45·00
		b. Greenish blue (*shades*)			£500	50·00
		c. Retouched (9 varieties)			£750	£120

Printed in sheets of 120 (12×10) produced from intermediate stones of 12 (6×2) on which the details of the veil were amended as described above.

The "void corner" error occurred on the printing stone. It is believed that only four examples still exist.

2d. Coarse border and background

(e) *Fourth state of 2d. die only: Coarse border and background. Veil details as in original die.*

15	1	2d. red-lilac (*shades*) (5.50)			£600	£180
		a. Lilac			£600	£180
		b. Grey			—	£275
		c. Dull brownish lilac			£400	£100
		d. Retouched lower label—value omitted			from	£1800
		e. Other retouches (17 varieties)			from £1000	£225

Printed in sheets of 120 (12×10) produced from an intermediate stone of 30 (6×5).

(f) *2d. as (e), but with veils altered to give effect of vertical drapes.*

16	1	2d. lilac-grey (1.51)			£750	£110
		a. Deep grey			£850	£110
		b. Brown-lilac (*shades*)			£600	60·00
17		2d. cinnamon (*shades*) (2.51)			£500	95·00
		a. Drab (*shades*)			£550	60·00
		b. Pale dull brown (*shades*)			£650	70·00
		c. Greenish grey			£500	60·00
		d. Olive-drab (*shades*)			£600	£120
		e. Buff			†	£130

Printed in sheets of 120 (12×10) produced from two successive intermediate stones of 30 (6×5) on which the details of the veils were amended as described above.

This was the final printing of the 2d. "Half Length" as the die for this value had been damaged. A replacement 2d. design was ordered from Thomas Ham.

For the later printings of the 1d. and 3d. in this design see Nos. 23/4, 26/31, 48/9 and 78/9.

2 Queen on Throne **3**

(Recess-printed by Thomas Ham)

1852 (27 Dec). *Imperf.*

18	2	2d. reddish brown			£160	22·00
		a. Chestnut			—	£110
		b. Purple-brown			£225	22·00

Printed in sheets of 50 (10×5) from a hand-engraved plate of the same size. Each stamp in the sheet had individual corner letters made-up of various combinations, none of which contained the letter "J".

Reprints were made in 1891 using the original plate, on paper wmk V over Crown, both imperf and perf 12½.

For later printings of this design see Nos. 19/22 and 36/9.

CAMPBELL & CO PRINTINGS. In May 1853 the Victoria postal authorities placed an order for 1d. and 6d. stamps in the "Queen on Throne" design with Perkins, Bacon in London. These would not arrive for some time, however, and supplies of Ham's printings were rapidly becoming exhausted. Local tenders were, therefore, solicited for further supplies of the 1d. and 3d. "Half Lengths" and the 2d. "Queen on Throne". That received from J. S. Campbell & Co was accepted. The stamps were produced by lithography, using transfers from either the "Half Length" engraved plate or the 2d. "Queen on Throne" engraved plate of 50. Stamps from the Campbell & Co printings can be distinguished from later printings in lithography by the good quality paper used.

(Lithographed by J. S. Campbell & Co, Melbourne, using transfers taken from Ham's engraved plate)

1854 (Jan–July). *Good quality white or toned paper. Imperf.*

(a) *Clear impressions with details around back of throne generally complete*

19	2	2d. brownish purple			£170	22·00
		a. Grey-brown			£250	22·00
		b. Purple-black			—	22·00
		c. Dull lilac-brown (toned paper only)			£300	40·00

(b) *Poor impressions with details around back of throne not fully defined*

20	2	2d. violet-black (2.54)			£250	22·00
		a. Grey-black			£350	24·00
		b. Grey-lilac			£250	24·00
		c. Dull brown (on toned)			£250	24·00
		ca. Substituted transfer (in pair)			—	£2000

(c) *Weak impressions with background generally white without details. Toned paper only*

21	2	2d. grey-purple (7.54)			£130	20·00
		a. Purple-black			£130	20·00

(d) *Printings using an intermediate stone. Impression flat and blurred. Background details usually complete. Toned paper only*

22	2	2d. grey-drab (*shades*) (5.54)			£225	19·00
		a. Black			—	£100

Nos. 19/21 were produced using transfers taken directly from the original Ham engraved plate. It is believed that the different strengths of the impressions were caused by the amount of pressure exerted when the tranfers were taken. The stamps were printed in sheets of 100 (2 panes 10×5). On one stone a block of four at bottom left, lettered "FL GM" over "QV RW", was damaged and the stone was repaired by using a block of four substituted transfers. These were lettered "VZ WA" over "FL GM". No. 20ca covers any one of these substituted transfers in pair with normal. As horizontal pairs these are lettered "WA HN" or "GM SX" and as vertical "VZ" over "VZ" or "WA" over "WA".

For No. 22 an intermediate stone was used to produce a printing stone of 300 (6 panes 10×5). The insertion of a further stage into the process caused the blurred appearance of stamps from this printing. No. 22a is believed to come from proof sheets issued to post offices for normal use. Examples are usually cancelled with Barred Oval 108 and Barred Numerals 1 and 2.

(Lithographed by J. S. Campbell & Co, Melbourne)

1854 (Feb–June). *Good quality wove paper. Imperf.*

23	1	1d. orange-red (*shades*)			£450	£110
		a. Rose			£2000	£275
24		3d. blue (*shades*) (6.54)			£475	32·00
		a. Retouch under "C" of "VICTORIA"			—	£120

The 1d. was produced in sheets of 192 (two panes of 96 (12×8)) and the 3d. in sheets of 320 (two panes of 160 (18×9)). Both printing stones were constructed from transfers taken from intermediate stones of 24 (6×4). The spacing between stamps is far wider than on the Ham printings. The 3d. panes of 160 were constructed using six complete transfers of 24 and three of 6 with the final impression in the bottom two rows removed.

The 1d. Campbell printings have the frame lines almost completely absent due to lack of pressure when taking transfers. The 3d. retouch, No. 24a, occurs on R.3/5 of the intermediate stone.

CAMPBELL AND FERGUSSON PRINTINGS. Increased postal rates in early 1854 led to a requirement for a 1s. value and in April a contract for this stamp was awarded to Campbell and Fergusson (the new corporate style of J. S. Campbell & Co). Further contracts to print the 1d. and 3d. "Half Lengths" and the 2d. "Queen on Throne" followed. All were produced by lithography with the two "Half Lengths" using transfers from the original engraved die and the 2d. "Queen on Throne" transfers from Ham's original engraved plate.

All Campbell and Fergusson printings were on paper of a poorer quality than that used for the earlier contract.

(Lithographed by Campbell & Fergusson)

1854 (6 July). *Poorer quality paper. Imperf.*

25	3	1s. blue (*shades*)			£650	22·00
		a. Greenish blue (*shades*)			£750	22·00
		b. Indigo-blue			—	£110

No. 25 was produced in sheets of 100 (8×12 with an additional stamp appearing at the end of Rows 6 to 9). The printing stones used each contained four such sheets. They were constructed from an intermediate stone of 40 (8×5) taken from a single engraved die. Each pane of 100 showed two complete transfers of 40, one of 20 and one of a vertical strip of 4.

For this stamp rouletted or perforated see Nos. 54 and 81.

(Lithographed by Campbell & Fergusson)

1854 (July)–**57**. *Poorer quality paper. Imperf.*

26	1	1d. brown (*shades*)			£450	95·00
		a. Brick-red (*shades*)			£600	75·00
		b. Dull red (*shades*)			£650	75·00
27		1d. orange-brown (*shades*) (8.55)			£400	£100
		a. Dull rose-red (*shades*)			£400	60·00
		b. Bright rose-pink			£500	£100
		c. Retouched (6 varieties)			£1400	£400

28	1	1d. pink (*shades*) (2.55)			£375	32·00
		a. Rose (*shades*)			£375	32·00
		b. Lilac-rose (*shades*)			£400	32·00
		c. Dull brown-red (*shades*)			—	£110
		d. Retouched (8 varieties)			£750	£325
29		3d. bright blue (*shades*) (7.57)			£425	50·00
		a. Greenish blue (*shades*)			£375	40·00
		b. Retouch under "C" of "VICTORIA"			—	95·00
30		3d. Prussian blue (*shades*) (11.56)			£500	70·00
		a. Milky blue			£750	£110
		b. Retouch under "C" of "VICTORIA"			—	£225
31		3d. steel-blue (*shades*) (*heavier impression*) (5.55)			—	42·00
		a. Greenish blue (*shades*)			£350	30·00
		b. Blue (*shades*)			£350	30·00
		c. Deep blue (*shades*)			£350	30·00
		d. Indigo (*shades*)			—	38·00

The 1d. was produced in sheets of 400 (2 panes 20×10) constructed from transfers originating from the J. S. Campbell & Co intermediate stone. Each pane contained six complete tranfers of 24, three of 12, two of 8 and one of 4.

The 3d. was produced in sheets of 320 (2 panes of 160) (No. 29), 200 (No. 30) or 400 (2 panes of 200) (No. 31). The stone for No. 29 was constructed from transfers taken from the J. S. Campbell intermediate stone with the retouch on R.3/5 present. The panes of 160 contained six transfers of 24 and three of 6 with the last impression in both rows 8 and 9 removed. Quality of impression is generally poor. The stone for No. 30, once again taken from the Campbell intermediate stone, was laid down in the same combination of transfers as the 1d. value. Impressions from it were, however, so poor that transfers from a new intermediate stone were used for No. 31. Impressions from this stone, on which the panes of 200 were in a similar layout to the 1d., were much further apart than those on the stones used to produce Nos. 29/30.

The Campbell and Fergusson printings of the "Half Lengths" are listed in the order in which they were printed.

CALVERT PRINTINGS. Contracts for the provision of other values required by the postal rate changes in 1853 were placed with Samuel Calvert of Melbourne who used typography as the printing process. Calvert continued to print, and later roulette, stamps for the Victoria Post Office until March 1858 when it was discovered that he had placed some of the stock in pawn.

4   **5**   **6**

(Typographed from woodblocks by Samuel Calvert)

1854 (1 Sept)–**55**. *Imperf.*

32	4	6d. reddish brown (13.9.54)			£225	23·00
		a. Dull orange			£180	18·00
		b. Orange-yellow			£180	19·00
33	5	6d. ("TOO LATE") lilac and green (1.1.55)			£650	£130
34	6	1s. ("REGISTERED") rose-pink and blue (1.12.54)			£800	95·00
35	4	2s. dull bluish green/*pale yellow*			£1100	£240

No. 33 was provided to pay the additional fee on letters posted after the normal closure of the mails. This service was only available in the larger towns; examples are usually postmarked Castlemaine, Geelong or Melbourne. The service was withdrawn on 30 June 1857 and remaining stocks of the "TOO LATE" stamps were used for normal postal purposes.

No. 34 was issued to pay the registration fee and was so used until 5 January 1858 after which remaining stocks were used for normal postage.

These four values were produced from individually-engraved boxwood woodblocks. The 6d. was in sheets of 100 printed by two impressions from two plates of 25. The 2s. was in sheets of 50 from a single plate of 25. The bicoloured "TOO LATE" and "REGISTERED" stamps are unusual in that Calvert used a common woodblock "key" plate of 25 for both values combined with "duty" plates made up from metal stereos. Both values were originally in sheets of 50, but the "REGISTERED" later appeared in sheets of 100 for which a second "key" plate of 25 was utilised.

For these stamps rouletted or perforated see Nos. 53, 55/8, 60/1 and 82.

(Lithographed by Campbell & Fergusson)

1855 (Mar)–**56**. *Poorer quality paper. Imperf.*

(a) *Printings from stones which were not over-used; background around top of throne generally full and detail good*

36	2	2d. lilac (*shades*) (7.55)			£140	19·00
		a. Purple (*shades*)			£140	19·00
		b. "TVO" for "TWO"			£2500	£600

(b) *Early printings from stones which were over-used. Similar characteristics to those above, though detail is not quite so full. Distinctive shades.*

37	2	2d. brown			—	70·00
		a. Brown-purple			£170	22·00
		b. Warm purple			—	22·00
		c. Rose-lilac			—	22·00
		d. Substituted transfer (pair)			—	£600

(c) *Later printings from the same stones used for No. 37 when in a worn condition. Impressions heavy, coarse and overcoloured; details blurred; generally white background around top of throne.*

38	2	2d. dull lilac-mauve (1856)			£170	22·00
		a. Dull mauve			£170	22·00
		b. Grey-violet			—	22·00
		c. Red-lilac			—	24·00
		d. Substituted transfer (pair)			—	£600

(d) *Printings from a stone giving blotchy and unpleasing results, with poor definition. Mainly shows in extra colour patches found on most stamps.*

39	2	2d. dull purple (7.55)			—	40·00
		a. Dull grey-lilac			£180	40·00
		b. On thick card paper			—	£500

The Campbell and Fergusson 2d. "Queen on Throne" printings were in sheets of 200 (4 panes 10 × 5) constructed from transfers taken from the original Ham engraved plate.

Four separate stones were used. On Stone A a creased transfer running through R.4/8, 4/9 and 5/8 caused the "TVO" variety on the stamp from the bottom row of one pane. On Stone C the impression in the first vertical row of one pane were found to be so faulty that they were replaced by substituted transfers taken from elsewhere on the sheet causing abnormal horizontal pairs lettered "UY BF", "TX MQ", "DI WA", "SW GM" and "CH RW". The vertical pairs from the substituted transfers are lettered "UY" over "TX" and "DI" over "SW".

7 Queen on Throne

8 "Emblems"

(Recess Perkins, Bacon & Co, London)

1856 (23 Oct). *Wmk Large Star, W w 1. Imperf.*
40   7   1d. yellow-green   ..   ..   £120   19·00

Supplies of this stamp, and the accompanying 6d. which was only issued rouletted (see No. 73), arrived in the colony at the end of 1854, but the 1d. was not placed on sale until almost two years later.

No. 40 was reprinted from the original plate in 1891. Examples, in either dull yellow-green or bright blue-green, are imperforate and on V over Crown watermarked paper.

(Typographed from electrotypes by Calvert)

1857 (26 Jan–6 Sept). *Imperf.* (a) *Wmk Large Star, W w 1*
41   8   1d. yellow-green (18 Feb) ..   ..   95·00   13·00
    a. Deep green   ..   ..   ..   £110   26·00
    b. Printed on both sides   ..   †   £700
42   4d. vermilion   ..   ..   ..   £250   10·00
    a. Brown-vermilion   ..   ..   £225   9·00
    b. Printed on both sides   ..   †   £700
43   4d. dull red (20 July)   ..   £160   7·50
44   4d. dull rose (6 Sept)   ..   £225   7·50
(b) *No wmk. Good quality medium wove paper*
45   8   2d. pale lilac (25 May)   ..   £170   10·00
    a. Grey-lilac   ..   ..   £170   10·00

Nos. 41/5 were produced in sheets of 120, arranged as four panes of 30 (6×5) (1d. and 4d.) or twelve panes of 10 (2×5) (2d.), using electrotypes taken from a single engraved die of each value. The setting of the 4d. was re-arranged before the printing of Nos. 43/4.

Only two examples of No. 41b and No. 42b have been recorded.

For this printing rouletted or perforated see Nos. 46/7, 50/2, 59, 74 and 77.

ROULETTES AND PERFORATIONS. In August 1857 a rouletting machine was provided at the G.P.O., Melbourne, to enable the counter clerks to separate stamp stocks before sale to the public. This machine produced roulettes of 7½–9 in one direction across six rows at a time. There was also a single wheel device which gauged 7–7½. Both were in use between the earliest known date of 12 August and the end of 1857.

Calvert was granted a separate contract in October 1857 to roulette the stamps he printed, but only Nos. 57/61 had been produced when it was found, in April 1858, that he had pawned a quantity of the sheets. His contracts were terminated and his successor, F. W. Robinson, used a roulette machine of a different gauge before switching to a gauge 12 perforating machine in January 1859.

1857 (12 Aug–Sept). *Rouletted 7–9 by counter clerks at G.P.O., Melbourne.*
46   8   1d. yellow-green (No. 41)   ..   £275   65·00
47   2d. pale lilac (No. 45)   ..   —   £225
    a. Grey-lilac   ..   ..   —   £225
48   1   3d. blue (shades) (No. 24)   ..   —   £180
    a. Retouch under "C" of "VICTORIA"
49   3d. bright blue (shades) (No. 29) ..   —   £190
    a. Greenish blue (shades)   ..   £1000   £170
    b. Retouch under "C" of "VICTORIA"
50   8   4d. vermilion (No. 42)   ..   —   £100
51   4d. dull red (No. 43)   ..   —   38·00
52   4d. dull rose (No. 44) (Sept)   ..   —   26·00
53   4   6d. reddish brown (No. 32)   ..   —   42·00
    a. Dull orange   ..   ..   —   35·00
    b. Orange-yellow   ..   ..   —   42·00
54   3   1s. blue (shades) (No. 25)   ..   —   80·00
    a. Greenish blue   ..   ..   —   80·00
55   6   1s. ("REGISTERED") rose-pink and blue
    (No. 34) £3500   £180
56   4   2s. dull bluish green/pale yellow (No. 35)   £3500   £350

With the exception of the 1s., Nos. 54/a, these stamps are normally found rouletted on one or two sides only.

1857 (Oct). *Rouletted by Calvert.* (a) *Rouletted 7–9 on all four sides and with finer points than No. 53b*
57   4   6d. orange-yellow (No. 32b)   ..   —   55·00
(b) *Serpentine roulette 10–10½*
58   4   6d. orange-yellow (No. 32b)   ..   —   55·00
(c) *Serrated 18–19*
59   8   2d. grey-lilac (No. 45a)   ..   £500   £350
60   4   6d. orange-yellow (No. 32b)   ..   —   55·00
(d) *Compound of serrated 18–19 and serpentine 10–10½*
61   4   6d. orange-yellow (No. 32b)   ..   —   55·00

No. 59 was not covered by the contract given to Calvert, but it is believed to be a test run for the rouletting machine. No. 61 always shows serrated 18–19 on three sides and the serpentine roulette at the top or bottom of the stamp.

(Typo from electrotypes by Calvert)

1858 (14 Jan–Apr). *No wmk. Good quality white wove paper.*
(a) *Rouletted 7–9 on all four sides*
62   8   1d. pale emerald   ..   ..   £300   14·00
    a. Emerald-green   ..   ..   £300   14·00
63   4d. rose-pink (18 Jan)   ..   £200   6·00
    a. Bright rose   ..   ..   £200   6·00
    b. Reddish pink   ..   ..   —   11·00
    c. Imperf horiz (vert pair)   ..   †   £400
(b) *Imperf* (Apr)
64   8   1d. pale emerald   ..   ..   £190   10·00
    a. Emerald-green   ..   ..   —   13·00
65   4d. rose-pink   ..   ..   £250   23·00
    a. Bright rose   ..   ..   —   23·00
    b. Reddish pink   ..   ..   —   30·00

Nos. 62/5 were produced in sheets of 120, arranged as four panes of 30 (6×5).

The Royal Collection contains a used horizontal pair of the 4d. showing the vertical roulettes omitted.

The majority of Nos. 64/5 were issued in April after Calvert's contracts had been terminated, although there is some evidence that imperforate sheets of the 4d., at least, were issued earlier.

For the 1d. of this issue perforated see No. 75.

ROBINSON PRINTINGS. Calvert's contracts were cancelled in April 1858 and the work was then placed with F. W. Robinson, who had unsuccessfully tendered in 1856. The same electrotypes were used, but a perforating machine was introduced from January 1859. Robinson continued to print and perforate stamps under contract until the end of 1859 when the Victoria Post Office purchased his equipment to set up a Stamp Printing Branch and appointed him Printer of Postage Stamps.

(Typo from electrotypes by Robinson)

1858 (May–Dec). (a) *Imperf.* (i) *Coarse quality wove paper.*
66   8   4d. dull rose (oily ink)   ..   —   60·00
(ii) *Smooth vertically-laid paper*
67   8   4d. dull rose (oily ink)   ..   —   23·00
    a. Dull rose-red   ..   ..   —   23·00
68   4d. dull rose-red (normal ink) (20 May)   £400   15·00
(b) *Rouletted 5½–6½.* (i) *Smooth laid paper*
69   8   2d. brown-lilac (shades) (horiz laid) (June)   £120   5·50
    a. Vert laid paper (21 Sept)   ..   £200   9·50
70   2d. violet (horiz laid) (27 Nov)   ..   £150   5·50
    a. Dull violet   ..   ..   £180   18·00
71   4d. pale dull rose (vert laid) (1 June)   £150   3·75
    a. Horiz laid paper   ..   ..   †   £800
    b. Dull rose-red   ..   ..   £120   3·75
    c. Rose-red   ..   ..   £120   3·50
    ca. Serrated 19   ..   ..   †   £350
(ii) *Good quality wove paper*
72   8   1d. yellow-green (24 Dec)   ..   £275   23·00

Nos. 66/72 were produced in sheets of 120, arranged as four panes of 30 (6 × 5).

For stamps of this issue perforated see Nos. 76 and 80.

(Recess Perkins, Bacon & Co, London)

1858 (1 Nov). *Wmk Large Star, W w 1. Rouletted 5½–6½.*
73   7   6d. bright blue   ..   ..   £120   12·00
    a. Light blue   ..   ..   £160   24·00

No. 73 was received from London at the same time as the 1d., No. 40, but was kept in store until November 1858 when the stock was rouletted by Robinson. When issued the gum was in a poor state.

Imperforate examples exist from Perkins, Bacon remainders. Imperforate reprints, in shades of indigo, were made from the original plate in 1891 on V over Crown watermarked paper.

1859 (Jan–May). *P* 12 *by Robinson.*
74   8   1d. yellow-green (No. 41)   ..   —   £275
75   1d. emerald-green (No. 64a)   ..   —   £275
    a. Imperf between (horiz pair)
76   1d. yellow-green (as No. 72) (11 Jan)   £160   11·00
    a. Imperf horiz (vert pair)   ..   —   £300
    b. Thin, glazed ("Bordeaux") paper   †   £150
77   2d. pale lilac (No. 45)   ..   —   £225
    a. Grey-lilac   ..   ..   —   £225
78   1   3d. blue (shades) (No. 24) (2 Feb)   £750   £110
    a. Retouch under "C" of "VICTORIA"   —   £250
79   3d. greenish blue (shades) (No. 29a)   †   £350
    a. Retouch under "C" of "VICTORIA"   † £1000
80   8   4d. dull rose-red (No. 68)   ..   —   £300
81   3   1s. blue (shades) (No. 25) (4 Feb)   £130   15·00
    a. Greenish blue   ..   ..   £150   12·00
    b. Indigo-blue   ..   ..   —   30·00
82   4   2s. dull bluish green/pale yellow (No. 35)
    (May)   ..   ..   ..   £250   30·00

The 1s. was reprinted in 1891 using transfers taken from the original die. These reprints were on V over Crown watermarked paper and perforated 12½.

For perforated 6d. black and 2s. blue both as Type 4 see Nos. 102 and 129/30.

(Typo from electrotypes by Robinson)

1859 (17 Feb–Dec). *P* 12. (a) *Good quality wove paper*
83   8   4d. dull rose   ..   ..   £150   3·00
    a. Roul 5½–6½   ..   ..   †   £800
(b) *Poorer quality wove paper*
84   8   1d. dull green (July)   ..   £120   7·50
    a. Green (11 Nov)   ..   ..   £120   7·50
85   4d. rose-carmine (16 July)   ..   £150   5·00
    a. Rose-pink (thick paper) (30 Nov)   —   9·00
(c) *Horizontally laid paper with the lines wide apart*
86   8   1d. dull green (July)   ..   ..
    a. Laid lines close together   ..   —   15·00
    b. Green (shades) (Oct)   ..   £130   9·50
87   4d. rose-pink (shades) (23 Dec)   £120   7·50
    a. Laid lines close together   ..   —   10·00

STAMP PRINTING BRANCH. On 1 January 1860 F. W. Robinson was appointed Printer of Postage Stamps and his equipment purchased by the Post Office to establish the Stamp Printing Branch. All later Victoria issues were printed by the Branch which became part of the Victoria Government Printing Office in December 1885. In 1909 the Commonwealth Stamp Printing Office under J. B. Cooke was established in Melbourne and produced stamps for both the states and Commonwealth until 1918.

9

10   11

(Des and eng F. Grosse. Typo from electrotypes)

1860 (31 Jan)–**66**. *P* 12. (a) *No wmk*
88   9   3d. deep blue (horiz laid paper)   ..   £300   23·00
    a. Light blue
89   4d. rose-pink (thin glazed Bordeaux paper)
    (21.4.60)   ..   ..   ..   —   8·00
    a. Rose   ..   ..   ..   £275   13·00
    ab. Thick coarse paper (7.60)   ..   £275   8·00
(b) *On paper made by T. H. Saunders of London wmkd with the appropriate value in words as W* 10
90   9   3d. pale blue (1.61)   ..   ..   £120   7·00
    a. Bright blue (10.61)   ..   ..   £120   6·00
    b. Blue (4.63)   ..   ..   £130   6·00
    c. Deep blue (4.64)   ..   ..   £130   6·00
    d. "TRREE" for "THREE" in wmk
91   3d. maroon (13.2.66)   ..   ..   £100   25·00
    a. Perf 13   ..   ..   ..   £120   28·00
92   4d. rose-pink (1.8.60)   ..   ..   —   3·25
    a. Rose-red   ..   ..   80·00   3·25
    b. Rose-carmine   ..   ..   —   8·00
    c. Dull rose   ..   ..   80·00   3·25
    d. Printed on "FIVE SHILLINGS"
    diagonal wmk paper (11.9.62) ..   £1500   20·00
93   6d. orange (25.10.60) £3000   £200
94   6d. black (20.8.61)   ..   ..   £110   5·50
    a. Grey-black   ..   ..   £110   5·50
(c) *On paper made by De La Rue wmkd with the appropriate value as a single-lined numeral as W* 11
95   9   4d. dull rose-pink (9.10.62)   ..   90·00   5·00
    a. Dull rose   ..   ..   95·00   5·50
    b. Rose-red   ..   ..   —   5·00
    c. Roul 8 (28.7.63)   ..   ..   —   £250
    d. Imperf (31.7.63)   ..   ..   —   60·00
    e. Perf 13×12

All three values were produced in sheets of 120, initially as four panes of 30 (6×5). Printings of the 3d. from 1864 were in a changed format of six panes of 20 (4×5).

The "TRREE" watermark error comes from early printings of No. 90 on R. 10/7.

Two examples of the 4d. on Saunders paper are known bisected in 1863, but such use was unauthorised.

Nos. 95c/e were issued during July and August 1863 when the normal perforating machine had broken down.

Reprints, from new plates, were made of the 3d. and 4d. in 1891 on "V over Crown" paper and perforated 12½.

1860 (Apr)–**63**. *P* 12. (a) *No wmk*
96   8   1d. bright green (horiz laid paper)
97   1d. bright green (thin, glazed Bordeaux
    paper) (25.5.60)   ..   ..   —   22·00
(b) *On paper made by T. H. Saunders of London wmkd with the appropriate value in words as W* 10
98   8   1d. pale yellowish green (8.7.60) ..   65·00   4·50
    a. Yellow-green   ..   ..   75·00   4·75
    b. Error. Wmkd "FOUR PENCE"   †   —
99   2d. brown-lilac (7.7.61)   ..   —   17·00
100   2d. bluish slate (8.61)   ..   £100   4·75
    a. Greyish lilac (9.61)   ..   £110   4·75
    b. Slate-grey (1.62)   ..   ..   —   4·75
    c. Printed on "THREE PENCE" wmkd
    paper. Pale slate (27.12.62)   ..   £110   10·00
    ca. Bluish grey (2.63)   ..   ..   £110   12·00
(c) *On paper made by De La Rue wmkd single-lined "2", W* 11
101   8   2d. dull reddish lilac (24.4.63)   ..   £160   5·50
    a. Grey-lilac (10.63)   ..   ..   £150   12·00
    ab. Error. Wmkd "6"   ..   ..   † £4000
    b. Grey-violet (11.63)   ..   ..   £100   9·00
    c. Slate (12.63)   ..   ..   £150   18·00

The only confirmed example of No. 98b is in the Royal Collection. There have been unconfirmed reports of the existence of another.

1861 (22 June). *On paper made by T. H. Saunders of London wmkd "SIX PENCE" as W* 10. *P* 12.
102   4   6d. black   ..   ..   ..   £160   38·00

No. 102 was produced as an emergency measure after the decision had been taken to change the colour of the current 6d. from orange (No. 93) to black (No. 94). During the changeover the old Calvert "woodblock" plates were pressed into service to provide two month's supply.

MINIMUM PRICE

The minimum price quote is 10p which represents a handling charge rather than a basis for valuing common stamps. For further notes about prices see introductory pages.

12   13

(Des, eng and electrotyped De Gruchy & Leigh, Melbourne. Typo)

1861 (1 Oct)–64. *P* 12. (*a*) *On paper made by T. H. Saunders of London wmkd "ONE PENNY" as* W 10

103 **12** 1d. pale green	75·00	6·00
a. Olive-green	—	6·50

(*b*) *On paper made by De La Rue wmkd single-lined "1" as* W 11

104 **12** 1d. olive-green (1.2.63)	60·00	5·00
a. Pale green (9.63)	60·00	5·00
b. Apple-green (4.64)	60·00	5·00

(*c*) *On paper supplied to Tasmania by Perkins, Bacon and wmkd double-lined "1", W 4 of Tasmania*

105 **12** 1d. yellow-green (10.12.63)	£110	7·50
a. Dull green	—	7·50
b. Imperf between (pair)	†	

All printings were in sheets of 120 containing four panes of 30 (6×5).

Reprints from new plates were made in 1891 on paper watermarked "V over Crown" and perforated 12½.

(Frame die eng F. Grosse. Typo from electrotypes)

1862 (26 Apr)–64. *Centre vignette cut from T* 9 *with a new frame as T* 13.

(*a*) *On paper made by T. H. Saunders of London wmkd "SIX PENCE" as* W 10. *P* 12

106 **13** 6d. grey	80·00	5·00
a. Grey-black	80·00	6·50
b. Jet-black	85·00	7·50

(*b*) *On paper made by De La Rue wmkd with single-lined "6" as* W 11

107 **13** 6d. grey (*p* 12) (18.6.63)	70·00	4·50
a. Jet-black	—	5·50
b. Grey-black	70·00	4·75
c. Perf 13. Jet-black	80·00	5·00
ca. Grey-black	80·00	5·50

Printings before August 1863 were in sheets of 120 containing four panes of 30 (6×5). For subsequent printings of No. 107 the format was changed to six panes of 20 (4×5).

Reprints from new plates were made in 1891 on paper watermarked "V over Crown" and perforated 12½.

SINGLE-LINED NUMERAL WATERMARK PAPERS.
The first consignment of this paper, showing watermarks as W 11, arrived in Victoria during October 1862. Four further consignments followed, all but the last supplied by De La Rue.

The complexity of the scheme for different watermarks for each value, together with the time required to obtain further supplies from Great Britain, resulted in the emergency use of paper obtained from Tasmania and of the wrong numeral watermark on certain printings.

The final order for this paper was placed, in error with the firm of T. H. Saunders of London. Although the actual watermarks are the same (the dandy rolls were the property of the Victoria Government and supplied to each firm in turn) there are considerable differences between the two types of paper. That manufactured by Saunders is of a more even quality and is smoother, thicker, less brittle and less white than the De La Rue type.

De La Rue supplied white paper watermarked "1", "2", "4", "6" and "8", blue paper watermarked "1" and green paper watermarked "2".

The Saunders consignment of October 1865 contained white paper watermarked "1", "4" and "6", blue paper watermarked "1", green paper watermarked "2" and pink paper watermarked "10".

It is helpful for comparison purposes to note that all white paper watermarked "2" or "8" can only be De La Rue and all pink paper watermarked "10" can only be Saunders.

14   15   16

17   18

(Des and eng F. Grosse. Typo from electrotypes)

1863–74. *"Laureated" series.*

(*a*) *On paper made by De La Rue wmkd with the appropriate value in single-lined numerals as* W 11

108 **14** 1d. pale green (*p* 12) (9.9.64)	75·00	7·00
a. Perf 12½×12 (9.64)		†
b. Perf 13 (10.10.64)	70·00	3·50
c. Bluish green (*p* 13) (12.64)	65·00	2·75
ca. Printed double		† £550
d. Green (*p* 12) (7.65)	70·00	3·00
da. Perf 13	65·00	3·50
e. Deep green (*p* 12) (12.65)	85·00	3·00
ea. Perf 13	—	3·00
eb. Perf 12×13	—	6·00
f. Bright yellow-green (*p* 13) (1.67)	—	15·00

109 **14** 2d. violet (*p* 12) (1.4.64)	65·00	4·75
a. Dull violet (*p* 12) (10.64)	70·00	5·00
ab. Perf 12½×12		
ac. Perf 12½		
ad. Perf 13	70·00	3·75
b. Dull lilac (*p* 13) (4.65)	55·00	3·50
ba. Perf 12 (7.66)	—	6·00
bb. Perf 12×13 (7.66)	—	7·50
c. Reddish mauve (*p* 13) (11.65)	60·00	3·50
d. Rose-lilac (*p* 13) (1.66)	55·00	4·75
da. Perf 12×13 or 13×12 (2.66)	55·00	4·75
e. Grey (*p* 12) (7.66)	85·00	6·00
ea. Perf 13	55·00	3·00
110 4d. deep rose (*p* 12) (11.9.63)	£110	3·50
a. Printed double	†	£500
b. Rose-pink (*p* 12) (9.63)	85·00	2·50
c. Pink (*p* 12) (7.5.64)	85·00	2·50
ca. Error. Wmkd single-lined "8"		† £2000
cb. Perf 12½×12 (9.64)		
d. Dull rose (*p* 13) (10.64)	75·00	2·50
e. Dull rose-red (*p* 13) (2.65)	75·00	2·50
ea. Perf 12 (8.65)	£120	75·00
111 **16** 6d. blue (*p* 12) (13.2.66)	30·00	4·50
a. Perf 13	30·00	2·75
b. Perf 12×13	28·00	2·00
112 **14** 8d. orange (*p* 13) (22.2.65)	£300	50·00
113 **17** 1s. blue/*blue* (*p* 13) (10.4.65)	£100	3·50
a. Perf 12×13 (4.66)	£100	3·50
ab. Imperf between (vert pair)		† £1200
b. Bright blue/*blue* (*p* 13) (6.67)	85·00	3·00
c. Indigo-blue/*blue* (*p* 13) (3.68)	—	2·75
d. Dull blue/*blue* (*p* 12) (6.74)	—	3·50

(*b*) *Emergency printings on Perkins, Bacon paper borrowed from Tasmania wmkd double-lined "4" as* W 4 *of Tasmania*

114 **14** 4d. deep rose (*p* 12) (7.1.64)	£110	3·75
a. Pale rose (*p* 12)	—	3·25
b. Dull reddish rose (*p* 13) (11.8.65)	£110	3·50
ba. Perf 12	—	3·75
bb. Perf 12×13	—	11·00
c. Red (*p* 13) (4.12.65)	£120	3·50

(*c*) *Emergency printings on De La Rue paper as* W 11, *but showing incorrect single-lined numeral. P* 13

115 **14** 1d. brt yellow-grn (*wmkd* "8") (27.12.66)	£120	10·00
116 1d. brt yellow-green (*wmkd* "6") (6.67)	—	15·00
117 2d. grey (*wmkd* "8") (18.1.67)	£110	5·00
118 **15** 3d. lilac (*wmkd* "8") (29.9.66)	£110	22·00
119 **16** 10d. grey (*wmkd* "8") (21.10.65)	£450	£100
a. Grey-black	£450	£100

(*d*) *On paper made by T. H. Saunders wmkd with the appropriate value in single-lined numerals as* W 11

120 **14** 1d. deep yellow-green (*p* 12×13) (1.66)	£120	6·00
a. Perf 13 (3.66)	65·00	3·00
b. Perf 12 (7.66)	—	7·00
121 4d. rose-red (*p* 13) (12.12.65)	75·00	3·00
a. Perf 12×13 or 13×12 (2.66)	£110	5·50
b. Perf 12 (4.66)	—	4·75
122 **16** 6d. blue (*p* 13) (28.5.66)	27·00	1·50
a. Perf 12	30·00	3·00
b. Perf 12×13	27·00	1·75
ba. Imperf between (horiz pair)	†	£600
123 10d. dull purple/*pink* (*p* 13) (22.3.66)	85·00	5·00
a. Perf 12×13	£120	5·50
b. Blackish brown/*pink* (*p* 13) (12.69)	90·00	5·50
c. Purple-brown/*pink* (*p* 13) (11.70)		
124 **17** 1s. bright blue/*blue* (*p* 13) (5.12.70)	55·00	2·50
a. Pale dull blue/*blue* (*p* 12) (1.73)	£120	3·25
ab. Perf 13	—	7·00
b. Indigo-blue/*blue* (*p* 12) (9.73)	—	5·00
ba. Perf 13	55·00	3·25

(*e*) *Emergency printings on Saunders paper as* W 11, *but showing incorrect single-lined numeral. P* 13

125 **14** 1d. brt yellow-green (*wmkd* "4") (6.3.67)	85·00	7·50
126 1d. brt yellow-green (*wmkd* "6") (6.67)	£120	13·00
127 2d. grey (*wmkd* "4") (21.2.67)	75·00	5·00
128 2d. grey (*wmkd* "6") (13.5.67)	£130	6·00

The 1d., 2d., 4d. and 8d. were originally produced in sheets of 120 containing eight panes of 15 (3×5). The 3d. and 6d. were in sheets of 120 (12×10) and the 1d. (from February 1866), 2d. (from July 1866) and 4d. (from April 1866) subsequently changed to this format. The 10d. was in sheets of 120 containing twenty panes of 6 (2×3). The 1s. was originally in sheets of 60 containing three panes of 20 (4×5), but this changed to 120 (12×10) in April 1866.

Only single examples are thought to exist of Nos. 110a, 110ca, 113ab, and 122ba and two of No. 108ca.

For later emergency printings on these papers see Nos.153/66.

(Typo from composite woodblock and electrotype plate)

1864 (22 Nov)–80. (*a*) *On De La Rue paper wmkd single-lined "2" as* W 11

129 **4** 2s. light blue/*green* (*p* 13) (22.11.64)	£150	5·50
a. Dark blue/*green* (*p* 12) (9.65)	£170	9·00
ab. Perf 13 (6.66)	£150	5·50
b. Blue/*green* (*p* 13) (6.68)	£140	4·75
c. Greenish blue/*green* (*p* 13) (7.73)	£140	4·75
ca. Perf 12	£160	6·00
d. Deep greenish blue/*green* (*p* 12½)	£140	4·75

(*b*) *On Saunders paper wmkd single-lined "2" as* W 11

130 **4** 2s. dark blue/*green* (*p* 13) (23.11.67)	£160	6·00
a. Blue/*green* (*p* 13) (10.71)	£160	4·75
ab. Perf 12 (8.74)	£180	6·00
c. Deep greenish blue/*green* (*p* 12½) (7.80)	£140	4·75

Nos. 129/30 were produced in sheets of 30 containing two panes of 15 (3×5). The plate contained eighteen of the original woodblock impressions and twelve electrotypes taken from them.

19   20

V OVER CROWN WATERMARKS. The changeover from the numeral watermarks to a general type to be used for all values was first suggested at the end of 1865, but the first supplies did not reach Melbourne until April 1867. Five different versions were used before the V over Crown watermark was superseded by the Commonwealth type in 1905. The five versions are listed as follows:

Type **19** De La Rue paper supplied 1867 to 1882. Shows four points at the top of the crown with the left and right ornaments diamond-shaped

Type **33** De La Rue paper supplied 1882 to 1895. No points at the top of the crown with the left and right ornaments oval-shaped

Type **82** Waterlow paper supplied 1896 to 1899. Wide base to crown

Type **85** Waterlow paper used for postal issues 1899 to 1905. Wide top to crown

Type **104** James Spicer and Sons paper used for postal issues August and September 1912. Narrow crown

(Typo from electrotypes)

1867–81. *Wmk V over Crown*, W 19. (*a*) *P* 13

131 **14** 1d. bright yellow-green (10.8.67)	65·00	2·50
a. Bright olive-green (1.69)	95·00	14·00
b. Yellow-green (4.69)	65·00	2·10
c. Dull green (3.70)	65·00	2·10
d. Pale green (10.70)	60·00	2·10
e. Grass-green (1871)	60·00	2·40
f. Bluish green (shades) (7.72)	60·00	2·40
g. Green (shades) (9.72)	60·00	2·25
132 2d. slate-grey (shades) (26.8.67)	70·00	3·50
a. Grey-lilac (29.1.68)	70·00	4·75
b. Lilac (26.8.68)	50·00	3·25
c. Dull mauve (shades) (10.68)	50·00	3·25
d. Lilac-grey (1.69)	—	3·50
e. Lilac-rose (2.69)	55·00	3·00
f. Mauve (4.69)	70·00	3·25
g. Red-lilac (5.69)	55·00	3·00
h. Dull lilac (6.69)	55·00	2·50
i. Silver-grey (9.69)	£110	7·00
133 **15** 3d. lilac (28.8.67)	£200	24·00
a. Grey-lilac (6.68)	£225	26·00
134 3d. yellow-orange (12.6.69)	20·00	5·00
a. Dull orange (6.70)	18·00	1·90
b. Orange (3.73)	—	2·25
c. Bright orange (3.73)	23·00	2·50
d. Orange-brown (glazed paper) (10.78)	23·00	5·50
135 **14** 4d. dull rose (28.11.67)	75·00	5·00
a. Aniline red (shades) (21.4.69)	—	6·50
b. Rose-pink (11.69)	—	5·00
c. Rose (shades) (8.71)	70·00	3·00
d. Dull rose (glazed paper) (5.3.79)	70·00	3·00
e. Dull rose-red (glazed paper) (11.79)	—	3·00
f. Bright lilac-rose (aniline) (glazed paper) (2.80)	75·00	3·75
g. Rosine (aniline) (glazed paper) (9.80)	£200	5·00
136 **16** 6d. deep blue (15.1.68)	—	3·00
a. Blue (21.12.68)	17·00	1·25
b. Indigo-blue (10.69)	17·00	1·25
c. Prussian blue (9.72)	16·00	1·25
d. Indigo (4.73)	17·00	1·40
e. Dull blue (worn plate) (3.74)	—	1·25
f. Dull ultramarine (2.12.75)	24·00	1·25
g. Light Prussian blue (12.75)	35·00	1·25
h. Dull violet-blue (7.77)	—	5·50
i. Blue (glazed paper) (6.78)	26·00	1·25
j. Dull milky-blue (glazed paper) (9.79)	24·00	1·25
k. Prussian blue (glazed paper) (4.80)	—	1·25
l. Light blue (glazed paper) (4.81)	26·00	1·25
m. Deep blue (glazed paper) (10.81)	24·00	1·25
137 **14** 8d. lilac-brown/*pink* (24.1.77)	75·00	5·50
a. Purple-brown/*pink* (2.78)	75·00	5·50
b. Chocolate/*pink* (8.78)	80·00	5·00
ba. Compound perf 13×12	†	£325
c. Red-brown/*pink* (12.78)	75·00	5·00
138 **17** 1s. light blue/*blue* (11.5.75)	£100	7·00
139 **18** 5s. blue/*yellow* (26.12.67)	£1600	£300
a. Wmk reversed	—	£500
140 5s. indigo-blue and carmine (I) (8.10.68)	£200	17·00
a. Blue and carmine (4.69)	£170	13·00
b. Pale bright blue and carmine (glazed paper) (24.7.77)	—	17·00
c. Grey-blue and carmine (glazed paper) (4.78)	£160	15·00
d. Wmk sideways. Deep lavender-blue and carmine (glazed paper) (4.6.80)	£160	15·00
141 5s. bright blue and red (II) (glazed paper) (12.5.81)	£140	13·00
a. Indigo-blue and red (glazed paper)	—	17·00

(*b*) *P* 12

142 **14** 1d. pale green (10.71)	70·00	2·40
a. Grass-green (1871)	60·00	2·40
b. Bluish green (shades) (7.72)	—	2·40
c. Green (shades) (9.72)	60·00	2·25
143 **15** 3d. dull orange (5.72)	18·00	20·00
a. Orange (3.73)	—	2·10
b. Bright orange (3.73)	—	2·50
c. Dull orange-yellow (glazed paper) (12.80)		
144 **14** 4d. rose (shades) (8.71)	70·00	3·00
a. Compound perf 12×13	—	£325
b. Dull rose (glazed paper) (3.79)	—	3·00
c. Dull rose-red (glazed paper) (11.79)	—	3·00
d. Bright lilac-rose (aniline) (glazed paper) (2.80)	—	6·50
e. Rosine (aniline) (glazed paper) (9.80)	80·00	4·75
145 **16** 6d. deep blue (2.2.72)	—	1·75
a. Prussian blue (9.72)	18·00	1·25
b. Indigo (4.73)	24·00	1·75
c. Dull blue (worn plate) (3.74)	—	1·25
d. Blue (glazed paper) (6.78)	—	1·25
e. Dull milky-blue (glazed paper) (9.79)	—	1·25
f. Light blue (glazed paper) (4.81)	—	2·40
146 **14** 8d. red-brn/*pink* (glazed paper) (11.80)	75·00	5·50
147 **17** 1s. light blue/*blue* (5.75)	—	6·50
148 **18** 5s. bright blue and red (II) (glazed paper) (5.81)	£130	13·00
a. Indigo-blue and red	£225	17·00

(*c*) *P* 12½

149 **15** 3d. dull orange-yellow (glazed paper) (12.80)	26·00	2·75
150 **14** 4d. rosine (aniline) (glazed paper) (9.80)		

151 **16** 6d. Prussian blue (*glazed paper*) (4.80) ..
    a. Light blue (glazed paper) (4.81) ..
    b. Deep blue (glazed paper) (10.81) .. 24.00 1.25
152 **14** 8d. lilac-brown/*pink* (8.77) 75.00 5.50
    a. Red-brown/pink (glazed paper) (11.80) † —

The same electrotypes as the previous issues were used for this series with the exception of the 5s. which was a new value. The 1d., 2d., 3d., 4d., 6d. and 1s. plates were arranged to print sheets of 120 (12×10) and the 8d. conformed to this when reintroduced in 1877. New plates for the 1d. (1868), 2d.(1869) and 6d. (1875) were constructed by Robinson's successor, J. P. Atkinson, using the improved facilities then available.

Atkinson was also responsible for the printing of the 5s. value. The original printings in blue on yellow paper were produced in sheets of 25, or possibly 50, using a vertical strip of five electrotypes. Due to its size the 5s. did not exactly fit the watermarked paper and, to avoid a preprinted sheet number, a proportion of the printing was made on the back of the paper creating the reversed watermark variety, No. 139a. These varieties occur in the first printing only as Atkinson created a plate of 25 for the second printing in March 1868. Printings of the 5s. bicoloured to April 1880 were made from electrotypes taken from the monocoloured plate. These showed a blue line beneath the crown (Type I). In early 1881 this plate was found to be too worn for further use and a new die was made from which a plate of 100 was constructed. Stamps from this plate are without the blue line beneath the crown (Type II).

PERFORATIONS. Various perforating machines were in use during this period. The use of line machines gauging 12 ceased around 1883. Of the line machines gauging 13 two were converted to comb types in 1873 and were eventually replaced by the 12½ gauge line and comb machines first used in 1876.

(Typo from electrotypes)

1867–70. *Emergency printings on various papers due to shortages of V over Crown paper.* P 13.

(a) Perkins, Bacon paper borrowed from Tasmania. Wmkd double-lined numerals as W 4 of Tasmania
153 **14** 1d. pale yellowish green (*wmkd "1"*)
    (24.9.67) 65.00 3.50
    a. Deep yellow-green (10.67) .. 65.00 3.50
154 1d. pale yellow-green (*wmkd "4"*) (27.5.68) £1300 80.00
155 1d. grey-lilac (*wmkd "4"*) (3.2.68) .. £110 4.25
    a. Slate (4.68) £110 3.50
    b. Mauve (7.68) 4.50
156 2d. mauve (*wmkd "1"*) (30.6.68) .. £110 5.50
157 **15** 3d. grey-lilac (*wmkd "1"*) (8.68) .. £150 35.00
158 **14** 4d. dull rose-red (*wmkd "4"*) (5.68) .. £110 5.00
159 **16** 6d. blue (*wmkd "4"*) (20.6.68) .. £150 13.00
    a. Indigo-blue 15.00
160 6d. blue (*wmkd "1"*) (28.7.68) .. 55.00 4.25
161 6d. dull blue (*wmkd "2"*) (1870) .. †£2250

(b) Saunders paper. Wmkd in words as W 10
162 **14** 1d. pale yellow-green (wmkd "SIX
    PENCE") (23.3.68) £375 16.00
163 2d. slate-grey (*wmkd "SIX PENCE"*)
    (6.68) .. .. .. †£2500
164 **16** 6d. blue (*wmkd "SIX PENCE"*) (20.5.68) £250 12.00
    a. Indigo-blue .. .. .. — 16.00
165 6d. dull blue (*wmkd "THREE PENCE"*)
    (6.12.69) £130 6.00
    a. Deep blue 7.00
166 6d. dull blue (*wmkd "FOUR PENCE"*)
    (21.5.70) £250 23.00
    a. Deep blue .. .. .. — 24.00

(c) V over Crown, W 19, coloured paper
167 **14** 2d. mauve/*lilac* (7.68) 65.00 6.50
    a. Lilac/lilac 65.00 6.00

(d) Saunders single-lined numeral "4" as W 11
168 **16** 6d. dull blue (21.5.70) .. .. †£1600
The supply of paper was so short during 1868 that many odds and ends were utilised. Nos. 161 (five known), 163 (one known) and 168 (ten known) are the rarest of these emergency printings.

(Printed in Melbourne from a double electrotyped plate of 240 supplied by D.L.R.)

1870 (28 Jan)–73. *Wmk V over Crown, W 19.*
169 **20** 2d. brown-lilac (*p 13*) 55.00 1.50
    a. Dull lilac-mauve (9.70) .. 45.00 1.00
    b. Mauve (worn plate) (3.73) .. 45.00 1.25
170 2d. dull lilac-mauve (*p 12*) (28.7.71) .. 55.00 1.50
    a. Mauve (worn plate) (3.73) .. 55.00 1.00

9   9

NINEPENCE
(21)

1871 (22 Apr). *No. 123c surch with T 21 in blue.*
171 **16** 9d. on 10d. purple-brown/*pink* .. £300 10.00
    a. Blackish brown/pink £400 12.00
    b. Surch double .. .. .. † £800

22	23	24
25	26	27

(Des and eng W. Bell. Typo from electrotyped plates)
1873 (25 Mar)–74. *Saunders paper wmkd single-lined "10" as W 11.*
172 **25** 9d. pale brown/*pink* (*p 13*) .. 60.00 7.50
    a. Red-brown/pink (7.74) .. 55.00 8.00
173 9d. pale brown/*pink* (*p 12*) .. 65.00 11.00

½   ½

HALF
(28)

1873 (25 June). *No. 131g surch with T 28 in red.*
174 **14** ½d. on 1d. green (*p 13*) 42.00 12.00
    a. Grass-green 45.00 12.00
    b. Short "1" at right (R. 1/3) .. — 70.00
175 ½d. on 1d. green (*p 12*) 55.00 14.00
    a. Grass-green 55.00 14.00
    b. Short "1" at right (R. 1/3) .. — 75.00

Die I   Die II

Two Dies of 2d.:
Die I. Single-lined outer oval
Die II. Double-lined outer oval

(Des and eng W. Bell. Typo from electrotyped plates)
1873–87. *Wmk V over Crown, W 19, (sideways on ½d.).*
(a) P 13
176 **22** ½d. rose-red (10.2.74) 6.50 70
    a. Lilac-rose (1874) 7.00 90
    b. Rosine (shades) (glazed paper)
    (12.80) 5.50 70
    c. Pale red (glazed paper) (1882) 6.50 60
    d. Mixed perf 13 and 12 .. † £250
177 **23** 1d. dull bluish green (14.12.75) .. 14.00 85
    a. Green (shades) (1877) .. 14.00 80
    b. Yellow-green (glazed paper) (1878) 14.00 65
178 **24** 2d. deep lilac-mauve (I) (1.10.73) .. 18.00 45
    a. Dull violet-mauve 18.00 45
    b. Dull mauve 18.00 45
    c. Pale mauve (worn plate) (glazed paper) (1.79) 19.00 60
    d. Mixed perf 13 and 12 .. £130 £100
179 2d. lilac-mauve (II) (*glazed paper*)
    (17.12.78) 17.00 45
    a. Grey-mauve (1.80) 50
    b. Pale mauve (6.80) .. 26.00 50
    c. Vert pair, lower stamp imperf horiz † £1200
180 **26** 1s. indigo-blue/*blue* (16.8.76) .. 48.00 3.00
    a. Deep blue/blue (7.77) .. 50.00 3.00
    b. Pale blue/blue (3.80) .. 55.00 3.00
    c. Bright blue/blue (9.80) .. 60.00 7.50
    d. Bright blue/blue (glazed paper)
    (21.11.83) 60.00 5.00
    e. Pale blue/blue (glazed paper) (7.84)
    f. Mixed perf 13 and 12 .. † —

(b) P 12
181 **22** ½d. rose-red (1874) 7.00 90
    a. Lilac-rose (1874) 6.50 90
    b. Rosine (shades) (glazed paper) (12.80) 6.50 60
    c. Pale red (glazed paper) (1882) 6.50 65
182 **23** 1d. dull bluish green (1875) .. 15.00 1.00
    a. Green (shades) (1877) .. 14.00 5.00
    b. Yellow-green (glazed paper) (1878) — 2.00
183 **24** 2d. deep lilac-mauve (I) (1873) .. — 1.75
    a. Dull violet-mauve .. .. — 1.60
    b. Dull mauve 22.00 60
    c. Pale mauve (worn plate) (glazed paper) (1879) .. .. — 75
184 2d. lilac-mauve (II) (*glazed paper*) (1878) 23.00 45
    a. Grey-mauve (glazed paper) (1880) .. — 50
    b. Pale mauve (glazed paper) (1880) .. — 1.50
185 **25** 9d. lilac-brown/*pink* (1.12.75) .. £100 12.00
186 **26** 1s. deep blue/*blue* (1880) .. .. — 7.50
    a. Bright blue/blue (1880) .. — 7.50

(c) P 12½
187 **22** ½d. rosine (*shades*) (*glazed paper*) (1880)
    a. Pale red (glazed paper) (1882) ..
188 **23** 1d. yellow-green (*glazed paper*) (1880)
189 **24** 2d. grey-mauve (II) (*glazed paper*) (1880)
    a. Pale mauve (1880) ..
190 **27** 2s. deep blue (*glazed paper*)
    (8.7.81) £120 18.00
    a. Pale blue/green (glazed paper) (4.83)
    ab. Wmk sideways £130 22.00
    b. Ultramarine/green (glazed paper)
    (6.84) .. .. .. — 28.00
    ba. Wmk sideways .. .. — 48.00

8d   8d

EIGHTPENCE
(29)

1876 (1 July). *No. 185 surch with T 29.*
191 **25** 8d. on 9d. lilac-brown/*pink* .. £160 15.00
    a. "F.IGHTPENCE" .. .. — £180
No. 191a was caused by a broken "E" and it occurred once in each sheet of 120.

1877 (24 Jan). *Saunders paper wmkd "10" as W 11.*
192 **14** 8d. lilac-brown/*pink* (*p 13*) .. — £500
    a. Purple-brown/pink (2.78) .. £100 8.00
    b. Chocolate/pink (8.78) .. † £600
    c. Red-brown/pink (8.79) .. 85.00 5.00
193 8d. red-brown/*pink* (*p 12*) (8.79) .. — 8.00
194 **23** 8d. red-brown/*pink* (*p 12½*) (8.79) .. — 50.00
Nos. 192/4 occur amongst the V over Crown printings, the two types of pink paper having become mixed.

1878. *Emergency printings on coloured papers wmkd V over Crown, W 19, (sideways on ½d.). P 13.*
195 **22** ½d. rose-red/*pink* (1.3.78) .. 23.00 10.00
196 **23** 1d. yellow-green/*yellow* (5.3.78) .. 75.00 11.00
197 1d. yellow-green/*drab* (5.4.78) .. £100 42.00
198 **24** 2d. dull violet-mauve/*lilac* (21.2.78) — £400
199 2d. dull violet-mauve/*green* (23.2.78) £130 11.00
200 2d. dull violet-mauve/*brown* (21.3.78) £120 11.00
There was a shortage of white V over Crown, W 19, watermarked paper in the early months of 1878 and various coloured papers were used for printings of the ½d., 1d. and 2d. values until fresh stocks of white paper were received.

30	31	32

(Des and eng C. Naish. Typo from electrotyped plates)
1880 (3 Nov)–84. *Wmk V over Crown, W 19.*
201 **30** 1d. green (*p 12½*) (2.84) 90.00 7.50
202 **31** 2d. sepia (*p 12½*) 18.00 55
    a. Sepia-brown (2.81) .. 16.00 55
    b. Brown (aniline) (5.81) .. 19.00 55
    c. Dull black-brown (10.81) .. — 55
    d. Dull grey-brown (3.82) .. 15.00 55
203 2d. sepia (*p 13*)
    a. Mixed perf 13 and 12 .. † £250
204 2d. sepia (*p 12*) .. .. — 38.00
    a. Sepia-brown (2.81) .. — 38.00
    b. Brown (aniline) (5.81) .. — 38.00
205 2d. mauve (*worn plate*) (*p 12½*) (2.84) .. — 5.00
206 **32** 4d. rose-carmine (*p 12½*) (10.81) .. 50.00 5.00
    a. Rosine (7.82) 50.00 4.50
Nos. 201 and 205 are subsequent printings of stamps first produced on watermark W 33.

33

1882–84. *Wmk V over Crown, W 33, (sideways on ½d.). P 12½.*
207 **22** ½d. rosine (3.83) 8.00 1.25
    a. Perf 12 .. .. .. — 15.00
208 **23** 1d. yellow-green (9.82) 15.00 1.25
    a. Perf 12 .. .. .. — 15.00
209 **30** 1d. yellow-green (29.10.83) .. 15.00 1.25
    a. Green (1.84) 13.00 1.25
    b. Pale green (5.84) 13.00 1.25
210 **31** 2d. dull grey-brown (15.8.82) .. 16.00 60
    a. Chocolate (3.83) 16.00 60
    ab. Perf 12 .. .. .. — 19.00
211 2d. mauve (20.12.83) 9.00 30
    a. Worn plate (2.84) 9.50 30
    b. Perf 12 .. .. .. † £250
    c. Mixed perf 12 and 12½ .. † £250
212 **15** 3d. yellow-orange (13.4.83) .. 26.00 5.50
    a. Dull brownish orange .. 30.00 7.00
213 **32** 4d. rose-red (3.83) 40.00 5.50
214 **16** 6d. dull violet-blue (10.11.82) .. 18.00 1.25
    a. Indigo-blue (11.83) 18.00 1.25
    b. Light ultramarine (8.84) .. 18.00 1.40
Reprints were made in 1891 of the "Laureated" 1d., 2d., 3d. (in yellow), 4d., 6d., 8d. (in orange-yellow), 10d. (in greenish slate) and 5s. (in blue and red), of the Bell ½d., 1d., 2d. (Die II) 9d. and 1s. and of the Naish 2d. (in brown), 4d. (in pale red) and 2s. With the exception of the Bell 9d., which was watermarked W 19, all were watermarked W 33 and perforated 12½. Some were from new plates.

THE POST OFFICE ACT OF 1883. Following official concern as to the number of different series of adhesive stamps, both fiscal and postal, used in Victoria it was decided that the system should be unified to the extent that the postage stamps, Stamp Statute fiscals and Stamp Duty fiscals should be replaced by a single series valid for all three purposes. As the Stamp Duty series contained the largest number of values it was adopted as the basis of the new range.

The regulations for the changeover were detailed in the Post Office Act of 1883 which came into force on 1 January 1884. From that date all existing Stamp Statute (first produced in 1871) and Stamp Duty (first produced in 1879) issues became valid for postal purposes, and the previous postage stamps could be used for fiscal fees.

Until matters could be organised printings of some of the existing postage values continued and these will be found included in the listings above.

Printing of the Stamp Statute series was discontinued in early 1884.

The existing Stamp Duty range was initially supplemented by postage stamps overprinted "STAMP DUTY" for those values where the available fiscal design was considered to be too large to be easily used on mail. These overprints were replaced by smaller designs inscribed "STAMP DUTY".

Stamp Statute and Stamp Duty values which became valid for postal purposes on 1 January 1884 have previously been listed in this catalogue as Postal Fiscals. Under the circumstances this distinction appears somewhat arbitrary and all such stamps are now shown in the main listing. Used prices quoted are for examples with postal cancellations. In some instances prices are also provided for fiscally used and these are marked "F.C.".

34   35   36

37

(Des and dies eng J. Turner (3d., 2s. 6d.), W. Bell (others). Typo from electrotypes)

1884 (1 Jan)*. *Stamp Statute series. Vert designs as T* **34/6**, *and others showing Queen Victoria, and T* **37**. *P* 13.

(a) Wmk single-lined numerals according to face value, as W **11**, *(sideways). Paper manufactured by T. H. Saunders unless otherwise stated*

215	1s. blue/*blue*	..	..	40·00 15·00
	a. Perf 12	..	..	50·00 20·00
216	2s. blue/*green* (D.L.R. paper)	..		55·00 45·00
	a. Perf 12	..	..	55·00 45·00
217	2s. deep blue/*green*	..	..	55·00
	a. Perf 12	..	..	— 45·00
	b. Wmk upright	..		
218	10s. brown-olive/*pink*	..		
219	10s. red-brown/*pink*	..	..	£500 £100
	a. Wmk upright. Perf 12			

(b) Wmk V over Crown, W **19**, *(sideways). P* 13

220	1d. pale green	..	..	15·00 15·00
	a. Green (wmk upright) (p 12½)			40·00 35·00
221	3d. mauve	..	..	£100 75·00
222	4d. rose	..	..	90·00 55·00
223	6d. blue	..	..	45·00 15·00
	a. Ultramarine	..	..	40·00 10·00
	ab. Perf 12	..	..	45·00 12·50
224	1s. blue/*blue*	..	..	40·00 15·00
	a. Perf 12	..	..	45·00 18·00
	b. Ultramarine/blue (p 12½)	..		— 25·00
	ba. Perf 12	..	..	— 20·00
	c. Deep blue/blue (p 12½)	..		40·00 15·00
	ca. Perf 12	..	..	— 15·00
225	2s. blue/*green*	..	..	50·00 35·00
	a. Perf 12	..	..	50·00
	b. Deep blue/blue-green (glazed paper)			50·00 40·00
	ba. Perf 12	..	..	50·00 45·00
226	2s. 6d. orange	..	..	— 50·00
	a. Perf 12	..	..	
	b. Yellow (glazed paper) ..	..		£100
	ba. Perf 12	..	..	£100 55·00
	c. Orange-yellow (glazed paper) (p 12½)			— 60·00
	ca. Perf 12	..	..	
227	5s. blue/*yellow*	..	..	£120 40·00
	a. Perf 12	..	..	£130
	b. Wmk upright ..	..		
	ba. Perf 12	..	..	
	c. Ultram/lemon (glazed paper) (p 12½)			£120 40·00
	ca. Perf 12	..	..	
228	10s. brown/*pink*	..	..	£500 £100
	a. Purple-brown/pink	..	..	£500 £100
	ab. Perf 12	..	..	
229	£1 slate-violet/*yellow*	..	..	£250 80·00
	a. Wmk upright ..	..		
	b. Mauve/yellow	..	..	
	ba. Perf 12	..	..	£250 80·00
	bb. Perf 12½	..	..	£250 80·00
230	£5 black and yellow-green	..		£2000 £400
	a. Perf 12	..	..	
	b. Wmk upright. Perf 12½			£2000 £400

(c) Wmk V over Crown, W **33**, *(sideways)*

231	1d. yellowish green (p 12½)	..		25·00 25·00
232	2s. 6d. pale orange-yellow (p 12)	..		£100 50·00
233	£5 black & yellow-grn (wmk upright) (p 12)			— £400

STANLEY GIBBONS STAMP COLLECTING SERIES

Introductory booklets on *How to Start, How to Identify Stamps* and *Collecting by Theme*. A series of well illustrated guides at a low price. Write for details.

½d

HALF

(38)

1884 (1 Jan)*. *No. 220 surch with T* **38** *in red.*

234	½d. on 1d. pale green	..	..	30·00 25·00

* The dates quoted are those on which the stamps became valid for postal purposes. The ½d., 1d., 4d., 6d., 1s., 5s. and £1 were issued for fiscal purposes on 26 April 1871. The 10s. was added to the series in June 1871, the £5 in September 1871, the 2s. 6d. in July 1876 and the 3d. in October 1879.

All values of the Stamp Statue series were reprinted in 1891 on paper watermarked W **19** (5s., 10s., £1) or W **33** (others). The £5 was pulled from the original plate, but the others were produced from new electrotypes taken from the original dies.

39   40   41

42   43   44

45   46   47

48   49   50

51   52   53

54   55

---

56   57

58   59

60

61

(Des H. Samson and F. Oxenbould (T **39**), C. Jackson and L. Lang (all others except T **40**). Dies eng C. Jackson, J. Turner, J. Whipple, A. Williams and other employees of Sands & MacDougall. T **40** die eng C. Naish)

1884 (1 Jan)*–96. *Existing Stamp Duty series.*

(a) Litho. Wmk V over Crown, W **19**, *(sideways). P* 13

235	39	1d. blue-green	..	..	40·00 7·50
		a. Perf 12	..		40·00 7·50
		b. Perf 12½	..		
236	43	1s. 6d. rosine	..	..	£110 16·00
		a. Perf 12	..		— 22·00
		b. Perf 12½	..		
237	45	3s. purple/*blue*	..	..	£300 24·00
		a. Perf 12	..		— 32·00
		b. Perf 12½	..		
238	46	4s. orange-red	..	..	60·00 15·00
		a. Perf 12	..		60·00 15·00
		b. Perf 12½	..		
239	48	6s. apple-green	..	..	£200 22·00
		a. Perf 12½	..		
240	49	10s. brown/*rose* (glazed paper)			£300 55·00
		a. Perf 12	..		
		b. Perf 12½	..		
		c. Wmk upright	..		
		cb. Perf 12½	..		
241	50	15s. mauve	..	..	£750 £120
242	51	£1 red-orange	..	..	£325 55·00
		a. Perf 12½	..		£325
243	52	£1 5s. dull rose (wmk upright)			£750 £120
244	53	£1 10s. deep grey-olive	..		£800 85·00
		a. Wmk upright	..		— £120
245	—	35s. grey-violet (wmk upright) (F.C. £150)			£3000
246	54	£2 blue	..	..	— 70·00
247	55	45s. dull brown-lilac	..		£1400 90·00
248	56	£5 rose-red (wmk upright)	..		£1100 £190
249	57	£6 blue/*pk* (wmk upright) (glazed paper)			— £450
250	58	£7 violet/*blue* (wmk upright)	..		— £450
251	59	£8 brownish red/*yellow* (wmk upright)			
		(glazed paper)	..		— £550
252	60	£9 yellow-green/*green* (wmk upright)			
		(glazed paper) (F.C. £100)	..		— £550

(b) Typo from electrotypes
(i) Wmk V over Crown, W **19**, *(sideways). P* 13

253	39	1d. yellowish green	..	..	25·00 7·00
		a. Perf 12	..		25·00 7·00
		b. Perf 12½	..		

254 40 1d. pale bistre .. .. 7·00 1·00
    a. Perf 12 .. .. 7·00 2·00
    b. Perf 12½
255 41 6d. dull blue .. .. 30·00 5·00
    a. Perf 12 .. .. 35·00 12·00
    b. Perf 12½
256 42 1s. deep blue/*blue* .. .. .. 55·00 4·00
    a. Perf 12 .. .. 55·00 5·00
    b. Perf 12½
    c. *Brt blue/blue (glazed paper)* (p 12½) 55·00 4·50
    ca. Perf 12 .. .. — 5·00
    d. *Ultramarine/blue (glazed paper)*
    (p 12½) (11.84) .. .. 90·00 5·00
257 1s. chalky blue/*lemon (glazed paper)*
    (p 12½) (3.3.85) .. 75·00 20·00
258 44 2s. deep blue/*green (glazed paper)* £100 12·00
    a. Perf 12½ .. .. .. — 14·00
    b. *Indigo/green*
    ca. Perf 12 .. .. .. 80·00 16·00
    c. Perf 12½ .. .. .. £120 17·00
259 45 3s. mar/bl *(glazed paper)* (p 12½) (8.8.84) £150 23·00
260 47 5s. claret/*yellow (glazed paper)* .. 50·00 4·00
    a. Perf 12 .. .. .. 60·00 9·00
    c. *Pale claret/yellow* (p 12½) 50·00 9·00
    ca. Perf 12 .. .. .. 70·00 9·00
    d. *Reddish purple/lemon* (p 12½) (6.87) 45·00 10·00
    e. *Brown-red/yellow* (p 12½) (5.93) 75·00 20·00
261 49 10s. chocolate/*rose (glazed paper)* .. — 55·00
    a. Perf 12
    b. Perf 12½
    c. Wmk upright
262 51 £1 yellow-orange/*yellow* (p 12) .. £550 75·00
    a. *Orange/yellow* (p 12½) (8.84) £500 55·00
    b. *Reddish orange/yellow* (p 12½) (9.88) £325 55·00
263 54 £2 deep blue (p 12) .. .. — 80·00
264 61 £10 dull mauve (p 12) .. .. £1500 80·00
    a. *Deep red-lilac* (p 12)

   (ii) *Wmk V over Crown*, W **33**, *(sideways). P* 12½
265 40 1d. ochre .. .. 15·00 2·00
    a. Perf 12 .. .. .. 15·00 2·00
266 41 6d. ultramarine .. .. .. 50·00 4·00
    a. Perf 12 .. .. .. 50·00 4·00
267 43 1s. 6d. pink (1.85) .. .. £130 25·00
    a. *Bright rose-carmine* (4.86) .. £150 25·00
268 45 3s. drab (20.10.85) .. .. 75·00 16·00
    a. *Olive-drab* (1.93) .. .. 70·00 16·00
269 46 4s. red-orange (5.86) .. .. 80·00 12·00
    a. *Yellow-orange* (12.94)
    ab. Wmk upright .. .. £100 8·50
270 47 5s. rosine (8.5.96) .. .. 75·00 19·00
271 48 6s. pea-green (12.11.91) .. £110 32·00
    a. *Apple-green (wmk upright)* (3.96) £180 32·00
272 49 10s. dull bluish green (10.85) .. £150 28·00
    a. *Grey-green* (5.86) .. .. £100 25·00
273 50 15s. purple-brown (12.85) .. £550 75·00
    a. *Brown (wmk upright)* (5.95) £550 80·00
274 52 £1 5s. pink (*wmk upright*) (6.8.90) £850 80·00
275 53 £1 10s. pale olive (6.88) .. £600 65·00
276 54 £2 bright blue .. .. .. — 75·00
    a. *Blue* (7.88) .. .. .. £750 75·00
277 55 45s. lilac (15.8.90) .. .. £2000 90·00
278 56 £5 rose-pink (p 12) .. .. — £180
    a. *Pink* (p 12½) .. .. .. — £300
279 61 £10 mauve (3.84) .. .. £1700 90·00
    a. *Lilac* (6.85) .. .. .. — £100

*This is the date on which the stamps became valid for postal use. The 1d., 6d., 1s., 1s.6d., 2s., 3s., 4s., 5s., 10s., 15s., £1, £1 10s., £2, £5 and £10 were issued for fiscal purposes on 18 December 1879 with the £1 5s., 35s., 45s., £6 and £9 added to the range later the same month and the 6s., £7 and £8 in January 1880.

Used prices for the £1 5s., £1 10s., £2 (No. 276a), 45s. and £10 watermarked W **33** are for examples from the cancelled-to-order sets sold to collectors by the Victoria postal authorities between September 1900 and 30 June 1902.

Similar Stamp Duty designs were prepared for 7s., 8s., 9s., 11s., 12s., 13s., 14s., 16s., 17s., 18s., and 19s., but were never issued.

The two different 1d. designs were reprinted in 1891 on W **33** paper.

For these designs with later watermarks see Nos. 345/50 and 369/71.

62

(Des C. Jackson and L. Lang. Dies eng C. Jackson)

1884 (1 Jan*)–1900. *High value Stamp Duty series.*

  (a) *Recess-printed direct from the die*
  (i) *Wmk V over Crown*, W **19**, *(sideways). P* 12½
280 62 £25 yellow-green (F.C. £55)
    a. Wmk upright
    b. Perf 13
    c. *Deep green* (F.C. £55)
    ca. Wmk upright
281 £50 bright mauve (F.C. £85)
    a. Wmk upright
    b. Perf 13
282 £100 crimson-lake (F.C. £110)
    a. Wmk upright
    b. Perf 13

  (ii) *Wmk V over Crown*, W **33**, *(sideways). P* 12½
283 62 £25 yellow-green
    a. Perf 12
    b. *Deep green* (1.85) (F.C. £55) — £350
    c. *Bright blue-green* (10.90) (F.C. £55)
    ca. Wmk upright
284 £50 dull lilac-mauve (*wmk upright*)
    (F.C.£85)
    a. *Black-violet* (10.90) (F.C. £65) — £350
    ab. Wmk upright

285 62 £100 crimson (F.C. £120)
    a. Wmk upright
    b. Perf 12 (F.C. £120)..
    c. *Aniline crimson (wmk upright)* (2.85)
    (F.C. £120) .. .. .. — £425
    d. *Scarlet-red (wmk upright)* (5.95) .. — £325

  (b) *Litho. Wmk V over Crown*, W **33**, *(sideways). P* 12½
286 62 £25 dull yellowish green (1.86) (F.C. £45)
    a. Wmk upright (11.87)
    b. *Dull blue-green* (9.88) (F.C. £45)
    ba. Wmk upright
287 £50 dull purple (1.86) (F.C. £60)
    a. Wmk upright
    b. *Bright violet* (11.89) (F.C. £60)
    ba. Wmk upright
288 £100 rosine (1.86) (F.C. £95)

  (c) *Typo from electrotyped plates. Wmk V over Crown*, W **33**.
    P 12½
289 62 £25 dull blue-green (12.97) .. — 90·00
290 £50 bright mauve (10.97) .. — £130
291 £100 pink-red (10.1900) .. .. — £180
*This is the date on which the stamps became valid for postal use. All three values were issued for fiscal purposes on 18 December 1879.

Used prices for Nos. 283b, 284a, 285c/d and 289/91 are for examples from the cancelled-to-order sets described beneath No. 279a. "F.C." indicates that the price quoted is for a stamp with a fiscal cancellation.

For the £25 and £50 with watermark W **82** see Nos. 351/2.

63

(Des and die eng C. Naish. Typo from electrotyped plates)

1884 (23 Apr)–**92.** *New design inscr* "STAMP DUTY". *Wmk V over Crown*, W **33** *(sideways). P* 12½.
292 63 2s. 6d. brown-orange .. .. 80·00 12·00
    a. *Yellow* (8.85) .. .. 75·00 11·00
    b. *Lemon-yellow* (2.92) .. 75·00 11·00
For this design on later watermarks see Nos. 344 and 368.

64   65   66

67   68

(Des and dies eng C. Naish. Typo from electrotyped plates)

1885 (1 Jan)–**95.** *New designs inscr* "STAMP DUTY". *P* 12½.

  (a) W **19**
293 68 8d. rose/*pink* .. .. .. 20·00 5·50
    a. *Rose-red/pink* (2.88) .. 22·00 5·50
294 66 1s. deep dull blue/*lemon* (11.85) .. 50·00 6·00
    a. *Dull blue/yellow* (6.86) .. 50·00 6·50
295 68 2s. olive/*bluish green* (12.85) .. 35·00 3·00

  (b) W **33**
296 64 ½d. pale rosine .. .. .. 6·50 65
    a. *Deep rosine* (7.85) .. .. 7·50 1·00
    b. *Salmon* (9.85) .. .. 8·00 1·25
297 65 1d. yellowish green (1.85) .. 7·00 50
    a. *Dull pea-green* (2.85) .. 11·00 1·75
298 66 2d. lilac .. .. 5·00 30
    a. *Mauve* (1886) .. .. 5·00 30
    b. *Rosy-mauve* (1886) .. 6·50 50
299 65 3d. yellowish brown .. .. 8·00 80
    a. *Pale ochre* (9.86) .. .. 7·50 80
    b. *Bistre-yellow* (9.92) .. 8·00 80
300 67 4d. magenta .. .. .. 32·00 3·00
    a. *Bright mauve-rose* (12.86) .. 35·00 3·50
    b. Error. Lilac (12.86) .. £2250 £400
301 65 6d. chalky blue (1.85) .. .. 45·00 2·50
    a. *Bright blue* (3.85) .. .. 28·00 2·10
    b. *Cobalt* (7.85) .. .. 28·00 2·10
302 68 8d. bright scarlet/*pink* (3.95) .. 28·00 7·50
303 2s. olive-green/*pale green* (1.90) 25·00 3·50
304 2s. apple-green (12.8.95) .. 25·00 28·00
    a. *Blue-green* (29.10.95) .. 18·00 5·50
The plates for the 1d., 6d., 1s. and 2s. were derived from the dies of the 2d. (1s.), 3d. (1d. and 6d.) and 8d. (2s.). In each instance lead moulds of six impressions were taken from the original die and the face values altered by hand creating six slightly different versions.

Two states of the 2d. die exist with the second showing a break in the top frame line near the righthand corner. This damaged die was used for seven impressions on Plate 1 and all 120 on Plate 2.

No. 300b occured during the December 1886 printing of the 4d. when about fifty sheets were printed in the colour of the 2d.

by mistake. The sheets were issued to Melbourne post offices and used examples are known postmarked between 21 December 1886 and 4 March 1887. Nine unused are also believed to exist.

Reprints of the ½d., 1d., 2d., 4d., 6d. and 1s. values were made in 1891 from the existing plates. The 1s. was watermarked W **19** and the remainder W **33**.

For some of these values used with later watermarks see Nos. 336, 343, 360, 368 and X362.

STAMP DUTY

(69)

1885 (Feb–Nov). *Optd with T* **69**. *P* 12½. (a) W **19**
305 15 3d. dull orge-yell (*glazed paper*) (B.) (Nov) .. — £130
306 26 1s. pale blue/*blue (glazed paper)* (p 13) 95·00 20·00
    a. *Deep blue/blue* .. .. — 22·00
    b. Blue opt (F.C. £14) £1200 £600
307 27 2s. ultramarine/*grn (glazed paper)* (Mar) 80·00 18·00
    a. Wmk sideways .. .. 90·00 20·00

  (b) W **33**
308 15 3d. yellow-orange (B.) (Nov) .. 60·00 22·00
    a. *Dull brownish orange* (B.) .. 65·00 24·00
309 32 4d. rose-red (B.) (Nov) .. .. 55·00 22·00
Unauthorised reprints of the 4d. and 1s., both with blue overprints and watermarked W **33**, were made during 1895–96. The 4d. reprint, which is in pale red, also exists without the overprint.

70   71   72

73   74   75

76   77   78

79   80

(Des S. Reading (1d. (No. 313), M. Tannenberg (2½d., 5d.), C. Naish (1s. 6d.), P. Astley (others). Dies eng C. Naish (2d., 4d. (both existing dies with lines added behind Queen's head) and 1s. 6d.), S. Reading (originally as an employee of Fergusson & Mitchell) (others). Typo from electrotyped plates)

1886 (26 July)–**96.** W **33** *(sideways on ½d., 1s., £5, £7 to £9). P* 12½.
310 70 ½d. lilac-grey (28.8.86) .. 17·00 3·00
    a. *Grey-black* .. .. — 35·00
311 ½d. pink (15.2.87) .. .. 6·00 30
    a. *Rosine (aniline)* (1889) .. 4·75 30
    b. *Rose-red* (1891) .. .. 4·50 30
    c. *Vermilion* (1896) .. .. 4·75 35
312 71 1d. green .. .. 5·25 30
    a. *Yellow-green* (1887) .. 5·25 30
313 72 1d. dull chestnut (1.1.90) .. 4·00 20
    a. *Deep red-brown* (1890) .. 4·00 40
    b. *Orange-brown* (1890) .. 4·00 20
    c. *Brown-red* (1890) .. .. 4·00 20
    d. *Yellow-brown* (1890) .. 4·00 20
    e. *Bright yellow-orange* (1893) 50·00 12·00
    f. *Brownish orange* (1894) .. 3·25 20
314 73 2d. pale lilac (17.12.86) .. 4·25 20
    a. *Pale mauve* (1887) .. .. 4·50 20
    b. *Deep lilac* (1888, 1892) .. 4·00 20
    c. *Purple* (1894) .. .. 3·00 25
    d. *Violet* (1895) .. .. 3·00 20
    e. Imperf .. .. .. — £700
315 74 2½d. red-brown/*lemon* (1.1.91) .. 11·00 1·50
    a. *Brown-red/yellow* (1892) .. 7·00 80
    b. *Red/yellow* (1893) .. 6·00 70
316 75 4d. rose-red (1.4.87) .. .. 10·00 1·00
    a. *Red* (1893) .. .. .. 5·75 90

317	76	5d. purple-brown (1.1.91)	8·50	85
		a. *Pale reddish brown* (1893)	6·50	80
318	77	6d. bright ultramarine (27.8.86)	9·50	80
		a. *Pale ultramarine* (1887)	8·00	50
		b. *Dull blue* (1891)	7·50	50
319	25	9d. apple-green (18.10.92)	20·00	9·00
320		9d. carmine-rose (15.10.95)	20·00	4·50
		a. *Rosine (aniline)* (1896)	22·00	4·75
321	78	1s. dull purple-brown (14.3.87)	30·00	2·00
		a. *Lake* (1890)	24·00	1·75
		b. *Carmine-lake* (1892)	14·00	1·00
		c. *Brownish red* (1896)	15·00	1·60
322	79	1s. 6d. pale blue (9.88)	£120	65·00
323		1s. 6d. orange (19.9.89)	15·00	4·50
		a. *Red-orange* (1893)	15·00	4·00
324	80	£5 pale blue and maroon (7.2.88) †	£1000	80·00
325		£6 yellow and pale lake (1.10.87)†	£1200	£100
326		£7 rosine and black (17.10.89)†	£1400	£120
327		£8 mauve & brown-orange (2.8.90)†	£1500	£150
328		£9 apple-green and rosine (21.8.88)†	£1800	£160

†The used prices provided for these stamps are for cancelled-to-order examples.

Unauthorised reprints of the ½d. lilac-grey and 1s. 6d. pale blue were made in 1894–95 on W 33 paper and perforated 12½. These differ in shade from the originals and have rougher perforations. It should be noted that the original printing of No. 322 does not occur with inverted watermark, but the reprint does.

A single example of No. 314e is known postmarked "737" (Foster). A second, postmarked "249" (Mortlake), was reported in 1892. It is known that an imperforate sheet was sold at Mortlake P.O. in 1890. Other examples are believed to be clandestine.

A £10 value as Type **80** was prepared, but not issued.

1891 (17 June). *W* **19**. *P* 12½.

329	72	1d. orange-brown/*pink*	4·00	1·75

No. 329 was an emergency printing during a shortage of white W 33 paper.

81   82

(Die eng A. Williams (1½d.). Typo from electrotyped plates)

1896 (11 June)–**99**. *W* **82** (*sideways on* ½d., 1½d., 1s., 2s. 6d. *to* 15s.). *P* 12½.

330	70	½d. light scarlet (1.7.96)	3·00	15
		a. *Carmine-rose* (1897)	3·25	15
		b. *Dp carmine-red* (coarse impression) (1899)	—	90
		c. Wmk upright		
331		½d. emerald (1.8.99)	6·00	80
332	72	1d. brown-red (13.6.96)	3·75	10
		a. *Brownish orange* (1897)	3·75	10
333	81	1½d. apple-green (7.10.97)	4·00	1·50
334	73	2d. violet	4·00	10
335	74	2½d. blue (1.8.99)	7·50	3·50
336	65	3d. ochre (11.96)	7·00	55
		a. *Buff* (1898)	6·50	50
337	75	4d. red (6.97)	8·00	90
338	76	5d. red-brown (7.97)	12·00	95
339	77	6d. dull blue (9.96)	8·50	55
340	25	9d. rosine (8.96)	22·00	2·75
		a. *Rose-carmine* (1898)	—	2·75
		b. *Dull rose* (1898)	17·00	2·75
341	78	1s. brownish red (1898)	11·00	1·50
342	79	1s. 6d. brown-orange (8.98)	25·00	9·00
343	68	2s. blue-green (4.97)	23·00	6·00
344	63	2s. 6d. yellow (9.96)	90·00	12·00
		a. Wmk upright (1898)	£100	12·00
345	45	3s. olive-drab (12.96)	55·00	17·00
		a. Wmk upright (1898)	55·00	16·00
346	46	4s. orange (9.97)	80·00	6·00
347	47	5s. rosine (2.97)	80·00	7·00
		a. *Rose-carmine* (1897)	80·00	7·00
		b. Wmk upright. *Rosine* (1899)	80·00	7·50
348	48	6s. pale yellow-green (4.99)†	80·00	23·00
349	49	10s. grey-green (4.97)	95·00	16·00
		a. *Blue-green* (1898)	95·00	16·00
350	50	15s. brown (4.97)†	£325	38·00
351	62	£25 dull bluish green (1897)†	—	95·00
352		£50 dull purple (1897)†	—	£120

†The used prices provided for these stamps are for cancelled-to-order examples.

83   84

(Des M. Tannenberg. Dies eng A. Mitchelhill. Typo from electrotyped plates)

1897 (22 Oct). *Hospital Charity Fund*. *W* **82** (*sideways*). *P* 12½.

353	83	1d. (1s.) blue	18·00	18·00
354	84	2½d. (2s. 6d.) red-brown	85·00	70·00
353/4		Optd "Specimen"	Set of 2	£140

These stamps were sold at 1s. and 2s. 6d., but only had postal validity for 1d. and 2½d. with the difference going to the Fund.

1899 (1 Aug). *W* **33** (*sideways*). *P* 12½.

355	81	1½d. brown-red/*yellow*	3·00	1·75

85

1899 (1 Aug)–**1901**. *W* **85** (*sideways on* ½d., 1s. *and* 2s. 6d. *to* 10s.). *P* 12½.

356	70	½d. emerald (12.99)	4·75	40
		a. *Deep blue-green*	5·00	40
		b. Wmk upright	†	
357	72	1d. rose-red	4·00	15
		a. *Rosine* (1900)	4·25	10
358		1d. olive (6.6.01)	5·00	4·00
359	73	2d. violet	5·00	10
		a. Wmk sideways	†	
360	74	2½d. blue (10.99)	6·00	1·50
361	65	3d. bistre-yellow (9.99)	7·00	65
362		3d. slate-green (20.6.01)	21·00	6·50
363	75	4d. rose-red (12.99)	4·75	95
364	76	5d. red-brown (12.99)	8·50	95
365	77	6d. dull ultramarine (1.00)	7·00	65
366	25	9d. rose-red (9.99)	11·00	1·75
367	78	1s. brown-red (5.00)	12·00	1·75
368	79	1s. 6d. orange (2.00)	14·00	6·00
369	68	2s. blue-green (6.00)	17·00	4·75
370	63	2s. 6d. yellow (1.00)	£300	12·00
371	45	3s. pale olive (4.00)†	£130	17·00
372	47	5s. rose-red (4.00)	£100	17·00
373	49	10s. green (3.00)†	£130	18·00

†The used prices provided for these stamps are for cancelled-to-order examples.

From 1 July 1901 stamps inscribed "STAMP DUTY" could only be used for fiscal purposes.

86 Victoria Cross   87 Australian Troops in South Africa

(Des Sands and MacDougall (1d.), J. Sutherland (2d.). Dies eng S. Reading. Typo from electrotyped plates)

1900 (22 May). *Empire Patriotic Fund*. *W* **85** (*sideways*). *P* 12½.

374	86	1d. (1s.) olive-brown	55·00	32·00
375	87	2d. (2s.) emerald-green	£110	£110

These stamps were sold at 1s. and 2s., but only had postal validity for 1d. and 2d. with the difference going to the Fund.

FEDERATION. The six Australian colonies were federated as the Commonwealth of Australia on 1 January 1901. Under the terms of the Post and Telegraph Act their postal services were amalgamated on 1 March 1901, but other clauses to safeguard the financial position of the individual States provided them with a large degree of independence until 13 October 1910 when issues of each state could be used throughout Australia. Postage stamps for the Commonwealth of Australia did not appear until January 1913.

It was agreed in 1901 that stamp printing should be centralised at Melbourne under J. B. Cooke of South Australia who was appointed Commonwealth Stamp Printer. By 1909 the Commonwealth Stamp Printing Branch in Melbourne was producing stamps for Papua, South Australia, Tasmania and Western Australia in addition to those of Victoria.

On federation it was decided to separate postal and fiscal stamp issues so Victoria needed urgent replacements for the current Stamp Duty series which reverted to fiscal use only on 30 June 1901.

1901 (29 Jan). *Re-use of previous designs without* "POSTAGE" *inscr*. *W* **82** (2s.) *or* **85** (*others*) (*sideways on* ½d.). *P* 12×12½.

376	22	½d. bluish green	2·00	85
		a. "VICTCRIA" (R. 7/19)	30·00	20·00
377	31	2d. reddish violet	5·50	60
378	15	3d. dull orange	15·00	1·25
379	32	4d. bistre-yellow	25·00	10·00
380	16	6d. emerald	9·00	5·50
381	26	1s. yellow	35·00	27·00
382	27	2s. blue/*pink*	40·00	14·00
383	18	5s. pale red and deep blue	45·00	27·00

88   89   90

---

91   92   93

94   95   96

97   98   99

100   101   102

I   II   III

Three die states of ½d.:

I. Outer vertical line of colour to left of "V" continuous except for a break opposite the top of "V". Triangles either end of "VICTORIA" are more or less solid colour.

II. Die re-engraved. Three breaks in outer line of colour left of "V". White lines added to left triangle.

III. Die re-engraved. As II, but equivalent triangle at right also contains white lines.

I

II

III

I and II   III

Three die states of 1d.:
I. Thick lines fill top of oval above Queen's head.
II. Die re-engraved. Lines thinner, showing white space between.
III. Die re-engraved. As II, but with bottom left value table recut to show full point separated from both "1" and the circular frame.

Two die states of 2d.:
I. Frame line complete at top right corner. Bottom right corner comes to a point.
II. Break in right frame line just below the top corner. Bottom right corner is blunted.

Two types of 1s.:
A. "POSTAGE" 6 mm long (produced by a hand punch applied twice to each impression on the previous 1s. electrotyped plate. Slight variations in position occur).
B. "POSTAGE" 7 mm long (produced from new electrotyped plates incorporating the "POSTAGE" inscriptions).

(Eng S. Reading after photo by W. Stuart (£1, £2))

1901 (29 Jan)–**10**. *Previous issues with "POSTAGE" added and new designs (£1, £2). W 85 (sideways on ¹/₂d., 1¹/₂d., £1, £2).*

(a) P 12×12¹/₂

384	88	¹/₂d. blue-green (I) (26.6.01)		1·90	20
		a. Wmk upright (1903)		1·90	20
		b. Die state II (6.04)		3·25	20
385	89	1d. rose (I)		2·50	15
		a. Dull red (12.02)		2·50	15
		b. Die state II (4.01)		1·25	15
		ba. Dull red (12.02)		1·25	15
		c. Die state III. Pale rose-red (4.05)		3·00	70
		ca. Wmk sideways		†	—
386	90	1¹/₂d. maroon/yellow (9.7.01)		5·50	2·50
		a. Wmk upright. Brn-red/yell (9.01)		2·10	55
		b. Dull red-brown/yellow (1906)		2·10	55
		ba. On yellow-buff back (1908)		2·75	1·00
387	91	2d. lilac (I) (26.6.01)		5·00	30
		a. Die state II		18·00	1·50
		b. Reddish violet (1902)		5·00	30
		ba. Die state II		18·00	1·50
		c. Bright purple (II) (1905)		6·00	30
		d. Rosy mauve (II) (1905)			
388	92	2¹/₂d. dull blue		5·00	35
		a. Deep blue (1902)		5·00	35
389	93	3d. dull orange-brown (5.7.01)		6·50	80
		a. Chestnut (1901)		5·50	55
		b. Yellowish brown (1903)		5·50	55
		ba. Wmk sideways		10·00	14·00
390	94	4d. bistre-yellow (26.6.01)		4·75	55
		a. Brownish bistre (1905)		7·50	70
391	95	5d. reddish brown		7·50	40
		a. Purple-brown (1903)		6·50	40
392	96	6d. emerald (5.7.01)		11·00	80
		a. Dull green (1904)		13·00	85
393	97	9d. dull rose-red (5.7.01)		11·00	1·40
		a. Wmk sideways (1901)		16·00	3·00
		b. Pale red (1901)		11·00	1·25
		c. Dull brownish red (1905)		15·00	2·00
394	98	1s. yellow-orange (A) (5.7.01)		13·00	1·75
		a. Yellow (1902)		15·00	1·75
		b. Type B (4.03)		15·00	3·00
		ba. Orange (1904)		13·00	2·50
		bb. Wmk sideways (1905)		22·00	5·00
395	99	2s. blue/rose (5.7.01)		22·00	2·00

(b) P 12¹/₂

396	88	¹/₂d. blue-green (III) (6.05)		6·50	50
397	92	2¹/₂d. dull blue (1901)		£250	£250
398	100	5s. rose-red and pale blue (5.7.01)		70·00	12·00
		a. Scarlet and deep blue (12.01)		65·00	10·00
		b. Rosine and blue (12.04)		65·00	10·00
399	101	£1 carmine-rose (18.11.01)		£225	£100
400	102	£2 deep blue (2.6.02)		£500	£250

(c) P 11

401	88	¹/₂d. blue-green (I) (9.02)		5·00	1·50
		a. Wmk upright (1903)		3·25	30
		b. Die state II (6.04)		3·50	30
		c. Die state III (6.05)		4·25	60
402	89	1d. dull red (I) (12.02)		55·00	40·00
		a. Die state II		45·00	18·00
		ab. Pale red (aniline) (3.03)		4·25	1·00
		ac. Pale rose (aniline) (1904)		25·00	3·50
		b. Die state III. Pale rose-red (7.05)		45·00	25·00
403	90	1¹/₂d. dull red-brown/yellow (1910)		40·00	40·00
404	91	2d. bright purple (II) (1905)		†	£180
		a. Rosy mauve (II) (1905)		†	—
405	93	3d. yellowish brown (1903)		5·50	3·75
		a. Wmk sideways		15·00	20·00
406	96	6d. emerald (2.03)		11·00	14·00
		a. Dull green (1905)		£325	£160
407	101	£1 rose (5.05)		£275	£130
408	102	£2 deep blue (1905)		£800	£700

(d) Compound or mixed perf 12¹/₂ and 11

409	88	¹/₂d. blue-green (I) (1901)		22·00	6·00
		a. Wmk upright (1903)		—	6·00
		b. Die state II (1904)		20·00	15·00
410	89	1d. dull red (I) (1902)		—	£180
		a. Die state II		£350	£140
		b. Die state II			
411	90	1¹/₂d. maroon/yellow (1903)		£500	£200
412	91	2d. reddish violet (I) (1903)		†	£300
413	93	3d. dull orange-brown (1902)		—	£450
414	96	6d. emerald (1903)		†	£400
415	100	5s. rosine and blue (12.04)		†	£800

Examples of the 1d. Die state II perforated 12¹/₂ exist with two black lines printed across the face of the stamp. These were prepared in connection with stamp-vending machine trials.

1905–13. *Wmk Crown over A, W w 11 (sideways on ¹/₂d., £1, £2).*

(a) P 12×12¹/₂

416	88	¹/₂d. blue-green (shades) (III) (21.10.05)	1·60	15
		a. Wmk upright. Thin, ready gummed paper (6.12)		3·25	2·50

417	89	1d. rose-red (III) (16.7.05)		80	10
		a. Pale rose (1907)		1·25	10
		b. Rose-carmine (1911)		3·50	85
		ba. Wmk sideways		10·00	4·00
		c. Thin, ready gummed paper (10.12)		4·50	1·25
418	91	2d. dull mauve (II) (13.9.05)		5·00	30
		a. Lilac (1906)		5·00	25
		b. Reddish violet (1907)		5·00	25
		c. Bright mauve (1910)		4·75	25
		ca. Thin, ready gummed paper (8.12)		26·00	3·50
419	92	2¹/₂d. blue (10.08)		3·00	40
		a. Indigo (1909)		4·50	60
420	93	3d. orange-brown (11.11.05)		6·50	85
		a. Yellow-orange (1908)		7·50	65
		b. Dull orange-buff (1909)		7·50	65
		c. Ochre (1912)		7·50	3·25
421	94	4d. yellow-bistre (15.1.06)		7·00	65
		a. Olive-bistre (1908)		7·00	65
		b. Yellow-olive (1912)		7·00	3·25
422	95	5d. chocolate (14.8.06)		7·00	1·00
		a. Dull reddish brown (1908)		7·00	75
		ab. Thin, ready gummed paper (19.10.12)		12·00	5·50
423	96	6d. dull green (25.10.05)		11·00	80
		a. Dull yellow-green (1907)		11·00	80
		b. Emerald (1909)		11·00	1·10
		c. Yellowish green (1911)		11·00	1·60
		d. Emerald. Thin, ready gummed paper (11.12)		17·00	8·00
424	97	9d. brown-red (11.12.05)		12·00	1·75
		a. Orange-brown (1906)		12·00	1·50
		b. Red-brown (1908)		12·00	1·50
		c. Pale dull rose (1909)		13·00	2·75
		d. Rose-carmine (1910)		9·50	1·25
425	98	1s. orange (B) (13.2.06)		8·00	2·00
		a. Yellow-orange (1906)		11·00	2·00
		b. Yellow (1908)		13·00	2·00
		ba. Thin, ready gummed paper (11.12)		25·00	15·00
		c. Pale orange. Thin, ready gummed paper (1913)		25·00	15·00

(b) P 12¹/₂

426	88	¹/₂d. blue-green (shades) (III) (1905)		2·00	20
		a. Wmk upright (1909)		10·00	2·00
		ab. Thin, ready gummed paper (1912)		3·25	2·50
427	89	1d. rose-red (III) (1905)		2·00	20
		a. Rose-carmine (1911)		5·00	1·25
428	92	2¹/₂d. indigo (1909)		8·00	1·00
429	96	6d. yellowish green (1911)		15·00	4·50
430	100	5s. rose-red and ultramarine (12.07)		70·00	13·00
		a. Rose-red and blue (1911)		80·00	13·00
		ab. Wmk sideways		80·00	16·00
431	101	£1 salmon (12.2.07)		£225	£100
		a. Dull rose (1910)		£225	£100
		ab. Wmk upright (1911)		£275	£120
432	102	£2 dull blue (18.7.06)		£500	£250

(c) P 11

433	88	¹/₂d. blue-green (shades) (III) (1905)		1·60	20
		a. Wmk upright. Thin, ready gummed paper (1912)		15·00	14·00
434	89	1d. rose-red (III) (1905)		3·50	75
		a. Pale rose (1907)		3·50	75
		b. Rose-carmine (1911)		7·00	3·25
		ba. Wmk sideways		15·00	4·50
		c. Thin, ready gummed paper (10.12)		7·50	4·50
435	91	2d. lilac (II) (1906)		†	£150
		a. Reddish violet (1907)		65·00	15·00
		b. Bright mauve (1910)		25·00	8·50
436	92	2¹/₂d. blue (1907)		60·00	7·50
		a. Indigo (1909)		9·00	4·50
437	93	3d. orange-brown (1905)		10·00	6·50
		a. Yellow-orange (1908)		†	£130
		b. Dull orange-buff (1909)		15·00	15·00
		c. Ochre (1912)		8·00	4·75
438	94	4d. yellow-bistre (1906)		9·00	15·00
		a. Olive-bistre (1909)			
		b. Yellow-olive (1912)		8·50	10·00
439	95	5d. chocolate (1906)		†	£475
		a. Dull reddish brown (1908)		†	£475
440	96	6d. emerald (1909)		10·00	13·00
		a. Yellowish green (1911)		15·00	16·00
441	97	9d. rose-carmine (1910)		†	£375
442	98	1s. yellow-orange (B) (1906)		†	£180
		a. Orange (1910)		£375	
443	100	5s. rose-red and ultramarine (12.07)		70·00	9·50
444	101	£1 salmon (12.2.07)		£275	£100
445	102	£2 dull blue (1.07)		£650	£275

(d) Compound or mixed perfs 12¹/₂ and 11

446	88	¹/₂d. blue-green (shades) (III) (1905)		17·00	16·00
		a. Wmk upright. Thin, ready gummed paper (1912)		£110	80·00
447	89	1d. rose-red (III) (1905)		32·00	32·00
		a. Pale rose (1907)		—	40·00
		b. Rose-carmine (1911)		—	40·00
448	91	2d. reddish violet (1907)		£350	£200
449	93	3d. orange-brown (1905)		†	£275
		a. Ochre (1912)		£250	
450	94	4d. bistre (1908)		†	£275
451	96	6d. emerald (1909)		—	£375
		a. Yellowish green (1911)		†	£250
452	97	9d. orange-brown (1906)		†	£450
		a. Red-brown (1908)		†	£450
453	98	1s. yellow-orange (1906)		£600	

(e) Rotary comb perf 11¹/₂×12¹/₄

454	89	1d. pale rose (III) (2.10)		6·50	1·25
		a. Rose-carmine (1911)			
		ab. Thin, ready gummed paper (7.12)		3·25	2·25
		b. Rose-red. Thin, ready gummed paper (10.12)		3·25	2·25
455	91	2d. lilac (II) (1910)		7·50	1·50

The original Crown over A watermark paper used by Victoria was of medium thickness and had toned gum applied after printing. Stocks of this paper lasted until 1912 when further supplies were ordered from a new papermakers, Cowan and Sons. This paper was much thinner and was supplied with white gum already applied. The first delivery arrived in June 1912 and a second in September the same year.

The rotary comb perforating gauging 11¹/₂×12¹/₄ was transferred from South Australia in 1909 when J. B. Cooke moved to Melbourne.

Examples of the 1d. perforated 12¹/₂ or 11 exist with two black lines across the face of the stamp. These were prepared in connection with stamp-vending machine trials.

ONE PENNY

(103)   104

1912 (29 June). *No. 455 surch with T 103 in red.*

456	91	1d. on 2d. lilac (II)		70	45

1912 (Aug–Sept). W 104. (a) P 12×12¹/₂

457	89	1d. rose-carmine (III)		2·75	1·50
		a. Wmk sideways		50·00	
458	91	2d. reddish violet (II) (Sept)		3·00	2·25
		a. Lilac		5·00	3·00
459	97	9d. rose-carmine		14·00	8·50

(b) P 12¹/₂

460	88	¹/₂d. bluish green (III)		3·00	2·75

(c) P 11

461	88	¹/₂d. bluish green (III)		18·00	18·00
462	89	1d. rose-carmine (III)		28·00	11·00
463	97	9d. rose-carmine		20·00	13·00

(d) Compound or mixed perfs 12¹/₂ and 11

464	97	9d. rose-carmine		†	£425

Nos. 457/64 were emergency printings caused by the non-arrival of stocks of the Cowan thin, ready gummed Crown over A watermarked paper. Paper watermarked W 104 had been introduced in 1911 and was normally used for Victoria fiscal stamps. This watermark can be easily distinguished from the previous W 85 by its narrow crown.

STAMP BOOKLETS

There are very few surviving examples of Nos. SB1/4. Listings are provided for those believed to have been issued with prices quoted for those known to still exist.

1904 (Mar)–**09**. *Black on red cover as No. SB1 of New South Wales. Stapled.*
SB1   £1 booklet containing two hundred and forty 1d. in four blocks of 30 and two blocks of 60 ..
      a. Red on pink cover (1909) £6000
      b. Blue on pink cover £5000

1904 (Mar). *Black on grey cover as No. SB1. Stapled.*
SB2   £1 booklet containing one hundred and twenty 2d. in four blocks of 30

1910 (May). *Black on white cover as No. SB3 of New South Wales. Stapled.*
SB3   2s. booklet containing eleven ¹/₂d. (No. 426, either in block of 6 plus block of 5 or block of 11, and eighteen 1d. (No. 427), either in three blocks of 6 or block of 6 plus block of 12 .. .. £2000
      a. Black on pale green cover £2000
Unsold stock of No. SB3 was uprated with one additional ¹/₂d. in May 1911.

1911 (Aug). *Red on pink cover as No. SB3. Stapled.*
SB4   2s. booklet containing twelve ¹/₂d. (No. 426), either in two blocks of 6 or block of 12, and eighteen 1d. (No. 427), either in three blocks of 6 or block of 6 plus block of 12 .. .. £1500

POSTAGE DUE STAMPS

D 1

(Dies eng A. Williams (values) and J. McWilliams (frame). Typo)

1890 (12 Oct)–**94**. *Wmk V over Crown, W 33. P 12×12¹/₂.*

D 1	D 1	¹/₂d. dull blue and brown-lake (24.12.90)	2·75	2·00
		a. Dull blue and deep claret	2·75	3·50
D 2		1d. dull blue and brown-lake	4·25	1·40
		a. Dull blue and brownish red (1.93)	5·50	1·10
D 3		2d. dull blue and brown-lake	7·00	1·10
		a. Dull blue and brownish red (3.93)	7·50	90
D 4		4d. dull blue and brown-lake	8·00	2·00
		a. Dull blue and pale claret (5.94)	9·50	6·50
D 5		5d. dull blue and brown-lake	7·50	2·00
D 6		6d. dull blue and brown-lake	8·50	1·75
D 7		10d. dull blue and brown-lake	70·00	35·00
D 8		1s. dull blue and brown-lake	48·00	6·50
D 9		2s. dull blue and brown-lake	£110	45·00
D10		5s. dull blue and brown-lake	£160	90·00
D1/10			Set of 10	£375	£160
D1a/10	Optd "Specimen"		Set of 10	£300	

A used example of the 6d. showing compound perforation of 12×12¹/₂ and 11 exists in the Royal Collection.

1895 (17 Jan)–**96**. *Colours changed. Wmk V over Crown, W 33. P 12×12¹/₂.*

D11	D 1	¹/₂d. rosine and bluish green	2·75	1·60
		a. Pale scarlet and yellow-green (3.96)	3·25	1·50
D12		1d. rosine and bluish green	2·50	40
		a. Pale scarlet and yellow-green (3.96)	2·75	50

D13	D 1	2d. rosine and bluish green	..	..	3·75	50
		a. Pale scarlet and yellow-green (3.96)			4·25	60
D14		4d. rosine and bluish green	..	..	7·00	1·50
		a. Pale scarlet and yellow-green (3.96)			8·50	1·00
D15		5d. rosine and bluish green	..	..	6·50	5·00
		a. Pale scarlet and yellow-green (3.96)			8·00	3·75
D16		6d. rosine and bluish green	..	..	7·00	3·00
D17		10d. rosine and bluish green	..	..	14·00	10·00
D18		1s. rosine and bluish green	..	..	8·50	3·25
D19		2s. pale red & yellowish green (28.3.95)		60·00	20·00
D20		5s. pale red & yellowish green (28.3.95)		£100	40·00
D11/20		..	..	Set of 10	£180	75·00

1897 (July)–**99**. *Wmk V over Crown.* W 82. *P* 12×12½.

D21	D 1	1d. pale scarlet and yellow-green	..	3·75	80
		a. Dull red and bluish green (8.99)		5·50	75
D22		2d. pale scarlet and yellow-green	..	5·50	80
		a. Dull red and bluish green (6.99)		6·50	75
D23		4d. pale scarlet and yellow-green	..	8·00	2·25
		a. Dull red and bluish green (8.99)		12·00	1·10
D24		5d. pale scarlet and yellow-green	..	8·00	2·50
D25		6d. pale scarlet and yellow-green	..	7·00	2·75
D21/5		..	..	Set of 5	29·00	7·00

1900 (June)–**04**. *Wmk V over Crown,* W 85. *P* 12×12½.

D26	D 1	½d. rose-red and pale green	..	4·25	3·50
		a. Pale red and deep green (8.01)		3·00	3·00
		b. Scarlet and deep green (1.03)		—	22·00
		c. Aniline rosine and green (6.04)		4·50	5·00
D27		1d. rose-red and pale green	..	4·50	75
		a. Pale red and deep green (9.01)		4·00	35
		b. Scarlet and deep green (2.02)		5·00	50
		c. Aniline rosine and green (9.03)		4·50	85
D28		2d. rose-red and pale green (7.00)		5·00	75
		a. Pale red and deep green (9.01)		5·50	70
		b. Scarlet and deep green (2.02)		5·50	50
		c. Aniline rosine and green (9.03)		5·50	85
D29		4d. rose-red and pale green (5.01)		11·00	3·75
		a. Pale red and deep green (9.01)		10·00	1·40
		b. Scarlet and deep green (6.03)		10·00	2·00
		c. Aniline rosine and green (6.04)		11·00	2·50
D30		5d. scarlet and deep green (1.03)		9·00	4·00
D31		1s. scarlet and deep green (3.02)		14·00	4·25
D32		2s. scarlet and deep green (1.03)		£110	65·00
D33		5s. scarlet and deep green (1.03)		£130	65·00
D26/33		..	..	Set of 8	£250	£130

1905 (Dec)–**09**. *Wmk Crown over A,* W w 11. *P* 12×12½.

D34	D 1	½d. aniline rosine and pale green (1.06)		6·00	6·00
		a. Scarlet & pale yellow-green (7.07)		3·50	3·25
		b. Dull scarlet and pea-green (3.09)		4·75	3·25
		ba. Compound perf 12×12½ and 11		£120	85·00
D35		1d. aniline rosine and pale green	..	32·00	4·25
		a. Scarlet & pale yellow-green (5.06)		4·00	90
		b. Dull scarlet and pea-green (1.07)		7·00	80
D36		2d. aniline scarlet & dp yell-grn (5.06)		5·00	1·10
		a. Dull scarlet and pea-green (11.07)		6·50	80
D37		4d. dull scarlet and pea-green (1908)		15·00	6·00
D34/7		..	..	Set of 4	25·00	9·50

A printing of the 5d. in dull scarlet and pea-green on this paper was prepared in 1907–08, but not put into use. A few examples have survived, either mint or cancelled-to-order from presentation sets (*Price £1000 mint, £750 cancelled-to-order*).

WESTERN AUSTRALIA

PRICES FOR STAMPS ON COVER

Nos. 1/6	from × 6
Nos. 15/32	from × 4
Nos. 33/46	from × 5
Nos. 49/51	from × 6
Nos. 52/62	from × 10
Nos. 63/a	from × 8
No. 67	from × 6
Nos. 68/92a	from × 10
Nos. 94/102	from × 40
Nos. 103/5	from × 8
Nos. 107/10a	from × 12
Nos. 111a/b	
Nos. 112/16	from × 25
Nos. 117/25	from × 10
Nos. 126/8	—
Nos. 129/34	from × 8
Nos. 135/6	—
Nos. 138/48	from × 12
Nos. 151/63	from × 5
Nos. 168/9	from × 20
Nos. 170/1	from × 4
Nos. 172/3	from × 40
Nos. F11/22	from × 10
Nos. T1/2	—

SPECIMEN OVERPRINTS. Those listed are from U.P.U. distributions between 1889 and 1892. Further "Specimen" overprints exist, but those were used for other purposes.

1

2

3

4

GUM. The 1854 issues are hardly ever seen with gum and so the unused prices quoted are for examples without gum.

(Eng W. Humphrys. Recess P.B.)

1854 (1 Aug). W 4 *(sideways).* (*a*) *Imperf.*

| 1 | 1 | 1d. black | .. | £800 | £180 |

(*b*) *Rouletted* 7½ *to* 14 *and compound*

| 2 | 1 | 1d. black | .. | £1100 | £350 |

In addition to the supplies received from London a further printing, using the original plate and watermarked paper from Perkins, Bacon, was made in the colony before the date of issue. The 1d. is also known pin-perforated.

(Litho H. Samson (later A. Hillman), Government Lithographer)

1854 (1 Aug)–**55**. W 4 *(sideways).* (*a*) *Imperf.*

3	2	4d. pale blue	..	£225	£150
		a. Blue		£225	£150
		b. Deep dull blue		£1200	£600
		c. Slate-blue (1855)		£1200	£650
4	3	1s. salmon	..	— £1400	
		a. Deep red-brown		£850	£400
		b. Grey-brown (1.55)		£450	£325
		c. Pale brown (10.55)		£325	£275

(*b*) *Rouletted* 7½ *to* 14 *and compound*

5	2	4d. pale blue	..	£1100	£400
		a. Blue		—	£400
		b. Slate-blue (1855)		—	£1100
6	3	1s. grey-brown (1.55)		£1400	£650
		a. Pale brown (10.55)		£1400	£650

The 1s. is also known pin-perforated.

The 4d. value was prepared from the Perkins, Bacon 1d. plate. A block of 60 (5 × 12) was taken as a transfer from this plate, the frames painted out and then individually replaced by transfers taken from a single impression master plate of the frame. Four transfers were then taken from this completed intermediate stone to construct the printing stone of 240 impressions. This first printing stone was used by H. Samson to print the initial supplies in July 1854.

The intermediate stone had carried several transfer errors, the most prominent of which was the "T" of "POSTAGE" sliced at foot, which appeared on four positions of the printing stone.

| 3d. "T" of "POSTAGE" shaved off to a point at foot (R.7/5, 7/10, 7/15, 7/20) | £650 | £475 |

The original printing stone also contained three scarce creased transfers, whose exact positions in the sheet have yet to be established. These were corrected during the first printing.

3e. Top of letters of "AUSTRALIA" cut off so that they are barely 1 mm high ..	— £6000
f. "PEICE" instead of "PENCE"	— £6000
g. "CE" of "Pence" close together	— £8000

Further supplies were required in January 1855 and A. Hillman, Samson's successor, found, after printing three further sheets from the first printing stone, that two of the impressions on the intermediate stone were defective giving one inverted and one tilted frame. A second printing stone was then prepared on which the four positions of the inverted frame were individually corrected.

| 3h. Frame inverted (R.8/1, 8/6, 8/11, 8/16) .. | † £60000 |
| i. Tilted border (R.7/4, 7/9, 7/14, 7/19).. .. | £750 £500 |

None of the creased transfers from the first printing stone appear on the second, which exhibits its own range of similar varieties.

3j. "WEST" in squeezed-down letters and "F" of "FOUR" with pointed foot (R.2/17) ..	£800 £550
k. "ESTERN" in squeezed-down letters and "U" of "FOUR" squeezed-up (R.3/17) ..	£1300 £1000
l. Small "S" in "POSTAGE" (R.4/17) ..	£800 £550
m. "EN" of "PENCE" shorter (R.6/4) ..	£700 £500
n. "N" of "PENCE" tilted to right with thin first downstroke (R.6/16)	£700 £500
o. Swan and water above "ENCE" damaged (R.6/20)	£700 £500
p. "F" of "FOUR" slanting to left (R.7/17)	£700 £500
q. "WESTERN" in squeezed-down letters only 1½ mm high (R.8/17)	£850 £600
r. "P" of "PENCE" with small head (R.9/15)	£700 £500
s. "RALIA" in squeezed-down letters only 1½ mm high (R.9/16)	£800 £550
t. "PE" of "PENCE" close together (R.10/15)	£700 £500
u. "N" of "PENCE" narrow (R.10/16) ..	£700 £500
v. Part of right cross-stroke and down-stroke of "T" of "POSTAGE" cut off (R.11/15)	£700 £500
w. "A" in "POSTAGE" with thin right limb (R.11/16)	£700 £500

For the third printing in October 1855 the impressions showing the inverted frame were replaced on the printing stone with fresh individual transfers of the frame. On two of the positions traces of the original frame transfer remained visible.

| 3x. Coloured line above "AGE" of "POSTAGE" (R.8/6) | £700 £500 |
| y. No outer line above "GE" of "POSTAGE" and coloured line under "FOU" of "FOUR" (R.8/11) .. .. .. | £750 £550 |

The same stone was used for a further printing in December 1855 and it is believed that the slate-blue shade occurred from one of the 1855 printings.

The above varieties, with the exception of Nos. 3e/g, also occur on the rouletted stamps.

The 1s. value was produced in much the same way, based on a transfer from the Perkins, Bacon 1d. plate.

5

(Litho A. Hillman, Government Lithographer)

1857 (7 Aug)–**59**. W 4 *(sideways).* (*a*) *Imperf.*

15	5	2d. brown-black/*red* (26.2.58)	..	£1700	£500
		a. Printed both sides..		£1900	£800
16		2d. brown-black/*Indian red* (26.2.58)		—	£800
		a. Printed both sides..		£1700	£850
17		6d. golden bronze	..	£3250 £1300	
18		6d. black-bronze	..	£1900	£600
19		6d. grey-black (1859)	..	£2000	£500

(*b*) *Rouletted* 7½ *to* 14 *and compound*

20	5	2d. brown-black/*red*	..	£2500 £1000	
		a. Printed both sides ..			
21		2d. brown-black/*Indian red*	..	— £1200	
22		6d. black-bronze	..	£2250	£750
23		6d. grey-black	..	—	£800

The 2d. and 6d. are known pin-perforated.

Prices quoted for Nos. 15/23 are for "cut-square" examples. Collectors are warned against "cut-round" copies with corners added.

(Recess in the colony from P.B. plates)

1860 (11 Aug)–**64**. W 4 *(sideways).* (*a*) *Imperf.*

24	1	2d. pale orange	..	..	70·00	55·00
25		2d. orange-vermilion	..	..	65·00	50·00
		a. Wmk upright	..	..	£225	£300
25b		2d. deep vermilion	..	..	£1100	
26		4d. blue (21.6.64)	..	..	£180 £1400	
		a. Wmk upright	..	..	£250	
27		4d. deep blue	..	..	£180 £1500	
28		6d. sage-green (27.7.61)	..	£1100	£400
28a		6d. deep sage-green	..	..	—	£500

(*b*) *Rouletted* 7½ *to* 14

29	1	2d. pale orange	..	..	£325	£140
30		2d. orange-vermilion	..	..	£400	£150
31		4d. deep blue	..	..	£1700	
32		6d. sage-green	..	..	£1200	£400

(Recess P.B.)

1861. W 4 *(sideways).* (*a*) *Intermediate perf* 14–16.

33	1	1d. rose	..	..	..	£250	80·00
34		2d. blue	..	..	..	£110	38·00
35		4d. vermilion	..	..	..	£450 £1100	
36		6d. purple-brown	..	..	£275	55·00
37		1s. yellow-green	..	..	£375	95·00

(*b*) *P* 14 *at Somerset House*

38	1	1d. rose	..	..	..	£140	40·00
39		2d. blue	..	..	..	60·00	25·00
40		4d. vermilion	..	..	..	£130	£120

(*c*) *Perf clean-cut* 14–16

41	1	2d. blue	..	..	..	60·00	24·00
		a. Imperf between (pair) ..			
42		6d. purple-brown	..	..	£170	32·00
43		1s. yellow-green	..	..	£300	50·00

(*d*) *P* 14–16 *very rough* (July)

44	1	1d. rose-carmine	..	..	£160	26·00
45		6d. purple/*blued*	..	..	£600	£120
46		1s. deep green	..	..	£900	£190

Perkins, Bacon experienced considerable problems with their perforating machine during the production of these stamps.

The initial printing showed intermediate perforation 14–16. Further supplies were then sent, in late December 1860, to Somerset House to be perforated on their comb 14 machine. The Inland Revenue Board were only able to process the three lower values, although the 6d. purple-brown and 1s. yellow-green are known from this perforation overprinted "SPECIMEN".

The Perkins, Bacon machine was repaired the following month and the 6d., 1s. and a further supply of the 2d. were perforated on it to give a clean-cut 14–16 gauge.

A final printing was produced in July 1861, but by this time the machine had deteriorated so that it produced a very rough 14–16.

(Recess D.L.R. from P.B. plates)

1863 (16 Dec)–**64**. *No wmk. P* 13.

49	1	1d. carmine-rose	..	..	42·00	3·50
50		1d. lake	..	..	..	42·00	3·50
51		6d. deep lilac (15.4.64)	..	..	80·00	35·00
51a		6d. dull violet (15.4.64)	..	..	£120	40·00

Both values exist on thin and on thick papers, the former being the scarcer.

Both grades of paper show a marginal sheet watermark, "T H SAUNDERS 1860" in double-lined large and small capitals, but parts of this watermark rarely occur on the stamps.

(Recess D.L.R. from P.B. plates)

1864 (27 Dec)–**79**. *Wmk Crown CC (sideways on* 1d.). *P* 12½.

52	1	1d. bistre	..	..	..	45·00	2·50
53		1d. yellow-ochre (16.10.74)	..	60·00	6·00
54		2d. chrome-yellow (18.1.65)	..	45·00	90
55		2d. yellow	..	..	..	45·00	90
		a. Wmk sideways (5.79)	..	—	15·00
		b. Error. Mauve (1879)	..	£5000 £3750	
56		4d. carmine (18.1.65)	..	..	50·00	4·00
		a. Doubly printed	..	..	£5000	
57		6d. violet (18.1.65)	..	..	60·00	6·00
		a. Doubly printed	..	..	† £7000	
		b. Wmk sideways	..	..	—	£150
58		6d. indigo-violet	..	..	£250	28·00
59		6d. lilac (1872)	..	..	£120	6·00
60		6d. mauve (12.5.75)	..	..	£110	6·00
61		1s. bright green (18.1.65) (H/S S. £85)	85·00	12·00
62		1s. sage-green (10.68)	..	..	£200	12·00

Beware of fakes of No. 55b made by altering the value tablet of No. 60.

ONE PENNY

7   (8)

(Typo D.L.R.)

1871 (29 Oct)–**73.** *Wmk Crown CC* (*sideways*). *P* 14.
63   7   3d. pale brown (H/S S. £75) .. .. 28·00 4·00
        a. *Cinnamon* (1873) .. .. .. 28·00 3·50

1874 (10 Dec). *No.* 55 *surch with T* **8** *by Govt Printer.*
67   1   1d. on 2d. yellow (G.) .. .. £160 45·00
        a. *Pair, one without surch* .. ..
        b. *Surch triple* .. .. † £1800
        c. "O" *of* "ONE" *omitted*
    Forged surcharges of T **8** are known on stamps wmk Crown CC
perf 14, and on Crown CA, perf 12 and 14.

(Recess D.L.R. from P.B. plates)

1876–81. *Wmk Crown CC* (*sideways*). *P* 14.
68   1   1d. ochre .. .. .. 42·00 1·25
69   1d. bistre (1878) .. .. 60·00 2·75
70   1d. yellow-ochre (1879) .. 45·00 70
71   2d. chrome-yellow .. .. 42·00 50
        a. *Wmk upright* (1877) .. 60·00 1·25
74   4d. carmine (1881) .. .. £275 75·00
75   6d. lilac (1877) .. .. 75·00 3·25
        a. *Wmk upright* (1879) .. £450 15·00
75b   6d. reddish lilac (1879) .. 75·00 5·50

(Recess D.L.R. from P.B. plates)

1882 (Mar)–**85.** *Wmk Crown CA* (*sideways*). (*a*) *P* 14.
76   1   1d. yellow-ochre .. .. 15·00 50
77   2d. chrome-yellow .. .. 19·00 50
        a. *Wmk upright* .. .. †
78   4d. carmine (8.82) .. .. 75·00 6·50
        a. *Wmk upright* (1885) .. 25·00
79   6d. reddish lilac (1882) .. 70·00 3·00
80   6d. lilac (1884) (H/S S. £75) .. 70·00 4·00

(*b*) *P* 12 × 14
81   1   1d. yellow-ochre (2.83) .. £1000 £150

(*c*) *P* 12
82   1   1d. yellow-ochre (2.83) .. 60·00 1·60
83   2d. chrome-yellow (6.83) .. 75·00 1·60
        a. *Imperf between* (*pair*) .. £120 25·00
84   4d. carmine (5.83) .. .. £120 25·00
85   6d. lilac (6.83) .. .. £190 25·00

(Typo D.L.R.)

1882 (July)–**95.** *Wmk Crown CA* (*sideways*). *P* 14.
86   7   3d. pale brown .. .. 13·00 1·50
87   3d. red-brown (12.95) .. 8·50 1·00
    The 3d. stamps in other colours, watermark Crown CA and
perforated 12, are colour trials dating from 1883.

$\frac{1}{2}$ **1d.**   **1d.**
(9)   (10)   (11)

1884 (19 Feb). *Surch with T* **9**, *in red, by Govt Printer.*
89   1   ½ on 1d. yellow-ochre (No. 76) .. 13·00 17·00
        a. *Thin bar* .. .. 70·00 85·00
90   ½ on 1d. yellow-ochre (No. 82) .. 9·00 13·00
    Inverted or double surcharges are forgeries made in London
about 1886.
    The "Thin bar" varieties occur on R12/3, R12/8, R12/13 and
R12/18, and show the bar only 0.2 mm thick.

1885 (May). *Nos.* 63/a *surch, in green, by Govt Printer.*
(*a*) *Thick* "1" *with slanting top, T* **10** (*Horizontal Rows* 1/5)
91   1d. on 3d. pale brown .. 45·00 10·00
        a. *Cinnamon* .. .. 35·00 8·00
        b. *Vert pair. Nos.* 91/2 .. £130

(*b*) *Thin* "1" *with straight top, T* **11** (*Horizontal Row* 6)
92   1d. on 3d. pale brown .. 95·00 18·00
        a. *Cinnamon* .. .. 75·00 19·00

12   13

14   15

(Typo D.L.R.)

1885 (May)–**93.** *Wmk Crown CA* (*sideways*). *P* 14.
94   12   ½d. yellow-green .. .. 3·00 30
94a   ½d. green .. .. 3·00 30
95   13   1d. carmine (2.90) .. .. 12·00 10
96   14   2d. bluish grey (6.90) .. 17·00 40
96a   2d. grey .. .. 16·00 40

---

97   15   2½d. deep blue (1.5.92) .. .. 7·00 35
97a   2½d. blue .. .. .. 6·50 35
98   4d. chestnut (7.90) .. .. 6·50 40
99   5d. bistre (1.5.92) .. .. 8·00 2·25
100   6d. bright violet (1.93) .. .. 14·00 1·00
101   1s. olive-green (4.90) .. 22·00 3·00
102   1s. olive-green .. .. 17·00 3·00
94, 96a, 97a/99, 101 Optd/H/S "Specimen" *Set of* 6 £225

(Recess D.L.R. from P.B. plates)

1888 (Mar–Apr). *Wmk Crown CA* (*sideways*). *P* 14.
103   1   1d. carmine-pink .. .. 12·00 1·50
104   2d. grey .. .. 32·00 1·00
105   4d. red-brown (April) .. 70·00 18·00
103/5 H/S "Specimen" .. .. *Set of* 3 £150

ONE PENNY   Half-penny

(16)   (17)

1893 (Feb). *Surch with T* **16**, *in green, by Govt Printer.*
107   7   1d. on 3d. pale brown (No. 63) .. 11·00 2·75
108   1d. on 3d. cinnamon (No. 63a) .. 11·00 3·00
        a. *Double surcharge* £475
109   1d. on 3d. pale brown (No. 86) .. 32·00 4·25

1895 (21 Nov). *Surch with T* **17** *by Govt Printer.* (*a*) *In green.*
110   7   ½d. on 3d. pale brown (No. 63) .. 7·50 18·00
110a   ½d. on 3d. cinnamon (No. 63a) .. 5·50 17·00
        b. *Surcharge double* .. £350

(*b*) *In red and in green*
111a 7   ½d. on 3d. cinnamon (No. 63a) .. 70·00 £150
111b   ½d. on 3d. red-brown (No. 87) .. 50·00 85·00
    Green was the adopted surcharge colour but a trial had earlier
been made in red on stamps watermarked Crown CC. As they
proved unsatisfactory they were given another surcharge in green.
The trial stamps were inadvertently issued and, to prevent speculation, a further printing of the duplicated surcharge was made, but
on both papers, Crown CC (No. 111a) and Crown CA (No. 111b).

18   19

20   21

(Typo D.L.R.)

1898 (Dec)–**1907.** *Wmk W Crown A, W* **18.** *P* 14.
112   13   1d. carmine .. .. 3·50 10
113   14   2d. bright yellow (1.99) .. 9·00 95
114   19   2½d. blue (1.01) .. .. 6·00 30
115   20   6d. bright violet (10.06) .. 17·00 50
116   21   1s. olive-green (4.07) .. 20·00 3·50

22   23   24

25   26   27

28   29   30

31   32   33

(Typo Victoria Govt Printer, Melbourne, Commonwealth Stamp
Ptg Branch from March, 1909)

1902 (Oct)–**12.** *Wmk V and Crown, W* **33** (*sideways on horiz
designs*).
(*a*) *P* 12½ *or* 12½ × 12 (*horiz*), 12 × 12½ (*vert*)
117   22   1d. carmine-rose (1.03) .. 8·00 10
        a. *Wmk upright* (10.02) .. 11·00 30
118   23   2d. yellow (4.1.03) .. .. 7·50 95
        a. *Wmk upright* (12.7.04) .. — 1·50
119   24   4d. chestnut (4.03) .. .. 7·50 90
        a. *Wmk upright* £160
120   15   5d. bistre (4.9.05) .. .. 70·00 42·00
121   25   8d. apple-green (3.03) .. 18·00 2·50
122   26   9d. yellow-orange (5.03) .. 26·00 4·75
        a. *Wmk upright* (11.03) .. 35·00 14·00
123   27   10d. red (3.03) .. .. 28·00 4·50
124   28   2s. bright red/*yellow* .. 75·00 15·00
        a. *Wmk sideways* .. £150 16·00
        b. *Orange/yellow* (7.06) .. 40·00 8·50
        c. *Brown-red/yellow* (5.11) .. 40·00 8·50
125   29   2s. 6d. deep blue/*rose* .. 40·00 8·00
126   30   5s. emerald-green .. .. 60·00 19·00
127   31   10s. deep mauve .. .. £140 55·00
        a. *Bright purple* (1910) .. £160 80·00
128   32   £1 orange-brown (1.11.02) .. £275 £150
        a. *Orange* (10.7.09) .. £550 £250

(*b*) *P* 11
129   22   1d. carmine-rose .. .. 80·00 9·00
        a. *Wmk upright* .. ..
130   23   2d. yellow .. .. £110 11·00
        a. *Wmk upright* .. ..
131   24   4d. chestnut £400 £120
132   15   5d. bistre .. .. 42·00 25·00
133   26   9d. yellow-orange .. .. 60·00 48·00
134   28   2s. bright red/*yellow* .. £120 70·00
        a. *Orange/yellow* £225 £110

(*c*) *Perf compound of* 12½ *or* 12 *and* 11
135   22   1d. carmine-rose £350 £160
136   23   2d. yellow £425 £200
137   24   4d. chestnut .. ..
    Type **22** is similar to Type **13** but larger.

34   35

1905–12. *Wmk Crown and A, W* **34** (*sideways*).
(*a*) *P* 12½ *or* 12½ × 12 (*horiz*), 12 × 12½ (*vert*)
138   12   ½d. green (6.10) .. .. 3·50 2·25
139   22   1d. rose-pink (10.05) .. 5·00 10
        a. *Wmk upright* (1.06) .. 4·50 10
        b. *Carmine* (1909) .. .. 6·50 20
        c. *Carmine-red* (1912) .. 7·50 3·50
140   23   2d. yellow (15.11.05) .. 4·00 85
        a. *Wmk upright* (4.10) ..
141   7   3d. brown (2.06) .. .. 10·00 50
142   24   4d. bistre-brown (12.06) .. 10·00 2·75
        a. *Pale chestnut* (1908) .. 10·00 2·25
        b. *Bright brown-red* (14.10.10) .. 7·50 80
143   15   5d. pale olive-bistre (8.05) .. 11·00 2·50
        a. *Olive-green* (1.09) .. 11·00 2·50
        b. *Pale greenish yellow* (5.12) .. 55·00 55·00
144   25   8d. apple-green (22.4.12) .. 17·00 26·00
145   26   9d. orange (11.5.06) .. 22·00 3·50
        a. *Red-orange* (6.10) .. 32·00 3·50
        b. *Wmk upright* (7.12) .. 38·00 24·00
146   27   10d. red-orange (16.2.10) .. 22·00 12·00
148   30   5s. emerald-grn (*wmk upright*) (9.07) .. 65·00 48·00

(*b*) *P* 11
150   12   ½d. green .. .. 18·00 4·50
151   22   1d. rose-pink .. .. 18·00 4·50
        a. *Carmine-red* .. .. 18·00 3·50
        b. *Wmk upright* .. .. 18·00 7·50
152   23   2d. yellow .. .. 17·00 7·00
153   7   3d. brown .. .. 13·00 2·00
154   24   4d. yellow-brown £425 £120
        a. *Pale chestnut* .. ..
155   15   5d. pale olive-bistre .. 28·00 10·00
        a. *Olive-green* .. .. 16·00 9·00
157   26   9d. orange .. .. 75·00 80·00
        a. *Red-orange* .. .. — 65·00
        b. *Wmk upright or inverted* (1912) .. † £275

(*c*) *Perf compound of* 12½ *or* 12 *and* 11
161   22   1d. rose-pink (*wmk upright*) .. £200 £100
162   23   2d. yellow .. .. £170 90·00
163   7   3d. brown £250 £150
164   26   9d. red-orange .. ..

1912 (Mar). *Wmk Crown and A* (*sideways*). *W* **35.** *P* 11½ × 12.
168   20   6d. bright violet .. .. 9·50 3·25
169   21   1s. sage-green .. .. 24·00 4·75
        a. *Perf* 12½ (*single line*) .. — £150

1912 (7 Aug). *W* **34** (*sideways*). *Thin paper and white gum* (*as
Victoria*).
170   7   3d. brown (*p* 12½) .. .. 40·00 40·00
        a. *Wmk upright* .. .. 40·00 40·00
171   3d. brown (*p* 11) .. ..
        a. *Wmk upright* .. ..

ONE PENNY

(36)

The Choice is Yours

MAX STERN & CO., AUSTRALIA'S BEST KNOWN STAMP DEALER

Complete Stocks of

Australia, Australian Antarctic, Cocos, Christmas, Norfolk, Nauru, Pitcairn, Papua New Guinea, New Zealand and Pacific Islands at Competitive prices.
BIG SAVINGS on Complete Country and Year Collections.
Wants lists (S.G.No.) welcome.

Price List available.
All items Guaranteed.
American Stamp Dealers Association Member since 1948.
Hon. Life Member A.S.D.A. Australia.
P.T.S. London.

You Cannot Afford To Deal With Anyone Else But . . .

MAX STERN & CO.

234 Flinders Street,
(Port Phillip Arcade)
Box 997H. GPO
Melbourne, 3001,
Australia

Tel: (61) 3 9654 6751
Fax: (61) 3 9650 7192
E-mail: maxstern@netspace.net.au

Introducing Quality Albums Featuring SG Catalogue Numbers

Stanley Gibbons 'One Country' Albums

Available for

● Great Britain ● Guernsey ● Jersey ● Isle of Man
● Australia ● New Zealand ● Canada

Ideal for the straightforward single country collection these popular albums are available as separate volumes or in a great value set. The high quality leaves feature illustrations, SG catalogue numbers and dates of issue with supplements produced yearly to keep your collection up-to-date.

Plus

● Padded leather finish maroon PVC binders
● Secure 4 and 22 ring locking mechanism
● High quality leaves with illustrations
● Includes self-adhesive album title sheet

Available from our London showroom, at 399 Strand and by Mail Order

 STANLEY GIBBONS

Stanley Gibbons Publications
5/7 Parkside, Christchurch Road,
Ringwood, Hants BH24 3SH
Tel: +44 (0)1425 472363 Fax: +44 (0)1425 470247
e.mail: sales@stangib.demon.co.uk
internet: http://www.stangib.com/

Phone Free On 0800 611 622 For Your Complimentary Colour Brochure

1912 (6 Nov). *Nos. 140 and 162 surch with T* **36** *in Melbourne.*

(a) P 12½ *or* 12 × 12½

172	**23**	1d. on 2d. yellow	..	80	30
		a. Wmk upright	..	1·75	1·75

(b) Perf compound of 12½ *and* 11

173	**23**	1d. on 2d. yellow	..	£300

STAMP BOOKLETS

There are very few surviving examples of Nos. SB1/4. Listings are provided for those believed to have been issued with prices quoted for those known to still exist.

1904 (1 Jan)–**09**. *Black on red cover as No. SB1 of New South Wales. Stapled.*
SB1 £1 booklet containing two hundred and forty 1d.
in four blocks of 30 and two blocks of 60 ..
    a. Red on pink cover (1909) £6000
    b. Blue on pink cover   ..   ..   ..

1904 (1 Jan). *Black on grey cover as No. SB1. Stapled.*
SB2 £1 booklet containing one hundred and twenty 2d.
in four blocks of 30 ..   ..

1910 (May). *Black on white cover as No. SB3 of New South Wales. Stapled.*
SB3 2s. booklet containing eleven ½d. (No. 138), either
in block of 6 plus block of 5 or block of 11, and
eighteen 1d. (No. 139) either in three blocks of
6 or block of 12 ..   ..   .. £2000
Unsold stock of No. SB3 was uprated with one additional ½d. in May 1911.

1911 (Aug). *Red on pink cover as No. SB3. Stapled.*
SB4 2s. booklet containing twelve ½d. (No. 138), either
in two blocks of 6 or block of 12, and eighteen
1d. (No. 139), either in three blocks of 6 or block
of 6 plus block of 12 ..   ..   .. £1500

POSTAL FISCAL STAMPS

By the Post and Telegraph Act of 5 September 1893 the current issue of fiscal stamps up to and including the 1s. value, Nos. F11/15, was authorised for postal use.

These stamps had been initially supplied, for fiscal purposes, in February 1882 and had been preceded by a series of "I R" surcharges and overprints on postage stamps which were in use for a period of about six months. Examples of these 1881–82 provisionals can be found postally used under the terms of the 1893 Act but, as they had not been current for fiscal purposes for over eleven years, we no longer list them.

F 3

(Typo D.L.R.)

1893 (5 Sept). *Definitive fiscal stamps of Feb* 1882. *Wmk CA over Crown. P* 14.

F11	F **3**	1d. dull purple	..	..	8·00	85
F12		2d. dull purple	..	..	80·00	32·00
F13		3d. dull purple	..	..	30·00	1·75
F14		6d. dull purple	..	..	32·00	3·00
F15	—	1s. dull purple	..	..	60·00	4·75

The 1s. value is as Type F **3** but with rectangular outer frame and circular frame surrounding swan.

Higher values in this series were not validated by the Act for postal use.

Two varieties of watermark exist on these stamps. Initial supplies showed an indistinct watermark with the base of the "A" 4 mm wide. From 1896 the paper used showed a clearer watermark on which the base of the "A" was 5 mm wide.

1897. *Wmk W Crown A, W* **18**. *P* 14.

F19	F **3**	1d. dull purple	..	..	4·50	85
F20		3d. dull purple	..	..	23·00	1·75
F21		6d. dull purple	..	..	23·00	1·75
F22	—	1s. dull purple	..	..	55·00	7·00

TELEGRAPH STAMPS USED FOR POSTAGE

The 1d. Telegraph stamps were authorised for postal purposes from 25 October 1886.

T 1

1886 (25 Oct). *Wmk Crown CC.*

T1	T **1**	1d. bistre (*p* 12½)	..	22·00	2·50
T2		1d. bistre (*p* 14)	..	24·00	4·00

Copies of a similar 6d. value are known postally used, but such use was unauthorised.

OFFICIAL STAMPS

Stamps of the various issues from 1854–85 are found with a circular hole punched out, the earlier size being about 3 mm. in diameter and the later 4 mm. These were used on official correspondence by the Commissariat and Convict Department, branches of the Imperial administration separate from the colonial government. This system of punching ceased by 1886. Subsequently many stamps between Nos. 94 and 148 may be found punctured, "PWD", "WA" or "OS".

Western Australia became part of the Commonwealth of Australia on 1 January 1901.

COMMONWEALTH OF AUSTRALIA

On 1 March 1901 control of the postal service passed to the federal administration although it was not until 13 October 1910 that the issues of the various states became valid for use throughout Australia. Postal rates were standardised on 1 May 1911.

The first national postage due stamps appeared in July 1902, but it was not until January 1913 that postage stamps inscribed "AUSTRALIA" were issued.

PRICES FOR STAMPS ON COVER TO 1945	
Nos. 1/19	*from* × 4
Nos. 20/3	*from* × 2
Nos. 24/30	*from* × 4
Nos. 35/47f	*from* × 3
Nos. 51/5a	*from* × 4
Nos. 55b/75	*from* × 3
Nos. 76/84	*from* × 4
Nos. 85/104	*from* × 3
Nos. 105/6	*from* × 4
Nos. 107/15	*from* × 3
No. 116	*from* × 5
Nos. 117/20	*from* × 4
Nos. 121/39a	*from* × 2
Nos. 140/a	*from* × 5
Nos. 141/4	*from* × 3
No. 146	*from* × 6
Nos. 147/53	*from* × 3
Nos. 153a/b	*from* × 2
Nos. 154/63	*from* × 3
Nos. 164/211	*from* × 2
Nos. D1/118	*from* × 8
Nos. O123/36	*from* × 5

PRINTERS. Except where otherwise stated, all Commonwealth stamps to No. 581 were printed under Government authority at Melbourne. Until 1918 there were two establishments (both of the Treasury Dept)—the Note Printing Branch and the Stamp Printing Branch. The former printed T **3** and 4.

In 1918 the Stamp Printing Branch was closed and all stamps were printed by the Note Printing Branch. In 1926 control was transferred from the Treasury to the Commonwealth Bank of Australia, and on 14 January 1960 the branch was attached to the newly established Reserve Bank of Australia.

Until 1942 stamps bore in the sheet margin the initials or names of successive managers and from 1942 to March 1952 the imprint "Printed by the Authority of the Government of the Commonwealth of Australia". After November 1952 (or Nos. D129/31 for Postage Dues) imprints were discontinued.

SPECIMEN OVERPRINTS. These come from Specimen sets, first produced in 1913. In these sets the lower values were cancelled-to-order, but stamps with a face value of 7s. 6d. or 75 c. were overprinted "Specimen" in different types. These overprints are listed as they could be purchased from the Australian Post Office.

It is, however, believed that examples of No. 112 overprinted "Specimen" were distributed by the U.P.U. in 1929. Supplies of the 1902 and 1902–04 postage due stamps overprinted "Specimen" were supplied to the U.P.U. by some of the states.

The sale of the cancelled-to-order sets ceased after 1966, but high value "Specimen" overprints were retained until the end of 1994 to support philatelic funds.

1   2

Die I   Die II

Dies of Type 1 (mono-coloured values only):—

Die I.	Break in inner frame line at lower left level with top of words of value.
Die II.	Die repaired showing no break.

Die I was only used for the ½d., 1d., 2d. and 3d. Several plates were produced for each except the 3d. When the second plate of the 3d. was being prepared the damage became aggravated after making 105 out of the 120 units when the die was returned for repair. This gave rise to the *se-tenant* pairs showing the two states of the die.

Die II was used until 1945 and deteriorated progressively with damage to the frame lines and rounding of the corners.

Specialists recognise seven states of this die, but we only list the two most major of the later versions.

Die IIA. This state is as Die II, but, in addition, shows a break in the inner left-hand frame line, 9 mm from the top of the design (occurs on 1d., 2d. and 6d.).

Die IIB. As Die IIA, but now also showing break in outer frame line above "ST", and (not illustrated) an incomplete corner to the inner frame line at top right (occurs on 3d., 6d., 9d., 1s. and £1 (No. 75)).

(Des B. Young. Eng S. Reading. Typo J. B. Cooke)

1913 (2 Jan)–**14**. *W* **2**. *P* 12.

1	1	½d. green (Die I) (16.1.13)		6·00	2·75
		a. Printed on the gummed side	..	£1000	
		bw. Wmk inverted	..	20·00	8·00
		c. Wmk sideways	..	† £3000	
2		1d. red (Die I)	..	8·50	85
		a. Wmk sideways	..	£550	£100
		b. Carmine	..	8·50	85
		cw. Wmk inverted	..	18·00	2·75
		d. Die II. *Red* (16.1.13)	..	9·00	85
		da. Wmk sideways	..	£600	£100
		db. Carmine	..	8·50	85
		dw. Wmk inverted	..	18·00	2·75
		e. Die IIA. *Red* (4.14)	..	14·00	95
		eb. Carmine	..	14·00	95
		ew. Wmk inverted	..	25·00	2·75
3		2d. grey (Die I) (15.1.13)	..	27·00	4·25
		w. Wmk inverted	..	50·00	9·00
4		2½d. indigo (Die II) (27.1.13)	..	28·00	12·00
5		3d. olive (Die I) (1.2.13)	..	48·00	7·50
		a. Imperf three sides (horiz pair)	..	£11000	
		b. In pair with Die II	..	£425	£160
		c. Yellow-olive	..	48·00	9·00
		ca. In pair with Die II	..	£425	£160
		dw. Wmk inverted	..	60·00	15·00
		e. Die II. *Olive*	..	£160	50·00
		ea. Yellow-olive	..	£160	50·00
		ew. Wmk inverted	..	£200	65·00
6		4d. orange (Die II) (15.2.13)	..	50·00	22·00
		a. Orange-yellow	..	£170	48·00
8		5d. chestnut (Die II) (18.1.13)	..	40·00	32·00
9		6d. ultramarine (Die II) (18.1.13)	..	48·00	20·00
		a. Retouched "E"	..	£1500	£500
		b. Die IIA (substituted cliché) (11.13)	..	£1000	£325
		w. Wmk inverted	..	90·00	45·00
10		9d. violet (Die II) (1.2.13)	..	45·00	22·00
11		1s. emerald (Die II) (25.1.13)	..	45·00	14·00
		a. Blue-green	..	45·00	14·00
		w. Wmk inverted	..	£100	45·00
12		2s. brown (Die II) (30.1.13)	..	£160	65·00
13		5s. grey and yellow (Die II) (20.3.13)	..	£250	£140
14		10s. grey and pink (Die II) (20.3.13)	..	£600	£450
15		£1 brown & ultram (Die II) (20.3.13)	..	£1100	£1000
16		£2 black and rose (Die II) (8.4.13)	..	£2250	£1600
1/16			Set of 15	£4250	£3000
14/16		Optd "Specimen" ..	Set of 3	£600	

Three examples, all used, are known of No. 1c.

The 3d. was printed from two plates, one of which contained 105 stamps as Die I and 15 as Die II. The other plate contained Die I stamps only.

No. 9a shows a badly distorted second "E" in "PENCE", which is unmistakable. It occurs on the Upper plate right pane R. 10/6 and was replaced by a substitute cliché in Type IIA (No. 9b) in the November 1913 printing.

See also Nos. 24/30 (*W* **5**), 35/45b (*W* **6**), 73/5 (*W* **6**, new colours), 107/14 (*W* **7**), 132/8 (*W* **15**), 212 (2s. re-engraved).

3   4 Laughing Kookaburra

(Des R. A. Harrison. Eng and recess T. S. Harrison)

1913 (8 Dec)–**14.** *No wmk. P* 11.

17	3	1d. red	2·50	4·50
		a. Imperf between (horiz pair)	£1700	
		b. Imperf horiz (vert pair)	£1300	
		c. Pale rose-red	7·00	10·00
		ca. Imperf between (vert pair)	£1500	
		cb. Imperf between (horiz pair)	£1900	
19	4	6d. claret (26.8.14)	70·00	38·00

All printings from Plate 1 of the 1d. were in the shade of No. 17c. This plate shows many retouches.

5   5a

1d. Die II

1d. Die II. The flaw distinguishing the so-called Die II, a white upward spur to the right of the base of the "1" in the left value tablet, is now known to be due to a defective roller-die. It occurred on all stamps in the second and third vertical rows of upper left plate right pane. Each of the twenty defective impressions differs slightly; a typical example is illustrated above.

(Dies eng P.B. Typo J. B. Cooke until May 1918, then T. S. Harrison)

1914 (17 July)–**20.** *W* 5. *P* 14.

20	5a	½d. bright green (22.2.15)	3·75	80
		a. Green (1916)	3·75	80
		b. Yellow-green (1916)	25·00	7·50
		c. Thin "1" in fraction at right (Pl 5 rt pane R. 8/1)	£2000	£850
		w. Wmk inverted	10·00	4·00
21		1d. carmine-red (*shades*) (Die I)	7·00	50
		a. Rusted cliché (Pl 2 rt pane R. 6/4 and 5) (9.16)	£5000	£300
		b. Substituted cliché (Pl 2 rt pane R. 6/5) (2.18)	£850	50·00
		c. Pale carmine (*shades*)	14·00	50
		d. Rose-red (1917)	11·00	2·50
		e. Carmine-pink (1918)	70·00	5·50
		f. Carmine (aniline) (1920)	16·00	3·25
		gw. Wmk inverted	12·00	2·00
		h. Die II. Carmine-red (*shades*)	£300	6·00
		hb. Substituted cliché (Pl 2 right pane R. 6/4) (2.18)	£850	50·00
		hc. Pale carmine (*shades*)	£300	7·00
		hw. Wmk inverted	£400	12·00
22		4d. orange (6.1.15)	32·00	2·50
		a. Yellow-orange (1915)	32·00	3·25
		b. Pale orange-yellow (1916)	75·00	11·00
		c. Lemon-yellow (1916)	£130	22·00
		d. Dull orange (1920)	50·00	3·25
		e. Line through "FOUR PENCE" (Pl 2 right pane R. 2/6) (*all shades*) From	£350	90·00
		w. Wmk inverted	45·00	12·00
23		5d. brown (22.2.15)	18·00	1·60
		a. Yellow-brown (1920)	25·00	2·25
		w. Wmk inverted	35·00	14·00

The variety No. 20c was caused by the engraving of a new fraction in a defective electro in 1918.

No. 21a was caused by rusting on two positions of the steel plate 2 and shows as white patches on the back of the King's neck and on, and besides, the top of the right frame (right pane R. 6/4) and on the left frame, wattles, head and ears of kangaroo (right pane R. 6/5). These were noticed in December 1916 when the damaged impressions were removed and replaced by a pair of copper electros (Die II for R. 6/4 and Die I for R. 6/5), showing rounded corners and some frame damage, the former also showing a white spot under tail of emu. In time the tops of the crown quickly wore away.

Most of Nos. 20/3 were perforated 14 by a comb machine (exact gauge 14.25×14), but printings of the ½d. in December 1915, of the 1d. in 1914 and of the 5d. until 1917 were perforated by a line machine measuring 14.2.

See also Nos. 47/fa (*W* 5, rough paper), 51/5a (*W* 6a), 55/ba (1d. Die III), 56/66b and 76/81 (*W* 5, new colours), 82 (*W* 6a), 83/4 (no wmk), 85/104 (*W* 7), 124/31 (*W* 15).

(Typo J. B. Cooke)

1915 (15 Jan–Aug). *W* 5. *P* 12.

24	1	2d. grey (Die I)	50·00	10·00
		w. Wmk inverted	†	£325
25		2½d. indigo (Die II) (July)	50·00	27·00
26		6d. ultramarine (Die II) (April)	£130	22·00
		a. Bright blue	£170	48·00
		b. Die IIA. Ultramarine (substituted cliché) (Upper plate rt pane R. 10/6)	£1000	£275
		ba. Bright blue	£1300	£350
		w. Wmk inverted	†	£850
27		9d. violet (Die II) (9 July)	£130	30·00
		w. Wmk inverted	£475	£140
28		1s. blue-green (Die II) (Aug)	£140	22·00
29		2s. brown (Die II) (April)	£425	90·00
30		5s. grey and yellow (Die II) (12 Feb)	£500	£250
		a. Yellow portion doubly printed	£5500	£1500
		w. Wmk inverted	£600	£300
24/30			Set of 7 £1300 £400	

The watermark in this issue is often misplaced as the paper was made for the portrait stamps.

---

6   6a

Nos. 38ca and 73a
(Upper plate lt pane R. 1/6)

(Typo J. B. Cooke (to May 1918), T. S. Harrison to February 1926), A. J. Mullett (to June 1927) and thereafter J. Ash)

1915 (12 Oct)–**28.** *W* 6 (*narrow Crown*). *P* 12.

35	1	2d. grey (Die I) (11.15)	25·00	5·00
		a. In pair with Die IIA (1917)*	£850	£375
		bw. Wmk inverted	30·00	8·00
		c. Silver-grey (shiny paper) (3.18)	26·00	6·00
		d. Die II. Silver-grey (shiny paper) (3.18)	35·00	8·50
		da. Grey (1920)	38·00	8·50
36		2½d. deep blue (Die II) (9.17)	22·00	9·50
		aw. Wmk inverted	50·00	20·00
		b. Deep indigo (1920)	26·00	5·00
		ba. "1" of fraction omitted (Lower plate left pane R. 6/3)	£9500	£3500
37		3d. yellow-olive (Die I)	27·00	3·50
		a. In pair with Die II	£200	80·00
		b. Olive-green (1917)	30·00	3·50
		ba. In pair with Die II	£200	80·00
		cw. Wmk inverted	35·00	7·00
		d. Die II. Yellow-olive	80·00	27·00
		da. Olive-green	80·00	27·00
		dw. Wmk inverted	£110	40·00
		e. Die IIB. Light olive (1.23)	35·00	10·00
38		6d. ultramarine (Die II) (15.12.15)	50·00	6·00
		a. Die IIA (substituted cliché) (Upper plate rt pane R. 10/6)	£850	£190
		b. Dull blue (6.18)	65·00	9·00
		ba. Die IIA (substituted cliché)	£950	£225
		cw. Wmk inverted	75·00	15·00
		d. Die IIB. Brt ultramarine (23.7.21)	55·00	6·00
		da. Leg of kangaroo broken	£2250	£450
		dw. Wmk inverted	—	40·00
39		9d. violet (Die II) (29.7.16)	38·00	6·00
		aw. Wmk inverted	60·00	15·00
		b. Die IIB. Violet (16.4.19)	35·00	6·00
		bw. Wmk inverted	50·00	14·00
40		1s. blue-green (Die II) (6.16)	35·00	3·00
		aw. Wmk inverted	60·00	15·00
		b. Die IIB (9.12.20)	35·00	3·00
		ba. Wmk sideways (12.27)	60·00	£100
		bw. Wmk inverted	55·00	14·00
41		2s. brown (Die II) (6.16)	£150	11·00
		a. Imperf three sides (horiz pair)	£14000	
		b. Red-brown (aniline)	£425	75·00
		c. Lemon brown	£225	75·00
42		5s. grey and yellow (Die II) (4.18)	£180	75·00
		a. Grey and orange (1920)	£190	75·00
		b. Grey and deep yellow	£180	75·00
		ba. Wmk sideways	† £5000	
		c. Grey and pale yellow (1928)	£180	75·00
		w. Wmk inverted	£225	£100
43		10s. grey and pink (Die II) (5.2.17)	£400	£180
		a. Grey and bright aniline pink (10.18)	£350	£150
		ab. Wmk sideways	£7000	£3500
		aw. Wmk inverted	£500	£200
		b. Grey and pale aniline pink (1928)	£425	£170
44		£1 chocolate & dull blue (Die II) (7.16)	£1300	£700
		a. Chestnut and bright blue (6.17)	£1400	£750
		ab. Wmk sideways	£10000	£4500
		aw. Wmk inverted	£1600	£850
		b. Bistre-brown and bright blue (7.19)	£1300	£700
45		£2 black and rose (Die II) (12.19)	£2250	£1300
		a. Grey and crimson (1921)	£2000	£1200
		b. Purple-black and pale rose (6.24)	£1800	£1100
35/45b			Set of 11 £3500 £1800	
43/5		Optd "Specimen"	Set of 3 £500	

*The Die IIA of No. 35a is a substituted cliché introduced to replace a cracked plate which occurred on R. 10/1 of the Upper plate left pane. The Die IIA characteristics are more pronounced in this cliché than on the sheet stamps from this die. The break at left, for instance, extends to the outer, in addition to the inner, frame line.

One plate of the 3d. contained mixed Die I and Die II stamps as described.

All values were printed by both Cooke and Harrison, and the 9d., 1s. and 5s. were also printed by Mullett and Ash.

1916 (14 Dec)–**18.** *Rough, unsurfaced paper, locally gummed. W* 5. *P* 14.

47	5a	1d. scarlet (Die I)	18·00	2·00
		a. Deep red (1917)	18·00	2·00
		b. Rose-red (1918)	28·00	2·00
		ba. Substituted cliché (Pl 2 rt pane R. 6/5)	£750	55·00
		c. Rosine (1918)	90·00	12·00
		ca. Substituted cliché (Pl 2 rt pane R. 6/5)	£1200	55·00
		dw. Wmk inverted	25·00	3·50
		e. Die II. Rose-red (1918)	£275	20·00
		ea. Substituted cliché (Pl 2 rt pane R. 6/4)	£750	55·00
		f. Die II. Rosine (1918)	£375	50·00
		fa. Substituted cliché (Pl 2 rt pane R. 6/4)	£1200	£140
		fw. Wmk inverted		

All examples of the 5d. on this paper were perforated "OS" and will be found listed as No. O60.

(Typo J. B. Cooke to May 1918 thereafter T. S. Harrison)

1918 (4 Jan)–**20.** *W* 6a (*Mult*). *P* 14.

51	5a	½d. green (*shades*)	5·00	2·00
		a. Thin 1 in fraction at right (Pl 5 rt pane R. 8/1)	£100	50·00
		b. Wmk sideways	† £3000	
		w. Wmk inverted	15·00	8·00
52		1d. carmine-pink (Die I) (23.1.18)	£100	55·00
		a. Deep red (1918)	£850	£275
		w. Wmk inverted	†	
53		1d. carmine (10.12.19)	35·00	6·00
		aw. Wmk inverted	£150	70·00
		b. Deep red (aniline) (1920)	£180	55·00
54		1½d. black-brown (30.1.19)	5·00	2·00
		a. Very thin paper (2.19)	25·00	13·00
		w. Wmk inverted	18·00	6·00
55		1½d. red-brown (4.19)	12·00	1·25
		a. Chocolate (1920)	11·00	1·25
		w. Wmk inverted	26·00	7·00

No. 51 was printed by Cooke and Harrison, Nos. 52/a by Cooke only and Nos. 53/55a by Harrison only. Nos. 52/a have rather yellowish gum, that of No. 53 being pure white.

1d. Die III

1d. Die III. In 1918 a printing (in sheets of 120) was made on paper originally prepared for printing War Savings Stamps, with watermark T 5. A special plate was made for this printing, differing in detail from those previously used. The shading round the head is even; the solid background of the words "ONE PENNY" is bounded at each end by a white vertical line; and there is a horizontal white line cutting the vertical shading lines at left on the King's neck.

(Typo J. B. Cooke)

1918 (15 July). *Printed from a new Die III plate on white unsurfaced paper, locally gummed. W* 5. *P* 14.

55b	5a	1d. rose-red	55·00	28·00
		ba. Rose-carmine	55·00	30·00
		bw. Wmk inverted	75·00	35·00

(Typo T. S. Harrison or A. J. Mullett (1s. 4d. from March 1926))

1918 (9 Nov)–**23.** *W* 5. *P* 14.

56	5a	½d. orange (9.11.23)	2·50	2·50
		w. Wmk inverted	5·00	5·00
57		1d. violet (*shades*) (12.2.22)	7·00	90
		a. Imperf three sides (horiz pair)	£8500	
		b. Red-violet	8·00	1·75
58		1½d. black-brown	8·50	70
		w. Wmk inverted	12·00	3·00
59		1½d. deep red-brown (4.19)	6·50	40
		a. Chocolate (1920)	6·50	45
		w. Wmk inverted	14·00	4·00
60		1½d. bright red-brown (20.1.22)	12·00	3·25
		w. Wmk inverted	† £750	
61		1½d. green (7.3.23)	4·00	55
		a. Rough unsurfaced paper	£110	45·00
		w. Wmk inverted	† £750	
62		2d. brown-orange (4.10.20)	15·00	55
		a. Dull orange (1921)	18·00	55
		w. Wmk inverted	† £750	
63		2d. bright rose-scarlet (19.1.22)	8·00	90
		a. Dull rose-scarlet	8·00	90
		w. Wmk inverted	£1000	
64		4d. violet (21.6.21)	13·00	13·00
		a. Line through "FOUR PENCE" (Pl 2 rt pane R. 2/6)	£6000	£2500
		b. "FOUR PENCE" in thinner letters (Pl 2 rt pane R. 2/6)	£400	£225
65		4d. ultramarine (*shades*) (23.3.22)	48·00	7·00
		a. "FOUR PENCE" in thinner letters (Pl 2 rt pane R. 2/6)	£400	£150
		b. Pale milky blue	70·00	11·00
		w. Wmk inverted	65·00	35·00
66		1s. 4d. pale blue (2.12.20)	65·00	19·00
		a. Dull greenish blue	65·00	19·00
		b. Deep turquoise (1922)	£850	£275
56/66			Set of 11 £160 42·00	

In addition to a number of mint pairs from two sheets purchased at Gumeracha, South Australia, with the bottom row imperforate on three sides, a single used example of No. 57 imperforate on three sides is known.

No. 61a was printed on a small residue of paper which had been employed for Nos. 47/ea.

The 4d. ultramarine was originally printed from the Cooke plates but the plates were worn in mid-1923 and Harrison prepared a new pair of plates. Stamps from these plates can only be distinguished by the minor flaws which are peculiar to them.

The variety of Nos. 64 and 65 with "FOUR PENCE" thinner, was caused by the correction of the line through "FOUR PENCE" flaw early in the printing of No. 64.

(Typo T. S. Harrison (to February 1926), A. J. Mullett (to June 1927), thereafter J. Ash)

1923 (6 Dec)–**24.** *W* 6. *P* 12.

73	1	6d. chestnut (Die IIB)	24·00	1·50
		a. Leg of kangaroo broken (Upper plate lt pane R. 1/6)	75·00	95·00
		w. Wmk inverted	† £1000	
74		2s. maroon (Die II) (1.5.24)	55·00	22·00
		w. Wmk inverted	£120	65·00
75		£1 grey (Die IIB) (1.5.24) (Optd S. £75)	£400	£225

The 6d. and 2s. were printed by all three printers, but the £1 only by Harrison.

No. 73a was corrected during the Ash printing.

(Typo T. S. Harrison (to February 1926), thereafter A. J. Mullett)

1924 (1 May–18 Aug). *P* 14. (*a*) *W* 5.
76 5a 1d. sage-green .. .. .. 3·00 65
　w. Wmk inverted .. .. 10·00 4·50
77 1½d. scarlet (*shades*) .. .. 2·25 30
　a. Very thin paper .. .. 40·00 17·00
　b. "HALEPENCE" (Pl 22 left pane R. 4/4) .. .. 35·00 17·00
　c "RAL" of "AUSTRALIA" thin (Pl 22 left pane R. 5/4) .. 35·00 17·00
　d. Curved "1" and thin fraction at left (Pl 24 rt pane R. 7/5) .. 35·00 17·00
　w. Wmk inverted .. .. 30·00 9·00
78 2d. red-brown .. .. .. 20·00 6·00
　a. *Bright red-brown* .. .. 26·00 7·50
　w. Wmk inverted .. .. † £850
79 3d. dull ultramarine .. .. 24·00 1·50
　a. Imperf three sides (horiz pair) .. £6000
80 4d. olive-yellow .. .. 26·00 4·25
　a. *Olive-green* .. .. .. 28·00 4·50
　w. Wmk inverted .. .. † £750
81 4½d. violet .. .. .. 23·00 2·75
(*b*) *W* 6a
82 5a 1d. sage-green (20 May) .. 8·00 7·50
　w. Wmk inverted .. .. † £650
(*c*) *No wmk*
83 5a 1d. sage-green (18 August) .. 5·50 9·00
84 1½d. scarlet (14 August) .. 11·00 9·50
76/84 Set of 9 £110 35·00

Nos. 78/a and 82/4 were printed by Harrison only but the remainder were printed by both Harrison and Mullett.

In the semi-transparent paper of Nos. 54a and 77a the watermark is almost indistinguishable.

Nos. 77b, 77c and 77d are typical examples of retouching of which there are many others in these issues. In No. 77c the letters "RAL" differ markedly from the normal. There is a white stroke cutting the oval frame-line above the "L", and the right-hand outer line of the Crown does not cut the white frame-line above the "A".

7

I

II

New Dies
1d. For differences see note above No. 20.
1½d. From new steel plates made from a new die. Nos. 87a and 96a are the Ash printings, the ink of which is shiny.
2d. Die I. Height of frame 25.6 mm. Left-hand frame-line thick and uneven behind Kangaroo. Pearls in Crown vary in size.
Die II. Height of frame 25.6 mm. Left-hand frame-line thin and even. Pearls in Crown are all the same size.
Die III. Height 25.1 mm; lettering and figures of value bolder than Die I.
3d. Die II has bolder letters and figures than Die I, as illustrated above.
5d. Die II has a bolder figure "5" with flat top compared with Die I of the earlier issues.

(Typo A. J. Mullett or J. Ash (from June 1927))
1926–30. *W* 7. (*a*) *P* 14.
85 5a ½d. orange (10.3.27) .. 7·00 7·00
　w. Wmk inverted .. .. 18·00 14·00
86 1d. sage-green (23.10.26) .. 3·25 75
　w. Wmk inverted .. .. 10·00 3·00
87 1½d. scarlet (5.11.26) .. 7·50 1·25
　a. *Golden scarlet* (1927) .. 11·00 1·75
　w. Wmk inverted .. .. 14·00 3·50
89 2d. red-brown (Die I) (17.8.27) .. 28·00 28·00
90 3d. dull ultramarine (12.26) .. 23·00 4·25
　w. Wmk inverted .. .. † £750
91 4d. yellow-olive (17.1.28) .. 48·00 29·00
92 4½d. violet (26.10.27) .. 18·00 3·50
93 1s. 4d. pale greenish blue (6.9.27) .. £100 75·00
　w. Wmk inverted .. .. † £750
85/93 .. .. Set of 8 £200 £130

(*b*) *P* 13½×12½
94 5a ½d. orange (21.11.28) .. 2·00 1·00
95 1d. sage-green (Die I) (23.12.26) .. 2·00 50
　aw. Wmk inverted .. .. 10·00 4·00
　b. Die II (6.28) .. .. 50·00 80·00
　bw. Wmk inverted £150
96 1½d. scarlet (14.1.27) .. 2·25 70
　a. *Golden scarlet* (1927) .. 2·25 80
　w. Wmk inverted .. .. 6·00 3·00
97 1½d. red-brown (16.9.30) .. 5·50 5·50
98 2d. red-brown (Die II) (28.4.28) .. 7·50 7·50

99 5a 2d. golden scarlet (Die II) (2.8.30) .. 11·00 1·25
　a. Die III (9.9.30) .. .. 9·00 60
　ab. No wmk £550 £600
　ac. *Tête-bêche* (pair) £30000
100 3d. dull ultramarine (Die I) (28.2.28) 45·00 4·75
　aw. Wmk inverted .. .. 85·00 £110
　b. Die II. *Deep ultramarine* (28.9.29) 23·00 1·25
　bw. Wmk inverted .. .. † £550
102 4d. yellow-olive (19.4.29) .. 23·00 2·75
　w. Wmk inverted .. .. † £750
103 4½d. violet (11.28) .. .. 48·00 22·00
103a 5d. orange-brown (Die II) (27.8.30) 22·00 5·00
104 1s. 4d. turquoise (30.9.28) .. 80·00 24·00
　w. Wmk inverted .. .. † £1000
94/104 Set of 11 £190 60·00

Owing to defective manufacture, part of a sheet of the 2d. (Die III), discovered in July 1931, escaped unwatermarked; while the watermark in other parts of the same sheet was faint or normal. Only one example of No. 99ac is known.

8 Parliament House, Canberra
9 "DH66" Biplane and Pastoral Scene

(Des R. A. Harrison. Die eng J. A. C. Harrison (Waterlow, London). Plates and printing by A. J. Mullett)
1927 (9 May). *Opening of Parliament House, Canberra. No wmk. P* 11.
105 8 1½d. brownish lake 50 50
　a. Imperf between (vert pair) .. £2250
　b. Imperf between (horiz pair) .. £3250 £3250

(Eng H. W. Bell. Recess J. Ash)
1928 (29 Oct). *4th National Stamp Exhibition, Melbourne. As T* 4. *No wmk. P* 11.
106 3d. blue .. .. .. 4·25 4·75
　a. Pane of four with margins .. £150 £225
　ab. Imperf (pane of four) .. £18000
No. 106a comes from special sheets of 60 stamps divided into 15 blocks of 4 (5 × 3) and separated by wide gutters perforated down the middle, printed and sold at the Exhibition.

(Typo J. Ash)
1929 (Feb)–30. *W* 7. *P* 12.
107 1 6d. chestnut (Die IIB) (25.9.29) .. 23·00 4·50
108 9d. violet (Die IIB) .. .. 35·00 12·00
109 1s. blue-green (Die IIB) (12.6.29) .. 35·00 5·00
　w. Wmk inverted .. .. † £1000
110 2s. maroon (Die II) (3.29) .. 50·00 15·00
111 5s. grey and yellow (Die II) (30.11.29) £190 80·00
112 10s. grey and pink (Die II) .. £275 £400
114 £2 black and rose (Die II) (11.30) .. £1900 £450
107/14 Set of 7 £2250 £850
112/14 Optd "Specimen" Set of 2 £325

(Des R. A. Harrison and H. Herbert. Eng A. Taylor. Recess J. Ash)
1929 (20 May). *Air. No wmk. P* 11.
115 9 3d. green (*shades*) .. .. 10·00 3·50
Variations of up to ¾ mm in the design size of No. 115 are due to paper shrinkage on the printings produced by the "wet" process. The last printing, in 1935, was printed by the "dry" method.

10 Black Swan
11 "Capt. Charles Sturt" (J. H. Crossland)

(Des G. Pitt Morrison. Eng F. D. Manley. Recess J. Ash)
1929 (28 Sept). *Centenary of Western Australia. No wmk. P* 11.
116 10 1½d. dull scarlet .. .. 1·25 1·40
　a. Re-entry ("T" of "AUSTRALIA" clearly double) (Pl 2 R. 7/4) .. 55·00 55·00

(Des R. A. Harrison. Eng F. D. Manley. Recess J. Ash)
1930 (2 June). *Centenary of Exploration of River Murray by Capt. Sturt. No wmk. P* 11.
117 11 1½d. scarlet .. .. .. 1·00 65
118 3d. blue .. .. 4·00 6·00
No. 117 with manuscript surcharge of "2d. paid P M L H I" was issued by the Postmaster of Lord Howe Island during a shortage of 2d. stamps between 23 August and 17 October 1930. A few copies of the 1½d. value No. 96a were also endorsed. These provisionals are not recognized by the Australian postal authorities. (*Price £500 un. or us., either stamp*).

TWO

PENCE

(12)

13 Fokker F.VIIa/3m Southern Cross above Hemispheres

1930 (31 July–2 Aug). *T* 5a *surch as T* 12. *W* 7. *P* 13½×12½.
119 2d. on 1½d. golden scarlet .. 1·00 50
120 5d. on 4½d. violet (2 Aug) .. 7·50 7·50
No. 120 is from a redrawn die in which the words "FOURPENCE HALFPENNY" are noticeably thicker than in the original die and the figure "4" has square instead of tapering serifs.
Stamps from the redrawn die without the surcharge were printed, but not issued thus. Some stamps, *cancelled to order*, were included in sets supplied by the post office. A few mint copies, which escaped the cancellation were found and some may have been used postally (*Price £2000 unused, £50 used c.t.o.*).

(Des and eng F. D. Manley. Recess John Ash)
1931 (19 Mar). *Kingsford Smith's Flights. No wmk. P* 11.
(*a*) *Postage.*
121 13 2d. rose-red 75 75
122 3d. blue .. .. 4·50 4·50
(*b*) *Air. Inscr* "AIR MAIL SERVICE" *at sides*
123 13 6d. violet .. .. .. 9·00 11·00
　a. Re-entry ("FO" and "LD" double) (Pl 1 R. 5/5) .. .. 55·00 70·00
121/3 Set of 3 13·00 14·50

15
17 Superb Lyrebird

(Typo John Ash)
1931–36. *W* 15. (*a*) *P* 13½×12½.
124 5a ½d. orange (2.33) .. .. 4·75 5·00
125 1d. green (Die I) (10.31) .. 1·75 10
　w. Wmk inverted .. .. 9·00 3·00
　x. Wmk reversed .. .. £100 40·00
　y. Wmk inverted and reversed .. £150 60·00
126 1½d. red-brown (10.36) .. 6·00 8·50
127 2d. golden scarlet (Die III) (18.12.31) 1·75 10
　w. Wmk inverted (*from booklets*) 2·25 50
128 3d. ultramarine (Die II) (30.9.32) 18·00 75
　w. Wmk inverted £750
129 4d. yellow-olive (2.33) .. 18·00 90
　w. Wmk inverted .. .. † £750
130 5d. orange-brown (Die II) (25.2.32) 15·00 15
　w. Wmk inverted .. .. † £550
131 1s. 4d. turquoise (18.8.32) .. 60·00 3·50
　w. Wmk inverted .. .. † £750
124/31 Set of 8 £110 16·00

(*b*) *P* 12
132 1 6d. chestnut (Die IIB) (20.4.32) .. 22·00 25·00
133 9d. violet (Die IIB) (20.4.32) .. 26·00 1·00
134 2s. maroon (Die II) (6.8.35) .. 5·00 45
135 5s. grey and yellow (Die II) (12.32) .. £110 12·00
136 10s. grey and pink (Die II) (31.7.32) .. £250 £100
137 £1 grey (Die IIB) (11.35) .. £425 £150
138 £2 black and rose (Die II) (6.34) .. £1600 £325
132/138 Set of 7 £2250 £550
136/138 Optd "Specimen" Set of 3 85·00
Stamps as No. 127, but without watermark and perforated 11, are forgeries made in 1932 to defraud the P.O.
For re-engraved type of No. 134, see No. 212.

(Des and eng F. D. Manley. Recess John Ash)
1931 (4 Nov). *Air Stamp. As T* 13 *but inscr* "AIR MAIL SERVICE" *in bottom tablet. No wmk. P* 11.
139 6d. sepia .. .. 16·00 12·00

1931 (17 Nov). *Air. No* 139 *optd with Type O* 4.
139a 6d. sepia .. .. 35·00 45·00
This stamp was not restricted to official use but was on general sale to the public.

(Des and eng F. D. Manley. Recess John Ash)
1932 (15 Feb). *No wmk. P* 11.
140 17 1s. green .. .. 42·00 1·25
　a. *Yellow-green* .. .. .. 45·00 2·50

18 Sydney Harbour Bridge
19 Laughing Kookaburra

(Des and eng F. D. Manley. Printed John Ash)
1932 (14 Mar). *Opening of Sydney Harbour Bridge. (a) Recess. No wmk. P* 11.
141 18 2d. scarlet .. .. .. 2·00 2·50
142 3d. blue .. .. 4·00 6·50
143 5s. blue-green £375 £180
(*b*) *Typo. W* 15. *P* 10½.
144 18 2d. scarlet .. .. .. 2·00 1·25
141/4 Set of 4 £375 £180
Stamps as No. 144 without wmk and perf 11 are forgeries made in 1932 to defraud the P.O.

(Des F. D. Manley. Die eng E. Broad. Typo John Ash)

1932 (1 June). *W* **15**. *P* 13½×12½.
146 **19** 6d. red-brown .. .. 25·00 55
   w. Wmk inverted .. .. † £750

20 Melbourne and R. Yarra   **21** Merino Ram

(Des and eng F. D. Manley. Recess John Ash)

1934 (2 July). *Centenary of Victoria. W* **15**.
                     I. *P* 10½. II. *P* 11½.
147 **20** 2d. orange-vermilion .. 2·50 1·75 4·50 1·50
148   3d. blue .. .. .. 6·00 5·50 7·50 8·00
149   1s. black .. .. .. 45·00 19·00 45·00 20·00
147/9 .. .. *Set of 3* 48·00 24·00 50·00 27·00
Stamps were originally issued perforated 10½, but the gauge was subsequently changed to 11½ in August 1934 due to difficulties in separating stamps in the first perforation.

(Des and eng F. D. Manley. Recess John Ash)

1934 (1 Nov). *Death Centenary of Capt. John Macarthur. W* **15**. *P* 11½.
150 **21** 2d. carmine-red (A) .. .. 4·00 1·50
150a   2d. carmine-red (B) .. .. 25·00 3·00
151   3d. blue .. .. .. 10·00 8·50
152   9d. bright purple .. .. 38·00 38·00
150/2 .. .. .. *Set of 3* 48·00 42·00
Type A of the 2d. shows shading on the hill in the background varying from light to dark (as illustrated). Type B has the shading almost uniformly dark.

22 Hermes   **23** Cenotaph, Whitehall

(Des F. D. Manley. Eng E. Broad and F. D. Manley. Recess John Ash until April 1940; W. C. G. McCracken thereafter)

1934 (1 Dec)–48. (*a*) *No wmk. P* 11.
153 **22** 1s. 6d. dull purple .. .. 32·00 1·00
    (*b*) *W* **15**. *Chalk-surfaced paper. P* 13½×14
153a **22** 1s. 6d dull purple (22.10.37) .. 12·00 45
   b. Thin rough ordinary paper (12.2.48) .. .. 4·75 1·10

(Des B. Cottier; adapted and eng F. D. Manley. Recess John Ash)

1935 (18 Mar). *20th Anniv of Gallipoli Landing. W* **15**. *P* 13½×12½ or 11 (1s.).
154 **23** 2d. scarlet 80 30
155   1s. black (*chalk-surfaced*) .. .. 48·00 38·00
   a. Perf 13½×12½ £1500

24 King George V   **25** Amphitrite and Telephone
on "Anzac"   Cable

(Des and eng F. D. Manley. Recess John Ash)

1935 (2 May). *Silver Jubilee. Chalk-surfaced paper. W* **15** (*sideways*). *P* 11½.
156 **24** 2d. scarlet .. .. .. 1·50 30
157   3d. blue .. .. .. 7·00 7·00
158   2s. bright violet .. .. 45·00 38·00
156/8 .. .. .. *Set of 3* 48·00 40·00

(Des and eng F. D. Manley. Recess John Ash)

1936 (1 Apr). *Opening of Submarine Telephone Link to Tasmania. W* **15**. *P* 11½.
159 **25** 2d. scarlet 75 50
160   3d. blue .. .. .. 2·75 2·75

26 Site of Adelaide, 1836; Old Gum Tree, Glenelg; King William St., Adelaide

---

(Des and eng F. D. Manley. Recess John Ash)

1936 (3 Aug). *Centenary of South Australia. W* **15**. *P* 11½.
161 **26** 2d. carmine .. .. .. 1·25 40
162   3d. blue .. .. .. 4·00 3·50
163   1s. green .. .. .. 10·00 8·00
161/3 .. .. .. *Set of 3* 14·00 11·00

27 Wallaroo   **28** Queen Elizabeth   **28a**

29   **30**   **30a**
King George VI

31 King   **32** Koala   **33** Merino Ram
George VI

34 Laughing Kookaburra   **35** Platypus   **36** Superb Lyrebird

38 Queen Elizabeth   **39** King George VI

40 King George VI and
Queen Elizabeth

Dies of 3d.:

Die I   Die Ia   Die II

Die I. The letters "TA" of "POSTAGE" at right are joined by a white flaw; the outline of the chin consists of separate strokes.
No. 168a is a preliminary printing made with unsuitable ink and may be detected by the absence of finer details; the King's face appears whitish and the wattles are blank. The greater part of this printing was distributed to the Press with advance notices of the issue.
Die Ia. As Die I, but "T" and "A" have been clearly separated by individual retouches made on the plates.
Die II. A completely new die. "T" and "A" are separate and a continuous line has been added to the chin. The outline of the cheek extends to about 1 mm above the lobe of the King's right ear.
Die III. Differs from Dies I and II in the King's left eyebrow which is shaded downwards from left to right instead of from right to left.

Line to Kangaroo's ear (Rt pane R. 6/8)

Medal flaw
(Right pane R. 2/5)

(Des R. A. Harrison (T **28**/30), F. D. Manley (T **27**, 31/6), H. Barr (T **38**/9), H. Barr and F. D. Manley (T **40**). Eng F. D. Manley and T. C Duffell (T **34**), T. C Duffell (revised lettering for T 28a, 30a), F. D. Manley (others). All recess with John Ash, W. C. G. McCracken or "By Authority ..." imprints)

1937–49. *W* **15** (*sideways on* 5d., 9d., 5s. *and* 10s.). *Chalk-surfaced paper* (3d. (*No.* 168), 5s., 10s., £1).
   (*a*) *P* 13½ × 14 (*vert designs*) *or* 14 × 13½ (*horiz*)
164 **27** ½d. orange (3.10.38) .. ..2·50 45
165 **28** 1d. emerald-green (10.5.37) .. 40 10
166 **29** 1½d. maroon (20.4.38) .. 9·00 3·00
167 **30** 2d. scarlet (10.5.37) .. 40 10
168 **31** 3d. blue (Die I) (2.8.37) .. 60·00 9·00
   a. "White wattles" (from 1st ptg) .. £120 70·00
   b. Die Ia .. .. .. £140 6·50
   c. Die II (3.38) .. .. 60·00 3·00
   ca. *Bright blue (ordinary thin paper)* (20.12.38) .. .. 60·00 2·50
170 **32** 4d. green (1.2.38) .. .. 14·00 75
171 **33** 5d. purple (1.12.38) .. .. 2·00 50
172 **34** 6d. purple-brown (2.8.37) .. 23·00 90
173 **35** 9d. chocolate (1.9.38) .. .. 5·00 90
174 **36** 1s. grey-green (2.8.37) .. 48·00 15·00
175 **31** 1s. 4d. pale magenta (3.10.38) .. 1·50 1·50
   a. *Deep magenta* (1943) .. 3·25 2·00
     (*b*) *P* 13½
176 **38** 5s. claret (1.4.38) .. .. 14·00 1·25
   a. Thin rough ordinary paper (4.2.48) .. .. 5·00 2·00
177 **39** 10s. dull purple (1.4.38) (Optd S. £30) 38·00 12·00
   a. Thin rough ordinary paper (11.48) .. .. 48·00 28·00
178 **40** £1 bl-slate (1.11.38) (Optd S. £400) 65·00 30·00
   a. Thin rough ordinary paper (4.4.49) .. .. 85·00 60·00
164/78 .. .. .. *Set of 14* £250 48·00

(*c*) *P* 15×14 (*vert designs*) *or* 14×15 (*horiz*) (1d. *and* 2d. *redrawn with background evenly shaded and lettering strengthened*)
179 **27** ½d. orange (28.1.42) 55 10
   a. Line to kangaroo's ear .. 10·00
   b. Coil pair (1942) .. .. 15·00 17·00
   ba. Coil block of four £130
180 **28a** 1d. emerald-green (1.8.38) .. 2·25 10
181   1d. maroon (10.12.41) .. 1·25 10
   a. Coil pair (1942) .. .. 12·00 16·00
182 **29** 1½d. maroon (21.11.41) .. 4·50 7·50
183   1½d. emerald-green (10.12.41) .. 1·00 60
184 **30a** 2d. scarlet (11.7.38) .. .. 2·50 10
   a. Coil pair (10.41) £325 £375
   b. Medal flaw .. .. 80·00
   w. Wmk inverted (*from booklets*) .. 4·00 50
185   2d. bright purple (10.12.41) .. 50 10
   a. Coil pair (1942) .. .. 42·00 48·00
   b. Medal flaw .. .. 30·00
   w. Wmk inverted (*from coils*) .. 60·00 20·00
186 **31** 3d. blue (Die III) (11.41) .. 45·00 2·25
187   3d. purple-brown (Die III) (10.12.41) 30 10
188 **32** 4d. green (10.42) .. .. 1·00 10
   w. Wmk inverted .. .. † £450
189 **33** 5d. purple (1.46) .. .. 45 1·50
190 **34** 6d. red-brown (6.42) .. .. 2·00 10
   a. *Purple-brown* (1944) .. 1·75 10
191 **35** 9d. chocolate (8.43) .. .. 1·00 20
192 **36** 1s. grey-green (3.41) .. .. 1·00 10
   w. Wmk inverted £500 £130
179/92 .. .. .. *Set of 14* 55·00 11·00
For unwmkd issue, see Nos. 228/30d.

Thin paper. Nos. 176a, 177a, 178a. In these varieties the watermark is more clearly visible on the back and the design is much less sharp. On early printings of No. 176a the paper appears tinted.

SPECIAL COIL PERFORATION. This special perforation of large and small holes on the narrow sides of the stamps was introduced after 1939 for stamps issued in coils and was intended to facilitate separation. Where they exist they are listed as "Coil pairs".
The following with "special coil" perforation were placed on sale in *sheets*: Nos. 179, 205, 222a (1952), 228, 230, 237, 262 (1953), 309, 311, and 314. These are listed as "Coil blocks of four".
Coils with "normal" perforations also exist for Nos. 180 and 184.

PRICES OF SETS

Set prices are given for many issues, generally those containing three stamps or more. Definitive sets include one of each value or major colour change, but do not cover different perforations, die types or minor shades. Where a choice is possible the set prices are based on the cheapest versions of the stamps included in the listings.

41 "Governor Phillip at Sydney Cove" (J. Allcot)

"Tail" flaw (Left pane R. 7/1)

(Des and eng E. Broad and F. D. Manley. Recess J. Ash)

1937 (1 Oct). *150th Anniv of Foundation of New South Wales.* W **15**. P 13½ × 14.

193	41	2d. scarlet	..	..	..	2·25	15
	a. "Tail" flaw	..	..	..	£200	50·00
194	3d. bright blue	..	..	..	7·50	2·75
195	9d. purple	..	..	..	15·00	9·50
193/5	..			*Set of 3*	22·00	11·00

42 A.I.F. and Nurse

(Des and eng F. D. Manley from drawing by Virgil Reilly. Recess W. C. G. McCracken)

1940 (15 July). *Australian Imperial Forces.* W **15** (*sideways*). P 14 × 13½.

196	42	1d. green	..	..	..	1·75	1·25
197	2d. scarlet	..	..	..	1·75	40
198	3d. blue	..	..	..	12·00	7·50
199	6d. brown-purple	..	..	..	22·00	13·00
196/9	..			*Set of 4*	35·00	20·00

(43)   (44)   (45)

(Opts designed by F. D. Manley)

1941 (10 Dec). *Nos. 184, 186 and 171 surch with T* **43/5**.

200	40b	2½d. on 2d. scarlet (V.)	..	..	60	40
	a. Pair, one without surcharge	..	£3500	
	b. Medal flaw	..	..	80·00	
201	31	3½d. on 3d. bright blue (Y. on Black)	75	1·50
202	33	5½d. on 5d. purple (V.)	..	3·50	4·00
200/2				*Set of 3*	4·25	5·50

Nos 200/2 were prepared in connection with the imposition of a ½d. "war tax" increase on most postage rates.

One sheet of the 2½d on 2d. was discovered showing the surcharge omitted on R.1/4 and R.1/5.

46 Queen Elizabeth   46a   47 King George VI

48 King George VI   49 King George VI   50 Emu

(Des F. D. Manley. Eng F. D. Manley and T. C. Duffell (T **46**/a) or F. D. Manley (others))

1942–48. *Recess.* W **15**. P 15×14.

203	46	1d. brown-purple (2.1.43)	..	40	10
	a. Coil pair (1944)	..	18·00	20·00
204	46a	1½d. green (1.12.42)	..	30	10
205	47	2d. bright blue (4.12.44)	..	45	40
	b. Coil pair (4.48)	..	85·00	90·00
	ba. Coil block of four	..	£800	
206	48	2½d. scarlet (7.1.42)	..	30	10
	a. Imperf (pair)*	..	£2500	
	w. Wmk inverted (*from booklets*)	..	3·25	30

207	49	3½d. bright blue (3.42)	..	..	30	10
	a. *Deep blue*	..	..	50	10
208	50	5½d. slate-blue (12.2.42)	..	65	10
203/8				*Set of 6*	2·25	50

*No. 206a comes in horizontal pair with the right-hand stamp completely imperforate and the left-hand stamp imperforate at right only.

Coils with normal perforations exist for 1d.

For stamps as Nos. 204/5 but without watermark see Nos. 229/30.

The following items are understood to have been the subject of unauthorised leakages from the Commonwealth Note and Stamp Printing Branch and are therefore not listed by us.

It is certain that none of this material was distributed to post offices for issue to the public.

Imperforate all round. 1d. Princess Elizabeth; 1½d. Queen; 2½d. King; 4d. Koala; 6d. Kookaburra; 9d. Platypus; 1s. Lyrebird (small) (also imperf three sides); 1s. 6d. Air Mail (Type 22); 2½d. Mitchell; 2½d. Newcastle (also imperf three sides or imperf vertically).

Also 2½d. Peace, unwatermarked; 2½d. King, *tête-bêche*; 3½d. Newcastle, in dull ultramarine; 2½d. King on "toned" paper.

---

52 Duke and Duchess of Gloucester

(Des F. D. Manley. Eng F. D. Manley and T. C. Duffell. Recess)

1945 (19 Feb). *Arrival of Duke and Duchess of Gloucester in Australia.* W **15**. P 14½.

209	52	2½d. lake	..	..	10	10
210	3½d. ultramarine	..	..	15	45
211	5½d. indigo	..	..	20	45
209/11			*Set of 3*	40	85

A   B

1945 (24 Dec). *Kangaroo type, as No. 134, but re-engraved as* B. W **15**. P 12.

212	1	2s. maroon	..	..	3·50	4·00
	w. Wmk inverted	..	..	†	£850

No. 134 has two background lines between the value circle and "TWO SHILLINGS"; No. 212 has only one line in this position. There are also differences in the shape of the letters.

53 Star and Wreath   56 Sir Thomas Mitchell and Queensland

(Des F. D. Manley (2½d.), F. D. Manley and G. Lissenden (3½d.), G. Lissenden (5½d.). Eng F. D. Manley. Recess)

1946 (18 Feb). *Victory Commemoration. T* **53** *and similar designs.* W **15** (*sideways on* 5½d.). P 14½.

213	2½d. scarlet	..	..	..	10	10
214	3½d. blue	..	..	..	25	75
215	5½d. green	..	..	..	30	50
213/15			*Set of 3*	60	1·25

Designs: Horiz—3½d. Flag and dove. Vert—5½d. Angel.

For these designs re-issued in 1995 with face values in decimal currency see Nos. 1542/4.

(Des F. D. Manley. Eng F. D. Manley and T. C. Duffell. Recess)

1946 (14 Oct). *Centenary of Mitchell's Exploration of Central Queensland.* W **15**. P 14½.

216	56	2½d. scarlet	..	..	10	10
217	3½d. blue	..	..	25	70
218	1s. grey-olive	..	..	30	25
216/18			*Set of 3*	60	90

57 Lt. John Shortland R.N.   58 Steel Foundry   59 Coal Carrier Cranes

(Des and eng G. Lissenden (5½d.), F. D. Manley (others). Recess)

1947 (8 Sept). *150th Anniv of City of Newcastle, New South Wales.* W **15** (*sideways on* 3½d.). P 14½ or 15×14 (2½d.).

219	57	2½d. lake	..	..	10	10
220	58	3½d. blue	..	..	25	55
221	59	5½d. green	..	..	25	35
219/21			*Set of 3*	55	85

60 Queen Elizabeth II when Princess

(Des R. A. Harrison. Eng F. D. Manley. Recess)

1947 (20 Nov)–**52**. *Marriage of Princess Elizabeth.* P 14×15.

(a) W **15** (*sideways*)

222	60	1d. purple	..	..	15	10

(b) No wmk

222a	60	1d. purple (8.48)	..	..	10	10
	b. Coil pair (1.50)	..	..	2·25	4·50
	c. Coil block of four (9.52)	..	4·50	

61 Hereford Bull   61a Hermes and Globe

62 Aboriginal Art   62a Commonwealth Coat of Arms

(Des G. Sellheim (T **62**), F. D. Manley (others). Eng G. Lissenden (T **62**), F. D. Manley (1s. 3d., 1s. 6d., 5s.), F. D. Manley and R. J. Becker (10s., £1, £2). Recess)

1948 (16 Feb)–**56.** *(a)* W **15** (*sideways*). P 14½

223	61	1s. 3d. brown-purple	..	1·75	95
223a	61a	1s. 6d. blackish brown (1.9.49)	..	1·25	10
224	62	2s. chocolate	..	..	2·00	10

(b) W **15**. P 14½×13½

224a	62a	5s. claret (11.4.49)	..	..	3·25	20
	ab. Thin paper (1951)	..	23·00	1·00
224b	10s. purple (3.10.49)	..	17·00	50
224c	£1 blue (28.11.49)	..	35·00	3·25
224d	£2 green (16.1.50)	..	£110	14·00
224b/d Optd "Specimen"	..	*Set of 3*	£150	

(c) No wmk. P 14½

224e	61a	1s. 6d. blackish brown (6.12.56)	..	16·00	1·25
224f	62	2s. chocolate (21.7.56)	..	16·00	50
223/4f			*Set of 9*	£180	19·00

No. 224ab is an emergency printing on white Harrison paper instead of the toned paper used for No. 224a.

63 William J. Farrer   64 F. von Mueller   65 Boy Scout

(Des and eng F. D. Manley. Recess)

1948 (12 July). *William J. Farrer* (*wheat research*) *Commemoration.* W **15**. P 15×14.

225	63	2½d. scarlet	..	..	10	10

(Des and eng F. D. Manley. Recess)

1948 (13 Sept). *Sir Ferdinand von Mueller* (*botanist*) *Commemoration.* W **15**. P 15×14.

226	64	2½d. lake	..	..	10	10

(Des and eng F. D. Manley. Recess)

1948 (15 Nov). *Pan-Pacific Scout Jamboree, Wonga Park.* W **15** (*sideways*). P 14 × 15.

227	65	2½d. lake	..	..	10	10

See also No. 254.

Sky retouch (normally unshaded near hill) (Rt pane R. 6/8) (No. 228a retouched in 1951)

"Green mist" retouch. A large area to the left of the bird's feathers is recut (upper plate left pane R. 9/3).

1948–56. No wmk. P 15×14 or 14×15 (9d.).
228	27	½d. orange (15.9.49)		20	10
		a. Line to kangaroo's ear		7·00	
		b. Sky retouch		18·00	
		c. Coil pair (1950)		75	2·25
		ca. Line to kangaroo's ear		27·00	
		cb. Sky retouch (in pair)		95·00	
		d. Coil block of four (1953)		2·50	
229	46a	1½d. green (17.8.49)		1·25	85
230	47	2d. bright purple (1.49)		80	80
		aa. Coil pair		3·00	5·50
230a	32	4d. green (18.8.56)		2·00	70
230b	34	6d. purple-brown (18.8.56)		4·75	50
230c	35	9d. chocolate (13.12.56)		20·00	2·50
230d	36	1s. grey green (13.12.56)		6·50	90
		da. "Green mist" retouch		£550	
228/30d			Set of 7	32·00	5·75

66 "Henry Lawson" (Sir Lionel Lindsay) | **67** Mounted Postman and Convair CV 240 Aircraft

(Des F. D. Manley. Eng. E. R. M. Jones. Recess)

1949 (17 June). *Henry Lawson (poet) Commemoration.* P 15×14.
231	66	2½d. maroon		15	10

(Des Sir Daryl Lindsay and F. D. Manley. Eng F. D. Manley. Recess)

1949 (10 Oct). *75th Anniv of Founding of U.P.U.* P 15 × 14.
232	67	3½d. ultramarine		20	30

68 Lord Forrest of Bunbury | **69** Queen Elizabeth | **70** King George VI

(Des and eng F. D. Manley. Recess)

1949 (28 Nov). *Lord Forrest of Bunbury (explorer and politician) Commemoration.* W **15**. P 15×14.
233	68	2½d. lake		15	10

(Des and eng F. D. Manley. Recess)

1950 (12 Apr)–53. P 15×14. (a) W **15**
234	70	2½d. scarlet (12.4.50)		10	10
235		3d. scarlet (28.2.51)		15	10
		aa. Coil pair (4.51)		17·00	19·00

(b) No wmk
236	69	1½d. green (19.6.50)		15	10
237		2d. yellow-green (28.3.51)		15	10
		a. Coil pair		5·00	7·50
		b. Coil block of four (8.53)		10·00	
237c	70	2½d. purple-brown (23.5.51)		15	15
237d		3d. grey-green (14.11.51)		15	10
		da. Coil pair (12.51)		24·00	30·00
234/7d			Set of 6	80	40

On 14 October 1951 No. 235 was placed on sale in sheets of 144 originally intended for use in stamp booklets. These sheets contain 3 panes of 48 (16×3) with horizontal gutter margin between.

71 Aborigine | **72** **73** Reproductions of First Stamps of New South Wales and Victoria

---

(Des and eng F. D. Manley. Recess)

1950 (14 Aug). W **15**. P 15×14.
238	71	8½d. brown		15	45

For T **71** in a larger size, see Nos. 253/b.

(Des and eng G. Lissenden (T **72**), E. R. M. Jones (T **73**). Recess)

1950 (27 Sept). *Centenary of First Adhesive Postage Stamps in Australia.* P 15×14.
239	72	2½d. maroon		15	10
		a. Horiz pair. Nos. 239/40		30	55
240	73	2½d. maroon		15	10

Nos. 239/40 were printed alternately in vertical columns throughout the sheet.

74 Sir Edmund Barton | **75** Sir Henry Parkes

76 "Opening First Federal Parliament" (T. Roberts) | **77** Federal Parliament House, Canberra

(Des and eng F. D. Manley. Recess)

1951 (1 May). *50th Anniv of Commonwealth of Australia.* P 15×14.
241	74	3d. lake		30	10
		a. Horiz pair. Nos. 241/2		1·75	2·25
242	75	3d. lake		30	10
243	76	5½d. blue		20	1·75
244	77	1s. 6d. purple-brown		35	50
241/4			Set of 4	2·00	2·25

Nos. 241/2 are printed alternately in vertical columns throughout the sheet.

78 E. H. Hargraves | **79** C. J. Latrobe

(Des and eng F. D. Manley. Recess)

1951 (2 July). *Centenaries of Discovery of Gold in Australia and of Responsible Government in Victoria.* P 15×14.
245	78	3d. maroon		30	10
		a. Horiz pair. Nos. 245/6		70	95
246	79	3d. maroon		30	10

Nos. 245/6 were printed alternately in vertical columns throughout the sheet.

80 | **81** King George VI | **82**

(Des and eng F. D. Manley. Recess)

1951–52. W **15** (sideways on 1s. 0½d.). P 14½ (1s. 0½d.) or 15×14 (others).
247	80	3½d. brown-purple (28.11.51)		10	10
		a. Imperf between (horiz pair)		£5500	
248		4½d. scarlet (20.2.52)		15	60
249		6½d. brown (20.2.52)		15	55
250		6½d. emerald-green (9.4.52)		10	15
251	81	7½d. blue (31.10.51)		15	45
		a. Imperf three sides (vert pr)		£7500	
252	82	1s. 0½d. indigo (19.3.52)		35	30
247/52			Set of 6	90	1·75

No. 251a occurs on the left-hand vertical row of one sheet.

(Des and eng F. D. Manley. Recess.)

1952 (19 Mar)–65. P 14½. (a) W **15** (sideways*)
253		2s. 6d. deep brown		1·50	35
		aw. Wmk Crown to left of C of A		†	£700

(b) No wmk
253b		2s. 6d. deep brown (30.1.57)		5·00	45
		ba. Sepia (10.65)		12·00	12·00

Design:—2s. 6d. As T **71** but larger (21×25½ mm).
*The normal sideways watermark on No. 253 shows Crown to right of C of A, *as seen from the back of the stamp.*
No. 253ba was an emergency printing and can easily be distinguished from No. 253b as it is on white Harrison paper, No. 253b being on toned paper.

(Des and eng F. D. Manley. Recess)

1952 (19 Nov). *Pan-Pacific Scout Jamboree, Greystanes. As T* **65***, but inscr* "1952–53" W **15** (sideways). P 14 × 15.
254		3½d. brown-lake		10	10

---

83 Butter | **84** Wheat | **85** Beef

(Des P.O. artists; adapted G. Lissenden. Typo)

1953 (11 Feb). *Food Production.* P 14½.
255	83	3d. emerald		30	10
		a. Strip of 3. Nos. 255/7		2·00	
256	84	3d. emerald		30	10
257	85	3d. emerald		30	10
258	83	3½d. scarlet		30	10
		a. Strip of 3. Nos. 258/60		2·00	
259	84	3½d. scarlet		30	10
260	85	3½d. scarlet		30	10
255/60			Set of 6	3·75	40

The three designs in each denomination appear in rotation, both horizontally and vertically, throughout the sheet.

86 Queen Elizabeth II | **87** Queen Elizabeth II

(Des F. D. Manley from photograph by Dorothy Wilding Ltd. Eng D. Cameron. Recess)

1953–56. P 15×14. (a) No wmk.
261	86	1d. purple (19.8.53)		15	10
261a		2½d. blue (23.6.54)		20	10
262		3d. deep green (17.6.53)		20	10
		aa. Coil pair		5·00	7·50
		ab. Coil block of four (9.53)		13·00	
262a		3½d. brown-red (2.7.56)		1·75	10
262b		6½d. orange (9.56)		2·25	90

(b) W **15**
263	86	3½d. brown-red (21.4.53)		20	10
263a		6½d. orange (23.6.54)		1·50	10
261/3a			Set of 7	5·50	1·10

(Des and eng F. D. Manley. Recess.)

1953 (25 May). *Coronation.* P 15 × 14.
264	87	3½d. scarlet		35	10
265		7½d. violet		75	1·00
266		2s. dull bluish green		2·50	75
264/6			Set of 3	3·25	1·60

88 Young Farmers and Calf

(Des P.O. artist; adapted P. E. Morriss. Eng E. R. M. Jones. Recess)

1953 (3 Sept). *25th Anniv of Australian Young Farmers' Clubs.* P 14½.
267	88	3½d. red-brown and deep green		10	10

89 Lt.-Gov. D. Collins | **90** Lt.-Gov. W. Paterson

91 Sullivan Cove, Hobart, 1804

(Des E. R. M. Jones, eng D. Cameron (T **89**/90); des and eng G. Lissenden (T **91**). Recess)

1953 (23 Sept). *150th Anniv of Settlement in Tasmania.* P 15 × 14.
268	89	3½d. brown-purple		30	10
		a. Horiz pair. Nos. 268/9		80	1·25
269	90	3½d. brown-purple		30	10
270	91	2s. green		1·50	2·50
268/70			Set of 3	2·10	2·50

Nos. 268/9 were printed alternately in vertical columns throughout the sheet.

NEW INFORMATION

The editor is always interested to correspond with people who have new information that will improve or correct the Catalogue.

92 Stamp of 1853

(Des R. L. Beck; eng G. Lissenden. Recess)

1953 (11 Nov). *Tasmanian Postage Stamp Centenary.* P 14½.
271   92   3d. rose-red   10   20

93 Queen Elizabeth II and Duke of Edinburgh

94 Queen Elizabeth II   Re-entry (lower plate left pane R. 8/2)

(Des and eng F. D. Manley; border and lettering on 7½d. des by R. M. Warner. Recess)

1954 (2 Feb). *Royal Visit.* P 14.
272   93   3½d. scarlet   20   10
     a. Re-entry   ..   ..   ..   38·00   12·00
273   94   7½d. purple   35   1·25
274   93   2s. dull bluish green   ..   85   65
272/4   ..   ..   ..   *Set of 3*   1·25   1·75

95 "Telegraphic Communications"   96 Red Cross and Globe

(Des R. M. Warner. Eng P. E. Morriss. Recess)

1954 (7 Apr). *Australian Telegraph System Centenary.* P 14.
275   95   3½d. brown-red   10   10

(Des B. Stewart. Eng P. E. Morriss. Design recess; cross typo)

1954 (9 June). *40th Anniv of Australian Red Cross Society.* P 14½.
276   96   3½d. ultramarine and scarlet   ..   10   10

97 Mute Swan   98 Locomotives of 1854 and 1954

(Des R. L. Beck. Eng G. Lissenden. Recess)

1954 (2 Aug). *Western Australian Postage Stamp Centenary.* P 14½.
277   97   3½d. black   15   10

(Des R. M. Warner. Eng G. Lissenden. Recess)

1954 (13 Sept). *Australian Railways Centenary.* P 14.
278   98   3½d. purple-brown   ..   30   10

99 Territory Badge   100 Olympic Games Symbol   101 Rotary Symbol, Globe and Flags

(Des F. D. Manley. Eng G. Lissenden. Recess)

1954 (17 Nov). *Australian Antarctic Research.* P 14½ × 13½.
279   99   3½d. grey-black   15   10

(Des R. L. Beck. Eng P. E. Morriss. Recess)

1954 (1 Dec)–**55.** *Olympic Games Propaganda.* P 14.
280   100   2s. deep bright blue   70   60
280a   2s. deep bluish green (30.11.55)   ..   1·75   1·25

(Des and eng D. Cameron. Recess)

1955 (23 Feb). *50th Anniv of Rotary International.* P 14 × 14½.
281   101   3½d. carmine   10   10

101a Queen Elizabeth II   101b Queen Elizabeth II   102 Queen Elizabeth II

(Des F. D. Manley from bas-relief by W. L. Bowles. Eng G. Lissenden. Recess)

1955 (9 Mar)–**57.** P 15×14 (*T* 101a/b) or 14½ (*T* 102).
(a) W 15 (*sideways*)
282   102   1s. 0½d. deep blue   ..   ..   2·50   60
(b) No wmk
282a   101a   4d. lake (13.3.57)   ..   30   10
     ab. Booklet pane of 6   ..   7·50
282b   101b   7½d. violet (13.11.57)   ..   60   1·25
     ba. Double print £1600
282c   101a   10d. deep grey-blue (6.3.57)   ..   60   65
282d   102   1s. 7d red-brown (13.3.57)   ..   2·75   20
282/d   ..   ..   ..   *Set of 5*   6·00   2·50
     No. 282ab has the outer edges of the pane imperforate, producing single stamps with one or two adjacent sides imperforate.

103 American Memorial, Canberra   104 Cobb & Co. Coach (from dry-print by Sir Lionel Lindsay)

(Des R. L. Beck (head by F. D. Manley). Eng F. D. Manley. Recess)

1955 (4 May). *Australian–American Friendship.* P 14 × 14½.
283   103   3½d. violet-blue   10   10

(Design adapted and eng by F. D. Manley. Recess)

1955 (6 July). *Mail-coach Pioneers Commemoration.* P 14½ × 14.
284   104   3½d. blackish brown   ..   25   10
285   2s. reddish brown   75   1·40

105 Y.M.C.A. Emblem and Map of the World   106 Florence Nightingale and Young Nurse

(Des E. Thake. Eng P. E. Morriss. Design recess; emblem typo)

1955 (10 Aug). *World Centenary of Y.M.C.A.* P 14½ × 14.
286   105   3½d. deep bluish green and red   ..   10   10
     a. Red (emblem) omitted   ..   £6500

(Des and eng F. D. Manley. Recess)

1955 (21 Sept). *Nursing Profession Commem.* P 14×14½.
287   106   3½d. reddish violet   10   10

107 Queen Victoria   108 Badges of New South Wales, Victoria and Tasmania

(Des and D. Cameron. Recess)

1955 (17 Oct). *Centenary of First South Australian Postage Stamps.* P 14½.
288   107   3½d. green   10   10

(Des and eng F. D. Manley. Recess)

1956 (26 Sept). *Centenary of Responsible Government in New South Wales, Victoria and Tasmania.* P 14½ × 14.
289   108   3½d. brown-lake   10   10

109 Arms of Melbourne   110 Olympic Torch and Symbol

111 Collins Street, Melbourne   112 Melbourne across R. Yarra

(Des P. E. Morriss; eng F. D. Manley (4d.). Des and eng F. D. Manley (7½d.). Recess. Des and photo Harrison from photographs by M. Murphy and sketches by L. Coles (1s.). Des and photo Courvoisier from photographs by M. Murphy (2s.))

1956 (31 Oct). *Olympic Games, Melbourne.* P 14½ (4d.), 14 × 14½ (7½d., 1s.) or 11½ (2s.).
290   109   4d. carmine-red   25   10
291   110   7½d. deep bright blue   ..   40   90
292   111   1s. multicoloured   40   30
293   112   2s. multicoloured   50   90
290/3   ..   ..   ..   *Set of 4*   1·40   2·00

115 South Australia Coat of Arms   116 Map of Australia and Caduceus

(Des and eng P. E. Morriss. Recess)

1957 (17 Apr). *Centenary of Responsible Government in South Australia.* P 14½.
296   115   4d. red-brown   10   10

(Des J. E. Lyle; adapted B. Stewart. Eng D. Cameron. Recess)

1957 (21 Aug). *Flying Doctor Service.* P 14½ × 14.
297   116   7d. ultramarine   15   10

117 "The Spirit of Christmas"

Re-entry (upper plate left pane R. 10/1)

(Des and eng D. Cameron from a painting by Sir Joshua Reynolds. Recess)

1957 (6 Nov). *Christmas.* P 14½ × 14.
298   117   3½d. scarlet   10   10
     a. Re-entry   ..   ..   ..   8·50   8·50
299   4d. purple   10   10

NEW INFORMATION

The editor is always interested to correspond with people who have new information that will improve or correct the Catalogue.

118 Lockheed L.1049
Super Constellation
Airliner

(Des and eng P. E. Morriss. Recess)

1958 (6 Jan). *Inauguration of Australian "Round the World" Air Service.* P 14½ × 14.
301　118　2s. deep blue　..　..　..　..　60　85

119 Hall of Memory, Sailor and Airman

120 Sir Charles Kingsford Smith and Fokker F.VIIa/3m *Southern Cross*

(Des and eng G. Lissenden. Recess)

1958 (10 Feb). *T* **119** *and similar horiz design.* P 14½ × 14.
302　119　5½d. brown-red　..　..　40　30
　　a. Horiz pair. Nos. 302/3　..　80　5·50
303　–　5½d. brown-red　..　..　40　30
　No. 303 shows a soldier and service-woman respectively in place of the sailor and airman. Nos. 302/3 are printed alternately in vertical columns throughout the sheet.

(Des J. E. Lyle. Eng F. D. Manley. Recess)

1958 (27 Aug). *30th Anniv of First Air Crossing of the Tasman Sea.* P 14 × 14½.
304　120　8d. deep ultramarine　..　..　60　85

121 Silver Mine, Broken Hill **122** The Nativity

(Des R. H. Evans; adapted and eng F. D. Manley. Recess)

1958 (10 Sept). *75th Anniv of Founding of Broken Hill.* P 14½ × 14.
305　121　4d. chocolate　..　..　..　30　10

(Des D. Cameron. Eng P. E. Morriss. Recess)

1958 (5 Nov). *Christmas.* P 14½ × 15.
306　122　3½d. deep scarlet　..　..　20　10
307　　　4d. deep violet　..　..　..　20　10

PHOSPHOR STAMPS ("Helecon"). "Helecon", a chemical substance of the zinc sulphide group, has been incorporated in stamps in two different ways, either in the ink with which the stamps are printed, or included in the surface coating of the stamp paper.
　Owing to the difficulty of identification without the use of a U.V. lamp we do not list the helecon stamps separately but when in stock can supply them after testing under the lamp.
　The first stamp to be issued was the 11d. Bandicoot from an experimental printing of four millions on helecon paper released to the public in December 1963. The next printing on ordinary paper was released in September 1964. The experimental printing was coarse, showing a lot of white dots and the colour is slate-blue, differing from both the ordinary and the later helecon paper.
　The following helecon printings have been reported: 2d. and 3d. (sheets, coils and coil sheets) and 5d. (No. 354) Queen Elizabeth II; 8d. Tiger Cat; 11d. Bandicoot; 1s. Colombo Plan; 1s. 2d. Tasmanian Tiger; 2s. 3d. Wattle (No. 324a); and 6d. (No. 363a), 9d. and 1s. 6d. Birds (the 2s., 2s. 6d. and 3s. Birds were only issued on helecon paper). The 5d. Queen Elizabeth II in red (No. 354b) exists ordinary and with helecon ink. The coil pair was only issued with helecon ink; the booklet is normally with helecon ink but some were printed with ordinary ink by mistake. The Churchill stamp was printed on ordinary and helecon paper. The I.T.U. Centenary, Monash and later commemorative stamps were printed on helecon paper and all issues from No. 382 onwards were on helecon paper or paper coated with Derby Luminescence.
　In 1982 a series of booklet stamps, Nos. 870/4, were printed by Enschedé on Harrison paper which gives a bluish white reaction under u.v. light.

123 **124** **126**

127 **128** **129**

Queen Elizabeth II

Type I
Short break in outer line to bottom right of "4"

Type II
Line unbroken

Type A
Four short lines inside "5"

Type B
Five short lines inside "5"

(Des G. Lissenden from photographs by Baron Studios. Eng F. D. Manley (2d.), D. Cameron (3d.). P. E. Morriss (others). Recess)

1959–63. P 14 × 15 (*horiz*) or 15 × 14 (*vert*).
308　123　1d. deep slate-purple (2.2.59)　..　10　10
　　a. Deep slate-lilac (1961)　..　85　20
309　124　2d. brown (21.3.62)　..　..　40　15
　　a. Coil pair (1962) ..　..　4·00　4·25
　　b. Coil block of four (1963)　..　8·00
311　126　3d. blue-green (20.5.59)　..　15　10
　　a. Coil pair (8.59)　..　4·00　4·75
　　b. Coil block of four (8.59)　..　10·00
312　127　3½d. deep green (18.3.59)　..　15　15
313　128　4d. carmine-lake (Type I) (2.2.59)　1·75　10
　　a. Carmine-red　..　..　1·75　10
　　ab. Booklet pane of 6 (18.3.59)　..　19·00
　　b. Type II　..　..　1·75　10
　　ba. Carmine-red　..　..　1·75　10
314　129　5d. deep blue (Type A or B) (1.10.59)　90　10
　　a. Vert se-tenant pair (A and B)　1·75　2·50
　　b. Coil pair (18.7.60)　..　8·00　10·00
　　c. Coil block of four (7.61)　..　35·00
　　d. Booklet pane of 6 (23.3.60)　..　10·00
308/14　　　　　Set of 6　3·00　30
　No. 313. Produced in printer's sheets, of 640 split into sheets of 160 for issue. Type I occurs on the two upper sheets from the printers' sheet and on ten positions from the left pane of the lower right sheet. Type II occurs on all stamps from the lower sheets except for ten positions from the left pane of lower right sheet.
　No. 314. Both types occur in alternate horizontal rows in the sheet (Type A in Row 1, Type B in Row 2, and so on), and their value is identical. Booklet pane No. 314d contains two Type A and four Type B.
　Nos. 309a/b, 311a/b and 314b/c have horizontal coil perforations as described after No. 191.
　Nos. 313ab and 314d have the outer edges of the panes imperforate, producing stamps with one or two adjacent sides imperforate.

131 Numbat **137** Christmas Bells

142 Aboriginal Stockman

(Des Eileen Mayo (6d., 8d., 9d., 11d., 1s., 1s. 2d.), B. Stewart (5s.), Margaret Stones (others). Eng P. Morriss (11d.), F. D. Manley (1s.), B. Stewart (others). Recess)

1959–64. *T* **131, 137, 142** *and similar designs.* W **15** (5s.), *no wmk* (others). P 14 × 15 (1s. 2d.), 15 × 14 (6d. to 1s.), 14½ × 14 (5s.) or 14½ (others).
316　6d. brown (30.9.60)　..　..　2·00　10
317　8d. red-brown (11.5.60)　..　75　10
　　a. Pale red-brown (9.61)　..　75　10
318　9d. deep sepia (21.10.59)　..　1·75　35
319　11d. deep blue (3.5.61)　..　1·00　15
320　1s. deep green (9.9.59)　..　4·00　30
321　1s. 2d. deep purple (21.3.62)　..　1·00　15
322　1s. 6d. crimson/yellow (3.2.60)　..　2·50　80
323　2s. grey-blue (8.59)　..　..　1·25　10
324　2s. 3d. green/maize (9.9.59)　..　1·75　10
324a　2s. 3d. yellow-green (28.10.64)　..　6·00　1·50

325　2s. 5d. brown/yellow (16.3.60)　..　7·00　45
326　3s. scarlet (15.7.59)　..　..　2·00　10
327　5s. red-brown (26.7.61)　..　20·00　75
　　a. White paper. Brown-red (17.6.64)　£100　7·00
316/327　　　　Set of 13　48·00　4·25
　Designs: (*As T* **131**) *Vert*—8d. Tiger Cat; 9d. Eastern Grey Kangaroos; 11d. Common Rabbit-Bandicoot; 1s. Platypus. *Horiz*—1s. 2d. Thylacine. (*As T* **137**) *Vert*—2s. Flannel Flower; 2s. 3d. Wattle; 2s. 5d. Banksia; 3s. Waratah.
　No. 327 is on toned paper. No. 327a was a late printing on the white paper referred to in the note below No. 360.
　See notes after No. 307 re helecon ink.

143 Postmaster Isaac Nichols boarding the brig *Experiment*

144 Parliament House, Brisbane, and Arms of Queensland

(Des R. Shackel; adapted and eng F. D. Manley. Recess)

1959 (22 Apr). *150th Anniv of the Australian Post Office.* P 14½ × 14.
331　143　4d. slate　..　..　..　15　10

(Des and eng G. Lissenden. Recess and typo)

1959 (5 June). *Centenary of Self-Government in Queensland.* P 14 × 14½.
332　144　4d. lilac and green　..　..　10　10

145 "The Approach of the Magi"

146 Girl Guide and Lord Baden-Powell

(Des and eng F. D. Manley. Recess)

1959 (4 Nov). *Christmas.* P 15 × 14.
333　145　5d. deep reddish violet ..　..　10　10

(Des and eng B. Stewart. Recess)

1960 (18 Aug). *50th Anniv of Girl Guide Movement.* P 14½ × 14.
334　146　5d. deep ultramarine　..　..　30　15

147 "The Overlanders" (Sir Daryl Lindsay)

148 "Archer" and Melbourne Cup

Two types:

I Mane rough　　II Mane smooth

　Type II occurs on Pane A, Row 2 Nos. 8 and 9, Row 4 Nos. 1 to 12, Row 5 Nos. 10 to 12, and on Pane C, Row 4 Nos. 5 to 12, Row 5 Nos. 1 to 9, and Rows 6 to 10 inclusive; the stamps in Row 4 Nos. 5 to 12 and Row 5 Nos. 1 to 9 are considered to be of an intermediate type with the mane as in Type II but the ear and rein being as in Type I. All the rest are Type I.

(Adapted and eng P. E. Morriss. Recess)

1960 (21 Sept). *Centenary of Northern Territory Exploration.* P 15 × 14½.
335　147　5d. magenta (I)　..　..　30　15
　　a. Type II ..　..　..　1·75　55

(Des F. D. Manley. Eng G. Lissenden. Recess)

1960 (12 Oct). *100th Melbourne Cup Race Commemoration.* P 14½.
336　148　5d. sepia　..　..　..　20　10

NEW INFORMATION

The editor is always interested to correspond with people who have new information that will improve or correct the Catalogue.

149 Queen Victoria

150 Open Bible and Candle

(Des F. D. Manley. Eng B. Stewart. Recess)

1960 (2 Nov). *Centenary of First Queensland Postage Stamp.*
P 14½ × 15.
337 149 5d. deep myrtle-green 25 10

(Des K. McKay. Adapted and eng B. Stewart. Recess)

1960 (9 Nov). *Christmas. P 15 × 14½.*
338 150 5d. carmine-red .. 10 10

151 Colombo Plan
Bureau Emblem

152 Melba (after bust by
Sir Bertram Mackennal)

(Des and eng G. Lissenden. Recess)

1961 (30 June). *Colombo Plan. P 14 × 14½.*
339 151 1s. red-brown 10 10
 See notes after No. 307 *re* helecon ink.

(Des and eng B. Stewart. Recess)

1961 (20 Sept). *Birth Centenary of Dame Nellie Melba (singer).*
P 14½×15.
340 152 5d. blue 30 15

153 Open Prayer Book
and Text

(Des G. Lissenden. Eng P. E. Morriss. Recess)

1961 (8 Nov). *Christmas. P 14½ × 14.*
341 153 5d. brown 10 10

154 J. M. Stuart

155 Flynn's Grave and
Nursing Sister

(Des W. Jardine. Eng P. E. Morriss. Recess)

1962 (25 July). *Centenary of Stuart's Crossing of Australia from
South to North. P 14½ × 15.*
342 154 5d. brown-red 15 10

(Des F. D. Manley. Photo)

1962 (5 Sept). *50th Anniv of Australian Inland Mission. P 13½.*
343 155 5d. multicoloured 30 15
 a. Red omitted.. .. .. † £500
 The note below No. 372b also applies to No. 343a.

156 "Woman"

157 "Madonna and
Child"

(Des D. Dundas. Eng G. Lissenden. Recess)

1962 (26 Sept). *"Associated Country Women of the World" Conference, Melbourne. P 14 × 14½.*
344 156 5d. deep green 10 10

(Des and eng G. Lissenden. Recess)

1962 (17 Oct). *Christmas. P 14½.*
345 157 5d. violet 15 10

158 Perth and Kangaroo Paw
(plant)

159 Arms of Perth and
Running Track

(Des R. M. Warner (5d.), G. Hamori (2s. 3d.). Photo Harrison)

1962 (1 Nov). *Seventh British Empire and Commonwealth
Games, Perth. P 14 (5d.) or 14½ × 14 (2s. 3d.).*
346 158 5d. multicoloured 40 10
 a. Red omitted.. .. .. £800
347 159 2s. 3d. black, red, blue and green .. 3·25 2·75

160 Queen Elizabeth II.

161 Queen Elizabeth II
and Duke of Edinburgh

(Des and eng after portraits by Anthony Buckley, P. E. Morriss
(5d.), B. Stewart (2s. 3d.). Recess)

1963 (18 Feb). *Royal Visit. P 14½.*
348 160 5d. deep green 35 10
349 161 2s. 3d. brown-lake .. .. 2·25 3·50

162 Arms of Canberra and
W. B. Griffin (architect)

163 Centenary Emblem

(Des and eng B. Stewart. Recess)

1963 (8 Mar). *50th Anniv of Canberra. P 14½ × 14.*
350 162 5d. deep green 15 10

(Des G. Hamori. Photo)

1963 (8 May). *Red Cross Centenary. P 13½ × 13.*
351 163 5d. red, grey-brown and blue 30 10

164 Blaxland, Lawson and Wentworth on Mt. York

(Des T. Alban. Eng P. E. Morriss. Recess)

1963 (28 May). *150th Anniv of First Crossing of Blue Mountains.
P 14½ × 14.*
352 164 5d. ultramarine 15 10

165 "Export"

166 Queen Elizabeth II

(Des and eng B. Stewart. Recess)

1963 (28 Aug). *Export Campaign. P 14½ × 14.*
353 165 5d. red 10 10

(Des and eng P. E. Morriss from photograph by Anthony Buckley.
Recess)

1963 (9 Oct)–65. *P 15×14.*
354 166 5d. deep green 65 10
 a. Booklet pane of 6 (17.6.64) .. 21·00
 b. Imperf between (horiz pair) (31.7.64) 1·75 2·50
354c 5d. red (30.6.65) 55 10
 ca. Coil pair .. .. .. 18·00 23·00
 cb. Booklet pane of 6 .. .. 21·00
 See notes after No. 307 *re* helicon ink.
 Nos. 354a and 354cb have the outer edges of the panes
imperforate producing single stamps with one or two adjacent
sides imperforate.

PRICES OF SETS

Set prices are given for many issues, generally
those containing three stamps or more. Definitive
sets include one of each value or major colour
change, but do not cover different perforations,
die types or minor shades. Where a choice is
possible the set prices are based on the cheapest
versions of the stamps included in the listings.

No. 354a comes from sheets of uncut booklet panes containing
288 stamps (16 × 18) with wide margins intersecting the sheet
horizontally below each third row, alternate rows of stamps imperforate between vertically and the outer left, right and bottom
margins imperforate. This means that in each sheet there are 126
pairs of stamps imperf between vertically, plus a number with wide
imperforate margins attached, as shown in the illustration.
 A 5d. in a similar design, printed in blue and brown with
vertical edges imperforate, was prepared, but not issued.

167 Tasman and *Heemskerk*

168 Dampier and *Roebuck*

(Des W. Jardine. Eng B. Stewart (4s., £1). E. R. M. Jones (10s.),
P. E. Morriss (others). Recess)

1963–65. *T 167/8 and similar designs. No wmk (4s.) or W 15
(others), (sideways on 5s., £1). P 14 or 14½ (5s., £1, £2).*
355 4s. ultramarine (9.10.63) .. .. 3·75 55
356 5s. red-brown (25.11.64) .. .. 5·00 85
357 7s. 6d. olive (26.8.64) .. .. 19·00 16·00
358 10s. brown-purple (26.2.64) .. .. 38·00 4·50
 a. White paper. *Deep brown-purple* (14.1.65) 40·00 7·50
359 £1 deep reddish violet (26.2.64) .. 38·00 15·00
 a. White paper. *Deep bluish violet* (16.11.64) 55·00 24·00
360 £2 sepia (26.8.64) .. .. 75·00 75·00
355/360 Set of 6 £160 £100
357/60 Optd "Specimen" Set of 4 £450
 Designs: *As T 167*—7s. 6d. Captain Cook; 10s. Flinders and
Investigator. As T 168—£1 Bass and whaleboat; £2 Admiral
King and *Mermaid* (survey cutter).
 Nos. 358 and 359 were printed on a toned paper but all the
other values are on white paper, the 4s. being on rather thicker
paper.

173 "Peace on Earth . . ."

174 "Commonwealth Cable"

(Des R. M. Warner. Eng B. Stewart. Recess)

1963 (25 Oct). *Christmas. P 14½.*
361 173 5d. greenish blue 10 10

(Des P. E. Morriss. Photo)

1963 (3 Dec). *Opening of COMPAC (Trans-Pacific Telephone
Cable). Chalky paper. P 13½.*
362 174 2s. 3d. red, blue, black and pale blue 2·25 3·50

175 Yellow-tailed
Thornbill

176 Black-backed
Magpie

(Des Mrs. H. Temple-Watts. Photo)

1964 (11 Mar)-**65.** *T 175/6 and similar designs showing birds. Chalky paper (except No. 367a).* P 13½.

363		6d. brown, yellow, black and bluish green (19.8.64)		70	25
	a.	Brown, yellow, black and emerald-green (6.65)		2·50	2·00
364		9d. black, grey and pale green		1·00	2·75
365		1s. 6d. pink, grey, dull purple and black		75	1·40
366		2s. yellow, black and pink (21.4.65)		1·75	50
367		2s. 5d. deep royal blue, light violet-blue, yellow-orange, grey and black		2·50	3·50
367a		2s. 5d. deep blue, light blue, orange-brown, blue-grey and black (8.65)		20·00	12·00
368		2s. 6d. black, red, grey and green (21.4.65)		4·50	3·00
	a.	Red omitted (white breast)		£1300	
369		3s. black, red, buff & yellow-green (21.4.65)		4·50	1·50
363/9			*Set of 8*	32·00	23·00

Designs: *Vert*—1s. 6d. Galah; 2s. Golden Whistler; 2s. 5d. Blue Wren; 3s. Straw-necked Ibis. *Horiz*—2s. 6d. Scarlet Robin.

No. 367a is from a printing on unsurfaced Wiggins Teape paper, the rest of the set being on chalk-surfaced Harrison paper. Apart from the differences in shade, the inscriptions, particularly "BLUE WREN", stand out very much more clearly on No. 367a. Although two colours are apparent in both stamps, the grey and black were printed from one plate.

See notes after No. 307 re helecon ink.

182 Bleriot XI Aircraft (type flown by M. Guillaux, 1914)

Re-entry (upper right plate, R. 4/4)

(Des K. McKay. Adapted and eng P. E. Morriss. Recess)

1964 (1 July). *50th Anniv of First Australian Airmail Flight.* P 14½ × 14.

370	182	5d. olive-green		40	10
	a.	Re-entry		£150	75·00
371		2s. 3d. scarlet		3·25	2·25

183 Child looking at Nativity Scene

184 "Simpson and his Donkey"

(Des P. E. Morriss and J. Mason. Photo)

1964 (21 Oct). *Christmas. Chalky paper.* P 13½.

372	183	5d. red, blue, buff and black		10	10
	a.	Red omitted		†	£500
	b.	Black omitted			£650

The red ink is soluble and can be removed by bleaching and it is therefore advisable to obtain a certificate from a recognised expert committee before purchasing No. 372a. The used price quoted is for an example on cover.

(Des C. Andrew (after statue, Shrine of Remembrance, Melbourne). Eng E. R. M. Jones. Recess)

1965 (14 Apr). *50th Anniv of Gallipoli Landing.* P 14 × 14½.

373	184	5d. drab		65	10
374		8d. blue		1·00	2·75
375		2s. 3d. reddish purple		1·50	2·25
373/5			*Set of 3*	2·75	4·25

185 "Telecommunications" **186** Sir Winston Churchill

(Des J. McMahon and G. Hamori. Photo)

1965 (10 May). *I.T.U. Centenary.* P 13½.

376	185	5d. black, brown, orange-brown & bl		30	10
	a.	Black (value and pylon) omitted		£850	

(Des P. E. Morriss from photo by Karsh. Photo)

1965 (24 May). *Churchill Commemoration. Chalky paper.* P 13½.

377	186	5d. black, pale grey, grey and light blue		15	10
	a.	Pale grey (facial shading) omitted		£850	

No. 377a occurred on stamps from the bottom row of one sheet.

Two used examples are known showing the grey ("AUSTRALIA") omitted.

About half the printing was on helecon impregnated paper, differing slightly in the shade of the blue.

187 General Monash **188** Hargrave and "Multiplane" Seaplane (1902)

(Des O. Foulkes and W. Walters. Photo)

1965 (23 June). *Birth Centenary of General Sir John Monash (engineer and soldier). Chalky paper.* P 13½.

378	187	5d. multicoloured		15	10

(Des G. Hamori. Photo)

1965 (4 Aug). *50th Death Anniv of Lawrence Hargrave (aviation pioneer). Chalky paper.* P 13½.

379	188	5d. purple-brown, blk, yell-ochre & pur		15	10
	a.	Purple (value) omitted		£225	

189 I.C.Y. Emblem **190** "Nativity Scene"

(Des H. Fallu from U.N. theme. Photo)

1965 (1 Sept). *International Co-operation Year. Chalky paper.* P 13½.

380	189	2s. 3d. emerald and light blue		1·25	1·75

(Des J. Mason. Photo)

1965 (20 Oct). *Christmas.* P 13½.

381	190	5d. multicoloured		15	10
	a.	Gold omitted		£850	
	b.	Blue omitted		£500	

No. 381a comes from the bottom row of a sheet in which the gold is completely omitted, the background appearing as black with "CHRISTMAS 1965" and "AUSTRALIA" omitted. The row above had the black missing from the lower two-fifths of the stamp.

(New Currency. 100 cents = 1 dollar)

191 Queen Elizabeth II **192** Blue-faced Honeyeater **193** White-tailed Dascyllus ("Humbug Fish")

Nos. 401 (top), 401a (centre) and 401b (bottom). No. 401b shows the final form of the variety with a plate crack visible in sky and across sail (Lower sheet left pane. R. 10/1)

(Des Mrs. H. Temple-Watts (6 c. (No. 387), 13 c., 24 c.), Eileen Mayo (7 c. (No. 388) to 10 c.). Recess (T **191**, 40 c. to $4). Photo Chalky paper (others))

1966 (14 Feb)-**73.** *Decimal currency. T 191/3 and similar designs, some reused from previous issues. No wmk.* P 15 × 14 (T **191**), 14 (40 c., 75 c., $1), 14½ (50 c., $2, $4) or 13½ (others).

382	191	1 c. deep red-brown		25	10
383		2 c. olive-green		70	10
384		3 c. slate-green		70	10
385		4 c. red		20	10
	a.	Booklet pane. Five stamps plus one printed label		22·00	
386	175	5 c. brown, yellow, black & emer-grn		25	10
	a.	Brown (plumage) omitted		£950	
	b.	*Brown, yellow, blk & bl-grn* (1.67)		25	20
386c	191	5 c. deep blue (29.9.67)		70	10
	ca.	Booklet pane. Five stamps plus one printed label		8·00	
	cb.	Imperf in horiz strip of 3*		£1300	
387	192	6 c. olive-yellow, blk, blue & pale grey		80	45
	aa.	Blue (eye markings) omitted		£225	
387a	191	6 c. orange (28.9.70)		55	10
388	193	7 c. black, grey, salmon and brown		85	10
388a	191	7 c. purple (1.10.71)		1·10	
389		8 c. red, yell, bl-grn & blackish green		85	25
390	—	9 c. brown-red, purple-brown, black and light yellow-olive		85	15
391	—	10 c. orange, blackish brown, pale turquoise-blue and olive-brown		85	10
392	—	13 c. red, black, grey & light turq-green		2·25	25
	a.	Red omitted		£950	
	b.	Grey (plumage and legs) omitted		£750	
393	—	15 c. rose-carmine, black, grey and light bluish green		2·00	70
	a.	Rose-carmine omitted		£2250	
394	—	20 c. yellow, black and pink		4·00	15
	a.	Yellow (plumage) omitted		£800	
395	—	24 c. ultramarine, yellow, blk & lt brn		90	85
396	—	25 c. black, red, grey and green		4·00	30
	a.	Red omitted		£1100	
397	—	30 c. black, red, buff & lt yellow-green		16·00	65
	a.	Red omitted		£950	
398	167	40 c. ultramarine		6·50	10
399	168	50 c. red-brown		8·00	10
400	—	75 c. olive		1·00	1·00
401	—	$1 brown-purple (*shades*)		2·25	15
	a.	Recut lines in sky		45·00	
	b.	Recut lines and plate crack		55·00	
	c.	Perf 15 × 14† (1973)		£110	22·00
402	—	$2 deep reddish violet		7·50	50
40_	—	$4 sepia		6·50	5·50
382/403			*Set of 25*	60·00	10·00
400/3 Optd "Specimen"			*Set of 4*	90·00	

Designs: *Vert* (as T **193**)—8 c. Copper-banded Butterflyfish ("Coral Fish"); 9 c. Hermit Crab; 10 c. Orange Clownfish ("Anemone Fish"). (As T **192**)—13 c. Red-necked Avocet; 15 c. Galah; 20 c. Golden Whistler; 30 c. Straw-necked Ibis. *Horiz* (as T **192**)—24 c. Azure Kingfisher; 25 c. Scarlet Robin. As T **167**—75 c. Captain Cook; $1 Flinders and *Investigator*. As T **168**—$2 Bass and whaleboat; $4 Admiral King and *Mermaid* (survey cutter).

*This comprises two stamps imperforate all round and one imperforate at left only.

†The note below No. 553 also applies to No. 401c, its exact gauge being 14.8×14.1. No. 401 is 14.25×13.95.

Nos. 385a and 386ca have the outer edges of the pane imperforate producing single stamps with one or two adjacent sides imperforate.

No. 385 is normally printed with helecon ink, the rest being on helecon paper. Early in 1967 experimental printings of No. 385 on different kinds of paper coated with helecon or Derby Luminescents phosphor were put on sale. They cannot be distinguished by the naked eye.

199 Queen Elizabeth II **200** "Saving Life"

1966 (14 Feb)-**67.** *Coil stamps. Photo.* P 15 × imperf.

404	199	3 c. black, light brown and green		20	50
405		4 c. black, light brown & lt vermilion		35	20
405a		4 c. black, light brown and new blue (29.9.67)		40	10
404/5a			*Set of 3*	85	70

(Des L. Mason. Photo)

1966 (6 July). *75th Anniv of Royal Life Saving Society.* P 13½.

406	200	4 c. black, bright blue and blue		15	10

201 "Adoration of the Shepherds" **202** Eendracht

(Des L. Stirling, after medieval engraving. Photo)

1966 (19 Oct). *Christmas.* P 13½.

407	201	4 c. black and yellow-olive		10	10
	a.	Value omitted		£1600	

No. 407a was caused by a shift of the yellow-olive which covered the white face value.

(Des F. Eidlitz. Photo)

1966 (24 Oct). *350th Anniv of Dirk Hartog's Landing in Australia.* P 13½.

408	202	4 c. multicoloured		10	10
	a.	Red (sphere) omitted		£1600	

203 Open Bible **204** Ancient Keys and Modern Lock

(Des L. Stirling. Photo)

1967 (7 Mar). *150th Anniv of British and Foreign Bible Society in Australia.* P 13½.

409	203	4 c. multicoloured		10	10

(Des G. Andrews. Photo)

1967 (5 Apr). *150th Anniv of Australian Banking.* P 13½.

410	204	4 c. black, light blue and emerald		10	10

205 Lions Badge and 50 Stars   **206** Y.W.C.A. Emblem

(Des M. Ripper. Photo)

1967 (7 June). *50th Anniv of Lions International.* P 13½.
411   205   4 c. black, gold and blue   10   10

(Des H. Williamson. Photo)

1967 (21 Aug). *World Y.W.C.A. Council Meeting. Monash University, Victoria.* P 13½.
412   206   4 c. dp blue, ultramarine, lt pur & lt bl   10   10

207 Anatomical Figures   (**208**)

(Des R. Ingpen. Photo)

1967 (20 Sept). *Fifth World Gynaecology and Obstetrics Congress, Sydney.* P 13½.
413   207   4 c. black, blue and light reddish violet   10   10

1967 (29 Sept). *No. 385 surch with T 208.*
414   191   5 c. on 4 c. red   45   10
  a. Booklet pane. Five stamps plus one
    printed label   ..   ..   ..   2·25
No. 414 was only issued in booklets with the outer edges of the pane imperforate so all stamps have one or two adjacent sides imperforate. It only exists printed with helecon ink on normal paper.

209 Christmas Bells and Gothic   **210** Religious Symbols
Arches

(Des M. Ripper (5 c.), Erica McGilchrist (25 c.). Photo)

1967. *Christmas.* P 13½.
415   209   5 c. multicoloured (18.10.67)   20   10
  a. Imperf three sides (vert pair)   ..   £3750
416   210   25 c. multicoloured (27.11.67) ..   ..   1·40   1·75

211 Satellite in Orbit   **212** World Weather Map

(Des J. Mason. Photo)

1968 (20 Mar). *World Weather Watch.* P 13½.
417   211   5 c. orange-brown, pl blue, blk & ochre   30   10
418   212   20 c. orange-brown, blue and black   ..   1·40   3·25
  a. White (radio waves) omitted   ..   £650
  b. Orange-brown (triangle) omitted £1500

213 Radar Antenna   **214** Kangaroo Paw
(Western Australia)

(Des R. Ingpen. Photo)

1968 (20 Mar). *World Telecommunications Intelsat II.* P 13½.
419   213   25 c. greenish blue, black & lt blue-green   1·75   3·00

(Des Nell Wilson (6c., 30 c.); R. and P. Warner (13 c., 25 c.); Dorothy Thornhill (15 c., 20 c.). Photo)

1968 (10 July)–**71.** *State Floral Emblems. T* **214** *and similar vert designs. Multicoloured.* P 13½.
420   6 c. Type 214   55   65
421   13 c. Pink Heath (Victoria)   ..   65   40
422   15 c. Tasmanian Blue Gum (Tasmania)   90   20
423   20 c. Sturt's Desert Pea (South Australia)   3·00   40
424   25 c. Cooktown Orchid (Queensland)   2·50   40
425   30 c. Waratah (New South Wales) (Type I)   80   10
  a. Green (leaves) omitted   ..   £750
  b. Type II (29.6.71)   ..   ..   4·75   1·50
420/5   ..   ..   ..   *Set of 6*   7·50   2·00
The 30 c. was reprinted in 1971 from new cylinders so that Type II shows greater areas of white in the pink tones of the petals.

220 Soil Sample Analysis

(Des R. Ingpen. Photo)

1968 (6 Aug). *International Soil Science Congress and World Medical Association Assembly. T* **220** *and similar horiz design.* P 13½.
426   220   5 c. orange-brn, stone, greenish bl & blk   10   10
  a. Nos. 426/7 *se-tenant* with gutter mar-
    gin between   ..   ..   ..   14·00   16·00
427   –   5 c. greenish blue, dull ol-yell, rose & blk   10   10
  Design:—No. 427, Rubber-gloved hands, syringe and head of Hippocrates.
The above were printed in sheets of 100 containing a pane of 50 of each design.
The major shades formerly listed have been deleted as there is a range of intermediate shades.

222 Athlete carrying Torch,   **223** Sunstone Symbol and
and Sunstone Symbol   Mexican Flag

(Des H. Williamson. Photo)

1968 (2 Oct). *Olympic Games, Mexico City.* P 13½.
428   222   5 c. multicoloured   30   10
429   223   25 c. multicoloured   60   1·50

224 Houses and   **225** Church Window and
Dollar Signs   View of Bethlehem

(Des Erica McGilchrist. Photo)

1968 (16 Oct). *Building and Savings Societies Congress.* P 13½.
430   224   5 c. multicoloured   10   40

(Des G. Hamori. Photo)

1968 (23 Oct). *Christmas.* P 13½.
431   225   5 c. multicoloured   10   10
  a. Green window (gold omitted)   ..   £475
  b. Red (inscr) omitted £650

226 Edgeworth
David (geologist)

(Des Note Ptg Branch (Nos. 432, 434), A. Cook (others). Recess, background litho)

1968 (6 Nov). *Famous Australians (1st series). T* **226** *and similar vert portraits.* P 15×14.
432   5 c. myrtle-green/*pale green*   45   20
  a. Booklet pane. Five stamps plus one
    printed label   ..   ..   ..   2·50
433   5 c. black/*pale blue*   45   20
  a. Booklet pane. Five stamps plus one
    printed label   ..   ..   ..   2·50

---

434   5 c. blackish brown/*pale buff*   ..   45   20
  a. Booklet pane. Five stamps plus one
    printed label   ..   ..   ..   2·50
435   5 c. deep violet/*pale lilac*   ..   45   20
  a. Booklet pane. Five stamps plus one
    printed label   ..   ..   ..   2·50
432/5   ..   ..   ..   *Set of 4*   1·60   70
  Designs:—No. 432, Type **226**; No. 433, A. B. Paterson (poet); No. 434, Albert Namatjira (artist); No. 435, Caroline Chisholm (social worker).
Nos. 432/5 were only issued in booklets with the outer edges of the pane imperforate so all stamps have one or two adjacent sides imperforate.
See also Nos. 446/9, 479/82, 505/8, 537/40, 590/5, 602/7 and 637/40.

230 Macquarie Lighthouse   **231** Pioneers and Modern
Building, Darwin

(Des and eng Note Ptg Branch. Recess; background litho)

1968 (27 Nov). *150th Anniv of Macquarie Lighthouse.* P 14½ × 13½.
436   230   5 c. black/*pale yellow*   10   40
Used examples are known with the pale yellow background colour omitted.

(Des Mrs. M. Lyon. Photo)

1969 (5 Feb). *Centenary of Northern Territory Settlement.* P 13½.
437   231   5 c. blackish brown, yellow-olive and
    yellow-ochre   10   10

232 Melbourne Harbour   **233** Concentric Circles
(symbolising Management,
Labour and Government)

(Des J. Mason. Photo)

1969 (26 Feb). *Sixth Biennial Conference of International Association of Ports and Harbours.* P 13½.
438   232   5 c. multicoloured   15   10

(Des G. Hamori. Photo.)

1969 (4 June). *50th Anniv of International Labour Organisation.* P 13½.
439   233   5 c. multicoloured   15   10
  a. Gold (middle circle) omitted   ..   £950

234 Sugar Cane   **238** "The Nativity"   **240** Edmund
(stained-glass window)   Barton

(Des R. Ingpen. Photo)

1969 (17 Sept). *Primary Industries. T* **234** *and similar vert designs. Multicoloured.* P 13½.
440   7 c. Type **234**   80   1·50
441   15 c. Timber   ..   ..   ..   1·75   3·50
  a. Black ("Australia" and value) omitted   ..   £950
442   20 c. Wheat   65   80
443   25 c. Wool   ..   ..   ..   1·25   2·00
440/3 ..   ..   *Set of 4*   4·00   7·00

(Des G. Hamori (5 c.), J. Coburn (25 c.). Photo)

1969 (15 Oct). *Christmas. T* **238** *and similar multicoloured designs.* P 13½.
444   5 c. Type **238**   25   10
  a. Magenta (robe) omitted   ..   £550
  b. Yellow omitted £450
445   25 c. "Tree of Life", Christ in Crib and
    Christmas Star (abstract)   ..   1·25   2·00

(Des from drawings by J. Santry. Recess, background litho)

1969 (22 Oct). *Famous Australians (2nd series). Prime Ministers. T* **240** *and similar vert designs each black on pale green.* P 15×14.
446   5 c. Type **240**   50   20
  a. Booklet pane. Five stamps plus one
    printed label   ..   ..   ..   2·75
447   5 c. Alfred Deakin   50   20
  a. Booklet pane. Five stamps plus one
    printed label   ..   ..   ..   2·75

448	5 c. J. C. Watson				50	20
	a. Booklet pane. Five stamps plus one					
	printed label	..	..		2·75	
449	5 c. G. H. Reid				50	20
	a. Booklet pane. Five stamps plus one					
	printed label	..	..		2·75	
446/9				Set of 4	1·75	70

Nos. 446/9 were only issued in booklets with the outer edges of the pane imperforate so all stamps have one or two adjacent sides imperforate.

244 Capt. Ross Smith's Vickers Vimy, 1919

247 Symbolic Track and Diesel Locomotive

(Des E. Thake. Photo)

1969 (12 Nov). *50th Anniv of First England–Australia Flight. T **244** and similar horiz designs. P 13½.*

450	5 c. olive-green, pale blue, black and red	..		15	10
	a. Strip of 3. Nos. 450/2	..	..	1·50	
451	5 c. black, red and olive-green			15	10
452	5 c. olive-green, black, pale blue and red	..		15	10
450/2			Set of 3	1·50	25

Designs:—No. 450, Type 244; No. 451, Lt. H. Fysh and Lt. P. McGinness on 1919 survey with Ford car; No. 452, Capt. Wrigley and Sgt. Murphy in Royal Aircraft Factory B.E.2E taking off to meet the Smiths.

The three designs appear *se-tenant*, both horizontally and vertically, throughout the sheet.

(Des B. Sadgrove. Photo)

1970 (11 Feb). *Sydney–Perth Standard Gauge Railway Link. P 13½.*

453	247	5 c. multicoloured	..	15	10

248 Australian Pavilion, Osaka

251 Australian Flag

(Des J. Copeland (5 c.), A. Leydin (20 c.). Photo)

1970 (16 Mar). *World Fair, Osaka. T **248** and similar horiz design. P 13½.*

454	5 c. multicoloured	..	..	15	10
455	20 c. orange-red and black	..	..	35	65

Design:—20 c. "Southern Cross" and "from the Country of the South with warm feelings" (message).

(Des P.O. Artists (5 c.), J. Mason (30 c.). Photo)

1970 (31 Mar). *Royal Visit. T **251** and similar horiz design. P 13½.*

456	5 c. black and deep ochre	..	..	25	15
457	30 c. multicoloured	..	..	75	2·00

Design:—5 c. Queen Elizabeth II and Prince Philip.

252 Lucerne Plant, Bull and Sun

253 Captain Cook and H.M.S. *Endeavour*

(Des R. Ingpen. Photo)

1970 (13 Apr). *Eleventh International Grasslands Congress. P 13½.*

458	252	5 c. multicoloured	..	10	40

(Des R. Ingpen and "Team" (T. Keneally, A. Leydin, J. R. Smith). Photo)

1970 (20 Apr). *Bicentenary of Captain Cook's Discovery of Australia's East Coast. T **253** and similar multicoloured designs. P 13½.*

459	5 c. Type 253	..	..	50	10
	a. Strip of 5. Nos. 459/63	..		2·25	
460	5 c. Sextant and H.M.S. *Endeavour*	..		50	10
461	5 c. Landing at Botany Bay	..		50	10
462	5 c. Charting and exploring	..		50	10
463	5 c. Claiming possession	..		50	10
464	30 c. Captain Cook, H.M.S. *Endeavour*,				
	sextant, aborigines and kangaroo (63 ×				
	30 *mm*)	..	..	1·40	2·50
459/64			Set of 6	3·25	2·75
MS465	157 × 129 mm. Nos. 459/64. Imperf			12·00	12·00

The 5 c. stamps were issued horizontally *se-tenant* within the sheet, to form a composite design in the order listed.

50,000 miniature sheets were made available by the Post Office to the organisers of the Australian National Philatelic Exhibition which overprinted them in the white margin at each side of the 30 c. stamp with "Souvenir Sheet AUSTRALIAN NATIONAL PHILATELIC EXHIBITION" at left and "ANPEX 1970 SYDNEY 27 APRIL–1 MAY" at right in light red-brown and they were also serially numbered. These were put on sale at the exhibition on the basis of one sheet to each visitor paying 30 c. for admission. Although still valid for postage, since the stamps themselves had not been defaced, these sheets were not sold at post offices.

Subsequently further supplies were purchased and similarly overprinted and numbered by a private firm without the authority of the Post Office and ANPEX took successful legal action to stop their further sale to the public. This firm also had the unoverprinted sheets rouletted in colour between the stamps whilst further supplies of the normal sheets were overprinted with reproductions of old coins and others with an inscription commemorating the opening of Melbourne Airport on 1st July 1970, but all these are private productions. Further private productions have been reported.

259 Sturt's Desert Rose

AUSTRALIA   AUSTRALIA
I.   II.

Two types of 2 c.
I. "AUSTRALIA" thin: "2c" thin; flower name lightly printed.
II. Redrawn. "AUSTRALIA" thicker; "2c" much more heavily printed; flower name thicker and bolder.

(Des Note Ptg Branch. Photo)

1970–75. *Coil Stamps. Vert designs as T **259**. Multicoloured. Perf 15 × imperf.*

465a	2 c. Type 259 (I) (1.10.71)			35	20
	ab. Type II (1973)	..	..	55	30
466	4 c. Type 259 (27.4.70)			70	1·25
467	5 c. Golden Wattle (27.4.70)	..		20	10
468	6 c. Type 259 (28.9.70)			1·25	1·00
	a. Green (leaves) omitted	..		£350	
468b	7 c. Sturt's Desert Pea (1.10.71)		40	40
	c. Green (leaves) omitted	..		75·00	
468d	10 c. As 7 c. (15.1.75)	..		40	40
465a/8d			Set of 6	3·00	3·00

Nos. 465a/8d have horizontal coil perforations described after No. 191.

The 2 c. (No. 465a), 5 c. and 7 c. also exist on fluorescent paper; the 2 c. (No. 465ab) and 10 c. exist only on fluorescent paper (see note after No. 504).

264 Snowy Mountains Scheme

265 Rising Flames

(Des L. Mason (7 c.), R. Ingpen (8 c., 9 c.), B. Sadgrove (10 c.). Photo)

1970 (31 Aug). *National Development (1st series). T **264** and similar horiz designs. Multicoloured. P 13½.*

469	7 c. Type 264	..	..	30	80
470	8 c. Ord River Scheme	..	..	15	15
471	9 c. Bauxite to aluminium	..	..	15	15
472	10 c. Oil and Natural Gas	..	..	40	10
469/72			Set of 4	90	1·10

See also Nos. 541/4.

(Des G. Hamori. Photo)

1970 (2 Oct). *16th Commonwealth Parliamentary Association Conference, Canberra. P 13½.*

473	265	6 c. multicoloured	..	10	10

266 Milk Analysis and Dairy Herd

267 "The Nativity"

(Des R. Honisett. Photo)

1970 (7 Oct). *18th International Dairy Congress, Sydney. P 13½.*

474	266	6 c. multicoloured	..	10	10

(Des W. Beasley. Photo)

1970 (14 Oct). *Christmas. P 13½.*

475	267	6 c. multicoloured	..	10	10

---

268 U.N. "Plant" and Dove of Peace

269 Boeing 707 and Avro 504

(Des Monad Ltd. Photo)

1970 (19 Oct). *25th Anniv of United Nations. P 13½.*

476	268	6 c. multicoloured	..	15	10

(Des G. Hamori. Photo)

1970 (2 Nov). *50th Anniv of QANTAS Airline. T **269** and similar horiz design. Multicoloured. P 13½.*

477	6 c. Type 269	..	..	25	10
478	30 c. Avro 504 and Boeing 707	..		70	1·25

270 The Duigan Brothers (Pioneer Aviators)

271 "Theatre"

(Des A. Cook (No. 480), T. Adams (No. 482), Note Ptg Branch (others). Recess (background litho))

1970 (16 Nov). *Famous Australians (3rd series). T **270** and similar vert designs. P 15 × 14.*

479	6 c. blue			85	20
	a. Booklet pane. Five stamps plus one				
	printed label	..	..	4·00	
480	6 c. black/*cinnamon*			85	20
	a. Booklet pane. Five stamps plus one				
	printed label	..	..	4·00	
481	6 c. purple/*pale pink*			85	20
	a. Booklet pane. Five stamps plus one				
	printed label	..	..	4·00	
482	6 c. brown-lake/*flesh*			85	20
	a. Booklet pane. Five stamps plus one				
	printed label	..		4·00	
479/82			Set of 4	3·00	75

Designs:—No. 479 Type 270; No. 480 Lachlan Macquarie (Governor of N.S.W.); No. 481 Adam Lindsay Gordon (poet); No. 482 E.J. Eyre (explorer).

Nos. 479/82 were only issued in booklets with the outer edges of the pane imperforate so all stamps have one or two adjacent sides imperforate.

(Des D. Annand. Photo)

1971 (6 Jan). *"Australia–Asia". T **271** and similar horiz designs. Multicoloured. P 13½.*

483	7 c. Type 271	..	..	45	60
484	15 c. "Music"	..	..	70	1·00
485	20 c. "Sea Craft"	..	..	65	90
483/5			Set of 3	1·60	2·25

272 The Southern Cross

273 Market "Graph"

(Des R. Beck. Photo)

1971 (21 Apr). *Centenary of Australian Natives' Association. P 13½.*

486	272	6 c. black, vermilion and bright blue	..	10	10

(Des Monad Ltd. Photo)

1971 (5 May). *Centenary of Sydney Stock Exchange. P 13½.*

487	273	6 c. multicoloured	..	10	10

274 Rotary Emblem

275 Dassault Mirage Jets and De Havilland D.H.9A Biplane

(Des H. Williamson. Photo)

1971 (17 May). *50th Anniv of Rotary International in Australia.*
P 13½.
288 274 6 c. multicoloured 15 10

(Des R. Honisett. Photo)

1971 (9 June). *50th Anniv of R.A.A.F.* P 13½.
289 275 6 c. multicoloured 15 10
  a. Black (face value and inscr) omitted £1100

276 Draught-horse,   277 Bark Painting
Cat and Dog

(Des R. Ingpen. Photo)

1971 (5 July). *Animals. T 276 and similar vert designs. Multi-coloured.* P 13½.
490 6 c. Type 276 .. .. .. 20 10
491 12 c. Vet and lamb ("Animal Science") .. 45 35
492 18 c. Red Kangaroo ("Fauna Conservation") .. 60 55
493 24 c. Guide-dog ("Animals Aid to Man") .. 1·00 1·40
490/3 .. .. .. *Set of 4* 2·00 2·25
The 6 c. commemorated the Centenary of the Australian R.S.P.C.A., and the others were short-term definitives.

(Des J. Mason. Photo)

1971 (29 Sept). *Aboriginal Art. T 277 and similar multicoloured designs.* P 13½.
494 20 c. Type 277 .. .. .. 20 20
495 25 c. Body decoration 20 50
  a. Black omitted* £700
496 30 c. Cave painting (vert) 30 20
497 35 c. Grave posts (vert) 30 15
494/7 .. .. .. *Set of 4* 90 95
*The omission of the black results in the stamp being without face-value and "AUSTRALIA".
Nos. 494/7 also exist on fluorescent paper and the 35 c. exists with both PVA gum and gum arabic.

278 The Three Kings and the Star 279 Andrew Fisher

(Des J. Lee. Photo)

1971 (13 Oct). *Christmas. Colours of star and colour of "AUSTRALIA" given.* P 13½.
498 278 7 c. royal blue, pl mauve & pl lake-brn 70 15
  a. Block of 7. Nos. 498/504 .. 25·00
499 7 c. pale mauve, pl lake-brown & white 70 15
500 7 c. pale mauve, white and black .. 4·50 80
501 7 c. black, green and black 70 15
502 7 c. lilac, green and lilac 70 15
503 7 c. black, pale lake-brown and white .. 70 15
504 7 c. royal blue, pale mauve and green .. 20·00 2·25
498/504 .. .. .. *Set of 7* 25·00 3·50
Nos. 498/504, which also exist on fluorescent paper, were issued in sheets having two panes of 50 stamps. Each half pane had its stamps arranged thus:—

498	499	500	499	498
503	502	501	502	503
504	501	500	501	504
503	502	501	502	503
498	499	500	499	498

FLUORESCENT VERY WHITE CHALKY PAPER. As an experiment 10% of the above issue was printed on very white paper which fluoresces back and front under an ultraviolet lamp; it also has a strong coating of chalk on the surface. Late in 1972 this paper began to be introduced more generally and a number of stamps exist on both types of paper. The normal helecon paper does not fluoresce under the lamp but does react to the chalky test to a lesser degree.
Stamps reprinted on the white fluorescent paper are recorded below in footnotes and are listed in the *Australia Concise Catalogue.*

(Des J. Sandry. Recess)

1972 (8 Mar). *Famous Australians (4th series). Prime Ministers. T 279 and similar vert designs.* P 15 × 14.
505 7 c. ultramarine (Type 279) 30 20
  a. Booklet pane. Five stamps plus one printed label .. .. .. 1·75
506 7 c. ultramarine. (W. M. Hughes) .. 30 20
  a. Booklet pane. Five stamps plus one printed label .. .. .. 1·75
507 7 c. red (Joseph Cook) 30 20
  a. Booklet pane. Five stamps plus one printed label .. .. .. 1·75
508 7 c. red (S. M. Bruce) 30 20
  a. Booklet pane. Five stamps plus one printed label .. .. .. 1·75
505/8 .. .. .. *Set of 4* 1·10 70
Nos. 505/8 were only issued in booklets with the outer edges of the pane imperforate so all stamps have one or two adjacent sides imperforate.

280 Cameo Brooch 281 Fruit

(Des Mrs. V. Mason. Photo)

1972 (18 Apr). *50th Anniv of Country Women's Association.* P 13½.
509 280 7 c. multicoloured 20 10

(Des D. Annand. Photo)

1972 (14 June). *Primary Industries. T 281 and similar horiz designs. Multicoloured.* P 13½.
510 20 c. Type 281 .. .. .. 1·50 3·00
511 25 c. Rice .. .. .. 1·50 5·00
512 30 c. Fish .. .. .. 1·50 2·00
513 35 c. Beef .. .. .. 4·50 1·00
510/13 .. .. *Set of 4* 8·00 10·00

282 Worker in Wheelchair 283 Telegraph Line

(Des from photographs by Barbara Ardizzone. Photo)

1972 (2 Aug). *Rehabilitation of the Disabled. T 282 and similar designs.* P 13½.
514 12 c. yellow-brown and emerald .. 10 10
515 18 c. sage-green and yellow-orange .. 60 35
516 24 c. blue and yellow-brown .. 15 10
514/16 .. .. *Set of 3* 70 50
Designs: Horiz—18 c. Patient and teacher. Vert—24 c. Boy playing with ball.
The 12 c. and 24 c. also exist on fluorescent paper.

(Des J. Copeland. Photo)

1972 (22 Aug). *Centenary of Overland Telegraph Line.* P 13½.
517 283 7 c. multicoloured 15 15

284 Athletics 285 Numerals and Computer Circuit

(Des B. Sadgrove. Photo)

1972 (28 Aug). *Olympic Games, Munich. T 284 and similar vert designs. Multicoloured.* P 13½.
518 7 c. Type 284 .. .. .. 25 25
519 7 c. Rowing 25 25
520 7 c. Swimming 25 25
521 35 c. Equestrian .. .. .. 1·50 3·50
518/21 .. .. *Set of 4* 2·00 3·75

(Des G. Andrews. Photo)

1972 (16 Oct). *Tenth International Congress of Accountants, Sydney.* P 13½.
522 285 7 c. multicoloured 15 15

286 Australian-built Harvester

(Des R. Ingpen. Photo)

1972 (15 Nov). *Pioneer Life. T 286 and similar multicoloured designs.* P 13½.
523 5 c. Pioneer family (vert) 15 10
524 10 c. Water-pump (vert) 40 10
525 15 c. Type 286 .. .. .. 15 10
  a. Black (face value and inscr) omitted £700
526 40 c. House 30 60
527 50 c. Stage-coach 80 20
528 60 c. Morse key (vert) .. .. 60 1·00
529 80 c. Gem (paddle-steamer) .. .. 60 1·00
  a. Black (face value and inscr) omitted £600
523/9 .. .. *Set of 7* 2·50 2·50
All values also exist on fluorescent paper and the 15 c. exists with both PVA gum and gum arabic.

287 Jesus with Children 288 "Length"

(Des from drawing by Wendy Tamlyn (7 c.), L. Stirling (35 c.). Photo)

1972 (29 Nov). *Christmas. T 287 and similar vert design. Multicoloured.* P 15 × 14 (7 c.) or 13½ (35 c.).
530 7 c. Type 287 .. .. .. 30 10
  a. Brown-red ("Australia 7c") omitted £450
  b. Red-brown (inscr) omitted .. £450
531 35 c. Dove and spectrum motif .. 4·00 6·00

(Des Weatherhead & Stitt Pty. Ltd. Photo)

1973 (7 Mar). *Metric Conversion. T 288 and similar multicoloured designs.* P 15 × 14. (No. 535) or 14 × 15 (others).
532 7 c. Type 288 .. .. .. 30 40
533 7 c. "Volume".. .. .. .. 30 40
  a. Yellow-olive omitted* .. £650
534 7 c. "Mass" 30 40
535 7 c. "Temperature" (horiz) 30 40
532/5 .. .. .. *Set of 4* 1·10 1·40
*This results in the man's drink and shorts appearing white, and the colour of the stool being the same as the background.

289 Caduceus and Laurel Wreath 290 William Wentworth
(statesman and explorer)

(Des H. Williamson. Photo)

1973 (4 Apr). *25th Anniv of W.H.O.* P 15 × 14.
536 289 7 c. multicoloured 30 15

(Des J. Santry. Recess and litho)

1973 (16 May). *Famous Australians (5th series). T 290 and similar vert designs.* P 15 × 14.
537 7 c. yellow-bistre and black 40 35
  a. Block of 4. Nos. 537/40 .. 1·75
538 7 c. lilac and black 40 35
539 7 c. yellow-bistre and black 40 35
540 7 c. lilac and black 40 35
537/40 .. .. *Set of 4* 1·75 1·25
Designs:—No. 537, Type 290; No. 538, Isaac Isaacs (first Australian-born Governor-General); No. 539, Mary Gilmore (writer); No. 540, Marcus Clarke (author).
Nos. 537/40 were printed in se-tenant blocks of four within the sheet. They also exist on fluorescent paper.

291 Shipping 292 Banded Coral Shrimp

(Des J. Copeland. Photo)

1973 (6 June). *National Development (2nd series). T 291 and similar vert designs. Multicoloured.* P 13½.
541 20 c. Type 291 .. .. .. 2·00 3·25
542 25 c. Iron ore and steel .. .. 2·00 3·25
543 30 c. Beef roads .. .. .. 2·00 3·25
544 35 c. Mapping .. .. .. 2·50 3·25
541/4 .. .. .. *Set of 4* 7·50 11·50

(Des Printing Bureau artists (1 to 4 c.), J. Mason (others). Photo)

1973 (11 July)–**74**. *Marine Life and Gemstones. T 292 and similar multicoloured designs.* P 14 × 15 (1 to 4 c.) or 15 × 14 (others).
545 1 c. Type 292 .. .. .. 10 10
  a. Black (inscr and face value) omitted £160
  b. Yellow-brown omitted .. £325
546 2 c. Fiddler crab 10 10
547 3 c. Coral crab 10 10
  a. Black (inscr and value) omitted £450
548 4 c. Mauve stinger 30 55
  a. Black (face value and inscr) omitted £400
549 6 c. Chrysoprase (vert) 30 10
550 7 c. Agate (vert) 30 10
  a. Black (value and "agate") omitted 90·00
551 8 c. Opal (vert) 30 10
  a. Black (face value and inscr) omitted £160
552 9 c. Rhodonite (vert) 60 15
552a 10 c. Star sapphire (vert) (16.10.74) 40 10
  ab. Black (value, inscr, etc.) omitted £140
  ac. Turquoise-blue omitted* .. £100
  ad. Printed on the gummed side 25·00
545/52a .. .. *Set of 9* 2·00 1·25

*The turquoise-blue occurs on the gemstones, and is normally partly covered by the black.

The 1, 3, 7 and 10 c. exist with PVA gum as well as gum arabic.

293 Children at Play   **294** John Baptising Jesus

(Des G. Hamori. Photo)

1973 (5 Sept). *50th Anniv of Legacy (Welfare Organisation).* P 13½.
553 **293** 7 c. cinnamon, deep claret and emerald   30   10

PERFORATIONS. From 1973 to 1975 two different perforating machines were used for some issues, giving gauges of 14½×14 or 15×14 (on horizontal stamps), the exact measurement being 14.4×14.1 or 14.8×14.1. The latter gauge was also used for a reprint of the $1 definitive (No. 401c).

(Des G. Hamori. Photo)

1973 (3 Oct). *Christmas.* T **294** *and similar vert design. Multicoloured.* P 14×14½ (7 c.) or 13½ (30 c.).
554   7 c. Type **294** ..   35   10
    a. Perf 14×15 ..   3·50   80
    ab. Printed on the gummed side   55·00
555   30 c. The Good Shepherd ..   1·75   2·00

295 Sydney Opera House   **296** Wireless Receiver and Speaker

(Des A. Leydin. Photo)

1973 (17 Oct). *Architecture.* T **295** *and similar designs.* P 14½×14 (7, 10 c.) or 13½ (40, 50 c.).
556   7 c. pale turquoise-blue and new blue ..   30   15
    a. Perf 15×14 ..   3·50   1·60
557   10 c. light ochre and sepia ..   80   70
558   40 c. black, drab and dull mauve ..   1·25   1·75
    a. Dull mauve (background) omitted .. £1100
559   50 c. multicoloured ..   1·25   2·50
556/9 ..   *Set of 4*   3·25   4·50
Designs: *Horiz*—10 c. Buchanan's Hotel, Townsville; 40 c. Como House, Melbourne. *Vert*—50 c. St. James' Church, Sydney.

(Des E. Thake. Photo)

1973 (21 Nov). *50th Anniv of Regular Radio Broadcasting.* P 13½.
560 **296** 7 c. lt turquoise-blue, brown-red & blk   15   10

297 Common Wombat   **298** "Sergeant of Light Horse" (G. Lambert)

(Des R. Bates. Photo)

1974 (13 Feb). *Animals.* T **297** *and similar vert designs. Multicoloured.* P 14×15 (20, 30 c.) or 13½ (others).
561   20 c. Type **297**..   35   10
562   25 c. Short-nosed Echidna ..   75   60
563   30 c. Brush-tailed Possum ..   50   15
    a. Carmine-red (face-value, etc) omitted .. £700
564   75 c. Pygmy Glider ..   1·00   85
561/4 ..   *Set of 4*   2·40   1·50
The 20 c. exists with gum arabic as well as PVA gum.

(Des P.O. artists. Litho Asher & Co, Melbourne ($5, $10). Photo R.B.A. (others))

565   $1 Type **298** ..   1·00   10
    a. Flesh omitted†
566   $2 "Red Gums of the Far North" (H. Heysen) (*horiz*)   1·50   25
566a $4 "Shearing the Rams" (Tom Roberts) (*horiz*)   3·00   2·25
567   $5 "McMahon's Point" (Sir Arthur Streeton) (14.3.79)   6·00   2·25
567a $10 "Coming South" (Tom Roberts) (19.10.77) ..   8·50   3·50
565/7a ..   *Set of 5* 18·00   7·50
567/a, 778 Optd "Specimen" ..   *Set of 3*   9·00

---

†The omission of the flesh colour results in much of the design appearing in different shades, most notably the shirt, which appears green (especially the folds), the hillside, which is green, and the man's skin, which has highlights in yellow.

The $1 and $2 exist with PVA gum as well as gum arabic.

Nos. 567/a and 778 optd "Specimen" come from a special "Ausipex 84" Presentation Pack issued on 9 February 1983.

299 Supreme Court Judge   **300** Rugby Football

(Des T. Thompson. Photo)

1974 (15 May). *150th Anniv of Australia's Third Charter of Justice.* P 14×15.
568 **299** 7 c. multicoloured ..   20   10

(Des A. Leydin from drawings by D. O'Brien. Photo)

1974 (24 July). *Non-Olympic Sports.* T **300** *and similar multicoloured designs.* P 15×14 (Nos. 569/70) or 14×15 (others).
569   7 c. Type **300** ..   40   40
570   7 c. Bowls ..   40   40
571   7 c. Australian football (*vert*)   40   40
572   7 c. Cricket (*vert*) ..   40   40
573   7 c. Golf (*vert*)..   40   40
574   7 c. Surfing (*vert*) ..   40   40
575   7 c. Tennis (*vert*) ..   40   40
569/75 ..   *Set of 7*   2·50   2·50

301 "Transport of Mails"   **302** Letter "A" and W. C. Wentworth (co-founder)

(Des J. Copeland. Photo)

1974 (9 Oct). *Centenary of Universal Postal Union.* T **301** *and similar vert designs. Multicoloured.* P 15×14 (7 c.) or 13½ (30 c.).
576   7 c. Type **301**..   40   20
    a. Perf 14½×14 ..   60   30
577   30 c. Three-part version of Type **301**   85   1·90

(Des I. Dalton. Typo and litho)

1974 (9 Oct). *150th Anniv of First Independent Newspaper, "The Australian".* P 14×15.
578 **302** 7 c. black/light cinnamon ..   30   30
    a. Perf 14×14½ ..   1·25   50

(303)   **304** "The Adoration of the Magi"

1974 (16 Oct). *No. 551 surch with* T **303**, *in red.*
579   9 c. on 8 c. Opal ..   15   15

(Des and recess R.B.A.)

1974 (13 Nov). *Christmas. Woodcuts by Dürer.* T **304** *and similar vert design.* P 14×15.
580   10 c. black/cream ..   25   10
581   35 c. black/cream ..   80   1·00
Design:—35 c. "The Flight into Egypt".

PROCESS. All the following issues to No. 772 were printed in photogravure, *except where otherwise stated.*

305 "Pre-School Education"   **306** "Road Safety"

(Des Vivienne Binns (5 c.), Erica McGilchrist (11 c.), E. Tanner (15 c.), J. Meldrum (60 c.))

1974 (20 Nov). *Education in Australia.* T **305** *and similar multicoloured designs.* P 13½.
582   5 c. Type **305** ..   25   40
583   11 c. "Correspondence Schools"   25   25
584   15 c. "Science Education" ..   40   40
585   60 c. "Advanced Education" (*vert*)   75   2·00
582/5 ..   *Set of 4*   1·50   2·75

(Des G. Andrews)

1975 (29 Jan). *Environment Dangers.* T **306** *and similar horiz designs. Multicoloured.* P 14×14½ (No. 586) or 14½×14 (others).
586   10 c. Type **306** ..   50   50
    a. Printed on the gummed side .. 30·00
587   10 c. "Pollution" ..   50   50
    a. Perf 15×14 ..   7·00   3·50
588   10 c. "Bush Fires" ..   50   50
    a. Perf 15×14 ..   1·40   1·10
586/8 ..   *Set of 3*   1·40   1·40

307 Australian Women's Year Emblem   **308** J. H. Scullin

(Des Leonora Howlett)

1975 (12 Mar). *International Women's Year.* P 14×15.
589 **307** 10 c. dp violet-blue, green & bluish vio ..   20   15
This stamp exists with PVA gum as well as gum arabic.

(Des B. Dunlop)

1975 (26 Mar). *Famous Australians (6th series). Prime Ministers* T **308** *and similar vert designs. Multicoloured.* P 14×15.
590   10 c. Type **308** ..   25   30
591   10 c. J. A. Lyons ..   25   30
    a. Printed on the gummed side .. 70·00
592   10 c. Earle Page ..   25   30
593   10 c. Arthur Fadden ..   25   30
594   10 c. John Curtin ..   25   30
595   10 c. J. B. Chifley ..   25   30
590/5 ..   *Set of 6*   1·40   1·60
Nos. 591/2 and 594 exist with both PVA gum and gum arabic.

309 Atomic Absorption Spectrophotometry   **310** Logo of Australian Postal Commission

(Des Weatherhead & Stitt)

1975 (14 May). *Scientific Development.* T **309** *and similar horiz designs. Multicoloured.* P 13½.
596   11 c. Type **309** ..   60   40
597   24 c. Radio astronomy..   1·40   1·90
598   33 c. Immunology ..   1·50   2·50
599   48 c. Oceanography ..   2·00   2·75
596/9 ..   *Set of 4*   5·00   6·75

(Des P. Huveneers)

1975 (1 July). *Inauguration of Australian Postal and Telecommunications Commissions.* T **310** *and similar horiz design.* P 14½×14.
600   10 c. black, rosine and pale grey ..   25   10
    a. Pair. Nos. 600/1 ..   85   1·40
    b. Perf 15×14 ..   25   10
    ba. Pair. Nos. 600b/lb ..   1·00   1·50
601   10 c. black, orange-yellow and pale grey ..   25   10
    b. Perf 15×14 ..   25   10
Design:—No. 601, Logo of Australian Telecommunications Commission.
Nos. 600/1 were printed together, *se-tenant* in horizontal and vertical pairs throughout the sheet.

311 Edith Cowan   **312** *Helichrysum thomsonii*   **313** "Tambaran" House and Sydney Opera House

(Des D. and J. O'Brien)

1975 (6 Aug). *Famous Australians (7th series). Australian Women. T* **311** *and similar vert designs. Multicoloured.* A. *P* 14×14½. B. *P* 14×15.

			A.		B.	
602	10 c. Type **311**		35	55	35	55
	c. Printed on the gummed side		†	60·00	†	
603	10 c. Louisa Lawson ..		35	55	60	55
604	10 c. Ethel Richardson		35	55	60	55
605	10 c. Catherine Spence		35	55	45	55
606	10 c. Constance Stone		50	55	35	55
607	10 c. Truganini		35	55	40	55
602/7		*Set of* 6	2·00	3·00	2·50	3·00

No. 604 is inscribed with the *nom de plume* "Henry Handel Richardson".

(Des F. Knight)

1975 (27 Aug). *Wild Flowers. T* **312** *and similar multicoloured design. P* 15×14 (18 c.) *or* 14×15 (45 c.).

608	18 c. Type **312**.	..	..	25	10
	a. Black omitted		..	30·00	
	b. Grey (stem, etc) omitted		..	40·00	
609	45 c. *Callistemon teretifolius* (*horiz*)..		..	50	10
	a. Black (face value and inscr) omitted		..	£400	
	b. Yellow-green (twigs) omitted ..		..	£120	

The 18 c. exists with both PVA gum and gum arabic.

(Des D. Annand (18 c.) or G. Hamori (25 c.))

1975 (16 Sept). *Papua New Guinea Independence. T* **313** *and similar horiz design. Multicoloured. P* 13½.

610	18 c. Type **313**.	..	..	20	10
611	25 c. "Freedom" (bird in flight)	..	..	50	1·25

314 Epiphany Scene   315 Australian Coat of Arms

(Des D. O'Brien (15 c.) or J. Milne (45 c.))

1975 (29 Oct). *Christmas. T* **314** *and similar horiz design. P* 14×15 (15 c.) *or* 13½ (45 c.).

612	15 c. multicoloured	..	25	10
613	45 c. reddish violet, greenish blue and silver		75	2·40

Design:—45 c. "Shining Star".

I   II

Two types of No. 614:
I. Emu's legs without toes.
II. Emu showing toes.
Other minor differences also occur.

(Des J. Spatchurst)

1976 (5 Jan). *75th Anniv of Nationhood. P* 15×14.

614	315 18 c. multicoloured (I) ..	..	40	20
	a. Buff (supporters) omitted	..	£400	
	b. Gold (shield and star) omitted	..	£180	
	c. Type II	..	75	30
	cb. Gold (shield and star) omitted	..	£650	

316 Telephone-user, *circa* 1878   317 John Oxley

(Des R. Ingpen)

1976 (10 Mar). *Telephone Centenary. P* 13½.

615	316 18 c. multicoloured	..	..	20	15

(Des B. Dunlop)

1976 (9 June). *19th Century Explorers. T* **317** *and similar horiz designs. Multicoloured. P* 13½.

616	18 c. Type **317**	..	..	30	40
617	18 c. Hume and Hovell	..	..	30	40
618	18 c. John Forrest	..	..	30	40
619	18 c. Ernest Giles	..	..	30	40
620	18 c. William Gosse	..	..	30	40
621	18 c. Peter Warburton	..	..	30	40
616/21			*Set of* 6	1·60	2·25

318 Measuring Stick, Graph   319 Football
and Computer Tape

(Des R. Ingpen)

1976 (15 June). *50th Anniv of Commonwealth Scientific and Industrial Research Organisation. P* 15×14.

622	318 18 c. multicoloured	..	..	20	15

(Des A. Leydin)

1976 (14 July). *Olympic Games, Montreal. T* **319** *and similar multicoloured designs. P* 13½.

623	18 c. Type **319** ..	..	..	30	20
624	18 c. Gymnastics (*vert*)	..	..	30	20
625	25 c. Diving (*vert*)	..	..	50	60
626	40 c. Cycling	..	..	70	80
623/6			*Set of* 4	1·60	1·60

The 25 c. exists with gum arabic as well as PVA gum.

320 Richmond Bridge,   321 Blamire Young (designer
Tasmania   of first Australian stamp)

(Des O. Borchert)

1976 (23 Aug). *Australian Scenes. T* **320** *and similar designs. Multicoloured. P* 14×15 (50 c.) *or* 15×14 (*others*).

627	5 c. Type **320** ..	..	..	15	10
628	25 c. Broken Bay, N.S.W.	..	..	45	20
629	35 c. Wittenoom Gorge, W.A...	..	..	35	20
630	50 c. Mt. Buffalo, Victoria (*vert*)	..	..	80	30
631	70 c. Barrier Reef	..	..	1·10	1·10
632	85 c. Ayers Rock, N.T...	..	..	1·10	1·75
627/32			*Set of* 6	3·50	3·50

(Des R. Honisett)

1976 (27 Sept). *National Stamp Week. P* 13½.

633	321 18 c. multicoloured	..	..	15	15
MS634	101 × 112 mm. No. 633 × 4	..	75	2·00	

MS634 contains one stamp coloured as No. 633; the others, showing the different colour separations used in the printing, are each differently coloured.
The miniature sheet exists with "AUSTRALIAN STAMP PROMOTION COUNCIL" overprinted in red on the margin from a privately produced booklet.

322 "Virgin and Child" (detail,   323 John Gould
Simone Cantarini)

(Des C. Medlycott (15 c.), Wendy Tamlyn (45 c.))

1976 (1 Nov). *Christmas. T* **322** *and similar horiz design. P* 15×14 (15 c.) *or* 13½ (45 c.).

635	15 c. bright magenta and light azure..	..	25	10
636	45 c. multicoloured	..	70	90

Design:—45 c. Toy koala bear and decorations.

(Des B. Weatherhead)

1976 (10 Nov). *Famous Australians (8th series). T* **323** *and similar horiz designs. Multicoloured. P* 15×14.

637	18 c. Type **323** ..	..	..	35	45
638	18 c. Thomas Laby	..	..	35	45
	a. Red-brown ("AUSTRALIA" etc.) omitted		£425		
639	18 c. Sir Baldwin Spencer	..	..	35	45
640	18 c. Griffith Taylor	..	..	35	45
637/40			*Set of* 4	1·25	1·60

324 "Music"   325 Queen Elizabeth II

1977 (19 Jan). *Performing Arts. T* **324** *and similar vert designs. Multicoloured. P* 14×15.

641	20 c. Type **324**	..	..	..	25	25
642	30 c. Drama	..	..	..	40	35
643	40 c. Dance	..	..	..	55	40
644	60 c. Opera	..	..	..	1·00	1·75
641/4 ..	..	..	..	*Set of* 4	2·00	2·50

(Des P.O. Artists. Litho Govt Printer, Sydney (2% of supplies) or by Norman J. Field, Melbourne)

1977 (2 Feb). *Silver Jubilee. T* **325** *and similar vert design. Multicoloured. P* 14×15.

645	18 c. Type **325**	..	..	20	10
646	45 c. The Queen and Prince Philip	..	..	50	80

326 Fielder and   327 Parliament House
Wicket Keeper

(Des B. Weatherhead)

1977 (9 Mar). *Australia–England Test Cricket Centenary. T* **326** *and similar vert designs. Multicoloured. P* 13½.

647	18 c. Type **326** ..	..	..	35	50
	a. Horiz strip of 5. Nos. 647/51	..	2·00		
648	18 c. Umpire, batsman and scoreboard		35	50	
649	18 c. Fielders	..	..	35	50
650	18 c. Batsman and umpire	..	..	35	50
651	18 c. Bowler and fielder	..	..	35	50
652	45 c. Batsman awaiting delivery	..	75	1·25	
647/52			*Set of* 6	2·50	3·25

Nos. 647/51 were printed together, *se-tenant*, in horizontal strips of 5 throughout the sheet, forming a composite design.

(Des R.B.A.)

1977 (13 Apr). *50th Anniv of Opening of Parliament House, Canberra. P* 15×14.

653	327 18 c. multicoloured	..	..	15	10
	a. Yellow (foreground) omitted	..	£1000		

328 Trade Unions Workers   329 Surfing Santa

(Des D. Lanyon; adapted B. Sadgrove)

1977 (9 May). *50th Anniv of Australian Council of Trade Unions. P* 13½.

654	328 18 c. multicoloured	..	..	15	10

(Des R. Roberts (15 c.), J. O'Brien (45 c.))

1977 (31 Oct). *Christmas. T* **329** *and similar vert design. Multicoloured. P* 14×15 (15 c.) *or* 13½ (45 c.).

655	15 c. Type **329**	..	..	25	10
656	45 c. Madonna and Child	..	..	75	90

330 National Flag   331 Harry Hawker and
Sopwith Atlantic

(Des Cato Hibberd Design)

1978 (26 Jan). *Australia Day. P* 13½.

657	330 18 c. multicoloured	..	..	20	15

(Litho Asher and Co, Melbourne)

1978 (19 Apr). *Early Australian Aviators. T* **331** *and similar horiz designs. Multicoloured. P* 15½.

658	18 c. Type **331**	..	35	45
	a. Imperf (horiz pair)	..	£550	
659	18 c. Bert Hinkler and Avro Type 581 Avian		35	45
	a. Imperf (horiz pair)	..	£600	
660	18 c. Sir Charles Kingsford Smith and Fokker F311a/3m *Southern Cross*		35	45
	a. Imperf (pair) ..	..	£110	
661	18 c. Charles Ulm and Fokker F311a/3m *Southern Cross*		35	45
658/61		*Set of* 4	1·25	1·60
MS662	100×112 mm. Nos. 660/1×2. Imperf	75	1·75	

Forgeries of No. MS662 have been reported. These can be detected, under strong magnification, by the lack of magenta screen on the blue panel at right and by the presence of magenta dots in the yellow background to No. 661.

332 Piper PA-31 Navajo   333 Illawarra
landing at Station   Flame Tree
Airstrip

1978 (15 May). *50th Anniv of Royal Flying Doctor Service.* P 13½.

663	332	18 c. multicoloured	..	20	15

(Des D. Rose)

1978 (1 June). *Trees. T 333 and similar vert designs. Multicoloured.* P 14 × 15 (18 c.) or 13½ (others).

664	18 c. Type 333	..	..	20	15
665	25 c. Ghost Gum	..	..	35	1·10
666	40 c. Grass Tree	..	..	45	1·75
667	45 c. Cootamundra Wattle	..	..	45	70
664/7 ..			*Set of 4*	1·25	3·25

334 Sturt's Desert Rose and Map

335 Hooded Plover

(Des D. Pitt. Litho Asher and Co, Melbourne)

1978 (19 June). *Establishment of State Government for the Northern Territory.* P 15½.

668	334	18 c. multicoloured	..	20	15

(Des Kay Breeden-Williams. Photo)

1978 (3 July)–80. *Birds (1st series). Multicoloured designs as T 335.* P 15 × 14 (20 c. (both)), 14 × 15 (22 c.) or 13½ (others).

669	1 c. Spotted-sided Finch (17.9.79)	..	10	20
670	2 c. Crimson Finch (17.9.79)	..	10	20
671	5 c. Type 335 (17.7.78)	..	30	10
	a. Grey-brown (bird's back) omitted		£250	
672	15 c. Forest Kingfisher (vert) (17.9.79)		20	20
673	20 c. Australian Dabchick ("Little Grebe") ..		60	10
	a. Yellow (beak and eye) omitted ..		£160	
674	20 c. Eastern Yellow Robin (17.9.79) ..		20	10
675	22 c. White-tailed Kingfisher (22 × 29 mm) (31.3.80) ..		30	10
676	25 c. Masked Plover (17.7.78) ..		80	35
677	30 c. Oystercatcher (17.7.78) ..		90	25
678	40 c. Variegated Wren (vert) (17.9.79) ..		30	45
679	50 c. Flame Robin (vert) (17.9.79) ..		40	50
680	55 c. Comb-crested Jacana ("Lotus-bird") ..		85	60
669/80		*Set of 12*	4·50	2·75

See also Nos. 734/40.

336 1928 3d. "National Stamp Exhibition" Commemorative

337 "The Madonna and Child" (after van Eyck)

(Des Cato Hibberd Design. Litho Asher and Co, Melbourne)

1978 (25 Sept). *National Stamp Week. 50th Anniv of National Stamp Exhibition, Melbourne.* P 15½.

694	336	20 c. multicoloured	..	15	15
MS695	78 × 113 mm. No. 694 × 4	..		75	1·75

(Litho Asher and Co, Melbourne)

1978 (3 Oct–1 Nov). *Christmas. Paintings. T 337 and similar vert designs. Multicoloured.* P 14½.

696	15 c. Type 337 (1.11)	..		30	10
697	25 c. "The Virgin and Child" (Marmion)	..		45	55
698	55 c. "The Holy Family" (del Vaga) (1.11)	..		70	90
696/8 ..	..	..	*Set of 3*	1·25	1·40

338 "Tulloch"

339 Raising the Flag, Sydney Cove, 26 January 1788

(Des B. Clinton)

1978 (18 Oct). *Race-horses. T 338 and similar multicoloured designs.* P 15 × 14 (20 c.) or 13½ (others).

699	20 c. Type 338	..	..	35	10
700	35 c. "Bernborough" (vert)	..		60	70
701	50 c. "Phar Lap" (vert) ..	..		85	1·10
702	55 c. "Peter Pan"	..		90	1·10
699/702			*Set of 4*	2·40	2·75

(Des B. Clinton. Litho Asher and Co, Melbourne)

1979 (26 Jan). *Australia Day.* P 15½.

703	339	20 c. multicoloured	..	15	15
		a. Yellow omitted	..		

340 P.S. *Canberra*

341 Port Campbell, Victoria

(Des O. Borchert)

1979 (14 Feb). *Ferries and Murray River Steamers. T 340 and similar horiz designs. Multicoloured.* P 15 × 14 (20 c.) or 13½ (others).

704	20 c. Type 340 ..		35	10
705	35 c. M.V. *Lady Denman*		60	85
706	50 c. P.S. *Murray River Queen*		80	1·25
707	55 c. H.V. *Curl Curl*		90	1·25
704/7 ..		*Set of 4*	2·40	3·00

(Des M. Robinson. Litho Asher and Co. Melbourne)

1979 (9 Apr). *National Parks. T 341 and similar multicoloured designs.* P 15½.

708	20 c. Type 341 ..		25	25
	a. Horiz strip of 5. Nos. 708/12		1·10	
709	20 c. Uluru, Northern Territory		25	25
710	20 c. Royal, New South Wales		25	25
711	20 c. Flinders Ranges, South Australia		25	25
712	20 c. Nambung, Western Australia		25	25
713	20 c. Girraween, Queensland (vert)		25	25
	a. Horiz pair. Nos. 713/14		50	50
	ab. Imperf (horiz pair)*		£600	
714	20 c. Mount Field, Tasmania (vert)		25	25
708/14		*Set of 7*	1·40	1·40

Nos. 708/14 were printed together, *se-tenant*; Nos. 708/12 in horizontal strips of 5 and Nos. 713/14 in horizontal pairs, throughout separate sheets.

*The imperforate error, No. 713ab, involves the two right-hand vertical columns of the sheet only, the left-hand stamp having vertical perforations at left.

342 "Double Fairlie" Type Locomotive, Western Australia

343 Symbolic Swan

(Des R. Honisett)

1979 (16 May). *Steam Railways. T 342 and similar horiz designs. Multicoloured.* P 14 × 15 (20 c.) or 13½ (others).

715	20 c. Type 342 ..		30	10
716	35 c. Locomotive, "Puffing Billy" Line, Victoria		60	70
717	50 c. Locomotive, Pichi Richi Line, South Australia ..		70	1·25
718	55 c. Locomotive, Zig Zag Railway, New South Wales		80	1·40
715/18		*Set of 4*	2·25	3·00

(Des B. Weatherhead)

1979 (6 June). *150th Anniv of Western Australia.* P 13½.

719	343	20 c. multicoloured	..	15	15

344 Children playing on Slide

345 Letters and Parcels

(Des Wendy Tamlyn. Litho Asher and Co, Melbourne)

1979 (13 Aug). *International Year of the Child.* P 13½ × 13.

720	344	20 c. multicoloured	..	15	10

(Des A. Collins. Litho Asher and Co, Melbourne)

1979 (24 Sept–1 Nov). *Christmas. T 345 and similar vert designs. Multicoloured.* P 13 × 13½.

721	15 c. Christ's Nativity (Eastern European icon) (1.11.79) ..		15	10
722	25 c. Type 345 ..		25	50
723	55 c. "Madonna and Child" (Buglioni) (1.11.79)		40	75
721/3 ..	..	*Set of 3*	70	1·25

MINIMUM PRICE

The minimum price quote is 10p which represents a handling charge rather than a basis for valuing common stamps. For further notes about prices see introductory pages.

---

346 Fly-fishing

347 Matthew Flinders

(Des B. Clinton)

1979 (24 Oct). *Fishing. T 346 and similar vert designs.* P 14 × 15 (20 c.) or 13½ (others).

724	20 c. multicoloured		20	10
725	35 c. black, deep grey-blue and violet-blue		35	70
726	50 c. multicoloured		40	90
727	55 c. multicoloured		45	85
724/7 ..		*Set of 4*	1·25	2·25

Designs:—35 c. Spinning; 50 c. Deep sea game-fishing; 55 c. Surf fishing.

(Des B. Weatherhead. Litho Asher and Co, Melbourne)

1980 (23 Jan). *Australia Day.* P 13½ × 13.

728	347	20 c. multicoloured	..	20	10

348 Dingo

349 Queen Elizabeth II

(Des Marg Towt. Litho Asher and Co, Melbourne)

1980 (20 Feb). *Dogs. T 348 and similar horiz designs. Multicoloured.* P 13½ × 13.

729	20 c. Type 348 ..		35	10
730	25 c. Border Collie		35	10
731	35 c. Australian Terrier		50	70
732	50 c. Australian Cattle Dog		1·10	1·75
733	55 c. Australian Kelpie		1·00	1·40
729/33		*Set of 5*	3·00	4·00

(Des Kay Breeden-Williams. Litho Asher and Co, Melbourne)

1980 (31 Mar)–82. *Birds (2nd series). Multicoloured designs as T 335.* P 12½.

734	10 c. Golden-shouldered Parrot (vert) (1.7.80)		30	10
	a. Perf 14½×14 (1982) ..		1·50	55
734b	18 c. Spotted Catbird (vert) (17.11.80)		70	1·10
735	28 c. Australian Bee Eater ("Rainbow Bird") (vert) ..		50	30
736	35 c. Regent Bowerbird (vert) (1.7.80)		35	10
737	45 c. Masked Wood Swallow (1.7.80)		40	10
	a. Perf 14½×14½ (1982) ..		2·00	90
738	60 c. Australian King Parrot (vert)		50	15
739	80 c. Rainbow Pitta (1.7.80)		85	75
740	$1 Black-backed Magpie (vert) (1.7.80)		85	10
734/40		*Set of 8*	4·00	2·25

Designs of Nos. 734/40 measure 22 × 29 mm (vert) or 29 × 22 mm (horiz).

(Des B. Weatherhead. Litho Asher and Co, Melbourne)

1980 (21 Apr). *Queen Elizabeth II's Birthday.* P 13 × 13½.

741	349	22 c. multicoloured	..	30	20

350 "Once a jolly Swagman camp'd by a Billabong"

351 High Court Buildings

(Des R. Roberts. Litho Asher and Co, Melbourne)

1980 (7 May). *Folklore. Scenes and Verses from the Folksong "Waltzing Matilda". T 350 and similar vert designs. Multicoloured.* P 13 × 13½.

742	22 c. Type 350 ..		30	10
	a. Horiz strip of 5. Nos. 742/6		1·40	
743	22 c. "And he sang as he shoved that Jumbuck in his Tuckerbag"		30	10
744	22 c. "Up rode the Squatter, mounted on his Thoroughbred"		30	10
745	22 c. "Down came the Troopers one, two, three"		30	10
746	22 c. "And his Ghost may be heard as you pass by that Billabong"		30	10
742/6 ..		*Set of 5*	1·40	

Nos. 742/6 were printed together, *se-tenant*, in horizontal strips of 5 throughout the sheet, forming a composite design.

(Des Cato Hibberd Design. Litho Asher and Co, Melbourne)

1980 (19 May). *Opening of High Court Building, Canberra.* P 13 × 13½.

747	351	22 c. multicoloured	..	20	20

352 Salvation Army   353 Postbox, *circa* 1900

(Des J. Spatchurst. Litho Asher and Co, Melbourne)

1980 (11 Aug). *Community Welfare. T* 352 *and similar multi-coloured designs.* P 13½ × 13 (*Nos.* 748, 751) *or* 13 × 13½ (*others*).

748	22 c. Type 352		40	40
749	22 c. St. Vincent de Paul Society (*vert*)		40	40
750	22 c. Meals on Wheels (*vert*)		40	40
751	22 c. "Life. Be in it"		40	40
748/51		*Set of 4*	1·40	1·40

(Des B. Weatherhead. Litho Asher and Co, Melbourne)

1980 (29 Sept). *National Stamp Week. T* 353 *and similar vert designs showing postal history, circa* 1900. *Multicoloured.* P 13 × 13½.

752	22 c. Type 353		30	10
	a. Horiz strip of 5. Nos. 752/6		1·40	
753	22 c. Postman (facing left)		30	10
754	22 c. Mail van		30	10
755	22 c. Postman and postbox		30	10
756	22 c. Postman (facing right)		30	10
752/6		*Set of 5*	1·40	45
MS757	95 × 130 mm. Nos. 752, 754 and 756		1·10	1·40
	a. Error. Imperf			

Nos. 752/6 were printed together, *se-tenant*, in horizontal strips of 5 throughout the sheet.
Stamps from No. **MS**757 have different backgrounds to the stamps from normal sheets.

354 "Holy Family" (painting, Prospero Fontana)   355 Commonwealth Aircraft Factory CA-6 Wackett, 1941

(Des B. Weatherhead. Litho Asher and Co, Melbourne)

1980 (1 Oct–3 Nov). *Christmas. Works of Art. T* 354 *and similar vert designs. Multicoloured.* P 13 × 13½.

758	15 c. "The Virgin Enthroned" (detail of painting by Justin O'Brien) (3.11)		15	10
759	28 c. Type 354		25	40
760	60 c. "Madonna and Child" (sculpture by School of M. Zuern) (3.11)		50	1·10
758/60		*Set of 3*	80	1·40

(Des O. Borchert. Litho Victorian Government Printer, Melbourne (22 c.), Asher and Co, Melbourne (others))

1980 (19 Nov). *Aircraft. T* 355 *and similar horiz designs. Multicoloured.* P 13½ × 14 (22 c.) *or* 13½ × 13 (*others*).

761	22 c. Type 355		35	10
762	40 c. Commonwealth Aircraft Factory CA-25 Winjeel, 1955		70	85
763	45 c. Commonwealth Aircraft Factory CA-13 Boomerang, 1944		70	95
764	60 c. Government Aircraft Factory N22B Nomad, 1975		80	1·40
761/4		*Set of 4*	2·25	3·00

356 Flag in shape of Australia   357 Caricature of Darby Munro (jockey)

(Des B. Weatherhead. Litho Asher and Co, Melbourne)

1981 (21 Jan). *Australia Day.* P 13½ × 13.

765	356 22 c. multicoloured		20	20

(Des T. Rafty. Litho Cambec Press, Melbourne)

1981 (18 Feb). *Sports Personalities. T* 357 *and similar vert designs showing caricatures. Multicoloured.* P 14 × 13½.

766	22 c. Type 357		30	10
767	35 c. Victor Trumper (cricketer)		65	70
768	55 c. Sir Norman Brookes (tennis player)		85	1·00
769	60 c. Walter Lindrum (billiards player)		90	1·50
766/9		*Set of 4*	2·40	3·00

358 1931 Kingsford Smith's Flights 6d. Commemorative   359 Apex Emblem and Map of Australia

(Des Cato Hibberd Design. Litho Asher and Co, Melbourne)

1981 (25 Mar). *50th Anniv of Official Australia–U.K. Airmail Service. T* 358 *and similar horiz design showing* 1931 *Kingsford Smith's Flights* 6d. *commemorative.* P 13 × 13½ (22 c.) *or* 13½ × 13 (60 c.).

770	22 c. blackish lilac, rosine and bright blue		20	10
771	60 c. blackish lilac, rosine and ultramarine		60	90

(Des P. Clark)

1981 (6 Apr). *50th Anniv of Apex (young men's service club).* P 13½.

772	359 22 c. multicoloured		20	20

ASHER AND CO. From April 1981 this firm was known as Leigh-Mardon Ltd, Melbourne.

360 Queen's Personal Standard for Australia   361 "Licence Inspected"

(Litho Leigh-Mardon Ltd, Melbourne)

1981 (21 Apr). *Queen Elizabeth II's Birthday.* P 13½ × 13.

773	360 22 c. multicoloured		20	20

(Des B. Weatherhead. Litho Leigh-Mardon Ltd, Melbourne)

1981 (20 May). *Gold Rush Era. Sketches by S. T. Gill. T* 361 *and similar vert designs. Multicoloured.* P 13 × 13½.

774	22 c. Type 361		20	25
775	22 c. "Puddling"		20	25
776	22 c. "Quality of washing stuff"		20	25
777	22 c. "On route to deposit gold"		20	25
774/7		*Set of 4*	70	90

362 "On the Wallaby Track" (Fred McCubbin)

(Litho Leigh-Mardon Ltd, Melbourne)

1981 (17 June)–84. *Paintings. T* 362 *and similar horiz design. Multicoloured.* P 15 × 14½.

778	$2 Type 362		1·50	30
779	$5 "A Holiday at Mentone, 1888" (Charles Conder) (4.4.84) (Optd S. £2·75)		4·75	1·25

For No. 778 overprinted "Specimen" see after No. 567a.

363 Thylacine   363a Blue Mountain Tree-Frog

363b Papilio ulysses (butterfly)

PRINTINGS OF THE 24 C. VALUE. (Nos. 788, 788b). Original printings of this stamp were produced by a combination of printing processes. The centre design was first printed in photogravure by the Note Printing Branch, Reserve Bank of Australia, and then the half-printed sheets were transferred to Leigh-Mardon Ltd for the inscriptions and face value to be added in lithography.

Further supplies of this value were required in late 1981, but these were printed by Leigh-Mardon Ltd entirely in lithography.

The work of the two printers can be identified by the usual differences exhibited by the processes concerned; the lithography version tending to be darker in appearance with much sharper outlines.

Other specific differences are as follows:

On the *photogravure* version the front legs show a diagonal pattern of screening dots which are replaced by vertical and horizontal lines on the *litho* stamp.

The animal's eye is highlighted on the *photogravure* stamp.

The fourth and sixth bands on the animal's back are much longer on the *litho* version.

The end of the right-hand twig is pointed on the *photogravure* and blunt on the *litho*.

Photogravure Centre

Lithography Centre

(Des C. McCubbin (4, 10, 20, 27 c. (No. 791), 30 c. (No. 792a), 35, 45, 60, 80 c., $1), F. Knight (5, 24, 25, 30 c. (No. 792)), 50, 55 c.) or Beverley Bruen (others). Photo Note Ptg Branch, Reserve Bank of Australia and litho Leigh-Mardon (24 c. (No. 788)), litho Leigh-Mardon (3, 5, 15, 24 c. (No. 788b)), 25, 27 c. (both), 30 c. (both), 40, 50, 55, 65, 75, 90 c.), Cambec Press (others))

1981 (19 July)–83. *Wildlife. Multicoloured designs as T* 363 (5, 24, 25, 30, 50, 55 c.), *T* 363a (1, 3, 5, 27 (*No.* 790), 40, 65, 70, 75, 85, 90, 95 c.) *or vert as T* 363b (*others*). P 13½ (1, 4, 10, 20, 24, 35, 45, 60, 70, 80, 85, 95 c., $1), 14½ × 14 (27 c. (*No.* 791), 30 c. (*No.* 792a)) *or* 12½ (*others*).

781	1 c. Lace Monitor (2.2.83)		10	20
782	3 c. Corroboree Frog (19.4.82)		10	10
	a. Perf 14×14½ (1983)		40	15
783	4 c. *Euschemon rafflesio* ("Regent Skipper") (butterfly) (*vert*) (15.6.83)		55	45
784	5 c. Queensland Hairy-nosed Wombat (*vert*) (15.7.81)		10	10
	a. Perf 14½×14 (12.83)		1·25	15
785	10 c. *Ornithoptera priamus* ("Cairns Bird-wing") (butterfly) (*vert*) (15.6.83)		60	10
786	15 c. Eastern Snake-necked Tortoise (16.6.82)		40	30
	a. Perf 14×14½ (12.83)		1·00	40
787	20 c. *Graphium macleayanus* ("MacLeay's Swallow Tail") (butterfly) (*vert*) (15.6.83)		80	35
788	24 c. Type 363 (centre photo, inscr litho)		35	10
	a. Imperf (pair)		£200	
	b. Centre and inscr litho (12.81)		55	65
789	25 c. Common Rabbit-Bandicoot (*vert*) (15.7.81)		35	10
	a. Perf 14×14½ (1982)		90	65
790	27 c. Type 363a (19.4.82)		35	20
	a. Perf 14×14½ (6.82)		65	20
791	27 c. Type 363b (15.6.83)		90	30
	a. Imperf (pair)		£375	
792	30 c. Bridle Nail-tailed Wallaby (*vert*) (15.7.81)		40	15
792a	30 c. *Pseudalmenus chlorinda* ("Chlorinda Hairstreak") (butterfly) (*vert*) (24.10.83)		1·00	20
793	35 c. *Danaus hamata* ("Blue Tiger") (butterfly) (*vert*) (15.6.83)		1·00	30
794	40 c. Smooth Knob-tailed Gecko (16.6.82)		45	30
	a. Perf 14×14½ (12.83)		2·50	75
795	45 c. *Cressida cressida* ("Big Greasy") (butterfly) (*vert*) (15.6.83)		1·00	30
796	50 c. Leadbeater's Possum (15.7.81)		50	10
	a. Perf 14×14½ (1983)		1·25	30
797	55 c. Stick-nest Rat (*vert*) (15.7.81)		50	30
798	60 c. *Delias aganippe* ("Wood White") (butterfly) (*vert*) (15.6.83)		1·10	30
799	65 c. Yellow-faced Whip Snake (19.4.82)		80	30
	a. Perf 14×14½ (1983)		1·50	75
800	70 c. Crucifix Toad (2.2.83)		65	1·00
801	75 c. Eastern Water Dragon (19.4.82)		1·00	40
	a. Perf 14×14½ (12.83)		1·75	1·00
802	80 c. *Ogyris amaryllis* ("Amaryllis Azure") (butterfly) (*vert*) (15.6.83)		1·40	1·25
803	85 c. Centralian Blue-tongued Lizard (2.2.83)		1·10	1·25
804	90 c. Freshwater Crocodile (16.6.82)		1·40	1·25
805	95 c. Thorny Devil (2.2.83)		1·00	1·40
806	$1 *Tisiphone abeona* ("Sword-grass Brown") (butterfly) (*vert*) (15.6.83)		1·40	30
781/806		*Set of 27*	17·00	9·50

A late printing of No. 781, issued July 1987, is on thicker paper with a creamier appearance.

364 Prince Charles and Lady Diana Spencer   **365** *Cortinarius cinnabarinus*

(Des B. Clinton. Litho Leigh-Mardon Ltd, Melbourne)

1981 (29 July). *Royal Wedding. P* 13½ × 13.

821	**364**	24 c. multicoloured	20	10
822		60 c. multicoloured	55	1·00

(Des Celia Rosser. Litho Leigh-Mardon Ltd, Melbourne)

1981 (19 Aug). *Australian Fungi. T* **365** *and similar vert designs. Multicoloured. P* 13 × 13½.

823	24 c. Type **365**		35	10
824	35 c. *Coprinus comatus*		60	70
825	55 c. *Armillaria luteobubalina*		80	1·10
826	60 c. *Cortinarius austrovenetus*		90	1·40
823/6		Set of 4	2·40	2·75

366 Disabled People playing Basketball   **367** "Christmas Bush for His Adorning"

(Des J. Spatchurst. Litho Cambec Press, Melbourne)

1981 (16 Sept). *International Year for Disabled Persons. P* 14 × 13½.

827	**366**	24 c. multicoloured	20	20

(Des F. Beck. Litho Leigh-Mardon Ltd, Melbourne)

1981 (28 Sept–2 Nov). *Christmas. Scenes and Verses from Carols by W. James and J. Wheeler. T* **367** *and similar vert designs. Multicoloured. P* 13 × 13½.

828	18 c. Type **367** (2 Nov)		25	10
829	30 c. "The Silver Stars are in the Sky"		35	25
830	60 c. "Noeltime" (2 Nov)		60	70
828/30		Set of 3	1·10	90

368 Globe depicting Australia   **369** Ocean Racing Yacht

(Des B. Weatherhead. Litho Leigh-Mardon Ltd, Melbourne)

1981 (30 Sept). *Commonwealth Heads of Government Meeting, Melbourne. P* 13 × 13½.

831	**368**	24 c. black, pale blue and gold	20	10
832		60 c. black, pale blue and silver	50	75

(Des R. Fletcher. Litho Leigh-Mardon Ltd, Melbourne)

1981 (14 Oct). *Yachts. T* **369** *and similar vert designs. Multicoloured. P* 13 × 13½.

833	24 c. Type **369**		35	10
834	35 c. "Sharpie"		50	50
835	55 c. "12 Metre"		75	85
836	60 c. "Sabot"		1·00	1·00
833/6		Set of 4	2·40	2·25

370 Aborigine, Governor Phillip (founder of N.S.W., 1788) and Post World War II Migrant   **371** Humpback Whale

(Des B. Clinton. Litho Cambec Press, Melbourne)

1982 (20 Jan). *Australia Day. "Three Great Waves of Migration". P* 13½ × 14.

837	**370**	24 c. multicoloured	35	25

(Des R. and Katrina Ingpen. Litho Cambec Press, Melbourne)

1982 (17 Feb). *Whales. T* **371** *and similar multicoloured designs. P* 13½ × 14 (24, 60 c.) or 14 × 13½ (others).

838	24 c. Sperm Whale		40	10
839	35 c. Black Right Whale (*vert*)		60	70
840	55 c. Blue Whale (*vert*)		1·10	1·60
841	60 c. Type **371** (new blue background)		1·25	1·75
	a. Solid greenish blue background		£250	£150
838/41		Set of 4	3·00	3·50

No. 841a comes from a small trial printing, some sheets of which were included amongst normal stock by mistake. The correct version of the 60 c. value shows the new blue background streaked with white at top left. On No. 841a the background is in greenish blue and is without the white streaks.

372 Queen Elizabeth II   **373** "Marjorie Atherton"

(Des R. Honisett. Litho Cambec Press, Melbourne)

1982 (21 Apr). *Queen Elizabeth II's Birthday. P* 14 × 13½.

842	**372**	27 c. multicoloured	35	15

(Des Betty Conabere. Litho Leigh-Mardon Ltd, Melbourne)

1982 (19 May). *Roses. T* **373** *and similar vert designs. Multicoloured. P* 13 × 13½.

843	27 c. Type **373**		40	15
844	40 c. "Imp"		65	75
845	65 c. "Minnie Watson"		1·10	1·75
846	75 c. "Satellite"		1·25	1·60
843/6		Set of 4	3·00	3·75

374 Radio Announcer and 1930-style Microphone   **375** Forbes Post Office

(Des Cato Hibberd Design. Litho Leigh-Mardon Ltd, Melbourne)

1982 (16 June). *50th Anniv of ABC (Australian Broadcasting Commission). T* **374** *and similar horiz design. Multicoloured. P* 13½ × 13.

847	27 c. Type **374**		30	45
	a. Pair. Nos. 847/8		60	90
848	27 c. ABC logo		30	45

Nos. 847/8 were printed together, *se-tenant*, in horizontal and vertical pairs throughout the sheet.

(Des F. Beck. Litho Cambec Press, Melbourne)

1982 (4 Aug). *Historic Australian Post Offices. T* **375** *and similar multicoloured designs. P* 14 × 13½ (*vert*) or 13½ × 14 (*horiz*).

849	27 c. Type **375**		40	40
850	27 c. Flemington Post Office		40	40
851	27 c. Rockhampton Post Office		40	40
852	27 c. Kingston S.E. Post Office (*horiz*)		40	40
853	27 c. York Post Office (*horiz*)		40	40
854	27 c. Launceston Post Office		40	40
855	27 c. Old Post and Telegraph Station, Alice Springs (*horiz*)		40	40
849/55		Set of 7	2·50	2·50

376 Early Australian Christmas Card   **377** Boxing

(Des B. Weatherhead. Litho Leigh-Mardon Ltd, Melbourne)

1982 (15 Sept–1 Nov). *Christmas. T* **376** *and similar multicoloured designs. P* 14½.

856	21 c. Bushman's Hotel, with Cobb's coach arriving (*horiz*) (1.11.82)		30	10
857	27 c. Type **376**		50	60
858	75 c. Little girl offering Christmas pudding to swagman (1.11.82)		75	1·40
856/8		Set of 3	1·40	1·90

(Des R. Carnielye. Litho Leigh-Mardon Ltd, Melbourne)

1982 (22 Sept). *Commonwealth Games, Brisbane. T* **377** *and similar horiz designs. P* 14½.

859	27 c. stone, lemon and bright carmine		25	20
860	27 c. lemon, stone and emerald		25	20
861	27 c. stone, lemon and yellow-brown		25	20
862	75 c. multicoloured		75	90
859/62		Set of 4	1·40	1·40
MS863	130 × 95 mm. Nos. 859/61. *P* 13½ × 13		1·25	1·60

Designs:—No. 859, Type **377**; No. 860, Archery; No. 861, Weight-lifting; No. 862, Pole-vaulting.

378 Sydney Harbour Bridge 5s. Stamp of 1932   **379** "Yirawala" Bark Painting

(Des Cato Hibberd Design. Litho Cambec Press, Melbourne)

1982 (27 Sept). *National Stamp Week. P* 13½ × 14.

864	**378**	27 c. multicoloured	35	30

(Des Australia Post Graphic Design Section. Litho Leigh-Mardon Ltd, Melbourne)

1982 (12 Oct). *Opening of Australian National Gallery. P* 14½.

865	**379**	27 c. multicoloured	30	25

380 Mimi Spirits Dancing   **381** *Eucalyptus calophylla* "Rosea"

(Des D. Milaybuma (27 c.), L. Nabardayal (40 c.), J. Galareya (65 c.), D. Nguleingulei-Murrumurru (75 c.). Litho Cambec Press, Melbourne)

1982 (17 Nov). *Aboriginal Culture. Music and Dance. T* **380** *and similar horiz designs depicting Aboriginal Bark Paintings of Mimi Spirits. P* 13½ × 14.

866	27 c. multicoloured		25	10
867	40 c. multicoloured		40	55
868	65 c. multicoloured		60	1·25
869	75 c. multicoloured		65	1·25
866/9		Set of 4	1·75	2·75

(Des Elizabeth Conabere. Photo Enschedé)

1982 (17 Nov). *Booklet stamps. Eucalyptus Flowers. T* **381** *and similar horiz designs. P* 12½ × 13½.

870	1 c. Type **381**		10	30
	a. Booklet pane. Nos. 870/1 and 874 each × 2	1·00	
	b. Booklet pane. Nos. 870/1 each × 2, 872/3 and 874 × 3	2·50	
871	2 c. *Eucalyptus casia*		10	30
872	3 c. *Eucalyptus ficifolia*		70	1·10
873	10 c. *Eucalyptus globulus*		70	1·10
874	27 c. *Eucalyptus forrestiana*		35	40
870/4		Set of 5	1·75	2·75

Nos. 870/4 only exist from 60 c. (pane No. 870a) and $1 (pane No. 870b) stamp booklets and the stamps have one or two adjacent sides imperforate.

382 Shand Mason Steam Fire Engine, 1891   **383** H.M.S. *Sirius*

(Des A. Puckett. Litho Cambec Press, Melbourne)

1983 (12 Jan). *Historic Fire Engines. T* **382** *and similar horiz designs. Multicoloured. P* 13½ × 14.

875	27 c. Type **382**		40	10
876	40 c. Hotchkiss fire engine, 1914		60	60
877	65 c. Ahrens-Fox PS2 fire engine, 1929		1·00	1·50
878	75 c. Merryweather manual fire appliance, 1851		1·00	1·40
875/8		Set of 4	2·75	3·25

(Des J. Spatchurst. Litho Leigh-Mardon Ltd, Melbourne)

1983 (26 Jan). *Australia Day. T* **383** *and similar horiz design. Multicoloured. P* 14½.

879	27 c. Type **383**		40	50
	a. Pair. Nos. 879/80		80	1·00
880	27 c. H.M.S. *Supply*		40	50

Nos. 879/80 were printed together, *se-tenant*, in horizontal and vertical pairs throughout the sheet.

| 384 Stylised Kangaroo and Kiwi | 385 Equality and Dignity |

(Des G. Emery. Litho Cambec Press, Melbourne)

1983 (2 Feb). *Closer Economic Relationship Agreement with New Zealand.* P 14 × 13½.
381 **384** 27 c. multicoloured 30 30

(Des G. Emery. Litho Leigh-Mardon Ltd, Melbourne)

1983 (9 Mar). *Commonwealth Day.* T **385** *and similar vert designs. Multicoloured.* P 14½.
882 27 c. Type **385** 20 25
883 27 c. Liberty and Freedom 20 25
884 27 c. Social Justice and Co-operation .. 20 25
885 75 c. Peace and Harmony .. .. 50 1·10
882/5 .. .. *Set of 4* 1·00 1·75

| 386 R.Y. *Britannia* passing Sydney Opera House | 387 "Postal and Telecommunications Services" |

(Des J. Richards. Litho Leigh-Mardon Ltd, Melbourne)

1983 (20 Apr). *Queen Elizabeth II's Birthday.* P 14½.
886 **386** 27 c. multicoloured 45 30

(Des B. Sadgrove. Litho Cambec Press, Melbourne)

1983 (18 May). *World Communications Year.* P 13 × 13½.
887 **387** 27 c. multicoloured 30 30

| 388 Badge of the Order of St. John | 389 Jaycee Members and Badge |

(Des T. McCauley. Litho Cambec Press, Melbourne)

1983 (8 June). *Centenary of St. John Ambulance in Australia.* P 14 × 13½.
888 **388** 27 c. black and deep turquoise-blue 35 30

(Des B. Clinton. Litho Cambec Press, Melbourne)

1983 (8 June). *50th Anniv of Australian Jaycees.* P 13½ × 14.
889 **389** 27 c. multicoloured 30 30

| 390 "The Bloke" | 391 Nativity Scene |

(Des B. Clinton. Litho Leigh-Mardon Ltd, Melbourne)

1983 (3 Aug). *Folklore. "The Sentimental Bloke" (humorous poem by C. J. Dennis).* T **390** *and similar vert designs. Multicoloured.* P 14½.
890 27 c. Type **390** 40 50
 a. Horiz strip of 5. Nos. 890/4 .. 1·75
891 27 c. "Doreen—The Intro" .. 40 50
892 27 c. "The Stror' at Coot" 40 50
893 27 c. "Hitched" 40 50
894 27 c. "The Mooch o'Life" 40 50
890/4 .. .. *Set of 5* 1·75 2·25
 Nos. 890/4 were printed together, *se-tenant*, in horizontal strips of 5 throughout the sheet.

(Des Holly Alvarez (24 c.), Deanne Head (35 c.), Justine Jacobi (85 c.). Litho Cambec Press, Melbourne)

1983 (14 Sept–2 Nov). *Christmas. Children's Paintings.* T **391** *and similar horiz designs. Multicoloured.* P 13½ × 14.
895 24 c. Type **391** (2 November) .. 20 10
896 35 c. Kookaburra 35 45
897 85 c. First Christmas in sleigh over beach (2 November) .. .. 90 1·40
895/7 .. .. *Set of 3* 1·25 1·75

| 392 Sir Paul Edmund de Strzelecki | 393 Cook Family Cottage, Melbourne |

(Des Dianne Quinn. Litho Leigh-Mardon Ltd, Melbourne)

1983 (26 Sept). *Explorers of Australia.* T **392** *and similar vert designs. Multicoloured.* P 14½.
898 30 c. Type **392** 35 40
899 30 c. Ludwig Leichardt 35 40
900 30 c. William John Wills and Robert O'Hara Burke 35 40
901 30 c. Alexander Forrest 35 40
898/901 .. .. .. *Set of 4* 1·25 1·40

(Des J. Quinn. Litho Cambec Press, Melbourne)

1984 (26 Jan). *Australia Day.* P 13½ × 14.
902 **393** 30 c. black and stone 30 35

MACHINE LABELS. From 22 February 1984 gummed labels in the above design, ranging in value from 1 c. to $9.99, were available from seven automatic machines. The postcode at the top of the label indicates the location of the machine from which it was issued; 2000, Sydney; 2601, Canberra; 3000, Melbourne; 4000, Brisbane; 5000, Adelaide, 5790 Darwin (from 29 July 1985); 6000, Perth; 7000, Hobart. Labels without code numbers appeared on 24 June 1985.

These were replaced by a further series, with a background pattern of kangaroos, on 22 October 1985. These exist with the same code numbers as before or without code.

On 25 August 1986 a further series, with a background pattern of platypuses, was issued. The design was again changed on 2 September 1987 to show Echidnas. During this issue the postcode for Darwin changed from 5790 to 0800. These were followed by Ringtail Possums on 28 September 1988, Frill-necked Lizards on 1 September 1989, Koalas on 3 September 1990, Emus on 2 January 1992 and the Waratah (flower) on 8 September 1994.

An overall pattern of geometric shapes, streamers and springs was introduced on 6 June 1996.

As the number of machines increased rapidly only those situated at the State, or Capital Territory, General Post Offices showed a postcode. Other machines eventually showed a code, letter followed by numbers at bottom left. Later machines had a top label value of either $10 or $20.

394 Charles Ulm, Avro Type 618 Ten *Faith in Australia* and Trans-Tasman Cover

(Des G. Beck and J. Quinn. Litho Leigh-Mardon Ltd, Melbourne)

1984 (22 Feb). *50th Anniv of First Official Airmail Flights, New Zealand–Australia and Australia–Papua New Guinea.* T **394** *and similar horiz design. Multicoloured.* P 13½.
903 45 c. Type **394** .. .. .. 1·00 1·25
 a. Horiz pair. Nos. 903/4 .. 2·00 2·50
904 45 c. As Type **394** but showing flown cover to Papua New Guinea .. 1·00 1·25
 Nos. 903/4 were printed together, *se-tenant*, in horizontal pairs throughout the sheet.

| 395 Thomson "Steamer", 1898 | 396 Queen Elizabeth II |

(Des A. Puckett. Litho Leigh-Mardon Ltd, Melbourne)

1984 (14 Mar). *Veteran and Vintage Cars.* T **395** *and similar horiz designs. Multicoloured.* P 14½.
905 30 c. Type **395** 45 60
 a. Vert strip of 5. Nos. 905/9 .. 2·00
906 30 c. Tarrant, 1906 .. .. 45 60
907 30 c. Gordon & Co "Australian Six", 1919 45 60
908 30 c. Summit, 1923 .. .. 45 60
909 30 c. Chic, 1924 .. .. .. 45 60
905/9 .. .. *Set of 5* 2·00 2·75
 Nos. 905/9 were printed together, *se-tenant*, in vertical strips of 5 throughout the sheet.

(Des B. Weatherhead. Litho Leigh-Mardon Ltd, Melbourne)

1984 (18 Apr). *Queen Elizabeth II's Birthday.* P 14½.
910 **396** 30 c. multicoloured 30 35
 a. Dull mauve (background) omitted £400

| 397 Cutty Sark | 398 Freestyle |

(Des J. Earl and J. Quinn. Litho Leigh-Mardon Ltd, Melbourne)

1984 (23 May). *Clipper Ships.* T **397** *and similar multicoloured designs.* P 14 × 13½ (30 c., 85 c.) or 13½ × 14 (others).
911 30 c. Type **397** 40 25
912 45 c. *Orient (horiz)* 70 70
913 75 c. *Sobraon (horiz)* .. .. 1·25 1·75
914 85 c. *Thermopylae* .. .. 1·25 1·50
911/14 .. .. *Set of 4* 3·25 3·75

(Des B. Clinton. Litho Leigh-Mardon Ltd, Melbourne)

1984 (6 June). *Skiing.* T **398** *and similar multicoloured designs.* P 14½.
915 30 c. Type **398** 40 45
916 30 c. Downhill racer 40 45
917 30 c. Slalom *(horiz)* 40 45
918 30 c. Nordic *(horiz)* 40 45
915/18 .. .. *Set of 4* 1·50 1·75

| 399 Coral Hopper | 400 Before the Event |

(Des G. Ryan and R. Fletcher (2, 25, 30, 50, 55, 85 c.) or G. Ryan (others). Litho Leigh-Mardon Ltd, Melbourne (30, 33 c.) or Cambec Press, Melbourne (others))

1984 (18 June)–86. *Marine Life.* T **399** *and similar horiz designs. Multicoloured.* P 14 × 14½ (30 c., 33 c.) or 13½ (others).
919 2 c. Type **399** 10 20
920 3 c. Jimble (11.6.86) 20 20
921 5 c. Tasselled Frogfish ("Anglerfish") (12.6.85) 15 10
922 10 c. Rough Stonefish (11.6.86) .. 20 10
923 20 c. Red Handfish (12.6.85) .. 55 30
924 25 c. Orange-lipped Cowrie .. 45 30
925 30 c. Choat's Wrasse 45 40
926 33 c. Leafy Seadragon (20.3.85) .. 55 10
927 40 c. Red Velvetfish (12.6.85) .. 75 60
928 45 c. Textile or Cloth of Gold Cone (11.6.86) 80 50
929 50 c. Clown Surgeonfish 80 50
930 55 c. Bennett's Nudibranch .. 80 50
 a. New blue ("BENNETT'S NUDI-BRANCH") omitted .. † —
931 60 c. Zebra Lionfish (11.6.86) .. 90 70
932 65 c. Banded Stingray (11.6.86) .. 90 70
933 70 c. Southern Blue-ringed Octopus (11.6.86) .. 90 65
934 80 c. Pineconefish ("Pineapple Fish") (12.6.85) .. .. 1·25 70
935 85 c. Royal Angelfish 90 70
936 90 c. Crab-eyed Goby (12.6.85) .. 1·40 75
937 $1 Crown of Thorns Starfish (11.6.86) (Optd S. 50p.) .. 1·50 80
919/37 .. .. .. *Set of 19* 12·00 8·00
 No. 930a only exists used on maximum card.

(Des O. Schmidinger and Christine Stead. Litho Cambec Press, Melbourne)

1984 (25 July). *Olympic Games, Los Angeles.* T **400** *and similar multicoloured designs.* P 14 × 13½ (No. 943) or 13½ × 14 (others).
941 30 c. Type **400** 35 35
942 30 c. During the event.. .. .. 35 35
943 30 c. After the event *(vert)* .. 35 35
941/3 .. .. *Set of 3* 95 95

| 401 Australian 1913 1d. Kangaroo Stamp | 402 "Angel" (stained-glass window, St. Francis' Church, Melbourne) |

(Des Ken Cato Design Studio. Litho Cambec Press, Melbourne)

1984 (22 Aug–21 Sept). *"Ausipex" International Stamp Exhibition, Melbourne.* T **401** *and similar vert designs. Multicoloured.* P 14½.
944 30 c. Type **401** 35 30
MS945 126 × 175 mm. 30 c. × 7, Victoria 1850 3d. "Half Length"; New South Wales 1850 1d. "Sydney View"; Tasmania 1853 1d.; South Australia 1855 1d.; Western Australia 1854 1d. "Black Swan"; Queensland 1860 6d.; Type **401** (21 Sept) .. 3·50 4·50
 On No. MS945 the emblem and inscription on the sheet margin are embossed.

(Des Ken Cato Design Studio. Litho Cambec Press, Melbourne)

1984 (17 Sept–31 Oct). *Christmas. Stained-glass Windows.* T **402** *and similar vert designs. Multicoloured.* P 14 × 13½.
946 24 c. "Angel and Child" (Holy Trinity Church, Sydney) (31.10.84) 25 20
947 30 c. "Veiled Virgin and Child" (St. Mary's Catholic Church, Geelong) (31.10.84) .. 35 20
948 40 c. Type **402** 50 60
949 50 c. "Three Kings" (St. Mary's Cathedral, Sydney) (31.10.84) 65 80
950 85 c. "Madonna and Child" (St. Bartholomew's Church, Norwood) (31.10.84) .. 80 1·25
946/50 .. .. *Set of 5* 2·25 2·75

403 "Stick Figures" (Cobar Region) **404** Yellow-tufted Honeyeater

(Des Elizabeth Innes. Litho Leigh-Mardon Ltd, Melbourne)

1984 (7 Nov). *Bicentenary of Australian Settlement (1988) (1st issue). The First Australians.* T **403** *and similar square designs showing aborigine rock paintings. Multicoloured.* P 14½.
951 30 c. Type **403** 35 45
952 30 c. "Bunjil" (large figure), Grampians .. 35 45
953 30 c. "Quikans" (tall figures), Cape York .. 35 45
954 30 c. "Wandjina Spirit and Baby Snakes" (Gibb River) 35 45
955 30 c. "Rock Python" (Gibb River) .. 35 45
956 30 c. "Silver Barramundi" (fish) (Kakadu National Park) 35 45
957 30 c. Bicentenary emblem 35 45
958 85 c. "Rock Possum" (Kakadu National Park) .. .. .. 80 1·40
951/8 .. .. .. *Set of 8* 3·00 4·00
See also Nos. 972/6, 993/6, 1002/7, 1019/22, 1059/63, 1064/6, 1077/81, 1090/2, 1105/9, 1110, 1137/41, 1145/8 and 1149.

(Des. G. Emery. Litho Leigh-Mardon Ltd, Melbourne)

1984 (19 Nov). *150th Anniv of Victoria.* T **404** *and similar vert design. Multicoloured.* P 14½.
959 30 c. Type **404** 40 65
a. Pair. Nos. 959/60.. .. .. 80 1·25
960 30 c. Leadbeater's Possum 40 65
Nos. 959/60 were printed together, *se-tenant*, in horizontal and vertical pairs throughout the sheet.

405 "Musgrave Ranges" (Sir Sidney Nolan) **406** Young People of Different Races, and Sun

(Des Sue Titcher. Litho Leigh-Mardon Ltd, Melbourne)

1985 (25 Jan). *Australia Day. Birth Centenary of Dorothea Mackellar (author of poem "My Country").* T **405** *and similar horiz design. Multicoloured.* P 14½.
961 30 c. Type **405** 45 70
a. *Tête-bêche* (vert pair) .. .. 1·50 2·25
b. Vert pair. Nos. 961/2 .. 90 1·40
962 30 c. "The Walls of China" (Russell Drysdale) 45 70
a. *Tête-bêche* (vert pair) .. 1·50 2·25
Nos. 961/2 were printed together, *se-tenant*, within the sheet of 100 (2 panes 50 (5×10)). In each pane No. 961 occurs in horizontal rows 1, 4, 5, 8 and 9, and No. 962 in rows 2, 3, 6, 7 and 10. Horizontal rows 3/4 and 7/8 are inverted forming *tête-bêche* pairs of the same design in addition to the vertical *se-tenant* pairs containing both designs.

(Des Derryn Vogelnest. Litho Cambec Press, Melbourne)

1985 (13 Feb). *International Youth Year.* P 14 × 13½.
963 **406** 30 c. multicoloured 40 30

407 Royal Victorian Volunteer Artillery **408** District Nurse of early 1900's

(Des Pam Andrews. Litho Leigh-Mardon Ltd, Melbourne)

1985 (25 Feb). *19th-Century Australian Military Uniforms.* T **407** *and similar vert designs. Multicoloured.* P 14½.
964 33 c. Type **407** 60 65
a. Horiz strip of 5. Nos. 964/8 .. 2·75
965 33 c. Western Australian Pinjarrah Cavalry .. 60 65

---

966 33 c. New South Wales Lancers .. 60 65
967 33 c. New South Wales Contingent to the Sudan 60 65
968 33 c. Victorian Mounted Rifles .. 60 65
964/8 .. .. .. *Set of 5* 2·75 3·00
Nos. 964/8 were printed together, *se-tenant*, in horizontal strips of 5 throughout the sheet.

(Des Wendy Tamlyn. Litho Leigh-Mardon Ltd, Melbourne)

1985 (13 Mar). *Centenary of District Nursing Services.* P 14½.
969 **408** 33 c. multicoloured 45 35

409 Sulphur-crested Cockatoos

(Des R. Bevers. Litho Leigh-Mardon Ltd, Melbourne)

1985 (13 Mar). *Booklet stamps. Multicoloured, background colour given.* P 14½ × imperf.
970 **409** 1 c. flesh .. .. .. 1·50 2·00
a. Booklet pane. Nos. 970, and 971×3 2·75
971 33 c. pale turquoise-green 45 55
Nos. 970/1 only exist from $1 stamp booklets. As stamps from these booklets have their outer edges imperforate, the end example of No. 971 is only perforated along one side.

410 Abel Tasman and Journal Entry **411** Sovereign's Badge of Order of Australia

(Des G. Emery. Litho Cambec Press, Melbourne)

1985 (10 Apr). *Bicentenary of Australian Settlement (1988) (2nd issue). Navigators.* T **410** *and similar square designs. Multicoloured.* P 13.
972 33 c. Type **410**.. .. .. 50 35
973 33 c. Dirk Hartog's *Eendracht* (detail, Aert Anthonisz) 50 35
974 33 c. "William Dampier" (detail, T. Murray) 50 35
975 90 c. Globe and hand with extract from Dampier's journal .. .. 1·25 1·75
972/5 .. .. .. *Set of 4* 2·50 2·50
MS976 150×115 mm. As Nos. 972/5, but with cream-coloured margins .. .. 3·25 4·00

(Des Elizabeth Innes. Litho Cambec Press, Melbourne)

1985 (22 Apr). *Queen Elizabeth II's Birthday.* P 14 × 13½.
977 **411** 33 c. multicoloured 40 30

412 Tree, and Soil running through Hourglass ("Soil") **413** *Elves and Fairies* (Annie Rentoul and Ida Rentoul Outhwaite)

(Des L. Whaite and G. Jorgensen. Litho Cambec Press, Melbourne)

1985 (15 May). *Conservation.* T **412** *and similar vert designs. Multicoloured.* P 14 × 13½.
978 33 c. Type **412**.. .. .. 45 20
979 50 c. Washing on line and smog ("air") .. 80 85
980 80 c. Tap and flower ("water") .. 1·25 1·50
981 90 c. Chain encircling flames ("energy") .. 1·40 2·00
978/81 .. .. .. *Set of 4* 3·50 4·00

(Des P. Leuver. Litho Leigh-Mardon Ltd, Melbourne)

1985 (17 July). *Classic Australian Children's Books.* T **413** *and similar vert designs. Multicoloured.* P 14½.
982 33 c. Type **413**.. .. .. 50 65
a. Horiz strip of 5. Nos. 982/6 .. 2·25
983 33 c. *The Magic Pudding* (Norman Lindsay) 50 65
984 33 c. *Ginger Meggs* (James Charles Bancks) 50 65
985 33 c. *Blinky Bill* (Dorothy Wall) .. 50 65
986 33 c. *Snugglepot and Cuddlepie* (May Gibbs) 50 65
982/6 .. .. .. *Set of 5* 2·25 3·00
Nos. 982/6 were printed together, *se-tenant*, in horizontal strips of 5 throughout the sheet.

---

414 Dish Aerials **415** Angel in Sailing Ship

(Des J. Ostoja-Kotkowski. Litho Leigh-Mardon Ltd, Melbourne)

1985 (18 Sept). *Electronic Mail Service.* P 14½.
987 **414** 33 c. multicoloured 35 30

(Des S. Hartshorne. Litho Leigh-Mardon Ltd, Melbourne)

1985 (18 Sept–1 Nov). *Christmas.* T **415** *and similar horiz designs. Multicoloured.* P 14½.
988 27 c. Angel with holly wings (1.11).. .. 35 15
989 33 c. Angel with bells (1.11) 40 15
990 45 c. Type **415**.. .. .. .. 60 50
991 55 c. Angel with star (1.11) 75 80
992 90 c. Angel with Christmas tree bauble (1.11) .. .. .. 1·40 1·50
988/92 .. .. .. *Set of 5* 3·25 2·75

416 Astrolabe (*Batavia*, 1629) **417** Aboriginal Wandjina Spirit, Map of Australia and Egg

(Des G. Emery. Litho Cambec Press, Melbourne)

1985 (2 Oct). *Bicentenary of Australian Settlement (1988) (3rd issue). Relics from Early Shipwrecks.* T **416** *and similar square designs. Multicoloured.* P 13.
993 33 c. Type **416**.. .. .. 40 15
994 50 c. German beardman jug (*Vergulde Draeck*, 1656) 80 90
995 90 c. Wooden bobbins (*Batavia*, 1629) and encrusted scissors (*Zeewijk*, 1727) 1·50 2·00
996 $1 Silver and brass buckle (*Zeewijk*, 1727) 1·75 2·00
993/6 .. .. .. *Set of 4* 4·00 4·50

(Des R. Meeks. Litho Leigh-Mardon Ltd, Melbourne)

1986 (24 Jan). *Australia Day.* P 14½.
997 **417** 33 c. multicoloured 40 30

418 AUSSAT Satellite, Moon and Earth's Surface **419** H.M.S. *Buffalo*

(Des O. Schmidinger and Christine Stead. Litho Leigh-Mardon Ltd, Melbourne)

1986 (24 Jan). *AUSSAT National Communications Satellite System.* T **418** *and similar vert design. Multicoloured.* P 14½.
998 33 c. Type **418**.. .. .. 50 15
999 80 c. AUSSAT satellite in orbit .. 1·50 2·00

(Des I. Kidd. Litho Cambec Press, Melbourne)

1986 (12 Feb). *150th Anniv of South Australia.* T **419** *and similar horiz design. Multicoloured.* P 13½ × 14.
1000 33 c. Type **419** 70 90
a. Pair. Nos. 1000/1 .. .. 1·40 1·75
1001 33 c. "City Sign" sculpture (Otto Hajek), Adelaide 70 90
Nos. 1000/1 were printed together, *se-tenant*, in horizontal and vertical pairs throughout the sheet, the background of each horizontal pair showing an extract from the colony's Letters Patent of 1836.

420 *Banksia serrata* **421** Radio Telescope, Parkes, and Diagram of Comet's Orbit

(Des Sue Titcher. Litho Cambec Press, Melbourne)

1986 (12 Mar). *Bicentenary of Australian Settlement* (1988) (4th issue). *Cook's Voyage to New Holland.* T **420** *and similar horiz designs. Multicoloured. P* 13.

1002	33 c. Type **420**	..	..	60	35
1003	33 c. *Hibiscus meraukensis*..		..	60	35
1004	50 c. *Dillenia alata*	..	..	90	80
1005	80 c. *Correa reflexa* ..	..	..	1·60	2·25
1006	90 c. "Joseph Banks" (botanist) (Reynolds) and Banks with Dr. Solander			2·00	2·00
1007	90 c. "Sydney Parkinson" (self-portrait) and Parkinson drawing			2·00	2·00
1002/7	..	..	*Set of 6*	7·00	7·00

(Des J. Passmore. Litho Cambec Press, Melbourne)

1986 (9 Apr). *Appearance of Halley's Comet. P* 14 × 13½.

1008	421	33 c. multicoloured	..	50	35

422 Queen Elizabeth II   **423** Brumbies (wild horses)

(Des Fay Plamka. Litho Leigh-Mardon Ltd, Melbourne)

1986 (21 Apr). *60th Birthday of Queen Elizabeth II. P* 14½.

1009	**422**	33 c. multicoloured	..	45	35

(Des R. Ingpen. Litho Leigh-Mardon Ltd, Melbourne)

1986 (21 May). *Australian Horses.* T **423** *and similar horiz designs. Multicoloured. P* 14½.

1010	33 c. Type **423**	..	..	60	15
1011	80 c. Mustering	..	..	1·50	1·75
1012	90 c. Show-jumping ..	..	..	1·75	2·00
1013	$1 Child on pony ..	..	..	2·00	2·00
1010/13	..	*Set of 4*		5·25	5·50

424 "The Old Shearer stands"   **425** "King George III" (A. Ramsay) and Convicts

(Des R. Ingpen. Litho Leigh-Mardon Ltd, Melbourne)

1986 (21 July). *Folklore. Scenes and Verses from the Folksong "Click go the Shears".* T **424** *and similar vert designs. Multicoloured. P* 14½.

1014	33 c. Type **424**	..	..	70	75
	a. Horiz strip of 5. Nos. 1014/18		..	3·25	
1015	33 c. "The ringer looks around"	..	70	75
1016	33 c. "The boss of the board"	..	70	75
1017	33 c. "The tar-boy is there"	..	70	75
1018	33 c. "Shearing is all over"..	..	70	75
1014/18	..		*Set of 5*	3·25	3·50

Nos. 1014/18 were printed together, *se-tenant*, in horizontal strips of 5 throughout the sheet, forming a composite design.

(Des D. Lancashire. Litho Cambec Press, Melbourne)

1986 (6 Aug). *Bicentenary of Australian Settlement* (1988) (5th issue). *Convict Settlement in New South Wales.* T **425** *and similar horiz designs. Multicoloured. P* 13.

1019	33 c. Type **425**	..	..	80	50
1020	33 c. "Lord Sydney" (Gilbert Stuart) and convicts			80	50
1021	33 c. "Captain Arthur Phillip" (F. Wheatley) and ship			80	50
1022	$1 "Captain John Hunter" (W. B. Bennett) and aborigines			3·25	4·25
1019/22	..	..	*Set of 4*	5·00	5·25

426 Red Kangaroo   **427** Royal Bluebell   **428** Pink Enamel Orchid

---

(Des D. Higgins. Litho Leigh-Mardon Ltd, Melbourne)

1986 (13 Aug). *Australian Wildlife* (1st series). T **426** *and similar vert designs. Multicoloured. P* 14½ × 14.

1023	36 c. Type **426**	..	..	55	70
	a. Horiz strip of 5. Nos. 1023/7 ..		..	2·50	
1024	36 c. Emu	..	..	55	70
1025	36 c. Koala	..	..	55	70
1026	36 c. Laughing Kookaburra	..	55	70
1027	36 c. Platypus	..	..	55	70
1023/7			*Set of 5*	2·50	3·25

Nos. 1023/7 were printed together, *se-tenant*, in horizontal strips of 5 throughout the sheet.
For 37 c. values see Nos. 1072/6.

(Des Betty Conabere. Litho Mercury-Walch Pty, Hobart)

1986 (25 Aug). *Booklet stamps. Alpine Wildflowers.* T **427** *and similar vert designs. Multicoloured. Roul.*

1028	3 c. Type **427**	..	..	25	25
	a. Booklet pane. Nos. 1028, 1029 and 1031 × 2			2·50	
	b. Booklet pane. Nos. 1028, 1030 and 1031 × 2			2·50	
1029	5 c. Alpine Marsh Marigold	..	1·40	2·25
1030	25 c. Mount Buffalo Sunray	..	1·40	2·25
1031	36 c. Silver Snow Daisy	..	60	30
1028/31			*Set of 4*	3·25	4·50

Nos. 1028/31 only exist from 80 c. (pane No. 1028a) and $1 (pane No. 1028b) stamp booklets. The outer edges of the booklet panes are imperforate.

(Des O. Schmidinger and Christine Stead. Litho Leigh-Mardon Ltd, Melbourne)

1986 (18 Sept). *Native Australian Orchids.* T **428** *and similar vert designs. Multicoloured. P* 14½.

1032	36 c. Type **428**	..	..	70	20
1033	55 c. *Dendrobium nindii*	..	..	1·25	1·00
1034	90 c. Duck Orchid	..	..	2·00	2·00
1035	$1 Queen of Sheba Orchid	..	2·00	2·00
1032/5	..	..	*Set of 4*	5·50	4·75

429 *Australia II* crossing Finishing Line   **430** Dove with Olive Branch and Sun

(Des J. Passmore and G. Rowan. Litho Cambec Press, Melbourne)

1986 (26 Sept). *Australian Victory in America's Cup, 1983.* T **429** *and similar vert designs. Multicoloured. P* 14 × 13½.

1036	36 c. Type **429**	..	..	75	75
1037	36 c. Boxing kangaroo flag of winning syndicate			75	75
	a. Grey (inscr and face value) omitted ..			£130	
1038	36 c. America's Cup trophy..	..	75	75
	a. Grey (inscr and face value) omitted ..			£130	
1036/8	..		*Set of 3*	2·00	2·00

(Des K. Cato. Litho Cambec Press, Melbourne)

1986 (22 Oct). *International Peace Year. P* 14 × 13½.

1039	**430**	36 c. multicoloured ..	..	65	40

Examples with the gutter margin overprinted to commemorate the Papal visit in November 1986 were not produced by the Australian Post Office.

431 Mary and Joseph   **432** Australian Flag on Printed Circuit Board

(Des B. Clinton. Litho Leigh-Mardon Ltd, Melbourne)

1986 (3 Nov–Dec). *Christmas.* T **431** *and similar multicoloured designs showing scenes from children's nativity play. P* 14½.

1040	30 c. Type **431**	..	..	40	30
	a. Perf 14 × 13½ (12.86) ..			75	50
1041	36 c. Three Wise Men leaving gifts	..	50	45
1042	60 c. Angels (*horiz*) ..	..	90	1·50
1040/2			*Set of 3*	1·60	2·00
MS1043	147 × 70 mm. 30 c. Three angels and shepherd (*horiz*); 30 c. Kneeling shepherds (*horiz*); 30 c. Mary, Joseph and three angels; 30 c. Innkeeper and two angels; 30 c. Three Wise Men (*horiz*)			2·75	3·00

No. 1040a was printed by Cambec Press after stocks of the original printing by Leigh-Mardon Ltd ran short. It is believed that this Cambec Press printing was distributed in New South Wales, Tasmania, Victoria and Western Australia.

(Des J. Passmore. Litho CPE Australia Ltd, Melbourne)

1987 (23 Jan). *Australia Day.* T **432** *and similar horiz design. Multicoloured. P* 13½ × 14.

1044	36 c. Type **432**	..	..	55	35
1045	36 c. "Australian Made" Campaign logos ..		55	35

---

433 Aerial View of Yacht   **434** Grapes and Melons

(Des O. Schmidinger and Christine Stead. Litho Leigh-Mardon Ltd, Melbourne)

1987 (28 Jan). *America's Cup Yachting Championship.* T **433** *and similar vert designs. Multicoloured. P* 14½.

1046	36 c. Type **433**	..	..	40	20
1047	55 c. Two yachts tacking	..	90	1·00
1048	90 c. Two yachts turning	..	1·40	2·00
1049	$1 Two yachts under full sail	..	1·50	1·75
1046/9	..		*Set of 4*	3·75	4·50

(Des Susan Tilley. Litho CPE Australia Ltd, Melbourne)

1987 (11 Feb). *Australian Fruit.* T **434** *and similar vert designs. Multicoloured. P* 14 × 13½.

1050	36 c. Type **434**	..	..	40	20
1051	65 c. Tropical and sub-tropical fruits	..	1·00	1·25
1052	90 c. Citrus fruit, apples and pears	..	1·40	1·90
1053	$1 Stone and berry fruits	..	1·40	1·60
1050/3			*Set of 4*	3·75	4·50

435 Livestock   **436** Queen Elizabeth in Australia, 1986

(Des D. Lancashire. Litho CPE Australia Ltd, Melbourne)

1987 (10 Apr). *Agricultural Shows.* T **435** *and similar vert designs. Multicoloured. P* 14 × 13½.

1054	36 c. Type **435**	..	..	60	20
1055	65 c. Produce	..	..	1·25	1·75
1056	90 c. Sideshows	..	..	1·75	2·40
1057	$1 Competitions	..	..	1·90	2·40
1054/7	..		*Set of 4*	5·00	6·00

(Des Janet Boschen. Litho CPE Australia Ltd, Melbourne)

1987 (21 Apr). *Queen Elizabeth II's Birthday. P* 13½ × 14.

1058	**436**	36 c. multicoloured	..	55	50

437 Convicts on Quay   **438** "At the Station"

(Des Sue Passmore. Litho CPE Australia Ltd, Melbourne)

1987 (13 May). *Bicentenary of Australian Settlement* (1988) (6th issue). *Departure of the First Fleet.* T **437** *and similar square designs. Multicoloured. P* 13.

1059	36 c. Type **437**	..	..	70	85
	a. Horiz strip of 5. Nos. 1059/63		..	3·25	
1060	36 c. Royal Marines officer and wife	..	70	85
1061	36 c. Sailors loading supplies	..	70	85
1062	36 c. Officers being ferried to ships	..	70	85
1063	36 c. Fleet in English Channel	..	70	85
1059/63			*Set of 5*	3·25	3·75

Nos. 1059/63 were printed together, *se-tenant*, in horizontal strips of 5 throughout the sheet.
See also Nos. 1064/6, 1077/81, 1090/2 and 1105/9.

(Des Sue Passmore. Litho CPE Australia Ltd, Melbourne)

1987 (3 June). *Bicentenary of Australian Settlement* (1988) (7th issue). *First Fleet at Tenerife. Square designs as* T **437**. *Multicoloured. P* 13.

1064	36 c. Ferrying supplies, Santa Cruz	..	75	90
	a. Horiz pair. Nos. 1064/5	..	1·50	1·75
1065	36 c. Canary Islands fishermen and departing fleet			75	90
1066	$1 Fleet arriving at Tenerife (Optd S. 50p) ..			1·90	2·00
1064/6			*Set of 3*	3·00	3·50

Nos. 1064/5 were printed together, *se-tenant*, in horizontal pairs throughout the sheet, forming a composite design.

(Des C. Lee. Litho CPE Australia Ltd, Melbourne)

1987 (24 June). *Folklore. Scenes and Verses from Poem "The Man from Snowy River".* T **438** *and similar vert designs. Multicoloured. P* 14 × 13½.

1067	36 c. Type **438**	.. ..	70	90
	a. Horiz strip of 5. Nos. 1067/71		3·25	
1068	36 c. "Mountain bred"	.. ..	70	90
1069	36 c. "That terrible descent"	.. ..	70	90
1070	36 c. "At their heels"	.. ..	70	90
1071	36 c. "Brought them back"	.. ..	70	90
1067/71		*Set of 5*	3·25	4·00

Nos. 1067/71 were printed together, *se-tenant*, in horizontal strips of five throughout the sheet, forming a composite background design of mountain scenery.

(Des D. Higgins. Litho Leigh-Mardon Ltd, Melbourne)

1987 (1 July). *Australian Wildlife* (2nd series). *Vert designs as* T **426**. *Multicoloured. P* 14½ × 14.

1072	37 c. Common Brushtail Possum		55	65
	a. Horiz strip of 5. Nos. 1072/6		2·50	
	ab. Pale orange (top panel) omitted		£1500	
1073	37 c. Sulphur-crested Cockatoo		55	65
1074	37 c. Common Wombat		55	65
1075	37 c. Crimson Rosella		55	65
1076	37 c. Echidna	.. ..	55	65
1072/6		*Set of 5*	2·50	3·00

Nos. 1072/6 were printed together, *se-tenant*, in horizontal strips of 5 throughout the sheet.

(Des Sue Passmore. Litho CPE Australia Ltd, Melbourne)

1987 (6 Aug). *Bicentenary of Australian Settlement* (1988) (8th issue). *First Fleet at Rio de Janeiro. Square designs as* T **437**. *Multicoloured. P* 13.

1077	37 c. Sperm Whale and fleet		70	85
	a. Horiz strip of 5. Nos. 1077/81		3·25	
1078	37 c. Brazilian coast..		70	85
1079	37 c. British officers in market		70	85
1080	37 c. Religious procession		70	85
1081	37 c. Fleet leaving Rio		70	85
1077/81		*Set of 5*	3·25	3·75

Nos. 1077/81 were printed together, *se-tenant*, in horizontal strips of 5, forming a composite design.

439 Bionic Ear   **440** Catching Crayfish

(Des. O. Schmidinger and Christine Stead. Litho Leigh-Mardon Ltd, Melbourne)

1987 (19 Aug). *Australian Achievements in Technology.* T **439** *and similar vert designs. Multicoloured. P* 14½.

1082	37 c. Type **439**		40	35
1083	53 c. Microchips	.. ..	75	60
1084	63 c. Robotics		85	70
1085	68 c. Ceramics		95	75
1082/5		*Set of 4*	2·75	2·25

(Des Elizabeth Honey. Litho Leigh-Mardon Ltd, Melbourne)

1987 (16 Sept). *"Aussie Kids".* T **440** *and similar horiz designs. Multicoloured. P* 14½.

1086	37 c. Type **440**		40	35
1087	55 c. Playing cat's cradle		1·00	65
1088	90 c. Young football supporters		1·40	1·10
1089	$1 Children with kangaroo (Optd S. 50p)		1·60	1·25
1086/9		*Set of 4*	4·00	3·00

(Des Sue Passmore. Litho CPE Australia Ltd, Melbourne)

1987 (13 Oct). *Bicentenary of Australian Settlement* (1988) (9th issue). *First Fleet at Cape of Good Hope. Square designs as* T **437**. *Multicoloured. P* 13.

1090	37 c. Marine checking list of livestock		65	75
	a. Horiz pair. Nos. 1090/1		1·25	1·50
1091	37 c. Loading livestock		65	75
1092	$1 First Fleet at Cape Town (Optd S. 50p)		1·40	1·60
1090/2		*Set of 3*	2·40	2·75

Nos. 1090/1 were printed together, *se-tenant*, in horizontal and vertical pairs throughout the sheet, the former showing a composite design.

441 Detail of Spearthrower, Western Australia   **442** Grandmother and Granddaughters with Candles

(Des J. Passmore. Litho Leigh-Mardon Ltd, Melbourne)

1987 (13 Oct). *Booklet stamps. Aboriginal Crafts.* T **441** *and similar horiz designs. Multicoloured. P* 15½ × imperf

1093	3 c. Type **441**		1·00	1·50
	a. Booklet pane. Nos. 1093 and 1095, each × 2		3·75	

1094	15 c. Shield pattern, New South Wales	3·75	4·75
	a. Booklet pane. Nos. 1094, 1096 × 3 and 1097 × 2		7·50
1095	37 c. Basket weave, Queensland	1·00	1·50
1096	37 c. Bowl pattern, Central Australia	90	1·25
1097	37 c. Belt pattern, Northern Territory	1·00	1·50
1093/7		*Set of 5*	7·00	9·50

Nos. 1093/7 only exist from 80 c. (pane No. 1093a) and $2 (pane No. 1094a) stamp booklets. The vertical edges of the booklet panes are imperforate.

(Des B. Clinton. Litho Leigh-Mardon Ltd, Melbourne (30 c.) or CPE Australia Ltd, Melbourne (37 c., 63 c.))

1987 (2 Nov). *Christmas.* T **442** *and similar multicoloured designs showing carol singing by candlelight. P* 14½ (30 c.) or 13½ × 14 (37 c., 63 c.).

1098	30 c. Type **442**		55	55
	a. Horiz strip of 5. Nos. 1098/102		2·50	
1099	30 c. Father and daughters..		55	55
1100	30 c. Four children ..		55	55
1101	30 c. Family ..		55	55
1102	30 c. Six teenagers ..		55	55
1103	37 c. Choir (*horiz*)		55	40
1104	63 c. Father and two children (*horiz*)		1·00	1·00
1098/104		*Set of 7*	3·75	3·75

Nos. 1098/1102 were printed together, *se-tenant*, in horizontal strips of five throughout the sheet.

(Des Sue Passmore. Litho CPE Australia Ltd, Melbourne)

1988 (26 Jan). *Bicentenary of Australian Settlement* (10th issue). *Arrival of First Fleet. Square designs as* T **437**. *Multicoloured. P* 13.

1105	37 c. Aborigines watching arrival of Fleet, Botany Bay		70	85
	a. Horiz strip of 5. Nos. 1105/9		3·25	
1106	37 c. Aborigine family and anchored ships	70	85
1107	37 c. Fleet arriving at Sydney Cove	70	85
1108	37 c. Ship's boat		70	85
1109	37 c. Raising the flag, Sydney Cove, 26 January 1788		70	85
1105/9		*Set of 5*	3·25	3·75

Nos. 1105/9 were printed together, *se-tenant*, in horizontal strips of five throughout the sheet, forming a composite design.

443 Koala with Stockman's Hat and Eagle dressed as Uncle Sam   **444** "Religion" (A. Horner)

(Des R. Harvey. Litho CPE Australia Ltd, Melbourne)

1988 (26 Jan). *Bicentenary of Australian Settlement* (11th issue). *Joint issue with U.S.A. P* 13.

1110	**443** 37 c. multicoloured	.. ..	60	35

NEW PRINTINGS. From the beginning of 1990 new printings of definitive stamps were identified by small koala or kangaroo symbols printed on the vertical sheet margins alongside alternate rows. One koala represented the first printing, two koalas the second and so on. The kangaroo symbol was used once four koalas had been reached.

(Litho Leigh-Mardon Ltd, Melbourne (4, 5, 20, 25, 30, 37, 39, 40, 50, 53, 70, 80, 90 c., $1) or CPE Australia Ltd, Melbourne (others))

1988 (17 Feb)–**95**. *"Living Together".* T **444** *and similar square designs showing cartoons. Multicoloured* (except 30 c.). *P* 14.

1111	1 c. Type **444** (16.3.88)		40	30
1112	2 c. "Industry" (P. Nicholson) (16.3.88) ..	40	30
1113	3 c. "Local Government" (A. Collette) (16.3.88)		40	30
1114	4 c. "Trade Unions" (Liz Honey)		10	10
1115	5 c. "Parliament" (Bronwyn Halls) (16.3.88)		50	30
1116	10 c. "Transport" (Meg Williams)		30	30
1117	15 c. "Sport" (G. Cook)		30	40
1118	20 c. "Commerce" (M. Atcherson)		70	30
1119	25 c. "Housing" (C. Smith)		35	30
	a. Perf 14½ (4.9.95)		25	30
1120	30 c. "Welfare" (R. Tandberg) (black and pale rose-lilac) (16.3.88)		45	40
1121	37 c. "Postal Services" (P. Viska)		60	50
	a. Booklet pane. No. 1121×10 (1.7.88)		6·00	
1121b	39 c. "Tourism" (J. Spooner) (28.9.88)		60	50
	ba. Booklet pane. No. 1121b×10		7·00	
1122	40 c. "Recreation" (R. Harvey) (16.3.88) ..	70	40
1123	45 c. "Health" (Jenny Coopes)		60	50
1124	50 c. "Mining" (G. Haddon)		55	50
1125	53 c. "Primary Industry" (S. Leahy)		1·75	85
1126	55 c. "Education" (Victoria Roberts) (16.3.88)		1·50	55
1127	60 c. "Armed Forces" (B. Green) (16.3.88)	1·25	70
1128	63 c. "Police" (J. Russell) (16.3.88)		2·00	85
1129	65 c. "Telecommunications" (B. Petty) (16.3.88)		1·25	75
1130	68 c. "The Media" (A. Langoulant) (16.3.88)	1·75	1·25
1131	70 c. "Science and Technology" (J. Hook)	1·75	1·00
1132	75 c. "Visual Arts" (G. Dazeley) (16.3.88)	1·00	1·00
1133	80 c. "Performing Arts" (A. Stitt)		1·25	1·00
1134	90 c. "Banking" (S. Billington)		1·50	90
1135	95 c. "Law" (C. Aslanis) (16.3.88)		1·00	1·00
1136	$1 "Rescue and Emergency" (M. Leunig) (Optd S. 50p.)		1·10	90
1111/36		*Set of 27*	22·00	14·00

Although Leigh-Mardon printed the 37 c. and 39 c. sheet stamps, and some of the 37 c. booklets, Nos. 1121a and 1121ba were produced by CPE with the upper and lower edges of the panes imperforate, so that stamps from them exist imperforate at top or bottom. These panes also show margins at both right and left.

Early in 1989 Leigh-Mardon Ltd, whose works were situated at Moorabbin, took over C.P.E Australia Ltd of Scoresby. Printings of the 45, 55, 60, 75, 80, 95 c. and $1 were made at both printing works.

No. 1119a comes from part of the 4 koala printing.

445 "Government House, Sydney, 1790" (George Raper)   **446** Queen Elizabeth II (from photo by Tim Graham)

(Des J. Passmore. Litho CPE Australia Ltd, Melbourne)

1988 (13 Apr). *Bicentenary of Australian Settlement* (12th issue). *"The Early Years, 1788–1809".* T **445** *and similar square designs showing paintings. Multicoloured. P* 13.

1137	37 c. Type **445**		65	65
	a. Horiz strip of 5. Nos. 1137/41		3·00	
1138	37 c. "Government Farm, Parramatta, 1791" ("The Port Jackson Painter") ..		65	65
1139	37 c. "Parramatta Road, 1796" (attr Thomas Watling)		65	65
1140	37 c. "View of Sydney Cove, c. 1800" (detail) (Edward Dayes)		65	65
1141	37 c. "Sydney Hospital, 1803", (detail) (George William Evans)		65	65
1137/41		*Set of 5*	3·00	3·00

Nos. 1137/41 were printed together, *se-tenant*, in horizontal strips of 5 throughout the sheet, each strip forming a composite background design from the painting, "View of Sydney from the East Side of the Cove, c. 1808" by John Eyre.

(Des Sandra Baker. Litho Leigh-Mardon Ltd, Melbourne)

1988 (21 Apr). *Queen Elizabeth II's Birthday. P* 14½.

1142	**446** 37 c. multicoloured	.. ..	50	40

447 Expo '88 Logo   **448** New Parliament House

(Des G. Emery. Litho CPE Australia Ltd, Melbourne)

1988 (29 Apr). *"Expo '88" World Fair, Brisbane. P* 13.

1143	**447** 37 c. multicoloured	.. ..	50	40

(Des B. Sadgrove. Litho Leigh-Mardon Ltd, Melbourne)

1988 (9 May). *Opening of New Parliament House, Canberra. P* 14½.

1144	**448** 37 c. multicoloured	.. ..	50	40

449 Early Settler and Sailing Clipper   **450** Kiwi and Koala at Campfire

(Des G. Emery. Litho CPE Australia Ltd, Melbourne)

1988 (21 June). *Bicentenary of Australian Settlement* (13th issue). T **449** *and similar square designs. Multicoloured. P* 13.

1145	37 c. Type **449**		75	1·00
	a. Pair. Nos. 1145/6		1·50	2·00
1146	37 c. Queen Elizabeth II with British and Australian Parliament Buildings		75	1·00
1147	$1 W. G. Grace (cricketer) and tennis racquet		1·50	2·25
	a. Pair. Nos. 1147/8		3·00	4·50
1148	$1 Shakespeare, John Lennon (entertainer) and Sydney Opera House		1·50	2·25
1145/8		*Set of 4*	4·00	6·00

Nos. 1145/6 and 1147/8 were printed together, *se-tenant*, in horizontal and vertical pairs throughout the sheets, each horizontal pair showing a background design of the Australian flag.

Stamps in similar designs were also issued by Great Britain.

(Des R. Harvey. Litho Leigh-Mardon Ltd, Melbourne)

1988 (21 June). *Bicentenary of Australian Settlement* (14th issue). *P* 14½.

1149	**450** 37 c. multicoloured	.. ..	65	40

A stamp in a similar design was also issued by New Zealand.

451 "Bush Potato Country"
(Turkey Tolsen Tjupurrula
and David Corby
Tjapaltjarri)

452 Basketball

(Des Janet Boschen. Litho CPE Australia Ltd, Melbourne)

1988 (1 Aug). *Art of the Desert. Aboriginal Paintings from Central Australia. T 451 and similar square designs. Multicoloured. P 13.*

1150	37 c. Type **451**		40	40
1151	55 c. "Courtship Rejected" (Limpi Puntungka Tjapangati)		80	60
1152	90 c. "Medicine Story" (artist unknown)		1·25	1·50
1153	$1 "Ancestor Dreaming" (Tim Leura Tjapaltjarri)		1·50	1·40
1150/3		*Set of 4*	3·50	3·50

(Des Sue Passmore. Litho Leigh-Mardon Ltd, Melbourne)

1988 (14 Sept). *Olympic Games, Seoul. T 452 and similar horiz designs. Multicoloured. P 14½.*

1154	37 c. Type **452**		40	40
1155	65 c. Athlete crossing finish line		80	80
1156	$1 Gymnast with hoop		1·25	1·40
1154/6		*Set of 3*	2·25	2·40

453 Rod and Mace

(Des K. Christos. Litho Leigh-Mardon Ltd, Melbourne)

1988 (19 Sept). *34th Commonwealth Parliamentary Conference, Canberra. P 14½.*

1157	**453** 37 c. multicoloured		50	60

454 Necklace by Peter Tully

(Des K. Christos. Litho Mercury-Walch Pty, Hobart)

1988 (28 Sept). *Booklet stamps. Australian Crafts. T 454 and similar horiz designs. Multicoloured. Roul × imperf.*

1158	2 c. Type **454**		3·00	3·75
	a. Booklet pane. Nos. 1158 and 1160 × 2		3·50	
1159	5 c. Vase by Colin Levy		3·00	3·75
	a. Booklet pane. Nos. 1159 and 1160 × 5		5·00	
1160	39 c. Teapot by Frank Bauer		50	35
1158/60		*Set of 3*	6·00	7·00

Nos. 1158/60 only exist from 80 c. (pane No. 1158a) and $2 (pane No. 1159a) stamp booklets. The vertical edges of the booklet panes are imperforate.

455 Pinnacles Desert

456 "The Nativity"
(Danielle Hush)

(Des K. Christos. Litho CPE Australia Ltd, Melbourne)

1988 (17 Oct). *Panorama of Australia. T 455 and similar horiz designs. Multicoloured. P 13.*

1161	39 c. Type **455**		60	40
1162	55 c. Flooded landscape, Arnhem Land		85	75
1163	65 c. Twelve Apostles, Victoria		1·10	1·00
1164	70 c. Mountain Ash wood		1·25	1·40
1161/4		*Set of 4*	3·50	3·25

(Des Sandra Baker. Litho CPE Australia Ltd, Melbourne (32, 39 c.) or Leigh-Mardon Ltd, Melbourne (63 c.))

1988 (31 Oct). *Christmas. T 456 and similar square designs. Multicoloured. P 14½ (63 c.) or 13 (others).*

1165	32 c. Type **456**		50	35
1166	39 c. "Koala as Father Christmas" (Kylie Courtney)		55	40
1167	63 c. "Christmas Cockatoo" (Benjamin Stevenson)		1·10	1·40
1165/7		*Set of 3*	1·90	1·90

PRINTERS. On 1 April 1989 Leigh-Mardon Ltd took over CPE Australia Ltd. Stamp printing continued at both the Moorabbin (original Leigh-Mardon) and Scoresby (ex-CPE) works with some stamps being printed at one and then perforated at the other. The Scoresby works closed at the end of 1991.

457 Sir Henry
Parkes

458 Bowls

(Des R. Bevers. Litho CPE Australia Ltd, Melbourne)

1989 (25 Jan). *Australia Day. Centenary of Federation Speech by Sir Henry Parkes (N.S.W. Prime Minister). P 14 × 13½.*

1168	**457** 39 c. multicoloured		45	40

(Des Sue Passmore (5, 10, 20, 41, 43, 65 c., $1, $1.20), N. Stapleton (75, 80, 85, 90 c.), G. Cook (others). Litho Printset Cambec Pty Ltd (5 c., (No. 1172a), 65 c. (No. 1186a) and ptgs of 1 c. (No. 1169), 3 c., 75 c., 80 c. (No. 1189) and $1 (No. 1192) from 1993) or Leigh-Mardon Ltd, Melbourne (others))

1989 (13 Feb)–94. *Sports. T 458 and similar horiz designs. Multicoloured. P 13½ (5, 10, 20, 65 c., $1.20) or 14×14½ (others).*

1169	1 c. Type **458**		10	10
	a. Perf 13½ (4.90)		30	30
1170	2 c. Tenpin-bowling		10	10
	a. Perf 13½ (9.89)		10	10
1171	3 c. Australian football		10	10
1172	5 c. Kayaking and canoeing (17.1.90)		15	10
	a. Perf 14×14½ (3.94)		30	10
1174	10 c. Sailboarding (17.1.90)		15	10
	a. Perf 14×14½ (2.92)		30	10
1176	20 c. Tennis (17.1.90)		20	25
	a. Perf 14×14½ (7.93)		1·25	40
1179	39 c. Fishing		35	40
	a. Booklet pane. No. 1179×10		7·50	
	b. Perf 13½ (6.89)		1·00	1·00
	ba. Booklet pane. No. 1179b×10		10·00	
1180	41 c. Cycling (23.8.89)		40	35
	a. Booklet pane. No. 1180×10		6·00	
1181	43 c. Skateboarding (27.8.90)		35	40
	a. Booklet pane. No. 1181×10		5·50	
1184	50 c. Kite-flying		50	55
1186	65 c. Rock-climbing (17.1.90)		70	60
	a. Perf 14×14½ (2.92)		55	60
1187	70 c. Cricket		85	80
1188	75 c. Netball (22.8.91)		1·40	80
1189	80 c. Squash (22.8.91)		1·40	85
1190	85 c. Diving (22.8.91)		1·50	80
1191	90 c. Soccer (22.8.91)		1·50	80
1192	$1 Fun-run (17.1.90)		1·00	95
	a. Perf 13½ (1.91)		3·50	3·00
1193	$1.10, Golf		95	1·00
1194	$1.20, Hang-gliding (27.8.90)		1·50	1·10
1169/94		*Set of 19*	11·50	8·50
1192/4	Optd "Specimen"	*Set of 3*	1·75	

The booklet panes have the upper and lower edges imperforate, so that the stamps from them are imperforate at top or bottom, and have margins at both left and right.

Nos. 1169a (1 koala ptg), 1170a (all ptgs except the first), 1179b (1st new ptg) and 1192a (1 koala ptg) are Scoresby printings of values originally produced at Moorabbin. Nos. 1174a (2, 3 and 4 koala ptgs) and 1176a (2 and 3 koala) are Moorabbin printings of values originally produced at Scoresby.

No. 1186a (2 koala ptg) was printed by Printset Cambec Pty Ltd. instead of Leigh-Mardon Ltd. There are minor differences in the arrangement of the inscriptions. Further supplies of the 1 c. (No. 1169) (2 koala), 3 c. (3 koala), 75 c. (1 and 2 koala), 80 c. (2 koala) and $1 (No. 1192) (2 koala) were also produced by Printset Cambec from 1993.

No. 1172a (4 koala ptg) was printed by McPherson's as were additional supplies of the 65 c. (No. 1186a) (3 koala) and $1 (No. 1192) (1 kangaroo +1 koala and 1 kangaroo + 2 koala ptgs).

For self-adhesive versions of Nos. 1180/1 see Nos. 1259/60a.

WARNING. The coating on a batch of paper used during 1989-90 was defective so that stamps lose parts of their design if immersed in water.

459 Merino

(Des K. McEwan. Litho CPE Australia Ltd, Melbourne)

1989 (27 Feb). *Sheep in Australia. T 459 and similar horiz designs. Multicoloured. P 13½ × 14.*

1195	39 c. Type **459**		70	40
1196	39 c. Poll Dorset		70	40
1197	85 c. Polwarth		1·40	1·75
1198	$1 Corriedale (Optd S. 70p.)		1·40	1·40
1195/8		*Set of 4*	3·75	3·50

460 Adelaide Botanic Garden

(Des J. Passmore. Eng B. Stewart. Litho Leigh-Mardon Ltd and die-stamped Avon Graphics, both of Melbourne ($20), litho CPE Australia Ltd, Melbourne ($2 later by Leigh-Mardon Ltd) and recess Note Ptg Branch, Reserve Bank of Australia (others))

1989 (12 Apr)–90. *Botanic Gardens. T 460 and similar horiz designs. Multicoloured. P 14 ($2 to $10) or 14½×14 ($20).*

1199	$2 Nooroo, New South Wales (13.9.89)		2·25	1·25
	a. Perf 13½		2·50	1·40
1200	$5 Mawarra, Victoria (13.9.89)		4·25	1·25
	a. Perf 13½		4·75	3·50
1201	$10 Flying		8·75	2·00
1201a	$20 "A View of the Artist's House and Garden in Mills Plains, Van Diemen's Land" (John Glover) (15.8.90)		17·00	11·00
1199/1201a		*Set of 4*	28·00	14·00
1199a/1201a Optd "Specimen"		*Set of 4*	14·00	

$10 Type **460**

461 "Queen
Elizabeth II"
(sculpture, John
Dowie)

462 Arrival of Immigrant
Ship, 1830's

(Des Sandra Baker. Litho Leigh-Mardon Ltd, Melbourne)

1989 (21 Apr). *Queen Elizabeth II's Birthday. P 14½.*

1202	**461** 39 c. multicoloured		55	50

(Des D. Lancashire. Litho Leigh-Mardon Ltd, Melbourne)

1989 (10 May). *Colonial Development (1st issue). Pastoral Era 1810–1850. T 462 and similar square designs. Multicoloured. P 14½.*

1203	39 c. Type **462**		55	55
	a. Horiz strip of 5. Nos. 1203/7		2·50	
1204	39 c. Pioneer cottage and wool dray		55	55
1205	39 c. Squatter's homestead		55	55
1206	39 c. Shepherd with flock (from Joseph Lycett's "Views of Australia")		55	55
1207	39 c. Explorer in desert (after watercolour by Edward Frome)		55	55
1203/7		*Set of 5*	2·50	2·50

Nos. 1203/7 were printed together, *se-tenant*, in horizontal strips of five throughout the sheet.

See also Nos. 1254/8 and 1264/8.

463 Gladys
Moncrieff and Roy
Rene

464 "Impression" (Tom
Roberts)

(Des Sue Passmore. Litho Leigh-Mardon Ltd, Melbourne)

1989 (12 July). *Australian Stage and Screen Personalities. T 463 and similar vert designs. Multicoloured. P 14½.*

1208	39 c. Type **463**		45	40
	a. Perf 14 × 13½		7·00	7·50
1209	85 c. Charles Chauvel and Chips Rafferty		1·25	1·40
1210	$1 Nellie Stewart and J. C. Williamson		1·25	1·10
1211	$1.10, Lottie Lyell and Raymond Longford		1·25	1·25
1208/11		*Set of 4*	3·75	3·75
1210/11 Optd "Specimen"		*Set of 2*	1·40	

No. 1208a was from a small first printing produced at the Scoresby (ex C.P.E.) plant and used in presentation packs or on first day covers. The rest of the 39 c. printing was perforated at the Moorabbin works.

(Des K. Christos. Litho Leigh-Mardon Ltd, Melbourne)

1989 (23 Aug). *Australian Impressionist Paintings. T 464 and similar multicoloured designs. P 14 × 13½ (No. 1214) or 13½ × 14 (others).*

1212	41 c. Type **464**		55	50
1213	41 c. "Impression for Golden Summer" (Sir Arthur Streeton)		55	50
1214	41 c. "All on a Summer's Day" (Charles Conder) (*vert*)		55	50
1215	41 c. "Petit Déjeuner" (Frederick McCubbin)		55	50
1212/15		*Set of 4*	2·00	1·75

465 Freeways

(Des Sally Newell and Carolyn Limonta. Litho Leigh-Mardon Ltd, Melbourne)

1989 (1 Sept). *Booklet stamps. The Urban Environment. T* **465** *and similar horiz designs.* P 15½×imperf.
1216 41 c. black, maroon and blue-green 65 90
    a. Booklet pane. Nos. 1216×2, 1217×3
    and 1218×2 .. .. .. 4·00
1217 41 c. black, maroon and magenta .. 65 90
1218 41 c. black, maroon and bright blue .. 65 90
1216/18 .. .. .. *Set of 3* 1·75 2·40
Designs:—No. 1217, City buildings, Melbourne; No. 1218, Commuter train at platform.
Nos. 1216/18 only exist from $3 stamp booklets in which the vertical edges of the pane are imperforate.

466 Hikers outside Youth   **467** Horse Tram, Adelaide,
Hostel   1878

(Des Priscilla Cutter. Litho Leigh-Mardon Ltd, Melbourne)

1989 (13 Sept). *50th Anniv of Australian Youth Hostels.* P 14½.
1219 **466** 41 c. multicoloured 55 50

(Des I. McKellar. Litho Leigh-Mardon Ltd, Melbourne)

1989 (11 Oct). *Historic Trams. T* **467** *and similar horiz designs. Multicoloured.* P 13½×14.
1220 41 c. Type **467** 60 60
1221 41 c. Steam tram, Sydney, 1884 .. 60 60
1222 41 c. Cable tram, Melbourne, 1886 .. 60 60
    a. Perf 14½ .. .. .. 1·00 1·00
    ab. Booklet pane. No. 1222a×10 .. 10·00
1223 41 c. Double-deck electric tram, Hobart,
    1893 .. .. 60 60
1224 41 c. Combination electric tram, Brisbane,
    1901 .. .. 60 60
1220/4 .. .. *Set of 5* 2·75 2·75
The upper and lower edges of booklet pane No. 1222ab are imperforate. It was printed and perforated at the Moorabbin plant.

468 "Annunciation"   **469** Radio Waves
(15th-century Book   and Globe
of Hours)

(Des Lynette Brown. Litho Leigh-Mardon Ltd, Melbourne)

1989 (1 Nov). *Christmas. Illuminated Manuscripts. T* **468** *and similar vert designs. Multicoloured.* P 14×13½ (36 c.) or 14½ (others).
1225 36 c. Type **468** 40 40
    a. Booklet pane. No. 1225×10 .. 4·00
1226 41 c. "Annunciation to the Shepherds"
    (Wharncliffe Book of Hours, c. 1475) 50 45
1227 80 c. "Adoration of the Magi" (15th-century
    Parisian Book of Hours) .. 1·25 1·40
1225/7 .. .. *Set of 3* 1·90 2·00
The vertical sides of booklet pane No. 1225a are imperforate.

(Des B. Sadgrove. Litho Leigh-Mardon Ltd, Melbourne)

1989 (1 Nov). *50th Anniv of Radio Australia.* P 14×13½.
1228 **469** 41 c. multicoloured 55 50

470 Golden   **471** Australian
Wattle   Wildflowers

(Des Celia Rosser. Litho Leigh-Mardon Ltd, Melbourne)

1990 (17 Jan). *Australia Day.* P 14½.
1229 **470** 41 c. multicoloured 55 50

(Des Beverley Graham and G. Rogers. Litho Leigh-Mardon Ltd, Melbourne)

1990 (7 Feb–3 Sept). *Greetings Stamps.* P 14×13½ (41 c.) or 14½ (43 c.).
1230 **471** 41 c. multicoloured 45 45
    a. Booklet pane. No. 1230×10 .. 5·50
    b. Perf 14½ (May) .. .. 1·00 1·00
    ba. Booklet pane. No. 1230b×10 .. 10·00

1231 **471** 43 c. multicoloured (3 Sept) 35 40
    a. Booklet pane. No. 1231×10 .. 4·00
The upper and lower edges of the booklet panes are imperforate.
No. 1230b is a Moorabbin (1 koala) printing which only exists from booklets. The remainder were printed at the Scoresby works.

472 Dr. Constance Stone   **473** Greater
(first Australian woman   Glider
doctor), Modern Doctor
and Nurses

(Des Priscilla Cutter. Litho Leigh-Mardon Ltd, Melbourne)

1990 (7 Feb). *Centenary of Women in Medical Practice.* P 14½.
1232 **472** 41 c. multicoloured 50 45

(Des D. Higgins. Litho Leigh-Mardon Ltd, Melbourne)

1990 (21 Feb). *Animals of the High Country. T* **473** *and similar vert designs. Multicoloured.* P 14×13½.
1233 41 c. Type **473** 60 45
1234 65 c. Tiger Cat ("Spotted-tailed Quoll") 90 85
1235 70 c. Mountain Pygmy-possum .. 95 90
1236 80 c. Brush-tailed Rock-wallaby .. 1·10 1·00
1233/6 .. .. *Set of 4* 3·25 2·75

474 "Stop   **475** Soldiers
Smoking"   from Two World
           Wars

(Des A. Stitt. Litho Leigh-Mardon Ltd, Melbourne)

1990 (14 Mar). *Community Health. T* **474** *and similar vert designs. Multicoloured.* P 14×13½.
1237 41 c. Type **474** 55 55
1238 41 c. "Drinking and driving don't mix" 55 55
1239 41 c. "No junk food, please" .. 55 55
1240 41 c. "Guess who's just had a checkup?" 55 55
1237/40 .. .. *Set of 4* 2·00 2·00

(Des O. Schmidinger and Christine Stead. Litho Leigh-Mardon Ltd, Melbourne)

1990 (12 Apr). *"The Anzac Tradition". T* **475** *and similar vert designs. Multicoloured.* P 14½.
1241 41 c. Type **475** 50 40
1242 41 c. Fighter pilots and munitions worker 50 40
1243 65 c. Veterans and Anzac Day parade 85 90
1244 $1 Casualty evacuation, Vietnam, and
    disabled veteran .. .. 1·25 1·40
1245 $1·10, Letters from home and returning
    troopships .. .. .. 1·40 1·50
1241/5 .. .. .. *Set of 5* 4·00 4·25
1244/5 Optd "Specimen" .. *Set of 2* 1·10

476 Queen at   **477** New South Wales
Australian Ballet   1861 5s. Stamp
Performance,
London, 1988

(Des Lynette Brown. Litho Leigh-Mardon Ltd, Melbourne)

1990 (19 Apr). *Queen Elizabeth II's Birthday.* P 14½.
1246 **476** 41 c. multicoloured 65 45

(Des J. Passmore. Litho Leigh-Mardon Ltd, Melbourne)

1990 (1 May). *150th Anniv of the Penny Black. T* **477** *and similar horiz designs showing stamps. Multicoloured.* P 13½×14.
1247 41 c. Type **477** 60 75
    a. Block of 6. Nos. 1247/52 .. 3·25
1248 41 c. South Australia 1855 unissued 1s. 60 75
1249 41 c. Tasmania 1853 4d. 60 75
1250 41 c. Victoria 1867 5s. 60 75
1251 41 c. Queensland 1897 unissued 6d. 60 75
1252 41 c. Western Australia 1855 4d. with
    inverted frame 60 75
1247/52 .. .. .. *Set of 6* 4·00 4·00
MS1253 122×85 mm. Nos. 1247/52 .. 3·25 4·00
Nos. 1247/52 were printed together, *se-tenant*, throughout the sheet of 100 (two panes 5×10). The first and fifth vertical rows

---

contained Nos. 1247 and 1250 alternately, the second and four[th] rows Nos. 1248 and 1251, and the third row Nos. 1249 and 125[2].
No. MS1253 also exists overprinted with the "Stamp Wor[ld] London 90" logo for sale at this international stamp exhibiti[on].

478 Gold Miners on way   **479** Glaciology Research
to Diggings

(Des B. Weatherhead. Litho Leigh-Mardon Ltd, Melbourne)

1990 (16 May). *Colonial Development* (2nd issue). *Gold Feve[r]. T* **478** *and similar square designs. Multicoloured.* P 13.
1254 41 c. Type **478** 55 55
    a. Horiz strip of 5. Nos. 1254/8 .. 2·50
1255 41 c. Mining camp .. .. 55 5[5]
1256 41 c. Panning and washing for gold .. 55 5[5]
1257 41 c. Gold Commissioner's tent .. 55 5[5]
1258 41 c. Moving gold under escort .. 55 5[5]
1254/8 .. .. *Set of 5* 2·50 2·5[0]
Nos. 1254/8 were printed together, *se-tenant*, in horizonta[l] strips of 5 throughout the sheet.

1990 (16 May)–**91**. *As Nos. 1180/1, but self-adhesive.* P 11½.
    (a) *Typo Pemara Labels, Victoria*
1259 41 c. Cycling .. .. .. 65 1·0[0]
1260 43 c. Skateboarding (27.8.90) .. 65 8[0]
    (b) *Litho Printset-Cambec Pty Ltd, Melbourne*
1260a 43 c. Skateboarding (26.6.91) .. 1·25 1·5[0]
Nos. 1259/60a were only available in rolls of 100, No. 1260[a] also initially in rolls of 200, from major post offices or as strips o[f] three from philatelic counters, each stamp, with die-cu[t] perforations, being separate on the imperforate backing strip.
No. 1260a can be identified by its screened colours: on No. 1260 these are solid. The lithography printing also shows [a] kangaroo on the reverse and is on plain, rather than waxe[d] backing paper.
Due to the type of adhesive used examples should be retaine[d] on piece.

(Des Janet Boschen and Yu. Artsimenev. Litho Leigh-Mardon Ltd, Melbourne)

1990 (13 June). *Australian-Soviet Scientific Co-operation in Antarctica. T* **479** *and similar horiz design. Multicoloured.* P 14½.
1261 41 c. Type **479** .. .. .. 55 4[0]
1262 $1·10, Krill (marine biology research)
    (Optd S. 55p) .. .. 1·40 1·5[0]
MS1263 85 × 65 mm. Nos. 1261/2 .. 1·90 1·9[0]
Stamps in similar designs were also issued by Russia.
Examples of No. MS1263 imperforate originate from the Russian postal archives.
No. MS1263 also exists overprinted with the "New Zealand 1990" logo for sale at this international stamp exhibition in Auckland.

480 Auctioning Building   **481** "Salmon
Plots   Gums" (Robert
             Juniper)

(Des B. Clinton. Litho Leigh-Mardon Ltd, Melbourne)

1990 (12 July). *Colonial Development* (3rd series). *Boomtime. T* **480** *and similar square designs. Multicoloured.* P 13.
1264 41 c. Type **480** 55 55
    a. Horiz strip of 5. Nos. 1264/8 .. 2·50
1265 41 c. Colonial mansion 55 55
1266 41 c. Stock exchange 55 55
1267 41 c. Fashionable society 55 55
1268 41 c. Factories 55 55
1264/8 .. .. *Set of 5* 2·50 2·50
Nos. 1264/8 were printed together, *se-tenant*, in horizontal strips of 5 throughout the sheet.

(Des Sandra Baker. Litho Leigh-Mardon Ltd, Melbourne)

1990 (3 Sept). *Booklet stamps. "Heidelberg and Heritage" Art Exhibition. T* **481** *and similar vert design. Multicoloured.* Imperf × p 14½.
1269 28 c. Type **481** .. .. .. 1·50 2·00
    a. Booklet pane. Nos. 1269 and 1270 × 4
    b. Imperf × p 15½ .. .. 3·50 4·25
    ba. Booklet pane. Nos. 1269b and 1270a
    × 4 .. .. 5·50
1270 43 c. "The Blue Dress" (Brian Dunlop) .. 45 45
    a. Imperf × p 15½ 85 85
Nos. 1269/70 only exist from $2 stamp booklets in which the horizontal edges of the pane are imperforate.

482 "Adelaide Town Hall" (Edmund Gouldsmith) 483 Laughing Kookaburras and Gifts

(Des Janet Boschen. Litho Leigh-Mardon Ltd, Melbourne)
1990 (31 Oct). 150th Anniv of Local Government. P 14¹/₂.
1271 482 43 c. multicoloured 55 50

(Des Marg Towt. Litho Leigh-Mardon Ltd, Melbourne)
1990 (31 Oct). Christmas. T 483 and similar multicoloured designs. P 14¹/₂.
1272 38 c. Type 483 .. .. .. 50 40
    a. Booklet pane. No. 1272 × 10 .. 5·50
1273 43 c. Baby Jesus with Koalas and Wallaby (vert) 50 40
1274 80 c. Possum on Christmas tree .. 1·50 1·25
1272/4 .. .. .. Set of 3 2·25 1·90
The upper and lower edges of booklet pane No. 1272a are imperforate, producing stamps imperforate top or bottom, and there are margins at left and right.

484 National Flag 485 Black-necked Stork

(Des Dianne Cook. Litho Leigh-Mardon Ltd, Melbourne)
1991 (10 Jan). Australia Day. 90th Anniv of Australian Flag. T 484 and similar horiz designs. P 14¹/₂.
1275 43 c. deep ultramarine, brt scarlet & grey 50 40
1276 90 c. multicoloured .. .. 1·10 45
1277 $1 multicoloured .. .. .. 1·25 1·40
1278 $1.20, brt scarlet, dp ultramarine & grey 1·60 1·75
1275/8 .. .. .. Set of 4 4·00 4·25
Designs:—90 c. Royal Australian Navy ensign; $1 Royal Australian Air Force standard; $1.20, Australian merchant marine ensign.

(Des P. Margocsy. Litho Leigh-Mardon Ltd, Melbourne)
1991 (14 Feb). Waterbirds. T 485 and similar multicoloured designs. P 14¹/₂.
1279 43 c. Type 485 .. .. 65 40
1280 43 c. Black Swan (horiz) 65 40
1281 85 c. Cereopsis Goose ("Cape Barren Goose") .. .. 1·50 2·25
1282 $1 Chestnut-breasted Teal (horiz) (Optd S. 55p) .. .. 1·60 1·75
1279/82 .. .. .. Set of 4 4·00 4·25

486 Recruitment Poster (Women's Services) 487 Queen Elizabeth at Royal Albert Hall, London

(Des Dianne Cook. Litho Leigh-Mardon Ltd, Melbourne)
1991 (14 Mar). Anzac Day. 50th Anniversaries. T 486 and similar horiz designs. P 14¹/₂.
1283 43 c. multicoloured 60 40
1284 43 c. black, brown-olive & pale grey-brown 60 40
1285 $1.20, multicoloured (Optd S. 55p) .. 2·25 2·00
1283/5 .. .. .. Set of 3 3·00 2·50
Designs:—43 c. (No. 1284) Patrol (Defence of Tobruk); $1.20, "V-P Day Canberra" (Harold Abbot) (Australian War Memorial).

(Des R. Bulach. Litho Leigh-Mardon Ltd, Melbourne)
1991 (11 Apr). Queen Elizabeth II's Birthday. P 14¹/₂.
1286 487 43 c. multicoloured 70 50

NEW INFORMATION
The editor is always interested to correspond with people who have new information that will improve or correct the Catalogue.

488 Tectocoris diophthalmus (bug) 489 "Bondi" (Max Dupain)

(Des D. Nelson. Litho Leigh-Mardon Ltd, Melbourne)
1991 (11 Apr). Insects. T 488 and similar horiz designs. Multicoloured. P 14¹/₂.
1287 43 c. Type 488 .. .. 70 45
1288 43 c. Cizara ardeniae (hawk moth) .. 70 45
1289 80 c. Petasida ephippigera (grasshopper) 1·75 2·00
1290 $1 Castiarina producta (beetle) .. 1·90 1·50
1287/90 .. .. .. Set of 4 4·50 4·00

(Des Janet Boschen. Litho Leigh-Mardon Ltd, Melbourne)
1991 (13 May). 150 Years of Photography in Australia. T 489 and similar vert designs. P 14¹/₂.
1291 43 c. black, chestnut and deep ultramarine 65 65
    a. Horiz pair. Nos. 1291/2 .. 1·25 1·25
1292 43 c. black, turquoise-green and chestnut 65 65
1293 70 c. black, yellow-green and chestnut 1·00 1·10
1294 $1.20, black, light brown and deep blue-green (Optd S. 55p) .. 1·60 1·50
1291/4 .. .. .. Set of 4 3·50 3·50
Designs:—No. 1292, "Gears for the Mining Industry, Vickers Ruwolt, Melbourne" (Wolfgang Sievers); No. 1293, "The Wheel of Youth" (Harold Cazneaux); No. 1294, "Teacup Ballet" (Olive Cotton).
Nos. 1291/2 were printed together, se-tenant, in horizontal pairs throughout the sheet.

490 Singing Group 491 Puppy

(Des O. Schmidinger and Christine Stead. Litho Leigh-Mardon Ltd, Melbourne)
1991 (13 June). Australian Radio Broadcasting. T 490 and similar vert designs showing listeners and scenes from radio programmes. Multicoloured. P 14¹/₂.
1295 43 c. Type 490 .. .. 50 45
1296 43 c. "Blue Hills" serial 50 45
1297 85 c. "The Quiz Kids" .. .. 1·10 1·25
1298 $1 "The Argonauts' Club" children's programme (Optd S. 55p). .. 1·25 1·40
1295/8 .. .. .. Set of 4 3·00 3·25

(Des Betina Ogden. Litho Leigh-Mardon Ltd, Melbourne)
1991 (25 July). Domestic Pets. T 491 and similar vert designs. Multicoloured. P 14¹/₂.
1299 43 c. Type 491 .. .. 70 45
1300 43 c. Kitten 70 45
1301 70 c. Pony .. .. 1·40 1·10
1302 $1 Sulphur-crested Cockatoo .. 1·90 1·40
1299/1302 .. .. Set of 4 4·25 3·00

492 George Vancouver (1791) and Edward Eyre (1841) 493 Seven Little Australians (Ethel Turner)

(Des D. Lancashire. Litho Leigh-Mardon Ltd, Melbourne)
1991 (25 Sept). Exploration of Western Australia. P 14¹/₂.
1303 492 $1.05, multicoloured 90 95
MS1304 100 × 65 mm. No. 1303 .. 90 95
No. MS1304 also exists overprinted with the "Philanippon '91" logo for sale at this international stamp exhibition in Tokyo.

(Des Dianne Cook. Litho Leigh-Mardon Ltd, Melbourne)
1991 (10 Oct). Australian Writers of the 1890s. T 493 and similar multicoloured designs. P 14¹/₂.
1305 43 c. Type 493 .. .. 50 45
1306 75 c. On Our Selection (Steele Rudd) .. 80 75
1307 $1 "Clancy of the Overflow" (poem, A. B. Paterson) (vert) .. .. 1·10 95
1308 $1.20, "The Drover's Wife" (short story, Henry Lawson) (vert) (Optd S. 55p) 1·25 1·40
1305/8 .. .. .. Set of 4 3·25 3·25

494 Shepherd 495 Parma Wallaby

(Des Sue Passmore. Litho Leigh-Mardon Ltd, Melbourne)
1991 (1 Nov). Christmas. T 494 and similar horiz designs. Multicoloured. P 14¹/₂.
1309 38 c. Type 494 .. .. 40 40
    a. Booklet pane. No. 1309 × 20 .. 9·00
1310 43 c. Infant Jesus 45 45
1311 90 c. Wise Man .. .. 1·10 1·25
1309/11 .. .. .. Set of 3 1·75 1·90
The vertical edges of booklet pane No. 1309a are imperforate, producing stamps imperforate at right or left, and there are margins at top and bottom.
Variations in the shades of all three values were caused by changes in the production method during printing.

(Des Betina Ogden. Litho Leigh-Mardon Ltd, Melbourne)
1992 (2 Jan). Threatened Species. T 495 and similar horiz designs. Multicoloured. P 14 × 14¹/₂.
1312 45 c. Type 495 .. .. 60 50
    a. Block of 6. Nos. 1312/17 .. 3·25
1313 45 c. Ghost Bat 60 50
1314 45 c. Long-tailed Dunnart .. 60 50
1315 45 c. Little Pygmy-possum .. 60 50
1316 45 c. Dusky Hopping-mouse .. 60 50
1317 45 c. Squirrel Glider 60 50
1312/17 .. .. .. Set of 6 3·25 2·75
Nos. 1312/17 were printed together, se-tenant, throughout the sheet of 100, giving fifteen blocks of 6 (3 × 2) and 10 single stamps.
For self-adhesive versions of these designs see Nos. 1321/32.

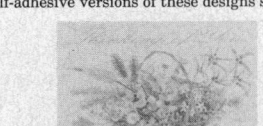

496 Basket of Wild Flowers

(Des Priscilla Cutter. Litho Leigh-Mardon Ltd, Melbourne)
1992 (2 Jan). Greetings Stamp. P 14¹/₂.
1318 496 45 c. multicoloured 40 45
    a. Booklet pane. No. 1318×10 .. 4·50
The upper and lower edges of booklet pane No. 1318a are imperforate, producing stamps imperforate at top or bottom, and there are margins at left and right.

497 Noosa River, Queensland

(Des Sue Passmore. Litho Leigh-Mardon Ltd, Melbourne)
1992 (2 Jan)–94. Booklet stamps. Wetlands and Waterways. T 497 and similar horiz design. P 14¹/₂×imperf.
1319 20 c. Type 497 .. .. 1·40 1·60
    a. Booklet pane. Nos. 1319 and 1320×4 2·75
    b. Perf 14×imperf (3.94) .. 2·50 3·00
    ba. Booklet pane. Nos. 1319b and 1320b×4 .. .. 3·75
1320 45 c. Lake Eildon, Victoria .. 40 45
    b. Perf 14×imperf (3.94) .. 40 45
Nos. 1319/20 only exist from $2 stamp booklets in which the vertical edges of the pane are imperforate.
Nos. 1319b/ba and 1320b (2 koala ptg) were printed by McPherson's Ptg Group.

1992 (2 Jan–24 Dec). As Nos. 1312/17, but self-adhesive.
(a) Typo Pemara Labels, Victoria. Phosphorised paper. P 11
1321 45 c. Type 495 .. .. 55 55
    a. Black (inscr, etc) omitted .. £100
1322 45 c. Squirrel Glider 55 55
    a. Black (inscr, etc) omitted .. £100
1323 45 c. Dusky Hopping-mouse .. 55 55
    a. Black (inscr, etc) omitted .. £100
1324 45 c. Little Pygmy-possum .. 55 55
    a. Black (inscr, etc) omitted .. £100
1325 45 c. Long-tailed Dunnart .. 55 55
    a. Black (inscr, etc) omitted .. £100
1326 45 c. Ghost Bat 55 55
    a. Black (inscr, etc) omitted .. £100
1321/6 .. .. .. Set of 6 3·00 3·00
(b) Litho Printset Cambec Pty Ltd. Phosphorised paper. P 11¹/₂
1327 45 c. Type 495 .. .. 60 60
    p. Broad phosphor band at right .. 1·40 1·60
    pa. Booklet pane. Nos. 1327p×2, 1328p/9p and 1330p/2p×2 .. 12·00
    q. Horiz phosphor bands at top, bottom and on animal (22.4.92) .. 1·40 1·40
    qa. Booklet pane. Nos. 1327q×2, 1328q/9q and 1330q/2q×2 .. 12·00
    qb. Booklet pane. As No. 1327qa, but imperf £300
1328 45 c. Squirrel Glider 60 60
    p. Broad phosphor band at right .. 1·40 1·60
    pa. Sheetlet of 5. Nos. 1328p/32p .. 6·50
    q. Horiz phosphor bands at top, bottom and on animal (22.4.92) .. 1·40 1·40
    qa. Sheetlet of 5. Nos. 1328q/32q (24.12.92) .. .. 6·50

1329	45 c. Dusky Hopping-mouse	..	..	60	60
	p. Broad phosphor band at right	..		1·40	1·60
	q. Horiz phosphor bands at top, bottom and on animal (22.4.92)	..		1·40	1·40
1330	45 c. Little Pygmy-possum	..	..	60	60
	p. Broad phosphor band at right	..		1·40	1·60
	q. Horiz phosphor bands at top, bottom and on animal (22.4.92)			1·40	1·40
1331	45 c. Long-tailed Dunnart	..	..	60	60
	p. Broad phosphor band at right	..		1·40	1·60
	q. Horiz phosphor bands at top, bottom and on animal (22.4.92)			1·40	1·40
1332	45 c. Ghost Bat	..	..	60	60
	p. Broad phosphor band at right	..		1·40	1·60
	q. Horiz phosphor bands at top, bottom and on animal (22.4.92)			1·40	1·40
1327/32	..	..	Set of 6	3·25	3·25
1327p/32p	..	..	Set of 6	7·50	8·50
1327q/32a	..	..	Set of 6	7·50	7·50

Nos. 1321/6 were only available in rolls of 100 with Nos. 1327/32 in rolls of 100 or 200, each stamp, with die-cut perforations, being separate on the imperforate backing strip.

Nos. 1321a/6a also show a horizontal red line across the stamp which normally occurs on the reverse. Examples are reported to have been purchased from Buxton, N.S.W., post office.

The booklet panes Nos. 1327pa and 1327qa are arranged as a block of eight and a separate vertical pair with backing card forming the booklet cover. Stamps from these panes and the sheetlet of 5, Nos. 1328pa and 1328qa, differ from the coil printing by retaining the surplus self-adhesive paper around the stamps.

Booklet pane No. 1327pa and sheetlet No. 1328pa have a broad phosphor band, which shows pink under U.V. light, over the right-hand half of each design. Nos. 1327qa and 1328qa show this phosphor as horizontal bands at the top and bottom of each design and also have the animal overprinted in phosphor ink.

No. 1328pa also exists overprinted with the "World Columbian Stamp Expo '92" logo for sale at this international stamp exhibition in Chicago.

498 *Young Endeavour* (cadet brigantine)   499 Bombing of Darwin

(Des Sue Passmore. Litho Leigh-Mardon Ltd, Melbourne)

1992 (15 Jan). *Australia Day and 500th Anniv of Discovery of America by Columbus (No. MS1337). Sailing Ships. T 498 and similar multicoloured designs.* P 14½.

1333	45 c. Type 498	..	..	70	45
1334	45 c. Britannia (yacht) (vert)	..	..	70	45
1335	$1.05, Akarana (cutter) (vert)	..	..	1·60	1·50
1336	$1.20, John Louis (pearling lugger) (Optd. S. 55p)	..	..	1·75	1·75
1333/6	..	..	Set of 4	4·25	3·75
MS1337	147×64 mm. Nos. 1333/6	..	..	4·25	4·75

No. MS1337 also exists overprinted with either the "World Columbian Stamp Expo '92" or "Genova '92" logos for sale at these international stamp exhibitions in Chicago or Genoa.

(Des B. Clinton. Litho Leigh-Mardon Ltd, Melbourne)

1992 (19 Feb). *50th Anniv of Second World War Battles. T 499 and similar horiz designs. Multicoloured.* P 14½.

1338	45 c. Type 499	..	..	70	45
1339	75 c. Anti-aircraft gun and fighters, Milne Bay	..	..	1·25	1·00
1340	75 c. Infantry on Kokoda Trail	..	..	1·25	1·00
1341	$1.05, H.M.A.S. Australia (cruiser) and American carrier, Coral Sea	..	..	1·50	1·50
1342	$1.20, Australians advancing, El Alamein (Optd. S. 55p)	..	..	1·75	1·60
1338/42	..	..	Set of 5	5·75	5·00

500 Helix Nebula   501 Hunter Valley, New South Wales

(Des Sandra Harman. Litho Leigh-Mardon Ltd, Melbourne)

1992 (19 Mar). *International Space Year. T 500 and similar horiz designs. Multicoloured.* P 14½.

1343	45 c. Type 500	..	..	50	45
1344	$1.05, The Pleiades	..	..	1·25	1·25
1345	$1.20, Spiral Galaxy, NGC 2997 (Optd. S. 55p)	..	..	1·50	1·60
1343/5	..	..	Set of 3	3·00	3·00
MS1346	133×70 mm. Nos. 1343/5	..	..	3·75	4·25

No. MS1346 also exists overprinted with the "World Columbian Stamp Expo '92" logo for sale at this international stamp exhibition in Chicago.

(Des P. Blizzard-Allen. Litho McPherson's Ptg Group, Mulgrave)

1992 (9 Apr). *Vineyard Regions. T 501 and similar horiz designs. Multicoloured.* P 14×14½.

1347	45 c. Type 501	..	..	60	50
1348	45 c. North-east Victoria	..	..	60	50
1349	45 c. Barossa Valley, South Australia	..	..	60	50
1350	45 c. Coonawarra, South Australia	..	..	60	50
1351	45 c. Margaret River, Western Australia	..	..	60	50
1347/51	..	..	Set of 5	2·75	2·25

502 3½d. Stamp of 1953   503 Salt Action

(Des Lynette Brown. Litho McPherson's Ptg Group, Mulgrave)

1992 (9 Apr). *Queen Elizabeth II's Birthday.* P 14×14½.
| 1352 | 502 | 45 c. multicoloured | .. | .. | 70 | 50 |

(Des J. Wolseley. Litho McPherson's Ptg Group, Mulgrave)

1992 (11 June). *Land Conservation. T 503 and similar vert designs. Multicoloured.* P 14½×14.

1353	45 c. Type 503	..	..	80	80
	a. Horiz strip of 5. Nos. 1353/7	..		3·50	
1354	45 c. Farm planning	..	..	80	80
1355	45 c. Erosion control	..	..	80	80
1356	45 c. Tree planting	..	..	80	80
1357	45 c. Dune care	..	..	80	80
1353/7	..	..	Set of 5	3·50	3·50

Nos. 1353/7 were printed together, *se-tenant*, in horizontal strips of 5 throughout the sheet.

504 Cycling   505 Echidna

(Des G. Emery. Litho Leigh-Mardon Ltd, Melbourne)

1992 (2 July). *Olympic Games and Paralympic Games (No. 1359), Barcelona. T 504 and similar horiz designs. Multicoloured.* P 14½.

1358	45 c. Type 504	..	..	60	45
1359	$1.20, High jumping	..	..	1·50	1·60
1360	$1.20, Weightlifting	..	..	1·50	1·60
1358/60	..	..	Set of 3	3·25	3·25
1359/60 Optd "Specimen"	..	Set of 2	1·10	

(Des Marg Towt (30, 85 c., $1.35), Betina Ogden (35, 50, 60, 95 c.), S. Morrell (others). Litho McPherson's Ptg Group, Mulgrave)

1992 (13 Aug)–96. *Australian Wildlife (1st series). T 505 and similar horiz designs. Multicoloured.* P 14½×14½.

1361	30 c. Saltwater Crocodile (10.3.94)	..	..	50	35
1362	35 c. Type 505	..	..	50	40
1363	40 c. Platypus (12.8.93)	..	..	60	45
1364	50 c. Koala	..	..	70	55
1365	60 c. Common Bushtail Possum	..	..	75	65
1366	70 c. Laughing Kookaburra ("70 c" and "AUSTRALIA" in orange) (12.8.93)	..	..	60	65
	a. "70 c" and "AUSTRALIA" in orange-brown (3.96)	..		1·50	1·75
1367	85 c. Australian Pelican (10.3.94)	..	..	75	80
1368	90 c. Eastern Grey Kangaroo (12.8.93)	..	..	80	85
1369	95 c. Common Wombat	..	..	85	90
1370	$1.20, Major Mitchell's Cockatoo (12.8.93)	..	..	1·00	1·10
1371	$1.35, Emu (10.3.94)	..	..	1·75	1·50
1361/71	..	..	Set of 11	8·00	7·50

No. 1366a is from the 3 koala printing.
See also Nos. 1453/64.

506 Sydney Harbour Tunnel (value at left)   507 Warden's Courthouse, Coolgardie

(Des Sandra Harman. Litho Leigh-Mardon Ltd, Melbourne)

1992 (28 Aug). *Opening of Sydney Harbour Tunnel. T 506 and similar vert design. Multicoloured.* P 14½.

1375	45 c. Type 506	..	..	2·25	2·25
	a. Horiz pair. Nos. 1375/6	..		4·50	4·50
	b. Perf 15½	..		1·75	1·75
	ba. Horiz pair. Nos. 1375b/6b	..		3·50	3·50
1376	45 c. Sydney Harbour Tunnel (value at right)	..	..	2·25	2·25
	b. Perf 15½	..		1·75	1·75

Nos. 1375/6 were printed together, *se-tenant*, in horizontal pairs throughout the sheet, each pair forming a composite design.

(Des Janet Boschen. Litho Printset Cambec Pty Ltd)

1992 (17 Sept). *Centenary of Discovery of Gold at Coolgardie and Kalgoorlie. T 507 and similar horiz designs. Multicoloured.* P 14×14½.

1377	45 c. Type 507	..	..	60	45
1378	45 c. Post Office, Kalgoorlie	..	..	60	45
1379	$1.05, York Hotel, Kalgoorlie	..	..	1·50	1·60
1380	$1.20, Town Hall, Kalgoorlie	..	..	1·75	1·90
1377/80	..	..	Set of 4	4·00	4·00

508 Bowler of 1892   509 Children's Nativity Play

(Des Janet Boschen and M. Sofilas. Litho Leigh-Mardon Ltd, Melbourne)

1992 (15 Oct). *Centenary of Sheffield Shield Cricket Tournament. T 508 and similar vert design. Multicoloured.* P 14½.

| 1381 | 45 c. Type 508 | .. | .. | 85 | 45 |
| 1382 | $1.20, Batsman and wicket-keeper | .. | .. | 1·90 | 1·60 |

(Des C. Smith. Litho McPherson's Ptg Group, Mulgrave)

1992 (30 Oct). *Christmas. T 509 and similar horiz designs. Multicoloured.* P 14×14½.

1383	40 c. Type 509	..	..	55	40
	a. Booklet pane. No. 1383×20	..		9·00	
1384	45 c. Child waking on Christmas Day	..	..	60	45
1385	$1 Children carol singing	..	..	1·50	1·60
1383/5	..	..	Set of 3	2·40	2·25

The vertical edges of booklet pane No. 1383a are imperforate and there are margins at top and bottom.

510 "Ghost Gum, Central Australia" (Namatjira)   511 "Wild Onion Dreaming" (Pauline Nakamarra Woods)

(Des Janet Boschen. Litho McPherson's Ptg Group, Mulgrave)

1993 (14 Jan). *Australia Day. Paintings by Albert Namatjira. T 510 and similar horiz design. Multicoloured.* P 14×14½.

1386	45 c. Type 510	..	..	75	90
	a. Pair. Nos. 1386/7	..		1·50	1·75
1387	45 c. "Across the Plain to Mount Giles"	..	..	75	90

Nos. 1386/7 were printed together, *se-tenant*, in horizontal and vertical pairs throughout the sheet.

(Des C. Atkinson. Litho Printset Cambec Pty Ltd)

1993 (4 Feb). *"Dreamings". Paintings by Aboriginal Artists. T 511 and similar multicoloured designs.* P 14×14½ (horiz) or 14½×14 (vert).

1388	45 c. Type 511	..	..	60	45
1389	75 c. "Yam Plants" (Jack Wunuwun) (vert)	..	..	1·10	95
1390	85 c. "Goose Egg Hunt" (George Milpurrurru) (vert)	..	..	1·25	1·25
1391	$1 "Kalumpiwarra-Ngulalintji" (Rover Thomas)	..	..	1·40	1·40
1388/91	..	..	Set of 4	4·00	3·50

512 Uluru (Ayers Rock) National Park   513 Queen Elizabeth II on Royal Visit, 1992

(Des Lynette Brown. Litho McPherson's Ptg Group, Mulgrave)

1993 (4 Mar). *World Heritage Sites (1st series). T 512 and similar horiz designs. Multicoloured.* P 14½×14.

1392	45 c. Type 512	..	..	70	45
1393	85 c. Rain forest, Fraser Island	..	..	1·75	1·60
1394	95 c. Beach, Shark Bay	..	..	1·75	1·60
1395	$2 Waterfall, Kakadu	..	..	2·00	1·90
1392/5	..	..	Set of 4	5·50	5·00

See also Nos. 1582/5.

(Des Dianne Cook. Litho Printset Cambec Pty Ltd)

1993 (7 Apr). *Queen Elizabeth II's Birthday.* P 14½×14.
| 1396 | 513 | 45 c. multicoloured | .. | .. | 60 | 60 |

514 H.M.A.S. *Sydney* (cruiser, launched 1934) in Action   515 "Work in the Home"

(Des R. Shardlow and Sue Passmore. Litho McPherson's Ptg Group, Mulgrave)

1993 (7 Apr). *Second World War Naval Vessels. T **514** and similar horiz designs. Multicoloured. P* 14×14½.
1397	45 c. Type **514**	..	80	45
1398	85 c. H.M.A.S. *Bathurst* (minesweeper)	..	1·60	1·75
1399	$1.05, H.M.A.S. *Arunta* (destroyer)	..	1·75	2·10
1400	$1.20, *Centaur* (hospital ship) and tug (Optd S. £2) ..		2·00	2·10
1397/1400	.. ..	*Set of 4*	5·50	5·75

(Des G. Hogg. Litho McPherson's Ptg Group, Mulgrave)

1993 (7 May). *Working Life in the 1890s. T **515** and similar vert designs. Multicoloured. P* 14½×14.
1401	45 c. Type **515**	..	55	45
1402	45 c. "Work in the Cities"	..	55	45
1403	$1 "Work in the Country"	..	1·10	1·10
1404	$1.20, Trade Union banner	..	1·50	1·75
1401/4	.. .. ..	*Set of 4*	3·25	3·25

516 Centenary Special
Train, Tasmania, 1971

(Des Sue Passmore and J. Richards. Litho Prinset Cambec Pty Ltd)

1993 (1 June). *Australian Trains. T **516** and similar horiz designs.* (a) *Phosphorised paper. P* 14×14½.
1405	45 c. Type **516**	..	60	60
	a. Block of 6. Nos. 1405/10	..	3·25	
1406	45 c. "Spirit of Progress", Victoria	..	60	60
1407	45 c. "Western Endeavour", Western Australia, 1970		60	60
1408	45 c. "Silver City Comet", New South Wales	..	60	60
1409	45 c. Kuranda tourist train, Queensland		60	60
1410	45 c. "The Ghan", Northern Territory		60	60
1405/10	.. .. ..	*Set of 6*	3·25	3·25

(b) *Self-adhesive. Phosphor frame. P* 11½.
1411	45 c. Type **516**	..	70	85
	a. Booklet pane. Nos. 1411/12×2, 1413, 1414/15×2 and 1416		6·00	
1412	45 c. "Spirit of Progress", Victoria	..	70	85
1413	45 c. "Western Endeavour", Western Australia, 1970		70	85
1414	45 c. "Silver City Comet", New South Wales	..	70	85
1415	45 c. Kuranda tourist train, Queensland		70	85
1416	45 c. "The Ghan", Northern Territory		70	85
1411/16	.. .. ..	*Set of 6*	3·75	4·50

Nos. 1405/10 were printed together, *se-tenant,* in sheets of 100 (2 panes of 50 5×10) each pane providing five blocks of 6 and twenty single stamps.

Nos. 1411/16 occur in rolls of 100, on which the surplus self-adhesive paper around each stamp was removed, or in $4.50 booklets, containing No. 1411a, on which the surplus paper was retained.

The phosphor on both rolls and booklets, which shows pink under U.V. light, extends from the frame onto sections of the centre design.

COUNTER-PRINTED LABELS. Since 1960 the Australian Post Office used a number of different franking machines at post office counters issuing "POSTAGE PAID" labels. On 21 June 1993 a further type of self-adhesive label was introduced which incorporated Threatened Species designs as Nos. 1312/17 with the machine-printed face value as value. Possible face values of these labels ranged from 45 c. to $9,999.99. This was subsequently restricted to a top value of $100.

The labels were initially available at the National Philatelic Centre, Melbourne showing code "NPCI" and were subsequently available from Canberra Parliament House post office ("ACT 93" and "CPH1") and Royal Exchange, Sydney ("RX1").

517 "Black
Cockatoo Feather"
(Fiona Foley)

518 Conference Emblem

(Des Lynette Brown. Litho McPherson's Ptg Group, Mulgrave)

1993 (1 July). *International Year of Indigenous Peoples. Aboriginal Art. T **517** and similar multicoloured designs. P* 14½×14 (vert) or 14×14½ (horiz).
1417	45 c. Type **517**	..	55	45
1418	75 c. "Ngarrgooroon Country" (Hector Jandany) (horiz)	..	1·10	1·10

1419	$1 "Ngak Ngak" (Ginger Riley Munduwalawala) (horiz)	1·25	1·25
1420	$1.05, "Untitled" (Robert Cole) (Optd S. £2) ..	1·50	1·50
1417/20	.. ..	*Set of 4*	4·00	4·00

(Des Dianne Cook. Litho Leigh-Mardon Ltd, Melbourne)

1993 (2 Sept). *Inter-Parliamentary Union Conference and 50th Anniv of Women in Federal Parliament. T **518** and similar square design. Multicoloured. P* 14½.
1421	45 c. Type **518**	..	90	1·00
	a. Pair. Nos. 1421/2	..	1·75	2·00
1422	45 c. Dame Enid Lyons and Senator Dorothy Tangney		90	1·00

Nos. 1421/2 were printed together, *se-tenant,* in sheets of 25 (5×5) with a block of nine examples of No. 1422 (R. 2/2-4, 3/2-4, 4/2-4) surrounded by sixteen examples of No. 1421 (R. 1/1-5, 2/1, 2/5, 3/1, 3/5, 4/1, 4/5, 5/1-5).

These stamps also exist in reverse format showing No. 1421 as the centre block of nine. Such panes were prepared for inclusion in the Eminent Women portfolio which was jointly produced by Note Printing Australia and Australia Post. Examples from the portfolio were numbered in red or black with unnumbered panes also available by mail order.

519 Ornithocheirus

520 "Goodwill"

(Des P. Trusler and Sue Passmore)

1993 (1 Oct). *Prehistoric Animals. T **519** and similar multicoloured designs.* (a) *Litho McPherson's Ptg Group, Mulgrave. Phosphorised paper. P* 14×14½ (Nos. 1423, 1427) or 14½×14 (Nos. 1424/6, 1428).
1423	45 c. Type **519**	..	60	50
1424	45 c. Leaellynasaura (25×30 mm)	..	60	50
1425	45 c. Timimus (26×33 mm)	..	60	50
1426	45 c. Allosaurus (26×33 mm)	..	60	50
1427	75 c. Muttaburrasaurus (30×50 mm)	..	1·00	90
1428	$1.05, Minmi (50×30 mm)	..	1·50	1·50
1423/8	.. ..	*Set of 6*	4·50	4·00
MS1429	166×73 mm. Nos. 1423/8. P 14½	..	5·00	6·00

(b) *Litho Printset Cambec Pty Ltd. Self-adhesive. Phosphor background. P* 11½.
1430	45 c. Type **519**	..	65	75
	a. Booklet pane. Nos. 1430/1, each × 5		6·00	
1431	45 c. Leaellynasaura (25×30 mm)	..	65	75

No. MS1429 exists overprinted with the logos of "Bangkok '93" or Sydney Stamp and Coin Fair, 1993, for sale at these exhibitions.

Nos. 1430/1 occur either in rolls of 100 and 200, on which the surplus self-adhesive paper around each stamp was removed, or in $4.50 booklets, containing No. 1430a, on which the surplus paper was retained.

The phosphor on both rolls and booklets, which shows pink under U.V. light, covers much of the background of each design.

(Des Sandra Harman. Litho McPherson's Ptg Group, Mulgrave)

1993 (1 Nov). *Christmas. T **520** and similar vert designs. Multicoloured. P* 14½×14.
1432	40 c. Type **520**	..	50	45
	a. Booklet pane. No. 1432×20		8·50	
1433	45 c. "Joy"	..	50	45
1434	$1 "Peace"	..	1·50	1·60
1432/4	.. ..	*Set of 3*	2·25	2·25

The horizontal edges of booklet pane No. 1432a are imperforate and there are margins at right and left.

521 "Shoalhaven River Bank –
Dawn" (Arthur Boyd)

(Des Lynette Brown. Litho McPherson's Ptg Group, Mulgrave)

1994 (13 Jan). *Australia Day. Landscape Paintings. T **521** and similar multicoloured designs. P* 14×14½ ($2) or 14½×14 (others).
1435	45 c. Type **521**	..	60	45
1436	85 c. "Wimmera" (Sir Sidney Nolan)	..	1·40	1·40
1437	$1.05, "Lagoon, Wimmera" (Nolan)	..	1·60	1·60
1438	$2 "White Cockatoos with Flame Trees" (Boyd) (vert)		2·50	2·50
1435/8	.. ..	*Set of 4*	5·50	5·50

MINIMUM PRICE

The minimum price quote is 10p which represents a handling charge rather than a basis for valuing common stamps. For further notes about prices see introductory pages.

---

522 Teaching Lifesaving
Techniques

523 Rose

(Des O. Schmidinger, Christine Stead and Lynette Brown. Litho Printset Cambec Pty Ltd)

1994 (20 Jan). *Centenary of Organised Life Saving in Australia. T **522** and similar horiz designs. Multicoloured.*

(a) *Phosphorised paper. P* 14×14½.
1439	45 c. Type **522**	..	60	45
1440	45 c. Lifeguard on watch ..	..	60	45
1441	95 c. Lifeguard team	..	1·25	1·40
1442	$1.20, Lifeguards on surf boards	..	1·60	1·75
1439/42	..	*Set of 4*	3·75	3·75

(b) *Self-adhesive. Phosphor frame. P* 11½.
1443	45 c. Type **522**	..	65	85
	a. Booklet pane. Nos. 1443/4, each × 5		6·00	
1444	45 c. Lifeguard on watch ..	..	65	85

Nos. 1443/4 occur either in rolls of 100, on which the surplus self-adhesive paper around each stamp was removed, or in $4.50 booklets containing No. 1443a, on which the surplus paper was retained.

The phosphor on the rolls and booklets, which shows pink under U.V. light, extends onto the left or right corner of the centre designs.

(Des Sandra Harman. Litho McPherson's Ptg Group, Mulgrave)

1994 (3 Feb). *Greetings Stamps. Flower photographs by Lariane Fonseca. T **523** and similar vert designs. Multicoloured. P* 14½×14.
1445	45 c. Type **523**	..	40	45
1446	45 c. Tulips	..	40	45
	a. Horiz pair. Nos. 1446/7		80	90
	b. Booklet pane. Nos. 1446/7 each × 5	4·00	
1447	45 c. Poppies	..	40	45
1445/7	..	*Set of 3*	1·10	1·25

Nos. 1446/7 were printed together, *se-tenant,* in horizontal pairs throughout the sheet.

The vertical edges of booklet pane No. 1446b are imperforate, producing stamps imperforate at left (No. 1446) or right (No. 1447), and there are margins at top and bottom.

524 Bridge and
National Flags

525 "Queen
Elizabeth II" (Sir
William Dargie)

(Des W. Crossett and Sue Passmore. Litho McPherson's Ptg Group, Mulgrave)

1994 (8 Apr). *Opening of Friendship Bridge between Thailand and Laos. P* 14½×14.
1448	**524** 95 c. multicoloured	..	1·25	1·40

(Des Sue Passmore. Litho Leigh-Mardon Ltd, Melbourne)

1994 (8 Apr). *Queen Elizabeth II's Birthday. P* 14½.
1449	**525** 45 c. multicoloured	..	70	70

526 "Family in Field"
(Bobbie-Lea Blackmore)

527 Suffragettes

(Des Lynette Brown. Litho Leigh-Mardon Ltd, Melbourne)

1994 (14 Apr). *International Year of the Family. Children's Paintings. T **526** and similar horiz designs. Multicoloured. P* 14½.
1450	45 c. Type **526**	..	55	45
1451	75 c. "Family on Beach" (Kathryn Teoh)	1·00	1·10
1452	$1 "Family around Fire" (Maree McCarthy)		1·25	1·50
1450/2	..	*Set of 3*	2·50	2·75

Two types of inscr on Nos. 1453/5:
Type I. "KANGAROO" 9 mm long with spaces between letters.
Type II. "KANGAROO" 7 mm long without spaces between letters.

(Des Janet Boschen)

1994 (12 May)–97. *Australian Wildlife (2nd series). Horiz designs as T 505. Multicoloured. (a) Litho Leigh-Mardon Ltd, Melbourne (Nos. 1453/8) or SNP Cambec (Nos. 1453b/8b, 1453c/8c). Phosphorised paper. P* 14×14¹/₂.

1453	45 c. Kangaroo (pale orange inscr) (I)		60	50
	a. Block of 6. Nos. 1453/8		3·25	
	b. Type II. Orange-brown inscr (1.96)		70	60
	ba. Block of 6. Nos. 1453b/8b		3·75	
	c. Type II. Pale orange inscr (8.97)		60	50
	ca. Block of 6. Nos. 1453c/5c and 1456/8		3·25	
1454	45 c. Female kangaroo with young (pale orange inscr) (I)		60	50
	b. Type II. Orange-brown inscr (1.96)		70	60
	c. Type II. Pale orange inscr (8.97)		60	50
1455	45 c. Two kangaroos (pale orange inscr) (I)		60	50
	b. Type II. Orange-brown inscr (1.96)		70	60
	c. Type II. Pale orange inscr (8.97)		60	50
1456	45 c. Family of koalas on branch (pale orange inscr)		60	50
	b. Orange-brown inscr (1.96)		70	60
1457	45 c. Koala on ground (pale orange inscr)		60	50
	b. Orange-brown inscr (1.96)		70	60
1458	45 c. Koala asleep in tree (pale orange inscr)		60	50
	b. Orange-brown inscr (1.96)		70	60
1453/8		*Set of 6*	3·25	3·00

(b) *Litho Printset Cambec Pty Ltd. Self-adhesive. Phosphor frame. P* 11¹/₂

1459	45 c. Kangaroo		60	65
	a. Booklet pane. Nos. 1459/60×2, 1461 1462/3×2 and 1464		5·50	
	ab. Imperf pane			
	b. Sheetlet of 5. Nos. 1459 and 1461/4 (24.3.95)		2·75	
1460	45 c. Female kangaroo with young		60	65
1461	45 c. Two kangaroos		60	65
1462	45 c. Family of koalas on branch		60	65
1463	45 c. Koala on ground		60	65
1464	45 c. Koala asleep in tree		60	65
1459/64		*Set of 6*	3·25	3·50

(c) *Typo Pemara Labels, Victoria. Self-adhesive. Phosphor frame. P* 11¹/₂.

1464a	45 c. Kangaroo (5.95)		2·25	2·25
	ap. Phosphorised mesh (9.95)		70	70
1464b	45 c. Female kangaroo with young (5.95)		2·25	2·25
	bp. Phosphorised mesh (9.95)		70	70
1464c	45 c. Two kangaroos (5.95)		2·25	2·25
	cp. Phosphorised mesh (9.95)		70	70
1464d	45 c. Family of koalas on branch (5.95)		2·25	2·25
	dp. Phosphorised mesh (9.95)		70	70
1464e	45 c. Koala on ground (5.95)		2·25	2·25
	ep. Phosphorised mesh (9.95)		70	70
1464f	45 c. Koala asleep in tree (5.95)		2·25	2·25
	fp. Phosphorised mesh (9.95)		70	70
1464a/f		*Set of 6*	12·00	12·00
1464ap/fp		*Set of 6*	3·75	3·75

Nos. 1453/8 were printed together, *se-tenant*, in sheets of 100 (2 panes of 50 5×10) each pane providing five blocks of 6 and twenty single stamps. They also exist as a *se-tenant* sheetlet of 6 with inscribed margins produced for sale at "Philakorea '94" Stamp Exhibition Seoul.

The colour of the "AUSTRALIA" inscription and face value is repeated on a horizontal band at the foot of each design.

Nos. 1453b/8b are from the 2 koala printing and Nos. 1453c/5c from the 3 koala printing.

Nos. 1459/64 occur either in rolls of 100, rolls of 200, booklets of 10 or sheetlets of 5. On all rolls the surplus self-adhesive paper around each stamp was removed, but this was retained on booklet pane No. 1459a and sheetlet No. 1459b.

The phosphor on Nos. 1459/64 and Nos. 1464a/f, which shows pink under U.V. light, extends from bars at top and bottom onto sections of the centre designs. On Nos. 1464ap/fp, which come from the 3 koala, 4 koala, 1 kangaroo and 1 kangaroo + 2 koala printings, the phosphor extends over the same area; but is broken up by a mesh pattern into small squares or diamonds.

The Pemara printings were produced in rolls only.

Counter-printed labels, as described beneath No. 1416, in designs as Nos. 1453/64, but 40×28 mm, were issued on 17 November 1994. Possible face values for these labels ranged from 45 c. to $100. Machines issuing the labels were located at National Philatelic Centre, Melbourne ("NPC"), Canberra Parliament House post office ("CPH"), Royal Exchange ("REX") and Haymarket ("HAYMKT") post offices, Sydney, and at the General Post Offices in Adelaide ("ADEL GPO"), Brisbane ("BRIS GPO"), Melbourne ("MELB GPO"), Perth ("PERTH GPO") (from 26 June 1995) and Bathurst Street, Hobart ("BTH ST HBT") (from 16 October 1995). Exhibition labels were issued at "AEROPEX 94", "AUSTRAPEX 95", "SINGAPORE 95", "SYDNEY 95", "CAPEX 96" and "HONG KONG 97".

Very similar labels were produced from experimental "Weigh & Pay" machines used in the Perth area from May 1996 onwards. Those from Perth itself are inscribed "GPO PERTH" or "PERTH GPO", but labels from other post offices are without inscription.

For Nos. 1453b, 1454b and 1455b in miniature sheet for "CHINA '96" see No. MS1638.

(Des Maire Smith. Litho McPherson's Ptg Group, Mulgrave)

1994 (9 June). *Centenary of Women's Emancipation in South Australia. P* 14×14¹/₂.

1465	527	45 c. multicoloured	60	60

528 Bunyip from Aboriginal Legend

529 "Robert Menzies" (Sir Ivor Hele)

(Des J. Morrison (No. 1466), D. Lancashire (No. 1467), R. Brooks (No. 1468), Marg Towt (No. 1470). Litho Leigh-Mardon Ltd, Melbourne)

1994 (14 July). *The Bunyip (mythological monster). T 528 and similar square designs. Multicoloured. P* 14¹/₂.

1466	45 c. Type 528		60	60
	a. Pair. Nos. 1466/7		1·10	1·10
1467	45 c. Nature spirit bunyip		60	60
1468	90 c. "The Bunyip of Berkeley's Creek" (book illustration)		1·50	1·50
1469	$1.35, Bunyip as natural history		1·90	1·90
1466/9		*Set of 4*	4·00	4·00

Nos. 1466/7 were printed together, *se-tenant*, in horizontal or vertical pairs throughout the sheet.

(Des FHA Design. Litho McPherson's Ptg Group, Mulgrave)

1994 (11 Aug). *Wartime Prime Ministers. T 529 and similar horiz designs. Multicoloured. P* 14×14¹/₂.

1470	45 c. Type 529		65	65
	a. Horiz strip of 5. Nos. 1470/4		3·00	
1471	45 c. "Arthur Fadden" (William Dargie)		65	65
1472	45 c. "John Curtin" (Anthony Dattilo-Rubbo)		65	65
1473	45 c. "Francis Forde" (Joshua Smith)		65	65
1474	45 c. "Joseph Chifley" (A. D. Colquhoun)		65	65
1470/4		*Set of 5*	3·00	3·00

Nos. 1470/4 were printed together, *se-tenant*, in horizontal strips of 5 throughout the sheet.

530 Lawrence Hargrave and Box Kites

531 Scarlet Macaw

(Des Janet Boschen. Eng C. Slania. Recess Royal Swedish Stamp Ptg Office, Stockholm)

1994 (29 Aug). *Aviation Pioneers. T 530 and similar vert designs. P* 12¹/₂.

1475	45 c. red-brown, blackish olive & cinnamon		70	45
1476	45 c. red-brown, deep carmine and lavender		70	45
1477	$1.35, red-brown, dp violet & greenish bl		2·25	2·50
1478	$1.80, red-brown, slate-green & sage-grn		2·50	2·75
1475/8		*Set of 4*	5·50	5·50

Designs:—No. 1475, Type 530; No. 1476, Ross and Keith Smith with Vickers Vimy (first England-Australia flight); No. 1477, Ivor McIntyre, Stanley Goble and Fairey IIID seaplane (first aerial circumnavigation of Australia); No. 1478, Freda Thompson and De Havilland Moth Major *Christopher Robin* (first Australian woman to fly solo from England to Australia).

No. 1475 also exists as a pane of 25 numbered in red or black from a limited issue Hargrave portfolio.

Two types of phosphor on self-adhesive Type 531:
Type I. Leaf below second tail feather covered by phosphor
Type II. Leaf without phosphor

(Des G. Cook)

1994 (28 Sept). *Australian Zoos. Endangered Species. T 531 and similar multicoloured designs. (a) Litho McPherson's Ptg Group, Mulgrave. Phosphorised paper. P* 14×14¹/₂ (No. 1479) or 14¹/₂×14 (others).

1479	45 c. Type 531		65	55
1480	45 c. Cheetah (25×30 mm)		65	55
1481	45 c. Orang-Utan (26×37 mm)		65	55
1482	45 c. Fijian Crested Iguana (26×37 mm)		65	55
1483	$1 Asian Elephants (49×28 mm)		1·75	1·60
1479/83		*Set of 5*	3·50	3·50
MS1484	166×73 mm. Nos. 1479/83. P 14¹/₂		4·00	4·25

(b) *Litho Printset Cambec Pty Ltd. Self-adhesive. Phosphor frame. P* 11¹/₂

1485	45 c. Type 531 (I)		1·00	1·25
	a. Type II		1·00	1·25
	b. Booklet pane. Nos. 1485×4, 1485a×2 and 1486×4		9·00	
1486	45 c. Cheetah		1·00	1·25

No. MS1484 exists overprinted with the logos of the Sydney Stamp and Coin Fair, Brisbane Stamp and Coin Fair, "Stampshow Melbourne '94" or "Swanpex '94" (including one with overprint inverted) for sale at these Australian exhibitions.

Nos. 1485/6 occur in $4.50 booklets, containing No. 1485b.

The phosphor on the booklets, which shows pink under U.V. light, appears as an irregular frame to each design.

532 "Madonna and Child" (detail, "The Adoration of the Magi") (Giovanni Toscani)

533 Yachts outside Sydney Harbour

(Des Lisa Christenson. Litho McPherson's Ptg Group, Mulgrave)

1994 (31 Oct). *Christmas. T 532 and similar designs showing "The Adoration of the Magi" by Giovanni Toscani. Multicoloured. P* 14¹/₂×14 (40 c., $1.80) or 14×14¹/₂ (45 c., $1).

1487	40 c. Type 532		60	40
	a. Booklet pane. No. 1487×20		8·50	
1488	45 c. "Wise Man and Horse" (detail) (horiz)		60	45
1489	$1 "Wise Man and St. Joseph" (detail) (horiz)		1·50	1·40
1490	$1.80, Complete painting (49×29 mm)		2·00	2·50
1487/90		*Set of 4*	4·25	4·25

The vertical edges of booklet pane No. 1487a are imperforate and there are margins at top and bottom.

(Des J. Spatchurst)

1994 (31 Oct). *50th Sydney to Hobart Yacht Race. T 533 and similar horiz design. (a) Litho Leigh-Mardon Ltd, Melbourne. Phosphorised paper. P* 14¹/₂.

1491	45 c. Type 533		50	55
	a. Pair. Nos. 1491/2		1·00	1·10
1492	45 c. Yachts passing Tasmania coastline		50	55

(b) *Litho Printset Cambec Pty Ltd. Self-adhesive. Phosphor frame. P* 11¹/₂.

1493	45 c. Type 533 (31×20 mm)		50	55
1494	45 c. Yachts passing Tasmania coastline (31×20 mm)		50	55

Nos. 1491/2 were printed together, *se-tenant*, in horizontal and vertical pairs throughout the sheet.

Nos. 1493/4 occur in rolls of 100. The phosphor, which shows pink under U.V. light, appears as an irregular frame to each design.

534 Symbolic Kangaroo

535 "Back Verandah" (Russell Drysdale)

(Des Sandra Harman and J. Passmore. Typo (gold die-stamped) Pemara Labels)

1994 (2 Nov)–96. *Self-adhesive. Automatic Cash Machine Stamps. Phosphorised paper. P* 16¹/₂.

1495	534	45 c. gold, emerald and dull blue-green	50	50
	a. Pane of 20. Nos. 1495/1502		9·00	
	ab. Pane of 20. Nos. 1495/7, 1498a, 1499/1501 and 1502a (11.4.96)		9·00	
1496		45 c. gold, emerald and cobalt	50	50
1497		45 c. gold, emerald and bright lilac	50	50
1498		45 c. gold, emerald and apple-green (grey-brown dots in background)	50	50
	a. Emerald dots in background (11.4.96)			
1499		45 c. gold, emerald & pale yellow-green	50	50
1500		45 c. gold, emerald and pink	50	50
1501		45 c. gold, emerald and rose	50	50
1502		45 c. gold, emerald and yellow-ochre (grey-brown dots in background)	50	50
	a. Emerald dots in background (11.4.96)			
1495/1502		*Set of 8*	4·00	4·00

Nos. 1495/1502 were issued in panes of 20 from automatic cash machines at Advance Bank branches in Australian Capital Territory, New South Wales and Queensland, and from the National Philatelic Centre, Melbourne. The stamps were arranged, *tête-bêche*, in horizontal rows of 3 or 4 with the pane containing two examples of Nos. 1495, 1497, 1499 and 1501 and three of Nos. 1496, 1498, 1500 and 1502. As originally issued the backing paper carried advertising for the Advance Bank. A second version advertising Postpak packaging was introduced on 11 April 1996 and contained Nos. 1495/7, 1498a, 1499/1501 and 1502a.

(Des Allnutt Graphics. Litho Leigh-Mardon Ltd, Melbourne)

1995 (12 Jan). *Australia Day. Paintings. T 535 and similar horiz designs. Multicoloured. P* 15×14¹/₂.

1503	45 c. Type 535		50	45
1504	45 c. "Skull Springs Country" (Guy Grey-Smith)		50	45
1505	$1.05, "Outcamp" (Robert Juniper)		1·40	1·50
1506	$1.20, "Kite Flying" (Ian Fairweather)		1·50	1·50
1503/6		*Set of 4*	3·50	3·50

536 Red Heart and Rose

537 Endeavour Replica at Sea

(Des Kim Roberts. Litho Printset Cambec Pty Ltd, (gold die-stamped Avon Graphics))

1995 (30 Jan). *St. Valentine's Day. T 536 and similar vert designs. Multicoloured. P* 14¹/₂×14.

1507	45 c. Type 536		45	55
	a. Horiz strip of 5. Nos. 1507/8×2 and 1509		2·10	
1508	45 c. Gold and red heart with rose		45	55
1509	45 c. Gold heart and roses		45	55
1507/9		*Set of 3*	1·25	1·50

Nos. 1507/9 were printed together, *se-tenant*, in horizontal strips of 5 throughout the sheet each containing two examples of Nos. 1507/8 and one of No. 1509.

(Des Michelle Gauci. Litho McPherson's Ptg Group, Mulgrave)

1995 (9 Feb). *Completion of* Endeavour *Replica.* T **537** *and similar horiz design. Multicoloured.* (a) *Sheet stamps,* 38×26 *mm.* P 14×14½.
1510	45 c. Type **537**	65	65
	a. Pair. Nos. 1510/11	1·25	1·25
1511	45 c. "Captain Cook's Endeavour" (detail) (Oswald Brett)	65	65

(b) *Booklet stamps,* 44×26 *mm.* P 14×*imperf*
1512	20 c. Type **537**	1·00	1·25
	a. Booklet pane. Nos. 1512 and 1513×4	2·50	
1513	45 c. As No. 1511	45	50

Nos. 1510/11 are printed together, *se-tenant*, in horizontal and vertical pairs throughout the sheet.
The 20 c. value was only available from $2 stamp booklets. The vertical edges of pane No. 1512a are imperforate and there are margins at top and bottom.

538 Coalport Plate and
Bracket Clock, Old
Government House,
Parramatta

(Des Janet Boschen. Recess Note Ptg Branch, Reserve Bank of Australia)

1995 (16 Mar). *50th Anniv of Australian National Trusts.* T **538** *and similar horiz designs.* P 14×14½.
1514	45 c. deep violet-blue and purple-brown	45	45
	a. Pair. Nos. 1514/15	90	90
1515	45 c. deep blue-green and purple-brown	45	45
1516	$1 brown-red and royal blue	1·00	95
1517	$2 blackish olive and royal blue	1·90	1·90
1514/17	*Set of* 4	3·50	3·75

Designs:—No. 1515, Steiner doll and Italian-style chair, Ayers House, Adelaide; No. 1516, "Advance Australia" teapot and parian-ware statuette, Victoria; No. 1517, Silver bowl and china urn, Old Observatory, Perth.
Nos. 1514/15 were printed together, *se-tenant*, in horizontal and vertical pairs throughout the sheet.

539 Light Opal

(Des Sue Passmore. Litho Printset Cambec Pty Ltd (exelgrams by Avon Graphics))

1995 (5 Apr). *Opals.* T **539** *and similar horiz design. Multicoloured.* P 14½×14.
1518	$1.20, Type **539**	1·60	1·25
1519	$2.50, Black opal	3·00	3·25

The opals depicted on Nos. 1518/19 are produced as exelgrams (holographic printing on an ultra thin plastic film) embossed onto the stamps.

540 Queen Elizabeth
II at Gala Concert,
1992

541 Sir Edward
Dunlop and P.O.W.
Association Badge

(Des Nuttshell Graphics. Litho Leigh-Mardon Ltd, Melbourne)

1995 (20 Apr). *Queen Elizabeth II's Birthday.* P 14½.
1520	**540** 45 c. multicoloured	65	75

Two types of phosphor on Nos. 1527/8:
Type I. Phosphor at right ends level with hat or cap (coils)
Type II. Phosphor at right extends to the ear (No. 1527a) or shoulder (No. 1528a) (booklets)

(Des Sue Passmore)

1995 (20 Apr). *Australian Second World War Heroes* (1st series). T **541** *and similar vert designs. Multicoloured.* (a) *Litho McPherson's Ptg Group, Mulgrave. Phosphorised paper.* P 14½×14.
1521	45 c. Type **541**	60	60
	a. Block of 4. Nos. 1521/4	2·25	
1522	45 c. Mrs. Jessie Vasey and War Widows' Guild badge	60	60
1523	45 c. Sgt. Tom Derrick and Victoria Cross	60	60
1524	45 c. Flt. Sgt. Rawdon Middleton and Victoria Cross	60	60
1521/4	*Set of* 4	2·25	2·25

(b) *Litho Printset Cambec Pty Ltd. Self-adhesive. Designs* 21×32½ *mm. Phosphor frame.* P 11½
1525	45 c. Type **541** (I)	60	70
	a. Booklet pane. Nos. 1525×4 and 1526, 1527a/8a, each × 2	6·00	
1526	45 c. Mrs. Jessie Vasey and War Widows' Guild badge	70	80
1527	45 c. Sgt. Tom Derrick and Victoria Cross (I)	70	80
	a. Type II	70	80
1528	45 c. Flt. Sgt. Rawdon Middleton and Victoria Cross (I)	70	80
	a. Type II	70	80
1525/8	*Set of* 4	2·40	2·75

Nos. 1521/4 were printed together, *se-tenant*, in sheets of 100 (2 panes of 50 10×5) each pane providing ten blocks of 4 and ten single stamps.
Nos. 1525/8 occur either in rolls of 100, on which the surplus self-adhesive paper around each stamp was removed, or in $4.50 booklets, containing No. 1525a, on which the surplus paper was retained.
The phosphor, which shows pink under U.V. light, covers the designs, with the exception of the portraits and emblems, and the backing paper on both the booklets and the rolls.
See also Nos. 1545/8

542 Children and Globe of
Flags

543 *The Story of
the Kelly Gang*

(Des FHA Design. Litho McPherson's Ptg Group, Mulgrave)

1995 (11 May). *50th Anniv of United Nations.* P 14×14½.
1529	**542** 45 c. multicoloured	75	75

No. 1529 was printed in sheets with *se-tenant* 10×26 *mm* labels. In rows 1, 3, 5, 7 and 9 these labels occur on the right of each stamp and commemorate either the 50th anniversary or the F.A.O. alternately. On rows 2, 4, 6, 8 and 10 the labels occur on the left of each stamp and are inscribed for either U.N.E.S.C.O. or U.N.I.C.E.F.

(Des J. Spatchurst)

1995 (8 June). *Centenary of Cinema.* T **543** *and similar vert designs showing scenes from films. Multicoloured.* (a) *Litho McPherson's Ptg Group, Mulgrave. Phosphorised paper.* P 14½×14.
1530	45 c. Type **543**	60	60
	a. Horiz strip of 5. Nos. 1530/4	2·75	
1531	45 c. *On Our Selection*	60	60
1532	45 c. *Jedda*	60	60
1533	45 c. *Picnic at Hanging Rock*	60	60
1534	45 c. *Strictly Ballroom*	60	60
1530/4	*Set of* 5	2·75	2·75

(b) *Litho Printset Cambec Pty Ltd. Self-adhesive. Designs* 19×30½ *mm. Phosphor frame.* P 11½.
1535	45 c. Type **543**	60	60
	a. Booklet pane. Nos. 1535/9 each × 2	5·50	
1536	45 c. *On Our Selection*	60	60
1537	45 c. *Jedda*	60	60
1538	45 c. *Picnic at Hanging Rock*	60	60
1539	45 c. *Strictly Ballroom*	60	60
1535/9	*Set of* 5	2·75	2·75

Nos. 1530/4 were printed together, *se-tenant*, in horizontal strips of 5 throughout the sheet.
Nos. 1535/9 occur either in rolls of 100, on which the surplus self-adhesive paper around each stamp was removed, or in $4.50 booklets, containing No. 1535a, on which the surplus paper was retained.

544 Man in
Wheelchair flying
Kite

545 Koala with Cub

(Des Tracie Grimwood. Litho McPherson's Ptg Group, Mulgrave)

1995 (13 July). *People with Disabilities.* T **544** *and similar vert design. Multicoloured.* P 14½×14.
1540	45 c. Type **544**	65	65
	a. Horiz pair. Nos. 1540/1	1·25	1·25
1541	45 c. Blind woman playing violin	65	65

Nos. 1540/1 were printed together, *se-tenant*, in horizontal pairs throughout the sheet.

(Adapted L. Dolan. Recess Note Ptg Branch, Reserve Bank of Australia)

1995 (10 Aug). *50th Anniv of Peace in the Pacific. Designs as* 1946 *Victory Commemoration* (Nos. 213/15) *redrawn with new face values.* P 14×14½ (*horiz*) *or* 14½×14 (*vert*).
1542	53	45 c. scarlet	60	60
1543	—	45 c. green	60	60
1544	—	$1.50, blue	1·75	2·25
1542/4		*Set of* 3	2·75	3·00

Designs: *Vert*—No. 1543, Angel. *Horiz*—No. 1544, Flag and dove.

(Des Sue Passmore. Litho McPherson's Ptg Group, Mulgrave)

1995 (10 Aug). *Australian Second World War Heroes* (2nd series). *Vert designs as* T **541**. *Multicoloured.* P 14½×14.
1545	45 c. Sister Ellen Savage and George Medal	60	60
	a. Block of 4. Nos. 1545/8	2·25	
1546	45 c. Chief Petty Officer Percy Collins and Distinguished Service Medal and Bar	60	60
1547	45 c. Lt-Comm. Leon Goldsworthy and George Cross	60	60
1548	45 c. Warrant Officer Len Waters and R.A.A.F. wings	60	60
1545/8	*Set of* 4	2·25	2·25

Nos. 1545/8 were printed together, *se-tenant*, in sheets of 100 (2 panes of 50 10×5) each pane providing ten blocks of 4 and ten single stamps.

PRINTERS. Leigh-Mardon Ltd ceased printing Australian stamps in May 1995. On 10 July 1995 Singapore National Printer Pty Ltd took over Printset Cambec and the firm was then known as SNP Cambec.

(Des Xu Yanbo and Lisa Christensen. Litho SNP Cambec (Nos. 1549/50) or Postage Stamp Ptg Works, Peking (No. **MS**1551))

1995 (1 Sept). *Australia–China Joint Issue. Endangered Species.* T **545** *and similar horiz design. Multicoloured.* P 14½×14.
1549	45 c. Type **545**	70	70
	a. Pair. Nos. 1549/50	1·40	1·40
1550	45 c. Giant Panda with cubs	70	70
MS1551	Two sheets, each 106×70 mm. (a) No. 1549. (b) No. 1550. P 11×11½ .. *Set of* 2 *sheets*	1·60	1·60

Nos. 1549/50 were printed together, *se-tenant*, in horizontal and vertical pairs throughout the sheet.
No. **MS**1551a also exists overprinted "AUSTRALIAN STAMP EXHIBITION" and No. **MS**1551b "INTERNATIONAL STAMP & COIN EXPO BEIJING" for sale at these exhibitions in China.

546 Father Joseph
Slattery, Thomas Lyle
and Walter Filmer
(Radiology)

547 Flatback Turtle

(Des O. Schmidinger, Christine Stead and Melinda Whitechurch. Litho McPherson's Ptg Group, Mulgrave)

1995 (7 Sept). *Medical Scientists.* T **546** *and similar multicoloured designs.* P 14×14½ (*horiz*) *or* 14½×14 (*vert*).
1552	45 c. Type **546**	60	70
	a. Pair. Nos. 1552/3	1·10	1·40
1553	45 c. Dame Jean Macnamara and Sir Macfarlane Burnet (viruses)	60	70
1554	45 c. Fred Hollows (ophthalmology) (*vert*)	60	60
1555	$2.50, Sir Howard Florey (antibiotics) (*vert*)	3·75	4·50
1552/5	*Set of* 4	5·00	6·00

Nos. 1552/3 were printed together, *se-tenant*, in horizontal and vertical pairs throughout the sheet.
It was intended that 45 c. gutter blocks for philatelic sale would be produced in special sheets, but these were withdrawn just prior to issue when it was found that the gutter pairs contained two examples of the same design, instead of one of each.
No. 1555 also exists as a pane of 10 numbered in red or black from a limited issue Howard Florey portfolio.

Two types of phosphor on self-adhesive Type **547**:
Type I. Outcrop at bottom left completely covered by phosphor (coils).
Type II. Only part of outcrop covered by phosphor (booklets)

(Des G. Ryan. Litho SNP Cambec)

1995 (3 Oct). *Marine Life.* T **547** *and similar horiz designs.* (a) *Phosphorised paper.* P 14×14½.
1556	45 c. Type **547**	45	55
	a. Vert pair. Nos. 1556/7	90	1·10
1557	45 c. Flame Angelfish and Nudibranch	45	55
1558	45 c. Potato Grouper ("Potato Cod") and Hump-headed Wrasse ("Maori Wrasse")	45	55
	a. Vert pair. Nos. 1558/9	90	1·10
1559	45 c. Giant Trevally	45	55
1560	45 c. Black Marlin	45	55
	a. Vert pair. Nos. 1560/1	90	1·10
1561	45 c. Mako and Tiger Sharks	45	55
1556/61	*Set of* 6	2·40	3·00
MS1562	166×73 mm. As Nos. 1556/61, but without lighter frame	3·00	3·00

(b) *Self-adhesive. Phosphor frame on three sides.* P 11½
1563	45 c. Type **547** (I)	45	60
	a. Type II	45	60
	ab. Booklet pane Nos. 1563a/6, each × 2, and Nos. 1567/8	4·25	
1564	45 c. Flame Angelfish and Nudibranch	45	60
1565	45 c. Potato Cod and Maori Wrasse	45	60
1566	45 c. Giant Trevally	45	60
1567	45 c. Black Marlin	45	60
1568	45 c. Mako and Tiger Sharks	45	60
1563/8	*Set of* 6	2·40	3·25

Nos. 1556/7, 1558/9 and 1560/1 were printed together, *se-tenant*, in vertical pairs throughout the sheets. Parts of No. **MS**1562 are printed in luminescent ink.
No. **MS**1562 also exists overprinted with the logos of the Adelaide Stamp and Collectables Fair, Sydney Centrepoint 95 National Stamp Exhibition, Brisbane Stamp Show, Melbourne Stamp and Coin Fair and "Swanpex WA", Perth, for sale at these Australian exhibitions.

Nos. 1563/8 occur either in rolls of 100, on which the surplus self-adhesive paper around each stamp was removed, or in $4.50 booklets, containing No. 1563ab, on which the surplus paper was retained.

The phosphor on both rolls and booklets shows pink under U.V. light.

548 "Madonna and Child"	**549** "West Australian Banksia" (Margaret Preston)

(Des Dianne Cook. Litho SNP Cambec)

1995 (1 Nov). *Christmas. Stained-glass Windows from Our Lady Help of Christians Church, Melbourne.* T **548** *and similar vert designs.* (a) *Phosphorised paper.* P 14½×14.

1569	40 c. Type **548**		45	45
1570	45 c. "Angel carrying the Gloria banner"		45	45
1571	$1 "Rejoicing Angels"		1·10	1·25
1569/71		Set of 3	1·75	1·90

(b) *Self-adhesive. Phosphor frame.* P 11½

1572	40 c. Type **548**		40	45
	a. Booklet pane. No. 1572×20		7·75	

No. 1572, on which the phosphor shows pink under U.V. light, was only issued in $8 booklets, on which the surplus self-adhesive paper was retained.

(Des Susan Horvath. Litho McPherson's Ptg Group, Mulgrave)

1996 (16 Jan). *Australia Day. Paintings.* T **549** *and similar multicoloured designs.* P 14×14½ (vert) or 14½×14 (horiz).

1573	45 c. Type **549**		55	45
1574	85 c. "The Babe is Wise" (Lina Bryans)		1·25	1·25
1575	$1 "The Bridge in Curve" (Grace Cossington Smith) (horiz)		1·40	1·25
1576	$1.20, "Beach Umbrellas" (Vida Lahey) (horiz)		1·50	1·50
1573/6		Set of 4	4·25	4·00

550 Gold Heart and Rose	**551** Bristol Type 156 Beaufighter and Curtiss P-40E Kittyhawk I

(Des Kim Roberts and Sandra Harman. Litho SNP Cambec (gold die-stamped Avon Graphics))

1996 (30 Jan). *St. Valentine's Day.* P 14×14½.

1577	**550** 45 c. multicoloured		50	50

(Des Melinda Whitechurch and N. Clifford. Litho SNP Cambec)

1996 (26 Feb). *Military Aviation.* T **551** *and similar horiz designs. Multicoloured.* P 14×14½.

1578	45 c. Type **551**		75	75
	a. Block of 4. Nos. 1578/81		2·75	
1579	45 c. Hawker Sea Fury and Fairey Firefly		75	75
1580	45 c. Bell Kiowa helicopters		75	75
1581	45 c. Government Aircraft Factory Hornets		75	75
1578/81		Set of 4	2·75	2·75

Nos. 1578/81 were printed together, *se-tenant*, in different combinations throughout the pane of 25, giving four blocks of 4 and nine single stamps.

552 Tasmanian Wilderness	**553** Australian Spotted Cuscus

(Des Dianne Cook. Litho SNP Cambec)

1996 (14 Mar). *World Heritage Sites (2nd series).* T **552** *and similar horiz designs. Multicoloured.* P 14½×14.

1582	45 c. Type **552**		50	45
1583	75 c. Willandra Lakes		90	90
1584	95 c. Naracoorte Fossil Cave		1·25	1·25
1585	$1 Lord Howe Island		1·50	1·60
1582/5		Set of 4	3·75	3·75

(Des Rosemary Ganf and Josephine Mure. Litho SNP Cambec)

1996 (22 Mar). *Australia–Indonesia Joint Issue.* T **553** *and similar vert design. Multicoloured.* P 14½×14.

1586	45 c. Type **553**		55	55
	a. Horiz pair. Nos. 1586/7		1·10	1·10
1587	45 c. Indonesian Bear Cuscus		55	55
MS1588	106×70 mm. Nos. 1586/7		1·25	1·25

Nos. 1586/7 were printed together, *se-tenant*, in horizontal pairs throughout the sheet.

No. MS1588 also exists overprinted "WORLD PHILATELIC YOUTH EXHIBITION PAMERAN FILATELI REMAJA DUNIA INDONESIA '96" and emblem for sale at this exhibition.

554 Head of Queen Elizabeth II	**555** North Melbourne Players

(Des Pendulum Design. Recess and litho Note Ptg Branch, Reserve Bank of Australia and SNP Cambec)

1996 (11 Apr). *Queen Elizabeth II's Birthday.* P 14×14½.

1589	**554** 45 c. multicoloured		55	55

Numbered gutter strips of ten, overprinted to commemorate the 30th anniversary of decimal currency in Australia, come from a limited issue Queen Elizabeth II portfolio.

(Des Rankin Bevers Design and B. Clinton. Litho SNP Cambec)

1996 (23 Apr). *Centenary of Australian Football League.* T **555** *and similar vert designs each showing players from a different team. Multicoloured.* (a) *Phosphorised paper.* P 14½×14.

1590	45 c. Type **555**		60	65
	a. Sheetlet. Nos. 1590/1605		8·75	
1591	45 c. Brisbane (red and yellow shirt)		60	65
1592	45 c. Sydney (red and white shirt)		60	65
1593	45 c. Carlton (black shirt with white emblem)		60	65
1594	45 c. Adelaide (black, red and yellow shirt)		60	65
1595	45 c. Fitzroy (yellow, red and blue shirt)		60	65
1596	45 c. Richmond (black shirt with yellow diagonal stripe)		60	65
1597	45 c. St. Kilda (red, white and black shirt)		60	65
1598	45 c. Melbourne (black shirt with red top)		60	65
1599	45 c. Collingwood (black and white vertical striped shirt)		60	65
1600	45 c. Fremantle (green, red, white and blue shirt)		60	65
1601	45 c. Footscray (blue, white and red shirt)		60	65
1602	45 c. West Coast (deep blue shirt with yellow stripes)		60	65
1603	45 c. Essendon (black shirt with red stripe)		60	65
1604	45 c. Geelong (black and white horizontal striped shirt)		60	65
1605	45 c. Hawthorn (black and yellow vertical striped shirt)		60	65
1590/1605		Set of 16	8·75	9·50

(b) *Self-adhesive. Phosphor frame at top and left.* P 11½.

1606	45 c. Type **555**		60	65
	a. Booklet pane. No. 1606×10		5·50	
1607	45 c. Brisbane		60	65
	a. Booklet pane. No. 1607×10		5·50	
1608	45 c. Sydney		60	65
	a. Booklet pane. No. 1608×10		5·50	
1609	45 c. Carlton		60	65
	a. Booklet pane. No. 1609×10		5·50	
1610	45 c. Adelaide		60	65
	a. Booklet pane. No. 1610×10		5·50	
1611	45 c. Fitzroy		60	65
	a. Booklet pane. No. 1611×10		5·50	
1612	45 c. Richmond		60	65
	a. Booklet pane. No. 1612×10		5·50	
1613	45 c. St. Kilda		60	65
	a. Booklet pane. No. 1613×10		5·50	
1614	45 c. Melbourne		60	65
	a. Booklet pane. No. 1614×10		5·50	
1615	45 c. Collingwood		60	65
	a. Booklet pane. No. 1615×10		5·50	
1616	45 c. Fremantle		60	65
	a. Booklet pane. No. 1616×10		5·50	
1617	45 c. Footscray		60	65
	a. Booklet pane. No. 1617×10		5·50	
1618	45 c. West Coast		60	65
	a. Booklet pane. No. 1618×10		5·50	
1619	45 c. Essendon		60	65
	a. Booklet pane. No. 1619×10		5·50	
1620	45 c. Geelong		60	65
	a. Booklet pane. No. 1620×10		5·50	
1621	45 c. Hawthorn		60	65
	a. Booklet pane. No. 1621×10		5·50	
1606/21		Set of 16	8·75	9·50

Nos. 1590/1605 were printed together, *se-tenant*, in sheetlets of 16.

Nos. 1606/21 were only available in $4.50 booklets. The phosphor shows pink under U.V. light.

556 Leadbeater's Possum	**557** Edwin Flack (800 and 1500 metres gold medal winner, 1896)

(Des Rankin Bevers Design).

1996 (9 May)–97. *Fauna and Flora.* T **556** *and similar multicoloured designs.*

(a) *Litho McPherson's Ptg Group, Mulgrave* (5 c., 10 c., $2, $5) *or SNP Cambec* (others) (gold on $10 die-stamped Avon Graphics). *Phosphorised paper.* P 14½×14 ($10) *or* 14×14½ (others).

1622	5 c. Type **556**		10	10
1623	10 c. Powerful Owl		10	15
1624	20 c. Saltwater Crocodile (10.4.97)		15	20
1625	25 c. Northern Dwarf Tree Frog (10.4.97)		20	25
1626	45 c. Comb-crested Jacana (2.6.97)		40	45
	a. Block of 4. Nos. 1626/9		1·60	
1627	45 c. Little Kingfisher (2.6.97)		40	45
1628	45 c. Brolga (2.6.97)		40	45
1629	45 c. Black-necked Stork ("Jabiru") (2.6.97)		40	45
1630	$1 Cressida cressida (butterfly) (10.4.97)		90	95
1631	$2 Blackwood Wattle		1·75	1·90
1632	$5 Soft Tree Fern and Mountain Ash (30×50 mm)		4·25	4·50
1633	$10 Kakadu Wetlands (50×30 mm) (10.4.97)		8·75	9·00
1622/33		Set of 12	17·50	18·50
MS1633a	106×70 mm. No. 1633 (10.4.97)		8·75	9·00

No. MS1633a was issued in connection with the forthcoming "Australia 99" International Stamp Exhibition. It also exists overprinted with the "PACIFIC 97" logo for sale at this International Stamp Exhibition in San Francisco.

A further miniature sheet containing Nos. 1628/9 was sold at the "International Stamp and Coin Exposition Shanghai 97" and from philatelic outlets.

(b) *Self-adhesive. Litho SNP Cambec* (Nos. 1634/7) *or Pemara* (Nos. 1634c/7c). *Phosphor frame.* P 11½

1634	45 c. Comb-crested Jacana (2.6.97)		40	45
	a. Booklet pane. Nos. 1634 and 1636, each × 3, and Nos. 1635 and 1637, each × 2		4·00	
	b. Sheetlet. Nos. 1634×2 and 1635/7		2·00	
	c. Perf 12½×13 (13.11.97)		40	45
1635	45 c. Little Kingfisher (2.6.97)		40	45
	c. Perf 12½×13 (13.11.97)		40	45
1636	45 c. Brolga (2.6.97)		40	45
	c. Perf 12½×13 (13.11.97)		40	45
1637	45 c. Black-necked Stork (2.6.97)		40	45
	c. Perf 12½×13 (13.11.97)		40	45
1634/7		Set of 4	1·60	1·75

Nos. 1634/7 and 1634c/7c were printed in rolls of 100 with the surplus paper around each stamp removed. Nos. 1634/7 also come in $4.50 booklets, containing No. 1634a, and sheetlets of 5, both of which have the surplus paper in place.

The phosphor shows orange-pink under U.V. light and appears as a broken frame around each stamp.

(Des Janet Boschen. Litho McPherson's Ptg Group, Mulgrave)

1996 (18 May). *"CHINA '96" 9th Asian International Stamp Exhibition, Peking. Sheet 120×65 mm, containing Nos. 1453b, 1454b and 1455b. Multicoloured.* P 14½×14½.

MS1638	45 c. Kangaroo; 45 c. Female kangaroo with young; 45 c. Two kangaroos		1·75	1·90

(Des Pendulum Design. Eng L. Dolan. Recess and litho Note Ptg Branch, Reserve Bank of Australia and SNP Cambec)

1996 (6 June). *Centennial Olympic Games and 10th Paralympic Games, Atlanta.* T **557** *and similar horiz designs. Multicoloured.* P 14×14½.

1639	45 c. Type **557**		70	70
	a. Pair. Nos. 1639/40		1·40	1·40
1640	45 c. Fanny Durack (100 metres freestyle swimming gold medal winner, 1912)		70	70
1641	$1.05, Wheelchair athletes		1·60	1·60
1639/41		Set of 3	2·75	2·75

Nos. 1639/40 were printed together, *se-tenant*, in horizontal and vertical pairs throughout the sheet.

558 Animalia (Graeme Base)	**559** American Bald Eagle, Kangaroo and Olympic Flame

(Des Pendulum Design. Litho SNP Cambec)

1996 (4 July). *50th Anniv of Children's Book Council Awards.* T **558** *and similar horiz designs taken from book covers.*

(a) *Phosphorised paper.* P 14×14½.

1642	45 c. Type **558**		60	60
	a. Block of 4. Nos. 1642/5		2·25	
1643	45 c. Greetings from Sandy Beach (Bob Graham)		60	60
1644	45 c. Who Sank the Boat? (Pamela Allen)		60	60
1645	45 c. John Brown, Rose and the Midnight Cat (Jenny Wagner, illustrated by Ron Brooks)		60	60
1642/5		Set of 4	2·25	2·25

(b) *Self-adhesive. Phosphor frame.* P 11½

1646	45 c. Type **558**		60	60
	a. Booklet pane. Nos. 1646×4 and 1647/9 each × 2		5·50	
1647	45 c. Greetings from Sandy Beach (Bob Graham)		60	60
1648	45 c. Who Sank the Boat? (Pamela Allen)		60	60
1649	45 c. John Brown, Rose and the Midnight Cat (Jenny Wagner, illustrated by Ron Brooks)		60	60
1649/9		Set of 4	2·25	2·25

Nos. 1642/5 were printed together, *se-tenant*, in sheets of 50 (2 panes of 25 5×5) each pane providing ten blocks of 4 and ten single stamps.

Nos. 1646/9 occur either in rolls of 100, on which the surplus self-adhesive paper around each stamp was removed, or in $4.50 booklets, containing No. 1646a, on which the surplus paper was retained.

The phosphor on both rolls and booklets shows pink under U.V. light.

(Des C. Ellett. Litho SNP Cambec (gold die-stamped Avon Graphics))

1996 (22 July). *Passing of Olympic Flag to Sydney.* P 14×14½.
1650 **559** 45 c. multicoloured 55 50

560 Margaret   **561** Pearl
Windeyer

(Des Mad House Design. Litho Canberra Press)

1996 (8 Aug). *Centenary of the National Council of Women.* T **560** and similar vert design. P 14½×14.
1651   45 c. deep reddish purple and lemon .. 45 50
1652 $1 blue and lemon .. .. .. 1·00 1·10
Design:—$1 Rose Scott.

(Des Janet Boschen. Litho SNP Cambec (exelgram (45c.) and hologram ($1.20) Avon Graphics))

1996 (5 Sept). *Pearls and Diamonds.* T **561** and similar horiz designs. Multicoloured. P 14½×14.
1653   45 c. Type **561** 55 50
1654 $1.20, Diamond .. .. .. 1·40 1·40
The pearl on the 45 c. is shown as an exelgram (holographic printing on ultra thin plastic film) and the diamond on the $1.20 as a hologram, each embossed on to the stamp.

562 Silhouettes of Female   **563** Ginger Cats
Dancer and Musician on Rural
Landscape

(Des A. Ashton. Litho McPherson's Ptg Group, Mulgrave)

1996 (12 Sept). *50th Anniv of Arts Councils.* T **562** and similar horiz design. Multicoloured. P 14×imperf.
1655   20 c. Type **562** 20 25
   a. Booklet pane. Nos. 1655 and 1656×4 2·00
1656   45 c. Silhouettes of musician and male dancer on landscape 45 50
Nos. 1655/6 only exist from $2 stamp booklets in which the vertical edges of the pane are imperforate.

(Des Dianne Cooke. Litho SNP Cambec)

1996 (1 Oct). *Australian Pets.* T **563** and similar multicoloured designs. (a) Phosphorised paper. P 14×14½ (Nos. 1659, 1662) or 14½×14 (others).
1657   45 c. Type **563** 60 60
   a. Pair. Nos. 1657/8 .. .. 1·10 1·10
1658   45 c. Blue Heeler dogs 60 60
1659   45 c. Cockatoo (30×25 *mm*) .. 60 60
1660   45 c. Duck with ducklings (25×30 *mm*) .. 60 60
   a. Horiz pair. Nos. 1660/1 .. 1·10 1·10
1661   45 c. Dog and cat (25×30 *mm*) .. 60 60
1662   45 c. Ponies (30×50 *mm*) .. 60 60
1657/62 .. .. .. *Set of* 6 3·25 3·50
MS1663   166×73 mm. Nos. 1657/62. P 14½ .. 3·25 3·50

(b) *Self-adhesive. Phosphor band.* P 11½
1664   45 c. Type **563** 60 60
   a. Booklet pane. Nos. 1664×4 and 1665×6 .. .. 5·50
1665   45 c. Blue Heeler dogs 60 60
Nos. 1657/8 and 1660/1 were each printed together, *se-tenant*, either in vertical and horizontal pairs (Nos. 1657/8) or in horizontal pairs (Nos. 1660/1) throughout the sheets.

Nos. 1664/5 were printed either in rolls of 100 on which the surplus self-adhesive paper around each stamp was removed, or in $4.50 booklets containing No. 1664a, on which the surplus paper was retained.

The phosphor on both rolls and booklets shows orange-pink under U.V. light and appears as a bar at the top and on the cats for No. 1664 and as a L-shaped frame for No. 1665.

No. MS1163 also exists overprinted with the logos of the ASDA Centrepoint '96 Sydney, St. Peter's Stamp and Coin Fair, "Melbourne '96", "TAIPEI '96", Queensland Stamp and Coin Expo, Stamp Show '96 Claremont and "HONG KONG '97" for sale at these exhibitions.

NEW INFORMATION

The editor is always interested to correspond with people who have new information that will improve or correct the Catalogue.

---

564 Ferdinand von Mueller   **565** Willem de Vlamingh

(Des J. Sellitto and D. Blyth. Litho State Ptg Wks, Berlin)

1996 (9 Oct). *Australia–Germany Joint Issue. Death Centenary of Ferdinand von Mueller (botanist).* P 14.
1666 **564** $1.20, multicoloured .. .. 1·25 1·40

(Des A. Donato. Litho McPherson's Ptg Group, Mulgrave)

1996 (1 Nov). *300th Anniv of the Visit of Willem de Vlamingh to Western Australia.* P 14×14½.
1667 **565** 45 c. multicoloured 55 55
   a. Horiz pair. No. 1667 and No. 433 of Christmas Island .. 1·10 1·10
No. 1667 and No. 433 of Christmas Island were printed together, *se-tenant*, in horizontal pairs throughout the sheet.

566 Madonna and   **567** "Landscape '74" (Fred
Child   Williams)

(Des Vivienne Goodman. Litho SNP Cambec)

1996 (1 Nov). *Christmas.* T **566** and similar vert designs. Multicoloured. (a) Phosphorised paper. P 14½×14.
1668   40 c. Type **566** 50 45
1669   45 c. Wise man with gift 50 50
1670 $1 Shepherd boy with lamb .. 1·25 1·10
1668/70 .. .. .. *Set of* 3 2·00 2·00

(b) *Self-adhesive. Phosphor on inscr panel and central figures.* P 11½
1671   40 c. Type **566** 40 45
   a. Booklet pane. No. 1671×20 .. 8·00
No. 1671, on which the phosphor shows pink under U.V. light was only issued in $8 booklets, on which the surplus self-adhesive paper was retained.

(Des Karina Weston. Litho McPherson's Ptg Group, Mulgrave)

1997 (16 Jan). *Australia Day. Contemporary Paintings.* T **567** and similar horiz designs. Multicoloured. P 14½×14.
1672   85 c. Type **567** 85 90
1673   90 c. "The Balcony 2" (Brett Whiteley) .. 90 95
1674 $1.20, "Fire Haze at Gerringong" (Lloyd Rees) .. .. .. 1·25 1·40
1672/4 .. .. .. *Set of* 3 3·00 3·25

568 Sir Donald Bradman   **569** Red Roses

(Des Sophie Byass. Litho SNP Cambec)

1997 (23 Jan). *Australian Legends (1st series). Sir Donald Bradman (cricketer).* T **568** and similar square design. Multicoloured. P 14½.
1675   45 c. Type **568** 55 55
   a. Horiz pair. Nos. 1675/6 .. 1·10 1·10
1676   45 c. Bradman playing stroke .. 55 55
Nos. 1675/6 were printed together, *se-tenant*, in horizontal pairs throughout the sheet of 10.
See also Nos. 1731/54.

(Des Kate Linton. Litho SNP Cambec)

1997 (29 Jan). *St. Valentine's Day.* (a) *Phosphorized paper.* P 14½×14.
1677 **569** 45 c. multicoloured 50 50

(b) *Self-adhesive. Phosphor on inscr panel and background.* P 11½
1678 **569** 45 c. multicoloured 50 50
   a. Booklet pane. No. 1678×10 .. 5·00
No. 1678, on which the phosphor shows pink under U.V. light, was only issued in $4.50 booklets on which the surplus self-adhesive paper was retained.

---

570 Ford Coupe Utility,   **571** May Wirth
1934   and Horse

(Des Sandra Harmon. Litho SNP Cambec)

1997 (27 Feb). *Classic Cars.* T **570** and similar horiz designs. Multicoloured. (a) *Phosphorised paper.* P 14×14½.
1679   45 c. Type **570** 55 60
   a. Block of 4. Nos. 1679/82 .. 2·00
   b. Booklet pane. No. 1679×4 with margins all round .. .. 2·00
1680   45 c. GMH Holden 48-215 (FX), 1948 55 60
   a. Booklet pane. No. 1680×4 with margins all round .. .. 2·00
1681   45 c. Austin Lancer, 1958 .. .. 55 60
   a. Booklet pane. No. 1681×4 with margins all round .. .. 2·00
1682   45 c. Chrysler Valiant "R" Series, 1962 55 60
   a. Booklet pane. No. 1682×4 with margins all round .. .. 2·00
1679/82 .. .. .. *Set of* 4 2·00 2·25

(b) *Self-adhesive. Designs 32½×21 mm. Phosphor frames.* P 11½
1683   45 c. Type **570** 55 60
   a. Booklet pane. Nos. 1683, 1685 each × 2 and 1684, 1686 each × 3 5·00
1684   45 c. GMH Holden 48-215 (FX), 1948 55 60
1685   45 c. Austin Lancer, 1958 .. .. 55 60
1686   45 c. Chrysler Valiant "R" Series, 1962 55 60
1683/6 .. .. .. *Set of* 4 2·00 2·25
Nos. 1679/82 were printed together, *se-tenant*, in sheets of 50 (2 panes 5×5) each sheet providing ten blocks of 4 and ten single stamps.
Nos. 1683/6, occur either in rolls of 100, on which the surplus self-adhesive paper was removed, or in $4.50 booklets, containing No. 1683a, on which the surplus paper was retained. The phosphor on both rolls and booklets shows pink under U.V. light.

(Des Cathleen Bryant. Litho McPherson's Ptg Group, Mulgrave)

1997 (13 Mar). *150th Anniv of the Circus in Australia.* T **571** and similar vert designs. Multicoloured. P 14½×14.
1687   45 c. Type **571** 50 55
   a. Block of 4. Nos. 1687/90 .. 1·75
1688   45 c. Con Colleano on tightrope .. 50 55
1689   45 c. Clowns 50 55
1690   45 c. Acrobats 50 55
1687/90 .. .. .. *Set of* 4 1·75 2·00
Nos. 1687/90 were printed together, *se-tenant*, in sheets of 50 (2 panes of 5×5), each sheet providing ten blocks of 4 and ten single stamps.

572 Royal Wedding 1d.   **573** Hand holding
Stamp of 1947   Globe and Lions
                        Emblem

(Des Cozzolino Ellett. Recess Note Ptg Branch, Reserve Bank of Australia)

1997 (17 Apr). *Queen Elizabeth II's Birthday.* P 14×14½.
1691 **572** 45 c. blackish purple 50 50

(Des Cozzolino Ellett. Recess Note Ptg Branch, Reserve Bank of Australia)

1997 (17 Apr). *50th Anniv of First Australian Lions Club.* P 14½×14.
1692 **573** 45 c. brt blue, chestnut & blackish pur 50 50

574 Doll holding   **575** Police Rescue
Teddy Bear (Kaye   Helicopter
Wiggs)

(Des Cathleen Bryant. Litho McPherson's Ptg Group, Mulgrave)

1997 (8 May). *Dolls and Teddy Bears.* T **574** and similar vert designs. Multicoloured. P 14½×14.
1693   45 c. Type **574** 40 45
   a. Horiz strip of 5. Nos. 1693/7 .. 2·00
1694   45 c. Teddy bear standing (Jennifer Laing) 40 45

1695	45 c. Doll wearing white dress with teddy bear (Susie McMahon)	40 45
1696	45 c. Doll in brown dress and bonnet (Lynda Jacobson)	40 45
1697	45 c. Teddy bear sitting (Helen Williams)	40 45
1693/7		Set of 5 2·00 2·00

Nos. 1693/7 were printed together in sheets of 10, containing two *se-tenant* strips of 5. Sheets exist overprinted for the 1997 Brisbane Stamp and Coin Expo.

(Des B. Sadgrove. Litho McPherson's Ptg Group, Mulgrave)

1997 (10 July). *Emergency Services.* T **575** *and similar horiz designs. Multicoloured.* P 14×14½.

1698	45 c. Type **575**	40 45
	a. Horiz pair. Nos. 1698/9	80
1699	45 c. Emergency Service volunteers carrying victim	40 45
1700	$1.05, Fire service at fire	90 95
1701	$1.20, Loading casualty into ambulance	1·00 1·10
1698/1701		Set of 4 2·75 3·00

Nos. 1698/9 were printed together, *se-tenant*, in horizontal pairs throughout the sheet.
Numbered gutter strips of ten of No. 1701, overprinted "Emergency Services", come from a limited issue portfolio.

576 George Peppin Jnr (breeder) and Merino Sheep   **577** Dumbi the Owl

(Des C. Shurey. Litho SNP Cambec)

1997 (7 Aug). *Bicentenary of Arrival of Merino Sheep in Australia.* T **576** *and similar horiz design. Multicoloured.* P 14×14½.

1702	45 c. Type **576**	40 45
	a. Horiz pair. Nos. 1702/3	80
1703	45 c. Pepe chair, cloth and wool logo	40 45

Nos. 1702/3 were printed together, *se-tenant*, as horizontal pairs in sheets of 10.

(Des Melinda Coombes. Litho SNP Cambec)

1997 (21 Aug). *"The Dreaming". Cartoons from Aboriginal Stories.* T **577** *and similar square designs. Multicoloured.* P 14½.

1704	45 c. Type **577**	40 45
1705	$1 The Two Willy-Willies	90 95
1706	$1.20, How Brolga became a Bird	1·00 1·10
1707	$1.80, Tuggan-Tuggan	1·50 1·60
1704/7		Set of 4 3·75 4·00

578 *Rhoetosaurus brownei*   **579** *Spotted-tailed Quoll*

(Des P. Schouten. Litho SNP Cambec)

1997 (4 Sept). *Prehistoric Animals.* T **578** *and similar vert designs. Multicoloured.* P 14½×14.

1708	45 c. Type **578**	40 45
	a. Horiz strip of 5. Nos. 1708/12	2·00
1709	45 c. *Mcnamaraspis kaprios*	40 45
1710	45 c. *Ninjemys oweni*	40 45
1711	45 c. *Paracylotosaurus davidi*	40 45
1712	45 c. *Woolungasaurus glendowerensis*	40 45
1708/12		Set of 5 2·00 2·25

Nos. 1708/12 were printed together, *se-tenant*, as horizontal strips of five in sheets of 10.

(Des P. Gouldthorpe. Litho SNP Cambec)

1997 (1 Oct). *Nocturnal Animals.* T **579** *and similar multicoloured designs.*

(a) *Phosphorised paper.* P 14×14½ (Nos. 1715/17) or 14½×14 (others)

1713	45 c. Type **579**	40 45
	a. Pair. Nos. 1713/14	80
1714	45 c. Barking Owl	40 45
1715	45 c. Platypus (30×25 *mm*)	40 45
	a. Horiz strip of 3. Nos. 1715/17	1·25
1716	45 c. Brown Antechinus (30×25 *mm*)	40 45
1717	45 c. Dingo (30×25 *mm*)	40 45
1718	45 c. Yellow-bellied Glider (50×30 *mm*)	40 45
1713/18		Set of 6 2·40 2·75
MS1719	166×73 mm. Nos. 1713/18. P 14½	2·40 2·50

(b) *Self-adhesive. Phosphor frame.* P 11½

1720	45 c. Type **579** (25×32 *mm*)	40 45
	a. Vert pair. Nos. 1720/1	80
	b. Booklet pane. Nos. 1720/1, each ×5	4·00
1721	45 c. Barking Owl (25×32 *mm*)	40 45

Nos. 1713/14 were printed together, *se-tenant*, in horizontal or vertical pairs and Nos. 1715/17 in horizontal strips of three throughout the sheets.
No. MS1719 shows a spider and web printed in green

phosphor, visible under U.V. light, across much of the sheet.
Nos. 1720/1, on which the phosphor frame appears pink under U.V. light, were printed either in rolls of 100 on which the surplus self-adhesive paper around each stamp was removed or in $4.50 booklets containing No. 1720b on which the surplus paper was retained.

580 Woman   **581** Two Angels

(Des Lynda Warner. Litho SNP Cambec)

1997 (27 Oct). *Breast Cancer Awareness Campaign.* P 14×14½.

1722	**580** 45 c. multicoloured	40 45

(Des Cathleen Bryant. Litho SNP Cambec)

1997 (3 Nov). *Christmas. Children's Nativity Play.* T **581** *and similar horiz designs. Multicoloured.*

(a) *Phosphorised paper.* P 14×14½

1723	40 c. Type **581**	35 40
1724	45 c. Mary	40 45
1725	$1 Three Kings	90 95
1723/5		Set of 3 1·60 1·75

(b) *Self-adhesive. Phosphor frame at right and foot.* P 11½

1726	40 c. Type **581**	35 40
	a. Booklet pane. No. 1726×20	7·00

No. 1726, on which the phosphor shows pink under U.V. light, was only issued in $8 booklets on which the surplus self-adhesive paper was retained.

582 *"Flying Cloud"* (clipper) (J. Scott)   **583** Betty Cuthbert (1956)

(Des B. Sadgrove. Litho McPherson's Ptg Group, Mulgrave)

1998 (15 Jan). *Ship Paintings.* T **582** *and similar square designs. Multicoloured.* P 14½×14.

1727	45 c. Type **582**	40 45
1728	85 c. "*Marco Polo*" (full-rigged ship) (T. Robertson)	75 80
1729	$1 "*Chusan*" (steam ship) (C. Gregory)	90 95
1730	$1.20, "*Heather Belle*" (clipper)	1·00 1·10
1727/30		Set of 4 3·00 3·25

(Des Sophie Byass. Litho SNP Cambec)

1998 (21 Jan). *Australian Legends (2nd series). Olympic Gold Medal Winners.* T **583** *and similar horiz designs.*

(a) *Phosphorised paper.* P 14×14½.

1731	45 c. Type **583**	40 45
	a. Sheetlet. Nos. 1731/42	4·75
1732	45 c. Betty Cuthbert running	40 45
1733	45 c. Herb Elliot (1960)	40 45
1734	45 c. Herb Elliot running	40 45
1735	45 c. Dawn Fraser (1956, 1960 and 1964)	40 45
1736	45 c. Dawn Fraser swimming	40 45
1737	45 c. Marjorie Jackson (1952)	40 45
1738	45 c. Marjorie Jackson running	40 45
1739	45 c. Murray Rose (1956)	40 45
1740	45 c. Murray Rose swimming	40 45
1741	45 c. Shirley Strickland (1952 and 1956)	40 45
1742	45 c. Shirley Strickland hurdling	40 45
1731/42		Set of 12 4·75 5·50

(b) *Self-adhesive. Two vertical phosphor bands.* P 11½

1743	45 c. Type **583**	40 45
	b. Booklet pane. Nos. 1743/54	4·75
1744	45 c. Betty Cuthbert running	40 45
1745	45 c. Herb Elliot	40 45
1746	45 c. Herb Elliot running	40 45
1747	45 c. Dawn Fraser	40 45
1748	45 c. Dawn Fraser swimming	40 45
1749	45 c. Marjorie Jackson	40 45
1750	45 c. Marjorie Jackson running	40 45
1751	45 c. Murray Rose	40 45
1752	45 c. Murray Rose swimming	40 45
1753	45 c. Shirley Strickland	40 45
1754	45 c. Shirley Strickland hurdling	40 45
1743/54		Set of 12 4·75 5·00

Nos. 1731/42 were printed together, *se-tenant*, in sheetlets of 12.
Nos. 1743/54, on which the phosphor bands appear pink under U.V. light, were printed in $5.40 stamp booklets containing No. 1743b on which the surplus paper around each stamp was retained.

1st CLASS STAMPS & SERVICE

Stanley Gibbons are pleased to offer a dedicated and completely free of charge service to today's discerning British Commonwealth collectors.

- Specialist database of clients' interests.
- Large stocks of specialised British Commonwealth material.
- Free advice from our team of experts.
- Regular advance lists and illustrated colour brochures.
- Private viewing facilities and postal approvals service.
- Specialist 'Wants List' service.
- We are always interested in buying quality collections and single items.

To take advantage of our free and highly specialised service contact us today on 0171 836 8444.

STANLEY GIBBONS

———FIRST CLASS———
STAMPS & SERVICE

Stanley Gibbons Limited
399 Strand, London WC2R 0LX

Index to Australian Stamp Designs from 1942

Index to Australian Stamp Designs from 1942—*Continued*

STAMP BOOKLETS

Illustrations of booklet covers are reduced to ½ size, *unless otherwise stated.*
All booklets from 1913 to 1949 were stapled.

1913 (17 Jan). *Red on pink cover (SB1) or blue on pink cover with map of Australia on front and picture of State G.P.O. on back (SB2)*
SB1 2s. booklet containing twelve ½d. and eighteen 1d.
(Nos. 1/2) in blocks of 6 .. .. £1000
SB2 £1 booklet containing two hundred and forty 1d.
(No. 2) in blocks of 30 .. .. £5000

1914 (6 Oct)–**18.** *Red on pink cover (Nos. SB2a/3), black on red cover (No. SB4) or blue on pink cover with map of Australia on front and picture of State G.P.O. on back (No. SB5).*
SB2a 2s. booklet containing twelve ½d. and eighteen 1d.
(Nos. 1, 21) in blocks of 6 .. £1500
SB3 2s. booklet containing twelve ½d. and eighteen 1d.
(Nos. 20/1) in blocks of 6 (1915) .. £1500
SB4 2s. booklet containing twenty-four 1d. (No. 21) in
blocks of 6 (10.5.17) £1800
a. Black on green cover £1800
b. Red on green cover £1800
SB5 £1 booklet containing two hundred and forty 1d.
(No. 21) in blocks of 30 .. .. £5000
a. Back cover without G.P.O. picture (1918)
Records show that a £1 booklet containing one hundred and twenty 2d. stamps was issued in very limited quantities during 1914. No examples are known to have survived.

1919 (Jan–Apr). *Black on pink (Nos. SB6/7) or black on green (Nos. SB8/9c) covers.*
SB6 2s. 3d. booklet containing eighteen 1½d. (No. 58)
in blocks of 6 .. .. .. £1300
a. Black on green cover £1300
SB7 2s. 3d. booklet containing eighteen 1½d. (No. 54)
in blocks of 6 .. .. .. £1300
a. Black on green cover £1300
SB8 2s. 3d. booklet containing eighteen 1½d. (No. 59)
in blocks of 6 (Apr) £1300
a. Black on pink cover £1300
SB9 2s. 3d. booklet containing eighteen 1½d. (No. 55)
in blocks of 6 (Apr) £1300
a. Black on pink cover £1300
b. Black on blue cover £1300
SB9c £1 booklet containing one hundred and sixty 1½d.
(No. 55) in blocks of 20 (Apr) .. £5000

1920 (Dec)–**22.** *Black on blue (Nos. SB10, SB12), black on white (No. SB11) or black on brown (No. SB14) covers.*
SB10 2s. booklet containing twelve 2d. (No. 62) in
blocks of 6 .. .. .. £1500
a. Black on pink cover £1500
b. Black on orange cover (3.22) .. £2000
SB11 2s. booklet containing twelve 2d. (No. 63) in
blocks of 6 (3.22) £1500
a. Black on orange cover (7.22) .. £2000
b. Black on pink cover £1500
c. Brown on buff cover £1500
d. Black on pink cover £1500
SB12 £1 booklet containing one hundred and twenty
2d. (No. 62) in blocks of 15 (1.21) .. £5000
a. Black on pink cover
SB13 £1 booklet containing ninety 2d. and fifteen 4d.
(Nos. 63, 65) in blocks of 15 (3.22)
SB14 £1 booklet containing one hundred and twenty
2d. (No. 63) in blocks of 15 (8.22) .. £2000

1923 (Oct)–**24.** *Black on rose (No. SB15), or green on pale green (Nos. SB16/18) covers.*
SB15 2s. 3d. booklet containing eighteen 1½d. (No. 61)
in blocks of 6 .. .. .. £1200
a. Black on pale green cover .. £1200
b. Green on pale green cover .. £1200
SB16 2s. 3d. booklet containing eighteen 1½d. (No. 77)
in blocks of 6 (5.24) £1200
SB17 £1 booklet containing one hundred and sixty
1½d. (No. 61) in blocks of 20 (3.24) .. £4000
SB18 £1 booklet containing one hundred and sixty
1½d. (No. 77) in blocks of 20 (5.24) .. £4000

1927 (Jan–June). *Green on pale green covers.*
SB19 2s. 3d. booklet containing eighteen 1½d. (No. 87)
in blocks of 6 .. .. .. £750
SB20 2s. 3d. booklet containing eighteen 1½d. (No. 96)
in blocks of 6 .. .. .. £750
SB21 £1 booklet containing one hundred and sixty
1½d. (No. 96) in blocks of 20 (June) .. £3750

1927 (9 May). *Opening of Parliament House, Canberra. Green on pale green cover with picture of H. M. S. Renown on back (2s.).*
SB22 2s. booklet containing sixteen 1½d. (No. 105) in
blocks of 8.. .. .. .. 80·00
SB22a 10s. booklet containing eighty 1½d. (No. 105) in
blocks of 8
Surviving examples of No. SB22a are without front cover and have a blank back cover.

1928 (Nov). *Green on pale green cover.*
SB23 2s. 3d. booklet containing eighteen 1½d. (No. 96a
or 96w) in blocks of 6 .. .. £325

1930 (July)–**35.** *Air. Black on blue cover inscr "AIR MAIL. SAVES TIME"*
SB24 3s. booklet containing twelve 3d. (No. 115) in
blocks of 4 plus two panes of air mail labels £650
a. Cover inscr "USE THE AIR MAIL" (5.35) .. £1200
b. Black on pale green cover inscr "USE THE
AIR MAIL" (5.35) £900

1930 (9 Sept)–**33.** *Green on pale green covers inscr "USE THE AIR MAIL" on the back (2s)*
SB25 2s. booklet containing twelve 2d. (No. 99a or
99aw) in blocks of 6 .. .. £300
SB25a 2s. booklet containing twelve 2d. (No. 127 or
127w) in blocks of 6 (1.32) .. £275
ab. Cover with parcel rates on back (1933) .. £375
SB26 £1 booklet containing one hundred and twenty
2d. (No. 99) in blocks of 20 .. £3750
SB26a £1 booklet containing one hundred and twenty
2d. (No. 99a) in blocks of 20 .. £3750

1934 (June). *Black on cream cover inscr "Address your mail fully..." on front.*
SB26b 2s. booklet containing twelve 2d. (No. 127 or
127w) in blocks of 6 .. .. £375

1935–38. *Black on green cover with Commonwealth Savings Bank advertisement on front inscr "WHEREVER THERE IS A MONEY ORDER POST OFFICE".*
SB26c 2s. booklet containing twelve 2d. (No. 127 or
127w) in blocks of 6 .. .. £325
ca. Front cover inscr "IN MOST MONEY
ORDER OFFICES" (1936) .. £275
cb. Ditto with waxed interleaves (1938) .. £325

1938 (Dec). *Black on green cover as No. SB26c.*
SB27 2s. booklet containing twelve 2d. (No. 184 or
184w) in blocks of 6 .. .. £350
a. With waxed interleaves £450
b. Black on buff cover £400

1942 (Aug). *Black on buff cover, size 73×47½ mm.*
SB28 2s. 6d. booklet containing twelve 2½d. (No. 206
or 206w) in blocks of 6, upright within the
booklet £110
a. With waxed interleaves £200

1949 (Sept). *Black on buff cover, size 79½×42½ mm including figure of Hermes.*
SB29 2s. 6d. booklet containing twelve 2½d. (No. 206)
in blocks of 6, sideways within the booklet 80·00

All booklets from 1952 to 1972 were stitched and stapled booklets of this period are remakes of defective stitched booklets with new covers. All subsequent booklets have their panes attached by selvedge *unless otherwise stated.*

B 1

1952 (24 June). *Vermilion and deep blue on green cover as Type B 1.*
SB30 3s. 6d. booklet containing twelve 3½d. (No. 247)
in blocks of 6 .. .. .. 17·00
a. With waxed interleaves .. .. 90·00

B 1a

1953 (8 July)–**56.** *Vermilion and deep blue on green cover as Type B 1a.*
SB31 3s. 6d. booklet containing twelve 3½d. (No. 263)
in blocks of 6 .. .. .. 11·00
a. With waxed interleaves .. .. 22·00
SB32 3s. 6d. booklet containing twelve 3½d. (No. 262a)
in blocks of 6 (7.56) .. .. 22·00
a. With waxed interleaves .. .. 80·00

B 2

1957 (13 Mar)–**59.** *Vermilion and deep blue on green cover as Type B 2.*
SB33 4s. booklet containing two panes of 6 4d. (No.
294a) .. .. 15·00
a. With waxed interleaves .. .. 35·00
SB34 4s. booklet containing two panes of 6 4d. (No.
313ab) (18.3.59) .. .. 38·00
a. With waxed interleaves .. .. 75·00

B 3

1960 (23 Mar). *Vermilion and deep blue on green cover as Type B 3.*
SB35 5s. booklet containing two panes of 6 5d. (No.
314d) .. .. 20·00
a. With waxed interleaves .. .. 42·00

B 4

1962 (July)–**65.** *Rose and emerald on green cover as Type B 4.*
SB36 5s. booklet containing two panes of 6 5d. (No.
314d) .. .. 45·00
a. With waxed interleaves (1963) .. £100
SB37 5s. booklet containing two panes of 6 5d. (No.
354a) (17.6.64) .. .. 45·00
a. With waxed interleaves £100
SB38 5s. booklet containing two panes of 6 5d. (No.
354cb) (13.7.65) .. .. 48·00
a. With waxed interleaves £110

B 5

1966 (14 Feb). *Greenish blue and black on yellow-olive cover as Type B 5.*
SB39 60 c. booklet containing three panes of 5 4 c. and
1 label (No. 385a) .. .. 60·00
a. With waxed interleaves £130

1967 (29 Sept). *Greenish blue and black on yellow-olive covers as Type B 5.* (a) *Surcharged covers*
SB40 50 c. booklet containing two panes of 5 5 c. on 4 c.
and 1 label (No. 414a) .. .. 12·00
SB41 $1 booklet containing four panes of 5 5 c. on 4 c.
and 1 label (No. 414a) .. .. 11·00
a. Normal cover as Type B 5 .. 11·00
ab. With waxed interleaves .. .. 55·00
(b) *Normal covers*
SB42 50 c. booklet containing two panes of 5 5 c. and 1
label (No. 386ca) .. .. 15·00
SB43 $1 booklet containing four panes of 5 5 c. and 1
label (No. 386ca) .. .. 30·00
a. With waxed interleaves .. .. 65·00
Booklets SB40/1ab were intended as provisional issues until supplies of the new 5 c. became available in booklet form, but in the event these were put on sale on the same date.

B 6

1968 (6 Nov). *Famous Australians (1st series). Black, red, white and blue cover as Type B 6.*
SB44 $1 booklet containing four panes of 5 5 c. and 1
label (Nos 432a, 433a, 434a, 435a) .. 10·00
a. With waxed interleaves .. .. 50·00

B 7

1969 (22 Oct). *Famous Australians (2nd series). Olive-green, gold and black cover as Type B 7.*
SB45 $1 booklet containing four panes of 5 5 c. and 1
label (Nos. 446a, 447a, 448a, 449a) .. 11·00
a. With waxed interleaves .. .. 60·00

B 8

1970 (16 Nov). *Famous Australians (3rd series). Multicoloured on white covers as Type* B **8.**

SB46 60 c. booklet containing two panes of 5 6 c. and 1 label (Nos. 479a, 480a) 10.00
SB47 60 c. booklet containing two panes of 5 6 c. and 1 label (Nos. 481a, 482a) 10.00
SB48 $1.20 booklet containing four panes of 5 6 c. and 1 label (Nos. 479a, 480a, 481a, 482a) 16.00
 a. With waxed interleaves 60.00

1972 (8 Mar). *Famous Australians (4th series). Covers in reddish violet (No.* SB49), *yellowish olive (No.* SB50) *or blue (No.* SB51), *each with inscr in yellow-brown and black as Type* B **7.**

SB49 70 c. booklet containing two panes of 5 7 c. and 1 label (Nos. 505a, 506a) 3.75
SB50 70 c. booklet containing two panes of 5 7 c. and 1 label (Nos. 507a, 508a) 3.75
SB51 $1.40, booklet containing four panes of 5 7 c. and 1 label (Nos. 505a, 506a, 507a, 508a) 6.50
 a. With waxed interleaves 50.00

The Australian Post Office discontinued the general use of stamp booklets in May 1973, but from 30 April 1979 tested two stamp-vending machines in Brisbane which issued 60 c. and 80 c. folders containing three or four examples of No. 673 taken from sheet stock. These folders were withdrawn on 30 January 1981.

During 1982 experimental stamp booklet vending machines were under test at the G.P.O.s in Melbourne and Sydney. These machines dispensed a cream card folder, without printing, containing two copies of Nos. 669/70 and 790a. The stamps, from normal sheets, were affixed to the folders by their selvedge. These 60 c. trial folders were replaced by booklets Nos. SB52/3 in November 1982.

From 1982 all booklets have folded covers with the stamps attached by their selvedge, *unless otherwise stated.*

B 9

1982 (17 Nov). *Eucalyptus Flowers. Covers in pale greenish yellow with olive-grey (60 c.) or rose-red ($1) as Type* B **9.**
SB52 60 c. booklet containing pane of 6 (No. 870a) .. 1.00
SB53 $1 booklet containing pane of 9 (No. 870b) .. 2.50
 Nos. SB52/3 were sold from vending machines.

B 10

1985 (13 Mar). *Turquoise-green on white cover as Type* B **10.**
SB54 $1 booklet containing pane of 4 (No. 970a) .. 2.75
 No. SB54 was sold from vending machines.

B 11

1986 (25 Aug). *Alpine Wildflowers. Apple-green* (80 *c.*) *or orange-yellow* ($1) *on white covers as Type* B **11.**
SB55 80 c. booklet containing pane of 4 (No. 1028a) 2.50
SB56 $1 booklet containing pane of 4 (No. 1028b) .. 2.50
 Nos. SB55/6 were sold from vending machines.

B 12

1987 (13 Oct). *Aboriginal Crafts. Orange-brown* (80 *c.*) *or orange-yellow* ($2) *on white covers as Type* B **12.**
SB57 80 c. booklet containing pane of 4 (No. 1093a) .. 3.75
SB58 $2 booklet containing pane of 6 (No. 1094a) .. 7.50
 Nos. SB57/8 were sold from vending machines.
 Trial versions of both booklets exist which differ considerably from the main supply. On the trial versions the outside back cover is headed "ABORIGINAL CRAFTS", there is no advertisement on the selvedge of the pane and the bottom stamp in each pane is imperforate at foot.

B 13

1988 (1 July–28 Sept). *Multicoloured covers as Type* B **13.**
SB59 $3.70, booklet containing pane of 37 c. (No. 1121) in block of 10 (printed by Leigh-Mardon Ltd) .. 6.00
SB60 $3.70, booklet containing pane of 10 37 c. (No. 1121a) (printed by CPE Australia Ltd) with upper and lower edges of the pane imperf and margins at left and right 6.00
SB61 $3.90, booklet containing pane of 10 39 c. (No. 1121ba) (28 Sept) 7.00

B 14

1988 (28 Sept). *Australian Crafts. Orange-yellow* (80 *c.*) *or bright purple* ($2) *on white covers as Type* B **14.**
SB62 80 c. booklet containing pane of 3 (No. 1158a) .. 3.50
SB63 $2 booklet containing pane of 6 (No. 1159a) .. 5.00
 Nos. SB62/3 were sold from vending machines.

B 15

1989 (13 Feb). *Multicoloured cover as Type* B **15.**
SB64 $3.90, booklet containing pane of 10 39 c. (No. 1179a) 7.50
 a. Containing pane No. 1179ba 10.00

B 16

1989 (23 Aug). *Multicoloured cover as Type* B **16.**
SB65 $4.10, booklet containing pane of 10 41 c. (No. 1180a) 6.00
 No. SB65 also exists overprinted with the "Austamp 90" logo for sale at this exhibition.

B 17

1989 (1 Sept). *Urban Environment. Black and grey-brown on white cover as Type* B **17.**
SB66 $3 booklet containing pane of 7 (No. 1216a) .. 4.00
 No. SB66 was sold from vending machines and only contained stamps to a face value of $2.87. A refund of 13 c. could, however, be obtained by returning the empty booklet cover to a post office.
 No. SB66 also exists overprinted with the "New Zealand 1990" logo for sale at this exhibition.

B 18
(Illustration reduced. Actual size 132×54 mm)

1989 (11 Oct). *"Stampshow '89" National Stamp Exhibition, Melbourne. Multicoloured cover as Type* B **18.** *Stapled.*
SB67 $8 booklet containing pane of 10 41 c. (No. 1222ab) 10.00
 Booklet No. SB67 also contains a Melbourne Metro travel pass and entrance ticket to "Stampshow '89".

B 19

1989 (1 Nov). *Christmas. Reddish brown on toned cover as Type* B **19.**
SB68 $3.60, booklet containing pane of 10 36 c. (No. 1225a) 4.00
 No. SB68 was also overprinted with the Sydney Stamp and Coin Show, 1989, or "World Stamp Expo", Washington logos for sale at these exhibitions.

B 20

1990 (7 Feb–May). *Greetings Stamps. Maroon and dull mauve cover as Type* B **20.**
SB69 $4.10, booklet containing pane of 10 41 c. (No. 1230a) and pane of 10 greetings labels 5.50
 a. Containing pane of 10 (No. 1230ba) and pane of 10 greetings labels (May) 10.00

For three months from May 1990 a series of provisional booklets was available from a vending machine at Sydney International Airport. These had plain covers, each handstamped with the airport post office's pictorial cancellation, and exist with the following contents:
 70 c. (No. 1187) × 5 (lemon cover).
 75 c. (No. 1132) × 5 (buff cover).
 80 c. (No. 1133) × 5 (buff cover).
 $1 (No. 1192) × 5 (buff cover).
 $1.10 (No. 1193) × 5 (buff cover).

1990 (27 Aug)–**91.** *Multicoloured cover as Type* B **16.**
SB70 $4.30, booklet containing pane of 10 43 c. (No. 1181a) 5.50
 a. Inscription changed and with additional slotted tab attached at right (2.91) .. 6.50

BARCODES. Barcodes appear on the back cover of booklet No. SB70 and later issues.

1990 (3 Sept). *Greetings Stamps. Maroon, brown-olive and pale olive cover as Type* B **20.**
SB71 $4.30, booklet containing pane of 10 43 c. (No. 1231a) and pane of 10 greetings labels 4.00

MINIMUM PRICE

The minimum price quote is 10p which represents a handling charge rather than a basis for valuing common stamps. For further notes about prices see introductory pages.

B 21 "Wild Life is Fun" (David Larwill)

1990 (3 Sept). *"Heidelberg and Heritage" Art Exhibition. Multicoloured cover as Type B 21.*
SB72 $2 booklet containing pane of 5 (No. 1269a) .. 3·00
    a. Containing pane of 5 (No. 1269ba) .. 5·50
    Nos. SB72/a were sold from vending machines. Both also exist overprinted with the Norpex 91, Newcastle, logo for sale at this exhibition.

B 22 "Parrot unwrapping Parcel"

1990 (31 Oct). *Christmas. Multicoloured cover as Type B 22.*
SB73 $3.80, booklet containing pane of 10 38 c. (No. 1272a) .. 5·50
    No. SB73 also exists overprinted with the Sydney Stamp and Coin Show, 1990, logo for sale at this exhibition.

1991 (Jan). *Red-brown and brown-olive cover as Type B 20, but inscr* "8 GREETINGS STICKERS".
SB74 $4.30, booklet containing pane of 10 43 c. (No. 1231a) and 8 self-adhesive greetings labels affixed to the inside back cover .. .. 10·00

B 23

1991 (1 Nov). *Christmas. Multicoloured cover as Type B 23.*
SB75 $7.60, booklet containing pane of 20 38 c. (No. 1309a) and 20 self-adhesive "Card Only" stickers affixed to the inside back cover .. 9·00

B 24

1992 (2 Jan)–**94.** *Wetlands and Waterways. Multicoloured cover as Type B 24.*
SB76 $2 booklet containing pane of 5 (No. 1319a) .. 2·75
    a. Containing pane No. 1319ba (3.94) .. 3·75
    Nos. SB76/a were sold from vending machines. No. SB76 was also overprinted with "N.P.C. Canberra 14–16 March 1992", "World Columbian Stamp Expo '92", Chicago, "Australian Stamp Exhibition 1993", Kaohsiung, and No. S76a with Queensland Stamp and Coin Show 94 logos for sale at these events.

1992 (2 Jan). *"Thinking of You". Orange-yellow, red-orange and grey-black cover as Type B 20, showing wild flowers.*
SB77 $4.50, booklet containing pane of 10 45 c. (No. 1318a) with 8 self-adhesive greetings labels affixed to the inside back cover .. .. 4·50
    No. SB77 was also overprinted with "Australian Stamp Exhibition 1993", Taichung, logo for sale at this exhibition.

ALTERED CATALOGUE NUMBERS

Any Catalogue numbers altered from the last edition are shown as a list in the introductory pages.

B 25

1992 (2 Jan)–**94.** *Threatened Species. Multicoloured covers as Type B 25. Self-adhesive.*
SB78 $4.50, booklet containing pane of 10 45 c. (No. 1327pa) (cover showing No. 1329 on front and Olympic draw details on back) .. .. 12·00
    a. Containing pane No. 1327qa (cover as Type B 25, but without Olympic draw flash and with National Philatelic Centre advertisement on back) (22.4.92) .. .. 12·00
    b. Containing pane No. 1327qa (cover as No. SB78a, but Stamp Collecting Kit advertisement on back) (7.11.92) .. .. 12·00
    c. Containing pane No. 1327qa (cover as Type B 25, but showing larger illustration (46×39 mm) of Dusky Hopping-mouse instead of stamp) (1.93) .. .. 12·00
    d. Containing pane No. 1327qa (cover as No. SB78c, but illustration (46×32 mm) of Little Pygmy Possum) (7.93) .. .. 12·00
    e. Containing pane No. 1327qa (cover as No. SB78c, but illustration (46×32 mm) of Ghost Bat) (1.94) .. .. 12·00
    These booklets can also be identified by the new printing symbols (koalas or kangaroos) which appear in the margin of the pane. No. SB78a shows 1 or 2 koalas, No. SB78b 3 koalas, No. SB78c 4 koalas, No. SB78d 1 kangaroo and No. SB78e 1 kangaroo and 1 koala.
    An example of No. SB78e has been reported showing the printing of the stamps omitted.
    No. SB78a (1 koala) was also overprinted with "National Stamp Show '92" logo, No. SB78a (2 koalas) with "Kuala Lumpur '92" and No. SB78c with "Australian Stamp Exhibition 1993", Taipeh, logo for sale at these exhibitions.

B 26

1992 (30 Oct). *Christmas. Multicoloured cover as Type B 26.*
SB79 $8 booklet containing pane of 20 40 c. (No. 1383a) and 20 self-adhesive "Card Only" stickers affixed to the inner cover .. .. 9·00
    No. SB79 was also overprinted with "Sydney Stamp and Coin Fair '92" logo for sale at this exhibition.

B 27

1993 (1 June). *Trains of Australia. Multicoloured cover as Type B 27. Self-adhesive.*
SB80 $4.50, booklet containing pane of 10 45 c. (No. 1411a) .. .. 6·00
    No. SB80 was also overprinted with "Indopex '93", Surabaya, or "Queensland Stamp and Coin Show" logos for sale at these exhibitions.

B 28

1993 (1 Oct). *Prehistoric Animals. Multicoloured cover as Type B 28. Self-adhesive.*
SB81 $4.50, booklet containing pane of 10 45 c. (No. 1430a) .. .. 6·00
    No. SB81 was also overprinted with the "Sydney Stamp and Coin Show 93" logo for sale at this exhibition.

B 29

1993 (1 Nov). *Christmas. Multicoloured cover as Type B 29.*
SB82 $8 booklet containing pane of 20 40 c. (No. 1432a) with 20 self-adhesive "Card only" stickers affixed to the inner cover .. .. 8·50

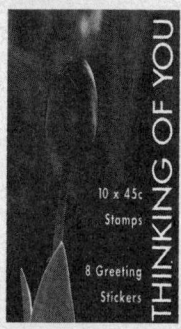

B 30   B 31

1994 (20 Jan). *Centenary of Organised Life Saving in Australia. Multicoloured cover as Type B 30. Self-adhesive.*
SB83 $4.50, booklet containing pane of 10 45 c. (No. 1443a) .. .. 6·00
    No. SB83 was also overprinted with the "Newcastle Mini-National Exhibition" logo for sale at this event.

1994 (3 Feb). *"Thinking of You". Multicoloured cover as Type B 31.*
SB84 $4.50, booklet containing pane of 10 45 c. (No. 1446b) with 8 self-adhesive greetings stickers affixed to the inner cover .. .. 4·00
    No. SB84 was also overprinted with "Melbourne Stamp and Coin Show" or "Canberra Stamp Show 94" logos for sale at these exhibitions.

B 32   B 33

1994 (12 May)–**96**. *Australian Wildlife (2nd series). Multi-coloured cover as Type B **32**. Self-adhesive.*

SB85 $4.50, booklet containing pane of 10 45 c. (No. 1459a) .. 5·50
 a. Cover with "BOOKABOUT" advert at foot (1.96) .. 5·50
 b. Cover with "WIN A TRIP FOR TWO TO THE ATLANTA OLYMPICS" advert at foot (16.3.96) .. 5·50

No. SB85a is from the 4 koala, 1 kangaroo + 1 koala, 1 kangaroo + 2 koala and 1 kangaroo + 3 koala printings.

No. SB85b is from the 1 kangaroo printing and also exists overprinted "CANBERRA STAMPSHOW 96 16–18 March 1996" in gold on the cover.

1994 (28 Sept). *Australian Zoos. Endangered Species. Multicoloured cover as Type B **33**. Self-adhesive.*

SB86 $4.50, booklet containing pane of 10 45 c. (No. 1485b) .. 9·00

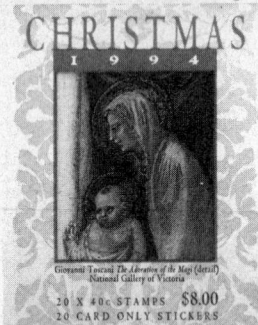

B 34

1994 (31 Oct). *Christmas. Multicoloured cover as Type B **34**.*

SB87 $8 booklet containing pane of 20 40 c. (No. 1487a) and 20 self-adhesive "CARD ONLY" stickers affixed to the inner cover .. 8·50

B 35

1995 (9 Feb). *Completion of* Endeavour *Replica. Multicoloured cover as Type B **35**.*

SB88 $2 booklet containing pane of 5 (No. 1512a) .. 2·50

B 36

1995 (20 Apr). *Australian Second World War Heroes. Multicoloured cover as Type B **36**. Self-adhesive.*

SB89 $4.50, booklet containing pane of 10 45 c. (No. 1525a) .. 6·00

B 37

1995 (8 June). *Centenary of Cinema. Multicoloured cover as Type B **37**. Self-adhesive.*

SB90 $4.50, booklet containing pane of 10 45 c. (No. 1535a) .. 5·50

No. SB90 was also overprinted with the "Queensland Stamp and Coin Show 1995" logo for sale at this exhibition.

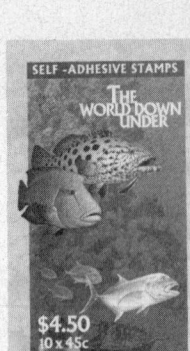

B 38   B 39

1995 (3 Oct). *Marine Life. Multicoloured cover as Type B **38**. Self-adhesive.*

SB91 $4.50, booklet containing pane of 10 45 c. (No. 1563ab) .. 4·25

1995 (1 Nov). *Christmas. Multicoloured cover as Type B **39**. Self-adhesive.*

SB92 $8 booklet containing pane of 20 40 c. (No. 1572a) and 20 self-adhesive "Card Only" labels affixed to the inner cover .. 7·75

Booklet No. SB92 shows either an advertisement for B.P. Australia or a selection of Christmas cards available from Australia Post on the back cover.

B 40 North Melbourne

(Des Janet Boschen)

1996 (23 Apr). *Centenary of Australian Football League. Multicoloured covers as Type B **40** showing team logos. Self-adhesive.*

SB 93 $4.50, booklet containing pane of ten 45 c. (No. 1606a) (Type B 40) .. 5·50
SB 94 $4.50, booklet containing pane of ten 45 c. (No. 1607a) (Brisbane) .. 5·50
SB 95 $4.50, booklet containing pane of ten 45 c. (No. 1608a) (Sydney) .. 5·50
SB 96 $4.50, booklet containing pane of ten 45 c. (No. 1609a) (Carlton) .. 5·50
SB 97 $4.50, booklet containing pane of ten 45 c. (No. 1610a) (Adelaide) .. 5·50
SB 98 $4.50, booklet containing pane of ten 45 c. (No. 1611a) (Fitzroy) .. 5·50
SB 99 $4.50, booklet containing pane of ten 45 c. (No. 1612a) (Richmond) .. 5·50
SB100 $4.50, booklet containing pane of ten 45 c. (No. 1613a) (St. Kilda) .. 5·50
SB101 $4.50, booklet containing pane of ten 45 c. (No. 1614a) (Melbourne) .. 5·50
SB102 $4.50, booklet containing pane of ten 45 c. (No. 1615a) (Collingwood) .. 5·50
SB103 $4.50, booklet containing pane of ten 45 c. (No. 1616a) (Fremantle) .. 5·50
SB104 $4.50, booklet containing pane of ten 45 c. (No. 1617a) (Footscray) .. 5·50
SB105 $4.50, booklet containing pane of ten 45 c. (No. 1618a) (West Coast) .. 5·50
SB106 $4.50, booklet containing pane of ten 45 c. (No. 1619a) (Essendon) .. 5·50
SB107 $4.50, booklet containing pane of ten 45 c. (No. 1620a) (Geelong) .. 5·50
SB108 $4.50, booklet containing pane of ten 45 c. (No. 1621a) (Hawthorn) .. 5·50

Nos. SB93/108 each exist with two different barcodes on the back.

No. SB94 also exists overprinted with "Queensland Stamp & Coin Expo 1996" for sale at this event.

B 41

1996 (4 July). *50th Anniv of Children's Book Council Awards. Multicoloured cover as Type B **41**. Self-adhesive.*

SB109 $4.50, booklet containing pane of 10 45 c. (No. 1646a) .. 5·50

B 42 Silhouettes on Landscape

1996 (12 Sept). *50th Anniv of Arts Councils. Multicoloured cover as Type B **42**.*

SB110 $2 booklet containing pane of 5 (No. 1655a) .. 2·00

B 43 Dog and Cat

1996 (1 Oct). *Australian Pets. Multicoloured cover as Type B **43**. Self-adhesive.*

SB111 $4.50, booklet containing pane of 10 45 c. (No. 1664a) .. 5·50

B 44 Madonna and Child

1996 (1 Nov). *Christmas. Multicoloured cover as Type B **44**. Self-adhesive.*

SB112 $8 booklet containing pane of 20 40 c. (No 1671a) and 20 self-adhesive "Card Only" labels affixed to the inner cover .. 8·00

B 45 Rose

1997 (29 Jan). *St. Valentine's Day. Multicoloured cover as Type* B **45**. *Self-adhesive.*
SB113 $4.50, booklet containing pane of 10 45 c. (No. 1678a) and 12 self-adhesive greetings stickers affixed to the inner cover .. 5·00

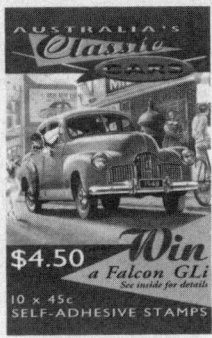

B 46 GMH Holden 48-215 (FX)

1997 (27 Feb). *Classic Cars. Multicoloured cover as Type* B **46**. *Self-adhesive.*
SB114 $4.50, booklet containing pane of 10 45 c. (No. 1683a) .. .. 5·00

B 47 Classic Cars
(Illustration reduced. Actual size 155×105 mm)

1997 (27 Feb). *Classic Cars Prestige Booklet. Multicoloured cover as Type* B **47**.
SB115 $9.95, booklet containing four panes of 4 45 c. (Nos. 1679b/82a), two pre-paid postcards and 16 self-adhesive labels .. .. .. 10·00

B 48 Wetland Birds

1997 (2 June). *Flora and Fauna. Multicoloured cover as Type* B **48**. *Self-adhesive.*
SB116 $4.50, booklet containing pane of 10 45 c. (No. 1634a) .. .. 4·00

COVER PRICES

Cover factors are quoted at the beginning of each country for most issues to 1945. An explanation of the system can be found on page x. The factors quoted do not, however, apply to philatelic covers.

B 49 Barking Owl

1997 (1 Oct). *Nocturnal Animals. Multicoloured cover as Type* B **49**. *Self-adhesive.*
SB117 $4.50, booklet containing pane of 10 45 c. (No. 1720b) .. .. 4·00

B 50 Two Angels

1997 (3 Nov). *Christmas. Children's Nativity Play. Multicoloured cover as Type* B **50**. *Self-adhesive.*
SB118 $8 booklet containing pane of 20 40 c. (No. 1726a) and 20 self-adhesive "Card Only" labels affixed to the inner cover .. .. 7·00

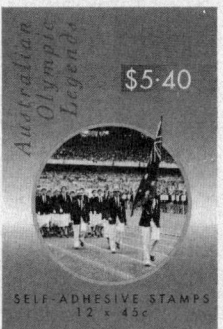

B 51 Australian Athletes

1998 (21 Jan). *Australian Legends (2nd series). Olympic Gold Medal Winners. Multicoloured cover as Type* B **51**. *Self-adhesive.*
SB119 $5.40, booklet containing pane of 12 45 c. (No. 1743b) .. .. 4·50

Military Post Booklets

Issued for the use of Australian Forces in Vietnam.

MB 1

1967 (30 May–Sept). *Yellow-green and black on white cover as Type* MB **1**. *Pane attached by selvedge.*
MB1 50 c. booklet containing 5 c. (No. 386) in block of 10 .. .. 80·00
  a. Containing No. 386b (Sept) .. .. 80·00

1968 (Mar). *Yellow-green and black on white cover as Type* MB **1**. *Pane attached by selvedge.*
MB2 50 c. booklet containing 5 c. (No. 386c) in block of 10 .. .. 55·00

POSTAGE DUE STAMPS

POSTAGE DUE PRINTERS. Nos. D1/62 were typographed at the New South Wales Government Printing Office, Sydney. They were not used in Victoria.

D 1	D 2	D 3

Type D 1 adapted from plates of New South Wales Type D 1. No letters at foot.

1902 (1 July). *Chalk-surfaced paper. Wmk Type D 2.*

(a) P 11½, 12

D 1	D 1	½d. emerald-green	..	..	2·75	3·50
D 2		1d. emerald-green		..	12·00	5·50
D 3		2d. emerald-green		..	28·00	6·00
D 4		3d. emerald-green		..	28·00	18·00
D 5		4d. emerald-green		..	40·00	11·00
D 6		6d. emerald-green		..	55·00	9·00
D 7		8d. emerald-green		..	95·00	70·00
D 8		5s. emerald-green	..	..	£180	70·00
D1/8				Set of 8	£400	£170
D1/7 Optd "Specimen"				Set of 7	£250	

(b) P 11½, 12, compound with 11

D 9	D 1	1d. emerald-green	..	..	£200	£110
D10		2d. emerald-green	..	..	£250	£110

(c) P 11

D12	D 1	1d. emerald-green	..	£700	£300

The ½d., 6d. and 8d. exist in dull green.
Stamps may be found showing portions of the letters "N S W" at foot.

1902–4. *Type D 3, space at foot filled in. Chalky paper. Wmk Type D 2.*

(a) P 11½, 12

D13	1d. emerald-green	..	£130	70·00
D14	2d. emerald-green	..	£130	55·00
D15	3d. emerald-green	..	£150	55·00
D17	4d. emerald-green	..	40·00	9·50
D18	10d. emerald-green	..	70·00	16·00
D19	1s. emerald-green	..	55·00	10·00
D20	2s. emerald-green	..	£100	16·00
D21	5s. emerald-green	..	£600	£160

(b) P 11½, 12, compound with 11

D22	½d. emerald-green	..	6·00	4·25
D23	1d. emerald-green	..	6·00	2·00
D24	2d. emerald-green	..	20·00	2·75
D25	3d. emerald-green	..	55·00	6·50
D26	4d. emerald-green	..	50·00	6·50
D27	5d. emerald-green	..	50·00	13·00
D28	6d. emerald-green	..	50·00	9·00
D29	8d. emerald-green	..	£120	35·00
D30	10d. emerald-green	..	90·00	18·00
D31	1s. emerald-green	..	85·00	18·00
D32	2s. emerald-green	..	£120	27·00
D33	5s. emerald-green	..	£180	21·00

(c) P 11

D34	½d. emerald-green	..	£180	£120
D35	1d. emerald-green	..	65·00	16·00
D36	2d. emerald-green	..	£100	16·00
D37	3d. emerald-green	..	65·00	24·00
D38	4d. emerald-green	..	£120	32·00
D39	5d. emerald-green	..	£160	16·00
D40	6d. emerald-green	..	85·00	14·00
D41	1s. emerald-green	..	£180	38·00
D42	5s. emerald-green	..	£475	95·00
D43	10s. emerald-green	..	£1600	£1300
D44	20s. emerald-green	..	£3250	£2250
D13/44		Set of 14	£5000	£3250
D13/44 Optd "Specimen"		Set of 14	£800	

Most values exist in dull green.

D 4	D 6

1906 (From Jan)–**08.** *Chalky paper. Wmk Type D 4.*

(a) P 11½, 12, compound with 11

D45	D 3	½d. green (1907)	..	9·00	7·00
D46		1d. green	..	10·00	2·25
D47		2d. green	..	28·00	3·25
D48		3d. green	..	£425	£180
D49		4d. green (1907)	..	55·00	20·00
D50		6d. green (1908)	..	£160	20·00
D45/50		..	Set of 6	£600	£200

(b) P 11

D51	D 3	1d. dull green	..	£700	£275
D52		6d. dull green	..	£1000	£450

Shades exist.

1907 (From July). *Chalky paper. Wmk Type w 11 (see Introduction). P 11½ × 11.*

D53	D 3	½d. dull green	..	20·00	55·00
D54		1d. dull green	..	60·00	27·00
D55		2d. dull green	..	£100	70·00
D56		4d. dull green	..	£150	80·00
D57		6d. dull green	..	£200	£100
D53/7	..	..	Set of 5	£450	£275

1908 (Sept)–**09.** *Stroke after figure of value. Chalky paper. Wmk Type D 4.*

(a) P 11½ × 11

D58	D 6	1s. dull green (1909)..		75·00	8·00
D59		5s. dull green	..	£200	48·00

(b) P 11

D60	D 6	2s. dull green (1909)	..	£850	£1200
D61		10s. dull green (1909)	..	£2000	£2250
D62		20s. dull green (1909)	..	£5000	£6000
D58/62			Set of 5	£7500	£8500

Nos. D61/2 were only issued in New South Wales.

D 7

Die I	Die II

1d.

Die I	Die II

2d.

(Typo J. B. Cooke, Melbourne)

1909 (July)–**1910.** *Type D 7. Wmk Crown over A, Type w 11.*

(a) P 12×12½ (comb) or 12½ (line)

D63	½d. rosine and yellow-green	..	12·00	24·00
D64	1d. rosine and yellow-green (I)	..	13·00	4·00
	a. Die II (7.10) ..		15·00	1·00
D65	2d. rosine and yellow-green (I)	..	24·00	3·50
	a. Die II (7.10) ..		18·00	1·25
D66	3d. rosine and yellow-green (1910)	..	23·00	10·00
D67	4d. rosine and yellow-green	..	22·00	4·50
D68	6d. rosine and yellow-green	..	27·00	7·00
D69	1s. rosine and yellow-green	..	30·00	4·00
D70	2s. rosine and yellow-green	..	70·00	16·00
D71	5s. rosine and yellow-green	..	85·00	17·00
D72	10s. rosine and yellow-green	..	£250	£150
D73	£1 rosine and yellow-green	..	£475	£275
D63/73		Set of 11	£900	£450

(b) P 11

D74	1d. rose and yellow-green (II)	..	£1200	£500
D74a	2d. rose and yellow-green (II)		
D75	6d. rose and yellow-green (II)	..	£5500	£2750

Only one unused example, without gum, and another pen-cancelled are known of No. D74a.

The 1d. of this printing is distinguishable from No. D78 by the colours, the green being very yellow and the rose having less of a carmine tone. The paper is thicker and slightly toned, that of No. D78 being pure white; the gum is thick and yellowish, No. D78 having thin white gum.

All later issues of the 1d. and 2d. are Die II.

(Typo J. B. Cooke and T. S. Harrison (from May 1918))

1912–23. *Type D 7. Thin paper. White gum. W w 11. (a) P 12½.*

D76	½d. scarlet and pale yellow-green (12.12)		22·00	26·00

(b) P 11

D77	½d. rosine and bright apple-green (10.14)		11·00	14·00
	a. Wmk sideways	..	6·00	7·00
D78	1d. rosine and bright apple-green (10.14)		5·00	1·25
	a. Wmk sideways	..	9·00	1·25

(c) P 14

D79	½d. rosine and bright apple-green (1914)		75·00	90·00
	a. Carmine and apple-green (Harrison) (1920)		9·00	16·00
D80	1d. rosine and bright apple-green (10.14)		55·00	12·00
	a. Scarlet and apple-green (1918)		20·00	3·50
	b. Carmine and apple-green (Harrison) (1919)		11·00	2·75
D81	2d. scarlet and pale yellow-green (1918)		17·00	6·00
	a. Carmine and apple-green (Harrison) (1920)		16·00	3·50
D82	3d. rosine and apple-green (5.16)		70·00	32·00
	a. Wmk sideways		£1600	£1000
D83	4d. carmine and apple-green (Harrison) (1918)		85·00	50·00
	a. Wmk sideways		£475	£325
	b. Carmine and pale yellow-green (Harrison) (26.4.21)		60·00	50·00
D85	1s. scarlet and pale yellow-green (7.23)		25·00	12·00
D86	10s. scarlet and pale yellow-green (5.21)		£850	£1100
D87	£1 scarlet and pale yellow-green (5.21)		£700	£900
D76/87		Set of 8	£1500	£1900

Although printed by Cooke, the three higher values were not issued until some years later.

(Typo T. S. Harrison (to Feb. 1926), A. J. Mullet (to June 1927) and J. Ash (later))

1919–30. *Type D 7. W 6. (a) P 14.*

D91	½d. carmine and yellow-green (5.23)	..	2·50	4·75
D92	1d. carmine and yellow-green (1.3.22)	..	4·00	65
D93	1½d. carmine and yellow-green (3.25)	..	1·50	9·00
D94	2d. carmine and yellow-green (20.3.22)	..	3·00	1·75
D95	3d. carmine and yellow-green (12.11.19)	..	9·50	3·50
D96	4d. carmine and yellow-green (13.2.22)	..	35·00	12·00
D97	6d. carmine and yellow-green (13.2.22)	..	26·00	11·00

(b) P 11

D98	4d. carmine and yellow-green (9.30)	..	4·00	4·25
D91/8		Set of 8	75·00	42·00

All values perf 14 were printed by Harrison and all except the 4d. by Mullett and Ash. There is a wide variation of shades in this issue.

(Typo J. Ash)

1931–37. *Type D 7. W 15. (a) P 14.*

D100	1d. carmine and yellow-green (10.31)		8·50	11·00
	a. Imperf between (horiz pair)		†	
D102	2d. carmine and yellow-green (19.10.31)		8·50	11·00

(b) P 11

D105	½d. carmine and yellow-green (4.34)		12·00	14·00
D106	1d. carmine and yellow-green (11.32)		7·50	1·00
D107	2d. carmine and yellow-green (29.9.32)		80	60
D108	3d. carmine and yellow-green (3.37)		70·00	70·00
D109	4d. carmine and yellow-green (26.7.34)		3·75	2·25
D110	6d. carmine and yellow-green (4.36)		£300	£275
D111	1s. carmine and yellow-green (8.34)		48·00	32·00
D105/11		Set of 7	£375	£350

D 8	D 9

A	B	C

The differences are found in the middle of the "D"

D	E

Type E. Larger "1" with only three background lines above; hyphen more upright.

(Frame recess. Value typo J. Ash)

1938–39. *W 15. P 14½ × 14.*

D112	D 8	½d. carmine and green (A) (1939)		3·75	2·50
D113		1d. carmine and green (A)	..	10·00	50
D114		2d. carmine and green (A)	..	10·00	1·25
D115		3d. carmine and green (B)	..	28·00	13·00
D116		4d. carmine and green (A)	..	12·00	40
D117		6d. carmine and green (A)	..	70·00	42·00
D118		1s. carmine and green (D)	..	60·00	12·00
D112/18			Set of 7	£170	65·00

Shades exist.

1946–57. *Redrawn as Type C and E (1s.). W 15. P 14½ × 14.*

D119	D 9	½d. carmine and green (9.56)		85	3·00
D120		1d. carmine and green (11.1.47)		90	80
D121		2d. carmine and green (9.46)		4·50	1·25
D122		3d. carmine and green (25.9.46)		6·00	1·25
D123		4d. carmine and green (11.52)		9·00	1·75
D124		5d. carmine and green (12.48)		12·00	3·00
D125		6d. carmine and green (9.47)		10·00	1·75
D126		7d. carmine and green (26.8.53)		4·25	8·50
D127		8d. carmine and green (24.4.57)		10·00	25·00
D128		1s. carmine and green (9.47)		18·00	1·60
D119/28			Set of 10	65·00	42·00

There are many shades in this issue.

D 10

1953 (26 Aug)–**60.** *W 15. P 14½ × 14.*

D129	D 10	1s. carmine & yellow-grn (17.2.54)		7·50	3·00
		a. Carmine and deep green	..	11·00	8·00
D130		2s. carmine and yellow-green		18·00	12·00
		a. Carmine and deep green	..	£170	60·00
D131		5s. carmine and green	..	18·00	6·00
		a. Carmine and deep green (1960)		12·00	70
D129/31			Set of 3	40·00	19·00
D129a/31a	..		Set of 3	£170	60·00

A new die was introduced for No. D131a. This differs from the original in having a distinct gap between the two arms of the "5". On No. D131 these two features are joined.

I	II

Type I. Numeral, "D" and stop, generally unoutlined.

Type II. Clear white line separates numeral, etc. from background.

1958–60. *No wmk. P* 14½ × 14.
D132	D **9**	½d. carmine and deep green (II) (27.2.58)		1·60	1·75
D133		1d. carmine and deep green (I) (25.2.58)		3·00	3·50
		a. Type II (6.59)		1·00	65
D134		3d. carmine and deep green (II) (25.5.60)		1·75	2·50
D135		4d. carmine and deep green (I) (27.2.58)		3·75	9·00
		a. Type II (6.59)		3·00	8·50
D136		5d. carmine and deep green (I) (27.2.58)		13·00	15·00
		a. Type II (6.59)		65·00	75·00
D137		6d. carmine and deep green (II) (25.5.60)		2·75	2·75
D138		8d. carmine and deep green (II) (25.2.58)		10·00	28·00
D139		10d. carmine and deep green (II) (9.12.59)		4·50	3·25
D140	D **10**	1s. carmine and deep green (8.9.58)		5·00	3·50
		a. Deep carmine & deep green (6.59)		4·50	4·00
D141		2s. deep carmine and deep green (8.3.60)		22·00	22·00
D132/41			Set of 10	55·00	80·00

Nos. D140*a* and D141. Value tablets are re-engraved and have thicker and sharper printed lines than before.
The use of Postage Due stamps ceased on 13 January 1963.

OFFICIAL STAMPS

From 1902 the departments of the Commonwealth government were issued with stamps of the various Australian States perforated "OS" to denote official use. These were replaced in 1913 by Commonwealth of Australia issues with similar perforated initials as listed below.

During the same period the administrations of the Australian States used their own stamps and those of the Commonwealth perforated with other initials for the same purpose. These States issues are outside the scope of this catalogue.

Most shades listed under the postage issues also exist perforated "OS". Only those which are worth more than the basic colours are included below.

(O 1)　(O 2)　(O 3)

1913 (Jan–Apr). *Nos.* 1/16 *punctured as Type* O 1. *W* 2. *P* 12.
O1	**1**	½d. green (Die I)		9·50	5·50
		w. Wmk inverted		† 50·00	
O2		1d. red (Die I)		9·50	1·75
		cw. Wmk inverted		50·00	5·00
		d. Die II		12·00	2·00
		dw. Wmk inverted		50·00	5·00
O3		2d. grey (Die I)		23·00	7·00
O4		2½d. indigo (Die II)		£140	85·00
O5		3d. olive (Die I)		65·00	27·00
		ca. In pair with Die II		£475	
		dw. Wmk inverted		75·00	32·00
		e. Die II		£180	50·00
		ew. Wmk inverted		£225	60·00
O6		4d. orange (Die II)		95·00	16·00
		a. Orange-yellow		£150	60·00
O7		5d. chestnut (Die II)		70·00	23·00
O8		6d. ultramarine (Die II)		65·00	14·00
		w. Wmk inverted		75·00	35·00
O9		9d. violet (Die II)		70·00	30·00
		w. Wmk inverted		† £400	
O10		1s. emerald (Die II)		95·00	19·00
		w. Wmk inverted		£130	35·00
O11		2s. brown (Die II)		£170	80·00
		a. Double print		† £1000	
O12		5s. grey and yellow		£375	£180
O13		10s. grey and pink		£1100	£650
O14		£1 brown and ultramarine		£1800	£1100
O15		£2 black and rose		£3250	£1800
O1/15			Set of 15	£6500	£3500

1914. *Nos.* 1/16 *punctured as Type* O 2. *W* 2. *P* 12.
O16	**1**	½d. green (Die I)		8·00	3·75
		w. Wmk inverted		† 30·00	
O17		1d. red (Die I)		9·00	3·00
		d. Die II		13·00	1·75
		e. Die IIA		11·00	2·25
O18		2d. grey (Die I)		35·00	4·50
		w. Wmk inverted		45·00	8·00
O19		2½d. indigo (Die II)		£120	65·00
O20		3d. olive (Die I)		48·00	5·50
		e. Die II		£130	40·00
		ew. Wmk inverted		£160	50·00
O21		4d. orange (Die II)		£100	50·00
		a. Orange-yellow		£150	70·00
O22		5d. chestnut (Die II)		85·00	32·00
O23		6d. ultramarine (Die II)		60·00	12·00
		w. Wmk inverted		75·00	30·00
O24		9d. violet (Die II)		60·00	17·00
O25		1s. emerald (Die II)		60·00	16·00
O26		2s. brown (Die II)		£135	65·00
O27		5s. grey and yellow		£375	£200
O28		10s. grey and pink		£1300	£800
O29		£1 brown and ultramarine		£2000	£1200
O30		£2 black and rose		£3500	£1900
O16/30			Set of 15	£7000	£3750

1915. *Nos.* 24 *and* 26/30 *punctured as Type* O 2. *W* 5. *P* 12.
O31	**1**	2d. grey (Die II)		55·00	11·00
O33		6d. ultramarine (Die II)		85·00	15·00
		b. Die IIA		£750	£170
O34		9d. violet (Die II)		£130	48·00
O35		1s. blue-green (Die II)		£120	27·00
O36		2s. brown (Die II)		£425	70·00
O37		5s. grey and yellow		£500	£100
		w. Wmk inverted		£600	£130

1914–21. *Nos.* 20/3 *punctured as Type* O 2. *W* 5. *P* 14.
O38	5a	½d. bright green		7·50	2·00
		w. Wmk inverted		12·00	5·00
O39		1d. carmine-red (I)		8·00	60
		gw. Wmk inverted		14·00	2·00
		h. Die II		£250	10·00
O41		4d. orange		38·00	3·50
		a. Yellow-orange		50·00	7·50
		b. Pale orange-yellow		70·00	15·00
		c. Lemon-yellow		£110	35·00
		w. Wmk inverted		50·00	15·00
O42		5d. brown		40·00	3·00
		w. Wmk inverted		75·00	18·00
		wa. Printed on the gummed side		£400	

1915–28. *Nos.* 35/45 *punctured as Type* O 2. *W* 6. *P* 12.
O43	**1**	2d. grey (Die I)		15·00	3·00
		bw. Wmk inverted		20·00	5·00
		b. Die II		22·00	4·75
O44		2½d. deep blue (Die II)		35·00	7·50
		w. Wmk inverted		† 20·00	
O45		3d. yellow-olive (Die I)		20·00	2·50
		cw. Wmk inverted		24·00	6·00
		d. Die II		75·00	38·00
		dw. Wmk inverted		£100	50·00
		e. Die IIB		20·00	6·00
		ew. Wmk inverted		30·00	10·00
O46		6d. ultramarine (Die II)		30·00	3·25
		a. Die IIA		£450	£110
		d. Die IIB		35·00	5·50
		dw. Wmk inverted		50·00	15·00
O47		9d. violet (Die II)		22·00	6·00
		b. Die IIB		22·00	5·00
		bw. Wmk inverted		† 13·00	
O48		1s. blue-green (Die II)		23·00	2·50
		aw. Wmk inverted		50·00	13·00
		b. Die IIB		23·00	3·50
O49		2s. brown (Die II)		£110	13·00
		b. Red-brown (aniline)		£225	40·00
		w. Wmk inverted		£180	60·00
O50		5s. grey and yellow		£150	40·00
		w. Wmk inverted		£225	75·00
O51		10s. grey and pink		£250	60·00
		w. Wmk inverted			
O52		£1 chocolate and dull blue		£1300	£850
		ab. Wmk sideways. Chestnut & brt blue		† £4000	
		aw. Wmk inverted			
O53		£2 black and rose		£2000	£850
O43/53			Set of 11	£3250	£1600

1916–20. *Nos.* 47/f *and* 5d. *as No.* 23 *punctured as Type* O 2. *W* 5. *Rough paper. P* 14.
O54	5a	1d. scarlet (Die I)		16·00	2·50
		a. Deep red		16·00	2·50
		b. Rose-red		16·00	2·50
		c. Rosine		55·00	8·50
		dw. Wmk inverted		20·00	4·00
		e. Die II. Rose-red		£200	11·00
		f. Die II. Rosine		£400	38·00
		fw. Wmk inverted			
O60		5d. bright chestnut (1920)		£1200	£100

All examples of the 5d. on this paper were perforated "OS".

1918–20. *Nos.* 51 *and* 53/5 *punctured as Type* O 2. *W* 6a. *P* 14.
O61	5a	½d. green		11·00	1·75
		w. Wmk inverted		15·00	8·00
O63		1d. carmine (I)		40·00	22·00
		w. Wmk inverted			
O64		1½d. black-brown		14·00	2·25
		a. Very thin paper		28·00	9·50
		w. Wmk inverted		35·00	8·00
O65		1½d. red-brown		14·00	1·75
		w. Wmk inverted		30·00	8·00
O61/5			Set of 4	70·00	25·00

1918–23. *Nos.* 56/9 *and* 61/6 *punctured as Type* O 2. *W* 5. *P* 14.
O66	5a	½d. orange		13·00	7·50
O67		1d. violet		19·00	6·00
O68		1½d. black-brown		19·00	2·25
		w. Wmk inverted		30·00	6·00
O69		1½d. deep red-brown		15·00	1·50
		w. Wmk inverted		28·00	6·00
O70		1½d. green		11·00	1·00
O71		2d. brown-orange		12·00	1·25
		w. Wmk inverted		26·00	8·00
O72		2d. bright rose-scarlet		11·00	2·00
		w. Wmk inverted		25·00	10·00
O73		4d. violet		32·00	13·00
O74		4d. ultramarine		50·00	9·00
O75		1s. 4d. pale blue		50·00	15·00
		b. Deep turquoise		£350	£200
O66/75			Set of 10	£200	50·00

1923–24. *Nos.* 73/5 *punctured as Type* O 2. *W* 6. *P* 12.
O76	**1**	6d. chestnut (Die IIB)		17·00	2·50
O77		2s. maroon (Die II)		55·00	12·00
O78		£1 grey (Die IIB)		£475	£275
O76/8			Set of 3	£500	£275

1924. *Nos.* 76/84 *punctured as Type* O 2. *P* 14. *(a) W* 5.
O79	5a	1d. sage-green		5·00	90
O80		1½d. scarlet		4·25	40
		w. Wmk inverted		40·00	10·00
		wa. Printed on the gummed side		£160	
O81		2d. red-brown		20·00	9·00
		a. Bright red-brown		35·00	17·00
O82		3d. dull ultramarine		30·00	4·50
O83		4d. olive-yellow		35·00	3·50
O84		4½d. violet		65·00	12·00
		w. Wmk inverted		† £650	

(b) W 6a
O85	5a	1d. sage-green		11·00	12·00

(c) No wmk
O86	5a	1d. sage-green		55·00	50·00
O87		1½d. scarlet		60·00	50·00
O79/87			Set of 9	£250	£130

1926–30. *Nos.* 85/104 *punctured as Type* O 2. *W* 7. *(a) P* 14
O88	5a	½d. orange		£130	60·00
O89		1d. sage-green		7·00	50
O90		1½d. scarlet		13·00	1·60
		a. Golden scarlet		16·00	3·75
		w. Wmk inverted		14·00	2·50
O92		2d. red-brown (Die I)		90·00	35·00
O93		3d. dull ultramarine		40·00	10·00
		w. Wmk inverted		40·00	10·00
O94		4d. yellow-olive		£100	35·00
O95		4½d. violet		85·00	28·00
O96		1s. 4d. pale greenish blue		£200	£110
O88/96			Set of 8	£600	£250

(b) P 13½×12½
O97	5a	½d. orange		2·25	60
O98		1d. sage-green (Die I)		2·25	60
		b. Die II		75·00	85·00
O100		1½d. scarlet		3·00	65
		a. Golden scarlet		2·75	85
		w. Wmk inverted		4·50	2·25
O102		1½d. red-brown		12·00	3·00
O103		2d. red-brown (Die I)		19·00	9·00
O104		2d. golden scarlet (Die II)		12·00	2·00
		a. Die II		9·50	1·50
		aw. Wmk inverted		15·00	6·00
O106		3d. dull ultramarine (Die I)		28·00	5·00
		aw. Wmk inverted		28·00	12·00
		b. Die II. Deep ultramarine		14·00	1·50
		bw. Wmk inverted			† £650
O108		4d. yellow-olive		18·00	3·50
O109		4½d. violet		60·00	60·00
O110		5d. orange-brown (Die II)		38·00	5·00
O111		1s. 4d. turquoise		£150	17·00
O97/111			Set of 11	£300	90·00

1927 (9 May). *Opening of Parliament House, Canberra. No.* 105 *punctured as Type* O 3.
O112	**8**	1½d. brownish lake		12·00	9·00

1928 (29 Oct). *National Stamp Exhibition, Melbourne. No.* 106 *punctured as Type* O 2.
O113		3d. blue		13·00	9·00

1929–30. *Nos.* 107/14 *punctured as Type* O 2. *W* 7. *P* 12.
O114	**1**	6d. chestnut (Die IIB)		17·00	2·50
O115		9d. violet (Die IIB)		30·00	5·50
O116		1s. blue-green (Die IIB)		23·00	3·00
O117		2s. maroon (Die II)		60·00	10·00
O118		5s. grey and yellow		£160	40·00
O118a		10s. grey and pink			
O118b		£2 black and rose		£2000	

1929 (20 May). *Air. No.* 115 *punctured as Type* O 3.
O119	**9**	3d. green		20·00	14·00

1929 (28 Sept). *Centenary of Western Australia. No.* 116 *punctured as Type* O 3.
O120	**10**	1½d. dull scarlet		13·00	9·00

1930 (2 June). *Centenary of Exploration of River Murray by Capt. Sturt. Nos.* 117/18 *punctured as Type* O 2.
O121	**11**	1½d. scarlet		6·50	4·50
O122		3d. blue		13·00	9·50

(O 4)

1931 (4 May). *Nos.* 121/3 *optd with Type* O 4.
O123	**13**	2d. rose-red		55·00	16·00
O124		3d. blue		£200	38·00

For No. 139 overprinted with Type O 4, see No. 139*a*.

1932 (Feb)–**33.** *Optd as Type* O 4. *(a) W* 7. *(i) P* 13½×12½.
O125	5a	2d. golden scarlet (Die III)		8·00	90
		a. Opt inverted			† £2750
O126		4d. yellow-olive (3.32)		16·00	5·00

(ii) P 12
O127	**1**	6d. chestnut (3.32)		40·00	40·00

(b) W 15. *(i) P* 13½×12½
O128	5a	½d. orange (11.7.32)		4·75	1·50
		a. Opt inverted		£3000	£1800
O129		1d. green (3.32)		3·25	45
		w. Wmk inverted		45·00	25·00
		x. Wmk reversed		£150	50·00
O130		2d. golden scarlet (Die III)		6·50	55
		a. Opt inverted			† £3000
O131		3d. ultramarine (Die II) (2.33)		7·50	5·00
O132		5d. orange-brown (7.32)		35·00	27·00

(ii) P 12
O133	**1**	6d. chestnut (9.32)		20·00	20·00
		a. Opt inverted			† £4250

(c) Recess. No wmk. P 11
O134	**18**	2d. scarlet (3.32)		6·00	2·00
O135		3d. blue (3.32)		17·00	7·00
O136	**17**	1s. green (3.32)		45·00	35·00

Issue of overprinted official stamps ceased in February 1933 and thereafter mail from the federal administration was carried free.

MINIMUM PRICE

The minimum price quote is 10p which represents a handling charge rather than a basis for valuing common stamps. For further notes about prices see introductory pages.

BRITISH COMMONWEALTH OCCUPATION FORCE (JAPAN)

Nos. J1/7 were used by the Australian forces occupying Japan after the Second World War. Initially their military post offices supplied unoverprinted Australian stamps, but it was decided to introduce the overprinted issue to prevent currency speculation.

B.C.O.F.
JAPAN
1946
(1)

B.C.O.F.
JAPAN
1946
(2)

Ͻ.F.Ͻ.F.
1946 AN AN

Wrong fount "6"   Normal   Narrow "N"
(left pane R. 9/4)   (right pane R. 1/8)

1946 (11 Oct)–48. *Stamps of Australia optd as T* **1** (1d., 3d.) or *T* **2** (others) at Hiroshima Printing Co, Japan.

J1	27	½d. orange (No. 179)			3·00	4·25
		a. Wrong fount "6"			55·00	65·00
		b. Narrow "N"			55·00	65·00
		c. Stop after "JAPAN" (right pane R.5/5)			55·00	65·00
J2	46	1d. brown-purple (No. 203)			2·50	1·75
		a. Blue-black overprint			55·00	95·00
J3	31	3d. purple-brown (No. 187)			2·00	2·00
		a. Opt double			£400	
J4	34	6d. purple-brown (No. 189a) (8.5.47)			15·00	9·00
		a. Wrong fount "6"			£160	£110
		b. Stop after "JAPAN" (right pane R. 5/5)			£160	£110
		c. Narrow "N"			£160	£110
J5	36	1s. grey-green (No. 191) (8.5.47)			15·00	11·00
		a. Wrong fount "6"			£170	£130
		b. Stop after "JAPAN" (right pane R.5/5)			£170	£130
		c. Narrow "N"			£170	£130
J6	1	2s. maroon (No. 212) (8.5.47)			42·00	45·00
J7	38	5s. claret (No. 176) (8.5.47)			£120	£130
		a. Thin rough paper (No. 176a) (1948)			£130	£150
J1/7				*Set of 7*	£180	£180

The ½d., 1d. and 3d. values were first issued on 11 October 1946, and withdrawn two days later, but were re-issued together with the other values on 8 May 1947.

The following values with T **2** in the colours given were from proof sheets which, however, were used for postage: ½d. (red), 1d. (red or black) and 3d. (gold, red or black). (*Prices for black opts* £100, *each, and for red or gold from* £300 *each, all un*)

The use of B.C.O.F. stamps ceased on 12 February 1949.

AUSTRALIAN ANTARCTIC TERRITORY

For use at the Antarctic bases of Casey (opened early 1969: used Wilkes postmark until early 1970), Davis (closed from 1965 until early 1969), Heard Island (seasonal occupation only), Macquarie Island, Mawson and Wilkes (closed January 1969). Stamps of Australia were used from the bases before the introduction of Australian Antarctic Territory issues.

The following are also valid for use in Australia, where they are put on sale for a limited period when first issued.

DATES OF ISSUE. The dates given refer to release dates in Australia. Local release dates are usually later and where known they are given in footnotes.

1 1954 Expedition at Vestfold Hills and Map

(Des. T. Lawrence: adapted by artist of the Printing Branch. Recess)

1957 (27 Mar). *P* 14½.

1	1	2s. ultramarine			1·25	50

Issued Macquarie Island 11.12.57, Davis 6.2.58, Mawson 18.2.58, Wilkes 1.2.59.

2 Members of Shackleton Expedition at South Magnetic Pole, 1909

3 Weazel and Team

1959 (16 Dec). *T* **2** *and designs as T* **3**. *Recess; new values surch typo* (5d., 8d.). *P* 14½ (5d.), 14½ × 14 (8d.) or 14 × 14½ (others).

2		5d. on 4d. black and sepia			60	15
3		8d. on 7d. black and indigo			4·50	2·25
4		1s. deep green			3·50	2·00
5		2s. 3d. green			9·00	4·00
2/5				*Set of 4*	16·00	7·50

Designs: Values—1s. Dog-team and iceberg; 2s. 3d. Map of Antarctica and Emperor Penguins. Issued Macquarie Island 26.12.59, Davis 30.1.60, Mawson 10.2.60, Wilkes 13.2.60.

6

7 Sir Douglas Mawson (Expedition leader)

1961 (5 July). *Recess. P* 14½.

6	6	5d. deep blue			1·25	20

Issued Macquarie Island 6.12.61, Wilkes 10.1.62, Davis 20.1.62, Mawson 30.1.62.

1961 (18 Oct). *50th Anniv of 1911–14 Australasian Antarctic Expedition. Recess. P* 14½.

7	7	5d. myrtle-green			35	20

Issued Macquarie Island 6.12.61, Wilkes 10.1.62, Davis 20.1.62, Mawson 30.1.62.

(New Currency. 100 cents = 1 Australian dollar)

8 Aurora and Camera Dome

9 Bell 47G Trooper Helicopter

(Des J. Mason. Photo)

1966 (28 Sept)–68. *T* **8/10** *and similar multicoloured designs. P* 13½.

8	1 c.	Type 8 (*shades*)			70	30
9	2 c.	Emperor Penguins (*shades*)			2·50	80
10	4 c.	Ship and iceberg			90	90
11	5 c.	Banding Elephant-seals (25.9.68)			2·75	1·75
12	7 c.	Measuring snow strata			80	80
13	10 c.	Wind gauges			1·00	90
14	15 c.	Weather balloon			4·50	2·00
15	20 c.	Type 9			5·00	2·25
16	25 c.	Radio operator			3·00	3·00
17	50 c.	Ice compression tests			5·50	5·50
18	$1	Parahelion ("mock sun")			27·00	12·00
8/18				*Set of 11*	48·00	27·00

The 1 c. to 15 c. are vert as Type **8**; the 25 c., 50 c. and $1 are horiz as Type **9**.

Nos. 8/10 and 12/18 placed on sale locally at Macquarie Island on 11.12.66, Wilkes 9.2.67 and Mawson 16.2.67.

No. 11 issued Macquarie Island 4.12.68, Mawson 13.1.69, Wilkes/Casey 9.2.69 and Davis 20.2.69.

11 Sastrugi (Snow Ridges)

12 Capt. Cook, Sextant and Compass

(Des J. Mason. Photo)

1971 (23 June). *Tenth Anniv of Antarctic Treaty. T* **11** *and similar horiz design. P* 13½.

19		6 c. blue and black			75	1·00
20		30 c. multicoloured (Pancake ice)			3·25	6·00

Issued Macquarie Island 23.11.71, Mawson 27.12.71, Davis 13.1.72 and Casey 17.1.72.

(Des J. Mason. Photo)

1972 (13 Sept). *Bicentenary of Cook's Circumnavigation of Antarctica. T* **12** *and similar horiz design. Multicoloured. P* 13½.

21		7 c. Type 12			1·25	75
22		35 c. Chart and H.M.S. *Resolution*			4·75	6·00

Issued Macquarie Island 19.11.72, Mawson 24.12.72, Davis 3.1.73 and Casey 22.1.73.

13 Plankton

14 Admiral Byrd (expedition leader), Ford 4-AT-B Trimotor *Floyd Bennett* and Map of South Pole

(Des G. Browning (1, 7, 9, 10, 20 c., $1), R. Honisett (others). Photo)

1973 (5 Aug). *T* **13** *and similar multicoloured designs. P* 13½.

23	1 c.	Type 13			30	15
24	5 c.	Mawson's De Havilland D.H.60G Gipsy Moth, 1931			50	50
25	7 c.	Adélie Penguin			2·25	70
26	8 c.	Rymill's De Havilland D.H.83 Fox Moth, 1934–7			75	70

27	9 c.	Leopard Seal (*horiz*)			40	70
28	10 c.	Killer Whale (*horiz*)			5·50	2·00
		a. Buff (overlay on seals) omitted			£850	
29	20 c.	Wandering Albatross (*horiz*)			1·25	1·00
30	25 c.	Wilkins's Lockheed X-3903 *San Francisco*, 1928 (*horiz*)			90	1·00
31	30 c.	Ellsworth's Northrop Gamma *Polar Star*, 1935			70	1·00
32	35 c.	Christensen's Avro Type 581 Avian, 1934 (*horiz*)			70	80
33	50 c.	Byrd's Ford 4-AT-B Trimotor *Floyd Bennett*, 1929			70	1·00
34	$1	Sperm Whale			1·25	1·40
23/34				*Set of 12*	13·50	9·75

Issued Macquarie Island 29.11.73, Mawson 30.12.73, Davis 10.1.74 and Casey 31.1.74.

(Des R. Honisett. Litho Asher and Co, Melbourne)

1979 (20 June). *50th Anniv of First Flight over South Pole. T* **14** *and similar horiz design. Multicoloured. P* 15½.

35	20 c.	Type 14			30	50
36	55 c.	Admiral Byrd, Ford 4-AT-B Trimotor *Floyd Bennett* and Antarctic terrain			80	1·50

Issued Macquarie Island 24.10.79, Davis 3.1.80, Mawson 13.1.80 and Casey 9.2.80.

15 *Thala Dan* (supply ship)

16 Sir Douglas Mawson in Antarctic Terrain

(Des R. Honisett, Litho Asher and Co, Melbourne)

1979 (29 Aug)–81. *Ships. Multicoloured designs as T* **15**. *P* 13½ × 13 (*horiz*) or 13 × 13½ (*vert*).

37	1 c.	Aurora (*horiz*) (21.5.80)			15	10
38	2 c.	Penola (Rymill) (9.9.81)			40	10
39	5 c.	Type 15			30	40
40	10 c.	H.M.S. *Challenger* (survey ship) (*horiz*) (9.9.81)			50	45
41	15 c.	*Morning** (bow view) (whaling ship) (*horiz*) (21.5.80)			2·00	3·00
42	15 c.	*Nimrod* (stern view) (Shackleton) (*horiz*) (9.9.81)			1·40	60
43	20 c.	Discovery II (supply ship) (*horiz*)			90	1·50
44	22 c.	Terra Nova (Scott) (21.5.80)			90	1·25
45	25 c.	Endurance (Shackleton)			60	1·00
46	30 c.	Fram (Amundsen) (*horiz*)			60	1·50
47	35 c.	Nella Dan (supply ship) (*horiz*) (21.5.80)			80	1·50
48	40 c.	Kista Dan (supply ship) (9.9.81)			1·25	1·00
49	45 c.	L'Astrolabe (D'Urville) (*horiz*) (9.9.81)			70	70
50	50 c.	Norvegia (supply ship) (9.9.81)			70	70
51	55 c.	Discovery (Scott)			85	2·00
52	$1	H.M.S. *Resolution* (Cook) (21.5.80)			1·75	2·50
37/52				*Set of 16*	12·00	16·00

*No. 41 is incorrectly inscribed "S.Y. *Nimrod*".

On No. 46 the S.S. *Fram* is shown flying the Icelandic ensign, instead of the Norwegian.

Nos. 37, 41, 44, 47 and 52 issued Macquarie Island 27.10.80, Casey 1.12.80, Mawson 5.12.80 and Davis 11.12.80.

Nos. 38, 40, 42 and 48/50 issued Macquarie Island 21.10.81, Mawson 25.11.81, Davis 11.1.82 and Casey 25.1.82.

Nos. 39, 43, 45/6 and 51 issued Macquarie Island 24.10.79, Davis 3.1.80, Mawson 13.1.80 and Casey 9.2.80.

(Des R. Honisett. Litho Cambec Press, Melbourne)

1982 (5 May). *Birth Centenary of Sir Douglas Mawson (Antarctic explorer). T* **16** *and similar vert design. Multicoloured. P* 14 × 13½.

53	27 c.	Type 16			35	30
54	75 c.	Sir Douglas Mawson and map of Australian Antarctic Territory			1·25	2·00

Issued Macquarie Island 26.10.82, Casey 16.1.83, Davis 10.2.83 and Mawson 2.3.83.

17 Light-mantled Sooty Albatross

18 Antarctic Scientist

(Des R. Honisett. Litho Leigh-Mardon Ltd, Melbourne)

1983 (6 Apr). *Regional Wildlife. T* **17** *and similar vert designs. Multicoloured. P* 14½.

55	27 c.	Type 17			85	90
		a. Horiz strip of 5. Nos. 55/9			3·75	
56	27 c.	King Cormorant			85	90
57	27 c.	Southern Elephant-Seal			85	90
58	27 c.	Royal Penguin			85	90
59	27 c.	Dove Prion			85	90
55/9				*Set of 5*	3·75	4·00

Nos. 55/9 were issued together, *se-tenant*, in horizontal strips of five, forming a composite design.

Issued Macquarie Island 21.10.83, Mawson 9.12.83, Casey 1.1.84 and Davis 2.1.84.

(Des R. Honisett. Litho Leigh-Mardon Ltd, Melbourne)

1983 (7 Sept). *12th Antarctic Treaty Consultative Meeting, Canberra. P* 14½.
60   18   27 c. multicoloured   55   55
    Issued Macquarie Island 21.10.83, Mawson 9.12.83, Casey 1.1.84 and Davis 2.1.84.

19 Prismatic Compass and   **20** Dog Team pulling Sledge
Lloyd-Creak Dip Circle

(Des R. Fletcher. Litho Leigh-Mardon Ltd, Melbourne)

1984 (16 Jan). *75th Anniv of Magnetic Pole Expedition. T* **19** *and similar horiz design. Multicoloured. P* 14½.
61   30 c. Type **19**   50   50
62   85 c. Aneroid barometer and theodolite   ..   1·25   1·50
    Issued Macquarie Island 23.10.84, Mawson 15.11.84, Casey 16.11.84 and Davis 1.2.85.

(Des G. Emery. Litho Leigh-Mardon Ltd (2, 10, 20, 36, 60 c.) or Cambec Press (others), both of Melbourne)

1984 (18 July)–**87**. *Antarctic Scenes. T* **20** *and similar multicoloured designs. P* 14½ *(2 c., 10 c., 20 c., 36 c., 60 c.), 14×13½ (45 c., 90 c.) or 13½×14 (others).*
63   2 c. Summer afternoon, Mawson Station
         (11.3.87)   10   30
64   5 c. Type **20**   15   15
65   10 c. Late summer evening, MacRobertson
         Land (11.3.87)   15   15
66   15 c. Prince Charles Mountains (7.8.85)   ..   15   20
67   20 c. Summer morning, Wilkes Land (11.3.87)   15   20
68   25 c. Sea-ice and iceberg   40   50
69   30 c. Mount Coates   25   30
70   33 c. "Iceberg Alley", Mawson (7.8.85)   ..   25   30
71   36 c. Early winter evening, Casey Station
         (11.3.87)   30   35
72   45 c. Brash ice (*vert*) (7.8.85)   70   1·00
73   60 c. Midwinter shadows, Casey Station
         (11.3.87)   50   55
74   75 c. Coastline   ..   ..   ..   2·00   2·50
75   85 c. Landing strip   ..   ..   ..   2·25   2·75
76   90 c. Pancake ice (*vert*) (7.8.85)   ..   75   80
77   $1 Emperor Penguins (7.8.85) (Optd S. 50p)   2·00   90
63/77   ..   ..   *Set of* 15   9·00   9·75
    Nos. 63, 65, 67, 71 and 73 issued Macquarie Island 6.10.87, Davis 25.11.87, Mawson 1.1.88 and Casey 13.1.88.
    Nos. 64, 68/9 and 74/5 issued Macquarie Island 23.10.84, Mawson 15.11.84, Casey 16.11.84 and Davis 1.2.85.
    Nos. 66, 70, 72 and 76/7 issued Heard Island 1.11.85, Casey 31.11.85, Mawson 6.12.85, Macquarie Island 6.12.85 and Davis 11.12.85.

21 Prince Charles Mountains   **22** Hourglass Dolphins
near Mawson Station   and *Nella Dan*

(Des A. McGregor. Litho Cambec Press, Melbourne)

1986 (17 Sept). *25th Anniv of Antarctic Treaty. P* 14×13½.
78   **21**   36 c. multicoloured   ..   ..   1·25   85
    Issued Mawson 9.11.86, Davis 15.11.86, Casey 23.11.86 and Macquarie Island 7.12.86.

(Des Trish Hart. Litho CPE Australia Ltd, Melbourne)

1988 (20 July). *Environment, Conservation and Technology. T* **22** *and similar square designs. Multicoloured. P* 13.
79   37 c. Type **22**   ..   ..   ..   1·00   1·10
    a. Horiz strip of 5. Nos. 79/83   ..   4·50
80   37 c. Emperor Penguins and Davis Station   1·00   1·10
81   37 c. Crabeater Seal and Hughes 500D
         helicopters   ..   ..   ..   1·00   1·10
82   37 c. Adelie Penguins and tracked vehicle   1·00   1·10
83   37 c. Grey-headed Albatross and photo-
         grapher   ..   ..   ..   1·00   1·10
79/83   ..   ..   *Set of* 5   4·50   5·00
    Nos. 79/83 were printed together, *se-tenant*, in horizontal strips of five throughout the sheet.
    Issued Macquarie Island 29.10.88, Casey 14.12.88, Mawson 21.12.88 and Davis 29.12.88.

23 "Antarctica"   **24** Aurora Australis

(Des Janet Boschen. Litho CPE Australia Ltd, Melbourne)

1989 (14 June). *Antarctic Landscape Paintings by Sir Sidney Nolan. T* **23** *and similar vert designs. Multicoloured. P* 14 × 13½.
84   39 c. Type **23**   ..   ..   ..   1·00   70
85   39 c. "Iceberg Alley"   ..   ..   1·00   70
86   60 c. "Glacial Flow"   ..   ..   1·75   1·25
87   80 c. "Frozen Sea"   ..   ..   2·25   1·40
84/7   ..   ..   ..   *Set of* 4   5·50   3·50
    Issued Casey 28.10.89, Davis 29.10.89, Mawson 17.11 89 and Macquarie Island 24.11.89.

    Supplies of Australia Nos. 1261/3 were sent to the Antarctic and were issued at Macquarie Island on 24.11.90, Mawson 10.12.90, Davis 14.12.90 and Casey 19.12.90

(Des Lynette Brown. Litho Leigh-Mardon Ltd, Melbourne)

1991 (20 June). *30th Anniv of Antarctic Treaty (43 c.) and Maiden Voyage of* Aurora Australis (*research ship*) ($1.20). *T* **24** *and similar horiz design. Multicoloured. P* 14½.
88   43 c. Type **24**   75   50
89   $1.20, *Aurora Australis* off Heard Island
         (optd S. 55p.)   ..   ..   2·50   2·25
    Issued Mawson 12.11.91, Casey 22.12.91, Macquarie Island 17.1.92 and Davis 9.2.92.

25 Adélie Penguin and   **26** Head of
Chick   Husky

(Des Janet Boschen. Litho McPherson's Ptg Group, Mulgrave ($1, $1.40, $1.50) or Printset Cambec Pty Ltd (others))

1992 (14 May)–**93**. *Antarctic Wildlife. T* **25** *and similar multicoloured designs. P* 14½×14 ($1.20, $1.50) *or* 14×14½ (*others*).
90   45 c. Type **25**   40   45
91   75 c. Elephant Seal with pup   ..   65   70
92   85 c. Hall's Giant Petrel on nest with
         fledgeling   75   80
93   95 c. Weddell Seal and pup   ..   80   85
94   $1 Royal Penguin (14.1.93)   ..   90   95
95   $1.20, Emperor Penguins with chicks (*vert*)
         (Optd. S. 55p)   ..   ..   1·00   1·10
96   $1.40, Fur Seal (14.1.93)   ..   ..   1·25   1·40
97   $1.50, King Penguin (*vert*) (14.1.93)   ..   1·25   1·40
90/7   ..   ..   ..   *Set of* 8   6·25   7·00
    Nos. 90/3 and 95 issued Mawson 2.11.92, Davis 11.11.92, Casey 27.11.92 and Macquarie Island 10.12.92.
    Nos. 94 and 96/7 issued Mawson 28.10.93, Casey 13.11.93, Davis 2.12.93 and Macquarie Island 19.12.93.

(Des FHA Design. Litho Leigh-Mardon Ltd, Melbourne)

1994 (13 Jan). *Departure of Huskies from Antarctica. T* **26** *and similar multicoloured designs. P* 14½.
104   45 c. Type **26**   60   50
105   75 c. Dogs pulling sledge (*horiz*)   ..   1·00   1·10
106   85 c. Husky in harness   ..   ..   1·25   1·40
107   $1.05, Dogs on leads (*horiz*)   ..   1·40   1·50
104/7   ..   ..   ..   *Set of* 4   3·75   4·00
    Issued Casey 31.10.94, Davis 11.11.94, Mawson 14.11.94 and Macquarie Island 4.12.94.

27 Humpback Whale with   **28** "Rafting Sea Ice"
Calf   (Christian Clare
                              Robertson)

(Des D. Nelson. Litho Leigh-Mardon Ltd, Melbourne)

1995 (15 June). *Whales and Dolphins. T* **27** *and similar multicoloured designs. P* 14½.
108   45 c. Type **27**   65   65
109   45 c. Pair of Hourglass Dolphins (*vert*)   ..   65   65
    a. Horiz pair. Nos. 109/10   ..   1·25   1·25
110   45 c. Pair of Minke Whales (*vert*)   ..   65   65
111   $1 Killer Whale   ..   ..   ..   1·50   1·50
108/11   ..   ..   ..   *Set of* 4   3·00   3·00
MS112   146×64 mm. Nos. 108/11   ..   3·00   3·00
    Nos. 109/10 were printed together, *se-tenant*, in horizontal pairs throughout the sheet, with the background forming a composite design.
    Issued Macquarie Island 18.11.95, Casey 5.12.95, Mawson 16.12.95 and Davis 20.12.95.
    No. **MS**112 also exists overprinted "Singapore 95 World Stamp Exhibition", "Philately and Collections Fair, Hong Kong '95" or "CAPEX '96 WORLD PHILATELIC EXHIBITION EXPOSITION PHILATELIQUE MONDIALE" for sale at these exhibitions.

(Des Melinda Whitechurch. Litho McPherson's Ptg Group, Mulgrave)

1996 (16 May). *Paintings by Christian Clare Robertson. T* **28** *and similar vert designs. Multicoloured. P* 14½×14.
113   45 c. Type **28**   55   55
    a. Horiz pair. Nos. 113/14   ..   1·10   1·10
114   45 c. "Shadow on the Plateau"   ..   55   55
115   $1 "Ice Cave"   ..   ..   ..   1·40   1·40
116   $1.20, "Twelve Lake"   ..   ..   1·60   1·60
113/16   ..   ..   ..   *Set of* 4   3·75   3·75
    Nos. 113/14 were printed together, *se-tenant*, in horizontal pairs throughout the sheet.
    Issued Macquarie Island 28.11.96, Mawson 23.12.96, Davis 29.12.96 and Casey 11.1.97.

29 Apple Huts

(Des Sophie Byass. Litho McPherson's Ptg Group, Mulgrave)

1997 (15 May). *50th Anniv of Australian National Antarctic Research Expeditions (A.N.A.R.E.). T* **29** *and similar horiz designs. Multicoloured. P* 14×14½.
117   45 c. Type **29**   50   55
    a. Pair. Nos. 117/18   ..   1·00   1·10
118   45 c. Tuning a radio receiver   ..   50   55
119   95 c. Summer surveying   90   1·10
120   $1.05, Scientists in cage above sea ice   ..   1·00   1·25
121   $1.20, Scientists and tents   ..   1·10   1·40
117/21   ..   ..   ..   *Set of* 5   3·50   4·25
    Nos. 117/18 were printed together, *se-tenant*, in horizontal and vertical pairs throughtout the sheet.

The Philatelic Register

LOOKING FOR A COMPLETE, CLASSIFIED, BUYERS GUIDE?

YOU'LL FIND OUR PHILATELIC REGISTER IN THE YELLOW SECTION AT THE BACK OF VOLUME ONE OF THIS CATALOGUE

EASY TO USE — CLASSIFIED TRADE DIRECTORY

CHRISTMAS ISLAND

Formerly a part of the Straits Settlements and then of the Colony of Singapore, Christmas Island was occupied by the Japanese from 31 March, 1942, until September, 1945. It reverted to Singapore after liberation, but subsequently became an Australian territory on 15 October 1958.

Stamps of the STRAITS SETTLEMENTS and later SINGAPORE were used on Christmas Island from 1901 until 1942 and subsequently from 1946 to 1958.

(Currency. 100 cents = 1 Malayan dollar)

1 Queen Elizabeth II

(Des G. Lissenden. Recess with name and value typo in black. Note Printing Branch, Commonwealth Bank, Melbourne)

1958 (15 Oct). *No wmk. P* 14½.

1	1	2 c. yellow-orange	..	..	55	70
2		4 c. brown	..	..	60	30
3		5 c. deep mauve	..	..	60	30
4		6 c. grey-blue	..	..	1·50	30
5		8 c. black-brown	..	..	3·00	50
6		10 c. violet	..	..	2·00	30
7		12 c. carmine	..	..	3·25	1·75
8		20 c. blue	..	..	2·50	1·75
9		50 c. yellow-green	..	..	4·00	1·75
10		$1 deep bluish green	..	..	5·00	1·75
1/10	..	..	..	*Set of* 10	21·00	8·50

PRINTERS. Nos. 11/32 were printed by the Note Printing Branch, Reserve Bank of Australia, Melbourne. Nos. 33/82 were printed in photogravure by Harrison and Sons, Ltd, London.

2 Map

11 White-tailed Tropic Bird

(Des G. Lissenden (2, 8c.), P. Morriss (4, 5, 10, 20 c.), B. Stewart (others). Recess)

1963 (28 Aug). *T* **2** *and similar designs and T* **11.** *P* 14½ × 14 ($1) *or* 14½ *(others).*

11		2 c. orange	..	..	90	55
12		4 c. red-brown	..	..	50	20
13		5 c. purple	..	..	50	20
14		6 c. indigo	..	..	40	30
15		8 c. black	..	..	3·25	60
16		10 c. violet	..	..	40	20
17		12 c. brown-red	..	..	40	30
18		20 c. blue	..	..	1·00	35
19		50 c. green	..	..	1·50	35
20		$1 yellow	..	..	3·50	60
11/20			..	*Set of* 10	11·00	3·25

Designs: *Vert*—4 c. Moonflower; 5 c. Robber Crab; 8 c. Phosphate train; 10 c. Raising phosphate. *Horiz*—6 c. Island scene; 12 c. Flying Fish Cove; 20 c. Loading cantilever; 50 c. Christmas Island Frigate Bird.

I

II

I Thick lettering

II Thinner lettering

1965. 50*th Anniversary of Gallipoli Landing. As T* **184** *of Australia, but slightly larger* (22×34½ *mm) and colour changed. Photo. P* 13½.

21		10 c. sepia, black and emerald (I) (14.4)		30	70
		a. Black-brown, black and light emerald (II)			
		(24.4)	..	..	2·00	2·00

(New Currency. 100 cents = 1 Australian dollar)

12 Golden-striped Grouper

13 "Angel" (mosaic)

(Des G. Hamori. Photo)

1968 (6 May)–70. *Fishes. T* **12** *and similar horiz designs. Multicoloured. P* 13½.

22		1 c. Type 12			45	45
23		2 c. Moorish Idol			60	20
24		3 c. Long-nosed Butterflyfish			60	30
25		4 c. Pink-tailed Triggerfish			60	20
		a. Deep blue (face value) omitted			£600	
26		5 c. Regal Angelfish			75	20
27		9 c. White-cheeked Surgeonfish			2·00	40
28		10 c. Lionfish			1·50	20
28a		15 c. Saddle Butterflyfish (14.12.70)		10·00	5·50
29		20 c. Ornate Butterflyfish			3·50	55
29a		30 c. Giant Ghost Pipefish (14.12.70)		10·00	5·50
30		50 c. Clown Surgeonfish			6·00	3·00
31		$1 Meyer's Butterflyfish			8·00	5·00
22/31				*Set of* 12	40·00	19·00

(Des G. Hamori. Photo)

1969 (10 Nov). *Christmas. P* 13½.

32	13	5 c. red, deep blue and gold	..	20	30

14 "The Ansidei Madonna" (Raphael)

15 "The Adoration of the Shepherds" (ascr to the School of Seville)

(Des Harrison)

1970 (26 Oct). *Christmas. Paintings. T* **14** *and similar vert design. Multicoloured. P* 14 × 14½.

33		3 c. Type 14			20	15
34		5 c. "The Virgin and Child, St. John the Baptist and an Angel" (Morando)		20	15

(Des Harrison)

1971 (4 Oct). *Christmas. T* **15** *and similar vert design. Multicoloured. W w* 12. *P* 14.

35		6 c. Type 15			30	50
36		20 c. "The Adoration of the Shepherds" (Reni)	70	1·00

16 H.M.S. *Flying Fish*, 1887

17 Angel of Peace

(Des V. Whiteley)

1972 (7 Feb)–73. *Ships. Horiz designs as T* **16**. *Multicoloured. P* 14×13½.

37		1 c. *Eagle* (merchantman), 1714 (5.6.72)	..	25	60
38		2 c. H.M.S. *Redpole* (gunboat), 1890 (5.6.72)	30	70
39		3 c. *Hoi Houw* (freighter), 1959 (5.6.72)	30	70
40		4 c. *Pigot* (sailing ship), 1771 (6.2.73)	40	75
41		5 c. *Valetta* (cargo-liner), 1968 (6.2.73)	40	75
42		6 c. Type 16			40	75
43		7 c. *Asia* (merchantman), 1805		40	75
44		8 c. *Islander* (freighter), 1929–60 ..	45	80
45		9 c. H.M.S. *Imperieuse* (armoured cruiser), 1888 (6.2.73)		65	70
46		10 c. H.M.S. *Cerberus* (coast defence turret ship), 1871 (4.6.73)		55	80
47		20 c. *Thomas* (galleon), 1615		70	90
48		25 c. Royal Navy sail sloop, 1864 (4.6.73)	1·00	1·00
49		30 c. *Cygnet* (flute), 1688 (4.6.73)	1·00	1·00
50		35 c. *Triadic* (freighter), 1958 (4.6.73)	1·00	1·00
51		50 c. H.M.S. *Amethyst* (frigate), 1857 (6.2.73)	1·00	1·50
52		$1 *Royal Mary* (warship), 1643 (5.6.72)	1·40	1·75
37/52				*Set of* 16	9·00	13·50

No. 45 is inscribed "H.M.S. *Imperious*", No. 46 "H.M.S. *Egeria*" and No. 48 "H.M.S. *Gordon*", all in error.

(Des Jennifer Toombs)

1972 (2 Oct). *Christmas. T* **17** *and similar vert design. Multicoloured. P* 14.

53		3 c. Type 17			30	50
		a. Pair. Nos. 53/4			60	1·00
54		3 c. Angel of Joy			30	50
55		7 c. Type 17			40	65
		a. Pair. Nos. 55/6			80	1·25
56		7 c. As No. 54			40	65
53/6				*Set of* 4	1·25	2·10

Nos. 53/4 and 55/6 have the two designs printed horizontally *se-tenant* within the sheet.

18 Virgin and Child, and Map

19 Mary and Holy Child within Christmas Star

(Des P. Law)

1973 (2 Oct). *Christmas. P* 14 × 13.

57	18	7 c. multicoloured	..	..	50	35
58		25 c. multicoloured	..	..	1·50	1·25

(Des Jennifer Toombs)

1974 (2 Oct). *Christmas. P* 13 × 14½.

59	19	7 c. mauve and grey-black			50	75
60		30 c. light orange, bright yell & grey-blk	1·50	2·75

20 "The Flight into Egypt"

21 Dove of Peace and Star of Bethlehem

(Des Jennifer Toombs)

1975 (2 Oct). *Christmas. P* 14 × 13.

61	20	10 c. light greenish yellow, agate and gold	40	35
62		35 c. bright rose, deep blue and gold	..	1·10	1·75

(Des R. Bates)

1976 (2 Oct). *Christmas. P* 13½.

63	21	10 c. cerise, lemon and bright mauve	..	25	60
		a. Pair. Nos. 63/4			50	1·10
64	–	10 c. cerise, lemon and bright mauve		25	60
65	21	35 c. reddish violet, light greenish blue and light yellow-green		40	75
		a. Pair. Nos. 65/6			80	1·50
66	–	35 c. reddish violet, light greenish blue and light yellow-green		40	75
63/6				*Set of* 4	1·10	2·40

Nos. 64 and 66 are "mirror-images" of T **21**, the two designs of each value being printed horizontally *se-tenant* throughout the sheet.

22 William Dampier (explorer)

23 Australian Coat of Arms on Map of Christmas Island

(Des V. Whiteley Studio)

1977 (30 Apr)–78. *Famous Visitors. Horiz designs as T* **22** *in black, vermilion and greenish yellow* (45 c.) *or multicoloured* (*others*). *P* 14 × 13.

67		1 c. Type 22			15	70
68		2 c. Capt. de Vlamingh (explorer) (22.2.78)	20	70
69		3 c. Vice-Admiral MacLear (22.2.78)	30	70
70		4 c. Sir John Murray (oceanographer) (22.2.78)		30	80
71		5 c. Admiral Aldrich (31.5.78)		30	40
72		6 c. Andrew Clunies Ross (first settler)	30	60
73		7 c. J. J. Lister (naturalist) (31.5.78)	30	60
74		8 c. Admiral of the Fleet Sir William May (1.9.78)		35	70
75		9 c. Henry Ridley (botanist)		40	75
76		10 c. George Clunies Ross (phosphate miner) (1.9.78)		35	55
77		20 c. Capt. Joshua Slocum (yachtsman) (1.9.78)		50	75
78		45 c. Charles Andrews (naturalist) (31.5.78) ..	85	45
79		50 c. Richard Hanitsch (biologist) (31.5.78)	95	60
80		75 c. Victor Purcell (scholar) (1.9.78)	..	85	1·25
81		$1 Fam Choo Beng (educator)	..	85	1·25
82		$2 Sir Harold Spencer-Jones (astronomer) (22.2.78)		1·00	2·25
67/82			..	*Set of* 16	7·00	11·50

(Des Mrs S. Muir. Litho Harrison)

1977 (2 June). *Silver Jubilee.* P 14½ × 13½.
83   23   45 c. multicoloured   45   55

24 "A Partridge in a Pear Tree"   25 Abbott's Booby

(Des Jennifer Toombs. Litho Questa)

1977 (20 Oct)–78. *Christmas. T 24 and similar vert designs depicting the carol "The Twelve Days of Christmas". Multicoloured.* P 14.

A. No wmk. B. W w 14 (27.1.78)

		A.		B.	
84	10 c. Type 24	10	20	25	30
	a. Sheetlet. Nos. 84/95	1·10		2·75	
85	10 c. "Two turtle doves"	10	20	25	30
86	10 c. "Three French hens"	10	20	25	30
87	10 c. "Four calling birds"	10	20	25	30
88	10 c. "Five gold rings"	10	20	25	30
89	10 c. "Six geese a-laying"	10	20	25	30
90	10 c. "Seven swans a-swimming"	10	20	25	30
91	10 c. "Eight maids a-milking"	10	20	25	30
92	10 c. "Nine ladies dancing"	10	20	25	30
93	10 c. "Ten lords a-leaping"	10	20	25	30
94	10 c. "Eleven pipers piping"	10	20	25	30
95	10 c. "Twelve drummers drumming"	10	20	25	30
84/95	Set of 12	1·10	2·25	2·75	3·25

Nos. 84/95 were printed as a *se-tenant* block within a sheetlet 142 × 170 mm.

(Des Jennifer Toombs. Litho Questa)

1978 (21 Apr). *25th Anniv of Coronation. T 25 and similar vert designs.* P 15.
96   45 c. black and bright ultramarine   ..   45   75
    a. Sheetlet. Nos. 96/8 × 2   ..   ..   2·50
97   45 c. multicoloured   45   75
98   45 c. black and bright ultramarine   ..   45   75
96/8   ..   ..   ..   Set of 3   1·25   2·00
Designs:—No. 96, White Swan of Bohun; No. 97, Queen Elizabeth II; No. 98, Type 25.
Nos. 96/8 were printed together in small sheets of 6, containing two *se-tenant* strips of 3 with horizontal gutter margin between.

26 "Christ Child"   27 Chinese Children

(Des Jennifer Toombs. Litho J.W.)

1978 (2 Oct). *Christmas. Scenes from "The Song of Christmas". T 26 and similar horiz designs. Multicoloured.* P 14.
99   10 c. Type 26   15   20
    a. Sheetlet. Nos. 99/107   ..   ..   1·25
100   10 c. "Herald Angels"   15   20
101   10 c. "Redeemer"   15   20
102   10 c. "Israel"   15   20
103   10 c. "Star"   15   20
104   10 c. "Three Wise Men"   15   20
105   10 c. "Manger"   15   20
106   10 c. "All He Stands For"   15   20
107   10 c. "Shepherds Came"   15   20
99/107   ..   ..   Set of 9   1·25   1·60
Nos. 99/107 were printed together, *se-tenant*, in a small sheet of 9.

(Des Jennifer Toombs. Litho Questa)

1979 (20 Apr). *International Year of the Child. T 27 and similar vert designs showing children of different races. Multicoloured, colour of inscr given.* P 14.
108   20 c. apple-green (Type 27)   30   45
    a. Horiz strip of 5. Nos. 108/12   ..   1·25
109   20 c. turquoise-green (Malay children)   ..   30   45
110   20 c. lilac (Indian children)   ..   30   45
111   20 c. rose (European children)   ..   30   45
112   20 c. orange-yellow ("Oranges and Lemons")   ..   30   45
108/12   ..   ..   Set of 5   1·25   2·00
Nos. 108/12 were printed together, *se-tenant*, in horizontal strips of 5 throughout the sheet, forming a composite design.

28 1958 2 c. Definitive   29 Wise Men following Star

(Des J.W. Litho Questa)

1979 (27 Aug). *Death Centenary of Sir Rowland Hill. T 28 and similar horiz designs showing stamps and Sir Rowland Hill. Multicoloured.* P 13½.
113   20 c. Type 28   25   40
    a. Horiz strip of 5. Nos. 113/17   ..   1·10
114   20 c. 1963 2 c. Map definitive   ..   25   40
115   20 c. 1965 50th anniversary of Gallipoli Landing 10 c. commemorative   25   40
116   20 c. 1968 4 c. Pink-tailed Triggerfish definitive   25   40
117   20 c. 1969 5 c. Christmas issue   ..   25   40
113/17   ..   ..   ..   Set of 5   1·10   1·75
Nos. 113/17 were printed together, *se-tenant*, in horizontal strips of 5 throughout the sheet.

(Des L. Curtis. Litho Walsall)

1979 (22 Oct). *Christmas. T 29 and similar horiz design. Multicoloured.* P 14 × 14½.
118   20 c. Type 29   20   30
119   55 c. Virgin and Child..   45   70

30 9th Green   31 Surveying

(Des R. Granger Barrett. Litho Format)

1980 (12 Feb). *25th Anniv of Christmas Island Golf Club. T 30 and similar horiz design. Multicoloured.* P 14½ × 14.
120   20 c. Type 30   50   50
121   55 c. Clubhouse   60   1·00

(Des L. Curtis. Litho Walsall)

1980 (6 May). *Phosphate Industry (1st issue). T 31 and similar horiz designs. Multicoloured.* P 14.
122   15 c. Type 31   15   25
123   22 c. Drilling for samples   20   30
124   40 c. Sample analysis   30   45
125   55 c. Mine planning   40   55
122/5   ..   ..   ..   Set of 4   95   1·40
See also Nos. 126/9, 136/9 and 140/3.

(Des L. Curtis. Litho Walsall)

1980 (14 July). *Phosphate Industry (2nd issue). Horiz designs as T 31. Multicoloured.* P 14.
126   15 c. Jungle clearing   15   15
127   22 c. Overburden removal   20   20
128   40 c. Open cut mining..   30   25
129   55 c. Restoration   35   30
126/9   ..   ..   ..   Set of 4   90   80

32 Angel with Harp   33 *Cryptoblepharus egeriae*

(Des Jennifer Toombs. Litho Walsall)

1980 (6 Oct). *Christmas. T 32 and similar vert designs. Multicoloured.* P 13½ × 13.
130   15 c. Type 32   15   25
    a. Sheetlet. Nos. 130/5   ..   ..   1·10
131   15 c. Angel with wounded soldier   ..   15   25
132   22 c. Virgin and Child..   15   30
133   22 c. Kneeling couple   15   30
134   60 c. Angel with harp (*different*)   ..   35   45
135   60 c. Angel with children   35   45
130/5   ..   ..   ..   Set of 6   1·10   1·75
Nos. 130/5 were printed together in small sheets of 6, containing two *se-tenant* strips of 3 (Nos. 130, 132, 134 and 131, 133, 135) with horizontal gutter margin between.

(Des L. Curtis. Litho Walsall)

1981 (9 Feb). *Phosphate Industry (3rd issue). Horiz designs as T 31. Multicoloured.* P 14.
136   15 c. Screening and stockpiling   20   20
137   28 c. Train loading   25   25
138   40 c. Railing   40   40
139   60 c. Drying   55   55
136/9   ..   ..   ..   Set of 4   1·25   1·25

(Des L. Curtis. Litho Walsall)

1981 (4 May). *Phosphate Industry (4th issue). Horiz designs as T 31. Multicoloured.* P 14.
140   22 c. Crushing   30   20
141   28 c. Conveying   40   25
142   40 c. Bulk storage   60   40
143   60 c. *Consolidated Venture* (bulk carrier) loading   70   55
140/3   ..   ..   ..   Set of 4   1·75   1·25

(Des L. Curtis. Litho Walsall)

1981 (10 Aug). *Reptiles. T 33 and similar horiz designs. Multicoloured.* P 13.
144   24 c. Type 33   25   25
145   30 c. *Emoia nativitata*   30   30
146   40 c. *Lepidodactylus listeri*   ..   45   45
147   60 c. *Cyrtodactylus sp. nov.*   ..   65   65
144/7   ..   ..   ..   Set of 4   1·50   1·50

34 Scene from Carol "Away in a Manger"   35 Eastern Reef Heron

(Des Jennifer Toombs. Litho Questa)

1981 (19 Oct). *Christmas. T 34 and similar horiz designs showing scenes from carol "Away in a Manger".* P 14½ × 14.
148   18 c. silver, deep blue and turquoise-blue   35   50
    a. Sheetlet. Nos. 148/51   ..   1·50
149   24 c. multicoloured   ..   40   55
150   40 c. multicoloured   ..   45   65
151   60 c. multicoloured   ..   50   75
148/51   ..   ..   Set of 4   1·50   2·25
Nos. 148/51 were printed together, *se-tenant*, in sheetlets of 4.

(Des N. Arlott. Litho Questa)

1982 (8 Mar)–83. *Birds. Multicoloured designs as T 35.* P 14.
152   1 c. Type 35   60   30
153   2 c. Common Noddy   60   30
154   3 c. White-bellied Swiftlet (14.6.82)   ..   60   70
155   4 c. Christmas Island Imperial Pigeon (14.6.82)   60   70
156   5 c. Christmas Island White Eye (21.2.83)   70   70
157   10 c. Island Thrush (14.6.82)   ..   55   70
158   25 c. Red-tailed Tropic Bird   ..   1·25   60
159   30 c. Emerald Dove (21.2.83)   ..   70   70
160   40 c. Brown Booby (23.8.82)   ..   70   55
161   50 c. Red-footed Booby (23.8.82)   ..   70   55
162   65 c. Christmas Island Frigate Bird (23.8.82)   70   65
163   75 c. White-tailed Tropic Bird (23.8.82)   90   65
164   80 c. Australian Kestrel (*vert*) (21.2.83)   1·25   1·40
165   $1 Indonesian Hawk Owl (*vert*) (21.2.83)·   2·00   1·40
166   $2 Australian Goshawk (*vert*) (14.6.82)   1·75   4·00
167   $4 Abbott's Booby (*vert*)   ..   3·00   3·25
152/67   ..   ..   ..   Set of 16   15·00   15·00

36 Joseph   37 "Mirror" Dinghy and Club House

(Des Jennifer Toombs. Litho and embossed Walsall)

1982 (18 Oct). *Christmas. Origami Paper Sculptures. T 36 and similar vert designs. Multicoloured.* P 14½ × 14.
168   27 c. Type 36   30   30
    a. Horiz strip of 3. Nos. 168/70   ..   1·25
169   50 c. Angel   45   45
170   75 c. Mary and baby Jesus   ..   65   65
168/70   ..   ..   Set of 3   1·25   1·25
Nos. 168/70 were printed together, *se-tenant*, in horiz strips of 3 throughout the sheet.

(Des L. McCombie. Litho Format)

1983 (2 May). *25th Anniv of Christmas Island Boat Club. T 37 and similar multicoloured designs.* P 14 × 14½ (27, 35 c.) or 14½ × 14 (*others*).
171   27 c. Type 37   30   35
172   35 c. Ocean-going yachts   ..   35   40
173   50 c. Fishing launch and cargo ship (*horiz*)   40   50
174   75 c. Dinghy-racing and cantilever (*horiz*)   60   70
171/4   ..   ..   ..   Set of 4   1·50   1·75

38 Maps of Christmas Island and Australia, Eastern Grey Kangaroo and White-tailed Tropic Bird   39 Candle and Holly

(Des A. Theobald. Litho Questa)

1983 (1 Oct). *25th Anniv of Christmas Island as an Australian Territory. T 38 and similar horiz designs. Multicoloured.* P 14.
175   24 c. Type 38   40   25
176   30 c. Christmas Island and Australian flag   45   45
177   85 c. Maps of Christmas Island and Australia, with Boeing 727   ..   1·25   1·25
175/7   ..   ..   Set of 3   1·90   1·75

(Des J.W. Litho Walsall)

1983 (31 Oct). *Christmas. Candles. T 39 and similar vert designs. Multicoloured.* P 13.
178   24 c. Type 39   20   20
179   30 c. Six gold candles   ..   30   40
180   85 c. Candles   70   1·00
178/80   ..   ..   Set of 3   1·10   1·40

40 Feeding on Leaf   **41** *Leucocoprinus fragilissimus*

(Des L. Curtis. Litho Questa)

1984 (20 Feb). *Red Land Crab. T* **40** *and similar horiz designs showing various aspects of crab's life. Multicoloured. P* 14 × 14½.

181	30 c. Type **40**			30	30
182	40 c. Migration			40	40
183	55 c. Development stages			50	50
184	85 c. Adult female and young			70	70
181/4			*Set of 4*	1·75	1·75

(Des I. Loe. Litho Format)

1984 (30 Apr). *Fungi. T* **41** *and similar vert designs. Multicoloured. P* 14 × 14½.

185	30 c. Type **41**			55	55
186	40 c. *Microporus xanthopus*			65	70
187	45 c. *Hydropus anthidepas* ("*Trogia anthidepas*")			75	80
188	55 c. *Haddowia longipes*			85	90
189	85 c. *Phillipsia domingensis*			1·00	1·25
185/9			*Set of 5*	3·50	3·75

42 Run-out   **43** Arrival of Father Christmas

(Des A. Theobald. Litho J.W.)

1984 (23 July). *25th Anniversary of Cricket on Christmas Island. T* **42** *and similar horiz designs. Multicoloured. P* 14.

190	30 c. Type **42**			75	85
191	40 c. Bowled-out			85	1·10
192	55 c. Batsman in action			1·10	1·50
193	85 c. Fielder diving for catch			1·25	1·75
190/3			*Set of 4*	3·50	4·75

(Des D. Slater. Litho B.D.T.)

1984 (21 Sept). *Christmas and "Ausipex" International Stamp Exhibition, Melbourne. Sheet* 100 × 100 *mm containing T* **43** *and similar horiz designs. Multicoloured. P* 13½.

MS194	30 c. Type **43**; 55 c. Distribution of presents; 85 c. Departure of Father Christmas			2·25	2·25

No. **MS**194 also contains three labels horizontally *se-tenant* with the stamps and forming composite designs with them.

44 Robber Crab   **45** "Once in Royal David's City"

(Des L. Curtis. Litho Walsall)

1985 (30 Jan). *Crabs (1st series). T* **44** *and similar horiz designs. Multicoloured. P* 13 × 13½.

195	30 c. Type **44**			90	70
196	40 c. Horn-eyed Ghost Crab			1·00	1·00
197	55 c. Purple Hermit Crab			1·40	1·40
198	85 c. Little Nipper			1·90	2·25
195/8			*Set of 4*	4·75	4·75

See also Nos. 199/202 and 203/6.

(Des L. Curtis. Litho Walsall)

1985 (29 Apr). *Crabs (2nd series). Horiz designs as T* **44**. *Multicoloured. P* 13 × 13½.

199	33 c. Blue Crab			90	55
200	45 c. Tawny Hermit Crab			1·00	1·00
201	60 c. Red Nipper			1·40	1·40
202	90 c. Smooth-handed Ghost Crab			1·90	2·25
199/202			*Set of 4*	4·75	4·75

(Des L. Curtis. Litho Walsall)

1985 (22 July). *Crabs (3rd series). Horiz designs as T* **44**. *Multicoloured. P* 13 × 13½.

203	33 c. Red Crab			1·00	60
204	45 c. Mottled Crab			1·40	1·40
205	60 c. Rock Hopper Crab			2·00	2·25
206	90 c. Yellow Nipper			2·50	3·25
203/6			*Set of 4*	6·25	6·75

(Des Jennifer Toombs. Litho Harrison)

1985 (28 Oct). *Christmas. Carols. T* **45** *and similar vert designs. Multicoloured. P* 14 × 14½.

207	27 c. Type **45**			90	1·10
	a. Horiz strip of 5. Nos. 207/11			5·50	
208	33 c. "While Shepherds Watched Their Flocks by Night"			1·00	1·25
209	45 c. "Away in a Manger"			1·25	1·50
210	60 c. "We Three Kings of Orient Are"			1·40	1·60
211	90 c. "Hark the Herald Angels Sing"			1·50	1·75
207/11			*Set of 5*	5·50	6·50

Nos. 207/11 were printed together, *se-tenant* in horizontal strips of 5 throughout the sheet.

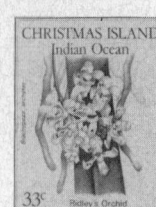

46 Halley's Comet over Christmas Island   **47** Ridley's Orchid

(Des L. Curtis. Litho Format)

1986 (30 Apr). *Appearance of Halley's Comet. T* **46** *and similar horiz designs. Multicoloured. P* 14.

212	33 c. Type **46**			65	80
213	45 c. Edmond Halley			80	1·10
214	60 c. Comet and *Consolidated Venture* (bulk carrier) loading phosphate			1·00	1·75
215	90 c. Comet over Flying Fish Cove			1·50	2·25
212/15			*Set of 4*	3·50	5·50

(Des I. Loe. Litho Format)

1986 (30 June). *Native Flowers. T* **47** *and similar vert designs. Multicoloured. P* 14.

216	33 c. Type **47**			50	55
217	45 c. Hanging Flower			65	85
218	60 c. Hoya			75	1·25
219	90 c. Sea Hibiscus			1·10	1·75
216/19			*Set of 4*	2·75	4·00

(Des D. Miller. Litho Walsall)

1986 (23 July). *Royal Wedding. Square designs as T* **112** *of Ascension. Multicoloured. P* 14½ × 14.

220	33 c. Prince Andrew and Miss Sarah Ferguson			45	50
221	90 c. Prince Andrew piloting helicopter, Digby, Canada, 1985			95	1·75

48 Father Christmas and Reindeer in Speed Boat

(Des G. Vasarhelyi. Litho Walsall)

1986 (30 Sept). *Christmas. T* **48** *and similar horiz designs. Multicoloured. P* 13 × 13½.

222	30 c. Type **48**			65	50
223	36 c. Father Christmas and reindeer on beach			75	60
224	55 c. Father Christmas fishing			1·25	1·40
225	70 c. Playing golf			1·75	2·25
226	$1 Sleeping in hammock			2·00	3·00
222/6			*Set of 5*	5·75	7·00

49 H.M.S. *Flying Fish* and Outline Map of Christmas Island

(Des L. Curtis. Litho Format)

1987 (21 Jan). *Centenary of Visits by H.M.S. "Flying Fish" and H.M.S. "Egeria". T* **49** *and similar horiz design. Multicoloured. P* 14½.

227	36 c. Type **49**			80	75
228	90 c. H.M.S. *Egeria* and outline map			1·60	3·00

PRICES OF SETS

Set prices are given for many issues, generally those containing three stamps or more. Definitive sets include one of each value or major colour change, but do not cover different perforations, die types or minor shades. Where a choice is possible the set prices are based on the cheapest versions of the stamps included in the listings.

50 Blind Snake   **51** Children watching Father Christmas in Sleigh

(Des G. Drummond. Litho Questa)

1987 (25 Mar)–**89**. *Wildlife. T* **50** *and similar horiz designs. Multicoloured. P* 14.

229	1 c. Type **50**			40	80
	a. Sheetlet of 16. Nos. 229/37 and 238/44 (1.3.88)			27·00	
230	2 c. Blue-tailed Skink			40	80
231	3 c. Insectivorous Bat (24.6.87)			80	80
232	5 c. Grasshopper (1.3.88)			80	80
233	10 c. Christmas Island Fruit Bat (24.6.87)			80	80
234	25 c. Gecko			80	80
235	30 c. *Mantis religiosa* (mantid) (1.3.88)			1·00	90
236	36 c. Indonesian Hawk Owl (24.6.87)			2·50	1·60
237	40 c. Bull-mouth Helmet (*Cypraecassis rufa*) (26.8.87)			1·00	90
237a	41 c. Nudibranch (*Phidiana* sp) (1.9.89)			1·00	70
238	50 c. Textile or Cloth of Gold Cone (*Conus textile*) (26.8.87)			1·10	1·00
239	65 c. Brittle Stars (26.8.87)			1·10	1·00
240	75 c. Regal Angelfish (26.8.87)			1·10	1·00
241	90 c. *Appias paulina* (butterfly) (1.3.88)			3·50	2·50
242	$1 *Hypolimnas misippus* (butterfly) (1.3.88)			3·50	2·50
243	$2 Shrew (*Crocidura attenuata trichura*) (24.6.87)			3·50	4·50
244	$5 Green Turtle			4·50	6·50
229/44			*Set of 17*	25·00	25·00

No. 229a was originally only available from a presentation pack, but was, subsequently, sold separately by the Christmas Island Post Office. Stamps from it show "1988" imprint date. Examples from the ordinary sheets are without imprint date.

(Des D. Miller. Litho CPE Australia Ltd, Melbourne)

1987 (7 Oct). *Christmas. Sheet,* 165 × 65 *mm, containing T* **51** *and similar multicoloured designs. P* 13½.

MS245	30 c. Type **51**; 37 c. Father Christmas distributing gifts (48 × 22 *mm*); 90 c. Children with presents (48 × 22 *mm*); $1 Singing carols			4·00	4·00
	a. Imperf between 37 c. and 90 c.				

The stamps within No. **MS**245 form a composite design of a beach scene.

(Des Sue Passmore. Litho CPE Australia Ltd, Melbourne)

1988 (26 Jan). *Bicentenary of Australian Settlement. Arrival of First Fleet. Square designs as Nos.* 1105/9 *of Australia, but each inscribed "CHRISTMAS ISLAND Indian Ocean" and "AUSTRALIA BICENTENARY".*

246	37 c. Aborigines watching arrival of Fleet, Botany Bay			1·40	1·60
	a. Horiz strip of 5. Nos. 246/50			6·25	
247	37 c. Aboriginal family and anchored ships			1·40	1·60
248	37 c. Fleet arriving at Sydney Cove			1·40	1·60
249	37 c. Ship's boat			1·40	1·60
250	37 c. Raising the flag, Sydney Cove, 26 January 1788			1·40	1·60
246/50			*Set of 5*	6·25	7·25

Nos. 246/50 were printed together, *se-tenant*, in horizontal strips of five throughout the sheet, forming a composite design.

52 Captain William May   **53** Pony and Trap, 1910

(Des Josephine Martin. Litho Questa)

1988 (8 June). *Centenary of British Annexation. T* **52** *and similar vert designs. Multicoloured. P* 14½ × 14.

251	37 c. Type **52**			35	40
252	53 c. Annexation ceremony			50	55
253	95 c. H.M.S. *Imperieuse* (armoured cruiser) firing salute			90	95
254	$1.50, Building commemorative cairn			1·40	1·50
251/4			*Set of 4*	2·50	3·00

(Des L. Curtis. Litho Walsall)

1988 (24 Aug). *Centenary of Permanent Settlement. T* **53** *and similar horiz designs. Multicoloured. P* 14 × 14½.

255	37 c. Type **53**			45	40
256	55 c. Phosphate mining, 1910			60	55
257	70 c. Steam locomotive, 1914			85	85
258	$1 Arrival of first aircraft, 1957			1·25	1·25
255/8			*Set of 4*	2·75	2·75

54 Beach Toys | **55** Food on Table ("Good Harvesting")

(Des N. Shewring. Litho Format)

988 (15 Nov). *Christmas. Toys and Gifts. T* **54** *and similar vert designs. Multicoloured. P* 14.

59	32 c. Type **54**			40	35
60	39 c. Flippers, snorkel and mask			50	40
61	90 c. Model soldier, doll and soft toys			1·10	1·10
62	$1 Models of racing car, lorry and jet aircraft			1·25	1·25
59/62			Set of 4	3·00	2·75

(Des D. Miller. Litho Questa)

989 (31 Jan). *Chinese New Year. T* **55** *and similar horiz designs. Multicoloured. P* 14 × 14¹/₂.

63	39 c. Type **55**			45	40
64	70 c. Decorations ("Prosperity")			80	70
65	90 c. Chinese girls ("Good Fortune")			1·10	90
66	$1 Lion dance ("Progress Every Year")			1·25	1·00
63/6			Set of 4	3·25	2·75

56 Sir John Murray | **57** Four Children

(Des S. Noon. Litho Walsall)

989 (16 Mar). *75th Death Anniv of Sir John Murray (oceanographer). T* **56** *and similar horiz designs. Multicoloured. P* 14 × 14¹/₂.

67	39 c. Type **56**			50	50
68	80 c. Map of Christmas Island showing Murray Hill			95	95
69	$1 Oceanographic equipment			1·25	1·25
70	$1.10, H.M.S. *Challenger* (survey ship), 1872			1·50	1·50
67/70			Set of 4	3·75	3·75

(Des C. Burke. Litho Questa)

989 (31 May). *Malay Hari Raya Festival. T* **57** *and similar vert designs. Multicoloured. P* 14.

271	39 c. Type **57**			50	50
272	55 c. Man playing tambourine			70	70
273	80 c. Girl in festival costume			1·00	1·00
274	$1.10, Christmas Island Mosque			1·40	1·40
271/4			Set of 4	3·25	3·25

58 *Huperzia phlegmaria* | **59** Virgin Mary and Star

(Des Kerrie Rockett. Litho Walsall)

989 (16 Aug). *Ferns. T* **58** *and similar vert designs. Multicoloured. P* 14.

275	41 c. Type **58**			60	60
276	65 c. *Asplenium polydon*			85	85
277	80 c. Common Bracken			1·00	1·00
278	$1.10, Birds-nest Fern			1·40	1·40
275/8			Set of 4	3·50	3·50

(Des G. Maynard. Litho Leigh-Mardon Ltd, Melbourne)

989 (4 Oct). *Christmas. T* **59** *and similar vert designs. Multicoloured. P* 14¹/₂.

279	36 c. Type **59**			50	40
280	41 c. Christ Child in manger			60	45
281	80 c. Shepherds and Star			1·25	80
282	$1.10, Three Wise Men following Star			1·40	1·10
279/82			Set of 4	3·25	2·50

COVER PRICES

Cover factors are quoted at the beginning of each country for most issues to 1945. An explanation of the system can be found on page x. The factors quoted do not, however, apply to philatelic covers.

---

(60) | **61** First Sighting, 1615

1989 (18 Oct). *"Melbourne Stampshow '89". No.* 237a *and as No.* 242, *but with imprint date, optd with T* **60**.

283	41 c. Nudibranch (*Phidiana* sp)			40	45
284	$1 *Hypolimnas misippus*			1·00	1·00

(Des R. Honisett. Litho Note Ptg Branch, Reserve Bank of Australia)

1990 (31 Jan). *375th Anniv of Discovery of Christmas Island. T* **61** *and similar vert design. Multicoloured. P* 14×15.

285	41 c. Type **61**			75	50
286	$1.10, Second sighting and naming, 1643		1·75	1·40

62 Miniature Tractor pulling Phosphate | **63** Male Abbott's Booby

(Des C. Lee. Litho Leigh-Mardon Ltd, Melbourne)

1990 (18 Apr–22 Aug). *Christmas Island Transport. T* **62** *and similar multicoloured designs. P* 13¹/₂×14 (*horiz*) *or* 14×13¹/₂ (*vert*).

287	1 c. Type **62**			15	20
288	2 c. Phosphate train (22 Aug)			40	40
289	3 c. Diesel railcar (*vert*)			20	20
290	5 c. Loading Road train (22 Aug)			40	40
291	10 c. Trishaw (*vert*)			30	30
292	15 c. Terex truck (22 Aug)			65	65
293	25 c. Articulated bus			30	30
294	30 c. Railway passenger rake (*vert*)			30	35
295	40 c. Passenger barge (*vert*)			35	40
296	50 c. Kolek (outrigger canoe)			55	55
297	65 c. Flying Doctor aircraft and ambulance (22 Aug)			2·00	1·50
298	75 c. Commercial van (22 Aug)			1·50	1·50
299	90 c. Vintage lorry (22 Aug)			1·75	1·75
300	$1 Water tanker (22 Aug)			1·75	1·75
301	$2 Traction engine (22 Aug)			3·25	3·25
302	$5 Steam locomotive and flat car			4·50	4·75
287/302			Set of 16	16·00	17·00

(Des N. Shewring. Litho Questa)

1990 (6 June). *Abbott's Booby. T* **63** *and similar vert designs. Multicoloured. P* 13¹/₂×14.

303	10 c. Type **63**			75	30
304	20 c. Juvenile male			1·25	50
305	29 c. Female with egg			1·50	55
306	41 c. Pair with chick			2·00	70
303/6			Set of 4	5·00	1·90

MS307 122×68 mm. 41 c. Male with wings spread; 41 c. Male on branch; 41 c. Female with fledgling. P 14¹/₂ .. .. .. 2·50 2·25

The three stamps within No. **MS**307 form a composite design and are without the W.W.F. logo.

64 1977 Famous Visitors 9 c. Stamp

(Des Elizabeth Innes. Litho Leigh-Mardon Ltd, Melbourne)

1990 (11 July). *Centenary of Henry Ridley's Visit. T* **64** *and similar multicoloured design. P* 15×14¹/₂ (41 c.) *or* 14¹/₂×15 (75 c.).

308	41 c. Type **64**			55	65
309	75 c. Ridley (botanist) in rainforest (*vert*)		85	1·75

1990 (24 Aug). *"New Zealand 1990" International Stamp Exhibition, Auckland. No.* **MS**307 *optd* "NZ 1990 WORLD STAMP EXHIBITION AUCKLAND, NEW ZEALAND, 24 AUGUST – 2 SEPTEMBER 1990" *in purple on the sheet margins.*

MS310 122×68 mm. 41 c. Male with wings spread; 41 c. Male on branch; 41 c. Female with fledgling .. .. 3·25 3·50
  a. Error. Imperf £1000

---

65 *Corymborkus veratrifolia* | **66** Islander (freighter), 1898

(Litho Leigh-Mardon Ltd, Melbourne)

1990 (3 Oct). *Christmas. Flowers. T* **65** *and similar horiz designs. Multicoloured. P* 14¹/₂.

311	38 c. Type **65**			90	60
312	43 c. *Hoya aldrichii*			95	65
313	80 c. *Quisqualis indica*			1·75	2·25
314	$1.20, *Barringtonia racemosa*			2·25	2·75
311/14			Set of 4	5·25	5·50

1990 (6 Dec). *"Birdpex '90" Stamp Exhibition, Christchurch. No.* **MS**307 *optd* "BIRDPEX '90 NATIONAL PHILATELIC EXHIBITION UNIVERSITY OF CANTERBURY CHRISTCHURCH NZ 6–9 DEC 1990 IN CONJUNCTION WITH THE 20th INTERNATIONAL ORNITHOLOGICAL CONGRESS" *in green on the sheet margins.*

MS315 122×68 mm. 41 c. Male with wings spread; 41 c. Male on branch; 41 c. Female with fledgling .. .. 4·00 4·50

(Des C. Lee. Litho Leigh-Mardon Ltd, Melbourne)

1991 (13 Feb). *Centenary of First Phosphate Mining Lease. T* **66** *and similar vert designs. Multicoloured. P* 14¹/₂.

316	43 c. Type **66**			60	60
	a. Horiz strip of 5. Nos. 316/20			5·00	
317	43 c. Miners loading rail wagons, 1908			60	60
318	85 c. Shay steam locomotive No. 4, 1925			1·00	1·00
319	$1.20, Extracting phosphate, 1951			1·40	1·40
320	$1.70, Land reclamation, 1990			1·90	1·90
316/20			Set of 5	5·00	5·00

Nos. 316/20 were printed together, *se-tenant*, in horizontal strips of 5 throughout the sheet, the background forming a composite forest design.

67 Teaching Children Road Safety | **68** Map of Christmas Island, 1991

(Des R. Honisett. Litho Leigh-Mardon Ltd, Melbourne)

1991 (17 Apr). *Christmas Island Police Force. T* **67** *and similar horiz designs. Multicoloured. P* 14¹/₂.

321	43 c. Type **67**			1·00	60
322	43 c. Traffic control			1·00	60
323	90 c. Airport customs			1·75	1·60
324	$1.20, Police launch *Fregata Andrews* towing rescued boat			2·25	1·90
321/4			Set of 4	5·50	4·25

MS325 135×88 mm. Nos. 321/4 .. .. 5·50 4·25

(Des D. Miller. Litho Questa)

1991 (19 June). *Maps of Christmas Island. T* **68** *and similar vert designs. Multicoloured. P* 14×13¹/₂.

326	43 c. Type **68**			75	65
327	75 c. Goos Atlas, 1666			1·25	1·10
328	$1.10, De Manevillette, 1745			1·90	1·60
329	$1.20, Comberford, 1667			1·90	1·90
326/9			Set of 4	5·25	4·75

69 *Bruguiera gymnorrhiza* | **70** "Family round Christmas Tree", (S'ng Yen Luiw)

(Des Jane Moore. Litho Leigh-Mardon Ltd, Melbourne)

1991 (21 Aug). *Local Trees. T* **69** *and similar horiz designs. Multicoloured. P* 14.

330	43 c. Type **69**			65	65
331	70 c. *Syzygium operculatum*			1·00	1·00
332	85 c. *Ficus microcarpa*			1·25	1·25
333	$1.20, *Arenga listeri*			1·60	1·60
330/3			Set of 4	4·00	4·00

(Des Liz Innes. Litho Leigh-Mardon Ltd, Melbourne)

1991 (2 Oct). *Christmas. Children's Paintings. T **70** and similar horiz designs. Multicoloured. P 14½.*

334	38 c. Type **70**	55	55
	a. Horiz strip of 5. Nos 334/8	2·50	
335	38 c. "Opening Presents" (Liew Ann Nee)	55	55
336	38 c. "Beach Party" (Foo Pang Chuan)	55	55
337	38 c. "Christmas Walk" (Too Lai Peng)	55	55
338	38 c. "Santa Claus and Christmas Tree" (Jesamine Wheeler)	55	55
339	43 c. "Santa Claus fishing" (Ho Puay Ha)	60	60
340	$1 "Santa Claus in Boat" (Ng Hooi Hua)	1·25	1·25
341	$1.20, "Santa Claus surfing" (Yani Kawi)	1·50	1·50
334/41	Set of 8	5·50	5·50

Nos. 334/8 were printed together, *se-tenant*, in horizontal strips of 5 throughout the sheet.

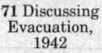

71 Discussing Evacuation, 1942

72 Snake's-head Cowrie (*Cypraea caputserpentis*)

(Des C. Lee. Litho Leigh-Mardon Ltd, Melbourne)

1992 (19 Feb). *50th Anniv of Partial Evacuation. T **71** and similar vert designs. Multicoloured. P 14½.*

342	45 c. Type **71**	75	75
343	45 c. Families waiting to embark	75	75
344	$1.05, Ferrying evacuees to *Islander*	2·00	2·00
345	$1.20, Departure of *Islander* (freighter)	2·25	2·25
342/5	Set of 4	5·25	5·25

(Des G. Ryan. Litho Leigh-Mardon Ltd, Melbourne)

1992 (15 Apr–19 Aug). *Shells. T **72** and similar vert designs. Multicoloured. P 14½.*

346	5 c. Tiger Cowrie (*Cypraea tigris*) (19 Aug)	20	30
347	10 c. Type **72**	30	30
348	15 c. Scorpion Conch (*Lambis scorpius*) (19 Aug)	40	30
349	20 c. Royal Oak Scallop (*Cryptopecten pallium*)	55	30
350	25 c. Striped Engina (*Engina mendicaria*) (19 Aug)	55	30
351	30 c. Prickly Pacific Drupe (*Drupa ricinus*)	70	45
352	40 c. Reticulate Distorsio (*Distorsio recticulata*) (19 Aug)	70	45
353	45 c. Tapestry Turban (*Turbo petholatus*)	90	60
354	50 c. Beautiful Goblet (*Pollia puchra*) (19 Aug)	90	55
355	60 c. Captain Cone (*Conus capitaneus*)	1·00	65
356	70 c. Lajonkaire's Turban (*Turbo lajonkairii*) (19 Aug)	1·00	75
357	80 c. Chiragra Spider Conch (*Lambis chiragra chiragra*)	1·25	85
358	90 c. Common Delphina (*Angaria delphinus*) (19 Aug)	1·40	1·10
359	$1 Ceramic Vase (*Vasum ceramicum*)	1·50	1·25
360	$2 Pacific Partridge Tun (*Tonna perdix*)	2·00	2·10
361	$5 Strawberry Drupe (*Drupa rubusidaeus*) (19 Aug)	5·00	5·25
346/61	Set of 16	16·00	13·00

73 Torpedoing of *Eidsvold*   (74)

(Des R. Watton. Litho Enschedé)

1992 (17 June). *50th Anniv of Sinkings of Eidsvold and Nissa Maru. T **73** and similar horiz designs. Multicoloured. P 14×13½.*

362	45 c. Type **73**	1·00	75
363	80 c. *Eidsvold* sinking	1·75	1·75
364	$1.05, *Nissa Maru* under attack	2·25	2·25
365	$1.20, *Nissa Maru* beached	2·25	2·50
362/5	Set of 4	6·50	6·50

1992 (1 Sept). *"Kuala Lumpur '92" International Philatelic Exhibition. No. 361 optd with T **74** in red.*

366	$5 Strawberry Drupe (*Drupa rubusidaeus*)	6·50	7·00

75 Jungle   76 Abbott's Booby

(Des Jane Moore and Elizabeth Innes. Litho Leigh-Mardon Ltd, Melbourne)

1992 (7 Oct). *Christmas. T **75** and similar vert designs. Multicoloured. P 14½.*

367	40 c. Type **75**	50	70
	a. Horiz strip of 5. Nos. 367/71	3·75	
368	40 c. Seabirds over rock	50	70
369	45 c. Brown Boobies on headland	55	70
370	$1.05, Seabirds and cliffs	1·25	1·40
371	$1.20, Cliffs	1·40	1·50
367/71	Set of 5	3·75	4·50

Nos. 367/71 were printed together, *se-tenant*, in horizontal strips of 5 throughout the sheet, each strip forming a composite coastal design.

On 2 March 1993 responsibility for the Christmas Island postal service passed from the territorial administration to Australia Post. In consequence Nos. 372/7 and all subsequent issues are valid for postal purposes in both Christmas Island and Australia.

(Des D. Nelson and Janet Boschen. Litho McPherson's Ptg Group, Mulgrave)

1993 (4 Mar). *Seabirds. T **76** and similar vert designs. Multicoloured. P 14½×14.*

372	45 c. Type **76**	55	70
	a. Horiz strip of 5. Nos. 372/6	2·50	
373	45 c. Christmas Island Frigate Bird	55	70
374	45 c. Common Noddy	55	70
375	45 c. White-tailed Tropic Bird ("Golden Bosunbird")	55	70
376	45 c. Brown Booby	55	70
372/6	Set of 5	2·50	3·25
MS377	140×70 mm. Nos. 372/6	2·75	3·50

Nos. 372/6 were printed together, *se-tenant*, in horizontal strips of 5 throughout the sheet, forming a composite design.
No. **MS**377 also exists overprinted with the "Indopex '93" or "Taipei '93" logos for sale at these stamp exhibitions in Surabaya, Indonesia, and Taiwan.

77 Dolly Beach   78 Turtle on Beach

(Des Jane Moore and Janet Boschen. Litho McPherson's Ptg Group, Mulgrave)

1993 (1 June). *Scenic Views of Christmas Island. T **77** and similar horiz designs. Multicoloured. P 14×14½.*

378	85 c. Type **77**	1·25	1·50
379	95 c. Blow Holes	1·50	1·75
380	$1.05, Merrial Beach	1·60	1·90
381	$1.20, Rainforest	1·75	2·00
378/81	Set of 4	5·50	6·50

(Des B. Wood and Sandra Harman. Litho McPherson's Ptg Group, Mulgrave)

1993 (2 Sept). *Christmas. T **78** and similar vert designs. Multicoloured. P 14½×14.*

382	40 c. Type **78**	70	50
383	45 c. Crabs and wave	70	50
384	$1 Christmas Island Frigate Bird and rainforest	1·50	2·00
382/4	Set of 3	2·50	2·75

79 Map of Christmas Island   80 Pekingese

(Des Betina Ogden. Litho McPherson's Ptg Group, Mulgrave)

1993 (1 Dec). *350th Anniv of Naming of Christmas Island. P 14×14½.*

385	79 $2 multicoloured	2·75	3·00

(Des Yen Lau. Litho McPherson's Ptg Group, Mulgrave)

1994 (20 Jan). *Chinese New Year ("Year of the Dog"). T **80** and similar horiz design. P 14×14½.*

386	45 c. Type **80**	80	90
	a. Pair. Nos. 386/7	1·60	1·75
387	45 c. Mickey (Christmas Island dog)	80	90
MS388	106×70 mm. Nos. 386/7	1·60	1·75

Nos. 386/7 were printed together, *se-tenant*, in horizontal or vertical pairs throughout the sheet.
No. **MS**388 also exists overprinted with "Melbourne Stamp & Coin Show 11–13 February 1994", "Hong Kong '94 Stamp Exhibition", "Canberra Stamp Show 94" or "Queensland Stamp and Coin Show 94" logos for sale at these exhibitions.

---

81 Locomotive No. 4   82 *Brachypeza archytas*

(Des J. Richards. Litho McPherson's Ptg Group, Mulgrave)

1994 (19 May). *Steam Locomotives. T **81** and similar horiz designs. Multicoloured. P 14×14½.*

389	85 c. Type **81**	1·25	1·40
390	95 c. Locomotive No. 9	1·25	1·40
391	$1.20, Locomotive No. 1	1·50	1·75
389/91	Set of 3	3·50	4·00

(Des Celia Rosser. Litho McPherson's Ptg Group, Mulgrave)

1994 (16 Aug). *Orchids. T **82** and similar vert designs. Multicoloured. P 14½×14.*

392	45 c. Type **82**	80	90
	a. Horiz strip of 5. Nos. 392/6	3·50	
393	45 c. *Thelasis capitata*	80	90
394	45 c. *Corymborkis veratrifolia*	80	90
395	45 c. *Flickingeria nativitatis*	80	90
396	45 c. *Dendrobium crumenatum*	80	90
392/6	Set of 5	3·50	4·00

Nos. 392/6 were printed together, *se-tenant*, in horizontal strips of 5 throughout the sheet.

83 Angel blowing Trumpet   84 Pig

(Des Tracie Grimwood. Litho McPherson's Ptg Group, Mulgrave)

1994 (8 Sept). *Christmas. T **83** and similar horiz designs. Multicoloured. P 14×14½.*

397	40 c. Type **83**	70	50
398	45 c. Wise Man holding gift	75	50
399	80 c. Star over Bethlehem	1·60	2·00
397/9	Set of 3	2·75	2·75

(Des J. Chan. Litho McPherson's Ptg Group, Mulgrave)

1995 (12 Jan). *Chinese New Year ("Year of the Pig"). T **84** and similar horiz design showing a different pig. P 14×14½.*

400	45 c. multicoloured	65	65
401	85 c. multicoloured	1·10	1·40
MS402	106×71 mm. Nos. 400/1		

No. **MS**402 also exists overprinted with "Melbourne Stamp & Coin Show 10–12 February 1995" logo for sale at this exhibition.

85 Golfer playing Shot   86 Father Christmas with Map on Christmas Island Frigate Bird

(Des N. Buchanan. Litho McPherson's Ptg Group, Mulgrave)

1995 (11 May). *40th Anniv of Christmas Island Golf Course. P 14×14½.*

403	85 $2.50, multicoloured	3·00	3·25

(Des B. Wood and Sophie Newman. Litho McPherson's Ptg Group, Mulgrave)

1995 (14 Sept). *Christmas. T **86** and similar horiz designs. Multicoloured. P 14×14½.*

404	40 c. Type **86**	60	50
405	45 c. Father Christmas distributing presents	65	50
406	80 c. Father Christmas waving goodbye	1·40	2·00
404/6	Set of 3	2·40	2·75

COVER PRICES

Cover factors are quoted at the beginning of each country for most issues to 1945. An explanation of the system can be found on page x. The factors quoted do not, however, apply to philatelic covers

87 De Havilland D.H.98   **88** Lemon-peel Angelfish
    Mosquito on
    Reconnaissance Mission

(Des B. Sadgrove. Recess and litho Note Ptg Branch, Reserve
Bank of Australia)

1995 (12 Oct). *50th Anniv of End of Second World War. T* **87** *and similar horiz design, each black, stone and vermilion. P* 14×14½.

407	45 c. Type **87**	..	..	..	50	65
	a. Pair. Nos. 407/8		..	..	1·00	1·25
408	45 c. H.M.S. *Rother* (frigate)		..	50	65

Nos. 407/8 were printed together, *se-tenant*, in horizontal and vertical pairs throughout the sheet.

(Des Lisa Christensen (85 c., 95 c., $1.20), Josephine Mure (others). Litho SNP Cambec (75 c., $1) or McPherson's Ptg Group, Mulgrave (others))

1995 (12 Oct)–**97**. *Marine Life. T* **88** *and similar horiz designs. Multicoloured. P* 14×14½.

412	20 c. Pink-tailed Triggerfish (18.4.96)	..	15	20
413	30 c. Japanese Inflator-filefish ("Longnose Filefish") (18.4.96)		25	30
414	45 c. Princess Anthias (18.4.96)	..	40	45
415	75 c. Type **88**			1·00	1·10
416	85 c. Moon Wrasse (17.7.97)		75	80
417	90 c. Spotted Boxfish (18.4.96)		80	85
418	95 c. Moorish Idol (17.7.97)		80	85
419	$1 Emperor Angelfish	..		1·40	1·50
420	$1.20, Glass-eyed Snapper ("Glass Bigeye") (17.7.97)		1·00	1·10
412/20	..	..	..	*Set of* 9	6·00	6·50

89 Rat with Drum   **90** Christmas
    Island White Eye

(Des L. Chiang. Litho SNP Cambec (gold die-stamped Avon Graphics))

1996 (9 Jan). *Chinese New Year ("Year of the Rat"). T* **89** *and similar horiz design. Multicoloured. P* 14×14½.

425	45 c. Type **89**	..	..	..	50	65
	a. Pair. Nos. 425/6	..	..	1·00	1·25
426	45 c. Rat with tambourine	..	50	65
MS427	106×70 mm. Nos. 425/6	..	1·00	1·25

Nos. 425/6 were printed together, *se-tenant*, in horizontal and vertical pairs throughout the sheet.

No. **MS427** also exists overprinted with the logo of the Melbourne Stamp and Coin Fair for sale at this Australian exhibition.

(Des T. Pridham and Susan Horvath. Litho McPherson's Ptg Group, Mulgrave)

1996 (11 July). *Christmas Island Land Birds. T* **90** *and similar vert design. Multicoloured. P* 14½×14.

428	45 c. Type **90**	..	..	50	50
429	85 c. Christmas Island Hawk Owl	..	1·25	1·50

91 Three Ships approaching Island   **92** Ox facing Right

(Des P. Gifford. Litho McPherson's Ptg Group, Mulgrave)

1996 (12 Sept). *Christmas. "I saw Three Ships" (carol). T* **91** *and similar square designs. Multicoloured. P* 14½.

430	40 c. Type **91**	..	..	50	50
431	45 c. Madonna and Child with ships at anchor	..	50	50
432	80 c. Ships leaving	..	1·25	1·50
430/2	..	..	*Set of* 3	2·00	2·25

(Des A. Donato. Litho McPherson's Ptg Group, Mulgrave)

1996 (1 Nov). *300th Anniv of Willem de Vlamingh's Discovery of Christmas Island. As No.* 1667 *of Australia. P* 14×14½.

433	45 c. multicoloured	..	..	55	55

Nos. 433 and No. 1667 of Australia were printed together, *se-tenant*, in horizontal pairs throughout the sheet which are listed as No. 1667a of Australia.

(Des L. Chiang. Litho SNP Cambec (gold die-stamped Avon Graphics))

1997 (6 Jan). *Chinese New Year ("Year of the Ox"). T* **92** *and similar horiz design. Multicoloured. P* 14×14½.

434	45 c. Type **92**	..	..	..	50	65
	a. Pair. Nos. 434/5	..	..	1·00	1·25
435	45 c. Ox facing left	..	..	50	65
MS436	106×70 mm. Nos. 434/5	..	1·00	1·25

Nos. 434/5 were printed together, *se-tenant*, in horizontal and vertical pairs throughout the sheet.

93 Father Christmas   **94** Tiger
    reading Letter

(Des A. Hopgood. Litho McPherson's Ptg Group, Mulgrave)

1997 (11 Sept). *Christmas. T* **93** *and similar horiz designs. Multicoloured. P* 14×14½.

437	40 c. Type **93**	..	45	45
438	45 c. Father Christmas carving wooden boat	45	45
439	80 c. Father Christmas in sleigh	..	90	1·10
437/9		*Set of* 3	1·60	1·75

(Des L. Chiang. Litho SNP Cambec)

1998 (5 Jan). *Chinese New Year ("Year of the Tiger"). T* **94** *and similar horiz design. Multicoloured. P* 14×14½.

440	45 c. Type **94**	..	..	40	45
	a. Pair. Nos. 440/1	..	..	80	
441	45 c. Tiger with head facing left	..	40	45
MS442	106×70 mm. Nos. 440/1	..	80	85

Nos. 440/1 were printed together, *se-tenant*, in horizontal and vertical pairs throughout the sheet.

STAMP BOOKLETS

Between mid-1995 and 25 June 1996 the Christmas Island Postmaster produced stamp booklets utilising card from surplus Presentation Packs. These booklets contained blocks of ten 45 c. stamps from whichever issue was currently available.

1996 (26 June). *Black on red cover,* 95×150 *mm, inscr* "CHRISTMAS ISLAND POST OFFICE STAMP BOOKLET" *and with Christmas Island postmark on front. Stapled.*

SB1	$4.50, booklet containing 45 c. (No. 414) in block of 10 ..	..	£140
	a. Containing 45 c. (No. 353)		

All examples of No. SB1a are postmarked 23 June 1996.

Keep This Catalogue up to Date With

Gibbons Stamp Monthly

FREE Bahamas WWF Stamps

Leeward Islands
GB—The perf 14
½d. Downey Head
Albania
WWF Collection
Falkland Airmails

Exclusive Interview with HRH The Prince Philip

The Magazine with the Stanley Gibbons Catalogue Supplement

Plus

■ More editorial than other magazines.

■ Regular features for all collectors from beginners to specialists.

■ Authoritatively written.

■ Regular special offers, competitions and free gifts.

Get Gibbons Stamp Monthly delivered direct to your door!

For a free sample copy and subscription details phone
01425 472363
or write to:

Hugh Jefferies
Gibbons Stamp Monthly
5 Parkside, Christchurch Road,
Ringwood, Hants BH24 3SH

COCOS (KEELING) ISLANDS

The Cocos (Keeling) Islands, which had been settled by the Clunies Ross family in the 1820s, were annexed by Great Britain in 1857. In 1878 the group was attached to Ceylon, but was transferred to the Straits Settlements on 7 February 1886. During the Second World War the islands were under British military control exercised from Ceylon. At the end of hostilities administration from Singapore was continued until the islands were transferred to Australia on 23 November 1955.

The stamps of the STRAITS SETTLEMENTS were used by a postal agency operating on Cocos (Keeling) Islands from 1 April 1933 until 1 March 1937. The postal agency reopened on 2 September 1952 and used the stamps of SINGAPORE until the islands were transferred to Australia in 1955. From 1955 until 1963 stamps of AUSTRALIA were in use.

PRINTERS. All the following stamps to No. 31 were printed by the Note Printing Branch, Reserve Bank of Australia, Melbourne.

1 Copra Industry   2 "Super Constellation"

(Des K. McKay and E. Jones (5d.), E. Jones (others). Eng E. Jones. Recess)

1963 (11 June). *T* **1/2** *and similar designs. P* 14½×14 (5d., 2s. 3d.) *or* 14½ (*others*).

1	3d. chocolate		1·25	1·50
2	5d. ultramarine		1·50	80
3	8d. scarlet		2·25	2·25
4	1s. green		1·25	55
5	2s. deep purple		11·00	3·25
6	2s. 3d. deep green		35·00	3·25
1/6		*Set of 6*	48·00	10·50

Designs: *Vert* (*as T* **1**)—8d. Map of islands; 2s. Jukong (sailboat). *Horiz* (*as T* **1**)—1s. Palms. (*as T* **2**)—2s. 3d. White Tern.

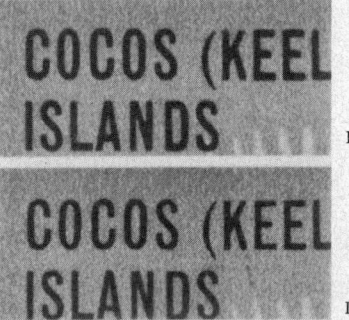

I Thick lettering

II Thinner lettering

1965 (14 Apr). *50th Anniv of Gallipoli Landing. As T* **184** *of Australia, but slightly larger* (22×34½ *mm*) *and colour changed. Photo. P* 13½.

7	5d. sepia, black and emerald (I)		60	45
	a. *Black-brown, black and light emerald* (II)		2·50	1·75

No. 7a comes from a second printing, using a new black cylinder, which was available from the end of April.

With the introduction of decimal currency on 14 February 1966, Australian stamps were used in Cocos Islands, until the appearance of the new definitives on 9 July 1969.

(New Currency. 100 cents = 1 Australian dollar)

7 Reef Clam   8 Great Frigate Bird
(*Tridacna derasa*)

(Des L. Annois (1 c. to 6 c.), P. Jones (10 c. to $1). Photo)

1969 (9 July). *Decimal Currency. T* **8** *or designs as T* **7**. *Multicoloured. P* 13½.

8	1 c.	Lajonkaines Turbo shell (*Turbo lajonkairii*) (*vert*)		30	60
9	2 c.	Elongate or Small Giant Clam (*Tridacna maxima*) (*vert*)		1·00	80
10	3 c.	Type **7**		40	20
11	4 c.	Floral Blenny (fish)		30	50
		a. *Salmon-pink omitted*		£650	
12	5 c.	*Porites cocosensis* (coral)		35	30
13	6 c.	Atrisignis Flyingfish		75	75
14	10 c.	Banded Rail		1·00	70
15	15 c.	Java Sparrow		1·00	30
16	20 c.	Red-tailed Tropic Bird		1·00	30
17	30 c.	Sooty Tern		1·00	30
18	50 c.	Eastern Reef Heron (*vert*)		1·00	30
19	$1	Type **8**		3·00	1·00
8/19			*Set of 12*	10·00	5·50

9 *Dragon*, 1609   10 Map of Cocos (Keeling) Islands Union Flag, Stars and Trees

(Des R. Honisett. Photo)

1976 (29 Mar). *Ships. Multicoloured designs as T* **9**. *P* 13½.

20	1 c.	Type **9**		30	40
21	2 c.	H.M.S. *Juno*, 1857		30	40
22	5 c.	H.M.S. *Beagle*, 1836		30	40
23	10 c.	H.M.A.S. *Sydney*, 1914		35	40
24	15 c.	S.M.S. *Emden*, 1914		1·00	55
25	20 c.	*Ayesha*, 1907		1·00	80
26	25 c.	T.S.S. *Islander*, 1927		1·00	1·00
27	30 c.	M.V. *Cheshire*, 1951		1·00	1·00
28	35 c.	Jukong (sailboat)		1·00	1·00
29	40 c.	C.S. *Scotia*, 1900		1·00	1·00
30	50 c.	R.M.S. *Orontes*, 1929		1·40	1·10
31	$1	Royal Yacht *Gothic*, 1954		2·00	1·40
20/31			*Set of 12*	9·50	8·50

The 2 c. to 20 c., 35 c. and 40 c. are horizontal designs.

(Des Marg Towt. Litho Asher and Co, Melbourne)

1979 (3 Sept). *Inauguration of Independent Postal Service* (20 c.) *and Establishment of First Statutory Council* (50 c.). *T* **10** *and similar horiz design. Multicoloured. P* 15½ × 15.

32	20 c. Type **10**		25	30
33	50 c. Council seal and jukong (sailboat)		35	50

11 Forceps Fish   12 "Peace on Earth"

(Des Marg Towt. Litho Asher and Co, Melbourne)

1979 (3 Sept)**—80.** *Fishes. Horiz designs as T* **11**. *Multicoloured. P* 13½ × 13 (22 c., 28 c., 60 c.) *or* 15½ × 15 (*others*).

34	1 c.	Type **11**		30	80
35	2 c.	Ornate Butterflyfish (19.11.79)		30	80
36	5 c.	Barbier		50	90
37	10 c.	Meyer's Butterflyfish (18.2.80)		30	55
38	15 c.	Pink Wrasse (19.11.79)		30	30
39	20 c.	Clark's Anemonefish (19.11.79)		45	30
39a	22 c.	Undulate Triggerfish (1.7.80)		45	30
40	25 c.	Red-breasted Wrasse (18.2.80)		45	60
40a	28 c.	Guineafowl Wrasse (1.7.80)		35	35
41	30 c.	Madagascar Butterflyfish (19.11.79)		65	45
42	35 c.	Cocos-Keeling Angelfish		65	1·40
43	40 c.	Coral Hogfish (19.11.79)		70	60
44	50 c.	Clown Wrasse (19.11.79)		85	75
45	55 c.	Yellow-tailed Tamarin (18.2.80)		75	1·00
45a	60 c.	Greasy Grouper (1.7.80)		75	75
46	$1	Palette Surgeonfish		1·75	3·50
47	$2	Melon Butterflyfish (18.2.80)		2·00	3·50
34/47			*Set of 17*	10·00	14·50

(Des D. Pitt. Litho Asher & Co, Melbourne)

1979 (22 Oct). *Christmas. T* **12** *and similar multicoloured design. P* 15 × 15½ (25 c.) *or* 15½ × 15 (55 c.).

48	25 c. Type **12**		25	35
49	55 c. "Goodwill Toward Men" (*horiz*)		40	55

13 Star, Map of Cocos (Keeling)   14 "Administered by the Islands and Island Landscape   British Government, 1857"

(Des P. Arnold. Litho Asher and Co, Melbourne)

1980 (22 Oct). *Christmas. T* **13** *and similar horiz designs. Multicoloured. P* 13.

50	15 c. Type **13**		10	10
51	28 c. Map and Wise Men following star		15	15
52	60 c. Map and Nativity scene		40	40
50/2		*Set of 3*	60	60

(Des Sue Wilson. Litho Asher and Co, Melbourne)

1980 (24 Nov). *25th Anniv of Cocos (Keeling) Islands as an Australian Territory. T* **14** *and similar horiz designs. Multicoloured. P* 13½ × 13.

53	22 c. Type **14**		15	15
	a. *Horiz strip of 5. Nos. 53/7*		70	
54	22 c. "Administered by the Government of Ceylon, 1878, 1942–6"		15	15
55	22 c. "Administered by the Straits Settlements, 1886"		15	15
56	22 c. "Administered by the Colony of Singapore, 1946"		15	15
57	22 c. "Administered by the Australian Government, 1955"		15	15
53/7		*Set of 5*	70	70

Nos. 53/7 were printed together, *se-tenant*, in horizontal strips of 5 throughout the sheet, forming a composite design.

15 *Eye of the Wind*   16 Aerial View of Animal
and Map of Cocos   Quarantine Station
(Keeling) Islands

(Des Sue Wilson. Litho Asher and Co, Melbourne)

1980 (18 Dec). *"Operation Drake" (round the world expedition and 400th Anniv of Sir Francis Drake's Circumnavigation of the World. T* **15** *and similar multicoloured designs. P* 13.

58	22 c. Type **15**		20	15
59	28 c. Map showing voyage routes (*horiz*)		20	15
60	35 c. Sir Francis Drake and *Golden Hind*		20	15
61	60 c. Prince Charles and *Eye of the Wind* (brigantine)		35	30
58/61		*Set of 4*	85	65

(Des Cato Hibberd Design. Litho Leigh-Mardon Ltd, Melbourne)

1981 (12 May). *Opening of Animal Quarantine Station. T* **16** *and similar horiz designs. Multicoloured. P* 13½ × 13.

62	22 c. Type **16**		15	15
63	45 c. Unloading livestock		30	30
64	60 c. Livestock in pen		35	35
62/4		*Set of 3*	70	70

17 Consolidated "Catalina"   18 Prince Charles and
Guba II Flying Boat   Lady Diana Spencer

(Des R. Honisett. Litho Leigh-Mardon Ltd, Melbourne)

1981 (23 June). *Aircraft. T* **17** *and similar horiz designs. Multicoloured. P* 13½ × 13.

65	22 c. Type **17**		25	25
	a. *Horiz strip of 5. Nos. 65/9*		1·10	
66	22 c. Consolidated "Liberator" and Avro "Lancastrian"		25	25
67	22 c. Douglas "DC4 (Skymaster)" and Lockheed "Constellation"		25	25
68	22 c. Lockheed "Electra"		25	25
69	22 c. Boeing "727" airliners		25	25
65/9		*Set of 5*	1·10	1·10

Nos. 65/9 were printed together, *se-tenant*, in horizontal strips of 5 throughout the sheet.

(Des B. Clinton. Litho Leigh-Mardon Ltd, Melbourne)

1981 (29 July). *Royal Wedding. P* 13½ × 13.

70	18	24 c. multicoloured	30	25
71		60 c. multicoloured	50	60

19 "Angels we have heard   20 *Pachyseris speciosa* and
on High"   *Heliofungia actiniformis* (corals)

(Des B. Weatherhead. Litho Leigh-Mardon Ltd, Melbourne)

1981 (22 Oct). *Christmas. Scenes and Lines from Carol "Angels we have heard on High". T* **19** *and similar horiz designs. Multicoloured. P* 13½ × 13.

72	18 c. Type **19**		10	10
73	30 c. "Shepherds why this Jubilee?"		20	20
74	60 c. "Come to Bethlehem and see Him"		30	30
72/4		*Set of 3*	60	60

(Des B. Weatherhead. Litho Leigh-Mardon Ltd, Melbourne)

1981 (28 Dec). *150th Anniv of Charles Darwin's Voyage. T* **20** *and similar horiz designs. Multicoloured. P* 13½ × 13.

75	24 c. Type **20**		35	15
76	45 c. Charles Darwin in 1853 and *Pavona cactus* (coral)		55	30
77	60 c. H.M.S. *Beagle*, 1832, and *Lobophyllia hemprichii* (coral)		70	35
75/7		*Set of 3*	1·40	75
MS78	130 × 95 mm. 24 c. Cross-section of West Island; 24 c. Cross-section of Home Island		75	90

21 Queen Victoria   22 Lord Baden-Powell

(Des B. Weatherhead. Litho Cambec Press, Melbourne)
1982 (31 Mar). 125th Anniv of Annexation of Cocos (Keeling) Islands to British Empire. T 21 and similar horiz designs. Multicoloured. P 13½ × 14.

79	24 c. Type 21	20	15
80	45 c. Union flag	35	25
81	60 c. Capt. S. Fremantle (annexation visit, 1857)	40	35
79/81	Set of 3	85	65

(Des B. Clinton. Litho Cambec Press, Melbourne)
1982 (21 July). 75th Anniv of Boy Scout Movement. T 22 and similar multicoloured design. P 13½ × 14 (27 c.) or 14 × 13½ (75 c.).

82	27 c. Type 22	30	25
83	75 c. "75" and map of Cocos (Keeling) Islands (vert)	1·10	1·00

23 *Precis villida*   24 "Call His Name Immanuel"

(Des B. Hargreaves. Litho Harrison)
1982 (6 Sept)–83. Butterflies and Moths. T 23 and similar multicoloured designs. P 14.

84	1 c. Type 23	1·00	60
85	2 c. Cephonodes picus (horiz) (6.1.83)	40	40
86	5 c. Macroglossum corythus (horiz)	1·50	70
87	10 c. Chasmina candida (6.1.83)	40	40
88	20 c. Nagia linteola (horiz) (6.4.83)	40	65
89	25 c. Eublemma rivula (1.7.83)	40	75
90	30 c. Eurrhyparodes tricoloralis (6.4.83)	40	65
91	35 c. Hippotion boerhaviae (horiz)	1·50	75
92	40 c. Euploea core (6.4.83)	40	80
93	45 c. Psara hipponalis (horiz) (6.4.83)	50	80
94	50 c. Danaus chrysippus (horiz) (1.7.83)	60	1·25
95	55 c. Hypolimnas misippus (6.1.83)	60	70
96	60 c. Spodoptera litura (1.7.83)	65	1·75
97	$1 Achaea janata	2·75	2·75
98	$2 Panacra velox (horiz) (1.7.83)	2·00	2·75
99	$3 Utetheisa pulchelloides (horiz) (6.1.83)	2·75	2·75
84/99	Set of 16	14·50	17·00

(Des G. Hamori. Litho Cambec Press, Melbourne)
1982 (25 Oct). Christmas. T 24 and similar horiz designs. Multicoloured. P 13½ × 14.

100	21 c. Type 24	20	20
101	35 c. "I bring you good tidings"	35	35
102	75 c. "Arise and flee into Egypt"	80	1·00
100/2	Set of 3	1·25	1·40

25 "God will look after us" (Matt. 1:20)   26 Hari Raya Celebrations

(Des R. Roberts. Litho Cambec Press, Melbourne)
1983 (25 Oct). Christmas. Extracts from the New Testament. T 25 and similar vert designs. Multicoloured. P 14 × 13½.

103	24 c. Type 25	30	30
	a. Horiz strip of 5. Nos. 103/7	1·40	
104	24 c. "Our baby King, Jesus" (Matthew 2:2)	30	30
105	24 c. "Your Saviour is born" (Luke 2:11)	30	30
106	24 c. "Wise men followed the Star" (Matthew 2:9–10)	30	30
107	24 c. "And worship the Lord" (Matthew 2:11)	30	30
103/7	Set of 5	1·40	1·40

Nos. 103/7 were printed together, se-tenant, in horizontal strips of 5 throughout the sheet.

(Des Marg Towt. Litho Cambec Press, Melbourne)
1984 (24 Jan). Cocos-Malay Culture. (1st series). Festivals. T 26 and similar vert designs. Multicoloured. P 13½ × 13.

108	45 c. Type 26	45	35
109	75 c. Melenggok dancing	65	50
110	85 c. Cocos-Malay wedding	75	55
108/10	Set of 3	1·75	1·25

See also Nos. 126/8.

27 Unpacking Barrel   28 Captain William Keeling

(Des R. Honisett. Litho Cambec Press, Melbourne)
1984 (20 Apr). 75th Anniv of Cocos Barrel Mail. T 27 and similar horiz designs. Multicoloured. P 13½ × 14.

111	35 c. Type 27	40	25
112	55 c. Jukong awaiting mail ship	75	50
113	70 c. P. & O. mail ship Morea	85	55
111/13	Set of 3	1·75	1·10
MS114	125 × 95 mm. $1 Retrieving barrel	90	1·25

(Des B. Clinton. Litho Cambec Press, Melbourne)
1984 (10 July). 375th Anniv of Discovery of Cocos (Keeling) Islands. T 28 and similar vert designs. Multicoloured. P 14.

115	30 c. Type 28	70	40
116	65 c. Keeling's ship Hector	1·50	90
117	95 c. Mariner's astrolabe	1·75	1·25
118	$1. 10, Map circa 1666	1·90	1·50
115/18	Set of 4	5·25	3·50

29 Malay Settlement, Home Island   30 "Rainbow" Fish

(Des E. Roberts. Litho Cambec Press, Melbourne)
1984 (21 Sept). "Ausipex" International Stamp Exhibition, Melbourne. T 29 and similar horiz designs. Multicoloured. P 13½ × 14.

119	45 c. Type 29	75	50
120	55 c. Airstrip, West Island	85	60
MS121	130 × 95 mm. $2 Jukongs (native craft) racing	2·75	2·50

(Des R. Roberts. Litho Cambec Press, Melbourne)
1984 (31 Oct). Christmas. T 30 and similar horiz designs. Multicoloured. P 13½ × 14.

122	24 c. Type 30	50	40
123	35 c. "Rainbow" butterfly	1·10	1·10
124	55 c. "Rainbow" bird	1·25	1·50
122/4	Set of 3	2·50	2·75

31 Cocos Islanders   32 Jukong building

(Des B. Weatherhead. Litho Cambec Press, Melbourne)
1984 (30 Nov). Integration of Cocos (Keeling) Islands with Australia. Sheet 90 × 52 mm. containing T 31 and similar horiz design. Multicoloured. P 13½ × 14.
MS125 30 c. Type 31: 30 c. Australian flag on island   1·50   1·25

(Des Marg Towt. Litho Cambec Press, Melbourne)
1985 (30 Jan). Cocos-Malay Culture (2nd series). Handicrafts. T 32 and similar vert designs. Multicoloured. P 14 × 13½.

126	30 c. Type 32	75	35
127	45 c. Blacksmithing	1·00	55
128	55 c. Woodcarving	1·25	65
126/8	Set of 3	2·75	1·40

33 C.S. Scotia   34 Red-footed Booby

(Des B. Clinton. Litho Cambec Press, Melbourne)
1985 (24 Apr). Cable-laying Ships. T 33 and similar horiz designs. Multicoloured. P 13½ × 14.

129	33 c. Type 33	1·25	40
130	65 c. C.S. Anglia	2·00	1·60
131	80 c. C.S. Patrol	2·25	2·25
129/31	Set of 3	5·00	3·75

(Des Marg Towt. Litho Cambec Press, Melbourne)
1985 (17 July). Birds of Cocos (Keeling) Islands. T 34 and similar multicoloured designs. P 13½.

132	33 c. Type 34	1·50	1·50
	a. Block of 3. Nos. 132/4	5·00	
	ab. Imperf vert (block of 3).	£600	
133	60 c. Rufous Night Heron (juvenile) (horiz)	1·75	1·75
134	$1 Banded Rail (horiz)	2·25	2·25
132/4	Set of 3	5·00	5·00

Nos. 132/4 were printed together, se-tenant, in blocks of 3 throughout the sheet, each block forming a composite design.

35 Mantled Top (*Trochus maculatus*)   36 Night Sky and Palm Trees

(Des G. Ryan. Litho Cambec Press, Melbourne)
1985 (18 Sept)–86. Shells and Molluscs. T 35 and similar horiz designs. Multicoloured. P 13½ × 14.

135	1 c. Type 35	30	60
136	2 c. Rang's Nerite (Smaragdia rangiana) (29.1.86)	40	65
137	3 c. Jewel Box (Chama sp) (29.1.86)	45	70
138	4 c. Money Cowrie (Cypraea moneta) (30.7.86)	45	70
139	5 c. Purple Pacific Drupe (Drupa morum)	45	70
140	10 c. Soldier Cone (Conus miles) (29.1.86)	50	75
141	15 c. Marlin-spike Auger (Terebra maculata) (30.4.86)	1·00	1·00
142	20 c. Pacific Strawberry Cockle (Fragum fragum) (30.4.86)	80	1·10
143	30 c. Lajonkaire's Turban (Turbo lajonkairii) (30.4.86)	85	1·25
144	33 c. Reticulate Mitre (Scabricola fissurata) (30.4.86)	1·10	1·25
145	40 c. Common Spider Conch (Lambis lambis) (30.4.86)	1·25	1·40
146	50 c. Fluted Giant Clam or Scaled Tridacna (Tridacna squamosa) (30.7.86)	1·10	1·50
147	60 c. Minstrel Cowrie (Cypraea histrio) (30.7.86)	1·40	2·00
148	$1 Varicose Nudibranch (Phyllidia varicosa)	2·75	3·00
149	$2 Tesselated Nudibranch (Halgerda tessellata) (30.7.86)	3·50	4·00
150	$3 Haminoea cymballum (29.1.86)	4·25	4·75
135/50	Set of 16	19·00	23·00

(Des D. Goodwin. Litho Cambec Press, Melbourne)
1985 (30 Oct). Christmas. Sheet 121 × 88 mm, containing T 36 and similar horiz designs. P 13½ × 14.
MS151   27 c. × 4 multicoloured   2·00   2·75

The stamps within MS151 show a composite design of the night sky seen through a grove of palm trees. The position of the face value on the four stamps varies. Type 36 shows the top left design. The top right stamp shows the face value at bottom right, the bottom left at top left and the bottom right at top right.

37 Charles Darwin, c 1840   38 Coconut Palm and Holly Sprigs

(Des B. Clinton. Litho Cambec Press, Melbourne)
1986 (1 Apr). 150th Anniv of Charles Darwin's Visit. T 37 and similar vert designs. Multicoloured. P 14 × 13½.

152	33 c. Type 37	70	50
153	60 c. Map of H.M.S. Beagle's route Australia to Cocos Islands	1·25	1·75
154	$1 H.M.S. Beagle	1·75	2·25
152/4	Set of 3	3·25	4·00

(Des S. Hartshorne. Litho Cambec Press, Melbourne)
1986 (29 Oct). Christmas. T 38 and similar horiz designs. Multicoloured. P 13½ × 14.

155	30 c. Type 38	60	40
156	90 c. Nautilus shell and Christmas tree bauble	1·75	2·25
157	$1 Tropical fish and bell	2·00	2·25
155/7	Set of 3	4·00	4·50

39 Jukong   40 Beach, Direction Island

(Des J. Earl. Litho Cambec Press, Melbourne)

1987 (28 Jan). *Sailing Craft.* T **39** *and similar horiz designs. Multicoloured. P* 13½×14.
158	36 c. Type **39**	..	1·10	1·25
	a. Horiz strip of 4. Nos. 158/61	..	4·00	
159	36 c. Ocean racing yachts	..	1·10	1·25
160	36 c. *Sarimanok* (replica of early dhow)	..	1·10	1·25
161	36 c. *Ayesha* (schooner)	..	1·10	1·25
158/61		*Set of* 4	4·00	4·50

Nos. 158/61 were printed together, *se-tenant*, in horizontal strips of 5 throughout the sheet, each strip forming a composite background design.

(Des H. Missingham and R. Fletcher. Litho CPE Australia Ltd, Melbourne)

1987 (8 Apr). *Cocos Islands Scenes.* T **40** *and similar horiz designs. P* 13½×14.
162	70 c. Type **40**	..	1·40	1·40
163	90 c. Palm forest, West Island	..	1·75	2·00
164	$1 Golf course	..	2·75	3·00
162/4		*Set of* 3	5·50	5·75

41 Radio Transmitter and Palm Trees at Sunset   **42** Batik Printing

(Des R. Fletcher. Litho CPE Australia Ltd, Melbourne)

1987 (29 July). *Communications.* T **41** *and similar horiz designs. Multicoloured. P* 13½×14.
165	70 c. Type **41**	..	1·25	1·50
166	75 c. Air liner at terminal	..	1·50	1·75
167	90 c. "Intelsat 5" satellite	..	1·75	2·25
168	$1 Airmail letter and globe	..	2·00	2·25
165/8		*Set of* 4	6·00	7·00

(Des B. Clinton. Litho CPE Australia Ltd, Melbourne)

1987 (16 Sept). *Cocos (Keeling) Islands Malay Industries.* T **42** *and similar horiz designs. Multicoloured. P* 13½×14.
169	45 c. Type **42**	..	1·25	1·50
170	65 c. Jukong building	..	1·75	2·00
171	75 c. Copra production	..	2·00	2·25
169/71		*Set of* 3	4·50	5·25

43 Hands releasing Peace Dove and Map of Islands   **44** Coconut Flower

(Des Marg Towt. Litho CPE Australia Ltd, Melbourne)

1987 (28 Oct). *Christmas.* T **43** *and similar vert designs. Multicoloured. P* 14×13½.
172	30 c. Type **43**	..	40	40
173	90 c. Local children at Christmas party	..	1·25	1·75
174	$1 Island family and Christmas star	..	1·50	1·75
172/4		*Set of* 3	2·75	3·50

(Des Sue Passmore. Litho CPE Australia Ltd, Melbourne)

1988 (26 Jan). *Bicentenary of Australian Settlement. Arrival of First Fleet. Square designs as Nos.* 1105/9 *of Australia but each inscribed* "COCOS (KEELING) ISLANDS" *and* "AUSTRALIA BICENTENARY".
175	37 c. Aborigines watching arrival of Fleet, Botany Bay	..	1·50	1·75
	a. Horiz strip of 5. Nos. 175/9	..	6·75	
176	37 c. Aboriginal family and anchored ships	..	1·50	1·75
177	37 c. Fleet arriving at Sydney Cove	..	1·50	1·75
178	37 c. Ship's boat	..	1·50	1·75
179	37 c. Raising the flag, Sydney Cove, 26 January 1788	..	1·50	1·75
175/9		*Set of* 5	6·75	8·00

Nos. 175/9 were printed together, *se-tenant*, in horizontal strips of five throughout the sheet, forming a composite design.

(Des Celia Rosser. Litho CPE Australia Ltd, Melbourne)

1988 (13 Apr). *Life Cycle of the Coconut.* T **44** *and similar vert designs. Multicoloured. P* 14×13½.
180	37 c. Type **44**	..	50	40
181	65 c. Immature nuts	..	75	1·00
182	90 c. Coconut palm and mature nuts	..	1·10	1·50
183	$1 Seedlings	..	1·25	1·50
180/3		*Set of* 4	3·25	4·00
MS184	102×91 mm. Nos. 180/3		4·00	4·00

MINIMUM PRICE

The minimum price quote is 10p which represents a handling charge rather than a basis for valuing common stamps. For further notes about prices see introductory pages.

45 Copra 3d. Stamp of 1963   **46** Pisonia grandis

(Des R. Fletcher. Recess and litho Note Printing Branch, Reserve Bank of Australia, Melbourne)

1988 (15 June). *25th Anniv of First Cocos (Keeling) Islands Stamps.* T **45** *and similar vert designs, each showing stamp from* 1963 *definitive set. P* 15×14.
185	37 c. chocolate, black and azure	..	1·00	75
186	55 c. green, black and pale drab	..	1·50	1·40
187	65 c. ultramarine, black and pale grey-lilac	..	1·75	1·75
188	70 c. scarlet, black and bluish grey	..	1·75	1·75
189	90 c. deep purple, black and greenish grey	..	1·90	2·00
190	$1 deep green, black and light brown	..	2·00	2·00
185/90		*Set of* 6	9·00	8·75

Designs:—55 c. Palms 1s.; 65 c. "Super Constellation" 5d.; 70 c. Map 8d.; 90 c. Jukong (sailboat) 2s.; $1 White Tern 2s. 3d.

(Des R. Fletcher. Litho CPE Australia Ltd, Melbourne)

1988 (29 July)–89. *Flora.* T **46** *and similar vert designs. Multicoloured. P* 14×13½.
191	1 c. Type **46**	..	20	50
192	2 c. *Cocos nucifera* (18.1.89)	..	30	60
193	5 c. *Morinda citrifolia*	..	55	70
194	10 c. *Cordia subcordata* (18.1.89)	..	60	70
195	30 c. *Argusia argentea* (18.1.89)	..	85	90
196	37 c. *Calophyllum inophyllum*	..	85	1·00
197	40 c. *Barringtonia asiatica* (19.4.89)	..	85	1·25
198	50 c. *Caesalpinia bonduc* (19.4.89)	..	1·00	1·50
199	90 c. *Terminalia catappa* (19.4.89)	..	1·40	2·25
200	$1 *Pemphis acidula* (19.4.89)	..	1·50	2·25
201	$2 *Scaevola sericea* (18.1.89)	..	2·50	2·50
202	$3 *Hibiscus tiliaceus*	..	3·50	3·75
191/202		*Set of* 12	12·50	16·00

(Des R. Fletcher. Litho CPE Australia Ltd, Melbourne)

1988 (30 July). *"Sydpex '88" National Stamp Exhibition, Sydney. Sheet* 70×85 *mm. Multicoloured. P* 14×13½.
MS203	$3 As No. 202	..	4·00	4·00

 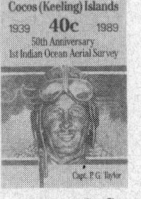

47 Beach at Sunset   **48** Capt. P. G. Taylor

(Des T. Bland. Litho CPE Australia Ltd, Melbourne)

1988 (12 Oct). *Christmas. P* 13½×14.
204	**47** 32 c. multicoloured	..	80	40
205	90 c. multicoloured	..	1·75	2·25
206	$1 multicoloured	..	2·00	2·25
204/6		*Set of* 3	4·00	4·50

(Des B. Clinton. Litho CPE Australia Ltd, Melbourne)

1989 (19 July). *50th Anniv of First Indian Ocean Aerial Survey.* T **48** *and similar vert designs. P* 14×13½.
207	40 c. multicoloured	..	80	65
208	70 c. multicoloured	..	1·50	1·75
209	$1 multicoloured	..	1·75	1·90
210	$1.10, deep ultramarine, pale lilac & black	..	2·00	2·25
207/10		*Set of* 4	5·50	6·00

Designs:—70 c. Consolidated Catalina "PBY2" *Guba II* and crew; $1 *Guba II* over Direction Island; $1.10, Unissued Australia 5s. stamp commemorating flight.

49 Jukong and Star   **50** H.M.A.S. *Sydney* (cruiser)

(Des T. Bland. Litho Leigh-Mardon Ltd, Melbourne)

1989 (18 Oct). *Christmas. P* 14×13½.
211	**49** 35 c. multicoloured	..	75	40
212	80 c. multicoloured	..	2·00	2·25
213	$1.10, multicoloured	..	2·00	2·25
211/13		*Set of* 3	4·25	4·50

(Des PCS Studios. Litho Leigh-Mardon Ltd, Melbourne)

1989 (9 Nov). *75th Anniv of Destruction of German Cruiser Emden.* T **50** *and similar horiz designs. Multicoloured. P* 13½×14.
214	40 c. Type **50**	..	1·60	1·60
	a. Horiz strip of 4, Nos. 214/17, with central label	..	6·75	
215	70 c. *Emden* (German cruiser)	..	1·90	1·90
216	$1 *Emden's* steam launch	..	2·00	2·00
217	$1.10, H.M.A.S. *Sydney*, (1914) and crest	..	2·00	2·00
214/17		*Set of* 4	6·75	6·75
MS218	145×90 mm. Nos. 214/17		6·75	7·00

Nos. 214/17 were printed together, *se-tenant*, in horizontal strips of four stamps and one label throughout the sheet.

51 Xanthid Crab   **52** Captain Keeling and *Hector*, 1609

(Des Jill Ruse. Litho Leigh-Mardon Ltd, Melbourne)

1990 (31 May). *Cocos Islands Crabs.* T **51** *and similar multicoloured designs. P* 14½.
219	45 c. Type **51**	..	1·25	70
220	75 c. Ghost Crab	..	1·75	1·75
221	$1 Red-backed Mud Crab	..	1·90	1·90
222	$1.30, Coconut Crab (*vert*)	..	2·25	2·50
219/22		*Set of* 4	6·50	6·25

(Des Elizabeth and R. Innes. Litho Note Ptg Branch, Reserve Bank of Australia)

1990 (24 Aug). *Navigators of the Pacific.* T **52** *and similar horiz designs. P* 14½.
223	45 c. dull mauve	..	1·75	85
224	75 c. dull mauve and pale azure	..	2·00	2·25
225	$1 dull mauve and pale stone	..	2·50	2·75
226	$1.30, dull mauve and pale buff	..	3·25	3·50
223/6		*Set of* 4	8·50	8·50
MS227	120×95 mm. As Nos. 223/6, but imperf		7·50	8·50

Designs—75 c. Captain Fitzroy and H.M.S. *Beagle*, 1836; $1 Captain Belcher and H.M.S. *Samarang*, 1846; $1.30, Captain Fremantle and H.M.S. *Juno*, 1857.

(53)   (54)

(Des Elizabeth Innes (No. MS229). Litho Western Australian Govt Ptg Division, Perth)

1990 (3 Sept). *"New Zealand 1990" International Stamp Exhibition, Auckland. No.* 188 *optd with* T **53** *in red and miniature sheet containing designs as Nos.* 194, 199 *and* 201.
228	70 c. scarlet, black and bluish grey	..	1·50	2·00
MS229	127×90 mm. As Nos. 194, 199 and 201, but self-adhesive. Roul 9		4·00	3·50

Nos. 228/9 were available at the Exhibition from 24 August 1990, but were not sold locally until 3 September.

1990 (11 Dec). *No.* 187 *surch with* T **54** *in deep ultramarine by Western Australian Govt Ptg Division, Perth.*
230	$5 on 65 c. ultram, black & pale grey-lilac		13·00	14·00

55 Cocos Atoll from West and Star

(Des Stylegraphics, Perth. Litho Scott Four-Colour Print, Perth)

1990 (12 Dec). *Christmas.* T **55** *and similar square designs. Multicoloured. Roul* 5.
231	40 c. Type **55**	..	50	70
	a. Booklet pane. No. 231×4 and No. 232×2 plus 6 labels	..	10·00	
	b. Booklet pane. No. 231×10 plus 2 labels		15·00	
232	70 c. Cocos atoll from south	..	1·50	2·00
233	$1.30, Cocos atoll from east	..	2·25	2·50
231/3		*Set of* 3	3·75	4·75

Booklet panes Nos. 231a/b have the upper and lower edges imperforate, producing stamps imperforate at top or bottom and there are margins at left and right.

MAINLAND POSTAGE PAID

(56)

LOCAL

POSTAGE PAID

(57)

990 (12 Dec)–91. *Nos. 140/1, 143 and 146/7 surch by Western Australian Govt Ptg Division.*

(a) With T **56** *in blue*

34	(43 c.) on 10 c. Soldier Cone (*Conus miles*)		20·00	2·25

(b) As T **57** *with original face value obliterated*

35	(1 c.) on 30 c. Lajonkaire's Turban (*Turbo lajonkairii*) (Type 57) (B.) (21.1.91)		80	1·25
36	(43 c.) on 10 c. Soldier Cone (*Conus miles*) ("MAINLAND") (B.) (7.3.91)		1·10	1·50
37	70 c. on 60 c. Minstrel Cowrie (*Cypraea histrio*) ("ZONE 1") (7.3.91)		1·25	2·00
38	80 c. on 50 c. Fluted Giant Clam or Scaled Tridacna (*Tridacna squamosa*) ("ZONE 2") (7.3.91)		1·50	2·50
39	$1.20 on 15 c. Marlin-spike Auger (*Terebra maculata*) ("ZONE 5") (7.3.91)		1·75	2·75
34/9		*Set of 6*	24·00	11·00

58 Beaded Sea Star   59 Cocos Islands

(Des Jill Ruse. Litho Leigh-Mardon Ltd, Melbourne)

1991 (28 Feb). *Starfish and Sea Urchins. T* **58** *and similar horiz designs. Multicoloured. P* 14½.

240	45 c. Type 58		70	60
241	75 c. Feather Star		1·40	1·60
242	$1 Slate Pencil Urchin		1·60	1·75
243	$1.30, Globose Sea Urchin		2·00	2·50
240/3		*Set of 4*	5·25	5·75

(Des P. Cunningham. Litho Leigh-Mardon Ltd, Melbourne)

1991 (16 Apr). *Malay Hari Raya Festival. T* **59** *and similar horiz designs. Multicoloured. P* 14½.

244	45 c. Type 59		70	60
245	75 c. Island house		1·40	1·60
246	$1.30, Islands scene		2·00	2·50
244/6		*Set of 3*	3·75	4·25

60 Child   61 *Lybia tessellata*
praying

(Des R. Honisett. Litho Leigh-Mardon Ltd, Melbourne)

1991 (6 Nov). *Christmas. T* **60** *and similar vert designs. Multicoloured. P* 15½.

247	38 c. Type 60		70	55
248	43 c. Child dreaming of Christmas Day		75	60
249	$1 Child singing		1·60	1·75
250	$1.20, Child fascinated by decorations		2·25	2·75
247/50		*Set of 4*	4·75	5·00
MS251	118×74 mm. 38 c., 43 c., $1, $1.20, Local children's choir		5·00	5·50

The four values in No. MS251 form a composite design.

(Des Jane Moore. Litho Leigh-Mardon Ltd, Melbourne)

1992 (28 Feb–11 Aug). *Crustaceans. T* **61** *and similar multicoloured designs. P* 14½.

252	5 c. Type 61		20	20
253	10 c. Pilodius areolatus (11 Aug)		25	25
254	20 c. Trizopagurus strigatus		40	40
255	30 c. Lophozozymus pulchellus (11 Aug)		70	70
256	40 c. Thalamitoides quadridens		70	70
257	45 c. Calcinus elegans (vert)		75	75
258	50 c. Clibarius humilis (11 Aug)		80	80
259	60 c. Trapezia rufopunctata (vert)		1·00	1·00
260	80 c. Pylopaguropsis magnimanus (vert) (11 Aug)		1·75	1·75
261	$1 Trapezia ferruginea (vert) (11 Aug)		1·50	1·50
262	$2 Trapezia guttata (vert) (11 Aug)		3·00	3·25
263	$3 Trapezia cymodoce (vert)		3·50	3·75
252/63		*Set of 12*	13·00	13·50

62 *Santa Maria*   63 Banded Rail searching for Food

(Des Philatelic Studios, Melbourne. Litho Leigh-Mardon Ltd, Melbourne)

1992 (22 May). *500th Anniv of Discovery of America by Columbus. P* 14½.

264	62	$1.05, multicoloured	2·25	2·50

(Des G. Drummond. Litho Questa)

1992 (11 June). *Endangered Species. Banded Rail. T* **63** *and similar horiz designs. Multicoloured. P* 14.

265	10 c. Type 63		50	60
	a. Strip of 4. Nos. 265/8		2·50	
266	15 c. Banded Rail with chick		65	75
267	30 c. Two Rails drinking		80	90
268	45 c. Rail and nest		90	1·10
265/8		*Set of 4*	2·50	3·00
MS269	165×78 mm. 45 c. Two Rails by pool; 85 c. Chick hatching; $1.20, Head of Rail		3·75	4·25

Nos. 265/8 were printed together, *se-tenant*, in horizontal or vertical strips of 4 throughout the sheet.

64 R.A.F. Spitfires on   65 Waves
Island Airstrip   breaking on Reef

(Des Philatelic Studios, Melbourne. Litho Leigh-Mardon Ltd, Melbourne)

1992 (13 Oct). *50th Anniv of Second World War. T* **64** *and similar horiz designs. Multicoloured. P* 14½.

270	45 c. Type 64		1·25	80
271	85 c. Japanese aircraft bombing Kampong		2·00	2·25
272	$1.20, R.A.F. Sunderland (flying boat)		2·50	3·00
270/2		*Set of 3*	5·25	5·50

(Des Philatelic Studios, Melbourne. Litho Leigh-Mardon Ltd, Melbourne)

1992 (11 Nov). *Christmas. T* **65** *and similar vert designs. Multicoloured. P* 14½.

273	40 c. Type 65		80	60
274	80 c. Direction Island		1·75	2·00
275	$1 Moorish Idols (fish) and coral		1·75	2·00
273/5		*Set of 3*	3·75	4·25

66 *Lobophyllia hemprichii*   67 Plastic 5 r. Token

(Litho Leigh-Mardon Ltd, Melbourne)

1993 (28 Jan). *Corals. T* **66** *and similar vert designs. Multicoloured. P* 14½.

276	45 c. Type 66		55	55
277	85 c. Pocillopora eydouxi		1·00	1·40
278	$1.05, Fungia scutaria		1·40	1·75
279	$1.20, Sarcophyton sp		1·50	2·00
276/9		*Set of 4*	4·00	5·00

(Des Sandra Harman. Litho Leigh-Mardon Ltd, Melbourne)

1993 (30 Mar). *Early Cocos (Keeling) Islands Currency. T* **67** *and similar vert designs. Multicoloured. P* 14½.

280	45 c. Type 67		65	55
281	85 c. 1968 1 r. plastic token		1·10	1·40
282	$1.05, 1977 150 r. commemorative gold coin		1·50	1·75
283	$1.20, 1910 plastic token		1·60	2·00
280/3		*Set of 4*	4·25	5·00

68 Primary   69 Lifeboat and Crippled
School Pupil   Yacht

(Des Philatelic Studios. Litho Leigh-Mardon Ltd, Melbourne)

1993 (1 June). *Education. T* **68** *and similar vert designs. Multicoloured. P* 14½.

284	5 c. Type 68		20	30
285	40 c. Secondary school pupil		65	50
286	85 c. Learning traditional crafts		1·25	1·40
287	$1.05, Learning office skills		1·50	2·00
288	$1.20, Seaman training		2·00	2·50
284/8		*Set of 5*	5·00	6·00

(Des Philatelic Studios. Litho Leigh-Mardon Ltd, Melbourne)

1993 (17 Aug). *Air-Sea Rescue. T* **69** *and similar horiz designs. Multicoloured. P* 14½.

289	45 c. Type 69		1·00	70
290	85 c. Westwind Seascan (aircraft)		2·00	2·25
291	$1.05, R.J. Hawke (ferry)		2·25	2·75
289/91		*Set of 3*	4·75	5·25
MS292	135×61 mm. Nos. 289/91		4·75	5·50

70 Peace Doves   71 Rectangle
Triggerfish and
Coral

(Des Philatelic Studios. Litho Leigh-Mardon Ltd, Melbourne)

1993 (26 Oct). *Christmas. P* 14½.

293	70	40 c. multicoloured	80	60
294		80 c. multicoloured	1·75	2·00
295		$1 multicoloured	1·75	2·00
293/5		*Set of 3*	3·75	4·25

On 1 January 1994 responsibility for the Cocos (Keeling) Islands postal service passed from the territorial administration to Australia Post. In consequence Nos. 296/315 and all subsequent issues are valid for postal purposes in both Cocos (Keeling) Islands and Australia.

(Des Sue Passmore. Litho McPherson's Ptg Group, Mulgrave)

1994 (17 Feb). *Transfer of Postal Service to Australia Post. T* **71** *and similar vert designs. Multicoloured. P* 14½×14.

296	5 c. Type 71		20	25
	a. Sheetlet. Nos. 296/315		5·00	
297	5 c. Three Rectangle Triggerfish and map section		20	25
298	5 c. Two Rectangle Triggerfish and map section		20	25
299	5 c. Two Rectangle Triggerfish, map section and red coral		20	25
300	5 c. Rectangle Triggerfish with red and brown corals		20	25
301	10 c. Green Turtles on beach		20	25
302	10 c. Two Green Turtles		20	25
303	10 c. Crowd of young Green Turtles		20	25
304	10 c. Green Turtle and map section		20	25
305	10 c. Green Turtle, Pyramid Butterflyfish and map section		20	25
306	20 c. Three Pyramid Butterflyfish and map section		30	35
307	20 c. Pyramid Butterflyfish with brown coral		30	35
308	20 c. Two Pyramid Butterflyfish and coral		30	35
309	20 c. Three Pyramid Butterflyfish and coral		30	35
310	20 c. Coral, Pyramid Butterflyfish and map section		30	35
311	45 c. Jukongs with map of airport		40	45
	a. Horiz strip of 5. Nos. 311/15		1·75	
312	45 c. Two jukongs with red or blue sails and map section		40	45
313	45 c. Jukong in shallows		40	45
314	45 c. Two jukongs with red or yellow sails and map section		40	45
315	45 c. Two jukongs, one with blue jib, and map section		40	45
296/315		*Set of 20*	5·00	5·50

Nos. 296/315 were printed together, *se-tenant*, in sheetlets of 20 with inscriptions on the sheet margins and the backgrounds forming a composite map. Nos. 311/15 were also avaliable printed together, *se-tenant*, in horizontal strips of 5 in sheets of 100.

72 Prabu Abjasa   73 Angel playing Harp
Puppet

(Des Josephine Muré. Litho McPherson's Ptg Group, Mulgrave)

1994 (16 June). *Shadow Puppets. T* **72** *and similar vert designs. Multicoloured. P* 14½×14.

316	45 c. Type 72		55	50
317	90 c. Prabu Pandu		1·00	1·25
318	$1 Judistra		1·10	1·25
319	$1.35, Abimanju		1·25	1·75
316/19		*Set of 4*	3·50	4·25

(Des Tracie Grimwood. Litho McPherson's Ptg Group, Mulgrave)

1994 (31 Oct). *Seasonal Festivals. T* **73** *and similar horiz designs. Multicoloured. P* 14×14½.

320	40 c. Type 73		50	50
321	45 c. Wise Man holding gift		55	50
322	80 c. Mosque at night		1·00	1·75
320/2		*Set of 3*	1·90	2·50

74 White-tailed Tropic   **75** Yellow Crazy
Bird and Blue-faced Booby   Ant

(Des Lisa Christensen and B. Wood. Litho McPherson's Ptg Group, Mulgrave)

1995 (16 Mar). *Sea-birds of North Keeling Island. T **74** and similar horiz design. Multicoloured. P 14×14½.*
323	45 c. Type **74**			60	45
324	85 c. Great Frigate Bird and White Tern			1·00	1·50
MS325	106×70 mm. Nos. 323/4.			1·60	2·00

No. **MS**325 also exists overprinted with the "JAKARTA 95" logo for sale at this exhibition.

(Des Sue Maddern. Litho McPherson's Ptg Group, Mulgrave)

1995 (13 July). *Insects. T **75** and similar vert designs. Multicoloured. P 14½×14.*
326	45 c. Type **75**			70	80
	a. Horiz strip of 5. Nos. 326/30			3·25	
327	45 c. Aedes Mosquito			70	80
328	45 c. Hawk Moth			70	80
329	45 c. Scarab Beetle			70	80
330	45 c. Lauxaniid Fly			70	80
331	$1.20, Common Eggfly (butterfly)			1·25	1·50
326/31			*Set of* 6	4·00	5·00

Nos. 326/30 were printed together, *se-tenant*, in horizontal strips of 5 throughout the sheet, with the backgrounds forming a composite design.

76 Saddle Butterflyfish   **77** Members of Malay
Community

(Des M. Baker and Sandra Harman (5 c., 75 c., 90 c., $1, $1.20), M. Baker and Sophie Byass (others). Litho SNP Cambec (40 c., 80 c., $1.05) or McPherson's Ptg Group, Mulgrave (others))

1995 (1 Nov)–97. *Marine Life. T **76** and similar horiz designs. Multicoloured. P 14×14½.*
332	5 c. Redspot Wrasse (14.8.97)		10	10
333	30 c. Blue-throated Triggerfish ("Gilded Triggerfish") (15.8.96)		25	30
334	40 c. Type **76**		40	45
335	45 c. Arc-eyed Hawkfish (15.8.96)		40	45
336	75 c. Orangespine Unicornfish (14.8.97)		65	70
337	80 c. Blue Tang		80	85
338	85 c. Juvenile Twin-spotted Wrasse ("Humphead Wrasse") (15.8.96)		75	80
339	90 c. Threadfin Butterflyfish (14.8.97)		80	85
340	$1 Bluestripe Snapper (14.8.97)		90	95
341	$1.05, Longnosed Butterflyfish		1·10	1·25
342	$1.20, Freckled Hawkfish (14.8.97)		1·00	1·10
343	$2 Powder-blue Surgeonfish (15.8.96)		1·75	1·90
332/43		*Set of* 12	8·00	8·75

(Des Melinda Whitechurch and Jacqui Young. Litho McPherson's Ptg Group, Mulgrave)

1996 (19 Feb). *Hari Raya Puasa Festival. T **77** and similar square designs. Multicoloured. P 14½.*
344	45 c. Type **77**		55	50
345	75 c. Beating drums		1·00	1·25
346	85 c. Preparing festival meal		1·10	1·50
344/6		*Set of* 3	2·40	3·00

78 Black Rhinoceros with Calf   **79** Dancers and
Tambourine

(Des Kerry Argent and Lisa Christensen. Litho Canberra Press)

1996 (13 June). *Cocos Quarantine Station. T **78** and similar vert designs. Multicoloured. P 14½×14.*
347	45 c. Type **78**		70	70
348	50 c. Alpacas		70	75
349	$1.05, Boran cattle		1·25	1·50
350	$1.20, Ostrich with chicks		1·50	1·75
347/50		*Set of* 4	3·75	4·25

(Des MYD Graphic. Litho SNP Cambec)

1997 (6 Jan). *Hari Raya Puasa Festival. T **79** and similar square designs. Multicoloured. P 14½.*
351	45 c. Type **79**		55	50
352	75 c. Girl clapping and sailing dinghies		90	1·00
353	85 c. Dancers on beach and food		1·00	1·25
351/3		*Set of* 3	2·25	2·50

80 "Wrapped Present"
(Lazina Brian)

(Adapted Dianne Cook. Litho SNP Cambec)

1998 (22 Jan). *Hari Raya Puasa Festival. T **80** and similar vert designs showing paintings by children. Multicoloured. P 14½×14.*
354	45 c. Type **80**		40	45
	a. Horiz strip of 5. Nos. 354/8		2·00	
355	45 c. "Mosque" (Azran Jim)		40	45
356	45 c. "Cocos Malay Woman" (Kate Gossage)		40	45
357	45 c. "Yacht" (Matt Harber)		40	45
358	45 c. "People dancing" (Rakin Chongkin)		40	45
354/8		*Set of* 5	2·00	2·25

Nos. 354/8 were printed together, *se-tenant*, in horizontal strips of five throughout the sheet.

STAMP BOOKLETS

COCOS (KEELING) ISLANDS
INDIAN OCEAN

PHILATELIC BUREAU

B 1 Prison Island

1990 (12 Dec). *Christmas. Multicoloured cover as Type B **1**. Panes attached by selvedge.*
SB1	$3 booklet containing *se-tenant* pane of 6 (No. 231a)			10·00
SB2	$4 booklet containing pane of 10 (No. 231b)			15·00

OFFICIAL STAMP

OFFICIAL PAID
MAINLAND
(O 1)

1991 (25 Jan). *No. 182 surch with Type O **1** in deep violet-blue.*
O1	(43 c.) on 90 c. Coconut palm and mature nuts	†	90·00

No. O1 was only sold to the public cancelled-to-order and not in unused condition.

1st CLASS STAMPS & SERVICE

Stanley Gibbons are pleased to offer a dedicated and completely free of charge service to today's discerning British Commonwealth collectors.

- Specialist database of clients' interests.
- Large stocks of specialised British Commonwealth material.
- Free advice from our team of experts.
- Regular advance lists and illustrated colour brochures.
- Private viewing facilities and postal approvals service.
- Specialist 'Wants List' service.
- We are always interested in buying quality collections and single items.

To take advantage of our free and highly specialised service contact us today on 0171 836 8444.

STANLEY GIBBONS

—FIRST CLASS—
STAMPS & SERVICE

**Stanley Gibbons Limited
399 Strand, London WC2R 0LX**

NORFOLK ISLAND

Norfolk Island, first settled in 1788, was previously part of Tasmania and then New South Wales. The island was declared an Australian Territory in 1913. Unlike the other External Territories it retains an independent postal administration.

The stamps of TASMANIA were used on Norfolk Island from mid-1854 until May 1855, such use being identified by the "72" numeral cancellation. From 1877 the stamps of NEW SOUTH WALES were in regular use, being replaced by issues for AUSTRALIA from 1913 to 1947.

PRINTERS. Nos. 1 to 42 were printed at the Note Printing Branch, Reserve Bank of Australia (until 14 Jan 1960, known as the Note Printing Branch, Commonwealth Bank) by recess. See note at the beginning of Australia *re* imprints.

1 Ball Bay

1947 (10 June)**-59.** *Toned paper. P* 14.
1	1	½d. orange	..	..	35	60
		a. White paper (11.56)	..	..	1·50	4·50
2		1d. bright violet	..	..	50	60
		a. White paper (11.56)	..	..	6·50	16·00
3		1½d. emerald-green	..	..	50	70
		a. White paper (11.56)	..	..	10·00	23·00
4		2d. reddish violet	..	..	55	40
		a. White paper (11.56)	..	..	£100	£130
5		2½d. scarlet	..	..	80	50
6		3d. chestnut	..	..	70	70
6a		3d. emerald-green (*white paper*) (6.7.59)		16·00	6·50
7		4d. claret	..	..	90	40
8		5½d. indigo	..	..	70	30
9		6d. purple-brown	..	..	70	40
10		9d. magenta	..	..	1·25	40
11		1s. grey-green	..	..	70	40
12		2s. yellow-bistre	..	..	1·50	1·00
12a		2s. deep blue (*white paper*) (6.7.59)		24·00	7·00
1/12a			*Set of* 14		45·00	17·00

Stamps of T **1**, perf 11, or in different colours, perf 11, are printer's waste which leaked from the Note Ptg Branch. They were never distributed to post offices for sale to the public.

2 Warder's Tower   **3 Airfield**

1953 (10 June). *T* **2/3** *and similar designs. P* 14½ × 15 (*vert*) *or* 15 × 14½ (*horiz*).
13	3½d. brown-lake	..	..	1·50	90
14	6½d. deep green	..	..	2·50	2·25
15	7½d. deep blue	..	..	2·00	3·00
16	8½d. chocolate	..	..	2·25	4·25
17	10d. reddish violet	..	..	1·50	75
18	5s. sepia	..	..	45·00	10·00
13/18			*Set of* 6	50·00	19·00

Designs: *Horiz* (as *T* **3**)—7½d. Old Stores (Crankmill); 5s. Bloody Bridge. *Vert* (as *T* **2**)—8½d. Barracks entrance; 10d. Salt House.

8 Norfolk Island Seal and Pitcairners Landing

Two types of 2s.:

Type I   Type II

Alternate stamps on each horizontal row are with or without a dot in bottom right corner.

1956 (8 June). *Centenary of Landing of Pitcairn Islanders on Norfolk Island. P* 15 × 14½.
19	8	3d. deep bluish green	..	..	1·50	40
20		2s. violet (I)	..	..	2·00	75
		a. Type II	..	..	2·00	75
		b. Deep violet (I)	..	..	3·50	2·25
		ba. Type II	..	..	3·50	2·25

7ᵈ   **NORFOLK ISLAND**

8ᵈ   **5ᴰ**

(9)   (10)   (11)

1958 (1 July). *Nos.* 15/16 *surch with T* **9/10**.
21	7d. on 7½d. deep blue	..	..	1·00	85
22	8d. on 8½d. chocolate	..	..	1·00	85

1959 (7 Dec). *150th Anniv of Australian Post Office. No.* 331 *of Australia surch with T* **11**.
23	5d. on 4d. slate (R.)	..	..	35	30

12 Hibiscus insularis   **14 White Tern**

16 Red Hibiscus   **17 Queen Elizabeth II and Cereus**

21 Rose Apple   **22 Red-tailed Tropic Bird**

(Design recess; centre typo (T **21**))

1960-62. *T* **12, 14, 16/17, 21/2** *and similar designs. P* 14½ *or* 14½ × 14 (10s.).
24	1d. bluish green (23.5.60)	..	..	15	10
25	2d. rose and myrtle-green (23.5.60)	..	20	10
26	3d. green (1.5.61)	..	..	70	15
27	5d. bright purple (20.6.60)	..	55	20
28	8d. red (20.6.60)	..	..	80	50
29	9d. ultramarine (23.5.60)	..	80	45
30	10d. brown and reddish violet (as No. 17) (27.2.61)	..	2·75	1·25
31	1s. carmine-red (16.10.61)	..	80	35
32	2s. sepia (1.5.61)	..	..	6·00	90
33	2s. 5d. deep violet (5.2.62)	..	1·00	40
34	2s. 8d. cinnamon and deep green (9.4.62)	..	2·75	55
35	5s. sepia and deep green (as No. 18) (27.2.61)	6·50	75
36	10s. emerald-green (14.8.61) (Optd S. £48) ..	60·00	26·00
24/36			*Set of* 13	70·00	28·00

Designs: *Vert* (as *T* **12**)—2d. *Lagunaria patersonii*; 5d. Lantana. (As *T* **21**); 1s. 1d. Fringed Hibiscus; 2s. 5d. Passion-flower. (As *T* **14**)—2s. Solander's Petrel.

Nos. 30 and 35 are redrawn.

The Specimen overprint on No. 36 is from sets sold by the Australian Post Office.

For Nos. 25 and 28 with face values in decimal currency see Nos. 600/1.

2'8

(23)   (24)   (25)

1960. *As Nos.* 13/15 *but colours changed, surch with T* **23/5**.
37	1s. 1d. on 3½d. deep ultramarine (26.9.60)	3·50	2·50
38	2s. 5d. on 6½d. bluish green (26.9.60)	..	4·00	1·50
39	2s. 8d. on 7½d. sepia (29.8.60)	..	10·00	4·25
37/9			*Set of* 3	16·00	7·50

26 Queen Elizabeth II and Map   **27 Open Bible and Candle**

1960 (24 Oct). *Introduction of Local Government. P* 14.
40	26	2s. 8d. reddish purple ..	..	..	16·00	9·00

(Des K. McKay. Adapted and eng B. Stewart. Recess)

1960 (21 Nov). *Christmas. P* 15×14½.
41	27	5d. bright purple ..	..	80	50

28 Open Prayer Book and Text   **29 Stripey (Atypichthys latus)**

(Des G. Lissenden. Eng P. Morriss. Recess)

1961 (20 Nov). *Christmas. P* 14½×14.
42	28	5d. slate-blue	..	..	30	40

PRINTERS. All the following issues to No. 233 were printed in photogravure by Harrison and Sons, Ltd, London, *except where otherwise stated*.

1962-63. *Fishes. Horiz designs as T* **29.** *P* 14½×14.
43	6d. sepia, yellow & dp bluish green (16.7.62)	75	25
44	11d. red-orange, brown and blue (25.2.63)	2·00	80
45	1s. blue, pink and yellow-olive (17.9.62)	75	25
46	1s. 3d. blue, red-brown and green (15.7.63)	2·00	1·75
47	1s. 6d. sepia, violet and light blue (6.5.63)	2·75	80
48	2s. 3d. dp blue, red & greenish yell (23.9.63)	5·00	80
43/8		*Set of* 6	12·00	4·25

Designs:—11d. Gold-mouthed Emperor (*Lethrinus chrysostomus*); 1s. Surge Wrasse ("Po'ov"); 1s. 3d. Seachub ("Dreamfish"); 1s. 6d. Giant Grouper (*Promicrops lanceolatus*); 2s. 3d. White Trevally (*Carangidae*).

30 "Madonna and Child"   **31 "Peace on Earth..."**

(Des and eng G. Lissenden. Recess Note Ptg Branch, Reserve Bank of Australia)

1962 (19 Nov). *Christmas. P* 14½.
49	30	5d. ultramarine	..	..	45	70

(Des R. Warner. Eng B. Stewart. Recess Note Ptg Branch, Reserve Bank of Australia)

1963 (11 Nov). *Christmas. P* 14½.
50	31	5d. red	..	..	40	60

32 Overlooking Kingston   **33 Norfolk Pine**

1964 (24 Feb–28 Sept). *Views. Horiz designs as T* **32.** *Multicoloured. P* 14½×14.
51	5d. Type **32**	..	..	75	30
52	8d. Kingston	..	..	1·00	85
53	9d. The Arches (Bumboras) (11.5)	..	3·00	30
54	10d. Slaughter Bay (28.9)	..	3·00	30
51/4		*Set of* 4	7·00	1·60

(Photo Note Ptg Branch, Reserve Bank of Australia, Melbourne)

1964 (1 July). *50th Anniv of Norfolk Island as Australian Territory. P* 13½.
55	33	5d. black, red and orange	..	..	40	15
56		8d. black, red and grey-green	..	..	40	70

34 Child looking at Nativity Scene   **35 Nativity Scene**

(Des P. Morriss and J. Mason. Photo Note Ptg Branch, Reserve Bank of Australia)

1964 (9 Nov). *Christmas. P* 13½.
57	34	5d. green, blue, buff and violet	..	..	30	40

1965 (14 Apr). *50th Anniv of Gallipoli Landing. As T* **22** *of Nauru. P* 13½.
58	5d. sepia, black and emerald	..	..	15	10

(Des J. Mason. Photo Note Ptg Branch, Reserve Bank of Australia)

1965 (25 Oct). *Christmas. Helecon paper. P* 13½.
59	35	5d. multicoloured ..	..	..	15	10

ALTERED CATALOGUE NUMBERS

Any Catalogue numbers altered from the last edition are shown as a list in the introductory pages.

(New Currency. 100 cents = 1 Australian dollar)

38 *Hibiscus insularis*   **39** Headstone Bridge

1966 (14 Feb). *Decimal currency. Various stamps surch in black on silver tablets, which vary slightly in size, obliterating old value as in T **38**. Surch typo.*

60	38	1 c. on 1d. bluish green *(value tablet 4×5 mm)*		20	10
		a. Value tablet larger, 5½×5½ mm		40	30
61	–	2 c. on 2d. rose & myrtle-green (No. 25)		20	10
62	14	3 c. on 3d. green		50	30
		a. Silver tablet omitted		£225	
63	–	4 c. on 5d. bright purple (No. 27)		25	10
64	16	5 c. on 8d. red		30	10
65	–	10 c. on 10d. brown & reddish vio (No. 30)		60	15
66	–	15 c. on 1s. 1d. carmine-red (No. 31)		45	30
67	–	20 c. on 2s. sepia (No. 32)		3·50	2·75
68	–	25 c. on 2s. 5d. deep violet (No. 33)		1·50	40
69	21	30 c. on 2s. 8d. cinnamon and deep green		1·00	50
70	–	50 c. on 5s. sepia and deep green (No. 35)		3·50	75
71	22	$1 on 10s. emerald-green *(value tablet 7×6½ mm)*		2·75	2·00
		a. Value tablet smaller, 6½×4 mm		2·75	2·00
60/71			*Set of 12*	13·00	6·50

1966 (27 June). *Horiz designs as T **39**. Multicoloured. P 14½ × 14.*

72	7 c. Type **39**			40	15
73	9 c. Cemetery Road			40	15

41 St. Barnabas' Chapel (interior)   **42** St. Barnabas' Chapel (exterior)

1966 (23 Aug). *Centenary of Melanesian Mission. P 14 × 14½.*

74	41	4 c. multicoloured		10	10
75	42	25 c. multicoloured		20	20

43 Star over Philip Island   **44** H.M.S. *Resolution*, 1774

(Des B. G. W. McCoy)

1966 (24 Oct). *Christmas. P 14½.*

76	43	4 c. multicoloured		10	10

(Des Harrison)

1967 (17 Apr)–**68**. *T **44** and similar horiz designs showing ships. Multicoloured. P 14 × 14½.*

77	1 c. Type **44**		10	10
78	2 c. *La Boussole* and *L'Astrolabe*, 1788		15	10
79	3 c. H.M.S. *Supply*, 1788		15	10
80	4 c. H.M.S. *Sirius*, 1790		30	10
81	5 c. *Norfolk* (cutter), 1798 (14.8.67)		20	10
82	7 c. H.M.S. *Mermaid* (survey cutter), 1825 (14.8.67)		20	10
83	9 c. *Lady Franklin*, 1853 (14.8.67)		20	10
84	10 c. *Morayshire*, 1856 (14.8.67)		20	20
85	15 c. *Southern Cross*, 1866 (18.3.68)		45	30
86	20 c. *Pitcairn*, 1891 (18.3.68)		60	40
87	25 c. *Black Billy* (Norfolk Island whaleboat), 1895 (18.3.68)		1·00	75
88	30 c. *Iris* (cable ship), 1907 (18.6.68)		1·50	2·00
89	50 c. *Resolution*, 1926 (18.6.68)		3·50	2·75
90	$1 *Morinda*, 1931 (18.6.68)		5·50	3·00
77/90		*Set of 14*	12·50	9·00

45 Lions Badge and 50 Stars   **46** Prayer of John Adams and Candle

(Des M. Ripper. Photo Note Ptg Branch, Reserve Bank of Australia)

1967 (7 June). *50th Anniv of Lions International. P 13½.*

91	45	4 c. black, bluish green and olive-yellow	10	10

(Des B. G. W. McCoy)

1967 (16 Oct). *Christmas. P 14.*

92	46	5 c. black, light yellow-olive and red	10	10

148

---

47 Queen Elizabeth II

(Photo Note Ptg Branch, Reserve Bank of Australia)

1968 (5 Aug)–**71**. *Coil stamps. P 15×imperf.*

93	47	3 c. black, light brown and vermilion		10	10
94		4 c. black, light brown and blue-green		10	10
95		5 c. black, light brown and deep violet		10	10
95a		6 c. black, lt brown & lake-brn (25.8.71)		30	35
93/5a			*Set of 4*	45	45

59 Avro Type 691 Lancastrian and Douglas DC-4 Aircraft   **60** Bethlehem Star and Flowers

(Des Harrison)

1968 (25 Sept). *21st Anniv of QANTAS Air Service, Sydney–Norfolk Island. P 14.*

96	59	5 c. bluish black, carmine-red & lt blue	15	10
97		7 c. blackish brown, carmine-red & turq	15	10

(Des Mrs. B. L. Laing)

1968 (24 Oct). *Christmas. P 14 × 14½.*

98	60	5 c. multicoloured	10	10

 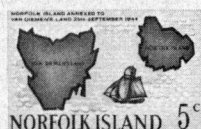

61 Captain Cook, Quadrant and Chart of Pacific Ocean   **62** Van Diemen's Land, Norfolk Island and Sailing Cutter

(Des V. Whiteley from sketch by J. Cowap)

1969 (3 June). *Captain Cook Bicentenary (1st issue). Observation of the transit of Venus across the Sun, from Tahiti. P 14.*

99	61	10 c. multicoloured	10	10

See also Nos. 118/19, 129, 152/5, 200/2 and 213/14.

(Des Mrs. A. Bathie and Mrs. M. J. McCoy)

1969 (29 Sept). *125th Anniv of the Annexation of Norfolk Island to Van Diemen's Land. P 14 × 14½.*

100	62	5 c. multicoloured	10	10
101		30 c. multicoloured	50	60
		a. Inscr "VAN DIFMEN'S LAND" (R. 8/5)	10·00	

63 "The Nativity" (carved mother-of-pearl plaque)   **64** New Zealand Grey Flyeater

(Des J. Cowap)

1969 (27 Oct). *Christmas. P 14½ × 14.*

102	63	5 c. multicoloured	10	10

(Des G. Mathews)

1970–71. *Birds. T **64** and similar multicoloured designs. Chalk-surfaced paper. P 14.*

103	1 c. Scarlet Robins (22.7.70)		30	10
104	2 c. Golden Whistler (24.2.71)		30	20
105	3 c. Type **64** (25.2.70)		30	10
106	4 c. Long-tailed Koels (25.2.70)		60	10
107	5 c. Red-fronted Parakeet (24.2.71)		1·50	45
108	7 c. Long-tailed Triller (22.7.70)		45	10
109	9 c. Island Thrush (25.2.70)		70	10
110	10 c. Boobook Owl (22.7.70)		1·75	90
111	15 c. Norfolk Island Pigeon (24.2.71)		1·50	65
112	20 c. White-chested White Eye (16.6.71)		6·00	3·25
113	25 c. New Zealand Parrots (22.7.70)		2·50	40
	a. Error. Glazed, ordinary paper		£350	
114	30 c. Collared Grey Fantail (16.6.71)		6·00	1·75
115	45 c. Norfolk Island Starlings (25.2.70)		3·50	80
116	50 c. Crimson Rosella (24.2.71)		4·00	1·75
117	$1 Sacred Kingfisher (16.6.71)		10·00	10·00
103/17		*Set of 15*	35·00	18·00

Nos. 105, 106, 109, 112, 114, 115 and 117 are horizontal, and the remainder vertical designs.

It is believed that only one sheet of No. 113a was issued.

---

65 Capt. Cook and Map of Australia   **66** First Christmas Service, 1788

(Des R. Bates)

1970 (29 Apr). *Captain Cook Bicentenary (2nd issue). Discovery of Australia's East Coast. T **65** and similar horiz design. Multi-coloured. P 14.*

118	5 c. Type **65**		15	10
119	10 c. H.M.S. *Endeavour* and aborigine		40	10

(Des R. Bates)

1970 (15 Oct). *Christmas. P 14.*

120	66	5 c. multicoloured	10	10

67 Bishop Patteson and Martyrdom of St. Stephen   **68** Rose Window, St. Barnabas Chapel, Kingston

(Des R. Bates)

1971 (20 Sept). *Death Centenary of Bishop Patteson. T **67** and similar horiz designs. Multicoloured. P 14 × 14½.*

121	6 c. Type **67**		10	10
	a. Pair. Nos. 121/2		15	30
122	6 c. Bible, Martyrdom of St. Stephen and knotted palm-frond		10	10
123	10 c. Bishop Patteson and stained-glass		10	15
	a. Pair. Nos. 123/4		20	30
124	10 c. Cross and Bishop's Arms		10	15
121/4		*Set of 4*	30	55

Nos. 121/2 and 123/4 were printed in *se-tenant* pairs throughout the sheet.

(Des G. Hitch. Photo Heraclio Fournier, Spain)

1971 (25 Oct). *Christmas. P 14 × 13½.*

125	68	6 c. multicoloured	10	10

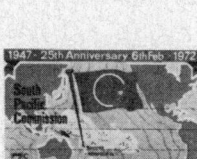

69 Map and Flag   **70** "St. Mark" (stained-glass window, All Saints, Norfolk Is)

(Des G. Hitch)

1972 (7 Feb). *25th Anniv of South Pacific Commission. P 14 × 14½.*

126	69	7 c. multicoloured	15	20

(Des Mrs. M. J. McCoy)

1972 (16 Oct). *Christmas. P 14.*

127	70	7 c. multicoloured	10	10

71 Cross and Pines. (stained-glass window, All Saints Church)   **72** H.M.S. *Resolution* in the Antarctic

(Des Harrison)

1972 (20 Nov). *Centenary of First Pitcairner-built Church. P 14.*

128	71	12 c. multicoloured	10	10
		a. Purple (background to dates) omitted	£500	

No. 128a occurred on the top row of one sheet.

(Des G. Hitch)

1973 (17 Jan). *Captain Cook Bicentenary (3rd issue). Crossing of the Antarctic Circle. P* 14.
129 **72** 35 c. multicoloured .. .. 3·00 2·25

73 Child and Christmas Tree   **74** Protestant Clergyman's Quarters

(Des B. G. W. McCoy (T **73**), R. Westwood (35 c.))

1973 (22 Oct). *Christmas. T* **73** *and similar vert design. Multicoloured. P* 14.
130   7 c. Type **73** 20   10
131 12 c. Type **73** 25   10
132 35 c. Fir trees and star 70   80
130/2 .. .. *Set of* 3   1·00   90

(Des G. Hitch)

1973 (19 Nov)–**75**. *Historic Buildings. T* **74** *and similar horiz designs. Multicoloured. P* 14 × 14½.
133   1 c. Type **74** 10   10
134   2 c. Royal Engineers' Office (1.5.74) .. 10   10
135   3 c. Double Quarters for Free Overseers (19.2.75) 25   30
136   4 c. Guard House (12.7.74) .. 20   20
137   5 c. Entrance to Pentagonal Gaol .. 25   15
138   7 c. Pentagonal Gaol (1.5.74) .. 35   35
139   8 c. Prisoners' Barracks (19.2.75) .. 1·25 1·25
140 10 c. Officers' Quarters, New Military Barracks 50   55
141 12 c. New Military Barracks (1.5.74) 50   30
142 14 c. Beach Stores (12.7.74) .. 60   70
143 15 c. The Magazine (19.2.75) .. 1·25   50
144 20 c. Entrance, Old Military Barracks (12.7.74) 70   90
145 25 c. Old Military Barracks (19.2.75).. 1·25 1·00
146 30 c. Old Stores (Crankmill) (1.5.74) .. 70   60
147 50 c. Commissariat Stores .. 70 2·00
148   $1 Government House (12.7.74) .. 1·50 4·00
133/48 .. .. .. *Set of* 16   9·00 11·00

75 Royal Couple and Map

(Des Harrison)

1974 (8 Feb). *Royal Visit. P* 14 × 14½.
149 **75**   7 c. multicoloured 40   15
150 25 c. multicoloured .. .. 1·25   75

76 Chichester's De Havilland D.H.60G Gipsy Moth Seaplane *Madame Elijah*

(Des B. G. W. McCoy. Litho State Bank Note Printing Works, Helsinki)

1974 (28 Mar). *First Aircraft Landing on Norfolk Island. P* 14.
151 **76** 14 c. multicoloured .. .. 1·00   70

77 "Captain Cook" (engraving by J. Basire)   **78** Nativity Scene (pearl-shell pew carving)

(Des C. I. Buffett. Litho Questa)

1974 (8 Oct). *Captain Cook Bicentenary (4th issue). Discovery of Norfolk Is. T* **77** *and similar vert designs. Multicoloured. P* 14.
152   7 c. Type **77** .. .. 1·25   75
153 10 c. "H.M.S. *Resolution*" (H. Roberts) 2·25 1·75
154 14 c. Norfolk Island Pine .. 2·25 2·25
155 25 c. "Norfolk Island flax" (G. Raper).. 2·50 3·00
152/5 .. .. .. *Set of* 4   7·50 7·00

(Des G. Hitch)

1974 (18 Oct). *Christmas. P* 14½.
156 **78**   7 c. multicoloured 15   10
157 30 c. multicoloured 60   75

79 Norfolk Pine

(Manufactured by Walsall)

1974 (16 Dec). *Centenary of Universal Postal Union. T* **79** *and similar "island"-shaped designs. Multicoloured. Imperf (backing-paper roul* 20). *Self-adhesive.*
158 10 c. Type **79** 25   40
159 15 c. Offshore islands 35   45
160 35 c. Crimson Rosella and Sacred Kingfisher 60   75
161 40 c. Pacific map 60   90
158/61 .. .. .. *Set of* 4   1·60 2·25
MS162   106 × 101 mm. Map of Norfolk Is. cut-to-shape with reduced-size replicas of Nos. 158/61   20·00 27·00

80 H.M.S. *Mermaid* (survey cutter)

(Manufactured by Walsall)

1975 (18 Aug). *150th Anniv of Second Settlement. T* **80** *and similar "island"-shaped design. Multicoloured. Imperf (backing-paper roul* 20). *Self-adhesive.*
163 10 c. Type **80** 40   60
164 35 c. Kingston, 1835 (from painting by T. Seller) 60   90

81 Star on Norfolk Island Pine   **82** Memorial Cross

(Des Harrison)

1975 (6 Oct). *Christmas. P* 14.
165 **81** 10 c. multicoloured 15   10
166 15 c. multicoloured 20   10
167 35 c. multicoloured 30   35
165/7 .. .. .. *Set of* 3   60   45

(Des Harrison)

1975 (24 Nov). *Centenary of St. Barnabas Chapel. T* **82** *and similar horiz design. Multicoloured. P* 14.
168 **82** 30 c. Type **82** 20   15
169 60 c. Laying foundation stone and Chapel in 1975 40   40

83 Launching of *Resolution*   **84** Whaleship *Charles W. Morgan*

(Des Harrison)

1975 (1 Dec). *50th Anniv of Launching of Schooner "Resolution". T* **83** *and similar horiz design. Multicoloured. P* 14.
170 25 c. Type **83** 25   40
171 45 c. *Resolution* at sea.. .. 40   70

(Des Harrison)

1976 (5 July). *Bicentenary of American Revolution. T* **84** *and similar horiz designs. Multicoloured. P* 14.
172 18 c. Type **84** 30   20
173 25 c. Thanksgiving Service .. 40   20
174 40 c. Boeing B-17 Flying Fortress over Norfolk Is 75   55
175 45 c. California Quail .. .. 1·00   75
172/5 .. .. .. *Set of* 4   2·25 1·50

85 Swallow-tailed Tern and Sun   **86** *Vanessa ita*

(Des Harrison)

1976 (4 Oct). *Christmas. P* 14.
176 **85** 18 c. multicoloured 30   15
177 25 c. multicoloured 55   20
178 45 c. multicoloured 90   50
176/8 .. .. .. *Set of* 3   1·60   75

(Des B. Hargreaves)

1976 (17 Nov)–**77**. *Butterflies and Moths. T* **86** *and similar horiz designs. Multicoloured. P* 14.
179   1 c. Type **86** 10   40
180   2 c. *Utetheisa pulchelloides* (moth) (22.2.77) 10   40
181   3 c. *Agathia asterias* (moth) (5.7.77) .. 10   20
182   4 c. *Cynthia kershawi* (5.7.77) .. 10   25
183   5 c. *Leucania loreyimima* (moth) .. 15   30
184 10 c. *Hypolimnas bolina* 30   35
185 15 c. *Pyrrhorachis pyrrhogona* (moth) (22.2.77) 30   30
186 16 c. *Austrocarea iocephala* (moth) .. 30   30
187 17 c. *Pseudocoremia christiani* (moth) (10.5.77) 35   30
188 18 c. *Cleora idiocrossa* (moth) .. 35   30
189 19 c. *Simplicia caeneusalis* (moth) (10.5.77) 35   30
190 20 c. *Austrocidaria ralstonae* (moth) (10.5.77) 40   30
191 30 c. *Hippotion scrofa* (moth) (22.2.77) 50   40
192 40 c. *Papilio amynthor* (ilioneus) (10.5.77) 55   40
193 50 c. *Tiracola plagiata* (moth) (22.2.77) 70   60
194   $1 *Precis villida* 75   75
195   $2 *Cepora perimale* (5.7.77) .. 1·25 1·40
179/95 .. .. .. *Set of* 17   5·75 6·50

87 Queen's View, Kingston

(Des Harrison)

1977 (10 June). *Silver Jubilee. P* 14.
196 **87** 25 c. multicoloured 35   30

88 Hibiscus Flowers and Oil Lamp   **89** Captain Cook (from a portrait by Nathaniel Dance)

(Des Marguerite M. J. McCoy)

1977 (4 Oct). *Christmas. P* 14 × 14½.
197 **88** 18 c. multicoloured 15   10
198 25 c. multicoloured 15   10
199 45 c. multicoloured 30   35
197/9 .. .. .. *Set of* 3   55   50

(Des Harrison)

1978 (18 Jan). *Captain Cook Bicentenary (5th issue). Discovery of Hawaii. T* **89** *and similar horiz designs. Multicoloured. P* 14½.
200 18 c. Type **89** 30   20
201 25 c. Discovery of Northern Hawaiian islands 40   30
202 80 c. British flag against island background .. 90   70
200/2 .. .. .. *Set of* 3   1·40 1·10

90 Guide Flag and Globe

(Manufactured by Walsall)

1978 (22 Feb). *50th Anniv of Girl Guides. T* **90** *and similar "island"-shaped designs. Multicoloured. Imperf (backing paper roul 20). Self-adhesive.*
203	18 c.	Type **90**	20	20
204	25 c.	Emblem and scarf badge	25	30
	a.	Horiz roul omitted (vert pair)		
205	35 c.	Emblem and Queen Elizabeth	35	45
	a.	Horiz roul omitted (vert pair)		
206	45 c.	Emblem and Lady Baden-Powell	45	55
203/6		*Set of* 4	1·10	1·40

Nos. 204a and 205a each come from sheets of 20 on which all the horizontal roulettes were omitted.

91 St. Edward's Crown

(Des Harrison)

1978 (29 June). *25th Anniv of Coronation. T* **91** *and similar horiz design. Multicoloured. P* 14½.
207	25 c.	Type **91**	15	15
208	70 c.	Coronation regalia	40	45

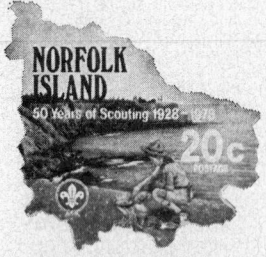

92 View of Duncombe Bay with Scout at Camp Fire

(Des S. Jensen. Manufactured by Walsall)

1978 (22 Aug). *50th Anniv of Boy Scouts. T* **92** *and similar "island"-shaped designs. Multicoloured. Imperf (backing paper roul 20). Self-adhesive.*
209	20 c.	Type **92**	30	40
210	25 c.	View from Kingston and emblem	35	50
211	35 c.	View of Anson Bay and Link Badge	50	80
212	45 c.	Sunset scene and Lord Baden-Powell	55	85
209/12		*Set of* 4	1·50	2·25

93 Chart showing Route of Arctic Voyage   94 Poinsettia and Bible

(Des G. Hitch)

1978 (29 Aug). *Captain Cook Bicentenary (6th issue). Northernmost Voyages. T* **93** *and similar horiz design. Multicoloured. P* 14½.
213	25 c.	Type **93**	40	30
214	90 c.	"H.M.S. *Resolution* and H.M.S. *Discovery* in Pack Ice" (painting by Webber)	1·00	80

(Des Marie L. McCoy)

1978 (3 Oct). *Christmas. T* **94** *and similar vert designs. Multicoloured. P* 14½ × 14.
215	20 c.	Type **94**	15	10
216	30 c.	Native Oak and Bible	20	15
217	55 c.	Hibiscus and Bible	30	30
215/17		*Set of* 3	60	50

95 Cook and Village of Staithes near Marton

(Des Harrison)

1978 (27 Oct). *250th Birth Anniv of Captain Cook. T* **95** *and similar horiz design. Multicoloured. P* 14½.
218	20 c.	Type **95**	30	25
219	80 c.	Cook and Whitby Harbour	1·00	1·25

MINIMUM PRICE

The minimum price quote is 10p which represents a handling charge rather than a basis for valuing common stamps. For further notes about prices see introductory pages.

96 H.M.S. *Resolution*   97 Assembly Building

(Des G. Hitch)

1979 (14 Feb). *Death Bicentenary of Captain Cook. T* **96** *and similar horiz designs. Multicoloured. P* 14.
220	20 c.	Type **96**	40	30
	a.	Pair. Nos. 220/1	80	60
221	20 c.	Cook (statue)	40	30
222	40 c.	Cook's death	45	50
	a.	Pair. Nos. 222/3	90	1·00
223	40 c.	Cook's death (*different*)	45	50
220/23		*Set of* 4	1·50	1·60

The 20 c. designs depict the *Resolution* and Cook's statue on a map showing the last voyage. The 40 c. designs show Cook's death from an aquatint by John Clevely.

Nos. 220/1 and 222/3 were each printed together, *se-tenant*, in horizontal pairs throughout the sheets, forming composite designs.

1979 (10 Aug). *First Norfolk Island Legislative Assembly. P* 14½ × 14.
224	97	$1 multicoloured	50	50

98   Tasmania 1853 1d. Stamp and Sir Rowland Hill

1979 (27 Aug). *Death Centenary of Sir Rowland Hill. T* **98** *and similar horiz designs showing stamps and Sir Rowland Hill. P* 14 × 14½.
225	20 c.	new blue and sepia	20	10
226	30 c.	brown-red and olive-grey	25	15
227	55 c.	violet and indigo	40	30
225/7		*Set of* 3	75	50
MS228	142 × 91 mm. No. 227. P 14		55	1·25

Designs:—30 c. Penny Red; 55 c. 1d. "Ball Bay".

99 I.Y.C. Emblem and Map of Pacific showing Norfolk Island as Pine Tree

(Des Claire Walters. Litho Asher and Co, Melbourne)

1979 (25 Sept). *International Year of the Child. P* 15.
229	99	80 c. multicoloured	40	45

100 Emily Bay   101 Lions International Emblem

1979 (5 Nov).* *Christmas. T* **100** *and similar horiz designs showing different aspects of Emily Bay. P* 12½ × 13.
230	15 c.	multicoloured	15	15
	a.	Horiz strip of 3. Nos. 230/2	40	
231	20 c.	multicoloured	15	15
232	30 c.	multicoloured	15	15
230/2		*Set of* 3	40	40
MS233	152 × 83 mm. Nos. 230/2. P 14 × 14½		1·00	1·60

Nos. 230/2 were printed together, *se-tenant*, in horizontal strips of 3 throughout the sheet, forming a composite design.

*Although released by the Crown Agents in London on 2 October the stamps were not released locally until 5 November.

(Des Norfolk Island Lions Club. Litho Asher and Co, Melbourne)

1980 (25 Jan). *Lions Convention. P* 15.
234	101	50 c. multicoloured	35	30

102 Rotary International Emblem

(Des E. Lenthall. Litho Asher and Co, Melbourne)

1980 (21 Feb). *75th Anniv of Rotary International. P* 15.
235	102	50 c. multicoloured	35	30
	a.	Black (face value and "NORFOLK ISLAND") omitted		

103 De Havilland D.H.60G Gipsy Moth Seaplane *Madame Elijah*

(Des G. Hitch and B. G. W. McCoy. Litho Harrison)

1980 (25 Mar)–81. *Airplanes. Horiz designs as T* **103**. *Multicoloured. P* 14½×14.
236	1 c.	Hawker Siddeley H.S.748 (3.3.81)	15	20
237	2 c.	Type **103**	15	20
238	3 c.	Curtiss P.40E Kittyhawk I	15	20
239	4 c.	Chance Vought F4U-1 Corsair (19.8.80)	15	30
240	5 c.	Grumman TBF Avenger (19.8.80)	15	30
241	15 c.	Douglas SBD-5 Dauntless (19.8.80)	30	30
242	20 c.	Cessna 172D Skyhawk	30	30
243	25 c.	Lockheed 414 Hudson (3.3.81)	30	35
244	30 c.	Lockheed PV-1 Ventura (13.1.81)	40	40
245	40 c.	Avro Type 685 York (3.3.81)	50	55
246	50 c.	Douglas DC-3 (13.1.81)	65	65
247	60 c.	Avro Type 691 Lancastrian (13.1.81)	75	75
248	80 c.	Douglas DC-4 (13.1.81)	95	95
249	$1	Beech 200 Super King Air (3.3.81)	1·25	
250	$2	Fokker F.27 Friendship (19.8.80)	2·50	2·25
251	$5	Lockheed C-130 Hercules	6·00	2·00
236/51		*Set of* 16	13·00	10·00

104 Queen Elizabeth the Queen Mother

(Des K. Williams. Litho Harrison)

1980 (4 Aug). *80th Birthday of Queen Elizabeth the Queen Mother. P* 14.
252	104	22 c. multicoloured	20	20
253		60 c. multicoloured	35	40

105 Red-tailed Tropic Birds

(Des K. Williams. Litho Harrison)

1980 (28 Oct). *Christmas. Birds. T* **105** *and similar horiz designs. Multicoloured. P* 14 × 14½.
254	15 c.	Type **105**	30	25
	a.	Horiz strip of 3. Nos. 254/6	80	
255	22 c.	White Terns	30	25
256	35 c.	White-capped Noddys	30	25
257	60 c.	White Terns (*different*)	40	45
254/7		*Set of* 4	1·10	1·10

Nos. 254/6 were printed together, *se-tenant*, in horizontal strips of 3 throughout the sheet.

106 *Morayshire* and View of Norfolk Island   107 Wedding Bouquet from Norfolk Island

(Des Jennifer Toombs. Litho Harrison)

1981 (5 June). *125th Anniv of Pitcairn Islanders' Migration to Norfolk Island. T* **106** *and similar horiz designs. Multicoloured. P* 14½.
258	5 c.	Type **106**	15	15
259	35 c.	Islanders arriving ashore	40	30
260	60 c.	View of new settlement	60	45
258/60		*Set of* 3	1·00	80
MS261	183 × 127 mm. Nos. 258/60		1·50	2·00

(Des J.W. Litho Harrison)

1981 (22 July). *Royal Wedding.* T 107 *and similar vert designs. Multicoloured.* P 14.

262	35 c. Type 107			15	15
263	55 c. Prince Charles at horse trials			25	25
264	60 c. Prince Charles and Lady Diana Spencer			25	35
262/4			Set of 3	60	65

108 Uniting Church in Australia   109 Pair of White-chested White Eyes

(Des K. Williams. Litho Harrison)

1981 (15 Sept). *Christmas. Churches.* T 108 *and similar horiz designs. Multicoloured.* P 14½ × 14.

265	18 c. Type 108			15	10
266	24 c. Seventh Day Adventist Church			15	15
267	30 c. Church of the Sacred Heart			20	20
268	$1 St. Barnabas Chapel			50	70
265/8			Set of 4	90	1·00

(Des P. Slater. Litho Questa)

1981 (10 Nov). *White-chested White Eye ("Silvereye").* T 109 *and similar horiz designs. Multicoloured.* P 14 × 14½.

269	35 c. Type 109			35	40
	a. Horiz strip of 5. Nos. 269/73			1·50	
270	35 c. Bird on nest			35	40
271	35 c. Bird with egg			35	40
272	35 c. Parents with chicks			35	40
273	35 c. Fledgelings			35	40
269/73			Set of 5	1·50	2·00

Nos. 269/73 were printed together, *se-tenant*, in horizontal strips of 5 throughout the sheet.

110 Aerial View of Philip Island

(Des local artist. Litho Harrison)

1982 (12 Jan). *Philip and Nepean Islands.* T 110 *and similar horiz designs. Multicoloured.* P 14 × 13½.

274	24 c. Type 110			25	25
	a. Horiz strip of 5. Nos. 274/8			1·10	
275	24 c. Close-up view of Philip Island landscape			25	25
276	24 c. Gecko (*Phyllodactylus guentheri*), Philip Island			25	25
277	24 c. Sooty Tern (*Sterna fuscata*), Philip Island			25	25
278	24 c. Philip Island Hibiscus (*Hibiscus insularis*)			25	25
279	35 c. Aerial view of Nepean Island			30	30
	a. Horiz strip of 5. Nos. 279/83			1·25	
280	35 c. Close-up view of Nepean Island landscape			30	30
281	35 c. Gecko (*Phyllodactylus guentheri*), Nepean Island			30	30
282	35 c. Blue-faced Boobies (*Sula dactylatra*), Nepean Island			30	30
283	35 c. *Carpobrotus glaucescens* (flower), Nepean Island			30	30
274/83			Set of 10	2·25	2·25

The five designs of each value were printed together, *se-tenant*, in horizontal strips of 5 throughout the sheet.

111 Sperm Whale

(Des Jennifer Toombs. Litho Harrison)

1982 (23 Feb). *Whales.* T 111 *and similar horiz designs.* P 14½.

284	24 c. multicoloured			45	35
285	55 c. multicoloured			85	85
286	80 c. black, mauve and stone			1·10	1·60
284/6			Set of 3	2·25	2·50

Designs:—55 c. Black Right Whale; 80 c. Humpback Whale.

112 *Diocet*, Wrecked 20 April 1873

(Litho Harrison)

1982 (18 May–27 July). *Shipwrecks.* T 112 *and similar horiz designs. Multicoloured.* P 14½ × 14.

287	24 c. H.M.S. *Sirius*, wrecked 19 March 1790 (27 July)			50	50
288	27 c. Type 112			50	50
289	35 c. *Friendship*, wrecked 17 May 1835 (27 July)			90	80
290	40 c. *Mary Hamilton*, wrecked 6 May 1873			90	90
291	55 c. *Fairlie*, wrecked 14 February 1840 (27 July)			1·25	1·25
292	65 c. *Warrigal*, wrecked 18 March 1918			1·25	1·50
287/92			Set of 6	4·75	5·00

C-KURITY PAPER. The following issues up to No. 342 were all printed on this type of security paper, *unless otherwise stated.* It shows a pattern of blue fluorescent markings, resembling rosettes, on the reverse beneath the gum.

113 R.N.Z.A.F. Lockheed 414 Hudson dropping Christmas Supplies, 1942   114 50th (Queen's Own) Regiment

(Des A. Theobald. Litho Walsall)

1982 (7 Sept). *Christmas. 40th Anniv of first Supply-plane Landings on Norfolk Island (Christmas Day 1942).* T 113 *and similar horiz designs. Multicoloured.* P 14.

293	27 c. Type 113			45	35
294	40 c. Lockheed 414 Hudson landing Christmas supplies, 1942			60	65
295	75 c. Christmas, 1942			90	1·40
293/5			Set of 3	1·75	2·25

(Des W. Fenton. Litho Questa)

1982 (9 Nov). *Military Uniforms.* T 114 *and similar vert designs. Multicoloured.* P 14½ × 14.

296	27 c. Type 114			30	35
297	40 c. 58th (Rutlandshire) Regiment			40	75
298	55 c. 80th (Staffordshire Volunteers) Battalion Company			50	95
299	65 c. 11th (North Devonshire) Regiment			60	1·25
296/9			Set of 4	1·60	3·00

115 *Panaeolus papilionaceus*   116 Beech 18 Aircraft

(Des Jane Thatcher. Litho Enschedé)

1983 (29 Mar). *Fungi.* T 115 *and similar vert designs. Multicoloured.* P 13½ × 13.

300	27 c. Type 115			45	35
301	40 c. *Coprinus domesticus*			70	50
302	55 c. *Marasmius niveus*			95	70
303	65 c. *Cymatoderma elegans* var *lamellatum*			1·25	85
300/3			Set of 4	3·00	2·25

(Des Walsall. Litho Format)

1983 (12 July). *Bicentenary of Manned Flight.* T 116 *and similar horiz designs. Multicoloured.* P 14½ × 14.

304	10 c. Type 116			15	15
305	27 c. Fokker F.28 Fellowship			25	35
306	45 c. French military Douglas C-54			40	60
307	75 c. Sikorsky S-61N helicopter			60	95
304/7			Set of 4	1·25	1·90
MS308	105×100 mm. Nos. 304/7			1·75	2·75

117 St. Matthew   118 Cable Ship *Chantik*

(Des McCombie-Skinner Studio. Litho Format)

1983 (13 Sept). *Christmas. 150th Birth Anniv of Sir Edward Burne-Jones.* T 117 *and similar vert designs showing stained-glass windows from St. Barnabas Chapel, Norfolk Island. Multicoloured.* P 14.

309	5 c. Type 117			10	10
310	24 c. St. Mark			20	30
311	30 c. Jesus Christ			25	40
312	45 c. St. Luke			35	55
313	85 c. St. John			55	1·10
309/13			Set of 5	1·25	2·25

(Des G. Drummond. Litho Format)

1983 (15 Nov). *World Communications Year. ANZCAN Cable.* T 118 *and similar horiz designs. Multicoloured. Ordinary paper.* P 14½ × 14.

314	30 c. Type 118			30	40
315	45 c. *Chantik* during in-shore operations			40	55
316	75 c. Cable ship *Mercury*			55	95
317	85 c. Diagram of cable route			55	1·10
314/17			Set of 4	1·60	2·75

119 Popwood   120 Morwong

(Des I. Loe. Litho B.D.T.)

1984 (10 Jan–27 Mar). *Flowers.* T 119 *and similar vert designs. Multicoloured.* P 14.

318	1 c. Type 119 (27.3)			30	60
319	2 c. Strand Morning Glory			40	60
320	3 c. Native Phreatia			45	60
321	4 c. Philip Island Wisteria (27.3)			45	60
322	5 c. Norfolk Island Palm (27.3)			45	60
323	10 c. Evergreen			50	60
324	15 c. Bastard Oak (27.3)			60	60
325	20 c. Devil's Guts			60	60
326	25 c. White Oak			70	70
327	30 c. Ti (27.3)			70	80
328	35 c. Philip Island Hibiscus (27.3)			70	80
329	40 c. Native Wisteria			80	90
330	50 c. Native Jasmine			1·25	1·00
331	$1 Norfolk Island Hibiscus (27.3)			1·25	1·50
332	$3 Native Oberonia (27.3)			2·75	3·50
333	$5 Norfolk Island Pine			3·75	4·25
318/33			Set of 16	14·00	16·00

(Des Marg Towt. Litho Cambec Press, Melbourne)

1984 (17 Apr). *Reef Fishes.* T 120 *and similar horiz designs. Multicoloured. Ordinary paper.* P 13½ × 14.

334	30 c. Type 120			40	45
335	45 c. Black-spotted Goatfish (*Pseudopeneus signatus*)			60	65
336	75 c. Surgeonfish (*Acanthuridae*)			1·00	1·10
337	85 c. Three-striped Butterflyfish (*Chaeton ancinetus*)			1·25	1·40
334/7			Set of 4	2·75	3·25

121 Owl with Eggs   122 1953 7½d. and 1974 Cook Bicent 10 c. Stamps

(Des P. Slater. Litho Questa)

1984 (17 July). *Boobook Owl.* T 121 *and similar vert designs. Multicoloured.* P 14.

338	30 c. Type 121			65	60
	a. Horiz strip of 5. Nos. 338/42			3·00	
339	30 c. Fledgeling			65	60
340	30 c. Young owl on stump			65	60
341	30 c. Adult on branch			65	60
342	30 c. Owl in flight			65	60
338/42			Set of 5	3·00	2·75

Nos. 338/42 were printed together, *se-tenant*, in horizontal strips of 5 throughout the sheet.

(Des D. Miller. Litho Harrison)

1984 (18 Sept). *"Ausipex" International Stamp Exhibition, Melbourne.* T 122 *and similar horiz designs. Multicoloured.* W w 14 *(sideways).* P 14.

343	30 c. Type 122			30	35
344	45 c. John Buffett commemorative postal stationery envelope			50	75
345	75 c. Design from Presentation Pack for 1982 Military Uniforms issue			90	1·75
343/5			Set of 3	1·50	2·50
MS346	151 × 93 mm. Nos. 343/5. P 14½			4·00	4·50

123 Font, Kingston Methodist   124 The Revd. Nobbs teaching
Church   Pitcairn Islanders

(Des R. Murphy. Litho Questa)

1984 (9 Oct).   *Christmas. Centenary of Methodist Church on
Norfolk Island. T* **123** *and similar vert designs. Multicoloured.
W w* 14. *P* 14.
347   5 c. Type **123** 10   10
348 24 c. Church service in Old Barracks, King-
     ston, late 1800's 25   40
349 30 c. The Revd. & Mrs. A. H. Phelps and sailing
     ship 35   45
350 45 c. The Revd. A. H. Phelps and First Congre-
     gational Church, Chester, U.S.A. .. 40   65
351 85 c. Interior of Kingston Methodist Church .. 80 1·40
347/51 .. .. *Set of 5* 1·60 2·50

(Des D. Hopkins. Litho B.D.T.)

1984 (6 Nov).   *Death Centenary of the Revd. George Hunn Nobbs
(leader of Pitcairn community). T* **124** *and similar vert designs.
Multicoloured. W w* 14. *P* 14 × 15.
352 30 c. Type **124** 30   45
353 45 c. The Revd. Nobbs with sick islander .. 45   65
354 75 c. Baptising baby .. .. 75 1·10
355 85 c. Presented to Queen Victoria, 1852 .. 80 1·40
352/5 .. .. *Set of 4* 2·10 3·25

125 *Fanny Fisher*   126 The Queen Mother (from
                         photo by Norman Parkinson)

(Des D. Hopkins. Litho Cambec Press, Melbourne)

1985 (19 Feb).   *19th-Century Whaling Ships* (1st series). *T* **125** *and
similar horiz designs. Multicoloured. P* 13½ × 14.
356   5 c. Type **125** 40   25
357 33 c. *Costa Rica Packet* .. .. .. 1·00   55
358 50 c. *Splendid* .. .. 1·50 1·25
359 90 c. *Onward* .. .. 1·90 2·00
356/9 .. .. *Set of 4* 4·25 3·50
   See also Nos. 360/3.

(Des D. Hopkins. Litho Cambec Press, Melbourne)

1985 (30 Apr).   *19th-Century Whaling Ships* (2nd series). *Horiz
designs as T* **125**. *Multicoloured. P* 13½ × 14.
360 15 c. *Waterwitch* 70   70
361 20 c. *Canton* 80   80
362 60 c. *Aladdin* .. .. 1·50 2·00
363 80 c. *California* .. .. 1·75 2·50
360/3 .. .. *Set of 4* 4·25 5·50

(Des A. Theobald ($1), C. Abbott (others). Litho Questa)

1985 (6 June).   *Life and Times of Queen Elizabeth the Queen
Mother. T* **126** *and similar vert designs. Multicoloured. W w* 16.
P 14½ × 14.
364   5 c. The Queen Mother (from photo by
     Dorothy Wilding) 10   10
365 33 c. With Princess Anne at Trooping the
     Colour 25   40
366 50 c. Type **126** 40   55
367 90 c. With Prince Henry at his christening
     (from photo by Lord Snowdon).. .. 60 1·00
364/7 .. .. *Set of 4* 1·25 1·75
MS368 91 × 73 mm. $1 With Princess Anne at
     Ascot Races. Wmk sideways .. .. 1·10 1·25

127 "Swimming"   128 Prize-winning Cow
                     and Owner

(Des from children's paintings. Litho Cambec Press, Melbourne)

1985 (9 July).   *International Youth Year. T* **127** *and similar
horiz design. Multicoloured. P* 13½ × 14.
369 33 c. Type **127** 40   40
370 50 c. "A Walk in the Country" 70   85

(Des Flett Henderson & Arnold. Litho Cambec Press,
Melbourne)

1985 (10 Sept).   *125th Anniv of Royal Norfolk Island Agricultural and Horticultural Show. T* **128** *and similar horiz design.
Multicoloured. P* 13½ × 14.
371 80 c. Type **128**.. 75   80
372 90 c. Show exhibits 85   90
MS373 132 × 85 mm. Nos. 371/2 .. .. 1·75 2·50

Christmas 1985
Norfolk Island **27ᶜ**

129 Shepherds with Flock   130 Long-spined Sea Urchin

(Des R. Murphy. Litho Cambec Press, Melbourne)

1985 (3 Oct).   *Christmas. T* **129** *and similar vert designs.
Multicoloured. P* 13½.
374 27 c. Type **129** 50   30
375 33 c. Mary and Joseph with donkey.. .. 60   40
376 50 c. The Three Wise Men .. .. 1·10   65
377 90 c. The Nativity .. .. .. 1·50 1·25
374/7 .. .. *Set of 4* 3·25 2·25

(Des L. Curtis. Litho Cambec Press, Melbourne)

1986 (14 Jan).   *Marine Life. T* **130** *and similar horiz designs.
Multicoloured. P* 13½ × 14.
378   5 c. Type **130** 10   10
379 33 c. Blue Starfish 30   35
380 55 c. Southern Eagle Ray 50   85
381 75 c. Snowflake Moray .. .. .. 70 1·25
378/81 .. .. *Set of 4* 1·40 2·25
MS382 100 × 95 mm. Nos. 378/81 .. .. 3·00 3·75

131 *Giotto* Spacecraft   132 Isaac Robinson
                              (U.S. Consul 1887–1908)

(Des G. Revell. Litho Leigh-Mardon Ltd, Melbourne)

1986 (11 Mar).   *Appearance of Halley's Comet. T* **131** *and
similar vert design. Multicoloured. P* 14½ × 15.
383 $1 Type **131** .. .. 75 1·50
     a. Horiz pair. Nos. 383/4 .. .. 1·50 3·00
384 $1 Halley's Comet .. .. .. 75 1·50
   Nos. 383/4 were printed together, *se-tenant*, in horizontal
pairs throughout the sheet, each pair forming a composite
design.

(Des G. Revell. Litho Cambec Press, Melbourne)

1986 (22 May).   *"Ameripex '86" International Stamp Exhibition,
Chicago. T* **132** *and similar multicoloured designs. P* 13½.
385 33 c. Type **132** 50   35
386 50 c. Ford "Model T" (first vehicle on island)
     (horiz) 70   50
387 80 c. Statue of Liberty 80   80
385/7 .. .. *Set of 3* 1·75 1·50
MS388 125 × 100 mm. Nos. 385/7 .. .. 2·00 2·25
   No. 387 also commemorates the Centenary of the Statue of
Liberty.

133 Princess Elizabeth   134 Stylized Dove and
    and Dog   Norfolk Island

(Des Allison Ryves. Litho Cambec Press, Melbourne)

1986 (12 June).   *60th Birthday of Queen Elizabeth II. T* **133** *and
similar vert designs. Multicoloured. P* 13½.
389   5 c. Type **133** 10   10
390 33 c. Queen Elizabeth II 40   35
391 80 c. Opening Norfolk Island Golf Club .. 1·25 1·40
392 90 c. With Duke of Edinburgh in carriage .. 1·25 1·60
389/92 .. .. *Set of 4* 2·75 3·00

(Des Lyn Studham. Litho Cambec Press, Melbourne)

1986 (23 Sept).   *Christmas. P* 13½ × 14.
393 **134** 30 c. multicoloured 30   30
394   40 c. multicoloured 40   45
395       $1 multicoloured .. .. .. 1·25 1·50
393/5 .. .. *Set of 3* 1·75 2·00

135 British Convicts, 1787   136 Stone Tools

(Des Josephine Martin. Litho Cambec Press, Melbourne)

1986 (14 Oct–16 Dec).   *Bicentenary of Norfolk Island Settlement
(1988) (1st issue). Governor Phillip's Commission. T* **135** *and
similar vert designs. Multicoloured. P* 14 × 13½.
396 36 c. Type **135**. 80   3
397 55 c. Judge passing sentence of trans-
     portation .. .. 1·50   8
398 90 c. Governor Phillip meeting Home Secre-
     tary (inscr "Home Society") .. 2·50 3·0
399 90 c. As No. 398, but correctly inscr "Home
     Secretary" (16.12) .. .. .. 2·25 2·7
400 $1 Captain Arthur Phillip.. .. .. 2·50 2·5
396/400 .. .. *Set of 5* 8·50 8·5
   See also Nos. 401/4, 421/4, 433/5, 436/7 and 438/43.

(Des B. Clinton. Litho Cambec Press, Melbourne)

1986 (16 Dec).   *Bicentenary of Norfolk Island Settlement* (1988)
(2nd issue). *Pre-European Occupation. T* **136** *and similar horiz
designs. Multicoloured. P* 13½.
401 36 c. Type **136**. 65   7
402 36 c. Bananas and taro 65   7
403 36 c. Polynesian outrigger canoe 65   7
404 36 c. Maori chief 65   7
401/4 .. .. *Set of 4* 2·40 2·7

137 Philip Island from   138 Male Red-fronted
    Point Ross   Parakeet

(Des C. Abbott. Litho CPE Australia Ltd, Melbourne)

1987 (17 Feb)–88.   *Norfolk Island Scenes. T* **137** *and similar
square designs. Multicoloured. P* 13½.
405   1 c. Cockpit Creek Bridge (17.5.88) .. 50   7
406   2 c. Cemetery Bay Beach (17.5.88) .. 50   7
407   3 c. Island guesthouse (17.5.88) .. 50   7
408   5 c. Type **137**.. 30   5
409 15 c. Cattle in pasture (27.7.87) .. .. 80 1·2
410 30 c. Rock fishing (7.4.87) .. .. 30 1·0
411 37 c. Old Pitcairner-style house (27.7.87) 1·40 1·5
412 40 c. Shopping centre (7.4.87) .. .. 35 1·2
413 50 c. Emily Bay .. .. 45 1·2
414 60 c. Bloody Bridge (27.7.87) .. .. 2·00 2·2
415 80 c. Pitcairner-style shop (7.4.87) .. 1·75 2·5
416 90 c. Government House .. .. .. 1·25 2·0
417 $1 Melanesian Memorial Chapel .. .. 1·00 1·7
418 $2 Convict Settlement, Kingston (7.4.87).. 1·75 3·5
419 $3 Ball Bay (27.7.87) .. .. .. 5·00 6·0
420 $5 Northern cliffs (17.5.88) .. .. 7·00 8·5
405/20 .. .. *Set of 16* 22·00 32·0

(Des Josephine Martin. Litho CPE Australia Ltd, Melbourne)

1987 (13 May).   *Bicentenary of Norfolk Island Settlement* (1988)
(3rd issue). *The First Fleet. Vert designs as T* **135**. *Multicoloured. P* 14 × 13½.
421   5 c. Loading supplies, Deptford 50   7
422 55 c. Fleet leaving Spithead .. .. 1·75 2·2
     a. Horiz pair. Nos. 422/3 .. .. 3·50 4·5
423 55 c. H.M.S. *Sirius* leaving Spithead .. 1·75 2·2
424 $1 Female convicts below decks .. .. 2·25 3·0
421/4 .. .. *Set of 4* 5·50 7·5
   Nos. 422/3 were printed together, *se-tenant*, in horizontal
pairs throughout the sheet, forming a composite design.

(Des P. Slater. Litho CPE Australia Ltd, Melbourne)

1987 (16 Sept).   *Red-fronted Parakeet ("Green Parrot"). T* **138**
and similar vert designs. Multicoloured. P 14 × 13½.
425   5 c. Type **138**.. .. .. .. 2·00 1·50
     a. Horiz strip of 4. Nos. 425/8 .. 11·00
426 15 c. Adult with fledgeling and egg.. .. 2·50 2·00
427 36 c. Young parakeets .. .. .. 3·50 3·00
428 55 c. Female parakeet .. .. .. 4·50 3·50
425/8 .. .. *Set of 4* 11·00 9·00
   Nos. 425/8 were printed together, *se-tenant*, in horizontal
strips of four throughout the sheet.

139 Christmas Tree and **140** Airliner, Container Ship
Restored Garrison Barracks and Sydney Harbour Bridge

(Des T. Bland and Alison Ryves. Litho CPE Australia Ltd,
Melbourne)

1987 (13 Oct). *Christmas. T 139 and similar horiz designs.
Multicoloured. P 13½ × 14.*
429	30 c. Type 139	30	30
430	42 c. Children opening presents	45	55
431	58 c. Father Christmas with children	60	75
432	63 c. Children's party	70	1·00
429/32	*Set of 4*	1·90	2·40

(Des Josephine Martin. Litho CPE Australia Ltd, Melbourne)

1987 (8 Dec). *Bicentenary of Norfolk Island Settlement* (1988)
(4th issue). *Visit of La Perouse* (navigator). *Vert designs as
T 135. Multicoloured. P 14 × 13½.*
433	37 c. La Perouse with King Louis XVI	95	55
434	90 c. *L'Astrolabe* and *La Boussole* off Norfolk Island	2·25	2·50
435	$1 *L'Astrolabe* wrecked in Solomon Islands	2·50	3·00
433/5	*Set of 3*	5·25	5·50

(Des Josephine Martin. Litho CPE Australia Ltd, Melbourne)

1988 (25 Jan). *Bicentenary of Norfolk Island Settlement* (5th
issue). *Arrival of First Fleet at Sydney. Vert designs as T 135.
Multicoloured. P 14 × 13½.*
436	37 c. Ship's cutter approaching Port Jackson	1·25	65
437	$1 Landing at Sydney Cove	2·75	3·00

(Des Josephine Martin. Litho CPE Australia Ltd, Melbourne)

1988 (4 Mar). *Bicentenary of Norfolk Island Settlement* (6th
issue). *Foundation of First Settlement. Vert designs as T 135.
Multicoloured. P 14 × 13½.*
438	5 c. Lt. Philip Gidley King	20	30
439	37 c. Raising the flag, March 1788	85	75
440	55 c. King exploring	1·75	1·50
441	70 c. Landing at Sydney Bay, Norfolk Island	2·00	2·25
442	90 c. H.M.S. *Supply* (brig)	2·25	2·50
443	$1 Sydney Bay settlement, 1788	2·25	2·50
438/43	*Set of 6*	8·50	9·00

(Des Janet Boschen. Litho CPE Australia Ltd, Melbourne)

1988 (30 July). *"Sydpex '88" National Stamp Exhibition,
Sydney. T 140 and similar multicoloured designs. P 14 × 13½
(vert) or 13½ × 14 (horiz).*
444	37 c. Type 140	95	95
445	37 c. Exhibition label under magnifying glass (horiz)	95	95
446	37 c. Telephone and dish aerial	95	95
444/6	*Set of 3*	2·50	2·50
MS447	118×84 mm. Nos. 444/6	3·50	4·25

In No. **MS447** the horizontal design is perforated 14 at foot
and 13½ on the other three sides.

141 Flowers and **142** Pier Store and Boat
Decorations Shed

(Des Sue Pearson. Litho CPE Australia Ltd, Melbourne)

1988 (27 Sept). *Christmas. T 141 and similar vert designs.
Multicoloured. P 14 × 13½.*
448	30 c. Type 141	50	40
449	42 c. Flowers	70	70
450	58 c. Fishes and beach	85	95
451	63 c. Norfolk Island	95	1·25
448/51	*Set of 4*	2·75	3·00

(Des R. Murphy. Litho CPE Australia Ltd, Melbourne)

1988 (6 Dec). *Restored Buildings from the Convict Era. T 142
and similar horiz designs. Multicoloured. P 13½ × 14.*
452	39 c. Type 142	45	40
453	55 c. Royal Engineers Building	60	60
454	90 c. Old Military Barracks	1·00	1·50
455	$1 Commissariat Store and New Military Barracks	1·10	1·50
452/5	*Set of 4*	2·75	3·50

ALTERED CATALOGUE NUMBERS

Any Catalogue numbers altered from the last
edition are shown as a list in the introductory
pages.

143 *Lamprima aenea* **144** H.M.S. *Bounty* off
Tasmania

(Des T. Nolan. Litho CPE Australia Ltd, Melbourne)

1989 (14 Feb). *Endemic Insects. T 143 and similar horiz
designs. Multicoloured. P 13½ × 14.*
456	39 c. Type 143	65	40
457	55 c. *Insulascirtus nythos*	90	75
458	90 c. *Caedicia araucariae*	1·40	1·75
459	$1 *Thrincophora aridela*	1·60	1·75
456/9	*Set of 4*	4·00	4·25

(Des C. Abbott. Litho CPE Australia Ltd, Melbourne (Nos.
460/3), B.D.T. (No. **MS464**))

1989 (28 Apr). *Bicentenary of the Mutiny on the Bounty. T 144
and similar horiz designs. Multicoloured. P 13½.*
460	5 c. Type 144	60	60
461	39 c. Mutineers and Polynesian women, Pitcairn Island	1·75	1·25
462	55 c. Lake Windermere, Cumbria (Christian's home county)	2·25	2·25
463	$1·10, "Mutineers casting Bligh adrift" (Robert Dodd)	3·50	4·50
460/3	*Set of 4*	7·25	7·75
MS464	110×85 mm. 39 c. No. 461; 90 c. Isle of Man 1989 Mutiny 35p., No. 414; $1 Pitcairn Islands 1989 Settlement Bicent 90 c., No. 345. P 14	5·00	7·00

145 Norfolk Island **146** Red Cross
Flag

(Des R. Fletcher. Litho CPE Australia Ltd, Melbourne)

1989 (10 Aug). *10th Anniv of Internal Self-Government. T 145
and similar vert designs. Multicoloured. P 14×13½.*
465	41 c. Type 145	70	55
466	55 c. Old ballot box	80	65
467	$1 Norfolk Island Act, 1979	1·60	1·75
468	$1·10, Island crest	1·75	2·50
465/8	*Set of 4*	4·25	5·00

(Des E. Lenthall. Litho CPE Australia Ltd, Melbourne)

1989 (25 Sept). *75th Anniv of Red Cross on Norfolk Island.
P 13½.*
469	146 $1 bright rose-red and ultramarine	2·75	2·75

147 "Gethsemane" **148** John Royle (first
announcer)

(Des Sue Pearson. Litho CPE Australia Ltd, Melbourne)

1989 (9 Oct). *Christmas. T 147 and similar horiz designs
showing opening lines of hymns and local scenes.
Multicoloured. P 13½×14.*
470	36 c. Type 147	90	40
471	60 c. "In the Sweet Bye and Bye"	1·75	1·75
472	75 c. "Let the Lower Lights Be Burning"	2·25	2·50
473	80 c. "The Beautiful Stream"	2·25	2·75
470/3	*Set of 4*	6·50	6·75

(Des Philatelic Studios. Litho Leigh-Mardon Ltd, Melbourne)

1989 (21 Nov). *50th Anniv of Radio Australia. T 148 and
similar vert designs each showing Kingston buildings.
Multicoloured. P 14×13½.*
474	41 c. Type 148	95	55
475	65 c. Radio waves linking Australia and Norfolk Island	1·75	2·00
476	$1·10, Anniversary kookaburra logo	2·75	3·50
474/6	*Set of 3*	5·00	5·50

149 H.M.S. *Bounty* **150** H.M.S. *Sirius* striking Reef
on fire, Pitcairn
Island, 1790

(Des G. Hitch. Litho Leigh-Mardon Ltd, Melbourne)

1990 (23 Jan). *History of the Norfolk Islanders* (1st series).
*Settlement on Pitcairn Island. T 149 and similar vert design.
Multicoloured. P 14½.*
477	70 c. Type 149	2·50	2·50
478	$1·10, Arms of Norfolk Island	2·75	3·00

See also Nos. 503/4 and 516/17.

(Des Maree Edmiston. Litho Leigh-Mardon Ltd, Melbourne)

1990 (19 Mar). *Bicentenary of Wreck of H.M.S. Sirius. T 150
and similar horiz designs. Multicoloured. P 13½.*
479	41 c. Type 150	1·75	2·00
	a. Horiz pair. Nos. 479/80	3·50	4·00
480	41 c. H.M.S. *Sirius* failing to clear bay	1·75	2·00
481	65 c. Divers at work on wreck	2·50	3·00
482	$1 Recovered artifacts and chart of site	2·75	3·25
479/82	*Set of 4*	8·00	9·25

Nos. 479/80 were printed together, *se-tenant*, in horizontal
pairs throughout the sheet, each pair forming a composite
design.

151 Unloading **152** *Ile de Lumiere*
Lighter, (freighter)
Kingston

(Des Philatelic Studios. Litho Leigh-Mardon Ltd, Melbourne)

1990 (17 July)–91. *Ships. T 151 and horiz designs as T 152.
P 14×14½ (5, 10 c.) or 14½ (others).*
483	151	5 c. purple-brown	20	30
484		10 c. ochre	20	30
485	–	45 c. multicoloured (19.2.91)	80	60
486	–	50 c. multicoloured (19.2.91)	90	1·00
487	–	65 c. multicoloured (19.2.91)	1·00	1·25
488	152	70 c. multicoloured	90	1·00
489	–	75 c. multicoloured (13.8.91)	1·50	1·75
490	–	80 c. multicoloured (13.8.91)	1·50	2·00
491	–	90 c. multicoloured (13.8.91)	1·50	2·00
492	–	$1 multicoloured (13.8.91)	1·50	1·75
493	–	$2 multicoloured	2·25	3·00
494	–	$5 multicoloured (19.2.91)	5·00	7·00
483/94		*Set of 12*	15·00	20·00

Designs: *Horiz* (as T 152)—45 c. *La Dunkerquoise* (French
patrol vessel); 50 c. *Dmitri Mendeleev* (Russian research vessel);
65 c. *Pacific Rover* (tanker); 75 c. *Norfolk Trader* (freighter);
80 c. *Roseville* (transport); 90 c. *Kalia* (container ship); $1
Bounty (replica); $2 H.M.A.S. *Success* (supply ship); $5 H.M.A.S.
Whyalla (patrol vessel).

153 Santa on **154** William
House Roof Charles
Wentworth

(Des G. Hitch, adapted Philatelic Studios. Litho Leigh-Mardon
Ltd, Melbourne)

1990 (25 Sept). *Christmas. T 153 and similar multicoloured
designs. P 14½.*
499	38 c. Type 153	75	45
500	43 c. Santa at Kingston Post Office	80	50
501	65 c. Santa over Sydney Bay, Kingston (horiz)	1·75	2·00
502	85 c. Santa on Officers' Quarters (horiz)	2·00	2·50
499/502	*Set of 4*	4·75	5·00

(Des G. Hitch. Litho Leigh-Mardon Ltd, Melbourne)

1990 (11 Oct). *History of the Norfolk Islanders* (2nd series).
The First Generation. T 154 and similar vert design. P 14½.
503	70 c. reddish brown and pale cinnamon	1·25	1·25
504	$1·20, reddish brown and pale cinnamon	2·00	2·50

Designs:—$1·20, Thursday October Christian.

155 Adult Robin and Chicks in Nest

156 Map of Norfolk Island

(Des E. Monks. Litho Leigh-Mardon Ltd, Melbourne)

1990 (3 Dec). *"Birdpex '90" Stamp Exhibition, Christchurch, New Zealand. Scarlet Robin. T 155 and similar vert designs. Multicoloured. P 14½.*

505	65 c. Type **155**	..	..	..	1·00	1·25
506	$1 Hen on branch		..	..	1·50	1·75
507	$1.20, Cock on branch		..	..	1·60	2·00
505/7				*Set of 3*	3·75	4·50
MS508	70×90 mm. $1 Hen; $1 Cock and hen		..		3·75	4·25

(Des Philatelic Studios. Litho Leigh-Mardon Ltd, Melbourne)

1991 (9 Apr). *Ham Radio Network. T 156 and similar vert designs. Multicoloured. P 14½.*

509	43 c. Type **156**	..	..	..	1·00	60
510	$1 Globe showing Norfolk Island		..		2·50	2·75
511	$1.20, Map of South-west Pacific		..		2·50	3·50
509/11				*Set of 3*	5·50	6·25

157 Display in *Sirius* Museum

158 H.M.S. *Pandora* wrecked on Great Barrier Reef (1791)

(Des Philatelic Studios. Litho Leigh-Mardon Ltd, Melbourne)

1991 (16 May). *Norfolk Island Museums. T 157 and similar multicoloured designs. P 14½.*

512	43 c. Type **157**				80	50
513	70 c. 19th-century sitting room, House Museum (*horiz*)		..		1·50	1·75
514	$1 Carronade, *Sirius* Museum (*horiz*)		..		2·25	2·50
515	$1.20, Reconstructed jug and beaker, Archaeological Museum		..		2·25	3·00
512/15		..	..	*Set of 4*	6·00	7·00

(Des Philatelic Studios. Litho Leigh-Mardon, Melbourne)

1991 (2 July). *History of the Norfolk Islanders (3rd series). Search for the* Bounty. *T 158 and similar horiz design. Multicoloured. P 13½×14.*

516	$1 Type **158**		..	..	2·00	2·25
517	$1.20, H.M.S. *Pandora* leaving bay		..		2·25	2·75

159 Hibiscus and Island Scene

160 Tank and Soldier in Jungle

(Des Philatelic Studios. Litho Leigh-Mardon Ltd, Melbourne)

1991 (23 Sept). *Christmas. P 14½.*

518	**159** 38 c. multicoloured		..		80	40
519	43 c. multicoloured		..		90	55
520	65 c. multicoloured		..		1·25	1·75
521	85 c. multicoloured		..		1·50	2·25
518/21		..	..	*Set of 4*	4·00	4·50

(Des Philatelic Studios. Litho Leigh-Mardon Ltd, Melbourne)

1991 (9 Dec). *50th Anniv of Outbreak of Pacific War. T 160 and similar horiz designs. Multicoloured. P 14½.*

522	43 c. Type **160**		..	..	85	55
523	70 c. Boeing B-17 Flying Fortress on jungle airstrip		..		1·75	2·25
524	$1 Warships		..	..	2·25	3·00
522/4				*Set of 3*	4·25	5·25

161 Coat of Arms

162 Deployment Map

(Des Philatelic Studios. Litho Leigh-Mardon Ltd, Melbourne)

1992 (11 Feb). *500th Anniv of Discovery of America by* Columbus. *T 161 and similar vert designs. Multicoloured. P 14½.*

525	45 c. Type **161**	..		..	85	45
526	$1.05, *Santa Maria*		..		2·00	2·50
527	$1.20, Columbus and globe		..		2·50	3·00
525/7				*Set of 3*	4·75	5·50

(Des Philatelic Studios. Litho Leigh-Mardon Ltd, Melbourne)

1992 (4 May). *50th Anniv of Battle of the Coral Sea. T 162 and similar vert designs. Multicoloured. P 14½.*

528	45 c. Type **162**		..		75	50
529	70 c. H.M.A.S. *Australia* (cruiser)		..		1·50	2·00
530	$1.05, U.S.S. *Yorktown* (aircraft carrier)			2·25	3·00
528/30				*Set of 3*	4·00	5·00

(Des Philatelic Studios. Litho Leigh-Mardon Ltd, Melbourne)

1992 (4 May). *50th Anniv of Battle of Midway. Vert designs as T 162. Multicoloured. P 14½.*

531	45 c. Battle area		..		75	50
532	70 c. Consolidated PBY-5 Catalina flying boat over task force			1·50	2·00
533	$1.05, Douglas SBD Dauntless dive bomber and burning Japanese aircraft carrier			2·25	3·00
531/3		..	..	*Set of 3*	4·00	5·00

(Des Philatelic Studios. Litho Leigh-Mardon Ltd, Melbourne)

1992 (6 Aug). *50th Anniv of Battle of Guadalcanal. Multicoloured designs as T 162, but horiz. P 14½.*

534	45 c. American troops landing		..		75	50
535	70 c. Machine-gun crew		..		1·50	2·00
536	$1.05, Map of Pacific with Japanese and American flags			2·25	3·00
534/6				*Set of 3*	4·00	5·00

163 Norfolk Pines above Ball Bay

164 Boat Shed and Flaghouses, Kingston

(Des Philatelic Studios. Litho Leigh-Mardon Ltd, Melbourne)

1992 (29 Oct). *Christmas. T 163 and similar vert designs. Multicoloured. P 14½.*

537	40 c. Type **163**		..		70	40
538	45 c. Headstone Creek		..		75	45
539	75 c. South side of Ball Bay		..		1·50	2·00
540	$1.20, Rocky Point Reserve		..		2·00	2·75
537/40				*Set of 4*	4·50	5·00

(Des Philatelic Studios. Litho Leigh-Mardon Ltd, Melbourne)

1993 (23 Feb). *Tourism. Historic Kingston. T 164 and similar horiz designs. Multicoloured. P 14½.*

541	45 c. Type **164**		..		80	1·00
	a. Horiz strip of 5. Nos. 541/5			3·50	
542	45 c. Old Military Barracks		..		80	1·00
543	45 c. All Saints Church		..		80	1·00
544	45 c. Officers' Quarters		..		80	1·00
545	45 c. Quality Row		..		80	1·00
541/5				*Set of 5*	3·50	4·50

Nos. 541/5 were printed together, *se-tenant*, in horizontal strips of 5 forming a composite design.

165 Fire Engine

166 Blue Sea Lizard (*Glaucus atlanticus*)

(Des Philatelic Studios, Melbourne. Litho Leigh-Mardon Ltd, Melbourne)

1993 (18 May). *Emergency Services. T 165 and similar horiz designs. Multicoloured. P 14½.*

546	45 c. Type **165**		..		80	50
547	70 c. Cliff rescue squad		..		1·00	1·50
548	75 c. Ambulance		..		1·25	1·60
549	$1.20, Police car		..		2·00	2·75
546/9				*Set of 4*	4·50	5·50

(Des Philatelic Studios. Litho Leigh-Mardon Ltd, Melbourne)

1993 (7 July). *Nudibranchs. T 166 and similar horiz designs. Multicoloured. P 14½.*

550	45 c. Type **166**		..		65	45
551	45 c. Ocellate Nudibranch (*Phyllidia ocellata*)			65	45
552	70 c. *Bornella* sp		..		1·25	1·50
553	85 c. *Glossodoris rubroannolata*			1·50	2·00
554	95 c. *Halgerda villeyi*		..		1·75	2·25
555	$1.05, *Ceratosoma amoena*		..		1·90	2·75
550/5				*Set of 6*	7·00	8·50

---

167 Christmas Wreath

168 Maori Stone Clubs

(Des Philatelic Studios. Litho Leigh-Mardon Ltd, Melbourne)

1993 (28 Oct). *Christmas. P 14½.*

556	**167** 40 c. multicoloured		..		60	45
557	45 c. multicoloured		..		60	45
558	75 c. multicoloured		..		1·00	1·50
559	$1.20, multicoloured		..		1·90	2·50
556/9				*Set of 4*	3·75	4·50

(Des Philatelic Studios. Litho Leigh-Mardon Ltd, Melbourne)

1993 (28 Oct). *Bicentenary of Contact with New Zealand. T 168 and similar vert design. Multicoloured. P 14½.*

560	70 c. Type **168**		..		1·25	1·50
561	$1.20, First Maori map of New Zealand, 1793		..		2·00	2·50

169 Alvaro de Saavedra, Route Map and *Florida*

170 Sooty Tern

(Des G. Hitch and Philatelic Consultative Services. Litho Leigh-Mardon Ltd, Melbourne)

1994 (8 Feb–26 July). *Pacific Explorers. T 169 and similar multicoloured designs. P 14½.*

562	5 c. Vasco Nunez de Balboa, map and *Barbara* (3 May)			10	10
563	10 c. Ferdinand Magellan, map and *Vitoria* (3 May)			10	10
564	20 c. Juan Sebastian del Cano, map and *Vitoria* (3 May)			15	20
565	50 c. Type **169**		..		45	50
566	70 c. Ruy Lopez de Villalobos, map and *San Juan*			60	65
567	75 c. Miguel Lopez de Legaspi, map and *San Lesmes*			65	70
568	80 c. Sir Francis Drake, map and *Golden Hind* (26 July)			70	75
569	85 c. Alvaro de Mendana, map and *Santiago* (26 July)			75	80
570	90 c. Pedro Fernandes de Quiros, map and *San Pedro y Pablo* (26 July)			80	85
571	$1 Luis Baez de Torres, map and *San Pedrico* (26 July)			90	95
572	$2 Abel Tasman, map and *Heemskerk*			1·75	1·90
573	$5 William Dampier, map and *Cygnet* (3 May)			4·25	4·50
562/73				*Set of 12*	10·00	11·00
MS574	100×80 mm. $1.20, *Golden Hind* (Drake) (32×52 mm). P 13		..		1·00	1·10

(Des Philatelic Studios. Litho Leigh-Mardon Ltd, Melbourne)

1994 (17 Aug). *Sea Birds. T 170 and similar vert designs. Multicoloured. P 14½.*

575	45 c. Type **170**		..		95	1·00
	a. Horiz strip of 5. Nos. 575/9			4·25	
576	45 c. Red-tailed Tropic Bird		..		95	1·00
577	45 c. Australian Gannet		..		95	1·00
578	45 c. Wedge-tailed Shearwater		..		95	1·00
579	45 c. Blue-faced Booby		..		95	1·00
575/9				*Set of 5*	4·25	4·50

Nos. 575/9 were printed together, *se-tenant*, in horizontal strips of 5 throughout the sheet with the backgrounds forming a composite design.

171 House and Star

172 Chevrolet, 1926

(Des Olive Gregory. Litho Walsall)

1994 (27 Oct). *Christmas.* T **171** *and similar vert designs. Multicoloured. Roul 9×imperf*. Self-adhesive.*

580	45 c. Type 171	70	55
581	75 c. Figures from stained-glass windows	1·25	1·75
582	$1.20, Rainbow and full-rigged sailing ship	2·25	2·75
580/2	*Set of 3*	3·75	4·50

*Nos. 580/2 were separated horizontally by roulette and vertically by rotary knife cuts which produce straight edges with two teeth between stamps.

(Litho McPherson's Ptg Group, Mulgrave)

1995 (7 Feb). *Vintage Motor Vehicles.* T **172** *and similar horiz designs. Multicoloured. P 14×14½.*

583	45 c. Type 172	75	55
584	75 c. Ford Model "A", 1928	1·25	1·50
585	$1.05, Ford Model "A A/C", 1929	1·60	1·75
586	$1.20, Ford Model "A", 1930	1·75	2·00
583/6	*Set of 4*	4·75	5·25

 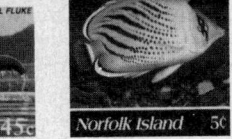

173 Tail Flukes of	174 Dot-and-Dash
Humpback Whale	Butterflyfish

(Des Mary Butterfield. Litho McPherson's Ptg Group, Mulgrave)

1995 (11 May). *Humpback Whale Conservation.* T **173** *and similar multicoloured designs. P 14½×14 ($1.05) or 14×14½ (others).*

587	45 c. Type 173	65	55
588	75 c. Mother and calf	1·00	1·50
589	$1.05, Whale breaching (*vert*)	1·40	2·00
587/9	*Set of 3*	2·75	3·50
MS590	107×84 mm. $1.20, Humpback Whale (29×49 mm). P 14×14½	1·60	2·00

(Des Mary Butterfield. Litho Leigh-Mardon Ltd, Melbourne)

1995 (15 June). *Butterflyfishes.* T **174** *and similar square designs. Multicoloured. P 14×14½.*

591	5 c. Type 174	30	40
592	45 c. Blue-spotted Butterflyfish (*Chaetodon plebeius*)	85	50
593	$1.20, Three-belted Butterflyfish (*Chaetodon tricinatus*)	2·25	2·50
594	$1.50, Thread-finned Butterflyfish (*Chaetodon auriga*)	2·50	2·75
591/4	*Set of 4*	5·50	5·50

1995 (19 July). *"JAKARTA '95" Stamp Exhibition, Indonesia. No.* **MS590** *optd "Selamat Hari Merdeka" and emblem on sheet margin in gold.*

MS595	107×84 mm. $1.20, Humpback Whale	1·60	2·00

175 International 4×4	176 Servicing Fighter
Refueller, 1942	

(Des G. Douran. Litho Southern Colour Print, Dunedin)

1995 (8 Aug). *Second World War Vehicles.* T **175** *and similar horiz designs. Multicoloured. P 14×14½.*

596	5 c. Type 175	15	15
597	45 c. Ford Sedan, 1942	55	45
598	$1.20, Ford 3 ton tipper, 1942	1·60	2·00
599	$2 D8 caterpillar with scraper	2·40	2·75
596/9	*Set of 4*	4·25	4·75

(Litho Photopress International, Norfolk Island)

1995 (1 Sept). *Flower designs as 1960 issues, but with face values in decimal currency. Roul 7.*

600	5 c. bright rose & dp blue-green (as No. 25)	10	10
	a. Booklet pane. No. 600×18	85	
601	5 c. bright rose-red (as No. 28)	10	10
	a. Booklet pane. No. 601×18	85	

Nos. 600/1 were only available in $1.80 stamp booklets containing panes of 18 (two blocks of 9 separated by a horizontal gutter and margins all round).

The original printing of Nos. 600a/1a had black inscriptions beneath each pane. These were subsequently changed to deep blue-green (No. 600a) or bright rose-red (No. 601a).

(Des Mary Butterfield (Nos. 602/5). Litho and die-stamped ($10) or litho (others) Southern Colour Print, Dunedin)

1995 (18 Sept). *50th Anniv of End of Second World War in the Pacific.* T **176** *and similar multicoloured designs. P 12.*

602	5 c. Type 176	15	20
603	45 c. Sgt. Tom Derrick, V.C. (*vert*)	60	45
604	75 c. Gen. Douglas MacArthur (*vert*)	1·00	1·25
605	$1.05, Girls celebrating victory	1·40	1·75
606	$10 Pacific War medals (50×30 mm)	14·00	16·00
602/6	*Set of 5*	15·00	18·00

The $10 also includes the "Singapore '95" International stamp exhibition logo.

177 Peace Dove	178 Skink on Bank
and Anniversary	
Emblem	

(Des Mary Butterfield. Litho SNP Cambec)

1995 (7 Nov). *Christmas. 50th Anniv of United Nations.* T **177** *and similar vert designs, each including U.N. anniversary emblem. P 14½×14.*

607	45 c. gold and new blue	60	45
608	75 c. gold and bright violet	1·00	1·25
609	$1.05, gold and bright rose-red	1·40	1·75
610	$1.20, gold and light green	1·60	2·00
607/10	*Set of 3*	4·25	5·00

Designs:—75 c. Star of Bethlehem; $1.05, Symbolic candles on cake; $1.20, Olive branch.

(Des Doreen McGuiness. Litho Questa)

1996 (6 Feb). *Endangered Species. Skinks and Geckos.* T **178** *and similar horiz designs. Multicoloured. P 14½×15.*

611	5 c. Type 178	40	45
	a. Strip of 4. Nos. 611/14	2·00	
612	5 c. Gecko on branch	40	45
613	45 c. Skink facing right	70	75
614	45 c. Gecko on flower	70	75
611/14	*Set of 4*	2·00	2·25

Nos. 611/14 were printed together, *se-tenant*, in horizontal and vertical strips of 4 throughout sheets of 16.

179 Sopwith Pup
Biplane and Emblem

(Des B. McCoy and B. Klemke. Litho Southern Colour Print, Dunedin)

1996 (22 Apr). *75th Anniv of Royal Australian Air Force.* T **179** *and similar vert designs showing aircraft. Multicoloured. P 14.*

615	45 c. Type 179	60	60
616	45 c. Wirraway fighter	60	60
617	75 c. F-111C jet fighter	1·00	1·40
618	85 c. F/A-18 Hornet jet fighter	1·10	1·50
615/18	*Set of 4*	3·00	3·50

180 Rat

(Des G. Douran. Litho Southern Colour Print, Dunedin)

1996 (18 May). *Chinese New Year ("Year of the Rat"). Sheet 100×75 mm. P 12.*

MS619	**180** $1 black, rosine and brown-ochre	1·25	1·60

181 *Naticarlus oncus*	182 Shopping

(Des Mary Butterfield. Litho Southern Colour Print, Dunedin)

1996 (2 July). *Shells.* T **181** *and similar square designs. Multicoloured. P 14.*

620	45 c. Type 181	70	80
621	45 c. *Janthina janthina*	70	80
622	45 c. *Cypraea caputserpentis*	70	80
623	45 c. *Argonauta nodosa*	70	80
620/3	*Set of 4*	2·50	2·75

(Des G. Douran. Litho Southern Colour Print, Dunedin)

1996 (17 Sept). *Tourism.* T **182** *and similar horiz designs. Multicoloured. P 13½×14.*

624	45 c. Type 182	50	50
625	75 c. Celebrating Bounty Day	1·00	1·00
626	$2.50, Horse riding	3·75	4·25
627	$3.70, Unloading lighter	4·50	5·25
624/7	*Set of 4*	8·75	10·00

183 The Nativity	184 Coat of Arms

(Des Mary Duke. Litho Questa)

1996 (5 Nov). *Christmas.* T **183** *and similar vert designs. Multicoloured. P 14½.*

628	45 c. Type 183	50	50
629	45 c. Star and boat sheds	50	50
630	75 c. Star, bungalow and ox	90	1·25
631	85 c. Star, fruit, flowers and ox	1·10	1·40
628/31	*Set of 4*	2·75	3·25

(Litho Photopress International, Norfolk Island)

1997 (22 Jan). *Booklet Stamps.* T **184** *and similar vert design. Roul 7.*

632	**184** 5 c. turquoise-blue and pale lemon	10	10
	a. Booklet pane of 10 with margins all round	50	
633	— 5 c. orange-brown	10	10
	a. Booklet pane of 10 with margins all round	50	

Designs:— No. 633, Great Seal of Norfolk Island

185 Calf	186 *Cepora perimale*

(Des G. Douran. Litho Southern Colour Print, Dunedin)

1997 (11 Feb). *Beef Cattle. Sheet 67×67 mm. P 13½×13.*

MS634	**185** $1.20, multicoloured	1·40	1·75

1997 (12 Feb). *"HONG KONG '97" International Stamp Exhibition. As No.* **MS634**, *but with exhibition emblem on sheet margin.*

MS635	67×67 mm. **185** $1.20, multicoloured	1·40	1·60

(Des Tracey Yager. Litho and gold die-stamped Southern Colour Print, Dunedin)

1997 (28 Mar). *Butterflies.* T **186** *and similar horiz designs. Multicoloured. P 14½.*

636	45 c. Type 186	1·00	85
637	90 c. *Danaus chrysippus*	1·25	1·25
638	$1 *Danaus hamata*	1·40	1·40
639	$1.20, *Danaus plexippus*	1·50	1·60
636/9	*Set of 4*	4·50	4·50

187 Dusky Dolphins

(Des Mary Butterfield. Litho Southern Colour Print, Dunedin)

1997 (29 May). *Dolphins.* T **187** *and similar horiz designs. Multicoloured. P 14.*

640	45 c. Type 187	60	50
641	75 c. Common dolphin and calf	80	90
MS642	106×80 mm. $1.05, Dolphin	1·10	1·25

1997 (29 May). *"Pacific '97" International Stamp Exhibition, San Francisco. As No.* **MS642**, *but with exhibition emblem on sheet margin.*

MS643	106×80 mm. $1.05, Dolphin	1·10	1·25

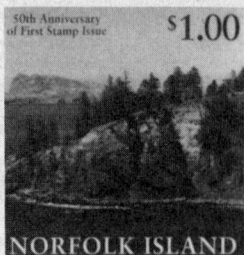

188 Ball Bay, Norfolk Island

(Litho Southern Colour Print, Dunedin)

1997 (30 June). *50th Anniv of Norfolk Island Stamps. T* **188** *and similar multicoloured designs. P* 12.

644	$1 Type **188**	..	..	1·50	1·75
	a. Horiz pair. Nos. 644/5	..		3·50	4·00
645	$1.50, 1947 2d. stamp	..		2·00	2·25
646	$8 Ball Bay and 1947 2s. yellow-bistre				
	stamp (90×45 *mm*)	..		10·00	10·50
644/6	..	..	*Set of* 3	12·00	13·00

Nos. 644/5 were printed together, *se-tenant*, in horizontal pairs with the backgrounds forming a composite design.

(Des N. Shewring (No. **MS651**), D. Miller (others). Litho Questa)

1997 (12 Aug). *Golden Wedding of Queen Elizabeth and Prince Philip. Multicoloured designs as T* **173** *of Ascension. P* 14½×14.

647	20 c. Queen Elizabeth	..	..	30	30
	a. Horiz pair. Nos. 647/8	..		60	60
648	25 c. Prince Philip in carriage-driving trials			30	30
649	25 c. Prince Philip ..			30	30
	a. Horiz pair. Nos. 649/50	..		90	90
650	50 c. Queen in phaeton at Trooping the				
	Colour	..	..	60	60
647/50	..	..	*Set of* 4	1·40	1·40

MS651 110×70 mm. $1.50, Queen Elizabeth and Prince Philip in landau (*horiz*). P 14×14½ .. 1·75 1·90

Nos. 647/8 and 649/50 were each printed together, *se-tenant*, in horizontal pairs throughout the sheets with the backgrounds forming composite designs.

189 Royal Yacht *Britannia* leaving Hong Kong

190 Christmas Tree

1997 (16 Sept). *Return of Hong Kong to China. Sheet* 126×91 *mm. Litho. P* 14.

MS652 **189** 45 c. multicoloured 40 45

No. **MS652** is inscribed "Brittania" in error

(Des Sue Wickison. Litho Southern Colour Print, Dunedin)

1997 (4 Nov). *Annual Festivals. T* **190** *and similar vert designs. Multicoloured. P* 13½.

653	45 c. Type **190**	..		40	45
654	75 c. Fireworks (New Year's Eve)	..		65	70
655	$1.20, Rose (Valentine's Day)	..		1·00	1·10
653/5	..	..	*Set of* 3	2·00	2·25

191 Oriental Pearl T.V. Tower, Shanghai

(Litho Questa)

1997 (18 Nov). *"Shanghai '97" International Stamp and Coin Exhibition, Shanghai. Sheet* 103×138 *mm. P* 14½.

MS656 **191** 45 c. multicoloured 40 45

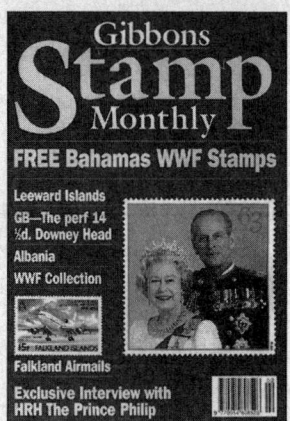

Keep This Catalogue up to Date With

Gibbons **Stamp** Monthly

FREE Bahamas WWF Stamps

Leeward Islands
GB—The perf 14 ½d. Downey Head
Albania
WWF Collection

Falkland Airmails

Exclusive Interview with HRH The Prince Philip

The Magazine with the Stanley Gibbons Catalogue Supplement

Plus

■ More editorial than other magazines.

■ Regular features for all collectors from beginners to specialists.

■ Authoritatively written.

■ Regular special offers, competitions and free gifts.

Get Gibbons Stamp Monthly delivered direct to your door!

For a free sample copy and subscription details phone 01425 472363 or write to:

Hugh Jefferies Gibbons Stamp Monthly 5 Parkside, Christchurch Road, Ringwood, Hants BH24 3SH

STAMP BOOKLETS

A \$4.10 booklet containing No. 465 in block of ten was prepared in 1989, but not issued.

B 1

1991 (9 Apr). *Ham Radio Network. Emerald on cinnamon cover as Type* B **1**. *Stamps attached by selvedge.*
SB1   \$4.30, booklet containing 43 c. (No. 509) in block
      of 10 .. ..   8·00

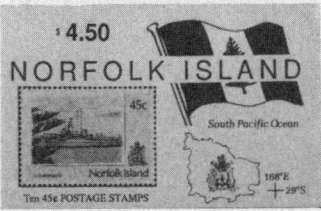

B 2

1991 (Dec). *Ships. Emerald on bluish grey (No.* SB2) *or cinnamon (No.* SB3) *covers as Type* B **2**. *Stamps attached by selvedge.*
SB2   \$4.50, booklet containing 45 c. (No. 485) in block
      of 10 .. ..   6·50
SB3   \$7 booklet containing 70 c. (No. 488) in block of 10   7·00

B 3

1993 (23 Feb). *Tourism. Emerald on white cover as Type* B **3**. *Stamps attached by selvedge.*
SB4   \$4.50, booklet containing five different 45 c. (Nos.
      541/5) in block of 10 .. ..   7·00

1993 (20 Aug). *Nudibranchs. Emerald on white cover as Type* B **3** *showing illustration of No. 550. Stamps attached by selvedge.*
SB5   \$4.50, booklet containing 45 c. (No. 550) in block
      of 10 .. ..   6·50

1994 (17 Aug). *Sea Birds. Emerald on white cover as Type* B **3**, *but showing illustration of No. 577. Stamps attached by selvedge.*
SB6   \$4.50, booklet containing horiz gutter strip of ten
      45 c. (No. 575a×2) .. ..   6·00

B 4
(Illustration reduced. Actual size 95×130 mm)

1995 (1 Sept). *Flowers. Rose and blue green cover as Type* B **4**. *Stamps attached by selvedge.*
SB7   \$1.80, booklet containing two different panes of
      eighteen 5 c. (Nos. 600a/1a) .. .. ..   2·25
      No. SB7 also exists overprinted with either the "Singapore '95" International Stamp Exhibition or Australian Stamp Dealers' Association logos.

B 5
(Illustration reduced. Actual size, 170×80 mm)

1997 (22 Jan). *Multicoloured cover as Type* B **5**. *Stamps attached by selvedge.*
SB8   \$2 booklet containing four panes of ten 5 c. (Nos
      632a/3a, each × 2) .. ..   2·00

HELP!

Even the most knowledgeable collector can be faced by philatelic terms of which he does not know the meaning – if this has ever been your problem then you need:

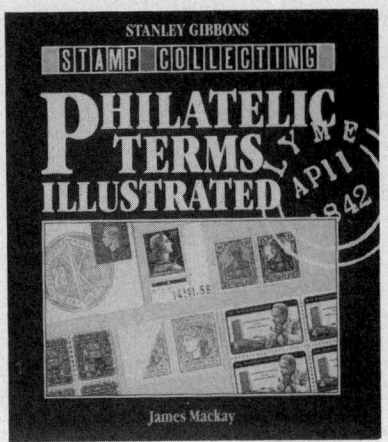

PHILATELIC TERMS ILLUSTRATED

Now completely revised and updated in a bright new format as part of the popular Stanley Gibbons 'Stamp Collecting' series.

The new edition of this useful book not only includes all the terms which have come into use since publication of the second edition in 1978 but also provides much new information on postal markings and services.

Noted philatelic author and journalist, James Mackay, has carefully updated and augmented the original text of Russell Bennett and James Watson to produce a work of great assistance to the postal historian and an indispensable aid to stamp identification.

Fully illustrated in colour or black and white, its encyclopedic style and helpful system of cross-referencing makes Philatelic Terms Illustrated extremely easy to use and provides a helpful work of reference for all collectors from the youngest beginner to the most advanced specialist.

Available direct from:

**Stanley Gibbons Publications,
Parkside, Christchurch Road,
Ringwood, Hampshire BH24 3SH
Telephone: 01425 472363**

Baghdad
see Iraq

Bahamas

The British Post Office at Nassau was established during the early days of the West Indies packet system, and was certainly operating by 1733. The first known local postmark dates from 1802.

The crowned-circle handstamp No. CC1 was issued in 1846 and was generally replaced, for the public mails, by various stamps of Great Britain in 1858.

Local mail deliveries were rudimentary until 1859 when Nos. 1/2 were issued by the colonial authorities for interisland mails. Examples used for this purpose are usually cancelled in manuscript or with a "27" postmark. The "local" 1d. stamp became valid for overseas mails in May, 1860, when the colonial authorities took over this service from the British G.P.O.

For illustrations of the handstamp and postmark types see BRITISH POST OFFICES ABROAD notes, following GREAT BRITAIN.

NASSAU

CROWNED-CIRCLE HANDSTAMPS

CC1 CC **2** BAHAMAS (Nassau) (18.5.1846) (R.)
Price on cover £1800

No. CC1 was later struck in black and used as an Offical Paid mark between July 1899 and September 1935. Handstamps as Types CC **1** and CC **3** (only three known) struck in black were used for the same purpose from 1933 until 1953; but it is believed that these were never employed during the pre-stamp period. *Price on cover from* £50.

Stamps of GREAT BRITAIN *cancelled* "A 05" *as Type* **2**.

1858 *to* **1860.**

Z1	1d. rose-red (1857), perf 14							£1600
Z2	2d. blue (1858) (Plate Nos. 7, 8)						£1300
Z3	4d. rose (1857)							£450
Z4	6d. lilac (1856)							£350
Z5	1s. green (1856)							£2250

PRICES FOR STAMPS ON COVER TO 1945

Nos. 1/2	—
Nos. 3/6	*from* × 6
No. 7	—
Nos. 8/19a	*from* × 6
Nos. 20/5	*from* × 10
Nos. 26/31	*from* × 4
No. 33	*from* × 20
Nos. 35/44a	*from* × 5
No. 45	*from* × 20
Nos. 47/57	*from* × 4
Nos. 58/89	*from* × 2
Nos. 90/130	*from* × 3
Nos. 131/2	*from* × 10
Nos. 141/5	*from* × 4
Nos. 146/8	*from* × 6
Nos. 149/57	*from* × 3
Nos. 158/60	*from* × 4
No. 161	*from* × 8
Nos. 162/75	*from* × 5
Nos. S1/3	*from* × 20

CROWN COLONY

1   2   3

(Eng and recess P.B.)

1859 (10 June). *No wmk. Imperf.* (*a*) *Thick paper.*

1	1	1d. reddish lake				£4500	£2250
		a. Brown-lake				£4500	£2250

(*b*) *Thin paper*

2	1	1d. dull lake				48.00	£1500

The handmade paper used for Nos. 1/a varies in thickness. Prices quoted for these stamps are for examples on thick paper. Unused remainders in brown-lake on thinner paper are worth about £250.

Collectors are warned against false postmarks upon the remainder stamps of 1d., imperf, on thin paper.

1860 (Oct). *No wmk. Clean-cut perf* 14 *to* 16.

3	1	1d. lake				£2250	£650

1861 (June)—**62.** *No wmk.* (*a*) *Rough perf* 14 *to* 16

4	1	1d. lake				£750	£300
5	2	4d. dull rose (Dec, 1861)			£1400	£375
		Imperf between (pair)				£19000	
6		6d. grey-lilac (Dec, 1861)			£2500	£450
		a. Pale dull lilac				£2750	£450

(*b*) *P* 11 *to* 12½ (1862)

7	1	1d. lake					£2000

No. 7 was a perforation trial on a new machine at Perkins, Bacon. It was not sent out to the Colony and is also known part perforated.

(Recess D.L.R.)

1862. *No wmk.** (*a*) *P* 11½, 12.

8	1	1d. carmine-lake				£800	£160
9		1d. lake				£850	£170
10	2	4d. dull rose				£3000	£400
11		6d. lavender-grey				£5000	£400

(*b*) *P* 11½, 12, *compound with* 11

12	1	1d. carmine-lake				£1800	£850
13		1d. lake				£1800	£850
14	2	4d. dull rose				£11000	£1800
15		6d. lavender-grey			£12000	£1600

(*c*) *P* 13

16	1	1d. lake				£650	£140
17		1d. brown-lake				£650	£120
18	2	4d. dull rose				£2500	£375
19		6d. lavender-grey			£2750	£400
		a. Lilac				£9500	£500

*Stamps exist with part of papermaker's sheet wmk ("T. H. SAUNDERS" and date).

(T **3** Typo D.L.R.)

1863–77. *Wmk Crown CC.* (*a*) *P* 12½

20	1	1d. brown-lake				90.00	55.00
21		1d. carmine-lake				£100	60.00
22		1d. carmine-lake (aniline)			£100	60.00
23		1d. rose-red				60.00	40.00
24		1d. red				60.00	40.00
25		1d. vermilion				65.00	40.00
26	2	4d. dull rose				£375	60.00
27		4d. bright rose				£225	60.00
28		4d. brownish rose				£400	80.00
28a		6d. rose-lilac				£5500	£1800
29		6d. lilac (shades)				£300	60.00
30		6d. deep violet				£160	60.00
31		6d. violet (aniline)				£250	90.00

No. 28a, believed to be the shade of the first printing only, is a very rare stamp, not to be confused with No. 29.

(*b*) *P* 14

33	1	1d. scarlet-vermilion (1877)			40.00	15.00
34		1d. scarlet (or scarlet-vermilion) (aniline) £1000				†
35	2	4d. bright rose (1876)				£350	40.00
36		4d. dull rose				£1500	40.00
37		4d. rose-lake				£350	40.00

No. 34 is not known postally used, although manuscript fiscal cancellations are recorded on this shade.

(Typo D.L.R.)

1863–80. *Wmk Crown CC.* (*a*) *P* 12½.

38	3	1s. green (1865)				£2500	£300

(*b*) *P* 14

39	3	1s. dark green				£100	35.00
39a		1s. green (thick paper) (1880)			7.50	7.00

1882 (March). *Wmk Crown CA.* (*a*) *P* 12.

40	1	1d. scarlet-vermilion				42.00	12.00
41	2	4d. rose				£550	45.00

(*b*) *P* 14

42	1	1d. scarlet-vermilion				£375	55.00
43	2	4d. rose				£750	60.00

1882 (Mar)—**98.** *Wmk Crown CA. P* 14.

44	3	1s. green				30.00	14.00
44a		1s. blue-green (1898)				35.00	21.00

FOURPENCE
(4)

5

1883. *No.* 30 *surch with T* **4.**

45	2	4d. on 6d. deep violet				£550	£400
		a. Surch inverted				£7500	£4500

Type 4 was applied by handstamp and occurs in various positions.

Caution is needed in buying Nos. 45 and 45a.

Sloping "2" (R. 10/6)   Malformed "E"

(Typo D.L.R.)

1884–90. *Wmk Crown CA. P* 14.

47	5	1d. pale rose				48.00	10.00
48		1d. carmine-rose				5.50	1.75
49		1d. bright carmine (aniline)			2.75	6.00
50		2½d. dull blue (1888)				50.00	16.00
51		2½d. blue				38.00	7.50
		a. Sloping "2"				£400	£120
52		2½d. ultramarine				9.00	1.75
		a. Sloping "2"				£130	70.00
53		4d. deep yellow				9.00	4.00
54		6d. mauve (1890)				4.50	26.00
		a. Malformed "E" (R. 6/6)			£160	£325
56		5s. sage-green				65.00	75.00
57		£1 Venetian red				£275	£225
47/57						*Set of* 6	£325	£300
50 & 54 Optd "Specimen"					*Set of* 2	£130

Examples of Nos. 54/7 are known showing a forged Bahamas postmark dated "AU 29 94".

---

6 Queen's Staircase, Nassau   7   8

(Recess D.L.R.)

1901 (23 Sept)—03. *Wmk Crown CC. P* 14.

58	6	1d. black and red				6.00	2.50
		w. Wmk inverted				75.00	
59		5d. black and orange (1.03)			8.00	42.00
		y. Wmk inverted and reversed			75.00	
60		2s. black and blue (1.03)			24.00	48.00
61		3s. black and green (1.03)			28.00	50.00
		w. Wmk inverted				£100	£110
		y. Wmk inverted and reversed		£100	£110
58/61						*Set of* 4	60.00	£130
58/61 Optd "Specimen"				*Set of* 4	£120

For stamps in this design, but with Mult Crown CA or Mult Script CA watermarks see Nos 75/80 and 111/14.

(Typo D.L.R.)

1902 (18 Dec)—10. *Wmk Crown CA. P* 14.

62	7	1d. carmine				1.50	2.25
63		2½d. ultramarine				6.50	1.25
64		4d. orange				13.00	45.00
65		4d. deep yellow (3.10)			17.00	55.00
66		6d. brown				3.50	15.00
		a. Malformed "E" (R.6/6)			£130	£180
67		1s. grey-black and carmine			17.00	45.00
68		1s. brownish grey and carmine (6.07)		18.00	45.00
69		5s. dull purple and blue			55.00	75.00
70		£1 green and black				£250	£325
62/70						*Set of* 7	£300	£425
62/70 Optd "Specimen"				*Set of* 7	£250

Examples of most values are known showing a forged Nassau postmark dated "2 MAR 10".

1906 (Apr)—11. *Wmk Mult Crown CA. P* 14.

71	7	½d. pale green (5.06) (Optd S. £50)		4.25	1.75
72		1d. carmine-rose				20.00	1.25
73		2½d. ultramarine (4.07)			20.00	24.00
		w. Wmk inverted				—	85.00
74		6d. bistre-brown (8.11)			16.00	48.00
		a. Malformed "E" (R. 6/6)			£275	£475
71/4						*Set of* 4	55.00	65.00

1911 (Feb)—19. *Wmk Mult Crown CA. P* 14.

75	6	1d. black and red				13.00	2.50
		a. Grey-black and scarlet (1916)		3.75	2.25
		b. Grey-black & deep carmine-red (1919)	4.25	4.25
76		3d. purple/yellow (thin paper) (18.5.17)	3.75	19.00
		a. Reddish purple/buff (thick paper) (1.19)	4.50	4.50
77		3d. black and brown (23.3.19)		1.50	2.25
		w. Wmk inverted					
78		5d. black and mauve (18.5.17)		2.75	5.50
79		2s. black and blue (11.16)		24.00	42.00
		w. Wmk inverted					
80		3s. black and green (8.17)		45.00	48.00
		w. Wmk inverted				—	£110
		y. Wmk inverted and reversed		£110	£110
75/80						*Set of* 6	70.00	95.00
76/8 Optd "Specimen"				*Set of* 3	£100

(Typo D.L.R.)

1912–19. *Wmk Mult Crown CA. Chalk-surfaced paper* (1s. to £1). *P* 14.

81	8	½d. green				80	6.50
		a. Yellow-green				2.25	8.50
82		1d. carmine (aniline)				2.25	30
		a. Deep rose				6.00	2.00
		b. Rose				10.00	2.25
		w. Wmk inverted				—	50.00
83		2d. grey (1919)				2.25	3.00
84		2½d. ultramarine				4.50	16.00
		a. Deep dull blue				13.00	26.00
85		4d. orange-yellow				5.50	17.00
		a. Yellow				2.25	9.50
86		6d. bistre-brown				1.75	4.00
		a. Malformed "E" (R. 6/6)			70.00	95.00
87		1s. grey-black and carmine			1.75	8.00
		a. Jet-black and carmine			14.00	22.00
88		5s. dull purple and blue			35.00	60.00
		a. Pale dull purple and deep blue	48.00	65.00
89		£1 dull green and black			£150	£275
		a. Green and black				£190	£300
81/9						*Set of* 9	£170	£350
81/9 Optd "Specimen"				*Set of* 9	£325

1.1.17.   **WAR TAX**
(9)   (10)

1917 (18 May). *No.* 75b *optd with T* **9** *in red by D.L.R.*

90	6	1d. grey-black and deep carmine-red (Optd S. £60)		40	1.40
		a. Long stroke to "7" (R.4/6)		40.00	75.00

It was originally intended to issue No. 90 on 1 January 1917, but the stamps were not received in the Bahamas until May. Half the proceeds from their sale were donated to the British Red Cross Society.

1918 (21 Feb–10 July). *Nos. 75/6, 81/2 and 87 optd at Nassau with T 10.*

91	8	½d. green	..	8·00	32·00
		a. Opt double	..	£1200	£1200
		b. Opt inverted	..	£1300	
92		1d. carmine (aniline)	..	70	50
		a. Opt double	..	£1300	£1300
		b. Opt inverted	..	£1300	
		w. Wmk inverted	..		
		x. Wmk reversed	..		
93	6	1d. black and red (10 July)	..	3·25	2·75
		a. Opt double, one inverted		£750	
		b. Opt double	..	£1500	£1600
		c. Opt inverted	..	£1300	£1400
		w. Wmk reversed	..		
94		3d. purple/*yellow* (*thin paper*)	..	2·25	2·25
		a. Opt double	..	£1200	£1300
		b. Opt inverted	..	£1000	£1100
95	8	1s. grey-black and carmine	..	80·00	£110
		a. Opt double	..	£2750	
91/5			*Set of 5*	85·00	£130

No. 93 was only on sale for ten days.

WAR CHARITY

WAR TAX (11)	**WAR TAX** (12)	**3.6.18.** (13)	

1918 (1 June–20 July). *Optd by D.L.R. in London with T 11 or 12 (3d.).*

96	8	½d. green	..	1·10	1·40
		w. Wmk inverted	..		
		x. Wmk reversed	..		
97		1d. carmine	..	40	35
		a. Wmk sideways	..	£350	
		w. Wmk inverted	..		
		y. Wmk inverted and reversed			
98	6	3d. purple/*yellow* (20 July)	..	50	1·50
		w. Wmk inverted	..		
99	8	1s. grey-black and carmine (R.)	..	6·50	2·75
96/9			*Set of 4*	7·75	5·50
96/9	Optd "Specimen"		*Set of 4*	£130	

1919 (21 Mar). *No. 77 optd with T 12 by D.L.R.*

100	6	3d. black and brown (Optd S. £45)		45	4·00
		a. "C" and "A" missing from wmk			
		w. Wmk inverted	..	50·00	

No. 100a shows the "C" omitted from one impression and the "A" missing from the next one to the right (as seen from the front of the stamp). The "C" is badly distorted in the second watermark.

1919 (1 Jan). *No. 75b optd with T 13 by D.L.R.*

101	6	1d. grey-black and deep carmine-red (R.) (Optd S. £50)		30	2·50
		a. Opt double	..	£1400	
		w. Wmk inverted	..	50·00	
		x. Wmk reversed	..	50·00	
		y. Wmk inverted and reversed		75·00	

The date that was originally fixed for the issue of the stamp. The year 1918 was also the bicentenary of the appointment of the first Royal governor.

WAR	**WAR**
TAX (14)	**TAX** (15)

1919 (14 July). (*a*) *Optd with T 14 by D.L.R.*

102	8	½d. green (R.)	..	30	1·25
103		1d. carmine	..	1·00	1·50
104		1s. grey-black and carmine (R.)		9·00	25·00

(*b*) *No. 77 optd with T 15*

105	6	3d. black and brown	..	55	5·50
		w. Wmk inverted	..	50·00	
		x. Wmk reversed	..	50·00	
		y. Wmk inverted and reversed		50·00	
102/5			*Set of 4*	9·75	30·00
102/5	Optd "Specimen"		*Set of 4*	£120	

16

17 Great Seal of the Bahamas.

(Recess D.L.R.)

1920 (1 Mar). *Peace Celebration. Wmk Mult Crown CA (sideways). P 14.*

106	16	½d. green	..	90	4·00
107		1d. carmine	..	2·75	90
		x. Wmk reversed	..	£300	
108		2d. slate-grey	..	2·75	7·00
109		3d. deep-brown	..	2·75	9·00
110		1s. deep myrtle-green	..	10·00	30·00
106/10			*Set of 5*	17·00	45·00
106/10	Optd "Specimen"		*Set of 5*	£150	

1921 (29 Mar)–*29*. *Wmk Script CA. P 14.*

111	6	1d. grey and rose-red	..	80	1·00
112		5d. black and purple (8.29)	..	3·50	35·00
113		2s. black and blue (11.22)	..	14·00	22·00
114		3s. black and green (9.24)	..	35·00	55·00
111/14			*Set of 4*	48·00	£100
111/14	Optd/Perf "Specimen"		*Set of 4*	£160	

F PENN

Elongated "E"
(left pane R. 9/6)

1921 (8 Sept)–*37*. *Wmk Mult Script CA. Chalk-surfaced paper (3d., 1s., 5s., £1). P 14.*

115	8	½d. green (1924)	..	45	40
		a. Elongated "E"	..	22·00	
116		1d. carmine	..	1·00	15
117		1½d. brown-red (1934)	..	1·60	1·00
118		2d. grey (1927)	..	95	2·75
119		2½d. ultramarine (1922)	..	80	2·75
120		3d. purple/*pale yellow* (1931)	..	5·00	16·00
		a. *Purple/orange-yellow* (1937)	..	5·00	15·00
121		4d. orange-yellow (1924)	..	90	5·00
122		6d. bistre-brown (1922)	..	70	1·25
		a. Malformed "E" (R.6/6)	..	65·00	95·00
123		1s. black and carmine (1926)	..	2·50	5·50
124		5s dull purple and blue (1924)	..	30·00	50·00
125		£1 green and black (1926)	..	£150	£275
115/25			*Set of 11*	£170	£325
115/25	Optd/Perf "Specimen"		*Set of 11*	£375	

(Recess B. W.)

1930 (2 Jan). *Tercentenary of Colony. Wmk Mult Script CA. P 12.*

126	17	1d. black and scarlet	..	2·00	2·50
127		3d. black and deep brown	..	3·75	13·00
128		5d. black and deep purple	..	3·75	13·00
129		2s. black and deep blue	..	18·00	40·00
130		3s. black and green	..	40·00	70·00
126/30			*Set of 5*	60·00	£120
126/30	Perf "Specimen"		*Set of 5*	£150	

18

(Recess B.W.)

1931 (14 July)–*46*. *Wmk Mult Script CA. P 12.*

131	18	2s. slate-purple and deep ultramarine	..	20·00	23·00
		a. *Slate-purple and indigo* (9.42)	..	55·00	38·00
		b. *Brownish black and indigo* (13.4.43)	..	5·00	2·50
		c. *Brownish black and steel-blue* (6.44)	..	8·00	1·25
132		3s. slate-purple and myrtle-green	..	28·00	24·00
		a. *Brownish black and green* (13.4.43)	..	6·50	2·00
		b. *Brownish blk & myrtle-grn* (1.10.46)	..	4·00	2·00
131/2	Perf "Specimen"		*Set of 2*	70·00	

Most of the stamps from the September 1942 printing (No. 131a and further stocks of the 3s. similar to No. 132) were used for the 1942 "LANDFALL" overprints

1935 (6 May). *Silver Jubilee. As Nos. 91/4 of Antigua. P 13½ × 14.*

141		1½d. deep blue and carmine..	..	1·00	2·25
		h. Dot by flagstaff..	..	65·00	
		i. Dash by turret	..	90·00	
142		2½d. brown and deep blue	..	4·00	6·00
		f. Diagonal line by turret	..	95·00	
		g. Dot to left of chapel	..	£120	
143		6d. light blue and olive-green	..	6·50	9·00
		g. Dot to left of chapel	..	£160	
144		1s. slate and purple	..	6·50	8·00
		h. Dot by flagstaff..	..	£170	
141/4			*Set of 4*	16·00	23·00
141/4	Perf "Specimen"		*Set of 4*	90·00	

For illustrations of plate varieties see Catalogue Introduction.

19 Greater Flamingos in flight

20 King George VI

(Recess Waterlow)

1935 (22 May). *Wmk Mult Script CA. P 12½.*

145	19	8d. ultramarine and scarlet	..	4·75	2·75
145	Perf "Specimen"..			42·00	

1937 (12 May). *Coronation. As Nos. 95/7 of Antigua, but printed by D.L.R. P 14.*

146		½d. green	..	15	15
147		1d. yellow-brown	..	30	45
148		2½d. bright blue	..	50	75
146/8			*Set of 3*	85	1·25
146/8	Perf "Specimen"		*Set of 3*	60·00	

Accent flaw (right pane R. 1/5) (1938 ptg only)

Short "T" in "TWO" (right pane R. 3/6) (Retouched on No. 152c, although bottom of letter is still pointed)

(Typo D.L.R.)

1938 (11 Mar)–*52*. *Wmk Mult Script CA. Chalk-surfaced paper (1s. to £1). P 14.*

149	20	½d. green	..	15	70
		a. Elongated "E"	..	32·00	
		b. Accent flaw	..	32·00	
		c. *Bluish green* (11.9.42)	..	1·50	1·00
		ca. Elongated "E"	..	75·00	
		d. *Myrtle-green* (11.12.46)	..	5·00	4·50
		da. Elongated "E"	..	£140	
149e		½d. brown-purple (18.2.52)	..	85	2·50
		ea. Error. Crown missing	..	£3000	
		eb. Error. St. Edward's Crown		£1800	
		ec. Elongated "E"	..	65·00	
150		1d. carmine	..	8·50	4·75
150a		1d. olive-grey (17.9.41)	..	3·00	3·00
		ab. *Pale slate* (11.9.42)	..	50	50
151		1½d. red-brown (19.4.38)	..	1·25	1·00
		a. *Pale red-brown* (19.4.48)	..	3·75	2·00
152		2d. pale slate (19.4.38)	..	18·00	6·00
		a. Short "T"	..	£350	
152b		2d. scarlet (17.9.41)	..	75	55
		ba. Short "T"	..	80·00	
		bb. "TWO PENCE" printed double		† £2750	
		bc. *Dull rose-red* (19.4.48)	..	2·25	2·25
152c		2d. green (1.5.51)	..	70	80
153		2½d. ultramarine	..	3·25	2·00
153a		2½d. violet (1.7.43)	..	1·25	70
		ab. "2½ PENNY" printed double		£2500	
154		3d. violet (19.4.38)	..	16·00	4·00
154a		3d. blue (4.43)	..	60	90
		ab. *Bright ultramarine* (19.4.48)		3·50	3·00
154b		3d. scarlet (1.2.52)	..	50	2·75
154c		10d. yellow-orange (18.11.46)	..	2·00	20
155		1s. grey-black and carmine (*thick paper*) (15.9.38)	..	13·00	4·50
		a. *Brownish grey and scarlet* (4.42)		£225	42·00
		b. Ordinary paper. *Black and carmine* (9.42)		15·00	5·50
		c. Ordinary paper. *Grey-black and bright crimson* (6.3.44)		7·00	50
		d. *Pale brownish grey and crimson* (19.4.48)	..	7·50	80
156		5s. lilac & blue (*thick paper*) (19.4.38)		£170	£100
		a. *Reddish lilac and blue* (4.42)		£900	£350
		b. Ordinary paper. *Purple & bl* (9.42)		26·00	11·00
		c. Ordinary paper. *Dull mauve and deep blue* (11.46)		65·00	25·00
		d. *Brown-purple & dp brt bl* (19.4.48)		26·00	8·00
		e. *Red-purple & dp bright blue* (8.51)		23·00	9·50
157		£1 deep grey-green and black (*thick paper*) (15.9.38)		£250	£140
		a. Ordinary paper. *Blue-green and black* (13.4.43)		60·00	45·00
		b. Ordinary paper. *Grey-green and black* (3.44)		85·00	55·00
149/57a			*Set of 17*	£130	70·00
149/57	Perf "Specimen"		*Set of 14*	£425	

Nos. 149/50a exist in coils, constructed from normal sheets.

No. 149eb occurs on a row in the watermark in which the crowns and letters "CA" alternate.

The thick chalk-surfaced paper, used for the initial printing of the 1s., 5s. and £1, was usually toned and had streaky gum. The April 1942 printing for the 1s. and 5s., which was mostly used for the "LANDFALL" overprints, was on thin, white chalk-surfaced paper with clear gum. Printings of the three values between September 1942 and November 1946 were on a thick, smooth, opaque ordinary paper.

21 Sea Garden, Nassau   22 Fort Charlotte

23 Greater Flamingos in Flight   **3d.** (24)

(Recess Waterlow)

1938 (1 July). *Wmk Mult Script CA. P 12½.*

158	21	4d. light blue and red-orange	..	1·00	70
159	22	6d. olive-green and light blue	..	60	70
160	23	8d. ultramarine and scarlet	..	5·00	2·00
158/60			*Set of 3*	6·00	3·00
158/60	Perf "Specimen"		*Set of 3*	£100	

1940 (28 Nov). *No. 153 surcharged with T 24 by The Nassau Guardian.*

161	20	3d. on 2½d. blue	..	65	40

NEW INFORMATION

The editor is always interested to correspond with people who have new information that will improve or correct the Catalogue.

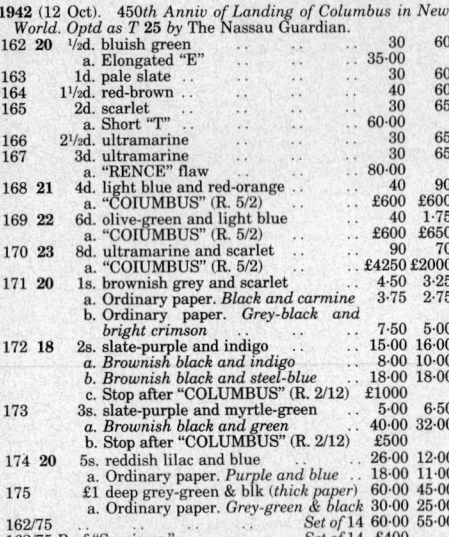

1 4 9 2
LANDFALL
OF
COLUMBUS
1 9 4 2

(25)

"RENCE" flaw (Right
pane R. 9/3. Later
corrected so that it does
not occur on No. 154a)

1942 (12 Oct). *450th Anniv of Landing of Columbus in New World. Optd as T* **25** *by The Nassau Guardian.*

162	20	½d. bluish green		30	60
		a. Elongated "E"	.. ..	35·00	
163		1d. pale slate	.. ..	30	60
164		1½d. red-brown	.. ..	40	60
165		2d. scarlet		30	65
		a. Short "T"	..	60·00	
166		2½d. ultramarine	..	30	65
167		3d. ultramarine	..	30	65
		a. "RENCE" flaw	..	80·00	
168	21	4d. light blue and red-orange		40	90
		a. "COIUMBUS" (R. 5/2)		£600	£600
169	22	6d. olive-green and light blue		40	1·75
		a. "COIUMBUS" (R. 5/2)		£600	£650
170	23	8d. ultramarine and scarlet		90	70
		a. "COIUMBUS" (R. 5/2)		£4250	£2000
171	20	1s. brownish grey and scarlet		4·50	3·25
		a. Ordinary paper. *Black and carmine*	3·75	2·75	
		b. Ordinary paper. *Grey-black and bright crimson*		7·50	5·00
172	18	2s. slate-purple and indigo		15·00	16·00
		a. *Brownish black and indigo*		8·00	10·00
		b. *Brownish black and steel-blue*	18·00	18·00	
		c. Stop after "COLUMBUS" (R. 2/12)	£1000		
173		3s. slate-purple and myrtle-green		5·00	6·50
		a. *Brownish black and green*		40·00	32·00
		b. Stop after "COLUMBUS" (R. 2/12)	£500		
174	20	5s. reddish lilac and blue		26·00	12·00
		a. Ordinary paper. *Purple and blue*	18·00	11·00	
175		£1 deep grey-green & blk (thick paper)	60·00	45·00	
		a. Ordinary paper. *Grey-green & black*	30·00	25·00	
162/75			*Set of 14*	60·00	55·00
162/75 Perf "Specimen"			*Set of 14*	£400	

These stamps replaced the definitive series for a period of six months. Initially stocks of existing printings were used, but when further supplies were required for overprinting a number of new printings were produced, some of which, including the new colour of the 3d., did not appear without overprint until much later.

1946 (11 Nov). *Victory. As Nos.* 110/11 *of Antigua.*

176	1½d. brown	..	10	20
177	3d. blue	..	10	20
176/7 Perf "Specimen"		*Set of*	55·00	

26 Infant Welfare Clinic

(Recess C.B.N.)

1948 (11 Oct). *Tercentenary of Settlement of Island of Eleuthera. T* **26** *and similar horiz designs. P* 12.

178	½d. orange	.. ..	30	60
179	1d. sage-green	..	30	35
180	1½d. yellow	..	30	80
181	2d. scarlet	.. ..	30	40
182	2½d. brown-lake	..	45	75
183	3d. ultramarine	..	65	85
184	4d. black	..	60	70
185	6d. emerald-green	..	1·75	80
186	8d. violet	..	60	70
187	10d. carmine	..	60	35
188	1s. sepia	..	90	50
189	2s. magenta	..	4·00	8·50
190	3s. blue	..	7·50	8·50
191	5s. mauve	..	5·50	4·50
192	10s. grey	..	9·50	9·00
193	£1 vermilion	..	13·00	14·00
178/93		*Set of 16*	40·00	45·00

Designs:—1d. Agriculture (combine harvester); 1½d. Sisal; 2d. Straw work; 2½d. Dairy farm; 3d. Fishing fleet; 4d. Island settlement; 6d. Tuna fishing; 8d. Paradise Beach; 10d. Modern hotels; 1s. Yacht racing; 2s. Water sports (skiing); 3s. Shipbuilding; 5s. Transportation; 10s. Salt production; £1, Parliament Buildings.

1948 (1 Dec). *Royal Silver Wedding. As Nos.* 112/13 *of Antigua.*

194	1½d. red-brown	..	20	25
195	£1 slate-green	..	32·00	32·00

1949 (10 Oct). *75th Anniv of Universal Postal Union. As Nos.* 114/17 *of Antigua.*

196	2½d. violet	..	35	40
197	3d. deep blue	..	1·50	1·75
198	6d. greenish blue	..	75	1·50
199	1s. carmine	..	75	75
196/9		*Set of 4*	3·00	4·00

1953 (3 June). *Coronation. As No.* 120 *of Antigua.*

200	6d. black and pale blue	.. ..	40	35

MINIMUM PRICE

The minimum price quote is 10p which represents a handling charge rather than a basis for valuing common stamps. For further notes about prices see introductory pages.

42 Infant Welfare Clinic   **43** Queen Elizabeth II

(Recess B.W.)

1954 (1 Jan)–63. *Designs previously used for King George VI issue, but with portrait of Queen Elizabeth II as in T* **42**, *and commemorative inscr omitted. Wmk Mult Script CA. P* 11 × 11½.

201	½d. black and red-orange	..	10	95
202	1d. olive-green and brown	..	10	10
203	1½d. blue and black	..	15	40
204	2d. yellow-brown and myrtle-green		15	15
	a. *Yellow-brn & dp myrtle-grn* (23.1.62)	4·50	5·00	
205	3d. black and carmine-red	..	55	55
206	4d. turquoise-green & deep reddish purple	30	30	
	a. *Turq-blue & dp reddish pur* (23.1.62)	8·00	9·00	
207	5d. red-brown and deep bright blue	1·40	2·25	
208	6d. light blue and black	..	75	10
	w. Wmk inverted	..	—	£500
209	8d. black and reddish lilac	..	70	40
	a. *Black and deep reddish lilac* (21.11.56)	1·40	1·50	
210	10d. black and ultramarine	..	30	10
	a. *Black and deep ultramarine* (8.1.63)	5·50	2·75	
211	1s. ultramarine and olive-brown	70	10	
	a. *Ultramarine & dp ol-sepia* (19.2.58)	1·75	30	
212	2s. orange-brown and black	..	2·00	70
	a. *Chestnut and black* (19.2.58)	9·00	1·50	
213	2s. 6d. black and deep blue	..	3·50	2·00
214	5s. bright emerald and orange	..	18·00	75
	a. *Brt emerald & reddish orange* (14.1.59)	38·00	4·50	
215	10s. black and slate-black	..	16·00	2·00
216	£1 slate-black and violet	..	18·00	6·00
201/16		*Set of 16*	55·00	14·50

Designs:—1d. Agriculture (combine harvester); 1½d. Island settlement; 2d. Straw work; 3d. Fishing fleet; 4d. Water sports (skiing); 5d. Dairy farm; 6d. Transportation; 8d. Paradise Beach; 10d. Modern hotels; 1s. Yacht racing; 2s. Sisal; 2s. 6d. Shipbuilding; 5s. Tuna fishing; 10s. Salt production; £1 Parliament Buildings.

Nos. 201/2, 205, 208 and 211 exist in coils, constructed from normal sheets.

See also No. 246.

(Recess Waterlow)

1959 (10 June). *Centenary of First Bahamas Postage Stamp. W w* **12**. *P* 13½.

217	**43**	1d. black and scarlet ..	..	35	15
218		2d. black and blue-green	..	35	70
219		6d. black and blue	..	45	30
220		10d. black and chocolate..		50	80
217/20			*Set of 4*	1·50	1·75

44 Christ Church Cathedral

(Photo Enschedé)

1962 (30 Jan). *Nassau Centenary. T* **44** *and similar horiz design. P* 14 × 13.

221	8d. green	..	45	55
222	10d. bluish violet	..	45	25

Design:—10d. Nassau Public Library.

1963 (4 June). *Freedom from Hunger. As No.* 146 *of Antigua.*

223	8d. sepia	..	40	40
	a. Name and value omitted	..	£900	

BAHAMAS TALKS 1962   **NEW CONSTITUTION 1964**

(46)   (47)

1963 (15 July). *Bahamas Talks, 1962. Nos.* 209/10 *optd with T* **46**.

224	8d. black and reddish lilac	..	40	60
225	10d. black and deep ultramarine		50	65

1963 (2 Sept). *Red Cross Centenary. As Nos.* 147/8 *of Antigua.*

226	1d. red and black	..	50	50
227	10d. red and blue	..	1·75	2·50

SELF GOVERNMENT

1964 (7 Jan). *New Constitution. As Nos.* 201/16 *but W w* **12**, *optd with T* **47**, *by B.W.*

228	½d. black and red-orange	..	15	60
229	1d. olive-green and brown	..	15	15
230	1½d. blue and black	..	70	60
231	2d. yellow-brown and deep myrtle-green	15	20	
232	3d. black and carmine-red	..	90	65
233	4d. turquoise-blue and deep reddish purple	40	45	
234	5d. red-brown and deep bright blue	40	1·00	
235	6d. light blue and black	..	1·00	30
236	8d. black and reddish lilac	..	70	30
237	10d. black and deep ultramarine	..	30	15
238	1s. ultramarine and olive-brown	..	80	15
239	2s. chestnut and black	..	1·50	1·75
240	2s. 6d. black and deep blue..		2·25	2·50
241	5s. bright emerald and orange	..	5·00	3·25
242	10s. black and slate black	..	5·00	5·50
243	£1 slate-black and violet	..	8·50	16·00
228/243		*Set of 16*	24·00	30·00

1964 (23 April). *400th Birth Anniv of William Shakespeare. As No.* 164 *of Antigua.*

244	6d. turquoise	..	10	10
	w. Wmk inverted	..	45·00	

(48)

1964 (1 Oct). *Olympic Games, Tokyo. As No.* 211 *but W w* **12**, *surch with T* **48**.

245	8d. on 1s. ultramarine and olive-brown	45	15

1964 (6 Oct). *As No.* 204a, *but wmk w* **12**.

246	2d. yellow-brown and deep myrtle-green	45	30

49 Colony's Badge   (64)

(Queen's portrait by Anthony Buckley. Litho and recess (portrait and "BAHAMAS") B.W.)

1965 (7 Jan–14 Sept). *Horiz designs as T* **49**. *W w* **12**. *P* 13½.

247	½d. multicoloured	..	15	90
248	1d. slate, light blue and orange	..	30	40
249	1½d. rose-red, green and brown	..	15	90
250	2d. slate, green and turquoise-blue	..	15	10
251	3d. red, light blue and purple	..	90	20
252	4d. green, blue and orange-brown ..		1·50	1·60
253	6d. dull green, light blue and rose ..		30	10
254	8d. reddish purple, light blue & bronze-green		50	30
255	10d. orange-brown, green and violet	..	25	10
256	1s. red, yellow, turquoise-blue & deep emer	50	20	
	a. *Red, yellow, dull blue & emer* (14.9.65)	30	10	
257	2s. brown, light blue and emerald	..	1·00	1·25
258	2s. 6d. yellow-olive, blue and carmine	2·25	2·75	
259	5s. orange-brown, ultramarine and green ..	2·25	1·00	
260	10s. rose, blue and chocolate	..	12·00	2·75
261	£1 chestnut, blue and rose-red	..	12·00	7·50
247/261		*Set of 15*	30·00	18·00

Designs:—1s. Out Island regatta; 1½d. Hospital; 2d. High School; 3d. Greater Flamingo; 4d. R.M.S. *Queen Elizabeth*; 6d. "Development"; 8d. Yachting; 10d. Public square; 1s. Sea garden; 2s. Old cannons at Fort Charlotte; 2s. 6d. Sikorsky S-38 flying boat, 1929, and Boeing 707 airliner; 5s. Williamson film project, 1914, and Undersea Post Office, 1939; 10s. Queen or Pink Conch; £1, Columbus's flagship.

Nos. 247/8, 251, 253 and 256 exist in coils, constructed from normal sheets.

1965 (17 May). *I.T.U Centenary. As Nos.* 166/7 *of Antigua.*

262	1d. light emerald and orange	..	15	10
	w. Wmk inverted	..	45·00	
263	2s. purple and yellow-olive	..	65	45
	w. Wmk inverted	..	16·00	

1965 (12 July). *No.* 254 *surch with T* **64**.

264	9d. on 8d. reddish purple, light blue and bronze-green	..	30	15

1965 (25 Oct). *International Co-operation Year. As Nos.* 168/9 *of Antigua.*

265	½d. reddish purple and turquoise-green	..	10	50
266	1s. deep bluish green and lavender ..		30	40

1966 (24 Jan). *Churchill Commemoration. As Nos.* 170/3 *of Antigua.*

267	½d. new blue	..	10	40
	w. Wmk inverted	..	25·00	
268	2d. deep green	..	30	30
269	10d. brown	..	65	85
270	1s. bluish violet	..	75	1·40
267/70		*Set of 4*	1·60	2·75

1966 (4 Feb). *Royal Visit. As Nos.* 174/5 *of Antigua, but inscr* "to the Caribbean" *omitted.*

271	6d. black and ultramarine	..	90	50
272	1s. black and magenta	..	1·60	1·25

(New Currency. 100 cents = 1 Bahamas dollar)

(65)   (66)

1966 (25 May). *Decimal Currency. Nos.* 247/61 *variously surch as T* 65/6, *by B.W.*

273	1 c. on ½d. multicoloured	..	10	30
274	2 c. on 1d. slate, light blue and orange	..	50	30
275	3 c. on 2d. slate, green and turquoise-blue	..	10	10
276	4 c. on 3d. red, light blue and purple	..	65	10
277	5 c. on 4d. green, blue and orange-brown	..	50	2·00
	a. Surch omitted (vert strip of 10)	..	£2250	
278	8 c. on 6d. dull green, light blue and rose	..	20	20
279	10 c. on 8d. reddish purple, light blue and bronze-green		30	75
280	11 c. on 1½d. rose-red, green and brown	..	30	30
281	12 c. on 10d. orange-brown, green and violet	15	10	
282	15 c. on 1s. multicoloured	..	25	10
283	22 c. on 2s. brown, light blue and emerald		60	80
284	50 c. on 2s. 6d. yellow-olive, blue and carmine	90	1·40	

285	$1 on 5s. orange-brown, ultram & green		1·25	1·50
286	$2 on 10s. rose, blue and chocolate ..		5·50	4·25
287	$3 on £1 chestnut, blue and rose-red		5·50	4·25
273/287		Set of 15	15·00	14·50

The above were made on new printings some of which vary slightly in shade and in No. 273 the shield appears as vermilion and green instead of carmine and blue-green due to a different combination of the printing colours.

No. 277a. One sheet exists and the stamp can be distinguished from No. 252 when in a vertical strip of ten as these were printed in sheets of 100 whereas No. 252 was printed in sheets of 60 (six rows of ten across).

1966 (1 July). *World Cup Football Championships. As Nos. 176/7 of Antigua.*

288	8 c. violet, yellow-green, lake & yell-brown		15	15
289	15 c. chocolate, blue-green, lake & yell-brown		25	25

1966 (20 Sept). *Inauguration of W.H.O. Headquarters, Geneva. As Nos. 178/9 of Antigua.*

290	11 c. black, yellow-green and light blue	..	40	40
291	15 c. black, light purple and yellow-brown	..	45	50

1966 (1 Dec). *20th Anniv of U.N.E.S.C.O. As Nos. 196/8 of Antigua.*

292	3 c. slate-violet, red, yellow and orange	..	10	10
293	15 c. orange-yellow, violet and deep olive	..	25	35
294	$1 black, bright purple and orange	..	1·00	2·50
292/4 ..		Set of 3	1·25	2·75

67 Oceanic

68 Conch Shell

(Portrait by Anthony Buckley. Litho and recess (portrait, "BAHAMAS" and value), B.W.)

1967 (25 May)–**71**. *T 67/8 or designs as Nos. 247/51, 253/9 and 261 but values in decimal currency and colours changed. Toned paper. W w 12. P 13½.*

295	1 c. multicoloured (as ½d.) ..	..	10	1·75
	a. Whiter paper (1970)	..	45	3·25
296	2 c. slate, light blue & deep emerald (as 1d.)		20	50
	a. Whiter paper (1970)	..	1·40	3·00
297	3 c. slate, green and violet (as 2d.) ..	..	10	10
	a. Whiter paper (1970)	..	55·00	5·00
298	4 c. red, light blue and ultramarine (as 3d.)		4·25	50
	a. Whiter paper (9.70*)	..	12·00	18·00
299	5 c. black, greenish blue and purple	..	75	1·50
	a. Whiter paper (1970)	..	1·50	4·00
300	8 c. dull green, light blue and sepia (as 6d.)		25	10
	a. Whiter paper (1970)	..	£170	17·00
301	10 c. reddish pur, greenish bl & carm (as 8d.)		30	70
	a. Whiter paper (1970)	..	1·00	2·50
302	11 c. rose-red, green and blue (as 1½d.)		25	80
	a. Whiter paper (1970)	..	80	2·25
303	12 c. orange-brown, green and olive (as 10d.)		25	10
	a. Whiter paper (4.71)	..	12·00	26·00
304	15 c. red, yellow, turquoise-bl & carm (as 1s.)		55	10
	a. Whiter paper (1970)	..	£170	22·00
305	22 c. brown, new blue and rose-red (as 2s.)		70	65
	a. Whiter paper (1970)	..	2·00	4·50
306	50 c. yellow-olive, new bl & emer (as 2s. 6d.)		2·00	75
	a. Whiter paper (1970)	..	2·25	3·75
307	$1 orange-brown, ultram & slate-pur (as 5s.)		2·00	60
	a. Whiter paper (4.71)	..	19·00	48·00
308	$2 multicoloured	..	10·00	3·00
	a. Whiter paper (4.71)	..	30·00	55·00
309	$3 chestnut, new blue and purple (as £1)		3·75	2·00
	a. Whiter paper (4.71)	..	30·00	55·00
295/309		Set of 15	22·00	11·50
295a/309a ..		Set of 15 (whiter paper)	£450	£250

*This is the earliest known date recorded in the Bahamas.
The 3 c. has the value at right instead of at as on No. 250.
The 1970–71 printings on whiter paper were released as needed, the 12 c., $1, $2 and $3 only a week or two before the issue was withdrawn. Due to the marked difference in paper and the use of some new plates there are marked differences in shade in nearly all values.

69 Bahamas Crest

(Des R. Granger Barrett. Photo Enschedé)

1967 (1 Sept). *Diamond Jubilee of World Scouting. T 69 and similar horiz design. Multicoloured. W w 12 (sideways*). P 14×13.*

310	3 c. Type 69		35	15
	w. Wmk Crown to left of CA	..	12·00	
311	15 c. Scout badge	..	40	15

*The normal sideways watermark shows Crown to right of CA, as seen from the back of the stamp.

71 Globe and Emblem   74 Golf

(Des R. Granger Barrett, Litho D.L.R)

1968 (13 May). *Human Rights Year. T 71 and similar horiz designs. Multicoloured. W w 12 (sideways*). P 14×13½.*

312	3 c. Type 71	..	10	10
313	12 c. Scales of Justice and emblem	..	20	10
314	$1 Bahamas Crest and emblem	..	70	80
312/14		Set of 3	90	85

*The normal sideways watermark shows Crown to right of CA on the 12 c. and Crown to left of CA on the others, *each when seen from the back of the stamp.*

(Litho B.W.)

1968 (20 Aug). *Tourism. T 74 and similar vert designs. Multicoloured. P 13.*

315	5 c. Type 74	..	1·25	1·00
316	11 c. Yachting	..	1·25	30
317	15 c. Horse-racing	..	1·50	35
318	50 c. Water-skiing	..	2·50	5·00
315/18		Set of 4	6·00	6·00

78 Racing Yacht and Olympic Monument

(Photo Harrison)

1968 (29 Sept). *Olympic Games, Mexico City. T 78 and similar horiz designs. No wmk. P 14½ × 13½.*

319	5 c. red-brown, orange-yellow & blue-green	25	15
320	11 c. multicoloured		35	25
321	50 c. multicoloured		80	1·40
322	$1 olive-grey, greenish blue and violet	..	2·00	3·00
319/22		Set of 4	3·00	4·25

Designs:—11 c. Long-jumping and Olympic Monument; 50 c. Running and Olympic Monument; $1, Type 78.
It is understood that the above were released by the Philatelic Agency in the U.S.A. on 1st September.

81 Legislative Building

(Des J. Cooter, Litho Format)

1968 (1 Nov). *14th Commonwealth Parliamentary Conference. T 81 and similar multicoloured designs. P 14.*

323	3 c. Type 81		10	10
324	10 c. Bahamas Mace and Westminster Clock-Tower (*vert*)	..	15	20
325	12 c. Local straw market (*vert*)	..	15	25
326	15 c. Horse-drawn Surrey	..	20	30
323/6 ..		Set of 4	55	75

85 Obverse and reverse of $100 Gold Coin

(Recess D.L.R.)

1968 (2 Dec). *Gold Coins commemorating the first General Election under the New Constitution. T 85 and similar "boomerang" shaped designs. P 13½.*

327	3 c. red/gold		30	25
328	12 c. blue-green/gold	..	50	50
329	15 c. dull purple/gold	..	60	60
330	$1 black/gold	..	1·75	2·50
327/30		Set of 4	2·75	3·50

Designs:—12 c. Obverse and reverse of $50 gold coin; 15 c. Obverse and reverse of $20 gold coin; $1, Obverse and reverse of $10 gold coin.

89 First Flight Postcard of 1919

90 Sikorsky S-38 Flying Boat of 1929

(Des V. Whiteley. Litho Format)

1969 (30 Jan). *50th Anniv of Bahamas Airmail Service. P 14.*

331	89	12 c. multicoloured	..	50	50
332	90	15 c. multicoloured	..	60	1·25

91 Game-fishing Boats   92 "The Adoration of the Shepherds" (Louis le Nain)

(Des J. Cooter. Litho Format)

1969 (26 Aug). *Tourism. One Millionth Visitor to Bahamas. T 91 and similar horiz designs. Multicoloured. W w 12 (sideways). P 14½.*

333	3 c. Type 91	..	25	10
334	11 c. Paradise Beach	..	35	15
335	12 c. "Sunfish" sailing boats ..		35	15
336	15 c. Rawson Square and Parade	..	45	25
333/6 ..		Set of 4	1·25	60
MS337	130 × 96 mm. Nos. 333/6 ..		2·50	3·00

(Des G. Drummond. Litho D.L.R.)

1969 (15 Oct). *Christmas. T 92 and similar vert designs. W w 12. P 12.*

338	3 c. Type 92		10	10
339	11 c. "The Adoration of the Shepherds" (Poussin) ..	..	15	15
340	12 c. "The Adoration of the Kings" (Gerard David)	..	15	20
341	15 c. "The Adoration of the Kings" (Vincenzo Foppa)	..	20	40
338/41		Set of 4	55	75

93 Badge of Girl Guides

(Des Mrs. R. Sands. Litho Harrison)

1970 (23 Feb). *Girl Guides Diamond Jubilee. T 93 and similar designs. Multicoloured. W w 12. P 14½.*

342	3 c. Type 93	..	30	10
	w. Wmk inverted	..		
343	12 c. Badge of Brownies	..	45	20
344	15 c. Badge of Rangers	..	50	35
	w. Wmk inverted	..		
342/4 ..		Set of 3	1·10	55

94 U.P.U. Headquarters and Emblem

(Des L. Curtis, Litho J.W.)

1970 (20 May). *New U.P.U. Headquarters Building. W w 12 (sideways). P 14.*

345	94	3 c. multicoloured	..	10	10
346		15 c. multicoloured	..	20	30

95 Coach and Globe

(Des G. Drummond. Litho B.W.)

1970 (14 July). *"Goodwill Caravan". T* **95** *and similar horiz designs. Multicoloured. W* w **12** *(sideways*). P* 13½×13.
347	3 c. Type **95**	..	..	75	15
	w. Wmk Crown to right of CA				
348	11 c. Train and globe			1·75	30
349	12 c. *Canberra* (liner), yacht and globe	..		1·75	40
	w. Wmk Crown to right of CA			3·50	
350	15 c. B.A.C. One Eleven airliner and globe			1·75	1·25
347/50			*Set of* 4	5·50	1·90
MS351	165×125 mm. Nos. 347/50			9·50	15·00

The normal sideways watermark shows Crown to left of CA, as seen from the back of the stamp.

96 Nurse, Patients and Greater Flamingo   **97 "The Nativity"** (detail, Pittoni)

(Photo Harrison)

1970 (1 Sept). *Centenary of British Red Cross. T* **96** *and similar horiz design. Multicoloured. W* w **12** *(sideways*). P* 14½.
352	3 c. Type **96**	..	..	80	50
	a. Gold ("EIIR", etc) omitted	..	£250		
	w. Wmk Crown to right of CA				
353	15 c. Hospital and Blue Marlin	..		80	1·25

The normal sideways watermark shows Crown to left of CA, as seen from back of the stamp.

(Des G. Drummond. Litho D.L.R.)

1970 (3 Nov). *Christmas. T* **97** *and similar vert designs. Multicoloured. W* w **12**. *P* 13.
354	3 c. Type **97**		15	10
355	11 c. "The Holy Family" (detail, Anton Raphael Mengs)		20	20
356	12 c. "The Adoration of the Shepherds" (detail, Giorgione)		20	20
357	15 c. "The Adoration of the Shepherds" (detail, School of Seville)		30	45
354/7	..	*Set of* 4	75	85
MS358	114 × 140 mm. Nos. 354/7 plus two labels		1·40	2·75

98 International Airport

(Des Mrs. W. Wasile. Litho Format)

1971 (27 Apr–1 Sept). *Multicoloured designs as T* **98**. *W* w **12** *(sideways on* $1 *to* $3). *P* 14½×14 (1 *to* 50 *c.) or* 14×14½ ($1 *to* $3).
359	1 c. Type **98**	..	..	10	30
360	2 c. Breadfruit	..	..	15	35
361	3 c. Straw market	..	..	15	30
362	4 c. Hawksbill turtle	..		1·75	6·50
363	5 c. Nassau Grouper	..		60	60
364	6 c. As 4 c. (21.9.71)	..		45	1·25
365	7 c. Hibiscus (21.9.71)	..		2·00	3·00
366	8 c. Yellow Elder	..		60	1·50
367	10 c. Bahamian sponge boat	..		55	30
368	11 c. Greater Flamingos	..		2·50	2·00
	w. Wmk inverted			11·00	
369	12 c. As 7 c.	..		2·00	3·00
370	15 c. Bonefish	..		40	55
	w. Wmk inverted				
371	18 c. Royal Poinciana (21.9.71)		65	65
	w. Wmk inverted				
372	22 c. As 18 c.	..		2·75	9·50
373	50 c. Post Office, Nassau	..		1·40	2·25
374	$1 Pineapple (*vert*)	..		5·00	3·00
375	$2 Crawfish (*vert*)	..		4·50	6·00
376	$3 Junkanoo (*vert*)	..		4·50	10·00
359/76		*Set of* 18	26·00	45·00

See also Nos. 395/400, 460/73 and 518/25.

NEW INFORMATION

The editor is always interested to correspond with people who have new information that will improve or correct the Catalogue.

99 Snowflake

(Litho (15 c. additionally die-stamped in gold) Walsall)

1971 (19 Oct). *Christmas. T* **99** *and similar horiz designs. W* w **12**. *P* 14 × 14½.
377	3 c. deep reddish purple, orange and gold		10	10
378	11 c. light ultramarine and gold		20	15
	w. Wmk inverted		1·00	
379	15 c. multicoloured		20	20
380	18 c. bluish green, royal blue and gold		25	25
377/80		*Set of* 4	65	60
MS381	126×95 mm. Nos. 377/80. P 15		1·25	1·50

Designs:—11 c. "Peace on Earth" (doves); 15 c. Arms of Bahamas and holly; 18 c. Starlit lagoon.

100 High jumping

(Des J. W. Litho B.W.)

1972 (11 July). *Olympic Games, Munich. T* **100** *and similar horiz designs. Multicoloured. W* w **12**. *P* 13½.
382	10 c. Type **100**	..		35	50
383	11 c. Cycling	..		1·25	65
384	15 c. Running	..		60	70
385	18 c. Sailing	..		95	1·10
382/5		*Set of* 4	2·75	2·75	
MS386	127 × 95 mm. Nos. 382/5	..	2·75	2·75	

101 Shepherd   **102 Northerly Bahama Islands**

(Des Jennifer Toombs. Litho (15 c. additionally embossed) J.W.)

1972 (3 Oct). *Christmas. T* **101** *and similar vert designs. Multicoloured. W* w **12** *(sideways on* 6 *and* 20 *c.) P* 14.
387	3 c. Type **101**	..	10	10
388	6 c. Bells	..	10	10
389	15 c. Holly and Cross	..	15	20
390	20 c. Poinsettia	..	25	45
387/90		*Set of* 4	50	70
MS391	108 × 140 mm. Nos. 387/90 (wmk sideways)		80	1·50

(Des M. Shamir. Litho Format)

1972 (1 Nov). *Tourism Year of the Americas. Sheet* 133 × 105 *mm, containing T* **102** *and similar vert designs. P* 15.
MS392	11, 15, 18 and 50 c. multicoloured	2·25	3·25

The four designs are printed horizontally *se-tenant* in **MS**392, forming a composite map design of the Bahamas.

103 Mace and Galleon

(Des (from photograph by D. Groves) and photo Harrison)

1972 (13 Nov). *Royal Silver Wedding. Multicoloured; background colour given. W* w **12**. *P* 14 × 14½.
393	103	11 c. rose	15	15
		w. Wmk inverted	50·00	
394		18 c. bluish violet	15	20
		w. Wmk inverted	1·75	

1972 (23 Nov)–73. *As Nos.* 363, 366 *and* 373/6 *but wmk sideways* on 5 *to* 50 *c.; upright on* $1 *to* $3.
395	5 c. Nassau Grouper	..	7·00	2·50
396	8 c. Yellow Elder (25.7.73)		2·75	2·00
397	50 c. Post Office, Nassau (25.7.73)		2·00	2·50
	w. Wmk Crown to left of CA		3·25	
398	$1 Pineapple (25.7.73)		3·00	4·00

399	$2 Crawfish (25.7.73)	..	3·00	6·00
400	$3 Junkanoo (1973)	..	4·00	14·00
395/400		*Set of* 6	20·00	28·00

The normal sideways watermark shows Crown to right of CA, as seen from the back of the stamp.

Nos. 401/9 vacant.

104 Weather Satellite

(Des C. Abbott. Litho Questa)

1973 (3 Apr). *I.M.O./W.M.O. Centenary. T* **104** *and similar horiz design. Multicoloured. W* w **12**. *P* 14.
410	15 c. Type **104**		50	25
411	18 c. Weather radar		60	35

INDEPENDENT

105 C. A. Bain (national hero)   **106 "The Virgin in Prayer"** (Sassoferrato)

(Des PAD Studio. Litho Questa)

1973 (10 July–1 Aug). *Independence. T* **105** *and similar vert designs. Multicoloured. W* w **12** *(sideways). P* 14½ × 14.
412	3 c. Type **105**		10	10
413	11 c. Coat of arms		15	10
414	15 c. Bahamas flag		20	15
415	$1 Governor-General, M. B. Butler (1 Aug)		65	1·00
412/15		*Set of* 4	1·00	1·10
MS416	86 × 121 mm. Nos. 412/15 (1 Aug)		1·25	1·75

(Des C. Abbott. Litho Format)

1973 (16 Oct). *Christmas. T* **106** *and similar vert designs. Multicoloured. W* w **12** *(sideways*). P* 14.
417	3 c. Type **106**		10	10
418	11 c. "Virgin and Child with St. John" (Filippino Lippi)		15	15
419	15 c. "A Choir of Angels" (Simon Marmion)		15	15
420	18 c. "The Two Trinities" (Murillo)	..	25	25
417/20		*Set of* 4	60	55
MS421	120×99 mm. Nos. 417/20		90	1·40
	w. Wmk Crown to right of CA		2·50	

The normal sideways watermark shows Crown to left of CA, as seen from the back of the stamp.

107 "Agriculture and Sciences"

(Des C. Abbott. Litho Questa)

1974 (5 Feb). *25th Anniv of University of West Indies. T* **107** *and similar horiz design. Multicoloured. W* w **12**. *P* 13½.
422	15 c. Type **107**		20	25
423	18 c. "Arts, Engineering and General Studies"		25	30

108 U.P.U. Monument, Berne

(Des P. Powell. Litho Questa)

1974 (23 Apr). *Centenary of Universal Postal Union. Designs as T* **108** *showing different arrangements of the U.P.U. Monument. W* w **12** *(upright on* 3 *c.,* 14 *c. and* **MS**428; *sideways on others). P* 14.
424	**108**	3 c. multicoloured	..	10	10
425	–	11 c. multicoloured	..	20	25
426	–	14 c. multicoloured		20	30
427	–	18 c. multicoloured (*vert*)		25	35
424/7			*Set of* 4	65	90
MS428	128×95 mm. Nos. 424/7			80	1·60
	w. Wmk inverted			£150	

109 Roseate Spoonbills

(Des G. Drummond. Litho Questa)

1974 (10 Sept). *15th Anniv of Bahamas National Trust. T* **109** *and similar horiz designs. Multicoloured. W w* **12** *(sideways). P* 13½.

429	13 c. Type 109 ..		1·10	85
430	14 c. White-crowned Pigeon		1·10	75
431	21 c. White-tailed Tropic Birds		1·50	1·25
432	36 c. Cuban Amazon		2·00	3·25
429/32		*Set of* 4	5·00	5·50
MS433	123 × 120 mm. Nos. 429/32		7·00	9·00

110 "The Holy Family" (Jacques de Stella)

(Des J. W. Litho Enschedé)

1974 (29 Oct). *Christmas. T* **110** *and similar horiz designs. Multicoloured. W w* **12** *(sideways). P* 13 × 13½.

434	8 c. Type 110 ..	10	10
435	10 c. "Madonna and Child" (16th-cent Brescian School)	15	15
436	12 c. "Virgin and Child with St. John the Baptist and St. Catherine" (Previtali)	15	15
437	21 c. "Virgin and Child with Angels" (Previtali)	25	30
434/7	*Set of* 4	60	60
MS438	126 × 105 mm. Nos. 434/7	80	1·40

111 *Anteos maerula*

(Des PAD Studio. Litho D.L.R.)

1975 (4 Feb). *Butterflies. T* **111** *and similar horiz designs. Multicoloured. W w* **12**. *P* 14 × 13½.

439	3 c. Type 111 ..	25	25
440	14 c. *Eurema nicippe*	80	50
441	18 c. *Papilio andraemon*	95	65
442	21 c. *Euptoieta hegesia*	1·10	85
	w. Wmk inverted	38·00	
439/42	*Set of* 4	2·75	2·00
MS443	119×94 mm. Nos. 439/42	6·50	6·50

112 Sheep Husbandry   113 Rowena Rand (evangelist)

(Des Daphne Padden. Litho Questa)

1975 (27 May). *Economic Diversification. T* **112** *and similar multicoloured designs. P* 14.

444	3 c. Type 112 ..	10	10
445	14 c. Electric-reel fishing (*vert*)	20	15
446	18 c. Farming	25	20
447	21 c. Oil Refinery (*vert*)	45	35
444/7	*Set of* 4	90	65
MS448	127 × 94 mm. Nos. 444/7 ..	90	1·50

(Des Jennifer Toombs. Litho Questa)

1975 (22 July). *International Women's Year. T* **113** *and similar vert design. W w* **14**. *P* 14.

449	14 c. bistre-brown, lt turquoise-blue & ultram	20	30
450	18 c. lemon, bright yellow-green and sepia	25	35

Design:—18 c. I.W.Y. symbol and Harvest symbol.

114 "Adoration of the Shepherds" (Perugino)

(Des Jennifer Toombs. Litho J.W.)

1975 (2 Dec). *Christmas. T* **114** *and similar horiz design. Multicoloured. W w* **14** *(sideways). P* 13.

451	3 c. Type 114 ..	15	30
452	8 c. "Adoration of the Magi" (Ghirlandaio) ..	20	10
453	18 c. As 8 c.	55	70
454	21 c. Type 114 ..	60	85
451/4	*Set of* 4	1·40	1·75
MS455	142 × 107 mm. Nos. 451/4. *P* 13½	2·25	3·50

115 Telephones, 1876 and 1976

(Des G. Vasarhelyi. Litho D.L.R.)

1976 (23 Mar). *Telephone Centenary. T* **115** *and similar horiz designs. Multicoloured. W w* **14** *(sideways*). P* 14.

456	3 c. Type 115	15	10
	w. Wmk Crown to right of CA	2·00	
457	16 c. Radio-telephone link, Deleporte	30	35
	w. Wmk Crown to right of CA	60·00	
458	21 c. Alexander Graham Bell	40	50
	w. Wmk Crown to right of CA	50·00	
459	25 c. Satellite	50	60
	w. Wmk Crown to right of CA	2·50	
456/9	*Set of* 4	1·25	1·40

*The normal sideways watermark shows Crown to left of CA, as seen from the back of the stamp.

1976 (30 May)–**79**. *Designs as Nos. 359/63, 365/7 and 373/6 (some with new face values). W w* **14** *(sideways on* $1 *to* $3). *Ordinary paper.*

460	1 c. Type 98 (1.11.76)	1·75	2·50
	a. Chalk-surfaced paper (1979)	14·00	15·00
461	2 c. Breadfruit	2·00	30
462	3 c. Straw market (1.11.76)	2·25	2·50
	a. Chalk-surfaced paper (1979)	60	60
463	5 c. Nassau Grouper (1.11.76)	3·75	2·25
	a. Chalk-surfaced paper (1979)	70	70
464	8 c. Yellow Elder	4·50	30
465	10 c. Bahamian sponge boat	80	30
466	16 c. As 7 c. (2.11.76)	70	35
	a. Chalk-surfaced paper (1979)	70	80
	aw. Wmk inverted	18·00	
467	21 c. As 2 c. (2.11.76)	3·00	1·50
	a. Chalk-surfaced paper (1979)	80	1·25
	aw. Wmk inverted	18·00	
468	25 c. As 4 c. (2.11.76)	90	40
	a. Chalk-surfaced paper (1979)	90	2·00
	aw. Wmk inverted	18·00	
469	40 c. As 10 c. (2.11.76)	3·25	75
470	50 c. Post Office, Nassau	1·75	1·75
471	$1 Pineapple	2·00	2·50
472	$2 Crawfish (2.5.76)	3·00	7·00
	a. Chalk-surfaced paper (1979)	20·00	27·00
473	$3 Junkanoo (1.11.76)	3·00	9·00
460/73	*Set of* 14	29·00	27·00
460a/72a ..	*Set of* 7	35·00	42·00

No. 474 vacant.

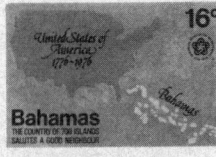

116 Map of North America

(Des and litho Walsall)

1976 (1 June). *Bicentenary of American Revolution. T* **116** *and similar horiz design. Multicoloured. W w* **14** *(sideways*). P* 14.

475	16 c. Type 116	30	30
476	$1 John Murray, Earl of Dunmore	1·50	1·75
MS477	127×100 mm. No. 476×4	5·50	7·50
	w. Wmk Crown to right of CA	16·00	

*The normal sideways watermark shows Crown to left of CA, as seen from the back of the stamp.

117 Cycling

118 "Virgin and Child" (detail, Lippi)

(Des J.W. Litho Questa)

1976 (13 July). *Olympic Games, Montreal. T* **117** *and similar vert designs. W w* **14**. *P* 14.

478	8 c. magenta, blue and pale cobalt	35	10
479	16 c. orange, brown and pale cobalt	35	25
480	25 c. blue, deep magenta and pale cobalt	40	45
481	40 c. brown, orange and pale cobalt	50	1·00
478/81	*Set of* 4	1·40	1·60
MS482	100 × 126 mm. Nos. 478/81	2·25	2·50

Designs:—16 c. Jumping; 25 c. Sailing; 40 c. Boxing.

(Des G. Drummond. Litho Questa)

1976 (5 Oct). *Christmas. T* **118** *and similar vert designs. Multicoloured. W w* **14**. *P* 14.

483	3 c. Type 118	10	10
484	21 c. "Adoration of the Shepherds" (School of Seville)	20	15
485	25 c. "Adoration of the Kings" (detail, Foppa)	20	20
486	40 c. "Virgin and Child" (detail, Vivarini)	35	40
483/6	*Set of* 4	75	75
MS487	107 × 127 mm. Nos. 483/6	1·00	2·00

119 Queen beneath Cloth of Gold Canopy

(Des G. Vasarhelyi. Litho Cartor)

1977 (7 Feb). *Silver Jubilee. T* **119** *and similar horiz designs. Multicoloured. No wmk. P* 12.

488	8 c. Type 119 ..	10	10
489	16 c. The Crowning	15	15
490	21 c. Taking the Oath ..	15	15
491	40 c. Queen with sceptre and orb	25	30
488/91	*Set of* 4	60	60
MS492	122 × 90 mm. Nos. 488/91	80	1·25

120 Featherduster

(Des BG Studio. Litho J.W.)

1977 (24 May). *Marine Life. T* **120** *and similar designs. Multicoloured. W w* **14** *(sideways). P* 13½.

493	3 c. Type 120	20	15
494	8 c. Porkfish and cave	35	20
495	16 c. Elkhorn Coral	60	40
496	21 c. Soft Coral and sponge	75	55
493/6	*Set of* 4	1·75	1·10
MS497	119×93 mm. Nos. 493/6. *P* 14½	2·50	4·00

121 Scouts around Campfire and Home-made Shower   (122)

(Des Harrison. Litho J.W.)

1977 (27 Sept). *Sixth Caribbean Scout Jamboree. T* **121** *and similar horiz design. Multicoloured. W w* **14** *(sideways). P* 13½.

498	16 c. Type 121	75	30
499	21 c. Boating scenes	85	35

One used example of No. 498 is known with the mauve (face value and inscription) omitted.

1977 (19 Oct). *Royal Visit. As Nos. 488/92, but W w* **14** *(sideways*), optd with T* **122**.

500	8 c. Type 119	15	10
501	16 c. The Crowning	20	15
	w. Wmk Crown to right of CA	40	
502	21 c. Taking the Oath	25	20
503	40 c. Queen with sceptre and orb	30	40
500/3	*Set of* 4	1·00	1·75
MS504	122×90 mm. Nos. 500/3	1·00	2·00
	w. Wmk Crown to right of CA	1·75	

*The normal sideways watermark shows Crown to right of CA on 8, 21, 40 c.; to left on 16 c. and miniature sheet; *all as seen from the back of the stamp.*

PRICES OF SETS

Set prices are given for many issues, generally those containing three stamps or more. Definitive sets include one of each value or major colour change, but do not cover different perforations, die types or minor shades. Where a choice is possible the set prices are based on the cheapest versions of the stamps included in the listings.

123 Virgin and Child　　124 Public Library, Nassau (Colonial)

(Des and litho J.W.)

1977 (25 Oct). *Christmas.* T **123** *and similar vert designs. Multi-coloured.* W w **14.** P 13½.

505	3 c. Type **123**		10	10
506	16 c. The Magi		20	25
507	21 c. Nativity scene		25	40
508	25 c. The Magi and star		30	45
505/8		*Set of 4*	75	1·10
MS509	136 × 74 mm. Nos. 505/8. P 14		75	1·75

(Des G. Drummond. Litho Questa)

1978 (28 Mar). *Architectural Heritage.* T **124** *and similar vert designs.* W w **14.** P 14½ × 14.

510	3 c. black and apple-green		10	10
511	8 c. black and pale greenish blue		15	10
512	16 c. black and mauve		20	20
513	18 c. black and salmon-pink		25	30
510/13		*Set of 4*	60	65
MS514	91×91 mm. Nos. 510/13		70	1·60

Designs:—8 c. St. Matthew's Church (Gothic); 16 c. Government House (Colonial); 18 c. Hermitage, Cat Island (Spanish).

125 Sceptre, St. Edward's Crown and Orb　　126 Coat of Arms within Wreath and Three Ships

(Des BG Studio. Litho Enschedé)

1978 (27 June). *25th Anniv of Coronation.* T **125** *and similar vert design. Multicoloured.* W w **14.** P 14 × 13½.

515	16 c. Type **125**		15	10
516	$1 Queen in Coronation regalia		50	65
MS517	147×96 mm. Nos. 515/16		1·00	1·00
	w. Wmk inverted		9·00	

1978 (June). *As Nos. 359/76, but no wmk.*

518	1 c. Type **98**		65	1·50
519	5 c. Nassau Grouper		1·00	1·00
520	16 c. Hibiscus		1·25	1·75
521	25 c. Hawksbill Turtle		3·75	1·75
522	50 c. Post Office, Nassau		2·50	3·00
523	$1 Pineapple		2·50	3·00
524	$2 Crawfish		4·00	8·00
525	$3 Junkanoo		4·50	8·00
518/25		*Set of 8*	18·00	25·00

Nos. 526/31 vacant.

(Des Jennifer Toombs. Litho Questa)

1978 (14 Nov). *Christmas.* T **126** *and similar horiz design.* W w **14** *(sideways).* P 14 × 14½.

532	5 c. gold, bright crimson and bright rose		20	10
533	21 c. gold, deep ultramarine and violet-blue		55	25
MS534	95 × 95 mm. Nos. 532/3		2·75	5·00

Design:—21 c. Three angels with trumpets.

127 Child reaching for Adult　　128 Sir Rowland Hill and Penny Black

(Litho J.W.)

1979 (15 May). *International Year of the Child.* T **127** *and similar vert designs. Multicoloured.* W w **14.** P 13.

535	5 c. Type **127**		20	15
536	16 c. Boys playing leap-frog		40	45
537	21 c. Girls skipping		50	60
538	25 c. Bricks with I.Y.C. emblem		50	75
535/8		*Set of 4*	1·40	1·75
MS539	101 × 125 mm. Nos. 535/8. P 14		1·40	2·75

(Des J. Cooter. Litho Walsall)

1979 (14 Aug). *Death Centenary of Sir Rowland Hill.* T **128** *and similar horiz designs. Multicoloured.* W w **14** *(sideways).* P 13½ × 14.

540	10 c. Type **128**		30	10
541	21 c. Printing press, 1840 and 6d. stamp of 1862		40	30
542	25 c. Great Britain 6d. stamp of 1856 with "A 05" (Nassau) cancellation and Two-penny blue		40	50
543	40 c. Early mailboat and 1d. stamp of 1859		45	70
540/3		*Set of 4*	1·40	1·40
MS544	115 × 80 mm. Nos. 540/3		2·00	2·50

129 Commemorative Plaque and Map of Bahamas　　130 Goombay Carnival Headdress

(Des G. Drummond. Litho Secura, Singapore)

1979 (27 Sept). *250th Anniv of Parliament.* T **129** *and similar horiz designs. Multicoloured.* W w **14** *(sideways*).* P 13½.

545	16 c. Type **129**		20	10
	w. Wmk Crown to right of CA		25	
546	21 c. Parliament Buildings		25	15
	w. Wmk Crown to right of CA		30	
547	25 c. Legislative Chamber		25	15
	w. Wmk Crown to right of CA		35	
548	$1 Senate Chamber		70	80
	w. Wmk Crown to right of CA		1·10	
545/8		*Set of 4*	1·25	1·00
MS549	116×89 mm. Nos. 545/8 (wmk upright)		2·25	3·00
	w. Wmk inverted		2·25	

*The normal sideways watermark shows Crown to left of CA, as seen from the back of the stamp.

(Des BG Studio. Litho J.W.)

1979 (6 Nov). *Christmas.* T **130** *and similar vert designs showing Goombay Carnival headdresses.* W w **14.** P 13.

550	5 c. multicoloured		10	10
551	10 c. multicoloured		10	10
552	16 c. multicoloured		15	10
553	21 c. multicoloured		20	20
554	25 c. multicoloured		20	20
	w. Wmk inverted		2·00	
555	40 c. multicoloured		30	35
550/5		*Set of 6*	90	85
MS556	50×88 mm. Nos. 550/5 (wmk sideways). P 13½		2·00	2·75

131 Landfall of Columbus, 1492　　132 Virgin and Child

(Des J.W. Litho Format)

1980 (9 July). *Horiz designs as T **131.** Multicoloured.* W w **14.** P 14½.

557	1 c. Type **131**		85	1·75
558	3 c. Blackbeard the Pirate, 1718		30	1·75
559	5 c. Eleutheran Adventurers (Articles and Orders, 1647)		30	30
560	10 c. Ceremonial mace		20	30
	w. Wmk inverted		†	—
561	12 c. The Loyalists, 1783–88 (Colonel Andrew Deveaux)		20	1·25
562	15 c. Slave trading, Vendue House		5·50	75
563	16 c. Wrecking in the 1800's		80	75
564	18 c. Blockade running (American Civil War)		90	1·50
565	21 c. Bootlegging, 1919–29		40	1·50
566	25 c. Pineapple cultivation		40	1·50
567	40 c. Sponge clipping		70	1·50
568	50 c. Tourist development		75	1·50
569	$1 Modern agriculture		1·10	3·75
570	$2 Modern air and sea transport		3·50	4·00
571	$3 Banking in the Bahamas (Central Bank)		1·75	4·00
572	$5 Independence, 10 July 1973 (Prince of Wales and Prime Minister L. O. Pindling)		2·00	6·00
557/72		*Set of 16*	17·00	28·00

See also Nos. 720/6 for stamps watermarked w **16.**

(Des B. Malone. Litho Walsall)

1980 (28 Oct). *Christmas. Straw-work.* T **132** *and similar vert designs. Multicoloured.* W w **14.** P 14½ × 14.

573	5 c. Type **132**		10	10
574	21 c. Three Kings		25	10
575	25 c. Angel		25	15
576	$1 Christmas Tree		75	70
573/6		*Set of 4*	1·25	80
MS577	168 × 105 mm. Nos. 573/6		1·25	2·25

133 Disabled Person with Walking-stick

(Des and litho Walsall)

1981 (10 Feb). *International Year for Disabled Persons.* T **133** *and similar horiz design. Multicoloured.* W w **14** *(sideways).* P 14½ × 14.

578	5 c. Type **133**		10	10
579	$1 Disabled person in wheelchair		1·25	1·25
MS580	120 × 60 mm. Nos. 578/9		1·40	2·50

134 Grand Bahama Tracking Site　　135 Prince Charles and Lady Diana Spencer

(Litho Enschedé)

1981 (21 Apr). *Space Exploration.* T **134** *and similar multicoloured designs.* W w **14** *(sideways* on 10 and 25 c.).* P 13½.

581	10 c. Type **134**		25	15
582	20 c. Satellite view of Bahamas *(vert)*		55	50
	w. Wmk inverted		20·00	
583	25 c. Satellite view of Eleuthera		60	60
	w. Wmk Crown to right of CA		1·60	
584	50 c. Satellite view of Andros and New Providence *(vert)*		85	1·25
581/4		*Set of 4*	2·00	2·25
MS585	115×99 mm. Nos. 581/4 (wmk sideways)		1·60	2·25

*The normal sideways watermark shows Crown to left of CA, as seen from the back of the stamp.

(Des C. Abbott. Litho Questa)

1981 (22 July). *Royal Wedding.* T **135** *and similar horiz design. Multicoloured.* W w **14** *(sideways*).* P 14×14½.

586	30 c. Type **135**		1·50	30
587	$2 Prince Charles and Prime Minister Pindling		2·00	1·75
MS588	142×120 mm. Nos. 586/7		5·00	1·75
	a. Upper stamp in miniature sheet imperf on 3 sides		£650	
	w. Wmk Crown to right of CA		30·00	

*The normal sideways watermark shows Crown to left of CA, as seen from the back of the stamp.
No. MS588a shows the upper stamp in the miniature sheet perforated at foot only.

136 Bahama Pintail

(Des Walsall. Litho Questa)

1981 (25 Aug). *Wildlife (1st series). Birds.* T **136** *and similar horiz designs. Multicoloured.* P 14.

589	5 c. Type **136**		80	20
590	20 c. Reddish Egret		1·50	50
591	25 c. Brown Booby		1·60	55
592	$1 Black-billed Whistling Duck		3·25	4·50
589/92		*Set of 4*	6·50	5·25
MS593	100 × 74 mm. Nos. 589/92		7·00	7·50

See also Nos. 626/30, 653/7 and 690/4.

COMMONWEALTH FINANCE MINISTERS' MEETING

(137)

1981 (21 Sept). *Commonwealth Finance Ministers' Meeting. Nos. 559/60, 566 and 568 optd with* T **137.**

594	5 c. Eleutheran Adventurers (Articles and Orders, 1647)		15	15
	a. Opt inverted		50·00	
595	10 c. Ceremonial mace		20	20
	w. Wmk inverted		6·50	
596	25 c. Pineapple cultivation		50	60
597	50 c. Tourist development		85	1·50
594/7		*Set of 4*	1·50	2·25

MINIMUM PRICE

The minimum price quote is 10p which represents a handling charge rather than a basis for valuing common stamps. For further notes about prices see introductory pages.

138 Poultry   **139** Father Christmas

(Des L. McCombie. Litho J.W.)

1981 (16 Oct). *World Food Day. T* **138** *and similar horiz designs. Multicoloured.* W w 14 (sideways). *P* 13.
598	5 c. Type 138		10	10
599	20 c. Sheep		30	35
600	30 c. Lobsters		40	50
601	50 c. Pigs		75	1·50
598/601		*Set of 4*	1·40	2·25
MS602	115 × 63 mm. Nos. 598/601. P 14		1·50	3·25

(Des local artists. Litho Format)

1981 (24 Nov). *Christmas. T* **139** *and similar vert designs. Multicoloured.* W w 14. *P* 13½ × 14.
603	5 c. Type 139		35	60
	a. Sheetlet of 9. Nos. 603/11		4·00	
604	5 c. Mother and child		35	60
605	5 c. St. Nicholas, Holland		35	60
606	25 c. Lussibruden, Sweden		50	85
607	25 c. Mother and child (*different*)		50	85
608	25 c. King Wenceslas, Czechoslovakia		50	85
609	30 c. Mother with child on knee		50	85
610	30 c. Mother carrying child		50	85
611	$1 Christkindl Angel, Germany		1·00	1·50
603/11		*Set of 9*	4·00	6·75

Nos. 603/11 were printed together, *se-tenant*, in a sheetlet of 9.

140 Robert Koch   **141** Male Flamingo (*Phoenicopterus ruber*)

(Des A. Theobald. Litho Harrison)

1982 (3 Feb). *Centenary of Discovery of Tubercle Bacillus by Robert Koch. T* **140** *and similar horiz designs.* W w 14 (sideways). *P* 14.
612	5 c. black, red-brown and rose-lilac		60	30
613	16 c. black, drab and dull orange		1·00	50
614	21 c. multicoloured		1·10	55
615	$1 multicoloured		2·75	6·00
612/15		*Set of 4*	5·00	6·50
MS616	94 × 97 mm. Nos. 612/15. P 14½		5·50	7·50

Designs:—16 c. Stylised infected person; 21 c. Early and modern microscopes; $1 Mantoux test.

(Des N. Arlott. Litho Questa)

1982 (28 Apr). *Greater Flamingos. T* **141** *and similar vert designs. Multicoloured.* W w 14. *P* 14 × 13½.
617	25 c. Type 141		1·25	1·00
	a. Horiz strip of 5. Nos. 617/21		5·50	
618	25 c. Female		1·25	1·00
619	25 c. Female with nestling		1·25	1·00
620	25 c. Juvenile		1·25	1·00
621	25 c. Immature bird		1·25	1·00
617/21		*Set of 5*	5·50	4·50

Nos. 617/21 were printed together, *se-tenant*, in horizontal strips of 5 throughout the sheet, forming a composite design.

142 Lady Diana Spencer at Ascot, June 1981   **143** House of Assembly Plaque

(Des C. Abbott. Litho Format)

1982 (1 July). *21st Birthday of Princess of Wales. T* **142** *and similar vert designs. Multicoloured.* W w 14. *P* 13½ × 14 (16 c., $1) *or* 13½ (others).
622	16 c. Bahamas coat of arms		20	10
	a. Perf 13½		1·00	1·25
623	25 c. Type 142		45	15
624	40 c. Bride and Earl Spencer arriving at St. Paul's		60	20
	w. Wmk inverted		11·00	
625	$1 Formal portrait		1·00	1·25
622/5		*Set of 4*	2·00	1·40

1982 (18 Aug). *Wildlife (2nd series). Mammals. Horiz designs as T* **136**. *Multicoloured.* W w 14 (sideways). *P* 14.
626	10 c. Buffy Flower Bat		60	15
627	16 c. Bahaman Hutia		80	25
628	21 c. Common Racoon		95	35
629	$1 Common Dolphin		2·50	1·75
626/9		*Set of 4*	4·25	2·25
MS630	115 × 76 mm. Nos. 626/9		4·25	3·50

(Des and litho Walsall)

1982 (16 Oct). *28th Commonwealth Parliamentary Association Conference. T* **143** *and similar vert designs. Multicoloured.* W w 14. *P* 14 × 13½.
631	5 c. Type 143		15	10
632	25 c. Association coat of arms		50	35
633	40 c. Coat of arms		80	60
634	50 c. House of Assembly		1·10	75
631/4		*Set of 4*	2·25	1·60

144 Wesley Methodist Church, Baillou Hill Road

(Des Jennifer Toombs. Litho Format)

1982 (3 Nov). *Christmas. Churches. T* **144** *and similar horiz designs. Multicoloured.* W w 14 (sideways). *P* 14.
635	5 c. Type 144		10	10
636	12 c. Centreville Seventh Day Adventist Church		15	20
637	15 c. The Church of God of Prophecy, East Street		20	30
638	21 c. Bethel Baptist Church, Meeting Street		25	30
639	25 c. St. Francis Xavier Catholic Church, Highbury Park		25	50
640	$1 Holy Cross Anglican Church, Highbury Park		75	2·75
635/40		*Set of 6*	1·50	3·75

145 Prime Minister Lynden O. Pindling

(Des Walsall. Litho Questa)

1983 (14 Mar). *Commonwealth Day T* **145** *and similar horiz designs. Multicoloured.* W w 14 (sideways). *P* 14.
641	5 c. Type 145		10	10
642	25 c. Bahamian and Commonwealth flags		30	40
643	35 c. Map showing position of Bahamas		40	50
644	$1 Ocean liner		1·10	1·40
641/4		*Set of 4*	1·60	2·10

= 20c

(146)

1983 (5 Apr). *Nos. 562/5 surch as T* **146**.
645	20 c. on 15 c. Slave trading, Vendue House		50	35
646	31 c. on 21 c. Bootlegging, 1919–29		60	55
	w. Wmk inverted		2·50	
647	35 c. on 16 c. Wrecking in the 1800's		1·00	60
648	80 c. on 18 c. Blockade running (American Civil War)		1·25	1·40
	w. Wmk inverted		7·00	
645/8		*Set of 4*	3·00	2·50

147 Customs Officers and Liner   **148** Raising the National Flag

(Des Walsall. Litho Harrison)

1983 (31 May). *30th Anniv of Customs Co-operation Council. T* **147** *and similar vert design. Multicoloured.* W w 14. *P* 13½ × 13.
649	31 c. Type 147		1·50	45
650	$1 Customs officers and Lockheed Jet Star 1 airliner		3·00	2·75

(Des L. Curtis. Litho Questa)

1983 (6 July). *10th Anniv of Independence.* W w 14. *P* 14.
651	148 $1 multicoloured		1·00	1·40
MS652	105 × 65 mm. No. 651. P 12		1·00	1·40

(Des F. Solomon, adapted N. Arlott. Litho Harrison)

1983 (24 Aug). *Wildlife (3rd series). Butterflies. Horiz designs as T* **136**. W w 14 (sideways). *P* 14½ × 14.
653	5 c. multicoloured		70	20
654	25 c. multicoloured		1·40	40
655	31 c. black, bistre-yellow and bright rose-red		1·40	55
656	50 c. multicoloured		1·40	85
653/6		*Set of 4*	4·50	1·75
MS657	120 × 80 mm. Nos. 653/6		4·50	4·50
	a. Perf 14		4·25	6·00

Designs:—5 c. *Atalopedes carteri*; 25 c. *Ascia monuste*; 31 c. *Phoebis agarithe*; 50 c. *Dryas julia*.

No. MS657a was perforated by Questa, the remainder of the issue by Harrison.

149 "Loyalist Dreams"   **150** Consolidated PBY-5 Catalina

(Des A. Lowe; adapted C. Abbott. Litho Questa)

1983 (28 Sept). *Bicentenary of Arrival of American Loyalists in the Bahamas. T* **149** *and similar multicoloured designs.* W w 14 (sideways on 31 c., 35 c.). *P* 14.
658	5 c. Type 149		10	10
659	31 c. New Plymouth, Abaco (*horiz*)		45	50
660	35 c. New Plymouth Hotel (*horiz*)		50	70
661	50 c. "Island Hope"		65	90
658/61		*Set of 4*	1·50	2·00
MS662	111 × 76 mm. Nos. 658/61. Wmk sideways		1·50	2·50

(Des and litho Harrison)

1983 (13 Oct). *Air Bicentenary of Manned Flight. T* **150** *and similar horiz designs. Multicoloured.* W w 14 (sideways). *P* 14.
663	10 c. Type 150		45	15
664	25 c. Avro Type 688 Tudor IV		65	40
665	31 c. Avro Type 691 Lancastrian		75	45
666	35 c. Consolidated Commodore		85	50
663/6		*Set of 4*	2·40	1·40

For these stamps without the Manned Flight logo see Nos. 699/702 (W w 14 (sideways)) and 752/3 (W w 16 (sideways)).

151 "Christmas Bells" (Monica Pinder)   **152** 1861 4d. Stamp

(Des local children, adapted G. Vasarhelyi. Litho Walsall)

1983 (1 Nov). *Christmas. Children's Paintings. T* **151** *and similar multicoloured designs.* W w 14 (sideways on 31 c. and 50 c.). *P* 14.
667	5 c. Type 151		10	10
668	20 c. "Flamingo" (Cory Bullard)		25	30
669	25 c. "Yellow Hibiscus with Christmas Candle" (Monique Bailey)		35	40
670	31 c. "Santa goes a Sailing" (Sabrina Seiler) (*horiz*)		40	45
671	35 c. "Silhouette scene with Palm Trees" (James Blake)		45	50
672	50 c. "Silhouette scene with Pelicans" (Erik Russell) (*horiz*)		65	70
667/72		*Set of 6*	1·90	2·25

(Des D. Miller. Litho Format)

1984 (22 Feb). *125th Anniv of First Bahamas Postage Stamp. T* **152** *and similar vert design. Multicoloured.* W w 14. *P* 14.
673	5 c. Type 152		25	10
674	$1 1859 1d. stamp		1·75	1·50

PRICES OF SETS

Set prices are given for many issues, generally those containing three stamps or more. Definitive sets include one of each value or major colour change, but do not cover different perforations, die types or minor shades. Where a choice is possible the set prices are based on the cheapest versions of the stamps included in the listings.

165

153 *Trent I* (paddle steamer)   154 Running

(Des L. Curtis. Litho Questa)

1984 (25 Apr). *250th Anniv of "Lloyd's List" (newspaper). T* **153** *and similar vert designs. Multicoloured.* W w **14**. P 14½ × 14.
675	5 c. Type **153**			20	10
676	31 c. *Orinoco II* (mailship), 1886			70	60
677	35 c. Cruise liners in Nassau harbour			80	75
678	50 c. *Oropesa* (container ship)			1·25	1·60
675/8			Set of 4	2·75	2·75

(Des McCombie Skinner Studio. Litho Questa)

1984 (20 June). *Olympic Games, Los Angeles. T* **154** *and similar horiz designs.* W w **14** (*sideways*). P 14 × 14½.
679	5 c. green, black and gold			15	10
680	25 c. new blue, black and gold			50	50
681	31 c. brown-lake, black and gold			55	60
682	$1 sepia, black and gold			3·25	3·75
679/82			Set of 4	4·00	4·50
MS683	115 × 80 mm. Nos. 679/82			4·00	5·50

Designs:— 25 c. Shot-putting; 31 c. Boxing; $1 Basketball.

155 Bahamas and Caribbean Community Flags   156 Bahama Woodstar

(Des McCombie Skinner Studio. Litho Questa)

1984 (4 July). *5th Conference of Caribbean Community Heads of Government.* W w **14**. P 14.
684	**155** 50 c. multicoloured			90	95

(Des N. Arlott. Litho Questa)

1984 (15 Aug). *25th Anniv of National Trust. T* **156** *and similar vert designs. Multicoloured.* W w **14**. P 14.
685	31 c. Type **156**..			2·50	2·50
	a. Horiz strip of 5. Nos. 685/9			11·00	
686	31 c. Belted Kingfishers, Greater Flamingos and *Eleutherodactylus planirostris* (frog)			2·50	2·50
687	31 c. Black-necked Stilts, Greater Flamingos and *Phoebis sennae* (butterfly)			2·50	2·50
688	31 c. *Urbanus proteus* (butterfly) and *Chelonia mydas* (turtle)			2·50	2·50
689	31 c. Osprey and Greater Flamingos			2·50	2·50
685/9			Set of 5	11·00	11·00

Nos. 685/9 were printed together, *se-tenant*, in horizontal strips of 5 throughout the sheet, forming a composite design.

(Des N. Arlott. Litho Questa)

1984 (18 Sept). *Wildlife (4th series). Reptiles and Amphibians. Horiz designs as T* **136**. W w **14** (*sideways*). P 14.
690	5 c. Allen's Cay Iguana			30	15
691	25 c. Curly-tailed Lizard			85	60
692	35 c. Greenhouse Frog			1·00	85
693	50 c. Atlantic Green Turtle			1·60	1·75
690/3			Set of 4	3·25	3·00
MS694	112 × 82 mm. Nos. 690/3			3·25	6·00

157 "The Holy Virgin with Jesus and Johannes" (19th-century porcelain plaque after Titian)   158 Brownie Emblem and Queen or Pink Conch

(Des D. Slater. Litho J.W.)

1984 (7 Nov). *Christmas. Religious Paintings. T* **157** *and similar vert designs. Multicoloured.* W w **14**. P 13½.
695	5 c. Type **157**			15	10
696	31 c. "Madonna with Child in Tropical Landscape" (aquarelle, Anais Colin)			65	60
	w. Wmk inverted			1·00	
697	35 c. "The Holy Virgin with the Child" (miniature on ivory, Elena Caula)			70	65
695/7			Set of 3	1·40	1·25
MS698	116 × 76 mm. Nos. 695/7. P 14			1·40	3·00

1985 (2 Jan). *Air. As Nos. 663/6, but without Manned Flight logo.* W w **14** (*sideways**). P 14.
699	10 c. Type **150**			60	20
700	25 c. Avro Type 688 Tudor IV			75	40
701	31 c. Avro Type 691 Lancastrian			75	55
	w. Wmk Crown to right of CA			18·00	
702	35 c. Consolidated Commodore			1·25	60
699/702			Set of 4	3·00	1·60

*The normal sideways watermark shows Crown to left of CA, as seen from the back of the stamp.
See also Nos. 752/3 for stamps watermarked w **16** (sideways).

(Des Berta Dallen Sands. Litho Walsall)

1985 (22 Feb). *International Youth Year. 75th Anniv of Girl Guide Movement. T* **158** *and similar horiz designs. Multicoloured.* W w **14** (*sideways*). P 14.
703	5 c. Type **158**			40	30
704	25 c. Tents and coconut palm			1·00	80
705	31 c. Guide salute and Greater Flamingos			1·25	80
706	35 c. Ranger emblem and marlin			1·40	1·10
703/6			Set of 4	3·50	2·75
MS707	95 × 74 mm. Nos. 703/6			3·50	4·50

159 Killdeer   160 The Queen Mother at the Christening of Peter Phillips, 1977

(Des Josephine Martin. Litho Walsall)

1985 (24 Apr). *Birth Bicentenary of John J. Audubon (ornithologist). T* **159** *and similar multicoloured designs.* W w **14** (*sideways on 5 c., $1*). P 14.
708	5 c. Type **159**..			80	20
709	31 c. Mourning Dove (*vert*)			2·00	55
710	35 c. "Mourning Dove" (John J. Audubon) (*vert*)			2·00	60
711	$1 "Killdeer" (John J. Audubon)			3·00	2·00
708/11			Set of 4	7·00	3·00

(Des A. Theobald ($1.25), C. Abbott (others). Litho Questa)

1985 (7 June). *Life and Times of Queen Elizabeth the Queen Mother. T* **160** *and similar vert designs. Multicoloured.* W w **16**. P 14½ × 14.
712	5 c. Visiting Auckland, New Zealand, 1927			10	10
713	25 c. Type **160**			40	40
714	35 c. The Queen Mother attending church			55	55
	w. Wmk inverted			80	
715	50 c. With Prince Henry at his christening (from photo by Lord Snowdon)			75	75
712/15			Set of 4	1·60	1·60
MS716	91 × 73 mm. $1.25, In horse-drawn carriage, Sark. Wmk sideways			1·75	1·90

161 Ears of Wheat and Emblems   162 Queen Elizabeth II

(Des A. Theobald. Litho Questa)

1985 (26 Aug). *40th Anniv of United Nations and F.A.O. (Food and Agriculture Organization).* W w **16** (*sideways*). P 14.
717	**161** 25 c. multicoloured			85	60

(Des L. Curtis. Litho Walsall)

1985 (16 Oct). *Commonwealth Heads of Government Meeting, Nassau. T* **162** *and similar vert design. Multicoloured.* W w **16**. P 14½.
718	31 c. Type **162**			1·75	2·00
	w. Wmk inverted			16·00	
719	35 c. Bahamas Prime Minister's flag and Commonwealth emblem			2·00	2·50
	w. Wmk inverted			16·00	

1985 (6 Nov). *As Nos. 557/8, 560 and 566, but* W w **16**. P 14½.
720	1 c. Type **131**			1·50	3·50
721	3 c. Blackbeard the Pirate, 1718			2·00	4·00
723	10 c. Ceremonial mace			2·50	1·75
726	25 c. Pineapple cultivation			6·00	6·50
720/6			Set of 4	11·00	14·00

163 "Grandma's Christmas Bouquet" (Alton Roland Lowe)

(Des D. Miller. Litho J.W.)

1985 (12 Nov). *Christmas. Paintings by Alton Roland Lowe. T* **163** *and similar multicoloured designs.* W w **16** (*sideways on 5, 35 c.*). P 13 × 13½ (5, 35 c.) or 13½ × 13 (others).
736	5 c. Type **163**.			25	10
737	25 c. "Junkanoo Romeo and Juliet" (*vert*)			85	75
738	31 c. "Bunce Gal" (*vert*)			1·10	1·25
739	35 c. "Home for Christmas"			1·40	1·50
736/9			Set of 4	3·25	3·25
MS740	110 × 68 mm. Nos. 736/9. Wmk sideways. P 14			2·00	3·00

(Des A. Theobald. Litho Harrison)

1986 (21 Apr). *60th Birthday of Queen Elizabeth II. Vert designs as T* **110** *of Ascension. Multicoloured.* W w **16**. P 14½ × 14.
741	10 c. Princess Elizabeth aged one, 1927			15	20
742	25 c. The Coronation, 1953			30	40
	w. Wmk inverted				
743	35 c. Queen making speech at Commonwealth Banquet, Bahamas, 1985			40	55
744	40 c. In Djakova, Yugoslavia, 1972			45	60
	w. Wmk inverted			8·00	
745	$1 At Crown Agents Head Office, London 1983			1·10	1·75
741/5			Set of 5	2·25	3·25

164 1980 1 c. and 18 c. Definitive Stamps

(Des G. Drummond. Litho Walsall)

1986 (19 May). *"Ameripex '86" International Stamp Exhibition, Chicago. T* **164** *and similar designs.* W w **16** (*sideways on 5 to 50 c.*). P 14.
746	5 c. multicoloured			35	15
747	25 c. multicoloured			90	50
748	31 c. multicoloured			1·00	60
749	50 c. multicoloured			1·50	2·25
750	$1 black, emerald and pale blue			1·75	1·00
746/50			Set of 5	5·00	6·00
MS751	80 × 80 mm. No. 750			3·00	3·50

Designs: Horiz (showing Bahamas stamps)—25 c. 1969 50th Anniversary of Bahamas Airmail Service pair; 31 c. 1976 Bicentenary of American Revolution 16 c.; 50 c. 1981 Space Exploration miniature sheet. *Vert*—$1 Statue of Liberty.
Nos. 750/1 also commemorate the Centenary of the Statue of Liberty.

1986 (17 June). *Air. As Nos. 699/700, but* W w **16** (*sideways*). P 14.
752	10 c. Type **150**			1·50	30
753	25 c. Avro Type 688 Tudor IV			1·75	1·25

(Des D. Miller. Litho Walsall)

1986 (23 July). *Royal Wedding. Square designs as T* **112** *of Ascension. Multicoloured.* W w **16**. P 14½ × 14.
756	10 c. Prince Andrew and Miss Sarah Ferguson			20	20
757	$1 Prince Andrew			1·25	2·10

165 Rock Beauty (juvenile)   166 Christ Church Cathedral, Nassau, 1861

(Des Harrison Studio. Litho Questa)

1986 (5 Aug)–**90**. *Fishes. T* **165** *and similar horiz designs. Multicoloured.* W w **16**. P 14. A. *Without imprint date at foot.* B. *With imprint date.*
			A		B	
758	5 c. Type **165**		75	75	†	
759	10 c. Stoplight Parrotfish		80	90	80	1·50
760	15 c. Jackknife-fish		1·50	1·50	†	
761	20 c. Flamefish		1·25	1·25	†	
762	25 c. Peppermint Basslet ("Swissguard Basslet")		1·50	1·50	1·00	2·00
763	30 c. Spot-finned Butterflyfish		1·10	1·50	†	
764	35 c. Queen Triggerfish		1·10	1·50	†	
765	40 c. Four-eyed Butterflyfish		1·50	1·25	1·10	1·60
766	45 c. Royal Gramma ("Fairy Basslet")		1·50	1·25	1·60	2·50
767	50 c. Queen Angelfish		2·00	2·25	1·60	2·50
768	60 c. Blue Chromis		3·50	4·00	†	
769	$1 Spanish Hogfish		3·50	4·00	2·75	3·00
770	$2 Harlequin Bass		8·00	9·00	11·00	9·50

771	$3 Black-barred Soldierfish	6·00	7·00	5·00	10·00
772	$5 Cherub Angelfish				
	("Pygmy Angelfish")		6·50 8·00	6·50	12·00
773	$10 Red Hind		14·00 18·00		†
758A/73A			*Set of 16* 48·00 55·00		
759B/72B			*Set of 9*	28·00	40·00

Dates of issue: 5.8.86, Nos. 758A/72A; 2.1.87 No. 773A;
15.8.88 Nos. 765B, 769B/70B; 8.90, Nos. 759B, 762B, 766B/7B,
771B/2B.
Imprint dates: "1988", Nos. 765B, 769B/70B; "1990", Nos.
759B, 762B, 765B/7B, 769B, 771B/2B.
For those designs watermarked w 14 see Nos. 791/9.

(Des L. Curtis. Litho Walsall)

1986 (16 Sept). *125th Anniv of City of Nassau, Diocese and
Cathedral. T 166 and similar vert design. Multicoloured.
W w 16. P 14½×14.*

774	10 c. Type 166..		20	20
775	40 c. Christ Church Cathedral, 1986		65	80
MS776	75×100 mm. Nos. 774/5 ..		2·25	4·25

167 Man and Boy   168 Great Isaac Lighthouse
looking at Crib

(Des Jennifer Toombs. Litho Questa)

1986 (4 Nov). *Christmas. International Peace Year. T 167 and
similar horiz designs. Multicoloured. W w 16 (sideways). P 14.*

777	10 c. Type 167..		25	20
778	40 c. Mary and Joseph journeying to Bethlehem		75	75
779	45 c. Children praying and Star of Bethlehem		85	1·00
780	50 c. Children exchanging gifts		90	1·75
777/80		*Set of 4*	2·50	3·25
MS781	95×90 mm. Nos. 777/80..		6·50	8·50

(Des A. Lowe, adapted L. Curtis. Litho Walsall)

1987 (31 Mar). *Lighthouses. T 168 and similar horiz designs.
Multicoloured. W w 16 (sideways). P 14×14½.*

782	10 c. Type 168..		1·25	50
783	40 c. Bird Rock Lighthouse		3·00	1·50
784	45 c. Castle Island Lighthouse		3·00	1·50
785	$1 "Hole in the Wall" Lighthouse		4·50	7·50
782/5		*Set of 4*	10·50	10·00

169 Anne Bonney   170 Boeing 737

(Des D. and Jane Hartley. Litho Questa)

1987 (2 June). *Pirates and Privateers of the Caribbean. T 169
and similar vert designs. Multicoloured. W w 16. P 14½.*

786	10 c. Type 169..		1·25	60
787	40 c. Edward Teach ("Blackbeard")..		3·00	2·25
788	45 c. Captain Edward England		3·00	2·25
789	50 c. Captain Woodes Rogers		3·25	3·25
786/9		*Set of 4*	9·50	7·50
MS790	75×95 mm. $1.25, Map of Bahamas and colonial coat of arms		4·00	3·00

1987 (25 June). *As Nos. 758/60 and 765/70, but W w 14. With
imprint date. P 14.*

791	5 c. Type 165		1·00	1·50
792	10 c. Stoplight Parrotfish		1·00	75
793	15 c. Jackknife-fish		1·75	2·00
794	40 c. Four-eyed Butterflyfish		1·75	2·00
795	45 c. Royal Gramma		2·00	2·00
796	50 c. Queen Angelfish		2·00	2·25
797	60 c. Blue Chromis		2·00	3·50
798	$1 Spanish Hogfish		2·25	3·75
799	$2 Harlequin Bass		2·75	6·50
791/9		*Set of 9*	15·00	22·00

Imprint dates: "1987", Nos. 791/9; "1988", No. 792; "1989", No.
791.

(Des A. Theobald. Litho Questa)

1987 (7 July). *Air. Aircraft. T 170 and similar horiz designs.
Multicoloured. W w 16. P 14.*

800	15 c. Type 170		1·00	55
801	40 c. Boeing 757-200		1·60	1·25
802	45 c. Airbus Industrie A300B4-200		1·60	1·25
803	50 c. Boeing 747-200		1·90	1·75
800/3		*Set of 4*	5·50	4·25

COVER PRICES

Cover factors are quoted at the beginning of each
country for most issues to 1945. An explanation of
the system can be found on page x. The factors
quoted do not, however, apply to philatelic covers.

---

171 *Norway* (liner)   172 *Cattleyopsis lindenii*
and Catamaran

(Des A. Theobald. Litho Questa)

1987 (26 Aug). *Tourist Transport. T 171 and similar vert
designs. Multicoloured. W w 16. P 14.*

804	40 c. Type 171..		1·25	1·00
	a. Horiz strip of 5. Nos. 804/8		5·50	
805	40 c. Liners and speedboat		1·25	1·00
806	40 c. Game fishing boat and cruising yacht ..		1·25	1·00
807	40 c. Game fishing boat and racing yachts ..		1·25	1·00
808	40 c. Fishing boat and schooner		1·25	1·00
809	40 c. Hawker Siddeley H.S.748 airliner		1·25	1·00
	a. Horiz strip of 5. Nos. 809/13		5·50	
810	40 c. Boeing 737 and Boeing 727-200 airliners ..		1·25	1·00
811	40 c. Beech 200 Super King Air aircraft and radio beacon		1·25	1·00
812	40 c. Aircraft and Nassau control tower		1·25	1·00
813	40 c. Helicopter and parked aircraft		1·25	1·00
804/13		*Set of 10*	11·00	9·00

Nos. 804/8 and 809/13 were each printed together, *se-tenant*,
in horizontal strips of 5 throughout the sheets, each strip
forming a composite design.

(Des A. Lowe; adapted L. Curtis. Litho Questa)

1987 (20 Oct). *Christmas. Orchids. T 172 and similar horiz
designs. Multicoloured. W w 16 (sideways). P 14×14½.*

814	10 c. Type 172..		90	20
815	40 c. *Encyclia lucayana*		1·90	80
816	45 c. *Encyclia hodgeana*		1·90	90
817	50 c. *Encyclia lleidae* ..		1·90	1·75
814/17		*Set of 4*	6·00	3·25
MS818	120×92 mm. Nos. 814/17		6·00	3·75

173 King Ferdinand and   174 Whistling Ducks
Queen Isabella of Spain   in Flight

(Des L. Curtis. Litho Format)

1988 (24 Feb). *500th Anniv of Discovery of America by
Columbus (1992) (1st issue). T 173 and similar vert designs.
Multicoloured. W w 14. P 14×14½.*

819	10 c. Type 173..		50	25
820	40 c. Columbus before Talavera Committee..		1·40	1·40
821	45 c. Lucayan village..		1·50	1·40
822	50 c. Lucayan potters..		1·50	1·75
819/22		*Set of 4*	4·50	4·25
MS823	65×50 mm. $1.50, Map of Antilles, c. 1500. Wmk sideways ..		5·50	3·75

See also Nos. 844/8, 870/4, 908/12, 933/7 and MS946.

(Des W. Oliver. Litho Walsall)

1988 (29 Apr). *Black-billed Whistling Duck. T 174 and similar
horiz designs. Multicoloured. W w 14 (sideways). P 14×14½.*

824	5 c. Type 174		1·60	65
825	10 c. Whistling Duck in reeds		1·75	65
826	20 c. Pair with brood		3·00	1·25
827	45 c. Pair wading		4·75	2·00
824/7		*Set of 4*	10·00	4·00

175 Grantstown Cabin,   176 Olympic Flame, High
c. 1820   Jumping, Hammer throwing,
   Basketball and Gymnastics

(Des N. Shewring. Litho B.D.T.)

1988 (9 Aug). *150th Anniv of Abolition of Slavery. T 175 and
similar horiz design. Multicoloured. W w 14 (sideways).
P 13½.*

828	10 c. Type 175		40	15
829	40 c. Basket-making, Grantstown		1·10	70

(Des D. Miller. Litho Walsall)

1988 (30 Aug). *Olympic Games, Seoul. T 176 and similar horiz
designs taken from painting by James Martin. Multicoloured.
W w 16 (sideways). P 14.*

830	10 c. Type 176		30	15
831	40 c. Athletics, archery, swimming, long jumping, weightlifting and boxing		60	60
832	45 c. Javelin throwing, gymnastics, hurdling and shot put		60	60
833	$1 Athletics, hurdling, gymnastics and cycling		2·00	1·60
830/3		*Set of 4*	3·25	2·75
MS834	113×85 mm. Nos. 830/3. W w 14 (sideways)		2·50	2·75

**(Des O. Bell and D. Miller (40 c.), E. Nisbet and D. Miller ($1),
D. Miller (others). Litho Questa)**

1988 (4 Oct). *300th Anniv of Lloyd's of London. Multicoloured
designs as T 123 of Ascension. W w 14 (sideways on 40, 45 c.).
P 14.*

835	10 c. Lloyd's List of 1740		30	15
836	40 c. Freeport Harbour (*horiz*)		1·00	60
837	45 c. Space shuttle over Bahamas (*horiz*)		1·10	60
838	$1 *Yarmouth Castle* (freighter) on fire		2·00	1·90
835/8		*Set of 4*	4·00	3·00

177 "Oh Little Town   178 Cuban Emerald
of Bethlehem"

(Des Josephine Martin. Litho Questa)

1988 (21 Nov). *Christmas. Carols. T 177 and similar vert
designs. Multicoloured. W w 16. P 14½×14.*

839	10 c. Type 177		25	15
840	40 c. "Little Donkey"		80	65
841	45 c. "Silent Night"		85	80
842	50 c. "Hark the Herald Angels Sing"		90	1·25
839/42		*Set of 4*	2·50	2·50
MS843	88×108 mm. Nos. 839/42. W w 14		2·25	2·50

(Des A. Lowe (50 c.), L. Curtis (others). Litho Questa)

1989 (25 Jan). *500th Anniv of Discovery of America by
Columbus (1992) (2nd issue). Vert designs as T 173.
Multicoloured. W w 16. P 14½×14.*

844	10 c. Columbus drawing chart		80	30
845	40 c. Types of caravel		2·25	1·10
846	45 c. Early navigational instruments		2·25	1·10
847	50 c. Arawak artefacts		2·25	2·25
844/7		*Set of 4*	6·75	4·25
MS848	64×64 mm. $1.50, Caravel under construction (from 15th-cent *Nuremburg Chronicles*)		2·25	1·90

(Des N. Shewring. Litho Questa)

1989 (29 Mar). *Hummingbirds. T 178 and similar vert
designs. Multicoloured. W w 16. P 14½ × 14.*

849	10 c. Type 178		1·25	50
850	40 c. Ruby-throated Hummingbird		2·50	1·75
851	45 c. Bahama Woodstar		2·50	1·75
852	50 c. Rufous Hummingbird		2·50	2·50
849/52		*Set of 4*	8·00	6·00

179 Teaching Water   180 Church of the
Safety   Nativity, Bethlehem

(Des S. Noon. Litho Questa)

1989 (31 May). *125th Anniv of International Red Cross. T 179
and similar horiz design. Multicoloured. W w 16 (sideways).
P 14×14½.*

853	10 c. Type 179		50	25
854	$1 Henri Dunant (founder) and Battle of Solferino		2·75	2·50

(Des A. Theobald ($2), D. Miller (others). Litho Questa)

1989 (20 July). *20th Anniv of First Manned Landing on Moon.
Multicoloured designs as T 126 of Ascension. W w 16
(sideways on 40, 45 c.). P 14×13½ (10 c., $1) or 14 (others).*

855	10 c. "Apollo 8" Communications Station, Grand Bahama		25	20
856	40 c. Crew of "Apollo 8" (30×30 mm)		60	55
857	45 c. "Apollo 8" emblem (30×30 mm)		65	60
858	$1 The Earth seen from "Apollo 8"		1·25	2·25
855/8		*Set of 4*	2·50	3·25
MS859	100×83 mm. $2 "Apollo 11" astronauts in training, Manned Spacecraft Centre, Houston. P 14×13½		2·50	3·50

(Des E. Weishoff. Litho Questa)

1989 (16 Oct). *Christmas. Churches of the Holy Land. T 180 and similar vert designs. Multicoloured. W w 14. P 14½×14.*
860	10 c. Type **180**		30	20
861	40 c. Basilica of the Annunciation, Nazareth		85	55
862	45 c. Tabgha Church, Galilee		90	60
863	$1 Church of the Holy Sepulchre, Jerusalem		1·75	2·50
860/3		*Set of 4*	3·50	3·50
MS864	92×109 mm. Nos. 860/3. Wmk sideways		2·75	5·00

181 1974 U.P.U. Centenary
13 c. Stamp and Globe

(Des J. Sayer. Litho Questa)

1989 (17 Nov). *"World Stamp Expo '89" International Stamp Exhibition, Washington. T 181 and similar multicoloured designs. W w 16 (sideways). P 14.*
865	10 c. Type **181**		50	30
866	40 c. 1970 New U.P.U. Headquarters Building 3 c. and building		1·25	75
867	45 c. 1986 "Ameripex '86" $1 and Capitol, Washington		1·25	80
868	$1 1949 75th anniversary of U.P.U. 2½d. and Boeing 737 airliner		3·75	4·75
865/8		*Set of 4*	6·00	6·00
MS869	107×80 mm. $2 Map showing route of Columbus, 1492 (30×38 mm). P 14½		7·00	9·00

(Des A. Lowe (50 c.), L. Curtis (others). Litho Questa)

1990 (24 Jan). *500th Anniversary of Discovery of America by Columbus (1992) (3rd issue). Vert designs as T 173. Multicoloured. W w 14. P 14½×14.*
870	10 c. Launching caravel		90	40
871	40 c. Provisioning ship		2·00	1·75
872	45 c. Shortening sail		2·00	1·25
873	50 c. Lucayan fishermen		2·00	2·50
870/3		*Set of 4*	6·25	5·75
MS874	70×61 mm. $1.50, Departure of Columbus, 1492		5·50	6·50

182 Bahamas Flag, O.A.S.
Headquarters and Centenary
Logo

(Des O. Bell. Litho Questa)

1990 (14 Mar). *Centenary of Organization of American States. W w 16 (sideways). P 14.*
875	**182** 40 c. multicoloured		1·60	1·50

183 Supermarine Spitfire Mk I
Bahamas I

(Des A. Theobald. Litho Questa)

1990 (3 May). *"Stamp World London 90" International Stamp Exhibition, London. Presentation Fighter Aircraft. Sheet 107×78 mm. containing T 183 and similar horiz design. Multicoloured. W w 16 (sideways). P 14.*
MS876	$1 Type **183**; $1 Hawker Hurricane Mk IIc *Bahamas V*		5·50	5·50

184 Teacher with Boy

185 Cuban Amazon preening

(Des G. Vasarhelyi. Litho Questa)

1990 (27 June). *International Literacy Year. T 184 and similar horiz designs. Multicoloured. W w 16 (sideways). P 14.*
877	10 c. Type **184**		60	35
878	40 c. Three boys in class		1·50	1·75
879	50 c. Teacher and children with books		1·50	2·00
877/9		*Set of 3*	3·25	3·25

(Des D. Miller. Litho Questa)

1990 (4 Aug). *90th Birthday of Queen Elizabeth the Queen Mother. Vert designs as T 134 (40 c.) or 135 ($1.50) of Ascension. W w 16. P 14×15 (40 c.) or 14½ ($1.50).*
880	40 c. multicoloured		75	50
881	$1.50, brownish black and ochre		2·00	2·75

Designs:—40 c. "Queen Elizabeth, 1938" (Sir Gerald Kelly); $1.50, Queen Elizabeth at garden party, France, 1938.

(Des N. Arlott. Litho Questa)

1990 (26 Sept). *Cuban Amazon (Bahamian Parrot). T 185 and similar vert designs. Multicoloured. W w 14. P 14.*
882	10 c. Type **185**		85	40
883	40 c. Pair in flight		1·75	80
884	45 c. Cuban Amazon's head		1·75	90
885	50 c. Perched on branch		1·90	1·75
882/5		*Set of 4*	5·50	3·50
MS886	73×63 mm. $1.50, Feeding on berries		4·75	6·00

186 The Annunciation

187 Green Heron

(Des Jennifer Toombs. Litho B.D.T.)

1990 (5 Nov). *Christmas. T 186 and similar vert designs. Multicoloured. W w 14. P 14×13½.*
887	10 c. Type **186**		30	15
888	40 c. The Nativity		75	55
889	45 c. Angel appearing to Shepherds		80	65
890	$1 The three Kings		2·00	3·00
887/90		*Set of 4*	3·50	4·00
MS891	94×110 mm. Nos. 887/90		4·50	5·50

(Des N. Arlott. Litho Questa)

1991 (4 Feb–1 July). *Birds. T 187 and similar vert designs. Multicoloured. W w 16 (sideways). "1991" imprint date. P 14.*
892	5 c. Type **187**		55	50
893	10 c. Turkey Vulture		70	60
894	15 c. Osprey		1·60	70
895	20 c. Clapper Rail		75	70
896	25 c. Royal Tern		1·10	75
897	30 c. Key West Quail Dove		1·25	75
898	40 c. Smooth-billed Ani		1·50	55
899	45 c. Burrowing Owl		2·00	80
900	50 c. Hairy Woodpecker		1·75	70
901	55 c. Mangrove Cuckoo		1·75	75
902	60 c. Bahama Mockingbird		1·75	1·40
903	70 c. Red-winged Blackbird		1·75	1·50
904	$1 Thick-billed Vireo		2·25	1·50
905	$2 Bahama Yellowthroat		4·50	4·50
906	$5 Stripe-headed Tanager		10·00	11·00
907	$10 Greater Antillean Bullfinch (1 July)		13·00	15·00
892/907		*Set of 16*	42·00	38·00

For these designs watermarked w 14 (sideways) see Nos. 975/88.

(Des A. Lowe (55 c.), L. Curtis (others). Litho Questa)

1991 (9 Apr). *500th Anniv of Discovery of America by Columbus (1992) (4th issue). Vert designs as T 173. Multicoloured. W w 16. P 14½ × 14.*
908	15 c. Columbus navigating by stars		1·00	50
909	40 c. Fleet in mid-Atlantic		1·75	1·50
910	55 c. Lucayan family worshipping at night		1·75	1·75
911	60 c. Map of First Voyage		2·25	3·00
908/11		*Set of 4*	6·00	6·00
MS912	56 × 61 mm. $1.50, Pinta's look-out sighting land		5·25	6·50

(Des D. Miller. Litho Questa)

1991 (17 June). *65th Birthday of Queen Elizabeth II and 70th Birthday of Prince Philip. Vert designs as T 139 of Ascension. Multicoloured. W w 16 (sideways). P 14½ × 14.*
913	15 c. Prince Philip		90	1·25
	a. Horiz pair. Nos. 913/14 separated by label		2·50	3·00
914	$1 Queen Elizabeth II		1·60	1·75

Nos. 913/14 were printed in the same sheet format as Nos. 539/40 of Ascension.

188 Radar Plot of Hurricane Hugo

189 The Annunciation

(Des A. Theobald. Litho B.D.T)

1991 (28 Aug). *International Decade for Natural Disaster Reduction. T 188 and similar horiz designs. Multicoloured. W w 16 (sideways). P 14.*
915	15 c. Type **188**		75	30
916	40 c. Diagram of hurricane		1·25	95
917	55 c. Flooding caused by Hurricane David, 1979		1·50	1·60
918	60 c. U.S. Dept of Commerce weather reconnaissance Lockheed WP-3D Orion		2·25	2·75
915/18		*Set of 4*	5·25	5·00

(Des Jennifer Toombs. Litho B.D.T.)

1991 (28 Oct). *Christmas. T 189 and similar vert designs. Multicoloured. W w 14. P 14.*
919	15 c. Type **189**		40	25
920	55 c. Mary and Joseph travelling to Bethlehem		1·00	1·00
921	60 c. Angel appearing to the shepherds		1·10	1·25
922	$1 Adoration of the Kings		2·00	3·00
919/22		*Set of 4*	4·00	5·00
MS923	92 × 108 mm. Nos. 919/22		5·50	6·50

190 First Progressive Liberal
Party Cabinet

(Des G. Vasarhelyi. Litho B.D.T.)

1992 (10 Jan). *25th Anniv of Majority Rule. T 190 and similar multicoloured designs. W w 14 (sideways on 15 c. and 40 c.). P 14.*
924	15 c. Type **190**		60	30
925	40 c. Signing of Independence Constitution		1·25	85
926	55 c. Prince of Wales handing over Constitutional Instrument (vert)		1·25	1·25
927	60 c. First Bahamian Governor-General, Sir Milo Butler (vert)		1·75	2·50
924/7		*Set of 4*	4·25	4·50

(Des D. Miller. Litho Questa ($1), B.D.T. (others))

1992 (6 Feb). *40th Anniv of Queen Elizabeth II's Accession. Horiz designs as T 143 of Ascension. Multicoloured. W w 14 (sideways). P 14.*
928	15 c. Queen Elizabeth with bouquet		40	20
929	40 c. Queen Elizabeth with flags		80	70
930	55 c. Queen Elizabeth at display		1·00	90
931	60 c. Three portraits of Queen Elizabeth		1·10	1·25
932	$1 Queen Elizabeth II		1·50	2·00
928/32		*Set of 5*	4·25	4·50

(Des A. Lowe and L. Curtis. Litho Questa)

1992 (17 Mar). *500th Anniv of Discovery of America by Columbus (5th issue). Vert designs as T 173. Multicoloured. W w 16. P 14½×14.*
933	15 c. Lucayans sighting fleet		75	50
934	40 c. Santa Maria and dolphins		1·40	1·25
935	55 c. Lucayan canoes approaching ships		1·50	1·50
936	60 c. Columbus giving thanks for landfall		2·00	2·50
933/6		*Set of 4*	5·00	5·25
MS937	61×57 mm. $1.50, Children at Columbus Monument		3·50	4·50

191 Templeton, Galbraith and Hansberger Ltd Building

192 Pole Vaulting

(Des O. Bell. Litho Questa)

1992 (22 Apr). *20th Anniv of Templeton Prize for Religion. W w 16 (sideways). P 14½.*
938	**191** 55 c. multicoloured		1·25	1·25

(Des O. Bell. Litho Questa)

1992 (2 June). *Olympic Games, Barcelona. T 192 and similar vert designs. Multicoloured. W w 14. P 14½.*
939	15 c. Type **192**		40	25
940	40 c. Javelin		80	85
941	55 c. Hurdling		1·00	1·10
942	60 c. Basketball		3·00	3·00
939/42		*Set of 4*	4·75	4·75
MS943	70×50 mm. $2 Sailing		5·00	6·00

COVER PRICES

Cover factors are quoted at the beginning of each country for most issues to 1945. An explanation of the system can be found on page x. The factors quoted do not, however, apply to philatelic covers.

193 Arid Landscape and Starving Child   **194** Mary visiting Elizabeth

(Des Jennifer Toombs. Litho Enschedé)

1992 (11 Aug). *International Conference on Nutrition. T* **193** *and similar horiz design. Multicoloured. W w* **14** (*sideways*). *P* 14½×13½.
944	15 c. Type 193	50	35
945	55 c. Seedling, cornfield and child	1·40	1·50

(Des L. Curtis. Litho B.D.T.)

1992 (12 Oct). *500th Anniv of Discovery of America by Columbus* (*6th issue*). *Sheet,* 65×65 *mm, containing vert design as T* **173**. *Multicoloured. W w* **16**. *P* 13½.
MS946 $2 Columbus landing in Bahamas   4·75   5·50

(Des Jennifer Toombs. Litho B.D.T.)

1992 (2 Nov). *Christmas. T* **194** *and similar vert designs. Multicoloured. W w* **14**. *P* 14×13½.
947	15 c. Type 194	40	20
948	55 c. The Nativity	1·10	1·00
949	60 c. Angel and Shepherds	1·25	1·50
950	70 c. Wise Men and star	1·40	2·00
947/50	*Set of* 4	3·75	4·25
MS951	95×110 mm. Nos. 947/50	5·00	6·00

(195)   **196** Flags of Bahamas and U.S.A. with Agricultural Worker

1992 (16 Nov). *Hurricane Relief. No.* MS876 *showing each stamp surch with T* **195**.
MS952 $1 + $1 Type **183**; $1 + $1 Hawker Hurricane MkIIc *Bahamas V*   7·50   10·00

(Des Lorraine Cox, adapted D. Miller. Litho Questa)

1993 (16 Mar). *50th Anniv of The Contract* (*U.S.A.–Bahamas farm labour programme*). *T* **196** *and similar horiz designs, each including national flags. Multicoloured. W w* **16** (*sideways*). *P* 14×14½.
953	15 c. Type 196	55	45
954	55 c. Onions	1·60	1·25
955	60 c. Citrus fruit	1·60	1·75
956	70 c. Apples	1·75	2·00
953/6	*Set of* 4	5·00	5·00

(Des A. Theobald. Litho Questa)

1993 (1 Apr). *75th Anniv of Royal Air Force. Horiz designs as T* **149** *of Ascension. Multicoloured. W w* **14** (*sideways*). *P* 14.
957	15 c. Westland Wapiti IIA	55	40
958	40 c. Gloster Gladiator I	1·25	80
959	55 c. De Havilland D.H.100 Vampire F.3	1·40	1·25
960	70 c. English Electric Lightning F.3	1·50	2·25
957/60	*Set of* 4	4·25	4·25
MS961	110×77 mm. 60 c. Avro Shackleton M.R.2; 60 c. Fairey Battle; 60 c. Douglas Boston III; 60 c. De Havilland D.H.9a	5·00	6·00

197 1978 Coronation Anniversary Stamps   **198** *Lignum vitae* (national tree)

(Des D. Miller. Litho Enschedé)

1993 (2 June). *40th Anniv of Coronation. T* **197** *and similar horiz designs. Multicoloured. W w* **14** (*sideways*). *P* 13½.
962	15 c. Type 197	50	40
963	55 c. Two examples of 1953 Coronation stamp	1·50	1·50
964	60 c. 1977 Silver Jubilee 8 c. and 16 c. stamps	1·60	1·75
965	70 c. 1977 Silver Jubilee 21 c. and 40 c. stamps	1·90	2·25
962/5	*Set of* 4	5·00	5·50

(Des N. Shewring. Litho B.D.T.)

1993 (8 July). *20th Anniv of Independence. T* **198** *and similar vert designs. Multicoloured. W w* **14**. *P* 14.
966	15 c. Type 198	20	20
967	55 c. Yellow Elder (national flower)	90	90
968	60 c. Blue Marlin (national fish)	1·00	1·25
969	70 c. Greater Flamingo (national bird)	1·40	1·90
966/9	*Set of* 4	3·25	3·75

199 Cordia   **200** The Annunciation

(Des D. Miller and A. Lowe. Litho B.D.T.)

1993 (8 Sept). *Environment Protection* (*1st issue*). *Wildflowers. T* **199** *and similar vert designs. Multicoloured. W w* **14**. *P* 13½.
970	15 c. Type 199	35	30
971	55 c. Seaside Morning Glory	1·25	1·00
972	60 c. Poinciana	1·40	1·50
973	70 c. Spider Lily	1·50	2·00
970/3	*Set of* 4	4·00	4·25

See also Nos. 1017/22, 1035/9 and 1084/8.

1993 (23 Sept)–**95**. *As Nos.* 893/4, 896/8, 901 *and* 906, *but W w* **14** (*sideways*). *With imprint date. P* 14.
975	10 c. Turkey Vulture	60	60
976	15 c. Osprey (4.95)	60	60
978	25 c. Royal Tern	60	60
979	30 c. Key West Quail Dove	1·00	80
980	40 c. Smooth-billed Ani (31.12.93)	1·25	1·50
983	55 c. Mangrove Cuckoo	1·25	80
988	$5 Stripe-headed Tanager	6·50	8·50
975/88	*Set of* 7	10·50	12·00

Imprint dates: "1993", Nos. 975, 978/80, 983, 988; "1995", Nos. 976, 978, 980, 983, 988.

(Des Jennifer Toombs. Litho B.D.T.)

1993 (1 Nov). *Christmas. T* **200** *and similar vert designs. Multicoloured. W w* **14**. *P* 13½.
990	15 c. Type 200	40	25
991	55 c. Angel and shepherds	1·40	1·40
992	60 c. Holy family	1·40	1·60
993	70 c. Three Kings	1·60	2·00
990/3	*Set of* 4	4·25	4·75
MS994	86×106 mm. $1 Virgin Mary with Child	3·50	4·25

201 Family   **202** Flags of Bahamas and Great Britain

(Des Jennifer Toombs. Litho B.D.T.)

1994 (18 Feb). *"Hong Kong '94" International Stamp Exhibition. International Year of the Family. T* **201** *and similar horiz designs. Multicoloured. W w* **16** (*sideways*). *P* 13½.
995	15 c. Type 201	40	25
996	55 c. Children doing homework	1·00	1·00
997	60 c. Grandfather and grandson fishing	1·25	1·25
998	70 c. Grandmother teaching grandchildren the Lord's Prayer	1·75	2·00
995/8	*Set of* 4	4·00	4·00

(Des D. Miller. Litho B.D.T.)

1994 (7 Mar). *Royal Visit. T* **202** *and similar vert designs. Multicoloured. W w* **14**. *P* 13½.
999	15 c. Type 202	35	25
1000	55 c. Royal Yacht *Britannia*	1·40	1·00
1001	60 c. Queen Elizabeth II	1·40	1·40
1002	70 c. Queen Elizabeth and Prince Philip	1·50	2·00
999/1002	*Set of* 4	4·25	4·25

203 Yachts   **204** Logo and Bahamas 1968 Olympic Games Stamps

(Des D. Miller and A. Lowe. Litho B.D.T.)

1994 (27 Apr). *40th Anniv of National Family Island Regatta. T* **203** *and similar multicoloured designs. W w* **14** (*sideways*). *P* 13½.
1003	15 c. Type 203	60	30
1004	55 c. Dinghy racing	1·40	1·10
1005	60 c. Working boats	1·50	1·75
1006	70 c. Sailing sloop	2·00	2·50
1003/6	*Set of* 4	5·00	5·00
MS1007	76×54 mm. $2 Launching sloop (*vert*). Wmk upright	4·25	5·00

(Des D. Miller. Litho Enschedé)

1994 (31 May). *Centenary of International Olympic Committee. T* **204** *and similar multicoloured designs. W w* **14** (*sideways on* 55 c. *and* 70 c.). *P* 13½.
1008	15 c. Type 204	70	30
1009	55 c. 1976 Olympic Games stamps (*vert*)	1·40	1·10
1010	60 c. 1984 Olympic Games stamps	1·50	1·75
1011	70 c. 1992 Olympic Games stamps (*vert*)	2·00	2·50
1008/11	*Set of* 4	5·00	5·00

205 Star of Order   **206** *Calpodes ethlius* and Canna

(Des D. Miller. Litho Enschedé)

1994 (5 July). *First Recipients of Order of the Caribbean Community. Sheet* 90×69 *mm. W w* **14**. *P* 13×14.
MS1012 **205** $2 multicoloured   3·75   4·50

(Des R. Watton. Litho Walsall)

1994 (16 Aug). *Butterflies and Flowers. T* **206** *and similar vert designs. Multicoloured. W w* **14**. *P* 14.
1013	15 c. Type 206	90	45
1014	55 c. *Phoebis sennae* and Cassia	1·75	1·25
1015	60 c. *Anartia jatrophae* and Passion Flower	1·90	2·00
1016	70 c. *Battus devilliersi* and Calico Flower	2·00	2·50
1013/16	*Set of* 4	6·00	5·50

207 Spot-finned Hogfish and Spanish Hogfish   **208** Angel

(Des A. Robinson. Litho Enschedé)

1994 (13 Sept). *Environment Protection* (*2nd issue*). *Marine Life. T* **207** *and similar vert designs. Multicoloured. W w* **14**. *P* 13×14½.
1017	40 c. Type 207	90	1·10
	a. Horiz strip of 5. Nos. 1017/21	4·00	
1018	40 c. Tomate and Long-spined Squirrelfish	90	1·10
1019	40 c. French Angelfish	90	1·10
1020	40 c. Queen Angelfish	90	1·10
1021	40 c. Rock Beauty	90	1·10
1017/21	*Set of* 5	4·00	5·00
MS1022	57×55 mm. $2 Rock Beauty, Queen Angelfish and windsurfer	3·50	4·50

Nos. 1017/21 were printed together, *se-tenant*, in horizontal strips of 5 throughout the sheet with the backgrounds forming a composite design.

(Des Jennifer Toombs. Litho B.D.T.)

1994 (31 Oct). *Christmas. T* **208** *and similar multicoloured designs. W w* **16** (*sideways*). *P* 14.
1023	15 c. Type 208	30	30
1024	55 c. Holy Family	90	1·10
1025	60 c. Shepherds	1·10	1·40
1026	70 c. Wise Men	1·25	1·60
1023/6	*Set of* 4	3·25	4·00
MS1027	73×85 mm. $2 Jesus in manger. Wmk upright	3·25	4·00

STANLEY GIBBONS STAMP COLLECTING SERIES

Introductory booklets on *How to Start, How to Identify Stamps* and *Collecting by Theme.* A series of well illustrated guides at a low price.
Write for details.

209 Lion and Emblem
210 Kirtland's Warbler on Nest

(Des D. Miller. Litho Enschedé)

1995 (8 Feb). *20th Anniv of the College of the Bahamas. T 209 and similar vert design. Multicoloured. W w 14. P 14×13½.*
1028 15 c. Type 209 .. .. .. 30 30
1029 70 c. Queen Elizabeth II and College building .. .. 1·25 1·60

(Des R. Watton. Litho Cartor (Nos. 1030/3) or Questa (No. MS1034))

1995 (8 May). *50th Anniv of End of Second World War. Multicoloured designs as T 161 of Ascension. W w 14 (sideways). P 13½.*
1030 15 c. Bahamian infantry drilling .. 40 30
1031 55 c. Consolidated PBY-5A Catalina flying boat .. .. .. 1·40 1·10
1032 60 c. Bahamian women in naval operations room .. .. 1·50 1·50
1033 70 c. Consolidated B-24 Liberator bomber 1·75 2·00
1030/3 .. .. .. *Set of 4* 4·50 4·50
MS1034 75×85 mm. $2 Reverse of 1939–45 War Medal (*vert*). Wmk upright. P 14 .. 3·00 4·00

(Des N. Arlott. Litho Cartor)

1995 (7 June). *Environment Protection (3rd issue). Endangered Species. Kirtland's Warbler. T 210 and similar vert designs. Multicoloured. W w 14. P 13½.*
1035 15 c. Type 210 .. .. .. 55 60
w. Wmk inverted 55 60
wa. Strip of 4. Nos. 1035/8 .. 2·00
1036 15 c. Singing on branch 55 60
w. Wmk inverted 55 60
1037 25 c. Feeding chicks 55 60
w. Wmk inverted 55 60
1038 25 c. Catching insects 55 60
w. Wmk inverted 55 60
1035/8 .. .. .. *Set of 4* 2·00 2·25
MS1039 73×67 mm. $2 On branch. Wmk sideways. P 13 .. .. .. 5·00 5·50
Nos. 1035/8 were issued in sheets of 50 of each design and Nos. 1035w/8w in sheets of 16 (4×4) containing horizontal and vertical *se-tenant* strips.
No. MS1039 does not show the W.W.F. Panda emblem.

211 Eleuthera Cliffs

(Des D. Miller. Litho Questa)

1995 (18 July). *Tourism. T 211 and similar horiz designs. Multicoloured. W w 16 (sideways). P 14½.*
1040 15 c. Type 211 .. .. .. 45 30
1041 55 c. Clarence Town, Long Island .. 1·10 1·10
1042 60 c. Albert Lowe Museum .. .. 1·25 1·40
1043 70 c. Yachts .. .. .. 1·50 1·75
1040/3 .. .. .. *Set of 4* 3·75 4·00

212 Pigs and Chick

(Des Jennifer Toombs. Litho Cartor)

1995 (5 Sept). *50th Anniv of Food and Agriculture Organization. T 212 and similar horiz designs. Multicoloured. W w 14 (sideways). P 13½×13.*
1044 15 c. Type 212 .. .. .. 30 30
1045 55 c. Seedling and hand holding seed .. 95 95
1046 60 c. Family with fruit and vegetables .. 1·00 1·25
1047 70 c. Fishes and crustaceans .. .. 1·25 1·50
1044/7 .. .. .. *Set of 4* 3·25 3·50

213 Sikorsky S-55 Helicopter, Sinai, 1957

(Des A. Theobald. Litho B.D.T.)

1995 (24 Oct). *50th Anniv of United Nations. T 213 and similar horiz designs. Multicoloured. W w 16 (sideways). P 14.*
1048 15 c. Type 213 .. .. .. 50 40
1049 55 c. Ferret armoured car, Sinai, 1957 .. 1·25 1·00
1050 60 c. Fokker F.27 Friendship (airliner), Cambodia, 1991–93 .. .. 1·25 1·25
1051 70 c. Lockheed C-130 Hercules (transport) 1·50 1·75
1048/51 .. .. .. *Set of 4* 4·00 4·00

214 St. Agnes Anglican Church

(Des R. Watton. Litho B.D.T.)

1995 (17 Nov). *Christmas. Churches. T 214 and similar horiz designs. Multicoloured. W w 16 (sideways). P 14.*
1052 15 c. Type 214 .. .. .. 30 25
1053 55 c. Church of God, East Street .. 90 90
1054 60 c. Sacred Heart Roman Catholic Church 95 1·10
1055 70 c. Salem Union Baptist Church .. 1·10 1·40
1052/5 .. .. .. *Set of 4* 3·00 3·25

215 Microscopic View of AIDS Virus

(Des N. Shewring. Litho B.D.T.)

1995 (1 Dec). *World AIDS Day. T 215 and similar horiz design. Multicoloured. W w 14 (sideways). P 14.*
1056 25 c. Type 215 .. .. .. 50 50
1057 70 c. Research into AIDS .. .. 90 1·25

216 Sunrise Tellin

(Des D. Miller. Litho Questa)

1996 (2 Jan–1 July). *Sea Shells. T 216 and similar horiz designs. Multicoloured. "1996" imprint date. W w 14 (sideways). P 14.*
1058 5 c. Type 216 .. .. .. 25 30
1059 10 c. Queen Conch 35 30
1060 15 c. Angular Triton 55 40
1061 20 c. True Tulip 70 40
1062 25 c. Reticulated Cowrie-helmet .. 70 45
1063 30 c. Sand Dollar 80 55
1064 40 c. Lace Short-frond Murex .. 1·00 60
1065 45 c. Inflated Sea Biscuit .. .. 1·00 60
1066 50 c. West Indian Top Shell .. 1·10 70
1067 55 c. Spiny Oyster .. .. .. 1·25 75
1068 60 c. King Helmet .. .. .. 1·50 80
1069 70 c. Lion's Paw .. .. .. 1·60 1·00
1070 $1 Crown Cone .. .. .. 2·25 1·75
1071 $2 Atlantic Partridge Tun .. 3·50 4·00
1072 $5 Wide-mouthed Purpura .. 8·00 8·50
1073 $10 Atlantic Trumpet Triton (1 July) .. 14·00 15·00
1058/73 .. .. .. *Set of 16* 35·00 32·00
For 70 c. in miniature sheet with "1997" imprint date see No. MS1097 and for the $1 with inverted watermark and "1997" imprint date see No. MS1096.
For these designs with watermark w 14 (upright) and "1997" imprint date see Nos. 1098/1113.

217 East Goodwin Lightship with Marconi Apparatus on Mast
218 Swimming

(Des N. Shewring. Litho B.D.T.)

1996 (2 Apr). *Centenary of Radio. T 217 and similar horiz designs. Multicoloured. W w 14 (sideways). P 13½×14.*
1074 15 c. Type 217 .. .. .. 45 35
1075 55 c. Newspaper headline concerning Dr. Crippen .. .. .. 1·10 1·10

1076 60 c. *Philadelphia* (liner) and first readable transatlantic message .. .. 1·25 1·40
1077 70 c. *Guglielmo Marconi* and *Elettra* (yacht) .. .. .. 1·50 1·75
1074/7 .. .. .. *Set of 4* 3·75 4·25
MS1078 80×47 mm. $2 *Titanic* and *Carpathia* (liners) .. .. .. 3·50 4·00

(Des S. Noon. Litho B.D.T.)

1996 (25 June). *Centenary of Modern Olympic Games. T 218 and similar vert designs. Multicoloured. W w 16. P 14×13½.*
1079 15 c. Type 218 .. .. .. 40 25
1080 55 c. Running 90 85
1081 60 c. Basketball .. .. .. 1·40 1·40
1082 70 c. Long jumping .. .. 1·40 1·75
1079/82 .. .. .. *Set of 4* 3·50 3·75
MS1083 73×68 mm. $2 Javelin throwing .. 3·00 3·50

219 Green Anole
220 The Annunciation

(Des Doreen McGuiness. Litho Questa)

1996 (3 Sept). *Environment Protection (4th issue). Reptiles. T 219 and similar vert designs. Multicoloured. W w 16. P 14.*
1084 15 c. Type 219 .. .. .. 55 40
1085 55 c. Little Bahama Bank Boa .. 1·10 85
1086 60 c. Inagua Freshwater Turtle .. 1·50 1·50
1087 70 c. Acklins Rock Iguana .. 1·75 2·00
1084/7 .. .. .. *Set of 4* 4·50 4·25
MS1088 85×105 mm. Nos. 1084/7 .. 4·50 4·75

(Des Jennifer Toombs. Litho B.D.T.)

1996 (4 Nov). *Christmas. T 220 and similar vert designs. Multicoloured. W w 14. P 14.*
1089 15 c. Type 220 .. .. .. 30 25
1090 55 c. Joseph and Mary travelling to Bethlehem 80 75
1091 60 c. Shepherds and Angel .. 1·10 1·40
1092 70 c. Adoration of the Magi .. 1·10 1·50
1089/92 .. .. .. *Set of 4* 3·00 3·50
MS1093 70×87 mm. $2 Presentation in the Temple .. .. .. 2·50 3·00

221 Department of Archives Building
222 Underwater Scene

(Des N. Shewring. Litho Questa)

1996 (9 Dec). *25th Anniv of Archives Department. T 221 and similar horiz design showing Archives Building. W w 16. P 14½×14.*
1094 221 55 c. multicoloured 80 80
MS1095 83×54 mm. $2 multicoloured. Wmk sideways. P 14 .. .. .. 3·00 3·50

(Des D. Miller. Litho Questa)

1997 (3 Feb). *"HONG KONG '97" International Stamp Exhibition. Sheet 130×90 mm, containing design as No. 1070, but with "1997" imprint date. Multicoloured. W w 14 (inverted). P 14.*
MS1096 $1 Crown Cone .. .. .. 1·50 2·00

(Des D. Miller. Litho Walsall)

1997 (20 June). *Return of Hong Kong to China. Sheet 130×90 mm containing design as No. 1069, but with "1997" imprint date.*
MS1097 70 c. Lion's Paw .. .. .. 1·25 1·50

1997 (1 July–22 Sept). *As Nos. 1058/73, but W w 14 (upright). "1997" imprint date. P 14.*
1098 5 c. Type 216 (22 Sept) 10 10
1099 10 c. Queen Conch (22 Sept) .. 10 10
1100 15 c. Angular Triton (22 Sept) .. 20 25
1101 20 c. True Tulip (22 Sept) .. 25 30
1102 25 c. Reticulated Cowrie-helmet (22 Sept) 30 35
1103 30 c. Sand Dollar (22 Sept) .. 35 40
1104 40 c. Lace Short-frond Murex (22 Sept) 50 45
1105 45 c. Inflated Sea Biscuit (22 Sept) .. 55 60
1106 50 c. West Indian Top Shell (22 Sept) 60 65
1107 55 c. Spiny Oyster (22 Sept) .. 65 70

1108	60 c. King Helmet (22 Sept)	.. ..	75	80
1109	70 c. Lion's Paw (22 Sept)	.. ..	85	90
1110	$1 Crown Cone	.. ..	1·25	1·40
1111	$2 Atlantic Partridge Tun	..	2·50	2·75
1112	$5 Wide-mouthed Purpura	..	6·25	6·50
1113	$10 Atlantic Trumpet Triton	..	12·50	13·00
1098/113	.. ..	Set of 16	28·00	29·00

(Des N. Shewring (No. **MS**1120), D. Miller (others). Litho Questa (No. **MS**1120) or Cartor (others))

1997 (9 July). *Golden Wedding of Queen Elizabeth and Prince Philip. Multicoloured designs as T **173** of Ascension. W w **14**. P 13.*

1114	50 c. Queen Elizabeth II in Bonn, 1992	..	80	90
	a. Horiz pair. Nos. 1114/15	..	1·60	1·75
1115	50 c. Prince Philip and Prince Charles at Trooping the Colour		80	90
1116	60 c. Prince Philip	..	90	1·00
	a. Horiz pair. Nos. 1116/17	..	1·75	2·00
1117	60 c. Queen at Trooping the Colour	..	90	1·00
1118	70 c. Queen Elizabeth and Prince Philip at polo, 1970	.. ..	1·25	1·40
	a. Horiz pair. Nos. 1118/19	..	2·50	2·75
1119	70 c. Prince Charles playing polo	..	1·25	1·40
1114/19	.. ..	Set of 6	5·50	6·00
MS1120	110×70 mm. $2 Queen Elizabeth and Prince Philip in landau (*horiz*). W w **14** (sideways). P 14×14¹/₂	.. ..	3·00	3·50

Nos. 1114/15, 1116/17 and 1118/19 were each printed together, *se-tenant*, in horizontal pairs throughout the sheets with the backgrounds forming composite designs.

(Des D. Miller. Litho Questa)

1997 (3 Sept). *International Year of the Reefs. T **222** and similar horiz designs showing different children's paintings of underwater scenes. W w **16** (sideways). P 14¹/₂.*

1121	15 c. multicoloured	.. .. ..	30	25
1122	55 c. multicoloured	.. .. ..	80	80
1123	60 c. multicoloured	.. .. ..	1·00	1·00
1124	70 c. multicoloured	.. .. ..	1·25	1·40
1121/4	.. .. ..	Set of 4	3·00	3·00

223 Angel

(Des Jennifer Toombs. Litho Cartor)

1997 (4 Nov). *Christmas. T **223** and similar vert designs. Multicoloured. W w **14** (inverted). P 13×13¹/₂.*

1125	15 c. Type **223**	.. ..	20	25
1126	55 c. Mary and Baby Jesus	.. ..	65	70
1127	60 c. Shepherd	.. .. ..	75	80
1128	70 c. King	.. .. ..	85	90
1125/8	.. ..	Set of 4	2·40	2·75
MS1129	74×94 mm. $2 Baby Jesus wrapped in swaddling-bands. Wmk upright	.. ..	2·50	2·75

STAMP BOOKLETS

1938. *Black on pink cover with map and "BAHAMAS ISLES OF JUNE" on reverse. Stapled.*

SB1 2s. booklet containing twelve 1d. (No. 150) in blocks of 6 and eight 1¹/₂d. (No. 151) in folded block of 8 .. ..£5000

1961 (15 Aug). *Brown-purple cover (3s.) or green cover (6s.). Stitched.*

SB2 3s. booklet containing eight each of 1d. 1¹/₂d. and 2d. (Nos. 202/4) in blocks of 4 .. 25·00

SB3 6s. booklet containing four each of 4d., 6d. and 8d. (Nos. 206, 208/9) in blocks of 4 .. .. 32·00

1965 (23 Mar). *Pink cover (3s.) or green cover (6s.). Stapled.*

SB4 3s. booklet containing eight each of 1d., 1¹/₂d. and 2d. (Nos. 248/50) in blocks of 4 .. 16·00

SB5 6s. booklet containing four each of 4d., 6d. and 8d. (Nos. 252/4) in blocks of 4 .. .. 19·00

SPECIAL DELIVERY STAMPS

SPECIAL DELIVERY

(S 1)

1916 (1 May). *No. 59 optd with Type S **1** by The Nassau Guardian.*

S1	**6** 5d. black and orange	.. ..	5·00	29·00
	a. Opt double	.. ..	£800	£1200
	b. Opt double, one inverted	..	£950	£1300
	c. Opt inverted	.. ..	£1300	£1400
	d. Pair, one without opt	..	£13000	£18000
	x. Wmk reversed	.. ..		

There were three printings from similar settings of 30, and each sheet had to pass through the press twice. The first printing of 600 was on sale from 1 May 1916 in Canada at Ottawa, Toronto, Westmount (Montreal) and Winnipeg; and under an agreement with the Canadian P.O. were used in combination with Canadian stamps and were cancelled in Canada. The second printing (number unknown) was made about the beginning of December 1916, and the third of 6000, issued probably on 1 March 1917, were on sale only in the Bahamas. These printings caused the revocation, in mid-December 1916, of the agreement by Canada, which no longer accepted the stamps as payment of the special delivery fee and left them to be cancelled in the Bahamas.

It is not possible to identify the printings of the normal stamps without plating both the basic stamp and the overprint, though, in general, the word "SPECIAL" is further to the right in relation to "DELIVERY" in the third printing than in the first or second. Our prices for No. S1 are for the third printing and any stamps which can be positively identified as being from the first or second printings would be worth about eight times as much unused, and any on cover are very rare. All the errors appear to be from the third printing.

SPECIAL DELIVERY	SPECIAL DELIVERY
(S 2)	(S 3)

1917 (2 July). *As No. 59, but Wmk Mult Crown CA. Optd with Type S **2** by D.L.R.*

S2	**6** 5d. black and orange (Optd S. £65)	..	45	4·50

1918. *No. 78 optd with Type S **3** by D.L.R.*

S3	**6** 5d. black and mauve (R.) (Optd S. £65)	..	30	1·50

Nos. S2/3 were only on sale in the Bahamas.

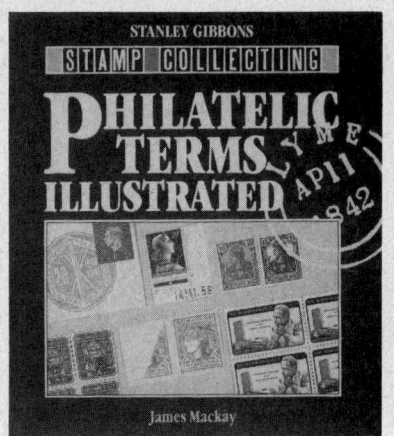

HELP!

Even the most knowledgeable collector can be faced by philatelic terms of which he does not know the meaning – if this has ever been your problem then you need:

STANLEY GIBBONS
STAMP COLLECTING
PHILATELIC TERMS ILLUSTRATED

James Mackay

PHILATELIC TERMS ILLUSTRATED

Now completely revised and updated in a bright new format as part of the popular Stanley Gibbons 'Stamp Collecting' series.

The new edition of this useful book not only includes all the terms which have come into use since publication of the second edition in 1978 but also provides much new information on postal markings and services.

Noted philatelic author and journalist, James Mackay, has carefully updated and augmented the original text of Russell Bennett and James Watson to produce a work of great assistance to the postal historian and an indispensable aid to stamp identification.

Fully illustrated in colour or black and white, its encyclopedic style and helpful system of cross-referencing makes Philatelic Terms Illustrated extremely easy to use and provides a helpful work of reference for all collectors from the youngest beginner to the most advanced specialist.

Available direct from:

Stanley Gibbons Publications, Parkside, Christchurch Road, Ringwood, Hampshire BH24 3SH Telephone: 01425 472363

Bahrain

An independent shaikhdom, with an Indian postal administration from 1884. A British postal administration operated from 1 April 1948 to 31 December 1965.

The first, and for 62 years the only, post office in Bahrain opened at the capital, Manama, on 1 August 1884 as a sub-office of the Indian Post Office at Bushire (Iran), both being part of the Bombay Postal Circle.

Unoverprinted postage stamps of India were supplied to the new office, continuing on sale there until 1933. Examples of the lower values can sometimes be found postmarked at Bahrain, but such cancellations on values over 4 a. are decidedly scarce. The occasional Official stamp can also be discovered, possibly used by the office of the Indian Political Agent.

The initial cancellation supplied showed a "B" against a circular background of horizontal lines, this being used in conjunction with a single ring date-stamp without any indication of the year of use.

1884 Cancellation and Date-stamp

This was followed by a squared-circle type, first seen in 1886, which was used into the early years of the 20th century. Its replacement was a single ring date-stamp, succeeded in turn by the first of a considerable number of Indian-style double-circle postmarks, all inscribed "BAHRAIN".

1886 Squared-circle

PRICES FOR STAMPS ON COVER TO 1945	
Nos. 1/14	from × 5
Nos. 15/19	from × 6
Nos. 20/37	from × 2
Nos. 38/50	from × 6

(Currency. 12 pies = 1 anna;
16 annas = 1 rupee)

BAHRAIN   BAHRAIN
(1)   (2)

Stamps of India overprinted with T 1 or T 2 (rupee values)

1933 (10 Aug–Dec). *King George V. Wmk Mult Star, T 69.*
1	55	3 p. slate (Dec)	..	2·75	45
2	56	½ a. green	..	7·50	3·25
3	80	9 p. deep green	..	3·75	90
4	57	1 a. chocolate	..	7·00	2·50
		w. Wmk inverted	..		
5	82	1 a. 3 p. mauve	..	3·75	70
		w. Wmk inverted	..	3·75	70
6	70	2 a. vermilion	..	10·00	7·50
		w. Wmk inverted	..	10·00	7·50
7	62	3 a. blue	..	19·00	40·00
8	83	3 a. 6 p. ultramarine	..	3·75	30
		w. Wmk inverted	..	5·50	30
9	71	4 a. sage-green	..	18·00	40·00
10	65	8 a. reddish purple	..	5·50	30
11	66	12 a. claret	..	7·50	1·00
12	67	1 r. chocolate and green	..	16·00	7·50
13		2 r. carmine and orange	..	32·00	38·00
14		5 r. ultramarine and purple	..	90·00	£120
		w. Wmk inverted	..	90·00	£120
1/14			*Set of 14*	£200	£225

The 9 p. exists both offset-litho and typo.

1934–37. *King George V. Wmk Mult Star, T 69.*
15	79	½ a. green (1935)	..	4·00	55
		w. Wmk inverted	..	6·00	55
16	81	1 a. chocolate	..	8·50	40
17	59	2 a. vermilion (1935)	..	35·00	7·50
17a		2 a. vermilion (small die) (1937)	..	45·00	25
18	62	3 a. carmine	..	4·75	40
19	63	4 a. sage-green (1935)	..	3·00	40
15/19			*Set of 6*	90·00	8·50

1938–41. *King George VI.*
20	91	3 p. slate (5.38)	..	7·00	2·75
21		½ a. red-brown (5.38)	..	3·00	10
22		9 p. green (5.38)	..	2·50	2·25
23		1 a. carmine (5.38)	..	2·25	10
24	92	2 a. vermilion (1939)	..	6·50	1·00
26		3 a. violet-blue (1941)	..	10·00	4·50
27		3 a. 6 p. bright blue (7.38)	..	4·25	2·75
28		4 a. brown (1941)	..	£120	55·00
30		8 a. slate-violet (1940)	..	£140	35·00
31		12 a. lake (1940)	..	£100	42·00

32	93	1 r. grey and red-brown (1940)	..	2·75	1·40
33		2 r. purple and brown (1940)	..	13·00	2·50
34		5 r. green and blue (1940)	..	15·00	13·00
35		10 r. purple and claret (1941)	..	65·00	27·00
36		15 r. brown and green (1941)	..	45·00	45·00
		w. Wmk inverted		45·00	45·00
37		25 r. slate-violet and purple (1941)		95·00	75·00
20/37			*Set of 16*	£550	£275

1942–45. *King George VI on white background.*
38	100a	3 p. slate	..	1·00	60
39		½ a. purple	..	3·50	90
40		9 p. green	..	11·00	11·00
41		1 a. carmine	..	3·50	50
42	101	1 a. 3 p. bistre	..	8·00	12·00
43		1½ a. dull violet	..	4·75	3·50
44		2 a. vermilion	..	3·50	1·50
45		3 a. bright violet	..	13·00	4·00
46		3½ a. bright blue	..	3·50	12·00
47	102	4 a. brown	..	2·00	1·25
48		6 a. turquoise-green	..	9·50	8·00
49		8 a. slate-violet	..	3·25	2·00
50		12 a. lake	..	5·00	3·50
38/50			*Set of 13*	65·00	55·00

Stamps of Great Britain surcharged
For similar surcharges without the name of the country, see
BRITISH POSTAL AGENCIES IN EASTERN ARABIA.

BAHRAIN
ANNA   RUPEES
BAHRAIN 1 ANNA (3)   BAHRAIN 5 RUPEES (4)

1948 (1 Apr)–**49.** *Surch as T 3, 4 (2 r. and 5 r.) or similar surch with bars at foot (10 r.).*
51	128	½ a. on ½d. pale green	..	40	65
52		1 a. on 1d. pale scarlet	..	40	85
53		1½ a. on 1½d. pale red-brown	..	40	90
54		2 a. on 2d. pale orange	..	40	20
55		2½ a. on 2½d. light ultramarine	..	50	2·00
56		3 a. on 3d. pale violet	..	40	10
57	129	6 a. on 6d. purple	..	40	10
58	130	1 r. on 1s. bistre-brown	..	1·25	10
59	131	2 r. on 2s. 6d. yellow-green	..	5·00	4·50
60		5 r. on 5s. red	..	5·50	4·50
60a	132	10 r. on 10s. ultramarine (4.7.49)	60·00	40·00
51/60a			*Set of 11*	65·00	48·00

BAHRAIN 2½ ANNAS (5)   BAHRAIN 15 RUPEES (6)

1948 (26 Apr). *Silver Wedding, surch as T 5 or 6.*
61	137	2½ a. on 2½d. ultramarine	..	50	30
62	138	15 r. on £1 blue	..	40·00	48·00

1948 (29 July). *Olympic Games, surch as T 5, but in one line (6 a.) or two lines (others); the 1 r. also has a square of dots as T 7.*
63	139	2½ a. on 2½d. ultramarine	..	55	1·00
		a. Surch double	..	£700	£1200
64	140	3 a. on 3d. violet	..	55	1·75
65	141	6 a. on 6d. bright purple	..	1·50	2·25
66	142	1 r. on 1s. brown	..	1·50	2·25
63/6			*Set of 4*	3·75	6·50

Fourteen used examples of No. 63a are known, of which twelve were postmarked at Experimental P.O. K-121 (Muharraq).

BAHRAIN 3 ANNAS

(7)

1949 (10 Oct). *75th Anniv of U.P.U., surch as T 7, in one line (2½ a.) or in two lines (others).*
67	143	2½ a. on 2½d. ultramarine	..	55	1·75
68	144	3 a. on 3d. violet	..	85	2·50
69	145	6 a. on 6d. bright purple	..	75	2·75
70	146	1 r. on 1s. brown	..	1·60	1·50
67/70			*Set of 4*	3·25	7·50

BAHRAIN   BAHRAIN

2 RUPEES   2 RUPEES
(7a)   Type II

BAHRAIN
Extra bar (R. 6/1)

Three Types of 2 r.:

Type I. As Type 7a showing "2" level with "RUPEES" and "BAHRAIN" sharp.

Type II. "2" raised. "BAHRAIN" worn. 15 mm between "BAHRAIN" and "2 RUPEES".

Type III. As Type II, but 16 mm between "BAHRAIN" and "2 RUPEES". Value is set more to the left of "BAHRAIN".

1950 (2 Oct)–**55.** *Surch as T 3 or 7a (rupee values).*
71	128	½ a. on ½d. pale orange (3.5.51)	60	60
72		1 a. on 1d. light ultramarine (3.5.51)	1·50	1·50
73		1½ a. on 1½d. pale green (3.5.51)	1·50	8·00
74		2 a. on 2d. pale red-brown (3.5.51)	60	30
75		2½ a. on 2½d. pale scarlet (3.5.51)	1·50	8·00
76	129	4 a. on 4d. light ultramarine	1·50	1·50
77	147	2 r. on 2s. 6d. yellow-green (3.5.51)	21·00	5·50
		a. Surch Type II (1953)	65·00	32·00
		b. Surch Type III (1955)	£700	75·00
		ba. "I" inverted and raised (R.2/1)	£2250	£550
78	148	5 r. on 5s. red (3.5.51)	13·00	3·75
		a. Extra bar	£200	
79	149	10 r. on 10s. ultramarine (3.5.51)	26·00	7·00
71/79			*Set of 9*	60·00	30·00

1952 (5 Dec)–**54.** *Q.E. II (W 153), surch as T 3 (in two lines on 2½ and 6 a.).*
80	154	½ a. on ½d. orange-red (31.8.53)	10	10
		a. Fraction "½" omitted	£100	£130
81		1 a. on 1d. ultramarine (31.8.53)	10	10
82		1½ a. on 1½d. green (31.8.53)	10	10
83		2 a. on 2d. red-brown (31.8.53)	20	10
84	155	2½ a. on 2½d. carmine-red	20	90
85		3 a. on 3d. deep lilac (B.) (18.1.54)	60	10
86	156	4 a. on 4d. ultramarine (2.11.53)	7·00	20
87	157	6 a. on 6d. reddish purple (18.1.54)	3·25	10
88	160	12 a. on 1s. green (2.11.53)	3·00	20
89	159	1 r. on 1s. 6d. grey-blue (2.11.53)	3·25	10
80/89			*Set of 10*	16·00	1·50

The word BAHRAIN is in taller letters on the 1½ a., 2½a., 3 a. and 6 a.

2½ BAHRAIN
ANNAS
(8)

1953 (3 June). *Coronation. Surch as T 8, or similarly.*
90	161	2½ a. on 2½d. carmine-red	..	1·25	75
91	162	4 a. on 4d. ultramarine	..	2·25	3·00
92	163	12 a. on 1s. 3d. deep yellow-green	..	3·25	3·00
93	164	1 r. on 1s. 6d. deep grey-blue	..	7·50	5·50
90/3			*Set of 4*	13·00	6·50

BAHRAIN 2 RUPEES   I

BAHRAIN 2 RUPEES   II

BAHRAIN 2 RUPEES   III

(9)

BAHRAIN 5 RUPEES   I

BAHRAIN 5 RUPEES   II

(10)

BAHRAIN 10 RUPEES   I

BAHRAIN 10 RUPEES   II

(11)

TYPE I (T 9/11). Type-set surch by Waterlow. Bold thick letters with sharp corners and straight edges.

TYPE II (T 9/11). Plate-printed surch by Harrison. Thinner letters, rounded corners and rough edges. Bars wider apart.

TYPE III (T 9). Plate-printed surch by Harrison. Similar to Type II as regards the position of the bars on all 40 stamps of the sheet, but the letters are thinner and with more rounded corners than in II, while the ink of the surcharge is less black.

The general characteristics of Type II of the 2 r. are less pronounced than in the other values, but a distinguishing test is in the relative position of the bars and the "U" of "RUPEES". In Type II (except for the 1st stamp, 5th row) the bars start immediately beneath the left-hand edge of the "U". In Type I they start more to the right.

In the 10 r. the "1" and the "0" are spaced 0.9 mm in Type I and only 0.6 mm in Type II.

1955 (23 Sept)–**60.** *T 166/8 (Waterlow ptgs) surch as T 9/11.*
94	166	2 r. on 2s. 6d. black-brown (Type I)	..	5·50	1·60
		a. Type II (13.5.58)	..	11·00	8·50
		b. Type III (No. 536a, D.L.R.) (29.1.60)	25·00	45·00
95	167	5 r. on 5s. rose-red (Type I)	..	11·00	2·75
		a. Type II (19.8.57)	..	11·00	8·00
96	168	10 r. on 10s. ultramarine (Type I)	..	20·00	2·75
		a. Type II (13.5.58)	..	50·00	95·00
		ab. Type II. Surch on No. 538a (D.L.R. ptg) (1960)	£110	
94/6			*Set of 3*	32·00	6·25
94a/6a			*Set of 3*	65·00	£100

1956–7. *Q.E. II (W 165), surch as T 3 (in two lines on 6 a.).*
97	154	½ a. on ½d. orange-red (1.57)	..	10	15
98	156	4 a. on 4d. ultramarine (8.6.56)	..	5·50	16·00
99	157	6 a. on 6d. reddish purple (5.12.56)	50	50
100	160	12 a. on 1s. green (28.6.56)	..	7·50	11·00
101	159	1 r. on 1s. 6d. grey-blue (4.3.57)	..	8·00	10
		a. Surch double	..	†£1700	
97/101			*Set of 5*	19·00	25·00

(New Currency. 100 naye paise = 1 rupee)

BAHRAIN BAHRAIN BAHRAIN

NP 1 NP	3 NP	75 NP
(12)	(13)	(14)

1957 (1 Apr)–59. *Q.E. II* (W 165), *surch as T* 12 (1 *n.p.*, 15 *n.p.*, 25 *n.p.*, 40 *n.p.*, *and* 50 *n.p.*), *T* 14 (75 *n.p.*) *or T* 13 (*others*).

102	157	1 n.p. on 5d. brown			10	10
103	154	3 n.p. on ½d. orange-red			30	1·25
104		6 n.p. on 1d. ultramarine			30	1·25
105		9 n.p. on 1½d. green			30	1·00
106		12 n.p. on 2d. light red-brown			30	30
107	155	15 n.p. on 2½d. carmine-red (Type I)			30	15
		a. Type II (1959)			1·00	1·75
108		20 n.p. on 3d. deep lilac (B.)			30	10
109	156	25 n.p. on 4d. ultramarine			75	1·50
110	157	40 n.p. on 6d. reddish purple			40	10
		a. Deep claret (1959)			55	10
111	158	50 n.p. on 9d. bronze-green			3·75	4·50
112	160	75 n.p. on 1s. 3d. green			2·25	50
102/112				Set of 11	8·00	9·50

BAHRAIN

15 NP

(15)

1957 (1 Aug). *World Scout Jubilee Jamboree. Surch in two lines as T* 15 (15 *n.p.*), *or in three lines* (*others*).

113	170	15 n.p. on 2½d. carmine-red			25	35
114	171	25 n.p. on 4d. ultramarine			30	35
115	172	75 n.p. on 1s. 3d. green			40	45
113/15				Set of 3	85	1·00

1960 (24 May). *Q.E. II* (W 179), *surch as T* 12.

116	155	15 n.p. on 2½d. carmine-red (Type II)		2·25	8·00

16   17
Shaikh Sulman bin Hamed al-Khalifa

(Des M. Farrar Bell. Photo Harrison (T 16). Des O. C. Meronti. Recess D.L.R. (T 17))

1960 (1 July). *P* 15 × 14 (T 16) *or* 13½ × 13 (T 17).

117	16	5 n.p. bright blue			10	10
118		15 n.p. red-orange			10	10
119		20 n.p. reddish violet			10	10
120		30 n.p. bistre-brown			10	10
121		40 n.p. grey			15	10
122		50 n.p. emerald-green			15	10
123		75 n.p. chocolate			30	15
124	17	1 r. black			1·50	30
125		2 r. rose-red			2·75	1·25
126		5 r. deep blue			4·50	2·00
127		10 r. bronze-green			12·00	3·25
117/127				Set of 11	19·00	6·50

18 Shaikh Isa bin   19 Air Terminal,
Sulman al-Khalifa   Muharraq

20 Deep Water Harbour

(Des M. Farrar Bell. Photo Harrison (5 to 75 n.p.). Des D. C. Rivett. Recess B.W. (others))

1964 (22 Feb). *P* 15 × 14 (T 18) *or* 13½ × 13 (T 19/20).

128	18	5 n.p. bright blue			10	10
129		15 n.p. orange red			10	10

130	18	20 n.p. reddish violet			10	10
131		30 n.p. olive-brown			10	10
132		40 n.p. slate			15	10
133		50 n.p. emerald-green			15	10
134		75 n.p. brown			25	10
135	19	1 r. black			4·75	90
136		2 r. carmine-red			8·50	90
137	20	5 r. ultramarine			9·50	7·50
138		10 r. myrtle-green			13·00	7·50
128/138				Set of 11	32·00	15·00

LOCAL STAMPS

The following stamps were issued primarily for postage within Bahrain, but apparently also had franking value when used on external mail.

L 1 Shaikh Sulman bin Hamed L 2
al-Khalifa

(Types L 1/2. Recess D.L.R.)

1953–56. *P* 12 × 12½.

L1	L 1	½ a. deep green (1.10.56)			3·75	75
L2		1 a. deep blue (1.10.56)			3·75	45
L3		1½ a. carmine (15.2.53)			50	3·00
L1/3				Set of 3	7·25	3·75

1957 (16 Oct). *As Nos. L 1/3 but values in new currency.*

L4		3 p. deep green			4·25	1·25
L5		6 p. carmine			4·25	1·25
L6		9 p. deep blue			4·25	1·25
L4/6				Set of 3	11·50	3·25

1961 (20 Mar). *P* 12 × 12½.

L 7	L 2	5 p. green			1·00	30
L 8		10 p. carmine-red			1·10	30
L 9		15 p. grey			1·00	25
L10		20 p. blue			1·25	25
L11		30 p. sepia			1·00	25
L12		40 p. ultramarine			1·50	30
L7/12				Set of 6	6·25	1·50

STAMP BOOKLETS

1934. *Red and black on tan cover. Mysore Sandal Soap advertisement on front.*

SB1	16 a. booklet containing sixteen 1 a. (No. 16) in blocks of 4		£750

The Bahrain Post Department took over the postal services on 1 January 1966. Later stamp issues will be found in Part 19 (*Middle East*) of the Stanley Gibbons catalogue.

Bangkok
see British Post Office in Siam

Bangladesh

In elections during December 1970 the Awami League party won all but two of the seats in the East Pakistan province and, in consequence, held a majority in the National Assembly. On 1 March 1971 the Federal Government postponed the sitting of the Assembly with the result that unrest spread throughout the eastern province. Pakistan army operations against the dissidents forced the leaders of the League to flee to India from where East Pakistan was proclaimed independent as Bangladesh. In early December the Indian army moved against Pakistan troops in Bangladesh and civilian government was re-established on 22 December 1971.

From 20 December 1971 various Pakistan issues were overprinted by local postmasters, mainly using handstamps. Their use was permitted until 30 April 1973. These are of philatelic interest, but are outside the scope of the catalogue.

(Currency. 100 paisa = 1 rupee)

1 Map of Bangladesh   (2)

(Des B. Mullick. Litho Format)

1971 (29 July). *Vert designs as T* 1. *P* 14 × 14½.

1		10 p. indigo-blue, red-orange and pale blue		10	10
2		20 p. multicoloured		10	10
3		50 p. multicoloured		10	10
4		1 r. multicoloured		10	10
5		2 r. deep greenish blue, light new blue and rose-magenta		25	35
6		3 r. apple-green, dull yellowish green and greenish blue		30	55
7		5 r. multicoloured		50	90
8		10 r. gold, rose-magenta & deep greenish blue		1·00	1·75
1/8			Set of 8	2·00	3·50

Designs:—20 p. "Dacca University Massacre"; 50 p. "75 Million People"; 1 r. Flag of Independence; 2 r. Ballot box; 3 r. Broken chain; 5 r. Shaikh Mujibur Rahman; 10 r. "Support Bangla Desh" and map.

Nos. 1/8 exist imperforate from stock dispersed by the liquidator of Format International Security Printers Ltd.

1971 (20 Dec). *Liberation. Nos. 1 and 7/8 optd with T* 2.

9		10 p. indigo-blue, red-orange and pale blue		10	10
10		5 r. multicoloured (O.)		1·50	1·75
11		10 r. gold, rose-magenta & deep greenish blue		2·00	2·50
9/11			Set of 3	3·25	3·75

The remaining values of the original issue were also overprinted and placed on sale in Great Britain but were not issued in Bangladesh. (*Price for the complete set £4 un.*)

On 1 February 1972 the Agency placed on sale a further issue in the flag, map and Shaikh Mujibur designs in new colours and new currency (100 paisas = 1 taka). This issue proved to be unacceptable to the Bangladesh authorities who declared them to be invalid for postal purposes, no supplies being sold within Bangladesh. The values comprise 1, 2, 3, 5, 7, 10, 15, 20, 25, 40, 50, 75 p., 1, 2 and 5 t. (*Price for set of 15 un., £1.*)

(New Currency. 100 paisa = 1 taka)

3 "Martyrdom"   4 Flames of Independence

(Des and photo Indian Security Printing Press, Nasik)

1972 (21 Feb). *In Memory of the Martyrs. P* 13.

12	3	20 p. dull green and rose-red			30	50

(Des N. Kundu. Photo Indian Security Printing Press, Nasik)

1972 (26 Mar). *First Anniv of Independence. P* 13.

13	4	20 p. brown-lake and red			15	10
14		60 p. dull ultramarine and red			20	35
15		75 p. reddish violet and red			25	45
13/15				Set of 3	55	80

5 Doves of Peace   6 "Homage to Martyrs"

(Litho B.W.)

1972 (16 Dec). *Victory Day. P* 13½.

16	5	20 p. multicoloured			15	10
17		60 p. multicoloured			20	45
18		75 p. multicoloured			20	45
16/18				Set of 3	50	90

(Des K. Mustafa. Litho B.W.)

1973 (25 Mar). *In Memory of the Martyrs. P* 13½.

19	6	20 p. multicoloured			15	10
20		60 p. multicoloured			30	35
21		1 t. 35, multicoloured			65	1·50
19/21				Set of 3	1·10	1·75

7 Embroidered Quilt   8 Court of Justice

(Litho B.W.)

1973 (30 Apr). *T* 7/8 *and similar designs. P* 14½ × 14 (50 p., 1 t., 5 t., 10 t.) *or* 14 × 14½ (*others*).

22		2 p. black			10	40
23		3 p. blue-green			20	30
		a. Imperf (pair)				

24	5 p. light brown	..	..	20	10
25	10 p. slate-black	..	..	20	10
26	20 p. yellow-green	..	..	50	10
27	25 p. bright reddish mauve	..	..	2·75	10
28	50 p. bright purple	..	..	1·50	30
29	60 p. greenish slate	..	..	75	50
30	75 p. yellow-orange	..	..	80	50
31	90 p. orange-brown	..	..	90	70
32	1 t. light violet	..	..	4·00	30
33	2 t. olive-green	..	..	4·00	55
34	5 t. grey-blue	..	..	5·50	1·50
35	10 t. rose	..	..	5·50	3·25
22/35 ..			Set of 14	24·00	7·50

Designs: *As T 7*—3 p. Jute field; 5 p. Jack fruit; 10 p. Bullocks ploughing; 20 p. Rakta jaba (flower); 25 p. Tiger; 60 p. Bamboo grove; 75 p. Plucking tea; 90 p. Handicrafts. *Horiz (28 × 22 mm)*—50 p. Hilsa (fish). *Horiz as T 8*—5 t. Fishing boat; 10 t. Sixty-dome mosque, Bagerhat. *Vert as T 8*—2 t. Date tree.
See also Nos. 49/51a and 64/75.

9 Flame Emblem   **10** Family, Map and Graph

(Des A. Karim. Litho B.W.)

1973 (10 Dec). *5th Anniv of Declaration of Human Rights.* P 13½.

36	**9**	10 p. multicoloured	.. ..	10	10
37		1 t. 25, multicoloured	..	20	20

(Des A. Karim. Litho B.W.)

1974 (10 Feb). *First Population Census.* P 13½.

38	**10**	20 p. multicoloured	.. ..	10	10
39		25 p. multicoloured	.. ..	10	10
40		75 p. multicoloured	.. ..	20	20
38/40 ..			Set of 3	30	30

11 Copernicus and Heliocentric System   **12** U.N. H.Q. and Bangladesh Flag

(Des K. Mustafa. Litho B.W.)

1974 (22 July). *500th Birth Anniv of Copernicus.* P 13½.

41	**11**	25 p. yellow-orange, bluish violet & blk	10	10
		a. Imperf (pair)		22·00	
42		75 p. orange, yellow-green and black	25	50

(Des A. Karim. Litho B.W.)

1974 (25 Sept). *Bangladesh's Admission to the U.N. Multicoloured; frame colour given.* P 13½.

43	**12**	25 p. light lilac	.. ..	10	10
44		1 t. light greenish blue	..	35	40

13 U.P.U. Emblem   **14** Courts of Justice

(Des K. Mustafa. Litho B.W.)

1974 (9 Oct). *Centenary of Universal Postal Union. T 13 and similar vert designs. Multicoloured; country name on a yellow background (Nos. 45/6) or a blue background (Nos. 47/8).* P 13½.

45	25 p. Type 13	..	..	10	10
46	1 t. 25, Mail runner	..	..	20	15
47	1 t. 75, Type 13	..	..	25	25
48	5 t. As 1 t. 25	..	..	80	1·60
45/8 ..			Set of 4	1·25	1·75

The above exist imperforate in a miniature sheet from a restricted printing.

1974–76. *Nos. 32/5 redrawn with revised value inscriptions as T 14.*

49	1 t. light violet	..	..	1·50	10
50	2 t. olive	..	..	2·00	70
51	5 t. grey-blue (1975)	..	..	5·00	70
51a	10 t. rose (1976)	..	..	10·50	7·00
49/51a			Set of 4	17·00	7·75

15 Royal Bengal Tiger   **16** Symbolic Family

(Des and litho B.W.)

1974 (4 Nov). *Wildlife Preservation. T 15 and similar vert designs. Multicoloured.* P 13½.

52	25 p. Type 15	..	..	70	10
53	50 p. Tiger whelp	..	..	1·25	70
54	2 t. Tiger in stream	..	..	2·75	3·50
52/4		Set of 3		4·25	3·75

(Des A. Karim. Litho B.W.)

1974 (30 Dec). *World Population Year. "Family Planning for All". T 16 and similar multicoloured designs.* P 14.

55	25 p. Type 16	..	..	15	10
56	70 p. Village family	..	..	25	50
57	1 t. 25, Heads of family (horiz)	..	40	1·10
55/7		Set of 3		70	1·50

The Bengali numerals on the 70 p. resemble "90".

17 Radar Antenna   **18** Woman's Head

(Des and litho B.W.)

1975 (14 June). *Inauguration of Betbunia Satellite Earth Station.* P 13½.

58	**17**	25 p. black, silver and dull red	..	10	10
59		1 t. black, silver and ultramarine	..	20	60

(Des A. Karim. Litho Asher & Co, Melbourne)

1975 (31 Dec). *International Women's Year.* P 15.

60	**18**	50 p. multicoloured	.. ..	10	10
61		2 t. multicoloured	.. ..	25	85
		a. Vert pair, bottom stamp imperf	..	75·00	

(Litho Asher & Co., Melbourne)

1976 (15 Jan)—77. *As Nos. 24/31 and 49/51a but redrawn in smaller size and colours changed (5, 75p.). P 14½×15 (50 p.), 14½ (1 to 10 t.) or 15×14½ (others). (a) 23×18 mm (50 p.) or 18×23 mm (others).*

64	5 p. deep yellow-green (11.2.76)	..	20	10
	a. Imperf (pair)		10·00	
65	10 p. slate-black (28.4.76)	..	20	10
66	20 p. yellow-green	..	70	10
	a. Imperf (pair)		10·00	
67	25 p. bright reddish mauve	..	2·00	10
	a. Imperf (pair)		10·00	
68	50 p. light purple (8.6.76)	..	1·75	10
69	60 p. greenish slate (10.11.76)	..	40	20
70	75 p. yellow-olive (10.11.76)	..	1·25	1·50
71	90 p. orange-brown (10.11.76)	..	40	20

(b) 20×32 mm (2 t.) or 32×20 mm (others)

72	1 t. light violet	..	2·00	10
73	2 t. olive-green (8.6.76)	..	5·00	10
	a. Imperf (pair)		35·00	
74	5 t. grey-blue (10.11.76)	..	3·25	1·75
75	10 t. rose (25.2.77)	..	7·50	1·75
64/75		Set of 12	22·00	5·50

19 Telephones, 1876 and 1976   **20** Eye and Nutriments

(Des A. Karim. Litho Asher & Co, Melbourne)

1976 (10 Mar). *Telephone Centenary. T 19 and similar vert design.* P 15.

76	2 t. 25, multicoloured	.. ..	25	20
77	5 t. dull vermilion, apple-green and black	..	55	65

Design:— 5 t. Alexander Graham Bell.

(Des A. Karim. Litho Asher & Co, Melbourne)

1976 (17 Apr). *Prevention of Blindness.* P 15.

78	**20**	30 p. multicoloured	.. ..	50	10
79		2 t. multicoloured	.. ..	1·40	2·00

21 Liberty Bell   **22** Industry, Science, Agriculture and Education

(Des E. Roberts. Photo Heraclio Fournier)

1976 (29 May). *Bicentenary of American Revolution. T 21 and similar horiz designs. Multicoloured.* P 14.

80	30 p. Type 21	..	..	10	10
81	2 t. 25, Statue of Liberty	..	..	30	25
82	5 t. Mayflower	..	..	80	50
83	10 t. Mount Rushmore	..	..	80	80
80/3		Set of 4		1·75	1·40
MS84	167 × 95 mm. Nos. 80/3			2·50	3·00

No. MS84 also exists imperforate from a restricted printing.

(Des K. Mustafa. Litho Asher & Co, Melbourne)

1976 (29 July). *25th Anniv of the Colombo Plan.* P 15.

85	**22**	30 p. multicoloured	.. ..	15	10
86		2 t. 25, multicoloured	.. ..	35	35

23 Hurdling   **24** The Blessing

(Des K. Mustafa. Litho Asher & Co, Melbourne)

1976 (29 Nov). *Olympic Games, Montreal. T 23 and similar multicoloured designs.* P 14½.

87	25 p. Type 23	..	..	10	10
88	30 p. Running (horiz)	..	..	10	10
	a. Imperf (pair)				
89	1 t. Pole vault	..	..	15	10
90	2 t. 25, Swimming (horiz)	..	..	40	35
91	3 t. 50, Gymnastics	..	..	75	1·00
92	5 t. Football	..	..	1·40	2·00
87/92 ..			Set of 6	2·50	3·25

(Des and litho Harrison)

1977 (7–17 Feb). *Silver Jubilee. T 24 and similar vert designs. Multicoloured.* P 14 × 14½.

93	30 p. Type 24	..	..	10	10
94	2 t. 25, Queen Elizabeth II	..	..	20	25
95	10 t. Queen Elizabeth and Prince Philip	..	70	85
93/5		Set of 3		80	1·00
MS96	114 × 127 mm. Nos. 93/5. P 14½ (17 Feb)		80	1·50

25 Qazi Nazrul Islam (poet)

(Des K. Mustafa. Litho Harrison)

1977 (29 Aug). *Qazi Nazrul Islam Commemoration. T 25 and similar design.* P 14.

97	40 p. blue-green and black	..	..	10	10
98	2 t. 25, sepia, stone and chestnut	..	30	30

Design: *Horiz*—2 t. 25, Head and shoulders portrait.

26 Bird with Letter

(Des A. Karim. Litho Harrison)

77 (29 Sept). *15th Anniv of Asian-Oceanic Postal Union.* P 14.
9 **26** 30 p. light rose, new blue and dull green .. 10 10
0 2 t. 25, light rose, new blue and light grey 20 25

27 Sloth Bear

28 Campfire and Tent

(Des K. Mustafa. Litho Harrison)

77 (9 Nov). *Animals. T* **27** *and similar multicoloured designs.* P 13.
1 40 p. Type **27** 20 10
2 1 t. Spotted Deer 30 10
3 2 t. 25, Leopard (*horiz*) 85 20
4 3 t. 50, Gaur (*horiz*).. .. .. 90 35
5 4 t. Indian Elephant (*horiz*) .. .. .. 1·75 50
6 5 t. Tiger (*horiz*) .. .. 2·00 75
1/6 .. .. *Set of* 6 5·50 1·75
The Bengali numerals on the 40 p. resemble "80", and that on the t. resembles "8".

(Des A. Karim. Litho Harrison)

78 (22 Jan). *First National Scout Jamboree. T* **28** *and similar designs.* P 13.
7 40 p. red, deep blue and light blue 30 10
8 3 t. 50, carmine, deep blue and green .. 1·25 30
9 5 t. reddish lilac, deep blue and bright green 1·40 45
7/9 .. .. *Set of* 3 2·75 70
Designs: *Horiz*—3 t. 50, Scout stretcher-team. *Vert*—5 t. Scout lute.

29 *Michelia champaca*

(Des and litho Harrison)

978 (29 Apr). *Flowers. T* **29** *and similar horiz designs. Multicoloured.* P 14.
10 40 p. Type **29** 30 10
11 1 t. *Cassia fistula* 55 15
12 2 t. 25, *Delonix regia* 85 30
13 3 t. 50, *Nymphaea nouchali* .. .. .. 1·00 60
14 4 t. *Butea monosperma* .. .. 1·10 80
15 5 t. *Anthocephalus indicus* .. .. .. 1·25 85
10/15 .. .. *Set of* 6 4·50 2·40

30 St. Edward's Crown and Sceptres **31** Sir Alan Cobham's De Havilland D.H.50J

(Des and litho Harrison)

978 (20 May). *25th Anniv of Coronation. T* **30** *and similar vert designs. Multicoloured.* P 14.
16 40 p. Type **30** 10 10
17 3 t. 50, Balcony scene 15 30
18 5 t. Queen Elizabeth and Prince Philip .. 25 50
19 10 t. Coronation portrait by Cecil Beaton .. 45 80
16/19 .. .. *Set of* 4 80 1·50
MS120 89×121 mm. Nos. 116/19. P 14½ .. 90 1·50

(Des and litho Harrison)

978 (15 June). *75th Anniv of Powered Flight. T* **31** *and similar horiz designs.* P 13.
21 40 p. multicoloured 15 10
22 2 t. 25, blackish brown and light new blue .. 50 45
23 3 t. 50, blackish brown and yellow 65 65
24 5 t. multicoloured .. .. 4·00 3·50
21/4 .. .. *Set of* 4 4·75 4·25
Designs:—2 t. 25, Captain Hans Bertram's Junkers W.33 eaplane *Atlantis*; 3 t. 50, Wright brothers' Flyer III; 5 t. Concorde.

32 Fenchuganj Fertilizer Factory **33** Tawaf-E-Ka'aba, Mecca

(Des P. Mandal (5 p.), A. Karim (10 p.), Harrison (30, 50 p., 1 t.). Photo Harrison)

1978 (6 Nov)–**82.** *Designs as T* **32.** P 14½.
125 5 p. deep brown (25.3.79) 10 10
126 10 p. turquoise-blue 10 10
127 15 p. orange (1.8.80) 10 10
128 20 p. brown-red (15.12.79) 10 10
129 25 p. grey-blue (1982) 15 10
130 30 p. deep green (10.12.80) 90 10
131 40 p. maroon (15.12.79) 30 10
132 50 p. black (1981) .. .. 3·00 1·50
134 80 p. brown (1.8.80) 20 10
136 1 t. reddish violet (6.81) .. .. .. 3·50 10
137 2 t. dull ultramarine (21.10.81) .. .. 50 1·50
125/37 .. .. *Set of* 11 8·00 3·00
Designs: *Horiz*—5 p. Lalbag Fort; 25 p. Jute on a boat; 40 p., 50 p. Baitul Mukarram Mosque; 1 t. Dotara (musical instrument); 2 t. Karnaphuli Dam. *Vert*—15 p. Pineapple; 20 p. Bangladesh gas; 30 p. Banana Tree; 80 p. Mohastan Garh.

(Des A. Karim. Litho J.W.)

1978 (9 Nov). *Holy Pilgrimage to Mecca. T* **33** *and similar multicoloured design.* P 13.
140 40 p. Type **33** 20 10
141 3 t. 50, Pilgrims in Wuquf, Arafat (*horiz*) .. 60 45

34 Jasim Uddin

(Des P. Mandal. Litho J.W.)

1979 (14 Mar). *3rd Death Anniv of Jasim Uddin (poet).* P 14.
142 **34** 40 p. multicoloured 20 30

35 Moulana Abdul Hamid Khan Bhashani **36** Sir Rowland Hill

(Des P. Mandal. Litho Harrison)

1979 (17 Nov). *3rd Death Anniv of Moulana Abdul Hamid Khan Bhashani (national leader).* P 12½.
143 **35** 40 p. multicoloured 40 20

(Des A. Karim. Litho Harrison)

1979 (26 Nov). *Death Centenary of Sir Rowland Hill. T* **36** *and similar designs.* P 14.
144 40 p. turquoise-blue, Venetian red and pale turquoise-blue 10 10
145 3 t. 50, multicoloured 35 30
146 10 t. multicoloured .. .. 80 1·00
144/6 .. .. *Set of* 3 1·10 1·25
MS147 176 × 96 mm. Nos. 144/6 .. .. .. 2·00 2·75
Designs: *Horiz*—3 t. 50, 1971 10 p. definitive stamp and Sir Rowland Hill; 10 t. 1974 1 t. 25, Centenary of U.P.U. commemorative stamp and Sir Rowland Hill.

37 Children with Hoops **38** Rotary International Emblem

(Des P. Mandal. Litho Harrison)

1979 (17 Dec). *International Year of the Child. T* **37** *and similar vert designs. Multicoloured.* P 14 × 14½.
148 40 p. Type **37** 10 10
149 3 t. 50, Child with kite 35 35
150 5 t. Children playing 50 50
148/50 .. .. *Set of* 3 80 80
MS151 170×120 mm. Nos. 148/50. P 14½ .. 1·50 2·75

(Des P. Mandal. Litho Rosenbaum Bros, Vienna)

1980 (23 Feb). *75th Anniv of Rotary International. T* **38** *and similar vert design showing club emblem.* P 13½×14.
152 40 p. black, vermilion and bistre-yellow .. 20 10
153 5 t. gold and bright blue 65 45

39 Canal Digging **40** A. K. Fazlul Huq

(Des A. Karim. Litho Rosenbaum Bros, Vienna)

1980 (27 Mar). *Mass Participation in Canal Digging.* P 14×13½.
154 **39** 40 p. multicoloured 40 30

(Des P. Mandal. Litho Rosenbaum Bros, Vienna)

1980 (27 Apr). *18th Death Anniv of A. K. Fazlul Huq (national leader).* P 13½×14.
155 **40** 40 p. multicoloured 30 30
On the face value the Bengali numerals resemble "80".

41 Early forms of Mail Transport **42** Dome of the Rock

(Des A. Karim. Litho Rosenbaum Bros, Vienna)

1980 (5 May). *"London 1980" International Stamp Exhibition. T* **41** *and similar horiz design. Multicoloured.* P 14×13½.
156 1 t. Type **41** 15 10
157 10 t. Modern forms of mail transport .. 1·25 85
MS158 140 × 95 mm. Nos. 156/7 .. .. .. 1·40 2·00

(Des A. Karim. Litho Harrison)

1980 (21 Aug). *Palestinian Welfare.* P 14½.
159 **42** 50 p. deep mauve 70 30
A similar stamp in grey, showing a Palestinian guerilla and the Dome of the Rock, printed by the State Printing Works, Moscow, was prepared in 1980, but not issued due to errors in the Arabic inscription. Quantities of the stamp were subsequently reported stolen. Examples were also issued by Comilla and Kotbari post offices on 27 September 1992 without authority.

43 Outdoor Class

(Des P. Mandal. Litho Rosenbaum Bros, Vienna)

1980 (23 Aug). *Education.* P 13½×14.
160 **43** 50 p. multicoloured 40 30

44 Beach Scene **45** Mecca

(Des A. Karim. Litho Rosenbaum Bros, Vienna)

1980 (27 Sept). *World Tourism Conference, Manila.* T **44** and *similar horiz design showing different beach scene.* P 14.
161 50 p. multicoloured 30 30
 a. Horiz pair. Nos. 161/2 .. .. 90 1·00
162 5 t. multicoloured 60 70
MS163 140 × 88 mm. Nos. 161/2 .. .. 90 1·50
 Nos. 161/2 were printed together, *se-tenant*, in horizontal pairs throughout the sheet.

(Des A. Karim. Litho Rosenbaum Bros, Vienna)

1980 (11 Nov). *Moslem Year 1400 A.H. Commemoration.* P 14×13½.
164 **45** 50 p. multicoloured 20 20

46 Begum Roquiah   **47** Spotted Deer and Scout Emblem

(Des A. Karim. Litho Rosenbaum Bros, Vienna)

1980 (9 Dec). *Birth Centenary of Begum Roquiah (campaigner for women's rights).* P 14.
165 **45** 50 p. multicoloured 10 10
166 2 t. multicoloured 35 20

(Des A. Karim. Litho Rosenbaum Bros, Vienna)

1981 (1 Jan). *5th Asia-Pacific/2nd Bangladesh Scout Jamboree.* P 13½×14.
167 **47** 50 p. multicoloured 40 15
168 5 t. multicoloured .. .. .. 1·25 2·00

2nd.
CENSUS
1981
(48)

49 Queen Elizabeth the Queen Mother

1981 (6 Mar). *Second Population Census. Nos. 38/40 optd with* T **48**.
169 **10** 20 p. multicoloured 10 10
170 25 p. multicoloured 10 10
171 75 p. multicoloured 20 30
169/71 .. .. .. *Set of 3* 30 40

(Des R. Granger Barrett. Litho Rosenbaum Bros, Vienna)

1981 (16 Mar). *80th Birthday of Queen Elizabeth the Queen Mother.* P 13½×14.
172 **49** 1 t. multicoloured 15 15
173 15 t. multicoloured .. .. .. 1·75 2·50
MS174 95 × 73 mm. Nos. 172/3 .. .. 2·40 2·50

50 Revolutionary with Flag and Sub-machine-gun   **51** Bangladesh Village and Farm Scenes

(Des P. Mandal. Litho Rosenbaum Bros, Vienna)

1981 (26 Mar). *Tenth Anniv of Independence.* T **50** and *similar vert design. Multicolourd.* P 13½×14.
175 50 p. Type **50** 15 10
176 2 t. Figures on map symbolising Bangladesh life-style 25 45

(Des A. Karim. Litho Rosenbaum Bros, Vienna)

1981 (1 Sept). *U.N. Conference on Least Developed Countries, Paris.* P 14×13½.
177 **51** 50 p. multicoloured 35 15

52 Kemal Atatürk in Civilian Dress   **53** Deaf People using Sign Language

(Des F. Karim and P. Mandal. Litho Rosenbaum Bros, Vienna)

1981 (10 Nov). *Birth Centenary of Kemal Atatürk (Turkish statesman).* T **52** and *similar vert design. Multicoloured.* P 13½×14.
178 50 p. Type **52** 45 20
179 1 t. Kemal Atatürk in uniform 80 50

(Des F. Karim. Litho Ueberreuter, Austria)

1981 (26 Dec). *International Year for Disabled Persons.* T **53** and *similar multicoloured design.* P 13½ × 14 (50 p.) or 14 × 13½ (2 t.).
180 50 p. Type **53** 40 20
181 2 t. Disabled person writing (*horiz*) .. .. 1·25 2·00

54 Farm Scene and Wheat Ear   **55** River Scene

(Des F. Karim. Litho Ueberreuter, Austria)

1981 (31 Dec). *World Food Day.* P 13½ × 14.
182 **54** 50 p. multicoloured 50 70

(Des P. Mandal. Litho Ueberreuter, Vienna)

1982 (22 May). *10th Anniv of Human Environment Conference.* P 13½ × 14.
183 **55** 50 p. multicoloured 50 70

56 Dr. M. Hussain   **57** Knotted Rope surrounding Bengali "75"

(Des F. Karim. Litho Ueberreuter, Vienna)

1982 (9 Oct). *First Death Anniv of Dr. Motahar Hussain (educationist).* P 13½.
184 **56** 50 p. multicoloured 50 70

(Des F. Karim and P. Mandal. Litho Ueberreuter, Vienna)

1982 (21 Oct). *75th Anniv of Boy Scout Movement and 125th Birth Anniv of Lord Baden-Powell.* T **57** and *similar multicoloured design.* P 14×13½ (50 p.) or 13½×14 (2 t.).
185 50 p. Type **57** .. .. 1·00 30
186 2 t. Lord Baden-Powell (*vert*) .. .. 3·25 4·50

সম্মিলিত
সমস্ত বাহিনী দিবস
২১ নভেম্বর, ৮২
(58)

59 Capt. Mohiuddin Jahangir

1982 (21 Nov). *Armed Forces' Day. No. 175 optd with* T **58**.
187 50 p. Type **50** .. .. .. 2·00 2·00

(Litho Ueberreuter, Vienna)

1982 (16 Dec). *Heroes and Martyrs of the Liberation.* T **59** and *similar horiz designs. Multicoloured: background colours of commemorative plaque given.* P 14×13½.
188 50 p. Type **59** (pale orange) 30 45
 a. Horiz strip of 7. Nos. 188/94 .. 1·90
189 50 p. Sepoy Hamidur Rahman (apple-green) 30 45

190 50 p. Sepoy Mohammed Mustafa Kamal (dull claret) 30 4
191 50 p. Muhammed Ruhul Amin (bistre-yellow) 30 4
192 50 p. Flt. Lt. M. Matiur Rahman (olive-bistre) 30 4
193 50 p. Lance-Naik Munshi Abdur Rob (chestnut) 30 4
194 50 p. Lance-Naik Nur Mouhammad (bright green) 30 4
188/94 .. .. .. *Set of 7* 1·90 2·7
 Nos. 188/94 were printed together, *se-tenant*, in horizonta strips of 7 throughout the sheet.

60 Metric Scales   **61** Dr. Robert Koch

(Des F. Karim. Litho Ueberreuter, Vienna)

1983 (10 Jan). *Introduction of Metric Weights and Measures* T **60** and *similar multicoloured design.* P 13½×14 (50 p.) o 14×13½ (2 t.).
195 50 p. Type **60** 40 3
196 2 t. Weights, jug and tap measure (*horiz*) .. 1·75 2·5

(Des F. Karim. Litho Ueberreuter, Vienna)

1983 (20 Feb). *Centenary (1982) of Robert Koch's Discovery Tubercle Bacillus.* T **61** and *similar vert design. Mult coloured.* P 13½×14.
197 50 p. Type **61** .. .. .. 1·00
198 1 t. Microscope, slide and X-ray .. .. 2·25 3·

62 Open Stage Theatre   **63** Dr. Muhammed Shahidulla

(Des F. Karim and P. Mandal. Litho Ueberreuter, Vienna)

1983 (14 Mar). *Commonwealth Day.* T **62** and *similar hor designs. Multicoloured.* P 14.
199 1 t. Type **62** 10 1
200 3 t. Boat race 20 3
201 10 t. Snake dance 50 9
202 15 t. Picking tea .. .. .. 60 1·5
199/202 .. .. .. *Set of 4* 1·25 2·5

(Litho Ueberreuter, Vienna)

1983 (10 July). *Dr. Muhammed Shahidulla (Bengali scholar Commemoration.* P 13½×14.
203 **63** 50 p. multicoloured 75 8

64 Magpie Robin

(Des F. Karim and P. Mandal. Litho Ueberreuter, Vienna)

1983 (17 Aug). *Birds of Bangladesh.* T **64** and *simila multicoloured designs.* P 14×13½ (50 p., 5 t.) or 13½×14 (2 t 3 t. 75).
204 50 p. Type **64** .. .. .. 1·25 4
205 2 t. White-breasted Kingfisher (*vert*) 2·25 2·
206 3 t. 75 Lesser Golden-backed Woodpecker (*vert*) .. .. .. 3·00 3·0
207 5 t. White-winged Wood Duck .. .. 3·50 3·
204/7 .. .. .. *Set of 4* 9·00 8·
MS208 165×110 mm. Nos. 204/7 (*sold at 13 t.*) .. 11·00 14·0

Visit of Queen

Nov. '83

65 *Macrobrachium rosenbergii*   (66)

(Litho Ueberreuter, Vienna)

1983 (31 Oct). *Marine Life. T 65 and similar horiz designs.*
Multicoloured. P 14×13½.

209	50 p. Type 65				80	30
210	2 t. White Pomfret	..	..		2·00	1·60
211	3 t. 75, Rohu		..		2·50	2·00
212	5 t. Climbing Perch		..		3·00	2·75
209/12				*Set of 4*	7·50	6·00
MS213	119×98 mm. Nos. 209/13. Imperf (*sold at*					
	13 t.)				5·00	6·00

1983 (14 Nov). *Visit of Queen Elizabeth II. No. 95 optd with*
T 66 in red.

214	10 t. Queen Elizabeth and Prince Philip	..	3·00	4·00
	a. Optd "Nov '83" (R. 3/10)	..		

67 Conference Hall, Dhaka

68 Early Mail Runner

(Des M. Begum and M. Shamim. Litho Ueberreuter, Vienna)

1983 (5 Dec). *14th Islamic Foreign Ministers' Conference, Dhaka.*
T 67 and similar horiz design. Multicoloured. P 14×13½.

215	50 p. Type 67		..		50	30
216	5 t. Old Fort, Dhaka	..	..		1·75	2·75

(Litho Ueberreuter, Vienna)

1983 (21 Dec). *World Communications Year. T 68 and similar*
multicoloured designs. P 14×13½ (10 t.) or 13½×14 (others).

217	50 p. Type 68				30	15
218	5 t. Sailing ship, steam train and Boeing					
	707 airliner	..	..		2·00	1·50
219	10 t. Mail runner and dish aerial (*horiz*)	..	2·75	2·50
	a. Gold (on dish aerial) omitted				£100	
217/19				*Set of 3*	4·50	3·75

69 Carrying Mail
by Boat　　　　　　(**70**)

(Des M. Akond, P. Mandal and M. Shamim. Litho State Ptg
Wks, Moscow)

1983 (21 Dec)–**86**. *Postal Communications. T 69 and similar*
designs. P 11½×12½ (5, 25 p.), 12×11½ (1, 2, 3, 5 t.) or
12½×11½ (others).

220	5 p. turquoise-blue	..	..		10	10
221	10 p. purple	..	..		10	10
222	15 p. new blue	..	..		10	10
223	20 p. grey-black	..	..		30	10
224	25 p. slate	..	..		15	10
225	30 p. brown	..	..		15	10
226	50 p. light brown	..			20	10
227	1 t. dull ultramarine	..	..		30	10
228	2 t. deep bluish green	..			30	10
228a	3 t. bistre (11.1.86)	..			75	30
229	5 t. bright purple	..			80	40
220/9				*Set of 11*	2·75	1·00

Designs: *Horiz (22 × 17 mm)*—10 p. Counter, Dhaka G.P.O.;
15 p. I.W.T.A. Terminal, Dhaka; 20 p. Inside railway travelling
post office; 30 p. Emptying pillar box; 50 p. Mobile post office van.
(30 × 19 mm)—1 t. Kamalapur Railway Station, Dhaka; 2 t. Zia
International Airport; 3 t. Sorting mail by machine; 5 t. Khulna
G.P.O. *Vert (17×22 mm)*—25 p. Delivering a letter.

1984 (1 Feb). *1st National Stamp Exhibition (1st issue). Nos.*
161/2 optd with T 70 (5 t.) or "First Bangladesh National
Philatelic Exhibition–1984" (50 p.), both in red.

230	44	50 p. multicoloured	..	..	60	85
		a. Horiz pair. Nos. 230/1	..		1·50	2·25
231	–	5 t. multicoloured	..	..	90	1·40

71 Girl with Stamp Album

(Des P. Mandal. Litho Harrison)

1984 (12 May). *1st National Stamp Exhibition (2nd issue). T 71*
and similar triangular design. Multicoloured. P 14.

232	50 p. Type 71	..	..		65	1·25
	a. Pair. Nos. 232/3 ..				1·75	2·75
233	7 t. 50, Boy with stamp album	..		1·10	1·60
MS234	98×117 mm. Nos. 232/3 (*sold at 10 t.*)	3·00	4·00

Nos. 232/3 were printed together, *se-tenant*, in pairs throughout the sheet.

---

72 Sarus Crane and Gavial

73 Eagle attacking
Hen with Chicks

(Des P. Mandal and M. Akond. Litho Ueberreuter, Vienna)

1984 (17 July). *Dhaka Zoo. T 72 and similar vert design.*
Multicoloured. P 13½×14.

235	1 t. Type 72		..		1·75	85
236	2 t. Common Peafowl and Tiger	..		2·50	3·25

(Des K. Mustafa. Litho Harrison)

1984 (3 Dec). *Centenary of Postal Life Insurance. T 73 and*
similar vert design. Multicoloured. P 14.

237	1 t. Type 73		..		50	20
238	5 t. Bangladesh family and postman's hand			
	with insurance cheque	..	..		1·50	1·50

74 Abbasuddin Ahmad　　　　　(**75**)

(Des K. Mustafa. Litho Harrison)

1984 (24 Dec). *Abbasuddin Ahmad (singer) Commemoration.*
P 14.

239	**74**	3 t. multicoloured	..	..	70	40

1984 (27 Dec). *"Khulnapex-84" Stamp Exhibition. No. 86 optd*
with T 75.

240	**22**	2 t. 25, multicoloured	..	..	70	60

76 Cycling

(Des M. Shamim. Litho Harrison)

1984 (31 Dec). *Olympic Games, Los Angeles. T 76 and similar*
horiz designs. Multicoloured. P 14.

241	1 t. Type 76		..		1·25	30
242	5 t. Hockey	..	..		2·50	2·25
243	10 t. Volleyball	..	..		2·75	3·00
241/3				*Set of 3*	6·00	5·00

77 Farmer with Rice and Sickle　　**78** Mother and Baby

(Des M. Shamim. Litho Harrison)

1985 (2 Feb). *9th Annual Meeting of Islamic Development*
Bank, Dhaka. T 77 and similar horiz design. Multicoloured.
P 14.

244	1 t. Type 77	..	..		35	15
245	5 t. Citizens of four races	..		1·25	1·25

(Des M. Akond. Litho Harrison)

1985 (14 Mar). *Child Survival Campaign. T 78 and similar vert*
design. Multicoloured. P 14.

246	1 t. Type 78		..		30	10
247	10 t. Young child and growth graph	..	2·50	2·00

উপজেলা নির্বাচন ১৯৮৫

(**79**)

1985 (16 May). *Local Elections. Nos. 110/15 optd with T 79.*

248	40 p. Type 29		..		10	15
249	1 t. Cassia fistula				10	20
250	2 t. 25, Delonix regia				15	35
251	3 t. 50, Nymphaea nouchali	..		20	45
252	4 t. Butea monosperma	..		20	45
253	5 t. Anthocephalus indicus ..			30	55
248/53			*Set of 6*	85	1·90

80 Women working at
Traditional Crafts

81 U.N. Building, New York,
Peace Doves and Flags

(Des M. Akond. Litho Harrison)

1985 (18 July). *United Nations Decade for Women. T 80 and*
similar vert design. Multicoloured. P 14.

254	1 t. Type 80	..	..		25	10
255	10 t. Women with microscope, computer ter-			
	minal and in classroom. ..	..		1·25	85

(Des M. Akond. Litho Harrison)

1985 (14 Sept). *40th Anniv of United Nations Organization and*
11th Anniv of Bangladesh Membership. T 81 and similar horiz
design. Multicoloured. P 14.

256	1 t. Type 81	..			10	10
257	10 t. Map of world and Bangladesh flag	..	80	90

82 Head of Youth,
Flowers and Symbols
of Commerce and
Agriculture

83 Emblem and Seven Doves

(Des M. Shamim. Litho Harrison)

1985 (2 Nov). *International Youth Year. T 82 and similar vert*
design. Multicoloured. P 14.

258	1 t. Type 82		..		10	10
259	5 t. Head of youth, flowers and symbols of			
	industry ..	..	..		40	60

(Des M. Akond. Litho Harrison)

1985 (8 Dec). *1st Summit Meeting of South Asian Association*
for Regional Co-operation, Dhaka. T 83 and similar vert
design. Multicoloured. P 14.

260	1 t. Type 83		..		10	10
261	5 t. Flags of member nations and lotus blos-			
	som	..	..		40	60

84 Zainul Abedin　　　　　(**85**)

(Des P. Mandal. Litho Harrison)

1985 (28 Dec). *10th Death Anniv of Zainul Abedin (artist).*
P 14.

262	**84**	3 t. multicoloured	..	..	75	30
		a. Red-brown ("BANGLADESH" and			
		face value) omitted				

1985 (29 Dec). *3rd National Scout Jamboree. No. 109 optd with*
T 85.

263	5 t. reddish lilac, deep blue and bright green	2·00	60

OMNIBUS ISSUES

Details, together with prices for complete sets,
of the various Omnibus issues from the 1935
Silver Jubilee series to date are included in a
special section following Zimbabwe at the end of
Volume 2.

86 "Fishing Net" (Safiuddin Ahmed)

(Litho Harrison)

1986 (6 Apr). *Bangladesh Paintings. T* **86** *and similar horiz designs. Multicoloured. P* 14.
264	1 t. Type **86** ..			15	10
265	5 t. "Happy Return" (Quamrul Hassan)			40	50
266	10 t. "Levelling the Ploughed Field" (Zainul				
	Abedin) ..			70	80
264/6	.. ..		Set of 3	1·10	1·25

87 Two Players competing for Ball   **88** General M. A. G. Osmani

(Des K. Mustafa. Litho Harrison)

1986 (29 June). *World Cup Football Championship, Mexico. T* **87** *and similar horiz design. Multicoloured. P* 15 × 14.
267	1 t. Type **87** ..			50	10
268	10 t. Goalkeeper and ball in net			2·25	2·00
MS269	105 × 75 mm. 20 t. Four players				
	(60 × 44 mm). Imperf. ..			4·00	4·00

(Des P. Mandal. Litho Harrison)

1986 (18 Sept). *General M. A. G. Osmani* (*army commander-in-chief*) *Commemoration. P* 14.
270	**88** 3 t. multicoloured ..			1·00	75

SAARC SEMINAR '86

(89)

90 Butterflies and Nuclear Explosion

1986 (3 Dec). *South Asian Association for Regional Co-operation Seminar. No.* 183 *optd with T* **89**.
271	**55** 50 p. multicoloured	..		1·50	2·00

(Des M. Shamim. Litho State Ptg Wks, Moscow)

1986 (29 Dec). *International Peace Year. T* **90** *and similar vert designs. Multicoloured. P* 12 × 12½.
272	1 t. Type **90**			50	25
273	10 t. Flowers and ruined buildings ..			2·75	3·00
MS274	109 × 80 mm. 20 t. Peace dove and soldier			1·50	2·00

TK. 1·00

CONFERENCE FOR
DEVELOPMENT '87

(91)

1987 (12 Jan). *Conference for Development. Nos.* 152/3 *surch or optd as T* **91**.
275	**38** 1 t. on 40 p. black, vermilion & bistre-yell			10	15
	a. Surch double	..			
	b. Surch triple	..			
	c. Surch sideways	..			
	d. Surch inverted	..			
276	– 5 t. gold and bright blue	..		30	60
	a. Opt double	..			
	b. Opt double, one inverted	..			
	c. Opt inverted ..				

Stamp booklets containing Nos. 275/6 in strips of three are private productions and were not sold by the Bangladesh Post Office.

92 Demonstrators with Placards   **93** Nurse giving Injection

(Des B. Sardar. Litho State Ptg Wks, Moscow)

1987 (21 Feb). *35th Anniv of Bangla Language Movement. T* **92** *and similar horiz design. Multicoloured. P* 12½ × 12.
277	3 t. Type **92** ..			80	1·25
	a. Horiz pair. Nos. 277/8 ..			1·60	2·50
278	3 t. Martyrs' Memorial			80	1·25

Nos. 277/8 were printed together, *se-tenant*, in horizontal pairs throughout the sheet, each pair forming a composite design.

(Litho State Ptg Wks, Moscow)

1987 (7 Apr). *World Health Day. P* 11½ × 12.
279	**93** 1 t. blue-black and deep blue	..		1·75	1·25

See also No. 295.

94 Pattern and Bengali Script   **95** Jute Shika

(Des M. Akond. Litho State Ptg Wks, Moscow)

1987 (16 Apr). *Bengali New Year. T* **94** *and similar vert design. Multicoloured. P* 12 × 12½.
280	1 t. Type **94**	..	..	10	10
281	10 t. Bengali woman ..		..	40	60

(Des P. Mandal, K. Mustafa and M. Akond. Photo State Ptg Wks, Moscow)

1987 (18 May). *Export Products. T* **95** *and similar multicoloured designs. P* 12½ × 12 (5 t.) *or* 12 × 12½ (*others*).
282	1 t. Type **95**	..	..	10	10
283	5 t. Jute carpet (*horiz*)	..	..	30	35
284	10 t. Cane table lamp	..	..	45	70
282/4	.. ..		Set of 3	70	1·00

96 Ustad Ayet Ali Khan and Surbahar   **97** Palanquin

(Litho State Ptg Wks, Moscow)

1987 (2 Sept). *20th Death Anniv of Ustad Ayet Ali Khan* (*musician and composer*). *P* 12 × 12½.
285	**96** 5 t. multicoloured ..		..	55	40

(Litho State Ptg Wks, Moscow)

1987 (24 Oct). *Transport. T* **97** *and similar horiz designs. Multicoloured. P* 12½ × 12.
286	2 t. Type **97** ..	..	..	20	15
287	3 t. Bicycle rickshaw	..	..	30	20
288	5 t. River steamer ..		..	70	35
289	7 t. Express diesel train	..	..	1·40	50
290	10 t. Bullock cart	..	..	50	75
286/90	.. ..		Set of 5	2·75	1·75

98 H. S. Suhrawardy   **99** Villagers fleeing from Typhoon

(Des P. Mandal. Litho State Ptg Wks, Moscow)

1987 (5 Dec). *Hossain Shahid Suhrawardy* (*politician*) *Commem. P* 12 × 12½.
291	**98** 3 t. multicoloured ..		..	20	3

(Des M. Akond. Litho State Ptg Wks, Moscow)

1987 (15 Dec). *International Year of Shelter for the Homeless. T* **99** *and similar horiz design. Multicoloured. P* 12½ × 12.
292	5 t. Type **99**	..	..	20	3
	a. Horiz pair. Nos. 292/3 ..		..	40	6
293	5 t. Villagers and modern houses	..	..	20	3

Nos. 292/3 were printed together, *se-tenant*, in horizontal pairs throughout the sheet.

100 President Ershad addressing Parliament

(Des K. Mustafa. Litho State Ptg Wks, Moscow)

1987 (31 Dec). *1st Anniv of Return to Democracy. P* 12½ × 12.
294	**100** 10 t. multicoloured	..	..	40	6

(Litho State Ptg Wks, Moscow)

1988 (16 Jan). *World Health Day. Vert design as T* **93**. *P* 11½ × 12.
295	25 p. brown ..		..	30	2

Design:—25 p. Oral rehydration.

101 Woman Planting Palm Saplings

(Des K. Mustafa. Litho State Ptg Wks, Moscow)

1988 (26 Jan). *I.F.A.D. Seminar on Agricultural Loans for Rural Women. T* **101** *and similar horiz design. Multicoloured. P* 12½ × 12.
296	3 t. Type **101**	..	..	15	20
297	5 t. Village woman milking cow	..	..	20	40

102 Basketball

(Litho State Ptg Wks, Moscow)

1988 (20 Sept). *Olympic Games, Seoul. T* **102** *and similar diamond-shaped designs. Multicoloured. P* 11½.
298	5 t. Type **102**	..	..	20	25
	a. Strip of 5. Nos. 298/302	..		90	
299	5 t. Weightlifting	..	..	20	25
300	5 t. Tennis	..	..	20	25
301	5 t. Rifle-shooting	..	..	20	25
302	5 t. Boxing	..	..	20	25
298/302			Set of 5	90	1·10

Nos. 298/302 were printed together, *se-tenant*, in horizontal and vertical strips of five throughout the sheet.

103 Interior of Shait Gumbaz Mosque, Bagerhat   **104** Henri Dunant (founder), Red Cross and Crescent

(Litho State Ptg Wks, Moscow)

988 (9 Oct). *Historical Buildings. T* **103** *and similar horiz designs. Multicoloured.* P 12½×12.

3	1 t.	Type 103		10	10
4	4 t.	Paharpur Monastery		10	10
5	5 t.	Kantanagar Temple, Dinajpur		10	15
6	10 t.	Lalbag Fort, Dhaka		15	15
3/6			*Set of* 4	30	30

(Litho State Ptg Wks, Moscow)

988 (26 Oct). *125th Anniv of International Red Cross and Red Crescent. T* **104** *and similar vert design. Multicoloured.* P 12 × 12½.

7	5 t.	Type 104		25	25
8	10 t.	Red Cross workers with patient		45	45

105 Dr. Qudrat-i-Khuda in Laboratory

106 Wicket-keeper

(Litho State Ptg Wks, Moscow)

988 (3 Nov). *Dr. Qudrat-i-Khuda (scientist) Commemoration.* P 12 × 12½.

09	**105**	5 t. multicoloured		20	25

(Litho State Ptg Wks, Moscow)

988 (27 Nov). *Asia Cup Cricket. T* **106** *and similar vert designs. Multicoloured.* P 12 × 12½.

10	1 t.	Type 106		70	90
	a. Horiz strip of 3. Nos. 310/12			2·40	
11	5 t.	Batsman		90	1·00
12	10 t.	Bowler		1·10	1·40
10/12			*Set of* 3	2·40	3·00

Nos. 310/12 were printed together, *se-tenant*, in horizontal strips of three throughout the sheet.

107 Labourers, Factory and Technician

(Litho State Ptg Wks, Moscow)

988 (29 Nov). *32nd Meeting of Colombo Plan Consultative Committee, Dhaka.* P 12×12½.

13	**107**	3 t. multicoloured		10	10
14		10 t. multicoloured		40	45

108 Dhaka G.P.O. Building

(Litho State Ptg Wks, Moscow)

988 (6 Dec). *25th Anniv of Dhaka G.P.O. Building. T* **108** *and similar horiz design. Multicoloured.* P 12.

315	1 t.	Type 108		10	10
316	5 t.	Post Office counter		20	25

৫ম জাতীয় রোভার মুট
১৯৮৮-৮৯

(**109**)

110 Bangladesh Airport

1988 (29 Dec). *5th National Rover Scout Moot.* No. 168 *optd with T* **109**.

317	47	5 t. multicoloured		90	90
	a. Opt inverted				

(Des K. Mustafa (3, 10 t.), N. Islam (5 t.), M. Akond (20 t.). Litho State Ptg Wks, Moscow)

1989 (1 Jan)–92. *Bangladesh Landmarks. T* **110** *and similar designs.* P 12×11½ (3 t.), 12×12½ (4, 20 t.), 12½×12 (5 t.) or 11½×12 (10 t.).

318	3 t. black and light blue			10	10
318a	4 t. steel blue (15.7.92)			15	20
319	5 t. black and orange-brown (31.3.89)			15	20
320	10 t. rosine (1.7.89)			30	35
321	20 t. multicoloured (1.7.89)			65	70
318/21			*Set of* 5	1·25	1·50

Designs: *Vert* (22×33 *mm*)—5 t. Curzon Hall. (19½×31½ *mm*) 10 t. Fertiliser factory, Chittagong. *Horiz* (33×23 *mm*)—4 t. Chittagong port. 20 t. Postal Academy. Rajshahi.

চতুর্থ দ্বিবার্ষিক এশীয়
চারুকলা প্রদর্শনী
বাংলাদেশ ১৯৮৯

(**111**)

112 Irrigation Methods and Student with Telescope

1989 (1 Mar). *4th Biennial Asian Art Exhibition.* No. 266 *optd with T* **111**.

322	10 t. "Levelling the Ploughed Field" (Zainul Abedin)			40	45

(Litho State Ptg Wks, Moscow)

1989 (7 Mar). *12th National Science and Technology Week.* P 12½×12½.

323	**112**	10 t. multicoloured		40	45

113 Academy Logo

114 Rejoicing Crowds, Paris, 1789

(Litho State Ptg Wks, Moscow)

1989 (13 Mar). *75th Anniv of Police Academy, Sardah.* P 12×12½.

324	**113**	10 t. multicoloured		40	45

(Des K. Mustafa (Nos. **MS327/8**). Litho Harrison)

1989 (12 July). *Bicentenary of French Revolution. T* **114** *and similar horiz design. Multicoloured.* P 14×14½.

325	17 t.	Type 114		70	75
	a. Horiz pair. Nos. 325/6 plus label			1·40	1·50
326	17 t.	Storming the Bastille, 1789		70	75
MS327	125×125 mm. 5 t. Men with pickaxes; 10 t. "Liberty guiding the People" (detail) (Delacroix); 10 t. Crowd with cannon. P 14			1·75	2·50
MS328	152×88 mm. 25 t. Storming the Bastille. Imperf			1·75	2·50

Nos. 325/6 were printed in sheets of 30 (6×5) with No. 325 in vertical columns one and four, labels showing the Bicentenary emblem in columns two and five, and No. 326 in columns three and six.

The design of No. **MS328** incorporates the three scenes featured on No. **MS327**.

115 Sowing and Harvesting

(Litho State Ptg Wks, Moscow)

1989 (10 Aug). *10th Anniv of Asia-Pacific Integrated Rural Development Centre. T* **115** *and similar horiz design. Multicoloured.* P 12½×12.

329	5 t.	Type 115		45	45
	a. Horiz pair. Nos. 329/30			95	95
330	10 t.	Rural activities		50	50

Nos. 329/30 were printed together, *se-tenant*, in horizontal pairs throughout the sheet, each pair forming a composite design.

STANLEY GIBBONS STAMP COLLECTING SERIES

Introductory booklets on *How to Start, How to Identify Stamps* and *Collecting by Theme.* A series of well illustrated guides at a low price.

Write for details.

---

116 Helper and Child playing with Baby

117 U.N. Soldier on Watch

(Litho State Ptg Wks, Moscow)

1989 (22 Aug). *40th Anniv of S.O.S. International Children's Village. T* **116** *and similar horiz design. Multicoloured.* P 12½ × 12.

331	1 t.	Type 116		15	10
332	10 t.	Foster mother with children		55	55

(Litho State Ptg Wks, Moscow)

1989 (12 Sept). *1st Anniv of Bangladesh Participation in U.N. Peace-keeping Force. T* **117** *and similar vert design. Multicoloured.* P 12×12½.

333	4 t.	Type 117		50	30
334	10 t.	Two soldiers checking positions		1·00	70

118 Festival Emblem

119 State Security Printing Press

(Litho State Ptg Wks, Moscow)

1989 (17 Nov). *2nd Asian Poetry Festival, Dhaka. T* **118** *and similar vert design.* P 12½×12½.

335	2 t. brt scarlet, dp carmine & myrtle-green			15	10
336	10 t. multicoloured			60	65

Design:—10 t. Festival emblem and hall.

(Litho State Security Ptg Press, Gazipur)

1989 (7 Dec). *Inauguration of State Security Printing Press, Gazipur.* P 13½.

337	**119**	10 t. multicoloured		65	65

120 Water Lilies and T.V. Emblem

(Litho State Ptg Wks, Moscow (5 t.), State Security Ptg Press, Gazipur (10 t.))

1989 (25 Dec). *25th Anniv of Bangladesh Television. T* **120** *and similar horiz design. Multicoloured.* P 12½×12 (5 t.) or 13½×12 (10 t.))

338	5 t.	Type 120		30	30
339	10 t.	Central emblem and water lilies		65	80

121 Gharial in Shallow Water

122 Symbolic Family

(Des K. Mustafa. Litho Harrison)

1990 (31 Jan). *Endangered Wildlife. Gharial. T* **121** *and similar horiz designs. Multicoloured.* P 14.

340	50 p.	Type 121		80	45
	a. Block of 4. Nos. 340/3			4·50	
341	1 t.	Gharial feeding		1·00	60
342	4 t.	Gharials basking on sand bank		1·40	70
343	10 t.	Two gharials resting		1·75	95
340/3			*Set of* 4	4·50	2·40

Nos. 340/3 were printed together, *se-tenant*, in blocks of four throughout the sheet.

(Litho State Ptg Press, Gazipur)

1990 (10 Feb). *Population Day.* P 13½.

344	**122**	6 t. multicoloured		55	35

123 Justice S.M. Murshed

124 Boy learning Alphabet

(Des P. Mandal. Litho State Ptg Wks, Moscow)

1990 (3 Apr). *10th Death Anniv of Justice Syed Mahbub Murshed.* P 12½×12.
345 **123** 5 t. multicoloured 90 35

(Litho State Ptg Wks, Moscow)

1990 (10 Apr). *International Literacy Year.* T **124** and similar vert design. Multicoloured. P 12×12½.
346 6 t. Type **124** .. .. .. 1·00 50
347 10 t. Boy teaching girl to write .. .. 1·50 1·00

125 Penny Black with "Stamp World London 90" Exhibition Emblem

126 Goalkeeper and Ball

(Des K. Mustafa. Litho State Security Ptg Press, Gazipur)

1990 (6 May). *150th Anniv of the Penny Black.* T **125** and similar vert design. Multicoloured. P 13½.
348 7 t. Type **125** .. .. .. 1·50 60
349 10 t. Penny Black, 1983 World Communications Year stamp and Bengali mail runner .. .. 1·75 1·00

(Des M. Shamim. Litho State Security Ptg Press, Gazipur)

1990 (12 June). *World Cup Football Championship, Italy.* T **126** and similar horiz designs. Multicoloured. P 13½.
350 8 t. Type **126** .. .. .. 1·75 90
351 10 t. Footballer with ball .. .. 2·00 1·00
MS352 104×79 mm. 25 t. Colosseum, Rome, with football. Imperf .. .. .. 4·50 4·75

127 Mango

128 Man gathering Wheat

(Des M. Shamim (1, 2t.), N. Islam (3, 4 t.), P. Mandal (5, 10 t). Litho State Ptg Wks, Moscow)

1990 (16 July). *Fruit.* T **127** and similar vert designs. Multicoloured. P 12×12½.
353 1 t. Type **127** 30 10
354 2 t. Guava 30 10
355 3 t. Water-melon 35 15
356 4 t. Papaya 40 25
357 5 t. Bread fruit 65 50
358 10 t. Carambola .. .. .. 1·25 1·25
353/8 .. .. .. *Set of 6* 3·00 2·00

PRINTERS. The following issues were printed in lithography by the State Security Printing Press, Gazipur, *unless otherwise stated.*

(Des M. Akond)

1990 (3 Sept). *U.N. Conference on Least Developed Countries, Paris.* P 14.
359 **128** 10 t. multicoloured .. .. 1·25 90
 a. Blue (U.N. emblem and inscr) inverted
On the evidence of the sheet marginal markings it would appear that the blue on No. 359a may be printed correctly and the remainder of the colours inverted. Unequal margins at top and bottom of the sheet also cause the country name and face value, in green, to be displaced.

MINIMUM PRICE

The minimum price quote is 10p which represents a handling charge rather than a basis for valuing common stamps. For further notes about prices see introductory pages.

129 Map of Asia with Stream of Letters

130 Canoe Racing

(Des K. Mustafa)

1990 (10 Sept). *20th Anniv of Asia–Pacific Postal Training Centre.* T **129** and similar vert design. Multicoloured. P 13½×14.
360 2 t. Type **129** 75 50
 a. Horiz pair. Nos. 360/1 .. 1·50 1·00
361 6 t. Map of Pacific with stream of letters 75 50
Nos. 360/1 were printed together, *se-tenant*, in horizontal pairs throughout the sheet, forming a composite map design.

(Des K. Mustafa)

1990 (22 Sept). *Asian Games, Beijing.* T **130** and similar horiz designs. Multicoloured. P 14×13½.
362 2 t. Type **130** 60 10
363 4 t. Kabaddi 75 25
364 6 t. Wrestling .. .. .. 1·25 75
365 10 t. Badminton .. .. .. 2·00 1·50
362/5 .. .. *Set of 4* 4·25 2·25

131 Lalan Shah

132 U.N. Logo and "40"

(Des K. Mustafa)

1990 (17 Oct). *1st Death Anniv of Lalan Shah (poet).* P 13½×14.
366 **131** 6 t. multicoloured .. .. 1·00 35

(Des M. Akond)

1990 (24 Oct). *40th Anniv of United Nations Development Programme.* P 14×13½.
367 **132** 6 t. multicoloured 80 35

133 Immunization

134 Salimullah Hall

(Des M. Akond (2 t.), P. Mandal (6 t.))

1990 (29 Nov)–**91**. P 14½×14.
368 **133** 2 t. brown 10 10
369 **134** 6 t. slate-blue & greenish yell (30.1.91) 20 25

135 Danaus chrysippus

136 Drugs attacking Bangladesh

(Des M. Shamim)

1990 (3 Dec). *Butterflies.* T **135** and similar square designs. Multicoloured. P 13½ × 12.
376 6 t. Type **135** .. .. .. 1·60 1·60
 a. Block of 4. Nos. 376/9 .. 6·00
 ab. Deep blue and chestnut inscr inverted (block of 4)
377 6 t. *Precis almana* .. .. 1·60 1·60
378 10 t. *Ixias pyrene* .. .. 1·75 1·75
379 10 t. *Danaus plexippus* .. .. 1·75 1·75
376/9 .. .. *Set of 4* 6·00 6·00
Nos. 376/9 were printed together, *se-tenant*, in blocks of four throughout the sheet.
On No. 376ab the printing of "BANGLADESH", in deep blue on No. 377 and in chestnut on No. 378, is inverted so that the inscription does not occur on these two designs. The inverted deep blue "BANGLADESH" appears on the left sheet margin or on No. 379 and the chestnut on No. 376.

(Des F. Karim (2 t.), M. Akond (4 t.))

1991 (1 Jan). *United Nations Anti-Drugs Decade.* T **136** and similar horiz design. Multicoloured. P 14.
380 2 t. Type **136** .. .. .. 1·00 50
381 4 t. "Drug" snake around globe .. 1·25 1·25

137 Silhouetted People on Map

138 "Invincible Bangla" (statue)

(Des P. Mandal)

1991 (12 Mar). *Third National Census.* P 14.
382 **137** 4 t. multicoloured 55 50

(Des M. Akond)

1991 (26 Mar). *20th Anniv of Independence.* T **138** and similar square designs. Multicoloured. P 13½.
383 4 t. Type **138** 55 65
 a. Horiz strip of 5. Nos. 383/7 .. 2·50
384 4 t. "Freedom Fighter" (statue) .. 55 65
385 4 t. Mujibnagar Memorial 55 65
386 4 t. Eternal Flame 55 65
387 4 t. National Martyrs' Memorial .. 55 65
383/7 .. .. *Set of 5* 2·50 3·00
Nos. 383/7 were printed together, *se-tenant*, in horizontal strips of five throughout the sheet, with the backgrounds forming a composite design.

139 Pres. Rahman Seated

140 Red Giant Flying Squirrel

(Des P. Mandal. Litho Ueberreuter, Austria)

1991 (30 May). *10th Death Anniv of President Ziaur Rahman.* T **139** and similar vert design. Multicoloured. P 13½×14.
388 50 p. Type **139** 20 15
389 2 t. President Rahman's head in circular decoration 65 85
MS390 146 × 75 mm. Nos. 388/9 (sold at 10 t.) 1·25 1·75

(Des K. Mustafa)

1991 (16 June). *Endangered Species.* T **140** and similar multicoloured designs. P 12.
391 2 t. Type **140** 80 80
 a. Vert pair. Nos. 391 and 394 .. 1·75 1·75
392 4 t. Black-faced Monkey (*vert*) .. 80 80
 a. Horiz pair. Nos. 392/3 .. 1·60 1·60
393 6 t. Great Indian Hornbill (*vert*) .. 1·00 1·00
394 10 t. Armoured Pangolin .. .. 1·10 1·10
391/4 .. .. *Set of 4* 3·25 3·25
Nos. 391 and 394, and 392/3 were printed together, *se-tenant*, in vertical (Nos. 391 and 394) or horizontal (Nos. 392/3) pairs throughout separate sheets.

141 Kaikobad

142 Rabindranath Tagore and Temple

(Des K. Mustafa)

1991 (21 July). *40th Death Anniv of Kaikobad (poet).* P 14.
395 **141** 6 t. multicoloured 60 60

(Des A. Karim)

1991 (7 Aug). *50th Death Anniv of Rabindranath Tagore (poet).* P 14.
396 **142** 4 t. multicoloured 70 55

143 Voluntary Blood
Donation Programme

144 Shahid
Naziruddin and
Crowd

(Des P. Mandal)

1991 (19 Sept). *14th Anniv of "Sandhani" (medical students' association). T 143 and similar vert design. P 14.*

197	3 t. black and bright carmine	..			75	50
198	5 t. multicoloured	..	..	..	1·00	1·00

Design:—5 t. Blind man and eye

1991 (10 Oct). *1st Death Anniv of Shahid Naziruddin Jahad (democrat). P 14.*

199	144	2 t. black, emerald and cinnamon		45	40
		a. Emerald ("BANGLADESH" and face value) omitted	..	£100	

145 Shaheed Noor
Hossain with Slogan
on Chest

146 Bronze Stupa

(Des K. Mustafa)

1991 (10 Nov). *4th Death Anniv of Shaheed Noor Hossain (democrat). P 14.*

200	145	2 t. multicoloured	..	..	..	45	40

(Des M. Akond)

1991 (26 Nov). *Archaeological Relics from Mainamati. T 146 and similar horiz designs. Multicoloured. P 13½.*

201	4 t. Type 146	..		70	80
	a. Horiz strip of 5. Nos. 401/5	..	3·25	
202	4 t. Earthenware and bronze pitchers	..	70	80
203	4 t. Remains of Salban Vihara Monastery	70	80
204	4 t. Gold coins	..	..	70	80
205	4 t. Terracotta plaque	..	..	70	80
401/5		Set of 5	3·25	3·50

Nos. 401/5 were printed together, *se-tenant*, in horizontal trips of 5 throughout the sheet.

147 Demonstrators

148 Munier
Chowdhury

(Des M. Muniruzzaman)

1991 (6 Dec). *1st Anniv of Mass Uprising. P 13½.*

406	147	4 t. multicoloured	..	..	55	40

1991 (14 Dec). *20th Anniv of Independence. Martyred Intellectuals (1st series). T 148 and similar vert designs. Each grey-black and reddish brown. P 13½.*

407	2 t. Type 148	..		20	20
	a. Sheetlet. Nos. 407/16	..	1·75	
408	2 t. Ghyasuddin Ahmad	..		20	20
409	2 t. Rashidul Hasan	..	..	20	20
410	2 t. Muhammad Anwar Pasha	..	20	20
411	2 t. Dr. Muhammad Mortaza	..	20	20
412	2 t. Shahid Saber	..	..	20	20
413	2 t. Fazlur Rahman Khan	..	20	20
414	2 t. Ranada Prasad Saha	..	20	20
415	2 t. Adhyaksha Joges Chandra Ghose	..	20	20
416	2 t. Santosh Chandra Bhattacharyya	..	20	20
417	2 t. Dr. Gobinda Chandra Deb	..	20	20
	a. Sheetlet. Nos. 417/26	..	1·75	
418	2 t. A. Muniruzzaman	..	20	20
419	2 t. Mufazzal Haider Chaudhury	..	20	20
420	2 t. Dr. Abdul Alim Choudhury	..	20	20
421	2 t. Sirajuddin Hossain	..	20	20
422	2 t. Shahidulla Kaiser	..	20	20

423	2 t. Altaf Mahmud	..		20	20
424	2 t. Dr. Jyotirmay Guha Thakurta	..	20	20
425	2 t. Dr. Muhammad Abul Khair	..	20	20
426	2 t. Dr. Serajul Haque Khan	..	20	20
427	2 t. Dr. Mohammad Fazle Rabbi	..	20	20
	a. Sheetlet. Nos. 427/36	..	1·75	
428	2 t. Mir Abdul Quyyum	..	20	20
429	2 t. Golam Mostafa	..	20	20
430	2 t. Dhirendranath Dutta	..	20	20
431	2 t. S. Mannan	..	20	20
432	2 t. Nizamuddin Ahmad	..	20	20
433	2 t. Abul Bashar Chowdhury	..	20	20
434	2 t. Selina Parveen	..	20	20
435	2 t. Dr. Abul Kalam Azad	..	20	20
436	2 t. Saidul Hassan	..	20	20
407/36		Set of 30	5·50	5·50

Nos. 407/16, 417/26 and 427/36 were printed together, *se-tenant*, in sheetlets of 10, the two horizontal rows in each sheetlet being separated by a row of inscribed labels.
See also Nos. 483/92, 525/40, 568/83, 620/35 and 656/71.

149 *Penaeus monodon*

1991 (31 Dec). *Shrimps. T 149 and similar horiz design. Multicoloured. P 14×13½.*

437	6 t. Type 149	..		1·25	1·50
	a. Horiz pair. Nos. 437/8	..	2·50	3·00
438	6 t. *Metapenaeus monoceros*	..	1·25	1·50

Nos. 437/8 were printed together, *se-tenant*, in horizontal pairs throughout the sheet.

150 Death of Raihan Jaglu

151 Rural and Urban
Scenes

(Des M. Muniruzzaman)

1992 (8 Feb). *5th Death Anniv of Shaheed Mirze Abu Raihan Jaglu. P 14×13½.*

439	150	2 t. multicoloured	..	60	50

(Des K. Mustafa (4 t.), A. Karim (10 t.))

1992 (5 June). *World Environment Day. T 151 and similar multicoloured design. P 14.*

440	4 t. Type 151	..		40	15
441	10 t. World Environment Day logo (*horiz*)	1·00	1·40

152 Nawab
Sirajuddaulah

153 Syed Ismail
Hossain Sirajee

(Des K. Mustafa)

1992 (2 July). *235th Death Anniv of Nawab Sirajuddaulah of Bengal. P 13½.*

442	152	10 t. multicoloured	..	70	70
		a. Emerald ("BANGLADESH" inscr) omitted	..	£100	

1992 (17 July). *61st Death Anniv of Syed Ismail Hossain Sirajee. P 14.*

443	153	4 t. multicoloured	..	50	30

154 Couple planting Seedling

(Des M. Huq and M. Muniruzzaman)

1992 (19 July). *Plant Week. T 154 and similar multicoloured design. P 14.*

444	2 t. Type 154	..	..	65	50
445	4 t. Birds on tree (*vert*)	..	65	50

155 Canoe Racing

Banglapex '92
(156)

(Des M. Akond, M. Mia and S. Datta)

1992 (25 July). *Olympic Games, Barcelona. T 155 and similar horiz designs. Multicoloured. P 14.*

446	4 t. Type 155	..		50	55
	a. Block of 4. Nos. 446/9	..	2·25	
447	6 t. Hands holding torch with Olympic rings	..	60	65
448	10 t. Olympic rings and doves	..	70	80
449	10 t. Olympic rings and multiracial handshake	..	70	80
446/9		Set of 4	2·25	2·50

Nos. 446/9 were printed together, *se-tenant*, in blocks of four throughout the sheet of 100 with the two 10 t. values occurring in the first, third, fifth, seventh and ninth horizontal rows.

1992 (18 Aug). *"Banglapex '92", National Philatelic Exhibition (1st issue). No. 290 optd with T 156.*

450	10 t. Bullock cart	..	75	1·00

157 Masnad-e-Ala Isa
Khan

158 Ceremonial Elephant
(19th-century ivory carving)

1992 (15 Sept). *393rd Death Anniv of Masnad-e-Ala Isa Khan. P 14.*

451	157	4 t. multicoloured	..	50	30

(Des M. Begum)

1992 (26 Sept). *"Banglapex '92", National Philatelic Exhibition (2nd issue). T 158 and similar horiz design. Multicoloured. P 14.*

452	10 t. Type 158	..		80	95
	a. Horiz pair. Nos. 452/3 plus label	1·60	1·90
453	10 t. Victorian pillarbox between early and modern postmen	80	95
MS454	145×92 mm. Nos. 452/3 plus label. Imperf (*sold at 25 t.*)	..	2·00	2·50

Nos. 452/3 were printed together, *se-tenant*, in sheets with No. 452 in vertical columns one and four, labels showing the exhibition emblem in columns two and five, and No. 453 in columns three and six.

159 Star Mosque

(Des Md. Jasimuddin)

1992 (29 Oct). *Star Mosque, Dhaka. P 14½×13½.*

455	159	10 t. multicoloured	..	75	75

160 Meer Nisar Ali Titumeer
and Fort

(Des M. Akond)

1992 (19 Nov). *161st Death Anniv of Meer Nisar Ali Titumeer. P 14½×13½.*

456	160	10 t. multicoloured	..	75	75

161 Terracotta Head and Seal

(Des M. Akond, M. Begum and M. Mia)

1992 (30 Nov). *Archaeological Relics from Mahasthangarh.*
T **161** *and similar horiz designs. Multicoloured. P* 14½×13½.
457	10 t. Type **161**		85	1·00
	a. Horiz strip of 4. Nos. 457/60		3·00	
458	10 t. Terracotta panel showing swan		85	1·00
459	10 t. Terracotta statue of Surya		85	1·00
460	10 t. Gupta stone column		85	1·00
457/60		*Set of 4*	3·00	3·50

Nos. 457/60 were printed together, *se-tenant*, in horizontal strips of 4 throughout the sheet.

162 Young Child and Food

163 National Flags

(Des M. Muniruzzaman)

1992 (5 Dec). *International Conference on Nutrition, Rome.*
P 14½×13½.
461	**162** 4 t. multicoloured		40	30

(Des N. Islam (6 t.), M. Akond (10 t.))

1992 (5 Dec). *7th South Asian Association for Regional*
Co-operation Summit Conference, Dhaka. T **163** *and similar*
vert design. Multicoloured. P 13½×14½.
462	6 t. Type **163**		40	40
463	10 t. S.A.A.R.C. emblem		60	85

164 Syed Abdus Samad

165 Haji Shariat Ullah

(Des P. Mandal)

1993 (2 Feb). *Syed Abdus Samad (footballer) Commemoration.*
P 14.
464	**164** 2 t. multicoloured		60	40

(Des M. Rahman)

1993 (10 Mar). *Haji Shariat Ullah Commemoration. P* 14½.
465	**165** 2 t. multicoloured		40	30

166 People digging Canal

(Des M. Rahman)

1993 (31 Mar). *Irrigation Canals Construction Project. T* **166**
and similar horiz design. Multicoloured. P 14.
466	2 t. Type **166**		45	55
	a. Horiz pair. Nos. 466/7		90	1·10
467	2 t. Completed canal and paddy-fields		45	55

Nos. 466/7 were printed together, *se-tenant*, in horizontal pairs throughout the sheet.

MINIMUM PRICE

The minimum price quote is 10p which represents a handling charge rather than a basis for valuing common stamps. For further notes about prices see introductory pages.

---

167 Accident Prevention

168 National Images

(Des A. Hussain (6 t.), N. Islam (10 t.))

1993 (7 Apr). *World Health Day. T* **167** *and similar*
multicoloured design. P 14.
468	6 t. Type **167**		1·00	75
469	10 t. Satellite photograph and symbols of trauma (*vert*)		1·25	1·50

(Des Md. Shamsuzzoha)

1993 (14 Apr). *1400th Year of Bengali Solar Calendar. P* 14.
470	**168** 2 t. multicoloured		40	30

169 Schoolchildren and Bengali Script

170 Nawab Sir Salimullah and Palace

(Des M. Huq (No. 471), M. Mia (No. 472))

1993 (26 May). *Compulsory Primary Education. T* **169** *and*
similar multicoloured design. P 14×14½ (*No.* 471) *or*
14½×14 (*No.* 472).
471	2 t. Type **169**		30	40
472	2 t. Books and slate (*horiz*)		30	40

(Des S. Shaheen)

1993 (7 June). *122nd Birth Anniv of Nawab Sir Salimullah.*
P 14½×14.
473	**170** 4 t. multicoloured		40	30

171 Fish Production

(Des M. Rahman)

1993 (15 Aug). *Fish Fortnight. P* 14½×14.
474	**171** 2 t. multicoloured		20	20

172 Sunderban

173 Exhibition Emblem

(Des M. Mia, M. Rahman and B. Biswas)

1993 (30 Oct). *Natural Beauty of Bangladesh. T* **172** *and*
similar multicoloured designs. P 14½×14 (*horiz*) *or* 14×14½
(*vert*).
475	10 t. Type **172**		60	70
476	10 t. Kuakata beach		60	70
477	10 t. Madhabkunda waterfall (*vert*)		60	70
478	10 t. River Piyain, Jaflang (*vert*)		60	70
475/8		*Set of 4*	2·25	2·50
MS479	174×102 mm. Nos. 475/8. Imperf. (*sold at 50 t.*)		2·75	3·25

(Des Q. Chowdhury)

1993 (2 Nov). *6th Asian Art Biennale. P* 14×14½.
480	**173** 10 t. multicoloured		60	70

---

174 Foy's Lake

175 Burdwan House

(Des A. Hussain)

1993 (6 Nov). *Tourism Month. P* 14½×14.
481	174 10 t. multicoloured		70	7

(Des N. Islam)

1993 (3 Dec). *Foundation Day, Bangla Academy. P* 14×14½.
482	175 2 t. deep brown and emerald		20	1

1993 (14 Dec). *Martyred Intellectuals (2nd series). Vert design*
as T **148**. *Each grey-black and reddish brown. P* 14½.
483	2 t. Lt. Cdr. Moazzam Hussain		15	2
	a. Sheetlet. Nos. 483/92		1·25	
484	2 t. Muhammad Habibur Rahman		15	2
485	2 t. Khandoker Abu Taleb		15	2
486	2 t. Moshiur Rahman		15	2
487	2 t. Md Abdul Muktadir		15	2
488	2 t. Nutan Chandra Sinha		15	2
489	2 t. Syed Nazmul Haque		15	2
490	2 t. Dr. Mohammed Amin Uddin		15	2
491	2 t. Dr. Faizul Mohee		15	2
492	2 t. Sukha Ranjan Somaddar		15	2
483/92		*Set of 10*	1·25	1·7

Nos. 483/92 were printed together, *se-tenant*, as a sheetlet of 10, the two horizontal rows being separated by a row of inscribed labels.

176 Throwing the Discus

1993 (19 Dec). *6th South Asian Federation Games, Dhaka.*
T **176** *and similar multicoloured design. P* 14½×14 (2 t.) *or*
14×14½ (4 t.).
493	2 t. Type **176**		15	1
	a. Rose-lilac, yellow-brown and orange (parts of logo) omitted			
494	4 t. Running (*vert*)		25	2
	a. Yellow-brown (part of logo) omitted		£100	

177 Tomb of Sultan Ghiyasuddin Azam Shah

178 Scouting Activities and Jamboree Emblem

(Des Md. Shamsuzzoha)

1993 (30 Dec). *Muslim Monuments. P* 14½×14.
495	177 10 t. multicoloured		60	6

(Des A. Hussain)

1994 (5 Jan). *14th Asian-Pacific and 5th Bangladesh National*
Scout Jamboree. P 14×14½.
496	178 2 t. multicoloured		30	2

179 Emblem and Mother giving Solution to Child

180 Interior of Chhota Sona Mosque, Nawabgonj

(Des Md. Shamsuzzoha)

1994 (5 Feb). *25th Anniv of Oral Rehydration Solution.*
P 14×14½.
497	179 2 t. multicoloured		30	2

(Des A. Hussain, M. Huq and M. Rahman)

1994 (30 Mar). *Ancient Mosques. T* 180 *and similar horiz designs. Multicoloured. P* 14½×14.

498	4 t. Type 180	15	15
499	6 t. Exterior of Chhota Sona Mosque	30	40
500	6 t. Exterior of Baba Adam's Mosque, Munshigonj	30	40
498/500	Set of 3	65	85

181 Agricultural Workers and Emblem

182 Priest releasing Peace Doves

(Des R. Hussain and M. Huq)

1994 (11 Apr). *75th Anniv of International Labour Organization. T* 181 *and similar multicoloured design. P* 14½×14 *(4 t.) or* 14×14½ *(10 t.).*

501	4 t. Type 181	15	15
	a. Bright blue ("BANGLADESH" inscr) omitted	£150	
502	10 t. Worker turning cog (*vert*)	60	60

(Des A. Hussain)

1994 (14 Apr). *1500th Year of Bengali Solar Calendar. P* 14×14½.

503	182	2 t. multicoloured	15	15

183 Scenes from Baishakhi Festival

184 Family, Globe and Logo

(Des A. Hussain)

1994 (12 May). *Folk Festivals. T* 183 *and similar horiz design. Multicoloured. P* 14½×14.

504	4 t. Type 183	25	25
505	4 t. Scenes from Nabanna and Paush Parvana Festivals	25	25

(Des M. Huq)

1994 (15 May). *International Year of the Family. P* 14×14½.

506	184	10 t. multicoloured	80	80

185 People planting Saplings

186 Player kicking Ball

(Des M. Mia and R. Hussain)

1994 (15 June). *Tree Planting Campaign. T* 185 *and similar vert design. Multicoloured. P* 14×14½.

507	4 t. Type 185	25	15
508	6 t. Hands holding saplings	40	40

(Des M. Shamim)

1994 (17 June). *World Cup Football Championship, U.S.A. T* 186 *and similar vert design. Multicoloured. P* 14½×14.

509	20 t. Type 186	1·50	1·75
	a. Horiz strip of 3. Nos. 509/10 and label	3·00	
510	20 t. Player heading ball	1·50	1·75

Nos. 509/10 were printed together, *se-tenant*, in sheets of 15 (3×5) with each horizontal row containing one of each design separated by a label showing the championship mascot.

NEW INFORMATION

The editor is always interested to correspond with people who have new information that will improve or correct the Catalogue.

187 Traffic on Bridge

188 Asian Black-headed Oriole

(Des A. Rouf)

1994 (24 July). *Inauguration of Jamuna Multi-purpose Bridge Project. P* 14½×14.

511	187	4 t. multicoloured	40	30

(Des A. Hussain)

1994 (31 Aug). *Birds. T* 188 *and similar vert designs. Multicoloured. P* 14×14½.

512	4 t. Type 188	40	40
513	6 t. Greater Racquet-tailed Drongo (*Dicrurus paradiseus*)	60	70
514	6 t. Indian Tree Pie (*Dendrocitta vagabunda*)	60	70
515	6 t. Red Junglefowl (*Gallus gallus*)	60	70
512/15	Set of 4	2·00	2·25
MS516	165×110 mm. Nos. 512/15 (*sold at 25 t.*)	2·00	2·75

189 Dr. Mohammad Ibrahim and Hospital

190 Nawab Faizunnessa Chowdharani

(Des M. Shamim)

1994 (6 Sept). *5th Death Anniv of Dr. Mohammad Ibrahim (diabetes treatment pioneer). P* 14½×14.

517	189	2 t. multicoloured	30	20

(Des M. Rahman)

1994 (23 Sept). *160th Birth Anniv of Nawab Faizunnessa Chowdhurani (social reformer). P* 14×14½.

518	190	2 t. multicoloured	10	10

191 Boxing

(Des A. Hussain)

1994 (2 Oct). *Asian Games, Hiroshima, Japan. P* 14½×14.

519	191	4 t. multicoloured	40	30

192 Pink and White Pearls with Windowpane Oysters

(Des M. Mia, M. Rahman and Md. Shamsuzzoha)

1994 (30 Oct). *Sea Shells. T* 192 *and similar multicoloured designs. P* 14×14½ *(No. 523) or* 14½×14 *(others).*

520	6 t. Type 192	60	70
521	6 t. Tranquelous Scallop and other shells	60	70
522	6 t. Lister's Conch, Asiatic Arabian Cowrie, Bladder Moon and Woodcock Murex	60	70
523	6 t. Spotted Tun, Spiny Frog Shell, Spiral Melongena and Gibbous Olive	60	70
520/3	Set of 4	2·25	2·50

193 Dr. Milon and Demonstrators

194 *Diplazium esculentum*

(Des M. Akond)

1994 (27 Nov). *4th Death Anniv of Dr. Shamsul Alam Khan Milon (medical reformer). P* 14½×14.

524	193	2 t. multicoloured	10	10

(Des M. Huq, A. Hussain, M. Mia, A. Moniruzzaman, M. Rahman and Md. Shamsuzzoha)

1994 (14 Dec). *Martyred Intellectuals* (3rd series). *Vert designs as T* 148. *Each grey-black and reddish brown. P* 14×14½.

525	2 t. Dr. Harinath Dey	10	10
	a. Sheetlet. Nos. 525/32	80	
526	2 t. Dr. A. F. Ziaur Rahman	10	10
527	2 t. Mamun Mahmud	10	10
528	2 t. Mohsin Ali Dewan	10	10
529	2 t. Dr. N. A. M. Jahangir	10	10
530	2 t. Shah Abdul Majid	10	10·
531	2 t. Muhammad Akhter	10	10
532	2 t. Meherunnesa	10	10
533	2 t. Dr. Kasiruddin Talukder	10	10
	a. Sheetlet. Nos. 533/40	80	
534	2 t. Fazlul Haque Choudhury	10	10
535	2 t. Md. Shamsuzzaman	10	10
536	2 t. A. K. M. Shamsuddin	10	10
537	2 t. Lt. Mohammad Anwarul Azim	10	10
538	2 t. Nurul Amin Khan	10	10
539	2 t. Mohammad Sadeque	10	10
540	2 t. Md. Araz Ali	10	10
525/40	Set of 16	1·60	1·60

Nos. 525/32 and 533/40 were printed together, *se-tenant*, in sheetlets of 8, the two horizontal rows in each sheetlet being separated by a row of inscribed labels.

(Des A. Hussain, N. Islam and Md. Shamsuzzoha)

1994 (24 Dec). *Vegetables. T* 194 *and similar multicoloured designs. P* 14½×14 *(No. 546) or* 14×14½ *(others).*

541	4 t. Type 194	25	20
542	4 t. *Momordica charantia*	25	20
543	6 t. *Lagenaria siceraria*	40	35
544	6 t. *Trichosanthes dioica*	40	35
545	10 t. *Solanum melongena*	70	90
546	10 t. *Cucurbita maxima* (*horiz*)	70	90
541/6	Set of 6	2·40	2·50

195 Sonargaon

(Des A. Hussain)

1995 (2 Jan). *20th Anniv of World Tourism Organization. P* 14½.

547	195	10 t. multicoloured	65	65

196 Exports

(Des M. Huq)

1995 (7 Jan). *Dhaka International Trade Fair '95. T* 196 *and similar horiz design. Multicoloured. P* 14½.

548	4 t. Type 196	20	20
549	6 t. Symbols of industry	45	45

197 Soldiers of Ramgarh Battalion (1795) and of Bangladesh Rifles (1995)

(Des M. Rahman and Md. Shamsuzzoha)

1995 (10 Jan). *Bicentenary of Bangladesh Rifles. T* **197** *and similar horiz design. Multicoloured. P* 14½.
550   2 t. Type 197   15   15
551   4 t. Riflemen on patrol   25   25

198 Surgical Equipment and Lightning attacking Crab (cancer)

199 Fresh Food and Boy injecting Insulin

(Des M. Rohana)

1995 (7 Apr). *Campaign against Cancer. P* 14×14½.
552 **198**   2 t. multicoloured   15   15

(Des N. Islam)

1995 (28 Feb). *National Diabetes Awareness Day. P* 14.
553 **199**   2 t. multicoloured   15   15

200 Munshi Mohammad Meherullah   (201)

(Des M. Huq)

1995 (7 June). *Munshi Mohammad Meherullah (Islamic educator) Commemoration. P* 14×14½
554 **200**   2 t. multicoloured   15   15

1995 (23 Aug). *"Rajshahipex '95" National Philatelic Exhibition. No.* 499 *optd with T* **201** *in red.*
555   6 t. Exterior of Chhota Sona Mosque   ..   40   40

202 *Lagerstroemia speciosa*

203 Aspects of Farming

(Des A. Hussain, Md. Shamsuzzoha, Md. Jasimuddin, M. Muniruzzaman)

1995 (9 Oct). *Flowers. T* **202** *and similar multicoloured designs. P* 14½.
556   6 t. Type 202   40   40
557   6 t. *Bombax ceiba* (*horiz*)   ..   40   40
558   10 t. *Passiflora incarnata*   ..   65   65
559   10 t. *Bauhina purpurea*   ..   65   65
560   10 t. *Canna indica*   ..   65   65
561   10 t. *Gloriosa superba*   ..   65   65
556/61   ..   ..   *Set of* 6   3·00   3·00

(Des A. Hussain)

1995 (16 Oct). *50th Anniv of Food and Agriculture Organization. P* 14×14½.
562 **203**   10 t. multicoloured   45   45

The new-issue supplement to this Catalogue appears each month in

GIBBONS
STAMP MONTHLY

—from your newsagent or by postal subscription— sample copy and details on request.

---

204 Anniversary Emblem, Peace Dove and U.N. Headquarters

(Des A. Hussain)

1995 (24 Oct). *50th Anniv of United Nations. T* **204** *and similar horiz designs. Multicoloured. P* 14½×14.
563   2 t. Type 204   15   15
564   10 t. Peace doves circling dates and Globe   65   65
565   10 t. Clasped hands and U.N. Headquarters   65   65
563/5   ..   ..   *Set of* 3   1·25   1·25

205 Diseased Lungs, Microscope, Family and Map

206 Peace Doves, Emblem and National Flags

(Des A. Hussain)

1995 (29 Oct). *18th Eastern Regional Conference on Tuberculosis, Dhaka. P* 14½×14.
566 **205**   6 t. multicoloured   40   35

(Des A. Hussain)

1995 (8 Dec). *10th Anniv of South Asian Association for Regional Co-operation. P* 14×14½.
567 **206**   2 t. multicoloured   15   15

1995 (14 Dec). *Martyred Intellectuals (4th series). Vert designs as T* **148**. *Each grey-black and reddish brown. P* 14×14½.
568   2 t. Abdul Ahad   10   10
    a. Sheetlet. Nos. 568/75   ..   1·00
569   2 t. Lt. Col. Mohammad Qadir   ..   10   10
570   2 t. Mozammel Hoque Chowdhury   ..   10   10
571   2 t. Rafiqul Haider Chowdhury   ..   10   10
572   2 t. Dr. Azharul Haque   ..   10   10
573   2 t. A. K. Shamsuddin   ..   10   10
574   2 t. Anudwaipayan Bhattacharjee   ..   10   10
575   2 t. Lutfunnahar Helena   ..   10   10
576   2 t. Shaikh Habibur Rahman   ..   10   10
    a. Sheetlet. Nos. 576/83   ..   1·00
577   2 t. Major Naimul Islam   ..   10   10
578   2 t. Md. Shahidullah   ..   10   10
579   2 t. Ataur Rahman Khan Khadim   ..   10   10
580   2 t. A. B. M. Ashraful Islam Bhuiyan   ..   10   10
581   2 t. Dr. Md. Sadat Ali   ..   10   10
582   2 t. Sarafat Ali   10   10
583   2 t. M. A. Sayeed   10   10
568/83   ..   ..   *Set of* 16   1·00   1·00
   Nos. 568/75 and 576/83 were printed together, *se-tenant*, in sheetlets of 8, the two horizontal rows in each sheetlet being separated by a row of inscribed labels.

207 Aspects of COMDECA Projects

208 Volleyball Players

(Des Md. Shamsuzzoha)

1995 (18 Dec). *2nd Asia-Pacific Community Development Scout Camp. P* 14×14½.
584 **207**   2 t. multicoloured   15   15

(Des A. Hussain)

1995 (25 Dec). *Centenary of Volleyball. P* 14×14½.
585 **208**   6 t. multicoloured   40   35

---

209 Man in Punjabi and Lungi

210 Shaheed Amanullah Mohammad Asaduzzaman

(Des M. Huq, A. Hussain, Md. Shamsuzzoha and M. Rahman)

1995 (25 Dec). *Traditional Costumes. T* **209** *and similar multicoloured designs. P* 14½.
586   6 t. Type 209   40   40
587   6 t. Woman in sari   ..   40   40
588   10 t. Christian bride and groom   ..   65   65
589   10 t. Muslim bride and groom   ..   65   65
590   10 t. Buddhist bride and groom (*horiz*)   65   65
591   10 t. Hindu bride and groom (*horiz*)   65   65
586/91   ..   ..   *Set of* 6   3·00   3·00

(Des A. Hussain)

1996 (20 Jan). *27th Death Anniv of Shaheed Amanullah Mohammad Asaduzzaman (student leader). P* 14×14½.
592 **210**   2 t. multicoloured   20   20

211 Bowler and Map

(Des M. Huq, A. Hussain and Md. Shamsuzzoha)

1996 (14 Feb). *World Cup Cricket Championship. T* **211** *and similar multicoloured designs. P* 14½×14 (10 t.) *or* 14×14½ (*others*).
593   4 t. Type 211   30   20
594   6 t. Batsman and wicket keeper   ..   40   30
595   10 t. Match in progress (*horiz*)   ..   65   65
593/5   ..   ..   *Set of* 3   1·25   1·00

212 Liberation Struggle, 1971

(Des A. Hussain, M. Huq, M. Rahman and Md. Shamsuzzoha)

1996 (26 Mar). *25th Anniv of Independence. T* **212** *and similar horiz designs. Multicoloured. P* 14½.
596   4 t. Type 212   15   20
597   4 t. National Martyrs Memorial   ..   15   20
598   4 t. Education   15   20
599   4 t. Health   15   20
600   4 t. Communications   ..   15   20
601   4 t. Industry   15   20
596/601   ..   ..   *Set of* 6   90   1·10

213 Michael Madhusudan Dutt

214 Gymnastics

(Des M. Huq)

1996 (29 June). *Michael Madhusudan Dutt (poet) Commemoration. P* 14×14½.
602 **213**   4 t. multicoloured   15   15

(Des M. Huq, Md. Shamsuzzoha and M. Rahman)

1996 (19 July). *Olympic Games, Atlanta. T* **214** *and similar multicoloured designs.* P 14×14¹/₂ (*vert*) or 14¹/₂×14 (*horiz*).
603   4 t. Type 214   15   20
604   6 t. Judo   20   25
605   10 t. Athletics (*horiz*)   30   35
606   10 t. High jumping (*horiz*)   .. 30   35
603/6   *Set of 4*   95   1·25
MS607   165×110 mm. Nos. 603/6. P 14×14¹/₂
(*sold at 40 t.*)   .. .. 1·25   1·40

1996 (29 July). *25th Anniv of Bangladesh Stamps. No.* **MS**234 *optd* "Silver Jubilee Bangladesh Postage Stamps 1971–96" *on sheet margin.*
MS608   98×117 mm. Nos. 232/3 (*sold at 10 t.*)   30   35

215 Bangabandhu   216 Maulana Mohammad
    Sheikh Mujibur   Akrum Khan
    Rahman

(Des M. Rahman)

1996 (15 Aug). *21st Death Anniv of Bangabandhu Sheikh Mujibur Rahman.* P 14×14¹/₂.
609 **215** 4 t. multicoloured   20   20

(Des Md. Muniruzzaman)

1996 (18 Aug). *28th Death Anniv of Maulana Mohammad Akrum Khan.* P 14×14¹/₂.
610 **216** 4 t. multicoloured   20   20

217 Ustad Alauddin   218 "Kingfisher"
    Khan   (Mayeesha Robbani)

(Des A. Hussain)

1996 (6 Sept). *24th Death Anniv of Ustad Alauddin Khan (musician).* P 14×14¹/₂.
611 **217** 4 t. multicoloured   20   20

1996 (9 Oct). *Children's Paintings. T* **218** *and similar multi-coloured design.* P 13¹/₂×14¹/₂ (2 t.) or 14¹/₂×13¹/₂ (4 t.).
612   2 t. Type 218   15   10
613   4 t. "River Crossing" (Iffat Panchlais) (*horiz*)   15   20

219 Syed Nazrul Islam   220 Children receiving
                               Medicine

(Des M. Rahman)

1996 (3 Nov). *21st Death Anniv of Jail Martyrs. T* **219** *and similar multicoloured.* P 14×14¹/₂.
614   4 t. Type 219   15   20
    a. Block of 4. Nos. 614/17   .. 69
615   4 t. Tajuddin Ahmad   15   20
616   4 t. M. Monsoor Ali   15   20
617   4 t. A. H. M. Quamaruzzaman   .. 15   20
614/17   *Set of 4*   60   80
Nos. 614/17 were printed together, *se-tenant*, in blocks of four throughout the sheet.

(Des A. Hussain)

1996 (11 Dec). *50th Anniv of U.N.I.C.E.F. T* **220** *and similar vert design. Multicoloured.* P 14×14¹/₂.
618   4 t. Type 220   15   20
619   10 t. Mother and child   30   35

(Des A. Hussain (Nos. 620/1, 625, 632/3), M. Huq (Nos. 622, 624, 627/9, 631) M. Rahman (Nos. 623, 630, 634), T. Hussain (No. 626), N. Islam (No. 635))

1996 (14 Dec). *Martyred Intellectuals (5th series). Vert designs as T* **148**. *Each grey-black and reddish brown.* P 14×14¹/₂.
620   2 t. Dr. Jekrul Haque   10   10
    a. Sheetlet. Nos. 620/7   55
621   2 t. Munshi Kabiruddin Ahmed   .. 10   10
622   2 t. Md. Abdul Jabbar   .. 10   10
623   2 t. Mohammad Amir   10   10
624   2 t. A. K. M. Shamsul Huq Khan   .. 10   10
625   2 t. Dr. Siddique Ahmed   .. 10   10
626   2 t. Dr. Soleman Khan   .. 10   10
627   2 t. S. B. M. Mizanur Rahman   .. 10   10
628   2 t. Aminuddin   10   10
    a. Sheetlet. Nos. 628/35   .. 55
629   2 t. Md. Nazrul Islam   .. 10   10
630   2 t. Zahirul Islam   10   10
631   2 t. A. K. Lutfor Rahman   .. 10   10
632   2 t. Afsar Hossain   10   10
633   2 t. Abul Hashem Mian   .. 10   10
634   2 t. A. T. M. Alamgir   .. 10   10
635   2 t. Baser Ali   10   10
620/35   *Set of 16*   1·10   1·25
Nos. 620/7 and 628/35 were each printed together, *se-tenant*, in sheetlets of 8, the two horizontal rows in each sheetlet being separated by a row of inscribed labels.

221 Celebrating Crowds   222 Paul P. Harris

(Des Md. Shamsuzzoha)

1996 (16 Dec). *25th Anniv of Victory Day. T* **221** *and similar multicoloured design.* P 14¹/₂×14 (4 t.) or 14×14¹/₂ (6 t.).
636   4 t. Type 221   15   20
637   6 t. Soldiers and statue (*vert*)   .. 20   25

(Des M. Huq)

1997 (18 Feb). *50th Death Anniv of Paul Harris (founder of Rotary).* P 14×14¹/₂.
638 **222** 4 t. multicoloured   15   20

223 Shaikh Mujibur Rahman
        making Speech

(Des A. Hussain)

1997 (7 Mar). *25th Anniv of Shaikh Mujibur's Speech of 7 March (1996).* P 12¹/₂.
639 **223** 4 t. multicoloured   15   20

224 Sheikh Mujibur   225 Sheikh Mujibur Rahman
    Rahman   and Crowd with Banners

(Des M. Mozammel)

1997 (17 Mar). *77th Birth Anniv of Sheikh Mujibur Rahman (first President).* P 14×14¹/₂.
640 **224** 4 t. multicoloured   15   20

(Des M. Rahman)

1997 (26 Mar). *25th Anniv (1996) of Independence.* P 12¹/₂.
641 **225** 4 t. multicoloured   15   20

---

226 Heinrich von   227 Sheep
    Stephan

(Des A. Hussain)

1997 (8 Apr). *Death Centenary of Heinrich von Stephan (founder of U.P.U.).* P 14×14¹/₂.
642 **226** 4 t. multicoloured   15   20

(Des A. Hussain)

1997 (10 Apr). *Livestock. T* **227** *and similar horiz designs. Multicoloured.* P 14¹/₂×14.
643   4 t. Type 227   15   20
644   4 t. Goat   15   20
645   6 t. Buffalo bull   20   25
646   6 t. Cow   20   25
643/6   *Set of 4*   70   90

228 "Tilling the Field – 2" (S. Sultan)

(Des A. Hussain)

1997 (26 June). *Bangladesh Paintings. T* **228** *and similar horiz design. Multicoloured.* P 12¹/₂.
647   6 t. Type 228   20   25
648   10 t. "Three Women" (Quamrul Hassan)   .. 30   35

229 Trophy, Flag and Cricket Ball

(Des A. Hussain)

1997 (4 Sept). *6th International Cricket Council Trophy Championship, Malaysia.* P 12¹/₂.
649 **229** 10 t. multicoloured   30   35

230 Kusumba Mosque,   231 Adul Karim
    Naogaon   Sahitya Vishard

(Des Md. Shamsuzzoha)

1997 (4 Sept). *Historic Mosques. T* **230** *and similar horiz designs. Multicoloured.* P 14¹/₂×14.
650   4 t. Type 230   15   20
651   6 t. Atiya Mosque, Tangail   .. 20   25
652   10 t. Bagha Mosque, Rajshahi   .. 30   35
650/2   *Set of 3*   65   80

(Des M. Rahman)

1997 (11 Oct). *126th Birth Anniv of Abdul Karim Sahitya Vishard (scholar).* P 14×14¹/₂.
653 **231** 4 t. multicoloured   15   20

OMNIBUS ISSUES

Details, together with prices for complete sets, of the various Omnibus issues from the 1935 Silver Jubilee series to date are included in a special section following Zimbabwe at the end of Volume 2.

232 Rover Moot
Emblem and Scouts
standing on top of
World

233 Officers and Flag

(Des M. Rahman)

1997 (25 Oct). *9th Asia-Pacific and 7th Bangladesh Rover Moot, Lakkatura. P 14×14½.*
654 **232** 2 t. multicoloured 10 10

(Des Md. Jasimuddin)

1997 (21 Nov). *25th Anniv of Armed Forces. P 14½×14.*
655 **233** 2 t. multicoloured 10 10

1997 (14 Dec). *Martyred Intellectuals (6th series). Vert designs as T 148. Each grey-black and reddish brown. P 14×14½.*
656 2 t. Dr. Shamsuddin Ahmed .. 10 10
    a. Sheetlet. Nos. 656/63 .. 60
657 2 t. Mohammad Salimullah .. 10 10
658 2 t. Mohiuddin Haider .. 10 10
659 2 t. Abdur Rahin 10 10
660 2 t. Nitya Nanda Paul .. 10 10
661 2 t. Abdel Jabber .. 10 10
662 2 t. Dr. Humayun Kabir .. 10 10
663 2 t. Khaja Nizamuddin Bhuiyan .. 10 10
664 2 t. Gulam Hossain .. 10 10
    a. Sheetlet. Nos. 664/71 .. 60
665 2 t. Ali Karim .. 10 10
666 2 t. Md. Moazzem Hossain .. 10 10
667 2 t. Rafiqul Islam .. 10 10
668 2 t. M. Nur Husain .. 10 10
669 2 t. Captain Mahmood Hossain Akonda .. 10 10
670 2 t. Abdul Wahab Talukder .. 10 10
671 2 t. Dr. Hasimoy Hazra .. 10 10
656/71 .. *Set of 16* 1·10 1·25

Nos. 656/63 and 664/71 were printed together, *se-tenant*, in sheetlets of 8, the two horizontal rows in each sheetlet being separated by a row of inscribed labels.

OFFICIAL STAMPS

SERVICE **SERVICE** **SERVICE**
(O 1) (O 2) (O 3)

1973 (30 Apr). *Nos. 22/7, 29/30, 32 and 34 optd with Type O 1.*
O 1 **7** 2 p. black (R.) 10 40
O 2 — 3 p. blue-green 10 40
O 3 — 5 p. light brown 15 10
O 4 — 10 p. slate-black (R.) .. 15 10
O 5 — 20 p. yellow-green .. 1·10 10
O 6 — 25 p. bright reddish mauve .. 2·75 10
O 7 — 60 p. greenish slate (R.) .. 2·75 1·25
O 8 — 75 p. yellow-orange .. 1·00 20
O 9 **8** 1 t. light violet .. .. 10·00 3·75
O10 — 5 t. grey-blue .. 4·50 6·00
O1/10 .. .. *Set of 10* 20·00 11·00

1974–75. *Nos. 49/51 optd with Type O 1.*
O11 **14** 1 t. light violet .. 3·50 30
O12 — 2 t. olive .. 4·50 1·50
O13 — 5 t. grey-blue (1975) .. 8·50 6·00
O11/13 .. *Set of 3* 15·00 7·00

1976. *Nos. 64/70 and 73 optd with Type O 2 and Nos. 72 and 74 optd with Type O 3.*
O14 5 p. deep yellow-green (11.2.76) .. 75 30
O15 10 p. slate-black (R.) (28.4.76) .. 1·25 30
O16 20 p. yellow-green (1.76) .. 1·50 30
O17 25 p. bright reddish mauve (1.76) .. 2·75 30
O18 50 p. light purple (8.6.76) .. 2·75 30
O19 60 p. greenish slate (R.) (10.11.76) .. 30 1·00
O20 75 p. yellow-olive (10.11.76) .. 30 1·40
O21 1 t. ultramarine (1.76) .. 2·00 30
O22 2 t. olive-green (8.6.76) .. 35 1·00
O23 5 t. grey-blue (10.11.76) .. 30 1·00
O14/23 .. *Set of 10* 11·00 5·75

1979–82. *Nos. 125/37 optd with Type O 1.*
O24 5 p. deep brown .. 80 90
O25 10 p. turquoise-blue .. 80 90
O26 15 p. orange (1980) .. 90 1·00
O27 20 p. brown-red .. 50 80
O28 25 p. grey-blue (1982) .. 80 1·50
O29 30 p. deep green .. 1·75 1·50
O30 40 p. maroon .. 1·50 15
O31 50 p. black (24.9.81) .. 30 10
O32 80 p. brown .. 70 15
O33 1 t. reddish violet (24.9.81) .. 30 10
O34 2 t. dull ultramarine (21.10.81) .. 35 1·50
O24/34 .. *Set of 11* 8·00 7·50

Service **Service** **সার্ভিস**
(O 4) (O 5) (O 6)

1983 (21 Dec)–**94.** *Nos. 220/9 and 318/a optd as Type O 4 in red, diagonally on 1 t. to 5 t.*
O35 5 p. turquoise-blue 10 10
O36 10 p. purple .. 10 10
O37 15 p. new blue .. 10 10
O38 20 p. grey-black .. 10 10
O39 25 p. slate .. 10 10
O40 30 p. brown .. 10 10
O41 50 p. light brown (opt horiz) .. 10 10
    a. Opt diagonal (1993) .. 10 10
O42 1 t. dull ultramarine .. 75 10
O43 2 t. deep bluish green .. 75 10
O44 3 t. black and light blue (16.7.94) .. 10 10
O45 4 t. slate-blue (28.6.90) .. 15 20
O46 5 t. bright purple (27.7.92) .. 15 20
O35/46 .. *Set of 12* 2·00 1·00

1990 (29 Nov)–**92.** *No. 368/9 optd as Type O 5 in red.*
O47 **133** 2 t. brown 10 10
O48 **134** 6 t. slate-blue and greenish yellow (opt horiz) (22.11.92) .. 20 25

1992 (16 Sept). *No. 227 optd with Type O 6 in red.*
O49 1 t. dull ultramarine 10 10

— URCH HARRIS —
ALL WORLD
NEW ISSUE SERVICE

Your 'First Choice' New Issue Supplier

Developed over the last 30 years Urch Harris 'All World' combines the widest choice of countries, themes and formats with a reliable individual service that helps develop and manage your collection.

■ 260 countries and 100 plus themes.

■ Choice of mint issues, reprints, yearpacks, used stamps, maxi cards, booklets, presentation packs, specimens and first day covers.

■ Regular distributions every 6 weeks.

■ Free magazine with every distribution.

■ Fully computerised invoices with descriptions.

■ Customer advice helpline.

■ Free gifts and regular special offers.

■ Supported by Stanley Gibbons, world leaders in philately.

FREE WELCOME PACK

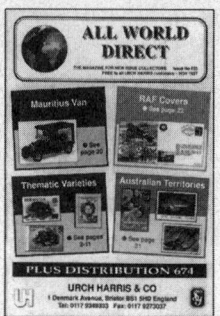

Containing full details of our unique service, a full list of countries and themes and a copy of 'All World Direct' magazine.

Telephone 0117 9349333 for a free pack.

Urch Harris & Co
1 Denmark Avenue
Bristol BS1 5HD
A Division of Stanley Gibbons Ltd

Barbados

Regular mails between Barbados and Great Britain were established at an early date in the island's development and it is believed that the British Mail Packet Agency at Bridgetown was opened in 1688 as part of the considerable expansion of the Packet Service in that year.

From 1 August 1851 the colonial authorities were responsible for the internal post system, but the British G.P.O. did not relinquish control of the overseas post until 1858.

For illustrations of the handstamp types see BRITISH POST OFFICES ABROAD notes, following GREAT BRITAIN.

CROWNED-CIRCLE HANDSTAMPS

CC1 CC 1 BARBADOES (3.10.1849) (R.) *Price on cover* £425
Combination covers exist with the local postage paid by a Barbados 1d. stamp and the overseas fee by an example of No. CC1.
During shortages of ½d. stamps in 1893 (17 February to 15 March) and of the ¼d. in 1896 (23 January to 4 May) No. CC1 was utilised, struck in black, on local mail. *Price on cover from* £85.

PRICES FOR STAMPS ON COVER TO 1945

Nos. 1/35	from × 5
Nos. 43/63	from × 4
Nos. 64/6	from × 10
Nos. 67/83	from × 5
Nos. 86/8	from × 3
Nos. 89/103	from × 4
No. 104	from × 20
Nos. 105/15	from × 4
Nos. 116/24	from × 8
Nos. 125/33	from × 5
Nos. 135/44	from × 4
Nos. 145/52	from × 6
No. 153	from × 8
Nos. 158/62	from × 5
Nos. 163/9	from × 3
Nos. 170/96	from × 4
Nos. 197/8	from × 10
Nos. 199/212	from × 6
Nos. 213/39	from × 3
No. 240	from × 10
Nos. 241/4	from × 5
Nos. 245/7	from × 6
Nos. 248/56a	from × 4
Nos. 257/61	from × 5
Nos. D1/3	from × 25

CROWN COLONY

1 Britannia 2

(Recess Perkins, Bacon & Co)

1852 (15 April)–**55**. *Paper blued. No wmk. Imperf.*
1	1	(½d.) yellow-green	—	£550
2		(½d.) deep green	80·00	£300
3		(1d.) blue	28·00	£190
4		(1d.) deep blue	17·00	65·00
4a		(2d.) greyish slate	£200	£1100
		b. Bisected (1d.) (on cover) (1854)		† £5500
5		(4d.) brownish red (1855)	60·00	£300

The bisect, No. 4b, was authorised for use between 4 August and 21 September 1854 during a shortage of 1d. stamps.
Nos. 5a/b were never sent to Barbados and come from the Perkins Bacon remainders sold in the 1880's.
Apart from the shade, which is distinctly paler, No. 4a can be distinguished from No. 5b by the smooth even gum, the gum of No. 5b being yellow and patchy, giving a mottled appearance to the back of the stamp. No. 5a also has the latter gum.

Prepared for use but not issued
5a	1	(No value), slate-blue (*shades*)	15·00	
5b		(No value), deep slate	£200	

1855–58. *White paper. No wmk. Imperf.*
7	1	(½d.) yellow-green (1857)	£375	£110
8		(½d.) green (1858)	85·00	£200
9		(1d.) pale blue	60·00	60·00
10		(1d.) deep blue	21·00	50·00

1858 (10 Nov). *No wmk. Imperf.*
11	2	6d. pale rose-red	£700	£110
11a		6d. deep rose-red	£700	£180
12		1s. brown-black	£225	£110
12a		1s. black	£160	70·00

1860. *No wmk. (a) Pin-perf 14.*
13	1	(½d.) yellow-green	£1500	£375
14		(1d.) pale blue	£1500	£150
15		(1d.) deep blue	£1500	£150

(b) Pin-perf 12½
16	1	(½d.) yellow-green	£3750	£600
16a		(1d.) blue	—	£1200

(c) Pin-perf 14 × 12½
16b	1	(½d.) yellow-green	—	£3250

1861. *No wmk. Clean-cut perf 14 to 16.*
17	1	(½d.) deep green	55·00	7·50
18		(1d.) pale blue	£500	45·00
19		(1d.) blue	£650	45·00
		a. Bisected (½d.) (on cover)		† £2750

1861–70. *No wmk. (a) Rough perf 14 to 16.*
20	1	(½d.) deep green	15·00	13·00
21		(½d.) green	9·50	8·00
21a		(½d.) blue-green	55·00	75·00
		b. Imperf (pair)	£475	
22		(½d.) grass-green	20·00	13·00
		a. Imperf (pair)	£550	
23		(1d.) blue (1861)	28·00	1·75
		a. Imperf (pair)	£450	
24		(1d.) deep blue	22·00	3·00
		a. Bisected diag (½d.) (on cover) (1863)		† £1700
25		(4d.) dull rose-red (1861)	60·00	27·00
		a. Imperf (pair)	£600	
26		(4d.) dull brown-red (1865)	80·00	38·00
		a. Imperf (pair)	£850	
27		(4d.) lake-rose (1868)	60·00	48·00
		a. Imperf (pair)	£850	
28		(4d.) dull vermilion (1869)	£160	50·00
		a. Imperf (pair)	£850	
29	2	6d. rose-red (1861)	£170	11·00
30		6d. orange-red (1864)	65·00	16·00
31		6d. bright orange-vermilion (1868)	55·00	16·00
32		6d. dull orange-vermilion (1870)	60·00	11·00
		a. Imperf (pair)	£600	
33		6d. orange (1870)	75·00	24·00
34		1s. brown-black (1863)	42·00	4·00
		a. Error. Blue	£12000	
35		1s. black (1866)	38·00	6·00
		a. Imperf between (horiz pair)	£5000	

(b) Prepared for use, but not issued. P 11 to 12
36	1	(½d.) grass-green	£6000	
37		(1d.) blue	£2250	

The bisect, No. 24a, was authorised for use in April 1863 and November 1866 during shortages of ½d. stamps.
No. 34a was an error on the part of the printer who supplied the first requisition of the 1s. value in the colour of the 1d. The 1s. blue stamps were never placed on sale, but the Barbados Colonial Secretary circulated some samples which were defaced by a manuscript corner-to-corner cross. A number of these samples subsequently had the cross removed.
Nos. 36/7 were never sent to Barbados and come from the Perkins Bacon remainders. It is believed that the imperforate pairs came from the same source.

1870. *Wmk Large Star, Type w 1. Rough perf 14 to 16.*
43	1	(½d.) green	65·00	4·50
		a. Imperf (pair)	£550	
43b		(½d.) yellow-green	90·00	40·00
44		(1d.) blue	£850	38·00
		a. Blue paper	—	75·00
45		(4d.) dull vermilion	£650	70·00
46	2	6d. orange-vermilion	£600	50·00
47		1s. black	£200	16·00

1871. *Wmk Small Star, Type w 2. Rough perf 14 to 16.*
48	1	(1d.) blue	75·00	1·25
49		(4d.) dull rose-red	£600	24·00
50	2	6d. orange-vermilion	£250	11·00
51		1s. black	£100	7·50

1872. *Wmk Small Star, Type w 2. (a) Clean-cut perf 14½ to 15½.*
52	1	(1d.) blue	£170	1·25
		a. Bisected diag (½d.) (on cover)		† £1500
53	2	6d. orange-vermilion	£500	50·00
54		1s. black	90·00	6·00

(b) P 11 to 13 × 14½ to 15½
56	1	(½d.) green	£200	25·00
57		(4d.) dull vermilion	£375	75·00

1873. *Wmk Large Star, Type w 1. (a) Clean-cut perf 14½ to 15½.*
58	1	(½d.) green	£160	10·00
59		(4d.) dull rose-red	£700	£110
60	2	6d. orange-vermilion	£500	50·00
		a. Imperf between (horiz pair)	£4000	
		b. Imperf (pair)	75·00	
61		1s. black	90·00	6·00
		a. Imperf between (horiz pair)	£4500	

(b) Prepared for use, but not issued. P 11 to 12
62	2	6d. orange-vermilion	£3500	

Only eight mint examples, in two strips of four, are known of No. 62.
Two used singles of No. 60b have been seen.

1873 (June). *Wmk Small Star, Type w 2 (sideways = two points upwards). P 14.*
63	2	3d. brown-purple	£325	£110

3

1873 (June). *Wmk Small Star, Type w 2 (sideways). P 15½×15.*
64	3	5s. dull rose (H/S S. £300)	£950	£300

1874 (May). *Wmk Large Star, Type w 1. (a) Perf 14.*
65	2	½d. deep green	18·00	4·00
66		1d. deep blue	55·00	1·25

(b) Clean-cut perf 14½ to 15½
66a	2	1d. deep blue		† £8000
		b. Imperf (pair)		

(Recess D.L.R.)

1875–80. *Wmk Crown CC (sideways on 6d., 1s.) (a) P 12½.*
67	2	½d. bright green	27·00	2·25
68		4d. deep red	£150	7·00
69		6d. bright yellow (aniline)	£750	70·00
70		6d. chrome-yellow	£400	65·00
		a. Wmk upright		† £1500
71		1s. violet (aniline)	£400	3·00

(b) P 14
72	2	½d. bright green (1876)	6·00	50
73		1d. dull blue	35·00	55
		a. Bisected (½d.) (on cover) (1877)		† £1300
74		1d. grey-blue	35·00	30
		a. Wmk sideways		† £850
75		3d. mauve-lilac (1878)	75·00	4·25
76		4d. red (1878)	75·00	7·00
77		4d. carmine	£120	1·75
78		4d. crimson-lake	£375	2·50
79		6d. chrome-yellow (1876)	90·00	1·00
80		6d. yellow	£250	5·00
81		1s. purple (1876)	£100	2·75
82		1s. violet (aniline)	£1500	32·00
83		1s. dull mauve	£250	2·00
		a. Bisected (6d.) (on cover) (1.80)		† £3750

(c) P 14 × 12½
84	2	4d. red		£5000
72/3 (in red), 75/6, 79, 81 (in red) Handstamped "Specimen"			Set of 6	£500
72/3 (in black) H/S "Specimen"			Set of 2	£150

Only two examples, both used, of No. 70a have been reported.
Very few examples of No. 84 have been found unused and only one used specimen is known.

4 ONE PENNY

HALF-PENNY

(5)

(Typo D.L.R.)

1882 (28 Aug)–**86**. *Wmk Crown CA. P 14.*
89	4	½d. dull green (1882)	9·00	90
90		½d. green	8·50	90
91		1d. rose (1882)	42·00	1·50
		a. Bisected (½d.) (on cover)..		† £900
92		1d. carmine	8·50	40
93		2½d. ultramarine (1882)	65·00	90
94		2½d. deep blue	70·00	85
95		3d. deep purple (1885)	85·00	25·00
96		3d. reddish purple	3·25	11·00
97		4d. grey (1882)	£190	2·00
98		4d. pale brown (1885)	5·00	2·25
99		4d. deep brown	3·50	75
100		6d. olive-black (1886)	60·00	32·00
102		1s. chestnut (1886)	22·00	21·00
103		5s. bistre (1886)	£140	£180
89/103			Set of 9	£450	£225
95/103, except 97, Optd "Specimen"			Set of 5	£375

1892 (July). *No. 99 surch with T 5 by West Indian Press.*
104	4	½d. on 4d. deep brown	1·60	2·50
		a. No hyphen	8·00	15·00
		b. Surch double (R.+Bk.)	£450	£700
		ba. Surch double (R.+Bk.) both without hyphen	£1300	£1300
		c. Surch double, one albino		
		d. Surch "PENNY HALF"	—	£200

Nos. 104b/ba come from a sheet with a trial surcharge in red which was subsequently surcharged again in black and put back into stock.
No. 104c is known in a horizontal pair with the left hand stamp showing the first two letters of the second impression inked. The right hand stamp shows a complete albino surcharge.

6 Seal of Colony 7

1D.

(3a) (3b) (3c)

1878 (28 Mar). *No. 64 surch by West Indian Press with T 3a/c sideways twice on each stamp and then divided vertically by 11½ to 13 perforations. The lower label, showing the original face value, was removed before use.*

(a) With T 3a. Large numeral "1", 7 mm high with curved serif, and large letter "D", 2¾ mm high.
86	3	1d. on half 5s. dull rose	£3250	£600
		a. No stop after "D"	£9500	£1600
		b. Unsevered pair (both No. 86)	£13000	£1800
		c. Ditto, Nos. 86 and 87	—	£3500
		ca. Pair without dividing perf		† £16000
		d. Ditto, Nos. 86 and 88	£22000	£5500

(b) With T 3b. As last, but numeral with straight serif
87	3	1d. on half 5s. dull rose	£3750	£700
		a. Unsevered pair		† £2500

(c) With T 3c. Smaller numeral "1", 6 mm high and smaller "D", 2½ mm high.
88	3	1d. on half 5s dull rose	£4500	£850
		a. Unsevered pair	£15000	£3500

All types of the surcharge are found reading upwards as well as downwards, and there are minor varieties of the type.

(Typo D.L.R.)

1892 (July)–**1903**. *Wmk Crown CA. P* 14.
105	**6**	¼d. slate-grey and carmine (5.5.96)		1·75	10
106		½d. dull green		1·00	10
107		1d. carmine		2·75	10
108		2d. slate-black and orange (5.99)		6·50	65
109		2½d. ultramarine		12·00	20
110		5d. grey-olive		5·50	4·50
111		6d. mauve and carmine		8·00	2·00
112		8d. orange and ultramarine		2·50	18·00
113		10d. dull blue-green and carmine		6·50	6·50
114		2s. blue-black and orange		42·00	45·00
115		2s. 6d. violet and green (29.5.03)		65·00	95·00
105/15			*Set of* 11	£140	£150
105/15 Optd "Specimen"			*Set of* 11	£170	

See also Nos. 135/44 and 163/9.

(Typo D.L.R.)

1897 (Dec)–**98**. *Diamond Jubilee. T* **7**. *Wmk Crown CC. P* 14.

(a) White paper
116		¼d. grey and carmine		2·00	40
117		½d. dull green		2·25	40
118		1d. rose		2·25	40
119		2½d. ultramarine		4·50	65
120		5d. olive-brown		12·00	12·00
121		6d. mauve and carmine		16·00	17·00
122		8d. orange and ultramarine		5·50	18·00
123		10d. blue-green and carmine		42·00	48·00
124		2s. 6d. blue-black and orange		45·00	48·00
116/124			*Set of* 9	£120	£130
116/124 Optd "Specimen"			*Set of* 9	£150	

(b) Paper blued
125		¼d. grey and carmine		26·00	30·00
126		½d. dull green		27·00	30·00
127		1d. carmine		35·00	40·00
128		2½d. ultramarine		38·00	45·00
129		5d. olive-brown		£225	£250
130		6d. mauve and carmine		£120	£130
131		8d. orange and ultramarine		£120	£140
132		10d. dull green and carmine		£180	£200
133		2s. 6d. blue-black and orange		£100	£110

1905. *Wmk Mult Crown CA. P* 14.
135	**6**	¼d. slate-grey and carmine		6·00	2·00
136		½d. dull green		10·00	10
137		1d. carmine		9·00	10
139		2½d. blue		6·00	15
141		6d. mauve and carmine		11·00	12·00
142		8d. orange and ultramarine		29·00	60·00
144		2s. 6d. violet and green		29·00	70·00
135/144			*Set of* 7	90·00	£130

See also Nos. 163/9.

8 Nelson Monument

(Des Mrs. G. Goodman. Recess D.L.R.)

1906 (1 Mar). *Nelson Centenary. Wmk Crown CC. P* 14.
145	**8**	¼d. black and grey		5·00	1·25
		w. Wmk inverted		25·00	
146		½d. black and pale green		7·00	15
		w. Wmk inverted			
		x. Wmk reversed			
147		1d. black and red		8·50	15
		w. Wmk inverted		25·00	
		x. Wmk reversed			
148		2d. black and yellow		1·75	4·25
149		2½d. black and bright blue		3·75	1·00
		w. Wmk inverted			
150		6d. black and mauve		17·00	23·00
151		1s. black and rose		18·00	42·00
145/51			*Set of* 7	55·00	65·00
145/51 Optd "Specimen"			*Set of* 7	£130	

Two sets may be made of the above: one on thick, opaque, creamy white paper; the other on thin, rather transparent, bluish white paper.

See also Nos. 158/62a.

9 Olive Blossom, 1605

Kingston
Relief
Fund.
1d.

(10)

(Des Lady Carter. Recess D.L.R.)

1906 (15 Aug). *Tercentenary of Annexation. Wmk Multiple Crown CA (sideways). P* 14.
152	**9**	1d. black, blue and green		10·00	25
152 Optd "Specimen"				65·00	

1907 (25 Jan–25 Feb). *Kingston Relief Fund. No.* 108 *surch with T* **10** *by T. E. King & Co., Barbados.*
153	**6**	1d. on 2d. slate-black and orange (R.)		1·50	4·25
		a. Surch inverted (25.2.07)		1·50	6·00
		b. Surch double		£550	£600
		c. Surch double, both inverted		£550	
		d. Surch *tête-bêche* (pair)		£700	
		e. No stop after "1d."		29·00	50·00
		ea. Do., surch inverted (25.2.07)		29·00	60·00
		eb. Do., surch double		—	£950
		f. Vert pair, one normal, one surch double		—	£750

The above stamp was sold for 2d. of which 1d. was retained for the postal revenue, and the other 1d. given to a fund for the relief of the sufferers by the earthquake in Jamaica.

An entire printing as No. 153a was created after a sheet of inverted surcharges was found in the initial supply.

1907 (6 July). *Nelson Centenary. Wmk Mult Crown CA. P* 14.
158	**8**	¼d. black and grey		5·00	2·75
161		2d. black and yellow		18·00	22·00
162		2½d. black and bright blue		10·00	18·00
		a. Black and indigo		£700	£800
158/62			*Set of* 3	30·00	38·00

1909 (July)–**10**. *Wmk Mult Crown CA. P* 14.
163	**6**	¼d. brown		2·00	30
164		½d. blue-green		17·00	60
165		1d. red		6·50	10
166		2d. greyish slate (8.10)		5·50	9·50
167		2½d. bright blue (1910)		35·00	5·00
168		6d. dull and bright purple (1910)		7·00	14·00
169		1s. black/*green* (8.10)		8·00	14·00
163/9			*Set of* 7	75·00	38·00
163, 165/6, 168/9 Optd "Specimen"			*Set of* 5	£100	

11   **12**   **13**

(Typo D.L.R.)

1912 (23 July)–**16**. *Wmk Mult Crown CA. P* 14.
170	**11**	¼d. brown		1·00	1·25
		a. Pale brown (1916)		65	1·40
		aw. Wmk inverted			
171		½d. green		2·50	10
		a. Wmk sideways		†	—
172		1d. red (13.8.12)		4·75	10
		a. Scarlet (1915)		14·00	2·25
173		2d. greyish slate (13.8.12)		2·00	11·00
174		2½d. bright blue (13.8.12)		1·25	30
175	**12**	3d. purple/*yellow* (13.8.12)		1·25	10·00
176		4d. red and black/*yellow* (13.8.12)		1·25	14·00
177		6d. purple and dull purple (13.8.12)		8·50	10·00
178	**13**	1s. black/*green* (13.8.12)		6·00	9·00
179		2s. blue and purple/*blue* (13.8.12)		35·00	38·00
180		3s. violet and green (13.8.12)		65·00	75·00
170/80			*Set of* 11	£110	£150
170/80 Optd "Specimen"			*Set of* 11	£140	

14

WAR TAX

(15)

(Recess D.L.R.)

1916 (16 June)–**19**. *Wmk Mult Crown CA. P* 14.
181	**14**	¼d. deep brown		75	30
		a. Chestnut-brown (9.17)		1·50	35
		b. Sepia-brown (4.18)		3·25	2·25
		w. Wmk inverted		15·00	15·00
		y. Wmk inverted and reversed		25·00	
182		½d. green		1·10	15
		a. Deep green (9.17)		1·40	15
		b. Pale green (4.18)		1·90	80
		w. Wmk inverted		20·00	
		y. Wmk inverted and reversed			
183		1d. deep red		17·00	6·00
		a. Bright carmine-red (4.17)		2·50	15
		b. Pale carmine-red (9.17)		6·00	65
		w. Wmk inverted		20·00	
		x. Wmk reversed			
		y. Wmk inverted and reversed		20·00	
184		2d. grey		3·50	13·00
		a. Grey-black (9.19)		23·00	55·00
		x. Wmk reversed			
		y. Wmk inverted and reversed			
185		2½d. deep ultramarine		2·00	1·25
		a. Royal blue (11.17)		2·00	1·25
		w. Wmk inverted			
		y. Wmk inverted and reversed		25·00	20·00
186		3d. purple/*yellow* (thin paper)		1·75	4·50
		a. Deep purple/yellow (thick paper) (9.19)		27·00	27·00
187		4d. red/*yellow*		70	14·00
		w. Wmk inverted			
		x. Wmk reversed			
188		6d. purple		2·50	3·50
		w. Wmk inverted			
		x. Wmk inverted and reversed			
189		1s. black/*green*		7·00	6·50
		x. Wmk reversed			
190		2s. purple/*blue*		16·00	7·50
		w. Wmk inverted			
		y. Wmk inverted and reversed		35·00	
191		3s. deep violet		42·00	80·00
181/91			*Set of* 11	70·00	£120
181/91 Optd "Specimen"			*Set of* 11	£180	

Dates quoted for shades are those of despatch from Great Britain.

Examples of the ½d. and 1d. values can be found perforated either by line or by comb machines.

See also Nos. 199/200a.

1917 (10 Oct)–**18**. *War Tax. Optd in London with T* **15**.
197	**11**	1d. bright red (Optd S. £55)		15	15
		w. Wmk inverted			
198		1d. pale red (*thicker bluish paper*) (4.18)		2·75	40

1918 (18 Feb)–**20**. *Colours changed. Wmk Mult Crown CA. P* 14.
199	**14**	4d. black and red		80	3·50
200		3s. green and deep violet		16·00	48·00
		a. Green and bright violet (1920)		£170	£225
199/200 Optd "Specimen"			*Set of* 2	£120	

The centres of these are from a new die having no circular border line.

16 Winged Victory   **17** Victory from
from the Louvre.   Victoria Memorial,
                        London

(Recess D.L.R.)

1920 (9 Sept)–**21**. *Victory. P* 14.

(a) Wmk Mult Crown CA (sideways* on T **17**)
201	**16**	¼d. black and bistre-brown		30	70
		a. "C" of "CA" missing from wmk		£180	
		w. Wmk inverted			
		x. Wmk reversed			
		y. Wmk inverted and reversed		35·00	
202		½d. black and bright yellow-green		90	15
		a. "C" of "CA" missing from wmk		£200	
		b. "A" of "CA" missing from wmk		£200	
		w. Wmk inverted			
		x. Wmk reversed			
		y. Wmk inverted and reversed			
203		1d. black and vermilion		2·50	10
		a. "A" of "CA" missing from wmk		†	£225
		w. Wmk inverted		30·00	
		y. Wmk inverted and reversed			
204		2d. black and grey		2·00	6·50
		a. "C" of "CA" missing from wmk		£250	
205		2½d. indigo and ultramarine		2·75	9·00
		a. "C" of "CA" missing from wmk		£250	
206		3d. black and purple		2·50	2·25
		w. Wmk inverted		25·00	25·00
207		4d. black and blue-green		2·50	4·50
208		6d. black and brown-orange		3·25	8·50
		w. Wmk inverted		45·00	
209	**17**	1s. black and bright green		8·50	20·00
		w. Wmk Crown to left of CA			
		x. Wmk sideways reversed		£100	
210		2s. black and brown		18·00	25·00
		w. Wmk Crown to left of CA		60·00	
211		3s. black and dull orange		22·00	32·00
		a. "C" of "CA" missing from wmk		£550	
		w. Wmk Crown to left of CA			

(b) Wmk Mult Script CA
212	**16**	1d. black and vermilion (22.8.21)		17·00	30
201/12			*Set of* 12	75·00	£100
201/12 Optd "Specimen"			*Set of* 12	£200	

*The normal sideways watermark on Nos. 209/11 shows Crown to right of CA, *as seen from the back of the stamp.*

18   **19**

(Recess D.L.R.)

1921 (14 Nov)–**24**. *P* 14. (*a*) *Wmk Mult Crown CA.*
213	**18**	3d. purple/*pale yellow*		2·00	5·50
214		4d. red/*pale yellow*		1·75	10·00
215		1s. black/*emerald*		4·50	11·00
		w. Wmk inverted			

(b) Wmk Mult Script CA
217	**18**	¼d. brown		15	10
		x. Wmk reversed		20·00	
		y. Wmk inverted and reversed		25·00	
219		½d. green		80	10
220		1d. red		80	10
		aw. Wmk inverted		20·00	
		ax. Wmk reversed			
		ay. Wmk inverted and reversed			
		b. Bright rose-carmine		5·00	1·00
		bw. Wmk inverted		20·00	
221		2d. grey		1·60	20
		x. Wmk reversed			
222		2½d. ultramarine		1·50	4·75
225		6d. reddish purple		3·50	4·75
226		1s. black/*emerald* (18.9.24)		48·00	70·00
227		2s. purple/*blue*		10·00	18·00
228		3s. deep violet		13·00	42·00
		y. Wmk inverted and reversed			
213/28			*Set of* 12	75·00	£150
213/28 Optd "Specimen"			*Set of* 12	£160	

1925 (1 Apr)–**35**. *Wmk Mult Script CA. P* 14.
229	**19**	¼d. brown		15	10
230		½d. green		30	10
		a. Perf 13½×12½ (2.32)		5·00	10
231		1d. scarlet		40	10
		a. Perf 13½×12½ (2.32)		4·50	30
231b		1½d. orange (1933)		7·50	1·75
		ba. Perf 13½×12½ (15.8.32)		2·00	1·00
232		2d. grey		50	2·50
233		2½d. blue		50	80
		a. Bright ultramarine (1933)		9·50	1·00
		ab. Perf 13½×12½ (2.32)		5·00	1·75
234		3d. purple/*pale yellow*		60	45
		a. Reddish purple/yellow (1935)		5·00	4·50

235	**19**	4d. red/*pale yellow*		75	95
236		6d. purple		75	50
237		1s. black/*emerald*		1·50	5·00
		a. Perf 13½×12½ (8.32)		38·00	20·00
		b. *Brownish black/bright yellow-green* (1934)		4·50	10·00
238		2s. purple/*blue*		7·00	6·50
238a		2s. 6d. carmine/*blue* (1.9.32)		22·00	24·00
239		3s. deep violet		11·00	13·00
229/39			*Set of 13*	42·00	50·00

229/39 Optd/Perf "Specimen"   *Set of 13* £170
Nos. 230/1 exist in coils constructed from normal sheets.

20 King Charles I and King George V   **21** Badge of the Colony

(Recess B.W.)

1927 (17 Feb). *Tercentenary of Settlement of Barbados. Wmk Mult Script CA. P 12½.*
240   **20**   1d. carmine (Optd S. £40)   75   60

1935 (6 May). *Silver Jubilee. As Nos. 91/4 of Antigua, but ptd by Waterlow. P 11 × 12.*

241	1d. deep blue and scarlet		30	20
	j. Damaged turret		65·00	
242	1½d. ultramarine and grey		2·75	4·50
	j. Damaged turret		90·00	
243	2½d. brown and deep blue		2·25	3·00
244	1s. slate and purple		15·00	16·00
	l. Kite and horizontal log		£180	
241/4		*Set of 4*	18·00	21·00

241/4 Perf "Specimen"   *Set of 4* 65·00
For illustrations of plate varieties see Catalogue Introduction.

1937 (14 May). *Coronation. As Nos. 95/7 of Antigua, but printed by D.L.R. P 14.*

245	1d. scarlet		30	15
246	1½d. yellow-brown		40	30
247	2½d. bright blue		70	45
245/7		*Set of 3*	1·25	80

245/7 Perf "Specimen"   *Set of 3* 50·00

Recut line (R. 10/6)   Extra frame line (R. 11/9)

Mark on central ornament (R. 1/3, 2/3, 3/3)   Vertical line over horse's head (R. 4/10) (corrected on Dec 1947 ptg)   "Flying mane" (R. 4/1) (corrected on Dec 1947 ptg)

Curved line at top right (R. 7/8)   Cracked plate (extends to top right ornament) (R. 6/10)

(Recess D.L.R.)

1938 (3 Jan)–47. *Wmk Mult Script CA. P 13½×13.*

248	**21**	½d. green	5·00	15
	a. Recut line		85·00	
	b. Perf 14 (8.42)		70·00	1·25
	c. Perf 14		£275	
248c	½d. yellow-bistre (16.10.42)		15	15
	ca. "A" of "CA" missing from wmk	£1100	
	cb. Recut line		16·00	
249	1d. scarlet (1941)		£275	4·00
	a. Perf 14 (3.1.38)		16·00	10
249b	1d. blue-green (1943)		2·50	60
	c. Perf 14 (16.10.42)		15	10
	ca. "A" of "CA" missing from wmk	£1100	

250   **21**   1½d. orange   15   40

	a. "A" of "CA" missing from wmk	£1100	
	b. Perf 14 (11.41)		4·00	50
250c	2d. claret (3.6.41)		40	1·50
	ca. Extra frame line		24·00	
250d	2d. carmine (20.9.43)		15	20
	da. Extra frame line		16·00	
	e. Perf 14 (11.9.44)		15	75
	ea. Extra frame line		16·00	
251	2½d. ultramarine		50	40
	a. Mark on central ornament	30·00	
	b. *Blue* (17.2.44)		1·10	4·25
	ba. "A" of "CA" missing from wmk	£1000	
	bb. Mark on central ornament	40·00	
252	3d. brown		20	1·90
	a. Vertical line over horse's head	70·00	
	b. Perf 14 (4.41)		20	20
	ba. Vertical line over horse's head	70·00	
252c	3d. blue (1.4.47)		20	1·00
	ca. Vertical line over horse's head	70·00	
253	4d. black		20	10
	a. Flying mane		70·00	
	b. Curved line at top right		60·00	
	c. Cracked plate		60·00	
	d. Perf 14 (11.9.44)		20	2·75
	da. Flying mane		70·00	
	db. Curved line at top right		60·00	
	dc. Cracked plate		60·00	
254	6d. violet		80	10
254a	8d. magenta (9.12.46)		55	1·40
255	1s. olive-green		16·00	2·00
	a. *Deep brown-olive* (19.11.45)	1·00	10
256	2s. 6d. purple		5·50	1·25
256a	5s. indigo (3.6.41)		3·25	5·00
	ab. "A" of "CA" missing from wmk	£1300	
248/56a		*Set of 16*	30·00	10·00

248/56a Perf "Specimen"   *Set of 16* £180
No. 249a was perforated by two machines, one gauging 13.8×14.1 (1938), the other 14.1 (1939).
Nos. 248/c and 249/c exist in coils constructed from normal sheets.
Nos. 249c and 256a both exist showing "A" of "CA" missing from a watermark on the sheet margin.

22 Kings Charles I, George VI, Assembly Chamber and Mace

(Recess D.L.R.)

1939 (27 June). *Tercentenary of General Assembly. Wmk Mult Script CA. P 13½ × 14.*

257	**22**	½d. green	1·75	30
258		1d. scarlet	1·75	30
259		1½d. orange	1·75	60
260		2½d. bright ultramarine	1·75	2·75
261		3d. brown	1·90	2·25
257/61		*Set of 5*	8·00	5·50

257/61 Perf "Specimen"   *Set of 5* £140

Two flags on tug (R. 5/2)

1946 (18 Sept). *Victory. As Nos. 110/11 of Antigua.*

262	1½d. red-orange		15	15
	a. Two flags on tug		20·00	
263	3d. brown		15	15
262/3	Perf "Specimen"	*Set of 2*	48·00	

ONE
PENNY
(23)

NY PEN

Short "Y" (R. 6/2)   Broken "E" (R. 7/4 and 11/4)

(Surch by Barbados Advocate Co)

1947 (21 Apr). *Surch with T 23. (a) P 14.*

264	**21**	1d. on 2d. carmine (No. 250e)	70	1·50
	a. Extra frame line		40·00	
	b. Short "Y"		40·00	
	c. Broken "E"		23·00	

(b) P 13½×13

264d	**21**	1d. on 2d. carmine (No. 250d)	4·50	5·00
	da. Extra frame line		£130	
	db. Short "Y"		£130	
	dc. Broken "E"		80·00	

The relationship of the two words in the surcharge differs on each position of the sheet.

1948 (24 Nov). *Royal Silver Wedding. As Nos. 112/13 of Antigua.*

265	1½d. orange		30	10
266	5s. indigo		9·50	6·00

1949 (10 Oct). *75th Anniv of Universal Postal Union. As Nos. 114/17 of Antigua.*

267	1½d. red-orange		30	35
268	3d. deep blue		1·25	1·25
269	4d. grey		50	1·50
270	1s. olive		50	60
267/70		*Set of 4*	2·25	3·25

(New Currency. 100 cents = 1 West Indian, later Barbados, dollar)

24 Dover Fort   **27** Statue of Nelson

(Recess B.W.)

1950 (1 May). *T 24, 27 and similar designs. Wmk Mult Script CA. P 11 × 11½ (horiz), 13½ (vert).*

271	1 c. indigo		15	2·00
272	2 c. emerald-green		15	1·50
273	3 c. reddish brown and blue-green		75	1·75
274	4 c. carmine		15	30
275	6 c. light blue		15	1·75
276	8 c. bright blue and purple-brown		65	1·25
277	12 c. greenish blue and brown-olive		90	70
278	24 c. scarlet and black		90	30
279	48 c. violet		8·00	4·50
280	60 c. green and claret		6·00	6·50
281	$1.20, carmine and olive-green		8·50	2·75
282	$2.40, black		15·00	10·00
271/282		*Set of 12*	35·00	30·00

Designs: *Horiz*—2 c. Sugar cane breeding; 3 c. Public buildings; 6 c. Casting net; 8 c. *Frances W. Smith* (schooner); 12 c. Four-winged Flyingfish; 24 c. Old Main Guard Garrison; 60 c. Careenage; $2.40, Seal of Barbados. *Vert*—48 c. St. Michael's Cathedral; $1.20, Map of Barbados and wireless mast.

1951 (16 Feb). *Inauguration of B.W.I. University College. As Nos. 118/19 of Antigua.*

283	3 c. brown and blue-green		30	30
284	12 c. blue-green and brown-olive		55	95

36 King George VI and Stamp of 1852

(Recess Waterlow)

1952 (15 Apr). *Barbados Stamp Centenary. Wmk Mult Script CA. P 13½.*

285	**36**	3 c. green and slate-green	15	30
286		4 c. blue and carmine	15	75
287		12 c. slate-green and bright green	15	75
288		24 c. red-brown and brownish black	15	30
285/8			*Set of 4*	55	1·90

37 Harbour Police

(Recess B.W.)

1953 (13 Apr)–61. *Designs previously used for King George VI issue, but with portrait or cypher ($2.40) of Queen Elizabeth II, as in T 37. Wmk Mult Script CA. P 11×11½ (horiz) or 13½ (vert).*

289	1 c. indigo		10	70
290	2 c. orange and deep turquoise (15.4.54)		15	40
291	3 c. black and emerald (15.4.54)		75	50
292	4 c. black and orange (15.4.54)		20	20
	a. *Black and reddish orange* (18.3.59)	1·75	90
293	5 c. blue and deep carmine-red (4.1.54)		65	40
294	6 c. red-brown (15.4.54)		30	40
	w. Wmk inverted			
295	8 c. black and blue (15.4.54)		2·00	40
296	12 c. turquoise-blue & brown-olive (15.4.54)	1·00	10
	a. *Turquoise-grn & brown-olive* (18.3.59)	11·00	2·75
	b. *Turquoise-blue & bronze-grn* (13.6.61)	11·00	2·00
297	24 c. rose-red and black (2.3.56)		45	10
298	48 c. deep violet (2.3.56)		3·50	1·00
299	60 c. blue-green and brown-purple (2.4.56)	1·00	4·50
	a. *Blue-green and pale maroon* (17.5.60)	25·00	6·50
300	$1.20, carmine and bronze-green (3.4.56)	19·00	2·25
301	$2.40, black (1.2.57)		7·50	1·25
289/301		*Set of 13*	48·00	11·00

Designs: *Horiz*—1 c. Dover Fort; 2 c. Sugar cane breeding; 3 c. Public buildings; 6 c. Casting net; 8 c. *Frances W. Smith* (schooner); 12 c. Flying fish; 24 c. Old Main Guard Garrison; 60 c. Careenage; $2.40, Seal of Barbados. *Vert*—4 c. Statue of Nelson; 48 c. St. Michael's Cathedral; $1.20, Map of Barbados and wireless mast.
See also Nos. 312/19.

1953 (4 June). *Coronation. As No. 120 of Antigua.*
302   4 c. black and red-orange   40   10

1958 (23 Apr). *Inauguration of British Caribbean Federation. As Nos. 135/7 of Antigua.*
303   3 c. deep green   45   20
304   6 c. blue   60   1·75
305   12 c. scarlet   60   30
303/5 ..   ..   *Set of 3*   1·50   2·00

38 Deep Water Harbour, Bridgetown

(Recess B.W.)

1961 (6 May). *Opening of Deep Water Harbour, Bridgetown. W w 12. P 11 × 12.*
306   **38**   4 c. black and red-orange   25   30
307   8 c. black and blue   25   40
308   24 c. carmine-red and black   25   40
306/8 ..   ..   *Set of 3*   65   1·00

SELF-GOVERNMENT

39 Scout Badge and Map of   40 Deep Sea Coral
    Barbados

(Recess B.W.)

1962 (9 Mar). *Golden Jubilee of Barbados Boy Scout Association. W w 12. P 11½ × 11.*
309   **39**   4 c. black and orange   40   10
310   12 c. blue and olive-brown   80   15
311    $1.20, carmine and olive-green..   ..   1·25   2·75
309/11   ..   ..   ..   *Set of 3*   2·25   2·75

1964 (14 Jan)–**65.** *As Nos. 289, etc., but wmk w 12.*
312   1 c. indigo (6.10.64)   50   1·00
313   4 c. black and orange   40   50
314   8 c. black and blue (29.6.65)   60   15
315   12 c. turquoise-blue and brown-olive (29.6.65)   90   50
316   24 c. rose-red and black (6.10.64)   70   35
317   48 c. deep violet   ..   ..   ..   3·00   2·00
318   60 c. blue-green and brown-purple (6.10.64) ..   12·00   4·00
319    $2.40, black (29.6.65)   ..   ..   1·75   2·25
312/19   ..   ..   ..   *Set of 8*   18·00   10·00
The above dates are for Crown Agents releases. The 14.1.64 printings were not released in Barbados until April 1964, the 6.10.64 printings until December 1964 and of the stamps released in London on 29 June 1965 the 8 c. and $2.40 were released from about 15 June 1965, but the 12 c. value was never put on sale in Barbados.

1965 (17 May). *I.T.U. Centenary. As Nos. 166/7 of Antigua.*
320   2 c. lilac and red   20   20
321   48 c. yellow and grey-brown   70   1·40

(Des V. Whiteley, from drawings by Mrs. J. Walker. Photo Harrison)

1965 (15 July). *Marine Life. Horiz designs as T 40. W w 12 (upright). P 14×13½.*
322   1 c. black, pink and blue   20   30
323   2 c. olive-brown, yellow and magenta   ..   20   15
324   3 c. olive-brown and orange   45   60
325   4 c. deep blue and olive-green   15   10
    a. Imperf (pair) £225   £150
    w. Wmk inverted   ..   ..   —   15·00
326   5 c. sepia, rose and lilac   30   20
327   6 c. multicoloured   45   20
    w. Wmk inverted   ..   ..   1·25
328   8 c. multicoloured   25   10
    w. Wmk inverted   ..   ..   2·75
329   12 c. multicoloured   35   10
    a. Grey printing double   ..   ..   45·00
    w. Wmk inverted
330   15 c. black, greenish yellow and red   ..   80   80
331   25 c. ultramarine and yellow-ochre   ..   95   75
332   35 c. brown-red and deep green   ..   1·50
    w. Wmk inverted
333   50 c. bright blue and apple-green ..   ..   2·00   40
334    $1 multicoloured   ..   ..   ..   2·75   1·25
335    $2.50, multicoloured   ..   ..   2·75   1·75
322/35   ..   ..   ..   *Set of 14*   12·00   6·00
Designs:—2 c. Lobster; 3 c. Lined Seahorse; 4 c. Sea Urchin; 5 c. Staghorn Coral; 6 c. Spot-finned Butterflyfish; 8 c. Rough File shell; 12 c. Porcupinefish ("Balloon Fish"); 15 c. Grey Angelfish; 25 c. Brain Coral; 35 c. Brittle Star; 50 c. Four-winged Flyingfish; $1 Queen or Pink Conch shell; $2.50 Fiddler Crab.
The 3 c. value is wrongly inscribed "Hippocanpus", the correct spelling "Hippocampus" was used for subsequent printings, see No. 344.
See also Nos. 342, etc.

1966 (24 Jan). *Churchill Commemoration. As Nos. 170/3 of Antigua.*
336   1 c. new blue   10   1·00
    w. Wmk inverted   ..   ..   15·00
337   4 c. deep green   30   10
338   25 c. brown   70   50
339   35 c. bluish violet   80   60
336/9   ..   ..   *Set of 4*   1·75   2·00

1966 (4 Feb). *Royal Visit. As Nos. 174/5 of Antigua.*
340   3 c. black and ultramarine   50   25
341   35 c. black and magenta   ..   ..   1·75   80

41 Dolphin   54 Arms of Barbados

1966 (15 Mar)–**69.** *As Nos. 322/35 but wmk w 12 (sideways*). New value and design (as T 41).*
342   1 c. black, pink and blue   10   20
    w. Wmk Crown to right of CA   ..
343   2 c. olive-brn, yellow & magenta (16.5.67)   30   60
344   3 c. olive-brown and orange (4.12.67)   30   1·75
345   4 c. deep blue and olive-green   ..   50   10
    w. Wmk Crown to right of CA   ..   35·00
346   5 c. sepia, rose and lilac (23.8.66)   45   10
347   6 c. multicoloured (31.1.67)   ..   70   10
348   8 c. multicoloured (19.9.67)   ..   75   10
349   12 c. multicoloured (31.1.67)   ..   45   10
350   15 c. black, greenish yellow and red   2·25   10
351   25 c. ultramarine and yellow-ochre   2·25   40
    a. Deep ultram & yellow-ochre (26.9.66)   8·00   2·25
352   35 c. brown-red and deep green (23.8.66)   2·50   65
    a. Chestnut and deep green (26.11.68)   6·50   3·00
353   50 c. bright blue and apple-green ..   1·75   2·50
    w. Wmk Crown to right of CA   ..   40·00
354    $1 multicoloured (23.8.66)   ..   6·00   1·00
355    $2.50, multicoloured (23.8.66)   ..   7·00   3·00
355a $5 multicoloured (9.1.69)   ..   12·00   7·00
342/55a   ..   ..   *Set of 15*   32·00   16·00
*The normal sideways watermark shows Crown to left of CA, as seen from the back of the stamp.
The 3 c. value is correctly inscribed "Hippocampus".
All values except the 50 c. exist with PVA gum as well as gum arabic but the $5 exists with PVA gum only.
The $5 was released by the Crown Agents on 6 January but was not put on sale locally until 9 January.

INDEPENDENT

(Des. V. Whiteley. Photo Harrison)

1966 (2 Dec). *Independence. T 54 and similar multicoloured designs. P 14.*
356   4 c. Type **54**   10   10
357   25 c. Hilton Hotel (*horiz*)   ..   15   10
358   35 c. G. Sobers (Test cricketer)   ..   1·50   40
359   50 c. Pine Hill Dairy (*horiz*)   ..   70   55
356/9   ..   ..   ..   *Set of 4*   2·00   1·00

1967 (6 Jan). *20th Anniv of U.N.E.S.CO. As Nos. 196/8 of Antigua.*
360   4 c. slate-violet, red, yellow and orange   30   10
361   12 c. orange-yellow, violet and deep olive   70   65
362   25 c. black, bright purple and orange..   1·00   1·50
360/2 ..   ..   *Set of 3*   1·75   2·00

58 Policeman and   62 Governor-General Sir Winston
    Anchor   Scott, G.C.M.G.

(Des V. Whiteley. Litho D.L.R.)

1967 (16 Oct). *Centenary of Harbour Police. T 58 and similar multicoloured designs. P 14.*
363   4 c. Type **58**   20   10
364   25 c. Policeman with telescope   ..   30   15
365   35 c. BP1 (police launch) (*horiz*)   ..   35   15
366   50 c. Policeman outside H.Q.   ..   40   80
363/6   ..   ..   ..   *Set of 4*   1·10   1·10

(Des V. Whiteley. Photo Harrison)

1967 (4 Dec). *First Anniv of Independence. T 62 and similar multicoloured designs. P 14½ × 14 (4 c.) or 14 × 14½ (others).*
367   4 c. Type **62**   10   10
368   25 c. Independence Arch (*horiz*)   ..   15   10
369   35 c. Treasury Building (*horiz*)   ..   20   10
370   50 c. Parliament Building (*horiz*)   ..   25   35
367/70   ..   ..   ..   *Set of 4*   55   45

66 U.N. Building, Santiago, Chile   67 Radar Antenna

(Des G. Vasarhelyi. Photo Harrison)

1968 (27 Feb). *20th Anniv of the Economic Commission for Latin America. P 14½.*
371   **66**   15 c. multicoloured   10   10

(Des G. Vasarhelyi. Photo Harrison)

1968 (4 June). *World Meteorological Day. T 67 and similar multi-coloured designs. P 14 × 14½ (25 c.) or 14½ × 14 (others).*
372   3 c. Type **67**   10   10
373   25 c. Meteorological Institute (*horiz*)   ..   25   10
374   50 c. Harp Gun and coat of arms   ..   30   50
372/4   ..   ..   ..   *Set of 3*   55   60

70 Lady Baden-Powell, and Guide at Camp Fire

(Des V. Whiteley (from local designs). Photo Harrison)

1968 (29 Aug). *50th Anniv of Girl Guiding in Barbados. T 70 and similar horiz designs. P 14.*
375   3 c. ultramarine, black and gold   ..   25   40
376   25 c. turquoise-blue, black and gold   ..   50   40
377   35 c. orange-yellow, black and gold   ..   65   40
375/7 ..   ..   ..   *Set of 3*   1·25   1·10
Designs:—25 c. Lady Baden-Powell and Pax Hill; 35 c. Lady Baden-Powell and Guide badge.

73 Hands breaking Chain, and Human Rights Emblem

(Des V. Whiteley. Litho B.W.)

1968 (10 Dec).* *Human Rights Year. T 73 and similar horiz designs. P 11 × 12.*
378   4 c. violet, brown and light green   ..   10   10
379   25 c. black, blue and orange-yellow ..   10   15
380   35 c. multicoloured   15   15
378/80   ..   ..   ..   *Set of 3*   20   30
Designs:—25 c. Human Rights emblem and family enchained; 35 c. Shadows of refugees beyond opening fence.
* This was the local release date but the Crown Agents issued the stamps on 29 October.

76 Racehorses in the Paddock

(Des J. Cooter. Litho Format)

1969 (20 Mar).* *Horse-Racing. T 76 and similar horiz designs. Multicoloured. P 14.*
381   4 c. Type **76**   20   10
382   25 c. Starting-gate   25   15
383   35 c. On the flat   25   15
384   50 c. Winning post   35   1·40
381/4 ..   ..   ..   *Set of 4*   95   1·60
MS385   117 × 85 mm. Nos. 381/4 ..   ..   2·00   2·75
*This was the local release date but the Crown Agents issued the stamps on 15 March.

The new-issue supplement to this Catalogue appears each month in

GIBBONS STAMP MONTHLY

—from your newsagent or by postal subscription— sample copy and details on request.

80 Map showing "CARIFTA" Countries | 81 "Strength in Unity"

(Des J. Cooter. Photo Harrison)

1969 (6 May). *First Anniv of CARIFTA (Caribbean Free Trade Area). W w 12 (sideways on T 80). P 14.*

386	80	5 c. multicoloured	..	10	10
387	81	12 c. multicoloured	..	10	10
388	80	25 c. multicoloured	..	10	10
389	81	50 c. multicoloured	..	15	20
386/9	..		Set of 4	30	30

82 I.L.O. Emblem and "1919-1969". | ONE CENT (83)

(Des Sylvia Goaman. Litho Enschedé)

1969 (12 Aug). *50th Anniv of International Labour Organisation. P 14 × 13.*

390	82	4 c. black, emerald and turquoise-blue		10	10
391		25 c. black, cerise and brown-red	..	20	10

Although released by the Crown Agents on 5 August, the above were not put on sale in Barbados until 12 August.

1969 (30 Aug). *No. 363 surch with T 83.*

392	1 c. on 4 c. Type 58	..	..	10	10
	a. Surch double	..	..	65·00	

84 National Scout Badge

(Des J. Cooter. Litho Enschedé)

1969 (16 Dec). *Independence of Barbados Boy Scouts Association and 50th Anniv of Barbados Sea Scouts. T 84 and similar horiz designs. Multicoloured. P 13 × 13½.*

393	5 c. Type 84	..	..	15	10
394	25 c. Sea Scouts rowing	..	..	45	10
395	35 c. Scouts around camp fire	..	..	55	10
396	50 c. Scouts and National Scout Headquarters		80	60
393/6	..		Set of 4	1·75	75
MS397	155 × 115 mm. Nos. 393/6	..	..	9·50	12·00

4 x (88) | 89 Lion at Gun Hill

1970 (11 Mar). *No. 346 surch locally with T 88.*

398	4 c. on 5 c. sepia, rose and lilac	..	10	10
	a. Vert pair, one without surch	..	35·00	
	b. Surch double	..	..	25·00	
	c. Vert pair, one normal, one surch double	50·00	
	d. Surch triple	..	..	£100	
	e. Surch normal on front, inverted on back	12·00	
	f. Surch omitted on front, inverted on back	16·00	

(Des J. W. Photo D.L.R.)

1970–71. *Multicoloured designs as T 89. W w 12 (sideways on 12 c. to $5). P 12½. A. Chalk-surfaced paper (4.5.70) B. Glazed, ordinary paper (13.12.71, 12 c., 15 c. and $2.50; 15.3.71, others).*

			A		B	
399	1 c. Type 89	..	10	30	10	75
400	2 c. Trafalgar Fountain	..	30	40	10	1·25
401	3 c. Montefiore Drinking Fountain	..	10	40	10	1·25
	w. Wmk inverted	..	†		6·50	—
402	4 c. St. James' Monument	..	60	15	10	10
403	5 c. St. Anne's Fort	..	10	10	10	10
404	6 c. Old Sugar Mill, Morgan Lewis	..	35	2·50		†
405	8 c. Cenotaph	..	10	10	10	10
406	10 c. South Point Lighthouse		2·00	50	85	15

407	12 c. Barbados Museum	..	60	10	2·25	30
408	15 c. Sharon Moravian Church	30	15	60	30
409	25 c. George Washington House	..	25	15	50	35
410	35 c. Nicholas Abbey	..	30	85	45	70
411	50 c. Bowmanston Pumping Station	..	40	95	70	2·75
412	$1 Queen Elizabeth Hospital	70	2·50	4·00	8·00
413	$2.50, Modern sugar factory	1·50	4·00	24·00	16·00
414	$5 Seawell International Airport ..	..	6·00	11·00	10·00	15·00
399A/414A		Set of 16	12·00	21·00		
399B/414B		Set of 15			40·00	42·00

The 2 to 10 c. values are vertical; the 12 c. to $5 horizontal. See also Nos. 455/67.

105 Primary Schoolgirl

(Des V. Whiteley. Litho J.W.)

1970 (26 June). *25th Anniv of United Nations. T 105 and similar horiz designs. Multicoloured. W w 12. P 14.*

415	4 c. Type 106	..	..	10	10
416	5 c. Secondary Schoolboy	..	10	10
417	25 c. Technical Student	..	..	35	10
418	50 c. University Buildings	..	55	1·00
415/18	..		Set of 4	90	1·10

106 Minnie Root

(Des and litho J.W.)

1970 (24 Aug). *Flowers of Barbados. T 106 and similar designs. Multicoloured. W w 12 (sideways on horiz designs). P 14½.*

419	1 c. Barbados Easter Lily (vert)	..	10	1·25
420	5 c. Type 106	..	..	40	10
421	10 c. Eyelash Orchid	..	..	1·50	20
422	25 c. Pride of Barbados (vert)	..	1·25	20
423	35 c. Christmas Hope	..	..	1·25	85
419/23	..		Set of 5	4·00	2·75
MS424	162 × 101 mm. Nos. 419/23. Imperf	2·00	5·50

107 "Via Dolorosa" (Window, St. Margaret's Church, St. John) | 108 "Sailfish" Craft

(Des Jennifer Toombs. Litho J.W.)

1971 (7 Apr). *Easter. T 107 and similar vert design. Multicoloured. W w 12. P 14.*

425	4 c. Type 107	..	..	10	10
426	10 c. "The Resurrection" (Benjamin West)	10	10
427	35 c. Type 107	..	..	15	10
428	50 c. As 10 c.	..	..	30	90
425/8	..		Set of 4	45	1·00

(Des and litho Harrison)

1971 (17 Aug). *Tourism. T 108 and similar horiz designs. Multicoloured. W w 12 (sideways on 5 c. and 25 c.). P 14.*

429	1 c. Type 108	..	..	10	20
	w. Wmk inverted	..	..	50	45
430	5 c. Tennis	..	..	15	10
431	12 c. Horse-riding	..	..	25	10
	w. Wmk inverted	..	..	1·75	1·25
432	25 c. Water-skiing ..	..	30	20
433	50 c. Scuba-diving	..	..	50	80
	w. Wmk inverted	..	..	80	80
429/33	..		Set of 5	1·10	1·25

109 S. J. Prescod (politician) | 110 Arms of Barbados

(Des J.W. litho Questa)

1971 (28 Sept).* *Death Centenary of Samuel Jackman Prescod. W w 12. P 14.*

434	109	3 c. multicoloured	..	..	10	15
435		35 c. multicoloured	..	..	15	15

*This is the local date but the Crown Agents released the stamps two days earlier.

(Des G. Drummond. Litho Questa)

1971 (23 Nov). *Fifth Anniv of Independence. T 110 and similar horiz design. Multicoloured. W w 12 (sideways). P 14.*

436	4 c. Type 110	..	..	15	10
437	15 c. National flag and map	..	35	10
438	25 c. Type 110	..	..	35	10
439	50 c. As 15 c.	..	..	80	80
436/9	..		Set of 4	1·50	95

111 Transmitting "Then and Now" | 112 Map and Badge

(Des Cable & Wireless Ltd. Litho J.W.)

1972 (28 Mar). *Cable Link Centenary. T 111 and similar horiz designs. Multicoloured. W w 12 (sideways). P 14.*

440	4 c. Type 111	..	..	10	10
441	10 c. Stanley Angwin (cable ship)	..	15	10
442	35 c. Barbados Earth Station and "Intelsat 4"	35	20
443	50 c. Mt. Misery and Tropospheric Scatter Station	..	50	1·10
440/3	..		Set of 4	95	1·25

(Des Mrs. C. Barrow (50 c.), Major L. Quintyne (others) and adapted by G. Drummond. Litho Questa)

1972 (1 Aug). *Diamond Jubilee of Scouts. T 112 and similar horiz designs. Multicoloured. W w 12 (sideways* on 5 c.). P 14.*

444	5 c. Type 112	..	..	10	10
	w. Wmk Crown to right of CA	..		
445	15 c. Pioneers of scouting	..	15	10
446	25 c. Scouts	..	..	30	15
447	50 c. Flags	..	..	50	75
444/7	..		Set of 4	90	90

*The normal sideways watermark shows Crown to left of CA, as seen from the back of the stamp.

113 Mobile Library

(Des PAD Studio. Litho Harrison)

1972 (31 Oct). *International Book Year. T 113 and similar horiz designs. Multicoloured. W w 12. P 14.*

448	4 c. Type 113	..	..	20	10
449	15 c. Visual-aids van	..	..	25	10
450	25 c. Public library	..	..	30	10
451	$1 Codrington College	..	..	1·25	1·50
448/51	..		Set of 4	1·75	1·50

1972 (17 Nov)–**74.** *As Nos. 402B/14B, but W w 12 (sideways on 4 to 10 c.; upright on 12 c. to $5).*

455	4 c. St. James' Monument	..	1·50	1·50
456	5 c. St. Anne's Fort	..	1·25	1·50
457	6 c. Old Sugar Mill, Morgan Lewis	3·75	8·00
458	8 c. Cenotaph	..	..	1·50	1·25
459	10 c. South Point Lighthouse (21.1.74)	3·50	6·00
460	12 c. Barbados Museum	..	2·25	3·00
461	15 c. Sharon Moravian Church	..	75	1·25
462	25 c. George Washington House	2·75	2·25
463	35 c. Nicholas Abbey	..	2·50	70
464	50 c. Bowmanston Pumping Station	4·25	1·50
465	$1 Queen Elizabeth Hospital	..	7·00	2·75
466	$2.50, Modern sugar factory (2.10.73)	4·00	6·50
467	$5 Seawell International Airport (2.10.73)	4·00	5·50
	w. Wmk inverted	..	..	6·50	
455/67	..		Set of 13	35·00	35·00

114 Potter's Wheel

(Des PAD Studio. Litho Questa)

1973 (1 Mar). *Pottery in Barbados. T 114 and similar horiz designs. Multicoloured. W w 12. P 14.*

468	5 c. Type 114	..	..	10	10
469	15 c. Kilns	..	..	20	10
470	25 c. Finished products	..	25	10
471	$1 Market scene	..	..	90	1·10
	w. Wmk inverted	..	..	25·00	
468/71	..		Set of 4	1·25	1·25

115 First Flight, 1911

(Des C. Abbott. Litho Enschedé)

1973 (25 July). *Aviation. T* **115** *and similar horiz designs. W* w **12** *(sideways). P* 12½ × 12.
472	5 c. multicoloured	..	..	30	10
473	15 c. multicoloured	..	..	90	10
474	25 c. grey-blue, black and cobalt		..	1·25	20
475	50 c. multicoloured	..	..	2·00	1·90
472/5	..		*Set of* 4	4·00	2·00

Designs:—15 c. De Havilland D.H.60 Cirrus Moth on first flight to Barbados, 1928; 25 c. Lockheed 14 Super Electra, 1939; 50 c. Vickers Super VC-10 airliner, 1973.

116 University Chancellor (117)

(Des J. W. Litho Enschedé)

1973 (11 Dec). *25th Anniv of University of West Indies. T* **116** *and similar horiz designs. Multicoloured. W* w **12**. *P* 13 × 14.
476	5 c. Type **116**	..	..	10	10
	w. Wmk inverted	..	..	22·00	
477	25 c. Sherlock Hall	..	..	25	15
478	35 c. Cave Hill Campus	..	..	30	25
476/8			*Set of* 3	55	40

1974 (30 Apr). *No.* 462 *surch with T* **117**.
479	4 c. on 25 c. George Washington House	..	15	15
	a. "4c." omitted	..	..		16·00

No. 479a occurs on R. 10/1, the overprint being applied to sheets consisting of two horizontal panes, 5 × 5. The variety occurs on plate 1A, and shows a clear albino impression of the "4c." on the reverse.

118 Old Sail Boat

(Des J. Cooter. Litho Questa)

1974 (11 June). *Fishing Boats of Barbados. T* **118** *and similar diamond-shaped designs. Multicoloured. W* w **12**. *P* 14.
480	15 c. Type **118**	..	..	30	15
481	35 c. Rowing-boat	..	..	55	25
482	50 c. Motor fishing-boat	..	..	70	70
483	$1 *Calamar* (fishing boat)	..	..	1·10	1·40
480/3	..		*Set of* 4	2·40	2·25
MS484	140 × 140 mm. Nos. 480/3	..	..	3·00	3·00

119 *Cattleya Gaskelliana Alba*

(Des PAD Studio. Photo Harrison)

1974 (16 Sept)–77. *Orchids. T* **119** *and similar multicoloured designs. W* w **12** *(upright on* 1, 20, 25 c., $1 *and* $10; *sideways* on others). P* 14½×14 ($1, $10), 14×14½ ($2.50, $5) *or* 14 *(others)*.
485	1 c. Type **119**	..	..	15	1·25
486	2 c. *Renanthera storiei*	..	..	20	1·25
487	3 c. *Dendrobium* "Rose Marie"	..	30	1·00
488	4 c. *Epidendrum ibaguense*	..	..	1·75	90
	w. Wmk Crown to right of CA	..	42·00	
489	5 c. *Schomburgkia humboldtii*	..	35	15
490	8 c. *Oncidium ampliatum*	..	..	1·00	90
	w. Wmk Crown to right of CA	..		
491	10 c. *Arachnis maggie oei*	..	..	55	20
492	12 c. *Dendrobium aggregatum*	..	45	1·50
	w. Wmk Crown to right of CA	..		
493	15 c. *Paphiopedilum puddle*	..	45	80
	aw. Wmk Crown to right of CA	..	6·00	
493*b*	20 c. *Spathoglottis* "The Gold" (3.5.77)	4·75	4·75
494	25 c. *Epidendrum ciliare* (Eyelash)	..	55	60
	w. Wmk inverted	..	..		
495	35 c. *Bletia patula*	..	..	2·00	1·75
	aw. Wmk Crown to right of CA	..	2·50	1·75
495*b*	45 c. *Phalaenopsis schilleriana* "Sunset Glow" (3.5.77)	..	..	4·75	4·50

496	50 c. As 45 c.	..	..	4·50	3·00
	w. Wmk Crown to left of CA	..	4·50	
497	$1 *Ascocenda* "Red Gem"	..	4·50	3·25
498	$2.50, *Brassolaeliocattleya* "Nugget"	3·50	4·50
499	$5 *Caularthron bicornutum*	..	3·50	6·00
500	$10 *Vanda* "Josephine Black"	..	4·00	13·00
485/500		*Set of* 18	32·00	42·00

The 1 c., 20 c., 25 c., $2.50 and $5 are horiz designs and the remainder are vert.

*The normal sideways watermark shows Crown to right of CA on the 50 c. and to left of CA on the others, *as seen from the back of the stamp.*

See also Nos. 510/24 and 543/51.

120 4d. Stamp of 1882, and U.P.U. Emblem

(Des Harrison. Litho Questa)

1974 (9 Oct). *Centenary of Universal Postal Union. T* **120** *and similar horiz designs. W* w **12** *(sideways*). P* 14.
501	8 c. magenta, light orange & lt grey-green	10	10
502	35 c. dp rose-red, dull orange & bistre-brown	20	10
503	50 c. ultramarine, cobalt and silver	..	25	30
504	$1 bright blue, dull brown and grey-black	55	80
	w. Wmk Crown to right of CA	..		12·00
501/4		*Set of* 4	1·00	1·10
MS505	126×101 mm. Nos. 501/4	..	1·50	2·25

Designs:—35 c. Letters encircling the globe; 50 c. U.P.U. emblem and arms of Barbados; $1 Map of Barbados, sailing ship and Boeing 747 airliner.

*The normal sideways watermark shows Crown to left of CA, *as seen from the back of the stamp.*

121 Royal Yacht *Britannia*

(Des Jennifer Toombs. Litho Harrison)

1975 (18 Feb). *Royal Visit. T* **121** *and similar horiz design. Multicoloured. W* w **12** *(sideways on* 8 *and* 25 c.) *P* 14.
506	8 c. Type **121**	..	..	40	20
507	25 c. Type **121**	..	..	75	30
508	35 c. Sunset and palms	..	..	60	35
509	$1 As 35 c.	..	..	1·75	2·50
506/9	..	..	*Set of* 4	3·25	3·00

1975 (30 Apr)–79. *As Nos.* 485 *etc.,* 491/3, 494 *and* 495*b*/500 *but W* w **14** *(sideways* on* 1, 25 c., $1 *and* $10).
510	1 c. Type **119**	..	..	15	1·00
511	2 c. *Renanthera storiei*	..	..	15	1·00
512	3 c. *Dendrobium* "Rose Marie"	..	15	1·00
513	4 c. *Epidendrum ibaguense*	..	..	50	2·50
514	5 c. *Schomburgkia humboldtii* (19.10.77)	35	15
515	10 c. *Arachnis maggie oei* (19.10.77)	..	35	10
	w. Wmk inverted	..	..		
516	12 c. *Dendrobium aggregatum* (19.10.77)	7·50	15
517	15 c. *Paphiopedilum puddle*	..	70	15
518	25 c. *Epidendrum ciliare* (Eyelash) (27.3.79)	70	10
519	45 c. *Phalaenopsis schilleriana* "Sunset Glow" (25.5.78)	..	60	15
	w. Wmk inverted	..	..		
520	50 c. As 45 c. (23.8.79)	..	6·00	6·00
521	$1 *Ascocenda* "Red Gem"	..	8·50	11·00
	w. Wmk Crown to right of CA	..	17·00	
522	$2.50, *Brassolaeliocattleya* "Nugget"	7·00	3·75
523	$5 *Caularthron bicornutum*	..	8·50	6·00
524	$10 *Vanda* "Josephine Black"	..	11·00	11·00
	a. Dull green (stems) omitted	..	£110	
510/24		*Set of* 15	48·00	40·00

*The normal sideways watermark shows Crown to left of CA, *as seen from the back of the stamp.*

No. 525 vacant.

122 St. Michael's Cathedral 123 Pony Float

(Des R. Granger Barrett. Litho Questa)

1975 (29 July). *150th Anniv of Anglican Diocese. T* **122** *and similar square designs. Multicoloured. W* w **12** *(sideways). P* 13½.
526	5 c. Type **122**	..	..	10	10
527	15 c. Bishop Coleridge	..	..	15	10
528	50 c. All Saints' Church	..	..	45	50
529	$1 "Archangel Michael and Satan" (stained-glass window, St. Michael's Cathedral, Bridgetown)	..	70	80
526/9	..	..	*Set of* 4	1·25	1·25
MS530	95 × 96 mm. Nos. 526/9 (wmk upright)	..	1·40	2·00

(Des R. Granger Barrett. Litho Questa)

1975 (18 Nov). *Crop-over Festival. T* **123** *and similar horiz designs. Multicoloured. W* w **14** *(sideways). P* 14.
531	8 c. Type **123**	..	..	10	10
532	25 c. Man on stilts	..	..	10	10
533	35 c. Maypole dancing	..	..	15	10
534	50 c. Cuban dancers	..	..	30	45
531/4			*Set of* 4	55	60
MS535	127 × 85 mm. Nos. 531/4	..	90	1·60

124 Barbados Coat 125 17th-Century
of Arms Sailing Ship

(Des and litho Harrison)

1975 (15 Dec). *Coil Definitives. W* w **12** *P* 15 × 14.
536	124	5 c. greenish blue	..	..	15	60
537		25 c. bluish violet	..	..	25	1·00

For 5 c. in this design, but watermarked W w **14**, see No. 743.

(Des PAD Studio. Litho J.W.)

1975 (17 Dec). *350th Anniv of First Settlement. T* **125** *and similar vert designs. Multicoloured. W* w **14**. *P* 13½.
538	4 c. Type **125**	..	..	50	10
539	10 c. Bearded fig tree and fruit	..	40	15
540	25 c. Ogilvy's 17th-century map	..	1·00	30
541	$1 Captain John Powell	..	..	2·00	4·50
538/41			*Set of* 4	3·50	4·50
MS542	105 × 115 mm. Nos. 538/41. *P* 14 × 14½	3·50	6·00

1976 (20 Feb). *As Nos.* 485 *etc., but W* w **12** *(sideways on* 1 c., 25 c., $1) *or upright (others).*
543	1 c. Type **119**	..	..	45	2·50
544	2 c. *Renanthera storiei*	..	..	60	2·50
545	3 c. *Dendrobium* "Rose Marie"	..	65	2·75
546	4 c. *Epidendrum ibaguense*	..	..	45	3·00
547	10 c. *Arachnis maggie oei*	..	..	85	2·75
548	15 c. *Paphiopedilum puddle*	..	..	75	1·00
549	25 c. *Epidendrum ciliare* "Eyelash"	..	1·50	1·00
550	35 c. *Bletia patula*	..	..	2·00	1·50
551	$1 *Ascocenda* "Red Gem"	..	..	5·00	5·00
543/51			*Set of* 9	11·00	20·00

Nos. 552/8 vacant.

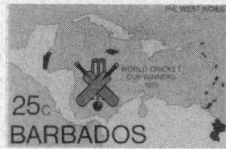

126 Map of the Caribbean

(Des PAD Studio. Litho Questa)

1976 (7 July). *West Indian Victory in World Cricket Cup. T* **126** *and similar design. No wmk. P* 14.
559	25 c. multicoloured	..	..	1·25	1·00
560	45 c. black and magenta	..	1·25	2·00

Design: *Vert*—45 c. The Prudential Cup.

127 Flag and Map of S. Carolina

(Des G. Vasarhelyi. Litho Walsall)

1976 (17 Aug). *Bicentenary of American Revolution. T* **127** *and similar horiz designs. Multicoloured. W* w **14** *(sideways). P* 13½.
561	15 c. Type **127**	..	..	40	15
562	25 c. George Washington and map of Bridgetown	..	..	45	15
563	50 c. Independence Declaration	..	70	90
564	$1 Prince Hall	..	..	95	2·75
561/4			*Set of* 4	2·25	3·50

128 Early Postman

(Des Jennifer Toombs. Litho Questa)

1976 (19 Oct). *125th Anniv of Post Office Act. T* **128** *and similar horiz designs. Multicoloured.* W w **14** (*sideways*) P 14.

565	8 c. Type **128**		10	10
566	35 c. Modern postman		25	10
567	50 c. Early letter		30	40
568	$1 Delivery van		50	1·25
565/8		*Set of* 4	1·00	1·60

129 Coast Guard Launches

(Des PAD Studio. Litho J.W.)

1976 (1 Dec).* *Tenth Anniv of Independence. T* **129** *and similar horiz designs. Multicoloured.* W w **14** (*sideways*). P 13 × 13½.

569	5 c. Type **129**		20	10
570	15 c. Reverse of currency note		20	10
571	25 c. National anthem		20	20
572	$1 Independence Day parade		75	2·00
569/72		*Set of* 4	1·25	2·00
MS573	90 × 125 mm. Nos. 569/72. P 14		1·75	3·00

*This is the local date of issue; the Crown Agents released the stamps a day earlier.

130 Arrival of Coronation Coach at Westminster Abbey

131 Underwater Park

(Des C. Abbott. Litho Walsall)

1977 (7 Feb). *Silver Jubilee. T* **130** *and similar vert designs. Multicoloured* W w **14**. P 13½.

574	15 c. Garfield Sobers being knighted, 1975		30	25
575	50 c. Type **130**		30	40
576	$1 Queen entering abbey		30	70
574/6		*Set of* 3	2·80	1·25

For the above with different inscription, see Nos. 590/2.

(Des R. Granger Barrett. Litho Questa)

1977 (3 May). *Natural Beauty of Barbados. T* **131** *and similar multicoloured designs.* W w **14** (*sideways on Nos. 577 and 579*). P 14.

577	5 c. Type **131**		15	10
578	35 c. Royal Palms (*vert*)		30	10
579	50 c. Underwater caves		40	50
580	$1 Stalagmite in Harrison's Cave (*vert*)		70	1·10
577/80		*Set of* 4	1·40	1·60
MS581	138 × 92 mm. Nos. 577/80 (wmk sideways)		2·00	2·75

132 Maces of the House of Commons

133 The Charter Scroll

(Des C. Abbott. Litho J. W.)

1977 (2 Aug). *13th Regional Conference of the Commonwealth Parliamentary Association. T* **132** *and similar designs.* W w **14** (*sideways on* $1). P 13½.

582	10 c. pale orange, yellow and lake-brown		10	10
583	25 c. apple-green, orange and deep green		10	10
584	50 c. multicoloured		20	20
	w. Wmk inverted		12·00	
585	$1 pale blue, orange and deep violet-blue		55	75
582/5		*Set of* 4	80	95

Designs: Vert—25 c. Speaker's Chair, 50 c. Senate Chamber. Horiz—$1 Sam Lord's Castle.

(Des Walsall. Litho J.W.)

1977 (11 Oct). *350th Anniv of Granting of Charter to Earl of Carlisle. T* **133** *and similar multicoloured designs.* W w **14** (*sideways on* 45 c. *and* $1). P 13.

586	12 c. Type **133**		15	10
587	25 c. The earl receiving charter		15	10
588	45 c. The earl and Charles I (*horiz*)		30	35
589	$1 Ligon's map, 1657 (*horiz*)		50	1·00
586/9		*Set of* 4	1·00	1·40

(Des C. Abbott. Litho Walsall)

1977 (31 Oct). *Royal Visit. As Nos. 574/6 but inscr at top* "SILVER JUBILEE ROYAL VISIT." W w **14**. *Roul* 5. *Self-adhesive.*

590	15 c. Garfield Sobers being knighted, 1975		30	40
	w. Wmk inverted		12·00	
591	50 c. Type **130**		35	50
	w. Wmk inverted		13·00	
592	$1 Queen entering abbey		45	75
	w. Wmk inverted		6·00	
590/2		*Set of* 3	1·00	1·50

134 Gibson's Map of Bridgetown, 1766

135 Brown Pelican

(Des J. W. Litho Questa)

1978 (1 Mar). *350th Anniv of Founding of Bridgetown. T* **134** *and similar horiz designs.* W w **14** (*sideways*). P 14.

593	12 c. multicoloured		15	10
594	25 c. black, light green and gold		20	10
595	45 c. multicoloured		25	15
596	$1 multicoloured		40	60
593/6		*Set of* 4	90	80

Designs:—25 c. "A Prospect of Bridgetown in Barbados" (engraving by S. Copens, 1695); 45 c. "Trafalgar Square, Bridgetown" (drawing by J. M. Carter, 1835); $1 The Bridges, 1978.

(Des C. Abbott. Litho Questa)

1978 (21 Apr). *25th Anniv of Coronation. T* **135** *and similar vert designs.* P 15.

597	50 c. yellow-olive, black and blue		25	50
	a. Sheetlet. Nos. 597/9 × 2		1·25	
598	50 c. multicoloured		25	50
599	50 c. yellow-olive, black and blue		25	50
597/9		*Set of* 3	65	1·40

Designs:—No. 597, Griffin of Edward III; No. 598, Queen Elizabeth II; No. 599, Type **135**.

Nos. 597/9 were printed together in small sheets of 6 containing two *se-tenant* strips of 3, with horizontal gutter margin between.

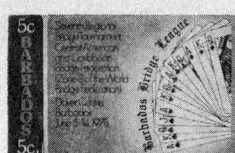

136 Barbados Bridge League Logo

(Des J.W. Litho Questa)

1978 (6 June). *7th Regional Bridge Tournament, Barbados. T* **136** *and similar horiz designs. Multicoloured.* W w **14** (*sideways**). P 14½.

600	5 c. Type **136**		10	10
601	10 c. Emblem of World Bridge Federation		15	10
602	45 c. Central American and Caribbean Bridge Federation emblem		25	10
603	$1 Playing cards on map of Caribbean		40	60
600/3		*Set of* 4	80	75
MS604	134×83 mm. Nos. 600/3		1·25	2·50
	w. Wmk Crown to right of CA		40·00	

*The normal sideways watermark shows Crown to left of CA, as seen from the back of the stamp.

137 Camp Scene

(Des and litho Harrison)

1978 (1 Aug). *Diamond Jubilee of Guiding. T* **137** *and similar diamond-shaped designs. Multicoloured.* W w **14** (*sideways on* 12, 28 c.). P 13½.

605	12 c. Type **137**		25	15
606	28 c. Community work		40	15
607	50 c. Badge and "60" (*vert*)		55	30
608	$1 Guide badge (*vert*)		75	1·00
605/8		*Set of* 4	1·75	1·40

138 Garment Industry

(Des Walsall. Litho Harrison)

1978 (14 Nov). *Industries. T* **138** *and similar multicoloured designs.* W w **14** (*sideways on* 12 *and* 50 c.). P 14.

609	12 c. Type **138**		15	10
610	28 c. Cooper (*vert*)		25	25
611	45 c. Blacksmith (*vert*)		35	65
612	50 c. Wrought iron working		40	65
609/12		*Set of* 4	1·00	1·50

139 Early Mail Steamer

(Des J. Cooter. Litho J. W.)

1979 (8 Feb). *Ships. T* **139** *and similar horiz designs. Multicoloured.* W w **14** (*sideways*). P 13.

613	12 c. Type **139**		35	10
614	25 c. *Queen Elizabeth 2* in Deep Water Harbour		55	15
615	50 c. *Ra II* nearing Barbados		75	90
616	$1 Early mail steamer (*different*)		1·00	2·25
613/16		*Set of* 4	2·40	3·00

140 1953 1 c. Definitive Stamp

(Des J.W. Litho Format)

1979 (8 May). *Death Centenary of Sir Rowland Hill. T* **140** *and similar multicoloured designs showing stamps.* W w **14** (*sideways** on 12 c.). P 14.

617	12 c. Type **140**		15	15
618	28 c. 1975 350th anniv of first settlement 25 c. commemorative (*vert*)		20	30
	a. Ultramarine (face value) omitted		£120	
619	45 c. Penny Black with Maltese Cross postmark (*vert*)		30	45
617/19		*Set of* 3	60	80
MS620	137×90 mm 50 c. Unissued "Britannia" blue (wmk sideways)		55	40
	w. Wmk Crown to left of CA			

*The normal sideways watermark on No. MS620 shows Crown to right of CA, *as seen from the back of the stamp.*

All examples of No. 618 show anniversary spelt as "anniverary".

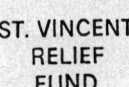

ST. VINCENT RELIEF FUND

(141)

142 Grassland Yellow Finch

1979 (29 May). *St. Vincent Relief Fund. No. 495 surch with T* **141**.

621	28 c. + 4 c. on 35 c. *Bletia patula*		50	60

(Des J.W. Photo Harrison)

1979 (7 Aug)–83. *Birds. Vert designs as T* **142**. *Multicoloured.* W w **14** (*sideways** on 1, 5, 10, 12, 15, 20, 25, 28, 40, 50, 55, 60, 70 c. *and* $1). P 14.

622	1 c. Type **142**		10	70
	w. Wmk Crown to right of CA		2·00	
623	2 c. Grey Kingbird		10	70
624	5 c. Lesser Antillean Bullfinch		10	70
625	8 c. Magnificent Frigate Bird		10	90
	w. Wmk inverted		24·00	
626	10 c. Cattle Egret (deep slate inscr)		10	40
	a. Slate-blue inscr		20	40
	w. Wmk Crown to right of CA		6·00	
627	12 c. Green Heron		15	60
627a	15 c. Carib Grackle (1.3.82)		4·50	5·00
628	20 c. Antillean Crested Hummingbird		20	55
	w. Wmk Crown to right of CA (14.3.83)		20	55
629	25 c. Scaly-breasted Ground Dove		20	60
630	28 c. As 15 c.		75	1·00
631	35 c. Green-throated Carib		30	70
	a. Yellow omitted		£200	
631b	40 c. Red-necked Pigeon (1.3.82)		4·50	5·00
632	45 c. Zenaida Dove		35	70
	w. Wmk inverted		10·00	
633	50 c. As 40 c.		55	1·00
633a	55 c. American Golden Plover (1.9.81)		3·50	2·75
	aw. Wmk Crown to right of CA		10·00	
633b	60 c. Bananaquit (1.3.82)		4·50	5·00
634	70 c. As 60 c.		55	1·75
635	$1 Caribbean Elaenia		1·00	1·50
636	$2.50. American Redstart		2·00	5·00

637	$5 Belted Kingfisher	.. ..	3·25	8·00
	w. Wmk inverted	.. ..		8·00
638	$10 Moorhen	.. ..	6·50	14·00
	w. Wmk inverted	.. ..		16·00
622/38		Set of 21	30·00	48·00

*The normal sideways watermark shows Crown to left of CA, as seen from the back of the stamp.

No. 626a occurred in the initial supply sent to Barbados.
No. 631a shows the birds' plumage in blue instead of green and has the background flowers omitted.

143 Gun aboard Landing Craft at Foul Bay

144 Family

(Des G. Vasarhelyi. Litho Format)

1979 (9 Oct). *Space Project Commemorations. T* **143** *and similar multicoloured designs. W* w **14** (*sideways on* 10, 28 *and* 45 c.). *P* 14.

639	10 c. Type 143 ..		15	10
640	12 c. Transporting launcher through Barbados (vert)		15	15
641	20 c. Firing of 16" launcher in daylight (vert)		15	20
642	28 c. Bath Earth Station and "Intelsat IV A"		15	30
643	45 c. "Intelsat V" over the Caribbean ..		25	50
644	50 c. "Intelsat IV A" over Atlantic (vert)		25	60
639/44		Set of 6	1·00	1·60
MS645	118 × 90 mm. $1 Lunar module descending on to Moon (wmk sideways)		65	80

Commemorations:—10 to 20 c. H.A.R.P. Gun experiment; 28 to 50 c. First use of "Intelsat" satellites; $1, 10th anniversary of Moon landing.

(Des R. Granger Barrett. Litho Questa)

1979 (27 Nov). *International Year of the Child. T* **144** *and similar vert designs. Multicoloured. W* w **14**. *P* 14.

646	12 c. Type 144 ..		10	10
647	28 c. Ring of children and map of Barbados ..		15	15
648	45 c. Child with teacher		20	20
649	50 c. Children playing ..		20	20
650	$1 Children and kite ..		35	45
646/50		Set of 5	80	90

145 Map of Barbados

146 Private, Artillery Company, Barbados Volunteer Force, circa 1909

(Des G. Hutchins. Litho Security Printers (M), Malaysia)

1980 (19 Feb). *75th Anniv of Rotary International. T* **145** *and similar horiz designs. Multicoloured. W* w **14** (*sideways*). *P* 13.

651	12 c. Type 145		15	10
652	28 c. Map of Caribbean ..		20	15
653	50 c. Rotary anniversary emblem ..		25	35
654	$1 Paul P. Harris (founder)..		40	95
651/4		Set of 4	90	1·40

(Des J.W. Litho Questa)

1980 (8 Apr). *Barbados Regiment. T* **146** *and similar vert designs. Multicoloured. W* w **14**. *P* 14×14½.

655	12 c. Type 146 ..		25	10
656	35 c. Drum Major, Zouave uniform		35	15
657	50 c. Sovereign's and Regimental colours ..		40	30
	w. Wmk inverted		10·00	
658	$1 Barbados Regiment Women's Corps ..		55	70
655/8		Set of 4	1·40	1·10

147 Early Postman

148 Yellow-tailed Snapper and other Fishes

(Des V. Whiteley Studio. Litho Walsall)

1980 (6 May). *"London 1980" International Stamp Exhibition. Two sheets each* 122 × 125 *mm containing T* **147** *or similar vert design. Multicoloured. W* w **14**. *P* 14 × 13½.

MS659	(a) 28 c. × 6, Type 147. (b) 50 c. × 6, Modern Postwoman and Inspector Set of 2 sheets	1·40	2·25

The two sheets each contain the stamp in full colour and in five different colour separations.

(Des G. Drummond. Litho Security Printers (M), Malaysia)

1980 (30 Sept). *Underwater Scenery. T* **148** *and similar horiz designs. Multicoloured. W* w **14** (*sideways**). *P* 13½.

660	12 c. Type 148		20	10
661	28 c. Banded Butterflyfish		35	15
	w. Wmk Crown to right of CA ..		30·00	
662	50 c. Male and female Blue-headed Wrasse and Princess Parrotfish		45	25
663	$1 French Grunt and French Angelfish		70	70
	w. Wmk Crown to right of CA		30·00	
660/3		Set of 4	1·50	1·00
MS664	136×110 mm. Nos. 660/3 (wmk upright)		2·50	3·25

*The normal sideways watermark shows Crown to left of CA, as seen from the back of the stamp.

149 Bathsheba Railway Station

(Des J. W. Litho Questa)

1981 (13 Jan). *Early Transport. T* **149** *and similar horiz designs. Multicoloured. W* w **14** (*sideways*). *P* 14½ × 14.

665	12 c. Type 149 ..		10	10
666	28 c. Cab stand at The Green ..		20	15
667	45 c. Animal-drawn tram		30	30
668	70 c. Horse-drawn bus ..		45	60
669	$1 Railway station in Fairchild Street		60	95
665/9	..	Set of 5	1·50	1·90

150 "The Blind at Work"

151 Prince Charles dressed for Polo

(Des BG Studio. Litho Walsall)

1981 (19 May). *International Year for Disabled Persons. T* **150** *and similar multicoloured designs. W* w **14** (*sideways on* 10 c. *and* $2.50). *P* 14.

670	10 c. Type 150		20	10
671	25 c. Sign language (vert) ..		25	15
672	45 c. "Be alert to the white cane" (vert)		40	25
673	$2.50, Children at play ..		1·25	3·00
670/3	..	Set of 4	1·90	3·00

(Des and litho J.W.)

1981 (22 July). *Royal Wedding. T* **151** *and similar vert designs. Multicoloured. W* w **14**. *P* 13½ × 13.

674	28 c. Wedding bouquet from Barbados		15	10
675	50 c. Type 151 ..		20	15
676	$2.50, Prince Charles and Lady Diana Spencer		55	1·25
674/6	..	Set of 3	80	1·25

152 Landship Manoeuvre

(153)

(Des C. Abbott. Litho Harrison)

1981 (11 Aug). *Carifesta (Caribbean Festival of Arts), Barbados. T* **152** *and similar vert designs. Multicoloured. W* w **14**. *P* 14½ × 14.

677	15 c. Type 152 ..		15	15
678	20 c. Yoruba dancers		15	15
679	40 c. Tuk band		20	25
680	55 c. Sculpture of Frank Collymore		25	35
	w. Wmk inverted ..		25·00	
681	$1 Harbour scene ..		50	75
677/81	..	Set of 5	1·10	1·50

1981 (1 Sept). *Nos.* 630, 632 *and* 634 *surch as T* **153**.

682	15 c. on 28 c. Carib Grackle ..		30	15
683	40 c. on 45 c. Zenaida Dove ..		30	35
684	60 c. on 70 c. Bananaquit ..		30	45
682/4	..	Set of 3	80	85

154 Satellite view of Hurricane

(Des A. Theobald. Litho Walsall)

1981 (29 Sept). *Hurricane Season. T* **154** *and similar horiz designs. W* w **14** (*sideways**). *P* 14.

685	35 c. black and blue ..		35	20
	w. Wmk Crown to right of CA		24·00	
686	50 c. multicoloured ..		45	35
	w. Wmk Crown to right of CA		24·00	
687	60 c. multicoloured ..		70	50
	w. Wmk Crown to right of CA		7·50	
688	$1 multicoloured		85	90
685/8		Set of 4	2·10	1·75

Designs:—50 c. Hurricane "Gladys" from "Apollo 7"; 60 c. Police Department on hurricane watch; $1 McDonnell F2H-2P Banshee "hurricane chaser" aircraft.

*The normal sideways watermark shows Crown to left of CA, as seen from the back of the stamp.

155 Twin Falls

156 Black Belly Ram

(Des L. Curtis. Litho Format)

1981 (1 Dec.) *Harrison's Cave. T* **155** *and similar vert designs. Multicoloured. W* w **14**. *P* 14 × 14½.

689	10 c. Type 155 ..		10	10
690	20 c. Stream in Rotunda Room ..		20	15
691	55 c. Formations in Rotunda Room ..		30	50
692	$2.50, Cascade Pool ..		80	2·25
689/92	..	Set of 4	1·25	2·75

(Des BG Studio. Litho Format)

1982 (9 Feb). *Black Belly Sheep. T* **156** *and similar horiz designs. Multicoloured. P* 14.

693	40 c. Type 156 ..		20	30
694	50 c. Black Belly ewe ..		20	35
695	60 c. Ewe with lambs ..		30	60
696	$1 Ram and ewe, with map of Barbados		50	1·50
693/6	..	Set of 4	1·10	2·50

157 Barbados Coat of Arms and Flag

(Des Harrison. Litho Format)

1982 (8 Apr). *President Reagan's Visit. T* **157** *and similar horiz design. Multicoloured. W* w **14** (*sideways*). *P* 14.

697	20 c. Type 157 ..		40	1·25
	a. Pair. Nos. 697/8 ..		80	2·50
698	20 c. U.S.A. coat of arms and flag ..		40	1·25
699	55 c. Type 157 ..		50	1·50
	a. Pair. Nos. 699/700 ..		1·00	3·00
700	55 c. As No. 698 ..		50	1·50
697/700	..	Set of 4	1·60	5·00

The two designs of each value were printed together, se-tenant, in horizontal and vertical pairs within small sheets of 8 stamps.

158 Lighter

159 Bride and Earl Spencer proceeding up Aisle

(Des J.W. Litho Harrison)

1982 (4 May). *Early Marine Transport. T* **158** *and similar horiz designs. Multicoloured. W* w **14** (*sideways*). *P* 14½.

701	20 c. Type 158 ..		20	15
702	35 c. Rowing boat ..		35	25
703	55 c. Speightstown schooner ..		50	40
704	$2.50, Inter-colonial schooner ..		1·75	2·50
701/4	..	Set of 4	2·50	3·00

(Des Jennifer Toombs. Litho Questa)

1982 (1 July). *21st Birthday of Princess of Wales. T* **159** *and similar vert designs. Multicoloured* W w **14**. *P* 14½ × 14.
705	20 c.	Barbados coat of arms	20	15
706	60 c.	Princess at Llanelwedd, October 1981	45	50
707	$1.20,	Type **159**	75	1·10
708	$2.50,	Formal portrait	1·25	1·90
705/8		*Set of 4*	2·40	3·25

160 "To Help other People" 161 Arms of George Washington

(Des G. Drummond. Litho Format)

1982 (7 Sept). *75th Anniv of Boy Scout Movement. T* **160** *and similar multicoloured designs.* W w **14** *(sideways on Nos.* 710/11). *P* 14.
709	15 c.	Type **160**	50	10
710	40 c.	"I Promise to do my Best" (*horiz*)	80	30
711	55 c.	"To do my Duty to God, the Queen and my Country" (*horiz*)	90	65
712	$1	National and Troop flags	1·40	1·75
709/12		*Set of 4*	3·25	2·50
MS713		119 × 93 mm. $1.50, The Scout Law	4·25	2·75

(Des and litho J.W.)

1982 (2 Nov). *250th Birth Anniv of George Washington. T* **161** *and similar vert designs. Multicoloured.* W w **14**. *P* 13½ × 13.
714	10 c.	Type **161**	10	10
715	55 c.	Washington House, Barbados	45	45
716	60 c.	Washington with troops	50	50
717	$2.50,	Washington taking Oath	1·60	1·60
714/17		*Set of 4*	2·40	2·40

162 *Agraulis vanillae*

(Des I. Loe. Litho J.W.)

1983 (8 Feb). *Butterflies. T* **162** *and similar horiz designs. Multicoloured.* W w **14** *(sideways). P* 13 × 13½.
718	20 c.	Type **162**	1·00	30
719	40 c.	*Danaus plexippus*	1·50	40
720	55 c.	*Hypolimnas misippus*	1·50	45
721	$2.50,	*Hemiargus hanno*	3·25	2·50
718/21		*Set of 4*	6·50	3·25

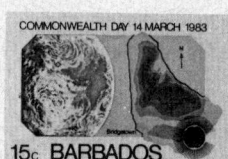

163 Map of Barbados and Satellite View

(Des D. Bowen. Litho J.W.)

1983 (14 Mar). *Commonwealth Day. T* **163** *and similar horiz designs. Multicoloured.* W w **14** *(sideways). P* 13.
722	15 c.	Type **163**	20	10
723	40 c.	Tourist beach	25	20
724	60 c.	Sugar cane harvesting	35	40
725	$1	Cricket match	1·25	1·10
722/5		*Set of 4*	1·75	1·60

164 U.S. Navy "M" Class Airship M-20

(Des L. Curtis. Litho Format)

1983 (14 June). *Bicentenary of Manned Flight. T* **164** *and similar horiz designs. Multicoloured.* W w **14** *(sideways). P* 14.
726	20 c.	Type **164**	50	15
727	40 c.	Douglas DC-3	70	40
728	55 c.	Vickers Viscount 837	80	80
729	$1	Lockheed L-1011 TriStar 500	1·50	2·50
726/9		*Set of 4*	3·25	3·50

165 Nash "600", 1941 166 Game in Progress

(Des and litho Harrison)

1983 (9 Aug). *Classic Cars. T* **165** *and similar horiz designs. Multicoloured.* W w **14** *(sideways). P* 14.
730	25 c.	Type **165**	50	20
731	45 c.	Dodge, 1938	65	30
732	75 c.	Ford "Model AA", 1930	85	1·25
733	$2.50,	Dodge "Four", 1918	2·25	3·75
730/3		*Set of 4*	3·75	5·00

(Des L. Curtis. Litho Questa)

1983 (30 Aug). *Table Tennis World Cup Competition. T* **166** *and similar vert designs. Multicoloured.* W w **14**. *P* 14.
734	20 c.	Type **166**	25	20
735	65 c.	Map of Barbados	50	55
736	$1	World Table Tennis Cup	75	1·00
734/6		*Set of 3*	1·40	1·60

167 Angel playing Lute (detail "The Virgin and Child" (Masaccio)) 168 Track and Field Events

(Des D. Miller. Litho Questa)

1983 (1 Nov). *Christmas. 50th Anniv of Barbados Museum. T* **167** *and similar multicoloured designs.* W w **14** *(sideways on 45 c., 75 c. and $2.50). P* 14.
737	10 c.	multicoloured	30	10
738	25 c.	multicoloured	60	20
739	45 c.	multicoloured	90	40
740	75 c.	black and gold	1·40	1·60
741	$2.50,	multicoloured	4·50	5·50
737/41		*Set of 5*	7·00	7·00
MS742		59 × 98 mm. $2 multicoloured	1·75	2·00

Designs: *Horiz*—45 c. "The Barbados Museum" (Richard Day); 75 c. "St. Ann's Garrison" (W. S. Hedges); $2.50, Needham's Point, Carlisle Bay. *Vert*—25 c., $2 Different details from "The Virgin and Child" (Masaccio).

1983 (Dec). *Coil Definitive. As No.* 536 *but* W w **14**.
743	**124**	5 c. greenish blue	1·00	1·50

No. 743 was also available from sheets.

(Des McCombie Skinner Studio. Litho Walsall)

1984 (28 Mar). *Olympic Games, Los Angeles. T* **168** *and similar horiz designs.* W w **14** *(sideways). P* 14.
745	50 c.	bright green, black and olive-sepia	60	45
746	65 c.	dull orange, black and drab	80	60
747	75 c.	greenish blue, black and deep cobalt	1·00	85
748	$1	light brown, black and yellow-ochre	2·50	1·75
745/8		*Set of 4*	4·50	3·25
MS749		115 × 97 mm. Nos. 745/8	6·50	8·00

Designs:—65 c. Shooting; 75 c. Sailing; $1 Cycling.

169 Global Coverage 170 U.P.U. 1943 3d. Stamp and Logo

(Des C. Abbott. Litho Questa)

1984 (25 Apr). *250th Anniv of Lloyd's List (newspaper). T* **169** *and similar vert designs. Multicoloured.* W w **14**. *P* 14½ × 14.
750	45 c.	Type **169**	70	40
751	50 c.	Bridgetown harbour	80	50
752	75 c.	*Philosopher* (full-rigged ship), 1857	1·10	90
753	$1	*Sea Princess* (liner), 1984	1·25	1·25
750/3		*Set of 4*	3·50	2·75

(Des McCombie Skinner Studio. Litho J.W.)

1984 (6 June). *Universal Postal Union Congress, Hamburg. Sheet* 90 × 75 *mm.* W w **14** *(sideways). P* 13½.
MS754	**170**	$2 multicoloured	2·50	2·50

171 Local Junior Match 172 Poinsettia

(Des L. Curtis. Litho Walsall)

1984 (8 Aug). *60th Anniv of World Chess Federation. T* **171** *and similar horiz designs. Multicoloured.* W w **14** *(sideways). P* 14½.
755	25 c.	Type **171**	1·25	30
756	45 c.	Staunton and 19th-century Knights	1·60	50
757	65 c.	Staunton Queen and 18th-century Queen from Macao	1·75	1·60
758	$2	Staunton and 17th-century Rooks	3·50	4·50
755/8		*Set of 4*	7·25	6·25

(Des I. Loe. Litho Questa)

1984 (24 Oct). *Christmas. Flowers. T* **172** *and similar vert designs. Multicoloured.* W w **14**. *P* 14.
759	50 c.	Type **172**	1·50	80
760	65 c.	Snow-on-the-Mountain	1·75	1·50
761	75 c.	Christmas Candle	2·00	2·75
762	$1	Christmas Hope	2·25	3·25
759/62		*Set of 4*	6·75	7·50

173 Pink-tipped Anemone 174 The Queen Mother at the Docks

(Des I. Loe. Litho Questa)

1985 (26 Feb)–87. *Marine Life. T* **173** *and similar horiz designs. Multicoloured.* W w **14** *(sideways). P* 14. A. *Without imprint date at foot.* B. *With imprint date* ("1987").
				A	B
763	1 c.	Bristle Worm		70	1·25	2·00	3·00
764	2 c.	Spotted Trunkfish		70	1·25	2·00	3·00
765	5 c.	Coney		1·75	75	†
766	10 c.	Type **173**		80	75	†
767	20 c.	Christmas Tree Worm		2·00	2·00	3·50	4·00
768	25 c.	Hermit Crab		1·50	70	†
769	35 c.	Animal Flower		3·00	75	†
770	40 c.	Vase Sponge		2·50	80	†
771	45 c.	Spotted Moray		1·50	90	†
772	50 c.	Ghost Crab		2·50	3·00	7·00	6·00
773	65 c.	Flamingo Tongue Snail		2·50	1·00	†
774	75 c.	Sergeant Major		2·00	8·00	7·50
775	$1	Caribbean Warty Anemone		2·75	1·25	†
776	$2.50,	Green Turtle		7·00	8·00	12·00	15·00
777	$5	Rock Beauty (fish)		8·00	9·00	16·00	19·00
778	$10	Elkhorn Coral		8·50	9·00	†
763/78A		*Set of 16*		40·00	38·00	
763/77B		*Set of 7*				45·00	50·00

Dates of issue:—26.2.85, Nos. 766A/8A, 772A, 776A/7A; 9.4.85, Nos. 765A, 769A/70A, 773A, 778A; 7.5.85, Nos. 763A/4A, 771A, 774A/5A; 15.9.87, 763B/77B.

For these designs watermarked w **16** (sideways) see Nos. 794/809.

(Des A. Theobald ($2), C. Abbott (others). Litho Questa)

1985 (7 June). *Life and Times of Queen Elizabeth the Queen Mother. T* **174** *and similar vert designs. Multicoloured.* W w **16**. *P* 14½ × 14.
779	25 c.	In the White Drawing Room, Buckingham Palace, 1930s	15	20
780	65 c.	With Lady Diana Spencer at Trooping the Colour, 1981	70	50
781	75 c.	Type **174**	55	60
782	$1	With Prince Henry at his christening (from photo by Lord Snowdon)	70	75
779/82		*Set of 4*	1·90	1·90
MS783		91 × 73 mm. $2 In Land Rover opening Syon House Garden Centre. Wmk sideways	1·40	1·50

175 Peregrine Falcon

(Des D. Miller. Litho Walsall)

1985 (6 Aug). *Birth Bicentenary of John J. Audubon (ornithologist). T* **175** *and similar multicoloured designs showing original paintings.* W w **14** *(sideways on 45 c.). P* 14.
784	45 c.	Type **175**	1·75	60
785	65 c.	Prairie Warbler (*vert*)	2·00	1·75
786	75 c.	Great Blue Heron (*vert*)	2·25	2·50
787	$1	Yellow Warbler (*vert*)	2·25	3·25
784/7		*Set of 4*	7·50	7·25

176 Intelsat Satellite orbitting   177 Traffic Policeman
Earth

(Des L. Curtis. Litho Harrison)

1985 (10 Sept).   20th Anniv of Intelsat Satellite System. W w **14**
(sideways). P 14.
788 **176** 75 c. multicoloured 75 60

(Des L. Curtis. Litho Format)

1985 (19 Nov).   150th Anniv of Royal Barbados Police. T **177**
and similar multicoloured designs. W w **16**. P 14.
789 25 c. Type **177**.. .. .. .. 80 20
790 50 c. Police Band on bandstand .. .. 1·40 80
791 65 c. Dog handler .. .. 2·00 1·40
792 $1 Mounted policeman in ceremonial uni-
form .. .. 2·25 2·00
789/92 .. .. Set of 4 5·75 4·00
MS793 85×60 mm. $2 Police Band on parade
(horiz). Wmk sideways .. .. .. 2·00 2·75

1986 (6 Jan)–**87**.   As Nos. 763/78 but W w **16** (sideways). P 14.
A. Without imprint date at foot. B. With imprint date.

		A		B	
794	1 c. Bristle Worm	..	†	20	1·00
795	2 c. Spotted Trunkfish	..	†	20	1·00
796	5 c. Coney	..	50	50	12·00	8·00
797	10 c. Type **173** ..	50	50	30	30
798	20 c. Christmas Tree Worm	..	70	75	30	30
799	25 c. Hermit Crab	..	70	50	40	40
800	35 c. Animal Flower	..	1·00	85	12·00	8·00
801	40 c. Vase Sponge	..	†	50	50
802	45 c. Spotted Moray	..	†	60	50
803	50 c. Ghost Crab	..	2·00	1·50	60	60
804	65 c. Flamingo Tongue Snail ..	†	65	70
805	75 c. Sergeant Major	..	†	70	75
806	$1 Caribbean Warty Anem-				
	one	..	†	85	85
807	$2.50, Green Turtle ..	..	3·50	3·50	2·00	3·50
808	$5 Rock Beauty (fish)	..	7·00	7·00	2·50	5·50
809	$10 Elkhorn Coral	..	10·00	10·00	4·25	8·00
796/809A		Set of 9	23·00	23·00	†
794/809B		Set of 16			35·00	35·00

Dates of issue:—6.1.86, Nos. 796A/800A, 803A, 807A/9A;
23.7.86, Nos. 794B/5B, 801B/2B; 18.8.86, Nos. 797B/9B,
803B/9B; 15.9.87, Nos. 796B, 800B.
Imprint dates: "1986", Nos. 794B/5B, 797B/9B, 801B/9B;
"1987", Nos. 796B/7B, 799B/802B, 804B, 806B, 809B; "1988",
No. 797B.

(Des A. Theobald. Litho Format)

1986 (21 Apr).   60th Birthday of Queen Elizabeth II. Vert
designs as T **110** of Ascension. Multicoloured. W w **16**.
P 14×14½.
810 25 c. Princess Elizabeth aged two, 1928 .. 15 20
811 50 c. At University College of West Indies,
Jamaica, 1953 .. .. .. 30 40
812 65 c. With Duke of Edinburgh, Barbados,
1985 .. .. 40 50
a. Silver (logo) omitted £300
813 75 c. At banquet in Sao Paulo, Brazil, 1968 .. 45 60
814 $2 At Crown Agents Head Office, London,
1983 .. .. 1·00 1·50
810/14 .. .. Set of 5 2·10 3·00

178 Canadair DC-4M2 North
Star of Trans-Canada Airlines

(Des L. Curtis. Litho Format)

1986 (2 May).   "Expo '86" World Fair, Vancouver. T **178** and
similar horiz design. Multicoloured. W w **16** (sideways). P 14.
815 50 c. Type **178** 50 50
816 $2.50, Lady Nelson (cargo liner) .. .. 2·00 2·50

(Des D. Miller. Litho Walsall)

1986 (22 May).   "Ameripex '86" International Stamp Exhibition,
Chicago. Horiz designs as T **164** of Bahamas, showing
Barbados stamps (Nos. 817/20). Multicoloured. W w **16**
(sideways). P 14.
817 45 c. 1976 Bicentenary of American Revolution 25 c... .. .. 85 35
818 50 c. 1976 Bicentenary of American Revolution 50 c... .. .. 95 55
819 65 c. 1981 Hurricane Season $1 .. .. 1·10 1·00
820 $1 1982 Visit of President Reagan
55 c. pair.. .. .. .. 1·25 1·75
817/20 .. .. Set of 4 3·75 3·25
MS821 90×80 mm. $2 Statue of Liberty and
liner Queen Elizabeth 2 .. .. .. 5·00 7·50
No. **MS**821 also commemorates the Centenary of the Statue of
Liberty.

(Des D. Miller. Litho Walsall)

1986 (23 July).   Royal Wedding. Square designs as T **112** of
Ascension. Multicoloured. W w **16**. P 14½×14.
822 45 c. Prince Andrew and Miss Sarah
Ferguson 60 35
823 $1 Prince Andrew in Midshipman's
uniform .. .. 1·00 75
w. Wmk inverted .. .. .. 12·00

179 Transporting   180 Alpinia
Electricity Poles, 1923   purpurata and
Church Window

(Des A. Theobald. Litho B.D.T.)

1986 (16 Sept).   75th Anniv of Electricity in Barbados. T **179**
and similar multicoloured designs. W w **16** (sideways on 10,
65 c.). P 13½.
824 10 c. Type **179**.. .. .. .. 15 10
825 25 c. Heathman Ladder, 1935 (vert).. .. 25 20
826 65 c. Transport fleet, 1941 .. .. 60 60
827 $2 Bucket truck, 1986 (vert) .. .. 1·60 2·00
824/7 .. .. Set of 4 2·40 2·50

(Des A. Atkinson. Litho Questa)

1986 (28 Oct).   Christmas. T **180** and similar vert designs
showing flowers and church windows. Multicoloured. W w **14**.
P 14.
828 25 c. Type **180**.. .. .. .. 20 20
829 50 c. Anthurium andraeanum 45 45
830 75 c. Heliconia rostrata 70 80
831 $2 Heliconia x psittacorum .. .. 1·50 2·50
828/31 .. .. Set of 4 2·50 3·50

181 Shot Putting   182 Barn Swallow

(Des G. Vasarhelyi. Litho Format)

1987 (27 Mar).   10th Anniv of Special Olympics. T **181** and
similar horiz designs. Multicoloured. W w **14** (sideways). P 14.
832 15 c. Type **181**.. .. .. .. 25 15
833 45 c. Wheelchair racing 45 30
834 65 c. Long jumping 60 65
835 $2 Logo and slogan .. .. .. 1·25 2·50
832/5 .. .. Set of 4 2·25 3·25

(Des P. Broadbent. Litho Walsall)

1987 (12 June).   "Capex '87" International Stamp Exhibition,
Toronto. Birds. T **182** and similar vert designs. Multicoloured.
W w **16**. P 14.
836 25 c. Type **182** .. .. 1·40 40
w. Wmk inverted .. .. .. 9·00
837 50 c. Yellow Warbler .. .. .. 1·60 1·25
838 65 c. Audubon's Shearwater .. .. 1·75 2·25
839 75 c. Black-whiskered Vireo .. .. 2·25 2·75
840 $1 Scarlet Tanager .. .. .. 2·25 3·25
836/40 .. .. Set of 5 8·50 9·00

183 Sea Scout saluting   184 Bridgetown Synagogue

(Des L. Curtis. Litho Format)

1987 (24 July).   75th Anniv of Scouting in Barbados. T **183** and
similar vert designs. Multicoloured. W w **16**. P 14.
841 10 c. Type **183**.. .. .. .. 20 10
842 25 c. Scout jamboree 30 20
843 65 c. Scout badges 65 45
844 $2 Scout band .. .. 1·60 1·75
841/4 .. .. Set of 4 2·50 2·25

(Des R. Edge. Litho Questa)

1987 (6 Oct).   Restoration of Bridgetown Synagogue. T **184** and
similar multicoloured designs. W w **16** (sideways on 50, 65 c.).
P 14×14½ (horiz) or 14½×14 (vert).
845 50 c. Type **184**. .. .. .. 1·40 1·40
846 65 c. Interior of Synagogue .. .. 1·60 1·60
847 75 c. Ten Commandments (vert) .. .. 1·90 1·90
848 $1 Marble laver (vert) .. .. .. 2·25 2·75
845/8 .. .. Set of 4 6·50 7·00

185 Arms and Colonial Seal

(Des D. Hartley. Litho Walsall)

1987 (24 Nov).   21st Anniv of Independence. T **185** and similar
multicoloured designs. W w **16** (sideways). P 14×14½.
849 25 c. Type **185**.. .. .. .. 30 20
850 45 c. Flags of Barbados and Great Britain .. 40 30
851 65 c. Silver dollar and one penny coins .. 70 45
852 $2 Colours of Barbados Regiment .. .. 1·50 1·40
849/52 .. .. Set of 4 2·50 2·10
MS853 94×56 mm. $1.50, Prime Minister E. W.
Barrow (vert). Wmk upright. P 14½×14 .. 1·00 1·25

186 Herman C. Griffith   186a

(Des D. Hartley. Litho Walsall)

1988 (6 June–11 July).   West Indian Cricket. T **186** and similar
horiz designs, each showing portrait, cricket equipment and
early belt buckle. Multicoloured. W w **14** (sideways). P 14.
854 15 c. E. A. (Manny) Martindale .. .. 1·50 40
855 45 c. George Challenor .. .. .. 2·25 75
856 50 c. Type **186** (11.7) .. .. .. 2·50 1·50
a. Error. Portrait as Type **186**a .. £150
857 75 c. Harold Austin .. .. .. 3·00 3·00
858 $2 Frank Worrell .. .. .. 4·00 7·50
854/8 .. .. Set of 5 12·00 12·00
As originally prepared the 50 c., inscribed "Herman C.
Griffith", showed the portrait of another Barbadian cricketer, E.
Lawson Bartlett, in error. The mistake was noticed two days
prior to issue and the 50 c. was delayed until 11 July while
supplies showing the correct portrait were printed. The
instructions to withdraw the stamps with the Bartlett portrait,
No. 856a, failed to reach the Parcel Post Department in time
and, it is reported, 101 examples were sold in the normal course
of business before the, belated, notification was received.

187 Kentropyx   188 Cycling
borckianus

(Des Doreen McGuinness. Litho B.D.T.)

1988 (13 June).   Lizards of Barbados. T **187** and similar vert
designs. Multicoloured. W w **14**. P 14.
859 10 c. Type **187** 85 30
860 50 c. Hemidactylus mabouia .. .. 2·00 60
861 65 c. Anolis extremus .. .. .. 2·00 1·00
862 $2 Gymnophthalmus underwoodii .. .. 4·00 5·00
859/62 .. .. Set of 4 8·00 6·00

(Des A. Edmonston. Litho Walsall)

1988 (2 Aug).   Olympic Games, Seoul. T **188** and similar vert
designs. Multicoloured. W w **14**. P 14½×14.
863 25 c. Type **188** 30 20
864 45 c. Athletics 40 30
865 75 c. Relay swimming 55 55
866 $2 Yachting .. .. 1·50 1·75
863/6 .. .. Set of 4 2·50 2·50
MS867 144×63 mm. Nos. 863/6. W w **16** .. .. 3·00 3·00

(Des S. Noon and D. Miller (50, 65 c.), D. Miller (others).
Litho Questa)

1988 (18 Oct).   300th Anniv of Lloyd's of London. Designs as
T **123** of Ascension. W w **14** (sideways on 50, 65 c.). P 14.
868 40 c. multicoloured 55 30
869 50 c. multicoloured 65 35
870 65 c. multicoloured .. .. .. 1·25 45
871 $2 steel-blue and brown-lake .. .. 2·50 2·00
868/71 .. .. Set of 4 4·50 2·75
Designs: Vert—40 c. Royal Exchange, 1774; $2 Sinking of
Titanic, 1912. Horiz—50 c. Early sugar mill; 65 c. Author
(container ship).

189 Harry Bayley and Observatory
190 L.I.A.T. Hawker Siddeley H.S.748

(Des Josephine Martin. Litho Walsall)

1988 (28 Nov). *25th Anniv of Harry Bayley Observatory. T 189 and similar horiz designs. Multicoloured. W w 16 (sideways). P 14×14½.*
872	25 c. Type 189			60	20
873	65 c. Observatory with North Star and Southern Cross constellations			1·00	55
874	75 c. Andromeda galaxy			1·25	70
875	$2 Orion constellation			2·75	3·25
872/5			Set of 4	5·00	4·25

(Des A. Theobald. Litho Walsall)

1989 (20 Mar). *50th Anniv of Commercial Aviation in Barbados. T 190 and similar horiz designs. Multicoloured. W w 16 (sideways). P 14.*
876	25 c. Type 190			1·25	30
877	65 c. Pan Am Douglas D.C.8-62			2·00	75
878	75 c. British Airways Concorde at Grantley Adams Airport			2·00	90
879	$2 Caribbean Air Cargo Boeing 707-351C			3·75	3·25
876/9			Set of 4	8·00	4·75

191 Assembly Chamber
192 Brown Hare

(Des A. Edmonston. Litho B.D.T.)

1989 (19 July). *350th Anniv of Parliament. T 191 and similar square designs. W w 16. P 13½.*
880	25 c. multicoloured			40	20
881	50 c. multicoloured			60	35
882	75 c. deep slate-blue and brownish black			1·00	90
883	$2·50, multicoloured			2·50	2·00
880/3			Set of 4	4·00	2·75

Designs:—50 c. The Speaker; 75 c. Parliament Buildings, c. 1882; $2·50, Queen Elizabeth II and Prince Philip in Parliament.

(Des R. Suffolk. Litho Questa)

1989 (1 Aug). *Wildlife Preservation. T 192 and similar multicoloured designs. W w 16 (sideways on 50 c., $2). P 14×13½ (vert) or 13½×14 (horiz).*
884	10 c. Type 192			40	20
885	50 c. Red-footed Tortoise (horiz)			85	60
886	65 c. Savanna "Green" Monkey			95	1·00
887	$2 Bufo marinus (toad) (horiz)			2·50	3·50
884/7			Set of 4	4·25	4·75
MS888	87×97 mm. $1 Small Indian Mongoose			75	80

(Des A. Edmonston. Litho B.D.T.)

1989 (9 Oct). *35th Commonwealth Parliamentary Conference. Square design as T 191. Multicoloured. W w 14. P 13½.*
MS889	108×69 mm. $1 Barbados Mace			75	1·00

193 Bread 'n Cheese
194 Water Skiing

(Des Rosanne Sanders. Litho Questa)

1989 (1 Nov)–**92**. *Wild Plants. T 193 and similar vert designs. Multicoloured. W w 14. P 14½.*
890	2 c. Type 193			50	90
891	5 c. Scarlet Cordia			30	30
892	10 c. Columnar Cactus			30	20
893	20 c. Spiderlily			40	30
894	25 c. Rock Balsam			70	80
895	30 c. Hollyhock			50	25
895a	35 c. Red Sage (9.6.92)			1·00	1·00
896	45 c. Yellow Shak-shak			85	1·00
897	50 c. Whitewood			85	1·00
898	55 c. Bluebell			70	55
899	65 c. Prickly Sage			1·00	1·50
900	70 c. Seaside Samphire			80	70

901	80 c. Flat-hand Dildo			90	80
901a	90 c. Herringbone (9.6.92)			1·50	1·75
902	$1.10, Lent Tree			1·25	1·75
903	$2.50, Rodwood			3·75	7·00
904	$5 Cowitch			6·50	10·00
905	$10 Maypole			11·00	16·00
890/905		Set of 18	29·00	42·00

Imprint dates: "1989", Nos. 890/5, 896/901, 902/5; "1991", Nos. 891/3, 895a, 900, 901a, 902.
For similar stamps but watermarked w 16, see Nos. 921/36.

(Des C. Burke. Litho Harrison)

1989 (17 Nov). *"World Stamp Expo '89" International Stamp Exhibition, Washington. Watersports. T 194 and similar vert designs. Multicoloured. W w 16. P 14.*
906	25 c. Type 194			80	30
907	50 c. Yachting			1·50	1·00
908	65 c. Scuba diving			1·60	1·60
909	$2.50, Surfing			4·75	6·50
906/9			Set of 4	7·75	8·50

195 Barbados 1852 1d. Stamp
196 Bugler and Jockeys

(Des D. Miller. Litho B.D.T.)

1990 (3 May). *150th Anniv of the Penny Black and "Stamp World London 90" International Stamp Exhibition. T 195 and similar vert designs showing stamps. W w 14. P 14.*
910	25 c. dp bluish green, blk & pale yell-ochre		80	30
911	50 c. multicoloured			1·25	1·00
912	65 c. multicoloured			1·40	1·25
913	$2.50, multicoloured			3·25	4·75
910/13			Set of 4	6·00	6·50
MS914	90×86 mm. 50 c. multicoloured; 50 c. multicoloured			1·50	2·50

Designs:—50 c. 1882 1d. Queen Victoria; 65 c. 1899 2d.; $2.50, 1912 3d.; miniature sheet, 50 c. Great Britain Penny Black, 50 c. Barbados 1906 Nelson Centenary 1s.

(Adapted G. Vasarhelyi. Litho B.D.T.)

1990 (3 May). *Horse Racing. T 196 and similar multicoloured designs. W w 14 (sideways on 25, 45 and 75 c.). P 14.*
915	25 c. Type 196			45	30
916	45 c. Horse and jockey in parade ring		70	50
917	75 c. At the finish			90	85
918	$2 Leading in the winner (vert)			2·50	3·50
915/18			Set of 4	4·00	4·75

(Des D. Miller. Litho Questa)

1990 (8 Aug). *90th Birthday of Queen Elizabeth the Queen Mother. Vert designs as T 134 (75 c.) or 135 ($2.50) of Ascension. W w 16. P 14×15 (75 c.) or 14½ ($2.50).*
919	75 c. multicoloured			60	60
920	$2.50, black and bronze-green			1·90	2·40

Designs:—75 c. Lady Elizabeth Bowes-Lyon, April 1923 (from painting by John Lander); $2.50, Lady Elizabeth Bowes-Lyon on her engagement, January 1923.

1990 (Sept). *As Nos. 890/4, 896/7, 903/5, but W w 16. "1990" imprint date. P 14½.*
921	2 c. Type 193			20	65
922	5 c. Scarlet Cordia			70	1·10
923	10 c. Columnar Cactus			70	1·10
924	20 c. Spiderlily			90	1·25
925	25 c. Rock Balsam			30	20
927	45 c. Yellow Shak-shak			45	35
928	50 c. Whitewood			50	40
930	65 c. Prickly Sage			60	55
934	$2.50, Rodwood			1·90	3·50
935	$5 Cowitch			3·25	5·50
936	$10 Maypole			6·50	8·50
921/36			Set of 11	14·50	21·00

197 Orthemis ferruginea (dragonfly)
VISIT OF HRH THE PRINCESS ROYAL OCTOBER 1990 (198)

(Des I. Loe. Litho Harrison)

1990 (16 Oct). *Insects. T 197 and similar horiz designs. Multicoloured. P 14.*
937	50 c. Type 197			1·00	70
938	65 c. Ligyrus tumulosus (beetle)			1·25	85
939	75 c. Neoconocephalus sp (grasshopper)		1·40	1·25
940	$2 Bostra maxwelli (stick-insect)			2·50	3·50
937/40			Set of 4	5·50	5·75

1990 (21 Nov). *Visit of the Princess Royal. Nos. 894, 901 and 903 optd with T 198.*
941	25 c. Rock Balsam			55	20
942	80 c. Flat-hand Dildo			1·10	1·10
943	$2.50, Rodwood			3·00	4·00
941/3			Set of 3	4·25	4·75

199 Star
200 Adult Male Yellow Warbler

(Des D. Miller. Litho B.D.T.)

1990 (4 Dec). *Christmas. T 199 and similar vert designs. Multicoloured. W w 14. P 14.*
944	20 c. Type 199			45	15
945	50 c. Figures from crib			75	50
946	$1 Stained glass window			1·40	1·10
947	$2 Angel (statue)			2·00	3·00
944/7			Set of 4	4·25	4·25

(Des G. Drummond. Litho B.D.T.)

1991 (4 Mar). *Endangered Species. Yellow Warbler. T 200 and similar horiz designs. Multicoloured. W w 14 (sideways). P 14.*
948	10 c. Type 200			85	55
949	20 c. Pair feeding chicks in nest			1·25	55
950	45 c. Female feeding chicks in nest		1·75	60
951	$1 Male with fledgeling			3·25	3·75
948/51			Set of 4	6·50	5·00

201 Sorting Daily Catch
202 Masonic Building, Bridgetown

(Des M. Maynard, adapted G. Vasarhelyi. Litho Cartor)

1991 (18 June). *Fishing in Barbados. T 201 and similar multicoloured designs. W w 14 (sideways on 50, 75 c.). P 13½×14 (5 c., $2.50) or 14×13½ (others).*
952	5 c. Type 201			30	30
953	50 c. Line fishing (horiz)			1·25	90
954	75 c. Fish cleaning (horiz)			1·75	1·25
955	$2.50, Game fishing			3·50	4·50
952/5			Set of 4	6·00	6·25

(Des N. Shewring. Litho B.D.T.)

1991 (17 Sept). *250th Anniv of Freemasonry in Barbados (1990). T 202 and similar vert designs. W w 14. P 14.*
956	25 c. multicoloured			75	30
957	65 c. multicoloured			1·40	1·00
958	75 c. black, greenish yellow & yellow-brown		1·40	1·00
959	$2.50, multicoloured			3·75	5·00
956/9			Set of 4	6·50	6·50

Designs:—65 c. Compass and Square (masonic symbols); 75 c. Royal Arch Jewel; $2.50, Ceremonial apron, columns and badge.

203 Battus polydamus

(Des I. Loe. Litho B.D.T.)

1991 (15 Nov). *"Phila Nippon '91" International Stamp Exhibition, Tokyo. Butterflies. T 203 and similar multicoloured designs. W w 16 (sideways on 20 c., 65 c.). P 14.*
960	20 c. Type 203			55	20
961	50 c. Urbanus proteus (vert)			90	65
962	65 c. Phoebis sennae			1·10	95
963	$2.50, Junonia evarete (vert)			3·00	4·00
960/3			Set of 4	5·00	5·25
MS964	87×86 mm. $4 Vanessa cardui. Wmk sideways			6·50	7·50

204 School Class
205 Jesus carrying Cross

(Des G. Vasarhelyi. Litho B.D.T.)

1991 (20 Nov). *25th Anniv of Independence. T* **204** *and similar multicoloured designs. W* w **14** *(sideways). P* 14.
965	10 c. Type **204**			15	15
966	25 c. Barbados Workers' Union Labour College			25	25
967	65 c. Building a house	..	..	60	70
968	75 c. Sugar cane harvesting		..	70	80
969	$1 Health clinic	..	..	90	1·50
965/9			*Set of* 5	2·40	3·00
MS970	123 × 97 mm. $2.50, Gordon Greenidge and Desmond Haynes (cricketers) (*vert*). Wmk upright..			4·50	5·50

(Des P. Argent. Litho B.D.T.)

1992 (7 Apr). *Easter. T* **205** *and similar vert designs. Multicoloured. W* w **16**. *P* 14.
971	35 c. Type **205**			55	30
972	70 c. Crucifixion	..	..	90	90
973	90 c. Descent from the Cross	..		1·10	1·10
974	$3 Risen Christ	..	..	3·25	4·00
971/4			*Set of* 4	5·25	5·75

206 Cannon Ball	**207** *Epidendrum* "Costa Rica"

(Des Jennifer Toombs. Litho Cartor)

1992 (9 June). *Conservation. Flowering Trees. T* **206** *and similar horiz designs. Multicoloured. W* w **14** *(sideways). P* 14×13½.
975	10 c. Type **206**	..	..	35	20
976	30 c. Golden Shower Tree ..	..	..	75	40
977	80 c. Frangipani	..	..	1·40	1·75
978	$1.10, Flamboyant	..	..	1·60	1·90
975/8			*Set of* 4	3·50	3·75

(Des Annette Robinson. Litho B.D.T.)

1992 (8 Sept). *Orchids. T* **207** *and similar horiz designs. Multicoloured. W* w **14** *(sideways). P* 13½×14.
979	55 c. Type **207**	..	..	65	50
980	65 c. *Cattleya guttaca*	..	..	80	80
981	70 c. *Laeliacattleya* "Splashing Around"	..		80	80
982	$1.40, *Phalaenopsis* "Kathy Saegert"	..		1·40	2·25
979/82			*Set of* 4	3·25	4·00

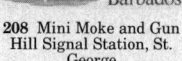

208 Mini Moke and Gun Hill Signal Station, St. George	**209** Barbados Gooseberry

(Des D. Miller. Litho Questa)

1992 (15 Dec). *Transport and Tourism. T* **208** *and similar horiz designs. Multicoloured. W* w **14** *(sideways). P* 14×14½.
983	5 c. Type **208**			30	30
984	35 c. Tour bus and Bathsheba Beach, St. Joseph			75	30
985	90 c. B.W.I.A. McDonnell Douglas MD-83 over Grantley Adams Airport			1·75	1·75
986	$2 *Festivale* (liner) and Bridgetown harbour			2·50	3·00
983/6			*Set of* 4	4·75	4·75

(Des I. Loe. Litho B.D.T.)

1993 (9 Feb). *Cacti and Succulents. T* **209** *and similar vert designs. Multicoloured. W* w **14**. *P* 14.
987	10 c. Type **209**			30	20
988	35 c. Night-blooming Cereus			75	35
989	$1.40, Aloe	..	..	2·25	3·00
990	$2 Scrunchineel ..	..		2·75	3·25
987/90			*Set of* 4	5·50	6·00

(Des A. Theobald. Litho Questa)

1993 (1 Apr). *75th Anniv of Royal Air Force. Horiz designs as T* **149** *of Ascension. Multicoloured. W* w **14** *(sideways). P* 14.
991	10 c. Hawker Hunter F.6			30	20
992	30 c. Handley Page H.P.80 Victor K2			50	30
993	70 c. Hawker Typhoon 1B ..			80	85
994	$3 Hawker Hurricane Mk 1			2·40	3·50
991/4			*Set of* 4	3·50	4·25
MS995	110×77 mm. 50 c. Armstrong Whitworth Siskin IIIA; 50 c. Supermarine S6B; 50 c. Supermarine Walrus Mk1; 50 c. Hawker Hart			1·75	2·25

NEW INFORMATION

The editor is always interested to correspond with people who have new information that will improve or correct the Catalogue.

WORLD ORCHID CONFERENCE 1993 (210)	**211** 18 pdr Culverin of 1625, Denmark Fort

1993 (1 Apr). *14th World Orchid Conference, Glasgow. Nos.* 979/82 *optd as T* **210**.
996	55 c. Type **207**			80	80
997	65 c. *Cattleya guttaca*			90	90
998	70 c. *Laeliacattleya* "Splashing Around"			90	90
999	$1.40, *Phalaenopsis* "Kathy Saegert"			1·60	2·25
996/9			*Set of* 4	3·75	4·25

The overprints on the 70 c. and $1.40 are in two lines.

(Des J. Batchelor. Litho Cartor)

1993 (8 June). *17th-century English Cannon. T* **211** *and similar horiz designs. Multicoloured. W* w **14** *(sideways). P* 13.
1000	5 c. Type **211**			20	30
1001	45 c. 6 pdr of 1649–60, St. Ann's Fort			60	50
1002	$1 9 pdr demi-culverin of 1691, The Main Guard			1·25	1·50
1003	$2.50, 32 pdr demi-cannon of 1693–94, Charles Fort			2·25	3·25
1000/3			*Set of* 4	3·75	5·00

212 Sailor's Shell-work Valentine and Carved Amerindian	**213** Plesiosaurus

(Des D. Miller. Litho B.D.T.)

1993 (14 Sept). *60th Anniv of Barbados Museum. T* **212** *and similar vert designs. Multicoloured. W* w **14**. *P* 13½.
1004	10 c. Type **212**			25	15
1005	75 c. "Barbados Mulatto Girl" (Agostino Brunias)			90	90
1006	90 c. Morris Cup and soldier of West India Regiment, 1858			1·25	1·40
1007	$1.10, Ogilby's map of Barbados, 1679, and Ashanti gold weights			1·60	2·00
1004/7			*Set of* 4	3·50	4·00

(Des N. Shewring. Litho Cartor)

1993 (28 Oct). *Prehistoric Aquatic Reptiles. T* **213** *and similar vert designs. Multicoloured. W* w **14**. *P* 13.
1008	90 c. Type **213**			1·10	1·40
	a. Horiz strip of 5. Nos. 1008/12	..		5·00	
1009	90 c. Ichthyosaurus	..	..	1·10	1·40
1010	90 c. Elasmosaurus	..	..	1·10	1·40
1011	90 c. Mosasaurus ..	..	..	1·10	1·40
1012	90 c. Archelon	..	..	1·10	1·40
1008/12			*Set of* 5	5·00	6·00

Nos. 1008/12 were printed together, *se-tenant*, in horizontal strips of 5 throughout the sheet with the background forming a composite design.

214 Cricket	**215** Whimbrel

(Des S. Noon. Litho B.D.T.)

1994 (11 Jan). *Sports and Tourism. T* **214** *and similar vert designs. Multicoloured. W* w **16**. *P* 14.
1013	10 c. Type **214**	..		60	30
1014	35 c. Rally driving	..		75	35
1015	50 c. Golf	..		1·25	1·00
1016	70 c. Long distance running	..		1·00	1·25
1017	$1.40, Swimming	..		1·50	2·25
1013/17			*Set of* 5	4·50	4·75

(Des N. Arlott. Litho B.D.T.)

1994 (18 Feb). *"Hong Kong '94" International Stamp Exhibition. Migratory Birds. T* **215** *and similar horiz designs. Multicoloured. W* w **14** *(sideways). P* 14.
1018	10 c. Type **215**			15	15
1019	35 c. American Golden Plover			40	35
1020	70 c. Turnstone			70	80
1021	$3 Louisiana Heron ("Tricoloured Heron")			2·75	3·50
1018/21			*Set of* 4	3·50	4·25

---

216 Bathsheba Beach and Logo	**217** William Demas

(Des D. Miller. Litho B.D.T.)

1994 (25 Apr). *First United Nations Conference of Small Island Developing States. T* **216** *and similar horiz designs showing scenery. Multicoloured. W* w **16** *(sideways). P* 14×15.
1022	10 c. Type **216**			15	10
1023	65 c. Pico Tenneriffe			60	60
1024	90 c. Ragged Point Lighthouse	..		85	95
1025	$2.50, Consett Bay			2·25	3·00
1022/5			*Set of* 4	3·50	4·25

(Des D. Miller. Litho Cot Printery Ltd, Newton, Barbados)

1994 (4 July). *First Recipients of Order of the Caribbean Community. T* **217** *and simlar vert designs. Multicoloured. W* w **14**. *P* 14.
1026	70 c. Type **217**			70	85
1027	70 c. Sir Shridath Ramphal	..		70	85
1028	70 c. Derek Walcott			70	85
1026/8			*Set of* 3	1·90	2·25

218 Dutch Flyut, 1695	**219** Private, 2nd West India Regt, 1860

(Des A. Theobald. Litho B.D.T.)

1994 (16 Aug). *Ships. T* **218** *and similar horiz designs. Multicoloured. W* w **14** *(sideways). P* 14.
1029	5 c. Type **218**			30	40
1030	10 c. *Geestport* (container ship), 1994			30	30
1031	25 c. H.M.S. *Victory* (ship of the line), 1805			15	20
1032	30 c. *Royal Viking Queen* (liner), 1994	..		60	40
1033	35 c. H.M.S. *Barbados* (frigate), 1945			65	45
1034	45 c. *Faraday* (cable ship), 1924	..		75	55
1035	50 c. U.S.C.G. *Hamilton* (coastguard cutter), 1974			80	60
1036	65 c. H.M.C.S. *Saguenay* (destroyer), 1939			90	75
1037	70 c. *Inanda* (cargo liner), 1928	..		90	75
1038	80 c. H.M.S. *Rodney* (battleship), 1944			1·00	1·00
1039	90 c. U.S.S. *John F. Kennedy* (aircraft carrier), 1982			1·25	1·25
1040	$1.10, *William and John* (immigrant ship), 1627			1·50	1·50
1041	$5 U.S.C.G. *Champlain* (coastguard cutter), 1931			6·00	6·50
1042	$10 *Artist* (full-rigged ship), 1877			6·25	6·50
1029/42			*Set of* 14	19·00	19·00

For these designs watermarked W w **16** (sideways) and with imprint date see Nos. 1075/88.

(Des D. Cribbs. Litho Enschedé)

1995 (21 Feb). *Bicentenary of Formation of West India Regiment. T* **219** *and similar vert designs. Multicoloured. W* w **14**. *P* 15×14.
1043	30 c. Type **219**			35	35
1044	50 c. Light Company private, 4th West India Regt, 1795			50	50
1045	70 c. Drum Major, 3rd West India Regt, 1860			65	85
1046	$1 Privates in undress and working dress, 5th West India Regt, 1815			90	1·10
	w. Wmk inverted			1·00	
1047	$1.10, Troops from 1st and 2nd West India Regts in Review Order, 1874 ..			95	1·25
1043/7			*Set of* 5	3·00	3·50

(Des R. Watton. Litho Cot Printery Ltd, Barbados)

1995 (8 May). *50th Anniv of End of Second World War. Multicoloured designs as T* **161** *of Ascension. W* w **14** *(sideways). P* 14.
1048	10 c. Barbadian Bren gun crew			30	20
1049	35 c. Avro Type 683 Lancaster bomber			50	30
1050	55 c. Supermarine Spitfire			70	55
1051	$2.50, *Davisian* (cargo liner)			2·25	3·00
1048/51			*Set of* 4	3·25	3·50
MS1052	75×85 mm. $2 Reverse of 1939–45 War Medal (*vert*). Wmk upright			1·50	2·25

220 Member of 1st Barbados
Combermere Scout Troop,
1912

221 Blue Beauty

(Des S. Noon. Litho Cot Printery Ltd, Barbados)

1995 (25 July). *300th Anniv of Combermere School. T **220** and
similar multicoloured designs.* W w **14** (sideways on horiz
designs). P 14.
1053	5 c. Type **220**		20	20
1054	20 c. Violin and sheet of music		30	20
1055	35 c. Sir Frank Worrell (cricketer) (*vert*)		70	40
1056	$3 Painting by pupil		2·25	3·25
1053/6		*Set of 4*	3·00	3·50
MS1057	174×105 mm. Nos. 1053/6 and 90 c.			
1981 Carifesta 55 c. stamp. Wmk sideways			4·00	4·75
a. All four horiz stamps imperforate				

(Des A. Theobald. Litho Cot Printery Ltd, Barbados)

1995 (24 Oct). *50th Anniv of United Nations. Horiz designs as
T **213** of Bahamas. Multicoloured.* W w **14** (sideways). P 14.
1058	30 c. Douglas C-124 Globemaster (transport), Korea, 1950–53		40	30
1059	45 c. Royal Navy Sea King helicopter		50	40
1060	$1.40, Westland Wessex helicopter, Cyprus, 1964		1·10	1·75
1061	$2 Sud Aviation SA 341 Gazelle helicopter, Cyprus, 1964		1·50	2·00
1058/61		*Set of 4*	3·25	4·00

(Des I. Loe. Litho Cot Printery Ltd, Barbados)

1995 (19 Dec). *Water Lilies. T **221** and similar vert designs.
Multicoloured.* W w **14** (inverted). P 14.
1062	10 c. Type **221**		20	20
1063	65 c. White Water Lily		60	60
1064	70 c. Sacred Lotus		60	60
1065	$3 Water Hyacinth		2·25	3·00
1062/5		*Set of 4*	3·25	4·00

222 Magnifying Glass,
Tweezers and 1896 Colony
Seal ¼d. Stamp

223 Football

(Des D. Miller. Litho Cot Printery Ltd, Barbados)

1996 (30 Jan). *Centenary of Barbados Philatelic Society. T **222**
and similar horiz designs, each showing magnifying glass,
tweezers and stamp. Multicoloured.* W w **14** (sideways). P 14.
1066	10 c. Type **222**		20	15
1067	55 c. 1906 Tercentenary of Annexation 1d.		45	45
1068	$1.10, 1920 Victory 1s.		85	1·10
1069	$1.40, 1937 Coronation 2½d.		1·25	1·60
1066/9		*Set of 4*	2·50	3·00

(Des S. Noon (Nos. 1070/3), G. Vasarhelyi (No. MS1074). Litho
Cot Printery Ltd)

1996 (2 Apr). *Centenary of Modern Olympic Games. T **223** and
similar vert designs. Multicoloured.* W w **14**. P 14.
1070	20 c. Type **223**		20	20
1071	30 c. Relay running		30	25
1072	55 c. Basketball		60	50
1073	$3 Rhythmic gymnastics		2·25	2·50
1070/3		*Set of 4*	3·00	3·00
MS1074	68×89 mm. $2.50, "The Discus Thrower" (Myron). Wmk inverted		2·00	2·50

1996 (May–1 Sept). *As Nos. 1029/30 and 1032/41, but* W w **16**
(sideways) and with imprint date. P 14.
1075	5 c. Type **218**		10	15
1076	10 c. *Geestport* (container ship), 1994		10	15
1078	30 c. *Royal Viking Queen* (liner), 1994 (1 Sept)		20	25
1079	35 c. H.M.S. *Barbados* (frigate), 1945 (1 Sept)		20	25
1080	45 c. *Faraday* (cable ship), 1996 (1 Sept)		30	35
1081	50 c. U.S.C.G. *Hamilton* (coastguard cutter), 1974		30	35
1082	65 c. H.M.C.S. *Saguenay* (destroyer), 1939 (1 Sept)		40	45
1083	70 c. *Inanda* (cargo liner), 1928 (1 Sept)		40	45
1084	80 c. H.M.S. *Rodney* (battleship), 1944 (1 Sept)		50	55
1085	90 c. U.S.S. *John F. Kennedy* (aircraft carrier), 1982 (1 Sept)		55	60
1086	$1.10, *William and John* (immigrant ship), 1627		65	70
1087	$5 U.S.C.G. *Champlain* (coastguard cutter), 1931		3·00	3·25
1075/87		*Set of 12*	6·00	6·75
Imprint date: "1996", Nos. 1075/6 and 1078/87.

224 Douglas DC-10 of
Canadian Airlines

(Des N. Shewring. Litho Cot Printery Ltd)

1996 (7 June). *"CAPEX '96" International Stamp Exhibition,
Toronto. Aircraft. T **224** and similar horiz designs.
Multicoloured.* W w **14** (sideways). P 14.
1089	10 c. Type **224**		20	20
1090	90 c. Boeing 767 of Air Canada		70	70
1091	$1 Airbus Industrie A320 of Air Canada		75	75
1092	$1.40, Boeing 767 of Canadian Airlines		1·10	1·40
1089/92		*Set of 4*	2·50	2·75

225 Chattel House

(Des G. Vasarhelyi. Litho Cot Printery Ltd)

1996 (7 June). *Chattel Houses. T **225** and similar horiz designs
showing different houses.* W w **14** (sideways). P 14.
1093	35 c. multicoloured		30	25
1094	70 c. multicoloured		55	50
1095	$1.10, multicoloured		80	90
1096	$2 multicoloured		1·60	2·00
1093/6		*Set of 4*	3·00	3·25

226 "Going to Church"

227 Doberman Pinscher

(Des Jennifer Toombs. Litho Cot Printery Ltd)

1996 (12 Nov). *Christmas. 50th Anniv of U.N.I.C.E.F.
Children's Paintings. T **226** and similar horiz designs.
Multicoloured.* W w **14** (sideways). P 14×14½.
1097	10 c. Type **226**		20	15
1098	30 c. "The Tuk Band"		35	25
1099	55 c. "Singing carols"		50	40
1100	$2.50, "Decorated house"		1·75	2·25
1097/1100		*Set of 4*	2·50	2·75

(Des N. Shewring. Litho Cot Printery Ltd)

1997 (12 Feb). *"HONG KONG '97" International Stamp
Exhibition. Dogs. T **227** and similar horiz designs.
Multicoloured.* W w **14** (sideways). P 14×14½.
1101	10 c. Type **227**		20	20
1102	30 c. German Shepherd		50	35
1103	90 c. Japanese Akita		1·10	1·10
1104	$3 Irish Red Setter		3·00	3·25
1101/4		*Set of 4*	4·25	4·50

228 Barbados Flag and State
Arms

229 Measled Cowrie

(Des A. Theobald. Litho Cot Printery Ltd)

1997 (9 May). *Visit of President Clinton of U.S.A.. T **228** and
similar horiz design. Multicoloured.* W w **14** (sideways). P 14.
1105	35 c. Type **228**		35	40
	a. Sheetlet. Nos. 1105/6 each × 4 and 2 labels		3·75	
1106	90 c. American flag and arms		60	70

Nos. 1105/6 were printed together, both horizontally and
vertically *se-tenant*, in sheetlets of 8 with the blocks of four
separated horizontally by two different stamp-sized illustrated
labels.
Sheetlet No. 1105a was re-issued on 29 May 1997 with the
bottom margin overprinted with two examples of the "PACIFIC
'97" International Stamp Exhibition logo.

(Des N. Shewring. Litho Cot Printery Ltd)

1997 (29 July). *Shells. T **229** and similar vert designs.
Multicoloured.* W w **14**. P 14.
1107	5 c. Type **229**		15	15
1108	35 c. Trumpet Triton		35	25
1109	90 c. Scotch Bonnet		75	75
1110	$2 West Indian Murex		1·50	1·75
1107/10		*Set of 4*	2·50	2·50
MS1111	71×76 mm. $2.50, Underwater scene. Wmk inverted		1·90	2·00

230 Lucas Manuscripts

231 Barbados Cherry

(Des O. Bell. Litho Cot Printery Ltd)

1997 (1 Oct). *150th Anniv of the Public Library Service. T **230**
and similar horiz designs. Multicoloured.* W w **14** (sideways).
P 14×14½.
1112	10 c. Type **230**		15	15
1113	30 c. Librarian reading to children		30	25
1114	70 c. Mobile library van		60	60
1115	$3 Man using computer		2·25	2·50
1112/15		*Set of 4*	3·00	3·25

(Des I. Loe. Litho Cot Printery)

1997 (16 Dec). *Local Fruits. T **231** and similar horiz designs.
Multicoloured.* W w **14** (sideways). P 14×14½.
1116	35 c. Type **231**		20	25
1117	40 c. Sugar Apple		25	30
1118	$1.15, Soursop		70	75
1119	$1.70, Pawpaw		1·00	1·10
1116/19		*Set of 4*	2·10	2·40

If you would like to ADVERTISE

in the next edition of this catalogue or any other catalogue published by Stanley Gibbons

Phone, write or fax

**Advertising Department
Stanley Gibbons Publications,
5 Parkside, Christchurch Road,
Ringwood, Hants BH24 3SH**

**Telephone: 01425 472363
Fax: 01425 470247**

STAMP BOOKLETS

1906 (Feb).
SB1   2s. ½d. booklet containing twenty-four 1d. (No.
      137) in blocks of 6   ..   ..

1909. *Black on red cover. Stapled.*
SB1*a* 1s. 6d. booklet containing eighteen 1d. (No. 165)
      in blocks of 6   ..   ..

1913 (June). *Black on red cover. Stapled.*
SB2   2s. booklet containing twelve ½d. and eighteen 1d.
      (Nos. 171/2) in blocks of 6   ..   ..   ..

1916 (16 June). *Black on red cover. Stapled.*
SB3   2s. booklet containing twelve ½d. and eighteen 1d.
      (Nos. 182/3) in pairs £650

1920 (Sept). *Black on red cover. Stapled.*
SB4   2s. booklet containing twelve ½d. and eighteen 1d.
      (Nos. 202/3) in pairs ..   ..

1932 (12 Nov). *Black on pale green cover. Austin Cars and Post
Office Guide advertisements on front. Stapled.*
SB5   2s. booklet containing ½d. and 1d. (Nos. 230a,
      231a) each in block of 10 and 1½d. (No. 231ba)
      in block of 6   ..   ..

1933 (4 Dec). *Black on pale green cover. Advocate Co. Ltd.
advertisement on front. Stapled.*
SB6   2s. booklet containing ½d. and 1d. (Nos. 230/1)
      each in block of 10 and 1½d. (No. 231*b*) in block
      of 6   ..   ..

1938 (3 Jan). *Black on light blue cover. Advocate Co. Ltd.
advertisement on front. Stapled.*
SB7   2s. booklet containing ½d. and 1d. (Nos. 248, 249a)
      each in block of 10 and 1½d. (No. 250) in block
      of 6   ..   .. £1300

POSTAGE DUE STAMPS

D 1   D 2

(Typo D.L.R.)

1934 (2 Jan)**–47.** *Wmk Mult Script CA. P* 14.
D1 D 1 ½d. green (10.2.35)   75   5·50
D2   1d. black   70   70
          a. Bisected (½d.) (on cover)   ..   † £600
D3   3d. carmine (13.3.47) ..   .. 18·00 16·00
D1/3   *Set of* 3 18·00 20·00
D1/3 Perf "Specimen"   *Set of* 3 65·00
   The bisected 1d. was officially authorised for use between
March 1934 and February 1935. Some specimens had the value
"½d." written across the half stamp in red or black ink (*Price on
cover* £700).

(Typo D.L.R.)

1950 (8 Dec)**–53.** *Values in cents. Wmk Mult Script CA.
Ordinary paper. P* 14.
D4 D 1 1 c. green   ..   ..   .. 3·00 14·00
          a. Chalk-surfaced paper. *Deep green*
             (29.11.51)   30   3·00
          ab. Error. Crown missing, W 9*a*   .. £250
          ac. Error. St. Edward's Crown, W 9*b* £160
D5   2 c. black   ..   ..   .. 5·50 8·50
          a. Chalk-surfaced paper (20.1.53) .. 40 3·75
          ac. Error. St. Edward's Crown, W 9*b* £250
D6   6 c. carmine   ..   ..   .. 13·00 14·00
          a. Chalk-surfaced paper (20.1.53) .. 1·00 8·50
          ab. Error. Crown missing, W 9*a*   .. £160
          ac. Error. St. Edward's Crown, W 9*b* £130
D4/6   ..   .. *Set of* 3 19·00 32·00
D4a/6a ..   .. *Set of* 3   1·50 13·50
   The 1 c. has no dot below "c".

1965 (3 Aug)**–68.** *As Nos.* D4/6 *but wmk w* **12** (*upright*).
Chalk-surfaced paper.
D7 D 1 1 c. deep green   30   3·50
          a. Missing top serif on "C" (R. 2/4) .. 6·00
          b. Green   ..   ..   ..   1·75 5·50
D8   2 c. black   30   3·50
D9   6 c. carmine   50   4·00
          a. Carmine-red (14.5.68)   ..   1·40 8·50
D7/9   ..   .. *Set of* 3   1·00 10·00

1974 (4 Feb). *As No.* D9 *but W w* **12** (*sideways*). *Glazed, ordinary
paper. P* 14 × 13½.
D10 D 1 6 c. carmine   ..   ..   .. 8·50 16·00

1974 (4 Dec). *W w* **12** (*sideways*). *P* 13.
D12 D 1 2 c. black   ..   ..   .. 3·75 15·00
D13   6 c. carmine   ..   ..   .. 3·75 15·00

(Des Jennifer Toombs. Litho Questa)

1976 (12 May)**–85.** *Different floral backgrounds as Type D* **2.**
W w **14.** *P* 14.
D14   1 c. deep mauve and light pink   ..   20   65
      a. Perf 15 × 14 (7.85)   10   10
D15   2 c. ultramarine and light cobalt .. 20   65
      a. Perf 15 × 14 (7.85)   10   10
D16   5 c. reddish brown and yellow   ..   20   70
      a. Perf 15 × 14 (7.85)   10   10
D17 10 c. royal blue and light lilac   .. 35   80
      a. Perf 15 × 14 (7.85)   10   10
D18 25 c. deep green and bright yellow-green 60 1·10
      a. Perf 15 × 14 (7.85)   15   20
D19 $1 rose-carmine and rose   65   70
D14/19 ..   .. *Set of* 6 2·00 4·00
D14a/18a ..   ..   ..   *Set of* 5   35   40

STANLEY GIBBONS

Auctions & Acquisitions

**LEADING
PHILATELIC AUCTIONEERS
SINCE 1901**

**A PROFESSIONAL
AUCTION SERVICE FROM
THE MOST FAMOUS
NAME IN PHILATELY**

A PROVEN PROGRAMME
OF SPECIALISED
INTERNATIONAL SALES

FREE ADVICE AND EXPERT
MARKET VALUATIONS

0% VENDOR COMMISSION
(on realisations over £5000)

FAST GUARANTEED PAYMENT

CASH ADVANCES AVAILABLE

SETTLEMENT IN ANY CURRENCY

THE INDUSTRY'S LARGEST
DATABASE OF SPECIALIST BUYERS

HIGH QUALITY CATALOGUES
DISTRIBUTED WORLDWIDE

REGULAR TELESALES CONTACT
WITH MAJOR BUYERS

SPECIALIST
SUBSCRIPTION SERVICE

REFINED VENUES AND
EXTENSIVE VIEWING TIMES

*TELEPHONE TODAY FOR A FULL
INFORMATION PACK.*

STANLEY GIBBONS AUCTIONS
399 STRAND • LONDON • WC2R 0LX
TELEPHONE: 0171 836 8444
FACSIMILE: 0171 836 7342

Barbuda
(see after Antigua)

Basutoland
see Lesotho

Batum

Batum, the outlet port on the Black Sea for the Russian Transcaucasian oilfields, was occupied by the Turks on 15 April 1918.

Under the terms of the armistice signed at Mudros on 30 October 1918 the Turks were to withdraw and be replaced by an Allied occupation of Batum, the Baku oilfields and the connecting Transcaucasia Railway. British forces arrived off Batum in early December and the oblast, or district, was declared a British military governorship on 25 December 1918. The Turkish withdrawal was completed five days later.

The provision of a civilian postal service was initially the responsibility of the Batum Town Council. Some form of mail service was in operation by February 1919 with the postage prepaid in cash. Letters are known showing a framed oblong handstamp, in Russian, to this effect. The Town Council was responsible for the production of the first issue, Nos. 1/6, but shortly after these stamps were placed on sale a strike by Council employees against the British military governor led to the postal service being placed under British Army control.

SURCHARGES. Types 2 and 4/8 were all applied by handstamp. Most values from No. 19 onwards are known showing the surcharge inverted, surcharge double or in pairs with surcharge *tête-bêche*.

BRITISH OCCUPATION

(Currency. 100 kopeks = 1 rouble)

PRICES FOR STAMPS ON COVER	
Nos. 1/6	from × 60
Nos. 7/10	from × 15
Nos. 11/18	from × 60
Nos. 19/20	from × 15
Nos. 21/44	—
Nos. 45/53	from × 200

БАТУМ. ОБ.

Руб **10** Руб

| | 1 Aloe Tree | | (2) |

1919 (4 Apr). *Litho. Imperf.*

1	1	5 k. green	..	..	..	4·50	6·00
2		10 k. ultramarine	..	..	..	4·50	6·00
3		50 k. yellow	..	..	..	1·50	2·00
4		1 r. chocolate	..	..	..	2·00	2·50
5		3 r. violet	..	..	..	7·00	8·50
6		5 r. brown	..	..	..	8·00	9·50
1/6				Set of 6		25·00	32·00

Nos. 1/6 were printed in sheets of 198 (18×11).

1919 (13 Apr). *Russian stamps (Arms types) handstamped with T 2.*

7	10 r. on 1 k. orange (imperf)	..	..	26·00	28·00
8	10 r. on 3 k. carmine-red (imperf)	..		14·00	16·00
9	10 r. on 5 k. brown-lilac (perf)	..	..	£250	£250
10	10 r. on 10 on 7 k. deep blue (perf)	..		£200	£200

A similar handstamped surcharge, showing the capital letters without serifs, is bogus.

BRITISH OCCUPATION

(3)

1919 (10 Nov.) *Colours changed and new values. Optd with T 3.*

11	1	5 k. yellow-green	..	..	..	6·50	6·50
12		10 k. bright blue	..	..	..	6·50	6·50
13		25 k. orange-yellow	..	..	..	6·50	6·00
14		1 r. pale blue	..	..	..	3·00	5·00
15		2 r. pink	..	..	..	90	1·00
16		3 r. bright violet	..	..	..	90	1·00
17		5 r. brown	..	..	..	1·25	1·40
		a. "CCUPATION" (R.5/1)	..	..		£250	
18		7 r. brownish red	..	..	..	2·75	3·75
11/18				Set of 8		25·00	28·00

Nos. 11/18 were printed in sheets of 432 (18×24).

---

(4)	(5)

1919 (27 Nov)–**20**. *Russian stamps (Arms types) handstamped with T 4 or 5. Imperf.*

19	10 r. on 3 k. carmine-red	..	..	..	10·00	12·00
20	15 r. on 1 k. orange ..		..	..	35·00	35·00
	a. Red surch	..	..	..	28·00	28·00
	b. Violet surch (10.3.20)	..	..	38·00	38·00

Nos. 20a/b have the handstamp in soluble ink.

1920 (12 Jan). *Russian stamps (Arms types) handstamped as T 4.*

(a) Imperf

21	50 r. on 1 k. orange ..	..	..	£250	£250
22	50 r. on 2 k. yellow-green (R.)	..	..	£350	£350

(b) Perf

23	50 r. on 2 k. yellow-green	..	..	£350	£350
24	50 r. on 3 k. carmine-red	..	..	£800	£800
25	50 r. on 4 k. red	..	..	£550	£550
26	50 r. on 5 k. brown-lilac	..	..	£350	£350
27	50 r. on 10 k. deep blue (R.)	..	..	£900	£900
28	50 r. on 15 k. blue and red-brown	..	£350	£350

(6)

1920 (30 Jan–21 Feb). *Russian stamps (Arms types) handstamped as T 6. (a) Perf*

29	25 r. on 5 k. brown-lilac (21 Feb)	..	..	28·00	28·00
	a. Blue surch	..	..	..	28·00	28·00
30	25 r. on 10 on 7 k. blue (21 Feb)	..	..	80·00	80·00
	a. Blue surch	..	..	..	45·00	45·00
31	25 r. on 20 on 14 k. dp carmine & bl (21 Feb)	48·00	48·00
	a. Blue surch	..	..	..	45·00	45·00
32	25 r. on 25 k. deep violet & lt green (21 Feb)	80·00	80·00
	a. Blue surch	..	..	..	65·00	65·00
33	25 r. on 50 k. green and copper-red (21 Feb)	45·00	45·00
	a. Blue surch	..	..	..	48·00	48·00
34	50 r. on 2 k. yellow-green	..	..	65·00	65·00
35	50 r. on 3 k. carmine-red	..	..	65·00	65·00
36	50 r. on 4 k. red	..	..	60·00	60·00
37	50 r. on 5 k. brown-lilac	..	..	45·00	45·00

(b) Imperf

38	50 r. on 2 k. yellow-green	..	..	£250	£250
39	50 r. on 3 k. carmine-red	..	..	£300	£300
40	50 r. on 5 k. brown-lilac	..	..	£950	£950

1920 (10 Mar). *Romanov issue, as T 25 of Russia, handstamped with T 6.*

41	50 r. on 4 k. rose-carmine (B.)	..	..	35·00	40·00

(7)	(8)

1920 (1 Apr). *Nos. 3, 11 and 13 handstamped with T 7 (Nos. 42/3) or 8 (No. 44).*

42	25 r. on 5 k. yellow-green	..	..	20·00	20·00
	a. Blue surch	..	..	..	22·00	22·00
43	25 r. on 25 k. orange-yellow	..	..	16·00	16·00
	a. Blue surch	..	..	..	60·00	60·00
44	50 r. on 50 k. yellow	..	..	12·00	12·00
	a. "50" cut	..	..	..	9·00	9·00
	b. Blue surch	..	..	..	65·00	65·00
	ba. "50" cut	..	..	..	£110	£110

Nos. 44a and 44ba show the figures broken by intentional file cuts applied as a protection against forgery. The "5" is cut at the base and on the right side of the loop. The "0" is chipped at top and foot, and has both vertical lines severed.

1920 (19 June). *Colours changed and new values. Optd with T 3. Imperf.*

45	1	1 r. chestnut	..	..	..	60	2·50
		a. "BPITISH"	..	..	..	42·00	
46		2 r. pale blue	..	..	..	70	2·50
		a. "BPITISH"	..	..	..	50·00	
47		3 r. pink	..	..	..	70	2·50
		a. "BPITISH"	..	..	..	50·00	
48		5 r. black-brown	..	..	..	70	2·50
		a. "BPITISH"	..	..	..	50·00	
49		7 r. yellow	..	..	..	70	2·50
		a. "BPITISH"	..	..	..	50·00	
50		10 r. myrtle-green	..	..	..	60	2·50
		a. "BPITISH"	..	..	..	50·00	
51		15 r. violet	..	..	..	90	3·75
		a. "BPITISH"	..	..	..	£100	

52	1	25 r. scarlet	..	..	..	80	3·25
		a. "BPITISH"	..	..	..	95·00	
53		50 r. deep blue	..	..	..	1·00	5·00
		a. "BPITISH"	..	..	..	£160	
45/53				Set of 9		6·00	24·00

Nos. 45/53 were printed in sheets of 308 (22×14). The "BPITISH" error occurs on R. 1/19 of the overprint.

POSTCARD STAMPS

When Nos. 7/10 were issued on 13 April 1919 a similar 35 k. surcharge was applied to stocks of various Russian postcards held by the post office. The majority of these had stamp impressions printed directly on to the card, but there were also a few cards, originally intended for overseas mail, on which Russia 4 k. stamps had been affixed.

PRICES. Those in the left-hand column are for unused examples on complete postcard; those on the right for used examples off card. Examples used on postcard are worth more.

1919 (13 Apr). *Russian stamps handstamped as T 2.*

P1	35 k. on 4 k. red (Arms type)	..	£2750	£3250
P2	35 k. on 4 k. carmine-red (Romanov issue)	£7500	£8500

Batum was handed over to the National Republic of Georgia on 7 July 1920.

Bechuanaland
see Botswana

Belize
(formerly British Honduras)

BRITISH HONDURAS

It is recorded that the first local post office was established by the inhabitants in 1809, but Belize did not become a regular packet port of call until 1829. A branch office of the British G.P.O. was established in 1857 and the stamps of Great Britain were supplied for use on overseas mail from 1858.

The colonial authorities took over the postal service on 1 April, 1860, the Great Britain stamps being withdrawn the following month. There was no inland postal service until 1862.

For illustrations of the handstamp and postmark types see BRITISH POST OFFICES ABROAD notes, following GREAT BRITAIN.

BELIZE

CROWNED-CIRCLE HANDSTAMPS

CC1	CC 1b BELIZE (R.)(13.11.1841)	..	Price on cover £4000

Stamps of GREAT BRITAIN cancelled "A 06" as Type 2.

1858 to 1860.

Z1	1d. rose-red (1857), perf 14 ..	..	..		£850
Z2	4d. rose (1857)	..	..	..		£350
Z3	6d. lilac (1856)	..	..	..		£350
Z4	1s. green (1856)	..	..	..		£1300

PRICES FOR STAMPS ON COVER TO 1945		
Nos. 1/4	from × 20	
Nos. 5/16	from × 25	
Nos. 17/22	from × 20	
Nos. 23/6	from × 10	
Nos. 27/30	from × 15	
Nos. 35/42	from × 20	
Nos. 43/4	from × 30	
Nos. 49/50	from × 25	
Nos. 51/69	from × 15	
Nos. 80/100	from × 6	
Nos. 101/10	from × 5	
Nos. 111/20	from × 15	
Nos. 121/2	from × 8	
No. 123	from × 10	
Nos. 124/37	from × 6	
Nos. 138/42	from × 10	
Nos. 143/9	from × 8	
Nos. 150/61	from × 5	
Nos. D1/3	from × 30	

CROWN COLONY

1

(Typo D.L.R.)

1865 (1 Dec). *No wmk. P* 14.
1	1	1d. pale blue		55·00	48·00
		a. Imperf between (pair)	..		
2		1d. blue	..	60·00	48·00
3		6d. rose	..	£250	£110
4		1s. green	..	£275	£100
		a. In horiz pair with 6d.		£16000	
		b. In vert pair with 1d.		£23000	

In the first printing all three values were printed in the same sheet separated by horizontal and vertical gutter margins. The sheet comprised two panes of 60 of the 1d. at the top with a pane of 60 of the 1s. at bottom left and another of 6d. at bottom right. Copies of 1d. *se-tenant* with the 6d. are not known. There were two later printings of the 1d. but they were in sheets without the 6d. and 1s.

1872–79. *Wmk Crown CC.* (a) *P* 12½.
5	1	1d. pale blue	..	60·00	16·00
6		1d. deep blue (1874)	..	65·00	16·00
7		3d. red-brown	..	£100	65·00
8		3d. chocolate (1874)	..	£120	80·00
9		6d. rose	..	£190	28·00
9a		6d. bright rose-carmine (1874)	..	£300	38·00
10		1s. green	..	£300	28·00
10a		1s. deep green (1874)	..	£250	20·00
		b. Imperf between (horiz pair)		† £13000	

(b) *P* 14 (1877–79)
11	1	1d. pale blue (1878)	..	55·00	15·00
12		1d. blue	..	50·00	10·00
		a. Imperf between (horiz pair)		£3750	
13		3d. chestnut	..	90·00	16·00
14		4d. mauve (1879) ..	..	£130	8·00
15		6d. rose (1878)	..	£275	£160
16		1s. green	..	£160	11·00
		a. Imperf between (pair)			

1882–87. *Wmk Crown CA. P* 14.
17	1	1d. blue (4.84)	..	38·00	13·00
18		1d. rose (1884)	..	18·00	11·00
		a. Bisected (½d.) (on cover)	..		
19		1d. carmine (1887)	..	50·00	15·00
20		4d. mauve (7.82)	..	70·00	4·50
21		6d. yellow (1885)	..	£275	£180
22		1s. grey (1.87)	..	£250	£150
18,22		Optd "Specimen"	..*Set of 2*	£200	

(New Currency. 100 cents = 1 British Honduras (later Belize) dollar)

2
CENTS
(2)

TWO
(3)

2
CENTS
(4)

1888 (1 Jan). *Stamps of 1872–79 (wmk Crown CC), surch locally as T* 2. (a) *P* 12½.
23	1	2 c. on 6d. rose	..	£140 95·00
24		3 c. on 3d. chocolate	..	£10000 £4750

(b) *P* 14
25	1	2 c. on 6d. rose	..	80·00 70·00
		a. Surch double	..	£1300
		b. Bisected (1 c.) (on cover)	†	£180
		c. Slanting "2" with curved foot	..	£850
26		3 c. on 3d. chestnut	..	60·00 60·00

There are very dangerous forgeries of these surcharges.

1888. *Stamps of 1882–87 (wmk Crown CA), surch locally as T* 2, *P* 14.
27	1	2 c. on 1d. rose	..	8·00 17·00
		a. Surch inverted	..	£1600 £1500
		b. Surch double	..	£900 £900
		c. Bisected (1 c.) (on cover)	†	£180
28		10 c. on 4d. mauve	..	38·00 15·00
29		20 c. on 6d. yellow	..	27·00 32·00
30		50 c. on 1s. grey	..	£325 £450
		a. Error. "5" for "50"	..	£7000

Various settings were used for the surcharges on Nos. 23/30, the most common of which was of 36 (6 × 6) impressions. For No. 29 this setting was so applied that an albino surcharge occurs in the margin above each stamp in the first horizontal row.

The same setting was subsequently amended, by altering the "2" to "1", to surcharge the 4d. value. As this was in sheets of 30 it was only necessary to alter the values on the bottom five rows of the setting. Albino surcharges once again occur in the top margin of the sheet, but, as the type in the first horizontal row remained unaltered, these read "20 CENTS" rather than the "10 CENTS" on the actual stamps.

1888 (Mar). *No.* 30 *further surch locally with T* 3.
35	1	"TWO" on 50c. on 1s. grey (R.)	..	40·00 80·00
		a. Bisected (1 c.) (on cover)	†	£200
		b. Surch in black	..	£8000 £7000
		c. Surch double (R. + Blk.)	..	£8000 £7000

1888 (July)–**91.** *Surch in London as T* 4. *Wmk Crown CA. P* 14.
36	1	1 c. on 1d. dull green (?12.91)	..	30 95
37		2 c. on 1d. carmine	..	30 1·25
		a. Bisected (1 c.) (on cover)	†	90·00
38		3 c. on 3d. red-brown	..	2·00 1·40
39		6 c. on 3d. ultramarine (?4.91)	..	1·90 9·00
40		10 c. on 4d. mauve	..	4·25 40
		a. Surch double	..	£1400
41		20 c. on 6d. yellow (2.89)	..	10·00 14·00
42		50 c. on 1s. grey (11.88)	..	25·00 65·00
36/42			.. *Set of 7*	38·00 80·00
36/42		Optd "Specimen"	*Set of 7*	£350

6
~~**10**~~
CENTS
(5)

FIVE   **15**
(6)   (7)

1891. *Stamps of 1888–9 surch locally.* (a) *With T* 5 (May).
43	1	6 c. on 10 c. on 4d. mauve (R.)		60	1·50
		a. "6" and bar inverted	..	£375	£375
		b. "6" only inverted	..	—	£2250
44		6 c. on 10 c. on 4d. mauve (Blk.)		60	1·50
		a. "6" and bar inverted	..	£2250	£650
		b. "6" only inverted	..	†	£2250

Of variety (b) only six copies of each can exist, as one of each of these errors came in the first six sheets, and the mistake was then corrected. Of variety (a) more copies exist.

Essays are known with "SIX" in place of "6", both with and without bars (*price £75 and £375 respectively*). Although not issued we mention them, as three contemporary covers franked with them are known.

(b) *With T* 6/7 (23 Oct)
49	1	5 c. on 3 c. on 3d. red-brown		70	1·40
		a. Wide space between "I" and "V"	..	45·00	65·00
		b. "FIVE" and bar double	..	£225	£250
50		15 c. on 6 c. on 3d. ultramarine (R.)		9·00	21·00
		a. Surch double	..		

8   9

10   11

(Typo D.L.R.)

1891 (July)–**1901.** *Wmk Crown CA. P* 14.
51	8	1 c. dull green (4.95)	..	1·50	80
		a. Malformed "S"	..	85·00	48·00
52		2 c. carmine-rose	..	1·25	10
		a. Malformed "S"	..	80·00	24·00
		b. Repaired "S"	..	65·00	24·00
53		3 c. brown	..	4·25	1·75
54		5 c. ultramarine (4.95)	..	12·00	40
		a. Malformed "S"	..	£200	45·00
55	11	5 c. grey-black & ultram/*blue* (10.00)	..	12·00	1·75
56	8	6 c. ultramarine	..	4·25	1·50
57	9	10 c. mauve and green (4.95)	..	8·50	8·50
58	10	10 c. dull purple and green (1901)	..	9·00	7·50
59	9	12 c. pale mauve and green	..	23·00	7·00
		a. *Violet and green*	..	2·50	2·00
60		24 c. yellow and blue	..	5·50	14·00
		a. *Orange and blue*	..	29·00	50·00
61		25 c. red-brown and green (4.95)	..	45·00	85·00
62	10	50 c. green and carmine (3.98)	..	19·00	48·00
63	11	$1 green and carmine (12.99)	..	50·00	90·00
64		$2 green and ultramarine (12.99)	..	70·00	£100
65		$5 green and black (12.99)	..	£200	£250
51/65			*Set of 15*	£400	£550
51/65		Optd "Specimen"	*Set of 15*	£300	

For illustrations of Nos. 51a, 52a/b and 54a see above Gambia No. 37.

1899 (1 July). *Optd "REVENUE" A. Opt 12 mm long. B. Opt 11 mm long.*
			A	B
66	5 c. (No. 54)	..	7·00 2·00	15·00 7·00
	a. "BEVENUE"	..	80·00 85·00	†
	b. Repaired "S" at right	..	£150	†
67	10 c. (No. 57)	..	3·00 11·00	18·00 40·00
	a. "BEVENUE"	..	£180 £225	†
	b. "REVENU"	..	£400 —	£425 £475
68	25 c. (No. 61)	..	2·75 30·00	4·00 48·00
	a. "BEVENUE"	..	£120 £275	†
	b. "REVE UE"	..		†
69	50 c. (No. 42)	..	£120 £275	£200 £375
	a. "BEVENUE"	..	£2750	—

Two minor varieties, a small "U" and a tall, narrow "U" are found in the word "REVENUE".

The overprint setting of 60 (6 × 10) contained 43 examples of the 12 mm size and 17 of the 11 mm. The smaller size overprints occur on R.8/1, R.8/3 to 6 and on all positions in Rows 9 and 10.

The "BEVENUE" error appears on R.6/4 and, it is believed, "REVE UE" comes from R.6/6. Both occur on parts of the printing only. The missing "E" developed during the overprinting and damage to this letter can be observed on at least eight positions in the setting. Examples of No. 67b are now known to exist on both sizes of the overprint.

14   15

(Typo D.L.R.)

1902 (10 Oct)–**04.** *Wmk Crown CA. P* 14.
80	14	1 c. grey-green and green (28.4.04)	..	1·75	19·00
81		2 c. purple and black/*red* (18.3.03)	..	75	25
		w. Wmk inverted	..	—	50·00
82		5 c. grey-black and blue/*blue*	..	4·50	30
		w. Wmk inverted	..		
83	15	20 c. dull and bright purple (28.4.04)	..	3·75	17·00
80/3			*Set of 4*	9·75	32·00
80/3		Optd "Specimen"	*Set of 4*	55·00	

1904 (Dec)–**07.** *Wmk Mult Crown CA. Ordinary paper* (1, 2 c.) *or chalk-surfaced paper* (*others*). *P* 14.
84	14	1 c. grey-green and green (8.05)	..	4·75	5·50
		a. Chalk-surfaced paper (1906)	..	65	1·25
85		2 c. purple and black/*red*	..	2·75	20
		a. Chalk-surfaced paper (1906)	..	65	10
86		5 c. grey-black and blue/*blue* (5.2.06)	..	1·75	20
87	15	10 c. dull purple & emerald-green (20.9.07)	..	5·00	11·00
89		25 c. dull purple and orange (20.9.07)	..	7·00	40·00
90		50 c. grey-green and carmine (20.9.07)	..	15·00	60·00
91	14	$1 grey-green and carmine (20.9.07)	..	40·00	60·00
92		$2 grey-green and blue (20.9.07)	..	75·00	£130
93		$5 grey-green and black (20.9.07)	..	£180	£250
84/93			*Set of 9*	£275	£500
87/93		Optd "Specimen"	*Set of 6*	£225	

Examples of most values are known showing a forged Belize postmark dated "OC 23 09".

1908 (7 Dec)–**11.** *Colours changed. Wmk Mult Crown CA. Chalk-surfaced paper* (25 c.). *P* 14.
95	14	1 c. blue-green (1.7.10)	..	7·50	30
96		2 c. carmine	..	7·00	10
		w. Wmk inverted	..		
97		5 c. ultramarine (1.6.09)	..	1·75	10
100	15	25 c. black/*green* (14.10.11)	..	2·75	42·00
95/100			*Set of 4*	17·00	42·00
95/100		Optd "Specimen"	*Set of 3*	70·00	

16   17   (18)

1913–21. *Wmk Mult Crown CA. Chalk-surfaced paper* (10 c. to $5). *P* 14.
101	16	1 c. blue-green	..	2·25	75
		a. *Yellow-green* (13.3.17)	..	3·75	1·60
		w. Wmk inverted	..		
102		2 c. red	..	1·50	75
		a. *Bright scarlet* (1915)	..	3·50	60
		b. *Dull scarlet* (8.17)	..	3·00	1·25
		c. *Red/bluish*	..	8·50	7·00
		w. Wmk inverted	..		
103		3 c. orange (16.4.17)	..	40	20
104		5 c. bright blue	..	2·00	40
105	17	10 c. dull purple and yellow-green	..	2·75	6·50
		a. *Dull purple and bright green* (1917)	..	9·00	20·00
106		25 c. black/*green*	..	1·25	10·00
		a. *On blue-green, olive back* (8.17)	..	3·25	8·50
		b. *On emerald back* (1921)	..	1·75	24·00
107		50 c. purple and blue/*blue*	..	7·00	10·00
108	16	$1 black and carmine	..	14·00	30·00
109		$2 purple and green	..	60·00	70·00
110		$5 purple and black/*red*	..	£190	£225
101/10			*Set of 10*	£250	£325
101/10		Optd "Specimen"	*Set of 10*	£225	

1915–16. *Optd with T* 18, *in violet.*
111	16	1 c. green (30.12.15)	..	2·00	14·00
		a. *Yellow-green* (6.6.16)	..	30	8·50
112		2 c. scarlet (3.11.15)	..	1·50	50
113		5 c. bright blue (29.7.15)	..	30	4·00
111/13		Optd "Specimen"	*Set of 3*	90·00	

These stamps were shipped early in the 1914–18 war, and were thus overprinted, so that if seized by the enemy, they could be distinguished and rendered invalid.

WAR   **WAR**
(19)   (20)   21

1916 (23 Aug). *No.* 111 *optd locally with T* 19.
114	16	1 c. green	..	10	40
		a. Opt inverted	..	£180	£200

1917. *Nos.* 101 *and* 103 *optd with T* 19.
116	16	1 c. blue-green	..	70	2·25
		aw. Wmk inverted			
		ax. Wmk reversed			
		b. *Yellow-green*	..	20	1·25
118		3 c. orange	..	1·50	3·25
		a. Opt double	..	£300	

1918. *Nos.* 101 *and* 103 *optd with T* 20.
119	16	1 c. blue-green	..	10	25
		a. *Yellow-green*	..	3·00	4·00
120		3 c. orange	..	30	95
		y. Wmk inverted and reversed			
119/20		Optd "Specimen"	*Set of 2*	£100	

1971 (14 June). *Racial Equality Year. As No. 264, but W w 12 (sideways*) and No. 277e optd with T 73.*

313	10 c. Paca	..	20	10
314	50 c. Mutton Snapper	..	40	20
	w. Wmk Crown to left of CA		6·50	

*The normal sideways watermark shows Crown to left of CA on the 10 c. and to the right on the 50 c., *both as seen from the back of the stamp.*

(Des Jennifer Toombs, Litho Questa)

1971 (16 Aug). *Indigenous Hardwoods (3rd series). T 74 and similar vert designs. Multicoloured. W w 12. P 13½.*

315	5 c. Type 74	..	40	10
	w. Wmk inverted		1·75	
316	15 c. Yemeri	..	60	30
317	26 c. Billywebb	..	85	35
318	50 c. Logwood	..	1·50	2·75
315/18		Set of 4	3·00	3·00
MS319	96×171 mm. Nos. 315/18	..	3·00	6·00
	a. Silver (Queen's head) omitted		£1500	

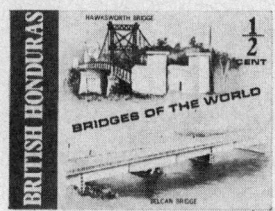

75 Hawksworth and Belcan Bridges

(Des and litho J.W.)

1971 (23 Sept). *Bridges of the World. T 75 and similar horiz designs. Multicoloured. W w 12 (sideways). P 13½.*

320	½c. Type 75	..	10	10
321	5 c. Narrows Bridge, N.Y. and Quebec Bridge		15	10
322	26 c. London Bridge (1871) and reconstructed, Arizona (1971)		40	10
323	50 c. Belize Mexican Bridge and Swing Bridge		50	60
320/3		Set of 4	95	75

76 *Petrae volubis*   77 Seated Figure

(Des G. Drummond. Litho Format)

1972 (28 Feb). *Easter. T 76 and similar vert designs showing wild flowers. Multicoloured. W w 12. P 14½.*

324	6 c. Type 76	..	15	10
325	15 c. Yemeri	..	35	30
326	26 c. Mayflower	..	50	45
327	50 c. Tiger's Claw	..	80	1·40
324/7		Set of 4	1·60	2·00

(Des Jennifer Toombs. Litho Questa)

1972 (22 May). *Mayan Artefacts. T 77 and similar multicoloured designs. W w 12 (sideways except 16 c.). P 13½ × 13 (16 c.) or 13 × 13½ (others).*

328	3 c. Type 77	..	15	10
329	6 c. Priest in "dancing" pose	..	20	10
330	16 c. Sun God's head (*horiz*)	..	35	15
331	26 c. Priest and Sun God	..	50	20
332	50 c. Full-front figure..	..	1·00	2·75
328/32		Set of 5	2·00	3·00

Nos. 328/32 are inscribed on the reverse with information about the artefacts depicted.

78 Banak   79 Orchids of Belize

(Des Jennifer Toombs. Litho Questa)

1972 (21 Aug). *Indigenous Hardwoods (4th series). T 78 and similar vert designs. Multicoloured. W w 12 (sideways). P 14½.*

333	3 c. Type 78	..	15	10
334	5 c. Quamwood	..	15	10
335	16 c. Waika Chewstick	..	40	15
336	26 c. Mamee-Apple	..	75	25
337	50 c. My Lady	..	1·40	2·75
333/7		Set of 5	2·50	3·00

1972 (17 Nov). *As Nos. 258 and 260/1, but W w 12 (upright).*

338	3 c. Misty Grouper	..	1·25	1·75
339	5 c. Bonefish	..	1·25	1·75
340	10 c. Paca	..	1·25	1·75
	w. Wmk inverted		6·00	
338/40		Set of 3	3·25	4·75

(Des (from photograph by D. Groves) and photo Harrison)

1972 (20 Nov). *Royal Silver Wedding. Multicoloured; background colour given. W w 12. P 14 × 14½.*

341	79	26 c. deep myrtle-green	..	25	10
		w. Wmk inverted	..	40·00	
342		50 c. bright bluish violet	..	40	55
		w. Wmk inverted	..	32·00	

80 Baron Bliss Day

(Des J.W. Litho Questa)

1973 (9 Mar). *Festivals of Belize. T 80 and similar horiz designs. Multicoloured. W w 12. P 14½ × 14.*

343	3 c. Type 80	..	15	10
344	10 c. Labour Day	..	15	10
345	26 c. Carib Settlement Day	..	30	15
346	50 c. Pan American Day	..	50	70
343/6	..	Set of 4	1·00	85

BELIZE

British Honduras was renamed Belize on 1 June 1973.

☀ B E L I Z E ☀

(81)

1973 (11 June*). *Designs as Nos. 256/7, 259, 262/7 and 277, but W w 12 (upright), and Nos. 338/40 optd with T 81 in black on silver by D.L.R. P 13×12½.*

347	½c. Mozambique Mouthbrooder ("Crana")	10	20
348	1 c. Spotted Jewfish	10	20
349	2 c. White-lipped Peccary ("Waree")	10	20
350	3 c. Misty Grouper	10	10
	a. Silver background to opt omitted	†	—
351	4 c. Collared Anteater	10	20
352	5 c. Bonefish	10	20
353	10 c. Paca ("Gibnut")	15	15
	a. Black (value etc.) omitted	£200	
354	15 c. Dolphin	20	20
355	25 c. Kinkajou ("Night Walker")	35	35
356	50 c. Mutton Snapper	65	75
357	$1 Tayra ("Bush Dog")	1·10	1·50
358	$2 Great Barracuda	2·00	2·75
359	$5 Puma	2·50	4·75
347/59	Set of 13	6·50	10·50

*This is the local date of issue: the Crown Agents released the stamps on 1 June.

No. 350a shows the silver background to the overprint omitted. Traces of the adhesive used to apply the silver are visible.

1973 (14 Nov). *Royal Wedding. As Nos. 165/6 of Anguilla. Centre multicoloured. W w 12 (sideways). P 13½.*

360	26 c. light turquoise-blue	..	15	10
361	50 c. ochre	..	15	20

82 Mozambique Mouthbrooder

1974 (1 Jan). *Designs as Nos. 256/67 and 277, but inscr "BELIZE" as in T 82. W w 12. P 13½.*

362	½c. Type 82	10	20
363	1 c. Spotted Jewfish	10	20
364	2 c. White-lipped Peccary ("Waree")	10	20
365	3 c. Misty Grouper	10	10
366	4 c. Collared Anteater	10	20
367	5 c. Bonefish	10	20
368	10 c. Paca ("Gibnut")	15	15
369	15 c. Dolphin	20	20
370	25 c. Kinkajou ("Night Walker")	35	35
371	50 c. Mutton Snapper	60	70
372	$1 Tayra ("Bush Dog")	1·00	1·50
373	$2 Great Barracuda	1·50	2·25
374	$5 Puma	3·50	5·50
362/74	Set of 13	7·00	10·50

83 Deer

(Des Mrs. Hosek; adapted PAD Studio, Litho Questa)

1974 (1 May). *Mayan Artefacts (1st series). T 83 and similar horiz designs showing pottery motifs. Multicoloured. W w 12. P 14½.*

375	3 c. Type 83	..	10	10
376	6 c. Jaguar deity	..	10	10
377	16 c. Sea monster	..	15	10
378	26 c. Cormorant	..	25	10
379	50 c. Scarlet macaw	..	40	40
375/9	..	Set of 5	85	65

See also Nos. 398/402.

84 *Parides arcas*

(Des J. Cooter from the collection of P.T. Hill. Litho Harrison)

1974 (2 Sept)–**76**. *Butterflies. Horiz designs as T 84. Multicoloured. W w 12 (sideways*). P 14 (½, 1, 2, 3, 4, 5, 10, 26 c.) or 14×14½ (others).*

380	½c. Type 84	..	90	2·25
381	1 c. *Evenus regalis*	..	90	1·75
382	2 c. *Colobura dirce*	..	1·25	1·75
383	3 c. *Catonephele numilia*	..	1·40	1·60
384	4 c. *Battus belus*	..	1·75	2·00
385	5 c. *Callicore patelina*	..	2·00	2·00
386	10 c. *Diaethria astala*	..	1·50	70
387	15 c. *Nessaea aglaura*	..	4·00	3·00
	w. Wmk Crown to right of CA		4·00	
388	16 c. *Prepona pseudojoiceyi*	..	4·00	4·50
389	25 c. *Papilio thoas*	..	4·00	80
	w. Wmk Crown to right of CA		38·00	
390	26 c. *Hamadryas arethusa*	..	2·50	4·25
391	50 c. *Panthiades bathildis*	..	2·75	65
392	$1 *Caligo uranus*	..	6·50	3·50
	w. Wmk Crown to right of CA		38·00	
393	$2 *Heliconius sapho*	..	4·00	1·25
394	$5 *Eurytides philolaus*	..	4·75	4·00
395	$10 *Philaethria dido* (2.1.75)	..	10·00	4·00
	w. Wmk Crown to left of CA (2.8.76)		12·00	9·00
380/95		Set of 16	48·00	32·00

*The normal sideways watermark shows Crown to right of CA on the 16 c. and $10 and to left on the others, *as seen from the back of the stamp.*

See also Nos. 403/13 and 426/33.

85 Churchill when Prime Minister,   86 The Actun Balam
and Coronation Scene   Vase

(Des J.W. Litho Questa)

1974 (30 Nov). *Birth Centenary of Sir Winston Churchill. T 85 and similar horiz design. Multicoloured. W w 14 (sideways). P 14.*

396	50 c. Type 85	..	20	20
397	$1 Churchill in stetson, and Williamsburg Liberty Bell	..	30	30

(Des Mrs. Hosek; adapted P. Powell. Litho Questa)

1975 (2 June). *Mayan Artefacts (2nd series). T 86 and similar vert designs showing decorated vessels. Multicoloured. W w 14. P 14.*

398	3 c. Type 86	..	10	10
399	6 c. Seated figure	..	10	10
400	16 c. Costumed priest	..	25	15
401	26 c. Head with headdress	..	35	20
402	50 c. Layman and priest	..	45	1·00
398/402		Set of 5	1·10	1·40

1975–78. *As Nos. 380, 382/7 and 389 and new value (35 c.), but W w 14 (sideways on ½, 2, 3, 4, 5, 10 and 35 c.). P 14 × 14½ (15, 25 c.) or 14 (others).*

403	½c. Type 84 (11.6.75)	..	2·00	6·50
405	2 c. *Colobura dirce* (17.5.77)	..	50	70
406	3 c. *Catonephele numulia* (17.5.77)	..	1·25	70
407	4 c. *Battus belus* (7.3.77)	..	3·00	30
408	5 c. *Callicore patelina* (11.2.77)	..	3·25	30
409	10 c. *Diaethria astala* (11.2.77)	..	3·25	30
410	15 c. *Nessaea aglaura* (17.5.77)	..	75	70
412	25 c. *Papilio thoas* (27.1.78)	..	1·50	40
413	35 c. Type 84 (25.7.77)	..	11·00	4·50
403/13		Set of 9	24·00	13·00

1975–77. *As Nos. 387, 389, 391 and 394 but W w 12 upright.*

426	15 c. *Nessaea aglaura* (20.10.75)	..	1·00	2·25
428	25 c. *Papilio thoas* (7.3.77)	..	4·50	1·75
429	50 c. *Panthiades bathildis* (7.3.77)	..	5·50	1·75
433	$5 *Eurytides philolaus* (20.10.75)	..	5·50	9·00
	w. Wmk inverted		35·00	
426/33	..	Set of 4	15·00	13·50

87 Musicians

(Des PAD Studio. Litho Harrison)

1975 (17 Nov). *Christmas. T 87 and similar multicoloured designs. W w 12 (upright on 6 c., 26 c.) or sideways (others). P 14 × 14½ (horiz) or 14½ × 14 (vert).*

435	6 c. Type 87	..	10	10
436	26 c. Children and "crib"	..	20	10
	w. Wmk inverted		5·00	3·00
437	50 c. Dancer and drummers (*vert*)	..	30	35
	a. Imperf (pair)		£100	
438	$1 Family and map (*vert*)	..	55	1·10
435/8	..	Set of 4	1·00	1·50

88 William Wrigley Jr. and Chicle Tapping

(Des PAD Studio. Litho Questa)

1976 (29 Mar). *Bicentenary of American Revolution. T **88** and similar horiz designs. Multicoloured. W w **14** (sideways). P **14**.

439	10 c. Type **88**		10	10
440	35 c. Charles Lindbergh and *Spirit of St. Louis*		20	40
441	$1 J. L. Stephens (archaeologist)		50	1·00
439/41		Set of 3	70	1·40

89 Cycling

(Des J.W. Litho Walsall)

1976 (17 July). *Olympic Games. Montreal. T **89** and similar horiz designs. Multicoloured. W w **14** (sideways). P **14**.

442	35 c. Type **89**		15	10
443	45 c. Running		20	15
444	$1 Shooting		35	50
442/4		Set of 3	65	65

(90)   (91)

1976 (30 Aug). *No. 390 surch with T **90** by Harrison.*

445	20 c. on 26 c. *Hamadryas arethusa*		1·50	80

1976 (18 Oct). *West Indian Victory in World Cricket Cup. As Nos. 559/60 of Barbados.*

446	35 c. Map of the Caribbean		50	50
447	$1 The Prudential Cup		1·10	2·00

1976 (2 Dec). *No. 426 surch with T **91** by the Govt Printery, Belize.*

448	5 c. on 15 c. *Nessaea aglaura*		1·50	2·25

92 Queen and Bishops

(Des R. Granger Barrett. Litho Enschedé)

1977 (7 Feb). *Silver Jubilee. T **92** and similar horiz designs. Multicoloured. W w **14** (sideways*). P 13×13½.*

449	10 c. Royal Visit, 1975		10	10
450	35 c. Queen and Rose Window		15	15
	w. Wmk Crown to right of CA		80·00	
451	$2 Type **92**		45	90
	w. Wmk Crown to right of CA		42·00	
449/51		Set of 3	60	1·00

The normal sideways watermark shows Crown to left of CA, as seen from the back of the stamp.

93 Red-capped Manakin   94 Laboratory Workers

(Des and litho J.W.)

1977 (3 Sept). *Birds (1st series). T **93** and similar vert designs. Multicoloured. W w **14**. P **14**.*

452	8 c. Type **93**		75	20
453	10 c. Hooded Oriole		90	25
454	25 c. Blue-crowned Motmot		1·25	55
455	35 c. Slaty-breasted Tinamou		1·50	75
456	45 c. Ocellated Turkey		1·75	1·25
457	$1 White Hawk		3·00	4·25
452/7		Set of 6	8·25	6·50
MS458	110 × 133 mm. Nos. 452/7.		8·25	11·00

See also Nos. 467/73, 488/94 and 561/7.

(Des G. Hutchins. Litho J.W.)

1977 (2 Dec). *75th Anniv of Pan-American Health Organisation. T **94** and similar horiz design. Multicoloured. W w **14** (sideways). P 13½.*

459	35 c. Type **94**		20	20
460	$1 Mobile medical unit		40	65
MS461	126 × 95 mm. Nos. 459/60. P 13		85	1·25

BELIZE DEFENCE FORCE
1ST JANUARY 1978
(95)

1978 (15 Feb). *Establishment of Belize Defence Force. Nos. 409 and 413 optd with T **95** in gold by Govt Printery, Belize.*

462	10 c. *Diaethria astala*		75	50
463	35 c. *Parides arcas*		1·50	1·50

96 White Lion of   97 *Russelia sarmentosa*
    Mortimer

(Des. C. Abbott. Litho Questa)

1978 (21 Apr). *25th Anniv of Coronation (1st issue). T **96** and similar vert designs. P 15.*

464	75 c. bistre, carmine and silver		20	30
	a. Sheetlet. Nos. 464/6 × 2		1·10	
465	75 c. multicoloured		20	30
466	75 c. bistre, carmine and silver		20	30
464/6		Set of 3	55	80

Designs:—No. 464, Type **96**; No. 465, Queen Elizabeth II; No 466, Jaguar (Maya god of Day and Night).

Nos. 464/6 were printed together in small sheets of 6, containing two *se-tenant* strips of 3 with horizontal gutter margin between. See also Nos. 495/503.

(Des. J.W. Litho Questa)

1978 (31 July). *Birds (2nd series). Vert designs as T **93**. Multicoloured. W w **14**. P 14½.*

467	10 c. White-capped Parrot		45	30
468	25 c. Crimson-collared Tanager		90	45
469	35 c. Citreoline Trogon		1·25	55
470	45 c. American Finfoot		1·40	1·75
471	50 c. Muscovy Duck		1·60	2·25
472	$1 King Vulture		2·25	4·00
467/72		Set of 6	7·00	8·50
MS473	111 × 133 mm. Nos. 467/72.		7·00	9·00

(Des. J. Cooter. Litho Questa)

1978 (16 Oct). *Christmas. Wild Flowers and Ferns. T **97** and similar vert designs. Multicoloured. W w **14**. P 14 × 13½.*

474	10 c. Type **97**		15	10
475	15 c. *Lygodium polymorphum*		20	15
476	35 c. *Heliconia aurantiaca*		25	20
477	45 c. *Adiantum tetraphyllum*		30	40
478	50 c. *Angelonia ciliaris*		30	50
479	$1 *Thelypteris obliterata*		50	1·00
474/79		Set of 6	1·50	2·00

98 Fairchild Monoplane of
Internal Airmail Service, 1937

(Des D. Bowen. Litho Questa)

1979 (15 Jan). *Centenary of U.P.U. Membership. T **98** and similar horiz designs. Multicoloured. W w **14** (sideways). P 13½ × 14.*

480	5 c. Type **98**		25	20
481	10 c. *Heron H* (mail boat), 1949		25	10
482	35 c. Internal mail service, 1920 (canoe)		30	20
483	45 c. Stann Creek Railway mail, 1910		60	55
484	50 c. Mounted mail courier, 1882		60	60
485	$2 *Eagle* (mail boat), 1856		1·10	2·25
480/5		Set of 6	2·75	3·50

15¢

(99)   (100)

1979. *No. 413 surch. (a) By typography, locally, with T **99**.*

486	15 c. on 35 c. Type 84 (March)		38·00	

(b) By lithography, in Great Britain, with T **100**

487	15 c. on 35 c. Type 84 (June)		1·25	1·75
	w. Wmk Crown to right of CA		20·00	

The normal sideways watermark shows Crown to left of CA, as seen from the back of the stamp.

(Des J.W. Litho Questa)

1979 (16 Apr). *Birds (3rd series). Vert designs as T **93**. Multicoloured. P 14.*

488	10 c. Boat-billed Heron		40	10
489	25 c. Grey-necked Wood Rail		65	25
490	35 c. Lineated Woodpecker		75	40
491	45 c. Blue-grey Tanager		80	60
492	50 c. Laughing Falcon		80	1·00
493	$1 Long-tailed Hermit		1·25	2·50
488/93		Set of 6	4·25	4·25
MS494	113 × 136 mm. Nos. 488/93.		4·25	6·00

PRINTER. The following issues to No. 742 were printed in lithography by Lito Nacional, Porto, Portugal.

AVAILABILITY. Certain values of some issues to No. 742 were only available in restricted quantities in Belize.

101 Paslow Building, Belize G.P.O.

(Des A. Medina)

1979 (31 May). *25th Anniv of Coronation (2nd issue). T **101** and similar multicoloured designs. P 14.*

495	25 c. Type **101**		40	10
496	50 c. Houses of Parliament		70	10
497	75 c. Coronation State Coach		1·10	10
498	$1 Queen on horseback (vert)		1·50	10
499	$2 Prince of Wales (vert)		2·00	15
500	$3 Queen and Duke of Edinburgh (vert)		2·40	20
501	$4 Portrait of Queen (vert)		3·00	25
502	$5 St. Edward's Crown (vert)		3·50	30
495/502		Set of 8	13·00	1·00
MS503	Two sheets, both 126 × 95 mm: (a) $5 Princess Anne on horseback at Montreal Olympics (vert), $10 Queen at Montreal Olympics (vert); (b) $15 As Type **101**			
		Set of 2 sheets	18·00	

Nos. 495/502 also exist imperforate from a restricted printing (price for set of 8 £15 mint).

102 Mortimer and Vaughan
"Safety" Airplane, 1910

(Des A. Medina)

1979 (30 July). *Death Centenary of Sir Rowland Hill and 60th Anniv of I.C.A.O. (International Civil Aviation Organization, previously International Commission for Air Navigation). T **102** and similar horiz designs. Multicoloured. P 14.*

504	4 c. Type **102**		20	10
505	25 c. Boeing 720		80	20
506	50 c. Concorde		2·25	30
507	75 c. Handley Page H.P.18 W8b (1922)		1·25	30
508	$1 Avro Type F (1912)		1·50	30
509	$1.50, Samuel Cody's biplane (1910)		2·00	30
510	$2 A. V. Roe Triplane I (1909)		2·25	40
511	$3 Santos Dumont's biplane 14 bis		2·50	45
512	$4 Wright Type A		3·00	65
504/12		Set of 9	14·00	2·75
MS513	Two sheets: (a) 115×95 mm. $5 Dunne D-5 (1910), $5 G.B. 1969 Concorde stamp; (b) 130×95 mm. $10 Boeing 720 (different)			
		Set of 2 sheets	20·00	

Nos. 504/12 also exist imperforate from a restricted printing (price for set of 9 £55 mint).

103 Handball   104 Olympic torch

(Des A. Medina)

1979 (10 Oct). *Olympic Games. Moscow* (1980). *T* **103** *and similar vert designs. Multicoloured. P* 14.

514	25 c. Type 103					30	10
515	50 c. Weightlifting					45	10
516	75 c. Athletics					65	10
517	$1 Football					80	10
518	$2 Yachting					1·60	15
519	$3 Swimming					1·90	20
520	$4 Boxing					2·25	25
521	$5 Cycling					3·00	30
514/21					*Set of 8*	10·00	1·00

MS522 Two sheets: (a) 126 × 92 mm. $5 Athletics (*different*), $10 Boxing (*different*); (b) 92 × 126 mm. $15 As $5 .. .. .. *Set of 2 sheets* 16·00

Nos. 514/21 also exist imperforate from a restricted printing (*price for set of 8 £55 mint*).

(Des A. Medina)

1979 (4 Dec). *Winter Olympic Games. Lake Placid* (1980). *T* **104** *and similar vert designs. Multicoloured. P* 14.

523	25 c. Type 104					20	10
524	50 c. Giant slalom					45	15
525	75 c. Figure-skating					65	15
526	$1 Slalom skiing					80	15
527	$2 Speed-skating					1·60	20
528	$3 Cross-country skiing					2·50	30
529	$4 Shooting					3·00	40
530	$5 Gold, Silver and Bronze medals					3·50	45
523/30					*Set of 8*	11·50	1·60

MS531 Two sheets: (a) 127 × 90 mm. $5 Lighting the Olympic Flame, $10 Gold, Silver and Bronze medals (*different*); (b) 90 × 127 mm. $15 Olympic Torch (*different*) .. .. *Set of 2 sheets* 20·00

Nos. 523/30 also exist imperforate from a restricted printing (*price for set of 8 £55 mint*).

105 Measled Cowrie	106 Girl and Flower
(*Cypraea zebra*)	Arrangement

(Des C. Abbott)

1980 (7 Jan). *Shells. Multicoloured designs as T* **105**. *P* 14.

532	1 c. Type 105			30	10
533	2 c. Callico Clam (*Macrocallista maculata*)			35	10
534	3 c. Atlantic Turkey Wing (*Arca zebra*) (*vert*)			40	10
535	4 c. Leafy Jewel Box (*Chama macerophylla*) (*vert*)			50	10
536	5 c. Trochlear Latirus (*Latirus cariniferus*)			50	10
537	10 c. Alphabet Cone (*Conus spurius*) (*vert*)			60	10
538	15 c. Cabrit's Murex (*Murex cabritii*) (*vert*)			90	10
539	20 c. Stiff Pen Shell (*Atrina rigida*) (*vert*)			1·00	10
540	25 c. Little Knobbed Scallop (*Chlamys imbricata*) (*vert*)			1·00	10
541	35 c. Glory of the Atlantic Cone (*Conus granulatus*)			1·25	10
542	45 c. Sunrise Tellin (*Tellina radiata*) (*vert*)			1·50	10
543	50 c. Leucozonia nassa leucozonalis			1·50	10
544	85 c. Triangular Typhis (*Tripterotyphis triangularis*)			2·25	10
545	$1 Queen or Pink Conch (*Strombus gigas*) (*vert*)			2·75	10
546	$2 Rooster-tail Conch (*Strombus gallus*) (*vert*)			4·00	30
547	$5 True Tulip (*Fasciolaria tulipa*)			6·50	75
548	$10 Star Arene (*Arene cruentata*)			8·50	1·25
532/48			*Set of 17*	30·00	2·50

MS549 Two sheets, each 125×90 mm. (a) Nos. 544 and 547; (b) Nos. 546 and 548 .. 23·00 15·00
Imprint dates: "1980", Nos. 532/49; "1981" Nos. 537, 543/5.

(Des A. Medina ($5), C. Mullin (*others*))

1980 (15 Mar). *International Year of the Child* (1st issue). *T* **106** *and similar vert designs. Multicoloured. P* 14.

550	25 c. Type 106			20	10
551	50 c. Boy holding football			30	10
552	75 c. Boy with butterfly			45	10
553	$1 Girl holding doll			60	10
554	$1.50, Boy carrying basket of fruit			95	15
555	$2 Boy holding Reticulated Cowrie-Helmet shell			1·25	20
556	$3 Girl holding posy			1·90	25
557	$4 Boy and girl wrapped in blanket			2·50	30
550/7			*Set of 8*	7·00	1·00

MS558 130×95 mm. $5 Three children of different races. $5 "Madonna with Cat" (A. Dürer) (*each 35×53 mm*). *P* 13 .. 7·00

MS559 111×151 mm. $10 Children and Christmas tree (73×110 *mm*). *P* 13 .. 7·00

Nos. 550/7 also exist imperforate from a restricted printing (*price for set of 8 £35 mint*).
See also Nos. 583/91.

NEW INFORMATION

The editor is always interested to correspond with people who have new information that will improve or correct the Catalogue.

(107)	108 Jabiru

1980 (10 Apr*). *No.* 412 *surch with T* **107**.

560	10 c. on 25 c. *Papilio thoas*			75	1·00
	a. Surch inverted			60·00	

* Earliest known date of use.

(Des J.W. Litho Questa)

1980 (16 June). *Birds* (4th series). *T* **108** *and similar vert designs. Multicoloured. P* 13.

561	10 c. Type 108			5·00	2·75
	a. Sheetlet. Nos. 561/6			32·00	
562	25 c. Barred Antshrike			5·50	2·75
563	35 c. Northern Royal Flycatcher			5·50	2·75
564	45 c. White-necked Puffbird			6·00	3·00
565	50 c. Ornate Hawk-eagle			6·00	3·00
566	$1 Golden-masked Tanager			6·50	3·75
561/6			*Set of 6*	32·00	16·00

MS567 85×90 mm. $2 Type 108, $3 As $1 .. 24·00 17·00

Nos. 561/6 were printed together, *se-tenant* in sheetlets of 6 or in "double" sheetlets of 12. Stamps from the "double" sheetlets have a red frame and red imprint at foot.

109 Speed Skating	(110)

1980 (20 Aug). *Medal Winners, Winter Olympic Games, Lake Placid. T* **109** *and similar vert designs. Multicoloured. P* 14.

568	25 c. Type 109			30	15
569	50 c. Ice hockey			50	15
570	75 c. Figure-skating			60	15
571	$1 Alpine skiing			85	15
572	$1.50, Giant slalom (women)			1·25	25
573	$2 Speed-skating (women)			1·50	30
574	$3 Cross-country skiing			2·25	40
575	$5 Giant slalom			3·50	55
568/75			*Set of 8*	9·75	1·90

MS576 Two sheets: (a) 126 × 91 mm. $5 Type 109; $10 Type 109; (b) 91 × 126 mm. $10 As 75 c. .. .. .. *Set of 2 sheets* 15·00

Nos. 568/75 were each printed in sheets of 30 (6×5) containing stamps in vertical rows 1, 3/4 and 6, and stamp-sized labels in rows 2 and 5.

Nos. 568/75 also exist imperforate from a restricted printing (*price for set of 8 £55 mint*).

1980 (3 Oct). *"ESPAMER" International Stamp Exhibition, Madrid. Nos.* 561/6 *optd* (*Nos.* 577/9) *or surch as T* **110**.

577	10 c. Type 107			3·75	2·50
	a. Sheetlet. Nos. 577/82			24·00	
578	25 c. Barred Antshrike			4·25	2·75
579	35 c. Northern Royal Flycatcher			4·25	2·75
580	40 c. on 45 c. White-necked Puffbird			4·75	3·00
581	40 c. on 50 c. Ornate Hawk-eagle			4·75	3·00
582	40 c. on $1 Golden-masked Tanager			4·75	3·00
577/82			*Set of 6*	24·00	15·00

111 Witch in Sky	112 Queen Elizabeth The Queen Mother

(Des C. Mullin)

1980 (24 Nov). *International Year of the Child* (2nd issue). *Sleeping Beauty. T* **111** *and similar vert designs illustrating the story. P* 14.

583	35 c. multicoloured				40	15
584	40 c. multicoloured				50	15
585	50 c. multicoloured				75	15
586	75 c. multicoloured				90	15
587	$1 multicoloured				1·00	20

588	$1.50, multicoloured				1·60	30
589	$3 multicoloured				2·75	35
590	$4 multicoloured				3·25	45
583/90				*Set of 8*	10·00	1·60

MS591 Two sheets; (a) 82 × 110 mm. $8 "Paumgartner Altar-piece" (Dürer); (b) 110 × 82 mm. $5 Marriage ceremony, $5 Sleeping Beauty and Prince on horseback .. *Set of 2 sheets* 14·00

Nos. 583/90 were printed in a similar sheet format to Nos. 568/75.

Nos. 583/90 also exist imperforate from a restricted printing (*price for set of 8 £55 mint*).

(Des C. Mullen)

1980 (12 Dec). *80th Birthday of Queen Elizabeth the Queen Mother. P* 13.

592	112	$1 multicoloured			1·25	40

MS593 82 ×110 mm, $5 As Type **112** (41 × 32 *mm*) 5·50 4·00

No. 592 exists imperforate from a restricted printing (*price £4.50 mint*).

113 The Annunciation	(114)

(Des C. Mullin)

1980 (30 Dec). *Christmas. T* **113** *and similar vert designs. Multicoloured. P* 14.

594	25 c. Type 113				25	10
595	50 c. Bethlehem				40	10
596	75 c. The Holy Family				65	10
597	$1 The Nativity				80	10
598	$1.50,The flight into Egypt				1·00	15
599	$2 Shepherds following the Star				1·10	20
600	$3 Virgin, Child and Angel				1·60	25
601	$4 Adoration of the Kings				1·90	30
594/601				*Set of 8*	7·00	1·00

MS602 Two sheets, each 82 × 111 mm: (a) $5 As $1; (b) $10 As $3 .. .. .. *Set of 2 sheets* 10·50

Nos. 594/601 were printed in a similar sheet format to Nos. 568/75.

1981 (22 May). *"WIPA" International Stamp Exhibition. Vienna. Nos.* 598 *and* 601/2b *surch with T* **114**.

603	$1 on $1.50, The flight into Egypt			1·50	65
604	$2 on $4 Adoration of the Kings			2·00	1·40

MS605 82 × 111 mm. $2 on $10 Virgin, Child and Angel .. .. 3·25 3·00

115 Paul Harris (founder)	116 Prince of Wales Coat of Arms

1981 (26 May). *75th Anniv of Rotary International. T* **115** *and similar multicoloured designs. P* 14.

606	25 c. Type 115				55	25
607	50 c. Emblems of Rotary activities				80	35
608	$1 75th Anniversary emblem				1·40	65
609	$1.50, Educational scholarship programme (*horiz*)				2·00	1·00
610	$2 "Project Hippocrates"				2·25	1·40
611	$3 Emblems (*horiz*)				3·00	2·00
612	$5 Emblem and handshake (*horiz*)				4·00	3·25
606/12				*Set of 7*	12·50	8·00

MS613 Two sheets: (a) 95 × 130 mm. $10 As 50 c.; (b) 130 × 95 mm, $5 As $1, $10 As $2 .. .. *Set of 2 sheets* 24·00

*Nos. 606/13, together with a 75 c. value showing a map, were originally issued on 30 March 1981, but were withdrawn from sale after two hours as there were objections to the colours used on the map. The stamps, without the offending 75 c., were reissued on 26 May. First Day covers carry the later date and there are no reports of examples used before 26 May.

(Des C. Mullin)

1981 (16 July). *Royal Wedding. T* **116** *and similar vert designs. Multicoloured.* (a) *Size* 22 × 38 *mm* (*from sheets of 27*). *P* 13½ × 14.

614	50 c. Type 116			35	40
	a. Horiz pair. Nos. 614/15			1·10	
615	$1 Prince Charles in military uniform			70	75
	a. Horiz pair. Nos. 615/16			1·90	
616	$1.50, Royal couple			1·10	1·25

(b) *Size 25 × 42 mm with gold borders (sheets of 6 stamps and 3 labels). P 13.*

617	50 c. Type **116**	..	..	..	35	15
618	$1 As No. 615	..	..	..	70	35
619	$1.50, As No. 616	..	..	..	1·10	45
614/19				*Set of 6*	3·75	3·00
MS620	145 × 85 mm. $3 × 3 As Nos 614/16, but					
	30 × 47 mm. P 14	..	..	..	2·50	4·25

Nos. 614/16 were each printed in blocks of 9 (3 × 3), the blocks *se-tenant* within the sheet.
Nos. 614/16 also exist imperforate from a restricted printing (*price for set of 3 £4 mint*).

(117)

1981 (22 Aug). *No. 538 surch with T* **117.**

621	10 c. on 15 c. Cabrit's Murex (*Murex cabritii*)			2·25	2·25
	a. Surch double	..	..	..	†	—

For a similar surcharge, but with rectangular obliterating panel see No. 728.

118 Athletics

(Des C. Mullin)

1981 (14 Sept). *History of the Olympic Games. T* **118** *and similar vert designs. Multicoloured. P 14.*

622	85 c. Type **118**	..	..	..	1·10	20
623	$1 Cycling	..	..	..	1·75	30
624	$1.50, Boxing	..	..	..	2·00	30
625	$2 1984 Games–Los Angeles and Sarajevo			2·25	30
626	$3 Baron Pierre de Coubertin	..	..	3·25	45
627	$5 Olympic Flame	..	..	..	4·50	60
622/7				*Set of 6*	13·50	1·75
MS628	Two sheets, each 175 × 123 mm: (a) $5 As					
	$3, $10 As $5 (*each 35 × 53 mm*). P 13½; (b) $15					
	As $2 (45 × 67 *mm*). P 14½ .. *Set of 2 sheets* 26·00					

The two miniature sheets of No. **MS628** also exist with the stamps and borders printed in gold from a restricted printing.

INDEPENDENCE

Independence
21 Sept.,1981 $1

(119)   (120)

1981 (21 Sept). *Independence Commemoration (1st issue). Optd as T* **119** *by Benex Press, Belize City.* (a) *On Nos. 532/44 and 546/9.*

629	1 c. Type **119**	..	..	..	20	10
630	2 c. Callico Clam (*Macrocallista maculata*)		20	10
631	3 c. Atlantic Turkey Wing (*Arca zebra*)				
	(*vert*) ..	..	..	..	25	10
632	4 c. Leafy Jewel Box (*Chama macero-phylla*) (*vert*) ..	..	..	25	10
	a. Opt inverted					
633	5 c. Trochlear Latirus (*Latirus cariniferus*)		25	10
634	10 c. Alphabet Cone (*Conus spurius*) (*vert*)		30	10
	a. Opt inverted					
635	15 c. Cabrit's Murex (*Murex cabritii*) (*vert*)		60	10
636	20 c. Stiff Pen Shell (*Atrina rigida*)	..		70	15
637	25 c. Little Knobbed Scallop (*Chlamys imbricata*) (*vert*)	..		80	25
638	35 c. Glory of the Atlantic Cone (*Conus granulatus*)	..	..		90	30
639	45 c. Sunrise Tellin (*Tellina radiata*) (*vert*)		1·25	40
640	50 c. *Leucozonia nassa leucozonalis*	..		1·25	40
641	85 c. Triangular Typhis (*Tripterotyphis triangularis*) ..	..	..		2·25	90
	a. Opt inverted					
642	$2 Rooster-tail Conch (*Strombus gallus*) (*vert*) ..	..	..		5·00	2·50
643	$5 True Tulip (*Fasciolaria tulipa*)	..		8·00	5·50
	a. Opt inverted				†	—
644	$10 Star Arene (*Arene cruentata*)	..		12·00	9·50
629/44				*Set of 16*	30·00	18·00
MS645	Two sheets, each 126 × 91 mm: (a) Nos. 641					
	and 643; (b) Nos. 642 and 644 .. *Set of 2 sheets* 20·00					

On the vertical designs and the miniature sheets the overprint is in roman type.
The 10 c. exists with either "1980" or "1981" imprint date.
Examples of the miniature sheets have been seen showing forged overprints apparently applied by rubber handstamp.

(b) *On Nos. 606/13*

646	25 c. Type **115** (Gold)	..	..		60	25
	a. Opt double					
647	50 c. Emblems of Rotary activities	..		90	35
648	$1 75th Anniversary emblem	..		1·25	65

649	$1.50, Educational scholarship programme		1·75	1·25
650	$2 "Project Hippocrates" (Gold)	..		2·25	1·60
651	$3 Emblems	..	..	..	3·25	2·50
652	$5 Emblems and handshake	..		5·00	3·75
646/52			*Set of 7*	13·50	9·25
MS653	Two sheets: (a) 95 × 130 mm. $10 As 50 c.;			
	(b) 130 × 95 mm. $5 As $1, $10 As $2 (Gold)			
			Set of 2 sheets 22·00		

See also Nos. 657/63.

1981 (13 Nov). *"ESPAMER" International Stamp Exhibition, Buenos Aires. Nos. 609 and MS613b surch with T* **120.**

654	$1 on $1.50, Educational scholarship			
	programme	..	..	2·25	1·75
MS655	95 × 130 mm. $1 on $5 75th anniversary			
	emblem, $1 on $10 "Project Hippocrates"..		5·00	4·25

14 · 18 · XI . 1981

(121)

1981 (14 Nov). *"Philatelia 81" International Stamp Exhibition, Frankfurt. No.* **MS**549 *surch with T* **121** *in red.*

MS656 Two sheets, each 125 × 90 mm: (a) $1 on 85 c. *Tripterotyphis triangularis*, $1 on $5 *Fasciolaria tulipa*; (b) $1 on $2 *Strombus gallus*. $1 on $10 *Arene cruentata* .. *Set of 2 sheets* 26·00

122 Black Orchid   123 Uruguayan Footballer

(Des C. Mullin)

1981 (18 Dec)–**82**. *Independence Commemoration (2nd issue) T* **122** *and similar multicoloured designs. P 14.*

657	10 c. Belize Coat of Arms (*horiz*) (10.2.82)	..		50	10
658	35 c. Map of Belize (10.2.82)	..	..		1·25	30
659	50 c. Type **122**	..	..	..	3·75	80
660	85 c. Baird's Tapir (*horiz*)	..	..		1·50	1·00
661	$1 Mahogany Tree	..	..	..	1·75	1·10
662	$2 Keel-billed Toucan (*horiz*)	..	..		6·00	2·75
657/62				*Set of 6*	13·00	5·50
MS663	130 × 98 mm. $5 As 10 c. P 14½ (10.2.82)		6·00	4·00

(Des C. Mullin)

1981 (28 Dec). *World Cup Football Championship, Spain (1st issue). T* **123** *and similar vert designs. Multicoloured. P 14.*

664	10 c. Type **123**	..	..	..	1·10	20
665	25 c. Italian footballer	..	..		1·75	20
666	50 c. German footballer	..	..		2·50	30
667	$1 Brazilian footballer	..	..		3·25	40
668	$1.50, Argentinian footballer	..		3·75	70
669	$2 English footballer	..	..		4·00	80
664/9				*Set of 6*	14·50	2·40
MS670	Two sheets: (a) 145 × 115 mm. $2 "SPAIN					
	'82" logo; (b) 155 × 115 mm. $3 Footballer					
	(46 × 76 *mm*) .. *Set of 2 sheets* 12·00			4·75		

See also Nos. 721/7.

124 British 19th-century Warship

(Des C. Mullin)

1982 (15 Mar). *Sailing Ships. T* **124** *and similar horiz designs. Multicoloured. P 14.*

671	10 c. Type **124**	..	..	..	1·50	35
672	25 c. Madagascar (1837)	..	..		2·50	45
673	35 c. Brig *Whitby* (1838)	..	..		2·75	50
674	50 c. China (1838)	..	..	..	3·25	75
675	85 c. Swiftsure (1850)	..	..		4·25	1·10
676	$2 Windsor Castle (1857)	..	..		7·00	2·00
671/6				*Set of 6*	18·00	4·75
MS677	110 × 87 mm. $5 Ships in battle ..			18·00	6·50

NEW INFORMATION

The editor is always interested to correspond with people who have new information that will improve or correct the Catalogue.

(125)   126 Princess Diana

1982 (28 Apr). *"ESSEN '82" International Stamp Exhibition, West Germany. Nos. 662 and 669 surch with T* **125.**

678	$1 on $2 Keel-billed Toucan	..	..		3·00	1·00
679	$1 on $2 English footballer ..	..	..		3·00	1·00

(Des C. Mullin)

1982 (20 May). *21st Birthday of Princess of Wales. T* **126** *and similar vert designs showing portrait of Princess of Wales with different backgrounds.* (a) *Size 22 × 38 mm (from sheets of 25).* P 13½ × 14.

680	50 c. multicoloured	..	..		25	35
	a. *Tête-bêche* (pair) ..				50	
681	$1 multicoloured	..	..		35	65
	a. *Tête-bêche* (pair) ..				70	
682	$1.50, multicoloured	..	..		50	1·00
	a. *Tête-bêche* (pair) ..				1·00	

(b) *Size 25 × 43 mm (from sheets of 6 stamps and 3 labels). P 13*

683	50 c. multicoloured	..	..		25	10
684	$1 multicoloured	..	..		35	20
685	$1.50, multicoloured	..	..		50	25
680/5				*Set of 6*	2·00	2·25
MS686	145 × 85 mm. $3 × 3 As Nos. 680/2, but					
	30 × 47 mm. P 14 ..	..			2·75	3·00

Stamps as Nos. 680/2, size 30×47 mm and perforated 14, exist from a limited printing. These have gold backgrounds to the central ovals and gold frames. In addition the Queen's head and the centre oval are embossed (*Price per set of 3 £7 mint*).

127 Lighting Camp-fire

(Des C. Mullin)

1982 (31 Aug). *125th Birth Anniv of Lord Baden-Powell. T* **127** *and similar horiz designs. Multicoloured. P 14.*

687	10 c. Type **127**	..	..		60	20
688	25 c. Bird watching	..	..		1·25	25
689	35 c. Three scouts, one playing guitar	..		1·25	30
690	50 c. Hiking	..	..	..	1·50	55
691	85 c. Scouts with flag	..	..		2·00	90
692	$2 Saluting	..	..	..	3·00	2·25
687/92				*Set of 6*	8·75	4·00
MS693	Two sheets: each 85 × 115 mm: (a) $2 Scout					
	with flag; (b) $3 Portrait of Lord Baden-Powell					
			Set of 2 sheets	12·00	8·00	

128 *Gorgonia ventalina*

(Des C. Mullin)

1982 (20 Sept). *First Anniv of Independence. Marine Life. T* **128** *and similar horiz designs. P 14.*

694	10 c. Type **128**	..	..		90	20
695	35 c. Carpiuis corallinus	..	..		2·00	20
696	50 c. Plexaura flexuasa	..	..		2·25	35
697	85 c. Candylactis gigantea	..	..		3·00	50
698	$1 Stenopus hispidus	..	..		3·25	70
699	$2 Sergeant Major ("Abudefduf saxatilis")	..		4·00	1·05
694/9				*Set of 6*	14·00	2·75
MS700	130×98 mm. $5 Schyllarides aequino-clialis. P 14½	..	..		16·00	7·00

(129)

982 (1 Oct). *"BELGICA 82" International Stamp Exhibition, Brussels. Nos 687/92 optd as T 129 in gold.*
01	10 c. Type 127		60	30
02	25 c. Bird watching		1·60	75
03	35 c. Three scouts, one playing guitar		2·00	1·00
04	50 c. Hiking		2·50	1·50
05	85 c. Scouts with flag		4·00	2·50
06	$2 Saluting		9·00	6·50
01/6		Set of 6	18·00	11·50

BIRTH OF H.R.H.

PRINCE WILLIAM ARTHUR PHILIP LOUIS 21ST JUNE 1982

(130)   131 Scotland v New Zealand

982 (21 Oct). *Birth of Prince William of Wales (1st issue). Nos. 680/6 optd as T 130 in silver. (a) Size 22 × 38 mm.*
07	50 c. multicoloured		25	35
	a. Tête-bêche (pair)		50	
	b. Opt double		55·00	
08	$1 multicoloured		35	50
	a. Tête-bêche (pair)		70	
09	$1.50, multicoloured		50	75
	a. Tête-bêche (pair)		1·00	
	(b) Size 25 × 43 mm			
10	50 c. multicoloured		25	35
	a. Opt double			
11	$1 multicoloured		35	50
12	$1.50, multicoloured		50	75
07/12		Set of 6	2·00	2·75
MS713	145 × 85 mm. $3 × 3 As Nos. 707/9, but 30 × 47 mm.		3·25	3·50

A similar overprint exists on the stamps from the limited printing described beneath No. MS686 (*Price per set of 3 £4 mint*).

982 (25 Oct). *Birth of Prince William of Wales (2nd issue). Nos 614/20 optd as T 130 in gold (a) Size 22 × 38 mm.*
714	50 c. Type 116		2·50	1·00
	a. Horiz pair. Nos. 714/15		7·50	
715	$1 Prince Charles in military uniform		5·00	2·00
	a. Horiz pair. Nos. 715/16		12·50	
716	$1.50, Royal couple		7·50	3·00
	(b) Size 25 × 42 mm			
717	50 c. Type 116		35	35
718	$1 As No. 715		70	70
719	$1.50, As No. 716		1·10	1·10
714/9		Set of 6	16·00	7·25
MS720	145 × 85 mm. $3 × 3 As Nos. 714/16 but 30 × 47 mm.		7·00	7·00

No. MS720 occurs with two different sizes of overprint. On the normal version the top line of the overprint, "BIRTH OF H.R.H." measures 19½ mm in length. On examples with the larger overprint this measures 22 mm. (*Price for miniature sheet with larger overprint £30 mint*).

(Des Baumann)

982 (10 Dec). *World Cup Football Championship, Spain (2nd issue). T 131 and similar horiz designs. Multicoloured. P 14.*
721	20 c. + 10 c. Type 131		80	65
722	30 c. + 15 c. Scotland v New Zealand (*different*)		90	65
723	40 c. + 20 c. Kuwait v France		1·00	65
724	60 c. + 30 c. Italy v Brazil		1·60	85
725	$1 + 50 c. France v Northern Ireland		2·50	1·10
726	$1.50 + 75 c. Austria v Chile		3·00	1·40
721/6		Set of 6	8·75	4·75
MS727	Two sheets: (a) 91 × 137 mm. $1 + 50 c. Germany v Italy (50 × 70 mm); (b) 122 × 116 mm. $2 + $1 England v France (50 × 70 mm)			
		Set of 2 sheets	7·50	5·50

10c

(132)   133 Belize Cathedral

1983 (28 Jan). *No. 538 surch with T 132.*
728	10 c. on 15 c. *Murex cabritii*			

No. 728 differs from the previous provisional, No. 621, in the size of the obliterating panel over the original face value. On No. 621 this measures 4½ × 4½ mm, but No. 728 shows it larger, 7 × 5½ mm.

1983 (7 March). *Visit of Pope John Paul II. P 13½.*
729	133 50 c. multicoloured		2·00	90
MS730	135 × 110 mm. $2.50, Pope John Paul II (30 × 47 mm). P 14		7·00	4·25

STANLEY GIBBONS STAMP COLLECTING SERIES

Introductory booklets on *How to Start, How to Identify Stamps* and *Collecting by Theme*. A series of well illustrated guides at a low price.
Write for details.

    10c

134 Map of Belize   (135)

1983 (14 Mar). *Commonwealth Day. T 134 and similar multi-coloured designs. P 13.*
731	35 c. Type 134		35	35
732	50 c. "Maya Stella" from Lamanai Indian church (*horiz*)		50	50
733	85 c. Supreme Court Building (*horiz*)		60	75
734	$2 University Centre, Belize (*horiz*)		1·25	2·00
731/4		Set of 4	2·40	3·25

1983 (15 Apr). *No. 658 surch with T 135.*
735	10 c. on 35 c. Map of Belize			

136 De Lana-Terzi's "Aerial Ship", 1670

(Des C. Mullin)

1983 (16 May). *Bicentenary of Manned Flight. T 136 and similar horiz designs. Multicoloured. P 14.*
736	10 c. Type 136		90	30
737	25 c. De Gusmao's *La Passarola*, 1709		1·50	40
738	50 c. Guyton de Morveau's balloon with oars, 1784		1·75	70
739	85 c. Early airship		2·25	1·10
740	$1 Airship *Clement Bayard*		2·50	1·50
741	$1.50, Beardmore airship R-34		2·75	2·25
736/41		Set of 6	10·50	5·50
MS742	Two sheets: (a) 125×84 mm. $3 Charles Green's balloon *Royal Vauxhall*; (b) 115×128 mm. $3 Montgolfier balloon, 1783 (*vert*)			
		Set of 2 sheets	10·00	4·50

$1.25

 $1.25

(137)   (138)

1983 (9 June). *Nos. 662 and 699 surch with T 137/8.*
743	$1.25 on $2 Keel-billed Toucan (surch T 137)		5·00	6·00
	a. Surch double		†	—
744	$1.25 on $2 Sergeant Major (surch T 138)		6·00	7·00

 10C   10C

(139)   (140)

1983 (28 Sept). *No. 541 surch with T 139/40.*
745	10 c. on 35 c. Glory of the Atlantic Cone (*Conus granulatus*) (surch T 139)		28·00	
	a. Surch inverted		38·00	
	b. Vert pair, lower stamp without "10 c"			
746	10 c. on 35 c. Glory of the Atlantic Cone (*Conus granulatus*) (surch T 140)		25·00	
	a. Surch triple		25·00	

141 Altun Ha

(Des G. Vasarhelyi. Litho Format)

1983 (14 Nov). *Maya Monuments. T 141 and similar horiz designs. Multicoloured. P 13½ × 14.*
747	10 c. Type 141		10	10
748	15 c. Xunantunich		10	10
749	75 c. Cerros		30	40
750	$2 Lamanai		70	80
747/50		Set of 4	1·00	1·25
MS751	102 × 72 mm. $3 Xunantunich (*different*)		1·00	1·75

Nos. 747/50 exist imperforate from stock dispersed by the liquidator of Format International Security Printers Ltd.

142 Belmopan Earth Station

(Des G. Vasarhelyi. Litho Format)

1983 (28 Nov). *World Communications Year. T 142 and similar horiz designs. Multicoloured. P 14.*
752	10 c. Type 142		30	10
753	15 c. *Telstar 2*		40	25
754	75 c. U.P.U. logo		1·25	1·75
755	$2 M.V. *Heron H* mail service		2·75	4·00
752/5		Set of 4	4·25	5·50

Nos. 752/5 exist imperforate from stock dispersed by the liquidator of Format International Security Printers Ltd.

143 Jaguar Cub

(Des G. Vasarhelyi. Litho Format)

1983 (9 Dec). *The Jaguar. T 143 and similar horiz designs. Multi-coloured. P 14.*
756	5 c. Type 143		30	25
757	10 c. Adult Jaguar		35	20
758	85 c. Jaguar in river		1·75	2·00
759	$1 Jaguar on rock		2·00	2·50
756/9		Set of 4	4·00	4·50
MS760	102 × 72 mm. $3 Jaguar in tree (44 × 28 mm). P 13½ × 14		2·50	2·50

Nos. 756/9 exist imperforate from stock dispersed by the liquidator of Format International Security Printers Ltd.

144 Pope John Paul II

(Des G. Vasarhelyi. Litho Format)

1983 (22 Dec). *Christmas. T 144 and similar designs showing Pope John Paul II at Papal Mass on 11 March 1983 in Belize. P 13½ × 14.*
761	10 c. multicoloured		25	10
762	15 c. multicoloured		25	10
763	75 c. multicoloured		60	60
764	$2 multicoloured		1·25	1·40
761/4		Set of 4	2·10	2·00
MS765	102 × 72 mm. $3 multicoloured		2·75	3·50

145 Four-eyed Butterflyfish

(Des G. Drummond. Litho Format)

1984 (27 Feb)–88. *Marine Life from the Belize Coral Reef. T 145 and similar horiz designs. Multicoloured. A. P 15. B. P 13½ (7.88).*
			A		B	
766	1 c. Type 145		15	20	†	
767	2 c. Cushion Star		20	30	—	
768	3 c. Flower Coral		25	30	†	
769	4 c. Royal Gramma ("Fairy Basslet")		25	30	†	
770	5 c. Spanish Hogfish		30	30	†	
771	6 c. Star-eyed Hermit Crab		30	30	†	
772	10 c. Sea Fans and Fire Sponge		70	40	35	35
773	15 c. Blue-headed Wrasse		80	70	50	60
774	25 c. Blue-striped Grunt		1·00	80	70	80
775	50 c. Coral Crab		2·00	1·50	1·25	1·25
776	60 c. Tube Sponge		2·00	1·50	1·25	1·75
777	75 c. Brain Coral		1·00	1·00	†	
778	$1 Yellow-tailed Snapper		1·25	1·25	1·50	2·00
779	$2 Common Lettuce Slug		1·75	1·25		
780	$5 Three-spotted Damselfish		2·00	1·75	†	
781	$10 Rock Beauty		3·00	5·00	†	
766A/81A		Set of 16	15·00	15·00		
772B/8B		Set of 6 (ex 2 c.)			5·00	6·50

Nos. 766/81 exist imperforate from stock dispersed by the liquidator of Format International Security Printers Ltd. Other values exist perforated 13½, but there is no evidence for their contemporary postal use.

Nos. 776A and 778A exist overprinted to commemorate the anniversary of Hurricane Hattie. These stamps were not issued, but exist from stock dispersed by the liquidator.

VISIT OF THE LORD ARCHBISHOP OF CANTERBURY 8th–11th MARCH 1984

(146)

1984 (8 Mar). *Visit of the Archbishop of Canterbury. Nos. 772A and 775A optd with T 146.*

782	10 c. Sea Fans and Fire Sponge		75	40
783	50 c. Coral Crab	.. ..	1·50	1·00

147 Shooting

(Des G. Vasarhelyi. Litho Format)

1984 (30 Apr). *Olympic Games, Los Angeles, (a) Sheet stamps. T 147 and similar horiz designs. Multicoloured. P 13½ × 14.*

784	25 c. Type **147**	..	30	25
785	75 c. Boxing	..	70	70
786	$1 Marathon	..	90	90
787	$2 Cycling	..	1·75	2·00
784/7		Set of 4	3·25	3·50
MS788	101 × 72 mm. $3 Statue of Discus-thrower	2·10	2·75

(b) Booklet stamps. Similar designs to T 147 but Royal cypher replaced by Queen's head. P 14½.

789	5 c. 1896 Marathon	..	15	30
	a. Booklet pane. No. 789 × 4		55	
790	20 c. Sprinting	..	25	50
	a. Booklet pane. No. 790 × 4		90	
791	25 c. Shot-putting	..	25	50
	a. Booklet pane. No. 791 × 4		90	
792	$2 Olympic torch	..	35	80
	a. Booklet pane. No. 792 × 4		1·25	
789/92		Set of 4	90	1·90

148 British Honduras 1866 1s. Stamp

149 Prince Albert

(Des G. Vasarhelyi. Litho Format)

1984 (26 Sept). *"Ausipex" International Stamp Exhibition, Melbourne. T 148 and similar horiz designs. Multicoloured. P 14 × 13½ ($2) or 15 (others).*

793	15 c. Type **148**..	..	15	15
794	30 c. Bath mail coach, 1784 ..	..	25	25
795	65 c. Sir Rowland Hill and Penny Black	..	55	65
796	75 c. British Honduras railway locomotive, 1910	..	65	75
797	$2 Royal Exhibition Buildings, Melbourne (46 × 28 mm)	..	1·50	2·00
793/7		Set of 5	2·75	3·50
MS798	103 × 73 mm. $3 Australia 1932 Sydney Harbour Bridge 5s. and British Honduras 1866 1s. stamps (44 × 28 mm). P 13½ × 14		1·40	2·00

(Des G. Vasarhelyi. Litho Format)

1984 (15 Oct). *500th Anniv of British Royal House of Tudor (1985). T 149 and similar vert designs showing members of the Royal Family. Multicoloured. P 14.*

799	50 c. Type **149**	..	25	35
	a. Sheetlet. Nos. 799/800 × 2		90	
800	50 c. Queen Victoria	..	25	35
801	75 c. King George VI	..	35	45
	a. Sheetlet. Nos. 801/2 × 2..		1·25	
802	75 c. Queen Elizabeth the Queen Mother	..	35	45
803	$1 Princess of Wales	..	50	70
	a. Sheetlet. Nos. 803/4 × 2..		1·75	
804	$1 Prince of Wales	..	50	70
799/804		Set of 6	2·00	2·75
MS805	147 × 97 mm. $1.50, Prince Philip; $1.50, Queen Elizabeth II		1·25	2·00

Nos. 799/804 were only issued in sheetlets of four stamps of one value, two of each design, with an illustrated vertical gutter margin

OMNIBUS ISSUES

Details, together with prices for complete sets, of the various Omnibus issues from the 1935 Silver Jubilee series to date are included in a special section following Zimbabwe at the end of Volume 2.

150 White-fronted Amazon

151 Effigy Censer, 1450 (Santa Rita Site)

(Des. G. Vasarhelyi. Litho Format)

1984 (1 Nov). *Parrots. T 150 and similar multicoloured designs. P 11.*

806	$1 Type **150**	..	1·50	1·50
	a. Block of 4. Nos. 806/9	..	5·50	
807	$1 White-capped Parrot (horiz)	..	1·50	1·50
808	$1 Mealy Amazon (horiz)	..	1·50	1·50
809	$1 Red-lored Amazon	..	1·50	1·50
806/9		Set of 4	5·50	5·50
MS810	102 × 73 mm. $3 Scarlet Macaw. P 13½ × 14	3·25	3·75

Nos. 806/9 were issued together, *se-tenant*, in blocks of 4 throughout the sheet, each block forming a composite design.

Nos. 806/9 exist imperforate from stock dispersed by the liquidator of Format International Security Printers Ltd.

(Des G. Vasarhelyi. Litho Format)

1984 (30 Nov). *Maya Artefacts. T 151 and similar vert designs. Multicoloured. P 15.*

811	25 c. Type **151**	..	25	25
812	75 c. Vase, 675 (Actun Chapat)	..	50	70
813	$1 Tripod Vase, 500 (Santa Rita site)	..	65	90
814	$2 Sun god Kinich Ahau, 600 (Altun Ha site)	1·40	2·25
811/14		Set of 4	2·50	3·75

152 Governor-General inspecting Girl Guides

153 White-tailed Kite

(Des R. Granger Barrett. Litho Format)

1985 (15 Mar). *International Youth Year and 75th Anniv of Girl Guide Movement. T 152 and similar horiz designs. Multicoloured. P 15.*

815	25 c. Type **152**..	..	30	30
816	50 c. Girl Guides camping	..	45	45
817	90 c. Checking map on hike ..	..	60	65
818	$1.25, Students in laboratory	..	70	80
819	$2 Lady Baden-Powell (founder)	..	90	1·10
815/19		Set of 5	2·75	3·00

(Des G. Vasarhelyi. Litho Format ($1, $5) Questa (others))

1985 (30 May)–**88**. *Birth Bicentenary of John J. Audubon (ornithologist). T 153 and similar multicoloured designs showing original paintings. P 15 ($1) or 14 (others).*

820	10 c. Type **153**..	..	70	30
821	15 c. Ruby-crowned Kinglet (horiz) ..	..	90	30
822	25 c. Painted Bunting	..	1·25	40
822a	60 c. As 25 c. (1988)	..	6·50	6·50
823	75 c. Belted Kingfisher	..	1·75	1·25
824	$1 Common Cardinal	..	1·75	2·00
825	$3 Long-billed Curlew (horiz)	..	3·00	3·50
820/5		Set of 7	14·00	11·00
MS826	139 × 99 mm. $5 "John James Audubon" (John Syme). P 13½ × 14..		3·00	3·25

154 The Queen Mother with Princess Elizabeth, 1928

INAUGURATION OF NEW GOVERNMENT – 21st. DECEMBER 1984

(155)

(Des G. Vasarhelyi. Litho Format)

1985 (20 June). *Life and Times of Queen Elizabeth the Queen Mother. T 154 and similar multicoloured designs. P 13½ × 14.*

827	10 c. Type **154**.	..	10	10
828	15 c. The Queen Mother, 1980	..	10	10
829	75 c. Waving to the crowd, 1982	..	40	40
830	$5 Four generations of Royal Family at Prince William's Christening ..		1·50	2·75
827/30		Set of 4	1·75	3·00
MS831	Two sheets, each 138 × 98 mm. (a) $2 The Queen Mother with Prince Henry (from photo by Lord Snowdon) (38 × 50 mm): (b) $5 The Queen Mother, 1984 (38 × 50 mm) .. Set of 2 sheets		3·75	4·50

1985 (24 June). *Inauguration of New Government. Nos. 772A/3A and 775A optd with T 155.*

832	10 c. Sea Fans and Fire Sponge	..	65	20
833	15 c. Blue-headed Wrasse ..		85	35
834	50 c. Coral Crab	..	1·50	2·00
832/4		Set of 3	2·75	2·25

156 British Honduras 1935 Silver Jubilee 25 c. stamp and King George V with Queen Mary in Carriage

(Des Harrison. Litho Format)

1985 (25 July). *50th Anniv of First Commonwealth Omnibus Issue. T 156 and similar horiz designs showing British Honduras/Belize stamps. Multicoloured. P 14.*

835	50 c. Type **156**	..	40	45
	a. Sheetlet. Nos. 835/44		3·50	
836	50 c. 1937 Coronation 3 c., and King George VI and Queen Elizabeth in Coronation robes	..	40	45
837	50 c. 1946 Victory 3 c., and Victory celebrations	..	40	45
838	50 c. 1948 Royal Silver Wedding 4 c., and King George VI and Queen Elizabeth at Westminster Abbey service	..	40	45
839	50 c. 1953 Coronation 4 c., and Queen Elizabeth II in Coronation robes	..	40	45
840	50 c. 1966 Churchill 25 c., Sir Winston Churchill and fighter aircraft ..		40	45
841	50 c. 1972 Royal Silver Wedding 50 c., and 1948 Wedding photograph	..	40	45
842	50 c. 1973 Royal Wedding 50 c., and Princess Anne and Capt. Mark Phillips at their Wedding..		40	45
843	50 c. 1977 Silver Jubilee $2, and Queen Elizabeth II during tour	..	40	45
844	50 c. 1978 25th anniv of Coronation 75 c. and Imperial Crown..		40	45
835/44		Set of 10	3·50	4·00
MS845	138 × 98 mm. $5 Queen Elizabeth II in Coronation robes (38 × 50 mm). P 13½ × 14 ..	4·50	4·50

Nos. 835/44 were printed together, *se-tenant*, in sheetlets of 10.

157 Mounted Postboy and Early Letter to Belize

COMMONWEALTH SUMMIT CONFERENCE, BAHAMAS 16th–22nd OCTOBER 1985

(158)

(Des G. Drummond. Litho Format)

1985 (1 Aug). *350th Anniv of the British Post Office. T 157 and similar horiz designs. Multicoloured. P 15.*

846	10 c. Type **157**	..	40	15
847	15 c. Hinchinbrook II (sailing packet) engaging Grand Turk (American privateer)	..	55	25
848	25 c. Duke of Marlborough II (sailing packet)		70	30
849	75 c. Diana (packet)	..	1·25	1·50
850	$1 Falmouth packet ship	..	1·50	1·75
851	$3 Conway (mail paddle-steamer)	..	3·75	4·50
846/51		Set of 6	7·25	7·25

A $5 miniature sheet was prepared, but not issued. Examples exist from stock dispersed by the liquidator of Format International Security Printers Ltd.

1985 (5 Sept). *Commonwealth Heads of Government Meeting, Nassau, Bahamas. Nos. 827/31 optd with T 158 in silver.*

852	10 c. Type **154**.	..	20	20
853	15 c. The Queen Mother, 1980	..	25	25
854	75 c. Waving to the crowd, 1980	..	60	70
855	$5 Four generations of Royal Family at Prince William's christening ..		2·50	3·50
852/5		Set of 4	3·25	4·25
MS856	Two sheets, each 138 × 98 mm. (a) $2 The Queen Mother with Prince Henry (from photo by Lord Snowdon) (38 × 50 mm): (b) $5 The Queen Mother, 1984 (38 × 50 mm) .. Set of 2 sheets		4·00	4·50

80TH ANNIVERSARY OF ROTARY INTERNATIONAL

(159)

160 Royal Standard and Belize Flag

1985 (25 Sept). *80th Anniv of Rotary International. Nos. 815/19 optd with T 159.*

357	25 c. Type 152.		50	30
358	50 c. Girl Guides camping		80	75
359	90 c. Checking map on hike		1·25	1·60
360	$1·25, Students in laboratory		1·75	2·25
361	$2 Lady Baden-Powell (founder)		2·25	2·75
357/61		*Set of 5*	6·00	7·00

(Des G. Vasarhelyi. Litho Format)

1985 (9 Oct). *Royal Visit. T 160 and similar multicoloured designs. P 15 × 14½.*

362	25 c. Type 160.		55	95
	a. Horiz strip of 3. Nos. 862/4		4·25	
363	75 c. Queen Elizabeth II		1·25	2·00
364	$4 Royal Yacht *Britannia* (81 × 39 mm)		3·00	3·25
362/4		*Set of 3*	4·25	5·50
MS865	138 × 98 mm. $5 Queen Elizabeth II (38 × 50 mm). P 13½ × 14		5·50	4·75

Nos. 862/4 were printed together, *se-tenant*, in horizontal strips of 3 within small sheets of 9 stamps.

161 Mountie in Canoe (Canada)

(Des Walt Disney Productions. Litho Format)

1985 (1 Nov). *Christmas. 30th Anniv of Disneyland, U.S.A. T 161 and similar vert designs showing dolls from "It's a Small World" exhibition. Multicoloured. P 11.*

866	1 c. Type 161.		10	10
867	2 c. Indian chief and squaw (U.S.A.)		10	10
868	3 c. Incas climbing Andes (South America)		10	10
869	4 c. Africans beating drums (Africa)		10	10
870	5 c. Snake-charmer and dancer (India and Far East)		10	10
871	6 c. Boy and girl with donkey (Belize)		10	10
872	50 c. Musician and dancer (Balkans)		70	80
873	$1.50, Boys with camel (Egypt and Saudi Arabia)		1·75	2·25
874	$3 Woman and girls playing with kite (Japan)		3·00	3·75
866/74		*Set of 9*	5·25	6·50
MS875	127 × 102 mm. $4 Beefeater and castle (Great Britain). P 13½ × 14		4·50	5·00

PRE"WORLD CUP FOOTBALL" MEXICO 1986

(162)

163 Indian Costume

1985 (20 Dec). *World Cup Football Championship, Mexico (1986) (1st issue). Nos. 835/45 optd with T 162.*

876	50 c. Type 156.		60	60
	a. Sheetlet. Nos. 876/85		5·50	
877	50 c. 1937 Coronation 3 c., and King George VI and Queen Elizabeth in Coronation robes		60	60
878	50 c. 1946 Victory 3 c., and Victory celebrations		60	60
879	50 c. 1948 Royal Silver Wedding 4 c., and King George VI and Queen Elizabeth at Westminster Abbey service		60	60
880	50 c. 1953 Coronation 4 c., and Queen Elizabeth II in Coronation robes		60	60
881	50 c. 1966 Churchill 25 c., Sir Winston Churchill and fighter aircraft		60	60
882	50 c. 1972 Royal Silver Wedding 50 c., and 1948 Wedding photograph		60	60
883	50 c. 1973 Royal Wedding 50 c., and Princess Anne and Capt. Mark Phillips at their Wedding		60	60
884	50 c. 1977 Silver Jubilee $2, and Queen Elizabeth II during tour		60	60
885	50 c. 1978 25th anniv of Coronation 75 c., and Imperial Crown		60	60
876/85		*Set of 10*	5·50	5·50
MS886	138 × 98 mm. $5 Queen Elizabeth II in Coronation robes		4·25	4·25

See also Nos. 936/40.

(Des Jane Clark. Litho Format)

1986 (15 Jan). *Costumes of Belize. T 163 and similar vert designs. Multicoloured. P 15.*

887	5 c. Type 163.		50	15
888	10 c. Maya		60	15
889	15 c. Garifuna		75	20
890	25 c. Creole		95	30
891	50 c. Chinese		1·40	1·00
892	75 c. Lebanese		1·75	1·75
893	$1 European *c* 1900		2·00	2·25
894	$2 Latin		2·75	3·00
887/94		*Set of 8*	9·50	8·00
MS895	139 × 98 mm. $5 Amerindian (38 × 50 mm). P 13½ × 14.		6·00	7·50

164 Pope Pius X **165** Princess Elizabeth aged Three

(Des G. Vasarhelyi. Litho Format)

1986 (15 Apr). *Easter. 20th-century Popes. T 164 and similar multicoloured designs. P 11.*

896	50 c. Type 164.		1·00	1·10
	a. Sheetlet. Nos. 896/903		7·25	
897	50 c. Benedict XV		1·00	1·10
898	50 c. Pius XI		1·00	1·10
899	50 c. Pius XII		1·00	1·10
900	50 c. John XXIII		1·00	1·10
901	50 c. Paul VI		1·00	1·10
902	50 c. John Paul I		1·00	1·10
903	50 c. John Paul II		1·00	1·10
896/903		*Set of 8*	7·25	8·00
MS904	147 × 92 mm. $4 Pope John Paul II preaching (*vert*). P 13½ × 14		8·50	8·50

Nos. 896/903 were printed together, *se-tenant*, in sheetlets of eight stamps and one stamp-size label.

(Des G. Vasarhelyi. Litho Format)

1986 (21 Apr). *60th Birthday of Queen Elizabeth II. T 165 and similar vert designs. Multicoloured. P 14 × 13½.*

905	25 c. Type 165.		15	20
	a. Sheetlet. Nos. 905/8, each × 2		4·00	
906	50 c. Queen wearing Imperial State Crown		35	40
907	75 c. At Trooping the Colour		50	55
908	$3 Queen wearing diadem		1·25	2·25
905/8		*Set of 4*	2·00	3·00
MS909	147 × 93 mm. $4 Queen Elizabeth II (37 × 50 mm). P 13½ × 14		2·50	3·25

Nos. 905/8 were printed together, *se-tenant*, in sheetlets of eight stamps, two of each value, and one stamp-size label.

166 Halley's Comet and Japanese *Planet A* Spacecraft

(Des G. Vasarhelyi. Litho Format)

1986 (30 Apr). *Appearance of Halley's Comet. T 166 and similar multicoloured designs. P 13½ × 14.*

910	10 c. Type 166.		20	35
	a. Sheetlet. Nos. 910/12, each × 3		2·40	
911	15 c. Halley's Comet, 1910		30	50
912	50 c. Comet and European *Giotto* space-craft		40	60
913	75 c. Belize Weather Bureau		70	80
	a. Sheetlet. Nos. 913/15, each × 3		8·50	
914	$1 Comet and U.S.A. space telescope		95	1·10
915	$2 Edmond Halley		1·50	1·60
910/15		*Set of 6*	3·50	4·25
MS916	147 × 93 mm. $4 Computer enhanced photograph of Comet (37 × 50 mm)		5·00	5·50

Nos. 910/12 and 913/15 were each printed together, *se-tenant*, in horizontal and vertical strips of 3, within the two sheetlets of nine.

167 George Washington

(Des G. Vasarhelyi. Litho Format)

1986 (7 May). *United States Presidents. T 167 and similar vert designs. Multicoloured. P 11.*

917	10 c. Type 167.		35	45
	a. Sheetlet. Nos. 917/22		3·00	
918	20 c. John Adams		35	55
919	30 c. Thomas Jefferson		40	60
920	50 c. James Madison		50	60
921	$1.50, James Monroe		80	1·25
922	$2 John Quincy Adams		1·00	1·50
917/22		*Set of 6*	3·00	4·50
MS923	147 × 93 mm. $4 George Washington (*different*). P 13½ × 14		5·00	5·50

Nos. 917/19 and 920/2 were printed together, *se-tenant*, in horizontal strips of 3, separated by three stamp-size labels, within the sheetlet of six stamps.

168 Auguste Bartholdi (sculptor) and Statue's Head

(Des G. Vasarhelyi. Litho Format)

1986 (15 May). *Centenary of Statue of Liberty. T 168 and similar multicoloured designs. P 13½ × 14.*

924	25 c. Type 168.		50	65
	a. Sheetlet. Nos. 924/7, each × 2		5·50	
925	50 c. Statue's head at U.S. Centennial Celebration, Philadelphia, 1876		60	85
926	75 c. Unveiling Ceremony, 1886		65	90
927	$3 Statue of Liberty and flags of Belize and U.S.A.		1·40	2·00
924/7		*Set of 4*	2·75	4·00
MS928	147 × 92 mm. $4 Statue of Liberty and New York skyline (37 × 50 mm)		3·75	5·00

Nos. 924/7 were printed together, *se-tenant*, in sheetlets of eight stamps, two of each value, and one stamp-size label.

169 British Honduras 1866 1s. Stamp

(Des G. Vasarhelyi. Litho Format)

1986 (22 May). *"Ameripex" International Stamp Exhibition, Chicago. T 169 and similar multicoloured designs. P 13½ × 14.*

929	10 c. Type 169.		40	55
	a. Sheetlet. Nos. 929/31, each × 3		4·50	
930	15 c. 1981 Royal Wedding $1.50 stamp		55	75
931	50 c. U.S.A. 1918 24 c. airmail inverted centre error		75	80
932	75 c. U.S.S. *Constitution* (frigate)		90	1·10
	a. Sheetlet. Nos. 932/4, each × 3		9·00	
933	$1 Liberty Bell		1·00	1·40
934	$2 White House		1·40	1·60
929/34		*Set of 6*	4·50	5·50
MS935	147 × 93 mm. $4 Capitol, Washington (37 × 50 mm)		3·25	4·00

Nos. 929/31 and 932/4 were each printed together, *se-tenant*, in horizontal and vertical strips of 3, within the two sheetlets of nine.

Nos. 929/34 exist imperforate from stock dispersed by the liquidator of Format International Security Printers Ltd.

170 English and Brazilian Players

(Des G. Vasarhelyi. Litho Format)

1986 (16 June) *World Cup Football Championship, Mexico (2nd issue). T 170 and similar multicoloured designs. P 11.*

936	25 c. Type 170.		1·00	1·25
	a. Sheetlet. Nos. 936/9, each × 2		13·00	
937	50 c. Mexican player and Maya statues		1·40	1·60
938	75 c. Two Belizean players		1·75	2·00
939	$3 Aztec stone calendar		3·00	3·50
936/9		*Set of 4*	6·50	7·50
MS940	147 × 92 mm. $4 Flags of competing nations on two footballs (37 × 50 mm). P 13½ × 14		7·50	8·00

Nos. 936/9 were printed together, *se-tenant*, in sheetlets of eight stamps, two of each value, and one stamp-size label.

No. 936a exists imperforate from stock dispersed by the liquidator of Format International Security Printers Ltd.

ARGENTINA-
WINNERS 1986

171 Miss Sarah   (172)
Ferguson

(Des G. Vasarhelyi. Litho Format)

1986 (23 July). *Royal Wedding. T* **171** *and similar multicoloured designs. P* 14½.
941	25 c. Type **171**..		40	40
	a. Horiz strip of 3. Nos. 941/3	..	2·25	
942	75 c. Prince Andrew	..	70	90
943	$3 Prince Andrew and Miss Sarah Ferguson (92×41 *mm*)	..	1·40	2·25
941/3		*Set of 3*	2·25	3·25
MS944	155×106 mm. $1 Miss Sarah Ferguson (*different*), $3 Prince Andrew (*different*)		3·25	5·00

Nos. 941/3 were printed together, *se-tenant*, in horizontal strips of 3 within small sheets of nine stamps.
No. MS944 exists imperforate from stock dispersed by the liquidator of Format International Security Printers Ltd.

1986 (15 Aug). *World Cup Football Championship Winners, Mexico. Nos. 936/40 optd with T* **172**.
945	25 c. Type **170** ..	..	1·00	1·00
	a. Sheetlet. Nos. 945/8, each×2	..	13·00	
946	50 c. Mexican player and Maya statues	..	1·40	1·40
947	75 c. Two Belizean players	..	1·75	1·75
948	$3 Aztec stone calendar	..	3·00	3·00
945/8		*Set of 4*	6·50	6·50
MS949	147×92 mm. $4 Flags of competing nations on two footballs (37×50 *mm*)	..	5·00	6·50

(173)   174 Amerindian Girl

1986 (28 Aug). *"Stockholmia '86" International Stamp Exhibition, Sweden. Nos. 929/35 optd with T* **173**.
950	10 c. Type **169**..	..	40	50
	a. Sheetlet. Nos. 950/2, each×3	..	4·75	
951	15 c. 1981 Royal Wedding $1.50 stamp	..	50	60
952	50 c. U.S.A. 1918 24 c. airmail inverted centre error	..	70	80
953	75 c. U.S.S. *Constitution*	..	90	1·10
	a. Sheetlet. Nos. 953/5, each×3	..	10·50	
954	$1 Liberty Bell	..	1·10	1·25
955	$2 White House	..	1·60	1·60
950/5		*Set of 6*	4·75	5·25
MS956	147×93 mm. $4 Capitol, Washington (37×50 *mm*)	..	4·50	6·00

(Des G. Vasarhelyi. Litho Format)

1986 (3 Oct). *International Peace Year. T* **174** *and similar multicoloured designs. P* 13½×14.
957	25 c. Type **174**..	..	45	60
	a. Sheetlet. Nos. 957/60, each×2	..	7·00	
958	50 c. European boy and girl ..	..	70	85
959	75 c. Japanese girl	..	1·00	1·25
960	$3 Indian boy and European girl ..	..	1·75	2·25
957/60		*Set of 4*	3·50	4·50
MS961	132 × 106 mm. $4 As 25 c. but vert (35 × 47 *mm*)	..	4·00	5·00

Nos. 957/60 were printed together, *se-tenant*, in sheetlets of eight stamps, two of each value, and one stamp-size label.
No. MS961 exists imperforate from stock dispersed by the liquidator of Format International Security Printers Ltd.

175 *Amanita lilloi*   176 Jose Carioca

(Des G. Drummond. Litho Format)

1986 (30 Oct). *Fungi and Toucans. T* **175** *and similar vert designs. Multicoloured. P* 14×13½.
962	5 c. Type **175**	..	75	75
	a. Sheetlet. Nos. 962, 964, 966 and 969, each × 2	..	11·00	

963	10 c. Keel-billed Toucan	..	90	90
	a. Sheetlet. Nos. 963, 965 and 967/8, each ×2	..	10·00	
964	20 c. *Boletellus cubensis*	..	1·25	1·25
965	25 c. Collared Aracari	..	1·25	1·25
966	75 c. *Psilocybe caerulescens*	..	1·50	1·50
967	$1 Emerald Toucanet	..	1·50	1·50
968	$1.25, Crimson-rumped Toucanet	..	1·50	1·50
969	$2 *Russula puiggarii*	..	2·00	2·00
962/9		*Set of 8*	9·50	9·50

Nos. 962, 964, 966 and 969, and Nos. 963, 965 and 967/8, were each printed together, *se-tenant*, in sheetlets of eight stamps, two of each value, and one stamp-size label.
No. 962a exists imperforate from stock dispersed by the liquidator of Format International Security Printers Ltd.

(Des Walt Disney Productions. Litho Format)

1986 (14 Nov). *Christmas. T* **176** *and similar vert designs showing Walt Disney cartoon characters in scenes from "Saludos Amigos". Multicoloured. P* 11.
970	2 c. Type **176**	..	20	10
	a. Sheetlet. Nos. 970/8	..	7·25	
971	3 c. Jose Carioca, Panchito and Donald Duck	..	20	10
972	4 c. Daisy Duck as Rio Carnival dancer	..	20	10
973	5 c. Mickey and Minnie Mouse as musician and dancer	..	20	10
974	6 c. Jose Carioca using umbrella as flute	..	20	10
975	50 c. Donald Duck and Panchito	..	1·00	1·25
976	65 c. Jose Carioca and Donald Duck playing hide and seek	..	1·25	1·50
977	$1.35, Donald Duck playing maracas	..	2·00	3·00
978	$2 Goofy as matador	..	2·75	3·50
970/8		*Set of 9*	7·25	8·50
MS979	131 × 111 mm. $4 Donald Duck. P 13½×14	..	6·00	8·00

Nos. 970/8 were printed together, *se-tenant*, in sheetlets of nine.

177 Princess Elizabeth in   178 *America II*
Wedding Dress, 1947

(Des G. Vasarhelyi. Litho Format)

1987 (7 Oct). *Royal Ruby Wedding. T* **177** *and similar vert designs. Multicoloured. P* 15.
980	25 c. Type **177**..	..	20	20
981	75 c. Queen and Duke of Edinburgh, 1972	..	35	40
982	$1 Queen on her 60th birthday	..	40	50
983	$4 In Garter robes ..	..	1·00	1·50
980/3		*Set of 4*	1·75	2·40
MS984	171×112 mm. $6 Queen and Duke of Edinburgh (44×50 *mm*). P 13½×14	..	5·00	6·50

(Des G. Vasarhelyi. Litho Format)

1987 (21 Oct). *America's Cup Yachting Championship. T* **178** *and similar multicoloured designs. P* 15.
985	25 c. Type **178**	..	20	25
986	75 c. *Stars and Stripes*	..	35	50
987	$1 *Australia II*, 1983	..	40	60
988	$4 *White Crusader*	..	1·00	1·60
985/8		*Set of 4*	1·75	2·75
MS989	171×112 mm. $6 Sails of *Australia II* (44×50 *mm*). P 13½×14	..	5·50	7·00

179 "Mother and   180 Black-handed
Child"   Spider Monkey

(Des G. Vasarhelyi. Litho Format)

1987 (4 Nov). *Wood Carvings by George Gabb. T* **179** *and similar vert designs. Multicoloured. P* 15.
990	25 c. Type **179**	..	15	25
991	75 c. "Standing Form"	..	35	50
992	$1 "Love-doves"	..	40	60
993	$4 "Depiction of Music"	..	1·10	1·60
990/3		*Set of 4*	1·75	2·75
MS994	173×114 mm. $6 "African Heritage" (44×50 *mm*). P 13½×14	..	3·50	5·00

(Des G. Drummond. Litho Format)

1987 (11 Nov). *Primates. T* **180** *and similar vert designs. Multicoloured. P* 15.
995	25 c. Type **180**	..	25	20
996	75 c. Black Howler Monkey	..	40	55
997	$1 Spider Monkeys with baby	..	45	65
998	$4 Two Black Howler Monkeys	..	1·10	2·00
995/8		*Set of 4*	2·00	3·00
MS999	171×112 mm. $6 Young Spider Monkey (41×48 *mm*). P 13½×14	..	4·00	6·00

181 Guides on Parade

(Des G. Vasarhelyi. Litho Format)

1987 (25 Nov). *50th Anniv of Girl Guide Movement in Belize. T* **181** *and similar multicoloured designs. P* 15.
1000	25 c. Type **181**	..	45	20
1001	75 c. Brownie camp	..	80	90
1002	$1 Guide camp	..	1·00	1·25
1003	$4 Olave, Lady Baden-Powell	..	3·00	4·25
1000/3		*Set of 4*	4·75	6·00
MS1004	173×114 mm. $6 As $4, but vert (44×50 *mm*). P 13½×14	..	4·50	5·50

182 Indian Refugee Camp   183 *Laelia euspatha*

(Des G. Vasarhelyi. Litho Format)

1987 (3 Dec). *International Year of Shelter for the Homeless. T* **182** *and similar horiz designs. Multicoloured. P* 15.
1005	25 c. Type **182**	..	50	25
1006	75 c. Filipino family and slum	..	90	90
1007	$1 Family in Middle East shanty town	..	1·10	1·25
1008	$4 Building modern house in Belize	..	3·00	4·25
1005/8		*Set of 4*	5·00	6·00

(Des G. Drummond. Litho Format)

1987 (16 Dec). *Christmas. Orchids. T* **183** *and similar vert designs showing illustrations from Sanders' Reichenbachia. Multicoloured. P* 13½×14.
1009	1 c. Type **183**	..	60	50
	a. Sheetlet. Nos. 1009/15, each × 2	..	7·50	
1010	2 c. *Cattleya citrina*	..	60	50
1011	3 c. *Masdevallia backhousiana*	..	60	50
1012	4 c. *Cypripedium tautzianum*	..	60	50
1013	5 c. *Trichopilia suavis alba*	..	60	50
1014	6 c. *Odontoglossum hebraicum*	..	60	50
1015	7 c. *Cattleya trianaei schroederiana*	..	60	50
1016	10 c. *Saccolabium giganteum*	..	75	65
	a. Sheetlet. Nos. 1016/22, each × 2	..	17·00	
1017	30 c. *Cattleya warscewiczii*	..	90	80
1018	50 c. *Chysis bractescens*	..	1·25	1·00
1019	70 c. *Cattleya rochellensis*	..	1·40	1·10
1020	$1 *Laelia elegans schilleriana*	..	1·50	1·10
1021	$1.50, *Laelia anceps percivaliana*	..	1·60	1·40
1022	$3 *Laelia gouldiana*	..	2·25	1·90
1009/22		*Set of 14*	12·50	10·50
MS1023	Two sheets, each 171×112 mm. (a) $3 *Odontoglossum roezlii* (40×47 *mm*). (b) $5 *Cattleya dowiana aurea* (40×47 *mm*)			
		Set of 2 sheets	7·50	10·00

Nos. 1009/1015 and 1016/22 were each printed together, *se-tenant*, in sheetlets of fourteen stamps, containing two of each value and one stamp-size label.
Examples of the $3 value from No. MS1023 with the orchid name incorrectly spelt are from stock dispersed by the liquidator of Format International Security Printers Ltd.

184 Christ condemned to   185 Basketball
Death

(Des G. Vasarhelyi. Litho Format)

1988 (21 Mar). *Easter. The Stations of the Cross. T* **184** *and similar vert designs. Multicoloured. P* 13½×14.
1024	40 c. Type **184**	..	30	40
	a. Sheetlet. Nos. 1024/37	..	3·75	
1025	40 c. Christ carrying the Cross	..	30	40
1026	40 c. Falling for the first time	..	30	40
1027	40 c. Christ meets Mary	..	30	40
1028	40 c. Simon of Cyrene helping to carry the Cross	..	30	40
1029	40 c. Veronica wiping the face of Christ	..	30	40
1030	40 c. Christ falling a second time	..	30	40

.031	40 c.	Consoling the women of Jerusalem	30	40
.032	40 c.	Falling for the third time	30	40
.033	40 c.	Christ being stripped	30	40
.034	40 c.	Christ nailed to the Cross	30	40
.035	40 c.	Dying on the Cross	30	40
.036	40 c.	Christ taken down from the Cross	30	40
.037	40 c.	Christ being laid in the sepulchre	30	40
.024/37		Set of 14	3·75	5·00

Nos. 1024/37 were printed together, *se-tenant*, in a sheetlet of 14 stamps and one stamp-size label which appears in the central position.

No. 1024a exists imperforate from stock dispersed by the liquidator of Format International Security Printers Ltd.

A $6 miniature sheet was prepared, but not issued. Examples exist from stock dispersed by the liquidator.

(Des J. McDaniel. Litho Questa)

1988 (15 Aug). *Olympic Games, Seoul.* T **185** *and similar vert designs. Multicoloured.* P 14.

1038	10 c.	Type **185**	50	30
1039	25 c.	Volleyball	55	30
1040	60 c.	Table tennis	60	60
1041	75 c.	Diving	70	70
1042	$1	Judo	80	85
1043	$2	Hockey	2·75	2·75
1038/43		Set of 6	5·50	5·00
MS1044	76×106 mm. $3 Gymnastics		2·75	3·75

186 Public Health Nurse, c. 1912   187 Collared Anteater ("Ants Bear")

(Des O. Fernandez. Litho Questa)

1988 (18 Nov). *125th Anniv of International Red Cross.* T **186** *and similar horiz designs. Multicoloured.* P 14.

1045	60 c.	Type **186**	1·25	1·00
1046	75 c.	Hospital ship and ambulance launch, 1937	1·50	1·50
1047	$1	Ambulance at hospital tent, 1956	2·00	1·75
1048	$2	Auster ambulance plane, 1940	2·75	3·50
1045/8		Set of 4	6·75	7·00

(Des J. Barberis. Litho Questa)

1989 (24 Feb)–**90**. *Small Animals of Belize.* T **187** *and similar multicoloured designs.* P 14. (a) W w 16 *(sideways on 25 c.)*.

1049	10 c.	Paca ("Gibnut") (30.6.89)	1·25	1·25
1049a	25 c.	Four-eyed Opossum (vert) (1.90)	1·50	1·50

(b) No wmk

1050	25 c.	Four-eyed Opossum (vert)	1·25	1·25
1051	50 c.	Type **187**	1·75	1·75
1052	60 c.	As 10 c.	1·75	1·75
1053	75 c.	Red Brocket	1·90	1·90
1054	$2	Collared Peccary	3·25	4·00
1049/54		Set of 7	11·50	12·00

(Des A. Theobald ($5), D. Miller (others). Litho Questa)

1989 (20 July). *20th Anniv of First Manned Landing on Moon. Multicoloured designs as* T **126** *of Ascension.* W w 16 *(sideways on 50, 75 c.).* P 14×13½ (25 c., $1) *or* 14 *(others).*

1055	25 c.	Docking of "Apollo 9" modules	35	20
1056	50 c.	"Apollo 9" command service module in space (30×30 mm)	55	55
1057	75 c.	"Apollo 9" emblem (30×30 mm)	75	80
1058	$1	"Apollo 9" lunar module in space	95	1·10
1055/8		Set of 4	2·40	2·40
MS1059	83×100 mm. $5 "Apollo 11" service module undergoing tests. P 14×13½.		4·50	5·50

WORLD STAMP EXPO '89™

United States Postal Service
Nov. 17 — 20 and
Nov. 24 — Dec. 3 1989
Washington Convention Center
Washington, DC

5c

(188)   (189)

1989 (15 Nov). *No.* 771A *surch with* T **188** *by Govt Printer, Belize.*

1060	5 c. on 6 c. Star-eyed Hermit Crab	10·00	1·25

1989 (17 Nov). *"World Stamp Expo '89" International Stamp Exhibition, Washington. No.* MS1059 *optd with* T **189**.

MS1061	83×100 mm. $5 "Apollo 11" command service module undergoing tests	4·75	5·50

**STANLEY GIBBONS
STAMP COLLECTING SERIES**

Introductory booklets on *How to Start, How to Identify Stamps* and *Collecting by Theme.* A series of well illustrated guides at a low price.
Write for details.

190 Wesley Church   191 White-winged Tanager and *Catonephele numilia*

(Des Jennifer Toombs. Litho B.D.T.)

1989 (13 Dec). *Christmas. Belize Churches.* T **190** *and similar vert designs.* W w 16. P 13½.

1062	10 c.	black, rose-pink and cinnamon	20	10
1063	25 c.	black, reddish lilac and rose-lilac	25	20
1064	60 c.	black, pale turquoise-blue and cobalt	50	60
1065	75 c.	black, pale blue-green and sage-green	65	80
1066	$1	blk, pale greenish yell & chrome-yell	80	1·10
1062/6		Set of 5	2·25	2·50

Designs:—25 c. Baptist Church; 60 c. St. John's Anglican Cathedral; 75 c. St. Andrew's Presbyterian Church; $1 Holy Redeemer Roman Catholic Cathedral.

(Des I. Loe. Litho Questa)

1990 (1 Mar)–**93**. *Birds and Butterflies.* T **191** *and similar vert designs. Multicoloured.* W w 14. P 14. A. *Without imprint date.* B. *With imprint date ("1993")* (5.7.93)

			A		B	
1067	5 c.	Type **191**	20	20	†	
1068	10 c.	Keel-billed Toucan and *Nessaea aglaura*	30	30	30	30
1069	15 c.	Magnificent Frigate Bird and *Eurytides philolaus*	30	30	†	
1070	25 c.	Jabiru and *Heliconius sapho*	40	40	†	
1071	30 c.	Great Blue Heron and *Colobura dirce*	40	40	†	
1072	50 c.	Northern Oriole and *Hamadryas arethusia*	50	50	†	
1073	60 c.	Scarlet Macaw and *Evenus regalis*	55	55	†	
1074	75 c.	Red-legged Honey-creeper and *Callicore patelina*	65	65	†	
1075	$1	Spectacled Owl and *Caligo uranus*	1·00	90	†	
1076	$2	Green Jay and *Philaethria dido*	1·75	2·00	†	
1077	$5	Turkey Vulture and *Battus belus*	3·50	4·50	†	
1078	$10	Osprey and *Papilio thoas*	7·00	8·00	†	
1067/78		Set of 12	15·00	17·00	†	

**FIRST DOLLAR
COIN
1990**

(192)   193 Green Turtle

1990 (1 Mar). *First Belize Dollar Coin. No.* 1075A *optd with* T **192** *in gold.*

1079	$1 Spectacled Owl and *Caligo uranus*	3·00	2·50

(Des G. Drummond. Litho B.D.T.)

1990 (8 Aug). *Turtles.* T **193** *and similar horiz designs. Multicoloured.* W w 14 *(sideways).* P 14.

1080	10 c.	Type **193**	45	25
1081	25 c.	Hawksbill Turtle	70	30
1082	60 c.	Saltwater Loggerhead Turtle	1·00	1·00
1083	75 c.	Freshwater Loggerhead Turtle	1·10	1·10
1084	$1	Bocatora Turtle	1·50	1·50
1085	$2	Hicatee Turtle	2·50	3·50
1080/5		Set of 6	6·50	7·00

194 Fairey Battle   195 *Cattleya bowringiana*

(Des A. Theobald. Litho B.D.T)

1990 (15 Sept). *50th Anniv of the Battle of Britain.* T **194** *and similar horiz designs. Multicoloured.* W w 16 *(sideways).* P 13½.

1086	10 c.	Type **194**	35	30
1087	25 c.	Bristol Type 152 Beaufort	60	30
1088	60 c.	Bristol Type 142 Blenheim Mk IV	1·25	1·50
1089	75 c.	Armstrong-Whitworth Whitley	1·40	1·60
1090	$1	Vickers-Armstrong Wellington Mk 1c	1·50	1·75
1091	$2	Handley-Page Hampden	1·75	2·75
1086/91		Set of 6	6·25	7·50

(Des Lynn Chadwick. Litho Questa)

1990 (1 Nov). *Christmas. Orchids.* T **195** *and similar vert designs. Multicoloured.* W w 14. P 14.

1092	25 c.	Type **195**	60	20
1093	50 c.	*Rhyncholaelia digbyana*	75	50
1094	60 c.	*Sobralia macrantha*	90	90
1095	75 c.	*Chysis bractescens*	1·00	1·00
1096	$1	*Vanilla planifolia*	1·25	1·25
1097	$2	*Epidendrum polyanthum*	2·00	2·75
1092/7		Set of 6	6·00	6·00

196 Common Iguana

(Des G. Drummond. Litho B.D.T.)

1991 (10 Apr). *Reptiles and Mammals.* T **196** *and similar horiz designs. Multicoloured.* W w 14 *(sideways).* P 14.

1098	25 c.	Type **196**	65	35
1099	50 c.	Morelet's Crocodile	1·00	90
1100	60 c.	American Manatee	1·25	1·25
1101	75 c.	Boa Constrictor	1·50	1·50
1102	$1	Baird's Tapir	1·75	1·75
1103	$2	Jaguar	2·50	3·25
1098/1103		Set of 6	7·75	8·00

(Des D. Miller. Litho Questa)

1991 (17 June). *65th Birthday of Queen Elizabeth II and 70th Birthday of Prince Philip. Vert designs as* T **139** *of Ascension. Multicoloured.* W w 16 *(sideways).* P 14½×14.

1104	$1	Queen Elizabeth II wearing tiara	1·00	1·25
	a.	Horiz pair. Nos. 1104/5 separated by label	2·00	2·50
1105	$1	Prince Philip wearing panama	1·00	1·25

Nos. 1104/5 were printed in a similar sheet format to Nos. 539/40 of Ascension

197 Weather Radar

(Des D. Miller. Litho Walsall)

1991 (31 July). *International Decade for Natural Disaster Reduction.* T **197** *and similar horiz designs.* W w 14 *(sideways).* P 14.

1106	60 c.	multicoloured	1·00	1·00
1107	75 c.	multicoloured	1·10	1·10
1108	$1	greenish blue and grey-black	1·25	1·25
1109	$2	multicoloured	2·00	2·50
1106/9		Set of 4	4·75	5·25

Designs:—75 c. Weather station; $1 Floods in Belize after Hurricane Hattie, 1961; $2 Satellite image of Hurricane Gilbert.

198 Thomas Ramos and Demonstration

(Des G. Vasarhelyi. Litho Questa)

1991 (4 Sept). *10th Anniv of Independence. Famous Belizians (1st series).* T **198** *and similar horiz designs. Multicoloured.* W w 16 *(sideways).* P 14.

1110	25 c.	Type **198**	50	20
1111	60 c.	Sir Isaiah Morter and palm trees	90	1·00
1112	75 c.	Antonio Soberanis and political meeting	1·00	1·25
1113	$1	Santiago Ricalde and cutting sugar-cane	1·25	1·50
1110/13		Set of 4	3·25	3·50

See also Nos. 1126/9 and 1148/51.

199 "Anansi the Spider"   200 *Gongora quinquenervis*

(Des G. Vasarhelyi. Litho B.D.T.)

1991 (6 Nov). *Christmas. Folklore. T **199** and similar multicoloured designs. W w **14** (sideways on horiz designs). P 14.*

1114	25 c.	Type **199**	50	20
1115	50 c.	"Jack-o-Lantern"	80	55
1116	60 c.	"Tata Duende" (vert)	90	90
1117	75 c.	"Xtabai"	1·00	1·00
1118	$1	"Warrie Massa" (vert)	1·25	1·25
1119	$2	"Old Heg"	2·25	3·00
1114/19		Set of 6	6·00	6·25

(Des Lynn Chadwick. Litho B.D.T.)

1992 (1 Apr). *Easter. Orchids. T **200** and similar vert designs. W w **14**. P 14×13½.*

1120	25 c.	Type **200**	75	20
1121	50 c.	Oncidium sphacelatum	1·25	70
1122	60 c.	Encyclia bratescens	1·50	1·40
1123	75 c.	Epidendrum ciliare	1·60	1·50
1124	$1	Psygmorchis pusilla	1·75	1·00
1125	$2	Galeandra batemanii	2·50	3·50
1120/5		Set of 6	8·50	8·00

(Des G. Vasarhelyi. Litho Enschedé)

1992 (26 Aug). *Famous Belizeans (2nd series). Horiz designs as T **198**, but inscr "EMINENT BELIZEANS" at top. Multicoloured. W w **14** (sideways). P 13×12½.*

1126	25 c.	Gwendolyn Lizarraga (politician) and High School	45	25
1127	60 c.	Rafael Fonseca (civil servant) and Government Offices, Belize	80	90
1128	75 c.	Vivian Seay (health worker) and nurses	95	1·10
1129	$1	Samuel Haynes (U.N.I.A. worker) and words of National Anthem	1·25	1·50
1126/9		Set of 4	3·00	3·25

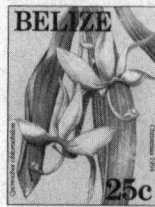

201 Xunantunich and National Assembly

(Des D. Miller. Litho Questa)

1992 (1 Oct). *500th Anniv of Discovery of America by Columbus. T **201** and similar horiz designs showing Mayan sites and modern buildings. Multicoloured. W w **16** (sideways). P 14.*

1130	25 c.	Type **201**	60	25
1131	60 c.	Altun Ha and Supreme Court	90	1·00
1132	75 c.	Santa Rita and Tower Hill Sugar Factory	1·10	1·25
1133	$5	Lamanai and Citrus Company works	5·50	6·50
1130/3		Set of 4	7·25	8·00

202 Hashishi Pampi   203 Lycaste aromatica

(Des G. Vasarhelyi. Litho Enschedé)

1992 (16 Nov). *Christmas. Folklore. T **202** and similar multicoloured designs. W w **14** (sideways on 25, 60 c., $5). P 12½×13 ($1) or 13×12½ (others).*

1134	25 c.	Type **202**	30	20
1135	60 c.	Cadejo	60	60
1136	$1	La Sucia (vert)	90	1·00
1137	$5	Sisimito	4·00	6·00
1134/7		Set of 4	5·25	7·00

(Des A. Theobald. Litho Questa)

1993 (1 Apr). *75th Anniv of Royal Air Force. Horiz designs as T **149** of Ascension. Multicoloured. W w **14** (sideways). P 14.*

1138	25 c.	Sud Aviation SA 330L Puma helicopter	55	30
1139	50 c.	Hawker Siddeley Harrier GR3	75	55
1140	60 c.	De Havilland DH98 Mosquito Mk XVIII	85	80
1141	75 c.	Avro Type 683 Lancaster	95	90
1142	$1	Consolidated Liberator I	1·25	1·10
1143	$3	Short Stirling Mk I	3·00	4·25
1138/43		Set of 6	6·50	7·00

(Des Annette Robinson. Litho Walsall)

1993 (23 Apr). *14th World Orchid Conference, Glasgow. T **203** and similar vert designs. Multicoloured. W w **16**. P 14½×14.*

1144	25 c.	Type **203**	25	25
1145	60 c.	Sobralia decora	60	80
1146	$1	Maxillaria alba	90	1·10
1147	$2	Brassavola nodosa	1·75	2·25
1144/7		Set of 4	3·25	4·00

(Des G. Vasarhelyi. Litho Questa)

1993 (11 Aug). *Famous Belizeans (3rd series). Horiz designs as T **198**, but inscr "EMINENT BELIZEANS" at top. Multicoloured. W w **16** (sideways). P 14.*

1148	25 c.	Herbert Watkin Beaumont, Post Office and postmark	40	25
1149	60 c.	Dr. Selvyn Walford Young and score of National Anthem	75	85
1150	75 c.	Cleopatra White and health centre	90	1·25
1151	$1	Dr. Karl Heusner and early car	1·10	1·40
1148/51		Set of 4	2·75	3·25

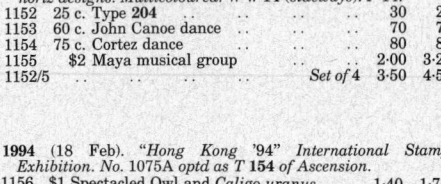

204 Boom and Chime Band

(Des Jennifer Toombs. Litho B.D.T.)

1993 (3 Nov). *Christmas. Local Customs. T **204** and similar horiz designs. Multicoloured. W w **14** (sideways). P 14.*

1152	25 c.	Type **204**	30	20
1153	60 c.	John Canoe dance	70	70
1154	75 c.	Cortez dance	80	80
1155	$2	Maya musical group	2·00	3·25
1152/5		Set of 4	3·50	4·50

1994 (18 Feb). *"Hong Kong '94" International Stamp Exhibition. No. 1075A optd as T **154** of Ascension.*

1156	$1 Spectacled Owl and Caligo uranus	1·40	1·75

(Des D. Miller. Litho Questa)

1994 (22 Feb). *Royal Visit. Vert designs as T **202** of Bahamas. Multicoloured. W w **16**. P 14½.*

1157	25 c.	Flags of Belize and Great Britain	25	20
1158	60 c.	Queen Elizabeth II in yellow coat and hat	55	65
1159	75 c.	Queen Elizabeth in evening dress	70	85
1160	$1	Queen Elizabeth, Prince Philip and Yeomen of the Guard	95	1·25
1157/60		Set of 4	2·25	2·75

10c

205 Lonchorhina aurita (bat)   (**206**)

(Des N. Arlott. Litho B.D.T.)·

1994 (30 May). *Bats. T **205** and similar horiz designs. Multicoloured. W w **16** (sideways). P 14.*

1161	25 c.	Type **205**	25	20
1162	60 c.	Vampyrodes caraccioli	55	60
1163	75 c.	Noctilio leporinus	70	75
1164	$2	Desmodus rotundus	1·90	2·75
1161/4		Set of 4	3·00	3·75

1994 (18 Aug). *75th Anniv of International Labour Organization. No. 1074A surch with T **206**.*

1165	10 c. on 75 c. Red-legged Honey-creeper and Callicore patelina	50	50

207 Cycnoches chlorochilon   208 Ground Beetle

(Des N. Shewring. Litho B.D.T.)

1994 (7 Nov). *Christmas. Orchids. T **207** and similar vert designs. Multicoloured. W w **16**. P 14×13½.*

1166	25 c.	Type **207**	25	20
1167	60 c.	Brassavola cucullata	55	70
1168	75 c.	Sobralia mucronata	70	90
1169	$1	Nidema boothii	95	1·25
1166/9		Set of 4	2·25	2·75

(Des I. Loe and D. Miller. Litho B.D.T.)

1995 (11 Jan)–**96**. *Insects. T **208** and similar horiz designs. Multicoloured. W w **14** (sideways*). P 14. A. Without imprint date at foot. B. With imprint date "1996" at bottom right (10.96).*

			A		B	
1170	5 c.	Type **208**	20	20	10	10
1171	10 c.	Harlequin Beetle	20	20	10	10
		w. Wmk Crown to right of CA	—	—	—	†
1172	15 c.	Giant Water Bug	20	20	10	10
1173	25 c.	Peanut-head Bug	30	20	15	20
1174	30 c.	Coconut Weevil	40	25	15	20
1175	50 c.	Mantis	50	40	30	35
1176	60 c.	Tarantula Wasp	60	50	35	40
1177	75 c.	Rhinoceros Beetle	70	60	45	50
1178	$1	Metallic Wood Borer	90	75	60	65
1179	$2	Dobson Fly	2·00	2·25	1·25	1·40
1180	$5	Click Beetle	4·25	5·00	3·00	3·25
1181	$10	Long-horned Beetle	7·50	8·00	6·00	6·50
1170/81		Set of 12	16·00	17·00	13·50	14·00

*The normal sideways watermark shows Crown to left of CA, as seen from the back of the stamp.

(Des R. Watton. Litho Cartor)

1995 (8 May). *50th Anniv of End of Second World War. Horiz designs as T **161** of Ascension. W w **14** (sideways). P 13½.*

1182	25 c.	War memorial	25	25
1183	60 c.	Remembrance Day parade	55	70
1184	75 c.	British Honduras forestry unit	65	90
1185	$1	Vickers-Armstrong Wellington bomber	75	1·10
1182/5		Set of 4	2·00	2·75

(**209**)   210 Male and Female Blue Ground Dove

1995 (1 Sept). *"Singapore '95" International Stamp Exhibition. Nos. 1166/9 optd with T **209** in blue.*

1186	25 c.	Type **207**	30	20
1187	60 c.	Brassavola cucullata	65	80
1188	75 c.	Sobralia mucronata	80	95
1189	$1	Nidema boothii	1·00	1·25
1186/9		Set of 4	2·50	2·75

(Des A. Theobald. Litho B.D.T.)

1995 (24 Oct). *50th Anniv of United Nations. Horiz designs as T **213** of Bahamas. W w **16** (sideways). P 14.*

1190	25 c.	M113-light reconnaisance vehicle	25	20
1191	60 c.	Sultan armoured command vehicle	60	65
1192	75 c.	Leyland-Daf 8×4 drops lorry	75	80
1193	$2	Warrior infantry combat vehicle	1·50	2·25
1190/3		Set of 4	2·75	3·50

(Des N. Arlott. Litho B.D.T.)

1995 (6 Nov). *Christmas. Doves. T **210** and similar vert designs. Multicoloured. W w **14**. P 14.*

1194	25 c.	Type **210**	25	20
1195	60 c.	White-fronted Doves	60	70
1196	75 c.	Pair of Ruddy Ground Doves	75	90
1197	$1	White-winged Doves	1·00	1·25
1194/7		Set of 4	2·40	2·75

(**211**)   212 Unloading Banana Train, Commerce Bight Pier

1996 (17 May). *"CHINA '96" 9th Asian International Stamp Exhibition, Peking. Nos. 1172A, 1174A/5A and 1179A optd with T **211**.*

1198	15 c.	Giant Water Bug	15	15
1199	30 c.	Coconut Weevil	30	30
1200	50 c.	Mantis	45	50
1201	$2	Dobson Fly	1·60	2·00
1198/1201		Set of 4	2·25	2·75

(Des A. Theobald. Litho Cartor)

1996 (7 June). *"CAPEX '96" International Stamp Exhibition, Toronto. Railways. T **212** and similar horiz designs. Multicoloured. W w **14** (sideways). P 13½×13.*

1202	25 c.	Type **212**	25	20
1203	60 c.	Locomotive No. 1, Stann Creek station	55	55
1204	75 c.	Locomotive No. 4 pulling mahogany log train	70	70
1205	$3	L.M.S. No. 5602 British Honduras locomotive	2·50	3·25
1202/5		Set of 4	3·50	4·25

213 *Epidendrum stamfordianum*

214 Red Poll

(Des Lynn Chadwick. Litho Cot Printery Ltd, Barbados)

1996 (6 Nov). *Christmas. Orchids. T 213 and similar vert designs. Multicoloured.* W w **14**. P 14.

1206	25 c. Type 213	..	..	30	20
1207	60 c. *Oncidium carthagenense*	..	..	60	70
1208	75 c. *Oerstedella verrucosa*	..	..	70	80
1209	$1 *Coryanthes speciosa*	..	..	95	1·10
1206/9			*Set of* 4	2·25	2·50

(Des G. Vasarhelyi. Litho Cot Printery Ltd, Barbados)

1997 (12 Feb). *"HONG KONG '97" International Stamp Exhibition. Chinese New Year ("Year of the Ox"). T 214 and similar horiz designs showing cattle breeds. Multicoloured.* W w **14** (sideways). P 14.

1210	25 c. Type 214	..	..	30	20
1211	60 c. Brahman	..	..	60	70
1212	75 c. Longhorn	..	..	70	80
1213	$1 Charbray	..	..	95	1·10
1210/13	..	..	*Set of* 4	2·25	2·50

215 Coral Snake

216 Adult Male Howler Monkey

(Des Doreen McGuiness. Litho Cot Printery, Barbados)

1997 (28 May). *Snakes. T 215 and similar vert designs. Multicoloured.* W w **14**. P 14.

1214	25 c. Type 215	..	..	25	20
1215	60 c. Green Vine Snake	..	..	50	50
1216	75 c. Yellow-jawed Tommygoff	..	..	60	60
1217	$1 Speckled Racer	..	..	75	80
1214/17	..	..	*Set of* 4	1·90	1·90

(Des N. Shewring. Litho Walsall)

1997 (13 Aug). *Endangered Species. Howler Monkey. T 216 and similar vert designs. Multicoloured.* W w **14**. P 14.

1218	10 c. Type 216	..	..	15	10
1219	25 c. Female feeding	..	..	25	20
1220	60 c. Female with young	..	..	55	55
1221	75 c. Juvenile monkey feeding	..	..	65	75
1218/21	..	..	*Set of* 4	1·40	1·40

217 *Maxillaria elatior*

(Des Lynn Chadwick. Litho B.D.T.)

1997 (21 Nov). *Christmas. Orchids. T 217 and similar vert designs. Multicoloured.* W w **16**. P 13½.

1222	25 c. Type 217	..	..	15	20
1223	60 c. *Dimerandra emarginata*	..	..	35	40
1224	75 c. *Macradenia brassavolae*	..	..	45	50
1225	$1 *Ornithocephalus gladiatus*	..	..	60	65
1222/5	..	..	*Set of* 4	1·50	1·75

STAMP BOOKLETS

1920. *Black on pink cover inscr "British Honduras–100–Two Cent Stamps". Stapled.*

SB1 $2 booklet containing one hundred 2 c. (No. 102b) in blocks of 10 (5×2) .. .. ..

1920. *Grey-blue cover inscr "British Honduras–100–Three Cent Stamps". Stapled.*

SB2 $3 booklet containing one hundred 3 c. (No. 103) in blocks of 10 (5×2) .. .. ..

1923. *Black on pink cover inscr "British Honduras–100–Two Cent Stamps". Stapled.*

SB3 $2 booklet containing one hundred 2 c. brown (No. 127) in blocks of 10 (5×2) .. .. ..

1927. *Black on pink cover inscr "British Honduras–100–Two Cent Stamps". Stapled.*

SB4 $2 booklet containing one hundred 2 c. rose-carmine (No. 128) in blocks of 10 (5×2) ..

1984 (30 Apr). *Olympic Games, Los Angeles. Multicoloured cover, 155×102 mm, showing athlete and chariot. Stitched.*

SB5 $10 booklet containing 5 c., 20 c., 25 c. and $2, each in pane of 4 (Nos. 789a, 790a, 791a, 792a) .. 3·25

POSTAGE DUE STAMPS

D 1

D 2

(Typo D.L.R.)

1923–64. *Wmk Mult Script CA. Ordinary paper.* P 14.

D1	D 1	1 c. black		1·75	11·00
		a. Chalk-surfaced paper (25.9.56)		50	15·00
		b. White uncoated paper (9.4.64)		14·00	27·00
D2		2 c. black		1·50	6·00
		a. Chalk-surfaced paper (25.9.56)		50	15·00
D3		4 c. black		1·25	6·00
		a. Missing top serif on "C" (R. 6/6)		7·00	
		b. Chalk-surfaced paper (25.9.56)		90	9·50
		ba. Missing top serif on "C" (R. 6/6)		5·50	
		w. Wmk inverted ..			
D1/3	..	.. ..	*Set of* 3	4·00	21·00
D1a/3b	..	..	*Set of* 3	1·75	35·00
D1/3	Optd "Specimen"		*Set of* 3	48·00	

The early ordinary paper printings were yellowish and quite distinct from No. D1b.

1965 (3 Aug)–**72.** *As Nos. D2a and D3b, but Wmk w 12 (sideways on 2 c.).* P 13½×13 (2 c.) or 13½×14 (4 c.)

D4	D 1	2 c. black (10.1.72)		2·00	4·50
D5		4 c. black		50	5·00

The missing top serif on "C" variety of R. 6/6 was corrected before No. D5 was printed.

(Des P. Powell. Litho Questa)

1976 (1 July). *Type D 2 and similar vert designs, but with different frames.* W w **14** (sideways). P 13½ x 14.

D 6	D 2	1 c. red and dull green ..		10	65
D 7	–	2 c. light magenta and bluish violet	..	10	65
D 8	–	5 c. dull green and orange-brown	..	15	75
D 9	–	15 c. apple-green and dull vermilion	..	25	1·10
D10	–	25 c. orange and olive-green	..	40	1·25
D6/10	..	.. ..	*Set of* 5	85	4·00

CAYES OF BELIZE

A chain of several hundred islands, coral atolls, reefs and sand-banks stretching along the eastern seaboard of Belize.

Appendix

The following issues for the Cayes of Belize fall outside the criteria for full listing as detailed on page xi.

1984

Marine Life, Map and Views. 1, 2, 5, 10, 15, 25, 75 c., $3, $5
250th Anniv of Lloyd's List (newspaper). 25, 75 c., $1, $2.
Olympic Games, Los Angeles. 10, 15, 75 c., $2
90th Anniv of "Caye Service" Local Stamps. 10, 15, 75 c., $2

1985

Birth Bicentenary of John J. Audubon (ornithologist). 25, 75 c., $1, $3
Shipwrecks. $1 × 4

Issues for the Cayes of Belize were discontinued after June 1985. It is reported that remainders, probably the 1984 definitive stamps, were later issued to other Belize post offices for postal purposes.

Quality British & Commonwealth Stamps Direct to Your Door

Irresistibly simple, exceptionally quick and reassuringly reliable. Stanley Gibbons Mail Order service enables you to build your collection economically from the comfort of your own home.

We Provide:

■ Free advice from our team of international specialists.

■ Large stocks of guaranteed quality material.

■ Fast 48 hour order despatch.

■ Regular well produced, illustrated brochures and lists.

■ Exclusive special offers mailed regularly.

■ Wants lists service available.

Telephone 0171 836 8444 for free copies of our latest Great Britain, Channel Islands, Australia, Canada, New Zealand and Falkland Islands brochures.

Or send your wants list to:
Stanley Gibbons Mail Order
399 Strand, London
WC2R 0LX
and we'll do our best to help.

STANLEY GIBBONS
Mail Order

• **OUR NAME IS YOUR GUARANTEE OF QUALITY** •

Bermuda

The first internal postal system for Bermuda was organised by Joseph Stockdale, the proprietor of the *Bermuda Gazette*, in 1784. This service competed with that of the colonial post office, set up in 1812, until 1818.

Control of the overseas postal service passed to the British G.P.O. in 1818. The internal delivery system was discontinued between 1821 and 1830. The overseas posts became a colonial responsibility in 1859.

For illustrations of the handstamp types see BRITISH POST OFFICES ABROAD notes, following GREAT BRITAIN.

CROWNED-CIRCLE HANDSTAMPS

CC1 CC1 ST. GEORGES BERMUDA (R.) (1.8.1845)
.. .. *Price on cover* £6500
CC2 IRELAND ISLE BERMUDA (R.) (1.8.1845)
.. .. *Price on cover* £6500
CC3 HAMILTON BERMUDA (R.) (13.11.1846)
.. .. *Price on cover* £3500
For Nos. CC1 and CC3 used as adhesive Postmasters' Stamps see Nos. O7 and O6.

PRICES FOR STAMPS ON COVER TO 1945	
Nos. 1/11	*from* × 5
Nos. 12/17	*from* × 10
Nos. 19/29a	*from* × 8
Nos. 30/a	*from* × 10
Nos. 31/4	*from* × 4
Nos. 34a/55	*from* × 3
Nos. 56/8	*from* × 10
Nos. 59/76	*from* × 4
Nos. 76a/93	*from* × 3
Nos. 94/7	*from* × 4
Nos. 98/106	*from* × 3
Nos. 107/15	*from* × 4
Nos. 116/21	*from* × 5
No. 122	*from* × 20

COLONY

O 1

O 2

1848–61. *Postmasters' Stamps. Adhesives prepared and issued by the postmasters at Hamilton and St. Georges. Dated as given in brackets.*

(a) By W. B. Perot at Hamilton
O1 O 1 1d. black/*bluish grey* (1848) .. .. — £80000
O2 1d. black/*bluish grey* (1849) .. .. — £110000
O3 1d. red/*thick white* (1853) .. .. — £80000
O4 1d. red/*bluish wove* (1854) .. .. — £250000
O5 1d. red/*bluish wove* (1856) .. .. — £160000
O6 O 2 (1d.) carmine-red/*bluish laid* (1861) .. — £70000

(b) By J. H. Thies at St. Georges
As Type O 2 but inscr "ST. GEORGES"
O7 — (1d.) carmine-red/*buff* (1860) .. .. † £60000
Stamps of Type O 1 bear manuscript value and signature, the dates being those shown on the eleven known examples. The stamps are distributed between the dates as follows: 1848 three examples, 1849 two examples, 1853 three examples, 1854 two examples, 1856 one example.

It is believed that the franking value of Nos. O6/7 was 1d., although this is not shown on the actual stamps. Four examples are known of this type used from Hamilton, from March 1861 (and one unused), and five used from St. Georges between July 1860 and January 1863, both issues being cancelled by pen.

Prices shown reflect our estimation of value based on known copies. For instance of the two copies known of No. O4, one is in the Royal collection and the other is on entire.

It is possible that a fourth postmaster's provisional was used by Robert Ward at Hamilton in late 1862 when two examples of Type O 2 on laid paper are known cancelled by blue crayon.

1

2

3

4

5

(Typo D.L.R.)

1865–1903. *Wmk Crown CC. (a) P* 14.
1	1	1d. rose-red (25.9.65) ..	..	85·00	1·25
2		1d. pale rose ..	..	£110	6·50
3	2	2d. dull blue (14.3.66) ..	..	£200	18·00
4		2d. bright blue ..	..	£225	11·00
5	3	3d. yellow-buff (10.3.73) ..	..	£450	65·00
5a	3	3d. orange	..	£700	85·00
6	4	6d. dull purple (25.9.65) ..	..	£800	75·00
7		6d. dull mauve	..	22·00	12·00
8	5	1s. green (25.9.65)	..	£225	42·00

(b) Imperf
9	1	1d. rose-red	..	£15000	£8500

(c) P 14 × 12½
10	3	3d. yellow-buff (1882) ..	..	£170	60·00
10a	4	6d. bright mauve (1903)	..	13·00	22·00
11	5	1s. green (1894)	..	11·00	£120
		a. Vert strip of 3, two stamps imperf			
		horiz	..	£12000	

Though manufactured early in 1880, stamps *P* 14 × 12½ were not issued until the dates given above.

THREE PENCE THREE PENCE
(6) (6a)

One
Penny.

THREE PENCE
(7) (8)

1874 (12 Mar–19 May). *Nos.* 1 *and* 8 *surch diagonally.*
(a) With T 6 ("P" *and* "R" *different type*)
12	1	3d. on 1d. rose-red ..	..	..	£10000
13	5	3d. on 1s. green..	..	£2000	£850

(b) With T 6a ("P" *same type as* "R")
13b	5	3d. on 1s. green..	..	£2000	£800

(c) With T 7 (19 May)
14	5	3d. on 1s. green..	..	£1200	£650

The 3d. on 1d. was a trial surcharge which was not regularly issued, though a few specimens were postally used before 1879. Nos. 13, 13b and 14, being handstamped, are found with double or partial double surcharges.

(Surch by Queen's Printer, Donald McPhee Lee)
1875 (March–May). *Surch with T* 8.
15	2	1d. on 2d. (No. 4) (23 Apr) ..	..	£700	£350
		a. No stop after "Penny"	..	£9000	£6000
16	3	1d. on 3d. (No. 5) (8 May) ..	..	£450	£350
17	5	1d. on 1s. (No. 8) (11 Mar) ..	..	£500	£250
		a. Surch inverted	..	†£15000	
		b. No stop after "Penny"	..	—	£8000

It is emphasised that the prices quoted for Nos. 12/17 are for fine examples. The many stamps from these provisional issues which are in inferior condition are worth much less.

BRITISH EMPIRE EXCLUSIVELY

WANTS LISTS WELCOMED FROM SERIOUS COLLECTORS OF <u>BERMUDA</u>. EMPHASIS ON PRE-1935. WE STOCK STAMPS, POSTAL HISTORY AND SPECIALIST MATERIAL. *REFERENCES ESSENTIAL.*

REQUEST A CATALOGUE FOR OUR NEXT PUBLIC AUCTION. PLEASE SPECIFY YOUR INTERESTS.

SELLING? ASK US ABOUT CONSIGNING TO A FUTURE SALE.

𝔙𝔦𝔠𝔱𝔬𝔯𝔦𝔞 𝔖𝔱𝔞𝔪𝔭 ℭ𝔬𝔪𝔭𝔞𝔫𝔶

Established 1962

PHOEBE A. MACGILLIVARY
P.O. BOX 745, RIDGEWOOD, NJ 07451, U.S.A.
Tel: 001-201-652-7283   Fax: 001-201-612-0024

9

10

11

(Typo D.L.R.)

1880 (23 Mar). *Wmk Crown CC. P* 14.
19	9	½d. stone	..	2·25	3·75
20	10	4d. orange-red	.. ..	15·00	1·75

(Typo D.L.R.)

1883–98. *Wmk Crown CA. P* 14.
21	9	½d. dull green (Oct, 1892)	..	2·25	2·25
21a		½d. deep grey-green (1893)	..	2·25	80
22	1	1d. dull rose (Dec. 1883)	..	£120	3·50
23		1d. rose-red	..	70·00	2·75
24		1d. carmine-rose (1886)	..	42·00	70
24a		1d. aniline carmine (1889)	..	7·00	20
25	2	2d. blue (Dec. 1886)	..	50·00	3·50
26		2d. aniline purple (July, 1893)	..	10·00	3·75
26a		2d. brown-purple (1898)	..	2·75	1·50
27	11	2½d. deep ultramarine (10.11.84)	..	12·00	2·25
27a		2½d. pale ultramarine	..	4·50	40
28	3	3d. grey (Jan, 1886)	..	22·00	6·00
29	5	1s. yellow-brown (1893)	..	15·00	15·00
29a		1s. olive-brown	..	13·00	14·00
21/9a			*Set of* 7	90·00	24·00
21, 26 & 29 Optd "Specimen"			*Set of* 3	£375	

1893 PROVISIONAL POSTCARD. Following the reduction of the postcard rate to 1d. in 1893 existing stocks of postal stationery postcards, including some from the September 1880 issue franked with Nos. 19 and 22, were surcharged "One Penny". This surcharge was applied by the *Royal Gazette* press. It is generally believed that an individual in the Post Office acquired all the examples showing Nos. 19 and 22, but provisional postcards are known used to Europe and, one example only, locally. *Price from* £550 *unused*, £1400 *used*.

ONE FARTHING

(12)

13 Dry Dock

14

1901. *As Nos.* 29/*a but colour changed, surch with T* 12 *by D.L.R.*
30	5	¼d. on 1s. dull grey (11.1.01) (Optd S. £75)		70	40
30a		¼d. on 1s. bluish grey (18.3.01)		1·25	85
		ab. "F" in "FARTHING" inserted by handstamp		£6000	£7000

Seven examples of No. 30ab are known, five unused (one being in the Royal Collection) and two used (one on postcard). It would appear that the "F" in position one of an unspecified horizontal row was either weak or missing and an additional impression of the letter was then inserted by a separate handstamp.

(Typo D.L.R.)

1902 (Nov)–**04.** *Wmk Crown CA. P* 14.
31	13	½d. black and green (12.03)	.. ..	9·00	1·25
32		1d. brown and carmine	..	8·00	10
33		3d. magenta and sage-green (9.03)	..	2·25	1·75
34	10	4d. orange-brown (18.1.04)	..	26·00	45·00
		x. Wmk reversed	..	£250	
31/4			*Set of* 4	40·00	45·00
31/3 Optd "Specimen"			*Set of* 3	£130	

1906–09. *Wmk Mult Crown CA. P* 14.
34a	13	¼d. brown and violet (9.08)	..	1·50	2·00
35		½d. black and green (12.06)	..	15·00	65
36		1d. brown and carmine (4.06)	..	18·00	20
		w. Wmk inverted	..	£250	£180
37		2d. grey and orange (10.07)	..	7·50	11·00
38		2½d. brown and ultramarine (12.06)	..	13·00	8·00
39		4d. blue and chocolate (11.09)	..	3·00	14·00
34a/9			*Set of* 6	50·00	32·00
34a, 37/9 Optd "Specimen"			*Set of* 4	£200	

1908–10. *Wmk Mult Crown CA. P* 14.
41	13	½d. green (3.09)	..	9·00	2·50
42		1d. red (5.08)	..	17·00	10
43		2½d. blue (14.2.10)	..	12·00	5·75
41/3			*Set of* 3	35·00	7·50
41/3 Optd "Specimen"			*Set of* 3	£180	

(Recess D.L.R.)

1910–25. *Wmk Mult Crown CA. P* 14.
44	14	¼d. brown (26.3.12)	..	1·50	2·50
		a. Pale brown	..	60	1·50
45		½d. green (4.6.10)	..	1·25	25
		a. Deep green (1918)	..	6·00	90
		w. Wmk inverted	..		
		x. Wmk reversed	..	—	£150
		y. Wmk inverted and reversed			
46		1d. red (I) (15.10.10)	..	13·00	30
		a. Rose-red	..	17·00	30
		b. Carmine (12.19)	..	48·00	8·00
		w. Wmk inverted	..	£300	
		x. Wmk reversed	..		
		y. Wmk inverted and reversed	..	£200	
47		2d. grey (1.13)	..	3·00	7·00
		x. Wmk reversed	..		

48	14	2½d. blue (27.3.12)	.. ..	3·50	60
		w. Wmk inverted	..		
		x. Wmk reversed	..	—	£150
		y. Wmk inverted and reversed	..	£110	75·00
49		3d. purple/*yellow* (1.13)	..	1·75	6·00
49a		4d. red/*yellow* (1.9.19)	..	4·75	8·00
50		6d. purple (26.3.12)	..	14·00	18·00
		a. Pale claret (2.6.24)	..	11·00	8·00
51		1s. black/*green* (26.3.12)	..	3·50	3·75
		a. Jet black/*olive* (1925)	..	4·00	12·00
44/51			*Set of* 9	40·00	32·00
44/51 Optd "Specimen"			*Set of* 9	£375	

Nos. 44 to 51a are comb-perforated 13.8×14 or 14. No. 45 exits also line-perforated 14, probably from the printing dispatched to Bermuda on 13 March 1911.
See also Nos. 76b/87a.

15

HIGH VALUE KEY TYPES. The reign of King Edward VII saw the appearance of the first in a new series of "key type" designs, initially on the issues of Malaya — Straits Settlements and Nyasaland, to be used for high value denominations where a smaller design was felt to be inappropriate. The system was extended during the reign of King George V, using the portrait as Bermuda Type 15, to cover Bermuda, Ceylon, Leeward Islands, Malaya — Straits Settlements, Malta and Nyasaland. A number of these territories continued to use the key type concept for high value King George VI stamps and one, Leeward Islands, for stamps of Queen Elizabeth II.

In each instance the King George V issues were printed in sheets of 60 (12×5) on various coloured papers. The system utilised a common "head" plate used with individual "duty" plates which printed the territory name and face value.

Two major plate flaws occur on the King George V head plate: the break in scroll on R.1/12 and the broken crown and scroll on R.2/12. Both of these occur in different states, having been repaired and then damaged once again, perhaps on several occasions. Later printings of R. 1/12 show additional damage to the crown and upper scrolls. The prices quoted in the listings are for examples approximately as illustrated.

Break in scroll (R. 1/12)

Broken crown and scroll (R. 2/12)

Break through scroll (R. 1/9. Ptgs from June 1929. Some show attempts at repair)

(Typo D.L.R.)

1918 (1 Apr)–**22.** *Wmk Mult Crown CA. Chalk-surfaced paper. P* 14.
51b	15	2s. purple and blue/*blue* (19.6.20)	..	15·00	45·00
		a. Break in scroll	..	£170	
		bb. Broken crown and scroll	..	£170	
		bx. Wmk reversed	..	£1300	
52		2s. 6d. black and red/*blue*	..	25·00	65·00
		a. Break in scroll	..	£225	
52b		4s. black and carmine (19.6.20)	..	60·00	£120
		ba. Break in scroll	..	£275	
		bb. Broken crown and scroll	..	£275	
53		5s. deep green and deep red/*yellow*	..	50·00	90·00
		a. Break in scroll	..	£275	
		c. Green & carmine-red/*pale yell* (1920)	38·00	75·00	
		ca. Break in scroll	..	£275	
		cb. Broken crown and scroll	..	£275	
		cw. Wmk inverted	..	£250	
		cy. Wmk inverted and reversed	..	£1500	
54		10s. green and carmine/*pale bluish green*	£150	£275	
		a. Break in scroll	..	£500	
		c. Green & red/*pale bluish green* (1922)	£180	£300	
		ca. Break in scroll	..	£550	
		cb. Broken crown and scroll	..	£550	
55		£1 purple and black/*red*	..	£350	£550
		a. Break in scroll	..	£800	
		b. Broken crown and scroll	..	£900	
		c. Break through scroll	..	£1100	
		w. Wmk inverted	..	£1500	
51b/5			*Set of* 6	£550	£1000
51b/5 Optd "Specimen"			*Set of* 6	£750	

Beware of cleaned copies of the 10s. with faked postmarks. Examples of Nos. 51b/5 are known showing a forged Hamilton double ring postmark dated "22 JAN 13".
See also Nos. 88/93.

WAR TAX
(16)

WAR TAX
(17)

1918 (4 May). *Nos.* 46 *and* 46a *optd locally with T* 16.
56	14	1d. red	.. ..	45	50
		a. Rose-red	.. ..	45	90

1920 (5 Feb). *No.* 46b *optd with T* 17.
58	14	1d. carmine	.. ..	75	1·25

The War Tax stamps represented a compulsory levy in addition to normal postal fees until 31 Dec 1920. Subsequently they were valid for ordinary postage.

18

19

(Des by the Governor (Gen. Sir James Willcocks). Typo D.L.R.)

1920 (11 Nov)–**21.** *Tercentenary of Representative Institutions* (1st issue). *Chalk-surfaced paper* (3d. to 1s.). *P* 14.
(a) Wmk Mult Crown CA (sideways)* (19.1.21)
59	18	¼d. brown	..	2·25	13·00
		a. "C" missing from wmk	..	£275	
		b. "A" missing from wmk	..	£275	
		w. Wmk Crown to right of CA	..	£100	
		x. Wmk sideways reversed	..	£130	
60		½d. green	..	2·25	7·00
		w. Wmk Crown to right of CA	..	£150	
		x. Wmk sideways reversed	..	£120	
		y. Wmk sideways inverted and reversed			
61		2d. grey	..	9·00	26·00
		a. "C" missing from wmk	..	£425	
		w. Wmk Crown to right of CA	..	£225	
		y. Wmk sideways inverted and reversed			
62		3d. dull and deep purple/*pale yellow*	..	8·50	25·00
63		4d. black and red/*pale yellow*	..	9·00	25·00
64		1s. black/*blue-green*	..	16·00	48·00

(b) Wmk Mult Script CA (sideways)
65	18	1d. carmine	..	2·25	30
66		2½d. bright blue	..	8·50	9·00
67		6d. dull and bright purple (19.1.21)	..	19·00	55·00
59/67			*Set of* 9	70·00	£190
59/67 Optd "Specimen"			*Set of* 9	£325	

The normal sideways watermark shows Crown to left of CA as seen from the back of the stamp.

(Des. H. J. Dale. Recess D.L.R.)

1921 (12 May). *Tercentenary of Representative Institutions* (2nd issue). *P* 14. (a) *Wmk Crown CA (sideways*).*
68	19	2d. slate-grey	..	4·50	21·00
		a. "C" of "CA" missing from wmk	..		
		w. Wmk Crown to left of CA	..	£300	
69		2½d. bright ultramarine	..	9·00	3·00
		a. "C" of "CA" missing from wmk	..	£425	
		b. "A" of "CA" missing from wmk	..	£425	
		x. Wmk sideways reversed	..	—	£250
70		3d. purple/*pale yellow*	..	4·00	14·00
71		4d. red/*pale yellow*	..	14·00	18·00
		x. Wmk sideways reversed	..	£150	
72		6d. purple	..	9·00	38·00
		a. "C" of "CA" missing from wmk	..	£475	
73		1s. black/*green*	..	21·00	45·00

(b) Wmk Mult Script CA (sideways)*
74	19	¼d. brown	..	80	2·75
		w. Wmk Crown to left of CA	..		
		x. Wmk sideways reversed	..		
75		½d. green	..	2·75	6·00
		w. Wmk Crown left of CA	..	90·00	£110
		y. Wmk sideways inverted and reversed	..	£180	

GREAT BRITAIN and BRITISH COMMONWEALTH

CLASSICS, RARITIES, ERRORS

Artists Designs, Essays, Proofs,
Thematic Varieties, Covers etc.

WANTS LISTS ALWAYS
WELCOMED

TOP QUALITY ITEMS FOR
THE ENTHUSIAST

Bermuda

PRIVATE TREATY. A top quality collection available.

Fine range of pre-adhesive covers including all the
rare crown circles, virtually all the listed stamps
and varieties, Q.V. - Q.E.II plus artists drawings,
proofs etc. Details on request.

S.G.30a

MUSCOTT'S

Established 1947

Meadrow, Godalming, Surrey GU7 3HL, U.K.
Tel: 01483 417884 Fax: 01483 860572

S.G.11a

Empire Philatelics

- POSTAGE STAMPS AND POSTAL HISTORY OF GREAT BRITAIN AND THE COMMONWEALTH

- WANTS LISTS SOLICITED FOR GENERAL OR SPECIALIZED MATERIAL FROM ALL REIGNS

- EXTENSIVE, SPECIALIZED STOCK 1840-1950, INCLUDING MANY RARITIES

- BUYING COLLECTIONS, ESTATES AND NOTEWORTHY INDIVIDUAL ITEMS

- PERIODIC POSTAL AUCTIONS AND PRICE LISTS

- CONSIGNMENTS SOUGHT FOR FUTURE SALES AND PRIVATE TREATY

- NEW IN 1998 - VISIT OUR WEB SITE FOR INFORMATION REGARDING: PRICE LISTS, OUR SHOW
  SCHEDULE, AND A LISTING OF ADDITIONAL SERVICES AND SPECIAL OFFERS

POSTAGE STAMPS:

Barry V. Banks
P. O. Box 9031
Ogden, UT 84409 USA
Tel and FAX: (801) 479-3764
E-Mail: BBANKS@EMAIL.STATE.UT.US

POSTAL HISTORY:

John Hart
P. O. Box 1162
Salt Lake City, UT 84110 USA
Tel: (801) 359-3459
Fax: (801) 521-9247

76 19 1d. deep carmine .. .. 2·50 35
  a. "C" of "CA" missing from wmk
38/76   *Set of 9* 60·00 £130
38/76 Optd "Specimen"   *Set of 9* £300
*The normal sideways watermark shows Crown to right of CA, *as seen from the back of the stamp.*

I   II   III

Three Types of the 1d.
I. Scroll at top left very weak and figure "1" has pointed serifs.
II. Scroll weak. "1" has square serifs and "1d" is heavy.
III. Redrawn. Scroll is completed by a strong line and "1" is thinner with long square serifs.

I   II

Two Types of the 2½d.
I. Short, thick figures, especially of the "1", small "d".
II. Figures taller and thinner, "d" larger.

1922–34. *Wmk Mult Script CA. P* 14.
76b 14 ¼d. brown (7.28) .. .. 1·25 2·00
77   ½d. green (11.22) 90 15
  w. Wmk inverted ..
  x. Wmk reversed ..
78   1d. scarlet (I) (11.22) .. 13·00 60
  a. Carmine (6.24) .. 17·00 60
  bx. Wmk reversed ..
78c   1d. carmine (II) (12.25) .. 30·00 4·50
  cx. Wmk reversed ..
  d. Scarlet (8.27) .. 9·00 80
79   1d. scarlet (III) (10.28) .. 12·00 30
  a. Carmine-lake (1934) .. 18·00 1·25
79b   1½d. red-brown (27.3.34) .. 7·50 35
80   2d. grey (12.23) .. .. 1·50 1·50
  x. Wmk reversed .. .. 50·00
81   2½d. pale sage-green (12.22) .. 2·00 1·50
  a. Deep sage-green (1924) .. 1·00 1·50
  aw. Wmk inverted ..
  ax. Wmk reversed ..
  ay. Wmk inverted and reversed ..
82   2½d. ultramarine (I) (1.12.26) .. 2·50 50
  aw. Wmk inverted .. 70·00
82b   2½d. ultramarine (II) (3.32) .. 1·75 50
83   3d. ultramarine (12.24) .. 15·00 26·00
  w. Wmk inverted .. 90·00
84   3d. purple/yellow (10.26) .. 3·00 1·00
85   4d. red/yellow (8.24) .. 1·50 1·00
  x. Wmk reversed ..
86   6d. purple (8.24) .. .. 1·00 80
87   1s. black/emerald (10.27) .. 4·75 7·00
  a. Brownish black/yellow-green (1934) 30·00 48·00
76b/87   *Set of* 12 42·00 38·00
76b/87 Optd/Perf "Specimen"   *Set of* 12 £475
Values to 1s. come perforated either comb (13.8×14) or line (13.75, 14, 13.75×14 or 14×13.75). Nos. 78/a and 83 only exist comb-perforated, Nos. 76b, 78c/9b, 81a, 82b and 87a line-perforated and the remainder come in both forms.

Breaks in scrolls at right (R. 1/3. Ptgs of 12s. 6d. from July 1932)

1924–32. *Wmk Mult Script CA. Chalk-surfaced paper. P* 14.
88 15 2s. purple and brt blue/pale blue (1.9.27) 38·00 60·00
  a. Break in scroll .. £180
  b. Broken crown and scroll .. £180
  c. Purple and blue/grey-blue (1931) 45·00 65·00
  ca. Break in scroll .. £200
  cb. Broken crown and scroll .. £200
  cc. Break through scroll .. £225
89   2s. 6d. black and carmine/pale blue (4.27) 50·00 95·00
  a. Break in scroll .. £225
  b. Broken crown and scroll .. £225
  c. Black and red/blue to deep blue (6.29) 60·00 95·00
  ca. Break in scroll .. £275
  cb. Broken crown and scroll .. £275
  cc. Break through scroll .. £300
  d. Grey-black and pale orange-vermilion/grey-blue (3.30) £2500 £2500

(89)   da. Break in scroll .. £3750
  db. Broken crown and scroll .. £3750
  dc. Break through scroll .. £3750
  e. Black and carmine-red/deep grey-blue (8.30) 60·00 95·00
  ea. Break in scroll .. £275
  eb. Broken crown and scroll .. £275
  ec. Break through scroll .. £300
  f. Black & scarlet-vermilion/dp bl (9.31) 65·00 95·00
  fa. Break in scroll .. £275
  fb. Broken crown and scroll .. £275
  fc. Break through scroll .. £300
  g. Black & brt orge-verm/dp blue (8.32) £2750 £2500
  ga. Broken crown and scroll .. £4000
  gb. Break through scroll .. £4000
92   10s. green and red/pale emerald (12.24) £120 £250
  b. Broken crown and scroll .. £450
  c. Break through scroll .. £450
  d. Green and red/deep emerald (1931) £120 £250
  da. Break in scroll .. £475
  db. Broken crown and scroll .. £450
  dc. Break through scroll .. £500
93   12s. 6d. grey and orange (8.32) .. £250 £350
  a. Break in scroll .. £650
  b. Broken crown and scroll .. £700
  c. Break through scroll .. £750
  d. Breaks in scrolls at right .. £750
  e. Error. Ordinary paper
88/93   *Set of* 4 £425 £650
88/93 Optd/Perf "Specimen"   *Set of* 4 £500
The true No. 89d is the only stamp on grey-blue paper; other deeper orange-vermilion shades exist on different papers.
Beware of fiscally used 2s. 6d. 10s. and 12s. 6d. stamps cleaned and bearing faked postmarks. Large quantities were used for a "head tax" levied on travellers leaving the country.
For 12s. 6d. design inscribed "Revenue" at both sides see No. F1 under POSTAL FISCAL.

1935 (6 May). *Silver Jubilee. As Nos.* 91/4 *of Antigua, but ptd by Waterlow. P* 11×12.
94   1d. deep blue and scarlet .. 45 55
  j. Damaged turret .. 75·00
  m. "Bird" by turret .. 75·00
95   1½d. ultramarine and grey .. 70 2·00
  m. "Bird" by turret .. 85·00
96   2½d. brown and deep blue .. 1·40 90
  m. "Bird" by turret .. £110
97   1s. slate and purple .. 11·00 20·00
  k. Kite and vertical log .. £130
  l. Kite and horizontal log .. £190
94/7   *Set of* 4 12·00 21·00
94/7 Perf "Specimen"   *Set of* 4 £160
For illustrations of plate varieties see Catalogue Introduction.

20 Red Hole, Paget   21 South Shore

22 *Lucie* (yacht)   23 Grape Bay, Paget Parish

24 Point House, Warwick Parish   25 Gardener's Cottage, Par-la-Ville, Hamilton

(Recess B.W.)

1936 (14 Apr)–47. *Wmk Mult Script CA* (sideways on horiz designs). *P* 12.
98 20 ½d. bright green 10 10
99 21 1d. black and scarlet 20 20
100   1½d. black and chocolate .. 90 30
101 22 2d. black and pale blue .. 4·50 2·00
102 23 2½d. light and deep blue .. 80 25
103 24 3d. black and scarlet .. 2·50 90
104 25 6d. carmine-lake and violet .. 80 10
  a. Claret and dull violet (6.47) 3·00 85
105 23 1s. green .. .. 3·50 7·00
106 20 1s. 6d. brown 50 10
98/106   *Set of* 9 12·50 9·50
98/106 Perf "Specimen"   *Set of* 9 £250
All are line-perf 11.9, except printings of the 6d. from July 1951 onwards, which are comb-perf 11.9 × 11.75.

1937 (14 May). *Coronation. As Nos.* 95/7 *of Antigua, but printed by D.L.R. P* 14.
107   1d. scarlet 50 50
108   1½d. yellow-brown .. 60 1·40
109   2½d. bright blue .. 70 1·50
107/9   *Set of* 3 1·60 3·00
107/9 Perf "Specimen"   *Set of* 3 £110

26 Ships in Hamilton Harbour   27 St. David's Lighthouse

28 White-tailed Tropic Bird, Arms of Bermuda and Native Flower

(Des Miss Higginbotham (T 28). Recess B.W.)

1938 (20 Jan)–1952. *T* 22, *T* 23 *(but with portrait of King George VI) and T* 26 *to* 28. *Wmk Mult Script CA. P* 12.
110 26 1d. black and red (a) (b) .. 65 20
111   1½d. deep blue and purple-brown (a) (b) 5·00 1·50
  a. Blue and brown (3.43) .. 5·50 2·50
  b. Lt blue & purple-brn (a) (b) (9.45) 2·25 35
  ba. "A" of "CA" missing from wmk ..
112 22 2d. light blue and sepia (a) .. 40·00 8·50
112a   2d. ultramarine and scarlet (a) (b) (8.11.40) .. 1·50 80
113 23 2½d. light and deep blue (a) .. 11·00 1·50
113a   2½d. lt blue & sepia-black (a) (18.12.41) 3·00 1·50
  b. Pale blue & sepia-black (a) (3.43) 2·75 1·25
  c. Bright blue and deep sepia-black (b) (23.9.52) 4·25 3·00
114 27 3d. black and rose-red (a) .. 12·00 1·50
114a   3d. black & deep blue (a) (b) (16.7.41) 1·75 40
114b 28 7½d. black, blue & brt grn (a) (18.12.41) 6·50 2·00
  c. Black, blue & yellow-grn (3.43) 4·50 2·25
115 23 1s. green (a)(b) .. .. 2·00 50
  a. Bluish green (b) (20.6.52) .. 6·50 5·00
Perforations. Two different perforating machines were used on the various printings of these stamps: (a) the original 11.9 line perforation; (b) 11.9 × 11.75 comb perforation, introduced in July 1950. These perforations occur as indicated above.

29 King George VI

Shading omitted from top right scroll (R. 1/1. March 1943 ptgs of 2s. and £1)   Lower right scroll with broken tail (R. 2/10. Line perforated printings only)

Broken top right scroll (R. 5/11. Line perforated ptgs only. A retouched state of the flaw is visible in later ptgs up to March 1943)   Broken lower right scroll (R. 5/12. Occurs on printings made between May 1941 and March 1943)

Gash in chin (R.2/5.   Missing pearl
Ptgs between May   (R.5/1, Nov 1945
1941 and March 1943   ptg of 5s. only)
(Typo D.L.R.)

1938 (20 Jan)–53. *T* **29**. *Wmk Mult Crown CA* (£1) *or Mult Script CA* (*others*). *Chalk-surfaced paper. P* 14 (comb).

116	2s. deep purple and ultramarine/grey-blue	£110	10·00
	a. *Deep reddish purple and ultram/ grey-blue* (10.40)	£225	20·00
	b. *Perf* 14¼ *line. Deep purple and ultram/ grey-blue* (14.11.41)*	£300	85·00
	bc. Lower right scroll with broken tail	£950	£400
	bd. Broken top right scroll	£850	£350
	be. Broken lower right scroll	£850	£350
	bf. Gash in chin	£850	£350
	c. *Ordinary paper. Pur & bl /dp bl* (7.6.42)	7·00	1·50
	ce. Broken lower right scroll	£180	65·00
	cf. Gash in chin	£180	65·00
	d. *Ordinary paper. Purple and deep blue/pale blue* (5.3.43)	11·00	1·50
	db. Shading omitted from top right scroll	£750	£400
	de. Broken lower right scroll	£475	£275
	df. Gash in chin	£475	£275
	e. *Perf* 13. *Ordinary paper. Dull purple and blue/pale blue* (15.2.50)	16·00	14·00
	f. *Perf* 13. *Ordinary paper. Reddish purple and blue/pale blue* (10.10.50)	8·50	12·00
117	2s. 6d. black and red/grey-blue	70·00	8·00
	a. *Perf* 14¼ *line. Black and red/grey-blue* (21.2.42)*	£475	£110
	ac. Lower right scroll with broken tail	£1100	£475
	ad. Broken top right scroll	£1000	£400
	ae. Broken lower right scroll	£1000	£400
	af. Gash in chin	£1000	£400
	b. *Ordinary paper. Black and red/pale blue* (5.3.43)	19·00	6·50
	be. Broken lower right scroll	£400	£180
	bf. Gash in chin	£400	£180
	c. *Perf* 13. *Ordinary paper. Black and orange-red/pale blue* (10.10.50)	19·00	11·00
	d. *Perf* 13. *Ordinary paper. Black and red/ pale blue* (18.6.52)	16·00	12·00
118	5s. green and red/yellow	£140	25·00
	a. *Pale green and red/yellow* (14.3.39)*	£275	60·00
	b. *Perf* 14¼ *line. Dull yellow-green and red/yellow* (5.1.43)*	£200	28·00
	bc. Lower right scroll with broken tail	£650	£250
	bd. Broken top right scroll	£600	£190
	be. Broken lower right scroll	£600	£190
	bf. Gash in chin	£600	£190
	c. *Ordinary paper. Dull yellow-green and carmine-red/pale yellow* (5.42)	£400	90·00
	ce. Broken lower right scroll	£2250	£800
	cf. Gash in chin	£2250	£800
	d. *Ordinary paper. Pale bluish green and carmine-red/pale yellow* (5.3.43)	£100	50·00
	de. Broken lower right scroll	£600	£350
	df. Gash in chin	£600	£350
	e. *Ordinary paper. Green and red/pale yellow* (11.45)*	50·00	20·00
	ea. Missing pearl	£550	
	f. *Perf* 13. *Ordinary paper. Yellow-green and red/pale yellow* (15.2.50)	21·00	16·00
	g. *Perf* 13. *Green and scarlet/yellow* (*chalk-surfaced*) (10.10.50)	27·00	27·00
119	10s. green and deep lake/pale emerald	£450	£250
	a. *Bluish green and deep red/green* (8.39)*	£200	£130
	b. *Perf* 14¼ *line. Ordinary paper. Yellow-green and carmine/green* (1942)*	£400	£140
	bc. Lower right scroll with broken tail	£1100	£600
	bd. Broken top right scroll	£950	£500
	be. Broken lower right scroll	£950	£500
	bf. Gash in chin	£950	£500
	c. *Ordinary paper. Yellowish green and deep carmine-red/green* (5.3.43)	80·00	55·00
	ce. Broken lower right scroll	£1800	
	cf. Gash in chin	£1600	
	d. *Ordinary paper. Deep green and dull red/green* (*emerald back*) (11.12.46)	85·00	60·00
	e. *Perf* 13. *Ordinary paper. Green and vermilion/green* (19.9.51)	30·00	35·00
	f. *Perf* 13. *Ordinary paper. Green and dull red/green* (16.4.53)	30·00	42·00
120	12s. 6d. deep grey and brownish orange	£475	£400
	a. *Grey and brownish orange* (*shades*)	£180	65·00
	b. *Grey and pale orange* (9.11.40)*	90·00	60·00
	c. *Ordinary paper* (2.3.44)*	£100	60·00
	ce. Broken lower right scroll	£1400	£1500
	cf. Gash in chin	£1400	
	d. *Ordinary paper. Grey & yell*† (7.9.47)*	£550	£450
	e. *Perf* 13. *Grey and pale orange* (*chalk-surfaced*) (10.10.50)	95·00	75·00
121	£1 purple and black/*red*	£275	£100
	a. *Pale purple & black/pale red* (13.3.43)*	80·00	60·00
	ab. Shading omitted from top right scroll	£1300	
	ae. Broken lower right scroll	£950	£800
	af. Gash in chin	£950	
	b. *Deep reddish purple and black/pale red* (29.3.45)*	70·00	45·00
	be. Broken lower right scroll	£1000	
	bf. Gash in chin	£1000	
	c. *Perf* 13. *Violet & black/scarlet* (7.12.51)	48·00	75·00
	d. *Perf* 13. *Brt violet & blk/scar* (10.12.52)	£160	£150
110/21c		*Set of* 16	£250	£140
110/21 *Perf* "Specimen"		*Set of* 16	£1500	

Following extensive damage to their printing works on 29 December 1940 much of De La Rue's work was transferred to other firms operating under their supervision. It is understood that Williams Lea & Co produced those new printings ordered for the Bermuda high value stamps during 1941. The first batch of these printings showed the emergency use, by Williams Lea, of a 14¼ line perforating machine (exact gauge 14.15) instead of the comb perforation (exact gauge 13.9 × 13.8).

Dates marked * are those of earliest known use.

In No. 116c the coloured surfacing of the paper is mottled with white specks sometimes accompanied by very close horizontal lines. In Nos. 116d, 117b and 118c/d the surfacing is the same colour as the back, sometimes applied in widely spaced horizontal lines giving the appearance of laid paper.

†No. 120d is the so-called "lemon" shade.

HALF PENNY

(30)   31 Postmaster Perot's Stamp

1940 (20 Dec). *No.* 110 *surch with T* **30**.

122	**26** ½d. on 1d. black and red (*shades*)	40	45

The spacing between "PENNY" and "X" varies from 12½ mm to 14 mm.

1946 (6 Nov). *Victory. As Nos.* 110/11 *of Antigua.*

123	1½d. brown	15	15
124	3d. blue	15	15
123/4 *Perf* "Specimen"		*Set of* 2	75·00

1948 (1 Dec). *Royal Silver Wedding. As Nos.* 112/13 *of Antigua.*

125	1½d. red-brown	30	50
126	£1 carmine	40·00	48·00

(Recess B.W.)

1949 (11 Apr). *Centenary of Postmaster Perot's Stamp. Wmk Mult Script CA. P* 13½.

127	**31** 2½d. blue and brown	15	15
128	3d. black and blue	15	15
129	6d. violet and green	15	15
127/9		*Set of* 3	40	40

1949 (10 Oct). *75th Anniv of Universal Postal Union. As Nos.* 114/17 *of Antigua.*

130	2½d. blue-black	60	75
131	3d. deep blue	1·75	85
132	6d. purple	60	75
133	1s. blue-green	60	75
130/3		*Set of* 4	3·25	2·75

1953 (4 June). *Coronation. As No.* 120 *of Antigia, but ptd by B.W.*

134	1½d. black and blue	60	15

32 Easter Lilies   34 Easter Lily

37 Map of Bermuda

Die I   Die II
"Sandy's"   "Sandys"

(Des C. Deakins (½d., 3d., 1s. 3d., 5s.), J. Berry (1d., 1½d., 2½d., 4d., 1s.). B. Brown (2d., 6d., 8d.), D. Haig (4½d., 9d.), Pamela Braley-Smith (2s. 6d.) and E. C. Leslie (10s.) Recess (except £1, centre typo), B.W.)

1953 (9 Nov)–**62**. *T* **32**, **34**, **37**, *and similar designs. Wmk Mult Script CA. P* 13½.

135	**32** ½d. olive-green	45	2·00
	a. *Yellow-olive* (19.5.54)	40	60
136	– 1d. black and red	1·00	50
	a. *Black and deep red* (19.5.54)	1·25	40
137	**34** 1½d. green	30	10
138	– 2d. ultramarine and brown-red	50	40
139	– 2½d. rose-red	2·00	50
140	**37** 3d. deep purple (I)	30	10
140a	3d. deep purple (II) (2.1.57)	1·00	20
141	– 4d. black and bright blue	30	40
142	– 4½d. emerald	45	1·00

143	– 6d. black and deep turquoise	5·00	60
143a	– 8d. black and red (16.5.55)	2·50	30
143b	– 9d. violet (6.1.58)	7·00	2·50
144	– 1s. orange	50	15
145	**37** 1s. 3d. blue (I)	3·50	30
	a. *Greenish blue* (21.9.54)	8·00	1·25
145b	1s. 3d. blue (II) (2.1.57)	7·00	50
	bc. *Bright blue* (14.8.62)	9·50	3·00
146	– 2s. brown	4·00	85
147	– 2s. 6d. scarlet	4·50	45
148	– 5s. carmine	16·00	85
149	– 10s. deep ultramarine	13·00	5·00
	a. *Ultramarine* (13.2.57)	40·00	14·00
150	– £1 brown, blue, red, grn & bronze-grn	23·00	21·00
135/150		*Set of* 18	70·00	32·00

Designs: *Horiz*—1d., 4d. Postmaster Perot's stamps; 2d. *Victory II* (racing dinghy); 2½d. Sir George Somers and *Sea Venture*; 4½d., 9d. *Sea Venture* (galleon), coin and Perot stamp; 6d., 8d. White-tailed Tropic Bird; 1s. Early Bermudian coinage; 2s. Arms of St. Georges; 5s. Hog coin; 10s. Obverse and reverse of hog coin; £1 Arms of Bermuda. *Vert*—2s. 6d. Warwick Fort.

Nos. 136, 138 and 143 exist in coils, constructed from normal sheets.

1953 (26 Nov). *Royal Visit. As No.* 143 *but inscr* "ROYAL VISIT 1953" *in top left corner.*

151	6d. black and deep turquoise	30	20

Three Power Talks December, 1953.   **Three Power Talks December, 1953.**

(46)   (46a)

First setting (Type 46). First line 24½ mm long.
Second setting (Type 46a). First line 25¼ mm long.

1953 (8 Dec). *Three Power Talks. Nos.* 140 *and* 145 *optd with T* **46**.

152	**37** 3d. deep purple (Type 46) (B.)	10	10
	a. Optd with Type 46a	45	15
153	1s. 3d. blue (Type 46) (R.)	10	10
	a. Optd with Type 46a	1·75	1·75

50TH ANNIVERSARY U S — BERMUDA OCEAN RACE 1956

(47)   48 Perot's Post Office

1956 (22 June). *50th Anniv of United States–Bermuda Yacht Race. Nos.* 143a *and* 145a *optd with T* **47** *by the Bermuda Press.*

154	8d. black and red (Bk.)	20	40
155	1s. 3d. greenish blue (R.)	20	55

(Des W. Harrington. Recess B.W.)

1959 (1 Jan). *Wmk Mult Script CA. P* 13½.

156	**48** 6d. black and deep mauve	70	15

49 Arms of King James I and Queen Elizabeth II

(Des W. Harrington. Recess; arms litho D.L.R.)

1959 (29 July). *350th Anniv of First Settlement. Arms, red, yellow and blue; frame colours below. W w* **12**. *P* 13.

157	**49** 1½d. grey-blue	25	10
158	3d. drab-grey	30	50
159	4d. reddish purple	35	55
160	8d. slate-violet	35	15
161	9d. olive-green	35	1·25
162	1s. 3d. brown	35	30
157/162		*Set of* 6	1·75	2·50

50 The Old Rectory, St. George's, circa 1730   67 *Tsotsi in the Bundu* (Finn class yacht)

(Des W. Harrington. Photo Harrison)

1962 (26 Oct)–**68**. *Horiz designs as T* **50**. *W w* **12** (*upright*). *P* 12½.

163	1d. reddish purple, black and orange	10	45
	w. Wmk inverted	†	—
164	2d. lilac, indigo, yellow and green	10	15
	a. Lilac omitted	£900	£650
	b. Green omitted	† £3750	
	c. Imperf (pair)	£1200	
	d. *Pale lilac, indigo, yell & grn* (22.10.68)	85	15
	w. Wmk inverted	—	£150
165	3d. yellow-brown and light blue	10	10
	a. Yellow-brown omitted	£2750	
166	4d. red-brown and magenta	20	40

.67	5d. grey-blue and rose	..	..	1·50	2·25
.68	6d. grey-blue, emerald and light blue		20	30
	w. Wmk inverted			80·00	
.69	8d. bright blue, bright green and orange		30	35
.70	9d. light blue and brown	..	..	25	30
170a	10d. violet and ochre (8.2.65)		8·00	1·00
	aw. Wmk inverted				
.71	1s. black, emerald, bright blue & orange		20	10
.72	1s. 3d. lake, grey and bistre	..	75	15
.73	1s. 6d. violet and ochre	..	1·75	1·75
.74	2s. red-brown and orange	..	3·00	1·25
.75	2s. 3d. bistre-brown and yellow-green	2·00	6·00
.76	2s. 6d. bistre-brn, bluish grn & olive-yell	55	50
.77	5s. brown-purple and blue-green	1·25	1·50
	w. Wmk inverted			60·00	
.78	10s. magenta, deep bluish green and buff	4·00	5·00
	w. Wmk inverted			£250	£300
.79	£1 black, yellow-olive and yellow-orange	14·00	14·00
163/79			Set of 18	35·00	32·00

Designs:—2d. Church of St. Peter, St. Georges; 3d.
Government House, 1892; 4d. The Cathedral, Hamilton, 1894;
5d. H.M. Dockyard, 1811; 6d. Perot's Post Office, 1848; 8d.
G.P.O. Hamilton, 1869; 9d. Library, Par-la-Ville; 10d., 1s. 6d.
Bermuda cottage, circa 1705; 1s. Christ Church, Warwick, 1719;
1s. 3d. City Hall, Hamilton, 1960; 2s. Town of St. George; 2s. 3d.
Bermuda house, circa 1710; 2s. 6d. Bermuda house, early
18th-century; 5s. Colonial Secretariat, 1833; 10s. Old Post
Office, Somerset, 1890; £1 The House of Assembly, 1815.
   Three examples of No. 164b are known, all used on piece.
   See also Nos. 195/200 and 246a.

1963 (4 June).	*Freedom from Hunger. As No. 146 of Antigua.*		
180	1s. 3d. sepia	.. .. ..	80	40

1963 (2 Sept).	*Red Cross Centenary. As Nos. 147/8 of Antigua.*		
181	3d. red and black	.. ..	75	25
182	1s. 3d. red and blue ..	.. ..	2·00	2·75

(Des V. Whiteley. Photo D.L.R.)

1964 (28 Sept).	*Olympic Games, Tokyo. W w* 12. *P* 14 × 13½.		
183	**67** 3d. red, violet and blue..		10	10

1965 (17 May).	*I.T.U. Centenary. As Nos. 166/7 of Antigua.*		
184	3d. light blue and emerald	.. ..	50	25
185	2s. yellow and ultramarine ..	..	1·00	1·25

68 Scout Badge and St. Edward's Crown

(Des W. Harrington. Photo Harrison)

1965 (24 July).	*50th Anniv of Bermuda Boy Scouts Association.*		
W w 12. *P* 12½.				
186	**68** 2s. multicoloured	.. ..	50	50
	w. Wmk inverted	.. ..	35·00	

1965 (25 Oct).	*International Co-operation Year. As Nos. 168/9 of Antigua.*		
187	4d. reddish purple and turquoise-green	50	20
188	2s. 6d. deep bluish green and lavender	..	1·10	80

1966 (24 Jan).	*Churchill Commemoration. As Nos. 170/3 of Antigua.*		
189	3d. new blue ..	.. ..	45	20
190	6d. deep green	.. ..	70	45
191	10d. brown	.. ..	90	75
192	1s. 3d. bluish violet	.. ..	1·25	2·00
189/92		Set of 4	3·00	3·00

1966 (1 July).	*World Cup Football Championships. As Nos. 176/7 of Antigua.*		
193	10d. violet, yellow-green, lake & yellow-brn ..	50	15
194	2s. 6d. chocolate, blue-grn, lake & yell-brn ..	75	65

1966 (25 Oct)–69.	*Designs as Nos. 164, 167 (1s. 6d.), 169,*		
170a/1 and 174 but W w 12 *(sideways*).*				
195	2d. lilac, indigo, yellow and green (20.5.69)	3·25	4·50
196	8d. brt blue, brt green & orange (14.2.67)	50	90
197	10d. violet and ochre (1.11.66)	..	75	60
	w. Wmk Crown to right of CA	..	†	
198	1s. black, emerald, brt bl & orge (14.2.67)	70	1·10
199	1s. 6d. grey-blue and rose (1.11.66)	..	2·75	1·25
	w. Wmk Crown to right of CA	..	48·00	
200	2s. red-brown and orange	..	2·75	2·75
195/200		Set of 6	9·50	10·00

*The normal sideways watermark shows Crown to left of CA,
as seen from the back of the stamp.
   The 2d. value exists with PVA gum only, and the 8d. exists
with PVA gum as well as gum arabic.

1966 (1 Dec).	*20th Anniv of U.N.E.S.C.O. As Nos. 196/8 of Antigua.*		
201	4d. slate-violet, red, yellow and orange	..	60	15
202	1s. 3d. orange-yellow, violet and deep olive	1·00	60
203	2s. black, bright purple and orange..		1·25	1·60
201/3	.. ..	Set of 3	2·50	2·25

NEW INFORMATION

The editor is always interested to correspond with
people who have new information that will
improve or correct the Catalogue.

---

69 G.P.O. Building

(Des G. Vasarhelyi. Photo Harrison)

1967 (23 June).	*Opening of New General Post Office. Hamilton.*		
W w 12. *P* 14½.				
204	**69** 3d. multicoloured	.. ..	10	10
205	1s. multicoloured	.. ..	10	10
206	1s. 6d. multicoloured	..	15	20
207	2s. 6d. multicoloured	..	45	40
204/7		Set of 4	45	65

70 Mercury (cable ship) and Chain Links

(Des V. Whiteley. Photo Harrison)

1967 (14 Sept).	*Inauguration of Bermuda–Tortola Telephone*		
Service. T 70 *and similar horiz designs. Multicoloured. W w* 12.			
P 14½ × 14.				
208	3d. Type **70**	.. ..	15	10
209	1s. Map, telephone and microphone..	20	10
210	1s. 6d. Telecommunications media ..	25	25
211	2s. 6d. Mercury (cable ship) and marine fauna		35	40
208/11		Set of 4	85	70

74 Human Rights Emblem and Doves

(Des M. Farrar Bell. Litho Harrison)

1968 (1 Feb).	*Human Rights Year. W w* 12. *P* 14 × 14½.		
212	**74** 3d. indigo, blue and dull green..	10	10
213	1s. yellow-brown, blue and light blue ..	10	10
214	1s. 6d. black, blue and rose	..	10	10
215	2s. 6d. grey-green, blue and yellow	15	15
212/15		Set of 4	30	30

REPRESENTATIVE GOVERNMENT

75 Mace and Queen's Profile

(Des R. Granger Barrett. Photo Harrison)

1968 (1 July).	*New Constitution. T* 75 *and similar horiz design.*		
W w 12. *P* 14.				
216	**75** 3d. multicoloured	.. ..	10	10
217	1s. multicoloured	.. ..	10	10
218	1s. 6d. greenish yellow, black & turq-bl	10	20
219	2s. 6d. lilac, black and orange-yellow ..	15	30
216/19		Set of 4	30	60

Design:—1s. 6d., 2s. 6d. Houses of Parliament and House of
Assembly, Bermuda.

77 Football, Athletics and Yachting

(Des V. Whiteley. Photo Harrison)

1968 (24 Sept).	*Olympic Games, Mexico. W w* 12. *P* 12½.		
220	**77** 3d. multicoloured	.. ..	10	10
	a. Red-brown ("BERMUDA" and value) omitted	..	£2500	
221	1s. multicoloured	.. ..	25	10
222	1s. 6d. multicoloured	..	35	20
223	2s. 6d. multicoloured	..	35	80
220/3	.. .. ..	Set of 4	1·00	1·10

---

78 Brownie and Guide | 80 Emerald-studded Gold Cross and Seaweed

(Des Harrison. Litho Format)

1969 (17 Feb).	*50th Anniv of Bermuda Girl Guides. P* 14.		
224	**78** 3d. multicoloured	.. ..	10	10
225	1s. multicoloured	.. ..	20	10
226	– 1s. 6d. multicoloured	..	25	40
227	– 2s. 6d. multicoloured	..	35	80
224/7		Set of 4	80	1·25

Design:—1s. 6d., 2s. 6d. Guides and badge.

(Des K. Giles adapted by V. Whiteley. Photo Harrison)

1969 (29 Sept).	*Underwater Treasure. T* 80 *and similar vert*		
design. Multicoloured. W w 12 *(sideways). P* 14½ × 14.			
228	4d. Type **80**	.. ..	20	10
229	1s. 3d. Emerald-studded gold cross and seabed		35	15
230	2s. Type **80**	.. ..	45	80
231	2s. 6d. As 1s. 3d.	..	45	1·25
228/31		Set of 4	1·25	2·00

(New Currency. 100 cents = 1 Bermuda dollar)

1c

2c

(82) Tall "2" (Pl 1A. R.2/2)

1970 (6 Feb).	*Decimal Currency. As Nos. 163, 165/6, 168, 170,*		
172, 175/9 and 195/200 surch as T 82. *W w* 12 *(sideways* on 2,		
5, 10, 12, 15, 18, 24, 30, 60 c., $1.20 and $2.40).			
232	1 c. on 1d. reddish purple, black and orange	10	1·25
	w. Wmk inverted	..	75·00	25·00
233	2 c. on 2d. lilac, indigo, yellow and green	10	10
	a. Lilac omitted ..	..	£800	
	b. Vert pair, one without surch	..	£3500	
	c. Tall "2"	..	4·25	
	dw. Wmk Crown to right of CA	..	50·00	
	e. Wmk upright (No. 164)	..	80	2·00
	ea. Tall "2"	..	6·50	
	f. Wmk upright (No. 164d)	..	90	2·75
	fa. Tall "2"	..	7·00	
234	3 c. on 3d. yellow-brown and light blue	10	10
235	4 c. on 4d. red-brown and magenta (Br.)	10	10
236	5 c. on 8d. bright blue, brt green & orange	15	1·25
237	6 c. on 6d. grey-blue, emerald & light blue	15	70
	a. Horiz pair, one with albino surch, the other with albino bar	†	£150
	w. Wmk inverted	..	£800	
238	9 c. on 9d. light blue and brown (Br.)	30	1·50
239	10 c. on 10d. violet and ochre	..	30	25
240	12 c. on 1s. black, emerald, brt blue & orge	30	30
241	15 c. on 1s. 3d. lake, grey and bistre	1·50	1·00
242	18 c. on 1s. 6d. grey-blue and rose	80	65
243	24 c. on 2s. red-brown and orange	85	85
	w. Wmk Crown to right of CA	..	70·00	
244	30 c. on 2s. 6d. bistre-brown, bluish green and olive-yellow		1·00	1·60
245	36 c. on 2s. 3d. bistre-brown & yellow-green	1·75	4·00
246	60 c. on 5s. brown-purple and blue-green	2·25	3·00
	a. Surch omitted†	..	£800	
247	$1.20. on 10s. mag, dp bluish green & buff	4·00	15·00
248	$2.40. on £1 black, yellow-olive & yell-orge	7·00	19·00
232/48		Set of 17	18·00	45·00

*The normal sideways watermark shows Crown to left of CA,
as seen from the back of the stamp.
†No. 246a differs from the normal No. 177 by its watermark,
which is sideways, and its gum, which is PVA.

83 Spathiphyllum

(Des W. Harrington. Photo D.L.R.)

1970 (6 July)–75.	*Flowers. Multicoloured designs as T* 83.		
W w 12 *(sideways on horiz designs). P* 14.			
249	1 c. Type **83**	.. ..	10	20
250	2 c. Bottlebrush	.. ..	20	25
251	3 c. Oleander (vert) ..	..	15	10
252	3 c. Bermudiana	.. ..	15	10
253	5 c. Poinsettia	.. ..	30	30
254	6 c. Hibiscus	.. ..	30	30
255	9 c. Cereus	.. ..	20	45
256	10 c. Bougainvillea (vert) ..	..	20	15
257	12 c. Jacaranda	.. ..	80	60

258	15 c. Passion-Flower				90	1·40
258a	17 c. As 15 c. (2.6.75)				2·75	3·25
259	18 c. Coralita				2·25	2·25
259a	20 c. As 18 c. (2.6.75)				2·75	3·25
260	24 c. Morning Glory				1·50	3·50
260a	25 c. As 24 c. (2.6.75)				2·75	4·00
261	30 c. Tecoma				1·00	1·25
262	36 c. Angel's Trumpet				1·25	2·25
262a	40 c. As 36 c. (2.6.75)				2·75	4·50
263	60 c. Plumbago				1·75	2·75
263a	$1 As 60 c. (2.6.75)				3·25	6·00
264	$1.20, Bird of Paradise flower				2·75	3·00
264a	$2 As $1.20 (2.6.75)				5·50	8·50
265	$2.40, Chalice Cup				5·50	7·00
265a	$3 As $2.40 (2.6.75)				10·00	11·00
249/65a				Set of 24	45·00	55·00

See also Nos. 303/6 and 340/1.

84 The State House, St. George's

(Des G. Drummond. Litho Questa)

1970 (12 Oct). *350th Anniv of Bermuda Parliament. T 84 and similar horiz designs. Multicoloured. W w 12 (sideways). P 14.*

266	4 c. Type 84				10	10
267	15 c. The Sessions House, Hamilton				25	15
268	18 c. St. Peter's Church, St George's				25	20
269	24 c. Town Hall, Hamilton				35	45
266/9				Set of 4	85	75
MS270	131 × 95 mm. Nos. 266/9				1·40	4·25

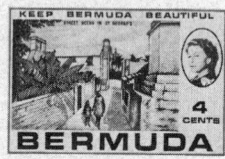

85 Street Scene, St. George's

(Des G. Drummond. Litho Questa)

1971 (8 Feb). *"Keep Bermuda Beautiful". T 85 and similar horiz designs. Multicoloured. W w 12 (sideways). P 14.*

271	4 c. Type 85				20	10
272	15 c. Horseshoe Bay				55	50
273	18 c. Gibb's Hill Lighthouse				1·00	1·50
274	24 c. Hamilton Harbour				1·25	2·25
271/4				Set of 4	2·75	3·75

86 Building of the *Deliverance*

(Des E. Amos. Adapted C. Abbott. Litho Questa)

1971 (10 May). *Voyage of the "Deliverance". T 86 and similar multicoloured designs. W w 12 (sideways on 4 c. and 24 c.). P 14.*

275	4 c. Type 86				50	20
276	15 c. *Deliverance* and *Patience* at Jamestown				1·50	1·75
277	18 c. Wreck of the *Sea Venture*				1·75	2·25
278	24 c. *Deliverance* and *Patience* on the high seas				1·90	2·50
275/8				Set of 4	5·00	6·00

The 15 c. and 18 c. are vert designs.

87 Green overlooking Ocean View

(Des G. Drummond. Litho D.L.R.)

1971 (1 Nov). *Golfing in Bermuda. T 87 and similar horiz designs. Multicoloured. W w 12 (sideways*). P 13.*

279	4 c. Type 87				70	10
	w. Wmk Crown to right of CA				80·00	50·00
280	15 c. Golfers at Port Royal				1·25	70
281	18 c. Castle Harbour				1·40	1·00
	w. Wmk Crown to right of CA				3·50	
282	24 c. Belmont				1·50	1·75
279/82				Set of 4	4·25	3·00

The normal sideways watermark shows Crown to left of CA, as seen from the back of the stamp.

HEATH · NIXON
DECEMBER 1971

(88)

1971 (20 Dec). *Anglo-American Talks. Nos. 252, 258, 259 and 260 optd with T 88 by Format.*

283	4 c. Bermudiana				10	10
284	15 c. Passion Glory				10	20
285	18 c. Coralita				15	65
286	24 c. Morning Glory				20	80
283/6				Set of 4	50	1·60

89 Bonefish

(Des Maynard Reece. Litho B.W.)

1972 (21 Aug). *World Fishing Records. T 89 and similar horiz designs. Multicoloured. W w 12. P 13½ × 14.*

287	4 c. Type 89				35	10
288	15 c. Wahoo				40	40
289	18 c. Yellow-finned Tuna				45	50
290	24 c. Greater Amberjack				60	80
287/90				Set of 4	1·60	1·60

90 "Admiralty Oar" and Mace

(Des from photograph by D. Groves) and photo Harrison)

1972 (20 Nov). *Royal Silver Wedding. Multicoloured; background colour given. W w 12. P 14 × 14½.*

291	90	4 c. bright bluish violet			15	10
292		15 c. rose-carmine			15	40
		w. Wmk inverted			2·00	

91 Palmetto

92 Bernard Park, Pembroke, 1973

(Des Jennifer Toombs. Litho J.W.)

1973 (3 Sept). *Tree Planting Year. T 91 and similar vert designs. Multicoloured. W w 12 (sideways). P 14.*

293	4 c. Type 91				30	10
294	15 c. Olivewood Bark				90	75
	a. Brown (Queen's head and value) omitted				£900	
295	18 c. Bermuda Cedar				1·00	1·25
296	24 c. Mahogany				1·10	1·60
293/6				Set of 4	3·00	3·25

1973 (21 Nov*). *Royal Wedding. As Nos. 165/6 of Anguilla. Centre multicoloured. W w 12 (sideways). P 13½.*

297	15 c. bright mauve				15	15
298	18 c. steel blue				15	15

*This is the local date of issue. The Crown Agents released the stamps on the 14 November.

(Des J.W. Litho Questa)

1973 (17 Dec). *Lawn Tennis Centenary. T 92 and similar horiz designs. Multicoloured. W w 12. P 14.*

299	4 c. Type 92				30	10
300	15 c. Clermont Court, 1873				60	65
301	18 c. Leamington Spa Court, 1872				70	1·25
302	24 c. Staten Island Courts, 1874				85	1·75
299/302				Set of 4	2·25	3·25

1974 (13 June)—76. *As Nos. 253/4, 257 and 261, but wmk upright.*

303	5 c. Poinsettia				90	4·25
304	6 c. Hibiscus				9·50	14·00
305	12 c. Jacaranda				1·75	4·00
	w. Wmk inverted				50·00	
306	30 c. Tecoma (11.6.76)				7·00	7·50
303/6				Set of 4	17·00	27·00

Nos. 307/19 vacant.

PRICES OF SETS

Set prices are given for many issues, generally those containing three stamps or more. Definitive sets include one of each value or major colour change, but do not cover different perforations, die types or minor shades. Where a choice is possible the set prices are based on the cheapest versions of the stamps included in the listings.

---

93 Weather Vane, City Hall

94 Jack of Clubs and "good bridge hand"

(Des G. Drummond. Litho Questa)

1974 (24 June). *50th Anniv of Rotary in Bermuda. T 93 and similar horiz designs. Multicoloured. W w 12 (sideways). P 14.*

320	5 c. Type 93				15	10
321	17 c. St. Peter's Church, St George's				45	35
322	20 c. Somerset Bridge				50	1·25
323	25 c. Map of Bermuda, 1626				60	2·00
320/3				Set of 4	1·50	3·25

(Des J.W. Litho Format)

1975 (27 Jan). *World Bridge Championships, Bermuda. T 94 and similar vert designs. Multicoloured. W w 12. P 14.*

324	5 c. Type 94				20	10
325	17 c. Queen of Diamonds and Bermuda Bowl				35	50
326	20 c. King of Hearts and Bermuda Bowl				40	1·75
327	25 c. Ace of Spades and Bermuda Bowl				40	2·25
324/7				Set of 4	1·25	4·00

95 Queen Elizabeth II and the Duke of Edinburgh

(Des and photo Harrison)

1975 (17 Feb). *Royal Visit. W w 14. P 14 × 14½.*

328	95	17 c. multicoloured			60	65
329		20 c. multicoloured			65	2·10

96 Short S.23 Flying Boat *Cavalier*, 1937

(Des R. Granger Barrett. Litho Questa)

1975 (28 Apr). *50th Anniv of Air-mail Service to Bermuda. T 96 and similar horiz designs. Multicoloured. W w 14 (sideways). P 14.*

330	5 c. Type 96				40	10
331	17 c. U.S.N. airship *Los Angeles*, 1925				1·25	85
332	20 c. Lockheed L.049 Constellation, 1946				1·40	2·75
333	25 c. Boeing 747-100, 1970				1·50	3·50
330/3				Set of 4	4·00	6·50
MS334	128 × 85 mm. Nos. 330/3				11·00	15·00

97 Supporters of American Army raiding Royal Magazine

98 Launching *Ready* (bathysphere)

(Des J. Cooter. Litho J.W.)

1975 (27 Oct). *Bicentenary of Gunpowder Plot, St George's. T 97 and similar horiz designs. Multicoloured. W w 14 (sideways*). P 13 × 13½.*

335	5 c. Type 97				20	10
336	17 c. Setting off for raid				40	30
337	20 c. Loading gunpowder aboard American ship				45	1·25
338	25 c. Gunpowder on beach				50	1·40
	w. Wmk Crown to left of CA				55·00	
335/8				Set of 4	1·40	2·75
MS339	165 × 138 mm. Nos. 335/8. P 14 (sold for 75 c.)				2·75	6·50

The normal sideways watermark shows Crown to right of CA, as seen from the back of the stamp.

1975 (8 Dec)—76. *As Nos. 250 and 254 but W w 14 (sideways).*

340	2 c. Bottlebrush				85	3·50
341	6 c. Hibiscus (11.6.76)				6·00	7·00

Nos. 342/56 vacant.

(Des G. Drummond. Litho Questa)

1976 (29 Mar). *50th Anniv of Bermuda Biological Station. T* **98** *and similar multicoloured designs. W w* **14** *(sideways on 17 and 20 c.). P* 14.

357	5 c. Type **98**		30	10
358	17 c. View from the sea (*horiz*)		60	60
359	20 c. H.M.S. *Challenger*, 1873 (*horiz*)..		65	2·25
360	25 c. Beebe's bathysphere descent, 1934		70	2·50
357/60		*Set of 4*	2·00	4·75

99 *Christian Radich* (cadet ship)

(Des R. Granger Barrett. Litho J.W.)

1976 (15 June). *Tall Ships Race, 1976. T* **99** *and similar horiz designs. Multicoloured. W w* **12** *(sideways). P* 13.

361	5 c. Type **99**		75	20
362	12 c. *Juan Sebastian de Elcano* (Spanish cadet schooner)		1·00	2·00
363	17 c. *Eagle* (U.S. coastguard cadet ship)		1·25	1·75
364	20 c. *Sir Winston Churchill* (cadet schooner)		1·40	2·50
365	20 c. *Kruzenshtern* (Russian cadet barque)		1·75	3·25
366	$1 *Cutty Sark* trophy		2·75	8·00
361/6		*Set of 6*	8·00	16·00

100 Silver Trophy and Club Flags

(Des C. Abbott. Litho Questa)

1976 (16 Aug). *75th Anniv of the St. George's v. Somerset Cricket Cup Match. T* **100** *and similar horiz designs. Multicoloured. W w* **14** *(sideways*). P* 14½×14.

367	5 c. Type **100**		35	10
	w. Wmk Crown to right of CA			
368	17 c. Badge and Pavilion, St. George's Club		60	65
369	20 c. Badge and Pavilion, Somerset Club..		80	2·75
370	25 c. Somerset playing field		1·25	3·75
367/70		*Set of 4*	2·75	6·50

*The normal sideways watermark shows Crown to left of CA, as seen from the back of the stamp.

101 Royal Visit, 1975   **102** Stockdale House, St. George's 1784–1812

(Des Harrison. Litho Walsall)

1977 (7 Feb). *Silver Jubilee. T* **101** *and similar vert designs. Multicoloured. W w* **14**. *P* 13½.

371	5 c. Type **101**		10	10
	w. Wmk inverted		£110	75·00
372	20 c. St. Edward's Crown		15	20
373	$1 Queen in Chair of Estate		40	1·25
371/3		*Set of 3*	55	1·40

(Des G. Drummond. Litho J.W.)

1977 (20 June). *Centenary of U.P.U. Membership. T* **102** *and similar horiz designs. Multicoloured. W w* **14** *(sideways). P* 13.

374	5 c. Type **102**		15	10
375	15 c. Perot Post Office and stamp		30	50
376	17 c. St. George's P.O. circa 1860		30	50
377	20 c. Old G.P.O., Hamilton, circa 1935		35	60
378	40 c. New G.P.O., Hamilton, 1967		60	1·10
374/8		*Set of 5*	1·50	2·50

103 17th-Century Ship approaching   **104** Great Seal of
Castle Island   Queen Elizabeth I

(Des R. Granger Barrett. Litho Questa)

1977 (26 Sept). *Piloting. T* **103** *and similar horiz designs. Multicoloured. W w* **14** *(sideways). P* 13½.

379	5 c. Type **103**		35	10
380	15 c. Pilot leaving ship, 1795		65	50
381	17 c. Pilots rowing out to paddle-steamer		75	50
382	20 c. Pilot gigs and brig *Harvest Queen*		80	2·25
383	40 c. Modern pilot cutter and R.M.S. *Queen Elizabeth 2*		1·25	3·25
379/83		*Set of 5*	3·50	6·00

(Des BG Studio. Litho Questa)

1978 (28 Aug). *25th Anniv of Coronation. T* **104** *and similar vert designs. Multicoloured. W w* **14**. *P* 14 × 13½.

384	8 c. Type **104**		10	10
385	50 c. Great Seal of Queen Elizabeth II		30	30
386	$1 Queen Elizabeth II		60	75
384/6		*Set of 3*	80	1·00

105 White-tailed Tropic Bird

(Des G. Drummond. Photo Harrison)

1978 (15 Nov)–83. *Wildlife. Horiz designs as T* **105**. *Multicoloured. W w* **14** *(sideways* on 8, 15, 20, 40 c. and* $1). *P* 14×14½ (4, 5 c., $2, $3, $5) or 14 (*others*).

387	3 c. Type **105**		1·50	1·75
	aw. Wmk inverted		15·00	
	b. Perf 14×14½ (3.8.83)†		2·75	2·50
388	4 c. White-eyed Vireo		1·25	1·75
	w. Wmk inverted		50·00	
389	5 c. Eastern Bluebird		1·25	1·50
	w. Wmk inverted		50·00	30·00
390	7 c. Whistling Frog (19.2.79)		50	1·25
391	8 c. Common Cardinal		1·25	55
392	10 c. Spiny Lobster (19.2.79)		20	10
393	12 c. Land Crab (19.2.79)		30	70
394	15 c. Lizard (Skink) (19.2.79)		30	15
395	20 c. Four-eyed Butterflyfish (12.3.79)		30	30
	w. Wmk Crown to right of CA		1·00	
396	25 c. Red Hind (12.3.79)		30	20
397	30 c. *Danaus plexippus* (butterfly) (19.2.79)		2·25	2·50
398	40 c. Rock Beauty (12.3.79)		45	1·50
399	50 c. Banded Butterflyfish (12.3.79)		55	85
400	$1 Blue Angelfish (12.3.79)		95	1·75
	w. Wmk Crown to right of CA		£250	
401	$2 Humpback Whale (12.3.79)		2·00	2·75
402	$3 Green Turtle (19.2.79)		2·75	3·00
403	$5 Cahow		6·50	6·00
387/403		*Set of 17*	20·00	24·00

*The normal sideways watermark shows Crown to left of CA, as seen from the back of the stamp.
†Earliest known postmark date.

106 Map by Sir George Somers, 1609   **107** Policeman and Policewoman

(Des J. Cooter. Litho Questa)

1979 (14 May). *Antique Maps. T* **106** *and similar multicoloured designs. W w* **14** *(sideways on 8, 15, 25 and 50 c.) P* 14 × 13½ (20 c.) or 13½ × 14 (*others*).

404	8 c. Type **106**		15	10
405	15 c. Map by John Seller, 1685		20	10
406	20 c. Map by H. Moll, 1729–40 (*vert*)		25	25
407	25 c. Map by Desbruslins, 1740		30	30
408	50 c. Map by Speed, 1626		45	80
404/8		*Set of 5*	1·25	1·40

(Des L. Curtis. Litho Questa)

1979 (26 Nov). *Centenary of Police Force. T* **107** *and similar multicoloured designs. W w* **14** *(sideways on 20 and 25 c.). P* 14.

409	8 c. Type **107**		20	10
	w. Wmk inverted		11·00	
410	20 c. Policeman directing traffic (*horiz*)		45	55
411	25 c. *Blue Heron* (police launch) (*horiz*)		50	65
412	50 c. Police car and motorcycle		90	1·50
409/12		*Set of 4*	1·90	2·50

108 1848 1d. "Perot" and Penny Black Stamps

(Des J.W. Litho Enschedé)

1980 (25 Feb). *Death Centenary of Sir Rowland Hill* (1979). *T* **108** *and similar horiz designs. Multicoloured. W w* **14** *(sideways). P* 13 × 13½.

413	8 c. Type **108**		15	10
414	20 c. 1848 1d. "Perot" stamp and Sir Rowland Hill		20	25
415	25 c. 1848 1d. "Perot" stamp and early letter		20	30
416	50 c. 1848 1d. "Perot" stamp and "Paid 1" cancellation		30	70
413/16		*Set of 4*	75	1·25

109 Lockheed L-1011 TriStar   **110** Gina Swainson
500 Airliner approaching   with Rose
Bermuda

(Des R. Granger Barrett. Litho Harrison)

1980 (6 May). *"London 1980" International Stamp Exhibition. Mail-carrying Transport. T* **109** *and similar horiz designs. Multicoloured. W w* **14** *(sideways*). P* 13×13½.

417	25 c. Type **109**		30	15
418	50 c. *Orduna I* (liner) in Grassy Bay		45	35
	w. Wmk Crown to right of CA		38·00	
419	$1 *Delta* (screw steamer) at St. George's Harbour		85	1·00
420	$2 *Lord Sidmouth* (sailing packet) in Old Ship Channel, St. George's		1·40	2·00
417/20		*Set of 4*	2·75	3·25

*The normal sideways watermark shows Crown to left of CA, as seen from the back of the stamp.

(Des Walsall. Litho Questa)

1980 (8 May). *"Miss World 1979–80" (Gina Swainson) Commemoration. T* **110** *and similar vert designs. Multicoloured. W w* **14**. *P* 14 × 13½.

421	8 c. Type **110**		15	10
422	20 c. After crowning ceremony		20	20
423	50 c. On Peacock Throne at "Welcome Home" party		35	35
424	$1 In Bermuda carriage		70	90
421/4		*Set of 4*	1·25	1·40

111 Queen Elizabeth the Queen Mother

(Des and litho Harrison)

1980 (4 Aug). *80th Birthday of Queen Elizabeth the Queen Mother. W w* **14** *(sideways). P* 14.

425	**111** 25 c. multicoloured		30	70

112 Bermuda from Satellite   **113** Kitchen, 18th-century

(Des L. Curtis. Litho Questa)

1980 (24 Sept). *Commonwealth Finance Ministers Meeting. T* **112** *and similar horiz designs. Multicoloured. W w* **14** *(sideways*). P* 14.

426	8 c. Type **112**		10	10
427	20 c. "Camden"		20	40
428	25 c. Princess Hotel, Hamilton		20	50
	w. Wmk Crown to right of CA		65·00	
429	50 c. Government House		35	1·25
426/9		*Set of 4*	75	2·00

*The normal sideways watermark shows Crown to left of CA, as seen from the back of the stamp.

(Des J.W. Litho Questa)

1981 (21 May). *Heritage Week. T* **113** *and similar horiz designs. Multicoloured. W w* **14** *(sideways*). P* 14.

430	8 c. Type **113**		15	10
	w. Wmk Crown to right of CA		8·00	
431	25 c. Gathering Easter lilies, 20th-century		40	50
432	30 c. Fishing, 20th-century		50	70
433	40 c. Stone cutting, 19th-century		55	1·00
	w. Wmk Crown to right of CA		1·50	
434	50 c. Onion shipping, 19th-century		35	1·25
435	$1 Privateering, 17th-century		1·60	2·75
430/5		*Set of 6*	3·50	5·50

*The normal sideways watermark shows Crown to left of CA, as seen from the back of the stamp.

114 Wedding Bouquet
from Bermuda

115 "Service", Hamilton

(Des J.W. Litho Questa)

1981 (22 July). *Royal Wedding. T* **114** *and similar vert designs. Multicoloured. W w* 14. *P* 14.

436	30 c. Type 114	20	20
437	50 c. Prince Charles as Royal Navy Commander	35	40
438	$1 Prince Charles and Lady Diana Spencer	55	80
436/8	Set of 3	1·00	1·25

(Des L. Curtis. Litho Questa)

1981 (28 Sept). *25th Anniv of Duke of Edinburgh Award Scheme. T* **115** *and similar vert designs. Multicoloured. W w* 14. *P* 14.

439	10 c. Type 115	15	10
440	25 c. "Outward Bound", Paget Island	20	20
441	30 c. "Expedition", St. David's Island	20	30
442	$1 Duke of Edinburgh	55	1·25
439/42	Set of 4	1·00	1·75

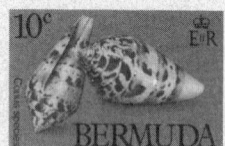

116 Lightbourne's Cone
(*Conus lightbourni*)

(Des Walsall. Litho Questa)

1982 (22 Apr). *Sea-shells. T* **116** *and similar horiz designs. Multicoloured. W w* 14 (*sideways*). *P* 14.

443	10 c. Type 116	30	10
444	25 c. Finlay's Frog Shell (*Bursa finlayi*)	70	75
445	30 c. Royal Bonnet (*Sconsia striata*)	75	85
446	$1 Lightbourne's Murex (*Murex lightbourni*)	2·00	3·25
443/6	Set of 4	3·25	4·50

117 Regimental Colours and
Colour Party

118 Charles Fort

(Des G. Drummond. Litho Questa)

1982 (17 June). *Bermuda Regiment. T* **117** *and similar horiz designs. Multicoloured. W w* 14 (*sideways*). *P* 14.

447	10 c. Type 117	45	10
448	25 c. Queen's Birthday Parade	90	80
449	30 c. Governor inspecting Guard of Honour	1·00	1·40
450	40 c. Beating the Retreat	1·25	1·75
451	50 c. Ceremonial gunners	1·40	2·00
452	$1 Guard of Honour, Royal visit, 1975	2·25	3·50
447/52	Set of 6	6·50	8·50

(Des L. Curtis. Litho Questa)

1982 (18 Nov) *Historic Bermuda Forts. T* **118** *and similar multicoloured designs. W w* 14 (*sideways on* 30 c. *and* $1). *P* 14.

453	10 c. Type 118	20	20
454	25 c. Pembroks Fort	50	85
455	30 c. Southampton Fort (*horiz*)	60	1·25
456	$1 Smiths Fort and Pagets Fort (*horiz*)	1·75	4·25
453/6	Set of 4	2·75	6·00

119 Arms of Sir Edwin Sandys

120 Early Fitted Dinghy

(Des Harrison. Litho J.W.)

1983 (14 Apr). *Coats of Arms (1st series). T* **119** *and similar vert designs. Multicoloured. W w* 14. *P* 13.

457	10 c. Type 119	45	15
458	25 c. Arms of the Bermuda Company	1·40	1·00
459	50 c. Arms of William Herbert, Earl of Pembroke	2·25	3·25
460	$1 Arms of Sir George Somers	3·00	5·00
457/60	Set of 4	6·50	8·50

See also Nos. 482/5 and 499/502.

(Des L. Curtis. Litho Harrison)

1983 (23 June). *Fitted Dinghies. T* **120** *and similar vert designs. Multicoloured. W w* 14 (*sideways*). *P* 14.

461	12 c. Type 120	45	15
462	30 c. Modern dinghy inshore	75	75
463	40 c. Early dinghy (*different*)	90	90
464	$1 Modern dinghy with red and white spinnaker	1·75	3·25
461/4	Set of 4	3·50	4·50

121 Curtiss N-9 Seaplane
(first flight over Bermuda)

122 Joseph Stockdale

(Des A. Theobald. Litho Walsall)

1983 (13 Oct). *Bicentenary of Manned Flight. T* **121** *and similar horiz designs. Multicoloured. W w* 14 (*sideways*). *P* 14.

465	12 c. Type 121	60	20
466	30 c. Stinson Pilot Radio seaplane (First completed flight between U.S.A. and Bermuda)	1·25	1·25
467	40 c. Short S.23 flying boat *Cavalier* (First scheduled passenger flight)	1·50	1·75
468	$1 U.S.N. *Los Angeles* (airship) moored to U.S.S. *Patoka*	2·50	4·50
465/8	Set of 4	5·25	7·00

(Des L. Curtis. Litho Harrison)

1984 (26 Jan). *Bicentenary of Bermuda's First Newspaper and Postal Service. T* **122** *and similar multicoloured designs. W w* 14 (*sideways* on* 40 c. *and* $1). *P* 14.

469	12 c. Type 122	30	15
470	30 c. *The Bermuda Gazette*	60	80
471	40 c. Stockdale's postal service (*horiz*)	80	1·10
	w. Wmk Crown to right of CA	£200	
472	$1 *Lady Hammond* (mail boat) (*horiz*)	2·50	3·25
469/72	Set of 4	3·75	4·75

The normal sideways watermark shows Crown to left of CA, as seen from the back of the stamp.

123 Sir Thomas Gates and Sir
George Somers

124 Swimming

(Des R. Granger Barrett. Litho Walsall)

1984 (3 May). *375th Anniv of First Settlement. T* **123** *and similar horiz designs. Multicoloured. W w* 14 (*sideways*). *P* 14.

473	12 c. Type 123	20	15
474	30 c. Jamestown, Virginia	50	1·25
475	40 c. Wreck of *Sea Venture*	90	1·25
476	$1 Fleet leaving Plymouth, Devon	2·00	4·50
473/6	Set of 4	3·25	6·50
MS477	130×73 mm. Nos. 474 and 476	3·50	8·00

(Des C. Collins. Litho J.W.)

1984 (19 July). *Olympic Games, Los Angeles. T* **124** *and similar multicoloured designs. W w* 14 (*sideways on* 30 c., $1). *P* 14.

478	12 c. Type 124	30	15
479	30 c. Track and field events (*horiz*)	60	85
480	40 c. Equestrian competition	1·00	1·25
481	$1 Sailing (*horiz*)	2·50	4·50
478/81	Set of 4	4·00	6·00

(Des Harrison. Litho J.W.)

1984 (27 Sept). *Coats of Arms (2nd series). Vert designs as T* **119**. *Multicoloured. W w* 14. *P* 13.

482	12 c. Arms of Henry Wriothesley, Earl of Southampton	50	15
483	30 c. Arms of Sir Thomas Smith	1·00	85
	w. Wmk inverted	1·25	
484	40 c. Arms of William Cavendish, Earl of Devonshire	1·25	1·50
485	$1 Town arms of St. George	2·75	4·00
482/5	Set of 4	5·00	6·00

---

125 Buttery

126 Osprey

(Des D. Miller. Litho Walsall)

1985 (24 Jan). *Bermuda Architecture. T* **125** *and similar multicoloured designs. W w* 14 (*inverted on* 12 c., $1.50, *sideways on* 30 c., 40 c.). *P* 13½ × 13 (12 c., $1.50) *or* 13 × 13½ (30 c., 40 c.).

486	12 c. Type 125	35	15
487	30 c. Limestone rooftops (*horiz*)	80	70
488	40 c. Chimneys (*horiz*)	95	1·00
489	$1.50, Entrance archway	3·00	3·75
486/9	Set of 4	4·75	5·00

(Des D. Miller. Litho Walsall)

1985 (28 Mar). *Birth Bicentenary of John J. Audubon (ornithologist). T* **126** *and similar multicoloured designs showing original drawings. W w* 14 (*sideways on* 40 c.). *P* 14.

490	12 c. Type 126	2·00	55
491	30 c. Yellow-crowned Night Heron	2·00	85
492	40 c. Great Egret (*horiz*)	2·25	1·25
493	$1.50, Eastern Bluebird	3·75	4·75
490/3	Set of 4	9·00	6·75

127 The Queen Mother
with Grandchildren,
1980

128 Halley's Comet and
Bermuda Archipelago

(Des A. Theobald ($1), C. Abbott (others). Litho Questa)

1985 (7 June). *Life and Times of Queen Elizabeth the Queen Mother. T* **127** *and similar vert designs. Multicoloured. W w* 16. *P* 14½×14.

494	12 c. Queen Consort, 1937	25	15
	w. Wmk inverted	†	—
495	30 c. Type 127	40	50
	w. Wmk inverted	1·50	
496	40 c. At Clarence House on 83rd birthday	50	60
497	$1.50, With Prince Henry at his christening (from photo by Lord Snowdon)	2·00	2·75
494/7	Set of 4	2·75	3·50
MS498	91×73 mm. $1 With Prince Charles at 80th birthday celebrations. Wmk sideways	1·50	2·25

(Des Harrison. Litho J.W.)

1985 (19 Sept). *Coats of Arms (3rd series). Vert designs as T* **119**. *Multicoloured. W w* 14. *P* 13 × 13½.

499	12 c. Hamilton	65	15
500	30 c. Paget	1·25	80
501	40 c. Warwick	1·50	1·40
502	$1.50, City of Hamilton	3·50	4·25
499/502	Set of 4	6·25	6·00

(Des Jennifer Toombs. Litho Walsall)

1985 (21 Nov). *Appearance of Halley's Comet. T* **128** *and similar horiz designs. Multicoloured. W w* 16 (*sideways*). *P* 14 × 14½.

503	15 c. Type 128	85	25
504	40 c. Halley's Comet, A.D. 684 (from Nuremberg Chronicles, 1493)	1·60	1·75
505	50 c. "Halley's Comet, 1531" (from Peter Apian woodcut, 1532)	1·90	2·50
506	$1.50, "Halley's Comet, 1759" (Samuel Scott)	3·50	5·00
503/6	Set of 4	7·00	8·50

129 *Constellation* (schooner),
1943

(Des L. Curtis. Litho Questa)

1986 (16 Jan)–**90**. *Ships Wrecked on Bermuda. T* **129** *and similar horiz designs. Multicoloured. W w* 16 (*sideways**). *P* 14. A. *Without imprint date at foot.* B. *With imprint date.*

		A		B	
507	3 c. Type 129	70	1·00	1·25	1·50
508	5 c. *Early Riser* (pilot boat), 1876	20	20	†	
509	7 c. *Madiana* (steamer), 1903	65	85	†	
510	10 c. *Curlew* (sail/steamer), 1856	30	30	†	

511	12 c.	*Warwick* (galleon), 1619	60	80	†
	w.	Wmk Crown to right of CA	—	—	†
512	15 c.	H.M.S. *Vixen* (gunboat), 1890	40	60	†
512c	18 c.	As 7 c.	3·50	2·00	†
513	20 c.	*San Pedro* (Spanish galleon), 1594	1·10	80	2·00 1·75
514	25 c.	*Alert* (fishing sloop), 1877	60	1·25	†
515	40 c.	*North Carolina* (barque), 1880	65	1·25	†
516	50 c.	*Mark Antonie* (Spanish privateer), 1777	1·50	1·75	†
517	60 c.	*Mary Celestia* (Confederate paddle-steamer), 1864	1·50	1·75	†
517c	70 c.	*Caesar* (brig), 1818	4·00	3·00	†
518	$1	*L'Herminie* (French frigate), 1839	4·00	4·50	1·50 1·60
519	$1.50,	As 70 c.	4·50	4·50	†
520	$2	*Lord Amherst* (transport), 1778	7·00	8·00	2·50 3·50
521	$3	*Minerva* (sailing ship), 1849	7·50	9·00	4·25 5·50
522	$5	*Caraquet* (cargo liner), 1923	7·50	10·00	†
523	$8	H.M.S. *Pallas* (frigate), 1783	9·00	12·00	†
507A/23A		*Set of 19*	48·00	55·00	†
507B/21B		*Set of 5*			10·50 12·50

*The normal sideways watermark shows Crown to left of CA, as seen from the back of the stamp.

It is reported that the vessel depicted on the 70 c. is the *Wolf* and not the *Caesar*.

Dates of issue: 16.1.86, Nos. 507A/8A, 510A/11A, 523A; 20.3.86, Nos. 509A, 513A, 517, 519A/21A; 18.9.86, Nos. 512A, 514A/16A, 518A, 522A; 22.9.88, Nos. 512cA; 27.10.88, No. 517cA; 7.89, Nos. 518B, 520B/1/B; 1.8.90, Nos. 507B, 513B.
Imprint dates: "1989", Nos. 518B, 520B/1/B; "1990", Nos. 507B, 513B.

No. 523A shows "BERMUDA" printed in yellow fluorescent ink as a security marking.

For some of these designs watermarked w 14 (sideways) see Nos. 664/78.

(Des A. Theobald. Litho Harrison)

1986 (21 Apr). *60th Birthday of Queen Elizabeth II. Vert designs as T 110 of Ascension. Multicoloured. W w 16. P 14½×14.*

524	15 c.	Princess Elizabeth aged three, 1929	30	30
	w.	Wmk inverted	17·00	
525	40 c.	With Earl of Rosebery at Oaks May Meeting, Epsom, 1954	50	60
526	50 c.	With Duke of Edinburgh, Bermuda, 1975	65	75
527	60 c.	At British Embassy, Paris, 1972	80	90
528	$1.50,	At Crown Agents Head Office, London, 1983	2·00	2·50
524/8		*Set of 5*	3·75	4·50

(Des G. Drummond. Litho Walsall)

1986 (22 May). *"Ameripex '86" International Stamp Exhibition, Chicago. Horiz designs as T 164 of Bahamas, showing Bermuda stamps (Nos. 529/32). Multicoloured. W w 16 (sideways). P 14.*

529	15 c.	1984 37th Anniv of Settlement miniature sheet	75	30
530	40 c.	1973 Lawn Tennis Centenary 24 c.	1·25	70
531	50 c.	1983 Bicentenary of Manned Flight 12 c.	1·50	1·00
532	$1	1976 Tall Ships Race 17 c.	2·50	2·50
529/32		*Set of 4*	5·50	4·00
MS533		80×80 mm. $1.50, Statue of Liberty and Monarch of Bermuda	5·00	5·00

No. MS533 also commemorates the Centenary of the Statue of Liberty.

90c

(130)

1986 (4 Dec). *25th Anniv of World Wildlife Fund. No. 402 surch with T 130 by J. W. Dunn Printers Ltd, Sutton, Surrey.*

534	90 c.	on $3 Green Turtle	2·25	3·25
	a.	Surch double		£100
	b.	Surch double, one inverted		£425
	c.	"90 c" omitted		

131 Train in Front Street, Hamilton, 1940

(Des A. Theobald. Litho Walsall)

1987 (22 Jan). *Transport (1st series). Bermuda Railway. T 131 and similar horiz designs. Multicoloured. W w 16 (sideways). P 14.*

535	15 c.	Type **131**.	1·00	25
536	40 c.	Train crossing Springfield Trestle	1·60	90
537	50 c.	"St. George Special" at Bailey's Bay Station	1·75	1·50
538	$1 50,	Boat train at St. George	3·00	4·00
535/8		*Set of 4*	6·50	6·00

See also Nos. 557/60, 574/7 and 624/9.

132 "Bermuda Settlers", 1901

(Des L. Curtis. Litho Walsall)

1987 (30 Apr). *Bermuda Paintings (1st series). Works by Winslow Homer. T 132 and similar horiz designs. Multicoloured. W w 16 (sideways). P 14×14½.*

(a) Sheet stamps (No. 541 with a buff frame).

539	15 c.	Type **132**.	60	25
540	30 c.	"Bermuda", 1900	85	45
541	40 c.	"Bermuda Landscape", 1901	95	55
542	50 c.	"Inland Water", 1901	1·10	70
543	$1.50,	"Salt Kettle", 1899	2·50	2·50
539/43		*Set of 5*	5·50	4·00

(b) Booklet stamps, each with grey frame

544	40 c.	Type **132**.	90	1·40
	a.	Booklet pane. Nos. 544/8, each × 2	8·00	
545	40 c.	As No. 540	90	1·40
546	40 c.	As No. 541	90	1·40
547	40 c.	As No. 542	90	1·40
548	40 c.	As No. 543	90	1·40
544/8		*Set of 5*	4·00	6·00

See also Nos. 607/10 and 630/3.

133 Sikorsky S-42B Flying Boat *Bermuda Clipper* of Pan Am

(Des A. Theobald. Litho Walsall)

1987 (18 June). *50th Anniv of Inauguration of Bermuda – U.S.A. Air Service. T 133 and similar horiz designs. Multicoloured. W w 16 (sideways). P 14.*

549	15 c.	Type **133**	1·10	15
550	40 c.	Short S.23 flying boat *Cavalier* of Imperial Airways	2·00	70
551	50 c.	*Bermuda Clipper* in flight over signpost	2·25	80
552	$1.50,	*Cavalier* on apron and *Bermuda Clipper* in flight	4·75	3·50
549/52		*Set of 4*	9·00	4·75

134 19th-century Wagon carrying Telephone Poles   135 Mail Wagon, c. 1869

(Des L. Curtis. Litho B.D.T.)

1987 (1 Oct). *Centenary of Bermuda Telephone Company. T 134 and similar horiz designs. Multicoloured. W w 16 (sideways). P 14×13½.*

553	15 c.	Type **134**.	75	15
554	40 c.	Early telephone exchange	1·40	60
555	50 c.	Early and modern telephones	1·75	70
556	$1.50,	Communications satellite orbiting Earth	2·75	3·00
553/6		*Set of 4*	6·00	4·50

(Des O. Bell. Litho Questa)

1988 (3 Mar). *Transport (2nd series). Horse-drawn Carts and Wagons. T 135 and similar horiz designs. Multicoloured. W w 16 (sideways). P 14.*

557	15 c.	Type **135**.	25	15
558	40 c.	Open cart, c. 1823	55	55
559	50 c.	Closed cart, c. 1823	65	65
560	$1.50,	Two-wheeled wagon, c. 1930	2·00	2·50
557/60		*Set of 4*	3·00	3·50

136 "Old Blush"   137 Devonshire Parish Militia, 1812

(Des R. Gorringe. Litho B.D.T.)

1988 (21 Apr). *Old Garden Roses (1st series). T 136 and similar multicoloured designs. W w 14 (sideways on horiz designs). P 14×13½ (vert) or 13½×14 (horiz).*

561	15 c.	Type **136**	35	25
562	30 c.	"Anna Olivier"	50	40
563	40 c.	*Rosa chinensis semperflorens* (vert)	65	55
564	50 c.	"Archduke Charles"	75	75
565	$1.50,	*Rosa chinensis viridiflora* (vert)	2·00	2·25
561/5		*Set of 5*	3·75	3·75

See also Nos. 584/8 and, for these designs with the royal cypher instead of the Queen's head, Nos. 589/98.

(Des D. Miller (18 c.), E. Nisbet and D. Miller (others). Litho Questa)

1988 (13 Oct). *300th Anniv of Lloyd's of London. Multicoloured designs as T 123 of Ascension. W w 16 (sideways* on 50, 60 c.). P 14.

566	18 c.	Loss of H.M.S. *Lutine* (frigate), 1799	45	25
	w.	Wmk inverted	10·00	
567	50 c.	*Sentinel* (cable ship) (horiz)	1·00	65
	w.	Wmk Crown to right of CA	15·00	
568	60 c.	*Bermuda* (liner), Hamilton, 1931 (horiz)	1·10	75
	w.	Wmk Crown to right of CA	12·00	
569	$2	Loss of H.M.S. *Valerian* (sloop) in hurricane, 1926	3·00	3·25
566/9		*Set of 4*	5·00	4·50

*The normal sideways watermark shows Crown to left of CA, as seen from the back of the stamp.

(Des A. Barbosa. Litho Harrison)

1988 (10 Nov). *Military Uniforms. T 137 and similar vert designs. Multicoloured. W w 14. P 14½.*

570	18 c.	Type **137**	65	25
571	50 c.	71st (Highland) Regiment, 1831-34	1·10	75
572	60 c.	Cameron Highlanders, 1942	1·25	85
573	$2	Troop of horse, 1774	3·50	3·75
570/3		*Set of 4*	6·00	5·00

138 *Corona* (ferry)   139 Morgan's Island

(Des C. Abbott, adapted L. Curtis. Litho Questa)

1989 (16 Feb). *Transport (3rd series). Ferry Services. T 138 and similar horiz designs. Multicoloured. W w 16 (sideways). P 14.*

574	18 c.	Type **138**	25	25
575	50 c.	Rowing boat ferry	65	65
576	60 c.	St. George's barge ferry	75	75
577	$2	*Laconia*	2·50	2·50
574/7		*Set of 4*	3·75	4·00

(Des A. Theobald. Litho Questa)

1989 (11 May). *150 Years of Photography. T 139 and similar horiz designs. Multicoloured. W w 14 (sideways). P 14×14½.*

578	18 c.	Type **139**	35	25
579	30 c.	Front Street, Hamilton	50	45
580	50 c.	Waterfront, Front Street, Hamilton	80	90
581	60 c.	Crow Lane from Hamilton Harbour	90	1·25
582	70 c.	Shipbuilding, Hamilton Harbour	1·10	1·40
583	$1	Dockyard	1·40	2·50
578/83		*Set of 6*	4·50	6·00

(Des R. Gorringe. Litho B.D.T.)

1989 (13 July). *Old Garden Roses (2nd series). Multicoloured designs as T 136. W w 14 (sideways on 50, 60 c. and $1.50). P 14×13½ (18, 30 c.) or 13½×14 (others).*

584	18 c.	"Agrippina" (vert)	40	25
585	30 c.	"Smith's Parish" (vert)	55	60
586	50 c.	"Champney's Pink Cluster"	90	1·25
587	60 c.	"Rosette Delizy"	1·00	1·60
588	$1.50,	*Rosa bracteata*	2·00	3·50
584/8		*Set of 5*	4·25	6·50

For these designs with the royal cypher instead of the Queen's head, see Nos. 589/98.

1989 (13 July). *Booklet stamps. Old Garden Roses designs as Nos. 561/5 and 584/8, but with royal cypher at top left instead of Queen's head. Multicoloured. W w 14 (sideways on horiz, inverted on vert designs). P 13½.*

589	50 c.	As No. 565 (vert)	1·00	1·25
	a.	Booklet pane. Nos. 589/98	9·00	
590	50 c.	As No. 563 (vert)	1·00	1·25
591	50 c.	Type **136**	1·00	1·25
592	50 c.	As No. 562	1·00	1·25
593	50 c.	As No. 564	1·00	1·25
594	50 c.	As No. 585 (vert)	1·00	1·25
595	50 c.	As No. 584 (vert)	1·00	1·25
596	50 c.	As No. 586	1·00	1·25
597	50 c.	As No. 587	1·00	1·25
598	50 c.	As No. 588	1·00	1·25
589/98		*Set of 10*	9·00	11·00

Booklet pane No. 589a has margins on three sides.

NEW INFORMATION

The editor is always interested to correspond with people who have new information that will improve or correct the Catalogue.

140 Main Library, Hamilton   141 1865 1d. Rose

(Des O. Bell. Litho B.D.T.)

1989 (5 Oct). *150th Anniv of Bermuda Library.* T **140** and similar horiz designs. Multicoloured. W w **14** (sideways). P 13½×14.

599	18 c. Type 140	20	25
600	50 c. The Old Rectory, St. George's	60	65
601	60 c. Somerset Library, Springfield	70	75
602	$2 Cabinet Building, Hamilton	2·40	2·75
599/602	*Set of 4*	3·50	4·00

(Des D. Miller. Litho Questa)

1989 (3 Nov). *Commonwealth Postal Conference.* T **141** and similar vert designs. Multicoloured. W w **14**. P 14.

603	18 c. brownish grey, brown-rose & brt scar	60	25
604	50 c. brownish grey, slate-bl & pale grey-bl	1·00	65
605	60 c. brownish grey, dull purple and purple	1·10	1·00
606	$2 brownish grey, dull green & brt emer	2·75	3·50
603/6	*Set of 4*	5·00	4·75

Designs:—50 c. 1866 2d. blue; 60 c. 1865 6d purple; $2 1865 1s. green.

142 "Fairylands, c. 1890"   (143)
(Ross Turner)

(Des L. Curtis. Litho B.D.T.)

1990 (19 Apr). *Bermuda Paintings (2nd series).* T **142** and similar horiz designs. Multicoloured. W w **16** (sideways). P 13½.

607	18 c. Type 142	40	25
608	50 c. "Shinebone Alley, c. 1953" (Ogden Pleissner)	85	1·10
609	60 c. "Salt Kettle, 1916" (Prosper Senat)	90	1·50
610	$2 "St. George's, 1934" (Jack Bush)	2·75	5·00
607/10	*Set of 4*	4·50	7·00

1990 (3 May). *"Stamp World London 90" International Stamp Exhibition, London.* Nos. 603/6 optd with T **143**.

611	18 c. brownish grey, brown-rose & brt scar	60	25
612	50 c. brownish grey, slate-bl & pale grey-bl	1·00	1·25
613	60 c. brownish grey, dull purple and purple	1·10	1·50
614	$2 brownish grey, dull green & brt emer	3·00	4·50
611/14	*Set of 4*	5·25	6·75

(144)   145 The Halifax and Bermudas Cable Company Office, Hamilton

1990 (13 Aug). Nos. 511A, 516A and 519A surch as T **144**.

615	30 c. on 12 c. *Warwick* (galleon), 1619	65	65
616	55 c. on 50 c. *Mark Antonie* (Spanish privateer), 1777	1·00	1·00
617	80 c. on $1.50 *Caesar* (brig), 1818	1·75	2·75
615/17	*Set of 3*	3·00	4·00

(Des C. Abbott. Litho Harrison)

1990 (18 Oct). *Centenary of Cable and Wireless in Bermuda.* T **145** and similar horiz designs. P 14.

618	20 c. light brown and black	50	25
619	55 c. light brown and black	1·50	1·25
620	70 c. multicoloured	1·75	2·00
621	$2 multicoloured	3·50	4·50
618/21	*Set of 4*	6·50	7·25

Designs:—55 c. *Westmeath* (cable ship), 1890; 70 c. Wireless transmitter station, St. George's, 1928; $2 *Sir Eric Sharp* (cable ship).

OMNIBUS ISSUES

Details, together with prices for complete sets, of the various Omnibus issues from the 1935 Silver Jubilee series to date are included in a special section following Zimbabwe at the end of Volume 2.

BUSH - MAJOR
16 MARCH 1991
(146)   147 Two-seater Pony Cart, 1805

1991 (16 Mar). *President Bush – Prime Minister Major Talks, Bermuda.* Nos. 618/19 optd with T **146** by Island Press.

622	**145** 20 c. light brown and black	1·25	75
623	– 55 c. light brown and black	1·75	2·50

(Des N. Shering. Litho Walsall)

1991 (21 Mar). *Transport (4th series). Horse-drawn Carriages.* T **147** and similar horiz designs. Multicoloured. W w **14** (sideways). P 14½.

624	20 c. Type 147	60	25
625	30 c. Varnished rockaway, 1830	70	50
626	55 c. Vis-a-Vis victoria, 1895	1·25	1·10
627	70 c. Semi-formal phaeton, 1900	1·75	1·60
628	80 c. Pony runabout, 1905	2·00	1·75
629	$1 Ladies phaeton, 1910	2·25	2·00
624/9	*Set of 6*	7·75	6·50

148 "Bermuda, 1916"   149 H.M.S. *Argonaut*
(Prosper Senat)   (cruiser) in Floating Dock

(Des L. Curtis. Litho Questa)

1991 (16 May). *Bermuda Paintings (3rd series).* T **148** and similar multicoloured designs. W w **14** (sideways on 55 c., $2). P 13½×14 (20, 70 c.) or 14×13½ (55 c., $2).

630	20 c. Type 148	70	30
631	55 c. "Bermuda Cottage", 1930 (Frank Allison) (horiz)	1·60	1·40
632	70 c. "Old Maid's Lane", 1934 (Jack Bush)	2·00	2·75
633	$2 "St. George's", 1953 (Ogden Pleissner) (horiz)	3·50	5·00
630/3	*Set of 4*	7·00	8·50

(Des D. Miller. Litho Questa)

1991 (20 June). *65th Birthday of Queen Elizabeth II and 70th Birthday of Prince Philip. Vert designs as* T **139** *of Ascension.* Multicoloured. W w **16** (sideways). P 14½×14.

634	55 c. Prince Philip in tropical naval uniform	90	1·25
	a. Horiz pair. Nos. 634/5 separated by label	2·00	2·50
635	70 c. Queen Elizabeth II in Bermuda	1·10	1·25

Nos. 634/5 were printed together in a similar sheet format to Nos. 539/40 of Ascension.

(Des N. Shewring. Litho Walsall)

1991 (19 Sept). *50th Anniv of Second World War.* T **149** and similar horiz designs. Multicoloured. W w **14** (sideways). P 14.

636	20 c. Type 149	1·00	30
637	55 c. Kindley Airfield	1·75	1·25
638	70 c. Boeing 314A flying boat and map of Atlantic route	2·25	2·50
639	$2 Censored trans-Atlantic mail	4·00	5·50
636/9	*Set of 4*	8·00	8·50

(Des D. Miller. Litho Questa ($1), B.D.T. (others))

1992 (6 Feb). *40th Anniv of Queen Elizabeth II's Accession.* Horiz designs as T **143** of Ascension. Multicoloured. W w **14** (sideways). P 14.

640	20 c. Old fort on beach	50	30
641	30 c. Public gardens	65	55
642	55 c. Cottage garden	1·00	90
643	70 c. Beach and hotels	1·40	1·60
644	$1 Queen Elizabeth II	1·75	2·25
640/4	*Set of 5*	4·75	5·00

150 Rings and Medallion

(Des N. Shewring. Litho Enschedé)

1992 (23 July). *500th Anniv of Discovery of America by Columbus. Spanish Artifacts.* T **150** and similar horiz designs. Multicoloured. W w **14** (sideways). P 13½.

645	25 c. Type 150	70	35
646	35 c. Ink wells	90	75
647	60 c. Gold ornaments	1·50	1·75
648	75 c. Bishop buttons and crucifix	1·75	2·50
649	85 c. Earrings and pearl buttons	2·00	2·75
650	$1 Jug and bowls	2·25	3·00
645/50	*Set of 6*	8·00	10·00

---

151 "Wreck of *Sea Venture*"

(Des D. Miller. Litho Questa)

1992 (24 Sept). *Stained Glass Windows.* T **151** and similar horiz designs. Multicoloured. W w **14** (sideways). P 13½×14.

651	25 c. Type 151	80	40
652	60 c. "Birds in tree"	1·75	2·00
653	75 c. "St. Francis feeding bird"	2·25	2·50
654	$2 "Shells"	4·50	5·00
651/4	*Set of 4*	8·50	9·00

152 German Shepherd   153 Policeman, Cyclist and Liner

(Des Jacqueline Murray-Hall, adapted D. Miller. Litho Enschedé)

1992 (12 Nov). *7th World Congress of Kennel Clubs.* T **152** and similar multicoloured designs. W w **14** (sideways on 25, 35 c.). P 13½.

655	25 c. Type 152	85	40
656	35 c. Irish Setter	1·00	70
657	60 c. Whippet (vert)	1·75	2·00
658	75 c. Border Terrier (vert)	1·90	2·50
659	85 c. Pomeranian (vert)	2·10	3·00
660	$1 Schipperke (vert)	2·25	3·25
655/60	*Set of 6*	8·75	10·50

1993 (25 Feb). *As Nos. 510, 512, 513/14, 517 and 522/3, but W w **14** (sideways). With "1992" imprint date. P 14.*

664	10 c. *Curlew* (sail/steamer), 1856	75	75
665	15 c. H.M.S. *Vixen* (gunboat), 1890	1·25	85
667	20 c. *San Pedro* (Spanish galleon), 1594	1·40	90
668	25 c. *Alert* (fishing sloop), 1877	1·40	60
672	60 c. *Mary Celestia* (Confederate paddle-steamer), 1864	2·50	1·75
677	$5 *Caraquet* (cargo liner), 1923	9·00	9·00
678	$8 H.M.S. *Pallas* (frigate), 1788	15·00	16·00
664/78	*Set of 7*	28·00	26·00

No. 678 does not have the fluorescent security marking present on the previous printing, as No. 523A.

(Des adapted D. Miller. Litho Questa)

1993 (25 Feb). *Tourism Posters by Adolph Treidler.* T **153** and similar vert designs. Multicoloured. W w **14**. P 14.

679	25 c. Type 153	75	45
680	60 c. Seaside golf course	1·75	2·00
681	75 c. Deserted beach	1·75	2·25
682	$2 Dancers in evening dress and liner	4·00	5·00
679/82	*Set of 4*	7·50	8·75

154 Duchesse de Brabant Rose and Bee

(Des D. Miller. Litho Questa)

1993 (1 Apr). *Booklet stamps.* W w **16** (sideways). P 14.

683	**154** 10 c. multicoloured	50	65
	a. Booklet pane. Nos. 683×2 and 685×3 with margins all round	3·25	
	b. Pane. No. 683×10 with margins all round	4·50	
684	25 c. multicoloured	30	35
	a. Booklet pane. No. 684×5 with margins all round	1·60	
685	50 c. multicoloured	80	1·00
686	60 c. multicoloured	75	95
	a. Booklet pane. No. 686×5 with margins all round	3·75	
683/6	*Set of 4*	2·10	2·75

The 10 c. was available as a loose pane of 10 and from $2.95 stamp booklets which also contained the 25 c. and 50 c. values. The 25 c. was also issued, together with the 60 c., in $4.25 booklets.

(Des A. Theobald. Litho Questa)

1993 (1 Apr). *75th Anniv of Royal Air Force. Horiz designs as* T **149** *of Ascension.* Multicoloured. W w **14** (sideways). P 14.

687	25 c. Consolidated PBY-5 Catalina	75	35
688	60 c. Supermarine Spitfire Mk IX	1·75	2·00
689	75 c. Bristol Type 156 Beaufighter Mk X	1·90	2·25
690	$2 Handley Page Halifax Mk III	3·50	4·50
687/90	*Set of 4*	7·00	8·00

155 Hamilton from the Sea

(Des R. Baxter and Sheila Semos (25 c.), N. Shewring and Sheila Semos (others). Litho Questa)

1993 (16 Sept). *Bicentenary of Hamilton. T* **155** *and similar horiz designs. Multicoloured. W* w **14** *(sideways). P* 14½.

691	25 c. Type 155	..	65	35
692	60 c. Waterfront ..	..	1·50	1·75
693	75 c. Barrel warehouse	..	1·75	2·25
694	$2 Sailing ships off Hamilton		3·50	4·50
691/4	.. .. ..	*Set of 4*	6·75	8·00

156 *Queen of Bermuda* (liner) at Hamilton

157 Queen Elizabeth II in Bermuda

(Des adapted D. Miller. Litho B.D.T.)

1994 (20 Jan). *75th Anniv of Furness Line's Bermuda Cruises. T* **156** *and similar multicoloured designs showing Adolph Treidler posters. W* w **16** *(sideways on 60 c. and 75 c.). P* 15×14 *(vert) or* 14×15 *(horiz).*

695	25 c. Type 156		45	35
696	60 c. *Monarch of Bermuda* entering port (horiz)		1·25	1·60
697	75 c. *Queen of Bermuda* and *Ocean Monarch* (liners) (horiz)		1·40	1·75
698	$2 Passengers on promenade deck at night ..		3·50	4·50
695/8	.. ..	*Set of 4*	6·00	7·50

The vessel depicted on the 60 c. was incorrectly identified as the *Queen of Bermuda* on the original, 1930s, travel poster.

(Des D. Miller. Litho Enschedé)

1994 (9 Mar). *Royal Visit. T* **157** *and similar vert designs. Multicoloured. W* w **14**. *P* 14.

699	25 c. Type 157		55	35
700	60 c. Queen Elizabeth and Prince Philip in open carriage ..		1·25	1·75
701	75 c. Royal Yacht *Britannia* ..		2·00	2·25
699/701	.. .. ..	*Set of 3*	3·50	4·00

158 Peach

159 Nurse with Mother and Baby

(Des Christine Phillips-Watlington and D. Miller. Litho Questa)

1994 (14 July)–**96**. *Flowering Fruits. T* **158** *and similar multicoloured designs. W* w **14** *(sideways on horiz designs). P* 14. A. *Without imprint date.* B. *Imprint date ("1996") at foot.*

			A		B	
702	5 c. Type 158	..	10	10	†	
703	7 c. Fig	..	10	10	†	
704	10 c. Calabash (*vert*) ..		10	15	†	
705	15 c. Natal Plum	..	20	25	†	
706	18 c. Locust and Wild Honey	25	30	25	30
707	20 c. Pomegranate	..	25	30	†	
708	25 c. Mulberry (*vert*) ..		30	35	†	
709	35 c. Grape (*vert*)	..	40	45	†	
710	55 c. Orange (*vert*)	..	65	70	†	
711	60 c. Surinam Cherry	..	75	80	†	
712	75 c. Loquat	..	90	95	†	
713	90 c. Sugar Apple	..	1·10	1·25	†	
714	$1 Prickly Pear (*vert*)	..	1·25	1·40	†	
715	$2 Paw Paw	..	2·50	2·75	†	
716	$3 Bay Grape	..	3·75	4·00	†	
717	$5 Banana (*vert*)	..	6·25	6·50	†	
718	$8 Lemon	..	10·00	10·50	†	
702/18	..	*Set of 17*	29·00	30·00	†	

Dates of issue: 14.7.94 Nos. 702A/3A, 705A, 707A, 718A; 6.10.94, Nos. 704A, 708A/10A, 714A, 717A; 23.3.95, Nos. 706A, 711A/13A, 715A/16A; 1.9.96, No.706B.

(Des S. Noon. Litho Enschedé)

1994 (15 Sept). *Centenary of Hospital Care. T* **159** *and similar vert designs. Multicoloured. W* w **14**. *P* 15×14.

719	25 c. Type 159	..	70	35
720	60 c. Patient on dialysis machine	..	1·60	1·75
721	75 c. Casualty on emergency trolley	1·75	2·00
722	$2 Elderly patient in wheelchair with physiotherapists	4·00	4·50
719/22	.. ..	*Set of 4*	7·25	7·75

160 Gombey Dancers

(Des Jennifer Toombs. Litho Enschedé)

1994 (10 Nov). *Cultural Heritage* (1st series). *T* **160** *and similar horiz designs. Multicoloured. W* w **14** *(sideways). P* 14×15.

723	25 c. Type 160	.. ..	55	35
724	60 c. Christmas carol singers	..	1·10	1·25
725	75 c. Marching band	..	1·40	1·75
726	$2 National Dance Group performers	3·50	4·25
723/6	..	*Set of 4*	6·00	7·00

See also Nos. 731/4.

161 Bermuda 1970 Flower 1 c. Stamps and 1 c. Coin

162 Bermuda Coat of Arms

(Des D. Miller. Litho Enschedé)

1995 (6 Feb). *25th Anniv of Decimal Currency. T* **161** *and similar horiz designs. Multicoloured. W* w **14** *(sideways). P* 13½×14.

727	25 c. Type 161	.. ..	45	35
728	60 c. 1970 5 c. stamps and coin	..	1·00	1·25
729	75 c. 1970 10 c. stamps and coin	..	1·25	1·75
730	$2 1970 25 c. stamps and coin	..	3·50	4·25
727/30	..	*Set of 4*	5·75	7·00

(Des Jennifer Toombs. Litho Enschedé)

1995 (30 May). *Cultural Heritage* (2nd series). *Horiz designs as T* **160**. *Multicoloured. W* w **14** *(sideways). P* 14×15.

731	25 c. Kite flying	.. ..	45	35
732	60 c. Majorettes	.. ..	1·25	1·25
733	75 c. Portuguese dancers	..	1·40	1·75
734	$2 Floral float ..	..	3·25	4·25
731/4	..	*Set of 4*	5·75	7·00

(Des Sheila Semas. Litho Enschedé)

1995 (3 Nov). *375th Anniv of Bermuda Parliament. W* w **14**. *P* 14×13½.

735	162 25 c. multicoloured	.. ..	40	35
736	$1 multicoloured	..	1·50	2·00

For design as No. 736, but inscr "Commonwealth Finance Ministers Meeting" see No. 765.

163 U.S. Navy Ordnance Island Submarine Base

164 Triple Jump

(Des R. Watton. Litho Walsall)

1995 (4 Dec). *Military Bases. T* **163** *and similar horiz designs. Multicoloured. W* w **14** *(sideways). P* 14.

737	20 c. Type 163	.. ..	40	30
738	25 c. Royal Naval Dockyard	..	50	35
739	60 c. U.S.A.F. Fort Bell and Kindley Field	1·00	1·00
740	75 c. R.A.F. Darrell's Island flying boat base	1·25	1·50
741	90 c. U.S. Navy operating base	..	1·50	2·00
742	$1 Canadian Forces Communications Station, Daniel's Head ..	1·60	2·00
737/42	..	*Set of 6*	5·50	6·50

(Des S. Noon. Litho B.D.T.)

1996 (21 May). *Olympic Games, Atlanta. T* **164** *and similar vert designs. Multicoloured. W* w **16**. *P* 14.

743	25 c. Type 164	.. ..	45	35
744	30 c. Cycling	.. ..	75	60
745	65 c. Yachting	..	1·25	1·60
746	80 c. Show jumping	..	1·50	1·90
743/6	.. ..	*Set of 4*	3·50	4·00

165 Jetty and Islets, Hamilton

(Des D. Miller. Litho Walsall)

1996 (21 May). *Booklet Stamps. Panoramic Paintings of Hamilton (Nos. 747/51) and St. George's (Nos. 752/6) by E. J. Holland. T* **165** *and similar horiz designs. Multicoloured. W* w **14** *(sideways). P* 14×14½.

747	60 c. Type 165	..	75	80
	a. Booklet pane. Nos. 747/56, with margins all round	7·50	
748	60 c. End of island and buildings ..	..	75	80
749	60 c. Yachts and hotel	..	75	80
750	60 c. Islet, hotel and cathedral	..	75	80
751	60 c. Cliff and houses by shore	..	75	80
752	60 c. Islet and end of main island ..	75	80
753	60 c. Yacht and houses on hillside	..	75	80
754	60 c. Yacht and St. George's Hotel on hilltop	75	80
755	60 c. Shoreline and fishing boats ..	75	80
756	60 c. Entrance to harbour channel	..	75	80
747/56	.. ..	*Set of 10*	7·50	8·00

Nos. 747/56 were only available from $6 booklets containing a pane of 10 (5×2) (No. 747a) showing the Hamilton panorama above that of St. George's.

166 Somerset Express Mail Cart, c. 1900

167 Hog Fish Beacon

(Des B. Dare. Litho Enschedé)

1996 (7 June). *"CAPEX '96" International Stamp Exhibition, Toronto. Local Transport. T* **166** *and similar horiz designs. Multicoloured. W* w **14** *(sideways). P* 13½×14.

757	25 c. Type 166	..	60	35
758	60 c. Victoria carriage and tram, 1930s	1·50	1·50
759	75 c. First bus, 1946	..	1·60	1·75
760	$2 Sightseeing bus, c. 1947	..	3·50	4·00
757/60	..	*Set of 4*	6·50	7·00

(Des N. Shewring. Litho Enschedé)

1996 (15 Aug). *Lighthouses. T* **167** *and similar vert designs. Multicoloured. W* w **14** *(inverted on* $2). *P* 14×13½.

761	30 c. Type 167	..	55	45
762	65 c. Gibbs Hill Lighthouse	..	1·10	1·10
763	80 c. St. David's Lighthouse	..	1·40	1·75
764	$2 North Rock Beacon	..	3·25	4·00
761/4	..	*Set of 4*	5·75	6·50

(Litho Enschedé)

1996 (24 Sept). *Commonwealth Finance Ministers' Meeting. As No. 736, but inscr "Commonwealth Finance Ministers Meeting" at top and with wider gold frame. W* w **14**. *P* 14×13½.

765	$1 multicoloured	..	1·50	1·75

168 Waterville

(Des D. Miller. Litho Walsall)

1996 (28 Nov). *Architectural Heritage. T* **168** *and similar horiz designs. Multicoloured. W* w **16** *(sideways). P* 14.

766	30 c. Type 168	..	60	45
767	65 c. Bridge House	..	1·10	1·25
768	80 c. Fannie Fox's Cottage	..	1·40	1·75
769	$2.50, Palmetto House	..	3·50	4·25
766/9	..	*Set of 4*	6·00	7·00

(Des N. Shewring. Litho Walsall)

1997 (12 Feb). *"HONG KONG '97" International Stamp Exhibition. Designs as Nos. 761/4, but incorporating "HONG KONG '97" logo and with one value changed. W w 14. P 14.*

770	30 c. As Type 167	..	..		60	45
771	65 c. Gibbs Hill Lighthouse				1·25	1·25
772	80 c. St David's Lighthouse		..		1·40	1·50
773	$2.50, North Rock Beacon		..		3·75	4·25
770/3	..	..	..	Set of 4	6·25	6·75

169 White-tailed Tropic Bird

(Des N. Arlott. Litho B.D.T.)

1997 (17 Apr). *Birds Conservation. T 169 and similar multicoloured designs. W w 16 (sideways on 30 c., $2.50). P 14.*

774	30 c. Type 169				50	40
775	60 c. White-tailed Tropic Bird and chick (*vert*)			..	1·00	1·00
776	80 c. Cahow and chick (*vert*)				1·40	1·50
777	$2.50, Cahow	..	..	..	3·75	4·00
774/7	..	..	..	Set of 4	6·00	6·25

170 Queen Elizabeth II with Crowd

171 Father playing with Children

(Des D. Miller. Litho Questa)

1997 (9 Oct). *Golden Wedding of Queen Elizabeth and Prince Philip. T 170 and similar horiz design. Multicoloured. W w 14 (sideways). P 14½.*

778	30 c. Type 170	..	..	..	50	40
779	$2 Queen Elizabeth and Prince Philip		..		2·75	3·00
MS780	90×56 mm. Nos. 778/9		..	..	3·25	3·50

(Litho Questa)

1997 (18 Dec). *Education. T 171 and similar horiz designs. Multicoloured. W w 14 (sideways). P 14.*

781	30 c. Type 171	..	..	..	35	40
782	40 c. Teacher and children with map				50	55
783	60 c. Boys holding sports trophy			..	75	80
784	65 c. Pupils outside Berkeley Institute		..		80	85
785	80 c. Scientific experiments			..	1·00	1·10
786	90 c. New graduates		..	..	1·10	1·25
781/6	..	..	..	Set of 6	4·50	5·00

STAMP BOOKLETS

1948 (5 Apr–10 May). *Pink (No. SB1), or light blue (No. SB2) covers. Stapled.*

SB1	5s. booklet containing six 1d., 1½d., 2d., 2½d. and 3d. (Nos. 110, 111*b*, 112*a*, 113*b*, 114*a*) in blocks of 6 (10 May) £130
SB2	10s. 6d. booklet containing six 3d. and eighteen 6d. (Nos. 114*a*, 104) in blocks of 6 with twelve air mail labels £150

B 1 "Window" Design (*Illustration reduced. Actual size 125×91 mm*)

1987 (30 Apr). *Paintings by Winslow Homer. Folded card covers, printed in gold. Pane attached by selvedge.*

SB3	$4 containing booklet pane of 10 40 c. (No. 544a)	8·50

1989 (13 July). *Old Garden Roses. Folded card cover, 125×91 mm, as Type B 1, printed in grey. Pane attached by selvedge.*

SB4	$5 containing booklet pane of 10 50 c. (No. 589a)	9·00

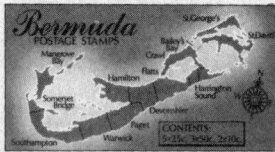

B 2 Map of Bermuda

1993 (1 Apr). *Folded card covers as Type B 2 printed in Venetian red, new blue and black. Panes attached by selvedge.*

SB5	$2.95, booklet containing panes Nos. 683a and 684a	4·75
SB6	$4.25, booklet containing panes Nos. 684a and 686a	5·25

B 3 Coats of Arms of Hamilton and St. George's

1996 (21 May). *Panoramic Paintings of Hamilton and St. George's. Pane attached by selvedge.*

SB7	$6 booklet containing pane No. 747a	7·75

EXPRESS LETTER STAMPS

E 1 Queen Elizabeth II

(Des D. Miller. Litho Enschedé)

1996 (7 Nov). *W w 14. P 14×13½.*

E1	E 1 $22 orange and royal blue	..	..	28·00 29·00

POSTAL FISCAL

1937 (1 Feb). *As T 15, but inscr "REVENUE" at each side. Wmk Mult Script CA. Chalk-surfaced paper. P 14.*

F1	12s. 6d. grey and orange £1000 £1100
	a. Break in scroll (R. 1/12) .. £2750
	b. Broken crown and scroll (R. 2/12) .. £2750
	c. Breaks in scrolls at right (R. 1/3) .. £2750

No. F1 was issued for fiscal purposes towards the end of 1936. Its use as a postage stamp was authorised from 1 February to April 1937. The used price quoted above is for examples postmarked during this period. Later in the same year postmarks with other dates were obtained by favour.

For illustration of No. F1a/c see above Nos. 44 and 88.

— URCH HARRIS —
ALL WORLD
NEW ISSUE SERVICE

Your 'First Choice' New Issue Supplier

Developed over the last 30 years Urch Harris 'All World' combines the widest choice of countries, themes and formats with a reliable individual service that helps develop and manage your collection.

- 260 countries and 100 plus themes.
- Choice of mint issues, reprints, yearpacks, used stamps, maxi cards, booklets, presentation packs, specimens and first day covers.
- Regular distributions every 6 weeks.
- Free magazine with every distribution.
- Fully computerised invoices with descriptions.
- Customer advice helpline.
- Free gifts and regular special offers.
- Supported by Stanley Gibbons, world leaders in philately.

FREE WELCOME PACK

Containing full details of our unique service, a full list of countries and themes and a copy of 'All World Direct' magazine.

Telephone 0117 9349333 for a free pack.

Urch Harris & Co
1 Denmark Avenue
Bristol BS1 5HD

A Division of Stanley Gibbons Ltd

Botswana

(*formerly* Bechuanaland)

Before the 1880s the only Europeans in the area which became Bechuanaland were scattered hunters and traders, together with the missionaries who were established at Kuruman as early as 1816.

Tribal conflicts in the early years of the decade led to the intervention of Boers from the Transvaal who established the independent republics of Goshen and Stellaland.

STELLALAND

The Boer republic of Stellaland was proclaimed towards the end of 1882. A postal service was organised from the capital, Vryburg, and stamps were ordered from a firm in Cape Town. These were only valid within the republic. Until June 1885 mail to other parts of South Africa was sent through Christiana, in the Transvaal, and was franked with both Stellaland and Transvaal stamps.

No date stamps or obliterators were used by the Stellaland Post Office. Stamps were pen-cancelled with the initials of a postal official and the date.

> **PRICES FOR STAMPS ON COVER**
> The issues of Stellaland are very rare on cover.

1 Arms of the Republic

(Litho by Van der Sandt, de Villiers & Co., Cape Town)

1884 (29 Feb). *P* 12.

1	**1**	1d. red		£170	£275
		a. Imperf between (horiz pair)		£2250	
		b. Imperf between (vert pair)		£2250	
2		3d. orange		20·00	£275
		a. Imperf between (horiz pair)		£600	
		b. Imperf between (vert pair)		£800	
3		4d. olive-grey		20·00	£300
		a. Imperf between (horiz pair)		£600	
4		6d. lilac-mauve		20·00	£300
		a. Imperf between (horiz pair)		£900	
		b. Imperf between (vert pair)		£1200	
5		1s. green		40·00	

In 1884 the British Government, following appeals from local chiefs for protection, decided to annex both Goshen and Stellaland. A force under Sir Charles Warren from the Cape reached Vryburg on 7 February 1885 and continued to Mafeking, the principal town of Goshen.

On 30 September 1885 Stellaland and other territory to the south of the Molopo River was constituted the Crown Colony of British Bechuanaland. A protectorate was also proclaimed over a vast tract of land to the north of the Molopo.

Stellaland stamps continued to be used until 2 December 1885 with external mail routed via Barkly West and Kimberley in Griqualand West franked with both Stellaland and Cape of Good Hope stamps. The latter were cancelled on arrival at Barkly West.

1885 (Oct). *Handstamped* "𝕭𝖜𝖈𝖈" *sideways in violet-lake.*

6	**1**	2d. on 4d. olive-grey		£3500

On 2 December 1885 Cape of Good Hope stamps overprinted "British Bechuanaland" were placed on sale at the Vryburg post office.

BRITISH BECHUANALAND

CROWN COLONY

> **PRICES FOR STAMPS ON COVER**
>
> | | |
> |---|---|
> | Nos. 1/8 | *from* × 12 |
> | No. 9 | *from* × 80 |
> | Nos. 10/21 | *from* × 8 |
> | Nos. 22/8 | *from* × 10 |
> | No. 29 | *from* × 10 |
> | No. 30 | *from* × 10 |
> | Nos. 31/2 | *from* × 12 |
> | Nos. 33/7 | *from* × 20 |
> | Nos. 38/9 | *from* × 25 |

BRITISH

British

Bechuanaland	BECHUANALAND
(1)	**(2)**

1885 (1 Dec)–87. *Stamps of Cape of Good Hope* ("*Hope*" *seated*) *optd with T* **1**, *by W. A. Richards & Sons, Cape Town.*

(a) Wmk Crown CC (No. 3) or Crown CA (others)

1	½d. grey-black (No. 40a) (R.)		11·00	15·00
	a. Opt in lake		£3000	
	b. Opt double (Lake+Black)		£600	
2	3d. pale claret (No. 43)		32·00	35·00
3	4d. dull blue (No. 30) (12.86?)		55·00	60·00

(b) Wmk Anchor (Cape of Good Hope). Type **13**)

4		½d. grey-black (No. 48a) (3.87)		7·00	11·00
		a. Error. "ritish"		£1700	
		b. Opt double		£2750	
5		1d. rose-red (No. 49)		9·00	9·00
		a. Error. "ritish"		£2250	£1800
		b. Opt double		† £1800	
6		2d. pale bistre (No. 50)		28·00	8·00
		a. Error. "ritish"		£4250	£3250
		b. Opt double		† £1500	
7		6d. reddish purple (No. 52)		75·00	38·00
8		1s. green (No. 53) (11.86?)		£200	£140
		a. Error. "ritish"		£12000	£9000

Nos. 1/8 were overprinted from settings of 120. The missing "B" errors are believed to have occurred on one position for one of these settings only.

Overprints with stop after "Bechuanaland" are forged.

1887 (1 Nov). *No. 197 of Great Britain optd with T* **2**, *by D.L.R.*

9	½d. vermilion (H/S S. £80)		70	1·25
	a. Opt double		£2250	

3	**4**	**5**

(Typo D.L.R.)

1887 (1 Nov). *(a) Wmk Orb (Great Britain Type* **48**). *P* 14.

10	**3**	1d. lilac and black		12·00	1·25
11		2d. lilac and black		55·00	1·25
		a. *Pale dull lilac and black*		35·00	22·00
12		3d. lilac and black		3·25	4·75
		a. *Pale reddish lilac and black*		50·00	14·00
13		4d. lilac and black		38·00	2·25
14		6d. lilac and black		48·00	2·50

(b) Wmk Script "V R" (*sideways, reading up*). *P* 13½

15	**4**	1s. green and black		28·00	4·50
16		2s. green and black		48·00	35·00
17		2s. 6d. green and black		60·00	42·00
18		5s. green and black		80·00	£130
19		10s. green and black		£170	£300

(c) Two Orbs (sideways). P 14×13½

20	**5**	£1 lilac and black		£900	£800
21		£5 lilac and black		£2750	£1300
10/21 H/S "Specimen"			*Set of* 12	£900	

Nos. 10/21 were produced by overprinting a series of "Unappropriated Die" designs originally produced by the Board of Inland Revenue for use as Great Britain fiscal stamps.

Several values are known on blued paper. No. 11a is the first printing of the 2d. (on safety paper?) and has a faded appearance.

When purchasing Nos. 20/21 in used condition beware of copies with fiscal cancellations cleaned off and bearing forged postmarks.

For No. 15 surcharged "£5" see No. F2.

1d.	**1s.**	**One Half-Penny**
(6)	(7)	(8)

1888 (7 Aug). *Nos. 10/11 and 13/15 surch as T* **6** *or* **7**, *by P. Townshend & Co, Vryburg.*

22	**3**	1d. on 1d. lilac and black		7·50	5·00
23		2d. on 2d. lilac and black (R.)		15·00	2·50
		a. *Pale dull lilac and black* (No. 11a)		70·00	48·00
		b. Curved foot to "2"		£200	£150
		c. Surch in green		† £2500	
25		4d. on 4d. lilac and black (R.)		£170	£225
26		6d. on 6d. lilac and black		75·00	10·00
		a. Surch in blue		† £5500	
28	**4**	1s. on 1s. green and black		£100	60·00

Nos. 23c and 26a are from two sheets of surcharge trials subsequently put into stock and used at Vryburg (2d.) or Mafeking (6d.) during 1888–89.

1888 (Dec). *No. 12a surch with T* **8**, *by P. Townshend & Co, Vryburg.*

29	**3**	½d. on 3d. pale reddish lilac and black		£130	£140
		a. Broken "f" in "Half"		£4000	

No. 29 was produced from a setting of 60 (12×5).

No. 29a shows the letter "f" almost completely missing and occurs on R. 5/11 of the setting. Five examples are known, one being in the Royal Collection.

Errors of spelling on this surcharge are bogus.

British		**BRITISH**
Bechuanaland.	**British Bechuanaland**	**BECHUANALAND**
(9)	(10)	(11)

1889 (Jan). *No. 48a of Cape of Good Hope (wmk Anchor) optd with T* **9**, *by P. Townshend & Co, Vryburg.*

30	½d. grey-black (G.)		3·25	19·00
	b. Opt double, one inverted		£1000	
	c. Opt double, one vertical		£500	
	ca. *Se-tenant* with stamp without opt		£2750	
	e. "British" omitted		£2000	

No. 30 was produced using a setting of 30 (6×5). No. 30e occurred on R. 5/1 of the setting on some sheets only.

1891 (Nov). *Nos. 49/50 of Cape of Good Hope (wmk Anchor), optd with T* **10**, *reading upwards.*

31		1d. rose-red		10·00	8·00
		a. Horiz pair, one without opt		£1800	
		b. "British" omitted		—	£1100
		c. "Bechuanaland" omitted		£1100	
32		2d. pale bistre		3·25	2·25
		a. No stop after "Bechuanaland"		£225	£275
31/2 H/S "Specimen"			*Set of* 2	£130	

Nos. 31/2 were produced from separate settings of 120 (12×10). No. 32a occurs on R. 3/3.

See also Nos. 38 and 39.

1891 (1 Dec)–1904. *Nos. 172, 200, 205, 208 and 211 of Great Britain optd with T* **11**, *by D.L.R.*

33	1d. lilac		6·00	85
34	2d. grey-green and carmine		3·50	3·00
35	4d. green and purple-brown		2·50	50
	a. Bisected (2d.) (on cover) (11.99)		† £2000	
36	6d. purple/*rose-red*		3·00	2·00
37	1s. green (7.94)		13·00	16·00
	a. Bisected (6d.) (on cover) (12.04)		†	
33/7			*Set of* 5	25·00	20·00
33/6 H/S "Specimen"			*Set of* 4	£170	

No. 35a was used at Palapye station and No. 37a at Kanye.

1893 (Dec)–95. *As Nos.* 31/2, *but T* **10** *reads downwards.*

38	1d. rose-red		2·25	2·25
	a. Pair, one without opt		£1000	
	b. "British" omitted		£1000	
	c. Optd "Bechuanaland. British"		£800	£900
	d. No dots to "i" of "British" (R. 1/10)		80·00	80·00
	e. Opt reading up, no dots to "i" of "British"		£1200	
39	2d. pale bistre (15.3.95)		4·50	2·25
	a. Opt double		£850	£550
	b. "British" omitted		£450	£450
	c. Optd "Bechuanaland. British"		£325	£200
	d. No dots to "i" of "British" (R. 1/10)		£100	£100
	e. Opt reading up, no dots to "i" of "British"			

A common setting of 120 (12×10) was used for Nos. 38/9. Some sheets of both values were overprinted the wrong way up, resulting in Nos. 38e and 39e.

On 16 November 1895 British Bechuanaland was annexed to the Cape of Good Hope and ceased to have its own stamps, but they remained in use in the Protectorate until superseded in 1897. The Postmaster-General of Cape Colony had assumed control of the Bechuanaland postal service on 1 April 1893 and the Cape, and subsequently the South African, postal authorities continued to be responsible for the postal affairs of the Bechuanaland Protectorate until 1963.

BECHUANALAND PROTECTORATE

> **PRICES FOR STAMPS ON COVER TO 1945**
>
> | | |
> |---|---|
> | Nos. 40/51 | *from* × 10 |
> | Nos. 52/71 | *from* × 6 |
> | Nos. 72/82 | *from* × 5 |
> | Nos. 83/98 | *from* × 4 |
> | Nos. 99/110 | *from* × 6 |
> | Nos. 111/17 | *from* × 10 |
> | Nos. 118/28 | *from* × 4 |
> | Nos. 129/31 | *from* × 10 |
> | | |
> | Nos. D1/3 | *from* × 50 |
> | Nos. D4/6 | *from* × 60 |
> | | |
> | No. F1 | *from* × 5 |
> | No. F2 | — |
> | No. F3 | *from* × 5 |

This large area north of the Molopo River was proclaimed a British Protectorate on 30 September 1885 at the request of the native chiefs.

A postal service using runners was inaugurated on 9 August 1888 and Nos. 40 to 55 were issued as a temporary measure with the object of assessing the cost of this service.

Protectorate	**Protectorate 1d**
(12) 15½ mm	(13)

1888 (7 Aug). *No. 9 optd with T* **12** *and Nos.* 10/19 *surch or optd only as T* **13**.

40		½d. vermilion (H/S S. £75)		2·75	20·00
		a. "Protectorate" double		£300	
41	**3**	1d. on 1d. lilac and black		6·50	12·00
		a. Small figure "1" (R. 5/4, 7/2, 10/2)		£275	£300
42		2d. on 2d. lilac and black		19·00	17·00
		b. Curved foot to "2"		£400	£375
43		3d. on 3d. pale reddish lilac and black		95·00	£140
44		4d. on 4d. lilac and black		£250	£250
		a. Small figure "4"		£2500	£2500
45		6d. on 6d. lilac and black		60·00	40·00
46	**4**	1s. green and black (H/S S. £100)		60·00	48·00
		a. First "o" omitted		£3500	£3000
47		2s. green and black		£500	£700
		a. First "o" omitted		£7500	
48		2s. 6d. green and black		£500	£650
		a. First "o" omitted		£7500	
49		5s. green and black		£1100	£1600
		a. First "o" omitted		£9500	
50		10s. green and black		£3000	£4250
		a. First "o" omitted		£14000	

Nos. 40/5 were produced from a basic setting of 120 (12×10) on which a faulty first "o" in "Protectorate" occurred on R.5/12. For Nos. 46/50 the setting was reduced to 84 (12×7) and on many sheets the first "o" on R.5/12 failed to print.

See also Nos. 54/5.

1888 (Dec). *No. 25 optd with T* **12** *by P. Townshend & Co, Vryburg.*

51	**3**	4d. on 4d. lilac and black		55·00	32·00

Bechuanaland

Protectorate

Protectorate. Fourpence

(14) (15)

1889 (Jan). *No. 48a of Cape of Good Hope (wmk Anchor), optd with T 14 by P. Townshend & Co., Vryburg.*
52	½d. grey-black (G.)	..	2·75	27·00
	a. Opt double		£400	£500
	ab. Ditto, one reading "Protectorate Bechuanaland"		£700	
	b. "Bechuanaland" omitted		£700	
	c. Optd "Protectorate Bechuanaland"		£350	£425

1889 (Aug). *No. 9 surch with T 15 by P. Townshend & Co., Vryburg.*
53	4d. on ½d. vermilion (H/S S. £120)		16·00	3·25
	a. "rpence" omitted (R. 9/2)		†	£6000
	b. "ourpence" omitted (R. 9/2)		£10000	
	c. Surch (T 15) inverted		†	£4000
	cb. Ditto. "ourpence" omitted		†	£11000

Examples of No. 53c are postmarked "679" (Tati).

Protectorate Protectorate

(16) 15 mm (17)

1890. *No. 9 optd.*
54	16	½d. vermilion		£120	£130
		a. Type 16 inverted		70·00	90·00
		b. Type 16 double		85·00	£110
		c. Type 16 double and inverted		£550	£550
		d. Optd "Portectorate" inverted		£2750	
55	17	½d. vermilion		£140	£200
		a. Type 17 double		£700	
		b. Optd "Protectorrte"		£700	
		c. Optd "Protectorrte" double		£12000	

These were trial printings made in 1888 which were subsequently issued.

In June 1890 the Bechuanaland Protectorate and the Colony of British Bechuanaland came under one postal administration and the stamps of British Bechuanaland were used in the Protectorate until 1897.

BRITISH

BECHUANALAND BECHUANALAND PROTECTORATE

(18) (19)

1897. *No. 59 of Cape of Good Hope (wmk Anchor), optd as T 18.*

(a) *Lines 13 mm apart, bottom line 16 mm long, by Taylor & Marshall, Cape Town*
56	½d. yellow-green (July?)	..	2·50	7·00

(b) *Lines 13½ mm apart, bottom line 15 mm long, by P. Townshend & Co, Vryburg*
57	½d. yellow-green (April)	..	18·00	60·00

(c) *Lines 10½ mm apart, bottom line 15 mm long, by W. A. Richards & Sons, Cape Govt Printers*
58	½d. yellow-green (July?)	..	8·00	32·00

Although issued only in the Protectorate, the above were presumably overprinted "BRITISH BECHUANALAND" because stamps bearing this inscription were in use there at the time.

1897 (Oct)–**1902.** *Nos. 172, 197, 200, 202, 205 and 208 of Great Britain (Queen Victoria) optd with T 19 by D.L.R.*
59	½d. vermilion		1·00	1·50
60	½d. blue-green (25.2.02)		1·40	2·25
61	1d. lilac		4·00	55
62	2d. grey-green and carmine		2·25	4·50
63	3d. purple/*yellow* (1898)		5·50	8·50
64	4d. green and purple-brown		11·00	11·00
65	6d. purple/*rose-red*		19·00	11·00
59/65		Set of 7	40·00	35·00
59/65 Optd/H.S. (No. 60) "Specimen"		Set of 7	£225	

BECHUANALAND PROTECTORATE

BECHUANALAND PROTECTORATE

(20) (21)

1904 (29 Nov)–**13.** *Nos. 216, 218/19, 230 and 313/14 (Somerset House ptgs) of Great Britain (King Edward VII) optd with T 20, by D.L.R.*
66	½d. blue-green (3.06)		90	90
67	½d. yellowish green (11.08)		2·50	3·50
68	1d. scarlet (4.05) (S. £60)		4·75	25
69	2½d. ultramarine		4·00	5·00
	a. Stop after "P" in "PROTECTORATE"		£800	£1200
70	1s. deep green and scarlet (10.12)		30·00	80·00
71	1s. green and carmine (1913) (S. £80)		30·00	85·00

No. 69a occurs on R.5/9 of the lower pane.

1912 (Sept). *No. 342 of Great Britain (King George V, wmk Crown) optd with T 20.*
72	1d. scarlet		55	60
	a. No cross on crown		—	75·00
	b. Aniline scarlet (No. 343)		£120	80·00

1913 (July)–**24.** *Stamps of Great Britain (King George V) optd.*

(a) *Nos. 351, 357, 362, 367, 370/1, 376, 379, 385 and 395 (wmk Simple Cypher, T 100) optd with T 20*
73	½d. green (shades)		1·25	1·75
74	1d. scarlet (shades) (4.15)		2·75	40
	a. Carmine-red (1922)		10·00	1·50
75	1½d. red-brown (12.20)		2·25	3·00
76	2d. reddish orange (Die I)		2·50	3·50
	a. Orange (Die I) (1921)		11·00	4·50
77	2d. orange (Die II) (1924)		35·00	5·00
78	2½d. cobalt-blue		3·00	16·00
	a. Blue (1915)		5·50	17·00
79	3d. bluish violet		5·50	12·00
80	4d. grey-green		6·00	14·00
81	6d. reddish purple (shades)		6·50	16·00
82	1s. bistre (S. £75)		9·00	18·00
	a. Bistre-brown (1923)		20·00	32·00
73/82		Set of 9	35·00	75·00

(b) *With T 21*

(i) *Waterlow printings (Nos. 399 and 401) (1914–15)*
83	2s. 6d. deep sepia-brown (1.15)		£100	£190
	a. Re-entry (R.2/1)		£900	£1200
	b. Opt double, one albino		£225	
84	5s. rose-carmine (1914)		£140	£325
	a. Opt double, one albino		£300	
83/4 Optd "Specimen"		Set of 2	£275	

(ii) *D.L.R. printings (Nos. 407/8 and 409) (1916–19)*
85	2s. 6d. pale brown (7.16)		£100	£190
	a. Re-entry (R. 2/1)		£950	
86	2s. 6d. sepia (1917)		£120	£190
	a. Opt treble, two albino			
	b. Re-entry (R. 2/1)			
87	5s. bright carmine (8.19)		£250	£375
	a. Opt double, one albino		£350	

(iii) *B.W. printings (Nos. 414 and 416) (1920–23)*
88	2s. 6d. chocolate-brown (7.23)		80·00	£150
	a. Major re-entry (R.1/2)		£1900	
	b. Opt double, one albino			
89	5s. rose-red (7.20)		£110	£225
	a. Opt treble, two albino			
	b. Opt double, one albino		£300	

1925 (July)–**27.** *Nos. 418/19, 421, 423/4, 426/a and 429 of Great Britain (wmk Block Cypher, T 111) optd with T 20.*
91	½d. green (1927)		80	1·75
92	1d. scarlet (8.25)		1·25	70
93	2d. orange (Die II)		1·50	1·00
94	3d. violet (10.26)		4·75	13·00
	a. Opt double, one albino		£225	
	w. Wmk inverted		£140	
95	4d. grey-green (10.26)		4·75	25·00
	a. Printed on the gummed side			
96	6d. reddish purple (chalk-surfaced paper) (12.25)		23·00	42·00
97	6d. purple (ordinary paper) (1926)		42·00	45·00
98	1s. bistre-brown (10.26)		9·00	24·00
	w. Wmk inverted		—	£250
91/8		Set of 8	80·00	£140

22 King George V, Baobab Tree and Cattle drinking

23 King George VI, Baobab Tree and Cattle drinking

(Des from photo by Resident Commissioner, Ngamiland, Recess Waterlow)

1932 (12 Dec). *Wmk Mult Script CA. P 12½.*
99	22	½d. green		1·00	30
		a. Imperf between (horiz pair)		£12000	
100		1d. scarlet		1·00	25
101		2d. brown		1·00	30
102		3d. ultramarine		1·00	50
103		4d. orange		1·25	4·00
104		6d. purple		2·50	2·00
105		1s. black and olive-green		3·00	7·00
106		2s. black and orange		24·00	38·00
107		2s.6d. black and scarlet		19·00	30·00
108		3s. black and purple		35·00	42·00
109		5s. black and ultramarine		48·00	50·00
110		10s. black and brown		95·00	£100
99/110			Set of 12	£200	£225
99/110 Perf "Specimen"			Set of 12	£250	

1935 (4 May). *Silver Jubilee. As Nos. 91/4 of Antigua but ptd by B.W.P. 11 × 12.*
111	1d. deep blue and scarlet		30	1·75
	a. Extra flagstaff		£180	
	b. Short extra flagstaff		£150	
	c. Lightning conductor		£150	
	d. Flagstaff on right-hand turret		£140	
	e. Double flagstaff		£140	
112	2d. ultramarine and grey-black		1·00	1·75
	a. Extra flagstaff		85·00	
	b. Short extra flagstaff		70·00	
	c. Lightning conductor		65·00	
113	3d. brown and deep blue		1·25	1·75
	a. Extra flagstaff		£120	
	b. Short extra flagstaff		85·00	
	c. Lightning conductor		85·00	
114	6d. slate and purple		2·75	1·75
	a. Extra flagstaff		£120	
	b. Short extra flagstaff		90·00	
	c. Lightning conductor		95·00	
111/14		Set of 4	4·75	6·25
111/14 Perf "Specimen"		Set of 4	80·00	

For illustrations of plate varieties see Catalogue Introduction.

1937 (12 May). *Coronation. As Nos. 95/7 of Antigua, but printed by D.L.R. P 14.*
115	1d. scarlet		45	40
116	2d. yellow-brown		85	65
117	3d. bright blue		85	80
115/17		Set of 3	1·90	1·75
115/17 Perf "Specimen"		Set of 3	55·00	

(Recess Waterlow)

1938 (1 Apr)–**52.** *Wmk Mult Script CA. P 12½.*
118	23	½d. green		2·00	2·25
		a. Light yellowish green (1941)		3·50	4·50
		b. Yellowish green (4.43)		2·75	3·00
		c. Deep green (4.49)		1·75	4·50
119		1d. scarlet		40	40
120		1½d. dull blue		8·50	1·75
		a. Light blue (4.43)		40	70
121		2d. chocolate-brown		40	40
122		3d. deep ultramarine		40	1·50
123		4d. orange		1·40	2·25
124		6d. reddish purple		3·50	3·00
		a. Purple (1944)		3·00	2·50
125		1s. black and brown-olive		3·00	2·75
		a. Grey-black and olive-green (21.5.52)		9·50	12·00
126		2s.6d. black and scarlet		14·00	8·50
127		5s. black and deep ultramarine		30·00	8·50
		a. Grey-black & dp ultramarine (10.46)		65·00	35·00
128		10s. black and red-brown		14·00	16·00
118/28			Set of 11	60·00	40·00
118/28 Perf "Specimen"			Set of 11	£170	

Bechuanaland

(24) 24a King George VI and Queen Elizabeth

1945 (3 Dec). *Victory. Stamps of South Africa optd with T 24. Inscr alternately in English and Afrikaans.*
				Un. pair	Used pair	Used single
129	55	1d. brown and carmine		50	35	10
130	56	2d. slate-blue and violet ..		50	65	10
131	57	3d. deep blue and blue		50	65	10
		a. Opt omitted (in vert pair with normal)		£4500		
129/31			Set of 3	1·40	1·50	25

No. 131a comes from a sheet on which the overprint was displaced downwards so that it is omitted from stamps in the top row and shown on the sheet margin at foot.

(Recess Waterlow)

1947 (17 Feb). *Royal Visit. T 24a and similar designs. Wmk Mult Script CA. P 12½.*
132	1d. scarlet		10	10
133	2d. green		10	10
134	3d. ultramarine		10	10
135	1s. mauve		10	10
132/5		Set of 4	35	30
132/5 Perf "Specimen"		Set of 4	80·00	

Designs: *Vert*—1d. King George VI. *Horiz*—3d. Princess Elizabeth and Princess Margaret; 1s. The Royal Family.

1948 (1 Dec). *Royal Silver Wedding. As Nos. 112/13 of Antigua.*
136	1½d. ultramarine		30	10
137	10s. black		27·00	35·00

1949 (10 Oct). *75th Anniv of Universal Postal Union. As Nos. 114/17 of Antigua.*
138	1½d. ultramarine		45	50
139	3d. deep blue ..		1·25	1·50
140	6d. magenta		90	80
141	1s. olive		95	80
138/41		Set of 4	3·25	3·25

1953 (3 June). *Coronation. As No. 120 of Antigua.*
142	2d. black and brown ..		30	30

25 Queen Elizabeth II, Baobab Tree and Cattle drinking

26 Queen Victoria, Queen Elizabeth II and Landscape

(Des from photo by Resident Commissioner, Ngamiland. Recess Waterlow)

1955 (3 Jan)–**58.** *Wmk Mult Script CA. P 13½ × 14.*
143	25	½d. green		50	30
144		1d. rose-red		80	10
145		2d. red-brown		1·25	30
146		3d. ultramarine		3·00	70
		a. Bright ultramarine (16.1.57)		6·00	2·50
146b		4d. red-orange (1.12.58)		6·50	7·00
147		4½d. blackish blue		1·50	35
148		6d. purple		1·25	60
149		1s. black and brown-olive		1·25	80
150		1s. 3d. black and lilac		11·00	9·50
151		2s. 6d. black and rose-red		10·00	9·50
152		5s. black and violet-blue		15·00	6·50
153		10s. black and red-brown		20·00	15·00
143/53			Set of 12	65·00	45·00

(Photo Harrison)

1960 (21 Jan). *75th Anniv of Bechuanaland Protectorate. W w* **12.**
P 14½ × 14.

154	**26**	1d. sepia and black	..	..	40	50
155		3d. magenta and black	..	..	40	30
156		6d. bright blue and black	..	..	40	50
154/6	..	..	..	*Set of 3*	1·10	1·10

(New Currency. 100 cents = 1 rand)

1c **1c 1c** **2½c 2½c**
(27) (I) (II) (I) (II)

3 3 3 **5c 5c** **R1 R1**
(I) (II) (III) (I) (II) (I) (II)
(3½ c. on 4d.)

2½ c

Spaced "c"
(R. 10/3)

1961 (14 Feb–June). *Nos.* 144/6a *and* 148/53 *surch as T* **27** *by South African Govt Printer, Pretoria.*

157	**25**	1 c. on 1d. rose-red (Type I)	..		30	10
		a. Type II (6 June)	..	..	40	10
158		2 c. on 2d. red-brown	..	..	20	10
159		2½ c. on 2d. red-brown (Type I)		..	30	10
		a. Type II (26 July)	..	..	85	65
		b. Vert pair, one without surch		..	£2000	
160		2½ c. on 3d. bright ultramarine	..	2·00	2·50
		a. Spaced "c" (R.10/3)	..	..	42·00	
161		3½ c. on 4d. red-orange (Type I)	..	50	20
		a. Type II	..	..	2·00	3·00
		b. Wide surch (I)	..	..	14·00	19·00
		c. Wide surch (II)	..	..	50·00	65·00
		d. Type III (6 June)	..	..	20	20
162		5 c. on 6d. purple (Type I)	..	65	30
		a. Type II (12 May)	..	..	20	10
163		10 c. on 1s. black and brown-olive	..	20	10
		a. Horiz pair, one without surch	..	£1400	
164		12½ c. on 1s. 3d. black and lilac	..	65	20
165		25 c. on 2s. 6d. black and rose-red	..	2·00	50
166		50 c. on 5s. black and violet-blue	..	3·00	2·00
167		1 r. on 10s. black & red-brown (Type I)	£250	90·00
		a. Type II (surch at bottom left) (17 Mar)	..	8·50	6·50
		b. Type II (surch at foot, either to right or central) (Apr)	..	7·00	2·25
157/67b		..	..	*Set of 11*	14·50	7·00

Nos. 161/c occur from the same printing each sheet containing thirty-three examples of Type I, five of Type I with wide spacing, nineteen of Type II and three of Type II with wide spacing. The wide surcharge measures 9½ mm overall (with "C" spaced 1½ mm from "1/2") and comes on 8 of the 10 stamps in the last vertical row. The surcharge on the remainder of the sheet varies between 8½ and 9½ mm.

A later printing of the 12½ c. on 1s. 3d. was from a fresh setting of type, but is insufficiently different for separate listing. Later printings of the 10 c. and 25 c. were identical with the originals.

28 African Golden Oriole

39 Bechuana Ox

(Des P. Jones. Photo Harrison)

1961 (2 Oct). *T* **28, 39** *and similar designs. W w* **12.** *P* 14½ × 14 (25, 50 c.) *or* 14 × 14½ (*others*).

168		1 c. yellow, red, black and lilac	..	1·00	40
169		2 c. orange, black and yellow-olive	..	1·00	2·00
170		2½ c. carmine, green, black and bistre	1·00	30
171		3½ c. yellow, black, sepia and pink	..	1·25	95
172		5 c. yellow, blue, black and buff	..	2·75	1·00
173		7½ c. brown, red, black and apple-green	1·50	1·50
174		10 c. red, yellow, sepia & turquoise-green	1·50	60
175		12½ c. buff, blue, red and grey-black	..	18·00	4·50
176		20 c. yellow-brown and drab	..	60	70
177		25 c. deep brown and lemon	..	80	85
178		35 c. deep blue and orange	..	80	1·50
179		50 c. sepia and olive	..	1·00	2·25
180		1 r. black and cinnamon	..	3·00	2·50
181		2 r. brown and turquoise-blue	..	18·00	9·00
168/81		..	..	*Set of 14*	45·00	25·00

Designs:—*Vert*—2 c. Hoopoe; 2½ c. Scarlet-chested Sunbird; 3½ c. Yellow-rumped Bishop; 5 c. Swallow-tailed Bee Eater; 7½ c. African Grey Hornbill; 10 c. Red-headed Weaver; 12½ c. Brown-hooded Kingfisher; 20 c. Woman musician; 35 c. Woman grinding maize; 1 r. Lion; 2 r. Police camel patrol. *Horiz*—25 c. Baobab Tree.

1963 (4 June). *Freedom from Hunger. As No.* 146 *of Antigua.*

182		12½ c. bluish green	..	30	15

1963 (2 Sept). *Red Cross Centenary. As Nos.* 147/8 *of Antigua.*

183		2½ c. red and black	..	20	10
184		12½ c. red and blue	..	40	50

1964 (23 April). *400th Birth Anniv of William Shakespeare. As No.* 164 *of Antigua.*

185		12½c. light brown	..	15	15

BECHUANALAND

INTERNAL SELF-GOVERNMENT

42 Map and Gaberones Dam

(Des Mrs. M. Townsend, adapted V. Whiteley. Photo Harrison)

1965 (1 Mar). *New Constitution. W w* **12.** *P* 14½×14.

186	**42**	2½ c. red and gold	..	..	10	10
		w. Wmk inverted	..	14·00	3·75
187		5 c. ultramarine and gold	..	15	30
188		12½ c. brown and gold	..	20	10
189		25 c. green and gold	..	20	40
186/9		..	..	*Set of 4*	55	95

1965 (17 May). *I.T.U. Centenary. As Nos.* 166/7 *of Antigua.*

190		2½ c. red and bistre-yellow	..	20	10
191		12½ c. mauve and brown	..	45	30

1965 (25 Oct). *International Co-operation Year. As Nos.* 168/9 *of Antigua.*

192		1 c. reddish purple and turquoise-green	10	10
193		12½ c. deep bluish green and lavender	..	60	55

1966 (24 Jan). *Churchill Commemoration. As Nos.* 170/3 *of Antigua.*

194		1 c. new blue	..	..	15	30
195		2½ c. deep green	..	..	35	10
196		12½ c. brown	..	..	70	30
197		20 c. bluish violet	..	..	75	40
194/7	..	..	..	*Set of 4*	1·75	90

43 Haslar Smoke Generator

(Des V. Whiteley. Photo Harrison)

1966 (1 June). *Bechuanaland Royal Pioneer Corps. T* **43** *and similar horiz designs. W w* **12.** *P* 14½.

198		2½ c. Prussian blue, red and light emerald	..	20	10
199		5 c. brown and light blue	..	..	20	20
200		15 c. Prussian blue, rosine and emerald	..	30	25
201		35 c. buff, blackish brown, red and green	..	30	80
198/201		..	..	*Set of 4*	90	1·25

Designs:—5 c. Bugler; 15 c. Gun-site; 35 c. Regimental cap badge.

BOTSWANA

INDEPENDENCE

Bechuanaland became the independent republic of Botswana, within the Commonwealth, on 30 September 1966.

47 National Assembly Building

(Des R. Granger Barrett. Photo Harrison)

1966 (30 Sept). *Independence. T* **47** *and similar horiz designs. Multicoloured. P* 14½.

202		2½ c. Type **47**	..	..	15	10
		a. Imperf (pair)	..	..	£250	
203		5 c. Abattoir, Lobatsi	..	20	10
204		15 c. National Airways Douglas DC-3	..	65	20
205		35 c. State House, Gaberones	..	40	30
202/5		..	..	*Set of 4*	1·25	55

REPUBLIC OF BOTSWANA
(51)

52 Golden Oriole

1966 (30 Sept). *Nos.* 168/81 *optd as T* **51.**

206		1 c. yellow, red, black and lilac	..	25	10
207		2 c. orange, black and yellow-olive	..	30	10
208		2½ c. carmine, green, black and bistre	..	30	10
209		3½ c. yellow, black, sepia and pink	..	40	15
		a. *Yellow, black, sepia and flesh*	..	1·00	75

210		5 c. yellow, blue, black and buff	..	40	90
211		7½ c. brown, red, black and apple-green	40	1·00
		a. Blue-green omitted		
212		10 c. red, yellow, sepia & turquoise-green	60	20
213		12½ c. buff, blue, red and grey-black	..	2·75	2·25
214		20 c. yellow-brown and drab	..	75	60
215		25 c. deep brown and lemon	..	75	1·50
216		35 c. deep blue and orange	..	85	1·75
217		50 c. sepia and olive	..	50	70
218		1 r. black and cinnamon	..	75	1·25
219		2 r. brown and turquoise-blue	..	1·25	2·50
206/19		..	..	*Set of 14*	9·00	11·50

No. 209a was a special printing produced to make up quantities. It does not exist without the overprint.

No. 211a shows the background in yellow instead of apple-green, the blue-green overlay being omitted.

52 Type 52

(Des D. M. Reid-Henry. Photo Harrison)

1967 (3 Jan). *Birds. Vert designs as T* **52.** *Multicoloured. P* 14×14½.

220		1 c. Type **52**	..	..	30	15
		a. Error. Wmk **105** of Malta	..	†	£700
221		2 c. Hoopoe	..	..	40	70
222		3 c. Groundscraper Thrush	..	55	10
223		4 c. Cordon-bleu ("Blue Waxbill")	..	55	10
224		5 c. Secretary Bird	..	..	55	10
225		7 c. Yellow-billed Hornbill	..	60	90
226		10 c. Burchell's Gonolek ("Crimson-breasted Shrike")	..	60	15
227		15 c. Malachite Kingfisher	..	7·00	2·25
228		20 c. African Fish Eagle	..	7·00	1·60
229		25 c. Go-away Bird ("Grey Loerie")	..	3·50	1·00
230		35 c. Scimitar-bill	..	..	7·00	1·75
231		50 c. Comb Duck	..	..	3·25	2·00
232		1 r. Levaillant's Barbet	..	8·00	3·50
233		2 r. Didric Cuckoo	..	..	9·50	15·00
220/33		..	..	*Set of 14*	45·00	26·00

A used copy of the 20 c. has been seen with the pale brown colour missing, resulting in the value (normally shown in white) being omitted.

The 1, 2, 4, 7 and 10 c. values exist with PVA gum as well as gum arabic.

66 Students and University

(Des V. Whiteley. Photo Harrison)

1967 (7 Apr). *First Conferment of University Degrees. P* 14 × 14½.

234	**66**	3 c. sepia, ultramarine & lt orange-yell	10	10
235		7 c. sepia, ultram & lt greenish bl	..	10	10
236		15 c. sepia, ultramarine and rose	..	10	10
237		35 c. sepia, ultramarine and light violet	20	20
234/7	..	..	..	*Set of 4*	30	30

67 Bushbuck

(Des G. Vasarhelyi. Photo Harrison)

1967 (2 Oct). *Chobe Game Reserve. T* **67** *and similar horiz designs. Multicoloured. P* 14.

238		3 c. Type **67**	..	..	10	20
239		5 c. Sable Antelope	..	..	15	30
240		35 c. Fishing on Chobe River	..	80	1·10
238/40		..	..	*Set of 3*	90	1·40

70 Arms of Botswana and Human Rights Emblem

(Litho D.L.R.)

1968 (8 Apr). *Human Rights Year. T* **70** *and similar horiz designs showing Arms of Botswana and Human Rights emblem arranged differently. P* 13½ × 13.

241		3 c. multicoloured	..	..	10	10
242		15 c. multicoloured	..	..	25	40
243		25 c. multicoloured	..	..	25	50
241/3		..	..	*Set of 3*	50	85

73 Eland and Giraffe Rock Paintings, Tsodilo Hills

75 "Baobab Trees" (Thomas Baines)

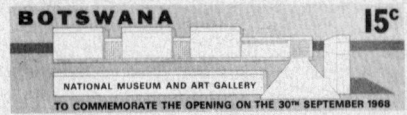

76 National Museum and Art Gallery

(Litho D.L.R.)

1968 (30 Sept). *Opening of National Museum and Art Gallery.*
T 73/6 and similar multicoloured design. P 12½ (7 c.),
12½ × 13½ (15 c.), or 13 × 13½ (others).

244	3 c. Type 73		20	20
245	7 c. Girl wearing ceremonial beads (30 × 48			
	mm)		35	20
246	10 c. Type 75		35	30
247	15 c. Type 76		50	1·40
244/7		Set of 4	1·25	1·90
MS248	132 × 82 mm. Nos. 244/7. P 13		1·25	2·00

77 African Family, and Star over Village

(Des Mrs M. E. Townsend, adapted J. Cooter. Litho Enschedé)

1968 (11 Nov). *Christmas. P 13 × 14.*

249	77	1 c. multicoloured		10	10
250		2 c. multicoloured		10	10
251		5 c. multicoloured		10	10
252		25 c. multicoloured		15	50
249/52			Set of 4	30	70

78 Scout, Lion and Badge in Frame

(Des D.L.R. Litho Format)

1969 (21 Aug). *22nd World Scout Conference, Helsinki. T 78 and*
similar multicoloured designs. P 13½.

253	3 c. Type 78		50	30
254	15 c. Scouts cooking over open fire (*vert*)		1·00	1·25
255	25 c. Scouts around camp fire		1·00	1·25
253/5		Set of 3	2·25	2·50

81 Woman, Child and   82 Diamond Treatment
   Christmas Star   Plant, Orapa

(Des A. Vale, adapted V. Whiteley. Litho Harrison)

1969 (6 Nov). *Christmas. P 14½ × 14.*

256	81	1 c. pale blue and chocolate		10	10
257		2 c. pale yellow-olive and chocolate		10	10
258		4 c. yellow and chocolate		10	10
259		35 c. chocolate and bluish violet		20	20
256/9			Set of 4	30	30
MS260	86 × 128 mm. Nos. 256/9. P 14½ (shades)			70	1·10

(Des J.W. Litho Harrison)

1970 (23 Mar). *Developing Botswana. T 82 and similar designs.*
Multicoloured. P 14½ × 14 (3 c., 7 c.) or 14 × 14½ (others).

261	3 c. Type 82		70	20
262	7 c. Copper-nickel mining		95	20
263	10 c. Copper-nickel mine, Selebi-Pikwe (*horiz*)		1·25	25
264	35 c. Orapa diamond mine, and diamonds			
	(*horiz*)		2·75	1·60
261/4		Set of 4	5·00	2·00

83 Mr. Micawber (*David Copperfield*)

(Des V. Whiteley. Litho Walsall)

1970 (6 July). *Death Centenary of Charles Dickens. T 83 and*
similar horiz designs. Multicoloured. P 11.

265	3 c. Type 83		25	10
266	7 c. Scrooge (*A Christmas Carol*)		35	10
267	15 c. Fagin (*Oliver Twist*)		60	40
268	25 c. Bill Sykes (*Oliver Twist*)		90	60
265/8		Set of 4	1·90	1·00
MS269	114 × 81 mm. Nos. 265/8		3·25	3·25

84 U.N. Building and Emblem

(Des J. Cooter. Litho Walsall)

1970 (24 Oct). *25th Anniv of United Nations. P 11.*

270	84	15 c. bright blue, chestnut and silver	70	30

85 Crocodile

(Des A. Vale. Litho Questa)

1970 (3 Nov). *Christmas. T 85 and similar horiz designs. Multi-*
coloured. P 14.

271	1 c. Type 85		10	10
272	2 c. Giraffe		10	10
273	7 c. Elephant		15	10
274	25 c. Rhinoceros		60	80
271/4		Set of 4	80	95
MS275	128 × 90 mm. Nos. 271/4		1·25	2·50

86 Sorghum

(Des J.W. Litho Questa)

1971 (6 April). *Important Crops. T 86 and similar horiz designs.*
Multicoloured. P 14.

276	3 c. Type 86		15	10
277	7 c. Millet		20	10
278	10 c. Maize		20	10
279	35 c. Groundnuts		70	40
276/9		Set of 4	1·10	50

87 Map and Head of Cow   88 King bringing Gift
                                   of Gold

(Des A. Vale, adapted L. Curtis. Litho Harrison)

1971 (30 Sept). *Fifth Anniv of Independence. T 87 and similar vert*
designs inscr "PULA" (local greeting). P 14½ × 14.

280	3 c. black, brown and apple-green		10	10
281	4 c. black, new blue and pale blue		10	10
282	7 c. black and red-orange		20	15
283	10 c. multicoloured		25	15
284	20 c. multicoloured		80	2·00
280/4		Set of 5	1·25	2·25

Designs:—4 c. Map and cogs; 7 c. Map and zebra; 10 c. Map and
sorghum stalk crossed by tusk; 20 c. Arms and map of Botswana.

(Des A. Vale. Litho Questa)

1971 (11 Nov). *Christmas. T 88 and similar vert designs. Multi-*
coloured. P 14.

285	2 c. Type 88		10	10
286	3 c. King bearing frankincense		10	10
287	7 c. King bearing myrrh		10	10
288	20 c. Three Kings behold the star		35	65
285/8		Set of 4	40	75
MS289	85 × 128 mm. Nos. 285/8		1·00	2·75

ALTERED CATALOGUE NUMBERS

Any Catalogue numbers altered from the last
edition are shown as a list in the introductory
pages.

89 Orion   90 Postmark and Map

(Des R. Granger Barrett. Litho Questa)

1972 (24 Apr). *"Night Sky". T 89 and similar vert designs. P 14.*

290	3 c. turquoise-blue, black and red		75	20
291	7 c. dull blue, black and yellow		1·10	60
292	10 c. dull green, black and orange		1·25	75
293	20 c. deep violet-blue, black and blue-green		1·75	2·25
290/3		Set of 4	4·25	3·50

Constellations:—7 c. The Scorpion; 10 c. The Centaur; 20 c. The
Cross.

(Des M. Bryan. Litho A. & M.)

1972 (21 Aug). *Mafeking-Gubulawayo Runner Post. T 90 and*
similar vert designs. Multicoloured. P 13½ × 13.

294	3 c. Type 90		30	10
	a. Imperf (vert pair)		£425	
295	4 c. Bechuanaland stamp and map		30	35
296	7 c. Runners and map		45	50
297	20 c. Mafeking postmark and map		1·10	1·25
294/7		Set of 4	2·00	2·00
MS298	84×216 mm. Nos. 294/7 vertically se-			

tenant, forming a composite map design .. 11·00 15·00
For these designs redrawn smaller with changed inscriptions
see Nos. 652/6.

91 Cross, Map and Bells   92 Thor

(Des M. Bryan. Litho Questa)

1972 (6 Nov). *Christmas. Vert designs each with Cross and Map*
as T 91. Multicoloured. P 14.

299	2 c. Type 91		10	75
300	3 c. Cross, map and candle		10	10
301	7 c. Cross, map and Christmas tree		15	25
302	20 c. Cross, map, star and holly		40	85
299/302		Set of 4	60	1·75
MS303	96 × 119 mm. Nos. 299/302		1·25	2·75

(Des Edna Elphick. Litho Questa)

1973 (23 Mar). *I.M.O./W.M.O. Centenary. T 92 and similar*
designs showing Norse myths. Multicoloured. P 14.

304	3 c. Type 92		20	10
305	4 c. Sun God's chariot (*horiz*)		25	15
306	7 c. Ymir, the frost giant		30	15
307	20 c. Odin and Sleipnir (*horiz*)		75	70
304/7		Set of 4	1·40	1·00

93 Livingstone and River Scene

(Des G. Vasarhelyi. Litho Walsall)

1973 (10 Sept). *Death Centenary of Dr. Livingstone. T 93 and*
similar horiz designs. Multicoloured. P 13½.

308	3 c. Type 93		20	10
309	20 c. Livingstone meeting Stanley		90	80

94 Donkey and Foal at   95 Gaborone Campus
   Village Trough

(Des M. Bryan. Litho Questa)

1973 (3 Dec). *Christmas. T **94** and similar multicoloured designs. P 14.*
310	3 c. Type **94**	..	..	10	10
311	4 c. Shepherd and flock (*horiz*)		..	10	10
312	7 c. Mother and child	..	..	10	10
313	20 c. Kgotla meeting (*horiz*)	..	..	40	80
310/13		..	*Set of 4*	55	90

(Des. M. Bryan, adapted P. Powell. Litho Questa)

1974 (8 May). *Tenth Anniv of University of Botswana, Lesotho and Swaziland. T **95** and similar horiz designs. Multicoloured. P 14.*
314	3 c. Type **95**	..	..	10	10
315	7 c. Kwaluseni Campus	..		10	10
316	20 c. Roma Campus	..	..	15	20
317	35 c. Map and flags of the three countries		..	20	35
314/17		..	*Set of 4*	35	55

96 Methods of Mail Transport

(Des. M. Bryan. Litho J.W.)

1974 (29 May). *Centenary of Universal Postal Union. T **96** and similar horiz designs. Multicoloured. P 14.*
318	2 c. Type **96**	..	..	55	35
319	3 c. Post Office, Palapye, *circa* 1889	..		55	35
320	7 c. Bechuanaland Police Camel Post, *circa* 1900			95	70
321	20 c. Hawker Siddeley H.S.748 and De Havilland D.H.9 mail planes of 1920 and 1974	..		2·75	2·50
318/21		..	*Set of 4*	4·25	3·50

97 Amethyst   **98** *Stapelia variegata*

(Des M. Bayliss, adapted PAD Studio. Photo Enschedé)

1974 (1 July). *Botswana Minerals. T **97** and similar horiz designs. Multicoloured. P 14×13.*
322	1 c. Type **97**	..	..	60	80
323	2 c. Agate—"Botswana Pink"	..		60	80
324	3 c. Quartz	..	..	65	80
325	4 c. Copper nickel	..	..	70	60
326	5 c. Moss agate	..	..	70	1·00
327	7 c. Agate	..	..	80	60
328	10 c. Stilbite	..	..	1·60	65
329	15 c. Moshaneng Banded Marble	..		2·00	3·00
330	20 c. Gem diamonds	..	..	4·00	3·25
331	25 c. Chrysotile	..	..	5·00	2·50
332	35 c. Jasper	..	..	5·00	3·75
333	50 c. Moss quartz	..	..	4·50	7·00
334	1 r. Citrine	..	..	7·50	10·00
335	2 r. Chalcopyrite	..	..	20·00	20·00
322/35		..	*Set of 14*	48·00	48·00

(Des M. Bryan. Litho Questa)

1974 (4 Nov). *Christmas. T **98** and similar vert designs showing flowers. Multicoloured. P 14.*
336	2 c. Type **98**	..	..	20	40
337	4 c. *Hibiscus lunarifolius*	..		50	20
338	15 c. *Ceratotheca triloba*	..		1·10	1·50
339	20 c. *Nerine laticoma*	..	..	1·25	1·75
336/9		..	*Set of 4*	2·75	3·50
MS340	85 × 130 mm. Nos. 336/9	..		3·50	4·25

99 President Sir Seretse Khama   **100** Ostrich

(Des M. Bryan, adapted G. Vasarhelyi. Photo Enschedé)

1975 (24 Mar). *Tenth Anniv of Self-Government. P 13½×13.*
341	**99**	4 c. multicoloured	..	10	10
342		10 c. multicoloured	..	15	10
343		20 c. multicoloured	..	25	25
344		35 c. multicoloured	..	45	50
341/4			*Set of 4*	85	85
MS345	93×130 mm. Nos. 341/4		..	1·00	1·50

(Des M. Bryan. Litho Questa)

1975 (23 June). *Rock Paintings, Tsodilo Hills. T **100** and similar horiz designs. Multicoloured. P 14.*
346	4 c. Type **100**	..	..	80	10
347	10 c. White Rhinoceros	..	..	1·40	10
348	25 c. Spotted Hyena	..	..	2·75	55
349	35 c. Scorpion	..	..	2·75	1·10
346/9		..	*Set of 4*	7·00	1·60
MS350	150 × 150 mm. Nos. 346/9	..		10·00	7·50

101 Map of British Bechuanaland, 1885   **102** *Aloe marlothii*

(Des M. Bryan, adapted G. Vasarhelyi. Litho Harrison)

1975 (13 Oct). *Anniversaries. T **101** and similar multicoloured designs. P 14 × 14½ (25 c.) or 14½ × 14 (others).*
351	6 c. Type **101**	..	..	30	20
352	10 c. Chief Khama, 1875	..	..	40	15
353	25 c. Chiefs Sebele, Bathoen and Khama, 1895 (*horiz*)			80	75
351/3		..	*Set of 3*	1·40	1·00

Events:—6 c. 90th Anniv of Protectorate; 10 c. Centenary of Khama's Accession; 25 c. 80th Anniv of Chiefs' visit to London.

(Des M. Bryan. Litho Questa)

1975 (3 Nov). *Christmas. T **102** and similar vert designs showing aloes. Multicoloured. P 14½.*
354	3 c. Type **102**	..	..	30	10
355	10 c. *Aloe lutescens*	..	..	75	20
356	15 c. *Aloe zebrina*	..	..	1·40	1·75
357	25 c. *Aloe littoralis*	..	..	1·60	2·75
354/7	..		*Set of 4*	3·50	4·25

103 Drum

(Des M. Bryan. Litho Questa)

1976 (1 Mar). *Traditional Musical Instruments. T **103** and similar horiz designs. Multicoloured. P 14.*
358	4 c. Type **103**	..	..	15	10
359	10 c. Hand Piano	..	..	20	10
360	15 c. Segankuru (violin)	..	..	25	50
361	25 c. Kudu Signal Horn	..	..	30	90
358/61		..	*Set of 4*	80	1·40

104 One Pula Note

(Des M. Bryan from banknotes by D.L.R. Litho Questa)

1976 (28 June). *First National Currency. T **104** and similar horiz designs. Multicoloured. P 14.*
362	4 c. Type **104**	..	..	15	10
363	10 c. Two pula note	..	..	20	10
364	15 c. Five pula note	..	..	35	20
365	25 c. Ten pula note	..	..	45	45
362/5	..		*Set of 4*	1·00	70
MS366	163 × 107 mm. Nos. 362/5	..		1·50	3·25

(New Currency. 100 thebe = 1 pula)

1t	**1t**	**2t**	**2t**
(105) (Type I)	(105) (Type II)	(I)	(II)
4t	**4t**	**5t**	**5t**
(I)	(II)	(I)	(II)
15t	**15t**	**20t**	**20t**
(I)	(II)	(I)	(II)

(Surch in letterpress by Govt Printer, Pretoria (Type I), or in lithography by Enschedé (Type II))

1976 (23 Aug)—77. *Nos. 322/35 surch as T **105**.*
367	1 t. on 1 c. Type **97** (I)	..	2·00	70
	a. Type II Surch (15.7.77)		2·50	80
368	2 t. on 2 c. Agate—"Botswana Pink" (I)		2·00	80
	a. Type II Surch (15.7.77)		2·50	80
369	3 t. on 3 c. Quartz (surch at top right) (Gold)		1·50	60
	a. Surch at bottom right (17.10.77)	..	50·00	

370	4 t. on 4 c. Copper nickel (I)	..	2·50	40
	a. Type II Surch (15.7.77)		2·75	80
371	5 t. on 5 c. Moss agate (I)		2·50	40
	a. Type II Surch (15.7.77)		2·75	70
372	7 t. on 7 c. Agate (surch at top right)		1·25	1·50
	a. Surch at bottom right (17.10.77)		60·00	
373	10 t. on 10 c. Stilbite		1·25	80
374	15 t. on 15 c. Moshaneng Banded Marble (I) (Gold)		4·25	1·10
	a. Type II Surch (15.7.77)		5·00	1·50
375	20 t. on 20 c. Gem diamonds (I)		7·50	80
	a. Type II Surch (15.7.77)		8·00	1·50
376	25 t. on 25 c. Chrysotile		5·00	1·25
377	35 t. on 35 c. Jasper		4·50	3·00
378	50 t. on 50 c. Moss quartz (surch at top right)		7·00	7·50
	a. Surch at bottom right (17.10.77)		£250	
379	1 p. on 1 r. Citrine (surch at top right)		8·00	8·00
	a. Surch at bottom left (17.10.77)		80·00	
380	2 p. on 2 r. Chalcopyrite (Gold)		11·00	11·00
367/80		*Set of 14*	50·00	35·00
367a/75a		*Set of 6*	21·00	5·50

Nos. 369a, 372a, 378a and 379a come from a second Pretoria printing on a small stock returned from the Crown Agents. By the time the stamps arrived in Pretoria the surcharge type for the 3 t., 7 t., 50 t. and 1 p. had been dispersed and when it was reset the position of the value figures was changed.

106 Botswanan Cattle   **107** *Colophospermum mopane*

(Des M. Bryan. Litho Questa)

1976 (30 Sept). *Tenth Anniv of Independence. T **106** and similar multicoloured designs. P 14.*
381	4 t. Type **106**	..	..	15	10
382	10 t. Deer, Okavango Delta (*vert*)	..		30	10
383	15 t. Schools and pupils	..	..	40	40
384	25 t. Rural weaving (*vert*)	..		55	50
385	35 t. Miner (*vert*)	..	..	1·25	85
381/5		..	*Set of 5*	2·40	1·75

Nos. 381/5 were printed on sand-grained paper which has an uneven surface.

(Des M. Bryan. Litho J.W.)

1976 (1 Nov). *Christmas. T **107** and similar horiz designs showing trees. Multicoloured. P 13.*
386	3 t. Type **107**	..	..	15	10
387	4 t. *Baikiaea plurijuga*	..		15	10
388	10 t. *Sterculia rogersii*	..		40	15
389	25 t. *Acacia nilotica*	..	..	80	50
390	40 t. *Kigelia africana*	..	..	1·25	1·25
386/90		..	*Set of 5*	2·50	1·75

108 Coronation Coach

(Des M. Bryan, adapted G. Vasarhelyi. Litho Cartor)

1977 (7 Feb). *Silver Jubilee. T **108** and similar horiz designs. Multicoloured. P 12.*
391	4 t. Queen and Sir Seretse Khama	..		10	10
392	25 t. Type **108**	..	..	20	15
393	40 t. The Recognition	..	..	35	80
391/3		..	*Set of 3*	60	90

Nos. 391/3 have matt, almost invisible gum.

109 African Clawless Otter   **110** Cwihaba Caves

(Des M. Bryan. Litho Questa)

1977 (7 June). *Diminishing Species. T **109** and similar horiz designs. Multicoloured. P 14.*
394	3 t. Type **109**	..	..	1·50	30
395	4 t. Serval	..	..	1·50	30
396	10 t. Bat-eared Fox	..	..	2·50	40
397	25 t. Temminck's Ground Pangolin	..		6·50	1·75
398	40 t. Brown Hyena	..	..	8·00	4·50
394/8	..		*Set of 5*	18·00	5·50

(Des M. Bryan. Litho J.W.)

1977 (22 Aug). *Historical Monuments. T **110** and similar horiz designs. Multicoloured. P 14.*
399	4 t. Type **110**	..	..	25	10
400	5 t. Khama Memorial	..	..	25	10
401	15 t. Green's Tree	..	..	55	40
402	20 t. Mmajojo Ruins	..	..	55	45
403	25 t. Ancient morabaraba board	..		55	50
404	35 t. Matsieng's footprint	..	..	70	60
399/404		..	*Set of 6*	2·50	2·00
MS405	154 × 105 mm. Nos. 399/404	..		3·00	3·25

111 Hypoxis nitida   112 Little Black Bustard

(Des M. Bryan. Litho Questa)

1977 (7 Nov). *Christmas. T* **111** *and similar vert designs showing lilies. Multicoloured. P* 14.

406	3 t. Type 111		15	10
407	5 t. *Haemanthus magnificus*		15	10
408	10 t. *Boophane disticha*		30	10
409	25 t. *Vellozia retinervis*		60	55
410	40 t. *Ammocharis coranica*		80	1·25
406/10		Set of 5	1·75	1·75

(Des M. Bryan. Photo Harrison)

1978 (3 July). *Birds. Vert designs as T* **112**. *Multicoloured. P* 14 × 14½ (1 to 20 t.) or 14 (25t to 5 p.).

411	1 t. Type 112		30	1·25
412	2 t. Marabou Stork		30	1·25
413	3 t. Green Wood Hoopoe		30	85
414	4 t. Carmine Bee Eater		30	75
415	5 t. African Jacana		30	40
416	7 t. African Paradise Flycatcher		40	1·50
417	10 t. Bennett's Woodpecker		1·75	50
418	15 t. Red Bishop		70	1·75
419	20 t. Crowned Plover		70	1·75
420	25 t. Giant Kingfisher		70	1·60
421	30 t. White-faced Whistling Duck		70	60
422	35 t. Green Heron		70	2·50
423	45 t. Black-headed Heron		70	2·00
424	50 t. Spotted Eagle Owl		5·50	4·00
425	1 p. Gabar Goshawk		2·00	4·00
426	2 p. Martial Eagle		2·25	7·50
427	5 p. Saddle-bill Stork		12·00	16·00
411/27		Set of 17	26·00	42·00

113 Tawana making Karos

(Des M. Bryan. Litho Questa)

1978 (11 Sept). *Okavango Delta. T* **113** *and similar horiz designs. Multicoloured. P* 14.

428	4 t. Type 113		15	10
429	5 t. Tribe localities		15	10
430	15 t. Bushmen collecting roots		35	40
431	20 t. Herero woman milking		40	55
432	25 t. Yei poling "mokoro" (canoe)		50	60
433	35 t. Mbukushu fishing		65	1·50
428/33		Set of 6	2·00	2·75
MS434	150 × 98 mm. Nos. 428/33		2·00	3·50

Nos. 428/34 were printed on sand-grained paper which has an uneven surface.

114 Caralluma lutea   115 Sip Well

(Des M. Bryan. Litho J.W.)

1978 (6 Nov). *Christmas. Flowers. T* **114** *and similar vert designs. Multicoloured. P* 14.

435	5 t. Type 114		35	10
436	10 t. *Hoodia lugardii*		50	15
437	15 t. *Ipomoea transvaalensis*		90	55
438	25 t. *Ansellia gigantea*		1·10	70
435/8		Set of 4	2·50	1·40

(Des M. Bryan. Litho Questa)

1979 (30 Mar). *Water Development. T* **115** *and similar vert designs. Multicoloured. P* 14.

439	3 t. Type 115		10	10
440	5 t. Watering pit		15	10
441	10 t. Hand dug well		15	10
442	25 t. Windmill		30	30
443	40 t. Modern drilling rig		55	55
439/43		Set of 5	1·10	1·00

ALTERED CATALOGUE NUMBERS

Any Catalogue numbers altered from the last edition are shown as a list in the introductory pages.

234

---

116 Pottery   117 1885 British Bechuanaland 1d. Stamp and Sir Rowland Hill

(Des M. Bryan. Litho Questa)

1979 (11 June). *Handicrafts. T* **116** *and similar vert designs. Multicoloured. P* 14½ × 14.

444	5 t. Type 116		10	10
445	10 t. Clay modelling		15	10
446	25 t. Basketry		30	25
447	40 t. Beadwork		50	50
444/7		Set of 4	95	80
MS448	123 × 96 mm. Nos. 444/7		95	2·25

(Des M. Bryan. Litho Secura, Singapore)

1979 (27 Aug). *Death Centenary of Sir Rowland Hill. T* **117** *and similar horiz designs showing stamps and Sir Rowland Hill. Multicoloured. P* 13½.

449	5 t. Type 117		20	10
450	25 t. 1932 Bechuanaland Protectorate 2d		45	50
451	45 t. 1967 2 c. definitive		55	75
449/51		Set of 3	1·10	1·25

118 Children Playing   119 Ximenia caffra

(Des K. Mosinyi (5 t.), M. Bryan (10 t.). Litho Questa)

1979 (24 Sept). *International Year of the Child. T* **118** *and similar multicoloured design. P* 14.

452	5 t. Type 118		20	10
453	10 t. Child playing with doll (*vert*)		30	20

(Des M. Bryan. Litho Questa)

1979 (12 Nov). *Christmas. Fruit. T* **119** *and similar vert designs. Multicoloured. P* 14.

454	5 t. Type 119		10	10
455	10 t. *Sclerocarya caffra*		20	20
456	15 t. *Hexalobus monopetalus*		35	35
457	25 t. *Ficus soldanella*		45	45
454/7		Set of 4	1·00	1·00

120 Flap-necked Chameleon   121 Rock Breaking

(Des M. Bryan. Litho Security Printers (M), Malaysia)

1980 (3 Mar). *Reptiles. T* **120** *and similar horiz designs. Multicoloured. P* 13½.

458	5 t. Type 120		40	10
459	10 t. Leopard Tortoise		40	10
460	25 t. Puff Adder		1·10	55
461	40 t. White-throated Monitor		1·25	2·00
458/61		Set of 4	2·75	2·50

(Des M. Bryan. Litho Secura, Singapore)

1980 (7 July). *Early Mining. T* **121** *and similar horiz designs. Multicoloured. P* 13½.

462	5 t. Type 121		25	15
463	10 t. Ore hoisting		30	15
464	15 t. Ore transport		70	60
465	20 t. Ore crushing		75	70
466	25 t. Smelting		80	90
467	35 t. Tools and products		1·00	1·40
462/7		Set of 6	3·50	3·50

122 "Chiwele and the Giant"

(Des W. Battiss. Litho Questa)

1980 (8 Sept). *Folktales. T* **122** *and similar multicoloured designs. P* 14 (5 t.), 14 × 13½ (45 t.) or 14½ × 14 (others).

468	5 t. Type 122 (35 × 22 mm)		10	10
469	10 t. "Kgori is not deceived" (28 × 37 mm)		15	10
470	30 t. "Nyambi's wife and Crocodile" (28 × 37 mm)		45	45
471	45 t. "Clever Hare" (44 × 27 mm)		60	60
468/71		Set of 4	1·10	1·10

---

123 Game watching. Makgadikgadi Pans

(Des M. Bryan. Litho Govt Printer, Pretoria)

1980 (6 Oct). *World Tourism Conference, Manila. P* 14.

472	**123** 5 t. multicoloured		45	20

124 Acacia gerrardii   125 Heinrich von Stephan with Bechuanaland 1949 3d. and Botswana 1974 3 c. U.P.U. Anniversary Commemoratives

(Des M. Bryan. Litho Govt Printer, Pretoria)

1980 (3 Nov). *Christmas. Flora. T* **124** *and similar vert designs. Multicoloured. P* 14 × 13½.

473	5 t. Type 124		10	10
474	10 t. *Acacia nilotica*		20	10
475	25 t. *Acacia erubescens*		45	30
476	40 t. *Dichrostachys cinerea*		70	70
473/6		Set of 4	1·25	1·00

(Des M. Bryan. Litho Govt Printer, Pretoria)

1981 (7 Jan). *150th Birth Anniv of Heinrich von Stephan (founder of U.P.U.). T* **125** *and similar horiz design showing Von Stephan and U.P.U. anniversary commemoratives. Multicoloured. P* 14.

477	6 t. Type 125		75	30
478	20 t. Bechuanaland 1949 6d. and Botswana 1974 7 c.		1·75	2·25

126 Anax imperator (dragonfly)   127 Camphill Community Ramkoromane, Otse

(Des M. Bryan. Litho Govt Printer, Pretoria)

1981 (23 Feb). *Insects. T* **126** *and similar vert designs. Multicoloured. P* 14.

479	6 t. Type 126		15	10
480	7 t. *Sphodromantis gastrica* (mantid)		15	10
481	10 t. *Zonocerus elegans* (grasshopper)		20	20
482	20 t. *Kheper nigroaeneus* (beetle)		35	50
483	30 t. *Papilio demodocus* (butterfly)		70	70
484	45 t. *Acanthocampa belina* (moth larva)		80	1·10
479/84		Set of 6	2·10	2·50
MS485	180×89 mm. Nos. 479/84		4·00	6·50

(Des M. Bryan. Litho Govt Printer, Pretoria)

1981 (6 Apr). *International Year for Disabled Persons. T* **127** *and similar horiz designs. Multicoloured. P* 14.

486	6 t. Type 127		20	10
487	20 t. Resource Centre for the Blind, Mochudi		55	35
488	30 t. Tlamelong Rehabilitation Centre, Tlokweng		75	45
486/8		Set of 3	1·40	80

128 Woman reading Letter   129 Sir Seretse Khama and Building

(Des Petra Rouendaal. Litho Govt Printer, Pretoria)

1981 (8 June). *Literacy Programme. T* **128** *and similar vert designs. Multicoloured. P* 14.

489	6 t. Type 128		20	10
490	7 t. Man filling in form		20	15
491	20 t. Boy reading newspaper		60	35
492	30 t. Child being taught to read		80	45
489/92		Set of 4	1·60	90

(Des G. Vasarhelyi. Litho Format)

1981 (13 July). *First Death Anniv of President Sir Seretse Khama.*
T **129** *and similar horiz designs. Multicoloured. P* 14.

493	6 t. Type **129**		..	15	10
494	10 t. Seretse Khama and building (*different*)			25	15
495	30 t. Seretse Khama and Botswana flag			40	45
496	45 t. Seretse Khama and building (*different*)			55	70
493/6	..	..	..	1·25	1·25

25t
(130)

131 Traditional Ploughing

1981 (1 Sept). *Nos. 417 and 422 surch as T* **130**.

497	25 t. on 35 t. Green Heron	..	2·50	2·00
498	30 t. on 10 t. Bennett's Woodpecker ..		2·50	2·00

(Des K. Mosinyi. Litho Format)

1981 (21 Sept). *Cattle Industry. T* **131** *and similar horiz designs.*
Multicoloured. P 14½.

499	6 t. Type **131**	..	..	10	10
500	20 t. Agricultural show			30	50
501	30 t. Botswana Meat Commission			35	60
502	45 t. Vaccine Institute, Botswana			50	1·00
499/502	..	..	Set of 4	1·10	2·00

132 *Nymphaea caerulea*   **133** "Cattle Post Scene"
(Boitumelo Golaakwena)

(Des M. Bryan. Litho Govt Printer, Pretoria)

1981 (11 Nov). *Christmas. Flowers. T* **132** *and similar vert designs. Multicoloured. P* 14.

503	6 t. Type **132**	..	..	20	10
504	10 t. *Nymphoides indica*			30	10
505	25 t. *Nymphaea lotus*			70	90
506	40 t. *Ottelia kunenensis*			1·00	2·25
503/6 ..			Set of 4	2·00	3·00

(Litho Govt Printer, Pretoria)

1982 (15 Feb). *Children's Art. T* **133** *and similar horiz designs. Multicoloured. P* 14.

507	6 t. Type **133**	..	..	40	10
508	10 t. "Kgotla Meeting" (Reginald Klinck)			50	15
509	30 t. "Village Water Supply" (Keromemang				
	Matswiri)			1·75	1·25
510	45 t. "With the Crops" (Kennedy Balemoge)			1·75	2·75
507/10	..	..	Set of 4	4·00	3·75

134 Common Type   **135** African Masked
Weaver

(Des K. Mosinyi and V. Moremi. Litho Govt Printer, Pretoria)

1982 (3 May). *Traditional Houses. T* **134** *and similar horiz designs. Multicoloured. P* 14.

511	6 t. Type **134**	..	..	40	15
512	10 t. Kgatleng type			50	15
513	30 t. North Eastern type			2·00	1·10
514	45 t. Sarwa type			2·00	3·00
511/14	..	..	Set of 4	4·50	4·00

(Des M. Bryan. Photo Harrison)

1982 (2 Aug). *Birds. T* **135** *and similar multicoloured designs. P* 14×14½ (1 t. to 10 t.) *or* 14½×14 (*others*).

515	1 t. Type **135**	..	70	1·25
516	2 t. Lesser Double-collared Sunbird ..		80	1·40
517	3 t. Red-throated Bee Eater ..		80	1·40
518	4 t. Ostrich		80	1·40
519	5 t. Grey-headed Gull		80	1·40
520	6 t. African Pygmy Goose		80	40
521	7 t. Cattle Egret		80	15
522	8 t. Lanner Falcon		1·75	1·25
523	10 t. Yellow-billed Stork		1·00	20
524	15 t. Red-billed Pintail (*horiz*)		2·00	25
525	20 t. Barn Owl (*horiz*) ..		4·50	3·50
526	25 t. Hammerkop (*horiz*)		2·50	70
527	30 t. South African Stilt (*horiz*)		3·25	90
528	35 t. Blacksmith Plover (*horiz*)		3·25	80
529	45 t. Senegal Wattled Plover (*horiz*)		3·50	1·75
530	50 t. Helmet Guineafowl (*horiz*)		4·50	2·50
531	1 p. Cape Vulture (*horiz*)		7·50	11·00
532	2 p. Augur Buzzard (*horiz*)		9·50	15·00
515/32	..	Set of 18	45·00	40·00

136 *Coprinus comatus*   **137** President Quett Masire

(Des Gillian Condy. Litho Mardon Printers Ltd, Zimbabwe)

1982 (2 Nov). *Christmas. Fungi. T* **136** *and similar vert designs. Multicoloured. P* 14½.

533	7 t. Type **136**				1·25	15
534	15 t. *Lactarius deliciosus*	..		..	2·25	55
535	35 t. *Amanita pantherina*		..		4·00	1·75
536	50 t. *Boletus edulis*		..		4·75	5·25
533/6	..			Set of 4	11·00	7·00

(Des G. Vasarhelyi. Litho Questa)

1983 (14 Mar). *Commonwealth Day. T* **137** *and similar horiz designs. Multicoloured. P* 14.

537	7 t. Type **137** ..			10	10
538	15 t. Native dancers			15	20
539	35 t. Melbourne conference centre			45	55
540	45 t. Meeting of Heads of State, Melbourne ..			55	80
537/40	..		Set of 4	1·00	1·50

138 Wattled Crane   **139** Wooden Spoons

(Des Petra Rouendaal (50 t.), Gillian Condy (others). Litho
Mardon Printers Ltd, Zimbabwe)

1983 (19 Apr). *Endangered Species. T* **138** *and similar vert designs. Multicoloured. P* 14×14½.

541	7 t. Type **138** ..			2·25	45
542	15 t. *Aloe lutescens*			2·00	80
543	35 t. Roan Antelope			2·25	2·75
544	50 t. Ivory Palm (*Hyphaene ventricosa*)			2·50	4·00
541/4	..		Set of 4	8·00	7·75

(Des M. Bryan. Litho Mardon Printers Ltd, Zimbabwe)

1983 (20 July). *Traditional Artifacts. T* **139** *and similar vert designs. Multicoloured. P* 14½.

545	7 t. Type **139** ..			25	10
546	15 t. Personal ornaments			45	30
547	35 t. Ox-hide milk bag			75	65
548	50 t. Decorated knives			1·00	1·10
545/8	..		Set of 4	2·25	1·90
MS549	115 × 102 mm. Nos. 545/8 ..			4·25	5·00

140 *Pantala flavescens*   **141** Sorting Diamonds

(Des Beverley Boudreau. Litho Mardon Printers Ltd, Zimbabwe)

1983 (7 Nov). *Christmas. Dragonflies. T* **140** *and similar designs. Multicoloured. P* 14½×14.

550	6 t. Type **140**			60	10
551	15 t. *Anax imperator*			1·10	40
552	25 t. *Trithemis arteriosa*			1·50	85
553	45 t. *Chlorolestes elegans*			2·00	3·25
550/3	..		Set of 4	4·75	4·25

(Des M. Kahn. Litho Mardon Printers Ltd, Zimbabwe)

1984 (19 Mar). *Mining Industry. T* **141** *and similar multicoloured designs. P* 14½.

554	7 t. Type **141**			2·00	50
555	15 t. Lime kiln..			2·00	75
556	35 t. Copper-nickel smelter plant (*vert*)			3·25	2·50
557	50 t. Stockpiled coal (*vert*)			3·75	5·00
554/7	..		Set of 4	10·00	8·00

142 Riding Cattle   **143** Avro 504 Aircraft

(Des S. Mogotsi. Litho Mardon Printers Ltd, Zimbabwe)

1984 (18 June). *Traditional Transport. T* **142** *and similar horiz designs. Multicoloured. P* 14½ × 14.

558	7 t. Type **142** ..			20	10
559	25 t. Sledge			65	45
560	35 t. Wagon			85	1·00
561	50 t. Two wheeled donkey cart			1·25	2·25
558/61	..		Set of 4	2·75	3·50

(Des V. Larsson. Litho Mardon Printers Ltd, Zimbabwe)

1984 (8 Oct). *40th Anniv of International Civil Aviation Organization. T* **143** *and similar horiz designs, each with I.C.A.O. emblem. Multicoloured. P* 14½ × 14.

562	7 t. Type **143**			60	15
563	10 t. Westland Wessex trimotor		..	75	20
564	15 t. Junkers Ju 52/3m			1·40	75
565	25 t. De Havilland D.H.89B Dominie			2·00	1·50
566	35 t. Douglas DC-3			2·25	2·75
567	50 t. Fokker F.27 Friendship			2·50	4·25
562/7	..		Set of 6	8·50	8·75

144 *Papilio demodocus*   **145** Seswaa (meat dish)

(Des M. Kahn. Litho Mardon Printers Ltd, Zimbabwe)

1984 (5 Nov). *Christmas. Butterflies. T* **144** *and similar horiz designs. Multicoloured. P* 14½ × 14.

568	7 t. Type **144**			1·50	30
569	25 t. *Byblia anvatara*			2·75	1·50
570	35 t. *Danaus chrysippus*			3·00	2·75
571	50 t. *Graphium taboranus*			4·00	6·00
568/71			Set of 4	10·00	9·50

No. 570 is incorrectly inscribed "Hypolimnas misippus".

(Des K. Mosinyi. Litho Mardon Printers Ltd, Zimbabwe)

1985 (18 Mar). *5th Anniv of Southern African Development Co-ordination Conference. Traditional Foods. T* **145** *and similar vert designs. Multicoloured. P* 14½.

572	7 t. Type **145** ..			25	10
573	15 t. Bogobe (cereal porridge)		..	45	35
574	25 t. Madila (soured coagulated cows milk)			70	55
575	50 t. Phane (caterpillars)			1·10	1·75
572/5	..		Set of 4	2·25	2·50
MS576	117 × 103 mm. Nos. 572/5		..	6·00	8·00

146 1885 British   **147** Bechuanaland
Bechuanaland   Border Police,
Overprint on Cape   1885–95
of Good Hope ½d.

(Des D. Finlay and J. Hodgson. Litho Mardon Printers Ltd, Zimbabwe)

1985 (24 June). *Centenary of First Bechuanaland Stamps. T* **146** *and similar designs. P* 14½.

577	7 t. black, grey-black and orange-vermilion			75	20
578	15 t. black, deep brown and greenish yellow			1·25	50
579	25 t. black and bright scarlet			1·75	80
580	35 t. black, ultramarine and gold ..			2·00	2·00
581	50 t. multicoloured			2·25	3·25
577/81	..		Set of 5	7·25	6·00

Designs: *Vert*—15 t. 1897 Bechuanaland Protectorate overprint on G.B. 3d.; 25 t. Bechuanaland Protectorate 1932 1d. definitive. *Horiz*—35 t. Bechuanaland 1965 Internal Self-Government 5 c.; 50 t. Botswana 1966 Independence 2½ c.

(Des V. Larsson. Litho Mardon Printers Ltd, Zimbabwe)

1985 (5 Aug). *Centenary of Botswana Police. T* **147** *and similar horiz designs. Multicoloured. P* 14½ × 14.

582	7 t. Type **147**			2·00	50
583	10 t. Bechuanaland Mounted Police, 1895–				
	1902			2·25	50
584	25 t. Bechuanaland Protectorate Police,				
	1903–66			3·25	2·00
585	50 t. Botswana Police, from 1966			4·50	6·00
582/5	..		Set of 4	11·00	8·00

MINIMUM PRICE

The minimum price quote is 10p which represents a handling charge rather than a basis for valuing common stamps. For further notes about prices see introductory pages.

148 Cucumis metuliferus

149 Mr. Shippard and Chief Gaseitsiwe of the Bangwaketse

(Des Audrey Renew. Litho Mardon Printers Ltd, Zimbabwe)

1985 (4 Nov). *Christmas. Edible Wild Cucumbers. T* **148** *and similar horiz designs. Multicoloured.* P 14½×14.

586	7 t. Type 148..				75	10
587	15 t. Acanthosicyos naudinianus				1·25	70
588	25 t. Coccinia sessifolia				2·00	1·10
589	50 t. Momordica balsamina				3·25	5·50
586/9 ..				Set of 4	6·50	6·50

(Des A. Campbell. Litho Mardon Printers Ltd, Zimbabwe)

1985 (30 Dec). *Centenary of Declaration of Bechuanaland Protectorate. T* **149** *and similar vert designs. Multicoloured.* P 14×14½.

590	7 t. Type 149..				35	10
591	15 t. Sir Charles Warren and Chief Sechele of the Bakwena ..				70	45
592	25 t. Revd. Mackenzie and Chief Khama of the Bamangwato				1·25	85
593	50 t. Map showing Protectorate				2·75	2·75
590/3 ..				Set of 4	4·50	3·75
MS594	130×133 mm. Nos. 590/3				6·50	8·00

150 Halley's Comet over Serowe

151 Milk Bag

(Des L. Hutchings. Litho Mardon Printers Ltd, Zimbabwe)

1986 (24 Mar). *Appearance of Halley's Comet. T* **150** *and similar horiz designs. Multicoloured.* P 14½×14.

595	7 t. Type 150..				80	15
596	15 t. Comet over Bobonong at sunset				1·50	70
597	35 t. Comet over Gomare at dawn				2·00	1·50
598	50 t. Comet over Thamaga and Letlhakeng				2·25	3·50
595/8 ..				Set of 4	6·00	5·25

(Des B. Mazebedi. Litho Mardon Printers Ltd, Zimbabwe)

1986 (23 June). *Traditional Milk Containers. T* **151** *and similar vert designs. Multicoloured.* P 14½.

599	8 t. Type 151..				15	10
600	15 t. Clay pot and calabashes				25	30
601	35 t. Wooden milk bucket				50	65
602	50 t. Milk churn				70	1·10
599/602				Set of 4	1·40	1·90

152 Map showing National Parks and Reserves

153 Ludwigia stogonifera

(Des K. Bogatsu, A. Campbell, I. Marshall and K. Mosinyi. Litho Govt Printer, Pretoria)

1986 (30 Sept). *20th Anniv of Independence. Sheet* 100×120 *mm, containing T* **152** *and similar vert designs. Multicoloured.* P 14.

MS603	20 t. Type 152; 20 t. Morupule Power Station; 20 t. Cattle breeding in Kgalagadi; 20 t. National Assembly Building	2·00	1·75

(Des Julia Cairns. Litho Mardon Printers Ltd, Zimbabwe)

1986 (3 Nov). *Christmas. Flowers of Okavango. T* **153** *and similar vert designs. Multicoloured.* P 14×14½.

604	8 t. Type 153..				1·25	10
605	15 t. Sopubia mannii..				2·25	1·10
606	35 t. Commelina diffusa				3·50	3·00
607	50 t. Hibiscus diversifolius				4·00	7·50
604/7 ..				Set of 4	10·00	10·50

154 Divining

(155)

156 Oral Rehydration Therapy

(Des K. Mosinyi. Litho Mardon Printers Ltd, Zimbabwe)

1987 (2 Mar). *Traditional Medicine. T* **154** *and similar horiz designs. Multicoloured.* P 14½×14.

608	8 t. Type 154..				80	10
609	15 t. Lightning prevention				1·50	80
610	35 t. Rain making				2·25	2·50
611	50 t. Blood letting				2·75	4·50
608/11				Set of 4	6·50	7·00

1987 (1 Apr). *Nos. 520, 523 and 530 surch as T* **155**.

612	3 t. on 6 t. African Pygmy Goose			1·00	60
613	5 t. on 10 t. Yellow-billed Stork			1·00	60
614	20 t. on 50 t. Helmet Guineafowl (horiz)			2·50	1·40
612/14			Set of 3	4·00	2·40

(Des A. Nunoo. Litho Govt Printer, Pretoria)

1987 (1 June). *U.N.I.C.E.F. Child Survival Campaign. T* **156** *and similar vert designs. Multicoloured.* P 14.

615	8 t. Type 156..				35	10
616	15 t. Growth monitoring				60	55
617	35 t. Immunization				1·25	1·75
618	50 t. Breast feeding				1·50	3·25
615/18 ..				Set of 4	3·25	5·00

157 Cape Fox

158 Cyperus articulatus

(Des P. Huebsch. Photo Harrison)

1987 (3 Aug). *Animals. T* **157** *and similar horiz designs. Multicoloured.* P 14.

619	1 t. Type 157..				10	50
620	2 t. Lechwe				10	50
621	3 t. Zebra				10	50
622	4 t. Duiker				10	50
623	5 t. Banded Mongoose				15	50
624	6 t. Rusty-spotted Genet				15	50
625	8 t. Hedgehog				30	10
626	10 t. Scrub Hare				25	10
627	12 t. Hippopotamus				1·00	1·25
628	15 t. Suricate				60	15
629	20 t. Caracal				70	65
630	25 t. Steenbok..				70	65
631	30 t. Gemsbok..				85	50
632	35 t. Square-lipped Rhinoceros				1·50	40
633	40 t. Mountain Reedbuck				1·10	65
634	50 t. Rock Dassie				90	80
635	1 p. Giraffe				2·50	2·50
636	2 p. Tsessebe				2·50	3·25
637	3 p. Side-striped Jackal				3·75	6·50
638	5 p. Hartebeest				6·00	10·00
619/38				Set of 20	20·00	27·00

(Des Julia Cairns. Litho National Printing & Packaging, Zimbabwe)

1987 (26 Oct). *Christmas. Grasses and Sedges of Okavango. T* **158** *and similar vert designs. Multicoloured.* P 14×14½.

639	8 t. Type 158..				40	10
640	15 t. Broomgrass				60	40
641	30 t. Cyperus alopurcides				1·25	75
642	1 p. Bulrush Sedge				2·50	4·00
639/42				Set of 4	4·25	4·75
MS643	88×99 mm. Nos. 639/42 ..				4·25	4·75
	a. 30 t. value imperf vert ..				40·00	

159 Planting Seeds with Digging Stick

160 Red Lechwe at Water-hole

(Des K. Mosinyi. Litho National Printing & Packaging, Zimbabwe)

1988 (14 Mar). *Early Cultivation. T* **159** *and similar horiz designs. Multicoloured.* P 14½×14.

644	8 t. Type 159..				40	10
645	15 t. Using iron hoe				60	35
646	35 t. Wooden ox-drawn plough				1·00	1·00
647	50 t. Villagers using lesotlas				1·40	2·00
644/7 ..				Set of 4	3·00	3·00

(Des P. Augustinus. Litho National Printing & Packaging, Zimbabwe)

1988 (6 June). *Red Lechwe. T* **160** *and similar horiz designs. Multicoloured.* P 14½×14.

648	10 t. Type 160				55	15
649	15 t. Red Lechwe and early morning sun				1·00	55
650	35 t. Female and calf				1·75	1·50
651	75 t. Herd on the move				3·00	4·25
648/51 ..				Set of 4	5·50	5·75

COVER PRICES

Cover factors are quoted at the beginning of each country for most issues to 1945. An explanation of the system can be found on page x. The factors quoted do not, however, apply to philatelic covers.

---

161 Gubulawayo Postmark and Route Southwards to Tati

162 Pope John Paul II and Outline Map of Botswana

(Des M. Bryan, adapted Lucy Phalayagae. Litho National Printing & Packaging, Zimbabwe)

1988 (22 Aug). *Centenary of Mafeking-Gubalawayo Runner Post. Designs as Nos. 294/8, but redrawn smaller with changed inscription as in T* **161**. *Multicoloured.* P 14½.

652	10 t. Type 161				35	10
653	15 t. Bechuanaland 1888 6d. on 6d. stamp and route from Tati southwards				55	30
654	30 t. Runners and twin routes south from Shoshong				95	75
655	60 t. Mafeking postmark and routes to Bechuanaland and Transvaal				1·60	2·75
652/5 ..				Set of 4	3·00	3·50
MS656	81×151 mm. Nos. 652/5 vertically se-tenant, forming a composite map design				5·50	6·50

(Des P. Lodoen. Litho National Printing & Packaging, Zimbabwe)

1988 (13 Sept). *Visit of Pope John Paul II. T* **162** *and similar vert designs. Multicoloured.* P 14×14½.

657	10 t. Type 162				60	10
658	15 t. Pope John Paul II				80	30
659	30 t. Pope giving blessing and outline map				1·25	70
660	80 t. Pope John Paul II (different) ..				2·00	2·75
657/60 ..				Set of 4	4·25	3·50

163 National Museum and Art Gallery

164 Grewia flava

(Des G. Mattsson and T. Sandberg (8 t.), A. Campbell (15 t.), K. Bogatsu (30 t.), T. Sandberg (60 t.). Litho National Printing & Packaging, Zimbabwe)

1988 (30 Sept). *20th Anniv of National Museum and Art Gallery, Gaborone. T* **163** *and similar vert designs. Multicoloured.* P 14½.

661	8 t. Type 163				15	10
662	15 t. Pottery				20	25
663	30 t. Blacksmith's buffalo bellows ..				35	40
664	60 t. Children and mobile museum van				70	1·00
661/4 ..				Set of 4	1·25	1·60

(Des Verena Blomberg-Ermatinger. Litho National Printing & Packaging, Zimbabwe)

1988 (31 Oct). *Flowering Plants of South-eastern Botswana. T* **164** *and similar vert designs. Multicoloured.* P 14×14½.

665	8 t. Type 164				20	10
666	15 t. Cienfuegosia digitata ..				30	25
667	40 t. Solanum seaforthianum				60	55
668	75 t. Carissa bispinosa				1·00	1·40
665/8 ..				Set of 4	1·90	2·00

165 Basket Granary

166 Female Red-throated Heron with Eggs

(Des K. Mosinyi. Litho National Printing & Packaging, Zimbabwe)

1989 (13 Mar). *Traditional Grain Storage. T* **165** *and similar vert designs. Multicoloured.* P 14 × 14½.

669	8 t. Type 165				30	10
670	15 t. Large letlole granary ..				50	30
671	30 t. Pot granary				85	60
672	60 t. Two types of serala				1·50	2·00
669/72 ..				Set of 4	2·75	2·75

The use of different paper stocks led to a wide range of shades in this issue.

(Des P. Augustinus. Litho Harrison)

1989 (5 July). *Red-throated Heron ("Slaty Egret"). T* **166** *and similar horiz designs. Multicoloured.* P 15×14.

673	8 t. Type 166				30	10
674	15 t. Chicks in nest				50	30
675	30 t. Red-throated Heron in flight				65	65
676	60 t. Pair building nest				95	1·50
673/6 ..				Set of 4	2·25	2·25
MS677	119×89 mm. Nos. 673/6				2·40	2·75

167 "My Work at Home"
(Ephraim Seeletso)

168 Eulophia
angolensis

(Litho Govt Printer, Pretoria)

1989 (4 Sept). *Children's Paintings.* T **167** *and similar multicoloured designs.* P 14.
678	10 t. Type **167**			35	10
679	15 t. "My Favourite Game" (hopscotch) (Neelma Bhatia) (*vert*)			50	35
680	30 t. "My Favourite Toy" (clay animals) (Thabo Habana)			75	70
681	1 p. "My School Day" (Thabo Olesitse)			2·00	3·25
678/81			*Set of 4*	3·25	4·00

(Des Julia Cairns. Litho Govt Printer, Pretoria)

1989 (30 Oct). *Christmas. Orchids.* T **168** *and similar vert designs.* Multicoloured. P 14.
682	8 t. Type **168**			60	10
683	15 t. Eulophia hereroensis ..			1·10	50
684	30 t. Eulophia speciosa			1·60	1·00
685	60 t. Eulophia petersii			2·25	4·00
682/5			*Set of 4*	5·00	5·00

169 Bechuanaland 1965 New
Constitution 25 c. Stamp
(25th anniv of Self
Government)

(170)

(Des K. Mosinyi. Litho National Printing & Packaging, Zimbabwe)

1990 (5 Mar). *Anniversaries.* T **169** *and similar horiz designs.* P 14½.
686	8 t. multicoloured			60	15
687	15 t. multicoloured			75	50
688	30 t. multicoloured			1·60	1·40
689	60 t. black, new blue and yellow-ochre			2·25	3·00
686/9			*Set of 4*	4·75	4·50

Designs:—15 t. Casting vote in ballot box (25th anniv of First Elections); 30 t. Outline map and flags of Southern African Development Coordination Conference countries (10th anniv); 60 t. Penny Black (150th anniv of first postage stamp).

1990 (27 Apr). *Nos. 619, 624 and 627 surch as* T **170.**
690	10 t. on 1 t. Type **157**			35	20
	a. Surch double ..			†	—
691	20 t. on 6 t. Rusty-spotted Genet			50	60
692	50 t. on 12 t. Hippopotamus			1·60	2·25
690/2			*Set of 3*	2·25	2·75

171 Telephone
Engineer

172 Young
Children

(Des M. Kahn. Litho National Printing & Packaging, Zimbabwe)

1990 (3 May). *"Stamp World London 90" International Stamp Exhibition.* T **171** *and similar vert designs.* Multicoloured. P 14½.
693	8 t. Type **171**			35	10
694	15 t. Transmission pylon			65	40
695	30 t. Public telephone			1·00	75
696	2 p. Testing circuit board ..			3·00	4·50
693/6			*Set of 4*	4·50	5·00

(Des K. Mosinyi. Litho National Printing & Packaging, Zimbabwe)

1990 (1 Aug). *Traditional Dress.* T **172** *and similar vert designs.* Multicoloured. P 14½.
697	8 t. Type **172**			35	10
698	15 t. Young woman			65	40
699	30 t. Adult man			1·00	70
700	2 p. Adult woman			3·00	4·50
697/700			*Set of 4*	4·50	5·00
MS701	104×150 mm. Nos. 697/700			4·50	5·50
	a. 30 t. and 2 p. imperf vert				

173 Acacia nigrescens

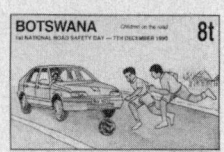
174 Children running in front
of Car

(Des Gillian Condy. Litho National Printing & Packaging, Zimbabwe)

1990 (30 Oct). *Christmas. Flowering Trees.* T **173** *and similar vert designs.* Multicoloured. P 14×14½.
702	8 t. Type **173**			35	10
703	15 t. Peltophorum africanum			65	30
704	30 t. Burkea africana			1·00	65
705	2 p. Pterocarpus angolensis			2·50	4·00
702/5			*Set of 4*	4·00	4·50

(Des B. Heman-Ackah. Litho National Printing & Packaging, Zimbabwe)

1990 (7 Dec). *First National Road Safety Day.* T **174** *and similar horiz designs.* Multicoloured. P 14½.
706	8 t. Type **174**			75	25
707	15 t. Careless overtaking			1·25	85
708	30 t. Cattle on road			2·00	2·25
706/8			*Set of 3*	3·50	3·00

175 Cattle

176 Children

(Des B. Mazebedi. Litho Questa)

1991 (4 Mar). *Rock Paintings.* T **175** *and similar horiz designs.* Multicoloured. P 14.
709	8 t. Type **175**			65	20
710	15 t. Cattle, drying frames and tree			1·10	60
711	30 t. Animal hides ..			1·50	1·25
712	2 p. Family herding cattle			3·25	4·50
709/12			*Set of 4*	6·00	6·00

Nos. 709/12 were printed on sand-grained paper which has an uneven surface.

(Des H. Methorst. Litho National Printing & Packaging, Zimbabwe)

1991 (3 June). *National Census.* T **176** *and similar vert designs.* Multicoloured. A. P 14. B. P 14½.
			A		B	
713	8 t. Type **176**		40	10	3·00	10
714	15 t. Village ..		2·00	60	75	55
715	30 t. School		85	75	85	75
716	2 p. Hospital		2·50	4·00	2·50	4·00
713/16		*Set of 4*	5·25	4·75	6·50	4·75

177 Tourists viewing
Elephants

178 Harpagophytum
procumbens

(Des P. Lodoen. Litho Govt Printer, Pretoria)

1991 (30 Sept). *African Tourism Year. Okavango Delta.* T **177** *and similar multicoloured designs.* P 14 (2 p.) or 14×14½ (*others*).
717	8 t. Type **177**			90	40
718	15 t. Crocodiles basking on river bank			1·25	70
719	35 t. African Fish Eagles and De Havilland D.H.C.7 Dash Seven aircraft			2·25	1·50
720	2 p. Okavango wildlife (26×44 mm)			4·25	5·50
717/20			*Set of 4*	7·75	7·25

(Des Gillian Condy. Litho Govt Printer, Pretoria)

1991 (4 Nov). *Christmas. Seed Pods.* T **178** *and similar vert designs.* Multicoloured. P 14.
721	8 t. Type **178**			50	10
722	15 t. Tylosema esculentum			75	40
723	30 t. Abrus precatorius			1·25	70
724	2 p. Kigelia africana			3·00	4·00
721/4			*Set of 4*	5·00	4·75

1992 (9 Mar). *Nos. 621, 624 and 627 surch as* T **170.**
725	8 t. on 12 t. Hippopotamus			70	30
726	10 t. on 12 t. Hippopotamus			70	30
727	25 t. on 6 t. Rusty-spotted Genet			1·00	1·00
728	40 t. on 3 t. Zebra			1·75	2·25
725/8			*Set of 4*	3·75	3·50

179 Cacosternum
boettgeri

180 Air-conditioned Coaches

(Des Julia Cairns. Litho Govt Printer, Pretoria)

1992 (23 Mar). *Climbing Frogs.* T **179** *and similar multicoloured designs.* P 14.
729	8 t. Type **179**			35	20
730	10 t. Hyperolius marmoratus angolensis (*vert*)			35	20
731	40 t. Bufo fenoulheti			1·25	1·00
732	1 p. Hyperolius sp (*vert*)			1·75	3·00
729/32			*Set of 4*	3·25	4·00

(Des P. Lodoen. Litho Harrison)

1992 (29 June). *Deluxe Railway Service.* T **180** *and similar multicoloured designs.* P 14.
733	10 t. Type **180**			60	30
734	25 t. Diesel locomotive No. BD001 (*vert*)			1·00	60
735	40 t. Coach interior (*vert*)			1·50	90
736	2 p. Diesel locomotive No. BD028..			3·25	4·50
733/6			*Set of 4*	5·75	5·75
MS737	127×127 mm. Nos. 733/6			6·00	7·00

181 Cheetah

182 Boxing

(Des Judith Penny. Photo Harrison)

1992 (3 Aug). *Animals.* T **181** *and similar horiz designs.* Multicoloured. P 14½×14.
738	1 t. Type **181**			15	30
739	2 t. Spring Hare			15	30
740	4 t. Blackfooted Cat			20	30
741	5 t. Striped Mouse			20	30
742	10 t. Oribi ..			20	10
743	12 t. Pangolin			30	40
744	15 t. Aardwolf			30	30
745	20 t. Warthog			30	30
746	25 t. Ground Squirrel			30	20
747	35 t. Honey Badger			35	30
748	40 t. Common Mole Rat			35	30
749	45 t. Wild Dog			35	30
750	50 t. Water Mongoose			40	35
751	80 t. Klipspringer			70	70
752	1 p. Lesser Bushbaby			80	80
753	2 p. Bushveld Elephant Shrew			1·50	1·75
754	5 p. Zorilla			3·25	3·75
755	10 p. Vervet Monkey			5·50	6·50
738/55			*Set of 18*	14·00	15·00

(Litho Harrison)

1992 (7 Aug). *Olympic Games, Barcelona.* T **182** *and similar vert designs.* Multicoloured. P 14×15.
756	10 t. Type **182**			20	10
757	50 t. Running			50	40
758	1 p. Boxing (*different*)			90	1·40
759	2 p. Running (*different*)			1·40	2·50
756/9			*Set of 4*	2·75	4·00
MS760	87×117 mm. Nos. 756/9			3·75	4·50

183 Adiantum
incisum

184 Helping
Blind Person
(Lions Club
International)

(Des Gillian Condy. Litho National Printing & Packaging, Zimbabwe)

1992 (23 Nov). *Christmas. Ferns.* T **183** *and similar vert designs.* Multicoloured. P 14½.
761	10 t. Type **183**			30	10
762	25 t. Actiniopteris radiata ..			55	35
763	40 t. Ceratopteris cornuta			70	45
764	1 p. 50, Pellaea calomelanos			2·25	3·50
761/4			*Set of 4*	3·50	4·00

(Des Ann Nilsson. Litho National Printing & Packaging, Zimbabwe)

1993 (29 Mar). *Charitable Organizations in Botswana.* T **184** *and similar multicoloured designs.* P 14.
765	10 t. Type **184**			25	10
766	15 t. Nurse carrying child (Red Cross Society) (*horiz*)			35	25

767	25 t.	Woman watering seedling (Ecumenical Decade)	45	40
768	35 t.	Deaf children (Round Table) (horiz)	60	75
769	40 t.	Crowd of people (Rotary International)	70	85
770	50 t.	Hands at prayer (Botswana Christian Council) (horiz)	85	1·25
765/70		Set of 6	2·75	3·25

185 Bechuanaland Railways Class "6" Locomotive No. 1   186 Long-crested Eagle

(Des P. Lodoen. Litho Harrison)

1993 (24 May). *Railway Centenary. T* **185** *and similar horiz designs. Multicoloured. P* 15×14.

771	10 t. Type 185	50	20
772	40 t. Class "19" locomotive No. 317	90	60
773	50 t. Class "12" locomotive No. 256	95	70
774	1 p. 50, Class "7" locomotive No. 71	1·40	2·50
771/4	Set of 4	3·25	3·50
MS775	190×100 mm. Nos. 771/4	3·25	4·25

(Des J. Leath. Litho National Printing & Packaging, Zimbabwe)

1993 (30 Aug). *Endangered Eagles. T* **186** *and similar vert designs. Multicoloured. P* 14½.

776	10 t. Type 186	45	20
777	25 t. Short-toed Eagle	80	60
778	50 t. Bateleur	1·25	1·50
779	1 p. 50, Secretary Bird	2·50	3·75
776/9	Set of 4	4·50	5·50

187 *Aloe zebrina*   188 Boy with String Puppet

(Des Gillian Condy. Litho National Printing & Packaging, Zimbabwe)

1993 (25 Oct). *Christmas. Flora. T* **187** *and similar vert designs. Multicoloured. P* 14×14½.

780	12 t. Type 187	25	10
781	25 t. Croton megalobotrys	40	25
782	50 t. Boophane disticha	65	70
783	1 p. Euphoria davyi	1·10	2·00
780/3	Set of 4	2·25	2·75

(Des K. Mosinyi. Litho National Printing & Packaging, Zimbabwe)

1994 (28 Mar). *Traditional Toys. T* **188** *and similar horiz designs. Multicoloured. P* 14½.

784	10 t. Type 188	15	10
785	40 t. Boys with clay cattle	35	30
786	50 t. Boy with spinner	40	50
787	1 p. Girls playing in make-believe houses	90	1·60
784/7	Set of 4	1·60	2·25

189 Interior of Control Tower, Gaborone Airport   (190)

(Des M. McArthur. Litho National Printing & Packaging, Zimbabwe)

1994 (30 June). *50th Anniv of International Civil Aviation Organization. T* **189** *and similar multicoloured designs. P* 14½.

788	10 t. Type 189	20	10
789	25 t. Crash tender	35	25
790	40 t. Loading supplies onto airliner (vert)	50	50
791	50 t. Control tower, Gaborone (vert)	60	1·00
788/91	Set of 4	1·50	1·60

1994 (1 Aug). *No. 743 surch with T* **190** *by Govt Printer, Pretoria.*

792	10 t. on 12 t. Pangolin	40	30

MINIMUM PRICE

The minimum price quote is 10p which represents a handling charge rather than a basis for valuing common stamps. For further notes about prices see introductory pages.

---

191 Lesser Flamingos at Sua Pan   192 *Ziziphus mucronata*

(Des P. Lodoen. Litho National Printing & Packaging, Zimbabwe)

1994 (26 Sept). *Environment Protection. Makgadikgadi Pans. T* **191** *and similar multicoloured designs. P* 14×14½ (*vert*) *or* 14½×14 (*horiz*).

793	10 t. Type 191	40	20
794	35 t. Baobab trees (horiz)	50	30
795	50 t. Zebra and palm trees	65	70
796	2 p. Map of area (horiz)	1·75	2·75
793/6	Set of 4	3·00	3·50

(Des Gillian Condy. Litho National Printing & Packaging, Zimbabwe)

1994 (24 Oct). *Christmas. Edible Fruits. T* **192** *and similar vert designs. Multicoloured. P* 14×14½.

797	10 t. Type 192	20	10
798	25 t. Strychnos cocculoides	30	25
799	40 t. Bauhinia petersiana	50	50
800	50 t. Schinziphyton rautoneii	60	70
797/800	Set of 4	1·40	1·40

193 Fisherman with Bow and Arrow   194 Boys watering Horses (F.A.O.)

(Des B. Mazebedi. Litho National Printing & Packaging, Zimbabwe)

1995 (3 Apr). *Traditional Fishing. T* **193** *and similar horiz designs. Multicoloured. P* 14½.

801	15 t. Type 193	20	15
802	40 t. Men in canoe and boy with fishing rod	35	30
803	65 t. Fisherman with net	50	60
804	80 t. Fisherman with basket fish trap	65	90
801/4	Set of 4	1·50	1·75

(Des M. McArthur. Litho National Printing & Packaging, Zimbabwe)

1995 (16 Oct). *50th Anniv of United Nations. T* **194** *and similar vert designs. Multicoloured. P* 14½.

805	20 t. Type 194	20	10
806	50 t. Schoolchildren queuing for soup (W.F.P.)	35	30
807	80 t. Letters and postman delivering to village (U.N.D.P.)	60	70
808	1 p. Weighing baby (U.N.I.C.E.F.)	70	90
805/8	Set of 4	1·60	1·75

195 Brown Hyena   196 *Adenia glauca*

(Des Judith Penny. Litho Questa)

1995 (6 Nov). *Endangered Species. Brown Hyena. T* **195** *and similar horiz designs. Multicoloured. P* 14½.

809	20 t. Type 195	25	35
	a. Strip of 4. Nos. 809/12	1·60	
810	50 t. Pair of Hyenas	40	50
811	80 t. Hyena stealing ostrich eggs	50	65
812	1 p. Adult Hyena and cubs	60	75
809/12	Set of 4	1·60	2·00

In addition to separate sheets of 50 Nos. 809/12 were also available in sheets of 16 (4×4) with the stamps arranged *se-tenant* both horizontally and vertically.

(Des Gillian Condy. Litho National Printing & Packaging, Zimbabwe)

1995 (27 Nov). *Christmas. Plants. T* **196** *and similar vert designs. Multicoloured. P* 14.

813	20 t. Type 196	20	10
814	50 t. Pterodiscus ngamicus	40	30
815	80 t. Sesamothamnus lugardii	65	70
816	1 p. Fockea multiflora	75	90
813/16	Set of 4	1·75	1·75

(197)   198 Spears

1996 (12 Feb). *Nos. 738/40 surch as T* **197**.

817	20 t. on 2 t. Spring Hare	20	20
818	30 t. on 1 t. Type 181	25	25
819	70 t. on 4 t. Blackfooted Cat	50	70
817/19	Set of 3	85	1·00

(Des B. Mazebedi. Litho National Printing & Packaging, Zimbabwe)

1996 (25 Mar). *Traditional Weapons. T* **198** *and similar horiz designs. Multicoloured. P* 14½×14.

820	20 t. Type 198	15	10
821	30 t. Axes	30	30
822	80 t. Shield and knobkerries	45	60
823	1 p. Knives and sheaths	50	75
820/3	Set of 4	1·25	1·60

199 Child with Basic Radio   200 Olympic Flame, Rings and Wreath

(Des P. Lodoen. Litho National Printing & Packaging, Zimbabwe)

1996 (3 June). *Centenary of Radio. T* **199** *and similar vert designs. Multicoloured. P* 14×14½.

824	20 t. Type 199	20	10
825	50 t. Radio Botswana's mobile transmitter	35	30
826	80 t. Police radio control	50	50
827	1 p. Listening to radio	65	75
824/7	Set of 4	1·50	1·50

(Des R. Andersson. Litho Govt Printer, Pretoria)

1996 (19 July). *Centenary of Modern Olympic Games. T* **200** *and similar vert designs. Multicoloured. P* 14.

828	20 t. Type 200	20	10
829	50 t. Pierre de Coubertin (founder of modern Olympics)	35	30
830	80 t. Map of Botswana with flags and athletes	50	60
831	1 p. Ruins of ancient stadium at Olympia	60	80
828/31	Set of 4	1·50	1·60

201 Family Planning Class (Botswana Family Welfare Association)   202 *Adansonia digitata* Leaf and Blossom

(Des K. Mosinyi. Litho National Printing and Packaging, Zimbabwe)

1996 (23 Sept). *Local Charities. T* **201** *and similar vert designs. Multicoloured. P* 14½.

832	20 t. Type 201	15	10
833	30 t. Blind workers (Pudulogong Rehabilitation Centre)	15	15
834	50 t. Collecting seeds (Forestry Association of Botswana)	25	30
835	70 t. Secretarial class (Y.W.C.A.)	35	45
836	80 t. Children's day centre (Botswana Council of Women)	40	50
837	1 p. Children's village, Tlokweng (S.O.S. Children's village)	50	60
832/7	Set of 6	1·60	1·75

(Des Gillian Condy. Litho National Printing and Packaging, Zimbabwe)

1996 (4 Nov). *Christmas. T* **202** *and similar vert designs showing parts of life cycle for Adansonia digitata. Multicoloured. P* 14.

838	20 t. Type **202**	..	..	15	10
839	50 t. Fruit	..	..	30	25
840	80 t. Tree in leaf	..	..	45	45
841	1 p. Tree with bare branches	..	..	50	60
838/41	..	..	Set of 4	1·25	1·25

203 Tati Hotel

204 Steam Locomotive, Bechuanaland Railway, 1897

(Des M. Smith. Litho National Printing and Packaging, Zimbabwe)

1997 (21 Apr). *Francistown Centenary. T* **203** *and similar horiz designs. Multicoloured. P* 14½×14.

842	20 t. Type **203**	..	..	15	10
843	50 t. Railway Station	..	..	30	25
844	80 t. Company Manager's House	..	40	40
845	1 p. Monarch Mine	..	..	50	60
842/5	..	..	Set of 4	1·25	1·25

(Des P. Lodoen. Litho National Printing and Packaging, Zimbabwe)

1997 (12 July). *Railway Centenary. T* **204** *and similar vert designs. Multicoloured. P* 14×14½.

846	35 t. Type **204**	..	..	20	15
847	50 t. Elephants crossing railway line		30	25
848	80 t. First locomotive in Bechuanaland, 1897	..		40	35
849	1 p. Beyer Garratt type steam locomotive No. 352	..		50	50
850	2 p. BD3 type diesel locomotive No. BD339		80	90
851	2 p. 50, Fantuzzi container stacker	..		90	1·10
846/51	..	..	Set of 6	2·75	3·00

205 Pel's Fishing Owl

206 Combretum zeyheri

(Des Helena Schüssel. Litho Enschedé)

1997 (4 Aug). *Birds. T* **205** *and similar multicoloured designs. P* 13½×13 (*vert*) *or* 13×13½ (*horiz*).

852	5 t. Type **205**	..	..	10	10
853	10 t. Gymnogene (*horiz*)	..	..	10	10
854	15 t. Meyer's Parrot	..	..	10	10
855	20 t. Harlequin Quail (*horiz*)	..	10	10
856	25 t. Marico Sunbird (*horiz*)	..	10	10
857	30 t. Kurrichane Thrush (*horiz*)	..	10	10
858	40 t. Redheaded Finch	..	..	10	10
859	50 t. Buffalo Weaver	..	..	15	20
860	60 t. Sacred Ibis (*horiz*)	..	..	20	25
861	70 t. Cape Shoveler (*horiz*)	..	20	25
862	80 t. Greater Honeyguide (*horiz*)	..	25	30
863	1 p. Woodland Kingfisher (*horiz*)	..	30	35
864	1 p. 25, Purple Heron	..	..	30	35
865	1 p. 50, Yellow-billed Oxpecker (*horiz*)		30	35
866	2 p. Shaft-tailed Whydah	..	..	60	65
867	2 p. 50, White Stork	..	..	65	70
868	5 p. Sparrowhawk	..	..	1·60	1·75
869	10 p. Spotted Crake	..	..	3·00	3·25
852/69	..	..	Set of 18	7·75	8·75

No. 861 is inscribed "Shoveller" in error.

(Des N. Shewring (No. **MS**876), D. Miller (others). Litho Questa (No. **MS**876), Cartor (others))

1997 (22 Sept). *Golden Wedding of Queen Elizabeth and Prince Philip. Multicoloured designs as T* **173** *of Ascension. W w* 14. *P* 13.

870	35 t. Prince Philip with carriage	..	20	20
	a. Horiz pair. Nos. 870/1	..	..	40	40
871	35 t. Queen Elizabeth with binoculars		20	20
872	2 p. Queen Elizabeth with horse team		90	1·00
	a. Horiz pair. Nos. 872/3	..	..	1·75	2·00
873	2 p. Prince Philip and horse	..	90	1·00
874	2 p. 50, Queen Elizabeth and Prince Philip		1·10	1·25
	a. Horiz pair. Nos. 874/5	..	..	2·10	2·50
875	2 p. 50, Princess Anne and Prince Edward		1·10	1·25
870/5	..	..	Set of 6	4·00	4·50
MS876	110×70 mm. 10 p. Queen Elizabeth and Prince Philip in landau (*horiz*). Wmk sideways. P 14×14½			4·00	4·25

Nos. 870/1, 872/3 and 874/5 were each printed together, *se-tenant*, in horizontal pairs throughout the sheets.

(Des Gillian Condy. Litho National Printing and Packaging, Zimbabwe)

1997 (10 Nov). *Christmas. Plants. T* **206** *and similar vert designs. Multicoloured. P* 14.

877	35 t. Type **206**	..	..	10	10
878	1 p. *Combretum apiculatum*	..	30	35
879	2 p. *Combretum molle*	..	..	60	65
880	2 p. 50, *Combretum imberbe*	..	65	70
877/80	..	..	Set of 4	1·60	1·75

STAMP BOOKLETS

B 1

1989 (1 Dec)–**92**. *Covers as Type* **B 1** *printed in blue on coloured card, each showing different stamp and postal logo. Stapled.*

SB1	20 t. booklet containing 2 t. (No. 620) in block of 10 (white cover) ..	50
SB2	40 t. booklet containing 2 t. (No. 620) in block of 20 (white cover) ..	75
SB3	50 t. booklet containing 5 t. (No. 623) in block of 10 (claret cover) ..	80
SB4	80 t. booklet containing 8 t. (No. 625) in block of 10 (grey cover) ..	1·10
	a. Containing 8 t. on 12 t. (No. 725) (1992)	
SB5	1 p. booklet containing 5 t. (No. 623) in block of 20 (claret cover) ..	1·25
SB6	1 p. booklet containing 10 t. (No. 626) in block of 10 (cinnamon cover) ..	1·25
	a. Containing 10 t. on 1 t. (No. 690) (1990) ..	
	b. Containing 10 t. on 12 t. (No. 726) (1992)	
SB7	1 p. 50, booklet containing 15 t. (No. 628) in block of 10 (pink cover) ..	2·00
SB8	1 p. 60, booklet containing 8 t. (No. 625) in block of 20 (grey cover) ..	2·00
	a. Containing 8 t. on 12 t. (No. 725) (1992) ..	
SB9	2 p. booklet containing 10 t. (No. 626) in block of 20 (cinnamon cover) ..	2·25
	a. Containing 10 t. on 1 t. (No. 690) (1990) ..	
	b. Containing 10 t. on 12 t. (No. 726) (1992) ..	
SB10	2 p. booklet containing 20 t. (No. 629) in block of 10 (pale blue cover) ..	2·25
	a. Containing 20 t. on 6 t. (No. 691) (1990) ..	
SB11	3 p. booklet containing 15 t. (No. 628) in block of 20 (pink cover) ..	3·25
SB12	3 p. booklet containing 30 t. (No. 631) in block of 10 (lemon cover) ..	3·25
SB13	4 p. booklet containing 20 t. (No. 629) in block of 20 (pale blue cover) ..	3·75
SB14	4 p. booklet containing 40 t. (No. 633) in block of 10 (pale green cover) ..	3·75
	a. Containing 40 t. on 3 t. (No. 728) (1992) ..	
	b. Error. Containing 50 t. on 12 t. (No. 692) (1990) ..	
SB15	6 p. booklet containing 30 t. (No. 631) in block of 20 (lemon cover) ..	5·50
SB16	8 p. booklet containing 40 t. (No. 633) in block of 20 (pale green cover) ..	7·00
	a. Containing 40 t. on 3 t. (No. 728) (1992) ..	

The booklets of twenty are larger, 81×69 mm.

No. SB14b, which was produced in error, has the face value of the booklet amended in manuscript.

B 2

1993 (4 Oct)–**94**. *Covers as Type* **B 2** *printed in black on coloured card, each showing different stamp with postal logo. Stapled.*

SB17	1 p. booklet containing 10 t. (No. 742) in strip of 10 (yellow cover) ..	75
	a. Containing 10 t. on 12 t. (No. 792) (1994)	75
SB18	1 p. 20, booklet containing 12 t. (No. 743) in strip of 10 (pale orange cover) ..	90
SB19	1 p. 50, booklet containing 15 t. (No. 744) in strip of 10 (orange cover) ..	1·10
SB20	2 p. booklet containing 10 t. (No. 742) in block of 20 (yellow cover) ..	1·40
	a. Containing 10 t. on 12 t. (No. 792) (1994)	1·40
SB21	2 p. booklet containing 20 t. (No. 745) in strip of 10 (white cover) ..	1·40
SB22	2 p. 40, booklet containing 12 t. (No. 743) in block of 20 (pale orange cover) ..	1·75
SB23	2 p. 50, booklet containing 25 t. (No. 746) in strip of 10 (pink cover) ..	1·75
SB24	3 p. booklet containing 15 t. (No. 744) in block of 20 (orange cover) ..	1·90
SB25	3 p. 50, booklet containing 35 t. (No. 747) in strip of 10 (green cover) ..	2·00
SB26	4 p. booklet containing 20 t. (No. 745) in block of 20 (white cover) ..	2·50
SB27	4 p. booklet containing 40 t. (No. 748) in strip of 10 (blue cover) ..	2·50
SB28	4 p. 50, booklet containing 45 t. (No. 749) in strip of 10 (pale rose-lilac cover) ..	2·75
SB29	5 p. booklet containing 25 t. (No. 746) in block of 20 (pink cover) ..	3·00
SB30	5 p. booklet containing 50 t. (No. 750) in strip of 10 (grey cover) ..	3·00
SB31	7 p. booklet containing 35 t. (No. 747) in block of 20 (green cover) ..	3·75
SB32	8 p. booklet containing 40 t. (No. 748) in block of 20 (blue cover) ..	4·00
SB33	9 p. booklet containing 45 t. (No. 749) in block of 20 (pale rose-lilac cover) ..	4·50
SB34	10 p. booklet containing 50 t. (No. 750) in block of 20 (grey cover) ..	5·00

The booklets of twenty are larger, 75×80 mm.

1996. *Covers as Nos. SB17 and SB21 cut down to 75×40 mm. Stamps attached by selvedge.*
SB35 1 p. booklet containing 5 t. and 15 t. (Nos. 741 and
       744) each in strip of 5 (yellow cover) ..
SB36 1 p. booklet containing 20 t. (No. 809) in strip of 5
       (white cover) ..

Nos. SB35/6 were issued from machines at Gaborone and Francistown Main Post Offices.

POSTAGE DUE STAMPS

(D 1)

(D 2)

BECHUANALAND
PROTECTORATE

1926 (Jan). *Nos. D9/10 and D13 of Great Britain, optd with Types D 1 or D 2 (2d.).*
D1 ½d. emerald (No. D10) .. .. .. 3·25 60·00
D2 1d. carmine (No. D9).. .. .. .. 3·25 45·00
D3 2d. agate (No. D13) .. .. 6·00 80·00
D1/3 .. .. Set of 3 11·00 £160

D 3   Normal   Large "d"
                         (R. 9/6, 10/6)

Serif on "d" (R.1/6)

(Typo D.L.R.)

1932 (12 Dec)–**58.** *Wmk Mult Script CA. Ordinary paper. P 14.*
D4 D 3 ½d. sage-green .. .. .. 6·00 28·00
D5   1d. carmine .. .. .. 5·50 8·50
         a. Chalk-surfaced paper (27.11.58) .. 1·00 11·00
D6   2d. violet .. .. .. 8·00 32·00
         a. Large "d" .. .. .. 75·00
         b. Chalk-surfaced paper (27.11.58) .. 1·50 16·00
         ba. Large "d" .. .. .. 20·00
         bb. Serif on "d" .. .. .. 20·00
D4/6b .. .. Set of 3 7·75 48·00
D4/6 Perf "Specimen" .. .. Set of 3 65·00
No. D6a first occurred on the 1947 printing.

1c **1c**

I (Small) II (Large)

1961 (14 Feb). *Surch as T 27. Chalk-surfaced paper (Nos. D7/8).*
D7 D 3 1 c. on 1d. (Type I) 25 50
         a. Type II (Apr) .. .. .. 15 1·75
         ab. Double surch £140
         ac. Ordinary paper .. .. 16·00 50·00
D8   2 c. on 2d. (Type I) .. .. .. 25 1·50
         a. Large "d" .. .. .. 6·00
         b. Serif on "d" .. .. .. 6·00
         c. Type II .. .. .. 15 2·00
         ca. Large "d" .. .. .. 4·50
         cb. Serif on "d" .. .. .. 4·50
         d. Ordinary paper. Type II .. 75·00 85·00
         da. Large "d" £250
D9   5 c. on ½d. 20 60
D7/9 .. .. .. Set of 3 45 2·40

1961 (15 Nov). *As Type D 3 but values in cents. Chalk-surfaced paper. Wmk Mult Script CA. P 14.*
D10 1 c. carmine .. .. .. 15 1·25
D11 2 c. violet .. .. .. 15 1·25
D12 5 c. green .. .. .. 30 1·50
D10/12 .. .. .. Set of 3 55 3·50

REPUBLIC OF

BOTSWANA

(D 4)

D 5 African
Elephant

D 6 Common Zebra

1967 (1 Mar). *Nos. D10/12 optd with Type D 4.*
D13 1 c. carmine .. .. .. 15 2·00
D14 2 c. violet .. .. .. 15 2·25
D15 5 c. green .. .. .. 20 2·25
D13/15 .. .. .. Set of 3 45 6·00

(Des and litho B.W.)

1971 (9 June). *P 13½.*
D16 D 5 1 c. carmine .. .. .. 1·10 3·00
D17   2 c. bluish violet .. .. 1·40 3·25
D18   6 c. sepia .. .. .. 2·50 4·75
D19   14 c. blue-green .. .. 2·75 7·00
D16/19 .. .. .. Set of 4 7·00 16·00

(Des M. Bryan. Litho Govt Printer, Pretoria)

1977 (18 Apr)–**84.** *P 12½.*
D20 D 6 1 t. black and vermilion (1978) .. 50 2·50
         a. Black and bright orange (1980) .. 90 2·50
         b. Perf 14 (1982?) .. .. 55 2·00
D21   2 t. black and emerald .. .. 40 2·75
         a. Perf 14 (5.8.81*) .. .. 60 2·25
D22   4 t. black and red .. .. 40 2·75
         a. Perf 14 (28.9.81*) .. 60 2·25
D23   10 t. black and deep ultramarine .. 40 2·75
         a. Perf 14 (7.3.84) .. 60 2·25
D24   16 t. black and chestnut .. 65 3·25
         a. Perf 14 (7.3.84) .. 75 2·75
D20/24 .. .. Set of 5 2·10 12·50
D20b/24a .. Set of 5 2·75 10·00
* First supplies of Nos. D20b, D21a and D22a were sent to Botswana in June 1981. The dates quoted for the 2 t. and 4 t. are earliest known dates of use. Early use of the 1 t. has yet to be identified.

Nos. D20b/4a are on white paper. A subsequent printing in September 1988 was on poorer grade paper.

(Litho National Printing & Packaging, Zimbabwe)

1989 (1 Apr)–**94.** *P 14½.*
D25 D 6 1 t. black and reddish orange .. 20 50
         a. Perf 14 (1.12.94) .. 10 10
D26   2 t. black and emerald .. 20 50
         a. Perf 14 (1.12.94) .. 10 10
D27   4 t. black and bright scarlet .. 20 50
         a. Perf 14 (1.12.94) .. 10 10
D28   10 t. black and deep ultramarine .. 25 50
         a. Perf 14 (1.12.94) .. 10 10
D29   16 t. black and reddish brown .. 35 80
         a. Perf 14 (1.12.94) .. 10 10
D25/9 .. .. Set of 5 1·10 2·50
D25a/9a .. Set of 5 25 25
Details on the zebra and of the grass stems are less distinct on Nos. D25/9 than on previous versions of Type D 6.

POSTAL FISCAL STAMPS

The following stamps issued for fiscal purposes were each allowed to be used for postal purposes for a short time. No. F2 was used by the public because the word "POSTAGE" had not been obliterated and No. F3 because the overprint did not include the words "Revenue only" as did the contemporary fiscal overprints for Basutoland and Swaziland.

Bechuanaland

Bechuanaland

Protectorate   £5   Bechuanaland
                                  Protectorate.

(F 1)   (F 2)   (F 3)

1910 (July). *No. 266a of Transvaal, optd with Type F 1 by Transvaal Govt Ptg Wks, Pretoria.*
F1 6d. black and brown-orange (Bl-Blk) .. £150 £300
No. F1 was supplied to Assistant Commissioners in January 1907 for revenue purposes. The "POSTAGE" inscription was not obliterated, however, and the stamp is known postally used for a period of a year from July 1910.

1918. *No. 15 surch with Type F 2 at top.*
F2 4 £5 on 1s. green and black £8500

1922. *No. 4b of South Africa optd with Type F 3, in varying positions.*
F3 1d. scarlet .. .. .. 42·00 £120
    a. Opt double, one albino £130

British Antarctic Territory

For use at the following bases:

Adelaide Island (Graham Land) (*closed 1977*)
Argentine Islands ("Faraday" *from* 1981), (Graham Land)
  (*closed 8 February* 1996 *and transferred to Ukraine*)
Brabant Island (Graham Land) (*opened* 1984, *closed* 1985)
Deception Island (South Shetlands) (*closed* 1967)
Halley Bay (Coats Land)
Hope Bay (Graham Land) (*closed 12 February* 1964)
Port Lockroy (Graham Land) (*opened 21 November* 1996)
Rothera Point (Graham Land) (*opened* 1977)
Signy Island (South Orkneys)
Stonington Island (Graham Land) (*closed February* 1975)

1 M.V. *Kista Dan*

(Des B.W. (No. 15*a*), M. Goaman (others). Recess B.W.)

1963 (1 Feb)–**69**. *Horiz designs as T* **1**, *W* w **12**. *P* 11 × 11½.

1	½d. deep blue	..	60	1·40
2	1d. brown	..	80	80
3	1½d. orange-red and brown-purple	..	80	1·00
4	2d. purple	..	1·25	80
5	2½d. myrtle-green	..	2·00	70
6	3d. deep blue	..	3·00	80
7	4d. sepia	..	2·25	1·25
8	6d. olive and deep ultramarine	..	3·75	1·75
9	9d. olive-green	..	3·25	1·50
10	1s. deep turquoise-blue	..	3·25	70
11	2s. deep violet and orange-sepia	..	17·00	6·50
12	2s. 6d. blue	..	15·00	6·50
13	5s. red-orange and rose-red	..	20·00	12·00
14	10s. deep ultramarine and emerald	..	45·00	25·00
15	£1 black and light blue	..	60·00	48·00
15*a*	£1 red and brownish black (1.12.69)	..	£150	£120
1/15*a*		*Set of* 16	£300	£200

Designs:—1d. Manhauling; 1½d. Muskeg (tractor); 2d. Skiing; 2½d. De Havilland D.H.C.2 Beaver (aircraft); 3d. R.R.S. *John Biscoe II*; 4d. Camp scene; 6d. H.M.S. *Protector*; 9d. Sledging; 1s. De Havilland D.H.C.3 Otter (aircraft); 2s. Huskies; 2s. 6d. Westland Whirlwind helicopter; 5s. Snocat (tractor); 10s. R.R.S. *Shackleton*; £1 (No. 15) Antarctic map; £1 (No. 15*a*) H.M.S. *Endurance*.

1966 (24 Jan). *Churchill Commemoration. As Nos.* 170/3 *of Antigua.*

16	½d. new blue	..	80	2·75
17	1d. deep green	..	3·00	2·75
18	1s. brown	..	21·00	6·50
19	2s. bluish violet	..	24·00	7·00
16/19		*Set of* 4	45·00	17·00

17 Lemaire Channel and Icebergs

(Des R. Granger Barrett. Litho Format)

1969 (6 Feb). *25th Anniv of Continuous Scientific Work. T* **17** *and similar horiz designs. W* w **12** (*sideways*). *P* 14.

20	3½d. black, pale blue and ultramarine	..	4·00	3·00
21	6d. multicoloured	..	3·50	2·50
22	1s. black, pale blue and vermilion	..	3·50	3·00
23	2s. black, orange and turquoise-blue	..	3·75	3·00
20/3		*Set of* 4	13·00	9·50

Designs:—6d. Radio Sonde balloon; 1s. Muskeg pulling tent equipment; 2s. Surveyors with theodolite.

(18) **19** Setting up Camp

1971 (15 Feb). *Decimal Currency. As Nos.* 1/14, *but glazed paper, colours changed and surch as T* **18**.

24	½p. on ½d. blue	..	60	2·50
25	1p. on 1d. pale brown	..	1·00	75
26	1½p. on 1½d. red and pale brown-purple	..	1·25	50
27	2p. on 2d. bright purple	..	1·25	30
28	2½p. on 2½d. green	..	1·75	1·00
29	3p. on 3d. blue	..	2·50	55
	w. Wmk inverted	..	60·00	
30	4p. on 4d. bistre-brown	..	2·25	55
31	5p. on 6d. olive and ultramarine	..	4·25	3·00
32	6p. on 9d. dull green	..	12·00	7·00

33	7½p. on 1s. turquoise-blue	..	13·00	7·50
34	10p. on 2s. violet and orange-sepia	..	18·00	13·00
	w. Wmk inverted	..	£550	
35	15p. on 2s. 6d. pale blue	..	18·00	13·00
36	25p. on 5s. orange and pale rose-red	..	24·00	16·00
37	50p. on 10s. ultramarine and emerald	..	48·00	35·00
	w. Wmk inverted	..	£120	
24/37		*Set of* 14	£130	85·00

(Des M. Goaman. Recess and litho Enschedé)

1971 (23 June). *10th Anniv of Antarctic Treaty. Vert designs each including Antarctic Map and Queen Elizabeth, as T* **19**. *Multicoloured. W* w **12** (*sideways*). *P* 14 × 13.

38	1½p. Type **19**	..	5·50	5·50
39	4p. Snow Petrels	..	14·00	8·00
40	5p. Weddell Seals	..	9·50	8·00
41	10p. Adelie Penguins	..	20·00	9·00
38/41		*Set of* 4	45·00	27·00

20 Kerguelen Fur Seals and Emperor Penguins   **21** James Cook and H.M.S. *Resolution*

(Des (from photograph by D. Groves) and photo Harrison)

1972 (13 Dec*). *Royal Silver Wedding. Multicoloured; background colour given. W* w **12**. *P* 14 × 14½.

42	**20** 5p. red-brown	..	3·00	3·00
	w. Wmk inverted	..	17·00	
43	10p. brown-olive	..	3·00	3·00
	w. Wmk inverted	..	£140	

*This is the local release date; they were issued by the Crown Agents on 20 November.

(Des J.W. Litho Questa)

1973 (14 Feb). *T* **21** *and similar vert designs. Multicoloured. W* w **12** (*sideways*). *P* 14 × 14½.

44	½p. Type **21** (*shades*)	..	1·25	2·00
45	1p. Thaddeus von Bellingshausen and *Vostok*	..	2·50	3·25
46	1½p. James Weddell and *Jane*	..	11·00	4·50
47	2p. John Biscoe and *Tula*	..	2·00	1·75
48	2½p. J. S. C. Dumont d'Urville and *L'Astrolabe*	..	1·50	1·75
49	3p. James Clark Ross and H.M.S. *Erebus*	..	95	1·75
50	4p. C. A. Larsen and *Jason*	..	95	1·75
51	5p. Adrien de Gerlache and *Belgica*	..	1·00	1·75
52	6p. Otto Nordenskjöld and *Antarctic*	..	1·25	1·75
53	7½p. W. S. Bruce and *Scotia*	..	1·50	2·25
54	10p. Jean-Baptiste Charcot and *Pourquoi Pas?*	..	2·75	3·00
55	15p. Ernest Shackleton and *Endurance*	..	5·00	4·00
56	25p. Hubert Wilkins and Lockheed Vega *San Francisco*	..	2·50	4·00
57	50p. Lincoln Ellsworth and Northrop Gamma *Polar Star*	..	2·50	4·50
58	£1 John Rymill and *Penola*	..	3·00	8·00
44/58		*Set of* 15	35·00	42·00

The 25 and 50p. show aircraft; the rest show ships.
See also Nos. 64/78.

1973 (23 Dec*). *Royal Wedding. As Nos.* 165/6 *of Anguilla. Centre multicoloured. W* w **12** (*sideways*). *P* 13½.

59	5p. ochre	..	40	20
60	15p. light turquoise-blue	..	70	30

*This is the local date of issue: the Crown Agents released the stamps on 14 November.

22 Churchill and Churchill Peninsula, B.A.T.

(Des G. Vasarhelyi. Litho Format)

1974 (10 Dec*). *Birth Centenary of Sir Winston Churchill. T* **22** *and similar horiz design. Multicoloured. W* w **12** (*sideways on* 5p). *P* 14.

61	5p. Type **22**	..	1·75	1·75
62	15p. Churchill and *Trepassey* ("Operation Tabarin", 1943)	..	2·25	2·25
MS63	114 × 88 mm. Nos. 61/2. Wmk upright	..	13·00	10·00

*This is the local date of issue: the Crown Agents released the stamps on 30 November.

1975 (11 June)–**81**. *As Nos.* 44/58 *but W* w **14**. *Ordinary paper* (½, 2, 2½, 3, 5, 10, 15, 25, 50p.) *or chalk-surfaced paper* (1, 1½, 4, 6, 7½p., £1). *P* 12 (4, 6, 7½p.) *or* 14 × 14½ (*others*).

64	½p. Type **21**	..	2·50	2·75
	a. Chalk-surfaced paper (14.3.78)		75	80
65	1p. Thaddeus von Bellingshausen and *Vostok* (14.3.78)	..	60	1·75
	a. Ordinary paper (11.12.79)		80	2·50
66	1½p. James Weddell and *Jane* (14.3.78)	..	60	1·50
	a. Ordinary paper (11.12.79)		80	2·50
67	2p. John Biscoe and *Tula* (11.12.79)	..	1·50	2·00
68	2½p. J. S. C. Dumont d'Urville and *L'Astrolabe* (11.12.79)	..	1·50	2·00
69	3p. James Clark Ross and H.M.S. *Erebus* (11.12.79)	..	2·50	2·25

70	4p. C. A. Larsen and *Jason* (5.12.80)	..	55	2·50
71	5p. Adrien de Gerlache and *Belgica* (11.12.79)	..	2·75	3·00
72	6p. Otto Nordenskjöld and *Antarctic* (5.12.80)	..	80	2·50
73	7½p. W. S. Bruce and *Scotia* (5.12.80)	..	1·25	3·00
74	10p. Jean-Baptiste Charcot and *Pourquoi Pas?* (11.12.79)	..	1·75	3·00
	a. Perf 12. Chalk-surfaced paper (25.11.81)		85	2·75
75	15p. Ernest Shackleton and *Endurance* (11.12.79)	..	1·25	1·50
	a. Perf 12. Chalk-surfaced paper (25.11.81)		85	2·75
76	25p. Hubert Wilkins and Lockheed Vega *San Francisco* (11.12.79)	..	1·25	1·50
	a. Perf 12. Chalk-surfaced paper (25.11.81)		85	3·00
77	50p. Lincoln Ellsworth and Northrop Gamma *Polar Star* (11.12.79)	..	1·25	2·75
	a. Perf 12. Chalk-surfaced paper (5.12.80)		85	2·75
78	£1 John Rymill and *Penola* (14.3.78)	..	3·25	2·00
	a. Perf 12 (5.12.80)		1·50	4·00
	aw. Wmk inverted		£425	
64*a*/78*a*		*Set of* 15	16·00	30·00

23 Sperm Whale

(Des J. Cooter. Litho Questa)

1977 (4 Jan). *Whale Conservation. T* **23** *and similar horiz designs. W* w **14** (*sideways*). *P* 13½.

79	2p. brownish black, slate and bright blue	..	5·50	3·00
80	8p. grey, brownish black and rosine	..	6·50	3·50
81	11p. multicoloured	..	7·00	3·50
82	25p. grey-blue, brownish blk & lt blue-green	..	8·00	4·50
79/82		*Set of* 4	24·00	13·00

Designs:—8p. Fin Whale; 11p. Humpback Whale; 25p. Blue Whale.

24 The Queen before Taking the Oath   **25** Emperor Penguin

(Des J.W. Litho Questa)

1977 (7 Feb). *Silver Jubilee. T* **24** *and similar horiz designs. Multicoloured. W* w **14** (*sideways**). *P* 13½.

83	6p. Prince Philip's visit, 1956/7	..	70	30
84	11p. Coronation Oath	..	80	40
	w. Wmk Crown to right of CA		10·00	10·00
85	33p. Type **24**	..	1·25	50
	w. Wmk Crown to right of CA		£140	
83/5		*Set of* 3	2·50	1·10

*The normal sideways watermark shows Crown to left of CA, as seen from the back of the stamp.

(Des C. Abbott. Litho Questa)

1978 (2 June). *25th Anniv of Coronation. T* **25** *and similar vert designs. P* 15.

86	25p. green, deep bluish green and silver	..	80	1·00
	a. Sheetlet Nos. 86/8 × 2		4·50	
87	25p. multicoloured	..	80	1·00
88	25p. green, deep bluish green and silver	..	80	1·00
86/8		*Set of* 3	2·25	2·75

Designs:— No. 86. Black Bull of Clarence; No. 87, Queen Elizabeth II; No. 88, Type **25**.
Nos. 86/8 were printed together in small sheets of 6, containing two *se-tenant* strips of 3 with a horizontal gutter margin between.

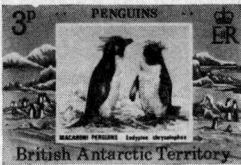

26 Macaroni Penguins

(Des G. Drummond. Litho Walsall)

1979 (14 Jan). *Penguins. T* **26** *and similar horiz designs. Multicoloured. W* w **14** (*sideways**). *P* 13½.

89	3p. Type **26**	..	11·00	11·00
	w. Wmk Crown to right of CA		£300	
90	8p. Gentoo penguins	..	3·00	3·00
91	11p. Adelie penguins	..	3·50	3·50
92	25p. Emperor penguins	..	4·50	4·50
89/92		*Set of* 4	20·00	20·00

*The normal sideways watermark shows Crown to left of CA, as seen from the back of the stamp.

27 Sir John Barrow and *Tula*

(Des A. Theobald. Litho Secura, Singapore)

1980 (14 Dec*). *150th Anniv of Royal Geographical Society. Former Presidents. T* **27** *and similar horiz designs. Multicoloured. W w* **14** *(sideways†). P* 13½.

93	3p. Type 27	..	..	20	15
94	7p. Sir Clement Markham and *Discovery*		25	25
	w. Wmk Crown to right of CA			5·50	
95	11p. Lord Curzon and whaleboat *James Caird*	..		30	30
	w. Wmk Crown to right of CA			4·00	
96	15p. Sir William Goodenough	..		35	35
97	22p. Sir James Wordie	..		50	55
	w. Wmk Crown to right of CA			65·00	
98	30p. Sir Raymond Priestley	..		60	65
93/8	..	..	*Set of 6*	2·00	2·00

*This is the local date of issue; the Crown Agents released the stamps on 1 December.

†The normal sideways watermark shows Crown to left of CA, as seen from the back of the stamp.

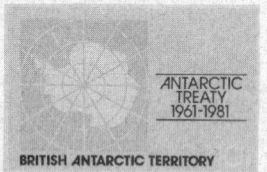

28 Map of Antarctic

(Des Walsall. Litho Questa)

1981 (1 Dec). *20th Anniv of Antarctic Treaty. T* **28** *and similar horiz designs. W w* **14** *(sideways*). P* 13½×14.

99	10p. black, new blue and azure	..		30	70
	w. Wmk Crown to right of CA	..		£180	
100	13p. black, new blue and apple-green	..	35	80
101	25p. black, new blue and mauve	..		50	90
102	26p. black, brown-ochre and rose-red	..	50	90
99/102		..	*Set of 4*	1·50	3·00

Designs:—13p. Conservation research ("scientific co-operation"); 25p. Satellite image mapping ("technical co-operation"); 26p Global geophysics ("scientific co-operation").

*The normal sideways watermark shows Crown to left of CA, as seen from the back of the stamp.

29 Map of Gondwana showing position of Continents 280 million years ago, and Contemporary Landscape Scene

30 British Antarctic Territory Coat of Arms

(Des C. Abbott. Litho Walsall)

1982 (8 Mar). *Gondwana—Continental Drift and Climatic Change. T* **29** *and similar horiz designs depicting maps of Gondwana showing position of continents, and contemporary landscape scenes. Multicoloured. W w* **14** *(sideways). P* 13½ × 14.

103	3p. Type 29	..		25	40
104	6p. 260 million years ago	..		30	50
105	10p. 230 million years ago	..		35	60
106	13p. 175 million years ago	..		45	70
107	25p. 50 million years ago	..		55	75
108	26p. Present day	..		55	75
	a. Gold (royal cypher) omitted				
103/8	..	..	*Set of 6*	2·25	3·25

(Des Jennifer Toombs. Litho Questa)

1982 (1 July). *21st Birthday of Princess of Wales. T* **30** *and similar vert designs. Multicoloured. W w* **14**. *P* 14½ × 14.

109	5p. Type 30	..		20	20
110	17p. Princess of Wales (detail of painting by Bryan Organ)	..		45	50
111	37p. Wedding ceremony	..		70	80
112	50p. Formal portrait	..		1·10	1·10
109/12	..	..	*Set of 4*	2·25	2·40

31 Leopard Seal

(Des R. Granger Barrett. Litho Walsall)

1983 (3 Jan). *10th Anniv (1982) of Antarctic Seal Conservation Convention. T* **31** *and similar horiz designs. Multicoloured. W w* **14** *(sideways). P* 11.

113	5p. Type 31	..		40	35
114	10p. Weddell Seals	..		45	40
115	13p. Southern Elephant Seals	..		50	45
116	17p. Kerguelen Fur Seals	..		60	55
117	25p. Ross Seal	..		70	65
118	34p. Crabeater Seals	..		95	85
113/18	..	..	*Set of 6*	3·25	3·00

32 De Havilland D.H.C.6 Twin Otter 200/300

(Des Harrison. Litho Questa)

1983 (20 Dec). *Bicentenary of Manned Flight. T* **32** *and similar horiz designs. Multicoloured. W w* **14** *(sideways). P* 14.

119	5p. Type 32	..		25	30
120	13p. De Havilland D.H.C.3 Otter	..	40	45
121	17p. Consolidated PBY-5A Canso	..	55	60
122	50p. Lockheed Vega *San Francisco*	..	1·10	1·25
119/22	..	..	*Set of 4*	2·10	2·40

33 *Corethron criophilum*

(Des I. Loe. Litho Walsall)

1984 (15 Mar). *Marine Life. T* **33** *and similar horiz designs. Multicoloured. W w* **14** *(sideways*). P* 14.

123	1p. Type 33	..		60	1·40
124	2p. *Desmonema gaudichaudi*	..		65	1·40
125	3p. *Tomopteris carpenteri*	..		65	1·40
126	4p. *Pareuchaeta antarctica*	..		70	1·50
127	5p. *Antarctomysis maxima*	..		70	1·50
128	6p. *Antarcturus signiensis*	..		70	1·50
129	7p. *Serolis cornuta*	..		70	1·50
130	8p. *Parathemisto gaudichaudii*	..		70	1·50
131	9p. *Bovallia gigantea*	..		70	1·50
132	10p. *Euphausia superba*	..		70	1·50
133	15p. *Colossendeis australis*	..		70	1·75
134	20p. *Todarodes sagittatus*	..		75	1·75
	w. Wmk Crown to right of CA	..		70·00	
135	25p. Antarctic Rockcod ("*Notothenia neglecta*")	..		80	1·75
136	50p. Black-finned Icefish ("*Chaenocephalus aceratus*")	..		1·25	2·00
137	£1 Crabeater Seal	..		1·75	2·50
138	£3 Antarctic marine food chain	..		5·00	6·50
123/38	..	..	*Set of 16*	15·00	28·00

*The normal sideways watermark shows Crown to left of CA on 1, 3, 4, 6, 7, 8, 9, 10, 20p. and to right on 2, 5, 15, 25, 50p., £1, £3, all as seen from the back of the stamp.

34 M.Y. *Penola* in Stella Creek

35 Robert McCormick and McCormick's Skua

(Des A. Theobald. Litho Questa)

1985 (23 Mar). *50th Anniv of British Graham Land Expedition. T* **34** *and similar horiz designs. Multicoloured. W w* **14** *(sideways). P* 14½.

139	7p. Type 34	..		40	65
140	22p. Northern Base, Winter Island	..	70	1·25
141	27p. De Havilland D.H.83 Fox Moth at Southern Base, Barry Island	..	80	1·40
142	54p. Dog team near Ablation Point, George VI Sound	..		1·50	2·25
139/42	..	..	*Set of 4*	3·00	5·00

(Des I. Strange. Litho Questa)

1985 (4 Nov). *Early Naturalists. T* **35** *and similar vert designs. Multicoloured. W w* **14**. *P* 14½ × 14.

143	7p. Type 35	..		1·25	1·50
144	22p. Sir Joseph Dalton Hooker and *Deschampsia antarctica*	..		1·75	2·75
145	27p. Jean René C. Quoy and Hourglass Dolphin	..		1·90	2·75
146	54p. James Weddell and Weddell Seal	..	2·75	4·00
143/6	..	..	*Set of 4*	7·00	10·00

NEW INFORMATION

The editor is always interested to correspond with people who have new information that will improve or correct the Catalogue.

36 Dr. Edmond Halley

37 Snow Crystal

(Des A. Theobald. Litho Questa)

1986 (6 Jan). *Appearance of Halley's Comet. T* **36** *and similar vert designs. Multicoloured. W w* **14**. *P* 14.

147	7p. Type 36	..		1·00	1·25
148	22p. Halley Station, Antarctica	..	1·75	2·25
149	27p. "Halley's Comet, 1531" (from Peter Apian woodcut, 1532)	..		2·00	2·50
150	54p. *Giotto* spacecraft	..		3·50	4·50
147/50	..	..	*Set of 4*	7·50	9·50

(Des C. Abbott. Litho Questa)

1986 (6 Dec). *50th Anniv of International Glaciological Society. T* **37** *and similar vert designs showing snow crystals. W w* **16**. *P* 14½.

151	10p. cobalt and deep ultramarine	..	50	75
152	24p. pale turquoise-green & dp bluish green	80	1·25
153	29p. mauve and deep mauve	..		90	1·40
154	58p. violet-blue and bright violet	..	1·25	2·25
151/4	..	..	*Set of 4*	3·00	5·00

38 Captain Scott, 1904

39 I.G.Y. Logo

(Des A. Theobald. Litho Questa)

1987 (19 Mar). *75th Anniv of Captain Scott's Arrival at South Pole. T* **38** *and similar horiz designs. Multicoloured. W w* **16** *(sideways). P* 14 × 14½.

155	10p. Type 38	..		75	95
156	24p. Hut Point and *Discovery*, Ross Island, 1902–4	..		1·25	1·75
157	29p. Cape Evans Hut, 1911–13	..	1·50	2·25
158	58p. Scott's Expedition at South Pole, 1912	2·00	2·75
155/8	..	..	*Set of 4*	5·00	7·00

(Des L. Curtis. Litho Questa)

1987 (25 Dec). *30th Anniv of International Geophysical Year. T* **39** *and similar vert designs. W w* **16**. *P* 14½ × 14.

159	10p. black and pale green	..		30	75
160	24p. multicoloured	..		60	1·40
161	29p. multicoloured	..		75	1·75
162	58p. multicoloured	..		1·40	2·50
159/62	..	..	*Set of 4*	2·75	5·75

Designs:—24p. Port Lockroy; 29p. Argentine Islands; 58p. Halley Bay.

40 Aurora over South Ice Plateau Station

41 *Xanthoria elegans*

(Des D. Hartley. Litho Questa)

1988 (19 Mar). *30th Anniv of Commonwealth Trans-Antarctic Expedition. T* **40** *and similar vert designs. Multicoloured. W w* **16**. *P* 14.

163	10p. Type 40	..		30	45
164	24p. "Otter" aircraft at Theron Mountains	..	60	80
165	29p. Seismic ice-depth sounding	..	70	95
166	58p. "Sno-cat" over crevasse	..		1·25	1·60
163/6	..	..	*Set of 4*	2·50	3·50

(Des I. Loe. Litho Walsall)

1989 (25 Mar). *Lichens. T* **41** *and similar horiz designs. Multicoloured. W w* **14** *(sideways). P* 14.

167	10p Type 41	..		75	75
168	24p *Usnea aurantiaco-atra*	..		1·40	1·40
169	29p *Cladonia chlorophaea*	..		1·50	1·50
170	58p *Umbilicaria antarctica*	..		2·25	2·50
167/70	..	..	*Set of 4*	5·50	5·50

42 Monocyathus (archaeocyath)	43 Late Cretaceous Forest and Southern Beech Fossil

(Des I. Loe. Litho Questa)

1990 (2 Apr). *Fossils. T* **42** *and similar horiz designs. Multicoloured.* W w **16** (*sideways*). P 14.

171	1p. Type **42**	..	..	40	70
172	2p. *Lingulella* (brachiopod)	..	..	40	70
173	3p. *Triplagnoslus* (trilobite)	..	50	70
174	4p. *Lyriaspis* (trilobite)	..	..	50	70
175	5p. *Glossopteris* leaf (gymnosperm)	..	50	70
176	6p. *Gonatosorus* (fern)	..	..	60	80
177	7p. *Belemnopsis aucklandica* (belemnite)	..	60	80
178	8p. *Sanmartinoceras africanum insignicostatum* (ammonite)	..	60	80
179	9p. *Pinna antarctica* (mussel)	..	70	80
180	10p. *Aucellina andina* (mussel)	..	70	80
181	20p. *Pterotrigonia malagninoi* (mussel)	..	1·00	1·40
182	25p. *Anchura* sp. (conch shell)	..	1·10	1·40
183	50p. *Ainoceras zinsmeisteri* (ammonite)	..	1·75	2·50
184	£1 *Gunnarites antarcticus* (ammonite)	..	3·50	4·25
185	£3 *Hoploparia* (crayfish)	..	7·00	8·00
171/85		Set of 15	18·00	22·00

(Des D. Miller. Litho Questa)

1990 (25 Dec*). *90th Birthday of Queen Elizabeth the Queen Mother. Vert designs as T* **134** (26p.) *or* **135** (£1) *of Ascension.* W w **16**. P 14×15 (26p.) *or* 14½ (£1).

186	26p. multicoloured	..	..	1·75	2·00
187	£1 brownish black and olive-bistre	..	3·75	4·00

Designs:—26p. Wedding of Prince Albert and Lady Elizabeth Bowes-Lyon, 1923; £1 The Royal Family, 1940.
*This is the local date of issue, the Crown Agents released the stamps on 4 August.

(Des N. Shewring. Litho Questa)

1991 (27 Mar). *Age of the Dinosaurs. T* **43** *and similar horiz designs. Multicoloured.* W w **14** (*sideways*). P 14×13½.

188	12p. Type **43**	..	..	1·00	1·00
189	26p. Hypsilophodont dinosaurs and skull	..	1·75	1·75
190	31p. Frilled Sharks and tooth	..	2·00	2·00
191	62p. Mosasaur, Plesiosaur, and Mosasaur vertebra	..	3·00	3·00
188/91		Set of 4	7·00	7·00

44 Launching Meteorological Balloon, Halley IV Station	45 Researching Dry Valley

(Des O. Bell. Litho Questa)

1991 (30 Mar). *Discovery of Antarctic Ozone Hole. T* **44** *and similar horiz designs. Multicoloured.* W w **16** (*sideways*). P 14×13½.

192	12p. Type **44**	..	..	75	75
193	26p. Measuring ozone with Dobson spectrophotometer	..	1·40	1·40
194	31p. Satellite map showing ozone hole	..	1·60	1·60
195	62p. Lockheed ER-2 aircraft and graph of chlorine monoxide and ozone levels	..	2·50	2·50
192/5		Set of 4	5·50	5·50

(Des O. Bell. Litho Questa)

1991 (2 Dec*). *30th Anniv of Antarctic Treaty. T* **45** *and similar vert designs.* W w **14**. P 13½×14 (31p.) *or* 14½×14 (*others*).

196	12p. multicoloured	..	..	75	75
197	26p. multicoloured	..	..	1·40	1·40
198	31p. black and blue-green	..	1·60	1·60
199	62p. multicoloured	..	..	2·50	2·50
196/9		Set of 4	5·50	5·50

Designs:—26p. Relief map of ice sheet; 31p. BIOMASS logo; 62p. Ross Seal.
*This is the local date of issue, the Crown Agents released the stamps on 24 June.

46 "H.M.S. *Erebus* and H.M.S. *Terror* in the Antarctic" (J. Carmichael)

(Des R. Watton. Litho Walsall)

1991 (10 Dec). *Maiden Voyage of* James Clark Ross (*research ship*). *T* **46** *and similar horiz designs. Multicoloured.* W w **14** (*sideways*). P 14½.

200	12p. Type **46**	..	..	75	75
201	26p. Launch of *James Clark Ross*	..	1·40	1·40
202	31p. *James Clark Ross* in Antarctica	..	1·60	1·60
203	62p. Scientific research	..	2·50	2·50
200/3		Set of 4	5·50	5·50

1991 (24 Dec). *Birth Bicentenary of Michael Faraday* (*scientist*). *Nos.* 200/3 *additionally inscr* "200th Anniversary M. Faraday 1791–1867" *in blue*.

204	12p. Type **46**	..	..	75	75
205	26p. Launch of *James Clark Ross*	..	1·40	1·40
206	31p. *James Clark Ross* in Antarctica	..	1·60	1·60
207	62p. Scientific research	..	2·50	2·50
204/7		Set of 4	5·50	5·50

47 Ross Seals

(Des A. Robinson. Litho B.D.T.)

1992 (10 Dec*). *Endangered Species. Seals and Penguins. T* **47** *and similar horiz designs. Multicoloured.* W w **14** (*sideways*). P 13½.

208	4p. Type **47**	..	..	40	30
209	5p. Adelie Penguins	..	..	40	30
210	7p. Weddell Seal with pup	..	45	35
211	29p. Emperor Penguins with chicks	..	1·25	1·00
212	34p. Crabeater Seals with pup	..	1·40	1·10
213	68p. Chinstrap Penguins with young	..	2·00	1·90
208/13		Set of 6	5·50	4·50

*This is the local date of issue, the Crown Agents released the stamps in London, and at the "Genova 92" International Thematic Stamp Exhibition, on 20 October.
Nos. 212/13 do not carry the W.W.F. Panda emblem.

48 Sun Pillar at Faraday	49 *Fitzroy* (mail and supply ship)

(Des N. Shewring. Litho Questa)

1992 (22 Dec). *Lower Atmospheric Phenomena. T* **48** *and similar horiz designs. Multicoloured.* W w **14** (*sideways*). P 14½.

214	14p. Type **48**	..	..	70	60
215	29p. Halo over iceberg	..	1·25	1·00
216	34p. Lee Wave Cloud	..	1·50	1·25
217	68p. Nacreous Clouds	..	2·50	1·90
214/17		Set of 4	5·50	4·25

(Des R. Watton. Litho Walsall)

1993 (13 Dec). *Antarctic Ships. T* **49** *and simlar horiz designs. Multicoloured.* W w **14** (*sideways*). P 14.

218	1p. Type **49**	..	..	10	10
219	2p. *William Scoresby* (research ship)	..	10	10
220	3p. *Eagle* (sealer)	..	..	10	10
221	4p. *Trepassey* (supply ship)	..	10	10
222	5p. *John Biscoe I* (research ship)	..	10	10
223	10p. *Norsel* (supply ship)	..	20	25
224	20p. H.M.S. *Protector* (ice patrol ship)	..	40	45
225	30p. *Oluf Sven* (supply ship)	..	60	65
226	50p. *John Biscoe II* and *Shackleton* (research ships)	..	1·00	1·10
227	£1 *Tottan* (supply ship)	..	2·00	2·10
228	£3 *Perla Dan* (supply ship)	..	6·00	6·25
229	£5 H.M.S. *Endurance I* (ice patrol ship)	..	10·00	10·50
218/29		Set of 12	20·00	21·00

For miniature sheets containing the 50p or £1 ("1997" imprint date) see Nos. **MS274/5**.

1994 (19 Mar*). *"Hong Kong '94" International Stamp Exhibition. Nos.* 240/5 *optd as T* **154** *of Ascension.*

230	15p. Type **51**	..	..	75	80
231	24p. De Havilland D.H.C.2 Turbo Beaver III aircraft	..	1·00	1·25
232	31p. De Havilland D.H.C.3 Otter aircraft and dog team	..	1·25	1·40
233	36p. De Havilland D.H.C.6 Twin Otter 200/300 aircraft and dog team	..	1·40	1·60
234	62p. De Havilland D.H.C.7 Dash Seven aircraft over landing strip, Rothera Point	..	2·00	2·50
235	72p. De Havilland D.H.C.7 Dash Seven aircraft on runway	..	2·00	2·50
230/5		Set of 6	7·50	9·00

*This is the local release date, the Crown Agents released the stamps in London and at the Exhibition on 18 February.

COVER PRICES

Cover factors are quoted at the beginning of each country for most issues to 1945. An explanation of the system can be found on page x. The factors quoted do not, however, apply to philatelic covers.

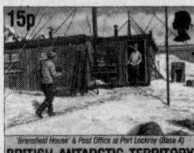

50 Bransfield House Post Office, Port Lockroy

(Des R. Watton. Litho Walsall)

1994 (19 Mar). *50th Anniv of Operation Tabarin. T* **50** *and similar horiz designs. Multicoloured.* W w **16** (*sideways*). P 14×14½.

236	15p. Type **50**	..	..	65	55
237	31p. Survey team, Hope Bay	..	1·10	95
238	36p. Dog team, Hope Bay	..	1·40	1·10
239	72p. *Fitzroy* (supply ship) and H.M.S. *William Scoresby* (minesweeper)	..	2·25	2·25
236/9		Set of 4	4·75	4·25

51 Huskies and Sledge

(Des D. Miller. Litho Walsall)

1994 (21 Mar). *Forms of Transportation. T* **51** *and similar horiz designs. Multicoloured.* W w **14** (*sideways*). P 14½.

240	15p. Type **51**	..	..	50	55
241	24p. De Havilland D.H.C.2 Turbo Beaver III aircraft	..	70	80
242	31p. De Havilland D.H.C.3 Otter aircraft and dog team	..	80	90
243	36p. De Havilland D.H.C.6 Twin Otter 200/300 aircraft and dog team	..	90	1·00
244	62p. De Havilland D.H.C.7 Dash Seven aircraft over landing strip, Rothera Point	..	1·75	2·25
245	72p. De Havilland D.H.C.7 Dash Seven aircraft on runway	..	1·90	2·50
240/5		Set of 6	6·00	7·00

52 Capt. James Cook and H.M.S. *Resolution*

(Des R. Watton. Litho Questa)

1994 (23 Nov). *Antarctic Heritage Fund. T* **52** *and similar horiz designs. Multicoloured.* W w **16** (*sideways*). P 14½×14.

246	17p. + 3p. Type **52**	..	1·50	1·40
247	35p. + 15p. Sir James Clark Ross with H.M.S. *Erebus* and H.M.S. *Terror*	1·75	1·60
248	40p. + 10p. Capt. Robert Falcon Scott and interior of hut	1·75	1·60
249	76p. + 4p. Sir Ernest Shackleton and H.M.S. *Endurance*	2·50	2·25
246/9		Set of 4	6·75	6·25

53 Pair of Crabeater Seals	54 Hauberg Mountains

(Des A. Robinson. Litho Questa)

1994 (29 Nov). *Antarctic Food Chain. T* **53** *and similar horiz designs. Multicoloured.* W w **14**. P 14×14½.

250	35p. Type **53**	..	..	95	1·10
	a. Sheetlet. Nos. 250/5	..	5·25	
251	35p. Blue Whale	..	..	95	1·10
252	35p. Wandering Albatross	..	95	1·10
253	35p. Mackerel Icefish	..	95	1·10
254	35p. Krill	..	..	95	1·10
255	35p. Seven Star Flying Squid (*Martialia hyadesi*)	..	95	1·10
250/5		Set of 6	5·25	6·00

Nos. 250/5 were printed together, *se-tenant*, in sheetlets of 6.

(Des N. Shewring. Litho Walsall)

1995 (28 Nov). *Geological Structures. T* **54** *and similar horiz designs. Multicoloured.* W w **14** (*sideways*). P 14×14½.

256	17p. Type **54**	..	..	65	60
257	35p. Arrowsmith Peninsula	..	1·25	1·10
258	40p. Colbert Mountains	..	1·50	1·40
259	76p. Succession Cliffs	..	2·25	2·25
256/9		Set of 4	5·00	4·75

55 World Map showing
Member Countries

(Des R. Watton. Litho Walsall)

1996 (23 Mar). *24th Meeting of Scientific Committee on Antarctic Research, Cambridge. T* **55** *and similar horiz designs. Multicoloured. W w* **16** *(sideways). P* 14.

260	17p. Type **55**	..			65	60
261	35p. Scientist analysing ice samples		..		1·25	1·10
262	40p. Releasing balloon	..	..		1·50	1·40
263	76p. Antarctic research ship catching marine life		..		2·25	2·00
260/3	..	..	..	*Set of 4*	5·00	4·50
MS264	100×90 mm. £1 S.C.A.R. logo. Wmk inverted				2·50	2·75

56 Killer Whales   **57** Penguins sledging

(Des Dafila Scott. Litho Questa)

1996 (25 Nov). *Whales. T* **56** *and similar horiz designs. Multicoloured. W w* **14** *(sideways). P* 14.

265	17p. Type **56**	..	..	..	50	60
266	35p. Sperm Whales		..	..	95	1·10
267	40p. Minke Whales		..	..	1·25	1·40
268	76p. Blue Whale and calf	..		..	1·75	2·00
265/8	..	..	..	*Set of 4*	4·00	4·50
MS269	105×82 mm. £1 Humpback Whale			..	2·50	2·75

(Des D. Miller. Litho Walsall)

1996 (25 Nov). *70th Birthday of Queen Elizabeth II. Vert designs as T* **165** *of Ascension, each incorporating a different photograph of the Queen. Multicoloured. W w* **16**. *P* 14½.

270	17p. At premiere of *Chaplin*, Leicester Square, 1992	..		50	60
271	35p. At Buckingham Palace dinner, 1991			95	1·10
272	40p. In Aberdeen, 1993	..	..	1·25	1·40
273	76p. At Royal Military School of Music, 1990		1·75	2·00
270/3	..	..	..	*Set of 4*	4·00	4·50

(Des D. Miller. Litho Questa)

1997 (3 Feb). *"HONG KONG '97" International Stamp Exhibition. Sheet* 130×90 *mm, containing design as No.* 226. *Multicoloured. W w* **14**. *P* 14.

MS274	50p. *John Biscoe II* and *Shackleton* (research ships)	..	..	1·40	1·40

(Des R. Watton. Litho Walsall)

1997 (20 June). *Return of Hong Kong to China. Sheet* 130×90 *mm containing design as No.* 227, *but with "*1997*" imprint date.*

MS275	£1 *Tottan*	..	..	2·75	3·00

(Des R. Watton. Litho Questa)

1997 (22 Dec). *Christmas. T* **57** *and similar vert designs. Multicoloured. W w* **16**. *P* 14½×14.

276	17p. Type **57**	..	..	..	35	40
277	35p. Penguins carol singing		..		70	75
278	40p. Penguins throwing snowballs		..	80	85
279	76p. Penguins ice-skating	..			1·50	1·60
276/9	..	..	..	*Set of 4*	3·25	3·50

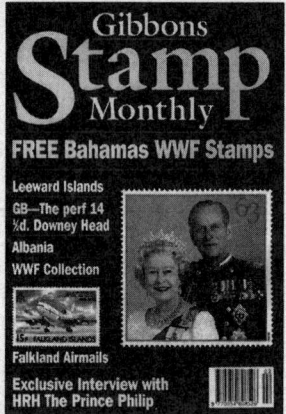

Keep This Catalogue up to Date With

Gibbons Stamp Monthly

FREE Bahamas WWF Stamps

Leeward Islands
GB—The perf 14 ½d. Downey Head
Albania
WWF Collection

Falkland Airmails

Exclusive Interview with HRH The Prince Philip

The Magazine with the Stanley Gibbons Catalogue Supplement

Plus

■ More editorial than other magazines.

■ Regular features for all collectors from beginners to specialists.

■ Authoritatively written.

■ Regular special offers, competitions and free gifts.

Get Gibbons Stamp Monthly delivered direct to your door!

For a free sample copy and subscription details phone
01425 472363
or write to:

Hugh Jefferies
Gibbons Stamp Monthly
5 Parkside, Christchurch Road,
Ringwood, Hants BH24 3SH

British Central Africa
see Nyasaland Protectorate

British Columbia and Vancouver Island
see Canada

British East Africa
see Kenya

British Forces in Egypt
see Egypt

British Guiana
see Guyana

British Honduras
see Belize

British Indian Ocean Territory

This Crown Colony was created on 8 November 1965 when it comprised the Chagos Archipelago, previously administered by Mauritius, together with the islands of Aldabra, Farquhar and Desroches, previously administered by Seychelles.

(Currency. 100 cents=1 rupee)

B.I.O.T.

(1)

1968 (17 Jan). As Nos. 196/200, 202/4 and 206/12 of Seychelles, optd with T **1**. W w **12** (sideways* on 5, 10, 15, 20, 25, 50, 75 c. and 10 r.).

1	5 c. multicoloured	..	40	40
	a. No stop after "I"	..	7·00	9·00
	b. No stop after "O"	..	4·75	7·50
	w. Wmk Crown to right of CA	..	24·00	
2	10 c. multicoloured ..		10	15
	a. No stop after "I"	..	8·00	8·00
	b. No stop after "O"	..	5·50	8·00
3	15 c. multicoloured ..		10	15
	a. No stop after "I"	..	8·00	8·00
	b. No stop after "O"	..	5·50	8·00
4	20 c. multicoloured ..		15	15
	a. No stop after "I"	..	8·00	10·00
	b. No stop after "O"	..	5·50	8·00
5	25 c. multicoloured ..		15	15
	a. No stop after "I"	..	8·50	11·00
	b. No stop after "O"	..	5·50	8·50

6	40 c. multicoloured	..	20	20
	a. No stop after "I"	..	12·00	15·00
	b. No stop after "O"	..	7·50	9·50
7	45 c. multicoloured ..		20	30
	a. No stop after "I"	..	12·00	15·00
	b. No stop after "B"	..	12·00	15·00
	c. No stop after "O"	..	12·00	15·00
8	50 c. multicoloured ..		20	30
	a. No stop after "I"	..	12·00	15·00
	b. No stop after "O"	..	7·00	9·00
9	75 c. multicoloured ..		20	35
10	1 r. multicoloured ..		40	35
	a. No stop after "I"	..	12·00	15·00
	b. No stop after "O"	..	7·00	9·00
11	1 r. 50, multicoloured	..	1·75	1·50
	a. No stop after "I"	..	22·00	25·00
	b. No stop after "O"	..	12·00	15·00
12	2 r. 25, multicoloured	..	3·00	3·75
	a. No stop after "I"	..	55·00	60·00
	b. No stop after "O"	..	27·00	32·00
13	3 r. 50, multicoloured	..	3·00	4·50
	a. No stop after "I"	..	55·00	60·00
	b. No stop after "O"	..	27·00	32·00
14	5 r. multicoloured	..	5·50	7·50
	a. No stop after "I"	..	70·00	75·00
	b. No stop after "O"	..	35·00	42·00
15	10 r. multicoloured	..	16·00	20·00
	a. No stop after "B"	..	£100	£110
	b. No stop after "I"	..	£100	£110
	c. No stop after "O"	..	65·00	75·00
1/15	..	Set of 15	28·00	35·00

*The normal sideways watermark shows Crown to left of CA, as seen from the back of the stamp.

These were issued by the Crown Agents on 15 January but owing to shipping delays they were not put on sale locally until 17 January.

The positions of the "no stop" varieties are as follows:

After "I": R. 2/4 on horiz stamps except 45 c. where it occurs on R. 3/3, and R. 8/5 on vert stamps except 10 r. where it occurs on R. 4/3.

After "O": R. 3/2 and 5/1 on vert stamps, R. 2/1 and 4/4 on horiz stamps (only occurs on R. 2/1 for 45 c.), and R. 2/7 and 5/9 on 10 r. value.

After "B": R. 10/4 (45 c.) or R. 1/8 (10 r.).

As sheets of all values from 5 c. to 50 c. are known with all stops in place the no stop varieties either developed during printing or their omission was discovered and replacements inserted.

2 Lascar

(Des G. Drummond, based on drawings by Mrs. W. Veevers-Carter. Litho D.L.R.)

1968 (23 Oct)–**70**. Marine Life. Multicoloured designs as T **2**. White paper (Nos. 20a, 23a, 24a) or cream paper (others). W w **12** (sideways on horiz, inverted on vert designs). P 14.

16	5 c. Type **2** ..	..	30	1·50
17	10 c. Smooth Hammerhead (vert)	..	30	1·25
18	15 c. Tiger Shark ..	..	30	1·50
19	20 c. Spotted Eagle Ray ("Bat Ray")	..	30	1·00
20	25 c. Yellow-finned Butterflyfish and Ear-spotted Angelfish (vert)		80	1·00
20a	30 c. Robber Crab (7.12.70)	..	3·50	2·75
21	40 c. Blue-finned Trevally ("Caranx")	..	40	40
22	45 c. Crocodile Needlefish ("Garfish") (vert)		2·25	2·50
23	50 c. Pickhandle Barracuda	..	45	30
23a	60 c. Spotted Pebble Crab (7.12.70)	..	3·50	3·25
24	75 c. Indian Ocean Steep-headed Parrotfish		2·50	2·75
24a	85 c. Rainbow Runner ("Dorade") (7.12.70)		6·00	3·50
25	1 r. Giant Hermit Crab ..	..	1·50	30
26	1 r. 50, Parrotfish ("Humphead")	..	2·50	2·50
27	2 r. 25, Yellow-edged Lyretail and Areolate Grouper ("Rock Cod")		7·00	8·50
28	3 r. 50, Black Marlin	..	4·00	3·75
29	5 r. black, blue-green and greenish blue (Whale Shark) (vert) ..		9·00	8·00
30	10 r. Lionfish ..	..	9·00	8·00
	a. Imperf (pair) ..	..	£500	
16/30	..	Set of 18	48·00	48·00

See also No. 52.

3 Sacred Ibis and Aldabra Coral Atoll

(Des and litho D.L.R.)

1969 (10 July). Coral Atolls. W w **12** (sideways). P 13½ × 13.

31	3	2 r. 25, multicoloured ..	1·50	45

4 Outrigger Canoe

(Des Mrs. M. Hayward adapted by V. Whiteley. Litho D.L.R.)

1969 (15 Dec.). Ships of the Islands. T **4** and similar horiz designs. Multicoloured. W w **12** (sideways). P 13½ × 14.

32	45 c. Type **4**	..	65	75
33	75 c. Pirogue ..	..	65	80
34	1 r. M. V. Nordvaer ..	..	70	90
35	1 r. 50, Isle of Farquhar	..	80	1·00
32/5	..	Set of 4	2·50	3·00

5 Giant Land Tortoise

(Des G. Drummond. Litho Format)

1971 (1 Feb). Aldabra Nature Reserve. T **5** and similar horiz designs. Multicoloured. W w **12** (sideways). P 13½.

36	45 c. Type **5** ..	..	2·50	2·25
37	75 c. Aldabra Lily ..	..	3·00	2·50
38	1 r. Aldabra Tree Snail (Rhachis aldabrae)	3·50	2·75
39	1 r. 50, Western Reef Herons	..	11·00	7·00
36/9	..	Set of 4	18·00	13·00

6 Arms of Royal Society and White-throated Rail

(Des V. Whiteley. Litho J.W.)

1971 (30 June). Opening of Royal Society Research Station on Aldabra. W w **12** (sideways). P 13½.

40	6	3 r. 50, multicoloured ..	..	15·00	8·50

7 Staghorn Coral

(Des V. Whiteley. Litho A. & M.)

1972 (1 Mar). Coral. T **7** and similar horiz designs. Multicoloured. W w **12** (sideways*). P 13½.

41	40 c. Type **7** ..	..	3·50	3·25
	w. Wmk Crown to left of CA	..	12·00	
42	60 c. Brain coral ..	..	4·00	3·75
	w. Wmk Crown to left of CA	..	8·00	
43	1 r. Mushroom coral ..	..	4·00	3·75
	w. Wmk Crown to left of CA	..	5·00	
44	1 r. 75, Organ Pipe coral ..	..	5·00	5·00
	w. Wmk Crown to left of CA	..	11·00	
41/4	..	Set of 4	15·00	14·00

*The normal sideways watermark shows Crown to right of CA, as seen from the back of the stamp.

On some sheets of No. 43 the inks have been applied in a different order, resulting in an almost total absence of blue.

8 White-throated Rail and Sacred Ibis

9 "Christ on the Cross"

(Des (from photograph by D. Groves) and photo Harrison)

1972 (20 Nov). Royal Silver Wedding. Multicoloured; background colour given. W w **12**. P 14 × 14½.

45	8	95 c. deep dull green	..	75	40
	a. Silver (frame and inscr) ptd double	£450	
	b. Slate-green	..	2·00	2·00
46	1 r. 50, bright bluish violet	..	75	40

(Des Jennifer Toombs. Litho Questa)

1973 (9 Apr). Easter. T **9** and similar vert design showing illustrations from 17th-century Ethiopian manuscript. Multicoloured. W w **12** (sideways). P 14.

47	45 c. Type **9** ..	..	25	40
48	75 c. Joseph and Nicodemus burying Jesus	35	55
49	1 r. Type **9** ..	..	35	60
50	1 r. 50. As 75 c. ..	..	40	70
47/50	..	Set of 4	1·25	2·00
MS51	126 × 110 mm. Nos. 47/50 ..		1·50	4·00

1973 (2 Oct). *As No. 16 but white paper and wmk upright.*
52   5 c. Type **2**   80   3·75
No. 52 differs in shade from No. 16 because of the change of paper.

10 Upsidedown Jellyfish   **11** M.V. *Nordvaer*

(Des G. Drummond. Litho Walsall)

1973 (12 Nov). *Wildlife (1st series). T* **10** *and similar vert designs. Multicoloured. W w* **12** (*sideways**). *P* 14.
53   50 c. Type **10** .. ..   3·25   3·00
54   1 r. *Hypolimnas misippus* and *Belenois*
         aldabrensis (butterflies) .. ..   3·25   3·00
55   1 r. 50, *Nephila madagascariensis* (spider)   4·00   3·00
     w. Wmk Crown to right of CA .. ..   6·50
53/5   .. ..   *Set of 3*   9·50   8·00
*The normal sideways watermark shows Crown to left of CA, as seen from the back of the stamp.
See also Nos. 58/61, 77/80 and 86/9.

(Des C. Abbott. Litho Walsall)

1974 (14 July). *Fifth Anniv of "Nordvaer" Travelling Post Office. T* **11** *and similar vert design. Multicoloured. W w* **12** (*sideways*). *P* 14.
56   85 c. Type **11**   75   75
57   2 r. 50, *Nordvaer off shore* .. ..   1·25   1·25

12 Red-cloud Auger (*Terebra nebulosa*) and Subulate Auger (*Terebra subulata*)

(Des PAD Studio. Litho J.W.)

1974 (12 Nov). *Wildlife (2nd series). T* **12** *and similar horiz designs showing shells. Multicoloured. W w* **12**. *P* 13½ × 14.
58   45 c. Type **12** .. ..   1·90   1·00
59   75 c. Great Green Turbo (*Turbo marmoratus*)   2·00   1·25
60   1 r. Strawberry Drupe (*Drupa rubusidaeus*)   2·40   1·50
61   1 r. 50, Bull-mouth Helmet (*Cypraecassis*
         rufa) .. ..   2·75   1·75
58/61   .. ..   *Set of 4*   8·00   5·00

13 Aldabra Drongo   **14** *Grewia salicifolia*

(Des R. Granger Barrett. Litho Questa)

1975 (28 Feb). *Birds. Multicoloured designs as T* **13**. *W w* **12** (*sideways* *on horiz designs*). *P* 14.
62   5 c. Type **13** .. ..   1·00   2·75
63   10 c. Black Coucal .. .. ..   1·00   2·75
64   20 c. Mascarene Fody .. .. ..   1·00   2·75
     w. Wmk inverted .. .. ..   85·00
65   25 c. White Tern .. .. ..   1·00   2·75
66   30 c. Crested Tern .. .. ..   1·00   2·75
67   40 c. Brown Booby .. .. ..   1·00   2·75
68   50 c. Common Noddy (*horiz*) .. ..   1·00   3·00
69   60 c. Grey Heron (*horiz*) .. ..   1·00   3·00
70   65 c. Blue-faced Booby (*horiz*) ..   1·00   3·00
71   95 c. Madagascar White Eye (*horiz*)   1·00   3·00
     w. Wmk Crown to right of CA .. ..   55·00
72   1 r. Green Heron (*horiz*) .. ..   1·25   3·00
73   1 r. 75, Lesser Frigate Bird (*horiz*)   2·00   4·75
74   3 r. 50, White-tailed Tropic Bird (*horiz*)   2·75   4·75
75   5 r. Souimanga Sunbird (*horiz*) ..   4·00   5·00
76   10 r. Madagascar Turtle Dove (*horiz*)   8·00   9·00
62/76   .. ..   *Set of 15*   25·00   48·00
*The normal sideways watermark shows Crown to left of CA, as seen from the back of the stamp.

(Des Sylvia Goaman. Litho Questa)

1975 (10 July). *Wildlife (3rd series). T* **14** *and similar vert designs showing seashore plants. Multicoloured. W w* **12** (*sideways*). *P* 14.
77   50 c. Type **14**   50   1·10
78   65 c. *Cassia aldabrensis*   55   1·25
79   1 r. *Hypoestes aldabrensis*   70   1·40
80   1 r. 60, *Euphorbia pyrifolia*   85   1·40
77/80   .. ..   *Set of 4*   2·40   4·75

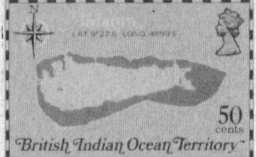

15 Map of Aldabra

(Des L. Curtis. Litho Questa)

1975 (8 Nov). *10th Anniv of Territory. Maps. T* **15** *and similar horiz designs. Multicoloured. W w* **12**. *P* 13½.
81   50 c. Type **15**   60   65
82   1 r. Desroches   75   85
83   1 r. 50, Farquhar   85   1·00
84   2 r. Diego Garcia   95   1·25
81/4   .. ..   *Set of 4*   2·75   3·25
MS85   147 × 147 mm. Nos. 81/4 (wmk sideways)   7·00   12·00

16 *Utetheisa pulchella* (moth)

(Des PAD Studio. Litho Questa)

1976 (22 Mar). *Wildlife (4th series). T* **16** *and similar horiz designs. Multicoloured. W w* **12** (*sideways*). *P* 13½.
86   65 c. Type **16**   60   1·10
87   1 r. 20, *Dysdercus fasciatus* (bug) ..   75   1·25
88   1 r. 50, *Sphex torridus* (wasp) ..   80   1·40
89   2 r. *Oryctes rhinoceros* (beetle) ..   85   1·40
86/9   .. ..   *Set of 4*   2·75   4·50

When the Seychelles achieved independence on 29 June 1976 the islands of Aldabra, Farquhar and Desroches reverted to its administration so that British Indian Ocean Territory from that date consisted of the Chagos Archipelago, an island group, the largest of whose five main atolls is Diego Garcia. The indigenous population was resettled on Mauritius and Diego Garcia was developed as a U.S. Navy base while remaining under British administration.
Nos. 62/76 were withdrawn in August 1979 and, until May 1990, base personnel used British and American forces mail facilities routed via the Philippines and San Francisco. From 1987 British mails were routed via Singapore. The growing number of civilian workers eventually led to the re-introduction of a public postal service in May 1990 using stamps with face values in sterling.

(New Currency. Sterling)

17 White-tailed   **18** 1974 Wildlife 1 r. 50 Stamp
Tropic Bird

(Des N. Arlott. Litho Questa)

1990 (3 May). *Birds. T* **17** *and similar vert designs. Multicoloured. W w* **16** (*sideways*). *P* 14.
90   15p. Type **17** .. ..   1·10   1·25
91   20p. Madagascar Turtle Dove ..   1·25   1·40
92   24p. Great Frigate Bird .. ..   1·40   1·50
93   30p. Green Heron .. .. ..   1·50   1·60
94   34p. Great Sand Plover .. ..   1·60   1·75
95   41p. Crab Plover .. .. ..   1·75   1·90
96   45p. Crested Tern .. .. ..   2·00   2·25
97   54p. Lesser Crested Tern .. ..   2·00   2·25
98   62p. White Tern .. .. ..   2·00   2·25
99   71p. Red-footed Booby .. ..   2·00   2·75
100   80p. Common Mynah .. ..   2·25   3·00
101   £1 Madagascar Red Fody .. ..   2·50   3·25
90/101   .. ..   *Set of 12*   19·00   23·00

(Des D. Miller. Litho Walsall)

1990 (3 May). *"Stamp World London 90" International Stamp Exhibition. T* **18** *and similar horiz designs showing stamps. Multicoloured. W w* **14** (*sideways*). *P* 14.
102   15p. Type **18** .. ..   1·75   1·75
103   20p. 1976 Wildlife 2 r. .. ..   2·25   2·25
104   34p. 1975 Diego Garcia map 2 r. ..   3·50   3·50
105   54p. 1969 *Nordvaer* 1 r. .. ..   5·00   5·00
102/5   .. ..   *Set of 4*   11·00   11·00

(Des D. Miller. Litho Questa)

1990 (4 Aug). *90th Birthday of Queen Elizabeth the Queen Mother. Vert designs as T* **134** (*24p.*) *or* **135** (*£1*) *of Ascension. W w* **16**. *P* 14×15 (24p.) *or* 14½ (£1).
106   24p. multicoloured .. .. ..   2·25   2·50
107   £1 brownish black and purple-brown   4·25   4·75
Designs:—24p. Lady Elizabeth Bowes-Lyon, 1923; £1 Queen Elizabeth and her daughters, 1940.

---

19 Territory Flag   **20** Postman emptying Pillar
                              Box

(Des D. Miller. Litho Questa)

1990 (8 Nov). *25th Anniv of British Indian Ocean Territory. T* **19** *and similar vert designs. Multicoloured. W w* **14**. *P* 14×13½.
108   20p. Type **19** .. ..   3·00   3·50
109   34p. Coat of arms .. .. ..   3·00   3·50
MS110   63×99 mm. £1 Map of Chagos Archipelago .. ..   7·00   8·50

(Des O. Bell. Litho Walsall)

1991 (3 June). *British Indian Ocean Territory Administration. T* **20** *and similar horiz designs. Multicoloured. W w* **14** (*sideways*). *P* 14.
111   20p. Type **20** .. ..   1·75   2·25
112   24p. Commissioner inspecting guard of
         Royal Marines .. .. ..   2·00   2·25
113   34p. Policemen outside station ..   3·00   3·50
114   54p. Customs officers boarding yacht ..   4·25   4·75
111/14   .. ..   *Set of 4*   10·00   11·50

21 *Experiment* (E.I.C. survey
        brig), 1786

(Des E. Nisbet. Litho Walsall)

1991 (8 Nov). *Visiting Ships. T* **21** *and similar horiz designs. Multicoloured. W w* **14** (*sideways*). *P* 14.
115   20p. Type **21** .. ..   2·00   2·50
116   24p. *Pickering* (American brig), 1819 ..   2·25   2·50
117   34p. *Emden* (German cruiser), 1914 ..   2·75   3·25
118   54p. H.M.S. *Edinburgh* (destroyer), 1988   3·50   4·25
115/18   .. ..   *Set of 4*   9·50   11·00

(Des D. Miller. Litho Questa (54p.), Walsall (others))

1992 (6 Feb). *40th Anniv of Queen Elizabeth II's Accession. Horiz designs as T* **143** *of Ascension. Multicoloured. W w* **14** (*sideways*). *P* 14.
119   15p. Catholic chapel, Diego Garcia ..   85   1·00
120   20p. Planter's house, Diego Garcia ..   95   1·10
121   24p. Railway tracks on wharf, Diego Garcia   1·50   1·50
122   34p. Three portraits of Queen Elizabeth ..   1·50   1·60
123   54p. Queen Elizabeth II .. ..   1·75   1·90
119/23   .. ..   *Set of 5*   6·00   6·25

22 R.A.F. Consolidated   **23** "The Mystical
PBY-5 Catalina (flying boat)   Marriage of St.
                                 Catherine"
                                 (Correggio)

(Des A. Theobald. Litho Walsall)

1992 (23 Oct). *Visiting Aircraft. T* **22** *and similar horiz designs. Multicoloured. W w* **16** (*sideways*). *P* 14.
124   20p. Type **22** .. ..   1·75   2·25
125   24p. R.A.F. Hawker Siddeley H.S.801
         Nimrod M.R.2 (maritime reconnais-
         sance aircraft) .. .. ..   1·90   2·25
126   34p. Lockheed P-3 Orion (transport aircraft)   2·25   2·75
127   54p. U.S.A.A.F. Boeing B-52 Stratofortress
         (heavy bomber) .. .. ..   3·00   4·00
124/7   .. ..   *Set of 4*   8·00   10·00

(Des D. Miller. Litho Walsall)

1992 (27 Nov). *Christmas. Religious Paintings. T* **23** *and similar vert designs. Multicoloured. W w* **16**. *P* 14½×14.
128   5p. Type **23**   60   65
129   24p. "Madonna" (anon) .. ..   1·40   1·50
130   34p. "Madonna" (anon) (*different*) ..   1·60   2·00
131   54p. "The Birth of Jesus" (Kaspar Jele)   2·25   3·00
128/31   .. ..   *Set of 4*   5·25   6·50

24 Coconut Crab and Rock

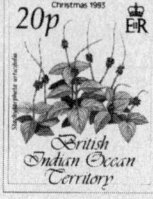

25 Stachytarpheta
urticifolia

(Des G. Vasarhelyi. Litho Questa)

1993 (5 Mar). *Endangered Species. Coconut Crab. T* **24** *and similar horiz designs. Multicoloured. W w* **16** *(sideways). P* 14.
132	10p. Type **24**	..	1·00	1·00
133	10p. Crab on beach	..	1·00	1·00
134	10p. Two crabs	..	1·00	1·00
135	15p. Crab climbing coconut tree	..	1·25	1·25
132/5		*Set of 4*	3·75	3·75

(Des A. Theobald. Litho Questa)

1993 (1 Apr). *75th Anniv of Royal Air Force. Horiz designs as T* **149** *of Ascension. Multicoloured. W w* **14** *(sideways). P* 14.
136	20p. Vickers Virginia Mk X	..	1·00	1·25
137	24p. Bristol Bulldog IIA	..	1·10	1·25
138	34p. Short S.25 Sunderland Mk III		1·50	1·75
139	54p. Bristol Type 142 Blenheim Mk IV	..	2·40	2·75
136/9		*Set of 4*	5·50	6·25
MS140	110×77 mm. 20p. Douglas DC-3 Dakota; 20p. Gloster G.41 Javelin; 20p. Blackburn Beverley C1; 20p. Vickers VC-10	..	5·50	6·50

(Des N. Shewring. Litho Questa)

1993 (22 Nov). *Christmas. Flowers. T* **25** *and similar vert designs. Multicoloured. W w* **14**. *P* 14½.
141	20p. Type **25**	..	80	90
142	24p. Ipomea pes-caprae	..	85	90
143	34p. Sida pusilla	..	1·25	1·75
144	54p. Catharanthus roseus	..	1·75	2·50
141/4		*Set of 4*	4·25	5·50

1994 (18 Feb). *"Hong Kong '94" International Stamp Exhibition. Nos. 92 and 101 optd as T* **154** *of Ascension.*
145	24p. Great Frigate Bird	..	1·00	1·25
146	£1 Madagascar Red Fody	..	2·75	3·50

26 Forrest's Map of
Diego Garcia, 1778

27 Junonia villida

(Des D. Miller. Litho Questa)

1994 (1 June). *18th-century Maps. T* **26** *and similar vert designs. Each black and cobalt. W w* **14**. *P* 14½.
147	20p. Type **26**	..	80	1·25
	a. Horiz strip of 5. Nos. 147/51	..	5·00	
148	24p. Blair's plan of Diego Garcia harbour, 1786–87	..	90	1·40
149	34p. Blair's chart of Chagos Archipelago, 1786–87	..	1·00	1·50
150	44p. Plan of part of Diego Garcia, 1774	..	1·25	1·60
151	54p. Fontaine's plan of Diego Garcia, 1770		1·50	1·75
147/51		*Set of 5*	5·00	6·75

Nos. 147/51 were printed together, *se-tenant*, in horizontal strips of 5 throughout the sheet.

(Des I. Loe. Litho Walsall)

1994 (16 Aug). *Butterflies. T* **27** *and similar vert designs. Multicoloured. W w* **16**. *P* 14½×14.
152	24p. Type **27**	..	1·25	1·25
153	30p. Petrelaea dana	..	1·75	2·00
154	56p. Hypolimnas misippus	..	2·50	2·75
152/4		*Set of 3*	5·00	5·50

28 Short-tailed Nurse Sharks

(Des N. Shewring. Litho Walsall)

1994 (1 Nov). *Sharks. T* **28** *and similar horiz designs. Multicoloured. W w* **14** *(sideways). P* 14.
155	15p. Type **28**	..	30	35
156	20p. Silver-tipped Sharks	..	40	45
157	24p. Black-finned Reef Shark	..	50	55
158	30p. Oceanic White-tipped Sharks	..	60	65

159	35p. Black-tipped Shark	..	..	70	75
160	41p. Smooth Hammerhead	..	..	80	85
161	46p. Sickle-finned Lemon Shark	..	90	95
162	55p. White-tipped Reef Shark	..	1·10	1·25
163	65p. Tiger Sharks	..	..	1·25	1·40
164	74p. Indian Sand Tiger	..	..	1·50	1·60
165	80p. Great Hammerhead	..	..	1·60	1·75
166	£1 Great White Shark	..	..	2·00	2·10
155/66		*Set of 12*	11·50	12·50

For miniature sheets containing the 65p. or 74p. (with "1997" imprint date) see Nos. MS193/4.

(Des R. Watton. Litho Walsall (Nos. 167/70) or Questa (No. MS171))

1995 (8 May). *50th Anniv of End of Second World War. Multicoloured designs as T* **161** *of Ascension. W w* **14** *(sideways). P* 14.
167	20p. Military cemetery	..	1·00	1·25
168	24p. Rusty 6-inch naval gun at Cannon Point	..	1·10	1·25
169	30p. Short S.25 Sunderland flying boat		1·40	1·60
170	56p. H.M.I.S. *Clive* (sloop)	..	2·25	2·75
167/70		*Set of 4*	5·25	6·25
MS171	75×85 mm. £1 Reverse of 1939–45 War Medal (*vert*). Wmk upright	..	2·50	3·00

29 Dolphin (fish)

30 Terebra crenulata

(Des K. McGee. Litho B.D.T.)

1995 (6 Oct). *Gamefish. T* **29** *and similar horiz designs. Multicoloured. W w* **16** *(sideways). P* 14.
172	20p. Type **29**	..	85	1·00
173	24p. Sailfish	..	95	1·00
174	30p. Wahoo	..	1·50	1·75
175	56p. Striped Marlin	..	2·25	2·75
172/5		*Set of 4*	5·00	6·00

(Des G. Drummond. Litho Walsall)

1996 (8 Jan). *Sea Shells. T* **30** *and similar horiz designs. Multicoloured. W w* **14** *(sideways). P* 14½.
176	20p. Type **30**	..	75	85
177	24p. Bursa bufonia	..	85	95
178	30p. Nassarius papillosus	..	1·25	1·50
179	56p. Lopha cristagalli	..	1·75	2·00
176/9		*Set of 4*	4·25	4·75

(Des D. Miller. Litho Walsall)

1996 (22 Apr). *70th Birthday of Queen Elizabeth II. Vert designs as T* **165** *of Ascension, each incorporating a different photograph of the Queen. Multicoloured. W w* **16**. *P* 14½.
180	20p. View of lagoon from south	..	60	80
181	24p. Manager's House, Peros Banhos		65	80
182	30p. Wireless Hut, Peros Banhos	..	80	1·10
183	56p. Sunset	..	..	1·25	1·60
180/3		*Set of 4*	3·00	3·75
MS184	64×66 mm. £1 Queen Elizabeth II	..	2·50	3·00

31 Loggerhead Turtle

32 Commissioner's
Representative (naval
officer)

(Des O. Bell. Litho Questa)

1996 (2 Sept). *Turtles. T* **31** *and similar horiz designs. Multicoloured. W w* **14** *(sideways). P* 14×14½.
185	20p. Type **31**	..	70	80
186	24p. Leatherback Turtle	..	75	80
187	30p. Hawksbill Turtle	..	95	1·25
188	56p. Green Turtle	..	1·40	1·75
185/8		*Set of 4*	3·50	4·25

(Des R. Watton. Litho Questa)

1996 (16 Dec). *Uniforms. T* **32** *and similar vert designs. Multicoloured. W w* **14**. *P* 14.
189	20p. Type **32**	..	70	80
190	24p. Royal Marine officer	..	75	80
191	30p. Royal Marine in battledress	..	95	1·25
192	56p. Police officers	..	1·40	1·75
189/92		*Set of 4*	3·50	4·25

(Des D. Miller. Litho Questa)

1997 (3 Feb). *"HONG KONG '97" International Stamp Exhibition. Sheet* 130×90 *mm, containing design as No. 163. Multicoloured. W w* **14**. *P* 14.
MS193	65p. Tiger Sharks	..	1·75	2·00

(Des N. Shewring. Litho Walsall)

1997 (20 June). *Return of Hong Kong to China. Sheet* 130×90 *mm containing design as No. 164, but with "1997" imprint date.*
MS194	74p. Indian Sand Tiger	..	1·75	2·00

(Des N. Shewring (No. MS201), D. Miller (others). Litho Questa)

1997 (10 July). *Golden Wedding of Queen Elizabeth and Prince Philip. Multicoloured designs as T* **173** *of Ascension. W w* **14**. *P* 14½.
195	20p. Queen Elizabeth at Bristol, 1994	..	60	70
	a. Horiz pair. Nos. 195/6	..	1·10	1·40
196	20p. Prince Philip competing in Royal Windsor Horse Show, 1996	..	60	70
197	24p. Queen Elizabeth in phaeton, Trooping the Colour, 1987	..	65	75
	a. Horiz pair. Nos. 197/8	..	1·25	1·50
198	24p. Prince Philip	..	65	75
199	30p. Queen Elizabeth and Prince Philip with Land Rover	..	70	80
	a. Horiz pair. Nos. 199/200	..	1·40	1·60
200	30p. Queen Elizabeth at Balmoral	..	70	80
195/200		*Set of 6*	3·50	4·00
MS201	110×71 mm. £1.50, Queen Elizabeth and Prince Philip in landau (*horiz*). Wmk sideways. P 14×14½	..	3·50	4·00

Nos. 195/6, 197/8 and 199/200 were each printed together, *se-tenant*, in horizontal pairs throughout the sheets with the backgrounds forming composite designs.

33 H.M.S. *Richmond*
(frigate) and H.M.S.
Beaver (frigate)

(Litho Questa)

1997 (1 Dec). *Exercise Ocean Wave. T* **33** *and similar horiz designs. Multicoloured. W w* **14** *(sideways). P* 14×14½.
202	24p. Type **33**	..	50	55
	a. Sheetlet. Nos. 202/13		6·00	
203	24p. H.M.S. *Illustrious* (aircraft carrier) launching aircraft	..	50	55
204	24p. H.M.S. *Beaver*	..	50	55
205	24p. R.Y. *Britannia*, R.F.A. *Sir Percival* and H.M.S. *Beaver*	..	50	55
206	24p. R.Y. *Britannia*	..	50	55
207	24p. H.M.S. *Richmond*, H.M.S. *Beaver* and H.M.S. *Gloucester* (destroyer)	..	50	55
208	24p. H.M.S. *Richmond*	..	50	55
209	24p. Aerial view of H.M.S. *Illustrious*	..	50	55
210	24p. H.M.S. *Sheffield* (destroyer)	..	50	55
211	24p. H.M.S. *Trenchant* (submarine) and R.F.A. *Diligence*	..	50	55
212	24p. R.F.A. *Fort George* replenishing H.M.S. *Illustrious* and H.M.S. *Gloucester*	..	50	55
213	24p. Aerial view of H.M.S. *Richmond*, H.M.S. *Beaver* and H.M.S. *Gloucester*	..	50	55
202/13		*Set of 12*	6·00	6·50

Nos. 202/13 were printed together, *se-tenant*, in sheetlets of 12.

British Levant

The term "British Levant" is used by stamp collectors to describe the issues made by various British Post Offices within the former Turkish Empire.

Arrangements for the first such service were included amongst the terms of a commercial treaty between the two countries in 1832, but the system did not start operations until September 1857 when a post office for civilian use was opened in Constantinople, replacing the Army Post Office which had existed there since June 1854.

Eventually the number of British Post Offices grew to five:

Beyrout (Beirut, Lebanon). Opened 1873, closed 30 September 1914.

Constantinople (Istanbul). Opened 1 September 1857, closed 30 September 1914, re-opened 4 February 1919, finally closed 27 September 1923.

Salonica (Thessalonika, Greece). Opened 1 May 1900, closed October 1914. The city was captured by Greek troops on 7 November 1912 and incorporated into Greece by the Treaty of London (July 1913).

Smyrna (Izmir). Opened 1872, closed 30 September 1914, re-opened 1 March 1919, finally closed September 1922. Between 15 May 1919 and 8 September 1922 the city was under Greek occupation.

Stamboul (a sub-office of Constantinople). Opened 1 April 1884, closed 25 August 1896, re-opened 10 February 1908, finally closed 30 September 1914.

Stamps from the two British Post Offices in Egypt, still technically part of the Turkish Empire, are listed under EGYPT.

A. BRITISH POST OFFICES IN TURKISH EMPIRE, 1857–1914

For illustrations of the postmark types see BRITISH POST OFFICES ABROAD notes, following GREAT BRITAIN.

From 1 August 1885 letter and registered charges were prepaid with surcharged stamps (No. 1 onwards). Until 14 August 1905 postcards and parcels continued to be franked with unoverprinted Great Britain stamps. Only a limited range of values were stocked for this purpose and these are listed. Other values exist with Levant postmarks, but these stamps did not originate from the local post offices.

After 15 August 1905 the post offices were supplied with Great Britain stamps overprinted "LEVANT". Subsequent examples of unoverprinted stamps with Levant postmarks are omitted from the listing. The use of such stamps during 1919–22 at Constantinople and Smyrna is, however, covered by a later note.

BEYROUT (BEIRUT)

Between 1873 and 1876 much of the mail from the British Post Office in Beyrout sent to European addresses was forwarded through the French or Italian Post Offices at Alexandria. Such covers show Great Britain stamps used in combination with those of French or Italian P.O's in the Turkish Empire.

Stamps of GREAT BRITAIN cancelled "G 06" or circular postmark as in Types 8, 18 or 20.

1873.

Z 1	½d. rose-red (1870–79) ..	..	From	26·00
	Plate Nos. 12, 13, 14, 19, 20.			
Z 2	1d. rose-red (1864–79) ..	..	From	11·00
	Plate Nos. 107, 118, 130, 140, 145, 148, 155, 157, 162, 167, 177, 179, 180, 184, 185, 186, 187, 195, 198, 200, 203, 204, 211, 213, 215, 218, 220, 222.			
Z 3	1½d. lake-red (1870–74) (Plate 3)			£200
Z 4	2d. blue (1858–69) ..	..	From	17·00
	Plate Nos. 13, 14, 15.			
Z 5	2½d. rosy mauve (1875) (blued paper)			70·00
	Plate No. 1.			
Z 6	2½d. rosy mauve (1875–76) ..	..	From	30·00
	Plate Nos. 1, 2, 3.			
Z 7	2½d. rosy mauve (1876–79) ..	..	From	25·00
	Plate Nos. 3, 4, 5, 6, 7, 8, 9, 10, 11, 12, 13, 14, 15, 16, 17.			
Z 8	2½d. blue (1880) ..	..		15·00
	Plate Nos. 17, 18, 19, 20.			
Z 9	2½d. blue (1881) ..	..	From	9·00
	Plate Nos. 21, 22, 23.			
Z10	3d. rose (1867–73) (Plate No. 10)	..		
Z11	3d. rose (1873–76) ..	..		30·00
	Plate Nos. 12, 15, 16, 18, 19, 20.			
Z12	3d. rose (1881) (Plate Nos. 20, 21)			
Z13	4d. vermilion (1865–73) ..	..	From	32·00
	Plate Nos. 11, 12, 13, 14.			
Z14	4d. vermilion (1876) (Plate No. 15)			£180
Z15	4d. sage-green (1877) ..	..		£120
	Plate Nos. 15, 16.			
Z16	4d. grey-brown (1880) wmk Large Garter (Plate No. 17)			
Z17	4d. grey-brown (1880) wmk Crown			40·00
	Plate Nos. 17, 18.			
Z18	6d. mauve (1870) (Plate Nos. 8, 9)			
Z19	6d. buff (1872–73) ..	..	From	75·00
	Plate Nos. 11, 12.			
Z20	6d. chestnut (1872) (Plate No. 11)			35·00
Z21	6d. grey (1873) (Plate No. 12)			
Z22	6d. grey (1874–80) ..	..	From	26·00
	Plate Nos. 13, 14, 15, 16, 17.			
Z23	8d. orange (1876) ..			£300
Z24	10d. red-brown (1867) ..	..		£160
Z25	1s. green (1867–73) ..	..		19·00
	Plate Nos. 6, 7.			
Z26	1s. green (1873–77) ..	..	From	32·00
	Plate Nos. 8, 9, 10, 12, 13.			
Z27	1s. orange-brown (1880) (Plate No. 13)			
Z28	1s. orange-brown (1881) ..	..		45·00
	Plate Nos. 13, 14.			
Z29	2s. blue (1867) ..	..		£130
Z30	5s. rose (1867) (Plate Nos. 1, 2)	..	From	£600

1880.

Z31	½d. deep green ..	..		8·00
Z32	½d. pale green ..	..		9·00
Z33	1d. Venetian red ..	..		10·00
Z34	1½d. Venetian red ..	..		£140
Z35	2d. pale rose ..	..		40·00
Z36	2d. deep rose ..	..		40·00
Z37	5d. indigo ..	..		65·00

1881.

Z38	1d. lilac (14 dots)			
Z39	1d. lilac (16 dots) ..	..		5·50

1884.

Z40	½d. slate-blue ..	..		10·00
Z41	1½d. lilac ..	..		50·00
Z42	2d. lilac ..	..		60·00
Z43	2½d. lilac ..	..		11·00
Z44	4d. dull green ..	..		£140
Z45	5d. dull green ..	..		£100
Z46	1s. dull green ..	..		£180

1887–92.

Z47	½d. vermilion ..	..		5·50
Z54	6d. purple/rose-red ..	..		17·00
Z55	1s. dull green ..	..		£100

1900.

Z56	½d. blue-green ..	..		7·50
Z57	1s. green and carmine ..	..		£120

1902–04. De La Rue ptgs.

Z58	½d. blue-green ..	..		4·50
Z59	½d. yellowish green ..	..		5·00
Z60	1d. scarlet ..	..		4·00
Z64	1s. dull green and carmine ..	..		24·00

CONSTANTINOPLE

Stamps of GREAT BRITAIN cancelled "C" or circular postmark as in Types 1, 10, 18 or 19.

1857.

Z 68	½d. rose-red (1870–79) ..	..	From	20·00
	Plate Nos. 5, 6, 10, 11, 12, 13, 14, 15, 20.			
Z 69	1d. red-brown (1854), Die I, wmk Small Crown, perf 16			
Z 70	1d. red-brown (1855), Die II, wmk Small Crown, perf 14			
Z 71	1d. red-brown, (1855), Die II, wmk Large Crown, perf 14			16·00
Z 72	1d. rose-red (1857) ..	..		6·50
Z 73	1d. rose-red (1861) Alphabet IV			
Z 74	1d. rose-red (1864–79) ..	..	From	5·50
	Plate Nos. 71, 72, 73, 74, 76, 78, 79, 80, 81, 83, 85, 87, 89, 90, 92, 93, 94, 95, 96, 97, 99, 101, 102, 105, 106, 108, 109, 110, 113, 116, 118, 119, 120, 121, 122, 123, 124, 125, 127, 129, 130, 131, 134, 135, 136, 137, 138, 140, 141, 143, 144, 145, 146, 147, 148, 149, 150, 151, 152, 155, 156, 157, 158, 159, 160, 161, 162, 163, 164, 166, 167, 170, 171, 172, 173, 174, 175, 176, 177, 178, 179, 180, 181, 183, 184, 186, 187, 188, 189, 190, 191, 192, 193, 194, 195, 196, 197, 198, 200, 201, 203, 204, 205, 206, 207, 208, 210, 212, 214, 215, 216, 220, 222, 224.			
Z 75	1½d. rose-red (1870) (Plate 1)	..		£180
Z 76	2d. blue (1855), wmk Large Crown, perf 14. (Plate Nos. 5, 6)			
Z 77	2d. blue (1858–69) ..	..	From	9·00
	Plate Nos. 7, 8, 9, 12, 13, 14, 15.			
Z 78	2½d. rosy mauve (1875–76) (blued paper) (Plate Nos. 1, 2)	..	From	50·00
Z 79	2½d. rosy mauve (1875–76) ..	..	From	27·00
	Plate Nos. 1, 2, 3.			
Z 80	2½d. rosy mauve (Error of Lettering)			
Z 81	2½d. rosy mauve (1876–79) ..	..	From	23·00
	Plate Nos. 3 to 17.			
Z 82	2½d. blue (1880–81) ..	..	From	11·00
	Plate Nos. 17, 18, 19, 20.			
Z 83	2½d. blue (1881) (Plate Nos. 21, 22, 23)			7·00
Z 84	3d. carmine-rose (1862) (Plate No. 2)			£110
Z 85	3d. rose (1865) (Plate No. 4)			65·00
Z 86	3d. rose (1867–73) (Plate Nos. 4 to 10)			65·00
Z 87	3d. rose (1873–76) ..	..		20·00
	Plates, 11, 12, 15, 16, 17, 18, 19.			
Z 88	3d. rose (1881) (Plate No. 21)			
Z 89	3d. on 3d. lilac (1883) (Plate No. 21)			
Z 90	4d. rose (1857) ..	..		40·00
	a. Rose-carmine			
Z 91	4d. red (1862) (Plate Nos. 3, 4)	..	From	35·00
Z 92	4d. vermilion (1865–73) ..	..	From	26·00
	Plate Nos. 7 to 14.			
Z 93	4d. vermilion (1876) (Plate No. 15)			£150
Z 94	4d. sage-green (1877) ..	..		85·00
	Plate Nos. 15, 16.			
Z 95	4d. grey-brown (1880) wmk Large Garter (Plate No. 17)			
Z 96	4d. grey-brown (1880) wmk Crown (Plate Nos. 17, 18)	..	From	25·00
Z 97	6d. lilac (1856) ..	..		50·00
Z 98	6d. lilac (1862) (Plate Nos. 3, 4)	..	From	35·00
Z 99	6d. lilac (1865–67) ..	..		32·00
	Plate Nos. 5, 6.			
Z100	6d. lilac (1867) (Plate No. 6)			40·00
Z101	6d. violet (1867–70) ..	..	From	32·00
	Plate Nos. 6, 8, 9.			
Z102	6d. buff (1872–73) ..	..		48·00
	Plate Nos. 11, 12.			
Z103	6d. chestnut (1872) (Plate No. 11)			26·00
Z104	6d. grey (1873) (Plate No. 12) ..			70·00
Z105	6d. grey (1874–76) ..	..	From	20·00
	Plate Nos. 13, 14, 15, 16.			
Z106	6d. grey (1881–82) (Plate Nos. 17, 18)			20·00
Z107	6d. on 6d. lilac (1883) ..	..		65·00
	a. Dots slanting (Letters MI or SJ)			£110
Z108	8d. orange (1876) ..	..		£275
Z109	10d. red-brown (1867), wmk Emblems	..		£12000
Z110	10d. red-brown (1867) ..	..		£160
Z111	1s. green (1856) ..	..		£100
Z112	1s. green (1862) ..	..		60·00
Z113	1s. green (1862) ("K" variety) ..			
Z114	1s. green (1862) (thick paper) ..			
Z115	1s. green (1865) (Plate No. 4) ..			60·00
Z116	1s. green (1867–73) ..	..	From	10·00
	Plate Nos. 4, 5, 6, 7.			
Z117	1s. green (1873–77) ..	..	From	26·00
	Plate Nos. 8, 9, 10, 11, 12, 13.			
Z118	1s. orange-brown (1880) (Plate No. 13)			£180
Z119	1s. orange-brown (1881) ..	..	From	40·00
	Plate Nos. 13, 14.			
Z120	2s. blue (1867) ..	..		85·00
Z121	5s. rose (1867–74) ..	..	From	£250
	Plate Nos. 1, 2.			
Z122	5s. rose (1882) (white paper) ..			£850
Z123	5s. rose (1882) (blued paper) ..			£1000

1880.

Z124	½d. deep green ..	..		4·50
Z125	½d. pale green ..	..		5·50
Z126	1d. Venetian red ..	..		4·00
Z127	2d. pale rose ..	..		32·00
Z128	2d. deep rose ..	..		32·00
Z129	5d. indigo ..	..		

1881.

Z130	1d. lilac (14 dots)			
Z131	1d. lilac (16 dots) ..	..		2·25

1883–84.

Z132	½d. slate-blue ..	..		5·50
Z133	1½d. lilac ..	..		
Z134	2d. lilac ..	..		50·00
Z135	2½d. lilac ..	..		7·00
Z136	3d. lilac ..	..		
Z137	4d. dull green ..	..		
Z138	5d. dull green ..	..		90·00
Z139	6d. dull green ..	..		
Z140	9d. dull green ..	..		
Z141	1s. dull green ..	..		£160
Z142	2s. 6d. lilac (blued paper) ..			£500
Z143	2s. 6d. lilac (white paper) ..			80·00
Z144	5s. rose (blued paper) ..			
Z145	5s. rose (white paper) ..			

1887–92.

Z146	½d. vermilion ..	..		2·50
Z154	6d. purple/rose-red ..	..		10·00
Z157	1s. dull green ..	..		70·00

1900.

Z158	½d. blue-green ..	..		4·00
Z159	1s. green and carmine ..	..		£110

1902–04. De La Rue ptgs.

Z160	½d. blue-green ..	..		3·00
Z161	½d. yellowish green ..	..		3·50
Z162	1d. scarlet ..	..		2·50
Z169	6d. purple ..	..		10·00
Z172	1s. green and carmine ..	..		15·00
Z173	2s. 6d. lilac ..	..		
Z174	5s. carmine ..	..		

POSTAL FISCAL

Z175	1d. purple (No. F19) (1868)			

SALONICA

Stamps of GREAT BRITAIN cancelled with circular postmark as in Type 18 or double-circle datestamp.

1900.

Z202	½d. vermilion (1887) ..	..		13·00
Z203	½d. blue-green (1900) ..	..		15·00
Z204	1d. lilac (1881) ..	..		15·00
Z205	6d. purple/red (1887) ..	..		19·00
Z206	1s. green and carmine (1900) ..			£110
Z207	5s. rose (white paper) (1883) ..			£600

1902.

Z208	½d. blue-green ..	..		19·00
Z209	½d. yellow-green ..	..		13·00
Z209a	1d. scarlet ..	..		13·00
Z209c	1s. green and carmine ..	..		32·00

SMYRNA (IZMIR)

Stamps of GREAT BRITAIN cancelled "F 87" or circular postmark as in Type 8, 16 or 18.

1872.

Z210	½d. rose-red (1870–79) ..	..	From	22·00
	Plates 11, 12, 13, 14, 15.			
Z211	1d. rose-red (1864–79) ..	..	From	9·00
	Plate Nos. 120, 124, 134, 137, 138, 139, 140, 142, 143, 145, 146, 148, 149, 150, 151, 152, 153, 155, 156, 157, 158, 159, 160, 161, 162, 163, 164, 166, 167, 168, 169, 170, 171, 172, 173, 174, 175, 176, 177, 178, 183, 184, 185, 186, 187, 188, 191, 193, 195, 196, 198, 200, 201, 204, 210, 212, 215, 217, 218.			
Z212	1½d. lake-red (1870–74) (Plate Nos. 1, 3)	..	From	£200
Z213	2d. blue (1858) wmk Large Crown, perf 16			
Z214	2d. blue (1858–69) ..	..	From	13·00
	Plate Nos. 13, 14, 15.			
Z215	2½d. rosy mauve (1875) (blued paper) ..			55·00
	Plate No. 1.			
Z216	2½d. rosy mauve (1875–76) ..	..	From	26·00
	Plate Nos. 1, 2, 3.			
Z217	2½d. rosy mauve (Error of lettering)			
Z218	2½d. rosy mauve (1876–79) ..	..	From	22·00
	Plate Nos. 3, 4, 5, 6, 7, 8, 9, 10, 11, 12, 13, 14, 15, 16, 17.			
Z219	2½d. blue (1880) ..	..	From	10·00
	Plate Nos. 17, 18, 19, 20.			

Z220	2½d. blue (1881) ..		8·50
	Plate Nos. 21, 22, 23.		
Z221	3d. rose (1867–73)		25·00
	Plate Nos. 5, 7, 9, 10.		
Z222	3d. rose (1873–76) (Plate No. 14)		
Z223	4d. vermilion (1865–73)		26·00
	Plate Nos. 12, 13, 14.		
Z224	4d. vermilion (1876) (Plate No. 15)		£150
Z225	4d. sage-green (1877)		90·00
	Plate Nos. 15, 16.		
Z226	4d. grey-brown (1880) wmk Large Garter		
	(Plate No. 17)		
Z227	4d. grey-brown (1880) wmk Crown (Plate Nos.		
	17, 18) .. .. From		26·00
Z228	4d. buff (1872–73) .. .. From		70·00
	Plate Nos. 11, 12.		
Z229	6d. chestnut (1872) (Plate No. 11)		75·00
Z230	6d. grey (1873) (Plate No. 12)		
Z231	6d. grey (1874–80) .. .. From		23·00
	Plate Nos. 13, 14, 15, 16, 17.		
Z232	6d. grey (1881–82) (Plate Nos. 17, 18)		50·00
Z233	6d. on 6d. lilac (1883)		70·00
Z234	8d. orange (1876)		
Z235	9d. straw (1867)		£180
Z236	10d. red-brown (1867)		£130
Z237	1s. green (1867–73) (Plate Nos. 6, 7)		£180
Z238	1s. green (1873–77) .. .. From		27·00
	Plate Nos. 8, 9, 10, 11, 12, 13.		
Z239	1s. orange-brown (1880) (Plate No. 13)		£160
Z240	1s. orange-brown (1881) (Plate Nos. 13, 14)		40·00
Z241	5s. rose (1867–74) (Plate No. 2)		

1880.

Z242	½d. deep green ..		6·00
Z243	½d. pale green ..		7·00
Z244	1d. Venetian red		8·50
Z245	1½d. Venetian red		70·00
Z246	2d. pale rose		32·00
Z247	2d. deep rose		32·00
Z248	5d. indigo		50·00

1881.

Z249	1d. lilac (16 dots)		4·25

1884.

Z250	½d. slate-blue		8·50
Z251	2d. lilac		60·00
Z252	2½d. lilac ..		10·00
Z253	4d. dull green		
Z254	5d. dull green		£100
Z255	1s. dull green		£180

1887.

Z256	½d. vermilion		4·75
Z263	6d. purple/rose-red		16·00
Z264	1s. dull green		£100

1900.

Z265	½d. blue-green		7·00
Z266	1s. green and carmine		

1902–04. De La Rue ptgs.

Z267	½d. blue-green		4·25
Z268	½d. yellowish green		4·75
Z269	1d. scarlet ..		3·75
Z276	6d. purple ..		12·00
Z279	1s. green and carmine		20·00
Z280	2s. 6d. purple ..		
Z281	5s. carmine ..		

STAMBOUL (CONSTANTINOPLE)

Stamps of GREAT BRITAIN cancelled "S" as Type 10, or circular postmarks inscribed either "BRITISH POST OFFICE CONSTANTINOPLE S" or "BRITISH POST OFFICE STAMBOUL" as Type 18.

1884.

Z296	½d. slate-blue		17·00
Z297	1d. lilac ..		8·00
Z298	2d. lilac ..		
Z299	2½d. lilac ..		11·00
Z300	5d. dull green		£100

1887–92.

Z306	½d. vermilion		8·00
Z314	6d. purple/rose-red		24·00
Z317	1s. dull green		

The "S" cancellation was in use from 1885 to 1891 and the "Stamboul" mark from 1892 to 1896, when the office was closed, and from its reopening in 1908 to 1914. The "CONSTANTINOPLE S" handstamp was normally used as a back stamp, but can be found cancelling stamps in the period 1885 to 1892.

PRICES FOR STAMPS ON COVER	
Nos. 1/3a	from × 8
Nos. 4/6a	from × 5
Nos. 7/40	from × 3
Nos. L1/10	from × 6
Nos. L11/17	from × 3

I. TURKISH CURRENCY

(40 paras = 1 piastre)

Following the depreciation of the Turkish piastre against sterling in 1884 it was decided to issue stamps surcharged in Turkish currency to avoid speculation. During the early period unsurcharged stamps of Great Britain remained on sale at the British Post Offices at the current rate of exchange until replaced by "LEVANT" overprints.

80 PARAS 4 PIASTRES 12 PIASTRES
(1) (2) (3)

PRINTERS. Nos. 1/24 were surcharged or overprinted by De La Rue, *unless otherwise stated.*

Stamps of Great Britain (Queen Victoria) surch as T 1 to 3

1885 (1 Aug)–88.

1	64	40 pa. on 2½d. lilac ..		85·00	1·00
2	62	80 pa. on 5d. green		£180	9·50
3	58	12 pi. on 2s. 6d. lilac/bluish		£275	£200
		a. On white paper (1888)		38·00	22·00

1887 (June)–96.

4	74	40 pa. on 2½d. purple/blue		1·75	10
		a. Surch double		£1900	£2500
5	78	80 pa. on 5d. purple and blue (6.90)		10·00	25
		a. Small "0" in "80"		£130	85·00
6	81	4 pi. on 10d. dull purple and carmine (11.96)		32·00	8·00
		a. Dull purple and deep bright carmine		32·00	11·00
		b. Large, wide "4"		£100	55·00

No. 5a occurs twice on each sheet in positions R.4/1 and R.4/7 of both the upper and the lower pane.

1893 (25 Feb). *Roughly handstamped at Constantinople, as T 1.*

7	71	40 pa. on ½d. vermilion ..		£425	£100

This provisional was in use for five days only at the Constantinople and Stamboul offices. As fraudulent copies were made with the original handstamp, and can be found "used" on piece cancelled by fraudulent use of the usual canceller, this stamp should only be purchased from undoubted sources. It is also known with genuine handstamp inverted (*Price £800 unused, £300 used*).

1902–5. *Stamps of King Edward VII surch as T 1 to 3.*

8	86	40 pa. on 2½d. ultramarine (3.02)		8·00	10
		a. Pale ultramarine ..		8·50	10
		ab. Surch double		† £2000	
9	89	80 pa. on 5d. dull purple & ultram (5.6.02)		3·25	1·75
		a. Small "0" in "80"		£180	£190
10	92	4 pi. on 10d. dull purple & carm (6.9.02)		8·50	4·00
		a. No cross on crown		90·00	90·00
		b. Chalk-surfaced paper ..		6·00	8·50
		ba. Chalk-surfaced paper. No cross on crown		85·00	£100
11	94	12 pi. on 2s. 6d. lilac (29.8.03) ..		30·00	32·00
		a. Chalk-surfaced paper. Pale dull pur		65·00	75·00
		b. Chalk-surfaced paper. Dull purple		32·00	32·00
12	95	24 pi. on 5s. bright carmine (15.8.05)		30·00	38·00
8/12			Set of 5	70·00	65·00
9/11		Optd "Specimen"	Set of 3	£150	

No. 9a only occurs on the first printing of 80 pa. on 5d.

1 PIASTRE
(4)

1905–08. *Surch in "PIASTRES" instead of "PARAS" as T 4 and 2.*

13	86	1 pi. on 2½d. ultramarine (17.4.06)		6·50	10
		a. Surch double		† £1300	
14	89	2 pi. on 5d. dull purple & ultram (11.11.05)	17·00	2·50
		a. Chalk-surfaced paper (1.08)		14·00	1·75
		ab. Slate-purple and ultramarine		18·00	6·00

1 PIASTRE
(5)

1 PIASTRE 10 PARAS
(6)

1906 (2 July). *Issued at Beyrout. No. L4 surch with T 5 by American Press, Beyrout.*

15	85	1 pi. on 2d. grey-green and carmine		£1300	£600

1909 (16 Nov–Dec.) *Stamps of King Edward VII surch as T 1 (30 pa.), 6, and 2 (5 pi). Ordinary paper (No. 19) or chalk-surfaced paper (others).*

16	84	30 pa. on 1½d. pale dull purple and green	7·00	1·25
		a. Surch double, one albino			
17	87	1 pi. 10 pa. on 3d. dull purple/orange-yell	10·00	24·00
18	88	1 pi. 30 pa. on 4d. green & chocolate-brn	5·00	14·00
19		1 pi. 30 pa. on 4d. pale orange (16.12.09)	12·00	32·00
20	83	2 pi. 20 pa. on 6d. dull purple		15·00	48·00
21	93	5 pi. on 1s. dull grn & carm (Optd S. £60)	3·75	7·00
16/21			Set of 6	48·00	£110

1¾ PIASTRE
(7)

4 Normal "4"   **4** Pointed "4"

1910 (24 Jan). *Stamps of King Edward VII surch as T 7. Chalk-surfaced paper (Nos. 22 and 24).*

22	87	1¾ pi. on 3d. dull purple/orange-yellow	40	1·00
23	88	1¾ pi. on 4d. pale orange		40	60
		a. Orange-red		4·50	5·50
		b. Thin, pointed "4" in fraction	5·50	6·00
24	83	2½ pi. on 6d. dull purple		90	65
22/4			Set of 3	1·50	2·00

No. 23b occurs in the first and seventh vertical rows of the sheet. The variety also occurs on No. 38, but not on No. 38b.

1 PIASTRE 1 PIASTRE
(8) (9)

TYPE DIFFERENCES. In T 4 the letters are tall and narrow and the space enclosed by the upper part of the "A" is small.

In T 8 the opening of the "A" is similar but the letters are shorter and broader, the "P" and the "E" being particularly noticeable.

In T 9 the letters are short and broad, but the "A" is thin and open.

1911–13. *Stamps of King Edward VII, Harrison or Somerset House ptgs, surch as T 4.*

(a) Surch with T 4 (20 July)

25	86	1 pi. on 2½d. bright blue (perf 14)	9·50	5·00
		a. Surch double, one albino		£200	
26		1 pi. on 2½d. bright blue (perf 15×14) (14.10.11)	7·00	1·90
		a. Dull blue		6·50	1·40

(b) Surch with T 8

27	86	1 pi. on 2½d. bright blue (perf 15×14) (3.12)	10·00	2·00
		a. Dull blue		16·00	3·00

(c) Surch with T 9 (7.12)

28	86	1 pi. on 2½d. bright blue (perf 15×14)	48·00	45
		a. Dull blue		48·00	45

(d) Surch with T 1 to 3 (1911–13)

29	84	30 pa. on 1½d. reddish purple and bright green (22.8.11)	4·25	55
		a. Slate-purple and green ..	7·50	2·25
		b. Surch double, one albino		50·00	
30	89	2 pi. on 5d. dull reddish purple and bright blue (13.5.12)	5·50	1·50
		a. Deep dull reddish purple and bright blue	6·50	2·00
31	92	4 pi. on 10d. dull purple & scar (26.6.12)	20·00	8·50
		a. Dull reddish purple & aniline pink	£150	70·00
		b. Dull reddish purple and carmine	9·00	11·00
		c. No cross on crown			
32	93	5 pi. on 1s. green and carmine (1913)..	17·00	5·00
		a. Surch double, one albino		£200	
33	94	12 pi. on 2s. 6d. dull reddish pur (3.2.12)	48·00	30·00
		a. Dull greyish purple		48·00	30·00
34	95	24 pi. on 5s. carmine (1913)	55·00	75·00
		a. Surch double, one albino..	£225	
29/34			Set of 6	£120	£110

1913 (Apr)–14. *Stamps of King George V, wmk Royal Cypher, surch as T 1 (30 pa.), 9 (1 pi.), 7 or 2 (4 and 5 pi.).*

35	105	30 pa. on 1½d. red-brown (4.13)	3·00	9·00
		a. Surch double, one albino		£100	
36	104	1 pi. on 2½d. cobalt-blue (6.13)	2·75	10
		a. Bright blue		1·50	15
37	106	1¼ pi. on 3d. dull reddish violet (9.13)	2·75	4·25
		a. Violet		3·25	5·00
		b. Surch double, one albino		£300	
38		1¾ pi. on 4d. deep grey-green (7.13)	3·00	5·50
		a. Thin, pointed "4" in fraction	45·00	80·00
		b. Grey-green		2·50	5·00
39	108	4 pi. on 10d. turquoise-blue (12.13)	5·50	13·00
40		5 pi. on 1s. bistre-brown (1.14)	29·00	48·00
35/40			Set of 6	40·00	70·00

II. BRITISH CURRENCY

Stamps overprinted "LEVANT" were for use on parcels, with the ½d. and 1d. principally used for printed paper and post cards. They replaced unoverprinted Great Britain stamps, Nos. Z58/64, Z160/74, Z208/9c and Z267/81, which had previously been used for these purposes.

From October 1907 the three lowest values were also used for certain other amended postal rates until Nos. 16/21 were introduced.

LEVANT
(L 1)

1905 (15 Aug)–12. *Stamps of King Edward VII optd with Type L 1.*

(a) De La Rue ptgs

L 1	83	½d. pale yellowish green	4·50	15
		a. Yellowish green ..		4·50	15
L 2		1d. scarlet ..		3·75	15
		a. Bright scarlet ..		3·75	90
L 3	84	1½d. dull purple and green	4·50	1·50
		a. Chalk-surfaced paper. Pale dull purple and green	11·00	2·00
L 4	85	2d. grey-green and carmine-red	3·00	17·00
		a. Chalk-surfaced paper. Pale grey-green and carmine-red	2·00	6·00
		ab. Dull blue-green and carmine	3·00	7·00
L 5	86	2½d. ultramarine		7·50	18·00
L 6	87	3d. dull purple/orange-yellow	5·50	11·00
L 7	88	4d. green and grey-brown	7·00	22·00
		a. Green and chocolate-brown	13·00	24·00
L 8	89	5d. dull purple and ultramarine	14·00	25·00
L 9	83	6d. pale dull purple		11·00	25·00
L10	93	1s. dull green and carmine	30·00	38·00
		a. Chalk-surfaced paper		30·00	38·00
			Set of 10	80·00	£130

(b) Harrison ptgs optd at Somerset House

L11	83	½d. dull yellow-green (p. 14) (2.12)	14·00	13·00
		a. Dull green ..		14·00	13·00
		b. Deep dull green		17·00	14·00

On 28 December 1909 all values, except for the ½d. and 1d. were withdrawn from sale. A further consignment of the 2d, No. L 4ab, probably ordered in error was, however, received, and, as there was no requirement for this value, sold mainly to collectors. Subsequently dated cancellations on the withdrawn values are philatelic, being worth only a fraction of the used prices quoted.

Distorted "N" (R. 2/10, 12/10)

1911–13. *Stamps of King George V optd with Type L 1 at Somerset House.* (a) *Die A, Wmk Crown.*

L12	98	½d. green (No. 322) (12.9.11)		40	90
		a. Distorted "N"		17·00	
L13	99	1d. carmine-red (No. 327) (1.1.12)		40	3·75
		a. No cross on crown		£150	
		b. Opt double, one albino		£100	
		c. Distorted "N"		17·00	

(b) *Redrawn types. Wmk Crown.*

L14	101	½d. green (No. 339) (19.3.12)		25	10
		a. Yellow-green		70	15
		b. Distorted "N"		13·00	
L15	102	1d. bright scarlet (No. 341) (24.2.12)		25	85
		a. Scarlet (No. 342)		1·25	85
		b. Opt triple, two albino		40·00	
		c. Distorted "N"		13·00	

(c) *New types. Wmk Royal Cypher* (7.13)

L16	105	½d. green (No. 351)		15	30
		a. Yellow-green		30	90
		b. Distorted "N"		11·00	
L17	104	1d. scarlet (No. 357)		15	2·75
		a. Vermilion		4·75	6·00
		b. Distorted "N"		11·00	

Similar overprints were issued when the British Post Offices reopened in 1919, and are listed below.

B. BRITISH POST OFFICES IN CONSTANTINOPLE AND SMYRNA, 1919–1923

CONSTANTINOPLE

Following the occupation of Constantinople by Allied forces a British Military Post Office was opened for civilian use on 4 February 1919. During the period of its existence stamps of Great Britain with face values to 10s. were available and such use can be identified by the following cancellations:

"FIELD POST OFFICE H12" (4 February 1919 to 18 March 1919)
"ARMY POST OFFICE Y" (20 March 1919 to May 1920)
"ARMY POST OFFICE S.X.3" (April 1919 to August 1920)
"BRITISH A.P.O. CONSTANTINOPLE" (5 July 1919 to 1 Sept 1920).

Of these four marks the first two types were also used for military mail.

The office reverted to civilian control in July 1920, Nos. 41/50 and L18/24 being intended for its use.

Z 1   Z 2

Z 3   Z 4

1919–20. *Used at the Army Post Office. Stamps of GREAT BRITAIN cancelled with Types Z 1, Z 2, Z 3, Z 4.*

Z176	½d. green					2·00
Z177	1d. scarlet					2·00
Z178	1½d. brown					3·25
Z179	2d. orange (Die I)					2·50
Z180	2½d. blue					4·00
Z181	4d. grey-green					8·50
Z182	6d. purple					4·50
Z183	9d. agate					22·00
Z184	1s. bistre					5·50
Z185	2s. 6d. brown					32·00
Z186	5s. rose-red					50·00
Z187	10s. dull grey-blue					90·00

1920–21. *Used at the Civilian Post Office. Stamps of GREAT BRITAIN cancelled with Type* **18** *or double-circle datestamp.*

Z188	½d. green					2·00
Z189	1d. scarlet					2·00
Z190	1½d. brown					3·25
Z191	2d. orange (Die I)					2·50
Z192	2½d. blue					4·00
Z193	3d. violet					6·50
Z194	4d. grey-green					8·50
Z195	5d. brown					13·00
Z196	6d. purple					4·50
Z197	10d. turquoise-blue					22·00
Z198	1s. bistre					5·50
Z199	2s. 6d. brown					32·00
Z200	5s. rose-red					50·00
Z201	10s. dull grey-blue					90·00

> ### PRICES FOR STAMPS ON COVER
>
> Nos. 41/50   *from* × 2
> Nos. L18/24   *from* × 5

Stamps of Great Britain surch at Somerset House

I. TURKISH CURRENCY

1½ PIASTRES
(10)

15 PIASTRES
(11)

18¾

Short hyphen bar
(R. 4/12, 14/12.)

1921 (Aug). *Stamps of King George V, wmk Royal Cypher, surch as T* 1 (30 pa.), **10** and **11** (15 and 18¾ pi.).

41	105	30 pa. on ½d. green		40	7·00
		a. Yellow-green		2·00	9·00
42	104	1½ pi. on 1d. bright scarlet		1·00	10
		a. Vermilion		3·25	2·25
		b. Scarlet-vermilion		2·50	2·25
43		3¾ pi. on 2½d. blue		1·00	25
		a. Dull Prussian blue		16·00	2·25
44	106	4½ pi. on 3d. violet		1·50	3·25
		a. Bluish violet		2·00	3·00
45	107	7½ pi. on 5d. brown		30	10
		a. Yellow-brown		1·25	20
46	108	15 pi. on 10d. turquoise-blue		55	15
47		18¾ pi. on 1s. bistre-brown		3·75	3·75
		a. Short hyphen bar		50·00	
		b. Olive-bistre		4·50	4·50
		ba. Short hyphen bar		60·00	

45 PIASTRES
(12)

45
Joined figures
(second stamp in
each horiz row)

1921. *Stamps of King George V (Bradbury, Wilkinson printing) surch as T* 12.

48	109	45 pi. on 2s. 6d. chocolate-brown		20·00	42·00
		a. Joined figures		30·00	60·00
		b. Olive-brown		48·00	60·00
		ba. Joined figures		65·00	80·00
49		90 pi. on 5s. rose-red		25·00	30·00
50		180 pi. on 10s. dull grey-blue		45·00	40·00
		a. Opt double, one albino		£225	
41/50			*Set of 10*	85·00	£110
47/50		Optd "Specimen"	*Set of 4*	£250	

II. BRITISH CURRENCY

1921. *Stamps of King George V optd as Type L* 1.

L18	106	2d. reddish orange (Die I)		1·25	22·00
		a. Bright orange		2·00	22·00
L19		3d. bluish violet		7·50	10·00
L20		4d. grey-green		4·50	13·00
L21	107	5d. yellow-brown		9·00	26·00
L22		6d. dull purple (chalk-surfaced paper)		22·00	35·00
		a. Reddish purple		20·00	8·50
L23	108	1s. bistre-brown (Optd £65)		10·00	7·00
		a. Olive-bistre		10·00	7·00
L24	109	2s. 6d. chocolate-brown (Optd S. £130)		35·00	75·00
		a. Olive-brown		65·00	£110
L18/24			*Set of 7*	75·00	£140

On No. L24 the letters of the overprint are shorter, being only 3 mm high.

Nos. 41/50 and L18/24 were used at the Constantinople office only.

SMYRNA

When the office re-opened on 1 March 1919 existing stocks of surcharged or overprinted issues were utilised until they were exhausted in mid-1920. During this period examples of Nos. 24, 29a, 30a, 33b/7, 39/40, L4b, L14/17 are known with commercial postmarks. These stamps were supplemented and finally replaced in mid-1920 by ordinary stamps of Great Britain.

Stamps of GREAT BRITAIN cancelled with circular postmark as Type **18** *or with* "REGISTERED" *oval.*

Z282	½d. green					2·50
Z283	1d. scarlet					2·50
Z284	1½d. brown					3·50
Z285	2d. orange (Die I)					3·00
Z286	2d. orange (Die II)					
Z287	2½d. blue					5·00
Z288	2½d. dull Prussian blue					
Z289	4d. grey-green					10·00
Z290	6d. purple					6·00
Z291	10d. turquoise-blue					27·00
Z292	1s. bistre					7·00
Z293	2s. 6d. brown					55·00
Z294	5s. rose-red					80·00
Z295	10s. dull grey-blue					£120

MINIMUM PRICE

The minimum price quote is 10p which represents a handling charge rather than a basis for valuing common stamps. For further notes about prices see introductory pages.

C. BRITISH FIELD OFFICE IN SALONICA

These overprints were originally prepared for use by a civilian post office to be set up on Mt Athos, Northern Greece. When the project was abandoned they were placed on sale at the Army Field Office in Salonica.

> ### PRICES FOR STAMPS ON COVER
>
> Nos. S1/8   *from* × 10

Levant
(S 1)

1916 (end Feb–9 Mar). *Stamps of Gt. Britain, optd with Type* S 1 *by Army Printing Office, Salonica.*

S 1	105	½d. green		30·00	£150
		a. Opt double		£1800	£2250
		b. Vert pair, one without opt		£900	£1200
S 2	104	1d. scarlet		30·00	£150
		a. Opt double		£1200	£1500
S 3	106	2d. reddish orange (Die I)		£120	£275
S 4		3d. bluish violet		90·00	£275
		a. Opt double			
S 5		4d. grey-green		£120	£275
S 6	107	6d. reddish pur (chalk-surfaced paper)		70·00	£225
		a. Vert pair, one without opt		£1000	£1400
S 7	108	9d. agate		£275	£475
		a. Opt double		£8000	£6500
S 8		1s. bistre-brown		£225	£425
S1/8			*Set of 8*	£850	£2000

There are numerous forgeries of this overprint.

All values can be found with an additional albino overprint, inverted on the gummed side.

British New Guinea
see Papua New Guinea

British Occupation of Iraq
see Iraq

British Occupation of Italian Colonies

> ### PRICES FOR STAMPS ON COVER TO 1945
>
> Nos. M1/21   *from* × 4
> Nos. MD1/5   *from* × 10
> Nos. S1/9   *from* × 4
>
> The above prices refer to covers from the territories concerned, not examples used in Great Britain.

MIDDLE EAST FORCES

For use in territory occupied by British Forces in Eritrea (1942), Italian Somaliland (from 13 April 1942), Cyrenaica (1943), Tripolitania (1943), and some of the Dodecanese Islands (1945).

PRICES. Our prices for used stamps with "M.E.F." overprints are for specimens with identifiable postmarks of the territories in which they were issued. These stamps were also used in the United Kingdom with official sanction, from the summer of 1950 onwards, and with U.K. postmarks are worth about 25 per cent less.

PRINTERS. Considerable research has been undertaken to discover the origins of Nos. M1/10. It is now suggested that Nos. M1/5, previously assigned to Harrison and Sons, were produced by the Army Printing Services, Cairo, and that the smaller printing, Nos. M6/10, previously identified as the work of the Army Printing Services, Cairo, was from an unidentified printer within the Middle East Forces area.

M.E.F. M.E.F.
(M 1) (M 2)

Opt. 14 mm long. Regular lettering and upright oblong stops.

Opt. 13½ mm long. Regular lettering and square stops.

M.E.F.
(M 2a)

Opt. 13½ mm long. Rough lettering and round stops.

(Illustrations twice actual size)

M.E.F.
Sliced "M"
(R.6/10)

1942 (2 Mar). *Stamps of Great Britain optd. W 127. P 15 × 14.*

(a) With Type M 1

M 1	**128**	1d. scarlet (No. 463)		..	50	1·00
		a. Sliced "M"		..	40·00	
M 2		2d. orange (No. 465)		..	20	1·75
		a. Sliced "M"		..	25·00	
M 3		2½d. ultramarine (No. 466)	..		20	30
		a. Sliced "M"		..	25·00	
M 4		3d. violet (No. 467)	..		20	10
		a. Opt double		..	—	£2000
M 5	**129**	5d. brown		..	20	15
		a. Sliced "M"		..	25·00	

(b) With Type M 2

M 6	**128**	1d. scarlet (No. 463)	..		45·00	9·50
		a. Optd. with Type M 2a			35·00	8·50
		b. Nos. M6/a *se-tenant* vert		£150	65·00	
M 7		2d. orange (No. 465)	..		55·00	65·00
		a. Optd with Type M 2a			48·00	55·00
		b. Nos. M7/a *se-tenant* vert		£200	£160	
M 8		2½d. ultramarine (No. 466)	..		28·00	6·50
		a. Optd with Type M 2a			26·00	5·00
		b. Nos. M8/a *se-tenant* vert		£120	48·00	
M 9		3d. violet (No. 467)	..		80·00	24·00
		a. Optd with Type M 2a			70·00	22·00
		b. Nos. M9/a *se-tenant* vert		£300	£120	
M10	**129**	5d. brown		..	£300	80·00
		a. Optd with Type M 2a			£275	70·00
		b. Nos. M10/a *se-tenant* vert		£950	£500	

See note after No. M21.

Nos. M6/10 were issued in panes of 60 (6 × 10), rows 2, 3, and 7 being overprinted with Type M 2 and the other seven rows with Type M 2a.

M.E.F.
(M 3)

Optd 13½ mm long. Regular lettering and upright oblong stops.

(Illustration twice actual size)

1943 (1 Jan)–1947. *Stamps of Great Britain optd with Type M 3 by Harrison & Sons. W 127, P 15 × 14 (1d. to 1s.); W 133, P 14 (others).*

M11	**128**	1d. pale scarlet (No. 486)	..		1·50	10
M12		2d. pale orange (No. 488)	..		1·50	75
M13		2½d. light ultramarine (No. 489)		..	45	10
M14		3d. pale violet (No. 490)	..		1·50	10
M15	**129**	5d. brown		..	2·25	10
M16		6d. purple		..	40	10
M17	**130**	9d. deep olive-green		..	85	10
M18		1s. bistre-brown		..	50	10
M19	**131**	2s. 6d. yellow-green		..	7·00	30
M20		5s. red (1947)		..	11·00	17·00
M21	**132**	10s. ultramarine (1947)	..		14·00	10·00
M11/21				*Set of 11*	35·00	25·00
M18/21 Optd "Specimen"				*Set of 4*	£500	

The overprint on No. M15 should not be confused with the other overprints on the 5d. value. It can be distinguished from No. M5 by the ½ mm difference in length; and from No. M10 by the more intense colour, thicker lettering and larger stops.

POSTAGE DUE STAMPS

M.E.F.
(MD 1)

1942. *Postage Due stamps of Great Britain. Nos. D27/30 and D33 optd with Type MD 1, in blue-black.*

MD1	D 1	½d. emerald		..	30	5·50
MD2		1d. carmine		..	30	1·50
MD3		2d. agate		..	1·25	1·00
MD4		3d. violet		..	50	4·25
MD5		1s. deep blue (Optd S. £150)			3·25	8·50
MD1/5				*Set of 5*	5·00	19·00

STANLEY GIBBONS STAMP COLLECTING SERIES

Introductory booklets on *How to Start, How to Identify Stamps* and *Collecting by Theme.* A series of well illustrated guides at a low price. Write for details.

CYRENAICA

In June 1949 the British authorities recognised the leader of the Senussi, Amir Mohammed Idris Al-Senussi, as Amir of Cyrenaica with autonomy in internal affairs.

(Currency. 10 millièmes = 1 piastre, 100 piastres = 1 Egyptian pound)

24 Mounted Warrior 25

(Recess Waterlow)

1950 (16 Jan). *P 12½.*

136	**24**	1 m. brown		..	55	1·25
137		2 m. carmine		..	70	1·00
138		3 m. orange-yellow		..	70	1·00
139		4 m. blue-green		..	1·25	2·50
140		5 m. grey-black		..	60	70
141		8 m. orange		..	75	65
142		10 m. violet		..	75	65
143		12 m. scarlet		..	75	65
144		20 m. blue		..	75	60
145	**25**	50 m. ultramarine and purple-brown		..	2·25	3·00
146		100 m. carmine and black		..	6·00	9·00
147		200 m. violet and deep blue		..	11·00	25·00
148		500 m. orange-yellow and green		..	42·00	65·00
136/148				*Set of 13*	60·00	£100

POSTAGE DUE STAMPS

D 26

(Recess Waterlow)

1950 (16 Jan). *P 12½*

D149	D 26	2 m. brown		..	45·00	80·00
D150		4 m. blue-green		..	45·00	80·00
D151		8 m. scarlet		..	45·00	80·00
D152		10 m. orange		..	45·00	80·00
D153		20 m. orange-yellow		..	45·00	80·00
D154		40 m. blue		..	45·00	80·00
D155		100 m. grey-brown		..	45·00	80·00
D149/155				*Set of 7*	£275	£500

On 24 December 1951 Cyrenaica united with Tripolitania, Fezzan and Ghadames to form the independent Kingdom of Libya, whose issues are listed in Part 13 *(Africa since Independence F–M)* of this catalogue.

ERITREA

From early 1950 examples of Nos. E1/32 exist precancelled in manuscript by a black or blue horizontal line for use by British troops on concession rate mail.

BRITISH MILITARY ADMINISTRATION

(Currency. 100 cents = 1 shilling)

B.M.A.
ERITREA **B.M.A.**
ERITREA

10 CENTS	5 SHILLINGS
(E 1)	(E 2)

SH. 50 SH .50

Normal	Misplaced Stop

1948–9. *Stamps of Great Britain surch as Types E 1 or E 2.*

E 1	**128**	5 c. on ½d. pale green	..		50	65
E 2		10 c. on 1d. pale scarlet	..		65	2·00
E 3		20 c. on 2d. pale orange	..		45	2·25
E 4		25 c. on 2½d. light ultramarine		..	40	60
E 5		30 c. on 3d. pale violet	..		1·25	4·00
E 6	**129**	40 c. on 5d. brown		..	30	4·00
E 7		50 c. on 6d. purple		..	30	60
E 7a	**130**	65 c. on 8d. bright carmine (1.2.49)			7·00	2·00
E 8		75 c. on 9d. deep olive-green		..	50	75
E 9		1 s. on 1s. bistre-brown	..		50	60
E10	**131**	2 s. 50 c. on 2s. 6d. yellow-green			6·50	10·00
		a. Misplaced stop (R. 4/7)		..	80·00	£110
E11		5 s. on 5s. red		..	6·50	16·00
E12	**132**	10 s. on 10s. ultramarine	..		16·00	21·00
E1/12				*Set of 13*	35·00	55·00

BRITISH ADMINISTRATION

1950 (6 Feb). *As Nos. E1/12, but surch "B.A. ERITREA" and new values instead of "B.M.A." etc.*

E13	**128**	5 c. on ½d. pale green		..	50	6·00
E14		10 c. on 1d. pale scarlet	..		30	2·75
E15		20 c. on 2d. pale orange	..		30	70
E16		25 c. on 2½d. light ultramarine	..		30	60

E17	**128**	30 c. on 3d. pale violet		..	30	1·00
E18	**129**	40 c. on 5d. brown		..	40	90
E19		50 c. on 6d. purple		..	30	20
E20	**130**	65 c. on 8d. bright carmine		..	40	1·00
E21		75 c. on 9d. deep olive-green		..	30	25
E22		1 s. on 1s. bistre-brown		..	30	15
E23	**131**	2 s. 50 c. on 2s. 6d. yellow-green		..	3·50	4·50
E24		5 s. on 5s. red		..	6·00	9·00
E25	**132**	10 s. on 10s. ultramarine		..	45·00	45·00
E13/25				*Set of 13*	50·00	65·00

1951 (28 May*). *Nos. 503/4, 506/7 and 509/11 of Great Britain surch "B.A. ERITREA" and new values.*

E26	**128**	5 c. on ½d. pale orange		..	30	60
E27		10 c. on 1d. light ultramarine		..	30	60
E28		20 c. on 2d. pale red-brown		..	30	30
E29		25 c. on 2½d. pale scarlet		..	30	30
E30	**147**	2 s. 50 c. on 2s. 6d. yellow-green			5·50	16·00
E31	**148**	5 s. on 5s. red		..	17·00	17·00
E32		10 s. on 10s. ultramarine		..	18·00	17·00
E26/32				*Set of 7*	38·00	45·00

*This is the local release date. The stamps were placed on sale in London on 3 May.

POSTAGE DUE STAMPS

B.M.A.
ERITREA

10 CENTS
(ED 1)

1948. *Postage Due stamps of Great Britain Nos. D27/30 and D33 surch as Type ED 1.*

ED1	D 1	5 c. on ½d. emerald	..		9·00	18·00
ED2		10 c. on 1d. carmine		..	8·00	18·00
		a. No stop after "B"		..	90·00	
ED3		20 c. on 2d. agate		..	7·00	13·00
		a. No stop after "A"		..	60·00	
		b. No stop after "B" (R. 1/9)		..	£100	
ED4		30 c. on 3d. violet		..	8·00	12·00
ED5		1 s. on 1s. deep blue	..		15·00	22·00
ED1/5				*Set of 5*	42·00	75·00

1950 (6 Feb). *As Nos. ED1/5, but surch "B.A. ERITREA" and new values instead of "B.M.A." etc.*

ED6	D 1	5 c. on ½d. emerald		..	11·00	30·00
ED7		10 c. on 1d. carmine		..	9·00	15·00
		a. "C" of "CENTS" omitted		..	£1300	
		ab. "C" omitted and vertical oblong for "E" of "CENTS"		..	£2250	
ED8		20 c. on 2d. agate		..	9·50	13·00
ED9		30 c. on 3d. violet		..	9·50	13·00
		w. Wmk sideways-inverted*				
ED10		1 s. on 1s. deep blue		..	15·00	22·00
		a. Stop after "A" omitted (R. 2/13)			£250	
ED6/10				*Set of 5*	48·00	85·00

No. ED7a, and probably No. ED7ab, occurred on R.7/20, but the error was quickly corrected.

*No. ED9w shows the Crowns pointing to the left, *as seen from the back of the stamp.*

Stamps of Ethiopia were used in Eritrea after 15 September 1952 following federation with Ethiopia.

SOMALIA

BRITISH OCCUPATION

E.A.F.
(S 1. "East Africa Forces")

1943 (15 Jan)–46. *Stamps of Great Britain optd with Type S 1, in blue.*

S1	**128**	1d. pale scarlet		..	60	40
S2		2d. pale orange		..	1·50	1·25
S3		2½d. light ultramarine	..		30	3·50
S4		3d. pale violet		..	50	15
S5	**129**	5d. brown		..	50	40
S6		6d. purple		..	30	90
S7	**130**	9d. deep olive-green		..	60	2·25
S8		1s. bistre-brown		..	1·25	15
S9	**131**	2s. 6d. yellow-green (1946)		..	6·00	6·50
S1/9				*Set of 9*	10·50	14·00
S8/9 Optd "Specimen"				*Set of 2*	£250	

The note *re* used prices above Type M 1 of Middle East Forces also applies to the above issue.

BRITISH MILITARY ADMINISTRATION

(Currency. 100 cents = 1 shilling)

1948 (27 May). *Stamps of Great Britain surch "B.M.A./ SOMALIA" and new values, as Types E 1 and E 2 of Eritrea.*

S10	**128**	5 c. on ½d. pale green		..	50	1·25
S11		15 c. on 1½d. pale red-brown		..	80	10·00
S12		20 c. on 2d. pale orange	..		1·00	3·25
S13		25 c. on 2½d. light ultramarine	..		60	4·00
S14		30 c. on 3d. pale violet		..	2·00	9·00
S15	**129**	40 c. on 5d. brown		..	40	20
S16		50 c. on 6d. purple		..	40	2·00
S17	**130**	75 c. on 9d. deep olive-green		..	2·00	14·00
S18		1 s. on 1s. bistre-brown		..	1·25	20
S19	**131**	2 s. 50 c. on 2s. 6d. yellow-green			3·25	18·00
		a. Misplaced stop (R. 4/7)		..	80·00	£180
S20		5 s. on 5s. red		..	8·00	26·00
S10/20				*Set of 11*	18·00	80·00

For illustration of No. S19a, see previous column above No. E1 of Eritrea.

BRITISH ADMINISTRATION

1950 (2 Jan). *As Nos. S10/20, but surch "B.A./SOMALIA" and new values, instead of "B.M.A." etc.*

S21	**128**	5 c. on ½d. pale green		..	20	2·25
S22		15 c. on 1½d. pale red-brown		..	60	13·00
S23		20 c. on 2d. pale orange		..	60	3·50
S24		25 c. on 2½d. light ultramarine		..	40	4·50
S25		30 c. on 3d. pale violet		..	1·00	3·00
S26	**129**	40 c. on 5d. brown		..	55	85
S27		50 c. on 6d. purple		..	40	1·00
S28	**130**	75 c. on 9d. deep olive-green		..	1·00	5·50
S29		1 s. on 1s. bistre-brown		..	60	1·50

S30	131	2 s. 50 c. on 2s. 6d. yellow-green	4·00	22·00
S31		5 s. on 5s. red	8·50	27·00
S21/31		Set of 11	16·00	75·00

Somalia reverted to Italian Administration on 1 April 1950 later becoming independent. Later issues will be found listed in Part 8 (*Italy and Switzerland*) of this catalogue.

TRIPOLITANIA

BRITISH MILITARY ADMINISTRATION

(Currency. 100 centesimi = 1 Military Administration lira)

4	4
M.A.L.	M.A.L.
Normal	Misaligned surcharge (R.8/8, 18/8)

1948 (1 July). *Stamps of Great Britain surch "B.M.A./TRIPOLITANIA" and new values, as Types E 1 and E 2 of Eritrea, but expressed in M(ilitary) A(dministration) L(ire).*

T 1	128	1 l. on ½d. pale green	30	80
T 2		2 l. on 1d. pale scarlet	20	15
T 3		3 l. on 1½d. pale red-brown	20	50
		a. Misaligned surch	20·00	
T 4		4 l. on 2d. pale orange	25	50
		a. Misaligned surch	23·00	
T 5		5 l. on 2½d. light ultramarine	30	20
T 6		6 l. on 3d. pale violet	20	40
T 7	129	10 l. on 5d. brown	20	15
T 8		12 l. on 6d. purple	30	20
T 9	130	18 l. on 9d. deep olive-green	50	65
T10		24 l. on 1s. bistre-brown	50	65
T11	131	60 l. on 2s. 6d. yellow-green	2·00	6·00
T12		120 l. on 5s. red	9·00	15·00
T13	132	240 l. on 10s. ultramarine	19·00	75·00
T1/13		Set of 13	30·00	90·00

BRITISH ADMINISTRATION

1950 (6 Feb). *As Nos. T1/13, but surch. "B.A. TRIPOLITANIA" and new values, instead of "B.M.A." etc.*

T14	128	1 l. on ½d. pale green	90	8·00
T15		2 l. on 1d. pale scarlet	1·00	40
T16		3 l. on 1½d. pale red-brown	35	7·00
		a. Misaligned surch	30·00	
T17		4 l. on 2d. pale orange	25	4·50
		a. Misaligned surch	23·00	
T18		5 l. on 2½d. light ultramarine	25	70
T19		6 l. on 3d. pale violet	90	1·75
T20	129	10 l. on 5d. brown	30	2·50
T21		12 l. on 6d. purple	75	50
T22	130	18 l. on 9d. deep olive-green	75	1·60
T23		24 l. on 1s. bistre-brown	75	3·50
T24	131	60 l. on 2s. 6d. yellow-green	3·75	11·00
T25		120 l. on 5s. red	15·00	21·00
T26	132	240 l. on 10s. ultramarine	22·00	42·00
T14/26		Set of 13	42·00	90·00

1951 (3 May). *Nos. 503/7 and 509/11 of Great Britain surch "B.A. TRIPOLITANIA" and new values.*

T27	128	1 l. on ½d. pale orange	20	3·50
T28		2 l. on 1d. light ultramarine	20	90
T29		3 l. on 1½d. pale green	30	6·50
T30		4 l. on 2d. pale red-brown	20	1·25
T31		5 l. on 2½d. pale scarlet	30	6·50
T32	147	60 l. on 2s. 6d. yellow-green	3·50	15·00
T33	148	120 l. on 5s. red	7·50	19·00
T34	149	240 l. on 10s. ultramarine	24·00	32·00
T27/34		Set of 8	32·00	75·00

POSTAGE DUE STAMPS

1948. *Postage Due stamps of Great Britain Nos. D27/30 and D33 surch. "B.M.A./TRIPOLITANIA" and new values, as Type ED 1 of Eritrea, but expressed in M(ilitary) A(dministration) L(ire).*

TD1	D 1	1 l. on ½d. emerald	4·50	32·00
		a. No stop after "A"	60·00	
TD2		2 l. on 1d. carmine	2·50	28·00
		a. No stop after "A"	42·00	
		b. No stop after "M" (R.1/17)	75·00	
TD3		4 l. on 2d. agate	7·00	22·00
		a. No stop after "A"	£110	
		b. No stop after "M"	£140	
TD4		6 l. on 3d. violet	7·50	20·00
TD5		24 l. on 1s. deep blue	28·00	85·00
TD1/5		Set of 5	45·00	£170

1950 (6 Feb). *As Nos. TD1/5, but surch "B.A. TRIPOLITANIA" and new values, instead of "B.M.A." etc.*

TD 6	D 1	1 l. on ½d. emerald	8·50	55·00
		a. No stop after "B"	£100	
TD 7		2 l. on 1d. carmine	2·50	24·00
		a. No stop after "B"	65·00	
TD 8		4 l. on 2d. agate	2·75	27·00
		a. No stop after "B"	70·00	
TD 9		6 l. on 3d. violet	16·00	60·00
		a. No stop after "B"	£140	
		w. Wmk sideways-inverted*		
TD10		24 l. on 1s. deep blue	35·00	£110
		a. No stop after "A"	£275	
		b. No stop after "B"	£275	
TD6/10		Set of 5	60·00	£250

*No. TD9w shows the Crowns pointing to the left, *as seen from the back of the stamp.*

Tripolitania became part of the independent kingdom of Libya on 24 December 1951.

British P.Os in Crete

BRITISH ADMINISTRATION OF CANDIA PROVINCE (HERAKLEION)

Crete, formerly part of the Turkish Empire, was made autonomous, under Turkish suzerainty, in November 1898 with British, French, Italian and Russian troops stationed in separate zones to keep the peace.

Overseas mail franked with Nos. B1/5 was forwarded through the Austrian post office at Canea, being additionally franked with stamps of the Austro-Hungarian Post Offices in the Turkish Empire.

(Currency. 40 paras = 1 piastre)

> **PRICES FOR STAMPS ON COVER**
>
> No. B1 *from* × 10
> Nos. B2/5 —

B 1	B 2

1898 (25 Nov). *Handstruck locally. Imperf.*

B1	B 1	20 pa. bright violet	£425	£225

1898 (3 Dec). *Litho by M. Grundmann, Athens. P 11½.*

B2	B 2	10 pa. blue	8·00	14·00
		a. Imperf (pair)	£250	
B3		20 pa. green	11·00	13·00
		a. Imperf (pair)	£250	

1899. *P 11½.*

B4	B 2	10 pa. brown	8·00	20·00
		a. Imperf (pair)	£250	
B5		20 pa. rose	15·00	15·00
		a. Imperf (pair)	£250	

The British postal service closed at the end of 1899.

British P.O. in Siam
(Bangkok)

An overseas postal service for foreign residents was operated by the British Consulate at Bangkok from 1858. Mail was despatched by steamer to Singapore and from 1876 onwards was increasingly franked with Straits Settlements stamps. These were initially cancelled on arrival at Singapore, but later an oval postmark inscribed "BRITISH CONSULATE BANGKOK" was used. In 1883 a circular "BANGKOK" datestamp was introduced for use with Nos. 1/23. Both cancellations can also be found used on Hong Kong stamps between 1881 and 1885.

(Currency. 100 cents = 1 Straits dollar)

Stamps of Straits Settlements (see Malaysia) cancelled with oval postmark inscribed "BRITISH CONSULATE BANGKOK" around Royal Arms.

1877 to **1882.** *Wmk Crown CC (Nos. 11/15, 33 and 35).*

Z1	2 c. brown		£325
Z2	4 c. rose		£325
Z3	6 c. dull lilac		£375
Z4	8 c. orange-yellow		£325
Z5	10 c. on 30 c. claret (thin "0") (No. 33)		£1000
Z6	10 c. on 30 c. claret (thick "10") (No. 34)		£1000
Z7	10 c. on 30 c. claret (thin "1", thick "0".) (No. 35)		£1000
Z8	12 c. blue		£425

Subsequent Straits Settlements values to 8 c. watermarked Crown CA are known used at Bangkok in 1883 and 1884. During this period the stamps overprinted "B" were on sale at the British Post Office.

> **PRICES FOR STAMPS ON COVER**
>
> The issues of the British Post Offices in Siam are worth from × 100 the prices quoted for used stamps when on cover.

B

(1)

1882 (May)–**85.** *Stamps of Straits Settlements optd with T 1.*

(a) On No. 9 of 1867

1	32 c. on 2 a. yellow (1885)		£35000

(b) On Nos. 11/13, 14a, 15/17 and 19 of 1867–72 and Nos. 48/9 of 1882. Wmk Crown CC

2	2 c. brown	£2500	£1400
3	4 c. rose	£2000	£1100
	a. Opt double	—	£7500
4	5 c. purple-brown	£250	£275
5	6 c. lilac	£160	£110
6	8 c. orange	£1700	£200
7	10 c. slate	£300	£125
8	12 c. blue	£900	£475
9	24 c. green	£700	£150
10	30 c. claret	£30000	£20000
11	96 c. grey	£4500	£2500

		(c) On Nos. 59/60 of April 1883		
12		2 c. on 32 c. pale red (*Wide "S"*)	£1900	£2250
13		2 c. on 32 c. pale red (*Wide "E"*)	£2250	£2500

(d) On Nos. 50/3 of 1882 and Nos. 63/7 of 1883–84. Wmk Crown CA

14		2 c. brown	£450	£325
15		2 c. pale rose (1883)	55·00	45·00
		a. Opt inverted	—	£9500
		b. Opt double	£2750	£2750
		c. Opt treble	£10000	
16		4 c. rose (1883)	£500	£300
17		4 c. pale brown (1883)	75·00	70·00
		a. Opt double	£3500	
		b. Broken oval	£900	£900
18		5 c. blue (1884)	£225	£160
19		6 c. lilac (1884)	£160	£110
20		8 c. orange (1883)	£140	£900
		a. Opt inverted	£17000	£10000
21		10 c. slate (1883)	£150	85·00
22		12 c. brown-purple (1883)	£275	£150
23		24 c. yellow-green (1884?)	£4000	£2250

The prices quoted for the overprint double errors, Nos. 3a, 15b and 17a, are for stamps showing two clear impressions of the overprint. Examples showing partial doubling, on these and other values, are worth a small premium over the price quoted for normal stamps.

No. 17b shows the edge of the central oval broken above the "O" of "POSTAGE". It occurs on R. 10/5 of the lower right pane.

The use of these stamps ceased on 30 June 1885. Siam joined the Universal Postal Union on 1 July 1885.

British Postal Agencies in Eastern Arabia

Certain Arab States in Eastern Arabia, whilst remaining independent, had British postal administrations.

Bahrain and Kuwait (from 1948) and Qatar (from 1957) used British stamps overprinted and surcharged in local currency. Abu Dhabi (from 1964) and Trucial States (from 1961 and used only in Dubai) had definitive issues made under the auspices of the British Agencies.

In addition, British stamps were surcharged with value only for use in Muscat and certain other states. They were formerly listed under Muscat as they were first put on sale there, but in view of their more extended use, the list has been transferred here, retaining the same numbering.

The stamps were used in Muscat from 1 April 1948 to 29 April 1966; in Dubai from 1 April 1948 to 6 January 1961; in Qatar: Doha from August 1950, Umm Said from February 1956, to 31 March 1957; and in Abu Dhabi from 30 March 1963 (Das Island from December 1960) to 29 March 1964.

Nos. 21/2 were placed on sale in Kuwait Post Offices in April and May 1951 and from February to November 1953 due to shortages of stamps with "KUWAIT" overprint. Isolated examples of other values can be found commercially used from Bahrain or Kuwait.

(Currency. 12 pies= 1 anna; 16 annas = 1 rupee)

Stamps of Great Britain surcharged

ANNA	2 RUPEES
(3)	(4)
I	II

Two types of 1½ a. surcharge:
I. "1" 3¼ mm high and aligns with top of "2" in "½" (Rows 1 to 10).
II. "1" 3½ mm high with foot of figure below top of "2" (Rows 11 to 20).

1948 (1 Apr). *Surch with T 3 (½ a. to 1 r.) or 4 (2 r.).*

16	128	½ a. on ½d. pale green	1·75	4·00
17		1 a. on 1d. pale scarlet	1·75	20
18		1½ a. on 1½d. pale red-brown (I)	3·00	40
		a. Type II	3·00	40
		b. Vert pair. Nos. 18/a	21·00	
19		2 a. on 2d. pale orange	1·50	55
20		2½ a. on 2½d. light ultramarine	2·00	3·50
21		3 a. on 3d. pale violet	2·00	10
22	129	6 a. on 6d. purple	2·00	10
23	130	1 r. on 1s. bistre-brown	3·00	50
24	131	2 r. on 2s. 6d. yellow-green	7·00	24·00
16/24		Set of 9	22·00	30·00

One example of No. 22 is known with the surcharge almost completely omitted from position R. 20/2 in the sheet.

2½ ANNAS	15 RUPEES
(5)	(6)

1948 (26 Apr). *Royal Silver Wedding. Nos. 493/4 surch with T 5 or 6.*

25	137	2½ a. on 2½d. ultramarine	1·00	50
26	138	15 r. on £1 blue	23·00	35·00

1948 (29 July). *Olympic Games. Nos. 495/8 surch with new values in "ANNAS" or "1 RUPEE", as T 5/6, but in one line on 2½ a. (vert) or 6 a. and 1 r. (horiz) and grills obliterating former values of all except 2½ a.*

27	139	2½ a. on 2½d. ultramarine	..	35	1·25
28	140	3 a. on 3d. violet	.. .. ..	45	1·60
29	141	6 a. on 6d. bright purple	..	45	1·60
30	142	1 r. on 1s. brown	..	1·25	1·90
		a. Surch double	..	£650	
27/30 ..			*Set of 4*	2·25	5·75

1949 (10 Oct). *75th Anniv of Universal Postal Union. Nos. 499/502 surch with new values in "ANNAS" or "1 RUPEE" as T 3/4, but all in one line, with grills obliterating former values.*

31	143	2½ a. on 2½d. ultramarine	..	60	2·25
32	144	3 a. on 3d. violet	..	60	2·25
33	145	6 a. on 6d. bright purple	..	60	1·75
34	146	1 r. on 1s. brown	..	3·00	2·50
31/4 ..			*Set of 4*	4·25	8·00

= 2 RUPEES = 2 RUPEES

(6a) (6b)

Type 6a. "2" and "RUPEES" level and in line with lower of the two bars.

Type 6b. "2" raised in relation to "RUPEES" and whole surcharge below the lower bar.

1950 (2 Oct)–55. *Nos. 503/8 surch as T 3 and No. 509 with T 6a.*

35	128	½ a. on ½d. pale orange (3.5.51)	..	30	6·50
36		1 a. on 1d. light ultramarine (3.5.51)	..	30	4·00
37		1½ a. on 1½d. pale green (I) (3.5.51)	..	2·50	16·00
		a. Type II	..	2·50	16·00
		b. Vert pair. Nos. 37/a	..	27·00	
38		2 a. on 2d. pale red-brown (3.5.51)	..	30	6·00
39		2½ a. on 2½d. pale scarlet (3.5.51)	..	30	13·00
40	129	4 a. on 4d. light ultramarine	..	30	2·00
41	147	2 r. on 2s. 6d. yellow-green (3.5.51)	..	22·00	5·50
		a. Surch with Type 6b (1955)	..	£110	65·00
35/41 ..			*Set of 7*	23·00	48·00

1952 (5 Dec)–54. *Stamps of Queen Elizabeth II wmk Tudor Crown, surch as T 3 (in one line on 2½ and 6 a.).*

42	154	½ a. on ½d. orange-red (31.8.53)	..	10	1·25
43		1 a. on 1d. light ultramarine (31.8.53)	..	10	1·25
44		1½ a. on 1½d. green	..	10	15
45		2 a. on 2d. red-brown (31.8.53)	..	10	10
46	155	2½ a. on 2½d. carmine-red (31.8.53)	..	10	10
47		3 a. on 3d. deep lilac (B.) (18.1.54)	..	20	10
48	156	4 a. on 4d. ultramarine (2.11.53)	..	55	2·75
49	157	6 a. on 6d. reddish purple (18.1.54)	..	35	10
50	160	12 a. on 1s. 3d. green (2.11.53).	..	2·00	30
51	159	1 r. on 1s. 6d. grey-blue (2.11.53)	..	2·00	10
42/51 ..			*Set of 10*	5·00	5·50

1953 (10 June). *Coronation. Nos. 532/5 surch with new values.*

52	161	2½ a. on 2½d. carmine-red	..	1·75	95
53	162	4 a. on 4d. ultramarine	..	1·75	95
54	163	12 a. on 1s. 3d. deep yellow-green	..	3·25	95
55	164	1 r. on 1s. 6d. deep grey-blue	..	4·50	45
52/5 ..			*Set of 4*	10·00	3·00

2 RUPEES
— I

2 RUPEES
— II

2 RUPEES
— III

(7)

5 RUPEES
— I

5 RUPEES
— II

(8)

Types of surcharges

2 rupees.

Type I. On *Waterlow ptg.* Top of "R" level with top of "2" and other letters of "RUPEES". Bars 7 mm long.

Type II. On *Waterlow ptg by Harrison:* "R" dropped out of alignment with "2" and other letters of "RUPEES". Bars 6½ mm long.

Type III. On *De La Rue ptg by Harrison.* Top of "R" below level of top of "2". Bars 7–7¼ mm long and with left sides aligned with "S".

5 rupees.

Type I. On *Waterlow ptg by Harrison.* Ends of letters square and sharp. There were two printings made in March and May 1957.

Type II. On *De La Rue ptg by Harrison.* Type is thicker and ends of letters are relatively rounded.

For differences between Waterlow and De La Rue printings of the basic stamps see notes in Great Britain after No. 539.

1955–60. *T 166/7 (Waterlow ptgs) (W 165, St. Edward's Crown) surch with T 7/8.*

56	166	2 r. on 2s. 6d. black-brown (Type I) (23.9.55)	..	3·25	70
		a. Type II (2.57)	..	5·50	2·75
		b. Type III (No. 536a D.L.R.) (6.60)	..	20·00	48·00

57	167	5 r. on 5s. rose-red (Type I) (1.3.57)	..	9·00	2·00
		a. Wide surcharge	..	£225	£200
		b. Type II (No. 537a D.L.R.) (27.1.60)	20·00	48·00

No. 57a ("5" and "R" spaced 2¼ mm instead of 1¼ mm) occurred on R. 8/4 of the first surcharging of No. 57 only.

1956–57. *Stamps of Queen Elizabeth II, W 165, St. Edward's Crown, surch as T 3 (in one line on 2½ and 6 a.).*

58	154	1 a. on 1d. ultramarine (4.3.57)	..	35	50
58a		1½ a. on 1½d. green (1956)	..	—	£550
59		2 a. on 2d. red-brown (8.6.56).	..	70	1·25
60	155	2½ a. on 2½d. carmine-red (8.6.56)	..	80	2·75
61		3 a. on 3d. deep lilac (B.) (3.2.57)	..	1·00	4·50
62	156	4 a. on 4d. ultramarine (9.12.56)	..	5·00	13·00
63	157	6 a. on 6d. red-purple (10.2.57)	..	1·10	5·50
64	159	1 r. on 1s. 6d. grey-blue (2.8.56)	..	3·25	15
58/64 (ex 58a).			*Set of 7*	11·00	25·00

No. 58a came from a few sheets of the St. Edward's Crown watermark included, in error, with a printing of No. 44. Most examples were used in Dubai, but two are known from Muscat and a pair on a cover from Bahrain. A single mint example also exists.

(New Currency. 100 naye paise = 1 rupee)

NP 1 NP **3 NP NP** **75 NP**
(9)   (10)   (11)

1957 (1 Apr)–59. *Value in naye paise. Stamps of Queen Elizabeth II, W 165, St. Edward's Crown, surch as T 9 (1, 15, 25, 40, 50 n.p.), 11 (75 n.p.) or 10 (others).*

65	157	1 n.p. on 5d. brown	..	10	30
66	154	3 n.p. on ½d. orange-red	..	20	1·50
67		6 n.p. on 1d. ultramarine	..	20	1·50
68		9 n.p. on 1½d. green	..	20	50
69		12 n.p. on 2d. light red-brown	..	30	70
70	155	15 n.p. on 2½d. carmine-red (Type I)	..	30	10
		a. Type II (4.59)	..	30	2·50
71		20 n.p. on 3d. deep lilac (B.)	..	20	10
72	156	25 n.p. on 4d. ultramarine	..	70	2·50
73	157	40 n.p. on 6d. reddish purple	..	30	10
		a. Deep claret (3.59)	..	35	10
74	158	50 n.p. on 9d. bronze-green	..	1·25	2·00
75	160	75 n.p. on 1s. 3d. green	..	2·00	35
65/75 ..			*Set of 11*	5·00	8·50

15 NP

(12)

1957 (1 Aug). *World Scout Jubilee Jamboree. Nos. 557/9 surch in one line as T 12 (15 n.p.), or in two lines (others).*

76		15 n.p. on 2½d. carmine-red	..	25	85
77		25 n.p. on 4d. ultramarine	..	30	85
78		75 n.p. on 1s. 3d. green.	..	35	85
76/8 ..			*Set of 3*	80	2·25

1960 (26 Apr)–61. *Stamps of Queen Elizabeth II, W 179, Mult Crown, surch as T 9 (1, 15, 30, 40, 50 n.p.), 11 (75 n.p.), 3 (1 r.), 7 (2 r., 5 r.) or 10 (others).*

79	157	1 n.p. on 5d. brown (30.8.60)	..	10	20
80	154	3 n.p. on ½d. orange-red (21.6.60)	..	55	80
81		5 n.p. on 1d. ultramarine (8.4.61)	..	80	40
82		6 n.p. on 1d. ultramarine (21.6.60)	..	1·25	90
83		10 n.p. on 1½d. green (8.4.61)	..	50	80
84		12 n.p. on 2d. light red-brown (21.6.60)	2·00	2·50
85	155	15 n.p. on 2½d. carmine-red (Type II)	..	25	10
86		20 n.p. on 3d. deep lilac (B.) (28.9.60)	..	25	10
87	156	30 n.p. on 4½d. chestnut (8.4.61)	..	40	40
88	157	40 n.p. on 6d. deep claret (28.9.60)	..	45	10
89	158	50 n.p. on 9d. bronze-green (8.4.61)	..	1·00	80
90	160	75 n.p. on 1s. 3d. green (8.4.61)	..	2·25	90
91	159	1 r. on 1s. 6d. grey-blue (8.4.61)	..	13·00	2·00
92	166	2 r. on 2s. 6d. black-brown (No. 595) (8.4.61)	..	7·00	22·00
93	167	5 r. on 5s. rose-red (No. 596) (8.4.61)	16·00	35·00
79/93 ..			*Set of 15*	42·00	60·00

British Solomon Islands
see **Solomon Islands**

British Somaliland
see **Somaliland Protectorate**

British South Africa Company
see Rhodesia

British Virgin Islands

CROWN COLONY

Apart from the 1951 Legislative Council issue, the word "BRITISH" did not appear regularly on the stamps until 1968 when it was introduced to avoid confusion with the nearby Virgin Islands of the United States (the former Danish West Indies).

Most mail from the early years of the islands' history was sent via the Danish island of St. Thomas.

It is not known exactly when the first post office, or agency, was established on Tortola, but an entry in a G.P.O. account book suggest that it was operating by 1787 and the earliest letter postmarked "TORTOLA" dates from June of that year. The stamps of Great Britain were used from 1858 to May 1860, when the colonial authorities assumed responsibility for the overseas mails from the British G.P.O.

For illustrations of the handstamp and postmark types see BRITISH POST OFFICES ABROAD notes, following GREAT BRITAIN.

TORTOLA

CROWNED-CIRCLE HANDSTAMPS

CC1	CC 1	TORTOLA (R.) (15.12.1842)	*Price on cover*	£4000
CC2	CC 5	TORTOLA (R.) (21.6.1854)	*Price on cover*	£7000

No. CC2 is known used as an Official Paid mark during the years 1900 to 1918. *Price on cover* £1200.

Stamps of GREAT BRITAIN *cancelled* "A 13" *as Type* **2.**

1858 to 1860.

Z1	1d. rose-red (1857), perf 14	..	..	£3000
Z2	4d. rose (1857)	..	..	£2750
Z3	6d. lilac (1856)	..	..	£1100
Z4	1s. green (1856)	..	..	

PRICES FOR STAMPS ON COVER TO 1945		
Nos. 1/7	*from* × 15	
Nos. 8/22	*from* × 12	
Nos. 24/31	*from* × 8	
Nos. 32/41	*from* × 10	
No. 42	*from* × 20	
Nos. 43/50	*from* × 6	
Nos. 54/77	*from* × 5	
Nos. 78/81	*from* × 6	
Nos. 82/101	*from* × 3	
Nos. 103/6	*from* × 4	
Nos. 107/9	*from* × 6	
Nos. 110/21	*from* × 2	

1   St. Ursula   2

(Litho Nissen & Parker from original dies by Waterlow)

1866 (Dec). *No wmk. P 12 (a) White wove paper.*

1	1	1d. green	..	45·00	60·00
2		1d. deep green	..	50·00	65·00
3	2	6d. rose	..	90·00	£110
4		6d. deep rose	..	£130	£140
		a. Large "V" in "VIRGIN"	..	£375	£475

(b) Toned paper

5	1	1d. green	..	45·00	60·00
		a. Perf 15 × 12	..	£4250	£5500
6		1d. deep green	..	£100	£120
7	2	6d. rose-red	..	60·00	90·00
		a. Large "V" in "VIRGIN" (R. 2/1)	£275	£375

The above were printed in sheets of 25.

6d. stamps showing part of the papermaker's watermark ("A. Cowan & Sons Extra Superfine A. C. & S.") are worth 50% more.

Beware of fakes of No. 5a made from perf 12 stamps.

3   4

Normal Variety

1s. Long-tailed "S" in "ISLANDS" (R. 3/1)

(Litho Nissen and Parker from original dies by Waterlow)

1867–70. *No wmk. P* 15. 1s. *with double-lined frame.*

(a) White wove paper
8	1	1d. yellow-green (1868)	80·00	80·00
9		1d. blue-green (1870)	65·00	70·00
10	2	pale rose	£475	£475
11	4	1s. black and rose-carmine	£225	£300
		a. Long-tailed "S"	£600	£650

(b) Toned paper
12	1	1d. yellow-green (1868)	85·00	80·00
13	2	6d. dull rose (1868)	£225	£275
14	4	1s. black and rose-carmine (*greyish paper*)	£225	£300
		aa. Long-tailed "S"	£600	£650
14a		1s. black and rose-carmine	£300	£325
		b. Long-tailed "S"	£650	£700

(c) Pale rose paper
15	3	4d. lake-red	50·00	70·00

(d) Buff paper
16	3	4d. lake-red	40·00	60·00
17		4d. lake-brown	40·00	60·00

The thin lines of the frame on the 1s. are close together and sometimes merge into one.

The 1d. from the 1868 printing was in sheets of 20 with narrow margins between the stamps. Later printings were in sheets of 12 with wider margins. The 4d. was in sheets of 25; and the remaining two values in sheets of 20.

In Type 4 the figure of the Virgin was printed by typography and the remainder of the design by lithography.

The greyish paper used for Nos. 14 and 20 often shows traces of blue.

1867. *As T* 4, *but with crimson frames superimposed with bands extending through margins. P* 15.
18	4	1s. black and rose-carmine (*white paper*)	48·00	60·00
		a. Long-tailed "S"	£160	£180
		b. Figure of Virgin omitted	£60000	
19		1s. black and rose-carmine (*toned paper*)	48·00	60·00
		a. Long-tailed "S"	£160	£180
20		1s. black and rose-carmine (*greyish paper*)	£700	£850
		a. Long-tailed "S"	£1600	£1600

1868. *Nos.* 11 *and* 14a *with frame lines retouched so as to make them single lines. Margins remain white. P* 15.
21	4	1s. black and rose-carmine (*white paper*)	£130	£160
		aa. Long-tailed "S"	£375	£450
21a		1s. black and rose-carmine (*toned paper*)	£130	£160
		b. Long-tailed "S"	£375	£450

(Litho D.L.R.)

1878. *Wmk Crown CC* (*sideways*). *P* 14.
22	1	1d. green	70·00	85·00
		a. Yellow-green	£170	£130
		ab. Wmk upright	90·00	£120

4D

6 (Die I)　　　　　　(7)

(Typo D.L.R.)

1879–80. *Wmk Crown CC. P* 14.
24	6	1d. emerald-green (1880)	65·00	85·00
25		2½d. red-brown	90·00	£120

1883 (June)**–84.** *Wmk Crown CA. P* 14.
26	6	½d. yellow-buff	80·00	80·00
27		½d. dull green (*shades*) (11.83)	3·25	8·00
		b. Top left triangle detached	85·00	
29		1d. pale rose (15.9.83)	22·00	50·00
		a. Deep rose (1884)	55·00	60·00
31		2½d. ultramarine (9.84)	2·50	13·00
		b. Top left triangle detached	85·00	

For illustration of "top left triangle detached" variety see above No. 21 of Antigua.

(Litho D.L.R.)

1887–89. *Wmk Crown CA. P* 14.
32	1	1d. red (5.89)	2·00	7·00
33		1d. rose-red	2·25	7·00
34		1d. rose	5·00	14·00
35	3	4d. chestnut	35·00	65·00
36		4d. pale chestnut	35·00	65·00
37		4d. brown-red	45·00	70·00
38	2	6d. dull violet	13·00	48·00
39		6d. deep violet	12·00	42·00
40	4	1s. sepia (2.89)	80·00	£100
41		1s. brown to deep brown	45·00	70·00
34/40		Optd "Specimen"	*Set of* 4	£300

The De La Rue transfers of T 1 to 4 are new transfers and differ from those of Messrs. Nissen and Parker, particularly T 4

1888 (July). *Nos.* 18/19 *surch with T* 7, *in violet, in Antigua.*
42	4	4d. on 1s. black and rose-carmine (*toned paper*)	£110	£150
		a. Surch double	£6500	
		b. Surch inverted (in pair with normal)	£40000	
		c. Long-tailed "S"	£400	£500
42d		4d. on 1s. black and rose-carmine (*white paper*)	£140	£180

The special issues for Virgin Islands were superseded on 31 October 1890, by the general issue for Leeward Islands. In 1899, however, a new special issue (given below) appeared; it did not supersede the general issue for Leeward Islands, but was used concurrently, as were all subsequent issues, until 1 July 1956, when the general Leeward Islands stamps were withdrawn.

8　　　　　　9　　　　　　10

(Recess D.L.R.)

1899 (Jan). *Wmk Crown CA. P* 14.
43	8	½d. yellow-green	75	55
		a. Error. "HALFPFNNY" (R. 10/1)	80·00	£120
		b. Error. "HALFPENNY" (R. 8/2)	80·00	£120
		c. Imperf between (horiz pair)	£7000	
44		1d. brick-red	2·25	2·75
45		2½d. ultramarine	12·00	4·00
46		4d. brown	4·00	16·00
		a. Error "FOURPENCF" (R.10/3)	£850	£1200
47		6d. dull violet	4·50	4·50
48		7d. deep green	7·00	8·00
49		1s. brown-yellow	19·00	32·00
50		5s. indigo	65·00	80·00
43/50			*Set of* 8	£100 £130
43/50		Optd "Specimen"	*Set of* 8	£160

Nos. 43a/b and 46a were corrected after the first printing.

(Typo D.L.R.)

1904 (1 June). *Wmk Mult Crown CA. P* 14.
54	9	½d. dull purple and green	60	40
55		1d. dull purple and scarlet	1·25	35
56	10	2d. dull purple and ochre	4·25	4·50
57	9	2½d. dull purple and ultramarine	1·75	2·00
58	10	3d. dull purple and black	2·75	3·00
59	9	6d. dull purple and brown	2·75	3·00
60	10	1s. green and scarlet	3·00	4·75
61		2s. 6d. green and black	21·00	48·00
62	9	5s. green and blue	45·00	65·00
54/62			*Set of* 9	75·00 £110
54/62		Optd "Specimen"	*Set of* 9	£140

11　　　　　　12

(Typo D.L.R.)

1913 (Feb)**–19.** *Die I. Wmk Mult Crown CA. Chalk-surfaced paper* (3d. *to* 5s.). *P* 14.
69	11	½d. green	1·50	2·75
		a. Yellow-green (8.16)	2·00	8·00
		b. Blue-green and deep green (3.19)	1·25	4·50
70		1d. deep red	7·50	9·50
		a. Deep red and carmine (10.17)	2·25	11·00
		b. Scarlet (10.17)	2·25	12·00
		c. Carmine-red (3.19)	42·00	25·00
71	12	2d. grey	3·75	17·00
		a. Slate-grey	48·00	22·00
72	11	2½d. bright blue	4·00	6·50
73	12	3d. purple/yellow	2·25	4·75
74	11	6d. dull and bright purple	3·75	6·00
75	12	1s. black/blue-green	3·25	6·50
76		2s. 6d. black and red/blue	48·00	45·00
77	11	5s. green and red/yellow	32·00	£100
69/77			*Set of* 9	90·00 £180
69/77		Optd "Specimen"	*Set of* 9	£180

Stock of the original printing of the ½d., No. 69, was exhausted by January 1916 and Leeward Islands ½d. stamps were used until the yellow-green printing, No. 69a, arrived in August 1916.

WAR STAMP

(13)　　　　　14

1916 (20 Oct)**–19.** *Optd with T* 13.
78	11	1d. carmine	1·60	15·00
		a. Watermark sideways	£900	
		b. Pale red/bluish	20	4·75
		bw. Wmk inverted	50·00	
		by. Wmk inverted and reversed		
		c. Scarlet (1918)	20	3·00
		d. Short opt (right pane R. 10/1)	20·00	
79	12	3d. purple/yellow	60	9·50
		a. Purple/lemon	2·50	7·50
		b. Purple/buff-yellow (11.3.19)	1·25	16·00
		bw. Wmk inverted	15·00	
		by. Wmk inverted and reversed		
		c. Short opt (right pane R. 10/1)	30·00	
78/9		Optd "Specimen"	*Set of* 2	70·00

Nos. 78d and 79c show the overprint 2 mm high instead of 2½ mm.

1921 (18 Nov). *As* 1913–19, *but Die II and wmk Mult Script CA.*
80	11	½d. green	1·75	22·00
81		1d. scarlet and deep carmine	1·25	18·00
80/1		Optd "Specimen"	*Set of* 2	70·00

(Typo D.L.R.)

1922 (15 June)**–29.** *P* 14. (a) *Wmk Mult Crown CA. Chalk-surfaced paper.*
82	14	3d. purple/pale yellow	50	12·00
83		1s. black/emerald	75	12·00
84		2s. 6d. black and red/blue	4·00	9·00
85		5s. green and red/pale yellow	30·00	85·00
82/5			*Set of* 4	32·00 £110
82/5		Optd "Specimen"	*Set of* 4	90·00

(b) *Wmk Mult Script CA. Chalk-surfaced paper* (5d. *to* 5s.)
86	14	½d. dull green	85	2·25
87		1d. rose-carmine	60	60
88		1d. bright violet (1927)	1·00	3·50
89		1d. scarlet (1929)	10·00	12·00
90		1½d. carmine-red (1927)	1·50	2·00
91		1½d. Venetian red (1928)	1·75	2·00
92		2d. grey	60	5·50
93		2½d. pale bright blue	1·50	11·00
94		2½d. dull orange (1.9.23)	1·25	1·25
95		2½d. bright blue (1927)	90	3·50
96		3d. purple/pale yellow (1928)	2·00	8·00
97		5d. dull purple and olive	5·00	45·00
98		6d. dull and bright purple	1·25	5·00
99		1s. black/emerald (1928)	1·25	11·00
100		2s. 6d. black and red/blue (1928)	19·00	40·00
101		5s. green and red/yellow (1.9.23)	19·00	60·00
86/101			*Set of* 16	60·00 £190
86/101		Optd/Perf "Specimen"	*Set of* 16	£275

In the 1½d. stamps the value is in colour on a white ground.

1935 (6 May). *Silver Jubilee. As Nos.* 91/4 *of Antigua but printed by Waterlow. P* 11 × 12.
103		1d. deep blue and scarlet	95	2·00
		k. Kite and vertical log	55·00	
		l. Kite and horizontal log	55·00	
104		1½d. ultramarine and grey	95	2·00
		k. Kite and vertical log	60·00	
		l. Kite and horizontal log	60·00	
105		2½d. brown and deep blue	95	2·00
		k. Kite and vertical log	65·00	
		l. Kite and horizontal log	65·00	
106		1s. slate and purple	5·50	11·50
		k. Kite and vertical log	£130	
		l. Kite and horizontal log	£130	
103/6			*Set of* 4	7·50 16·00
103/6		Perf "Specimen"	*Set of* 4	85·00

For illustrations of plate varieties see Catalogue Introduction.

1937 (12 May). *Coronation. As Nos.* 95/7 *of Antigua. P* 11×11½.
107		1d. carmine	20	80
108		1½d. yellow-brown	40	2·25
109		2½d. blue	45	80
107/9			*Set of* 3	95 3·50
107/9		Perf "Specimen"	*Set of* 3	55·00

15 King George VI and Badge of Colony　　　　16 Map

(Photo Harrison)

1938 (1 Aug)**–47.** *Wmk Mult Script CA. Chalk-surfaced paper. P* 14.
110	15	½d. green	2·25	1·75
		a. Ordinary paper (10.43)	30	90
111		1d. scarlet	2·25	1·25
		a. Ordinary paper (10.43)	30	60
112		1½d. red-brown	3·00	3·25
		a. Ordinary paper (10.43)	65	95
		w. Wmk inverted	†	
113		2d. grey	4·00	1·50
		a. Ordinary paper (10.43)	40	90
114		2½d. ultramarine	3·25	1·25
		a. Ordinary paper (10.43)	60	1·50
115		3d. orange	5·50	70
		a. Ordinary paper (10.43)	40	80
116		6d. mauve	3·50	90
		a. Ordinary paper (10.43)	1·50	80
117		1s. olive-brown	7·00	2·50
		a. Ordinary paper (10.43)	1·50	70
118		2s. 6d. sepia	20·00	4·50
		a. Ordinary paper (8.42)	14·00	3·00
119		5s. carmine	40·00	5·50
		a. Ordinary paper (8.42)	13·00	4·00
120		10s. blue (1.12 47)	7·00	8·00
121		£1 black (1.12.47)	11·00	20·00
110/21			*Set of* 12	45·00 38·00
110/21		Perf "Specimen"	*Set of* 12	£225

The ordinary paper, used as a substitute for the chalk-surfaced paper for printings between 1942 and 1945, is thick, smooth and opaque.

1946 (1 Nov). *Victory. As Nos.* 110/11 *of Antigua.*
122		1½d. lake-brown	10	10
123		3d. orange	10	10
122/3		Perf "Specimen"	*Set of* 2	55·00

1949 (3 Jan). *Royal Silver Wedding. As Nos.* 112/13 *of Antigua.*
124		2½d. ultramarine	10	10
125		£1 black	11·00	13·00

1949 (10 Oct). *75th Anniv of U.P.U. As Nos.* 114/17 *of Antigua.*
126		2½d. ultramarine	30	45
127		3d. orange	80	1·60
128		6d. magenta	50	40
129		1s. olive	50	40
126/9			*Set of* 4	1·90 2·50

(New Currency. 100 cents = 1 B.W.I. dollar)

1951. *Inauguration of B.W.I. University College. As Nos. 118/19 of Antigua.*
130   3 c. black and brown-red (10.4) 40   40
131   12 c. black and reddish violet (16.2) .. 40   50

(Recess Waterlow)

1951 (2 Apr). *Restoration of Legislative Council. Wmk Mult Script CA. P 14½ x 14.*
132 16   6 c. orange 20   50
133   12 c. purple 20   50
134   24 c. olive 20   50
135    $1.20 carmine 45   75
132/5 .. .. *Set of 4* 95 2·00

17 Sombrero   18 Map of Jost Van Dyke
Lighthouse

(Recess D.L.R.)

1952 (15 Apr). *T 17/18 and similar designs. Wmk Mult Script CA. P 12½ × 13 (vert) or 13 × 12½ (horiz).*
136   1 c. black 40   90
137   2 c. deep green 35   30
138   3 c. black and brown 30   80
139   4 c. carmine-red 35   40
140   5 c. claret and black 90   50
141   8 c. bright blue 35   75
142   12 c. dull violet 45   85
143   24 c. deep brown 35   30
144   60 c. yellow-green and blue .. 2·50 11·00
145    $1.20, black and bright blue .. 3·75 12·00
146    $2.40, yellowish green and red-brown 10·00 11·00
147    $4.80, bright blue and carmine .. 11·00 14·00
136/47 .. .. .. *Set of 12* 27·00 48·00
Designs: *Horiz*—3 c. Sheep industry; 4 c. Map of Anegada; 5 c. Cattle industry; 8 c. Map of Virgin Gorda; 12 c. Map of Tortola; 60 c. Dead Man's Chest; $1.20, Sir Francis Drake Channel; $2.40, Road Town; $4.80, Map of Virgin Islands. *Vert*—24 c. Badge of the Presidency.

1953 (2 June). *Coronation. As No. 120 of Antigua.*
148   2 c. black and green 30   85

29 Map of Tortola   30 Brown Pelican

(Recess D.L.R.)

1956 (1 Nov)–**62.** *Designs as T 29/30. Wmk Mult Script CA. P 13×12½ (½ c. to $1.20) or 12×11½ ($2.40 and $4.80).*
149   ½ c. black and reddish purple .. 40   20
    a. Black and deep reddish purple (19.4.60) 65 2·00
150   1 c. turquoise-blue and slate .. 2·00   75
    a. Turquoise and slate-violet (26.11.62) 11·00 4·75
151   2 c. vermilion and black 30   10
152   3 c. blue and deep olive 30   30
153   4 c. deep brown and turquoise-green 35   40
154   5 c. grey-black 45   10
155   8 c. yellow-orange and deep blue .. 60   40
156   12 c. ultramarine and rose-red .. 1·75   75
157   24 c. myrtle-green and brown-orange 1·00   65
158   60 c. indigo and yellow-orange .. 8·00 8·00
159    $1.20, deep yellow-green and carmine-red 2·00 10·00
160    $2.40, lemon and deep dull purple 28·00 13·00
161    $4.80, blackish brown and turquoise-blue 28·00 13·00
149/61 .. .. .. *Set of 13* 65·00 38·00
Designs: *Size as T 29*—1 c. Virgin Islands Sloop; 2 c. Nelthrop Red Poll Bull; 3 c. Road Harbour; 4 c. Mountain travel; 5 c. Badge of the Presidency; 8 c. Beach scene; 12 c. *New Idea* (sloop) under construction; 24 c. White Cedar tree; 60 c. Skipjack Tuna ("Bonito"); $1.20, Treasury Square. *Size as T 30*—$4.80, Magnificent Frigate Bird.

(New Currency. 100 cents = 1 U.S. dollar)

1¢

(42)

1962 (10 Dec). *As Nos. 149/53 and 155/61, but W w 12, surch in U.S. currency as T 42 by D.L.R.*
162   1 c. on ½ c. black and deep reddish purple 30   10
163   2 c. on 1 c. turquoise and slate-violet .. 1·25   10
164   3 c. on 2 c. vermilion and black .. 30   10
165   4 c. on 3 c. black and deep olive .. 30   10
166   5 c. on 4 c. deep brown and turquoise-green 30   10
167   8 c. on 8 c. yellow-orange and deep blue 30   10
168   10 c. on 12 c. ultramarine and rose-red 40   10
169   12 c. on 24 c. myrtle-green and brown-orange 30   10
170   25 c. on 60 c. indigo and yellow-orange 2·25   45
171   70 c. on $1.20, dp yellow-green & carmine-red 35   45
    a. Stop to right of C in surcharge instead of beneath it (in pair with normal). .. 9·50 7·50
172    $1.40 on $2.40, lemon and deep dull purple 6·50 3·50
173    $2.80 on $4.80, blackish brown and turquoise-blue .. .. 7·00 3·50
162/73 .. .. .. *Set of 12* 17·00 7·50
No. 171a occurs on the first stamp on Rows 1 to 10.

1963 (4 June). *Freedom from Hunger. As No. 146 of Antigua.*
174   25 c. reddish violet 20   10

1963 (2 Sept). *Red Cross Centenary. As Nos. 147/8 of Antigua.*
175   2 c. red and black 15   20
176   25 c. red and blue 40   20

1964 (23 Apr). *400th Birth Anniv of William Shakespeare. As No. 164 of Antigua.*
177   10 c. bright blue 15   10

43 Skipjack Tuna

44 Map of Tortola   45 Badge of the Colony

(Des and recess D.L.R.)

1964 (2 Nov)–**68.** *Designs as T 43/5. W w 12. P 11½×12 ($2.80), 13×13½ (70 c., $1, $1.40), or 13×12½ (others).*
178   1 c. blue and olive-green .. 30 1·00
179   2 c. yellow-olive and rose-red .. 15   30
180   3 c. sepia and turquoise-blue .. 3·00 1·25
181   4 c. black and carmine-red .. 80   90
182   5 c. black and deep bluish green .. 65 1·00
183   6 c. black and brown-orange .. 30   85
184   8 c. black and magenta 30   45
185   10 c. lake and deep lilac .. 1·25   30
    a. Bright lake and reddish lilac (26.11.68) 7·50 2·00
186   12 c. deep bluish green and deep violet-blue 2·00 1·50
187   15 c. yellow-green and grey-black .. 35 1·50
188   25 c. green and purple .. .. 11·00 1·60
189   70 c. black and yellow-brown .. 3·50 3·50
190    $1 yellow-green and chestnut .. 3·00 1·50
191    $1.40, light blue and rose .. 17·00 7·00
192    $2.80, black and bright purple .. 17·00 8·00
178/92 .. .. .. *Set of 15* 55·00 27·00
Designs: *Horiz as T 43*—2 c. Soper's Hole; 3 c. Brown Pelican; 4 c. Dead Man's Chest; 5 c. Road Harbour; 8 c. Fallen Jerusalem; 8 c. The Baths, Virgin Gorda; 10 c. Map of Virgin Islands; 12 c. Youth of Tortola (Tortola-St. Thomas ferry); 15 c. The Towers, Tortola; 25 c. Beef Island Airfield. *Vert as T 44*—$1 Virgin Gorda; $1.40, Yachts at anchor.

1965 (17 May). *I.T.U. Centenary. As Nos. 166/7 of Antigua.*
193   4 c. yellow and turquoise .. 15   10
194   25 c. light blue and orange-buff .. 35   20

1965 (25 Oct). *International Co-operation Year. As Nos. 168/9 of Antigua.*
195   1 c. reddish purple and turquoise-green 10   15
196   25 c. deep bluish green and lavender .. 30   15

1966 (24 Jan). *Churchill Commemoration. As Nos. 170/3 of Antigua.*
197   1 c. new blue 10   10
198   2 c. deep green 15   10
199   10 c. brown 30   10
200   25 c. bluish violet 60   25
197/200 .. .. .. *Set of 4* 1·00   40

1966 (22 Feb). *Royal Visit. As Nos. 174/5 of Antigua.*
201   4 c. black and ultramarine .. 40   10
202   70 c. black and magenta .. 1·40   45

58 Atrato I (paddle-steamer), 1866

(Des R. Granger Barrett. Litho B.W.)

1966 (25 Apr). *Stamp Centenary. T 58 and similar horiz designs. W w 12 (sideways). P 13.*
203   5 c. black, red, yellow and emerald .. 30   10
204   10 c. black, green and rose-red/cream.. 30   10
205   25 c. black, rose-red and blue/pale green 55   10
206   60 c. black, red and green/pale blue .. 85 1·50
203/6 .. .. .. *Set of 4* 1·75 1·50
Design:—10 c. 1d. and 6d. stamps of 1866; 25 c. Air mail transport, Beef Island, and 6d. stamp of 1866; 60 c. Landing mail at Roadtown, 1866 and 1d. stamp of 1866.

50c.

(62)

1966 (15 Sept). *As Nos. 189 and 191/2 but wmk sideways, surch as T 62.*
207   50 c. on 70 c. black and yellow-brown.. 1·00   90
208    $1.50 on $1.40, light blue and rose .. 2·50 2·00
209    $3 on $2.80, black and bright purple .. 2·50 2·75
207/9 .. .. .. *Set of 3* 5·50 5·00

1966 (1 Dec). *20th Anniv of U.N.E.S.C.O. As Nos. 196/8 of Antigua.*
210   2 c. slate-violet, red, yellow and orange 10   10
211   12 c. orange-yellow, violet and deep olive .. 20   10
212   60 c. black, bright purple and orange.. 50   45
210/12 .. .. .. *Set of 3* 65   60

63 Map of Virgin Islands

(Des G. Vasarhelyi. Photo Harrison)

1967 (18 Apr). *New Constitution. W w 12. P 14½.*
213 63   2 c. multicoloured 10   10
214   10 c. multicoloured 15   10
    w. Wmk inverted .. .. 15·00
215   25 c. multicoloured 15   10
    w. Wmk inverted .. .. 9·00
216    $1 multicoloured 55   40
213/16 .. .. .. *Set of 4* 75   55

64 Mercury (cable ship) and Bermuda-Tortola Link

(Des G. Drummond, Photo Harrison)

1967 (14 Sept). *Inauguration of Bermuda-Tortola Telephone Service. T 64 and similar horiz designs. Multicoloured. W w 12. P 14½.*
217   4 c. Type 64 15   10
218   10 c. Chalwell Telecommunications Station 15   10
219   50 c. Mercury (cable ship) .. 40   30
217/19 .. .. .. *Set of 3* 60   40

67 Blue Marlin

(Des V. Whiteley. Photo Enschedé)

1968 (2 Jan). *Game Fishing. T 67 and similar horiz designs. W w 12 (sideways). P 12½ × 12.*
220   2 c. multicoloured 10   55
221   10 c. multicoloured 25   10
222   25 c. black, blue and bright violet .. 55   10
223   40 c. multicoloured 85   70
220/3 .. .. .. *Set of 4* 1·60 1·25
Designs—10 c. Cobia; 25 c. Wahoo; 40 c. Fishing launch and map.

1968
INTERNATIONAL
YEAR FOR
HUMAN RIGHTS

(71)

72 Dr. Martin Luther King, Bible, Sword and Armour Gauntlet

1968 (29 July). *Human Rights Year. Nos. 185 and 188 optd with T 71.*
224   10 c. lake and deep lilac .. 20   10
225   25 c. green and purple .. 30   40
29 July was the date of issue in the islands. The Crown Agents supplies went on sale in London on 1 July, the local consignment being delayed in transit.

(Des V. Whiteley. Litho Format)

1968 (15 Oct). *Martin Luther King Commemoration. W w 12 (sideways). P 14.*
226 72   4 c. multicoloured 20   20
227   25 c. multicoloured 30   40

73 De Havilland D.H.C.6
Twin Otter 100

(Des R. Granger Barrett. Litho Format)

1968 (16 Dec). *Opening of Beef Island Airport Extension. T* **73** *and similar horiz designs. Multicoloured. P* 14.

228	2 c.	Type **73**		15	60
229	10 c.	Hawker Siddeley H.S.748 airliner		20	10
230	25 c.	De Havilland D.H.114 Heron 2		55	10
231	$1	Royal Engineers cap badge		75	2·00
228/31			*Set of* 4	1·50	2·50

77 Long John Silver and Jim Hawkins   78 Jim Hawkins escaping from the Pirates

(Des Jennifer Toombs. Photo Enschedé)

1969 (18 Mar). *75th Death Anniv of Robert Louis Stevenson. Scenes from* Treasure Island. *T* **77/8** *and similar designs. W* w **12** *(sideways on* 10 c., $1*). P* 13½×13 (4 c., 40 c.) or 13×13½ *(others).*

232	4 c.	indigo, pale yellow and carmine-red		25	15
233	10 c.	multicoloured		25	10
234	40 c.	brown, black and blue		30	30
235	$1	multicoloured		60	1·40
232/5			*Set of* 4	1·25	1·75

Designs:— *Vert—*40 c. The fight with Israel Hands. *Horiz—*$1 Treasure trove.

82 Yachts in Road Harbour, Tortola

(Des J. Cooter, Litho P.B.)

1969 (20 Oct). *Tourism. T* **82** *and similar multicoloured designs. W* w **12** *(sideways on* 2 c., $1*). P* 12½.

236	2 c.	Tourist and Yellow-finned Grouper (fish) *(vert)*		15	50
237	10 c.	Type **82**		30	10
238	20 c.	Sun-bathing at Virgin Gorda National Park		40	20
239	$1	Tourist and Pipe Organ Cactus at Virgin Gorda *(vert)*		90	1·50
236/9			*Set of* 4	1·60	2·00

85 Carib Canoe

(Des and litho J.W.)

1970 (16 Feb)–**74.** *Horiz designs as T* **85.** *W* w **12** *(sideways*). P* 14.

240	½ c.	buff, red-brown and sepia		10	85
241	1 c.	new blue, apple-green and chalky blue		15	30
		a. Perf 13½ (12.11.74)		1·25	2·00
242	2 c.	yellow-orange, red-brown and slate		40	1·00
243	3 c.	orange-red, cobalt and sepia		30	1·25
244	4 c.	greenish blue, chalky blue & bistre-brn		30	50
		w. Wmk Crown to right of CA			
245	5 c.	emerald, pink and black		30	10
246	6 c.	reddish violet mauve and myrtle-green		40	1·75
247	8 c.	apple-green, greenish yellow and sepia		50	2·00
248	10 c.	greenish blue, yellow-brown & red-brn		50	15
		a. Perf 13½ (12.11.74)		2·50	2·25
249	12 c.	yellow, crimson and brown		65	1·00
		a. Perf 13½ (12.11.74)		2·50	3·25
250	15 c.	turquoise-green, orange & bistre-brn		5·00	85
		a. Perf 13½ (12.11.74)		4·50	3·25
251	25 c.	grey-green, steel-blue and plum		6·00	1·75
252	50 c.	magenta, dull green and purple-brown		3·50	1·50
253	$1	salmon, olive-green and red-brown		4·00	4·75
254	$2	buff, slate and grey		8·00	9·00
255	$3	ochre, deep blue and sepia		5·00	6·50
256	$5	violet and grey		8·00	9·00
240/56			*Set of* 17	38·00	38·00

Designs:—1 c. *Santa Maria* (Columbus' flagship); 2 c. *Elizabeth Bonaventure* (Drake's flagship); 3 c. Dutch Buccaneer, circa 1660; 4 c. *Thetis,* 1827 (after etching by E. W. Cooke); 5 c. Henry Morgan's ship (17th century); 6 c. H.M.S. *Boreas* (Captain Nelson, 1784); 8 c. H.M.S. *Éclair,* 1804; 10 c. H.M.S. *Formidable,* 1782; 12 c. H.M.S. *Nymph,* 1778; 15 c. *Windsor Castle* (sailing packet) engaging *Jeune Richard* (French brig), 1807; 25 c. H.M.S. *Astrea,* 1808; 50 c. Wreck of R.M.S. *Rhone,* 1867; $1 Tortola sloop; $2 H.M.S. *Frobisher;* $3 *Booker Viking* (cargo liner), 1967; $5 Hydrofoil *Sun Arrow.*

*The normal sideways watermark shows Crown to left of CA, *as seen from the back of the stamp.*

See also Nos. 295/300.

---

102 *A Tale of Two Cities*

(Des W. G. Brown. Litho D.L.R.)

1970 (4 May). *Death Centenary of Charles Dickens. T* **102** *and similar horiz designs showing original book illustrations. W* w **12** *(sideways). P* 14.

257	5 c.	black, light rose and grey		10	15
258	10 c.	black, light blue and pale green		20	10
259	25 c.	black, light green and pale yellow		30	40
257/9			*Set of* 3	55	55

Designs:—10 c. *Oliver Twist;* 25 c. *Great Expectations.*

103 Hospital Visit

(Des R. Granger Barrett. Litho Questa)

1970 (10 Aug). *Centenary of British Red Cross. T* **103** *and similar horiz designs. Multicoloured. W* w **12** *(sideways*).*

260	4 c.	Type **103**		25	10
261	10 c.	First Aid Class		35	10
262	25 c.	Red Cross and Coat of Arms		80	45
		w. Wmk Crown to right of CA		35·00	
260/2			*Set of* 3	1·25	60

*The normal sideways watermark shows Crown to left of CA, *as seen from the back of the stamp.*

104 Mary Read   105 Children and "UNICEF"

(Des and litho J.W.)

1970 (16 Nov). *Pirates. T* **104** *and similar vert designs. Multicoloured. W* w **12.** *P* 14 × 14½.

263	½ c.	Type **104**		10	15
264	10 c.	George Lowther		35	10
265	30 c.	Edward Teach (Blackbeard)		85	25
266	60 c.	Henry Morgan		1·25	1·00
263/6			*Set of* 4	2·25	1·40

(Des L. Curtis. Litho Format)

1971 (13 Dec). *25th Anniv of UNICEF. W* w **12** *(sideways). P* 13½ × 14.

267	**106**	15 c. multicoloured		10	10
268		30 c. multicoloured		20	25

VISIT OF H.R.H.

THE

PRINCESS MARGARET

1972   1972

(106)

1972 (7 Mar). *Royal Visit of Princess Margaret. Nos.* 244 *and* 251 *optd with T* **106.**

269	4 c.	greenish blue, chalky blue & bistre-brn		20	15
270	25 c.	grey-green, steel-blue and plum		30	45

107 Seaman of 1800   108 Sailfish and *Sir Winston Churchill* (cadet schooner)

(Des J.W. Litho Questa)

1972 (17 Mar). *"Interpex" Stamp Exhibition, New York. T* **107** *and similar vert designs showing Naval Uniforms. Multicoloured. W* w **12** *(sideways*). P* 13½.

271	½ c.	Type **107**		10	15
		w. Wmk Crown to left of CA		1·75	
272	10 c.	Boatswain, 1787–1807		35	10
273	30 c.	Captain, 1795–1812		85	55
274	60 c.	Admiral, 1787–95		1·50	2·00
271/4			*Set of* 4	2·50	2·50

*The normal sideways watermark shows Crown to right of CA, *as seen from the back of the stamp.*

(Des (from photograph by D. Groves) and photo Harrison)

1972 (24 Nov). *Royal Silver Wedding. Multicoloured; background colour given. W* w **12.** *P* 14 × 14½.

275	**108**	15 c. bright blue		20	15
276		25 c. turquoise-blue		20	15
		a. Blue omitted*		£300	
		w. Wmk inverted		26·00	

*The omission of the blue colour results in the Duke's suit appearing sepia instead of deep blue.

109 Blue Marlin

(Des G. Drummond. Litho Questa)

1972 (12 Dec). *Game Fish. T* **109** *and similar horiz designs. Multicoloured. W* w **12.** *P* 13½.

277	½ c.	Type **109**		10	30
		a. Pair. Nos. 277/8		15	60
278	½ c.	Wahoo		10	30
279	15 c.	Yellow-finned Tuna ("Allison Tuna")		55	55
280	25 c.	White Marlin		60	30
281	50 c.	Sailfish		1·25	1·00
282	$1	Dolphin		2·00	2·25
277/82			*Set of* 6	4·00	4·00
MS283	194×158 mm. Nos. 277/82			8·50	8·50

Nos. 277/8 were printed horizontally and vertically *se-tenant* within the sheet.

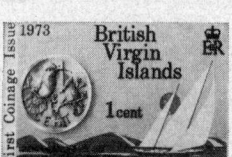

110 J. C. Lettsom   111 Green-throated Carib and Antillean Crested Hummingbird

(Des J. Cooter. Litho Questa)

1973 (9 Mar). *"Interpex 1973" (Quakers). T* **110** *and similar multicoloured designs. W* w **12** *(sideways on* ½ c. *and* 15 c.*). P* 13½.

284	½ c.	Type **110**		10	10
285	10 c.	Lettsom House *(horiz)*		15	10
286	15 c.	Dr. W. Thornton		20	10
287	30 c.	Dr. Thornton and Capitol, Washington *(horiz)*		25	20
288	$1	William Penn *(horiz)*		70	85
284/8			*Set of* 5	1·25	1·10

(Des G. Drummond. Litho Questa)

1973 (30 June). *First Issue of Coinage. T* **111** *and similar horiz designs showing coins and local scenery. Multicoloured. W* w **12.** *P* 14.

289	1 c.	Type **111**		10	10
290	5 c.	Zenaida Dove		50	10
291	10 c.	Ringed Kingfisher		65	10
292	25 c.	Mangrove Cuckoo		85	15
293	50 c.	Brown Pelican		95	1·00
294	$1	Magnificent Frigate Bird		1·40	1·75
289/94			*Set of* 6	4·00	2·75

1973 (17 Oct). *As Nos.* 240, 243/5 *and* 248/9, *but wmk upright.*

295	½ c.	buff, red-brown and sepia		50	4·00
296	3 c.	orange-red, cobalt and sepia		1·25	2·25
297	4 c.	greenish blue, chalky blue & bistre-brn		1·25	2·25
298	5 c.	emerald, pink and black		1·25	2·25
299	10 c.	greenish blue, yellow-brown & red-brn		1·50	2·50
		w. Wmk inverted			
300	12 c.	yellow, dull crimson and light brown		2·00	3·50
295/300			*Set of* 6	7·00	17·00

1973 (14 Nov). *Royal Wedding. As Nos.* 165/6 *of Anguilla. Centre multicoloured. W* w **12** *(sideways). P* 13½.

301	5 c.	brown-ochre		10	10
302	50 c.	light turquoise-blue		20	10

112 "The Virgin and Child"
(Pintoricchio)

113 Crest of the *Canopus*
(French)

(Des G. Drummond. Litho Questa)

1973 (7 Dec). *Christmas. T* **112** *and similar vert designs Multi coloured. W* w **12**. *P* 14.

303	½ c. Type 112		10	10
304	3 c. "Virgin and Child" (Lorenzo di Credi)		10	10
305	25 c. "Virgin and Child" (Crivelli)		15	10
306	50 c. "Virgin and Child with St. John" (Luini)		30	40
303/6		*Set of 4*	50	50

(Des J. Cooter. Litho Questa)

1974 (22 Mar). *"Interpex 1974" (Naval Crests). T* **113** *and similar vert designs. Multicoloured. W* w **12**. *P* 14.

307	5 c. Type 113		20	10
308	18 c. U.S.S. *Saginaw*		35	25
309	25 c. H.M.S. *Rothesay*		40	30
310	50 c. H.M.C.S. *Ottawa*		60	60
307/10		*Set of 4*	1·40	1·10
MS311	196 × 128 mm. Nos. 307/10		1·75	3·25

114 Christopher
Columbus

115 Atlantic Trumpet Triton
(*Charonia variegata*)

(Des J. W. Litho Format)

1974 (19 Aug). *Historical Figures. T* **114** *and similar vert designs. W* w **12**. *P* 14.

312	5 c. orange and black		20	10
	w. Wmk inverted		2·25	
313	10 c. greenish blue and black		30	10
314	25 c. reddish violet and black		35	25
315	40 c. yellow-brown and sepia		60	75
312/15		*Set of 4*	1·25	1·00
MS316	84×119 mm. Nos. 312/15		1·25	2·25

Portraits:—10 c. Sir Walter Raleigh; 25 c. Sir Martin Frobisher; 40 c. Sir Francis Drake.

(Des G. Drummond. Litho Harrison)

1974 (30 Sept). *Seashells. T* **115** *and similar horiz designs. Multicoloured. W* w **12**. *P* 13 × 13½.

317	5 c. Type 115		30	15
	a. Wmk T 53 of Lesotho (sideways)		£140	
	w. Wmk inverted		70·00	
318	18 c. West Indian Murex (*Murex brevifrons*)		60	30
319	25 c. Bleeding Tooth (*Nerita peloranta*)		75	35
320	75 c. Virgin Islands Latirus (*Latirus virginensis*)		1·75	2·00
317/20		*Set of 4*	3·00	2·50
MS321	146×95 mm. Nos. 317/20		3·00	5·50
	a. Printed on the gummed side		£500	
	w. Wmk inverted		32·00	

116 Churchill and St. Mary,
Aldermanbury, London

117 H.M.S. *Boreas*

(Des J. W. Litho Questa)

1974 (30 Nov). *Birth Centenary of Sir Winston Churchill. T* **116** *and similar horiz design. Multicoloured. W* w **14** *(sideways*)*. P* 14.

322	10 c. Type 116		15	10
	w. Wmk Crown to right of CA		3·75	
323	50 c. St. Mary, Fulton, Missouri		35	50
MS324	141×108 mm. Nos. 322/3		80	1·40

*The normal sideways watermark shows Crown to left of CA, as seen from the back of the stamp.

(Des J. Cooter. Litho J. W.)

1975 (14 Mar). *"Interpex 1975" Stamp Exhibition, New York. Ships' Figureheads. T* **117** *and similar vert designs. Multicoloured. W* w **12**. *P* 13.

325	5 c. Type 117		20	10
326	18 c. *Golden Hind*		50	15
327	40 c. H.M.S. *Superb*		70	25
328	85 c. H.M.S. *Formidable*		1·50	1·50
325/8		*Set of 4*	2·50	1·75
MS329	192×127 mm. Nos. 325/8 (Wmk inverted). P 14		2·50	7·00
	w. Wmk upright		80·00	

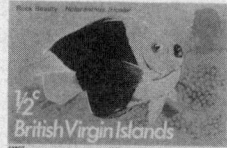

118 Rock Beauty

(Des C. Abbott. Litho Questa)

1975 (16 June–15 Aug). *Fishes. Horiz designs as T* **118**. *Multicoloured. W* w **14** *(sideways*)*. P* 14.

330	½ c. Type 118		15	40
	w. Wmk Crown to right of CA		6·00	
331	1 c. Long-spined Squirrelfish		40	1·25
332	3 c. Queen Triggerfish		90	1·25
333	5 c. Blue Angelfish		30	20
334	8 c. Spotlight Parrotfish		30	25
335	10 c. Queen Angelfish		30	25
336	12 c. Nassau Grouper		40	30
337	13 c. Blue Tang		40	30
338	15 c. Sergeant Major		40	35
339	18 c. Spotted Jewfish		70	80
340	20 c. Bluehead Wrasse		60	80
	w. Wmk Crown to right of CA		45·00	
341	25 c. Grey Angelfish		1·00	60
342	60 c. Glass-eyed Snapper		1·25	2·25
343	$1 Blue Chromis		1·75	1·75
	w. Wmk Crown to right of CA		3·50	
344	$2.50, French Angelfish		3·50	4·00
345	$3 Queen Parrotfish		4·25	5·00
346	$5 Four-eyed Butterflyfish (15.8)		8·00	7·50
330/46		*Set of 17*	22·00	25·00

*The normal sideways watermark shows Crown to left of CA, as seen from the back of the stamp.

Imprint dates: "1975", Nos. 330/46; "1977", Nos. 330, 333/8, 340.

The imprints on all the stamps show the designer's name as "Abbot".

119 St. George's Parish School (First meeting-place, 1950)

(Des R. Granger Barrett. Litho Questa)

1975 (27 Nov). *25th Anniv of Restoration of Legislative Council. T* **119** *and similar horiz designs. Multicoloured. W* w **14** *(sideways). P* 14.

347	5 c. Type 119		10	10
348	25 c. Legislative Council Building		25	10
349	40 c. Mace and gavel		35	15
350	75 c. Commemorative scroll		55	65
347/50		*Set of 4*	1·10	80

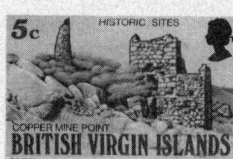

120 Copper Mine Point

(Des PAD Studio. Litho Walsall)

1976 (12 Mar). *Historic Sites. T* **120** *and similar horiz designs. Multicoloured. W* w **14** *(sideways). P* 14½.

351	5 c. Type 120		10	10
352	18 c. Pleasant Valley		20	10
353	50 c. Callwood Distillery		40	30
354	75 c. The Dungeon		60	65
351/4		*Set of 4*	1·10	1·00

121 Massachusetts Brig *Hazard*

(Des J. W. Litho Questa)

1976 (29 May). *Bicentenary of American Revolution. T* **121** *and similar horiz designs. Multicoloured, W* w **14** *(sideways). P* 14.

355	8 c. Type 121		60	15
356	22 c. American Privateer *Spy*		85	45
357	40 c. *Raleigh* (American frigate)		1·40	1·00
358	75 c. Frigate *Alliance* and H.M.S. *Trepassy*		1·60	1·90
355/8		*Set of 4*	4·00	3·25
MS359	114×89 mm. Nos. 355/8		5·50	11·00

122 Government House, Tortola

123 Royal Visit, 1966

(Des Walsall. Litho Questa)

1976 (29 Oct). *Fifth Anniv of Friendship Day with U.S. Virgin Is. T* **122** *and similar multicoloured designs. W* w **14** *(sideways on 8 and 75 c.). P* 14.

360	8 c. Type 122		10	10
361	15 c. Government House, St. Croix (*vert*)		10	10
362	30 c. Flags (*vert*)		15	10
363	75 c. Government seals		30	40
360/3		*Set of 4*	50	55

(Des J. Cooter. Litho Walsall)

1977 (7 Feb). *Silver Jubilee. T* **123** *and similar vert designs (inscr "SILVER JUBILEE" at top). Multicoloured. W* w **14**. *P* 13½.

364	8 c. Type 123		10	10
365	30 c. The Holy Bible		15	15
366	60 c. Presentation of Holy Bible		25	40
364/6		*Set of 3*	40	50

For stamps with different inscription, see Nos. 371/3.

The imprint at the stamp's foot gives the designer (wrongly) as "Waddington Studio".

124 Chart of 1739

(Des J. Cooter. Litho Walsall)

1977 (13 June). *18th-Century Maps. T* **124** *and similar horiz designs. Multicoloured. W* w **14**. *P* 13½.

367	8 c. Type 124		40	10
368	22 c. French Map, 1758		65	30
369	30 c. Map from English and Danish surveys, 1775		80	65
370	75 c. Map of 1779		1·25	1·50
367/70		*Set of 4*	2·75	2·25

1977 (26 Oct). *Royal Visit. Designs as Nos. 364/6 but inscr "SILVER JUBILEE ROYAL VISIT" at top, and face-values changed.*

371	5 c. Type 123		10	10
372	30 c. The Holy Bible		20	10
373	50 c. Presentation of Holy Bible		35	25
	w. Wmk inverted		5·50	
371/3		*Set of 3*	55	35

The above also differ from Nos. 364/6 in having the silver frame removed and the silver lettering replaced by white. The imprint at foot now has the designer's name correctly given as "J. E. Cooter".

125 Divers checking Equipment

126 Fire Coral

(Des J. W. Litho Rosenbaum Bros, Vienna)

1978 (10 Feb). *Tourism. T* **125** *and similar vert designs. Multicoloured. W* w **14**. *P* 13½.

374	½ c. Type 125		10	10
	w. Wmk inverted		8·00	
375	5 c. Cup coral on wreck of *Rhone*		20	10
	w. Wmk inverted		1·00	
376	8 c. Sponge formation on wreck of *Rhone*		25	10
	w. Wmk inverted		70	
377	22 c. Cup coral and sponges		60	15
	w. Wmk inverted		1·00	
378	30 c. Sponges inside cave		75	20
	w. Wmk inverted		1·25	
379	75 c. Marine life		1·25	85
	w. Wmk inverted		2·00	
374/9		*Set of 6*	2·75	1·25

(Des G. Drummond. Litho Harrison)

1978 (27 Feb). *Corals. T* 126 *and similar horiz designs. Multicoloured. W w* 14 (*sideways*). *P* 14.

380	8 c. Type 126	..	..	25	15
381	15 c. Staghorn coral	..	..	40	30
382	40 c. Brain coral	..	..	75	85
383	75 c. Elkhorn coral	..	..	1·50	1·60
380/3	..		*Set of* 4	2·50	2·50

127 Iguana   128 Lignum Vitae

(Des Jennifer Toombs. Litho Questa)

1978 (2 June). *25th Anniv of Coronation. T* 127 *and similar vert designs. P* 15.

384	50 c. brown-ochre, green and silver	..	..	20	40
	a. Sheetlet. Nos. 384/6 × 2	..		1·00	
385	50 c. multicoloured	..	..	20	40
386	50 c. brown-ochre, green and silver	..	..	20	40
384/6			*Set of* 3	55	1·10

Designs:—No. 384, Plantagenet Falcon; No. 385, Queen Elizabeth II; No. 386, Type 127.

(Des and litho J.W.)

1978 (4 Sept). *Flowering Trees. T* 128 *and similar horiz designs. Multicoloured. W w* 14 (*sideways**). *P* 13.

387	8 c. Type 128	..	..	15	10
388	22 c. Ginger Thomas	..	..	25	15
389	40 c. Dog Almond	..	..	35	20
390	75 c. White Cedar	..		60	70
387/90			*Set of* 4	1·25	1·00
MS391	131×95 mm. Nos. 387/90. P 14	..		1·50	3·00
	w. Wmk Crown to left of CA	..		60·00	

*The normal sideways watermark shows Crown to right of CA, *as seen from the back of the stamp.*

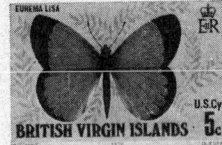

129 *Eurema lisa*

(Des G. Hutchins. Litho Questa)

1978 (4 Dec). *Butterflies. T* 129 *and similar horiz designs. Multicoloured. W w* 14 (*sideways*). *P* 14.

392	5 c. Type 129	..	..	25	10
393	22 c. *Agraulis vanillae*	..	..	75	20
394	30 c. *Heliconius charithonia*	..	..	1·00	30
395	75 c. *Hemiargus hanno*	..	..	1·40	1·25
392/5			*Set of* 4	3·00	1·75
MS396	159×113 mm. No. 392×6 and 393×3			2·50	5·50

130 Spiny Lobster

(Des Picton Print. Litho Harrison)

1979 (10 Feb). *Wildlife Conservation. T* 130 *and similar multicoloured designs. W w* 14 (*sideways on* 5 *and* 22 c.). *P* 14.

397	5 c. Type 130	..	..	15	10
398	15 c. Large Iguana (*vert*)	..	..	30	10
399	22 c. Hawksbill Turtle	..	..	50	15
400	75 c. Black Coral (*vert*)	..	..	1·10	90
397/400			*Set of* 4	1·90	1·10
MS401	130 × 153 mm. Nos. 397/400 (wmk sideways)	..	..	2·25	3·75

131 Strawberry Cactus   132 West Indian Girl

(Des BG Studio. Litho Format)

1979 (7 May). *Cacti. T* 131 *and similar vert designs. Multicoloured. W w* 14. *P* 14.

402	½ c. Type 131	..	..	10	10
403	5 c. Snowy Cactus	..	..	15	10
404	13 c. Barrel Cactus	..	..	20	20
405	22 c. Tree Cactus	..	..	30	35
406	30 c. Prickly Pear	..	..	35	40
407	75 c. Dildo Cactus	..	..	60	1·00
402/7			*Set of* 6	1·40	1·90

(Des R. Granger Barrett. Litho Questa)

1979 (9 July). *International Year of the Child. T* 132 *and similar vert designs. Multicoloured. W w* 14 (*inverted*). *P* 14½ × 14.

408	5 c. Type 132	..	..	10	10
409	10 c. African boy	..	..	10	10
410	13 c. Asian girl	..	..	10	10
411	$1 European boy	..	..	50	85
408/11			*Set of* 4	65	1·00
MS412	91 × 114 mm. Nos. 408/11	..		70	1·50

133 1956 Road Harbour 3 c. Definitive Stamp   134 Pencil Urchin

(Des J. W. Photo Heraclio Fournier)

1979 (1 Oct). *Death Centenary of Sir Rowland Hill. T* 133 *and similar designs showing stamps. P* 13½.

413	5 c. deep blue, new blue and brown-olive	..		10	10
414	13 c. deep blue and claret	..		10	10
415	75 c. deep blue and bright purple	..		45	50
413/15			*Set of* 3	55	55
MS416	37 × 91 mm. $1 deep blue & carm-red. P 13			70	1·25

Designs: (39 × 27 *mm*)—13 c. 1889 2½d.; 75 c. Great Britain unissued 1910 2d. Tyrian plum. (40 × 28 *mm*)—$1. 1867 1s. "Missing Virgin" error.

(Des BG Studio. Litho Questa)

1979 (17 Dec)–82. *Marine Life. Vert designs as T* 134. *Multicoloured. W w* 14. *Ordinary paper. P* 14.

417	½ c. Calcified Algae (1.4.80)	..	..	40	1·25
418	1 c. Purple-tipped Sea Anemone (1.4.80)			55	1·25
419	3 c. Common Starfish (1.4.80)	..		60	1·25
420	5 c. Type 134	..	..	60	80
	a. Chalk-surfaced paper (27.8.82)			75	60
421	8 c. Atlantic Trumpet Triton (*Charonia variegata*)			85	80
	a. Chalk-surfaced paper (27.8.82)			1·25	60
422	10 c. Christmas Tree Worms	..		30	75
423	13 c. Flamingo Tongue (*Cyphoma gibbosus*) (1.4.80)			1·50	2·00
	a. Chalk-surfaced paper (27.8.82)			1·50	75
424	15 c. Spider Crab	..	..	40	60
	a. Chalk-surfaced paper (27.8.82)			1·50	55
425	18 c. Sea Squirts (1.4.80)	..		2·00	2·25
426	20 c. True Tulip (*Fasciolaria tulipa*)			55	85
	a. Chalk-surfaced paper (27.8.82)			1·25	65
427	25 c. Rooster-tail Conch (*Strombus gallus*)			1·25	2·50
	w. Wmk inverted				
428	30 c. West Indian Fighting Conch (*Strombus pugilis*) (1.4.80)			1·75	1·25
	a. Chalk-surfaced paper (27.8.82)			2·00	1·00
429	60 c. Mangrove Crab (1.4.80)	..		1·75	2·50
430	$1 Coral Polyps (1.4.80)	..		2·00	3·25
431	$2.50, Peppermint Shrimp	..		2·50	5·00
432	$3 West Indian Murex (*Murex brevifrons*)			2·50	6·00
433	$5 Carpet Anemone (1.4.80)	..		3·25	7·50
417/33			*Set of* 17	20·00	32·00

Imprint dates: "1979", Nos. 420/2, 424, 426/7, 431/2; "1980", Nos. 417/19, 423, 425, 428/30, 433; "1982", Nos. 420a/1a, 423a/4a, 426a, 428a.

135 Rotary Athletics Meeting, Tortola   136 Brown Booby

(Des J. W. Litho Enschedé)

1980 (23 Feb). *75th Anniv of Rotary International. T* 135 *and similar horiz designs. Multicoloured. W w* 14 (*sideways*). *P* 13½ × 14.

434	8 c. Type 135	..	..	10	10
435	22 c. Paul P. Harris (founder) and Rotary emblem			15	10
436	60 c. "Creation of a National Park", Mount Sage, Tortola			40	40
437	$1 Rotary anniversary emblem	..		70	75
434/7			*Set of* 4	1·25	1·25
MS438	149 × 148 mm. Nos. 434/7.			1·25	3·00

(Des K. Penny. Litho Secura, Singapore)

1980 (6 May). *"London 1980" International Stamp Exhibition. Birds. T* 136 *and similar horiz designs. Multicoloured. W w* 14 (*sideways**). *P* 13½.

439	20 c. Type 136	..	..	20	20
	aw. Wmk Crown to right of CA				
	b. Wmk upright	..		40	40
	bw. Wmk inverted	..		50	50
440	25 c. Magnificent Frigate Bird	..		25	25
	b. Wmk upright	..		1·75	1·75
	bw. Wmk inverted	..		1·75	1·75
441	50 c. White-tailed Tropic Bird	..		40	40
	b. Wmk upright	..		65	65
	bw. Wmk inverted	..		80	80
442	75 c. Brown Pelican	..		55	55
	w. Wmk Crown to right of CA	..		5·00	
439/42			*Set of* 4	1·25	1·25
MS443	152×130 mm. Nos. 439/42	..		1·25	2·25
	w. Wmk Crown to left of CA	..		15·00	

*The normal sideways watermark shows Crown to left of CA on the sheet stamps and to right of CA on the miniature sheet; *both as seen from the back.* Singles of Nos. 439aw and 442w cannot be identified as the listed variety unless part of the sheet margin is attached to distinguish them from stamps originating in No. MS443.

CARIBBEAN
COMMONWEALTH
PARLIAMENTARY
ASSOCIATION
MEETING
TORTOLA   *11-19 JULY 1980*

(137)   138 Sir Francis Drake

1980 (7 July). *Caribbean Commonwealth Parliamentary Association Meeting, Tortola. Nos.* 414/15 *optd with T* 137.

444	13 c. deep blue and claret	..		15	10
445	75 c. deep blue and bright blue	..		40	40

(Des Franklin Mint. Litho Questa)

1980 (26 Sept). *Sir Francis Drake Commemoration. T* 138 *and similar vert designs. Multicoloured. W w* 14 (*inverted on* 75 c.). *P* 14 × 14½.

446	8 c. Type 138	..	..	50	10
447	15 c. Queen Elizabeth I	..	..	70	15
448	30 c. Drake receiving knighthood	..		90	30
449	75 c. *Golden Hind* and coat of arms	..		1·75	45
446/9			*Set of* 4	3·50	1·60
MS450	171 × 121 mm. Nos. 446/9. Wmk inverted			3·50	5·50
	a. 75 c. value in miniature sheet imperf	..		£150	
	b. 30 c. value in miniature sheet imperf	..		£150	

139 Jost van Dyke

(Des Jennifer Toombs. Litho Rosenbaum Bros, Vienna)

1980 (1 Dec). *Island Profiles. T* 139 *and similar horiz designs. Multicoloured. W w* 14 (*sideways**). *P* 13½.

451	2 c. Type 139	..	..	10	10
	w. Wmk Crown to right of CA	..		10	
452	5 c. Peter Island	..	..	10	10
	w. Wmk Crown to right of CA	..		10	
453	13 c. Virgin Gorda	..	..	15	10
	w. Wmk Crown to right of CA	..		20	
454	22 c. Anegada	..	..	20	10
	w. Wmk Crown to right of CA	..		30	
455	30 c. Norman Island	..	..	25	15
	w. Wmk Crown to right of CA	..		45	
456	$1 Tortola	..	..	70	1·00
	w. Wmk Crown to right of CA	..		1·10	
451/6			*Set of* 6	1·25	1·10
MS457	95×88 mm. No. 456 (wmk upright)	..		85	1·50
	a. Error. Imperf	..		£325	
	b. Gold and black omitted	..		£325	
	w. Wmk inverted	..		1·25	

*The normal sideways watermark shows Crown to left of CA as seen from the back of the stamp.

140 Dancing Lady   141 Wedding Bouquet from British Virgin Islands

(Des C. Abbott. Litho Walsall)

1981 (3 Mar). *Flowers. T* **140** *and similar vert designs. Multi-coloured. W w* 14 (*sideways*). *P* 11.

458	5 c. Type **140**	..	15	10
459	20 c. Love in the Mist	..	40	25
460	22 c. *Pitcairnia angustifolia*	..	40	25
461	75 c. Dutchman's Pipe	..	75	1·10
462	$1 Maiden Apple	..	90	1·40
458/62		*Set of 5*	2·40	2·75

(Des J. W. Litho Harrison)

1981 (22 July). *Royal Wedding. T* **141** *and similar vert designs. Multicoloured. W w* 14. *P* 14.

463	10 c. Type **141**	..	10	10
	w. Wmk inverted	..	4·00	
464	35 c. Prince Charles and Queen Elizabeth the Queen Mother in Garter robes	..	20	15
	w. Wmk inverted	..	4·00	
465	$1.25, Prince Charles and Lady Diana Spencer	..	60	80
463/5		*Set of 3*	80	90

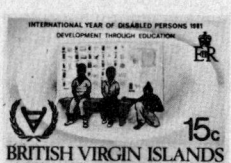

142 Stamp Collecting

143 "Development through Education"

(Des BG Studio. Litho Questa)

1981 (10 Oct). *25th Anniv of Duke of Edinburgh Award Scheme. T* **142** *and similar vert designs. Multicoloured. W w* 14. *P* 14.

466	10 c. Type **142**	..	10	10
467	15 c. Athletics	..	10	10
468	50 c. Camping	..	25	25
469	$1 Duke of Edinburgh	..	40	45
466/9		*Set of 4*	65	80

(Des G. Vasarhelyi. Litho Walsall)

1981 (19 Oct). *International Year for Disabled Persons. T* **143** *and similar horiz designs. Multicoloured. W w* 14 (*sideways*). *P* 14.

470	15 c. Type **143**	..	15	15
471	20 c. Fort Charlotte Children's Centre	..	20	20
472	30 c. "Developing cultural awareness"	..	30	30
473	$1 Fort Charlotte Children's Centre (different)	..	85	1·25
470/3		*Set of 4*	1·40	1·75

144 Detail from "The Adoration of the Shepherds" (Rubens)

145 Green-throated Caribs and Erythrina

(Des J. W. Litho Questa)

1981 (30 Nov). *Christmas. T* **144** *and similar designs showing details from "The Adoration of the Shepherds" by Rubens. W w* 14. *P* 14.

474	5 c. multicoloured	..	15	10
475	15 c. multicoloured	..	25	10
476	30 c. multicoloured	..	45	15
477	$1 multicoloured	..	1·10	1·10
474/7		*Set of 4*	1·75	1·25
MS478	117 × 90 mm. 50 c. multicoloured (*horiz*) (wmk sideways)		1·40	85

(Des Walsall. Litho Format)

1982 (5 Apr). *Hummingbirds. T* **145** *and similar vert designs. Multicoloured. W w* 14. *P* 14 × 14½.

479	15 c. Type **145**	..	50	15
480	30 c. Green-throated Carib and Bougainvillea	..	75	45
481	35 c. Antillean Crested Hummingbirds and Granadilla passiflora	..	85	55
482	$1.25, Antillean Crested Hummingbird and Hibiscus	..	2·50	3·00
479/82		*Set of 4*	4·25	3·75

146 "People caring for People"

147 Princess at Victoria and Albert Museum, November 1981

(Des Harrison. Litho Format)

1982 (3 May). *Tenth Anniv of Lions Club of Tortola. T* **146** *and similar horiz designs. Multicoloured. W w* 14 (*sideways*). *P* 13½ × 14.

483	10 c. Type **146**	..	25	15
484	20 c. Tortola Headquarters	..	35	20
485	30 c. "We Serve"	..	45	30
486	$1.50, "Lions" symbol	..	1·25	1·75
483/6		*Set of 4*	2·10	2·25
MS487	124 × 102 mm. Nos. 483/6	..	3·25	4·75

(Des C. Abbott. Litho Harrison)

1982 (2 July*). *21st Birthday of Princess of Wales. T* **147** *and similar vert designs. Multicoloured. W w* 14. *P* 14½ × 14.

488	10 c. British Virgin Islands coat of arms	..	15	10
489	35 c. Type **147**	..	30	25
490	50 c. Bride and groom proceeding into Vestry	..	45	45
491	$1.50, Formal portrait	..	1·10	1·40
488/91		*Set of 4*	1·75	2·00

*This is the local release date. The Crown Agents released the stamps on 1 July.

148 Douglas DC-3

(Des A. Theobald. Litho Questa)

1982 (10 Sept). *10th Anniv of Air BVI. T* **148** *and similar horiz designs. Multicoloured. W w* 14 (*sideways*). *P* 14.

492	10 c. Type **148**	..	35	15
493	15 c. Britten Norman Islander	..	50	20
494	60 c. Hawker Siddeley H.S.748	..	1·00	75
495	75 c. Runway scene	..	1·25	90
492/5		*Set of 4*	2·75	1·75

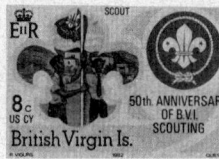

149 Scouts raising Flag

(Des R. Vigurs. Litho Questa)

1982 (18 Nov). *75th Anniv of Boy Scout Movement* ($1) *and 50th Anniv of Scouting in B.V.I.* (others). *T* **149** *and similar horiz designs. Multicoloured. W w* 14 (*sideways**). *P* 14.

496	8 c. Type **149**	..	20	10
497	20 c. Cub Scout	..	45	25
498	50 c. Sea Scout	..	85	55
	w. Wmk Crown to right of CA	..	11·00	
499	$1 First camp, Brownsea Island, and portrait of Lord Baden-Powell	..	1·50	1·50
	w. Wmk Crown to right of CA	..	11·00	
496/9		*Set of 4*	2·75	2·25

*The normal sideways watermark shows Crown to left of CA, as seen from the back of the stamp.

150 Legislature in Session

151 Florence Nightingale

(Des G. Vasarhelyi. Litho Enschedé)

1983 (10 Mar). *Commonwealth Day. T* **150** *and similar horiz designs. Multicoloured. W w* 14 (*sideways*). *P* 13 × 13½.

500	10 c. Type **150**	..	10	10
501	30 c. Tourism	..	25	20
502	35 c. Satellite view of Earth showing Virgin Islands	..	25	25
503	75 c. B.V.I. and Commonwealth flags	..	70	90
500/3		*Set of 4*	1·10	1·25

(Des L. Curtis. Litho Questa)

1983 (9 May). *Nursing Week. T* **151** *and similar multicoloured designs. W w* 14 (*sideways on* 60 c. *and* 75 c.). *P* 14.

504	10 c. Type **151**	..	50	15
505	30 c. Staff nurse and assistant nurse	..	90	45
506	60 c. Public Health nurses testing blood pressure (*horiz*)	..	1·75	1·25
507	75 c. Peebles Hospital (*horiz*)	..	1·90	1·75
504/7		*Set of 4*	4·50	3·25

152 Frame Construction

(Des R. Burnett. Litho Harrison)

1983 (25 July). *Traditional Boat-building. T* **152** *and similar horiz designs. Multicoloured. W w* 14 (*sideways*). *P* 14.

508	15 c. Type **152**	..	35	25
509	25 c. Planking	..	50	45
510	50 c. Launching	..	80	80
511	$1 Maiden voyage	..	1·25	1·75
508/11		*Set of 4*	2·50	3·00
MS512	127 × 101 mm. Nos. 508/11	..	2·50	3·75

153 Grumman G-21 Goose Amphibian

154 "Madonna and Child with the Infant Baptist"

(Des Walsall. Litho Questa)

1983 (15 Sept). *Bicentenary of Manned Flight. T* **153** *and similar horiz designs. Multicoloured. W w* 14 (*sideways*). *P* 14.

513	10 c. Type **153**	..	20	15
514	30 c. Riley Turbo Skyliner	..	45	45
515	60 c. Embraer EMB-110 Bandeirante	..	85	85
516	$1.25, Hawker Siddeley H.S.748	..	1·50	1·60
513/16		*Set of 4*	2·75	2·75

(Des M. Joyce. Litho Questa)

1983 (7 Nov). *Christmas. 500th Birth Anniv of Raphael. T* **154** *and similar vert designs showing details of different paintings. Multicoloured. W w* 14. *P* 14½ × 14.

517	8 c. Type **154**	..	10	10
518	15 c. "La Belle Jardiniére"	..	20	25
519	50 c. "Madonna Del Granduca"	..	65	70
520	$1 "The Terranuova Madonna"	..	1·25	1·40
517/20		*Set of 4*	2·00	2·25
MS521	108 × 101 mm. Nos. 517/20	..	2·50	3·75

155 Local Tournament

156 Port Purcell

(Des L. Curtis. Litho Questa)

1984 (20 Feb). *60th Anniv of World Chess Federation. T* **155** *and similar multicoloured designs. W w* 14 (*sideways on* 10 c. *and* $1, *inverted on* 35 c.). *P* 14.

522	10 c. Type **155**	..	1·00	40
523	35 c. Staunton chess pieces (*vert*)	..	2·00	1·50
524	75 c. Karpov's winning position, 1980 Chess Olympiad (*vert*)	..	3·75	4·25
525	$1 B.V.I. Gold Medal won by Bill Hook at 1980 Chess Olympiad	..	4·25	5·50
522/5		*Set of 4*	10·00	10·50

(Des L. Curtis. Litho Questa)

1984 (16 Apr). *250th Anniv of "Lloyd's List" (newspaper). T* **156** *and similar vert designs. Multicoloured. W w* 14. *P* 14½ × 14.

526	15 c. Type **156**	..	25	30
527	25 c. Boeing 747-100	..	45	50
528	50 c. Wreck of *Rhone* (mail steamer), 1867	..	90	95
529	$1 *Booker Viking* (cargo liner)	..	1·50	1·60
526/9		*Set of 4*	2·75	3·00

157 Mail Ship *Boyne*, Boeing 747-100 and U.P.U. Logo

(Des L. Curtis. Litho Walsall)

1984 (16 May). *Universal Postal Union Congress, Hamburg. Sheet* 90 × 69 mm. *W w* 14 (*sideways*). *P* 14.

MS530	**157** $1 pale blue and black	..	2·75	3·00

158 Running   **159** Steel Band

(Des R. Granger Barrett. Litho Walsall)

1984 (3 July). *Olympic Games, Los Angeles. T 158 and similar horiz designs. Multicoloured. W w 14 (sideways*). P 14.*

531	15 c. Type **158**		..	..	40	40
	a. Pair. Nos. 531/2		..	..	80	80
	aw. Wmk Crown to right of CA		..	6·00	
532	15 c. Runner	..	..	..	40	40
533	20 c. Wind-surfing	..	..	..	45	45
	a. Pair. Nos. 533/4		..	..	90	90
534	20 c. Surfer	..	..	..	45	45
535	30 c. Sailing	..	..	..	65	65
	a. Pair. Nos. 535/6		..	..	1·25	1·25
536	30 c. Yacht	..	..	..	65	65
531/6			..	*Set of 6*	2·75	2·75
MS537	97×69 mm. $1 Torch bearer. Wmk upright			..	1·50	1·90

The normal sideways watermark shows Crown to left of CA, as seen from the back of the stamp.

Nos. 531/2, 533/4 and 535/6 were printed together, *se-tenant*, in horizontal and vertical pairs throughout the sheets.

(Des D. Miller. Litho Format)

1984 (14 Aug). *150th Anniv of Abolition of Slavery. T 159 and similar vert designs showing various aspects of Emancipation Festival. Multicoloured. W w 14. P 14.*

538	10 c. Type **159**	..	..	..	30	35
	a. Horiz strip of 5. Nos. 538/42			..	1·40	
539	10 c. Dancing girls	..	..	..	30	35
540	10 c. Men in traditional costumes	..	..	30	35
541	10 c. Girl in traditional costume	..	..	30	35
542	10 c. Festival Queen	..	..	..	30	35
543	30 c. Green and yellow dinghies	..	..	45	50
	a. Horiz strip of 5. Nos. 543/7			..	2·00	
544	30 c. Blue and red dinghies	..	..	45	50
545	30 c. White and blue dinghies	..	..	45	50
546	30 c. Red and yellow dinghies	..	..	45	50
547	30 c. Blue and white dinghies	..	..	45	50
538/47			..	*Set of 10*	3·00	3·50

Nos. 538/42 and 543/7 were each printed together, *se-tenant*, in horizontal strips of 5 throughout the sheet, forming composite designs. On Nos. 543/7 the sail colours of the dinghies are described to assist identification.

160 Sloop

(Des R. Burnett. Litho J .W.)

1984 (15 Nov). *Boats. T 160 and similar horiz designs. Multicoloured. W w 14 (sideways). P 13 × 13½.*

548	10 c. Type **160**	..	..	..	40	20
549	35 c. Fishing boat	..	..	..	1·25	65
550	60 c. Schooner	..	..	..	1·75	1·25
551	75 c. Cargo boat	..	..	..	1·75	1·60
548/51				*Set of 4*	4·50	3·25
MS552	125 × 90 mm. Nos. 548/51. P 14		..	4·50	4·00

161 One Cent Coin and Aerial View   **162** Red-billed Tropic Bird

(Litho Walsall)

1985 (15 Jan). *New Coinage. T 161 and similar horiz designs showing coins and local scenery. Multicoloured. W w 14 (sideways). P 14½.*

553	1 c. Type **161**	..	..	..	10	10
554	5 c. Five cent coin and boulders on beach	..	10	10
555	10 c. Ten cent coin and scuba diving	..	..	20	20
556	25 c. Twenty-five cent coin and yachts	..	45	50
557	50 c. Fifty cent coin and jetty	..	..	90	1·25
558	$1 One dollar coin and beach at night	..	1·75	2·25
553/8				*Set of 6*	3·00	4·00
MS559	103 × 156 mm. Nos. 553/8		..	..	3·00	4·00

A set of stamps, 55 c. and $1·50 each × 2, showing Michael Jackson the entertainer was prepared in 1985, but was never released for postal use. Samples of the $1·50 values were, however, distributed for publicity purposes and both values exist from stock dispersed by the liquidator of Format International Security Printers Ltd.

(Des N. Arlott. Litho Questa)

1985 (3 July). *Birds of the British Virgin Islands. T 162 and similar vert designs. Multicoloured. W w 14. "1985" imprint date. P 14.*

560	1 c. Type **162**	..	..	..	60	80
561	2 c. Yellow-crowned Night Heron	..	..	60	80
562	5 c. Mangrove Cuckoo	..	..	70	60
563	8 c. Northern Mockingbird	..	..	75	85
564	10 c. Grey Kingbird	..	..	..	75	40
565	12 c. Red-necked Pigeon	..	..	1·00	55
566	15 c. Least Bittern	..	..	1·25	55
567	18 c. Smooth-billed Ani	..	..	1·40	1·00
568	20 c. Clapper Rail	..	..	1·40	1·00
569	25 c. American Kestrel	..	..	1·50	1·00
570	30 c. Pearly-eyed Thrasher	..	..	1·50	1·10
571	35 c. Bridled Quail Dove	..	..	1·75	1·25
572	40 c. Green Heron	..	..	1·75	1·50
573	50 c. Scaly-breasted Ground Dove	..	2·00	2·00
574	60 c. Little Blue Heron	..	..	2·25	2·50
575	$1 Audubon's Shearwater	..	..	3·00	3·00
576	$2 Blue-faced Booby	..	..	3·50	5·00
577	$3 Cattle Egret	..	..	4·75	7·50
578	$5 Zenaida Dove	..	..	7·00	10·00
560/78			*Set of 19*	35·00	38·00

For these stamps watermarked w 16 see Nos. 647/60.

IMPERFORATES AND MISSING COLOURS. Various issues between Nos. 579 and 609 exist either imperforate or with colours omitted. Many originate from stock dispersed by the liquidator of Format International Security Printers Ltd. Such items are not listed as there is no evidence that they fulfil the criteria outlined on page xi of this catalogue.

163 The Queen Mother at Festival of Remembrance   **164** Seaside Sparrow

(Des Maxine Marsh. Litho Format)

1985 (26 Aug). *Life and Times of Queen Elizabeth the Queen Mother. Various vertical portraits as T 163. Multicoloured. P 12½. A. W w 15 (sideways). B. No wmk.*

			A.		B.	
579	10 c. Type **163**	..	10	20	2·50	2·50
	a. Horiz pair. Nos. 579/80		20	40	5·00	5·00
580	10 c. At Victoria Palace Theatre, 1984		10	20	2·50	2·50
581	25 c. At the engagement of the Prince of Wales, 1981		15	40	2·50	2·50
	a. Horiz pair. Nos. 581/2		30	80	5·00	5·00
582	25 c. Opening Celia Johnson Theatre, 1985		15	40	2·50	2·50
583	50 c. The Queen Mother on her 82nd birthday		20	70	3·00	3·00
	a. Horiz pair. Nos. 583/4		40	1·40	6·00	1·40
584	50 c. At the Tate Gallery, 1983		20	70	3·00	3·00
585	75 c. At the Royal Smithfield Show, 1983		25	1·00	3·00	3·00
	a. Horiz pair. Nos. 585/6		50	2·00	1·75	2·00
586	75 c. Unveiling Mountbatten statue, 1983		25	1·00	3·00	3·00
579/86		*Set of 8*	1·25	4·25	20·00	20·00
MS587	85 × 114 mm. $1 At Columbia University; $1 At a Wedding, St. Margaret's Westminster, 1983			85	4·00	†

The two designs of each value were issued, *se-tenant*, in horizontal pairs within the sheets.

Each *se-tenant* pair shows a floral pattern across the bottom of the portraits which stops short of the left-hand edge on the left-hand stamp and of the right-hand edge on the right-hand stamp.

Sets of four miniature sheets, containing the two designs of each value, were prepared, but not issued. Examples exist from stock dispersed by the liquidator of Format International Security Printers Ltd.

Designs as Nos. 583/4 and 585/6, but with face values of $2·50×2 and $1×2, also exist in additional miniature sheets from a restricted printing issued 18 December 1985.

(Des R. Vigurs. Litho Format)

1985 (17 Dec). *Birth Bicentenary of John J. Audubon (ornithologist). T 164 and similar vert designs. showing original paintings. Multicoloured. P 15.*

588	5 c. Type **164**	..	..	..	40	20
589	30 c. Passenger Pigeon	..	..	70	70
590	50 c. Yellow-breasted Chat	..	..	80	1·75
591	$1 American Kestrel	..	..	1·25	2·75
588/91				*Set of 4*	2·75	4·75

165 S.V. *Flying Cloud*   **(166)**

(Des G. Drummond. Litho Format)

1986 (27 Jan). *Visiting Cruise Ships. T 165 and similar horiz designs. Multicoloured. W w 15. P 15.*

592	35 c. Type **165**	..	..	80	8
	w. Wmk inverted		..	10·00	
593	50 c. M.V. *Newport Clipper*	..	1·10	1·5
	w. Wmk inverted		..	9·00	
594	75 c. M.V. *Cunard Countess*	..	1·40	2·5
595	$1 M.V. *Sea Goddess*	..	1·50	3·0
	w. Wmk inverted		..	17·00	
592/5			*Set of 4*	4·25	7·0

1986 (17 Apr). *Inaugural Flight of Miami–Beef Island A Service. Nos. 581/2 and 585/6 optd with T 166. A. W w 1 (sideways). B. No wmk.*

			A.		B.	
596	25 c. At the engagement of the Prince of Wales, 1981		40	50	1·75	2·2
	a. Horiz pair. Nos. 596/7		80	1·00	3·50	4·5
597	25 c. Opening Celia Johnson theatre, 1985		40	50	1·75	2·2
598	75 c. At the Royal Smithfield Show, 1983		1·25	1·50	1·75	2·2
	a. Horiz pair. Nos. 598/9		2·50	3·00	3·50	4·5
599	75 c. Unveiling Mountbatten statue, 1983		1·25	1·50	1·75	2·2
596/9		*Set of 4*	3·00	3·50	6·00	8·0

167 Queen Elizabeth II in 1958

(Des Court House Studio. Litho Format)

1986 (21 Apr). *60th Birthday of Queen Elizabeth II. T 167 an similar multicoloured designs. P 12½.*

600	12 c. Type **167**	..	..	15	2
601	35 c. At a Maundy Service	..	..	20	4
	a. Wmk w 15 (sideways)		..	2·00	
602	$1.50. Queen Elizabeth	..	..	45	1·7
	a. Wmk w 15 (sideways)		..	3·25	
603	$2 During a visit to Canberra, 1982 (*vert*)		..	60	2·2
600/3			*Set of 4*	1·25	5·5
MS604	85 × 115 mm $3 Queen with bouquet	..	4·00	5·5

Examples of the 12 c., 35 c. and $1.50 values with the blu (ribbons and frame) omitted are from stock dispersed by th liquidator of Format International Security Printers Ltd.

Unissued sets of five miniature sheets, each containing on value, come from the same source.

168 Miss Sarah Ferguson   **169** Harvesting Sugar Cane

(Des Court House Studio. Litho Format)

1986 (23 July–15 Oct). *Royal Wedding. T 168 and simila multicoloured designs. P 12½.*

605	35 c. Type **168**	..	..	25	5
	a. Pair. Nos. 605/6		..	50	1·1
	b. Wmk w 15		..	3·00	
	ba. Pair. Nos. 605/6b		..	6·00	
606	35 c. Prince Andrew and Miss Sarah Ferguson		25	5
	b. Wmk w 15		..	3·00	
607	$1 Prince Andrew in morning dress (*horiz*)		40	1·2
	a. Pair. Nos. 607/8		..	80	2·5
608	$1 Miss Sarah Ferguson (*different*) (*horiz*)		40	1·2
605/8			*Set of 4*	1·10	3·2
MS609	115 × 85 mm. $4 Duke and Duchess of York in carriage after wedding (*horiz*) (15.10.86)				

Nos. 605/6 and 607/8 were each printed together, *se-tenant*, in horizontal and vertical pairs throughout the sheets.

Nos. 605/8 imperforate come from souvenir stamp booklets.

Nos. 605/8 overprinted "Congratulations to T.R.H. The Duk & Duchess of York" were not issued.

(Des Toni Lance. Litho Questa)

1986 (30 July). *History of Rum Making. T 169 and simila horiz designs. Multicoloured. W w 15. P 14.*

610	12 c. Type **169**	..	..	80	4
611	40 c. Bringing sugar cane to mill	..	1·50	1·2
612	60 c. Rum distillery	..	..	2·00	2·7
613	$1 Delivering barrels of rum to ship	..	3·25	4·0
610/13			*Set of 4*	6·75	7·5
MS614	115×84 mm. $2 Royal Navy rum issue. Wmk sideways		..	6·50	8·5

170 C.S. *Sentinel*   **171** Statue of Liberty at Sunset

(Des Court House Studio. Litho Format)

1986 (28 Oct). *20th Anniv of Cable and Wireless Caribbean Headquarters, Tortola. T* **170** *and similar horiz designs. Multicoloured.* W w 15. *P* 12½.

615	35 c. Type **170**.		60	80
	a. Vert pair. Nos. 615/16		1·10	1·60
616	35 c. C.S. *Retriever* (1961)		60	80
617	60 c. C.S. *Cable Enterprise* (1964)		1·00	1·50
	a. Vert pair. Nos. 617/18		2·00	3·00
618	60 c. C.S. *Mercury* (1962)		1·00	1·50
619	75 c. C.S. *Recorder* (1955)		1·10	1·75
	a. Vert pair. Nos. 619/20		2·10	3·50
620	75 c. C.S. *Pacific Guardian* (1984)		1·10	1·75
621	$1 S.S. *Great Eastern* (1860's)		1·25	2·00
	a. Vert pair. Nos. 621/2		2·50	4·00
622	$1 C.S. *Cable Venture* (1977)		1·25	2·00
615/22		*Set of 8*	7·00	11·00
MS623	Four sheets, each 102 × 131 mm. (a) 40 c. × 2 As 35 c. (b) 50 c. × 2 As 60 c. (c) 80 c. × 2 As 75 c. (d) $1.50 × 2 As $1	*Set of 4 sheets*	6·00	12·00

The two designs of each value were printed, *se-tenant*, in vertical pairs throughout the sheets.

(Des Court House Studio. Litho Format)

1986 (15 Dec). *Centenary of Statue of Liberty. T* **171** *and similar vert views of Statue in separate miniature sheets. Multicoloured. P* 14 × 13½.

MS624	Nine sheets, each 85 × 115 mm. 50 c.; 75 c.; 90 c.; $1; $1.25; $1.50; $1.75; $2; $2.50	*Set of 9 sheets*	9·00	18·00

172 18th-century Spanish Galleon   **173** Outline Map and Flag of Montserrrat

(Des J. Batchelor. Litho Questa)

1987 (15 Apr). *Shipwrecks. T* **172** *and similar horiz designs. Multicoloured.* W w 15. *P* 14.

625	12 c. Type **172**		1·25	45
626	35 c. H.M.S. *Astrea* (frigate), 1808		2·50	1·40
627	75 c. *Rhone* (mail steamer), 1867		3·75	4·00
628	$1.50 *Captain Rokos* (freighter), 1929		5·00	7·50
625/8		*Set of 4*	11·50	12·00
MS629	86 × 65 mm. $1.50, *Volvart*, 1819		11·00	13·00

(Des R. Burnett. Litho Walsall)

1987 (28 May). *11th Meeting of Organization of Eastern Caribbean States. T* **173** *and similar vert designs, each showing outline map and flag. Multicoloured.* W w **16**. *P* 14.

630	10 c. Type **173**.		70	60
631	15 c. Grenada		80	60
632	20 c. Dominica		85	65
633	25 c. St. Kitts–Nevis		90	70
634	35 c. St. Vincent and Grenadines		1·40	1·00
635	50 c. British Virgin Islands		2·00	2·50
636	75 c. Antigua and Barbuda		2·25	3·00
637	$1 St. Lucia		2·75	3·25
630/7		*Set of 8*	10·50	11·00

174 Spider Lily   **175** Early Mail Packet and 1867 1s. Stamp

(Des Jennifer Toombs. Litho Questa)

1987 (20 Aug). *Opening of Botanical Gardens. T* **174** *and similar vert designs. Multicoloured.* W w **16**. *P* 14.

638	12 c. Type **174**.		80	35
639	35 c. Barrel Cactus		1·75	1·00
640	$1 Wild Plantain		2·75	3·25
641	$1.50, Little Butterfly Orchid		8·00	8·50
638/41		*Set of 4*	12·00	12·00
MS642	139 × 104 mm. $2.50, White Cedar		3·75	6·00

1987 (28 Oct). *As Nos. 564, 566, 568/9, 571, 575 and 577 but* W w **16**. "1987" *imprint date. P* 14.

647	10 c. Grey Kingbird		60	70
649	15 c. Least Bittern		80	70
651	20 c. Clapper Rail		80	70
652	25 c. American Kestrel		90	75
654	35 c. Bridled Quail Dove		90	85
658	$1 Audubon's Shearwater		2·00	3·00
660	$3 Cattle Egret		6·00	9·00
647/60		*Set of 7*	11·00	14·00

(Des and litho Walsall)

1987 (17 Dec). *Bicentenary of Postal Services. T* **175** *and similar horiz designs, each including stamp and cancellation. Multicoloured.* W w **16** *(sideways). P* 14½.

662	10 c. Type **175**.		1·00	55
663	20 c. Map and 1899 1d.		1·50	95
664	35 c. Road Town Post Office and Customs House, 1913, and 1867 4d.		2·00	1·50
665	$1.50, Piper PA-23 Apache mail plane and 1964 25 c. definitive		6·00	8·00
662/5		*Set of 4*	9·50	10·00
MS666	70 × 60 mm. $2.50, Mail ship, 1880's, and 1880 1d.		6·00	8·50

(Litho Questa)

1988 (11 Aug). *500th Birth Anniv of Titian (artist). Vert designs as T* **238** *of Antigua. Multicoloured. P* 13½ × 14.

667	10 c. "Salome"		55	55
668	12 c. "Man with the Glove"		60	60
669	20 c. "Fabrizio Salvaresio"		80	80
670	25 c. "Daughter of Roberto Strozzi"		90	90
671	40 c. "Pope Julius II"		1·40	1·75
672	50 c. "Bishop Ludovico Beccadelli"		1·60	1·75
673	60 c. "King Philip II"		1·75	2·00
674	$1 "Empress Isabella of Portugal"		2·25	2·50
667/74		*Set of 8*	9·00	9·75
MS675	Two sheets, each 110 × 95 mm. (a) $2 "Emperor Charles V at Muhlberg" (detail). (b) $2 "Pope Paul III and his Grandsons" (detail)	*Set of 2 sheets*	8·50	11·00

176 De Havilland D.H.C.5 over Sir Francis Drake Channel and Staunton Pawn

(Des B. Bundock. Litho Questa)

1988 (25 Aug). *First British Virgin Islands Open Chess Tournament. T* **176** *and similar horiz designs. Multicoloured. P* 14.

676	35 c. Type **176**		3·50	1·50
677	$1 Jose Capablanca (former World Champion) and Staunton king		7·00	7·50
MS678	109 × 81 mm. $2 Chess match		8·00	10·00

177 Hurdling

(Des L. Fried. Litho B.D.T.)

1988 (8 Sept). *Olympic Games, Seoul. T* **177** *and similar horiz designs. Multicoloured. P* 14.

679	12 c. Type **177**		30	25
680	20 c. Windsurfing		45	45
681	75 c. Basketball		2·75	3·00
682	$1 Tennis		3·25	3·50
679/82		*Set of 4*	6·00	6·50
MS683	71 × 102 mm. $2 Athletics		3·00	4·25

178 Swimmer ("Don't Swim Alone")   **179** Princess Alexandra

(Des I. Arbell. Litho Questa)

1988 (26 Sept). *125th Anniv of International Red Cross. T* **178** *and similar designs. P* 14.

684	12 c. black, bright scarlet and cobalt		85	40
685	30 c. black, bright scarlet and cobalt		1·50	80
686	60 c. black, bright scarlet and cobalt		2·50	3·00
687	$1 black, bright scarlet and cobalt		3·00	4·00
684/7		*Set of 4*	7·00	7·50
MS688	68 × 96 mm. 50 c. × 4 black and bright scarlet		5·00	6·50

Designs: *Horiz*—30 c. Swimmers ("No swimming during electrical storms"); 60 c. Beach picnic ("Don't eat before swimming"); $1 Boat and equipment ("Proper equipment for boating"). *Vert*—50 c. × 4 Recovery position; clearing airway; mouth-to-mouth resuscitation; cardiac massage.

(Litho Questa)

1988 (9 Nov). *Visit of Princess Alexandra. T* **179** *and similar vert designs showing different portraits. P* 14.

689	40 c. multicoloured		1·75	75
690	$1.50, multicoloured		3·75	4·75
MS691	102 × 98 mm. $2 multicoloured		5·00	6·50

180 Brown Pelican in Flight   **181** Anegada Rock Iguana

(Des S. Barlowe. Litho Questa)

1988 (30 Nov). *Wildlife (1st series). Aquatic Birds. T* **180** *and similar multicoloured designs. P* 14.

692	10 c. Type **180**		1·10	50
693	12 c. Brown Pelican perched on post		1·25	55
694	15 c. Brown Pelican		1·40	1·10
695	35 c. Brown Pelican swallowing fish		2·75	3·00
692/5		*Set of 4*	6·00	4·75
MS696	106 × 76 mm. $2 Common Shoveler (*horiz*)		7·50	9·00

No. **MS**696 is without the WWF logo.

(Des S. Barlowe. Litho Questa)

1988 (15 Dec). *Wildlife (2nd series). Endangered Species. T* **181** *and similar multicoloured designs. P* 14.

697	20 c. Type **181**		1·25	75
698	40 c. Virgin Gorda Dwarf Gecko		1·50	1·40
699	60 c. Hawksbill Turtle		2·50	3·25
700	$1 Humpback Whale		6·00	7·00
697/700		*Set of 4*	10·00	11·00
MS701	106 × 77 mm. $2 Trunk Turtle (*vert*)		5·00	7·00

182 Yachts at Start   **183** "Apollo 11" Emblem

(Des D. Miller. Litho Questa)

1989 (7 Apr). *Spring Regatta. T* **182** *and similar multicoloured designs. P* 14.

702	12 c. Type **182**		45	40
703	40 c. Yacht tacking (*horiz*)		1·00	1·00
704	75 c. Yachts at sunset		1·60	2·50
705	$1 Yachts rounding buoy (*horiz*)		2·00	2·75
702/5		*Set of 4*	4·50	6·00
MS706	83 × 69 mm. $2 Yacht under full sail		4·75	6·00

(Des D. Miller. Litho Questa)

1989 (8 May). *500th Anniv of Discovery of America by Columbus (1992) (1st issue). Pre-Columbian Arawak Society. Multicoloured designs as T* **247** *of Antigua, but horiz. P* 14.

707	10 c. Arawak in hammock		50	30
708	20 c. Making fire		75	50
709	25 c. Making implements		80	60
710	$1.50, Arawak family		3·75	6·00
707/10		*Set of 4*	5·25	6·75
MS711	85 × 70 mm. $2 Religious ceremony		5·50	7·00

See also Nos. 741/5, 793/7 and 818/26.

(Des W. Hanson. Litho Questa)

1989 (28 Sept). *20th Anniv of First Manned Landing on Moon. T* **183** *and similar multicoloured designs. P* 14.

712	15 c. Type **183**		80	50
713	30 c. Edwin Aldrin deploying scientific experiments		1·50	1·00
714	65 c. Aldrin and U.S. flag on Moon		2·25	3·00
715	$1 "Apollo 11" capsule after splashdown		3·00	3·25
712/15		*Set of 4*	6·75	7·00
MS716	102 × 77 mm. $2 Neil Armstrong (38 × 50 mm). *P* 13½ × 14		5·50	7·50

184 Black Harry and Nathaniel Gilbert preaching to Slaves   **185** Player tackling

(Des R. Vigurs. Litho Questa)

1989 (24 Oct). *Bicentenary of Methodist Church in British Virgin Islands. T 184 and similar multicoloured designs.* P 14.
717	12 c. Type 184	..	65	30
718	25 c. Methodist school exercise book		85	60
719	35 c. East End Methodist Church, 1810		95	75
720	$1.25, Revd. John Wesley (founder of Methodism) and church youth choir		3·00	4·50
717/20		*Set of 4*	5·00	5·50
MS721	100×69 mm. $2 Dr. Thomas Coke	..	4·50	7·00

(Des R. Vigurs. Litho Questa)

1989 (6 Nov). *World Cup Football Championship, Italy, 1990. T 185 and similar vert designs. Multicoloured.* P 14.
722	5 c. Type 185		60	60
723	10 c. Player dribbling ball		60	60
724	20 c. Two players chasing ball		1·00	70
725	$1.75, Goalkeeper diving for ball		5·50	6·50
722/5		*Set of 4*	7·00	7·50
MS726	100×70 mm. $2 British Virgin Islands team captain		6·50	8·00

186 Princess Alexandra and Sunset House

(Litho Questa)

1990 (3 May). *"Stamp World London 90" International Stamp Exhibition. Royal Visitors. T 186 and similar horiz designs. Multicoloured.* P 14.
727	50 c. Type 186		1·40	1·50
	a. Sheetlet. Nos. 727/30		5·00	
728	50 c. Princess Margaret and Government House		1·40	1·50
729	50 c. Hon. Angus Ogilvy and Little Dix Bay Hotel		1·40	1·50
730	50 c. Princess Diana with Princes William and Harry and Necker Island Resort	..	1·40	1·50
727/30			5·00	5·50
MS731	89×80 mm. $2 Royal Yacht *Britannia*		5·00	5·50

Nos. 727/30 were printed together, *se-tenant*, in sheetlets of four.

187 Audubon's Shearwater   **188** Queen Elizabeth the Queen Mother

(Litho Questa)

1990 (15 May). *Birds. T 187 and similar multicoloured designs showing birds and eggs.* P 14.
732	5 c. Type 187		30	40
733	12 c. Red-necked Pigeon		45	30
734	20 c. Moorhen ("Common Gallinule")		60	40
735	25 c. Green Heron		75	50
736	40 c. Yellow Warbler		1·10	1·10
737	60 c. Smooth-billed Ani		1·50	2·00
738	$1 Antillean Crested Hummingbird		1·75	2·00
739	$1.25, Black-faced Grassquit		2·00	2·50
732/9		*Set of 8*	7·50	8·25
MS740	Two sheets, each 98×70 mm. (a) $2 Royal Tern egg (*vert*). (b) $2 Red-billed Tropicbird egg (*vert*) .. .. .. *Set of 2 sheets*		6·50	6·50

(Des Mary Walters. Litho Questa)

1990 (18 June). *500th Anniv of Discovery of America by Columbus (1992) (2nd issue). New World Natural History—Fishes. Multicoloured designs as T 260 of Antigua, but horiz.* P 14.
741	10 c. Blue Tang	..	55	40
742	35 c. Glass-eyed Snapper		1·00	70
743	50 c. Slippery Dick		1·50	2·00
744	$1 Porkfish		2·50	2·75
741/4		*Set of 4*	5·00	5·25
MS745	100×70 mm. $2 Yellow-tailed Snapper		3·50	4·50

(Litho Questa)

1990 (30 Aug). *90th Birthday of Queen Elizabeth the Queen Mother. T 188 and similar vert designs showing recent photographs.* P 14.
746	12 c. multicoloured		35	20
747	25 c. multicoloured		65	45
748	60 c. multicoloured		1·40	2·00
749	$1 multicoloured		1·75	2·25
746/9		*Set of 4*	3·75	4·50
MS750	75×75 mm. $2 multicoloured		2·75	2·75

189 Footballers   **190** Judo

(Litho Questa)

1990 (10 Dec). *World Cup Football Championship, Italy. T 189 and similar vert designs showing footballers.* P 14.
751	12 c. multicoloured		60	35
752	20 c. multicoloured		90	50
753	50 c. multicoloured		1·75	2·00
754	$1.25, multicoloured		2·50	3·00
751/4		*Set of 4*	5·25	5·25
MS755	91×76 mm. $2 multicoloured		4·00	4·00

(Litho Questa)

1990 (20 Dec). *Olympic Games, Barcelona (1992). T 190 and similar horiz designs. Multicoloured.* P 14.
756	12 c. Type 190		60	35
757	40 c. Yachting		1·25	1·25
758	60 c. Hurdling		1·75	2·00
759	$1 Show jumping		2·50	3·00
756/9		*Set of 4*	5·50	6·00
MS760	78×105 mm. $2 Windsurfing		3·50	3·50

191 Tree-fern, Sage Mountain National Park   **192** Haiti Haiti

(Litho Questa)

1991 (1 Mar). *30th Anniv of National Parks Trust. T 191 and similar multicoloured designs.* P 14.
761	10 c. Type 191		40	40
762	25 c. Coppermine ruins, Virgin Gorda (*horiz*)		65	45
763	35 c. Ruined windmill, Mount Healthy	..	75	60
764	$2 The Baths (rock formation), Virgin Gorda (*horiz*)		4·75	6·00
761/4	.. .. ..	*Set of 4*	6·00	6·75

(Des Wendy Smith-Griswold. Litho Questa)

1991 (1 May)–95. *Flowers. T 192 and similar vert designs. Multicoloured. Without imprint date.* P 14.
765	1 c. Type 192		20	30
766	2 c. Lobster Claw		20	30
767	5 c. Frangipani		20	30
768	10 c. Autograph Tree		60	60
769	12 c. Yellow Allamanda		40	30
770	15 c. Lantana		70	70
771	20 c. Jerusalem Thorn		50	30
772	25 c. Turk's Cap		55	40
773	30 c. Swamp Immortelle		80	80
774	35 c. White Cedar		90	90
775	40 c. Mahoe Tree		75	65
776	45 c. Pinguin		1·25	1·25
777	50 c. Christmas Orchid		2·00	1·50
	a. Perf 12 (8.95)		2·00	2·00
778	70 c. Lignum Vitae		1·10	1·40
779	$1 African Tulip Tree		1·25	1·50
	a. Perf 12 (8.95)		1·75	2·00
780	$2 Beach Morning Glory		4·00	5·00
	a. Perf 12 (8.95)		4·00	5·00
781	$3 Organ Pipe Cactus		4·00	5·50
	a. Perf 12½×11½ (8.95)		4·00	5·50
782	$5 Tall Ground Orchid		11·00	12·00
783	$10 Ground Orchid (1.5.92)		14·00	15·00
765/83		*Set of 19*	40·00	42·00

No. 781a shows a larger hole on every sixth perforation, both vertically and horizontally.

Nos. 777a, 779a and 780a/1a are known to have been sold for postal purposes by the B.V.I. post offices.

For some of these designs watermarked w 14 (sideways) and with imprint date see Nos. 887/901.

193 *Phoebis sennae*   **194** *Agaricus bisporus*

(Litho Questa)

1991 (28 June). *Butterflies. T 193 and similar multicoloured designs.* P 14.
784	5 c. Type 193		40	50
785	10 c. *Dryas iulia*		45	50
786	15 c. *Junonia evarete*		65	65
787	20 c. *Dione vanillae*		75	75
788	25 c. *Battus polydamus*		85	85
789	30 c. *Eurema lisa*		95	95
790	35 c. *Heliconius charitonius*		1·10	1·10
791	$1.50, *Siproeta stelenes*		3·50	4·50
784/91		*Set of 8*	7·75	9·00
MS792	Two sheets. (a) 77×117 mm. $2 *Danaus plexippus* (*horiz*). (b) 117×77 mm. $2 *Biblis hyperia* (*horiz*) .. .. *Set of 2 sheets*		11·00	12·00

(Des T. Agans. Litho Questa)

1991 (20 Sept). *500th Anniv of Discovery of America by Columbus (1992) (3rd issue). History of Exploration. Designs as T 277 of Antigua.* P 14.
793	12 c. multicoloured		60	40
794	50 c. multicoloured		1·50	1·60
795	75 c. multicoloured		2·00	2·25
796	$1 multicoloured		2·50	3·00
793/6		*Set of 4*	6·00	6·50
MS797	105×76 mm. $2 black and red-orange		6·00	6·50

Designs: *Horiz*—12 c. *Vitoria* in Pacific (Magellan, 1519–21); 50 c. La Salle on the Mississippi, 1682, 75 c. John Cabot landing in Nova Scotia, 1497–98; $1 Cartier discovering the St. Lawrence, 1534. *Vert*—$2 *Santa Maria* (woodcut).

(Litho B.D.T.)

1991 (1 Nov). *Death Centenary of Vincent van Gogh (artist) (1990). Multicoloured designs as T 278 of Antigua.* P 13.
798	15 c. "Cottage with Decrepit Barn and Stooping Woman" (*horiz*)		65	40
799	30 c. "Paul Gauguin's Armchair"		1·10	80
800	75 c. "Breton Women" (*horiz*)		2·00	2·50
801	$1 "Vase with Red Gladioli"		2·50	3·00
798/801		*Set of 4*	5·50	6·00
MS802	103×81 mm. $2 "Dance Hall in Arles" (detail) (*horiz*) ..		6·00	7·00

(Litho Walsall)

1991 (12 Dec). *Christmas. Religious Paintings by Quinten Massys. Vert designs as T 291 of Antigua. Multicoloured.* P 12.
803	15 c. "The Virgin and Child Enthroned" (detail)		65	25
804	30 c. "The Virgin and Child Enthroned" (different detail)		1·10	50
805	60 c. "Adoration of the Magi" (detail)		2·50	3·00
806	$1 "Virgin in Adoration"		3·00	3·25
803/6		*Set of 4*	6·50	6·25
MS807	Two sheets, each 102×127 mm. (a) $2 "The Virgin standing with Angels"; (b) $2 "The Adoration of the Magi". P 14×14½. *Set of 2 sheets*		8·50	10·00

(Litho Questa)

1992 (15 Jan). *Fungi. T 194 and similar multicoloured designs.* P 14.
808	12 c. Type 194		85	45
809	30 c. *Lentinula edodes* (*horiz*)		1·40	85
810	45 c. *Hygrocybe acutoconica*		1·60	1·00
811	$1 *Gymnopilus chrysopellus* (*horiz*)		3·25	4·50
808/11		*Set of 4*	6·50	6·00
MS812	94×68 mm. $2 *Pleurotus ostreatus* (*horiz*)		6·50	6·50

(Des D. Miller. Litho Questa)

1992 (12 Mar). *40th Anniv of Queen Elizabeth II's Accession. Horiz designs as T 292 of Antigua. Multicoloured.* P 14.
813	12 c. Little Dix Bay, Virgin Gorda		35	30
814	45 c. Deadchest Bay, Peter Island		1·00	90
815	60 c. Pond Bay, Virgin Gorda		1·25	1·75
816	$1 Cane Garden Bay, Tortola		1·75	2·25
813/16		*Set of 4*	4·00	4·75
MS817	75×97 mm. $2 Long Bay, Beef Island	..	4·00	5·00

195 Queen Isabella of Spain   **196** Basketball

(Des W. Hanson. Litho B.D.T.)

1992 (26 May). *500th Anniv of Discovery of America by Columbus (4th issue). T 195 and similar multicoloured designs.* P 14.
818	10 c. Type 195		40	40
819	15 c. Fleet of Columbus (*horiz*)		70	70
820	20 c. Arms awarded to Columbus		70	70
821	30 c. Landing Monument, Watling Island and Columbus' signature (*horiz*)		85	85
822	45 c. Christopher Columbus		1·25	1·25
823	50 c. Landing in New World and Spanish royal standard (*horiz*)		1·25	1·40
824	70 c. Convent at La Rabida		2·00	2·75
825	$1.50, Replica of *Santa Maria* and Caribbean Pavilion, New York World's Fair (*horiz*)		3·50	4·00
818/25		*Set of 8*	9·50	11·00
MS826	Two sheets. (a) 116×86 mm. $2 Ships of second voyage at Virgin Gorda (*horiz*). (b) 86×116 mm. $2 De la Cosa's map of New World (*horiz*) .. .. *Set of 2 sheets*		8·00	10·00

(Litho Questa)

1992 (26 Oct). *Olympic Games, Barcelona. T* **196** *and similar vert designs. Multicoloured. P* 14.

827	15 c. Type **196**	..	..	..	1·00	55
828	30 c. Tennis				1·50	90
829	60 c. Volleyball				2·25	2·75
830	$1 Football				2·75	3·50
827/30				*Set of* 4	6·75	7·00
MS831	100×70 mm. $2 Olympic flame			..	5·50	7·00

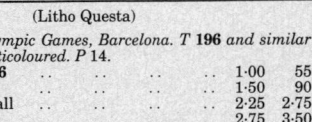

197 Issuing Social Security
Cheque

(Litho Questa)

1993 (14 May). *25th Anniv of Ministerial Government. T* **197** *and similar horiz designs. Multicoloured. P* 14.

832	12 c. Type **197**	..	..	25	25
833	15 c. Map of British Virgin Islands			35	30
834	45 c. Administration building	..		60	70
835	$1.30, International currency abbreviations			1·75	3·00
832/5			*Set of* 4	2·75	3·75

198 Cruising Yacht and
Swimmers, The Baths, Virgin
Gorda

(Litho Questa)

1993 (23 July). *Tourism. T* **198** *and similar multicoloured designs. P* 14.

836	15 c. Type **198**			50	30
837	30 c. Cruising yacht under sail (*vert*)	..		75	60
838	60 c. Scuba diving ..			1·25	1·60
839	$1 Cruising yacht at anchor and snorklers (*vert*)			1·60	1·90
836/9			*Set of* 4	3·50	4·00
MS840	79×108 mm. $1 *Promenade* (trimaran) (*vert*); $1 Scuba diving (*different*) (*vert*)			4·00	4·50

(Des Kerri Schiff. Litho Questa)

1993 (27 Aug). *40th Anniv of Coronation. Vert designs as T* **307** *of Antigua. P* 13½×14.

841	12 c. multicoloured			60	75
	a. Sheetlet. Nos. 841/4×2			6·50	
842	45 c. multicoloured			80	1·00
843	60 c. bluish grey and black	..		95	1·25
844	$1 multicoloured			1·40	1·75
841/4			*Set of* 4	3·25	4·25

Designs:—12 c. Queen Elizabeth II at Coronation (photograph by Cecil Beaton); 45 c. Orb; 60 c. Queen with Prince Philip, Queen Mother and Princess Margaret, 1953; $1 Queen Elizabeth II on official visit.

Nos. 841/4 were printed in sheetlets of 8, containing two *se-tenant* blocks of 4.

A $2 miniature sheet showing "Queen Elizabeth II" (Sir Herbert James) was prepared, but not issued in British Virgin Islands.

200 Columbus with King
Ferdinand and Queen Isabella

(Des G. Vasarhelyi. Litho Questa)

1993 (24 Sept). *500th Anniv of Discovery of Virgin Islands by Columbus. T* **200** *and similar horiz designs. Multicoloured. P* 14.

846	3 c. Type **200**			15	40
847	12 c. Columbus's ship leaving port			40	40
848	15 c. Blessing the fleet			45	45
849	25 c. Arms and flag of B.V.I.			60	60
850	30 c. Columbus and *Santa Maria*			70	70
851	45 c. Ships of second voyage	..		95	95
852	60 c. Columbus in ship's boat			1·50	2·25
853	$1 Landing of Columbus			2·00	2·50
846/53			*Set of* 8	6·00	7·50
MS854	Two sheets, each 120×80 mm. (a) $2 Amerindians sighting fleet. (b) $2 Christopher Columbus and ships		*Set of 2 sheets*	6·00	8·00

NEW INFORMATION

The editor is always interested to correspond with people who have new information that will improve or correct the Catalogue.

---

201 Library Services
Publications

202 Anegada Ground
Iguana

1993 (20 Dec). *50th Anniv of Secondary Education and Library Services. T* **201** *and similar multicoloured designs. Litho. P* 14×13½ (*horiz*) *or* 13½×14 (*vert*).

855	5 c. Type **201**			30	40
856	10 c. Secondary school sports			40	40
857	15 c. Stanley Nibbs (school teacher) (*vert*)			50	45
858	20 c. Mobile library			60	50
859	30 c. Dr. Norwell Harrigan (adminstrator and lecturer) (*vert*)			75	60
860	35 c. Children in library			80	65
861	70 c. Commemorative inscription on book			1·60	2·25
862	$1 B.V.I. High School			1·75	2·25
855/62			*Set of* 8	6·00	6·75

(Litho Questa)

1994 (18 Mar). *Endangered Species. Anegada Ground Iguana. T* **202** *and similar vert designs showing iguanas. P* 14.

863	5 c. multicoloured			30	40
864	10 c. multicoloured			30	40
865	15 c. multicoloured			40	40
866	45 c. multicoloured			1·10	1·25
863/6			*Set of* 4	1·90	2·25
MS867	106×77 mm. $2 multicoloured			3·00	4·00

No. MS867 does not carry the W.W.F. Panda emblem.

203 Loading Disaster Relief
Aircraft

204 Argentina v.
Netherlands, 1978

(Litho Questa)

1994 (3 June). *Centenary of Rotary International in B.V.I. T* **203** *and similar horiz designs. Multicoloured. P* 14.

868	15 c. Type **203**			35	35
869	45 c. Training children in marine safety			85	85
870	50 c. Donated operating table			90	1·00
871	90 c. Paul Harris (founder) and emblem			1·60	2·25
868/71			*Set of* 4	3·25	4·00

(Des W. Hanson. Litho Questa)

1994 (30 Sept). *25th Anniv of First Moon Landing. Horiz designs as T* **326** *of Antigua. Multicoloured. P* 14.

872	50 c. Anniversary logo			1·50	1·75
	a. Sheetlet. Nos. 872/7			8·00	
873	50 c. Lunar landing training vehicle			1·50	1·75
874	50 c. Launch of "Apollo 11"			1·50	1·75
875	50 c. Lunar module *Eagle* in flight			1·50	1·75
876	50 c. Moon's surface			1·50	1·75
877	50 c. Neil Armstrong (astronaut) taking first step			1·50	1·75
872/7			*Set of* 6	8·00	9·50
MS878	106×76 mm. $2 Signatures and mission logo			4·00	5·00

Nos. 872/7 were printed together, *se-tenant*, in sheetlets of 6.

(Des J. Iskowitz. Litho Questa)

1994 (16 Dec). *World Cup Football Championship, U.S.A. Previous Winners. T* **204** *and similar multicoloured designs. P* 14.

879	15 c. Type **204**			65	40
880	35 c. Italy v. West Germany, 1982			1·00	70
881	50 c. Argentina v. West Germany, 1986			1·75	1·75
882	$1.30, West Germany v. Argentina, 1990			3·75	4·50
879/82			*Set of* 4	6·50	6·50
MS883	74×101 mm. $2 U.S. flag and World Cup trophy (*horiz*)			4·50	5·50

1995 (June). *As Nos.* 768, 770, 773/4, 776/7, 780 *and* 782, *but W* w 14 (*sideways*) *and with* "1995" *imprint date. P* 14.

887	10 c. Autograph Tree			30	40
889	15 c. Lantana			40	35
892	30 c. Swamp Immortelle			60	50
893	35 c. White Cedar			65	55
895	45 c. Pinguin			75	70
896	50 c. Christmas Orchid			1·25	1·25
899	$2 Beach Morning Glory			2·75	3·75
901	$5 Tall Ground Orchid			8·00	8·50
887/901			*Set of* 8	13·00	14·50

(Des A. Theobald. Litho Questa)

1995 (24 Oct). *50th Anniv of United Nations. Horiz designs as T* **213** *of Bahamas. Multicoloured. W* w 16 (*sideways*). *P* 14.

903	15 c. Peugeot P4 all-purpose field cars			45	30
904	30 c. Foden medium road tanker	..		75	60
905	45 c. SISU all-terrain vehicle			1·00	90
906	$2 Westland Lynx AH7 helicopter			3·75	4·50
903/6			*Set of* 4	5·50	5·75

205 Pair of Juvenile
Flamingos

206 "Tortola House with
Christmas Tree" (Maureen
Walters)

(Des N. Arlott. Litho Cartor)

1995 (15 Nov). *Anegada Flamingos Restoration Project. T* **205** *and similar vert designs. Multicoloured. W* w 14. *P* 13×13½.

907	15 c. Type **205**			50	40
908	20 c. Pair of adults			55	45
909	60 c. Adult feeding			1·25	1·50
910	$1.45, Adult feeding chick			2·25	3·00
907/10			*Set of* 4	4·00	4·75
MS911	80×70 mm. $2 Chicks. P 13			3·00	4·00

(Adapted G. Vasarhelyi. Litho Walsall)

1995 (1 Dec). *Christmas. Children's Paintings. T* **206** *and similar horiz designs. Multicoloured. W* w 16 (*sideways*). *P* 13½×14.

912	15 c. Type **206**			60	30
913	50 c. "Father Christmas in Rowing Boat" (Collin Collins)			1·50	1·40
914	70 c. "Christmas Tree and Gifts" (Clare Wassell)			1·75	2·00
915	$1.30, "Peace Dove" (Nicholas Scott)			2·75	3·00
912/15			*Set of* 4	6·00	6·00

207 Seine Fishing

(Des G. Vasarhelyi. Litho Cartor)

1996 (14 Feb). *Island Profiles. Jost Van Dyke. T* **207** *and similar horiz designs. Multicoloured. W* w 14 (*sideways*). *P* 13½×13.

916	15 c. Type **207**			50	35
917	35 c. Sandy Spit			70	55
918	90 c. Map			2·00	2·00
919	$1.50, Foxy's Regatta			2·50	3·25
916/19			*Set of* 4	5·25	5·50

(Des D. Miller. Litho Cartor)

1996 (22 Apr). *70th Birthday of Queen Elizabeth II. Vert designs as T* **165** *of Ascension, each incorporating a different photograph of the Queen. Multicoloured. W* w 14. *P* 13½×14.

920	10 c. Government House, Tortola	..		20	20
921	30 c. Legislative Council Building	..		55	55
922	45 c. Liner in Road Harbour			1·00	70
923	$1.50, Map of British Virgin Islands			2·75	3·25
920/3			*Set of* 4	4·00	4·25
MS924	63×65 mm. $2 Queen Elizabeth II. P 13×13½			3·00	3·50

208 Hurdling

(Des S. Noon. Litho Cartor)

1996 (22 May). *Centenary of Modern Olympic Games. T* **208** *and similar horiz designs. Multicoloured. W* w 14 (*sideways*). *P* 13.

925	20 c. Type **208**			35	30
926	35 c. Volleyball			60	60
927	50 c. Swimming			90	1·25
928	$1 Yachting			1·75	3·00
925/8			*Set of* 4	3·25	4·00

209 Mercedes-Benz "500 K A",
1934

(Des R. Watton. Litho B.D.T.)

1996 (8 June). *"CAPEX '96" International Stamp Exhibition, Toronto. Early Motor Cars. T 209 and similar horiz designs. Multicoloured. W w 14 (sideways*). P 13½.*
929	15 c. Type 209		30	25
930	40 c. Citröen "12", 1934		70	70
931	60 c. Cadillac "V-8 Sport Phaeton", 1932		1·00	1·25
	w. Wmk Crown to right of CA		2·75	
932	$1.35, Rolls Royce "Phantom II", 1934		2·25	2·75
	w. Wmk Crown to right of CA		2·75	
929/32		*Set of 4*	3·75	4·50
MS933	79×62 mm. $2 Ford "Sport Coupé", 1932		3·00	4·00

*The normal sideways watermark shows Crown to left of CA, as seen from the back of the stamp.

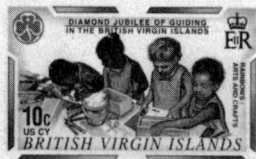

210 Children with
Computer

(Des R. Watton. Litho Cot Printery Ltd, Barbados)

1996 (16 Sept). *50th Anniv of U.N.I.C.E.F. T 210 and similar horiz designs. Multicoloured. W w 14 (sideways). P 14×14½.*
934	10 c. Type 210		25	25
935	15 c. Carnival costume		35	35
936	30 c. Children on Scales of Justice		60	60
937	45 c. Children on beach		90	90
934/7		*Set of 4*	1·90	1·90

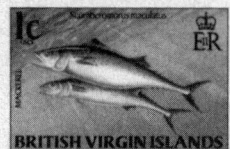

211 Young Rainbows in Art Class

(Des G. Vasarhelyi. Litho Cartor)

1996 (30 Dec). *75th Anniv of Guiding in the British Virgin Islands. T 211 and similar horiz designs. Multicoloured. W w 14 (sideways). P 13½.*
938	10 c. Type 211		20	20
939	15 c. Brownies serving meals		30	25
940	30 c. Guides around campfire		50	45
941	45 c. Rangers on parade		65	60
942	$2 Lady Baden-Powell		2·75	3·50
938/42		*Set of 5*	4·00	4·50

212 Spanish Mackerel

(Des A. Robinson. Litho Walsall)

1997 (6 Jan). *Game Fishes. T 212 and similar horiz designs. Multicoloured. W w 16 (sideways). P 14.*
943	1 c. Type 212		10	10
944	10 c. Wahoo		10	15
945	15 c. Great Barracuda		20	25
946	20 c. Tarpon		25	30
947	25 c. Tiger Shark		30	35
948	35 c. Sailfish		40	45
949	40 c. Dolphin		50	55
950	50 c. Black-finned Tuna		60	65
951	60 c. Yellow-finned Tuna		75	80
952	75 c. King Mackerel ("Kingfish")		90	95
953	$1.50, White Marlin		1·75	1·90
954	$1.85, Amberjack		2·25	2·40
955	$2 Atlantic Bonito		2·50	2·75
956	$5 Bonefish		6·25	6·50
957	$10 Blue Marlin		12·50	13·00
943/57		*Set of 15*	29·00	31·00

(Des D. Miller. Litho Questa)

1997 (3 Feb). *"HONG KONG '97" International Stamp Exhibition. Sheet 130×90 mm, containing design as No. 953, but with "1997" imprint date. Multicoloured. W w 14 (inverted). P 14.*
MS958	$1.50, White Marlin		2·25	2·75

(Des N. Shewring (No. **MS**965), D. Miller (others). Litho Questa (No. **MS**965), Cartor (others))

1997 (10 July). *Golden Wedding of Queen Elizabeth and Prince Philip. Multicoloured designs as T 173 of Ascension. W w 14. P 13.*
959	30 c. Prince Philip with horse		60	65
	a. Horiz pair. Nos. 959/60		1·10	1·25
960	30 c. Queen Elizabeth at Windsor, 1989		60	65
961	45 c. Queen in phaeton, Trooping the Colour		80	90
	a. Horiz pair. Nos. 961/2		1·60	1·75
962	45 c. Prince Philip in Scots Guards uniform		80	90
963	70 c. Queen Elizabeth and Prince Philip at the Derby, 1993		1·10	1·25
	a. Horiz pair. Nos. 963/4		2·10	2·50
964	70 c. Prince Charles playing polo, Mexico 1993		1·10	1·25
959/64		*Set of 6*	4·50	5·00
MS965	110×70 mm. $2 Queen Elizabeth and Prince Philip in landau (horiz). Wmk sideways. P 14×14½		2·75	3·00

Nos. 959/60, 961/2 and 963/4 were each printed together, *se-tenant,* in horizontal pairs throughout the sheets with the backgrounds forming composite designs.

213 Fiddler Crab

(Des Jennifer Toombs. Litho Cartor)

1997 (11 Sept). *Crabs. T 213 and similar horiz designs. Multicoloured. W w 14 (sideways). P 13.*
966	12 c. Type 213		30	25
967	15 c. Coral Crab		35	30
968	35 c. Blue Crab		70	60
969	$1 Giant Hermit Crab		1·50	1·75
966/9		*Set of 4*	2·50	2·50
MS970	76×67 mm. $2 Arrow Crab		3·00	3·25

214 *Psychilis macconnelliae*

(Des I. Loe. Litho Cot Printery Ltd, Barbados)

1997 (26 Nov). *Orchids of the World. T 214 and similar multicoloured designs. W w 14 (sideways). P 14.*
971	20 c. Type 214		25	30
	a. Horiz strip of 4. Nos. 971/4		2·50	
972	50 c. *Tolumnia prionochila*		60	65
973	60 c. *Tetramicra canaliculata*		75	80
974	75 c. *Liparis elata*		90	95
971/4		*Set of 4*	2·50	2·75
MS975	59×79 mm. $2 *Dendrobium crumenatum* (vert). Wmk upright		2·50	2·75

Nos. 971/4 were printed together, *se-tenant,* in horizontal strips of four throughout the sheet.

215 Sir Francis Drake and
Signature

(Des E. Nisbet. Litho Questa)

1997 (13 Dec). *420th Anniv of Drake's Circumnavigation of the World. T 215 and similar horiz designs. Multicoloured. W w 14 (sideways). P 14½.*
976	40 c. Type 215		50	55
	a. Sheetlet. Nos. 976/87		6·00	
977	40 c. Drake's coat of arms		50	55
978	40 c. Queen Elizabeth I and signature		50	55
979	40 c. *Christopher* and *Marigold*		50	55
980	40 c. *Golden Hind*		50	55
981	40 c. *Swan*		50	55
982	40 c. *Cacafuego* (Spanish galleon)		50	55
983	40 c. *Elizabeth*		50	55
984	40 c. *Maria*		50	55
985	40 c. Drake's astrolabe		50	55
986	40 c. *Golden Hind's* figurehead		50	55
987	40 c. Compass rose		50	55
976/87		*Set of 12*	6·00	6·50
MS988	96×76 mm. $2 *Sir Francis Drake* (ketch)		2·50	2·75

Nos. 976/87 were printed together, *se-tenant,* in sheetlets of 12 with the backgrounds forming a composite map of Drake's route.

STAMP BOOKLETS

1981 (22 July). *Royal Wedding. Gold on blue cover, 75×50 mm, showing Royal coat of arms on front and St. Paul's Cathedral on back. Stapled.*
SB1	$3.50, booklet containing 10 c., 35 c., $1.25 (Nos. 463/5), in pairs		2·25

No. SB1 was sold at a 10 c. premium above the total face value of the stamps it contained.

1986 (23 July). *Royal Wedding. Gold (No. SB2) or silver (No. SB3) on new blue covers. Stapled.*
SB2	$4.20, booklet (Westminster Abbey cover) containing twelve 35 c. (Nos. 605/6) in blocks of four		5·50
SB3	$5.40, booklet (State Coach cover) containing four 35 c. (Nos. 605/6) and four $1 (Nos. 607/8), each in block of four		5·50

The stamps from No. SB3 are imperforate.

OFFICIAL STAMPS

OFFICIAL

(O 1)

Two varieties of overprint:
Type I. Foot of "OFFICIAL" 15–16 mm from top of design. Light impression with little or no black outline to letters.
Type II. Foot of "OFFICIAL" 20 mm from top of design. Heavy impression with thick black outline to letters.

1985 (Feb). *Nos. 418/19, 420a/1a, 423a/4a, 425, 426a, 427, 428a and 429/33 optd as Type O 1 in silver by Questa.*
O 1	1 c. Purple-tipped Sea Anemone (I)		30	70
	a. Opt Type II		30·00	35·00
O 2	3 c. Common Starfish (I)		45	70
	a. Opt Type II		35·00	40·00
O 3	5 c. Type 134 (II)		45	30
O 4	8 c. Atlantic Trumpet Triton (*Charonia variegata*) (I)		55	30
	a. Opt Type II		75·00	
O 5	13 c. Flamingo Tongue (*Cyphoma gibbosus*) (II)		80	50
O 6	15 c. Spider Crab (I)		85	70
O 7	18 c. Sea Squirts (I)		90	1·00
	a. Opt Type II		75·00	
O 8	20 c. True Tulip (*Fasciolaria tulipa*) (I)		90	80
O 9	25 c. Rooster-tail Conch (*Strombus gallus*) (I)		1·25	1·25
	w. Wmk inverted			
O10	30 c. West Indian Fighting Conch (*Strombus pugilis*) (I)		1·40	1·00
	a. Optd on No. 428		7·00	13·00
O11	60 c. Mangrove Crab (I)		2·00	2·50
O12	$1 Coral Polyps (I)		3·00	3·75
O13	$2.50, Peppermint Shrimp (I)		4·50	9·00
O14	$3 West Indian Murex (*Murex brevifrons*) (I)		5·50	10·00
	a. Opt inverted		£100	£110
O15	$5 Carpet Anemone (I)		7·50	12·00
O1/15		*Set of 15*	27·00	40·00

Postally used examples of No. O14a are known.
Examples of the ½ c. and 10 c. overprinted in silver and of all seventeen values overprinted in gold also exist, but were not issued in British Virgin Islands.

OFFICIAL **OFFICIAL**

(O 2) (O 3)

1986 (10 Feb–Sept). *Nos. 560/78 optd with Type O 2 by Questa.*
O16	1 c. Type 162 (9.86)		20	20
O17	2 c. Yellow-crowned Night Heron		20	20
O18	5 c. Mangrove Cuckoo (9.86)		30	30
O19	8 c. Northern Mockingbird		30	30
O20	10 c. Grey Kingbird (9.86)		40	40
O21	12 c. Red-necked Pigeon		40	40
O22	15 c. Least Bittern (9.86)		40	40
O23	18 c. Smooth-billed Ani		45	45
O24	20 c. Clapper Rail (9.86)		70	70
O25	25 c. American Kestrel (9.86)		70	70
O26	30 c. Pearly-eyed Thrasher (9.86)		1·00	1·00
O27	35 c. Bridled Quail Dove (9.86)		1·00	1·00
O28	40 c. Green Heron		1·00	1·00
O29	50 c. Scaly-breasted Ground Dove		1·40	1·40
O30	60 c. Little Blue Heron		1·50	1·50
O31	$1 Audubon's Shearwater		2·25	2·25
O32	$2 Blue-faced Booby		2·50	2·75
O33	$3 Cattle Egret		6·00	6·50
O34	$5 Zenaida Dove (9.86)		6·50	6·75
O16/34		*Set of 19*	24·00	25·00

1991 (Sept). *Nos. 767/8, 771, 773/9 and 781 optd with Type O 3.*
O35	5 c. Frangipani		30	30
O36	10 c. Autograph Tree		30	30
O37	20 c. Jerusalem Thorn		35	40
O38	30 c. Swamp Immortelle		50	50
O39	35 c. White Cedar		55	55
O40	40 c. Mahoe Tree		60	60
O41	45 c. Pinguin		70	65
O42	50 c. Christmas Orchid		75	75
O43	70 c. Lignum Vitae		1·00	1·40
O44	$1 African Tulip Tree		1·25	1·60
O45	$3 Organ Pipe Cactus		4·00	4·75
O35/45		*Set of 11*	9·25	11·00

The same stamps, except for the 30 c., exist overprinted with Type O 2, but such overprints were not placed on sale in British Virgin Islands.

Brunei

Sultan Hashim Jalil-ul-alam Akamudin, 1885–1906

(Currency. 100 cents = 1 Straits, later Malayan and Brunei, dollar)

For many years the status of the 1895 issue remained uncertain to such an extent that the 1906 provisionals on Labuan were taken to be the first issue of Brunei.

The 1895 "Star and Crescent" design stamps were, from their first appearance, considered bogus or, at best, as an issue made purely for philatelic purposes. Research into the background of the events surrounding the set led to the publication, in 1933, of the original agreement between Sultan Hashim and J. C. Robertson dated 20 August 1894 which made clear that the stamps fulfilled a genuine postal purpose. Although Robertson and his partners intended to exploit the philatelic sales for their own benefit the agreement testifies, as does other evidence, to the use of the stamps by the Sultan for his postal service. As Brunei did not, at that time, belong to any local or international postal union the stamps were only valid within the state or on mail to Labuan or Sarawak. Items for further afield required franking with Labuan stamps in addition. Although most covers surviving are addressed to Robertson's associates enough commercial covers and cards exist to show that there was, indeed, a postal service.

> **PRICES FOR STAMPS ON COVER TO 1945**
>
> Nos. 1/10 are rare used on cover.
> Nos. 11/22 *from* × 30
> Nos. 23/33 *from* × 25
> Nos. 34/50 *from* × 10
> Nos. 51/9 *from* × 12
> Nos. 60/78 *from* × 8

The Sarawak Government maintained a post office at the coal mining centre of Brooketon, and the stamps of SARAWAK were used there from 1893 until the office was handed over to Brunei in February 1907.

1 Star and Local Scene

(Litho in Glasgow)

1895 (22 July). P 13–13½.

1	1	½ c. brown		2·00	18·00
2		1 c. brown-lake		2·50	13·00
3		2 c. black		3·75	13·00
4		3 c. deep blue		3·00	12·00
5		5 c. deep blue-green		6·00	14·00
6		8 c. plum		6·00	23·00
7		10 c. orange-red		7·50	23·00
		a. Imperf (pair)		£1200	
8		25 c. turquoise-green		42·00	60·00
9		50 c. yellow-green		18·00	75·00
10		$1 yellow-olive		20·00	90·00
1/10			*Set of 10*	£100	£300

BRUNEI. (2)   **BRUNEI.** (3)

BRUNEI.   **TWO CENTS.** (3)   **25 CENTS.** (4)

Line through "B" (R.5/10)

(Optd by Govt Printer, Singapore)

1906 (1 Oct). *Nos. 117/26 of Labuan (see Malaysia), optd with* T 2, *or surch as* T 3 *or* 4 (25 c.), *in red.* P 13½/2 *or* 14 (1 c.).

11		1 c. black and purple		24·00	48·00
		a. Error. Opt in black		£1700	£2500
		b. Line through "B"		£250	
12		2 c. on 3 c. black and sepia		1·50	7·50
		a. "BRUNEI" double		£3750	£2500
		b. "TWO CENTS" double		£9000	
		c. Line through "B"		80·00	
13		2 c. on 8 c. black and vermilion		26·00	75·00
		a. "TWO CENTS" double		£8000	
		b. "TWO CENTS" omitted (in vert pair with normal)		£9000	
		c. Line through "B"		£250	
14		3 c. black and sepia		27·00	75·00
		a. Line through "B"		£250	

15		4 c. on 12 c. black and yellow		2·00	5·00
		a. Line through "B"		80·00	
16		5 c. on 16 c. green and brown		38·00	65·00
		a. Line through "B"		£275	
17		8 c. black and vermilion		8·50	26·00
		a. Line through "B"		£160	
18		10 c. on 16 c. green and brown		6·50	19·00
		a. Line through "B"		£140	
19		25 c. on 16 c. green and brown		95·00	£130
		a. Line through "B"		£500	
20		30 c. on 16 c. green and brown		85·00	£120
		a. Line through "B"		£500	
21		50 c. on 16 c. green and brown		85·00	£120
		a. Line through "B"		£500	
22		$1 on 8 c. black and vermilion		85·00	£120
		a. Line through "B"		£500	
11/22			*Set of 12*	£400	£700

Only one sheet of the 1 c. received the black overprint. The surcharges were applied in settings of 50. Nos. 13a/b occur from one sheet on which the surcharge from the second impression of the setting was misplaced to give two surcharges on row five and none on row ten.

Examples of all values are known showing a forged Brunei postmark dated "13 JUL".

Sultan Mohamed Jemal-ul-Alam, 1906–1924

PRINTERS. All Brunei stamps from Nos. 23 to 113 were recess-printed by De La Rue.

5 View on Brunei River

1907 (26 Feb)–**10**. *Wmk Mult Crown CA.* P 14.

23	5	1 c. grey-black and pale green		2·25	10·00
		x. Wmk reversed		15·00	
24		2 c. grey-black and scarlet		2·50	4·50
		x. Wmk reversed		25·00	
25		3 c. grey-black and chocolate		10·00	20·00
		x. Wmk reversed		30·00	
26		4 c. grey-black and mauve		7·50	10·00
		a. Grey-black and reddish purple (1910)		70·00	60·00
		y. Wmk inverted and reversed		50·00	
27		5 c. grey-black and blue		48·00	85·00
		x. Wmk reversed		85·00	
28		8 c. grey-black and orange		7·50	23·00
29		10 c. grey-black and deep green		4·50	7·00
30		25 c. pale blue and ochre-brown		29·00	48·00
31		30 c. violet and black		18·00	22·00
32		50 c. green and deep brown		15·00	22·00
33		$1 red and grey		55·00	85·00
23/33			*Set of 11*	£180	£300
23/33		Optd "Specimen"	*Set of 11*	£275	

I

II

I Double plate. Lowest line of shading on water is dotted.
II Single plate. Dotted line of shading removed.

Stamps printed in two colours are as I.

1908 (12 June)–**22**. *Colours changed. Double or single plates. Wmk Mult Crown CA.* P 14.

34	5	1 c. green (I)		80	2·25
35		1 c. green (II) (1911)		60	1·50
		a. "A" missing from wmk		£200	
		b. "C" missing from wmk		£200	
36		2 c. black and brown (5.4.11)		2·00	1·25
		w. Wmk inverted		40·00	
37		3 c. scarlet (I)		2·25	1·25
38		3 c. scarlet (II) (1916)		65·00	35·00
39		4 c. claret (II)		2·00	75
40		5 c. black and orange		7·00	7·00
41		8 c. blue and indigo-blue (10.08)		7·00	11·00
42		10 c. purple/yellow (II) (1912)		1·50	1·25
		a. On pale yellow (1922) (Optd S. £38)		1·25	4·00
		w. Wmk inverted		75·00	
		x. Wmk reversed		50·00	
43		25 c. deep lilac (II) (30.5.12)		3·25	12·00
		a. Deep dull purple (1920)			
44		30 c. purple and orange-yellow (18.3.12)		8·50	12·00
45		50 c. black/green (II) (1912)		26·00	65·00
		a. On blue-green (1920)		8·50	32·00
46		$1 black and red/blue (18.3.12)		20·00	48·00
47		$5 carmine/green (I) (1910)		90·00	£150
48		$25 black/red (I) (1910)		£450	£800
34/47			*Set of 12*	£130	£250
34/48		Optd "Specimen"	*Set of 13*	£500	

The used price for No. 48 is for a cancelled-by-favour example, dated before December 1941; there being no actual postal rate for which this value could be used. Examples dated after 1945 are worth much less.

Retouch   Normal   (6)

MALAYA-BORNEO EXHIBITION, 1922.

RETOUCHES. We list the very distinctive 5 c. Retouch (top left value tablet, 1st row, 8th stamp) but there are others of interest, notably in the clouds.

1916. *Colours changed. Single plates. Wmk Mult Crown CA.* P 14.

49	5	5 c. orange		12·00	12·00
		a. "5 c." retouch		£325	£325
50		8 c. ultramarine		5·00	22·00
49/50		Optd "Specimen"	*Set of 2*	£100	

MALAYA-BORNEO EXHIBITION OVERPRINTS. These were produced from a setting of 30 examples, applied twice to overprint the complete sheet of 60 stamps. Three prominent overprint flaws exist, each occurring on all the stamps in two vertical rows of the sheet.

HI   **EX**   **NE**

Short "I"	Broken "E"	Broken "N"
(all stamps in 2nd and 8th vertical rows)	(all stamps in 4th and 10th vertical rows)	(all stamps in 6th and 12th vertical rows)

(Optd by Govt Printer, Singapore)

1922 (31 Mar). *Optd with* T **6**, *in black.*

51	5	1 c. green (II)		2·50	22·00
		a. Short "I"		6·00	32·00
		b. Broken "E"		6·00	32·00
		c. Broken "N"		6·00	32·00
52		2 c. black and brown		3·75	27·00
		a. Short "I"		10·00	38·00
		b. Broken "E"		10·00	38·00
		c. Broken "N"		10·00	38·00
53		3 c. scarlet (II)		5·50	35·00
		a. Short "I"		12·00	48·00
		b. Broken "E"		12·00	48·00
		c. Broken "N"		12·00	48·00
54		4 c. claret (II)		5·50	42·00
		a. Short "I"		12·00	60·00
		b. Broken "E"		12·00	60·00
		c. Broken "N"		12·00	60·00
55		5 c. orange (II)		8·50	55·00
		a. "5 c." retouch (and short "I")		£300	£650
		b. Short "I"		16·00	80·00
		c. Broken "E"		16·00	80·00
		d. Broken "N"		16·00	80·00
56		10 c. purple/yellow (II)		6·50	55·00
		a. Short "I"		14·00	80·00
		b. Broken "E"		14·00	80·00
		c. Broken "N"		14·00	80·00
57		25 c. deep dull purple (II)		14·00	80·00
		a. Short "I"		30·00	£120
		b. Broken "E"		30·00	£120
		c. Broken "N"		30·00	£120
58		50 c. black/blue-green (II)		45·00	£150
		a. Short "I"		80·00	£200
		b. Broken "E"		80·00	£200
		c. Broken "N"		80·00	£200
59		$1 black and red/blue		70·00	£190
		a. Short "I"		£120	£250
		b. Broken "E"		£120	£250
		c. Broken "N"		£120	£250
51/9			*Set of 9*	£140	£550

Examples of all values are known showing a forged Brunei postmark dated "13 JUL".

Sultan Ahmed Tajudin Akhazul Khairi Wadin, 1924–1950

7 Native houses, Water Village

1924 (Feb)–**37**. *Printed from single plates as Type II, except 30 c. and $1 as Type I. Wmk Mult Script CA.* P 14.

60	5	1 c. black (9.26)		60	35
61		2 c. brown (3.24)		90	4·25
62		2 c. green (3.33)		60	30
63		3 c. green (3.24)		80	4·75
64		4 c. maroon (3.24)		1·50	75
65		4 c. orange (1929)		1·00	50
66		5 c. orange-yellow* (3.24)		3·25	1·00
		a. "5 c." retouch		£150	£110
67		5 c. grey (1931)		9·00	8·50
		a. "5 c." retouch		£325	£275
68		5 c. chocolate (1933)		6·50	20
		a. "5 c." retouch		£170	50·00
69	7	6 c. intense black** (3.24)		12·00	10·00
70		6 c. scarlet (1931)		3·75	11·00
71	5	8 c. ultramarine (9.27)		6·00	5·00
72		8 c. grey-black (1933)		6·50	55
73		10 c. purple/yellow (3.37)		12·00	24·00
74	7	12 c. blue		4·50	9·00
		a. Pale greenish blue (1927)		£130	£250
75	5	25 c. slate-purple (1931)		5·00	11·00
76		30 c. purple and orange-yellow (1931)		7·00	16·00
77		50 c. black/emerald (1931)		7·00	15·00
78		$1 black and red/blue (1931)		24·00	70·00
60/78			*Set of 19*	£100	£170
60/72, 74/8		Optd/Perf "Specimen"	*Set of 18*	£350	

*For 5 c. orange, see No. 82. No. 66 is a "Wet" printing and No. 82 a "Dry".

**For 6 c. black, see No. 83. Apart from the difference in shade there is a variation in size, No. 69 being 37¾ mm long and No. 82 39 mm.

The 2 c. orange and 3 c. blue-green in Type **5**, and the 6 c. greenish grey, 8 c. red and 15 c. ultramarine in Type **7** were not issued without the Japanese Occupation overprint although unoverprinted examples exist. It is believed that these printings were produced and possibly perforated, by other firms in Great Britain following bomb damage to the De La Rue works at the end of 1940 (*Price for set of 5, £450 un*).

During the life of this issue De La Rue changed the method of production from a "Wet" to a "Dry" process. Initially the stamps were printed on ungummed paper which was dampened before being put on the press. Once the paper had dried, and contracted in the process, the gum was then applied. "Dry" printings, introduced around 1934, were on pre-gummed paper. The contraction of the "Wet" printings was considerable and usually involves a difference of between 0.5 mm and 1 mm when compared with the larger "Dry" printings. The following listings occur from both "Wet" and "Dry" versions: 1 c., 2 c. green, 4 c. orange, 5 c. chocolate, 6 c. scarlet, 8 c. grey-black, 10 c. and 25 c.

Stamps of this issue can be found either line or comb perforated.

Brunei was occupied by the Japanese Army in January 1942 and remained under Japanese administration until liberated by the 9th Australian Division in June 1945.

After the cessation of hostilities with the Japanese postal services were re-introduced by the British Military Administration. Post offices under B.M.A. control were opened at Brunei Town and Kuala Belait on 17 December 1945 where B.M.A. overprints on the stamps of NORTH BORNEO and SARAWAK were used until the reappearance of Brunei issues on 2 January 1947.

Redrawn clouds (R. 1/1 of No. 80*ab* only)

1947 (2 Jan)–51. *Colours changed and new values. Wmk Mult Script CA. P 14.*

79	**5**	1 c. chocolate	50	1·25
		a. "A" of "CA" missing from wmk	£1100	
80		2 c. grey	90	1·50
		a. Perf 14½×13½ (25.9.50)	1·50	3·75
		ab. Black (27.6.51)	2·00	5·50
		ac. Redrawn clouds	65·00	
81	**7**	3 c. green	1·00	3·00
82	**5**	5 c. orange*	80	1·25
		a. "5 c." retouch	55·00	75·00
		b. Perf 14½×13½ (25.9.50)	4·00	11·00
		c. Ditto "5 c." retouch	£120	£180
83	**7**	6 c. black*	1·00	2·75
84	**5**	8 c. scarlet	40	70
		a. Perf 13 (25.1.51)	55	8·50
85		10 c. violet	70	20
		a. Perf 14½×13½ (25.9.50)	2·00	4·50
86		15 c. ultramarine	50	60
87		25 c. deep claret	1·25	70
		a. Perf 14½×13½ (25.1.51)	1·50	6·50
88		30 c. black and orange	1·00	1·00
		a. Perf 14½×13½ (25.1.51)	1·50	11·00
89		50 c. black	1·75	55
		a. Perf 13 (25.9.50)	1·75	13·00
90		$1 black and scarlet	4·00	75
91		$5 green and red-orange (2.2.48)	16·00	14·00
92		$10 black and purple (2.2.48)	42·00	30·00
79/92		Set of 14	65·00	50·00
79/92	Perf "Specimen"	Set of 14	£200	

*See also Nos. 66 and 69.

The 1, 2, 3, 5, 6, 10 and 25 c. values utilised the plates of the pre-war issue and were line perforated until the introduction of the 14½×13½ comb machine for some values in 1950–51. The 8, 15, 50 c., $1, $5 and $10 were from new plates with the sheets comb perforated. The 30 c. was initially a pre-war plate, but it is believed that a new plate was introduced in 1951.

8 Sultan Ahmed Tajudin and Water Village

1949 (22 Sept). *Sultan's Silver Jubilee. Wmk Mult Script CA. P 13.*

93	**8**	8 c. black and carmine	55	60
94		25 c. purple and red-orange	55	1·10
95		50 c. black and blue	70	1·10
93/5		Set of 3	1·60	2·50

1949 (10 Oct). *75th Anniv of Universal Postal Union. As Nos. 114/17 of Antigua.*

96		8 c. carmine	1·50	1·25
97		15 c. deep blue	2·50	1·50
98		25 c. magenta	1·50	1·50
99		50 c. blue-black	1·75	1·25
96/9		Set of 4	6·50	5·00

Sultan Sir Omar Ali Saifuddin-Wasa'adul Khairi Wadin, 1950–1967

9 Sultan Omar Ali Saifuddin   **10** Native houses, Water Village

1952 (1 Mar)–58. *Wmk Mult Script CA. P 13.*

100	**9**	1 c. black	10	50
101		2 c. black and orange	10	50
102		3 c. black and lake-brown	10	30
103		4 c. black and green	10	20
104		6 c. black and grey	10	10
105		8 c. black and crimson	50	60
		a. Black and crimson-lake (15.2.56)	4·00	20
106		10 c. black and sepia	15	10
107		12 c. black and violet	3·50	10
108		15 c. black and pale blue	3·25	10
109		25 c. black and purple	2·50	10
		a. Black and reddish purple (8.10.53)	4·50	90
110		50 c. black and ultramarine	1·50	10
		a. Black and blue (22.6.55)	3·25	10
111	**10**	$1 black and green	1·50	95
		a. Black and bronze-green (23.7.58)	3·50	2·50
112		$2 black and scarlet	4·50	2·25
113		$5 black and maroon	11·00	4·75
		a. Black and brown-purple (15.2.56)	14·00	4·50
100/13		Set of 14	25·00	8·75

No. 106 exists in coils constructed from normal sheets.
See also Nos. 118/31 and 202/9.

11 Brunei Mosque and Sultan Omar

(Recess B.W.)

1958 (24 Sept). *Opening of Brunei Mosque. W w **12**. P 13½.*

114	**11**	8 c. black and myrtle-green	20	50
115		15 c. black and carmine	25	15
116		35 c. black and deep lilac	30	80
114/16		Set of 3	65	1·25

12 "Protein Foods"

(Des M. Goaman. Photo Harrison)

1963 (4 June). *Freedom from Hunger. W w **12**. P 14 × 14½.*

117	**12**	12 c. sepia	2·75	90

1964–72. *As Nos. 100/13, but W w **12**. Glazed paper ($2, 5) or ordinary paper (others).*

118	**9**	1 c. black (17.3.64)	50	70
		a. Glazed paper. Grey (28.11.69)	1·10	2·00
		ab. Slate-grey (30.6.72)	15	1·25
119		2 c. black and orange (17.3.64)	1·50	20
		a. Glazed paper (27.5.70)	1·50	10
120		3 c. black and lake-brown (10.11.64)	1·50	20
		a. Glazed paper (27.5.70)	1·50	10
121		4 c. black and green (12.5.64)	30	15
		a. Glazed paper (22.4.70)	50	10
		ab. Black and emerald (19.11.71)	60	3·00
122		6 c. black and grey (12.5.64)	2·00	10
		a. Black (28.11.69)	5·00	5·00
		b. Glazed paper (28.11.69)	35	30
		ba. Light grey (19.11.71)	2·00	3·25
123		8 c. black and crimson-lake (12.5.64)	60	10
		a. Glazed paper (27.5.70)	75	15
		ab. Black and brown-red (19.11.71)	1·75	3·25
124		10 c. black and sepia (12.5.64)	50	10
		a. Glazed paper (31.3.70)	2·75	10
		ab. Grey and pale brown (coil) (11.10.71)	3·25	3·25
125		12 c. black and violet (12.5.64)	1·50	10
		a. Glazed paper (5.11.70)	9·00	1·00
126		15 c. black and pale blue (12.5.64)	55	10
		a. Glazed paper (28.11.69)	65	20
127		25 c. black and purple (12.5.64)	4·50	10
		a. Glazed paper (18.5.70)	8·50	4·00
		ab. Glazed paper. Black and reddish violet (30.4.71)	10·00	85
128		50 c. black and ultramarine (10.11.64)	2·50	10
		a. Black & brt ultramarine (17.3.69)	4·50	65
		b. Glazed paper (5.11.70)	10·00	2·50
		ba. Grey and indigo (21.12.71)	11·00	2·50
129	**10**	$1 black and bronze-green (14.5.68)	3·00	5·00
		a. Glazed paper (5.11.70)	4·50	4·50
130		$2 black and scarlet (5.11.70)	35·00	20·00
131		$5 black and maroon (5.11.70)	42·00	28·00
118/29		Set of 12	17·00	6·00
118a/29a, 130/1		Set of 14	£100	50·00

Printings of the 6 and 15 c. issued on 28 November 1969 were on both ordinary and glazed paper, the 6 c. on ordinary producing a distinct shade.

No. 124a exists in coils constructed from normal sheets.

---

13 I.T.U. Emblem

(Des M. Goaman. Litho Enschedé)

1965 (17 May). *I.T.U. Centenary. W w **12**. P 11 × 11½.*

132	**13**	4 c. mauve and orange-brown	35	10
133		75 c. orange-yellow and light emerald	1·00	75

14 I.C.Y. Emblem

(Des V. Whiteley. Litho Harrison)

1965 (25 Oct). *International Co-operation Year. W w **12**. P 14.*

134	**14**	4 c. reddish purple and turquoise-green	20	10
135		15 c. deep bluish green and lavender	55	35

15 Sir Winston Churchill and St. Paul's Cathedral in Wartime

(Des Jennifer Toombs. Photo Harrison)

1966 (24 Jan). *Churchill Commemoration. W w **12**. P 14.*

136	**15**	3 c. black, cerise, gold and new blue	30	20
137		10 c. black, cerise, gold and deep green	1·50	20
138		15 c. black, cerise, gold and brown	1·75	35
139		75 c. black, cerise, gold and bluish violet	4·25	2·25
136/9		Set of 4	7·00	2·50

16 Footballer's Legs, Ball and Jules Rimet Cup

(Des V. Whiteley. Litho Harrison)

1966 (4 July). *World Cup Football Championships. W w **12** (sideways). P 14.*

140	**16**	4 c. violet, yellow-green, lake & yell-brn	20	15
141		75 c. chocolate, blue-grn, lake & yell-brn	75	60

17 W.H.O. Building

(Des M. Goaman. Litho Harrison)

1966 (20 Sept). *Inauguration of W.H.O. Headquarters, Geneva. W w **12** (sideways). P 14.*

142	**17**	12 c. black, yellow-green and light blue	35	40
143		25 c. black, light purple and yellow-brown	55	85

18 "Education"

19 "Science"

20 "Culture"

(Des Jennifer Toombs. Litho Harrison)

1966 (1 Dec). 20th Anniv of U.N.E.S.C.O. W w **12** (sideways). P 14.
144	18	4 c. slate-violet, red, yellow and orange		35	10
145	19	15 c. orange-yellow, violet and deep olive		75	50
146	20	75 c. black, bright purple and orange		2·50	5·50
144/6			Set of 3	3·25	5·50

Sultan Sir Hassanal Bolkiah Mu'izzadin Waddaulah, 1967

21 Religious Headquarters Building

(Des and photo Harrison)

1967 (19 Dec). 1400th Anniv of Revelation of the Koran. W w **12** (sideways). P 12½.
147	21	4 c. multicoloured		10	10
148		10 c. multicoloured		15	10
149	–	25 c. multicoloured		20	30
150	–	50 c. multicoloured		35	1·50
147/50			Set of 4	70	1·75

Nos. 149/50 are as T **21** but have sprigs of laurel flanking the main design (which has a smaller circle) in place of flagpoles.

22 Sultan of Brunei, Mosque and Flags

(Des V. Whiteley. Photo Enschedé)

1968 (9 July). Installation of Y.T.M. Seri Paduka Duli Pengiran Temenggong. T **22** and similar multicoloured design. P 14 × 13 (12 c.) or 13 × 14 (others).
151		4 c. Type **22**		15	30
152		12 c. Sultan of Brunei, Mosque and Flags (horiz)		40	75
153		25 c. Type **22**		50	1·25
151/3			Set of 3	95	2·10

23 Sultan of Brunei   24 Sultan of Brunei

(Des V. Whiteley. Litho D.L.R.)

1968 (15 July). Sultan's Birthday. W w **12** (sideways). P 12.
154	23	4 c. multicoloured		10	20
155		12 c. multicoloured		20	40
156		25 c. multicoloured		30	75
154/6			Set of 3	55	1·25

(Des V. Whiteley. Photo Harrison)

1968 (1 Aug). Coronation of the Sultan of Brunei. W w **12** (sideways). P 14½ × 14.
157	24	4 c. multicoloured		15	15
158		12 c. multicoloured		25	45
159		25 c. multicoloured		40	65
157/9			Set of 3	70	1·10

25 New Building and Sultan's Portrait

26 New Building and Sultan's Portrait

(Photo Enschedé)

1968 (29 Sept). Opening of Language and Literature Bureau. W w **12** (sideways). P 13½ (10 c.) or 12½ × 13½ (others).
160	25	10 c. multicoloured		20	1·25
		a. Tête-bêche (pair)		40	2·50
161	26	15 c. multicoloured		20	35
162		30 c. multicoloured		45	85
160/2			Set of 3	75	2·25

The above were scheduled for release in 1967, and when finally issued had the year altered by overprinting.

27 Human Rights   28 Sultan of Brunei and W.H.O.
Emblem and   Emblem
struggling Man

(Des V. Whiteley. Litho Harrison)

1968 (16 Dec). Human Rights Year. W w **12**. P 14.
163	27	12 c. black, yellow and green		10	20
164		25 c. black, yellow and blue		15	25
165		75 c. black, yellow and dull purple		45	1·50
163/5			Set of 3	65	1·75

(Des V. Whiteley. Litho Format)

1968 (19 Dec). 20th Anniv of World Health Organization. P 14.
166	28	4 c. yellow, black and cobalt		30	30
167		15 c. yellow, black and deep bluish violet		55	65
168		25 c. yellow, black and pale yellow-olive		65	1·25
166/8			Set of 3	1·40	2·00

29 Deep Sea Oil-Rig, Sultan of Brunei and
inset portrait of Pengiran Di-Gadong

(Des adapted by V. Whiteley. Photo Enschedé)

1969 (10 July). Installation (9th May, 1968) of Pengiran Shah-bandar as Y.T.M. Seri Paduka Duli Pengiran Di-Gadong Sahibol Mal. W w **12**. P 14 × 13.
169	29	12 c. multicoloured		85	40
170		40 c. multicoloured		1·25	1·75
171		50 c. multicoloured		1·25	1·75
169/71			Set of 3	3·00	3·50

30 Aerial View of Parliament Buildings

(Des Harrison. Litho D.L.R.)

1969 (23 Sept). Opening of Royal Audience Hall and Legislative Council Chamber. P 15.
172	30	12 c. multicoloured		20	25
173		25 c. multicoloured		30	45
174	–	50 c. rose-red and bluish violet		60	1·25
172/4			Set of 3	1·00	1·75

Design:—50 c. Elevation of new buildings.

32 Youth Centre and Sultan's Portrait

(Des V. Whiteley. Litho D.L.R.)

1969 (20 Dec). Opening of the New Youth Centre. W w **12**. P 15 × 14½.
175	32	6 c. flesh, slate-lilac and black		20	75
176		10 c. olive-yellow, grey-green and blackish brown		25	10
177		30 c. yellow-olive, yellow-brown & black		70	1·00
175/7			Set of 3	1·00	1·60

33 Soldier, Sultan and   34 Badge, and Officer in
Badge   Full-dress Uniform

(Des Maj. M. A. Bowman. Adapted V. Whiteley. Litho Questa)

1971 (3 May). Tenth Anniv of Royal Brunei Malay Regiment. Multicoloured designs, each with Badge and Sultan's portrait as T **33**. W w **12** (sideways on 15 and 75 c.). P 14½.
178		10 c. Type **33**		70	30
179		15 c. Bell 205 UH-1H Iroquois helicopter (horiz)		90	70
180		75 c. Pahlawan (patrol boat) (horiz)		2·75	5·50
178/80			Set of 3	4·00	6·00

(Des Supt. T. Swan. Litho Format)

1971 (14 Aug). 50th Anniv of Royal Brunei Police Force. T **34** and similar vert designs. Multicoloured. W w **12** (sideways). P 14½.
181		10 c. Type **34**		50	30
182		15 c. Badge and Patrol Constable		60	80
183		50 c. Badge and Traffic Constable		1·75	5·00
181/3			Set of 3	2·50	5·50

35 Perdana Wazir, Sultan of Brunei and view
of Water Village

(Des and litho Harrison)

1971 (27 Aug). Installation of the Yang Teramat Mulia as the Perdana Wazir (1970). T **35** and similar horiz designs showing different views of Brunei Town. W w **12**. P 14.
184	35	15 c. multicoloured		40	50
185	–	25 c. multicoloured		70	1·00
186	–	50 c. multicoloured		1·40	4·00
184/6			Set of 3	2·25	5·00

36 Pottery

(Des C. Abbott. Litho Questa)

1972 (29 Feb). Opening of Brunei Museum. T **36** and similar horiz designs. Multicoloured. W w **12** (sideways). P 13½.
187		10 c. Type **36**		30	10
188		12 c. Straw-work		40	20
189		15 c. Leather-work		45	20
190		25 c. Gold-work		1·25	1·10
191		50 c. Museum Building (58 × 21 mm)		2·25	3·50
187/91			Set of 5	4·25	4·50

37 Brunei Museum, Queen Elizabeth and
Sultan of Brunei

(Des locally. Photo Enschedé)

1972 (29 Feb). Royal Visit. T **37** and similar horiz designs each with portraits of Queen and Sultan. Multicoloured. W w **12** (sideways*). P 13 × 13½.
192		10 c. Type **37**		60	20
193		15 c. Native houses		85	55
		w. Wmk Crown to right of CA			
194		25 c. Mosque		1·75	1·60
195		50 c. Royal Assembly Hall		3·50	5·50
192/5			Set of 4	6·00	7·00

*The normal sideways watermark shows Crown to left of CA, as seen from the back of the stamp.

38 Secretariat Building

(Des Harrison. Litho J.W.)

1972 (4 Oct). *Renaming of Brunei Town as Bandar Seri Begawan. T* **38** *and similar horiz designs.* W w **12** *(sideways).* P 13½.
196		10 c. multicoloured		30	15
197		15 c. green, light yellow and black		35	15
198		25 c. ultramarine, lemon and black		60	50
199		50 c. rosine, pale turquoise-blue and black		95	1·75
196/9			*Set of* 4	2·00	2·25

Views:—15 c. Darul Hana Palace; 25 c. Old Brunei Town; 50 c. Town and Water Village.

39 Blackburn Beverley C1 parachuting Supplies

(Des Trident Artists. Litho Questa)

1972 (15 Nov). *Opening of R.A.F. Museum, Hendon. T* **39** *and similar horiz design.* Multicoloured. W w **12** *(sideways on* 75 c.). P 14 × 13½ (25 c.) *or* 13½ × 14 (75 c.).
200	25 c. Type **39**		1·75	1·25
201	75 c. Blackburn Beverley C1 landing		3·25	3·75

1972 (17 Nov)–**74**. *As Nos.* 119/26, *but* W w **12** *(sideways*).* Glazed paper.
202	**9**	2 c. black and orange (9.5.73)		1·50	5·00
203		3 c. black and lake-brown		1·75	40
204		4 c. black and green		50	80
205		6 c. black and grey		2·75	30
206		8 c. black and brown-red (9.5.73)		1·75	3·00
207		10 c. black and sepia		80	30
	a.	Black and bistre-brown (24.7.74)		80	2·75
	aw.	Wmk Crown to right of CA		5·00	
208		12 c. black and violet		1·50	2·25
209		15 c. black and pale blue		1·75	2·25
202/9			*Set of* 8	11·00	13·00

*The normal sideways watermark shows Crown to left of CA, *as seen from the back of the stamp.*

40 Girl with Traditional Flower-pot, and Boy with Bowl and Pipe

(Des (from photograph by D. Groves) and photo Harrison)

1972 (20 Nov). *Royal Silver Wedding.* Multicoloured; background colour given. P 14 × 14½.
210	**40**	12 c. carmine-red		10	10
	w.	Wmk inverted		22·00	
211		75 c. deep myrtle-green		20	50

41 Interpol H.Q., Paris

(Des Shamir Bros. Litho Harrison)

1973 (7 Sept). *50th Anniv of Interpol. T* **41** *and similar horiz design.* W w **12** *(inverted on* 50 c.). P 14 × 14½.
212	25 c. bright green, purple and dull blue-black		1·50	1·25
213	50 c. pale greenish blue, ultramarine & carm		1·50	1·25

The 50 c. shows a different view of the H.Q.

42 Sultan, Princess Anne and Capt. Phillips

(Des PAD Studio. Litho Format)

1973 (14 Nov). *Royal Wedding.* W w **12**. P 14.
214	**42**	25 c. multicoloured	15	10
215		50 c. multicoloured	15	25

43 Churchill Painting

44 Sultan Sir Hassanal Bolkiah Mu'izzaddin Waddaulah

(Des C. Abbott. Litho Questa)

1973 (31 Dec). *Opening of Churchill Memorial Building. T* **43** *and similar vert design.* Multicoloured. W w **12** *(sideways).* P 14 × 13½.
216	12 c. Type **43**		10	20
217	50 c. Churchill Statue		30	1·40

(Des Staff Artists, Dept of Language and Literature. Photo Harrison)

1974 (15 July*). *Multicoloured; background colour given.* W w **12** *(sideways†).* P 13½ × 14½.
218	**44**	4 c. turquoise-green		20	20
219		5 c. pale blue		20	30
220		6 c. olive		70	1·25
221		10 c. lavender		30	10
222		15 c. light brown		55	10
223		20 c. stone		30	20
	w.	Wmk Crown to right of CA		1·40	
224		25 c. sage-green		40	15
225		30 c. bright blue		40	15
226		35 c. grey		40	20
227		40 c. bright purple		40	20
228		50 c. cinnamon		40	20
229		75 c. light yellow-green		60	2·50
230		$1 pale salmon		1·25	4·00
231		$2 greenish yellow		2·25	8·50
232		$5 silver		4·50	17·00
233		$10 gold		7·00	28·00
218/33			*Set of* 16	17·00	55·00

*This was the London release date. The stamps were not put on sale locally until 29 August 1974, but First Day Covers were cancelled with the 15 July date.
†The normal sideways watermark shows Crown to left of CA, *as seen from the back of the stamp.*
See also Nos. 244/59 and 260/2.

45 Aerial View of Airport

(Des Harrison. Litho B.W.)

1974 (18 July). *Inauguration of Brunei International Airport. T* **45** *and similar horiz design.* Multicoloured. W w **12** *(sideways on* 75 c.). P 14 × 14½ (50 c.) *or* 12½ × 13 (75 c.).
234	50 c. Type **45**		1·25	1·00
235	75 c. Sultan in Army uniform, and airport (48 × 36 mm)		1·50	1·50

46 U.P.U. Emblem and Sultan

(Des J.W. Litho Harrison)

1974 (28 Oct). *Centenary of Universal Postal Union.* W w **12** *(sideways).* P 14½.
236	**46**	12 c. multicoloured		20	20
237		50 c. multicoloured		40	1·40
238		75 c. multicoloured		50	1·75
236/8			*Set of* 3	1·00	3·00

47 Sir Winston Churchill

(Des C. Abbott. Litho Questa)

1974 (30 Nov). *Birth Centenary of Sir Winston Churchill. T* **47** *and similar horiz design.* Multicoloured. W w **14** *(sideways).* P 14.
239	12 c. Type **47**		25	20
240	75 c. Churchill smoking cigar (profile)		45	1·25

A set of four, 12, 20, 25 and 75 c., was prepared during this period to mark the opening of new port facilities at Muara, but these stamps were never issued.

48 Boeing 737 and R.B.A. Crest

(Des PAD Studio. Litho Enschedé)

1975 (14 May). *Inauguration of Royal Brunei Airlines. T* **48** *and similar horiz designs.* Multicoloured. No wmk. P 12½ × 12.
241	12 c. Type **48**		85	25
242	35 c. Boeing 737 over Bandar Seri Begawan Mosque		1·60	1·25
243	75 c. Boeing 737 in flight		2·25	2·50
241/3		*Set of* 3	4·25	3·50

1975 (13 Aug)–**78**. *As Nos.* 218/33, *but* W w **14** *(sideways*).*
244	**44**	4 c. turquoise-green		30	1·50
245		5 c. pale blue		30	1·50
246		6 c. olive		2·25	2·50
247		10 c. lavender		30	10
	a.	Pale bluish violet (19.4.77)		30	10
248		15 c. light brown		60	90
249		20 c. stone		60	75
250		25 c. sage-green		70	90
	a.	Grey-olive (25.5.78)		30	1·00
251		30 c. bright blue		35	1·25
	w.	Wmk Crown to right of CA		1·25	
252		35 c. grey		45	1·25
253		40 c. bright purple		55	1·50
254		50 c. cinnamon		90	50
	a.	Blue omitted†		50·00	
255		75 c. light yellow-green		80	2·75
256		$1 pale salmon		1·50	2·75
	w.	Wmk Crown to right of CA		2·00	3·00
257		$2 greenish yellow		4·00	8·50
258		$5 silver		5·50	17·00
259		$10 gold		23·00	28·00
244/59			*Set of* 16	38·00	65·00

*The normal sideways watermark shows Crown to left of CA, *as seen from the back of the stamp.*
†The blue colour on the 50 c. value is only evident in the bluish green stripes of the sash and on several of the medal ribbons.

1976 (12 Apr). *As Nos.* 221 *and* 223/4 *but* W w **12** *(upright).*
260	**44**	10 c. lavender		3·50	1·50
261		20 c. stone		3·50	3·50
262		25 c. sage-green		3·50	4·50
260/2			*Set of* 3	9·50	8·50

(49)

50 Royal Coat of Arms

(Surchd by Govt Printer, Brunei)

1976 (16 Aug). *No.* 246 *surch with T* **49** *in silver.*
263	**44**	10 c. on 6 c. olive		1·75	60
	a.	Surch on No. 220		2·25	85

(Des C. Abbott. Litho D.L.R.)

1977 (7 June). *Silver Jubilee. T* **50** *and similar vert designs.* Multicoloured. W w **14**. P 13½ × 14.
264	10 c. Type **50**		15	15
265	20 c. Imperial State Crown		20	20
	a. Silver omitted		£200	
266	75 c. Queen Elizabeth (portrait by Annigoni)		45	60
264/6		*Set of* 3	70	85

51 The Moment of Crowning   **52** Royal Crest

(Des J. Cooter. Litho Enschedé)

1978 (2 June). *25th Anniv of Coronation. T* **51** *and similar vert designs.* Multicoloured. W w **14**. P 13½ × 13.
267	10 c. Type **51**		15	10
268	20 c. Queen in Coronation regalia		20	20
	w. Wmk inverted		75·00	
269	75 c. Queen's departure from Abbey		55	85
267/9		*Set of* 3	80	1·00

(Des local artist; adapted BG Studio. Litho Cartor)

1978 (1 Aug). *10th Anniv of Sultan's Coronation. T 52 and similar vert designs.* W w 14 (*inverted*). *P* 12.

270	10 c. black, scarlet and greenish yellow	..	15	10
271	20 c. multicoloured	..	30	25
272	75 c. multicoloured	.. .. ..	90	1·75
270/2	..	Set of 3	1·25	1·75
MS273	182 × 77 mm. Nos. 270/2	.. ..	10·00	14·00

Designs:—20 c. Coronation ceremony; 75 c. Royal Crown.

53 Human Rights Emblem and struggling Man

54 Smiling Children

(Des V. Whiteley; adapted L. McCombie. Litho Questa)

1978 (10 Dec). *Human Rights Year.* W w 14. *P* 14½.

274	53	10 c. black, yellow and scarlet	10	10
275		20 c. black, yellow and violet	20	35
276		75 c. black, yellow and bistre	50	1·50
274/6	..	Set of 3	70	1·75

Type 53 is similar to the design used for the 1968 Human Rights Year issue.

(Des L. Curtis. Litho Harrison)

1979 (30 June). *International Year of the Child. T 54 and similar horiz design.* W w 14 (*sideways*). *P* 14.

277	10 c. multicoloured	..	20	10
278	$1 black and dull green	.. ..	1·25	2·50

Design:—$1 I.Y.C. emblem.

55 Earth Satellite Station   56 Hegira Symbol

(Des A. Theobald. Litho Questa)

1979 (23 Sept). *Telisai Earth Satellite Station. T 55 and similar horiz designs. Multicoloured.* W w 14 (*sideways*). *P* 14.

279	10 c. Type 55	..	20	15
280	20 c. Satellite and antenna	..	35	35
281	75 c. Television camera, telex machine and telephone	..	75	2·25
279/81		Set of 3	1·10	2·50

(Litho Secura, Singapore)

1979 (21 Nov). *Moslem Year 1400 AH Commemoration.* W w 14. *P* 13 × 13½.

282	56	10 c. black, yellow and emerald	10	15
283		20 c. black, yellow and light blue	15	30
284		75 c. black, yellow and violet	45	1·75
282/4		Set of 3	60	2·00
MS285	178×200 mm. Nos. 282/4	.. ..	3·00	5·50
	w. Wmk inverted	.. ..	3·00	

57 Installation Ceremony   58 Royal Umbrella and Sash

(Des BG Studio. Litho Questa)

1980 (8 Nov). *1st Anniv of Prince Sufri Bolkiah's Installation as First Wazir. T 57 and similar vert design. Multicoloured.* W w 14. *P* 13½.

286	10 c. Type 57	..	15	10
287	75 c. Prince Sufri	.. ..	85	1·75

Nos. 286/7 have blue borders.

(Des BG Studio. Litho Secura, Singapore)

1980 (6 Dec). *1st Anniv of Prince Jefri Bolkiah's Installation as Second Wazir. Vert designs as T 57. Multicoloured.* W w 14. *P* 13½.

288	10 c. Installation ceremony	..	15	10
	w. Wmk inverted	..	22·00	
289	75 c. Prince Jefri	.. ..	45	1·50

Nos. 288/9 have green borders.

(Des BG Studio. Litho Security Printers (M), Malaysia)

1981 (18 Jan*). *Royal Regalia (1st series). T 58 and similar multi-coloured designs. P* 13½ × 13 (50 c.) or 12 × 11½ (others).

290	10 c. Type 58	..	20	15
291	15 c. Sword and Shield	..	30	25
292	20 c. Lance and Sheath	..	40	35
293	30 c. Betel-leaf Container	..	60	1·00
294	50 c. Coronation Crown (23 × 40 mm)	..	1·00	3·75
290/4		Set of 5	2·25	5·00
MS295	98 × 142 mm. Nos. 290/4	..	3·50	5·50

*This is the local release date. The Crown Agents released the stamps on 19 January.

See also Nos. 298/303, 314/19 and 320/5.

59 I.T.U. and W.H.O. Emblems   60 Shield and Broadsword

(Litho Security Printers (M), Malaysia)

1981 (17 May). *World Telecommunications and Health Day. P* 13 × 13½.

296	59	10 c. black and bright crimson	50	25
297		75 c. black, chalky blue & pale violet-bl	2·25	4·25

(Des BG Studio. Litho Security Printers (M), Malaysia)

1981 (15 July). *Royal Regalia (2nd series). T 60 and similar multicoloured designs. P* 12.

298	10 c. Type 60	..	10	10
299	15 c. Blunderbuss and Pouch	..	20	30
300	20 c. Crossed Lances and Sash	..	30	30
301	30 c. Sword, Shield and Sash	..	40	65
302	50 c. Forked Lance	..	60	2·00
303	75 c. Royal Drum (29 × 45 mm)	..	80	3·25
298/303		Set of 6	2·10	6·00

61 Prince Charles as Colonel of the Welsh Guards   62 Fishing

(Des J.W. Litho Format)

1981 (29 July). *Royal Wedding. T 61 and similar vert designs. Multicoloured.* W w 14. *P* 14.

304	10 c. Wedding bouquet from Brunei	..	15	15
305	$1 Type 61	..	50	1·50
306	$2 Prince Charles and Lady Diana Spencer	70	2·50
	w. Wmk inverted	..	40·00	
304/6	.. .. ..	Set of 3	1·25	3·75

(Des local artist. Litho Secura, Singapore)

1981 (16 Oct). *World Food Day. T 62 and similar vert design. Multicoloured. P* 12 × 11½.

307	10 c. Type 62	..	50	15
308	$1 Farm produce and machinery	..	4·50	6·00

63 Blind Man and Braille Alphabet   64 Drawing of Infected Lungs

(Des local artist. Litho Security Printers (M), Malaysia)

1981 (16 Dec). *International Year for Disabled Persons. T 63 and similar vert designs. Multicoloured.* W w 14. *P* 12.

309	10 c. Type 63	..	65	20
	w. Wmk inverted	..	11·00	
310	20 c. Deaf people and sign language	..	1·50	80
	a. Wmk sideways	..	1·75	1·75
311	75 c. Disabled person and wheelchairs	..	3·00	5·50
309/11	.. ..	Set of 3	4·75	6·00

(Des local artist. Litho Security Printers (M), Malaysia)

1982 (24 May). *Centenary of Robert Koch's Discovery of Tubercle Bacillus. T 64 and similar horiz design. Multicoloured.* W w 14. *P* 12 (10 c.) or 13½ (75 c.).

312	10 c. Type 64	..	50	25
313	75 c. Magnified tubercle bacillus and microscope	..	3·00	4·50

(Des PAD Studio. Litho Security Printers (M), Malaysia)

1982 (31 May). *Royal Regalia (3rd series). Multicoloured designs as T 60.* W w 14 (*sideways*). *P* 13½ (75 c.) or 12 × 11½ (others).

314	10 c. Ceremonial Ornament	..	10	10
315	15 c. Silver Betel Caddy	..	20	20
316	20 c. Traditional Flower-pot	..	25	25
317	30 c. Solitary Candle	..	50	70
318	50 c. Golden Pipe	..	70	2·00
319	75 c. Royal Chin Support (28 × 45 mm)	90	3·25
314/19		Set of 6	2·40	5·75

(Des BG Studio. Litho Security Printers (M), Malaysia)

1982 (15 July). *Royal Regalia (4th series). Multicoloured designs as T 60.* W w 14 (*sideways**). *P* 12 (75 c.) or 12×11½ (others).

320	10 c. Royal Mace	..	25	10
321	15 c. Ceremonial Shield and Spears	..	35	20
322	20 c. Embroidered Ornament	..	45	30
323	30 c. Golden-tasselled Cushion	..	75	1·25
324	50 c. Ceremonial Dagger and Sheath	..	1·25	3·00
325	75 c. Religious Mace (28×45 mm)	..	1·60	4·00
	w. Wmk Crown to left of CA	..	18·00	
320/5		Set of 6	4·25	8·00

*The normal sideways watermark shows Crown to right of CA, *as seen from the back of the stamp.*

65 Brunei Flag

(Des Siti Zaleha Haji Kaprawi. Litho Secura, Singapore)

1983 (14 Mar). *Commonwealth Day. T 65 and similar horiz designs. P* 13 × 13½.

326	10 c. multicoloured	..	15	35
	a. Horiz strip of 4. Nos. 326/9	..	1·75	
327	20 c. bright blue, black and buff	..	20	40
328	75 c. bright blue, black and bright green	45	75
329	$2 bright blue, black and lemon	..	1·10	1·75
326/9	..	Set of 4	1·75	3·00

Designs:—20 c. Brunei Mosque; 75 c. Machinery; $2 Sultan of Brunei.

Nos. 326/9 were printed together, *se-tenant*, in horizontal strips of four throughout the sheet.

66 "Postal Service"   67 Football

(Litho Secura, Singapore)

1983 (15 Aug). *World Communications Year. T 66 and similar horiz designs. P* 13½.

330	10 c. multicoloured	..	15	10
331	75 c. yellow, orange-brown and black	..	60	75
332	$2 multicoloured	..	1·75	2·25
330/2		Set of 3	2·25	2·75

Designs:—75 c. "Telephone Service"; $2 "Communications".

(Litho Security Printers (M), Malaysia)

1983 (23 Sept). *Official Opening of the Negara Hassanal Bolkiah Stadium. T 67 and similar multicoloured designs. P* 12.

333	10 c. Type 67	..	55	15
334	75 c. Athletics	..	2·25	1·50
335	$1 View of stadium (44 × 27 mm)	..	2·75	3·00
333/5	..	Set of 3	5·00	4·25

68 Fishermen and Crustacea

(Litho Secura, Singapore)

1983 (23 Sept). *Fishery Resources. T 68 and similar horiz designs. Multicoloured. P* 13½ × 14.

336	10 c. Type 68	..	75	15
337	50 c. Fishermen with net	..	1·75	1·00
338	75 c. Fishing trawler	..	2·00	1·75
339	$1 Fishing with hook and tackle	..	2·25	2·50
336/9	..	Set of 4	6·00	4·75

INDEPENDENCE

From No. 349 onwards issues are inscribed "BRUNEI DARUSSALAM".

69 Royal Assembly Hall

(Des Haji Salleh bin Haji Ibrahim (No. 346), Pengiran Haji Muhammed bin Pengiran Duraman (No. MS348) or Siti Zaleha Haji Kaprawi (others). Litho Cartor)

1984 (1 Jan). *Independence. T* **69** *and similar designs. P* 13.

340	10 c. pale stone and bright orange	..	..	20	10
341	20 c. flesh and brown-red			30	20
342	35 c. rose-pink and plum	..	..	60	60
343	50 c. pale blue and new blue	..	..	1·50	1·00
344	75 c. bright yellow-green and emerald			1·50	1·75
345	$1 light brownish grey and light brown			2·00	2·25
346	$3 multicoloured	..	..	4·50	7·50
340/6	..	..	*Set of* 7	9·50	12·00

MS347 150 × 120 mm. Nos. 340/6 .. .. 9·50 14·00

MS348 Two sheets each 150 × 120 mm. containing 4 stamps (34 × 69 mm.). (a) 25 c. × 4 grey-black and new blue (Signing of the Brunei Constitution). (b) 25 c. × 4 multicoloured (Signing of Brunei-U.K. Friendship Agreement) .. *Set of 2 sheets* 1·75 3·25

Designs:—34×25 mm. 20 c. Government Secretariat Building; 35 c. New Supreme Court; 50 c. Natural gas well; 75 c. Omar Ali Saifuddin Mosque; $1 Sultan's Palace; 68×24 mm. $3 Brunei flag and map of South-East Asia.

70 Natural Forests and Enrichment Planting

(Des Awang Nor Ariffin bin Md. Yassin. Litho Secura, Singapore)

1984 (21 Apr). *Forestry Resources. T* **70** *and similar horiz designs. Multicoloured. P* 13½ × 14.

349	10 c. Type **70**	..	..	90	25
350	50 c. Forests and water resources	..	..	2·00	2·25
351	75 c. Recreation forests	..	..	2·75	3·50
352	$1 Forests and wildlife	..	..	4·00	4·50
349/52			*Set of* 4	8·75	9·50

71 Sultan Omar Saifuddin 50 c. Stamp of 1952

(Recess and litho D.L.R.)

1984 (22 Oct). *"Philakorea" International Stamp Exhibition, Seoul. T* **71** *and similar vert designs. Multicoloured. P* 13.

353	10 c. Type **71**	..	..	50	15
354	75 c. Brunei River view 10 c. stamp of 1907			1·75	2·00
355	$2 Star and view ½ c. stamp of 1895	..	..	2·50	4·50
353/5			*Set of* 3	4·25	6·00

MS356 Three sheets, 117 × 100 mm, each containing one stamp as Nos. 353/5 *Set of 3 sheets* 3·75 5·50
a. Line perf 14 at left *Set of 3 sheets* 4·50 7·50

The stamps within the miniature sheets were perforated by means of a three-sided comb gauging 13 and completed by a line perforation at left. Normally this line perforation is also 13, but on **MS356a** it measures 14.

72 United Nations Emblem   **73** Young People and Brunei Flag

(Des Awang Nor Ariffin bin Md. Yassin (No. 357, 359), Haji Salleh bin Haji Ibrahim (358) or Siti Zaleha Haji Kaprawi (360). Litho Cartor)

1985 (23 Sept). *Admission of Brunei to World Organizations (1st issue). T* **72** *and similar horiz designs. W w* 17 (*sideways**). *P* 13.

357	50 c. black, gold and pale greenish blue	..		50	70
358	50 c. multicoloured			50	70
359	50 c. multicoloured			50	70
360	50 c. multicoloured	..		50	70
357/60			*Set of* 4	1·75	2·50

MS361 110×151 mm. Nos. 357/60 .. .. 2·00 3·00
w. Wmk reading upwards .. .. 2·00 3·00

Designs—No. 357, Type **72**; No. 358, Islamic Conference Organization logo; No. 359, Commonwealth logo; No. 360 A.S.E.A.N. emblem.

*The normal sideways version of the watermark shows the words reading downwards.
See also Nos. 383/7.

(Des Siti Zaleha Haji Kaprawi. Litho Security Printers (M), Malaysia)

1985 (17 Oct). *International Youth Year. T* **73** *and similar horiz designs. Multicoloured. P* 12.

362	10 c. Type **73**	..	..	80	20
363	75 c. Young people at work	..	..	3·50	4·50
364	$1 Young people serving the community			4·00	5·00
362/4			*Set of* 3	7·50	8·75

74 Palestinian Emblem   **75** Early and Modern Scout Uniforms

(Des Haji Salleh bin Haji Ibrahim. Litho Secura, Singapore)

1985 (29 Nov). *International Palestinian Solidarity Day. P* 12 × 12½.

365	**74** 10 c. multicoloured	..	..	85	20
366	50 c. multicoloured	..	..	2·75	1·50
367	$1 multicoloured	..	..	3·25	3·00
365/7	..	..	*Set of* 3	6·25	4·25

(Des Awang Nor Ariffin bin Md. Yassin. Litho Secura, Singapore)

1985 (14 Dec). *National Scout Jamboree. T* **75** *and similar vert designs. Multicoloured. P* 13½.

368	10 c. Type **75**	..	..	40	10
369	20 c. Scout on tower signalling with flag	..		65	40
370	$2 Jamboree emblem	..	..	2·25	3·25
368/70			*Set of* 3	3·00	3·25

76 Sultan Sir Hassanal Bolkiah Mu'izzaddin Waddaulah

77

(Des Awang Nor Ariffin bin Md. Yassin. Photo Harrison)

1985 (23 Dec)—86. *W* **77**. *P* 13½ × 14½ (10 *to* 75 *c.*) *or* 14 ($1 *to* $10).

371	**76** 10 c. multicoloured	..		20	15
372	15 c. multicoloured	..		30	15
373	20 c. multicoloured	..		40	25
374	25 c. multicoloured	..		45	30
375	35 c. multicoloured (15.1.86)	..		55	35
376	40 c. multicoloured (15.1.86)	..		60	40
377	50 c. multicoloured (15.1.86)	..		70	50
378	75 c. multicoloured (15.1.86)	..		1·00	75
379	$1 multicoloured (23.2.86)	..		1·25	95
	a. Wmk sideways				
380	$2 multicoloured (23.2.86)	..		2·25	2·50
381	$5 multicoloured (23.2.86)	..		4·50	5·50
382	$10 multicoloured (29.3.86)	..		9·25	11·00
371/82			*Set of* 12	19·00	20·00

Nos. 379/82 are larger, size 32×39 mm.

(Des Awang Nor Ariffin bin Md. Yassin. Litho Cartor)

1986 (30 Apr). *Admission of Brunei to World Organizations (2nd issue). Horiz designs as T* **72**. *W w* 17 (*sideways*). *P* 13.

383	50 c. black, gold and bright yellow-green	..		40	60
384	50 c. black, gold and bright pinkish mauve	..		40	60
385	50 c. black, gold and orange-red	..		40	60
386	50 c. black, gold and dull ultramarine	..		40	60
383/6			*Set of* 4	1·40	2·25

MS387 105 × 155 mm. Nos. 383/6. Wmk upright 1·50 3·00

Designs:—No. 383, World Meteorological Organization emblem; 384, International Telecommunication Union emblem; 385, Universal Postal Union emblem; 386, International Civil Aviation Organization emblem.

78 Soldiers on Assault Course and Bell 205 UH-1H Iroquois Helicopter   **79** Tunggul Charok Buritan, Alam Bernaga (Alam Besar), Pisang-Pisang and Sandaran

(Des Awang Nor Ariffin bin Md. Yassin. Litho Secura, Singapore)

1986 (31 May). *25th Anniv of Brunei Armed Forces. T* **78** *and similar horiz designs. Multicoloured. P* 13½.

388	10 c. Type **78**			2·00	2·00
	a. Horiz strip of 4. Nos. 388/91 ..			10·00	
389	20 c. Operating computer	..		2·50	2·50
390	50 c. Anti-aircraft missile, MBB-Bolkow Bo 105L helicopter and missile boat			3·00	3·00
391	75 c. Army commanders and parade			3·50	3·50
388/91			*Set of* 4	10·00	10·00

Nos. 388/91 were printed together, *se-tenant*, in horizontal strips of 4 throughout the sheet, forming a composite design.

(Des Awang Nor Ariffin bin Md. Yassin. Litho Secura, Singapore)

1986 (15 July). *Royal Ensigns (1st series). T* **79** *and similar vert designs. P* 12.

392	10 c. black, greenish yellow and red			30	10
393	75 c. multicoloured	..		1·10	1·10
394	$2 black, greenish yellow and green	..		2·25	2·75
392/4			*Set of* 3	3·25	3·50

Designs:—75 c. Ula-Ula Besar, Sumbu Layang and Payong Haram; $2 Panji-Panji, Chogan Istiadat (Chogan Di-Raja) and Chogan Ugama.

(Des Awang Nor Ariffin bin Md. Yassin. Litho Secura, Singapore)

1986 (30 Sept). *Royal Ensigns (2nd series). Vert designs as T* **79**. *P* 12.

395	10 c. multicoloured	..		30	10
396	75 c. black, red and greenish yellow			1·10	1·10
397	$2 multicoloured	..		2·25	2·75
395/7			*Set of* 3	3·25	3·50

Designs:—10 c. Dadap, Tunggul Kawan, Ambal, Payong Ubor-Ubor, Sapu-Sapu Ayeng and Rawai Lidah; 75 c. Payong Tinggi and Payong Ubor-Ubor Tiga Ringkat; $2 Lambang Duli Yang Maha Mulia and Mahligai.

80 Stylised Peace Doves   **81** Drug Addict in Cage and Syringe (poster by Othman bin Ramboh)

(Des Zainal Abidin Haji Ibrahim. Litho Security Printers (M), Malaysia)

1986 (24 Oct). *International Peace Year. T* **80** *and similar horiz designs. Multicoloured. P* 12.

398	50 c. Type **80**	..	..	75	75
399	75 c. Stylised hands and "1986"			1·00	1·10
400	$1 International Peace Year emblem and arms of Brunei	..		1·25	1·50
398/400			*Set of* 3	2·75	3·00

(Litho Security Printers (M), Malaysia)

1987 (15 Mar). *National Anti-drug Campaign. Children's Posters. T* **81** *and similar vert designs. Multicoloured. P* 12.

401	10 c. Type **81**			70	25
402	75 c. Drug addict and noose (Arman bin Mohd. Zaman)			2·00	2·75
403	$1 Blindfolded drug addict and noose (Abidin bin Hj. Rashid)			2·50	3·50
401/3			*Set of* 3	4·75	6·00

82 Cannon ("badil")   **83** Map showing Member Countries

(Des Haji Salleh bin Haji Ibrahim. Litho Security Printers (M),
Malaysia)

1987 (15 July). *Brassware (1st series). T 82 and similar vert
designs. Multicoloured. P 12.*

404	50 c. Type 82		50	50
405	50 c. Lamp ("pelita")		50	50
406	50 c. Betel container ("langguai")		50	50
407	50 c. Water jug ("kiri")		50	50
404/7		*Set of 4*	1·75	1·75

See also Nos. 434/7.

(Des Zainal Abidin bin Haji Ibrahim. Litho Security Printers
(M), Malaysia)

1987 (8 Aug). *20th Anniv of Association of South East Asian
Nations. T 83 and similar horiz designs. Multicoloured.
P 14 × 13½.*

408	20 c. Type 83		25	20
409	50 c. Dates and figures "20"		50	50
410	$1 Flags of member states		1·00	1·00
408/10		*Set of 3*	1·60	1·50

84 Brunei Citizens

(Des Pengiran Haji Muhammad bin Pengiran Duraman. Litho
Secura, Singapore)

1987 (29 Sept). *25th Anniv of Language and Literature Bureau
(1986). T 84 and similar horiz designs. Multicoloured.
P 13 × 12½.*

411	10 c. Type 84		25	25
	a. Horiz strip of 3. Nos. 411/13		2·00	
412	50 c. Flame emblem and hands holding open book		50	50
413	$2 Scenes of village life		1·50	1·50
411/13		*Set of 3*	2·00	2·00

Nos. 411/13 were printed together, *se-tenant*, in horizontal
strips of three throughout the sheet, each strip forming a
composite design taken from a mural.

85 *Artocarpus odoratissima*

(Litho Security Printers (M), Malaysia)

1987 (31 Oct). *Local Fruits (1st series). T 85 and similar horiz
designs. Multicoloured. P 12.*

414	50 c. Type 85		45	55
	a. Horiz strip of 4. Nos. 414/17		1·60	
415	50 c. *Canarium odontophyllum mig.*		45	55
416	50 c. *Litsea garciae*		45	55
417	50 c. *Mangifera foetida lour*		45	55
414/17		*Set of 4*	1·60	2·00

Nos. 414/17 were printed together, *se-tenant*, in horizontal
strips of 4 throughout the sheet.
See also Nos. 421/4, 459/62, 480/2 and 525/8.

86 Modern House   87 Wooden Lathe

(Litho Security Printers (M), Malaysia)

1987 (28 Nov). *International Year of Shelter for the Homeless.
T 86 and similar horiz designs, each showing modern Brunei
housing. P 13 × 12½.*

418	50 c. multicoloured		40	50
419	75 c. multicoloured		55	65
420	$1 multicoloured		80	90
418/20		*Set of 3*	1·60	1·90

(Des Awang Nor Ariffin bin Md. Yassin. Litho Security Printers
(M), Malaysia)

1988 (30 Jan). *Local Fruits (2nd series). Horiz designs as T 85.
Multicoloured. P 12.*

421	50 c. *Durio spp*		40	50
	a. Horiz strip of 4. Nos. 421/4		1·40	
422	50 c. *Durio oxleyanus*		40	50
423	50 c. *Durio graveolens* (blue background)		40	50
424	50 c. *Durio graveolens* (white background)		40	50
421/4		*Set of 4*	1·40	1·75

Nos. 421/4 were printed together, *se-tenant*, in horizontal
strips of four throughout the sheet.

(Des Awang Padzil bin Haji Ahmad. Litho Security Printers (M),
Malaysia)

1988 (29 Feb). *Opening of Malay Technology Museum. T 87
and similar vert designs. Multicoloured. P 12.*

425	10 c. Type 87		15	10
426	75 c. Crushing sugar cane		55	70
427	$1 Bird scarer		70	85
425/7		*Set of 3*	1·25	1·50

88 Beragi Bunga Sakah-Sakah   89 Sultan reading
dan Bunga Cengkih Cloth   Proclamation

(Des Awang Nor Ariffin bin Md. Yassin. Litho Security Printers
(M), Malaysia)

1988 (30 Apr). *Handwoven Material (1st series). T 88 and
similar horiz designs showing different patterns. Multicoloured. P 12.*

428	10 c. Type 88		10	10
429	20 c. Jong Sarat cloth		15	15
430	25 c. Si Pugut cloth		20	25
431	40 c. Si Pugut Bunga Berlapis cloth		30	35
432	75 c. Si Lobang Bangsi Bunga Belitang Kipas cloth		55	80
428/32		*Set of 5*	1·10	1·50
MS433	150×204 mm. Nos. 428/32		2·00	2·50

See also Nos. 442/7.

(Des Haji Salleh bin Haji Ibrahim. Litho Security Printers (M),
Malaysia)

1988 (30 June). *Brassware (2nd series). Vert designs as T 82.
Multicoloured. P 12.*

434	50 c. Lidded two-handled pot ("periok")		40	50
435	50 c. Candlestick ("lampong")		40	50
436	50 c. Shallow circular dish with stand ("gangsa")		40	50
437	50 c. Repousse box with lid ("celapa")		40	50
434/7		*Set of 4*	1·40	1·75

(Des Awang Nor Ariffin bin Md. Yassin. Litho Security Printers
(M), Malaysia)

1988 (1 Aug). *20th Anniv of Sultan's Coronation. T 89 and
similar vert designs. Multicoloured. P 14 (20, 75 c.) or
12½ × 13 ($2).*

438	20 c. Type 89		10	10
439	75 c. Sultan reading from Koran		45	60
440	$2 In Coronation robes (26×63 mm)		1·50	1·60
438/40		*Set of 3*	1·75	2·00
MS441	164×125 mm. Nos. 438/40		1·75	2·50

In No. MS441 the perforations of the stamps are as Nos.
438/40 except for the 75 c. which is perforated 13 at right.

(Des Awang Nor Ariffin bin Md. Yassin. Litho Security Printers
(M), Malaysia)

1988 (29 Sept). *Handwoven Material (2nd series). Horiz
designs as T 88. Multicoloured. P 12.*

442	10 c. Beragi cloth		10	10
443	20 c. Bertabur cloth		10	15
444	25 c. Sukma Indra cloth		15	20
445	40 c. Si Pugut Bunga cloth		25	35
446	75 c. Beragi Si Lobang Bangsi Bunga Cendera Kesuma cloth		45	70
442/6		*Set of 5*	90	1·40
MS447	150×204 mm. Nos. 442/6		2·00	2·75

90 Malaria-carrying Mosquito

(Litho Cartor)

1988 (17 Dec). *40th Anniv of World Health Organization. T 90
and similar horiz designs. Multicoloured. P 14 × 13½.*

448	25 c. Type 90		60	30
449	35 c. Man with insecticide spray and sample on slide		70	45
450	$2 Microscope and magnified malaria cells	2·25	2·00
448/50		*Set of 3*	3·25	2·50

91 Sultan and Council of   92 Dove escaping from
Ministers   Cage

(Des Awang Nor Ariffin bin Md Yassin. Litho Security Printers
(M), Malaysia)

1989 (23 Feb). *5th Anniv of National Day. T 91 and similar
multicoloured designs. P 12.*

451	20 c. Type 91		20	15
452	30 c. Guard of honour		30	25
453	60 c. Firework display (27 × 55 mm)		50	40
454	$2 Congregation in mosque		1·50	1·75
451/4		*Set of 4*	2·25	2·25
MS455	164 × 124 mm. Nos. 451/4		2·25	2·75

(Des Haji Salleh bin Haji Ibrahim. Litho Secura, Singapore)

1989 (1 Apr). *"Freedom of Palestine". T 92 and similar horiz
designs. Multicoloured. P 13½.*

456	20 c. Type 92		30	20
457	75 c. Map and Palestinian flag		90	85
458	$1 Dome of the Rock, Jerusalem		1·10	1·25
456/8		*Set of 3*	2·10	2·10

(Des Awang Nor Ariffin bin Md. Yassin. Litho Secura,
Singapore)

1989 (31 Oct). *Local Fruits (3rd series). Horiz designs as T 85.
Multicoloured. P 12.*

459	60 c. *Daemonorops fissa*		1·25	1·50
	a. Horiz strip of 4. Nos. 459/62		4·50	
460	60 c. *Eleiodoxa conferta*		1·25	1·50
461	60 c. *Salacca zalacca*		1·25	1·50
462	60 c. *Calamus ornatus*		1·25	1·50
459/62		*Set of 4*	4·50	5·50

Nos. 459/62 were printed together, *se-tenant*, in horizontal
strips of four throughout the sheet.

93 Oil Pump

(Des Brunei Shell Petroleum Co. Litho Secura, Singapore)

1989 (28 Dec). *60th Anniv of Brunei Oil and Gas Industry.
T 93 and similar horiz designs. Multicoloured. P 13½.*

463	20 c. Type 93		75	30
464	60 c. Loading tanker		1·75	1·75
465	90 c. Oil well at sunset		2·00	2·25
466	$1 Pipe laying		2·25	2·25
467	$2 Oil terminal		3·75	5·00
463/7		*Set of 5*	9·50	10·50

94 Museum Building and
Exhibits

(Des Awang Padzil bin Haji Ahmad ($1), Mohd Yamin bin Haji
Abd. Momin (others). Litho Security Printers (M), Malaysia)

1990 (1 Jan). *25th Anniv of Brunei Museum. T 94 and similar
horiz designs. Multicoloured. P 12.*

468	30 c. Type 94		75	60
469	60 c. Official opening, 1965		1·40	1·75
470	$1 Brunei Museum		2·00	2·25
468/70		*Set of 3*	3·75	4·25

95 Letters from Malay   96 Tarsier in Tree
Alphabet

(Des Pengiran Haji Muhammad bin Pengiran Duraman. Litho
Security Printers (M), Malaysia)

1990 (15 July). *International Literacy Year. T 95 and similar
horiz designs. Multicoloured. P 12.*

471	15 c. Type 95		50	20
472	90 c. English alphabet		1·90	2·50
473	$1 Literacy Year emblem and letters		2·00	2·75
471/3		*Set of 3*	4·00	5·00

(Des Haji Salleh bin Haji Ibrahim. Litho Security Printers (M),
Malaysia)

1990 (29 Sept). *Endangered Species. Western Tarsier. T 96
and similar vert designs. Multicoloured. P 12 (20 c.) or
12½ × 13 (others).*

474	20 c. Western Tarsier on branch		90	35
475	60 c. Western Tarsier feeding		1·75	2·00
476	90 c. Type 96		2·50	3·25
474/6		*Set of 3*	4·75	5·00

97 Symbolic Family   98 Proboscis Monkey on Ground

(Litho Security Printers (M), Malaysia)

1990 (1 Dec). *Worldwide Campaign against AIDS. T* **97** *and similar vert designs. Multicoloured. P* 12½.
477 20 c. Type **97** 80 60
478 30 c. Sources of infection .. .. 1·50 1·25
479 90 c. "AIDS" headstone surrounded by skulls 3·75 4·50
477/9 .. .. *Set of* 3 5·50 5·75

(Litho Security Printers (M), Malaysia)

1990 (31 Dec). *Local Fruits* (4th series). *Horiz designs as T* **85**. *Multicoloured. P* 12.
480 60 c. *Willoughbea* sp. (brown fruit) .. 2·00 2·50
    a. Horiz strip of three. Nos. 480/2 .. 5·50
481 60 c. Ripe *Willoughbea* sp. (yellow fruit) 2·00 2·50
482 60 c. *Willoughbea angustifolia* .. 2·00 2·50
480/2 .. .. *Set of* 3 5·50 6·50
Nos. 480/2 were printed together, *se-tenant*, in horizontal strips of three throughout the sheet.

(Des Haji Salleh bin Haji Ibrahim. Litho Cartor)

1991 (30 Mar). *Endangered Species. Proboscis Monkey. T* **98** *and similar vert designs. Multicoloured. P* 13½×14.
483 15 c. Type **98** 85 50
484 20 c. Head of monkey 95 60
485 50 c. Monkey sitting on branch .. 2·25 2·50
486 60 c. Female monkey with baby climbing tree .. .. 2·50 3·00
483/6 .. .. *Set of* 4 6·00 6·00

99 Junior School Classes   100 Young Brunei Beauty

(Des Awang Nor Ariffin bin Md Yassin. Litho, Secura Singapore)

1991 (23 Sept). *Teachers' Day. T* **99** *and similar horiz design. Multicoloured. P* 13½×14.
487 60 c. Type **99** .. .. .. 2·00 2·25
488 90 c. Secondary school class .. 2·25 2·75

(Des Awang Padzil bin Haji Ahmad. Litho Security Printers (M), Malaysia)

1991 (1 Oct). *Fishes. Brunei Beauty. T* **100** *and similar horiz designs. Multicoloured. P* 12½.
489 30 c. Type **100** .. .. .. 1·50 85
490 60 c. Female fish .. .. .. 2·50 3·00
491 $1 Male fish .. .. .. 3·00 3·50
489/91 .. .. *Set of* 3 6·25 6·50

101 Graduate with Family   102 Symbolic Heart and Trace

(Des A. Mansur. Litho Cartor)

1991 (30 Nov). *Happy Family Campaign. T* **101** *and similar vert designs. Multicoloured. P* 13.
492 20 c. Type **101** 60 50
493 60 c. Mothers with children .. 1·50 2·00
494 90 c. Family .. .. .. 2·25 3·00
492/4 .. .. *Set of* 3 4·00 5·00

(Des Siti Zaleha Haji Kaprawi. Litho Cartor)

1992 (7 Apr). *World Health Day. T* **102** *and similar horiz designs showing heart and heartbeat trace. P* 13.
495 20 c. multicoloured 75 50
496 50 c. multicoloured .. .. 1·75 2·00
497 75 c. multicoloured .. .. 2·50 3·25
495/7 .. .. *Set of* 3 4·50 5·25
The 75 c. is larger, 48 × 27 mm.

---

103 Map of Cable System

(Des Awang Nor Ariffin bin Md. Yassin. Litho Security Printers (M), Malaysia)

1992 (28 Apr). *Launching of Singapore–Borneo–Philippines Fibre Optic Submarine Cable System. T* **103** *and similar horiz designs. P* 12.
498 20 c. Type **103** 90 50
499 30 c. Diagram of Brunei connection .. 1·25 1·10
500 90 c. Submarine cable .. .. 2·75 3·50
498/500 .. .. *Set of* 3 4·50 4·50

 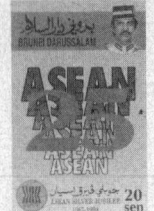

104 Modern Sculptures   105 "A.S.E.A.N. 25" and Logo

(Des Awang Nor Ariffin bin Md. Yassin. Litho Enschedé)

1992 (30 June). *Visit A.S.E.A.N. Year. T* **104** *and similar horiz designs. Multicoloured. P* 13½×14.
501 20 c. Type **104** .. .. .. 1·00 1·50
    a. Horiz strip of 3. *Nos.* 501/3 .. 3·75
502 60 c. Traditional martial arts .. 1·50 2·00
503 $1 Modern sculptures (*different*) .. 1·75 2·25
501/3 .. .. *Set of* 3 3·75 5·25
Nos. 501/3 were printed together, *se-tenant*, in horizontal strips of 3 throughout the sheet with the backgrounds forming a composite design.

(Des Mohd. Yamin bin Haji Abd. Momin. Litho Questa)

1992 (8 Aug). *25th Anniv of A.S.E.A.N (Association of South East Asian Nations). T* **105** *and similar vert designs. Multicoloured. P* 14.
504 20 c. Type **105** 70 50
505 60 c. Headquarters building .. 1·75 2·25
506 90 c. National landmarks .. .. 2·50 3·25
504/6 .. .. *Set of* 3 4·50 5·50

106 Sultan in Procession   107 Crested Wood Partridge

(Des Awang Padzil bin Haji Ahmad. Litho Enschedé)

1992 (5 Oct). *25th Anniv of Sultan's Accession. T* **106** *and similar vert designs. Multicoloured. P* 14×13½.
507 25 c. Type **106** .. .. .. 85 1·00
    a. Horiz strip of 5. *Nos.* 507/11 .. 3·75
508 25 c. Brunei International Airport .. 85 1·00
509 25 c. Sultan's Palace .. .. 85 1·00
510 25 c. Docks and Brunei University .. 85 1·00
511 25 c. Mosque .. .. .. 85 1·00
507/11 .. .. *Set of* 5 3·75 4·50
Nos. 507/11 were printed together, *se-tenant*, in horizontal strips of 5 throughout the sheet, each strip forming a composite design.

(Des Awang Padzil bin Haji Ahmad. Litho Enschedé)

1992 (30 Dec). *Birds* (1st series). *T* **107** *and similar vert designs. Multicoloured. P* 14×13½.
512 30 c. Type **107** 65 50
513 60 c. Asiatic Paradise Flycatcher .. 1·25 1·60
514 $1 Great Argus Pheasant .. .. 1·75 2·50
512/14 .. .. *Set of* 3 3·25 4·25

(Des Awang Padzil bin Haji Ahmad (60 c.), Kassim bin Haji Ismail (others). Litho Enschedé)

1993 (27 Jan). *Birds* (2nd series). *Vert designs as T* **107**. *Multicoloured. P* 14×13½.
515 30 c. Long-tailed Parakeet 65 50
516 60 c. Magpie Robin .. .. 1·25 1·60
517 $1 Blue-crowned Hanging Parrot .. 2·00 2·50
515/17 .. .. *Set of* 3 3·50 4·25

(Des Kassim bin Haji Ismail. Litho Enschedé)

1993 (3 May). *Birds* (3rd series). *Multicoloured designs as T* **107**. *P* 13½×14 (*horiz*) *or* 14×13½ (*vert*).
518 30 c. Chesnut-breasted Malkoha .. 75 50
519 60 c. White-rumped Shama .. 1·40 1·60
520 $1 Black and Red Broadbill (*vert*) .. 2·25 2·50
518/20 .. .. *Set of* 3 4·00 4·25

---

108 National Flag and "10"   109 Cigarette burning Heart and Deformed Baby in Womb

(Des Awang Nor Ariffin bin Md. Yassin. Litho Cartor)

1994 (16 June). *10th Anniv of National Day. T* **108** *and similar vert designs. Multicoloured. P* 13.
521 10 c. Type **108** 30 45
    a. Horiz strip of 4. *Nos.* 521/4 .. 1·75
522 20 c. Symbolic hands 40 55
523 30 c. Previous National Day symbols .. 55 70
524 60 c. Coat of arms 75 90
521/4 .. .. *Set of* 4 1·75 2·40
Nos. 521/4 were printed together, *se-tenant*, in horizontal strips of 4 throughout the sheet.

(Des Al bin Haji Abd Rahim. Litho Cartor)

1994 (8 Aug). *Local Fruits* (5th issue). *Horiz designs as T* **85**, *but each* 36×26 *mm. Multicoloured. P* 13½.
525 60 c. *Nephelium mutabile* .. .. 85 1·00
526 60 c. *Nephelium xerospermoides* .. 85 1·00
527 60 c. *Nephelium* spp .. .. 85 1·00
528 60 c. *Nephelium macrophyllum* .. 85 1·00
525/8 .. .. *Set of* 4 3·00 3·50

(Litho Enschedé)

1994 (1 Sept). *World No Tobacco Day. T* **109** *and similar vert designs. Multicoloured. P* 14×13½.
529 10 c. Type **109** 15 10
530 15 c. Symbols of smoking over crowd of people 15 10
531 $2 Globe crushing cigarettes .. 2·75 3·50
529/31 .. .. *Set of* 3 2·75 3·50

110 Girl Guide   111 Turbo-prop Airliner on Runway

(Des Awang Nor Ariffin bin Md. Yassin. Litho Enschedé)

1994 (7 Oct). *40th Anniv of Brunei Girl Guides' Association. T* **110** *and similar vert designs. Multicoloured. P* 14×13½.
532 40 c. Type **110** 70 80
    a. Horiz strip of 5. *Nos.* 532/6 .. 3·25
533 40 c. Guide receiving award .. 70 80
534 40 c. Guide reading 70 80
535 40 c. Group of guides 70 80
536 40 c. Guides erecting tent 70 80
532/6 .. .. *Set of* 5 3·25 3·50
Nos. 532/6 were printed together, *se-tenant*, in horizontal strips of 5 throughout the sheet.

(Des Mohd Yamin bin Haji Abd Momin. Litho Cartor)

1994 (18 Nov). *20th Anniv of Royal Brunei Airlines. T* **111** *and similar horiz designs. Multicoloured. P* 13½.
537 10 c. Type **111** 30 20
538 20 c. Jet airliner on runway .. 55 30
539 $1 Jet airliner in the air .. .. 1·75 2·50
537/9 .. .. *Set of* 3 2·40 2·75

112 Malay Family   113 Aerial View of City, 1970

(Des Awang Padzil bin Haji Ahmad. Litho Cartor)

1994 (30 Dec). *International Day against Drug Abuse and Trafficking.* T **112** *and similar vert designs.* P 13½×14.

540	20 c. Type 112	..	60	70
	a. Horiz strip of 3. Nos. 540/2	..	2·50	
541	60 c. Chinese family	..	1·00	1·25
542	$1 Doctor, police officers and members of youth organizations	..	1·25	1·50
540/2		*Set of 3*	2·50	3·00

Nos. 540/2 were printed together, *se-tenant*, in horizontal strips of 3 throughout the sheet, each strip forming a composite design.

(Des Awang Padzil bin Haji Ahmad. Litho Cartor)

1995 (4 Oct). *25th Anniv of Bandar Seri Begawan.* T **113** *and similar horiz designs. Multicoloured.* P 13½.

543	30 c. Type 113	..	45	45
544	50 c. City in 1980	..	70	75
545	$1 City in 1990	..	1·50	1·75
543/5		*Set of 3*	2·40	2·75

114 United Nations General Assembly   **115** Students in Laboratory

(Des Mohd Yamin bin Haji Abd Momin. Litho Walsall)

1995 (24 Oct). *50th Anniv of United Nations.* T **114** *and similar vert designs. Multicoloured.* P 14½×14.

546	20 c. Type 114	..	30	25
547	60 c. Security Council in session	..	65	80
548	90 c. United Nations Building, New York (27×44 *mm*)	..	1·00	1·50
546/8		*Set of 3*	1·75	2·25

(Des Mahadi bin Haji Matzain. Litho Cartor)

1995 (28 Oct). *10th Anniv of University of Brunei.* T **115** *and similar vert designs. Multicoloured.* P 13×13½.

549	30 c. Type 115	..	35	35
550	50 c. University building	..	55	65
551	90 c. Sultan visiting University	..	1·10	1·50
549/51		*Set of 3*	1·75	2·25

116 Police Officers   **117** Telephones

(Des Awang Nor Affin bin Md. Yassin. Litho Enschedé)

1996 (10 Feb). *25th Anniv of Royal Brunei Police Force.* T **116** *and similar vert designs. Multicoloured.* P 13½×13.

552	25 c. Type 116	..	50	30
553	50 c. Aspects of police work	..	75	80
554	75 c. Sultan inspecting parade	..	1·25	1·60
552/4		*Set of 3*	2·25	2·40

(Litho Cartor)

1996 (17 May). *World Telecommunications Day. Children's Paintings.* T **117** *and similar vert designs. Multicoloured.* P 13½.

555	20 c. Type 117	..	40	25
556	35 c. Telephone dial and aspects of telecommunications	..	55	45
557	$1 Globe and aspects of telecommunications	..	1·50	1·75
555/7		*Set of 3*	2·25	2·25

118 Sultan and Crowd   **119** Sultan Hassanal Bolkiah Mu'izzaddin Waddaulah

120

(Des Awang Nor Ariffin bin Md. Yassin. Litho Cartor)

1996 (15 July). *50th Birthday of Sultan Hassanal Bolkiah Mu'izzaddin Waddaulah.* T **118** *and similar vert designs. Multicoloured.* P 13×13½.

558	50 c. Type 118	..	70	85
559	50 c. Sultan in ceremonial dress	..	70	85
560	50 c. Sultan receiving dignitaries at mosque		70	85
561	50 c. Sultan with subjects	..	70	85
558/61		*Set of 4*	2·50	3·00
MS562	152×100 mm. $1 Sultan in ceremonial dress (*different*). P 13		1·50	2·00

A larger miniature sheet, 176×128 mm, containing five vertical $50 values was produced in a limited printing for presentation purposes.

(Des A. Robinson. Litho Walsall)

1996 (9 Oct). T **119** *and similar vert design.* W **120**. P 14×13½.

563	119	10 c. multicoloured	..	10	15
564		15 c. multicoloured	..	10	15
565		20 c. multicoloured	..	15	20
566		30 c. multicoloured	..	20	25
567		50 c. multicoloured	..	40	45
568		60 c. multicoloured	..	45	50
569		75 c. multicoloured	..	55	60
570		90 c. multicoloured	..	70	75
571	—	$1 multicoloured	..	75	80
572	—	$2 multicoloured	..	1·50	1·60
573	—	$5 multicoloured	..	3·75	4·00
574	—	$10 multicoloured	..	7·50	8·00
563/74			*Set of 12*	16·00	17·00

Design: (27×39 *mm*)—$1 to $10 Sultan in ceremonial robes.

121 Black-naped Tern   **122** *Acanthus ebracteatus*

(Des Siti Zaleha Haji Kaprawi. Litho Enschedé)

1996 (11 Nov). *Sea Birds.* T **121** *and similar vert designs. Multicoloured.* P 14×13½.

575	20 c. Type 121	..	35	30
576	30 c. Roseate Tern	..	45	40
577	$1 Bridled Tern	..	1·25	1·40
575/7		*Set of 3*	1·90	1·90

No. 576 is inscribed "ROSLATE TERN" in error.

(Des J. Lee. Litho Security Printers (M), Malaysia)

1997 (29 May). *Mangrove Flowers.* T **122** *and similar horiz designs. Multicoloured.* P 12.

578	20 c. Type 122	..	25	20
579	30 c. *Lumnitzera littorea*	..	35	30
580	$1 *Nypa fruticans*	..	1·10	1·25
578/80		*Set of 3*	1·50	1·60

123 *Heterocentrotus mammillatus*

(Des Esther Lee. Litho Southern Colour Print, Dunedin)

1997 (15 Dec). *Marine Life.* T **123** *and similar horiz designs. Multicoloured.* P 12.

581	60 c. Type 123	..	45	50
582	60 c. *Linckia laevigata* (starfish)	..	45	50
583	60 c. *Oxycomanthus bennetti* (plant)	..	45	50
584	60 c. *Bohadschia argus* (sea slug)	..	45	50
581/4		*Set of 4*	1·75	2·00

NEW INFORMATION

The editor is always interested to correspond with people who have new information that will improve or correct the Catalogue.

STAMP BOOKLETS

1976 (23 Feb). *Buff card cover showing Sultan's arms. Stitched.*

SB1	$1 booklet containing four 5 c. and eight 10 c. (Nos. 245, 247) in blocks of 4	2·50

1986. *Black and bright scarlet printed cover showing Post Office emblem. Stitched.*

SB2	$1 booklet containing four 10 c. and four 15 c. (Nos. 371/2) in blocks of 4	1·25

JAPANESE OCCUPATION OF BRUNEI

Japanese forces landed in Northern Borneo on 15 December 1941 and the whole of Brunei had been occupied by 6 January 1942.

Brunei, North Borneo, Sarawak and, after a short period, Labuan, were administered as a single territory by the Japanese. Until September–October 1942, previous stamp issues, without overprint, continued to be used in conjunction with existing postmarks. From the Autumn of 1942 onwards unoverprinted stamps of Japan were made available and examples can be found used from the area for much of the remainder of the War. Japanese Occupation issues for Brunei, North Borneo and Sarawak were equally valid throughout the combined territory but not, in practice, equally available.

PRICES FOR STAMPS ON COVER	
Nos. J1/16	*from* × 8
Nos. J17/20	—

(1)	(2)
("Imperial Japanese Government")	("Imperial Japanese Postal Service $3")

1942 (Oct)–**44**. *Stamps of Brunei handstamped with* T **1** *in violet to blue.* Wmk Mult Script CA (*except Nos.* J18/19, *Mult Crown CA).* P 14.

J 1	5	1 c. black	..	6·00	23·00
		a. Red opt	..	45·00	60·00
J 2		2 c. green	..	45·00	£100
J 3		2 c. orange (1943)	..	2·50	9·00
J 4		3 c. green	..	28·00	75·00
J 5		4 c. orange	..	3·00	13·00
J 6		5 c. chocolate	..	3·00	13·00
		a. "5 c." retouch	..	£150	£375
J 7	7	6 c. greenish grey (*p* 14×11½) (1944)	50·00	£200
J 8		6 c. scarlet	..	£550	£550
J 9	5	8 c. grey-black	..	£650	£850
J10	7	8 c. red	..	3·75	12·00
		a. Opt omitted (in pair with normal)		£850	
J11	5	10 c. purple/*yellow*	..	8·50	26·00
J12	7	12 c. blue	..	20·00	26·00
		a. Red opt	..	£120	£180
J13		15 c. ultramarine (1944)	..	13·00	26·00
J14	5	25 c. slate-purple	..	23·00	50·00
		a. Red opt	..	£180	£250
J15		30 c. purple and orange-yellow	..	90·00	£180
J16		50 c. black/*emerald*	..	38·00	60·00
		a. Red opt	..	£200	
J17		$1 black and red/*blue* (1944)	..	55·00	70·00
		a. Red opt	..	—	£450
J18		$5 carmine/*green* (1944)	..	£800	£1600
J19		$25 black/*red* (1944)	..	£850	£1600

The overprint varies in shade from violet to blue, and being handstamped, exists double, double one inverted and treble.

Nos. J3, J7, J10 and J13 were not issued without the overprint.

1944 (11 May). *No.* J1 *surch with* T **2** *in orange-red.*

J20	5	$3 on 1 c. black	..	£5500	£5000
		a. Surch on No. 60 of Brunei	..	£6500	

Three separate handstamps were used to apply Type **2**, one for the top line, one for the bottom and the third for the two central characters.

Burma

(Currency. 12 pies = 1 anna; 16 annas = 1 rupee)

Stamps of India were used in Burma from 1854 and, after 1856, individual examples can be identified by the use of the concentric octagonal postmarks of the Bengal Postal Circle of which the following were supplied to Burmese post offices:

Type A
No. B 156
(Rangoon)

Type B
No. B 5
(Akyab)

B5	Akyab	B146	Pegu
B12*	Bassein	B150	Prome
B22	Nga Thine Khyoung	B156*	Rangoon
B56	Amherst	B159	Sandoway
B108	Kyouk Phyoo	B165	Sarawah (to 1860)
B111	Meeaday	B165	Henzada (from 1861)
B112	Mengyee	B171	Shoay Gyeen
B127	Moulmein	B173	Sittang
B128	Mergui	B179	Thayetmyo
B129	Tavoy	B181	Toungoo
B133	Myanoung	B227	Port Blair
B136	Namayan		

*Exists in black or blue. Remainder in black only.

Akyab, Moulmein and Rangoon used postmarks as both Type A and Type B, Port Blair as Type B only and the remainder as Type A only.

From 1860 various types of duplex cancellations were introduced and Burmese examples can be identified when sufficient of the left-hand portion is visible on the stamp. Such marks were issued for the following offices:

Akyab	Rangoon
Bassein	Rangoon C.R.H.
Mandalay	(Cantonment Receiving House)
Moulmein	Thayetmyo
Port Blair	Toungoo
Prome	

1862 Duplex from
Toungoo

1865 Duplex from
Akyab

During 1875, a further series of duplex marks was introduced in which the right-hand portion of the cancellation included the office code number, prefixed by the letter "R" for Rangoon:

R–1	Rangoon	1/R–8	Amherst
R–1/1	Rangoon Cantonment	R–9	Myanoung
R–2	Akyab	R–10	Port Blair
R–3	Bassein	R–11	Prome
R–4	Henzada	R–12	Sandoway
R–5	Kyouk Phyoo	R–13	Shwegyeen
R–6	Mandalay	R–14	Tavoy
R–7	Mergui	R–15	Thayetmyo
R–8	Moulmein	R–16	Toughhoo

1875 type from
Rangoon

1875 type from Rangoon
Cantonment Receiving House

From 1886 the whole of Burma was united under the Crown and the post offices were supplied with circular date stamps giving the name of the town.

Most Indian stamps, both postage and official, issued during the period were supplied to post offices in Burma. None of the imperforates printed by De La Rue have been seen however, and from the later issues the following have not been recorded with Burma postmarks:

Nos. 39a, 66a, 68, 85a, 92a, 110a/b, 148a, 155a, 165, 192a/c, 195a/b, O15, O38, O40b, O50a/b, O76a, O101a, O102, O103/a, O104/5 and O142.

The value of most India stamps used in Burma coincides proportionally with the used prices quoted for India, but some, especially the provisional surcharges, are extremely rare with Burmese postmarks. Stamps of the face value of 2 r. and above from the reigns of Victoria and Edward VII are more common with telegraph cancellations than with those of the postal service.

PRICES FOR STAMPS ON COVER TO 1945	
Nos. 1/18	from × 6
Nos. 18a/33	from × 4
No. 34	from × 5
Nos. 35/50	from × 8
Nos. O1/27	from × 15

BRITISH ADMINISTRATION

From 1 January 1886 Burma was a province of the Indian Empire but was separated from India and came under direct British administration on 1 April 1937.

BURMA   BURMA
(1)   (1a)

1937 (1 Apr). Stamps of India (King George V inscr "INDIA POSTAGE") optd with T **1** or **1a** (rupee values). W **69**. P 14.

1	3 p. slate		30	10
	w. Wmk inverted		1·00	50
2	½ a. green		50	10
	w. Wmk inverted		1·50	50
3	9 p. deep green		75	10
	w. Wmk inverted		1·00	50
4	1 a. chocolate		40	10
	w. Wmk inverted		1·25	50
5	2 a. vermilion (small die)		40	10
6	2½ a. orange		30	10
	w. Wmk inverted		1·25	50
7	3 a. carmine		75	30
	w. Wmk inverted		2·50	1·00
8	3½ a. deep blue		65	10
	aw. Wmk inverted		1·00	20
	b. Dull blue		6·00	6·00
	bw. Wmk inverted		4·00	4·00
9	4 a. sage-green		70	10
	w. Wmk inverted		—	20·00
10	6 a. bistre		60	35
	w. Wmk inverted		—	20·00
11	8 a. reddish purple		1·50	10
12	12 a. claret		2·50	85
	w. Wmk inverted		6·00	1·75
13	1 r. chocolate and green		16·00	2·00
14	2 r. carmine and orange		20·00	8·00
	w. Wmk inverted		30·00	12·00
15	5 r. ultramarine and purple		35·00	14·00
16	10 r. green and scarlet		60·00	45·00
17	15 r. blue and olive (wmk inverted)		£190	85·00
18	25 r. orange and blue		£375	£180
	w. Wmk inverted		£450	£225
1/18		Set of 18	£650	£300

The opt is at top on all values except the 3 a.

2 King George VI
and "Chinthes"

3 King George VI
and "Nagas"

4 Royal Barge

8 King George VI
and Peacock

10 Elephants' Heads

Extra trees flaw (R. 11/8)

(Des Maung Kyi (2 a. 6 p.), Maung Hline (3 a.), Maung Ohn Pe (3 a. 6 p.) and N. K. D. Naigamwalla (8 a.). Litho Security Ptg Press, Nasik.)

1938 (15 Nov)–**40**. T **2/4**, **8** and similar designs. W **10**. P 14 (vert) or 13½ × 13 (horiz).

18a	2	1 p. red-orange (1.8.40)	3·00	80
19		3 p. bright violet	20	30
20		6 p. bright blue	20	10
21		9 p. yellow-green	1·00	80
22	3	1 a. purple-brown	20	10
23		1½ a. turquoise-green	20	60
24		2 a. carmine	45	10
25	4	2 a. 6 p. claret	14·00	90
26	—	3 a. dull violet	14·00	1·25
27	—	3 a. 6 p. light blue and blue	1·25	3·75
		a. Extra trees flaw	38·00	
28	3	4 a. greenish blue	60	10
29		8 a. myrtle-green	5·00	30
30	8	1 r. purple and blue	9·00	20
31		2 r. brown and purple	15·00	1·75
32	—	5 r. violet and scarlet	48·00	20·00
33	—	10 r. brown and myrtle	60·00	40·00
18a/33			Set of 16	£150 60·00

Designs: Horiz (as T **4**)—3 a. Burma teak; 3 a. 6 p. Burma rice; 8 a. River Irrawaddy. Vert (as T **8**)—5 r., 10 r. King George VI and "Nats".

The 1 a. exists lithographed and typographed, the latter having a "Jubilee" line in the sheet margin.

COMMEMORATION
POSTAGE STAMP
6ᵗʰ MAY 1840

(11)

1940 (6 May) Centenary of First Adhesive Postage Stamps. No. 25 surch with T **11**.
34	4	1 a. on 2 a. 6 p. claret	3·25	85

For stamps issued in 1942–45 see under Japanese Occupation.

CHIN HILLS DISTRICT. This area, in the far north-west of the country, remained in British hands when the Japanese overran Burma in May 1942.

During the period July to December 1942 the local officials were authorised to produce provisional stamps and the letters "OHMS" are known overprinted by typewriter on Nos. 3, 20, 22/4, 28/9 and 31 of Burma or handstamped, in violet, on Nos. 25, 27 and 29. The two types can also occur together or in combination with a handstamped "SERVICE".

From early in 1943 ordinary postage stamps of India were used from the Chin Hills post offices of Falam, Haka, Fort White and Tiddim, this expedient continuing until the fall of Falam to the Japanese on 7 November 1943.

The provisional stamps should only be collected on Official cover where dates and the sender's handwriting can be authenticated.

BRITISH MILITARY ADMINISTRATION

MILY ADMN   MILY ADMN
(12)   (13)

1945 (from 16 June). Nos. 18a to 33 optd with T **12** (small stamps) or **13** (others) by Security Printing Press, Nasik.

35	2	1 p. red-orange	10	10
		a. Opt omitted (in pair with normal)	£1400	
36		3 p. bright violet	10	30
37		6 p. bright blue	10	30
38		9 p. yellow-green	30	30
39	3	1 a. purple-brown (16.6)	10	10
40		1½ a. turquoise-green (16.6)	10	15
41		2 a. carmine	10	15
42	4	2 a. 6 p. claret	1·50	60
43	—	3 a. dull violet	1·50	20
44	—	3 a. 6 p. light blue and blue	10	70
		a. Extra trees flaw	13·00	
45	3	4 a. greenish blue	10	25
46	—	8 a. myrtle-green	10	40

47	8	1 r. purple and blue	..	50	50
48		2 r. brown and purple	..	50	1·00
49		5 r. violet and scarlet	..	50	1·00
50		10 r. brown and myrtle	..	50	1·00
35/50			Set of 16	4·75	6·25

Only the typographed version of the 1 a., No. 22, received this overprint.

BRITISH CIVIL ADMINISTRATION

1946 (1 Jan). *As Nos. 19/33, but colours changed.*

51	2	3 p. brown	..	10	90
52		6 p. deep violet	..	10	30
53		9 p. green	..	15	1·60
54	3	1 a. blue	..	15	20
55		1½ a. orange	..	15	10
56		2 a. claret	..	15	40
57	4	2 a. 6 p. greenish blue	..	60	2·50
57a		— 3 a. blue-violet	..	6·50	2·75
57b		— 3 a. 6 p. black and ultramarine	..	30	1·00
		ba. Extra trees flaw	..	25·00	
58	3	4 a. purple	..	30	30
59		8 a. maroon	..	1·75	1·50
60	8	1 r. violet and maroon	..	1·00	40
61		2 r. brown and orange	..	6·00	1·75
62		— 5 r. green and brown	..	6·00	9·00
63		— 10 r. claret and violet	..	6·00	15·00
51/63			Set of 15	26·00	35·00

No. 54 was printed in typography only.

14 Burman

(Des A. G. I. McGeogh. Litho Nasik)

1946 (2 May). *Victory. T* **14** *and similar vert designs. W* **10** (*sideways*). *P* 13.

64		9 p. turquoise-green	..	20	20
65		1½ a. violet	..	20	10
66		2 a. carmine	..	20	10
67		3 a. 6 p. ultramarine	..	30	20
64/7			Set of 4	80	50

Designs:—1½ a. Burmese woman; 2 a. Chinthe; 3 a. 6 p. Elephant.

INTERIM BURMESE GOVERNMENT

(**18** Trans. "Interim Government")	**18a**	**18b**

Type **18a** shows the first character transposed to the end of the top line (R. 6/15).

Type **18b** shows the last two characters transposed to the front of the top line (R. 14/14).

Some sheets of the 3 p. show both errors corrected by a handstamp as Type **18**.

1947 (1 Oct). *Stamps of 1946 optd with T* **18** (*small stamps*) *or larger opt* (*others*).

68	2	3 p. brown	..	70	70
		a. Opt Type **18a**	..	17·00	
		ab. Corrected by handstamp as Type **18**			
		b. Opt Type **18b**	..	17·00	
		ba. Corrected by handstamp as Type **18**			
69		6 p. deep violet	..	10	30
		a. Opt Type **18a**	..	9·00	
70		9 p. green	..	10	30
		a. Opt inverted	..	19·00	21·00
71	3	1 a. blue	..	10	30
		a. Vert pair, one with opt omitted			
72		1½ a. orange	..	90	10
73		2 a. claret	..	30	15
		a. Horiz pair, one with opt omitted			
		b. Opt Type **18a**	..	18·00	
74	4	2 a. 6 p. greenish blue	..	1·75	95
75		— 3 a. blue-violet	..	2·50	1·50
76		— 3 a. 6 p. black and ultramarine	..	45	1·25
		a. Extra trees flaw	..	22·00	
77	3	4 a. purple	..	1·75	30
78		8 a. maroon	..	1·75	90
79	8	1 r. violet and maroon	..	2·50	30
80		2 r. brown and orange	..	3·25	2·50
81		— 5 r. green and brown	..	3·25	3·25
82		— 10 r. claret and violet	..	3·25	3·25
68/82			Set of 15	20·00	14·00

The 3 p., 6 p., 2 a., 2 a. 6 p., 3 a. 6 p. and 1 r. are also known with overprint inverted.

OFFICIAL STAMPS

BURMA **BURMA**

SERVICE **SERVICE**

(O 1) (O 1a)

1937 (Apr–June). *Stamps of India* (*King George V inscr* "INDIA POSTAGE") *optd with Type* O **1** *or* O **1a** (*rupee values*). *W* **69**. *P* 14.

O 1		3 p. slate	..	90	10
		w. Wmk inverted	..	—	10·00
O 2		½ a. green	..	4·50	10
O 3		9 p. deep green	..	3·25	30
O 4		1 a. chocolate	..	3·25	10
O 5		2 a. vermilion (*small die*)	..	4·50	35
		w. Wmk inverted	..	—	10·00
O 6		2½ a. orange	..	4·00	1·50
O 7		4 a. sage-green	..	3·25	10
O 8		6 a. bistre	..	4·00	5·50
O 9		8 a. reddish purple (1.4.37)	..	2·75	80
O10		12 a. claret (1.4.37)	..	2·75	3·00
O11		1 r. chocolate and green (1.4.37)	..	20·00	3·75
O12		2 r. carmine and orange	..	35·00	25·00
		w. Wmk inverted	..	45·00	32·00
O13		5 r. ultramarine and purple	..	80·00	40·00
O14		10 r. green and scarlet	..	£250	£100
O1/14			Set of 14	£375	£160

For the above issue the stamps were either overprinted "BURMA" and "SERVICE" at one operation or had the two words applied separately. Research has yet to establish if all values exist with both forms of overprinting.

SERVICE **SERVICE**

(O 2) (O 3)

1939. *Nos. 19/24 and 28 optd with Type* O **2** (*typo*) *and Nos. 25 and 29/33 optd with Type* O **3** (*litho*).

O15	2	3 p. bright violet	..	15	20
O16		6 p. bright blue	..	15	20
O17		9 p. yellow-green	..	5·00	1·60
O18	3	1 a. purple-brown	..	15	15
O19		1½ a. turquoise-green	..	4·50	85
O20		2 a. carmine	..	1·25	20
O21	4	2 a. 6 p. claret	..	25·00	8·00
O22	3	4 a. greenish blue	..	5·50	45
O23		— 8 a. myrtle-green	..	25·00	3·75
O24	8	1 r. purple and blue	..	38·00	4·75
O25		2 r. brown and purple	..	45·00	9·00
O26		— 5 r. violet and scarlet	..	42·00	28·00
O27		— 10 r. brown and myrtle	..	£120	38·00
O15/27			Set of 13	£275	85·00

Both versions of the 1 a. value exist with this overprint.

1946. *British Civil Administration. Nos. 51/6 and 58 optd with Type* O **2** (*typo*) *and Nos. 57 and 59/63 optd with Type* O **3** (*litho*).

O28	2	3 p. brown	..	60	2·00
O29		6 p. deep violet	..	60	1·50
O30		9 p. green	..	20	2·25
O31	3	1 a. blue	..	20	1·50
O32		1½ a. orange	..	20	20
O33		2 a. claret	..	20	1·50
O34	4	2 a. 6 p. greenish blue	..	1·00	3·50
O35	3	4 a. purple	..	20	70
O36		— 8 a. maroon	..	90	2·25
O37	8	1 r. violet and maroon	..	60	2·25
O38		2 r. brown and orange	..	7·00	29·00
O39		— 5 r. green and brown	..	9·00	35·00
O40		— 10 r. claret and violet	..	17·00	48·00
O28/40			Set of 13	35·00	£120

1947. *Interim Burmese Government. Nos.* O28/40 *optd with T* **18** (*small stamps*) *or larger opt* (*others*).

O41	2	3 p. brown	..	15	40
O42		6 p. deep violet	..	50	10
O43		9 p. green	..	75	90
O44	3	1 a. blue	..	1·75	80
O45		1½ a. orange	..	3·00	20
O46		2 a. claret	..	1·25	15
O47	4	2 a. 6 p. greenish blue	..	16·00	6·00
O48	3	4 a. purple	..	4·75	40
O49		— 8 a. maroon	..	4·75	3·00
O50	8	1 r. violet and maroon	..	13·00	2·25
O51		2 r. brown and orange	..	14·00	17·00
O52		— 5 r. green and brown	..	14·00	18·00
O53		— 10 r. claret and violet	..	14·00	28·00
O41/53			Set of 13	80·00	70·00

Later stamp issues will be found listed in Part 21 (*South-East Asia*) of this catalogue.

JAPANESE OCCUPATION OF BURMA

PRICES FOR STAMPS ON COVER	
Nos. J1/44	—
Nos. J45/72	*from* × 6
Nos. J73/94	*from* × 12
Nos. J95/101	—
Nos. J102/8	*from* × 25

BURMA INDEPENDENCE ARMY ADMINISTRATION

The Burma Independence Army, formed by Aung San in 1941, took control of the Delta area of the Irrawaddy in May 1942. They reopened a postal service in the area and were authorised by the Japanese to overprint local stocks of stamps with the Burmese emblem of a peacock.

Postage and Official stamps with the peacock overprints or handstamps were used for ordinary postal purposes with the probable exception of No. J44.

DISTINGUISHING FEATURES. Type **1**. Body and head of Peacock always clearly outlined by broad uncoloured band. There are four slightly different sub-types of overprint Type **1**.

Type **2**. Peacock with slender neck and more delicately detailed tail. Clear spur on leg at right. Heavy fist-shaped blob of ink below and parallel to beak and neck.

Type **4**. No basic curve. Each feather separately outlined. Straight, short legs.

Type **5**. Much fine detail in wings and tail in clearly printed overprints. Thin, long legs ending in claws which, with the basic arc, enclose clear white spaces in well-printed copies. Blob of colour below beak shows shaded detail and never has the heavy fist-like appearance of this portion in Type **2**.

Two sub-types may be distinguished in Type **5**, the basic arc of one having a chord of 14–15 mm and the other 12½–13 mm.

Type **6**. Similar to Type **5**, but with arc deeply curved and reaching nearly to the top of the wings. Single diagonal line parallel to neck below beak.

Collectors are warned against forgeries of these overprints, often in the wrong colours or on the wrong values.

(1) (2)

(3)

1942 (May). *Stamps of Burma overprinted with the national device of a Peacock.*

I. *Overprinted at Myaungmya*

A. *With Type* **1** *in black*

		On Postage Stamps of King George V		
J 1		9 p. deep green (No. 3)	..	£100
J 2		3½ a. deep blue (No. 8)	..	45·00

		On Official Stamp of King George V		
J 3		6 a. bistre (No. O8)	..	70·00

		On Postage Stamps of King George VI		
J 4	2	9 p. yellow-green	..	£150
J 5	3	1 a. purple-brown	..	£450
J 6		4 a. greenish blue (opt black on red)	..	£160
		a. Triple opt, black on double red	..	£425

		On Official Stamps of King George VI		
J 7	2	3 p. bright violet	..	19·00	65·00
J 8		6 p. bright blue	..	14·00	45·00
J 9	3	1 a. purple-brown	..	13·00	38·00
J 9a		1½ a. turquoise-green	..	£650	
J10		2 a. carmine	..	19·00	65·00
J11		4 a. greenish blue	..	19·00	55·00

The overprint on No. J6 was apparently first done in red in error, and then corrected in black. Some stamps have the black overprint so accurately superimposed that the red hardly shows. These are rare.

Nos. J5 and J9 exist with the Peacock overprint on both the typographed and the litho printings of the original stamps.

B. *With Types* **2** *or* **3** (*rupee values*), *in black*

		On Postage Stamps of King George VI			
J12	2	3 p. bright violet	..	17·00	55·00
J13		6 p. bright blue	..	40·00	75·00
J14		9 p. yellow-green	..	16·00	50·00
J15	3	1 a. purple-brown	..	14·00	45·00
J16		2 a. carmine	..	15·00	50·00
J17		4 a. greenish blue	..	32·00	75·00
		a. Opt double	..		
		b. Opt inverted	..	£500	
		c. Opt double, one inverted	..	£350	
		d. Opt double, both inverted	..	£500	
J18		1 r. purple and blue	..	£225	
J19		2 r. brown and purple	..	£140	

The Myaungmya overprints (including No. J44) are usually clearly printed.

(4) (5) (6)

Type **5** generally shows the details of the peacock much less clearly and, due to heavy inking, or careless impression, sometimes appears as almost solid colour.

Type **6** was officially applied only to postal stationery. However, the handstamp remained in the possession of a postal official who used it on postage stamps after the war. These stamps are no longer listed.

II. *Handstamped* (*at Pyapon?*) *with T* **4**, *in black* (*so-called experimental type*)

		On Postage Stamps of King George VI			
J19a	2	6 p. bright blue	..	£180	
J19b	3	1 a. purple-brown	..	95·00	
J20		2 a. carmine	..	95·00	
J21		4 a. greenish blue	..	£600	£600

Unused specimens of these stamps are usually in poor condition.

III. *Overprinted at Henzada with T* **5** *in blue, or blue-black*

		On Postage Stamps of King George V			
J22		3 p. slate (No. 1)	..	3·00	17·00
		a. Opt double	..	10·00	45·00
J23		9 p. deep green (No. 3)	..	21·00	60·00
		a. Opt double	..	80·00	
J24		2 a. vermilion (No. 5)	..	£100	£180

On Postage Stamps of King George VI

J25	2	1 p. red-orange		£170	£250
J26		3 p. bright violet		27·00	70·00
J27		6 p. bright blue		24·00	50·00
		a. Opt double		£100	
		b. Clear opt, on back and front		£250	
J28		9 p. yellow-green		£600	
J29	3	1 a. purple-brown		9·00	35·00
		a. Opt inverted		£375	
J30		1½ a. turquoise-green		21·00	60·00
		a. Opt omitted (in pair with normal)		£1300	
J31		2 a. carmine		21·00	60·00
J32		4 a. greenish blue		42·00	90·00
		a. Opt double		£250	
		b. Opt inverted		£850	

On Official Stamps of King George VI

J33	2	3 p. bright violet		£100	£190
J34		6 p. bright violet		£130	£190
J35	3	1½ a. turquoise-green		£130	£190
J35a		2 a. carmine		£325	£350
J36		4 a. greenish blue		£850	

(6a)

("Yon Thon" = "Office use")

V. *Official Stamp of King George VI optd at Myaungmya with Type 6a in black*

J44	7	8 a. myrtle-green		80·00	

No. J44 was probably for official use.

There are two types of T 6a, one with base of peacock 8 mm long and the other with base about 5 mm long. The neck and other details also vary. The two types are found *se-tenant* in the sheet.

Stocks of the peacock types were withdrawn when the Japanese Directorate-General took control of the postal services in the Delta in August 1942.

JAPANESE ARMY ADMINISTRATION

7   **8 Farmer**

1942 (1 June). *Impressed by hand. Thick yellowish paper. P* 12 × 11. *No gum.*

J45	7	(1 a.) red		38·00	65·00

This device was the personal seal of Yano Sitza, the Japanese official in charge of the Posts and Telegraphs department of the Japanese Army Administration. It was impressed on paper already perforated by a line machine. Some stamps show part of the papermaker's watermark, either "ABSORBO DUPLICATOR" or "ELEPHANT BRAND", each with an elephant.

Other impressions of this seal on different papers, and showing signs of wear, were not valid for postal purposes.

(Des T. Kato. Typo *Rangoon Gazette* Press)

1942 (15 June). *Value in annas. P* 11 *or* 11 × 11½. *Laid bâtonné paper. No gum.*

J46	8	1 a. scarlet		15·00	15·00

Some stamps show part of the papermaker's watermark, either "ELEPHANT BRAND" or "TITAGHUR SUPERFINE", each with an elephant.

   1R.

(9)   **(10)**

1942 (22 Sept). (*a*) *Nos.* 314/17, 320/2, 325, 327 *and* 396 *of Japan surch as T* 9/10.

J47	9	¼ a. on 1 s. chestnut (Rice harvesting)		20·00	25·00
		a. Surch inverted		90·00	90·00
		b. Surch double, one inverted		£130	
J48		½ a. on 2 s. bright scarlet (General Nogi)		20·00	25·00
		a. Surch inverted		80·00	85·00
		b. Surch double, one inverted		£130	
J49		¾ a. on 3 s. green (Power station)		42·00	45·00
		a. Surch inverted		£100	£100
		b. Surch double, one inverted		—	£150
J50		1 a. on 5 s. claret (Admiral Togo)		35·00	38·00
		a. Surch inverted		£130	£130
		b. Surch double, one inverted		£150	£150
		c. Surch omitted (in pair with normal)		—	£180
J51		3 a. on 7 s. green (Diamond Mts)		70·00	80·00
		a. Surch inverted		£130	
J52		4 a. on 4 s. emerald (Togo)		35·00	40·00
		a. Surch inverted		£130	
J53		8 a. on 8 s. violet (Meiji Shrine)		£140	£140
		a. Surch inverted		£200	£200
		b. Surch double, one inverted		£325	
		c. Surch in red		£225	£250
		d. Red surch inverted		£325	
		e. Surch double (black and red)		£475	
J54	10	1 r. on 10 s. deep carmine (Yomei Gate)		15·00	24·00
		a. Surch inverted		80·00	100·00
		b. Surch double		80·00	£100
		c. Surch double (black and red)		£350	
		d. Surch omitted (in pair with normal)		£170	£170
		e. Surch omitted (in pair with inverted surch)		£250	

J55	10	2 r. on 20 s. ultramarine (Mt Fuji)		42·00	42·00
		a. Surch inverted		£110	£110
		b. Surch double, one inverted		£120	
		c. Surch omitted in pair with normal black surch)		£160	£160
		d. Surch in red		40·00	40·00
		e. Red surch inverted		£110	£110
		f. Red surch double		£110	£110
		g. Surch omitted (in pair with normal red surch)		£200	£200
		ga. Surch omitted (in pair with double red surch)			
		h. Surch double (black and red)		£275	
J56	9	5 r. on 30 s. turquoise (Torii Shrine)		12·00	27·00
		a. Surch inverted		85·00	
		b. Surch double		£110	
		c. Surch double, one inverted		£150	
		d. Surch omitted (in pair with normal surch)		£170	£170
		e. Surch omitted (in pair with inverted black surch)		£225	
		f. Surch in red		23·00	32·00
		fa. Red surch inverted		90·00	90·00
		fb. J56a and J56fa *se-tenant*		£350	£350
		fc. Surch omitted (in pair with normal red surch)		£170	£170

(*b*) *No.* 386 *of Japan commemorating the fall of Singapore similarly surch*

J56g	9	4 a. on 4 + 2 s. green and red		£150	£160
		h. Surch omitted (in pair with normal)		£500	
		ha. Surch omitted (in pair with inverted surch)		£550	
		i. Surch inverted		£350	

(New Currency. 100 cents = 1 rupee)

15 C.   15 C.   15 C.

(11)   **(12)**   **(13)**

1942 (15 Oct). *Previous issues, with "anna" surcharges obliterated, handstamped with new value in cents, as T* 11 *and* 12 (*No.* J57 *handstamped with new value only*).

(*a*) *On No.* J46

J57		5 c. on 1 a. scarlet		11·00	15·00

(*b*) *On Nos.* J47/53

J58		1 c. on ¼ a. on 1 s. chestnut		38·00	38·00
		a. "1 c." omitted (in pair with normal)		£475	
		b. "¼ a." inverted		£250	
J59		2 c. on ½ a. on 2 s. bright scarlet		38·00	38·00
J60		3 c. on ¾ a. on 3 s. green		40·00	40·00
		a. Surch in blue		£160	
J61		5 c. on 1 a. on 5 s. claret		60·00	65·00
J62		10 c. on 3 a. on 7 s. green		95·00	95·00
J63		15 c. on 4 a. on 4 s. emerald		28·00	30·00
J64		20 c. on 8 a. on 8 s. violet		£300	£250
		a. Surch on No. J53c (surch in red)		£200	£140

The "anna" surcharges were obliterated by any means available, in some cases by a bar or bars, and in others by the butt of a pencil dipped in ink. In the case of the fractional surcharges, the letter "A" and one figure of the fraction, were sometimes barred out, leaving the remainder of the fraction to represent the new value, e.g. the "1" of "½" deleted to create the 2 c. surcharge or the "4" of "¾" to create the 3 c. surcharge.

1942. *Nos.* 314/17, 320/1 *and* 396 *of Japan surcharged in cents only as T* 13.

J65		1 c. on 1 s. chestnut (Rice harvesting)		17·00	20·00
		a. Surch inverted		£110	£110
J66		2 c. on 2 s. brt scarlet (General Nogi)		32·00	32·00
J67		3 c. on 3 s. green (Power station)		35·00	35·00
		a. Pair, with and without surch		—	£180
		b. Surch inverted		£120	
		c. Surch in blue		85·00	95·00
		d. Surch in blue inverted		£200	£225
J68		5 c. on 5 s. claret (Admiral Togo)		38·00	38·00
		a. Pair, with and without surch		£250	
		b. Surch in violet		£130	£150
		ba. Surch inverted		—	£225
J69		10 c. on 3 s. green (Diamond Mts)		42·00	48·00
J70		15 c. on 4 s. emerald (Togo)		14·00	20·00
		a. Surch inverted		£120	£130
		b. Pair, with and without surch		—	£170
J71		20 c. on 8 s. violet (Meiji Shrine)		£110	85·00

Nos. J67c and J68b were issued for use in the Shan States.

BURMESE GOVERNMENT

On 1 November 1942 the Japanese Army Administration handed over the control of the postal department to the Burmese Government. On 1 August 1943 Burma was declared by the Japanese to be independent.

14 Burma State Crest   **15 Farmer**

(Des U Tun Tin and Maung Tin from drawing by U Ba Than. Typo Rangoon)

1943 (15 Feb). *P* 11. *No gum.*

J72	14	5 c. scarlet		13·00	17·00
		a. Imperf		14·00	18·00
		ab. Printed on both sides		80·00	

No. J72 was usually sold affixed to envelopes, particularly those with the embossed 1 a. King George VI stamp, which it covered. Unused specimens off cover are not often seen and blocks are rare.

1943. *Typo. No gum. P* 11½.

J73	15	1 c. orange (22 March)		1·00	3·00
		a. Brown-orange		70	3·25
J74		2 c. yellow-green (24 March)		60	1·00
		a. "3" for "2" in face value (R.2/10)		£150	
		b. Blue-green		6·50	
J75		3 c. light blue (25 March)		70	85
		a. On laid paper		18·00	24·00
		b. Imperf between (horiz pair)		—	£250
J76		5 c. carmine (small "c") (17 March)		12·00	8·50
J77		5 c. carmine (large "C")		1·25	2·50
		a. Imperf (pair)		£160	
		b. "G" for "C" (R.2/6)		£170	
J78		10 c. grey-brown (25 March)		2·50	3·00
		a. Imperf (pair)		£200	
		b. Imperf between (horiz pair)		—	£250
J79		15 c. magenta (26 March)		30	90
		a. Imperf between (vert strip of 3)			
		b. On laid paper		6·00	14·00
		c. Inverted "C" in value (R.2/3)		£120	
J80		20 c. grey-lilac (29 March)		30	65
J81		30 c. deep blue-green (29 March)		30	70

The 1 c., 2 c. and 3 c. have large "C" in value as illustrated. The 10 c. and higher values have small "c". Nos. J73/81 had the face values inserted individually into the plate used for No. J46 with the original face value removed. There were a number of printings for each value, often showing differences such as missing stops, various founts of figures or "c", etc., in the value tablets.

The face value error, No. J74a, was later corrected.

Some sheets of No. J75a show a sheet watermark of Britannia seated within a crowned oval spread across fifteen stamps in each sheet. Examples showing part of this sheet watermark are rare.

No. J79a shows the horizontal perforations omitted between rows 3/4 and 4/5.

There are marked varieties of shade in this issue.

16 Soldier carving   **17 Rejoicing**
word "Independence"   **Peasant**

18 Boy with National Flag

Normal   **Skyline flaw (R. 5/6)**

(Des Maung Ba Thit (**16**), Naung Ohn Maung (**17**), and Maung Soi Yi (**18**). Typo State Press, Rangoon)

1943 (1 Aug). *Independence Day.* (*a*) *P* 11.

J82	16	1 c. orange		6·50	11·00
J83	17	3 c. light blue		7·00	12·00
J84	18	5 c. carmine		13·00	8·00
		a. Skyline flaw		50·00	
J82/4			*Set of 3*	24·00	28·00

(*b*) *Rouletted*

J85	16	1 c. orange		1·00	1·50
		b. Perf×roul		80·00	85·00
		c. Imperf (pair)		45·00	55·00
J86	17	3 c. light blue		1·00	1·50
		b. Perf×roul		80·00	85·00
		c. Imperf (pair)		45·00	55·00
J87	18	5 c. carmine		1·00	1·50
		a. Horiz roulette omitted (vert pair)			
		b. Perf×roul		50·00	55·00
		c. Imperf (pair)		45·00	55·00
		d. Skyline flaw		7·00	
J85/7			*Set of 3*	2·75	4·00

The stamps perf × rouletted may have one, two or three sides perforated.

The rouletted stamps often appear to be roughly perforated owing to failure to make clean cuts. These apparent perforations are very small and quite unlike the large, clean holes of the stamps perforated 11.

A few imperforate sets, mounted on a special card folder and cancelled with the commemorative postmark were presented to officials. These are rare.

19 Burmese   **20 Elephant carrying**   **21 Watch Tower,**
Woman   Log   Mandalay

(Litho G. Kolff & Co, Batavia)

1943 (1 Oct).		P 12½.			
J88 **19**	1 c. red-orange	..	..	17·00	15·00
J89	2 c. yellow-green	..	..	50	2·00
J90	3 c. deep violet	..	..	50	2·25
	a. *Bright violet*		..	70	2·25
J91 **20**	5 c. carmine	..	..	55	60
J92	10 c. blue	..	..	65	95
J93	15 c. red-orange	..	..	65	1·75
J94	20 c. yellow-green	..	..	65	1·75
J95	30 c. olive-brown	..	..	65	1·75
J96 **21**	1 r. red-orange	..	..	30	2·00
J97	2 r. bright violet	..	..	30	2·25
J88/97	..	..	Set of 10	20·00	27·00

22 Bullock Cart	**23** Shan Woman	(**24** "Burma State" and value)

(Litho G. Kolff & Co, Batavia)

1943 (1 Oct). *Issue for Shan States.* P 12½.

J 98 **22**	1 c. olive-brown	..	..	20·00	28·00
J 99	2 c. yellow-green	..	..	20·00	28·00
J100	3 c. bright violet	..	..	2·75	8·50
J101	5 c. ultramarine	..	..	2·00	5·50
J102 **23**	10 c. blue	..	..	8·00	17·00
J103	20 c. carmine	..	..	22·00	17·00
J104	30 c. olive-brown	..	..	13·00	27·00
J98/104	..	..	Set of 7	80·00	£120

The Shan States, except for the frontier area around Keng Tung which was ceded to Thailand, were placed under the administration of the Burmese Government on 24 December 1943, and these stamps were later overprinted as T **24** for use throughout Burma.

1944 (1 Nov). *Optd as T* **24** (*the lower characters differ for each value*).

J105 **22**	1 c. olive-brown	..	..	2·50	6·00
J106	2 c. yellow-green	..	..	40	1·50
	a. Opt inverted	..	..	£300	£500
J107	3 c. bright violet	..	..	1·50	7·00
J108	5 c. ultramarine	..	..	80	1·00
J109 **23**	10 c. blue	..	..	1·75	2·00
J110	20 c. carmine	..	..	40	1·50
J111	30 c. olive-brown	..	..	40	1·75
J105/11	..	..	Set of 7	7·00	18·00

The British 14th Army recaptured Mandalay on 20 March 1945 and Rangoon on 6 May.

Bushire

BRITISH OCCUPATION

(Currency. 20 chahis = 1 kran; 10 kran = 1 toman)

Bushire, a seaport town of Persia, was occupied by the British on 8 August 1915. The Persian postal authorities resumed control on 18 October 1915. British forces returned to Bushire during 1916, but mail from this period was carried by Indian Army F.P.O. No. 319.

PRICES FOR STAMPS ON COVER	
Nos. 1/14	*from* × 10
Nos. 15/29	*from* × 5

Types of Iran (Persia) overprinted

57	66

67	68

BUSHIRE
Under British
Occupation.
(1)

1915 (15 Aug). *Nos. 361/3, 365, 367/70, 372, 374/6 and 378/9 of Iran optd with T* **1** *at the British Residency.*

1 **57**	1 ch. orange and green	..	26·00	30·00
	a. No stop	..	70·00	80·00
2	2 ch. sepia and carmine	..	26·00	24·00
	a. No stop	..	70·00	70·00
3	3 ch. green and grey	..	32·00	40·00
	a. No stop	..	90·00	£120
4	5 ch. carmine and brown	..	£250	£250
5	6 ch. brown-lake and green	..	25·00	20·00
	a. No stop	..	70·00	65·00
6	9 ch. indigo-lilac and brown	..	26·00	30·00
	a. No stop	..	80·00	85·00
	b. Opt double			
7	10 ch. brown and carmine	..	28·00	28·00
	a. No stop	..	85·00	85·00
8	12 ch. blue and green	..	35·00	40·00
	a. No stop	..	£100	£120
9	24 ch. green and purple	..	50·00	40·00
	a. No stop	..	£150	£120
10	1 kr. carmine and blue	..	50·00	26·00
	a. Double overprint	..	£5000	
	b. No stop	..	£150	80·00
11	2 kr. claret and green	..	£170	£120
	a. No stop	..	£450	£325
12	3 kr. black and lilac	..	£150	£150
	a. No stop	..	£400	£400
13	5 kr. blue and red	..	80·00	75·00
	a. No stop	..	£275	£250
14	10 kr. rose and bistre-brown	..	70·00	70·00
	a. No stop	..	£225	£225

Nos. 1/3 and 5/14 were overprinted in horizontal strips of 10 and No. 4 in horizontal strips of 5. Eight different settings are recognized, with the "No stop" variety occurring on stamp 9 from the four settings with 3 mm between "Under" and "British" and on stamp 10 from one setting where the gap is 2 mm.

1915 (Sept). *Nos. 426/40 and 441 of Iran optd with T* **1**.

15 **66**	1 ch. deep blue and carmine	..	£300	£300
16	2 ch. carmine and deep blue	..	£5000	£5500
17	3 ch. deep green	..	£375	£400
18	5 ch. vermilion	..	£3750	£4000
19	6 ch. carmine and green	..	£3000	£3250
20	9 ch. deep violet and brown	..	£475	£500
21	10 ch. brown and deep green	..	£800	£850
22	12 ch. ultramarine	..	£900	£1000
23	24 ch. sepia and brown	..	£375	£400
24 **67**	1 kr. black, brown and silver	..	£350	£375
25	2 kr. carmine, slate and silver	..	£300	£325
26	3 kr. sepia, dull lilac and silver	..	£425	£450
27	5 kr. slate, sepia and silver	..	£400	£425
	a. Opt inverted	..	—	£9000
28 **68**	1 t. black, violet and gold	..	£350	£400
29	3 t. red, crimson and gold	..	£2250	£2500

Nos. 15/29 were overprinted in strips of 5.

Examples of overprint Type 1 on Iran No. 414, 1 ch. on 5 ch. (previously No. 30), are now believed to be forged.

Cameroon

I. CAMEROONS EXPEDITIONARY FORCE

Allied operations against the German protectorate of Kamerun commenced in September 1914 and were completed on 18 February 1916. The territory was divided, under an Anglo-French agreement, on 31 March 1916 with the British administering the area in the west along the Nigerian border. League of Nations mandates were issued for the two sections of Cameroon, which were converted into United Nations trusteeships in 1946.

Supplies of Kamerun stamps were found on the German steamer *Professor Woermann* captured at Freetown and these were surcharged, probably in Sierra Leone, and issued by the Cameroons Expeditionary Force at Duala in July 1915.

A French Post Office opened in Duala on 10 November 1915 using stamps of Gabon overprinted "Corps Expeditionnaire Franco-Anglais Cameroun". Although under the overall control of the British combined force commander this office remained part of the French postal system.

PRICES FOR STAMPS ON COVER
The stamps of British Occupation of Cameroons are rare used on cover.

A	B

C.E.F.	**C.E.F.**
1d.	1s.
(1)	(2)

SETTINGS. Nos. B1/3 were surcharged from a setting of 100 (10×10) with the face value changed for the 1d.

Nos. B4 and B6/9 were surcharged from a common setting of 50 (5×10) with the face value amended.

No. B5 was surcharged from a setting of 10 in a vertical strip repeated across the sheet. The figures of the surcharge on this value are in a different style from the remainder of the pence stamps.

Nos. B10/13 were surcharged from a common setting of 20 (4×5) with the face value amended.

Different fount "d"	"1" with thin serifs
(R. 1/10, 6/9, 10/10)	(R. 5/1)

Large "3"	Short "4"
(R. 3/5, 3/10)	(R. 10/2, 10/7)

"s" inverted
(R. 3/4)

5 *s*

"s" broken at top (R. 3/1)

1915 (12 July). *Stamps of German Kamerun. Types A and B, surch as T* **1** (*Nos. B1/9*) *or* **2** (*Nos. B10/13*) *in black or blue.*

B1	A	½d. on 3 pf. (No. K7) (B.)	..		9·00	22·00
		a. Different fount "d"	..		85·00	£170
B2		½d. on 5 pf. (No. K21 *wmk lozenges*) (B.	1·75	8·00
		a. Different fount "d"	..	23·00	70·00
		b. Surch double	..	—	£600
		ba. Surch double, one albino	..	£160	
B3		1d. on 10 pf. (No. K22 *wmk lozenges* (B.)	..	1·25	8·00
		a. "1" with thin serifs	..	12·00	60·00
		b. Surch double	..	£200	
		ba. Surch double, one albino	..	85·00	
		c. "1d." only double	..	£1700	
		d. Surch triple, two albino	..	£180	
		e. Surch in black	..	14·00	55·00
		ea. "1" with thin serifs	..	£140	
		eb. "C.E.F." omitted	..	£2500	
B4		2d. on 20 pf. (No. K23 *wmk lozenges*)	3·50	17·00
		a. Surch double, one albino	..	£180	
B5		2½d. on 25 pf. (No. K11)	..	12·00	35·00
		a. Surch double	..	£6500	
		ab. Surch double, one albino			
B6		3d. on 30 pf. (No. K12)	..	12·00	35·00
		a. Large "3"	..	£650	
		b. Surch triple, two albino	..	£190	
B7		4d. on 40 pf. (No. K13)	..	12·00	35·00
		a. Short "4"	..	£475	£750
		b. Surch triple, two albino	..	£180	
		c. Surch quadruple, three albino	..	£1500	
B8		6d. on 50 pf. (No. K14)	..	12·00	35·00
		a. Surch double, one albino	..	£170	
B9		8d. on 80 pf. (No. K15)	..	12·00	35·00
B10	B	1s. on 1 m. (No. K16)	..	£140	£500
		a. "s" inverted	..	£550	£1700
B11		2s. on 2 m. (No. K17)	..	£140	£500
		a. "s" inverted	..	£550	£1700
		b. Surch double, one albino	..	£950	
B12		3s. on 3 m. (No. K18)	..	£140	£500
		a. "s" inverted	..	£550	£1700
		b. "s" broken at top	..	£400	
		c. Surch double	..	£5500	
		ca. Surch double, one albino	..	£950	
B13		5s. on 5 m. (No. K25a *wmk lozenges*)	£170	£550
		a. "s" inverted	..	£650	£1800
		b. "s" broken at top	..	£450	
B1/13			Set of 13	£600	£2000

Examples of all values exist showing a forged Duala Kamerun postmark dated "11 10 15". Another forged cancel dated "16 11 15" is also known. This can be identified by the lack of a serif on the index letter "b".

The stamps of Nigeria were subsequently used in British Cameroons and the area was administered as part of Nigeria from February 1924.

For issues of Cameroon under French administration see *Part 6 (France)* and for the Cameroon Republic (1960–1995) *Part 12 (Africa since Independence A to E)*.

II. CAMEROONS TRUST TERRITORY

Following the independence of the French Trust Territory of Cameroun on 1 January 1960 the United Nations directed that a plebiscite should be held in the British Trust Territory. The northern area voted to join Nigeria, but the southern part of the territory decided to join the Cameroun Republic.

The following issue, although administered by the Southern Cameroons authorities, was also on sale in Northern Cameroons, until the latter joined Nigeria on 1 June 1961. The stamps therefore can be found with Nigerian postmarks.

CAMEROONS
U.K.T.T.
(1)

1960 (1 Oct)–**61**. *Nos. 69/71, 72ca/cc and 73/80 of Nigeria optd with T* **1**, *in red.*

T 1 **18**	½d. black and orange	..	..	..	10	60
T 2	–	1d. black and bronze-green	..	..	10	40
		a. *Grey-black and dull bronze-green* (19.9.61)	..	60	1·50
T 3	–	1½d. blue-green	..	..	10	15
T 4 **21**	2d. grey (Type B)	..	..	..	10	30
		a. *Slate-blue* (Type A)	..	£750	£250
		b. *Bluish grey* (Type B)	..	40·00	14·00
		c. *Pale grey* (Type B) (19.9.61)	..	10	20
T 5	–	3d. black and deep lilac	..	..	15	10
T 6	–	4d. black and blue	..	..	10	60
T 7 **24**	6d. orange-brown and black (*p* 14)	..	30	10
		a. Perf 13×13½ (19.9.61)	..	20	1·50
T 8	–	1s. black and maroon	..	..	15	10
T 9 **26**	2s. 6d. black and green	..	..	1·10	80

T10	–	5s. black and red-orange	..	..	1·60 3·50
T11	–	10s. black and red-brown	..	..	2·50 4·50
T12	**29**	£1 black and violet	..	..	8·50 15·00
T1/12				*Set of* 12	13·00 23·00

Nos. T2 and T4/*b* were overprinted on stamps printed by Waterlows' subsidiary, Imprimerie Belge de Securité.

Nos. T2*a*, T4*c* and T7*a* were from new printings produced by De La Rue instead of Waterlow.

The above stamps were withdrawn on 30 September 1961, when Southern Cameroons became part of the Cameroun Republic.

III. REPUBLIC OF CAMEROON

COMMONWEALTH MEMBER

1 November 1995

The Republic of Cameroon joined the Commonwealth on 1 November 1995 and issues from that date will be listed below when details and examples are received.

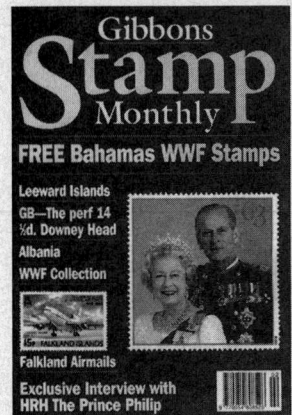

Keep This Catalogue up to Date With

Gibbons Stamp Monthly

FREE Bahamas WWF Stamps

Leeward Islands
GB—The perf 14 ½d. Downey Head
Albania
WWF Collection

Falkland Airmails

Exclusive Interview with HRH The Prince Philip

The Magazine with the Stanley Gibbons Catalogue Supplement

Plus

■ More editorial than other magazines.

■ Regular features for all collectors from beginners to specialists.

■ Authoritatively written.

■ Regular special offers, competitions and free gifts.

Get Gibbons Stamp Monthly delivered direct to your door!

For a free sample copy and subscription details phone
01425 472363
or write to:

Hugh Jefferies
Gibbons Stamp Monthly
5 Parkside, Christchurch Road,
Ringwood, Hants BH24 3SH

Canada

Separate stamp issues appeared for British Columbia and Vancouver Island, Canada, New Brunswick, Newfoundland, Nova Scotia and Prince Edward Island before these colonies joined the Dominion of Canada.

BRITISH COLUMBIA & VANCOUVER ISLAND

Vancouver Island was organised as a Crown Colony in 1849 and the mainland territory was proclaimed a separate colony as British Columbia, in 1858. The two colonies combined, as British Columbia, on 19 November 1866.

```
PRICES FOR STAMPS ON COVER

Nos. 2/3        from × 6
Nos. 11/12      from × 2
Nos. 13/14      from × 6
Nos. 21/2       from × 10
Nos. 23/7       from × 6
Nos. 28/9       from × 10
No. 30          —
No. 31          from × 10
Nos. 32/3       —
```

1

(Typo D.L.R.)

1860. *No wmk. P* 14.
| 2 | 1 | 2½d. deep reddish rose | .. | .. | .. | £275 | £180 |
| 3 | | 2½d. pale reddish rose | .. | .. | | £275 | £180 |

When Vancouver Island adopted the dollar currency in 1862 the 2½d. was sold at 5 c. From 18 May until 1 November 1865 examples of Nos. 2/3 were used to prepay mail from Vancouver Island to British Columbia at the price of 15 cents a pair.

From 20 June 1864 to 1 November 1865, the 2½d. was sold in British Columbia for 3d. and was subsequently used for the same purpose during a shortage of 3d. stamps in 1867.

Imperforate plate proofs exist in pale dull red (*Price* £2500 *un*)

VANCOUVER ISLAND
(New Currency. 100 cents = 1 dollar)

2　　　　　3

(Typo D.L.R.)

1865 (19 Sept). *Wmk Crown CC.* (*a*) *Imperf* (1866)
| 11 | 2 | 5 c. rose | .. | .. | .. | .. | £20000 | £8000 |
| 12 | 3 | 10 c. blue | .. | .. | .. | .. | £1400 | £850 |

(*b*) *P* 14
| 13 | 2 | 5 c. rose | .. | .. | .. | £225 | £140 |
| 14 | 3 | 10 c. blue | .. | .. | .. | £200 | £140 |

Medium or poor copies of Nos. 11 and 12 can be supplied at much lower prices, when in stock.

After the two colonies combined Nos. 13/14 were also used in British Columbia.

BRITISH COLUMBIA

4

(Typo D.L.R.)

1865 (1 Nov)–**67.** *Wmk Crown CC. P* 14.
| 21 | 4 | 3d. deep blue | .. | .. | 70·00 | 60·00 |
| 22 | | 3d. pale blue (19.7.67) | .. | | 70·00 | 60·00 |

British Columbia changed to the dollar currency on 1 January 1866. Remaining stocks of No. 21 and the supply of No. 22, when it finally arrived, were sold at 12½ c. a pair.

(New Currency. 100 cents = 1 dollar)

TWO CENTS　　5.CENTS.5

(5)　　　　　　　(6)

1868–71. *T* 4 *in various colours. Wmk Crown CC. Surch as T* 5 *or* 6. (*a*) *P* 12½ (3.69)
23		5 c. red (Bk.)	..		..	..	£550	£550
24		10 c. lake (B.)	..		..	..	£450	£425
25		25 c. yellow (V.)	..		..	..	£350	£350
26		50 c. mauve (R.)	..		..	..	£425	£375
27		$1 green (G.)	..	..	..	..	£650	£700

(*b*) *P* 14
28		2 c. brown (Bk.) (1.68)	..	..	..	90·00	90·00
29		5 c. pale red (Bk.) (5.69)	..	..	£120	£120
30		10 c. lake (B.)	..	..		£650	
31		25 c. yellow (V.) (21.7.69)	..	..	£120	£120
32		50 c. mauve (R.) (23.2.71)	..	..	£400	£750
33		$1 green (G.)	..	..	..	£600	

Nos. 30 and 33 were not issued.

British Columbia joined the Dominion of Canada on 20 July 1871.

COLONY OF CANADA

The first British post offices in what was to become the colony of Canada were opened at Quebec, Montreal and Trois Rivières during 1763. These, and subsequent, offices remained part of the British G.P.O. system until 6 April 1851.

The two provinces of Upper Canada (Ontario) and Lower Canada (Quebec) were united in 1840.

For illustration of the handstamp types see BRITISH POST OFFICES ABROAD notes, following GREAT BRITAIN.

NEW CARLISLE, GASPÉ

POSTMASTER'S PROVISIONAL ENVELOPE

1

1851 (7 April).
| 1 | 1 | 3d. black | .. | .. | .. | .. | .. |

Only one example is known, with the impression cancelled by the signature of the postmaster, R. W. Kelly.

QUEBEC

CROWNED-CIRCLE HANDSTAMPS

CC1　CC 1*b* QUEBEC L.C. (R.) (13.1.1842)　*Price on cover* £150

```
PRICES FOR STAMPS ON COVER

Nos. 1/23       from × 2
Nos. 25/8       from × 3
Nos. 29/43a     from × 3
Nos. 44/5       from × 8
```

1 American Beaver　　2 Prince Albert　　3
(Designed by
Sir Sandford Fleming)

Major re-entry: Line though "EE PEN" (Upper pane R. 5/7)

(*T* 1/6. Eng and recess Rawdon, Wright, Hatch and Edson, New York)

1851. *Imperf. Laid paper.*
1	1	3d. red (23 April)	..	..	..	£11000	£650
1*a*		3d. orange-vermilion	..	..	£11000	£650
		b. Major re-entry	..	..		—	£1600
2	2	6d. slate-violet (15 May)	..	..	£14000	£900
3		6d. brown-purple	..	..	£15000	£1200
		a. Bisected (3d.) on cover	..		† £20000
4	3	12d. black (14 June)	..	..	£60000	£40000

There are several re-entries on the plate of the 3d. in addition to the major re-entry listed. All re-entries occur in this stamp on all papers.

Forgeries of the 3d. are known without the full stop after "PENCE". They also omit the foliage in the corners, as do similar forgeries of the 6d.

4　　　　　　5　　　　　6 Jacques Cartier

1852–57. *Imperf.*
A. *Handmade wove paper, varying in thickness* (1852–56)
5	1	3d. red	..	..	..	£1100	£160
		a. Bisected (1½d.) on cover (1856)		† £22000
6		3d. deep red	..	..	..	£1200	£160
7		3d. scarlet-vermilion	..	..	£1500	£170
8		3d. brown-red	..	..	..	£1200	£160
		a. Bisected (1½d.) on cover (1856)	..	†	—
		b. Major re-entry (*all shades*)	*from* £2500	£650

9	2	6d. slate-violet	..	..	£12000	£950
		a. Bisected (3d.) on cover	..		† £12000
10		6d. greenish grey	..	..	£12000	£950
11		6d. brownish grey	..	..	£13000	£1100
12	5	7½d. yellow-green (*shades*) (2.6.57)	..	£7000	£1500
13	6	10d. bright blue (1.55)	..	..	£7000	£1200
14		10d. dull blue	..	..	£6500	£1100
15		10d. blue *to* deep blue	..	..	£7000	£1200
		a. Major re-entry (*all shades*) *from*	—	£45000
16	3	12d. black	..	..	..	..	† £12000

B. *Machine-made medium to thick wove paper of a more even hard texture with more visible mesh. Clearer impressions* (1857)
17	4	½d. deep rose (1.8.57)	..	..	£650	£400
18	1	3d. red	..	..	..	£1600	£450
		a. Bisected (1½d.) on cover	..		† £20000
		b. Major re-entry	..	..		—	£1200
19	2	6d. grey-lilac	..	..	..	£14000	£2000
20	6	10d. blue *to* deep blue	..	..	£7000	£2000
		a. Major re-entry	..	..	£11000	£2500

C. *Thin soft horizontally ribbed paper* (1857)
21	4	½d. deep rose	..	..	£5500	£1600
		a. Vertically ribbed paper	..	..	£6000	£2250
22	1	3d. red	..	..	..	£3000	£400
		a. Major re-entry	..	..		—	£1100

D. *Very thick soft wove paper* (1857)
| 23 | 2 | 6d. reddish purple | .. | .. | £14000 | £2500 |
| | | a. Bisected (3d.) on cover | .. | | † £18000 |

Bisected examples of the 3d. value were used to make up the 7½d. Canadian Packet rate to England from May 1856 until the introduction of the 7½d. value on 2 June 1857.

The 7½d. and 10d. values can be found in wide and narrow versions. These differences are due to shrinkage of the paper, which was wetted before printing and then contracted unevenly during drying. The width of these stamps varies between 17 and 18 mm.

The listed major re-entry on the 10d. occurs on R.3/5 and shows strong doubling of the top frame line and the left-hand "8d. stg." with a line through the lower parts of "ANAD" and "ENCE". Smaller re-entries occur on all values.

Examples of the 12d. on wove paper come from a proof sheet used for postal purposes by the postal authorities.

The 3d. is known perforated 14 and also *percé en scie* 13. Both are contemporary, but were unofficial.

1858–59. *P* 11¾. A. *Machine-made medium to thick wove paper with a more even hard texture.*
25	4	½d. deep rose (12.58)	..	..	£1700	£600
		a. Lilac-rose	..	..	£1900	£650
26	1	3d. red (1.59)	..	..	£2500	£300
		a. Major re-entry	..	..		—	£1000
27	2	6d. brownish grey (1.59)	..	£6500	£2200
		a. Slate-violet	..	..	£6500	£2250

B. *Thin soft horizontally ribbed paper*
27*b*	4	½d. deep rose-red	..	..		—	£3250
28	1	3d. red	..	..	..		—	£1200
		a. Major re-entry	..	..	

(New Currency. 100 cents = 1 dollar)

7　　　　　　8 American Beaver

9 Prince Albert　　10　　11 Jacques Cartier

(Recess A.B.N. Co)

(On 1 May 1858, Messrs. Rawdon, Wright, Hatch and Edson joined with eight other firms to form "The American Bank Note Co" and the "imprint" on sheets of the following stamps has the new title of the firm with "New York" added.)

1859 (1 July). *P* 12.
29	7	1 c. pale rose (to rose-red)	..	£225	24·00
30		1 c. deep rose (to carmine-rose)	..	£300	42·00
		a. Imperf (pair)	..	..	£2500
		b. Imperf × perf	..		
31	8	5 c. pale red	..	..	£250	11·00
32		5 c. deep red	..	..	£250	11·00
		a. Re-entry* (R.3/8)	..	£2500	£450
		b. Imperf (pair)	..		£7000
		c. Bisected (2½ c.) with 10 c. on cover	† £4000
33	9	10 c. black-brown	..	..	£6000	£1300
		a. Bisected (5 c.), on cover	..	† £5500
33*b*		10 c. deep red-purple	..	..	£2500	£500
		ba. Bisected (5 c.), on cover	..	† £3750
34		10 c. purple (*shades*)	..	..	£750	40·00
		a. Bisected (5 c.), on cover	..	† £3750
35		10 c. brownish purple	..	..	£700	40·00
36		10 c. brown (to pale)	..	..	£700	40·00
		a. Bisected (5 c.), on cover	..	† £4500
37		10 c. dull violet	..	..	£750	45·00
38		10 c. bright red-purple	..	..	£750	40·00
		a. Imperf (pair)	..	..	£6000
39	10	12½ c. deep yellow-green	..	£600	38·00
40		12½ c. pale yellow-green	..	£550	38·00
41		12½ c. blue-green	..	..	£650	45·00
		a. Imperf (pair)	..	..	£2500
		b. Imperf between (vert pair)	..	

CONTEMPLATING CANADA?

Then contact Eastern Auctions today! Canada's most trusted auction house is internationally recognised as a primary source of specialized Canada, Newfoundland and Provinces. Our sales contain thousands of auction lots from classics to modern major errors. You'll find stamps, plate blocks, sheets, booklets, covers and postal history, essays, proofs, forgeries, etc. Accumulations and entire collections are also included. We regularly feature Commonwealth and foreign material as well. Send in £15 for a one year (12 auctions) subscription to our public and mail auctions.

We also maintain a very active retail division where you can find anything from inexpensive varieties to high priced rarities. It's the perfect way to fill in those empty album spaces. Ask for a free monthly price list.

Thinking of selling? Let Gary Lyon guide you through a profitable and worry-free experience. Take advantage of the strong North american market. Our expert auction lotting and full colour catalogue will achieve top realizations for you stamps. We guarantee competitive commission rates and prompt settlement after the auction. Outright purchase can also be arranged if you prefer.

Contact Canada's only full service stamp dealer today.

EASTERN AUCTIONS LTD

CANADA'S LEADING STAMP DEALERS

P.O. BOX 250G, BATHURST, N.B., E2A 3Z4 CANADA

Members: PTS, CPSofGB, ASDA, APS, CSDA, BNAPS, RPSC, IFSDA

 Telephone 1-506-548-8986. Fax 1-506-546-6627. Or E-mail: glstamps@nbnet.nb.ca

---

FREE SAMPLE

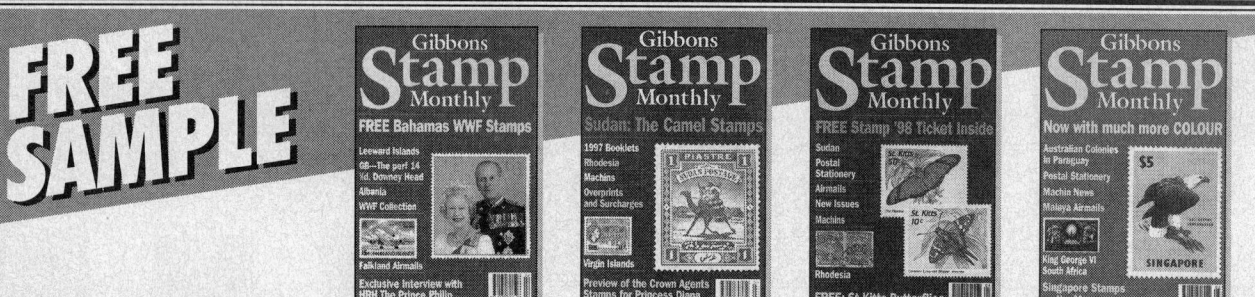

No Stamp Magazine Offers More For The GB & Commonwealth Collector

● Varied GB and Commonwealth articles written by acknowledged experts in their fields.

● GB articles on stamps, postal history, Machins and much, much more.

● Regular features include King George VI varieties, Postal Stationary, Queen Elizabeth II and much more.

● Notable GB and Commonwealth auction results and a monthly 'Tipster' column.

● Read by thousands of subscribers in over 80 countries world-wide.

● Exceptional value for money with 50% more editorial than other magazines.

Gibbons Stamp Monthly
5/7 Parkside, Christchurch Road,
Ringwood, Hants BH24 3SH
Tel: +44 (0)1425 472363
Fax: +44 (0)1425 470247

e.mail: sales@stangib.demon.co.uk
internet: http://www.stangib.com/

But don't just take our word for it - write to the Editor requesting a sample copy and subscription details.

42	11	17 c. deep blue ..	..	..	..	£700	60·00
		a. Imperf (pair)		..	..	£3000	
43		17 c. slate-blue ..		..	..	£850	90·00
43a		17 c. indigo	..	..	..	£750	65·00
		b. Imperf (pair)		..	..	£3000	

*The price of No. 32a is for the very marked re-entry showing oval frame line doubled above "CANADA". Slighter re-entries are worth from £30 upwards in used condition.

As there were numerous P.O. Dept. orders for the 10 c., 12½ c. and 17 c. and some of these were executed by more than one separate printing, with no special care to ensure uniformity of colour, there is a wide range of shade, especially in the 10 c., and some shades recur at intervals after periods during which other shades predominated. The colour-names given in the above list therefore represent groups only.

It has been proved by leading Canadian specialists that the perforations may be an aid to the approximate dating of a particular stamp, the gauge used measuring 11¾ × 11¾ from mid-July, 1859 to mid 1863, 12 × 11¾ from March 1863 to mid 1865 and 12 × 12 from April 1865 to 1868. Exceptionally in the 5 c. value many sheets were perforated 12 × 12 between May and October, 1862, whilst the last printings of the 12½ c. and 17 c. perf 11¾ × 11¾ were in July 1863, the perf 12 × 11¾ starting towards the end of 1863.

12

(Recess A.B.N. Co)

1864	(1 Aug).	*P* 12.					
44	12	2 c. rose-red	..	..	..	£400	£140
45		2 c. bright rose ..	..	..	..	£400	£140
		a. Imperf (pair)	..	..	..	£1600	

The Colony of Canada became part of the Dominion of Canada on 1 July 1867.

NEW BRUNSWICK

New Brunswick, previously part of Nova Scotia, became a separate colony in June 1784.

PRICES FOR STAMPS ON COVER

Nos. 1/4	*from* × 2
Nos. 5/6	*from* × 3
Nos. 7/9	*from* × 10
Nos. 10/12	*from* × 30
No. 13	—
Nos. 14/17	*from* × 2
No. 18	*from* × 5
No. 19	*from* × 100

1 Royal Crown and Heraldic Flowers
of the United Kingdom

(Recess P.B.)

1851	(5 Sept).	*Blue paper. Imperf.*					
1	1	3d. bright red	..	..	..	£1600	£300
2		3d. dull red	..	..	..	£1800	£300
		a. Bisected (1½d.) (on cover) ..		..	†	£2750	
2b		6d. mustard-yellow	..	..	..	£6000	£1500
3		6d. yellow	..	..	..	£4500	£800
4		6d. olive-yellow	..	..	..	£4500	£700
		a. Bisected (3d.) (on cover)	..		†	£3000	
		b. Quartered (1½d.) (on cover)			†	£20000	
5		1s. reddish mauve	..	..	..	£13000	£4000
6		1s. dull mauve ..	..	..	..	£14000	£4500
		a. Bisected (6d.) (on cover) ..			†	£20000	
		b. Quartered (3d.) (on cover) ..			†	£20000	

Reprints of all three values were made in 1890 on thin, hard, white paper. The 3d. is bright orange, the 6d. and 1s. violet-black.

Nos. 2a and 4b were to make up the 7½d. rate to Great Britain, introduced on 1 August 1854.

(New Currency. 100 cents = 1 dollar)

2 Locomotive 3 3a Charles
Connell

---

4 5 6 Paddle-steamer
Washington

7 King Edward VII when Prince of Wales

(Recess A.B.N. Co)

1860	(15 May)–63.	*No wmk. P* 12.					
7	2	1 c. brown-purple	..	..	..	48·00	35·00
8		1 c. purple	..	..	..	28·00	28·00
9		1 c. dull claret	..	..	..	28·00	28·00
		a. Imperf vert (horiz pair)	..	..		£500	
10	3	2 c. orange (1863)	..	..	..	14·00	14·00
11		2 c. orange-yellow	..	..	..	15·00	14·00
12		2 c. deep orange	..	..	..	18·00	14·00
		a. Imperf horiz (vert pair)	..	..		£450	
13	3a	5 c. brown	..	..	..	£4000	
14		5 c. yellow-green	..	..	..	12·00	12·00
15		5 c. deep green	..	..	..	12·00	12·00
16		5 c. sap-green (deep yellowish green)		..		£300	40·00
17	5	10 c. red	..	..	..	35·00	35·00
		a. Bisected (5 c.) (on cover) (1860)		..	†	£600	
18	6	12½ c. indigo	..	..	..	50·00	40·00
19	7	17 c. black	..	..	..	32·00	40·00

Beware of forged cancellations.

New Brunswick joined the Dominion of Canada on 1 July 1867 and its stamps were withdrawn in March of the following year.

NEWFOUNDLAND

Newfoundland became a self-governing colony in 1855 and a Dominion in 1917. In 1934 the adverse financial situation led to the suspension of the constitution.

The first local postmaster, at St. John's, was appointed in 1805, the overseas mails being routed via Halifax, Nova Scotia. A regular packet service was established between these two ports in 1840, the British G.P.O. assuming control of the overseas mails at the same time.

The responsibility for the overseas postal service reverted to the colonial administration on 1 July 1851.

For illustrations of the handstamp types see BRITISH POST OFFICES ABROAD notes, following GREAT BRITAIN.

ST. JOHN'S

CROWNED-CIRCLE HANDSTAMPS

CC1	CC 1a	ST. JOHNS NEWFOUNDLAND (R.)		
		(27.6.1846)	.. ..	*Price on cover* £900

PRICES FOR STAMPS ON COVER TO 1945

No. 1	*from* × 30
Nos. 2/4	*from* × 3
No. 5	*from* × 20
No. 6	*from* × 10
No. 7	*from* × 3
No. 8	*from* × 30
No. 9	*from* × 8
No. 10	—
No. 11	*from* × 8
No. 12	*from* × 3
Nos. 13/14	*from* × 20
No. 15	—
Nos. 16/19	*from* × 15
No. 20	—
Nos. 21/4c	*from* × 15
Nos. 24d/e	—
No. 25	*from* × 30
No. 26	*from* × 5
No. 27	*from* × 8
No. 28	*from* × 3
Nos. 29/30	*from* × 10
No. 31	*from* × 30
No. 32	*from* × 8
No. 33	*from* × 5
No. 33a	—
Nos. 34/9	*from* × 8
Nos. 40/1	*from* × 5
Nos. 42/3	*from* × 30
Nos. 44/8	*from* × 8
No. 49	*from* × 50
Nos. 50/3	*from* × 10
No. 54	*from* × 4
Nos. 55/8b	*from* × 10
No. 59	*from* × 100
No. 59a	*from* × 10
Nos. 60/1	*from* × 4
Nos. 62/5	*from* × 8
Nos. 65a/79	*from* × 3
Nos. 83/90	*from* × 10
Nos. 91/3	*from* × 2
No. 94	*from* × 50
Nos. 95/141	*from* × 10
Nos. 142/3	—
Nos. 144/8f	*from* × 2
Nos. 149/62	*from* × 3

No. 163				*from* × 2	—
Nos. 164/78			*from* × 2		
Nos. 179/90			*from* × 3		
No. 191					—
Nos. 192/220			*from* × 2		
No. 221					—
Nos. 222/9			*from* × 3		
Nos. 230/4			*from* × 2		
No. 235					—
Nos. 236/91			*from* × 2		
Nos. D1/6			*from* × 10		

1 2 4

3 5

Royal Crown and Heraldic flowers of the United Kingdom

(Recess P.B.)

1857	(1 Jan–15 Feb).	*No wmk. Thick, machine-made paper with a distinct mesh. Imperf.*					
1	1	1d. brown-purple	..	..	..	85·00	£140
		a. Bisected (½d.) (on cover)		..	†	£11000	
2	2	2d. scarlet-vermilion (15 Feb)		..	£9000	£4500	
3	3	3d. yellowish green	..	..	..	£700	£400
4	4	4d. scarlet-vermilion	..	..	£6000	£2500	
		a. Bisected (2d.) (on cover)	..	..	†	£15000	
5	1	5d. brown-purple	..	..	..	£180	£350
6	4	6d. scarlet-vermilion	..	..	£12000	£3000	
7	5	6½d. scarlet-vermilion	..	..	£2250	£2250	
8	4	8d. scarlet-vermilion	..	..	£225	£300	
		a. Bisected (4d.) (on cover)	..		†	£3250	
9	2	1s. scarlet-vermilion	..	..	£13000	£4750	
		a. Bisected (6d.) (on cover)	..		†	£12000	

The 6d. and 8d. differ from the 4d. in many details, as does also the 1s. from the 2d.

1860	(Aug).	*Medium, hand-made paper without mesh. Imperf.*					
10	2	2d. orange-vermilion ..		..	..	£300	£375
11	3	3d. green *to* deep green*		..	..	65·00	£150
12	4	4d. orange-vermilion	..	..	..	£2250	£750
		a. Bisected (2d.) (on cover)	..		†	£12000	
13	1	5d. Venetian red	..	..	..	90·00	£275
14	4	6d. orange-vermilion	..	..	..	£2750	£600
15	2	1s. orange-vermilion	..	..	£19000	£8000	
		a. Bisected (6d.) (on cover)	..		†	£40000	

*No. 11 includes stamps from the November 1861 printing which are very difficult to distinguish.

The 1s. on horizontally or vertically *laid* paper is now considered to be a proof (*Price* £10000).

BISECTS. Collectors are warned against buying bisected stamps of these issues without a reliable guarantee.

1861.	*New colours. Imperf.* (a) *1st printing. Soft, hand-made paper without mesh* (July).						
16	2	2d. deep rose-lake	..	..	..	£190	£500
17	4	4d. deep rose-lake	..	..	..	£100	£180
		a. Bisected (2d.) (on cover) ..					
18		6d. deep rose-lake	..	..	..	£100	£190
		a. Bisected (3d.) (on cover) ..			†	£9000	
19	5	6½d. deep rose-lake	..	..	..	£225	£700
20	2	1s. deep rose-lake	..	..	..	£225	£650
		a. Bisected (6d.) (on cover) ..			†	£14000	
		(b) *2nd printing. Hard, hand-made paper without mesh* (Nov)					
21	1	1d. chocolate-brown	..	..	..	£150	£225
		a. Red-brown	..	..	..	£4000	
22	2	2d. pale rose-lake	..	..	..	£150	£375
23	4	4d. pale rose-lake	..	..	..	25·00	90·00
24	1	5d. chocolate-brown	..	..	..	50·00	£300
		a. Red-brown	..	..	..	42·00	£190
24b	4	6d. pale rose-lake	..	..	..	19·00	£100
24c	5	6½d. pale rose-lake	..	..	..	65·00	£225
24d	4	8d. pale rose-lake	..	..	..	70·00	£475
24e	2	1s. pale rose-lake	..	..	..	32·00	£300

Stamps of the second printing of the pale rose-lake shades have a more transparent look due to the paper being generally thinner, but paper thickness alone is not a sure test for distinguishing the printings.

Stamps of this issue may be found with part of the paper-maker's watermark "STACEY WISE 1858".

Beware of buying used specimens of the stamps which are worth much less in unused condition, as many unused stamps have been provided with faked postmarks. A guarantee should be obtained.

STANLEY GIBBONS STAMP COLLECTING SERIES

Introductory booklets on *How to Start, How to Identify Stamps* and *Collecting by Theme.* A series of well illustrated guides at a low price.
Write for details.

STAMPS AUCTION NEWS
2 Jan. 1989

Record Prices Set for Canada Pence in Charles Firby Auction

The famed 12 penny pair of Canada realized $165,000 ($203,000 Canadian) when sold by Charles G. Firby Auctions on Oct. 29. The mint pair of black stamps was issued in 1851.

The pair was offered as part of the 450-lot auction of a Canadian first-issue collection formed by Sam C. Nickle of Calgary, Alberta. This was the highest price ever paid for a Canadian philatelic item sold at public auction.

The bidding began at $135,000 and increased by $5,000 increments. Five bids later, the piece was knocked down at...

Acting as agent for a Toronto commission brought the total... "I was pleased," Jamie... price." He would... "This piece is... by any me... The... believe...

Philatelic Literature Review 37:1/7

Year's Major U.S. Auction Had Something for Everyone

by Steven J. Rod

The major American philatelic literature auction of the past year seems to have been the October 31, 1987, Charles G. Firby "Rarities of Philatelic Literature Sale" held at Southfield, Michigan. This sale truly seems to have had something for everyone with prices realized ranging from $2.50 to $4,200. Well, okay, if you take away one expensive lot, the prices ranged from $2.50 to $1,150. Take away those figure lots and there were eight lots at $400 to $725 and nineteen lots...

Philatelic Literature Review 37:4/179

Prices 'Out of Sight' at Firby's 2nd 'Rarities' Sale

by William Hagan

Chuck Firby's second "Rarities" sale featured Roger Koerber's Philatelic li... also a portion of his retail stock. Of the four sessions (three on Mond 29, and one on Tuesday, August 30), I was able to attend only the secon and I spent only about thirty minutes examining material.

Probably the most exciting lot was No. 803, Roger's p... titles ... masters and templates ... buyer ac... quires rights to Postilion name ... 650 imprint binders ... A tremendous number of potent buyers (more than twenty) refused to be scar... by the $5,000 estimate. The lot was... $14,000 and, after the sale, the won...

Canadian Stamp News
May 20, 1986

Record prices set at Firby a...

Collectors and agents alike witnessed record prices at the Charles G. Firby March 18 public auction held near the Detroit Metropolitan Airport.

All prices quoted are in United States dollars and include the buyers premium.

The auction began with Ray Simrak Gold Medal Canadian Airmail Collection. The very first lot set the tone of the sale. An orange ABN sample proof...

international route cover on the North American Continent is listed by AAMC at cv $1,000 and was estimated at $1,250 plus. After some healthy floor bidding it was finally knocked down at $6,700 plus 10 per cent, a total realization of $7,370 — almost 600 per cent of estimate. Another item is the Grand Ar... cover. ... surviving titive...

sold fo 125. "... Haileybu cv $25($412.50 The SCADTA covers also standing pe Lot 228, on estimated plus, close Lot 229

Before You Sell Your Stamps
Talk To Us.

This 12 Pence Pair realized $165,000.00 in our OCTOBER 29, 1989 AUCTION. Highest price ever paid for a Canadian Stamp at auction.

We understand what it takes to Establish Records. We've done it Again & Again & Again & Again . . .

You spent much time & money forming your collection & we feel that it is important to present your material in the same way: professionally & with great care.

Our lotting, presentation & international buyers assure you of the highest possible realization. The kind of realization that makes headlines.

After all, when the experts review our sales & prices realized it becomes obvious that we know how to sell your stamps.

No collection is too small to receive our individual attention. We encourage you to call Collect to learn more about how best to offer your collection or to request our "Auction Consignment Information" brochure which describes the auction process.

That way you may very well come up with some records of your own.

If an outright sale is more to your liking, you can count on us for a prompt response & "instant" payment. Just Ask.

Charles G. Firby
AUCTIONS

QUALIFIED AUCTIONEER

LICENSED and BONDED

6695 Highland Road, Waterford, MI 48327-1967
Phone: 248 666 5333   Fax: 248 666 5020

(New Currency. 100 cents = 1 dollar)

6 Atlantic Cod   **7** Common Seal on Ice-floe

8 Prince Consort   **9** Queen Victoria

10 Schooner   **11** Queen Victoria

(Recess A.B.N. Co)

1865 (15 Nov)–**75**. *P* 12. (*a*) *Thin yellowish paper.*

25	6	2 c. yellowish green	..	£100	35·00
		a Bisected (1 c.) (on cover) (1870)		†	£3750
26	7	5 c. brown	..	£450	£170
		a. Bisected (2½ c.) (on cover)			
27	8	10 c. black	..	£250	60·00
		a. Bisected (5 c.) (on cover) (1869)		†	£2750
28	9	12 c. red-brown	..	£400	£150
		a. Bisected (6 c.) (on cover)		†	£2750
29	10	13 c. orange-yellow	..	85·00	60·00
30	11	24 c. blue	..	32·00	32·00

(*b*) *Medium white paper*

31	6	2 c. bluish green (*to* deep) (1870)	..	65·00	28·00
32	8	10 c. black (1875)	..	£150	32·00
33	9	12 c. chestnut (1870)	..	40·00	40·00
33a	11	24 c. blue (1870?)	..	£800	£275

The inland postage rate was reduced to 3 c. on 8 May, 1870. Until the 3 c. value became available examples of No. 25 were bisected to provide 1 c. stamps.

12 King Edward VII when Prince of Wales   **14** Queen Victoria

I

II

In Type II the white oval frame line is unbroken by the scroll containing the words "ONE CENT", the letters "N.F." are smaller and closer to the scroll, and there are other minor differences.

(Recess National Bank Note Co, New York)

1868 (Nov). *P* 12.

34	12	1 c. dull purple (I)	.. ..	48·00	45·00

(Recess A.B.N. Co)

1868 (Nov)–**73**. *P* 12.

35	12	1 c. brown-purple (II) (5.71)	..	75·00	50·00
36	14	3 c. vermilion (7.70)	..	£250	£100
37		3 c. blue (1.4.73)	..	£275	18·00
38	7	5 c. black	..	£200	£100
39	14	5 c. rose (7.70)	..	6·50	16·00

1876–79. *Rouletted.*

40	12	1 c. lake-purple (II) (1877)	..	85·00	38·00
41	6	2 c. bluish green (1879)	..	£120	45·00
42	14	3 c. blue (1877)	..	£250	3·50
43	7	5 c. blue	..	£170	2·75
		a. Imperf (pair)	.. ..		

15 King Edward VII when Prince of Wales   **16** Atlantic Cod

17   **18** Common Seal on Ice-floe

(Recess British American Bank Note Co, Montreal)

1880–82. *P* 12.

44	15	1 c. dull grey-brown	..	22·00	7·00
		a. Dull brown	..	20·00	7·00
		b. Red-brown	..	24·00	12·00
46	16	2 c. yellow-green (1882)	..	42·00	20·00
47	17	3 c. pale dull blue	..	60·00	5·00
		a. Bright blue	..	65·00	2·00
48	18	5 c. pale dull blue	..	£200	7·00

19 Newfoundland Dog   **20** Atlantic Brigantine   **21** Queen Victoria

(Recess British American Bank Note Co, Montreal)

1888 (Jan). *New colours and values. P* 12.

49	19	½ c. rose-red	..	7·50	6·00
50	15	1 c. blue-green	..	9·50	4·50
		a. Green	..	5·50	2·00
		b. Yellow-green	..	9·50	6·50
51	16	2 c. orange-vermilion	..	11·00	3·50
52	17	3 c. deep brown	..	55·00	80
53	18	5 c. deep blue	..	85·00	4·00
54	20	10 c. black	..	45·00	48·00
49/54			*Set of* 6	£190	55·00

For reissues of 1880/87 stamps in similar colours, see Nos. 62/65a.

(Recess B.A.B.N.)

1890 (Nov). *P* 12.

55	21	3 c. deep slate	..	23·00	90
		a. Imperf (pair)	..		
56		3 c. slate-grey (*to* grey)	..	24·00	90
		a. Imperf horiz (vert pair)	..	£400	
57		3 c. slate-violet	..	27·00	3·00
58		3 c. grey-lilac	..	27·00	90
58a		3 c. brown-grey	..	27·00	6·50
58b		3 c. purple-grey	..	32·00	5·00

There is a very wide range of shades in this stamp, and those given only cover the main groups.

Stamps on pink paper are from a consignment recovered from the sea and which were affected by the salt water.

(Recess British American Bank Note Co, Montreal)

1894 (Aug–Dec). *Changes of colour. P* 12.

59	19	½ c. black (11.94)	..	7·00	3·50
59a	18	5 c. bright blue (12.94)	..	55·00	2·00
60	14	6 c. crimson-lake (12.94)	..	13·00	14·00
61	9	12 c. deep brown	..	42·00	48·00

The 6 c. is printed from the old American Bank Note Company's plates.

1896–97. *Reissues. P* 12.

62	19	½ c. orange-vermilion	..	38·00	48·00
63	15	1 c. deep green	..	14·00	7·00
63a		1 c. deep brown	..	48·00	48·00
64	16	2 c. green	..	65·00	35·00
65	17	3 c. deep blue	..	55·00	12·00
65a		3 c. chocolate-brown	..	70·00	65·00
62/65a			*Set of* 6	£250	£190

The above were *reissued* for postal purposes. The colours were generally brighter than those of the original stamps.

22 Queen Victoria   **23** Jean Cabot   **24** Cape Bonavista

25 Reindeer-hunting   **26** Mining

27 Logging   **28** Fishing

29 *Matthew* (Cabot)   **30** Willow Grouse

31 Group of Grey Seals   **32** Salmon-fishing

33 Seal of the Colony   **34** Iceberg off St. John's   **35** Henry VII

(Recess A.B.N. Co)

1897 (24 June). *400th Anniv of Discovery of Newfoundland and 60th year of Queen Victoria's reign. P* 12.

66	22	1 c. green	..	2·00	3·75
67	23	2 c. bright rose	..	1·00	2·00
		a. Bisected (1 c.) on cover		†	£250
68	24	3 c. bright blue	..	2·75	40
		a. Bisected (1½ c.) on cover		†	£250
69	25	4 c. olive-green	..	8·50	2·75
70	26	5 c. violet	..	10·00	2·75
71	27	6 c. red-brown	..	7·50	2·75
		a. Bisected (3 c.) on cover		†	£250
72	28	8 c. orange	..	15·00	7·50
73	29	10 c. sepia	..	30·00	4·50
74	30	12 c. deep blue	..	32·00	4·50
75	31	15 c. bright scarlet	..	17·00	14·00
76	32	24 c. dull violet-blue	..	20·00	18·00
77	33	30 c. slate-blue	..	42·00	50·00
78	34	35 c. red	..	60·00	50·00
79	35	60 c. black	..	15·00	10·00
66/79			*Set of* 14	£225	£150

The 60 c. surcharged "TWO—2—CENTS" in three lines is an essay made in December 1918 (*Price* £250).

36 Prince Edward later Duke of Windsor   **37** Queen Victoria   **38** King Edward VII when Prince of Wales

39 Queen Alexandra when Princess of Wales   **40** Queen Mary when Duchess of York   **41** King George V when Duke of York

(Recess A.B.N. Co)

1897–1918. *P* 12.

83	36	½ c. olive (8.97)	..	2·00	1·00
		a. Imperf (pair)	..	£275	
84	37	1 c. carmine (4.12.97)	..	2·50	2·50
85		1 c. blue-green (6.98)	..	6·00	10
		a. Yellow-green	..	5·50	10
		b. Imperf horiz (vert pair)	..	£170	

86 38	2 c. orange (4.12.97)	..	..	2·50	1·40
	a. Imperf (pair)	..	..	—	£300
87	2 c. scarlet (6.98)	..	..	11·00	30
	a. Imperf (pair)	..	..	£225	£225
	b. Imperf between (pair)	..		£300	
88 39	3 c. orange (6.98)	..	..	11·00	20
	a. Imperf horiz (vert pair)	..		£250	
	b. Imperf (pair)	..		£225	£225
	c. Red-orange/bluish (6.18)	..		28·00	2·75
89 40	4 c. violet (10.01)	..	..	22·00	3·50
	a. Imperf (pair)	..		£300	
90 41	5 c. blue (6.99)	..	..	35·00	2·75
83/90		..	Set of 8	80·00	10·00

No. 88c was an emergency war-time printing made by the American Bank Note Co from the old plate, pending receipt of the then current 3 c. from England.

The imperforate errors of this issue are found used, but only as philatelic "by favour" items. It is possible that No. 86a only exists in this condition.

ONE CENT   **ONE CENT**

(42)   (43)

ONE CENT

(44)

1897 (Oct). *T* **21** *surch with T* **42** *to T* **44** *by Royal Gazette, St. Johns, on stamps of various shades.*

91 42	1 c. on 3 c. grey-purple	..	..	38·00	16·00
	a. Surch double, one diagonal	..		£1100	
	d. Vert pair, one without lower bar and "ONE CENT"	..	..	£3500	
92 43	1 c. on 3 c. grey-purple	..	..	95·00	80·00
93 44	1 c. on 3 c. grey-purple	..	..	£450	£350

Nos. 91/3 occur in the same setting of 50 (10×5) applied twice to each sheet. Type **42** appeared in the first four horizontal rows. Type **43** on R. 5/1–8 and Type **44** on R. 5/9 and 10.

Trial surcharges in red or red and black were not issued. (*Price: Type* **42** *in red* £750, *in red and black* £750: *Type* **43** *in red* £2250, *in red and black* £2500: *Type* **44** *in red* £5000, *in red and black* £6000).

These surcharges exist on stamps of various shades, but those on brown-grey are clandestine forgeries, having been produced by one of the printers at the *Royal Gazette*.

45 Map of Newfoundland

(Recess A.B.N. Co)

1908 (Sept). *P* 12.

94 45	2 c. lake	..	..	25·00	60

46 King James I   47 Arms of Colonisation Co   48 John Guy

49 *Endeavour* (immigrant ship), 1610   50 Cupids

51 Sir Francis Bacon   52 View of Mosquito

53 Logging Camp   54 Paper Mills

55 King Edward VII   56 King George V

(Litho Whitehead, Morris & Co, Ltd)

1910 (15 Aug). (a) *P* 12.

95 46	1 c. green	..	..	5·00	1·50
	a. "NFWFOUNDLAND" (Right pane R. 5/1)	..		45·00	70·00
	b. "JANES" (Right pane R. 5/2)	..		45·00	70·00
	c. Imperf between (horiz pair)	..		£275	£300
96 47	2 c. rose-carmine	..		8·00	1·50
97 48	3 c. olive	..		4·50	14·00
98 49	4 c. violet	..		11·00	12·00
99 50	5 c. bright blue	..		17·00	5·50
100 51	6 c. claret (A)	..		45·00	£120
100a	6 c. claret (B)	..		18·00	60·00
101 52	8 c. bistre-brown	..		48·00	85·00
102 53	9 c. olive-green	..		40·00	75·00
103 54	10 c. purple-slate	..		55·00	95·00
104 55	12 c. pale red-brown	..		55·00	70·00
	a. Imperf (pair)	..		£300	
105 56	15 c. black	..		65·00	95·00
95/105		..	Set of 11	£275	£450

6 c. (A) "Z" in "COLONIZATION" reversed. (B) "Z" correct.

(b) *P* 12×14

106 46	1 c. green	..		3·75	6·00
	a. "NFWFOUNDLAND"	..		42·00	80·00
	b. "JANES"	..		42·00	80·00
	c. Imperf between (horiz pair)	..		£475	£500
107 47	2 c. rose-carmine	..		3·50	35
	a. Imperf between (horiz pair)	..		£450	
108 50	5 c. bright blue (*p* 14×12)	..		8·00	2·50

(c) *P* 12×11

109 46	1 c. green	..		1·25	20
	a. Imperf between (horiz pair)	..		£250	
	b. Imperf between (vert pair)	..		£300	
	c. "NFWFOUNDLAND"	..		22·00	40·00
	e. "JANES"	..		22·00	40·00

(d) *P* 12 × 11½

110 47	2 c. rose-carmine	..		£180	£170

(Dies eng Macdonald & Sons. Recess A. Alexander & Sons, Ltd)

1911 (7 Feb). *As T* **51** *to* **56**, *but recess printed. P* 14.

111	6 c. claret (B)	..		17·00	40·00
112	8 c. yellow-brown	..		48·00	55·00
	a. Imperf between (horiz pair)	..		£400	
	b. Imperf (pair)	..		£300	
113	9 c. sage-green	..		40·00	80·00
	a. Imperf between (horiz pair)	..		£350	
114	10 c. purple-black	..		80·00	£110
	a. Imperf between (horiz pair)	..		£350	
	b. Imperf (pair)	..		£250	
115	12 c. red-brown	..		60·00	60·00
116	15 c. slate-green	..		55·00	£110
111/16		..	Set of 6	£275	£400

The 9 c. and 15 c. exist with papermaker's watermark "E. TOWGOOD FINE".

57 Queen Mary   58 King George V   59 Duke of Windsor when Prince of Wales

60 King George VI when Prince Albert   61 Princess Mary, the Princess Royal   62 Prince Henry Duke of Gloucester

63 Prince George, Duke of Kent   64 Prince John   65 Queen Alexandra

66 Duke of Connaught   67 Seal of Newfoundland

(1 c. to 5 c., 10 c. eng and recess D.L.R.; others eng Macdonald & Co, recess A. Alexander & Sons)

1911 (19 June)–**16**. *Coronation. P* 13½ × 14 (*comb*) (1 c. to 5 c., 10 c.) *or* 14 (*line*) (*others*).

117 57	1 c. yellow-green	..		5·00	20
	a. Blue-green (1915)	..		6·00	30
118 58	2 c. carmine	..		2·75	20
	a. Rose-red (*blurred impression*). Perf 14 (1916)			6·00	55
119 59	3 c. red-brown	..		16·00	25·00
120 60	4 c. purple	..		16·00	24·00
121 61	5 c. ultramarine	..		4·50	1·25
122 62	6 c. slate-grey	..		10·00	24·00
123 63	8 c. aniline blue	..		48·00	75·00
	a. Greenish blue	..		55·00	90·00
124 64	9 c. violet-blue	..		13·00	40·00
125 65	10 c. deep green	..		25·00	35·00
126 66	12 c. plum	..		18·00	35·00
127 67	15 c. lake	..		15·00	42·00
117/27		..	Set of 11	£150	£250

The 2 c. rose-red, No. 118a is a poor war-time printing by Alexander & Sons.

Although No. 123 has a typical aniline appearance it is believed that the shade results from the thinning of non-aniline ink.

FIRST TRANS-ATLANTIC AIR POST April, 1919.

68 Reindeer   (69)

(Des J. H. Noonan. Recess D.L.R.)

1919 (2 Jan). *Newfoundland Contingent, 1914–1918. P* 14.

130 68	1 c. green (*a*) (*b*)	..		2·75	20
131	2 c. scarlet (*a*) (*b*)	..		2·50	85
	a. Carmine-red (*b*)			7·50	45
132	3 c. brown (*a*) (*b*)	..		3·75	20
	a. Red-brown (*b*)			4·50	30
133	4 c. mauve (*a*)	..		3·75	60
	a. Purple (*b*)			7·50	30
134	5 c. ultramarine (*a*) (*b*)	..		3·50	95
135	6 c. slate-grey (*a*)	..		4·50	28·00
136	8 c. bright magenta (*a*)	..		7·00	38·00
137	10 c. deep grey-green (*a*)	..		4·50	3·25
138	12 c. orange (*a*)	..		18·00	42·00
139	15 c. indigo (*a*)	..		15·00	55·00
	a. Prussian blue (*a*)			80·00	£140
140	24 c. bistre-brown (*a*)	..		22·00	25·00
141	36 c. sage-green (*a*)	..		10·00	23·00
130/41		..	Set of 12	85·00	£190

Each value bears with "Trail of the Caribou" the name of a different action: 1 c. Suvla Bay; 3 c. Gueudecourt; 4 c. Beaumont Hamel; 6 c. Monchy; 10 c. Steenbeck; 15 c. Langemarck; 24 c. Cambrai; 36 c. Combles; 2 c., 5 c., 8 c., and 12 c. inscribed "Royal Naval Reserve-Ubique".

Perforations. Two perforating heads were used: (*a*) comb 14 × 13.9; (*b*) line 14.1 × 14.1.

1919 (12 Apr). *Air. No.* 132 *optd with T* **69**, *by Robinson & Co Ltd, at the offices of the "Daily News".*

142 68	3 c. brown	..		£15000	£8000

These stamps franked correspondence carried by Lieut. H. Hawker on his Atlantic flight. 18 were damaged and destroyed, 95 used on letters, 11 given as presentation copies, and the remaining 76 were sold in aid of the Marine Disasters Fund.

1919 (19 April). *Nos.* 132 *optd in MS.* "Aerial Atlantic Mail. J.A.R."

142a 68	3 c. brown	..		—	£20000

This provisional was made by W. C. Campbell, the Secretary of the Postal Department, and the initials are those of the Postmaster, J. A. Robinson, for use on correspondence intended to be carried on the abortive Morgan-Raynham Trans-Atlantic flight. The mail was eventually delivered by sea.

In addition to the 25 to 30 used examples, one unused, no gum, copy of No. 142a is known.

A single example of a similar overprint on the 2 c., No. 131, is known used on cover together with an unoverprinted example of the same value.

Trans-Atlantic AIR POST, 1919. ONE DOLLAR.   **THREE CENTS**

(70)   (71)

1919 (9 June). *Air. No.* 75 *surch with T* **70** *by Royal Gazette, St. Johns.*

143 31	$1 on 15 c. bright scarlet	..		£110	£110
	a. No comma after "AIR POST"	..		£140	£150
	b. As Var a and no stop after "1919"	..		£350	£350
	c. As Var a and "A" of "AIR" under "a" of "Trans"	..		£350	£350

These stamps were issued for use on the mail carried on the first successful flight across the Atlantic by Capt. J. Alcock and Lieut. A. Brown, and on other projected Trans-Atlantic flights (Alcock flown cover, *Price* £3000).

The surcharge was applied in a setting of which 16 were normal, 7 as No. 143a, 1 as No. 143b and 1 as No. 143c.

1920 (Sept). *Nos. 75 and 77/8 surch as T* **71**, *by Royal Gazette* (2 c. with only one bar, at top of stamp).

A. Bars of surch 10½ mm apart. B. Bars 13½ mm apart.

44	33	2 c. on 30 c. slate-blue (23 Sept)	..	..	3·50	14·00
		a. Surch inverted			£400	£425
45	31	3 c. on 15 c. bright scarlet (A) (13 Sept)		£140	£140
		a. Surch inverted				£900
46		3 c. on 15 c. bright scarlet (B) (13 Sept)		11·00	9·00
47	34	3 c. on 35 c. red (15 Sept)	..	..	4·75	8·50
		a. Surch inverted				
		b. Lower bar omitted	..	..	£120	£130
		c. "THREE" omitted	..	..		£1100

Our prices for Nos. 147b and 147c are for stamps with lower bar or "THREE" entirely missing. The bar may be found in all stages of incompleteness and stamps showing broken bar are not of much value.

On the other hand, stamps showing either only the top or bottom of the letters "THREE" are scarce, though not as rare as No. 147c.

The 6 c. T **27** surcharged "THREE CENTS", in red or black, is an essay (*Price* £375). The 2 c. on 30 c. with red surcharge is a colour trial (*Price* £325).

AIR MAIL
to Halifax, N.S.
1921.
(72)

1921 (16 Nov). *Air. No. 78 optd with T* **72** *by Royal Gazette*.

I. 2¾ *mm between* "AIR" *and* "MAIL"

148	34	35 c. red	..	..	90·00	90·00
		a. No stop after "1921"	..	..	80·00	80·00
		b. No stop and first "1" of "1921" below "f" of "Halifax"	..	£180	£180
		c. As No. 148, inverted	..	..	£4000	
		d. As No. 148a, inverted	..	..	£3750	
		e. As No. 148b, inverted	..	..	£8000	

148f | 34 | 35 c. red.. | .. | .. | £100 | £100 |
		g. No stop after "1921"	..	..	£120	£120
		h. No stop and first "1" of "1921" below "f" of "Halifax"	..	£180	£180
		i. As No. 148f, inverted	..	..	£4500	
		k. As No. 148g, inverted	..	..	£5500	
		l. As No. 148h, inverted	..	..	£8000	

II. 1½ *mm between* "AIR" *and* "MAIL"

Type **72** was applied as a setting of 25 which contained ten stamps as No. 148a, seven as No. 148, four as No. 148f, two as No. 148g, one as No. 148b and one as No. 148h.

73 Twin Hills, Tor's Cove   **74** South-West Arm, Trinity   **75** Statue of the Fighting Newfoundlander, St. John's

(Recess D.L.R.)

1923 (9 July)–**26**. *T* **73/5** *and similar designs. P* 14 (*comb or line*).

149		1 c. green	..	..	60	10
150		2 c. carmine	..	..	60	10
		a. Imperf (pair)	..	..	£160	
151		3 c. brown	..	..	60	10
152		4 c. deep purple	..	..	90	30
153		5 c. ultramarine	..	..	1·50	1·25
154		6 c. slate	..	..	2·50	7·00
155		8 c. purple	..	..	2·50	3·25
156		9 c. slate-green	..	..	17·00	28·00
157		10 c. violet	..	..	4·00	2·50
		a. Purple	..	..	4·50	2·50
158		11 c. sage-green	..	..	2·25	14·00
159		12 c. lake	..	..	2·50	8·00
160		15 c. Prussian blue	..	..	2·50	12·00
161		20 c. chestnut (28.4.24)	..	..	4·25	10·00
162		24 c. sepia (22.4.24)	..	..	45·00	75·00
149/62				*Set of 14*	75·00	£140

Designs: *Horiz* (as *T* **73**)—6 c. Upper Steadies, Humber River; 11 c. Shell Bird Island; 20 c. Placentia. (As *T* **74**)—8 c. Quidi Vidi, near St. John's; 9 c. Reindeer crossing lake; 12 c. Mount Moriah, Bay of Islands. *Vert* (as *T* **75**)—4 c. Humber River; 5 c. Coast at Trinity; 10 c. Humber River Cañon; 15 c. Humber River near Little Rapids; 24 c. Topsail Falls.

Perforations. Three perforating heads were used: comb 13.8 × 14 (all values); line 13.7 and 14, and combinations of these two (for all except 6, 8, 9 and 11 c.).

Air Mail
DE PINEDO
1927
(87)

1927 (18 May). *Air. No. 79 optd with T* **87**, *by Robinson & Co, Ltd.*

163	35	60 c. black (R.)	..	..	£23000	£6500

For the mail carried by De Pinedo to Europe 300 stamps were overprinted, 230 used on correspondence, 66 presented to De Pinedo, Government Officials, etc., and 4 damaged and destroyed. Stamps without overprint were also used.

NEW INFORMATION

The editor is always interested to correspond with people who have new information that will improve or correct the Catalogue.

---

88 Newfoundland and Labrador

89 S.S. *Caribou*

90 King George V and Queen Mary

91 Duke of Windsor when Prince of Wales

92 Express Train

93 Newfoundland Hotel, St. John's

94 Heart's Content

95 Cabot Tower, St. John's

96 War Memorial, St. John's

97 G.P.O., St. John's

98 Vickers "Vimy" Aircraft

99 Parliament House, St. John's

100 Grand Falls, Labrador

(Recess D.L.R.)

1928 (3 Jan)–**29**. *"Publicity" issue. A. P* 14 (1 c.), 13½×13 (*horiz designs*) *or* 13×13½ (*vert designs*), *all comb. B. P* 14–13½ *line*.

				A		B	
164	88	1 c. deep green	..	1·75	80	†	
165	89	2 c. carmine	..	2·25	40	†	
166	90	3 c. brown	..	2·75	75	2·25	75
167	91	4 c. mauve	..	4·50	2·25	†	
		a. Rose-purple (1929)	..	5·00	5·00	†	
168	92	5 c. slate-grey	..	13·00	4·00	20·00	4·75
169	93	6 c. ultramarine	..	2·00	15·00	4·75	15·00
170	94	8 c. red-brown	..		†	2·00	21·00
171	95	9 c. deep green	..		†	2·00	10·00
172	96	10 c. deep violet	..	9·00	9·50	6·00	10·00
173	97	12 c. carmine-lake	..		†	2·00	17·00
174	95	14 c. brown-purple	..	8·50	9·00	5·00	7·50
175	98	15 c. deep blue	..		†	2·75	26·00
176	99	20 c. grey-black	..	7·50	8·50	2·50	6·50
177	97	28 c. deep green	..		†	27·00	48·00
178	100	30 c. sepia	..		†	6·00	14·00
164/78 (*cheapest*)			*Set of 15*	70·00	£160		

Exact gauges for the various perforations are: 14 comb = 14×13.9; 13½×13 comb = 13.5×12.75; 14–13½ line = 14–13.75.

See also Nos. 179/87 and 198/208.

D   1 c.   P   D   2 c.   P

D   3 c.   P   D   4 c.   P

D   5 c.   P

D   6 c.   P   D   10 c.   P

D   15 c.   P

D   20 c.   P

D. De La Rue printing

P. Perkins, Bacon printing

1929 (10 Aug)–**31**. *Perkins, Bacon printing. Former types re-engraved. No wmk. P* 14 (*comb*) (1 c.), 13½ (*comb*) (2, 6 c.), 14–13½ (*line*) (20 c.) *or* 13½×14 (*comb*) (*others*).

179	88	1 c. green (26.9.29)	..	..	3·50	20
		a. Perf 14–13½ (line)	..	..	3·50	30
		b. Imperf between (vert pair)	..	£130	
		c. Imperf (pair)	..	..	£110	
180	89	2 c. scarlet	..	..	1·50	20
		a. Imperf (pair)	..	..	85·00	
		b. Perf 14–13½ (line)	..	..	2·00	80
181	90	3 c. red-brown	..	..	1·00	10
		a. Imperf (pair)	..	..	95·00	
182	91	4 c. reddish purple (26.8.29)	..	2·75	50
		a. Imperf (pair)	..	..	£110	
183	92	5 c. deep grey-green (14.9.29)	..	5·50	2·00
184	93	6 c. ultramarine (8.11.29)	..	5·00	10·00
		a. Perf 14–13½ (line)	..	..	2·25	11·00
185	96	10 c. violet (5.10.29)	..	..	3·25	3·00
186	98	15 c. blue (1.30)	..	..	17·00	75·00
187	99	20 c. black (1.1.31)	..	..	40·00	40·00
179/87		.. .. ..	*Set of 9*	70·00	£120

Exact gauges for the various perforations are: 14 comb = 14×13.9; 13½ comb = 13.6×13.5; 14–13½ line = 14–13.75; 13½×14 comb = 13.6×13.8.

Trans-Atlantic
AIR MAIL
By B. M.
"Columbia"
September
1930

THREE CENTS	Fifty Cents
(101)	(102)

(Surch by Messrs D. R. Thistle, St. John's)

1929 (23 Aug). *No. 154 surch with T* **101**.

188		3 c. on 6 c. slate (R.)	..	..	85	3·75
		a. Surch inverted	..	..	£600	£900
		b. Surch in black	..	..	£700	

1930 (25 Sept). *Air. No. 141 surch with T* **102** *by Messrs D. R. Thistle.*

191	68	50 c. on 36 c. sage-green	..	£4500	£4250

103 Aeroplane and Dog-team   **104** Vickers-Vimy Biplane and early Sailing Packet

105 Routes of historic Transatlantic Flights

106

(Des A. B. Perlin. Recess P.B.)

1931. *Air.* P 14. (*a*) *Without wmk* (2.1.31)
192	103	15 c. chocolate ..	..	..	3·75	9·50
		a. Imperf between (horiz or vert pair)			£600	
		b. Imperf (pair)	..	..	£375	
193	104	50 c. green	..	..	24·00	40·00
		a. Imperf between (horiz or vert pair)			£650	£500
		b. Imperf (pair)	..	..	£500	
194	105	$1 deep blue	..	..	45·00	85·00
		a. Imperf between (horiz or vert pair)			£600	
		b. Imperf (pair)	..	..	£500	
192/4				*Set of* 3	65·00	£120

(*b*) *Wmk* W **106**, (*sideways*) (13.3.31)
195	103	15 c. chocolate ..	..	..	4·50	14·00
		a. Pair, with and without wmk			30·00	
		b. Imperf between (horiz or vert pair)			£550	
		ba. Ditto, one without wmk (vert pair)			£800	
		c. Imperf (pair)	..	..	£375	
		d. Wmk Cross (pair)	..	..	85·00	
196	104	50 c. green	..	..	20·00	60·00
		a. Imperf between (horiz or vert pair)			£600	
		b. Imperf (pair)	..	..	£500	
		c. Pair, with and without wmk			£170	
197	105	$1 deep blue ..	..	..	70·00	£130
		a. Imperf between (horiz or vert pair)			£600	
		b. Imperf horiz (vert pair)	..	..	£475	
		c. Pair, with and without wmk			£300	
		d. Imperf (pair)	..	..	£225	
195/7		..	..	*Set of* 3	85·00	£180

"WITH AND WITHOUT WMK" PAIRS listed in the issues from No. 195a onwards must have one stamp *completely* without any trace of watermark.

1931 (25 March–July). *Perkins, Bacon printing* (*re-engraved types*). W **106** (*sideways on* 1 c., 4 c., 30 c.). P 13½ (1 c.) or 13½×14 (*others*), *both comb**.
198	88	1 c. green (7.31)	..	..	4·50	3·00
		a. Imperf between (horiz pair)		..	£500	
199	89	2 c. scarlet (7.31)	..	..	4·75	2·75
200	90	3 c. red-brown (7.31)	..	..	1·75	1·50
201	91	4 c. reddish purple (7.31)	..	..	1·75	70
202	92	5 c. deep grey-green (7.31)	..	..	7·00	8·50
203	93	6 c. ultramarine	..	..	10·00	19·00
204	94	8 c. chestnut (1.4.31)	..	..	18·00	26·00
		w. Wmk inverted	..	..	55·00	
205	96	10 c. violet (1.4.31)	..	..	5·50	8·00
206	98	15 c. blue (1.7.31)	..	..	21·00	48·00
207	99	20 c. black (1.7.31)	..	..	45·00	12·00
208	100	30 c. sepia (1.7.31)	..	..	27·00	35·00
198/208		..	..	*Set of* 11	£130	£150

*Exact gauges for the two perforations are: 13½ = 13.6×13.5; 13½×14 = 13.6×13.8.

107 Atlantic Cod

108 King George V

109 Queen Mary

110 Duke of Windsor when Prince of Wales

111 Reindeer

112 Queen Elizabeth II when Princess

113 Atlantic Salmon

114 Newfoundland Dog

115 Harp Seal

116 Cape Race

117 Sealing Fleet

118 Fishing Fleet

(Recess P.B.)

1932 (2 Jan). W **106** (*sideways* on vert designs*). P 13½ (*comb*).
209	107	1 c. green	..	..	2·00	15
		a. Imperf (pair)	..	..	90·00	
		b. Perf 13 (line)	..	..	22·00	32·00
		ba. Imperf between (vert pair)			£110	
210	108	2 c. carmine ..	..	..	1·50	10
		a. Imperf (pair)	..	..	95·00	
		c. Perf 13 (line)	..	..	15·00	23·00
211	109	3 c. orange-brown	..	..	1·50	10
		a. Imperf (pair)	..	..	85·00	
		c. Perf 13 (line)	..	..	24·00	26·00
		d. Perf 14 (line). Small holes			18·00	20·00
		da. Imperf between (vert pair)			£140	
212	110	4 c. bright violet	..	..	4·75	1·50
213	111	5 c. maroon	..	..	2·25	80
		a. Imperf (pair)	..	..	£150	
		w. Wmk top of shield to right				
214	112	6 c. light blue	..	..	4·00	13·00
215	113	10 c. black-brown	..	..	70	30
		a. Imperf (pair)	..	..	70·00	
		w. Wmk inverted	..	..	10·00	
216	114	14 c. black	..	..	3·00	3·25
		a. Imperf (pair)	..	..	£120	
217	115	15 c. claret	..	..	1·25	1·75
		a. Imperf (pair)	..	..	£130	
		b. Perf 14 (line)	..	..	8·00	10·00
218	116	20 c. green	..	..	1·00	80
		a. Imperf (pair)	..	..	£120	
		b. Perf 14 (line)	..	..	50·00	48·00
		w. Wmk inverted	..	..	20·00	
219	117	25 c. slate	..	..	2·00	2·00
		a. Imperf (pair)	..	..	£130	
		b. Perf 14 (line)	..	..	20·00	35·00
		ba. Imperf between (vert pair)			£275	
220	118	30 c. ultramarine	..	..	25·00	25·00
		a. Imperf (pair)	..	..	£325	
		b. Imperf between (vert pair)			£600	
		c. Perf 14 (line)	..	..	£225	
209/20			..	*Set of* 12	45·00	42·00

*The normal sideways watermark shows the top of the shield to left, *as seen from the back of the stamp*.

Nos. 209b, 210c and 211c were only issued in stamp booklets. For similar stamps in different perforations see Nos. 222/8c and 276/89.

TRANS-ATLANTIC WEST TO EAST Per Dornier DO-X May, 1932. One Dollar and Fifty Cents

(119)

1932 (19 May). *Air. No.* 197 *surch as* T **119**, *by Messrs. D. R. Thistle.* P 14.
221	105	$1.50 on $1 deep blue (R.)	..		£180	£225
		a. Surch inverted	..	..	£9500	

120 Queen Mother, when Duchess of York

121 Paper Mills

122 Bell Island

(Recess P.B.)

1932 (15 Aug)–**38**. W **106** (*sideways* on vert designs*). P 13½ (*comb*).
222	107	1 c. grey	..	..	70	10
		a. Imperf (pair)	..	..	40·00	
		c. Perf 14 (line)	..	..	6·00	8·00
		d. Perf 14 (line). Small holes			15·00	22·00
		e. Pair, with and without wmk			40·00	
		w. Wmk top of shield to right			50·00	
223	108	2 c. green ..	..	..	40	10
		a. Imperf (pair)	..	..	35·00	
		c. Perf 14 (line)	..	..	7·00	8·00
		ca. Imperf between (horiz pair)			£250	
		d. Perf 14 (line). Small holes			17·00	20·00
		e. Pair, with and without wmk			40·00	
		w. Wmk top of shield to right			35·00	
224	110	4 c. carmine (21.7.34)	..	..	1·60	30
		a. Imperf (pair)	..	..	50·00	
		b. Perf 14 (line)	..	..	3·25	4·00
		ba. Imperf between (horiz or vert pair)			£120	
		w. Wmk top of shield to right			50·00	
225	111	5 c. violet (Die I)	..	..	2·00	1·50
		a. Imperf (pair)	..	..	55·00	
		b. Perf 14 (line). Small holes			23·00	19·00
		c. Die II	..	..	70	80
		ca. Imperf (pair)	..	..	60·00	
		cb. Perf 14 (line)	..	..	20·00	16·00
		cc. Imperf between (horiz pair)			£190	
		cd. Pair, with and without wmk			£120	
		cw. Wmk top of shield to right				
226	120	7 c. red-brown	..	..	2·00	2·75
		b. Perf 14 (line)	..	..	£120	
		ba. Imperf between (horiz pair)			£450	
		c. Pair, with and without wmk			£140	
227	121	8 c. brownish red	..	..	3·00	1·75
		a. Imperf (pair)	..	..	85·00	
228	122	24 c. bright blue	..	..	60	2·50
		a. Imperf (pair)	..	..	£180	
		b. Doubly printed	..	..	£750	
228c	118	48 c. red-brown (1.1.38)	..	..	4·50	9·50
		ca. Imperf (pair)	..	..	85·00	
222/8c				*Set of* 8	12·00	15·00

*The normal sideways watermark shows the top of the shield to left, *as seen from the back of the stamp*.

No. 223. Two dies exist of the 2 c. Die I was used for No. 210 and both dies for No. 223. The differences, though numerous, are very slight.

No. 225. There are also two dies of the 5 c., Die I only being used for No. 213 and both dies for the violet stamp. In Die II the antler pointing to the "T" of "POSTAGE" is taller than the one pointing to the "S" and the individual hairs on the underside of the caribou's tail are distinct.

For similar stamps in a slightly larger size and perforated 12½ or 13½ (5 c.) see Nos. 276/89.

(123) "L.&S."—Land and Sea

1933 (9 Feb). *No.* 195 *optd with* T **123** *for ordinary postal use, by Messrs D. R. Thistle.* W **106** (*sideways*). P 14.
229	103	15 c. chocolate	..	..	2·50	8·00
		a. Pair, one without wmk	..		23·00	
		b. Opt reading up	..	..	£1400	
		c. Vertical pair, one without surch			£2250	

124 Put to Flight

125 Land of Hearts Delight

(Des J. Scott. Recess P.B.)

1933 (31 May). *Air.* T **124/5** *and similar horiz designs.* W **106** (*sideways*). P 14 (5, 30, 75 c.) or 11½ (10, 60 c.).
230		5 c. red-brown	..	..	12·00	15·00
		a. Imperf (pair)	..	..	£160	
		b. Imperf between (horiz or vert pair)			£900	
231		10 c. orange-yellow	..	..	8·00	22·00
		a. Imperf (pair)	..	..	£130	
232		30 c. light blue	..	..	27·00	38·00
		a. Imperf (pair)	..	..	£375	
233		60 c. green	..	..	45·00	75·00
		a. Imperf (pair)	..	..	£425	
234		75 c. yellow-brown ..	..	..	45·00	70·00
		a. Imperf (pair)	..	..	£375	
		b. Imperf between (horiz or vert pair)			£1600	
230/4				*Set of* 5	£110	£200

Designs:—30 c. Spotting the herd; 60 c. News from home; 75 c. Labrador.

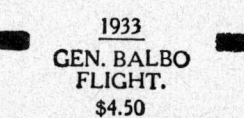

1933 GEN. BALBO FLIGHT. $4.50

(129)

(Surch by Robinson & Co, St. John's)

1933 (24 July). *Air. Balbo Transatlantic Mass Formation Flight. No.* 234 *surch with* T **129.** W **106.** P 14.
235		$4.50 on 75 c. yellow-brown ..	..	..	£250	£300
		a. Surch inverted	..	..	£23000	
		b. Surch on 10 c. (No. 231).	..		£23000	

No. 235a. When this error was discovered the stamps were ordered to be officially destroyed but four copies which had been torn were recovered and skilfully repaired. In addition four undamaged examples exist and the price quoted is for one of these.

130 Sir Humphrey Gilbert   131 Compton Castle, Devon   132 Gilbert Coat of Arms

(Recess P.B.)

1933 (3 Aug). *350th Anniv of the Annexation by Sir Humphrey Gilbert. T* **130/2** *and similar designs. W* **106** *(sideways* on vert designs). P* 13½ *(comb†).*

236	1 c. slate	..	..	..	70	90
	a. Imperf (pair)	..			45·00	
237	2 c. green	..			1·00	50
	a. Imperf (pair)	..			48·00	
	b. Doubly printed	..	..		£300	
238	3 c. chestnut	..	..		1·75	1·00
239	4 c. carmine	..			80	40
	a. Imperf (pair)	..			45·00	
240	5 c. violet	..			2·00	70
241	7 c. greenish blue	..			9·00	14·00
	a. Perf 14 (line)	..			10·00	35·00
242	8 c. vermilion	..			7·00	10·00
	a. *Brownish red*	..	..		£275	
	b. Bisected (4 c.) (on cover)	..		†	£375
243	9 c. ultramarine	..			7·00	8·00
	a. Imperf (pair)	..			£190	
	b. Perf 14 (line)	..			38·00	48·00
244	10 c. brown-lake	..			4·00	6·50
	a. Imperf (pair)	..			£300	
	b. Perf 14 (line)	..			48·00	50·00
245	14 c. grey-black	..			12·00	30·00
	a. Perf 14 (line)	..			17·00	48·00
246	15 c. claret	..			7·50	14·00
247	20 c. grey-green	..			13·00	14·00
	a. Perf 14 (line)	..			18·00	28·00
248	24 c. maroon	..			11·00	22·00
	a. Imperf (pair)	..			£110	
	b. Perf 14 (line)	..			22·00	35·00
	w. Wmk top of shield to right	..		35·00	
249	32 c. olive-black	..			7·00	45·00
	a. Perf 14 (line)	..			22·00	60·00
	w. Wmk top of shield to right	..		40·00	
236/49				*Set of* 14	65·00	£150

Designs: *Horiz*—4 c. Eton College; 7 c. Gilbert commissioned by Elizabeth; 8 c. Fleet leaving Plymouth, 1583; 9 c. Arrival at St. John's; 10 c. Annexation, 5 August 1583; 20 c. Map of Newfoundland. *Vert*—5 c. Anchor token; 14 c. Royal Arms; 15 c. Gilbert in the *Squirrel*; 24 c. Queen Elizabeth I. 32 c. Gilbert's statue at Truro.

*The normal sideways watermark shows the top of the shield to left, *as seen from the back of the stamp.*

†Exact gauges for the two perforations are: 13½ comb = 13.4; 14 line = 13.8.

1935 (6 May). *Silver Jubilee. As Nos.* 91/4 *of Antigua, but ptd by B.W. P* 11 × 12.

250	4 c. rosine	..	..	1·00	1·60
251	5 c. bright violet	..	..	1·25	1·60
252	7 c. blue	..	..	1·50	5·50
253	24 c. olive-green	..	..	5·00	5·50
250/3	..	..	*Set of* 4	8·00	13·00
250/3 Perf "Specimen"		*Set of* 4	£120	

1937 (12 May). *Coronation Issue. As Nos.* 95/7 *of Antigua, but name and value uncoloured on coloured background. P* 11×11½.

254	2 c. green	..	..	1·00	2·25
255	4 c. carmine	..	..	1·60	2·75
256	5 c. purple	..	..	3·00	2·75
254/6			*Set of* 3	5·00	7·00
254/6 Perf "Specimen"		*Set of* 3	70·00	

144 Atlantic Cod

Die I   Die II

No. 258. In Die II the shading of the King's face is heavier and dots have been added down the ridge of the nose. The top frame line is thicker and more uniform.

NEW INFORMATION

The editor is always interested to correspond with people who have new information that will improve or correct the Catalogue.

Fish-hook flaw (R. 1/7 or 3/3)

Re-entry to right of design (inscr oval, tree and value) (R.4/8)

Extra chimney (R. 6/5)

(Recess P.B.)

1937 (12 May). *Additional Coronation Issue. T* **144** *and similar horiz designs. W* **106**. A. *P* 14–13½ *(line).* B. *P* 13 *(comb)*.*

				A		B	
257	1 c. grey	..	..	1·75	20	23·00	40·00
	a. Pair, with and without wmk		19·00	—	—	—
	b. Fish-hook flaw	..	..	16·00	—	£170	—
258	3 c. orange-brown (I)	..	3·75	2·00	3·00	2·00
	a. Pair, with and without wmk		50·00	—		†
	b. Die I. Imperf between (horiz or vert pair)	..	£350	—		†
	c. Die II	..	..	3·00	2·75	4·50	2·00
	d. Die II. Imperf between (horiz or vert pair)	..	£450	—		†
	e. Die II. Pair, with and without wmk		—	—	85·00	—
259	7 c. bright ultramarine	..	2·00	75	£250	£325
	a. Pair, with and without wmk		—	—		†
	b. Re-entry at right	..	40·00	—		†
260	8 c. scarlet	..	..	1·75	2·25	6·00	7·00
	a. Pair, with and without wmk		50·00	—		†
	b. Imperf between (horiz or vert pair)	..	£500	—		†
	c. Imperf (pair)	..	..	£250	—		†
261	10 c. blackish brown	..	3·25	5·50	3·25	9·00
	a. Pair, with and without wmk		60·00	—		†
	w. Wmk inverted	..	..	—	†	75·00	—
262	14 c. black	..	..	1·40	2·00	£4250	£2250
	a. Pair, with and without wmk		45·00	—		†
263	15 c. claret	..	..	8·50	4·00	17·00	18·00
	a. Pair, with and without wmk		60·00	—	90·00	—
	b. Imperf between (vert pair)	..	£350	—		†
	w. Wmk inverted	..	..	75·00	—		†
264	20 c. green	..	..	2·25	4·75	2·50	7·00
	a. Pair, with and without wmk		£100	—		†
	b. Imperf between (vert pair)	..	£600	—		†
	c. Extra chimney	..	35·00	—	38·00	—
	w. Wmk inverted	..	85·00	—		†
265	24 c. light blue	..	..	2·25	2·50	19·00	19·00
	a. Pair, with and without wmk		£100	—		†
	b. Imperf between (vert pair)	..	£600	—		†
266	25 c. slate	..	..	2·75	1·75	20·00	35·00
	a. Pair, with and without wmk		£100	—		†
267	48 c. slate-purple	..	8·50	4·50	29·00	48·00
	a. Pair, with and without wmk		£140	—		†
	b. Imperf between (vert pair)	..	£600	—		†
257/67			*Set of* 11	32·00	27·00		

Designs:—3 c. Map of Newfoundland; 7 c. Reindeer; 8 c. Corner Brook paper mills; 10 c. Atlantic Salmon; 14 c. Newfoundland dog; 15 c. Harp Seal; 20 c. Cape Race; 24 c. Bell Island; 25 c. Sealing fleet; 48 c. The Banks fishing fleet.

*The line perforation A was produced by two machines measuring respectively 13.7 and 14.1. The comb perforation B measures 13.3×13.2.

Four used examples of No. 259B have now been identified on separate covers.

The paper used had the watermarks spaced for smaller format stamps. In consequence the individual watermarks are out of alignment so that stamps from the second vertical row were frequently without watermark.

155 King George VI   156 Queen Mother

Damaged "A" (R. 5/9)

(Recess P.B.)

1938 (12 May). *T.* **155/6** *and similar vert designs. W* **106** *(sideways). P* 13½ *(comb).*

268	2 c. green	..	..	1·50	50
	a. Pair, with and without wmk	..	£130	
	b. Imperf (pair)	..	..	75·00	
269	3 c. carmine	..	..	1·00	50·
	a. Perf 14 (line)	..	..	£325	£190
	b. Pair, with and without wmk	..	£180	
	c. Imperf (pair)	..	..	70·00	
	d. Damaged "A"	..	..	38·00	
270	4 c. light blue	..	..	1·75	20
	a. Pair, with and without wmk	..	80·00	
	b. Imperf (pair)	..	..	70·00	
	w. Wmk inverted	..	..	65·00	
271	7 c. deep ultramarine	..	75	3·50
	a. Imperf (pair)	..	..	95·00	
268/71			*Set of* 4	4·50	4·25

Designs:— 4 c. Queen Elizabeth II as princess; 7 c. Queen Mary. For similar designs, perf 12½, see Nos. 277/281.

159 King George VI and Queen Elizabeth

(Recess B.W.)

1939 (17 June). *Royal Visit. No wmk. P* 13½.

272	159	5 c. deep ultramarine	..	1·25	30

2

▲   **CENTS**   ▲

(160)

1939 (20 Nov). *No.* 272 *surch as T* **160**, *at St. John's.*

273	159	2 c. on 5 c. deep ultramarine (Br.)	1·75	30
274		4 c. on 5 c. deep ultramarine (C.)	..	90	50

161 Grenfell on the *Strathcona* (after painting by Gribble)   162 Memorial University College

(Recess C.B.N.)

1941 (1 Dec). *Sir Wilfred Grenfell's Labrador Mission. P* 12.

275	161	5 c. blue	..	30	50

(Recess Waterlow)

1941–44. *W* **106** *(sideways* on vert designs). P* 12½ *(line).*

276	107	1 c. grey	..	20	30
277	155	2 c. green	..	30	20
		w. Wmk top of shield to right	35·00	
278	156	3 c. carmine	..	30	10
		a. Pair, with and without wmk	75·00	
		w. Wmk top of shield to right	35·00	
279	—	4 c. blue (As No. 270)	2·25	20
		a. Pair, with and without wmk	£140	
		w. Wmk top of shield to right	35·00	
280	111	5 c. violet (Die I) (*p* 13½ comb)	90·00	
		a. Perf 12½ (line) (6.42)	..	2·75	30
		ab. Pair, with and without wmk	£120	
		ac. Printed double	..	£300	
		ad. Imperf vert (horiz pair)	..	£325	
		b. Imperf (pair)	..	£120	
281	—	7 c. deep ultramarine (As No. 271)	6·00	8·50
		a. Pair, with and without wmk	£150	
282	121	8 c. rose-red	..	1·00	1·75
		a. Pair, with and without wmk	£140	
283	113	10 c. black-brown	..	1·75	75
284	114	14 c. black	..	2·00	5·00
285	115	15 c. claret	..	5·50	7·00
286	116	20 c. green	..	5·50	5·50
287	122	24 c. blue	..	3·25	10·00
		w. Wmk top of shield to right	55·00	

288	117	25 c. slate	.. ..	6·50	7·50
289	118	48 c. red-brown (1944)	..	3·00	5·50
276/89			*Set of* 14	35·00	48·00

*The normal sideways watermark shows the top of the shield to left, *as seen from the back of the stamp.*

Nos. 276/89 are redrawn versions of previous designs with slightly larger dimensions; the 5 c. for example, measures 21 mm in width as opposed to the 20.4 mm of the Perkins Bacon printings.

No. 280. For Die I see note relating to No. 225.

(Recess C.B.N.)

1943 (2 Jan). *P* 12.

290	162	30 c. carmine	.. ..	1·00	1·10

163 St. John's

TWO CENTS

(164)

(Recess C.B.N.)

1943 (1 June). *Air. P* 12.

291	163	7 c. ultramarine	.. ..	40	55

1946 (21 Mar). *No. 290 surch locally with T* 164.

292	162	2 c. on 30 c. carmine	..	30	55

165 Queen Elizabeth II when Princess   166 Cabot off Cape Bonavista

(Recess Waterlow)

1947 (21 Apr). *Princess Elizabeth's 21st Birthday. W* 106 (*sideways*). *P* 12½.

293	165	4 c. light blue	.. ..	30	55
		a. Imperf vert (horiz pair) ..	..	£250	

(Recess Waterlow)

1947 (23 June). *450th Anniv of Cabot's Discovery of Newfoundland. W* 106 (*sideways*). *P* 12½.

294	166	5 c. mauve	.. ..	20	70
		a. Imperf between (horiz pair)	..	£1200	

STAMP BOOKLETS

1926. *Black on pink cover with Ayers and Sons advertisement on front. Stapled.*

SB1   40 c. booklet containing eight 1 c. and sixteen 2 c. (Nos. 149/50) in blocks of 8 .. .. £1200

B 1

1932 (2 Jan). *Black on buff cover as Type B* 1. *Stapled.*

SB2   40 c. booklet containing four 1 c., twelve 2 c. and four 3 c. (Nos. 209b, 210c, 211c) in blocks of 4 £400
   a. Contents as No. SB2, but containing Nos. 209b, 210 and 211c £475
   b. Contents as No. SB2, but containing Nos. 222d, 223d and 211d £425

B 2

1932. *Black on cream cover as Type B* 2. *Stapled.*

SB3   40 c. booklet containing four 1 c., twelve 2 c. and four 3 c. (Nos. 222, 223, 211) in blocks of 4 £350

POSTAGE DUE STAMPS

D 1   D 6ac

(Litho John Dickinson & Co, Ltd)

1939 (1 May)–49. *P* 10.

D1	D 1	1 c. green	.. ..	2·00	7·50
		a. Perf 11 (1949) ..	..	3·00	8·50
D2		2 c. vermilion	..	9·00	6·50
		a. Perf 11 × 9 (1946) ..		9·00	17·00
D3		3 c. ultramarine	..	4·50	18·00
		a. Perf 11 × 9 (1949)	..	10·00	25·00
		b. Perf 9	..	£475	
D4		4 c. orange	..	8·00	15·00
		a. Perf 11 × 9 (May 1948)		11·00	45·00
D5		5 c. brown	..	5·50	22·00
D6		10 c. violet	..	6·00	15·00
		a. Perf 11 (W 106) (1949)	..	22·00	70·00
		ab. Ditto. Imperf between (vert pair)	..	£650	
		ac. "POSTAGE LUE" (R 3/3 or 3/8)	..	£100	£250
D1/6			*Set of* 6	32·00	75·00

Newfoundland joined the Dominion of Canada on 31 March 1949.

NOVA SCOTIA

Organised postal services in Nova Scotia date from April 1754 when the first of a series of Deputy Postmasters was appointed, under the authority of the British G.P.O. This arrangement continued until 6 July 1851 when the colony assumed responsibility for its postal affairs.

For illustrations of the handstamp types see BRITISH POST OFFICES ABROAD notes, following GREAT BRITAIN.

AMHERST

CROWNED-CIRCLE HANDSTAMPS

CC1   CC 1   AMHERST. N.S.(R) (25.2.1845)
     Price on cover   £1000

ST. MARGARETS BAY

CROWNED-CIRCLE HANDSTAMPS

CC2   CC 1   ST. MARGARETS BAY. N.S.(R) (30.6.1845)
     Price on cover   £9000

Nos. CC1/2 were later used during temporary shortages of stamps, struck in red or black.

PRICES FOR STAMPS ON COVER	
No. 1	*from* × 5
Nos. 2/4	*from* × 2
Nos. 5/8	*from* × 4
Nos. 9/10	*from* × 10
Nos. 11/13	*from* × 2
Nos. 14/15	—
No. 16	*from* × 4
Nos. 17/19	*from* × 10
Nos. 20/5	*from* × 2
No. 26	*from* × 50
Nos. 27/8	*from* × 4
No. 29	*from* × 10

1   2

Crown and Heraldic Flowers of United Kingdom and Mayflower of Nova Scotia.

(Recess P.B.)

1851 (1 Sept)–57. *Bluish paper. Imperf.*

1	1	1d. red-brown (12.5.53)	..	£2000	£400
		a. Bisected (½d.) (on cover)	..	†£50000	
2	2	3d. deep blue	..	£1200	£200
		a. Bisected (1½d.) (on cover)	..	† £2250	
3		3d. bright blue	..	£900	£110
		a. Bisected (1½d.) (on cover)	..	† £2250	
4		3d. pale blue (1857)	..	£700	£130
		a. Bisected (1½d.) (on cover)	..	† £2250	
5		6d. yellow-green	..	£4000	£400
		a. Bisected (3d.) (on cover)	..	† £3000	
6		6d. deep green (1857)	..	£10000	£750
		a. Bisected (3d.) (on cover)	..	† £5000	
		b. Quartered (1½d.) (on cover)	..	†£38000	

7	2	1s. cold violet..	..	£19000	£600
		a. Bisected (6d.) (on cover)	..	†£4200	
		b. Quartered (3d.) (on cover)	..	†£5500	
7c		1s. deep purple (1851)	..	£15000	£375
		d. Watermarked	..	£20000	£600
8		1s. purple (1857)	..	£14000	£250
		a. Bisected (6d.) (on cover)	..	†£32000	

The watermark on No. 7d consists of the whole or part of a letter from the name "P. H. SAUNDERS" (the papermakers).

The stamps formerly catalogued on almost white paper are probably some from which the bluish paper has been discharged.

Reprints of all four values were made in 1890 on thin, hard, white paper. The 1d. is brown, the 3d. blue, the 6d. deep green, and the 1s. violet-black.

The 3d. bisects are usually found used on cover to make up the 7½d. rate.

(New Currency. 100 cents = 1 dollar)

3   4   5

(Recess American Bank Note Co, New York)

1860–63. *P* 12. (a) *Yellowish paper.*

9	3	1 c. jet black	..	3·00	12·00
		a. Bisected (½ c.) (on cover)		†	£1000
10		1 c. grey-black	..	3·00	12·00
11		2 c. grey-purple	..	11·00	15·00
11a		2 c. purple	..	17·00	14·00
12		5 c. blue	..	£275	16·00
13		5 c. deep blue	..	£275	16·00
14	4	8½ c. deep green	..		2·50
15		8½ c. yellow-green	..		2·50
16		10 c. scarlet	..	12·00	23·00
17	5	12½ c. black	..	26·00	26·00
17a		12½ c. greyish black	..	—	26·00

(b) *White paper*

18	3	1 c. black	..	3·00	12·00
		a. Imperf vert (horiz pair) ..		£150	
19		1 c. grey	..	3·00	12·00
20		2 c. dull purple	..	3·25	14·00
21		2 c. purple	..	3·25	14·00
22		2 c. grey-purple	..	3·25	14·00
		a. Bisected (1 c.) (on cover)		†	£4500
23		2 c. slate-purple	..	3·25	12·00
24		5 c. blue	..	£300	16·00
25		5 c. deep blue	..	£300	16·00
26	4	8½ c. deep green	..	17·00	40·00
27		10 c. scarlet	..	4·00	20·00
28		10 c. vermilion	..	4·00	20·00
		a. Bisected (5 c.) (on cover)		†	£750
29	5	12½ c. black	..	32·00	28·00

Nova Scotia joined the Dominion of Canada on 1 July 1867.

PRINCE EDWARD ISLAND

Prince Edward Island, previously administered as part of Nova Scotia, became a separate colony in 1769.

PRICES FOR STAMPS ON COVER	
Nos. 1/4	*from* × 3
Nos. 5/6	—
Nos. 7/8	*from* × 5
Nos. 9/20	*from* × 6
Nos. 21/6	*from* × 3
Nos. 27/31	*from* × 6
Nos. 32/3	*from* × 50
Nos. 34/45	*from* × 6
Nos. 46/7	*from* × 5

1   2   3

4   5   6

Two Dies of 2d:

Die I. Left-hand frame and circle merge at centre left (all stamps in the sheet of 60 (10×6) except R. 2/5)

Die II. Left-hand frame and circle separate at centre left (R. 2/5). There is also a break in the top frame line.

(Typo Charles Whiting, London)

1861 (1 Jan). *Yellowish toned paper.* (a) *P* 9.

1	1	2d. rose (I)	..	£225	£120
		a. Imperf between (horiz pair)	..	£4000	
		b. Imperf horiz (vert pair)	..		
		c. Bisected (1d.) (on cover)	..		
		d. Die II	..		

2	1	2d. rose-carmine (I)		£250	£130
		a. Die II		£450	£225
3	2	3d. blue		£450	£225
		a. Bisected (1½d.) (on cover)		†	£2750
		b. Double print		£1200	
4	3	6d. yellow-green		£650	£325

(b) Rouletted

5	1	2d. rose (I)		£2500	£1800

The 2d. and 3d., perf 9, were authorised to be bisected and used for half their normal value.

1862. *Yellowish toned paper.* P 11.

6	4	1d. brown-orange		28·00	50·00
7	6	9d. bluish lilac (29.3.62)		60·00	40·00
8		9d. dull mauve		60·00	40·00

1863–68. *Yellowish toned paper.* (a) P 11½–12

9	4	1d. yellow-orange		22·00	27·00
		a. Bisected (½d.) (on cover)		†	£1600
		b. Imperf between (horiz pair)		£250	
10		1d. orange-buff		23·00	27·00
11		1d. yellow		24·00	27·00
12	1	2d. rose (I)		8·00	8·50
		a. Imperf vert (horiz pair)			
		b. Bisected (1d.) (on cover)		†	£1400
		c. Die II		75·00	80·00
13		2d. deep rose (I)		8·50	11·00
		a. Die II		80·00	90·00
14	2	3d. blue		14·00	14·00
		a. Imperf horiz (vert pair)			
		b. Bisected (1½d.) (on cover)			
15		3d. deep blue		14·00	12·00
16	5	4d. black (1867)		14·00	18·00
		a. Imperf vert (horiz pair)			
		b. Bisected (2d.) (on cover)		†	£1400
17	3	6d. yellow-green (15.12.66)		70·00	55·00
		a. Bisected (3d.) (on cover)		†	£2250
18		6d. blue-green (1868)		55·00	60·00
19	6	9d. lilac		45·00	40·00
20		9d. reddish mauve		40·00	40·00
		a. Imperf vert (horiz pair)		£350	
		b. Bisected (4½d.) (on cover)		†	£1800

(b) Perf compound of 11 and 11½–12

21	4	1d. yellow-orange		£150	65·00
22	1	2d. rose (I)		£150	65·00
		a. Die II			
23	2	3d. blue		£170	65·00
24	5	4d. black		£190	£180
25	3	6d. yellow-green		£170	£180
26	6	9d. reddish mauve		£180	£180

1870. *Coarse, wove bluish white paper.* P 11½–12.

27	1	2d. rose (I)		9·00	10·00
		a. Die II		85·00	95·00
28		2d. rose-pink (I)		5·50	8·00
		a. Die II		65·00	70·00
		b. "TWC" (R. 6/4)		65·00	75·00
		c. Imperf between (horiz pair)		£120	
29	2	3d. pale blue		8·00	9·00
30		3d. blue		8·00	9·00
		a. Imperf between (horiz pair)		£275	
31	5	4d. black		4·00	26·00
		a. Imperf between (horiz pair)		£120	
		b. Bisected (2d.) (on cover)		†	£1500
		c. Perf compound 11 and 11½–12			

7

(Recess British-American Bank Note Co., Montreal and Ottawa)

1870 (1 June). P 12.

32	7	4½d. (3d. stg), yellow-brown		35·00	42·00
33		4½d. (3d. stg), deep brown		38·00	45·00

(New Currency. 100 cents = 1 dollar)

8	9	10

11	12	13

(Typo Charles Whiting, London)

1872 (1 Jan). (a) P 11½–12.

34	8	1 c. orange		3·50	11·00
35		1 c. yellow-orange		3·50	9·00
36		1 c. brown-orange		4·00	12·00
37	10	3 c. rose		17·00	17·00
		a. Stop between "PRINCE. EDWARD"		38·00	45·00
		b. Bisected (1½ c.) (on cover)			
		c. Imperf horiz (vert pair)		£325	

(b) Perf 12 to 12¼, large holes

38	9	2 c. blue		10·00	30·00
		a. Bisected (1 c.) (on cover)			
39	11	4 c. yellow-green		4·00	15·00
40		4 c. deep green		4·50	13·00
		a. Bisected (2 c.) (on cover)		†	£2000
41	12	6 c. black		3·50	14·00
		a. Bisected (3 c.) (on cover)		†	£950
		b. Imperf between (horiz pair)		£200	
		c. Imperf vert (horiz pair)			
42	13	12 c. reddish mauve		3·50	25·00

(c) P 12½–13, smaller holes

43	8	1 c. orange		12·00	
44		1 c. brown-orange		4·00	11·00
45	10	3 c. rose		13·00	20·00
		a. Stop between "PRINCE. EDWARD"		50·00	65·00
45b	12	6 c. black		—	£250

(d) Perf compound of (a) and (c) 11½–12 × 12½–13

46	8	1 c. orange		30·00	32·00
47	10	3 c. rose		32·00	32·00
		a. Stop between "PRINCE. EDWARD"		£170	£180

Prince Edward Island joined the Dominion of Canada on 1 July 1873.

DOMINION OF CANADA

On July 1867, Canada, Nova Scotia and New Brunswick were united to form the Dominion of Canada.

The provinces of Manitoba (1870), British Columbia (1871), Prince Edward Island (1873), Alberta (1905), Saskatchewan (1905), and Newfoundland (1949) were subsequently added, as were the Northwest Territories (1870) and Yukon Territory (1898).

PRICES FOR STAMPS ON COVER TO 1945	
Nos. 46/61c	*from* × 2
Nos. 62/7b	*from* × 3
Nos. 68/75b	*from* × 2
No. 76/c	*from* × 10
No. 77/a	*from* × 3
Nos. 78/83	*from* × 3
Nos. 115/20	*from* × 6
Nos. 121/49	*from* × 3
Nos. 150/65	*from* × 2
Nos. 166/72	*from* × 3
Nos. 173/87	*from* × 5
Nos. 188/95	*from* × 2
Nos. 196/215	*from* × 3
Nos. 219/224b	*from* × 4
Nos. 225/45	*from* × 2
Nos. 246/55	*from* × 8
Nos. 256/310	*from* × 2
No. 312	*from* × 20
No. 313	*from* × 10
Nos. 315/18	*from* × 2
Nos. 319/28	*from* × 3
Nos. 329/40	*from* × 2
Nos. 341/400	*from* × 1
Nos. R1/11	*from* × 5
Nos. S1/3	*from* × 8
No. S4	*from* × 6
No. S5	*from* × 5
Nos. S6/11	*from* × 3
Nos. S12/14	*from* × 5
Nos. D1/8	*from* × 4
Nos. D9/13	*from* × 5
Nos. D14/24	*from* × 4

13	14

Large types

PRINTERS. Nos. 46/120 were recess-printed by the British American Bank Note Co at Ottawa or Montreal.

1868 (Mar)–**71.** *As T* 13 *and* 14 *(various frames). Ottawa printings.* P 12.

(a) Thin rather transparent crisp paper

46	13	½ c. black		65·00	50·00
47	14	1 c. red-brown		£325	48·00
48		2 c. grass-green		£350	38·00
49		3 c. red-brown		£600	20·00
50		6 c. blackish brown		£850	£250
51		12½ c. bright blue		£500	£150
52		15 c. deep reddish purple		£750	£200

In these first printings the impression is generally blurred and the lines of the background are less clearly defined than in later printings.

(b) Medium to stout wove paper (1868–71)

53	13	½ c. black		45·00	45·00
54		½ c. grey-black		45·00	45·00
		a. Imperf between (pair)			
		b. Watermarked		£14000	£9000
55	14	1 c. red-brown		£300	40·00
		a. Laid paper		£6500	£1600
		b. Watermarked (1868)		£1800	£190
56		1 c. deep orange (Jan. 1869)		£700	75·00
56a		1 c. orange-yellow (May (?), 1869)		£650	60·00
56b		1 c. pale orange-yellow		£750	70·00
		ba. Imperf			

57	14	2 c. deep green		£325	25·00
57a		2 c. pale emerald-green (1871)		£375	32·00
		ab. Bisected (1 c. with 2 c. to make 3 c. rate) on cover		†	£4000
		ac. Laid paper		†	£50000
57d		2 c. bluish green		£325	25·00
		da. Watermarked (1868)		£1500	£200
58		3 c. brown-red		£650	15·00
		a. Laid paper		£6000	£300
		b. Watermarked (1868)		£2250	£160
59		6 c. blackish brown (to chocolate)		£700	32·00
		a. Watermarked (1868)		£3000	£600
59b		6 c. yellow-brown (1870)		£650	32·00
		ba. Bisected (3 c.), on cover		†	£2000
60		12½ c. bright blue		£400	35·00
		a. Imperf horiz (vert pair)		†	£6000
		b. Watermarked (1868)		£1600	£225
60c		12½ c. pale dull blue (milky)		£425	35·00
61		15 c. deep reddish purple		£450	60·00
61a		15 c. pale reddish purple		£400	60·00
		ab. Watermarked (1868)		—	£1200
61b		15 c. dull violet-grey		£200	28·00
		ba. Watermarked (1868)		£3000	£500
61c		15 c. dull grey-purple		£300	28·00

The watermark on the stout paper stamps consists of the words "E & G BOTHWELL CLUTHA MILLS," in large double-lined capitals. Portions of one or two letters only may be found on these stamps, which occur in the early printings of 1868.

The papers may, in most cases, be easily divided if the stamps are laid face downwards and carefully compared. The thin hard paper is more or less transparent and shows the design through the stamp; the thicker paper is softer to the feel and more opaque.

The paper of this issue may be still further subdivided in several values into sets on—(a) *Medium to stout wove.* (b) *Thin, soft, very white.* and (c) *Thinner and poorer quality, sometimes greyish or yellowish (from 1878 to end of issue).*

Of the 2 c. laid paper No. 57ac two examples only are known.

21

Small type

1870–91. *As T* 21 *(various frames). Ottawa (1870–73) and Montreal printings.* P 12 (or slightly under).
Papers (a) 1870–80. *Medium to stout wove.*
(b) 1870–72. *Thin, soft, very white.*
(c) 1878–97. *Thinner and poorer quality.*

62	21	1 c. bright orange (a, b) (1870–73)		£120	20·00
		a. Thick soft paper (1871)		£350	£120
62b		1 c. orange-yellow (a) (1876–79)		42·00	1·25
62c		1 c. pale dull yellow (a) (1877–79)		27·00	75
62d		1 c. bright yellow (a, c) (1878–97)		20·00	70
		da. Imperf (pair) (c)		£300	
		db. Bisected (½ c.) (on *Railway News*)		†	£3000
		dc. Printed both sides		£1400	
62e		1 c. lemon-yellow (c) (1880)		75·00	15·00
63		2 c. dp green (a, b) (1872–73 & 1876–78)		70·00	1·00
63a		2 c. grass-green (c) (1878–88)		40·00	70
		ab. Imperf (pair) (1891–93?)		£325	
		ac. Bisected (1 c. with 2 c. to make 3 c. rate) on cover		†	£1400
64		3 c. Indian red (a) (1.70)		£850	50·00
		a. Perf 12½ (2.70)		£4250	£500
64b		3 c. pale rose-red (9.70)		£275	8·00
64c		3 c. deep rose-red (a, b) (1870–73)		£300	8·50
		ca. Thick soft paper (Jan. 1871)		—	£150
64d		3 c. dull red (a, c) (1876–88)		55·00	1·25
64e		3 c. orange-red (a, c) (1876–88) (*shades*)		45·00	80
64f		3 c. rose-carm (c) (Oct 1888–April 1889)		£350	11·00
65		5 c. olive-green (a, c) (Feb, 1876–88)		£200	7·00
66		6 c. yellowish brown (a, b, e) (1872–73) and 1876–90)		£180	9·50
		a. Bisected (3 c.) on cover		†	£1600
		b. Perf 12×11½ (1873)		†	—
67		10 c. pale lilac-magenta (a) (1876–?)		£450	48·00
67a		10 c. deep lilac-magenta (a, c) (March, 1876–88)		£425	48·00
67b		10 c. lilac-pink (March, 1888)		£200	28·00

Nos. 62d and 63a were printed in the same shades during the second Ottawa period.

Examples of paper (a) can often be found showing traces of ribbing, especially on the 2 c. value.

No. 64a was issued in New Brunswick and Nova Scotia.

One used copy of the 10 c. perf 12½ has been reported.

22

1873–79. *As T* 13, 14, 21 *and* 22. *Montreal printings. Medium to stout wove paper.* P 11½×12 or 11¾×12.

68	13	½ c. black		55·00	55·00
69	21	1 c. bright orange		£180	22·00
69a		1 c. orange-yellow (1873–79)		£150	9·00
69b		1 c. pale dull yellow (1877–79)		£140	14·00
69c		1 c. lemon-yellow (1879)		£170	14·00
70		2 c. deep green (1873–78)		£190	15·00
71		3 c. dull red (1875–79)		£200	11·00
71a		3 c. orange-red (1873–79)		£200	11·00
72	22	5 c. olive-green (1 Oct, 1875)		£700	65·00
		a. Perf 12		£3500	£800
72b	21	5 c. olive-green (1876–79)		£375	22·00
73		6 c. yellowish brown (1873–79)		£375	24·00
74		10 c. very pale lilac-magenta (1874)		£850	£250
74a		10 c. deep lilac-magenta (1876–79)		£550	£170

289

75	14	15 c. dull grey-purple (1874)	..	£650	£225
75a		15 c. lilac-grey (Mar, 1877)	..	£850	£225
		ab. Script Wmk*	..	£9000	£2500
		ac. "BOTHWELL" watermark†		†	—
75b		15 c. slate	..	£850	£450

*The watermark on No. 75ab is part of the words "Alexr. Pirie & Sons" in script lettering, a very small quantity of paper thus watermarked having been used for printing this stamp.

†For description of this watermark see below No. 61c.

Several used examples of the 12½ c. have been reported in these perforations.

No. 72a gauges 12 or above on all four sides.

1879–88. *Montreal printings. Medium to stout wove paper. P 12.*

76	14	15 c. clear deep violet	..	.£2250	£500
76a		15 c. deep slate (1881)	..	£130	25·00
76b		15 c. slaty blue (1887)	..	£130	25·00
76c		15 c. slate-purple (*shades*) (July, 1888–92)		60·00	16·00

The last printing of No. 76c took place at Ottawa.

27

1882–97. *Montreal (to March 1889) and Ottawa printings. Thinnish paper of poor quality. P 12.*

77	27	½ c. black (July, 1882–97)	..	7·00	5·50
77a		½ c. grey-black	..	7·00	5·50
		ab. Imperf (pair) (1891–93?)		£400	
		ac. Imperf between (pair)	..	£700	

1889–97. *As T 14 and 21 (various frames). Ottawa printings. Thinnish paper of poor quality, often toned grey or yellowish. P 12.*

78	21	2 c. dull sea-green	..	35·00	70
78a		2 c. blue-green (July, 1889–91)		30·00	90
79		3 c. bright vermilion (April, 1889–97)		22·00	50
		a. Imperf (pair) (1891–93?)		£300	
80		5 c. brownish grey (May, 1889)	..	55·00	1·00
		a. Imperf (pair) (1891–93)		£400	
81		6 c. deep chestnut (Oct, 1890)	..	30·00	7·50
		a. "5 c." re-entry*		£2000	£1300
		b. Imperf (pair) (1891–93?)		£450	
81c		6 c. pale chestnut	..	30·00	7·50
82		10 c. salmon-pink	..	£225	£110
82a		10 c. carmine-pink (April, 1890)		£150	20·00
		ab. Imperf (pair) (1891–93?)		£450	
82b		10 c. brownish red (1894?)	..	£130	20·00
		ba. Imperf (pair)	..	£400	
83	14	15 c. slate-violet (*shades*) (May, 1890)		60·00	20·00
		a. Imperf (brown-purple) (pair)		£1000	

The 1 c. showed no change in the Ottawa printings, so is not included. The 2 c. reverted to its previous grass-green shade in 1891. The 15 c. stamps are generally found with yellowish streaky gum.

The 3 c. is known bisected and used as a ⅔ stamp for the 2 c. "drop letter" rate at Halifax in 1892.

28   29

(Recess B.A.B.N.)

1893 (17 Feb). *P 12.*

115	28	20 c. vermilion	..	£160	42·00
		a. Imperf (pair)		£1400	
116		50 c. blue	..	£225	24·00
		a. Imperf (Prussian blue) (pair)		£1400	

1893 (1 Aug). *P 12.*

117	29	8 c. pale bluish grey	..	80·00	3·50
		a. Imperf (pair)	..	£475	
118		8 c. bluish slate	..	85·00	3·50
119		8 c. slate-purple	..	75·00	3·50
120		8 c. blackish purple	..	70·00	3·50
		a. Imperf (pair)	..	£500	

PRINTERS. The following stamps to No. 287 were recess-printed by the American Bank Note Co, Ottawa, which in 1923 became the Canadian Bank Note Co.

30

(Des L. Pereira and F. Brownell)

1897 (19 June). *Jubilee issue. P 12.*

121	30	½ c. black	..	48·00	48·00
122		1 c. orange	..	8·50	3·25
123		1 c. orange-yellow	..	8·50	3·25
		a. Bisected (½ c.) on cover		£475	
124		2 c. green	..	12·00	7·00
125		2 c. deep green	..	12·00	7·00
126		3 c. carmine	..	8·50	1·75

127	30	5 c. slate-blue	..	32·00	12·00
128		5 c. deep blue	..	30·00	11·00
129		6 c. brown	..	85·00	85·00
130		8 c. slate-violet	..	32·00	29·00
131		10 c. purple	..	50·00	38·00
132		15 c. slate	..	85·00	85·00
133		20 c. vermilion	..	85·00	85·00
134		50 c. pale ultramarine		£120	95·00
135		50 c. bright ultramarine	..	£120	95·00
136		$1 lake	..	£400	£400
137		$2 deep violet	..	£700	£325
138		$3 bistre	..	£800	£650
139		$4 violet	..	£800	£600
140		$5 olive-green	..	£800	£600
121/40			*Set of 16*	£3500	£2500
133/40		Handstamped "Specimen"	*Set of 7*	£1800	

No 123a was used on issues of the *Railway News* of 5, 6 and 8 November 1897 and must be on a large part of the original newspaper with New Glasgow postmark.

31   32

(From photograph by W. & D. Downey, London)

1897–98. *P 12.*

141	31	½ c. grey-black (9.11.97)	..	5·00	3·50
142		½ c. black	..	6·50	4·25
		a. Imperf (pair)		£375	
143		1 c. blue-green (12.97)	..	17·00	60
		a. Imperf (pair)		£375	
144		2 c. violet (12.97)	..	17·00	1·00
		a. Imperf (pair)		£375	
145		3 c. carmine (1.98)	..	20·00	40
		a. Imperf (pair)		£700	
146		5 c. deep blue/*bluish* (12.97)		60·00	2·00
		a. Imperf (pair)		£375	
147		6 c. brown (12.97)	..	55·00	18·00
		a. Imperf (pair)		£700	
148		8 c. orange (12.97)	..	75·00	6·50
		a. Imperf (pair)		£400	
149		10 c. brownish purple (1.98)		£130	55·00
		a. Imperf (pair)		£425	
141/9			*Set of 8*	£325	75·00

BOOKLET PANES. Most definitive booklets issued from 1900 onwards had either the two horizontal sides or all three outer edges imperforate. Stamps from the panes show one side or two adjacent sides imperforate.

Two types of the 2 c.
Die Ia. Frame consists of four fine lines.
Die Ib. Frame has one thick line between two fine lines.

The die was retouched in 1900 for Plates 11 and 12 producing weak vertical frame lines and then retouched again in 1902 for Plates 15 to 20 resulting in much thicker frame lines. No. 155b covers both states of the retouching.

1898–1902. *P 12.*

150	32	½ c. black (9.98)	..	2·50	95
		a. Imperf (pair)		£375	
151		1 c. blue-green (6.98)	..	21·00	30
152		1 c. deep green/*toned paper*		21·00	30
		a. Imperf (pair)		£700	
153		2 c. dull purple (Die Ia) (9.98)		22·00	30
		a. Thick paper (6.99)		90·00	10·00
154		2 c. violet (Die Ia)	..	22·00	30
154a		2 c. reddish purple (Die Ia)		55·00	1·50
155		2 c. rose-carmine (Die Ia) (20.8.99)		28·00	30
		a. Imperf (pair)		£300	
155b		2 c. rose-carmine (Die Ib) (1900)		35·00	40
		ba. Booklet pane of 6 (11.6.00)		£750	
156		3 c. rose-carmine (6.98)		35·00	60
		a. Imperf (pair)		£750	
157		5 c. slate-blue/*bluish*	..	85·00	1·25
		a. Imperf (pair)		£750	
158		5 c. Prussian blue/*bluish*		90·00	1·25
159		6 c. brown (9.98)	..	85·00	48·00
		a. Imperf (pair)		£650	
160		7 c. greenish yellow (23.12.02)		50·00	10·00
161		8 c. orange-yellow (10.98)		£110	22·00
162		8 c. brownish orange	..	£100	22·00
		a. Imperf (pair)		£650	
163		10 c. pale brownish purple (11.98)		£160	13·00
164		10 c. deep brownish purple		£160	13·00
		a. Imperf (pair)		£650	
165		20 c. olive-green (29.12.00)		£325	48·00
150/65			*Set of 11*	£750	£120

The 7 c. and 20 c. also exist imperforate, but unlike the values listed in this condition, they have no gum. (Price, 7 c. £300, 20 c. £1400 *pair, un*).

33

(Des R. Weir Crouch, G. Hahn, A. H. Howard and R. Holmes. Eng C. Skinner. Design recess, colours added by typo)

1898 (7 Dec). *Imperial Penny Postage. Design in black. British possessions in red. Oceans in colours given. P 12.*

166	33	2 c. lavender	..	28·00	5·00
167		2 c. greenish blue	..	22·00	4·50
168		2 c. blue	..	22·00	4·25
		a. Imperf (pair)		£350	

Forgeries of Type 33 are without horizontal lines across the continents and have a forged Montreal postmark of 24.12.98.

1899 (4 Jan). *Provisionals used at Port Hood, Nova Scotia. No 156 divided vertically and handstamped.*

169	32	"1" in blue, on ⅓ of 3 c.	..	—	£350
170		"2" in violet, on ⅔ of 3 c.	..	—	£300

Nos. 169/70 were prepared by the local postmaster during shortage of 2 c. stamps caused by a change in postage rates.

2 CENTS

(34)   35 King Edward VII

1899. *Surch with T 34, by Public Printing Office.*

171	31	2 c. on 3 c. carmine (8 Aug)	..	11·00	7·0
		a. Surch inverted	..	£275	
172	32	2 c. on 3 c. rose-carmine (28 July)		15·00	3·5
		a. Surch inverted	..	£275	

(Des King George V when Prince of Wales and J. A. Tilleard)

1903 (1 July)–**12.** *P 12.*

173	35	1 c. pale green	..	19·00	3
174		1 c. deep green	..	17·00	3
175		1 c. green	..	17·00	3
176		2 c. rose-carmine	..	17·00	2
		a. Booklet pane of 6	..	£750	
177		2 c. pale rose-carmine	..	17·00	2
		a. Imperf (pair) (18.7.09)		28·00	32·0
178		5 c. blue/*bluish*	..	70·00	2·0
179		5 c. indigo/*bluish*	..	70·00	2·2
180		7 c. yellow-olive	..	55·00	2·2
181		7 c. greenish bistre	..	65·00	2·5
181a		7 c. straw (1.12)	..	£110	35·0
182		10 c. brown-lilac	..	£110	7·5
183		10 c. pale dull purple	..	£110	7·5
184		10 c. dull purple	..	£110	7·5
185		20 c. pale olive-green (27.9.04)		£225	22·0
186		20 c. deep olive-green (H/S S. £75)		£250	22·0
187		50 c. deep violet (19.11.08)		£350	75·0
173/87			*Set of 7*	£700	£10

The 1 c., 5 c., 7 c. and 10 c. exist imperforate but are believe to be proofs. (*Prices per pair*, 1 c. £400, 5 c. £600, 7 c. £400, 10 £600).

IMPERFORATE AND PART-PERFORATED SHEETS
Prior to 1946 many Canadian issues exist imperforate, or with other perforation varieties, in the colours of the issued stamps and usually, with gum. In the years before 1927 such examples ar believed to come from imprimatur sheets, removed from th Canadian Post Office archives. From 1927 until 1946 it is know that the printers involved in the production of the various issue submitted several imperforate plate proof sheets of each stamp t the Post Office authorities for approval. Some of these sheets or par sheets were retained for record purposes, but the remainder foun their way onto the philatelic market.

Part-perforated sheets also occur from 1927–29 issues.

From 1908 until 1946 we now only list and price such varietie of this type which are known to be genuine errors, sold from pos offices. Where other imperforate or similar varieties are know they are recorded in footnotes.

It is possible, and in some cases probable, that some imperforat varieties listed before 1908 may have also been removed from th archives as mentioned above, but it is far harder to be explicit ove the status of this earlier material.

36 King George V and Queen Mary when Prince and Princess of Wales   37 Jacques Cartier and Samuel Champlain

(Des Machado)

1908 (16 July). *Quebec Tercentenary T 36/7 and similar hori designs. P 12.*

188		½ c. sepia	..	3·25	2·7
189		1 c. blue-green	..	10·00	2·0
190		2 c. carmine	..	16·00	8
191		5 c. indigo	..	45·00	15·0
192		7 c. olive-green	..	48·00	32·0
193		10 c. violet	..	55·00	40·0
194		15 c. brown-orange	..	75·00	60·0
195		20 c. dull brown	..	£100	70·0
188/95			*Set of 8*	£300	£20

Designs:—2 c. King Edward VII and Queen Alexandra; 5 Champlain's House in Quebec; 7 c. Generals Montcalm and Wolfe 10 c. Quebec in 1700; 15 c. Champlain's departure for the Wes 20 c. Cartier's arrival before Quebec.

Some values exist on both toned and white papers.

Nos. 188/95 exist imperforate. (*Price £325, un, for each pair*)

WET AND DRY PRINTINGS. Until the end of December 192 all Canadian stamps were produced by the "wet" method of recess printing in which the paper was dampened before printing, drie and then gummed.

In late December 1922 the Canadian Bank Note Co. began to us the "dry" process in which the paper was gummed before printing Late printings of the 3 c. brown were the first stamps to be produce by this method, but the changeover was not completed unt January 1926.

"Dry" printings have a sharper appearance and can often b found with a degree of embossing showing on the reverse. Stamp from "wet" printings shrink during drying and are narrower tha "dry" examples. In many cases the difference can be as great as 0.

nm. On some early booklet panes the difference is in the vertical, rather than the horizontal, measurement.

On Nos. 196/215 all values only exist from "wet" printings except the 3 c., 20 c. and 50 c. which come from both types of printing.

44

1911–22. *P* 12.

196	44	1 c. yellow-green (22.12.11)			5·50	20
		a. With fine horiz lines across stamp			35·00	8·50
197		1 c. bluish green			5·50	30
		a. Booklet pane of 6 (1.5.13)			50·00	
198		1 c. deep bluish green			6·00	30
199		1 c. deep yellow-green			6·00	30
		a. Booklet pane of 6			18·00	
200		2 c. rose-red (22.12.11)			4·50	20
201		2 c. deep rose-red			4·75	20
		a. Booklet pane of 6 (1.12)			32·00	
202		2 c. pale rose-red			4·50	20
		a. With fine horiz lines across stamp			25·00	6·50
203		2 c. carmine			5·50	20
204		3 c. brown (6.8.18)			6·00	20
205		3 c. deep brown			5·00	20
		a. Booklet pane of 4 + 2 labels (2.22)			50·00	
205b		5 c. deep blue (17.1.12)			60·00	50
206		5 c. indigo			85·00	1·50
206a		5 c. grey-blue			75·00	1·25
206b		7 c. straw (12.1.12)			75·00	12·00
207		7 c. pale sage-green (1914)			£180	30·00
208		7 c. olive-yellow (1915)			20·00	2·50
209		7 c. yellow-ochre (1916)			20·00	2·50
210		10 c. brownish purple (12.1.12)			80·00	2·00
211		10 c. reddish purple			90·00	2·25
212		20 c. olive-green (23.1.12)			28·00	1·25
213		20 c. olive			28·00	1·50
214		50 c. grey-black (26.1.12)			£100	8·00
215		50 c. sepia			48·00	3·25
196/215				*Set of 8*	£225	9·00

The 20 c. and 50 c. values exist imperforate (*Price £1100 un, for each pair*).

1912 (Nov)–**21.** *For use in coil-machines.* (a) *P* 12×imperf.

216	44	1 c. yellow-green (1914)			3·50	9·00
217		1 c. blue-green			12·00	23·00
		a. Two large holes at top and bottom (vert pair) (7.18)			60·00	75·00
218		2 c. deep rose-red (1914)			25·00	16·00
218a		3 c. brown (1921)			3·50	5·50

No. 217a has two large holes about 3½ mm in diameter in the top and bottom margins. They were for experimental use in a vending machine at Toronto in July 1918 and were only in use for two days. The 1 c. and 2 c. also exist with two small "V" shaped holes about 9.5 mm apart at top which are gripper marks due to modifications made in vending machines in 1917.

(b) *Imperf* × *perf* 8

219	44	1 c. yellow-green (9.12)			11·00	2·75
220		1 c. blue-green			14·00	3·00
		a. With fine horiz lines across stamp			55·00	
221		2 c. carmine (9.12)			11·00	70
222		2 c. rose-red			12·00	2·00
223		2 c. scarlet			32·00	4·75
224		3 c. brown (8.18)			5·00	1·00

(c) *P* 8 × *imperf*

224a	44	1 c. blue-green (15.2.13)			60·00	48·00
224b		2 c. carmine (15.2.13)			60·00	48·00

The stamps imperf × perf 8 were sold in coils over the counter; those perf 8 × imperf were on sale in automatic machines. Varieties showing perf 12 on 2 or 3 adjacent sides and 1 or 2 sides imperf are from booklets, or the margins of sheets.

(45)   46   47

1915 (12 Feb). *Optd with T* **45.**

225	44	5 c. blue			£110	£180
226		20 c. olive-green			55·00	90·00
227		50 c. sepia (R.)			£110	£140
225/7				*Set of 3*	£250	£375

These stamps were intended for tax purposes, but owing to ambiguity in an official circular dated 16 April 1915, it was for a time believed that their use for postal purposes was authorised. The position was clarified by a further circular on 20 May 1916 which made clear that Nos. 225/7 were for fiscal use only.

1915. *P* 12.

228	46	1 c. green (15.4.15)			7·50	20
229		2 c. carmine-red (16.4.15)			7·50	30
230		2 c. rose-carmine			9·00	2·50

STANLEY GIBBONS STAMP COLLECTING SERIES

Introductory booklets on *How to Start, How to Identify Stamps* and *Collecting by Theme.* A series of well illustrated guides at a low price.
Write for details.

Die I   Die II

In Die I there is a long horizontal coloured line under the foot of the "T", and a solid bar of colour runs upwards from the "1" to the "T".

In Die II this solid bar of colour is absent, and there is a short horizontal line under the left side of the "T", with two short vertical dashes and a number of dots under the right-hand side.

1916 (1 Jan). *P* 12.

231	47	2 c. + 1 c. rose-red (Die I)			18·00	75
232		2 c. + 1 c. bright carmine (Die I)			18·00	75
233		2 c. + 1 c. scarlet (Die I)			15·00	75

1916 (Feb). *Imperf × perf* 8 (coils).

234	47	2 c. + 1 c. rose-red (Die I)			48·00	8·50

1916 (July). *P* 12 × 8.

235	47	2 c. + 1 c. carmine-red (Die I)			14·00	45·00
236		2 c. + 1 c. bright rose-red (Die I)			14·00	45·00

1916 (Aug). *P* 12.

237	47	2 c. + 1 c. carmine-red (Die II)			85·00	16·00

1916 (Aug). *Colour changed.* (a) *P* 12.

238	47	2 c. + 1 c. brown (Die I)			£180	20·00
239		2 c. + 1 c. yellow-brown (Die II)			4·00	20
		a. Imperf (pair)			£750	
240		2 c. + 1 c. deep brown (Die II)			10·00	20

(b) *Imperf × perf* 8

241	47	2 c. + 1 c. brown (Die I)			90·00	7·00
		a. Pair, 241 and 243			£325	
243		2 c. + 1 c. deep brown (Die II)			32·00	2·75

No. 239a, which is a genuine error, should not be confused with ungummed proofs of the Die I stamp, No. 238 (*Price per pair, £130*).

This value also exists p 12×imperf or imperf×p 12, but was not issued with these perforations (*Price, in either instance, £225, un, per pair*).

48 Quebec Conference, 1864, from painting "The Fathers of Confederation", by Robert Harris

1917 (15 Sept). *50th Anniv of Confederation. P* 12.

224	48	3 c. bistre-brown			16·00	1·25
245		3 c. deep brown			18·00	1·50

No. 244 exists imperforate (*Price per pair, £250 un*).

I

II

Die I. Space between top of "N" and oval frame line and space between "CENT" and lower frame line.
Die II. "ONE CENT" appears larger so that "N" touches oval and "CENT" almost touches frame line. There are other differences but this is the most obvious one.

I

II

Die I. The lowest of the three horizontal lines of shading below the medals does not touch the three heavy diagonal lines; three complete white spaces over both "E's" of "THREE"; long centre bar to figures "3". Vertical spandrel lines fine.
Die II. The lowest horizontal line of shading touches the first of the three diagonal lines; two and a half spaces over first "E" and spaces over second "E" partly filled by stem of maple leaf; short centre bar to figures "3". Vertical spandrel lines thick. There are numerous other minor differences.

WET AND DRY PRINTINGS. See notes above No. 196.
On Nos. 246/63 all listed items occur from both "wet" and "dry" printings except Nos. 246aa/ab, 248aa, 256, 259, 260 and 262 which come "wet" only, and Nos. 246a, 248/a, 252/4a, 256b and 263 which are "dry" only.

1922–31. As *T* 44. (a) *P* 12.

246	44	1 c. chrome-yellow (Die I) (7.6.22)			2·50	20
		aa. Booklet pane of 4 + 2 labels (7.22)			48·00	
		ab. Booklet pane of 6 (12.22)			27·00	
		a. Die II (1925)			5·50	10
247		2 c. deep green (6.6.22)			2·25	10
		aa. Booklet pane of 4 + 2 labels (7.22)			27·00	
		ab. Booklet pane of 6 (12.22)			£250	
		b. Thin paper (9.24)			2·75	3·75
248		3 c. carmine (Die I) (18.12.23)			3·75	10
		aa. Booklet pane of 4 + 2 labels (12.23)			28·00	
		a. Die II (11.24)			19·00	30
249		4 c. olive-yellow (7.7.22)			8·00	3·25
		a. Yellow-ochre			8·00	3·25
250		5 c. violet (2.2.22)			5·00	1·00
		a. Thin paper (9.24)			5·00	8·00
		b. Reddish violet (1925)			7·00	1·25
251		7 c. red-brown (12.12.24)			12·00	6·50
		a. Thin paper			£120	30·00
252		8 c. blue (1.9.25)			19·00	9·00
253		10 c. blue (20.2.22)			20·00	2·00
254		10 c. bistre-brown (1.8.25)			18·00	2·00
		a. Yellow-brown			18·00	2·00
255		$1 brown-orange (22.7.23)			50·00	6·00
246/55				*Set of 10*	£130	27·00

The $1 differs from T 44 in that the value tablets are oval.
Nos. 249/55 exist imperforate (*Prices per un pair 4 c. to 8 c. £850 each, 10 c. £900, $1 £1000*).

(b) *Imperf × perf* 8

256	44	1 c. chrome-yellow (Die I) (1922)			4·00	4·75
		a. Imperf horiz (vert pair) (1924)			£200	
		b. Die II (1925)			4·50	7·00
		c. Do. Imperf horiz (vert pair) (1927)			11·00	27·00
257		2 c. deep green (26.7.22)			7·50	1·00
		b. Imperf horiz (vert pair) (1927)			12·00	27·00
258		3 c. carmine (Die I) (9.4.24)			55·00	8·00
		a. Imperf horiz (vert pair) (1924)			£250	
		b. Die II (1925)			75·00	19·00
256/8				*Set of 3*	60·00	12·00

Nos. 256a, 256c, 257b and 258a come from coil printings sold in sheet form. Those issued in 1924 were from "wet" printings and those in 1927 from "dry". A "wet" printing of No. 257b, issued in 1924, also exists (*Price £200 mint*), but cannot be identified from that issued in 1927 except by the differences between "wet" and "dry" stamps.

(c) *Imperf (pairs)*

259	44	1 c. chrome-yellow (Die I) (6.10.24)			50·00	70·00
260		2 c. deep green (6.10.24)			50·00	70·00
261		3 c. carmine (Die I) (31.12.23)†			28·00	40·00

(d) *P* 12 × *imperf*

262	44	2 c. deep green (9.24)			65·00	60·00

(e) *P* 12 × 8

263	44	3 c. carmine (Die II) (24.6.31)			2·00	3·00

Nos. 259 to 261 were on sale only at the Philatelic Branch P.O. Dept, Ottawa.
†Earliest known postmark.

(49)   (50)

1926. *No.* 248 *surch.*

(a) *With T* **49,** *by the Govt Printing Bureau*

264	44	2 c. on 3 c. carmine (12.10.26)			38·00	48·00
		a. Pair, one without surch			£300	
		b. On Die II			£350	

(b) *With T* **50,** *by the Canadian Bank Note Co*

265	44	2 c. on 3 c. carmine (4.11.26)			13·00	18·00
		a. Surch double (partly treble)			£200	

51 Sir J. A. Macdonald   **52** "The Fathers of Confederation"

53 Parliament Buildings, Ottawa   **54** Sir W. Laurier

55 Canada, Map 1867–1927

1927 (29 June). *60th Anniv of Confederation. P* 12. I. *Commemorative Issue. Inscr* "1867–1927 CANADA CONFEDERATION".

266	51	1 c. orange			2·00	95
267	52	2 c. green			2·00	10
268	53	3 c. carmine			6·00	95
269	54	5 c. violet			3·25	3·00
270	55	12 c. blue			18·00	4·50
266/70				*Set of 5*	28·00	11·00

Nos. 266/70 exist imperforate, imperf×perf or perf×imperf (*Prices from £60, un, per pair*).

56 Darcy McGee **57** Sir W. Laurier and Sir J. A. Macdonald

58 R. Baldwin and L. H. Lafontaine

II. *Historical Issue*

271	56	5 c. violet		..	3·00	1·75
272	57	12 c. green		..	14·00	4·00
273	58	20 c. carmine		..	14·00	10·00
271/3				*Set of* 3	28·00	14·00

Nos. 271/3 exist imperforate, imperf×perf or perf×imperf (*Prices from* £60, *un, per pair*).

59

(Des H. Schwartz)

1928 (21 Sept). *Air. P* 12.
274 **59** 5 c. olive-brown ..   ..   3·75 2·50
No. 274 exists imperforate, imperf×perf or perf×imperf (*Price per pair*, £130, *un*).

60 King George V **61** Mt Hurd and Indian Totem Poles

62 Quebec Bridge **63** Harvesting with Horses

64 *Bluenose* (fishing schooner) **65** Parliament Buildings, Ottawa

1928–29. (*a*) *P* 12.
275	60	1 c. orange (25.10.28)	..	..	2·25	40
		a. Booklet pane of 6	..	..	18·00	
276		2 c. green (16.10.28)	..	..	1·00	10
		a. Booklet pane of 6	..	..	18·00	
277		3 c. lake (12.12.28)	..	..	13·00	13·00
278		4 c. olive-bistre (16.8.29)	..	..	13·00	5·50
279		5 c. violet (12.12.28)	..	..	5·00	2·50
		a. Booklet pane of 6 (6.1.29)	..	..	90·00	
280		8 c. blue (21.12.28)	..	..	7·50	3·50
281	61	10 c. green (5.12.28)	..	..	7·00	85
282	62	12 c. grey-black (8.1.29)	..	..	17·00	8·50
283	63	20 c. lake (8.1.29)	..	..	27·00	9·00
284	64	50 c. blue (8.1.29)	..	..	£100	35·00
285	65	$1 olive-green (8.1.29)	..	..	£110	50·00
		a. Brown-olive	..	..	£250	£110
275/85		..	..	*Set of* 11	£250	£110

(*b*) *Imperf* × *perf* 8 (5.11.28)
286	60	1 c. orange	..	..	13·00	21·00
287		2 c. green	..	..	13·00	3·25

Slight differences in the size of many Canadian stamps, due to paper shrinkage, are to be found.

Nos. 275/85 exist imperforate, imperf×perf or perf×imperf (*Prices per unused pair*, 1 c. to 8 c., *from* £60, 10 c. to 20 c., *from* £90, 50 c. and $1, *from* £350). *Tête-bêche* horizontal pairs of the 1 c., 2 c. and 5 c. are also known from uncut booklet sheets (*Prices per pair*, £200, *un*).

PRINTERS. The following stamps to No. 334 were recess-printed by the British American Bank Note Co, Ottawa.

---

66 **67** Parliamentary Library, Ottawa

68 The Old Citadel, Quebec **69** Harvesting with Tractor

70 Acadian Memorial Church and Statue of "Evangeline", Grand Pre, Nova Scotia **71** Mt Edith Cavell, Canadian Rockies

Die I 1 c. Die II Die I 2 c. Die II

1 c. Die I. Three thick coloured lines and one thin between "P" and ornament, at right. Curved line in ball-ornament short.
Die II. Four thick lines. Curved line longer.

2 c. Die I. Three thick coloured lines between "P" and ornament, at left. Short line in ball.
Die II. Four thick lines. Curved line longer.

1930–31. (*a*) *P* 11.
288	66	1 c. orange (I) (17.7.30)	..	..	90	60
289		2 c. green (I) (6.7.30)	..	..	1·10	10
		a. Booklet pane of 6 (17.6.30)	..	35·00	
290		4 c. yellow-bistre (5.11.30)	..	..	6·00	3·00
291		5 c. violet (18.6.30)	..	..	2·50	3·50
292		8 c. blue (13.8.30)	..	..	6·00	12·00
293	67	10 c. olive-green (15.9.30)	..	..	12·00	85
		a. Imperf (pair)	..	..	£900	
294	68	12 c. grey-black (4.12.30)	..	..	10·00	3·50
295	69	20 c. red (4.12.30)	..	..	22·00	60
296	70	50 c. blue (4.12.30)	..	..	80·00	17·00
297	71	$1 olive-green (4.12.30)	..	..	95·00	23·00
288/97				*Set of* 10	£200	55·00

Nos. 294/7 exist imperforate (*Prices per unused pair*, 12 c. £500, 20 c. £500, 50 c. £600, $1 £650).

(*b*) *Imperf* × *perf* 8½
298	66	1 c. orange (I)	..	..	9·50	12·00
299		2 c. green (I)	..	..	3·75	4·25

Colours changed and new value. (*a*) *P* 11
300	66	1 c. green (I) (6.12.30)	..	..	90	10
		a. Imperf (pair)	..	..	£750	
		b. Booklet pane of 6 (21.7.31)	..	25·00	
		c. Booklet pane of 4 + 2 labels (13.11.31)	..	75·00	
		d. Die II	..	..	1·00	10
301		2 c. scarlet (I) (17.11.30)	..	..	70	30
		a. Booklet pane of 6 (17.11.30)	..	23·00	
		b. Die II	..	..	90	10
302		2 c. deep brown (I) (4.7.31)	..	..	1·00	2·50
		a. Booklet pane of 6 (23.7.31)	..	35·00	
		b. Die II	..	..	70	10
		ba. Booklet pane of 4 + 2 labels (13.11.31)	..	£100	
303		3 c. scarlet (13.7.31)	..	..	90	10
		a. Booklet pane of 4 + 2 labels	..	35·00	
304		5 c. deep slate-blue (13.11.30)	..	5·00	20
		a. Dull blue	..	..	12·00	40
305		8 c. red-orange (5.11.30)	..	..	6·50	4·50
300/5				*Set of* 6	13·00	4·50

(*b*) *Imperf* × *perf* 8½
306	66	1 c. green (I)	..	..	6·00	7·00
307		2 c. scarlet (I)	..	..	4·50	3·25
308		2 c. deep brown (I) (4.7.31)	..	9·00	1·25
309		3 c. scarlet (13.7.31)	..	..	14·00	1·00
306/9				*Set of* 4	30·00	11·00

Some low values in the above and subsequent issues have been printed by both Rotary and "Flat plate" processes. The former can be distinguished by the gum, which has a striped appearance.
For 13 c. bright violet, T **68**, see No. 325.

ALTERED CATALOGUE NUMBERS

Any Catalogue numbers altered from the last edition are shown as a list in the introductory pages.

---

72 Mercury and Western Hemisphere **73** Sir Georges Etienne Cartier

(Des H. Schwartz)

1930 (4 Dec). *Air. P* 11.
310 **72** 5 c. deep brown ..   ..   15·00 17·00

1931 (30 Sept). *P* 11.
312 **73** 10 c. olive-green ..   ..   2·75 10
No. 312 exists imperforate (*Price per pair*, £300, *un*).

(74)   (75)

1932 (22 Feb). *Air. No.* 274 surch with T **74**.
313 **59** 6 c. on 5 c. olive-brown ..   ..   2·25 2·00
Examples of this stamp with surcharge inverted, surcharge double, surcharge triple or surcharge omitted in pair with normal are not now believed to have been regularly issued. Such "errors" have also been forged and collectors are warned against forged examples, some of which bear unauthorized markings which purport to be the guarantee of Stanley Gibbons Ltd.

1932 (21 June). *Nos.* 301/b surch with T **75**.
314	66	3 c. on 2 c. scarlet (I)	..	..	1·75	2·25
		a. Die II	..	..	1·00	40

76 King George V **77** Duke of Windsor when Prince of Wales

78 Allegory of British Empire

OTTAWA CONFERENCE 1932

(79)

1932 (12 July). *Ottawa Conference. P* 11. (*a*) *Postage stamps.*
315	76	3 c. scarlet	..	..	70	60
316	77	6 c. blue ..	..	..	6·00	3·50
317	78	13 c. green	..	..	8·50	6·00

(*b*) *Air. No.* 310 surch with T **79**.
318	72	6 c. on 5 c. deep brown (B.)	..	10·00	12·00
315/18		..	..	*Set of* 4	23·00	20·00

80 King George V "3" level Die I "3" raised Die II

1932 (1 Dec)–**33**. (*a*) *P* 11.
319	80	1 c. green	..	..	60	10
		a. Booklet pane of 6 (28.12.33)	..	15·00	
		b. Booklet pane of 4 + 2 labels (19.9.33)	75·00	
320		2 c. sepia	..	..	70	10
		a. Booklet pane of 6 (7.9.33)	..	15·00	
		b. Booklet pane of 4 + 2 labels (19.9.33)	75·00	
321		3 c. scarlet (Die I)	..	..	1·00	10
		a. Booklet pane of 4 + 2 labels (22.8.33)	40·00	
		b. Die II (29.11.32)	..	..	85	10
		ba. Booklet pane of 4 + 2 labels (19.9.33)	30·00	
322		4 c. yellow-brown	..	..	35·00	7·50
323		5 c. blue	..	..	10·00	10
		a. Imperf vert (horiz pair)	..	£850	
324		8 c. red-orange	..	..	22·00	3·50
325	68	13 c. bright violet	..	..	32·00	2·00
319/25				*Set of* 7	90·00	12·00

A plate block of four from Plate 1 exists printed in varnish ink.
Nos. 319/25 exist imperforate (*Prices per unused pair*, 1 c. to 8 c. £140, 13 c. £400)

(b) Imperf × perf 8½ (1933)

326	80	1 c. green	13·00	2·25
327		2 c. sepia	19·00	1·75
328		3 c. scarlet (Die II)	12·00	85
326/8		*Set of 3*	40·00	4·25

81 Parliament Buildings, Ottawa

1933 (18 May). *U.P.U. Congress Preliminary Meeting. P* 11.
329 81 5 c. blue .. 5·00 2·50
No. 329 exists imperforate (*Price per pair £425, un*).

WORLD'S GRAIN EXHIBITION & CONFERENCE

REGINA 1933
(82)

1933 (24 July). *World's Grain Exhibition and Conference, Regina. No.* 295 *optd with T* 82 *in blue.*
330 69 20 c. red .. 16·00 6·50
No. 330 exists imperforate (*Price per pair £425, un*).

83 S.S. Royal William (after S. Skillett)   **84 Jacques Cartier approaching Land**

1933 (17 Aug). *Centenary of First Trans-Atlantic Steamboat Crossing. P* 11.
331 83 5 c. blue .. 7·50 2·50
No. 331 exists imperforate (*Price per pair £425, un*).

1934 (1 July). *Fourth Centenary of Discovery of Canada. P* 11.
332 84 3 c. blue .. 2·00 1·25
No. 332 exists imperforate (*Price per pair £425, un*).

85 U.E.L. Statue, Hamilton   **86 Seal of New Brunswick**

1934 (1 July). *150th Anniv of Arrival of United Empire Loyalists. P* 11.
333 85 10 c. olive-green .. 8·50 4·50
No. 333 exists imperforate (*Price per pair £750, un*).

1934 (16 Aug). *150th Anniv of Province of New Brunswick. P* 11.
334 86 2 c. red-brown .. 1·50 2·00
No. 334 exists imperforate (*Price per pair £375, un*).

PRINTERS. The following stamps were recess-printed (except where otherwise stated) by the Canadian Bank Note Co, Ottawa, until No. 616.

87 Queen Elizabeth II when Princess   **89 King George V and Queen Mary**

1935 (4 May). *Silver Jubilee. T* 87, 89 *and similar designs. P* 12.

335	1 c. green	55	40
336	2 c. brown	60	30
337	3 c. carmine-red	1·75	30
338	5 c. blue	4·00	3·75
339	10 c. green	3·25	2·75
340	13 c. blue	6·00	4·00
335/40	*Set of 6*	14·00	10·50

Designs: *Vert (as T* 87)—2 c. King George VI when Duke of York; 5 c. King Edward VIII when Prince of Wales. *Horiz (as T* 89)—10 c. Windsor Castle; 13 c. Royal Yacht *Britannia*.
Nos. 335/40 exist imperforate (*Price £160, un, for each pair*).

93 King George V   **94 Royal Canadian Mounted Policeman**

99 Daedalus

1935 (1 June–5 Nov). *T* 93/4, 99 *and similar designs.* (a) *Postage.* (i) *P* 12.
341 93 1 c. green .. 30 10
  a. Booklet pane of 6 (19.8.35) .. 22·00
  b. Booklet pane of 4+2 labels (22.7.35) .. 55·00
342 2 c. brown .. 50 10
  a. Booklet pane of 6 (16.11.35) .. 26·00
  b. Booklet pane of 4+2 labels (22.7.35) .. 55·00
343 3 c. scarlet .. 60 10
  a. Booklet pane of 4+2 labels .. 28·00
  b. Printed on the gummed side .. £120
344 4 c. yellow .. 2·50 90
345 5 c. blue .. 1·75 10
  a. Imperf vert (horiz pair) .. £200
346 8 c. orange .. 1·75 2·50
347 94 10 c. carmine .. 5·00 30
348 13 c. purple .. 4·75 45
349 — 20 c. olive-green .. 17·00 70
350 — 50 c. deep violet .. 25·00 4·25
351 — $1 bright blue .. 40·00 9·00
341/51 *Set of 11* 90·00 16·00

(ii) *Coil stamps. Imperf × perf 8*
352 93 1 c. green (5.11.35) .. 13·00 3·00
353 2 c. brown (14.10.35) .. 9·00 2·75
354 3 c. scarlet (20.7.35) .. 9·00 85
352/4 .. *Set of 3* 28·00 6·00

(b) *Air. P* 12
355 99 6 c. red-brown .. 2·50 60
  a. Imperf vert (horiz pair) .. £4500
Designs: *Horiz (as T* 94)—13 c. Confederation Conference, Charlottetown, 1864; 20 c. Niagara Falls; 50 c. Parliament Buildings, Victoria, British Columbia; $1 Champlain Monument, Quebec.
Nos. 341/51 (*Prices per pair*, 1 c. to 8 c. each £95, 10 c. to $1 each £190, *un*.) and 355 (*Price per pair £375, un*) exist imperforate.

100 King George VI and Queen Elizabeth

1937 (10 May). *Coronation. P* 12.
356 100 3 c. carmine .. 85 30
No. 356 exists imperforate (*Price per pair £400, un*).

101 King George VI   **102 Memorial Chamber Parliament Buildings, Ottawa**

(*T* 101. Photograph by Bertram Park)

1937–38. *T* 101/2, 107 *and similar designs.* (a) *Postage.* (i) *P* 12.
357 101 1 c. green (1.4.37) .. 1·50 10
  a. Booklet pane of 4 + 2 labels (14.4.37) .. 28·00
  b. Booklet pane of 6 (18.5.37) .. 3·50
358 2 c. brown (1.4.37) .. 1·75 10
  a. Booklet pane of 4 + 2 labels (14.4.37) .. 45·00
  b. Booklet pane of 6 (3.5.38) .. 11·00

107 Fairchild 45-80 Sekani Seaplane over Distributor on River Mackenzie

359 101 3 c. scarlet (1.4.37) .. 2·25 10
  a. Booklet pane of 4 + 2 labels (14.4.37) .. 4·25
360 4 c. yellow (10.5.37) .. 3·75 1·50
361 5 c. blue (10.5.37) .. 4·00 10
362 8 c. orange (10.5.37) .. 3·75 1·50
363 102 10 c. rose-carmine (15.6.38) .. 5·00 10
  a. Red .. 5·00 10
364 — 13 c. blue (15.11.38) .. 14·00 80
365 — 20 c. red-brown (15.6.38) .. 22·00 50
366 — 50 c. green (15.6.38) .. 45·00 6·50
367 — $1 violet (15.6.38) .. 60·00 8·00
  a. Imperf horiz (vert pair) .. £2500
357/67 *Set of 11* £150 17·00
Nos. 357/67 exist imperforate (*Prices per pair* 1 c. to 50 c. each £160, $1 £250 *un*).

(ii) *Coil stamps. Imperf × perf 8*
368 101 1 c. green (15.6.37) .. 3·50 1·50
369 2 c. brown (18.6.37) .. 3·50 10
370 3 c. scarlet (15.4.37) .. 17·00 60
368/70 *Set of 3* 22·00 4·00

(b) *Air. P* 12
371 107 6 c. blue (15.6.38) .. 9·00 50
Designs: *Horiz (as T* 107)—13 c. Entrance to Halifax Harbour; 20 c. Fort Garry Gate, Winnipeg; 50 c. Entrance, Vancouver Harbour; $1 Chateau de Ramezay, Montreal.
No. 371 exists imperforate (*Price per pair £325, un*).

108 Queen Elizabeth II when Princess and Princess Margaret   **109 National War Memorial, Ottawa**

110 King George VI and Queen Elizabeth

1939 (15 May). *Royal Visit. P* 12.
372 108 1 c. black and green .. 1·75 10
373 109 2 c. black and brown .. 60 40
374 110 3 c. black and carmine .. 60 10
372/4 *Set of 3* 2·75 50
Nos. 372/4 exist imperforate (*Price £250, un, for each pair*).

111 King George VI in Naval uniform   **112 King George VI in Military uniform**   **113 King George VI in Air Force uniform**

114 Grain Elevator   **116 Parliament Buildings**

117 Ram Tank   **121 Air Training Camp**

1942 (1 July)–48. *War Effort. T* 111/14, 116/17, 121 *and similar designs.* (a) *Postage.* (i) *P* 12.
375 111 1 c. green .. 1·50 10
  a. Booklet pane of 4 + 2 labels (12.9.42) .. 20·00
  b. Booklet pane of 6 (24.11.42) .. 2·50
376 112 2 c. brown .. 1·75 10
  a. Booklet pane of 4 + 2 labels (12.9.42) .. 24·00
  b. Booklet pane of 6 (6.10.42) .. 18·00
377 113 3 c. carmine-lake .. 1·25 60
  a. Booklet pane of 4 + 2 labels (20.8.42) .. 4·25

378	113	3 c. purple (30.6.43)	..	..	90	10
		a. Booklet pane of 4 + 2 labels (28.8.43)		..	5·50	
		b. Booklet pane of 6 (24.11.47)		..	11·00	
379	114	4 c. slate	..	..	5·50	90
380	112	4 c. carmine-lake (9.4.43)		..	70	10
		a. Booklet pane of 6 (3.5.43)		..	3·50	
381	111	5 c. blue	..	..	3·00	10
382	—	8 c. red-brown	..	..	5·50	75
383	116	10 c. brown	..	..	5·00	10
384	117	13 c. dull green	..	..	6·00	6·00
385	—	14 c. dull green (16.4.43)		..	13·00	65
386	—	20 c. chocolate	..	..	13·00	15
387	—	50 c. violet	..	..	24·00	2·25
388	—	$1 blue	..	..	42·00	4·75
375/88				Set of 14	£110	14·00

Nos. 375/88 exist imperforate (*Prices per pair* 1 c. to 8 c. *each* £180, 10 c. to 20 c. *each* £250, 50 c. and $1 *each* £325, *un*).

(ii) *Coil stamps. Imperf* × *perf* 8

389	111	1 c. green (9.2.43)	..	..	1·00	1·50
390	112	2 c. brown (24.11.42)		..	2·25	1·00
391	113	3 c. carmine-lake (23.9.42)		..	1·75	4·25
392	—	3 c. purple (19.8.43)	..	..	4·75	2·75
393	112	4 c. carmine-lake (13.5.43)		..	5·50	10·00
389/93				Set of 5	13·00	10·00

(iii) *Booklet stamps. Imperf* × *perf* 12 (1.9.43)

394	111	1 c. green	..	..	3·00	80
		a. Booklet pane of 3 ..		..	9·00	
395	113	3 c. purple	..	..	3·00	1·00
		a. Booklet pane of 3 ..		..	9·00	
396	112	4 c. carmine-lake	..	..	3·00	1·25
		a. Booklet pane of 3 ..		..	9·00	
394/6	..			Set of 3	8·00	2·75

Nos. 394/6 are from booklets in which the stamps are in strips of three, imperforate at top and bottom and right-hand end.

(iv) *Coil stamps. Imperf* × *perf* 9½

397	111	1 c. green (13.7.48)	..	..	3·00	4·00
397a	112	2 c. brown (1.10.48)	..	..	7·50	19·00
398	113	3 c. purple (2.7.48)	..	..	4·75	6·00
398a	112	4 c. carmine-lake (22.7.48)		..	7·00	3·50
397/8a				Set of 4	20·00	29·00

(b) *Air. P* 12

399	121	6 c. blue (1.7.42)	..	..	12·00	4·00
400	—	7 c. blue (16.4.43)	..	..	2·25	10

Designs: *Horiz* (*as* T 114)—8 c. Farm scene. (As T 117)—20 c. Launching of corvette H.M.C.S. *La Malbaie*, Sorel; 50 c. Munitions factory; $1 H.M.S. *Cossack* (destroyer).
Nos. 399/400 exist imperforate (*Price* £400, *un*, for each pair).

122 Ontario Farm Scene

129 Alexander Graham Bell and "Fame"

1946 (16 Sept)–47. *Peace Re-conversion. T* **122** *and similar horiz designs. P* 12. (*a*) *Postage.*

401		8 c. brown	..	..	1·25	1·50
402		10 c. olive-green	..	..	1·75	10
403		14 c. sepia	..	..	4·00	80
404		20 c. slate	..	..	3·00	10
405		50 c. green	..	..	17·00	2·25
406		$1 purple	..	..	27·00	2·25

(b) *Air*

407		7 c. blue	..	..	3·75	10
		a. Booklet pane of 4 (24.11.47) ..			9·00	
401/7				Set of 7	50·00	6·00

Designs:—7 c. Canada Geese in flight; 10 c. Great Bear Lake; 14 c. St. Maurice River Power Station; 20 c. Combine Harvester; 50 c. Lumbering in British Columbia; $1 *Abegweit* (train ferry), Prince Edward Is.

1947 (3 Mar). *Birth Centenary of Bell* (inventor of telephone). *P* 12.

408	129	4 c. blue ..	..	..	15	10

130 "Canadian Citizenship".

131 Queen Elizabeth II when Princess

1947 (1 July). *Advent of Canadian Citizenship and Eightieth Anniv of Confederation. P* 12.

409	130	4 c. blue	..	..	10	10

(From photograph by Dorothy Wilding)

1948 (16 Feb). *Princess Elizabeth's Marriage. P* 12.

410	131	4 c. blue	..	..	10	10

NEW INFORMATION

The editor is always interested to correspond with people who have new information that will improve or correct the Catalogue.

132 Queen Victoria, Parliament Building, Ottawa, and King George VI

133 Cabot's Ship *Matthew*

1948 (1 Oct). *One Hundred Years of Responsible Government. P* 12.

411	132	4 c. grey ..	..	..	10	10

1949 (1 Apr). *Entry of Newfoundland into Canadian Confederation. P* 12.

412	133	4 c. green	..	..	30	10

134 "Founding of Halifax, 1749" (C. W. Jefferys)

1949 (21 June). *Bicentenary of Halifax, Nova Scotia. P* 12.

413	134	4 c. violet	..	..	10	10

135 **136** **137**

138 King George VI **139**

(From photographs by Dorothy Wilding)

1949 (15 Nov)–**51.** (i) *P* 12.

414	135	1 c. green	..	..	..	10	10
415	136	2 c. sepia	..	..	..	30	30
415a		2 c. olive-green (25.7.51)		..	..	30	10
416	137	3 c. purple	..	..	..	30	10
		a. Booklet pane of 4 + 2 labels (12.4.50)				2·25	
417	138	4 c. carmine-lake	..	..	..	20	10
		a. Booklet pane of 6 (5.5.50)..				27·00	
417b		4 c. vermilion (2.6.51)	..	..		40	10
		ba. Booklet pane of 6	..			6·00	
418	139	5 c. blue	..	..	..	1·50	10
414/18					Set of 7	2·75	40

(ii) *Imperf* × *perf* 9½ (*coil stamps*)

419	135	1 c. green (18.5.50)	..	..	90	1·00
420	136	2 c. sepia (18.5.50)	..	..	4·50	4·25
420a		2 c. olive-green (9.10.51)		..	1·75	1·40
421	137	3 c. purple (18.5.50)	..	..	2·25	2·00
422	138	4 c. carmine-lake (20.4.50)		..	14·00	7·50
422a		4 c. vermilion (27.11.51)		..	1·50	2·00
419/22a				Set of 6	22·00	16·00

(iii) *Imperf* × *perf* 12 (*booklets*)

422b	135	1 c. green (18.5.50)	..	..	50	1·60
		ba. Booklet pane of 3 ..		..	1·50	
423	137	3 c. purple (18.5.50)	..	..	1·25	85
		a. Booklet pane of 3 ..		..	3·75	
423b	138	4 c. carmine-lake (18.5.50)		..	15·00	7·00
		ba. Booklet pane of 3 ..		..	45·00	
423c		4 c. vermilion (25.10.51)		..	7·00	7·00
		ca. Booklet pane of 3 ..		..	21·00	
422b/3c				Set of 4	21·00	14·50

These booklet panes are imperforate at top, bottom and right-hand end.

140 King George VI **141** Oil Wells in Alberta

(From photograph by Dorothy Wilding)

1950 (19 Jan). *As T* 135/9 *but without* "POSTES POSTAGE", *as T* 140. (i) *P* 12.

424		1 c. green	..	..	10	50
425		2 c. sepia	..	..	10	60
426		3 c. purple	..	..	10	90
427		4 c. carmine-lake	..	..	10	20
428		5 c. blue	..	..	30	1·25
424/8				Set of 5	60	3·00

(ii) *Imperf* × *perf* 9½ (*coil stamps*)

429		1 c. green	..	..	30	1·00
430		3 c. purple	..	..	80	1·50

142 Drying Furs **143** Fisherman

1950 (1 Mar). *P* 12.

431	141	50 c. green	..	..	7·50	1·00

1950 (2 Oct). *P* 12.

432	142	10 c. brown-purple	..	..	1·00	10

1951 (1 Feb). *P* 12.

433	143	$1 ultramarine	..	..	38·00	5·00

144 Sir R. L. Borden **145** W. L. Mackenzie King

1951 (25 June). *Prime Ministers* (1st issue). *P* 12.

434	144	3 c. blue-green	..	..	10	50
435	145	4 c. rose-carmine	..	..	10	10

See also Nos. 444/5, 475/6 and 483/4.

146 Mail Trains, 1851 and 1951

147 SS. *City of Toronto* and SS. *Prince George*

148 Mail Coach and DC-4M North Star

149 Reproduction of 3d., 1851

1951 (24 Sept). *Canadian Stamp Centenary. P* 12.

436	146	4 c. black	..	..	35	10
437	147	5 c. violet	..	..	65	1·75
438	148	7 c. blue	..	..	35	10
439	149	15 c. scarlet	..	..	1·10	10
436/9				Set of 4	2·25	2·75

150 Queen Elizabeth II when Princess and Duke of Edinburgh

151 Forestry Products

1951 (26 Oct). *Royal Visit. P* 12.

440	150	4 c. violet	..	..	10	10

(Des A. L. Pollock)

1952 (1 Apr). *P* 12.

441	151	20 c. grey ..	..	..	1·00	10

152 Red Cross Emblem

1952 (26 July). *18th International Red Cross Conference, Toronto. Design recess; cross litho. P* 12.

442	152	4 c. scarlet and blue	..	..	15	10

153 Canada Goose

154 Pacific Coast Indian House and Totem Pole

(Des E. Hahn)

952 (3 Nov). P 12.
43 153 7 c. blue 50 10

952 (3 Nov). *Prime Ministers (2nd issue). Various portraits as* T 144. P 12.
4 3 c. reddish purple 15 20
5 4 c. orange-red 15 10
Portraits:—3 c. Sir John J. C. Abbott; 4 c. A. Mackenzie.

(Des E. Hahn)

953 (2 Feb). P 12.
46 154 $1 black .. .. .. 5·50 20

55 Polar Bear   156 Elk   157 American Bighorn

(Des J. Crosby (2 c.), E. Hahn (others))

953 (1 Apr). *National Wild Life Week.* P 12.
47 155 2 c. blue 10 10
48 156 3 c. sepia 10 20
49 157 4 c. slate 15 10
47/9 .. .. .. *Set of 3* 30 30

158   Queen Elizabeth II   159

(From photograph by Karsh, Ottawa)

953 (1 May–3 Sept). (a) *Sheet stamps.* P 12.
450 158 1 c. purple-brown 10 10
451 2 c. green 15 10
452 3 c. carmine 15 15
a. Booklet pane of 4+2 labels (17.7) 1·25
453 4 c. violet 20 10
a. Booklet pane of 6 (6.7) 3·00
454 5 c. ultramarine 20 10
450/4 .. .. .. *Set of 5* 70 30

(b) *Coil stamps. Imperf × perf* 9½
455 158 2 c. green (30.7) .. .. 1·75 1·00
456 3 c. carmine (27.7) .. 1·75 1·00
457 4 c. violet (3.9) .. .. 1·50 1·00
455/7 .. .. .. *Set of 3* 4·50 2·75

(c) *Booklet stamps. Imperf × perf* 12
458 158 1 c. purple-brown (12.8) .. 2·00 1·50
a. Booklet pane of 3 5·50
459 3 c. carmine (17.7) .. .. 2·00 1·50
a. Booklet pane of 3 5·50
460 4 c. violet (6.7) .. .. 2·00 1·50
a. Booklet pane of 3 5·50
458/60 .. .. .. *Set of 3* 5·50 4·00
These booklet stamps have top and bottom or top, bottom and right-hand sides imperforate.

(Des E. Hahn)

1953 (1 June). *Coronation.* P 12.
461 159 4 c. violet 10 10

160 Textile Industry   161 Queen Elizabeth II

(Des A. L. Pollock)

1953 (2 Nov). P 12.
462 160 50 c. deep bluish green .. .. 1·25 10

(From photograph by Dorothy Wilding)

1954–62. (i) P 12.
463 161 1 c. purple-brown (10.6.54) .. 10 10
a. Booklet pane. Five stamps plus printed label (1.6.56) .. 1·00
p. Two phosphor bands (13.1.62) .. 80 2·50
464 2 c. green (10.6.54) 20 10
a. Pack. Two blocks of 25 (12.61) .. 6·00
p. Two phosphor bands (13.1.62) .. 80 2·75
465 3 c. carmine (10.6.54) .. 60
a. Imperf vert (horiz pair) .. £1300
p. Two phosphor bands (13.1.62) .. 1·50 2·75
466 4 c. violet (10.6.54) .. 30 10
a. Booklet pane of 6 (7.7.55) .. 4·25
b. Booklet pane. Five stamps plus printed label (1.6.56) .. 1·75
p. One phosphor band (13.1.62) .. 2·00 7·50

467 161 5 c. bright blue (1.4.54) .. 30 10
a. Booklet pane. Five stamps plus printed label (14.7.54) .. 1·75
b. Pack. One block of 20 (12.61) .. 5·00
c. Imperf vert (horiz pair) ..
p. Two phosphor bands (13.1.62) .. 2·00 7·50
468 6 c. red-orange (10.6.54) .. 1·00 30
463/8 *Set of 6* 2·25 45
463p/7p *Set of 5* 6·50 21·00
(ii) *Imperf × perf* 9½ *(coil stamps)*
469 161 2 c. green (9.9.54) .. 55 75
470 4 c. violet (23.8.54) .. 55 80
471 5 c. bright blue (6.7.54) .. 1·75 30
469/71 *Set of 3* 2·50 1·75
No. 467c is from the left side of a sheet and shows perforations between the stamps and the sheet margin.
Nos. 464a and 467b are blocks with the outer edges imperf. These come from "One Dollar Plastic Packages" sold at post offices.

WINNIPEG PHOSPHOR BANDS. In 1962 facer-cancelling machines were introduced in Winnipeg which were activated by phosphor bands on the stamps. Under long or short wave ultra-violet light the phosphor glows and there is also a short after-glow when the lamp is turned off. This should not be confused with the fluorescent bands introduced in Ottawa in 1971.

162 Walrus   163 American Beaver   164 Northern Gannet

(Des E. Hahn)

1954 (1 Apr). *National Wild Life Week.* P 12.
472 162 4 c. slate-black 35 10
473 163 5 c. ultramarine 35 10
a. Booklet pane. Five stamps plus one printed label .. .. 1·75

(Des L. Hyde)

1954 (1 Apr). P 12.
474 164 15 c. black 50 10

1954 (1 Nov). *Prime Ministers (3rd issue). Various portraits as* T 144. P 12.
475 4 c. violet 15 10
476 5 c. bright blue 15 10
Portraits:—4 c. Sir John Thompson; 5 c. Sir Mackenzie Bowell.

165 Eskimo Hunter

(Des H. Beament)

1955 (21 Feb). P 12.
477 165 10 c. purple-brown 20 10

166 Musk Ox

167 Whooping Cranes

(Des E. Hahn (4 c.), Dr. W. Rowan (5 c.))

1955 (4 Apr). *National Wild Life Week.* P 12.
478 166 4 c. violet 30 10
479 167 5 c. ultramarine 80 10

168 Dove and Torch

169 Pioneer Settlers

(Des W. Lohse)

1955 (1 June). *Tenth Anniv of International Civil Aviation Organisation.* P 12.
480 168 5 c. ultramarine 10 10

(Des L. Hyde)

1955 (30 June). *50th Anniv of Alberta and Saskatchewan Provinces.* P 12.
481 169 5 c. ultramarine 15 15

170 Scout Badge and Globe

173 Ice-hockey Players

(Des L. Hyde)

1955 (20 Aug). *Eighth World Scout Jamboree, Niagara-on-the-Lake.* P 12.
482 170 5 c. orange-brown and green .. 20 10

1955 (8 Nov). *Prime Ministers (4th issue). Various portraits as* T 144. P 12.
483 4 c. violet 10 20
484 5 c. bright blue 10 10
Portraits:—4 c. R. B. Bennett; 5 c. Sir Charles Tupper.

(Des J. Simpkins)

1956 (23 Jan). *Ice-hockey Commemoration.* P 12.
485 173 5 c. ultramarine 15 15

174 Reindeer

175 Mountain Goat

(Des E. Hahn)

1956 (12 Apr). *National Wild Life Week.* P 12.
486 174 4 c. violet 20 15
487 175 5 c. bright blue 20 10

176 Pulp and Paper Industry

177 Chemical Industry

(Des A. J. Casson (20 c.), A. L. Pollock (25 c.))

1956 (7 June). P 12.
488 176 20 c. green 40 10
489 177 25 c. red 55 10

178

(Des A. Price)

1956 (9 Oct). *Fire Prevention Week.* P 12
490 178 5 c. red and black 30 10

179 Fishing   180 Swimming

(Des L. Hyde)

1957 (7 Mar). *Outdoor Recreation.* T 179/180 *and similar horiz designs.* P 12.
491 179 5 c. ultramarine 25 10
a. Block of 4. Nos. 491/4 .. .. 1·25
492 180 5 c. ultramarine 25 10
493 5 c. ultramarine 25 10
494 5 c. ultramarine 25 10
491/4 .. .. .. *Set of 4* 1·25 35
Designs:— No. 493, Hunting. No. 494, Skiing.
No. 491/4 are printed together in sheets of 50 (5 × 10). In the first, second, fourth and fifth vertical rows the four different designs are arranged in se-tenant blocks, whilst the central row is made up as follows (reading downwards):—Nos. 491/4, 491/2 (or 493/4), 491/4.

The new-issue supplement to this Catalogue appears each month in

GIBBONS STAMP MONTHLY

—from your newsagent or by postal subscription— sample copy and details on request.

CANADA — 1957

183 White-billed Diver   184 Thompson with Sextant, and North American Map

(Des L. Hyde)
1957 (10 Apr). National Wild Life Week. P 12.
495 183 5 c. black 20 10

(Des G. A. Gundersen)
1957 (5 June). Death Centenary of David Thompson (explorer). P 12.
496 184 5 c. ultramarine 15 30

185 Parliament Buildings, Ottawa   186 Globe within Posthorn

(Des Carl Mangold)
1957 (14 Aug). 14th U.P.U. Congress, Ottawa. P 12.
497 185 5 c. grey-blue 15 10
498 186 15 c. blackish blue .. .. 45 1·50

187 Miner   188 Queen Elizabeth II and Duke of Edinburgh

(Des A. J. Casson)
1957 (5 Sept). Mining Industry. P 12.
499 187 5 c. black 35 10

(From photographs by Karsh, Ottawa)
1957 (10 Oct). Royal Visit. P 12.
500 188 5 c. black 30 10

189 "A Free Press"   190 Microscope

(Des A. L. Pollock)
1958 (22 Jan). The Canadian Press. P 12.
501 189 5 c. black 15 30

(Des A. L. Pollock)
1958 (5 Mar). International Geophysical Year. P 12.
502 190 5 c. blue 20 10

191 Miner panning for Gold   192 La Verendrye (statue)

(Des J. Harman)
1958 (8 May). Centenary of British Columbia. P 12.
503 191 5 c. deep turquoise-green 20 10

(Des G. Trottier)
1958 (4 June). La Verendrye (explorer) Commemoration. P 12.
504 192 5 c. ultramarine 15 10

193 Samuel de Champlain and the Heights of Quebec   194 Nurse

(Des G. Trottier)
1958 (26 June). 350th Anniv of Founding of Quebec. P 12.
505 193 5 c. brown-ochre and deep green .. 30 10

(Des G. Trottier)
1958 (30 July). National Health. P 12.
506 194 5 c. reddish purple 30 10

195 "Petroleum 1858–1958"   196 Speaker's Chair and Mace

(Des A. L. Pollock)
1958 (10 Sept). Centenary of Canadian Oil Industry. P 12.
507 195 5 c. scarlet and olive 30 10

(Des G. Trottier and C. Dair)
1958 (2 Oct). Bicentenary of First Elected Assembly. P 12.
508 196 5 c. deep slate 30 10

197 John McCurdy's Silver Dart Biplane   198 Globe showing N.A.T.O. Countries

1959 (23 Feb). 50th Anniv of First Flight of the Silver Dart in Canada. P 12.
509 197 5 c. black and ultramarine 30 10

(Des P. Weiss)
1959 (2 Apr). Tenth Anniv of North Atlantic Treaty Organisation. P 12.
510 198 5 c. ultramarine 40 10

199   200 Queen Elizabeth II

(Des Helen Fitzgerald)
1959 (13 May). "Associated Country Women of the World" Commemoration. P 12.
511 199 5 c. black and yellow-olive 15 10

(Des after painting by Annigoni)
1959 (18 June). Royal Visit. P 12.
512 200 5 c. lake-red 30 10

201 Maple Leaf linked with American Eagle   202 Maple Leaves

(Des A. L. Pollock, G. Trottier (of Canada); W. H. Buckley, A. J. Copeland, E. Metzl (of the United States))
1959 (26 June). Opening of St. Lawrence Seaway. P 12.
513 201 5 c. ultramarine and red 20 10
a. Centre inverted £9000 £5000
It is believed that No. 513a occurred on two printer's sheets, each of 200 stamps. About 230 examples have been discovered.

(Des P. Weiss)
1959 (10 Sept). Bicentenary of Battle of Plains of Abraham (Quebec). P 12.
514 202 5 c. deep green and red 30 10

203   204 Dollard des Ormeaux

(Des Helen Fitzgerald)
1960 (20 Apr). Golden Jubilee of Canadian Girl Guides Movement. P 12.
515 203 5 c. ultramarine and orange-brown .. 20 10

(Des P. Weiss)
1960 (19 May). Tercentenary of Battle of the Long Sault. P 12.
516 204 5 c. ultramarine and light brown .. 20 10

205 Surveyor, Bull-dozer and Compass Rose   206 E. Pauline Johnson

(Des B. J. Reddie)
1961 (8 Feb). Northern Development. P 12.
517 205 5 c. emerald and red 15 10

(Des B. J. Reddie)
1961 (10 Mar). Birth Centenary of E. Pauline Johnson (Mohawk poetess). P 12.
518 206 5 c. green and red 15 10

207 Arthur Meighen (statesman)   208 Engineers and Dam

(Des B. J. Reddie)
1961 (19 Apr). Arthur Meighen Commemoration. P 12.
519 207 5 c. ultramarine 15 10

(Des B. J. Reddie)
1961 (28 June). Tenth Anniv of Colombo Plan. P 12.
520 208 5 c. blue and brown 30 10

209 "Resources for Tomorrow"   210 "Education"

(Des A. L. Pollock)
1961 (12 Oct). Natural Resources. P 12.
521 209 5 c. blue-green and brown 15 10

(Des Helen Fitzgerald)
1962 (28 Feb). Education Year. P 12.
522 210 5 c. black and orange-brown 15 10

211 Lord Selkirk and Farmer   212 Talon bestowing Gifts on Married Couple

(Des Phillips-Gutkin Ltd)
1962 (3 May). 150th Anniv of Red River Settlement. P 12.
523 211 5 c. chocolate and green 20 10

(Des P. Weiss)
1962 (13 June). Jean Talon Commemoration. P 12.
524 212 5 c. blue 20 10

213 Br Columbia & Vancouver Is 2½d. stamp of 1860, and Parliament Buildings, B.C.   214 Highway (map version) and Provincial Arms

296

(Des Helen Bacon)

1962 (22 Aug). *Centenary of Victoria, B.C. P* 12.
525 213 5 c. red and black 30 10

(Des A. L. Pollock)

1962 (31 Aug). *Opening of Trans-Canada Highway. P* 12.
526 214 5 c. black and orange-brown 15 10

215 Queen Elizabeth II and Wheat (agriculture) Symbol   216 Sir Casimir Gzowski

(From drawing by Ernst Roch)

1962–64. *Horiz designs as T* **215** *showing Queen Elizabeth II and industry symbols.* (i) *P* 12
527 1 c. chocolate (4.2.63) 10 10
    a. Booklet pane. Five stamps plus one printed label (15.5.63) .. .. 3·50
    p. Two phosphor bands (15.5.63) .. 15 45
528 2 c. green (2.5.63) 15 10
    a. Pack. Two blocks of 25 .. .. 8·50
    p. Two phosphor bands (15.5.63) .. 20 45
529 3 c. reddish violet† (2.5.63) .. 15 10
    p. Two phosphor bands (15.5.63) .. 30 60
530 4 c. carmine-red (4.2.63) 15 10
    a. Booklet pane. Five stamps plus one printed label (15.5.63) .. 3·50
    b. Pack. One block of 25 .. .. 4·25
    p. One centre phosphor band (*narrow*)* (2.63) .. .. 50 2·50
    pa. One centre phosphor band (*wide*) (8.64) 3·75 4·75
    pb. One side phosphor band (12.64) 40 2·00
531 5 c. ultramarine (3.10.62) 15 10
    a. Booklet pane. Five stamps plus one printed label (5.63) .. 3·00
    b. Pack. One block of 20 .. .. 4·75
    c. Imperf horiz (vert pair) £2000 £600
    p. Two phosphor bands (31.1.63?) .. 35 45
    pa. Pack. One block of 20 .. ..14·00
    pb. Imperf (pair) ..
527/31 .. .. Set of 5 65 15
527p/31p .. .. Set of 5 1·25 3·50

    (ii) *P* 9½× *imperf (coil stamps)*
532 2 c. green (1963) .. .. .. 6·50 7·50
532a 3 c. reddish violet (1964) .. .. 4·75 3·00
533 4 c. carmine-red (15.5.63) .. 1·75 2·75
    a. Imperf (pair) ..
534 5 c. ultramarine (15.5.63) .. .. 4·00 80
532/4 .. .. Set of 4 15·00 12·50

Symbols:–1 c. Crystals (Mining); 2 c. Tree (Forestry); 3 c. Fish (Fisheries); 4 c. Electricity pylon (Industrial power).
Nos. 528a, 530b, 531b and 531pa are blocks with the outer edges imperf. These come from "One Dollar Plastic Packages" sold at post offices.
†This is a fugitive colour which tends to become reddish on drying. In successive printings the violet colour became more and more reddish as the printer tried to match the shade of each previous printing instead of referring back to the original shade. A deep reddish violet is also known from Plate 3. As there is such a range of shades it is not practical to list them.
*On No. 530p the band is 4 mm wide as against 8 mm on No. 530pa. No. 530pb exists with the band at either left or right side of the stamp, the bands being applied across alternate vertical perforations.
Postal forgeries are known of the 4 c. showing a coarser background and lack of shading on the Queen's face.

(Des P. Weiss)

1963 (5 Mar). *150th Birth Anniv of Sir Casimir Gzowski (engineer). P* 12.
535 216 5 c. reddish purple 10 10

217 "Export Trade"   218 Frobisher and barque *Gabriel*

(Des A. L. Pollock)

1963 (14 June). *P* 12.
536 217 $1 carmine .. .. .. 4·75 2·00

(Des P. Weiss)

1963 (21 Aug). *Sir Martin Frobisher Commemoration. P* 12.
537 218 5 c. ultramarine 20 10

219 Horseman and Map   220 Canada Geese

(Des B. J. Reddie)

1963 (25 Sept). *Bicentenary of Quebec–Trois-Rivieres–Montreal Postal Service. P* 12.
538 219 5 c. red-brown and deep green .. 15 10

(Des A. Short and P. Arthur)

1963 (30 Oct). *P* 12.
539 220 15 c. blue 85 10

221 Douglas DC-9 Airliner and Uplands Airport, Ottawa   222 "Peace on Earth"

1964. *P* 12.
540 221 7 c. blue (11 Mar) 35 70
540a 8 c. blue (18 Nov) 50 40

1964 (8 Apr). *"Peace". Litho and recess. P* 12.
541 222 5 c. ochre, blue and turquoise-blue 15 10

223 Maple Leaves

1964 (14 May). *"Canadian Unity". P* 12.
542 223 5 c. lake-red and light blue .. 10 10

224 White Trillium and Arms of Ontario   236 Maple Leaf and Arms of Canada

1964–66. *Provincial Emblems. T* **224**, **236** *and similar horiz designs. Recess (No. 555) or litho and recess (others). P* 12.
543 5 c. green, brown and orange (30.6.64) 40 20
544 5 c. green, orange-brown and yellow (30.6.64) 40 20
545 5 c. carmine-red, green and bluish violet (3.2.65) 30 20
546 5 c. blue, red and green (3.2.65) .. 30 20
547 5 c. purple, green and yellow-brown (28.4.65) 30 20
548 5 c. red-brown, deep bluish green and mauve (28.4.65) 30 20
549 5 c. slate-lilac, green and light reddish purple (21.7.65) 50 20
550 5 c. green, yellow and rose-red (19.1.66) 30 20
551 5 c. sepia, orange and green (19.1.66) 30 20
552 5 c. black, green and red (23.2.66) .. 30 20
553 5 c. drab, green and yellow (23.3.66). . 30 20
554 5 c. blue, green and rose-red (23.3.66) 30 20
555 5 c. red and blue (30.6.66) .. 30 20
543/55 .. Set of 13 4·00 2·40

Designs:—No. 543, Type **224**; No. 544, Madonna Lily and Arms of Quebec; No. 545, Purple Violet and Arms of New Brunswick; No. 546, Mayflower and Arms of Nova Scotia; No. 547, Dogwood and Arms of British Columbia; No. 548, Prairie Crocus and Arms of Manitoba; No. 549, Lady's Slipper and Arms of Prince Edward Island; No. 550, Wild Rose and Arms of Alberta; No. 551, Prairie Lily and Arms of Saskatchewan; No. 552, Pitcher Plant and Arms of Newfoundland; No. 553, Mountain Avens and Arms of Northwest Territories; No. 554, Fireweed and Arms of Yukon Territory; No. 555, Type **236**.

(237)   238 Fathers of the Confederation Memorial, Charlottetown

1964 (15 July). *No.* 540 *surch with T* **237**.
556 221 8 c. on 7 c. blue 15 15
    a. Surch omitted (left-hand stamp of horiz pair) £6000

(Des P. Weiss)

1964 (29 July). *Centenary of Charlottetown Conference. P* 12.
557 238 5 c. black 10 10

239 Maple Leaf and Hand with Quill Pen   240 Queen Elizabeth II

(Des P. Weiss)

1964 (9 Sept). *Centenary of Quebec Conference. P* 12.
558 239 5 c. light red and chocolate .. 15 10

(Portrait by Anthony Buckley)

1964 (5 Oct). *Royal Visit. P* 12.
559 240 5 c. reddish purple 15 10

241 "Canadian Family"   242 "Co-operation"

1964 (14 Oct). *Christmas. P* 12.
560 241 3 c. scarlet 10 10
    a. Pack. Two blocks of 25 .. 7·00
    p. Two phosphor bands .. 60 2·25
    pa. Pack. Two blocks of 25 .. 13·00
561 5 c. ultramarine 10 10
    p. Two phosphor bands .. 90 2·25
Nos. 560a and 560pa are blocks with the outer edges imperf. These come from "$1.50 Plastic Packages" sold at post offices.

1965 (3 Mar). *International Co-operation Year. P* 12.
562 242 5 c. grey-green 35 10

243 Sir W. Grenfell   244 National Flag

1965 (9 June). *Birth Centenary of Sir Wilfred Grenfell (missionary). P* 12.
563 243 5 c. deep bluish green 20 10

1965 (30 June). *Inauguration of National Flag. P* 12.
564 244 5 c. red and blue 15 10

245 Sir Winston Churchill   246 Peace Tower, Parliament Buildings, Ottawa

(Des P. Weiss from photo by Karsh. Litho)

1965 (12 Aug). *Churchill Commemoration. P* 12.
565 245 5 c. purple-brown 15 10

(Des Philips-Gutkin)

1965 (8 Sept). *Inter-Parliamentary Union Conference, Ottawa. P* 12.
566 246 5 c. deep green 10 10

247 Parliament Buildings, Ottawa, 1865   248 "Gold, Frankincense and Myrrh"

(Des G. Trottier)

1965 (8 Sept). *Centenary of Proclamation of Ottawa as Capital. P* 12.
567 247 5 c. brown 10 10

(Des Helen Fitzgerald)

1965 (13 Oct). *Christmas. P* 12.
568 248 3 c. olive-green 10 10
    a. Pack. Two blocks of 25 .. 5·00
    p. Two phosphor bands .. 10 45
    pa. Pack. Two blocks of 25 .. 5·50
569 5 c. ultramarine 10 10
    p. Two phosphor bands .. 20 35
Nos. 568a and 568pa are blocks with the outer edges imperf. These come from "$1.50 Plastic Packages" sold at post offices.

249 "Alouette 2" over Canada   250 La Salle

1966 (5 Jan). *Launching of Canadian Satellite, "Alouette 2". P* 12.
570 249 5 c. ultramarine 15 10

(Des Brigdens Ltd., Toronto)

1966 (13 Apr). *300th Anniv of La Salle's Arrival in Canada.* P 12.
571 **250** 5 c. deep bluish green 15 10

251 Road Signs   **252** Canadian Delegation and Houses of Parliament

(Des Helen Fitzgerald)

1966 (2 May). *Highway Safety. Invisible gum.* P 12.
572 **251** 5 c. yellow, blue and black .. 15 10

(Des P. Pederson (Brigdens Ltd))

1966 (26 May). *London Conference Centenary.* P 12.
573 **252** 5 c. red-brown 10 10

253 Douglas Point Nuclear Power Station   **254** Parliamentary Library, Ottawa

(Des A. L. Pollock)

1966 (27 July). *Peaceful Uses of Atomic Energy.* P 12.
574 **253** 5 c. ultramarine 10 10

(Des Brigdens Ltd)

1966 (8 Sept). *Commonwealth Parliamentary Association Conference, Ottawa.* P 12.
575 **254** 5 c. purple 10 10

255 "Praying Hands", after Dürer   **256** Flag and Canada on Globe

(Des G. Holloway)

1966 (12 Oct). *Christmas.* P 12.
576 **255** 3 c. carmine 10 10
  a. Pack. Two blocks of 25 .. .. 4·00
  p. Two phosphor bands 20 65
  pa. Pack. Two blocks of 25 .. 6·50
577 5 c. orange 10 10
  p. Two phosphor bands 20 95
Nos. 576a and 576pa are blocks with the outer edges imperf. These come from "$1.50 Plastic Packages" sold at post offices.

(Des Brigdens Ltd)

1967 (11 Jan). *Canadian Centennial. Invisible gum.* P 12.
578 **256** 5 c. scarlet and blue 10 10
  p. Two phosphor bands .. .. 30 1·00

257 Northern Lights and Dog-team   **263** "The Jack Pine" (T. Thomson)

1967 (8 Feb)–73. T **257**, **263** and similar horiz designs.

A. Recess C.B.N.

(i) P 12

579 1 c. brown 10 10
  a. Booklet pane. Five stamps plus one printed label (2.67) 50
  b. Printed on the gummed side .. £450
  p. Two phosphor bands 30 80
  pa. Centre phosphor band (12.68) 30 70
  q. Two fluorescent bands (11.71) 30 10
580 2 c. green 10 10
  a. Booklet pane. No. 580×4 *se-tenant* with No. 581×4 with gutter margin between (26.10.70) .. .. 2·50
  p. Two phosphor bands 30 70
  pa. Centre phosphor band (12.68) 30 70
  q. Two fluorescent bands (12.72) 40 10
581 3 c. slate-purple 30 10
  p. Two phosphor bands 30 90
  q. Two fluorescent bands (1972?)

582 4 c. red 20 10
  a. Booklet pane. Five stamps plus one printed label (2.67) .. .. 1·75
  b. Pack. One block of 25 (8.2.67) .. 10·00
  p. One side phosphor band .. 1·60 2·00
  pa. Centre phosphor band (3.69) .. 30 70
  q. Two fluorescent bands (4.73) .. 40 10
583 5 c. blue 20 10
  a. Booklet pane. Five stamps plus one printed label (3.67) .. .. 6·50
  b. Pack. One block of 20 (2.67) .. 17·00
  p. Two phosphor bands 45 65
  pa. Pack. One block of 20 (8.2.67) .. 35·00
  pb. Centre phosphor band (12.68) 30 65
583c 6 c. black (2.72) .. .. 1·50 30
  ca. Printed on the gummed side .. 9·50
  cp. Centre phosphor band .. 2·50 2·25
  cq. Two fluorescent bands .. 40 30
584 8 c. purple-brown 35 30
585 10 c. olive-green 30 10
  p. Two phosphor bands (9.12.69) .. 1·50 1·75
  q. Two fluorescent bands (1.72) .. 75 50
586 15 c. dull purple 30 10
  p. Two phosphor bands (9.12.69) .. 2·25 2·75
  q. Two fluorescent bands (2.72) .. 1·25 1·00
587 20 c. deep blue 80 10
  p. Two phosphor bands (9.12.69) .. 2·25 2·75
588 25 c. myrtle-green .. .. 1·50 10
  p. Two phosphor bands (9.12.69) .. 4·75 5·50
589 50 c. cinnamon .. .. 2·00 10
590 $1 scarlet .. .. 3·00 65
579/90 .. .. Set of 13 9·50 1·60
579pa/588p .. .. Set of 10 13·50 16·00

(ii) Perf 9½ × imperf (coil stamps)

591 3 c. slate-purple (3.67) .. .. 2·50 2·50
592 4 c. red (3.67) .. .. 2·50 1·50
593 5 c. blue (2.67) .. .. 2·50 1·40

(iii) Perf 10×imperf (coil stamps)

594 6 c. orange-red (1.69) 90 35
  a. Imperf (vert pair) £200
595 6 c. black (8.70) 35 30
  a. Imperf (vert pair) £500
596 7 c. green (30.6.71) 40 50
  a. Imperf (vert pair) £550
597 8 c. black (30.12.71) 40 30
  a. Imperf (vert pair) £225
  q. Two fluorescent bands .. 30 30
  qa. Imperf (vert pair) £225

B. Recess B.A.B.N.

(i) P 10 (sheets (601/p) or booklets)

598 1 c. brown (9.68) .. .. 40 1·75
  a. Booklet pane. No. 598 × 5 *se-tenant* with No. 599 × 5 (9.68) .. .. 2·50
  b. Booklet pane. No. 601 × 4 *se-tenant* with No. 598 plus one printed label (10.68) .. 2·50
599 4 c. red (9.68) 30 90
  a. Booklet pane. 25 stamps plus two printed labels .. .. 9·00
600 5 c. blue (9.68) 30 90
  a. Booklet pane of 20 .. .. 6·50
601 6 c. orange-red (10.68) 45 10
  a. Booklet pane. 25 stamps plus two printed labels (1.69) .. .. 11·00
  p. Two phosphor bands (1.11.68) .. 75 85
602 6 c. black (1.70) .. .. 1·40 85
  a. Booklet pane. 25 stamps plus two printed labels .. .. 20·00
603 6 c. black (re-engraved die) (8.70) .. 4·25 3·00
  a. Booklet pane of 4 .. .. 13·00

(ii) P 12½×12 (sheets (606/10) or booklets)

604 1 c. brown (30.6.71) .. .. 80 1·40
  a. Booklet pane. Nos. 604×4, 605×4 and 609×12 *se-tenant* .. 14·00
  b. Booklet pane. Nos. 604/5 and 609×3 *se-tenant* plus one printed label .. 5·50
  c. Booklet pane. Nos. 604×3, 608 and 610×2 *se-tenant* (30.12.71) .. 2·00
  d. Booklet pane. Nos. 604×6, 608 and 610×11 *se-tenant* (30.12.71) .. 7·50
  e. Booklet pane. Nos. 604×4, 608 and 610×5 *se-tenant* (8.72) .. 4·50
  q. Two fluorescent bands (30.12.71) .. 40 10
  qc. Booklet pane. Nos. 604q×3, 608q and 610q×2 *se-tenant* .. 2·50
  qd. Booklet pane. Nos. 604q×6, 608q and 610q×11 *se-tenant* .. 7·00
  qe. Booklet pane. Nos. 604q×4, 608q and 610q×5 *se-tenant* (8.72) .. 4·50
605 3 c. slate-purple (30.6.71) .. .. 3·50 4·25
606 6 c. orange-red (3.69) .. .. 1·00 10
  p. Two phosphor bands .. .. 1·00 1·25
607 6 c. black (7.1.70) 30 10
  a. Booklet pane. 25 stamps plus two printed labels (8.70) .. .. 16·00
  p. Two phosphor bands .. .. 90 1·50
608 6 c. black (re-engraved die) (9.70) .. 80 10
  a. Booklet pane of 4 (11.70) .. 5·50
  p. One centre phosphor band (9.71) .. 1·75 2·50
  q. Two fluorescent bands (30.12.71) .. 75 10
609 7 c. myrtle-green (30.6.71) 30 10
  p. Two phosphor bands .. .. 60 1·60
610 8 c. slate-black (30.12.71) 30 10
  p. Two phosphor bands .. .. 60 1·00
  q. Two fluorescent bands (30.12.71) .. 45 15

Designs: (as T **257**)—2 c. Totem pole; 3 c. Combine-harvester and oil derrick; 4 c. Ship in lock; 5 c. Harbour scene; 6 c., 7 c. "Transport"; 8 c. (Nos. 597, 610) Library of Parliament. (as T **263**)—8 c. (No. 584) "Alaska Highway" (A. Y. Jackson); 15 c. "Bylot Island" (L. Harris); 20 c. "Quebec Ferry" (J. W. Morrice); 25 c. "The Solemn Land" (J. E. H. MacDonald); 50 c. "Summer's Stores" (grain elevators) (J. Ensor); $1 "Oilfield" (near Edmonton) (H. G. Glyde).
No. 581q only exists as a pre-cancel.
Nos. 582b, 583b and 583pa are blocks with the outer edges imperf. These come from "One Dollar Plastic Packages" sold at post offices.
No. 592p comes with the band to the left or right of the stamp, the phosphor having been applied across alternate vertical perforations.
Postal forgeries exist of the 6 c. orange printed in lithography and perforated 12½.

Normal

Re-engraved

When the basic postal rate was changed to 6 c. the C.B.N. lent their die to B.A.B.N. who made a duplicate die from it by transfer. Parts of this proved to be weak, but it was used for Nos. 601/2 and 606/7. B.A.B.N. later re-engraved their die to make fresh plates which were used for Nos. 603 and 608. No. 608 first appeared on sheets from Plate 4.
There are no records of dates of issue of the booklets, packs and coils, but supplies of these were distributed to depots in the months indicated.

IMPERF BETWEEN PAIRS FROM COIL STAMPS. Nos. 594/7 are known in blocks or horizontal pairs imperf between vertically. Coils are supplied to post offices in batches of ten coils held together by roulettes between every fourth stamp so that they can easily be split apart. If two or more unsplit coils are purchased it is possible to obtain blocks or pairs imperf between vertically.
Vertical coil stamps are also known imperf between horizontally or with some stamps apparently completely imperf. These can result from blind perforations identifiable by slight indentations.

WHITE FLUORESCENT PAPER. Different papers with varying degrees of whiteness have been used for Canadian stamps, but during 1968–70 a distinctive very white and highly fluorescent paper was used known as "hybrite"; this fluoresces on the back and front. This paper has also been employed for commemorative issues, some of which exist on more than one type of paper. The white fluorescent papers are recorded in the Stanley Gibbons *Elizabethan Catalogue.*

FLUORESCENT BANDS. During the second half of 1971 new sorting machines were installed in the Ottawa area which were activated by stamps bearing fluorescent bands. These differ from the Winnipeg phosphor bands in that they react green and have no after-glow. To the naked eye the fluorescent bands appear shiny when compared with the remainder of the stamp when looking along its surface. Winnipeg phosphor bands appear matt.
The experiments were successful and what was at first called "Ottawa tagging" has since come into more general use and the Winnipeg phosphor was phased out. However, the substance at first used (known as OP–4) was found to migrate to envelopes, documents, album pages, etc. as well as to adjoining stamps. Late in 1972 this fault was cured by using another substance (called OP–2). The migrating bands were used on early printings of Nos. 604q, 608q and 610q as well as certain stamps referred to in a footnote after No. 692. It is most advisable to use plastic mounts for housing stamps with migrating bands or else clear acetate should be affixed to the album leaves.

269 Canadian Pavilion   **270** Allegory of "Womanhood" on Ballot-box

(Des C.B.N.)

1967 (28 Apr). *World Fair, Montreal.* P 12.
611 **269** 5 c. blue and red 10 10

(Des Helen Fitzgerald. Litho)

1967 (24 May). *50th Anniv of Women's Franchise.* P 12.
612 **270** 5 c. reddish purple and black .. 10 10

271 Queen Elizabeth II and Centennial Emblem   **272** Athlete

(Portrait from photo by Anthony Buckley)

1967 (30 June). *Royal Visit.* P 12.
613 **271** 5 c. plum and orange-brown .. 15 10

(Des Brigdens Ltd)

1967 (19 July). *Fifth Pan-American Games, Winnipeg.* P 12.
614 **272** 5 c. rose-red 10 10

273 "World News"   274 Governor-General Vanier

(Des W. McLauchlan)

1967 (31 Aug). *50th Anniv of the Canadian Press. P* 12.
615 273 5 c. blue 10 10

(Des from photo by Karsh)

1967 (15 Sept). *Vanier Commemoration. P* 12.
616 274 5 c. black 10 10

PRINTERS. The following were printed either by the Canadian Bank Note Co, Ottawa (C.B.N.) or the British American Bank Note Co, Ottawa (B.A.B.N.), *except where otherwise stated.*

275 People of 1867 and Toronto, 1967   276 Carol Singers

(Des and recess C.B.N.)

1967 (28 Sept). *Centenary of Toronto as Capital City of Ontario. P* 12.
617 275 5 c. myrtle-green and vermilion .. 10 10

(Des and recess B.A.B.N.)

1967 (11 Oct). *Christmas. P* 12.
618 276 3 c. scarlet 10 10
  a. Pack. Two blocks of 25 .. .. 3·25
  p. Two phosphor bands 15 50
  pa. Pack. Two blocks of 25 .. .. 3·25
619 5 c. emerald-green 10 10
  p. Two phosphor bands 30 50
Nos. 618a and 618pa are blocks with the outer edges imperf. These come from "$1.50 Plastic Packs" sold at post offices.

277 Grey Jays   278 Weather Map and Instruments

(Des M. G. Loates. Litho C.B.N.)

1968 (15 Feb). *Wild Life. P* 12.
620 277 5 c. multicoloured 30 10
See also Nos. 638/40.

(Des and litho B.A.B.N.)

1968 (13 Mar). *Bicentenary of First Meteorological Readings. P* 11.
621 278 5 c. multicoloured 15 10

279 Narwhal   280 Globe, Maple Leaf and Rain Gauge

(Des J. A. Crosby. Litho B.A.B.N.)

1968 (10 Apr). *Wildlife. P* 11.
622 279 5 c. multicoloured 15 10
No. 622 has a background of yellow-green and pale blue but copies are known with the yellow-green apparently missing. This "yellow-green" is produced by an overlay of yellow on the blue but we have not come across any copies where the yellow is completely missing and the wide range of colour variation is due to technical dificulties in maintaining an exact blend of the two colours.

(Des I. von Mosdossy. Litho B.A.B.N.)

1968 (8 May). *International Hydrological Decade. P* 11.
623 280 5 c. multicoloured 15 10

IMPERF EDGES. On Nos. 624/54, 657 and 659 (stamps printed by the B.A.B.N. Co.) the outer edges of the sheets were guillotined to remove the imprints for P.O. stock so that single stamps may, therefore, be found with either one, or two adjacent sides imperforate.

281 Nonsuch   282 Lacrosse Players

(Recess and photo B.A.B.N.)

1968 (5 June). *300th Anniv of Voyage of the "Nonsuch". P* 10.
624 281 5 c. multicoloured 20 10

(Des J. E. Aldridge. Recess and photo B.A.B.N.)

1968 (3 July). *Lacrosse. P* 10.
625 282 5 c. black, red and lemon 15 10

283 Front Page of *The Globe*, George Brown and Legislative Building   284 H. Bourassa

(Des N. Sabolotny. Recess and photo B.A.B.N.)

1968 (21 Aug). *150th Birth Anniv of George Brown (politician and journalist). P* 10.
626 283 5 c. multicoloured 10 10

(Des, recess and litho C.B.N.)

1968 (4 Sept). *Birth Centenary of Henri Bourassa (journalist and politician). P* 12.
627 284 5 c. black, red and pale cream .. 10 10

285 John McCrae, Battlefield and First Lines of "In Flanders Fields"   286 Armistice Monument, Vimy

(Des I. von Mosdossy. Litho C.B.N.)

1968 (15 Oct). *50th Death Anniv of John McCrae (soldier and poet). P* 12.
628 285 5 c. multicoloured 10 10

(Des and recess C.B.N.)

1968 (15 Oct). *50th Anniversary of 1918 Armistice. P* 12.
629 286 15 c. slate-black 30 40

287 Eskimo Family (carving)   288 "Mother and Child" (carving)

(Designs from Eskimo carvings by Munamee (6 c.) and unknown carver (5 c.). Photo C.B.N.)

1968. *Christmas. P* 12.
630 287 5 c. black and new blue (1.11.68) .. 10 10
  a. Booklet pane of 10 (15.11.68) .. 2·50
  p. One centre phosphor band .. 10 50
  pa. Booklet pane of 10 (15.11.68) .. 3·50
631 288 6 c. black and ochre (15.11.68) .. 10 10
  p. Two phosphor bands .. 20 50

289 Curling   290 Vincent Massey

(Des D. Eales. Recess and photo B.A.B.N.)

1969 (15 Jan). *Curling. P* 10.
632 289 6 c. black, new blue and scarlet .. 15 10

(Des I. von Mosdossy. Recess and litho C.B.N.)

1969 (20 Feb). *Vincent Massey, First Canadian-born Governor-General. P* 12.
633 290 6 c. sepia and yellow-ochre .. 10 10

291 "Return from the Harvest Field" (Suzor-Côté)   292 Globe and Tools

(Photo C.B.N.)

1969 (14 Mar). *Birth Centenary of Marc Aurèle de Foy Suzor-Côté (painter). P* 12.
634 291 50 c. multicoloured .. .. 70 2·00

(Des J. Hébert. Recess B.A.B.N.)

1969 (21 May). *50th Anniv of International Labour Organisation. P* 12½ × 12.
635 292 6 c. bronze-green 10 10

293 Vickers FB-27 Vimy Aircraft over Atlantic Ocean   294 "Sir William Osler" (J. S. Sargent)

(Des R. W. Bradford. Recess and photo B.A.B.N.)

1969 (13 June). *50th Anniv of First Non-stop Transatlantic Flight. P* 12 × 12½.
636 293 15 c. chocolate, bright green & pale blue 40 55

(Des, recess and photo B.A.B.N.)

1969 (23 June). *50th Death Anniv of Sir William Osler (physician). P* 12½ × 12.
637 294 6 c. deep blue, light blue and chestnut 20 10

295 White-throated Sparrows   298 Flags of Winter and Summer Games

(Des M. G. Loates. Litho C.B.N.)

1969 (23 July). *Birds. T* 295 *and similar multicoloured designs. P* 12.
638 6 c. Type 295 .. .. 25 10
639 10 c. Savannah Sparrow (horiz) .. 50 95
640 25 c. Hermit Thrush (horiz) .. .. 1·60 2·50
638/40 .. .. .. Set of 3 2·10 3·25

(Des C. McDiarmid. Recess and litho C.B.N.)

1969 (15 Aug). *Canadian Games. P* 12.
641 298 6 c. emerald, scarlet and blue .. 10 10

299 Outline of Prince Edward Island showing Charlottetown   300 Sir Isaac Brock and Memorial Column

(Des L. Fitzgerald. Recess and photo B.A.B.N.)

1969 (15 Aug). *Bicentenary of Charlottetown as Capital of Prince Edward Island. P* 12 × 12½.
642 299 6 c. yellow-brown, black and blue 20 10

(Des I. von Mosdossy. Recess and litho C.B.N.)

1969 (12 Sept). *Birth Bicentenary of Sir Isaac Brock. P* 12.
643 300 6 c. orange, bistre and bistre-brown 10 10

301 Children of the   302 Stephen Butler Leacock, Mask
World in Prayer   and "Mariposa"

(Des Rapid Grip and Batten Ltd. Litho C.B.N.)

1969 (8 Oct). *Christmas.* P 12.
644	301	5 c. multicoloured	..	..	10	10
		a. Booklet pane of 10	..	..	1·75	
		p. One centre phosphor band	..	..	10	60
		pa. Booklet pane of 10			2·50	
645		6 c. multicoloured	..	..	10	10
		a. Black (inscr, value and frame omitted			£1200	
		p. Two phosphor bands	..	..	20	60

(Des, recess and photo B.A.B.N.)

1969 (12 Nov). *Birth Centenary of Stephen Butler Leacock (humorist).* P 12 × 12½.
646	302	6 c. multicoloured	..	..	10	10

303 Symbolic Cross-roads   304 "Enchanted Owl"
(Kenojuak)

(Des K. C. Lochhead. Litho C.B.N.)

1970 (27 Jan). *Centenary of Manitoba.* P 12.
647	303	6 c. ultramarine, lemon and vermilion		15	10
		p. Two phosphor bands	..	..	15	70

(Des N. E. Hallendy and Miss S. Van Raalte. Recess C.B.N.)

1970 (27 Jan). *Centenary of Northwest Territories.* P 12.
648	304	6 c. carmine-red and black	..	..	10	10

305 Microscopic View of   306 Expo 67 Emblem and
Inside of Leaf   Stylized Cherry Blossom

(Des I. Charney. Recess and photo B.A.B.N.)

1970 (18 Feb). *International Biological Programme.* P 12 × 12½.
649	305	6 c. emerald, orange-yellow & ultram	..	15	10

(Des E. R. C. Bethune. Litho C.B.N.)

1970 (18 Mar). *World Fair, Osaka.* T 306 *and similar horiz designs. Multicoloured; colour of Cherry Blossom given.* P 12.
650	25 c. red	..	..	1·50	2·00
	a. Block of 4. Nos. 650/3	..	..	5·50	
	p. Two phosphor bands	..	1·50	2·25
	pa. Block of 4. Nos. 650p/3p	..	5·50	
651	25 c. violet	..	..	1·50	2·00
	p. Two phosphor bands	..	1·50	2·25
652	25 c. green	..	..	1·50	2·00
	p. Two phosphor bands	..	1·50	2·25
653	25 c. blue	..	..	1·50	2·00
	p. Two phosphor bands	..	1·50	2·25
650/3			Set of 4	5·50	7·00
650p/3p			Set of 4	5·50	8·00

Designs:—No. 650, Type 306; No. 651, Dogwood and stylized cherry blossom; No. 652, White Trillium and stylized cherry blossom; No. 653, White Garden Lily and stylized cherry blossom. Nos. 650/3 and 650p/3p are printed together in sheets of 50 (5 × 10). In the first, second, fourth and fifth vertical rows the four different designs are arranged in *se-tenant* blocks, whilst the centre row is composed as follows (reading downwards:—650(p)/3(p), 650(p) × 2, 653(p), 651(p), 652(p) and 650(p).

310 Henry Kelsey   311 "Towards Unification"

(Des D. Burton. Recess and photo B.A.B.N.)

1970 (15 Apr). *300th Birth Anniv of Henry Kelsey (explorer).* P 12 × 12½.
654	310	6 c. multicoloured	..	..	10	10

(Des B. Fisher. Litho B.A.B.N.)

1970 (13 May). *25th Anniv of United Nations.* P 11.
655	311	10 c. blue	..	..	40	30
		p. Two phosphor bands	..	60	2·00
656		15 c. magenta and bluish lilac	..	40	35
		p. Two phosphor bands	..	70	2·00

312 Louis Riel (Métis   313 Mackenzie's Inscription,
leader)   Dean Channel

(Des R. Derreth. Photo B.A.B.N.)

1970 (19 June). *Louis Riel Commemoration.* P 12½ × 12.
657	312	6 c. greenish blue and vermilion	..	10	10

(Design from Government Archives photo. Recess C.B.N.)

1970 (25 June). *Sir Alexander Mackenzie (explorer).* P 12 × 11½.
658	313	6 c. bistre-brown	..	..	15	10

314 Sir Oliver Mowat (statesman)   315 "Isles of Spruce"
(A. Lismer)

(Des E. Roch. Recess and photo B.A.B.N.)

1970 (12 Aug). *Sir Oliver Mowat Commemoration.* P 12×12½.
659	314	6 c. vermilion and black	..	..	10	10

(Litho Ashton-Potter)

1970 (18 Sept). *50th Anniv of "Group of Seven" (artists).* P 11.
660	315	6 c. multicoloured	..	..	10	10

316 "Horse-drawn Sleigh"   317 "Christ in Manger"
(D. Niskala)   (C. Fortier)

(Des from children's drawings. Litho C.B.N.)

1970 (7 Oct). *Christmas. Horiz designs as* T 316/17, *showing children's drawings. Multicoloured.* P 12.
661	5 c. Type 316	..	..	50	20
	a. Strip of 5. Nos. 661/5	..	2·25	
	p. One centre phosphor band	..	90	1·25
	pa. Strip of 5. Nos. 661p/5p	..	4·00	
662	5 c. "Stable" and Star of Bethlehem" (L. Wilson) (26 × 21 *mm*)	50	20
	p. One centre phosphor band	..	90	1·25
663	5 c. "Snowmen" (M. Lecompte) (26 × 21 *mm*)	50	20
	p. One centre phosphor band	..	90	1·25
664	5 c. "Skiing" (D. Durham) (26 × 21 *mm*)	50	20
	p. One centre phosphor band	..	90	1·25
665	5 c. "Santa Claus" (A. Martin) (26 × 21 *mm*)	50	20
	p. One centre phosphor band	..	90	1·25
666	6 c. "Santa Claus" (E. Bhattacharya) (26 × 21 *mm*)	50	20
	a. Strip of 5. Nos. 666/70	..	2·25	
	p. Two phosphor bands	..	90	1·25
	pa. Strip of 5. Nos. 666p/70p..	..	4·00	
667	6 c. "Christ in Manger" (J. McKinney) (26 × 21 *mm*)	50	20
	p. Two phosphor bands	..	90	1·25
668	6 c. "Toy Shop" (N. Whateley) (26 × 21 *mm*)	50	20
	p. Two phosphor bands	..	90	1·25
669	6 c. "Christmas Tree" (J. Pomperleau) (26 × 21 *mm*)	50	20
	p. Two phosphor bands	..	90	1·25
670	6 c. "Church" (J. McMillan) (26 × 21 *mm*)	50	20
	p. Two phosphor bands	..	90	1·25
671	10 c. Type 317	..	..	30	30
	p. Two phosphor bands	..	55	1·25
672	15 c. "Trees and Sledge" (J. Dojcak) (35 × 21 *mm*)	45	60
	p. Two phosphor bands	..	70	1·75
661/72		Set of 12	4·75	2·50
661p/672p		Set of 12	8·50	12·50

The designs of the 5 c. and 6 c. were each issued with the various designs *se-tenant* in a diamond shaped arrangement within the sheet. This generally results in *se-tenant* pairs both vert and horiz, but due to the sheet arrangement vert and horiz pairs of the same design exist from the two centre vert and horiz rows.

328 Sir Donald A.   329 "Big Raven"
Smith   (E. Carr)

(Des Dora de Pédery-Hunt. Litho C.B.N.)

1970 (4 Nov). *150th Birth Anniv of Sir Donald Alexander Smith.* P 12.
673	328	6 c. yellow, brown and bronze-green	..	15	10

(Litho C.B.N.)

1971 (12 Feb). *Birth Centenary of Emily Carr (painter).* P 12.
674	329	6 c. multicoloured	..	..	20	20

330 Laboratory   331 "The Atom"
Equipment

(Des R. Webber. Litho B.A.B.N.)

1971 (3 Mar). *50th Anniv of Discovery of Insulin.* P 10½.
675	330	6 c. multicoloured	..	..	30	20

(Des R. Webber. Litho B.A.B.N.)

1971 (24 Mar). *Birth Centenary of Lord Rutherford (scientist).* P 11.
676	331	6 c. yellow, red and deep chocolate	20	10

332 Maple "Keys"   333 Louis Papineau

(Des Alma Duncan. Litho Ashton-Potter)

1971. *"The Maple Leaf in Four Seasons". T 332 and similar vert designs. Multicoloured.* P 11.
677	6 c. Type 332 (Spring) (14.4)	..	20	15
	a. Imperf (pair)	..	..	£600	
678	6 c. Green leaves (Summer) (16.6)	..	20	15
679	7 c. Autumn leaves (3.9)	..	20	15
	a. Grey (inscr and value) omitted	..	£2000	
680	7 c. Withered leaves and snow (Winter) (19.11)	20	15
677/80		Set of 4	70	55

(Des L. Marquart. Recess and photo B.A.B.N.)

1971 (7 May). *Death Centenary of Louis-Joseph Papineau (politician).* P 12½ × 12.
681	333	6 c. multicoloured	..	..	15	15

334 Chart of Coppermine River   335 "People" and
Computer Tapes

(Des L. Marquart. Recess and photo B.A.B.N.)

1971 (7 May). *Bicentenary of Samuel Hearne's Expedition to Coppermine River.* P 12 × 12½.
682	334	6 c. red, sepia and pale buff	..	40	40

(Des H. Kleefeld. Litho C.B.N.)

1971 (1 June). *Centenary of First Canadian Census.* P 11½.
683	335	6 c. blue, red and black	..	..	30	10

336 Maple Leaves

(Des B. Kramer. Litho C.B.N.)

1971 (1 June). *Radio Canada International.* P 12.
684	336	15 c. red, yellow and black	..	50	1·25
		p. Two phosphor bands	..	1·75	3·50

337 "BC"

(Des E. R. C. Bethune. Litho C.B.N.)

1971 (20 July). *Centenary of British Columbia's Entry into the Confederation.* P 12.
685	337	7 c. multicoloured	..	..	15	10

338 "Indian Encampment on Lake Huron" (Kane)

339 "Snowflake"

(Des and litho B.A.B.N.)

1971 (11 Aug). *Death Centenary of Paul Kane (painter).* P 12½.
586 338 7 c. multicoloured 20 10

(Des Lisl Levinsohn. Recess (6 c., 7 c.) or recess and litho (others) C.B.N.)

1971 (6 Oct). *Christmas.* T **379** *and similar design.* P 12.
687 339 6 c. deep blue 10 10
    p. One centre phosphor band 30 60
688 7 c. deep emerald 15 10
    p. Two phosphor bands 40 65
689 — 10 c. silver and cerise .. .. 55 1·25
    p. Two phosphor bands .. 1·00 2·25
690 — 15 c. silver, brown-purple and lavender 85 1·50
    p. Two phosphor bands .. 1·25 2·75
687/90 .. .. .. *Set of* 4 1·50 2·75
687p/90p .. .. .. *Set of* 4 2·75 5·50
Design:—10 c., 15 c. "Snowflake" design similar to Type **339**, but square (26×26 mm).

340 Pierre Laporte (Quebec Cabinet Minister)

341 Skaters

(Des G. Gundersen. Recess and litho B.A.B.N.)

1971 (20 Oct). *First Anniv of the Assassination of Pierre Laporte.* P 12½ × 12.
691 340 7 c. black/pale buff 15 10

(Des Design Workshop, Toronto. Litho C.B.N.)

1972 (1 Mar). *World Figure Skating Championships, Calgary.* P 12.
692 341 8 c. purple 15 10

MIGRATING FLUORESCENT BANDS. These are referred to in the notes after No. 610. In the following issues they exist on Nos. 719q/22q, 731q/2q and on early printings only of Nos. 702/6.

342 J. A. MacDonald

343 Forest, Central Canada

344 Vancouver

Type I

Type II

Two types of 10 c. (No. 702):
Type I. Light impression of green recess colour. Cross-hatching around "Canada" clearly visible (plate 1).
Type II. Green recess colour much more deeply etched. Cross-hatching around "Canada" entirely obscured (plates 2 and 3).

Type I

Type II

Two types of 15 c.:
Type I. Trees on hillside, shown in blue, clearly detailed (plate 1).
Type II. Trees shown in solid colour (plate 2).

Two types of 25 c.:
Type I. Bears' shadows evenly shaded.
Type II. Shadows have a solid central area.

(Des D. Annesley (1 to 10 c. (701)), R. Derreth (others))

1972–77. *Various designs as* T **342/4.**

(a) T **342** *and similar vert portraits. Recess C.B.N.* (1 *to* 6 c. *and last ptgs of* 7 *and* 8 c. (No. 700), B.A.B.N. (7, 8, 10 c. *and booklet panes*). *Two fluorescent bands.* P 12 × 12½ (1 *to* 8 c.) *or* 13 (10 c.). (17.10.73)
693 1 c. orange 10 10
  a. Booklet pane. Nos. 693×3, 698 and 700×2 (10.4.74) .. 65
  b. Booklet pane. Nos. 693×6, 698 and 700×11 (17.1.75) .. 2·25
  c. Booklet pane. Nos. 693×2, 694×4 and 701a×4 (1.9.76) .. 1·50
  d. Printed on the gummed side .. £150
694 2 c. deep green 10 10
695 3 c. agate 10 30
696 4 c. black 10 10
697 5 c. deep magenta 10 10
698 6 c. Indian red 10 10
  a. Printed on the gummed side .. 75·00
699 7 c. reddish brown (8.4.74) .. 10 30
700 8 c. dull ultramarine 15 10
  a. Perf 13 (12.76) .. .. 1·25 60
701 10 c. brown-lake (1.9.76) .. 40 10
  a. Perf 12×12½ (booklets) .. 80 90

(b) T **343** *and similar vert designs. Recess and photo B.A.B.N. Two fluorescent bands.* P 12½×12 (8.9.72)
702 10 c. dp green, blue-green & yellow-orge (I) 60 10
  a. Type II (7.74) .. 40 15
  b. Perf 13½ (2.76) .. 50 10
  p. Two phosphor bands .. 1·00 2·00
703 15 c. dull ultramarine and orange-brown (I) 90 15
  a. Type II (1975) .. 2·25 1·00
  b. Perf 13½ (2.76) .. 40 10
  p. Two phosphor bands .. 1·50 2·75
704 20 c. pale orange, reddish violet & ultram 65 10
  a. Perf 13½ (30.1.76) .. 30 10
  p. Two phosphor bands .. 2·00 3·00
705 25 c. deep ultramarine and pale blue (I) 85 10
  a. Type II (1975) .. 6·00 2·25
  b. Perf 13½ (2.76) .. 75 10
  p. Two phosphor bands .. 3·00 4·25
706 50 c. blue-green, royal blue and buff 45 30
  a. *Blue-green, ultramarine and buff* (8.74) 65 20
  b. Perf 13½ (2.76) .. .. 1·25 10

(c) T **344** *and similar horiz design. Recess B.A.B.N. and litho Ashton-Potter. No fluorescent bands.* P 11 (17.3.72)
707 $1 multicoloured .. .. 4·50 4·50
708 $2 multicoloured .. .. 1·50 2·00

(d) T **344.** *Recess and photo B.A.B.N. Two fluorescent bands.* P 12½ × 12 (24.10.73)
709 $1 multicoloured .. .. 2·25 1·00
  a. Perf 13½ (4.77) 85 40

(e) *As Nos.* 700/1. *Recess C.B.N. Imperf × perf* 10 (*coil stamps*)
710 8 c. dull ultramarine (10.4.74) .. 75 20
  a. Imperf (horiz pair) .. 80·00
711 10 c. brown-lake (1.9.76) .. 30 20
  a. Imperf (horiz pair) .. £110

CANADA — 1971

Designs (1 to 7c. show Canadian Prime Ministers):—2 c. W. Laurier; 3 c. R. Borden; 4 c. W. L. Mackenzie King; 5 c. R. B. Bennett; 6 c. L. B. Pearson; 7 c. Louis St. Laurent; 8 and 10 c. (Nos. 701/a, 711), Queen Elizabeth II; 15 c. American Bighorn sheep; 20 c. Prairie landscape from the air; 25 c. Polar Bears; 50 c. Seashore, Eastern Canada; $2 Quebec.

Stamps from booklets exist with one or two adjacent sides imperforate.

345 Heart

(Des Joyce Wieland. Recess B.A.B.N.)

1972 (7 Apr). *Heart Disease (World Health Day).* P 12×12½.
719 345 8 c. carmine 30 10
  q. Two fluorescent bands .. 60 25
The chemical used on No. 719q migrates.

346 Frontenac and Fort Saint-Louis, Quebec

(Des L. Marquart. Recess and photo B.A.B.N.)

1972 (17 May). *300th Anniv of Governor Frontenac's Appointment to New France.* P 12 × 12½.
720 346 8 c. brown-red, orange-brn & dp ultram 15 15
  q. Two fluorescent bands 15 15
The chemical used on No. 720q migrates.

347 Plains Indians' Artefacts

347a Buffalo Chase

(Des G. Beaupré. Litho Ashton-Potter (721/2, 725/6 and 729/30), B.A.B.N. (723/4), C.B.N. (727/8))

1972–76. *Canadian Indians. Two fluorescent bands* (Nos. 723/30 *and* 733/40). P 12×12½ (721/2, 725/6), 12 (723/4), 13 (727/30), 12½×12 (731/6) *or* 12½ (737/40).

(a) *Horiz designs issued in se-tenant pairs, the first showing Artefacts as* T **347**, *the second showing Scenes from Indian Life as* T **347a.**
721 8 c. multicoloured (6.7.72) 40 10
  a. Pair. Nos. 721/2 .. .. 85 1·00
  q. Two fluorescent bands 40 15
  qa. Pair. Nos. 721q/2q .. 85 1·00
722 8 c. dp brown, yellow & grey-black (6.7.72) 40 10
  q. Two fluorescent bands 40 15
723 8 c. multicoloured (21.2.73) 40 10
  a. Pair. Nos. 723/4 .. .. 85 1·00
724 8 c. multicoloured (21.2.73) 40 10
725 8 c. multicoloured (16.1.74) 40 10
  a. Pair. Nos. 725/6 .. .. 85 1·25
726 8 c. dp brown, yellow & grey-black (16.1.74) 40 10
727 8 c. multicoloured (4.4.75) 40 10
  a. Pair. Nos. 727/8 .. .. 85 1·25
728 8 c. multicoloured (4.4.75) 40 10
729 10 c. multicoloured (17.9.76) 40 20
  a. Pair. Nos. 729/30 .. .. 85 1·00
730 10 c. light stone and black (17.9.76) .. 40 20
Designs show the following tribes: Nos. 721/2 (T **347**/a), Plains Indians; 723/4, Algonkians; 725/6, Pacific Coast Indians; 727/8, Subarctic Indians; 729/30, Iroquoians.

348 Thunderbird and Tribal Pattern

348a Dancer in Ceremonial Costume

(Des G. Beaupré. Recess and photo B.A.B.N. (731/6). Litho and embossed Ashton-Potter (737, 739). Litho Ashton-Potter (738, 740))

(b) *Vert designs issued in se-tenant pairs, the first showing Thunderbird and pattern as* T **348**, *the second Costumes as* T **348a.**
731 8 c. lt yellow-orge, rose-red & blk (4.10.72) 40 15
  a. Pair. Nos. 731/2 .. .. 85 1·00
  q. Two fluorescent bands 40 15
  qa. Pair. Nos. 731q/2q .. .. 85 1·00
732 8 c. multicoloured (4.10.72) 40 15
  q. Two fluorescent bands 40 15
733 8 c. light rose-red, violet & black (28.11.73) 40 10
  a. Pair. Nos. 733/4 .. .. 85 1·00
734 8 c. turq-green, lake-brn & blk (28.11.73) 40 10

301

735	8 c. rose-red and black (22.2.74)	..	..	40	10
	a. Pair. Nos. 735/6		..	85	1·00
736	8 c. multicoloured (22.2.74)	..	..	40	10
737	8 c. myrtle-green, grey-brn & blk (4.4.75)			40	10
	a. Pair. Nos. 737/8		..	85	1·25
738	8 c. multicoloured (4.4.75)	..	..	40	10
739	10 c. olive-bistre, reddish orange and black				
	(17.9.76)	..	..	40	20
	a. Pair. Nos. 739/40		..	85	1·00
740	10 c. multicoloured (17.9.76)	..	..	40	20
721/40			Set of 20	7·50	2·10

Designs show the following tribes: Nos. 731/2 (T **348**(a)), Plains Indians; 733/4, Algonkians; 735/6, Pacific Coast Indians; 737/8, Subarctic Indians; 739/40, Iroquoians.

The fluorescent bands on Nos. 721q/2q and 731q/2q migrate.

349 Earth's Crust   **350** Candles

(Des Gottschalk and Ash Ltd. Litho Ashton-Potter)

1972 (2 Aug). *Earth Sciences. T* **349** *and similar square designs.* P 12.

741	15 c. multicoloured	..	..	1·40	1·75
	a. Block of 4. Nos. 741/4		..	5·00	
	q. Two fluorescent bands	..		1·50	2·00
	qa. Block of 4. Nos. 741q/4q			5·50	
742	15 c. pale grey, dull ultramarine and black			1·40	1·75
	q. Two fluorescent bands			1·50	2·00
743	15 c. multicoloured	..	..	1·40	1·75
	q. Two fluorescent bands			1·50	2·00
744	15 c. light emerald, red-orange and black			1·40	1·75
	q. Two fluorescent bands			1·50	2·00
741/4	..	..	Set of 4	5·00	6·00
741q/4q	..		Set of 4	5·50	7·50

Designs and Events:—No. 741, Photogrammetric surveying (12th Congress of International Society of Photogrammetry); No. 742, "Siegfried" lines (6th Conference of International Cartographic Association); No. 743, Type **349** (24th International Geological Congress); No. 744, Diagram of village at road-intersection (22nd International Geographical Congress).

Nos. 741/4 were issued in sheets of 64, made up of 4 panes of 16, each pane having a marginal commemorative inscription. Within a pane are 4 copies of each design, arranged in *se-tenant* blocks of 4.

(Des R. Webber. Litho Ashton-Potter)

1972 (1 Nov). *Christmas. T* **350** *and similar designs.* P 12½ × 12 (6 *and* 8 c.) *or* 11 × 10½ (*others*).

745	**350**	6 c. multicoloured	..	..	15	10
		p. One centre phosphor band	..	35	60
		q. Two fluorescent bands	..	20	15
746		8 c. multicoloured	..	..	20	10
		p. Two phosphor bands	..	40	70
		q. Two fluorescent bands	..	25	15
747	—	10 c. multicoloured	..	..	60	85
		p. Two phosphor bands	..	1·25	1·75
		q. Two fluorescent bands	..	60	90
748	—	15 c. multicoloured	..	..	80	1·25
		p. Two phosphor bands	..	1·50	2·50
		q. Two fluorescent bands	..	90	1·50
745/8	..	..	..	Set of 4	1·60	2·00
745p/8p	..	..		Set of 4	3·25	5·00
745q/8q	..	..		Set of 4	1·75	2·40

Designs: *Horiz* (36 × 20 *mm*)—10 c. Candles with fruits and pine boughs; 15 c. Candles with prayer-book, caskets and vase.

351 "The Blacksmith's Shop"   **352** François de
(Krieghoff)   Montmorency-Laval

(Des and litho B.A.B.N. and Saults & Pollard Ltd., Winnipeg)

1972 (29 Nov). *Death Centenary of Cornelius Krieghoff (painter).* P 12½.

| 749 | **351** | 8 c. multicoloured | .. | .. | 30 | 15 |
| | | q. Two fluorescent bands | .. | .. | 30 | 40 |

FLUORESCENT BANDS. Stamps from No. 750 onwards were issued only with two fluorescent bands, *unless otherwise stated.* Examples are known with the bands omitted in error, but such varieties are outside the scope of the catalogue.

(Des M. Fog and G. Lorange. Litho Ashton-Potter)

1973 (31 Jan). *350th Birth Anniv of Monsignor de Laval (First Bishop of Quebec).* P 11.

| 750 | **352** | 8 c. ultramarine, gold and silver | .. | 20 | 40 |

353 Commissioner French and Route of the March West

(Des Dallaire Morin DeVito Inc. Litho Ashton-Potter)

1973 (9 Mar). *Centenary of Royal Canadian Mounted Police.* T **353** *and similar horiz designs. Multicoloured (except* 8 c.). P 11.

751	8 c. Type **353** (deep reddish brown, dull			
	orange and orange-vermilion)		35	20
752	10 c. Spectrograph	..	1·00	1·25
753	15 c. Mounted policeman		1·40	2·00
751/3	..		Set of 3	2·50	3·00

354 Jeanne Mance

(Des R. Bellemare. Litho Ashton-Potter)

1973 (18 Apr). *300th Death Anniv of Jeanne Mance (nurse).* P 11.

| 754 | **354** | 8 c. multicoloured | .. | .. | 20 | 40 |

355 Joseph Howe   **356** "Mist Fantasy"
                       (MacDonald)

(Des A. Fleming. Litho Ashton-Potter)

1973 (16 May). *Death Centenary of Joseph Howe (Nova Scotian politician).* P 11.

| 755 | **355** | 8 c. gold and black | .. | .. | 20 | 40 |

(Des and litho Ashton-Potter)

1973 (8 June). *Birth Centenary of J. E. H. MacDonald (artist).* P 12½.

| 756 | **356** | 15 c. multicoloured | .. | .. | 30 | 55 |

357 Oaks and Harbour

(Des A. Mann. Recess and photo B.A.B.N.)

1973 (22 June). *Centenary of Prince Edward Island's Entry into the Confederation.* P 12.

| 757 | **357** | 8 c. pale orange and brown-red | .. | 20 | 30 |

358 Scottish Settlers   **359** Queen Elizabeth II

(Des P. Swan. Litho Ashton-Potter)

1973 (20 July). *Bicentennial of Arrival of Scottish Settlers at Pictou, Nova Scotia.* P 12 × 12½.

| 758 | **358** | 8 c. multicoloured | .. | .. | 25 | 20 |

(Des A. Fleming from photograph by Anthony Buckley. Eng G. A. Gundersen. Recess and photo B.A.B.N.)

1973 (2 Aug). *Royal Visit and Commonwealth Heads of Government Meeting, Ottawa.* P 12 × 12½.

759	**359**	8 c. multicoloured	..	25	20
760		15 c. red, black and bright gold	..	80	1·50
		a. Red, black and pale dull gold	..	1·10	1·90

360 Nellie McClung   **361** Emblem of 1976
                         Olympics

(Des S. Mennie. Litho Ashton-Potter)

1973 (29 Aug). *Birth Centenary of Nellie McClung (feminist).* P 10½ × 11.

| 761 | **360** | 8 c. multicoloured | .. | .. | 20 | 40 |

(Des Wallis and Matanovic. Litho Ashton-Potter)

1973 (20 Sept). *Olympic Games, Montreal* (1976) (1st issue). P 12 × 12½.

| 762 | **361** | 8 c. multicoloured | .. | .. | 25 | 15 |
| 763 | | 15 c. multicoloured | .. | .. | 45 | 1·25 |

See also Nos. 768/71, 772/4, 786/9, 798/802, 809/11, 814/16, 829/31, 833/7 and 842/4.

362 Ice-skate   **363** Diving

(Des A. Maggs. Litho Ashton-Potter)

1973 (7 Nov). *Christmas. T* **362** *and similar vert designs. Multicoloured.* P 12½ × 12 (6, 8 c.) *or* 11 (*others*).

764	6 c. Type **362**	..	..	15	10
765	8 c. Bird decoration	..	..	20	10
766	10 c. Santa Claus (20 × 36 mm)	..	70	1·40
767	15 c. Shepherd (20 × 36 mm)	..	80	1·75
764/7	..		Set of 4	1·75	3·00

(Des Hunter, Straker, Templeton Ltd. Recess C.B.N.)

1974 (22 Mar). *Olympic Games, Montreal* (1976) (2nd issue). *"Summer Activities". T* **363** *and similar vert designs. Each deep blue.* P 12.

768	8 c. Type **363**	..	..	25	50
	a. Block of 4. Nos. 768/71			90	
769	8 c. "Jogging"	..	..	25	50
770	8 c. Cycling	..	..	25	50
771	8 c. Hiking	..	..	25	50
768/71	..		Set of 4	90	1·75

Nos. 768/71 were printed in *se-tenant* blocks of four throughout the sheet. Each design has a second (latent) image—the Canadian Olympic Games symbol—which appears when the stamp is viewed obliquely to the light.

See also Nos. 786/9.

(Des Wallis and Matanovic. Litho Ashton-Potter)

1974 (17 Apr). *Olympic Games, Montreal* (1976) (3rd issue). *As T* **361** *but smaller* (20 × 36½ *mm*). P 12½.

772	**361**	8 c. + 2 c. multicoloured	..	25	45
773		10 c. + 5 c. multicoloured	..	35	1·00
774		15 c. + 5 c. multicoloured	..	40	1·40
772/4	..		Set of 3	90	2·50

364 Winnipeg Signpost, 1872   **365** Postmaster and Customer

(Des J. R. MacDonald. Litho and embossed Ashton-Potter)

1974 (3 May). *Winnipeg Centennial.* P 12½ × 12.

| 775 | **364** | 8 c. multicoloured | .. | .. | 20 | 15 |

(Des S. Mennie. Litho Ashton-Potter)

1974 (11 June). *Centenary of Canadian Letter Carrier Delivery Service. T* **365** *and similar horiz designs. Multicoloured.* P 13½.

776	8 c. Type **365**	..	..	50	80
	a. Block of 6. Nos. 776/81			2·75	
777	8 c. Postman collecting mail	..	50	80
778	8 c. Mail handler	..	..	50	80
779	8 c. Mail sorters	..	..	50	80
780	8 c. Postman making delivery	..	50	80
781	8 c. Rural delivery by car	..	50	80
776/81	..		Set of 6	2·75	4·25

Nos. 776/81 were printed in *se-tenant* combinations throughout a sheet of 50, giving 6 blocks of 6 and 14 single stamps.

366 "Canada's Contribution   **367** Telephone Development
to Agriculture"

(Des M. Brett, P. Cowley-Brown, and A. McAllister. Litho Ashton-Potter)

1974 (12 July). *"Agricultural Education". Centenary of Ontario Agricultural College.* P 12½ × 12.

| 782 | **366** | 8 c. multicoloured | .. | .. | 20 | 20 |

(Des R. Webber. Litho Ashton-Potter)

1974 (26 July). *Centenary of Invention of Telephone by Alexander Graham Bell.* P 12½.

| 783 | **367** | 8 c. multicoloured | .. | .. | 20 | 20 |

368 Bicycle Wheel

(Des Burns and Cooper. Recess and photo B.A.B.N.)

1974 (7 Aug). *World Cycling Championships, Montreal.* P 12 × 12½.
784 368 8 c. black, rosine and silver 20 30

369 Mennonite Settlers

(Des W. Davies. Litho Ashton-Potter)

1974 (28 Aug). *Centenary of Arrival of Mennonites in Manitoba.* P 12½.
785 369 8 c. multicoloured 20 20

(Des Hunter, Straker, Templeton Ltd. Recess C.B.N.)

1974 (23 Sept). *Olympic Games, Montreal (1976) (4th issue).* "Winter Activities". Horiz designs as T 363, each rosine. P 13½ × 13.
786 8 c. Snow-shoeing 50 60
  a. Block of 4. Nos. 786/9 .. .. 1·75
  ab. Printed on the gummed side (block of four) £650
787 8 c. Skiing 50 60
788 8 c. Skating 50 60
789 8 c. Curling 50 60
786/9 .. .. .. *Set of 4* 1·75 2·25

370 Mercury, Winged Horses and U.P.U. Emblem

(Des G. Gundersen. Recess and photo B.A.B.N.)

1974 (9 Oct). *Centenary of Universal Postal Union.* P 12 × 12½.
790 370 8 c. violet, red-orange and cobalt .. 15 15
791 15 c. red-orange, violet and cobalt .. 50 1·50

371 "The Nativity" 372 Marconi and St. John's
(J. P. Lemieux) Harbour, Newfoundland

(Des Wallis and Matanovic. Litho Ashton-Potter)

1974 (1 Nov). *Christmas. T 371 and similar horiz designs showing paintings.* Multicoloured. P 13½.
792 6 c. Type 371 .. .. .. 10 10
793 8 c. "Skaters in Hull" (H. Masson) (34 × 31 mm) 10 10
794 10 c. "The Ice Cone, Montmorency Falls" (R. C. Todd) 20 75
795 15 c. "Village in the Laurentian Mountains" (C. A. Gagnon) .. .. 30 1·10
792/5 .. .. .. *Set of 4* 60 1·75

(Des J. Boyle. Litho Ashton-Potter)

1974 (15 Nov). *Birth Centenary of Guglielmo Marconi (radio pioneer).* P 13.
796 372 8 c. multicoloured 20 20

373 Merritt and Welland Canal 374 Swimming

(Des W. Rueter. Recess (B.A.B.N.) and litho (C.B.N.))

1974 (29 Nov). *William Merritt Commemoration.* P 13 × 13½.
797 373 8 c. multicoloured 20 30

(Des Wallis and Matanovic. Litho C.B.N.)

1975 (5 Feb). *Olympic Games, Montreal (1976) (5th issue). T 374 and similar horiz designs.* Multicoloured.
798 8 c. + 2 c. Type 374 .. .. 30 50
799 10 c. + 5 c. Rowing 40 90
800 15 c. + 5 c. Sailing .. .. 45 1·00
798/800 .. .. .. *Set of 3* 1·00 2·25

375 "The Sprinter" 376 "Anne of Green Gables"
(Lucy Maud Montgomery)

(Des A. R. Fleming. Litho and embossed Ashton-Potter)

1975 (14 Mar). *Olympic Games, Montreal (1976) (6th issue). T 375 and similar multicoloured design showing sculpture by R. T. McKenzie.* P 12½ × 12 ($1) or 12 × 12½ ($2).
801 $1 Type 375 .. .. .. 2·00 2·75
802 $2 "The Diver" (vert) .. .. 2·75 4·75

(Des P. Swan (No. 803), C. Gagnon (No. 804). Litho Ashton-Potter)

1975 (15 May). *Canadian Writers (1st series). T 376 and similar vert design.* Multicoloured. P 13½.
803 8 c. Type 376 .. .. .. 30 10
  a. Pair. Nos. 803/4 .. .. 60 80
804 8 c. "Maria Chapdelaine" (Louis Hémon) .. 30 10
Nos. 803/4 were printed horizontally and vertically *se-tenant* throughout the sheet.
See also Nos. 846/7, 940/1 and 1085/6.

377 Marguerite Bourgeoys 378 S. D. Chown
(founder of the Order (founder of United Church
of Notre Dame) of Canada)

(Des Design and Communication, Montreal. Litho Ashton-Potter (Nos. 805/6). Des W. Southern. Eng G. Gundersen. Recess and photo B.A.B.N. (Nos. 807/8))

1975 (30 May). *Canadian Celebrities. T 377/8 and similar vert designs.*

(a) As T 377. P 12½ × 12
805 8 c. multicoloured 50 40
806 8 c. multicoloured 50 40

(b) As T 378. P 12 × 12½
807 8 c. sepia, flesh and light yellow .. 30 75
  a. Pair. Nos. 807/8 .. .. 60 2·25
808 8 c. sepia, flesh and light yellow .. 30 75
805/8 .. .. .. *Set of 4* 1·40 1·40
Designs:—No. 805, Type 377; No. 806, Alphonse Desjardins (leader of Credit Union movement); No. 807, Type 378; No. 808, Dr. J. Cook (first moderator of Presbyterian Church in Canada).
Nos. 807/8 were printed together in the sheet horizontally and vertically *se-tenant*.

379 Pole-vaulting 380 "Untamed"
(photo by Walt Petrigo)

(Des P. Swan. Litho Ashton-Potter)

1975 (11 June). *Olympic Games, Montreal (1976) (7th issue). T 379 and similar vert designs.* Multicoloured. P 12 × 12½.
809 20 c. Type 379 .. .. 35 50
810 25 c. Marathon-running 50 80
811 50 c. Hurdling .. .. 60 1·25
809/11 .. .. .. *Set of 3* 1·25 2·25

(Des B. Reilander. Litho C.B.N.)

1975 (3 July). *Centenary of Calgary.* P 12 × 12½.
812 380 8 c. multicoloured 20 30

381 I.W.Y. Symbol 382 Fencing

(Des Susan McPhee. Recess and photo B.A.B.N.)

1975 (14 July). *International Women's Year.* P 13.
813 381 8 c. lt grey-brown, bistre-yellow & blk 20 30

(Des J. Hill. Litho C.B.N.)

1975 (6 Aug). *Olympic Games, Montreal (1976) (8th issue). T 382 and similar vert designs showing combat sports.* Multicoloured. P 13.
814 8 c. + 2 c. Type 382 .. .. 30 45
815 10 c. + 5 c. Boxing .. .. 35 1·00
816 15 c. + 5 c. Judo .. .. 40 1·25
814/16 .. .. .. *Set of 3* 95 2·40

383 "Justice-Justitia" 384 William D. Lawrence
(statue by W. S. Allward) (full-rigged ship)

(Des A. Fleming. Litho Ashton-Potter)

1975 (2 Sept). *Centenary of Canadian Supreme Court.* P 12½.
817 383 8 c. multicoloured 20 30

(Des T. Bjarnason. Recess and photo B.A.B.N.)

1975 (24 Sept). *Canadian Ships (1st series). T 384 and similar horiz designs showing coastal ships.* P 13.
818 8 c. yellow-brown and black 60 75
  a. Block of 4. Nos. 818/21 .. 2·25
819 8 c. blue-green and black 60 75
820 8 c. yellow-green and black 60 75
821 8 c. yellow-brown and black 60 75
818/21 .. .. *Set of 4* 2·25 2·75
Designs:—No. 819, *Neptune* (steamer). No. 820, *Beaver* (paddle-steamer). No. 821, *Quadra* (steamer).
Nos. 818/21 were printed together, *se-tenant*, in different combinations throughout the sheet, giving ten blocks of 4 and ten single stamps.
See also Nos. 851/4, 902/5 and 931/4.

 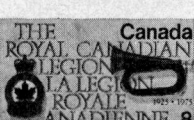

385 "Santa Claus" 386 Text, Badge and Bugle
(G. Kelly)

(Des B. Reilander from children's paintings. Litho Ashton-Potter)

1975 (22 Oct). *Christmas. T 385 and similar multicoloured designs.* P 13.
822 6 c. Type 385 .. .. 15 10
  a. Pair. Nos. 822/3 .. .. 30 40
823 6 c. "Skater" (Bill Cawsey) 15 10
824 8 c. "Child" (D. Hébert) 15 10
  a. Pair. Nos. 824/5 .. .. 30 45
825 8 c. "Family" (L. Caldwell) 15 10
826 10 c. "Gift" (D. Lovely) 30 50
827 15 c. "Trees" (R. Kowalski) (horiz) .. 40 75
822/7 .. .. .. *Set of 6* 1·10 1·90
Nos. 822/3 and 824/5 were respectively issued together *se-tenant* in an alternate arrangement within the sheet.

(Des R. Kavach. Recess and photo B.A.B.N.)

1975 (10 Nov). *50th Anniv of Royal Canadian Legion.* P 12½ × 13.
828 386 8 c. multicoloured 20 20

387 Basketball

(Des J. Hill. Litho Ashton-Potter)

1976 (7 Jan). *Olympic Games, Montreal (9th issue). T 387 and similar vert designs.* Multicoloured. P 13.
829 8 c. + 2 c. Type 387 .. .. 40 55
830 10 c. + 5 c. Gymnastics 45 90
831 20 c. + 5 c. Soccer .. .. 50 1·25
829/31 .. .. .. *Set of 3* 1·25 2·40

388 Games Symbol and Snow Crystal   389 "Communications Arts"

(Des R. Harder. Litho Ashton-Potter)

1976 (6 Feb). *12th Winter Olympic Games, Innsbruck.* P 12½.
832 388 20 c. multicoloured   20   40

(Des R. Webber. Litho C.B.N.)

1976 (6 Feb). *Olympic Games, Montreal* (10th issue). T **389** *and similar vert designs. Multicoloured.* P 12 × 12½.
833 20 c. Type **389**   30   25
834 25 c. "Handicrafts"   55   75
835 50 c. "Performing Arts"   70   1·60
833/5   *Set of 3* 1·40   2·40

390 Place Ville Marie and Notre-Dame Church

(Des J. and P. Mercier. Recess and photo B.A.B.N.)

1976 (12 Mar). *Olympic Games, Montreal* (11th issue). T **390** *and similar horiz design. Multicoloured.* P 13.
836 $1 Type **390**   2·00   4·50
837 $2 Olympic Stadium and flags   2·50   5·50

391 Flower and Urban Sprawl   392 Benjamin Franklin and Map

(Des I. McLeod. Litho Ashton-Potter)

1976 (12 May). *U.N. Conference on Human Settlements (HABITAT), Vancouver.* P 12 × 12½.
838 391 20 c. multicoloured   20   30

(Des B. Reilander. Recess and photo B.A.B.N.)

1976 (1 June). *Bicentenary of American Revolution.* P 13.
839 392 10 c. multicoloured   20   35

393 Wing Parade before Mackenzie Building   394 Transfer of Olympic Flame by Satellite

(Des W. Davies. Litho C.B.N.)

1976 (1 June). *Royal Military College Centenary.* T **393** *and similar vert design. Multicoloured.* P 12 × 12½.
840 8 c. Colour party and Memorial Arch   15   20
    a. Pair. Nos. 840/1   30   80
    ab. Printed double (pair)
841 8 c. Type **393**   15   20
Nos. 840/1 were printed horizontally and vertically *se-tenant* throughout the sheet.

(Des P. Swan. Litho Ashton-Potter)

1976 (18 June). *Olympic Games, Montreal* (12th issue). T **394** *and similar horiz designs. Multicoloured.* P 13½.
842 8 c. Type **394**   15   10
843 20 c. Carrying the Olympic flag   35   60
844 25 c. Athletes with medals   35   85
842/4   *Set of 3* 75   1·40

395 Archer

(Des T. Bjarnason. Litho C.B.N.)

1976 (3 Aug). *Olympiad for the Physically Disabled.* P 12 × 12½.
845 395 20 c. multicoloured   20   30

396 "Sam McGee" (Robert W. Service)   397 "Nativity" (F. Mayer)

(Des D. Bierk (No. 846), A. Dumas (No. 847). Litho Ashton-Potter)

1976 (17 Aug). *Canadian Writers* (2nd series). T **396** *and similar vert design. Multicoloured.* P 13.
846 8 c. Type **396**   15   30
    a. Pair. Nos. 846/7   30   1·00
847 8 c. "Le Survenant" (Germaine Guèvremont)   15   30
Nos. 846/7 were printed horizontally and vertically *se-tenant* throughout the sheet.

(Des B. Reilander. Litho Ashton-Potter)

1976 (3 Nov). *Christmas.* T **397** *and similar vert designs showing stained-glass windows. Multicoloured.* P 13½.
848 8 c. Type **397**   10   10
849 10 c. "Nativity" (G. Maile & Son)   10   10
850 20 c. "Nativity" (Yvonne Williams)   20   60
848/50   *Set of 3* 30   60

398 Northcote (paddle-steamer)   399 Queen Elizabeth II

(Des T. Bjarnason. Recess and litho C.B.N.)

1976 (19 Nov). *Canadian Ships* (2nd series). T **398** *and similar horiz designs showing inland vessels.* P 12 × 12½.
851 10 c. ochre, chestnut and black   40   55
    a. Block of 4. Nos. 851/4   1·40
852 10 c. violet-blue and black   40   55
853 10 c. bright blue and black   40   55
854 10 c. apple-green, olive-green and black   40   55
851/4   *Set of 4* 1·40   2·00
Designs:— No. 851, Type **398**; No. 852, *Passport* (paddle-steamer); No. 853, *Chicora* (paddle-steamer); No. 854, *Athabasca* (steamer).
Nos. 851/4 were printed together, *se-tenant*, in different combinations throughout the sheet, giving ten blocks of 4 and ten single stamps.

(Des K. Rodmell from photograph by P. Grugeon. Litho ("25" die-stamped) Ashton-Potter)

1977 (4 Feb). *Silver Jubilee.* P 12½ × 12.
855 399 25 c. multicoloured   30   50
    a. Silver (die-stamped "25") omitted £650 £325

400 Bottle Gentian   401 Queen Elizabeth II (bas-relief by J. Huta)   402 Houses of Parliament

403 Trembling Aspen   404 Prairie Town Main Street

405 Fundy National Park

(Des R. Derreth (Nos. 870/4). T. Bjarnason (880/3a), R. Bolt (884), B. Laycock and W. Tibbles (884b), B. Laycock (884c), A. Collier (885), W. Tibbles and G. Weber (No. 885a), W. Terry and W. Tibbles (885b), L. Marois and W. Tibbles (885c), Heather Cooper (others). Eng Y. Baril (880/3a))

1977 (1 Mar)–**86**. *(a) Vert designs as T* **400** *showing flowers. Multicoloured.* (i) *Recess and litho C.B.N. Sheet stamps.* P 12 × 12½.
856 1 c. Type **400** (22.4.77)   10   10
    a. Printed on the gummed side (pre-cancelled only)   £500
857 2 c. Red Columbine (22.4.77)   10   10
    a. Printed on the gummed side   £130
858 3 c. Canada Lily (22.4.77)   10   10
859 4 c. Hepatica (22.4.77)   10   10
    a. Printed on the gummed side   £130
860 5 c. Shooting Star (22.4.77)   10   10
861 10 c. Franklin's Lady's Slipper Orchid (22.4.77)   15   10
    a. Perf 13 × 13½ (5.10.78)   40   30

(ii) *Recess and photo B.A.B.N. Booklet stamps* (1, 2 c.) *or sheet stamps* (others). *Chalk-surfaced paper.* P 12 × 12½ (1, 2 c.) *or* 13 × 13½ (others)
862 1 c. Type **400** (1.11.77)   65   2·25
    a. Booklet pane. Nos. 862 × 2 and 867a × 4   2·75
    b. Perf 13 × 13½ (from sheets) (16.6.79) 10   10
863 2 c. Red Columbine (1.4.78)   65   90
    a. Booklet pane. Nos. 863 × 4 and 868a × 3 plus one printed label   3·25
    b. Perf 13 × 13½ (from sheets) (2.8.79) 10   10
864 3 c. Canada Lily (11.4.79)   20   10
864a 4 c. Hepatica (3.7.79)   20   10
865 5 c. Shooting Star (24.1.79)   20   10
865a 10 c. Franklin's Lady's Slipper Orchid (4.10.79)   60   10
866 12 c. Jewelweed (6.7.78)   15   40
866a 15 c. Canada Violet (16.8.79)   15   15

(b) T **401**. *Recess and photo B.A.B.N. Chalk-surfaced paper.* P 13 × 13½
867 12 c. black, grey and cobalt (1.3.77)   15   10
    a. Perf 12 × 12½ (from booklets) (1.11.77)   70   1·00
868 14 c. black, grey and rose-red (7.3.78)   20   10
    a. Perf 12 × 12½ (from booklets) (1.4.78)   50   85
    ab. Booklet pane. No. 868a × 25, plus two printed labels (13.11.78)   11·00
869 17 c. black, grey & yellowish green (8.3.79)   50   10
    a. Perf 12 × 12½ (from booklets) (3.7.79)   50   30
    ab. Booklet pane. No. 869a × 25, plus two printed labels (3.7.79)   11·00
869b 30 c. maroon, grey & reddish pur (11.5.82)   50   50
    ba. Maroon, grey and bright mauve (9.83) 1·60   80
869c 32 c. black, grey and light blue (24.5.83)   45   60
    ca. Grey printed double   †

(c) T **402**. (i) *Recess C.B.N.* (Nos. 872a, 873/4) *or B.A.B.N.* (others). *Booklet stamps* (Nos. 870/1) *or sheet stamps* (others). *Chalk-surfaced paper* (1, 5, 12 c.). P 12 × 12½ (1, 5 c.) *or* 13 × 13½ (others)
870 1 c. indigo (28.3.79)   1·25   2·50
    a. Booklet pane. Nos. 869a × 2, 870 and 871 × 3   2·50
871 5 c. deep rose-lilac (28.3.79)   35   40
872 12 c. blue (chalk-surfaced paper) (3.5.77)   30   10
    a. New blue (ordinary paper) (4.78)   50   10
    ab. Printed on the gummed side   £130
873 14 c. scarlet (7.3.78)   15   10
    a. Printed on the gummed side   18·00
874 17 c. deep green (8.3.79)   30   10
    a. Printed on the gummed side   19·00
(ii) *Recess C.B.N. Coil stamps. Imperf × perf* 10
874b 12 c. new blue (3.5.77)   30   30
    ba. Imperf (horiz pair)   90·00
874c 14 c. scarlet (7.3.78)   60   40
    ca. Imperf (horiz pair)   90·00
874d 17 c. deep green (8.3.79)   50   20
    da. Imperf (horiz pair)   £100

(d) Vert designs as T **403** *showing leaves. Multicoloured. Recess and photo B.A.B.N. Chalk-surfaced paper.* P 13½
875 15 c. Type **403** (8.8.77)   15   10
876 20 c. Douglas Fir (8.8.77)   15   10
877 25 c. Sugar Maple (8.8.77)   15   10
878 30 c. Red Oak (7.3.78)   20   10
879 35 c. White Pine (8.3.79)   25   10

(e) Horiz designs at T **404** *showing city streets. Multicoloured.* P 13½
(i) *Recess and photo B.A.B.N. Chalk-surfaced paper. No fluorescent bands* (75, 80 c.). (6.7.78)
880 50 c. Type **404**   1·00   90
881 75 c. Eastern city street   85   1·00
882 80 c. Maritimes street   85   90
(ii) *Recess and litho C.B.N.*
883 50 c. Type **404** (13.12.78)   85   60
883a 60 c. Ontario city street (11.5.82)   65   50

(f) Horiz designs as T **405** *showing national parks. Multicoloured. Recess and litho C.B.N. or B.A.B.N.* (ptgs of Nos. 884ba, 885c and 885e from 26 Sept 1986). No. 884 with or without fluorescent bands, others only exist without. P 13½
884 $1 Type **405** (fluorescent bands) (24.1.79)   90   50
    a. No fluorescent bands (4.3.81)   1·10   55
    ab. Black (inscr and value) ptd albino   £400
884b $1 Glacier (chalk-surfaced paper) (15.8.84)   85   45
    ba. Ordinary paper (12.7.85)   1·50   80
884c $1.50, Waterton Lakes (18.6.82)   2·50   2·50

885	$2 Kluane (27.4.79)	1·50	45
	a. Silver (inscr and value) omitted	£250	
	b. Chalk-surfaced paper (14.12.84)	4·00	2·00
885c	$2 Banff (21.6.85)	3·75	90
	ca. Bottle-green (inscr and value) omitted	£600	
885d	$5 Point Pelee (10.1.83)	5·50	2·25
	da. Chalk-surfaced paper (14.12.84)	7·00	3·50
885e	$5 La Mauricie (14.3.86)	7·00	4·00

The main differences between No. 861a and No. 865a are in the background. On No. 865a this is toned and has the blurred edges typical of photogravure. No. 861a has a background of solid appearance with the edges clean. The B.A.B.N. version also has stronger lines on the recess part of the design.

No. 883 can be identified from 880 in that the brown printing from the recess plate of the former is deeper and the detail more defined; the registration plate of the car in the foreground can clearly be seen under a glass as "1978". The "hidden date" (1977) occurs alongside the grain elevator door on No. 880. Also the colours from the lithographic plates of No. 883 are much bolder than those from the photogravure cylinders of 880. In addition the paper of No. 883 has a shiny appearance.

No. 884ab shows an uninked impression of the recess-printed part of the design.

Stamps with one or two adjacent sides imperforate come from booklets.

406 Puma   **407** "April in Algonquin Park"

(Des R. Bateman. Litho Ashton-Potter)

1977 (30 Mar). *Endangered Wildlife* (1st series). P 12½.

886	406	12 c. multicoloured	20	20

See also Nos. 906, 936/7, 976/7 and 1006/7.

(Litho Ashton-Potter)

1977 (26 May). *Birth Centenary of Tom Thomson (painter)*. T 407 *and similar square design. Multicoloured.* P 12.

887	12 c. Type 407	15	10
	a. Pair. Nos. 887/8	30	70
888	12 c. "Autumn Birches"	15	10

Nos. 887/8 were printed horizontally and vertically *se-tenant* throughout the sheet.

408 Crown and Lion   **409** Peace Bridge, Niagara River

(Des A. Hobbs. Litho (No. 890 also embossed) Ashton-Potter)

1977 (30 June). *Anniversaries.* T 408 *and similar horiz design. Multicoloured.* P 12½.

889	12 c. Type 408	15	20
890	12 c. Order of Canada	15	20

Events:—No. 889, 25th Anniv of first Canadian-born Governor-General; No. 890, Tenth Anniv of Order of Canada.

(Des R. Harder. Litho Ashton-Potter)

1977 (4 Aug). *50th Anniv of Opening of Peace Bridge.* P 12½.

891	409	12 c. multicoloured	15	15

410 Sir Sandford Fleming (engineer)

(Des W. Davies. Recess B.A.B.N.)

1977 (16 Sept). *Famous Canadians.* T 410 *and similar horiz design.* P 13.

892	12 c. grey-blue	20	10
	a. Pair. Nos. 892/3	40	70
893	12 c. reddish brown	20	10

Design:—No. 892, Joseph E. Bernier (explorer) and *Arctic* (survey ship).

The above were printed together, horizontally and vertically *se-tenant* throughout the sheet.

411 Peace Tower, Parliament Buildings, Ottawa   **412** Hunter Braves following Star

(Des S. Ash. Litho Ashton-Potter)

1977 (19 Sept). *23rd Commonwealth Parliamentary Conference.* P 12½.

894	411	25 c. multicoloured	20	30

(Des R. G. White. Litho C.B.N.)

1977 (26 Oct). *Christmas.* T 412 *and similar horiz designs depicting Canada's first Christmas carol "Jesous Ahatonhia". Multicoloured.* P 13½ × 13.

895	10 c. Type 412	10	10
	a. Printed on the gummed side	£200	
896	12 c. Angelic choir and the Northern Lights	10	10
	a. Imperf (vert pair)	£500	
897	25 c. Christ Child and chiefs ..	20	45
895/7	.. .. *Set of* 3	35	45

413 Seal Hunter (soapstone sculpture)   **414** Pinky (fishing boat)

(Des R. Derreth. Litho Ashton-Potter)

1977 (18 Nov). *Canadian Eskimos ("Inuits") (1st series). Hunting.* T 413 *and similar horiz designs. Multicoloured.* P 12 × 12½.

898	12 c. Type 413	25	25
	a. Pair. Nos. 898/9 ..	50	70
899	12 c. Fishing with spear	25	25
900	12 c. Disguised archer ..	25	25
	a. Pair. Nos. 900/1 ..	50	70
901	12 c. Walrus hunting	25	25
898/901	.. .. .. *Set of* 4	90	90

Nos. 898/9 and 900/1 were each printed together, *se-tenant*, in horizontal and vertical pairs throughout the sheet.

See also Nos. 924/7, 958/61 and 989/92.

(Des T. Bjarnason. Recess and litho C.B.N.)

1977 (18 Nov). *Canadian Ships (3rd series).* T 414 *and similar horiz designs, showing sailing craft. Multicoloured.* P 12 × 12½.

902	12 c. Type 414	20	30
	a. Block of 4. Nos. 902/5 ..	70	
	ab. Imperf (block of 4)		
903	12 c. *Malahat* (schooner)	20	30
904	12 c. Tern schooner	20	30
905	12 c. Mackinaw boat	20	30
902/5	.. .. .. *Set of* 4	70	1·00

Nos. 902/5 were printed together, *se-tenant*, in different combinations throughout the sheet, giving ten blocks of 4 and ten single stamps.

415 Peregrine Falcon   **416** Pair of 1851 12d. Black Stamps

(Des R. Bateman. Litho Ashton-Potter)

1978 (18 Jan). *Endangered Wildlife (2nd series).* P 12½.

906	415	12 c. multicoloured	30	20

(Des C. Brett. Recess and photo B.A.B.N.)

1978 (18 Jan). *"CAPEX 78" International Stamp Exhibition, Toronto (1st issue).* P 13.

907	416	12 c. black and brownish grey ..	10	10

See also Nos. 914/17.

417 Games Emblem   **418** "Captain Cook" (Nathaniel Dance)

(Des S. Ash. Litho Ashton-Potter)

1978 (31 Mar). *Commonwealth Games. Edmonton (1st issue).* T 417 *and similar horiz design. Multicoloured.* P 12½.

908	14 c. Type 417	10	10
909	30 c. Badminton	20	50

See also Nos. 918/21.

(Des W. Rueter. Litho Ashton-Potter)

1978 (26 Apr). *Bicentenary of Cook's Third Voyage.* T 418 *and similar vert design. Multicoloured.* P 13½.

910	14 c. Type 418	20	20
	a. Pair. Nos. 910/11	40	70
911	14 c. "Nootka Sound" (J. Webber) ..	20	20

Nos. 910/11 were printed together, *se-tenant*, in horizontal and vertical pairs throughout the sheet.

419 Hardrock Silver Mine, Cobalt, Ontario   **420** Princes' Gate (Exhibition entrance)

(Des W. Davies. Litho Ashton-Potter)

1978 (19 May). *Resource Development.* T 419 *and similar horiz design. Multicoloured.* P 12½.

912	14 c. Type 419	15	20
	a. Pair. Nos. 912/13 ..	30	70
913	14 c. Giant excavators, Athabasca Tar Sands	15	20

Nos. 912/13 were printed together, *se-tenant*, in horizontal and vertical pairs throughout the sheet.

(Des C. Brett. Eng R. Couture. Recess and photo B.A.B.N.)

1978 (10 June). *"CAPEX 78" International Stamp Exhibition, Toronto (2nd issue). Horiz designs as* T 416. *Two fluorescent bands (none on $1.25 from miniature sheet).* P 13.

914	14 c. Prussian blue, pale grey and brownish grey	15	10
915	30 c. deep rose, pale grey and brownish grey	25	35
916	$1.25, slate-violet, pale grey & brnish grey	1·00	1·40
914/16	.. .. .. *Set of* 3	1·25	1·60
MS917	101 × 76 mm. Nos. 914/16	1·50	2·50

Designs:—14 c. Pair of 1855 10d. Cartier stamps; 30 c. Pair of 1857 ½d. deep rose stamps; $1.25, Pair of 1851 6d. Prince Albert stamps.

(Des S. Ash. Litho Ashton-Potter)

1978 (3 Aug). *Commonwealth Games, Edmonton (2nd issue). Horiz designs as* T 417. *Multicoloured.* P 12½.

918	14 c. Games stadium	20	20
	a. Pair. Nos. 918/19 ..	40	70
919	14 c. Running	20	20
920	30 c. Alberta Legislature building ..	40	50
	a. Pair. Nos. 920/1 ..	80	1·50
921	30 c. Bowls	40	50
918/21	.. .. .. *Set of* 4	1·10	1·10

Nos. 918/19 and 920/1 were each printed together, *se-tenant*, in horizontal and vertical pairs throughout the sheet.

(Des T. Dimson, Litho Ashton-Potter)

1978 (16 Aug). *Centenary of National Exhibition.* P 12½.

922	420	14 c. multicoloured	15	30

421 Marguerite d'Youville   **422** "Madonna of the Flowering Pea" (Cologne School)

(Des A. Dumas. Litho C.B.N.)

1978 (21 Sept). *Marguerite d'Youville (founder of Grey Nuns) Commemoration.* P 13.

923	421	14 c. multicoloured	15	30

(Des R. Derreth. Litho Ashton-Potter)

1978 (27 Sept). *Canadian Eskimos ("Inuits") (2nd series). Travel. Horiz designs as* T 413. *Multicoloured.* P 12½.

924	14 c. Woman on foot (painting by Pitseolak) ..	15	15
	a. Pair. Nos. 924/5 ..	30	65
925	14 c. "Migration" (soapstone sculpture of sailing umiak by Joe Talurinili) ..	15	15
926	14 c. Aeroplane (stonecut and stencil print by Pudlo) ..	15	15
	a. Pair. Nos. 926/7 ..	30	65
927	14 c. Dogteam and dogsled (ivory sculpture by Abraham Kingmeatook) ..	15	15
924/7	.. .. .. *Set of* 4	60	55

Nos. 924/5 and 926/7 were each printed together, *se-tenant*, in horizontal and vertical pairs throughout the sheet.

(Des J. Morin. Litho Ashton-Potter)

1978 (20 Oct). *Christmas. Paintings.* T 422 *and similar vert designs. Multicoloured.* P 12½.

928	12 c. Type 422	10	10
929	14 c. "The Virgin and Child with St. Anthony and Donor" (detail, Hans Memling) ..	10	10
930	30 c. "The Virgin and Child" (Jacopo di Cione)	25	60
928/30	.. .. .. *Set of* 3	35	65

423 *Chief Justice Robinson* (paddle-steamer)   **424** Carnival Revellers

(Des T. Bjarnason. Recess and litho C.B.N.)

1978 (15 Nov). *Canadian Ships (4th series).* T 423 *and similar horiz designs showing ice vessels. Multicoloured.* P 13.

931	14 c. Type 423	45	65
	a. Block of 4. Nos. 931/4 ..	1·60	
932	14 c. *St. Roch* (steamer)	45	65
933	14 c. *Northern Light* (steamer) ..	45	65
934	14 c. *Labrador* (steamer)	45	65
931/4	.. .. .. *Set of* 4	1·60	2·40

Nos. 931/4 were printed together, *se-tenant*, in different combinations throughout the sheet, giving ten block of 4 and ten single stamps.

(Des A. Dumas. Litho Ashton-Potter)

1979 (1 Feb). *Quebec Carnival.* P 13.
935 424 14 c. multicoloured 20 20

Canada 17
POSTAL
CODE
CODE
POSTAL

Canada

17

425 Eastern Spiny Soft-shelled Turtle (*Trionyx spinifera*) **426** Knotted Ribbon round Woman's Finger

(Des G. Lowe (17 c.), R. Bateman (35 c.). Litho Ashton-Potter)

1979 (10 Apr). *Endangered Wildlife* (3rd series). T **425** and similar horiz design. Multicoloured. P 12½.
936 17 c. Type **425** 20 10
937 35 c. Bowhead Whale (*Balaena mysticetus*) .. 70 90

(Des D. Haws. Litho Ashton-Potter)

1979 (27 Apr). *Postal Code Publicity.* T **426** and similar vert design. Multicoloured. P 13.
938 17 c. Type **426** 15 10
  a. Pair. Nos. 938/9 .. .. .. 30 80
939 17 c. Knotted string round man's finger 15 10
Nos. 938/9 were printed together, *se-tenant*, in horizontal and vertical pairs throughout the sheet.

427 Scene from "Fruits of the Earth" by Frederick Philip Grove **428** Charles-Michel de Salaberry (military hero)

(Des Rosemary Kilbourne (No. 940), Monique Charbonneau (941). Litho C.B.N.)

1979 (3 May). *Canadian Writers* (3rd series). T **427** and similar horiz design. Multicoloured. P 13.
940 17 c. Type **427** 15 15
  a. Pair. Nos. 940/1 .. .. .. 30 85
  ab. Imperf (vert pair)
941 17 c. Scene from "Le Vaisseau d'Or" by Emile Nelligan 15 15
Nos. 940/1 were printed together, *se-tenant*, in horizontal and vertical pairs throughout the sheet.

(Des T. Dimson. Litho and embossed Ashton-Potter)

1979 (11 May). *Famous Canadians.* T **428** and similar vert design. Multicoloured. P 13.
942 17 c. Type **428** 25 15
  a. Pair. Nos. 942/3 .. .. .. 50 80
943 17 c. John By (engineer) 25 15
Nos. 942/3 were printed together, *se-tenant*, in horizontal and vertical pairs throughout the sheet.

Canada 17

429 Ontario **430** Paddling Kayak

(Des R. Bellemare. Litho Ashton-Potter)

1979 (15 June). *Canada Day. Flags.* Sheet 128 × 140 *mm* containing T **429** and similar horiz designs. Multicoloured. P 13.
MS944 17 c. × 12; Type **429**; Quebec; Nova Scotia; New Brunswick; Manitoba; British Columbia; Prince Edward Island; Saskatchewan; Alberta; Newfoundland; Northwest Territories; Yukon Territory .. .. 3·25 4·25

(Des J. Eby. Litho Ashton-Potter)

1979 (3 July). *Canoe-Kayak Championships.* P 12½
956 430 17 c. multicoloured 15 30

431 Hockey Players **432** Toy Train

(Des J. Eby. Litho Ashton-Potter)

1979 (16 Aug). *Women's Field Hockey Championships, Vancouver.* P 12½.
957 431 17 c. black, yellow and emerald .. 15 30

(Des R. Derreth. Litho Ashton-Potter)

1979 (13 Sept). *Canadian Eskimos* ("*Inuits*") (3rd series). "Shelter" (Nos. 958/9) and "Community" (Nos. 960/1). Horiz designs as T **413**. Multicoloured. P 13.
958 17 c. "Summer Tent" (print by Kiakshuk) .. 15 15
  a. Pair. Nos. 958/9 .. .. .. 30 80
959 17 c. "Five Eskimos building an Igloo" (soapstone sculpture by Abraham) 15 15
960 17 c. "The Dance" (print by Kalvak) .. 15 15
  a. Pair. Nos. 960/1 .. .. .. 30 80
961 17 c. "Inuit drum dance" (soapstone sculptures by Madeleine Isserkut and Jean Mapsalak) 15 15
958/61 .. .. Set of 4 60 55
Nos. 958/9 and 960/1 were each printed together, *se-tenant*, in horizontal and vertical pairs throughout the sheet.

(Des A. Maggs. Litho C.B.N.)

1979 (17 Oct). *Christmas.* T **432** and similar multicoloured designs showing toys. Fluorescent frame (35 c.) or two fluorescent bands (others). P 13.
962 15 c. Type **432** 10 10
963 17 c. Hobby-horse 10 10
964 35 c. Rag-doll (*vert*) 25 50
962/4 .. .. Set of 3 35 50

Canada 17

17

433 "Child watering Tree of Life" (painting by Marie-Annick Viatour) **434** Canadair CL-215

(Des J. Morin. Litho Ashton-Potter)

1979 (24 Oct). *International Year of the Child.* P 13.
965 433 17 c. multicoloured 15 30

(Des R. Bradford and J. Charette. Litho Ashton-Potter)

1979 (15 Nov). *Canadian Aircraft* (1st series). *Flying Boats.* T **434** and similar horiz designs. Multicoloured. P 12½.
966 17 c. Type **434** 20 15
  a. Pair. Nos. 966/7 .. .. .. 40 70
967 17 c. Curtiss HS-2L 20 15
968 35 c. Vickers Vedette 50 55
  a. Pair. Nos. 968/9 .. .. .. 1·00 1·40
969 35 c. Consolidated PBY-5A Canso .. 50 55
966/9 .. .. Set of 4 1·25 1·10
Nos. 966/7 and 968/9 were each printed together, *se-tenant*, in horizontal and vertical pairs throughout the sheet.
See also Nos. 996/9, 1026/9 and 1050/3.

Canada 17 Canada 35

435 Map of Arctic Islands **436** Skiing

(Des Gottschalk and Ash Ltd. Litho Ashton-Potter)

1980 (23 Jan). *Centenary of Arctic Islands Acquisition.* P 13.
970 435 17 c. multicoloured 15 30

(Des C. Malenfant. Litho C.B.N.)

1980 (23 Jan). *Winter Olympic Games, Lake Placid, U.S.A.* P 13.
971 436 35 c. multicoloured 55 65

CANADA 17 17

437 "A Meeting of the School Trustees" (painting by Robert Harris) **438** Canadian Whitefish (*Coregonus canadenis*)

(Des J. Morin. Litho Ashton-Potter)

1980 (6 Mar). *Centenary of Royal Canadian Academy of Arts.* T **437** and similar horiz designs. Multicoloured. P 13.
972 17 c. Type **437** 25 15
  a. Pair. Nos. 972/3 .. .. .. 50 50
973 17 c. "Inspiration" (sculpture by Philippe Hébert) 25 15
974 35 c. "Sunrise on the Saguenay" (painting by Lucius O'Brien) 50 35
  a. Pair. Nos. 974/5 .. .. .. 1·00 1·50
975 35 c. Sketch of design for original Parliament Buildings by Thomas Fuller .. 50 35
972/5 .. .. Set of 4 1·40 90
Nos. 972/3 and 974/5 were each printed together, *se-tenant*, in horizontal and vertical pairs throughout the sheet.

(Des M. Dumas (No. 976), R. Bateman (No. 977). Litho Ashton-Potter)

1980 (6 May). *Endangered Wildlife* (4th series). T **438** and similar horiz design. Multicoloured. P 12½.
976 17 c. Type **438** 15 15
977 17 c. Prairie Chicken (*Tympanuchus cupido pinnatus*) 15 15

---

439 Garden Flowers **440** "Helping Hand"

(Des Heather Cooper. Litho Ashton-Potter)

1980 (29 May). *International Flower Show, Montreal.* P 13.
978 439 17 c. multicoloured 15 20

(Des R. Harder. Litho and embossed Ashton-Potter)

1980 (29 May). *Rehabilitation.* P 12½.
979 440 17 c. gold and ultramarine 15 20

Canada

CANADA 17

441 Opening Bars of "Ô Canada" **442** John G. Diefenbaker

(Des F. Peter. Litho Ashton-Potter)

1980 (6 June). *Centenary of "O Canada"* (national song). T **441** and similar horiz design. Multicoloured. P 12½.
980 17 c. Type **441** 15 15
  a. Pair. Nos. 980/1 .. .. .. 30 40
981 17 c. Calixa Lavallee (composer), Adolphe-Basile Routhier (original writer) and Robert Stanley Weir (writer of English version) 15 15
Nos. 980/1 were printed together, *se-tenant*, in horizontal and vertical pairs throughout the sheet.

(Des B. Reilander. Eng Y. Baril. Recess C.B.N.)

1980 (20 June). *John G. Diefenbaker* (former Prime Minister) *Commemoration.* P 13½ × 13.
982 442 17 c. deep ultramarine 15 20

CANADA 17 CANADA 17

443 Emma Albani (singer) **444** Alberta

(Des C. Webster (No. 985), H. Brown (others). Litho Ashton-Potter)

1980 (4 July). *Famous Canadians.* T **443** and similar multicoloured designs. P 13.
983 17 c. Type **443** 15 25
  a. Pair. Nos. 983/4 .. .. .. 30 85
984 17 c. Healey Willan (composer) 15 25
985 17 c. Ned Hanlan (oarsman) (*horiz*) .. 15 15
983/5 .. .. Set of 3 40 60
Nos. 983/4 were printed together, *se-tenant*, in horizontal and vertical pairs throughout the sheet.

(Des G. Hunter and C. Yaneff. Litho Ashton-Potter)

1980 (27 Aug). *75th Anniv of Alberta and Saskatchewan Provinces.* T **444** and similar horiz design. Multicoloured. P 13.
986 17 c. Type **444** 15 15
987 17 c. Saskatchewan 15 15

Canada .35 CANADA

445 Uraninite Molecular Structure **446** "Christmas Morning" (J. S. Hallam)

(Des J. Charette. Litho C.B.N.)

1980 (3 Sept). *Uranium Resources.* P 13.
988 445 35 c. multicoloured 30 30

(Des R. Derreth. Litho C.B.N.)

1980 (25 Sept). *Canadian Eskimos* ("*Inuits*") (4th series). *Spirits.* Horiz designs as T **413**. Multicoloured. P 13½.
989 17 c. "Return of the Sun" (print by Kenojouak) 20 15
  a. Pair. Nos. 989/90 .. .. .. 40 55
990 17 c. "Sedna" (sculpture by Ashoona Kiawak) 20 15
991 35 c. "Shaman" (print by Simon Tookoome) .. 35 30
  a. Pair. Nos. 991/2 .. .. .. 70 1·00
992 35 c. "Bird Spirit" (sculpture by Doris Hagiolok) 35 30
989/92 .. .. Set of 4 1·00 80
Nos. 989/90 and 991/2 were each printed together, *se-tenant*, in horizontal and vertical pairs throughout the sheet.

(Des Yvon Laroche. Litho Ashton-Potter)

1980 (22 Oct). *Christmas. Paintings. T 446 and similar vert designs. Multicoloured. P 12½ × 12.*
993	15 c. Type 446	.. ..	10	10
994	17 c. "Sleigh Ride" (Frank Hennessy)..		15	10
995	35 c. "McGill Cab Stand" (Kathleen Morris) ..		30	90
993/5	.. ..	*Set of* 3	50	90

447 Avro (Canada) CF-100
Canuck Mk 5

(Des R. Bradford and J. Charette. Litho C.B.N.)

1980 (10 Nov). *Canadian Aircraft (2nd series). T 447 and similar horiz designs. Multicoloured. P 13.*
996	17 c. Type 447	.. ..	15	15
	a. Pair. Nos. 996/7	.. ..	30	60
997	17 c. Avro Type 683 Lancaster	..	15	15
998	35 c. Curtiss JN-4 Canuck	..	30	60
	a. Pair. Nos. 998/9	.. ..	60	1·25
999	35 c. Hawker Hurricane Mk 1	..	30	50
996/9	.. ..	*Set of* 4	80	1·10

Nos. 996/7 and 998/9 were each printed together, *se-tenant*, in horizontal and vertical pairs throughout the sheet.

448 Emmanuel-Persillier
Lachapelle
449 Mandora Instrument
(18th-century)

(Des J. Morin. Litho Ashton-Potter)

1980 (5 Dec). *Dr. Emmanuel-Persillier Lachapelle (founder of Notre-Dame Hospital, Montreal) Commemoration. P 13½.*
1000	448 17 c. cobalt, chocolate and brown		15	15

(Des C. Webster. Litho Ashton-Potter)

1981 (19 Jan). *"The Look of Music" Exhibition, Vancouver. P 12½.*
1001	449 17 c. multicoloured	.. ..	15	15

450 Henrietta Edwards
451 Vancouver Marmot
(*Marmota vancouverensis*)

(Des Muriel Wood and D. Goddard. Litho C.B.N.)

1981 (4 Mar). *Feminists. T 450 and similar horiz designs. Multicoloured. P 13.*
1002	17 c. Type 450	..	15	15
	a. Block of 4. Nos. 1002/5	..	55	
1003	17 c. Louise McKinney	..	15	15
1004	17 c. Idola Saint-Jean	..	15	15
1005	17 c. Emily Stowe	..	15	15
1002/5	..	*Set of* 4	55	55

Nos. 1002/5 were printed together, *se-tenant*, in different combinations throughout the sheet, giving ten blocks of 4 and ten single stamps.

(Des M. Dumas (17 c.), R. Bateman (35 c.). Litho C.B.N.)

1981 (6 Apr). *Endangered Wildlife (5th series). T 451 and similar horiz design. Multicoloured. P 13.*
1006	17 c. Type 451	..	15	10
1007	35 c. American Bison (*Bison bison athabascae*)	..	35	30

452 Kateri Tekakwitha
453 "Self Portrait"
(Frederick H. Varley)

(Des L. Marquart. Litho Ashton-Potter)

1981 (24 Apr). *17th-century Canadian Catholic Women. Statues by Emile Brunet. T 452 and similar vert design. P 12½.*
1008	17 c. red-brown and pale grey-olive ..		15	15
	a. Pair. Nos. 1008/9..		30	40
1009	17 c. steel blue and new blue		15	15

Designs:—No. 1008, Type 452; No. 1009, Marie de l'Incarnation. Nos. 1008/9 were printed together, *se-tenant*, in horizontal and vertical pairs throughout the sheet.

(Des P. Fontaine. Litho Ashton-Potter (17 c. (*both*)), B.A.B.N. (35 c.))

1981 (22 May). *Canadian Paintings. T 453 and similar multi-coloured designs. P 12½ (17 c. (both)) or 13 × 13½ (35 c.).*
1010	17 c. Type 453	..	15	10
1011	17 c. "At Baie Saint-Paul" (Marc-Aurele Fortin) (*horiz*)		15	10
1012	35 c. "Untitled No. 6" (Paul-Emile Borduas) ..		30	30
1010/12	..	*Set of* 3	55	45

454 Canada in 1867
455 Frère Marie-Victorin

(Des R. Bellemare. Litho B.A.B.N.)

1981 (30 June). *Canada Day. Maps showing evolution of Canada from Confederation to present day. T 454 and similar horiz designs. Multicoloured. P 13½.*
1013	17 c. Type 454	..	15	20
	a. Horiz strip of 4. Nos. 1013/16	..	55	
1014	17 c. Canada in 1873	..	15	20
1015	17 c. Canada in 1905	..	15	20
1016	17 c. Canada since 1949	..	15	20
1013/16	..	*Set of* 4	55	70

Nos. 1013/16 were printed together, *se-tenant*, in horizontal strips of 4 throughout the sheet.

(Des R. Hill. Litho and embossed Ashton-Potter)

1981 (22 July). *Canadian Botanists. T 455 and similar vert design. Multicoloured. P 12½ × 12.*
1017	17 c. Type 455	..	15	15
	a. Pair. Nos. 1017/18	..	30	50
1018	17 c. John Macoun	..	15	15

Nos. 1017/18 were printed together, *se-tenant*, in horizontal and vertical pairs throughout the sheet.

456 The Montreal Rose
457 Drawing of
Niagara-on-the-Lake

(Des J.-P. Beaudin, J. Morin and T. Yakobina. Litho C.B.N.)

1981 (22 July). *Montreal Flower Show. P 13½.*
1019	456 17 c. multicoloured	.. ..	15	20

(Des J. Mardon. Recess and litho B.A.B.N.)

1981 (31 July). *Bicentenary of Niagara-on-the-Lake (town). P 13 × 13½.*
1020	457 17 c. multicoloured	.. ..	15	20

458 Acadian Community
459 Aaron R. Mosher

(Des N. DeGrâce. Litho Ashton-Potter)

1981 (14 Aug). *Centenary of first Acadia (community) Convention. P 13½.*
1021	458 17 c. multicoloured	.. ..	15	20

(Des R. Hill. Litho Ashton-Potter)

1981 (8 Sept). *Birth Centenary of Aaron R. Mosher (founder of Canadian Labour Congress). P 13½.*
1022	459 17 c. multicoloured	.. ..	15	20

NEW INFORMATION
The editor is always interested to correspond with people who have new information that will improve or correct the Catalogue.

460 Christmas Tree, 1781
461 De Havilland D.H.82C
Tiger Moth

(Des Anita Kunz and W. Tibbles. Litho Ashton-Potter)

1981 (16 Nov). *Christmas. Bicentenary of First Illuminated Christmas Tree in Canada. T 460 and similar vert designs. Multicoloured. P 13½.*
1023	15 c. Type 460	..	20	15
1024	15 c. Christmas Tree, 1881	..	20	15
1025	15 c. Christmas Tree, 1981	..	20	15
1023/5	..	*Set of* 3	55	40

(Des R. Bradford and J. Charette. Litho Ashton-Potter)

1981 (24 Nov). *Canadian Aircraft (3rd series). T 461 and similar horiz designs. Multicoloured. P 12½.*
1026	17 c. Type 461	..	20	15
	a. Pair. Nos. 1026/7	..	40	40
1027	17 c. Canadair CL-41 Tutor	..	20	15
1028	35 c. Avro (Canada) CF-102 jet airliner	..	35	35
	a. Pair. Nos. 1028/9	..	70	70
1029	35 c. De Havilland D.H.C.7 Dash Seven ..		35	35
1026/9	..	*Set of* 4	1·10	90

The two designs of each value were printed together, *se-tenant*, in horizontal and vertical pairs throughout the sheet.

462 Canadian Maple
Leaf Emblem
463 1851 3d. Stamp

(Des R. Bellemare, Recess B.A.B.N. (No. 1030a), C.B.N. (others))

1981 (29 Dec). *Ordinary paper. (a) Sheet stamp. P 13×13½.*
1030	462 A (30 c.), bright scarlet	..	20	30
	a. Carmine-red, chalk-surfaced paper		20	25
	b. Printed on the gummed side		£300	

(b) Coil stamp, Imperf×perf 10
1031	462 A (30 c.), bright scarlet	..	40	70
	a. Imperf (pair)	..	£250	£140

Nos. 1030/1 were printed before a new first class domestic letter rate had been agreed, "A" representing the face value of the stamp later decided at 30 c. Because of U.P.U. regulations these stamps were only intended for use within Canada.

(Recess, or recess and photo (Nos. 1032/b), B.A.B.N. (Nos. 1032/5b) or C.B.N. (Nos. 1036/a))

1982 (1 Mar)–83. *Designs as Nos. 1030/1 but including face values.*

(a) Sheet stamps (Nos. 1032, 1032b) or from booklets (Nos. 1032a, 1032ba). Chalk-surfaced paper. P 13×13½.
1032	462 30 c. verm, slate-blue & azure (11.5.82)		30	40
	a. Perf 12 × 12½ (from booklets) (30.6.82)	..	70	1·00
	ab. Booklet pane. No. 1032a × 20 plus one printed label	..	14·00	
1032b	32 c. verm, orge-brn & stone (10.2.83)		45	45
	ba. Perf 12 × 12½ (from booklets) (8.4.83)	..	60	1·00
	bb. Booklet pane. No. 1032ba × 25 plus two printed labels..		17·00	

(b) Booklet stamps. Ordinary paper. P 12 × 12½*
1033	462 5 c. maroon	..	10	20
	a. Booklet pane. Nos. 1033 × 2, 1034 and 1035 plus two printed labels in bottom row	..	1·75	
	ab. Ditto. Printed labels in top row (10.82)	..	2·00	
	b. Chalk-surfaced paper (8.82)		40	50
	ba. Booklet pane. Nos. 1033b × 2, 1034a and 1035a plus two printed labels in bottom row	..	6·50	
	bb. Ditto. Printed labels in top row (10.82)	..	6·50	
	c. Booklet pane. Nos. 1033 × 2, 1033d and 1035b plus two printed labels (15.2.83)	..	2·50	
1033d	8 c. indigo (15.2.83)	..	1·00	1·50
1034	10 c. bottle green	..	1·00	1·40
	a. Chalk-surfaced paper	..	3·50	3·50
1035	30 c. carmine-red	..	1·25	1·60
	a. Chalk-surfaced paper	..	3·50	3·50
1035b	32 c. Indian red (15.2.83)	..	1·50	2·00

(c) Coil stamps. Ordinary paper. Imperf×perf 10
1036	462 30 c. bright scarlet (20.5.82)†	..	35	30
	a. Imperf (pair)	..	£180	
1036b	32 c. Indian red (10.2.83)	..	1·50	1·50
	ba. Imperf (pair)	..	90·00	

*The 30 c. and 32 c. values are perforated on two sides, the other values on three.
†The 30 c. coil stamp was originally intended for release on 11 May, but, due to production difficulties, it was not placed on sale until 20 May; F.D.C.s, however, carry the 11 May postmark.

(Des Gottschalk and Ash Ltd. Litho C.B.N.)

1982 (11 Mar–20 May). *"Canada 82" International Philatelic Youth Exhibition, Toronto. Stamps on Stamps.* T **463** *and similar horiz designs. Multicoloured.* P 13½.
1037 30 c. Type 463 .. .. 30 25
1038 30 c. 1908 Centenary of Quebec 15 c. commemorative (20.5.82) 30 25
1039 35 c. 1985 10 c. 30 40
1040 35 c. 1928 10 c. (20.5.82) 30 40
1041 60 c. 1929 50 c. (20.5.82) 60 85
1037/41 .. .. .. *Set of 5* 1·60 2·00
MS1042 159 × 108 mm. Nos. 1037/41 (20.5.82) .. 2·25 3·25

464 Jules Léger   465 Stylised Drawing
of Terry Fox

(Des P. Fontaine from photograph by M. Bedford. Litho Ashton-Potter)

1982 (2 Apr). *Jules Léger (politician) Commemoration.* P 13½.
1043 464 30 c. multicoloured 20 20

(Des F. Peter. Litho Ashton-Potter)

1982 (13 Apr). *Cancer-victim Terry Fox's "Marathon of Hope" (Trans-Canada fund-raising run)· Commemoration. Fluorescent frame.* P 12½.
1044 465 30 c. multicoloured 20 20

466 Stylised Open Book

(Des F. Peter. Litho Ashton-Potter)

1982 (16 Apr). *Patriation of Constitution.* P 12 × 12½.
1045 466 30 c. multicoloured 20 20

467 1880's Male and Female   468 "The Highway
Salvationists with Street Scene   near Kluane Lake"
(Yukon Territory) (Jackson)

(Des T. Dimson. Litho C.B.N.)

1982 (25 June). *Centenary of the Salvation Army in Canada.* P 13½.
1046 467 30 c. multicoloured 20 20

(Des J. Morin and P. Sasseville. Litho Ashton-Potter)

1982 (30 June). *Canada Day. Paintings of Canadian Landscapes. Sheet,* 139 × 139 *mm, containing* T **468** *and similar horiz designs. Multicoloured.* P 12½ × 12.
MS1047 30 c. × 12, Type **468**; "Street Scene, Montreal" (Quebec) (Hébert); "Breakwater" (Newfoundland) (Pratt); "Along Great Slave Lake" (Northwest Territories) (Richard); "Till Hill" (Prince Edward Island) (Lamb); "Family and Rainstorm" (Nova Scotia) (Colville); "Brown Shadows" (Saskatchewan) (Knowles); "The Red Brick House" (Ontario) (Milne); "Campus Gates" (New Brunswick) (Bobak); "Prairie Town—Early Morning" (Alberta) (Kerr); "Totems at Ninstints" (British Columbia) (Plaskett); "Doc Snider's House" (Manitoba) (FitzGerald) .. .. 4·25 4·75

469 Regina Legislature   470 Finish of Race
Building

(Des Kim Martin and R. Russell. Litho Ashton-Potter)

1982 (3 Aug). *Regina Centenary.* P 13½ × 13.
1048 469 30 c. multicoloured 20 20

(Des B. Reilander. Litho Ashton-Potter)

1982 (4 Aug). *Centenary of Royal Canadian Henley Regatta.* P 12½.
1049 470 30 c. multicoloured 20 25

---

471 Fairchild FC-2W1   472 Decoy

(Des R. Bradford. Litho Ashton-Potter)

1982 (5 Oct). *Canadian Aircraft (4th series). Bush Aircraft.* T **471** *and similar horiz designs. Multicoloured.* P 12½.
1050 30 c. Type 471 .. .. 35 20
a. Pair. Nos. 1050/1 .. .. 70 95
1051 30 c. De Havilland D.H.C.2 Beaver .. 35 20
1052 60 c. Fokker Super Universal .. 65 85
a. Pair. Nos. 1052/3 .. .. 1·25 2·00
1053 60 c. Noorduyn Norseman .. 65 85
1050/3 .. .. .. *Set of 4* 1·90 1·90
Nos. 1050/1 and 1052/3 were each printed together, *se-tenant,* in horiz and vert pairs throughout the sheet.

(Des J. P. Beaudin and J. Morin. Litho C.B.N. (Nos. 1054b/ba, 1055b/bc, 1056b, 1057b/ba, 1058b) or Ashton-Potter (others))

1982 (19 Oct)–87. *Heritage Artifacts.* T **472** *and similar designs. No fluorescent bands (1 c. to 5 c.). Chalk-surfaced paper (25, 42, 50, 72 c.).* P 12×12½ (37 c. to 72 c.) or 14×13½ (others).
1054 1 c. black, grey-brown and brown 10 10
a. Chalk-surfaced paper (4.7.86) 10 10
b. Perf 13×13½ (10.1.85) .. 30 30
ba. Chalk-surfaced paper (6.8.85) 1·25 1·00
1055 2 c. black, pale turquoise-blue & dp bl-grn 10 10
a. Chalk-surfaced paper (4.7.86) 20 20
b. Perf 13×13½ (10.2.84) .. 30 30
ba. Imperf (horiz pair) .. £500
bb. Printed on the gummed side .. 35·00
bc. Ordinary paper (23.1.86) .. 10 10
1056 3 c. black, dull violet-blue and chalky blue 10 10
a. Chalk-surfaced paper (4.7.86) 30 10
b. Perf 13×13½ (10.1.85) .. 30 40
1057 5 c. black, flesh and chestnut .. 10 10
a. Chalk-surfaced paper (15.8.86) 10 10
b. Perf 13×13½ (*chalk-surfaced paper*)
(6.7.84) 20 20
ba. Ordinary paper (1.3.85) .. 20 30
1058 10 c. black, light blue & dp turquoise-blue 10 10
a. Chalk-surfaced paper (22.8.86) 15 30
b. Perf 13×13½ (15.3.85) .. 60 30
1059 20 c. black, brownish grey and sepia 20 10
a. Chalk-surfaced paper (4.7.86) 50 50
1060 25 c. multicoloured (6.5.87) .. 35 10
1061 37 c. grey-black, deep yellow-green and
sage-green (8.4.83) .. 50 40
a. Chalk-surfaced paper (18.5.84) 1·00 90
1062 39 c. brownish black, violet-grey and
slate-violet (1.8.85) .. 1·60 60
1063 42 c. multicoloured (6.5.87) .. 50 15
1064 48 c. blackish brown, red-brown and pale
pink (8.4.83) .. 70 40
a. Chalk-surfaced paper (19.12.83) 80 70
1065 50 c. black, dull turq-blue & turq-bl (1.8.85) 1·50 20
1066 55 c. multicoloured (6.5.87) .. 65 30
1067 64 c. grey-black, black & pale grey (8.4.83) 80 35
a. Chalk-surfaced paper (29.6.84) 1·50 1·10
1068 68 c. black, pale brn & reddish brn (1.8.85) 1·60 50
1069 72 c. multicoloured (6.5.87) .. 85 35
1054/69 .. .. *Set of 16* 8·50 3·00
Designs: *Vert* (as T **472**)—2 c. Fishing spear; 3 c. Stable lantern; 5 c. Bucket; 10 c. Weathercock; 20 c. Skates; 25 c. Butter stamp. *Horiz* (26×20 mm)—37 c. Plough; 39 c. Settle-bed; 42 c. Linen chest; 48 c. Cradle; 50 c. Sleigh; 55 c. Iron kettle; 64 c. Kitchen stove; 68 c. Spinning wheel; 72 c. Hand-drawn cart.
No. 1058b has a fluorescent frame instead of bands.

475 Mary, Joseph and   476 Globes forming
Baby Jesus   Symbolic Designs

(Des J. Eby. Litho C.B.N.)

1982 (3 Nov). *Christmas. Nativity Scenes.* T **475** *and similar vert designs. Multicoloured.* P 13.
1080 30 c. Type 475 .. .. .. 20 10
1081 35 c. The Shepherds 25 55
1082 60 c. The Three Wise Men 45 80
1080/2 .. .. .. *Set of 3* 80 1·25

(Des R. Bellemare. Litho Ashton-Potter)

1983 (10 Mar). *World Communications Year. Fluorescent frame.* P 12 × 12½.
1083 476 32 c. multicoloured 30 25

STANLEY GIBBONS
STAMP COLLECTING SERIES

Introductory booklets on *How to Start, How to Identify Stamps* and *Collecting by Theme.* A series of well illustrated guides at a low price.
Write for details.

---

477 Map of World showing Canada

(Des R. Harder. Litho Ashton-Potter)

1983 (14 Mar). *Commonwealth Day. Without fluorescent bands.* P 12½.
1084 477 $2 multicoloured .. .. 2·00 3·00

478 Scene from Novel   479 St. John Ambulance
"Angéline de Montbrun" by   Badge and "100"
Laure Conan (Félicité Angers)

(Des R. Milot (No. 1085), Claire Pratt (No. 1086), adapted W. Tibbles. Litho C.B.N.)

1983 (22 Apr). *Canadian Writers (4th series).* T **478** *and similar horiz design. Multicoloured.* P 13.
1085 32 c. Type 478 .. .. .. 30 75
a. Pair. Nos. 1085/6 .. .. 60 1·50
1086 32 c. Woodcut illustrating "Sea-gulls" (poem by
E. J. Pratt) 30 75
Nos. 1085/6 were printed together, *se-tenant,* in horizontal and vertical pairs throughout the sheet.

(Des L. Fishauf. Litho Ashton-Potter)

1983 (3 June). *Centenary of St. John Ambulance in Canada.* P 13.
1087 479 32 c. brt rose-red, gold & dp chocolate 30 20

480 Victory Pictogram   481 Fort William, Ontario

(Des Krista Huebner, D. Kilvert and P.-Y. Pelletier. Litho C.B.N.)

1983 (28 June). *"Universiade 83" World University Games, Edmonton.* P 13.
1088 480 32 c. multicoloured 25 15
a. Printed on the gummed side .. £400
1089 64 c. multicoloured 50 70

(Des R. Harder. Litho Ashton-Potter)

1983 (30 June). *Canada Day. Forts (1st series).* T **481** *and similar horiz designs. Multicoloured.* P 12½ × 13.
1090 32 c. Fort Henry, Ontario (44 × 22 mm) 55 75
a. Booklet pane. Nos. 1090/9 .. 5·00
1091 32 c. Type 481 .. .. .. 55 75
1092 32 c. Fort Rodd Hill, British Columbia 55 75
1093 32 c. Fort Wellington, Ontario (28 × 22 mm) 55 75
1094 32 c. Fort Prince of Wales, Manitoba (28 × 22
mm) 55 75
1095 32 c. Halifax Citadel, Nova Scotia (44 × 22 mm) 55 75
1096 32 c. Fort Chambly, Quebec 55 75
1097 32 c. Fort No. 1, Point Levis, Quebec .. 55 75
1098 32 c. Coteau-du-Lac Fort, Quebec (28 × 22 mm) 55 75
1099 32 c. Fort Beauséjour, New Brunswick (28 × 22
mm) 55 75
1090/9 .. .. .. *Set of 10* 5·00 6·50
Nos. 1090/9 were only available from $3.20 stamp booklets containing the *se-tenant* pane, No. 1090a.
See also Nos. 1163/72.

482 Scouting Poster by   483 Cross Symbol
Marc Fournier (aged 12)

(Des F. Dallaire. Litho Ashton-Potter)

1983 (6 July). *75th Anniv of Scouting in Canada and 15th World Scout Jamboree, Alberta.* P 13.
1100 482 32 c. multicoloured 30 30

(Des G. Tsetsekas. Recess and photo B.A.B.N.)

1983 (22 July). *6th Assembly of the World Council of Churches, Vancouver.* P 13.
1101 **483** 32 c. blue-green and grey-lilac 30 20

484 Sir Humphrey Gilbert   **485** "NICKEL" Deposits
(founder)

(Des R. Hill. Litho C.B.N.)

1983 (3 Aug). *400th Anniv of Newfoundland.* P 13.
1102 **484** 32 c. multicoloured 30 20

(Des J. Capon. Litho ("NICKEL" die-stamped) C.B.N.)

1983 (12 Aug). *Centenary of Discovery of Sudbury Nickel Deposits.* P 13.
1103 **485** 32 c. multicoloured 30 20
　　　a. Silver ("NICKEL") omitted .. £650

486 Josiah Henson and   **487** Type 0-4-0, *Dorchester*
Escaping Slaves   *Locomotive*

(Des T. Kew and J. Hamel. Litho B.A.B.N.)

1983 (16 Sept). *Nineteenth-century Social Reformers.* T **486** *and similar horiz design. Multicoloured.* P 13 × 13½ (No. 1104) or 13 (No. 1105).
1104 32 c. Type **486** 35 25
1105 32 c. Father Antoine Labelle and rural village
　　　(32 × 26 mm) 35 25

(Des E. Roch. Litho Ashton-Potter)

1983 (3 Oct). *Railway Locomotives. (1st series).* T **487** *and similar horiz designs. Multicoloured.* P 12½ × 13.
1106 32 c. Type **487** 90 90
　　　a. Pair. Nos. 1106/7 .. .. .. 1·75 1·75
1107 32 c. Type 4-4-0, *Toronto* 90 90
1108 37 c. Type 0-6-0, *Samson* .. .. 90 1·00
1109 64 c. Type 4-4-0, *Adam Brown* .. .. 1·40 2·00
1106/9 .. .. *Set of 4* 3·75 4·25
Nos. 1106/7 were printed together, *se-tenant*, in horizontal and vertical pairs throughout the sheet.
See also Nos. 1132/6, 1185/8 and 1223/6.

 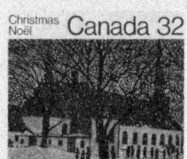

488 School Coat of Arms   **489** City Church

(Des Denise Saulnier. Litho C.B.N.)

1983 (28 Oct). *Centenary of Dalhousie Law School.* P 13.
1110 **488** 32 c. multicoloured 30 30

(Des C. Simard. Litho Ashton-Potter)

1983 (3 Nov). *Christmas. Churches.* T **489** *and similar horiz designs. Multicoloured.* P 13.
1111 32 c. Type **489** 40 10
1112 37 c. Family walking to church 55 70
1113 64 c. Country chapel .. .. .. 1·25 1·75
1111/13 .. .. .. *Set of 3* 2·00 2·25

490 Royal Canadian Regiment
and British Columbia Regiment

(Des W. Southern and R. Tibbles. Litho C.B.N.)

1983 (10 Nov). *Canadian Army Regiments.* T **490** *and similar vert design. Multicoloured. Fluorescent frame.* P 13.
1114 32 c. Type **490** 75 90
　　　a. Pair. Nos. 1114/15 .. .. 1·50 1·75
1115 32 c. Royal Winnipeg Rifles and Royal
　　　Canadian Dragoons 75 90
Nos. 1114/15 were printed together, *se-tenant*, in horizontal and vertical pairs throughout the sheet.

(Illustration reduced: actual size 112 × 88 mm)

"STICK 'N TICK" POSTAGE LABELS. Prepaid labels in the above design, printed in a combination of red, green and black, were tested by the Canadian Post Office in Winnipeg, Manitoba, between 21 November and 17 December 1983. These self-adhesive labels were sold to the public in kits of 12 or 25, at a saving of 35 c. or $1.11 on the normal postage. They were primarily intended for use on Christmas cards and were only valid on mail posted to Canadian addresses.

The label was affixed to normally addressed envelopes, but the user was then required to mark the postal code on the three lines at the foot. It was hoped that this incentive would increase the use of the postal codes and so speed automatic mail sorting.

The system was extended to seven other cities in 1984. The second version had separate postage paid and Postal Code labels, being available from 5 November until 17 December 1984.

491 Gold Mine in Prospecting   **492** Montreal Symphony
Pan   Orchestra

(Des K. Hughes. Litho Ashton-Potter)

1984 (15 Mar). *50th Anniv of Yellowknife.* P 13½.
1116 **491** 32 c. multicoloured 30 30

(Des J. Delisle and P. Kohler. Litho Ashton-Potter)

1984 (24 Mar). *50th Anniv of Montreal Symphony Orchestra.* P 12½.
1117 **492** 32 c. multicoloured 35 30

493 Jacques Cartier   **494** *Eagle* (U.S. Coastguard
cadet ship)

(Des Y. Paquin, Engraved C. Haley. Recess French Govt Ptg Wks, Perigueux)

1984 (20 Apr). *450th Anniv of Jacques Cartier's Voyage to Canada.* P 13.
1118 **493** 32 c. multicoloured 40 30

(Des O. Schenk. Litho Ashton-Potter)

1984 (18 May). *Tall Ships Visit. Fluorescent frame.* P 12×12½.
1119 **494** 32 c. multicoloured 35 30

495 Service Medal   **496** Oared Galleys

(Des W. Tibbles and C. Webster. Litho Ashton-Potter)

1984 (28 May). *75th Anniv of Canadian Red Cross Society.* P 13½.
1120 **495** 32 c. multicoloured 35 30

(Des P. Dorn. Photo and recess B.A.B.N.)

1984 (18 June). *Bicentenary of New Brunswick.* P 13½.
1121 **496** 32 c. multicoloured 35 30

497 St. Lawrence Seaway

(Des E. Barenscher. Litho C.B.N.)

1984 (26 June). *25th Anniv of St. Lawrence Seaway. Fluorescent frame.* P 13.
1122 **497** 32 c. multicoloured 45 30

498 New Brunswick   **499** Loyalists of 1784

(Des J. Morin and T. Yakobina. Litho C.B.N.)

1984 (29 June). *Canada Day. Paintings by Jean Paul Lemieux. Sheet,* 138 × 122 mm, *containing* T **498** *and similar multi-coloured designs.* P 13.
MS1123 32 c. × 12, Type **498**; British Columbia; Northwest Territories; Quebec; Manitoba; Alberta; Prince Edward Island; Saskatchewan; Nova Scotia (*vert*); Yukon Territory, Newfoundland; Ontario (*vert*) .. .. .. 6·00 6·50
The captions on the Northwest Territories and Yukon Territory paintings were transposed at the design stage.

(Des W. Davies. Litho B.A.B.N.)

1984 (3 July). *Bicentenary of Arrival of United Empire Loyalists.* P 13 × 13½.
1124 **499** 32 c. multicoloured 30 30

500 St. John's Basilica   **501** Coat of Arms of
Pope John Paul II

(Des J. Morin and R. Ethier. Litho C.B.N.)

1984 (17 Aug). *Bicentenary of Roman Catholic Church in Newfoundland.* P 13½.
1125 **500** 32 c. multicoloured 30 25

(Des L. Rivard. Litho Ashton-Potter)

1984 (31 Aug). *Papal Visit.* P 12½.
1126 **501** 32 c. multicoloured 40 20
1127 　　　64 c. multicoloured .. .. .. 85 1·10

502 Louisbourg Lighthouse, 1734

(Des D. Noble and K. Rodmell. Litho Ashton-Potter)

1984 (21 Sept). *Canadian Lighthouses* (1st series). T **502** *and similar horiz designs. Multicoloured.* P 12½.
1128 32 c. Type **502** .. .. .. 1·10 1·25
　　　a. Block of 4. Nos. 1128/31 .. .. 4·00
1129 32 c. Fisgard Lighthouse, 1860 .. .. 1·10 1·25
1130 32 c. Ile Verte Lighthouse, 1809 .. .. 1·10 1·25
1131 32 c. Gibraltar Point Lighthouse, 1808 .. 1·10 1·25
1128/31 .. .. .. *Set of 4* 4·00 4·50
Nos. 1128/31 were printed together, *se-tenant*, in different combinations throughout the sheet, giving ten blocks of 4 and ten single stamps.
See also Nos. 1176/80.

503 Type 0-6-0, *Scotia* Locomotive

(Des E. Roch. Litho Ashton-Potter)

1984 (25 Oct). *Railway Locomotives* (2nd series). T **503** *and similar horiz designs. Multicoloured.* P 12½ × 13.
1132 32 c. Type **503** 90 90
　　　a. Pair. Nos. 1132/3 .. .. .. 1·75 1·75
1133 32 c. Type 4-4-0, *Countess of Dufferin* .. 90 90
1134 37 c. Type 2-6-0, GT Class E3 .. .. 90 1·40
1135 64 c. Type 4-6-0, CP Class D10a .. .. 1·40 2·00
1132/5 .. .. .. *Set of 4* 3·75 4·75
MS1136 153 × 104 mm. As Nos. 1132/5, but with background colour changed from pale green to pale grey-blue .. .. 4·75 6·00
Nos. 1132/3 were issued together, *se-tenant*, in horizontal and vertical pairs throughout the sheet.
No. **MS**1136 commemorates "CANADA 84" National Stamp Exhibition, Montreal.
See also Nos. 1185/8 and 1223/6.

504 "The Annunciation"
(Jean Dallaire)

505 Pilots of 1914–18,
1939–45 and 1984

(Des J. Morin and T. Yakobina. Litho Ashton-Potter)

1984 (2 Nov). *Christmas. Religious Paintings. T* **504** *and similar horiz designs. Multicoloured. P* 13½.
1137	32 c. Type **504**	40	10
1138	37 c. "The Three Kings" (Simone Bouchard)	45	65
1139	64 c. "Snow in Bethlehem" (David Milne)	70	1·50
1137/9	*Set of 3*	1·40	2·00

(Des W. Southern and R. Tibbles. Litho Ashton-Potter)

1984 (9 Nov). *60th Anniv of Royal Canadian Air Force. Fluorescent frame. P* 12×12½.
1140	**505** 32 c. multicoloured	35	30

506 Treffle Berthiaume (editor)

507 Heart and Arrow

(Des P.-Y. Pelletier. Litho Ashton-Potter)

1984 (16 Nov). *Centenary of La Presse* (*newspaper*). *Fluorescent frame. P* 13×13½.
1141	**506** 32 c. agate, vermilion & pale grey-brn	35	30

(Des F. Dallaire. Litho Ashton-Potter)

1985 (8 Feb). *International Youth Year. P* 12½.
1142	**507** 32 c. multicoloured	30	30

508 Astronaut in Space,
and Planet Earth

509 Emily Murphy

(Des L. Holloway. Litho Ashton-Potter)

1985 (15 Mar). *Canadian Space Programme. P* 13½.
1143	**508** 32 c. multicoloured	40	30

(Des Muriel Wood and R. Tibbles. Litho Ashton-Potter)

1985 (17 Apr). *Women's Rights Activists. T* **509** *and similar horiz design. Multicoloured. P* 13½.
1144	32 c. Type **509**	40	70
	a. Horiz pair. Nos. 1144/5	80	1·40
1145	32 c. Therese Casgrain	40	70

Nos. 1144/5 were printed together, *se-tenant*, in horizontal pairs throughout the sheet.

510 Gabriel Dumont (Métis leader)
and Battle of Batoche, 1885

(Des R. Derreth. Litho Ashton-Potter)

1985 (6 May). *Centenary of the North-West Rebellion. P* 14×13½.
1146	**510** 32 c. blue, carmine and grey	30	30

511 Rear View,
Parliament Building,
Ottawa

512 Queen
Elizabeth II

512a Queen Elizabeth
II in 1984 (from photo
by Karsh)

(Des R. Bellemare. Eng R. Couture (Nos. 1161/2). Des T. Yakobina and C. Candlish (Nos. 1162a/g), R. Harder (others))

1985 (21 June)–95. *No fluorescent bands* (1 *c.* to 6 *c.*) *or fluorescent frame* (34 *c.*, 36 *c.*, 39 *c.*, 40 *c.*, 42 *c.*, 43 *c.*, 45 *c.*).

(a) T 511 *and similar horiz designs*

(i) *Booklet stamps. Recess B.A.B.N. Chalk-surfaced paper* (6 *c.* (*No.* 1150*b*), 37 *c.*, 38 *c.*) *or ordinary paper* (*others*). *P* 12½×12.
1147	–	1 c. grey-olive (30.3.87)	70	1·60
	a. Booklet pane. Nos. 1147×2, 1150×2, 1152 and label		4·50	
	b. Chalk-surfaced paper (1.10.87)		40	70
	ba. Booklet pane. Nos. 1147b×2, 1150a×2, 1153 and label		4·00	
	bb. Booklet pane. Nos. 1147b, 1150a×2, 1153 and two labels (3.2.88)		2·00	
1148	–	2 c. bottle green	10	40
	a. Booklet pane. Nos. 1148×3, 1149×2 and 1151		2·00	
	b. Chalk-surfaced paper (18.1.89)		30	40
	ba. Booklet pane. Nos. 1148b×3, 1150b, 1154 and label		1·90	
1149	–	5 c. sepia	20	50
1150	–	6 c. chestnut (30.3.87)	80	1·00
	a. Chalk-surfaced paper (1.10.87)		40	30
1150b	–	6 c. blackish purple (18.1.89)	65	95
1151	511	34 c. blue-black	1·00	1·50
1152		36 c. reddish purple (30.3.87)	2·25	2·50
	a. Chalk-surfaced paper (1.10.87)		3·00	3·00
1153		37 c. dull ultramarine (3.2.88)	75	30
1154		38 c. deep blue (18.1.89)	75	1·25

(ii) *Litho C.B.N.* (*Nos.* 1155 (*from sheets*), 1156/7*c*), *B.A.B.N.* (*No.* 1155 (*from booklets*)) *or Ashton-Potter* (*Nos.* 1155*b*, 1156*a*, 1157*a/ba*, 1157*ca/cb*). *Chalk-surfaced paper* (*Nos.* 1155*b/ba*, 1156, 1156*b/bb and* 1157*c/cb*). *P* 13×13½ (*No.* 1157*c*) *or* 13½×13 (*others*).
1155	511	34 c. multicoloured	50	10
	a. Booklet pane. No. 1155×25 (1.8.85)		11·50	
	b. Perf 13½×14 (4.7.86)		45	1·25
	ba. Booklet pane. No. 1155b×25		26·00	
1156		36 c. multicoloured (30.3.87)	30	30
	a. Ordinary paper		30	45
	b. Perf 13½×14		1·40	1·40
	ba. Booklet pane. No. 1156a×10		9·00	
	bb. Booklet pane. No. 1156a×25 (19.5.87)		20·00	
	c. Imperf (vert pair)		35·00	
1157	–	37 c. multicoloured (30.12.87)	85	10
	a. Perf 13½×14 (5.1.88)		1·00	1·00
	ab. Booklet pane. No. 1157a×10		11·00	
	ac. Booklet pane. No. 1157a×25 (2.5.88)		15·00	
	ad. Chalk-surfaced paper (5.1.88)		1·50	1·75
	ae. Booklet pane. No. 1157ad×25		25·00	
1157c	–	38 c. multicoloured (29.12.88)	35	10
	ca. Booklet pane. No. 1157c×10 and two labels		3·50	
	cb. Booklet pane. No. 1157c×25 and two labels		12·00	
	cc. Printed on the gummed side		35·00	

(iii) *Coil stamps. Recess C.B.N. P* 10×*imperf*
1158	511	34 c. purple-brown (1.8.85)	2·25	2·75
	a. Imperf (pair)		£110	
1159		36 c. carmine-vermilion (19.5.87)	90	55
	a. Imperf (pair)			
1160		37 c. deep ultramarine (22.2.88)	60	40
	a. Imperf (pair)		£110	
1160b		38 c. bottle green (1.2.89)	40	30
	ba. Imperf (pair)			

(b) Recess and photo B.A.B.N. P 13×13½
1161	512	34 c. black and cobalt (2.7.85)	45	30
1162		36 c. reddish purple (1.10.87)	2·75	1·10

(c) Litho B.A.B.N. (*Nos.* 1162*a/c*), *Ashton-Potter* (*Nos.* 1162*bc*, 1162*ca*, 1162*d/e*, 1162*fa*) *or C.B.N.* (*Nos.* 1162*f/g*). *Chalk-surfaced paper* (40 *c.*, 42 *c.*, 43 *c.*, 45 *c.*). *P* 13½×13 (*No.* 1162*a*) 13×12½ (*No.* 1162*b*) *or* 13×13½ (*Nos.* 1162*c*, 1162*d/g*).
1162a	512a	37 c. multicoloured (30.12.87)	1·75	10
1162b		38 c. multicoloured (29.12.88)	35	20
	ba. Imperf (horiz pair)		£275	
	bb. Imperf at top and sides (horiz pair)		£225	
	bc. Perf 13×13½. Chalk-surfaced paper		45	65
	bd. Booklet pane. No. 1162bc×10 and two labels		4·50	
	be. Imperf between (horiz pair) (from pane No. 1162bd)			
1162c		39 c. multicoloured (12.1.90)	1·00	20
	ca. Chalk-surfaced paper		1·25	55
	cb. Booklet pane. No. 1162ca×10 and two labels		12·00	
	cc. Perf 13×12½ (2.90)		7·00	1·00
1162d		40 c. multicoloured (28.12.90)	55	20
	da. Booklet pane. No. 1162d×10 and two labels		6·00	
1162e		42 c. multicoloured (27.12.91)	60	20
	ea. Booklet pane. No. 1162e×10		7·00	
1162f		43 c. multicoloured (30.12.92)	70	45
	fa. Booklet pane. No. 1162f×10		7·00	
1162g		45 c. multicoloured (31.7.95)	35	40
	ga. Booklet pane. No. 1162g×10		3·50	

Designs:—1 c., 5 c., 6 c. (No. 1150b) East Block, Parliament Building; 2 c., 6 c. (No. 1150) West Block, Parliament Building; 37 c. (No. 1157) Front view, Parliament Building; 38 c. (No. 1157c) Side view, Parliament Building.

Stamps from booklet panes Nos. 1147a, 1147ba/bb and 1148a/b have one or two adjacent sides imperforate. Stamps from the first and last vertical columns of booklet panes Nos. 1155a, 1155ba, 1156ba/bb, 1157ab/ac, 1157ae, 1157ca/cb, 1162bd, 1162cb, 1162da, 1162ea, 1162fa and 1162ga are imperforate at left or right. Those from the bottom row of No. 1157ac are also imperforate at foot.

Nos. 1157c and 1162b/g have a slightly larger design image 21×17 mm.

Printings of booklet pane No. 1162fa from booklet No. SB164 were initially by Ashton-Potter. On 7 January 1994 the printer changed to C.B.N. and the booklet cover to Type B 37. This booklet is listed as No. SB177. There were further printings by

---

C.B.N. before production reverted to Ashton-Potter Canada for supplies released on 27 March 1995.

Nos. 1162g/ga were reissued on 6 October 1995 showing a change of printer to Ashton-Potter Canada. There are no listable differences between these stamps and the previous printings.

(Des R. Harder. Litho Ashton-Potter)

1985 (28 June). *Canada Day. Forts* (2nd series). *Horiz designs as T* **481**. *Multicoloured. P* 12½×13.
1163	34 c. Lower Fort Garry, Manitoba (44×22 mm)	50	60
	a. Booklet pane. Nos. 1163/72	4·50	
1164	34 c. Fort Anne, Nova Scotia	50	60
1165	34 c. Fort York, Ontario	50	60
1166	34 c. Castle Hill, Newfoundland (28×22 mm)	50	60
1167	34 c. Fort Whoop Up, Alberta (28×22 mm)	50	60
1168	34 c. Fort Erie, Ontario (44×22 mm)	50	60
1169	34 c. Fort Walsh, Saskatchewan	50	60
1170	34 c. Fort Lennox, Quebec	50	60
1171	34 c. York Redoubt, Nova Scotia (28×22 mm)	50	60
1172	34 c. Fort Frederick, Ontario (28×22 mm)	50	60
1163/72	*Set of 10*	4·50	5·50

Nos. 1163/72 were only available from $3·40 stamp booklets containing the *se-tenant* pane, No. 1163a.

513 Louis Hébert
(apothecary)

514 Parliament
Buildings and Map
of World

515 Guide and
Brownie Saluting

(Des C. Malenfant. Litho Ashton-Potter)

1985 (30 Aug). *45th International Pharmaceutical Sciences Congress of Pharmaceutical Federation, Montreal. Fluorescent frame. P* 12½.
1173	**513** 34 c. multicoloured	45	35

(Des E. Barenscher. Litho Ashton-Potter)

1985 (3 Sept). *74th Conference of Inter-Parliamentary Union, Ottawa. P* 13½.
1174	**514** 34 c. multicoloured	45	35

(Des Barbara Griffin. Recess and photo B.A.B.N.)

1985 (12 Sept). *75th Anniv of Girl Guide Movement. Fluorescent frame. P* 13½×13.
1175	**515** 34 c. multicoloured	45	35

516 Sisters Islets
Lighthouse

517 Santa Claus in
Reindeer-drawn Sleigh

(Des B. Reilander (No. **MS**1180), L. Rivard (others). Litho Ashton-Potter)

1985 (3 Oct). *Canadian Lighthouses* (2nd series). *T* **516** *and similar horiz designs. Multicoloured. P* 13½.
1176	34 c. Type **516**	1·40	1·40
	a. Block of 4. Nos. 1176/9	5·00	
1177	34 c. Pelee Passage Lighthouse	1·40	1·40
1178	34 c. Haut-fond Prince Lighthouse	1·40	1·40
1179	34 c. Rose Blanche Lighthouse, Cains Island	1·40	1·40
1176/9	*Set of 4*	5·00	5·00
MS1180	109×90 mm. Nos. 1176/9	6·00	7·00

Nos. 1176/9 were printed together, *se-tenant*, in different combinations throughout the sheet, giving ten blocks of 4 and ten single stamps.

No. **MS**1180 Publicises "Capex 87" International Stamp Exhibition, Toronto.

(Des Barbara Carroll and C. Yaneff. Litho Ashton-Potter)

1985 (23 Oct). *Christmas. Santa Claus Parade. T* **517** *and similar horiz designs. Multicoloured. P* 13½.
1181	32 c. Canada Post's parade float	70	40
	a. Booklet pane. No. 1181×10	5·00	
1182	34 c. Type **517**	60	15
1183	39 c. Acrobats and horse-drawn carriage	70	80
1184	68 c. Christmas tree, pudding and goose on float	1·50	1·40
1181/4	*Set of 4*	3·25	2·50

No. 1181 was only available from $3·20 stamp booklets, which had the upper and lower edges of the pane imperforate. This value was intended for use on greeting cards posted on or before 31 January 1986, and represented a 2 c. saving of postage. After this date these stamps could be used for any postal purpose in conjunction with other values.

(Des E. Roch. Litho Ashton-Potter)

1985 (7 Nov). *Railway Locomotives (3rd series). Horiz designs as T 503. Multicoloured. P 12½ × 13.*

1185	34 c. Class "K2"	..	..	80	80
	a. Pair. Nos. 1185/6	..	..	1·60	1·60
1186	34 c. Class "P2a"	..	..	80	80
1187	39 c. Class "O10a"	..	..	95	95
1188	68 c. Class "H4D"	..	..	1·60	1·75
1185/8			*Set of 4*	3·75	3·75

Nos. 1185/6 were printed together, *se-tenant*, in horizontal and vertical pairs throughout the sheet.

518 Naval Personnel of 1910, 1939–45 and 1985

519 "The Old Holton House, Montreal" (James Wilson Morrice)

(Des W. Southern and R. Tibbles. Litho C.B.N.)

1985 (8 Nov). *75th Anniv of Royal Canadian Navy. Fluorescent frame. P 13½ × 13.*

| 1189 | 518 | 34 c. multicoloured | .. | .. | 65 | 55 |

(Des L. Parent and J. Morin. Litho C.B.N.)

1985 (15 Nov). *125th Anniv of Montreal Museum of Fine Arts. P 13½.*

| 1190 | 519 | 34 c. multicoloured | .. | .. | 40 | 35 |

520 Map of Alberta showing Olympic Sites

(Des P.-Y. Pelletier. Litho Ashton-Potter)

1986 (13 Feb). *Winter Olympic Games, Calgary (1988) (1st issue). Fluorescent frame. P 12½ × 13.*

| 1191 | 520 | 34 c. multicoloured | .. | .. | 40 | 50 |

See also Nos. 1216/17, 1236/7, 1258/9 and 1281/4.

521 Canada Pavilion

522 Molly Brant

(Des Debbie Adams. Recess and photo B.A.B.N.)

1986 (7 Mar). *"Expo '86" World Fair, Vancouver (1st issue). T 521 and similar horiz design. Multicoloured. Fluorescent frame. P 13 × 13½.*

| 1192 | 34 c. Type 521 | .. | .. | 1·00 | 50 |
| 1193 | 39 c. Early telephone, dish aerial and satellite | .. | .. | 1·25 | 2·00 |

See also Nos. 1196/7.

(Des Sara Tyson. Litho Ashton-Potter)

1986 (14 Apr). *250th Birth Anniv of Molly Brant (Iroquois leader). P 13½.*

| 1194 | 522 | 34 c. multicoloured | .. | .. | 40 | 40 |

523 Philippe Aubert de Gaspé and Scene from *Les Anciens Canadiens*

524 Canadian Field Post Office and Cancellation, 1944

(Des P. Fontaine and Y. Paquin. Litho Ashton-Potter)

1986 (14 Apr). *Birth Bicentenary of Philippe Aubert de Gaspé (author). Fluorescent frame. P 12½.*

| 1195 | 523 | 34 c. multicoloured | .. | .. | 40 | 40 |

(Des Debbie Adams. Recess and photo B.A.B.N.)

1986 (28 Apr). *"Expo '86" World Fair, Vancouver (2nd issue). Multicoloured designs as T 521. Fluorescent frame. P 13½ × 13 (34 c.) or 13 × 13½ (68 c.).*

| 1196 | 34 c. Expo Centre, Vancouver (vert) | .. | 65 | 40 |
| 1197 | 68 c. Early and modern trains | .. | 1·25 | 2·00 |

(Des J. DesRosiers. Litho Ashton-Potter)

1986 (9 May). *75th Anniv of Canadian Forces Postal Service. P 13½.*

| 1198 | 524 | 34 c. multicoloured | .. | .. | 75 | 40 |

525 Great Blue Heron

526 Railway Rotary Snowplough

(Des P. Fontaine and J.-L. Grondin. Litho Ashton-Potter)

1986 (22 May). *Birds of Canada. T 525 and similar horiz designs. Multicoloured. P 13½.*

1199	34 c. Type 525	..	..	1·25	1·25
	a. Block of 4. Nos. 1199/1202	..	4·50	
1200	34 c. Snow Goose	..	..	1·25	1·25
1201	34 c. Great Horned Owl	..	1·25	1·25
1202	34 c. Spruce Grouse ..	..	1·25	1·25
1199/1202		*Set of 4*	4·50	4·50

Nos. 1199/1202 were printed together, *se-tenant*, in different combinations throughout the sheet, giving ten blocks of 4 and ten single stamps.

(Des R. Hill. Litho C.B.N.)

1986 (27 June). *Canada Day. Science and Technology. Canadian Inventions (1st series). T 526 and similar vert designs. Multicoloured. P 13½.*

1203	34 c. Type 526	..	..	1·10	1·25
	a. Block of 4. Nos. 1203/6	..	4·00	
1204	34 c. Space shuttle *Challenger* launching satellite with Canadarm	1·10	1·25
1205	34 c. Pilot wearing anti-gravity flight suit and Supermarine Spitfire	..	1·10	1·25
1206	34 c. Variable-pitch propellor and Avro 504 airplane	..	..	1·10	1·25
1203/6		*Set of 4*	4·00	4·50

Nos. 1203/6 were printed together, *se-tenant*, in blocks of 4 throughout the sheet.

See also Nos. 1241/4 and 1292/5.

527 C.B.C. Logos over Map of Canada

528 Ice Age Artefacts, Tools and Settlement

(Des R. Mah and G. Tsetsekas. Litho Ashton-Potter)

1986 (23 July). *50th Anniv of Canadian Broadcasting Corporation. P 12½.*

| 1207 | 527 | 34 c. multicoloured | .. | .. | 40 | 45 |

(Des F. Hagan. Litho Ashton-Potter)

1986 (29 Aug–1 Oct). *Exploration of Canada (1st series). Discoverers. T 528 and similar horiz designs. Multicoloured. P 12½ × 13.*

1208	34 c. Type 528	..	..	60	70
	a. Block of 4. Nos. 1208/11	..	2·25	
1209	34 c. Viking ships	..	..	60	70
1210	34 c. John Cabot's *Matthew*, 1497, compass and Arctic Char (fish)	..	60	70
1211	34 c. Henry Hudson cast adrift, 1611	..	60	70
1208/11		*Set of 4*	2·25	2·50
MS1212	119×84 mm. Nos. 1208/11 (1 Oct)	..	3·00	3·50

Nos. 1208/11 were printed together, *se-tenant*, in different combinations throughout the sheet, giving ten blocks of 4 and ten single stamps.

No. MS1212 publicises "Capex '87" International Stamp Exhibition, Toronto.

See also Nos. 1232/5, 1285/8 and 1319/22.

529 Crowfoot (Blackfoot Chief) and Indian Village

530 Peace Dove and Globe

(Des Wanda Lewicka and J. Morin. Litho C.B.N.)

1986 (5 Sept). *Founders of the Canadian West. T 529 and similar horiz design. Multicoloured. P 13 × 13½.*

1213	34 c. Type 529	..	..	35	55
	a. Pair. Nos. 1213/14	..	70	1·10
1214	34 c. James Macleod of the North West Mounted Police and Fort Macleod	35	55

Nos. 1213/4 were printed together, *se-tenant*, in horizontal and vertical pairs throughout the sheet.

(Des Carole Jeghers. Litho and embossed Ashton-Potter)

1986 (16 Sept). *International Peace Year. P 13½.*

| 1215 | 530 | 34 c. multicoloured | .. | .. | 40 | 45 |

531 Ice Hockey

532 Angel with Crown

(Des P.-Y. Pelletier. Litho C.B.N.)

1986 (15 Oct). *Winter Olympic Games, Calgary (1988) (2nd issue). T 531 and similar vert design. Multicoloured. P 13½ × 13.*

1216	34 c. Type 531	..	..	1·25	1·40
	a. Pair. Nos. 1216/17	..	2·50	2·75
1217	34 c. Biathlon	..	..	1·25	1·40

Nos. 1216/17 were printed together, *se-tenant*, in horizontal and vertical pairs throughout the sheet.

See also Nos. 1236/7, 1258/9 and 1281/4.

(Des T. Dimson. Litho Ashton-Potter)

1986 (29 Oct). *Christmas. T 532 and similar multicoloured designs. Fluorescent frame (34 to 68 c.). P 13½ × imperf (29 c.) or 12½ × 13.*

1218	29 c. Angel singing carol (36×22 mm)	..	40	30
	a. Booklet pane. No. 1218×10	..	4·00	
	b. Perf 12½ × imperf ..	..	5·00	30
	ba. Booklet pane. No. 1218b×10	..	50·00	
1219	34 c. Type 532	..	..	60	25
1220	39 c. Angel playing lute ..	..	1·00	90
1221	68 c. Angel with ribbon ..	..	1·50	2·25
1218/21		*Set of 4*	3·25	3·25

Nos. 1218/b were only available from $2.90 stamp booklets, which had the sides of the pane imperforate. In addition to the design each stamp in the pane included an integral horizontal label showing a bar code. This value was intended for use on greeting cards posted on or before 31 January 1987, and represented a 5 c. saving when used in conjunction with special postcoded envelopes. These stamps were valid for normal postal purposes after 31 January when used with other values.

533 John Molson with Theatre Royal, Montreal, *Accommodation* (paddle-steamer) and Railway Train

534 Toronto's First Post Office

(Des C. Malenfant. Litho Ashton-Potter)

1986 (4 Nov). *150th Death Anniv of John Molson (businessman). P 12½.*

| 1222 | 533 | 34 c. multicoloured | .. | .. | 50 | 50 |

(Des E. Roch. Litho Ashton-Potter)

1986 (21 Nov). *Railway Locomotives (4th series). Horiz designs as T 503, but size 60 × 22 mm. Multicoloured. P 12½ × 13.*

1223	34 c. Class "V-1-a" ..	..	..	1·25	1·25
	a. Pair. Nos. 1223/4	..	2·50	2·50
1224	34 c. Class "T1a"	..	..	1·25	1·25
1225	39 c. Class "U-2-a" ..	..	1·40	1·00
1226	68 c. Class "H1c"	..	..	2·25	2·75
1223/6		*Set of 4*	5·50	5·75

Nos. 1223/6 were issued together, *se-tenant*, in horizontal and vertical pairs throughout the sheet.

(Des J. Mardon (stamps) and B. Reilander (sheet). Recess and litho B.A.B.N.)

1987 (16 Feb–12 June). *"Capex '87" International Stamp Exhibition, Toronto. T 534 and similar horiz designs showing Post Offices. Fluorescent frame. P 13 × 13½.*

1227	34 c. Type 534	..	..	60	20
1228	36 c. Nelson-Miramichi, New Brunswick (12.6)	..	..	65	45
1229	42 c. Saint-Ours, Quebec (12.6)	..	70	65
1230	72 c. Battleford, Saskatchewan (12.6)	..	1·00	1·25
1227/30		*Set of 4*	2·75	2·25
MS1231	155×92 mm. 36 c. As No. 1227 and Nos. 1228/30, but main inscr in brt green (12.6)	..	2·25	2·25

535 Étienne Brûlé exploring Lake Superior

(Des J. Britton and F. Hagan. Litho Ashton-Potter)

1987 (13 Mar). *Exploration of Canada (2nd series). Pioneers of New France. T 535 and similar horiz designs. Multicoloured. P 12½ × 13.*

1232	34 c. Type 535	..	..	85	85
	a. Block of 4. Nos. 1232/5	..	3·00	
1233	34 c. Radisson and des Groseilliers with British and French flags	..	85	85
1234	34 c. Jolliet and Father Marquette on the Mississippi	..	..	85	85
1235	34 c. Jesuit missionary preaching to Indians..	..	..	85	85
1232/5		*Set of 4*	3·00	3·00

Nos. 1232/5 were printed together, *se-tenant*, in different combinations throughout the sheet, giving ten blocks of 4 and ten single stamps.

(Des P.-Y. Pelletier. Litho C.B.N.)

1987 (3 Apr). *Winter Olympic Games, Calgary* (1988) (3rd issue). *Vert designs as* T **531**. *Multicoloured. P* 13½ × 13.
1236	36 c. Speed skating ..	..	..	50	40
1237	42 c. Bobsleighing ..	..	..	75	60

536 Volunteer Activities   **537** Canadian Coat of Arms

(Des W. Davies. Litho Ashton-Potter)

1987 (13 Apr). *National Volunteer Week. P* 12½ × 13.
1238	**536** 36 c. multicoloured	..	..	30	35

(Des R. Tibbles. Litho Ashton-Potter)

1987 (15 Apr). *5th Anniv of Canadian Charter of Rights and Freedoms. Fluorescent frame. P* 14 × 13½.
1239	**537** 36 c. multicoloured	..	..	35	35

538 Steel Girder, Gear Wheel and Microchip   **539** R. A. Fessenden (AM Radio)

(Des L. Holloway, R. Kerr and Nita Wallace. Litho Ashton-Potter)

1987 (19 May). *Centenary of Engineering Institute of Canada. P* 12½ × 13.
1240	**538** 36 c. multicoloured	..	..	35	40

(Des R. Hill. Litho C.B.N.)

1987 (25 June). *Canada Day. Science and Technology. Canadian Inventors* (2nd series). T **539** *and similar vert designs. Multicoloured. P* 13½.
1241	36 c. Type **539**	..	..	80	60
	a. Block of four. Nos. 1241/4	..	..	2·75	
1242	36 c. C. Fenerty (newsprint pulp) ..	..	80	60
1243	36 c. G.-E. Desbarats and W. Leggo (half-tone engraving)	..	80	60
1244	36 c. F. N. Gisborne (first North American undersea telegraph) ..	80	60
1241/4		*Set of* 4	2·75	2·25

Nos. 1241/4 were printed together, *se-tenant*, in blocks of four throughout the sheet.

540 *Segwun*   **541** Figurehead from *Hamilton*, 1813

(Des D. Champion. Litho C.B.N.)

1987 (20 July). *Canadian Steamships.* T **540** *and similar multicoloured design. P* 13.
1245	36 c. Type **540**	..	..	1·25	1·75
	a. Horiz pair. Nos. 1245/6	..	2·50	3·50
1246	36 c. *Princess Marguerite* (52 × 22 *mm*)	1·25	1·75

Nos. 1245/6 were printed together horizontally, *se-tenant*, throughout the sheet of 25, with No. 1245 occurring in columns 1, 3 and 5 and No. 1246 in columns 2 and 4.

(Des L.-A. Rivard. Litho Ashton-Potter)

1987 (7 Aug). *Historic Shipwrecks.* T **541** *and similar horiz designs. Multicoloured. P* 13½ × 13.
1247	36 c. Type **541**	..	..	70	85
	a. Block of four. Nos. 1247/50 ..	..	2·50	
1248	36 c. Hull of *San Juan*, 1565	..	70	85
1249	36 c. Wheel from *Breadalbane*, 1853	70	85
1250	36 c. Bell from *Ericsson*, 1892	..	70	85
1247/50		*Set of* 4	2·50	3·00

Nos. 1247/50 were printed together, *se-tenant*, in different combinations throughout the sheet, giving ten blocks of 4 and ten single stamps.

The new-issue supplement to this Catalogue appears each month in

GIBBONS STAMP MONTHLY

—from your newsagent or by postal subscription— sample copy and details on request.

542 Air Canada Boeing 767-200 and Globe   **543** Summit Symbol

(Des Debbie Adams and D. Carter. Litho C.B.N.)

1987 (1 Sept). *50th Anniv of Air Canada. P* 13½.
1251	**542** 36 c. multicoloured	..	..	55	35

(Des C. Gaudreau. Litho Ashton-Potter)

1987 (2 Sept). *2nd International Francophone Summit, Quebec. Fluorescent frame. P* 13 × 12½.
1252	**543** 36 c. multicoloured	..	..	30	35

544 Commonwealth Symbol   **545** Poinsettia

(Des G. Tsetsekas. Litho Ashton-Potter)

1987 (13 Oct). *Commonwealth Heads of Government Meeting, Vancouver. Fluorescent frame. P* 13 × 12½.
1253	**544** 36 c. multicoloured	..	..	35	40

(Des C. Simard. Litho Ashton-Potter)

1987 (2 Nov). *Christmas. Christmas Plants.* T **545** *and similar multicoloured designs. Fluorescent frame. P* 12½ × 13 (31 c.) *or* 13½ (*others*).
1254	31 c. Decorated Christmas tree and presents (36 × 20 *mm*)	..	45	35
	a. Booklet pane. No. 1254 × 10	..	4·50	
	b. Imperf between (horiz pair) (from booklet)			
1255	36 c. Type **545**	..	..	35	40
1256	42 c. Holly wreath	..	..	40	45
1257	72 c. Mistletoe and decorated tree	65	70
1254/7		*Set of* 4	1·75	1·75

On No. 1254 the left-hand third of the design area is taken up by a bar code which has fluorescent bands between the bars. This value was only available from $3.10 stamp booklets which had the sides of the pane imperforate. This value was intended for use on greeting cards posted on or before 31 January 1988 and represented a 5 c. saving when used in conjunction with special postcoded envelopes.

(Des P.-Y. Pelletier. Litho C.B.N.)

1987 (13 Nov). *Winter Olympic Games, Calgary* (1988) (4th issue). *Vert designs as* T **531**. *Multicoloured. Fluorescent frame. P* 13½ × 13.
1258	36 c. Cross-country skiing ..	..	50	40
	a. Pair. Nos. 1258/9	..	1·00	80
1259	36 c. Ski-jumping	..	..	50	40

Nos. 1258/9 were printed together, *se-tenant*, in horizontal and vertical pairs throughout the sheet.

546 Football, Grey Cup and Spectators

(Des L. Holloway. Litho Ashton-Potter)

1987 (20 Nov). *75th Grey Cup Final* (*Canadian football championship*), *Vancouver. Fluorescent frame. P* 12½.
1260	**546** 36 c. multicoloured	..	..	35	40

547 Flying Squirrel   **548** Lynx

548a Runnymede Library, Toronto

(Des Gottschalk & Ash International (1 c. to 25 c.), B. Tsang (43 c. to 80 c.), R. Bellemare ($1, $2, $5). Litho Ashton-Potter (1 c. to 80 c.), Recess and litho B.A.B.N. to June 1992, thereafter C.B.N. ($1, $2, $5))

1988 (18 Jan)–**93**. *Canadian Mammals and Architecture. Multicoloured. Fluorescent frame* (10 c. (*ptgs to Sept 1991 only*), 25 c. (*ptgs to March 1992 only*) *and* 43 c. *to* 80 c.) *or no fluorescent frame* (*others*).

(*a*) *Horiz designs as* T **547**. *Chalk-surfaced paper. P* 13 × 13½.
1261	1 c. Type **547** (3.10.88)	..	10	10
	a. Perf 13 × 12½ (1.92)	..	1·25	95
1262	2 c. Porcupine (3.10.88)	..	10	10
1263	3 c. Muskrat (3.10.88)	..	10	10
1264	5 c. Varying Hare (3.10.88)	..	10	10
1265	6 c. Red Fox (3.10.88)	..	10	10
1266	10 c. Striped Skunk (3.10.88)	..	10	10
	a. Perf 13 × 12½ (2.91)	..	3·25	1·50
1267	25 c. American Beaver (3.10.88)	..	30	15

(*b*) *Horiz designs as* T **548**. *Chalk-surfaced paper* (45, 46, 57, 61, 63, 78, 80 c.) *or ordinary paper* (*others*). *P* 12 × 12½ (43, 57, 74 c.) *or* 14½ × 14 (*others*)
1268	43 c. Type **548**	..	..	1·40	30
1269	44 c. Walrus (18.1.89)	..	45	20
	a. Perf 12½ × 13. Chalk-surfaced paper	1·00	55
	ab. Booklet pane. No. 1269a × 5 and label with margins all round	..	5·00	
	b. Chalk-surfaced paper (9.6.89)	2·00	1·25
	c. Perf 13½ × 13. Chalk-surfaced paper (1989)	£120	11·00
1270	45 c. Pronghorn (12.1.90)	..	35	20
	a. Perf 12½ × 13	..	1·00	30
	ab. Booklet pane. No. 1270a × 5 and label with margins all round	..	5·00	
	b. Perf 13 (6.90)	..	7·00	50
1270c	46 c. Wolverine (28.12.90)	..	45	30
	ca. Perf 13	..	2·00	50
	cb. Perf 12½ × 13	..	1·25	40
	cc. Booklet pane. No. 1270cb × 5 and label with margins all round	..	4·00	
1271	57 c. Killer Whale	..	2·00	55
	a. Ordinary paper (26.9.88)	..	3·25	1·75
1272	59 c. Musk Ox (18.1.89)	..	1·50	45
	a. Chalk-surfaced paper (1.11.89)	3·75	2·25
	b. Perf 13. Chalk-surfaced paper (1.11.89)	..	6·00	3·50
1273	61 c. Wolf (12.1.90)	..	60	65
	a. Perf 13 (7.90)	..	27·00	1·50
1273b	63 c. Harbour Porpoise (28.12.90)	65	60
	ba. Perf 13	..	3·50	1·00
1274	74 c. Wapiti	..	1·60	
	a. Chalk-surfaced paper	85·00	5·00
1275	76 c. Brown Bear (18.1.89)	..	90	60
	a. Perf 12½ × 13. Chalk-surfaced paper	1·75	70
	ab. Booklet pane. No. 1275a × 5 and label with margins all round	..	8·50	
	b. Chalk-surfaced paper (25.8.89)	3·00	2·25
	c. Perf 13. Chalk-surfaced paper (1989)	17·00	3·25
1276	78 c. White Whale (12.1.90)	..	90	55
	a. Perf 12½ × 13	..	1·60	
	ab. Booklet pane. No. 1276a × 5 and label with margins all round	..	8·00	
	b. Perf 13 (4.90)	..	14·00	2·25
1276c	80 c. Peary Caribou (28.12.90)	..	80	60
	ca. Perf 13	..	2·00	80
	cb. Perf 12½ × 13	..	1·25	60
	cc. Booklet pane. No. 1276cb × 5 and label with margins all round	..	7·00	

(*c*) *Horiz designs as* T **548a**. *Chalk-surfaced paper* ($5) *or ordinary paper* (*others*). *P* 13½
1277	$1 Type **548a** (brown roof)	..	1·25	30
	a. Chalk-surfaced paper (28.8.92)	2·50	1·10
	ab. Black (recess inscr) inverted	£6000	
	ac. Imperf (horiz pair)		
	ad. Black roof (1993)	..	10·00	1·25
1278	$2 McAdam Railway Station, New Brunswick (5.5.89)	2·00	50
	a. Chalk-surfaced paper (29.7.92)	4·25	2·10
	ab. Imperf (pair)		
1279	$5 Bonsecours Market, Montreal (28.5.90)	..	4·75	5·00
1261/79		*Set of* 22	17·00	8·50

The later issues of the mammal series are slightly larger than the original three, measuring 27 × 21 mm.

Nos. 1269a, 1270a, 1270cb, 1275a, 1276a and 1276cb were only issued in stamp booklets.

Nos. 1277a/ac and 1278a were printed by C.B.N. There was also a further printing of the $5, also by C.B.N. in September 1992, but this does not differ from the B.A.B.N. version. All C.B.N. printings are on thinner paper, less crisp than the initial printings.

No. 1277ad aapears to be from new plates. In addition to the differences in the roof colour it shows a less solid blue background around the building.

For further designs as Type **548a**, but in a changed format, see Nos. 1479/81.

(Des P.-Y. Pelletier. Litho Ashton-Potter)

1988 (12 Feb). *Winter Olympic Games, Calgary* (5th issue). *Vert designs as* T **531**. *Multicoloured. Fluorescent frame. P* 12 × 12½ (37 c.) *or* 12½ (*others*).
1281	37 c. Slalom skiing ..	..	65	40
	a. Pair. Nos. 1281/2	..	1·25	80
1282	37 c. Curling	..	..	65	40
1283	43 c. Figure skating..	..	75	45
1284	74 c. Luge	..	..	1·25	70
1281/4		*Set of* 4	3·00	1·75

Nos. 1281/2 were printed together, *se-tenant*, in horizontal and vertical pairs throughout the sheet.

549 Trade Goods, Blackfoot Encampment and Page from Anthony Henday's Journal

(Des F. Hagan. Litho Ashton-Potter)

1988 (17 Mar). *Exploration of Canada (3rd series). Explorers of the West. T* **549** *and similar horiz designs. Multicoloured. Fluorescent frame. P* 12¹/₂×13.

1285	37 c. Type **549**			65	50
	a. Block of 4. Nos. 1285/8			2·40	
1286	37 c. *Discovery* and map of George Vancouver's voyage			65	50
1287	37 c. Simon Fraser's expedition portaging canoes			65	50
1288	37 c. John Palliser's surveying equipment and view of prairie			65	50
1285/8			*Set of 4*	2·40	1·75

Nos. 1285/8 were printed together, *se-tenant*, in different combinations throughout the sheet, giving ten blocks of 4 and ten single stamps.

550 "The Young Reader" (Ozias Leduc)

551 Mallard landing on Marsh

(Des P.-Y. Pelletier. Eng G. Prosser. Recess and photo B.A.B.N.)

1988 (20 May). *Canadian Art (1st series). No fluorescent bands. P* 13×13¹/₂.

1289	**550**	50 c. multicoloured		70	70

No. 1289 was issued in sheets of 16 with descriptive texts on the margins.
See also Nos. 1327, 1384, 1421, 1504, 1539, 1589, 1629, 1681 and 1721.

(Des J. Gault and T. Telmet. Litho C.B.N.)

1988 (1 June). *Wildlife and Habitat Conservation. T* **551** *and similar horiz design. Multicoloured. Fluorescent frame. P* 13 × 13¹/₂.

1290	37 c. Type **551**			75	40
	a. Pair. Nos. 1290/1			1·50	80
1291	37 c. Moose feeding in marsh			75	40

Nos. 1290/1 were printed together, *se-tenant*, in horizontal and vertical pairs throughout the sheet.

552 Kerosene Lamp and Diagram of Distillation Plant

553 *Papilio brevicauda*

(Des R. Hill. Litho Ashton-Potter)

1988 (17 June). *Canada Day. Science and Technology. Canadian Inventions (3rd series). T* **552** *and similar vert designs. Multicoloured. Fluorescent frame. P* 12¹/₂×13.

1292	37 c. Type **552**			50	40
	a. Block of 4. Nos. 1292/5			1·75	
1293	37 c. Ears of Marquis wheat			50	40
1294	37 c. Electron microscope and magnified image			50	40
1295	37 c. Patient under "Cobalt 60" cancer therapy			50	40
1292/5			*Set of 4*	1·75	1·40

Nos. 1292/5 were printed together, *se-tenant*, in blocks of 4 throughout the sheet.

(Des Heather Cooper. Litho Ashton-Potter)

1988 (4 July). *Canadian Butterflies. T* **553** *and similar vert designs. Multicoloured. Fluorescent frame. P* 12×12¹/₂.

1296	37 c. Type **553**			60	60
	a. Block of four. Nos. 1296/9			2·25	
1297	37 c. *Lycaeides idas*			60	60
1298	37 c. *Oeneis macounii*			60	60
1299	37 c. *Papilio glaucus*			60	60
1296/9			*Set of 4*	2·25	2·25

Nos. 1296/9 were printed together, *se-tenant*, in different combinations throughout the sheet, giving ten blocks of 4 and ten single stamps.

554 St. John's Harbour Entrance and Skyline

555 Club Members working on Forestry Project and Rural Scene

(Des L.-A. Rivard. Litho Ashton-Potter)

1988 (22 July). *Centenary of Incorporation of St. John's, Newfoundland. Fluorescent frame. P* 13¹/₂×13.

1300	**554**	37 c. multicoloured		35	40

(Des Debbie Adams. Litho Ashton-Potter)

1988 (5 Aug). *75th Anniv of 4-H Clubs. Fluorescent frame. P* 13¹/₂×13.

1301	**555**	37 c. multicoloured		35	40

556 Saint-Maurice Ironworks

557 Tahltan Bear Dog

(Des Michèle Cayer and Hélène Racicot. Eng. Y. Baril. Recess and litho C.B.N.)

1988 (19 Aug). *250th Anniv of Saint-Maurice Ironworks, Québec. Fluorescent frame. P* 13¹/₂.

1302	**556**	37 c. black, pale orange and cinnamon	35	40	

(Des Mia Lane and D. Nethercott. Litho Ashton-Potter)

1988 (26 Aug). *Canadian Dogs. T* **557** *and similar horiz designs. Multicoloured. Fluorescent frame. P* 12¹/₂×12.

1303	37 c. Type **557**			85	50
	a. Block of 4. Nos. 1303/6			3·00	
1304	37 c. Nova Scotia Duck Tolling Retriever			85	50
1305	37 c. Canadian Eskimo Dog			85	50
1306	37 c. Newfoundland			85	50
1303/6			*Set of 4*	3·00	1·75

Nos. 1303/6 were printed together, *se-tenant*, in different combinations throughout the sheet, giving ten blocks of 4 and ten single stamps.

558 Baseball, Glove and Pitch

559 Virgin with Inset of Holy Child

(Des L. Holloway. Litho C.B.N.)

1988 (14 Sept). *150th Anniv of Baseball in Canada. Fluorescent frame. P* 13¹/₂ × 13.

1307	**558**	37 c. multicoloured		35	40

(Des E. Roch and T. Yakobina. Litho Ashton-Potter)

1988 (27 Oct). *Christmas. Icons. T* **559** *and similar multicoloured designs. Fluorescent frame. P* 12¹/₂×13 *(32 c.) or* 13¹/₂ *(others).*

1308	32 c. Holy Family (36×21 *mm*)			35	35
	a. Booklet pane. No. 1308×10			3·50	
1309	37 c. Type **559**			35	40
1310	43 c. Virgin and Child			40	45
1311	74 c. Virgin and Child (*different*)			70	75
1308/11			*Set of 4*	1·60	1·75

On No. 1308 the left-hand third of the design area is taken up by a bar code which has fluorescent bands between the bars. This value was only available from $3.20 stamp booklets which had the sides and bottom of the pane imperforate. It was intended for use on greeting cards posted on or before 31 January 1989.
No. 1309 also commemorates the Millenium of Ukrainian Christianity.

560 Bishop Inglis and Nova Scotia Church

561 Frances Ann Hopkins and "Canoe manned by Voyageurs"

(Des S. Slipp and K. Sollows. Litho Ashton-Potter)

1988 (1 Nov). *Bicentenary of Consecration of Charles Inglis (first Canadian Anglican bishop) (1987). Fluorescent frame. P* 12¹/₂ × 12.

1312	**560**	37 c. multicoloured		35	40

(Des D. Nethercott. Litho Ashton-Potter)

1988 (18 Nov). *150th Birth Anniv of Frances Ann Hopkins (artist). Fluorescent frame. P* 13¹/₂ × 13.

1313	**561**	37 c. multicoloured		35	40

562 Angus Walters and *Bluenose* (yacht)

563 Chipewyan Canoe

(Des R. Hill. Litho Ashton-Potter)

1988 (18 Nov). *20th Death Anniv of Angus Walters (yachtsman). Fluorescent frame. P* 13¹/₂.

1314	**562**	37 c. multicoloured		35	40

(Des B. Leduc and L.-A. Rivard. Litho Ashton-Potter)

1989 (1 Feb). *Small Craft of Canada (1st series). Native Canoes. T* **563** *and similar horiz designs. Multicoloured. Fluorescent frame. P* 13¹/₂ × 13.

1315	38 c. Type **563**			60	50
	a. Block of 4. Nos. 1315/18			2·25	
1316	38 c. Haida canoe			60	50
1317	38 c. Inuit kayak			60	50
1318	38 c. Micmac canoe			60	50
1315/18			*Set of 4*	2·25	1·75

Nos. 1315/18 were printed together, *se-tenant*, throughout the sheet, giving ten blocks of 4 and ten single stamps.
See also Nos. 1377/80 and 1428/31.

564 Matonabbee and Hearne's Expedition

565 Construction of Victoria Bridge, Montreal and William Notman

(Des F. Hagan. Litho Ashton-Potter)

1989 (22 Mar). *Exploration of Canada (4th series). Explorers of the North. T* **564** *and similar horiz designs. Multicoloured. Fluorescent frame. P* 12¹/₂×13.

1319	38 c. Type **564**			65	65
	a. Block of 4. Nos. 1319/22			2·40	
1320	38 c. Relics of Franklin's expedition and White Ensign			65	65
1321	38 c. Joseph Tyrrell's compass, hammer and fossil			65	65
1322	38 c. Vilhjalmur Stefansson, camera on tripod and sledge dog team			65	65
1319/22			*Set of 4*	2·40	2·40

Nos. 1319/22 were printed together, *se-tenant*, in different combinations throughout the sheet, giving ten blocks of 4 and ten single stamps.

(Des J. Morin and T. Yakobina. Litho Ashton-Potter)

1989 (23 June). *Canada Day. "150 Years of Canadian Photography". T* **565** *and similar horiz designs, each showing early photograph and photographer. Multicoloured. P* 12¹/₂×12.

1323	38 c. Type **565**			50	50
	a. Block of 4. Nos. 1323/6			1·75	
1324	38 c. Plains Indian village and W. Hanson Boorne			50	50
1325	38 c. Horse-drawn sleigh and Alexander Henderson			50	50
1326	38 c. Quebec street scene and Jules-Ernest Livernois			50	50
1323/6			*Set of 4*	1·75	1·75

Nos. 1323/6 were printed together, *se-tenant*, in blocks of 4 throughout the sheet.

566 Tsimshian Ceremonial Frontlet, c 1900

567 Canadian Flag and Forest

(Des P.-Y. Pelletier. Litho and die-stamped Ashton-Potter)

1989 (29 June). *Canadian Art (2nd series). No fluorescent bands. P* 12¹/₂×13.

1327	**566**	50 c. multicoloured		55	60

No. 1327 was issued in a similar sheet format to No. 1289

(Des Gottschalk & Ash International. Litho Ashton-Potter)

1989 (30 June)–93. *Self-adhesive booklet stamps.* T **567** and similar horiz designs. Multicoloured. Fluorescent frame. Die-cut.

1328	38 c. Type **567** ..	90	1·40
	a. Booklet pane. No. 1328×12 ..	10·00	
1328*b*	39 c. Canadian flag and prairie (8.2.90)	1·00	1·50
	ba. Booklet pane. No. 1328*b*×12 ..	11·00	
1328*c*	40 c. Canadian flag and sea (11.1.91)	1·00	1·25
	ca. Booklet pane. No. 1328*c*×12 ..	11·00	
1328*d*	42 c. Canadian flag and mountains (28.1.92) ..	80	1·10
	da. Booklet pane. No. 1328*d*×12	9·00	
1328*e*	45 c. Canadian flag over lake (15.2.93) ..	70	85
	ea. Booklet pane. No. 1328*e*×12	8·50	
1328/*e*	*Set of 5*	4·00	5·50

Nos. 1328, 1328*b*, 1328*c*, 1328*d* and 1328*e* were only available from self-adhesive booklets in which the backing card forms the booklet cover.

568 Archibald Lampman   **569** *Clavulinopsis fusiformis*

(Des R. Milot. Litho Ashton-Potter)

1989 (7 July). *Canadian Poets.* T **568** and similar horiz design. Multicoloured. Fluorescent frame. P 13½.

1329	38 c. Type **568** ..	40	45
	a. Pair. Nos. 1329/30 ..	80	90
1330	38 c. Louis-Honoré Fréchette ..	40	45

Nos. 1329/30 were printed together, *se-tenant*, in horizontal and vertical pairs throughout the sheet.

(Des E. Roch. Litho Ashton-Potter)

1989 (4 Aug). *Mushrooms.* T **569** and similar vert designs. Multicoloured. Fluorescent frame. P 13½.

1331	38 c. Type **569** ..	70	60
	a. Block of 4. Nos. 1331/4 ..	2·50	
1332	38 c. *Boletus mirabilis* ..	70	60
1333	38 c. *Cantharellus cinnabarinus* ..	70	60
1334	38 c. *Morchella esculenta* ..	70	60
1331/4	*Set of 4*	2·50	2·25

Nos. 1331/4 were printed together, *se-tenant*, in different combinations throughout the sheet, giving ten blocks of 4 and ten single stamps.

570 Night Patrol, Korea   **571** Globe in Box

(Des N. Fontaine, J. Gault and T. Telmet. Eng Y. Baril. Recess and litho C.B.N.)

1989 (8 Sept). *75th Anniv of Canadian Regiments.* T **570** and similar horiz design. Multicoloured. Fluorescent frame. P 13.

1335	38 c. Type **570** (Princess Patricia's Canadian Light Infantry) ..	70	70
	a. Vert pair. Nos. 1335/6	1·40	1·40
1336	38 c. Trench raid, France, 1914-18 (Royal 22e Régiment) ..	70	70

Nos. 1335/6 were printed together, *se-tenant*, in vertical pairs throughout the sheet.

(Des L. Holloway and Nita Wallace. Litho Ashton-Potter)

1989 (2 Oct). *Canada Export Trade Month.* Fluorescent frame. P 13½×13.

1337	571 38 c. multicoloured ..	40	45

572 Film Director   **573** "Snow II" (Lawren S. Harris)

(Des W. Tibbles from paper sculptures by J. Milne. Litho Ashton-Potter)

1989 (4 Oct). *Arts and Entertainment.* T **572** and similar vert designs. Fluorescent frame. P 13×13½.

1338	38 c. grey-brown, blackish brown and bright reddish violet ..	40	45
	a. Block of 4. Nos. 1338/41 ..	1·50	
1339	38 c. grey-brown, blackish brown & brt grn	40	45
1340	38 c. grey-brn, blackish brn & brt magenta	40	45
1341	38 c. grey-brown, blackish brown & new bl	40	45
1338/41	*Set of 4*	1·50	1·60

Designs:—No. 1339, Actors; No. 1340, Dancers; No. 1341, Musicians.

Nos. 1338/41 were printed together, *se-tenant*, in different combinations throughout the sheet, giving ten blocks of 4 and ten single stamps.

(Des D. Nethercott and Viviane Warburton. Litho Ashton-Potter)

1989 (26 Oct). *Christmas. Paintings of Winter Landscapes.* T **573** and similar multicoloured designs. Fluorescent frame. P 12½×13 (33 c.), 13×13½ (38 c.) or 13½ (others).

1342	33 c. "Champ-de-Mars, Winter" (William Brymner) (35×21 *mm*) ..	35	40
	a. Booklet pane. No. 1342×10	6·50	
	b. Imperf between (horiz pair) (from booklet) ..		
1343	38 c. "Bend in the Gosselin River" (Marc-Aurèle Suzor-Coté) (21×35 *mm*)	40	45
	a. Perf 13×12½ ..	2·50	3·00
	ab. Booklet pane. No. 1343a×10	26·00	
1344	44 c. Type **573** ..	45	50
	a. Booklet pane. No. 1344×5 plus one printed label ..	9·00	
1345	76 c. "Ste. Agnès" (A. H. Robinson) ..	80	85
	a. Booklet pane. No. 1345×5 plus one printed label..	17·00	
1342/5	*Set of 4*	1·75	2·00

On No. 1342 the left-hand third of the design area is taken up by a bar code which has fluorescent bands between the bars. This value was only available from $3.30 stamp booklets which had the sides and bottom of the pane imperforate. It was intended for use on greeting cards posted on or before 31 January 1990.

No. 1343a was only issued in $3.80 stamp booklets.

Booklet pane No. 1343ab has the outer edges of the pane imperforate while Nos. 1344a and 1345a have the vertical edges imperforate.

574 Canadians listening to Declaration of War, 1939

(Des J.-P. Armanville and P.-Y. Pelletier. Litho C.B.N.)

1989 (10 Nov). *50th Anniv of Second World War (1st issue).* T **574** and similar horiz designs. Fluorescent frame. P 13½.

1346	38 c. black, silver and slate-purple	55	55
	a. Block of 4. Nos. 1346/9 ..	2·00	
1347	38 c. black, silver and olive-grey ..	55	55
1348	38 c. black, silver and grey-green	55	55
1349	38 c. black, silver and azure	55	55
1346/9	*Set of 4*	2·00	2·00

Designs:—No. 1347, Army mobilization; No. 1348, British Commonwealth air crew training; No. 1349, North Atlantic convoy.

Nos. 1346/9 were printed together, *se-tenant*, in different combinations throughout the sheet, giving four blocks of 4.

See also Nos. 1409/12, 1456/9, 1521/4, 1576/9, 1621/4 and 1625/8.

575   Canadian Flag   **576**

1989 (28 Dec)–95. *No fluorescent bands (1, 5 c.) or fluorescent frame (39, 40, 42, 43, 45 c.).*

(a) Booklet stamps. T **575** and similar horiz designs, each showing Canadian flag. Litho Ashton-Potter. Chalk-surfaced paper. P 13½×14.

1350	575	1 c. multicoloured (12.1.90) ..	20	85
		a. Booklet panes. Nos. 1350, 1351×2 and 1352 ..	1·40	
		b. Perf 12½×13	13·00	13·00
		ba. Booklet pane. Nos. 1350*b*, 1351a×2 and 1352a	25·00	
		c. Booklet pane. Nos. 1350×2, 1351 and 1353 (28.12.90)	1·25	
1351	—	5 c. multicoloured (12.1.90) ..	20	30
		a. Perf 12½×13	4·00	4·00
1352	—	39 c. multicoloured (12.1.90) ..	1·25	1·50
		a. Perf 12½×13	13·00	13·00
1353	—	40 c. multicoloured (28.12.90)	1·25	1·75

(b) Litho (for printers see below). Chalk-surfaced paper. P 14½ (45 c.) or 13½×13 (others)

1354	576	39 c. multicoloured ..	50	10
		a. Booklet pane. No. 1354×10 and two labels ..	6·50	
		b. Booklet pane. No. 1354×25 and two labels ..	14·00	
		c. Perf 12½×13 (2.90) ..	4·00	3·25
1355	—	40 c. multicoloured (28.12.90) ..	50	10
		a. Booklet pane. No. 1355×10 and two labels ..	5·50	
		b. Booklet pane. No. 1355×25 and two labels ..	14·00	
1356	—	42 c. multicoloured (27.12.91) ..	60	15
		a. Booklet pane. No. 1356×10	6·50	
		b. Booklet pane. No. 1356×25 and two labels ..	14·00	
		c. Booklet pane. No. 1356×50 and two labels ..	45·00	
1357	—	43 c. multicoloured (30.12.92)	60	60
		a. Booklet pane. No. 1357×10	6·00	
		b. Booklet pane. No. 1357×25 and two labels ..	15·00	
		c. Perf 14½ (18.1.94)	90	90
		ca. Booklet pane. No. 1357c×10	6·00	
		cb. Booklet pane. No. 1357c×25 and two labels ..	15·00	
		cc. Imperf between (vert pair) ..		

1358	— 45 c. multicoloured (31.7.95) ..	55	65
	a. Booklet pane. No. 1358×10	4·75	
	b. Booklet pane. No. 1358×25 and two labels ..	12·00	
	c. Perf 13½×13 (6.10.95) ..	35	40
	ca. Booklet pane. No. 1358c×10	3·50	
	cb. Booklet pane. No. 1358c×25 and two labels ..	8·75	

(c) Coil stamps. Designs as T **575**, but different folds in flag. Recess C.B.N. P 10×*imperf*.

1359	— 39 c. deep purple (8.2.90) ..	60	75
	a. Imperf (pair) ..	55·00	
1360	— 40 c. indigo (28.12.90)	40	45
	a. Imperf (pair) ..	£100	
1361	— 42 c. scarlet-vermilion (27.12.91)	40	45
	a. Imperf (pair) ..	55·00	
1362	— 43 c. deep olive (30.12.92)	55	70
	a. Imperf (pair) ..	55·00	
1363	— 45 c. bluish green (31.7.95)	35	40
	a. Imperf (pair) ..	55·00	

Designs:—40 c. (No. 1355) Canadian flag over forest; 42 c. (No. 1356) Flag over mountains; 43 c. (No. 1357) Flag over prairie; 45 c. (No. 1358) Flag and skyscraper.

Booklet panes Nos. 1350a/b, 1356a/c, 1357ca/cb, 1358a/b and 1358ca/cb have the vertical edges of the panes imperforate and each shows a margin at foot. Booklet panes Nos. 1354a/b, 1355a/b and 1357a/b are imperforate at top and bottom.

Due to changes in the Canada Post contracts the printing history of Nos. 1354/8 is very complex. Details are provided below with Ashton-Potter Ltd printings shown as AP, Canadian Bank Note Co as CBN and Leigh-Mardon Ltd as LM.

39 c. (No. 1354) CBN (28.12.89), AP (14.2.90)
    (Nos. 1354a/b) AP (28.12.89)
    (No. 1354c) AP (2.90)
40 c. (No. 1355) CBN (28.12.90), AP (28.12.89)
    (Nos. 1355a/b) AP (28.12.90)
42 c. (No. 1356/c) AP (27.12.91)
43 c. (Nos. 1357/b) AP (30.12.92), CBN (14.11.94)
    (Nos. 1357c/cb) LM (18.1.94)
45 c. (Nos. 1358/b) LM (31.7.95)
    (Nos. 1358c/cb) CBN (6.10.95).

The C.B.N. printings of the 45 c. (No. 1358c) show the copyright date on flag changed from "1990" to "1995".

Postal forgeries of Nos. 1359 and 1362 exist showing heavier printing across the foot of the design.

577 Norman Bethune in 1937, and performing Operation, Montreal   **578** Maple Leaf Mosaic

(Des Wanda Lewicka, J. Morin and Liu Xiang Ping. Eng Hu Zhenyuan and Yan Bingwu. Recess and litho C.B.N.)

1990 (2 Mar). *Birth Centenary of Dr. Norman Bethune (surgeon).* T **577** and similar horiz design. Multicoloured. Fluorescent frame. P 13×13½.

1375	39 c. Type **577** ..	45	65
	a. Pair. Nos. 1375/6 ..	90	1·25
1376	39 c. Bethune in 1939, and treating wounded Chinese soldiers	45	65

Nos. 1375/6 were printed together, *se-tenant*, in horizontal and vertical pairs throughout the sheet.

(Des B. Leduc and L.-A. Rivard. Litho Ashton-Potter)

1990 (15 Mar). *Small Craft of Canada (2nd series). Early Work Boats.* Horiz designs as T **563**. Multicoloured. Fluorescent frame. P 13½×13.

1377	39 c. Fishing dory ..	50	55
	a. Block of 4. Nos. 1377/80 ..	1·75	
1378	39 c. Logging pointer ..	50	55
1379	39 c. York boat ..	50	55
1380	39 c. North canoe ..	50	55
1377/80	*Set of 4*	1·75	2·00

Nos. 1377/80 were printed together, *se-tenant*, throughout the sheet, giving ten blocks of 4 and ten single stamps.

(Des F. Peter. Recess and litho C.B.N.)

1990 (5 Apr). *Multiculturalism.* P 13.

1381	578 39 c. multicoloured ..	35	40

579 Mail Van (facing left)   **580** Amerindian and Inuit Dolls

(Des J. Morin and A. Rochon. Litho Ashton-Potter)

1990 (3 May). *"Moving the Mail".* T **579** and similar horiz design. Multicoloured. Fluorescent frame. P 13½.

1382	39 c. Type **579** ..	45	55
	a. Booklet pane. Nos. 1382/3, each × 4	3·50	
	b. Booklet pane. Nos. 1382×5, 1383×4 and 3 labels ..	7·00	
1383	39 c. Mail van (facing right) ..	45	55

Nos. 1382/3 were only issued in $9.75 stamp booklets.

(Des P.-Y. Pelletier. Litho and die-stamped Ashton-Potter)

1990 (3 May). *Canadian Art (3rd series).* Vert design as T **550**. Multicoloured. No fluorescent bands. P 12½×13.

1384	50 c. "The West Wind" (Tom Thomson) ..	55	65

No. 1384 was issued in a similar sheet format to No. 1289.

(Des Nita Wallace. Litho Ashton-Potter)

1990 (8 June). *Dolls. T **580** and similar horiz designs. Multicoloured. Fluorescent frame. P 12½×12.*

1385	39 c. Type **580**		55	60
	a. Block of 4. Nos. 1385/8		2·00	
1386	39 c. 19th-century settlers' dolls		55	60
1387	39 c. Commercial dolls, 1917–36		55	60
1388	39 c. Commercial dolls, 1940–60		55	60
1385/8		*Set of 4*	2·00	2·10

Nos. 1385/8 were printed together, *se-tenant*, in different combinations throughout the sheet, giving ten blocks of 4 and en single stamps.

581 Canadian Flag and Fireworks

582 *Stromatolites* (fossil algae)

(Des C. Malenfont. Litho Ashton-Potter)

1990 (1 July*). *Canada Day. Fluorescent frame. P 13×12½*
1389 **581** 39 c. multicoloured .. 45 50

No. 1389 was issued in sheets of 16 with descriptive texts on the coloured margins.
*First day covers of No. 1389 are postmarked 29 June 1990. The stamp was available from two temporary post offices in Ottawa on Sunday 1 July, but was not sold throughout Canada until 3 July.

(Des R. Harder. Eng Y. Baril. Recess and litho C.B.N.)

1990 (12 July). *Prehistoric Canada (1st series). Primitive Life. T **582** and similar horiz designs. Multicoloured. Fluorescent frame. P 13×13½.*

1390	39 c. Type **582**		60	70
	a. Block of 4. Nos. 1390/3		2·25	
1391	39 c. *Opabinia regalis* (soft invertebrate)		60	70
1392	39 c. *Paradoxides davidis* (trilobite)		60	70
1393	39 c. *Eurypterus remipes* (sea scorpion)		60	70
1390/3		*Set of 4*	2·25	2·50

Nos. 1390/3 were printed together, *se-tenant*, in different combinations throughout the sheet, giving four blocks of 4 and four single stamps.
See also Nos. 1417/20, 1568/71 and 1613/16.

583 Acadian Forest

584 Clouds and Rainbow

(Des M. and Jan Waddell. Litho Ashton-Potter)

1990 (7 Aug). *Canadian Forests. T **583** and similar horiz designs. Multicoloured. Fluorescent frame. P 12½×13.*

1394	39 c. Type **583**		60	70
	a. Block of 4. Nos. 1394/7		2·25	
1395	39 c. Great Lakes–St. Lawrence forest		60	70
1396	39 c. Pacific Coast forest		60	70
1397	39 c. Boreal forest		60	70
1394/7		*Set of 4*	2·25	2·50

Nos. 1394/7 were printed together, *se-tenant*, in different combinations throughout the sheet, giving four blocks of 4 and four single stamps.

Nos. 1394/7 also exist as blocks of four of the same design surrounded by margins. Such blocks were not available from post offices, but could be obtained for $1 each at Petro-Canada filling stations by using a previously-distributed voucher in conjunction with the purchase of 25 litres of petrol. They could also be obtained, at face value, from the Canadian Philatelic Service by post.

(Des D. L'Allier and Dominique Trudeau. Litho Ashton-Potter)

1990 (5 Sept). *150th Anniv of Weather Observing in Canada. Fluorescent frame. P 12½×13½.*
1398 **584** 39 c. multicoloured .. 40 50

No. 1398 has a break in the lower vertical sides of the fluorescent frame to allow the clouds to run on to the margins.

585 "Alphabet" Bird

586 Sasquatch

(Des Debbie Adams. Recess and litho C.B.N.)

1990 (7 Sept). *International Literacy Year. Fluorescent frame. P 13½×13.*
1399 **585** 39 c. multicoloured 40 50

(Des A. Cormack, Deborah Drew-Brook and R. Tibbles. Litho Ashton-Potter)

1990 (1 Oct). *Legendary Creatures. T **586** and similar horiz designs. Multicoloured. Fluorescent frame. P 12½×13½.*

1400	39 c. Type **586**		70	70
	a. Block of 4. Nos. 1400/3		2·50	
	b. Perf 12½×12		5·50	5·00
	ba. Block of 4. Nos. 1400b/3b		20·00	
1401	39 c. Kraken		70	70
	b. Perf 12½×12		5·50	5·00
1402	39 c. Werewolf		70	70
	b. Perf 12½×12		5·50	5·00
1403	39 c. Ogopogo		70	70
	b. Perf 12½×12		5·50	5·00
1400/3		*Set of 4*	2·50	2·50

Nos. 1400/3 were printed together, *se-tenant*, in different combinations throughout the sheet, giving ten blocks of four and ten single stamps.

Stamps perforated 12½×12 come from a small percentage of the "non-philatelic" stock without imprints. Examples have also been found on official First Day Covers included in Presentation Packs.

587 Agnes Macphail

588 "Virgin Mary with Christ Child and St. John the Baptist" (Norval Morrisseau)

(Des M. and Jan Waddell. Litho Ashton-Potter)

1990 (9 Oct). *Birth Centenary of Agnes Macphail (first woman elected to Parliament). Fluorescent frame. P 13×13½.*
1404 **587** 39 c. multicoloured 40 50

(Des C. Malenfant. Litho Ashton-Potter)

1990 (25 Oct). *Christmas. Native Art. T **588** and similar designs. Fluorescent frame. P 12½×13 (34 c.) or 13½ (others).*

1405	34 c. multicoloured (35×21 mm) ..		40	35
	a. Booklet pane. No. 1405×10 ..		4·00	
1406	39 c. multicoloured		40	40
	a. Booklet pane. No. 1406×10 ..		6·00	
1407	45 c. multicoloured		40	45
	a. Booklet pane. No. 1407×5 plus one printed label		3·50	
1408	78 c. black, bright scarlet and violet-grey		70	75
	a. Booklet pane. No. 1408×5 plus one printed label		6·00	
1405/8		*Set of 4*	1·75	1·75

Designs:—34 c. "Rebirth" (Jackson Beardy); 45 c. "Mother and Child" (Inuit sculpture, Cape Dorset); 78 c. "Children of the Raven" (Bill Reid).
On No. 1405 the left-hand third of the design area is taken up by a bar code which has fluorescent bands between the bars. This value was only available from $3.40 stamp booklets which had the sides and bottom of the pane imperforate. It was intended for use on greeting cards posted on or before 31 January 1991.
Booklet panes Nos. 1406a, 1407a and 1408a also have the side and bottom edges imperforate.

(Des J.-P. Armanville and P.-Y. Pelletier. Litho Ashton-Potter)

1990 (9 Nov). *50th Anniv of Second World War (2nd issue). Horiz designs as T **574**. Fluorescent frame. P 12½×12.*

1409	39 c. black, silver and grey-olive ..		85	85
	a. Block of 4. Nos. 1409/12		3·00	
1410	39 c. black, silver and red-brown ..		85	85
1411	39 c. black, silver and bistre-brown		85	85
1412	39 c. black, silver and dull mauve		85	85
1409/12		*Set of 4*	3·00	3·00

Designs:—No. 1409, Canadian family at home, 1940; No. 1410, Packing parcels for the troops; No. 1411, Harvesting; No. 1412, Testing anti-gravity flying suit.
Nos. 1409/12 were printed together, *se-tenant*, in different combinations throughout the sheet, giving four blocks of 4.

589 Jennie Trout (first woman physician) and Women's Medical College, Kingston

590 Blue Poppies and Butchart Gardens, Victoria

(Des R. Milot. Litho Ashton-Potter)

1991 (15 Mar). *Medical Pioneers. T **589** and similar vert designs. Multicoloured. Fluorescent frame. P 13½.*

1413	40 c. Type **589**		85	85
	a. Block of 4. Nos. 1413/16		3·00	
1414	40 c. Wilder Penfield (neurosurgeon) and Montreal Neurological Institute		85	85

1415	40 c. Frederick Banting (discoverer of insulin) and University of Toronto medical faculty		85	85
1416	40 c. Harold Griffith (anesthesiologist) and Queen Elizabeth Hospital, Montreal		85	85
1413/16		*Set of 4*	3·00	3·00

Nos. 1413/16 were printed together, *se-tenant*, in different combinations throughout the sheet, giving ten blocks of 4 and ten single stamps.

(Des R. Harder. Eng L. Bloss. Recess and litho Ashton-Potter)

1991 (5 Apr). *Prehistoric Canada (2nd series). Primitive Vertebrates. Horiz designs as T **582**. Multicoloured. Fluorescent frame. P 12½×13½.*

1417	40 c. Foord's Crossopt (*Eusthenopteron foordi*) (fish fossil)		1·25	1·40
	a. Block of 4. Nos. 1417/20		4·50	
1418	40 c. *Hylonomus lyelli* (land reptile)		1·25	1·40
1419	40 c. Fossil Conodonts (fossil teeth)		1·25	1·40
1420	40 c. *Archaeopteris halliana* (early tree)		1·25	1·40
1417/20		*Set of 4*	4·50	5·00

Nos. 1417/20 were printed together, *se-tenant*, in different combinations throughout the sheet, giving four blocks of 4 and four single stamps.

(Des P.-Y. Pelletier. Litho and die-stamped Ashton-Potter)

1991 (7 May). *Canadian Art (4th series). Vert design as T **550**. Multicoloured. No fluorescent bands. P 12½×13.*
1421 50 c. "Forest, British Columbia" (Emily Carr) .. .. 80 1·00

No. 1421 was issued in a similar sheet format to No. 1289.

(Des G. Gauci and D. Wyman. Litho Ashton-Potter)

1991 (22 May). *Public Gardens. T **590** and similar vert designs. Multicoloured. Fluorescent frame. P 13×12½.*

1422	40 c. Type **590**		55	55
	a. Booklet pane. Nos. 1422/6, each × 2		5·50	
1423	40 c. Marigolds and International Peace Garden, Boissevain		55	55
1424	40 c. Lilac and Royal Botanical Gardens, Hamilton		55	55
1425	40 c. Roses and Montreal Botanical Gardens		55	55
1426	40 c. Rhododendrons and Halifax Public Gardens		55	55
1422/6		*Set of 5*	2·50	2·50

Nos. 1422/6 were only available from $4 stamp booklets containing No. 1422a, which is imperforate at top and bottom.

591 Maple Leaf

592 South Nahanni River

(Des Lisa Miller, R. Séguin and J.-P. Veilleux. Litho C.B.N.)

1991 (28 June). *Canada Day. Fluorescent frame. P 13½×13.*
1427 **591** 40 c. multicoloured 50 60

No. 1427 was issued in sheets of 20 with inscribed and decorated margins.

(Des B. Leduc and L.-A. Rivard. Litho Ashton-Potter)

1991 (18 July). *Small Craft of Canada (3rd series). Horiz designs as T **563**. Multicoloured. Fluorescent frame. P 13½×13.*

1428	40 c. Verchère rowboat		85	85
	a. Block of 4. Nos. 1428/31		3·00	
1429	40 c. Touring kayak		85	85
1430	40 c. Sailing dinghy		85	85
1431	40 c. Cedar strip canoe		85	85
1428/31		*Set of 4*	3·00	3·00

Nos. 1428/31 were printed together, *se-tenant*, throughout the sheet, giving ten blocks of 4 and ten single stamps.

(Des M. and Jan Waddell. Litho Ashton-Potter)

1991 (20 Aug). *Canadian Rivers (1st series). T **592** and similar vert designs. Multicoloured. Fluorescent frame. P 13×12½.*

1432	40 c. Type **592**		80	90
	a. Booklet pane. Nos. 1432/6, each × 2 with margins all round		7·50	
1433	40 c. Athabasca River		80	90
1434	40 c. Boundary Waters, Voyageur Waterway		80	90
1435	40 c. Jacques-Cartier River		80	90
1436	40 c. Main River ..		80	90
1432/6		*Set of 5*	3·50	4·00

Nos. 1432/6 were only issued in $4 stamp booklets.
See also Nos. 1492/6, 1558/62 and 1584/8.

593 "Leaving Europe"

594 Ski Patrol rescuing Climber

(Des J. Gault and T. Telmet. Litho C.B.N.)

1991 (29 Aug). *Centenary of Ukrainian Immigration. Panels from "The Ukrainian Pioneer" by William Kurelek. T **593** and similar vert designs. Multicoloured. Fluorescent frame. P* 13½×13.

1437	40 c.	Type **593**	..	80	85
	a.	Block of 4. Nos. 1437/40		2·75	
1438	40 c.	"Canadian Winter"	..	80	85
1439	40 c.	"Clearing the Land"	..	80	85
1440	40 c.	"Harvest"	..	80	85
1437/40			*Set of* 4	2·75	3·00

Nos. 1437/40 were printed together, *se-tenant*, in different combinations throughout the sheet, giving four blocks of 4 and four single stamps.

(Des Suzanne Duranceau. Litho C.B.N.)

1991 (23 Sept). *Emergency Services. T **594** and similar vert designs. Multicoloured. Fluorescent frame. P* 13½.

1441	40 c.	Type **594**	..	90	1·00
	a.	Block of 4. Nos 1441/4		3·25	
1442	40 c.	Police at road traffic accident		90	1·00
1443	40 c.	Firemen on extending ladder		90	1·00
1444	40 c.	Boeing-Vertol CH-147 Chinook rescue helicopter and lifeboat		90	1·00
1441/4			*Set of* 4	3·25	3·50

Nos. 1441/4 were printed together, *se-tenant*, in different combinations throughout the sheet, giving ten blocks of 4 and ten single stamps.

595 "The Witched Canoe"	**596** Grant Hall Tower

(Des A. Cormack, Deborah Drew-Brook and R. Tibbles. Litho Ashton-Potter)

1991 (1 Oct). *Canadian Folktales. T **595** and similar vert designs. Multicoloured. Fluorescent frame. P* 13½×12½.

1445	40 c.	Type **595**	..	85	85
	a.	Block of 4. Nos. 1445/8	..	3·00	
1446	40 c.	"The Orphan Boy"	..	85	85
1447	40 c.	"Chinook"	..	85	85
1448	40 c.	"Buried Treasure"	..	85	85
1445/8			*Set of* 4	3·00	3·00

Nos. 1445/8 were printed together, *se-tenant*, in different combinations throughout the sheet, giving ten blocks of 4 and ten single stamps.

(Des L. Holloway and R. Kerr. Litho Ashton-Potter)

1991 (16 Oct). *150th Anniv of Queen's University, Kingston. Fluorescent frame. P* 13×12½.

1449	**596** 40 c.	multicoloured		65	1·00
	a.	Booklet pane. No. 1449×10 plus two printed labels with margins all round		6·50	

No. 1449 was only issued in $4 stamp booklets.

597 North American Santa Claus	**598** Players jumping for Ball

(Des S. Slipp. Litho Ashton-Potter)

1991 (23 Oct). *Christmas. T **597** and similar multicoloured designs. Fluorescent frame. P* 12½×13 (35 c.) *or* 13½ (others).

1450	35 c.	British Father Christmas (35×21 mm)		60	40
	a.	Booklet pane. No. 1450×10	..	6·00	
1451	40 c.	Type **597**		70	20
	a.	Booklet pane. No. 1451×10		7·00	
1452	46 c.	French Bonhomme Noel		75	90
	a.	Booklet pane. No. 1452×5 plus one printed label		3·50	
1453	80 c.	Dutch Sinterklaas		1·40	2·00
	a.	Booklet pane. No. 1453×5 plus one printed label		7·00	
1450/3			*Set of* 4	3·25	3·25

On No. 1450 the left-hand third of the design area is taken up by a bar code which has fluorescent bands between the bars. This value was only available from $3.50 stamp booklets which had the edges of the pane imperforate. It was intended for use on greeting cards posted on or before 31 January 1992.

Nos. 1451a, 1452a and 1453a also have the vertical edges of the panes imperforate.

(Des J. Gault, C. Reynolds and T. Telmet. Litho Ashton-Potter)

1991 (25 Oct). *Basketball Centenary. T **598** and similar vert designs. Multicoloured. Fluorescent frame. P* 13×13½.

1454	40 c.	Type **598**	..	90	75
MS1455	155×90 mm. 40 c. Type **598**, but with shorter inscr below face value; 46 c. Player taking shot; 80 c. Player challenging opponent			5·00	5·00

(Des J.-P. Armanville and P.-Y. Pelletier. Litho C.B.N)

1991 (8 Nov). *50th Anniv of Second World War (3rd issue). Horiz designs as T **574**. Fluorescent frame. P* 13½.

1456	40 c.	black, silver and greenish blue		90	90
	a.	Block of 4. Nos. 1456/9		3·25	
1457	40 c.	black, silver and brown		90	90
1458	40 c.	black, silver and lilac		90	90
1459	40 c.	black, silver and ochre		90	90
1456/9			*Set of* 4	3·25	3·25

Designs:—No. 1456, Women's services, 1941; No. 1457, Armament factory; No. 1458, Cadets and veterans; No. 1459, Defence of Hong Kong.

Nos. 1456/9 were printed together, *se-tenant*, in different combinations throughout the sheet, giving four blocks of 4.

599 Blueberry	**600** McIntosh Apple

600a Court House, Yorkton

(Des Tania Craan and D. Noble (1 c. to 25 c.), C. Malenfant (48 c. to 90 c.), R. Bellemare ($1, $2, $5))

1991 (27 Dec)–96. *Multicoloured. Chalk-surfaced paper.*

(a) *Edible Berries. Litho (for printers see below). T **599** and similar horiz designs. No fluorescent frame. P* 13×13½ (5.8.92).

1460	1 c.	Type **599**	..	..	10	10
1461	2 c.	Wild Strawberry	..	..	10	10
1462	3 c.	Black Crowberry	..	..	10	10
1463	5 c.	Rose Hip	..	..	10	10
1464	6 c.	Black Raspberry	..	..	10	10
1465	10 c.	Kinnikinnick	..	..	10	10
	a.	Imperf (horiz pair)				
1466	25 c.	Saskatoon Berry	..	..	20	25

(b) *Fruit and Nut Trees. Litho (for printers see below). T **600** and similar horiz designs. Three fluorescent bands (90 c.) or fluorescent frame (others). P* 13.

1467	48 c.	Delicious Apple		50	35
	a.	Perf 14½×14		80	80
	ab.	Booklet pane. No. 1467a×5 and label	3·75	
1468	49 c.	Delicious Apple (30.12.92)		65	80
	a.	Booklet pane. No. 1468×5 and label (7.1.94)		4·50	
	b.	Perf 14½×14		90	1·00
	ba.	Booklet pane. No. 1468b×5 and label	4·50	
1469	50 c.	Snow Apple (25.2.94)		80	80
	a.	Booklet pane. No. 1469×5 and label		4·00	
	b.	Perf 14½×14 (27.3.95)		80	1·00
	ba.	Booklet pane. No. 1469b×5 and label	4·00	
1470	52 c.	Gravenstein Apple (31.7.95)		40	45
	a.	Booklet pane. No. 1470×5 and label	2·00	
	b.	Perf 14½×14 (6.10.95)		40	45
	ba.	Booklet pane. No. 1470b×5 and label	4·00	
1471	65 c.	Black Walnut		70	50
1472	67 c.	Beaked Hazelnut (30.12.92)		1·00	1·00
1473	69 c.	Shagbark Hickory (25.2.94)		1·00	1·00
1474	71 c.	American Chestnut (31.7.95)		80	1·00
	a.	Perf 14½×14 (6.10.95)		2·50	70
1475	84 c.	Stanley Plum		90	75
	a.	Perf 14½×14		1·40	1·50
	ab.	Booklet pane. No. 1475a×5 and label	7·00	
1476	86 c.	Bartlett Pear (30.12.92)		85	1·00
	a.	Booklet pane. No. 1476×5 and label (7.1.94)		7·50	
	b.	Perf 14½×14		1·60	1·75
	ba.	Booklet pane. No. 1476b×5 and label	7·50	
1477	88 c.	Westcot Apricot (25.2.94)		90	1·25
	a.	Booklet pane. No. 1477×5 and label	6·00	
	b.	Three fluorescent bands (14.11.94)	1·50	1·75
	ba.	Booklet pane. No. 1477b×5 and label	7·50	
	c.	Perf 14½×14. Three fluorescent bands (27.3.95)		1·50	1·75
	ca.	Booklet pane. No. 1477c×5 and label	7·50	
1478	90 c.	Elberta Peach (31.7.95)		75	80
	a.	Booklet pane. No. 1478×5 and label	3·75	
	b.	Perf 14½×14 (6.10.95)		75	80
	ba.	Booklet pane. No. 1478b×5 and label	7·00	

(c) *Architecture. Recess and litho Leigh-Mardon Ltd, Melbourne (Nos. 1479/80) or C.B.N. (Nos. 1479a, 1480a, 1481). T **600a** and similar horiz designs. P* 14½×14 ($1, $2) *or* 13½×13 ($5)

1479	$1	Type **600a** (21.2.94)		90	95
	a.	Perf 13½×13 (20.2.95)		1·50	90
1480	$2	Provincial Normal School, Truro (21.2.94)		1·90	2·00
	a.	Perf 13½×13 (20.2.95)		2·25	1·90
	ab.	Deep turquoise-blue (recess inscr) omitted			£650
	ac.	Deep turquoise-blue (recess inscr) inverted			
1481	$5	Public Library, Victoria (29.2.96)		4·00	4·25
1460/81			*Set of* 22	15·00	15·00

Nos. 1460/6 were so printed that each horizontal row formed a composite design.

Nos. 1467a, 1468b, 1469b, 1475a, 1476b and 1477c were only issued in stamp booklets.

Booklet panes Nos. 1467ab, 1468a, 1468ba, 1475ab, 1476a,

1476ab, 1477a and 1477ba each have the vertical edges of the pane imperforate and margins at top and bottom.

Due to changes in the Canada Post contracts the printing history of Nos. 1460/80 is very complex. Details are provided below with Ashton-Potter Ltd printings shown as AP, Canadian Bank Note Co as CBN, Leigh-Mardon Ltd as LM and Ashton-Potter Canada Ltd as APC.

1 c.	No. 1460 AP (5.8.92), CBN (19.8.94), APC (3.4.95)
2 c.	No. 1461 AP (5.8.92), CBN (22.4.94), APC (31.7.95)
3 c.	No. 1462 AP (5.8.92), CBN (22.4.94), APC (2.5.97)
5 c.	No. 1463 AP (5.8.92), CBN (25.2.94), APC (20.9.95)
6 c.	No. 1464 AP (5.8.92), CBN (25.2.94)
10 c.	No. 1465 AP (5.8.92), CBN (25.2.94), APC (1.9.95)
25 c.	No. 1466 AP (5.8.92), CBN (22.4.94), APC (1.5.96)
48 c.	Nos. 1467/ab (27.12.91)
49 c.	No. 1468 AP (30.12.92), CBN (7.1.94)
	No. 1468a CBN (7.1.94)
	Nos. 1468b/ba AP (30.12.92)
50 c.	No. 1469 CBN (25.2.94), APC (10.4.95)
	No. 1469a CBN (25.2.94)
	Nos. 1469b/ba APC (27.3.95)
52 c.	No. 1470 CBN (31.7.95), APC (6.10.95)
	No. 1470a CBN (31.7.95), APC (1997)
	Nos. 1470b/ba APC (6.10.95)
65 c.	No. 1471 AP (27.12.91)
67 c.	No. 1472 AP (30.12.92)
69 c.	No. 1473 CBN (25.2.94), APC (10.4.95)
71 c.	No. 1474 CBN (31.7.95), APC (6.10.95)
	No. 1474a APC (6.10.95)
84 c.	Nos. 1475/ab (27.12.91)
86 c.	No. 1476 AP (30.12.92), CBN (7.1.94)
	No. 1476a CBN (7.1.94)
	Nos. 1476b/ba AP (30.12.92)
88 c.	Nos. 1477/a CBN (25.2.94)
	No. 1477b CBN (14.11.94), APC (10.4.95)
	No. 1477ba CBN (14.11.94)
	Nos. 1477c/ca APC (27.3.95)
90 c.	No. 1478 CBN (31.7.95), APC (6.10.95)
	No. 1478a CBN (31.7.95), APC (1997)
	Nos. 1478b/ba APC (6.10.95)
$1	No. 1479 LM (21.2.94)
	No. 1479a CBN (20.2.95)
$2	No. 1480 LM (21.2.294)
	No. 1480a CBN (20.2.95)
$5	No. 1481 CBN (29.2.96)

601 Ski Jumping

(Des Gottschalk & Ash International. Litho Ashton-Potter)

1992 (7 Feb). *Winter Olympic Games, Albertville. T **601** and similar horiz designs. Multicoloured. Fluorescent frame. P* 12½×13.

1482	42 c.	Type **601**		70	70
	a.	Booklet pane. Nos. 1482/6, each × 2 with margins all round		6·50	
1483	42 c.	Figure skating		70	70
1484	42 c.	Ice hockey		70	70
1485	42 c.	Bobsleighing		70	70
1486	42 c.	Alpine skiing		70	70
1482/6			*Set of* 5	3·25	3·25

Nos. 1482/6 were only available from $4.20 stamp booklets.

602 Ville-Marie in 17th Century	**603** Road Bed Construction and Route Map

(Des Suzanne Duranceau and P.-Y. Pelletier. Litho C.B.N.)

1992 (25 Mar). *"CANADA 92" International Youth Stamp Exhibition, Montreal. T **602** and similar horiz designs. Multicoloured. Fluorescent frame. P* 13½.

1487	42 c.	Type **602**	..	80	80
	a.	Pair. Nos. 1487/8		1·60	1·60
1488	42 c.	Modern Montreal		80	80
1489	48 c.	Compass rose, snow shoe and crow's nest of Cartier's ship *Grande Hermine*	90	90
1490	84 c.	Atlantic map, Aztec "calendar stone" and navigational instrument		1·75	2·00
1487/90			*Set of* 4	3·75	4·00
MS1491	181×120 mm. Nos. 1487/90			4·00	4·50

Nos. 1487/8 were printed together, *se-tenant*, in horizontal and vertical pairs throughout the sheet.

Nos. MS1491 also exists showing the facsimile signature of Paul Chomedy de Maisonneuve printed at bottom right. These miniature sheets were prepared in connection with "CANADA '92", but were not sold by the Canadian Post Office.

(Des M. and Jan Waddell. Litho Ashton-Potter)

1992 (22 Apr). *Canadian Rivers (2nd series). Multicoloured designs as T **592**, but horiz. Fluorescent frame. P* 12½×13.

1492	42 c.	Magaree River		70	90
	a.	Booklet pane. Nos. 1492/6, each × 2	6·50	
1493	42 c.	West (Eliot) River		70	90
1494	42 c.	Ottawa River		70	90
1495	42 c.	Niagara River		70	90
1496	42 c.	South Saskatchewan River		70	90
1492/6			*Set of* 5	3·25	4·00

Nos. 1492/6 were only issued in $4.20 stamp booklets.

Booklet pane No. 1492a has the horizontal edges of the pane imperforate.

(Des J. Charette and Vivian Laliberté. Litho C.B.N.)

1992 (15 May). *50th Anniv of Alaska Highway. Fluorescent frame.* P 13½.
1497 603 42 c. multicoloured 70 70

(Des Gottschalk & Ash International. Litho Ashton-Potter)

1992 (15 June). *Olympic Games, Barcelona. Horiz designs as T 601. Multicoloured. Fluorescent frame.* P 12½×13.
1498 42 c. Gymnastics 80 90
    a. Booklet pane. Nos. 1498/1502 each
      × 2 with margins all round .. 7·00
1499 42 c. Athletics 80 90
1500 42 c. Diving 80 90
1501 42 c. Cycling 80 90
1502 42 c. Swimming 80 90
1498/1502 .. .. .. *Set of 5* 3·50 4·00
Nos. 1482/1502 were only available from $4.20 stamp booklets.

604 "Quebec, Patrimoine Mondial" (A. Dumas)   **605** Jerry Potts (scout)

(Des P.-Y. Pelletier. Litho Ashton-Potter)

1992 (29 June). *Canada Day. Paintings. Sheet, 190 × 256 mm, containing T 604 and similar diamond-shaped designs. Multicoloured. Fluorescent frame.* P 13×12½.
MS1503 42 c. Type 604; 42 c. "Christie Passage, Hurst Island, British Columbia" (E. J. Hughes); 42 c. "Toronto, Landmarks of Time" (Ontario) (V. McIndoe); 42 c. "Near the Forks" (Manitoba) (S. Gouthro); 42 c. "Off Cape St. Francis" (Newfoundland) (R. Shepherd); 42 c. "Crowd at City Hall" (New Brunswick) (Molly Bobak); 42 c. "Across the Tracks to Shop" (Alberta) (Janet Mitchell); 42 c. "Cove Scene" (Nova Scotia) (J. Norris); 42 c. "Untitled" (Saskatchewan) (D. Thauberger); 42 c. "Town Life" (Yukon) (T. Harrison); 42 c. "Country Scene" (Prince Edward Island) (Erica Rutherford); 42 c. "Playing on an Igloo" (Northwest Territories) (Agnes Nanogak) .. .. .. 12·00 12·00

(Des P.-Y. Pelletier. Litho and die-stamped Ashton-Potter)

1992 (29 June). *Canadian Art (5th series). Vert design as T 550. Multicoloured. No fluorescent bands.* P 12½×13.
1504 50 c. "Red Nasturtiums" (David Milne) .. 90 90
No. 1504 was issued in a similar sheet format to No. 1289

(Des A. Cormack, Deborah Cormack and R. Tibbles. Litho Ashton-Potter)

1992 (8 Sept). *Folk Heroes. T 605 and similar vert designs. Multicoloured. Fluorescent frame.* P 12½.
1505 42 c. Type 605 .. .. .. 90 1·00
    a. Block of 4. Nos. 1505/8 .. .. 3·25
1506 42 c. Capt. William Jackman and wreck of
    Sea Clipper, 1867 .. .. 90 1·00
1507 42 c. Laura Secord (messenger) .. 90 1·00
1508 42 c. Jos Montferrand (lumberjack) .. 90 1·00
1505/8 .. .. .. *Set of 4* 3·25 3·50
Nos. 1505/8 were printed together, *se-tenant*, in different combinations throughout the sheet, giving ten blocks of 4 and ten single stamps.

606 Copper   **607** Satellite and Photographs from Space

(Des R. Bellamare. Litho Ashton-Potter)

1992 (21 Sept). *150th Anniv of Geological Survey of Canada. Minerals. T 606 and similar horiz designs. Multicoloured. Fluorescent frame.* P 12½.
1509 42 c. Type 606 .. .. .. 85 90
    a. Booklet pane. Nos. 1509/13, each × 2
      with margins all round .. 7·50
1510 42 c. Sodalite 85 90
1511 42 c. Gold 85 90
1512 42 c. Galena 85 90
1513 42 c. Grossular 85 90
1509/13 .. .. .. *Set of 5* 3·75 4·00
Nos. 1509/13 were only issued in $4.20 stamp booklets.

(Des Debbie Adams. Litho C.B.N.)

1992 (1 Oct). *Canadian Space Programme. T 607 and similar horiz design. Multicoloured.* P 13.
1514 42 c. Type 607 .. .. .. 80 90
    a. Horiz pair. Nos. 1514/15 .. 1·60 1·75
1515 42 c. Space Shuttle over Canada
    (hologram) (32×26 mm) .. 80 90
    a. Hologram omitted
Nos. 1514/15 were printed together, *se-tenant*, in horizontal pairs throughout the sheet of 20 with No. 1514 occurring in the first and fourth vertical rows and No. 1515 on the second and third.

608 Babe Siebert, Skates and Stick   **609** Companion of the Order of Canada Insignia

(Des L. Holloway and R. Kerr. Litho Ashton-Potter)

1992 (9 Oct). *75th Anniv of National Ice Hockey League. T 608 and similar horiz designs. Multicoloured. Fluorescent frame.* P 13×12½.
1516 42 c. Type 608 .. .. .. 85 1·00
    a. Booklet pane. No. 1516×8 plus one
      printed label with margins all round 6·00
1517 42 c. Claude Provost, Terry Sawchuck and
    team badges .. .. .. 85 1·00
    a. Booklet pane. No. 1517×8 plus one
      printed label with margins all round 6·00
1518 42 c. Hockey mask, gloves and modern
    player .. .. .. 85 1·00
    a. Booklet pane. No. 1518×9 with
      margins all round 6·00
1516/18 .. .. .. *Set of 3* 2·25 2·75
Nos. 1516/18 were only issued in $10.50 stamp booklets. Booklet pane Nos. 1516a/18a only exist folded between the first and second vertical rows.

(Des Tania Craan. Litho Ashton-Potter)

1992 (21 Oct). *25th Anniv of the Order of Canada and Daniel Roland Michener (former Governor-General) Commemoration. T 609 and similar vert design. Multicoloured. Fluorescent frame.* P 12½.
1519 42 c. Type 609 .. .. .. 80 80
    a. Pair. Nos. 1519/20 .. .. 1·60 1·60
1520 42 c. Daniel Roland Michener .. 80 80
Nos. 1519/20 were printed together, *se-tenant*, within the sheet of 25 (5×5) with sixteen examples of No. 1519 (R. 1/1-5, 2/1, 2/5, 3/1, 3/5, 4/1, 4/5, 5/1-5) and nine of No. 1520 (R. 2/2-4, 3/2-4, 4/2-4).

(Des J.-P. Armanville and P.-Y. Pelletier. Litho C.B.N)

1992 (10 Nov). *50th Anniv of Second World War (4th issue). Horiz designs as T 574. Fluorescent frame.* P 13½.
1521 42 c. black, silver and sepia .. 90 1·00
    a. Block of 4. Nos. 1521/4 .. 3·25
1522 42 c. black, silver and dull blue-green .. 90 1·00
1523 42 c. black, silver and brown .. 90 1·00
1524 42 c. black, silver and light blue .. 90 1·00
1521/4 .. .. .. *Set of 4* 3·25 3·50
Designs:—No. 1521, Reporters and soldiers, 1942; No. 1522, Consolidated Liberator bombers over Newfoundland; No. 1523, Dieppe raid; No. 1524, U-boat sinking merchant ship.
Nos. 1521/4 were printed together, *se-tenant*, in different combinations throughout the sheet, giving four blocks of 4.

610 Estonian Jouluvana   **611** Adelaide Hoodless (women's movement pioneer)

(Des R. MacDonald (37 c.), Anita Kunz (42 c.), J. Bennett (48 c.), S. Ng (84 c.), adapted L. Fishauf and Stephanie Power. Litho Ashton-Potter)

1992 (13 Nov). *Christmas. T 610 and similar multicoloured designs. Fluorescent frame.* P 12½×imperf (37 c.), 12½ (42 c.) or 13½ (others).
1525 37 c. North American Santa Claus (35×21
    mm) 50 50
    a. Booklet pane. No. 1525×10 .. 6·00
1526 42 c. Type 610 .. .. .. 40 20
    a. Perf 13½ 70 75
    ab. Booklet pane. No. 1526a×10 .. 7·00
1527 48 c. Italian La Befana 60 60
    a. Booklet pane. No. 1527×5 plus one
      printed label 4·00
1528 84 c. German Weihnachtsmann .. 1·00 1·25
    a. Booklet pane. No. 1528×5 plus one
      printed label 7·00
1525/8 .. .. .. *Set of 4* 2·25 2·25
On No. 1525 the left-hand third of the design area is taken up by a bar code which has fluorescent bands between the bars.

This value was only available from $3.70 stamp booklets which had the vertical edges of the pane imperforate. It was intended for use on greeting cards posted on or before 31 January 1993.
No. 1526a was only issued in $4.20 stamp booklets. Nos. 1526ab, 1527a and 1528a have the vertical edges of the panes imperforate.

(Des Heather Cooper. Litho Ashton-Potter)

1993 (8 Mar). *Prominent Canadian Women. T 611 and similar vert designs. Multicoloured. Fluorescent frame.* P 12½.
1529 43 c. Type 611 .. .. .. 85 85
    a. Block of 4. Nos. 1529/32 .. 3·00
1530 43 c. Marie-Josephine Gérin-Lajoie (social
    reformer) 85 85
1531 43 c. Pitseolak Ashoona (Inuit artist) .. 85 85
1532 43 c. Helen Kinnear (lawyer) .. 85 85
1529/32 .. .. .. *Set of 4* 3·00 3·00
Nos. 1529/32 were printed together, *se-tenant*, in different combinations throughout the sheet, giving ten blocks of 4 and ten single stamps.

612 Ice Hockey Players with Cup   **613** Coverlet, New Brunswick

(Des F. Dallaire and Lise Giguère. Litho C.B.N.)

1993 (16 Apr). *Centenary of Stanley Cup. Fluorescent frame.* P 13½.
1533 612 43 c. multicoloured 75 60

(Des P. Adam. Litho Ashton-Potter)

1993 (30 Apr). *Hand-crafted Textiles. T 613 and similar square designs. Multicoloured. Fluorescent frame.* P 13×12½.
1534 43 c. Type 613 .. .. .. 60 80
    a. Booklet pane. Nos. 1534/8, each × 2 6·00
1535 43 c. Pieced quilt, Ontario .. 60 80
1536 43 c. Doukhobor bedcover, Saskatchewan .. 60 80
1537 43 c. Ceremonial robe, Kwakwaka'wakw .. 60 80
1538 43 c. Boutonné coverlet, Quebec .. 60 80
1534/8 .. .. .. *Set of 5* 2·75 3·50
Nos. 1534/8 were only available from $4.30 stamp booklets. Booklet pane No. 1534a has the horizontal edges of the pane imperforate and margins at both left and right.

(Des P.-Y. Pelletier. Litho and die-stamped Ashton-Potter)

1993 (17 May). *Canadian Art (6th series). Vert design as T 550. Multicoloured. Fluorescent frame.* P 12½×13.
1539 86 c. "The Owl" (Kenojuak Ashevak) .. 1·50 1·60
No. 1539 was issued in a similar sheet format to No. 1289.

614 Empress Hotel, Victoria   **615** Algonquin Park, Ontario

(Des G. Tsetsekas. Litho Ashton-Potter)

1993 (14 June). *Historic Hotels. T 614 and similar horiz designs. Multicoloured. Fluorescent frame.* P 13½.
1540 43 c. Type 614 .. .. .. 60 80
    a. Booklet pane. Nos. 1540/4, each × 2 6·00
1541 43 c. Banff Springs Hotel .. 60 80
1542 43 c. Royal York Hotel, Toronto .. 60 80
1543 43 c. Le Chateau Frontenac, Quebec .. 60 80
1544 43 c. Algonquin Hotel, St. Andrews .. 60 80
1540/4 .. .. .. *Set of 5* 2·75 3·50
Nos. 1540/4 were only issued in $4.30 stamp booklets. Booklet pane No. 1540a has the horizontal edges of the pane imperforate and margins at both left and right.

(Des M. and Jan Waddell. Litho C.B.N.)

1993 (30 June). *Canada Day. Provincial and Territorial Parks. T 615 and similar horiz designs. Multicoloured. Fluorescent frame.* P 13.
1545 43 c. Type 615 .. .. .. 60 70
    a. Sheetlet. Nos. 1545/56 .. 6·00
1546 43 c. De La Gaspésie Park, Québec .. 60 70
1547 43 c. Cedar Dunes Park, Prince Edward
    Island 60 70
1548 43 c. Cape St. Mary's Seabird Reserve,
    Newfoundland 60 70
1549 43 c. Mount Robson Park, British Columbia 60 70
1550 43 c. Writing-on-Stone Park, Alberta .. 60 70
1551 43 c. Spruce Woods Park, Manitoba .. 60 70
1552 43 c. Herschel Island Park, Yukon .. 60 70
1553 43 c. Cypress Hills Park, Saskatchewan .. 60 70
1554 43 c. The Rocks Park, New Brunswick .. 60 70
1555 43 c. Blomidon Park, Nova Scotia .. 60 70
1556 43 c. Katannilik Park, Northwest
    Territories 60 70
1545/56 .. .. .. *Set of 12* 6·00 7·00
Nos. 1545/56 were printed together, *se-tenant*, in sheetlets of 12, which come with or without a large illustrated and inscribed margin at top.

616 Toronto Skyscrapers   **617** Taylor's Steam Buggy, 1867

(Des R. Heeney and V. McIndoe. Litho C.B.N.)

1993 (6 Aug). *Bicentenary of Toronto. Fluorescent frame. P 13½×13.*

1557	**616**	43 c. multicoloured	70	50

(Des M. and Jan Waddell. Litho Ashton-Potter)

1993 (10 Aug). *Canadian Rivers (3rd series). Vert designs as T 592. Multicoloured. Fluorescent frame. P 13×12½.*

1558	43 c. Fraser River		60	80
	a. Booklet pane. Nos. 1558/62, each × 2	6·00		
1559	43 c. Yukon River		60	80
1560	43 c. Red River		60	80
1561	43 c. St. Lawrence River		60	80
1562	43 c. St. John River		60	80
1558/62		*Set of 5*	2·75	3·50

Nos. 1558/62 were only issued in $4.30 stamp booklets.

(Des J. Gault, T. Telmet and C. Wykes. Litho C.B.N.)

1993 (23 Aug). *Historic Automobiles (1st series). Sheet, 177×125 mm, containing T 617 and similar horiz designs. Multicoloured. Fluorescent frame. P 12½×13.*

MS1563   43 c. Type **617**; 43 c. Russel "Model L" touring car, 1908; 49 c. Ford "Model T" touring car, 1914 (43×22 *mm*); 49 c. Studebaker "Champion Deluxe Starlight" coupe, 1950 (43×22 *mm*); 86 c. McLaughlin-Buick "28-496 special", 1928 (43×22 *mm*); 86 c. Gray-Dort "25 SM" luxury sedan, 1923 (43×22 *mm*) .. 6·50 7·00

See also Nos. MS1611, MS1636 and MS1683/4.

618 "The Alberta Homesteader"   **619** Polish Swiety Mikolaj

(Des Deborah Cormack, A. Cormack and R. Tibbles. Litho Ashton-Potter)

1993 (7 Sept). *Folk Songs. T 618 and similar horiz designs. Multicoloured. Fluorescent frame. P 12½.*

1564	43 c. Type **618**		70	85
	a. Block of 4. Nos. 1564/7	2·50		
1565	43 c. "Les Raftmans" (Quebec)		70	85
1566	43 c. "Tse the B'y that Builds the Boat" (Newfoundland)		70	85
1567	43 c. "Onkwá:ri Tenhanónniahkwe" (Mohawk Indian)		70	85
1564/7		*Set of 4*	2·50	3·00

Nos. 1564/7 were printed together, *se-tenant*, in different combinations throughout the sheet, giving ten blocks of 4 and ten single stamps.

(Des R. Harder. Litho Ashton-Potter)

1993 (1 Oct). *Prehistoric Canada (3rd series). Dinosaurs. Horiz designs as T 582, but 40×28 mm. Multicoloured. Fluorescent frame. P 13½.*

1568	43 c. Massospondylus		60	60
	a. Block of 4. Nos. 1568/71	2·25		
1569	43 c. Stryacosaurus		60	60
1570	43 c. Albertosaurus		60	60
1571	43 c. Platecarpus		60	60
1568/71		*Set of 4*	2·25	2·25

Nos. 1568/71 were printed together, *se-tenant*, in different combinations throughout the sheet, giving four blocks of 4 and four single stamps.

(Des J. Bennett (38 c.), J. Jackson (43 c.), B. Dawson (49 c.), B. Blitt (86 c.), adapted L. Fishauf and Stephanie Power. Litho C.B.N.)

1993 (4 Nov). *Christmas. T 619 and similar multicoloured designs. Fluorescent frame. P 13×imperf (38 c.) or 13½ (others).*

1572	38 c. North American Santa Claus (35×22 mm)		60	55
	a. Booklet pane. No. 1572×10	6·00		
1573	43 c. Type **619**		50	20
	a. Booklet pane. No. 1573×10	7·00		
	b. Imperf between (horiz pair)	£750		
1574	49 c. Russian Ded Moroz		70	70
	a. Booklet pane. No. 1574×5 plus one printed label	4·00		
1575	86 c. Australian Father Christmas		1·00	1·50
	a. Booklet pane. No. 1575×5 plus one printed label	7·00		
1572/5		*Set of 4*	2·50	2·75

On No. 1572 the left-hand third of the design area is taken up by a barcode which has fluorescent bands between the bars. This value was only available from $3.80, stamp booklets which had the vertical edges of the pane imperforate. It was intended for use on greeting cards posted before 31 January 1994.

Nos. 1573a/5a have the vertical edges of the panes imperforate.

No. 1573b appears to originate from the incorrect use of the booklet pane perforation on ordinary sheet stock.

(Des J.-P. Armanville and P.-Y. Pelletier. Litho C.B.N.)

1993 (8 Nov). *50th Anniv of Second World War (5th issue). Horiz designs as T 574. Fluorescent frame. P 13½.*

1576	43 c. black, silver and brown-olive		90	90
	a. Block of 4. Nos. 1576/9	3·25		
1577	43 c. black, silver and slate-blue		90	90
1578	43 c. black, silver and dull-violet blue		90	90
1579	43 c. black, silver and chestnut		90	90
1576/9		*Set of 4*	3·25	3·25

Designs:—No. 1576, Loading munitions for Russia, 1943; No. 1577, Loading bombs on Avro Type 683 Lancaster; No. 1578, Escorts attacking U-boat; No. 1579, Infantry advancing, Italy.

Nos. 1576/9 were printed together, *se-tenant*, in different combinations throughout the sheet, giving four blocks of 4.

620 (face value at right)

(Des Tarzan Communication Graphique, Litho Leigh-Mardon Ltd, Melbourne)

1994 (28 Jan). *Self-adhesive Greetings booklet stamps. T 620 and similar horiz design. Multicoloured. Inscriptions behind face value and "CANADA" show names of family events. Fluorescent outline. Die-cut.*

1580	43 c. Type **620**		60	70
	a. Booklet pane. Nos. 1580/1, each × 5, and 35 circular greetings labels	5·50		
1581	43 c. As Type 620, but face value at left		60	70

Nos. 1580/1 were only available from $4.50 self-adhesive booklets in which the backing card formed the cover. It was intended that the sender should insert the appropriate greetings label into the circular space on each stamp before use.

For 45 c. values in this design see Nos. 1654/5.

621 Jeanne Sauvé   **622** Timothy Eaton, Toronto Store of 1869 and Merchandise

(Des J. Morin and T. Yakobina. Litho C.B.N.)

1994 (8 Mar). *Jeanne Sauvé (former Governor-General) Commemoration. Fluorescent frame. P 12½×12½×13.*

1582	**621**	43 c. multicoloured	60	60

No. 1582 was printed in sheets of 20 (4×5), the horizontal rows containing four stamps, each with a differently-inscribed 6×22½ mm *se-tenant* label. These are at the right of the stamps on rows 1, 3 and 5 and at left on rows 2 and 4.

(Des L. Fishauf. Litho C.B.N.)

1994 (17 Mar). *125th Anniv of T. Eaton Company Ltd (department store group). Fluorescent frame. P 13½×13.*

1583	**622**	43 c. multicoloured	55	75
	a. Booklet pane. No. 1583×10 and 2 labels with margins all round	5·50		

No. 1583 was only available from $4.30 stamp booklets.

(Des M. and Jan Waddell. Litho C.B.N.)

1994 (22 Apr). *Canadian Rivers (4th series). Horiz designs as T 592. Multicoloured. Fluorescent frame. P 13½×13.*

1584	43 c. Saguenay River		60	75
	a. Booklet pane. Nos. 1584/8 each × 2	5·50		
1585	43 c. French River		60	75
1586	43 c. Mackenzie River		60	75
1587	43 c. Churchill River		60	75
1588	43 c. Columbia River		60	75
1584/8		*Set of 5*	2·75	3·25

Nos. 1584/8 were only issued in $4.30 stamp booklets.

Booklet pane No. 1584a has the vertical edges of the pane imperforate.

(Des P.-Y. Pelletier. Litho and die-stamped Leigh-Mardon Ltd, Melbourne)

1994 (6 May). *Canadian Art (7th series). Vert design as T 550. Multicoloured. Fluorescent frame. P 14×14½.*

1589	88 c. "Vera" (detail) (Frederick Varley)	1·00	1·40

No. 1589 was issued in a similar sheet format to No. 1289.

623 Lawn Bowls   **624** Mother and Baby

(Des D. Coates and R. Roodenburg. Litho and die-stamped Leigh-Mardon Ltd, Melbourne)

1994 (20 May–5 Aug). *15th Commonwealth Games, Victoria. T 623 and similar horiz designs. Multicoloured. Fluorescent frame. P 14.*

1590	43 c. Type **623**		40	50
	a. Pair. Nos. 1590/1	80	1·00	
1591	43 c. Lacrosse		40	50
1592	43 c. Wheelchair race (5 Aug)		40	50
	a. Pair. Nos. 1592/3	80	1·00	
1593	43 c. High jumping (5 Aug)		40	50
1594	50 c. Diving (5 Aug)		45	60
1595	88 c. Cycling (5 Aug)		80	95
1590/5		*Set of 6*	2·75	3·25

Nos. 1590/1 and 1592/3 were printed together, *se-tenant*, in horizontal and vertical pairs throughout the sheets.

(Des Suzanne Duranceau. Litho Leigh-Mardon Ltd, Melbourne)

1994 (2 June). *International Year of the Family. Sheet 178×134 mm, containing T 624 and similar vert designs. Multicoloured. Fluorescent paper. P 14×14½.*

MS1596   43 c. Type **624**; 43 c. Family outing; 43 c. Grandmother and granddaughter; 43 c. Computer class; 43 c. Play group, nurse with patient and female lawyer .. 2·50 3·00

625 Big Leaf Maple Tree   **626** Billy Bishop (fighter ace) and Nieuport 17

(Des D. Noble. Litho C.B.N.)

1994 (30 June). *Canada Day. Maple Trees. T 625 and similar horiz designs. Multicoloured. Fluorescent frame. P 13×13½.*

1597	43 c. Type **625**		55	60
	a. Sheetlet. Nos. 1597/1608	5·75		
1598	43 c. Sugar Maple		55	60
1599	43 c. Silver Maple		55	60
1600	43 c. Striped Maple		55	60
1601	43 c. Norway Maple		55	60
1602	43 c. Manitoba Maple		55	60
1603	43 c. Black Maple		55	60
1604	43 c. Douglas Maple		55	60
1605	43 c. Mountain Maple		55	60
1606	43 c. Vine Maple		55	60
1607	43 c. Hedge Maple		55	60
1608	43 c. Red Maple		55	60
1597/1608		*Set of 12*	5·75	6·50

Nos. 1597/1608 were printed together, *se-tenant*, in sheetlets of 12, which come with or without a large illustrated and inscribed margin at top.

(Des P. Fontaine and B. Leduc. Litho C.B.N.)

1994 (12 Aug). *Birth Centenaries. T 626 and similar horiz design. Multicoloured. Fluorescent frame. P 13½.*

1609	43 c. Type **626**		75	80
	a. Pair. Nos. 1609/10	1·50	1·60	
1610	43 c. Mary Travers ("La Bolduc") (singer) and musicians		75	80

Nos. 1609/10 were printed together, *se-tenant*, in horizontal and vertical pairs throughout the sheet.

(Des J. Gault, T. Telmet, and C. Wickes. Litho C.B.N.)

1994 (19 Aug). *Historic Automobiles (2nd issue). Sheet 177×125 mm, containing horiz designs as T 617. Multicoloured. Fluorescent frame. P 12½×13.*

MS1611   43 c. Ford "Model F60L-AMB" military ambulance, 1942–43; 43 c. Winnipeg police wagon, 1925; 50 c. Sicard snowblower, 1927 (43×22 *mm*); 50 c. Bickle "Chieftain" fire engine, 1936 (43×22 *mm*); 88 c. Ottawa Car Company tram, 1894 (51×22 *mm*); 88 c. Motor Coach Industries "Courier 50 Skyview" coach, 1950 (51×22 *mm*) .. 6·00 6·50

No. MS1611 was sold in a protective pack.

627 Symbolic Aircraft, Radar Screen and Clouds   **628** Carol Singing around Christmas Tree

(Des Gottschalk & Ash International, Katalin Kovats and S. Napoleone. Litho C.B.N.)

1994 (16 Sept). *50th Anniv of International Civil Aviation Organization. Fluorescent frame. P 13.*

1612	**627**	43 c. multicoloured	60	60

(Des R. Harder. Litho C.B.N.)

1994 (26 Sept). *Prehistoric Canada (4th series). Mammals. Multicoloured designs as T **582**, but 40×28 mm. Fluorescent frame. P* 13½.

1613	43 c. Coryphodon		90	1·00
	a. Block of 4. Nos. 1613/16		3·25	
1614	43 c. Megacerops		90	1·00
1615	43 c. Arctodus simus (bear)		90	1·00
1616	43 c. Mammuthus primigenius (mammoth)		90	1·00
1613/16		*Set of* 4	3·25	3·50

Nos. 1613/16 were printed together, *se-tenant*, in different combinations throughout the sheet, giving four blocks of 4 and four single stamps.

(Des Nina Berkson, Diti Katona and J. Pylypczak. Litho C.B.N.)

1994 (3 Nov). *Christmas. T **628** and similar multicoloured designs. Fluorescent frame. P* 13×imperf (No. 1617) or 13½ (others).

1617	(–) c. Carol singer (35×21 mm)		40	40
	a. Booklet pane. No. 1617×10		4·50	
1618	43 c. Type **628**		45	20
	a. Booklet pane. No. 1618×10		5·00	
1619	50 c. Choir (*vert*)		55	70
	a. Booklet pane. No. 1619×5 plus one printed label		3·50	
1620	88 c. Couple carol singing in snow (*vert*)		1·40	1·75
	a. Booklet pane. No. 1620×5 plus one printed label		5·00	
1617/20		*Set of* 4	2·50	2·75

No. 1617 was only available from $3.80 stamp booklets with the vertical edges of the pane imperforate. The stamp is without face value, but was intended for use as a 38 c. on internal greetings cards posted before 31 January 1995. The design shows a barcode at left with fluorescent bands between the bars. Nos. 1617a/20a have the vertical edges of the panes imperforate.

(Des J.-P. Armanville and P.-Y. Pelletier. Litho C.B.N.)

1994 (7 Nov). *50th Anniv of Second World War (6th issue). Horiz designs as T **574**. Fluorescent frame. P* 13½.

1621	43 c. black, silver and dull green		70	80
	a. Block of 4. Nos. 1621/4		2·50	
1622	43 c. black, silver and Venetian red		70	80
1623	43 c. black, silver and light blue		70	80
1624	43 c. black, silver and violet-grey		70	80
1621/4		*Set of* 4	2·50	2·75

Designs:—No. 1621, D-Day landings, Normandy; No. 1622, Canadian artillery, Normandy; No. 1623, Hawker Typhoons on patrol; No. 1624, Canadian infantry and disabled German self-propelled gun, Walcheren.

Nos. 1621/4 were printed together, *se-tenant*, in different combinations throughout the sheet, giving four blocks of 4.

(Des J.-P. Armanville and P.-Y. Pelletier. Litho C.B.N.)

1995 (20 Mar). *50th Anniv of Second World War (7th issue). Horiz designs as T **574**. Fluorescent frame. P* 13½.

1625	43 c. black, silver and reddish purple		70	80
	a. Block of 4. Nos. 1625/8		2·50	
1626	43 c. black, silver and yellow-brown		70	80
1627	43 c. black, silver and dull yellowish green		70	80
1628	43 c. black, silver and light greenish blue		70	80
1625/8		*Set of* 4	2·50	2·75

Designs:—No. 1625, Returning troopship; No. 1626, Canadian P.O.W's celebrating freedom; No. 1627, Canadian tank liberating Dutch town; No. 1628, Parachute drop in support of Rhine Crossing.

Nos. 1625/8 were printed together, *se-tenant*, in different combinations throughout the sheet, giving four blocks of 4.

(Des P.-Y. Pelletier. Litho and die-stamped C.B.N.)

1995 (21 Apr). *Canadian Art (8th series). Vert design as T **550**. Multicoloured. Fluorescent frame. P* 13×13½.

1629	88 c. "Floraison" (Alfred Pellan)		1·00	1·40

No. 1629 was issued in a similar sheet format to No. 1289.

629 Flag and Lake

(Des Gottschalk & Ash International. Litho C.B.N.)

1995 (1 May). *30th Anniv of National Flag. Fluorescent frame. P* 13½×13.

1630	629	43 (c.) multicoloured		50	50

No. 1630 is without any indication of face value, but was sold for 43 c.

PRINTER. Following a change in ownership, and the awarding of a further Canada Post contract, the previous Ashton Potter Ltd was known as Ashton Potter Canada Ltd from 1995.

630 Louisbourg Harbour

(Des R. Harder. Litho Ashton-Potter Canada)

1995 (5 May). *275th Anniv of Fortress of Louisbourg. T **630** and similar horiz designs. Multicoloured. "All-over" fluorescent. P* 12½×13.

1631	(43 c.) Type **630**		40	55
	a. Booklet pane. Nos. 1631/5 each × 2 with margins all round		4·00	
1632	(43 c.) Barracks (32×29 mm)		40	55
1633	(43 c.) King's Bastion (40×29 mm)		40	55
1634	(43 c.) Site of King's Garden, convent and hospital (56×29 mm)		40	55
1635	(43 c.) Site of coastal fortifications		40	55
1631/5		*Set of* 5	2·00	2·50

Nos. 1631/5 are without any indication of face value, but were sold in booklets of 10 for $4.30.

(Des J. Gault, T. Telmet and C. Wykes. Litho C.B.N.)

1995 (26 May). *Historic Automobiles (3rd issue). Sheet 177×25 mm, containing horiz designs as T **617**. Multicoloured. Fluorescent frame. P* 12½×13.

MS1636 43 c. Cockshutt "30" farm tractor, 1950; 43 c. Bombardier "Ski-Doo Olympique 335" snowmobile, 1970; 50 c. Bombardier "B-12 CS" multi-passenger snowmobile, 1948 (43×22 mm); 50 c. Gotfredson "Model 20" farm truck, 1924 (43×22 mm); 88 c. Robin-Nodwell "RN 110" tracked carrier, 1962 (43×22 mm); 88 c. Massey-Harris "No. 21" self-propelled combine-harvester, 1942 (43×22 mm) .. 4·00 4·50

No. **MS1636** was sold in a protective pack.

631 Banff Springs Golf Club, Alberta

(Des P. Adam. Litho Ashton-Potter Canada)

1995 (6 June). *Centenaries of Canadian Amateur Golf Championship and of the Royal Canadian Golf Association. T **631** and similar horiz designs. Fluorescent frame. P* 13½×13.

1637	43 c. Type **631**		50	60
	a. Booklet pane. Nos. 1637/41 each × 2		4·50	
1638	43 c. Riverside Country Club, New Brunswick		50	60
1639	43 c. Glen Abbey Golf Club, Ontario		50	60
1640	43 c. Victoria Golf Club, British Columbia		50	60
1641	43 c. Royal Montreal Golf Club, Quebec		50	60
1637/41		*Set of* 5	2·25	2·75

Nos. 1637/41 were only issued in $4.30 stamp booklets. Booklet pane No. 1637a has the vertical edges of the pane imperforate.

632 "October Gold" (Franklin Carmichael) **633** Academy Building and Ship Plan

(Des A. Leduc. Litho C.B.N.)

1995 (29 June). *Canada Day. 75th Anniv of "Group of Seven" (artists). Three sheets, each 180×80 mm, containing T **632** and similar square designs. Multicoloured. Fluorescent paper. P* 13.

MS1642 (a) 43 c. Type **632**; 43 c. "From the North Shore, Lake Superior" (Lawren Harris); 43 c. "Evening, Les Eboulements, Quebec" (A. Jackson). (b) 43 c. "Serenity, Lake of the Woods" (Frank Johnston); 43 c. "A September Gale, Georgian Bay" (Arthur Lismer); 43 c. "Falls, Montreal River" (J. E. H. MacDonald); 43 c. "Open Window" (Frederick Varley). (c) 43 c. "Mill Houses" (Alfred Casson); 43 c. "Pembina Valley" (Lionel FitzGerald); 43 c. "The Lumberjack" (Edwin Holgate) .. *Set of 3 sheets* 6·50 7·50

The three sheets of No. **MS1642** were sold together in an envelope which also includes a small descriptive booklet.

(Des B. Mackay-Lyons and S. Slipp. Litho C.B.N.)

1995 (29 June). *Centenary of Lunenburg Academy. Fluorescent frame. P* 13.

1643	633	43 c. multicoloured		40	45

STANLEY GIBBONS STAMP COLLECTING SERIES

Introductory booklets on *How to Start, How to Identify Stamps* and *Collecting by Theme.* A series of well illustrated guides at a low price.
Write for details.

634 Aspects of Manitoba **635** Monarch Butterfly

(Des T. Gallagher and S. Rosenberg. Litho Ashton-Potter Canada)

1995 (14 July). *125th Anniv of Manitoba as Canadian Province. Fluorescent frame. P* 13½×13.

1644	634	43 c. multicoloured		40	45

Two Types of Belted Kingfisher design:

Type I. Inscr "aune migratrice" in error.
Type II. Inscr corrected to "faune migratrice".

(Des Debbie Adams. Litho C.B.N.)

1995 (15 Aug–26 Sept). *Migratory Wildlife. T **635** and similar vert designs. Fluorescent paper. P* 13×12½.

1645	45 c. Type **635**		65	70
	a. Block of 4. Nos. 1645/6, 1648/9		2·40	
	b. Block of 4. Nos. 1645, 1647/9 (26 Sept)		2·40	
1646	45 c. Belted Kingfisher (I)		65	70
1647	45 c. Belted Kingfisher (II) (26 Sept)		65	70
1648	45 c. Pintail		65	70
1649	45 c. Hoary Bat		65	70
1645/9		*Set of* 5	3·00	3·25

The inscription error on No. 1646 was corrected in a new printing issued 26 September 1995.

The four different designs were printed together, *se-tenant*, throughout the sheet, giving four blocks of 4 and four single stamps, showing an overall background design of migration routes.

636 Quebec Bridge

(Des J. Gault, T. Telmet and C. Wykes. Litho Ashton-Potter Canada)

1995 (1 Sept). *20th World Road Congress, Montreal. Bridges. T **636** and similar horiz designs. Multicoloured. Fluorescent paper. P* 12½×13.

1650	45 c. Type **636**		70	80
	a. Block of 4. Nos. 1650/3		2·50	
1651	45 c. 401-403-410 Interchange, Mississauga		70	80
1652	45 c. Hartland Bridge, New Brunswick		70	80
1653	45 c. Alex Fraser Bridge, British Columbia		70	80
1650/3		*Set of* 4	2·50	2·75

Nos. 1650/3 were printed together, *se-tenant*, throughout the sheet, giving four blocks of 4 and four single stamps.

Two Types of Background to Nos. 1654/5:

Type I. Inscriptions behind face value and "CANADA" show names of Canadian Provinces.
Type II. Inscription behind face value and "CANADA" show names of family events.

(Des Tarzan Communication Graphique. Litho Ashton-Potter Canada (Nos. 1654/5) or Leigh-Mardon Ltd, Melbourne (Nos. 1654b/5b)).

1995 (1 Sept)–96. *Self-adhesive Greetings booklet stamps. Horiz designs as T **620**. Multicoloured. Fluorescent outline. Die-cut.*

1654	45 c. Face value at right (I)		35	40
	a. Booklet pane. Nos. 1654/5, each × 5		3·50	
	b. Type II (15.1.96)		40	45
	ba. Booklet pane. Nos. 1654b and 1655b each × 5		4·00	
1655	45 c. Face value at left (I)		35	40
	b. Type II (15.1.96)		40	45

Nos. 1654/5 were only available from $4.70 self-adhesive booklets in which the backing card formed the cover. Booklets containing Nos. 1654/5 also include a separate pane of 15 self-adhesive labels which it was intended the sender should insert in the circular space on each stamp before use. Booklets containing Nos. 1654b/5b included 35 circular greetings labels on the same pane as the stamps.

637 Mountain, Baffin Island, Polar Bear and Caribou **638** Superman

(Des Eskind Waddell. Litho C.B.N.)

1995 (15 Sept). *50th Anniv of Arctic Institute of North America. T* **637** *and similar horiz designs. Multicoloured. Fluorescent paper. P* 13×12½.

1656	45 c. Type **637**		50	60
	a. Booklet pane. Nos. 1656/60, each × 2, with margins all round	..	4·50	
1657	45 c. Arctic poppy, Auyuittuq National Park and cargo canoe	..	50	60
1658	45 c. Inuk man and igloo ..	..	50	60
1659	45 c. Ogilvie Mountains, dog team and ski-equipped airplane	..	50	60
1660	45 c. Inuit children	..	50	60
1656/60		*Set of 5*	2·25	2·75

Nos. 1656/60 were only issued in $4.50 stamp booklets.

(Des L. Fishauf. Litho Ashton-Potter Canada)

1995 (2 Oct). *Comic Book Superheroes. T* **638** *and similar vert designs. Multicoloured. Fluorescent frame. P* 13×12½.

1661	45 c. Type **638**		40	45
	a. Booklet pane. Nos. 1661/5, each × 2, with margins all round	..	4·25	
1662	45 c. Johnny Canuck	..	40	45
1663	45 c. Nelvana	..	40	45
1664	45 c. Captain Canuck	..	40	45
1665	45 c. Fleur de Lys	..	40	45
1661/5		*Set of 5*	2·00	2·25

Nos. 1661/5 were only issued in $4.50 stamp booklets.

639 Prime Minister MacKenzie King signing U.N. Charter, 1945

640 "The Nativity"

(Des L. Holloway and R. Kerr. Litho and die-stamped C.B.N.)

1995 (24 Oct). *50th Anniv of United Nations. Fluorescent frame. P* 13½.

1666	**639** 45 c. multicoloured	..	50	50

No. 1666 was issued in sheets of 10 with a large illustrated and inscribed margin at top.

(Des F. Dallaire. Litho Ashton-Potter Canada (40 c.) or C.B.N. (others))

1995 (2 Nov). *Christmas. T* **640** *and similar multicoloured designs showing sculptured capitals from Ste.-Anne-de-Beaupré Basilica designed by Emilé Brunet (Nos.* 1668/70)*. Fluorescent frames. P* 12½×13 (40 c.) *or* 13½ (*others*).

1667	40 c. Sprig of holly (35×22 *mm*)	..	45	50
	a. Booklet pane. No. 1667×10	..	4·50	
1668	45 c. Type **640**	..	50	20
	a. Booklet pane. No. 1668×10	..	4·75	
1669	52 c. "The Annunciation"	..	75	80
	a. Booklet pane. No. 1669×5 plus one printed label	..	3·00	
1670	90 c. "The Flight to Egypt"	..	1·25	1·50
	a. Booklet pane. No. 1670×5 plus one printed label	..	4·75	
1667/70		*Set of 4*	2·50	2·75

On No. 1667 the left-hand third of the design area is taken up by a barcode which has fluorescent bands between the bars. This value was only available from $4 stamp booklets which had the vertical edges of the pane imperforate. It was intended for use on greetings cards posted before 31 January 1996.

Nos. 1668a/70a have the vertical edges of the panes imperforate.

641 World Map and Emblem

(Des A. Leduc. Litho Ashton-Potter Canada)

1995 (6 Nov). *25th Anniv of La Francophonie and The Agency for Cultural and Technical Co-operation. Fluorescent frame. P* 13×13½.

1671	**641** 45 c. multicoloured	..	50	50

642 Concentration Camp Victims, Uniform and Identity Card

(Des Q30 Design. Litho Ashton-Potter Canada)

1995 (9 Nov). *50th Anniv of the End of The Holocaust. Fluorescent paper. P* 12½×13.

1672	**642** 45 c. multicoloured	..	50	50

Horizontal strips of No. 1672 form a continuous design which is carried over onto the vertical sheet margins.

643 American Kestrel

(Des R. Bellemare and P. Leduc. Litho C.B.N.)

1996 (9 Jan). *Birds (1st issue). T* **643** *and similar horiz designs. Multicoloured. Fluorescent frame. P* 13½.

1673	45 c. Type **643**	..	55	65
	a. Horiz strip of 4. Nos. 1673/6		2·00	
1674	45 c. Atlantic Puffin	..	55	65
1675	45 c. Pileated Woodpecker		55	65
1676	45 c. Ruby-throated Hummingbird		55	65
1673/6		*Set of 4*	2·00	2·40

Nos. 1673/6 were printed together, *se-tenant*, in panes of 12 (4×3) containing three examples of No. 1673a. Those panes intended for philatelic sale had inscribed margins so arranged as to produce a diamond-shaped format.

See also Nos. 1717/20.

644 *Louis R. Desmarais* (tanker), Three-dimensional Map and Radar Screen

(Des Q30 Design Inc. Litho C.B.N.)

1996 (15 Feb). *High Technology Industries. T* **644** *and similar horiz designs. Multicoloured. Fluorescent paper. P* 13½.

1677	45 c. Type **644**	..	65	70
	a. Booklet pane. Nos. 1677/80, each × 3	6·75	
1678	45 c. Canadair Challenger 601-3R, jet engine and navigational aid	..	65	70
1679	45 c. Map of North America and eye	..	65	70
1680	45 c. Genetic engineering experiment and Canola (plant)	..	65	70
1677/80		*Set of 4*	2·40	2·50

Nos. 1677/80 were only available from $5.40 stamp booklets which had the vertical edges of the pane imperforate.

(Des P.-Y. Pelletier. Litho and die-stamped Ashton-Potter Canada)

1996 (30 Apr). *Canadian Art (9th series). Vert design as T* **550**. *Multicoloured. Fluorescent paper. P* 12½×13.

1681	90 c. "The Spirit of Haida Gwaii" (sculpture) (Bill Reid)		1·40	1·40

No. 1681 was issued in a similar sheet format to No. 1289.

645 "One World, One Hope" (Joe Average)

(Des G. Tsetsekas. Litho Ashton-Potter Canada)

1996 (8 May). *11th International Conference on AIDS, Vancouver. Fluorescent frame. P* 13½.

1682	**645** 45 c. multicoloured	..	60	60

(Des J. Gault, T. Telmet and C. Wickes. Litho C.B.N.)

1996 (8 June). *Historic Automobiles (4th issue). Sheet* 177×125 *mm, containing horiz designs as T* **617**. *Multicoloured. Fluorescent frame. P* 12½×13.

MS1683   45 c. Still Motor Co. electric van, 1899; 45 c. Waterous Engine Works steam roller, 1914; 52 c. International "D.35" delivery truck, 1938; 52 c. Champion road grader, 1936; 90 c. White "Model WA 122" articulated lorry, 1947 (51×22 *mm*); 90 c. Hayes "HDX 45-115" logging truck, 1975 (51×22 *mm*) .. .. 4·50 4·75

No. MS1683 also includes the "CAPEX '96" International Stamp Exhibition logo on the sheet margin and was sold in a protective pack.

(Des J. Gault, T. Telmet and C. Wickes. Litho C.B.N.)

1996 (8 June). *"CAPEX '96" International Stamp Exhibition, Toronto. Sheet,* 368×182 *mm, containing horiz designs as Nos.* MS1563, MS1611, MS1636, MS1683, *but with different face values, and one new design* (45 c.)*. P* 12½×13.

MS1684   5 c. Bombardier "Ski-Doo Olympique 335" snowmobile, 1970; 5 c. Cockshutt "30" farm tractor, 1950; 5 c. Type **617**; 5 c. Ford "Model F160L-AMB" military ambulance, 1942; 5 c. Still Motor Co. electric van, 1895; 5 c. International "D.35" delivery truck, 1936; 5 c. Russel "Model L" touring car, 1908; 5 c. Winnipeg police wagon, 1925; 5 c. Waterous Engine Works steam roller,

1914; 5 c. Champion road grader, 1936; 10 c. White "Model WA 122" articulated lorry, 1947 (51×22 *mm*); 10 c. Ottawa Car Company tram, 1894 (51×22 *mm*); 10 c. Hayes "HDX 45-115" logging truck, 1975 (51×22 *mm*); 10 c. Motor Coach Industries "Courier 50 Skyview" coach, 1950 (51×22 *mm*); 20 c. Ford "Model T" touring car, 1914 (43×22 *mm*); 20 c. McLaughlin-Buick "28-496 special", 1928 (43×22 *mm*); 20 c. Bombardier "B-12 CS" multi-passenger snow-mobile, 1948 (43×22 *mm*); 20 c. Robin-Nodwell "RN 110" tracked carrier, 1962 (43×22 *mm*); 20 c. Studebaker "Champion Deluxe Starlight" coupe, 1950 (43×22 *mm*); 20 c. Gray-Dort "25 SM" luxury sedan, 1923 (43×22 *mm*); 20 c. Gotfredson "Model 20" farm truck, 1924 (43×22 *mm*); 20 c. Massey-Harris "No. 21" self-propelled combine-harvester, 1942 (43×22 *mm*); 20 c. Bickle "Chieftain" fire engine, 1936 (43×22 *mm*); 20 c. Sicard snowblower, 1927 (43×22 *mm*); 20 c. Bricklin "SV-1" sports car, 1975 (51×22 *mm*)   5·00 6·00

No. MS1684 was sold folded within a special pack at $3.75, a premium of 40 c. over the face value. It was only possible to obtain an unfolded example by purchasing an uncut press sheet, containing three miniature sheets, of which only 25000 were made available. The price quoted for No. MS1684 is for a folded example.

646 Skookum Jim Mason and Bonanza Creek

647 Patchwork Quilt Maple Leaf

(Des S. Slipp. Litho and gold die-stamped Ashton-Potter Canada)

1996 (13 June). *Centenary of Yukon Gold Rush. T* **646** *and similar horiz designs. Multicoloured. Fluorescent paper. P* 13½.

1685	45 c. Type **646**	..	60	60
	a. Horiz strip of 5. Nos. 1685/9	..	2·75	
1686	45 c. Prospector and boats on Lake Laberge	60	60
1687	45 c. Superintendent Sam Steele (N.W. M.P.) and U.S.A.–Canada border	..	60	60
1688	45 c. Dawson saloon	..	60	60
1689	45 c. Miner with rocker box and sluice	..	60	60
1685/9		*Set of 5*	2·75	2·75

Nos. 1685/9 were printed together, *se-tenant*, in sheetlets of 10, containing two examples of No. 1685a.

(Des R. Bellemare. Litho Ashton-Potter Canada)

1996 (28 June). *Canada Day. Self-adhesive. Fluorescent frame. Die-cut.*

1690	**647** 45 c. multicoloured	..	50	50

No. 1690 was printed in sheets of 12 with each stamp separate on the backing paper.

648 Ethel Catherwood (high jump), 1928

649 Indian Totems, City Skyline, Forest and Mountains

(Des M. Koudys. Litho and die-stamped Ashton-Potter Canada)

1996 (8 July). *Canadian Olympic Gold Medal Winners. T* **648** *and similar vert designs. Multicoloured. Fluorescent paper. P* 13×12½.

1691	45 c. Type **648**	..	55	60
	a. Booklet pane. Nos. 1691/5, each × 2 with margins all round	..	5·00	
1692	45 c. Etienne Desmarteau (56lb weight throw), 1904		55	60
1693	45 c. Fanny Rosenfeld (400 metres relay), 1928		55	60
1694	45 c. Gerald Ouellette (small bore rifle, prone), 1956		55	60
1695	45 c. Percy Williams (100 and 200 metres), 1928		55	60
1691/5		*Set of 5*	2·50	2·75

Nos. 1691/5 were only issued in $4.50 stamp booklets.

(Des M. Warburton. Litho Ashton-Potter Canada)

1996 (19 July). *125th Anniv of British Columbia. Fluorescent paper. P* 13×12½.

1696	**649** 45 c. multicoloured	..	50	50

NEW INFORMATION

The editor is always interested to correspond with people who have new information that will improve or correct the Catalogue.

650 Canadian
Heraldic Symbols

651 *L'Arrivee d'un
Train en Gare* (1896)

(Des D. Sarty and R. Gaynor. Litho Ashton-Potter Canada)

1996 (19 Aug). *22nd International Congress of Genealogical
and Heraldic Sciences, Ottawa. Fluorescent paper.* P 12½.
1697 **650** 45 c. multicoloured 50 50

(Des P.-Y. Pelletier. Litho C.B.N.)

1996 (22 Aug). *Centenary of Cinema. Two sheets, each
180×100 mm containing T **651** and similar vert designs.
Multicoloured. Self-adhesive. Fluorescent paper. Die-cut.*
MS1698 Two sheets. (a) 45 c. Type **651**; 45 c.
Back to God's Country (1919); 45 c. *Hen Hop!*
(1942); 45 c. *Pour la Suite du Monde* (1963); 45 c.
Goin' Down the Road (1970). (b) 45 c. *Mon Oncle
Antoine* (1971); 45 c. *The Apprenticeship of
Duddy Kravitz* (1974); 45 c. *Les Ordres* (1974);
45 c. *Les Bons Debarras* (1980); 45 c. *The Grey
Fox* (1982) .. .. 5·50 6·50
The two sheets of No. MS1698 were sold together in an
envelope with a descriptive booklet.

652 Interlocking Jigsaw
Pieces and Hands

653 Edouard Montpetit
and Montreal University

(Des Debbie Adam. Litho Ashton-Potter Canada)

1996 (9 Sept). *Literacy Campaign. Fluorescent paper.*
P 13×12½.
1699 **652** 45 c. + 5 c. multicoloured .. 60 65
a. Booklet pane. No. 1699×10 with
margins all round .. .. 5·50
No. 1699 has one piece of the jigsaw removed by die-cutting
and was only issued in $5 stamp booklet

(Des J. Beauchesne. Litho Ashton-Potter Canada)

1996 (26 Sept). *Edouard Montpetit (academic) Commemoration. Fluorescent frame.* P 12×12½.
1700 **653** 45 c. multicoloured 50 50

654 Winnie and Lt.
Colebourn, 1914

655 Margaret
Laurence

(Des Wai Poon. Litho Ashton-Potter Canada)

1996 (1 Oct). *Stamp Collecting Month. Winnie the Pooh. T **654**
and similar horiz designs. Multicoloured. Fluorescent frame.*
P 12½×13.
1701 **654** 45 c. Type **654** 50 55
a. Double sheetlet of 16. Nos. 1701/4
each × 4 .. .. .. 6·50
1702 45 c. Christopher Robin Milne and teddy
bear, 1925 .. .. .. 50 55
1703 45 c. Illustration from *Winnie the Pooh*,
1926 .. .. 50 55
1704 45 c. Winnie the Pooh at Walt Disney
World, 1996 .. .. .. 50 55
1701/4 .. .. *Set of 4* 1·75 2·00
MS1705 152×112 mm. Nos. 1701/4 .. 2·25 2·75
Nos. 1701/4 were printed together, *se-tenant*, as blocks of 4 in
double sheetlets, used as a cover to "The True Story of Winnie
the Pooh" booklet.

(Des A. Leduc. Recess and litho C.B.N.)

1996 (10 Oct). *Canadian Authors. T **655** and similar vert
designs. Fluorescent paper.* P 13½×13.
1706 45 c. multicoloured 60 65
a. Booklet pane. Nos. 1706/10 each × 2 5·25
1707 45 c. black, greenish grey & scarlet-verm 60 65
1708 45 c. multicoloured 60 65

1709 45 c. multicoloured 60 65
1710 45 c. multicoloured 60 65
1706/10 .. .. *Set of 5* 2·75 3·00
Designs:—No. 1706, Type **655**; No. 1707, Donald G.
Creighton; No. 1708, Gabrielle Roy; No. 1709, Felix-Antoine
Savard; No. 1710, Thomas C. Haliburton.
Nos. 1706/10 were only issued in $4.50 stamp booklets with
the horizontal edges of the pane imperforate and margins at left
and right.

656 Children tobogganing

657 Head of Ox

(Des T. Harrison (45 c.), Pauline Paquin (52 c.), Joan Bacquie
(90 c.). Litho C.B.N. (45 c.) or Ashton-Potter Canada (others))

1996 (1 Nov). *Christmas. 50th Anniv of U.N.I.C.E.F. T **656**
and similar vert designs. Multicoloured. Fluorescent frame.*
P 13½ (45 c.) or 12½×12 (others).
1711 45 c. Type **656** 50 20
a. Booklet pane. No. 1711×10 .. 4·00
1712 52 c. Father Christmas skiing .. 60 70
a. Perf 13½ 60 70
ab. Booklet pane. No. 1712a×5 plus one
printed label .. .. 2·75
1713 90 c. Couple ice-skating .. .. 90 1·25
a. Perf 13½ .. .. .. 90 1·25
ab. Booklet pane. No. 1713a×5 plus one
printed label .. .. 4·25
1711/13 .. .. *Set of 3* 1·75 1·90
Nos. 1712a and 1713a were only issued in stamp booklets.
Nos. 1711a, 1712ab and 1713ab have the vertical edges of the
panes imperforate and margins at top and bottom.

(Des Ivy Li and Liu Xiang-Ping. Litho Ashton-Potter Canada)

1997 (7 Jan). *Chinese New Year ("Year of the Ox"). Fluorescent
frame.* P 13×12½.
1714 45 c. multicoloured 85 90
MS1715 155×75 mm*. No. 1714×2 .. 2·00 2·50
No. MS1715 is an extended fan shape with overall
measurements as quoted.
Two examples of No. 1714, taken from the miniature sheet,
have been found with the gold ("Canada, 45", etc.) omitted.

1997 (7 Jan). *"HONG KONG '97" International Stamp
Exhibition. As No. MS1715, but with exhibition logo added to
the sheet margin in gold. Fluorescent frame.* P 13×12½.
MS1716 155×75 mm. No. 1714×2 .. 2·75 3·25

(Des R. Bellemare and P. Leduc. Litho Ashton-Potter, Canada)

1997 (10 Jan). *Birds (2nd series). Horiz designs as T **643**.
Multicoloured. Fluorescent frame.* P 12½×13.
1717 45 c. Mountain Bluebird 55 55
a. Horiz strip of 4. Nos. 1717/20 .. 2·00
1718 45 c. Western Grebe 55 55
1719 45 c. Northern Gannet 55 55
1720 45 c. Scarlet Tanager 55 55
1717/20 .. .. *Set of 4* 2·00 2·00
Nos. 1717/20 printed together, *se-tenant*, in sheets of 20 (4×5)
containing five examples of No. 1717a.

(Des P.-Y. Pelletier. Litho and die-stamped Ashton-Potter,
Canada)

1997 (17 Feb). *Canadian Art (10th series). Vert design as
T **550**. Multicoloured. Fluorescent paper.* P 12½×13½.
1721 90 c. "York Boat on Lake Winnipeg, 1930"
(Walter Phillips) .. .. 1·00 1·25
No. 1721 was issued in a similar sheet format to No. 1289

658 Man and Boy with
Bike, and A. J. and J. W.
Billes (company founders)

659 Abbé Charles-Emile
Gadbois

(Des Fuel Design. Litho Ashton-Potter Canada)

1997 (3 Mar). *75th Anniv of Canadian Tire Corporation.
Fluorescent frame.* P 13×13½.
1722 **658** 45 c. multicoloured 50 50
No. 1722 was printed in sheets of 12 which were supplied in
special envelopes each with a pamphlet on the history of the
company.

(Des Marie Lessard. Litho C.B.N.)

1997 (20 Mar). *Abbé Charles-Emile Gadbois (musicologist)
Commemoration. Fluorescent frame.* P 13½×13.
1723 **659** 45 c. multicoloured 50 50

660 Blue Poppy **661** Nurse attending Patient

(Des C. Simard. Litho Ashton-Potter Canada)

1997 (4 Apr). *"Quebec in Bloom" International Floral Festival.
Fluorescent paper.* P 13×12½.
1724 **660** 45 c. multicoloured 35 40
a. Booklet pane. No. 1724×12 .. 4·25
No. 1724 was only issued in $5.40 booklets. No. 1724a has the
horizontal edges of the pane imperforate and margins at left and
right.

(Des Margaret Issenman. Litho Ashton-Potter Canada)

1997 (12 May). *Centenary of Victorian Order of Nurses.
Fluorescent frame.* P 12½×13.
1725 **661** 45 c. multicoloured 50 50

662 Osgoode Hall
and Seal of Law
Society

663 Great White Shark

(Des L. Holloway. Litho C.B.N.)

1997 (23 May). *Bicentenary of Law Society of Upper Canada.
Fluorescent frame.* P 13½×13.
1726 **662** 45 c. multicoloured 50 50

(Des Q30 Design. Litho Ashton-Potter Canada)

1997 (30 May). *Ocean Fishes. T **663** and similar horiz designs.
Multicoloured. Fluorescent frame.* P 12½×13.
1727 45 c. Type **663** 50 50
a. Block of 4. Nos. 1727/30 .. 1·75
1728 45 c. Pacific Halibut 50 50
1729 45 c. Common Sturgeon 50 50
1730 45 c. Blue-finned Tuna 50 50
1727/30 .. .. *Set of 4* 1·75 1·75
Nos. 1727/30 were printed together, *se-tenant*, throughout the
sheet giving four blocks of 4 and four single stamps.

664 Lighthouse and
Confederation Bridge

(Des C. Burke and J. Hudson. Litho C.B.N.)

1997 (31 May). *Opening of Confederation Bridge, Northumberland Strait. T **664** and similar horiz design. Multicoloured.
Fluorescent frame.* P 12½×13.
1731 45 c. Type **664** 50 50
a. Horiz pair. Nos. 1731/2 and centre
label .. .. .. 1·00
1732 45 c. Confederation Bridge and Great Blue
Heron 50 50
Nos. 1731/2 were printed together, horizontally *se-tenant*, in
sheets of 20 (4×5) with labels measuring 16×23½ mm between
vertical rows 1 and 2 and 3 and 4 which link the two designs.

665 Gilles Villeneuve in Ferrari
T-3

(Des J. Gault and N. Skinner. Litho C.B.N.)

1997 (12 June). *15th Death Anniv of Gilles Villeneuve (racing
car driver). T **665** and similar horiz design. Multicoloured.
Fluorescent frame.* P 12½×13.
1733 45 c. Type **665** 50 50
1734 90 c. Villeneuve in Ferrari T-4 .. 1·00 1·00
MS1735 203×115 mm. Nos. 1733/4 each × 4 5·50 6·00
No. MS1735 was sold in an illustrated folder.

666 Globe and the *Matthew*

(Des Susan Warr. Litho Ashton-Potter Canada)

1997 (24 June). *500th Anniv of John Cabot's Discovery of North America. Fluorescent paper.* P 12½×13.
1736 **666** 45 c. multicoloured 50 50

667 Sea to Sky Highway, British Columbia, and Skier

(Des L. Cable. Litho C.B.N.)

1997 (30 June). *Scenic Highways.* T **667** *and similar horiz designs. Multicoloured. Fluorescent frame.* P 12½×13.
1737 45 c. Type **667** 50 50
  a. Block of 4. Nos. 1737/40 .. 1·75
1738 45 c. Cabot Trail, Nova Scotia, and rug-making 50 50
1739 45 c. Wine route, Ontario, and glasses of wine 50 50
1740 45 c. Highway 34, Saskatchewan, and cowboy 50 50
1737/40 .. .. .. *Set of* 4 1·75 1·75
Nos. 1737/40 were printed together, *se-tenant*, in sheets of 20 containing four blocks of 4 and four single stamps.

668 Kettle, Ski-bike, Lounger and Plastic Cases

(Des F. Dallaire. Litho C.B.N.)

1997 (23 July). *20th Congress of International Council of Societies for Industrial Design. Fluorescent frame.* P 12½×13.
1741 **668** 45 c. multicoloured 50 50
No. 1741 was printed in sheets of 24 (4×6), the horizontal rows containing four stamps each with a different 11½×24 mm *se-tenant* label showing examples of Canadian industrial design. These labels are on the right of the stamps in rows 1, 3 and 5 and to the left in rows 2, 4 and 6.

669 Caber Thrower, Bagpiper, Drummer and Highland Dancer

670 Knights of Columbus Emblem

(Des F. Ross. Litho C.B.N.)

1997 (1 Aug). *50th Anniv of Glengarry Highland Games, Ontario. Fluorescent frame.* P 12½×13.
1742 **669** 45 c. multicoloured 50 50

(Des A. Leduc. Litho C.B.N.)

1997 (5 Aug). *Centenary of Knights of Columbus (welfare charity) in Canada. Fluorescent frame.* P 13.
1743 **670** 45 c. multicoloured 50 50

671 Postal and Telephone Workers with P.T.T.I. Emblem

(Des Epicentre. Litho C.B.N.)

1997 (18 Aug). *28th World Congress of Postal, Telegraph and Telephone International Staff Federation, Montreal. Fluorescent frame.* P 13.
1744 **671** 45 c. multicoloured 50 50

672 C.Y.A.P. Logo

(Des K. Fung. Litho C.B.N.)

1997 (25 Aug). *Canada's Year of Asia Pacific. Fluorescent frame.* P 13½.
1745 **672** 45 c. multicoloured 50 50

673 Paul Henderson celebrating Goal

674 Martha Black

(Des C. Vinh. Litho Ashton-Potter Canada)

1997 (20 Sept). *25th Anniv of Canada–U.S.S.R. Ice Hockey Series.* T **673** *and similar horiz design. Multicoloured. Fluorescent frame.* P 12½×13.
1746 45 c. Type **673** 35 40
  a. Booklet pane. Nos. 1746/7, each × 5 with margins all round .. 3·50
1747 45 c. Canadian team celebrating .. 35 40
Nos. 1746/7 were only issued in $4.50 stamp booklets with a partial fluorescent frame around each stamp.

(Des S. Hepburn. Litho C.B.N.)

1997 (26 Sept). *Federal Politicians.* T **674** *and similar vert designs. Multicoloured. Fluorescent frame.* P 13½×13.
1748 45 c. Type **674** 35 40
  a. Block of 4. Nos. 1748/51 .. 1·40
1749 45 c. Lionel Chevrier 35 40
1750 45 c. Judy LaMarsh 35 40
1751 45 c. Réal Caouette 35 40
1748/51 .. .. *Set of* 4 1·40 1·60
The four different designs were printed together, *se-tenant*, throughout the sheet, giving four blocks of 4 and four single stamps.

675 Vampire and Bat

(Des L. Fishauf, J. Bennett, B. Drawson, T. Hunt, S. Ng. Litho Ashton-Potter Canada)

1997 (1 Oct). *The Supernatural. Centenary of Publication of Bram Stoker's* Dracula. T **675** *and similar square designs. Multicoloured. Fluorescent paper.* P 12½×13.
1752 45 c. Type **675** 35 40
  a. Block of 4. Nos. 1752/5 .. 1·40
1753 45 c. Werewolf 35 40
1754 45 c. Ghost 35 40
1755 45 c. Goblin 35 40
1752/5 .. .. *Set of* 4 1·40 1·60
Nos. 1752/5 were printed together, *se-tenant*, in blocks of 4 throughout the sheet.

676 Grizzly Bear

(Des A. Leduc. Eng G. Peral. Recess and litho C.B.N.)

1997 (15 Oct). *Mammals.* P 12½×13.
1756 **676** $8 multicoloured .. .. 6·50 6·75
No. 1756 was printed in sheets of 4.

677 "Our Lady of the Rosary" (detail, Holy Rosary Cathedral, Vancouver)

(Des G. Nincheri (45 c.), Ellen Simon (52 c.), C. Wallis (90 c.). Litho Ashton-Potter Canada)

1997 (3 Nov). *Christmas. Stained Glass Windows.* T **677** *and similar horiz designs. Multicoloured. Fluorescent frame.* P 12½×13.
1763 45 c. Type **677** 35 40
  a. Perf 12½×imperf 35 40
  ab. Booklet pane. No. 1763a×10 3·50
1764 52 c. "Nativity" (detail, Leith United Church, Ontario) .. 40 45
  a. Perf 12½×imperf 40 45
  ab. Booklet pane. No. 1764a×5 2·00
1765 90 c. "Life of the Blessed Virgin" (detail, St. Stephen's Ukrainian Catholic Church, Calgary) 75 80
  a. Perf 12½×imperf 75 80
  ab. Booklet pane. No. 1765a×5 3·75
1736/5 .. .. .. *Set of* 3 1·50 1·60
Nos. 1763a/5a were only issued in stamp booklets with the vertical edges of the panes imperforate and margins at top and bottom.

678 Livestock and Produce

(Des Heather Lafleur and Shelagh Armstrong. Litho C.B.N.)

1997 (6 Nov). *75th Anniv of Royal Agricultural Winter Fair, Toronto. Fluorescent frame.* P 12½×13.
1766 **678** 45 c. multicoloured 35 40

679 Tiger

(Des R. Mah. Litho Ashton-Potter Canada)

1998 (8 Jan). *Chinese New Year ("Year of the Tiger"). Fluorescent frame.* P 13½×12½.
1767 **679** 45 c. multicoloured 35 40
MS1768 130×110 mm. As No. 1767×2. P 13×12½ 70 75
No. **MS1768** is diamond-shaped with overall measurements as quoted.
As originally issued the miniature sheet was surrounded by a plain gold margin. Examples from the "Lunar New Year" pack issued on 28 January were additionally inscribed with design and printing information on this gold margin at foot.

Index to Canada Stamp Designs from 1942

The following index is intended to facilitate the identification of Canadian issues from 1942. Portrait stamps are usually listed under surnames only, views under the name of the town or city and other issues under the main subject or a prominent word and date chosen from the inscription. Simple abbreviations have occasionally been resorted to and when the same design or subject appears on more than one stamp, only the first of each series is indicated.

STAMP BOOKLETS

Booklet Nos. SB1/60 are stapled, all subsequent booklets have their panes attached by selvedge, *unless otherwise stated.*

All booklets up to and including No. SB41 contain panes consisting of two rows of three (3×2).

B 1

1900 (11 June). *Red on pink cover. Two panes of six 2 c. (No. 155ba).*
SB1   25 c. booklet. Cover as Type B **1** with English text £1700

1903 (1 July). *Red on pink cover. Two panes of six 2 c. (No. 176a).*
SB2   25 c. booklet. Cover as Type B **1** with English text £1800

1912 (Jan)–**16**. *Red on pink cover. Two panes of six 2 c. (No. 201a).*
SB3   25 c. booklet. Cover as Type B **1** with English text   60·00
      a. Cover handstamped "NOTICE Change in Postal Rates For New Rates See Postmaster"   60·00
      b. French text (4.16) £100
      ba. Cover handstamped "AVIS Changement des tarifs Postaux Pour les nouveaux tarifs consulter le maitre de poste" £100

1913 (1 May)–**16**. *Green on pale green cover. Four panes of six 1 c. (No. 197a).*
SB4   25 c. booklet. Cover as Type B **1** with English text   £350
      a. Containing pane No. 199a .. ..   65·00
      ab. Cover handstamped "NOTICE Change in Postal Rates For New Rates See Postmaster"   65·00
      b. French text (28.4.16) £500
      ba. Containing pane No. 199a £130
      bb. Cover handstamped "AVIS Changement des tarifs Postaux Pour les nouveaux tarifs consulter le maitre de poste" £275

1922 (Mar). *Black on brown cover. Two panes of four 3 c. and 2 labels (No. 205a).*
SB5   25 c. booklet. Cover as Type B **1** with English text   £300
      a. French text £600

1922 (July–Dec). *Black on blue cover. Panes of four 1 c., 2 c. and 3 c. (Nos. 246aa, 247aa, 205a) and 2 labels.*
SB6   25 c. booklet. Cover as Type B **1** with English text   £300
      a. French text (Dec) £475

1922 (Dec). *Black on orange cover. Four panes of six 1 c. (No. 246ab).*
SB7   25 c. booklet. Cover as Type B **1** with English text   £100
      a. French text £130

1922 (Dec). *Black on green cover. Two panes of six 2 c. (No. 247ab).*
SB8   25 c. booklet. Cover as Type B **1** with English text   £600
      a. French text £700

1923 (Dec). *Black on blue cover. Panes of four 1 c., 2 c. and 3 c. (Nos. 246aa, 247aa, 248aa) and 2 labels.*
SB9   25 c. booklet. Cover as Type B **1** with English text   £200
      a. French text £325

1923 (Dec)–**24**. *Black on brown cover. Two panes of four 3 c. (No. 248aa) and 2 labels.*
SB10 25 c. booklet. Cover as Type B **1** with English text   £180
      a. French text (5.24) £275

B 2

1928 (16 Oct). *Black on green cover. Two panes of six 2 c. (No. 276a).*
SB11 25 c. booklet. Cover as Type B **2** with English text   55·00
      a. French text .. ..   75·00

1928 (25 Oct). *Black on orange cover. Four panes of six 1 c. (No. 275a).*
SB12 25 c. booklet. Cover as Type B **2** with English text   £100
      a. French text £190

1929 (6 June). *Plain manilla cover. Three panes of six 1 c., two panes of six 2 c. and one pane of six 5 c. (Nos. 275a, 276a, 279a).*
SB13 72 c. booklet. Plain cover £300
      a. With "Philatelic Div., Fin. Br. P.O. Dept., Ottawa" circular cachet on front cover ..   £800
      b. With code number in the centre of the circular cachet £900

1930 (17 June). *Black on green cover. Two panes of six 2 c. (No. 289a).*
SB14 25 c. booklet. Cover as Type B **2** with English text   80·00
      a. French text £110

1930 (17 Nov). *Black on red cover. Two panes of six 2 c. (No. 301a).*
SB15 25 c. booklet. Cover as Type B **2** with English text   55·00
      a. French text .. .. ..   75·00

1931 (13 July). *Black on red cover. Two panes of four 3 c. (No. 303a) and 2 labels.*
SB16 25 c. booklet. Cover as Type B **2** with English text   80·00
      a. French text £110

1931 (21 July). *Black on green cover. Four panes of six 1 c. (No. 300b).*
SB17 25 c. booklet. Cover as Type B **2** with English text   £120
      a. French text £160

1931 (23 July). *Black on brown cover. Two panes of six 2 c. (No. 302a).*
SB18 25 c. booklet. Cover as Type B **2** with English text   80·00
      a. French text £110

1931 (13 Nov). *Black on blue cover. Panes of four 1 c., 2 c. and 3 c. (Nos. 300c, 302ba, 303a) and 2 labels.*
SB19 25 c. booklet. Cover as Type B **2** with English text   £250
      a. French text £350

1933 (22 Aug–13 Nov). *Black on red cover. Two panes of four 3 c. (No. 321a) and 2 labels.*
SB20 25 c. booklet. Cover as Type B **2** with English text (13 Nov) .. ..   85·00
      a. French text (22 Aug) £160

1933 (7 Sept). *Black on brown cover. Two panes of six 2 c. (No. 320a).*
SB21 25 c. booklet. Cover as Type B **2** with English text   60·00
      a. French text £100

1933 (19 Sept–5 Dec). *Black on blue cover. Panes of four 1 c., 2 c. and 3 c. (Nos. 319b, 320b, 321ba) and 2 labels.*
SB22 25 c. booklet. Cover as Type B **2** with English text   £200
      a. French text (5 Dec) £300

1933 (28 Dec)–**34**. *Black on green cover. Four panes of six 1 c. (No. 319a).*
SB23 25 c. booklet. Cover as Type B **2** with English text   85·00
      a. French text (26.3.34) £120

B 3

1935 (1 June–8 Aug). *Red on white cover. Two panes of four 3 c. (No. 343a) and 2 labels.*
SB24 25 c. booklet. Cover as Type B **3** with English text (8 Aug) .. .. ..   55·00
      a. French text (1 June) .. ..   70·00

1935 (22 July–1 Sept). *Blue on white cover. Panes of four 1 c., 2 c. and 3 c. (Nos. 341b, 342b, 343a) and 2 labels.*
SB25 25 c. booklet. Cover as Type B **3** with English text   £140
      a. French text (1 Sept) £180

1935 (19 Aug–18 Oct). *Green on white cover. Four panes of six 1 c. (No. 341a).*
SB26 25 c. booklet. Cover as Type B **3** with English text   90·00
      a. French text (18 Oct) £130

1935 (16–18 Mar). *Brown on white cover. Two panes of six 2 c. (No. 342a).*
SB27 25 c. booklet. Cover as Type B **3** with English text   70·00
      a. French text (18 Mar) £120

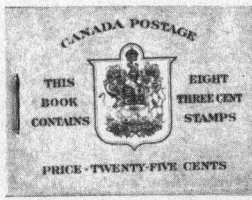

B 4

1937 (14 Apr)–**38**. *Blue and white cover. Panes of four 1 c., 2 c. and 3 c. (Nos. 357a, 358a, 359a) and 2 labels.*
SB28 25 c. booklet. Cover as Type B **3** with English text   80·00
      a. French text (4.1.38) .. ..   90·00
SB29 25 c. booklet. Cover as Type B **4** with English text 57 mm wide .. .. ..   55·00
      a. English text 63 mm wide .. ..   80·00
      b. French text 57 mm wide (4.1.38) ..   85·00
      ba. French text 63 mm wide £130

1937 (23–27 Apr). *Red and white cover. Two panes of four 3 c. (No. 359a) and 2 labels.*
SB30 25 c. booklet. Cover as Type B **3** with English text (27 Apr) .. .. ..   16·00
      a. French text (23 Apr) .. ..   23·00
SB31 25 c. booklet. Cover as Type B **4** with English text 57 mm wide (27 Apr) .. ..   10·00
      a. English text 63 mm wide .. ..   25·00
      b. French text 57 mm wide (23 Apr) ..   13·00
      ba. French text 63 mm wide £120

1937 (18 May)–**38**. *Green and white cover. Four panes of six 1 c. (No. 357b).*
SB32 25 c. booklet. Cover as Type B **3** with English text   25·00
      a. French text (14.10.38) .. ..   35·00
SB33 25 c. booklet. Cover as Type B **4** with English text 57 mm wide .. .. ..   16·00
      a. English text 63 mm wide .. ..   48·00
      b. French text 57 mm wide (14.10.38) ..   18·00
      ba. French text 63 mm wide £110

1938 (3 May)–**39**. *Brown and white cover. Two panes of six 2 c. (No. 358b).*
SB34 25 c. booklet. Cover as Type B **3** with English text   32·00
      a. French text (3.3.39) .. ..   40·00
SB35 25 c. booklet. Cover as Type B **4** with English text 57 mm wide .. .. ..   23·00
      a. English text 63 mm wide .. ..   55·00
      b. French text 57 mm wide .. ..   35·00
      ba. French text 63 mm wide .. ..   80·00

1942 (20–29 Aug) *Red and white cover. Two panes of four 3 c. (No. 377a) and 2 labels.*
SB36 25 c. booklet. Cover as Type B **4** with English text   8·50
      a. French text (29 Aug) .. ..   12·00

1942 (12–14 Sept). *Violet and white cover. Panes of four 1 c., 2 c. and 3 c. (Nos. 375a, 376a, 377a), each with 2 labels.*
SB37 25 c. booklet. Cover as Type B **4** with English text (14 Sept) .. .. ..   45·00
      a. French text (12 Sept) .. ..   90·00

1942 (6 Oct)–**43**. *Brown and white cover. Two panes of six 2 c. (No. 376b).*
SB38 25 c. booklet. Cover as Type B **4** with English text   38·00
      a. French text (6.4.43) .. ..   65·00

1942 (24 Nov)–**46**. *Green and white cover. Four panes of six 1 c. (No. 375b).*
SB39 25 c. booklet. Cover as Type B **4** with English text   11·00
      a. French text (16.2.43) .. ..   17·00
      b. Bilingual text (8.1.46) .. ..   17·00

1943 (3 May)–**46**. *Orange and white cover. One pane of six 4 c. (No. 380a).*
SB40 25 c. booklet. Cover as Type B **4** with English text   4·00
      a. French text (12.5.43) .. ..   9·00
      b. Bilingual text (8.1.46) .. ..   13·00

1943 (28 Aug)–**46**. *Purple and white cover. Two panes of four 3 c. (No. 378a) and 2 labels.*
SB41 25 c. booklet. Cover as Type B **4** with English text   10·00
      a. French text (7.9.43) .. ..   24·00
      b. Bilingual text (8.1.46) .. ..   17·00

B 5

1943 (1 Sept)–**46**. *Black and white cover. Panes of three 1 c., 3 c. and 4 c. (Nos. 394a, 395a, 396a) (3×1).*
SB42 25 c. booklet. Cover as Type B **5** with English text   26·00
      a. French text (18.9.43) .. ..   30·00
      c. Bilingual text (23.1.46) .. ..   28·00

B 6

1947 (24 Nov). *Brown on orange cover. Panes of six 3 c. and 4 c. (3×2) and two panes of four 7 c. (2×2) (Nos. 378b, 380a, 407a).*
SB43 $1 booklet. Cover as Type B **6** with English text   25·00
      a. French text .. .. ..   38·00

1950 (12 Apr–18 May). *Purple and white cover. Two panes of four 3 c. (No. 416a) and 2 labels (3×2).*
SB44   25 c. booklet. Cover as Type B 4 with English text   5·00
   a. Bilingual text (18 May) .. .. .. 5·00

1950 (5–10 May). *Orange and white cover. One pane of six 4 c. (No. 417a) (3×2).*
SB45   25 c. booklet. Cover as Type B 4 with English text   28·00
   a. Stitched .. .. ..60·00
   b. Bilingual text (10 May) .. .. 30·00

1950 (18 May). *Black and white cover. Panes of three 1 c., 3 c. and 4 c. (Nos. 422ba, 423a, 423a) (3×1).*
SB46   25 c. booklet. Cover as Type B 5 with English text   50·00
   a. Bilingual text .. .. 55·00

1951 (2 June). *Orange and white cover. One pane of six 4 c. (No. 417ba) (3×2).*
SB47   25 c. booklet. Cover as Type B 4 with English text   6·00
   a. Stitched .. .. .. 11·00
   b. Bilingual text .. .. 7·50

1951 (25 Oct)–52. *Black and white cover. Panes of three 1 c., 3 c. and 4 c. (Nos. 422ba, 423a, 423ca) (3×1).*
SB48   25 c. booklet. Cover as Type B 5 with English text   26·00
   a. Bilingual text (9.7.52) .. 28·00

1953 (6 July–19 Aug). *Orange cover. One pane of six 4 c. (No. 453a) (3×2).*
SB49   25 c. booklet. Cover as Type B 4 with English text   3·50
   a. Bilingual text (19 Aug) .. .. .. 4·25

1953 (17 July–20 Oct). *Purple cover. Two panes of four 3 c. (No. 452a) and 2 labels (3×2).*
SB50   25 c. booklet. Cover as Type B 4 with English text   3·75
   a. Bilingual text (20 Oct) .. .. 7·50

1953 (12 Aug). *Grey cover. Panes of three 1 c., 3 c. and 4 c. (Nos. 458a, 459a, 460a) (3×1).*
SB51   25 c. booklet. Cover as Type B 5 with English text   16·00
   a. Bilingual text .. .. 16·00

All the following booklets are bilingual

1954 (1 Apr–Nov). *Blue cover as Type B 4.*
SB52   25 c. booklet containing pane of five 5 c. and 1 label (No. 473a) (3×2) .. .. .. 2·00
   a. Stitched (Nov) .. .. 3·25

1954 (14 July–Nov). *Blue cover as Type B 4.*
SB53   25 c. booklet containing pane of five 5 c. and 1 label (No. 467a) (3×2) .. .. 2·00
   a. Stitched (Nov) .. .. 3·25

1955 (7 July). *Violet cover as Type B 4.*
SB54   25 c. booklet containing pane of six 4 c. (No. 466a) (3×2) .. .. 4·75

B 7

1956 (1 June). *Red and white cover as Type B 7.*
SB55   25 c. booklet containing two panes of five 1 c. and five 4 c., each with 1 label (Nos. 463a, 466b) (3×2) .. .. 3·00

1956 (July). *Blue and white cover as Type B 7.*
SB56   25 c. booklet containing pane of five 5 c. and 1 label (No. 467a) (3×2) .. .. 2·50

B 8

1963 (May)–**67**. *Blue and white cover as Type B 7.*
SB57   25 c. booklet containing pane of five 5 c. and 1 label (No. 531a) (2×3) .. .. 3·50
   a. Cover Type B 8 (1.67) .. .. 30·00

1963 (15 May). *Red and white cover as Type B 7.*
SB58   25 c. booklet containing two panes of five 1 c. and five 4 c., each with 1 label (Nos. 527a, 530a) (2×3) .. .. 7·00

1967 (Feb). *Red cover as Type B 8.*
SB59   25 c. booklet containing two panes of five 1 c. and five 4 c., each with 1 label (Nos. 579a, 582a) (2×3) .. .. 2·50

1967 (Mar). *Blue cover as Type B 8.*
SB60   25 c. booklet containing pane of five 5 c. and 1 label (No. 583a) (2×3) .. .. 7·00

B 9

1968 (Sept). *Brown and cream cover, 70×48 mm, as Type B 9.*
SB61   25 c. booklet containing se-tenant pane of five 1 c. and five 4 c. (No. 598a) (2×5) .. .. 2·50

1968 (Sept). *Red and cream cover as Type B 9.*
SB62 $1 booklet containing pane of twenty-five 4 c. and 2 labels (No. 599a) (3×9) .. .. 9·00

1968 (Sept). *Blue and cream cover, 82×48 mm, as Type B 9.*
SB63 $1 booklet containing pane of twenty 5 c. (No. 600a) (2×10) .. .. 6·50

1968 (Oct). *Orange and cream cover, 70×48 mm, as Type B 9, but without border.*
SB64   25 c. booklet containing se-tenant pane of one 1 c., four 6 c. and 1 label (No. 598b) (2×3) .. 2·50

B 10 (*Illustration reduced. Actual size 128×60 mm*)

1968 (15 Nov). *Christmas. Red and green cover as Type B 10.*
SB65 $1 booklet containing two panes of ten 5 c. (No. 630a) (5×2) .. .. .. 6·00
   p. Phosphor (No. 630pa) .. .. 7·50
Nos. SB65/p exist with left or right opening (i.e. with selvedge at left or right of pane).

1969 (Jan). *Orange-red on cream cover as Type B 9, but without border.*
SB66 $1.50, booklet containing pane of twenty-five 6 c. and 2 labels (No. 601a) (3×9) .. .. 11·00

1969 (8 Oct). *Christmas. Red cover size as Type B 10.*
SB67 $1 booklet containing two panes of ten 5 c. (No. 644a) (5×2) .. .. .. 3·75
   p. Phosphor (No. 644pa) .. .. 6·00

1970 (Jan). *Black on cream cover as Type B 9, but without border.*
SB68 $1.50, booklet containing pane of twenty-five 6 c. and 2 labels (No. 602a) (3×9) .. 20·00

1970 (Aug). *Black on cream cover, 70×48 mm, as Type B 9, but without border.*
SB69   25 c. booklet containing pane of four 6 c. (No. 603a) (2×2) .. .. .. 13·00

1970 (Aug). *Black on cream cover as Type B 9, but without border.*
SB70 $1.50, booklet containing pane of twenty-five 6 c. and 2 labels (No. 607a) (3×9) .. 16·00

1970 (26 Oct). *Indigo on cream cover, 70×50 mm. Inscr* "CANADIAN POSTAGE STAMPS...MADE EXPRESSLY FOR OPAL MANUFACTURING CO. LIMITED".
SB71   25 c. booklet containing four 2 c. and four 3 c. (No. 580a) (2×2) with gutter margin between   2·50
No. SB71 was produced by the Canadian Bank Note Co for use in the private stamp-vending machines owned by the Opal Manufacturing Co Ltd, Toronto. To cover the cost of manufacture and installation these booklets were sold at 25 c. each. They were not available from the Canadian Post Office.

1970 (Nov). *Black on cream cover, 70×48 mm, as Type B 9, but without border.*
SB72   25 c. booklet containing pane of four 6 c. (No. 608a) (2×2) .. .. .. 5·50

1971 (30 June). *Green on cream cover, 70×48 mm, as Type B 9, but without border.*
SB73   25 c. booklet containing se-tenant pane of one 1 c., one 3 c., three 7 c. and 1 label (No. 604b) (2×3) .. .. 5·50
This exists with or without a black sealing strip inside the cover.

1971 (30 June). *Green and buff cover, 82×47 mm, as Type B 9, but without border.*
SB74 $1 booklet containing se-tenant pane of four 1 c., four 3 c. and twelve 7 c. (No. 604a) (2×10)   14·00

1971 (Aug). *Booklet No. SB73 with label affixed giving the new contents. Sold as an experiment in Toronto for 50 c.*
SB75   50 c. booklet. Contents as No. SB73, but containing two panes .. 11·00
The experiment was later continued by the use of machines which issued two 25 c. booklets for 50 c.

1971 (30 Dec). *Grey on cream cover, 70×48 mm, as Type B 9, but without border.*
SB76   25 c. booklet containing se-tenant pane of three 1 c., one 6 c. and two 8 c. (No. 604c) (2×3)   2·00
   q. With fluorescent bands (No. 604qc) .. 4·00

1971 (30 Dec). *Grey on cream cover, 77×48 mm, as Type B 9, but without border.*
SB77 $1 booklet containing se-tenant pane of six 1 c., one 6 c. and eleven 8 c. (No. 604d) (2×9) .. 7·50
   q. With fluorescent bands (No. 604qd) .. 7·00

B 11

1972 (Mar). *As No. SB76, but with brown on cream illustrated covers as Type B 11. Ten different designs showing Mail Transport:*
(a) Post Office, 1816   (b) Stage Coach, c 1820
(c) Paddle Steamer, 1855   (d) Rural postman, c 1900
(e) Motor car, 1910   (f) Ford Model "T", 1914
(g) Curtis "JN4", 1918   (h) Mail truck, 1921
(i) Motorcycle, 1923   (j) Horse-drawn mail wagon, 1926
SB78   25 c. booklet. Contents as No. SB76 (any cover)   2·00
   q. With fluorescent bands .. .. 2·50
   Set of 10 different cover designs .. 18·00
   Set of 10 different cover designs (fluorescent bands on stamps) .. .. 22·00

1972 (Aug). *Ten cover designs as No. SB78, but in blue on cream.*
SB79   50 c. booklet (any cover) containing se-tenant pane of one 6 c., four 1 c. and five 8 c. (No. 604e) (2×5) .. .. 4·50
   q. With fluorescent bands (No. 604qe) .. 4·50
   Set of 10 different cover designs .. 42·00
   Set of 10 different cover designs (fluorescent bands on stamps) .. .. 42·00
This exists with black or white sealing strip inside the cover.

1974 (10 Apr). *Red on cream covers as Type B 11. Ten different designs showing aircraft:*
(a) Gibson "Twin-plane"   (f) Fokker "Super Universal"
(b) Burgess Dunne seaplane (g) "Mosquito"
(c) Nieuport "Scout"   (h) "Stranraer" flying-boat
(d) Curtiss "HS-2L"   (i) "CF-100 Canuck"
(e) Junkers "W-34"   (j) "Argus"
SB80   25 c. booklet (any cover) containing se-tenant pane of three 1 c., one 6 c. and two 8 c. (No. 693a) (3×2)   65
   Set of 10 different cover designs ..   6·00

B 12

1975 (17 Jan). *Violet on cream cover as Type B 12.*
SB81 $1 booklet containing se-tenant pane of six 1 c., one 6 c. and eleven 8 c. (No. 693b) (9×2) .. 2·25

1976 (1 Sept). *Violet on cream cover. Designs as No. SB80.*
SB82   50 c. booklet (any cover) containing se-tenant pane of two 1 c., four 2 c. and four 10 c. (No. 693c) (5×2) .. .. .. 1·50
   Set of 10 different cover designs .. 14·00

1977 (1 Nov). *Brown on cream covers, similar to Type B 11, but vert. Ten different designs showing flowers or trees:*
(a) Bottle Gentian   (g) Trembling Aspen
(b) Western Columbine   (h) Douglas Fir
(c) Canada Lily   (i) Sugar Maple
(d) Hepatica   (j) Rose, Thistle, Shamrock,
(e) Shooting Star   Lily and Maple leaf
(f) Lady's Slipper

SB83 50 c. booklet (*any cover*) containing *se-tenant*
pane of two 1 c. and four 12 c. (No. 862a)
(3×2) .. .. 2·75
Set of 10 different cover designs .. 25·00

1978 (17 May). *Green on cream covers. Designs as No. SB83.*
SB84 50 c. booklet (*any cover*) containing *se-tenant*
pane of four 2 c., three 14 c. and 1 label (No.
863a) (4×2) .. .. 3·25
Set of 10 different cover designs .. 30·00

B 13

1978 (13 Nov). *Black on cream covers as Type B 13. Five
different designs showing postcode publicity cartoons:*
(a) Talking post box
(b) Woman throwing letter
  to man
(c) Running letters
(d) Letter running to post
  box
(e) Womam with letter and
  laughing post box
SB85 $3.50, booklet (*any cover*) containing pane of
twenty-five 14 c. and 2 labels (No. 868ab)
(9×3) .. .. 11·00
Set of 5 different cover designs .. 50·00

1979 (28 Mar). *Blue on cream covers. Designs as No. SB83.*
SB86 50 c. booklet (*any cover*) containing *se-tenant*
pane of one 1 c., three 5 c. and two 17 c. (No.
870a) (3×2) .. .. 2·50
Set of 10 different cover designs .. 23·00

1979 (3 July)–**81.** *Violet on cream covers. Designs as No. SB85.*
SB87 $4.25, booklet (*any cover*) containing pane of
twenty-five 17 c. and 2 labels (No. 869ab)
(9×3) (cover without wavy lines) .. 11·00
Set of 5 different cover designs .. 50·00
SB88 $4.25, booklet (*any cover*) containing No. 869ab
(horizontal wavy lines across cover) (4.2.81) 12·00
Set of 5 different cover designs .. 55·00

B 14

1982 (1 Mar). *Black on cream covers as Type B 14. Ten
different designs showing provincial legislature buildings:*
(a) Victoria, British
  Columbia
(b) Fredericton, New
  Brunswick
(c) Halifax, Nova Scotia
(d) Charlottetown, Prince
  Edward Island
(e) Quebec
(f) Edmonton, Alberta
(g) Toronto, Ontario
(h) Regina, Saskatchewan
(i) Winnipeg, Manitoba
(j) St. John's, Newfoundland
SB89 50 c. booklet (*any cover*) containing *se-tenant*
pane of two 5 c., one 10 c., one 30 c. and 2
labels (No. 1033a) (3×2) .. .. 1·75
a. Containing pane No. 1033ab .. .. 2·00
b. Containing pane No. 1033ba .. 6·50
c. Containing pane No. 1033bb .. 6·50
Set of 10 different cover designs (No. SB89) 16·00

B 15 Parliament Buildings, Ottawa

1982 (30 June). *Black on cream cover as Type B 15.*
SB90 $6 booklet containing pane of twenty 30 c. and 1
label (No. 1032ab) (7×3) .. .. 14·00

1983 (15 Feb)–**85.** *Indian red on cream covers as Type B 14.
Designs as No. SB89.*
SB91 50 c. booklet (*any cover*) containing *se-tenant*
pane of two 5 c., one 8 c., one 32 c. and 2
labels (No. 1033c) (3×2) .. .. 2·50
Set of 10 different cover designs .. 22·00
a. Indian red on surfaced yellow cover (3.4.85) 2·50
Set of 10 different cover designs .. 22·00

1983 (8 Apr). *Indian red on cream cover as Type B 15.*
SB92 $8 booklet containing pane of twenty-five 32 c.
and 2 labels (No. 1032bb) (9×3) .. 15·00

1983 (30 June). *Canada Day. Multicoloured cover, 100×78
mm, showing location map of various forts.*
SB93 $3.20, booklet containing *se-tenant* pane of ten
32 c. (No. 1090a) (5×2) .. .. 5·00

1984 (15 Feb). *Cover as Type B 15, but additionally inscribed
"1984" below "POSTES".*
SB94 $8 booklet containing pane of twenty-five 32 c.
and 2 labels (No. 1032bb) (9×3) .. 20·00

1985 (21 June). *Reddish brown on grey-brown covers similar
to Type B 14. Ten different designs showing architectural or
ornamental details from Parliament Buildings, Ottawa:*
(a) Clock from Peace Tower
(b) Library entrance
(c) Gargoyle from Peace Tower
(d) Indian mask sculpture
(e) Stone carving at Memorial Chamber entrance
(f) Door to House of Commons
(g) Stone ornament at House of Commons main entrance
(h) Carved head, Senate Chamber
(i) Windows, Centre Block
(j) Window and war memorial, Peace Tower
SB95 50 c. booklet (*any cover*) containing *se-tenant*
pane of three 2 c., two 5 c. and one 34 c.
(No. 1148a) (2×3) .. .. .. 2·00
Set of 10 different cover designs .. 18·00
a. "R" on bottom left-hand corner of back cover 2·00
Set of 10 different cover designs .. 18·00

1985 (28 June). *Canada Day. Black, pale brown and pale
grey-brown cover, 100×78 mm, showing location map of
various forts.*
SB96 $3.40, booklet containing *se-tenant* pane of ten
34 c. (No. 1163a) (5×2) .. .. 4·50

B 16 Parliament Buildings, Ottawa
(*Illustration reduced. Actual size 120×70 mm*)

1985 (1 Aug)–**86.** *White on agate cover as Type B 16.*
SB97 $8.50, booklet containing pane of twenty-five
34 c. (No. 1155a) (5×5) .. .. 11·50
a. Containing pane No. 1155ba (4.7.86) .. 26·00

B 17
(*Illustration reduced. Actual size 121×61 mm*)

1985 (23 Oct). *Christmas. Rosine and emerald cover as Type
B 17.*
SB98 $3.20, booklet containing pane of ten 32 c. (No.
1181a) (5×2) .. .. .. 5·00

B 18
(*Illustration reduced. Actual size 150×72 mm*)

1986 (29 Oct). *Christmas. Black and brown-red cover as
Type B 18.*
SB99 $2.90, booklet containing pane of ten 29 c. (No.
1218a) (1×10) .. .. .. 4·00
a. Containing pane No. 1218ba .. .. 50·00

1987 (30 Mar). *Ten cover designs as No. SB95 but in blackish
olive on grey-brown.*
SB100 50 c. booklet (*any cover*) containing *se-tenant*
pane of two 1 c., two 6 c., one 36 c. and 1
label (No. 1147a) (2×3) .. .. 4·50
Set of 10 different cover designs .. 40·00
a. Containing pane No. 1147ba (1.10.87) .. 4·00
Set of 10 different cover designs .. 35·00

1987 (30 Mar). *Yellow-orange on agate cover similar to Type
B 16, but 48×74 mm.*
SB101 $3.60, booklet containing pane of ten 36 c. (No.
1156ba) (2×5) .. .. .. 9·00

1987 (19 May). *Yellow-orange on agate cover as Type B 16.*
SB102 $9 booklet containing pane of twenty-five 36 c.
(No. 1156bb) (5×5) .. .. 20·00

1987 (2 Nov). *Christmas. Christmas Plants. Black and
magenta cover as Type B 18, but 148×80 mm.*
SB103 $3.10, booklet containing pane of ten 31 c. (No.
1254a) (2×5) .. .. .. 4·50

B 19

1988 (5 Jan). *White and black on bright green cover as Type
B 19.*
SB104 $3.70, booklet (49×73 mm) containing pane of
ten 37 c. (No. 1157ab) .. .. 11·00
SB105 $9.25, booklet (120×73 mm) containing pane of
twenty-five 37 c. (No. 1157ae) (5×5) .. 25·00

1988 (15 Jan). *Covers as Type B 19, but inscribed "LUNCH
SAVER".*
SB106 $3.70, booklet (49×73 mm) containing pane of
ten 37 c. (No. 1157ab) (2×5) .. 11·00
SB107 $9.25, booklet (120×73 mm) containing pane of
twenty-five 37 c. (No. 1157ae) (5×5) .. 25·00

1988 (3 Feb). *Deep blue on grey-brown covers as Type B 14.
Ten different designs as No. SB95.*
SB108 50 c. booklet (*any cover*) containing *se-tenant*
pane of one 1 c., two 6 c., one 37 c. and 2
labels (No. 1147bb) (2×3) .. .. 2·00
Set of 10 different cover designs .. 18·00

1988 (27 Oct). *Christmas. Icons. Multicoloured cover as Type
B 18, but 150×80 mm, showing stamp illustration on the
front.*
SB109 $3.20, booklet containing pane of ten 32 c. (No.
1308a) (2×5) .. .. .. 3·50

B 20   B 21
(*Illustrations reduced. Actual size 79×152 mm*)

1988 (29 Dec)–**89.** *Multicoloured stamps on bright scarlet and
violet-blue covers (Type B 20) or on scarlet with white inscr
(Type B 21).*
SB110 $2.20, booklet containing pane of five 44 c. and
1 label (No. 1269ab) (2×3) (18.1.89) .. 5·00
a. Cover Type B 21 (17.3.89) .. .. 5·00
SB111 $3.80, booklet containing pane of ten 38 c. and
2 labels (No. 1157ca) (3×4) .. .. 5·00
a. Cover Type B 21 (17.3.89) .. .. 5·00
SB112 $3.80, booklet containing pane of ten 38 c. and
2 labels (No. 1162bd) (3×4) .. .. 4·50
a. Cover Type B 21 (17.3.89) .. .. 4·50
SB113 $3.80, booklet containing pane of five 76 c. and
1 label (No. 1275ab) (2×3) (18.1.89) .. 8·50
a. Cover Type B 21 (17.3.89) .. .. 8·50

SB114 $9.50, booklet containing pane of twenty-five 38 c. and 2 labels (No. 1157cb) (3×9) .. 12·00
   a. Cover Type B 21 (17.3.89) .. .. 12·00
Booklet Nos. SB110/14 each exist with either "Lunch Savers" or "Would it be more convenient" advertisement on the reverse. Booklet Nos. SB110a/14a also exist with "Your "Rush" Connection" advertisement on the reverse.

1989 (18 Jan). *Brown-purple on grey-brown covers as Type B 14. Ten different designs as No. SB95.*
SB115 50 c. booklet (*any cover*) containing *se-tenant* pane of three 2 c., one 6 c., one 38 c. and 1 label (No. 1148ba) (2×3) .. .. 1·90
   Set of 10 different cover designs .. .. 17·00

B 22
(*Illustration reduced. Actual size 85 × 155 mm*)

1989 (30 June). *Multicoloured cover as Type B 22.*
SB116 $5 booklet containing pane of twelve self-adhesive 38 c. (No. 1328ea) (6×2) .. 10·00
Two types of cover exist for No. SB116 with one being the mirror image of the other.

1989 (26 Oct). *Christmas. Paintings of Winter Landscapes. Multicoloured covers as Type B 21.*
SB117 $2.20, booklet containing pane of five 44 c. and 1 label (No. 1344a) (2×3) (*cover 60×155 mm*) 9·00
SB118 $3.30, booklet containing pane of ten 33 c. (No. 1342a) (2×5) (80×155 mm) .. 6·50
SB119 $3.80, booklet containing pane of ten 38 c. (No. 1343ab) (5×2) (80×155 mm) .. 26·00
SB120 $3.80, booklet containing pane of five 76 c. and 1 label (No. 1345a) (2×3) (60×155 mm) 17·00

1989 (28 Dec). *Multicoloured covers as Type B 21.*
SB121 $3.90, booklet containing pane of ten 39 c. and 2 labels (No. 1354c) (4×3) .. .. 6·50
SB122 $9.75, booklet containing pane of twenty-five 39 c. and 2 labels (No. 1354b) (9×3) 14·00

CANADA

B 23 Park Corner, Prince Edward Island

1990 (12 Jan). *Multicoloured cover as Type B 23.*
SB123 50 c. booklet containing *se-tenant* pane of one 1 c., two 5 c. and one 39 c. (No. 1350a) (2×2) (*p* 13½×14) .. .. 1·40
   a. Containing pane No. 1350ba (*p* 12½×13) 25·00

1990 (12 Jan). *Multicoloured covers as Type B 21.*
SB124 $2.25, booklet containing pane of five 45 c. and 1 label (No. 1270ab) (2×3) .. .. 5·00
SB125 $3.90, booklet containing pane of ten 39 c. and 2 labels (No. 1162cb) (3×4) .. 12·00
SB126 $3.90, booklet containing pane of five 78 c. and 1 label (No. 1276ab) (2×3) .. .. 8·00

1990 (8 Feb). *Multicoloured cover as Type B 22 showing wheatfield.*
SB127 $5 booklet containing pane of twelve self-adhesive 39 c. (No. 1328ba) (2×6) .. 11·00
Two types of cover exist for No. SB127 with one being the mirror image of the other.

B 24
(*Illustration reduced. Actual size 170 × 100 mm*)

1990 (3 May). *"Moving the Mail". Multicoloured cover as Type B 24. Booklet contains text and illustrations on labels attached to the panes and on interleaving pages. Stitched.*
SB128 $9.75, booklet containing two panes of eight 39 c. (No. 1382a) (2×4) and one pane of nine 39 c. (No. 1382b) (3×4) .. .. 15·00

1990 (25 Oct). *Christmas. Native Art. Multicoloured covers as Type B 21.*
SB129 $2.25, booklet containing pane of five 45 c. (No. 1407a) (2×3) (*cover 60×155 mm*) .. 3·50
SB130 $3.40, booklet containing pane of ten 34 c. (No. 1405a) (2×5) (80×155 mm) .. 4·00
SB131 $3.90, booklet containing pane of ten 39 c. (No. 1406a) (2×5) (60×155 mm) .. 6·00
SB132 $3.90, booklet containing pane of five 78 c. (No. 1408a) (2×3) (60×155 mm) .. 6·00

1990 (28 Dec). *Multicoloured cover as Type B 23, but showing Point Atkinson, British Columbia.*
SB133 50 c. booklet containing *se-tenant* pane of two 1 c., one 5 c. and one 40 c. (No. 1350c) (2×2) 1·25
The face value of No. SB133 included 3 c. Goods and Service Tax.

1990 (28 Dec). *Covers as Type B 21 showing multicoloured stamps on scarlet background with white inscriptions.*
SB134 $2.30, booklet containing pane of five 46 c. and 1 label (No. 1270cc) (2×3) .. .. 4·00
SB135 $4 booklet containing pane of ten 40 c. and 2 labels (No. 1162da) (3×4) .. .. 6·00
SB136 $4 booklet containing pane of five 80 c. and 1 label (No. 1276cc) (2×3) .. .. 7·00
SB137 $4 booklet containing pane of ten 40 c. and 2 labels (No. 1355a) (4×3) .. .. 6·00
SB138 $10 booklet containing pane of twenty-five 40 c. and 2 labels (No. 1355b) (9×3) .. 15·00

1991 (11 Jan). *Multicoloured cover as Type B 22, but showing coastal scene.*
SB139 $5.25, booklet containing pane of twelve self-adhesive 40 c. (No. 1328ca) (2×6) .. 11·00
Two types of cover exist for No. SB139 with one being the mirror image of the other.

B 25 (*Illustration reduced. Actual size 80×125 mm*)

B 26 (*Illustration reduced. Actual size 64×156 mm*)

1991 (22 May). *Public Gardens. Multicoloured cover as Type B 25.*
SB140 $4 booklet containing *se-tenant* pane of ten 40 c. (No. 1422a) (5×2) .. .. 5·50

1991 (20 Aug). *Canadian Rivers (1st series). Multicoloured cover as Type B 26.*
SB141 $4 booklet containing *se-tenant* pane of ten 40 c. (No. 1432a) (10×1) .. .. 7·50

B 27
(*Illustration reduced. Actual size 150×81 mm*)

1991 (16 Oct). *150th Anniv of Queen's University. Multi-coloured cover as Type B 27. Booklet contains text and illustrations on labels attached to the pane and on interleaving pages. Stitched.*
SB142 $4 booklet containing pane of ten 40 c. and 2 labels (No. 1449a) (4×3) .. .. 6·50

B 28 Christmas Tree   **B 29**

1991 (23 Oct). *Christmas. Multicoloured covers as Type B 28.*
SB143 $2.30, booklet containing pane of five 46 c. and 1 label (No. 1452a) (2×3) .. .. 3·50
SB144 $3.50, booklet containing pane of ten 35 c. (No. 1450a) (2×5) (punch bowl and candles cover design, 80×155 mm) .. .. 6·00
SB145 $4 booklet containing pane of ten 40 c. (No. 1451a) (2×5) (Christmas stocking cover design) .. .. 7·00
SB146 $4 booklet containing pane of five 80 c. and 1 label (No. 1453a) (2×3) (Christmas presents cover design) .. .. .. 7·00

1991 (27 Dec). *Covers as Type B 29 showing multicoloured stamps on scarlet background with Olympic logo in black.*
SB147 $2.40, booklet containing pane of five 48 c. and 1 label (No. 1467ab) (2×3) .. 3·75
SB148 $4.20, booklet containing pane of five 84 c. and 1 label (No. 1475ab) (2×3) .. 7·00
SB149 $4.20, booklet containing pane of ten 42 c. (No. 1162ea) (2×5) .. .. .. 7·00
SB150 $4.20, booklet containing pane of ten 42 c. (No. 1356a) (2×5) .. .. .. 6·00
SB151 $10.50, booklet containing pane of twenty-five 42 c. and 2 labels (No. 1356b) (3×9) .. 14·00
SB152 $21 booklet containing pane of fifty 42 c. and 2 labels (No. 1356c) (4×13) .. 45·00
The cover of booklet No. SB152 is made up of two $10.50 covers rouletted down the centre. It was issued in connection with a Canada Post special offer of a $1 coupon towards the cost of its purchase.

1992 (28 Jan). *Multicoloured cover as Type B 22, but showing mountain peaks.*
SB153 $5.25, booklet containing pane of twelve self-adhesive 42 c. stamps (No. 1328da) (2×6) 9·00
Two types of cover exist for No. SB153 with one being the mirror image of the other.

B 30 Olympic Flame
(*Illustration reduced. Actual size 83×151 mm*)

1992 (7 Feb). *Winter Olympic Games, Albertville. Multi-coloured cover as Type B 30.*
SB154 $4.20, booklet containing *se-tenant* pane of ten 42 c. (No. 1482a) (5×2) .. .. 6·50
Two types of cover exist for No. SB154 with one being the mirror image of the other.

1992 (22 Apr). *Canadian Rivers (2nd series). Multicoloured vert cover as Type B 26.*
SB155 $4.20, booklet containing *se-tenant* pane of ten 42 c. (No. 1492a) (5×2) .. .. 6·50

1992 (15 June). *Olympic Games, Barcelona. Multicoloured cover as Type B 30, but showing Olympic flag.*
SB156 $4.20, booklet containing *se-tenant* pane of ten 42 c. (No. 1498a) (5×2) .. .. 7·00
Two types of cover exist for No. SB156 with one being the mirror image of the other.

B 31 Prospecting Equipment
(Illustration reduced. Actual size 90×151 mm)

1992 (21 Sept). *150th Anniv of Geological Survey of Canada. Multicoloured cover as Type B* **31**.
SB157 $4.20, booklet containing *se-tenant* pane of ten
       42 c. (No. 1509a) (5×2)   ..   ..   7·50

B 32 Hockey Players
(Illustration reduced. Actual size 171×105 mm)

1992 (9 Oct). *75th Anniv of National Ice Hockey League. Multicoloured cover as Type B* **32**. *Booklet contains text and illustrations on labels attached to the pane and on interleaving pages. Stitched.*
SB158 $10.50, booklet containing twenty-five 42 c.
       stamps in two panes of 8 and 1 label and one
       pane of 9 (Nos. 1516a, 1517a, 1518a) (each
       3×3)   ..   ..   17·00

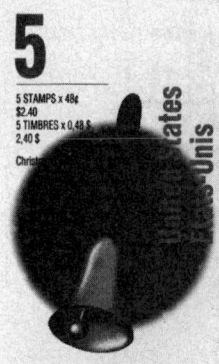

B 33 Hand Bell

1992 (13 Nov). *Christmas. Multicoloured covers as Type B* **33**.
SB159 $2.40, booklet containing pane of five 48 c. and
       1 label (No. 1527a) (2×3) ..   4·00
SB160 $3.70, booklet containing pane of ten 37 c. (No.
       1525a) (2×5) (candle and cookies cover
       design, 80×156 mm)   ..   ..   6·00
SB161 $4.20, booklet containing pane of ten 42 c. (No.
       1526ab) (2×5) (hobby horse cover design)   7·00
SB162 $4.20, booklet containing pane of five 84 c. and
       1 label (No. 1528a) (2×3) (Christmas tree
       cover design)   ..   ..   ..   7·00

1992 (30 Dec). *Multicoloured covers as Type B* **29**, *but without Olympic symbol at top right.*
SB163 $2.45, booklet containing pane of five 49 c. and
       1 label (No. 1468ba) (2×3)   ..   4·50
SB164 $4.30, booklet containing pane of ten 43 c. (No.
       1162fa) (2×5)   ..   ..   ..   7·00
SB165 $4.30, booklet containing pane of ten 43 c. (No.
       1357a) (2×5)   ..   ..   ..   7·00
SB166 $4.30, booklet containing pane of five 86 c. and
       1 label (No. 1476ba) (2×3)   ..   7·50
SB167 $10.75, booklet containing pane of twenty-five
       43 c. and 2 labels (No. 1357b) (3×9)   ..   15·00

1993 (15 Feb). *Multicoloured cover as Type B* **22**, *but showing lake.*
SB168 $5.25, booklet containing pane of twelve
       self-adhesive 43 c. stamps (2×6) (No.
       1328ea)   ..   ..   ..   8·50
Two types of cover exist for No. SB168 with one being the mirror image of the other.

B 34 Hand-crafting   **B 35** Postcards and
Techniques *(Illustration*   Stamps *(Illustration*
reduced. Actual size   *reduced. Actual size*
81×156 mm)   *60×155 mm)*

1993 (30 Apr). *Hand-crafted Textiles. Multicoloured cover as Type B* **34**.
SB169 $4.30, booklet containing *se-tenant* pane of ten
       43 c. (5×2) (No. 1534a)   ..   ..   6·00

1993 (14 June). *Historic Hotels. Multicoloured cover as Type B* **35**.
SB170 $4.30, booklet containing *se-tenant* pane of ten
       43 c. (5×2) (No. 1540a)   ..   ..   6·00

1993 (10 Aug). *Canadian Rivers (3rd series). Multicoloured vert cover as Type B* **26**.
SB171 $4.30, booklet containing *se-tenant* pane of ten
       43 c. (10×1) (No. 1558a)   ..   ..   6·00

B 36 Rabbit and Present   **B 37**

1993 (4 Nov). *Christmas. Multicoloured covers as Type B* **36**.
SB172 $2.45, booklet containing pane of five 49 c. and
       1 label (2×3) (No. 1574a)   ..   4·00
SB173 $3.80, booklet containing pane of ten 38 c.
       (2×5) (No. 1572a) (wooden puppet cover
       design, 80×156 mm)   ..   ..   6·00
SB174 $4.30, booklet containing pane of ten 43 c.
       (2×5) (No. 1573a) (angel cover design)   ..   7·00
SB175 $4.30, booklet containing pane of five 86 c. and
       1 label (2×3) (No. 1575a) (kangaroo cover
       design)   ..   ..   ..   7·00

1994 (7 Jan–14 Nov). *Covers as Type B* **37**, *each showing multicoloured stamps in a continuous pattern on scarlet background.*
SB176 $2.45, booklet containing pane of five 49 c. and
       1 label (No. 1468a) (2×3)   ..   4·50
SB177 $4.30, booklet containing pane of ten 43 c. (No.
       1162fa) (2×5)   ..   ..   ..   7·00
SB178 $4.30, booklet containing pane of ten 43 c. (No.
       1357ca) (p 14¹/₂) (18 Jan)   ..   6·00
       a. Containing pane No. 1357a (p 13¹/₂×13)
         (14 Nov)   ..   ..   ..   6·00
SB179 $4.30, booklet containing pane of five 86 c.
       (No. 1476a) and 1 label (2×3)   ..   7·50
SB180 $10.75, booklet containing pane of twenty-five
       43 c. and 2 labels (No. 1357cb) (p 14¹/₂)
       (3×9) (18 Jan)   ..   ..   ..   15·00
       a. Containing pane No. 1357b (p 13¹/₂×13)
         (14 Nov) ..   ..   ..   15·00

ALTERED CATALOGUE NUMBERS

Any Catalogue numbers altered from the last edition are shown as a list in the introductory pages.

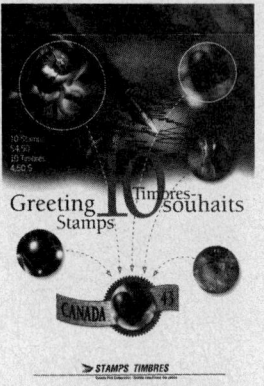

B 38
(Illustration reduced. Actual size 106×157 mm)

1994 (28 Jan). *Greetings. Multicoloured cover as Type B* **38**.
SB181 $4.50, booklet containing pane of ten self-
       adhesive 43 c. (No. 1580a) and 35 circular
       greetings labels   ..   ..   ..   5·50

1994 (25 Feb)–**95**. *Covers as Type B* **37** *showing multicoloured stamps in a continuous pattern on scarlet backgrounds.*
SB182 $2.50, booklet containing pane of five 50 c. and 1
       label (No. 1469a) (p 13) (2×3)   ..   4·00
       a. Containing pane No. 1469ba (p 14¹/₂×14)
         (27.3.95)   ..   ..   ..   4·00
SB183 $4.40, booklet containing pane of five 88 c. and 1
       label (No. 1477a) (fluorescent frame) (p 13)
       (2×3)   ..   ..   ..   6·00
       a. Containing pane No. 1477ba (three
         fluorescent bands) (p 13) (14.11.94)   7·50
       b. Containing pane No. 1477ca (three
         fluorescent bands) (p 14¹/₂×14) (27.3.95)   ..   7·50

B 39 Images of T. Eaton Company Ltd
(Illustration reduced. Actual size 151×101 mm)

1994 (17 Mar). *125th Anniv of T. Eaton Company Ltd. Multicoloured cover as Type B* **39**. *Booklet containing text and illustrations on label attached to the pane and on interleaving pages. Stitched.*
SB184 $4.30, booklet containing ten 43 c. stamps and
       2 labels (No. 1583a) (6×2)   ..   ..   5·50

1994 (22 Apr). *Canadian Rivers (4th series). Multicoloured vert cover as Type B* **26**.
SB185 $4.30, booklet containing *se-tenant* pane of ten
       43 c. (No. 1584a) (2×5)   ..   ..   5·50

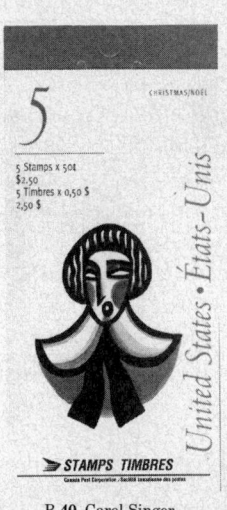

B 40 Carol Singer

1994 (3 Nov). *Christmas. Multicoloured covers as Type B* **40**.
SB186 $2.50, booklet containing pane of five 50 c. and
        1 label (2×3) (No. 1619a) .. .. .. 3·50
SB187 $3.80, booklet containing pane of ten (38 c.)
        (2×5) (No. 1617a) (chorister wearing ruff
        cover design, 80×156 mm) .. .. 4·50
SB188 $4.30, booklet containing pane of ten 43 c. (2×5)
        (No. 1618a) (pair of singers cover design) 5·00
SB189 $4.40, booklet containing pane of five 88 c. and
        1 label (2×3) (No. 1620a) (singer in hat and
        scarf cover design) .. .. .. 5·00

B **41** Fortress Gateway
*(Illustration reduced. Actual size
96×157 mm)*

1995 (5 May). *275th Anniv of Fortress of Louisbourg.
Multicoloured cover as Type B* **41**.
SB190 $4.30, booklet containing pane of ten (43 c.)
        (5×2) (No. 1631a) .. .. .. 4·00

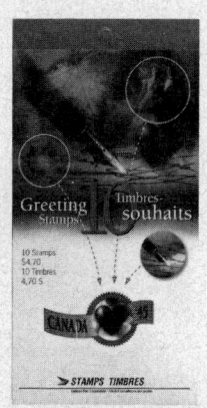

B **42** Player and Bunker   B **43** Fountain Pen
(Illustration reduced.   *(Illustration reduced.*
Actual size 52×156 mm.)   *Actual size 78×156 mm.)*

1995 (6 June). *Centenaries of Canadian Amateur Golf
Championship and of the Royal Canadian Golf Association.
Multicoloured cover as Type B* **42**.
SB191 $4.30, booklet containing *se-tenant* pane of ten
        43 c. (5×2) (No. 1637a) .. .. 4·50

1995 (31 July–6 Oct). *Covers as Type B* **37**, *each showing
multicoloured stamps in a continuous pattern on scarlet
background.*
SB192 $2.60, booklet containing pane of five 52 c. and
        1 label (No. 1470a) (*p* 13) (2×3) .. 2·00
        a. Containing pane No. 1470ba (*p* 14½×14)
        (6 Oct) 4·00
SB193 $4.50, booklet containing pane of ten 45 c. (No.
        1162ga) (2×5) .. .. .. 3·50
SB194 $4.50, booklet containing pane of ten 45 c. (No.
        1358a) (*p* 14½) (2×5) .. .. 4·25
        a. Containing pane No. 1358ca (*p* 13½×13)
        (6 Oct) 3·50
SB195 $4.50, booklet containing pane of five 90 c. and
        1 label (No. 1478a) (*p* 13) (2×3) .. 3·75
        a. Containing pane No. 1478ba (*p* 14½×14)
        (6 Oct) 7·00
SB196 $11.25, booklet containing pane of twenty-five
        45 c. and 2 labels (No. 1358b) (*p* 14½) (3×9) 12·00
        a. Containing pane No. 1358cb (*p* 13½×13)
        (6 Oct) 8·75
    Nos. SB192a, SB194a, SB195a and SB196a, together with a
new printing of No. SB193 issued on the same date, show a
revised back cover layout including a customer service phone
number.

1995 (1 Sept). *Greetings. Multicoloured cover as Type B* **43**.
SB197 $4.70, booklet containing pane of ten self-
        adhesive 45 c. (No. 1654a) and 15 circular
        greetings labels .. .. .. 4·00

B **44** Aspects of Chiropractic
Healing *(Illustration reduced.
Actual size 78×156 mm)*

1995 (15 Sept). *Centenary of Chiropractic Healing in Canada.
Multicoloured cover as Type B* **44**.
SB198 $4.70, booklet containing pane of ten self-
        adhesive 45 c. (No. 1654a) and 15 circular
        commemorative labels .. .. .. 4·50

1995 (15 Sept). *50th Anniv of Arctic Institute of North
America. Multicoloured cover as Type B* **26**, *but showing Inuk
woman and Arctic scene.*
SB199 $4.50, booklet containing *se-tenant* pane of ten
        45 c. (No. 1656a) (5×2) .. .. 4·50

B **45** Superman
*(Illustration reduced. Actual size
105×169 mm)*

1995 (2 Oct). *Comic Book Superheroes. Multicoloured cover as
Type B* **45**.
SB200 $4.50, booklet containing *se-tenant* pane of ten
        45 c. (No. 1661a) (5×2) .. .. 4·25

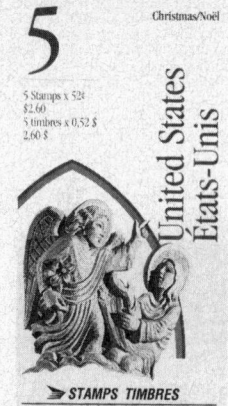

B **46** "The Annunciation"

1995 (2 Nov). *Christmas. Multicoloured covers as Type B* **46**.
SB201 $2.60, booklet containing pane of five 52 c. and
        1 label (2×3) (No. 1669a) .. .. 3·00
SB202 $4 booklet containing pane of ten 40 c. (2×5)
        (No. 1667a) (Sprig of holly cover design,
        80×156 mm) .. .. .. 4·50
SB203 $4.50, booklet containing pane of ten 45 c. (2×5)
        (No. 1668a) ("The Nativity" cover design) 4·75
SB204 $4.50, booklet containing pane of five 90 c. and
        1 label (2×3) (No. 1670a) ("The Flight to
        Egypt" cover design) .. .. 4·75

1996 (15 Jan). *Greetings. Multicoloured cover as Type B* **38**.
SB205 $4.70, booklet containing pane of ten self-
        adhesive 45 c. (No. 1654ba) and 35 circular
        greetings labels .. .. .. 4·00

B **47** Binary Codes and Globe
(Illustration reduced. Actual size 90×155 mm)

1996 (15 Feb). *High Technology Industries. Multicoloured
cover as Type B* **47**.
SB206 $5.40, booklet containing pane of twelve 45 c.
        (No. 1677a) (2×6) .. .. .. 6·75

B **48** Ethel Catherwood
*(Illustration reduced. Actual
size 95×155 mm)*

1996 (8 July). *Canadian Olympic Gold Medal Winners. Multicoloured cover as Type B* **48**.
SB207 $4.50, booklet containing pane of ten 45 c. (No.
        1691a) (5×2) .. .. .. 5·00

B **49** Father reading to Children
*(Illustration reduced. Actual size
95×155 mm)*

1996 (9 Sept). *Literacy Campaign. Multicoloured cover as Type
B* **49**.
SB208 $5 booklet containing pane of ten 45 + 5 c.
        (5×2) (No. 1699a) .. .. .. 5·50

PRICES OF SETS

Set prices are given for many issues, generally
those containing three stamps or more. Definitive
sets include one of each value or major colour
change, but do not cover different perforations,
die types or minor shades. Where a choice is
possible the set prices are based on the cheapest
versions of the stamps included in the listings.

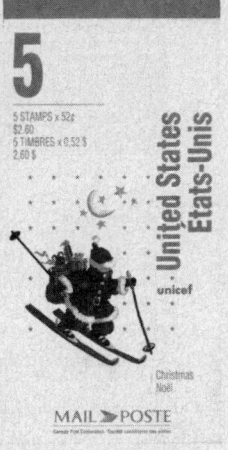

B 50 Canadian Authors
(Illustration reduced.
Actual size 80×155 mm)

B 51 Father Christmas

1996 (10 Oct). *Canadian Authors. Multicoloured cover as Type B 50.*
SB209 $4.50, booklet containing pane of ten 45 c. (5×2)
(No. 1706a)   ..   ..   ..   5·25

1996 (1 Nov). *Christmas. 50th Anniv of U.N.I.C.E.F. Multi-coloured covers as Type B 51.*
SB210 $2.60, booklet containing pane of five 52 c. and 1
label (2×3) (No. 1712ab)   ..   2·40
SB211 $4.50, booklet containing pane of ten 45 c. (2×5)
(No. 1711a) (Child tobogganing design)   4·25
SB212 $4.50, booklet containing pane of five 90 c. and 1
label (2×3) (No. 1713ab) (Couple ice-skating
design)   ..   ..   4·25

B 52 Blue Poppy

1997 (4 Apr). *"Quebec in Bloom" International Floral Festival. Multicoloured cover as Type B 52.*
SB213 $5.40, booklet containing pane of twelve 45 c.
(6×2) (No. 1724a) ..   ..   ..   4·25

PRICES OF SETS

Set prices are given for many issues, generally those containing three stamps or more. Definitive sets include one of each value or major colour change, but do not cover different perforations, die types or minor shades. Where a choice is possible the set prices are based on the cheapest versions of the stamps included in the listings.

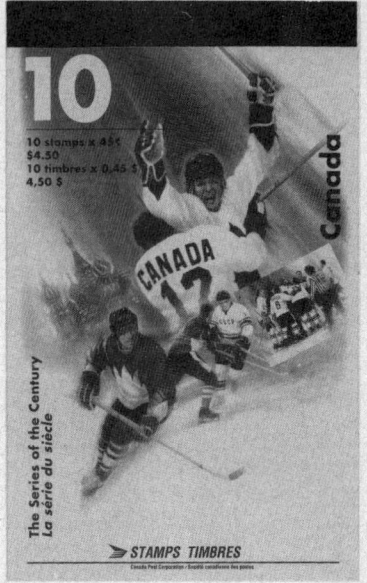

B 53 Paul Henderson celebrating

1997 (20 Sept). *25th Anniv of the Canada–U.S.S.R Ice Hockey Series. Multicoloured cover as Type B 53.*
SB214 $4.50, booklet containing pane of ten 45 c. (2×5)
(No. 1746a)   ..   ..   ..   3·50

B 54 "The Holy Family"

1997 (3 Nov). *Christmas. Stained Glass Windows. Multi-coloured covers as Type B 54.*
SB215 $2.60, booklet containing pane of five 52 c. (No.
1764ab)   ..   ..   ..   2·25
SB216 $4.50, booklet containing pane of ten 45 c. (No.
1763ab) (cover showing "Regina SSi Rosarii")   3·75
SB217 $4.50, booklet containing pane of five 90 c. (No.
1765ab) (cover showing "Madonna and
Child")   ..   ..   3·75

— URCH HARRIS —
ALL WORLD
NEW ISSUE SERVICE

Your 'First Choice' New Issue Supplier

Developed over the last 30 years Urch Harris 'All World' combines the widest choice of countries, themes and formats with a reliable individual service that helps develop and manage your collection.

- 260 countries and 100 plus themes.
- Choice of mint issues, reprints, yearpacks, used stamps, maxi cards, booklets, presentation packs, specimens and first day covers.
- Regular distributions every 6 weeks.
- Free magazine with every distribution.
- Fully computerised invoices with descriptions.
- Customer advice helpline.
- Free gifts and regular special offers.
- Supported by Stanley Gibbons, world leaders in philately.

FREE WELCOME PACK

Containing full details of our unique service, a full list of countries and themes and a copy of 'All World Direct' magazine.

Telephone 0117 9349333 for a free pack.

**Urch Harris & Co
1 Denmark Avenue
Bristol BS1 5HD**

A Division of Stanley Gibbons Ltd

REGISTRATION STAMPS

R 1

(Eng and recess – printed British-American Bank Note Co, Montreal and Ottawa)

1875 (15 Nov)–**92.** *White wove paper. (a) P* 12 *(or slightly under).*

R 1	R 1	2 c. orange	60·00	1·00
R 2		2 c. orange-red (1889)	70·00	6·00
R 3		2 c. vermilion	75·00	7·50
		a. Imperf (pair)	†	—
R 4		2 c. rose-carmine (1888)	£150	55·00
R 5		5 c. yellow-green (1878)	£100	1·25
R 6		5 c. deep green	80·00	1·00
		a. Imperf (pair)	£650	
R 7		5 c. blue-green (1888)	90·00	1·25
R 7a		5 c. dull sea-green (1892)	£130	3·25
R 8		8 c. bright blue	£325	£225
R 9		8 c. dull blue	£300	£200

(b) P 12 × 11½ *or* 12 × 11¾

R10	R 1	2 c. orange	£300	60·00
R11		5 c. green (*shades*)	£750	£150

SPECIAL DELIVERY STAMPS

PRINTERS. The following Special Delivery and Postage Due Stamps were recess-printed by the American Bank Note Co (to 1928), the British American Bank Note Co (to 1934), and the Canadian Bank Note Co (1935 onwards).

S 1

1898–1920. *P* 12.

S1	S 1	10 c. blue-green (28.6.98)	80·00	6·50
S2		10 c. deep green (12.13)	45·00	5·50
S3		10 c. yellowish green (8.20)	55·00	5·00

The differences between Types I and II (figures "10" with and without shading) formerly illustrated were due to wear of the plate. There was only one die.

S 2   S 3 Mail-carrying, 1867 and 1927

1922 (21 Aug). *P* 12.

S4	S 2	20 c. carmine-red	35·00	5·00

No. S4 exists in two slightly different sizes due to the use of "wet" or "dry" printing processes. See note below No. 195.

1927 (29 June). *60th Anniversary of Confederation. P* 12.

S5	S 3	20 c. orange	11·00	10·00

No. S5 exists imperforate, imperf×perf or perf×imperf (*Price, in each instance, £120 per pair, un*).

S 4

1930 (2 Sept). *P* 11.

S6	S 4	20 c. brown-red	40·00	7·00

1932 (24 Dec). *Type as S* 4, *but inscr* "CENTS" *in place of* "TWENTY CENTS". *P* 11.

S7		20 c. brown-red	45·00	12·00

No. S7 exists imperforate (*Price per pair £275, un*).

MINIMUM PRICE

The minimum price quote is 10p which represents a handling charge rather than a basis for valuing common stamps. For further notes about prices see introductory pages.

S 5 Allegory of Progress

(Des A. Foringer)

1935 (1 June). *P* 12.

S8	S 5	20 c. scarlet	3·50	2·00

No. S8 exists imperforate (*Price per pair £325, un*).

S 6 Canadian Coat of Arms

1938–39. *P* 12.

S 9	S 6	10 c. green (1.4.39)	18·00	3·00
S10		20 c. scarlet (15.6.38)	40·00	23·00

Nos. S9/10 exist imperforate (*Price £350, un, for each pair*).

$$\equiv 10 \qquad 10 \equiv$$

(S 7)

1939 (1 Mar). *Surch with Type S* 7.

S11	S 6	10 c. on 20 c. scarlet	9·00	8·00

S 8 Coat of Arms and Flags

S 9 Lockheed L.18 Lodestar

1942 (1 July)–**1943.** *War Effort. P* 12. *(a) Postage.*

S12	S 8	10 c. green	4·25	30

(b) Air

S13	S 9	16 c. ultramarine	3·75	45
S14		17 c. ultramarine (1.4.43)	4·00	55

Nos. S12/14 exist imperforate (*Prices per un pair 10 c. £325, 16 c. £375, 17 c. £375*).

S 10 Arms of Canada and Peace Symbols

S 11 Canadair DC-4M North Star

1946 (16 Sept–5 Dec). *P* 12. *(a) Postage*

S15	S 10	10 c. green	2·00	30

(b) Air. (i) *Circumflex accent in* "EXPRÊS"

S16	S 11	17 c. ultramarine	4·00	3·50

(ii) *Grave accent in* "EXPRÈS"

S17	S 11	17 c. ultramarine (5.12.46)	5·00	4·00

POSTAGE DUE STAMPS

PRINTERS. See note under "Special Delivery Stamps".

D 1   D 2

1906 (1 July)–**28.** *P* 12.

D1	D 1	1 c. dull violet	8·00	2·50
D2		1 c. red violet (1916)	10·00	3·00
		a. Thin paper (10.24)	15·00	18·00
D3		2 c. dull violet	15·00	90
D4		2 c. red-violet (1917)	11·00	1·25
		a. Thin paper (10.24)	27·00	18·00
D5		4 c. violet (3.7.28)	45·00	50·00
D6		5 c. dull violet	20·00	2·25
D7		5 c. red-violet (1917)	19·00	2·25
		a. Thin paper (10.24)	16·00	24·00
D8		10 c. violet (3.7.28)	32·00	15·00
D1/8			Set of 5 £100	65·00

The 1 c., 2 c. and 5 c. values exist imperforate (*Price £250 for each un pair*).

Printings up to October 1924 used the "wet" method, those from mid 1925 onwards the "dry". For details of the differences between these two methods, see above No. 196.

1930–2. *P* 11.

D 9	D 2	1 c. bright violet (14.7.30)	8·50	10·00
D10		1 c. bright violet (21.8.30)	7·50	1·40
D11		4 c. bright violet (14.10.30)	15·00	6·50
D12		5 c. bright violet (12.12.31)	15·00	25·00
D13		10 c. bright violet (24.8.32)	65·00	26·00
D9/13			Set of 5 £100	60·00

Nos. D9/11 and D13 exist imperforate, No. D13 also exists imperf×perf (*Price for vertical pair £450, un*).

D 3   D 4   D 5

1933–4. *P* 11.

D14	D 3	1 c. violet (5.5.34)	9·00	13·00
D15		2 c. violet (20.12.33)	6·50	3·50
D16		4 c. violet (12.12.33)	11·00	11·00
D17		10 c. violet (20.12.33)	23·00	26·00
D14/17			Set of 4 45·00	48·00

No. D14 exists imperforate (*Price per pair £275, un*).

1935–65. *P* 12.

D18	D 4	1 c. violet (14.10.35)	50	10
D19		2 c. violet (9.9.35)	50	10
D20		3 c. violet (4.65)	3·00	80
D21		4 c. violet (2.7.35)	1·25	10
D22		5 c. violet (12.48)	2·75	45
D23		6 c. violet (1957)	1·50	3·00
D24		10 c. violet (16.9.35)	60	10
D18/24			Set of 7 9·00	8·00

The 1 c., 2 c., 4 c. and 10 c. exist imperforate (*Price £140 for each un pair*).

1967–78. *Litho. P* 12½ × 12 (20 c., 24 c., 50 c.) *or* 12 (*others*).

(a) Size 20 × 17½ mm

D25	D 5	1 c. scarlet (3.67)	1·50	3·25
D26		2 c. scarlet (3.67)	1·00	80
D27		3 c. scarlet (3.67)	1·00	4·00
D28		4 c. scarlet (2.67)	2·25	1·25
D29		5 c. scarlet (3.67)	3·50	3·25
D30		6 c. scarlet (2.67)	1·60	3·75
D31		10 c. scarlet (1.67)	2·00	2·00
D25/31			Set of 7 11·50	17·00

(b) Size 19½×16 mm

D32	D 5	1 c. scarlet (12.70)	30	30
		a. Perf 12½×12 (11.77)	15	90
D33		2 c. scarlet (1972)	75	90
D34		3 c. scarlet (1.74)	2·50	3·00
D35		4 c. scarlet (4.69)	30	40
		a. Printed on the gummed side	£325	
		b. Perf 12½×12 (11.77)	30	90
D36		5 c. scarlet (2.69)	20·00	35·00
		a. Perf 12½×12 (11.77)	30	1·50
D37		6 c. scarlet (1972)	2·75	3·50
D38		8 c. scarlet (1.69)	30	45
		a. Perf 12½×12 (28.6.78)	75	1·40
D39		10 c. scarlet (4.69)	30	45
		a. Perf 12½×12 (9.77)	40	60
D40		12 c. scarlet (1.69)	40	60
		a. Perf 12½×12 (9.77)	80	1·50
D41		16 c. scarlet (1.74)	70	2·75
D42		20 c. scarlet (10.77)	40	1·25
D43		24 c. scarlet (10.77)	40	1·75
D44		50 c. scarlet (10.77)	60	2·25
D32a/44			Set of 13 8·50	18·00

There are no records of dates of issue of the above but supplies were distributed to depots in the months indicated.

Both white and ordinary papers have been used for Nos. D32/41.

The last Postage Due stamps were withdrawn on 30 June 1982.

OFFICIAL STAMPS

Stamps perforated "O H M S" were introduced in May 1923 for use by the Receiver General's department in Ottawa and by the Assistant Receiver Generals' offices in provincial cities. From 1 July 1939 this use was extended to all departments of the federal government and such stamps continued to be produced until replaced by the "O.H.M.S." overprinted issue of 1949.

The perforated initials can appear either upright, inverted or sideways on individual stamps. The prices quoted are for the cheapest version. Stamps perforated with Type O 1 are only priced used. Only isolated examples are known mint and these are very rare.

A number of forged examples of the perforated "O.H.M.S." are known, in particular of Type O 1. Many of these forged perforated initials were applied to stamps which had already been used and this can aid their detection. Genuine examples, postmarked after the perforated initials were applied, often show the cancellation ink bleeding into the holes.

(O 1)	(O 2)
(Five holes in vertical bars of "H")	(Four holes in vertical bars of "H")

1923 (May). *Nos. 196/215 punctured as Type O 1.*

O1	44	1 c. yellow-green	..	..	— 20·00
O2		2 c. carmine	..	..	— 18·00
O3		3 c. deep brown	..	..	— 16·00
O4		5 c. deep blue	..	..	— 20·00
O5		7 c. yellow-ochre	..	..	— 35·00
O6		10 c. reddish purple	..	..	— 35·00
O7		20 c. olive	..	..	— 22·00
O8		50 c. sepia	..	..	— 35·00
O1/8			*Set of 8*		— £180

1923 (May). *50th Anniv of Confederation. No. 244 punctured as Type O 1.*

O9	48	3 c. bistre-brown ..	..	..	— £110

1923 (May)–**31**. *Nos. 246/55 and 263 punctured as Type O 1.*

(a) P 12

O10	44	1 c. chrome-yellow (Die I)	..	..	— 18·00
		a. Die II (1925)	..	..	— 18·00
O11		2 c. deep green	..	..	— 13·00
O12		3 c. carmine (Die I) (12.23)	..	..	— 13·00
		a. Die II (1924)	..	..	— 16·00
O13		4 c. olive-yellow	..	..	— 18·00
O14		5 c. violet	..	..	— 18·00
		a. Thin paper (1924)	..	..	— 22·00
O15		7 c. red-brown (1924) ..	..	..	— 27·00
O16		8 c. blue (1925)	..	..	— 32·00
O17		10 c. blue	..	..	— 22·00
O18		10 c. bistre-brown (1925)	..	..	— 13·00
O19		$1 brown-orange (7.23)	..	..	— 55·00
O10/19			*Set of 10*		— £200

(b) P 12×8

O20	44	3 c. carmine (Die II) (1931)	..	..	— 42·00

1927 (29 June). *60th Anniv of Confederation. Nos. 266/73 punctured as Type O 1. (a) Commemorative issue.*

O21	51	1 c. orange	..	..	— 18·00
O22	52	2 c. green	..	..	— 25·00
O23	53	3 c. carmine	..	..	— 35·00
O24	54	5 c. violet	..	..	— 23·00
O25	55	12 c. blue	..	..	— £140
O21/5			*Set of 5*		— £225

(b) Historical issue

O26	56	5 c. violet	..	..	— 18·00
O27	57	12 c. green	..	..	— £110
O28	58	20 c. carmine	..	..	— 70·00
O26/8			*Set of 3*		— £180

1928 (21 Sept). *Air. No. 274 punctured as Type O 1.*

O29	59	5 c. olive-brown ..	..	..	— 90·00

1928–29. *Nos. 275/85 punctured as Type O 1.*

O30	60	1 c. orange	..	..	— 23·00
O31		2 c. green	..	..	— 15·00
O32		3 c. lake	..	..	— 40·00
O33		4 c. olive-bistre	..	..	— 48·00
O34		5 c. violet	..	..	— 16·00
O35		8 c. blue	..	..	— 45·00
O36	61	10 c. green	..	..	— 13·00
O37	62	12 c. grey-black	..	..	— £120
O38	63	20 c. lake	..	..	— 38·00
O39	64	50 c. blue	..	..	— £110
O40	65	$1 olive-green	..	..	— £100
O30/40			*Set of 11*		— £500

1930–31. *Nos. 288/97, and 300/5 punctured as Type O 1.*

O41	66	1 c. orange (Die I)	..	..	— 23·00
O42		1 c. green (Die I)	..	..	— 13·00
		a. Die II	..	..	— 11·00
O43		2 c. green (Die I)	..	..	— 35·00
O44		2 c. scarlet (Die I)	..	..	— 18·00
		a. Die II	..	..	— 16·00
O45		2 c. deep brown (Die I)	..	..	— 22·00
		a. Die II	..	..	— 18·00
O46		3 c. scarlet	..	..	— 13·00
O47		4 c. yellow-bistre	..	..	— 42·00
O48		5 c. violet	..	..	— 29·00
O49		5 c. deep slate-blue	..	..	— 23·00
O50		8 c. blue	..	..	— 55·00
O51		8 c. red-orange	..	..	— 40·00
O52	67	10 c. olive-green	..	..	— 18·00
O53	68	12 c. grey-black	..	..	— 75·00
O54	69	20 c. red	..	..	— 38·00

O55	70	50 c. blue	..	..	..	— 55·00
O56	71	$1 olive-green	..	..	..	— £130
O41/56			..	*Set of 15*		— £500

1930 (4 Dec). *Air. No. 310 punctured as Type O 1.*

O57	72	5 c. deep brown ..	..	..	— £140

1931 (30 Sept). *No. 312 punctured as Type O 1.*

O58	73	10 c. olive-green	..	..	— 18·00

1932 (22 Feb). *Air. No. 313 punctured as Type O 1.*

O59	59	6 c. on 5 c. olive-brown ..	..	..	— 95·00

1932 (21 June). *Nos. 314/a punctured as Type O 1.*

O60	66	3 c. on 2 c. scarlet (Die I)	..	..	— 30·00
		a. Die II	..	..	— 23·00

1932 (12 July). *Ottawa Conference. Nos. 315/18 punctured as Type O 1. (a) Postage.*

O61	76	3 c. scarlet	..	..	— 15·00
O62	77	5 c. blue	..	..	— 27·00
O63	78	13 c. green	..	..	— £160

(b) Air

O64	72	6 c. on 5 c. deep brown	..	— £120
O61/4			*Set of 4*	— £300

1932–33. *Nos. 319/25 punctured as Type O 1.*

O65	80	1 c. green	..	..	— 13·00
O66		2 c. sepia	..	..	— 13·00
O67		3 c. scarlet	..	..	— 13·00
O68		4 c. yellow-brown	..	..	— 45·00
O69		5 c. blue	..	..	— 20·00
O70		8 c. red-orange	..	..	— 45·00
O71	68	13 c. bright violet	..	..	— 45·00
O65/71			*Set of 7*		— £180

1933 (18 May). *U.P.U. Congress Preliminary Meeting. No. 329 punctured as Type O 1.*

O72	81	5 c. blue	..	..	— 38·00

1933 (24 July). *World's Grain Exhibition and Conference, Regina. No. 330 punctured as Type O 1.*

O73	69	20 c. red	..	..	— 45·00

1933 (17 Aug). *Centenary of First Trans-Atlantic Steamboat Crossing. No. 331 punctured as Type O 1.*

O74	83	5 c. blue..	..	..	— 40·00

1934 (1 July). *Fourth Centenary of Discovery of Canada. No. 332 punctured as Type O 1.*

O75	84	3 c. blue..	..	..	— 45·00

1934 (1 July). *150th Anniv of Arrival of United Empire Loyalists. No. 333 punctured as Type O 1.*

O76	85	10 c. olive-green	..	..	— 48·00

1934 (16 Aug). *150th Anniv of Province of New Brunswick. No. 334 punctured as Type O 1.*

O77	86	2 c. red-brown	..	..	— 60·00

1935 (4 May). *Silver Jubilee. Nos. 335/40 punctured as Type O 1.*

O78	87	1 c. green	..	..	— 25·00
O79	—	2 c. brown	..	..	— 32·00
O80	89	3 c. carmine-red	..	..	— 40·00
O81	—	5 c. blue	..	..	— 38·00
O82	—	10 c. green	..	..	— £110
O83	—	13 c. blue	..	..	— £110
O78/83			*Set of 6*		— £325

1935. *Nos. 341/51 and 355 punctured as Type O 1. (a) Postage*

O84	93	1 c. green	..	..	— 15·00
O85		2 c. brown	..	..	— 28·00
O86		3 c. scarlet	..	..	— 25·00
O87		4 c. yellow	..	..	— 45·00
O88		5 c. blue	..	..	— 25·00
O89		8 c. orange	..	..	— 45·00
O90	94	10 c. carmine	..	..	— 35·00
O91	—	13 c. purple	..	..	— 45·00
O92	—	20 c. olive-green	..	..	— 48·00
O93	—	50 c. deep violet	..	..	— 35·00
O94	—	$1 bright blue	..	..	— 95·00

(b) Air

O95	99	6 c. red-brown	..	..	— 75·00
O84/95			*Set of 12*		— £475

1937 (10 May). *Coronation. No. 356 punctured as Type O 1.*

O96	100	3 c. carmine	..	..	— 40·00

1937–38. *Nos. 357/67, 370 and 371 punctured as Type O 1.*

(a) Postage

O 97	101	1 c. green	..	..	— 2·50
O 98		2 c. brown	..	..	— 2·75
O 99		3 c. scarlet	..	..	— 2·50
O100		4 c. yellow	..	..	— 8·00
O101		5 c. blue	..	..	— 6·50
O102		8 c. orange	..	..	— 13·00
O103	102	10 c. rose-carmine	..	..	— 20·00
		a. Red	..	..	— 23·00

O104	—	13 c. blue	..	..	..	— 28·00
O105	—	20 c. red-brown	..	..	..	— 28·00
O106	—	50 c. green	..	..	..	— 65·00
O107	—	$1 violet	..	..	..	— 95·00
O97/107			..	*Set of 11*		— £250

(b) Coil stamp

O108	101	3 c. scarlet	..	..	..	— 65·00

(c) Air

O109	107	6 c. blue	..	..	..	— 28·00

1939 (15 May). *Royal Visit. Nos. 372/4 punctured as Type O 1.*

O110	108	1 c. black and green	..	..	— 32·00
O111	109	2 c. black and brown	..	..	— 42·00
O112	110	3 c. black and carmine	..	..	— 32·00
O110/12			*Set of 3*		— 95·00

1939 (1 July). *Air. No. 274 punctured as Type O 2.*

O113	59	5 c. olive-brown	..	..	20·00 14·00

1939 (1 July). *Nos. 347/50 and 355 punctured as Type O 2.*

(a) Postage

O114	94	10 c. carmine	..	55·00 38·00
O115	—	13 c. purple	..	60·00 38·00
O116	—	20 c. olive-green	..	75·00 48·00
O117	—	50 c. deep violet	..	60·00 38·00

(b) Air

O118	99	6 c. red-brown	..	50·00 42·00
O114/18			*Set of 5*	£275 £180

1939 (1 July). *Coronation. No. 356 punctured as Type O 2.*

O119	100	3 c. carmine	..	..	70·00 45·00

1939 (1 July). *Nos. 357/67, 369/70 and 371 punctured as Type O 2. (a) Postage*

O120	101	1 c. green	..	..	1·50	10
O121		2 c. brown	..	..	2·25	10
O122		3 c. scarlet	..	..	2·50	10
O123		4 c. yellow	..	..	5·00	2·25
O124		5 c. blue	..	..	3·50	20
O125		8 c. orange	..	..	13·00	4·25
O126	102	10 c. rose-carmine	..	..	48·00	3·25
		a. Red	..	..	7·00	30
O127	—	13 c. blue	..	..	13·00	1·50
O128	—	20 c. red-brown	..	..	35·00	2·00
O129	—	50 c. green	..	..	40·00	8·00
O130	—	$1 violet	..	..	£110	30·00
O120/30			*Set of 11*		£200	42·00

(b) Coil stamps

O131	101	2 c. brown	..	..	70·00 45·00
O132		3 c. scarlet	..	..	70·00 45·00

(c) Air

O133	107	6 c. blue	..	..	3·00	80

1939 (1 July). *Royal Visit. Nos. 372/4 punctured as Type O 2.*

O134	108	1 c. black and green ..	..	80·00 38·00
O135	109	2 c. black and brown	..	80·00 38·00
O136	110	3 c. black and carmine	..	80·00 38·00
O134/6			*Set of 3*	£225 £100

1942–43. *War Effort. Nos. 375/88 and 399/400 punctured as Type O 2. (a) Postage*

O137	111	1 c. green	..	..	40	10
O138	112	2 c. brown	..	..	50	10
O139	113	3 c. carmine-lake	..	..	1·10	40
O140	—	3 c. purple	..	..	60	10
O141	114	4 c. slate	..	..	2·75	75
O142	112	4 c. carmine-lake	..	..	55	10
O143	111	5 c. blue	..	..	1·25	15
O144	—	8 c. red-brown	..	..	7·50	2·00
O145	116	10 c. brown	..	..	4·50	20
O146	117	13 c. dull green	..	..	5·50	5·50
O147	—	14 c. dull green	..	..	9·00	85
O148	—	20 c. chocolate	..	..	11·00	70
O149	—	50 c. violet	..	..	35·00	5·50
O150	—	$1 blue	..	..	90·00	25·00

(b) Air

O151	121	6 c. blue	..	..	3·50	2·00
O152	—	7 c. blue	..	..	3·00	25
O137/52			*Set of 16*		£160	40·00

1946. *Peace Re-conversion. Nos. 401/7 punctured as Type O 2.*

(a) Postage

O153	122	8 c. brown	..	..	9·00	3·50
O154	—	10 c. olive-green	..	..	3·00	15
O155	—	14 c. sepia	..	..	3·75	65
O156	—	20 c. slate	..	..	4·00	50
O157	—	50 c. green	..	..	22·00	5·00
O158	—	$1 purple	..	..	60·00	15·00

(b) Air

O159	—	7 c. blue	..	..	2·50	40
O153/9			*Set of 7*		95·00	23·00

1949. *Nos. 415 and 416 punctured as Type O 2.*

O160	136	2 c. sepia	..	..	75	75
O161	137	3 c. purple	..	..	75	75

STANLEY GIBBONS STAMP COLLECTING SERIES

Introductory booklets on *How to Start, How to Identify Stamps* and *Collecting by Theme.* A series of well illustrated guides at a low price.

Write for details.

O.H.M.S.

(O 3)

1949. *Nos. 375/6, 378, 380 and 402/7 optd as Type O 3 by typography.*

(a) Postage

O162	111	1 c. green	..	1·75	2·00
		a. Missing stop after "S"	..	£140	45·00
O163	112	2 c. brown	..	12·00	12·00
		a. Missing stop after "S"	..	£140	85·00
O164	113	3 c. purple	..	1·25	1·10
O165	112	4 c. carmine-lake	..	2·00	80
O166	—	10 c. olive-green	..	3·75	15
		a. Missing stop after "S"	..	70·00	35·00
O167	—	14 c. sepia	..	4·50	1·75
		a. Missing stop after "S"	..	90·00	45·00
O168	—	20 c. slate	..	12·00	60
		a. Missing stop after "S"	..	£130	50·00
O169	—	50 c. green	..	£160	£120
		a. Missing stop after "S"	..	£800	£500
O170	—	$1 purple	..	45·00	45·00
		a. Missing stop after "S"	..	£1300	

(b) Air

O171	—	7 c. blue	..	24·00	7·00
		a. Missing stop after "S"	..	£130	60·00
O162/71	..		*Set of 10*	£225	£140

Forgeries exist of this overprint. Genuine examples are 2.3×15 mm and show the tops of all letters aligned, as are the stops.

Only a few sheets of the $1 showed the variety, No. O170a.

MISSING STOP VARIETIES. These occur on R. 6/2 of the lower left pane (Nos. O162a, O163a and O176a) or R. 10/2 of the lower left pane (O166a, O167a, O168a, O169a, O170a and O171a). No. O176a also occurs on R. 8/8 of the upper left pane in addition to R. 6/2 of the lower left pane.

1949–50. *Nos. 414/15, 416/17, 418 and 431 optd as Type O 3 by typography.*

O172	135	1 c. green	..	85	85
O173	136	2 c. sepia	..	1·75	1·50
O174	137	3 c. purple	..	1·00	70
O175	138	4 c. carmine-lake	..	1·50	15
O176	139	5 c. blue (1949)	..	2·50	2·00
		a. Missing stop after "S"	..	80·00	38·00
O177	141	50 c. green (1950)	..	32·00	28·00
O172/7	..		*Set of 6*	35·00	30·00

G G G

(O 4)   (O 5)   (O 6)

Type O 6 differs from Type O 5 in having a thinner appearance and an upward sloping left serif to the lower arm. It results from a new plate introduced in 1961/62. Variations in thickness are known in Type O 4 but these are due to wear and subsequent cleaning of the plate. All are produced by typography. Examples showing the "G" applied by lithography are forgeries.

1950 (2 Oct)–52. *Nos. 402/4, 406/7, 414/18 and 431 optd with Type O 4 (1 to 5 c.) or O 5 (7 c. to $1). (a) Postage.*

O178	135	1 c. green	..	70	10
O179	136	2 c. sepia	..	1·50	1·60
O180		2 c. olive-green (11.51)	..	1·75	10
O181	137	3 c. purple	..	1·50	10
O182	138	4 c. carmine-lake	..	1·50	30
O183		4 c. vermilion (1.5.52)	..	1·60	10
O184	139	5 c. blue	..	2·50	30
O185	—	10 c. olive-green	..	3·00	10
O186	—	14 c. sepia	..	11·00	2·25
O187	—	20 c. slate	..	14·00	20
O188	141	50 c. green	..	10·00	8·00
O189	—	$1 purple	..	60·00	55·00

(b) Air

O190	—	7 c. blue	..	24·00	12·00
O178/90	..		*Set of 13*	£120	70·00

1950–51. *Nos. 432/3 optd with Type O 5.*

O191	142	10 c. brown-purple	..	2·25	10
		a. Opt omitted in pair with normal	..	£400	£350
O192	143	$1 ultramarine (1.2.51)	..	55·00	60·00

1952–53. *Nos. 441, 443 and 446 optd with Type O 5.*

O193	153	7 c. blue (3.11.52)	..	1·40	1·25
O194	151	20 c. grey (1.4.52)	..	1·40	10
O195	154	$1 black (2.2.53)	..	10·00	11·00
O193/5	..		*Set of 3*	11·50	11·00

1953 (1 Sept)–61. *Nos. 450/4 and 462 optd with Type O 4 (1 to 5 c.) or O 5 (50 c.).*

O196	158	1 c. purple-brown	..	15	10
O197		2 c. green	..	20	10
O198		3 c. carmine	..	20	10
O199		4 c. violet	..	30	10
O200		5 c. ultramarine	..	30	10
O201	160	50 c. deep bluish green (2.11.53)	..	3·00	1·50
		a. Opt Type O 6 (24.4.61*)	..	2·25	2·25
O196/201	..		*Set of 6*	3·00	1·60

*Earliest recorded date.

1955–56. *Nos. 463/4 and 466/7 optd with Type O 4.*

O202	161	1 c. purple-brown (12.11.56)	..	20	20
O203		2 c. green (19.1.56)	..	15	10
O204		4 c. violet (23.7.56)	..	40	10
O205		5 c. bright blue (11.1.55)	..	15	10
O202/5	..		*Set of 5*	80	30

1955–62. *Nos. 477 and 488 optd with Type O 5.*

O206	165	10 c. purple-brown (21.2.55)	..	40	10
		a. Opt Type O 6 (28.3.62*)	..	40	90
O207	176	20 c. green (4.12.56)	..	1·75	10
		a. Opt Type O 6 (10.4.62*)	..	5·00	40

*Earliest recorded date.

1963 (15 May). *Nos. 527/8 and 530/1 optd as Type O 4.*

O208		1 c. chocolate		40	3·75
O209		2 c. green		40	3·50
		a. Type O 4 omitted (vert pair with normal)		£600	
O210		4 c. carmine-red		40	1·75
O211		5 c. ultramarine		40	90
O208/11			*Set of 4*	1·40	9·00

No. O209a comes from the top row of an upper pane on which the overprint was misplaced downwards by one row. Owing to the margin between the panes the top row of the bottom pane had the overprint at the top of the stamp.

OFFICIAL SPECIAL DELIVERY STAMPS

1923 (May). *Nos. S3/4 punctured as Type O 1.*

OS1	S 1	10 c. yellowish green	..	—	85·00
OS2	S 2	20 c. carmine-red	..	—	70·00

1927 (29 June). *60th Anniv of Confederation. No. S5 punctured as Type O 1.*

OS3	S 3	20 c. orange	..	—	80·00

1930 (2 Sept). *Inscr "TWENTY CENTS" at foot. No. S6 punctured as Type O 1.*

OS4	S 4	20 c. brown-red	..	—	65·00

1932 (24 Dec). *Inscr "CENTS" at foot. No. S7 punctured as Type O 1.*

OS5	S 4	20 c. brown-red	..	—	65·00

1935 (1 June). *No. S8 punctured as Type O 1.*

OS6	S 5	20 c. scarlet	..	—	65·00

1938–39. *Nos. S9/10 punctured as Type O 1.*

OS7	S 6	10 c. green	..	—	32·00
OS8		20 c. scarlet	..	—	60·00

1939 (1 Mar). *No. S11 punctured as Type O 1.*

OS9	S 6	10 c. on 20 c. scarlet	..	—	60·00

1939 (1 July). *Inscr "CENTS" at foot. No. S7 punctured as Type O 2.*

OS10	S 4	20 c. brown-red	..	£150	80·00

1939 (1 July). *No. S8 punctured as Type O 2.*

OS11	S 5	20 c. scarlet	..	85·00	38·00

1939 (1 July). *No. S9 punctured as Type O 2.*

OS12	S 6	10 c. green	..	7·00	4·50

1939 (1 July). *No. S11 punctured as Type O 2.*

OS13	S 6	10 c. on 20 c. scarlet	..	£100	50·00

1942–43. *Nos. S12/14 punctured as Type O 2. (a) Postage*

OS14	S 8	10 c. green	..	9·00	6·50

(b) Air

OS15	S 9	16 c. ultramarine	..	17·00	13·00
OS16		17 c. ultramarine	..	10·00	8·00

1946–47. *Nos. S15/17 punctured as Type O 2. (a) Postage*

OS17	S 10	10 c. green	..	6·50	4·50

(b) Air

OS18	S 11	17 c. ultramarine (circumflex accent)	26·00	22·00
OS19		17 c. ultramarine (grave accent)	..	55·00	55·00

1950. *No. S15 optd as Type O 3, but larger.*

OS20	S 10	10 c. green	..	17·00	21·00

1950 (2 Oct). *No. S15 optd as Type O 4, but larger.*

OS21	S 10	10 c. green	..	26·00	27·00

The use of official stamps was discontinued on 31 December 1963.

The new-issue supplement to this Catalogue appears each month in

GIBBONS STAMP MONTHLY

—from your newsagent or by postal subscription— sample copy and details on request.

Cape of Good Hope *see* South Africa

Cayman Islands

The first post office was opened at Georgetown in April 1889. The stamps of Jamaica with the following cancellations were used until 19 February 1901. At some stage, probably around 1891, a supply of the Jamaica 1889 1d., No. 27, was overprinted "CAYMAN ISLANDS", but these stamps were never issued. Two surviving examples are known, one unused and the other cancelled at Richmond in Jamaica.

Types of Jamaica

2   3   4

8   11

13

PRICES OF NOS. Z1/27. These are for a single stamp showing a clear impression of the postmark. Nos. Z1, 2, 6/8, 11/13, 18, 22 and Z25 are known used on cover and these are worth considerably more.

GEORGETOWN, GRAND CAYMAN

Z 1

Z 2   Z 3

Stamps of JAMAICA cancelled with Type Z 1 in purple.

1889 to 1894.

Z1	8	½d. yellow-green (No. 16)	..		£400
Z2	11	1d. purple and mauve (No. 27)	..		£400
Z2a	2	2d. slate (No. 20a)	..		£3250
Z3	11	2d. green (No. 28)	..		£750
Z4		2½d. dull purple and blue (No. 29)	..		£900
Z5	4	4d. red-orange (No. 22)	..		£1800

Stamps of JAMAICA cancelled with Type Z 2 in purple or black.

1895 to 1898.

Z6	8	½d. yellow-green (No. 16)	..		£450
Z7	11	1d. purple and mauve (No. 27)	..		£375
Z8		2½d. dull purple and blue (No. 29)	..		£650
Z9	3	3d. sage-green (No. 21)	..		£2500

Stamps of JAMAICA cancelled with Type Z 3.

1898 to 1901.

Z10	8	½d. yellow-green (No. 16)	..	..	£375
		a. *Green* (No. 16a)	..	..	£375
Z11	11	1d. purple and mauve (No. 27)	..	..	£375
Z12	13	1d. red (No. 31) (1900)	..	..	£375
Z13	11	2½d. dull purple and blue (No. 29)	..	..	£550

OFFICIAL STAMPS

Stamps of JAMAICA cancelled with Type Z 1 in purple.

1890 to 1894.

Z14	8	½d. green (No. O1) (opt 17–17½ mm long)	..	£750
Z15		½d. green (No. O3) (opt 16 mm long) (1893)		£1200
Z16	11	1d. rose (No. O4)	..	..	£900
Z17		2d. grey (No. O5)	..	..	£1800

Stamps of JAMAICA cancelled with Type Z 2 in purple or black.

1895 to 1898.

Z18	8	½d. green (No. O3)	..	..	£1300
Z19	11	1d. rose (No. O4)	..	..	£2500
Z20		2d. grey (No. O5)	..	..	£2500

STAKE BAY, CAYMAN BRAC

Z 4   Z 5

Stamps of JAMAICA cancelled with Type Z 4.

1898 to 1900.

Z21	8	½d. yellow-green (No. 16)	..	..	£2250
Z22	11	1d. purple and mauve (No. 27)	..	..	£2500
Z23		2d. green (No. 28)	..	..	£3000
Z24		2½d. dull purple and blue (No. 29)	..	..	£2500

Stamps of JAMAICA cancelled with Type Z 5.

1900 to 1901.

Z25	8	½d. yellow-green (No. 16)	..	..	£2500
Z26	11	1d. purple and mauve (No. 27)	..	..	£2000
Z27	13	1d. red (No. 31)	..	..	£2000
Z28	11	2½d. dull purple and blue (No. 29)	..	..	£1800

PRICES FOR STAMPS ON COVER TO 1945

Nos. 1/2	*from* × 25
Nos. 3/12	*from* × 5
Nos. 13/16	*from* × 4
Nos. 17/19	*from* × 10
Nos. 25/34	*from* × 5
Nos. 35/52b	*from* × 4
Nos. 53/67	*from* × 5
Nos. 69/83	*from* × 4
Nos. 84/95	*from* × 6
Nos. 96/9	*from* × 5
Nos. 100/11	*from* × 4
Nos. 112/14	*from* × 6
Nos. 115/26	*from* × 2

DEPENDENCY OF JAMAICA

1   2   3

(T 1/3, 8/9 and 12/13 typo D.L.R.)

1900 (Nov). *Wmk Crown CA. P 14.*

1	1	½d. deep green	..	6·50	15·00
		a. *Pale green*	..	3·00	11·00
2		1d. rose-carmine	..	2·50	1·40
		a. *Pale carmine*	..	8·00	7·50
1/2	Optd "Specimen"	..		90·00	

Dented frame under "A" (R. 1/6 of left pane)

1902 (Jan)–**03**. *Wmk Crown CA. P 14.*

3	2	½d. green (15.9.02)	..	4·00	23·00
		a. Dented frame	..	70·00	
4		1d. carmine (6.3.03)	..	7·50	7·00
		a. Dented frame	..	95·00	

5	2	2½d. bright blue	..	..	7·00	10·00
		a. Dented frame	..	£100	
6		6d. brown ..	..	25·00	50·00
		a. Dented frame	..	£200	
7	3	1s. orange	..	60·00	£100
		a. Dented frame	..	£300	
3/7			Set of 5	95·00	£170
3/7	Optd "Specimen"		Set of 5	£160	

1905 (Feb–18 Oct). *Wmk Mult Crown CA. P 14.*

8	2	½d. green	..	4·00	5·50
		a. Dented frame	..	60·00	
9		1d. carmine (18 Oct)	..	12·00	16·00
		a. Dented frame	..	£150	
10		2½d. bright blue	..	4·25	3·00
		a. Dented frame	..	75·00	
11		6d. brown	..	16·00	35·00
		a. Dented frame	..	£190	
12	3	1s. orange	..	32·00	48·00
		a. Dented frame	..	£250	
8/12			Set of 5	60·00	95·00

1907 (13 Mar). *Wmk Mult Crown CA. P 14.*

13	3	4d. brown and blue	..	25·00	45·00
		a. Dented frame ..	..	£200	
14	2	6d. olive and rose	..	25·00	50·00
		a. Dented frame	..	£200	
15	3	1s. violet and green	..	42·00	60·00
		a. Dented frame	..	£275	
16		5s. salmon and green	..	£170	£275
		a. Dented frame ..	..	£950	
13/16			Set of 4	£225	£375
13/16	Optd "Specimen"	..	Set of 4	£180	

One Halfpenny.   ½D   1D

(4)   (5)   (6)

1907 (30 Aug). *No. 9 surch at Govt Printing Office, Kingston, with T 4.*

17	2	½d. on 1d. carmine	..	38·00	55·00
		a. Dented frame	..	£325	

1907 (Nov). *No. 16 handstamped at Georgetown P.O. with T 5 or 6.*

18	3	½d. on 5s. salmon and green (26 Nov)	£225	£300
		a. Surch inverted	..	£22000	
		b. Surch double	..	£9000	£9000
		c. Surch double, one inverted ..		
		d. Surch omitted (in pair with normal)	£32000	
		e. Dented frame	..	£900	
19		1d. on 5s. salmon and green (23 Nov)	£225	£300
		a. Surch double	..	£14000	
		b. Surch inverted	..	£35000	
		c. Dented frame	..	£950	

The ½d. on 5s. may be found with the figures "1" or "2" omitted, owing to defective handstamping.

8   9   2½D

(10)

1907 (27 Dec)–**09**. *Chalk-surfaced paper (3d. to 10s.). P 14.*

(a) Wmk Mult Crown CA

25	8	½d. green	..	1·25	3·25
26		1d. carmine	..	1·00	65
27		2½d. ultramarine (30.3.08)	..	2·75	3·50
28	9	3d. purple/*yellow* (30.3.08)	..	2·75	6·50
29		4d. black and red/*yellow* (30.3.08)	..	48·00	60·00
30	8	6d. dull and bright purple (2.10.08)	..	6·50	28·00
		a. *Dull purple and violet-purple*	..	27·00	45·00
31	9	1s. black/*green* (5.4.09)	..	5·50	17·00
32		5s. green and red/*yellow* (30.3.08)	..	35·00	55·00

(b) Wmk Crown CA (30.3.08)

33	9	1s. black/*green* ..	..	48·00	70·00
34	8	10s. green and red/*green*	..	£160	£225
25/34			Set of 10	£250	£400
25/34	(except 31) Optd "Specimen" ..	Set of 9	£275	

1908 (12 Feb). *No. 13 handstamped locally with T 10.*

35	3	2½d. on 4d. brown and blue	£1500	£2250
		a. Surch double	..	£30000	£18000
		b. Dented frame	..	£7500	

No. 35 should only be purchased when accompanied by an expert committee's certificate or similar form of guarantee.

MANUSCRIPT PROVISIONALS. During May and June 1908 supplies of ½d. and 1d. stamps became exhausted, and the payment of postage was indicated by the Postmistress, Miss Gwendolyn Parsons, using a manuscript endorsement. Such endorsements were in use from 12 May to 1 June.

Price on cover

MP1	"(Postage Paid G.A.P.)" (12 May to 1 June)	..	£2500
MP1a	"(Postage Paid G.A.P.)" (½ or 1d." (23 May)		£3750

In October of the same year there was a further shortage of ¼d. stamps and the manuscript endorsements were again applied by either the new Postmaster, William Graham McCausland, or by Miss Parsons who remained as his assistant.

MP2	"Pd W.G. McC." (4 to 27 October) ..	..	£1500
MP2a	"¼ Pd./W.G. McC" (14 October)	..	£1000
MP3	"Paid" (7 October)	..	£5500
MP4	"Pd ¼" (8 October)	..	£4500
MP5	"(Paid ¼GAP. asst.)" (15 October)	..	£4000

No. MP2 exists in different inks and formats.

Manuscript endorsement for the 2½d. rate is also known, but this is thought to have been done by oversight.

A 1d. surcharge on 4d. (No. 29), issued in mid-May, was intended as a revenue stamp and was never authorised for postal use (*price £225 un.*). Used examples were either cancelled by favour or passed through the post in error. Exists with surcharge inverted (*price £1600 un.*), surcharge double (*price £2500 un.*) or surcharge double, both inverted (*price £2500 un.*).

11   12   13

1908 (30 June)–**09**. *Wmk Mult Crown CA. Litho. P 14.*

38	11	¼d. brown (Optd S. £65)	..	75	30
		a. *Grey-brown* (2.09)	..	1·50	75

1912 (24 Apr)–**20**. *Die I. Wmk Mult Crown CA. Chalk-surfaced paper (3d. to 10s.). P 14.*

40	13	¼d. brown (10.2.13)	..	60	30
41	12	½d. green	..	2·50	4·00
42		1d. red (25.2.13)	..	3·25	2·00
43	13	2d. pale grey	..	80	7·00
44	12	2½d. bright blue (26.8.14)	..	7·00	8·00
		a. *Deep bright blue* (9.11.17)	..	15·00	22·00
45	13	3d. purple/*yellow* (26.11.14)	..	11·00	35·00
		a. *White back* (19.11.13)	..	3·00	
		b. *On lemon* (12.3.18) (Optd S. £50)	..	2·00	16·00
		c. *On orange-buff* (1920)	..	9·00	27·00
		d. *On buff* (1920)	..		
		e. *On pale yellow* (1920)	..	3·50	27·00
46		4d. black and red/*yellow* (25.2.13)	..	75	7·00
47	12	6d. dull and bright purple (25.2.13)	..	3·00	6·00
48	13	1s. black/*green* (15.5.16) (Optd S. £50)	..	3·50	23·00
		a. *White back* (19.11.13)	..	2·25	2·75
49		2s. purple and bright blue/*blue*	..	9·50	45·00
50		3s. green and violet	..	19·00	60·00
51		5s. green and red/*yellow* (26.8.14)	..	70·00	£130
52	12	10s. deep green and red/*green* (26.11.14) (Optd S. £80)	..	85·00	£160
		a. *White back* (19.11.13)	..	80·00	£140
		b. *On blue-green, olive back* (5.10.18)	70·00	£160
40/52b			Set of 13	£170	£375
40/4, 45a, 46/7, 48a, 49/51, 52a Optd "Specimen"	Set of 13	£325			

WAR STAMP.   WAR STAMP.

1½d   1½d   1½d

(14)   (15)   Straight serif (Left-hand pane R. 10/2)

1917 (26 Feb). *T 12 surch with T 14 or 15 at Kingston, Jamaica.*

53	14	1½d. on 2½d. deep blue	..	4·25	7·50
		a. No fraction bar	..	70·00	£120
		b. Missing stop after "STAMP" (R.1/4)	£275	
54	15	1½d. on 2½d. deep blue	..	1·00	4·25
		a. No fraction bar	..	42·00	85·00
		b. Straight serif	..	50·00	£100

On No. 53 "WAR STAMP" and "1½d." were applied separately.

WAR STAMP   WAR STAMP   WAR STAMP

1½d   1½ᵈ   1½d.

(16)   (17)   (18)

1917 (4 Sept). *T 12 surch with T 16 or 17 by D.L.R.*

55	16	1½d. on 2½d. deep blue	..	£650	£1800
56	17	1½d. on 2½d. deep blue (Optd S. £100)	20	40
		x. Wmk reversed	..	75·00	

De La Rue replaced surcharge Type 16 by Type 17 after only a few sheets as it did not adequately obliterate the original face value. A small quantity, said to be 3½ sheets, of Type 16 was included in the consignment in error.

1919–20. *T 12 and 13 (2½d. special printing), optd only, or surch in addition at Kingston (No. 58) or by D.L.R. (others).*

57	16	½d. green (4.2.19)	..	20	1·50
		a. Short opt (right pane R. 10/1)	..	20·00	
58	18	1½d. on 2d. grey (10.3.20)	..	1·25	6·00
59	17	1½d. on 2½d. orange (4.12.19)	..	60	80
57, 59	Optd "Specimen"		Set of 2	£80·00	

In T 16 the "R" of "WAR" has a curved foot and the other letters vary slightly from T 17. "1½d." is in thin type. In T 17 the "R" has a straight foot, and the "1½d." differs.

The ½d. stamps on *buff* paper, and later consignments of the 2d. T 13 on *pink*ish, derived their colour from the paper in which they were packed for despatch from England.

No. 57a shows the overprint 2 mm high instead of 2½ mm.

A further surcharge as No. 58, but in red, was prepared in Jamaica during April 1920, but these were not issued.

19   20 King William IV and King George V

1921 (4 Apr)–26. P 14. (a) Wmk Mult Crown CA.
60	19	3d. purple/orange-buff ..	..	1·50	7·00
		aw. Wmk inverted	..	50·00	
		ay. Wmk inverted and reversed		50·00	
		b. Purple/pale yellow	..	45·00	60·00
		bw. Wmk inverted	..		
62		4d. red/yellow (1.4.22)	..	80	3·75
63		1s. black/green	..	1·25	8·50
		x. Wmk reversed	..		
64		5s. yellow-green/pale yellow	..	16·00	60·00
		a. Deep green/pale yellow	..	55·00	90·00
		b. Blue-green/pale yellow	..	60·00	£100
		c. Deep green/orange-buff (19.11.21)		85·00	£140
67		10s. carmine/green (19.11.21)	..	55·00	90·00
60/7			Set of 5	70·00	£150
60/7 Optd "Specimen"			Set of 5	£180	

(b) Wmk Mult Script CA
69	19	¼d. yellow-brown (1.4.22)	..	40	1·00
		w. Wmk inverted			
70		½d. pale grey-green (1.4.22)	..	50	25
		w. Wmk inverted			
		y. Wmk inverted and reversed			
71		1d. deep carmine-red (1.4.22)	..	95	85
72		1½d. orange-brown	..	1·75	20
73		2d. slate-grey (1.4.22)	..	1·75	3·25
74		2½d. bright blue (1.4.22)	..	50	45
		x. Wmk reversed			
75		3d. purple/yellow (29.6.23)	..	50	2·50
		w. Wmk inverted			
		y. Wmk inverted and reversed		50·00	
76		4½d. sage-green (29.6.23)	..	1·50	3·00
77		6d. claret (1.4.22)	..	5·50	27·00
		a. Deep claret ..		19·00	35·00
79		1s. black/green (15.5.25)	..	7·00	28·00
80		2s. violet (1.4.22) ..	..	13·00	18·00
81		3s. violet (1.4.22)	..	21·00	15·00
82		5s. green/yellow (15.2.25)	..	24·00	40·00
83		10s. carmine/green (5.9.26)	..	55·00	70·00
69/83			Set of 14	£120	£180
69/83 Optd "Specimen"			Set of 14	£325	

"A.S.R." PROVISIONAL. On the night of 9/10 November 1932 the Cayman Brac Post Office at Stake Bay, and its contents, was destroyed by a hurricane. Pending the arrival of replacement stamp stocks and cancellation the Postmaster, Mr. A. S. Rutty, initialled covers to indicate that postage had been paid. Those destined for overseas addresses additionally received a "Postage Paid" machine postmark in red when they passed through Kingston, Jamaica.

Price on cover

MP6 Endorsed "A.S.R." in manuscript .. £4000
MP7 Endorsed "A.S.R." in manuscript and "Postage Paid" machine postmark in red .. £6500
These emergency arrangements lasted until 19 December.

(Recess Waterlow)

1932 (5 Dec). Centenary of the "Assembly of Justices and Vestry". Wmk Mult Script CA. P 12½.
84	20	¼d. brown	..	1·00	90
		a. "A" of "CA" missing from wmk	£1000	
85		½d. green	..	2·25	7·00
		a. "A" of "CA" reversed in wmk	£1200	
86		1d. scarlet	..	2·25	5·00
87		1½d. red-orange	..	2·00	1·75
88		2d. grey	..	1·75	2·25
89		2½d. ultramarine	..	1·75	1·00
90		3d. olive-green	..	2·25	3·50
91		6d. purple	..	8·00	18·00
92		1s. black and brown	..	15·00	27·00
93		2s. black and ultramarine	..	42·00	70·00
94		5s. black and green	..	80·00	£120
95		10s. black and scarlet	..	£250	£350
84/95			Set of 12	£350	£500
84/95 Perf "Specimen"			Set of 12	£450	

No. 85a shows one "A" of the watermark reversed so that its head points to right when seen from the back. It is believed that this stamp may also exist with the "A" missing. An example of the 1½d., No. 87, is known with the "A" missing from a watermark in the right-hand sheet margin.

Examples of all values are known showing a forged George Town postmark dated "DE 31 1932".

21 Cayman Islands   24 Queen or Pink Conch Shells

(Recess Waterlow)

1935 (1 May)–36. T 21, 24 and similar designs. Wmk Mult Script CA. P 12½.
96	21	¼d. black and brown	..	30	80
97		½d. ultramarine & yellow-green (1.1.36)	1·00	1·00
98		1d. ultramarine and scarlet	..	2·75	2·25
99	24	1½d. black and orange	..	1·50	1·75
100		2d. ultramarine and purple	..	3·00	1·10
101		2½d. blue and black (1.1.36)	..	3·00	1·25
102	21	3d. black and olive-green	..	2·00	2·75
103		6d. bright purple and black (1.1.36)	8·50	4·00
104		1s. ultramarine and orange (1.1.36)	5·50	6·50
105		2s. ultramarine and black	..	45·00	32·00
106		5s. green and black	..	48·00	48·00
107	24	10s. black and scarlet	..	65·00	80·00
96/107			Set of 12	£150	£160
96/107 Perf "Specimen"			Set of 12	£180	

Designs: Horiz—½d., 2d., 1s. Cat boat; 1d., 2s. Red-footed Booby; 2½d., 6d. 5s. Hawksbill Turtles.

Examples of all values are known showing a forged George Town postmark dated "AU 23 1936"

1935 (6 May). Silver Jubilee. As Nos. 91/4 of Antigua.
108		½d. black and green	..	15	50
		f. Diagonal line by turret	..	23·00	
		h. Dot by flagstaff	..	35·00	
109		2½d. brown and deep blue	..	90	1·00
110		6d. light blue and olive-green	..	1·00	3·00
		h. Dot by flagstaff	..	£110	
		i. Dash by turret	..	£110	
111		1s. slate and purple	..	5·50	5·50
		h. Dot by flagstaff	..	£170	
		i. Dash by turret	..	£180	
108/11			Set of 4	7·00	9·00
108/11 Perf "Specimen"			Set of 4	85·00	

For illustrations of plate varieties see Catalogue Introduction.

1937 (13 May). Coronation Issue. As Nos. 95/7 of Antigua. P 11×11½.
112		½d. green	..	30	20
113		1d. carmine ..	..	50	20
114		2½d. blue ..	..	30	20
112/14			Set of 3	1·60	70
112/14 Perf "Specimen"			Set of 3	75·00	

26 Beach View   27 Dolphin (fish) (Coryphaena hippurus)

(Recess D.L.R. (½d., 2d., 6d., 1s., 10s.), Waterlow (others))

1938 (5 May)–48. T 26/7 and similar designs. Wmk Mult Script CA (sideways on ¼d., 1d., 1½d., 2½d., 3d., 2s., 5s.). Various perfs.
115	26	¼d. red-orange (p 12½)	..	30	55
		a. Perf 13½×12½ (16.7.43)	10	55
116	27	½d. green (p 13×11½)	..	75	55
		a. Perf 14 (16.7.43)	1·25	1·40
		ab. "A" of "CA" missing from wmk	£1000	
117	—	1d. scarlet (p 12½)	..	30	75
118	26	1½d. black (p 12½)	..	30	10
119	—	2d. violet (p 11½×13)	..	1·75	40
		a. Perf 14 (16.7.43)	60	30
120	—	2½d. bright blue (p 12½)	..	40	20
120a		2½d. orange (p 12½) (25.8.47)	1·50	50
121	—	3d. orange (p 12½)	..	40	15
121a		3d. bright blue (p 12½) (25.8.47)	1·50	30
122	—	6d. olive-green (p 11½×13)	8·00	4·00
		a. Perf 14 (16.7.43)	2·00	1·25
		b. Brownish olive (p 11½×13) (8.7.47)	3·00	1·50
123	27	1s. red-brown (p 13×11½)	4·25	1·50
		a. Perf 14 (16.7.43)	4·00	2·00
124	26	2s. yellow-green (shades) (p 12½)	48·00	14·00
		a. Deep green (16.7.43)	25·00	9·00
125	—	5s. carmine-lake (p 12½)	32·00	15·00
		a. Crimson (1948)	50·00	21·00
126	—	10s. chocolate (p 11½×13)	23·00	9·00
		a. Perf 14 (16.7.43)	21·00	9·00
115/26a			Set of 14	80·00	35·00
115/26 Perf "Specimen"			Set of 14	£275	

Designs: Horiz (as T 26)—1d., 3d. Cayman Islands map; 2½d., 5s. Rembro (schooner). Vert (as T 27)—2d., 6d., 10s. Hawksbill Turtles.

Stop after "1946" (R.2/1)

1946 (26 Aug). Victory. As Nos. 110/11 of Antigua.
127		1½d. black	..	20	10
128		3d. orange-yellow	..	20	10
		a. Stop after "1946"	..	14·00	
127/8 Perf "Specimen"			Set of 2	65·00	

1948 (29 Nov). Royal Silver Wedding. As Nos. 112/13 of Antigua.
129		½d. green	..	10	10
130		10s. violet-blue	..	12·00	10·00

1949 (10 Oct). 75th Anniv of Universal Postal Union. As Nos. 114/17 of Antigua.
131		2½d. orange	..	30	30
132		3d. deep blue	..	1·50	90
133		6d. olive	..	60	1·00
134		1s. red-brown	..	60	30
131/4			Set of 4	2·75	2·25

31 Cat Boat   32 Coconut Grove, Cayman Brac

(Recess B.W.)

1950 (2 Oct). T 31/2 and similar horiz designs. Wmk Mult Script CA. P 11½ × 11.
135		¼d. bright blue and pale scarlet	..	15	60
136		½d. reddish violet and emerald-green	15	1·25
137		1d. olive-green and deep blue	..	60	50
138		1½d. green and brown	..	30	75
139		2d. reddish violet and rose-carmine	1·00	1·50
140		2½d. turquoise and black	..	60	50
141		3d. bright green and light blue	..	1·40	1·50
142		6d. red-brown and blue	..	2·00	1·25
143		9d. scarlet and grey-green ..	..	3·50	2·00
144		1s. brown and orange	..	3·25	2·75
145		2s. violet and reddish purple	..	7·50	8·50
146		5s. olive-green and violet ..	..	11·00	75
147		10s. black and scarlet	..	14·00	12·00
135/47			Set of 13	40·00	35·00

Designs:—1d. Green Turtle; 1½d. Thatch rope industry; 2d. Cayman seamen; 2½d. Map of Cayman Islands; 3d. Parrotfish; 6d. Bluff, Cayman Brac; 9d. Georgetown harbour; 1s. Turtle in "crawl"; 2s. Ziroma (schooner); 5s. Boat-building; 10s. Government Offices, Grand Cayman.

44 South Sound Lighthouse, Grand Cayman   45 Queen Elizabeth II

1953 (2 Mar)–62. Designs previously used for King George VI issue but with portrait of Queen Elizabeth II as in T 44/5. Wmk Mult Script CA. P 11½×11 or 11×11½ (4d., £1).
148		¼d. deep bright blue & rose-red (21.2.55)	85	50
		a. Bright blue and bright rose-red (5.12.56)	1·50	90
149		½d. purple and bluish green (7.7.54)	20	50
150		1d. brown-olive and indigo (7.7.54)	70	40
151		1½d. deep green and red-brown (7.7.54)	50	20
152		2d. reddish violet and cerise (2.6.54)	3·00	55
153		2½d. turquoise-blue and black (2.6.54)	3·50	80
154		3d. bright green and blue (21.2.55)	4·00	60
155		4d. black and deep blue	..	2·00	40
		a. Black and greenish blue (13.10.54)	17·00	17·00
		b. Black and deep bright blue (10.7.62)	14·00	14·00
156		6d. lake-brown and deep blue (7.7.54)	1·75	30
157		9d. scarlet and bluish green (2.6.54)	3·50	30
158		1s. brown and red-orange (21.2.55)	3·25	20
159		2s. slate-violet & reddish purple (21.2.55)	11·00	7·50
160		5s. olive-green and slate-violet (21.2.55)	14·00	4·50
161		10s. black and rose-red (21.2.55) ..	14·00	7·50
161a		£1 blue (6.1.59) ..	..	32·00	10·00
148/61a			Set of 15	90·00	35·00

Designs: Horiz—¼d. Cat boat; ½d. Coconut grove, Cayman Brac; 1d. Green Turtle; 1½d. Thatch rope industry; 2d. Cayman seamen; 2½d. Map of Cayman Islands; 3d. Parrotfish; 6d. Bluff, Cayman Brac; 9d. Georgetown harbour; 1s. Turtle in "crawl"; 2s. Ziroma (schooner); 5s. Boat-building; 10s. Government Offices, Grand Cayman.

1953 (2 June). Coronation. As No. 120 of Antigua, but ptd by B.W.
162		1d. black and emerald	..	30	80

46 Arms of the Cayman Islands

(Photo D.L.R.)

1959 (4 July). New Constitution. Wmk Mult Script CA. P 12.
163	46	2½d. black and light blue	..	45	1·10
164		1s. black and orange	..	55	30

CROWN COLONY

47 Cuban Amazon   48 Cat Boat

(Recess B.W.)

1962 (28 Nov)–64. T 47/8 and similar designs. W w 12. P 11×11½ (vert) or 11½×11 (horiz).
165		¼d. emerald and red	..	30	70
		a. Emerald and rose (18.2.64)	1·75	2·00
166		1d. black and yellow-olive	..	50	20
167		1½d. yellow and purple	..	2·75	80
168		2d. blue and deep brown	..	60	30
169		2½d. violet and bluish green	..	85	80
170		3d. bright blue and carmine	..	30	10
171		4d. deep green and purple	..	80	60
172		6d. bluish green and sepia	..	3·25	30

173	9d. ultramarine and purple	.. ..		1·25	40
174	1s. sepia and rose-red	.. ..		80	10
175	1s. 3d. bluish green and orange-brown			3·50	1·75
176	1s. 9d. deep turquoise and violet	..		12·00	1·10
177	5s. plum and deep green	.. ..		7·00	4·75
178	10s. olive and blue	.. ..		13·00	8·00
179	£1 carmine and black	.. ..		19·00	15·00
165/79			Set of 15	55·00	30·00

Designs: Horiz—1½d. Schomburgkia thomsoniana (orchid); 2d. Map of Cayman Islands; 2½d. Fisherman casting net; 3d. West Bay Beach; 4d. Green Turtle; 6d. Lydia E. Wilson (schooner); 1s. Iguana; 1s. 3d. Swimming Pool, Cayman Brac; 1s. 9d. Water sports; 5s. Fort George. Vert—9d. Angler with King Mackerel; 10s. Coat of Arms; £1 Queen Elizabeth II.

1963 (4 June). Freedom from Hunger. As No. 146 of Antigua.
180	1s. 9d. carmine	.. ..	30	15

1963 (2 Sept). Red Cross Centenary. As Nos. 147/8 of Antigua.
181	1d. red and black	.. ..	15	40
182	1s. 9d. red and blue	.. ..	70	1·50

1964 (23 April). 400th Birth Anniv of William Shakespeare. As No. 164 of Antigua.
183	6d. magenta	.. ..	10	10

1965 (17 May). I.T.U. Centenary. As Nos. 166/7 of Antigua.
184	1d. blue and light purple	..	15	10
185	1s. 3d. bright purple and green	..	40	25

1965 (25 Oct). International Co-operation Year. As Nos. 168/9 of Antigua.
186	1d. reddish purple and turquoise-green	10	10
187	1s. deep bluish green and lavender	..	40	25

1966 (24 Jan). Churchill Commemoration. As Nos. 170/3 of Antigua.
188	¼d. new blue	.. ..	10	65
	w. Wmk inverted	.. ..	22·00	
189	1d. deep green	.. ..	20	10
190	1s. brown	..	50	10
	w. Wmk inverted	..	4·50	5·00
191	1s. 9d. bluish violet	..	70	65
188/91		Set of 4	1·25	1·25

1966 (4 Feb). Royal Visit. As Nos. 174/5 of Antigua.
192	1d. black and ultramarine	..	60	10
193	1s. 9d. black and magenta	..	2·25	45

1966 (1 July). World Cup Football Championships. As Nos. 176/7 of Antigua.
194	1½d. violet, yellow-green, lake & yellow-brn	10	10
195	1s. 9d. chocolate, blue-grn, lake & yell-brn	40	25

1966 (20 Sept). Inauguration of W.H.O. Headquarters, Geneva. As Nos. 178/9 of Antigua.
196	2d. black, yellow-green and light blue	50	15
197	1s. 3d. black, light purple and yellow-brown	1·25	60

62 Telephone and Map

(Des V. Whiteley. Litho Harrison)

1966 (5 Dec). International Telephone Links. W w **12**. P 14½ × 14.
198	**62** 4d. red, black, greenish blue & ol-grn	20	15
199	9d. violet-blue, black, brown-red & lt grn	20	15

1966 (12 Dec*). 20th Anniv of U.N.E.S.C.O. As Nos. 196/8 of Antigua.
200	1d. slate-violet, red, yellow and orange	15	10
201	1s. 9d. orange-yellow, violet and deep olive	45	10
202	5s. black, bright purple and orange	1·25	55
200/2		Set of 3	1·75	65

*This is the local date of issue; the Crown Agents released the stamps on 1 December.

63 B.A.C. One Eleven 200/400 Airliner over Cayman Schooner

(Des V. Whiteley. Photo Harrison)

1966 (17 Dec). Opening of Cayman Jet Service. W w **12**. P 14½.
203	**63** 1s. black, new blue and olive-green	40	30
204	1s. 9d. deep purple-brown, ultramarine and emerald	40	35

64 Water-skiing

(Des G. Vasarhelyi. Photo Harrison)

1967 (1 Dec). International Tourist Year. T **64** and similar horiz designs. Multicoloured. W w **12**. P 14½ × 14.
205	4d. Type 64	..	40	10
	a. Gold omitted	..	£180	
206	6d. Skin diving	..	40	25
207	1s. Sport fishing	..	40	25
208	1s. 9d. Sailing	..	55	55
205/8		Set of 4	1·60	1·00

A used copy of No. 207 is known with yellow omitted.

68 Former Slaves and Emblem

(Des and photo Harrison)

1968 (3 June). Human Rights Year. W w **12**. P 14½ × 14.
209	**68** 3d. deep bluish green, black and gold	10	10
	w. Wmk inverted		60	80
210	9d. brown, gold and myrtle-green	10	10
211	5s. ultramarine, gold and myrtle-green	30	55
209/11		Set of 3	40	65

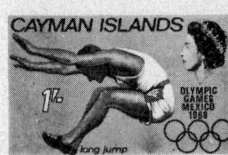

69 Long-jumping

(Des R. Granger Barrett. Litho P.B.)

1968 (1 Oct). Olympic Games, Mexico. T **69** and similar multicoloured designs. W w **12**. P 13½.
212	1s. Type 69	..	10	10
213	1s. 3d. High jumping	..	15	25
214	2s. Pole vaulting (vert)	..	15	30
212/14		Set of 3	30	50

72 "The Adoration of the Shepherds" (Fabritius)

(Des and photo Harrison)

1968–69. Christmas. T **72** and similar horiz design. Centres multicoloured; country name and frames in gold; value and background in colours given. P 14 × 14½.

(a) W w **12**. (18.11.68)
215	**72** ¼d. brown	..	10	20
	a. Gold omitted	..	£190	
216	1d. bluish violet	..	10	10
217	**72** 6d. bright blue	..	15	10
218	8d. cerise	..	15	15
219	**72** 1s. 3d. bright green	..	20	25
220	2s. grey	..	25	35

(b) No wmk (8.1.69)
221	**72** ¼d. bright purple	..	10	20
215/21		Set of 7	80	1·10

Design:—1d., 8d., 2s. "The Adoration of the Shepherds" (Rembrandt).

74 Grand Cayman Thrush

76 Arms of the Cayman Islands

(Des G. Vasarhelyi. Litho Format)

1969 (5 June). Designs as T **74** and T **76** in black, ochre and red (£1) or multicoloured (others). No wmk. P 14.
222	¼d. Type 74	..	10	75
223	1d. Brahmin Cattle (horiz)	..	10	10
224	2d. Blowholes on the coast (horiz)	10	10
225	2½d. Map of Grand Cayman (horiz)	15	10
226	3d. Georgetown scene (horiz)	15	10
227	4d. Royal Poinciana (horiz)	30	10
228	6d. Cayman Brac and Little Cayman on Chart (horiz)	30	10
229	8d. Motor vessels at berth (horiz)	40	10
230	1s. Basket-making (horiz)	20	10
231	1s. 3d. Beach scene (horiz)	35	1·50
232	1s. 6d. Straw-rope making (horiz)	50	1·25
233	2s. Great Barracuda (horiz)	1·25	80
234	4s. Government House (horiz)	50	80
235	10s. Type 76	..	1·00	2·25
236	£1 Queen Elizabeth II (vert)	1·75	2·50
222/36		Set of 15	6·00	9·00

1969 (11 Aug). As No. 222, but wmk w **12** (sideways).
237	**74** ¼d. multicoloured	..	30	65

(New Currency. 100 cents = 1 dollar.)

C·DAY
8th September 1969   ¼c=

(89)

1969 (8 Sept). Decimal Currency. No. 237, and as Nos. 223/36, but wmk w **12** (sideways on horiz designs), surch as T **89**.
238	¼ c. on ¼d. Type 74	..	10	75
239	1 c. on 1d. Brahmin Cattle	..	10	10
240	2 c. on 2d. Blowholes on the coast	10	10
241	3 c. on 4d. Royal Poinciana	..	10	10
242	4 c. on 2½d. Map of Grand Cayman	10	10
243	5 c. on 6d. Cayman Brac and Little Cayman on Chart	10	10
244	7 c. on 8d. Motor vessels at berth	10	10
245	8 c. on 3d. Georgetown scene	15	10
246	10 c. on 1s. Basket-making	25	10
247	12 c. on 1s. 3d. Beach scene	35	90
248	15 c. on 1s. 6d. Straw-rope making	45	60
249	20 c. on 2s. Great Barracuda	1·25	1·50
250	40 c. on 4s. Government House	45	80
251	$1 on 10s. Type 76	..	1·50	2·25
	w. Wmk inverted			
252	$2 on £1 Queen Elizabeth II	2·00	3·25
238/52		Set of 15	6·00	9·00

90 "Virgin and Child" (Vivarini)

92 "Noli me tangere" (Titian)

(Des adapted by G. Drummond. Photo Harrison)

1969 (14 Nov*). Christmas. Multicoloured; background colours given. W w **12** (sideways on 1, 7 and 20 c.). P 14½.
253	**90** ¼ c. orange-red	..	10	10
	w. Wmk inverted	..	3·50	5·00
254	¼ c. magenta	..	10	10
	w. Wmk inverted	..	3·50	5·00
255	¼ c. emerald	..	10	10
	a. Gold frame omitted		£150	
	w. Wmk inverted	..	1·00	1·75
256	¼ c. new blue	..	10	10
	w. Wmk inverted	..	3·50	5·00
257	— 1 c. ultramarine	..	10	10
258	**90** 5 c. orange-red	..	10	10
259	— 7 c. myrtle-green	..	10	10
260	**90** 12 c. emerald	..	15	15
261	— 20 c. brown-purple	..	20	25
253/61		Set of 9	45	45

Design:—1, 7, 20 c. "The Adoration of the Kings" (Gossaert).

*This is the local release date. The Crown Agents released the stamps on 4 November.

(Des L. Curtis. Litho D.L.R.)

1970 (23 Mar). Easter. Paintings multicoloured; frame colours given. P 14.
262	**92** ¼ c. carmine-red	..	10	10
263	¼ c. deep green	..	10	10
264	¼ c. yellow-brown	..	10	10
265	¼ c. pale violet	..	10	10
266	10 c. chalky blue	..	25	10
267	12 c. chestnut	..	30	10
268	40 c. plum	..	40	45
262/8		Set of 7	90	60

STANLEY GIBBONS STAMP COLLECTING SERIES

Introductory booklets on How to Start, How to Identify Stamps and Collecting by Theme. A series of well illustrated guides at a low price.
Write for details.

93 Barnaby (*Barnaby Rudge*)

97 Grand Cayman Thrush

(Des Jennifer Toombs. Photo Harrison)

1970 (17 June). *Death Centenary of Charles Dickens. T 93 and similar vert designs. W w 12 (sideways*). P 14½×14.*

269	1 c. black, olive-green and greenish yellow	10	10
	w. Wmk Crown to right of CA	—	3·00
270	12 c. black, lake-brown and red	20	10
271	20 c. black, ochre-brown and gold	25	10
272	40 c. black, bright ultramarine and new blue	30	10
269/72	*Set of 4*	70	35

Designs:—12 c. Sairey Gamp (*Martin Chuzzlewit*); 20 c. Mr. Micawber and David (*David Copperfield*); 40 c. The "Marchioness" (*The Old Curiosity Shop*).

*The normal sideways watermark shows Crown to left of CA, as seen from the back of the stamp.

1970 (8 Sept). *Decimal Currency. Designs as Nos. 223/37, but with values inscr in decimal currency as T 97. W w 12 (sideways* on cent values).*

273	¼ c. Type 97	10	10
274	1 c. Brahmin Cattle	10	10
275	2 c. Blowholes on the coast	10	10
276	3 c. Royal Poinciana	20	10
277	4 c. Map of Grand Cayman	20	10
278	5 c. Cayman Brac and Little Cayman on Chart	35	10
	w. Wmk Crown to right of CA	9·00	
279	7 c. Motor vessels at berth	30	10
280	8 c. Georgetown scene	30	10
281	10 c. Basket-making	30	10
282	12 c. Beach scene	90	45
283	15 c. Straw-rope making	1·25	2·25
284	20 c. Great Barracuda	2·50	1·25
285	40 c. Government House	85	75
286	$1 Type 76	1·25	4·00
	w. Wmk inverted	9·00	
287	$2 Queen Elizabeth II	2·00	4·50
273/87	*Set of 15*	9·50	12·00

*The normal sideways watermark shows Crown to left of CA, as seen from the back of the stamp.

98 The Three Wise Men

(Des G. Drummond. Litho Format)

1970 (8 Oct). *Christmas. T 98 and similar horiz design. W w 12 (sideways*). P 14.*

288	98	¼ c. apple-green, grey and emerald	10	10
	w. Wmk Crown to right of CA	5·00	5·00
289	98	1 c. black, lemon and turquoise-green	10	10
290	98	5 c. grey, red-orange and crimson	10	10
291	98	10 c. black, lemon and orange-red	10	10
292	98	12 c. grey, pale turquoise & ultramarine	15	10
293	98	20 c. black, lemon and green	20	15
288/93	*Set of 6*	55	30

Design:—1, 10, 20 c. Nativity scene and Globe.

*The normal sideways watermark shows Crown to left of CA, as seen from the back of the stamp.

100 Grand Cayman Terrapin

(Des V. Whiteley. Photo Harrison)

1971 (28 Jan). *Turtles. T 100 and similar diamond-shaped designs. W w 12 (sideways*, reading from inscr to "ISLANDS"). P 14½×14.*

294	5 c. Type 100	30	25
	w. Wmk Crown to right of CA	13·00	
295	7 c. Green Turtle	35	25
	w. Wmk Crown to right of CA	50·00	
296	12 c. Hawksbill Turtle	55	30
297	20 c. Turtle Farm	1·00	1·40
294/7	*Set of 4*	2·00	2·00

*The normal sideways watermark shows Crown to left of CA, as seen from the back of the stamp.

101 *Dendrophylax fawcettii*

102 "Adoration of the Kings" (French, 15th Cent)

(Des Sylvia Goaman. Litho Questa)

1971 (7 Apr). *Orchids. T 101 and similar vert designs. Multicoloured. W w 12. P 14.*

298	¼ c. Type 101	10	70
299	2 c. *Schomburgkia thomsoniana*	40	60
300	10 c. *Vanilla claviculata*	90	50
301	40 c. *Oncidium variegatum*	3·00	3·50
298/301	*Set of 4*	4·00	4·75

(Des Jennifer Toombs. Litho Questa)

1971 (15 Oct*). *Christmas. T 102 and similar vert designs. Multicoloured. W w 12. P 14.*

302	¼ c. Type 102	10	10
	w. Wmk inverted	2·00	
303	1 c. "The Nativity" (Parisian, 14th Cent.)	10	10
304	5 c. "Adoration of the Magi" (Burgundian, 15th Cent.)	10	10
305	12 c. Type 102	20	15
306	15 c. As 1 c.	20	25
307	20 c. As 5 c.	25	35
302/7	*Set of 6*	70	80
MS308	113×115 mm. Nos. 302/7.	1·25	2·25
	w. Wmk inverted	£225	

*This is the local date of issue. The Crown Agents released the stamps on 27 September.

103 Turtle and Telephone Cable

(Des Anglo Arts Associates. Litho Walsall)

1972 (10 Jan). *Co-Axial Telephone Cable. W w 12 (sideways*). P 14.*

309	103	2 c. multicoloured	10	10
310		10 c. multicoloured	15	10
		w. Wmk Crown to right of CA	8·00	
311		40 c. multicoloured	30	40
		w. Wmk Crown to right of CA	75	
309/11		*Set of 3*	45	45

*The normal sideways watermark shows Crown to left of CA, as seen from the back of the stamp.

104 Court House Building

(Des C. Abbott. Litho Questa)

1972 (15 Aug). *New Government Buildings. T 104 and similar horiz design. Multicoloured. W w 12. P 13½.*

312	5 c. Type 104	10	10
313	15 c. Legislative Assembly Building	10	10
314	25 c. Type 104	15	15
315	40 c. As 15 c.	20	30
312/15	*Set of 4*	35	45
MS316	121×108 mm. Nos. 312/15.	70	2·00
	w. Wmk inverted	30·00	

105 Hawksbill Turtle and Queen or Pink Conch

(Des (from photograph by D. Groves) and photo Harrison)

1972 (20 Nov). *Royal Silver Wedding. Multicoloured; background colour given. W w 12. P 14 × 14½.*

317	105	12 c. deep slate-violet	15	10
318		30 c. yellow-olive	15	20
		a. Blue omitted*	£400	
		w. Wmk inverted	3·00	

*The omission of the blue colour results in the Duke's suit appearing sepia instead of deep blue.

106 $1 Coin and Note

107 "The Way of Sorrow"

(Des and photo D.L.R.)

1973 (15 Jan). *First Issue of Currency. T 106 and similar horiz designs. Multicoloured. W w 12 (sideways*). P 13.*

319	3 c. Type 106	20	10
320	6 c. $5 Coin and note	20	10
321	15 c. $10 Coin and note	60	20
322	25 c. $25 Coin and note	80	35
319/22	*Set of 4*	1·60	60
MS323	128×107 mm. Nos. 319/22	3·00	3·00
	w. Wmk Crown to right of CA	70·00	

*The normal sideways watermark shows Crown to left of CA, as seen from the back of the stamp.

(Des G. Drummond. Litho Questa)

1973 (11 Apr*). *Easter. T 107 and similar multicoloured designs showing stained-glass windows. W w 12 (sideways on 10 and 12 c.). P 14½.*

324	10 c. Type 107	15	10
325	12 c. "Christ Resurrected"	20	10
326	20 c. "The Last Supper" (*horiz*)	25	15
327	30 c. "Christ on the Cross" (*horiz*)	30	25
324/7	*Set of 4*	80	45
MS328	122 × 105 mm. Nos. 324/7. Imperf	1·00	1·60

*This is the local date of issue; the Crown Agents released the stamps on 15 March.

108 "The Nativity" (Sforza Book of Hours)

109 White-winged Dove

(Des J. Cooter. Litho Questa)

1973 (2 Oct). *Christmas. T 108 and similar vert design. W w 12 (sideways). P 14.*

329	108	3 c. multicoloured	10	10
330		5 c. multicoloured	10	10
331	108	9 c. multicoloured	15	10
332		12 c. multicoloured	15	10
333	108	15 c. multicoloured	15	15
334		25 c. multicoloured	20	25
329/34		*Set of 6*	65	50

Design:—5, 12, 25 c. "The Adoration of the Magi" (Breviary of Queen Isabella).

1973 (14 Nov). *Royal Wedding. As Nos. 165/6 of Anguilla. Centre multicoloured. W w 12 (sideways). P 13½.*

335	10 c. sage-green	10	10
336	30 c. bright mauve	15	10

(Des M. Goaman. Litho Walsall)

1974 (2 Jan). *Birds (1st series). T 109 and similar vert designs. Multicoloured. W w 12 (sideways). P 14.*

337	3 c. Type 109	1·75	20
338	10 c. Vitelline Warbler	2·50	20
339	12 c. Antillean Grackle	2·50	20
340	20 c. West Indian Red-bellied Woodpecker	4·00	65
341	30 c. Stripe-headed Tanager	5·50	1·50
342	50 c. Yucatan Vireo	7·00	2·75
337/42	*Set of 6*	21·00	5·00

See also Nos. 383/8.

110 Old School Building

(Des PAD Studio. Litho Questa)

1974 (1 May). *25th Anniv of University of West Indies. T 110 and similar horiz designs. Multicoloured. W w 12 (sideways). P 14.*

343	12 c. Type 110	10	10
344	20 c. New Comprehensive School	15	10
345	30 c. Creative Arts Centre, Mona	15	35
343/5	*Set of 3*	30	40

111 Hermit Crab and Staghorn Coral

(Des J.W. Litho Kynoch Press)

1974 (1 Aug). *Multicoloured designs as T 111 (size 41½ × 27 mm). W w 12 (sideways on $1 and $2). P 14.*
346	1 c. Type 111	..	3·50	1·25
347	3 c. Treasure-chest and Lion's Paw	..	3·50	75
348	4 c. Treasure and Spotted Scorpionfish		50	70
349	5 c. Flintlock pistol and Brain Coral	..	3·00	75
350	6 c. Blackbeard and Green Turtle	..	35	2·25
351	9 c. Jewelled pomander and Porkfish	..	3·50	6·00
352	10 c. Spiny Lobster and treasure	..	4·50	80
353	12 c. Jewelled sword and dagger, and Seafan	..	35	1·40
354	15 c. Cabrit's Murex (*Murex cabritii*) and treasure		45	1·25
355	20 c. Queen or Pink Conch (*Strombus gigas*) and treasure	..	10·00	1·75
356	25 c. Hogfish and Treasure	..	45	70
357	40 c. Gold chalice and sea-whip	..	2·75	1·25
358	$1 Coat of arms (*vert*)	..	2·75	3·25
359	$2 Queen Elizabeth II (*vert*)	..	4·00	13·00
346/59		*Set of* 14	35·00	32·00

See also Nos. 364/6, 412/19 and 445/52.

112 Sea Captain and Ship (Shipbuilding)

(Des G. Vasarhelyi. Litho D.L.R.)

1974 (7 Oct). *Local Industries. T 112 and similar horiz designs. Multicoloured. W w 12. P 14×13½.*
360	8 c. Type 112	..	15	10
	w. Wmk inverted	..	20	20
361	12 c. Thatcher and cottages	..	15	10
	w. Wmk inverted	..	30	30
362	20 c. Farmer and plantation	..	25	20
	w. Wmk inverted	..	40	40
360/2		*Set of* 3	50	35
MS363	92×132 mm. Nos. 360/2	..	1·50	2·50
	w. Wmk inverted	..	2·25	

1974–75. *As Nos. 346/7 and design of 351, but wmk sideways*.*
364	1 c. Type 111 (29.9.75)	..	2·50	1·50
365	3 c. Treasure-chest and Lions-paw (12.11.74)	..	4·50	2·00
	w. Wmk Crown to right of CA		4·50	
366	8 c. Jewelled pomander and Porkfish (16.12.74)	..	2·50	8·50
364/6		*Set of* 3	8·50	11·00

*The normal sideways watermark shows Crown to left of CA, as seen from the back of the stamp.
Nos. 367/79 vacant.

113 Arms of Cinque Ports and Lord Warden's Flag

114 "The Crucifixion"

(Des P. Powell. Litho D.L.R.)

1974 (30 Nov). *Birth Centenary of Sir Winston Churchill. T 113 and similar vert design. Multicoloured. W w 12 (sideways*). P 13½×14.*
380	12 c. Type 113	..	15	10
381	50 c. Churchill's coat of arms	..	45	70
	w. Wmk Crown to right of CA (pair)	..	30·00	
MS382	98×86 mm. Nos. 380/1	..	60	1·60

*The normal sideways watermark shows Crown to left of CA on Nos. 380/1 or Crown to right of CA on **MS**382, as seen from the back of the stamp.

(Des M. Goaman. Litho Questa)

1975 (1 Jan). *Birds (2nd series). Multicoloured designs as T 109. W w 12 (sideways). P 14.*
383	3 c. Common Flicker	..	70	45
384	10 c. Black-billed Whistling Duck	..	1·25	45
385	12 c. Yellow Warbler	..	1·40	65
386	20 c. White-bellied Dove	..	2·00	2·00
387	30 c. Magnificent Frigate Bird	..	3·25	4·00
388	50 c. Cuban Amazon	..	3·75	9·00
	a. Error. Wmk Lesotho W 53 (inverted)	£600	
383/8		*Set of* 6	11·00	15·00

(Des PAD Studio. Litho D.L.R.)

1975 (24 Mar). *Easter. French Pastoral Staffs. T 114 and similar vert design showing "The Crucifixion" (different). Multicoloured. W w 12 (sideways). P 13½ × 14.*
389	114 15 c. multicoloured	..	10	15
390	– 35 c. multicoloured	..	20	30
MS391	128 × 98 mm. Nos. 389/90. W w 12 (*upright*)	65	2·50
	a. Error. Imperf		

See also Nos. 396/**MS**398.

115 Israel Hands

(Des J.W. Litho Harrison)

1975 (25 July). *Pirates. T 115 and similar horiz designs. Multicoloured. W w 12 (sideways*). P 14.*
392	10 c. Type 115	..	20	10
393	12 c. John Fenn	..	20	10
394	20 c. Thomas Anstis	..	40	35
	w. Wmk Crown to right of CA	50·00	
395	30 c. Edward Low	..	55	1·00
392/5		*Set of* 4	1·25	1·40

*The normal sideways watermark shows Crown to left of CA, as seen from the back of the stamp.

(Des PAD Studio. Litho Questa)

1975 (31 Oct). *Christmas. Vert designs as T 114 showing "Virgin and Child with Angels" (both different). W w 14. P 14.*
396	12 c. multicoloured	..	10	10
397	50 c. multicoloured	..	30	30
MS398	113 × 85 mm. Nos. 396/7	..	1·00	2·25

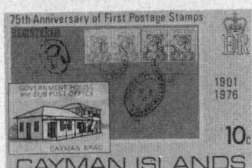

116 Registered Cover, Government House and Sub-Post Office

(Des J. Cooter. Litho Questa)

1976 (12 Mar). *75th Anniv of First Cayman Is. Postage Stamp. T 116 and similar horiz designs. Multicoloured. W w 14 (sideways). P 13½.*
399	10 c. Type 116	..	15	10
400	20 c. ½d. stamp and 1890–94 postmark	..	20	15
401	30 c. 1d. stamp and 1908 surcharge	..	30	25
402	50 c. ½d. and 1d. stamps	..	45	50
399/402		*Set of* 4	1·00	85
MS403	117 × 147 mm. Nos. 399/402	..	2·50	3·00

117 Seals of Georgia, Delaware and New Hampshire

(Des P. Powell. Litho J.W.)

1976 (29 May). *Bicentenary of American Revolution. T 117 and similar horiz designs showing seals of the States given. Multicoloured. W w 14 (sideways). P 13½ × 14.*
404	10 c. Type 117	..	50	15
405	15 c. S. Carolina, New Jersey and Maryland	..	65	20
406	20 c. Virginia, Rhode Is. and Massachusetts	..	75	25
407	25 c. New York, Connecticut and N. Carolina	..	75	35
408	30 c. Pennsylvania seal, Liberty Bell and U.S. Great Seal	..	90	40
404/8		*Set of* 5	3·25	1·25
MS409	166 × 124 mm. Nos. 404/8. P 14	..	5·00	8·00

118 Racing Dinghies

119 Queen Elizabeth II and Westminster Abbey

(Des C. Abbott. Litho D.L.R.)

1976 (16 Aug). *Olympic Games, Montreal. T 118 and similar vert design. Multicoloured. W w 14. P 14.*
410	20 c. Type 118	..	40	10
411	50 c. Racing dinghy	..	70	50

1976 (3 Sept)–78. *As Nos. 347/9, 352, 355, 358/9 and 366, but W 14 (upright on $1, inverted on $2, sideways on others). Chalk-surfaced paper (4, 5 c. and $1) or ordinary paper (others).*
412	3 c. Treasure-chest and Lion's Paw	..	1·00	3·00
	a. Chalk-surfaced paper (19.10.77)	4·50	4·50
413	4 c. Treasure and Spotted Scorpionfish (19.10.77)	..	1·10	3·00
414	5 c. Flintlock pistol and Brain Coral (19.10.77)	..	3·50	4·00
415	8 c. Jewelled pomander and Porkfish	..	6·50	2·75
	a. Chalk-surfaced paper (19.10.77)	8·00	4·75
416	10 c. Spiny Lobster and treasure	..	1·75	2·50
	a. Chalk-surfaced paper (27.1.78)	1·75	3·00
417	20 c. Queen or Pink Conch (*Strombus gigas*) and treasure	..	3·50	5·00
	a. Chalk-surfaced paper (27.1.78)	3·50	5·00
418	$1 Coat of arms (19.10.77)	..	6·50	8·50
419	$2 Queen Elizabeth II	..	7·50	6·50
	a. Chalk-surfaced paper (19.10.77)	11·00	17·00
412/19		*Set of* 8	28·00	30·00

Nos. 420/6 vacant.

(Des BG Studio. Litho Questa)

1977 (7 Feb). *Silver Jubilee. T 119 and similar multicoloured designs. W w 14 (sideways on 50 c.). P 13½.*
427	8 c. Prince of Wales' visit, 1973	..	10	20
	w. Wmk inverted	..	8·00	
428	30 c. Type 119	..	15	40
	w. Wmk inverted	..	27·00	
429	50 c. Preparation for the Anointing (*horiz*)	30	75
427/9		*Set of* 3	50	1·25

120 Scuba Diving

(Des Jennifer Toombs. Litho J.W.)

1977 (25 July). *Tourism. T 120 and similar horiz designs. Multicoloured. W w 14 (sideways). P 13½.*
430	5 c. Type 120	..	10	10
431	10 c. Exploring a wreck	..	15	10
432	20 c. Royal Gramma ("Fairy Basslet") (fish)	45	20
433	25 c. Sergeant Major (fish)	..	55	35
430/3		*Set of* 4	1·10	60
MS434	146×89 mm. Nos. 430/3. P 14½	..	2·00	3·25

121 *Composia fidelissima* (moth)

(Des J. Cooter. Litho Enschedé)

1977 (2 Dec). *Butterflies and Moth. T 121 and similar horiz designs. Multicoloured. W w 14 (sideways). P 14×13.*
435	5 c. Type 121	..	55	10
436	8 c. *Heliconius charithonia*	..	60	15
437	10 c. *Danaus gilippus*	..	60	15
438	15 c. *Agraulis vanillae*	..	90	40
439	20 c. *Junonia evarete*	..	1·00	45
440	30 c. *Anartia jatrophae*	..	1·25	70
435/40		*Set of* 6	4·50	1·75

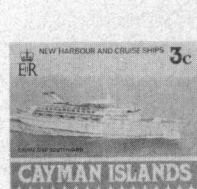

122 *Southward* (liner)

123 "The Crucifixion" (Dürer)

(Des G. Hutchins. Litho Questa)

1978 (23 Jan). *New Harbour and Cruise Ships. T 122 and similar multicoloured designs. W w 14 (sideways* on 3, 5 c.). P 14×14½ (3, 5 c.) or 14½×14 (others).*
441	3 c. Type 122	..	20	10
	w. Wmk Crown to right of CA	..	15·00	
442	5 c. *Renaissance* (liner)	..	20	10
443	30 c. New harbour (*vert*)	..	80	25
444	50 c. *Daphne* (liner) (*vert*)	..	1·00	55
441/4		*Set of* 4	2·00	85

*The normal sideways watermark shows Crown to left of CA, as seen from the back of the stamp.

339

(Litho Walsall)

1978 (16 Mar)–**80**. *Designs as Nos. 346/7, 349, 352, 355 and 357/9 but smaller, 40 × 26 or 26 × 40 mm. W w **14** (sideways on 1 to 40 c.). Chalk-surfaced paper.*

445	1 c. Type **111**			1·00	1·25
446	3 c. Treasure-chest and Lion's Paw			80	50
447	5 c. Flintlock pistol and Brain Coral (11.12.79)			2·00	2·50
448	10 c. Spiny Lobster and treasure (25.5.78)			1·60	60
449	20 c. Queen or Pink Conch (*Strombus gigas*) and treasure (25.5.78)			3·25	1·25
450	30 c. Gold chalice and sea-whip (1979*)			15·00	20·00
451	$1 Coat of arms (30.7.80)			14·00	8·00
452	$2 Queen Elizabeth II (3.4.80)			6·00	22·00
445/52			*Set of 8*	40·00	50·00

*Supplies of No. 450 were sent to Cayman Islands on 7 May 1979. It is not known when these stamps were first placed on sale.

Nos. 453/8 vacant.

(Des Jennifer Toombs. Litho Cartor)

1978 (20 Mar). *Easter and 450th Death Anniv of Dürer. T* **123** *and similar vert designs. W w* **14** *(inverted on 20 c.). P 12.*

459	10 c. magenta and black			20	10
	w. Wmk inverted			14·00	
460	15 c. yellow and black			30	15
	w. Wmk inverted			12·00	
461	20 c. turquoise-green and black			40	20
	w. Wmk upright				
462	30 c. lilac and black			55	35
	w. Wmk inverted			1·75	
459/62			*Set of 4*	1·25	70
MS463	120×108 mm. Nos. 459/62			3·50	4·50
	w. Wmk inverted			4·50	

Designs:—15 c. "Christ at Emmaus"; 20 c. "The Entry into Jerusalem"; 30 c. "Christ washing Peter's Feet".

124 "Explorers" Singing Game

125 Yale of Beaufort

(Des Walsall. Litho Questa)

1978 (25 Apr). *3rd International Council Meeting of Girls' Brigade. T* **124** *and similar vert designs. Multicoloured. W w* **14**. *P 14.*

464	3 c. Type **124**			20	10
465	10 c. Colour party			30	10
466	20 c. Girls and Duke of Edinburgh Award interests			60	20
467	50 c. Girls using domestic skills			1·10	80
464/7			*Set of 4*	2·00	1·10

(Des C. Abbott. Litho Questa)

1978 (2 June). *25th Anniv of Coronation. T* **125** *and similar vert designs. P 15.*

468	30 c. apple-green, deep magenta and silver			20	25
	a. Sheetlet. Nos. 468/70 × 2			1·10	
469	30 c. multicoloured			20	25
470	30 c. apple-green, deep magenta and silver			20	25
468/70			*Set of 3*	55	65

Designs:—No. 468, Type **125**; No. 469, Queen Elizabeth II; No. 470, Barn Owl.

Nos. 468/70 were printed together in small sheets of 6, containing two *se-tenant* strips of 3, with horizontal gutter margin between.

126 Four-eyed Butterflyfish

(Des G. Hutchins, Litho Walsall)

1978 (29 Aug). *Fish (1st series). T* **126** *and similar horiz designs. Multicoloured. W w* **14** *(sideways). P 14.*

471	3 c. Type **126**			25	10
472	5 c. Grey Angelfish			30	10
473	10 c. Squirrelfish			45	10
474	15 c. Queen Parrotfish			60	30
475	20 c. Spanish Hogfish			70	35
476	30 c. Queen Angelfish			80	50
471/6			*Set of 6*	2·75	1·25

Examples of the 15 c. value inscribed "SERGEANT MAJOR FISH" and 20 c. inscribed "PARROT FISH" were prepared, but not issued for postal purposes.
See also Nos. 483/8.

127 Lockheed L.18 Lodestar

(Des A. Theobald. Litho Format)

1979 (5 Feb). *25th Anniv of Owen Roberts Airfield. T* **127** *and similar horiz designs. Multicoloured. W w* **14** *(sideways). P 14½ × 14.*

477	3 c. Type **127**			20	10
478	5 c. Consolidated PBY-5A Catalina			20	10
479	10 c. Vickers Viking 1B			25	10
480	15 c. B.A.C. One Eleven 475 on tarmac			45	20
481	20 c. Piper PA-31 Cheyenne II, Bell 47G Trooper helicopter and Hawker Siddeley H.S.125			55	30
482	30 c. B.A.C. One Eleven 475 over airfield			80	45
477/82			*Set of 6*	2·25	1·10

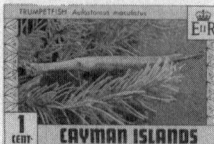

128 Trumpetfish

(Des R. Granger Barrett. Litho Questa)

1979 (20 Apr). *Fish (2nd series). T* **128** *and similar horiz designs. Multicoloured. W w* **14** *(sideways*). P 14.*

483	1 c. Type **128**			10	10
	w. Wmk Crown to right of CA			26·00	
484	3 c. Nassau Grouper			25	10
485	5 c. French Angelfish			25	10
	w. Wmk Crown to right of CA			3·50	
486	10 c. Schoolmaster Snapper			35	10
487	20 c. Banded Butterflyfish			55	25
488	50 c. Black-barred Soldierfish			1·00	70
483/8			*Set of 6*	2·25	1·25

*The normal sideways watermark shows Crown to left of CA, as seen from the back of the stamp.

129 1900 1d. Stamp

(Des J.W. Litho Walsall)

1979 (15 Aug). *Death Centenary of Sir Rowland Hill. T* **129** *and similar horiz designs showing stamps and Sir Rowland Hill. W w* **14** *(sideways). P 13½.*

489	5 c. black, rose-carmine and grey-blue			10	10
490	10 c. multicoloured			15	10
491	20 c. multicoloured			20	25
489/91			*Set of 3*	30	30
MS492	138 × 90 mm. 50 c. multicoloured			55	65

Designs:—10 c. Great Britain 1902 3d.; 20 c. 1955 £1 definitive; 50 c. 1908 2½d.

130 Holy Family and Angels

(Des G. Vasarhelyi. Litho Secura, Singapore)

1979 (20 Nov). *Christmas. T* **130** *and similar horiz designs. Multicoloured. W w* **14** *(sideways*). P 13½×13.*

493	10 c. Type **130**			15	10
	w. Wmk Crown to right of CA			25	
494	20 c. Angels appearing before shepherds			20	10
	w. Wmk Crown to right of CA			35	
495	30 c. Nativity scene			30	20
	w. Wmk Crown to right of CA			50	
496	40 c. Wise men following star			40	30
	w. Wmk Crown to right of CA			70	
493/6			*Set of 4*	95	60

*The normal sideways watermark shows Crown to left of CA, as seen from the back of the stamp.

131 Local Rotary Project

(Des Walsall. Litho Secura, Singapore)

1980 (14 Feb). *75th Anniv of Rotary International. T* **131** *and similar designs in black, bistre-yellow and deep ultramarine. W w* **14** *(sideways on 20 c.). P 13½ × 13 (20 c.) or 13 × 13½ (others).*

497	20 c. Type **131**			20	15
498	30 c. Paul P. Harris (founder) (*vert*)			25	20
499	50 c. Rotary anniversary emblem (*vert*)			35	30
	a. Black (Royal cypher, and face value) omitted			£750	
497/9			*Set of 3*	70	60

132 Walking Mail Carrier (late 19th-century)

(Des J.W. Litho Walsall)

1980 (6 May). *"London 1980" International Stamp Exhibition. T* **132** *and similar horiz designs. Multicoloured. W w* **14** *(sideways). P 14.*

500	5 c. Type **132**			10	10
501	10 c. Delivering mail by cat boat (late 19th-century)			15	10
502	15 c. Mounted mail carrier (early 20th-century)			20	10
503	30 c. Horse-drawn waggonette (early 20th-century)			30	15
504	40 c. Postman on bicycle (mid 20th-century)			30	15
505	$1 Motor transport (late 20th-century)			65	55
500/5			*Set of 6*	1·50	1·00

133 Queen Elizabeth the Queen Mother at the Derby, 1976

134 American Thorny Oyster (*Spondylus americanus*)

(Des and litho Harrison)

1980 (4 Aug). *80th Birthday of Queen Elizabeth the Queen Mother. W w* **14** *(sideways). P 14.*

506	**133** 20 c. multicoloured			20	25

(Des J.W. Litho Walsall)

1980 (12 Aug). *Shells (1st series). T* **134** *and similar horiz designs. Multicoloured. W w* **14** *(sideways). P 14½ × 14.*

507	5 c. Type **134**			40	10
508	10 c. West Indian Murex (*Murex brevifrons*)			40	10
509	30 c. Angular Triton (*Cymatium femorale*)			75	40
510	50 c. Caribbean Vase (*Vasum muricatum*)			90	80
507/10			*Set of 4*	2·25	1·25

See also Nos. 565/8 and 582/5.

135 Lantana

136 Juvenile Tarpon and Fire Sponge

(Des G. Hutchins. Litho Rosenbaum Bros, Vienna)

1980 (21 Oct). *Flowers (1st series). T* **135** *and similar horiz designs. Multicoloured. W w* **14** *(sideways). P 13½.*

511	5 c. Type **135**			10	10
512	15 c. Bauhinia			25	10
513	30 c. Hibiscus Rosa			35	10
514	$1 Milk and Wine Lily			1·00	75
511/14			*Set of 4*	1·50	85

See also Nos. 541/4.

(Des G. Drummond. Litho J.W.)

1980 (9 Dec)–**82**. *Flora and Fauna of the Mangrove Swamp. Vert designs as T* **136**. *Multicoloured. W w* **14**. *P 13½ × 13.*
A. *Without imprint date.*
B. *Printed with imprint date at foot of designs (14.6.82).*

		A		B	
515	3 c. Type **136**	50	1·50	4·00	3·50
516	5 c. Flat Tree or Mangrove-root Oyster (*Isognomon alatus*)	60	1·00	1·00	70
517	10 c. Mangrove Crab	40	80	1·25	80
518	15 c. Lizard and *Phyciodes phaon* (butterfly)	1·00	1·50	4·00	1·75
519	20 c. Louisiana Heron	1·50	2·00	2·50	2·00
520	30 c. Red Mangrove Flower	70	1·00	1·50	1·50
521	40 c. Red Mangrove Seeds	75	1·00	1·50	1·50
522	50 c. Waterhouse's Leaf-nosed Bat	1·25	1·50	2·00	2·00
523	$1 Black-crowned Night Heron	4·50	4·50	4·50	4·50
524	$2 Cayman Islands coat of arms	1·50	3·75	3·75	4·00
525	$4 Queen Elizabeth II	2·25	4·75	6·50	11·00
515/25	*Set of 11*	13·00	21·00	29·00	30·00

Imprint dates: "1982", Nos. 515/25B; "1984", No. 516B; "1985", Nos. 516B/24B.
For stamps in these designs, but watermark w **16**, see Nos. 626 and 631/2.

EASTER 1981

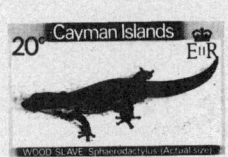

137 Eucharist   138 Wood Slave

(Des Jennifer Toombs. Litho Questa)

1981 (17 Mar). *Easter. T* **137** *and similar vert designs. Multi-coloured. W w* **14**. *P* 14.
526	3 c.	Type 137	..	..	10	10
527	10 c.	Crown of thorns	..	..	10	10
528	20 c.	Crucifix	..	..	20	10
529	$1	Lord Jesus Christ	..	..	70	80
526/9	..			*Set of* 4	90	90

(Des R. Granger Barrett. Litho Rosenbaum Bros, Vienna)

1981 (16 June). *Reptiles and Amphibians. T* **138** *and similar horiz designs. Multicoloured. W w* **14** (*sideways**). *P* 13½.
530	20 c.	Type 138			30	20
	w.	Wmk Crown to left of CA			50	
531	30 c.	Cayman Iguana			45	35
	w.	Wmk Crown to left of CA			70	
532	40 c.	Lion Lizard			55	45
	w.	Wmk Crown to left of CA			80	
533	50 c.	Terrapin ("Hickatee")			65	55
	w.	Wmk Crown to right of CA			1·00	
530/3	..			*Set of* 4	1·75	1·40

*The normal sideways watermark shows Crown to right of CA on Nos. 530/2 and to left on No. 533, *as seen from the back of the stamp.*

139 Prince Charles   140 Disabled Scuba Divers

(Des J.W. Litho Walsall)

1981 (22 July). *Royal Wedding. T* **139** *and similar vert designs. Multicoloured. W w* **14**. *P* 14.
534	20 c.	Wedding bouquet from Cayman Islands		15	10
535	30 c.	Type 139			20	10
536	$1	Prince Charles and Lady Diana Spencer		50	75
534/6	..			*Set of* 3	75	80

(Des J.W. Litho Walsall)

1981 (29 Sept). *International Year for Disabled Persons. T* **140** *and similar horiz designs. Multicoloured. W w* **14** (*sideways*). *P* 14.
537	5 c.	Type 140			10	10
538	15 c.	Old School for the Handicapped		25	20
539	20 c.	New School for the Handicapped		30	25
540	$1	Disabled people in wheelchairs, by the sea	1·25	85
537/40				*Set of* 4	1·60	1·25

(Des G. Hutchins. Litho Questa)

1981 (20 Oct). *Flowers* (2nd series). *Horiz designs as T* **135**. *Multi-coloured. W w* **14** (*sideways*). *P* 13½.
541	3 c.	Bougainvillea	..	..	10	10
542	10 c.	Morning Glory	..	..	20	10
543	20 c.	Wild Amaryllis	..	..	45	25
544	$1	Cordia	..	..	1·75	1·75
541/4	..			*Set of* 4	2·25	2·00

141 Dr. Robert Koch and Microscope   142 Bride and Groom walking down Aisle

(Des and litho Walsall)

1982 (24 Mar). *Centenary of Robert Koch's Discovery of Tubercle Bacillus. T* **141** *and similar multicoloured designs. W w* **14** (*sideways on* 15 c, *inverted on* 30 c.). *P* 14½.
545	15 c.	Type 141	..	..	25	25
546	30 c.	Koch looking through microscope (*vert*)	45	45
547	40 c.	Microscope (*vert*)	..	..	70	70
548	50 c.	Dr. Robert Koch (*vert*)	..	80	80
545/8	..			*Set of* 4	2·00	2·00

(Des Jennifer Toombs. Litho J.W.)

1982 (1 July). *21st Birthday of Princess of Wales. T* **142** *and similar vert designs. Multicoloured. W w* **14**. *P* 13.
549	20 c.	Cayman Islands coat of arms		30	35
550	30 c.	Lady Diana Spencer in London, June 1981		60	45
	w.	Wmk inverted			3·50	
551	40 c.	Type 142			60	65
552	50 c.	Formal portrait			1·75	90
	w.	Wmk inverted			6·00	
549/52				*Set of* 4	3·00	2·10

CAYMAN ISLANDS   CAYMAN ISLANDS

143 Pitching Tent   144 "Madonna and Child with the Infant Baptist"

(Des L. Walker. Litho Questa)

1982 (24 Aug). *75th Anniv of Boy Scout Movement. T* **143** *and similar horiz designs. Multicoloured. W w* **14** (*sideways*). *P* 14.
553	3 c.	Type 143	..	..	15	10
554	20 c.	Scouts camping	..	..	55	40
555	30 c.	Cub Scouts and Leaders	..	70	55
556	50 c.	Boating skills	..	..	1·10	85
553/6	..			*Set of* 4	2·25	1·75

(Des PAD Studio. Litho Questa)

1982 (26 Oct). *Christmas. Raphael Paintings. T* **144** *and similar vert designs. Multicoloured. W w* **14**. *P* 14½ × 14.
557	3 c.	Type 144	..	..	10	10
558	10 c.	"Madonna of the Tower"	..	20	20
	w.	Wmk inverted				
559	20 c.	"Ansidei Madonna"	..	35	35
560	30 c.	"Madonna and Child"	..	50	50
	w.	Wmk inverted				
557/60				*Set of* 4	1·00	1·00

145 Mace

(Des and litho Walsall)

1982 (9 Nov). *150th Anniv of Representative Government. T* **145** *and similar horiz designs. Multicoloured. W w* **14** (*sideways*). *P* 14½ × 14.
561	3 c.	Type 145	..	..	10	20
562	10 c.	Old Courthouse	..	..	20	20
563	20 c.	Commonwealth Parliamentary Association coat of arms		35	45
564	30 c.	Legislative Assembly building		50	90
561/4	..			*Set of* 4	1·00	1·60

(Des J.W. Litho Format)

1983 (11 Jan). *Shells* (2nd series). *Horiz designs as T* **134**. *Multi-coloured. W w* **14** (*sideways*). *P* 13½ × 13.
565	5 c.	Colourful Atlantic Moon (*Natica canrena*)		15	10
566	10 c.	King Helmet (*Cassis tuberosa*)		25	20
567	20 c.	Rooster-tail Conch (*Strombus gallus*)	45	40
568	$1	Reticulated Cowrie-helmet (*Cypraecassis testiculus*)	1·75	3·25
565/8	..			*Set of* 4	2·40	3·50

146 Legislative Building, Cayman Brac

(Des C. Abbott. Litho Questa)

1983 (15 Feb). *Royal Visit. T* **146** *and similar multicoloured designs. W w* **14** (*sideways on* 20 c., 30 c.). *P* 14.
569	20 c.	Type 146	..	..	45	35
570	30 c.	Legislative Building, Grand Cayman	60	50
571	50 c.	Duke of Edinburgh (*vert*)	..	1·25	90
572	$1	Queen Elizabeth II (*vert*)	..	2·00	2·00
569/72				*Set of* 4	4·00	3·25
MS573	113 × 94 mm. Nos. 569/72 (wmk sideways)	4·00	4·25

MINIMUM PRICE

The minimum price quote is 10p which represents a handling charge rather than a basis for valuing common stamps. For further notes about prices see introductory pages.

Commonwealth Day 14 March 1983 CAYMAN ISLANDS 3c

147 Satellite View of Earth

(Des J.W. Litho Questa)

1983 (14 Mar). *Commonwealth Day. T* **147** *and similar horiz designs. Multicoloured. W w* **14** (*sideways*). *P* 14.
574	3 c.	Type 147	..	..	10	10
575	15 c.	Cayman Islands and Commonwealth flags		25	30
576	20 c.	Fishing	..	..	30	35
577	40 c.	Portrait of Queen Elizabeth II	60	65
574/7				*Set of* 4	1·10	1·25

CAYMAN ISLANDS

148 MRCU Cessna 188 Ag Wagon Aircraft   149 Song of Norway (cruise liner)

(Des Harrison. Litho Questa)

1983 (10 Oct). *Bicentenary of Manned Flight. T* **148** *and similar horiz designs. Multicoloured. W w* **14** (*sideways*). *P* 14.
578	3 c.	Type 148	..	..	40	20
579	10 c.	Consolidated PBY-5A Catalina	60	20
580	20 c.	Boeing 727-200	..	1·25	1·25
581	40 c.	Hawker Siddeley H.S. 748	1·75	2·75
578/81				*Set of* 4	3·50	4·00

(Des J.W. Litho Questa)

1984 (18 Jan). *Shells* (3rd series). *Horiz designs as T* **134**. *Multi-coloured. W w* **14** (*sideways*). *P* 14 × 14½.
582	3 c.	Florida Moon (*Natica floridana*)	60	25
583	10 c.	Austin's Cone (*Conus atractus austini*)	85	25
584	30 c.	Leaning Dwarf Triton (*Colubraria obscura*)	2·25	2·50
585	50 c.	Filose or Threaded Turban (*Turbo cailletii*)	2·50	3·50
582/5	..			*Set of* 4	5·50	6·00

(Des G. Vasarhelyi and L. Curtis. Litho Questa)

1984 (18 June). *250th Anniv of "Lloyd's List" (newspaper). T* **149** *and similar vert designs. Multicoloured. W w* **14**. *P* 14½ × 14.
586	5 c.	Type 149	..	..	25	20
587	10 c.	View of old harbour	..	35	25
588	25 c.	Wreck of *Ridgefield* (freighter)	1·00	1·00
589	50 c.	*Goldfield* (schooner)	..	1·60	2·25
586/9				*Set of* 4	2·75	3·25
MS590	105×75 mm. $1 *Goldfield* (schooner) (*different*)	2·10	2·25

U. P. U. CONGRESS HAMBURG 1984

(150)   151 Snowy Egret

1984 (18 June). *Universal Postal Union Congress, Hamburg. No.* 589 *optd with T* **150**.
591	50 c.	Schooner *Goldfield*	..	1·00	1·50

(Des Josephine Martin. Litho Questa)

1984 (15 Aug). *Birds of the Cayman Islands* (1st series). *T* **151** *and similar horiz designs. Multicoloured. W w* **14** (*sideways*). *P* 14 × 14½.
592	5 c.	Type 151	..	..	75	35
593	10 c.	Bananaquit	..	..	85	35
594	35 c.	Belted Kingfisher	..	2·75	2·25
595	$1	Brown Booby	..	..	5·00	7·00
592/5	..			*Set of* 4	8·50	9·00

See also Nos. 627/30.

152 Couple on Beach at Sunset   153 *Schomburgkia thomsoniana (var. minor)*

(Des G. Wilby. Litho Questa)

1984 (17 Oct). *Christmas. Local Festivities. T* **152** *and similar vert designs. Multicoloured. W* w **14** *(sideways). P* 14.

596	5 c. Type 152		50	75
	a. Horiz strip of 4. Nos. 596/9		1·75	
597	5 c. Family and schooner		50	75
598	5 c. Carol singers		50	75
599	5 c. East End bonfire		50	75
600	25 c. Yachts		70	85
	a. Horiz strip of 4. Nos. 600/3		2·50	
601	25 c. Father Christmas in power-boat		70	85
602	25 c. Children on beach		70	85
603	25 c. Beach party		70	85
596/603		*Set of 8*	4·25	5·75
MS604	59×79 mm. $1 As No. 599, but larger, 27×41 mm		2·10	2·25

Nos. 596/9 and 600/3 were each printed together, *se-tenant*, in horizontal strips of 4 throughout the sheets, the four designs of each value forming a composite picture of a beach scene at night (5 c.) or in the daytime (25 c.).

(Des Liza Horstman. Litho J.W.)

1985 (13 Mar). *Orchids. T* **153** *and similar vert designs. Multicoloured. W* w **14**. *P* 14×13½.

605	5 c. Type 153		65	20
606	10 c. Schomburgkia thomsoniana		85	20
607	25 c. Encyclia plicata		1·90	1·00
608	50 c. Dendrophylax fawcettii		2·50	2·75
605/8		*Set of 4*	5·50	3·75

154 Freighter Aground   155 Athletics

(Des Walsall. Litho J.W.)

1985 (22 May). *Shipwrecks. T* **154** *and similar horiz designs. Multicoloured. W* w **14** *(sideways). P* 14.

609	5 c. Type 154		70	30
610	25 c. Submerged sailing ship		2·25	2·25
611	35 c. Wrecked trawler		2·50	2·25
612	40 c. Submerged wreck on its side		2·75	3·00
609/12		*Set of 4*	7·50	6·00

(Des Harrison. Litho Walsall)

1985 (14 Aug). *International Youth Year. T* **155** *and similar multicoloured designs. W* w **14** *(sideways on 5 c., 15 c.). P* 14×14½ (5, 15 c.) *or* 14½×14 *(others).*

613	5 c. Type 155		20	20
614	15 c. Students in library		35	30
615	25 c. Football (*vert*)		65	55
616	50 c. Netball (*vert*)		1·25	2·00
613/16		*Set of 4*	2·25	2·75

156 Morse Key (1935)   157 Magnificent Frigate Bird

(Des G. Vasarhelyi. Litho Walsall)

1985 (25 Oct). *50th Anniv of Telecommunications System. T* **156** *and similar vert designs. Multicoloured. W* w **16**. *P* 14.

617	5 c. Type 156		40	30
618	10 c. Hand cranked telephone		45	30
619	25 c. Tropospheric scatter dish (1966)		1·10	80
	w. Wmk inverted			
620	50 c. Earth station dish aerial (1979)		1·75	2·50
617/20		*Set of 4*	3·25	3·50

(Des A. Theobald. Litho Format)

1986 (21 Apr). *60th Birthday of Queen Elizabeth II. Vert designs as T* **110** *of Ascension. Multicoloured. W* w **16**. *P* 14×14½.

621	5 c. Princess Elizabeth at wedding of Lady May Cambridge, 1931		10	20
622	10 c. In Norway, 1955		15	20
623	25 c. Queen inspecting Royal Cayman Islands Police, 1983		1·00	60
624	50 c. During Gulf tour, 1979		75	1·00
625	$1 At Crown Agents Head Office, London, 1983		1·10	2·25
621/5		*Set of 5*	2·75	3·75

(Litho J.W.)

1986 (Apr). *As No. 516B, but W* w **16**. "1986" *imprint date. P* 13½×13.

626	5 c. Mangrove Root Oyster		3·75	4·00

(Des Harrison. Litho Questa)

1986 (21 May). *Birds of the Cayman Islands (2nd series). T* **157** *and similar multicoloured designs. W* w **16** *(sideways on 10, 40 c.). P* 14.

627	10 c. Type 157		1·00	40
628	25 c. Black-billed Whistling Duck (*vert*)		1·60	1·10
629	35 c. La Sagra's Flycatcher (*vert*)		1·75	1·90
630	40 c. Yellow-faced Grassquit		1·90	2·50
627/30		*Set of 4*	5·50	5·50

(Litho Questa)

1986 (June). *As Nos. 516B/17B, but different printer and W* w **16**. "1986" *imprint date. P* 14.

631	5 c. Mangrove Root Oyster		4·25	4·00
632	10 c. Mangrove Crab		4·25	4·00

(Des D. Miller. Litho Walsall)

1986 (23 July) *Royal Wedding. Square designs as T* **112** *of Ascension. Multicoloured. W* w **16**. *P* 14½×14.

633	5 c. Prince Andrew and Miss Sarah Ferguson		25	10
634	50 c. Prince Andrew aboard H.M.S. *Brazen*		1·25	1·40

158 Red Coral Shrimp   159 Golf

(Des D. Miller. Litho Walsall)

1986 (15 Sept). *Marine Life. T* **158** *and similar vert designs. Multicoloured. W* w **14**. *P* 13½×13.

635	5 c. Type 158		40	50
636	10 c. Yellow Crinoid		40	50
637	15 c. Calcinus tibicen (hermit crab)		35	60
638	20 c. Tube dwelling Anemone		35	60
639	25 c. Christmas Tree Worm		45	1·50
640	35 c. Porcupinefish		70	1·75
641	50 c. Orangeball Anemone		80	3·00
642	60 c. Astrophyton muricatum (basket starfish)		2·50	4·50
643	75 c. Flamingo Tongue (Cyphoma gibbosus)		4·50	5·50
644	$1 Condylactis gigantea (sea anemone)		1·40	2·50
645	$2 Diamond Blenny		2·25	4·25
646	$4 Rough File Shell (Lima scabra)		4·75	6·50
635/46		*Set of 12*	17·00	28·00

No. 644 is incorrectly inscribed "Conolylactis gigantea".
Imprint dates: "1986", Nos. 635/46; "1987", Nos. 635/8, 644/6; "1990", Nos. 635/41, 644/5.
For the 10 c. value with watermark w **16** see No. 696.

(Des L. Curtis. Litho Walsall)

1987 (26 Jan). *Tourism. T* **159** *and similar horiz designs. Multicoloured. W* w **16** *(sideways). P* 13×13½.

647	10 c. Type 159		1·25	65
648	15 c. Sailing		1·50	75
649	25 c. Snorkelling		1·60	1·25
650	35 c. Paragliding		1·75	1·40
651	$1 Game fishing		3·25	5·50
647/51		*Set of 5*	8·50	8·50

160 Ackee   161 Lion Lizard

(Des Jennifer Toombs. Litho Questa)

1987 (20 May). *Cayman Islands Fruits. T* **160** *and similar vert designs. Multicoloured. W* w **16**. *P* 14½×14.

652	5 c. Type 160		10	10
	w. Wmk inverted			
653	25 c. Breadfruit		45	45
	w. Wmk inverted		8·50	
654	35 c. Pawpaw		60	60
655	$1 Soursop		1·60	2·75
652/5		*Set of 4*	2·50	3·50

(Des I. Loe. Litho Questa)

1987 (26 Aug). *Lizards. T* **161** *and similar horiz designs. Multicoloured. W* w **16** *(sideways). P* 13½×14.

656	10 c. Type 161		60	20
657	50 c. Iguana		1·75	1·40
658	$1 Anole		2·50	2·50
656/8		*Set of 3*	4·25	3·75

162 Poinsettia   163 *Hemiargus ammon* and *Strymon martialis*

(Des Annette Robinson. Litho Walsall)

1987 (18 Nov). *Flowers. T* **162** *and similar square designs. Multicoloured. W* w **16**. *P* 14½×14.

659	5 c. Type 162		30	15
660	25 c. Periwinkle		1·00	60
661	35 c. Yellow Allamanda		1·25	1·00
662	75 c. Blood Lily		2·25	2·50
659/62		*Set of 4*	4·25	3·75

(Des Jane Thatcher. Litho Questa)

1988 (29 Mar). *Butterflies. T* **163** *and similar horiz designs. Multicoloured. W* w **16**. *P* 14.

663	5 c. Type 163		90	35
664	25 c. Phocides pigmalion		2·00	75
665	50 c. Anaea troglodyta		3·25	2·50
666	$1 Papilio andraemon		4·00	3·00
663/6		*Set of 4*	9·00	6·00

164 Green Heron   165 Cycling

(Des Jane Thatcher. Litho Walsall)

1988 (27 July). *Herons. T* **164** *and similar vert designs. Multicoloured. W* w **16**. *P* 14.

667	5 c. Type 164		80	40
668	25 c. Louisiana Heron		1·75	65
669	50 c. Yellow-crowned Night Heron		2·25	2·25
670	$1 Little Blue Heron		3·00	3·50
667/70		*Set of 4*	7·00	6·00

(Des L. Curtis. Litho Walsall)

1988 (21 Sept). *Olympic Games, Seoul. T* **165** *and similar horiz designs. Multicoloured. W* w **16** *(sideways). P* 14×14½.

671	10 c. Type 165		65	30
672	50 c. Cayman Airways Boeing 727 airliner and national team		1·50	1·10
673	$1 Sailing		1·75	2·00
671/3		*Set of 3*	3·50	3·00
MS674	53×60 mm. $1 Tennis. W w 14 (sideways)		3·00	2·75

166 Princess Alexandra   167 George Town Post Office and Cayman Postmark on Jamaica 1d., 1889

(Des N. Harvey. Litho B.D.T.)

1988 (1 Nov). *Visit of Princess Alexandra. T* **166** *and similar vert design. Multicoloured. W* w **14**. *P* 15×14.

675	5 c. Type 166		60	40
676	$1 Princess Alexandra in evening dress		3·75	2·50

(Des L. Curtis. Litho Questa)

1989 (12 Apr). *Centenary of Cayman Islands Postal Service. T* **167** *and similar horiz designs. Multicoloured. W* w **16** *(sideways). P* 14×14½.

677	5 c. multicoloured		40	25
678	25 c. yellowish green, black and new blue		1·25	70
679	35 c. multicoloured		1·25	90
680	$1 multicoloured		3·50	3·00
677/80		*Set of 4*	5·75	4·25

Designs:—25 c. *Orinoco* (mail steamer) and 1900 ½d. stamp; 35 c. G.P.O., Grand Cayman and "London 1980" $1 stamp; $1 Cayman Airways B.A.C. One Eleven 200/400 and 1966 1s. Jet Service stamp.

 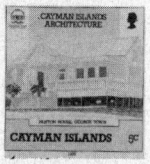

168 Captain Bligh ashore in West Indies   169 Panton House

(Des Jane Hartley. Litho B.D.T.)

1989 (24 May). *Captain Bligh's Second Breadfruit Voyage, 1791-93.* T **168** *and similar vert designs. Multicoloured.* W w **16**. P 14.

681	50 c. Type **168**		2·50	2·75
	a. Horiz strip of 5. Nos. 681/5		11·00	
682	50 c. H.M.S. *Providence* (sloop) at anchor		2·50	2·75
683	50 c. Breadfruit in tubs and H.M.S. *Assistant* (transport)		2·50	2·75
684	50 c. Sailors moving tubs of breadfruit		2·50	2·75
685	50 c. Midshipman and stores		2·50	2·75
681/5		*Set of 5*	11·00	12·00

Nos. 681/5 were printed together, *se-tenant* as a composite design, in horizontal strips of five throughout the sheet.

(Des S. Conlin. Litho Walsall)

1989 (18 Oct). *Architecture.* T **169** *and similar square designs showing George Town buildings. Multicoloured.* W w **14**. P 14½×14.

686	5 c. Type **169**		15	15
687	10 c. Town Hall and Clock Tower		20	20
688	25 c. Old Court House		50	50
689	35 c. Elmslie Memorial Church		65	70
690	$1 Post Office		1·75	2·25
686/90		*Set of 5*	3·00	3·50

170 Map of Grand Cayman, 1773, and Surveying Instruments   171 French Angelfish

(Des N. Shewring. Litho Walsall)

1989 (15 Nov). *Island Maps and Survey Ships.* T **170** *and similar horiz designs. Multicoloured.* W w **16** (*sideways*). P 14×14½.

691	5 c. Type **170**		60	60
692	25 c. Map of Cayman Islands, 1956, and surveying instruments		1·75	1·25
693	50 c. H.M.S. *Mutine*, 1914		2·50	3·00
694	$1 H.M.S. *Vidal*, 1956		4·00	4·50
691/4		*Set of 4*	8·00	8·50

1990 (Mar). *As No. 636, but* W w **16**. "1990" *imprint date.* P 13½×13.

696	10 c. Yellow Crinoid		1·40	1·75

(Des D. Miller. Litho Questa)

1990 (25 Apr). *Angelfishes.* T **171** *and similar horiz designs. Multicoloured.* W w **16** (*sideways*). P 14.

707	10 c. Type **171**		85	40
708	25 c. Grey Angelfish		1·75	90
709	50 c. Queen Angelfish		2·50	3·00
710	$1 Rock Beauty		4·00	4·50
707/10		*Set of 4*	8·25	8·00

(Des D. Miller. Litho Questa)

1990 (4 Aug). *90th Birthday of Queen Elizabeth the Queen Mother. Vert designs as* T **134** (50 c.) *or* **135** ($1) *of Ascension.* W w **16**. P 14×15 (50 c.) *or* 14½ ($1).

711	50 c. multicoloured		1·25	1·75
712	$1 black and blue		2·25	4·00

Designs:—50 c. Silver Wedding photograph, 1948; $1 King George VI and Queen Elizabeth with Winston Churchill, 1940.

172 *Danaus eresimus*   173 Goes Weather Satellite

(Des G. Drummond. Litho Questa)

1990 (24 Oct). *"EXPO 90" International Garden and Greenery Exhibition, Osaka. Butterflies.* T **172** *and similar horiz designs. Multicoloured.* W w **16** (*sideways*). P 14.

713	5 c. Type **172**		65	40
714	25 c. *Brephidium exilis*		1·50	1·10
715	35 c. *Phyciodes phaon*		1·75	1·25
716	$1 *Agraulis vanillae*		4·00	5·50
713/16		*Set of 4*	7·00	7·50

(Des A. Theobald. Litho Questa)

1991 (8 Aug). *International Decade for Natural Disaster Reduction.* T **173** *and similar horiz designs. Multicoloured.* W w **16** (*sideways*). P 14.

717	5 c. Type **173**		65	40
718	30 c. Meteorologist tracking hurricane		1·50	1·10
719	40 c. Damaged buildings		1·75	1·25
720	$1 U.S. Dept of Commerce weather reconnaisance Lockheed WP-3D Orion		4·00	5·50
717/20		*Set of 4*	7·00	7·50

174 Angels and *Datura candida*   175 Coconut Palm

(Des Jennifer Toombs. Litho Questa)

1991 (6 Nov). *Christmas.* T **174** *and similar horiz designs. Multicoloured.* W w **16** (*sideways*). P 14.

721	5 c. Type **174**		30	30
722	30 c. Mary and Joseph going to Bethlehem and *Allamanda cathartica*		90	60
723	40 c. Adoration of the Kings and *Euphorbia pulcherrima*		1·25	90
724	60 c. Holy Family and *Guaiacum officinale*		1·75	2·50
721/4		*Set of 4*	3·75	3·75

(Des D. Miller. Litho Enschede)

1991 (11 Dec). *Island Scenes.* T **175** *and similar multicoloured designs.* W w **16** (*sideways on horiz designs*). P 12½×13 (*vert*) *or* 13×12½ (*horiz*).

725	5 c. Type **175**		30	30
726	15 c. Beach scene (*horiz*)		45	30
727	20 c. Poincianas in bloom (*horiz*)		60	35
728	30 c. Blowholes (*horiz*)		70	50
	a. Silver (inscr and face value) omitted			
729	40 c. Police band (*horiz*)		2·50	1·40
730	50 c. *Song of Norway* (liner) at George Town		1·75	1·40
731	60 c. The Bluff, Cayman Brac (*horiz*)		1·50	1·75
732	80 c. Coat of arms		1·50	2·00
733	90 c. View of Hell (*horiz*)		1·60	2·00
734	$1 Game fishing (*horiz*)		2·00	2·00
735	$2 *Nieuw Amsterdam* (1983) and *Holiday* (liners) in harbour		4·25	4·50
736	$8 Queen Elizabeth II		13·00	15·00
725/36		*Set of 12*	27·00	28·00

Imprint dates: "1991", Nos. 725/36; "1994", No. 725.

(Des D. Miller. Litho Questa ($1), Leigh-Mardon Ltd, Melbourne (others))

1992 (6 Feb). *40th Anniv of Queen Elizabeth II's Accession. Horiz designs as* T **143** *of Ascension.* W w **16** (*sideways*) (30, 40 c.) *or* w **14** (*sideways*) (*others*). P 14.

737	5 c. Caymans' house		25	30
738	20 c. Sunset over islands		70	50
739	30 c. Beach		80	65
740	40 c. Three portraits of Queen Elizabeth		90	90
741	$1 Queen Elizabeth II		2·00	3·25
737/41		*Set of 5*	4·25	5·00

176 Single Cyclist   177 Woman and Donkey with Panniers

(Des G. Vasarhelyi. Litho Questa)

1992 (5 Aug). *Olympic Games, Barcelona. Cycling.* T **176** *and similar horiz designs. Multicoloured.* W w **14** (*sideways*). P 14.

742	15 c. Type **176**		85	45
743	40 c. Two cyclists		1·50	1·25
744	60 c. Cyclist's legs		2·00	2·50
745	$1 Two pursuit cyclists		2·75	3·25
742/5		*Set of 4*	6·25	6·75

(Des O. Ball. Litho Enschedé)

1992 (21 Oct). *Island Heritage.* T **177** *and similar vert designs. Multicoloured.* W w **14**. P 14×13½.

746	5 c. Type **177**		30	20
747	30 c. Fisherman weaving net		85	75
748	40 c. Maypole dancing		1·10	95
749	60 c. Basket making		2·00	2·75
750	$1 Cooking on caboose		2·50	3·25
746/50		*Set of 5*	6·00	7·00

178 Yellow Stingray   179 Turtle and Sailing Dinghies

(Des G. Drummond. Litho Cartor)

1993 (16 June). *Rays.* T **178** *and similar horiz designs. Multicoloured.* W w **14** (*sideways*). P 13½.

751	5 c. Type **178**		50	40
752	30 c. Southern Stingray		1·25	1·00
753	40 c. Spotted Eagle-ray		1·40	1·25
754	$1 Manta		3·25	4·25
751/4		*Set of 4*	5·75	6·25

(Des D. Miller. Litho B.D.T.)

1993 (30 Sept). *Tourism.* T **179** *and similar vert designs. Multicoloured.* W w **14**. P 13½.

755	15 c. Type **179**		40	55
	a. Horiz strip of 5. Nos. 755/9		1·75	
	b. Booklet pane. Nos. 755/64		6·00	
756	15 c. Tourist boat, fishing launch and scuba diver		40	55
757	15 c. Golf		40	55
758	15 c. Tennis		40	55
759	15 c. Pirates and ship		40	55
760	30 c. Liner, tourist launch and yacht		75	90
	a. Horiz strip of 5. Nos. 760/4		3·25	
761	30 c. George Town street		75	90
762	30 c. Tourist submarine		75	90
763	30 c. Motor-scooter riders and cyclists		75	90
764	30 c. Cayman Airways Boeing 737 airliners		75	90
755/64		*Set of 10*	5·00	6·50

Nos. 755/9 and 760/4 were each printed together, *se-tenant*, in horizontal strips of 5 throughout the sheets. Booklet pane No. 755b contains both *se-tenant* strips as a block of 10 with the horizontal edges of the pane imperforate and margins at left and right.

180 Cuban Amazon with Wings spread   181 *Ionopsis utricularioides* and Manger

(Des O. Ball. Litho Leigh-Mardon Ltd, Melbourne)

1993 (29 Oct). *Endangered Species. Cuban Amazon ("Grand Cayman Parrot").* T **180** *and similar square designs. Multicoloured.* W w **14**. P 14.

765	5 c. Type **180**		40	40
766	5 c. On branch with wings folded		40	40
767	30 c. Head of parrot		1·40	1·60
768	30 c. Pair of parrots		1·40	1·60
765/8		*Set of 4*	3·25	3·50

(Des Jennifer Toombs. Litho B.D.T.)

1993 (6 Dec). *Christmas. Orchids.* T **181** *and similar horiz designs. Multicoloured.* W w **16** (*sideways*). P 13½×14.

769	5 c. Type **181**		50	35
770	40 c. *Encyclia cochleata* and shepherd		1·25	85
771	60 c. *Vanilla pompona* and wise men		1·75	2·50
772	$1 *Oncidium caymanense* and Virgin Mary		3·00	3·50
769/72		*Set of 4*	6·00	6·50

182 Queen Angelfish   183 Flags of Great Britain and Cayman Islands

(Des D. Miller and A. Robinson. Litho Enschedé)

1994 (18 Feb). *"Hong Kong '94" International Stamp Exhibition. Reef Life. Sheet* 121×85 mm *containing* T **182** *and similar vert designs. Multicoloured.* W w **14** (*sideways*). P 14½×13.

MS773	60 c. Type **182**; 60 c. Diver with Porkfish and Spot-finned Hogfish; 60 c. Rock Beauty and Royal Gramma; 60 c. French Angelfish and Banded Butterflyfish		6·00	7·00

(Des D. Miller. Litho Questa)

1994 (22 Feb). *Royal Visit.* T **183** *and similar vert designs. Multicoloured.* W w **14**. P 14½×14.

774	5 c. Type **183**		30	25
775	15 c. Royal Yacht *Britannia*		75	50
776	30 c. Queen Elizabeth II		90	90
777	$2 Queen Elizabeth and Prince Philip disembarking		4·25	5·50
774/7		*Set of 4*	5·50	6·50

NEW INFORMATION

The editor is always interested to correspond with people who have new information that will improve or correct the Catalogue.

184 Black-billed Whistling Duck

185 *Electrostrymon angelia*

(Des Josephine Martin. Litho Walsall)

1994 (21 Apr). *Black-billed Whistling Duck ("West Indian Whistling Duck"). T 184 and similar multicoloured designs. W w 16 (sideways) on 15 c., 20 c.). P 14½.*

778	5 c. Type 184		45	40
779	15 c. Duck landing on water (*horiz*)		75	60
780	20 c. Duck preening (*horiz*)		85	70
781	80 c. Duck flapping wings		2·50	3·25
782	$1 Adult and duckling		3·00	3·50
778/82		*Set of 5*	6·75	7·50

MS783 71×45 mm. $1 As No. 782, but including Cayman Islands National Trust symbol .. 5·00 6·00

(Des K. McGee. Litho Enschedé)

1994 (16 Aug). *Butterflies. T 185 and similar vert designs. Multicoloured. W w 14 (sideways). P 13½×14.*

784	10 c. Type 185		40	65
	a. Vert pair. Nos. 784/5		80	1·25
785	10 c. *Eumaeus atala*		40	65
786	$1 *Eurema daira*		2·50	3·25
	a. Vert pair. Nos. 786/7		5·00	6·50
787	$1 *Urbanus dorantes*		2·50	3·25
784/7		*Set of 4*	5·25	7·00

Nos. 784/5 and 786/7 were printed together, *se-tenant*, in vertical pairs throughout the sheets.

186 H.M.S. *Convert* (frigate)

187 Young Green Turtles

(Des B. Dare. Litho Enschedé)

1994 (12 Oct). *Bicentenary of Wreck of Ten Sail off Grand Cayman. T 186 and similar square designs. Multicoloured. W w 14 (sideways). P 13×14.*

788	10 c. Type 186		35	35
789	10 c. Merchant brig and full-rigged ship		35	35
790	15 c. Full-rigged ship near rock		55	45
791	20 c. Long boat leaving full-rigged ship		65	55
792	$2 Merchant brig		4·00	6·00
788/92		*Set of 5*	5·50	7·00

(Des Doreen McGuiness. Litho Questa)

1995 (28 Feb). *Sea Turtles. T 187 and similar horiz designs. Multicoloured. W w 16 (sideways). P 14.*

793	10 c. Type 187		35	30
794	20 c. Kemp's Ridley Turtle		60	45
795	25 c. Hawksbill Turtle		70	50
796	30 c. Leatherback Turtle		75	60
797	$1.30, Loggerhead Turtle		3·00	3·25
798	$2 Pacific Ridley Turtles		4·00	4·50
793/8		*Set of 6*	8·50	8·75

MS799 167×94 mm. Nos. 793/8 .. 8·50 9·50

188 Running

189 Queen Elizabeth the Queen Mother

(Des B. Dare. Litho Questa)

1995 (15 Apr). *C.A.R.I.F.T.A. and I.A.A.F. Games, George Town. T 188 and similar horiz designs. Multicoloured. W w 14 (sideways). P 14½.*

800	10 c. Type 188		40	30
801	20 c. High jumping		70	50
802	30 c. Javelin throwing		90	70
803	$1.30, Yachting		3·25	4·50
800/3		*Set of 4*	4·75	5·50

MS804 100×70 $2 Athletes with medals .. 3·75 4·75

(Des R. Watton. Litho Cartor (Nos. 805/8) or Questa (No. MS809))

1995 (8 May). *50th Anniv of End of Second World War. Multicoloured designs as T 161 of Ascension. W w 14 (sideways). P 13½.*

805	10 c. Members of Cayman Home Guard		50	30
806	25 c. *Comayagua* (freighter)		1·25	70

807	40 c. U-boat *U125*		1·60	1·25
808	$1 U.S. Navy *L-3* airship		3·00	4·25
805/8		*Set of 4*	5·75	6·00

MS809 75×85 mm. $1.30, Reverse of 1939–45 War Medal (*vert*). Wmk upright. P 14 .. 2·50 3·00

(Des N. Shewring. Litho Walsall)

1995 (25 Aug). *95th Birthday of Queen Elizabeth the Queen Mother. Sheet 70×90 mm. W w 14 (sideways). P 14½.*

MS810 189 $4 multicoloured .. 8·00 9·00

190 Ox and Christ Child

191 Sea Grape

(Des Doreen McGuiness. Litho Walsall)

1995 (1 Nov). *Christmas. Nativity Animals. T 190 and similar vert designs. Multicoloured. W w 14. P 14×13½.*

811	10 c. Type 190		35	20
812	20 c. Sheep and lamb		60	45
813	30 c. Donkey		80	60
814	$2 Camels		4·25	5·50
811/14		*Set of 4*	5·50	6·00

MS815 160×75 mm. Nos. 811/14 .. 5·50 6·00

(Des I. Loe. Litho B.D.T.)

1996 (21 Mar). *Wild Fruit. T 191 and similar vert designs. Multicoloured. W w 16. P 14.*

816	10 c. Type 191		30	30
817	25 c. Guava		65	50
818	40 c. West Indian Cherry		90	70
819	$1 Tamarind		2·00	2·75
816/19		*Set of 4*	3·50	3·75

192 Dinghy Sailing

193 Guitar and Score of National Song

(Des G. Vasarhelyi. Litho Walsall)

1996 (19 June). *Centenary of Modern Olympic Games. T 192 and similar vert designs. Multicoloured. W w 16. P 14×13½.*

820	10 c. Type 192		25	20
821	20 c. Sailboarding		50	50
822	30 c. Dinghy sailing (*different*)		70	70
823	$2 Running		3·75	4·50
820/3		*Set of 4*	4·75	5·50

(Des N. Shewring. Litho Questa)

1996 (26 Sept). *National Identity. T 193 and similar square designs. Multicoloured. W w 14. P 14.*

824	10 c. Type 193		15	30
825	20 c. Cayman Airways Boeing 737-200		30	35
826	25 c. Queen Elizabeth opening Legislative Assembly		35	40
827	30 c. Seven Mile Beach		40	45
828	40 c. Scuba diver and Stingrays		55	60
829	60 c. Children at turtle farm		85	90
830	80 c. Cuban Amazon ("Cayman Parrot") (national bird)		1·10	1·25
831	90 c. Silver Thatch Palm (national tree)		1·25	1·40
832	$1 Cayman Islands flag		1·40	1·50
833	$2 Wild Banana Orchid (national flower)		2·75	3·00
834	$4 Cayman Islands coat of arms		5·75	6·00
835	$6 Cayman Islands currency		8·50	8·75
824/35		*Set of 12*	23·00	25·00

Imprint dates: "1996", Nos. 824/35; "1997", No. 824.
For miniature sheet containing No. 830 with "1997" imprint date see No. MS840.

OMNIBUS ISSUES

Details, together with prices for complete sets, of the various Omnibus issues from the 1935 Silver Jubilee series to date are included in a special section following Zimbabwe at the end of Volume 2.

194 "Christmas Time on North Church Street" (Joanne Sibley)

195 Children accessing Internet

(Des D. Miller. Litho Questa)

1996 (12 Nov). *Christmas. Paintings. T 194 and similar square designs. Multicoloured. W w 14 (sideways). P 14.*

836	10 c. Type 194		25	20
837	25 c. "Gone Fishing" (Lois Brezinsky)		50	50
838	30 c. "Claus Encounters" (John Doak)		60	70
839	$2 "A Caymanian Christmas" (Debbie van der Bol)		3·75	4·50
836/9		*Set of 4*	4·50	5·50

(Des D. Miller. Litho Questa)

1997 (3 Feb). *"HONG KONG '97" International Stamp Exhibition. Sheet 130×90 mm, containing design as No. 830 with "1997" imprint date. Multicoloured. W w 14 (inverted). P 14.*

MS840 80 c. Cuban Amazon ("Cayman Parrot") 1·50 2·00

(Des N. Shewring (No. MS847), D. Miller (others). Litho Questa (No. MS847), B.D.T.(others))

1997 (10 July). *Golden Wedding of Queen Elizabeth and Prince Philip. Multicoloured designs as T 173 of Ascension. W w 14. P 13½.*

841	10 c. Queen Elizabeth		25	25
	a. Horiz pair. Nos. 841/2		50	50
842	10 c. Prince Philip and Prince Charles at Trooping the Colour		25	25
843	30 c. Prince William horse riding, 1989		65	75
	a. Horiz pair. Nos. 843/4		1·25	1·50
844	30 c. Queen Elizabeth and Prince Philip at Royal Ascot		65	75
845	40 c. Prince Philip at the Brighton Driving Trials		70	80
	a. Horiz pair. Nos. 845/6		1·40	1·60
846	40 c. Queen Elizabeth at Windsor Horse Show, 1993		70	80
841/6		*Set of 6*	2·75	3·25

MS847 110×70 mm. $1 Queen Elizabeth and Prince Philip in landau (*horiz*). Wmk sideways. P 14×14½ .. 1·75 2·00

Nos. 841/2, 843/4 and 845/6 were each printed together, *se-tenant*, in horizontal pairs throughout the sheets with the backgrounds forming a composite design.

(Des O. Bell. Litho Walsall)

1997 (10 Oct). *Telecommunications. T 195 and similar horiz designs. Multicoloured. W w 16 (sideways). P 14×14½.*

848	10 c. Type 195		25	20
849	25 c. Cable & Wireless cable ship		50	45
850	30 c. New area code "345" on children's T-shirts		60	60
851	60 c. Satellite dish		1·10	1·40
848/51		*Set of 4*	2·25	2·40

196 Santa in Hammock

(Des R. Watton. Litho Cartor)

1997 (3 Dec). *Christmas. T 196 and similar vert designs. Multicoloured. W w 14. P 13.*

852	10 c. Type 196		15	20
853	30 c. Santa with children on the Bluff		40	45
854	40 c. Santa playing golf		55	60
855	$1 Santa scuba diving		1·40	1·50
852/5		*Set of 4*	2·50	2·75

STAMP BOOKLETS

B 1

1993 (30 Sept). *Tourism. Deep ultramarine and bright greenish blue cover as Type B 1. Pane attached by selvedge.*
SB1 $2.25, booklet containing pane of five 15 c. and five
    30 c. (No. 755b)   ..   ..   6·00

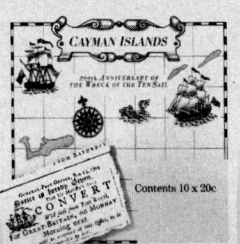

B 2

1994 (12 Oct). *Bicentenary of Wreck of Ten Sail off Grand Cayman. Multicoloured covers as Type B 2. Stamps attached by selvedge.*
SB2 $1 booklet containing block of ten 10 c. stamps
    (No. 788)   ..   ..   1·60
SB3 $1.50, booklet containing block of ten 15 c. stamps
    (No. 790)   ..   ..   2·40
SB4 $2 booklet containing block of ten 20 c. stamps
    (No. 791)   ..   ..   3·25

B 3

1996 (26 Sept). *National Identity. Multicoloured covers as Type B 3 illustrating stamp design enclosed. Stamps attached by selvedge.*
SB5 $1 booklet containing block of ten 10 c. stamps
    (No. 824)   ..   ..   1·40
SB6 $3 booklet containing block of ten 30 c. stamps
    (No. 827)   ..   ..   4·25
SB7 $4 booklet containing block of ten 40 c. stamps
    (No. 828)   ..   ..   5·75

STANLEY GIBBONS
Auctions & Acquisitions

LEADING
PHILATELIC AUCTIONEERS
SINCE 1901

A PROFESSIONAL AUCTION SERVICE FROM THE MOST FAMOUS NAME IN PHILATELY

A PROVEN PROGRAMME OF SPECIALISED INTERNATIONAL SALES

FREE ADVICE AND EXPERT MARKET VALUATIONS

0% VENDOR COMMISSION
(on realisations over £5000)

FAST GUARANTEED PAYMENT

CASH ADVANCES AVAILABLE

SETTLEMENT IN ANY CURRENCY

THE INDUSTRY'S LARGEST DATABASE OF SPECIALIST BUYERS

HIGH QUALITY CATALOGUES DISTRIBUTED WORLDWIDE

REGULAR TELESALES CONTACT WITH MAJOR BUYERS

SPECIALIST SUBSCRIPTION SERVICE

REFINED VENUES AND EXTENSIVE VIEWING TIMES

TELEPHONE TODAY FOR A FULL INFORMATION PACK.

STANLEY GIBBONS AUCTIONS
399 STRAND • LONDON • WC2R 0LX
TELEPHONE: 0171 836 8444
FACSIMILE: 0171 836 7342

Ceylon *see* Sri Lanka

Channel Islands

These issues are now listed under GREAT BRITAIN after the Postal Fiscal Issues.

China—British Post Offices *see after* Hong Kong

Christmas Island *see after* Australia

Cocos (Keeling) Islands *see after* Australia

Cook Islands

(Rarotonga)

This group of fifteen islands was originally also known as the Hervey Islands. A British Protectorate was declared over the group by the local Vice-Consul on 20 September 1888.

Before the introduction of the Cook Islands Post Office mail was forwarded via Auckland, New Zealand.

PRICES FOR STAMPS ON COVER TO 1945

Nos. 1/4	from × 5
Nos. 5/74	from × 4
Nos. 75/145	from × 3

Watermarks of New Zealand used for Cook Islands (including Aitutaki and Penrhyn Island)

W 12*b*

W 38

W 43

W 98

Types of New Zealand Definitives overprinted or surcharged for Cook Islands (including Aitutaki and Penrhyn Island)

23 27 28

31 34 42

51 52 53

60 61 72

F 4 F 6

BRITISH PROTECTORATE

1 2 Queen Makea Takau 3 White Tern or Torea

(Des F. Moss. Typo Govt Printing Office, Wellington)

1892 (19 Apr). *No wmk. P* 12½.

A. Toned paper. B. White paper.

				A.	B.
1	1	1d. black		27·00 26·00	26·00 26·00
		a. Imperf between (vert pair)		† £8500	—
2		1½d. mauve		40·00 38·00	40·00 38·00
		a. Imperf (pair)		£9000	†
3		2½d. blue		40·00 38·00	40·00 38·00
4		10d. carmine		£140 £130	£160 £130
1/4		*Set of* 4 £200 £200		£225 £200	

Nos. 1/4 were printed in sheets of 60 (6×10) from plates constructed from a matrix of 6 slightly different types.

(Eng A. E. Cousins. Typo Govt Printing Office, Wellington)

1893 (28 July)–**1900.** *W* 12*b of New Zealand* (N Z *and Star wide apart*) *(sideways on T* 3*). (a) P* 12 × 11½.

5	2	1d. brown				30·00 45·00
6		1d. blue (3.4.94)				6·50 1·75
		a. Perf 12×11½ and 12½ mixed			†	£950
7		1½d. mauve				6·50 6·00
8		2½d. rose				35·00 23·00
		a. Rose-carmine				60·00 55·00
		ab. Perf 12×11½ and 12½ mixed				£1700
9		5d. olive-black				14·00 13·00
10		10d. green				65·00 48·00
5/10					*Set of* 6	£140 £110

(b) P 11 (July 1896–1900)

11	3	½d. steel blue (1st setting) (11.99)			28·00 45·00
		a. Upper right "d" omitted			£1400
		b. Second setting			18·00 22·00
		ba. Deep blue (1900)			3·75 4·75
12	2	1d. blue			4·00 4·50
13		1d. deep brown/*cream* (4.99)			13·00 13·00
		a. Wmk sideways			
		b. Bistre-brown (1900)			16·00 17·00
14		1½d. deep lilac			8·00 6·50
		a. Deep mauve (1900)			8·00 6·50
15	3	2d. brown/*thin toned* (7.98)			9·00 6·50
		a. Deep brown (1900)			7·50 6·50
16	2	2½d. pale rose			45·00 38·00
		a. Deep rose (1900)			13·00 9·00
17		5d. olive-black			23·00 17·00
18	3	6d. purple/*thin toned* (7.98)			23·00 28·00
		a. Bright purple (1900)			18·00 20·00
19	2	10d. green			16·00 40·00
20	3	1s. red/*thin toned* (7.98)			60·00 70·00
		a. Deep carmine (1900)			48·00 48·00
11/20a				*Set of* 10	£140 £150

Examples of the 1d., 1½d., 2½d. and 5d. perforated 11 and on laid paper are perforation trials.

On the 1st setting of the ½d. the face values are misplaced in each corner. As corrected in the second setting the face values are correctly positioned in each corner.

ONE

HALF

PENNY

(4)

(5)

1899 (24 Apr). *No.* 12 *surch with T* 4 *by Govt Printer, Rarotonga.*

21	2	½d. on 1d. blue				32·00 40·00
		a. Surch inverted				£800 £850
		b. Surch double				£950 £750

NEW ZEALAND TERRITORY

On 8 and 9 October 1900 the chiefs of all the main islands, except Aitutaki, ceded their territory to the British Crown. On 11 June 1901 all the islands, including Aitutaki, were transferred by Great Britain to New Zealand control.

1901 (8 Oct). *No.* 13 *optd with T* 5 *by Govt Printer, Rarotonga.*

22	2	1d. brown			£170 £140
		a. Crown inverted			£1800 £1400
		c. Optd with crown twice			£1500 £1500

1902. *No wmk. P* 11.

(a) Medium white Cowan paper (Feb)

23	3	½d. blue-green			5·50 6·50
24	2	1d. dull rose			8·00 10·00

(b) Thick white Pirie paper (May)

25	3	½d. yellow-green			3·75 4·00
		a. Imperf horiz (vert pair)			£1100
26	2	1d. rose-red			10·00 10·00
		a. Rose-lake			9·50 6·50
27		2½d. dull blue			10·00 21·00

NEW ZEALAND WATERMARKS. In W 43 the wmk units are in vertical columns widely spaced and the sheet margins are unwatermarked or wmkd "NEW ZEALAND POSTAGE" in large letters.

In W **98** the wmk units are arranged alternately in horizontal rows closely spaced and are continued into the sheet margins. Stamps with W **98** sideways show the star to the left of NZ, *as seen from the back.* Sideways inverted varieties have the star to the right, *as seen from the back.*

1902 (Sept). *W* 43 *of New Zealand* (*single-lined NZ and Star, close together; sideways on T* 2). P 11.

28	3	½d. yellow-green			2·00 3·25
		a. Grey-green			17·00 32·00
29	2	1d. rose-pink			3·50 3·00
30		1½d. deep mauve			3·00 7·50
31	3	2d. deep brown			3·75 10·00
		a. No figures of value			£1800 £2750
		b. Perf 11 × 14			£1000
32	2	2½d. deep blue			3·75 6·50
33		5d. olive-black			35·00 45·00
34	3	6d. purple			32·00 28·00
35	2	10d. green			48·00 85·00
36	3	1s. carmine			48·00 65·00
		a. Perf 11 × 14			£1200
28/36				*Set of* 9	£150 £225

Stamps in Type 3 were printed from a master plate with the value added by a series of separate duty plates. One sheet of the 2d. missed this second pass through the press and was issued without value.

1909–11. *W* 43 *of New Zealand.*

37	3	½d. green (*p* 14½×14) (1911)			5·00 6·50
38	2	1d. deep red (*p* 14)			27·00 25·00
		a. Wmk sideways (24.12.09)			10·00 9·00

1913–19. W 43 of New Zealand (sideways on T 3). Chalk-surfaced paper.

9	3	½d. deep green (p 14) (1915)	..	3·50	12·00
		a. Wmk upright	..	4·50	10·00
0	2	1d. red (p 14) (7.13)	..	3·25	3·75
1		1d. red (p 14 × 14½) (1914)	..	4·75	5·00
2		1½d. deep mauve (p 14) (1915)	..	85·00	45·00
3		1½d. deep mauve (p 14 × 15) (1916)	..	7·00	3·75
4	3	2d. deep brown (p 15 × 14) (1919)	..	5·00	42·00
5	2	10d. green (p 14 × 15) (1918)	..	13·00	75·00
6	3	1s. carmine (p 15 × 14) (1919)	..	27·00	75·00
9/46	..	..	Set of 6	50·00	£180

RAROTONGA

APA PENE
(8)

1919 (Apr–July). Stamps of New Zealand surch as T 8.

(a) T 53. W 43. De La Rue chalk-surfaced paper. P 14×15

47		1d. carmine (No. 405) (B.) (June)	..	75	1·50

(b) T 60 (recess). W 43. Cowan unsurfaced paper. P 14×13½.

48		2½d. blue (No. 419) (R.) (June)	..	2·25	6·00
		a. Perf 14×14½	..	2·00	2·25
		b. Vert pair. Nos. 48/a	..	20·00	45·00
49		3d. chocolate (No. 420) (B.)	..	2·00	7·00
		a. Perf 14×14½	..	2·00	1·50
		b. Vert pair. Nos. 49/a	..	22·00	50·00
50		4d. bright violet (No. 422) (B.)	..	2·00	5·50
		a. Re-entry (Pl 20 R. 1/6)	..	60·00	
		b. Re-entry (Pl 20 R. 4/10)	..	60·00	
		c. Perf 14×14½	..	1·75	4·00
		d. Vert pair. Nos. 50 and 50c	..	20·00	55·00
51		4½d. deep green (No. 423) (B.)	..	2·00	6·50
		a. Perf 14×14½	..	1·75	6·50
		b. Vert pair. Nos. 51/a	..	20·00	65·00
52		6d. carmine (No. 425) (B.) (June)	..	3·00	8·00
		a. Perf 14×14½	..	1·75	5·00
		b. Vert pair. Nos. 52/a	..	38·00	80·00
53		7½d. red-brown (No. 426a) (B.)	..	1·50	5·50
54		9d. sage-green (No. 429) (R.)	..	3·25	11·00
		a. Perf 14×14½	..	2·00	11·00
		b. Vert pair. Nos. 54/a	..	38·00	95·00
55		1s. vermilion (No. 430) (B.) (June)	..	11·00	29·00
		a. Perf 14×14½	..	2·75	14·00
		b. Vert pair. Nos. 55/a	..	48·00	£110

(c) T 61 (typo). W 43. De La Rue chalk-surfaced paper. P 14×15

56		½d. green (No. 435) (R.) (June)	..	40	80
57		1½d. orange-brown (No. 438) (R.) (June)	..	40	75
58		2d. yellow (No. 439) (R.)	..	1·00	1·00
59		3d. chocolate (No. 440) (B.) (July)	..	2·00	7·50
47/59	..	..	Set of 13	18·00	55·00

9 Capt. Cook landing
10 Wharf at Avarua

11 "Capt. Cook" (Dance)
12 Palm Tree

13 Huts at Arorangi
14 Avarua Harbour

R.2/8 R.3/6 R.5/2
Double derrick flaws

(Des, eng and recess Perkins, Bacon & Co)

1920 (23 Aug). No wmk. P 14.

70	9	½d. black and green	..	4·00	13·00
71	10	1d. black and carmine-red	..	3·50	10·00
		a. Double derrick flaw (R.2/8, 3/6 or 5/2)	11·00	
72	11	1½d. black and dull blue	..	7·50	8·50
73	12	3d. black and chocolate	..	2·25	5·50
74	13	6d. brown and yellow-orange	..	1·75	8·50
75	14	1s. black and violet	..	5·00	17·00
70/5	..	..	Set of 6	22·00	55·00

Examples of the 1d. and 1s. with centre inverted were not supplied to the Post Office.

RAROTONGA
(15)
RAROTONGA

Trimmed overprint (R. 1/6 and R. 3/7)

1921 (Oct)–23. Postal Fiscal stamps as Type F 4 of New Zealand optd with T 15. W 43 (sideways). Chalk-surfaced "De La Rue" paper. P 14½×14.

76		2s. deep blue (No. F111) (R.)	..	26·00	50·00
		a. Trimmed opt	..	85·00	
		b. Carmine opt (1923)	..	£140	£160
		ba. Trimmed opt	..	£400	
77		2s. 6d. grey-brown (No. F112) (B.)	..	18·00	50·00
		a. Trimmed opt	..	65·00	
78		5s. yellow-green (No. F115) (R.)	..	26·00	65·00
		a. Trimmed opt	..	85·00	
79		10s. maroon (No. F120) (B.)	..	48·00	80·00
		a. Trimmed opt	..	£150	
80		£1 rose-carmine (No. F123) (B.)	..	80·00	£130
		a. Trimmed opt	..	£250	
76/80			Set of 5	£180	£325

See also Nos. 85/9.

16 Te Po, Rarotongan Chief
17 Harbour, Rarotonga and Mt Ikurangi

(2½d. from a print; 4d. des A. H. Messenger. Plates by P.B. Recess Govt Ptg Office, Wellington)

1924–27. W 43 of New Zealand. P 14.

81	9	½d. black and green (13.5.26)	..	4·50	7·00
82	10	1d. black and deep carmine (10.11.24)	6·00	1·50
		a. Double derrick flaw (R.2/8, 3/6 or 5/2)	16·00	
83	16	2½d. red-brown and steel blue (15.10.27)	4·50	19·00
84	17	4d. green and violet (15.10.27)	..	7·50	15·00
81/4			Set of 4	20·00	38·00

1926 (Feb–May). As Nos. 76/80, but on thick, opaque white chalk-surfaced "Cowan" paper.

85		2s. blue (No. F131) (C.)	..	£100	£150
		a. Trimmed opt	..	£300	
86		2s. 6d. deep grey-brown (No. F132) (B.)	50·00	80·00
87		5s. yellow-green (No. F135) (R.) (May)	48·00	70·00
		a. Trimmed opt	..	£130	
88		10s. brown-red (No. F139) (B.) (May)	55·00	85·00
89		£1 rose-pink (No. F142) (B.) (May)	80·00	£120
85/9			Set of 5	£300	£450

1926 (Oct)–28. T 72 of New Zealand, overprinted with T 15.

(a) Jones chalk-surfaced paper.

90		2s. deep blue (No. 466) (R.)	..	10·00	38·00

(b) Cowan thick, opaque chalk-surfaced paper

91		2s. light blue (No. 469) (R.) (18.6.27)	15·00	38·00
92		3s. pale mauve (No. 470) (R.) (30.1.28)	16·00	40·00
90/2			Set of 3	38·00	£100

TWO PENCE   COOK ISLANDS.
(18)   (19)

1931 (Mar). Surch with T 18. P 14. (a) No wmk.

93	11	2d. on 1½d. black and blue (R.)	..	8·50	2·75

(b) W 43 of New Zealand

94	11	2d. on 1½d. black and mauve (R.)	..	3·75	8·00

1931 (12 Nov)–32. Postal Fiscal stamps as Type F 6 of New Zealand. W 43. Thick, opaque, white chalk-surfaced Cowan paper. P 14.

(a) Optd with T 15

95		2s. 6d. deep brown (No. F147) (B.)	..	9·50	19·00
96		5s. green (No. F149) (R.) ..	..	16·00	48·00
97		10s. carmine-lake (No. F155) (B.) ..	35·00	80·00
98		£1 pink (No. F158) (B.)	..	80·00	£130

(b) Optd with T 19 (3.32)

98a		£3 green (No. F164) (R.)	..	£140	£300
98b		£5 indigo-blue (No. F168) (R.)	..	£170	£300

The £3 and £5 values were mainly used for fiscal purposes.

20 Capt. Cook landing
21 Capt. Cook

22 Double Maori Canoe
23 Natives working Cargo

24 Port of Avarua
25 R.M.S. Monowai

26 King George V

(Des L. C. Mitchell. Recess P.B.)

1932 (15 Mar–2 May). No wmk. P 13.

99	20	½d. black and deep green	..	3·50	14·00
		a. Perf 14	..	28·00	90·00
100	21	1d. black and lake	..	4·50	3·75
		a. Centre inverted	..	£2500	£2500
		b. Perf compound of 13 and 14	£180	£200
		c. Perf 14	..	15·00	18·00
101	22	2d. black and brown	..	2·50	4·50
		a. Perf 14	..	8·50	17·00
102	23	2½d. black and deep blue	..	6·00	48·00
		a. Perf 14	..	12·00	48·00
103	24	4d. black and bright blue	..	19·00	55·00
		a. Perf 14	..	9·50	45·00
		b. Perf 14×13	..	30·00	90·00
		c. Perf compound of 14 and 13	50·00	£100
104	25	6d. black and orange	..	24·00	48·00
		a. Perf 14	..	3·50	12·00
105	26	1s. black and violet (p 14) (2 May)	7·50	19·00
99/105			Set of 7	32·00	£130

Nos. 100b and 103c come from sheets reperforated 14 on arrival at Wellington. No. 100b comes from the first vertical column of a sheet and has 14 at left and No. 103c from the third or fourth vertical column with 13 at left or right.

Other major errors exist on this issue, but these are not listed as they originated from printer's waste which appeared on the market in 1935.

(Recess from P.B. plates at Govt Printing Office, Wellington)

1933–36. W 43 of New Zealand (Single N Z and Star). P 14.

106	20	½d. black and deep green	..	75	3·00
		w. Wmk inverted	..	—	75·00
107	21	1d. black and scarlet (1935) ..	..	80	1·50
		w. Wmk inverted and reversed		
108	22	2d. black and brown (1936)	..	1·00	30
109	23	2½d. black and deep blue	..	1·25	2·25
110	24	4d. black and bright blue	..	1·00	35
111	25	6d. black and orange-yellow (1936)	1·50	2·25
112	26	1s. black and violet (1936)	..	25·00	26·00
106/12			Set of 7	28·00	32·00

SILVER JUBILEE OF KING GEORGE V. 1910 - 1935.
(27)

Normal letters B K E N
Narrow letters B K E N

1935 (7 May). Silver Jubilee. Optd with T 27 (wider vertical spacing on 6d.). Colours changed. W 43 of New Zealand. P 14.

113	21	1d. red-brown and lake	..	60	85
		a. Narrow "K" in "KING"	..	2·75	
		b. Narrow "B" in "JUBILEE"	..	4·50	
114	23	2½d. dull and deep blue (R.)	..	1·00	1·75
		a. Narrow first "E" in "GEORGE"	3·50	5·00
115	25	6d. green and orange	..	3·50	4·75
		a. Narrow "N" in "KING"	..	16·00	
113/15			Set of 3	4·50	6·50

1936 (15 July)–44. Stamps of New Zealand optd with T 19. W 43. P 14.

(a) T 72. Cowan thick, opaque chalk-surfaced paper

116		2s. light blue (No. 469)	..	12·00	45·00
117		3s. pale mauve (No. 470)	..	13·00	65·00

(b) Type F 6. Cowan thick, opaque chalk-surfaced paper

118		2s. 6d. deep brown (No. F147)	..	17·00	60·00
119		5s. green (No. F149) (R.)	..	20·00	80·00
120		10s. carmine-lake (No. F155)	..	40·00	£130
121		£1 pink (No. F158)	..	60·00	£160
118/21			Set of 4	£120	£375

(c) Type F 6. Thin, hard, chalk-surfaced Wiggins, Teape paper

122		2s. 6d. dull brown (No. F170) (12.40)	85·00	85·00
123		5s. green (No. F172) (R.) (10.40)	..	£300	£300
123a		10s. pale carmine-lake (No. F177) (11.44)	£120	£160
123b		£3 green (No. F183) (R.) (date?)	..	£325	£550
122/3b			Set of 4	£700	£1000

COOK IS'DS.
(28)

IS'DS.
Small second "S" (R. 1/2)

1937 (1 June). Coronation. Nos. 599/601 of New Zealand (inscr "12th MAY 1937") optd with T 28.

124		1d. carmine	..	40	20
		a. Small second "S"	..	10·00	
125		2½d. Prussian blue..	..	80	20
		a. Small second "S"	..	18·00	
126		6d. red-orange	..	80	20
		a. Small second "S"	..	18·00	
124/6			Set of 3	1·75	55

29 King George VI   **30** Native Village

31 Native Canoe   **32** Tropical Landscape

(Des J. Berry (2s., 3s., and frame of 1s.). Eng B.W. Recess Govt Ptg. Office, Wellington)

1938 (2 May). *W* **43** *of New Zealand. P* 14.
127	29	1s. black and violet	..	6·00	8·00
128	30	2s. black and red-brown	..	17·00	9·00
		w. Wmk inverted			
129	31	3s. light blue and emerald-green	..	40·00	30·00
127/9		.. .. ..	*Set of* 3	55·00	42·00

(Recess B.W.)

1940 (2 Sept). *Surch as in T* **32**. *W* **98** *of New Zealand. P* 13½ × 14.
130	32	3d. on 1½d. black and purple ..	30	40

Type 32 was not issued without surcharge.

1943–54. *Postal Fiscal stamps as Type F* **6** *of New Zealand optd with T* **19**. *W* **98** *of New Zealand. Wiggins, Teape chalk-surfaced paper. P* 14.
131	2s. 6d. dull brown (No. F170) (3.46)	..	24·00	38·00
	w. Wmk inverted (2.4.51)	..	12·00	16·00
132	5s. green (No. F172) (R.) (11.43)	..	7·00	17·00
	w. Wmk inverted (5.54)	..	15·00	18·00
133	10s. pale carmine-lake (No. F177) (10.48)		48·00	65·00
	w. Wmk inverted (10.51)	..	38·00	60·00
134	£1 pink (No. F179) (11.47)	..	42·00	65·00
	w. Wmk inverted (19.5.54)	..	42·00	65·00
135	£3 green (No. F183) (R.) (1946?)	..	£375	£550
	w. Wmk inverted (28.5.53)	..	55·00	£160
136	£5 indigo-blue (No. F184) (R.) (25.10.50)		£225	£350
	w. Wmk inverted (19.5.54)	..	£250	£375
131/6	.. ..	*Set of* 6	£350	£600

The £3 and £5 were mainly used for fiscal purposes.

(Recess Govt Ptg Office, Wellington)

1944–46. *W* **98** *of New Zealand (sideways on ½d. 1d., 1s., and 2s.). P* 14.
137	20	½d. black and deep green (11.44)	..	1·00	3·50
		w. Wmk sideways inverted ..		7·00	
138	21	1d. black and scarlet (3.45)	..	2·00	35
		w. Wmk sideways inverted ..		10·00	
139	22	2d. black and brown (2.46)	..	1·25	4·25
140	23	2½d. black and deep blue (5.45)		65	1·75
141	24	4d. black and blue (4.44)	..	3·50	7·00
		y. Wmk inverted and reversed	..	40·00	40·00
142	25	6d. black and orange (6.44)	..	1·25	1·50
143	29	1s. black and violet (9.44)	..	1·25	2·25
144	30	2s. black and red-brown (8.45)		23·00	20·00
145	31	3s. light blue & emerald-green (6.45)	27·00	20·00
137/45		..	*Set of* 9	55·00	55·00

COOK ISLANDS

(33)

34 Ngatangiia Channel,   **41** Map and Statue
Rarotonga   of Capt. Cook

(Des J. Berry. Recess Waterlow)

1949 (1 Aug)–**61.** *T* **34**, **41** *and similar designs. W* **98** *of New Zealand (sideways on shilling values). P* 13½ × 13 *(horiz) or* 13 × 13½ *(vert).*
150		½d. violet and brown	..	10	1·00
151		1d. chestnut and green	..	3·00	2·00
152		2d. reddish brown and scarlet	..	90	2·00
153		3d. green and ultramarine	..	1·00	2·00
		aw. Wmk inverted	..	£100	
		b. Wmk sideways (white opaque paper) (22.5.61)		3·50	2·50
154		6d. emerald-green and violet	..	3·50	1·50
155		6d. black and carmine	..	3·75	2·75
156		8d. olive-green and orange	..	40	3·75
		w. Wmk inverted	..	85·00	50·00
157		1s. light blue and chocolate	..	4·25	3·75

158		2s. yellow-brown and carmine	..	3·00	9·00
		w. Wmk sideways inverted	..	..	
159		3s. light blue and bluish green	..	7·50	14·00
150/9			*Set of* 10	25·00	38·00

Designs: *Horiz*—1d. Capt. Cook and map of Hervey Islands; 2d. Rarotonga and Revd. John Williams; 3d. Aitutaki and palm trees; 5d. Rarotonga Airfield; 6d. Penrhyn village; 8d. Native hut. *Vert*—2s. Native hut and palms; 3s. *Matua* (inter-island freighter).
See note on white opaque paper below No. 736 of New Zealand.

42 Queen
Elizabeth II

(Des J. Berry. Photo Harrison)

1953 (25 May). *Coronation. T* **42** *and similar vert design. W* **98**. *P* 14×14½.
160		3d. brown	..	1·00	75
161		6d. slate-grey	..	1·25	1·25

Design:—6d. Westminster Abbey.

1/6

(44)

1960 (1 Apr). *No.* 154 *surch with T* **44**.
162		1s. 6d. on 5d. emerald-green and violet	..	30	30

45 Tiare Maori   **48** White Tern

52 Queen Elizabeth II   **53** Island Scene

(Des J. Berry. Recess (1s. 6d.), litho (others) B.W.)

1963 (4 June). *T* **45**, **48**, **52**/**3** *and similar designs. W* **98** *of New Zealand (sideways). P* 13½×13 *(1d., 2d., 8d.),* 13×13½ *(3d., 5d., 6d., 1s.) or* 13½×13½ *(others).*
163		1d. emerald-green and yellow	..	45	40
164		2d. brown-red and yellow	..	20	40
165		3d. yellow, yellow-green & reddish violet	70	40
166		5d. blue and black	..	7·00	75
167		6d. red, yellow and green	..	1·00	30
168		8d. black and blue	..	3·25	1·25
169		1s. orange-yellow and yellow-green..	40	30
170		1s. 6d. bluish violet	..	2·75	2·00
171		2s. bistre-brown and grey-blue	..	85	75
172		3s. black and yellow-green	..	1·25	1·00
173		5s. bistre-brown and blue	..	9·00	3·25
163/73			*Set of* 11	24·00	9·50

Designs: *Vert (as T* **45**)—2d. Fishing god; 8d. Long-tailed Tuna. *Horiz (as T* **48**)—3d. Frangipani; 6d. Hibiscus; 1s. Oranges. (*As T* **53**)—3s. Administration Centre, Mangaia; 5s. Rarotonga.

56 Eclipse and Palm   **57** N.Z. Ensign and Map

(Des L. C. Mitchell. Litho B.W.)

1965 (31 May). *Solar Eclipse Observation, Manuae Island. W* **98** *of New Zealand. P* 13½.
174	56	6d. black, yellow and light blue	..	20	10

SELF-GOVERNMENT

(Des R. M. Conly (4d.), L. C. Mitchell (10d., 1s.), J. Berry (1s. 9d.) Litho B.W.)

1965 (16 Sept). *Internal Self-Government. T* **57** *and similar horiz designs. W* **98** *of New Zealand (sideways). P* 13½.
175		4d. red and blue	..	..	20	15
176		10d. multicoloured	..	..	20	15
177		1s. multicoloured	..	..	20	15
178		1s. 9d. multicoloured	..		50	1·00
175/8		..	*Set of* 4	1·00	1·25

Designs:—10d. London Missionary Society Church; 1s. Proclamation of Cession, 1900; 1s. 9d. Nikao School.

In Memoriam
SIR WINSTON CHURCHILL
1874 - 1965   **Airmail**
(61)   (62)

1966 (24 Jan). *Churchill Commemoration. Nos.* 171/3 *and* 175/7 *optd with T* **61**, *in red.*
179		4d. red and blue	..		75	30
		a. "l" for "1" in "1874"	..	..	3·00	
180		10d. multicoloured	..		1·50	45
		a. Opt inverted	..		£160	
		b. "l" for "1" in "1874"	..		5·00	
181		1s. multicoloured	..		1·50	65
		a. Opt inverted	..		£100	
		b. "l" for "1" in "1874"	..		5·00	
182		2s. bistre-brown and grey-blue	..	1·50	1·25
		a. "l" for "1" in "1874"	..		5·00	
183		3s. black and yellow-green	..	1·50	1·25
		a. "l" for "1" in "1874"	..		5·00	
184		5s. bistre-brown and blue	..	2·00	1·75
		a. "l" for "1" in "1874"	..		10·00	
179/84		..	*Set of* 6	8·00	5·00

The lower case "l" for "1" in "1874" occurred on R. 6/5 for all values and additionally on R. 12/5 for the 2s., 3s. and 5s.

1966 (22 Apr). *Air. Various stamps optd with T* **62** *or surch also.*
185		6d. red, yellow and green (No. 167)	..	1·25	20
186		7d. on 8d. black and blue (No. 168)	..	1·50	25
187		10d. on 3d. yellow, yellow-green and reddish violet (No. 165)		1·00	15
188		1s. orange-yellow & yellow-green (No. 169)	1·00	15
189		1s. 6d. bluish violet (No. 170)	..	1·50	1·25
190		2s. 3d. on 3s. black & yellow-grn (No. 172)	1·00	65
191		5s. bistre-brown and blue (No. 173)	..	1·75	1·50
192		10s. on 2s. bistre-brown & grey-bl (No. 171)	1·75	10·00
193		£1 pink (No. 134)	..	..	12·00	17·00
		a. Aeroplane omitted	..		27·00	40·00
		w. Wmk inverted	..		12·00	16·00
185/93		..	*Set of* 9	20·00	27·00

No. 193a occurred in all stamps of the last vertical row as insufficient aeroplane symbols were available. There are also numerous other varieties on all values, notably aeroplanes of different sizes and broken first "i" with dot missing owing to damaged type.

PRINTERS. The following stamps were printed by Heraclio Fournier, Spain except *where otherwise stated.* The process used was photogravure until No. **MS**1247 and lithography thereafter.

63 "Adoration of the Magi" (Fra Angelico)

1966 (28 Nov). *Christmas. T* **63** *and similar multicoloured designs.*
A. *P* 13 × 12 *(horiz) or* 12 × 13 *(vert).*
B. *P* 13 × 14½ *(horiz) or* 14½ × 13 *(vert).*
			A		B	
194		1d. Type 63	50	60	10	10
195		2d. "The Nativity" (Memling) (*vert*)	11·00	11·00	20	10
196		4d. "Adoration of the Magi" (Velazquez) (*horiz*)	1·00	1·00	30	15
197		10d. "Adoration of the Magi" (Bosch) (*horiz*)	2·00	4·50	30	20
198		1s. 6d. "Adoration of the Shepherds" (J. de Ribera) (*vert*)	20·00	6·50	40	35
194/8		..	*Set of* 5	30·00	21·00	1·10	70

68 Tennis, and Queen Elizabeth II

(Des V. Whiteley)

1967 (12 Jan). *2nd South Pacific Games, Nouméa. T* **68** *and similar horiz designs in orange-brown, black and new blue (1d.) or multicoloured (others). P* 13½. *(a) Postage.*

199	½d. Type **68**	10	10
200	1d. Netball and Games emblem	10	10
201	4d. Boxing and Cook Islands' team badge	10	10
202	7d. Football and Queen Elizabeth II	15	10

(b) Air

203	10d. Running and Games emblem	15	10
204	2s. 3d. Running and Cook Islands' team badge	20	20
199/204	*Set of 6*	60	45

(New Currency, 100 cents = 1 dollar)

1c   2½c (I)   2½c (II)

(74)

1967 (3 Apr–6 June). *Decimal Currency. Nos.* 134, 135w, 136, 163/70 *and* 172/5 *surch as T* **74** *by the Government Printer. Sterling values unobliterated except No.* 218.

205	1 c. on 1d. emerald-green and yellow (4.5)		45	1·25
206	2 c. on 2d. brown-red and yellow		10	10
207	2½ c. on 3d. yell, yellow-grn & reddish vio (I)		20	10
	a. Horiz pair. Nos. 207/8		40	20
208	2½ c. on 3d. yellow, yellow-green & reddish violet (II)		20	10
209	3 c. on 4d. red and blue		15	10
210	4 c. on 5d. blue and black (4.5)		3·50	30
211	5 c. on 6d. red, yellow and green		15	10
212	5 c. on 6d. black, yellow and light blue		4·75	40
213	7 c. on 8d. black and blue		30	10
214	10 c. on 1s. orange-yellow and yellow-green		15	10
215	5 c. on 1s. 6d. bluish violet (R.) (4.5.67)		2·00	1·00
216	30 c. on 3s. black & yellow-green (R.) (4.5.67)		15·00	4·50
217	50 c. on 5s. bistre-brown & blue (R.) (4.5.67)		4·00	1·25
218	$1 and 10s. on 10d. mult (R.) (4.5.67)		15·00	6·50
219	$2 on £1 pink (R.) (6.6.67)		50·00	70·00
220	$6 on £3 green (R.) (6.6.67)		95·00	£110
221	$10 on £5 blue (R.) (6.6.67)		£150	£170
	w. Wmk inverted		£150	£170
205/18	*Set of 14*		40·00	13·00

The two types of the 2½ c. occur on alternate vertical rows within the sheet.

The surcharge on No. 218 is $1 and its equivalent of 10s. in the old currency. The "10d." is obliterated by three bars.

A large number of minor varieties exist in these surcharges, such as wrong fount letter "C" and figures.

75 Village Scene. Cook Islands 1d. Stamp of 1892 and Queen Victoria (from "Penny Black")

(Des V. Whiteley)

1967 (3 July). *75th Anniv of First Cook Islands Stamps. T* **75** *and similar horiz designs. Multicoloured. P* 13½.

222	1 c. (1d.) Type **75**	10	10
223	3 c. (4d.) Post Office, Avarua, Rarotonga and Queen Elizabeth II	15	10
224	8 c. (10d.) Avarua, Rarotonga and Cook Islands 10d. stamp of 1892	30	10
225	18 c. (1s. 9d.) *Moana Roa* (inter-island ship), Douglas DC-3 aircraft, map and Captain Cook	1·40	25
222/5	*Set of 4*	1·75	40
MS226	134×109 mm. Nos. 222/5	2·25	2·75

The face values are expressed in decimal currency and in the sterling equivalent.

Each value was issued in sheets of 8 stamps and 1 label.

79 Hibiscus   **80** Queen Elizabeth II

81 Queen Elizabeth and Flowers

Two types of $4

I. Value 32½ mm long. Coarse screen.
II. Value 33½ mm long. Finer screen.

(Floral designs from paintings by Mrs. Kay W. Billings)

1967–71. *Multicoloured designs as T* **79**/81. *P* 14 × 13½. A. *Without fluorescent security markings.* B. *With fluorescent security markings.*

			A		B	
227	½ c. Type **79**		10	10	20	10
228	1 c. *Hibiscus syriacus* (27 × 37 mm)		10	10	20	10
229	2 c. *Frangipani* (27 × 37 mm)		10	10	20	10
230	2½ c. *Clitoria ternatea* (27 × 37 mm)		20	10	20	10
231	3 c. "Suva Queen" (27 × 37 mm)		55	10	40	10
232	4 c. Water Lily ("WALTER LILY") (27 × 37 mm)		70	1·00	†	
233	4 c. Water Lily (27 × 37 mm)		2·00	2·50	2·50	10
234	5 c. *Bauhinia bipinnata rosea* (27 × 37 mm)		35	10	30	10
235	6 c. *Hibiscus* (27 × 37 mm)		40	10	30	10
236	8 c. *Allamanda cathartica* (27 × 37 mm)		40	10	30	10
237	9 c. *Stephanotis* (27 × 37 mm)		40	10	30	10
238	10 c. *Poinciana regia flamboyant* (27 × 37 mm)		40	10	30	10
239	15 c. *Frangipani* (27 × 37 mm)		40	10	30	10
240	20 c. *Thunbergia* (27 × 37 mm)		4·00	1·25	3·50	75
241	25 c. *Canna Lily* (27 × 37 mm)		80	30	1·00	15
242	30 c. *Euphorbia pulcherrima poinsettia* (27 × 37 mm)		65	50	2·00	40
243	50 c. *Gardinia taitensis* (27 × 37 mm)		1·00	55	2·00	40
244	$1 Type **80**		2·25	80	1·75	80
245	$2 Type **80**		4·75	1·50	3·50	1·50
246	$4 Type **81** (I)		2·50	4·00	35·00	48·00
246c	$4 Type **81** (II)			†	7·00	8·50
247	$6 Type **81**		3·00	5·50	11·00	6·00
247c	$8 Type **81**		7·00	14·00	15·00	10·00
248	$10 Type **81**		6·00	12·00	17·00	12·00
227/48	*Set of 22*		32·00	38·00	60·00	35·00

Dates of issue:—Nos. 227/238A, 31.7.67; Nos. 239/243A, 11.8.67; Nos. 244/245A, 31.8.67; Nos. 246/247A, 30.4.68; No. 248A, 12.7.68; No. 247cA, 21.4.69; Nos. 227/243B, 9.2.70; Nos. 244/245B, 12.10.70; No. 246cB, 14.7.71; No. 246B, 11.11.70; No. 247B, 12.2.71; No. 247cB, 3.5.71; No. 248B, 14.6.71.

The "WALTER" spelling error occurred on all stamps in one of the four post office sheets which went to make up the printing sheet and this was corrected in later supplies.

FLUORESCENT PAPER. This is on paper treated with fluorescent security markings, in the form of faint multiple coats of arms. Stamps exist with these markings inverted. In addition an invisible synthetic gum has been used which prevents curling and is suitable for use in the tropics without interleaving the sheets.

Some of the above are known with these markings omitted and can be distinguished when in unused condition from the original printings without markings by their synthetic invisible gum.

97 "Ia Orana Maria"

1967 (24 Oct). *Gauguin's Polynesian Paintings. T* **97** *and similar designs. Multicoloured. P* 13.

249	1 c. Type **97**	10	10
250	3 c. "Riders on the Beach"	15	10
251	5 c. "Still Life with Flowers"	20	10
252	8 c. "Whispered Words"	25	10
253	15 c. "Maternity"	50	15
254	22 c. "Why are you angry?"	65	20
249/54	*Set of 6*	1·60	55
MS255	156 × 132 mm. Nos. 249/54	1·75	1·25

The 5 c. includes an inset portrait of Queen Elizabeth.

98 "The Holy Family" (Rubens)

HURRICANE RELIEF PLUS 5c

(99)

1967 (4 Dec). *Christmas. Renaissance Paintings. T* **98** *and similar designs. Multicoloured. P* 12 × 13.

256	1 c. Type **98**	10	10
257	3 c. "Adoration of the Magi" (Dürer)	10	10
258	4 c. "The Lucca Madonna" (J. van Eyck)	10	10
259	8 c. "The Adoration of the Shepherds" (J. da Bassano)	15	10
260	15 c. "Adoration of the Shepherds" (El Greco)	30	10
261	25 c. "Madonna and Child" (Correggio)	35	10
256/61	*Set of 6*	90	30

1968 (12 Feb). *Hurricane Relief. Nos.* 231A, 233A, 251, 238A, 241A *and* 243/4A *surch as T* **99** *by Govt Printer, Rarotonga.*

262	3 c. + 1 c. "Suva Queen"	15	10
263	4 c. + 1 c. Water Lily	15	10
264	5 c. + 2 c. "Still Life with Flowers"	20	10
	a. Black surch albino		
265	10 c. + 2 c. *Poinciana regia flamboyant*	20	10
266	25 c. + 5 c. Canna Lily	25	10
267	50 c. + 10 c. *Gardinia taitensis*	30	20
268	$1 + 10 c. Type **80**	50	40
262/8	*Set of 7*	1·60	95

The surcharge on No. 268 is as T **99**, but with seriffed letters. On No. 264 silver blocking obliterates the design area around the lettering.

100 "Matavai Bay, Tahiti" (J. Barralet)

101 "*Resolution* and *Discovery*" (J. Webber)

(Des J. Berry)

1968 (12 Sept). *Bicentenary of Captain Cook's First Voyage of Discovery. Multicoloured. Invisible gum. P* 13.

(a) Postage. Vert designs as T **100**

269	½ c. Type **100**	10	10
270	1 c. "Island of Huaheine" (John Cleveley)	15	10
271	2 c. "Town of St. Peter and St. Paul, Kamchatka" (J. Webber)	45	35
272	4 c. "The Ice Islands" (Antarctica: W. Hodges)	60	35

(b) Air. Horiz designs as T **101**

273	6 c. Type **101**	1·00	65
274	10 c. "The Island of Tahiti" (W. Hodges)	1·25	75
275	15 c. "Karakakooa, Hawaii" (J. Webber)	1·75	90
276	25 c. "The Landing at Middleburg" (J. Sherwin)	2·00	1·25
269/76	*Set of 8*	6·50	4·00

Each value was issued in sheets of 10 stamps and 2 labels.

FLUORESCENT PAPER. From No. 277, *unless otherwise stated,* all issues are printed on paper treated with fluorescent security markings with invisible synthetic gum. These markings may be inverted or omitted in error.

102 Sailing   **103** "Madonna and Child" (Titian)

1968 (21 Oct). *Olympic Games, Mexico. T* **102** *and similar horiz designs. Multicoloured. P* 13.

277	1 c. Type **102**	10	10
278	5 c. Gymnastics	10	10
279	15 c. High-jumping	20	10
280	20 c. High-diving	20	10
281	30 c. Cycling	40	20
282	50 c. Hurdling	40	25
277/82	*Set of 6*	1·10	60

Each value was issued in sheets of 10 stamps and 2 labels.

1968 (2 Dec). *Christmas. Paintings. T* **103** *and similar vert designs. Multicoloured. P* 13½.

283	1 c. Type **103**	10	10
284	4 c. "The Holy Family with Lamb" (Raphael)	15	10
285	10 c. "The Virgin of the Rosary" (Murillo)	25	10
286	20 c. "Adoration of the Kings" (Memling)	40	10
287	30 c. "Adoration of the Magi" (Ghirlandaio)	45	10
283/7	*Set of 5*	1·25	30
MS288	114 × 177 mm. Nos. 283/7 plus label	1·60	1·60

NEW INFORMATION

The editor is always interested to correspond with people who have new information that will improve or correct the Catalogue.

104 Camp-fire Cooking

1969 (6 Feb). *Diamond Jubilee of New Zealand Scout Movement and Fifth National (New Zealand) Jamboree.* T **104** *and similar square designs. Multicoloured.* P 13½.

289	½ c. Type **104**	..	..	10	10
290	1 c. Descent by rope	..	..	10	10
291	5 c. Semaphore	..	..	10	10
292	10 c. Tree-planting	..	..	15	10
293	20 c. Constructing a shelter	..	25	10
294	30 c. Lord Baden-Powell and island scene	40	15
289/94			*Set of 6*	90	35

Each value was optd in sheets of 10 stamps and 2 labels.

105 High Jumping

1969 (7 July). *Third South Pacific Games, Port Moresby.* T **105** *and similar triangular designs. Multicoloured. Without fluorescent security markings.* P 13 × 13½.

295	½ c. Type **105**	..	..	10	20
296	½ c. Footballer	..	..	10	20
297	1 c. Basketball	..	..	40	30
298	1 c. Weightlifter	..	..	40	30
299	4 c. Tennis-player	..	..	50	40
300	4 c. Hurdler	..	..	50	40
301	10 c. Javelin-thrower	..	55	40
302	10 c. Runner	..	..	55	40
303	15 c. Golfer	..	..	1·50	1·25
304	15 c. Boxer	..	..	1·50	1·25
295/304			*Set of 10*	5·50	4·50
MS305	174 × 129 mm. Nos. 295/304 plus two labels		5·50	4·50

Each value was issued in sheets containing 5 *se-tenant* pairs of both designs and 2 labels.

106 Flowers, Map and Captain Cook

1969 (8 Oct). *South Pacific Conference, Nouméa.* T **106** *and similar horiz designs. Multicoloured. Without fluorescent security markings.* P 13.

306	5 c. Flowers, map and Premier Albert Henry	75	20
307	10 c. Type **106**	..	1·40	75
308	25 c. Flowers, map and N.Z. arms	..	1·40	95
309	30 c. Queen Elizabeth II, map and flowers	1·40	1·10
306/9	..	..	*Set of 4*	4·50	2·75

107 "Virgin and Child with Saints Jerome and Dominic" (Lippi)

108 "The Resurrection of Christ" (Raphael)

1969 (21 Nov). *Christmas. Paintings.* T **107** *and similar designs. Multicoloured. Without fluorescent security markings.* P 13.

310	1 c. Type **107**	..	..	10	10
311	4 c. "The Holy Family" (Fra Bartolomeo)	10	10
312	10 c. "The Adoration of the Shepherds" (A. Mengs)		15	10
313	20 c. "Madonna and Child with Saints" (R. Campin)		25	20
314	30 c. "The Madonna of the Basket" (Correggio)	25	30
310/14			*Set of 5*	70	60
MS315	132 × 97 mm. Nos. 310/14		1·50	1·50

Each value was issued in sheets of 9 stamps and 1 label.

1970 (12 Mar). *Easter. Paintings.* T **108** *and similar vert designs showing "The Resurrection of Christ" by the artists named. Multicoloured.* P 13.

316	4 c. Type **108**	..	10	10
317	8 c. Dirk Bouts	..	10	10
318	20 c. Altdorfer	..	15	10
319	25 c. Murillo	..	20	10
316/19		*Set of 4*	50	20
MS320	132 × 162 mm. Nos. 316/19		1·25	1·25

Each value was issued in sheets of 8 stamps and 1 label.

KIA ORANA
APOLLO 13
ASTRONAUTS
Te Atua to
Tatou Irinakianga
(109)

1970 (17–30 Apr). *Apollo 13. Nos. 233, 236, 239/40, 242 and 245/6 optd with* T **109** (4 c. to $2) *or with first three lines only in larger type* ($4), *by Govt Printer.* A. *Without fluorescent security markings.* B. *With fluorescent security markings.*

				A	B	
321	4 c. Water Lily	..	..	10	10	†
	a. Opt albino	..	..	25·00	—	†
322	8 c. *Allamanda cathartica*		10	10	†
323	15 c. Frangipani	..	..	10	10	†
324	20 c. Thunbergia	..	..	15	15	†
325	30 c. *Euphorbia pulcherrima poinsettia*	..	20	20	†
326	$2 Type **80**	..	..	60	90	†
327	$4 Type **81** (30.4)	..	28·00	45·00	1·25	2·75
321/6A, 327B		*Set of 7*	2·00	3·75	

110 The Royal Family

(Des V. Whiteley (5 c.), J. Berry ($1))

1970 (12 June). *Royal Visit to New Zealand.* T **110** *and similar horiz designs. Multicoloured.* P 13.

328	5 c. Type **110**	..	65	30
329	30 c. Captain Cook and H.M.S. *Endeavour*	..	2·75	1·75
330	$1 Royal Visit commemorative coin	..	4·00	3·00
328/30		*Set of 3*	6·75	4·50
MS331	145 × 97 mm. Nos. 328/30		9·00	9·50

Each value was issued in sheets of 8 stamps and 1 label.

FOUR DOLLARS

FIFTH ANNIVERSARY SELF-GOVERNMENT AUGUST 1970	**$4.00**
(113)	(114)

1970 (27 Aug). *5th Anniv of Self-Government Nos. 328/30 optd with* T **113** (30 c. and $1), *or in single line in silver around frame of stamp* (5 c.).

332	5 c. Type **110**	..	40	15
333	30 c. Captain Cook and H.M.S. *Endeavour*	..	1·25	35
334	$1 Royal Visit commemorative coin	..	2·00	90
332/4	..	..	*Set of 3*	3·25	1·25

1970 (11 Nov). *Nos. 247c and 248 surch with* T **114** *by Govt Printer, Rarotonga.* A. *Without fluorescent security markings.* B. *With fluorescent security markings.*

			A	B	
335	81	$4 on $8 multicoloured	35·00 28·00	2·50	3·00
336		$4 on $10 multicoloured	40·00 48·00	1·50	1·75

There are variations in the setting of this surcharge and also in the rule.

	PLUS 20c
	UNITED KINGDOM
	SPECIAL MAIL SERVICE
115 Mary, Joseph and Christ in Manger	(116)

(Des from De Lisle Psalter)

1970 (30 Nov). *Christmas.* T **115** *and similar square designs. Multicoloured.* P 13.

337	1 c. Type **115**	..	10	10
338	4 c. Shepherds and Apparition of the Angel	10	10
339	10 c. Mary showing Child to Joseph	..	15	10
340	20 c. The Wise Men bearing Gifts	..	20	10
341	30 c. Parents wrapping Child in swaddling clothes		25	15
337/41		*Set of 5*	65	35
MS342	100 × 139 mm. Nos. 337/41 plus label	90	1·50

Each value was issued in sheets of 5 stamps and 1 label. Stamps from the miniature sheet are smaller, since they do not have the buff parchment border as on the stamps from the sheets.

1971. *Nos. 242B and 243B surch as* T **116**.

343	30 c. + 20 c. *Euphorbia pulcherrima poinsettia* (25.2)		40	50
344	50 c. + 20 c. *Gardinia taitensis* (8.3)	1·25	1·75

The premium of 20 c. was to prepay a private delivery service fee in Great Britain during the postal strike. The mail was sent by air to a forwarding address in the Netherlands. No. 343 was intended for ordinary airmail ½ oz letters, and No. 344 included registration fee.

The postal strike ended on 8 March and both stamps were withdrawn on 12 March.

117 Wedding of Princess Elizabeth and Prince Philip

(Des from photographs. Litho Format)

1971 (11 Mar). *Royal Visit of H.R.H. The Duke of Edinburgh.* T **117** *and similar horiz designs. Multicoloured.* P 13½.

345	1 c. Type **117**	..	20	50
346	4 c. Queen Elizabeth, Prince Philip, Princess Anne and Prince Charles at Windsor	60	1·10
347	10 c. Prince Philip sailing	..	80	1·25
348	15 c. Prince Philip in polo gear	..	80	1·25
349	25 c. Prince Philip in naval uniform, and the Royal Yacht *Britannia*	..	1·50	2·00
345/9		*Set of 5*	3·50	5·50
MS350	168 × 122 mm. Nos 345/9 plus printed labels in positions 1, 3, 4, and 6	4·25	8·00

Each value was issued in sheets of 7 stamps and 2 labels.

Fourth South Pacific Games Papeete	Fourth South Pacific Games Papeete
(118)	(119)

1971 (8 Sept). *Fourth South Pacific Games, Tahiti. Nos. 238B, 241B and 242B optd with* T **118** *in black, or surch as* T **119** *in blue.*

351	10 c. *Poinciana regia flamboyant*	..	10	10
352	10 c. + 1 c. *Poinciana regia flamboyant*	10	10
353	10 c. + 3 c. *Poinciana regia flamboyant*	10	10
354	25 c. Canna Lily	..	..	15	10
355	25 c. + 1 c. Canna Lily	..	15	10
356	25 c. + 3 c. Canna Lily	..	15	10
357	30 c. *Euphorbia pulcherrima poinsettia*	15	10
358	30 c. + 1 c. *Euphorbia pulcherrima poinsettia*	15	10
359	30 c. + 3 c. *Euphorbia pulcherrima poinsettia*	15	10
351/9		*Set of 9*	1·10	50

The stamps additionally surcharged 1 c. or 3 c. helped to finance the Cook Islands' team at the games.

10c ≡	
(120)	121 "Virgin and Child" (Bellini)

1971 (20 Oct). *Nos. 230B, 233B, 236B/7B and 239B surch with* T **120**.

360	10 c. on 2½ c. *Clitoria ternatea*	..	15	25
361	10 c. on 4 c. Water Lily	..	15	25
362	10 c. on 8 c. *Allamanda cathartica*	..	15	25
	a. Surch inverted		£140	
363	10 c. on 9 c. Stephanotis	..	15	25
364	10 c. on 15 c. Frangipani	..	15	25
	a. Surch double		95·00	
360/4	..	..	*Set of 5*	65	1·10

1971 (30 Nov). *Christmas. T 121 and similar vert designs showing different paintings of the "Virgin and Child", by Bellini.* P 13.

365	1 c. multicoloured	10	10
366	4 c. multicoloured	10	10
367	10 c. multicoloured	25	10
368	20 c. multicoloured	50	10
369	30 c. multicoloured	50	20
365/9	*Set of 5*	1·25	35
MS370	135 × 147 mm. Nos. 365/9	1·75	2·25
MS371	92 × 98 mm. 50 c. + 5 c. "The Holy Family in a Garland of Flowers (Jan Brueghel and Pieter van Avont) (41 × 41 *mm*)	75	1·40

Each value was issued in sheets of 8 stamps and 1 label.

SOUTH PACIFIC COMMISSION
FEB. 1947 - 1972
(122)

123 St. John

1972 (17 Feb). *25th Anniv of South Pacific Commission.* No. 244B optd with T 122.

372	**80** $1 multicoloured	40	75

(Des from De Lisle Psalter)

1972 (6 Mar). *Easter. T 123 and similar vert designs. Multicoloured.* P 13.

373	5 c. Type **123**	10	10
374	10 c. Christ on the Cross	10	10
375	30 c. Mary, Mother of Jesus	25	25
373/5	*Set of 3*	35	35
MS376	79 × 112 mm. Nos. 373/5 forming triptych of "The Crucifixion"	80	2·25

Stamps from the miniature sheet do not have a border around the perforations, and are therefore smaller than stamps from sheets.

HURRICANE RELIEF PLUS 2c
(124)

Hurricane Relief Plus 5c
(125)

1972 (30 Mar). *Hurricane Relief. Nos. 373/5 surch as T 124, and Nos. 239B, 241B and 243B surch as T 125, by Govt Printer, Rarotonga.*

377	5 c. + 2 c. Type **123** (R.)	10	10
	a. Albino surch	50·00	
378	10 c. + 2 c. Christ on the Cross (R.)	15	15
379	15 c. + 5 c. Frangipani	20	20
380	25 c. + 5 c. Canna Lily	20	20
381	30 c. + 5 c. Mary, Mother of Jesus	20	20
	a. Albino surch	25	25
382	50 c. + 10 c. *Gardinia taitensis*	25	25
377/82	*Set of 6*	90	90

10c

126 Rocket heading for Moon 127

1972 (17 Apr). *Apollo Moon Exploration Flights. T 126/7 and similar horiz designs. Multicoloured.* P 13.

383	5 c. Type **126**	20	10
384	5 c. Type **127**	20	10
385	10 c. Lunar module and astronaut	20	10
386	10 c. Astronaut and experiment	20	10
387	25 c. Command capsule and Earth	25	15
388	25 c. Lunar Rover	25	15
389	30 c. Sikorsky S-61B SH-3 Sea King helicopter	35	15
390	30 c. Splashdown	35	15
383/90	*Set of 8*	3·25	4·75
MS391	83×205 mm. Nos. 383/90		

These were issued in horizontal *se-tenant* pairs of each value, forming one composite design.

ALTERED CATALOGUE NUMBERS

Any Catalogue numbers altered from the last edition are shown as a list in the introductory pages.

HURRICANE RELIEF
Plus 2c
(128)

129 High-jumping

1972 (24 May). *Hurricane Relief. Nos. 383/91 surch as T 128.*

392	5 c. + 2 c. Type **126**	10	10
393	5 c. + 2 c. Type **127**	10	10
394	10 c. + 2 c. Lunar module and astronaut	10	10
395	10 c. + 2 c. Astronaut and experiment	10	10
396	25 c. + 2 c. Command capsule and Earth	15	15
397	25 c. + 2 c. Lunar Rover	15	15
398	30 c. + 2 c. Sikorsky S-61B SH-3 Sea King helicopter	15	15
399	30 c. + 2 c. Splashdown	15	15
392/9	*Set of 8*	75	75
MS400	83×205 mm. No. **MS391** surch 3 c. on each stamp	2·50	3·50

1972 (26 June). *Olympic Games, Munich. T 129 and similar vert designs. Multicoloured.* P 13½.

401	10 c. Type **129**	20	10
402	25 c. Running	40	15
403	30 c. Boxing	40	20
401/3	*Set of 3*	90	40
MS404	88 × 78 mm. 50 c. + 5 c. Pierre de Coubertin	1·00	2·00
MS405	84 × 133 mm. Nos. 401/3 plus *se-tenant* label	1·25	2·00

Each value was issued in sheets of 8 stamps and 1 label.

130 "The Rest on the Flight into Egypt" (Caravaggio)   131 Marriage Ceremony

1972 (11 Oct). *Christmas T 130 and similar vert designs. Multicoloured.* P 13.

406	1 c. Type **130**	10	10
407	5 c. "Madonna of the Swallow" (Guercino)	25	10
408	10 c. "Madonna of the Green Cushion" (Solario)	35	10
409	20 c. "Madonna and Child" (di Credi)	55	20
410	30 c. "Madonna and Child" (Bellini)	85	30
406/10	*Set of 5*	1·90	60
MS411	141 × 152 mm. Nos. 406/10 plus *se-tenant* label in position 1	2·75	2·75
MS412	101 × 82 mm. 50 c + 5 c. "The Holy Night" (Correggio) (31 × 43 *mm*)	75	1·50

Each value was issued in sheets of 9 stamps and 1 label.

1972 (20 Nov). *Royal Silver Wedding. T 131 and similar black and silver designs.* P 13.

413	5 c. Type **131**	25	15
414	10 c. Leaving Westminster Abbey	35	40
415	15 c. Bride and Bridegroom (40 × 41 *mm*)	45	65
416	30 c. Family Group (67 × 40 *mm*)	55	90
413/16	*Set of 4*	1·40	1·90

The 5, 10 and 15 c. values were each issued in sheets of 8 stamps and 1 label.

132 Taro Leaf   133 "Noli me Tangere" (Titian)

1973 (15 Mar). *Silver Wedding Coinage. T 132 and similar designs showing coins.* P 13.

417	1 c. black, rosy carmine and gold	10	10
418	2 c. black, bright blue and gold	10	10
419	5 c. black, green and silver	10	10
420	10 c. black, royal blue and silver	25	10
421	20 c. black, deep blue-green and silver	35	10
422	50 c. black, carmine and silver	65	15
423	$1 black, bright blue and silver	1·10	30
417/23	*Set of 7*	2·25	50

Designs: As T **132**—2 c. Pineapple; 5 c. Hibiscus. 46×30 *mm*—10 c. Oranges; 20 c. White Tern; 50 c. Striped Bonito. 32×55 *mm*—$1 Tangaroa.

Each value was issued in sheets of 20 stamps and 1 label.

1973 (9 Apr). *Easter. T 133 and similar vert designs. Multicoloured.* P 13.

424	5 c. Type **133**	15	10
425	10 c. "The Descent from the Cross" (Rubens)	20	10
426	30 c. "The Lamentation of Christ" (Dürer)	25	10
424/6	*Set of 3*	55	20
MS427	132 × 67 mm. Nos. 424/6	55	1·25

Each value was issued in sheets of 15 stamps and 1 label.

1973 (30 Apr). *Easter. Children's Charity. Designs as Nos. 424/6 in separate Miniature Sheets 67 × 87 mm, each with a face value of 50 c. + 5 c. P 13 × 14.*

MS428	As Nos. 424/6	*Set of 3 sheets* 90	1·75

10c

TENTH ANNIVERSARY CESSATION OF NUCLEAR TESTING TREATY

134 Queen Elizabeth II in Coronation Regalia   (135)

1973 (1 June). *20th Anniv of Queen Elizabeth's Coronation.* P 14 × 13½.

429	**134** 10 c. multicoloured	50	90
MS430	64 × 89 mm. 50 c. as 10 c. P 13 × 14	2·50	2·25

The perforated portion of MS430 is similar to No. 429, but has no borders.

No. 429 was issued in sheets of 5 stamps and 1 label.

1973 (25 July). *Tenth Anniv of Treaty Banning Nuclear Testing. Nos. 234B, 236B, 238B, and 240B/242B optd with T 135.*

431	5 c. *Bauhinia bi-pinnata rosea*	10	10
432	8 c. *Allamanda cathartica*	10	10
433	10 c. *Poinciana regia flamboyant*	10	10
434	20 c. *Thunbergia*	15	15
435	25 c. *Canna Lily*	20	15
436	30 c. *Euphorbia pulcherrima poinsettia*	20	15
431/6	*Set of 6*	70	65

136 Tipairua

1973 (17 Sept). *Maori Exploration of the Pacific. T 136 and similar horiz designs showing sailing craft. Multicoloured.* P 13.

437	½ c. Type **136**	10	10
438	1 c. Wa'a Kaulua	10	10
439	1½ c. Tainui	10	15
440	5 c. War canoe	50	15
441	10 c. Pahi	70	15
442	15 c. Amastasi	1·25	65
443	25 c. Vaka	1·50	80
437/443	*Set of 7*	3·75	1·75

137 The Annunciation   138 Princess Anne

1973 (30 Oct). *Christmas. T 137 and similar vert designs showing scenes from a 15th-century Flemish "Book of Hours". Multicoloured.* P 13.

444	1 c. Type **137**	10	10
445	5 c. The Visitation	10	10
446	10 c. Annunciation to the Shepherds	10	10
447	20 c. Epiphany	15	10
448	30 c. The Slaughter of the Innocents	20	15
444/8	*Set of 5*	40	30
MS449	121 × 128 mm. Nos. 444/8 plus *se-tenant* label	55	1·40

Each value was issued in sheets of 14 stamps and 1 label.
See also No. MS454.

1973 (14 Nov). *Royal Wedding. T 138 and similar vert designs. Multicoloured.* P 14 × 13½.

450	25 c. Type **138**	20	10
451	30 c. Capt. Mark Phillips	25	10
452	50 c. Princess Anne and Capt. Phillips	30	15
450/2	*Set of 3*	65	30
MS453	119 × 100 mm. No. 450/2 plus *se-tenant* label. P 13	55	35

Each value was issued in sheets of 8 stamps and 1 label.

1973 (3 Dec).. *Christmas. Children's Charity. Designs as Nos. 444/8 in separate Miniature Sheets 50 × 70 mm, each with a face value of 50 c. + 5 c.*
MS454 As Nos. 444/8 .. .. .. *Set of 5 sheets* 75 80

139 Running

140 "Jesus carrying the Cross" (Raphael)

1974 (24 Jan). *Commonwealth Games, Christchurch. T 139 and similar multicoloured designs. P 14 × 13½ (1 and 3 c.) or 13½ × 14 (others).*
455	1 c. Diving (*vert*)	..	..	10 10
456	3 c. Boxing (*vert*)	..	..	10 10
457	5 c. Type **139**	..	..	10 10
458	10 c. Weightlifting	..	..	10 10
459	30 c. Cycling	..	..	20 25
455/9		*Set of 5*		40 40

MS460 115 × 90 mm. 50 c. Discobolus 40 55
Each value was issued in sheets of 15 stamps and 1 label.

1974 (25 Mar). *Easter. T 140 and similar vert designs. Multicoloured. P 13½.*
461	5 c. Type **140**	..	..	10 10
462	10 c. "The Holy Trinity" (El Greco)	..	15 10
463	30 c. "The Deposition of Christ" (Caravaggio)	..	..	25 20
461/3		*Set of 3*		40 30

MS464 130 × 70 mm. Nos. 461/3 .. .. 1·50 50
Each value was issued in sheets of 20 stamps and 1 label.

1974 (22 Apr). *Easter. Children's Charity. Designs as Nos. 461/3 in separate Miniature Sheets 59 × 87 mm, each with a face value of 50 c. + 5 c.*
MS465 As Nos. 461/3 .. .. *Set of 3 sheets* 70 1·40

141 Grey Bonnet (*Phalium glaucum*)

142 Queen Elizabeth II

1974 (17 May)–75. *Horiz designs as T 141 showing sea-shells (½ to 60 c.), T 142 or larger horiz design ($4 to $10). Multicoloured. P 14×13½ ($4 to $10) or 13½ (others).*
466	½ c. Type **141**	..	30 10
467	1 c. Common Pacific Vase (*Vasum turbinellum*)		30 10
468	1½ c. True Heart Cockle (*Corculum cardissa*)		30 10
469	2 c. Terebellum Conch (*Terebellum terebellum*)		30 10
470	3 c. Bat Volute (*Cymbiola vespertilio*)		45 10
471	4 c. Gibbose Conch (*Strombus gibberulus gibbosus*)		50 10
472	5 c. Common Hairy Triton (*Cymatium pileare*)		50 10
473	6 c. Serpent's-head Cowrie (*Cypraea caputserpentis*)		50 90
474	8 c. Granulate Frog Shell (*Bursa granularis*)		60 10
475	10 c. Fly-spotted Auger (*Terebra areolata*)		60 10
476	15 c. Episcopan Mitre (*Mitra mitra*)		70 20
477	20 c. Butterfly Moon (*Natica alapapilionis*)		1·00 20
478	25 c. Royal Oak Scallop (*Cryptopecten pallium*)		1·00 30
479	30 c. Soldier Cone (*Conus miles*)		1·00 30
480	50 c. Textile or Cloth of Gold Cone (*Conus textile*) (26.8.74)		7·00 4·50
481	60 c. Red-mouth Olive (*Oliva miniacea miniacea*) (26.8.74)		7·00 4·50
482	$1 Type **142** (26.8.74)		3·00 4·50
483	$2 Type **142** (27.1.75)		2·50 2·25
484	$4 Queen Elizabeth II and seashells (17.3.75)		3·50 5·50
485	$6 As $4 (29.4.75)		14·00 7·00
486	$8 As $4 (30.5.75)		15·00 8·50
487	$10 As $4 (30.6.75)		18·00 9·00
466/87		*Set of 22*	70·00 42·00

Nos. 484/7 are larger, 60×39 mm.

OMNIBUS ISSUES

Details, together with prices for complete sets, of the various Omnibus issues from the 1935 Silver Jubilee series to date are included in a special section following Zimbabwe at the end of Volume 2.

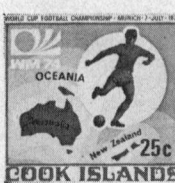
143 Footballer and Australasian Map

144 Obverse and Reverse of Commemorative $2·50 Silver Coin

1974 (5 July). *World Cup Football Championships, West Germany. T 143 and similar horiz designs. Multicoloured. P 13.*
488	25 c. Type **143**	..	15 10
489	50 c. Map and Munich Stadium	..	30 25
490	$1 Footballer, stadium and World Cup	..	50 45
488/90		*Set of 3*	85 70

MS491 89 × 100 mm. Nos. 488/90 .. .. 1·00 2·75
Each value was issued in sheets of 8 stamps and 1 label.

1974 (22 July). *Bicentenary of Capt. Cook's Second Voyage of Discovery. T 144 and similar vert design. P 14.*
492	$2.50, silver, black and violet		13·00 7·00
493	$7.50, silver, black and deep turquoise-green	27·00 13·00

MS494 73 × 73 mm. Nos. 492/3 .. 48·00 48·00
Design:—$7.50. As T **144** but showing $7.50 coin.
Each value was issued in sheets of 5 stamps and 1 label.

145 Early Stamps of Cook Islands

146 "Madonna of the Goldfinch" (Raphael)

1974 (16 Sept). *Centenary of Universal Postal Union. T 145 and similar horiz designs. Multicoloured. P 13½ × 14.*
495	10 c. Type **145**	..	20 15
496	25 c. Old landing strip, Rarotonga, and stamp of 1898		35 40
497	30 c. Post Office, Rarotonga, and stamp of 1920		40 40
498	50 c. U.P.U. emblem and stamps		45 65
495/8		*Set of 4*	1·25 1·40

MS499 118 × 79 mm. Nos. 495/8. P 13 .. 1·00 1·75
Each value was issued in sheets of 8 stamps and 1 label.

1974 (15 Oct). *Christmas. T 146 and similar vert designs. Multicoloured. P 13.*
500	1 c. Type **146**	..	10 10
501	5 c. "The Sacred Family" (Andrea del Sarto)		20 10
502	10 c. "The Virgin adoring the Child" (Correggio)		25 10
503	20 c. "The Holy Family" (Rembrandt)		40 20
504	30 c. "The Virgin and Child" (Rogier Van Der Weyden)		50 30
500/504		*Set of 5*	1·25 60

MS505 114 × 133 mm. Nos. 500/4 plus *se-tenant* label .. .. .. 1·75 2·00
Each value was issued in sheets of 15 stamps and 1 label.
See also No. MS512.

147 Churchill and Blenheim Palace

1974 (20 Nov). *Birth Centenary of Sir Winston Churchill. T 147 and similar horiz designs. Multicoloured. P 13 × 14.*
506	5 c. Type **147**	..	20 10
507	10 c. Churchill and Houses of Parliament	..	20 10
508	25 c. Churchill and Chartwell	..	40 20
509	30 c. Churchill and Buckingham Palace	..	40 25
510	50 c. Churchill and St. Paul's Cathedral	..	50 50
506/10		*Set of 5*	1·50 1·00

MS511 108 × 114 mm. Nos. 506/10 plus *se-tenant* label .. .. .. 3·00 1·25
Each value was issued in sheets of 5 stamps and 1 label.

1974 (9 Dec). *Christmas. Children's Charity. Designs as Nos. 500/504 in separate miniature sheets 53 × 69 mm, each with a face value of 50 c. + 5 c.*
MS512 As Nos. 500/4 .. .. *Set of 5 sheets* 1·25 1·25

---

148 Vasco Nuñez de Balboa and Discovery of Pacific Ocean (1513).

1975 (3 Feb). *Pacific Explorers. T 148 and similar horiz designs. Multicoloured. P 13.*
513	1 c. Type **148**		15 10
514	5 c. Fernando de Magellanes and map (1520)		65 20
515	10 c. Juan Sebastian del Cano and *Vitoria* (1520)		1·25 20
516	25 c. Friar de Urdaneta and ship (1564–67)		2·25 75
517	30 c. Miguel Lopez de Legazpi and ship (1564–67)		2·25 80
513/17		*Set of 5*	6·00 1·90

149 "Apollo" Capsule

1975 (15 July). *"Apollo-Soyuz" Space Project. T 149 and similar horiz designs. Multicoloured. P 13½.*
518	25 c. Type **149**	..	30 15
519	25 c. "Soyuz" capsule	..	30 15
520	30 c. "Soyuz" crew	..	35 15
521	30 c. "Apollo" crew	..	35 15
522	50 c. Cosmonaut within "Soyuz"	..	40 25
523	50 c. Astronauts within "Apollo"	..	40 25
518/23		*Set of 6*	1·90 1·00

MS524 119 × 119 mm. Nos. 518/23. P 13 × 14 .. 2·25 2·00
Each value was issued in sheets containing 9 horizontal *setenant* pairs of the two designs, together with 2 labels.

150 $100 Commemorative Gold Coin

1975 (8 Aug). *Bicentenary of Captain Cook's Second Voyage. P 13.*
525 **150** $2 brown, gold and bluish violet .. 4·50 1·75
No. 525 was issued in sheets of 5 stamps and 1 label.

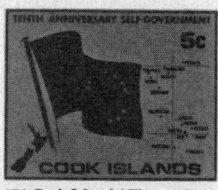
151 Cook Islands' Flag and Map

1975 (8 Aug). *Tenth Anniv of Self-Government. T 151 and similar multicoloured designs. P 13.*
526	5 c. Type **151**	..	40 10
527	10 c. Premier Sir Albert Henry and flag (*vert*)		45 10
528	25 c. Rarotonga and flag	..	80 30
526/8		*Set of 3*	1·50 45

152 "Madonna by the Fireside" (R. Campin)

153 "Entombment of Christ" (Raphael)

1975 (1 Dec). *Christmas. T 152 and similar vert designs. Multicoloured. P 13½.*
529	6 c. Type **152**	..	15 10
530	10 c. "Madonna in the Meadow" (Raphael)		20 10
531	15 c. "Madonna of the Oak" (attrib Raphael)		25 10
532	20 c. "Adoration of the Shepherds" (J. B. Maino)		30 15
533	35 c. "The Annunciation" (Murillo)		45 20
529/33		*Set of 5*	1·25 45

MS534 110 × 124 mm. Nos. 529/33 .. .. 1·25 90

1975 (15 Dec). *Christmas. Children's Charity. Designs as Nos. 529/33 in separate miniature sheets 53 × 71 mm, each with a face value of 75 c. + 5 c.*

MS535	As Nos. 529/33	*..Set of 5 sheets*	1·10 1·25
a. Error. Miniature sheet as No. 531 imperf			£250

1976 (29 Mar). *Easter. T 153 and similar square designs. Multicoloured. P 13.*

536	7 c. Type 153	..	..	..	..	30	10
537	15 c. "Pieta" (Veronese)					50	15
538	35 c. "Pieta" (El Greco)					75	25
536/8				*Set of 3*		1·40	40
MS539	144 × 57 mm. Nos. 536/8 ..					1·50	85

Each value was issued in sheets of 20 stamps and 1 label.

1976 (3 May). *Easter. Children's Charity. Designs as Nos. 536/8 in separate miniature sheets 69 × 69 mm. each with a face value of 60 c. + 5 c.*

MS540	As Nos. 536/8	*.. Set of 3 sheets*	1·10 1·40

154 Benjamin Franklin and H.M.S. *Resolution*

1976 (29 May). *Bicentenary of American Revolution. T 154 and similar horiz designs. Multicoloured. P 13.*

541	$1 Type 154	..	..	..	7·50	1·50
542	$2 Captain Cook and H.M.S. *Resolution*				9·50	2·50
MS543	118 × 58 mm. $3 Cook, Franklin and H.M.S. *Resolution* (74 × 31 mm) ..		..	..	17·00	8·00

Each value was issued in sheets of 5 stamps and 1 label.

Royal Visit July 1976

(155)

1976 (9 July). *Visit of Queen Elizabeth to the U.S.A. Nos. 541/3 optd with T 155.*

544	$1 Type 154	..	..	..	5·00	1·50
545	$2 Captain Cook and H.M.S. *Resolution*		..		7·00	2·50
MS546	$3 Cook, Franklin and H.M.S. *Resolution*				8·00	5·50

156 Hurdling   157 "The Visitation"

1976 (22 July). *Olympic Games, Montreal. T 156 and similar square designs. Multicoloured. P 13.*

547	7 c.	} Type 156	20	10
548	7 c.		20	10
549	15 c.	} Hockey	40	15
550	15 c.		40	15
551	30 c.	} Fencing	40	15
552	30 c.		40	15
553	35 c.	} Football ..	40	20
554	35 c.		40	20
547/54		*Set of 8*	2·40	1·10
MS555	104 × 146 mm. Nos. 547/54		2·40	2·40

Each value was issued in sheets containing 5 horizontal se-tenant pairs and 2 labels. In each pair the first stamp has the face value on the right, the second has it on the left. Illustrated is the left-hand stamp of the 7 c. design.

1976 (12 Oct). *Christmas. T 157 and similar vert designs showing Renaissance sculptures. Multicoloured. P 14 × 13½.*

556	6 c. Type 157	..	..	10	10
557	10 c. "Adoration of the Shepherds"			10	10
558	15 c. "Adoration of the Shepherds" (*different*)			15	10
559	20 c. "The Epiphany" ..			20	20
560	35 c. "The Holy Family"		..	25	25
556/60			*Set of 5*	70	60
MS561	116 × 110 mm. Nos. 556/60. P 13.			85	1·75

Each value was issued in sheets of 20 stamps and 1 label.

1976 (2 Nov.) *Christmas. Children's Charity. Designs as Nos. 556/60 in separate miniature sheets 66 × 80 mm, with a face value of 75 c. + 5 c.*

MS562	As Nos. 556/60	*.. Set of 5 sheets*	1·10 1·10

158 Obverse and Reverse of $5 Mangaia Kingfisher Coin

1976 (15 Nov). *National Wildlife and Conservation Day. P 13.*

563	158	$1 multicoloured	..	..	2·25	1·25

No. 563 was issued in sheets of 5 stamps and 1 label.

159 Imperial State Crown   160 "Christ on the Cross"

1977 (7 Feb). *Silver Jubilee. T 159 and similar vert designs. Multicoloured. P 13.*

564	25 c. Type 159	..	..	40	40
565	25 c. Queen with regalia	..		40	40
566	50 c. Westminster Abbey	..		50	50
567	50 c. Coronation Coach	..		50	50
568	$1 Queen and Prince Philip			80	80
569	$1 Royal Visit, 1974			80	80
564/9			*Set of 6*	3·00	3·00
MS570	130 × 136 mm. As Nos. 564/9 (borders and "COOK ISLANDS" in a different colour).			2·75	2·00

The two designs of each value are printed horizontally se-tenant throughout the sheet, and stamps from MS570 have borders and "COOK ISLANDS" in a different colour.

1977 (28 Mar). *Easter and 400th Birth Anniv of Rubens. T 160 and similar vert designs. Multicoloured. P 14 × 13½.*

571	7 c. Type 160	..	..	35	10
572	15 c. "Christ on the Cross"			55	15
573	35 c. "The Deposition of Christ"			1·10	30
571/3			*Set of 3*	1·75	50
MS574	118 × 65 mm. Nos. 571/3. P 13			1·75	1·60

Each value was issued in sheets of 24 stamps and 1 label.

1977 (18 Apr). *Easter. Children's Charity. Designs as Nos. 571/3 in separate miniature sheets 60 × 79 mm, each with a face value of 60 c. + 5 c. P 13 × 14.*

MS575	As Nos. 571/3	*.. Set of 3 sheets*	1·00 1·00

161 "Virgin and Child" (Memling)   162 Obverse and Reverse of $5 Cook Islands Swiftlet Coin

1977 (3 Oct). *Christmas. T 161 and similar vert designs. Multicoloured. P 14.*

576	6 c. Type 161 ..	..	..	20	10
577	10 c. "Madonna and Child with Saints and Donors" (Memling)			20	10
578	15 c. "Adoration of the Kings" (Geertgen)			30	10
579	20 c. "Virgin and Child with Saints" (Crivelli)			40	15
580	35 c. "Adoration of the Magi" (16th-cent Flemish School)			50	20
576/80			*Set of 5*	1·40	50
MS581	118 × 111 mm. Nos. 576/80. P 13½			1·40	1·75

Each value was issued in sheets of 24 stamps and 1 label.

1977 (31 Oct). *Christmas. Children's Charity. Designs as Nos. 576/80 in separate miniature sheets 69 × 69 mm, each with a face value of 75 c. + 5 c.*

MS582	As Nos. 576/80	*.. Set of 5 sheets*	1·00 1·25

1977 (15 Nov). *National Wildlife and Conservation Day. P 13.*

583	162	$1 multicoloured	..	..	2·25	1·25

No. 583 was issued in sheets containing 10 stamps and 2 labels.

163 Captain Cook and H.M.S. *Resolution* (from paintings by N. Dance and H. Roberts)

1978 (20 Jan). *Bicentenary of Discovery of Hawaii. T 163 and similar horiz designs. Multicoloured. P 13½.*

584	50 c. Type 163 ..	..		1·50	60
585	$1 Earl of Sandwich, and Cook landing at Owhyhee (from paintings by Thomas Gainsborough and J. Cleveley) ..			2·00	1·00
586	$2 Obverse and reverse of $200 coin and Cook monument, Hawaii			3·25	1·75
584/6			*Set of 3*	6·00	3·00
MS587	118 × 95 mm. Nos. 584/86 ..			7·00	9·00

Each value was issued in sheets of 5 stamps and 1 label.

164 "Pieta" (Van der Weyden)   165 Queen Elizabeth II

1978 (20 Mar). *Easter. Paintings from National Gallery, London. T 164 and similar horiz designs. Multicoloured. P 13.*

588	15 c. Type 164	..	..	40	15
589	35 c. "The Entombment" (Michelangelo)			50	30
590	75 c. "The Supper at Emmaus" (Caravaggio)			75	55
588/90			*Set of 3*	1·50	90
MS591	114 × 96 mm. Nos. 588/90.			1·50	2·00

Each value was issued in sheets of 5 stamps and 1 label.

1978 (10 Apr). *Easter. Children's Charity. Designs as Nos. 588/90 in separate miniature sheets, 85 × 72 mm, each with a face value of 60 c. + 5 c. P 13½.*

MS592	As Nos. 588/90	*.. Set of 3 sheets*	1·10 1·10

1978 (6 June). *25th Anniv of Coronation. T 165 and similar vert designs. Multicoloured. P 13.*

593	50 c. Type 165	..	..	25	30
594	50 c. The Lion of England	..		25	30
595	50 c. Imperial State Crown	..		25	30
596	50 c. Statue of Tangaroa (god)	..		25	30
597	70 c. Type 165	..		25	30
598	70 c. Sceptre with Cross	..		25	30
599	70 c. St. Edward's Crown	..		25	30
600	70 c. Rarotongan staff god	..		25	30
593/600		*Set of 8*	1·75	2·00
MS601	103 × 142 mm. Nos. 593/600*.			1·00	1·50

Each value was issued in sheets containing the 4 designs and 2 labels.

* In No MS601 the designs of Nos. 595 and 599 are transposed.

5c

(166)

1978 (10 Nov). *Nos. 466, 468, 473/4 and 478/81 surch as T 166.*

602	5 c. on 1½ c. True Heart Cockle (*Corculum cardissa*) (Silver)	..		40	10
603	7 c. on ½ c. Type 141	..		45	15
604	10 c. on 6 c. Serpent's-head Cowrie (*Cypraea caputserpentis*) (Gold)			50	15
605	10 c. on 8 c. Granulate Frog Shell (*Bursa granularis*) (Gold)			50	15
606	15 c. on ½ c. Type 141			50	20
607	15 c. on 25 c. Royal Oak Scallop (*Cryptopecten pallium*) (Silver)			50	20
608	15 c. on 30 c. Soldier Cone (*Conus miles*)			50	20
609	15 c. on 50 c. Textile or Cloth of Gold Cone (*Conus textile*) (Silver)			50	20
610	15 c. on 60 c. Red-mouth Olive (*Oliva miniacea miniacea*) (Gold)			50	20
611	17 c. on ½ c. Type 141			80	25
612	17 c. on 50 c. Textile or Cloth of Gold Cone (*Conus textile*) (Silver)			80	25
602/12	..	..	*Set of 11*	5·50	1·75

1728 · 250th ANNIVERSARY OF COOK'S BIRTH · 1978

(167)

1978 (13 Nov). *250th Birth Anniv of Captain Cook. Nos. 584/7 optd with T 167 on silver.*

613	50 c. Type 163	..	..	2·00	75
614	$1 Earl of Sandwich, and Cook landing at Owhyhee (from paintings by Thomas Gainsborough and J. Cleveley)			2·25	1·00
615	$2 Obverse and reverse of $200 coin and Cook monument, Hawaii			2·50	2·00
613/15			*Set of 3*	6·00	3·25
MS616	Nos. 613/15	..		17·00	17·00

168 Obverse and Reverse of $5 Pitcairn Warblers Coin

1978 (15 Nov). *National Wildlife and Conservation Day. P 13.*

617	168	$1 multicoloured	..	..	1·60	1·00

COVER PRICES

Cover factors are quoted at the beginning of each country for most issues to 1945. An explanation of the system can be found on page x. The factors quoted do not, however, apply to philatelic covers.

169 "The Virgin and Child"
(Van der Weyden)

170 Virgin with Body
of Christ

1978 (8 Dec). *Christmas. Paintings. T* **169** *and similar vert designs. Multicoloured. P* 13.

618	15 c. Type **169**		35	10
619	17 c. "The Virgin and Child" (Crivelli)		35	15
620	35 c. "The Virgin and Child" (Murillo)		65	30
618/20		*Set of 3*	1·25	50
MS621	107 x 70 mm. Nos. 618/20..		1·50	1·50

1979 (12 Jan). *Christmas. Children's Charity. Designs as Nos. 618/20 in separate miniature sheets* 57 x 87 mm. *each with a face value of* 75 c. + 5 c. *P* 13½

MS622	As Nos. 618/20	*Set of 3 sheets*	1·00	1·00

1979 (5 Apr). *Easter. Details of Painting "Descent" by Gaspar de Crayar. T* **170** *and similar vert designs. Multicoloured. P* 13.

623	10 c. Type **170** ..		25	10
624	12 c. St. John		30	20
625	15 c. Mary Magdalene		35	25
626	20 c. Weeping angels ..		45	30
623/6		*Set of 4*	1·25	75
MS627	83 × 100 mm. As Nos. 623/6, but each with charity premium of 2 c.		65	75

Stamps from No. **MS**627 are slightly smaller, 32 × 40 mm, and are without borders.

171 "Captain Cook"
(James Weber)

172 Post-Rider

1979 (23 July). *Death Bicentenary of Captain Cook. T* **171** *and similar vert designs. Multicoloured. P* 14 × 13.

628	20 c. Type **171**		50	20
629	30 c. H.M.S. *Resolution*		80	35
630	35 c. H.M.S. *Royal George* (ship of the line)		90	45
631	50 c. "Death of Captain Cook" (George Carter)		95	60
628/31		*Set of 4*	2·75	1·40
MS632	78×112 mm. Nos. 628/31		2·25	1·50

Stamps from No. **MS**632 have black borders.

1979 (10 Sept). *Death Centenary of Sir Rowland Hill. History of Mail Transport. T* **172** *and similar square designs. Multicoloured. P* 14.

633	30 c. Type **172**	..	25	20
634	30 c. Mail coach		25	20
635	30 c. Automobile		25	20
636	30 c. Railway train		25	20
637	30 c. *Cap-Hornier* (full-rigged ship)		30	20
638	30 c. River steamer		30	20
639	30 c. *Deutschland* (liner)		30	20
640	35 c. *United States* (liner) ..		30	20
641	50 c. Balloon *Le Neptune*		40	25
642	50 c. Junkers F13 airplane		40	25
643	50 c. Airship LZ-127 *Graf Zeppelin*		40	25
644	50 c. Concorde		40	25
633/44		*Set of 12*	3·50	2·40
MS645	132×104 mm. Nos. 633/44		3·50	5·50

Nos. 633/6, 637/40 and 641/4 were each printed together, *se-tenant*, in blocks of 4 throughout the sheets.

(173)

1979 (12 Sept). *Nos.* 466, 468 *and* 481 *surch as T* **173**.

646	6 c. on ½ c. Type **141** (Gold)		20	30
647	10 c. on 1½ c. Cockle shell (Silver)		25	20
	a. Surch inverted		90·00	
648	15 c. on 60 c. Olive shell (Gold)		40	40
646/8		*Set of 3*	75	80

MINIMUM PRICE

The minimum price quote is 10p which represents a handling charge rather than a basis for valuing common stamps. For further notes about prices see introductory pages.

174 Brother and Sister

175 "Apollo 11" Emblem

1979 (10 Oct). *International Year of the Child. T* **174** *and similar horiz designs. Multicoloured. P* 13.

649	30 c. Type **174**		25	25
650	50 c. Boy with tree drum		40	40
651	65 c. Children dancing		50	50
649/51		*Set of 3*	1·00	1·00
MS652	102 × 75 mm. As Nos. 649/51, but each with charity premium of 5 c. P 13½ × 13		1·00	1·50

Designs for stamps from No. **MS**652 are as Nos. 649/51 but have I.Y.C. emblem in red.

1979 (7 Nov). *10th Anniv of Moon Landing. T* **175** *and similar vert designs. Multicoloured. P* 14.

653	30 c. Type **175**		40	50
654	50 c. Crew of "Apollo 11"		50	70
655	60 c. Astronaut on Moon		65	75
656	65 c. Command module after splashdown		70	85
653/6		*Set of 4*	2·00	2·50
MS657	119 × 105 mm. Nos. 653/6. P 13½		2·50	2·50

176 Obverse and Reverse of
$5 Rarotongan Fruit Dove Coin

177 Glass Christmas Tree
Ornaments

1979 (15 Nov). *National Wildlife and Conservation Day. P* 13 × 14.

658	**176** $1 multicoloured		1·60	2·50

1979 (14 Dec). *Christmas. T* **177** *and similar vert designs. Multicoloured. P* 13½. (*a*) *Postage.*

659	6 c. Type **177**		10	10
660	10 c. Hibiscus flower and star		10	10
661	12 c. Poinsettia flower, bells and candle		15	10
662	15 c. Poinsettia leaves and Tiki (god).		15	15

(*b*) *Air*

663	20 c. Type **177** ..		20	15
664	25 c. As 10 c.		25	20
665	30 c. As 12 c.		30	25
666	35 c. As 15 c.		35	30
659/66		*Set of 8*	1·40	1·10

1980 (15 Jan). *Christmas. Children's Charity. Designs as Nos.* 659/66 *with additional premiums.* (*a*) *Postage.*

667	6 c. + 2 c. Type **177**		10	10
668	10 c. + 2 c. Hibiscus flower and star		15	15
669	12 c. + 2 c. Poinsettia flower, bells and candle		15	20
670	15 c. + 2 c. Poinsettia leaves and Tiki (god)		15	20

(*b*) *Air*

671	20 c. + 4 c. Type **177**		15	25
672	25 c. + 4 c. As 10 c.		15	25
673	30 c. + 4 c. As 12 c.		20	30
674	35 c. + 4 c. As 15 c.		25	35
667/74		*Set of 8*	1·00	1·60

178 "Flagellation"

179 Dove with Olive Twig

1980 (31 Mar). *Easter. Illustrations by Gustave Doré. T* **178** *and similar vert designs in sepia and gold. P* 13.

675	20 c. Type **178** ..		25	20
676	20 c. "Crown of Thorns"		25	20
677	30 c. "Jesus Insulted"		35	30
678	30 c. "Jesus Falls"		35	30
679	35 c. "The Crucifixion"		40	30
680	35 c. "The Descent from the Cross"		40	30
675/80		*Set of 6*	1·75	1·40
MS681	120 × 110 mm. As Nos. 675/80, but each with charity premium of 2 c.		1·10	1·50

Nos. 675/6, 677/8 and 679/80 were each printed together, *se-tenant*, in vertical pairs throughout the sheet.

1980 (23 Apr). *Easter. Children's Charity. Designs as Nos.* 675/80 *in separate miniature sheets* 60 × 71 mm, *each with a face value of* 75 c. + 5 c. *P* 13.

MS682	As Nos. 675/80	*Set of 6 sheets*	90	1·50

1980 (27 May). *75th Anniv of Rotary International. T* **179** *and similar horiz designs. Multicoloured. P* 14.

683	30 c. Type **179**		35	35
684	35 c. Hibiscus flower ..		40	40
685	50 c. Ribbons		50	50
683/5		*Set of 3*	1·10	1·10
MS686	72 × 113 mm. Nos. 683/5 but each with premium of 3 c. P 13½ ..		1·10	1·50

(180)

181 Queen Elizabeth
the Queen Mother

1980 (22 Aug). *"Zeapex 80" International Stamp Exhibition, Auckland. Nos.* 633/45 *optd with T* **180** *in black on silver background.*

687	30 c. Type **172**		30	25
688	30 c. Mail coach		30	25
689	30 c. Automobile		30	25
690	30 c. Railway train		30	25
691	35 c. *Cap-Hornier* (full-rigged ship)		35	30
692	35 c. River steamer		35	30
693	35 c. *Deutschland* (liner)		35	30
694	35 c. *United States* (liner)		35	30
695	50 c. Balloon *Le Neptune*		45	35
696	50 c. Junkers F13 airplane		45	35
697	50 c. Airship LZ-127 *Graf Zeppelin*		45	35
698	50 c. Concorde		45	35
687/98		*Set of 12*	4·00	3·25
MS699	132×104 mm. Nos. 687/98		6·00	6·00

1980 (22 Aug). *"Zeapex 80" International Stamp Exhibition, Auckland. As No.* **MS**681 *but containing stamps without charity premium of 2 c. optd "Zeapex '80 Auckland + 10 c" in black on gold background.*

MS700	120 × 110 mm. Nos. 675/80 (*sold at* $1.80)		80	1·75

Stamps from No. **MS**700 are unaffected by the overprint which appears on the sheet margin.

1980 (23 Sept). *80th Birthday of Queen Elizabeth the Queen Mother. P* 13.

701	**181** 50 c. multicoloured		80	90
MS702	64× 78 mm. **181** $2 multicoloured		1·25	1·75

182 Satellites orbiting Moon

183 Scene from novel *From
the Earth to the Moon*

1980 (7 Nov). *350th Death Anniv of Johannes Kepler (astronomer). T* **182** *and similar horiz designs. Multicoloured. P* 13.

703	12 c. Type **182** ..		50	35
704	12 c. Space-craft orbiting Moon		50	35
705	50 c. Space-craft orbiting Moon (*different*)		1·00	80
706	50 c. Astronaut and Moon vehicle		1·00	80
703/6		*Set of 4*	2·75	2·10
MS707	121 × 122 mm. Nos. 703/6		2·75	2·75

Nos. 703/4 and 705/6 were each printed together, *se-tenant*, in horizontal pairs throughout the sheet.

1980 (7 Nov). *75th Death Anniv of Jules Verne (author). T* **183** *and similar vert designs showing scenes from the novel "From the Earth to the Moon". P* 13.

708	20 c. multicoloured (green background)		45	35
709	20 c. multicoloured (brown background)		45	35
710	30 c. multicoloured (mauve background)		55	45
711	30 c. multicoloured (blue background)		55	45
708/11		*Set of 4*	1·75	1·40
MS712	121 × 122 mm. Nos. 708/11		2·00	2·00

Nos. 708/9 and 710/11 were each printed together, *se-tenant*, in horizontal pairs throughout the sheet.

184 Siphonogorgia   **185** Annunciation

186 "The Crucifixion" (from book of Saint-Amand)   **187** Prince Charles

1980 (21 Nov)–82. *Corals (1st series). Multicoloured designs as T* **184**. *P* 13 (1 c. to $1) or 14×13½ ($2 to $10).

13	1 c. Type **184**	..	20	20
14	1 c. Pavona praetorta	..	20	20
15	1 c. Stylaster echinatus	..	20	20
16	1 c. Tubastraea	..	20	20
17	3 c. Millepora alcicornis	..	25	20
18	3 c. Junceella gemmacea	..	25	20
19	3 c. Fungia fungites	..	25	20
20	3 c. Heliofungia actiniformis	..	25	20
21	4 c. Distichopora violacea	..	25	20
22	4 c. Stylaster	..	25	20
23	4 c. Goniopora	..	25	20
24	4 c. Caulastraea echinulata	..	25	20
25	5 c. Ptilosarcus gurneyi	..	25	20
26	5 c. Stylophora pistillata	..	25	20
27	5 c. Melithaea squamata	..	25	20
28	5 c. Porites andrewsi	..	25	20
29	6 c. Lobophyllia bemprichii	..	25	20
30	6 c. Palauastrea ramosa	..	25	20
31	6 c. Bellonella indica	..	25	20
32	6 c. Pectinia alcicornis	..	25	20
33	8 c. Sarcophyton digitatum	..	25	20
34	8 c. Melithaea albitincta	..	25	20
35	8 c. Plerogyra sinuosa	..	25	20
36	8 c. Dendrophyllia gracilis	..	25	20
37	10 c. Type **184** (19.12.80)	..	30	20
38	10 c. As No. 714 (19.12.80)	..	30	40
39	10 c. As No. 715 (19.12.80)	..	30	40
40	10 c. As No. 716 (19.12.80)	..	30	40
41	12 c. As No. 717 (19.12.80)	..	30	40
42	12 c. As No. 718 (19.12.80)	..	30	40
43	12 c. As No. 719 (19.12.80)	..	30	40
44	12 c. As No. 720 (19.12.80)	..	30	40
45	15 c. As No. 721 (19.12.80)	..	30	20
46	15 c. As No. 722 (19.12.80)	..	30	20
47	15 c. As No. 723 (19.12.80)	..	30	20
48	15 c. As No. 724 (19.12.80)	..	30	20
49	20 c. As No. 725 (19.12.80)	..	35	30
50	20 c. As No. 726 (19.12.80)	..	35	30
51	20 c. As No. 727 (19.12.80)	..	35	30
52	20 c. As No. 728 (19.12.80)	..	35	30
53	25 c. As No. 729 (19.12.80)	..	35	30
54	25 c. As No. 730 (19.12.80)	..	35	30
55	25 c. As No. 731 (19.12.80)	..	35	30
56	25 c. As No. 732 (19.12.80)	..	35	30
57	30 c. As No. 733 (19.12.80)	..	40	30
58	30 c. As No. 734 (19.12.80)	..	40	30
59	30 c. As No. 735 (19.12.80)	..	40	30
60	30 c. As No. 736 (19.12.80)	..	40	30
61	35 c. Type **184** (16.3.81)	..	45	35
62	35 c. As No. 714 (16.3.81)	..	45	35
63	35 c. As No. 715 (16.3.81)	..	45	35
64	35 c. As No. 716 (16.3.81)	..	45	35
65	50 c. As No. 717 (16.3.81)	..	65	75
66	50 c. As No. 718 (16.3.81)	..	65	75
67	50 c. As No. 719 (16.3.81)	..	65	75
68	50 c. As No. 720 (16.3.81)	..	65	75
69	60 c. As No. 721 (16.3.81)	..	75	75
70	60 c. As No. 722 (16.3.81)	..	75	75
71	60 c. As No. 723 (16.3.81)	..	75	75
72	60 c. As No. 724 (16.3.81)	..	75	75
73	70 c. As No. 725 (13.4.81)	..	2·50	75
74	70 c. As No. 726 (13.4.81)	..	2·50	75
75	70 c. As No. 727 (13.4.81)	..	2·50	75
76	70 c. As No. 728 (13.4.81)	..	2·50	75
77	80 c. As No. 729 (13.4.81)	..	2·50	80
78	80 c. As No. 730 (13.4.81)	..	2·50	80
79	80 c. As No. 731 (13.4.81)	..	2·50	80
80	80 c. As No. 732 (13.4.81)	..	2·50	80
81	$1 As No. 733 (20.5.81)	..	3·75	1·00
82	$1 As No. 734 (20.5.81)	..	3·75	1·00
83	$1 As No. 735 (20.5.81)	..	3·75	1·00
84	$1 As No. 736 (20.5.81)	..	3·75	1·00
85	$2 As No. 723 (27.11.81)	..	11·00	4·00
86	$3 As No. 720 (27.11.81)	..	11·00	4·00
87	$4 As No. 726 (11.1.82)	..	4·50	9·00
88	$6 As No. 715 (11.1.82)	..	6·00	12·00
89	$10 As No. 734 (5.3.82)	..	27·00	32·00
713/89		Set of 77	£100	80·00

Nos. 761/84 are 30 × 40 mm and Nos. 785/9, which include a portrait of Queen Elizabeth II in each design, are 55 × 35 mm in size.

The four designs of each value were printed together, *se-tenant*, in horizontal strips of 4 (Nos. 713/60) or in blocks of 4 (Nos. 761/84) throughout the sheet.

For similar designs with redrawn frames and inscriptions see Nos. 966/94.

1980 (1 Dec). *Christmas. Illustrations from 13th-century French Prayer Book. T* **185** *and similar vert designs. Multicoloured. P* 14 × 13½.

801	15 c. Type **185**	..	25	15
802	30 c. Visitation	..	35	25
803	40 c. Nativity	..	45	30
804	50 c. Epiphany	..	60	40
801/4		Set of 4	1·50	1·00
MS805	89 × 114 mm. Nos. 801/4. P 13½		1·50	1·50

1981 (9 Jan). *Christmas. Children's Charity. Designs as Nos. 801/4 in separate miniature sheets 55 × 68 mm, each with a face value of 75 c. + 5 c. Imperf.*

MS806	As Nos. 801/4	.. Set of 4 sheets	1·50	1·50

1981 (10 Apr). *Easter. Illustrations from 12th-century French Prayer Books. T* **186** *and similar horiz designs. Multicoloured. P* 13½ × 14.

807	15 c. Type **186**	..	20	20
808	25 c. "Placing in Tomb" (from book of Ingeburge)		30	30
809	40 c. "Mourning at the Sepulchre" (from book of Ingeburge)		40	40
807/9		Set of 3	80	80
MS810	72 × 116 mm. As Nos. 807/9 but each with charity premium of 2 c. P 13½		90	90

1981 (28 Apr). *Easter. Children's Charity. Designs as Nos. 807/9 in separate miniature sheets 64 × 53 mm, each with a face value of 75 c. + 5 c. Imperf.*

MS811	As Nos. 807/9	.. Set of 3 sheets	1·10	1·10

1981 (29 July). *Royal Wedding. T* **187** *and similar vert design. Multicoloured. P* 14.

812	$1 Type **187**	..	50	1·10
813	$2 Prince Charles and Lady Diana Spencer		60	1·40
MS814	106 × 59 mm. Nos. 812/13. P 13½		1·40	2·50

Nos. 812/13 were each printed in small sheets of 4.

188 Footballers   **(189)**

1981 (20 Oct). *World Cup Football Championship, Spain (1982). T* **188** *and similar horiz designs showing footballers. Multicoloured. P* 13½ × 14.

815	20 c. Type **188**	..	40	20
816	20 c. Figures to right of stamp	..	40	20
817	30 c. Figures to left	..	50	30
818	30 c. Figures to right	..	50	30
819	35 c. Figures to left	..	50	35
820	35 c. Figures to right	..	50	35
821	50 c. Figures to left	..	65	45
822	50 c. Figures to right	..	65	45
815/22		Set of 8	3·75	2·40
MS823	180 × 94 mm. As Nos. 815/22, but each stamp with a charity premium of 3 c. P 13½		4·50	6·00

The two designs of each value were printed together, *se-tenant*, in horizontal pairs throughout the sheet, forming composite designs.

1981 (10 Nov). *International Year for Disabled Persons. Nos. 812/14 surch as T* **189**.

824	$1 + 5 c. Type **187**	..	1·00	2·00
825	$2 + 5 c. Prince Charles and Lady Diana Spencer		1·40	3·00
MS826	106 × 59 mm. $1 + 10 c., $2 + 10 c. As Nos. 824/5		2·75	5·00

Nos. 824/6 have commemorative inscriptions overprinted on the sheet margins.

190 "Holy Virgin with Child"   **191** Princess of Wales (inscr "21st Birthday")

1981 (14 Dec). *Christmas. Details from Paintings by Rubens. T* **190** *and similar vert designs. Multicoloured. P* 14 × 13½.

827	8 c. Type **190**	..	55	20
828	15 c. "Coronation of St. Catherine"	..	65	35
829	40 c. "Adoration of the Shepherds"	..	90	80
830	50 c. "Adoration of the Magi"	..	1·00	1·00
827/30		Set of 4	2·75	2·00
MS831	86 × 110 mm. As Nos. 827/30, but each with a charity premium of 3 c. P 13½		3·00	3·50

1982 (18 Jan). *Christmas. Children's Charity. Designs as Nos. 827/30 in separate miniature sheets 62 × 78 mm, each with a face value of 75 c. + 5 c.*

MS832	As Nos. 827/30	.. Set of 4 sheets	3·50	4·00

1982 (21 June). *21st Birthday of Princess of Wales. T* **191** *and similar horiz designs. Multicoloured. P* 14.

833	$1.25, Type **191**	..	1·25	1·50
	a. Pair. Nos. 833/4	..	2·50	3·00
834	$1.25, As Type **191**, but inscr "1 July 1982"		1·25	1·50
835	$2.50, Princess (*different*) (inscr "21st Birthday")		2·00	2·25
	a. Pair. Nos. 835/6	..	4·00	4·50
836	$2.50, As No. 835, but inscr "1 July 1982"		2·00	2·25
833/6		Set of 4	6·00	6·50
MS837	92 × 72 mm. $1.25, Type **191**; $2.50, As No. 835. Both inscribed "21st Birthday 1 July 1982". P 13½		3·50	3·75

The two designs for each value were printed together, *se-tenant*, in small sheets of 4.

ROYAL BIRTH · 21 JUNE 1982

(192)

1982 (12 July). *Birth of Prince William of Wales (1st issue). Nos. 812/14 optd as T* **192**.

838	$1 Type **187** (optd with T **192**)		1·50	1·25
	a. Pair. Nos. 838/9	..	3·00	2·50
839	$1 Type **187** (optd "PRINCE WILLIAM OF WALES")		1·50	1·25
840	$2 Prince Charles and Lady Diana Spencer (optd with T **192**)		2·50	2·00
	a. Pair. Nos. 840/1	..	5·00	4·00
841	$2 Prince Charles and Lady Diana Spencer (optd. "PRINCE WILLIAM OF WALES")		2·50	2·00
838/41		Set of 4	7·00	6·00
MS842	106 × 59mm. Nos. 812/13 optd "21 JUNE 1982. ROYAL BIRTH"		4·50	4·50

1982 (3 Aug). *Birth of Prince William of Wales (2nd issue). Designs as Nos. 833/7 but with changed inscriptions. Multicoloured. P* 14.

843	$1.25, As Type **191** (inscr "Royal Birth")		1·40	1·00
	a. Pair. Nos. 843/4	..	2·75	2·00
844	$1.25, As Type **191** (inscr "21 June 1982")		1·40	1·00
845	$2.50, As No. 835 (inscr "Royal Birth")		2·00	1·50
	a. Pair. Nos. 845/6	..	4·00	3·00
846	$2.50, As No. 835 (inscr "21 June 1982")		2·00	1·50
843/6		Set of 4	6·00	4·50
MS847	92 × 73 mm. $1.25, As Type **191**; $2.50, As No. 835. Both inscribed "Royal Birth 21 June 1982". P 13½		2·75	2·75

193 "The Accordionist" (inscr "Serenade")   **194** Franklin D. Roosevelt

(Litho Format)

1982 (10 Sept). *Norman Rockwell (painter) Commemoration. T* **193** *and similar vert designs. Multicoloured. P* 13½ × 14.

848	5 c. Type **193**	..	15	10
849	10 c. "Spring" (inscr "The Hikers")	..	20	15
850	20 c. "The Doctor and the Doll"	..	25	25
851	30 c. "Home from Camp"	..	25	30
848/51		Set of 4	75	70

1982 (30 Sept). *Air. American Anniversaries. T* **194** *and similar vert designs. Multicoloured. P* 14.

852	60 c. Type **194**	..	1·50	80
853	80 c. Benjamin Franklin	..	1·75	1·00
854	$1.40, George Washington	..	2·00	1·50
852/4		Set of 3	4·75	3·00
MS855	116 × 60 mm. Nos. 852/4. P 13½		4·75	3·00

Anniversaries:—60 c. Roosevelt birth centenary; 80 c. "Articles of Peace" negotiations bicentenary; $1.40, Washington 250th birth anniv.

195 "Virgin with Garlands" (detail) (Rubens) and Princess Diana with Prince William   **196** Princess Diana and Prince William

1982 (30 Nov). *Christmas. T* **195** *and similar horiz designs depicting different details from Rubens' painting "Virgin with Garlands". P* 13½ × 14.

856	35 c. multicoloured	..	95	60
857	48 c. multicoloured	..	1·50	1·00
858	60 c. multicoloured	..	1·75	1·75
859	$1.70, multicoloured	..	2·50	3·25
856/9		*Set of 4*	6·00	6·00

MS860 104 × 83 mm. 60 c × 4. Designs, each 27 × 32 mm, forming complete painting "Virgin with Garlands". P 13 × 13½ .. .. .. 3·50 4·25

1982 (30 Nov). *Christmas. Birth of Prince William of Wales. Children's Charity. Sheet* 73 × 59 *mm. P* 13.

MS861 **196** 75 c. + 5 c. multicoloured .. 1·60 2·50

No. **MS**861 comes with 4 different background designs showing details from painting "Virgin with Garlands" (Rubens).

197 Statue of Tangaroa

198 Scouts using Map and Compass

1983 (14 Mar). *Commonwealth Day. T* **197** *and similar vert designs. Multicoloured. P* 14 × 13½.

862	60 c. Type **197**		55	60
863	60 c. Rarotonga oranges		55	60
864	60 c. Rarotonga Airport		55	60
865	60 c. Prime Minister Sir Thomas Davis		55	60
862/5		*Set of 4*	2·00	2·10

Nos. 862/5 were issued together, *se-tenant*, in blocks of four throughout the sheet.

1983 (5 Apr). *75th Anniv of Boy Scout Movement and 125th Birth Anniv of Lord Baden-Powell. T* **198** *and similar vert designs. Multicoloured. P* 13.

866	12 c. Type **198**	..	60	20
867	12 c. Hiking	..	60	20
868	36 c. Campfire cooking	..	90	40
869	36 c. Erecting tent	..	90	40
870	48 c. Hauling on rope	..	1·10	55
871	48 c. Using bos'n's chair	..	1·10	55
872	60 c. Digging hole for sapling	..	1·25	70
873	60 c. Planting sapling	..	1·25	70
866/73		*Set of 8*	7·00	3·25

MS874 161 × 132 mm. As Nos. 866/73, but each with a premium of 2 c. .. .. 4·50 5·50

The two designs of each value were printed together, *se-tenant*, in horizontal pairs throughout the sheets.

XV WORLD JAMBOREE
(199)

1983 (4 July). *15th World Scout Jamboree, Alberta, Canada. Nos. 866/74 optd with T* **199** *(Nos. 875, 877, 879, 881) or with* "ALBERTA, CANADA 1983" (*others*).

875	12 c. Type **198** ..	..	50	20
876	12 c. Hiking	..	50	20
877	36 c. Campfire cooking	..	70	40
878	36 c. Erecting tent	..	70	40
879	48 c. Hauling on rope	..	85	55
880	48 c. Using bos'n's chair	..	85	55
881	60 c. Digging hole for sapling	..	1·00	70
882	60 c. Planting sapling	..	1·00	70
875/82		*Set of 8*	5·50	3·25

MS883 161 × 132 mm. As Nos. 875/82, but each with a premium of 2 c. .. .. 2·75 3·25

The two designs of each value were printed together, *se-tenant*, in horizontal pairs throughout the sheet. In each such pair the left-hand design is overprinted with Type **199** and the right-hand with "ALBERTA, CANADA 1983".

18c ═══ **$5.60**

(200)   (201)

1983 (12–30 Aug). *Various stamps surch. (a) Nos.* 733/6, 745/8, 753/64 *and* 773/6 *as T* **200**.

884	18 c. on 8 c. multicoloured (No. 733)	..	75	50
885	18 c. on 8 c. multicoloured (No. 734)	..	75	50
886	18 c. on 8 c. multicoloured (No. 735)	..	75	50
887	18 c. on 8 c. multicoloured (No. 736)	..	75	50
888	36 c. on 15 c. multicoloured (No. 745)	..	1·25	85
889	36 c. on 15 c. multicoloured (No. 746)	..	1·25	85
890	36 c. on 15 c. multicoloured (No. 747)	..	1·25	85
891	36 c. on 15 c. multicoloured (No. 748)	..	1·25	85
892	36 c. on 30 c. multicoloured (No. 757)	..	1·25	85
893	36 c. on 30 c. multicoloured (No. 758)	..	1·25	85
894	36 c. on 30 c. multicoloured (No. 759)	..	1·25	85
895	36 c. on 30 c. multicoloured (No. 760)	..	1·25	85
896	36 c. on 35 c. multicoloured (No. 761) (30.8.83)	..	1·25	85
897	36 c. on 35 c. multicoloured (No. 762) (30.8.83)	..	1·25	85
898	36 c. on 35 c. multicoloured (No. 763) (30.8.83)	..	1·25	85
899	36 c. on 35 c. multicoloured (No. 764) (30.8.83)	..	1·25	85

202 Union Flag

203 Dish Aerial, Satellite Earth Station

900	48 c. on 25 c. multicoloured (No. 753)	..	1·50	1·25
901	48 c. on 25 c. multicoloured (No. 754)	..	1·50	1·25
902	48 c. on 25 c. multicoloured (No. 755)	..	1·50	1·25
903	48 c. on 25 c. multicoloured (No. 756)	..	1·50	1·25
904	72 c. on 70 c. multicoloured (No. 773)	..	2·50	1·75
905	72 c. on 70 c. multicoloured (No. 774)	..	2·50	1·75
906	72 c. on 70 c. multicoloured (No. 775)	..	2·50	1·75
907	72 c. on 70 c. multicoloured (No. 776)	..	2·50	1·75

(*b*) *Nos.* 788/9, 813, 835/6 *and* 854, *as T* **201** *in gold*

908	96 c. on $1.40, George Washington	..	2·00	2·00
909	96 c. on $2 Prince Charles and Lady Diana Spencer	..	8·50	5·50
	a. Surch double		£130	
	b. Error. Surch on No. 840	..	16·00	
	ba. Pair, Nos. 909 b/c	..	32·00	
	c. Error. Surch on No. 841	..	16·00	
910	96 c. on $2.50 Princess Diana (inscr "21st Birthday") (30.8.83)	..	3·00	3·00
911	96 c. on $2.50. As No. 910 but inscr "1 July 1982" (30.8.83)	..	3·00	3·00
912	$5.60 on $6 Stylaster echinatus	..	23·00	18·00
913	$5.60 on $10 Melithaea albitincta (30.8.83)	..	23·00	18·00
884/913		*Set of 30*	85·00	65·00

The surcharge on No. 908 is printed in gold on a black background, over the old value.

204 "La Belle Jardinière"

205 Montgolfier Balloon 1783

1983 (9 Sept). *Cook Islands Flags and Ensigns. T* **202** *and similar horiz designs. Multicoloured. P* 13½ × 14. (*a*) *Postage. Gold frames.*

914	6 c. Type **202** ..	..	35	20
915	6 c. Group Federal flag	..	35	20
916	12 c. Raratonga ensign	..	50	25
917	12 c. Flag of New Zealand	..	50	25
918	15 c. Cook Islands' flag (1973–79)	..	50	25
919	15 c. Cook Islands' National flag	..	50	25

(*b*) *Air. Silver frames and backgrounds changed*

920	20 c. Type **202** ..	..	60	35
921	20 c. Group Federal flag	..	60	35
922	30 c. Raratonga ensign	..	70	40
923	30 c. Flag of New Zealand	..	70	40
924	35 c. Cook Islands' flag (1973–79)	..	75	45
925	35 c. Cook Islands' National flag	..	75	45
914/25		*Set of 12*	6·00	3·50

MS926 Two sheets, each 132 × 120 mm. (*a*) Nos. 914/19; (*b*) Nos. 920/5. P 13 .. 2·25 4·00

The two designs of each value were issued as *se-tenant* horizontal pairs within the sheets.

1983 (10 Oct). *World Communications Year. T* **203** *and similar vert designs showing satellites. P* 13.

927	36 c. multicoloured	..	50	40
928	48 c. multicoloured	..	65	55
929	60 c. multicoloured	..	85	90
930	96 c. multicoloured	..	1·40	1·75
927/30		*Set of 4*	3·00	3·25

MS931 90 × 65 mm. $2 multicoloured .. 2·00 3·00

1983 (14 Nov). *Christmas. 500th Birth Anniv of Raphael. T* **204** *and similar vert designs. Multicoloured. P* 14 × 13½.

932	12 c. Type **204** ..	..	60	30
933	18 c. "Madonna and Child with Five Saints"	..	85	50
934	36 c. "Madonna and Child with St. John"	..	1·60	1·40
935	48 c. "Madonna of the Fish"	..	1·75	2·00
936	60 c. "The Madonna of the Baldacchino"	..	2·25	3·25
932/6		*Set of 5*	6·25	6·75

MS937 139 × 113 mm. As Nos. 932/6 but each with a premium of 3 c. .. 2·00 2·50

Nos. 932/6 were each printed in small sheets of 5 stamps and 1 label.

1983 (9 Dec). *Christmas. 500th Birth Anniv of Raphael. Children's Charity. Designs as Nos.* 932/6 *in separate miniature sheets* 66 × 82 *mm., each with a face value of* 85 c. + 5 c. *P* 13.

MS938 As Nos. 932/6 .. *Set of 5 sheets* 4·00 3·75

206 Cuvier's Beaked Whale   207 Athens, 1896

1984 (16 Jan). *Bicentenary of Manned Flight* (1983). *T* **205** *and similar vert designs. Multicoloured. P* 13.

939	36 c. Type **205** ..	..	50	50
940	48 c. Adorne's ascent, Strasbourg, 1784	..	60	60
941	60 c. Balloon driven by sails, 1785	..	75	75
942	72 c. Ascent of man on horse, 1798	..	90	90
943	96 c. Godard's aerial acrobatics, 1850	..	1·00	1·00
939/43		*Set of 5*	3·25	3·25

MS944 104 × 85 mm. $2.50, Blanchard and Jeffries crossing Channel, 1785 .. 1·50 2·25

MS945 122 × 132 mm. As Nos. 939/43 but each with a premium of 5 c. .. 1·50 2·25

Nos. 939/43 were each printed in small sheets of 5 stamps and 1 label.

1984 (10 Feb). *Save the Whales. T* **206** *and similar horiz designs. Multicoloured. P* 13.

946	10 c. Type **206**	..	50	50
947	18 c. Risso's Dolphin	..	75	75
948	20 c. True's Beaked Whale	..	75	75
949	24 c. Long-finned Pilot Whale	..	80	80
950	30 c. Narwhal	..	90	90
951	36 c. White Whale (Beluga)	..	1·10	1·10
952	42 c. Common Dolphin	..	1·40	1·40
953	48 c. Commerson's Dolphin	..	1·60	1·60
954	60 c. Bottle-nosed Dolphin	..	1·90	1·90
955	72 c. Sowerby's Beaked Whale	..	2·00	2·00
956	96 c. Common Porpoise	..	2·50	2·50
957	$2 Boutu	..	3·25	3·25
946/57		*Set of 12*	16·00	16·00

1984 (8 Mar). *Olympic Games, Los Angeles. T* **207** *and similar vert designs showing official posters of earlier Games. Multicoloured. P* 13½.

958	18 c. Type **207**	..	40	40
959	24 c. Paris, 1900	..	45	45
960	36 c. St. Louis, 1904	..	55	55
961	48 c. London, 1948	..	65	65
962	60 c. Tokyo, 1964	..	75	75
963	72 c. Berlin, 1936	..	90	90
964	96 c. Rome, 1960	..	1·00	1·00
965	$1.20 Los Angeles, 1930	..	1·25	1·25
958/65		*Set of 8*	5·50	5·50

208 Siphonogorgia

$3.60

(209)

1984 (23 Mar–10 Aug). *Corals (2nd series). (a) Designs as No.* 713 *etc, but with redrawn frames and inscriptions as in T* **208**. *Multicoloured. P* 13.

966	1 c. Type **208**	..	20	10
967	2 c. Millepora alcicornis	..	20	10
968	3 c. Distichopora violacea	..	30	10
969	5 c. Ptilosarcus gurneyi	..	35	10
970	10 c. Lobophyllia bemprichii	..	40	10
971	12 c. Sarcophyton digitatum	..	45	15
972	14 c. Pavona praetorta	..	45	15
973	18 c. Junceella gemmacea	..	50	20
974	20 c. Stylaster	..	55	20
975	24 c. Stylophora pistillata	..	55	20
976	30 c. Palauastrea ramosa	..	80	25
977	36 c. Melithaea albitincta	..	90	30

978	40 c. *Stylaster echinatus*	.. ..	90	30
979	42 c. *Fungia fungites*	..	90	35
980	48 c. *Goniopora*	.. ..	90	35
981	50 c. *Melithaea squamata* (15 May)	..	1·25	45
982	52 c. *Bellonella indica* (15 May)	..	1·25	60
983	55 c. *Plerogyra sinuosa* (15 May)	..	1·25	65
984	60 c. *Tubastraea* (15 May)	..	1·40	70
985	70 c. *Heliofungia actiniformis* (15 May)		1·60	85
986	85 c. *Caulastraea echinulata* (15 May)		1·75	1·00
987	96 c. *Porites andrewsi* (15 May)	..	1·90	1·10
988	$1.10, *Pectinia alcicornis* (15 May)		2·00	1·40
989	$1.20, *Dendrophyllia gracilis* (15 May)		2·25	1·50

(*b*) Nos. 785/9 surch as T **209** in gold on black

990	$3.60 on $2 *Gonipora* (28 June)	..		
991	$4.20 on $3 *Heliofungia actiniformis* (28 June) ..	..	5·50	4·00
			6·00	5·00
992	$5 on $4 *Stylophora pistillata* (28 June) ..		6·50	5·50
993	$7.20 on $6 *Stylaster echinatus* (20 July)		8·50	8·50
994	$9.60 on $10 *Melithaea albitincta* (10 Aug)		10·00	10·00
966/94	.. ..	*Set of 29*	55·00	40·00

Equestrian Team Dressage Germany
(210)

1984 (24 Aug). *Olympic Gold Medal Winners. Nos. 963/5 optd as T* **210**.

995	72 c. Berlin, 1936 (optd T **210**)		60	65
996	96 c. Rome, 1960 (optd "Decathlon Daley Thompson Great Britain")		80	85
997	$1.20 Los Angeles, 1930 (optd "Four Gold Medals Carl Lewis U.S.A."		1·00	1·10
995/7	..	*Set of 3*	2·25	2·40

211 Capt. Cook's Cottage, Melbourne

1984 (20 Sept). *"Ausipex" International Stamp Exhibition, Melbourne. T* **211** *and similar horiz designs. Multicoloured. P* 13.

998	36 c. Type **211**	..	1·25	1·25
999	48 c. "H.M.S. Endeavour careened for Repairs" (Sydney Parkinson)..		2·00	2·00
1000	60 c. "Cook's landing at Botany Bay" (E. Phillips Fox) ..		2·75	2·75
1001	$2 "Capt. James Cook" (John Webber) ..		3·50	3·50
998/1001		*Set of 4*	8·50	8·50
MS1002	140 × 100 mm. As Nos. 998/1001, but each stamp with a face value of 90 c.		7·50	7·50

Commemorating-
15 Sept. 1984
(212)

213 "Virgin on Throne with Child" (Giovanni Bellini)

1984 (15 Oct). *Birth of Prince Henry. Nos. 812 and 833/6 optd or surch (No. 1007) as T* **212**.

1003	$1.25, Type **191** (optd with T **212**) (Gold) ..		1·50	1·10
	a. Pair. Nos. 1003/4.	..	3·00	2·25
1004	$1.25, As Type **191**, but inscr "1 July 1982" (optd "Birth H.R.H. Prince Henry") (Gold)		1·50	1·10
1005	$2.50, Princess Diana (inscr "21st Birthday") (optd with T **212**) (Gold)		2·25	2·00
	a. Pair. Nos. 1005/6.	..	4·50	4·00
1006	$2.50, As No. 835, but inscr "1 July 1982" (optd "Birth H.R.H. Prince Henry") (Gold)		2·25	2·00
1007	$3 on $1 Type **187** (surch "Royal Birth Prince Henry 15 Sept. 1984") (Sil.)		4·50	4·00
1003/7		*Set of 5*	11·00	9·25

1984 (21 Nov). *Christmas. T* **213** *and similar vert designs. Multicoloured. P* 14.

1008	36 c. Type **213**		90	40
1009	48 c. "Virgin and Child" (anonymous, 15th century) ..		1·00	60
1010	60 c. "Virgin and Child with Saints" (Alvise Vivarini) ..		1·25	80
1011	96 c. "Virgin and Child with Angels" (H. Memling) ..		1·60	1·60
1012	$1.20, "Adoration of Magi" (G. Tiepolo) ..		1·75	2·00
1008/12		*Set of 5*	6·00	4·75
MS1013	120 × 113 mm. As Nos. 1008/12, but each with a premium of 5 c. P 13½.		2·75	3·00

1984 (10 Dec). *Christmas. Designs as Nos. 1008/12 in separate miniature sheets, 62 × 76 mm, each with a face value of 95 c. + 5 c. P* 13½.

MS1014	As Nos. 1008/12 ..	*Set of 5 sheets*	4·00	4·50

214 Downy Woodpecker

1985 (23 Apr). *Birth Bicentenary of John J. Audubon (ornithologist). T* **214** *and similar vert designs showing original paintings. Multicoloured. P* 13 × 13½.

1015	30 c. Type **214**		2·00	1·00
1016	55 c. Black-throated Blue Warbler	..	2·25	1·50
1017	65 c. Yellow-throated Warbler	..	2·50	2·00
1018	75 c. Chestnut-sided Warbler	..	2·75	2·50
1019	95 c. Dickcissel	..	3·00	2·75
1020	$1.15, White-crowned Sparrow	..	3·00	3·25
1015/20		*Set of 6*	14·00	11·50
MS1021	Three sheets, each 76 × 75 mm. (a) $1.30, Red-cockaded Woodpecker. (b) $2.80, Seaside Sparrow. (c) $5.30, Zenaida Dove	*Set of 3 sheets*	11·00	8·50

215 "The Kingston Flyer" (New Zealand)

(Des and litho Format)

1985 (14 May). *Famous Trains. T* **215** *and similar horiz designs. Multicoloured. Ordinary paper. P* 14 × 13½.

1022	20 c. Type **215**	..	50	50
1023	55 c. Class "640" (Italy) ..	..	75	85
1024	65 c. "Gotthard" type (Switzerland)	..	80	90
1025	75 c. Union Pacific No. 6900 (U.S.A.)	..	1·00	1·10
1026	95 c. "Super Continental" type (Canada)	..	1·10	1·25
1027	$1.15, "TGV" type (France) ..	..	1·10	1·50
1028	$2.20, "The Flying Scotsman" (Great Britain)	..	1·25	2·50
1029	$3.40, "The Orient Express" ..	..	1·40	3·75
1022/9		*Set of 8*	7·00	11·00

Nos. 1022/9 exist imperforate from stock dispersed by the liquidator of Format International Security Printers Ltd.

216 "Helena Fourment" (Peter Paul Rubens)

217 "Lady Elizabeth, 1908" (Mabel Hankey)

1985 (θ June). *International Youth Year. T* **216** *and similar vert designs. Multicoloured. P* 13.

1030	55 c. Type **216**		2·25	2·00
1031	65 c. "Vigee-Lebrun and Daughter" (E. Vigee-Lebrun) ..		2·50	2·50
1032	75 c. "On the Terrace" (P. Renoir) ..		2·75	2·75
1033	$1.30, "Young Mother Sewing" (M. Cassatt)		3·50	3·75
1030/3		*Set of 4*	10·00	10·00
MS1034	103 × 106 mm. As Nos. 1030/3, but each with a premium of 10 c. ..		4·50	4·50

1985 (28 June). *Life and Times of Queen Elizabeth the Queen Mother. T* **217** *and similar vert designs showing paintings. Multicoloured. P* 13.

1035	65 c. Type **217**		40	50
1036	75 c. "Duchess of York, 1923" (Savely Sorine) ..		45	60
1037	$1.15, "Duchess of York, 1925" (Philip de Laszlo) ..		55	85
1038	$2.80, "Queen Elizabeth, 1938" (Sir Gerald Kelly) ..		1·40	2·25
1035/8		*Set of 4*	2·50	3·75
MS1039	69 × 81 mm. $5.30, As $2.80 ..		2·50	3·50

Nos. 1035/8 were each printed in small sheets of 4 stamps. For these designs in a miniature sheet, each with a face value of 55 c., see No. **MS**1079.

218 Albert Henry (Prime Minister, 1965–78)

219 Golf

1985 (29 July). *20th Anniv of Self-Government. T* **218** *and similar vert designs. Multicoloured. P* 13.

1040	30 c. Type **218**		60	40
1041	50 c. Sir Thomas Davis (Prime Minister, 1978–Apr 1983 and from Nov 1983)..		90	60
1042	65 c. Geoffrey Henry (Prime Minister, Apr–Nov 1983) ..		1·00	1·00
1040/2		*Set of 3*	2·25	1·75
MS1043	134 × 70 mm. As Nos. 1040/2, but each stamp with a face value of 55 c.		1·25	1·40

1985 (29 July). *South Pacific Mini Games, Rarotonga. T* **219** *and similar vert designs. Multicoloured. P* 14.

1044	55 c. Type **219**		4·00	3·50
1045	65 c. Rugby		4·00	4·00
1046	75 c. Tennis		5·50	6·00
1044/6		*Set of 3*	12·00	12·00
MS1047	126 × 70 mm. Nos. 1044/6, but each with a premium of 10 c. P 13½.		9·00	10·00

220 Sea Horse, Gearwheel and Leaves

221 "Madonna of the Magnificat"

1985 (29 July). *Pacific Conferences, Rarotonga. P* 13.

1048	**220** 55 c. black, gold and rosine ..		75	65
1049	65 c. black, gold and violet ..		85	80
1050	75 c. black, gold and blue-green ..		1·00	1·10
1048/50		*Set of 3*	2·40	2·25
MS1051	126 × 81 mm. As Nos. 1048/50, but each stamp with a face value of 50 c. ..		1·25	1·40

No. 1048 shows the South Pacific Bureau for Economic Co-operation logo and is inscribed "S.P.E.C. Meeting, 30 July–1 Aug 1985, Rarotonga". No. 1049 also shows the S.P.E.C. logo, but is inscribed "South Pacific Forum, 4–6 Aug 1985, Rarotonga". No. 1050 shows the Pacific Islands Conference logo and the inscription "Pacific Islands Conference, 7–10 Aug 1985, Rarotonga".

1985 (18 Nov). *Christmas. Virgin and Child Paintings by Botticelli. T* **221** *and similar vert designs. Multicoloured. P* 14.

1052	55 c. Type **221**		1·60	60
1053	65 c. "Madonna with Pomegranate" ..		1·75	65
1054	75 c. "Madonna and Child with Six Angels".. ..		2·00	1·00
1055	95 c. "Madonna and Child with St. John" ..		2·25	1·40
1052/5		*Set of 4*	7·00	3·25
MS1056	90 × 104 mm. As Nos. 1052/5, but each stamp with a face value of 50 c. P 13½..		3·50	3·50

1985 (9 Dec). *Christmas. Virgin and Child Paintings by Botticelli. Square designs (46 × 46 mm) as Nos. 1052/5 in separate miniature sheets, 50 × 51 mm, with face values of $1.20, $1.45, $2.20 and $2.75. Imperf.*

MS1057	As Nos. 1052/5 ..	*Set of 4 sheets*	9·00	11·00

222 "The Eve of the Deluge" (John Martin)

223 Queen Elizabeth II

1986 (13 Mar). *Appearance of Halley's Comet. Paintings. T* **222** *and similar vert designs. Multicoloured. P* 14.

1058	55 c. Type **222**		1·25	1·25
1059	65 c. "Lot and his Daughters" (Lucas van Leyden) ..		1·40	1·40
1060	75 c. "Auspicious Comet" (from treatise c 1587) ..		1·50	1·50
1061	$1.25, "Events following Charles I" (Herman Saftleven)		2·25	2·25

1062	$2 "Ossian receiving Napoleonic Officers" (Anne Louis Girodet-Trioson) ..		3·00	3·00
1058/62		Set of 5	8·50	8·50
MS1063	130×100 mm. As Nos. 1058/62, but each with a face value of 70 c. P 13½		3·75	5·00
MS1064	84×63 mm. $4 "Halley's Comet of 1759 over the Thames" (Samuel Scott). P 13½		4·50	6·00

1986 (21 Apr). *60th Birthday of Queen Elizabeth II. T* **223** *and similar vert designs showing formal portraits.* P 13 × 13½.

1065	95 c. multicoloured		1·10	1·50
1066	$1.25, multicoloured ..		1·40	1·75
1067	$1.50, multicoloured ..		1·50	2·00
1065/7		Set of 3	3·50	4·75
MS1068	Three sheets, each 44×75 mm. As Nos. 1065/7, but with face values of $1.10, $1.95 and $2.45 ..	Set of 3 sheets	8·00	9·00

224 U.S.A. 1847 Franklin 5 c. Stamp and H.M.S. *Resolution* at Rarotonga

225 Head of Statue of Liberty

1986 (21 May). *"Ameripex '86" International Stamp Exhibition, Chicago. T* **224** *and similar horiz designs. Multicoloured.* P 14.

1069	$1 Type **224** ..		4·00	3·50
1070	$1.50, Chicago ..		3·50	4·00
1071	$2 1975 definitive $2, Benjamin Franklin and H.M.S. *Resolution* ..		5·00	5·00
1069/71		Set of 3	11·00	11·00

1986 (4 July). *Centenary of Statue of Liberty. T* **225** *and similar vert designs. Multicoloured.* P 14.

1072	$1 Type **225**..		75	85
1073	$1.25, Hand and torch of Statue ..		90	1·10
1074	$2.75, Statue of Liberty ..		2·00	2·50
1072/4		Set of 3	3·25	4·00

226 Miss Sarah Ferguson

(**227**)

1986 (23 July). *Royal Wedding. T* **226** *and similar multicoloured designs.* P 14 ($1, $2) or 13½ × 13 ($3).

1075	$1 Type **226** ..		1·00	1·25
1076	$2 Prince Andrew ..		1·75	2·25
1077	$3 Prince Andrew and Miss Sarah Ferguson (57×31 mm)..		2·50	3·00
1075/7		Set of 3	4·75	6·00

Nos. 1075/7 were each printed in small sheets of 4 stamps.

1986 (4 Aug). *"Stampex '86" Stamp Exhibition, Adelaide. No.* MS1002 *optd with T* **227** *in gold (circle) and black (inscr) only on design as No. 1001.*

MS1078	90 c.×4 multicoloured ..		5·50	6·50

The "Stampex '86" exhibition emblem is also overprinted on the sheet margin.

1986 (4 Aug). *86th Birthday of Queen Elizabeth the Queen Mother. Designs as Nos.* 1035/8 *in miniature sheet,* 91×116 *mm, each stamp with a face value of 55 c. Multicoloured.* P 13×13½.

MS1079	55 c.×4. As Nos. 1035/8 ..		4·25	4·75

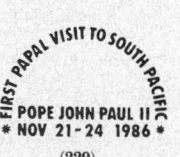

228 "The Holy Family with St. John the Baptist and St. Elizabeth"

(**229**)

1986 (17 Nov). *Christmas. Paintings by Rubens. T* **228** *and similar vert designs. Multicoloured.* P 13½.

1080	55 c. Type **228** ..		1·00	85
1081	$1.30, "Virgin with the Garland"		2·00	1·75
1082	$2.75, "The Adoration of the Magi" (detail) ..		3·75	3·50
1080/2		Set of 3	6·00	5·50
MS1083	140×100 mm. As Nos. 1080/2, but each size 36×46 mm with a face value of $2.40		11·00	12·00
MS1084	80×70 mm. $6.40, As No. 1081 but size 32×50 mm		11·00	12·00

1986 (21 Nov). *Visit of Pope John Paul II to South Pacific. Nos.* 1080/4 *surch as T* **229** *in silver.*

1085	55 c. + 10 c. Type **228**		2·50	1·75
1086	$1.30 + 10 c. "Virgin with the Garland"		3·25	2·25
1087	$2.75 + 10 c. "The Adoration of the Magi" (detail) ..		5·50	3·75
1085/7		Set of 3	10·00	7·00
MS1088	140×100 mm. As Nos. 1085/7, but each size 36×46 mm with a face value of $2.40 + 10 c.		11·00	12·00
MS1089	80×70 mm. $6.40 + 50 c. As No. 1086 but size 32×50 mm		11·00	12·00

═══

HURRICANE RELIEF

10c	**+50c**
(**230**)	(**231**)

1987 (10–12 Feb). *Various stamps surch as T* **230** *by N.Z. Govt Printer.*

(a) On Nos. 741/56, 761/76 and 787/8

1090	10 c. on 15 c. *Distichopora violacea* (11.2) ..		10	10
1091	10 c. on 15 c. *Stylaster* (11.2) ..		10	10
1092	10 c. on 15 c. *Gonipora* (11.2) ..		10	10
1093	10 c. on 15 c. *Caulastraea echinulata* (11.2)		10	10
1094	10 c. on 15 c. *Lobophyllia bemprichii* (11.2)		10	10
1095	10 c. on 25 c. *Palauastrea ramosa* (11.2) ..		10	10
1096	10 c. on 25 c. *Bellonella indica* (11.2)		10	10
1097	10 c. on 25 c. *Pectinia alcicornis* (11.2)		10	10
1098	18 c. on 12 c. *Millepora alcicornis* (11.2)		15	15
1099	18 c. on 12 c. *Junceella gemmacea* (11.2)		15	15
1100	18 c. on 12 c. *Fungia fungites* (11.2)		15	15
1101	18 c. on 12 c. *Heliofungia actiniformis* (11.2)		15	15
1102	18 c. on 20 c. *Ptilosarcus gurneyi* (11.2)		15	15
1103	18 c. on 20 c. *Stylophora pistillata* (11.2)		15	15
1104	18 c. on 20 c. *Melithaea squamata* (11.2)		15	15
1105	18 c. on 20 c. *Porites andrewsi* (11.2)		15	15
1106	55 c. on 35 c. Type **184** (11.2)		40	45
1107	55 c. on 35 c. *Pavona praetorta* (11.2)		40	45
1108	55 c. on 35 c. *Stylaster echinatus* (11.2)		40	45
1109	55 c. on 35 c. *Tubastraea* (11.2)		40	45
1110	65 c. on 50 c. As No. 1098 (11.2)		45	50
1111	65 c. on 50 c. As No. 1099 (11.2)		45	50
1112	65 c. on 50 c. As No. 1100 (11.2)		45	50
1113	65 c. on 50 c. As No. 1101 (11.2)		45	50
1114	65 c. on 60 c. As No. 1090 (11.2)		45	50
1115	65 c. on 60 c. As No. 1091 (11.2)		45	50
1116	65 c. on 60 c. As No. 1092 (11.2)		45	50
1117	65 c. on 60 c. As No. 1093 (11.2)		45	50
1118	75 c. on 70 c. As No. 1102 (11.2)		55	60
1119	75 c. on 70 c. As No. 1103 (11.2)		55	60
1120	75 c. on 70 c. As No. 1104 (11.2)		55	60
1121	75 c. on 70 c. As No. 1105 (11.2)		55	60
1122	$6.40 on $4 *Stylophora pistillata*		4·50	4·75
1123	$7.20 on $6 *Stylaster echinatus* ..		5·00	5·25

(b) On Nos. 812/13 in gold (12 Feb)

1124	$9.40 on $1 Type **187** ..		15·00	16·00
1125	$9.40 on $2 Prince Charles and Lady Diana Spencer..		15·00	16·00

(c) On Nos. 835/6 in gold (12 Feb)

1126	$9.40 on $2.50 Princess of Wales (inscr "21st Birthday") ..		15·00	16·00
1127	$9.40 on $2.50 As No. 1126, but inscr "1 July 1982" ..		15·00	16·00

(d) On Nos. 966/8, 971/2, 975, 979/80, 982 and 987/9

1128	5 c. on 1 c. Type **208** ..		10	10
1129	5 c. on 2 c. *Millepora alcicornis* ..		10	10
1130	5 c. on 3 c. *Distichopora violacea* ..		10	10
1131	5 c. on 12 c. *Sarcophyton digitatum* ..		10	10
1132	5 c. on 14 c. *Pavona praetorta* ..		10	10
1133	18 c. on 24 c. *Stylophora pistillata* ..		15	15
1134	55 c. on 52 c. *Bellonella indica* ..		40	45
1135	65 c. on 42 c. *Fungia fungites* ..		45	50
1136	75 c. on 48 c. *Gonipora* ..		55	60
1137	95 c. on 96 c. *Porites andrewsi* ..		70	75
1138	95 c. on $1.10 *Pectinia alcicornis* ..		70	75
1139	95 c. on $1.20 *Dendrophyllia gracilis* ..		70	75

(e) On Nos. 998/1001 in gold (No. 1143) or gold (value) and black (bars) (others) (12 Feb)

1140	$1.30 on 36 c. Type **211** ..		1·40	1·50
1141	$1.30 on 48 c. "The *Endeavour* careened for Repairs" (Sydney Parkinson) ..		1·40	1·50
1142	$1.30 on 60 c. "Cook's landing at Botany Bay" (E. Phillips Fox)..		1·40	1·50
1143	$1.30 on $2 "Capt. James Cook" (John Webber) ..		1·40	1·50

(f) On Nos. 1065/7 in gold (12 Feb)

1144	**223** $2.80 on 95 c. multicoloured		7·00	7·50
1145	– $2.80 on $1.25 multicoloured ..		7·00	7·50
1146	– $2.80 on $1.50 multicoloured ..		7·00	7·50

(g) On Nos. 1075/7 in gold (value) and black (bars) (12 Feb)

1147	$2.80 on $1 Type **226** ..		6·00	6·50
	a. Black opt (bars) omitted		£110	
1148	$2.80 on $2 Prince Andrew ..		6·00	6·50
1149	$2.80 on $3 Prince Andrew and Miss Sarah Ferguson (57×31 mm) ..		6·00	6·50
1090/149 ..		Set of 60	£100	£120

1987 (17 June). *Various stamps surch as T* **230**.

(a) On Nos. 785/6 and 789

1150	$2.80 on $2 *Gonipora* ..		2·10	2·25
1151	$5 on $3 *Heliofungia actiniformis* ..		4·00	4·25
1152	$9.40 on $10 *Melithaea albitincta* ..		7·50	7·75

(b) On Nos. 838/42 (in gold on Nos. 1153/6)

1153	$9.40 on $1 Type **187** (No. 838)		7·50	7·75
	a. Pair. Nos. 1153/4 ..		15·00	16·00
1154	$9.40 on $1 Type **187** (No. 839)		7·50	7·75
1155	$9.40 on $2 Prince Charles and Lady Diana Spencer (No. 840) ..		7·50	7·75
	a. Pair. Nos. 1155/6 ..		15·00	16·00
1156	$9.40 on $2 Prince Charles and Lady Diana Spencer (No. 841) ..		7·50	7·75
1150/6		Set of 7	40·00	40·00
MS1157	106×59 mm. $9.20 on $1 Type **187**; $9.20 on $2 Prince Charles and Lady Diana Spencer ..		12·00	15·00

1987 (30 June–31 July). *Hurricane Relief Fund. Various stamps surch as T* **231**.

(a) On Nos. 1035/9 in silver

1158	65 c. + 50 c. Type **217** ..		80	85
1159	75 c. + 50 c. "Duchess of York, 1923" (Savely Sorine) ..		85	1·00
1160	$1.15 + 50 c. "Duchess of York, 1925" (Philip de Laszlo) ..		1·10	1·40
1161	$2.80 + 50 c. "Queen Elizabeth, 1938" (Sir Gerald Kelly) ..		2·25	2·75
MS1162	69×81 mm. $5.30 + 50 c. As $2.80 + 50 c. ..		4·50	6·00

(b) On Nos. 1058/62 (in silver on Nos. 1164/6)

1163	55 c. + 50 c. Type **222** ..		75	80
1164	65 c. + 50 c. "Lot and his Daughters" (Lucas van Leyden) ..		80	85
1165	75 c. + 50 c. "Auspicious Comet" (from treatise c 1587) ..		85	90
1166	$1.25 + 50 c. "Events following Charles I" (Herman Saftleven) ..		1·25	1·40
1167	$2 + 50 c. "Ossian receiving Napoleonic Officers" (Anne Louis Girodet-Trioson) ..		1·75	2·00

(c) On Nos. 1065/8 (in silver on No. 1169) (31 July)

1168	**223** 95 c. + 50 c. multicoloured ..		1·00	1·10
1169	– $1.25 + 50 c. multicoloured ..		1·25	1·40
1170	– $1.50 + 50 c. multicoloured ..		1·40	1·50
MS1171	Three sheets, each 44×75 mm. As Nos. 1168/70, but with face values of $1.10 + 50 c., $1.95 + 50 c., $2.45 + 50 c. Set of 3 sheets		7·00	8·50

(d) On Nos. 1069/71 (in silver on No. 1172)

1172	$1 + 50 c. Type **224** ..		2·00	2·00
1173	$1.50 + 50 c. Chicago ..		1·75	2·00
1174	$2 + 50 c. 1975 definitive $2, Benjamin Franklin and H.M.S. *Resolution* ..		2·75	2·75

(e) On Nos. 1072/4 (in silver on Nos. 1175 and 1177)

1175	$1 + 50 c. Type **225** ..		1·00	1·25
1176	$1.25 + 50 c. Hand and torch of Statue ..		1·25	1·50
1177	$2.75 + 50 c. Statue of Liberty ..		2·25	2·75

(f) On Nos. 1075/7 in silver (31 July)

1178	$1 + 50 c. Type **226**..		1·00	1·25
1179	$2 + 50 c. Prince Andrew ..		1·75	2·00
1180	$3 + 50 c. Prince Andrew and Miss Sarah Ferguson (57×31 mm) ..		2·40	2·75

(g) On Nos. 1080/4 in silver

1181	55 c. + 50 c. Type **228** ..		75	80
1182	$1.30 + 50 c. "Virgin with the Garland"..		1·25	1·40
1183	$2.75 + 50 c. "The Adoration of the Magi" (detail) ..		2·25	2·40
MS1184	140×100 mm. As No. 1181/3, but each size 36×46 mm with a face value of $2.40 + 50 c.		7·00	8·50
MS1185	80×70 mm. $6.40 + 50 c. As No. 1182, but size 32×50 mm.		4·75	6·00

(h) On Nos. 1122, 1134/7 and 1150/1

1186	55 c. + 25 c. on 52 c. *Bellonella indica*		70	70
1187	65 c. + 25 c. on 42 c. *Fungia fungites* ..		80	80
1188	75 c. + 25 c. on 48 c. *Gonipora* ..		90	90
1189	95 c. + 25 c. on 96 c. *Porites andrewsi* ..		1·10	1·10
1190	$2.80 + 50 c. on $2 *Gonipora* ..		2·75	2·75
1191	$5 + 50 c. on $3 *Heliofungia actiniformis* ..		4·50	4·50
1192	$6.40 + 50 c. on $4 *Stylophora pistillata* ..		6·00	6·00
1158/92 ..		Set of 31	45·00	48·00

ROYAL WEDDING FORTIETH ANNIVERSARY

(**232**)

1987 (20 Nov). *Royal Ruby Wedding. Nos. 484 and 787 optd with T* **232** *in black on gold.*

1193	$4 Queen Elizabeth II and seashells ..		4·50	4·50
1194	$4 Queen Elizabeth II and *Stylophora pistillata* ..		4·50	4·50

233 "The Holy Family" (Rembrandt)

1987 (7 Dec). *Christmas. T **233** and similar horiz designs showing different paintings of the Holy Family by Rembrandt.* P 13½.

1195	$1.25, multicoloured	2·25	2·00
1196	$1.50, multicoloured	2·75	2·25
1197	$1.95, multicoloured	4·00	3·50
1195/7	*Set of 3*	8·00	7·00
MS1198	100×140 mm. As Nos. 1195/7, but each size 47×36 mm with a face value of $1.15	5·50	7·00
MS1199	70×80 mm. $6 As No. 1196, but size 40×31 mm. P 13×13½	8·00	9·00

234 Olympic Commemorative $50 Coin

(Des G. Vasarhelyi)

1988 (26 Apr). *Olympic Games, Seoul. T **234** and similar vert designs. Multicoloured.* P 13½×14.

1200	$1.50, Type **234**	2·50	2·00
	a. Horiz strip of 3. Nos. 1200/2	6·50	
1201	$1.50, Olympic torch and Seoul Olympic Park	2·50	2·00
1202	$1.50, Steffi Graf playing tennis and Olympic medal	2·50	2·00
1200/2	*Set of 3*	6·50	5·50
MS1203	131×81 mm. $10 Combined design as Nos. 1200/2, but measuring 114×47 mm. P 13½	11·00	12·00

Nos. 1200/2 were printed together, *se-tenant*, in horizontal strips of 3 throughout the sheet, each strip forming a composite design.

MILOSLAV MECIR CZECHOSLOVAKIA GOLD MEDAL WINNER MEN'S TENNIS
(235)

1988 (12 Oct). *Olympic Tennis Medal Winners, Seoul. Nos. 1200/3 optd as T **235**.*

1204	$1.50, Type **234** (optd with T **235**)	2·00	2·00
	a. Horiz strip of 3. Nos. 1204/6	5·50	
1205	$1.50, Olympic torch and Seoul Olympic Park (optd "TIM MAYOTTE UNITED STATES GABRIELA SABATINI ARGENTINA SILVER MEDAL WINNERS")	2·00	2·00
1206	$1.50, Steffi Graf playing tennis and Olympic medal (optd "GOLD MEDAL WINNER STEFFI GRAF WEST GERMANY")	2·00	2·00
1204/6	*Set of 3*	5·50	5·50
MS1207	131×81 mm. $10 Combined design as Nos. 1200/2, but measuring 114×47 mm. (optd "GOLD MEDAL WINNER SEOUL OLYMPIC GAMES STEFFI GRAF -WEST GERMANY")	10·00	11·00

236 "Virgin and Child"   237 "Apollo II" leaving Earth

1988 (11 Nov). *Christmas. T **236** and similar vert designs showing paintings of "The Nativity" ($6.40) or different versions of "Virgin and Child" by Dürer.* P 13½.

1208	70 c. multicoloured	1·75	1·75
1209	85 c. multicoloured	2·00	2·00
1210	95 c. multicoloured	2·25	2·25
1211	$1.25, multicoloured	2·75	2·75
1208/11	*Set of 4*	8·00	8·00
MS1212	80 × 100 mm. $6.40, multicoloured (45 × 60 mm)	6·00	8·00

(Des G. Vasarhelyi)

1989 (14 July). *20th Anniv of First Manned Landing on Moon. T **237** and similar horiz designs. Multicoloured.* P 13.

1213	40 c. Type **237**	1·00	1·00
	a. Horiz pair. Nos. 1213/14	2·00	2·00
1214	40 c. Lunar module over Moon	1·00	1·00
1215	55 c. Armstrong stepping onto Moon	1·25	1·25
	a. Horiz pair. Nos. 1215/16	2·50	2·50
1216	55 c. Astronaut on Moon	1·25	1·25

1217	65 c. Working on lunar surface	1·50	1·50
	a. Horiz pair. Nos. 1217/18	3·00	3·00
1218	65 c. Conducting experiment	1·50	1·50
1219	75 c. "Apollo 11" leaving Moon	1·60	1·60
	a. Horiz pair. Nos. 1219/20	3·00	3·00
1220	75 c. Splashdown in South Pacific	1·60	1·60
1213/20	*Set of 8*	9·50	9·50
MS1221	108×91 mm. $4.20, Astronauts on Moon	4·50	5·50

Nos. 1213/14, 1215/16, 1217/18 and 1219/20 were each printed together, horizontally *se-tenant*, in sheets of 12.

238 Rarotonga Flycatcher

(Des G. Drummond)

1989 (4 Oct). *Endangered Birds of the Cook Islands. T **238** and similar horiz designs. Multicoloured. (a) Postage.* P 13½×13

1222	15 c. Type **238**	1·75	1·75
1223	20 c. Pair of Rarotonga Flycatchers	1·75	1·75
1224	65 c. Pair of Rarotongan Fruit Doves	2·75	2·75
1225	70 c. Rarotongan Fruit Dove	2·75	2·75
1222/5	*Set of 4*	8·00	8·00

(b) Air. P 13½

MS1226	Four sheets, each 70×53 mm. As Nos. 1222/5, but with face values of $1, $1.25, $1.50, $1.75 and each size 50×32 mm. *Set of 4 sheets*	5·50	7·50

239 Villagers

1989 (24 Nov). *Christmas. T **239** and similar multicoloured designs showing details from "Adoration of the Magi" by Rubens.* P 13.

1227	70 c. Type **239**	1·00	1·00
1228	85 c. Virgin Mary	1·25	1·50
1229	95 c. Christ Child	1·40	1·60
1230	$1.50, Boy with gift	2·00	2·50
1227/30	*Set of 4*	5·00	6·00
MS1231	85×120 mm. $6.40, "Adoration of the Magi" (45×60 mm). P 13½	8·50	9·00

240 Revd. John Williams   241 "Woman writing and L.M.S. Church   Letter" (Terborch)

(Des Jennifer Toombs)

1990 (19 Feb). *Christianity in the Cook Islands. T **240** and similar square designs. Multicoloured.* P 13.

1232	70 c. Type **240**	75	80
1233	85 c. Mgr. Bernardine Castanié and Roman Catholic Church	90	1·10
1234	95 c. Elder Osborne Widstoe and Mormon Church	1·00	1·40
1235	$1.60, Dr. J. E. Caldwell and Seventh Day Adventist Church	1·75	2·00
1232/5	*Set of 4*	4·00	5·25
MS1236	90×90 mm. As Nos. 1232/5, but each with a face value of 90 c. P 13½	4·75	6·00

1990 (2 May). *150th Anniv of the Penny Black. T **241** and similar vert designs showing paintings. Multicoloured.* P 13½.

1237	85 c. Type **241**	1·10	1·25
1238	$1.15, "George Gisze" (Holbein the Younger)	1·50	1·75
1239	$1.55, "Mrs. John Douglas" (Gainsborough)	1·90	2·25
1240	$1.85, "Portrait of a Gentleman" (Dürer)	2·25	2·50
1237/40	*Set of 4*	6·00	7·00
MS1241	82×150 mm. As Nos. 1237/40, but each with a face value of $1.05	8·00	9·00

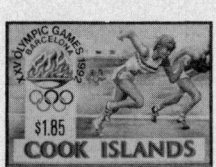

242 Sprinting   243 Queen Elizabeth the Queen Mother

(Des G. Vasarhelyi)

1990 (15 June)–**91**. *Olympic Games, Barcelona, and Winter Olympic Games, Albertville (1st issue) (1992). T **242** and similar horiz designs. Multicoloured.* P 14.

1242	$1.85, Type **242**	3·50	4·00
	a. Horiz strip of 3. Nos. 1242/4	9·50	
1243	$1.85, Cook Islands $50 commemorative coin	3·50	4·00
1244	$1.85, Skiing	3·50	4·00
1242/4	*Set of 3*	9·50	11·00
MS1245	109×52 mm. $6.40, As Nos. 1242/4, but 80×26 mm. P 13½ (12.2.91)	10·50	12·00

Nos. 1242/4 were printed together, *se-tenant*, in horizontal strips of 3 throughout the sheet of 18.
See also Nos. 1304/10.

1990 (20 July). *90th Birthday of Queen Elizabeth the Queen Mother.* P 13½.

1246	**243** $1.85, multicoloured	3·50	4·00
MS1247	66×101 mm. **243** $6.40, multicoloured	8·50	10·00

244 "Adoration of the Magi"   (245)
(Memling)

(Litho Questa)

1990 (29 Nov). *Christmas. Religious Paintings. T **244** and similar multicoloured designs. Ordinary paper.* P 14.

1248	70 c. Type **244**	95	95
1249	85 c. "Holy Family" (Lotto)	1·10	1·10
1250	95 c. "Madonna and Child with Saints John and Catherine" (Titian)	1·40	1·60
1251	$1.50, "Holy Family" (Titian)	2·50	3·00
1248/51	*Set of 4*	5·50	6·00
MS1252	98×110 mm, $6.40, "Madonna and Child enthroned, surrounded by Saints" (Vivarini) (vert)	7·00	8·00

1990 (5 Dec). *"Birdpex '90" Stamp Exhibition, Christchurch, New Zealand. No.* MS1226 *optd with T **245**.*

MS1253	Four sheets, each 70×53 mm. As Nos. 1222/5, but with face values of $1, $1.25, $1.50, $1.75 and each size 50×32 mm . *Set of 4 sheets*	10·00	11·00

246 Columbus   (247)
(engraving by Theodoro de Bry)

1991 (14 Feb). *500th Anniv of Discovery of America by Columbus (1992) (1st issue).* P 13½×13.

1254	**246** $1 multicoloured	1·75	2·00

See also Nos. 1302/3.

1991 (22 Apr). *65th Birthday of Queen Elizabeth II. No.* 789 *optd with T **247** in gold.*

1255	$10 *Melithaea albitincta*	12·00	13·00

248 "Adoration of the Child"
(G. delle Notti)

359

(Des G. Vasarhelyi. Litho Questa)

1991 (12 Nov). *Christmas. Religious Paintings. T 248 and similar multicoloured designs. Ordinary paper. P 14.*

1256	70 c.	Type 248	1·25	1·25
1257	85 c.	"The Birth of the Virgin" (B. Murillo)	1·50	1·50
1258	$1.15,	"Adoration of the Shepherds" (Rembrandt)	2·00	2·00
1259	$1.50,	"Adoration of the Shepherds" (L. le Nain)	2·75	3·25
1256/9		Set of 4	6·75	7·25
MS1260	79×103 mm. $6.40, "Madonna and Child" (Lippi) (vert)		8·00	9·00

249 Red-breasted Wrasse

250 Tiger

(Litho Questa (5 c. to $2), Fournier ($3 to $15))

1992 (22 Jan)–94. *Reef Life* (1st series). *T 249 and similar horiz designs. Multicoloured with white borders. Ordinary paper (5 c. to $2) or fluorescent security markings ($3 to $15). P 14 (5 c. to $2) or 14×13½ ($3 to $15).*

1261	5 c.	Type 249	30	30
1262	10 c.	Blue Sea Star	10	15
1263	15 c.	Bicoloured Angelfish ("Black and Gold Angelfish")	45	45
1264	20 c.	Spotted Pebble Crab	55	55
1265	25 c.	Black-tipped Grouper ("Black-tipped Cod")	60	60
1266	30 c.	Spanish Dancer	60	60
1267	50 c.	Regal Angelfish	90	90
1268	80 c.	Big-scaled Soldierfish ("Squirrel Fish")	1·25	1·25
1269	85 c.	Red Pencil Sea Urchin (23.3.92)	1·75	1·75
1270	90 c.	Red-spotted Rainbowfish (23.3.92)	2·00	2·00
1271	$1	Cheek-lined Wrasse (23.3.92)	2·00	2·00
1272	$2	Long-nosed Butterflyfish (23.3.92)	1·50	1·60
1273	$3	Red-spotted Rainbowfish (25.10.93)	2·25	2·40
1274	$5	Blue Sea Star (25.10.93)	3·75	4·00
1275	$7	*Pygoplites diacanthus* (6.12.93)	5·00	5·25
1276	$10	Spotted Pebble Crab (31.1.94)	7·25	7·50
1277	$15	Red Pencil Sea Urchin (9.9.94)	11·00	11·50
1261/77		Set of 17	38·00	38·00

The 25 c., 50 c., $1 and $2 include a silhouette of the Queen's head.

Nos. 1273/7 are larger, 55×34 mm, and show a portrait of Queen Elizabeth II at left.

For some of these designs in a larger size, 40×30 mm, and with light cinnamon borders, see Nos. 1342/52.

(Litho B.D.T.)

1992 (6 June)–93. *Endangered Wildlife. T 250 and similar horiz designs. Multicoloured. Ordinary paper. P 14.*

1279	$1.15,	Type 250	1·25	1·25
1280	$1.15,	Indian Elephant (7.6.92)	1·25	1·25
1281	$1.15,	Brown Bear (8.6.92)	1·25	1·25
1282	$1.15,	Black Rhinoceros (9.6.92)	1·25	1·25
1283	$1.15,	Chimpanzee (10.6.92)	1·25	1·25
1284	$1.15,	Argali (11.6.92)	1·25	1·25
1285	$1.15,	Heaviside's Dolphin (13.7.92)	1·25	1·25
1286	$1.15,	Eagle Owl (14.7.92)	1·25	1·25
1287	$1.15,	Bee Hummingbird (15.7.92)	1·25	1·25
1288	$1.15,	Puma (16.7.92)	1·25	1·25
1289	$1.15,	European Otter (17.7.92)	1·25	1·25
1290	$1.15,	Red Kangaroo (18.7.92)	1·25	1·25
1291	$1.15,	Jackass Penguin (2.11.92)	1·25	1·25
1292	$1.15,	Asian Lion (3.11.92)	1·25	1·25
1293	$1.15,	Peregrine Falcon (4.11.92)	1·25	1·25
1294	$1.15,	Persian Fallow Deer (5.11.92)	1·25	1·25
1295	$1.15,	Key Deer (6.11.92)	1·25	1·25
1296	$1.15,	Alpine Ibex (7.11.92)	1·25	1·25
1297	$1.15,	Mandrill (1.2.93)	1·25	1·25
1298	$1.15,	Gorilla (2.2.93)	1·25	1·25
1299	$1.15,	*Vanessa atalanta* (butterfly) (3.2.93)	1·25	1·25
1300	$1.15,	Takin (4.2.93)	1·25	1·25
1301	$1.15,	Ring-tailed Lemur (5.2.93)	1·25	1·25
1279/1301		Set of 23	26·00	26·00

251 Columbus and Landing in New World

(Des G. Vasarhelyi. Litho B.D.T.)

1992 (22 May–21 Sept). *500th Anniv of Discovery of America by Columbus (2nd issue). Ordinary paper. P 14×14½.*

1302	251	$6 multicoloured	6·50	7·50
MS1303	128×84 mm. $10 As T 251, but detail of landing party only (40×29 mm). P 15×14 (21 Sept)		7·00	8·50

MINIMUM PRICE

The minimum price quote is 10p which represents a handling charge rather than a basis for valuing common stamps. For further notes about prices see introductory pages.

---

252 Football and $50 Commemorative Coin

(Des G. Vasarhelyi. Litho B.D.T.)

1992 (24 July). *Olympic Games, Barcelona (2nd issue). T 252 and similar horiz designs. Multicoloured. Ordinary paper. P 13.*

1304	$1.75,	Type 252	2·50	2·50
	a.	Horiz strip of 3. Nos. 1304/06	6·75	
1305	$1.75,	Olympic Gold medal	2·50	2·50
1306	$1.75,	Basketball and $10 coin	2·50	2·50
1307	$2.25,	Running	3·50	3·50
	a.	Horiz strip of 3. Nos. 1307/09	9·50	
1308	$2.25,	$10 and $50 coins	3·50	3·50
1309	$2.25,	Cycling	3·50	3·50
1304/09		Set of 6	16·00	16·00
MS1310	155×91 mm. $6.40, Javelin throwing		8·00	9·00

Nos. 1304/06 and 1307/09 were each printed together, *se-tenant*, in horizontal strips of 3 throughout the sheets.

253 Festival Poster

ROYAL VISIT

(254)

(Litho B.D.T.)

1992 (16 Oct). *6th Festival of Pacific Arts, Rarotonga. T 253 and similar vert designs. Multicoloured. Ordinary paper. P 15×14.*

1311	80 c.	Type 253	80	85
1312	85 c.	Seated Tangaroa carving	80	85
1313	$1	Seated Tangaroa carving (different)	95	1·10
1314	$1.75,	Standing Tangaroa carving	1·75	2·25
1311/14		Set of 4	3·75	4·50

1992 (16 Oct). *Royal Visit by Prince Edward. Nos. 1311/14 optd with T 254.*

1315	80 c.	Type 253	1·10	1·10
1316	85 c.	Seated Tangaroa carving	1·10	1·10
1317	$1	Seated Tangaroa carving (different)	1·25	1·25
1318	$1.75,	Standing Tangaroa carving	2·25	2·25
1315/18		Set of 4	5·00	5·00

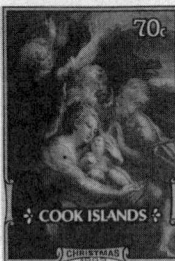
255 "Worship of Shepherds" (Parmigianino)

256 Queen in Garter Robes

1992 (20 Nov). *Christmas. Religious Paintings by Parmigianino. T 255 and similar vert designs. Multicoloured. Ordinary paper. P 13½.*

1319	70 c.	Type 255	1·00	1·00
1320	85 c.	"Virgin with Long Neck"	1·25	1·25
1321	$1.15,	"Virgin with Rose"	1·50	1·75
1322	$1.90,	"St. Margaret's Virgin"	2·75	3·75
1319/22		Set of 4	6·00	7·00
MS1323	86×102 mm. $6.40, As 85 c., but larger (36×46 mm)		7·50	8·50

(Litho B.D.T.)

1992 (10 Dec). *40th Anniv of Queen Elizabeth II's Accession. T 256 and similar vert designs. Multicoloured. Ordinary paper. P 13½.*

1324	80 c.	Type 256	1·25	1·25
1325	$1.15,	Queen at Trooping the Colour	1·60	1·75
1326	$1.50,	Queen in evening dress	2·25	2·50
1327	$1.95,	Queen with bouquet	2·75	3·00
1324/7		Set of 4	7·00	7·75

---

257 Coronation Ceremony

(Des G. Vasarhelyi. Litho B.D.T.)

1993 (2 June). *40th Anniv of Coronation. T 257 and similar horiz designs. Multicoloured. P 14.*

1328	$1	Type 257	1·60	1·60
1329	$2	Coronation photograph by Cecil Beaton	2·75	3·00
1330	$3	Royal family on balcony	4·00	4·25
1328/30		Set of 3	7·50	8·00

258 "Virgin with Child" (Filippo Lippi)

1993 (8 Nov). *Christmas. Religious Paintings. T 258 and similar vert designs. Multicoloured. Ordinary paper. P 13½ ($4) or 14 (others).*

1331	70 c.	Type 258	80	80
1332	85 c.	"Bargellini Madonna" (Lodovico Carracci)	95	95
1333	$1.15,	"Virgin of the Curtain" (Rafael Sanzio)	1·40	1·60
1334	$2.50,	"Holy Family" (Agnolo Bronzino)	3·25	3·75
1335	$4	"Saint Zachary Virgin" (Parmigianino) (32×47 mm)	4·00	5·00
1331/5		Set of 5	9·50	11·00

259 Skiing, Flags and Ice Skating
(*illustration further reduced. Actual size 94×28 mm*)

(Litho Questa)

1994 (11 Feb). *Winter Olympic Games, Lillehammer. P 13½×14.*

1336	259	$5 multicoloured	5·00	6·00

260 Cup on Logo with German and Argentinian Players

(Des G. Vasarhelyi. Litho B.D.T.)

1994 (17 June). *World Cup Football Championship, U.S.A. P 14×14½.*

1337	260	$4.50, multicoloured	4·50	5·50

261 Neil Armstrong taking First Step on Moon

(Litho B.D.T.)

994 (20 July). *25th Anniv of First Moon Landing. T 261 and similar horiz designs. Multicoloured. P 14.*

338	$2.25, Type 261	..	..	3·50	3·50
	a. Sheetlet. Nos. 1338/41×2			25·00	
339	$2.25, Astronaut on Moon and view of Earth ..	..	..	3·50	3·50
340	$2.25, Astronaut and flag	..	..	3·50	3·50
341	$2.25, Astronaut with reflection in helmet visor ..	..	..	3·50	3·50
338/41	..	..	*Set of 4*	12·50	12·50

Nos. 1338/41 were printed together, *se-tenant*, in sheetlets of (2×4), containing two of each design, with Nos. 1338/9 in the op two rows and Nos. 1340/1 in the bottom two. Each row shows wo different designs with a half stamp-size *se-tenant* label in he centre.

(Litho B.D.T.)

994 (24 Oct). *Reef Life* (2nd series). *As Nos. 1261 and 1263/71, but each 40×30 mm and with light cinnamon borders. P 15×14.*

342	5 c. Type 249	..	..	10	10
344	15 c. Bicoloured Angelfish	..	..	15	20
345	20 c. Spotted Pebble Crab	..	..	15	20
346	25 c. Black-tipped Grouper	..	..	20	25
347	30 c. Spanish Dancer	..	..	20	25
348	50 c. Regal Angelfish	..	..	35	40
349	80 c. Big-scaled Soldierfish	..	..	60	65
350	85 c. Red Pencil Sea Urchin	..	..	60	65
351	90 c. Red-spotted Rainbowfish	..	..	65	70
352	$1 Cheek-lined Wrasse	..	..	75	80
342/52	..	..	*Set of 10*	3·75	4·25

Nos. 1261 and 1263/71, which were printed by Questa, are 5×27 mm and have white borders.

262 Actors in Outrigger Canoe

263 "The Virgin and Child" (Morales)

(Litho B.D.T.)

994 (23 Nov)–**97**. *Release of* The Return of Tommy Tricker *(film shot in Cook Islands). T 262 and similar horiz designs showing scenes from film. Multicoloured. P 14.*

1359	85 c. Type 262	..	..	1·10	1·25
	a. Sheetlet. Nos. 1359/64	..		6·00	
1360	85 c. Male and female dancers	..		1·10	1·25
1361	85 c. European couple on beach	..		1·10	1·25
1362	85 c. Aerial view of island	..		1·10	1·25
1363	85 c. Two female dancers	..		1·10	1·25
1364	85 c. Cook Islands couple on beach	..		1·10	1·25
1364a	90 c. Type 262 (28.8.97)	..		65	70
	ab. Sheetlet. Nos. 1364a/f	..		4·00	
1364b	90 c. As No. 1360 (28.8.97)	..		65	70
1364c	90 c. As No. 1361 (28.8.97)	..		65	70
1364d	90 c. As No. 1362 (28.8.97)	..		65	70
1364e	90 c. As No. 1363 (28.8.97)	..		65	70
1364f	90 c. As No. 1364 (28.8.97)	..		65	70
1359/64f	..		*Set of 12*	10·00	11·50

Nos. 1359/64 and 1364a/f were each printed together, *se-tenant*, in sheetlets of 6.

(Litho B.D.T.)

1994 (30 Nov). *Christmas. Religious Paintings. T 263 and similar vert designs. Multicoloured. P 14.*

1365	85 c. Type 263	..	..	1·10	1·25
	a. Block of 4. Nos. 1365/8	..		4·00	
1366	85 c. "Adoration of the Kings" (Gerard David)	..		1·10	1·25
1367	85 c. "Adoration of the Kings" (Foppa)	..		1·10	1·25
1368	85 c. "The Madonna and Child with St. Joseph and Infant Baptist" (Baroccio)			1·10	1·25
1369	$1 "Madonna with Iris" (Dürer)	..		1·25	1·40
	a. Block of 4. Nos. 1369/72	..		4·50	
1370	$1 "Adoration of the Shepherds" (Le Nain)			1·25	1·40
1371	$1 "The Virgin and Child" (school of Leonardo)			1·25	1·40
1372	$1 "The Mystic Nativity" (Botticelli)			1·25	1·40
1365/72	..		*Set of 8*	8·50	9·50

Nos. 1365/8 and 1369/72 were printed together, *se-tenant*, in blocks of 4 throughout the sheets.

264 Pirates (*Treasure Island*)

(Des G. Vasarhelyi. Litho B.D.T.)

1994 (12 Dec). *Death Centenary of Robert Louis Stevenson (author). T 264 and similar horiz designs. Multicoloured. P 14×15.*

1373	$1.50, Type 264	..	..	1·60	1·90
	a. Block of 4. Nos. 1373/6	..		5·75	
1374	$1.50, Duel (*David Balfour*)	..		1·60	1·90
1375	$1.50, Mr. Hyde (*Dr. Jekyll and Mr. Hyde*)		1·60	1·90
1376	$1.50, Rowing boat and sailing ship (*Kidnapped*) ..		1·60	1·90
1373/6	..		*Set of 4*	5·75	7·00

Nos. 1373/6 were printed together, *se-tenant*, in blocks of 4 throughout the sheet.

265 U.N. and National Flags with Peace Doves

(Des G. Vasarhelyi. Litho B.D.T.)

1995 (17 July). *50th Anniv of United Nations. P 13.*

| 1377 | **265** $4.75, multicoloured .. | .. | .. | 4·75 | 6·00 |

266 Queen Elizabeth the Queen Mother and Coat of Arms

(Des G. Vasarhelyi. Litho B.D.T.)

1995 (31 Aug). *95th Birthday of Queen Elizabeth the Queen Mother. P 13.*

| 1378 | **266** $5 multicoloured | .. | .. | 6·00 | 7·00 |

267 German Delegation signing Unconditional Surrender at Rheims

(Litho B.D.T.)

1995 (4 Sept). *50th Anniv of End of Second World War. T 267 and similar horiz design. Multicoloured. P 13.*

1379	$3.50, Type 267	..	..	4·75	5·50
	a. Pair. Nos. 1379/80	..		9·50	11·00
1380	$3.50, Japanese delegation on U.S.S. Missouri, Tokyo Bay ..	..	4·75	5·50

Nos. 1379/80 were printed together, *se-tenant* horizontally and vertically, in sheets of 4.

(Des G. Vasarhelyi. Litho B.D.T.)

1995 (12 Oct). *50th Anniv of Food and Agriculture Organization. Horiz design as T 265. Multicoloured. P 13×13½.*

| 1381 | $4.50, F.A.O. and U.N. emblems | .. | .. | 4·75 | 6·00 |

268 Green Turtle

269 Emblem and Throwing the Discus

(Litho B.D.T.)

1995 (20 Nov). *Year of the Sea Turtle. T 268 and similar horiz designs. Multicoloured. P 13½×14.*

1382	85 c. Type 268	..	..	1·40	1·40
1383	$1 Hawksbill Turtle	..	..	1·60	1·60
1384	$1.75, Green Turtle on beach	..		2·50	2·50
1385	$2.25, Young Hawksbill Turtles hatching		2·75	2·75
1382/5	..		*Set of 4*	7·50	7·50

(Litho B.D.T.)

1996 (12 Jan). *Olympic Games, Atlanta. T 269 and similar horiz designs. Multicoloured. P 14.*

1386	85 c. Type 269	..	..	1·10	1·10
1387	$1 Athlete with Olympic Torch	..		1·40	1·40
1388	$1.50, Running	..	..	1·90	1·90
1389	$1.85, Gymnastics	..	..	2·25	2·25
1390	$2.10, Ancient archery	..	..	2·50	2·50
1391	$2.50, Throwing the javelin	..		2·75	2·75
1386/91	..		*Set of 6*	10·50	10·50

28th South Pacific Forum

270 Queen Elizabeth II   (**271**)

(Des G. Vasarhelyi. Litho)

1996 (21 June). *70th Birthday of Queen Elizabeth II. T 270 and similar vert designs. Multicoloured. P 14.*

1392	$1.90, Type 270	..	..	2·25	2·25
1393	$2.25, Wearing tiara	..	..	2·75	2·75
1394	$2.75, In Garter robes	..	..	3·00	3·00
1392/4	..		*Set of 3*	7·25	7·25
MS1395	103×152 mm. Designs as Nos. 1392/4, but each with a face value of $2.50	..	8·50	9·00

1997 (12 Sept). *28th South Pacific Forum. Nos. 1364a/f optd with T 271 (Nos. 1396, 1399/400) or "12–22 September 1997" (Nos. 1397/8 and 1401), all in silver.*

1396	90 c. Type 262	..	..	65	70
	a. Sheetlet. Nos. 1396/1401	..		4·00	
1397	90 c. As No. 1360	..	..	65	70
1398	90 c. As No. 1361	..	..	65	70
1399	90 c. As No. 1362	..	..	65	70
1400	90 c. As No. 1363	..	..	65	70
1401	90 c. As No. 1364	..	..	65	70
1396/1401	..		*Set of 6*	4·00	4·25

272 *Lampides boeticus* (female)

(Litho B.D.T.)

1997 (22 Oct–12 Nov). *Butterflies. T 272 and similar horiz designs. Multicoloured. P 13×13½.*

1402	5 c. Type 272	..	..	10	10
1403	10 c. Vanessa atalanta	..	..	10	15
1404	15 c. Lampides boeticus (male)	..		15	20
1405	20 c. Papilio godeffroyi	..	..	15	20
1406	25 c. Danaus hamata	..	..	20	25
1407	30 c. Xois sesara	..	..	20	25
1408	50 c. Vagrans egista	..	..	35	40
1409	70 c. Parthenos sylvia	..	..	50	55
1410	80 c. Hyblaea sanguinea (12.11.97)	..		60	65
1411	85 c. Melanitis leda (12.11.97)	..		60	65
1412	90 c. Ascalapha odorata (12.11.97)	..		65	70
1413	$1 Precis villida (12.11.97)	..		75	80
1402/13	..		*Set of 11*	4·25	5·00

273 Queen Elizabeth and Prince Philip

1997 (20 Nov). *Golden Wedding of Queen Elizabeth and Prince Philip. P 14.*

| 1419 | **273** $2 multicoloured | .. | .. | 1·50 | 1·60 |
| MS1420 | 76×102 mm. **273** $5 multicoloured | .. | 3·75 | 4·00 |

STAMP BOOKLETS

1982 (June). *Royal Wedding. Multicoloured cover, 130×74 mm, showing Prince and Princess of Wales. Stitched.*
SB1 $6 booklet containing $1 and $2 (Nos. 812/13), each in pair .. .. 4·25

OFFICIAL STAMPS

O.H.M.S.	O.H.M.S.
(O 1)	(O 2)

1975 (17 Mar–19 May). *Nos. 228/31, 233, 235/7, 239/40, 243/5 and 246c/7 optd with Type O 1 (5, 10, 18, 25 and 30 c. surch also), in black and silver*

O 1	1 c. Hibiscus syriacus	..		
O 2	2 c. Frangipani	..		
O 3	3 c. "Suva Queen"	..		
O 4	4 c. Water Lily			
O 5	5 c. on 2½ c. Clitoria ternatea	..		
O 6	8 c. Allamanda cathartica	..		
O 7	10 c. on 6 c. Hibiscus	..		
O 8	18 c. on 20 c. Thunbergia	..		
O 9	25 c. on 9 c. Stephanotis	..		
O10	30 c. on 15 c. Frangipani	..		
O11	50 c. Gardinia taitensis	..		
O12	$1 Type **80**	..		
O13	$2 Type **80**	..		
O14	$4 Type **81** (19 May)	..		
O15	$6 Type **81** (19 May)	..		
O1/15		Set of 15	† 15·00	

These stamps were only sold to the public cancelled-to-order and not in unused condition.

1978 (19 Oct)–**79**. *Nos. 466/7, 474, 478/81, 484/5, 542 and 568/9 optd or surch (2, 5, 10, 15, 18 and 35 c.) as Type O 2.*

O16	1 c. Common Pacific Vase (*Vasum turbinellum*) (Silver)	..	50	10
O17	2 c. on ½ c. Type **141**	..	50	10
O18	5 c. on ½ c. Type **141**	..	60	10
O19	10 c. on 8 c. Granulate Frog Shell (*Bursa granularis*) (Silver)	..	65	10
O20	15 c. on 50 c. Textile or Cloth of Gold Cone (*Conus textile*) (Silver)		90	10
O21	18 c. on 60 c. Red-mouth Olive (*Oliva miniacea miniacea*) (Silver)	..	90	15
O22	25 c. Royal Oak Scallop (*Cryptopecten pallium*)	..	1·00	20
O23	30 c. Soldier Cone (*Conus miles*) (Silver)	..	1·00	25
O24	35 c. on 60 c. Red-mouth Olive (*Oliva miniacea miniacea*) (Silver)	..	1·25	30
O25	50 c. Textile or Cloth of Gold Cone (*Conus textile*) (Silver)	..	1·75	35
O26	60 c. Red-mouth Oliva (*Oliva miniacea miniacea*) (Silver)	..	2·00	45
O27	$1 Queen and Prince Philip (Silver)	..	4·00	65
O28	$1 Royal Visit, 1974 (Silver)	..	4·00	65
O29	$2 Captain Cook and H.M.S. *Resolution*		7·00	2·25
O30	$4 Queen Elizabeth II and seashells (15.2.79)	..	11·00	2·25
O31	$6 As $4 (15.2.79)	..	11·00	3·50
O16/31	.. ..	Set of 16	42·00	10·00

These stamps were originally only sold to the public cancelled-to-order and not in unused condition. They were made available to overseas collectors in mint condition during 1980.

75c

O.H.M.S.	*O.H.M.S.*
(O 3)	(O 4)

O.H.M.S.

(O 5)

1985 (10 July)–**90**. (*a*) *Nos. 969/74, 976, 978, 981, 984/6 and 988/9 optd or surch as Type O 3 by silver foil embossing.*

O32	5 c. Ptilosarcus gurneyi	..	50	50
O33	10 c. Lobophyllia bemprichii	..	50	50
	a. Opt double, one albino..	..	50·00	
O34	12 c. Sarcophyton digitatum (5.5.86)	..	1·25	60
O35	14 c. Pavona praetorta (5.5.86)	..	1·25	60
O36	18 c. Junceella gemmacea (5.5.86)	..	1·25	60
O37	20 c. Stylaster	..	60	50
O38	30 c. Palauastrea ramosa	..	60	50
O39	40 c. Stylaster echinatus	..	60	50
O40	50 c. Melithaea squamata (5.5.86)	..	2·00	70
O41	55 c. on 85 c. Caulastraea echinulata		70	50
	a. "O.H.M.S." albino	..	†	
O42	60 c. Tubastraea	..	70	60
O43	70 c. Heliofungia actiniformis (5.5.86)	..	2·25	85
O44	$1.10, Pectinia alcicornis ..	..	1·10	90
O45	$2 on $1.20, Dendrophyllia gracilis	..	2·00	1·75

(*b*) *Nos. 862/5 surch with Type O 4 by gold foil embossing*

O46	75 c. on 60 c. Type **197** (5.5.86)	..	2·50	1·00
O47	75 c. on 60 c. Rarotonga oranges (5.5.86)	..	2·50	1·00
O48	75 c. on 60 c. Rarotonga Airport (5.5.86)	..	2·50	1·00
O49	75 c. on 60 c. Prime Minister Sir Thomas Davis (5.5.86)	..	2·50	1·00

(*c*) *Nos. 786/9 surch as T* **209** *in silver and black further optd with Type O* **5** *by silver foil embossing.*

O50	$5 on $3 Heliofungia actiniformis (5.5.86)		6·50	4·75
O51	$9 on $4 Stylophora pistillata (30.5.89)		8·00	8·25
O52	$14 on $6 Stylaster echinatus (12.7.89)	..	12·50	13·00
O53	$18 on $10 Melithaea albitincta (4.6.90)	..	17·00	17·00
O32/53	.. .. ..	Set of 22	65·00	50·00

1995 (24 Feb–15 May). *Nos. 1261/72 optd with Type O 3 by silver foil embossing.*

O54	5 c. Type **249**	..	10	10
O55	10 c. Blue Sea Star	..	10	10
O56	15 c. Bicoloured Angelfish	..	15	20
O57	20 c. Spotted Pebble Crab	..	15	20
O58	25 c. Black-tipped Grouper	..	20	25
O59	30 c. Spanish Dancer	..	20	25
O60	50 c. Regal Angelfish	..	35	40
O61	80 c. Big-scaled Soldierfish	..	60	65
O62	85 c. Red Pencil Sea Urchin	..	60	65
O63	90 c. Red-spotted Rainbowfish	..	65	70
O64	$1 Cheek-lined Wrasse (15 May)	..	75	80
O65	$2 Long-nosed Butterflyfish (15 May)	..	1·50	1·60
O54/65	.. ..	Set of 12	5·25	5·75

STANLEY GIBBONS

Auctions & Acquisitions

LEADING PHILATELIC AUCTIONEERS SINCE 1901

A PROFESSIONAL AUCTION SERVICE FROM THE MOST FAMOUS NAME IN PHILATELY

A PROVEN PROGRAMME OF SPECIALISED INTERNATIONAL SALES

FREE ADVICE AND EXPERT MARKET VALUATIONS

0% VENDOR COMMISSION
(on realisations over £5000)

FAST GUARANTEED PAYMENT

CASH ADVANCES AVAILABLE

SETTLEMENT IN ANY CURRENCY

THE INDUSTRY'S LARGEST DATABASE OF SPECIALIST BUYERS

HIGH QUALITY CATALOGUES DISTRIBUTED WORLDWIDE

REGULAR TELESALES CONTACT WITH MAJOR BUYERS

SPECIALIST SUBSCRIPTION SERVICE

REFINED VENUES AND EXTENSIVE VIEWING TIMES

TELEPHONE TODAY FOR A FULL INFORMATION PACK.

STANLEY GIBBONS AUCTIONS
399 STRAND • LONDON • WC2R 0LX
TELEPHONE: 0171 836 8444
FACSIMILE: 0171 836 7342

AITUTAKI

Stamps of COOK ISLANDS were used in Aitutaki from 1892 until 1903.

> **PRICES FOR STAMPS ON COVER TO 1945**
> Nos. 1/7   *from* × 4
> Nos. 9/14   *from* × 3
> Nos. 15/29   *from* × 4
> Nos. 30/2   *from* × 6

A. NEW ZEALAND DEPENDENCY

The island of Aitutaki, under British protection from 1888, was annexed by New Zealand on 11 June 1901.

Stamps of New Zealand overprinted or surcharged. For illustrations of New Zealand watermarks and definitive types see the beginning of Cook Islands.

AITUTAKI. (1)   **Ava Pene.** (2) ½d.

Tai Pene. (3) 1d.   **Rua Pene Ma Te Ava.** (4) 2½d.

Toru Pene. (5) 3d.   **Ono Pene.** (6) 6d.

Tai Tiringi. (7) 1s.

1903 (29 June)–11. *T* **23**, **27/8**, **31**, **34** *and* **42** *surch with T* **1** *at top and T* **2** *to* **7** *at foot. Thin, hard Cowan paper. W* **43**.

(a) P 14
1	½d. green (No. 302) (R.)	..	..	4·00 6·50
2	1d. carmine (No. 303) (B.)	..	..	4·75 5·50
3	2½d. deep blue (No. 320a) (R.) (9.11)		8·00 18·00
	a. "Ava" without stop	..	£130 £170
1/3			*Set of 3*	15·00 27·00

(b) P 11
4	2½d. blue (No. 308) (R.)	..	..	10·00 12·00
5	3d. yellow-brown (No. 309) (B.)	..	13·00 15·00
6	6d. rose-red (No. 312a) (B.)	..	27·00 25·00
7	1s. bright red (No. 315a) (B.)	..	55·00 85·00
	a. "Tiringi" without stop (R. 7/12)	£400 £700
	b. *Orange-red*	..	65·00 95·00
	ba. "Tiringi" without stop (R. 7/12)	£550 £650
	c. *Orange-brown*	..	£140 £160
	ca. "Tiringi" without stop (R. 7/12)	£1000 £1200
4/7			*Set of 4*	95·00 £120

Nos. 1/2 and 4/7 were placed on sale in Auckland on 12 June 1903.

There were four states of the overprint used for No. 3. On the first the "no stop" variety (No. 3a) occurs on R. 6/8, on the second it appears on R. 1/4, 2/4 and 6/8, on the third on R. 5/8 and 6/8, and on the fourth all stops are present.

AITUTAKI.

Ono Pene. (8)

1911–16. *T* **51** *and* **53** *surch with T* **1** *at top and T* **2** *or* **3** *at foot and T* **52** *surch as T* **8**. P 14×15 (½d., 1d.) *or* 14×14½ (*others*).
9	½d. green (No. 387) (R.) (9.11)	..	1·00 2·50
10	1d. carmine (No. 405) (B.) (2.13)	..	3·00 9·50
11	6d. carmine (No. 392) (B.) (23.5.16)	38·00 90·00
12	1s. vermilion (No. 394) (B.) (9.14)	55·00 £140
9/12			*Set of 4*	85·00 £225

1916–17. *T* **60** (*recess*) *surch as T* **8**. *W* **43**. *P* 14×13½.
13	6d. carmine (No. 425) (B.) (6.6.16)	14·00 50·00
	a. Perf 14×14½	..	7·50 25·00
	b. Vert pair. Nos. 13/13a	..	50·00 £150
14	1s. vermilion (No. 430) (B.) (3.17)	28·00 90·00
	a. Perf 14×14½	..	35·00 90·00
	ab. "Tai" without dot	..	£225 £425
	ac. "Tiringi" without dot on second "i"	£275 £475
	ad. "Tiringi" without dot on third "i"	£350 £550
	b. Vert pair. Nos. 14/14a	..	£140 £350

1917–18. *T* **60** (*recess*) *optd* "AITUTAKI" *only, as in T* **8**. *W* **43**. *P* 14×13½.
15	2½d. blue (No. 419) (R.) (12.18)	..	2·00 15·00
	a. Perf 14×14½	..	1·75 15·00
	b. Vert pair. Nos. 15/15a	..	50·00 £130
16	3d. chocolate (No. 420) (B.) (1.18)	..	1·75 17·00
	a. Perf 14×14½	..	1·50 17·00
	b. Vert pair. Nos. 16/16a	..	45·00 £140
17	6d. carmine (No. 425) (B.) (11.17)	7·50 20·00
	a. Perf 14×14½	..	4·75 18·00
	b. Vert pair. Nos. 17/17a	..	60·00 £140
18	1s. vermilion (No. 430) (B.) (11.17)	17·00 38·00
	a. Perf 14×14½	..	12·00 26·00
	b. Vert pair. Nos. 18/18a	..	85·00 £180
15/18			*Set of 4*	18·00 70·00

1917–20. *T* **53** *and* **61** (*typo*) *optd* "AITUTAKI" *only, as in T* **8**. *W* **43**. *P* 14×15.
19	½d. green (No. 435) (R.) (2.20)	..	1·00 5·00
20	1d. carmine (No. 405) (B.) (5.20)	..	2·75 18·00

21	1½d. slate (No. 437) (R.) (11.17)	..	3·75 30·00
22	1½d. orange-brown (No. 438) (R.) (2.19)	..	80 7·00
23	3d. chocolate (No. 440) (B.) (6.19)	..	3·50 13·00
19/23		*Set of 5*	10·50 65·00

(Des and recess Perkins, Bacon & Co)

1920 (23 Aug). *T* **9/14** *of Cook Islands, but inscr* "AITUTAKI". *No wmk.* P 14.
24	½d. black and green	..	3·50 24·00
25	1d. black and dull carmine	..	3·50 15·00
	a. Double derrick flaw (R.2/8, 3/6 or 5/2)	11·00
26	1½d. black and sepia	..	6·00 12·00
27	3d. black and deep blue	..	2·00 13·00
28	6d. red-brown and slate	..	5·00 14·00
29	1s. black and purple	..	9·50 16·00
24/9		*Set of 6*	26·00 85·00

(Recess Govt Printing Office, Wellington)

1924–27. *T* **9/10** *and* **16** *of Cook Islands, but inscr* "AITUTAKI". *W* **43** *of New Zealand.* P 14.
30	½d. black and green (5.27)	..	2·00 8·50
31	1d. black and deep carmine (10.24)	5·50 6·50
	a. Double derrick flaw (R.2/8, 3/6 or 5/2)	14·00
32	2½d. black and dull blue (10.27)	..	7·50 50·00
30/2		*Set of 3*	13·50 60·00

> Cook Islands stamps superseded those of Aitutaki on 15 March 1932. Separate issues were resumed in 1972.

B. PART OF COOK ISLANDS

On 9 August 1972, Aitutaki became a Port of Entry into the Cook Islands, and at the close of business on the previous day, Cook Islands stamps were withdrawn from sale there. Whilst remaining part of the Cook Islands, Aitutaki has a separate postal service.

(New Currency. 100 cents = 1 dollar)

PRINTERS. The following stamps, *unless otherwise stated*, were printed, in photogravure until No. **MS613** and in lithography thereafter, by Heraclio Fournier, Spain. All such issues are, *unless otherwise stated*, on paper treated with fluorescent security markings, and with synthetic gum. The fluorescent markings can be found inverted or omitted.

Aitutaki (9)   **Aitutaki** (10)

(Optd by Govt Printer, Wellington)

1972 (9 Aug). *Nos.* 227B *etc. of Cook Is. optd with T* **9** (*applied horizontally on* $1), *by New Zealand Govt Printer.*
33	½ c. Type **79**	..	..	30 80
34	1 c. *Hibiscus syriacus*	..	70 1·40
35	2½ c. *Clitoria ternatea*	..	2·25 7·00
36	4 c. Water Lily (No. 233B)	..	70 85
37	5 c. *Bauhinia bi-pinnata rosea*	2·50 7·50
38	10 c. *Poinciana regia flamboyant*	2·50 5·50
39	20 c. Thunbergia	..	1·25 1·00
40	25 c. Canna Lily	..	70 1·00
41	50 c. *Gardinia taitensis*	..	2·75 2·75
42	$1 Type **80** *	..	4·00 5·50
	a. *Shade* *	..	20·00
33/42		*Set of 10*	16·00 30·00

* No. 42a has the border flowers predominantly in a carmine colour instead of scarlet, and may be due to a missing yellow colour.

1972 (27 Oct). *Christmas. Nos.* 406/8 *of Cook. Is. optd in silver with T* **10**.
43	**130**	1 c. multicoloured	..	10 10
44		5 c. multicoloured	..	15 15
45		10 c. multicoloured	..	15 25
43/5			*Set of 3*	30 40

1972 (20 Nov). *Royal Silver Wedding. As Nos.* 413 *and* 415 *of Cook Is., but inscr* "COOK ISLANDS Aitutaki".
46	**131**	5 c. black and silver	..	4·00 2·75
47		15 c. black and silver	..	2·00 1·50

AITUTAKI (11)   **AITUTAKI** (12)

1972 (24 Nov). *No.* 245B *of Cook Is. optd with T* **11** *by Govt Printer, Rarotonga.*
48	**80**	$2 multicoloured	..	50 75
	a. Optd "AJTUTAKI" for "AITUTAKI" (R. 2/4)		25·00
	b. On No. 245A (gum arabic printing)	50·00
	ba. Optd "AJTUTAKI" for "AITUTAKI" (R. 2/4)	50·00

1972 (11 Dec). *Nos.* 227B *etc of Cook Is. optd with T* **12**, *by Heraclio Fournier.*
49	½ c. Type **79**	..	..	15 10
50	1 c. *Hibiscus syriacus*	..	15 10
51	2½ c. *Clitoria ternatea*	..	20 10
52	4 c. Water Lily (No. 233B)	..	25 15
53	5 c. *Bauhinia bi-pinnata rosea*	25 15
54	10 c. *Poinciana regia flamboyant*	35 25
55	20 c. Thunbergia	..	1·00 50
56	25 c. Canna Lily	..	50 55
57	50 c. *Gardinia taitensis*	..	75 90
58	$1 Type **80**	..	1·25 1·75
49/58		*Set of 10*	4·25 4·00

---

13 "Christ Mocked" (Grünewald)   (14)

1973 (6 Apr). *Easter. T* **13** *and similar vert designs. Multicoloured.* P 13.
59	1 c. Type **13**		15 10
60	1 c. "St. Veronica" (Van der Weyden)	15 10
61	1 c. "The Crucified Christ with Virgin Mary, Saints and Angels" (Raphael)	15 10
62	1 c. "Resurrection" (Piero della Francesca)	15 10
63	5 c. "The Last Supper" (Master of Amiens)	20 15
64	5 c. "Condemnation" (Holbein)	20 15
65	5 c. "Christ on the Cross" (Rubens)	20 15
66	5 c. "Resurrection" (El Greco)	20 15
67	10 c. "Disrobing of Christ" (El Greco)	25 15
68	10 c. "St. Veronica" (Van Oostsanen)	25 15
69	10 c. "Christ on the Cross" (Rubens)	25 15
70	10 c. "Resurrection" (Bouts)	25 15
59/70		*Set of 12*	2·25 1·25

Nos. 59/62, 63/6 and 67/70 were each printed together, *se-tenant*, in blocks of 4 throughout the sheet.

1973 (14 May). *Silver Wedding Coinage. Nos.* 417/23 *of Cook Is. optd in silver and black as T* **14**.
71	1 c. black, rosy carmine and gold	10 10
72	2 c. black, bright blue and gold	10 10
73	5 c. black, green and silver	15 10
74	10 c. black, royal blue and silver	20 10
75	20 c. black, deep blue-green and silver	30 15
76	50 c. black, carmine and silver	50 30
77	$1 black, bright blue and silver	70 45
71/7		*Set of 7*	1·90 1·00

TENTH ANNIVERSARY CESSATION OF NUCLEAR TESTING TREATY (15)   16 Red Hibiscus and Princess Anne

1973 (13 Aug). *Tenth Anniv of Treaty Banning Nuclear Testing. Nos.* 236B, 238B, 240B *and* 243B *of Cook Is. optd with T* **15** *and T* **12** *together.*
78	8 c. *Allamanda cathartica*	..	15 15
79	10 c. *Poinciana regia flamboyant*	15 15
80	20 c. Thunbergia	..	30 30
81	50 c. *Gardinia taitensis*	..	70 50
78/81		*Set of 4*	1·10 90

1973 (14 Nov). *Royal Wedding. T* **16** *and similar horiz design. Multicoloured.* P 13½ × 14.
82	25 c. Type **16**	..	25 10
83	30 c. Capt. Phillips and Blue Hibiscus	25 10
MS84	114 × 65 mm. Nos. 82/3. P 13	50 40

17 "Virgin and Child" (Montagna)   18 Rose-branch Murex (*Murex ramosus*)

1973 (10 Dec). *Christmas. T* **17** *and similar vert designs showing* "The Virgin and Child" *by the artists listed. Multicoloured.* P 13½.
85	1 c. Type **17**	..	10 10
86	1 c. Crivelli	..	10 10
87	1 c. Van Dyck	..	10 10
88	1 c. Perugino	..	10 10
89	5 c. Veronese (child at shoulder)	25 10
90	5 c. Veronese (child on lap)	25 10
91	5 c. Cima	..	25 10
92	5 c. Memling	..	25 10
93	10 c. Memling	..	25 10
94	10 c. Del Colle	..	25 10
95	10 c. Raphael	..	25 10
96	10 c. Lotto	..	25 10
85/96		*Set of 12*	2·00 80

Nos. 85/8, 89/92 and 93/6 were each printed together, *se-tenant*, in blocks of 4 throughout the sheet.

1974 (31 Jan)–75. *T* **18** *and similar horiz designs showing sea-shells. Multicoloured.* P 13.
97	½ c. Type **18**	..	90 80
98	1 c. New Caledonia Nautilus (*Nautilus macromphallus*)	90 80

99	2 c.	Common or Major Harp (*Harpa major*)	90	80
100	3 c.	Striped Bonnet (*Phalium flammiferum*)	90	80
101	4 c.	Mole Cowrie (*Cypraea talpa*)	90	80
102	5 c.	Pontifical Mitre (*Mitra stictica*)	90	80
103	8 c.	Trumpet Triton (*Charonia tritonis*)	90	80
104	10 c.	Venus Comb Murex (*Murex pecten*)	90	80
105	20 c.	Red-mouth Olive (*Oliva miniacea marrati*)	1·25	80
106	25 c.	Ruddy Frog Shell (*Bursa rubeta*)	1·25	80
107	60 c.	Widest Pacific Conch (*Strombus latissimus*)	3·00	1·25
108	$1	Maple-leaf Triton or Marlin-spike Auger (*Biplex perca*)	2·50	1·40
109	$2	Queen Elizabeth II and Marlin-spike Auger (*Terebra maculata*) (20.1.75)	6·00	9·00
110	$5	Queen Elizabeth II and Tiger Cowrie (*Cypraea tigris*) (28.2.75)	27·00	10·00
97/110		*Set of 14*	42·00	27·00

Nos. 109/110 are larger, 53×25 mm.

19 Bligh and H.M.S. *Bounty*

(Des G. Vasarhelyi)

1974 (11 Apr). *William Bligh's Discovery of Aitutaki. T* **19** *and similar horiz designs. Multicoloured. P* 13½.

114	1 c.	Type **19**	25	25
115	1 c.	H.M.S. *Bounty*	25	25
116	5 c.	Bligh, and H.M.S. *Bounty* at Aitutaki	55	30
117	5 c.	Aitutaki chart of 1856	55	30
118	8 c.	Capt. Cook and H.M.S. *Resolution*	85	40
119	8 c.	Map of Aitutaki and inset location map	85	40
114/19		*Set of 6*	3·00	1·60

Nos. 114/15, 116/17 and 118/19 were each printed together, *se-tenant*, in horizontal and vertical pairs throughout the sheet. See also Nos. 123/8.

20 Aitutaki Stamps of 1903, and Map

21 "Virgin and Child" (Hugo van der Goes)

1974 (15 July). *Centenary of Universal Postal Union. T* **20** *and similar horiz design. Multicoloured. P* 13½ × 14.

120	25 c.	Type **20**	65	40
121	50 c.	Stamps of 1903 and 1920, and map	85	60
MS122		66 × 75 mm. Nos. 120/1. P 13	1·50	2·50

Each value was issued in sheets of 5 stamps and 1 label.

1974 (9 Sept). *Air. As Nos.* 114/119, *but larger* (46 × 26 *mm*), *denominations changed, and inscr* "AIR MAIL".

123	10 c.	Type **19**	60	20
124	10 c.	H.M.S. *Bounty*	60	20
125	25 c.	Bligh, and H.M.S. *Bounty* at Aitutaki	70	30
126	25 c.	Aitutaki chart of 1856	70	30
127	30 c.	Capt. Cook and H.M.S. *Resolution*	80	30
128	30 c.	Map of Aitutaki and inset location map	80	30
123/8		*Set of 6*	3·75	1·40

Nos. 123/4, 125/6 and 127/8 were each printed together, *se-tenant*, in horizontal and vertical pairs throughout the sheet.

1974 (11 Oct). *Christmas. T* **21** *and similar vert designs showing "Virgin and Child" by the artists listed. Multicoloured. P* 13.

129	1 c.	Type **21**	10	10
130	5 c.	Bellini	10	10
131	8 c.	Gerard David	10	10
132	10 c.	Antonello da Messina	10	10
133	25 c.	Joos van Cleve	20	20
134	30 c.	Master of the Life of St. Catherine	20	20
129/34		*Set of 6*	65	65
MS135		127 × 134 mm. Nos. 129/34	1·40	1·60

Each value was issued in sheets of 15 stamps and 1 label.

22 Churchill as Schoolboy

+1c

(23)

1974 (29 Nov). *Birth Centenary of Sir Winston Churchill. T* **22** *and similar vert designs. Multicoloured. P* 13½.

136	10 c.	Type **22**	30	25
137	25 c.	Churchill as young man	40	40
138	30 c.	Churchill with troops	45	45
139	50 c.	Churchill painting	60	60
140	$1	Giving "V" sign	1·10	1·10
136/40		*Set of 5*	2·50	2·50
MS141		115 × 108 mm. Nos. 136/40 plus *se-tenant* label. P 13	2·75	2·00

Each value was issued in sheets of 5 stamps and 1 label.

1974 (2 Dec). *Children's Christmas Fund. Nos.* 129/34 *surch with T* **23**.

142	1 c. + 1 c.	multicoloured	10	10
143	5 c. + 1 c.	multicoloured	10	10
144	8 c. + 1 c.	multicoloured	10	10
145	10 c. + 1 c.	multicoloured	10	10
146	25 c. + 1 c.	multicoloured	20	20
147	30 c. + 1 c.	multicoloured	20	20
142/7		*Set of 6*	55	55

24 Soviet and U.S. Flags

25 "Madonna and Child with Saints Francis and John" (Lorenzetti)

1975 (24 July). *"Apollo-Soyuz" Space Project. T* **24** *and similar horiz design. Multicoloured. P* 13 × 14.

148	25 c.	Type **24**	30	20
149	50 c.	Daedalus and space capsule	40	30
MS150		123 × 61 mm. Nos. 148/9	1·25	1·10

Each value was issued in sheets of 8 stamps and 1 label.

1975 (24 Nov). *Christmas. T* **25** *and similar vert designs. Multicoloured. P* 13½.

151	6 c.	} Type **25**	10	10
152	6 c.		10	10
153	6 c.		10	10
154	7 c.	} "Adoration of the Kings" (Van der Weyden)	10	10
155	7 c.		10	10
156	7 c.		10	10
157	15 c.	} "Madonna and Child Enthroneth with Saints Onufrius and John the Baptist" (Montagna)	15	15
158	15 c.		15	15
159	15 c.		15	15
160	20 c.	} "Adoration of the Shepherds" (Reni)	20	15
161	20 c.		20	15
162	20 c.		20	15
151/62		*Set of 12*	1·50	1·40
MS163		104 × 201 mm. Nos. 151/62. P 13	2·25	2·50

Nos. 151/3, 154/6, 157/9 and 160/2 were each printed together, *se-tenant*, in horizontal strips of 3 throughout the sheet, forming composite designs. Type **25** shows the left-hand stamp of the 6 c. design.

1975 (19 Dec). *Children's Christmas Fund. Nos.* 151/62 *surch as T* **23**, *in silver*.

164	6 c. + 1 c.	} Type **25**	10	10
165	6 c. + 1 c.		10	10
166	6 c. + 1 c.		10	10
167	7 c. + 1 c.	} "Adoration of the Kings" (Van der Weyden)	10	10
168	7 c. + 1 c.		10	10
169	7 c. + 1 c.		10	10
170	15 c. + 1 c.	} "Madonna and Child" (Montagna)	15	15
171	15 c. + 1 c.		15	15
172	15 c. + 1 c.		15	15
173	20 c. + 1 c.	} "Adoration of the Shepherds" (Reni)	20	20
174	20 c. + 1 c.		20	20
175	20 c. + 1 c.		20	20
164/75		*Set of 12*	1·50	1·50

26 "The Descent" (detail, 15th-cent Flemish School)

27 "The Declaration of Independence" (detail)

1976 (5 Apr). *Easter. Various vert designs showing portions of "The Descent" as in T* **26**. *P* 13.

176	**26**	15 c. multicoloured	15	10
177	–	30 c. multicoloured	20	15
178	–	35 c. multicoloured	25	20
176/8		*Set of 3*	55	40
MS179		87 × 67 mm. Nos. 176/8 forming a complete picture of "The Descent". P 12½ × 13	1·00	1·25

Stamps from No. MS179 have no borders and are therefore smaller than stamps from the sheets.

Each value was issued in sheets of 8 stamps and 1 label.

1976 (1 June). *Bicentenary of American Revolution. T* **27** *and similar vert designs showing paintings by John Trumbull. Multicoloured. P* 13.

180	30 c.	} Type **27**	35	20
181	30 c.		35	20
182	30 c.		35	20
183	35 c.	} "The Surrender of Lord Cornwallis at Yorktown"	40	20
184	35 c.		40	20
185	35 c.		40	20
186	50 c.	} "The Resignation of General Washington"	50	25
187	50 c.		50	25
188	50 c.		50	25
180/8		*Set of 9*	3·25	1·75
MS189		132 × 120 mm. Nos. 180/8. P 13	3·25	2·25

Nos. 180/2, 183/5 and 186/8 were each printed together, *se-tenant*, in horizontal strips of 3 throughout the sheet, forming composite designs. Each sheet includes 3 stamp-size labels. Type **27** shows the left-hand stamp of the 30 c. design.

Stamps from No. MS189 have their borders in a different colour and come with a different inscription.

28 Cycling

1976 (15 July). *Olympic Games, Montreal. T* **28** *and similar horiz designs. Multicoloured. P* 13 × 14.

190	15 c.	Type **28**	30	15
191	35 c.	Sailing	45	20
192	60 c.	Hockey	70	25
193	70 c.	Sprinting	70	30
190/3		*Set of 4*	1·90	80
MS194		107 × 97 mm. Nos. 190/3	1·90	1·60

Stamps from No. MS194 have borders of a different colour. Each value was issued in sheets of 5 stamps and 1 label.

ROYAL VISIT JULY 1976

(29)

30 "The Visitation"

1976 (30 July). *Visit of Queen Elizabeth to the U.S.A. Nos.* 190/MS194 *optd with T* **29**.

195	15 c.	Type **28**	25	15
196	35 c.	Sailing	40	25
197	60 c.	Hockey	60	40
198	70 c.	Sprinting	70	45
195/8		*Set of 4*	1·75	1·10
MS199		107 × 97 mm. Nos. 195/8	2·00	2·50

1976 (18 Oct). *Christmas. T* **30** *and similar vert designs. Figures in gold; background colours given. P* 13.

200	6 c.	} deep bluish green	10	10
201	6 c.		10	10
202	7 c.	} dull brown-purple	10	10
203	7 c.		10	10
204	15 c.	} deep blue	10	10
205	15 c.		10	10
206	20 c.	} reddish violet	15	15
207	20 c.		15	15
200/207		*Set of 8*	60	60
MS208		128 × 96 mm. As Nos. 200/207 but with borders on three sides	1·00	1·40

Designs:—No. 201, Angel: No. 202, Angel; No. 203, Shepherds; No. 204, Joseph; No. 205, Mary and the Child; No. 206, Wise Man; No. 207, Two Wise Men.

Nos. 200/1, 202/3, 204/5 and 206/7 were each printed together, *se-tenant*, in horizontal pairs throughout the sheet, forming composite designs. Type **30** shows the left-hand stamp of the 6 c. design.

+1c

(31)

32 Alexander Graham Bell and First Telephone

1976 (19 Nov). *Children's Christmas Fund. Nos.* 200/MS208 *surch in silver as T* **31**.

209	6 c. + 1 c.	} "The Visitation"	10	10
210	6 c. + 1 c.		10	10
211	7 c. + 1 c.	} "Angel and Shepherds"	10	10
212	7 c. + 1 c.		10	10
213	15 c. + 1 c.	} "The Holy Family"	15	15
214	15 c. + 1 c.		15	15
215	20 c. + 1 c.	} "The Magi"	15	15
216	20 c. + 1 c.		15	15
209/16		*Set of 8*	70	70
MS217		128 × 96 mm. As Nos. 209/216 but with a premium of "+ 2 c." and borders on three sides	80	1·40

977 (3 Mar).   *Telephone Centenary* (1976). *T* **32** *and similar horiz design. P* 13.

18	25 c. black, gold and dull scarlet	..	20	15
19	70 c. black, gold and lilac	..	40	40
MS220	116 × 59 mm. As Nos. 218/19 but with different colours		70	1·00

Design:—70 c. Earth Station and satellite.

33 "Christ on the Cross" (detail)

977 (31 Mar).   *Easter and 400th Birth Anniv of Rubens. T* **33** *and similar horiz designs. Multicoloured. P* 13½ × 14.

21	15 c. Type **33**	..	45	15
22	20 c. "Lamentation for Christ"	..	60	20
23	35 c. "Christ with Straw"	..	75	25
21/3		*Set of 3*	1·60	55
MS224	115 × 57 mm. Nos. 221/3. P 13 × 12½		2·00	2·00

Each value was issued in sheets of 8 stamps and 1 label.

34 Capt. Bligh, George III and H.M.S. *Bounty*

977 (21 Apr).   *Silver Jubilee. T* **34** *and similar horiz designs. Multicoloured. P* 13.

225	25 c. Type **34**	..	35	35
226	35 c. Rev. Williams, George IV and Aitutaki Church	..	40	40
227	50 c. Union Jack, Queen Victoria and island map	..	45	45
228	$1 Balcony scene, 1953	..	50	50
225/8		*Set of 4*	1·50	1·50
MS229	130 × 87 mm. Nos. 225/8 but with gold borders. P 13½ × 13		1·25	1·25

Each value was issued in sheets of 5 stamps and 1 label.

35 The Shepherds   (36)

1977 (14 Oct).   *Christmas. T* **35** *and similar vert designs. Multicoloured. P* 13½ × 14.

230	6 c. Type **35**	..	10	10
231	6 c. Angel	..	10	10
232	7 c. Mary, Jesus and ox	..	10	10
233	7 c. Joseph and donkey	..	10	10
234	7 c. Three Kings	..	10	10
235	15 c. Virgin and Child	..	10	10
236	20 c. Joseph	..	10	10
237	20 c. Mary and Jesus on donkey	..	10	10
230/7		*Set of 8*	55	55
MS238	130 × 95 mm. Nos. 230/7		70	1·25

Each design covers two stamps; Type **35** shows the left-hand stamp of the 6 c. design.

1977 (15 Nov).   *Children's Christmas Fund. Nos. 230/7 surch with T* **36**.

239	6 c. + 1 c. }		10	10
240	6 c. + 1 c. } Type **35**		10	10
241	7 c. + 1 c. }		10	10
242	7 c. + 1 c. } The Holy Family		10	10
243	15 c. + 1 c. } The Three Kings with Virgin		15	10
244	15 c. + 1 c. } and Child		15	10
245	20 c. + 1 c. } Flight into Egypt		15	10
246	20 c. + 1 c. }		15	10
239/46		*Set of 8*	75	55
MS247	130 × 95 mm. As Nos. 239/46 but each with premium of "+ 2 c."		70	85

37 Hawaiian Goddess

38 "Christ on the Way to Calvary" (Martini)

1978 (19 Jan).   *Bicentenary of Discovery of Hawaii. T* **37** *and similar multicoloured designs. P* 13½.

248	35 c. Type **37**	..	35	25
249	50 c. Figurehead of H.M.S. *Resolution (horiz)*		60	40
250	$1 Hawaiian temple figure	..	70	70
248/50		*Set of 3*	1·50	1·25
MS251	168 × 75 mm. Nos. 248/50		1·50	2·25

1978 (17 Mar).   *Easter. Details of Paintings from Louvre, Paris. T* **38** *and similar horiz designs. Multicoloured. P* 13½ × 14.

252	15 c. Type **38**	..	15	10
253	20 c. "Piéta of Avignon" (E. Quarton)	..	20	10
254	35 c. "Pilgrims at Emmaus" (Rembrandt)	..	25	15
252/4		*Set of 3*	55	30
MS255	108 × 83 mm. Nos. 252/4		75	75

Each value was printed in two panes of 9 within the sheet, both panes including one se-tenant stamp-size label.

1978 (17 Mar).   *Easter. Children's Charity. Designs as Nos. 252/4, but smaller (34 × 26 mm) and without margins, in separate miniature sheets 75 × 58 mm, each with a face value of 50 c. + 5 c. P* 14.

MS256	As Nos. 252/4	..	*Set of 3 sheets* 1·40	1·00

39 Yale of Beaufort

40 "Adoration of the Infant Jesus"

1978 (15 June).   *25th Anniv of Coronation. T* **39** *and similar vert designs. Multicoloured. P* 13½ × 13.

257	$1 Type **39**	..	30	50
258	$1 Queen Elizabeth II	..	30	50
259	$1 Aitutaki ancestral statue	..	30	50
257/9		*Set of 3*	80	1·40
MS260	98 × 127 mm. Nos. 257/9 × 2		75	75

Stamps from No. MS260 have coloured borders, the upper row in lavender and the lower in apple-green.

Nos. 257/9 were printed together, se-tenant, in small sheets of 6, containing two horizontal strips of 3.

1978 (4 Dec).   *Christmas. 450th Death Anniv of Dürer. T* **40** *and similar vert designs. Multicoloured. P* 13 × 14.

261	15 c. Type **40**	..	35	15
262	17 c. "The Madonna with Child"	..	40	15
263	30 c. "The Madonna with the Iris"	..	55	20
264	35 c. "The Madonna of the Siskin"	..	60	25
261/4		*Set of 4*	1·75	65
MS265	101 × 109 mm. As Nos. 261/4 but each with premium of "+ 2 c."		1·50	1·00

Nos. 261/4 were each printed in small sheets of 6, including 1 se-tenant stamp-size label.

41 "Captain Cook" (Nathaniel Dance)

42 Girl with Flowers

1979 (20 July).   *Death Bicentenary of Captain Cook. Paintings. T* **41** *and similar vert designs. Multicoloured. P* 14 × 13½.

266	50 c. Type **41**	..	1·00	80
267	75 c. "H.M.S. *Resolution* and *Adventure* at Matavai Bay" (William Hodges)		1·75	95
MS268	94 × 58 mm. Nos. 266/7. P 13½		2·00	2·25

1979 (1 Oct).   *International Year of the Child. T* **42** *and similar vert designs. Multicoloured. P* 14 × 13½.

269	30 c. Type **42**	..	15	15
270	35 c. Boy playing guitar	..	20	20
271	65 c. Children in canoe	..	30	30
269/71		*Set of 3*	60	60
MS272	104 × 80 mm. As Nos. 269/71, but each with a premium of "+ 3 c."		70	1·00

43 "Man writing a Letter" (painting by G. Metsu)

44 "The Burial of Christ" (detail, Quentin Metsys)

1979 (14 Nov).   *Death Centenary of Sir Rowland Hill. T* **43** *and similar horiz designs. Multicoloured. P* 13.

273	50 c. Type **43**	..	45	45
274	50 c. Sir Rowland Hill with Penny Black, 1903 ½d. and 1911 1d. stamps		45	45
275	50 c. "Girl in Blue reading a Letter" (painting by J. Vermeer)		45	45
276	65 c. "Woman writing a Letter" (painting by G. Terborch)		50	50
277	65 c. Sir Rowland Hill with Penny Black, 1903 3d. and 1920 ½d. stamps		50	50
278	65 c. "Lady reading a Letter" (painting by J. Vermeer)		50	50
273/8		*Set of 6*	2·50	2·50
MS279	151 × 85 mm. 30 c. × 6. As Nos. 273/8		1·75	2·00

Nos. 273/5 and 276/8 were printed together, se-tenant, in horizontal strips of 3, the sheet having two panes separated by margin, one containing 273/5 × 3, the other containing 276/8 × 3.

1980 (3 Apr).   *Easter. T* **44** *and similar vert designs showing different details of painting "The Burial of Christ" by Quentin Metsys. P* 13.

280	20 c. multicoloured	..	40	25
281	30 c. multicoloured	..	50	35
282	35 c. multicoloured	..	65	45
280/2		*Set of 3*	1·40	95
MS283	93 × 71 mm. As Nos. 280/2, but each with premium of "+ 2 c."		75	75

45 Einstein as Young Man

46 Ancestor Figure, Aitutaki

1980 (21 July).   *25th Death Anniv of Albert Einstein (physicist). T* **45** *and similar vert designs. Multicoloured. P* 14 × 13½.

284	12 c. Type **45**	..	50	50
285	12 c. Atom and "E=mc²" equation	..	50	50
286	15 c. Einstein as middle-aged man	..	55	55
287	15 c. Cross over nuclear explosion (Nuclear Test Ban Treaty, 1963)		55	55
288	20 c. Einstein as old man	..	65	65
289	20 c. Hand over bomb explosion (Nuclear Test Ban Treaty, 1963)		65	65
284/9		*Set of 6*	3·00	3·00
MS290	113 × 118 mm. Nos. 284/9. P 13½		3·00	3·00

Nos. 284/5, 286/7 and 288/9 were each printed together, se-tenant, in horizontal pairs throughout the sheet.

1980 (26 Sept).   *South Pacific Festival of Arts. T* **46** *and similar vert designs. Multicoloured. P* 13½.

291	6 c. Type **46**	..	10	10
292	6 c. Staff god image, Rarotonga	..	10	10
293	6 c. Trade adze, Mangaia	..	10	10
294	6 c. Carved image of Tangaroa, Rarotonga	..	10	10
295	12 c. Wooden image, Aitutaki	..	10	10
296	12 c. Hand club, Rarotonga	..	10	10
297	12 c. Carved mace "god", Mangaia	..	10	10
298	12 c. Fisherman's god, Rarotonga	..	10	10
299	15 c. Ti'i image, Aitutaki	..	15	15
300	15 c. Fisherman's god, Rarotonga (*different*) ..		15	15
301	15 c. Carved mace "god", Cook Islands	..	15	15
302	15 c. Carved image of Tangaroa, Rarotonga (*different*)		15	15
303	20 c. Chief's headdress, Aitutaki	..	15	15
304	20 c. Carved "mace" god, Cook Islands (*different*)		15	15
305	20 c. Staff god image, Rarotonga (*different*) ..		15	15
306	20 c. Carved image of Tangaroa, Rarotonga (*different*)		15	15
291/306		*Set of 16*	1·60	1·60
MS307	134 × 194 mm. Nos. 291/306		1·60	1·75

The four designs of each value were printed together, se-tenant, in blocks of 4 throughout the sheet.

47 Virgin and Child (13th-century)

48 "Mourning Virgin"

1980 (21 Nov).   *Christmas. Sculptures. T* **47** *and similar vert designs showing various Virgin and Child works from the periods given. Multicoloured. P* 13.

308	15 c. Type **47**	..	15	15
309	15 c. 14th-century	..	15	15
310	25 c. 15th-century	..	20	20
311	35 c. 15th-century (*different*)	..	20	20
308/11		*Set of 4*	60	60
MS312	82 × 120 mm. As Nos. 306/11 but each with premium of 2 c.		70	80

1981 (31 Mar). *Easter. Details of Sculpture "Burial of Christ" by Pedro Roldan. T* 48 *and similar vert designs. P* 14.

313	30 c. gold and myrtle-green			25	25
314	40 c. gold and deep reddish lilac			30	30
315	50 c. gold and Prussian blue			30	30
313/15			*Set of 3*	75	75
MS316	107 × 60 mm. As Nos. 313/15 but each with premium of 2 c.			75	85

Designs:—40 c. "Christ"; 50 c. "Saint John".

49 Gouldian Finch (*Poephila gouldiae*)

50 Prince Charles

1981 (6 Apr)–*82. Birds (1st series). Multicoloured designs as T* 49. *P* 14 × 13½ (1 *to* 10 c.), 13½ × 14 (15 *to* 70 c.) *or* 13 ($1 *to* $4).

317	1 c. Type **49**		45	30
318	1 c. Common Starling (*Sturnus vulgaris*)		45	30
319	2 c. Golden Whistler (*Pachycephala pectoralis*)		50	30
320	2 c. Scarlet Robin (*Petroica multicolor*)		50	30
321	3 c. Rufous Fantail (*Rhipidura rufifrous*)		60	30
322	3 c. Peregrine Falcon (*Falco peregrinus*)		60	30
323	4 c. Java Sparrow (*Padda oryzivora*)		70	30
324	4 c. Barn Owl (*Tyto alba*)		70	30
325	5 c. Tahitian Lory (*Vini peruviana*)		70	30
326	5 c. White-breasted Wood Swallow (*Artamus leucorhynchus*)		70	30
327	6 c. Purple Swamphen (*Porphyrio porphyrio*)		70	30
328	6 c. Rock Dove (*Columba livia*)		70	30
329	10 c. Chestnut-breasted Mannikin (*Lonchura castaneothorax*)		90	30
330	10 c. Zebra Dove (*Geopelia striata*)		90	30
331	12 c. Eastern Reef Heron (*Egretta sacra*)		1·00	40
332	12 c. Common Mynah (*Acridotheres tristis*)		1·00	40
333	15 c. Whimbrel (*Numenius phaeopus*) (horiz) (8.5.81)		1·25	40
334	15 c. Black-browed Albatross (*Diomeda melanophris*) (horiz) (8.5.81)		1·25	40
335	20 c. American Golden Plover (*Pluvialis dominica*) (horiz) (8.5.81)		1·50	55
336	20 c. White Tern (*Gygis alba*) (horiz) (8.5.81)		1·50	55
337	25 c. Spotbill Duck (*Anas superciliosa*) (horiz) (8.5.81)		1·75	70
338	25 c. Brown Booby (*Sula leucogaster*) (horiz) (8.5.81)		1·75	70
339	30 c. Great Frigate Bird (*Fregata minor*) (horiz) (8.5.81)		2·00	85
340	30 c. Pintail (*Anas acuta*) (horiz) (8.5.81)		2·00	85
341	35 c. Long-billed Reed Warbler (*Conopoderas caffra caffra*) (14.1.82)		2·25	1·00
342	35 c. Pomarine Skua (*Stercorarius pomarinus*) (14.1.82)		2·25	1·00
343	40 c. Banded Rail (*Gallirallus philippensis goodsoni*) (14.1.82)		2·75	1·25
344	40 c. Spotted Triller (*Lalage maculosa pumila*) (14.1.82)		2·75	1·25
345	50 c. Royal Albatross (*Diomedea epomophora*) (14.1.82)		3·00	1·50
346	50 c. Stephen's Lory (*Vini stepheni*) (14.1.82)		3·00	1·50
347	70 c. Red-headed Parrot Finch (*Erythrura cyaneovirens*) (14.1.82)		5·50	3·00
348	70 c. Orange Dove (*Ptilinopus victor victor*) (14.1.82)		5·50	3·00
349	$1 Blue-headed Flycatcher (*Myiagra azureo-capilla whitneyi*) (15.2.82)		5·50	3·75
350	$2 Red-bellied Flycatcher (*Myiagra vanikorensis rufiventris*) (15.5.82)		8·00	8·00
351	$4 Red Munia (*Amandava amandava*) (19.3.82)		14·00	14·00
352	$5 Flat-billed Kingfisher (*Halcyon recurvirostris*) (19.3.82)		15·00	16·00
317/52		*Set of 36*	80·00	60·00

The two designs of each value (1 c. to 70 c.) were printed together, *se-tenant*, in horizontal and vertical pairs throughout the sheet.

Nos. 341/8 are 35 × 27 mm and Nos. 349/52, which include a portrait of Queen Elizabeth II, 35 × 48 mm in size.

See also Nos. 475/94 for redrawn designs as Type **65**.

Nos. 353/90 are vacant.

1981 (10 June). *Royal Wedding. T* 50 *and similar multicoloured designs. P* 14 ($1.40) *or* 13 × 13½ (*others*).

391	60 c. Type **50**		30	40
392	80 c. Lady Diana Spencer		40	55
393	$1.40, Prince Charles and Lady Diana (87 × 70 mm)		60	80
391/3		*Set of 3*	1·10	1·60

(51)   **52** Footballers

53 "The Holy Family"

1981 (23 Nov). *International Year for Disabled Persons. Nos. 391/3 surch with T* 51 *on gold background.*

394	60 c. + 5 c. Type **50**		80	1·25
395	80 c. + 5 c. Lady Diana Spencer		1·25	1·75
396	$1.40 + 5 c.Prince Charles and Lady Diana		2·25	3·25
394/6		*Set of 3*	3·75	5·50

Nos. 394/6 have commemorative inscriptions overprinted on the sheet margins.

1981 (30 Nov). *World Cup Football Championship, Spain* (1982). *T* 52 *and similar horiz designs showing footballers. Multicoloured. P* 14.

397	12 c. Ball to left of stamp		40	35
398	12 c. Ball to right		40	35
399	15 c. Ball to right		45	40
400	15 c. Ball to left		45	40
401	20 c. Ball to left		55	50
402	20 c. Ball to right		55	50
403	25 c. Type **52**		60	55
404	25 c. "ESPANA 82" inscr on printed background		60	55
397/404		*Set of 8*	3·50	3·25
MS405	100 × 137 mm. 12 c. + 2 c., 15 c. + 2 c., 20 c. + 2 c., 25 c. + 2 c., each × 2. As Nos. 397/404		3·25	3·00

The two designs of each value were printed together, *se-tenant*, in horizontal pairs throughout the sheet.

1981 (10 Dec). *Christmas. Details from Etchings by Rembrandt. T* 53 *and similar designs in purple-brown and gold. P* 14.

406	15 c. Type **53**		45	45
407	30 c. "Virgin with Child"		70	70
408	40 c. "Adoration of the Shepherds" (*horiz*)		95	95
409	50 c. "The Holy Family" (*horiz*)		1·25	1·25
406/9		*Set of 4*	3·00	3·00
MS410	Designs as Nos. 406/9 in separate miniature sheets, 65 × 82 mm or 82 × 65 mm, each with a face value of 80 c. + 5 c. P 14 × 13½ *Set of 4 sheets*		3·25	3·00

54 Princess of Wales   **(55)**

1982 (24 June). *21st Birthday of Princess of Wales. T* 54 *and similar vert designs. Multicoloured. P* 14.

411	70 c. Type **54**		60	60
412	$1 Prince and Princess of Wales		75	75
413	$2 Princess Diana (*different*)		1·50	1·50
411/13		*Set of 3*	2·75	2·75
MS414	82 × 91 mm. Nos. 411/13		3·00	2·75

Nos. 411/13 were each printed in small sheets of 6 including two *se-tenant* stamp-size labels. The silver markings in the margins of the individual stamps differ for each position in the sheetlet.

1982 (13 July). *Birth of Prince William of Wales* (1st issue). *Nos. 391/3 optd as T* 55.

415	60 c. Type **50** (optd with T **55**)		1·25	1·00
	a. Pair. Nos. 415/16		2·50	2·00
416	60 c. Type **50** (optd "COMMEMORATING THE ROYAL BIRTH")		1·25	1·00
417	80 c. Lady Diana Spencer (optd with T **55**)		1·40	1·10
	a. Pair. Nos. 417/18		2·75	2·10
418	80 c. Lady Diana Spencer (optd "COMMEMORATING THE ROYAL BIRTH")		1·40	1·10
419	$1.40, Prince Charles and Lady Diana (87 × 70 mm) (optd as T **55**)		1·75	1·40
	a. Pair. Nos. 419/20		3·50	2·75
420	$1.40, Prince Charles and Lady Diana (87 × 70 mm) (optd "COMMEMORATING THE ROYAL BIRTH")		1·75	1·40
415/20		*Set of 6*	8·00	6·25

Nos. 415/16, 417/18 and 419/20 were each printed together in *se-tenant* pairs, horiz and vert, throughout the sheets.

1982 (5 Aug). *Birth of Prince William of Wales* (2nd issue). *As Nos. 411/14, but inscr* "ROYAL BIRTH 21 JUNE 1982 PRINCE WILLIAM OF WALES". *Multicoloured. P* 14.

421	70 c. Type **54**		50	60
422	$1 Prince and Princess of Wales		60	75
423	$2 Princess Diana (*different*)		1·00	1·50
421/3		*Set of 3*	1·90	2·75
MS424	81 × 91 mm. Nos. 421/3		2·75	3·00

56 "Virgin and Child" (12th-century sculpture)

57 Aitutaki Bananas

1982 (10 Dec). *Christmas. Religious Sculptures. T* 56 *and similar vert designs. Multicoloured. P* 13.

425	18 c. Type **56**		60	6
426	36 c. "Virgin and Child" (12th-century)		75	7
427	48 c. "Virgin and Child" (13th-century)		90	9
428	60 c. "Virgin and Child" (15th-century)		1·25	1·2
425/8		*Set of 4*	3·25	3·2
MS429	99 × 115 mm. As Nos. 425/8 but each with 2 c. charity premium		2·25	2·7

Nos. 425/8 were each printed in small sheets of 6 including one *se-tenant*, stamp size, label, depicting the Prince and Princess o Wales with Prince William.

1983 (14 Mar). *Commonwealth Day. T* 57 *and similar horiz designs. Multicoloured. P* 13.

430	48 c. Type **57**		1·10	5
431	48 c. Ancient Ti'i image		1·10	5
432	48 c. Tourist canoeing		1·10	5
433	48 c. Captain William Bligh and chart		1·10	5
430/3		*Set of 4*	4·00	1·7

Nos. 430/3 were issued together, *se-tenant*, in blocks of fou throughout the sheet.

58 Scouts around Campfire   **(59)**

1983 (18 Apr). *75th Anniv of Boy Scout Movement, T* 58 *an similar horiz designs. Multicoloured. P* 13½ × 14.

434	36 c. Type **58**		55	55
435	48 c. Scout saluting		70	70
436	60 c. Scouts hiking		75	75
434/6		*Set of 3*	1·75	1·75
MS437	78 × 107 mm. As Nos. 434/6 but each with premium of 3 c. P 13		2·00	2·25

1983 (11 July). *15th World Scout Jamboree, Alberta, Canada Nos. 434/7 optd with T* 59.

438	36 c. Type **58**		80	4
439	48 c. Scout saluting		1·00	5
440	60 c. Scouts hiking		1·25	7
438/40		*Set of 3*	2·75	1·6
MS441	78 × 107 mm. As Nos. 438/40 but each with a premium of 3 c.		2·00	2·5

60 Modern Sport Balloon   **(61)**   **(62)**

1983 (22 July). *Bicentenary of Manned Flight. T* 60 *and simila vert designs showing different modern sport balloons. P* 14 × 13.

442	18 c. multicoloured		55	3
443	36 c. multicoloured		75	5
444	48 c. multicoloured		90	6
445	60 c. multicoloured		1·00	8
442/5		*Set of 4*	2·75	2·0
MS446	64 × 80 mm. $2.50, multicoloured (48½ × 28½ mm)		1·90	2·5

Nos. 442/5 were each issued in small sheets of 4 stamps.

1983 (22 Sept). *Various stamps surch.*

(a) *Nos. 335/48 and* 352 *as T* 61

447	18 c. on 20 c. American Golden Plover (*Pluvialis dominica*)		2·00	7
448	18 c. on 20 c. White Tern (*Gygis alba*)		2·00	7
449	36 c. on 25 c. Spotbill Duck (*Anas superciliosa*)		3·00	1·00
450	36 c. on 25 c. Brown Booby (*Sula leucogaster*)		3·00	1·00
451	36 c. on 30 c. Great Frigate Bird (*Fregata minor*)		3·00	1·00
452	36 c. on 30 c. Pintail (*Anas acuta*)		3·00	1·00
453	36 c. on 35 c. Long-billed Reed Warbler (*Conopoderas caffra caffra*)		3·00	1·00
454	36 c. on 35 c. Pomarine Skua (*Stercorarius pomarinus*)		3·00	1·00
455	48 c. on 40 c. Banded Rail (*Gallirallus philippensis goodsoni*)		4·00	1·2
456	48 c. on 40 c. Spotted Triller (*Lalage maculosa pumila*)		4·00	1·2
457	48 c. on 50 c. Royal Albatross (*Diomedea epomophora*)		4·00	1·25
458	48 c. on 50 c. Stephen's Lory (*Vini stepheni*)		4·00	1·25
459	72 c. on 70 c. Red-headed Parrot Finch (*Erythrura cyaneovirens*)		7·00	2·00
460	72 c. on 70 c. Orange Dove (*Ptilinopus victor victor*)		7·00	2·00
461	$5.60 on $5 Flat-billed Kingfisher (*Halcyon recurvirostris*)		20·00	8·50

(b) *Nos. 392/3 and* 412/13 *as T* 62

462	96 c. on 80 c. Lady Diana Spencer (Gold)		4·00	2·5
	a. Error. Surch on No. 417		12·00	
	ab. Pair. Nos. 462/a/b		25·00	
	b. Error. Surch on No. 418		12·00	

63	96 c. on $1 Prince and Princess of Wales	3·50	2·00
64	$1.20 on $1.40, Prince Charles and Lady Diana (Gold)	4·00	2·50
	a. Error. Surch on No. 419	12·00	
	ab. Pair. Nos. 464a/b	25·00	
	b. Error. Surch on No. 420	12·00	
65	$1.20 on $2, Princess Diana	3·50	2·00
47/65	Set of 19	75·00	30·00

On Nos. 462 and 464 the gold surcharge is printed on a black obliterating panel over the original face value.

63 International Mail   **64** "Madonna of the Chair"

1983 (29 Sept). *World Communications Year. T 63 and similar vert designs. Multicoloured. P 14 × 13½.*

466	48 c. Type 63	65	50
467	60 c. Telecommunications	95	70
468	96 c. Space satellites	1·40	1·00
466/8	Set of 3	2·75	2·00
MS469	126 × 53 mm. Nos. 466/8. P 13	2·50	2·50

1983 (21 Nov). *Christmas. 500th Birth Anniv of Raphael. T 64 and similar horiz designs. Multicoloured. P 13½ × 14.*

470	36 c. Type 64	65	30
471	48 c. "The Alba Madonna"	80	40
472	60 c. "Conestabile Madonna"	1·10	55
470/2	Set of 3	2·25	1·10
MS473	95 × 116 mm. As Nos. 470/2, but each with a premium of 3 c. P 13	2·00	1·40

1983 (15 Dec). *Christmas. 500th Birth Anniv of Raphael. Children's Charity. Designs as Nos. 470/2 in separate miniature sheets 46 × 47 mm, but each with different frames and a face value of 85 c. + 5 c. Imperf.*

MS474	As Nos. 470/2 Set of 3 sheets	3·00	2·75

65 Gouldian Finch   **66** Javelin-throwing

1984 (13 Feb–2 July). *Birds (2nd series). Designs as Nos. 317 etc. but with redrawn frames and inscriptions as in T 65. Multicoloured. P 13 × 13½ ($3 to $9.60) or 14 (others).*

475	2 c. Type 65	85	60
476	3 c. Common Starling	85	60
477	5 c. Scarlet Robin	1·00	70
478	10 c. Golden Whistler	1·00	80
479	12 c. Rufous Fantail	1·00	80
480	18 c. Peregrine Falcon	1·40	90
481	24 c. Barn Owl	1·40	90
482	30 c. Java Sparrow	1·40	90
483	36 c. White-breasted Wood Swallow	1·40	90
484	48 c. Tahitian Lory	1·40	1·00
485	50 c. Rock Dove (26 Mar)	1·90	1·40
486	60 c. Purple Swamphen (26 Mar)	1·90	1·40
487	72 c. Zebra Dove (26 Mar)	1·90	1·40
488	96 c. Chestnut-breasted Mannikin (26 Mar)	1·90	1·60
489	$1.20, Common Mynah (26 Mar)	2·00	2·25
490	$2.10, Eastern Reef Heron (30 Apr)	2·50	2·75
491	$3 Blue-headed Flycatcher (30 × 42 mm) (30 Apr)	6·00	5·00
492	$4.20, Red-bellied Flycatcher (30 × 42 mm) (5 June)	3·75	6·00
493	$5.60, Red Munia (30 × 42 mm) (5 June)	4·50	7·00
494	$9.60, Flat-billed Kingfisher (30 × 42 mm) (2 July)	7·50	10·00
475/94	Set of 20	40·00	42·00

1984 (24 July). *Olympic Games, Los Angeles. T 66 and similar vert designs showing Memorial Coliseum and various events. Multicoloured. P 13 × 13½.*

495	36 c. Type 66	30	35
496	48 c. Shot-putting	40	45
497	60 c. Hurdling	45	55
498	$2 Basketball	1·10	1·50
495/8	Set of 4	2·00	2·50
MS499	88 × 117 mm. As Nos. 495/8, but each with a charity premium of 5 c.	2·75	3·00

1984 (21 Aug). *Olympic Gold Medal Winners. Nos. 495/8 optd as T 209 of Cook Islands in gold on black background.*

500	36 c. Type 66 (optd "Javelin Throw Tessa Sanderson Great Britain")	30	35
501	48 c. Shot-putting (optd "Shot Put Claudia Losch Germany")	40	45
502	60 c. Hurdling (optd "Heptathlon Glynis Nunn Australia")	45	55
503	$2 Basketball (optd "Team Basketball United States")	1·10	1·50
500/3	Set of 4	2·00	2·50

15.9.84 Birth   **Prince Henry**   **$3**

67 Capt. William Bligh and Chart   (**68**)

1984 (14 Sept). *"Ausipex" International Stamp Exhibition, Melbourne. T 67 and similar horiz designs. Multicoloured. P 14.*

504	60 c. Type 67	3·25	3·25
505	96 c. H.M.S. *Bounty* and map	3·50	3·50
506	$1.40, Aitutaki stamps of 1974, 1979 and 1981 with map	3·50	3·50
504/6	Set of 3	9·00	9·00
MS507	85 × 113 mm. As Nos. 504/6, but each with a premium of 5 c. P 13½.	5·50	4·00

1984 (10 Oct). *Birth of Prince Henry (1st issue). No. 391 surch with T 68 in gold.*

508	$3 on 60 c. Type 50	2·75	3·25

On No. 508 the gold surcharge is printed on a black obliterating panel over the original face value.

69 The Annunciation   **70** Princess Diana with Prince Henry

1984 (16 Nov). *Christmas. Details from Altarpiece, St. Paul's Church, Palencia, Spain. T 69 and similar vert designs. Multicoloured. P 13½ × 13.*

509	36 c. Type 69	30	35
510	48 c. The Nativity	40	45
511	60 c. The Epiphany	45	50
512	96 c. The Flight into Egypt	75	80
509/12	Set of 4	1·75	1·90
MS513	Designs as Nos. 509/12 in separate miniature sheets, each 45 × 53 mm and with a face value of 90 c. + 7 c. Imperf. Set of 4 sheets	2·50	3·25

1984 (10 Dec). *Birth of Prince Henry (2nd issue). T 70 and similar vert designs. Multicoloured. P 14.*

514	48 c. Type 70	85	95
515	60 c. Prince William with Prince Henry	95	1·10
516	$2.10, Prince and Princess of Wales with children	2·50	2·50
514/16	Set of 3	3·75	4·00
MS517	113 × 65 mm. As Nos. 514/16, but each with a face value of 96 c. + 7 c. P13½.	2·75	2·75

71 Grey Kingbird   **72** The Queen Mother, aged Seven

1985 (22 Mar). *Birth Bicentenary of John J. Audubon (ornithologist). T 71 and similar vert designs showing original paintings. Multicoloured. P 13.*

518	55 c. Type 71	1·10	1·10
519	65 c. Bohemian Waxwing	1·25	1·25
520	75 c. Summer Tanager	1·40	1·40
521	95 c. Common Cardinal	1·50	1·50
522	$1.15, White-winged Crossbill	1·90	1·90
518/22	Set of 5	6·50	6·50

1985 (14 June). *Life and Times of Queen Elizabeth the Queen Mother. T 72 and similar horiz designs. Multicoloured. P 13.*

523	55 c. Type 72	45	50
524	65 c. Engagement photograph, 1922	50	55
525	75 c. With young Princess Elizabeth	60	65
526	$1.30, With baby Prince Charles	1·00	1·10
523/6	Set of 4	2·25	2·50
MS527	75 × 49 mm. $3 Queen Mother on her 63rd birthday	2·25	2·40

Nos. 523/6 were each printed in sheetlets of 4.
For these stamps in a miniature sheet see No. MS550.

73 "The Calmady Children" (T. Lawrence)

1985 (16 Sept). *International Youth Year. T 73 and similar horiz designs. Multicoloured. P 13.*

528	75 c. Type 73	2·00	1·25
529	90 c. "Madame Charpentier's Children" (Renoir)	2·00	1·50
530	$1.40, "Young Girls at Piano" (Renoir)	2·50	2·50
528/30	Set of 3	6·00	4·75
MS531	103 × 104 mm. As Nos. 528/30, but each with a premium of 10 c.	4·00	3·00

74 "Adoration of the Magi" (Giotto) and *Giotto* Spacecraft

1985 (15 Nov). *Christmas. Appearance of Halley's Comet (1st issue). T 74 and similar multicoloured designs. P 13.*

532	95 c. Type 74	1·25	1·25
533	95 c. As Type 74 but showing *Planet A* spacecraft	1·25	1·25
534	$1.15, Type 74	1·50	1·50
535	$1.15, As No. 533	1·50	1·50
532/5	Set of 4	5·00	5·00
MS536	52 × 55 mm. $6.40, As Type 74 but without spacecraft (30 × 31 mm). Imperf	11·00	8·50

Nos. 532/3 and 534/5 were each printed together, *se-tenant*, in horizontal pairs throughout the sheets.

75 Halley's Comet, A.D. 684 (from "Nuremberg Chronicle")   **76** Queen Elizabeth II on Coronation Day (from photo by Cecil Beaton)

1986 (25 Feb). *Appearance of Halley's Comet (2nd issue). T 75 and similar multicoloured designs. P 13½ × 13.*

537	90 c. Type 75	65	70
538	$1.25, Halley's Comet, 1066 (from Bayeux Tapestry)	85	90
539	$1.75, Halley's Comet, 1456 (from "Lucerne Chronicles")	1·25	1·40
537/9	Set of 3	2·50	2·75
MS540	107 × 82 mm. As Nos. 537/9, but each with a face value of 95 c.	2·50	2·50
MS541	65 × 80 mm. $4.20, "Melencolia I" (Albrecht Dürer woodcut) (61 × 76 mm). Imperf	4·00	3·50

1986 (21 Apr). *60th Birthday of Queen Elizabeth II. T 76 and similar vert design. Multicoloured. P 14.*

542	95 c. Type 76	85	1·00
MS543	58 × 68 mm. $4.20, As T 76, but showing more of the portrait without oval frame. P 13½	5·50	5·50

No. 542 was printed in sheetlets of five stamps and one stamp-size label at top left.

77 Head of Statue of Liberty   **78** Prince Andrew and Miss Sarah Ferguson

1986 (27 June). *Centenary of Statue of Liberty. T 77 and similar horiz design. Multicoloured. P 14.*

544	$1 Type 77	1·25	1·25
545	$2.75, Statue of Liberty at sunset	2·75	2·75
MS546	91 × 79 mm. As Nos. 544/5, but each with a face value of $1.25. P 13½	2·50	2·50

1986 (23 July). *Royal Wedding.* P 14.
547 **78** $2 multicoloured .. .. .. 2·00 2·00
MS548 85×70 mm. **78** $5 mult. P 13½ .. .. 6·50 8·00
No. 547 was printed in sheetlets of 5 stamps and one stamp-size label at top left.

1986 (4 Aug). *"Stampex '86" Stamp Exhibition, Adelaide. No.* MS507 *with "Ausipex" emblems obliterated in gold.*
MS549 As Nos. 504/6, but each with a premium of 5 c. .. .. 8·00 9·50
The "Stampex '86" exhibition emblem is overprinted on the sheet margin.

1986 (4 Aug). *86th Birthday of Queen Elizabeth the Queen Mother. Nos. 523/6 in miniature sheet,* 132×82 *mm.* P 13½×13.
MS550 Nos. 523/6 .. .. 7·50 8·50

79 "St. Anne with Virgin and Child" (80)

1986 (21 Nov). *Christmas. Paintings by Dürer. T* **79** *and similar vert designs. Multicoloured.* P 13½.
551 75 c. Type **79** .. .. .. 1·25 1·25
552 $1.35, "Virgin and Child" .. .. 1·75 1·75
553 $1.95, "The Adoration of the Magi" .. 2·25 2·25
554 $2.75, "Madonna of the Rosary" .. 3·00 3·00
551/4 .. .. .. *Set of 4* 7·50 7·50
MS555 88×125 mm. As Nos. 551/4, but each stamp with a face value of $1.65 .. 11·00 12·00

1986 (25 Nov). *Visit of Pope John Paul II to South Pacific. Nos.* 551/5 *surch with T* **80** *in silver.*
556 75 c. + 10 c. Type **79** .. .. 2·25 2·25
557 $1.35 + 10 c. "Virgin and Child" .. 2·75 2·75
558 $1.95 + 10 c. "The Adoration of the Magi" 3·25 3·25
559 $2.75 + 10 c. "Madonna of the Rosary" .. 4·50 4·50
556/9 .. .. .. *Set of 4* 11·50 11·50
MS560 88 × 125 mm. As Nos. 556/9, but each stamp with a face value of $1.65 + 10 c. .. 13·00 13·00

HURRICANE RELIEF +50c

(81) (82)

1987 (29 Apr). *Hurricane Relief Fund. Nos. 544/5, 547, 551/4 and* 556/9 *surch with T* **81** *in black (Nos. 563, 569) or silver (others).*
561 75 c. + 50 c. Type **79** .. .. 1·75 1·75
562 75 c. + 10 c. + 50 c. Type **79** .. 2·00 2·00
563 $1 + 50 c. Type **77** .. .. 2·25 2·25
564 $1.35 + 50 c. "Virgin and Child" (Dürer) .. 2·40 2·40
565 $1.35 + 10 c. + 50 c. "Virgin and Child" (Dürer) .. .. .. 2·50 2·50
566 $1.95 + 50 c. "The Adoration of the Magi" (Dürer) .. .. .. 3·00 3·00
567 $1.95 + 10 c. + 50 c. "The Adoration of the Magi" (Dürer) .. .. 3·00 3·00
568 $2 + 50 c. Type **78** .. .. 3·00 3·00
569 $2.75 + 50 c. Statue of Liberty at sunset .. 3·50 3·50
570 $2.75 + 50 c. "Madonna of the Rosary" (Dürer) .. .. .. 3·50 3·50
571 $2.75 + 10 c. + 50 c. "Madonna of the Rosary" (Dürer) .. .. 3·50 3·50
561/71 .. .. .. *Set of 11* 27·00 27·00

1987 (20 Nov). *Royal Ruby Wedding. Nos. 391/3 surch as T* **82**.
572 $2.50 on 60 c. Type **50** .. .. 2·50 2·50
573 $2.50 on 80 c. Lady Diana Spencer .. 2·50 2·50
574 $2.50 on $1.40, Prince Charles and Lady Diana (87×70 *mm*) .. .. 2·50 2·50
572/4 .. .. .. *Set of 3* 6·75 6·75
On Nos. 572/4 the original values are obliterated in gold.

STANLEY GIBBONS STAMP COLLECTING SERIES

Introductory booklets on *How to Start, How to Identify Stamps* and *Collecting by Theme.* A series of well illustrated guides at a low price.
Write for details.

---

83 "Angels" (detail from "Virgin with Garland")

1987 (10 Dec). *Christmas. T* **83** *and similar designs showing different details of angels from "Virgin with Garland" by Rubens.* P 13×13½.
575 70 c. multicoloured .. .. 1·25 1·25
576 85 c. multicoloured .. .. 1·25 1·25
577 $1.50, multicoloured .. .. 2·25 2·25
578 $1.85, multicoloured .. .. 2·50 2·50
575/8 .. .. .. *Set of 4* 6·50 6·50
MS579 92×120 mm. As Nos. 575/8, but each with a face value of 95 c. .. .. 8·00 9·00
MS580 96×85 mm. $6 "Virgin with Garland" (*diamond,* 56×56 *mm*). P 13 .. 10·00 11·00

84 Chariot Racing and Athletics

(Des G. Vasarhelyi. Litho Questa)

1988 (22 Aug). *Olympic Games, Seoul. T* **84** *and similar horiz designs showing ancient and modern Olympic sports. Multicoloured.* P 14½.
581 70 c. Type **84** .. .. .. 1·25 1·25
582 85 c. Greek runners and football .. 1·40 1·40
583 95 c. Greek wrestling and handball .. 1·60 1·60
584 $1.40, Greek hoplites and tennis .. 2·25 2·25
581/4 .. .. .. *Set of 4* 6·00 6·00
MS585 103×101 mm. As Nos. 581 and 584, but each with face value of $2 .. .. 6·00 7·00

1988 (10 Oct). *Olympic Medal Winners, Los Angeles. Nos.* 581/4 *optd as T* **235** *of Cook Islands.*
586 70 c. Type **84** (optd "FLORENCE GRIFFTH JOYNER UNITED STATES 100 M AND 200 M") .. .. .. 1·10 1·25
587 85 c. Greek runners and football (optd "GELINDO BORDIN ITALY MARA-THON") .. .. 1·25 1·40
588 95 c. Greek wrestling and handball (optd "HITOSHI SAITO JAPAN JUDO") .. 1·40 1·60
589 $1.40, Greek hoplites and tennis (optd "STEFFI GRAF WEST GERMANY WOMEN'S TENNIS") .. .. 2·00 2·25
586/9 .. .. .. *Set of 4* 5·25 6·00

85 "Adoration of the Shepherds" (detail)

1988 (2 Nov). *Christmas. T* **85** *and similar multicoloured designs showing paintings by Rembrandt.* P 13½.
590 55 c. Type **85** .. .. .. 1·25 1·25
591 70 c. "The Holy Family" .. .. 1·50 1·50
592 85 c. "Presentation in the Temple" .. 1·60 1·60
593 95 c. "The Holy Family" (*different*) .. 1·75 1·75
594 $1.15, "Presentation in the Temple" (*different*) .. .. .. 1·90 1·90
590/4 .. .. .. *Set of 5* 7·25 7·25
MS595 85 × 101 mm. $4.50, As Type **85** but 52 × 34 mm. P 14 .. .. 5·50 6·50

86 H.M.S. *Bounty* leaving Spithead and King George III

(Des Jennifer Toombs)

1989 (3 July). *Bicentenary of Discovery of Aitutaki by Capt. Bligh. T* **86** *and similar horiz designs. Multicoloured.* P 13½×13.
596 55 c. Type **86** .. .. .. 1·75 1·75
597 65 c. Breadfruit plants .. .. 2·00 2·00
598 75 c. Old chart showing Aitutaki and Capt. Bligh .. .. 2·25 2·25
599 95 c. Native outrigger and H.M.S. *Bounty* off Aitutaki .. .. .. 2·50 2·50
600 $1.65, Fletcher Christian confronting Bligh .. .. 3·00 3·00
596/600 .. .. .. *Set of 5* 10·50 10·50
MS601 94×72 mm. $4.20, "Mutineers casting Bligh adrift" (Robert Dodd) (60×45 *mm*). P 13½ 7·50 8·50

87 "Apollo 11" Astronaut on Moon   88 Virgin Mary

1989 (28 July). *20th Anniv of First Manned Landing on Moon. T* **87** *and similar horiz designs. Multicoloured.* P 13½×13.
602 75 c. Type **87** .. .. .. 1·25 1·25
603 $1.15, Conducting experiment on Moon .. 1·75 1·75
604 $1.80, Astronaut on Moon carrying equipment .. .. .. 2·50 2·50
602/4 .. .. .. *Set of 3* 5·00 5·00
MS605 105×86 mm. $6.40, Astronaut on Moon with U.S. flag (40×27 *mm*). P 13½ .. 6·00 7·50

1989 (20 Nov). *Christmas. T* **88** *and similar vert designs showing details from "Virgin in the Glory" by Titian. Multicoloured.* P 13½×13.
606 70 c. Type **88** .. .. .. 1·60 1·60
607 85 c. Christ Child .. .. 2·00 2·00
608 95 c. Angel .. .. .. 2·25 2·25
609 $1.25, Cherubs .. .. .. 2·75 2·75
606/9 .. .. .. *Set of 4* 7·75 7·75
MS610 80×100 mm. $6 "Virgin in the Glory" (45×60 *mm*). P 13½ .. .. 8·00 9·00

89 Human Comet striking Earth   (90) Ninetieth Birthday

1990 (16 Feb). *Protection of the Environment. T* **89** *and similar horiz design. Multicoloured.* P 13½×13.
611 $1.75, Type **89** .. .. .. 2·25 2·25
  a. Horiz pair. Nos. 611/12 .. 4·50 4·50
612 $1.75, Comet's tail .. .. 2·25 2·25
MS613 108×43 mm. $3 As Nos. 611/12 .. 3·50 4·50
Nos. 611/12 were printed together, *se-tenant,* in horizontal pairs throughout the sheet, each pair forming a composite design.

1990 (16 July). *90th Birthday of Queen Elizabeth the Queen Mother. No.* MS550 *optd with T* **90** *in black on gold on each stamp.*
MS614 132×82 mm. Nos. 523/6 .. .. 8·00 9·00

91 "Madonna of the Basket" (Correggio)   (92) COMMEMORATING 65th BIRTHDAY OF H.M. QUEEN ELIZABETH II

(Litho Questa)

1990 (28 Nov). *Christmas. Religious Paintings. T* **91** *and similar multicoloured designs. Ordinary paper.* P 14.
615 70 c. Type **91** .. .. .. 1·25 1·25
616 85 c. "Virgin and Child" (Morando) .. 1·40 1·40
617 95 c. "Adoration of the Child" (Tiepolo) .. 1·50 1·50
618 $1.75, "Mystic Marriage of St. Catherine" (Memling) .. .. .. 2·25 2·25
615/18 .. .. .. *Set of 4* 5·75 5·75
MS619 165×93 mm. $6 "Donne Triptych" (Memling) (*horiz*) .. .. 7·00 8·00

1990 (5 Dec). *"Birdpex '90" Stamp Exhibition, Christchurch, New Zealand. Nos. 349/50 optd as T* **245** *of Cook Islands.*
620 $1 Blue-headed Flycatcher .. .. 2·50 2·50
621 $2 Red-bellied Flycatcher .. .. 3·50 3·50

1991 (22 Apr). *65th Birthday of Queen Elizabeth II. No. 352 optd with T 92.*

522 $5 Flat-billed Kingfisher (*Halcyon recurvirostris*) .. .. 7·00 8·00

93 "The Holy Family" 94 Hurdling
(A. Mengs)

(Des G. Vasarhelyi. Litho Questa)

1991 (13 Nov). *Christmas. Religious Paintings. T 93 and similar vert designs. Multicoloured. Ordinary paper. P 14.*

623 80 c. Type 93 .. .. .. 1·25 1·25
624 90 c. "Virgin and the Child" (Lippi) .. 1·40 1·40
625 $1.05, "Virgin and Child" (A. Dürer) .. 1·60 1·60
626 $1.75, "Adoration of the Shepherds" (G. de la Tour) .. .. .. 2·25 2·25
623/6 .. .. .. *Set of 4* 6·00 6·00
MS627 79×103 mm. $6 "The Holy Family" (Michelangelo) .. .. .. 8·00 9·00

(Des G. Vasarhelyi. Litho B.D.T.)

1992 (29 July). *Olympic Games, Barcelona. T 94 and similar horiz designs. Multicoloured. Ordinary paper. P 14.*

628 95 c. Type 94 .. .. .. 1·25 1·25
629 $1.25, Weightlifting .. .. 1·60 1·60
630 $1.50, Judo .. .. .. 2·00 2·00
631 $1.95, Football .. .. .. 2·40 2·40
628/31 .. .. .. *Set of 4* 6·50 6·50

95 Vaka Motu Canoe 96 "Virgin's Nativity"
(detail) (Reni)

(Litho B.D.T.)

1992 (16 Oct). *6th Festival of Pacific Arts, Rarotonga. T 95 and similar horiz designs showing sailing canoes. Multicoloured. Ordinary paper. P 14×15.*

632 30 c. Type 95 .. .. .. 65 65
633 50 c. Hamatafua 80 80
634 95 c. Alia Kalia Ndrua .. .. 1·50 1·50
635 $1.75, Hokule'a Hawaiian .. .. 2·25 2·50
636 $1.95, Tuamotu Pahi .. .. 2·50 2·75
632/6 .. .. .. *Set of 5* 7·00 7·50

1992 (16 Oct). *Royal Visit by Prince Edward. Nos. 632/6 optd with T 254 of Cook Islands.*

637 30 c. Type 95 .. .. .. 75 75
638 50 c. Hamatafua .. .. .. 1·00 1·00
639 95 c. Alia Kalia Ndrua .. .. 1·75 1·75
640 $1.75, Hokule'a Hawaiian .. .. 2·50 2·75
641 $1.95, Tuamotu Pahi .. .. 2·50 2·75
637/41 .. .. .. *Set of 5* 7·75 8·00

1992 (19 Nov). *Christmas. Different details from "Virgin's Nativity" by Guido Reni. T 96 and similar vert designs. Ordinary paper. P 13½.*

642 80 c. multicoloured .. .. 1·25 1·25
643 90 c. multicoloured .. .. 1·40 1·40
644 $1.05, multicoloured .. .. 1·60 1·60
645 $1.75, multicoloured .. .. 2·25 2·25
642/5 .. .. .. *Set of 4* 6·00 6·00
MS646 101×86 mm. $6 multicoloured (as $1.05, but larger (36×46 mm)) .. .. 5·50 6·50

97 The Departure from Palos

(Litho B.D.T.)

1992 (11 Dec). *500th Anniv of Discovery of America by Columbus. T 97 and similar horiz designs. Multicoloured. Ordinary paper. P 14×15.*

647 $1.25, Type 97 .. .. .. 2·00 2·25
648 $1.75, Map of voyages .. .. 2·50 2·75
649 $1.95, Columbus and crew in New World 2·75 3·00
647/9 .. .. .. *Set of 3* 6·50 7·00

98 Queen Victoria and King
Edward VII

(Litho B.D.T.)

1993 (4 June). *40th Anniv of Coronation. T 98 and similar horiz designs. Multicoloured. P 14.*

650 $1.75, Type 98 .. .. .. 2·25 2·25
  a. Horiz strip. Nos. 650/2 .. 6·00
651 $1.75, King George V and King George VI 2·25 2·25
652 $1.75, Queen Elizabeth II in 1953 and 1993 2·25 2·25
650/2 .. .. .. *Set of 3* 6·00 6·00
  Nos. 650/2 were printed together, *se-tenant*, in horizontal strips of 3 throughout the sheet.

99 "Madonna and 100 Ice Hockey
Child" (Nino Pisano)

1993 (29 Oct). *Christmas. Religious Sculptures. T 99 and similar vert designs. Multicoloured. Ordinary paper. P 13½ ($3) or 14 (others).*

653 80 c. Type 99 .. .. .. 80 80
654 90 c. "Virgin on Rosebush" (Luca della Robbia) 85 85
655 $1.15, "Virgin with Child and St. John" (Juan Francisco Rustici) .. 1·25 1·25
656 $1.95, "Virgin with Child" (Miguel Angel) 2·00 2·00
657 $3 "Madonna and Child" (Jacopo della Quercia) (32×47 mm) .. 3·00 3·00
653/7 .. .. .. *Set of 7* 7·00 7·00

(Litho B.D.T.)

1994 (11 Feb). *Winter Olympic Games, Lillehammer. T 100 and similar horiz designs. Multicoloured. P 14.*

658 $1.15, Type 100 .. .. .. 1·75 1·75
  a. Horiz strip of 3. Nos. 658/60 .. 4·75
659 $1.15, Ski-jumping .. .. 1·75 1·75
660 $1.15, Cross-country skiing .. 1·75 1·75
658/60 .. .. .. *Set of 3* 4·75 4·75
  Nos. 658/60 were printed together, *se-tenant*, in horizontal strips of 3 throughout the sheet.

101 *Ipomoea pes-caprae* 102 Cook Islands and U.S.A.
Flags with Astronauts Collins,
Armstrong and Aldrin

(Des G. Drummond. Litho Questa ($3, $5, $8), B.D.T. (others))

1994 (17 Feb)–97. *Flowers. T 101 and similar vert designs. Multicoloured. P 13½×14 ($3, $5, $8) or 13½ (others).*

661 5 c. Type 101 .. .. .. 10 10
662 10 c. *Plumeria alba* 10 10
663 15 c. *Hibiscus rosa-sinensis* .. 15 20
664 20 c. *Allamanda cathartica* .. 15 20
665 25 c. *Delonix regia* 20 25
666 30 c. *Gardenia taitensis* 20 25
667 50 c. *Plumeria rubra* 35 40
668 80 c. *Ipomoea littoralis* 60 65
669 85 c. *Hibiscus tiliaceus* 60 65
670 90 c. *Erythrina variegata* 65 70
671 $1 *Solandra nitida* (29.4.94) .. 75 80
672 $2 *Cordia subcordata* (29.4.94) .. 1·50 1·60
673 $3 *Hibiscus rosa-sinensis* (*different*) (34×47 mm) (18.11.94) .. 2·25 2·40
674 $5 As $3 (34×47 mm) (18.11.94) .. 3·75 4·00
675 $8 As $3 (34×47 mm) (21.11.97) .. 6·00 6·25
661/75 .. .. .. *Set of 15* 17·00 18·00
  Nos. 671/5 include a portrait of Queen Elizabeth II at top right.

(Des G. Vasarhelyi. Litho B.D.T.)

1994 (20 July). *25th Anniv of First Moon Landing. T 102 and similar horiz design. Multicoloured. P 14.*

676 $2 Type 102 .. .. .. 3·00 3·00
  a. Pair. Nos. 676/7 .. .. 6·00 6·00
677 $2 "Apollo 11" re-entering atmosphere and landing in sea .. .. 3·00 3·00
  Nos. 676/7 were printed together, *se-tenant*, in horizontal or vertical pairs throughout the sheet.

103 "The Madonna 104 Battle of Britain
of the Basket"
(Correggio)

(Litho B.D.T.)

1994 (30 Nov). *Christmas. Religious Paintings. T 103 and similar vert designs. Multicoloured. P 14.*

678 85 c. Type 103 .. .. .. 1·00 1·10
  a. Block of 4. Nos. 678/81 .. 3·50
679 85 c. "The Virgin and Child with Saints" (Memling) .. .. .. 1·00 1·10
680 85 c. "The Virgin and Child with Flowers" (Dolci) .. .. .. 1·00 1·10
681 85 c. "The Virgin and Child with Angels" (Bergognone) .. .. 1·00 1·10
682 90 c. "Adoration of the Kings" (Dosso) 1·00 1·10
  a. Block of 4. Nos. 682/5 .. 3·50
683 90 c. "The Virgin and Child" (Bellini) 1·00 1·10
684 90 c. "The Virgin and Child" (Schiavone) 1·00 1·10
685 90 c. "Adoration of the Kings" (Dolci) 1·00 1·10
678/85 .. .. .. *Set of 8* 7·00 8·00
  Nos. 678/81 and 682/5 were printed together, *se-tenant*, in blocks of 4 throughout the sheets.
  No. 678 is inscribed "Corregio" in error.

(Litho B.D.T.)

1995 (4 Sept). *50th Anniv of End of Second World War. T 104 and similar horiz design. Multicoloured. P 13.*

686 $4 Type 104 .. .. .. 5·50 6·00
  a. Pair. Nos. 686/7 .. .. 11·00 12·00
687 $4 Battle of Midway .. .. 5·50 6·00
  Nos. 686/7 were printed together, *se-tenant* horizontally and vertically, in sheets of 4.

105 Queen Elizabeth the
Queen Mother

(Des G. Vasarhelyi. Litho B.D.T.)

1995 (14 Sept). *95th Birthday of Queen Elizabeth the Queen Mother. P 13.*

688 105 $4 multicoloured .. .. 5·00 5·50

106 Globe, Doves, United Nations
Emblem and Headquarters

(Des G. Vasarhelyi. Litho B.D.T.)

1995 (18 Oct). *50th Anniv of United Nations. P 13×13½.*

689 106 $4.25, multicoloured .. .. 4·50 5·00

107 Green Turtle

(Litho B.D.T.)

1995 (1 Dec). *Year of the Sea Turtle. T* **107** *and similar horiz designs. Multicoloured. P* 13½×14.

690	95 c. Type **107**	..	..	1·50	1·50
691	$1.15, Leatherback Turtle		..	1·75	1·75
692	$1.50, Olive Ridley Turtle		..	2·00	2·00
693	$1.75, Loggerhead Turtle		..	2·50	2·50
690/3	..	..	*Set of* 4	7·00	7·00

108 Queen Elizabeth II

(Des G. Vasarhelyi. Litho)

1996 (24 June). *70th Birthday of Queen Elizabeth II. P* 14.

694	**108**	$4.50, multicoloured	..	..	6·00	6·50

109 Baron Pierre de Coubertin, Torch and Opening of 1896 Olympic Games

(Des G. Vasarhelyi. Litho)

1996 (11 July). *Centenary of Modern Olympic Games. T* **109** *and similar horiz design. Multicoloured. P* 14.

695	$2 Type **109**		..	2·75	3·00
	a. Pair. Nos. 695/6		..	5·50	6·00
696	$2 Athletes and American flag, 1996		..	2·75	3·00

Nos. 695/6 were printed together, *se-tenant*, in horizontal and vertical pairs within sheets of four.

110 Princess Elizabeth and Lieut. Philip Mountbatten with King George VI and Queen Elizabeth, 1947

1997 (20 Nov). *Golden Wedding of Queen Elizabeth and Prince Philip. P* 14.

697	**110**	$2.50, multicoloured	..	1·75	1·90
MS698	76×102 mm. **110** $6 multicoloured		..	4·50	4·75

STAMP BOOKLETS

1982 (June). *Royal Wedding. Cover as No. SB1 of Cook Islands, but inscr* "Aitutaki".

SB1	$5.60, booklet containing 60 c. and 80 c. (Nos. 391/2), each in block of 4	..	..	5·50

OFFICIAL STAMPS

O.H.M.S.

(O 1)

1978 (3 Nov)–**79**. *Nos.* 98/105, 107/10 *and* 227/8 *optd or surch (Nos. O8/9 and O15) as Type O* 1.

O 1	1 c. New Caledonia Nautilus (*Nautilus macromphallus*)		90	10
O 2	2 c. Common or Major Harp (*Harpa major*)	1·00	10
O 3	3 c. Striped Bonnet (*Phalium flammiferum*)	..	1·00	10
O 4	4 c. Mole Cowrie (*Cypraea talpa*) (Gold)	1·00	10
O 5	5 c. Pontifical Mitre (*Mitra stictica*)	..	1·00	10
O 6	8 c. Trumpet Triton (*Charonia tritonis*)	..	1·25	10
O 7	10 c. Venus Comb Murex (*Murex pecten*)	1·50	15
O 8	15 c. on 60 c. Widest Pacific Conch (*Strombus latissimus*)	..	2·50	20
O 9	18 c. on 60 c. Widest Pacific Conch (*Strombus latissimus*)	..	2·50	20
O10	20 c. Red-mouth Olive (*Oliva miniacea miniacea*) (Gold)	..	2·50	20
O11	50 c. Union Jack, Queen Victoria and island map	..	1·00	55
O12	60 c. Widest Pacific Conch (*Strombus latissimus*)	..	9·00	70
O13	$1 Maple-leaf Triton or Winged Frog Shell (*Biplex perca*)	..	9·00	85
O14	$2 Queen Elizabeth II and Marlin-spike Auger (*Terebra maculata*) (20.2.79)	9·00	1·00
O15	$4 on $1 Balcony scene, 1953 (Sil.) (20.2.79)	..	2·50	1·00
O16	$5 Queen Elizabeth II and Tiger Cowrie (*Cypraea tigris*) (20.2.79)	11·00	1·75
O1/16	..	..	*Set of* 16	50·00	6·00

These stamps were originally only sold to the public cancelled-to-order and not in unused condition.

They were made available to overseas collectors in mint condition during 1980.

75c

O.H.M.S. O.H.M.S.

(O 2)   (O 3)

1985 (9 Aug)–**90**. (*a*) *Nos.* 351/2, 475 *and* 477/94 *optd or surch as Type O* **2** *by foil embossing in blue* ($14, $18) *or emerald (others).*

O17	2 c. Type **65**	..	..	..	10	10
O18	5 c. Scarlet Robin	..	..	..	10	10
O19	10 c. Golden Whistler	..	..	10	10
O20	12 c. Rufous Fantail	..	..	10	10
O21	18 c. Peregrine Falcon	..	..	15	20
O22	20 c. on 24 c. Barn Owl	..	..	15	20
O23	30 c. Java Sparrow	..	..	20	25
O24	40 c. on 36 c. White-breasted Wood Swallow	30	35
O25	50 c. Rock Dove	..	..	35	40
O26	55 c. on 48 c. Tahitian Lory	..	..	40	45
O27	60 c. Purple Swamphen	..	..	45	50
O28	65 c. on 72 c. Zebra Dove	..	..	50	55
O29	80 c. on 96 c. Chestnut-breasted Mannikin	50	55
O30	$1.20, Common Mynah (15.6.88)	..	1·00	1·10
O31	$2.10, Eastern Reef Heron (15.6.88)	..	1·50	1·60
O32	$3 Blue-headed Flycatcher (30×42 *mm*) (1.10.86)		2·25	2·50
O33	$4.20, Red-bellied Flycatcher (30×42 *mm*) (1.10.86)		3·25	3·50
O34	$5.60, Red Munia (30×42 *mm*) (1.10.86)	4·00	4·25
O35	$9.60, Flat-billed Kingfisher (30×42 *mm*) (1.10.86)		7·00	7·25
O36	$14 on $4 Red Munia (35×48 *mm*)	10·50	11·00
O37	$18 on $5 Flat-billed Kingfisher (35×48 *mm*) (2.7.90)	13·00	13·50

(*b*) *Nos.* 430/3 *surch as Type O* **3** *by gold foil embossing*

O38	75 c. on 48 c. Type **57**	..	..	55	60
O39	75 c. on 48 c. Ancient Ti'i image	..	55	60
O40	75 c. on 48 c. Tourist canoeing	..	55	60
O41	75 c. on 48 c. Captain William Bligh and chart	..	..	55	60
O17/41	..	..	..	*Set of* 25	48·00	50·00

1st CLASS STAMPS & SERVICE

Stanley Gibbons are pleased to offer a dedicated and completely free of charge service to today's discerning British Commonwealth collectors.

- Specialist database of clients' interests.
- Large stocks of specialised British Commonwealth material.
- Free advice from our team of experts.
- Regular advance lists and illustrated colour brochures.
- Private viewing facilities and postal approvals service.
- Specialist 'Wants List' service.
- We are always interested in buying quality collections and single items.

To take advantage of our free and highly specialised service contact us today on 0171 836 8444.

STANLEY GIBBONS

—— FIRST CLASS ——
STAMPS & SERVICE

**Stanley Gibbons Limited
399 Strand, London WC2R 0LX**

PENRHYN ISLAND

Stamps of COOK ISLANDS were used on Penrhyn Island from late 1901 until the issue of the surcharged stamps in May 1902.

PRICES FOR STAMPS ON COVER TO 1945

No. 1	*from* × 25
No. 3	—
Nos. 4/5	*from* × 25
Nos. 6/8	—
Nos. 9/10	*from* × 50
Nos. 11/13	—
Nos. 14/18	*from* × 3
Nos. 19/23	*from* × 2
Nos. 24/37	*from* × 3
Nos. 38/40	*from* × 5

A. NEW ZEALAND DEPENDENCY

The island of Penrhyn, under British protection from 20 September 1888, was annexed by New Zealand on 11 June 1901.

Stamps of New Zealand overprinted or surcharged. For illustrations of New Zealand watermarks and definitive types see the beginning of Cook Islands.

PENRHYN ISLAND.

½ PENI.

(1)

PENRHYN ISLAND.

TAI PENI.

(2) 1d.

PENRHYN ISLAND.

2½ PENI.

(3)

1902 (5 May). *T* **23, 27** *and* **42** *surch with T* **1, 2** *and* **3.**

(a) *Thick, soft Pirie paper. No wmk. P* 11

1	2½d. blue (No. 260) (R.)	..	2·25	6·00
	a. "½"and "P" spaced (all stamps in 8th vert row)	..	13·00	27·00

(b) *Thin, hard Basted Mills paper. W* **38** *of New Zealand.*

(i) *P* 11

3	1d. carmine (No. 286) (Br.)	..	..	£850	£900

(iii) *P* 14

4	½d. green (No. 287) (R.)	..	..	80	4·00
	a. No stop after "ISLAND"	..	£140	£180
5	1d. carmine (No. 288) (Br.)	..	..	3·25	13·00

(iii) *Perf compound of* 11 *and* 14

6	1d. carmine (No. 290) (Br.)	..	..	£750	£800

(iv) *Mixed perfs*

7	½d. green (No. 291) (R.)	..	..		£1000
8	1d. carmine (No. 292) (Br.)	..	..		£1200

(c) *Thin, hard Cowan paper. W* **43** *of New Zealand.* (i) *P* 14

9	½d. green (No. 302) (R.)	..		1·25	4·00
	a. No stop after "ISLAND" (R. 10/6)	..	£120	£150
10	1d. carmine (No. 303) (B.)	..		1·00	2·75
	a. No stop after "ISLAND" (R. 10/6)	..	45·00	70·00

(ii) *Perf compound of* 11 *and* 14

11	1d. carmine (No. 305) (B.)	..	..		£6000

(iii) *Mixed perfs*

12	½d. green (No. 306) (R.)	..	..	£1100	£1200
13	1d. carmine (No. 307) (B.)	..	..	£425	£475

PENRHYN ISLAND.

(4)

Toru Pene.

(5) 3d.

Ono Pene.

(6) 6d.

Tahi Silingi.

(7) 1s.

1903 (28 Feb). *T* **28, 31** *and* **34** *surch with name at top, T* **4,** *and values at foot, T* **5/7.** *Thin, hard Cowan paper. W* **43** *(sideways) of New Zealand. P* 11.

14	3d. yellow-brown (No. 309) (B.)	..	9·00	20·00
15	6d. rose-red (No. 312a) (B.)	..	15·00	32·00
16	1s. brown-red (No. 315) (B.)	..	48·00	55·00
	a. Bright red	..	45·00	48·00
	b. Orange-red	..	55·00	55·00
14/16		*Set of* 3	60·00	90·00

1914 (May)–**15.** *T* **51/2** *surch with T* **1** *(½d.) or optd with T* **4** *at top and surch with T* **6/7** *at foot.*

19	½d. yellow-green (No. 387) (C.) (5.14)	..	80	6·00
	a. No stop after "ISLAND"	..	30·00	70·00
	b. No stop after "PENI" (R. 3/17)	..	90·00	£160
	c. Vermilion opt (1.15)	..	80	6·00
	ca. No stop after "ISLAND"	..	10·00	42·00
	cb. No stop after "PENI" (R. 3/5, 3/17)	..	40·00	90·00
22	6d. carmine (No. 393) (B.) (8.14)	..	27·00	70·00
23	1s. vermilion (No. 394) (B.) (8.14)	..	45·00	95·00
19/23		*Set of* 3	65·00	£150

The "no stop after ISLAND" variety occurs on R. 1/4, 1/10, 1/16, 1/22, 6/4, 6/10, 6/16 and 6/22 of the carmine surcharge, No. 19, and on these positions plus R. 1/12, 1/24, 6/12 and 6/24 for the vermilion, No. 19c.

1917 (Nov)–**20.** *Optd as T* **4.**

(a) *T* **60** *(recess). W* **43** *of New Zealand. P* 14×13½.

24	2½d. blue (No. 419) (R.) (10.20)	..	3·00	7·00
	a. Perf 14×14½	..	2·00	4·25
	ab. No stop after "ISLAND" (R. 10/8)	..	£140	£250
	b. Vert pair. Nos. 24/4a	..	50·00	80·00
25	3d. chocolate (No. 420) (B.) (6.18)	..	12·00	60·00
	a. Perf 14×14½	..	9·50	60·00
	b. Vert pair. Nos. 25/5a	..	70·00	£190
26	6d. carmine (No. 425) (B.) (1.18)	..	8·00	23·00
	a. Perf 14×14½	..	5·00	15·00
	ab. No stop after "ISLAND" (R. 10/8)	..	£300	£450
	b. Vert pair. Nos. 26/6a	..	55·00	£120
27	1s. vermilion (No. 430) (B.) (12.17)	..	15·00	38·00
	a. Perf 14×14½	..	12·00	28·00
	ab. No stop after "ISLAND" (R. 10/8)	..	£325	£475
	b. Vert pair. Nos. 27/7a	..	£110	£200
24/7		*Set of* 4	25·00	95·00

(b) *T* **61** *(typo). W* **43** *of New Zealand. P* 14×15

28	½d. green (No. 435) (R.) (2.20)	..	1·00	2·00
	a. No stop after "ISLAND" (R. 2/24)	..	85·00	£120
	b. Narrow spacing	..	6·00	8·50
29	1½d. slate (No. 437) (R.)	..	6·50	13·00
	a. Narrow spacing	..	18·00	35·00
30	1½d. orange-brown (No. 438) (R.) (2.19)	..	60	13·00
	a. Narrow spacing	..	5·00	35·00
31	3d. chocolate (No. 440) (B.) (6.19)	..	3·50	15·00
	a. Narrow spacing	..	15·00	45·00
28/31		*Set of* 4	10·50	38·00

The narrow spacing variety occurs on R. 1/5–8, 4/21–4, 7/5–8 and 9/21–4.

(Recess P.B.)

1920 (23 Aug). *As T* **9/14** *of Cook Islands, but inscr* "PENRHYN". *No wmk. P* 14.

32	½d. black and emerald	..	1·00	11·00
	a. Part imperf block of 4	..	£1200	
33	1d. black and deep red	..	1·50	11·00
	a. Double derrick flaw (R.2/8, 3/6 or 5/2)	5·50	
34	1½d. black and deep violet	..	6·50	17·00
35	3d. black and red	..	2·50	7·50
36	6d. red-brown and sepia	..	3·25	20·00
37	1s. black and slate-blue	..	10·00	22·00
32/7		*Set of* 6	22·00	80·00

No. 32a comes from sheets on which two rows were imperforate between horizontally and the second row additionally imperforate vertically.

Examples of the ½d. and 1d. with centre inverted were not supplied to the Post Office.

(Recess Govt Printing Office, Wellington)

1927–29. *As T* **9/10** *and* **16** *of Cook Islands, but inscr* "PENRHYN". *W* **43.** *P* 14.

38	½d. black and green (5.29)	..	5·00	17·00
39	1d. black and deep carmine (14.3.28)	..	5·50	13·00
	a. Double derrick flaw (R.2/8, 3/6 or 5/2)	16·00	
40	2½d. red-brown and dull blue (10.27)	..	2·75	21·00
38/40	..	*Set of* 3	12·00	45·00

> Cook Islands stamps superseded those of Penrhyn Islands on 15 March 1932. Separate issues were resumed in 1973.

B. PART OF COOK ISLANDS

The following issues are for use in all the islands of the Northern Cook Islands group.

(New Currency. 100 cents = 1 dollar)

PRINTERS. The notes above No. 33 of Aitutaki concerning printers and gum also apply here. Stamps printed by Fournier from No. 472 onwards are in lithography.

PENRHYN

NORTHERN

(8)

PENRHYN

NORTHERN

(9)

1973 (24 Oct–14 Nov). *Nos.* **228/45** *of Cook Is optd with T* **8** *(without "NORTHERN" on* $1, $2).
A. *Without fluorescent security markings. Gum arabic*
B. *With fluorescent security markings. PVA gum*

				A.		B.	
41	1 c. multicoloured	..	..	80	—	10	10
42	2 c. multicoloured	..	..	1·25	—	10	10
43	3 c. multicoloured	..	..	1·75	—	20	10
44	4 c. multicoloured (No. 233)	..	2·00	—	10	10
	a. Optd on Cook Is No. 232	..	24·00	—		†
45	5 c. multicoloured	..	..	2·50	—	10	10
46	6 c. multicoloured	..	..	2·50	—	20	30
47	8 c. multicoloured	..	..	2·75	—	30	40
48	15 c. multicoloured	..	..	4·25	—	45	50
49	20 c. multicoloured	..	..		†	1·50	80
50	50 c. multicoloured	..	..	10·00	—	90	1·75
51	$1 multicoloured	..	..	12·00	—	90	2·25
52	$2 multicoloured (14.11)	..	15·00	—	90	2·50
41A/52A	..	*Set of* 11	50·00	—		†
41B/52B	..	*Set of* 12		†	5·00	7·50

1973 (14 Nov). *Royal Wedding. Nos.* **450/2** *of Cook Is optd as T* **9,** *in silver.*

53	138 25 c. multicoloured	..	30	30
54	— 30 c. multicoloured	..	30	20
55	— 50 c. multicoloured	..	30	30
53/5	..	*Set of* 3	80	55

10 Yellow Boxfish	**11** Penrhyn Stamps of 1902

1974 (15 Aug)–**75.** *Multicoloured.* (a) *T* **10** *and similar horiz designs showing fishes. P* 13½.

56	½ c. Type 10	..	..	50	50
57	1 c. Diamond Fingerfish	..	..	70	50
58	2 c. Emperor Angelfish	..	..	80	50
59	3 c. Copper-banded Butterflyfish	..	80	50
60	4 c. Ornate Butterflyfish	..	..	80	50
61	5 c. Black-backed Butterflyfish	..	80	50
62	8 c. Latticed Butterflyfish	..	..	80	50
63	10 c. Saddle Butterflyfish	..	..	85	50
64	20 c. Regal Angelfish	..	..	1·75	50
65	25 c. Pennant Coralfish	..	..	1·75	50
66	60 c. Harlequin Sweetlips	..	..	2·50	90
67	$1 *Balistipus undulatus*	..	..	2·75	1·25

(b) *Larger designs,* 63×25 *mm. P* 13×12½.

68	$2 Birds-eye view of Penrhyn (12.2.75)	..	4·50	12·00
69	$5 Satellite view of Australasia (12.3.75)	..	4·50	6·00
56/69	..	..	..	*Set of* 14	21·00 23·00

1974 (27 Sept). *Centenary of Universal Postal Union. T* **11** *and similar vert design. Multicoloured. P* 13.

70	25 c. Type 11	..	..	20	20
71	50 c. Stamps of 1920	..	..	35	35

Each value was issued in sheets of 8 stamps and 1 label.

12 "Adoration of the Kings" (Memling)

1974 (30 Oct). *Christmas. T* **12** *and similar horiz designs. Multicoloured. P* 13.

72	5 c. Type 12	..	..	25	25
73	10 c. "Adoration of the Shepherds" (Hugo van der Goes)	..	30	25
74	25 c. "Adoration of the Magi" (Rubens)	..	50	35
75	30 c. "The Holy Family" (Borgianni)	..	60	50
72/5	..		*Set of* 4	1·50	1·25

13 Churchill giving "V" Sign	**(14)**

1974 (30 Nov). *Birth Centenary of Sir Winston Churchill. T* **13** *and similar vert design. P* 13.

76	30 c. agate and gold	..	..	35	85
77	50 c. myrtle-green and gold	..	..	45	90

Design:—50 c. Full-face portrait.

1975 (24 July). *"Apollo-Soyuz" Space Project. No.* **69** *optd with T* **14.**

78	$5 Satellite view of Australasia	..	2·00	2·75

15 "Virgin and Child" (Bouts)	**16** "Pietà"

1975 (21 Nov). *Christmas. T* **15** *and similar vert designs showing the "Virgin and Child". Multicoloured. P* 14 × 13.

79	7 c. Type 15	..	..	40	10
80	15 c. Leonardo da Vinci	..	..	70	20
81	35 c. Raphael	..	..	1·10	35
79/81	..		*Set of* 3	2·00	60

1976 (19 Mar). *Easter and 500th Birth Anniv of Michelangelo. T* **16** *and similar vert designs. P* 14 × 13.

82	15 c. sepia and gold		25	15
83	20 c. blackish purple and gold		30	15
84	35 c. myrtle-green and gold		40	20
82/4		*Set of 3*	85	45

MS85 112 × 72 mm. Nos. 82/4 .. .. 85 1·25
Each value was issued in sheets of 8 stamps and 1 label.

17 "Washington crossing the **18** Running
Delaware" (E. Leutze)

1976 (20 May). *Bicentenary of American Revolution. T* **17** *and similar vert designs. Multicoloured. P* 13.

86	30 c.		30	15
87	30 c.	Type **17**	30	15
88	30 c.		30	15
89	50 c.		40	20
90	50 c.	"The Spirit of '76" (A. M. Willard)	40	20
91	50 c.		40	20
86/91		*Set of 6*	1·90	95

MS92 103 × 103 mm. Nos. 86/91. P 13 .. 2·50 3·00
Nos. 86/8 and 89/91 were each printed together, *se-tenant*, in horizontal strips of 3 throughout the sheet, forming composite designs. Each sheet includes 3 stamp-size labels. Type **17** shows the left-hand stamp of the 30 c. design.

1976 (9 July). *Olympic Games, Montreal. T* **18** *and similar horiz designs. Multicoloured. P* 14.

93	25 c. Type **18**		25	15
94	30 c. Long Jumping		30	15
95	75 c. Throwing the Javelin		55	25
93/5		*Set of 3*	1·00	50

MS96 86 × 128 mm. Nos. 93/5. P 14 × 13 1·50 2·00

19 "The Flight into Egypt" **20** The Queen in
Coronation Robes

1976 (20 Oct). *Christmas. Dürer Engravings. T* **19** *and similar horiz designs. P* 13.

97	7 c. black and silver		15	10
98	15 c. steel blue and silver		25	15
99	35 c. violet and silver		35	25
97/9		*Set of 3*	65	45

Designs:—15 c. "Adoration of the Magi"; 35 c. "The Nativity".

1977 (24 Mar). *Silver Jubilee. T* **20** *and similar vert designs. Multicoloured. P* 13.

100	50 c. Type **20**		25	60
101	$1 Queen and Prince Philip		35	65
102	$2 Queen Elizabeth II		50	80
100/2		*Set of 3*	1·00	1·90

MS103 128 × 87 mm. Nos. 100/2. P 13 1·00 1·50
Stamps from the miniature sheet have silver borders.

21 "The Annunciation" **22** Iiwi

1977 (23 Sept). *Christmas. T* **21** *and similar designs showing illustrations by J. S. von Carolsfeld. P* 13.

104	7 c. light stone, purple-brown and gold		40	15
105	15 c. pale rose, deep maroon and gold		60	15
106	35 c. blackish green, pale green and gold		90	30
104/6		*Set of 3*	1·75	55

Designs:—15 c. "The Announcement to the Shepherds"; 35 c. "The Nativity".

1978 (19 Jan). *Bicentenary of Discovery of Hawaii. T* **22** *and similar vert designs showing Hawaiian birds or artefacts. Multicoloured. P* 13.

107	20 c. Type **22**		80	30
108	20 c. Elgin cloak		80	30
109	30 c. Apapane		90	40
110	30 c. Feather image of a god		90	40
111	35 c. Moorhen		90	45

112	35 c. Feather cape, helmet and staff		90	45
113	75 c. Hawaii O-o		1·50	80
114	75 c. Feather image and cloak		1·50	80
107/14		*Set of 8*	7·50	3·50

MS115 Two sheets each 78 × 119 mm containing
(a) Nos. 107, 109, 111, 113; (b) Nos. 108, 110, 112,
114 .. .. 6·50 8·50
Nos. 107/8, 109/10, 111/12 and 113/14 were each printed together, *se-tenant*, in horizontal and vertical pairs throughout the sheet.

23 "The Road to **24** Royal Coat of Arms
Calvary"

1978 (10 Mar). *Easter and 400th Birth Anniv of Rubens. T* **23** *and similar vert designs. Multicoloured. P* 13.

116	10 c. Type **23**		20	10
117	15 c. "Christ on the Cross"		25	15
118	35 c. "Christ with Straw"		45	25
116/18		*Set of 3*	80	45

MS119 87 × 138 mm. Nos. 116/18 .. 1·00 1·40
Stamps from No. MS119 are slightly larger (28 × 36 mm.)

1978 (17 Apr). *Easter. Children's Charity. Designs as Nos. 116/18 in separate miniature sheets. 49 × 68 mm, each with a face value of* 60 *c.* + 5 *c. P* 12½–13.
MS120 As Nos. 116/18 .. *Set of 3 sheets* 90 1·50

1978 (24 May). *25th Anniv of Coronation. T* **24** *and similar vert designs. P* 13.

121	90 c. black, gold and deep lilac		30	60
122	90 c. multicoloured		30	60
123	90 c. black, gold and deep bluish green		30	60
121/3		*Set of 3*	80	1·60

MS124 75 × 122 mm. Nos. 121/3 .. 1·10 2·00
Designs:—No. 122, Queen Elizabeth II; No. 123, New Zealand coat of arms.
Nos. 121/3 were printed together in small sheets of 6, containing two *se-tenant* strips of 3, with horizontal gutter margin between.

25 "Madonna of the **26** Sir Rowland Hill and G.B.
Pear" Penny Black Stamp

1978 (29 Nov). *Christmas. 450th Death Anniv of Dürer. T* **25** *and similar vert design. Multicoloured. P* 14.

125	30 c. Type **25**		65	30
126	35 c. "The Virgin and Child with St. Anne"		65	30

MS127 101 × 60 mm. Nos. 125/6. P 13½ .. 1·50 1·75
Nos. 125/6 were each printed in small sheets of 6.

1979 (26 Sept). *Death Centenary of Sir Rowland Hill. T* **26** *and similar vert designs. Multicoloured. P* 13½ × 14.

128	75 c. Type **26**		60	65
129	75 c. 1974 Centenary of Universal Postal Union 25 c. and 50 c. commemoratives		60	65
130	90 c. Sir Rowland Hill		70	80
131	90 c. 1978 25th anniv of Coronation 90 c. (Queen Elizabeth II) commemorative		70	80
128/31		*Set of 4*	2·40	2·75

MS132 116 × 58 mm. Nos. 128/31 .. 1·90 2·75
Stamps from No. MS132 have cream backgrounds.
Nos. 128/9 and 130/1 were each printed together, *se-tenant*, in horizontal and vertical pairs throughout small sheets of 8.

27 Max and Moritz **28** "Christ carrying Cross"
(Book of Ferdinand II)

1979 (20 Nov). *International Year of the Child. Illustrations from Max and Moritz stories by Wilhelm Busch. T* **27** *and similar horiz designs. Multicoloured. P* 13.

133	12 c. Type **27**		20	10
134	12 c. Max and Moritz looking down chimney		20	10
135	12 c. Max and Moritz making off with food		20	10
136	12 c. Cook about to beat dog		20	10
137	15 c. Max sawing through bridge		25	10

138	15 c. Pursuer approaching bridge		25	10
139	15 c. Bridge collapsing under pursuer		25	10
140	15 c. Pursuer in river		25	10
141	20 c. Baker locking shop		30	20
142	20 c. Max and Moritz coming out of hiding		30	20
143	20 c. Max and Moritz falling in dough		30	20
144	20 c. Max and Moritz after being rolled into buns by baker		30	20
133/44		*Set of 12*	2·75	1·50

Nos. 133/6, 137/40 and 141/4 were each printed together, *se-tenant*, in sheets of 4, either with or without labels containing extracts from the books on the top and bottom selvedge.

1980 (28 Mar). *Easter. Scenes from 15th-century Prayer Books. T* **28** *and similar vert designs. Multicoloured. P* 13.

145	12 c. Type **28**		15	20
146	20 c. "The Crucifixion" (William Vrelant, Book of Duke of Burgundy)		20	25
147	35 c. "Descent from the Cross" (Book of Ferdinand II)		30	45
145/7		*Set of 3*	55	80

MS148 111×65 mm. Nos. 145/7 .. 55 1·00
Stamps from No. MS148 have cream borders.

1980 (28 Mar). *Easter. Children's Charity. Designs as Nos. 145/7 in separate miniature sheets* 54 × 85 *mm, each with a face value of* 70 *c.* + 5 *c.*
MS149 As Nos. 145/7 .. *Set of 3 sheets* 75 1·00

29 "Queen Elizabeth, **30** Falk Hoffman, D.D.R.
1937" (Sir Gerald Kelly) (platform diving) (gold)

1980 (17 Sept). *80th Birthday of Queen Elizabeth the Queen Mother. P* 13.

150	**29** $1 multicoloured		1·25	1·25

MS151 55 × 84 mm. **29** $2.50 multicoloured .. 1·60 1·60

1980 (14 Nov). *Olympic Games, Moscow. Medal Winners. T* **30** *and similar vert designs. Multicoloured. P* 13½.

152	10 c. Type **30**		10	10
153	10 c. Martina Jaschke, D.D.R. (platform diving) (gold)		10	10
154	20 c. Tomi Polkolainen, Finland (archery) (gold)		15	15
155	20 c. Kete Losaberidse, U.S.S.R. (archery) (gold)		15	15
156	30 c. Czechoslovakia (football) (gold)		20	20
157	30 c. D.D.R. (football) (silver)		20	20
158	50 c. Barbel Wockel, D.D.R. (200-metre dash) (gold)		30	30
159	50 c. Pietro Mennea, Italy (200-metre dash) (gold)		30	30
152/9		*Set of 8*	1·40	1·40

MS160 150 × 106 mm. Nos. 152/9. P 13 .. 1·40 1·75
Stamps from No. MS160 have gold borders.
Nos. 152/3, 154/5, 156/7 and 158/9 were each printed together, *se-tenant*, in horizontal pairs throughout the sheet.

31 "The Virgin of Counsellors" **32** Amatasi
(Luis Dalmau)

1980 (5 Dec). *Christmas. Paintings. T* **31** *and similar vert designs. Multicoloured. P* 13.

161	20 c. Type **31**		15	15
162	35 c. "Virgin and Child" (Serra brothers)		20	20
163	50 c. "The Virgin of Albocacer" (Master of the Porciuncula)		30	30
161/3		*Set of 3*	60	60

MS164 135 × 75 mm. Nos. 161/3 .. 1·50 1·50

1980 (5 Dec). *Christmas. Children's Charity. Designs as Nos. 161/3 in separate miniature sheets,* 54 × 77 *mm, each with a face value of* 70 *c.* + 5 *c.*
MS165 As Nos. 161/3 .. *Set of 3 sheets* 1·50 1·50

1981 (16 Feb-21 Sept). *Sailing Craft and Ships (1st series). Multicoloured designs as T* **32**. *P* 14 *(Nos. 166/85),* 13 × 14½ *(Nos. 186/205) or* 13½ *(Nos. 206/8).*

166	1 c. Type **32**		20	15
167	1 c. Ndrua		20	15
168	1 c. Waka		20	15
169	1 c. Tongiaki		20	15
170	3 c. Va'a Teu'ua		40	15
171	3 c. *Vitoria,* 1500		40	15
172	3 c. *Golden Hind,* 1560		40	15
173	3 c. *Boudeuse,* 1760		40	15
174	4 c. H.M.S. *Bounty,* 1787		50	15
175	4 c. *L'Astrolabe,* 1811		50	15

176	4 c.	*Star of India*, 1861	.. .. ..	50	15
177	4 c.	*Great Republic*, 1853	.. ..	50	15
178	6 c.	*Balcutha*, 1886	..	50	20
179	6 c.	*Coonatto*, 1863	.. ..	50	20
180	6 c.	*Antiope*, 1866	..	50	20
181	6 c.	*Teaping*, 1863	..	50	20
182	10 c.	*Preussen*, 1902	.. ..	50	75
183	10 c.	*Pamir*, 1921	..	50	75
184	10 c.	*Cap Hornier*, 1910	..	50	75
185	10 c.	*Patriarch*, 1869	..	50	75
186	15 c.	As Type *32* (16 Mar)	..	50	85
187	15 c.	As No. 167 (16 Mar)	..	50	85
188	15 c.	As No. 168 (16 Mar)	..	50	85
189	15 c.	As No. 169 (16 Mar)	..	50	85
190	20 c.	As No. 170 (16 Mar)	..	50	85
191	20 c.	As No. 171 (16 Mar)	..	50	85
192	20 c.	As No. 172 (16 Mar)	..	50	85
193	20 c.	As No. 173 (16 Mar)	..	50	85
194	30 c.	As No. 174 (16 Mar)	..	50	95
195	30 c.	As No. 175 (16 Mar)	..	50	95
196	30 c.	As No. 176 (16 Mar)	..	50	95
197	30 c.	As No. 177 (16 Mar)	..	50	95
198	50 c.	As No. 178 (16 Mar)	..	1·00	1·75
199	50 c.	As No. 179 (16 Mar)	..	1·00	1·75
200	50 c.	As No. 180 (16 Mar)	..	1·00	1·75
201	50 c.	As No. 181 (16 Mar)	..	1·00	1·75
202	$1	As No. 182 (15 May)	..	2·00	1·50
203	$1	As No. 183 (15 May)	..	2·00	1·50
204	$1	As No. 184 (15 May)	..	2·00	1·50
205	$1	As No. 185 (15 May)	..	2·00	1·50
206	$2	*Cutty Sark*, 1869 (26 June)		4·50	3·25
207	$4	*Mermerus*, 1872 (26 June)		9·00	5·00
208	$6	H.M.S. *Resolution* and *Discovery*, 1776– 80 (21 Sept)	.. ..	15·00	12·00
166/208			*Set of 43*	48·00	42·00

Nos. 186/205 are 41 × 25 mm and Nos. 206/8 47 × 33 mm in size.
On Nos. 166/205 the four designs of each value were printed together, *se-tenant*, in blocks of 4 throughout the sheet.

For redrawn versions of these designs in other face values see Nos. 337/55.

33 "Jesus at the Grove" (Veronese)

34 Prince Charles as Young Child

1981 (5 Apr). *Easter. Paintings. T* **33** *and similar vert designs. Multicoloured. P* 14.

218	30 c.	Type *33*	..	40	20
219	40 c.	"Christ with Crown of Thorns" (Titian)	..	55	25
220	50 c.	"Pietá" (Van Dyck)	..	60	30
218/20			*Set of 3*	1·40	65
MS221		110 × 68 mm. Nos. 218/20. P 13½		2·75	2·00

1981 (5 Apr). *Easter. Children's Charity. Designs as Nos.* 218/20 *in separate miniature sheets* 70 × 86 *mm., each with a face value of* 70 c. + 5 c. P 13½.

MS222	As Nos. 218/20	..	*Set of 3 sheets* 1·50	1·50

1981 (10 July). *Royal Wedding. T* **34** *and similar vert designs. Multicoloured. P* 14.

223	40 c.	Type *34*	..	20	35
224	50 c.	Prince Charles as schoolboy	..	25	40
225	60 c.	Prince Charles as young man	..	25	40
226	70 c.	Prince Charles in ceremonial Naval uniform	..	25	45
227	80 c.	Prince Charles as Colonel-in-Chief, Royal Regiment of Wales	..	25	45
223/7			*Set of 5*	1·10	1·90
MS228		99 × 89 mm. Nos. 223/7		1·25	2·00

Nos. 223/7 were each printed in small sheets of 6 including one *se-tenant* stamp-size label.

1981 (30 Nov). *International Year for Disabled Persons. Nos.* 223/8 *surch as T* **51** *of Aitutaki.*

229	40 c.+ 5 c.	Type *34*	..	25	60
230	50 c.+ 5 c.	Prince Charles as schoolboy	..	30	65
231	60 c.+ 5 c.	Prince Charles as young man	..	30	65
232	70 c.+ 5 c.	Prince Charles in ceremonial Naval uniform	..	35	75
233	80 c.+ 5 c.	Prince Charles as Colonel-in-Chief, Royal Regiment of Wales	..	35	85
229/33			*Set of 5*	1·40	3·25
MS234		99 × 89 mm. As Nos. 229/33, but 10 c. premium on each stamp	..	1·40	3·50

Nos. 229/34 have commemorative inscriptions overprinted on the sheet margins.

35 Footballer

36 "The Virgin on a Crescent"

1981 (7 Dec). *World Cup Football Championship, Spain* (1982). *T* **35** *and similar vert designs showing footballers. Multicoloured. P* 13.

235	15 c.	Type **35**	..	15	15
236	15 c.	Footballer wearing orange jersey with black and mauve stripes	..	15	15
237	15 c.	Player in blue jersey	..	15	15
238	35 c.	Player in blue jersey	..	25	25
239	35 c.	Player in red jersey	..	25	25
240	35 c.	Player in yellow jersey with green stripes		25	25
241	50 c.	Player in orange jersey	..	35	35
242	50 c.	Player in mauve jersey	..	35	35
243	50 c.	Player in black jersey	..	35	35
235/43			*Set of 9*	2·00	2·00
MS244		113 × 151 mm. As Nos. 235/43, but each stamp with a premium of 3 c.		4·75	2·75

The three designs of each value were printed together, *se-tenant*, in horizontal strips of 3 throughout the sheet.

1981 (15 Dec). *Christmas. Details from Engravings by Dürer. T* **36** *and similar vert designs in violet, deep reddish purple and stone. P* 13 × 13½.

245	30 c.	Type **36**	..	90	1·00
246	40 c.	"The Virgin at the Fence"	..	1·25	1·40
247	50 c.	"The Holy Virgin and Child"	..	1·50	1·75
245/7			*Set of 3*	3·25	3·75
MS248		134 × 75 mm. As Nos. 245/7, but each stamp with a premium of 2 c.		2·25	2·25
MS249		Designs as Nos. 245/7 in separate miniature sheets, 58 × 85 mm, each with a face value of 70 c. + 5 c. P 14 × 13½	*Set of 3 sheets*	1·75	1·75

37 Lady Diana Spencer   (38)
as Baby

1982 (1 July). *21st Birthday of Princess of Wales. T* **37** *and similar vert designs. Multicoloured. P* 14.

250	30 c.	Type *37*	..	30	30
251	50 c.	As young child	..	40	45
252	70 c.	As schoolgirl	..	60	60
253	80 c.	As teenager	..	70	80
254	$1.40,	As young lady	..	1·10	1·25
250/4			*Set of 5*	2·75	3·00
MS255		87 × 110 mm. Nos. 250/4	..	2·75	3·50

1982 (30 July). *Birth of Prince William of Wales. Nos.* 223/8 *optd with T* **38**.

256	40 c.	Type *34*	..	40	45
257	50 c.	Prince Charles as schoolboy	..	50	60
258	60 c.	Prince Charles as young man	..	55	65
259	70 c.	Prince Charles in ceremonial Naval uniform	..	60	70
260	80 c.	Prince Charles as Colonel-in-Chief, Royal Regiment of Wales	..	70	80
256/60			*Set of 5*	2·50	3·00
MS261		99 × 89 mm. Nos. 256/60	..	6·00	7·00

1982 (6 Sept). *Birth of Prince William of Wales. As Nos.* 250/5 *but with changed inscriptions. Multicoloured. P* 13½ × 14.

262	30 c.	As Type *37* (inscr "21 JUNE 1982. BIRTH OF PRINCE WILLIAM OF WALES")	25	30
263	30 c.	As Type *37* (inscr "COMMEMORATING THE BIRTH OF PRINCE WILLIAM OF WALES")	25	30
264	50 c.	As No. 251 (inscr "21 JUNE 1982. BIRTH OF PRINCE WILLIAM OF WALES")	35	45
265	50 c.	As No. 251 (inscr "COMMEMORATING THE BIRTH OF PRINCE WILLIAM OF WALES")	35	45
266	70 c.	As No. 252 (inscr "21 JUNE 1982. BIRTH OF PRINCE WILLIAM OF WALES")	50	65
267	70 c.	As No. 252 (inscr "COMMEMORATING THE BIRTH OF PRINCE WILLIAM OF WALES")	50	65
268	80 c.	As No. 253 (inscr "21 JUNE 1982. BIRTH OF PRINCE WILLIAM OF WALES")	50	65
269	80 c.	As No. 253 (inscr "COMMEMORATING THE BIRTH OF PRINCE WILLIAM OF WALES")	50	65
270	$1.40,	As No. 254 (inscr "21 JUNE 1982. BIRTH OF PRINCE WILLIAM OF WALES")	90	1·25
271	$1.40,	As No. 254 (inscr "COMMEMORATING THE BIRTH OF PRINCE WILLIAM OF WALES")	90	1·25
262/71			*Set of 10* 4·50	6·00
MS272		88 × 109 mm. As **MS255** (stamps inscr "21 JUNE 1982. ROYAL BIRTH PRINCE WILLIAM OF WALES")	2·75	3·25

Nos. 262/3, 264/5, 266/7, 268/9 and 270/1 were printed together, *se-tenant*, in sheets of 5 stamps and 1 label, there being three examples of the "21 JUNE 1982..." and two of the "COMMEMORATING..." in each sheet.

ALTERED CATALOGUE NUMBERS

Any Catalogue numbers altered from the last edition are shown as a list in the introductory pages.

---

39 "Virgin and Child"   **40** Red Coral
(detail, Joos Van Cleve)

1982 (10 Dec). *Christmas. Details from Renaissance Paintings of "Virgin and Child". T* **39** *and similar vert designs. Multicoloured. P* 14 × 13½.

273	35 c.	Type **39**	..	30	40
274	48 c.	"Virgin and Child" (Filippino Lippi)	..	45	55
275	60 c.	"Virgin and Child" (Cima da Conegliano)	60	70
273/5			*Set of 3*	1·25	1·50
MS276		134 × 73 mm. As Nos. 273/5 but each with 2 c. charity premium. P 13		1·00	2·00

Nos. 273/5 were each printed in small sheets of 6 including one *se-tenant*, stamp size, label, depicting the Prince and Princess of Wales with Prince William.

1982 (10 Dec). *Christmas. Children's Charity. Designs as Nos.* 273/5, *but without frames, in separate miniature sheets,* 60 × 85 *mm, each with a face value of* 70 c. + 5 c. P 13.

MS277	As Nos. 273/5	..	*Set of 3 sheets* 1·25	1·60

1983 (14 Mar). *Commonwealth Day. T* **40** *and similar vert designs. Multicoloured. P* 13.

278	60 c.	Type **40**	..	60	70
279	60 c.	Aerial view of Penrhyn atoll	..	60	70
280	60 c.	Eleanor Roosevelt on Penrhyn during Second World War		60	70
281	60 c.	Map of South Pacific	..	60	70
278/81			*Set of 4*	2·25	2·50

Nos. 278/81 were issued together, *se-tenant*, in blocks of four throughout the sheet.

41 Scout Emblem and Blue   (42)
Tropical Flower

1983 (5 Apr). *75th Anniv of Boy Scout Movement. T* **41** *and similar horiz designs. Multicoloured. P* 13 × 14.

282	36 c.	Type **41**	..	1·50	65
283	48 c.	Emblem and pink flower	..	1·75	75
284	60 c.	Emblem and orange flower	..	1·75	1·00
282/4			*Set of 3*	4·50	2·25
MS285		86 × 46 mm. $2 As 48 c., but with elements of design reversed	..	2·40	3·00

1983 (8 July). *15th World Scout Jamboree, Alberta, Canada. Nos.* 282/5 *optd with T* **42**.

286	36 c.	Type **41**	..	1·25	40
287	48 c.	Emblem and pink flower	..	1·50	55
288	60 c.	Emblem and orange flower	..	1·75	75
286/8			*Set of 3*	4·00	1·60
MS289		86 × 46 mm. $2 As 48 c., but with elements of design reversed	..	2·40	3·50

43 School of Sperm   **44** *Mercury* (cable ship)
Whales

1983 (29 July). *Whale Conservation. T* **43** *and similar vert designs. Multicoloured. P* 13.

290	8 c.	Type **43**	..	1·00	70
291	15 c.	Harpooner preparing to strike	..	1·40	95
292	35 c.	Whale attacking boat	..	2·00	1·40
293	60 c.	Dead whales marked with flags	..	3·00	2·00
294	$1	Dead whales on slipway	..	3·75	3·00
290/4			*Set of 5*	10·00	7·25

1983 (23 Sept). *World Communications Year. T* **44** *and similar horiz designs. Multicoloured. P* 13.

295	36 c.	Type **44**	..	80	35
296	48 c.	Men watching cable being laid	..	85	45
297	60 c.	*Mercury* (different)	..	1·10	60
295/7			*Set of 3*	2·50	1·25
MS298		115 × 90 mm. As Nos. 295/7 but each with charity premium of 3 c.	..	1·50	1·60

On No. **MS298** the values are printed in black and have been transposed with the World Communications Year logo.

1983 (26 Sept). *Various stamps surch as T* **200** *of Cook Islands.*

(a) Nos. 182/5, 190/7 and 206

299	18 c. on 10 c. *Preussen*, 1902		20	20
300	18 c. on 10 c. *Pamir*, 1921		20	20
301	18 c. on 10 c. *Cap Hornier*, 1910		20	20
302	18 c. on 10 c. *Patriarch*, 1869		20	20
303	36 c. on 20 c. *Va'a Teu'ua*		35	35
304	36 c. on 20 c. *Vitoria*, 1500		35	35
305	36 c. on 20 c. *Golden Hind*, 1560		35	35
306	36 c. on 20 c. *Boudeuse*, 1760		35	35
307	36 c. on 30 c. H.M.S. *Bounty*, 1787		35	35
308	36 c. on 30 c. *L'Astrolabe*, 1811		35	35
309	36 c. on 30 c. *Star of India*, 1861		35	35
310	36 c. on 30 c. *Great Republic*, 1853		35	35
311	$1.20 on $2 *Cutty Sark*, 1869		1·40	1·40

(b) Nos. 252/3

312	72 c. on 70 c. Princess Diana as schoolgirl		2·00	1·50
313	96 c. on 80 c. Princess Diana as teenager		2·25	1·75
299/313		Set of 15	8·50	7·00

1983 (28 Oct). *Nos. 208, 225/6, 254 and 268/9 surch as T* **200** *of Cook Islands.*

314	48 c. on 60 c. Prince Charles as young man (Gold)		3·50	1·50
	a. Error. Surch on No. 258		6·00	5·00
315	72 c. on 70 c. Prince Charles in ceremonial Naval uniform		4·00	1·75
	a. Error. Surch on No. 259		7·00	5·00
316	96 c. on 80 c. As No. 253 (inscr "21 JUNE 1982 . . .")		2·75	1·00
	a. Error. Surch on No. 260		8·00	5·50
317	96 c. on 80 c. As No. 253 (inscr "COMMEMORATING. . .")		1·75	1·00
318	$1.20 on $1.40, Princess Diana as young lady		3·25	1·50
319	$5.60 on $6, H.M.S. *Resolution* and *Discovery*, 1776–80		15·00	6·50
314/19		Set of 6	27·00	12·00

45 George Cayley's Airship Design, 1837

1983 (31 Oct). *Bicentenary of Manned Flight. T* **45** *and similar horiz designs. Multicoloured. P* 13. A. *Inscr* "NORTHERN COOK ISLANS". B. *Corrected spelling optd in black on silver over original inscription.*

			A		B	
320	36 c. Type **45**	1·00	80	30	35
321	48 c. Dupuy de Lome's man-powered airship, 1872	1·25	90	40	45
322	60 c. Santos Dumont's *Airship No. 6*, 1901	1·50	1·25	45	50
323	96 c. Lebaudy-Juillot's practical airship No. 1 *La Jaune*, 1902	2·25	1·75	75	80
324	$1.32, Airship LZ-127 *Graf Zeppelin*, 1929	3·00	2·50	1·00	1·10
320/4	Set of 5	8·00	6·50	2·75	3·00
MS325	113×138 mm. Nos. 320/4	6·50	11·00	2·25	4·25

46 "Madonna in the Meadow"

47 Waka

1983 (30 Nov). *Christmas. 500th Birth Anniv of Raphael. T* **46** *and similar vert designs. Multicoloured. P* 13.

326	36 c. Type **46**		60	40
327	42 c. "Tempi Madonna"		60	40
328	48 c. "The Smaller Cowper Madonna"		80	50
329	60 c. "Madonna della Tenda"		95	60
326/9		Set of 4	2·75	1·75
MS330	87 × 115 mm. As Nos. 326/9 but each with a charity premium of 3 c.		2·50	2·50

1983 (1 Dec). *Nos. 266/7, 227 and 270/1 surch as T* **200** *of Cook Islands.*

331	72 c. on 70 c. As No. 252 (inscr "21 JUNE 1982. . .")		1·50	80
332	72 c. on 70 c. As No. 252 (inscr "COMMEMORATING. . .")		80	60
333	96 c. on 80 c. Prince Charles as Colonel-in-Chief, Royal Regiment of Wales		1·50	65
334	$1.20 on $1.40, As No. 254 (inscr "21 JUNE 1982. . .")		1·75	70
335	$1.20 on $1.40, As No. 254 (inscr "COMMEMORATING. . .")		1·25	65
331/5		Set of 5	6·00	3·00

1983 (28 Dec). *Christmas. 500th Birth Anniv of Raphael. Children's Charity. Designs as Nos.* 326/9 *in separate miniature sheets,* 65 × 84 *mm, each with a face value of* 75 c. + 5 c. P 13.

MS336	As Nos. 326/9	Set of 4 sheets	2·00 3·00

1984 (8 Feb–15 June). *Sailing Craft and Ships (2nd series). Designs as Nos.* 166, *etc. but with redrawn frames, inscriptions and compass rose at top right as in T* **47**. *Multicoloured.* P 13 × 13½ ($9.60), 13 ($3, $5) or 11 *(others).*

337	2 c. Type **47**		20	50
338	4 c. *Amatasi*		30	50
339	5 c. *Ndrua*		30	50
340	8 c. *Tongiaki*		40	60
341	10 c. *Vitoria*		40	60
342	18 c. *Golden Hind*		50	70
343	20 c. *Boudeuse*		50	70
344	30 c. H.M.S. *Bounty*		60	70
345	36 c. *L'Astrolabe*		60	70
346	48 c. *Great Republic*		60	70
347	50 c. *Star of India* (21 Mar)		60	70
348	60 c. *Coonatto* (21 Mar)		60	70
349	72 c. *Antiope* (21 Mar)		60	70
350	80 c. *Balcutha* (21 Mar)		70	70
351	96 c. *Cap Hornier* (21 Mar)		85	85
352	$1.20, *Pamir* (21 Mar)		2·50	1·40
353	$3 *Mermerus* (41 × 31 *mm*) (4 May)		5·00	3·00
354	$5 *Cutty Sark* (41 × 31 *mm*) (4 May)		5·50	5·00
355	$9.60, H.M.S. *Resolution* and *Discovery* (41 ×31 *mm*) (15 June)		12·00	12·00
337/55		Set of 19	29·00	28·00

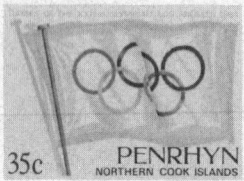

48 Olympic Flag

1984 (20 July). *Olympic Games, Los Angeles. T* **48** *and similar horiz designs. Multicoloured.* P 13½ × 13.

356	35 c. Type **48**		30	35
357	60 c. Olympic torch and flags		50	55
358	$1.80, Ancient athletes and Coliseum		1·50	1·60
356/8		Set of 3	2·10	2·25
MS359	103×86 mm. As Nos. 356/8 but each with a charity premium of 5 c.		2·40	2·50

49 Penrhyn Stamps of 1978, 1979 and 1981

1984 (20 Sept). *"Ausipex" International Stamp Exhibition, Melbourne. T* **49** *and similar horiz design. Multicoloured.* P 13½ × 13.

360	60 c. Type **49**		50	75
361	$1.20, Location map of Penrhyn		1·00	1·25
MS362	90 × 90 mm. As Nos. 360/1, but each with a face value of 96 c.		1·75	2·00

 $2

Birth of
Prince Henry
15 Sept. 1984

(50)

51 "Virgin and Child"
(Giovanni Bellini)

1984 (18 Oct). *Birth of Prince Henry. Nos.* 223/4 *and* 250/1 *surch as T* **50**.

363	$2 on 30 c. Type **37**		1·40	1·50
364	$2 on 40 c. Type **34**		1·60	1·75
365	$2 on 50 c. Prince Charles as schoolboy		1·60	1·75
366	$2 on 50 c. Lady Diana as young child (Gold)		1·40	1·50
363/6		Set of 4	5·50	6·00

1984 (15 Nov). *Christmas. Paintings of the Virgin and Child by different artists. T* **51** *and similar vert designs. Multicoloured.* P 13 × 13½.

367	36 c. Type **51**		55	35
368	48 c. Lorenzo di Credi		65	45
369	60 c. Palma the Older		70	50
370	96 c. Raphael		1·00	80
367/70		Set of 4	2·50	1·90
MS371	93 × 118 mm. As Nos. 367/70, but each with a charity premium of 5 c.		2·50	3·00

1984 (10 Dec). *Christmas. Children's Charity. Designs as Nos.* 367/70, *but without frames, in separate miniature sheets* 67 × 81 *mm, each with a face value of* 96 c. + 10 c. P 13½.

MS372	As Nos. 367/70	Set of 4 sheets	3·25 3·25

52 Harlequin Duck

1985 (9 Apr). *Birth Bicentenary of John J. Audubon (ornithologist). T* **52** *and similar horiz designs showing original paintings. Multicoloured.* P 13.

373	20 c. Type **52**		2·00	1·75
374	55 c. Sage Grouse		2·75	2·75
375	65 c. Solitary Sandpiper		3·00	3·00
376	75 c. Dunlin		3·25	3·50
373/6		Set of 4	10·00	10·00
MS377	Four sheets, each 70 × 53 mm. As Nos. 373/6, but each with a face value of 95 c.		7·00	6·00

53 Lady Elizabeth
Bowes-Lyon, 1921

54 "The House in the Wood"

1985 (24 June). *Life and Times of Queen Elizabeth the Queen Mother. T* **53** *and similar vert designs, each deep bluish violet, silver and yellow.* P 13.

378	75 c. Type **53**		40	65
379	95 c. With baby Princess Elizabeth, 1926		50	80
380	$1.20, Coronation Day, 1937		65	1·00
381	$2.80, On her 70th birthday		1·25	2·00
378/81		Set of 4	2·50	4·00
MS382	66 × 90 mm. $5 The Queen Mother		2·40	3·25

Nos. 378/81 were each printed in small sheets of 4 stamps. For these stamps in a miniature sheet see No. **MS403**.

1985 (10 Sept). *International Youth Year and Birth Centenary of Jacob Grimm (folklorist). T* **54** *and similar vert designs. Multicoloured.* P 13 × 13½.

383	75 c. Type **54**		1·75	1·75
384	95 c. "Snow-White and Rose-Red"		2·00	2·00
385	$1.15, "The Goose Girl"		2·25	2·25
383/5		Set of 3	5·50	5·50

55 "The Annunciation"

1985 (25 Nov). *Christmas. Paintings by Murillo. T* **55** *and similar horiz designs. Multicoloured.* P 14.

386	75 c. Type **55**		1·25	1·25
387	$1.15, "Adoration of the Shepherds"		1·75	1·75
388	$1.80, "The Holy Family"		2·50	2·50
386/8		Set of 3	5·00	5·00
MS389	66 × 131 mm. As Nos. 386/8, but each with a face value of 95 c. P 13½		2·75	3·00
MS390	Three sheets, each 66 × 72 mm. As Nos. 386/8, but with face values of $1.20, $1.45 and $2.75. P 13½	Set of 3 sheets	4·50	4·75

56 Halley's Comet

1986 (4 Feb). *Appearance of Halley's Comet. T* **56** *and similar horiz design showing details of the painting "Fire and Ice" by Camille Rendal. Multicoloured.* P 13½ × 13.

391	$1.50, Type **56**		1·75	1·50
392	$1.50, Stylised *Giotto* spacecraft		1·75	1·50
MS393	108 × 43 mm. $3 As Nos. 391/2 (104 × 39 mm). Imperf		2·25	2·50

Nos. 391/2 were printed together, *se-tenant*, in horizontal pairs throughout the sheet, forming a composite design of the complete painting.

57 Princess Elizabeth aged Three, 1929, and Bouquet   **58** Statue of Liberty under Construction, Paris

1986 (21 Apr). *60th Birthday of Queen Elizabeth II. T* **57** *and similar horiz designs. Multicoloured. P* 13½ × 13 ($2.50) *or* 14 (*others*).

394	95 c. Type **57**	.. .. ..	80	80
395	$1.45, Profile of Queen Elizabeth and St. Edward's Crown	..	1·25	1·25
396	$2.50, Queen Elizabeth aged three and in profile with Imperial State Crown (56 × 30 *mm*)	..	2·00	2·00
394/6	.. ..	*Set of* 3	3·50	3·50

1986 (27 June). *Centenary of Statue of Liberty* (*1st issue*). *T* **58** *and similar vert designs, each black, gold and yellow-green. P* 13 × 13½.

397	95 c. Type **58**	.. ..	65	70
398	$1.75, Erection of Statue, New York	..	1·10	1·25
399	$3 Artist's impression of Statue, 1876	..	2·10	2·25
397/9	.. .. ..	*Set of* 3	3·50	3·75

See also No. **MS412**.

$2.00

59 Prince Andrew and Miss Sarah Ferguson   (**60**)

1986 (23 July). *Royal Wedding. T* **59** *and similar vert design. Multicoloured. P* 13.

400	$2.50, Type **59**	.. ..	3·50	3·50
401	$3.50, Profiles of Prince Andrew and Miss Sarah Ferguson	..	4·00	4·00

Nos. 400/1 were each printed in sheetlets of 4 stamps and 2 stamp-size labels.

1986 (4 Aug). *"Stampex '86" Stamp Exhibition, Adelaide. No.* **MS362** *surch with T* **60** *in black on gold.*

MS402	$2 on 96 c. × 2	.. ..	6·00	7·00

The "Stampex '86" exhibition emblem is overprinted on the sheet margin.

1986 (4 Aug). *86th Birthday of Queen Elizabeth the Queen Mother. Nos.* 378/81 *in miniature sheet,* 90 × 120 *mm. P* 13 × 13½.

MS403	Nos. 378/81	.. ..	8·50	9·00

+10c

61 "The Adoration of the Shepherds"   (**62**)

1986 (20 Nov). *Christmas. Engravings by Rembrandt. T* **61** *and similar vert designs, each red-brown, yellow-ochre and gold. P* 13.

404	65 c. Type **61**	.. ..	1·75	1·75
405	$1.75 "Virgin and Child"	.. ..	3·00	3·00
406	$2.50 "The Holy Family"	..	4·25	4·25
404/6	.. .. ..	*Set of* 3	8·00	8·00
MS407	120 × 87 mm. As Nos. 404/6, but size 31 × 39 mm with a face value of $1.50. P 13½ × 13		8·50	9·00

1986 (24 Nov). *Visit of Pope John Paul II to South Pacific. Nos.* 404/7 *surch as T* **62** *in greenish blue.*

408	65 c. + 10 c. Type **61**	..	2·25	2·00
409	$1.75 + 10 c. "Virgin and Child"	..	3·75	3·50
410	$2.50 + 10 c. "The Holy Family"	..	4·50	4·00
408/10	.. ..	*Set of* 3	9·50	8·50
MS411	120 × 87 mm. As Nos. 408/10, but each size 31 × 39 mm with a face value of $1.50 + 10 c. ..		9·50	9·00

63 Head and Torch of Statue of Liberty

1987 (15 Apr). *Centenary of Statue of Liberty* (1986) (*2nd issue*). *Two sheets, each* 122 × 122 *mm, containing T* **63** *and similar multicoloured designs. Litho. P* 14 × 13½ (*vert*) *or* 13½ × 14 (*horiz*).

MS412 Two sheets (a) 65 c. Type **63**; 65 c. Torch at sunset; 65 c. Restoration workers with flag; 65 c. Statue and Manhattan skyline; 65 c. Workers and scaffolding. (b) 65 c. Workers on Statue crown (*horiz*); 65 c. Aerial view of Ellis Island (*horiz*); 65 c. Ellis Island Immigration Centre (*horiz*); 65 c. View from Statue to Ellis Island and Manhattan (*horiz*); 65 c. Restoration workers (*horiz*) .. .. .. *Set of* 2 *sheets* 9·00 11·00

Fortieth Royal Wedding
Anniversary 1947–87

(**64**)

1987 (20 Nov). *Royal Ruby Wedding. Nos.* 68/9 *optd with T* **64** *in magenta.*

413	$2 Birds-eye view of Penrhyn	..	2·00	2·25
414	$5 Satellite view of Australasia	..	3·50	4·25

65 "The Garvagh Madonna"   **66** Athletics

1987 (11 Dec). *Christmas. Religious Paintings by Raphael. T* **65** *and similar vert designs. Multicoloured. P* 13½.

415	95 c. Type **65**	..	1·50	1·50
416	$1.60, "The Alba Madonna"	..	2·00	2·00
417	$2.25, "The Madonna of the Fish"	..	3·00	3·00
415/17	.. ..	*Set of* 3	6·00	6·00
MS418	91 × 126 mm. As Nos. 415/17, but each with a face value of $1.15		10·00	10·50
MS419	70 × 86 mm. $4.80, As No. 417, but size 36 × 39 mm		11·00	11·50

1988 (29 July). *Olympic Games, Seoul. T* **66** *and similar horiz designs. Multicoloured. P* 13½ × 13 (*horiz*) *or* 13 × 13½ (*vert*).

420	55 c. Type **66**	..	65	65
421	95 c. Pole vaulting (*vert*)	..	1·00	1·00
422	$1.25, Shotputting	..	1·40	1·40
423	$1.50, Lawn Tennis (*vert*)	..	2·25	1·75
421/3	..	*Set of* 4	4·75	4·25
MS424	110 × 70 mm. As Nos. 421 and 423, but each with a face value of $2.50 ..		4·00	5·00

1988 (14 Oct). *Olympic Gold Medal Winners, Seoul. Nos.* 420/4 *optd as T* **235** *of Cook Islands.*

425	55 c. Type **66** (optd "CARL LEWIS UNITED STATES 100 METERS")		60	60
426	95 c. Pole vaulting (optd "LOUISE RITTER UNITED STATES HIGH JUMP")		90	90
427	$1.25, Shot putting (optd "ULF TIMMERMANN EAST GERMANY SHOT-PUT") ..		1·25	1·25
428	$1.50, Lawn Tennis (optd "STEFFI GRAF WEST GERMANY WOMEN'S TENNIS") ..		2·25	1·40
425/8	..	*Set of* 4	4·50	3·75
MS429	110 × 70 mm. $2.50, As No. 421 (optd "JACKIE JOYNER-KERSEE United States Heptathlon"); $2.50, As No. 423 (optd "STEFFI GRAF West Germany Women's Tennis MILOSLAV MECIR Czechoslovakia Men's Tennis")		4·50	5·50

STANLEY GIBBONS
STAMP COLLECTING SERIES

Introductory booklets on *How to Start, How to Identify Stamps* and *Collecting by Theme*. A series of well illustrated guides at a low price.
Write for details.

67 "Virgin and Child"   **68** Neil Armstrong stepping onto Moon

1988 (9 Nov). *Christmas. T* **67** *and similar designs showing different "Virgin and Child" paintings by Titian. P* 13 × 13½.

430	70 c. multicoloured	..	90	90
431	85 c. multicoloured	..	1·00	1·00
432	95 c. multicoloured	..	1·25	1·25
433	$1.25, multicoloured	..	1·50	1·50
430/3	..	*Set of* 4	4·25	4·25
MS434	100 × 80 mm. $6.40, As Type **67**, but diamond-shaped (57 × 57 *mm*). P 13		6·00	7·00

(Des G. Vasarhelyi)

1989 (24 July). *20th Anniv of First Manned Landing on Moon. T* **68** *and similar horiz designs. Multicoloured. P* 14.

435	55 c. Type **68**	..	60	60
436	75 c. Astronaut on Moon carrying equipment	..	75	75
437	95 c. Conducting experiment on Moon		95	95
438	$1.25, Crew of "Apollo 11"	..	1·25	1·25
439	$1.75, Crew inside "Apollo 11"	..	1·60	1·60
435/9	..	*Set of* 5	4·75	4·75

69 Virgin Mary

1989 (17 Nov). *Christmas. T* **69** *and similar multicoloured designs showing details from "The Nativity" by Dürer. P* 13.

440	55 c. Type **69**	..	80	80
441	70 c. Christ Child and cherubs	..	90	90
442	85 c. Joseph	..	1·25	1·25
443	$1.25, Three women	..	1·60	1·60
440/3	..	*Set of* 4	4·00	4·00
MS444	88 × 95 mm. $6.40, "The Nativity" (31 × 50 *mm*)		6·50	7·50

$2.25

70 Queen Elizabeth the Queen Mother

1990 (24 July). *90th Birthday of Queen Elizabeth the Queen Mother. P* 13½.

445	70 $2.25, multicoloured	..	2·50	2·50
MS446	85 × 73 mm. **70** $7.50, multicoloured	..	10·00	11·00

$1.50

71 "Adoration of the Magi" (Veronese)   (**72**)

(Litho Questa)

1990 (26 Nov). *Christmas. Religious Paintings. T* **71** *and similar vert designs. Multicoloured. Ordinary paper. P* 14.

447	55 c. Type **71**	..	1·00	1·00
448	70 c. "Virgin and Child" (Quentin Metsys)	1·40	1·40
449	85 c. "Virgin and Child Jesus" (Hugo van der Goes)	..	1·60	1·60
450	$1.50, "Adoration of the Kings" (Jan Gossaert)	..	2·50	2·50
447/50	..	*Set of* 4	6·00	6·00
MS451	108 × 132 mm. $6.40, "Virgin and Child with Saints, Francis, John the Baptist, Zenobius and Lucy" (Domenico Veneziano)		6·00	7·00

1990 (5 Dec). *"Birdpex '90" Stamp Exhibition, Christchurch, New Zealand. Nos.* 373/6 *surch as T* **72** *in red* (*Nos* 452, 455) *or black* (*others*).

452	$1.50 on 20 c. Type **52**	..	1·50	1·75
453	$1.50 on 55 c. Sage Grouse	..	1·50	1·75
454	$1.50 on 65 c. Solitary Sandpiper	..	1·50	1·75
455	$1.50 on 75 c. Dunlin	..	1·50	1·75
452/5	..	*Set of* 4	5·50	6·25

COMMEMORATING 65th BIRTHDAY OF H.M. QUEEN ELIZABETH II

(73)

1991 (22 Apr). *65th Birthday of Queen Elizabeth II. No. 208 optd with T* **73.**
456    $6 H.M.S. *Resolution* and *Discovery,* 1776–80 ..   ..   ..   9·00   10·00

74 "The Virgin and Child with Saints" (G. David)

(Des G. Vasarhelyi. Litho Questa)

1991 (11 Nov). *Christmas. Religious Paintings. T* **74** *and similar multicoloured designs. Ordinary paper. P* 14.
457   55 c. Type **74** ..   ..   ..   1·00   1·00
458   85 c. "Nativity" (Tintoretto) ..   1·50   1·50
459   $1.15, "Mystic Nativity" (Botticelli)   1·75   1·75
460   $1.85, "Adoration of the Shepherds" (B. Murillo) ..   ..   2·75   3·25
457/60   ..   ..   *Set of 4*   6·25   6·75
MS461   79×103 mm. $6.40, "The Madonna of the Chair" (Raphael) (*vert*) ..   8·50   9·50

(Des G. Vasarhelyi. Litho B.D.T.)

1992 (27 July). *Olympic Games, Barcelona. Horiz designs as T* **94** *of Aitutaki. Multicoloured. Ordinary paper. P* 14.
462   75 c. Running ..   ..   ..   1·00   1·00
463   95 c. Boxing ..   ..   ..   1·25   1·25
464   $1.15, Swimming ..   ..   1·40   1·40
465   $1.50, Wrestling ..   ..   1·60   1·60
462/5   ..   ..   *Set of 4*   4·75   4·75

75 Marquesan Canoe

(Litho B.D.T.)

1992 (16 Oct). *6th Festival of Pacific Arts, Rarotonga. T* **75** *and similar horiz designs. Multicoloured. Ordinary paper. P* 14×15.
466   $1.15, Type **75** ..   ..   1·40   1·40
467   $1.75, Tangaroa statue from Rarotonga   1·90   1·90
468   $1.95, Manihiki canoe ..   ..   2·00   2·00
466/8   ..   ..   *Set of 3*   4·75   4·75

1992 (16 Oct). *Royal Visit by Prince Edward. Nos. 466/8 optd with T* **254** *of Cook Islands.*
469   $1.15, Type **75** ..   ..   1·75   1·75
470   $1.75, Tangaroa statue from Rarotonga   2·50   2·50
471   $1.95, Manihiki canoe ..   ..   3·00   3·00
469/71   ..   ..   *Set of 3*   6·50   6·50

76 "Virgin with Child and Saints" (Borgognone)   **77** Vincente Pinzon and *Nina*

1992 (18 Nov). *Christmas. Religious Paintings by Ambrogio Borgognone. T* **76** *and similar vert designs. Multicoloured. Ordinary paper. P* 13½.
472   55 c. Type **76**   75   75
473   85 c. "Virgin on Throne" ..   ..   1·10   1·10
474   $1.05, "Virgin on Carpet" ..   1·40   1·40
475   $1.85, "Virgin of the Milk" ..   2·25   2·25
472/5   ..   ..   *Set of 4*   5·00   5·00
MS476   101×86 mm. $6.40, As 55 c., but larger (36×46 *mm*) ..   ..   6·50   7·50

(Litho B.D.T.)

1992 (4 Dec). *500th Anniv of Discovery of America by Columbus. T* **77** *and similar vert designs. Multicoloured. Ordinary paper. P* 15×14.
477   $1.15, Type **77** ..   ..   2·00   2·00
478   $1.35, Martin Pinzon and *Pinta*   2·25   2·25
479   $1.75, Christopher Columbus and *Santa Maria* ..   ..   3·00   3·00
477/9   ..   ..   *Set of 3*   6·50   6·50

78 Queen Elizabeth II   **79** Bull-mouth Helmet
in 1953

(Des G. Vasarhelyi. Litho B.D.T.)

1993 (4 June). *40th Anniv of Coronation. P* 14.
480 **78** $6 multicoloured ..   ..   6·50   8·00

(Des G. Drummond. Litho Questa ($3, $5, $8), B.D.T. (others))

1993 (18 Oct)–**97.** *Marine Life. T* **79** *and similar horiz designs. Multicoloured. P* 14×13½ ($3, $5, $8) *or* 13½×14 (*others*).
481   5 c. Type **79**   10   10
482   10 c. Daisy Coral   10   10
483   15 c. Hydroid Coral   15   20
484   20 c. Feather-star   15   20
485   20 c. Sea Star   15   20
486   30 c. Varicose Nudibranch ..   20   25
487   50 c. Smooth Sea Star   35   40
488   70 c. Black-lip Pearl Oyster ..   50   55
489   80 c. Four-coloured Nudibranch (3.12.93)   60   65
490   85 c. Prickly Sea Cucumber (3.12.93)   60   65
491   90 c. Organ Pipe Coral (3.12.93) ..   65   70
492   $1 Blue Sea Lizard (3.12.93) ..   75   80
493   $2 Textile Cone shell (3.12.93) ..   1·50   1·60
494   $3 Starfish (21.11.94) ..   ..   2·25   2·40
495   $5 As $3 (21.11.94) ..   ..   3·75   4·00
496   $8 As $3 (17.11.97) ..   ..   6·00   6·25
481/96   ..   ..   *Set of 16*   18·00   19·00
Nos. 494/6 are larger, 47×34 mm, and include a portrait of Queen Elizabeth II at top right.

80 "Virgin on Throne   **81** Neil Armstrong stepping
with Child" (detail)   onto Moon
(Tura)

1993 (2 Nov). *Christmas. T* **80** *and similar vert designs showing different details from "Virgin on Throne with Child" (Cosme Tura). Ordinary paper. P* 13½ ($4.50) *or* 14 (*others*).
499   55 c. multicoloured ..   ..   1·00   1·00
500   85 c. multicoloured ..   ..   1·50   1·50
501   $1.05, multicoloured ..   ..   1·75   1·75
502   $1.95, multicoloured ..   ..   2·75   3·00
503   $4.50, multicoloured (32×47 *mm*)   6·00   7·00
499/503   ..   ..   *Set of 5*   11·50   13·00

(Des G. Vasarhelyi. Litho B.D.T.)

1994 (20 July). *25th Anniv of First Moon Landing. P* 14.
504 **81** $3.25, multicoloured ..   ..   4·75   5·00

82 "The Virgin and Child with Sts. Paul and Jerome" (Vivarini)

(Litho B.D.T.)

1994 (30 Nov). *Christmas. Religious Paintings. T* **82** *and similar vert designs. Multicoloured. P* 14.
505   90 c. Type **82** ..   ..   1·10   1·25
   a. Block of 4. Nos. 505/8   ..   4·00
506   90 c. "The Virgin and Child with St. John" (Luini) ..   ..   ..   1·10   1·25
507   90 c. "The Virgin and Child with Sts. Jerome and Dominic" (Lippi) ..   1·10   1·25
508   90 c. "Adoration of the Shepherds" (Murillo)   1·10   1·25
509   $1 "Adoration of the Kings" (detail of angels) (Reni) ..   ..   1·10   1·25
   a. Block of 4. Nos. 509/12   ..   4·00
510   $1 "Madonna and Child with the Infant Baptist" (Raphael) ..   ..   1·10   1·25
511   $1 "Adoration of the Kings" (detail of manger) (Reni) ..   ..   1·10   1·25
512   $1 "Virgin and Child" (Borgognone)   1·10   1·25
505/12   ..   ..   *Set of 8*   8·00   9·00
Nos. 505/8 and 509/12 were printed together, *se-tenant*, in blocks of 4 throughout the sheets.

83 Battleship Row burning, Pearl Harbor

(Litho B.D.T.)

1995 (4 Sept). *50th Anniv of End of Second World War. T* **83** *and similar horiz design. Multicoloured. P* 13.
513   $3.75, Type **83** ..   ..   4·25   4·75
   a. Pair. Nos. 686/7   ..   ..   8·50   9·50
514   $3.75, Boeing B-25 Superfortress *Enola Gay* over Hiroshima ..   ..   4·25   4·75
Nos. 513/14 were printed together, *se-tenant* horizontally and vertically, in sheets of 4.

84 Queen Elizabeth the Queen Mother at Remembrance Day Ceremony

(Des G. Vasarhelyi. Litho B.D.T.)

1995 (14 Sept). *95th Birthday of Queen Elizabeth the Queen Mother. P* 13.
515 **84** $4.50, multicoloured ..   ..   6·00   7·00

85 Anniversary Emblem, United Nations Flag and Headquarters

(Des G. Vasarhelyi. Litho B.D.T.)

1995 (20 Oct). *50th Anniv of United Nations. P* 13×13½.
516 **85** $4 multicoloured ..   ..   4·00   5·00

86 Loggerhead Turtle   **87** Queen Elizabeth II and Rose

(Litho B.D.T.)

1995 (7 Dec). *Year of the Sea Turtle. T* **86** *and similar vert designs. Multicoloured. P* 13½×14.
517   $1.15, Type **86** ..   ..   1·75   2·00
   a. Horiz pair. Nos. 517/18   ..   3·50   4·00
518   $1.15, Hawksbill Turtle ..   ..   1·75   2·00
519   $1.65, Olive Ridley Turtle ..   2·25   2·50
   a. Horiz pair. Nos. 519/20   ..   4·50   5·00
520   $1.65, Green Turtle ..   ..   2·25   2·50
517/20   ..   ..   *Set of 4*   7·25   8·00
Nos. 517/18 and 519/20 were printed together, *se-tenant*, in horizontal pairs throughout the sheets.

(Des G. Vasarhelyi. Litho)

1996 (20 June). *70th Birthday of Queen Elizabeth II.* P 14.
521 **87** $4.25, multicoloured .. .. .. 4·75 5·50

88 Olympic Flame, National
Flags and Sports

(Des G. Vasarhelyi. Litho B.D.T.)

1996 (12 July). *Centenary of Modern Olympic Games.* P 14.
522 **88** $5 multicoloured .. .. .. 5·50 6·00

89 Royal Wedding, 1947

1997 (20 Nov). *Golden Wedding of Queen Elizabeth and Prince
Philip.* P 14.
523 **89** $3 multicoloured .. .. .. 2·25 2·40
MS524 42×28 mm. **89** $4 multicoloured .. 3·00 3·25

STAMP BOOKLETS

1982 (June). *Royal Wedding. Cover as No. SB1 of Cook
Islands, but inscr* "Penrhyn".
SB1 $4.50, booklet containing 40 c. and 50 c. (Nos.
223/4), each in block of 5 and 1 label 4·75

OFFICIAL STAMPS

O.H.M.S.

(O 1)

1978 (14 Nov). *Nos. 57/66, 89/91 and 101/2 optd or surch (Nos.
O8/9 and O12) as Type O 1.*
O 1 1 c. Diamond Fingerfish 15 10
O 2 2 c. Emperor Angelfish 15 10
O 3 3 c. Copper-banded Butterflyfish .. 25 10
O 4 4 c. Ornate Butterflyfish 25 10
O 5 5 c. Black-backed Butterflyfish .. 30 10
O 6 8 c. Latticed Butterflyfish 35 15
O 7 10 c. Saddle Butterflyfish 40 15
O 8 15 c. on 60 c. Harlequin Sweetlips .. 45 25
O 9 18 c. on 60 c. Harlequin Sweetlips .. 50 25
O10 20 c. Regal Angelfish 50 25
O11 25 c. Pennant Coralfish (Silver) .. 55 30
O12 30 c. on 60 c. Harlequin Sweetlips .. 55 35
O13 50 c. .. 90 55
O14 50 c. } "The Spirit of '76" (A. M. Willard) (Gold) 90 55
O15 50 c. .. 90 55
O16 $1 Queen and Prince Philip (Silver) .. 2·25 65
O17 $2 Queen Elizabeth II (Gold) .. 4·00 80
O1/17.. .. .. .. *Set of* 17 12·00 4·50
These stamps were originally only sold to the public cancelled-
to-order and not in unused condition. They were made available to
overseas collectors in mint condition during 1980.

65c

O.H.M.S.

O.H.M.S.

(O 2)   (O 3)

1985 (15 Aug)–**87**. (a) *Nos. 206/8, 337/47 and 349/55 optd or
surch as Type O 2 by foil embossing in red ($2, $4, $6) or silver
(others)*
O18 2 c. Type 47 .. .. 10 10
O19 4 c. Amatasi 10 10
O20 5 c. Ndrua 10 10
O21 8 c. Tongiaki 10 10
O22 10 c. Vitoria 10 10
O23 18 c. Golden Hind 15 20
O24 20 c. Boudeuse 15 20
O25 30 c. H.M.S. Bounty 20 25
O26 40 c. on 36 c. L'Astrolabe 30 35
O27 50 c. Star of India 35 40
O28 55 c. on 48 c. Great Republic .. 40 45
O29 75 c. on 72 c. Antiope (29.4.86) .. 55 60
O30 75 c. on 96 c. Cap Hornier (29.4.86) .. 55 60
O31 80 c. Balcutha (29.4.86) 60 65
O32 $1.20, Pamir (29.4.86) 90 95
O33 $2 Cutty Sark (29.4.86) .. .. 1·50 1·60
O34 $3 Mermerus (29.4.86) .. .. 2·25 2·40

O35 $4 *Mermerus* (29.4.86) .. .. .. 3·00 3·25
O36 $5 *Cutty Sark* (2.11.87) .. .. 3·75 4·00
O37 $6 H.M.S. *Resolution* and *Discovery*
(2.11.87) .. .. 4·50 5·00
O38 $9.60, H.M.S. *Resolution* and *Discovery*
(2.11.87) .. .. 7·00 7·25
(b) *Nos. 278/81 surch as Type O 3 by silver foil embossing*
O39 65 c. on 60 c. Type **40** .. 50 55
O40 65 c. on 60 c. Aerial view of Penrhyn atoll .. 50 55
O41 65 c. on 60 c. Eleanor Roosevelt on Penrhyn
during Second World War .. 50 55
O42 65 c. on 60 c. Map of South Pacific .. 50 55
O18/42 .. .. *Set of* 25 28·00 30·00

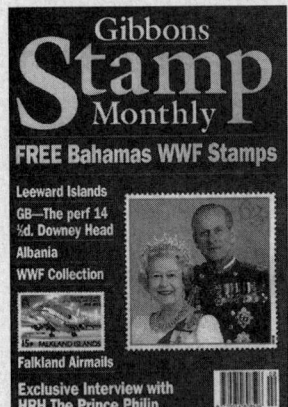

Keep This Catalogue up to Date With

Gibbons **Stamp** Monthly

FREE Bahamas WWF Stamps

Leeward Islands
GB—The perf 14
½d. Downey Head
Albania
WWF Collection
Falkland Airmails

**Exclusive Interview with
HRH The Prince Philip**

The Magazine with the Stanley Gibbons Catalogue Supplement

Plus

■ More editorial than other magazines.

■ Regular features for all collectors from beginners to specialists.

■ Authoritatively written.

■ Regular special offers, competitions and free gifts.

Get Gibbons Stamp Monthly delivered direct to your door!

For a free sample copy and subscription details phone
01425 472363
or write to:

**Hugh Jefferies
Gibbons Stamp Monthly
5 Parkside, Christchurch Road,
Ringwood, Hants BH24 3SH**

Cyprus

Cyprus was part of the Turkish Ottoman Empire from 1571.

The first records of an organised postal service date from 1871 when a post office was opened at Nicosia (Lefkosa) under the jurisdiction of the Damascus Head Post Office. Various stamps of Turkey from the 1868 issue onwards are known used from this office, cancelled "KIBRIS", in Arabic, within a double-lined oblong. Manuscript cancellations have also been reported. The records report the opening of a further office at Larnaca (Tuzla) in 1873, but no cancellation for this office has been identified.

To provide an overseas postal service the Austrian Empire opened a post office in Larnaca during 1845. Stamps of the Austrian Post Offices in the Turkish Empire were placed on sale there from 1 June 1864 and were cancelled with an unframed straight-line mark or circular date stamp. This Austrian post office closed on 6 August 1878.

BRITISH ADMINISTRATION

Following the convention with Turkey, Great Britain assumed the administration of Cyprus on 11 July 1878 and the first post office, as part of the British G.P.O. system, was opened at Larnaca on 27 July 1878. Further offices as Famagusta, Kyrenia, Limassol, Nicosia and Paphos followed in September 1878.

The stamps of Great Britain were supplied to the various offices as they opened and continued to be used until the Cyprus Administration assumed responsibility for the postal service on 1 April 1880. With the exception of "969" (Nicosia) similar numeral cancellations had previously been used at offices in Great Britain.

Numeral postmarks for Headquarters Camp, Nicosia ("D48") and Polymedia (Polemidhia) Camp, Limassol ("D47") were supplied by the G.P.O. in London during January 1881. These cancellations had three bars above and three bars below the numeral. Similar marks, but with four bars above and below, had previously been used in London on newspapers and bulk mail.

Although both three bar cancellations subsequently occur on Cyprus issues only isolated examples have been found on loose Great Britain stamps and there are no known covers or pieces which confirm such usage in Cyprus.

For illustrations of the postmark types see BRITISH POST OFFICES ABROAD notes, following GREAT BRITAIN.

FAMAGUSTA

Stamps of GREAT BRITAIN *cancelled* "982" *as Type* 9

1878 *to* **1880–81.**

Z1	½d. rose-red (1870–79) (Plate Nos. 11, 13)	..	£700
Z2	1d. rose-red (1864–79) ..	..	£475
	Plate Nos. 145, 174, 181, 193, 202, 206, 215.		
Z3	2d. blue (1858–69) (Plate Nos. 13, 14, 15)	..	£950
Z4	2½d. rosy mauve (1876) (Plate Nos. 13, 16)	..	£1100
Z5	6d. grey (1874–80) (Plate No. 15)	..	
Z6	1s. green (1873–77) (Plate No. 12)	..	£1900
Z7	1s. orange-brown (1881) (Plate No. 14)	..	£2500

KYRENIA

Stamps of GREAT BRITAIN *cancelled* "974" *as Type* 9

1878 *to* **1880.**

Z 8	½d. rose-red (1870–79) (Plate No. 13)	..		
Z 9	1d. rose-red (1864–79) ..	..	*From*	£500
	Plate Nos. 168, 171, 193, 196, 206, 207, 209, 220.			
Z10	2d. blue (1858–69) (Plate Nos. 13, 15)	*From*	£800	
Z11	2½d. rosy mauve (1876–79) ..	*From*	£950	
	Plate Nos. 12, 13, 14, 15.			
Z12	4d. sage-green (1877) (Plate No. 16)	..		
Z13	6d. grey (1874–80) (Plate No. 16)	..	..	

LARNACA

Stamps of GREAT BRITAIN *cancelled* "942" *as Type* 9

1878 *to* **1880–81.**

Z14	½d. rose-red (1870–79) ..	..	*From*	£250
	Plate Nos. 11, 12, 13, 14, 15, 19, 20.			
Z15	1d. rose-red (1864–79) ..	..	*From*	£170
	Plate Nos. 129, 131, 146, 154, 170, 171, 174, 175, 176, 177, 178, 179, 181, 182, 183, 184, 187, 188, 190, 191, 192, 193, 194, 195, 196, 197, 198, 199, 200, 201, 202, 203, 204, 205, 206, 207, 208, 209, 210, 212, 213, 214, 215, 216, 217, 218, 220, 221, 222, 225.			
Z16	1½d. lake-red (1870) (Plate No. 3)	..		£1700
Z17	2d. blue (1858–69) (Plate Nos. 9, 13, 14, 15)	..		£200
Z18	2½d. rosy mauve (1876–79) ..		*From*	50·00
	Plate Nos. 4, 5, 6, 8, 10, 11, 12, 13, 14, 15, 16, 17.			
Z19	2½d. blue (1880–81) (Plate Nos. 17, 18, 19, 20)	..		£500
Z20	2½d. blue (1881) (Plate No. 21)	..		£500
Z21	4d. sage-green (1877) (Plate Nos. 15, 16)	..		£550
Z22	6d. grey (1874–76) (Plate Nos. 15, 16, 17)	..		£500
Z23	6d. pale buff (1872–73) (Plate No. 11)	..		£1900
Z24	8d. orange (1876)	..		£4250
Z25	1s. green (1873–77) (Plate Nos. 12, 13)	..		£900
Z26	1s. orange-brown (1881) (Plate No. 14)	..		£1800
Z27	5s. rose (1874) (Plate No. 2)	..		£4500

LIMASSOL

Stamps of GREAT BRITAIN *cancelled* "975" *as Type* 9

1878 *to* **1880.**

Z28	½d. rose-red (1870–79) (Plate Nos. 11, 13, 15, 19)		£450
Z29	1d. rose-red (1864–79) ..		£275
	Plate Nos. 160, 171, 173, 174, 177, 179, 184, 187, 190, 193, 196, 197, 198, 200, 202, 206, 207, 208, 209, 210, 213, 215, 216, 218, 220, 221, 222, 225.		
Z30	1½d. lake-red (1870–74) (Plate No. 3)	..	£1800
Z31	2d. blue (1858–69) (Plate Nos. 14, 15)	*From*	£375

Z32	2½d. rosy-mauve (1876–80) ..	..	*From*	£150
	Plate Nos. 11, 12, 13, 14, 15, 16.			
Z33	2½d. blue (1880) (Plate Nos. 17, 19, 20)	*From*	£1200	
Z34	4d. sage-green (Plate No. 16)	..	..	£700

NICOSIA

Stamps of GREAT BRITAIN *cancelled* "969" *as Type* 9

1878 *to* **1880–81.**

Z35	½d. rose-red (1870–79) ..	..	£450
	Plate Nos. 12, 13, 14, 15, 20.		
Z36	1d. rose-red (1864–79) ..	*From*	£275
	Plate Nos. 170, 171, 174, 189, 190, 192, 193, 195, 196, 198, 200, 202, 203, 205, 206, 207, 210, 212, 214, 215, 218, 221, 222, 225.		
Z37	2d. blue (1858–69) (Plate Nos. 14, 15)	..	£450
Z38	2½d. rosy mauve (1876–79) ..	*From*	£170
	Plate Nos. 10, 11, 12, 13, 14, 15, 16.		
Z39	2½d. blue (1880) (Plate No. 20)	..	
Z42	4d. sage-green (1877) (Plate No. 16)	..	£800
Z43	6d. grey (1873) (Plate No. 16)	..	£800

PAPHOS

Stamps of GREAT BRITAIN *cancelled* "981" *as Type* 9

1878 *to* **1880.**

Z44	½d. rose-red (1870–79) (Plate Nos. 13, 15)		
Z45	1d. rose-red (1864–79) ..	*From*	£500
	Plate Nos. 196, 201, 202, 204, 206, 213, 217.		
Z46	2d. blue (1858–69) (Plate No. 15)	..	£850
Z47	2½d. rosy mauve (1876–79) ..	*From*	£500
	Plate Nos. 13, 14, 15, 16.		

PRICES FOR STAMPS ON COVER TO 1945

No. 1	*from* × 10
No. 2	*from* × 50
No. 3	*from* × 100
No. 4	*from* × 8
Nos. 5/6	—
Nos. 7/10	*from* × 15
Nos. 11/15	*from* × 5
No. 16	—
Nos. 16a/24	*from* × 10
No. 25	*from* × 40
No. 26	—
No. 27	*from* × 10
No. 28	—
No. 29	*from* × 30
Nos. 31/5a	*from* × 10
Nos. 36/7	—
Nos. 40/9	*from* × 8
Nos. 50/71	*from* × 5
Nos. 74/99	*from* × 4
Nos. 100/2	—
Nos. 103/17	*from* × 4
No. 117a	—
Nos. 118/31	*from* × 5
No. 132	—
Nos. 133/43	*from* × 5
Nos. 144/7	*from* × 6
Nos. 148/63	*from* × 5

PERFORATION. Nos. 1/122 are perf 14.

Stamps of Great Britain overprinted

CYPRUS
(1)

CYPRUS
(2)

(Optd by D.L.R.)

1880 (1 Apr.)

1	1	½d. rose ..	..	£100	£100
		a. Opt double (Plate 15)	..	†	£10000

Plate No.	Un. Used.	Plate No.	Un. Used
12..	£170 £250	19..	£4250 £700
15..	£100 £100		

2	2	1d. red	9·00	28·00
		a. Opt double (Plate 208)		£13000
		aa. Opt double (Plate 218)		£4250
		b. Vert pair, top stamp without opt (Plate 208)		£15000

174..	£1200 £1200	208..	90·00 48·00
181..	£325 £170	215..	9·50 42·00
184..	£10000 £2250	216..	12·00 28·00
193..	£600 †	217..	9·00 42·00
196..	£550 †	218..	14·00 42·00
201..	9·00 45·00	220..	£350 £375
205..	40·00 40·00		

3	2	2½d. rosy mauve	2·00	6·00
		a. Large thin "C" (Plate 14) (BK, JK)	35·00	£140
		b. Large thin "C" (Plate 15) (BK, JK)	55·00	£325
		14..	2·00 6·00	15..	2·75 18·00

4	2	4d. sage-green (Plate 16)	£120	£200
5		6d. grey (Plate 16)	£500	£650
6		1s. green (Plate 13)	£650	£450

No. 3 has been reported from Plate 9.

HALF-PENNY
(3) 18 mm

HALF-PENNY
(4) 16 or 16½ mm

HALF-PENNY
(5) 13 mm

30 PARAS
(6)

(Optd by Govt Ptg Office, Nicosia)

1881 (Feb–June). *No.* 2 *surch.*

7	3	½d. on 1d. red (Feb)	..	70·00	85·00
		a. "HALFPENN" (BG, LG) (*all plates*) ..	..	*From*	£1700 £1700

Plate No.	Un.	Used.	Plate No.	Un.	Used.
174..	£150	£300	215..	£600	£650
181..	£140	£160	216..	70·00	85·00
201..	85·00	£110	217..	£750	£650
205..	70·00	85·00	218..	£425	£550
208..	£160	£275	220..	£250	£300

8	4	½d. on 1d. red (Apr)	..	£120	£160
		a. Surch double (Plates 201 and 216)		£2250 £2250	

201..	£120 £160	218..	
216..	£350 £400		

9	5	½d. on 1d. red (1 June)	..	45·00	65·00
		aa. Surch double (Plate 205)	..	£650	
		ab. Surch double (Plate 215)	..	£450 £550	
		b. Surch treble (Plate 205)	..	£3000	
		ba. Surch treble (Plate 215)	..	£650	
		bc. Surch treble (Plate 218)	..	£2750	
		c. Surch quadruple (Plate 205)	..	£3250	
		ca. Surch quadruple (Plate 215)	..	£3250	

205..	£190 —	217..	£120 75·00
215..	45·00 65·00	218..	65·00 90·00

The surcharge on No. 8 was handstamped; the others were applied by lithography.

(New Currency: 40 paras = 1 piastre, 180 piastres = £1)

1881 (June). *No.* 2 *surch with* T **6** *by lithography.*

10	6	30 paras on 1d. red	..	£100	80·00
		aa. Surch double, one invtd (Plate 216)	£3250	
		aa. Surch double, one invtd (Plate 220)	£1300 £1000	

201..	£120 85·00	217..	£170 £160
216..	£100 80·00	220..	£150 £160

½ ½ 30 PARAS

7 (8) (9)

(Typo D.L.R.)

1881 (1 July). *Die I. Wmk Crown CC.*

11	7	½ pi. emerald-green	..	£180	42·00
12		1 pi. rose	..	£350	30·00
13		2 pi. blue	..	£450	30·00
14		4 pi. pale olive-green	..	£900	£275
15		6 pi. olive-grey	..	£1300	£425

Stamps of Queen Victoria initialled "J.A.B." or overprinted "POSTAL SURCHARGE" with or without the same initials were employed for accounting purposes between the Chief Post Office and sub-offices, the initials are those of the then Postmaster, Mr. J. A. Bulmer.

1882 (May)–86. *Die I*. Wmk Crown CA.*

16	7	½ pi. emerald-green (5.82)	..	£4000	£350
		a. Dull green (4.83)	..	9·00	90·00
		b. Top left triangle detached ..	—	90·00	
17		30 pa. pale mauve (7.6.82)	..	55·00	18·00
18		1 pi. rose (3.83)	..	70·00	1·25
		a. Top left triangle detached ..	—	£100	
19		2 pi. blue (4.83)	..	95·00	1·25
		a. Top left triangle detached ..	—	£100	
20		4 pi. deep olive-green (10.83)	..	£475	28·00
		a. Pale olive-green	..	£350	22·00
		b. Top left triangle detached ..			
21		6 pi. olive-grey (7.82)	..	35·00	16·00
		a. Top left triangle detached ..			
22		12 pi. orange-brown (1886) (Optd S. £650)	£160	32·00
16a/22		..	*Set of* 7	£700	80·00

*For description and illustrations of Dies I and II see Introduction.

For illustration of "top left triangle detached" variety see above No. 21 of Antigua.

See also Nos. 31/7.

(Surch litho by Govt Ptg Office, Nicosia)

1882. *Surch with* T **8/9.** (a) *Wmk Crown CC.*

23	7	½ on ½ pi. emerald-green (6.82)	..	£475	75·00
24		30 pa. on 1 pi. rose (22.5.82)	..	£1400	£100

(b) *Wmk Crown CA*

25	7	½ on ½ pi. emerald-green (27.5.82)	..	£120	6·50
		a. Surch double ..	..	†	£2750

1/2 1/2

(10)

11

Varieties of numerals:

1 1 1

Normal Large Small

2 2

Normal Large

1886 (Apr). *Surch with T 10 (fractions approx 6 mm apart) in typography.*

(a) *Wmk Crown CC*

26	7	½ on ½ pi. emerald-green	..	£12000

(b) *Wmk Crown CA*

27	7	½ on ½ pi. emerald-green	£225	70·00
		a. Large "2" at right	—	£700

1886 (May–June). *Surch with T 10 (fractions approx 8 mm apart) in typography.*

(a) *Wmk Crown CC*

28	7	½ on ½ pi. emerald-green	£6500	£425
		a. Large "1" at left	—	£1700
		b. Small "1" at left	£11000	£2250

(b) *Wmk Crown CA*

29	7	½ on ½ pi. emerald-green (June)	£300	7·50
		a. Large "1" at left	£2000	£200
		b. Small "1" at right	£2750	£275
		c. Large "2" at left	£2500	£275
		d. Large "2" at right	£2500	£275

Nos. 28/9 were surcharged in a setting of 60. The large "1" at left and large "2" at right both occur in the fourth vertical row, the large "2" at left in the fifth vertical row and the small "1" at right in the top horizontal row.

A third type of this surcharge is known with the fractions spaced approximately 10 mm apart on CA paper with postmarks from August 1886. This may be due to the shifting of type.

1892–94. *Die II. Wmk Crown CA.*

31	7	½ pi. dull green	3·00	50
32		30 pa. mauve	3·25	3·25
33		1 pi. carmine	8·00	1·00
34		2 pi. ultramarine	10·00	1·00
35		4 pi. olive-green	50·00	24·00
		a. Pale olive-green	16·00	20·00
36		6 pi. olive-grey (1894) ..	£120	£500
37		12 pi. orange-brown (1893) ..	£120	£325
31/37		*Set of 7*	£250	£750

1894 (14 Aug)**–96.** *Colours changed and new values. Die II. Wmk Crown CA.*

40	7	½ pi. green and carmine (1896)	4·00	60
41		30 pa. bright mauve and green (1896)	2·00	65
42		1 pi. carmine and blue (1896)	4·00	70
43		2 pi. blue and purple (1896)	4·50	80
44		4 pi. sage-green and purple (1896)	11·00	3·75
45		6 pi. sepia and green (1896)	8·00	9·00
46		9 pi. brown and carmine ..	15·00	11·00
47		12 pi. orange-brown and black (1896)	14·00	48·00
48		18 pi. greyish slate and brown	42·00	42·00
49		45 pi. grey-purple and blue ..	90·00	£120
40/49		*Set of 10*	£170	£200
40/49 Optd "Specimen"		*Set of 10*	£300	

(Typo D.L.R.)

1902–04. *Wmk Crown CA.*

50	11	½ pi. green and carmine (12.02)	2·75	50
		w. Wmk inverted	60·00	40·00
51		30 pa. violet and green (2.03) ..	4·25	1·75
		a. Mauve and green	12·00	5·00
52		1 pi. carmine and blue (9.03) ..	10·00	2·25
53		2 pi. blue and purple (2.03) ..	38·00	7·50
54		4 pi. olive-green and purple (9.03)	26·00	15·00
55		6 pi. sepia and green (9.03) ..	38·00	90·00
56		9 pi. brown and carmine (5.04)	95·00	£180
57		12 pi. chestnut and black (4.03)	12·00	40·00
58		18 pi. black and brown (5.04) ..	65·00	£120
59		45 pi. dull purple and ultramarine (10.03)	£200	£500
50/9		*Set of 10*	£450	£850
50/9 Optd "Specimen"		*Set of 10*	£450	

Broken top left triangle
(Left pane R.7/5)

1904–10. *Wmk Mult Crown CA.*

60	11	5 pa. bistre and black (14.1.08)	60	30
		a. Broken top left triangle ..	38·00	
61		10 pa. orange and green (12.06) ..	2·00	30
		a. Yellow and green ..	32·00	5·50
		b. Broken top left triangle ..	48·00	
		w. Wmk inverted	—	65·00
62		½ pi. green and carmine (1.7.04)	3·25	15
		a. Broken top left triangle ..	65·00	
		w. Wmk inverted	75·00	50·00
63		30 pa. purple and green (1.7.04) ..	9·50	1·00
		a. Violet and green (1910) ..	9·00	1·50
		b. Broken top left triangle ..	£110	
64		1 pi. carmine and blue (11.04) ..	3·00	70
		a. Broken top left triangle ..	75·00	
65		2 pi. blue and purple (11.04) ..	4·25	1·00
		a. Broken top left triangle ..	95·00	
66		4 pi. olive-green and purple (2.05)	9·00	6·00
		a. Broken top left triangle ..	£140	
67		6 pi. sepia and green (17.7.04) ..	8·50	9·50
		a. Broken top left triangle ..	£140	
68		9 pi. brown and carmine (30.5.04)	23·00	7·00
		a. Yellow-brown and carmine	17·00	17·00
		b. Broken top left triangle ..	£200	
		w. Wmk inverted	90·00	60·00
69		12 pi. chestnut and black (4.06) ..	21·00	28·00
70		18 pi. black and brown (16.6.04) ..	27·00	9·50
		a. Broken top left triangle ..	£300	
71		45 pi. dull purple and ultram (15.6.04)	65·00	£120
60/71		*Set of 12*	£150	£160
60/1 Optd "Specimen"		*Set of 2*	£120	

12   13

Broken bottom left triangle (Right pane R.10/6)

(Typo D.L.R.)

1912 (July)**–15.** *Wmk Mult Crown CA.*

74	12	10 pa. orange and green (11.12) ..	3·00	1·40
		a. Wmk sideways	†	£2000
		b. Orange-yellow & bright green (8.15)	2·25	50
		ba. Broken bottom left triangle ..	50·00	
75		½ pi. green and carmine ..	1·75	20
		a. Yellow-green and carmine ..	5·00	1·40
		ab. Broken bottom left triangle ..	65·00	
76		30 pa. violet and green (3.13) ..	1·50	50
		a. Broken bottom left triangle ..	50·00	
		w. Wmk inverted		
77		1 pi. rose-red and blue (9.12) ..	3·75	1·25
		a. Carmine and blue (1.15?) ..	12·00	4·00
		ab. Broken bottom left triangle ..	95·00	
78		2 pi. blue and purple (7.13) ..	6·50	1·00
		a. Broken bottom left triangle ..	85·00	
79		4 pi. olive-green and purple ..	3·25	3·50
		a. Broken bottom left triangle ..	60·00	
80		6 pi. sepia and green	2·75	7·00
		a. Broken bottom left triangle ..	60·00	
81		9 pi. brown and carmine (3.15) ..	19·00	20·00
		a. Yellow-brown and carmine ..	22·00	23·00
82		12 pi. chestnut and black (7.13) ..	9·00	22·00
83		18 pi. black and brown (3.15) ..	22·00	22·00
		a. Broken bottom left triangle ..	£190	
84		45 pi. dull purple and ultramarine (3.15)	65·00	£110
		a. Broken bottom left triangle ..	£350	
74/84		*Set of 11*	£120	£170
74/84 Optd "Specimen" ..		*Set of 11*	£350	

1921–23. (a) *Wmk Mult Script CA.*

85	12	10 pa. orange and green ..	3·00	3·25
		a. Broken bottom left triangle ..	60·00	
86		10 pa. grey and yellow (1923) ..	10·00	6·50
		a. Broken bottom left triangle ..	£140	
87		30 pa. violet and green ..	2·50	40
		a. Broken bottom left triangle ..	55·00	
		w. Wmk inverted		
		y. Wmk inverted and reversed ..	†	£500
88		30 pa. green (1923)	5·50	40
		a. Broken bottom left triangle ..	80·00	
		w. Wmk inverted		
89		1 pi. carmine and blue ..	10·00	18·00
		a. Broken bottom left triangle ..	£110	
90		1 pi. violet and red (1922) ..	3·00	3·25
		a. Broken bottom left triangle ..	60·00	
91		1½ pi. yellow and black (1922) ..	3·25	3·75
		a. Broken bottom left triangle ..	65·00	
92		2 pi. blue and purple ..	12·00	8·00
		a. Broken bottom left triangle ..	£140	
93		2 pi. carmine and blue (1922) ..	9·00	22·00
		a. Broken bottom left triangle ..	£130	
94		2¾ pi. blue and purple (1922) ..	7·00	10·00
		a. Broken bottom left triangle ..	£120	
95		4 pi. olive-green and purple ..	7·00	12·00
		a. Broken bottom left triangle ..	£120	
		w. Wmk inverted	†	£500
96		6 pi. sepia and green (1923) ..	11·00	50·00
		a. Broken bottom left triangle ..	£140	
97		9 pi. brown and carmine (1922) ..	25·00	55·00
		a. Yellow-brown and carmine ..	60·00	85·00
		b. Broken bottom left triangle ..	£250	
98		18 pi. black and brown (1923) ..	55·00	£130
		a. Broken bottom left triangle ..	£350	
99		45 pi. dull purple and ultramarine (1923)	£150	£250
		a. Broken bottom left triangle ..	£650	
85/99		*Set of 15*	£275	£500
85/99 Optd "Specimen" ..		*Set of 15*	£475	

(b) *Wmk Mult Crown CA (1923)*

100	12	10s. green and red/pale yellow ..	£350	£650
		a. Broken bottom left triangle ..	£1700	
101		£1 purple and black/red ..	£1000	£1400
		a. Broken bottom left triangle ..	£3500	
100/1 Optd "Specimen" ..		*Set of 2*	£500	

Examples of Nos. 96/101 are known showing a forged Limassol postmark dated "14 MR 25".

1924–28. *Chalk-surfaced paper.* (a) *Wmk Mult Crown CA.*

102	13	£1 purple and black/red ..	£300	£550

(b) *Wmk Mult Script CA*

103	13	¼ pi. grey and chestnut ..	65	15
104		½ pi. black	1·75	85
105		¾ pi. green	1·50	90
106		1 pi. purple and chestnut ..	1·25	40
107		1½ pi. orange and black.. ..	1·25	4·50
108		2 pi. carmine and green ..	1·75	7·00
109		2¾ pi. bright blue and purple ..	2·50	2·00
110		4 pi. sage-green and purple ..	2·25	1·75
111		4½ pi. black and orange/emerald ..	2·75	3·00
112		6 pi. olive-brown and green ..	2·75	4·00
113		9 pi. brown and purple ..	4·25	3·25
114		12 pi. chestnut and black ..	6·50	45·00
115		18 pi. black and orange.. ..	17·00	4·50

116	13	45 pi. purple and blue	28·00	35·00
117		90 pi. green and red/yellow ..	70·00	£150
117a		£5 black/yellow (1928) (Optd S.900) ..	£2750	£5500
102/122		*Set of 21 to £1*	£400	£700
102/22 Optd "Specimen"		*Set of 21*	£600	

Examples of No. 117a are known showing a forged Registered Nicosia postmark dated "6 MAY 35".

CROWN COLONY

1925. *Wmk Mult Script CA. Chalk-surfaced paper (½, ¾ and 2 pi.).*

118	13	½ pi. green	1·75	85
119		¾ pi. brownish black	1·75	10
120		1½ pi. scarlet	2·25	30
121		2 pi. yellow and black ..	4·25	2·00
122		2½ pi. bright blue	1·75	30

In the above set the fraction bar in the value is horizontal. In Nos. 91, 94, 107 and 109 it is diagonal.

14 Silver Coin of   16 Map of Cyprus
Amathus, 6th-cent B.C.

(Recess B.W.)

1928 (1 Feb). *50th Anniv of British Rule. T 14, 16 and similar designs. Wmk Mult Script CA. P 12.*

123		¾ pi. deep dull purple	2·25	70
124		1 pi. black and greenish blue ..	2·50	85
125		1½ pi. scarlet	3·75	2·00
126		2½ pi. light blue	2·75	2·00
127		4 pi. deep brown	4·00	6·00
128		6 pi. blue	5·00	17·00
129		9 pi. maroon	5·50	10·00
130		18 pi. black and brown ..	16·00	17·00
131		45 pi. violet and blue	32·00	45·00
132		£1 blue and bistre-brown	£200	£300
123/132		*Set of 10*	£225	£350
123/32 Optd "Specimen"		*Set of 10*	£500	

Designs: *Vert*—1 pi. Zeno (philosopher); 2½ pi. Discovery of body of St Barnabas; 4 pi. Cloister, Abbey of Bella Paise; 9 pi. Tekke of Umm Haram; 18 pi. Statue of Richard I, Westminster; 45 pi. St. Nicholas Cathedral, Famagusta (now Lala Mustafa Pasha Mosque); £1 King George V. *Horiz*—6 pi. Badge of Cyprus.

24 Ruins of Vouni Palace   25 Small Marble Forum, Salamis

30 St. Sophia   31 Bayraktar Mosque,
Cathedral, Nicosia   Nicosia
(now Selimiye
Mosque)

(Recess Waterlow)

1934 (1 Dec). *T 24/5, 30/1 and similar designs. Wmk Mult Script CA (sideways on ½ pi., 1½ pi., 2½ pi., 4½ pi., 6 pi., 9 pi. and 18 pi.). P 12½.*

133		¼ pi. ultramarine and orange-brown ..	60	50
		a. Imperf between (vert pair) ..	£18000	£15000
134		½ pi. green	70	80
		a. Imperf between (vert pair) ..	£10000	£11000
135		¾ pi. black and violet	80	10
		a. Imperf between (vert pair) ..	£20000	
136		1 pi. black and red-brown ..	70	80
		a. Imperf between (vert pair) ..	£12000	£12000
		b. Imperf between (horiz pair) ..	£10000	
137		1½ pi. carmine	70	55
138		2½ pi. ultramarine	1·25	1·25
139		4½ pi. black and crimson ..	3·00	3·00
140		6 pi. black and blue	7·00	12·00
141		9 pi. sepia and violet	4·50	3·75
142		18 pi. black and olive-green ..	40·00	27·00
143		45 pi. green and black	55·00	45·00
133/43		*Set of 11*	£100	85·00
133/43 Perf "Specimen" ..		*Set of 11*	£275	

Designs: *Horiz*.—¾ pi. Church of St. Barnabas and St. Hilarion, Peristerona; 1 pi. Roman theatre, Soli; 1½ pi. Kyrenia Harbour; 2½ pi. Kolossi Castle; 45 pi. Forest scene, Troodos. *Vert*.—9 pi. Queen's Window, St. Hilarion Castle; 18 pi. Buyuk Khan, Nicosia.

1935 (6 May). *Silver Jubilee. As Nos. 91/4 of Antigua, but ptd by Waterlow & Sons. P 11 × 12.*

144		¾ pi. ultramarine and grey ..	1·25	40
145		1½ pi. deep blue and scarlet ..	3·00	2·50
		l. Kite and horizontal log ..	£140	
146		2½ pi. deep blue and deep blue ..	3·75	1·50
147		9 pi. slate and purple	13·00	11·00
144/7		*Set of 4*	19·00	14·00
144/7 Perf "Specimen" ..		*Set of 4*	£130	

For illustration of plate variety see Catalogue Introduction.

1937 (12 May). *Coronation. As Nos. 95/7 of Antigua.*
P 11×11½.

148	¾ pi. grey	.. ..	75	20
149	1½ pi. carmine	.. ..	1·25	80
150	2½ pi. blue	.. ..	2·50	1·25
148/50		*Set of 3*	4·00	2·00
148/50 Perf "Specimen"		*Set of 3*	£100	

35 Vouni Palace   36 Map of Cyprus

37 Othello's Tower,   38 King George VI
Famagusta

(Recess Waterlow)

1938 (12 May)–**1951**. *T 35 to 38 and other designs as 1934, but with portrait of King George VI. Wmk Mult Script CA. P 12½.*

151	35	¼ pi. ultramarine and orange-brown ..	20	20
152	25	½ pi. green ..	30	10
152a	–	½ pi. violet (2.7.51) ..	1·75	20
153	–	¾ pi. black and violet ..	13·00	40
154	–	1 pi. orange ..	40	10
		a. Perf 13½ × 12½ (1944) ..	£375	26·00
155	–	1½ pi. carmine ..	5·00	1·50
155a	–	1½ pi. violet (15.3.43) ..	30	30
155ab	–	1½ pi. green (2.7.51) ..	2·25	40
155b	–	2 pi. black and carmine (2.2.42)	30	10
		c. Perf 12½×13½ (10.44) ..	1·75	5·00
156	–	2½ pi. ultramarine ..	16·00	3·00
156a	–	3 pi. ultramarine (2.2.42) ..	80	15
156b	–	4 pi. ultramarine (2.7.51) ..	3·00	30
157	36	4½ pi. grey ..	40	10
158	31	6 pi. black and blue ..	65	1·00
159	37	9 pi. black and purple ..	1·75	20
160	–	18 pi. green and olive-green ..	5·00	85
		a. Black and sage-green (19.8.47)	7·50	1·50
161	–	45 pi. green and black ..	14·00	2·50
162	38	90 pi. mauve and black ..	20·00	4·50
163	–	£1 scarlet and indigo ..	45·00	21·00
151/63		*Set of 19*	£110	32·00
151/63 Perf "Specimen"		*Set of 16*	£375	

Designs: *Horiz*—¾ pi., 2 pi. Peristerona Church; 1 pi. Soli Theatre; 1½ pi. Kyrenia Harbour; 2½ pi., 3 pi., 4 pi. Kolossi Castle; 45 pi. Forest scene. *Vert*—18 pi. Buyuk Khan, Nicosia.

1946 (21 Oct). *Victory. As Nos. 110/11 of Antigua.*

164	1½ pi. deep violet	.. ..	15	10
165	3 pi. blue	.. ..	15	15
164/5 Perf "Specimen"		*Set of 2*	90·00	

Extra decoration
(R. 3/5)

1948 (20 Dec). *Royal Silver Wedding. As Nos. 112/13 of Antigua.*

166	1½ pi. violet	.. ..	50	20
	a. Extra decoration	..	30·00	
167	£1 indigo	.. ..	42·00	48·00

1949 (10 Oct). *75th Anniv of Universal Postal Union. As Nos. 114/ 17 of Antigua but inscr "CYPRUS" (recess).*

168	1½ pi. violet	.. ..	90	70
169	2 pi. carmine-red	.. ..	1·75	1·50
170	3 pi. deep blue	.. ..	1·25	1·00
171	9 pi. purple	.. ..	1·75	1·10
168/71		*Set of 4*	5·00	3·75

1953 (2 June). *Coronation. As No. 120 of Antigua, but ptd by B.W.*

172	1½ pi. black and emerald	.. ..	65	10

(New Currency. 1000 mils. = £1)

39 Carobs   42 Mavrovouni Copper
Pyrites Mine

---

49 St. Hilarion Castle   52 Coins of Salamis, Paphos,
Citium and Idalium

(Recess B.W.)

1955 (1 Aug)–**60**. *T 39, 42, 49, 52 and similar designs. Wmk Mult Script CA. P 13½ (Nos. 183/5) or 11½ (others).*

173	2 m. blackish brown	..	10	40
174	3 m. blue-violet	..	10	15
175	5 m. brown-orange	..	50	10
	a. Orange-brown (17.9.58)	..	2·00	30
176	10 m. deep brown and deep green	..	65	10
177	15 m. olive-green and indigo	..	2·50	45
	aa. Yellow-olive and indigo (17.9.58)	10·00	2·00
	a. Bistre and indigo (14.6.60)	17·00	6·00
178	20 m. brown and deep bright blue	..	80	15
179	25 m. deep turquoise-blue	..	1·50	60
	a. Greenish blue (17.9.58)	..	7·50	3·50
180	30 m. black and carmine-lake	..	1·00	10
181	35 m. orange-brown & deep turquoise-blue	55	40
182	40 m. deep green and sepia	..	1·00	60
183	50 m. turquoise-blue and reddish brown	85	30
184	100 m. mauve and bluish green	..	11·00	60
185	250 m. deep grey-blue and brown	..	9·00	6·00
186	500 m. slate and purple	..	24·00	11·00
187	£1 brown-lake and slate	..	24·00	26·00
173/87		*Set of 15*	70·00	42·00

Designs: *Vert* (as *T 40*)—3 m. Grapes; 5 m. Oranges. (as *T 52*)—£1 Arms of Byzantium, Lusignan, Ottoman Empire and Venice. *Horiz* (as *T 42*)—15 m. Troodos Forest; 20 m. Beach of Aphrodite; 25 m. 5th-century B.C. coin of Paphos; 30 m. Kyrenia; 35 m. Harvest in Mesaoria; 40 m. Famagusta Harbour. (as *T 50*)—100 m. Hala Sultan Tekke; 250 m. Kanakaria Church.

(54 "Cyprus Republic")   55 Map of Cyprus

1960 (16 Aug)–**61**. *Nos. 173/87 optd as T 54, in blue by B.W. Opt larger on Nos. 191/7 and in two lines on Nos. 198/202.*

188	2 m. blackish brown	..	20	30
189	3 m. blue-violet	..	20	15
190	5 m. brown-orange	..	1·00	10
	a. Orange-brown (15.8.61)	..	1·75	10
191	10 m. deep brown and deep green	..	70	10
192	15 m. yellow-bistre and indigo	..	75	10
	a. Olive-green and indigo	£100	24·00
	b. Brownish bis & dp ind (10.10.61)	4·25	2·00
193	20 m. brown and deep bright blue	..	40	50
	a. Opt double		†	£9000
194	25 m. deep turquoise-blue	..	1·25	45
	a. Greenish blue (7.2.61)	12·00	5·50
195	30 m. black and carmine-lake	..	1·75	10
	a. Opt double		†£15000
196	35 m. orange-brown & dp turquoise-blue	1·75	20
197	40 m. deep green and sepia	..	2·00	1·00
198	50 m. turquoise-blue and reddish brown	2·00	40
199	100 m. mauve and bluish green	..	9·00	40
200	250 m. deep grey-blue and brown	..	25·00	2·00
201	500 m. slate and purple	..	40·00	15·00
202	£1 brown-lake and slate	..	60·00	48·00
188/202	..	*Set of 15*	£130	60·00

Only two used examples of No. 195a are known.

(Recess B.W.)

1960 (16 Aug). *Constitution of Republic. W w 12. P 11½.*

203	55	10 m. sepia and deep green	..	30	10
204		30 m. ultramarine and deep brown	..	65	10
205		100 m. purple and deep slate	..	2·00	1·50
203/5			*Set of 3*	2·75	1·50

PRINTERS. All the following stamps to No. 715 were designed by A. Tassos and lithographed by Aspioti-Elka, Athens, *unless otherwise stated.*

56 Doves

(Des T. Kurpershoek)

1962 (19 Mar). *Europa. P 14 × 13.*

206	56	10 m. purple and mauve	..	10	10
207		40 m. ultramarine and cobalt	..	20	15
208		100 m. emerald and pale green	..	20	20
206/8		..	*Set of 3*	40	40

57 Campaign Emblem

1962 (14 May). *Malaria Eradication. P 14 × 13½.*

209	57	10 m. black and olive-green	..	20	15
210		30 m. black and brown	..	40	15

58 Mult K C K Δ and Map

WATERMARK VARIETIES. The issues printed by Aspioti-Elka with W 58 are known with the vertical stamps having the watermark normal or inverted and the horizontal stamps with the watermark reading upwards or downwards. Such varieties are not given separate listing.

62 Selimiye Mosque,   63 St. Barnabas's Church
Nicosia

1962 (17 Sept). *T 62/3 and similar designs. W 58 (sideways on 25, 30, 40, 50, 250 m., £1). P 13½ × 14 (vert) or 14 × 13½ (horiz).*

211	3 m. deep brown and orange-brown	..	10	10
212	5 m. purple and grey-green	..	10	10
213	10 m. black and yellow-green	..	15	10
214	15 m. black and reddish purple	..	20	15
215	25 m. deep brown and chestnut	..	30	20
216	30 m. deep blue and light blue	..	20	10
217	35 m. light green and blue	..	35	10
218	40 m. black and violet-blue	..	1·25	1·50
219	50 m. bronze-green and bistre	..	50	10
220	100 m. deep brown and yellow-brown	..	3·50	30
221	250 m. black and cinnamon	..	8·00	2·25
222	500 m. deep brown and light green	..	15·00	10·00
223	£1 bronze-green and grey	..	16·00	26·00
211/23		*Set of 13*	40·00	35·00

Designs: *Vert*—3 m. Iron Age jug; 5 m. Grapes; 10 m. Bronze head of Apollo; 35 m. Head of Aphrodite; 100 m. Hala Sultan Tekke; 500 m. Mouflon. *Horiz*—30 m. Temple of Apollo Hylates; 40 m. Skiing, Troodos; 50 m. Salamis Gymnasium; 250 m. Bella Paise Abbey; £1 St. Hilarion Castle.

72 Europa "Tree"

(Des L. Weyer)

1963 (28 Jan). *Europa. W 58 (sideways). P 14 × 13½.*

224	72	10 m. bright blue and black	..	75	20
225		40 m. carmine-red and black	..	3·50	2·25
226		150 m. emerald-green and black	..	14·00	7·50
224/6			*Set of 3*	16·00	9·00

73 Harvester   75 Wolf Cub in Camp

1963 (21 Mar). *Freedom from Hunger. T 73 and similar vert design. W 58. P 13½ × 14.*

227	25 m. ochre, sepia and bright blue	..	35	25
228	75 m. grey, black and lake	..	2·25	1·00

Design:— 75 m. Demeter, Goddess of Corn.

1963 (21 Aug). *50th Anniv of Cyprus Scout Movement and Third Commonwealth Scout Conference, Platres. T 75 and similar vert designs. Multicoloured. W 58. P 13½ × 14.*

229	3 m. Type 75	..	10	20
230	20 m. Sea Scout	..	45	10
231	150 m. Scout with Mouflon	..	1·50	2·25
229/31		*Set of 3*	1·75	2·25
MS231a	110×90 mm. Nos. 229/31 (sold at 250 m.). Imperf	..	£120	£225

78 Nurse tending Child   **79** Children's Centre, Kyrenia

90 Dionysus and Acme

91 Silenus (satyr)

(Des H. Karlsson)

1965 (27 Sept). *Europa.* W **58** (*sideways*). P 14×13½.
267 100   5 m. black, orange-brown and orange   20   10
268   45 m. black, orange-brown & lt emer   1·40   1·50
269   150 m. black, orange-brown & lt grey   4·00   3·75
267/9   ..   ..   *Set of 3* 5·00   4·75

1966 (31 Jan). *U.N. General Assembly's Cyprus Resolution, 18 December 1965. Nos.* 211, 213, 216 *and* 221 *optd with T* **101**, *in blue by Govt Printing Office, Nicosia.*
270   3 m. deep brown and orange-brown   10   25
271   10 m. black and yellow-green   10   10
272   30 m. deep blue and light blue   10   15
273 250 m. black and cinnamon   55   1·75
270/3   ..   ..   *Set of 4* 70   2·00

102 Discovery of St. Barnabas's Body   **104** St. Barnabas (icon)

1963 (9 Sept). *Centenary of Red Cross.* W **58** (*sideways on* 100 *m.*). P 13½ × 14 (10 *m.*) *or* 14 × 13½ (100 *m.*).
232 78   10 m. red, blue, grey-bl, chestnut & blk   50   15
233 79   100 m. red, green, black and blue   ..   3·00   3·50

80 "Co-operation" (emblem)   (81)

(Des A. Holm)

1963 (4 Nov). *Europa.* W **58** (*sideways*).P 14 × 13½.
234 80   20 m. buff, blue and violet   ..   1·50   40
235   30 m. grey, yellow and blue   ..   2·25   40
236   150 m. buff, blue and orange-brown   10·00 10·00
234/6   ..   ..   *Set of 3* 12·00 10·00

1964 (5 May). *U.N. Security Council's Cyprus Resolutions, March, 1964, Nos.* 213, 216, 218/20, *optd with T* **81** *in blue by Govt Printing Office, Nicosia.*
237   10 m. black and yellow-green   20   10
238   30 m. deep blue and light blue   20   10
239   40 m. black and violet-blue   20   20
240   50 m. bronze-green and bistre   20   10
241 100 m. deep brown and yellow-brown   25   50
237/41   ..   ..   ..   *Set of 5* 95   85

82 Soli Theatre

1964 (15 June). *400th Birth Anniv of Shakespeare. T* **82** *and similar horiz designs. Multicoloured.* W **58**.*P* 13½ × 13.
242   15 m. Type **82**   40   15
243   35 m. Curium Theatre   ..   40   15
244   50 m. Salamis Theatre   ..   40   15
245 100 m. Othello Tower and scene from *Othello*   1·00   2·00
242/5   ..   ..   *Set of 4* 2·00   2·25

86 Running   **89** Europa "Flower"

1964 (6 July). *Olympic Games, Tokyo. T* **86** *and similar designs.* W **58** (*sideways,* 25 *m.* 75 *m.*). P 13½ × 14 (10 *m.*) *or* 14 × 13½ (*others*).
246   10 m. brown, black and yellow   ..   15   10
247   25 m. brown, blue and blue-grey   ..   35   10
248   75 m. brown, black and orange-red   ..   50   65
246/8   ..   ..   ..   *Set of 3* 90   75
MS248a 110 × 90 mm. Nos. 246/8 (*sold at* 250 *m.*).
Imperf   6·00 14·00
Designs: *Horiz*—25 m. Boxing; 75 m. Charioteers.

(Des G. Bétemps)

1964 (14 Sept). *Europa.* W **58**. P 13½ × 14.
249 89   20 m. chestnut and light ochre   ..   60   10
250   30 m. ultramarine and light blue   ..   1·00   10
251   150 m. olive and light blue-green   6·25   8·00
249/51   ..   ..   *Set of 3* 7·00   8·00

STANLEY GIBBONS STAMP COLLECTING SERIES

Introductory booklets on *How to Start, How to Identify Stamps* and *Collecting by Theme.* A series of well illustrated guides at a low price.
Write for details.

1964 (26 Oct). *Cyprus Wines. T* **90/1** *and similar multicoloured designs.* W **58** (*sideways,* 10 *m.,* or 100 *m.*). P 14 × 13½ (*horiz*) 13½ × 14 (*vert*).
252   10 m. Type **90**   25   10
253   40 m. Type **91**   65   75
254   50 m. Commandaria Wine (*vert*)   75   10
255 100 m. Wine factory (*horiz*)   2·50   1·60
252/5   ..   ..   *Set of 4* 3·75   2·25

94 President Kennedy

1965 (15 Feb). *President Kennedy Commemoration.* W **58** (*sideways*). P 14 × 13½.
256 94   10 m. ultramarine   ..   10   10
257   40 m. green   ..   25   20
258   100 m. carmine-lake   30   10
256/8   ..   *Set of 3* 55   40
MS258a 110 × 90 mm. Nos. 256/8 (*sold at* 250 *m.*).
Imperf   3·00   6·50

95 "Old Age"   **96** "Maternity"

1965 (12 Apr). *Introduction of Social Insurance Law. T* **95/6** *and similar design.* W **58**. P 13½×12 (75 *m.*) *or* 13½×14 (*others*).
259   30 m. drab and dull green   20   10
260   45 m. light grey-green, blue & dp ultramarine   30   10
261   75 m. red-brown and flesh   1·50   2·00
259/61   ..   *Set of 3* 1·75   2·00
Design: *Vert as T* **95**—45 m. "Accident".

98 I.T.U. Emblem and Symbols

1965 (17 May). *I.T.U. Centenary.* W **58** (*sideways*).P 14 × 13½.
262 98   15 m. black, brown and yellow   ..   75   20
263   60 m. black, green and light green   4·75   2·00
264   75 m. black, indigo and light blue   5·50   3·75
262/4   ..   ..   *Set of 3* 10·00   5·50

99 I.C.Y. Emblem

1965 (17 May). *International Co-operation Year.* W **58** (*sideways*). P 14 × 13½.
265 99   50 m. brown, dp green & lt yellow-brown   75   10
266   100 m. purple, dp green & lt purple   1·25   70

100 Europa "Sprig"

U. N.
Resolution on Cyprus
18 Dec. 1965
(101)

103 St. Barnabas's Chapel

105 "Privileges of Cyprus Church"
(*Actual size* 102 × 82 *mm*)

1966 (25 Apr). *1900th Death Anniv of St. Barnabas.* W **58** (*sideways on* 15 *m.,* 100 *m.,* 250 *m.*). P 14 × 13 (25 *m.*) *or* 13 × 14 (*others*).
274 102   15 m. multicoloured   ..   10   10
275 103   25 m. drab, black and blue   20   10
276 104   100 m. multicoloured   55   1·50
274/6   ..   *Set of 3* 70   1·50
MS277 110 × 91 mm. **105** 250 m. mult. Imperf   4·25 13·00

5 M

(106)   **107** General K. S. Thimayya and U. N. Emblem

1966 (30 May). *No.* 211 *surch with T* **106** *by Govt Printing Office, Nicosia.*
278   5 m. on 3 m. deep brown & orange-brown   10   10

1966 (6 June). *General Thimayya Commemoration.* W **58** (*sideways*).P 14 × 13.
279 107   50 m. black and light orange-brown   ..   30   10

EUROPA CEPT

108 Europa "Ship"

(Des G. and J. Bender)

1966 (26 Sept). *Europa. W* **58**. *P* 13½ × 14.

280	**108**	20 m. green and blue	..	25	10
281		30 m. bright purple and blue	.. ..	25	10
282		150 m. bistre and blue	.. ..	1·75	3·00
280/2	..		*Set of 3*	2·00	3·00

110 Church of
St. James, Trikomo

119 Vase of
7th Century B.C.

120 Bronze Ingot-stand

1966 (21 Nov)–69. *T* **110**, **119/20** *and similar designs. W* **58** (*sideways on 3, 15, 25, 50, 250, 500 m.*, £1). *P* 12×13 (3 *m.*), 13×12 (5, 10 *m.*), 14×13½ (15, 25, 50 *m.*), 13½×14 (20, 30, 35, 40, 100 *m.*) *or* 13×14 (*others*).

283	3 m. grey-green, buff, black & light blue			40	20
284	5 m. bistre, black and steel-blue			10	10
	a. Brownish bistre, black and steel-blue				
	(18.4.69)			45	20
285	10 m. black and bistre	..		15	15
286	15 m. black, chestnut & light orange-brown			15	10
287	20 m. black, slate and brown	..		1·25	90
288	25 m. black, drab and lake-brown	..		30	10
289	30 m. black, yellow-ochre and turquoise	..		50	20
290	35 m. yellow, black and carmine-red	..		50	30
291	40 m. black, grey and new blue	..		70	30
	a. Grey (background) omitted				
292	50 m. black, slate and brown	..		90	10
293	100 m. black, red, pale buff and grey	..		3·75	15
294	250 m. olive-green, black & lt yellow-ochre			1·50	40
295	500 m. multicoloured	..		2·25	70
296	£1 black, drab and slate	..		2·50	6·00
283/96		*Set of 14*		13·00	8·50

Designs: *Horiz* (as *T* **110**)—3 m. Stavrovouni Monastery. (*As T* **119**)—15 m. Minoan wine ship of 700 B.C. (painting); 25 m. Sleeping Eros (marble statue); 50 m. Silver coin of Alexander the Great. *Vert* (as *T* **110**)—10 m. Zeno of Cibium (marble bust). (*As T* **119**)—20 m. Silver coin of Evagoras I; 30 m. St. Nicholas Cathedral, Famagusta; 35 m. Gold sceptre from Curium; 40 m. Silver dish from 7th century. (*As T* **120**)—500 m. "The Rape of Ganymede" (mosaic); £1 Aphrodite (marble statue).

123 Power Station,
Limassol

124 Cogwheels

1967 (10 Apr). *First Development Programme. T* **123** *and similar designs but horiz. Multicoloured. W* **58** (*sideways on* 15 *to* 100 *m.*). *P* 13½ × 14 (10 *m.*) *or* 14 × 13½ (*others*).

297	10 m. Type **123**	..	..	10	10
298	15 m. Arghaka-Maghounda Dam	..		15	10
299	35 m. Troodos Highway	..		20	10
300	50 m. Hilton Hotel, Nicosia	..		20	10
301	100 m. Famagusta Harbour	..		20	90
297/301		*Set of 5*		75	1·10

(Des O. Bonnevalle)

1967 (2 May). *Europa. W* **58**. *P* 13½ × 14.

302	**124**	20 m. olive-green, green & pale yell-grn	25	10
303		30 m. reddish violet, lilac and pale lilac	25	10
304		150 m. brown, light reddish brown and		
		pale yellow-brown	..	1·00	2·00
302/4	..	.. .. ..	*Set of 3*	1·40	2·00

OMNIBUS ISSUES

Details, together with prices for complete sets, of the various Omnibus issues from the 1935 Silver Jubilee series to date are included in a special section following Zimbabwe at the end of Volume 2.

125 Throwing the Javelin

126 Running (amphora) and Map of Eastern
Mediterranean
(*Actual size* 97 × 77 *mm*)

1967 (4 Sept). *Athletic Games, Nicosia. T* **125** *and similar designs and T* **126**. *Multicoloured. W* **58**. *P* 13½ × 13.

305	15 m. Type **125**	..		20	10
306	35 m. Running	..		20	35
307	100 m. High-jumping	..		30	85
		Set of 3		60	1·10
MS308	110×90 mm. 250 m. Type **126** (wmk sideways). Imperf			1·60	6·50

127 Ancient Monuments

128 St. Andrew Mosaic

1967 (16 Oct). *International Tourist Year. T* **127** *and similar horiz designs. Multicoloured. W* **58**. *P* 13 × 13½.

309	10 m. Type **127**	..		10	10
310	40 m. Famagusta Beach	..		15	70
311	50 m. Hawker Siddeley Comet 4 at Nicosia				
	Airport	..		15	10
312	100 m. Skier and youth hostel	..		20	75
309/12	..		*Set of 4*	50	1·50

1967 (8 Nov). *Centenary of St. Andrew's Monastery. W* **58** (*sideways*). *P* 13 × 13½.

313	**128**	25 m. multicoloured	..	10	10

129 "The Crucifixion" (icon)

130 The Three Magi

(Photo French Govt Ptg Wks, Paris)

1967 (8 Nov). *Cyprus Art Exhibition, Paris. P* 12½ × 13½.

314	**129**	50 m. multicoloured	..	10	10

1967 (8 Nov). *20th Anniv of U.N.E.S.C.O. W* **58** (*sideways*). *P* 13 × 13½.

315	**130**	75 m. multicoloured	..	20	20

131 Human Rights
Emblem over Stars

132 Human Rights
and U.N. Emblems

133 Scroll of Declaration
(*Actual size* 95 × 75½ *mm*)

1968 (18 Mar). *Human Rights Year. W* **58**. *P* 13 × 14.

316	**131**	50 m. multicoloured		10	10
317	**132**	90 m. multicoloured		30	70
MS318	95 × 75½ mm. **133** 250 m. multicoloured.				
	W **58** (*sideways*). Imperf.	..	..	1·00	4·75

134 Europa "Key"

(Des H. Schwarzenbach)

1968 (29 Apr). *Europa. W* **58** (*sideways*). *P* 14 × 13.

319	**134**	20 m. multicoloured	..	20	10
320		30 m. multicoloured	..	20	10
321		150 m. multicoloured	..	60	2·00
319/21			*Set of 3*	90	2·00

135 U.N. Children's Fund Symbol
and Boy drinking Milk

136 Aesculapius

1968 (2 Sept). *21st Anniv of U.N.I.C.E.F. W* **58** (*sideways*). *P* 14 × 13.

322	**135**	35 m. yellow-brown, carmine-red & blk	10	10

1968 (2 Sept). *20th Anniv of W.H.O. W* **58**. *P* 13 × 14.

323	**136**	50 m. black, green and light olive	..	10	10

137 Throwing the
Discus

138 I.L.O. Emblem

1968 (24 Oct). *Olympic Games, Mexico. T* **137** *and similar designs. Multicoloured. W* **58** (*sideways on* 100 *m.*). *P* 14 × 13 (100 *m.*) *or* 13 × 14 (*others*).

324	10 m. Type **137**	..		10	10
325	25 m. Sprint finish	..		10	10
326	100 m. Olympic Stadium (*horiz*)	..		20	10
324/6	..	..	*Set of 3*	30	1·00

1969 (3 Mar). *50th Anniv of International Labour Organization. W* **58**. *P* 12 × 13½.

327	**138**	50 m. yellow-brown, blue and light blue	15	10
328		90 m. yellow-brown, black and pale grey	15	25

139 Mercator's Map of Cyprus, 1554

140 Blaeu's Map of Cyprus, 1635

1969 (7 Apr). *First International Congress of Cypriot Studies. W* 58 *(sideways). P* 14 × 14½.

329	139	35 m. multicoloured	..	20	30
330	140	50 m. multicoloured	..	20	10
		a. Wmk upright		—	2·75
		ab. Grey (shading on boats and cartouche) omitted			£225

141 Europa Emblem   142 Common Roller

(Des L. Gasbarra and G. Belli)

1969 (28 Apr). *Europa. W* 58 *(sideways). P* 14 × 13½.

331	141	20 m. multicoloured	..	20	10
332		30 m. multicoloured	..	20	10
333		150 m. multicoloured	..	80	2·00
331/3			*Set of* 3	1·10	2·00

1969 (7 July). *Birds of Cyprus. T* 142 *and similar designs. Multicoloured. W* 58 *(sideways on horiz designs). P* 13½ × 12 *(horiz designs) or* 12 × 13½ *(vert designs).*

334		5 m. Type 142	..	40	15
335		15 m. Audouin's Gull	..	60	15
336		20 m. Cyprus Warbler	..	65	15
337		30 m. Jay (*vert*)	..	70	15
338		40 m. Hoopoe (*vert*)	..	80	30
339		90 m. Eleanora's Falcon (*vert*)	..	2·25	5·00
334/9			*Set of* 6	4·75	5·50

The above were printed on glazed Samuel Jones paper with very faint watermark.

143 "The Nativity" (12th-century Wall Painting)

145 "Virgin and Child between Archangels Michael and Gabriel" (6th–7th-century Mosaic) (*Actual size* 102 × 81 *mm*)

1969 (24 Nov). *Christmas. T* 143 *and similar horiz design, and T* 145. *Multicoloured. W* 58 *(sideways). P* 13½ × 13.

340		20 m. Type 143	..	15	10
341		45 m. "The Nativity" (14th-century wall painting)	..	15	20
MS342		110 × 90 mm. 250 m. Type 145. Imperf	..	4·00	12·00
		a. Grey and light brown omitted ..		£1600	

146 Mahatma Gandhi

1970 (26 Jan). *Birth Centenary of Mahatma Gandhi. W* 58 *(sideways). P* 14 × 13½.

343	146	25 m. ultramarine, drab and black	15	10
344		75 m. yellow-brown, drab and black	..	20	65

147 "Flaming Sun"   148 Gladioli

(Des L. le Brocquy)

1970 (4 May). *Europa. W* 58 *(sideways). P* 14 × 13.

345	147	20 m. brown, greenish yellow & orange	20	10
346		30 m. new blue, greenish yellow & orge	20	10
347		150 m. bright purple, greenish yell & orge	80	2·25
345/7			*Set of* 3	1·10	2·25

1970 (3 Aug). *European Conservation Year. T* 148 *and similar vert designs. Multicoloured. W* 58. *P* 13 × 13½.

348		10 m. Type 148	..	10	10
349		50 m. Poppies	..	20	10
350		90 m. Giant fennel	..	65	1·75
348/50			*Set of* 3	85	1·75

149 I.E.Y. Emblem   150 Mosaic

151 Globe, Dove and U.N. Emblem

(Des G. Simonis (75 m.))

1970 (7 Sept). *Anniversaries and Events. W* 58 *(sideways on horiz designs). P* 13×14 *(5 m.), or* 14×13 *(others).*

351	149	5 m. black, red-brown & lt yellow-brn	10	10
352	150	15 m. multicoloured	..	10	10
353	151	75 m. multicoloured	..	15	50
351/3			*Set of* 3	30	60

Events:—5 m. International Education Year; 15 m. 50th General Assembly of International Vine and Wine Office; 75 m. 25th anniv of United Nations.

152 Virgin and Child   153 Cotton Napkin

(Photo Harrison)

1970 (23 Nov). *Christmas. Wall-painting from Church of Panayia Podhythou, Galata. T* 152 *and similar multicoloured designs. P* 14 × 14½.

354		25 m. Archangel (facing right)	..	15	20
		a. Horiz strip of 3. Nos. 354/6	..	40	
355		25 m. Type 152	..	15	20
356		25 m. Archangel (facing left)	..	15	20
357		75 m. Virgin and Child between Archangels	15	30
354/7			*Set of* 4	55	80

The 75 m. is horiz, size 42 × 30 mm, and the 25 m. values are vert, size as T 152.

Nos. 354/6 were issued in *se-tenant* strips of three, throughout the sheet. The triptych thus formed is depicted in its entirety on the 75 m. value.

1971 (22 Feb). *Multicoloured designs as T* 153. *W* 58 *(sideways on horiz designs).* (*a*) *Vert designs* 23 × 33 *mm. P* 12 × 13½.

358		3 m. Type 153	..	30	55
359		5 m. St. George and Dragon (19th-cent bas-relief)	..	10	10

(*b*) *Vert* (10, 20, 25, 40, 50, 75 m.) *or horiz* (15, 30, 90 m.) *designs, each* 24 × 37 *or* 37 × 24 *mm. P* 13 × 14 (15, 30, 90 m) *or* 14 × 13 (*others*)

360		10 m. Woman in festival costume	..	15	30
361		15 m. Archaic Bichrome Kylix (cup)	..	20	10
		a. Vert laid paper	..	1·00	

362		20 m. A pair of donors (St. Mamas Church)	35	50
363		25 m. "The Creation" (6th-cent mosaic)	..	30	10
364		30 m. Athena and horse-drawn chariot (4th-cent B.C. terracotta)	..	30	10
365		40 m. Shepherd playing pipe (14th-cent fresco)	..	1·00	90
366		50 m. Hellenistic head (3rd cent B.C.)	..	80	10
367		75 m. "Angel" (mosaic detail), Kanakaria Church	..	1·75	1·00
368		90 m. Mycenaean silver bowl	..	2·00	1·50

(*c*) *Horiz* (250, 500 *m*.) *or vert* (£1) *designs, each* 41 × 28 *or* 28 × 41 *mm. P* 13½ × 13 (250, 500 *m*.) *or* 13 × 13½ (£1)

369		250 m. Moufflon (detail of 3rd-cent mosaic) (shades) ..		1·50	30
370		500 m. Ladies and sacred tree (detail, 6th-cent amphora)	..	80	40
371		£1 Horned god from Enkomi (12th-cent bronze statue)	..	1·50	60
358/71			*Set of* 14	10·00	5·50

154 Europa Chain   155 Archbishop Kyprianos

(Des H. Haflidason)

1971 (3 May). *Europa, W* 58 *(sideways). P* 14 × 13

372	154	20 m. pale blue, ultramarine and black	20	10
373		30 m. apple green, myrtle-green & blk	20	10
374		150 m. lemon, bright green and black	90	2·25
372/4			*Set of* 3	1·10	2·25

The above were printed on glazed paper with very faint watermark.

1971 (9 July). *150th Anniv. of Greek War of Independence. T* 155 *and similar multicoloured designs. W* 58 *(sideways on* 30 *m*.). *P* 13½ × 12½ (30 *m*.) *or* 12½ × 13½ (*others*).

375	155	15 m. Type 155	..	10	10
376		30 m. "Taking the Oath" (*horiz*)	..	10	10
377		100 m. Bishop Germanos, flag and freedom-fighters	..	20	50
375/7			*Set of* 3	30	55

156 Kyrenia Castle   157 Madonna and Child in Stable

1971 (20 Sept). *Tourism. T* 156 *and similar multicoloured designs. W* 58 *(sideways on* 15 *and* 100 *m*.). *P* 13½ × 13 (15 *m*., 100 *m*.) *or* 13 × 13½ (*others*).

378		15 m. Type 156	..	10	10
379		25 m. Gourd on sunny beach (*vert*)	..	10	10
380		60 m. Mountain scenery (*vert*)	..	20	60
381		100 m. Church of St. Evlalios, Lambousa	..	20	65
378/81			*Set of* 4	45	1·25

1971 (22 Nov). *Christmas. T* 157 *and similar vert designs. Multicoloured. W* 58. *P* 13 × 14.

382		10 m. Type 157	..	10	10
		a. Horiz strip of 3. Nos. 382/4	..	35	
383		50 m. The Three Wise Men	..	15	35
384		100 m. The Shepherds	..	20	35
382/4			*Set of* 3	35	70

The 10 m. was issued in sheets of 100, and all three values were printed horizontally *se-tenant* in sheets of 36, the order being 50, 10 and 100 m.

158 Heart   159 "Communications"

1972 (11 Apr). *World Heart Month. W* 58 *(sideways). P* 13½×12.

385	158	15 m. multicoloured	..	10	10
386		50 m. multicoloured	..	20	45

(Des P. Huovinen)

1972 (22 May). *Europa. W* 58. *P* 12½ × 13½.

387	159	20 m. yell-orge, sepia & pale grey-brn	20	15
388		30 m. yell-orge, brt dp ultram & cobalt	20	15
389		150 m. yellow-orange, myrtle-green and pale-turquoise-green	1·60	3·25
387/9			*Set of* 3	1·75	3·25

160 Archery

1972 (24 July). *Olympic Games, Munich. T* **160** *and similar horiz designs. Multicoloured. W* **58** (*sideways*). *P* 14×13.

390	10 m. Type **160**		10	10
391	40 m. Wrestling		15	15
392	100 m. Football ..		35	1·10
390/2	..	*Set of 3*	50	1·25

161 Stater of Marion   162 Bathing the Child Jesus

1972 (25 Sept). *Ancient Coins of Cyprus* (1*st series*), *T* **161** *and similar horiz designs. W* **58** (*sideways*), *P* 14 × 13.

393	20 m. pale turquoise-blue, black and silver		20	10
394	30 m. pale violet-blue, black and silver		20	10
395	40 m. brownish stone, black and silver		20	20
396	100 m. light salmon-pink, black and silver		60	1·00
393/6		*Set of 4*	1·10	1·25

Coins:—30 m. Stater of Paphos; 40 m. Stater of Lapithos, 100 m. Stater of Idalion.
See also Nos. 486/9.

1972 (20 Nov). *Christmas. T* **162** *and similar vert designs showing portions of a mural in the Church of the Holy Cross of Agiasmati. Multicoloured. W* **58** (*sideways on MS400*). *P* 13 × 14.

397	10 m. Type **162**		10	10
398	20 m. The Magi		10	10
399	100 m. The Nativity		15	30
397/9		*Set of 3*	30	35
MS400	100×90 mm. 250 m. Showing the mural in full. Imperf ..		1·10	4·50

163 Mount Olympus, Troodos

1973 (13 Mar). *29th International Ski Federation Congress. T* **163** *and similar horiz design. Multicoloured. W* **58** (*sideways*). *P* 14 × 13.

401	20 m. Type **163**		10	10
402	100 m. Congress emblem		25	35

164 Europa "Posthorn"

(*Des I. Anisdahl*)

1973 (7 May). *Europa. W* **58** (*sideways*). *P* 14 × 13.

403	**164**	20 m. multicoloured	20	10
404		30 m. multicoloured	20	10
405		150 m. multicoloured	1·60	3·25
403/5	..	*Set of 3*	1·75	3·25

165 Archbishop's Palace, Nicosia   (166)

1973 (23 July). *Traditional Architecture. T* **165** *and similar multicoloured designs. W* **58** (*sideways on 20 and 100 m.*). *P* 14 × 13 (*20 and 100 m.*) *or* 13 × 14 (*others*).

406	20 m. Type **165**		10	10
407	30 m. House of Hajigeorgajis Cornessios, Nicosia (*vert*)		10	10
408	50 m. House at Gourri, 1850 (*vert*)		15	10
409	100 m. House at Rizokarpaso, 1772 ..		40	75
406/9		*Set of 4*	65	90

1973 (24 Sept). *No.* 361 *surch with T* **166**.

410	20 m. on 15 m. Archaic Bichrome Kylix (cup)		15	15
	a. Vert laid paper		80	
	b. Surch inverted			

167 Scout Emblem   168 Archangel Gabriel

1973 (24 Sept). *Anniversaries and Events. T* **167** *and similar designs. W* **58** (*sideways on 25 and 35 m.*). *P* 13×14 (10, 50 *and* 100 *m.*) *or* 14×13 (*others*).

411	10 m. yellow-olive and deep brown		20	10
412	25 m. deep blue, and slate-lilac		20	10
413	35 m. light brown-olive, stone and sage-green		20	25
414	50 m. dull blue and indigo		20	10
415	100 m. brown and sepia..		50	80
411/15		*Set of 5*	1·10	1·10

Designs and Events: *Vert*—10 m. Type **167** (60th anniv of Cyprus Boy Scouts); 50 m. Airline emblem (25th anniv of Cyprus Airways); 100 m. Interpol emblem (50th anniv of Interpol). *Horiz*—25 m. Outline of Cyprus and E.E.C. nations (Association of Cyprus with the E.E.C.); 35 m. F.A.O. emblem (Tenth anniv of F.A.O.).

1973 (26 Nov). *Christmas. Murals from Araka Church. T* **168** *and similar multicoloured designs. W* **58** (*sideways on 100 m.*). *P* 14 × 13 (100 *m.*) *or* 13 × 14 (*others*).

416	10 m. Type **168**		10	10
417	20 m. Madonna and Child		10	10
418	100 m. Araka Church (*horiz*)		40	75
416/18		*Set of 3*	45	75

169 Grapes   170 "The Rape of Europa" (Silver Stater of Marion)

1974 (18 Mar). *Products of Cyprus. T* **169** *and similar vert designs. Multicoloured. W* **58**. *P* 13 × 14.

419	25 m. Type **169**		10	15
420	50 m. Grapefruit		20	50
	a. Horiz strip of 3, Nos. 420/2		55	
421	50 m. Oranges ..		20	50
422	50 m. Lemons ..		20	50
419/22		*Set of 4*	65	1·50

Nos. 420/2 were printed together, horizontally *se-tenant* throughout the sheet.

1974 (29 Apr). *Europa. W* **58**. *P* 13½ × 14.

423	**170**	10 m. multicoloured	15	10
424		40 m. multicoloured	35	30
425		150 m. multicoloured	1·40	3·00
423/5	..	*Set of 3*	1·75	3·00

171 Title Page of A.   (172)
Kyprianos' "History of Cyprus" (1788)

1974 (22 July*). *Second International Congress of Cypriot Studies. T* **171** *and similar multicoloured designs. W* **58** (*sideways on 25 m. and MS429*). *P* 14 × 13½ (25 *m.*) *or* 13½ × 14 (*others*).

426	10 m. Type **171**		10	10
427	25 m. Solon (philosopher) in mosaic (*horiz*)		15	10
428	100 m. "St. Neophytos" (wall painting) .		60	75
426/8		*Set of 3*	70	80
MS429	111 × 90 mm. 250 m. Ortelius' map of Cyprus and Greek Islands, 1584. Imperf ..		1·75	6·00

*Although this is the date appearing on first day covers the stamps were not put on sale until the 24th.

1974 (1 Oct). *Obligatory Tax. Refugee Fund No.* 359 *surch with T* **172**.

430	10 m. on 5 m. St. George and Dragon ..		10	10

MINIMUM PRICE

The minimum price quote is 10p which represents a handling charge rather than a basis for valuing common stamps. For further notes about prices see introductory pages.

---

(173)   174 "Refugees"

1974 (14 Oct). *U.N. Security Council Resolution 353. Nos.* 360, 365, 366 *and* 369 *optd as T* **173**.

431	10 m. Woman in festival costume		20	10
432	40 m. Shepherd playing pipe ..		25	50
433	50 m. Hellenistic head..		25	10
434	250 m. Moufflon (*shades*)		60	2·50
431/4		*Set of 4*	1·10	2·75

1974 (2 Dec). *Obligatory Tax. Refugee Fund. W* **58** (*sideways*). *P* 12 × 12½.

435	**174**	10 m. black and light grey	10	10

175 "Virgin and Child between Two Angels", Stavros Church

1974 (2 Dec). *Christmas. T* **175** *and similar multicoloured designs showing wall-paintings. W* **58** (*sideways on 10 m. and 100 m.*). *P* 13 × 14 (50 *m.*) *or* 14 × 13 (*others*).

436	10 m. Type **175**		10	10
437	50 m. "Adoration of the Magi", Ayios Neophytos Monastery (*vert*) ..		20	10
438	100 m. "Flight into Egypt", Ayios Neophytos Monastery ..		25	45
436/8	..	*Set of 3*	45	50

176 Larnaca–Nicosia   177 "The Distaff"
Mail-coach, 1878   (M. Kashalos)

(*Photo Harrison*)

1975 (17 Feb). *Anniversaries and Events. T* **176** *and similar designs. No wmk. P* 14.

439	**176**	20 m. multicoloured	30	10
440		30 m. ultramarine, slate-blk & dull orge	30	75
441	**176**	50 m. multicoloured	30	15
442		100 m. multicoloured	55	1·60
439/42		*Set of 4*	1·40	2·40

Designs and Events:—20 m., 50 m. Type **176** (Centenary of Universal Postal Union). *Vert*—30 m. "Disabled Persons" (Eighth European Meeting of International Society for the Rehabilitation of Disabled Persons); 100 m. Council flag (25th anniv of Council of Europe).

(*Photo Harrison*)

1975 (28 Apr). *Europa. T* **177** *and similar vert designs. Multicoloured. P* 13½ × 14½.

443	20 m. Type **177**		35	50
	a. Horiz strip of 3. Nos. 443/5		1·10	
444	30 m. "Nature Morte" (C. Savva)		35	60
445	150 m. "Virgin and Child of Liopetri" (G. P. Georghiou) ..		50	1·00
443/5		*Set of 3*	1·10	1·90

Nos. 443/5 were printed horizontally *se-tenant* throughout the sheet.

178 Red Cross Flag   179 Submarine Cable
over Map   Links

1975 (4 Aug). *Anniversaries and Events. T* **178** *and similar horiz designs. P* 12½×13½ (25 *m.*) *or* 13½×12½ (*others*).

446	25 m. multicoloured		25	10
447	30 m. turquoise-green and greenish blue ..		25	10
448	75 m. red-brown, orge-brn & pale blue-grey		35	90
446/8		*Set of 3*	1·00	

Designs and Events: *Vert*—25 m. Type **178** (25th anniversary of Cyprus Red Cross). *Horiz*—30 m. Nurse and lamp (International Nurses' Day); 75 m. Woman's Steatite Idol (International Women's Year).

1975 (13 Oct). *Telecommunications Achievements. T* **179** *and similar design. W* **58** (*sideways on* 100 *m.*). *P* 12 × 13½ (50 *m.*) *or* 13½ × 12 (100 *m.*).

449	50 m. multicoloured	40	10
450	100 m. orange-yellow, dull violet and lilac	50	90

Design: *Horiz*—100 m. International subscriber dialling.

(180)

181 Human-figured Vessel, 19th-Century

1976 (5 Jan). *No.* 358 *surch with T* **180**.

451	10 m. on 3 m. Cotton napkin	20	50

1976 (3 May). *Europa. Ceramics. T* **181** *and similar vert designs. Multicoloured. W* **58**. *P* 13×14.

452	20 m. Type 181	20	10
453	60 m. Composite vessel, 2100–2000 B.C.	50	80
454	100 m. Byzantine goblet	90	1·75
452/4	*Set of* 3	1·40	2·40

182 Self-help Housing   183 Terracotta Statue of Youth

1976 (3 May). *Economic Reactivation. T* **182** *and similar horiz designs. Multicoloured. W* **58** (*sideways*). *P* 14 × 13.

455	10 m. Type 182	10	10
456	25 m. Handicrafts	20	20
457	30 m. Reafforestation	20	20
458	60 m. Air Communications	35	55
455/8	*Set of* 4	75	90

1976 (7 June). *Cypriot Treasures. T* **183** *and similar designs. W* **58** (*sideways on horiz designs, upright on vert designs*). *Ordinary cream paper. P* 12 × 13½ (5, 10 *m.*), 13 × 14 (20, 25, 30 *m.*), 14 × 13 (40, 50, 60 *m.*), 13½ × 12 (100 *m.*) *or* 13 × 13½ (250 *m. to* £1).

459	5 m. multicoloured	10	60
460	10 m. multicoloured	15	40
461	20 m. red, yellow and black	30	40
462	25 m. multicoloured	30	10
463	30 m. multicoloured	30	10
464	40 m. grey-green, light olive-bistre and black	45	45
465	50 m. buff, brown and black	45	10
466	60 m. multicoloured	45	20
467	100 m. multicoloured	50	40
468	250 m. deep dull blue, grey and black	80	1·50
469	500 m. black, stone and deep blue-green	80	2·00
470	£1 multicoloured	1·25	2·25
459/70	*Set of* 12	5·25	7·50

Sizes:—23 × 34 *mm*, 5 m., 10 m.; 34 × 23 *mm*, 100 m.; 24 × 37 *mm*, 20, 25, 30 m.; 37 × 24 *mm*, 40, 50, 60 m.; 28 × 41 *mm*, others.

Designs:—10 m. Limestone head; 20 m. Gold necklace from Lambousa; 25 m. Terracotta warrior; 30 m. Statue of a priest of Aphrodite; 40 m. Bronze tablet; 50 m. Mycenaean crater; 60 m. Limestone sarcophagus; 100 m. Gold bracelet from Lambousa; 250 m. Silver dish from Lambousa; 500 m. Bronze stand; £1 Statue of Artemis.

184 Olympic Symbol   185 "George Washington" (G. Stuart)

(Litho Harrison)

1976 (5 July). *Olympic Games, Montreal. T* **184** *and similar designs. P* 14.

471	20 m. carmine-red, black and yellow	10	10
472	60 m. multicoloured	20	30
473	100 m. multicoloured	30	55
471/3	*Set of* 3	55	80

Designs: *Horiz*—60, 100 m. Olympic symbols (*different*).

1976 (5 July). *Bicentenary of American Revolution. W* **58**. *P* 13 × 13½.

474	185 100 m. multicoloured	40	30

186 Children in Library   187 Archangel Michael

1976 (27 Sept). *Anniversaries and Events. T* **186** *and similar vert designs. W* **58**. *P* 13½×12½ (50 *m.*) *or* 13½ (*others*).

475	40 m. multicoloured	20	15
476	50 m. yellow-brown and black	20	10
477	80 m. multicoloured	45	60
475/7	*Set of* 3	75	75

Designs and Events:—40 m. Type 186 (Promotion of Children's Books); 50 m. Low-cost housing (HABITAT Conference, Vancouver); 80 m. Eye protected by hands (World Health Day).

(Litho Harrison)

1976 (15 Nov). *Christmas. T* **187** *and similar vert designs, showing icons from Ayios Neophytis Monastery. Multicoloured. P* 12½.

478	10 m. Type 187	15	10
479	15 m. Archangel Gabriel	15	10
480	150 m. The Nativity	60	80
478/80	*Set of* 3	80	80

188 "Cyprus 74"   189 "View of Prodhromos"
(wood-engraving   (A. Diamantis)
by A. Tassos)

1977 (10 Jan)–**82**. *Obligatory Tax. Refugee Fund. W* **58**. *Ordinary cream paper. P* 13 × 12½.

481	188 10 m. grey-black	20	10
	a. Chalk-surfaced cream paper (3.5.82)*		

*Earliest known date of use.
For 1 c. value, see Nos. 634/b, 729 and 747.

1977 (2 May). *Europa. Paintings. T* **189** *and similar horiz designs. Multicoloured. No wmk. P* 13½×13.

482	20 m. Type 189	15	10
483	60 m. "Springtime at Monagroulli" (T. Kanthos)	30	60
484	120 m. "Old Port, Limassol" (V. Ioannides)	60	1·50
482/4	*Set of* 3	95	2·00

190 Overprinted 500 m.   191 Bronze Coin of Emperor
Stamp of 1960   Trajan

1977 (13 June). *Silver Jubilee. W* **58**. *P* 13 × 13½.

485	190 120 m. multicoloured	30	30

(Litho Harrison)

1977 (13 June). *Ancient Coins of Cyprus* (2nd series). *T* **191** *and similar horiz designs. P* 14.

486	10 m. brownish black, gold and ultramarine	15	10
487	40 m. brownish black, silver and pale blue	30	30
488	60 m. brownish black, silver and dull orange	35	35
489	100 m. brownish black, gold and blue-green	50	95
486/9	*Set of* 4	1·10	1·50

Designs:—40 m. Silver tetradrachm of Demetrios Poliorcetes; 60 m. Silver tetradrachm of Ptolemy VIII; 100 m. Gold Octadrachm of Arsinoe II.

PRICES OF SETS

Set prices are given for many issues, generally those containing three stamps or more. Definitive sets include one of each value or major colour change, but do not cover different perforations, die types or minor shades. Where a choice is possible the set prices are based on the cheapest versions of the stamps included in the listings.

192 Archbishop Makarios   193 Embroidery, Pottery and
in Ceremonial Robes   Weaving

1977 (10 Sept). *Death of Archbishop Makarios. T* **192** *and similar vert designs. Multicoloured. P* 13 × 13½.

490	20 m. Type 192	15	10
491	60 m. Archbishop and doorway	20	10
492	250 m. Head and shoulders portrait	50	1·10
490/2	*Set of* 3	75	1·10

1977 (17 Oct). *Anniversaries and Events. T* **193** *and similar horiz designs. Multicoloured. W* **58** (*sideways*). *P* 13½ × 13.

493	20 m. Type 193	10	10
494	40 m. Map of Mediterranean	15	20
495	60 m. Gold medals	20	20
496	80 m. "Sputnik"	20	85
493/6	*Set of* 4	60	1·25

Events:—20 m. Revitalisation of handicrafts; 40 m. "Man and the Biosphere" Programme in the Mediterranean region; 60 m. Gold medals won by Cypriot students in the Orleans Gymnasiade; 80 m. 60th anniv of Russian October Revolution.

194 "Nativity"

(Litho Harrison)

1977 (21 Nov). *Christmas. T* **194** *and similar horiz designs showing children's paintings. Multicoloured. P* 14 × 13½.

497	10 m. Type 194	10	10
498	40 m. "The Three Kings"	10	10
499	150 m. "Flight into Egypt"	25	80
497/9	*Set of* 3	35	90

195 Demetrios Libertis   196 Chrysorrhogiatissa
Monastery Courtyard

(Des A. Ioannides)

1978 (6 Mar). *Cypriot Poets. T* **195** *and similar horiz design. W* **58** (*sideways*). *P* 14 × 13.

500	40 m. dull brown and olive-bistre	10	10
501	150 m. grey, grey-black and light red	30	80

Design:—150 m. Vasilis Michaelides.

(Litho Harrison)

1978 (24 Apr). *Europa. Architecture. T* **196** *and similar horiz designs. Multicoloured. P* 14 × 13½.

502	25 m. Type 196	15	10
503	75 m. Kolossi Castle	25	35
504	125 m. Municipal Library, Paphos	45	1·50
502/4	*Set of* 3	75	1·75

197 Archbishop of   198 Affected Blood
Cyprus, 1950–77   Corpuscles (Prevention
of Thalassaemia)

(Des A. Ioannides (300 m.). Photo Harrison)

1978 (3 Aug). *Archbishop Makarios Commemoration. T* **197** *and similar vert designs. Multicoloured. P* 14 × 15.

505	15 m. Type 197	15	20
	a. Silver (inscr and emblem) omitted	†	
	b. Horiz strip of 5. Nos. 505/9	85	
	ba. Imperf (horiz strip of 5)		
	bb. Silver omitted (horiz strip of 5)		

506	25 m. Exiled in Seychelles, 9 March 1956–28 March 1957		15	20
507	50 m. President of the Republic, 1960–77 ..		20	25
508	75 m. "Soldier of Christ"		20	30
509	100 m. "Fighter for Freedom"		25	35
	a. Silver (inscr and emblem) omitted			
505/9		Set of 5	85	1·10
MS510	110 × 80 mm. 300 m. "The Great Leader". Imperf		1·40	3·00

Nos. 505/9 were printed together, *se-tenant*, in horizontal strips of 5 throughout the sheet.

Sheets of this issue are known with the silver omitted completely or only from the first or last vertical rows.

(Des A. Ioannides)

1978 (23 Oct). *Anniversaries and Events. T* **198** *and similar designs. P* 13½×14 (15, 35 m.) *or* 14×13½ *(others).*

511	15 m. multicoloured		10	10
512	35 m. multicoloured		15	10
513	75 m. black and grey		20	30
514	125 m. multicoloured		35	80
511/14		Set of 4	70	1·10

Designs and Events. *Vert*—35 m. Aristotle (sculpture) (2300th death anniversary). *Horiz*—75 m. "Heads" (Human Rights); 125 m. Wright brothers and Wright Flyer I (75th anniversary of powered flight).

199 Icon Stand

200 Aphrodite (statue from Soli)

(Litho Harrison)

1978 (4 Dec). *Christmas. T* **199** *and similar vert designs showing icon stands. P* 14 × 14½.

515	15 m. multicoloured		10	10
516	35 m. multicoloured		15	10
517	150 m. multicoloured		40	60
515/17		Set of 3	60	65

(Des G. Simonis. Litho Harrison)

1979 (12 Mar). *Aphrodite (Greek goddess of love and beauty) Commemoration* (1st issue). *T* **200** *and similar horiz design showing Aphrodite emerging from the sea at Paphos (legendary birthplace). Multicoloured. P* 14×13½.

518	75 m. Type **200**		25	10
519	125 m. Aphrodite on a shell (detail from "Birth of Venus" by Botticelli)		35	25

See also Nos. 584/5.

201 Van, Larnaca–Nicosia Mail-coach and Envelope

202 Peacock Wrasse (*thalassoma pavo*)

(Des G. Simonis)

1979 (30 Apr). *Europa. Communications. T* **201** *and similar horiz designs. Multicoloured. W* **58** *(sideways). P* 14 × 13.

520	25 m. Type **201**		15	10
521	75 m. Radar, satellite and early telephone		30	20
522	125 m. Aircraft, ship and envelopes		65	80
520/2		Set of 3	1·00	1·00

1979 (25 June). *Flora and Fauna. T* **202** *and similar multicoloured designs. W* **58** *(sideways on* 25 *and* 125 m.*). P* 13½ × 12 (25, 125 m.) *or* 12 × 13½ *(others).*

523	25 m. Type **202**		15	10
524	50 m. Black Partridge (*Francolinus francolinus*) (*vert*)		45	30
525	75 m. Cedar (*Cedar brevifolia*) (*vert*)		45	20
526	125 m. Mule (*Equus mulus*)		50	1·10
523/6		Set of 4	1·40	1·50

203 I.B.E. and U.N.E.S.C.O. Emblems

204 "Jesus" (from Church of the Virgin Mary of Arakas, Lagoudhera)

(Des Mrs. A. Kalathia (25 m.), A. Ioannides (others). Litho Harrison)

1979 (1 Oct). *Anniversaries and Events. T* **203** *and similar designs in black, yellow-brown and yellow-ochre* (50 m.) *or multicoloured* (others). *P* 12½.

527	15 m. Type **203**		10	10
528	25 m. Graphic design of dove and stamp album (*horiz*)		10	10
529	50 m. Lord Kitchener and map of Cyprus (*horiz*)		20	15
530	75 m. Child's face (*horiz*)		25	10
531	100 m. Graphic design of footballers (*horiz*)		30	20
532	125 m. Rotary International emblem and "75"		30	75
527/32		Set of 6	1·10	1·25

Events:—15 m. 50th anniversary of International Bureau of Education; 25 m. 20th anniversary of Cyprus Philatelic Society; 50 m. Centenary of Cyprus Survey; 75 m. International Year of the Child; 100 m. 25th anniversary of U.E.F.A. (European Football Association); 125 m. 75th anniversary of Rotary International.

1979 (5 Nov). *Christmas. Icons. T* **204** *and similar vert designs. Multicoloured. W* **58**. *P* 13 × 13½ (35 m.) *or* 13½ × 14 *(others).*

533	15 m. Type **204**		10	10
534	35 m. "Nativity" (from the Iconostasis of the Church of St. Nicholas, Famagusta District) (29 × 41 mm)		10	10
535	150 m. "Holy Mary" (from Church of the Virgin Mary of Arakas, Lagoudhera)		25	30
533/5		Set of 3	35	40

205 1880 ½d. Stamp with "969" (Nicosia) Postmark

206 St. Barnabas (Patron Saint of Cyprus)

1980 (17 Mar). *Cyprus Stamp Centenary. T* **205** *and similar horiz designs. Multicoloured. W* **58** *(sideways). P* 13½ × 13.

536	40 m. Type **205**		10	10
537	125 m. 1880 2½d. stamp with "974" (Kyrenia) postmark		15	15
538	175 m. 1880 1s. stamp with "942" (Larnaca) postmark		15	20
536/8		Set of 3	30	35
MS539	105 × 85 mm. 500 m. 1880 1d., ½d., 2½d., 4d., 6d. and 1s. stamps (90 × 75 mm). Imperf		70	85

(Photo Harrison)

1980 (28 Apr). *Europa. Personalities. T* **206** *and similar vert design. Multicoloured. P* 12½.

540	40 m. Type **206**		15	10
541	125 m. Zeno of Citium (founder of the Stoic philosophy)		30	20
	a. Pale Venetian red omitted ..		£100	

The pale Venetian red colour on No. 541 appears as an overlay on the bust. On No. 541a the bust is pure grey.

207 Sailing

208 Gold Necklace, Arsos (7th-century BC)

(Des A. Ioannides)

1980 (23 June). *Olympic Games, Moscow. T* **207** *and similar horiz designs. Multicoloured. W* **58** *(sideways). P* 13½ × 13.

542	40 m. Type **207**		10	10
543	125 m. Swimming		20	20
544	200 m. Gymnastics		25	25
542/4		Set of 3	50	50

1980 (15 Sept). *Archaeological Treasures. Multicoloured designs as T* **208**. *W* **58** *(sideways on* 15, 40, 150 *and* 500 m.*). Chalk-surfaced cream paper. P* 14 × 13 (15, 40, 150 *and* 500 m.) *or* 13 × 14 *(others).*

545	10 m. Type **208**		30	45
546	15 m. Bronze cow, Vouni Palace (5th-century B.C.)		30	45
547	25 m. Amphora, Salamis (6th-century B.C.) ..		30	10
548	40 m. Gold finger-ring, Enkomi (13th-century B.C.) (*horiz*)		40	30
549	50 m. Bronze cauldron, Salamis (8th-century B.C.)		40	10
550	75 m. Funerary stele, Marion (5th-century B.C.)		80	55
551	100 m. Jug (15–14th-century B.C.)		85	15
552	125 m. Warrior (Terracotta) (6–5th-century B.C.)		85	15
553	150 m. Lions attacking bull (bronze relief), Vouni Palace (5th-century B.C.) (*horiz*)		1·00	15
554	175 m. Faience rhyton, Kition (13th-century B.C.)		1·00	55

555	200 m. Bronze statue of Ingot God, Enkomi (12th-century B.C.)		1·00	30
556	500 m. Stone bowl, Khirokitia (6th-millennium B.C.) (*horiz*)		1·00	1·00
557	£1 Ivory plaque, Salamis (7th-century B.C.)		1·25	1·25
558	£2 "Leda and the Swan" (mosaic), Kouklia (3rd-century A.D.)		2·50	2·00
545/58		Set of 14	10·50	6·50

209 Cyprus Flag

210 Peace Dove and Head Silhouettes

1980 (1 Oct). *20th Anniv of Republic. T* **209** *and similar multicoloured designs. P* 13½ × 13 (125 m.) *or* 13 × 14 *(others).*

559	40 m. Type **209**		10	10
560	125 m. Signing Treaty of Establishment (41 × 29 mm)		20	15
561	175 m. Archbishop Makarios		35	25
559/61		Set of 3	60	45

(Des A. Ioannides)

1980 (29 Nov). *International Palestinian Solidarity Day. T* **210** *and similar horiz design showing Peace Dove and head silhouettes. W* **58** *(sideways). P* 13½ × 13.

562	40 m. grey and black		20	20
	a. Horiz pair. Nos. 562/3		55	55
563	125 m. grey and black		35	35

Nos. 562/3 were printed together, *se-tenant*, in horizontal pairs throughout the sheet.

211 Pulpit, Tripiotis Church, Nicosia

212 Folk-dancing

1980 (29 Nov). *Christmas. T* **211** *and similar vert designs. Multicoloured. W* **58**. *P* 13 × 14.

564	25 m. Type **211**		10	10
565	100 m. Holy Doors, Panayia Church, Paralimni (24 × 37 mm)		15	15
566	125 m. Pulpit, Ayios Lazaros Church, Larnaca		15	15
564/6		Set of 3	30	30

(Litho Harrison)

1981 (4 May). *Europa. Folklore. T* **212** *and similar vert design showing folk-dancing from paintings by T. Photiades. P* 14.

567	40 m. multicoloured		40	10
568	175 m. multicoloured		1·00	50

213 Self-portrait

214 *Ophrys kotschyi*

1981 (15 June). *500th Anniv of Leonardo da Vinci's Visit. T* **213** *and similar multicoloured designs. W* **58** *(sideways on* 125 m.*). P* 12 × 14 (125 m.) *or* 13½ × 14 *(others).*

569	40 m. Type **213**		40	10
570	125 m. "The Last Supper" (50 × 25 mm) ..		70	40
571	175 m. Cyprus lace and Milan Cathedral ..		95	60
569/71		Set of 3	1·90	1·00

(Des A. Tassos)

1981 (6 July). *Cypriot Wild Orchids. T* **214** *and similar vert designs. Multicoloured. W* **58**. *P* 13½ × 14.

572	25 m. Type **214**		50	60
	a. Block of 4. Nos. 572/5		2·25	
573	50 m. *Orchis punctulata*		60	70
574	75 m. *Ophrys argolica elegans*		70	80
575	150 m. *Epipactis veratrifolia*		75	90
572/5		Set of 4	2·25	2·75

Nos. 572/5 were printed together, *se-tenant*, in blocks of 4 throughout the sheet.

215 Heinrich von Stephan

216 "The Lady of the Angels" (from Church of the Transfiguration of Christ, Palekhori)

(Des A. Tassos (200 m.), A. Ioannides (others))

1981 (28 Sept). *Anniversaries and Events. T 215 and similar horiz designs. W 58 (sideways). P 13½×13.*

576	25 m. brown-olive, dp yellow-green & brt bl	..		20	10
577	40 m. multicoloured	..	..	20	10
578	125 m. black, vermilion and deep yellow-green		35	25
579	150 m. multicoloured	..	..	45	30
580	200 m. multicoloured	..	..	50	35
576/80	..	..	*Set of 5*	1·50	95

Designs and Events:—25 m. Type 215 (150th birth anniversary of Henrich von Stephan (founder of U.P.U.); 40 m. Stylised man holding dish of food (World Food Day); 125 m. Stylised hands (International Year for Disabled Persons); 150 m. Stylised building and flower (European Campaign for Urban Renaissance); 200 m. Prince Charles, Lady Diana Spencer and St. Paul's Cathedral (Royal Wedding).

1981 (16 Nov). *Christmas. Murals from Nicosia District Churches. T 216 and similar multicoloured designs. W 58 (sideways on 25 and 125 m.). P 12½.*

581	25 m. Type 216			20	10
582	100 m. "Christ Pantokrator" (from Church of Madonna of Arakas, Lagoudera) (*vert*)		60	20
583	125 m. "Baptism of Christ" (from Church of Our Lady of Assinou, Nikitari)	..	70	30
581/3	..	..	*Set of 3*	1·25	50

217 "Louomene" (statue of Aphrodite bathing, 250 B.C.)

218 Naval Battle with Greek Fire, 985 A.D.

1982 (12 Apr). *Aphrodite (Greek goddess of love and beauty) Commemoration (2nd issue). T 217 and similar vert design. Multicoloured. W 58. P 13½×14.*

584	125 m. Type 217	..	..	80	45
585	175 m. "Änadyomene" (Aphrodite emerging from the waters) (Titian)	..	95	65

(Des G. Simonis. Photo Harrison)

1982 (3 May). *Europa. Historical Events. T 218 and similar horiz design. Multicoloured. P 12½.*

586	40 m. Type 218		75	10
587	175 m. Conversion of Roman Proconsul Sergius Paulus to Christianity, Paphos, 45 A.D.	1·40	3·00

219 Monogram of Christ (mosaic)   **100** **=** **(220)**

1982 (5 July). *World Cultural Heritage. T 219 and similar multicoloured designs. W 58 (sideways on 50 and 225 m.). P 13½×14 (125 m.) or 12½ (others).*

588	50 m. Type 219			25	10
589	125 m. Head of priest-king of Paphos (sculpture) (24×37 mm)	..	50	25
590	225 m. Theseus (Greek god) (mosaic)	..	75	95
588/90	..	..	*Set of 3*	1·40	1·10

1982 (6 Sept). *No. 550 surch with T 220 by Govt Ptg Office, Nicosia.*

591	100 m. on 75 m. Funerary stele, Marion (5th-century B.C.)	..	50	50

221 Cyprus and Stylised "75"

222 Holy Communion— The Bread

1982 (8 Nov). *75th Anniv of Boy Scout Movement. T 221 and similar multicoloured designs. W 58 (sideways on 100 m. and 175 m.). P 12½ × 13½ (125 m.) or 13½ × 12½ (others).*

592	100 m. Type 221			40	20
593	125 m. Lord Baden-Powell (*vert*)		45	30
594	175 m. Camp-site	..	..	55	55
592/4	..	..	*Set of 3*	1·25	95

1982 (6 Dec). *Christmas. T 222 and similar designs. W 58 (sideways on 25 and 250 m.). P 12½ × 12 (25 and 250 m.) or 13½ × 14 (100 m.).*

595	25 m. multicoloured	..	..	10	10
596	100 m. gold and black	..	..	30	15
597	250 m. multicoloured	..	..	70	75
595/7	..	..	*Set of 3*	1·00	85

Designs: *Vert*—100 m. Holy Chalice. *Horiz*—250 m. Holy Communion—The Wine.

223 Cyprus Forest Industries' Sawmill

1983 (14 Mar). *Commonwealth Day. T 223 and similar horiz designs. Multicoloured. W 58 (sideways). P 14 × 13½.*

598	50 m. Type 223			10	10
599	125 m. "Ikarios and the Discovery of Wine" (3rd-cent mosaic)	..	20	25
600	150 m. Folk-dancers, Commonwealth Film and Television Festival, 1980	25	35
601	175 m. Royal Exhibition Building, Melbourne (Commonwealth Heads of Government Meeting, 1981)	..	25	40
598/601	..	..	*Set of 4*	70	1·00

224 Cyprosyllabic Inscription (6th-cent B.C.)

225 *Pararge aegeria*

(Des G. Simonis. Photo Harrison)

1983 (3 May). *Europa. T 224 and similar horiz design. Multicoloured. P 14½ × 14.*

602	50 m. Type 224			40	10
603	200 m. Copper ore, ingot (Enkomi 1400-1250 B.C.) and bronze jug (2nd-cent A.D.)	1·10	2·40

1983 (28 June). *Butterflies. T 225 and similar horiz designs. Multicoloured. W w 58. P 12½.*

604	60 m. Type 225	..		25	20
605	130 m. *Aricia agestis*	..	..	45	25
606	250 m. *Glaucopsyche melanops*	..	85	1·75
604/6	..	..	*Set of 3*	1·40	2·00

(New Currency: 100 cents = £1 (Cyprus))

1c

=

(226)   227 View of Power Station

1983 (3 Oct). *Nos. 545/56 surch as T 226 by Govt Printing Office, Nicosia.*

607	1 c. on 10 m. Type 208		35	40
608	2 c. on 15 m. Bronze cow, Vouni Palace (5th-century B.C.)	35	40
609	3 c. on 25 m. Amphora, Salamis (6th-century B.C.)	35	20
610	4 c. on 40 m. Gold finger-ring, Enkomi (13th-century B.C.)	40	20
611	5 c. on 50 m. Bronze cauldron, Salamis (8th-century B.C.)	50	50
612	6 c. on 75 m. Funerary stele, Marion (5th-century B.C.)	50	20
613	10 c. on 100 m. Jug (15–14th-century B.C.)	..	50	40
614	13 c. on 125 m. Warrior (Terracotta) (6–5th-century B.C.)	60	50
615	15 c. on 150 m. Lions attacking bull (bronze relief), Vouni Palace (5th-century B.C.)	70	55
616	20 c. on 200 m. Bronze statue of Ingot God, Enkomi (12th-century B.C.)	70	65
617	25 c. on 175 m. Faience rhyton, Kition (13th-century B.C.)	80	1·10
618	50 c. on 500 m. Stone bowl, Khirokitia (6th-millennium B.C.)	1·00	2·00
607/18	..	..	*Set of 12*	6·00	6·50

1983 (27 Oct). *Anniversaries and Events. T 227 and similar vert designs. Multicoloured. W 58. P 13 × 14.*

619	3 c. Type 227	..	..	10	20
620	6 c. W.C.Y. logo	..	..	20	15
621	13 c. *Sol Olympia* (liner) and *Polys* (tanker)	40	35
622	15 c. Human Rights emblem and map of Europe	..	40	25
623	20 c. Nicos Kazantzakis (poet)	..	45	75
624	25 c. Archbishop Makarios in church	..	50	75
619/24	..	..	*Set of 6*	1·75	2·25

Events:—3 c. 30th anniv of the Cyprus Electricity Authority; 6 c. World Communications Year; 13 c. 25th anniv of International Maritime Organization; 15 c. 35th anniv of Universal Declaration of Human Rights; 20 c. Birth centenary; 25 c. 70th birth anniv.

228 St. Lazaros Church, Larnaca

229 Waterside Cafe, Larnaca

1983 (12 Dec). *Christmas. Church Towers. T 228 and similar vert designs. Multicoloured. W 58. P 12×13½.*

625	4 c. Type 228	..		15	10
626	13 c. St. Varvara Church, Kaimakli, Nicosia	40	35
627	20 c. St. Ioannis Church, Larnaca	..	70	1·50
625/7	..	..	*Set of 3*	1·10	1·75

(Litho Harrison)

1984 (6 Mar). *Old Engravings. T 229 and similar horiz designs. Each pale stone and black. P 14½ × 14 (6 c.) or 14 (others).*

628	6 c. Type 229	..		15	10
629	20 c. Bazaar at Larnaca (30 × 25 mm)	..	40	85
630	30 c. Famagusta Gate, Nicosia (30×25 mm)	65	1·50
628/30	..	..	*Set of 3*	1·10	2·25
MS631	110×85 mm. 75 c. "The Confession" (St. Lazarus Church, Larnaca)		1·60	2·00

230 C.E.P.T. 25th Anniversary Logo

(Des J. Larrivière. Litho Harrison)

1984 (30 Apr). *Europa. W 58. P 12½.*

632	230 6 c. apple-green, deep bl-green & blk	..	50	10
633	15 c. light blue, dull ultram & blk	1·10	2·50

A. Waddington ptgs (Nos. 634/a)

B. Aspioti-Elka ptg (No. 634b)

(Des A. Tassos)

1984 (18 June)–**87**. *Obligatory Tax. Refugee Fund. Design as T 188 but new value and "1984" date. P 13×12½.*

(a) Litho J.W. W 58. Chalk-surfaced cream paper

634	1 c. grey-black (A)	..	..	10	10
	a. Wmk sideways. Ordinary paper (21.2.87)*	..	70	70

(b) Litho Aspioti-Elka. W 58. Chalk-surfaced cream paper

634b	1 c. grey-black (B) (3.11.87*)	..	65	65

*Earliest known date of use.

In addition to the redrawn inscriptions there are other minor differences between the work of the two printers.

For a further version of this design, showing "1974" at top right, see Nos. 729, 747 and 807.

231 Running

(Des. K. Haine. Litho Harrison)

1984 (18 June). *Olympic Games. Los Angeles. T 231 and similar horiz designs. Multicoloured. W 58 (sideways). P 14.*

635	3 c. Type 231	..	..	20	10
636	4 c. Olympic column	..	..	20	20
637	13 c. Swimming	..	..	55	75
638	20 c. Gymnastics	..	..	80	1·50
635/8	..	..	*Set of 4*	1·60	2·25

232 Prisoners-of-War

233 Open Stamp Album
(25th Anniv of Cyprus
Philatelic Society)

1984 (20 July).   *10th Anniv of Turkish Landings in Cyprus. T 232 and similar horiz design. Multicoloured. P 14 × 13½.*

639	15 c. Type 232	40	45
640	20 c. Map and burning buildings	50	55

(Des P. St. Antoniades (6 c.), A. Ioannides (10 c.), Harrison (others). Litho Harrison)

1984 (15 Oct).   *Anniversaries and Events. T 233 and similar multicoloured designs. W 58 (sideways on horiz designs). P 12½.*

641	6 c. Type 233	30	20
642	10 c. Football in motion (*horiz*) (50th anniv of Cyprus Football Association)	45	30
643	15 c. "Dr. George Papanicolaou" (medical scientist – birth cent)	60	50
644	25 c. Antique map of Cyprus and ikon (*horiz*) (International Symposia on Cartography and Medieval Paleography)	1·00	2·00
641/4		*Set of 4* 2·10	2·75

234 St. Mark
(miniature from
11th-century Gospel)

235 Autumn at
Platania, Troodos
Mountains

(Des and litho Harrison)

1984 (26 Nov).   *Christmas. Illuminated Gospels. T 234 and similar vert designs. Multicoloured. W 58. P 12½.*

645	4 c. Type 234	30	10
646	13 c. Beginning of St. Mark's Gospel	75	50
647	20 c. St. Luke (miniature from 11th-century Gospel)	1·25	2·00
645/7		*Set of 3* 2·10	2·40

(Des and litho Harrison)

1985 (18 Mar.)   *Cyprus Scenes and Landscapes. T 235 and similar multicoloured designs. Ordinary white paper. P 14 × 15 (6 c., 20 c., 25 c., £1, £5) or 15 × 14 (others).*

648	1 c. Type 235	20	40
649	2 c. Ayia Napa Monastery	20	40
650	3 c. Phini Village—panoramic view	20	30
651	4 c. Kykko Monastery	20	20
652	5 c. Beach at Makronissos, Ayia Napa	20	20
653	6 c. Village street, Omodhos (*vert*)	30	20
654	10 c. Panoramic sea view	40	35
655	13 c. Windsurfing	55	25
656	15 c. Beach at Protaras	65	25
657	20 c. Forestry for development (*vert*)	80	50
658	25 c. Sunrise at Protaras (*vert*)	1·00	1·00
659	30 c. Village house, Pera	1·25	1·25
660	50 c. Apollo Hylates Sanctuary, Curium	2·00	1·75
661	£1 Snow on Troodos Mountains (*vert*)	3·50	3·00
662	£5 Personification of Autumn, House of Dionyssos, Paphos (*vert*)	13·00	15·00
648/62		*Set of 15* 22·00	23·00

236 Clay Idols of
Musicians (7/6th
Century B.C.)

237 Cyprus Coat of
Arms (25th Anniv of
Republic)

(Des and litho Harrison)

1985 (6 May). *Europa. European Music Year. T 236 and similar horiz design. Multicoloured. W 58 (sideways). P 12½.*

663	6 c. Type 236	85	35
664	15 c. Violin, lute, flute and score from the "Cyprus Suite"	1·40	2·00

(Des G. Simonis (4 c., 13 c.), Harrison (others). Litho Harrison)

1985 (23 Sept).   *Anniversaries and Events. T 237 and similar designs. P 14½ (4, 20 c.) or 14 × 13½ (others).*

665	4 c. multicoloured	30	15
666	6 c. multicoloured	35	15
667	13 c. multicoloured	75	1·25
668	15 c. black, olive-black and yellow-orange	1·25	1·25
669	20 c. multicoloured	80	2·00
665/9		*Set of 5* 3·00	4·25

Designs and Events: *Horiz* (43×30 *mm*)—6 c. "Barn of Liopetri" (detail) (Pol. Georghiou) (30th anniv of EOKA Campaign); 13 c. Three profiles (International Youth Year); 15 c. Solon Michaelides (composer and conductor) (European Music Year). *Vert* (as T 237)—20 c. U.N. Building, New York, and flags (40th anniv of United Nations Organization).

238 "The Visit of the
Madonna to Elizabeth"
(Lambadistis Monastery,
Kalopanayiotis)

239 Figure from
Hellenistic Spoon Handle

(Des and litho Harrison)

1985 (18 Nov).   *Christmas. Frescoes from Cypriot Churches. T 238 and similar vert designs. Multicoloured. P 12½.*

670	4 c. Type 238	30	10
671	13 c. "The Nativity" (Lambadistis Monastery, Kalopanayiotis)	1·00	65
672	20 c. "Candlemas-day" (Asinou Church)	1·50	2·00
670/2		*Set of 3* 2·50	2·50

(Des A. Ioannides. Litho Harrison)

1986 (17 Feb).   *New Archaeological Museum Fund. T 239 and similar horiz designs. Multicoloured. P 15 × 14.*

673	15 c. Type 239	70	45
674	20 c. Pattern from early Ionian helmet and foot from statue	80	75
675	25 c. Roman statue of Eros and Psyche	1·00	95
676	30 c. Head of statue	1·25	1·10
673/6		*Set of 4* 3·25	3·00
MS677	111 × 90 mm. Nos. 673/6 (*sold at £1*)	12·00	16·00

Two-thirds of the amount received from sales of Nos. 673/7 was devoted to the construction of a new Archaeological Museum, Nicosia.

No. 676 also commemorates the 50th anniversary of the Department of Antiquities.

240 Cyprus Moufflon and Cedars

(Des G. Simonis)

1986 (28 Apr).   *Europa. Protection of Nature and the Environment. T 240 and similar horiz design. Multicoloured. W 58 (sideways). P 14 × 13.*

678	7 c. Type 240	50	30
679	17 c. Greater Flamingos at Larnaca Salt Lake	1·75	2·50

241 Cat's-paw Scallop
(*Manupecten pesfelis*)

(242)

7c

(Des T. Katsoulides)

1986 (1 July).   *Sea Shells. T 241 and similar horiz designs. Multicoloured. W 58 (sideways). P 14 × 13½.*

680	5 c. Type 241	40	15
681	7 c. Atlantic Trumpet Triton (*Charonia variegata*)	45	15
682	15 c. Purple Dye Murex (*Murex brandaris*)	1·00	70
683	25 c. Yellow Cowrie (*Cypraea spurca*)	1·50	2·00
680/3		*Set of 4* 3·00	2·75

1986 (13 Oct).   *Nos. 653 and 655 surch as T 242.*

684	7 c. on 6 c. Village street, Omodhos (*vert*)	40	30
685	18 c. on 13 c. Windsurfing	1·10	60

For 15 c. on 4 c. see No. 730.

243 Globe, Outline Map of
Cyprus and Barn Swallows
(Overseas Cypriots' Year)

(Des T. Katsoulides)

1986 (13 Oct).   *Anniversaries and Events. T 243 and similar horiz designs. Multicoloured. W 58 (sideways). P 13½ × 13.*

686	15 c. Type 243	1·25	45
687	18 c. Halley's Comet over Cyprus beach (40 × 23 *mm*)	1·50	2·25
	a. Horiz pair. Nos. 687/8	3·00	4·50
688	18 c. Comet's tail over sea and Edmond Halley (40 × 23 *mm*)	1·50	2·25
686/8		*Set of 3* 3·75	4·50

Nos. 687/8 were printed together, *se-tenant*, in horizontal pairs throughout the sheet, each pair forming a composite design.

244 Pedestrian Crossing

245 "The Nativity"
(Church of Panayia tou
Araka)

(Des A. Ioannides)

1986 (10 Nov).   *Road Safety Campaign. T 244 and similar horiz designs. Multicoloured. W 58 (sideways). P 14 × 13.*

689	5 c. Type 244	1·00	30
690	7 c. Motor cycle crash helmet	1·10	30
691	18 c. Hands fastening car seat belt	2·25	3·00
689/91		*Set of 3* 4·00	3·50

(Des G. Simonis)

1986 (24 Nov).   *Christmas. International Peace Year. T 245 and similar vert designs showing details of Nativity frescoes from Cypriot churches. Multicoloured. W 58 (inverted). P 13½ × 14.*

692	5 c. Type 245	40	15
693	15 c. Church of Panayia tou Moutoulla	1·25	30
694	17 c. Church of St. Nicholas tis Steyis	1·50	2·00
692/4		*Set of 3* 2·75	2·25

246 Church of Virgin Mary, Asinou

(Des and photo Harrison)

1987 (22 Apr).   *Troodos Churches on the World Heritage List. T 246 and similar horiz designs. Multicoloured. P 12½.*

695	15 c. Type 246	1·00	1·10
	a. Sheetlet. Nos. 695/703	8·00	
696	15 c. Fresco of Virgin Mary, Moutoulla's Church	1·00	1·10
697	15 c. Church of Virgin Mary, Podithou	1·00	1·10
698	15 c. Fresco of Three Apostles, St. Ioannis Lampadistis Monastery	1·00	1·10
699	15 c. Annunciation fresco, Church of the Holy Cross, Pelentriou	1·00	1·10
700	15 c. Fresco of Saints, Church of the Cross, Ayiasmati	1·00	1·10
701	15 c. Fresco of Archangel Michael and Donor, Pedoula's Church of St. Michael	1·00	1·10
702	15 c. Church of St. Nicolaos, Steyis	1·00	1·10
703	15 c. Fresco of Prophets, Church of Virgin Mary, Araka	1·00	1·10
695/703		*Set of 9* 8·00	9·00

Nos. 695/703 were printed together, *se-tenant*, in sheetlets of nine.

247 Proposed Central Bank of Cyprus Building

(Des G. Simonis)

1987 (11 May).   *Europa. Modern Architecture. T 247 and similar horiz design. W 58 (sideways). P 14 × 13½.*

704	7 c. multicoloured	60	30
705	18 c. black, brownish grey and sage-green	1·40	2·00

Design:—18 c. Headquarters complex, Cyprus Telecommunications Authority.

248 Remains of Ancient Ship and Kyrenia Castle

(Des Y. Pantsopoulos)

1987 (3 Oct). *Voyage of "Kyrenia II" (replica of ancient ship).
T 248 and similar horiz designs. Multicoloured. W 58
(sideways).* P 14×13½.
706   2 c. Type 248. 30   20
707   3 c. *Kyrenia II* under construction, 1982–5   30   90
708   5 c. *Kyrenia II* at Paphos, 1986 55   20
709   17 c. *Kyrenia II* at New York, 1986 . . 1·40   90
706/9 . . . . *Set of 4* 2·25   2·00

249 Hands (from
Michelangelo's *Creation*)
and Emblem (10th anniv
of Blood Donation Co-
ordinating Committee)

250 Nativity Crib

(Des A. Ioannides)

1987 (2 Nov). *Anniversaries and Events. T 249 and similar
horiz designs. Multicoloured. W 58 (sideways).* P 14×13½.
710   7 c. Type 249. 60   25
711   15 c. Snail with flowered shell and countryside (European Countryside Campaign) 1·40   40
712   20 c. Symbols of ocean bed and Earth's crust
("Troodos '87" Ophiolites and Oceanic
Lithosphere Symposium) . . 1·75   3·50
710/12 . . . . *Set of 3* 3·25   3·75

(Des A. Ioannides)

1987 (30 Nov). *Christmas. Traditional Customs. T 250 and
similar square designs. Multicoloured. W 58 (sideways).* P 14.
713   5 c. Type 250. 35   15
714   15 c. Door knocker decorated with foliage . . 1·10   35
715   17 c. Bowl of fruit and nuts . . . . 1·25   2·00
713/15 . . . . *Set of 3* 2·40   2·25

251 Flags of Cyprus and
E.E.C.

(Des G. Simonis. Litho Alexandros Matsoukis, Athens)

1988 (11 Jan). *Cypriot–E.E.C. Customs Union. T 251 and
similar horiz design. Multicoloured. W 58.* P 13×13½.
716   15 c. Type 251 . . . . . 1·10   1·75
717   18 c. Outline maps of Cyprus and E.E.C.
countries . . . . . . 1·10   1·10

252 Intelpost Telefax Terminal

(Des A. Ioannides. Litho Alexandros Matsoukis, Athens)

1988 (9 May). *Europa. Transport and Communications. T 252
and similar horiz designs. Multicoloured. W 58.* P 14×14½.
718   7 c. Type 252 65   75
   a. Horiz pair. Nos. 718/19 . . 1·25   1·50
719   7 c. Car driver using mobile telephone 65   75
720   18 c. Nose of Cyprus Airways airliner and
Greater Flamingos . . . . 1·75   2·25
   a. Horiz pair. Nos. 720/1 . . 3·50   4·50
721   18 c. Boeing 737 airliner in flight and
Greater Flamingos . . . . 1·75   2·25
718/21 . . . . . . *Set of 4* 4·25   5·50
The two designs of each value were printed together,
se-tenant, in horizontal pairs throughout the sheet of ten.

253 Sailing   254 Conference Emblem

(Des A. Ioannides. Photo Courvoisier)

1988 (27 June). *Olympic Games, Seoul. T 253 and similar vert
designs. Multicoloured. Granite paper.* P 12.
722   5 c. Type 253 30   20
723   7 c. Athletes at start 35   40
724   10 c. Shooting 40   70
725   20 c. Judo 90   1·50
722/5 . . . . . . *Set of 4* 1·75   2·50

(Des A. Ioannides. Litho M. A. Moatsos, Athens)

1988 (5 Sept). *Non-Aligned Foreign Ministers' Conference,
Nicosia. T 254 and similar horiz designs. W 58 (sideways).*
P 14×13½.
726   1 c. black, pale blue and emerald . . 10   10
727   10 c. multicoloured 45   70
728   50 c. multicoloured . . . . 2·25   2·50
726/8 . . . . . . *Set of 3* 2·50   3·00
Designs:— 10 c. Emblem of Republic of Cyprus; 50 c. Nehru,
Tito, Nasser and Makarios.

255 "Cyprus 74"
(wood-engraving
by A. Tassos)

256 "Presentation of
Christ at the Temple"
(Church of Holy
Cross tou Agiasmati)

(Des A. Tassos. Litho M. A. Moatsos, Athens)

1988 (12 Sept). *Obligatory Tax. Refugee Fund. Design as Nos.
634/b, but with upper and lower inscriptions redrawn and
"1974" added as in T 255. W 58. Chalk-surfaced paper.*
P 13×12½.
729 255   1 c. brownish black and brownish grey . . 20   20
For this design printed in photogravure and perforated 11½
see No. 747, in lithography perforated 13 see No. 807 and in
lithography perforated 14½×13½ see No. 892.

1988 (3 Oct). *No. 651 surch as T 242.*
730   15 c. on 4 c. Kykko Monastery 90   70

(Des G. Simonis. Litho M. A. Moatsos, Athens)

1988 (28 Nov). *Christmas. T 256 and similar vert designs
showing frescoes from Cypriot churches. Multicoloured. W 58.*
P 13½×14.
731   5 c. Type 256 30   20
732   15 c. "Virgin and Child" (St. John Lampadistis Monastery) 70   25
733   17 c. "Adoration of the Magi" (St. John
Lampadistis Monastery) . . 1·00   1·75
731/3 . . . . . . *Set of 3* 1·75   2·00

257 Human Rights
Logo

258 Basketball

(Des G. Simonis. Litho M. A. Moatsos, Athens)

1988 (10 Dec). *40th Anniv of Universal Declaration of Human
Rights. W 58 (inverted).* P 13½ × 14.
734 257   25 c. azure, dull violet-blue and cobalt . . 90   1·25

(Des A. Ioannides. Litho Alexandros Matsoukis, Athens)

1989 (10 Apr). *Third Small European States' Games, Nicosia.
T 258 and similar horiz designs. Multicoloured.* P 13½.
735   1 c. Type 258 10   15
736   5 c. Javelin 20   15
737   15 c. Wrestling 45   20
738   18 c. Athletics 60   1·00
735/8 . . . . . . *Set of 4* 1·25   1·40
MS739 109×80 mm. £1 Angel and laurel wreath
(99×73 mm). Imperf . . . . 4·50   6·00

259 Lingri Stick Game

(Des S. Michael. Litho Alexandros Matsoukis, Athens)

1989 (8 May). *Europa. Children's Games. T 259 and similar
horiz designs. Multicoloured.* P 13×13½.
740   7 c. Type 259 65   75
   a. Horiz pair. Nos. 740/1 . . 1·25   1·50
741   7 c. Ziziros 65   75
742   18 c. Sitsia 80   1·00
   a. Horiz pair. Nos. 742/3 . . 1·60   2·00
743   18 c. Leapfrog 80   1·00
740/3 . . . . . . *Set of 4* 2·50   3·25
Nos. 740/1 and 742/3 were each printed together, *se-tenant*, in
horizontal pairs throughout the sheets.

MACHINE LABELS. From 29 May 1989 gummed labels in
the above design, ranging in value from 1 c. to £99.99, were
available from machines at Eleftheria Square P.O., Nicosia
("001") and District P.O., Limassol ("002").

260 "Universal Man"   261 Stylized Human
Figures

(Des A. Ioannides. Photo Courvoisier)

1989 (7 July). *Bicentenary of the French Revolution. Granite
paper.* P 11½.
744 260   18 c. multicoloured 60   60

(Des A. Ioannides. Litho Alexandros Matsoukis, Athens)

1989 (4 Sept). *Centenary of Interparliamentary Union (15 c.)
and 9th Non-Aligned Summit Conference, Belgrade (30 c.).
T 261 and similar vert design. Multicoloured.* P 13½.
745   15 c. Type 261 50   40
746   30 c. Conference logo . . . . 1·00   1·10

(Photo Courvoisier)

1989 (4 Sept). *Obligatory Tax. Refugee Fund. As T 255, but
inscr "1989" or "1990". Granite paper.* P 11½.
747 255   1 c. brownish black and brownish grey . . 45   30

262 Worker Bees
tending Larvae

263 Outstretched
Hand and Profile (aid
for Armenian
earthquake victims)

(Litho Alexandros Matsoukis, Athens)

1989 (16 Oct). *Bee-keeping. T 262 and similar vert designs.
Multicoloured.* P 13½.
748   3 c. Type 262 15   20
749   10 c. Bee on Rock-rose flower . . 40   50
750   15 c. Bee on Lemon flower . . 60   50
751   18 c. Queen and worker bees . . 65   90
748/51 . . . . . . *Set of 4* 1·60   1·90

(Des A. Ioannides. Litho Alexandros Matsoukis, Athens)

1989 (13 Nov). *Anniversaries and Events. T 263 and similar
vert designs. Multicoloured.* P 13½.
752   3 c. Type 263 15   40
753   5 c. Airmail envelope (Cyprus Philatelic
Society F.I.P. membership) . . 25   10
754   7 c. Crab symbol and daisy (European
Cancer Year) 45   90
755   17 c. Vegetables and fish (World Food Day) 75   90
752/5 . . . . . . *Set of 4* 1·40   2·00

282 School Building and Laurel Wreath

283 "Motherhood" (bronze sculpture, Nicos Dymiotis)

(Des A. Ladommates. Litho Alexandros Matsoukis, Athens)

1993 (15 Feb). *Centenary of Pancyprian Gymnasium (secondary school). P* 14.
830 282 10 c. multicoloured 60 50

(Litho Alexandros Matsoukis, Athens)

1993 (5 Apr). *Europa. Contemporary Art. T* **283** *and similar multicoloured design. P* 13½.
831 10 c. Type 283 .. .. .. 50 40
832 30 c. "Motherhood" (painting, Christoforos Savva) (*horiz*) .. .. 1·25 1·75

284 Women Athletes (13th European Cup for Women)

285 Red Squirrelfish

Two types of 20 c.:
I. Incorrectly inscribed "MUFFLON ENCOURAGEMENT CUP"
II. Inscription corrected to "MOUFFLON ENCOURAGEMENT CUP"

(Des Maria Trillidou (10 c.), G. Simonis (25 c.), M. Christou (others). Litho Alexandros Matsoukis, Athens)

1993 (24 May–24 June). *Anniversaries and Events. T* **284** *and similar multicoloured designs. P* 14.
833 7 c. Type 234 .. .. .. 40 30
834 10 c. Scout symbols (80th anniv of Scouting in Cyprus) (*vert*) 55 40
835 20 c. Water-skier, dolphin and gull (Moufflon Encouragement Cup) (I) 10·00 10·00
  a. Type II (24 June) 95 95
836 25 c. Archbishop Makarios III and monastery (80th birth anniv) .. 1·40 1·75
833/6 .. .. .. *Set of 4* 3·00 3·00
No. 835 was withdrawn on 2 June 1993, after the spelling error had been spotted. No. 835a, with the spelling corrected, was placed on sale from 24 June.

(Des A. Ioannides. Litho Alexandros Matsoukis, Athens)

1993 (6 Sept). *Fishes. T* **285** *and similar horiz designs. Multicoloured. P* 13½.
837 7 c. Type 285 .. .. .. 40 25
838 15 c. Red Scorpionfish 65 55
839 20 c. Painted Comber 75 85
840 30 c. Grey Triggerfish .. .. 1·40 1·75
837/40 .. .. .. *Set of 4* 2·75 3·00

286 Conference Emblem

(Des A. Ioannides. Litho Alexandros Matsoukis, Athens)

1993 (4 Oct). *12th Commonwealth Summit Conference. P* 13½.
841 286 35 c. orange-brown and pale ochre 1·60 1·90
842 40 c. bistre-brown and ochre .. 1·90 2·40

287 Ancient Sailing Ship and Modern Coaster

288 Cross from Stavrovouni Monastery

(Des G. Simonis. Litho Alexandros Matsoukis, Athens)

1993 (4 Oct). *"Maritime Cyprus '93" International Shipping Conference, Nicosia. P* 13½×14.
843 287 25 c. multicoloured .. .. 1·40 1·40

(Litho Alexandros Matsoukis, Athens)

1993 (22 Nov). *Christmas. Church Crosses. T* **288** *and similar multicoloured designs. P* 13½.
844 7 c. Type 288 .. .. .. 30 25
845 20 c. Cross from Lefkara 75 75
846 25 c. Cross from Pedoulas (*horiz*) 1·00 1·75
844/6 .. .. .. *Set of 3* 1·90 2·50

289 Copper Smelting

290 Symbols of Disability (Persons with Special Needs Campaign)

(Des G. Simonis. Litho Alexandros Matsoukis, Athens)

1994 (1 Mar). *Europa. Discoveries. Ancient Copper Industry. T* **289** *and similar horiz design. Multicoloured. P* 13×13½.
847 10 c. Type 289 .. .. .. 50 35
848 30 c. Ingot, ancient ship and map of Cyprus 1·25 1·50

(Des E. Hadjimichael (7 c., 25 c.), S. Karamallakis (others). Litho Alexandros Matsoukis, Athens)

1994 (9 May). *Anniversaries and Events. T* **290** *and similar vert designs. Multicoloured. P* 13½.
849 7 c. Type 290 .. .. .. 40 25
850 15 c. Olympic rings in flame (Centenary of International Olympic Committee) .. 65 55
851 20 c. Peace Doves (World Gymnasiade, Nicosia) 80 80
852 25 c. Adults and unborn baby in tulip (International Year of the Family) 1·10 1·50
849/52 .. .. .. *Set of 4* 2·75 2·75

291 Houses, Soldier and Family

292 Black Pine

(Des A. Ioannides. Litho Alexandros Matsoukis, Athens)

1994 (27 June). *20th Anniv of Turkish Landings in Cyprus. T* **291** *and similar horiz design. Multicoloured. P* 14.
853 10 c. Type 291 .. .. .. 50 40
854 50 c. Soldier and ancient columns .. 2·00 2·50

(Des A. Ioannides. Litho Alexandros Matsoukis, Athens)

1994 (10 Oct). *Trees. T* **292** *and similar vert designs. Multicoloured. P* 13½×14.
855 7 c. Type 292 .. .. .. 30 25
856 15 c. Cyprus Cedar 55 55
857 20 c. Golden Oak 70 80
858 30 c. Strawberry Tree .. .. 1·10 1·50
855/8 .. .. .. *Set of 4* 2·40 2·75

293 Airliner, Route Map and Emblem

294 "Virgin Mary" (detail) (Philip Goul)

(Des G. Simonis. Litho Alexandros Matsoukis, Athens)

1994 (21 Nov). *50th Anniv of International Civil Aviation Organization. P* 14.
859 293 30 c. multicoloured .. .. 1·50 1·50

(Litho Alexandros Matsoukis, Athens)

1994 (21 Nov). *Christmas. Church Paintings. T* **294** *and similar horiz designs. Multicoloured. P* 13½.
860 7 c. Type 294 .. .. .. 35 25
861 20 c. "The Nativity" (detail) (Byzantine) .. 85 70
862 25 c. "Archangel Michael" (detail) (Goul) 1·10 1·50
860/2 .. .. .. *Set of 3* 2·10 2·25

295 Woman from Paphos wearing Foustani

296 "Hearth Room" Excavation, Alassa, and Frieze

(Des A. Ioannides. Litho Alexandros Matsoukis, Athens)

1994 (27 Dec). *Traditional Costumes. T* **295** *and similar vert designs. Multicoloured. P* 13½×13.
863 1 c. Type 295 .. .. .. 10 10
864 2 c. Bride from Karpass 10 10
865 3 c. Woman from Paphos wearing sayia .. 10 10
866 5 c. Woman from Messaoria wearing foustani 10 10
867 7 c. Bridegroom 15 20
868 10 c. Shepherd from Messaoria .. 20 25
869 15 c. Woman from Nicosia in festive costume 35 40
870 20 c. Woman from Karpass wearing festive sayia 50 55
871 25 c. Woman from Pitsillia 60 65
872 30 c. Woman from Karpass wearing festive doupletti 70 75
873 35 c. Countryman 80 85
874 40 c. Man from Messaoria in festive costume 90 95
875 50 c. Townsman .. .. .. 1·10 1·25
876 £1 Townswoman wearing festive sarka 2·25 2·40
863/76 .. .. .. *Set of 14* 7·75 8·50

(Des A. Ladommatos. Litho Alexandros Matsoukis, Athens)

1995 (27 Feb). *3rd International Congress of Cypriot Studies, Nicosia. T* **296** *and similar multicoloured designs. P* 14.
877 20 c. Type 296 .. .. .. 75 75
878 30 c. Hypostyle hall, Kalavasos, and Mycenaean amphora .. 1·00 1·25
MS879 110×80 mm. £1 Old Archbishop's Palace, Nicosia (107×71 *mm*). Imperf .. 3·50 4·50

297 Statue of Liberty, Nicosia (left detail)

298 Nazi Heads on Peace Dove over Map of Europe

(Des G. Simonis. Litho Alexandros Matsoukis, Athens)

1995 (31 Mar). *40th Anniv of Start of E.O.K.A. Campaign. T* **297** *and similar vert designs showing different details of the statue. Multicoloured. P* 13×13½.
880 20 c. Type 297 .. .. .. 90 1·00
  a. Horiz strip of 3. Nos. 880/2 .. 2·40
881 20 c. Centre detail (face value at top right) 90 1·00
882 20 c. Right detail (face value at bottom right) 90 1·00
880/2 .. .. .. *Set of 3* 2·40 2·75
Nos. 880/2 were printed together, *se-tenant*, in horizontal strips of 3 forming a composite design.

(Des Toulla Paphitis. Litho Alexandros Matsoukis, Athens)

1995 (8 May). *Europa. Peace and Freedom. T* **298** *and similar vert design. Multicoloured. P* 13½.
883 10 c. Type 298 .. .. .. 50 35
884 30 c. Concentration camp prisoner and peace dove .. .. .. 1·25 1·40

299 Symbolic Figure holding Healthy Food

300 European Union Flag and European Culture Month Logo

(Des Liza Petridou-Mala. Litho Alexandros Matsoukis, Athens)

1995 (26 June). *Healthy Living. T* **299** *and similar multicoloured designs. P* 13½.
885 7 c. Type 299 .. .. .. 25 25
886 10 c. "AIDS" and patients (*horiz*) .. 40 40
887 15 c. Drug addict (*horiz*) 55 55
888 20 c. Smoker and barbed wire .. 75 85
885/8 .. .. .. *Set of 4* 1·75 1·90

(Des G. Simonis (Nos. 889/90), N. Rangos (No. **MS891**). Litho Oriental Press, Bahrain (Nos. 889/90) or Alexandros Matsoukis, Athens (No. **MS891**))

1995 (18 Sept). *European Culture Month and "Europhilex '95" International Stamp Exhibition, Nicosia.* T **300** and similar horiz designs. Royal blue, orange-yellow and pale stone (No. **MS891**) or multicoloured (others). P 13×13½.

889	20 c. Type **300**			55	60
890	25 c. Map of Europe and Cypriot church			70	75

MS891 95×86 mm. 50 c. Peace dove (42×30 mm); 50 c. European Cultural Month symbol (42×30 mm). P 14 ... 3·75 4·50

A limited quantity of No. MS891 was surcharged "£5" on each stamp and sold at "Europhilex '95" on 27 and 28 October 1995.

(Litho Oriental Press, Bahrain)

1995 (24 Oct). *Obligatory Tax. Refugee Fund.* As T **255**, but inscr "1995", "1996" or "1997". Chalk-surfaced paper. P 14½×14½.

892 **255** 1 c. brownish black and olive-grey .. 10 10

301 Peace Dove with Flags of Cyprus and United Nations　302 Reliquary from Kykko Monastery

(Des S. Hadjimichael (10, 25 c.), S. Karamallakis (15 c.), E. Georgiades (20 c.), Litho Oriental Press, Bahrain)

1995 (24 Oct). *Anniversaries and Events.* T **301** and similar multicoloured designs. P 13×13½ (horiz) or 13½×13 (vert).

893	10 c. Type **301** (50th anniv of United Nations)	30	35
894	15 c. Hand pushing ball over net (Centenary of volleyball) (vert)	45	50
895	20 c. Safety pin on leaf (European Nature Conservation Year) (vert)	55	60
896	25 c. Clay pigeon contestant (World Clay Target Shooting Championship)	70	75
893/6	Set of 4	2·00	2·25

(Des S. Karamallakis. Litho Oriental Press, Bahrain)

1995 (27 Nov). *Christmas.* T **302** and similar vert designs showing different reliquaries of Virgin and Child from Kykko Monastery. P 13½×13.

897	7 c. multicoloured	20	25
898	20 c. multicoloured	55	60
899	25 c. multicoloured	70	75
897/9	Set of 3	1·40	1·60

303 Family (25th anniv of Pancyprian Organisation of Large Families)　304 Maria Synglitiki

(Des Liza Petridou-Mala. Litho Oriental Press, Bahrain)

1996 (4 Jan). *Anniversaries and Events.* T **303** and similar vert designs. Multicoloured. P 13½×13.

900	10 c. Type **303**	45	35
901	20 c. Film camera (Centenary of cinema)	75	70
902	35 c. Silhouette of parent and child in globe (50th anniv of U.N.I.C.E.F.)	1·40	1·40
903	40 c. "13" and Commonwealth emblem (13th Conference of Commonwealth Speakers and Presiding Officers)	1·50	1·60
900/3	Set of 4	3·75	3·50

(Des G. Simonis. Litho Oriental Press, Bahrain)

1996 (8 Apr). *Europa. Famous Women.* T **304** and similar vert design. Multicoloured. P 14.

904	10 c. Type **304**	40	30
905	30 c. Queen Caterina Cornaro	1·00	1·10

305 High Jump　306 Watermill

(Des M. Christou. Litho Oriental Press, Bahrain)

1996 (10 June). *Centennial Olympic Games, Atlanta.* T **305** and similar horiz designs. Multicoloured. P 13×13½.

906	10 c. Type **305**	40	30
907	20 c. Javelin	75	65
908	25 c. Wrestling	85	95
909	30 c. Swimming	95	1·10
906/9	Set of 4	2·75	2·75

(Des E. Georgiades. Litho Oriental Press, Bahrain)

1996 (23 Sept). *Mills.* T **306** and similar vert designs. Multicoloured. P 13½×13.

910	10 c. Type **306**	40	30
911	15 c. Olivemill	55	50
912	20 c. Windmill	70	70
913	25 c. Handmill	80	90
910/13	Set of 4	2·25	2·25

307 Icon of Our Lady of Iberia, Moscow　308 "The Nativity" (detail)

(Des D. Komissarov (Nos. 914,917), G. Simonis (Nos. 915/16). Litho State Ptg Wks, Moscow)

1996 (13 Nov). *Cyprus–Russia Joint Issue. Orthodox Religion.* T **307** and similar square designs. Multicoloured. P 11½.

914	30 c. Type **307**	80	85
	a. Block of 4. Nos. 914/17	3·00	
915	30 c. Stravrovouni Monastery, Cyprus	80	85
916	30 c. Icon of St. Nicholas, Cyprus	80	85
917	30 c. Iberia Gate, Moscow	80	85
914/17	Set of 4	3·00	3·25

Nos. 914/17 were printed together, se-tenant, in blocks of 4 throughout the sheet.

(Des G. Koumouros. Litho Oriental Press, Bahrain)

1996 (2 Dec). *Christmas. Religious Murals.* T **308** and similar multicoloured designs. P 13½×13 (25 c.) or 13×13½ (others).

918	7 c. Type **308**	20	25
919	20 c. "Virgin Mary between the Archangels Gabriel and Michael"	55	60
920	25 c. "Christ bestowing Blessing" (vert)	65	70
918/20	Set of 3	1·40	1·50

309 Basketball　310 "The Last Supper"

(Des S. Karamallakis. Litho Oriental Press, Bahrain)

1997 (24 Mar). *Final of European Basketball Cup.* P 13½×13.
921 **309** 30 c. multicoloured .. 90 90

(Litho Oriental Press, Bahrain)

1997 (24 Apr). *Easter. Religious Frescoes from Monastery of St. John Lambadestis.* T **310** and similar horiz design. Multicoloured. P 13×13½.

922	15 c. Type **310**	50	50
923	25 c. "The Crucifixion"	75	75

311 Kori Kourelleni and Prince　312 Oedipoda miniata (grasshopper)

(Des Liza Petridou-Mala. Litho Oriental Press, Bahrain)

1997 (5 May). *Europa. Tales and Legends.* T **311** and similar vert design. Multicoloured. P 13½×13.

924	15 c. Type **311**	50	40
925	30 c. Digenis and Charon	90	1·00

(Des A. Ladommatos. Litho Oriental Press, Bahrain)

1997 (30 June). *Insects.* T **312** and similar horiz designs. Multicoloured. P 13×13½.

926	10 c. Type **312**	30	30
927	15 c. Acherontia atropos (hawk moth)	50	40
928	25 c. Daphnis nerii (hawk moth)	90	95
929	35 c. Ascalaphus macaronius (owl-fly)	1·10	1·25
926/9	Set of 4	2·50	2·75

313 Archbishop Makarios III and Chapel　314 The Nativity

(Des C. Sophocleous. Litho Oriental Press, Bahrain)

1997 (1 Aug). *20th Death Anniv of Archbishop Makarios III.* P 13½×13½.
930 **313** 15 c. multicoloured .. 35 40

(Des G. Koumouros. Litho Oriental Press, Bahrain)

1997 (17 Nov). *Christmas. Byzantine Frescos from the Monastery of St. John Lambadestis.* T **314** and similar vert designs. Multicoloured. P 13½×13.

931	10 c. Type **314**	20	25
932	25 c. Three Kings following the star	60	65
933	30 c. Flight into Egypt	70	75
931/3	Set of 3	1·50	1·60

STAMP BOOKLETS

Stamp-vending machines were introduced by the Cyprus Post Office in 1962. These were originally fitted to provide stamps to the value of 50 m., but in 1979 some were converted to accept 100 m. coins and, a year later, others were altered to supply 150 m. worth of stamps in exchange for three 50 m. coins.

The stamps contained in these booklets were a haphazard selection of low values to the required amount, attached by their sheet margins to the cardboard covers. From 1968 these covers carried commercial advertising and details of postage rates.

Following the change of currency in 1983 the machines were converted to supply 10 c., 20 c. or 30 c. booklets against one, two or three 10 c. coins.

TURKISH CYPRIOT POSTS

After the inter-communal clashes during December 1963, a separate postal service was established on 6 January 1964 between some of the Turkish Cypriot areas, using handstamps inscribed KIBRIS TURK POSTALARI". During 1964, however, an agreement was reached between representatives of the two communities for the restoration of postal services. This agreement, to which the United Nations representatives were a party, was ratified in November 1966 by the Republic's Council of Ministers. Under the scheme postal services were provided for the Turkish Cypriot communities in Famagusta, Larnaca, Limassol, Lefka, Nicosia and Paphos staffed by Turkish Cypriot employees of the Cypriot Department of Posts.

On 8 April 1970 5 m. and 15 m. locally-produced labels, originally designated "Social Aid Stamps", were issued by the Turkish Cypriot community and these can be found on commercial covers. These local stamps are outside the scope of this catalogue.

On 29 October 1973 Nos. 1/7 were placed on sale, but were used only on mail between the Turkish Cypriot areas.

Following the intervention by the Republic of Turkey on 20 July 1974 these stamps replaced issues of the Republic of Cyprus in that part of the island, north and east of the Attila Line, controlled by the Autonomous Turkish Cypriot Administration.

(Currency. 1000 mils = £1)

1 50th Anniversary Emblem   (2)

Des F. Direkoglu Miss E. Ata and G. Pir. Litho Darbhane, Istanbul)

1974 (27 July*). *50th Anniv of Republic of Turkey. T 1 and similar designs in vermilion and black (15 m.) or multicoloured (others). P 12 × 11½ (vert) or 11½ × 12 (horiz).*

1	3 m. Woman sentry (vert)	..	30·00	30·00
2	5 m. Military Parade, Nicosia	..	60	40
3	10 m. Man and woman with Turkish flags (vert)		50	20
4	15 m. Type 1	..	2·50	1·50
5	20 m. Atatürk statue, Kyrenia Gate, Nicosia (vert)		70	20
6	50 m. "The Fallen" (vert)	..	2·00	1·50
7	70 m. Turkish flag and map of Cyprus		16·00	16·00
1/7		Set of 7	48·00	48·00

*This is the date on which Nos. 1/7 became valid for international mail.

On 13 February 1975 a Turkish Cypriot Federated State was proclaimed in that part of Cyprus under Turkish occupation and later 9,000 Turkish Cypriots were transferred from the South to the North of the island.

1975 (3 Mar). *Proclamation of the Turkish Federated State of Cyprus. Nos. 3 and 5 surch as T 2 by Halkin Sesi, Nicosia.*

8	30 m. on 20 m. Atatürk statue, Kyrenia Gate, Nicosia		1·00	1·00
9	100 m. on 10 m. Man and woman with Turkish flags		1·50	2·25

On No. 9 the surcharge appears at the top of the stamp and the inscription at the bottom.

3 Namik Kemal's Bust,   4 Map of Cyprus
Famagusta

(Des I. Özişik. Litho Güzel Sanatlar Matbaasi, Ankara)

1975 (21 Apr). *Multicoloured designs as T 3. Imprint at foot with date "1975". P 13.*

10	3 m. Type 3	..	15	40
11	10 m. Atatürk Statue, Nicosia		15	10
12	15 m. St. Hilarion Castle	..	25	20
13	20 m. Atatürk Square, Nicosia		35	20
14	25 m. Famagusta Beach	..	35	30
15	30 m. Kyrenia Harbour	..	45	10
16	50 m. Lala Mustafa Pasha Mosque, Famagusta (vert)		50	10
17	100 m. Interior, Kyrenia Castle		1·00	90
18	250 m. Castle walls, Kyrenia		1·75	2·75
19	500 m. Othello Tower, Famagusta (vert)		3·50	5·00
10/19		Set of 10	7·50	9·00

See also Nos. 37/8.

(Des B. Erkmen (30 m.), S. Tuga (50 m.), N. Cüneş (150 m.). Litho Ajans-Türk Matbassi, Ankara)

1975 (20 July). *"Peace in Cyprus". T 4 and similar multicoloured designs. P 13.*

20	30 m. Type 4	..	30	15
21	50 m. Map, laurel and broken chain	..	35	20
22	150 m. Map and laurel-sprig on globe (vert)		90	1·00
20/2		Set of 3	1·40	1·25

5 "Pomegranates" (I. V. Guney)

(Litho Güzel Sanatlar Matbaasi, Ankara)

1975 (29 Dec). *Europa. Paintings. T 5 and similar horiz design. Multicoloured. P 13.*

23	90 m. Type 5	..	80	60
24	100 m. "Harvest Time" (F. Direkoglu) ..		95	60

10 M ——
(6)   7 "Expectation"

1976 (28 Apr). *Nos. 16/17 surch as T 6 at Govt Printing House, Nicosia in horizontal clichés of 10.*

25	10 m. on 50 m. Lala Mustafa Pasha Mosque, Famagusta		50	70
26	30 m. on 100 m. Interior, Kyrenia Castle		50	80

(Litho Ajans-Türk Matbassi, Ankara)

1976 (3 May). *Europa. T 7 and similar vert design showing ceramic statuette. Multicoloured. P 13.*

27	60 m. Type 7	..	40	80
28	120 m. "Man in Meditation"	..	60	90

8 Carob   9 Olympic Symbol "Flower"

(Des S. Atlihan. Litho Güzel Sanatlar Matbaasi, Ankara)

1976 (28 June). *Export Products—Fruits. T 8 and similar horiz designs. Multicoloured. P 13.*

29	10 m. Type 8	..	25	10
30	25 m. Mandarin	..	40	10
31	40 m. Strawberry	..	50	25
32	60 m. Orange	..	60	65
33	80 m. Lemon	..	70	1·75
29/33		Set of 5	2·25	2·50

(Des C. Mutver (60 m.), A. B. Kocamanoglu (100 m.). Litho Güzel Sanatlar Matbaasi, Ankara)

1976 (17 July). *Olympic Games. Montreal. T 9 and similar horiz design. Multicoloured. P 13.*

34	60 m. Type 9	..	25	20
35	100 m. Olympic symbol and doves	..	35	25

10 Kyrenia Harbour   11 Liberation Monument, Karaeglanoglu (Ay. Georghios)

(Des I. Özişik. Litho Ajans-Türk Matbassi, Ankara)

1976 (2 Aug). *New design (5 m.) or as Nos. 12/13 but redrawn with lettering altered and new imprint at foot with date "1976". P 13.*

36	5 m. Type 10	..	40	15
37	15 m. St. Hilarion Castle	..	40	15
38	20 m. Atatürk Square, Nicosia	..	40	15
36/8		Set of 3	1·10	40

Nos. 39/46 vacant.

(Des D. Erimez and C. Gizer. Litho Ajans-Türk Matbassi, Ankara)

1976 (1 Nov). *Liberation Monument. T 11 and similar vert design. P 13.*

47	11	30 m. lt turquoise-blue, lt flesh & black	15	20
48		70 m. light verm, light flesh & blk	35	45

No. 48 shows a different view of the Monument.

12 Hotel, Salamis Bay

(Litho Türk Tarih Kurumu Basimevi, Ankara)

1977 (2 May). *Europa. T 12 and similar horiz design. Multicoloured. P 13.*

49	80 m. Type 12	..	65	80
50	100 m. Kyrenia Port	..	75	80

13 Pottery   14 Arap Ahmet Pasha Mosque, Nicosia

(Litho Güzel Sanatlar Matbaasi, Ankara)

1977 (27 June). *Handicrafts. T 13 and similar designs. Multicoloured. P 13.*

51	15 m. Type 13	..	10	10
52	30 m. Decorated gourds (vert)	..	10	10
53	125 m. Basketware	..	30	50
51/3		Set of 3	40	65

(Litho APA Ofset Basimevi, Istanbul)

1977 (2 Dec). *Turkish Buildings in Cyprus. T 14 and similar horiz designs. Multicoloured. P 13.*

54	20 m. Type 14	..	10	10
55	40 m. Paphos Castle	..	10	10
56	70 m. Bekir Pasha aqueduct	..	15	20
57	80 m. Sultan Mahmut library ..		15	25
54/7		Set of 4	45	60

15 Namik Kemal (bust) and   16 Old Man and House, Famagusta   Woman

(Des B. Ozak. Litho Ticaret Matbaacilik TAS, Izmir)

1977 (21 Dec). *Namik Kemal (patriotic poet). T 15 and similar multicoloured design. P 12½ × 13 (30 m.) or 13 × 12½ (140 m.).*

58	30 m. Type 15	..	15	15
59	140 m. Namik Kemal (portrait) (vert) ..		35	60

(New Currency. 100 kurus = 1 lira)

(Des G. Pir. Litho Ajans-Türk Matbassi, Ankara)

1978 (17 Apr). *Social Security. T 16 and similar vert designs. P 13 × 13½.*

60	150 k. black, yellow and blue ..		10	10
61	275 k. black, red-orange and green	..	15	15
62	375 k. black, blue and red-orange	..	25	20
60/2		Set of 3	45	40

Designs:—275 k. Injured man with crutch; 375 k. Woman with family.

17 Oratory in Büyük   18 Motorway Junction
Han, Nicosia

(Des I. Özisik. Litho APA Ofset Basimevi, Istanbul)

1978 (2 May). *Europa. T 17 and similar horiz design. Multicoloured. P 13.*

63	225 k. Type 17	..	30	30
64	450 k. Cistern in Selimiye Mosque, Nicosia ..		60	70

(Litho APA Ofset Basimevi, Istanbul)

1978 (10 July). *Communications. T 18 and similar horiz designs. Multicoloured. P 13.*

65	75 k. Type 18	..	15	10
66	100 k. Hydrofoil	..	15	10
67	650 k. Boeing 720 at Ercan Airport	..	50	35
65/7		Set of 3	70	45

19 Dove with Laurel Branch   20 Kemal Atatürk

(Des E. Kaya (725 k.), C. Kirkbesoglu (others). Litho APA Ofset Basimevi, Istanbul)

1978 (13 Sept). *National Oath.* T **19** *and similar designs.* P 13.
68	150 k. orange-yellow, violet and black.		10	10
69	225 k. black, Indian red and orange-yellow		10	10
70	725 k. black, cobalt and orange-yellow		20	20
68/70		Set of 3	35	35

Designs: *Vert*—225 k. "Taking the Oath". *Horiz*—725 k. Symbolic dove.

(Des C. Mutver. Litho Türk Tarih Kurumu Basimevi, Ankara)

1978 (10 Nov). *Kemal Atatürk Commemoration.* P 13.
71	**20**	75 k. pale turquoise-grn & turq-grn	10	10
72		450 k. pale flesh and light brown	15	15
73		650 k. pale blue and light blue	20	25
71/3		Set of 3	40	40

50 Krs.

(21)

22 Gun Barrel with Olive Branch and Map of Cyprus

1979 (4 June). *Nos. 30/3 surch as* T **21**, *by Govt Printing Office, Lefkosa*
74	50 k. on 25 m. Mandarin		10	10
75	1 l. on 40 m. Strawberry		15	10
76	3 l. on 60 m. Orange		15	10
77	5 l. on 80 m. Lemon		35	15
74/7		Set of 4	65	30

(Des N. Dündar. Litho Ajans-Türk Matbassi, Ankara)

1979 (20 July). *5th Anniv of Turkish Peace Operation in Cyprus. Sheet 72 × 52 mm. Imperf.*
MS78 **22** 15 l. black, deep turquoise-blue and pale green .. .. 80 1·25

23 Postage Stamp and Map of Cyprus

24 Symbolised Microwave Antenna

(Des S. Mumcu. Litho Ajans-Türk Matbassi, Ankara)

1979 (20 Aug). *Europa. Communications.* T **23** *and similar horiz designs. Multicoloured.* P 13.
79	2 l. Type **23**		10	10
80	3 l. Postage stamps, building and map		10	10
81	8 l. Telephones, Earth and satellite		20	30
79/81		Set of 3	35	45

(Litho Ticaret Matbaacilik TAS, Izmir)

1979 (24 Sept). *50th Anniv of International Consultative Radio Committee.* P 13 × 12½.
82	**24**	2 l. multicoloured	20	10
83		5 l. multicoloured	20	10
84		6 l. multicoloured	25	15
82/4		Set of 3	60	30

25 School Children

26 Lala Mustafa Pasha Mosque, Magusa

(Des H. Hastürk (1½ l.), G. Akansel (4½ l.), P. Yalyali (6 l.). Litho APA Ofset Basimevi, Istanbul)

1979 (29 Oct). *International Year of the Child. Children's Drawings.* T **25** *and similar multicoloured designs.* P 13.
85	1½ l. Type **25**		25	15
86	4½ l. Children and globe (*horiz*)		40	20
87	6 l. College children		60	20
85/7		Set of 3	1·10	50

(Des S. Mumcu (20 l.), I. Ozisik (others). Litho Ajans-Türk Matbassi, Ankara)

1980 (23 Mar). *Islamic Commemorations.* T **26** *and similar vert designs. Multicoloured.* P 13.
88	2½ l. Type **26**		10	10
89	10 l. Arap Ahmet Pasha Mosque, Lefkosa		30	15
90	20 l. Mecca and Medina		50	20
88/90		Set of 3	80	40

Commemorations:—2½ l. 1st Islamic Conference in Turkish Cyprus; 10 l. General Assembly of World Islam Congress; 20 l. Moslem Year 1400AH.

27 Ebu-Su'ud Efendi (philosopher)

28 Omer's Shrine, Kyrenia

(Litho Ajans-Türk Matbassi, Ankara)

1980 (23 May). *Europa. Personalities.* T **27** *and similar vert. design. Multicoloured.* P 13.
91	5 l. Type **27**		20	10
92	30 l. Sultan Selim II		70	40

(Litho Guzel Sanatlar Matbaasi, Ankara)

1980 (25 June). *Ancient Monuments,* T **28** *and similar horiz designs.* P 13.
93	2½ l. new blue and stone		10	10
94	3½ l. grey-green and pale rose-pink		10	10
95	5 l. lake and pale blue-green		15	10
96	10 l. deep mauve and pale green		30	10
97	20 l. dull ultramarine & pale greenish yellow		50	25
93/7		Set of 5	95	45

Designs:—3½ l. Entrance gate, Famagusta; 5 l. Funerary monuments (16th-century), Famagusta; 10 l. Bella Paise Abbey, Kyrenia; 20 l. Selimiye Mosque, Nicosia.

29 Cyprus 1880 6d.

30 Dome of the Rock

31 Extract from World Muslim Congress Statement in Turkish

(Des S. Mumcu. Litho Ajans-Türk Matbassi, Ankara)

1980 (16 Aug). *Cyprus Stamp Centenary.* T **29** *and similar designs showing stamps.* P 14.
98	7½ l. black, drab and grey-olive		20	10
99	15 l. brown, grey-blue and blue		25	15
100	50 l. black, rose and grey		65	55
98/100		Set of 3	1·00	70

Designs: *Horiz*—15 l. Cyprus 1960 Constitution of the Republic 30 m. commemorative. *Vert*—50 l. Social Aid local, 1970.

(Litho Guzel Sanatlar Matbaasi, Ankara)

1980 (16 Oct). *Palestinian Solidarity.* T **30** *and similar multicoloured design.* P 13.
101	15 l. Type **30**		25	15
102	35 l. Dome of the Rock (*horiz*).		65	30

(Des S. Mumcu. Litho Turk Tarih Kurumu Basimevi, Ankara)

1981 (24 Mar). *Solidarity with Islamic Countries Day.* T **31** *and similar vert design showing extract from World Muslim Congress statement.* P 13.
103	1 l. rosine, stone and olive-sepia		15	15
104	35 l. black, pale blue-green and myrtle-green		55	85

Design:—35 l. Extract in English

32 "Atatürk" (F. Duran)

33 Folk-dancing

(Litho Ajans-Türk Matbassi, Ankara)

1981 (19 May). *Atatürk Stamp Exhibition, Lefkosa.* P 13.
105	**32**	20 l. multicoloured	25	35

No. 105 was printed in sheets of 100, including 50 *se-tenant* stamp-size labels.

(Litho Ticaret Matbaacilik TAS, Izmir)

1981 (29 June). *Europa, Folklore.* T **33** *and similar horiz design showing folk-dancing.* P 12½ × 13.
106	10 l. multicoloured		35	15
107	30 l. multicoloured		60	35

MINIMUM PRICE

The minimum price quote is 10p which represents a handling charge rather than a basis for valuing common stamps. For further notes about prices see introductory pages.

34 "Kemal Atatürk" (I. Calli)

35 Wild Convolvulus

(Litho Basim Ofset, Ankara)

1981 (23 July). *Birth Centenary of Kemal Atatürk. Sheet 70 × 95 mm. Imperf.*
MS108 **34** 150 l. multicoloured .. .. 1·10 1·25

(Litho Turk Tarih Kurumu Basimevi, Ankara)

1981 (28 Sept)–**82**. *Flowers, Multicoloured designs as* T **35**. P 13.
109	1 l. Type **35**.		10	10
110	5 l. Persian Cyclamen (*horiz*) (22.1.82)		10	10
111	10 l. Spring Mandrake (*horiz*)		10	10
112	25 l. Corn Poppy		15	10
113	30 l. Wild Arum (22.1.82)		20	10
114	50 l. Sage-leaved Rock Rose (*horiz*) (22.1.82)		40	20
115	100 l. *Cistus salviaefolius* L. (22.1.82)		75	30
116	150 l. Giant Fennel (*horiz*)		1·40	90
109/16		Set of 8	2·75	1·50

36 Stylized Disabled Person in Wheelchair

37 Turkish and Palestinian Flags

(Des H. Ulucam (7½ l.), N. Kozal (others). Litho Türk Tarih Kurumu Basimevi, Ankara)

1981 (16 Oct). *Commemorations.* T **36** *and similar multicoloured designs.* P 13.
117	7½ l. Type **36**		30	35
118	10 l. Heads of people of different races, peace dove and barbed wire (*vert*)		50	55
119	20 l. People of different races reaching out from globe, with dishes (*vert*)		75	85
117/19		Set of 3	1·40	1·60

Commemorations:—7½ l. International Year for Disabled Persons; 10 l. Anti-apartheid Publicity; 20 l. World Food Day.

(Des H. Ulucam. Litho Türk Tarih Kurumu Basimevi, Ankara)

1981 (29 Nov). *Palestinian Solidarity.* P 13.
120	**37**	10 l. multicoloured	30	40

38 Prince Charles and Lady Diana Spencer

39 Charter issued by Sultan Abdul Aziz to Archbishop Sophronios

(Des H. Ulucam. Litho Türk Tarih Kurumu Basimevi, Ankara)

1981 (30 Nov). *Royal Wedding.* P 13
121	**38**	50 l. multicoloured	1·00	85

(Des H. Ulucam, Litho Tezel Ofset, Lefkosa)

1982 (30 July). *Europa (CEPT). Sheet 83 × 124 mm containing* T **39** *and similar vert design. Multicoloured.* P 12½ × 13.
MS122 30 l. × 2. Type **39**; 70 l. × 2, Turkish forces landing at Tuzla, 1571 .. .. .. 4·50 5·00

40 Buffavento Castle

41 "Wedding" (A. Örek)

(Des H. Ulucam (Nos. 123/5). Litho Tezel Ofset, Lefkosa)

1982 (20 Aug). *Tourism. T 40 and similar multicoloured designs. P 12.*

123	5 l.	Type **40**	..	..	10	10
124	10 l.	Windsurfing (*horiz*)	..	..	15	10
125	15 l.	Kantara Castle (*horiz*)	..	..	25	15
126	30 l.	Shipwreck (300 B.C.) (*horiz*)	..		50	40
123/6	..			*Set of 4*	90	65

(Litho Ajans-Türk Matbassi, Ankara)

1982 (3 Dec). *Paintings (1st series). T 41 and similar multicoloured design. P 13.*

127	30 l.	Type **41**	..	..	15	30
128	50 l.	"Carob Pickers" (O. Naxim Selenge) (*vert*)			30	70

See also Nos. 132/3, 157/8, 176/7, 185/6, 208/9, 225/7, 248/50, 284/5, 315/16, 328/9, 369/70 and 432/3.

42 Cross of Lorraine, Koch and Bacillus (Cent of Koch's Discovery of Tubercle Bacillus)

43 "Calloused Hands" (Salih Oral)

(Des H. Ulucam. Litho Tezel Ofset, Lefkosa)

1982 (15 Dec). *Anniversaries and Events. T 42 and similar multicoloured designs. P 12.*

129	10 l.	Type **42**	..	..	85	40
130	30 l.	Spectrum on football pitch (World Cup Football Championships, Spain)			1·50	85
131	70 l.	"75" and Lord Baden-Powell (75th anniv of Boy Scout movement and 125th birth anniv) (*vert*)	..	..	2·25	3·00
129/31				*Set of 3*	4·25	3·75

(Litho Ajans-Türk Matbassi, Ankara)

1983 (16 May). *Paintings (2nd series). T 43 and similar vert design. Multicoloured. P 13.*

132	30 l.	Type **43**	..	..	90	1·40
133	35 l.	"Malya—Limassol Bus" (Emin Cizenel)			90	1·40

44 Old Map of Cyprus by Piri Reis

45 First Turkish Cypriot 10 m. Stamp

(Litho Türk Tarih Kurumu Basimevi, Ankara)

1983 (30 June). *Europa. Sheet 82 × 78 mm, containing T 44 and similar horiz design. Multicoloured. P 13.*

MS134	100 l.	Type **44**; 100 l. Cyprus as seen from "Skylab"	..	..	2·25	3·25

(Des E. Ata (15 l.), A. Hasan (20 l.), G. Pir (25 l.), H. Ulucam (others). Litho Ajans-Türk Matbassi, Ankara)

1983 (1 Aug). *Anniversaries and Events. T 45 and similar multicoloured designs commemorating World Communications Year (30, 50 l). or 25th Anniv. of T.M.T. (Turkish Cypriot Resistance Organization). P 13.*

135	15 l.	Type **45**	..	..	50	50
136	20 l.	"Turkish Achievements in Cyprus" (*horiz*)			60	60
137	25 l.	"Liberation Fighters"	..	..	70	70
138	30 l.	Dish aerial and telegraph pole (*horiz*)	..	85	90
139	50 l.	Dove and envelopes (*horiz*)	..	1·75	2·00
135/9	..			*Set of 5*	4·00	4·25

Kuzey Kıbrıs Türk Cumhuriyeti 15.11.1983

46 European Bee Eater   (47)

(Des E. Cizenel. Litho Ajans-Türks Matbassi, Ankara)

1983 (10 Oct). *Birds of Cyprus. T 46 and similar horiz designs. Multicoloured. P 13.*

140	10 l.	Type **46**	..	..	80	1·00
		a. Block of 4. Nos. 140/3	..	..	4·00	
141	15 l.	Goldfinch	..	..	1·00	1·10
142	50 l.	European Robin	..	..	1·25	1·40
143	65 l.	Golden Oriole	..	..	1·40	1·50
140/3				*Set of 4*	4·00	4·50

Nos. 140/3 were printed together, *se-tenant*, in blocks of 4 throughout the sheet.

1983 (7 Dec). *Establishment of the Republic. Nos. 109, 111/12 and 116 surch as T 47 (No. 145) or optd only.*

144	10 l.	Spring Mandrake	..	..	20	15
145	15 l.	on 1 l. Type **35**			30	15
		a. Surch inverted	..	..	75·00	
146	25 l.	Corn Poppy	..	..	40	25
147	150 l.	Giant Fennel	..	..	2·25	3·25
144/7	..			*Set of 4*	2·75	3·50

48 C.E.P.T. 25th Anniversary Logo.   49 Olympic Flame

(Des J. Larrivière. Litho Tezel Ofset, Lefkosa)

1984 (30 May). *Europa. P 12 × 12½.*

148	48	50 l. lemon, chestnut and black	..	2·25	3·00
		a. Pair. Nos. 148/9	..	4·50	6·00
149		100 l. pale blue, bright blue and black	..	2·25	3·00

Nos. 148/9 were printed together, *se-tenant*, in horizontal and vertical pairs throughout the sheet.

(Des H. Ulucam. Litho Tezel Ofset, Lefkosa)

1984 (19 June). *Olympic Games, Los Angeles. T 49 and similar multicoloured designs. P 12½ × 12 (10 l.) or 12 × 12½ (others).*

150	10 l.	Type **49**	..	..	15	10
151	20 l.	Olympic events within rings (*horiz*)		25	25
152	70 l.	Martial arts event (*horiz*)	..	50	1·50
150/2	..			*Set of 3*	80	1·60

50 Atatürk Cultural Centre

51

(Des H. Ulucam. Litho Tezel Ofset, Lefkosa)

1984 (20 July). *Opening of Atatürk Cultural Centre, Lefkosa. W 51. P 12 × 12½.*

153	50	120 l. stone, black and chestnut	..	1·25	1·75

52 Turkish Cypriot Flag and Map

(Des C. Guzeloglu (20 l.), M. Gozbebek (70 l.). Litho Tezel Ofset Lefkosa)

1984 (20 July). *10th Anniv of Turkish Landings in Cyprus. T 52 and similar horiz design. W 51. Multicoloured. P 12 × 12½.*

154	20 l.	Type **52**	..	..	50	25
155	70 l.	Turkish Cypriot flag within book	..	1·00	2·00

53 Burnt and Replanted Forests

(Des H. Ulucam. Litho Tezel Ofset, Lefkosa)

1984 (20 Aug). *World Forestry Resources. W 51. P 12 × 12½.*

156	53	90 l. multicoloured	..	..	1·25	1·75

ALTERED CATALOGUE NUMBERS

Any Catalogue numbers altered from the last edition are shown as a list in the introductory pages.

---

54 "Old Turkish Houses, Nicosia" (Cevdet Cagdas)

55 Kemal Atatürk, Flag and Crown

(Litho Tezel Ofset, Lefkosa)

1984 (21 Sept). *Paintings (3rd series). T 54 and similar horiz design. Multicoloured. W 51. P 13 × 12½.*

157	20 l.	Type **54**	..	..	50	40
158	70 l.	"Scenery" (Olga Rauf)	..	..	1·10	2·00

See also Nos. 176/7, 185/6, 208/9, 225/7, 248/50, 284/5, 315/16 and 328/9.

(Des H. Ulucam (20 l.), F. Isiman (70 l.). Litho Tezel Ofset, Lefkosa)

1984 (15 Nov). *1st Anniv of Turkish Republic of Northern Cyprus. T 55 and similar multicoloured design. W 51 (sideways on 20 l., inverted on 70 l.). P 12½.*

159	20 l.	Type **55**	..	..	50	40
160	70 l.	Legislative Assembly voting for Republic (*horiz*)	..	1·10	2·00

56 Taekwondo Bout

57 "Le Regard" (Saulo Mercader)

(Des H. Ulucam. Litho Tezel Ofset, Lefkosa)

1984 (10 Dec). *International Taekwondo Championship, Girne. T 56 and similar horiz design. W 51 (sideways on 10 l.). P 12½.*

161	10 l.	black, pale cinnamon and grey-black	..	40	25
162	70 l.	multicoloured	..	..	1·60	2·50

Design:—70 l. Emblem and flags of competing nations.

(Litho Tezel Ofset, Lefkosa)

1984 (10 Dec). *Exhibition by Saulo Mercader (artist). T 57 and similar multicoloured design. W 51 (sideways on 20 l.). P 12½ × 13 (20 l.) or 13 × 12½ (70 l.).*

163	20 l.	Type **57**	..	..	30	25
164	70 l.	"L'equilibre de L'esprit (*horiz*)..	..	1·10	2·25

58 Musical Instruments and Music

59 Dr. Fazil Kucuk (politician)

(Des H. Ulucam. Litho Tezel Ofset, Lefkosa)

1984 (10 Dec). *Visit of Nurnberg Chamber Orchestra. W 51 (sideways). P 12½.*

165	58	70 l. multicoloured	..	..	1·50	2·25

(Des Y. Calli (20 l.), E. Cizenel (70 l.). Litho Tezel Ofset, Lefkosa)

1985 (15 Jan). *1st Death Anniv of Dr. Fazil Kucuk (politician). T 59 and similar vert design. Multicoloured. W 51 (inverted on 70 l.) P 12½ × 12.*

166	20 l.	Type **59**	..	..	30	30
167	70 l.	Dr. Fazil Kucuk reading newspaper	..	95	2·00

60 Goat

61 George Frederick Handel

(Des E. Cizenel. Litho Tezel Ofset, Lefkosa)

1985 (29 May). *Domestic Animals. T* **60** *and similar horiz designs. Multicoloured. W* **51**. *P* 12×12½.
168	100 l. Type **60**..	..	..	55	30
169	200 l. Cow and calf	..	..	90	80
170	300 l. Ram	..	..	1·25	2·00
171	500 l. Donkey..	..	..	2·00	3·25
168/71	..	..	*Set of* 4	4·25	5·75

(Litho Tezel Ofset, Lefkosa)

1985 (26 June). *Europa. Composers. T* **61** *and similar vert designs. W* **51** (*sideways*). *P* 12½×12.
172	20 l. brown-purple, myrtle-green & pale grn	2·00	2·50
	a. Block of 4. Nos. 172/5 ..	8·00	
173	20 l. brown-purple, lake-brown & pale pink	2·00	2·50
174	100 l. brown-purple, steel blue & pale grey-bl	2·50	3·00
175	100 l. brown-purple, bistre-brown & pale cinn	2·50	3·00
172/5 ..		*Set of* 4	8·00	10·00

Designs:—No. 172, Type **61**; 173, Guiseppe Domenico Scarlatti; 174, Johann Sebastian Bach; 175, Buhurizade Mustafa Itri Efendi.

Nos. 172/5 were printed together, *se-tenant*, in blocks of four throughout the sheet.

(Litho Tezel Ofset, Lefkosa)

1985 (15 Aug). *Paintings (4th series). Vert designs as T* **54**. *Multicoloured. W* **51**. *P* 12½×13.
176	20 l. "Village Life" (Ali Atakan)	..	60	50
177	50 l. "Woman carrying Water" (Ismet V. Güney)	..	..	1·40	2·50

62 Heads of Three Youths   **63** Parachutist (Aviation League)

(Des H. Uluçam. Litho Tezel Ofset, Lefkosa)

1985 (29 Oct). *International Youth Year. T* **62** *and similar horiz design. Multicoloured. W* **51** (*sideways*). *P* 12×12½.
178	20 l. Type **62**..	..	..	75	40
179	100 l. Dove and globe	..	..	3·50	4·00

(Des H. Uluçam. Litho Tezel Ofset, Lefkosa)

1985 (29 Nov). *Anniversaries and Events. T* **63** *and similar designs. W* **51** (*inverted on Nos.* 181/2, *sideways on Nos.* 183/4). *P* 12×12½ (*Nos.* 183/4) *or* 12½×12 (*others*).
180	20 l. multicoloured	..	..	1·00	30
181	50 l. grey-black, light brown and dull ultramarine ..	..	..	1·50	1·00
182	100 l. light brown	..	..	1·75	2·50
183	100 l. multicoloured	..	..	1·75	2·50
184	100 l. multicoloured	..	..	1·75	2·50
180/4 ..		..	*Set of* 5	7·00	8·00

Designs: *Vert*—No. 181, Louis Pasteur (Centenary of Discovery of Rabies vaccine); 182, İsmet İnönü (Turkish statesman) (birth centenary (1984)). *Horiz*—183, "40" in figures and symbolic flower (40th anniv of United Nations Organization); 184, Patient receiving blood transfusion (Prevention of Thalassaemia).

(Litho Tezel Ofset, Lefkosa)

1986 (20 June). *Paintings (5th series). Horiz designs as T* **54**. *Multicoloured. W* **51** (*sideways*). *P* 13×12½.
185	20 l. "House with Arches" (Gönen Atakol)..	50	30
186	100 l. "Atatürk Square" (Yalkin Muhtaroğlu)	..	..	1·75	1·75

64 Griffon Vulture   **65** Karagöz Show Puppets

(Des E. Çizenel (100 l.), H. Uluçam (200 l.). Litho Tezel Ofset, Lefkosa)

1986 (20 June). *Europa. Protection of Nature and the Environment. Sheet* 82×76 *mm. containing T* **64** *and similar horiz design. Multicoloured. W* **51** (*sideways*). *P* 12×12½.
MS187	100 l. Type **64**: 200 l. Litter on Cyprus landscape ..	..	..	6·00	5·50

(Des Y. Yazgin. Litho Tezel Ofset, Lefkosa)

1986 (25 July). *Karagöz Folk Puppets. W* **51** (*inverted*). *P* 12½×13.
188	**65** 100 l. multicoloured	..	..	2·00	2·00

66 Old Bronze Age Composite Pottery   **67** Soldiers, Defence Force Badge and Atatürk (10th anniv of Defence Forces)

(Litho Tezel Ofset, Lefkosa)

1986 (15 Sept). *Archaeological Artifacts. Cultural Links with Anatolia. T* **66** *and similar multicoloured designs. W* **51** (*sideways on* 10, 50 *l., inverted on* 20, 100 *l.). P* 12×12½ (10, 50 *l.*) *or* 12½×12 (20, 100 *l.*).
189	10 l. Type **66**..	..	..	55	20
190	20 l. Late Bronze Age bird jug (*vert*)	90	30
191	50 l. Neolithic earthenware pot	..	1·50	1·50
192	100 l. Roman statue of Artemis (*vert*)	2·00	3·00
189/92			*Set of* 4	4·50	4·50

(Des. H. Uluçam (No. 196). Litho Tezel Ofset, Lefkosa)

1986 (13 Oct). *Anniversaries and Events. T* **67** *and similar multicoloured designs. W* **51** (*inverted on* 20, 50 *l., sideways on others*). *P* 12½×12 (*vert*) *or* 12×12½ (*horiz*).
193	20 l. Type **67**..	..	..	80	30
194	50 l. Woman and two children (40th anniv of Food and Agriculture Organization) ..	1·40	1·40
195	100 l. Football and world map (World Cup Football Championship, Mexico) (*horiz*)	2·75	3·25
196	100 l. Orbit of Halley's Comet and *Giotto* spacecraft (*horiz*)	..	..	2·75	3·25
193/6 ..	..	..	*Set of* 4	7·00	7·50

68 Güzelyurt Dam and Power Station   **69** Prince Andrew and Miss Sarah Ferguson

(Litho Tezel Ofset, Lefkosa)

1986 (17 Nov). *Modern Development* (1st series). *T* **68** *and similar horiz designs. Multicoloured. W* **51** (*sideways*). *P* 12½×12½.
197	20 l. Type **68**..	..	..	1·25	30
198	50 l. Low cost housing project, Lefkosa	..	1·40	1·25
199	100 l. Kyrenia Airport	..	..	2·75	3·25
197/9 ..	..	..	*Set of* 3	4·75	4·25

See also Nos. 223/4 and 258/63.

(Litho Tezel Ofset, Lefkosa)

1986 (20 Nov). *60th Birthday of Queen Elizabeth II and Royal Wedding. T* **69** *and similar vert design. Multicoloured. W* **51** (*inverted*). *P* 12½×13.
200	100 l. Type **69**..	..	..	1·40	1·75
	a. Pair. Nos. 200/1	..	..	2·75	3·50
201	100 l. Queen Elizabeth II	..	..	1·40	1·75

Nos. 200/1 were printed together, *se-tenant*, in horizontal and vertical pairs throughout the sheet.

(Litho Tezel Ofset, Lefkosa)

1986 (31 Dec). *Cyprus Railway. T* **70** *and similar horiz design. Multicoloured. W* **51** (*sideways*). *P* 12×12½.
202	50 l. Type **70**..	..	..	2·75	2·75
203	100 l. Locomotive No. 1	..	..	3·25	3·75

༄ི༅ི༄ི༅ི༄ི༅ི༄ི༅ི༄ི༅ི༄ི༅ི

Kuzey Kıbrıs Türk Cumhuriyeti

(71)

1987 (18 May). *Nos.* 94, 96/7 *and* 113 *optd as T* **71** *or surch also.*
204	10 l. deep mauve and pale green	50	70
205	15 l. on 3½ l. grey-green and pale rose-pink	50	70
206	20 l. dull ultramarine & pale greenish yellow	55	75
207	30 l. multicoloured	..	..	70	1·10
204/7 ..		*Set of* 4	2·00	3·00

(Litho Tezel Ofset, Lefkosa)

1987 (27 May). *Paintings* (6th series). *Vert designs as T* **54**. *Multicoloured. W* **51** (*inverted*). *P* 12½×13.
208	50 l. "Shepherd" (Feridun Işiman)..	1·25	1·25
209	125 l. "Pear Woman" (Mehmet Uluhan)	..	1·75	2·50

72 Modern House (architect A. Vural Behaeddin)   **73** Kneeling Folk Dancer

(Des H. Uluçam (50 l.). Litho Tezel Ofset, Lefkosa)

1987 (30 June). *Europa. Modern Architecture. T* **72** *and similar horiz design. Multicoloured. W* **51** (*sideways*). *P* 12×12½.
210	50 l. Type **72**..	..	..	1·00	80
	a. Perf 12×imperf	..	..	1·75	3·00
	ab. Booklet pane. Nos. 210a/11a, each × 2	7·00	
211	200 l. Modern house (architect Necdet Turgay)	..	..	1·75	3·00
	a. Perf 12 × imperf	..	..	1·75	3·00

Nos. 210a and 211a come from 500 l. stamp booklets containing *se-tenant* pane No. 210ab.

(Des B. Ruhi. Litho Tezel Ofset, Lefkosa)

1987 (20 Aug). *Folk Dancers. T* **73** *and similar vert designs. Multicoloured. W* **51** (*inverted*). *P* 12½×12.
212	20 l. Type **73**	..	..	50	20
213	50 l. Standing male dancer	..	..	75	40
214	200 l. Standing female dancer	..	..	1·75	1·50
215	1000 l. Woman's headdress ..	..	..	4·50	6·00
212/15	..	..	*Set of* 4	6·75	7·25

74 Regimental Colour (1st Anniv of Infantry Regiment)   **75** Ahmet Beliğ Pasha (Egyptian judge)

(Des H. Uluçam. Litho Tezel Ofset, Lefkosa)

1987 (30 Sept–2 Nov). *Anniversaries and Events. T* **74** *and similar multicoloured designs. W* **51** (*inverted on vert designs, sideways on horiz*). *P* 12½×12 (*vert*) *or* 12×12½ (*horiz*).
216	50 l. Type **74**..	..	..	1·00	60
217	50 l. Pres. Denktash and Turgut Özal (1st anniv. of Turkish Prime Minister's visit) (*horiz*) (2.11)	..	1·00	60
218	200 l. Emblem and Crescent (5th Islamic Summit Conference, Kuwait)..	2·00	3·00
219	200 l. Emblem and laurel leaves (Membership of Pharmaceutical Federation) (*horiz*)	..	..	2·00	3·00
216/19	..	..	*Set of* 4	5·50	6·50

(Des H. Uluçam. Litho Tezel Ofset, Lefkosa)

1987 (22 Oct). *Turkish Cypriot Personalities. T* **75** *and similar vert designs. W* **51** (*inverted*). *P* 12½×12.
220	75	50 l. brown and greenish yellow	..	65	40
221	–	50 l. multicoloured	..	..	65	40
222	–	125 l. multicoloured	..	..	1·50	3·00
220/2 ..			*Set of* 3	2·50	3·50

Designs:—50 l. (No. 221) Mehmet Emin Pasha (Ottoman Grand Vizier); 125 l. Mehmet Kâmil Pasha (Ottoman Grand Vizier).

76 Tourist Hotel, Girne   **77** Piyale Pasha (tug)

(Des A. Erduran. Litho Tezel Ofset, Lefkosa)

1987 (20 Nov). *Modern Development* (2nd series). *T* **76** *and similar horiz design. Multicoloured. W* **51** (*sideways*). *P* 12×12½.
223	150 l. Type **76**..	..	..	1·50	1·50
224	200 l. Dogu Akdeniz University	..	..	1·75	2·25

(Litho Tezel Ofset, Lefkosa)

1988 (2 May). *Paintings (7th series). Multicoloured designs as T **54**. W **51** (inverted on 20, 150 l, sideways on 50 l.). P 12½×13 (20, 150 l.) or 13×12½ (50 l.).*

225	20 l. "Woman making Pastry" (Ayhan Mentes)(vert)		50	20
226	50 l. "Chair Weaver" (Osman Güvenir)		75	75
227	150 l. "Woman weaving a Rug" (Zekäi Yesiladali)(vert)		1·75	3·00
225/7		Set of 3	2·75	3·50

(Des H. Uluçam. Litho Tezel Ofset, Lefkosa)

1988 (31 May). *Europa. Transport and Communications. T **77** and similar multicoloured design. W **51** (sideways on 200 l., inverted on 500 l.). P 12×12½ (200 l.) or 12½×12 (500 l.).*

228	200 l. Type **77**		1·75	75
229	500 l. Dish aerial and antenna tower, Selvilitepe(vert)		2·50	3·50

No. 229 also commemorates the 25th anniversary of Bayrak Radio and Television Corporation.

78 Lefkosa   79 Bülent Ecevit

(Litho Tezel Ofset, Lefkosa)

1988 (17 June). *Tourism. T **78** and similar horiz designs. Multicoloured. W **51** (sideways). P 12×12½.*

230	150 l. Type **78**		80	80
231	200 l. Gazi-Magusa		90	1·00
232	300 l. Girne		1·50	2·00
230/2		Set of 3	2·75	3·50

(Litho Tezel Ofset, Lefkosa)

1988 (20 July). *Turkish Prime Ministers. T **79** and similar vert designs. Multicoloured. W **51**. P 12½×12.*

233	50 l. Type **79**		60	60
234	50 l. Bülent Ulusu		60	60
235	50 l. Turgut Ozal		60	60
233/5		Set of 3	1·60	1·60

80 Red Crescent Members on Exercise   81 Hodori the Tiger (Games mascot) and Fireworks

(Des N. Kozal. Litho Tezel Ofset, Lefkosa)

1988 (8 Aug). *Civil Defence. W **51** (sideways). P 12×12½.*

236	80 150 l. multicoloured		1·25	1·50

(Des E. Cizenel (200 l.), N. Kozal (250 l.), H. Uluçam (400 l.). Litho Tezel Ofset, Lefkosa)

1988 (17 Sept). *Olympic Games, Seoul. T **81** and similar horiz designs. Multicoloured. W **51** (sideways). P 12×12½.*

237	200 l. Type **81**		80	1·00
	a. Imperf (pair)		70·00	
238	250 l. Athletics		1·00	1·25
239	400 l. Shot and running track with letters spelling "SEOUL"		1·50	2·00
237/9		Set of 3	3·00	3·75

82 Sedat Simavi (journalist)   83 "Kemal Atatürk" (I. Calli)

(Des H. Uluçam (Nos. 241/3). Litho Tezel Ofset, Lefkosa)

1988 (17 Oct). *Anniversaries and Events. T **82** and similar designs. W **51** (inverted on Nos. 240, 243 and 245, sideways on Nos. 241 and 244). P 12½×12 (vert) or 12×12½ (horiz).*

240	50 l. olive-green		25	25
241	100 l. multicoloured		50	45
242	300 l. multicoloured		70	1·00
243	400 l. multicoloured		1·50	1·75
244	400 l. multicoloured		1·00	1·75
245	600 l. multicoloured		2·00	2·50
240/5		Set of 6	5·50	7·00

Designs: *Horiz*—No. 241, Stylised figures around table and flags of participating countries (International Girne Conferences); 244, Presidents Gorbachev and Reagan signing treaty (Summit Meeting). *Vert*—No. 242, Cogwheels as flowers (North Cyprus Industrial Fair); 243, Globe (125th anniv of International Red Cross); 245, "Medical Services" (40th anniv of W.H.O.).

(Litho Tezel Ofset, Lefkosa)

1988 (10 Nov). *50th Death Anniv of Kemal Atatürk. Sheet 72 × 102 mm containing T **83** and similar vert designs. Multicoloured. W **51** (inverted). P 12½ × 12.*

MS246	250 l. Type **83**; 250 l. "Kemal Atatürk" (N. Ismail); 250 l. In army uniform; 250 l. In profile		2·00	2·00

84 Abstract Design

(Des E. Cizenel. Litho Tezel Ofset, Lefkosa)

1988 (15 Nov). *5th Anniv of Turkish Republic of Northern Cyprus. Sheet 98 × 76 mm. W **51** (sideways). Imperf.*

MS247	84 500 l. multicoloured		2·25	1·75

(Litho Tezel Ofset, Lefkosa)

1989 (28 Apr). *Paintings (8th series). Multicoloured designs as T **54**. W **51** (sideways on 150, 400 l., inverted on 600 l.). P 12½×13 (600 l.) or 13×12½ (others).*

248	150 l. "Dervis Pasa Mansion, Lefkosa" (Inci Kansu)		75	55
249	400 l. "Gamblers' Inn, Lefkosa" (Osman Güvenir)		1·50	2·00
250	600 l. "Mosque, Paphos" (Hikmet Ulucam)(vert)		2·25	2·75
248/50		Set of 3	4·00	4·75

85 Girl with Doll   86 Meeting of Presidents Vassiliou and Denktash

(Des N. Kozal. Litho Tezel Ofset, Lefkosa)

1989 (31 May). *Europa. Children's Games. T **85** and similar vert design. Multicoloured. W **51**. P 12½×12.*

251	600 l. Type **85**		1·75	1·25
	a. Imperf × p 12		3·00	3·00
	ab. Booklet pane. Nos. 251a/2a, each ×2		7·50	
252	1000 l. Boy with kite		2·00	3·00
	a. Imperf × p 12		2·00	3·00

Nos. 251a and 252a come from 3200 l. stamp booklets containing *se-tenant* pane No. 251ab.

(Litho Tezel Ofset, Lefkosa)

1989 (30 June). *Cyprus Peace Summit, Geneva, 1988. W **51** (sideways). P 12½×12.*

253	86 500 l. deep rose-red and black		1·25	1·25

87 Chukar Partridge   88 Road Construction

(Des E. Cizenel. Litho Tezel Ofset, Lefkosa)

1989 (31 July). *Wildlife. T **87** and similar horiz designs. Multicoloured. W **51** (sideways). P 12×12½.*

254	100 l. Type **87**		65	25
255	200 l. Cyprus Hare		70	35
256	700 l. Black Partridge		2·50	1·75
257	2000 l. Red Fox		3·00	3·50
254/7		Set of 4	6·00	5·25

(Litho Tezel Ofset, Lefkosa)

1989 (29 Sept). *Modern Development (3rd series). T **88** and similar multicoloured designs. W **51** (sideways on 100, 700 l.). P 12×12½ (100, 700 l.) or 12½×12 (others).*

258	100 l. Type **88**		15	10
259	150 l. Laying water pipeline(vert)		20	20
260	200 l. Seedling trees(vert)		30	30
261	450 l. Modern telephone exchange(vert)		75	1·00
262	650 l. Steam turbine power station(vert)		1·00	1·50
263	700 l. Irrigation reservoir		1·25	1·75
258/63		Set of 6	3·25	4·25

MINIMUM PRICE

The minimum price quote is 10p which represents a handling charge rather than a basis for valuing common stamps. For further notes about prices see introductory pages.

89 Unloading Freighter at Quayside (15th anniv of Gazi Magusa Free Port)   90 Erdal Inonu

(Des E. Çizenel (450, 600 l.), Ö. Özünalp (500 l.), S. Oral (1000 l.). Litho Tezel Ofset, Lefkosa)

1989 (17 Nov). *Anniversaries. T **89** and similar designs. W **51** (inverted on 450 l., sideways on others). P 12½×13 (450 l.) or 12×12½ (others).*

264	100 l. multicoloured		35	20
265	450 l. black, dull ultramarine & scar- verm		80	80
266	500 l. black, yellow-ochre and olive-grey		80	80
267	600 l. black, vermilion and new blue		1·10	1·25
268	1000 l. multicoloured		2·00	2·50
264/8		Set of 5	4·50	5·00

Designs: *Vert* (26×47 mm)—450 l. Airmail letter and stylized bird (25th anniv of Turkish Cypriot postal service). *Horiz* (as T **89**)—500 l. Newspaper and printing press (centenary of *Saded* newspaper); 600 l. Statue of Aphrodite, lifebelt and seabird (30th anniv of International Maritime Organization); 1000 l. Soldiers (25th anniv of Turkish Cypriot resistance).

(Litho Tezel Ofset, Lefkosa)

1989 (15 Dec). *Visit of Professor Erdal Inonu (Turkish politician). W **51** (inverted). P 12½×12.*

269	90 700 l. multicoloured		50	70

91 Mule-drawn Plough   92 Smoking Ashtray and Drinks

(Des N. Kozal. Litho Tezel Ofset, Lefkosa)

1989 (25 Dec). *Traditional Agricultural Implements. T **91** and similar multicoloured designs. W **51** (sideways on 150, 450 l.). P 12½×12 (550 l.) or 12×12½ (others).*

270	150 l. Type **91**		15	20
271	450 l. Ox-drawn threshing sledge		50	65
272	550 l. Olive press(vert)		60	80
270/2		Set of 3	1·10	1·50

(Des O. Ozünalp (200 l.), H. Ulucam (700 l). Litho Tezel Ofset, Lefkosa)

1990 (19 Apr). *World Health Day. T **92** and similar horiz design. Multicoloured. W **51** (sideways). P 12×12½.*

273	200 l. Type **92**		50	40
274	700 l. Smoking cigarette and heart		1·00	1·50

93 Yenierenköy Post Office   94 Song Thrush

(Des H. Billur. Litho Tezel Ofset, Lefkosa)

1990 (31 May). *Europa. Post Office Buildings. T **93** and similar horiz design. Multicoloured. W **51** (sideways). P 12½×12.*

275	1000 t. Type **93**		90	75
276	1500 t. Atatürk Meydani Post Office		1·60	2·25
MS277	105×72 mm. Nos. 275/6, each × 2		5·50	6·50

(Des H. Billur. Litho Tezel Ofset, Lefkosa)

1990 (5 June). *World Environment Day. T **94** and similar vert designs showing birds. Multicoloured. W **51** (inverted). P 12½×12.*

278	150 l. Type **94**		75	45
279	300 l. Blackcap		1·25	75
280	900 l. Black Redstart		2·00	2·50
281	1000 l. Chiff-chaff		2·00	2·75
278/81		Set of 4	5·50	5·75

95 Two Football Teams   **96** Amphitheatre, Soli

(Des H. Billur (1000 l.). Litho Tezel Ofset, Lefkosa)

1990 (8 June). *World Cup Football Championship, Italy. T* **95** *and similar horiz design. Multicoloured. W* **51** (*sideways*). *P* 12×12½.

282	300 l. Type **95**	..	75	50
283	1000 l. Championship symbol, globe and ball	2·50	3·00

(Litho Tezel Ofset, Lefkosa)

1990 (31 July). *Paintings* (9th series). *Multicoloured designs as T* **54**. *W* **51** (*sideways on* 300 *l.*). *P* 13×12½ (300 *l.*) *or* 12½×13 (1000 *l.*).

284	300 l. "Abstract" (Filiz Ankaçç)	..	25	25
285	1000 l. Wooden sculpture (S. Tekman) (*vert*)	85	1·50

(Litho Tezel Ofset, Lefkosa)

1990 (24 Aug). *Tourism. T* **96** *and similar vert design. Multicoloured. W* **51**. *P* 12½.

286	150 l. Type **96**	..	40	20
287	1000 l. Swan mosaic, Soli	..	1·75	2·50

97 Kenan Evren and Rauf Denktas   **98** Road Signs and Heart wearing Seat Belt

(Litho Tezel Ofset, Lefkosa)

1990 (19 Sept). *Visit of President Kenan Evren of Turkey. W* **51** (*sideways*). *P* 12½.

288	**97** 500 l. multicoloured	.. 1·00	1·00

(Des H. Billur. Litho Tezel Ofset, Lefkosa)

1990 (21 Sept). *Traffic Safety Campaign. T* **98** *and similar horiz designs. Multicoloured. W* **51** (*sideways*). *P* 12½.

289	150 l. Type **98**	..	50	25
290	300 l. Road signs, speeding car and spots of blood	75	50
291	1000 l. Traffic lights and road signs	2·25	2·75
289/91	..	*Set of 3*	3·25	3·25

99 Yildirim Akbulut   **100** *Rosularia cypria*

(Litho Tezel Ofset, Lefkosa)

1990 (1 Oct). *Visit of Turkish Prime Minister Yildirim Akbulut. W* **51** (*inverted*). *P* 12½.

292	**99** 1000 l. multicoloured	.. 1·10	1·10

(Des D. Viney and P. Jacobs (200, 1500 l.), D. Viney and C. Hessenberg (others). Litho Tezel Ofset, Lefkosa)

1990 (31 Oct). *Plants. T* **100** *and similar vert designs. Multicoloured. W* **51**. *P* 12½.

293	150 l. Type **100**	..	30	20
294	200 l. *Silene fraudratrix*	..	40	30
295	300 l. *Scutellaria sibthorpii*	..	45	35
296	600 l. *Sedum lampusae*	..	65	70
297	1000 l. *Onosma caespitosum*	..	90	1·10
298	1500 l. *Arabis cypria*	..	1·25	1·50
293/8	..	*Set of 6*	3·50	3·75

The new-issue supplement to this Catalogue appears each month in

GIBBONS
STAMP MONTHLY

—from your newsagent or by postal subscription—
sample copy and details on request.

---

101 Kemal Atatürk at Easel (wood carving)   (**102**)

(Des M. Uzel (300 l.), H. Billur (750 l.). Litho Tezel Ofset, Lefkosa)

1990 (24 Nov). *International Literacy Year. T* **101** *and similar horiz design. Multicoloured. W* **51** (*sideways*). *P* 12½.

299	300 l. Type **101**	..	40	35
300	750 l. Globe, letters and books	..	1·00	1·40

1991 (3 June). *Nos.* 189, 212 *and* 293 *surch as T* **102**.

301	250 l. on 10 l. Type **66**	..	40	40
302	250 l. on 20 l. Type **73**	..	40	40
303	500 l. on 150 l. Type **100**	..	60	60
	a. Surch inverted	..	50·00	
301/3	..	*Set of 3*	1·25	1·25

PRINTER. Issues from Nos. 304/5 onwards were printed in lithography by the State Printing Works, Lefkosa, *unless otherwise stated.*

103 *Ophrys lapethica*   **104** Hermes (projected shuttle)

1991 (8 July). *Orchids* (1st series). *T* **103** *and similar vert design. Multicoloured. W* **51** (*inverted*). *P* 14.

304	250 l. Type **103**	..	90	60
305	500 l. *Ophrys kotschyi*	..	1·50	1·75

See also Nos. 311/14.

1991 (29 July). *Europa. Europe in Space. Sheet* 78×82 *mm containing T* **104** *and similar vert design. Multicoloured. W* **51**. *P* 12½.

MS306	2000 l. Type **104**; 2000 l. *Ulysses* (satellite)	..	4·00	4·00

105 Kucuk Medrese Fountain, Lefkosa   **106** Symbolic Roots (Year of Love to Yunus Emre)

(Des H. Billur)

1991 (9 Sept). *Fountains. T* **105** *and similar horiz designs. Multicoloured. W* **51** (*sideways*). *P* 12½.

307	250 l. Type **105**	..	30	15
308	500 l. Cafer Pasa Fountain, Magusa	..	40	30
309	1500 l. Sarayönü Square Fountain, Lefkosa	70	80
310	5000 l. Arabahmet Mosque Fountain, Lefkosa	1·75	2·50
307/10	..	*Set of 4*	2·75	3·25

1991 (10 Oct). *Orchids* (2nd series). *Vert designs as T* **103**. *Multicoloured. W* **51**. *P* 14.

311	100 l. *Serapias levantina*	..	30	20
312	500 l. *Dactylorhiza romana*	..	70	50
313	2000 l. *Orchis simia*	..	2·00	2·50
314	3000 l. *Orchis sancta*	..	2·50	3·00
311/14	..	*Set of 4*	5·00	5·75

1991 (5 Nov). *Paintings* (10th series). *Multicoloured designs as T* **54**. *W* **51**. *P* 12½×13.

315	250 l. "Hindiler" (S. Çizel) (*vert*)	..	50	35
316	500 l. "Düsme" (A. Mene) (*vert*)	..	1·00	1·25

(Des K. Sarikavak (250 l.), H. Billur (500, 1500 l.))

1991 (20 Nov). *Anniversaries and Events. T* **106** *and similar designs. W* **51** (*sideways on* 1500 *l., inverted on others*). *P* 12×12½ (1500 *l.*) *or* 12½×12 (*others*).

317	250 l. greenish yellow, black & brt mag	..	25	25
318	500 l. multicoloured	..	45	50
319	500 l. multicoloured	..	45	50

320	1500 l. multicoloured	.. 1·75	2·00
317/20		*Set of 4* 2·75	3·00

Designs: *Vert*—No. 318, Mustafa Cagatay commemoration; No. 319, University building (5th anniv of Eastern Mediterranean University). *Horiz*—No. 320, Mozart (death bicent).

107 Four Sources of Infection   **108** Lighthouse, Gazimagusa

1991 (13 Dec). *AIDS Day. W* **51** (*sideways*). *P* 12×12½.

321	**107** 1000 l. multicoloured	.. 1·10	1·10

(Des H. Billur)

1991 (16 Dec). *Lighthouses. T* **108** *and similar horiz designs. Multicoloured. W* **51** (*sideways*). *P* 12×12½.

322	250 l. Type **108**	..	55	35
323	500 l. Ancient lighthouses, Girne harbour	80	65
324	1500 l. Modern lighthouse, Girne harbour	2·00	2·25
322/4		*Set of 3*	3·00	3·00

109 Elephant and Hippopotamus Fossils, Karaoglanoglu

1991 (27 Dec). *Tourism* (1st series). *T* **109** *and similar horiz designs. Multicoloured. W* **51** (*sideways*). *P* 12.

325	250 l. Type **109**	..	50	30
326	500 l. Roman fish ponds, Lambusa	..	65	45
327	1500 l. Roman remains, Lambusa	..	1·50	2·00
325/7		*Set of 3*	2·40	2·50

See also Nos. 330/3 and 351/2.

1992 (31 Mar). *Paintings* (11th series). *Multicoloured designs as T* **54**, *but* 31×49 *mm. W* **51** (*sideways*). *P* 14.

328	500 l. "Ebru" (A. Kandulu)	..	30	20
329	3500 l. "Street in Lefkosa" (I. Tatar)	..	1·50	2·00

1992 (21 Apr). *Tourism* (2nd series). *Multicoloured designs as T* **109**. *W* **51** (*sideways*). *P* 14×13½ (1500 *l.*) *or* 13½×14 (*others*).

330	500 l. Bugday Camii, Gazimagusa	..	30	20
331	500 l. Clay pigeon shooting	..	30	20
332	1000 l. Salamis Bay Hotel, Gazimagusa	..	60	70
333	1500 l. Casino, Girne (*vert*)	..	90	1·25
330/3	..	*Set of 4*	1·90	2·10

110 Fleet of Columbus and Early Map

(Des H. Billur)

1992 (29 May). *Europa. 500th Anniv of Discovery of America by Columbus. Sheet,* 80×76 *mm, containing T* **110** *and similar horiz design. Multicoloured. W* **51** (*sideways*). *P* 13½×14.

MS334	1500 l. Type **110**; 3500 l. Christopher Columbus and signature	..	2·00	2·50

111 Green Turtle   **112** Gymnastics

(Des H. Billur)

1992 (30 June). *World Environment Day. Sea Turtles. Sheet,* 105×75 *mm, containing T* **111** *and similar horiz design. W* **51** (*sideways*). *P* 13½×14.

MS335	1000 l. × 2, Type **111**; 1500 l. × 2, Loggerhead Turtle	..	3·00	3·25

(Des H. Billur)

1992 (25 July). *Olympic Games, Barcelona. T* **112** *and similar multicoloured designs. W* **51** *(inverted on* 500 *l., sideways on* 1000, 1500 *l.). P* 14×13½ (500 *l.)* or 13½×14 *(others).*

336	500 l.	Type 112		30	40
		a. Horiz pair. Nos. 336/7	..	60	80
337	500 l.	Tennis	..	30	40
338	1000 l.	High jumping (*horiz*)		40	50
339	1500 l.	Cycling (*horiz*)		75	1·00
336/9			*Set of 4*	1·60	2·10

Nos. 336/7 were printed together, *se-tenant,* in horizontal pairs throughout the sheet.

113 New Generating Station, Girne

(Des H. Billur (Nos. 341/2), Therese Coustry (No. 343))

1992 (30 Sept). *Anniversaries and Events (1st series). T* **113** *and similar horiz designs. Multicoloured. W* **51** *(sideways). P* 14.

340	500 l.	Type 113	..	30	20
341	500 l.	Symbol of Housing Association (15th anniv)		30	20
342	1500 l.	Domestic animals and birds (30th anniv of Veterinary Service)		1·50	1·75
343	1500 l.	Cat (International Federation of Cat Societies Conference)	..	1·50	1·75
340/3			*Set of 4*	3·25	3·50

114 Airliner over Runway

(Des H. Billur)

1992 (20 Nov). *Anniversaries and Events (2nd series). T* **114** *and similar horiz designs. Multicoloured. W* **51** *(sideways). P* 13½×14.

344	1000 l.	Type 114 (17th anniv of civil aviation)		70	70
345	1000 l.	Meteorological instruments and weather (18th anniv of Meteorological Service)		70	70
346	1200 l.	Surveying equipment and map (14th anniv of Survey Department)		80	1·00
344/6			*Set of 3*	2·00	2·25

115 Zübiye   116 Painting by Turksal Ince

(Des A. Erduran)

1992 (14 Dec). *International Conference on Nutrition, Rome. Turkish Cypriot Cuisine. T* **115** *and similar horiz designs. W* **51** *(sideways). P* 13½×14.

347	2000 l.	Type 115	..	50	70
348	2500 l.	Çiçek Dolmasi	..	60	80
349	3000 l.	Tatar Böregi	..	70	90
350	4000 l.	Seftali Kebabi		80	1·25
347/50			*Set of 4*	2·40	3·25

1993 (1 Apr). *Tourism (3rd series). Horiz designs as T* **109.** *Multicoloured. W* **51** *(sideways). P* 13½×14.

351	500 l.	Saint Barnabas Church and Monastery, Salamis	..	15	15
352	10000 l.	Ancient pot	..	1·60	2·25

(Des T. Ince and I. Onsoy)

1993 (5 May). *Europa. Contemporary Art. Sheet* 79×69 *mm containing T* **116** *and similar vert design. Multicoloured. W* **51.** *P* 14.

MS353	2000 l.	Type 116; 3000 l. Painting by Ilkay Onsoy	..	1·50	1·75

ALTERED CATALOGUE NUMBERS

Any Catalogue numbers altered from the last edition are shown as a list in the introductory pages.

117 Olive Tree, Girne

118 Traditional Houses

1993 (11 June). *Ancient Trees. T* **117** *and similar vert designs. Multicoloured. W* **51** *(inverted). P* 14.

354	500 l.	Type 117		15	15
355	1000 l.	River red gum, Kyrenia Gate, Lefkosa		25	25
356	3000 l.	Oriental plane, Lapta	..	70	90
357	4000 l.	Calabrian pine, Cinarli		85	1·25
354/7	..		*Set of 4*	1·75	2·25

(Des H. Billur)

1993 (20 Sept). *Arabahmet District Conservation Project, Lefkosa. T* **118** *and similar horiz design. Multicoloured. W* **51** *(sideways). P* 13½×14.

358	1000 l.	Type 118	..	50	40
359	3000 l.	Arabahmet street	..	1·50	2·00

119 National Flags turning into Doves

120 Kemal Atatürk

(Des H. Ulucam (5000 l.), H. Billur (others))

1993 (15 Nov). *10th Anniv of Proclamation of Turkish Republic of Northern Cyprus. T* **119** *and similar designs. W* **51** *(sideways on Nos.* 361/3). *P* 14×13½ (*No.* 360) *or* 13½×14 *(others).*

360	500 l.	carmine-red, black and new blue		20	15
361	500 l.	rosine and new blue	..	20	15
362	1000 l.	carmine-red, black and new blue		30	30
363	5000 l.	multicoloured		1·40	2·00
360/3	..	..	*Set of 4*	1·90	2·40

Designs: *Horiz*—No. 361, National flag forming figure "10"; No. 362, Dove carrying national flag; No. 363, Map of Cyprus and figure "10" wreath.

(Des H. Billur (Nos. 365/8))

1993 (27 Dec). *Anniversaries. T* **120** *and similar multicoloured designs. W* **51** *(inverted on No.* 364 *or sideways on others). P* 14×13½ (*No.* 364) *or* 13½×14 *(others).*

364	500 l.	Type 120 (55th death anniv)	..	15	15
365	500 l.	Stage and emblem (30th anniv of Turkish Cypriot theatre) (*horiz*)		15	15
366	1500 l.	Branch badges (35th anniv of T.M.T. organization) (*horiz*)		25	35
367	2000 l.	World map and computer (20th anniv of Turkish Cypriot news agency) (*horiz*)		35	45
368	5000 l.	Ballet dancers and Caykovski'nin (Death centenary) (*horiz*)		1·10	1·60
364/8	..		*Set of 5*	1·75	2·40

121 "Söyle Falci" (Göral Ozkan)

1994 (31 Mar). *Art (12th series). T* **121** *and similar vert design. Multicoloured. W* **51.** *P* 14.

369	1000 l.	Type 121		15	20
370	6500 l.	"IV. Hareket" (sculpture) (Senol Ozdevrim)	..	85	1·40

See also Nos. 432/3.

122 Dr. Kucuk and Memorial

1994 (1 Apr). *10th Death Anniv of Dr. Fazil Kucuk (politician). W* **51** *(sideways). P* 14.

371	122	1500 l. multicoloured	..	30	40

123 Neolithic Village, Girne

(Des H. Billur)

1994 (16 May). *Europa. Archaeological Discoveries. Sheet* 73×79 *mm containing T* **123** *and similar horiz design. Multicoloured. W* **51** *(sideways). P* 13½×14.

MS372	8500 l.	Type 123; 8500 l. Neolithic man and implements	..	4·00	4·00

124 Peace Doves and Letters over Pillar Box

125 World Cup Trophy

(Des H. Billur)

1994 (30 June). *30th Anniv of Turkish Cypriot Postal Service. W* **51** *(sideways). P* 13½×14.

373	124	50000 l. multicoloured	..	2·75	3·50

(Des H. Billur)

1994 (30 June). *World Cup Football Championship, U.S.A. T* **125** *and similar multicoloured design. W* **51** *(sideways on* 10000 *l.). P* 14×13½ (2500 *l.) or* 13½×14 (10000 *l.).*

374	2500 l.	Type 125		15	15
375	10000 l.	Footballs on map of U.S.A. (*horiz*)		75	1·00

126 Peace Emblem

127 Cyprus 1934 4½ pi. Stamp and Karpas Postmark

(Des H. Billur (2500, 8500 l.))

1994 (20 July). *20th Anniv of Turkish Landings in Cyprus. T* **126** *and similar designs. W* **51** *(sideways on horiz designs). P* 14×13½ (2500 *l.) or* 13½×14 *(others).*

376	2500 l.	greenish yellow, emerald and black		15	15
377	5000 l.	multicoloured	..	25	25
378	7000 l.	multicoloured	..	40	50
379	8500 l.	multicoloured	..	60	75
376/9			*Set of 4*	1·25	1·50

Designs: *Horiz*—5000 l. Memorial; 7000 l. Sculpture; 8500 l. Peace doves forming map of Cyprus and flame.

1994 (15 Aug). *Postal Centenary. T* **127** *and similar horiz designs. Multicoloured. W* **51** *(sideways). P* 13½×14.

380	1500 l.	Type 127		15	15
381	2500 l.	Turkish Cypriot Posts 1979 Europa 2 l. and Gazimagusa postmark	..	20	20
382	5000 l.	Cyprus 1938 6 pi. and Bey Keuy postmark		35	45
383	7000 l.	Cyprus 1955 100 m. and Aloa postmark		45	65
384	8500 l.	Cyprus 1938 18 pi. and Pyla postmark		55	75
380/4	..		*Set of 5*	1·50	2·00

128 Trumpet Triton   **(129)**
(*Charonia tritonis*)

***

1994 (15 Nov). *Sea Shells. T* **128** *and similar horiz designs.*
Multicoloured. W **51** *(sideways).* P 13¹/₂×14.
385   2500 l. Type **128**   30   20
386   12500 l. Mole Cowrie (*Cypraea talpa*) ..   1·00   1·25
387   12500 l. Giant Tun (*Tonna galea*) ..   1·00   1·25
385/7   ..   ..   ..   *Set of 3*   2·10   2·40

1994 (12 Dec)–**95.** *Nos.* 280, 295, 315 *and* 317 *surch as T* **129.**
388   1500 l. on 250 l. Type **106**   ..   10   10
389   2000 l. on 900 l. Black Redstart (21.4.95) ..   20   20
390   2500 l. on 250 l. "Hindiler" (S. Cizel)   20   20
391   3500 l. on 300 l. *Scutellaria sibthorpii*
    (21.4.95)   25   25
388/91   ..   ..   ..   *Set of 4*   65   65
Nos. 389/90 show the surcharge value horizontally.

130 Donkeys on Mountain   **131** Peace Dove and Globe

1995 (10 Feb). *European Conservation Year. T* **130** *and similar*
horiz designs. W **51** *(sideways).* P 13¹/₂×14.
392   2000 l. Type **130**   15   15
393   3500 l. Coastline   20   20
394   15000 l. Donkeys in field   ..   1·00   1·25
392/4   ..   ..   ..   *Set of 3*   1·25   1·40

(Des H. Billur)

1995 (20 Apr). *Europa. Peace and Freedom. Sheet* 72×78 *mm*
containing T **131** *and similar horiz design. W* **51** *(sideways).*
P 13¹/₂×14.
MS395   15000 l. Type **131**; 15000 l. Peace doves
   over map of Europe   ..   ..   1·60   1·75

132 Sini Katmeri   **133** *Papilio machaon*

1995 (29 May). *Turkish Cypriot Cuisine. T* **132** *and similar*
horiz designs. Multicoloured. W **51** *(sideways).* P 13¹/₂×14.
396   3500 l. Type **132**   15   15
397   10000 l. Kolokas musakka and bullez
    kizartma   45   45
398   14000 l. Enginar dolmasi   70   80
396/8   ..   ..   ..   *Set of 3*   1·10   1·25

(Des H. Billur)

1995 (30 June). *Butterflies. T* **133** *and similar horiz designs.*
Multicoloured. W **51** *(sideways).* P 13¹/₂×14.
399   3500 l. Type **133**   20   15
400   4500 l. *Charaxes jasius*   25   20
401   15000 l. *Cynthia cardui*   75   80
402   30000 l. *Vanessa atalanta*   ..   1·50   1·60
399/402   ..   ..   ..   *Set of 4*   2·40   2·50

134 Forest   **135** Beach, Girne

1995 (7 Aug). *Obligatory Tax. Forest Regeneration Fund.*
P 14×13¹/₂.
403   **134**   1000 l. emerald and black   ..   40   20
No. 403 was for compulsory use on all mail, in addition to the
normal postage, between 7 August and 6 February 1996. It was
intended to provide funds for the replanting of those forests
destroyed by fire in June 1995.

1995 (21 Aug). *Tourism. T* **135** *and similar multicoloured*
designs. W **51** *(sideways on horiz designs).* P 13¹/₂×14 (*horiz*)
or 14×13¹/₂ (*vert*).
404   3500 l. Type **135**   10   10
405   7500 l. Sail boards   25   30
406   15000 l. Ruins of Salamis (*vert*)   ..   50   55
407   20000 l. St. George's Cathedral, Gazimagusa
    (*vert*)   70   75
404/7   ..   ..   ..   *Set of 4*   1·50   1·75

136 Süleyman Demirel and   **137** Stamp Printing Press
     Rauf Denktas

1995 (21 Aug). *Visit of President Süleyman Demirel of Turkey.*
W **51** *(sideways).* P 14.
408   **136**   5000 l. multicoloured   20   20

(Des H. Billur (Nos. 410/14))

1995 (7 Nov). *Anniversaries. T* **137** *and similar designs. W* **51**
(sideways on horiz designs). P 14×13¹/₂ (*No.* 414) *or* 13¹/₂×14
(*others*).
409   3000 l. multicoloured   20   20
410   3000 l. multicoloured   20   20
411   5000 l. multicoloured   40   40
412   22000 l. dull ultramarine, new blue & black   80   1·00
413   30000 l. multicoloured   ..   ..   1·25   1·50
414   30000 l. multicoloured   ..   ..   1·25   1·50
409/14   ..   ..   ..   *Set of 6*   3·50   4·25
Designs: *Horiz*—No. 409, Type **137** (20th anniv od State
Printing Works); No. 410, Map of Turkey (75th anniv of Turkish
National Assembly); No. 411, Louis Pasteur (chemist) and
microscope (Death centenary); No. 412, United Nations
anniversary emblem (50th anniv); No. 413, Guglielmo Marconi
(radio pioneer) and dial (Centenary of first radio transmissions).
Vert—No. 414, Stars and reel of film (Centenary of cinema).

138 Kültegin   **139** "Bosnia"
   Epitaph and   (sculpture)
   Sculpture

(Des H. Billur)

1995 (28 Dec). *Centenary of Deciphering of Orhon Epitaphs.*
T **138** *and similar vert design. W* **51.** P 14.
415   5000 l. Type **138**   25   25
416   10000 l. Epitaph and tombstone   ..   45   55

(Des S. Ozdevrim)

1996 (31 Jan). *Support for Moslems in Bosnia and Herze-*
govina. W **51** *(inverted).* P 14×13¹/₂.
417   **139**   10000 l. multicoloured   ..   50   50

140 Striped Red Mullet   **141** Palm Trees

(Des H. Billur)

1996 (29 Mar). *Fishes. T* **140** *and similar horiz designs.*
Multicoloured. W **51** *(sideways).* P 13¹/₂×14.
418   5000 l. Type **140**   40   30
419   10000 l. Peacock Wrasse   60   45
420   28000 l. Common Two-banded Seabream   1·00   1·25
421   40000 l. Dusky Grouper   ..   ..   1·50   1·75
418/21   ..   ..   ..   *Set of 4*   3·25   3·25

1996 (26 Apr). *Tourism. T* **141** *and similar multicoloured*
designs. W **51** *(sideways on horiz designs).* P 14×13¹/₂ (*vert*) *or*
13¹/₂×14 (*horiz*).
422   100000 l. Type **141**   60   65
423   150000 l. Pomegranate   95   1·00
424   250000 l. Ruins of Bella Paise Abbey (*horiz*)   1·50   1·60
425   500000 l. Traditional dancers (*horiz*)   ..   3·00   3·25
422/5   ..   ..   ..   *Set of 4*   6·00   6·50

142 Beria Remzi Ozoran   **143** Established Forest

(Des H. Billur)

1996 (31 May). *Europa. Famous Women. T* **142** *and simila*
horiz design. Multicoloured. W **51** *(sideways).* P 13¹/₂×14.
426   15000 l. Type **142**   50   2‡
427   50000 l. Kadriye Hulusi Hacibulgur   ..   1·40   1·7‡

1996 (28 June). *World Environment Day. Sheet* 72×78 *mm*
containing T **143** *and similar horiz design. Multicoloured.*
W **51** *(sideways).* P 13¹/₂×14.
MS428   50000 l. Type **143**; 50000 l. Conifer
   plantation   ..   ..   ..   2·75   3·0‡

144 Basketball   **145** Symbolic Footballs

(Des H. Billur)

1996 (31 July). *Olympic Games, Atlanta. Sheet* 105×74 *mm*
containing T **144** *and similar horiz designs. Multicoloured.*
W **51** *(sideways).* P 13¹/₂×14.
MS429   15000 l. Type **144**; 15000 l. Discus
   throwing; 50000 l. Javelin throwing; 50000 l.
   Volleyball   ..   ..   ..   2·75   3·0‡

(Des H. Billur)

1996 (31 Oct). *European Football Championship, England.*
T **145** *and similar horiz design. Multicoloured. W* **51**
(sideways). P 13¹/₂×14.
430   15000 l. Type **145**   40   35
    a. Pair. Nos. 430/1   ..   ..   1·10   1·25
431   35000 l. Football and flags of participating
    nations   70   90
In addition to separate sheets Nos. 430/1 were also available
in pairs, *se-tenant* horizontally and vertically.

1996 (3 Nov). *Arts* (13th *series). Multicoloured designs as*
T **121.** *W* **51** *(sideways).* P 14.
432   25000 l. "City" (Lebibe Sonuc) (*horiz*)   ..   40   30
433   70000 l. "Woman opening Letter" (Ruzen
    Atakan) (*horiz*)   ..   ..   1·10   1·10

146 Houses on Fire   **147** *Amanita*
   (Auxiliary Fire Service)   *phalloides*

(Des O. Oker (10000 l.), H. Billur (50000, 75000 l.))

1996 (23 Dec). *Anniversaries and Events. T* **146** *and similar*
multicoloured designs. W **51** *(inverted on* 20000 *l., sideways on*
others). P 14×13¹/₂ (20000 *l.*) *or* 13¹/₂×14 (*others*).
434   10000 l. Type **146**   30   30
435   20000 l. Colour party (20th anniv of Defence
    Forces) (*vert*)   40   40
436   50000 l. Children by lake (Nasreddin-Hoca
    Year)   85   85
437   75000 l. Flowers (Children's Rights)   ..   1·25   1·25
434/7   ..   ..   ..   *Set of 4*   2·50   2·50

(Des H. Billur)

1997 (31 Mar). *Fungi. T* **147** *and similar vert designs.*
Multicoloured. W **51** *(inverted).* P 14×13¹/₂.
438   15000 l. Type **147**   30   30
439   25000 l. *Morchella esculenta*   45   45
440   25000 l. *Pleurotus eryngii*   45   45
441   70000 l. *Amanita muscaria*   ..   ..   1·25   1·25
438/41   ..   ..   ..   *Set of 4*   2·25   2·25

148 Flag on   **149** Mother and Children
   Hillside   playing Leapfrog

(Des H. Billur)

1997 (23 Apr). *Besparmak Mountains Flag Sculpture. W* **51**
(inverted). P 14×13¹/₂.
442   **148**   60000 l. multicoloured   ..   ..   1·00   1·00

(Des H. Billur)

1997 (30 May). *Europa. Tales and Legends.* T **149** *and similar horiz design. Multicoloured.* W **51** (*sideways*). P 13½×14.

443	25000 l. Type **149** ..	..	45	30
444	70000 l. Apple tree and well	..	1·25	1·50

150 Prime Minister Necmettin Erbakan of Turkey	151 Golden Eagle

1997 (20 June). *Visit of the President and the Prime Minister of Turkey.* T **150** *and similar multicoloured design.* W **51** (*sideways on* 80000 l.). P 14×13½ (*vert*) or 13½×14 (*horiz*).

445	15000 l. Type **150** ..	..	30	20
446	80000 l. President Suleyman Demirel of Turkey (*horiz*) ..	..	1·25	1·50

(Des H. Billur)

1997 (31 July). *Birds of Prey.* T **151** *and similar vert designs. Multicoloured.* W **51**. P 14×13½.

447	40000 l. Type **151**	..	60	60
448	40000 l. Eleonora's Falcon	..	60	60
449	75000 l. Common Kestrel	..	1·00	1·10
450	100000 l. Honey Buzzard ..	..	1·25	1·40
447/50	.. .. ..	Set of 4	3·00	3·25

152 Coin of Sultan Abdulaziz, 1861–76

1997 (28 Oct). *Rare Coins.* T **152** *and similar vert designs. Multicoloured.* W **51**. P 14×13½.

451	25000 l. Type **152** ..	..	15	20
452	40000 l. Coin of Sultan Mahmud II, 1808–39 ..		25	30
453	75000 l. Coin of Sultan Selim II, 1566–74		45	50
454	100000 l. Coin of Sultan Mehmed V, 1909–18 ..		60	65
451/4	.. .. ..	Set of 4	1·40	1·60

STAMP BOOKLETS

Following the inauguration of the Turkish Cypriot postal service in 1974 several postmasters continued to use the covers previously supplied by the Cyprus Post Office in conjunction with Turkish Cypriot Posts issues.

1987 (30 June). *Europa. Modern Architecture. Black on bluish grey cover,* 61×50 *mm, showing Europa symbols. Pane attached by selvedge.*

SB1	500 l. booklet containing *se-tenant* pane of 4 (No. 210ab)	..	7·00

1989 (31 May). *Europa. Children's Games. Black on pale blue-green cover,* 62×48 *mm, showing Europa symbols. Pane attached by selvedge.*

SB2	3200 l. booklet containing *se-tenant* pane of 4 (No. 251ab)	..	7·50

— URCH HARRIS —

ALL WORLD

NEW ISSUE SERVICE

Your 'First Choice' New Issue Supplier

Developed over the last 30 years Urch Harris 'All World' combines the widest choice of countries, themes and formats with a reliable individual service that helps develop and manage your collection.

- 260 countries and 100 plus themes.
- Choice of mint issues, reprints, yearpacks, used stamps, maxi cards, booklets, presentation packs, specimens and first day covers.
- Regular distributions every 6 weeks.
- Free magazine with every distribution.
- Fully computerised invoices with descriptions.
- Customer advice helpline.
- Free gifts and regular special offers.
- Supported by Stanley Gibbons, world leaders in philately.

FREE WELCOME PACK

Containing full details of our unique service, a full list of countries and themes and a copy of 'All World Direct' magazine.

Telephone 0117 9349333 for a free pack.

Urch Harris & Co
1 Denmark Avenue
Bristol BS1 5HD

A Division of Stanley Gibbons Ltd

Cyrenaica
see British Occupation of Italian Colonies

Dominica

CROWN COLONY

A British packet agency was operating on Dominica from about 1778, the date of the earliest known use of a postal marking. This was replaced by a branch office of the British G.P.O. which opened at Roseau on 8 May 1858. The stamps of Great Britain were used from that date until 1 May 1860, after which the colonial authorities assumed responsibility for the postal service. Until the introduction of Nos. 1/3 in 1874 No. CC1 and later handstamps were utilised.

For illustrations of handstamp and postmark types see BRITISH POST OFFICES ABROAD notes, following GREAT BRITAIN.

ROSEAU

CROWNED/CIRCLE HANDSTAMPS

CC1 CC 1 DOMINICA (Black or R.) (17.5.1845)
                      Price on cover £500
No. CC1 is also known struck in black on various adhesive stamps as late as 1883.

Stamps of GREAT BRITAIN *cancelled* "A 07" *as Type* **2**.

1858 to 1860
Z1	1d. rose-red (1857), *perf* 14		£190
Z2	2d. blue (1858) (Plate No. 7)		£650
Z3	4d. rose (1857)		£275
Z4	6d. lilac (1856)		£275
Z5	1s. green		£1100

PRICES FOR STAMPS ON COVER TO 1945
Nos. 1/3	*from* × 25
No. 4	*from* × 40
No. 5	*from* × 100
No. 6	*from* × 40
Nos. 7/8	*from* × 100
No. 9	*from* × 40
Nos. 10/12	*from* × 15
Nos. 13/15	*from* × 100
No. 17	*from* × 50
No. 18/a	—
No. 19	*from* × 40
Nos. 20/5	*from* × 30
No. 26	—
Nos. 27/90	*from* × 5
No. 91	—
Nos. 92/8	*from* × 10
Nos. 99/109	*from* × 3
Nos. R1/3	*from* × 15
No. R4	*from* × 50
No. R6	*from* × 3

1	**(2)**	**(3)**	**(4)**

(Typo D.L.R.)

1874 (4 May). *Wmk Crown CC. P* 12½.
1	1	1d. lilac	£150	40·00
2		6d. green	£550	85·00
3		1s. dull magenta	£325	65·00

N C E   N C E

Normal   Malformed "CE" (R.10/6)

1877–79. *Wmk Crown CC. P* 14.
4	1	½d. olive-yellow (1879)	8·50	40·00
5		1d. lilac	4·50	1·75
		a. Bisected vert or diag (½d.) (on cover or card)	† £1600	
6		2½d. red-brown (1879)	£225	25·00
7		4d. blue (1879)	£110	2·50
		a. Malformed "CE" in "PENCE"	£1500	£225
8		6d. green	£150	20·00
9		1s. magenta	£120	48·00

1882 (25 Nov)–**83.** *No.* 5 *bisected vertically and surch.*
10	2	½ (d.), in *black*, on half 1d.	£140	35·00
		a. Surch inverted	£950	£800
		b. Surcharges *tête-bêche* (pair)	£1600	
11	3	½ (d.) in *red*, on half 1d. (12.82)	28·00	12·00
		a. Surch inverted	£950	£450
		c. Surch double	£1600	£650
12	4	½d. in *black*, on half 1d. (3.83)	45·00	20·00
		b. Surch double	£800	

Type **4** is found reading up or down.

1883–86. *Wmk Crown CA. P* 14.
13	1	½d. olive-yellow	2·00	8·00
14		1d. lilac (1886)	22·00	8·00
		a. Bisected (½d.) (on cover)	† £1800	
15		2½d. red-brown (1884)	£140	2·00

Half Penny   One Penny

(5)	**(6)**

1886 (Mar). *Nos.* 8 *and* 9 *surch locally.*
17	5	½d. on 6d. green	4·00	3·50
18	6	1d. on 6d. green	£20000	£10000
		a. Thick bar (approx 1 mm)	† £16000	
19		1d. on 1s. magenta	14·00	14·00
		b. Surch double	£5000	£2750

It is believed that only two sheets of the 1d. on 6d. were surcharged. On one of these sheets the six stamps in the top row showed the thick bar variety, No. 18a.

1886–90. *Wmk Crown CA. P* 14.
20	1	½d. dull green	1·50	4·25
22		1d. rose (1887)	11·00	11·00
		a. *Deep carmine* (1889)	2·75	4·00
		b. Bisected (½d.) (on cover)	† £1800	
23		2½d. ultramarine (1888)	3·75	4·25
24		4d. grey	2·00	3·50
		a. Malformed "CE" in "PENCE"	£160	£200
25		6d. orange (1888)	6·00	28·00
26		1s. dull magenta (1890)	£150	£250
20/6			*Set of* 6 £150 £250	
20/5		Optd "Specimen"	*Set of* 5 £225	

The stamps of Dominica were superseded by the general issue for Leeward Islands on 31 October 1890, but the sets following were in concurrent use with the stamps inscribed "LEEWARD ISLANDS" until 31 December 1939, when the island came under the administration of the Windward Islands.

9 "Roseau from the Sea" (Lt. Caddy)	**10**

(T **9** to **11** typo D.L.R.)

1903 (1 Sept)–**07.** *Wmk Crown CC* (sideways* *on* T **9**). *Ordinary paper. P* 14.
27	9	½d. green and grey-green	3·75	2·25
		a. Chalk-surfaced paper (1906)	11·00	14·00
28		1d. grey and red	7·50	75
		a. Chalk-surfaced paper (1906)	23·00	5·50
29		2d. green and brown	2·50	4·50
		a. Chalk-surfaced paper (1906)	22·00	28·00
30		2½d. grey and bright blue	4·50	3·75
		a. Chalk-surfaced paper (3.9.07)	18·00	28·00
31		3d. dull purple and grey-black	8·00	2·75
		a. Chalk-surfaced paper (1906)	30·00	24·00
32		6d. grey and chestnut	4·25	15·00
33		1s. magenta and grey-green	24·00	32·00
		a. Chalk-surfaced paper (1906)	70·00	£130
34		2s. grey-black and purple	24·00	26·00
35		2s. 6d. grey-green and maize	17·00	70·00
36	10	5s. black and brown	90·00	£140
27/36			*Set of* 10 £170 £275	
27/36		Optd "Specimen"	*Set of* 10 £130	

*The normal sideways watermark shows Crown to right of CC, *as seen from the back of the stamp.*

1907–08. *Wmk Mult Crown to CA* (sideways* *on* T **9**). *Chalk-surfaced paper. P* 14.
37	9	½d. green	1·50	2·25
38		1d. grey and red	2·00	30
39		2d. green and brown	5·00	5·00
40		2½d. grey and bright blue	4·50	19·00
41		3d. dull purple and grey-black	4·00	13·00
42		6d. black and chestnut	48·00	75·00
43		1s. magenta and grey-green (1908)	3·75	45·00
44		2s. grey-black and purple (1908)	22·00	32·00
45		2s. 6d. grey-green and maize (1908)	22·00	55·00
46	10	5s. black and brown (1908)	60·00	60·00
37/46			*Set of* 10 £160 £275	

*The normal sideways watermark shows Crown to right of CA, *as seen from the back of the stamp.*
Examples of Nos. 27/36 and 37/46 are known showing a forged Gen. Post Office Dominica postmark dated "JU 1 11".

WAR TAX

ONE HALFPENNY

11	**(12)**

1908–21. *Wmk Mult Crown CA* (sideways* *on* T **9**), *Chalk-surfaced paper (3d., 6d., 1s.). P* 14.
47	9	½d. blue-green	3·00	3·00
		aw. Wmk Crown to left of CA	2·50	2·00
		b. *Deep green* (wmk Crown to left of CA) (1918)	3·50	1·75
48		1d. carmine-red	3·00	30
		aw. Wmk Crown to left of CA	3·50	40
		b. *Scarlet* (1916)	1·50	40
		bw. Wmk Crown to left of CA	1·00	50

49	9	2d. grey (1909)	3·00	12·00
		aw. Wmk Crown to left of CA	—	15·00
		b. *Slate* (wmk Crown to left of CA) (1918)	3·50	12·00
50		2½d. blue	8·50	6·00
		aw. Wmk Crown to left of CA	—	9·00
		b. *Bright blue* (1918)	5·00	9·00
		bw. Wmk Crown to left of CA	6·00	12·00
51		3d. purple/yellow (1909)	3·00	4·50
		a. Ordinary paper (wmk Crown to left of CA) (1912)	3·00	4·50
		ab. *On pale yellow* (1920)	8·50	12·00
52		6d. dull and bright purple (1909)	10·00	15·00
		a. Ordinary paper. *Dull purple* (wmk Crown to left of CA) (1915)	3·50	15·00
53		1s. black/green (1910)	2·50	2·75
		a. Ordinary paper (wmk Crown to left of CA) (1912) (Optd S. in red) £35)	3·00	4·00
53b		2s. purple and deep blue/*blue* (wmk Crown to left of CA) (1919)	25·00	65·00
53c		2s. 6d. black and red/*blue* (wmk Crown to left of CA) (1921)	25·00	75·00
54	11	5s. red and green/*yellow* (1914)	55·00	75·00
47/54			*Set of* 10 £110 £225	
48/54		Optd "Specimen" (1s. optd in black)	*Set of* 9 £180	

*The normal sideways watermark shows Crown to right of CA, *as seen from the back of the stamp.*

1916 (Sept). *No.* 47b *surch with* T **12** *by De La Rue.*
55	9	½d. on ½d. deep green (R.)	10	75
		a. Small "O" in "ONE"	6·50	16·00

No. 55a occurs on ten stamps within each sheet of 60.

1918 (18 Mar). *No.* 47b *optd with* T **12** *locally, from D.L.R. plate, but with* "ONE HALF-PENNY" *blanked out.*
56	9	½d. deep green (Blk.)	1·50	4·50

The blanking out of the surcharge was not completely successful so that it almost always appears as an albino to a greater or lesser extent.

WAR TAX
(14)

1918 (June)–**19.** *Nos.* 47b *and* 51a *optd with* T **14** *by De La Rue.*
57	9	½d. deep green	10	30
58		3d. purple/*yellow* (R.) (1919)	65	3·00

WAR TAX = 1½D. =   1½D.

(15)	Short Fraction Bar (R.6/4)

1919. *As No.* 50aw, *but colour changed, surch with* T **15** *by De La Rue.*
59	9	1½d. on 2½d. orange (R.)	10	55
		a. Short fraction bar	7·50	28·00
		b. "C" and "A" missing from wmk		

No. 59b shows the "C" omitted from one impression with the "A" missing from the next one to the right (as seen from the front of the stamp). The "C" is badly distorted in the second watermark.

1920 (1 June). *As No.* 59, *but without* "WAR TAX".
60	9	1½d. on 2½d. orange (Blk.)	1·75	3·75
		a. Short fraction bar	55·00	65·00
55/60		Optd "Specimen"	*Set of* 6 £170	

1921–22. *Wmk Mult Script CA* (sideways*). *Chalk-surfaced paper* (6d.). *P* 14.
62	9	½d. blue-green	1·75	11·00
63		1d. carmine-red	1·25	2·75
		w. Wmk Crown to right of CA	—	10·00
64		1½d. orange	3·50	9·00
65		2d. grey	2·75	3·25
66		2½d. bright blue	1·75	8·50
67		6d. purple	2·50	35·00
69		2s. purple and blue/*blue* (1922)	28·00	65·00
70		2s. 6d. black and red/*blue*	28·00	65·00
62/70			*Set of* 8 65·00 £180	
62/70		Optd "Specimen"	*Set of* 8 £140	

*The normal sideways watermark shows Crown to left of CA, *as seen from the back of the stamp.*
The 1½d. has figures of value in the lower corner and no ornamentation below words of value.

16

(Typo D.L.R.)

1923 (1 Mar)–**33.** *Chalk-surfaced paper. P* 14.
    (*a*) *Wmk Mult Script CA* (sideways*)
71	16	½d. black and green	1·50	30
72		1d. black and bright violet	1·75	1·00
73		1d. black and scarlet (1933)	9·00	90
74		1½d. black and scarlet	1·75	65
75		1½d. black and red-brown (1933)	9·00	60
76		2d. black and grey	1·50	40
77		2½d. black and orange-yellow	1·00	8·50
78		2½d. black and ultramarine (1927)	3·25	1·50
79		3d. black and ultramarine	1·00	11·00
80		3d. black and red/*yellow* (1927)	1·25	1·00
81		4d. black and brown	2·00	4·50
82		6d. black and bright magenta	3·50	5·00
83		1s. black/*emerald*	2·00	2·75
84		2s. black and blue/*blue*	7·00	14·00
85		2s. 6d. black and red/*blue*	17·00	14·00
86		3s. black and purple/*yellow* (1927)	3·00	9·00
87		4s. black and red/*emerald*	9·00	16·00
88		5s. black and green/*yellow* (1927)	22·00	42·00

(b) Wmk Mult Crown CA (sideways*)

89	16	3s. black and purple/yellow	..	4·00	55·00
90		5s. black and green/yellow	..	9·00	42·00
91		£1 black and purple/red	..	£225	£325
71/91			Set of 21	£300	£500
71/91	Optd/Perf "Specimen"		Set of 21	£350	

*The normal sideways watermark shows Crown to left of CA, as seen from the back of the stamp.

Examples of most values are known showing a forged G.P.O. Dominica postmark dated "MY 19 27".

1935 (6 May). *Silver Jubilee. As Nos. 91/4 of Antigua.*

92		1d. deep blue and carmine	..	75	20
		f. Diagonal line by turret	..	32·00	
		h. Dot by flagstaff	..	45·00	
93		1½d. ultramarine and grey ..		1·00	55
		f. Diagonal line by turret	..	40·00	
		h. Dot by flagstaff	..	55·00	
94		2½d. brown and deep blue	..	1·40	2·25
95		1s. slate and purple	..	1·50	3·25
		h. Dot by flagstaff	..	£100	
		i. Dash by turret	..	£100	
92/5			Set of 4	4·25	5·50
92/5	Perf "Specimen"		Set of 4	75·00	

For illustrations of plate varieties see Catalogue Introduction.

1937 (12 May). *Coronation. As Nos. 95/7 of Antigua.* P 11×11½.

96		1d. carmine	..	40	10
97		1½d. yellow-brown	..	40	10
98		2½d. blue	..	60	1·00
96/8			Set of 3	1·25	1·10
96/8	Perf "Specimen" ..		Set of 3	55·00	

17 Fresh Water Lake **18 Layou River**

(Recess Waterlow)

1938 (15 Aug)—47. *T 17/18 and similar horiz designs. Wmk Mult Script CA. P 12½.*

99	17	½d. brown and green	..	10	15
100	18	1d. grey and scarlet	..	20	20
101	—	1½d. green and purple..	..	30	70
102	—	2d. carmine and grey-black ..		50	70
103	—	2½d. purple and bright blue	..	4·00	1·75
		a. Purple & bright ultramarine (8.42)		20	1·25
104	18	3d. olive-green and brown	..	30	40
104a	—	3d. ultramarine and purple (15.10.47)		1·50	85
105	17	6d. emerald-green and violet	..	1·75	80
105a	—	7d. green and yellow-brown (15.10.47)		1·50	90
106	—	1s. violet and olive-green	..	2·25	65
106a	18	2s. slate and purple (15.10.47)	..	4·50	7·00
107	17	2s. 6d. black and vermilion	..	12·00	4·75
108	18	5s. light blue and sepia	..	7·50	7·00
108a	—	10s. black and brown-orange (15.10.47)		12·00	14·00
99/108a			Set of 14	40·00	35·00

Designs:—1½d., 2½d., 3½d. Picking limes; 2d., 1s., 10s. Boiling Lake.

21 King George VI

(Photo Harrison)

1940 (15 Apr)—42. *Wmk Mult Script CA. Chalk-surfaced paper. P 15×14.*

109	21	¼d. chocolate	..	60	15
		a. Ordinary paper (1942)	..	10	10
99/109	Perf "Specimen" ..		Set of 15	£225	

1946 (14 Oct). *Victory. As Nos. 110/11 of Antigua.*

110		1d. carmine ..	..	20	10
111		3½d. blue	..	20	10
110/11	Perf "Specimen"		Set of 2	48·00	

1948 (1 Dec). *Royal Silver Wedding. As Nos. 112/13 of Antigua.*

112		1d. scarlet	..	15	10
113		10s. red-brown	..	7·00	19·00

(New Currency. 100 cents = 1 B.W.I., later East Caribbean dollar)

1949 (10 Oct). *75th Anniv of Universal Postal Union. As Nos. 114/17 of Antigua.*

114		5c. blue	..	15	15
115		6c. brown	..	75	1·25
116		12c. purple	..	30	70
117		24c. olive	..	30	30
114/17			Set of 4	1·40	2·25

1951 (16 Feb). *Inauguration of B.W.I. University College. As Nos. 118/19 of Antigua.*

118		3c. yellow-green and reddish violet ..		75	30
119		12c. deep green and carmine ..	..	75	20

22 King George VI **23 Drying Cocoa**

(Photo Harrison (½ c.). Recess B.W. (others))

1951 (1 July). *T 22 and designs as T 23. Wmk Mult Script CA. Chalk-surfaced paper (½ c.). P 15×14 (½ c.), 13½×13 ($2.40), 13×13½ (others).*

120		½c. chocolate	..	10	15
121		1c. black and vermilion	..	10	30
		b. "A" of "CA" missing from wmk		£500	
		c. "JA" for "CA" in wmk		£500	
122		2c. red-brown and deep green	..	10	20
		a. "C" of "CA" missing from wmk	..	†	—
		b. "A" of "CA" missing from wmk		£600	
123		3c. green and reddish violet	..	15	70
		a. "C" of "CA" missing from wmk		£500	
		c. "JA" for "CA" in wmk		£500	
124		4c. brown-orange and sepia	..	30	60
		a. "C" of "CA" missing from wmk		£600	
		b. "A" of "CA" missing from wmk		£600	
125		5c. black and carmine	..	85	30
		a. "C" of "CA" missing from wmk		£800	
		b. "A" of "CA" missing from wmk		£800	
126		6c. olive and chestnut	..	90	30
		a. "C" of "CA" missing from wmk		£1000	
		b. "A" of "CA" missing from wmk	.. £1000		
127		8c. blue-green and blue	..	60	60
128		12c. black and bright green	..	45	1·25
		a. "C" of "CA" missing from wmk	.. £1200		
129		14c. blue and violet	..	95	1·25
		a. "C" of "CA" missing from wmk	.. £1200		
		b. "A" of "CA" missing from wmk		†	—
130		24c. reddish violet and rose-carmine	..	75	30
		a. "C" of "CA" missing from wmk	.. £1200		
131		48c. bright green and red-orange	..	2·50	6·00
		a. "C" of "CA" missing from wmk	.. £1200		
		b. "A" of "CA" missing from wmk	.. £1200		
132		60c. carmine and black	..	2·50	4·00
133		$1.20, emerald and black	..	4·00	4·00
		a. "C" of "CA" missing from wmk	.. £1400		
		b. "A" of "CA" missing from wmk	.. £1400		
134		$2.40, orange and black	..	22·00	28·00
120/34			Set of 15	30·00	42·00

Designs: *Horiz*—2 c., 60 c. Making Carib baskets; 3 c., 48 c. Lime plantation; 4 c. Picking oranges; 5 c. Bananas; 6 c. Botanical Gardens; 8 c. Drying vanilla beans; 12 c., $1.20, Fresh Water Lake; 14 c. Layou River; 24 c. Boiling Lake. *Vert*—$2.40, Picking oranges.

Examples of Nos. 121b, 122b, 124b, 125b, 126b, 129b, 131b and 133b show traces of the *right leg* of the "A", as seen from the front of the stamp.

Nos. 121c and 123c may represent an attempt to repair the missing "C" variety.

NEW CONSTITUTION 1951

(34)

1951 (15 Oct). *New Constitution. Nos. 123, 125, 127 and 129 optd with T 34 by B.W.*

135		3c. green and reddish violet	..	15	70
136		5c. black and carmine	..	15	70
137		8c. blue-green and blue (R.)	..	15	15
		a. "JA" for "CA" in wmk			
138		14c. blue and violet (R.)	..	15	20
		b. "A" of "CA" missing from wmk	..	£900	
135/8			Set of 4	55	1·60

1953 (2 June). *Coronation. As No. 120 of Antigua.*

139		2c. black and deep green	..	20	10

35 Queen Elizabeth II **36 Mat Making**

37 Picking Oranges **38 Canoe Making**

(Photo Harrison (½ c.). Recess B.W. (others))

1954 (1 Oct)—62. *Designs previously used for King George VI issue, but with portrait of Queen Elizabeth II as in T 35/8. Wmk Mult Script CA. P 15×14 (½ c.), 13½×13 ($2.40), 13×13½ (others).*

140	35	½c. brown	..	10	30
141	—	1c. black and vermilion	..	10	10
142	—	2c. chocolate and myrtle-green	..	55	75
		a. Chocolate and grey-green (13.3.62)		5·50	6·00
143	—	3c. green and purple	..	1·25	30
144	36	3c. black and carmine (15.10.57)		3·25	1·25
145	37	4c. brown-orange and sepia	..	20	10
146	—	5c. black and carmine-red	..	1·25	30
147	38	5c. light blue & sepia-brown (15.10.57)		10·00	90
		a. Blue and sepia (13.3.62)		17·00	5·00
148	—	6c. bronze-green and red-brown	..	40	10
149	—	8c. deep green and deep blue	..	60	10
150	—	10c. green and brown (15.10.57)	..	5·00	1·75
		a. Green and brown (17.7.62)		6·00	80
151	—	12c. black and emerald	..	50	10
152	—	14c. blue and purple	..	30	10
153	—	24c. purple and carmine	..	40	10
154	—	48c. green and red-orange	..	1·25	6·00
155	36	48c. deep brown and violet (15.10.57)		1·25	80
156	—	60c. rose-red and black	..	1·00	1·50
157	—	$1.20, emerald and black	..	16·00	6·00
158	—	$2.40, yellow-orange and black	..	16·00	14·00
140/58			Set of 19	55·00	29·00

Designs: *Horiz*—1 c. Drying cocoa; 2 c., 60 c. Making Carib

---

baskets; 3 c. (No. 143), 48 c. (No. 154) Lime plantation; 5 c. (No. 146) Bananas; 6 c. Botanical Gardens; 8 c. Drying vanilla beans; 10 c. Bananas (different); 12 c., $1.20, Fresh Water Lake; 14 c. Layou River; 24 c. Boiling Lake. *Vert*—$2.40, Picking oranges.

1958 (22 Apr). *Inauguration of British Caribbean Federation. As Nos. 135/7 of Antigua.*

159		3c. deep green	..	35	10
160		6c. blue	..	50	70
161		12c. scarlet	..	70	10
159/61			Set of 3	1·40	80

40 Seashore at Rosalie **48 Traditional Costume**

Two types of 14 c.

I. Eyes of model looking straight ahead.
II. Eyes looking to her right.

(Des S. Scott. Photo Harrison)

1963 (16 May)—65. *T 40, 48 and similar designs. W w 12 (upright). P 14×14½ (vert) or 14½×14 (horiz).*

162		1c. green, blue and sepia	..	10	55
163		2c. bright blue	..	30	10
		w. Wmk inverted	..	—	10·00
164		3c. blackish brown and blue	..	90	70
165		4c. green, sepia and slate-violet	..	10	10
166		5c. magenta	..	30	10
167		6c. green, bistre and violet	..	10	10
168		8c. green, sepia and black	..	10	10
169		10c. sepia and pink	..	10	10
170		12c. green, blue and blackish brown	..	45	10
171		14c. multicoloured (I)	..	70	10
171a		14c. multicoloured (II) (1.4.65)	..	2·50	1·50
172		15c. yellow, green and brown	..	1·00	10
		w. Wmk inverted	..	—	18·00
173		24c. multicoloured	..	8·00	10
174		48c. green, blue and black	..	75	25
175		60c. orange, green and black	..	1·00	50
176		$1.20, multicoloured	..	6·50	70
177		$2.40, blue, turquoise and brown	..	3·25	2·00
178		$4.80, green, blue and brown	..	9·00	20·00
162/78			Set of 17	29·00	22·00

Designs: *Vert*—2 c., 5 c. Queen Elizabeth II; 24 c. Imperial Amazon; $2.40, Trafalgar Falls; $4.80, Coconut Palm. *Horiz*—3 c. Sailing canoe; 4 c. Sulphur springs; 6 c. Road making; 8 c. Dug-out canoe; 10 c. Crapaud (toad); 12 c. Scott's Head; 15 c. Bananas; 48 c. Goodwill; 60 c. Cocoa tree; $1.20, Coat of Arms. See also Nos. 200/4.

1963 (4 June). *Freedom from Hunger. As No. 146 of Antigua.*

179		15c. reddish violet	..	15	10

1963 (2 Sept). *Red Cross Centenary. As Nos. 147/8 of Antigua.*

180		5c. red and black	..	15	10
181		15c. red and blue	..	30	55·

1964 (23 April). *400th Birth Anniv of William Shakespeare. As No. 164 of Antigua.*

182		15c. bright purple ..	..	10	10
		w. Wmk inverted	..	1·50	

1965 (17 May). *I.T.U. Centenary. As Nos. 166/7 of Antigua.*

183		2c. light emerald and blue	..	10	10
184		48c. turquoise-blue and grey	..	30	20

1965 (25 Oct). *International Co-operation Year. As Nos. 168/9 of Antigua.*

185		1c. reddish purple and turquoise-green	..	10	20
186		15c. deep bluish green and lavender ..		20	10

1966 (24 Jan). *Churchill Commemoration. As Nos. 170/3 of Antigua.*

187		1c. new blue	..	10	10
		a. Gold omitted	..	£550	
188		5c. deep green	..	10	10
189		15c. brown	..	20	10
190		24c. bluish violet	..	30	20
187/90			Set of 4	55	30

No. 187a occured on the bottom row of a sheet.
An example of the 1 c. is known showing the gold face value printed double.

1966 (4 Feb). *Royal Visit. As Nos. 174/5 of Antigua.*

191		5c. black and ultramarine	..	1·00	10
192		15c. black and magenta	..	1·50	20

1966 (1 July). *World Cup Football Championships. As Nos. 176/7 of Antigua.*

193		5c. violet, yellow-green, lake & yellow-brown		20	15
194		24c. chocolate, blue-green, lake & yell-brown		65	15

1966 (20 Sept). *Inauguration of W.H.O. Headquarters, Geneva. As Nos. 178/9 of Antigua.*

195		5c. black, yellow-green and light blue	..	10	15
196		24c. black, light purple and yellow-brown	..	20	15

1966 (1 Dec). *20th Anniv of U.N.E.S.C.O. As Nos. 196/8 of Antigua.*

197		5c. slate-violet, red, yellow and orange	..	15	15
198		15c. orange-yellow, violet and deep olive	..	30	10
199		24c. black, bright purple and orange..	..	35	15
197/9			Set of 3	70	30

1966 (30 Dec)—67. *As Nos. 165, 167/9 and 172 but wmk w 12 sideways.*

200		4c. green, sepia and slate-violet (16.5.67)		1·25	90
201		6c. green, bistre and violet	..	20	15
202		8c. green, sepia and black	..	40	10
203		10c. sepia and pink (16.5.67) ..		70	10
204		15c. yellow, green and brown (16.5.67)		70	10
200/4			Set of 5	3·00	1·25

ASSOCIATED STATEHOOD

56 Children of Three Races

(Des and photo Harrison)

1967 (2 Nov). *National Day. T* **56** *and similar horiz designs. Multicoloured.* W w **12**. P 14½.
205	5 c. Type 56		10	10
206	10 c. The *Santa Maria* and motto		30	10
207	15 c. Hands holding motto ribbon		15	15
208	24 c. Belaire dancing		15	15
205/8		*Set of 4*	60	30

57 John F. Kennedy

(Des G. Vasarhelyi. Litho D.L.R.)

1968 (20 Apr). *Human Rights Year. T* **57** *and similar horiz designs. Multicoloured.* W w **12** (*sideways*). P 14 × 13½.
209	1 c. Type 57		10	10
210	10 c. Cecil A. E. Rawle		10	10
	a. Imperf (pair)		90·00	
211	12 c. Pope John XXIII		50	15
212	48 c. Florence Nightingale		35	20
213	60 c. Albert Schweitzer		35	20
209/13		*Set of 5*	1·25	65

ASSOCIATED STATEHOOD	NATIONAL DAY 3 NOVEMBER 1968
(58)	(59)

1968 (8 July). *Associated Statehood. As Nos.* 162, 170 *and* 174, *but wmk sideways, or Nos.* 163/4, 166, 170, 171a, 173, 175/8 *and* 200/4 *optd with T* **58**.
214	1 c. green, blue and sepia (Sil.)		10	10
215	2 c. bright blue (Sil.)		10	10
216	3 c. blackish brown and blue (Sil.)		10	10
217	4 c. green, sepia and slate-violet (Sil.)		10	10
218	5 c. magenta (Sil.)		10	10
219	6 c. green, bistre and violet		10	10
220	8 c. green, sepia and black		10	10
221	10 c. sepia and pink (Sil.)		55	10
222	12 c. green, blue and blackish brown (Sil.) (wmk sideways)		10	10
	a. Wmk upright		10	10
224	14 c. multicoloured (II) (Sil.)		10	10
225	15 c. yellow, green and brown (Sil.)		10	10
226	24 c. multicoloured (Sil.)		3·50	10
227	48 c. green, bl & blk (Sil.) (wmk sideways)		55	90
	a. Wmk upright		40	75
228	60 c. orange, green and black		90	70
229	$1.20, multicoloured		1·00	1·75
230	$2.40, blue, turquoise and brown (Sil.)		1·25	2·25
231	$4.80, green, blue and brown (Sil.)		1·25	4·50
214/31		*Set of 17*	8·50	9·50

The 2, 5, 6, 8 and 10 c. values exist with PVA gum as well as gum arabic.

1968 (3 Nov). *National Day. Nos.* 162/4, 171 *and* 176 *optd with T* **58**.
232	1 c. green, blue and sepia		10	10
	a. Opt inverted		45·00	
233	2 c. bright blue		10	10
	a. Opt double		30·00	
234	3 c. blackish brown and blue		10	10
	a. Opt inverted		30·00	
235	14 c. multicoloured (I)		10	10
	a. Opt double		70·00	
236	$1.20, multicoloured		55	40
	a. Opt double		30·00	
	b. Vert pair, one opt omitted, other opt double		£150	
232/6		*Set of 5*	60	40

The above set was put on sale by the New York Agency on 1 November but not sold locally until the 3 November.

60 Forward shooting at Goal

(Des M. Shamir (1 c., 60 c.), K. Plowitz (5 c., 48 c.). Litho B.W.)

1968 (25 Nov). *Olympic Games, Mexico. T* **60** *and similar horiz designs. Multicoloured.* P 11½ × 11.
237	1 c. Type 60		10	10
	a. Horiz pair. Nos. 237/8		10	10
238	1 c. Goalkeeper trying to save goal		10	10
239	5 c. Swimmers about to dive		10	10
	a. Horiz pair. Nos. 239/40		10	10
240	5 c. Swimmers diving		10	10
241	48 c. Javelin-throwing		15	15
	a. Horiz pair. Nos. 241/2		30	30

242	48 c. Hurdling		15	15
243	60 c. Basketball		50	15
	a. Horiz pair. Nos. 243/4		1·00	30
244	60 c. Basketball players		50	15
237/44		*Set of 8*	1·25	70

Nos. 237/44 were issued in sheets of 40 containing two panes of *se-tenant* pairs.

61 "The Small Cowper Madonna" (Raphael)   **62** "Venus and Adonis" (Rubens)

(Photo Delrieu, Paris)

1968 (23 Dec). *Christmas.* P 12½ × 12.
245	61	5 c. multicoloured	10	10

Three other values were issued: 12 c. "Madonna of the Chair" (Raphael); 24 c. "Madonna and Child" (Italo-Byzantine, XVI century); $1.20 "Madonna and Child" (Byzantine, XIII century). Sizes as *T* **61**.

These only come from miniature sheets, containing two *se-tenant* strips of each value.

(Litho D.L.R.)

1969 (30 Jan). *20th Anniv of World Health Organisation. Paintings. T* **62** *and similar vert designs. Multicoloured.* W w **12**. P 15.
246	5 c. Type 62		20	10
247	15 c. "The Death of Socrates" (J.-L. David)		30	10
248	24 c. "Christ and the Pilgrims of Emmaus" (Velasquez)		30	10
249	50 c. "Pilate washing his Hands" (Rembrandt)		50	40
246/9		*Set of 4*	1·10	50

66 Picking Oranges   **67** "Strength in Unity" Emblem and Fruit Trees

(Des K. Plowitz. Litho Harrison)

1969 (10 Mar). *Tourism. T* **66** *and similar horiz designs. Multicoloured.* W w **12**. P 14½.
250	10 c. Type 66		15	10
	a. Horiz pair. Nos. 250/1		30	15
251	10 c. Woman, child and ocean scene		15	10
252	12 c. Fort Yeoung Hotel		30	10
	a. Horiz pair. Nos. 252/3		60	20
253	12 c. Red-necked Amazons		30	10
254	24 c. Calypso band		30	15
	a. Horiz pair. Nos. 254/5		60	30
	w. Wmk inverted		26·00	
255	24 c. Women dancing		30	15
	w. Wmk inverted		26·00	
256	48 c. Underwater life		30	25
	a. Horiz pair. Nos. 256/7		60	50
257	48 c. Skin-diver and turtle		30	25
250/7		*Set of 8*	1·90	1·00

Each denomination was printed *se-tenant* throughout the sheet. The 12 c. values are on cream coloured paper.

(Litho B.W.)

1969 (July). *First Anniv of CARIFTA (Caribbean Free Trade Area). T* **67** *and similar horiz designs. Multicoloured.* P 13½ × 13.
258	5 c. Type 67		10	10
259	8 c. Hawker Siddeley H.S.748 aircraft, emblem and island		25	10
260	12 c. Chart of Caribbean Sea and emblem		25	15
261	24 c. Steamship unloading, tug and emblem		30	15
258/61		*Set of 4*	75	40

71 "Spinning"   **72** Mahatma Gandhi Weaving and Clock Tower, Westminster

(Litho B.W.)

1969 (10 July). *50th Anniv of International Labour Organisation. T* **71** *and similar vert designs showing paintings of people at work by J. Millet, bordered by flags of member-nations of the I.L.O. Multicoloured. No wmk.* P 13 × 13½.
262	15 c. Type 71		10	10
263	30 c. "Threshing"		15	15
264	38 c. "Flax-pulling"		15	15
262/4		*Set of 3*	30	30

(Des G. Vasarhelyi. Litho Format)

1969 (20 Oct). *Birth Centenary of Mahatma Gandhi. T* **72** *and similar horiz designs. Multicoloured.* P 14½.
265	6 c. Type 72		30	10
266	38 c. Gandhi, Nehru and Mausoleum		50	15
267	$1.20, Gandhi and Taj Mahal		1·40	75
265/7		*Set of 3*	2·00	90

Nos. 265/7 are incorrectly inscribed "Ghandi".

75 "Saint Joseph"

(Des G. Vasarhelyi. Litho Govt Printer, Jerusalem)

1969 (3 Nov). *National Day. Stained Glass Windows. T* **75** *and similar vert designs. Multicoloured.* P 14.
268	6 c. Type 75		10	10
269	8 c. "Saint John"		10	10
270	12 c. "Saint Peter"		10	10
271	60 c. "Saint Paul"		30	50
268/71		*Set of 4*	40	60

Nos. 268/71 were printed in sheets of 16 (4 × 4) containing 12 stamps and four printed labels in the top row. The labels each contain two lines of a patriotic poem by W. O. M. Pond, the first letter from each line spelling "DOMINICA".

79 Queen Elizabeth II   **80** Purple-throated Carib and Flowe[r]

81 Government Headquarters

82 Coat of Arms

(Photo D.L.R.)

1969–72. *T* **79/82** *and similar horiz designs. Multicoloured.* W **41** *of Singapore* (60 c. to $4.80) *or no wmk* (*others*). P 13½ × 14 (½ c.), 14 × 13½ (1 to 50 c.) *or* 14 (60 c. to $4.80).

A. *Chalk-surfaced paper* (26.11.69)
B. *Glazed paper* (1972)

		A		B	
272	½ c. Type 79	10	1·25	30	60
273	1 c. Type 80	30	1·25	1·50	60
274	2 c. Poinsettia	15	10	50	60
275	3 c. Red-necked Pigeon	1·75	1·75	1·75	60
276	4 c. Imperial Amazon	1·75	1·75	1·75	60
277	5 c. *Battus polydamas* (butterfly)	1·75	65	1·75	60
278	6 c. *Dryas julia* (butterfly)	1·75	2·25	1·75	2·00
279	8 c. Shipping Bananas	20	10	40	20
280	10 c. Portsmouth Harbour	20	10	35	20
281	12 c. Copra Processing Plant	20	10	35	20
282	15 c. Straw Workers	20	10	35	25
283	25 c. Timber Plant	30	10	40	25
284	30 c. Pumice Mine	1·50	90	1·50	70
285	38 c. Grammar School and Playing Field	8·00	1·75	7·50	13·00
286	50 c. Roseau Cathedral	50	45	80	80
287	60 c. Type 81	55	1·00	†	
288	$1.20, Melville Hall Airport (40 × 27 mm)	1·00	1·75	†	
289	$2.40, Type 82	1·00	3·50	†	
290	$4.80, Type 79 (26 × 39 mm)	1·75	6·50	†	
272A/90A		*Set of 19*	20·00	22·00	
272B/86B		*Set of 15*		19·00	19·00

99 "Virgin and Child with St. John" (Perugino)

101 Astronaut's First Step onto the Moon

(Des G. Vasarhelyi. Litho B.W.)

1969 (19 Dec). *Christmas. Paintings. T 99 and similar vert designs. Multicoloured. P 14 × 14½.*
291	6 c. "Virgin and Child with St. John" (Lippi)		10	10
292	10 c. "Holy Family with the Lamb" (Raphael)		10	10
293	15 c. Type 99		10	10
294	$1.20, "Madonna of the Rose Hedge" (Botticelli)		35	40
291/4		*Set of 4*	35	40
MS295	89 × 76 mm. Nos. 293/4. Imperf		1·25	90

(Des G. Vasarhelyi. Photo Banknote Printing Office, Helsinki)

1970 (6 Feb*). *Moon Landing. T 101 and similar horiz designs. Multicoloured. P 12½.*
296	½ c. Type 101		10	10
297	5 c. Scientific Experiment on the Moon, and Flag		15	10
298	8 c. Astronauts collecting Rocks		15	10
299	30 c. Module over the Moon		30	15
300	50 c. Moon Plaque		40	25
301	60 c. Astronauts		40	30
296/301		*Set of 6*	1·25	80
MS302	116 × 112 mm. Nos. 298/301. Imperf		2·00	2·00

*This is the date of release in Dominica, but the above were released by the Philatelic Agency in the U.S.A. on 2 February.

107 Giant Green Turtle

(Des G. Drummond. Litho Kyodo Printing Co, Tokyo)

1970 (7 Sept). *Flora and Fauna. T 107 and similar horiz designs. Multicoloured. P 13.*
303	6 c. Type 107		50	20
304	24 c. Atlantic Flyingfish		60	40
305	38 c. Anthurium lily		70	65
306	60 c. Imperial and Red-necked Amazons		3·25	4·25
303/6		*Set of 4*	4·50	5·00
MS307	160×111 mm. Nos. 303/6		5·50	6·00

108 18th-Century National Costume

109 Scrooge and Marley's Ghost

(Des G. Drummond from local designs. Litho Questa)

1970 (30 Oct). *National Day. T 108 and similar horiz designs. Multicoloured. P 14.*
308	5 c. Type 108		10	10
309	8 c. Carib Basketry		10	10
310	$1 Flag and Chart of Dominica		30	40
308/10		*Set of 3*	30	40
MS311	150 × 85 mm. Nos. 308/10 plus three labels	50	1·40

(Des R. Granger Barrett. Litho Questa)

1970 (23 Nov). *Christmas and Charles Dickens' Death Centenary. T 109 and similar vert designs showing scenes from "A Christmas Carol". Multicoloured. P 14 × 14½.*
312	5 c. Type 109		10	10
313	15 c. Fezziwig's Ball		20	10
314	24 c. Scrooge and his Nephew's Party		20	10
315	$1.20, Scrooge and the Ghost of Christmas Present		65	60
312/15		*Set of 4*	1·00	70
MS316	142 × 87 mm. Nos. 312/15		1·50	3·25

110 "The Doctor" (Sir Luke Fildes)

(Des G. Vasarhelyi. Litho Questa)

1970 (28 Dec). *Centenary of British Red Cross. T 110 and similar horiz designs. Multicoloured. P 14½ × 14.*
317	8 c. Type 110		10	10
318	10 c. Hands and Red Cross		10	10
319	15 c. Flag of Dominica and Red Cross Emblem	15	10
320	50 c. "The Sick Child" (E. Munch)		50	35
317/20		*Set of 4*	75	40
MS321	108 × 76 mm. Nos. 317/20		1·25	2·50

111 Marigot School

(Des G. Vasarhelyi. Litho Questa)

1971 (1 Mar). *International Education Year (1970). T 111 and similar horiz designs. Multicoloured. P 13½.*
322	5 c. Type 111		10	10
323	8 c. Goodwill Junior High School		10	10
324	14 c. University of West Indies (Jamaica)	10	10
325	$1 Trinity College, Cambridge		25	30
322/5		*Set of 4*	30	30
MS326	85 × 85 mm. Nos. 324/5		50	1·00

112 Waterfall

(Des O. Bonnevalle. Litho Questa)

1971 (22 Mar). *Tourism. T 112 and similar horiz designs. Multicoloured. P 13½.*
327	5 c. Type 112		15	10
328	10 c. Boat-building		15	10
329	30 c. Sailing		25	10
330	50 c. Yacht and motor launch		40	30
327/30		*Set of 4*	85	45
MS331	130 × 86 mm. Nos. 327/30		85	1·00

113 UNICEF Symbol in "D"

114 German Boy Scout

(Des G. Drummond. Litho Questa)

1971 (14 June). *25th Anniv of UNICEF. P 14.*
332	113	5 c. bluish violet, black and gold	10	10
333		10 c. yellow, black and gold	10	10
334		38 c. green, black and gold	10	10
335		$1.20 orange, black and gold	30	45
332/5		*Set of 4*	40	55
MS336	84 × 79 mm. Nos. 333 and 335		50	1·10

(Litho Format)

1971 (18 Oct). *World Scout Jamboree, Asagiri, Japan. T 114 and similar vert designs showing Boy Scouts from the nations listed. Multicoloured. W w 12. P 11.*
337	20 c. Type 114		15	10
338	24 c. Great Britain		20	10
339	30 c. Japan		25	10
340	$1 Dominica		50	1·40
337/40		*Set of 4*	1·00	1·50
MS341	114 × 102 mm. Nos. 339/40		1·25	2·00

The above were printed on thick paper and the watermark is very faint.
Both No. 340 and the $1 value from the miniature sheet show the national flag of the Dominican Republic in error.
"Dominica" on the scout's shirt pocket is omitted on the $1 value from the miniature sheet.

115 Groine at Portsmouth

(Des V. Whiteley. Litho Format)

1971 (15 Nov). *National Day. T 115 and similar multicoloured designs. P 13½.*
342	8 c. Type 115		10	10
343	15 c. Carnival scene		10	10
344	20 c. Carifta Queen (vert)		10	10
345	50 c. Rock of Atkinson (vert)		20	25
342/5		*Set of 4*	30	30
MS346	63 × 89 mm. $1.20, As 20 c. P 15		45	70

116 Eight Reals Piece, 1761

(Des G. Drummond. Litho Questa)

1972 (7 Feb). *Coins. T 116 and similar designs. P 14.*
347	10 c. black, silver and violet		10	10
348	30 c. black, silver and yellowish green	15	15
349	35 c. black, silver and bright blue	20	20
350	50 c. black, silver and vermilion		40	1·10
347/50		*Set of 4*	75	1·40
MS351	86 × 90 mm. Nos. 349/50		1·00	1·40

Designs: *Horiz*—30 c. Eleven and three bitt pieces, 1798. *Vert*—35 c. Two reals and two bitt pieces, 1770; 50 c. Mocos, Pieces-of-eight and eight reals-eleven bitts piece, 1798.

117 Common Opossum

(Des R. Granger Barrett. Litho Questa)

1972 (3 June). *U.N. Conference on the Human Environment, Stockholm. T 117 and similar horiz designs. Multicoloured. W w 12 (sideways). P 14.*
352	½ c. Type 117		10	10
353	35 c. Brazilian Agouti (rodent)		40	15
354	60 c. Orchid		2·50	50
355	$1.20, Hibiscus		2·50	1·60
352/5		*Set of 4*	5·00	2·00
MS356	139×94 mm. Nos. 352/5		7·00	9·00

118 Sprinter

(Des R. Granger Barrett. Litho Format)

1972 (16 Oct*). *Olympic Games, Munich. T 118 and similar multicoloured designs. P 14.*
357	30 c. Type 118		10	10
358	35 c. Hurdler		15	15
359	58 c. Hammer-thrower (vert)		20	20
360	72 c. Long-jumper (vert)		40	40
357/60		*Set of 4*	75	75
MS361	98 × 96 mm. Nos. 359/60. P 15	75	90

*This is the local release date; the American philatelic agency released the stamps on 9 October.

119 General Post Office

(Des G. Vasarhelyi. Litho Format)

1972 (1 Nov). *National Day. T 119 and similar horiz designs. Multicoloured. P 13½.*
362	10 c. Type 119		10	10
363	20 c. Morne Diablotin		10	10
364	30 c. Rodney's Rock		15	15
362/4		*Set of 3*	30	30
MS365	83 × 96 mm. Nos. 363/4. P 15	50	70

120 Bananas and Imperial Amazon

(Des (from photograph by D. Groves) and photo Harrison)

1972 (20 Nov). *Royal Silver Wedding. Multicoloured; background colour given.* W w **12**. P 14 × 14½.

366	120	5 c. yellow-olive	..	15	10
		a. Deep yellow-olive	..	40	25
367		$1 myrtle-green	..	50	40
		w. Wmk inverted	..	3·50	

121 "The Adoration of the Shepherds" (Caravaggio)   **122** Launching of Weather Satellite

(Des G. Vasarhelyi. Litho Format)

1972 (4 Dec*). *Christmas. T* **121** *and similar vert designs. Multicoloured.* P 13½.

368	8 c. Type **121**			10	10
369	14 c. "The Myosotis Virgin" (Rubens)..			10	10
370	30 c. "Madonna and Child with St. Francesca Romana" (Gentileschi)			15	10
371	$1 "Adoration of the Kings" (Mostaert)			50	70
368/71			*Set of 4*	70	85
MS372	102 × 79 mm. Nos. 370/1. Imperf.			90	80

* This is the date of release in Dominica; the stamps were put on sale by the Philatelic agency in the U.S.A. on 27 November.
No. 368 is wrongly attributed to Boccaccino in the design.

(Des G. Vasarhelyi. Litho Format)

1973 (16 July). *I.M.O/W.M.O. Centenary. T* **122** *and similar multicoloured designs.* P 14½.

373	½ c. Type **122**			10	10
374	1 c. Nimbus satellite			10	10
375	2 c. Radiosonde balloon			10	10
376	30 c. Radarscope (*horiz*)			15	15
377	35 c. Diagram of pressure zones (*horiz*)			20	20
378	50 c. Hurricane shown by satellite (*horiz*)			30	35
379	$1 Computer weather-map (*horiz*)			60	65
373/9			*Set of 7*	1·25	1·40
MS380	90 × 105 mm. Nos. 378/9			90	1·75

123 Going to Hospital   **124** Cyrique Crab

(Des G. Vasarhelyi. Litho Format)

1973 (20 Aug). *25th Anniv of W.H.O. T* **123** *and similar horiz designs. Multicoloured.* P 14½.

381	½ c. Type **123**			10	10
382	1 c. Maternity care			10	10
383	2 c. Smallpox inoculation			10	10
384	30 c. Emergency service			30	15
385	35 c. Waiting for the doctor			35	15
386	50 c. Medical examination			45	25
387	$1 Travelling doctor			65	60
381/7			*Set of 7*	1·75	1·10
MS388	112 × 110 mm. Nos. 386/7. P 14 × 14½			75	1·25
	a. Perf 14½			45·00	45·00

(Des G. Drummond. Litho Format)

1973 (15 Oct). *Flora and Fauna. T* **124** *and similar vert designs. Multicoloured.* P 14½.

389	½ c. Type **124**			10	10
390	22 c. Blue Land-crab			35	10
391	25 c. Bread Fruit			35	15
392	$1.20, Sunflower			1·00	2·00
389/92			*Set of 4*	1·50	2·00
MS393	91 × 127 mm. Nos. 389/92			3·25	4·50

125 Princess Anne and Captain Mark Phillips

126 "Adoration of the Kings" (Brueghel)

(Des M. Shamir. Litho Format)

1973 (26 Nov). *Christmas. T* **126** *and similar horiz designs. Multicoloured.* P 14½.

397	½ c. Type **126**			10	10
398	1 c. "Adoration of the Magi" (Botticelli)			10	10
399	2 c. "Adoration of the Magi" (Dürer)			10	10
400	12 c. "Mystic Nativity" (Botticelli)			20	10
401	22 c. "Adoration of the Magi" (Rubens)			25	10
402	35 c. "The Nativity" (Dürer)			25	10
403	$1 "Adoration of the Shepherds" (Giorgione)			90	55
397/403			*Set of 7*	1·60	80
MS404	122 × 98 mm. Nos. 402/3			1·25	1·10

127 Carib Basket-weaving

(Des G. Drummond. Litho Format)

1973 (17 Dec). *National Day. T* **127** *and similar multicoloured designs.* P 13½.

405	5 c. Type **127**			10	10
406	10 c. Staircase of the Snake			10	10
407	50 c. Miss Caribbean Queen (*vert*)			15	15
408	50 c. Miss Carifta Queen (*vert*)			15	15
409	$1 Dance group			25	30
405/9			*Set of 5*	50	60
MS410	95 × 127 mm. Nos. 405/6 and 409			40	65

128 University Centre, Dominica

(Des G. Drummond. Litho Format)

1974 (21 Jan). *25th Anniv of West Indies University. T* **128** *and similar horiz designs. Multicoloured.* P 14½.

411	12 c. Type **128**			10	10
412	30 c. Graduation ceremony			10	10
413	$1 University coat of arms			25	35
411/13			*Set of 3*	30	35
MS414	97 × 131 mm. Nos. 411/13			30	55

129 Dominicia 1d. Stamp of 1874 and Map   **130** Footballer and Flag of Brazil

(Des G. Drummond. Litho Format)

1974 (27 May). *Stamp Centenary. T* **129** *and similar horiz designs. Multicoloured.* P 14½.

415	½ c. Type **129**			10	10
416	1 c. 6d. stamp of 1874 and posthorn			10	10
417	2 c. 1s. stamp of 1874 and arms			10	10
418	10 c. Type **129**			20	10
419	50 c. As 1 c.			75	30
420	$1.20, As 2 c.			1·00	70
415/20			*Set of 6*	1·75	1·00
MS421	105 × 121 mm. Nos. 418/20			1·50	1·50

(Des V. Whiteley. Litho Format)

1974 (12 Aug). *World Cup Football Championship, West Germany. T* **130** *and similar vert designs, showing footballers and flags of the countries given. Multicoloured.* P 14½.

422	½ c. Type **130**			10	10
423	1 c. West Germany			10	10
424	2 c. Italy			10	10
425	30 c. Scotland			50	10
426	40 c. Sweden			50	10
427	50 c. Netherlands			55	25
428	$1 Yugoslavia			90	65
422/8			*Set of 7*	2·25	1·00
MS429	89 × 87 mm. Nos. 427/8			70	80

131 Indian Hole

(Des G. Vasarhelyi. Litho Format)

1974 (1 Nov). *National Day. T* **131** *and similar horiz designs. Multicoloured.* P 13½.

430	10 c. Type **131**			10	10
431	40 c. Teachers' Training College			10	10
432	$1 Bay Oil distillery plant, Petite Savanne			50	45
430/2			*Set of 3*	60	45
MS433	96 × 143 mm. Nos. 430/2			60	65

132 Churchill with "Colonist"

(Des G. Drummond. Litho Format)

1974 (25 Nov). *Birth Centenary of Sir Winston Churchill. T* **132** *and similar horiz designs. Multicoloured.* P 14½.

434	½ c. Type **132**			10	10
435	1 c. Churchill and Eisenhower			10	10
436	2 c. Churchill and Roosevelt			10	10
437	20 c. Churchill and troops on assault-course			15	10
438	45 c. Painting at Marrakesh			25	10
439	$2 Giving the "V" sign			80	1·00
434/9			*Set of 6*	1·10	1·10
MS440	126 × 100 mm. Nos. 438/9. P 13			1·10	1·75

133 Mailboats *Orinoco* (1851) and *Geesthaven* (1974)   **134** "The Virgin and Child" (Tiso)

(Des G. Drummond. Litho Format)

1974 (4 Dec). *Centenary of Universal Postal Union. T* **133** *and similar horiz designs. Multicoloured.* P 13.

441	10 c. Type **133**			20	10
442	$2 De Havilland D.H.4 (1918) and Boeing 747-100 (1974)			80	1·00
MS443	107×93 mm. $1.20 as 10 c. and $2.40 as $2			1·50	1·90

Nos. 442 and MS443 are inscr "De Haviland"
Nos. 441/2 were issued either in sheets of 50 or in sheets of five stamps and one inscribed label.

(Des M. Shamir. Litho Questa)

1974 (16 Dec). *Christmas. T* **134** *and similar vert designs. Multicoloured.* P 14.

444	½ c. Type **134**			10	10
445	1 c. "Madonna and Child with Saints" (Costa)			10	10
446	2 c. "The Nativity" (School of Rimini, 14th-cent)			10	10
447	10 c. "The Rest on the Flight into Egypt' (Romanelli)			20	10
448	25 c. "Adoration of the Shepherds" (da Sermoneta)			35	10
449	45 c. "The Nativity" (Guido Reni)			45	10
450	$1 "The Adoration of the Magi" (Caselli)			65	40
444/50			*Set of 7*	1·60	60
MS451	114 × 78 mm. Nos. 449/50			60	1·00

135 Queen Triggerfish

(Des G. Drummond. Litho Format)

1973 (14 Nov). *Royal Wedding.* P 13½.

394	125	25 c. multicoloured		10	10
395	–	$2 multicoloured		30	30
MS396	79 × 100 mm. 75 c. as 25 c. and $1.20 as $2			40	30

No. 395 is as T **125**, but the portrait has a different frame.
Nos. 394/5 were each issued in small sheets of five stamps and one stamp-size label.

(Des G. Vasarhelyi. Litho Format)

1975 (2 June). *Fishes. T 135 and similar horiz designs. Multicoloured. P 14.*

452	½ c. Type 135		10	10
453	1 c. Porkfish		10	10
454	2 c. Sailfish		10	10
455	3 c. Swordfish		10	10
456	20 c. Great Barracuda		1·00	50
457	$2 Nassau Grouper		4·25	2·75
452/7		Set of 6	5·00	3·25
MS458	104×80 mm. No. 457. P 13		4·00	6·00

136 Myscelia antholia

(Des J. W. Litho Format)

1975 (28 July). *Dominican Butterflies. T 136 and similar horiz designs. Multicoloured. P 14½.*

459	½ c. Type 136		10	40
460	1 c. Lycorea ceres		10	40
461	2 c. Anaea marthesia ("Siderone nemesis")		15	40
462	6 c. Battus polydamas		60	55
463	30 c. Anartia lytrea		1·75	70
464	40 c. Morpho peleides		2·00	75
465	$2 Dryas julia		3·75	7·50
459/65		Set of 7	7·50	9·50
MS466	108 × 80 mm. No. 465. P 13		3·00	4·25

137 Yare (cargo liner)

(Des J. W. Litho Questa)

1975 (1 Sept). *"Ships Tied to Dominica's History". T 137 and similar horiz designs. Multicoloured. P 14.*

467	½ c. Type 137		20	30
468	1 c. Thames II (liner), 1890		20	30
469	2 c. Lady Nelson (cargo liner)		20	30
470	20 c. Lady Rodney (cargo liner)		1·00	35
471	45 c. Statesman (freighter)		1·25	55
472	50 c. Geestcape (freighter)		1·25	65
473	$2 Geeststar (freighter)		4·25	4·00
467/73		Set of 7	7·50	5·75
MS474	78×103 mm. Nos. 472/3		4·00	5·75

138 "Women in Agriculture"   *139 Miss Caribbean Queen, 1975*

(Litho Questa)

1975 (20 Oct). *International Women's Year. T 138 and similar horiz design. Multicoloured. P 14.*

475	10 c. Type 138		10	10
476	$2 "Women in Industry and Commerce"		40	60

(Litho Format)

1975 (6 Nov). *National Day. T 139 and similar multicoloured designs. P 14 × 13½ (vert) or 13½ × 14 (horiz).*

477	5 c. Type 139		10	10
478	10 c. Public Library (horiz)		10	10
479	30 c. Citrus Factory (horiz)		10	10
480	$1 National Day Trophy		25	50
477/80		Set of 4	35	60
MS481	130×98 mm. Nos. 478/80. Imperf		50	1·40

140 "Virgin and Child" (Mantegna)   *141 Hibiscus*

(Des M. Shamir. Litho Questa)

1975 (24 Nov). *Christmas. T 140 and similar vert designs showing "Virgin and Child". Multicoloured. P 14.*

482	½ c. Type 140		10	10
483	1 c. Fra Filippo Lippi		10	10
484	2 c. Bellini		10	10
485	10 c. Botticelli		15	10
486	25 c. Bellini		25	10
487	45 c. Correggio		30	10
488	$1 Dürer		55	50
482/88		Set of 7	1·10	70
MS489	139 × 85 mm. Nos. 487/88		1·00	1·50

(Des J.W. Litho Format)

1975 (8 Dec)–78. *T 141 and similar multicoloured designs.*

(a) Size as T 141. P 14½

490	½ c. Type 141		10	50
491	1 c. African Tulip		15	50
492	2 c. Castor Oil Tree		15	50
493	3 c. White Cedar Flower		15	50
494	4 c. Egg Plant		15	50
495	5 c. Needlefish ("Gare")		20	50
496	6 c. Ochro		20	60
497	8 c. Zenaida Dove		1·75	60
498	10 c. Screw Pine		20	15
	a. Perf 13½ (1978)		25·00	
499	20 c. Mango Longue		30	15
500	25 c. Crayfish		35	15
501	30 c. Common Opossum ("Manicou")		90	80

(b) Size 28 × 44 mm ($10) or 44 × 28 mm (others). P 13½

502	40 c. Bay Leaf Groves		90	80
503	50 c. Tomatoes		55	50
504	$1 Lime Factory		75	65
505	$2 Rum Distillery		2·00	3·50
506	$5 Bay Oil Distillery		2·50	5·00
507	$10 Queen Elizabeth II		3·25	15·00
490/507		Set of 18	13·00	27·00

Nos. 490/2, 494/9 and 501/7 exist imperforate from stock dispersed by the liquidator of Format International Security Printers Ltd.

142 American Infantry   *143 Rowing*

(Des J.W. Litho Format)

1976 (12 Apr). *Bicentenary of American Revolution. T 142 and similar vert designs. Multicoloured. P 14½.*

508	½ c. Type 142		10	10
509	1 c. British three-decker, 1782		10	10
510	2 c. George Washington		10	10
511	45 c. British sailors		70	15
512	75 c. British ensign		1·00	50
513	$2 Admiral Hood		1·50	1·50
508/13		Set of 6	3·00	2·25
MS514	105 × 92 mm. Nos. 512/13. P 13		2·50	4·00

(Des J.W. Litho Format)

1976 (24 May). *Olympic Games, Montreal. T 143 and similar vert designs. Multicoloured. P 14½.*

515	½ c. Type 143		10	10
516	1 c. Shot putting		10	10
517	2 c. Swimming		10	10
518	40 c. Relay		15	10
519	45 c. Gymnastics		15	10
520	60 c. Sailing		20	20
521	$2 Archery		55	80
515/21		Set of 7	1·10	1·10
MS522	90 × 104 mm. Nos. 520/1. P 13		1·25	1·75

Nos. 516/21 exist imperforate from stock dispersed by the liquidator of Format International Security Printers Ltd.

144 Ringed Kingfisher   *145 Viking Spacecraft System*

(Des G. Drummond. Litho Format)

1976 (28 June). *Wild Birds. T 144 and similar multicoloured designs. P 14½.*

523	½ c. Type 144		10	50
524	1 c. Mourning Dove		15	50
525	2 c. Green Heron		15	50
526	15 c. Broad-winged Hawk		1·25	45
527	30 c. Blue-headed Hummingbird		1·75	80
528	45 c. Bananaquit		2·50	1·00
529	$2 Imperial Amazon		9·00	14·00
523/9		Set of 7	13·50	16·00
MS530	133 ×101 mm. Nos. 527/9. P 13		11·00	16·00

Nos. 523/5 exist imperforate from stock dispersed by the liquidator of Format International Security Printers Ltd.

1976 (26 July). *West Indian Victory in World Cricket Cup. As Nos. 559/60 of Barbados.*

531	15 c. Map of the Caribbean		75	1·25
532	25 c. Prudential Cup		75	1·75

(Des PAD Studio. Litho Format)

1976 (20 Sept). *Viking Space Mission. T 145 and similar multicoloured designs. P 14½.*

533	½ c. Type 145		10	10
534	1 c. Launching pad (horiz)		10	10
535	2 c. Titan IIID and Centaur DII		10	10
536	3 c. Orbiter and lander capsule		10	10
537	45 c. Capsule, parachute unopened		30	15
538	75 c. Capsule, parachute opened		40	50
539	$1 Lander descending (horiz)		45	60
540	$2 Space vehicle on Mars (horiz)		60	1·60
533/40		Set of 8	1·75	2·75
MS541	104 × 78 mm. Nos. 539/40. P 13		1·10	2·25

146 "Virgin and Child with Saints Anthony of Padua and Roch" (Giorgione)   *147 Island Craft Co-operative*

(Des M. Shamir. Litho Questa)

1976 (1 Nov). *Christmas. T 146 and similar vert designs showing "Virgin and Child" by the artists named. Multicoloured. P 14.*

542	½ c. Type 146		10	10
543	1 c. Bellini		10	10
544	2 c. Mantegna		10	10
545	6 c. Mantegna (different)		10	10
546	25 c. Memling		15	10
547	45 c. Correggio		20	10
548	$3 Raphael		1·00	1·00
542/8		Set of 7	1·40	1·10
MS549	140 × 85 mm. 50 c. as No. 547 and $1 as No. 548		1·00	1·10

(Des G. Drummond. Litho Questa)

1976 (22 Nov). *National Day. T 147 and similar horiz designs. Multicoloured. P 13½.*

550	10 c. Type 147		10	10
551	50 c. Harvesting bananas		15	10
552	$1 Boxing plant		30	35
550/2		Set of 3	45	45
MS553	96 × 122 mm. Nos. 550/2		50	90

148 American Giant Sundial (Architectonica nobilis)   *149 The Queen Crowned and Enthroned*

(Des J.W. Litho Questa)

1976 (20 Dec). *Shells. T 148 and similar vert designs. Multicoloured. P 14.*

554	½ c. Type 148		10	10
555	1 c. Flame Helmet (Cassis flammea)		10	10
556	2 c. Mouse Cone (Conus mus)		10	10
557	20 c. Caribbean Vase (Vasum muricatum)		45	10
558	40 c. West Indian Fighting Conch (Strombus pugilis)		70	25
559	50 c. Short Coral Shell (Coralliophila abbreviata)		70	25
560	$3 Apple Murex (Murex pomum)		3·50	2·75
554/60		Set of 7	5·00	3·00
MS561	101×55 mm. $2 Long-spined Star Shell (Astraea phoebia)		2·50	3·00

(Des J.W. Litho Questa)

1977 (7 Feb). *Silver Jubilee. T 149 and similar horiz designs. Multicoloured. P 14 × 13½.*

562	½ c. Type 149		10	10
563	1 c. Imperial State Crown		10	10
564	45 c. Queen Elizabeth and Princess Anne		15	10
565	$2 Coronation Ring		25	30
566	$2.50, Ampulla and Spoon		30	40
562/6		Set of 5	60	70
MS567	104 × 79 mm. $5 Queen Elizabeth and Prince Philip		75	1·25

Nos. 562/6 also exist perf 12×11½ (Price for set of 5 50p mint or used) from additional sheetlets of 5 stamps and one label. Stamps perforated 14×13½ are from normal sheets of 40. Stamps from the sheets of 5 have the arch at left in a different colour.

150 Joseph Haydn   **151** Hiking

(Des J.W. Litho Questa)

1977 (25 Apr). *150th Death Anniv of Ludwig van Beethoven. T* **150** *and similar vert designs. Multicoloured. P* 14.

568	½ c. Type **150**		10	10
569	1 c. Scene from "Fidelio"		10	10
570	2 c. Maria Casentini (dancer)		10	10
571	15 c. Beethoven and pastoral scene		25	10
572	30 c. "Wellington's Victory"		35	10
573	40 c. Henriette Sontag (singer)		45	10
574	$2 The young Beethoven		1·50	2·00
568/74		*Set of 7*	2·25	2·25
MS575	138 × 93 mm. Nos. 572/4		2·00	3·25

(Des J.W. Litho Questa)

1977 (8 Aug). *Caribbean Scout Jamboree, Jamaica. T* **151** *and similar horiz designs. Multicoloured. P* 14.

576	½ c. Type **151**		10	10
577	1 c. First-aid		10	10
578	2 c. Camping		10	10
579	45 c. Rock climbing		35	15
580	50 c. Canoeing		40	20
581	$3 Sailing		2·00	1·75
576/81		*Set of 6*	2·50	2·00
MS582	111 × 113 mm. 75 c. Map reading and $2 Campfire singsong		1·60	1·75

ROYAL VISIT
W.I. 1977

152 Holy Family   **(153)**

(Des G. Vasarhelyi. Litho Questa)

1977 (17 Nov). *Christmas. T* **152** *and similar horiz designs showing book miniatures from Foix Book of Hours* ($3) *or De Lisle Psalter* (*others*). *Multicoloured. P* 14.

583	½ c. Type **152**		10	10
584	1 c. Angel and Shepherds		10	10
585	2 c. Holy Baptism		10	10
586	6 c. Flight into Egypt		15	10
587	15 c. Three Kings with gifts		15	10
588	45 c. Holy Family in the Temple		30	10
589	$3 Flight into Egypt (*different*)		1·25	1·10
583/9		*Set of 7*	1·75	1·40
MS590	113 × 85 mm. 50 c. Virgin and Child; $2 Flight into Egypt (*different*)		60	75

1977 (28 Nov). *Royal Visit. Nos. 562/7 optd with T* **153**. A. *In top left-hand corner**. P 14 × 13½. B. *Above* "JUBILEE". *P* 12 × 11½.

		A.		B.	
591	½ c. Type **149**		†	10	10
592	1 c. Imperial State Crown		†	10	10
593	45 c. Queen Elizabeth and Princess Anne	15	10	15	10
594	$2 Coronation Ring	30	30	45	55
595	$2.50, Ampulla and Spoon	35	35	50	70
591/5		*Set of 5*	†	1·00	1·40
MS596	104 × 79 mm. $5 Queen Elizabeth and Prince Philip	1·00	1·50	†	
	a. Optd "W.I. 1977" only on stamp	12·00	15·00	†	

*Stamp from No. **MS596** has the overprint to left of face-value.

No. **MS596a** is overprinted "W.I. 1977" beneath "ROYAL VISIT" inscription to left of stamp design. Overprint as T **153**, but in one line, appears at top left of *miniature sheet*.

154 "Sousouelle Souris"

(Des L. Honychurch and J.W. Litho Questa)

1978 (9 Jan). *"History of Carnival". T* **154** *and similar horiz designs. Multicoloured. P* 14.

597	½ c. Type **154**		10	10
598	1 c. Sensay costume		10	10
599	2 c. Street musicians		10	10
600	45 c. Douiette band		15	10
601	50 c. Pappy Show wedding		15	10
602	$2 Masquerade band		45	60
597/602		*Set of 6*	75	75
MS603	104 × 88 mm. $2.50 as No. 602		60	85

---

155 Col. Charles Lindbergh and Ryan NYP Special *Spirit of St. Louis*   **156** Queen receiving Homage

(Des G. Drummond. Litho Format)

1978 (13 Mar). *Aviation Anniversaries. T* **155** *and similar horiz designs. Multicoloured. P* 14½.

604	6 c. Type **155**		20	10
605	10 c. Ryan NYP Special *Spirit of St. Louis*, New York, 20 May 1927		25	10
606	15 c. Lindbergh and map of Atlantic		35	10
607	20 c. Lindbergh reaches Paris, 21 May 1927		45	10
608	40 c. Airship LZ-1, Lake Constance, 1900		55	20
609	60 c. Count F. von Zeppelin and airship LZ-2, 1906		65	30
610	$3 Airship LZ-127 *Graf Zeppelin*, 1928		1·40	1·10
604/10		*Set of 7*	3·50	1·75
MS611	139×108 mm. 50 c. Ryan NYP Special *Spirit of St. Louis* in mid-Atlantic; $2 Airship LZ-127 *Graf Zeppelin*, 1928		80	1·10

The 6, 10, 15, 20 and 50 c. values commemorate the 50th anniversary of first solo transatlantic flight by Col. Charles Lindbergh; the other values commemorate anniversaries of various Zeppelin airships.

No. **MS611** exists imperforate from stock dispersed by the liquidator of Format International Security Printers Ltd.

(Des J.W. Litho Questa)

1978 (2 June). *25th Anniv of Coronation. T* **156** *and similar vert designs. Multicoloured. P* 14.

612	45 c. Type **156**		15	10
613	$2 Balcony scene		30	30
614	$2.50, Queen and Prince Philip		40	40
612/14		*Set of 3*	75	75
MS615	76 × 107 mm. $5 Queen Elizabeth II		75	75

Nos. 612/14 also exist perf 12 (*Price for set of 3* 75p *mint or used*) from additional sheetlets of 3 stamps and 1 label. Stamps perforated 14 come from sheets of 50. The stamps from sheetlets have changed background or inscription colours.

157 Wright Flyer III   **158** "Two Apostles" (Rubens)

(Des G. Vasarhelyi. Litho Format)

1978 (10 July). *75th Anniv of Powered Flight. T* **157** *and similar horiz designs. Multicoloured. P* 14½.

616	30 c. Type **157**		15	15
617	40 c. Wright Type A, 1908		20	20
618	60 c. Flyer I		25	25
619	$2 Flyer I (*different*)		85	85
616/19		*Set of 4*	1·25	1·25
MS620	116×89 mm. $3 Wilbur and Orville Wright		90	1·00

Nos. 616/20 exist imperforate from stock dispersed by the liquidator of Format International Security Printers Ltd.

(Des BG Studio. Litho Questa)

1978 (16 Oct). *Christmas. Paintings. T* **158** *and similar vert designs. Multicoloured. P* 14.

621	20 c. Type **158**		10	10
622	45 c. "The Descent from the Cross" (Rubens)		15	10
623	50 c. "St Ildefonso receiving the Chasuble" (Rubens)		15	10
624	$3 "The Assumption of the Virgin" (Rubens)		35	80
621/4		*Set of 4*	60	90
MS625	113 × 83 mm. $2 "The Holy Family" (Sebastiano del Piombo*)		75	75

*This painting was incorrectly attributed to Rubens on the stamp.

INDEPENDENT

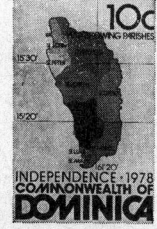

INDEPENDENCE 3rd NOVEMBER 1978

159 Map showing Parishes   **(160)**

(Des J.W. Litho Questa)

1978 (3 Nov). *Independence. T* **159** *and similar vert designs. Multicoloured. P* 14.

626	10 c. Type **159**		30	10
627	25 c. *Sabinea carinalis* (National flower)		35	10
628	45 c. New National flag		40	15
629	50 c. Coat of arms		40	20
630	$2 Patrick John (Prime Minister)		50	1·25
626/30		*Set of 5*	1·75	1·60
MS631	113 × 90 mm. $2.50, Type **159**		1·00	1·25

1978 (3 Nov)–79. *Independence. Nos. 490/507* (10 c. *now perf* 13½) *optd as T* **160** *by typography.*

632	½ c. Type **141**		40	10
633	1 c. African Tulip		45	10
634	2 c. Castor Oil Tree		45	10
635	3 c. White Cedar Flower		50	15
636	4 c. Egg Plant		50	15
637	5 c. Needlefish		50	15
638	6 c. Ochro		50	15
639	8 c. Zenaida Dove		1·75	20
640	10 c. Screw Pine		50	10
	a. Perf 14½. Litho opt (7.79)		1·00	45
641	20 c. Mango Longue		60	15
642	25 c. Crayfish		70	20
643	30 c. Common Opossum		70	20
644	40 c. Bay Leaf Groves		70	25
	a. Litho opt (7.79)		70	40
645	50 c. Tomatoes		80	30
646	$1 Lime Factory		80	65
647	$2 Rum Distillery		1·00	1·00
648	$5 Bay Oil Distillery		1·75	2·25
649	$10 Queen Elizabeth II		2·25	4·50
	a. Litho opt (7.79)		2·75	6·50
632/49		*Set of 18*	13·00	10·00

For History of Aviation gold foil stamps see Appendix at the end of the Dominica listing.

161 Sir Rowland Hill   **162** Children and Canoe

(Des BG Studio. Litho Questa)

1979 (19 Mar). *Death Centenary of Sir Rowland Hill. T* **161** *and similar vert designs. P* 14.

650	25 c. multicoloured		10	10
651	45 c. multicoloured		15	10
652	50 c. black, reddish violet and magenta		15	10
653	$2 black, magenta and yellow		35	65
650/3		*Set of 4*	65	80
MS654	186 × 96 mm. $5 black and vermilion		1·00	1·25

Designs:—45 c. Great Britain 1840 2d. blue; 50 c. 1874 1d. stamp; $2 Maltese Cross cancellations; $5 Penny Black.

Nos. 650/3 also exist perf 12 (*Price for set of 4* 80p *mint or used*) from additional sheetlets of 5 stamps and 1 label. Shades of these stamps differ from those perforated 14 which come from sheets of 40.

(Des BG Studio. Litho Questa)

1979 (23 Apr). *International Year of the Child. T* **162** *and similar horiz designs. Multicoloured. P* 14.

655	30 c. Type **162**		25	15
656	40 c. Children with bananas		25	25
657	50 c. Children playing cricket		1·25	80
658	$3 Child feeding rabbits		1·75	2·00
655/8		*Set of 4*	3·25	2·75
MS659	117 × 85 mm. $5 Child with catch of fish		1·00	1·50

163 Nassau Grouper

(Des G. Drummond. Litho Questa)

1979 (21 May). *Marine Wildlife. T* **163** *and similar horiz designs. Multicoloured. P* 14.

660	10 c. Type **163**		40	15
661	30 c. Striped Dolphin		70	35
662	50 c. White-tailed Tropic Bird		2·25	65
663	60 c. Brown Pelican		2·25	1·25
664	$1 Long-finned Pilot Whale		2·50	1·50
665	$2 Brown Booby		3·00	3·75
660/5		*Set of 6*	10·00	7·00
MS666	120 × 94 mm. $3 Elkhorn Coral		2·00	1·75

No. 661 is inscribed "SPOTTED DOLPHIN" in error.

164 H.M.S. *Endeavour*

1979 (16 July). *Death Bicentenary of Captain Cook. T* **164** *and similar horiz designs. Multicoloured. P* 14.
667	10 c. Type **164**	65	30
668	50 c. H.M.S. *Resolution* ..	1·10	90
669	60 c. H.M.S. *Discovery*	1·25	1·25
670	$2 Detail of Cook's chart of New Zealand, 1770	1·60	2·25
667/70	*Set of* 4	4·25	4·25
MS671	97 × 90 mm. $5 Captain Cook and signature	1·50	2·00

165 Cooking at Camp-fire

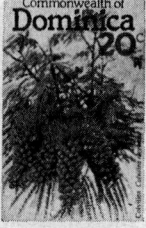

166 Colvillea

(Des M. Diamond. Litho Questa)

1979 (30 July). *50th Anniv of Girl Guide Movement in Dominica. T* **165** *and similar horiz designs. Multicoloured. P* 14.
672	10 c. Type **165**	25	10
673	20 c. Pitching emergency rain tent	30	10
674	50 c. Raising Dominican flag ..	45	10
675	$2.50, Singing and dancing to accordion	1·25	80
672/5 ..	*Set of* 4	2·00	85
MS676	110 × 86 mm. $3 Guides of different age-groups	75	1·25

(Des J.W. Litho Questa)

1979 (3 Sept). *Flowering Trees. T* **166** *and similar vert designs. Multicoloured. P* 14.
677	20 c. Type **166**	15	10
678	40 c. Lignum Vitae	20	15
679	60 c. Dwarf Poinciana ..	30	25
680	$2 Fern Tree	70	90
677/80	*Set of* 4	1·25	1·25
MS681	114 × 89 mm. $3 Perfume Tree ..	75	1·10

167 Cathedral of the Assumption, Roseau

(Des W. Grout. Litho Questa)

1979 (11 Oct). *Christmas. Cathedrals. T* **167** *and similar multicoloured designs. P* 14.
682	6 c. Type **167**	10	10
683	45 c. St. Paul's, London (*vert*) ..	15	10
684	60 c. St. Peter's, Rome	15	10
685	$3 Notre Dame, Paris (*vert*)..	55	60
682/5 ..	*Set of* 4	75	70
MS686	113 × 85 mm. 40 c. St. Patrick's, New York; $2 Cologne Cathedral (*both vert*) ..	50	80

HURRICANE RELIEF

(168)

169 Mickey Mouse and Octopus playing Xylophone

1979 (29 Oct). *Hurricane Relief. Nos.* 495, 502 *and* 506/7 *optd as T* **168**.
687	5 c. Gare	10	10
688	40 c. Bay Leaf Groves	10	10
689	$5 Bay Oil Distillery	1·00	1·25
690	$10 Queen Elizabeth II	1·25	1·75
687/90	*Set of* 4	2·25	2·75

(Litho Format)

1979 (2 Nov). *International Year of the Child. Walt Disney Cartoon Characters. T* **169** *and similar vert designs showing characters playing musical instruments. Multicoloured. P* 11.
691	½ c. Type **169**	10	10
692	1 c. Goofy playing guitar on rocking-horse ..	10	10
693	2 c. Mickey Mouse playing violin and Goofy playing bagpipes..	10	10
694	3 c. Donald Duck playing drum with pneumatic drill	10	10
695	4 c. Minnie Mouse playing saxophone on roller-skates	10	10
696	5 c. Goofy as one-man-band ..	10	10
697	10 c. Dale being blown from French horn by Horace Horsecollar ..	10	10
698	$2 Huey, Dewey and Louie playing bass	2·00	2·00

699	$2.50, Donald Duck playing piano and Huey playing trumpet	2·00	2·25
691/9	*Set of* 9	4·00	4·25
MS700	127 × 102 mm. $3 Mickey Mouse playing piano. P 13½	2·50	3·00

170 Hospital Ward

(Des BG Studio. Litho Questa)

1980 (31 Mar). *75th Anniv of Rotary International. T* **170** *and similar horiz designs. Multicoloured. P* 14.
701	10 c. Type **170**	10	10
702	20 c. Electric-cardiogram ..	15	10
703	40 c. Site for mental hospital ..	20	15
704	$2.50, Paul P. Harris (founder) ..	55	90
701/4 ..	*Set of* 4	80	1·10
MS705	128 × 113 mm. $3 Interlocking cogs of Rotary emblem and globe.. ..	60	80

1980 (6 May). *"London 1980" International Stamp Exhibition. As Nos.* 650/3 *optd with T* **262** *of Grenada. P* 12.
706	25 c. multicoloured	25	10
707	45 c. multicoloured	30	15
708	50 c. olive-brown, blue and rose-red ..	30	15
709	$2 olive-brown, vermilion and yellow	80	60
706/9 ..	*Set of* 4	1·50	80

171 Shot Putting

(Des J.W. Litho Questa)

1980 (27 May). *Olympic Games, Moscow. T* **171** *and similar horiz designs. Multicoloured. P* 14.
710	30 c. Type **171**	25	10
711	40 c. Basketball	60	15
712	60 c. Swimming	45	20
713	$2 Gymnastics	80	65
710/13	*Set of* 4	1·90	90
MS714	114 × 86 mm. $3 The Marathon ..	70	90

172 "Supper at Emmaus" (Caravaggio)

(Des J.W. Litho Questa)

1980 (22 July). *Famous Paintings. T* **172** *and similar multicoloured designs. P* 13½.
715	20 c. Type **172**	20	10
716	25 c. "Portrait of Charles I Hunting" (Van Dyck) (*vert*) ..	20	10
717	30 c. "The Maids of Honour" (Velasquez) (*vert*)	25	10
718	45 c. "The Rape of the Sabine Women" (Poussin) ..	25	10
719	$1 "Embarkation for Cythera" (Watteau) ..	50	35
720	$5 "Girl before a Mirror" (Picasso) (*vert*)	1·40	1·50
715/20	*Set of* 6	2·50	2·00
MS721	114 × 111 mm. $3 "The Holy Family" (Rembrandt) (*vert*).. ..	60	80

173 Scene from "Peter Pan"

(Litho Walsall)

1980 (1 Oct). *Christmas. Scenes from Walt Disney's Cartoon Film "Peter Pan". T* **173** *and similar horiz designs. P* 11.
722	½ c. multicoloured	10	10
723	1 c. multicoloured	10	10
724	2 c. multicoloured	10	10
725	3 c. multicoloured	10	10
726	4 c. multicoloured	10	10
727	5 c. multicoloured	10	10
728	10 c. multicoloured	10	10
729	$2 multicoloured	2·25	1·50
730	$2.50, multicoloured	2·25	1·75
722/30	*Set of* 9	4·50	3·25
MS731	124 × 98 mm. $4 multicoloured (*vert*) ..	3·50	3·50

174 Queen Elizabeth the Queen Mother in Doorway

(Litho Questa)

1980 (20 Oct). *80th Birthday of Queen Elizabeth the Queen Mother. P* 12.
732	**174** 40 c. multicoloured	25	15
	a. Perf 14	15	15
733	$2.50, multicoloured	65	60
	a. Perf 14	45	60
MS734	85×66 mm. **174** $3 multicoloured	75	2·00

Stamps perforated 12 are from normal sheets of 50. Those perforated 14 come either from similar sheets or from sheetlets of nine with inscribed sheet margins.

175 Douglas Bay

(Des G. Drummond. Litho Questa)

1981 (12 Feb). *Dominica Safari. T* **175** *and similar multicoloured designs. P* 14.
735	20 c. Type **175**	10	10
736	30 c. Valley of Desolation ..	10	10
737	40 c. Emerald Pool (*vert*) ..	10	10
738	$3 Indian River (*vert*)	75	1·10
735/8 ..	*Set of* 4	85	1·25
MS739	84 × 104 mm. $4 Trafalgar Falls (*vert*)	1·10	1·40

(Litho Format)

1981 (30 Apr). *50th Anniv of Walt Disney's Cartoon Character, Pluto. Vert designs as T* **169**. *Multicoloured. P* 13½ × 14.
740	$2 Pluto and Fifi	1·25	1·50
MS741	128 × 102 mm. $4 Pluto in scene from film *Pluto's Blue Note*	2·40	2·75

COMMONWEALTH OF DOMINICA

176 Forest Thrush

177 Windsor Castle

(Des P. Barrett. Litho Questa)

1981 (30 Apr). *Birds. T* **176** *and similar horiz designs. Multicoloured. P* 14.
742	20 c. Type **176**	55	30
743	30 c. Wied's Crested Flycatcher ..	65	35
744	40 c. Blue-hooded Euphonia ..	75	45
745	$5 Lesser Antillean Pewee	3·50	4·75
742/5 ..	*Set of* 4	5·00	5·25
MS746	121 × 95 mm. $3 Imperial Amazon ..	2·50	1·75

(Des J.W. Litho Questa)

1981 (23 June). *Royal Wedding. T* **177** *and similar vert designs. Multicoloured. A. P* 14. *B. P* 12.
	A		B	
747	45 c. Prince Charles and Lady Diana Spencer	10	10	40	65
748	60 c. Type **177** ..	15	15	40	65
749	$4 Prince Charles as helicopter pilot	50	75	40	65
747/9 ..	*Set of* 3	65	85	1·10	1·75
MS750	96×82 mm. $5 Westland HU Mk 5 Wessex helicopter of Queen's Flight	85	90		†

Nos. 747B/9B also exist from additional sheetlets of five stamps and one label with changed background colours.

178 Lady Diana Spencer   **179** Ixora

(Manufactured by Walsall)

1981 (23 June). *Royal Wedding. Booklet stamps.* T **178** *and similar vert designs. Multicoloured. Roul 5 × imperf*. Self-adhesive.*

751	25 c. Type **178**	20	35
	a. Booklet pane. Nos. 751/2, each × 3	2·50	
752	$2 Prince Charles	70	1·00
753	$5 Prince Charles and Lady Diana Spencer	1·75	2·50
	a. Booklet pane of 1.	1·75	
751/3	*Set of 3*	2·40	3·50

*The 25 c. and $2 values were separated by various combinations of rotary knife (giving a straight edge) and roulette. The $5 value exists only with straight edges.

(Litho Questa)

1981 (2 Nov). *Christmas. Horiz designs as* T **169** *showing scenes from Walt Disney's cartoon film "Santa's Workshop". P* 13½.

754	½ c. multicoloured	10	10
755	1 c. multicoloured	10	10
756	2 c. multicoloured	10	10
757	3 c. multicoloured	10	10
758	4 c. multicoloured	15	10
759	5 c. multicoloured	15	10
760	10 c. multicoloured	20	10
761	45 c. multicoloured	1·50	30
762	$5 multicoloured	4·25	4·50
754/62	*Set of 9*	5·75	4·75
MS763	129 × 103 mm. $4 multicoloured	4·00	3·50

(Des P. Barrett. Litho Questa)

1981 (1 Dec)–**85**. *Plant·Life. Horiz designs as* T **179**. *Multicoloured. A. Without imprint date. P* 14

764A	1 c. Type **179**	10	50
765A	2 c. Flamboyant	10	50
766A	4 c. Poinsettia	15	40
767A	5 c. Bois Caribe (national flower of Dominica)	15	20
768A	8 c. Annatto or Roucou	20	20
769A	10 c. Passion Fruit	30	10
770A	15 c. Breadfruit or Yampain	55	15
771A	20 c. Allamanda or Buttercup	40	15
772A	25 c. Cashew Nut	40	15
773A	35 c. Soursop or Couassol	45	30
774A	40 c. Bougainvillea	45	30
775A	45 c. Anthurium	50	35
776A	60 c. Cacao or Cocoa	1·25	70
777A	90 c. Pawpaw Tree or Papay	70	1·00
778A	$1 Coconut Palm	1·50	1·00
779A	$2 Coffee Tree or Café	1·00	2·75
780A	$5 Heliconia or Lobster Claw	3·50	9·50
781A	$10 Banana/Fig	4·75	13·00
764A/81A	*Set of 18*	15·00	27·00

B. *With imprint date at foot of design. P* 14 (15, 60 c.) *or* 12 (*others*)

769B	10 c. Passion Fruit (1984)	85	30
	a. Perf 14 (7.85)	1·00	60
770B	15 c. Breadfruit or Yampain (7.85)	2·25	80
776B	60 c. Cacao or Cocoa (7.85)	3·50	1·75
778B	$1 Coconut Palm (1984)	1·25	1·50
780B	$5 Heliconia or Lobster Claw (1984)	3·25	5·00
781B	$10 Banana Fig (1984)	5·00	9·50
769B/81B	*Set of 6*	14·50	17·00

Imprint dates: "1984", Nos. 769B, 778B, 780B, 781B; "1985", Nos. 769Ba, 770B, 776B, 780B.

180 Curb slope for Wheelchairs

181 "Olga Picasso in an Armchair"

(Des BG Studio. Litho Format)

1981 (22 Dec). *International Year for Disabled Persons.* T **180** *and similar vert designs. Multicoloured. P* 14½.

782	45 c. Type **180**	55	25
783	60 c. Bus with invalid step	60	35
784	75 c. Motor car controls adapted for handicapped	70	40
785	$4 Bus with wheelchair ramp	2·00	2·50
782/5	*Set of 4*	3·50	3·25
MS786	82 × 96 mm. $5 Specially designed elevator control panel	4·25	3·00

(Des J.W. Litho Format)

1981 (30 Dec). *Birth Centenary of Picasso.* T **181** *and similar vert designs. Multicoloured. P* 14½.

787	45 c. Type **181**	65	25
788	60 c. "Bathers"	75	50
789	75 c. "Woman in Spanish Costume"	80	60
790	$4 "Detail of Dog and Cock"	1·75	3·00
787/90	*Set of 4*	3·50	4·00
MS791	140 × 115 mm. $5 "Sleeping Peasants" (detail)	4·00	3·50

(Litho Questa)

1982 (29 Jan). *World Cup Football Championship, Spain. Walt Disney Cartoon Characters. Horiz designs as* T **169**. *Multicoloured. P* 14 × 13½.

792	½ c. Goofy chasing ball with butterfly net	10	10
793	1 c. Donald Duck with ball in beak	10	10
794	2 c. Goofy as goalkeeper	10	10
795	3 c. Goofy looking for ball	10	10
796	4 c. Goofy as park attendant puncturing ball with litter spike	10	10

797	5 c. Pete and Donald Duck playing	10	10
798	10 c. Donald Duck after kicking rock instead of ball	15	10
799	60 c. Donald Duck feeling effects of a hard game and Daisy Duck dusting ball	1·50	1·25
800	$5 Goofy hiding ball under his jersey from Mickey Mouse	5·50	5·50
792/800	*Set of 9*	6·75	6·50
MS801	132 × 105 mm. $4 Dale making off with ball	3·75	3·25

182 "Gone Fishing"

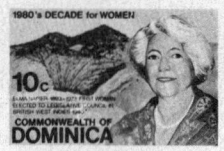

183 Elma Napier (first woman elected to B.W.I. Legislative Council)

(Des M.B.I. Studios. Litho Questa)

1982 (10 Mar). *Norman Rockwell (painter) Commemoration.* T **182** *and similar vert designs. Multicoloured. P* 14 × 13½.

802	10 c. Type **182**	10	10
803	25 c. "Breakfast"	15	10
804	45 c. "The Marbles Champ"	30	30
805	$1 "Speeding Along"	55	55
802/5	*Set of 4*	95	95

No. 802 is inscribed "Golden Days" and No. 803 "The Morning News".

(Des BG Studio. Litho Questa)

1982 (15 Apr). *Decade for Women.* T **183** *and similar horiz designs. Multicoloured. P* 14.

806	10 c. Type **183**	10	10
807	45 c. Margaret Mead (anthropologist)	30	30
808	$1 Mabel ("Cissy") Caudeiron (folk song composer and historian)	55	55
809	$4 Eleanor Roosevelt	2·25	2·25
806/9	*Set of 4*	2·75	2·75
MS810	92 × 63 mm. $3 Florence Nightingale	2·00	3·00

184 George Washington and Independence Hall, Philadelphia

185 *Anaea dominicana*

(Des J.W. Litho Format)

1982 (1 May). *250th Birth Anniv of George Washington* (45, 90 c.) *and Birth Centenary of Franklin D. Roosevelt* (60 c., $2). T **184** *and similar horiz designs. Multicoloured. P* 14½.

811	45 c. Type **184**	40	25
812	60 c. Franklin D. Roosevelt and Capitol, Washington D.C.	50	35
813	90 c. Washington at Yorktown (detail, "The Surrender of Cornwallis" by Trumbull)	70	55
814	$2 Construction of dam (from W. Gropper's mural commemorating Roosevelt's "New Deal")	1·25	1·60
811/14	*Set of 4*	2·50	2·50
MS815	115 × 90 mm. $5 Washington and Roosevelt with U.S.A. flags of 1777 and 1933	3·75	3·25

Nos. 813 and MS815 exist imperforate from stock dispersed by the liquidator of Format International Security Printers Ltd.

(Des P. Barrett. Litho Questa)

1982 (1 June). *Butterflies.* T **185** *and similar vert designs. Multicoloured. P* 14.

816	15 c. Type **185**	1·25	35
817	45 c. *Heliconius charithonia*	2·25	65
818	60 c. *Hypolimnas misippus*	2·50	1·75
819	$3 *Biblis hyperia*	5·00	6·00
816/19	*Set of 4*	10·00	8·00
MS820	77 × 105 mm. $5 *Marpesia petreus*	7·00	5·00

186 Prince and Princess of Wales

187 Scouts around Campfire

(Des PAD Studio. Litho Questa)

1982 (1 July). *21st Birthday of Princess of Wales.* T **186** *and similar vert designs. Multicoloured. P* 14½ × 14.

821	45 c. Buckingham Palace	20	10
822	$2 Type **186**	50	70
823	$4 Princess of Wales	80	1·25
821/3	*Set of 3*	1·40	1·75
MS824	103 × 75 mm. $5 Princess Diana (*different*)	2·00	2·25

Nos. 821/3 also exist in sheetlets of 5 stamps and 1 label.

(Des R. Sauber. Litho Questa)

1982 (3 Aug). *75th Anniv of Boy Scout Movement.* T **187** *and similar multicoloured designs. P* 14.

825	45 c. Type **187**	1·25	50
826	60 c. Temperature study, Valley of Desolation	1·75	1·25
827	75 c. Learning about native birds	2·25	1·50
828	$3 Canoe trip along Indian River	4·25	5·50
825/8	*Set of 4*	8·50	8·00
MS829	99 × 70 mm. $5 Dominican scouts saluting the flag (*vert*)	2·75	3·25

1982 (30 Aug). *Birth of Prince William of Wales. Nos.* 821/4 *optd with* T **171** *of Antigua.*

830	45 c. Buckingham Palace	30	30
831	$2 Type **186**	80	1·10
832	$4 Princess of Wales	1·40	1·90
830/2	*Set of 3*	2·25	3·00
MS833	103 × 75 mm. $5 Princess Diana (*different*)	2·00	2·75

Nos. 830/2 also exist in sheetlets of 5 stamps and 1 label.

188 "Holy Family of Francis I"

189 Cuvier's Beaked Whale

(Des Design Images. Litho Questa)

1982 (3 Nov). *Christmas. Raphael Paintings.* T **188** *and similar vert designs. Multicoloured. P* 13½ × 14.

834	25 c. Type **188**	15	10
835	30 c. "Holy Family of the Pearl"	20	15
836	90 c. "Canigiani Holy Family"	55	55
837	$4 "Holy Family of the Oak Tree"	1·90	1·90
834/7	*Set of 4*	2·50	2·40
MS838	95 × 125 mm. $5 "Holy Family of the Lamb"	2·40	2·50

(Des J. Cooter. Litho Questa)

1983 (15 Feb). *Save the Whales.* T **189** *and similar horiz designs. Multicoloured. P* 14.

839	45 c. Type **189**	2·00	65
840	60 c. Humpback Whale	2·25	1·75
841	75 c. Black Right Whale	2·25	2·25
842	$3 Melon-headed Whale	4·50	6·50
839/42	*Set of 4*	10·00	10·00
MS843	99 × 72 mm. $5 Pygmy Sperm Whale	4·00	4·00

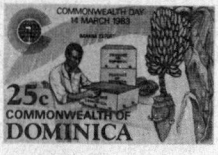

190 Banana Export

(Des R. Vigurs. Litho Questa)

1983 (14 Mar). *Commonwealth Day.* T **190** *and similar horiz designs. Multicoloured. P* 14.

844	25 c. Type **190**	15	15
845	30 c. Road building	15	20
846	90 c. Community nursing	40	45
847	$3 Tourism—handicrafts	1·00	1·50
844/7	*Set of 4*	1·50	2·10

191 Map and Satellite Picture of Hurricane

(Des G. Vasarhelyi. Litho Questa)

1983 (18 Apr). *World Communications Year.* T **191** *and similar horiz designs. Multicoloured. P* 14.

848	45 c. Type **191**	20	25
849	60 c. Aircraft-to-ship transmission	30	35
850	90 c. Satellite communications	40	45
851	$2 Shortwave radio	95	1·00
848/51	*Set of 4*	1·75	1·90
MS852	110 × 85 mm. $5 Communications satellite	2·50	2·75

192 Short-Mayo Composite

(Des W. Wright. Litho Format)

1983 (19 July). *Bicentenary of Manned Flight. T* **192** *and similar horiz designs. Multicoloured.* P 14½.
853	45 c. Type **192**		50	30
854	60 c. Macchi M.39 Schneider Trophy seaplane		75	85
855	90 c. Fairey Swordfish torpedo bomber		1·10	1·40
856	$4 Airship LZ-3		3·25	4·75
853/6		*Set of 4*	5·00	6·50
MS857	105×79 mm. $5 *Double Eagle II* (balloon)		1·50	2·75

Nos. 856/7 exist imperforate from stock dispersed by the liquidator of Format International Security Printers Ltd.

193 Duesenberg "SJ", 1935

(Des R. Sauber. Litho Questa)

1983 (1 Sept). *Classic Motor Cars. T* **193** *and similar horiz designs. Multicoloured.* P 14.
858	10 c. Type **193**		30	15
859	45 c. Studebaker "Avanti", 1962		50	25
860	60 c. Cord "812", 1936		60	35
861	75 c. MG "TC", 1945		65	50
862	90 c. Camaro "350 SS", 1967		75	60
863	$3 Porsch "356", 1948		1·50	1·60
858/63		*Set of 6*	3·75	3·00
MS864	110 × 75 mm. $5 *Ferrari* "312 T", 1975		2·50	2·75

194 "Charity"

(Des Design Images. Litho Format)

1983 (4 Oct). *Christmas. 500th Birth Anniv of Raphael. T* **194** *and similar horiz designs. Multicoloured.* P 13½.
865	45 c. Type **194**		50	30
866	60 c. "Hope"		60	50
867	90 c. "Faith"		80	60
868	$4 "The Cardinal Virtues"		2·00	3·00
865/8		*Set of 4*	3·50	4·00
MS869	101 × 127 mm. $5 "Justice"		2·00	2·75

Nos. 867 and MS869 exist imperforate from stock dispersed by the liquidator of Format International Security Printers Ltd.

195 Plumbeous Warbler   196 Donald Duck

(Des Jennifer Toombs. Litho Questa)

1984 (24 Apr). *Birds. T* **195** *and similar horiz designs. Multicoloured.* P 14.
870	5 c. Type **195**		1·40	70
871	45 c. Imperial Amazon		3·00	65
872	60 c. Blue-headed Hummingbird		3·25	2·75
873	90 c. Red-necked Amazon		4·00	5·00
870/3		*Set of 4*	10·50	8·00
MS874	72×72 mm. $5 *Greater Flamingos*		3·75	4·50

(Litho Format)

1984 (1 May). *Easter. T* **196** *and similar vert designs showing Disney cartoon characters and eggs. Multicoloured.* P 11.
875	½ c. Type **196**		10	10
876	1 c. Mickey Mouse		10	10
877	2 c. Tortoise and Hare		10	10
878	3 c. Brer Rabbit and Brer Bear		10	10
879	4 c. Donald Duck (*different*)		10	10
880	5 c. White Rabbit		10	10

881	10 c. Thumper		10	10
882	$2 Pluto		3·25	2·75
883	$4 Pluto (*different*)		4·50	4·00
875/83		*Set of 9*	7·50	6·50
MS884	126 × 100 mm. $5 *Chip and Dale.*			
	P 13½ × 14		3·50	4·00

197 Gymnastics   198 Atlantic Star

(Des R. Sauber. Litho Questa)

1984 (14 May). *Olympic Games, Los Angeles. T* **197** *and similar vert designs. Multicoloured.* P 14.
885	30 c. Type **197**		20	25
886	45 c. Javelin-throwing		30	35
887	60 c. High diving		40	45
888	$4 Fencing		2·00	2·50
885/8		*Set of 4*	2·50	3·25
MS889	104 × 85 mm. $5 *Equestrian event*		3·25	3·25

(Des W. Wright. Litho Questa)

1984 (14 June). *Shipping. T* **198** *and similar horiz designs. Multicoloured.* P 14.
890	45 c. Type **198**		1·75	75
891	60 c. Atlantic (liner)		2·00	1·75
892	90 c. Carib fishing boat		2·50	2·50
893	$4 Norway (liner)		6·00	8·00
890/3		*Set of 4*	11·00	11·50
MS894	106×79 mm. $5 *Santa Maria, 1492*		4·50	5·50

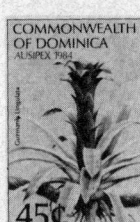

19th UPU
CONGRESS HAMBURG

(199)   200 *Guzmania lingulata*

1984 (19 June). *Universal Postal Union Congress, Hamburg.* Nos. 769A *and* 780A *optd with T* **199**.
895	10 c. Passion Fruit		10	10
896	$5 Heliconia or Lobster Claw		2·75	3·50

(Des P. Barrett. Litho Questa)

1984 (13 Aug). "Ausipex" International Stamp Exhibition, Melbourne. Bromilaids. T **200** and similar vert designs. Multicoloured. P 14.
897	45 c. Type **200**		30	35
898	60 c. Pitcairnia angustifolia		40	55
899	75 c. Tillandsia fasciculata		50	75
900	$3 Aechmea smithiorum		2·00	3·25
897/900		*Set of 4*	2·75	4·50
MS901	75 × 105 mm. $5 Tillandsia utriculata		2·75	4·25

201 "The Virgin and Child with   202 "Before the Start"
Young St John" (Correggio)   (Edgar Degas)

(Litho Format)

1984 (30 Oct). 450th Death Anniv of Correggio (painter). T **201** and similar vert designs. Multicoloured. P 15.
902	25 c. Type **201**		45	20
903	60 c. "Christ bids Farewell to the Virgin Mary"		80	40
904	90 c. "Do not Touch Me"		1·10	80
905	$4 "The Mystical Marriage of St Catherine"		2·50	3·25
902/5		*Set of 4*	4·25	4·25
MS906	89 × 60 mm. $5 "The Adoration of the Magi"		1·75	3·50

(Litho Format)

1984 (30 Oct). 150th Birth Anniv of Edgar Degas (painter). T **202** and similar multicoloured designs. P 15.
907	30 c. Type **202**		45	25
908	45 c. "Race on the Racecourse"		60	35
909	$1 "Jockeys at the Flagpole"		1·10	85
910	$3 "Racehorses at Longchamp"		2·50	3·00
907/10		*Set of 4*	4·25	4·00
MS911	89 × 60 mm. $5 "Self-portrait" (vert)		2·00	3·75

203 Tabby   204 Hawker
Siddeley H.S.748

(Des I. MacLaury. Litho Format)

1984 (12 Nov). Cats. T **203** and similar horiz designs. Multicoloured. P 15.
912	10 c. Type **203**		20	10
913	15 c. Calico Shorthair		25	10
914	20 c. Siamese		35	15
915	25 c. Manx		40	20
916	45 c. Abyssinian		65	30
917	60 c. Tortoise-shell Longhair		80	55
918	$1 Cornish Rex		1·40	90
919	$2 Persian		2·00	2·50
920	$3 Himalayan		2·75	3·75
921	$5 Burmese		3·75	6·50
912/21		*Set of 10*	11·50	13·50
MS922	105 × 75 mm. $5 Grey Burmese, Persian and American Shorthair		3·25	6·00

Nos. 912, 916 and MS922 exist imperforate from stock dispersed by the liquidator of Format International Security Printers Ltd.

(Des Bonny Redecker. Litho Questa)

1984 (26 Nov). 40th Anniv of International Civil Aviation Organisation. T **204** and similar vert designs. Multicoloured. P 14.
923	30 c. Type **204**		1·25	35
924	60 c. De Havilland D.H.C.6 Twin Otter 100		2·00	80
925	$1 Britten Norman Islander		2·25	1·40
926	$3 De Havilland D.H.C.6 Twin Otter 100 (*different*)		4·00	4·50
923/6		*Set of 4*	8·50	6·25
MS927	102×75 mm. $5 *Boeing 747-200*		3·25	3·50

205 Donald Duck, Mickey   206 Mrs. M. Bascom presenting
Mouse and Goofy with   Trefoil to Chief Guide Lady
Father Christmas   Baden-Powell

(Litho Questa)

1984 (30 Nov). Christmas. Walt Disney Cartoon Characters. T **205** and similar vert designs. Multicoloured. P 12 ($2) or 13½ × 14 (others).
928	45 c. Type **205**		1·25	30
929	60 c. Donald Duck as Father Christmas with toy train		1·50	70
930	90 c. Donald Duck as Father Christmas in sleigh		2·00	1·75
931	$2 Donald Duck and nephews in sledge		3·25	3·75
932	$4 Donald Duck in snow with Christmas tree		4·25	5·50
928/32		*Set of 5*	11·00	11·00
MS933	127 × 102 mm. $5 Donald Duck and nephews opening present		3·50	4·00

No. 931 was printed in sheetlets of 8 stamps.

(Des Marlise Najaka. Litho Questa)

1985 (28 Feb). 75th Anniv of Girl Guide Movement. T **206** and similar multicoloured designs. P 14.
934	35 c. Type **206**		60	30
935	45 c. Lady Baden-Powell inspecting Dominician Brownies		80	35
936	60 c. Lady Baden-Powell with Mrs. M. Bascom and Mrs. A. Robinson (Guide leaders)		1·00	65
937	$3 Lord and Lady Baden-Powell (vert)		2·50	3·25
934/7		*Set of 4*	4·50	4·00
MS938	77 × 105 mm. $5 Flags of Dominica and Girl Guide Movement		3·50	4·00

(Litho Questa)

1985 (4 Apr). Birth Bicentenary of John J. Audubon (ornithologist) (1st issue). Multicoloured designs as T **198** of Antigua showing original paintings. P 14.
939	45 c. Clapper Rail		1·10	80
940	$1 Black and White Warbler (vert)		2·00	1·10
941	$2 Broad-winged Hawk (vert)		2·75	2·50
942	$3 Ring-necked Duck		3·50	3·00
939/42		*Set of 4*	8·50	6·25
MS943	101 × 73 mm. $5 Reddish Egret		3·50	3·75

Nos. 939/42 were each printed in sheetlets of five stamps and one stamp-size label which appears in the centre of the bottom row.

See also Nos. 1013/17.

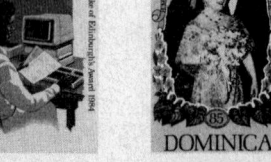

207 Student with Computer

208 The Queen Mother visiting Sadlers Wells Opera

(Des BG Studio. Litho Questa)

1985 (30 Apr). *Duke of Edinburgh's Award Scheme. T 207 and similar vert designs. Multicoloured. P 14.*

944	45 c. Type 207.		35	30
945	60 c. Assisting doctor in hospital		55	40
946	90 c. Two youths hiking		75	80
947	$4 Family jogging		2·75	3·50
944/7		Set of 4	4·00	4·50
MS948	100 × 98 mm. $5 Duke of Edinburgh		2·75	3·00

(Des J.W. Litho Questa)

1985 (15 July). *Life and Times of Queen Elizabeth the Queen Mother. T 208 and similar vert designs. Multicoloured. P 14.*

949	60 c. Type 208.		50	40
950	$1 Fishing in Scotland		70	60
951	$3 On her 84th birthday		1·90	2·00
949/51		Set of 3	2·75	2·75
MS952	56 × 85 mm. $5 Attending Garter ceremony, Windsor Castle		3·00	3·00

209 Cricket Match ("Sports")

210 Two Players competing for Ball

(Des S. Heinmann. Litho Questa)

1985 (22 July). *International Youth Year. T 209 and similar horiz designs. Multicoloured. P 14.*

953	45 c. Type 209.		3·50	1·50
954	60 c. Bird-watching ("Environmental Study")		3·75	2·25
955	$1 Stamp collecting ("Education")		4·00	3·25
956	$3 Boating ("Leisure")		5·50	7·50
953/6		Set of 4	15·00	13·00
MS957	96 × 65 mm. $5 Young people linking hands		2·75	4·00

(Des Susan David. Litho Questa)

1985 (2 Sept). *300th Birth Anniv of Johann Sebastian Bach (composer). Vert designs as T 206 of Antigua showing antique musical instruments. P 14.*

958	45 c. multicoloured		1·50	40
959	60 c. multicoloured		1·75	60
960	$1 multicoloured		2·25	1·00
961	$3 multicoloured		4·00	3·50
958/61		Set of 4	8·50	5·00
MS962	109 × 75 mm. $5 black		4·00	4·50

Designs:—45 c. Cornett; 60 c. Coiled trumpet; $1 Piccolo; $3 Violoncello piccolo; $5 Johann Sebastian Bach.

(Litho Format)

1985 (25 Oct). *Royal Visit. Multicoloured designs as T 207 of Antigua. P 14½.*

963	60 c. Flags of Great Britain and Dominica		1·00	70
964	$1 Queen Elizabeth II (*vert*)		1·25	1·75
965	$4 Royal Yacht *Britannia*		2·75	5·50
963/5		Set of 3	4·50	7·00
MS966	111 × 83 mm. $5 Map of Dominica		3·50	4·00

(Litho Questa)

1985 (11 Nov). *150th Birth Anniv of Mark Twain (author). Horiz designs as T 118 of Anguilla showing Walt Disney cartoon characters in scenes from "Tom Sawyer". Multicoloured. P 14 × 13½.*

967	20 c. "The glorious whitewasher"		65	30
968	60 c. "Aunt Polly's home dentistry".		1·25	75
969	$1 "Aunt Polly's pain killer"		1·75	1·25
970	$1.50, Mickey Mouse balancing on fence		2·25	3·00
971	$2 "Lost in the cave with Becky".		2·75	3·50
967/71		Set of 5	7·75	8·00
MS972	126 × 101 mm. $5 Mickey Mouse as pirate		5·50	6·50

(Des Walt Disney Productions. Litho Questa)

1985 (11 Nov). *Birth Bicentenaries of Grimm Brothers (folklorists). Horiz designs as T 119 of Anguilla showing Walt Disney cartoon characters in scenes from "Little Red Cap". Multicoloured. P 14 × 13½.*

973	10 c. Little Red Cap (Daisy Duck) meeting the Wolf		30	20
974	45 c. The Wolf at the door		85	30
975	90 c. The Wolf in Grandmother's bed		1·75	1·75
976	$1 The Wolf lunging at Little Red Cap		2·00	1·75

977	$3 The Woodsman (Donald Duck) chasing the Wolf		3·75	5·00
973/7		Set of 5	7·75	8·00
MS978	126 × 101 mm. $5 The Wolf falling into cooking pot		5·00	5·50

(Litho Format)

1985 (27 Nov). *40th Anniv of United Nations Organization. Horiz designs as T 208 of Antigua showing United Nations (New York) stamps. Multicoloured. P 14½.*

979	45 c. Lord Baden-Powell and 1984 International Youth Year 35 c.		70	50
980	$2 Maimonides (physician) and 1966 W.H.O Building 11 c.		3·00	3·25
981	$3 Sir Rowland Hill (postal reformer) and 1976 25th anniv of U.N. Postal Administration 13 c.		3·00	3·50
979/81		Set of 3	6·00	6·50
MS982	110 × 85 mm. $5 "Apollo" spacecraft		2·75	3·25

(Des J. Iskowitz. Litho Questa)

1986 (26 Mar). *World Cup Football Championship, Mexico. T 210 and similar vert designs. Multicoloured. P 14.*

983	45 c. Type 210.		1·75	40
984	60 c. Player heading ball		2·00	1·50
985	$1 Two players competing for ball (*different*)		2·25	1·75
986	$3 Player with ball		4·50	6·00
983/6		Set of 4	9·50	8·75
MS987	114 × 84 mm. $5 Three players		8·00	10·00

211 Police in Rowing Boat pursuing River Pirates, 1890

(Des J. Iskowitz. Litho Questa)

1986 (27 Mar). *Centenary of Statue of Liberty. T 211 and similar multicoloured designs. P 14.*

988	15 c. Type 211.		1·50	65
989	25 c. Police patrol launch, 1986		2·00	85
990	45 c. Hoboken Ferry Terminal, c 1890		2·00	85
991	$4 Holland Tunnel entrance and staff, 1986		4·50	6·00
988/91		Set of 4	9·00	7·50
MS992	104 × 76 mm. $5 Statue of Liberty (*vert*)		5·50	6·50

(Des W. Hanson. Litho Questa)

1986 (17 Apr). *Appearance of Halley's Comet (1st issue). Horiz designs as T 123 of Anguilla. Multicoloured. P 14.*

993	5 c. Nasir al Din al Tusi (Persian astronomer) and Jantal Mantar Observatory, Delhi		15	15
994	10 c. Bell XS-1 Rocket Plane breaking sound barrier for first time, 1947		20	15
995	45 c. Halley's Comet of 1531 (from "Astronomicum Caesareum", 1540)		55	30
996	$4 Mark Twain and quotation, 1910		2·75	3·75
993/6		Set of 4	3·25	4·00
MS997	104 × 71 mm. $5 Halley's Comet over Dominica		3·00	3·50

See also Nos. 1032/6.

(Des and litho Questa)

1986 (5 May). *60th Birthday of Queen Elizabeth II. Vert designs as T 125 of Anguilla. P 14.*

998	2 c. multicoloured		10	15
999	$1 multicoloured		70	80
1000	$4 multicoloured		2·00	3·00
998/1000		Set of 3	2·50	3·50
MS1001	120 × 85mm. $5 black and grey-brown		2·75	3·75

Designs:—2 c. Wedding photograph, 1947; $1 Queen meeting Pope John Paul II, 1982; $4 Queen on royal visit, 1971; $5 Princess Elizabeth with corgis, 1936.

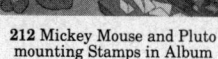

212 Mickey Mouse and Pluto mounting Stamps in Album

213 William I

(Des Walt Disney Productions. Litho Format)

1986 (22 May). *"Ameripex" International Stamp Exhibition, Chicago. T 212 and similar horiz designs showing Walt Disney cartoon characters. Multicoloured. P 11.*

1002	15 c. Type 212		60	40
1003	45 c. Donald Duck examining stamp under magnifying glass		80	65
1004	60 c. Chip n'Dale soaking and drying stamps		1·10	1·50
1005	$4 Donald Duck as scoutmaster awarding merit badges to Nephews		3·50	6·00
1002/5		Set of 4	5·50	7·75
MS1006	127 × 101 mm. $5 Uncle Scrooge conducting stamp auction. P 14 × 13½		5·00	8·00

No. 1003 exists imperforate from stock dispersed by the liquidator of Format International Security Printers Ltd.

(Des Mary Walters. Litho Questa)

1986 (9 June). *500th Anniv of Succession of House of Tudor to English Throne (1985). T 213 and similar vert designs. Multicoloured. P 14.*

1007	10 c. Type 213		40	40
1008	40 c. Richard II		80	80
1009	50 c. Henry VIII		90	90
1010	$1 Charles II		1·75	1·75
1011	$2 Queen Anne		2·75	3·00
1012	$4 Queen Victoria		3·75	4·50
1007/12		Set of 6	9·25	10·00

Nos. 1007/12 were each issued in sheetlets of five stamps and one stamp-size label showing the monarch's consort.

(Litho Questa)

1986 (18 June). *Birth Bicentenary of John J. Audubon (ornithologist) (1985) (2nd issue). Multicoloured designs as T 198 of Antigua showing original paintings. P 12½ × 12 (25 c., $4) or 12 × 12½ (others).*

1013	25 c. Black-throated Diver		1·50	50
1014	60 c. Great Blue Heron (*vert*)		2·00	1·50
1015	90 c. Yellow-crowned Night Heron (*vert*)		2·00	2·25
1016	$4 Common Shoveler		4·50	6·50
1013/16		Set of 4	9·00	9·75
MS1017	73 × 103 mm. $5 Canada Goose. P 14		10·00	12·00

Nos. 1013/16 were each issued in sheetlets of five stamps and one stamp-size label, which appears in the centre of the bottom row.

(Litho Questa)

1986 (1 July). *Royal Wedding. Vert designs as T 213 of Antigua. Multicoloured. P 14.*

1018	45 c. Prince Andrew and Miss Sarah Ferguson		35	30
1019	60 c. Prince Andrew.		45	45
1020	$4 Prince Andrew climbing aboard aircraft		2·00	2·75
1018/20		Set of 3	2·50	3·25
MS1021	88 × 88 mm. $5 Prince Andrew and Miss Sarah Ferguson (*different*)		3·50	4·50

1986 (15 Sept). *World Cup Football Championship Winners, Mexico. Nos. 983/7 optd with T 216 of Antigua in gold.*

1022	45 c. Type 210		1·50	55
1023	60 c. Player heading ball		1·75	1·50
1024	$1 Two players competing for ball		2·25	2·50
1025	$3 Player with ball		5·00	7·00
1022/5		Set of 4	9·50	10·50
MS1026	114 × 84 mm. $5 Three players.		8·50	11·00

214 "The Virgin at Prayer"

215 Broad-winged Hawk

(Litho Questa)

1986 (2 Dec). *Christmas. Paintings by Dürer. T 214 and similar vert designs. Multicoloured. P 14.*

1027	45 c. Type 214		1·00	35
1028	60 c. "Madonna and Child"		1·50	1·25
1029	$1 "The Madonna with the Pear"		2·00	2·25
1030	$3 "Madonna and Child with St. Anne"		5·50	7·50
1027/30		Set of 4	9·00	10·00
MS1031	76 × 102 mm. $5 "The Nativity"		8·00	10·00

1986 (16 Dec). *Appearance of Halley's Comet (2nd issue). Nos. 993/7 optd as T 218 of Antigua (in silver on $5).*

1032	5 c. Nasir al Din al Tusi (Persian astronomer) and Jantal Mantar Observatory, Delhi		15	15
1033	10 c. Bell XS-1 Rocket Plane breaking sound barrier for first time, 1947		20	15
1034	45 c. Halley's Comet of 1531 (from "Astronomicum Caesareum", 1540)		55	30
1035	$4 Mark Twain and quotation, 1910		2·75	3·50
1032/5		Set of 4	3·25	3·75
MS1036	104 × 71 mm. $5 Halley's Comet over Dominica		3·25	3·50

(Des S. Heinmann. Litho Format)

1987 (20 Jan). *Birds of Dominica. T 215 and similar vert designs. Multicoloured. Without imprint date. P 15.*

1037	1 c. Type 215		10	40
1038	2 c. Ruddy Quail Dove		10	40
1039	5 c. Red-necked Pigeon		15	40
1040	10 c. Green Heron		20	15
1041	15 c. Moorhen		25	20
1042	20 c. Ringed Kingfisher		30	20
1043	25 c. Brown Pelican.		30	20
1044	35 c. White-tailed Tropic Bird		30	30
1045	45 c. Red-legged Thrush		40	30
1046	60 c. Purple-throated Carib		55	45
1047	90 c. Magnificent Frigate Bird		70	70
1048	$1 Brown Trembler		80	80
1049	$2 Black-capped Petrel		1·25	3·00
1050	$5 Barn Owl		3·00	5·00
1051	$10 Imperial Amazon		5·00	9·00
1037/51		Set of 15	12·00	19·00

For similar stamps, with imprint date and perforated 14, 12 or 12½ × 11½ see Nos. 1241/54.

(Des J. Iskowitz. Litho Format)

1987 (16 Feb). *America's Cup Yachting Championship. Multicoloured designs as T 222 of Antigua. P 15.*

1052	45 c. *Reliance*, 1903		50	30
1053	60 c. *Freedom*, 1980		60	55
1054	$1 *Mischief*, 1881		80	90
1055	$3 *Australia*, 1977		1·75	3·00
1052/5		*Set of 4*	3·25	4·25
MS1056	113×83 mm. $5 *Courageous*, 1977 (*horiz*)		4·00	7·00

(Litho Questa)

1987 (24 Mar). *Birth Centenary of Marc Chagall (artist). Multicoloured designs as T 225 of Antigua. P 13½×14.*

1057	25 c. "Artist and His Model"		40	15
1058	35 c. "Midsummer Night's Dream"		40	15
1059	45 c. "Joseph the Shepherd"		50	25
1060	60 c. "The Cellist"		70	50
1061	90 c. "Woman with Pigs"		1·00	1·00
1062	$1 "The Blue Circus"		1·00	1·00
1063	$3 "For Vava"		2·25	3·00
1064	$4 "The Rider"		2·50	3·00
1057/64		*Set of 8*	8·00	8·00

MS1065 Two sheets, each 110×95 mm. (a) $5 "Purim" (104×89 mm). (b) $5 "Firebird" (stage design) (104×89 mm) .. *Set of 2 sheets* 4·50 6·00

216 Poulsen's Triton   **217** *Cantharellus cinnabarinus*

(Des L. Birmingham. Litho Format)

1987 (11 May). *Sea Shells. T 216 and similar designs. P 15.*

1066	35 c. multicoloured		20	20
1067	45 c. bluish violet, black and bright rose		25	25
1068	60 c. multicoloured		30	40
1069	$5 multicoloured		2·40	4·00
1066/9		*Set of 4*	2·75	4·25
MS1070	109×75 mm. $5 multicoloured		3·25	5·50

Designs: *Vert*—45 c. Elongate Janthina; 60 c. Banded Tulip; $5 (No. 1069) Deltoid Rock Shell. *Horiz*—$5 (No. MS1070) Junonia Volute.
No. 1066 is inscribed "TIRITON" in error.

(Des BG Studio. Litho Questa)

1987 (15 June). *"Capex '87" International Stamp Exhibition, Toronto. Mushrooms of Dominica. T 217 and similar horiz designs. Multicoloured. P 14.*

1071	45 c. Type 217		1·50	50
1072	60 c. *Boletellus cubensis*		2·00	1·25
1073	$2 *Eccilia cystiophorus*		4·25	4·50
1074	$3 *Xerocomus guadelupae*		4·50	5·00
1071/4		*Set of 4*	11·00	10·00
MS1075	85×85 mm. $5 *Gymnopilus chrysopellus*		8·00	10·00

218 Discovery of Dominica, 1493   **219** "Virgin and Child with St. Anne" (Dürer)

(Des I. MacLaury. Litho Format)

1987 (27 July). *500th Anniv of Discovery of America (1992) (1st issue). T 218 and similar horiz designs. Multicoloured. P 15.*

1076	10 c. Type 218		40	25
1077	15 c. Caribs greeting Columbus's fleet		50	30
1078	45 c. Claiming the New World for Spain		65	35
1079	60 c. Wreck of *Santa Maria*		80	60
1080	90 c. Fleet leaving Spain		1·00	1·00
1081	$1 Sighting the New World		1·10	1·25
1082	$3 Trading with Indians		2·25	3·00
1083	$5 Building settlement		3·25	4·00
1076/83		*Set of 8*	9·00	9·75

MS1084 Two sheets, each 109×79 mm. (a) $5 Fleet off Dominica, 1493. (b) $5 Map showing Columbus's route, 1493 .. *Set of 2 sheets* 5·00 7·00
See also Nos. 1221/5, 1355/63, 1406/14, 1547/53 and 1612/13.

(Des G. Welker. Litho Questa)

1987 (28 Sept). *Milestones of Transportation. Multicoloured designs as T 226 of Antigua. P 14.*

1085	10 c. H.M.S. *Warrior* (first ironclad warship), 1860		50	50
1086	15 c. MAGLEV-MLU 001 (fastest passenger train), 1979		60	60
1087	25 c. *Flying Cloud* (fastest clipper passage New York–San Francisco) (*vert*)		70	70
1088	35 c. First elevated railway, New York, 1868 (*vert*)		80	80
1089	45 c. *Tom Thumb* (first U.S. passenger locomotive), 1830		80	80

1090	60 c. *Spray* (Slocum's solo circumnavigation), 1895–8 (*vert*)		90	90
1091	90 c. *Sea-Land Commerce* (fastest Pacific passage), 1973 (*vert*)		1·25	1·25
1092	$1 First cable cars, San Francisco, 1873		1·40	1·40
1093	$3 "Orient Express", 1883		3·00	3·00
1094	$4 *Clermont* (first commercial paddlesteamer), 1807		3·25	3·25
1085/94		*Set of 10*	12·00	12·00

(Litho Questa)

1987 (16 Nov). *Christmas. Religious Paintings. T 219 and similar vert designs. Multicoloured. P 14.*

1095	20 c. Type 219		30	15
1096	25 c. "Virgin and Child" (Murillo)		30	15
1097	$2 "Madonna and Child" (Foppa)		1·50	2·25
1098	$4 "Madonna and Child" (Da Verona)		2·75	4·00
1095/8		*Set of 4*	4·25	6·00
MS1099	100×78 mm. $5 "Angel of the Annunciation" (anon, Renaissance period)		2·50	3·50

220 Three Little Pigs in People Mover, Walt Disney World   **221** Kayak Canoeing

(Des Walt Disney Company. Litho Questa)

1987 (22 Dec). *60th Anniv of Mickey Mouse (Walt Disney cartoon character). T 220 and similar multicoloured designs showing cartoon characters in trains. P 13½×14.*

1100	20 c. Type 220		45	35
1101	25 c. Goofy driving horse tram, Disneyland		45	35
1102	45 c. Donald Duck in *Roger E. Broggie*, Walt Disney World		75	65
1103	60 c. Goofy, Mickey Mouse, Donald Duck and Chip n'Dale aboard Big Thunder Mountain train, Disneyland		85	75
1104	90 c. Mickey Mouse in *Walter E. Disney*, Disneyland		1·40	1·25
1105	$1 Mickey and Minnie Mouse, Goofy, Donald and Daisy Duck in monorail, Walt Disney World		1·50	1·40
1106	$3 Dumbo flying over *Casey Jr*		3·25	3·75
1107	$4 Daisy Duck and Minnie Mouse in *Lilly Belle*, Walt Disney World		3·75	4·50
1100/7		*Set of 8*	11·00	11·50

MS1108 Two sheets, each 127×101 mm. (a) $5 Seven Dwarfs in Rainbow Caverns Mine train, Disneyland (*horiz*). (b) $5 Donald Duck and Chip n'Dale on toy train (from film *Out of Scale*) (*horiz*). P 14×13½ .. *Set of 2 sheets* 5·50 7·00

(Des D. Miller. Litho Questa)

1988 (15 Feb). *Royal Ruby Wedding. Vert designs as T 234 of Antigua. P 14.*

1109	45 c. multicoloured		85	30
1110	60 c. deep brown, black and light green		1·00	70
1111	$1 multicoloured		1·25	1·00
1112	$3 multicoloured		2·50	3·50
1109/12		*Set of 4*	5·00	5·00
MS1113	102×76 mm. $5 multicoloured		3·00	3·75

Designs:— 45 c. Wedding portrait with attendants, 1947; 60 c. Princess Elizabeth with Prince Charles, *c.* 1950; $1 Princess Elizabeth and Prince Philip with Prince Charles and Princess Anne, 1950; $3 Queen Elizabeth; $5 Princess Elizabeth in wedding dress, 1947.

(Des D. Miller. Litho Questa)

1988 (14 Mar). *Olympic Games, Seoul. T 221 and similar vert designs. Multicoloured. P 14.*

1114	45 c. Type 221		75	35
1115	60 c. Taekwon-do		1·00	1·00
1116	$1 High diving		1·10	1·25
1117	$3 Gymnastics on bars		2·25	4·00
1114/17		*Set of 4*	4·50	6·00
MS1118	81×110 mm. $5 Football		2·50	3·50

222 Carib Indian   **223** White-tailed Tropic Bird

(Des K. Gromell. Litho Format)

1988 (13 Apr). *"Reunion '88" Tourism Programme. T 222 and similar multicoloured designs. P 15.*

1119	10 c. Type 222		10	10
1120	25 c. Mountainous interior (*horiz*)		10	15
1121	35 c. Indian River		10	15
1122	60 c. Belaire dancer and tourists		15	30
1123	90 c. Boiling Lake		20	60
1124	$3 Coral reef (*horiz*)		60	1·60
1119/24		*Set of 6*	85	2·50
MS1125	112×82 mm. $5 Belaire dancer		1·75	4·00

1988 (1 June). *Stamp Exhibitions. Nos. MS1084 and 1092/3 optd as T 241 of Antigua showing various emblems.*

1126	$1 First cable cars, San Francisco, 1873 (optd "FINLANDIA 88", Helsinki)		75	70
1127	$3 "Orient Express", 1883 (optd "INDEPENDENCE 40", Israel)		1·75	2·00
	a. Opt albino			

MS1128 Two sheets, each 109 × 79 mm. (a) $5 Fleet off Dominica, 1493 (optd "OLYMPHILEX '88", Seoul). (b) $5 Map showing Columbus's route, 1493 (optd "Praga '88", Prague) .. *Set of 2 sheets* 4·25 5·50

(Des S. Barlow. Litho Questa)

1988 (25 July). *Dominica Rain Forest Flora and Fauna. T 223 and similar vert designs. Multicoloured. P 14½×14.*

1129	45 c. Type 223		50	50
	a. Sheetlet. Nos. 1129/48		9·00	
1130	45 c. Blue-hooded Euphonia		50	50
1131	45 c. Smooth-billed Ani		50	50
1132	45 c. Scaly-breasted Thrasher		50	50
1133	45 c. Purple-throated Carib		50	50
1134	45 c. *Marpesia petreus* and *Strymon maesites* (butterflies)		50	50
1135	45 c. Brown Trembler		50	50
1136	45 c. Imperial Amazon		50	50
1137	45 c. Mangrove Cuckoo		50	50
1138	45 c. *Dynastes hercules* (beetle)		50	50
1139	45 c. *Historis odius* (butterfly)		50	50
1140	45 c. Red-necked Amazon		50	50
1141	45 c. Tillandsia (plant)		50	50
1142	45 c. Bananaquit and *Polystacha luteola* (plant)		50	50
1143	45 c. False Chameleon		50	50
1144	45 c. Iguana		50	50
1145	45 c. *Hypolimnas misippus* (butterfly)		50	50
1146	45 c. Green-throated Carib		50	50
1147	45 c. Heliconia (plant)		50	50
1148	45 c. Agouti		50	50
1129/48		*Set of 20*	9·00	9·00

Nos. 1129/48 were printed together, *se-tenant*, in a sheetlet of 20 forming a composite design.

224 Battery Hens   **225** Gary Cooper

(Des J. Martin. Litho Questa)

1988 (5 Sept). *10th Anniv of International Fund for Agricultural Development. T 224 and similar multicoloured designs. P 14.*

1149	45 c. Type 224		50	30
1150	60 c. Pig		70	65
1151	90 c. Cattle		95	1·25
1152	$3 Black Belly Sheep		2·25	4·00
1149/52		*Set of 4*	4·00	5·50
MS1153	95×68 mm. $5 Tropical fruits (*vert*)		2·25	3·50

(Des Lynda Bruscheni. Litho Questa)

1988 (8 Sept). *Entertainers. T 225 and similar vert designs. Multicoloured. P 14.*

1154	10 c. Type 225		40	20
1155	35 c. Josephine Baker		50	35
1156	45 c. Maurice Chevalier		55	35
1157	60 c. James Cagney		60	50
1158	$1 Clark Gable		80	70
1159	$2 Louis Armstrong		1·25	1·50
1160	$3 Liberace		1·75	2·25
1161	$4 Spencer Tracy		2·25	3·00
1154/61		*Set of 8*	7·25	8·00

MS1162 Two sheets, each 105×75 mm. (a) $5 Humphrey Bogart. (b) $5 Elvis Presley. .. *Set of 2 sheets* 6·50 7·50

(Des Mary Walters. Litho Questa)

1988 (29 Sept). *Flowering Trees. Horiz designs as T 242 of Antigua. Multicoloured. P 14.*

1163	15 c. Sapodilla		10	10
1164	20 c. Tangerine		10	10
1165	25 c. Avocado Pear		10	10
1166	45 c. Amherstia		20	25
1167	90 c. Lipstick Tree		40	55
1168	$1 Cannonball Tree		45	55
1169	$3 Saman		1·25	1·75
1170	$4 Pineapple		1·60	2·00
1163/70		*Set of 8*	3·75	4·75

MS1171 Two sheets, each 96 × 66 mm. (a) $5 Lignum Vitae. (b) $5 Sea Grape *Set of 2 sheets* 4·50 6·00

(Litho Questa)

1988 (10 Oct). *500th Birth Anniv of Titian (artist). Vert designs as T* **238** *of Antigua. Multicoloured. P* 13½ × 14.
1172	25 c.	"Jacopo Strada"		15	15
1173	35 c.	"Titian's Daughter Lavinia"		20	20
1174	45 c.	"Andrea Navagero"		25	25
1175	60 c.	"Judith with Head of Holoferenes"		30	30
1176	$1	"Emilia di Spilimbergo"		50	50
1177	$2	"Martyrdom of St. Lawrence"		1·00	1·25
1178	$3	"Salome"		1·60	2·00
1179	$4	"St. John the Baptist"		1·90	2·50
1172/9			*Set of 8*	5·50	6·50

MS1180 Two sheets, each 110 × 95 mm. (a) $5 "Self Portrait". (b) $5 "Sisyphus" *Set of 2 sheets* 4·25 6·00

226 Imperial Amazon

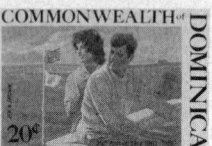
227 President and Mrs. Kennedy

(Des K. Gromell. Litho Questa)

1988 (31 Oct). *10th Anniv of Independence. T* **226** *and similar multicoloured designs. P* 14.
1181	20 c.	Type **226**		90	40
1182	45 c.	Dominica 1874 1d. stamp and landscape *(horiz)*		90	30
1183	$2	1978 Independence 10 c. stamp and landscape *(horiz)*		1·50	2·75
1184	$3	Carib Wood (national flower)		1·75	3·25
1181/4			*Set of 4*	4·50	6·00

MS1185 116 × 85 mm. $5 Government Band *(horiz)* 2·25 3·50

(Des J. Martin. Litho Questa)

1988 (22 Nov). *25th Death Anniv of John F. Kennedy (American statesman). T* **227** *and similar multicoloured designs. P* 14.
1186	20 c.	Type **227**		10	10
1187	25 c.	Kennedy sailing		10	10
1188	$2	Outside Hyannis Port house		80	1·50
1189	$4	Speaking in Berlin *(vert)*		1·60	2·50
1186/9			*Set of 4*	2·40	3·75

MS1190 100 × 71 mm. $5 President Kennedy *(vert)* 2·10 3·50

228 Donald Duck's Nephews decorating Christmas Tree

229 Raoul Wallenberg (diplomat) and Swedish Flag

(Des Walt Disney Co. Litho Questa)

1988 (1 Dec). *Christmas. "Mickey's Christmas Mall". T* **228** *and similar vert designs showing Walt Disney cartoon characters. Multicoloured. P* 13½ × 14.
1191	60 c.	Type **228**		55	65
		a. Sheetlet. Nos. 1191/8		4·00	
1192	60 c.	Daisy Duck outside clothes shop		55	65
1193	60 c.	Winnie the Pooh in shop window		55	65
1194	60 c.	Goofy with parcels		55	65
1195	60 c.	Donald Duck as Father Christmas		55	65
1196	60 c.	Mickey Mouse contributing to collection		55	65
1197	60 c.	Minnie Mouse		55	65
1198	60 c.	Chip n' Dale with peanut		55	65
1191/8			*Set of 8*	4·00	4·75

MS1199 Two sheets, each 127 × 102 mm. (a) $6 Mordie Mouse with Father Christmas. (b) $6 Mickey Mouse at West Indian market *Set of 2 sheets* 6·50 8·00

Nos. 1191/8 were printed together, *se-tenant* as a composite design, in sheetlets of eight.

(Des J. Genzo. Litho B.D.T.)

1988 (9 Dec). *40th Anniv of Universal Declaration of Human Rights. T* **229** *and similar multicoloured design. P* 14.
1200	$3	Type **229**	2·00	2·50

MS1201 92 × 62 mm. $5 Human Rights Day logo *(vert)* 2·50 3·25

NEW INFORMATION

The editor is always interested to correspond with people who have new information that will improve or correct the Catalogue.

---

230 Greater Amberjack

(Des J. Iskowitz. Litho Questa)

1988 (22 Dec). *Game Fishes. T* **230** *and similar horiz designs. Multicoloured. P* 14.
1202	10 c.	Type **230**		20	15
1203	15 c.	Blue Marlin		20	15
1204	35 c.	Cobia		35	30
1205	45 c.	Dolphin (fish)		45	30
1206	60 c.	Cero		60	55
1207	90 c.	Mahogany Snapper		85	95
1208	$3	Yellow-finned Tuna		2·50	3·25
1209	$4	Rainbow Parrotfish		3·00	3·75
1202/9			*Set of 8*	7·50	8·50

MS1210 Two sheets, each 104×74 mm. (a) $5 Manta. (b) $5 Tarpon *Set of 2 sheets* 7·00 8·50

231 Leatherback Turtle   (**232**)

(Des W. Wright. Litho Questa)

1988 (29 Dec). *Insects and Reptiles. T* **231** *and similar horiz designs. Multicoloured. P* 14.
1211	10 c.	Type **231**		45	35
1212	25 c.	*Danaus plexippus* (butterfly)		1·25	75
1213	60 c.	Green Anole (lizard)		1·60	1·25
1214	$3	*Mantis religiosa* (mantid)		4·00	6·50
1211/14			*Set of 4*	6·50	8·00

MS1215 119×90 mm. $5 *Dynastes hercules* (beetle) 3·00 4·50

1989 (20 Mar). *Olympic Medal Winners, Seoul. Nos.* 1114/18 *optd as T* **232** *(horizontally on No.* **MS**1220).
1216	45 c.	Type **221** (optd with T **232**)		20	25
1217	60 c.	Taekwon-do (optd "Women's Flyweight N. Y. Choo S. Korea")		25	35
1218	$1	High diving (optd "Women's Platform Y. Xu China")		40	60
1219	$3	Gymnastics on bars (optd "V. Artemov USSR")		1·25	1·75
1216/19			*Set of 4*	1·90	2·75

MS1220 81×110 mm. $5 Football (optd "USSR defeated Brazil 3-2 on penalty kicks after a 1-1 tie") 2·75 3·50

(Des D. Miller. Litho Questa)

1989 (8 May). *500th Anniv of Discovery of America by Columbus (1992) (2nd issue). Pre-Columbian Carib Society. Designs as T* **247** *of Antigua, but horiz. Multicoloured. P* 14.
1221	20 c.	Carib canoe		20	20
1222	35 c.	Hunting with bows and arrows		30	20
1223	$1	Dugout canoe making		70	90
1224	$3	Shield contest		1·75	2·75
1221/4			*Set of 4*	2·75	3·50

MS1225 87×71 mm. $6 Ceremonial dance 2·75 4·00

233 Map of Dominica, 1766

234 *Papilio homerus*

(Des U. Purins. Litho B.D.T.)

1989 (17 July). *"Philexfrance 89" International Stamp Exhibition, Paris. T* **233** *and similar multicoloured designs. P* 14.
1226	10 c.	Type **233**		45	30
1227	35 c.	French coin of 1653 *(horiz)*		65	40
1228	$1	French warship, 1720 *(horiz)*		1·40	1·25
1229	$4	Coffee plant *(horiz)*		2·00	3·00
1226/9			*Set of 4*	4·00	4·50

MS1230 98×98 mm. $5 Exhibition inscription *(horiz)* (black, grey and greenish yellow) 3·00 4·00

(Litho Questa)

1989 (31 Aug). *Japanese Art. Paintings by Taikan. Designs as T* **250** *of Antigua, but vert. Multicoloured. P* 13½×14.
1231	10 c.	"Lao-tzu" (detail)		10	10
1232	20 c.	"Red Maple Leaves" (panels 1 and 2)		10	10
1233	$1	"King Wen Hui learns a Lesson from his Cook" (detail)		20	25
1234	60 c.	"Red Maple Leaves" (panels 3 and 4)		25	35
1235	$1	"Wild Flowers" (detail)		40	50
1236	$2	"Red Maple Leaves" (panels 5 and 6)		85	1·00
1237	$3	"Red Maple Leaves" (panels 7 and 8)		1·25	1·60

1238	$4	"Indian Ceremony of Floating Lamps on the River" (detail)		1·75	2·10
1231/8			*Set of 8*	4·25	5·50

MS1239 Two sheets (a) 78×102 mm. $5 "Innocence" (detail). (b) 101×77 mm. $5 "Red Maple Leaves" (detail) *Set of 2 sheets* 5·50 6·50

Nos. 1231/8 were each printed in sheetlets of 10 containing two vertical strips of 5 stamps separated by printed labels commemorating Emperor Hirohito.

(Litho Questa)

1989 (31 Aug)–91. *As Nos.* 1038/46 *and* 1048/51 *but with "1989" imprint date.* A. *P* 14 (1989). B. *P* 12 (1989 ($10) or 1990 (others)).

				A		B	
1241	2 c.	Ruddy Quail Dove		40	60	40	60
1242	5 c.	Red-necked Pigeon		50	40	50	40
1243	10 c.	Green Heron		50	15	50	15
1244	15 c.	Moorhen		60	30	60	30
1245	20 c.	Ringed Kingfisher		65	40	65	40
1246	25 c.	Brown Pelican		65	40	65	40
1247	35 c.	White-tailed Tropic Bird		80	30	80	30
1248	45 c.	Red-legged Thrush		1·00	30	1·00	30
1249	60 c.	Purple-throated Carib		1·50	70	1·50	70
1251	$1	Brown Trembler		1·60	1·25	1·60	1·25
1252	$2	Black-capped Petrel		2·50	3·50	2·50	3·50
1253	$5	Barn Owl		5·50	7·00	5·50	7·00
1254	$10	Imperial Amazon		7·50	11·00	7·50	11·00
1241/54			*Set of 13*	21·00	23·00	21·00	23·00

C. *P* 12½×11½ (1991).

				C	
1241	2 c.	Ruddy Quail Dove		40	60
1242	5 c.	Red-necked Pigeon		50	40
1243	10 c.	Green Heron		50	15
1244	15 c.	Moorhen		60	30
1245	20 c.	Ringed Kingfisher		65	40
1246	25 c.	Brown Pelican		65	40
1247	35 c.	White-tailed Tropic Bird		80	30
1248	45 c.	Red-legged Thrush		1·00	30
1249	60 c.	Purple-throated Carib		1·50	70
1251	$1	Brown Trembler		1·60	1·25
1252	$2	Black-capped Petrel		2·50	3·50
1253	$5	Barn Owl		5·50	7·00
1254	$10	Imperial Amazon		7·50	11·00
1241/54			*Set of 13*	21·00	23·00

Nos. 1241C/54C show a larger hole on every sixth perforation, both vertically and horizontally.

(Des W. Wright. Litho Questa)

1989 (11 Sept). *Butterflies. T* **234** *and similar horiz designs. Multicoloured. P* 14.
1255	10 c.	Type **234**		40	30
1256	15 c.	*Morpho peleides*		45	30
1257	25 c.	*Dryas julia*		65	30
1258	35 c.	*Parides gundlachianus*		70	30
1259	60 c.	*Danaus plexippus*		1·00	75
1260	$1	*Agraulis vanillae*		1·25	1·25
1261	$3	*Phoebis avellaneda*		2·75	3·25
1262	$5	*Papilio andraemon*		3·75	5·00
1255/62			*Set of 8*	10·00	10·00

MS1263 Two sheets. (a) 105×74 mm. $6 *Adelpha cytherea*. (b) 105×79 mm. $6 *Adelpha iphicla* *Set of 2 sheets* 8·00 9·00

235 *Oncidium pusillum*

236 "Apollo 11" Command Module in Lunar Orbit

(Des W. Hanson Studio. Litho Questa)

1989 (28 Sept). *Orchids. T* **235** *and similar vert designs. Multicoloured. P* 14.
1264	10 c.	Type **235**		35	30
1265	35 c.	*Epidendrum cochleata*		70	30
1266	45 c.	*Epidendrum ciliare*		75	40
1267	60 c.	*Cyrtopodium andersonii*		1·00	80
1268	$1	*Habenaria pauciflora*		1·25	1·25
1269	$2	*Maxillaria alba*		2·00	2·25
1270	$3	*Selenipedium palmifolium*		2·50	2·75
1271	$4	*Brassavola cucullata*		3·25	3·75
1264/71			*Set of 8*	10·50	10·50

MS1272 Two sheets, each 108×77 mm. (a) $5 *Oncidium lanceanum*. (b) $5 *Comparettia falcata* *Set of 2 sheets* 8·00 9·00

(Litho Questa)

1989 (31 Oct). *20th Anniv of First Manned Landing on Moon. T* **236** *and similar multicoloured designs. P* 14.
1273	10 c.	Type **236**		30	30
1274	60 c.	Neil Armstrong leaving lunar module		70	70
1275	$2	Edwin Aldrin at Sea of Tranquility		1·60	2·00
1276	$3	Astronauts Armstrong and Aldrin with U.S. flag		2·00	2·50
1273/6			*Set of 4*	4·25	5·00

MS1277 62×77 mm. $6 Launch of "Apollo 11" *(vert)* 4·50 6·00

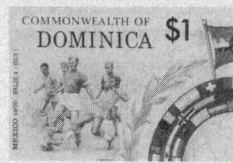

237 Brazil v Italy Final, 1970

(Des G. Vasarhelyi. Litho Questa)

1989 (8 Nov). *World Cup Football Championship, Italy (1st issue). T* **237** *and similar horiz designs. Multicoloured. P* 14.

1278	$1 Type **237**	..	1·25	1·50
	a. Sheetlet. Nos. 1278/81	..	4·50	
1279	$1 England v. West Germany, 1966	1·25	1·50
1280	$1 West Germany v. Holland, 1974	1·25	1·50
1281	$1 Italy v. West Germany, 1982	1·25	1·50
1278/81	.. ..	*Set of* 4	4·50	5·50
MS1282	106×86 mm. $6 Two players competing			
	for ball	.. ..	4·00	4·75

Nos. 1278/81 were printed together, *se-tenant*, in a sheetlet of 4 stamps, forming a composite central design of a football surrounded by flags of competing nations.
See also Nos. 1383/7.

238 George Washington and Inauguration, 1789

(Des W. Hanson Studio. Litho Questa)

1989 (17 Nov). *"World Stamp Expo '89" International Stamp Exhibition, Washington (1st issue). Bicentenary of the U.S. Presidency. T* **238** *and similar horiz designs. Multicoloured. P* 14.

1283	60 c. Type **238**	.. ..	50	50
	a. Sheetlet. Nos. 1283/8	..	2·75	
1284	60 c. John Adams and Presidential Mansion, 1800		50	50
1285	60 c. Thomas Jefferson, Graff House, Philadelphia and Declaration of Independence		50	50
1286	60 c. James Madison and U.S.S. *Constitution* defeating H.M.S. *Guerriere*, 1812		50	50
1287	60 c. James Monroe and freed slaves landing in Liberia		50	50
1288	60 c. John Quincy Adams and barge on Erie Canal		50	50
1289	60 c. Millard Fillmore and Perry's fleet off Japan		50	50
	a. Sheetlet. Nos. 1289/94	..	2·75	
1290	60 c. Franklin Pierce, Jefferson Davis and San Xavier Mission, Tucson		50	50
1291	60 c. James Buchanan, "Buffalo Bill" Cody carrying mail and Wells Fargo Pony Express stamp		50	50
1292	60 c. Abraham Lincoln and U.P.U. Monument, Berne		50	50
1293	60 c. Andrew Johnson, polar bear and Mt. McKinley, Alaska		50	50
1294	60 c. Ulysses S. Grant and Golden Spike Ceremony, 1869		50	50
1295	60 c. Theodore Roosevelt and steam shovel excavating Panama Canal		50	50
	a. Sheetlet. Nos. 1295/1300	..	2·75	
1296	60 c. William H. Taft and Admiral Peary at North Pole		50	50
1297	60 c. Woodrow Wilson and Curtiss JN-4 "Jenny" on first scheduled airmail flight, 1918 ..		50	50
1298	60 c. Warren G. Harding and airship U.S.S. *Shenandoah* at Lakehurst		50	50
1299	60 c. Calvin Coolidge and Lindbergh's Ryan NYP Special *Spirit of St. Louis* on trans-Atlantic flight..		50	50
1300	60 c. Mt. Rushmore National Monument		50	50
1301	60 c. Lyndon B. Johnson and Earth from Moon as seen by "Apollo 8" crew		50	50
	a. Sheetlet. Nos. 1301/6	..	2·75	
1302	60 c. Richard Nixon and visit to Great Wall of China		50	50
1303	60 c. Gerald Ford and *Gorch Fock* (German cadet barque) at Bicentenary of Revolution celebrations		50	50
1304	60 c. Jimmy Carter and Pres. Sadat of Egypt with Prime Minister Begin of Israel		50	50
1305	60 c. Ronald Reagan and space shuttle *Columbia*		50	50
1306	60 c. George Bush and Grumman TBF Avenger (fighter-bomber)		50	50
1283/1306		*Set of* 24	11·00	11·00

Nos. 1283/8, 1289/94, 1295/1300 and 1301/6 were printed together, *se-tenant*, in sheetlets of six stamps.

(Des Design Element. Litho Questa)

1989 (17 Nov). *"Expo '89" International Stamp Exhibition, Washington (2nd issue). Landmarks of Washington. Sheet* 77×62 *mm. containing horiz design as T* **257** *of Antigua. Multicoloured. P* 14.

MS1307	$4 The Capitol	.. ..	2·50	3·25

(Des Walt Disney Co. Litho Questa)

1989 (30 Nov). *Mickey Mouse in Hollywood. Horiz designs as T* **267** *of Antigua showing Walt Disney cartoon characters. Multicoloured. P* 14×13½.

1308	20 c. Mickey Mouse reading script	..	40	40
1309	35 c. Mickey Mouse giving interview		55	55
1310	45 c. Mickey and Minnie Mouse with newspaper and magazines		65	65
1311	60 c. Mickey Mouse signing autographs		75	75
1312	$1 Trapped in dressing room	..	1·25	1·25
1313	$2 Mickey and Minnie Mouse with Pluto in limousine		2·00	2·00
1314	$3 Arriving at Awards ceremony		2·25	2·25
1315	$4 Mickey Mouse accepting award		2·40	2·40
1308/15		*Set of* 8	9·00	9·00
MS1316	Two sheets, each 127×102 mm. (a) $5 Mickey Mouse leaving footprints at cinema. (b) $5 Goofy interviewing	..	*Set of* 2 *sheets*	7·50	8·50

(Litho Questa)

1989 (4 Dec). *Christmas. Paintings by Botticelli. Vert designs as T* **259** *of Antigua. Multicoloured. P* 14.

1317	20 c. "Madonna in Glory with Seraphim"		40	30
1318	25 c. "The Annunciation"	..	40	30
1319	35 c. "Madonna of the Pomegranate"	..	55	40
1320	45 c. "Madonna of the Rosegarden"		65	45
1321	60 c. "Madonna of the Book"	..	80	60
1322	$1 "Madonna under a Baldachin"		1·00	90
1323	$4 "Madonna and Child with Angels"		3·00	100
1324	$5 "Bardi Madonna"	..	3·50	4·25
1317/24		*Set of* 8	9·25	10·00
MS1325	Two sheets, each 71×96 mm. (a) $5 "The Mystic Nativity". (b) $5 "The Adoration of the Magi"	..	*Set of* 2 *sheets*	7·00	9·00

240 Lady Olave Baden-Powell and Agatha Robinson

241 Jawaharlal Nehru

(Des A. Fagbohun. Litho Questa)

1989 (27 Dec). *60th Anniv of Girl Guides in Dominica. T* **240** *and similar multicoloured design showing Guide leaders. P* 14.

1326	60 c. Type **240**	..	1·00	1·00
MS1327	70×99 mm. $5 Dorris Stockmann and Judith Pestaina (*horiz*)	..	3·50	4·00

(Des A. Fagbohun. Litho Questa)

1989 (29 Dec). *Birth Centenary of Jawaharlal Nehru (Indian statesman). T* **241** *and similar multicoloured design. P* 14.

1328	60 c. Type **241**	..	1·50	1·25
MS1329	101×72 mm. $5 Parliament House, New Delhi (*horiz*)	..	3·50	4·00

242 Cocoa Damselfish

(Des P. Chinelli. Litho Questa)

1990 (21 May). *Tropical Fishes. T* **242** *and similar horiz designs. Multicoloured. P* 14.

1330	45 c. Type **242**	..	45	50
	a. Sheetlet. Nos. 1330/47	..	7·00	
1331	45 c. Stinging Jellyfish	..	45	50
1332	45 c. Dolphin (fish)	..	45	50
1333	45 c. Atlantic Spadefish and Queen Angelfish		45	50
1334	45 c. French Angelfish	..	45	50
1335	45 c. Blue-striped Grunt	..	45	50
1336	45 c. Porkfish	..	45	50
1337	45 c. Great Hammerhead	..	45	50
1338	45 c. Atlantic Spadefish	..	45	50
1339	45 c. Great Barracuda	..	45	50
1340	45 c. Southern Stingray	..	45	50
1341	45 c. Black Grunt	..	45	50
1342	45 c. Spot-finned Butterflyfish		45	50
1343	45 c. Dog Snapper	..	45	50
1344	45 c. Band-tailed Puffer	..	45	50
1345	45 c. Four-eyed Butterflyfish		45	50
1346	45 c. Lane Snapper	..	45	50
1347	45 c. Green Moray	..	45	50
1330/47		*Set of* 18	7·00	8·00

Nos. 1330/47 were printed together, *se-tenant*, in sheetlets of 18, forming a composite design.

NEW INFORMATION

The editor is always interested to correspond with people who have new information that will improve or correct the Catalogue.

---

243 St. Paul's Cathedral, London, c. 1840

244 Blue-headed Hummingbird

(Des M. Pollard. Litho B.D.T.)

1990 (18 June). *150th Anniv of the Penny Black and "Stamp World London 90" International Stamp Exhibition. T* **243** *and similar square designs. P* 13½.

1348	45 c. deep blue-green and black	..	50	25
1349	50 c. greenish blue and black	..	55	35
1350	60 c. greenish blue and black	..	65	45
1351	90 c. deep blue-green and black	..	85	85
1352	$3 deep ultramarine and black	..	2·25	3·00
1353	$4 deep ultramarine and black	..	2·75	3·50
1348/53		*Set of* 6	6·75	7·50
MS1354	Two sheets. (a) 103×79 mm. $5 brown-ochre and black. (b) 85×86 mm. $5 dull vermilion and blackish brown	*Set of* 2 *sheets*	6·50	7·50

Designs:—50 c. British Post Office "accelerator" carriage, 1830; 60 c. St. Paul's and City of London; 90 c. Travelling post office, 1838; $3 "Hen and chickens" delivery cycle, 1883; $4 London skyline; $5 (a) As Type **243**; (b) Motor mail van, 1899.

(Des Mary Walters. Litho B.D.T.)

1990 (19 July). *500th Anniv of Discovery of America by Columbus (1992) (3rd issue). New World Natural History–Seashells. Vert designs as T* **260** *of Antigua. Multicoloured. P* 14.

1355	10 c. Reticulated Cowrie-helmet (*Cypraecassis testiculus*)		30	30
1356	20 c. West Indian Chank (*Turbinella angulata*)		40	40
1357	35 c. West Indian Fighting Conch (*Strombus pugilis*)		50	35
1358	60 c. True Tulip (*Fasciolaria tulipa*)		75	60
1359	$1 Sunrise Tellin (*Tellina radiata*)		1·00	1·00
1360	$2 Crown Cone (*Conus regius*)		1·75	2·25
1361	$3 Common Dove Shell (*Columbella mercatoria*)		2·50	3·00
1362	$4 Common or Atlantic Fig Shell (*Ficus communis*)		2·75	3·25
1355/62		*Set of* 8	9·00	10·00
MS1363	Two sheets, each 102×70 mm. (a) $5 King Helmet (*Cassis tuberosa*). (b) $5 Giant Tun (*Tonna galea*)	*Set of* 2 *sheets*	6·50	7·50

(Des Mary Walters. Litho B.D.T.)

1990 (26 July). *Birds. T* **244** *and similar vert designs. Multicoloured. P* 14.

1364	10 c. Type **244**		35	35
1365	20 c. Black-capped Petrel	..	45	45
1366	45 c. Red-necked Amazon	..	65	40
1367	60 c. Black Swift	..	80	70
1368	$1 Troupial	..	1·25	1·25
1369	$2 Common Noddy	..	2·00	2·50
1370	$4 Lesser Antillean Pewee	..	3·25	3·50
1371	$5 Little Blue Heron	..	3·75	4·25
1364/71		*Set of* 8	11·00	12·00
MS1372	Two sheets, each 103×70 mm. (a) $5 Imperial Amazon. (b) $6 House Wren	*Set of* 2 *sheets*	7·00	8·00

(Litho Questa)

1990 (10 Sept). *90th Birthday of Queen Elizabeth the Queen Mother. Vert designs as T* **266** *of Antigua showing recent photographs of The Queen Mother. P* 14.

1373	20 c. multicoloured	..	20	15
1374	45 c. multicoloured	..	35	25
1375	60 c. multicoloured	..	60	60
1376	$3 multicoloured	..	2·25	3·00
1373/6		*Set of* 4	3·00	3·50
MS1377	80×90 mm. $5 multicoloured	..	2·75	3·50

(Des B. Grout. Litho Questa)

1990 (6 Nov). *Olympic Games, Barcelona (1992) (1st issue). Vert designs as T* **268** *of Antigua. Multicoloured. P* 14.

1378	45 c. Tennis	..	75	40
1379	60 c. Fencing	..	75	50
1380	$2 Swimming	..	1·60	2·25
1381	$3 Yachting	..	2·25	2·75
1378/81		*Set of* 4	4·75	5·50
MS1382	100×70 mm. $5 Rowing	..	4·25	5·50

See also Nos. 1603/11.

245 Barnes, England

(Des Young Phillips Studio. Litho Questa)

1990 (6 Nov). *World Cup Football Championship, Italy (2nd issue). T 245 and similar multicoloured designs.* P 14.
1383	15 c. Type 245		40	30
1384	45 c. Romario, Brazil		70	30
1385	60 c. Franz Beckenbauer, West Germany manager		85	70
1386	$4 Lindenberger, Austria		3·25	4·50
1383/6		*Set of 4*	4·75	5·25

MS1387 Two sheets, each 105×90 mm. (a) $6 McGrath, Ireland (*vert*). (b) $6 Litovchenko, Soviet Union (*vert*) .. .. *Set of 2 sheets* 7·50 8·50

246 Mickey Mouse riding Herschell-Spillman Frog

247 *Craterellus cornucopioides*

(Des Walt Disney Co. Litho Questa)

1990 (13 Dec). *Christmas. T 246 and similar multicoloured designs showing Walt Disney cartoon characters and American carousel animals.* P 13½×14.
1388	10 c. Type 246		30	20
1389	15 c. Huey, Duey and Louie on Allan Herschell elephant		35	25
1390	25 c. Donald Duck on Allan Herschell polar bear		45	30
1391	45 c. Goofy on Dentzel goat		70	30
1392	$1 Donald Duck on Zalar giraffe		1·00	1·00
1393	$2 Daisy Duck on Herschell-Spillman stork		1·75	2·25
1394	$4 Goofy on Dentzel lion		3·00	3·75
1395	$5 Daisy Duck on Stein and Goldstein palomino stander		3·50	4·00
1388/95		*Set of 8*	10·00	11·00

MS1396 Two sheets, each 127×101mm. (a) $6 Mickey, Morty and Ferdie Mouse on Philadelphia Toboggan Company swan chariot (*horiz*). P 14×13½. (b) $6 Mickey and Minnie Mouse with Goofy on Philadelphia Toboggan Company winged griffin chariot. P 13½×14
Set of 2 sheets 8·00 10·00

(Des W. Hanson Studio. Litho Walsall)

1991 (26 Mar). *Cog Railways. Multicoloured designs as T 275 of Antigua.* P 14.
1397	10 c. Glion-Roches De Naye locomotive, 1890		30	30
1398	35 c. Electric railcar on Mt Pilatus		45	30
1399	45 c. Cog railway line to Schynige Platte		50	30
1400	60 c. Bugnli Viaduct, Furka-Oberalp line (*vert*)		75	75
1401	$1 Jungfrau train, 1910		1·00	1·25
1402	$2 Testing Pike's Peak railcar, Switzerland, 1983		1·75	2·25
1403	$4 Brienz-Rothorn steam train, 1991		3·00	4·00
1404	$5 Arth-Rigi steam locomotive, 1890		3·50	4·25
1397/404		*Set of 8*	10·00	12·00

MS1405 Two sheets. (a) 100×70 mm. $6 Swiss Europa stamps of 1983 showing Riggenbach's locomotive of 1871 (50×37 *mm*). (b) 90×68 mm. $6 Brunig line train and Sherlock Holmes (50×37 *mm*). P 13½ .. .. *Set of 2 sheets* 8·00 9·50

(Des T. Agans. Litho Questa)

1991 (8 Apr). *500th Anniv of Discovery of America by Columbus (1992) (4th issue). History of Exploration. Horiz designs as T 277 of Antigua. Multicoloured.* P 14.
1406	10 c. Gil Eannes sailing south of Cape Bojador, 1433–34		25	25
1407	25 c. Alfonso Baldaya sailing south to Cape Blanc, 1436		35	35
1408	45 c. Bartolomeu Dias in Table Bay, 1487		45	35
1409	60 c. Vasco da Gama on voyage to India, 1497–99		55	50
1410	$1 Vallarte the Dane off African coast		75	90
1411	$2 Aloisio Cadamosto in Cape Verde Islands, 1456–58		1·40	1·75
1412	$4 Diogo Gomes on River Gambia, 1457		2·75	3·50
1413	$5 Diogo Cao off African coast, 1482–85		3·25	3·75
1406/13		*Set of 8*	8·50	10·00

MS1414 Two sheets, each 105×71 mm. (a) $6 Green-winged Macaw and bow of *Santa Maria.* (b) $6 Blue and Yellow Macaw and caravel
Set of 2 sheets 7·50 8·50

(Des Walt Disney Co. Litho Questa)

1991 (22 May). *"Phila Nippon '91" International Stamp Exhibition, Tokyo. Multicoloured designs as T 279 of Antigua showing Walt Disney cartoon characters in Japanese costumes.* P 14×13½ (*horiz*) or 13½×14 (*vert*).
1415	10 c. Donald Duck as Shogun's guard (*horiz*)		20	20
1416	15 c. Mickey Mouse as Kabuki actor (*horiz*)		25	25
1417	25 c. Minnie and Mickey Mouse as bride and groom (*horiz*)		35	25
1418	45 c. Daisy Duck as geisha (*horiz*)		45	25
1419	$1 Mickey Mouse in Sokutai court dress		85	85
1420	$2 Goofy as Mino farmer		1·60	2·00

1421	$4 Pete as Shogun		2·75	3·25
1422	$5 Donald Duck as Samurai (*horiz*)		3·25	3·75
1415/22		*Set of 8*	8·75	9·75

MS1423 Two sheets, each 127×112 mm. (a) $6 Mickey Mouse as Noh actor. (b) $6 Goofy as Kabubei-jishi dancer .. *Set of 2 sheets* 8·50 10·00

(Litho Questa)

1991 (3 June). *Fungi. T 247 and similar vert designs. Multicoloured.* P 14.
1424	10 c. Type 247		40	40
1425	15 c. Coprinus comatus		50	40
1426	45 c. Morchella esculenta		75	40
1427	60 c. Cantharellus cibarius		1·00	70
1428	$1 Lepista nuda		1·25	1·10
1429	$2 Suillus luteus		1·75	2·00
1430	$4 Russula emetica		3·00	3·50
1431	$5 Armillaria mellea		3·25	3·75
1424/31		*Set of 8*	10·50	11·00

MS1432 Two sheets, each 100×70 mm. (a) $6 *Fistulina hepatica.* (b) $6 *Lactarius volemus*
Set of 2 sheets 8·50 10·00

(Des D. Miller. Litho Walsall)

1991 (17 June). *65th Birthday of Queen Elizabeth II. Horiz designs as T 280 of Antigua. Multicoloured.* P 14.
1433	10 c. Queen and Prince William on Buckingham Palace Balcony, 1990		30	20
1434	60 c. The Queen at Westminster Abbey, 1988		75	50
1435	$2 Queen and Prince Philip in Italy, 1990		1·60	2·00
1436	$4 The Queen at Ascot, 1986		2·50	3·00
1433/6		*Set of 4*	4·75	5·00

MS1437 68×90 mm. $5 Separate portraits of Queen and Prince Philip .. .. 3·75 4·25

(Des D. Miller. Litho Walsall)

1991 (17 June). *10th Wedding Anniv of the Prince and Princess of Wales. Horiz designs as T 280 of Antigua. Multicoloured.* P 14.
1438	15 c. Prince and Princess of Wales in West Germany, 1987		30	25
1439	40 c. Separate photographs of Prince, Princess and sons		50	25
1440	$1 Separate photographs of Prince William and Prince Henry		95	95
1441	$5 Prince Charles at Caister and Princess Diana in Thailand		3·25	4·00
1438/41		*Set of 4*	4·50	5·00

MS1442 68×90 mm. $5 Prince Charles, and Princess Diana with sons on holiday .. 3·75 4·25

(Litho Walsall)

1991 (8 July). *Death Centenary of Vincent van Gogh (artist) (1990). Multicoloured designs as T 278 of Antigua.* P 13½.
1443	10 c. "Thatched Cottages" (*horiz*)		30	30
1444	25 c. "The House of Père Eloi" (*horiz*)		45	30
1445	45 c. "The Midday Siesta" (*horiz*)		65	30
1446	60 c. "Portrait of a Young Peasant" (*horiz*)		85	70
1447	$1 "Still Life: Vase with Irises against a Yellow Background"		1·25	1·10
1448	$2 "Still Life: Vase with Irises" (*horiz*)		1·75	2·00
1449	$4 "Blossoming Almond Tree" (*horiz*)		3·00	3·75
1450	$5 "Irises" (*horiz*)		3·25	4·25
1443/50		*Set of 8*	10·50	11·00

MS1451 Two sheets, (a) 77×102 mm. $6 "Doctor Gachet's Garden in Auvers". (b) 102×77 mm. $6 "A Meadow in the Mountains: Le Mas de Saint-Paul" (*horiz*). Imperf .. *Set of 2 sheets* 7·50 8·50

(Des Walt Disney Co. Litho Questa)

1991 (6 Aug). *International Literacy Year (1990). Multicoloured designs as T 269 of Antigua showing scenes from Disney cartoon film The Little Mermaid.* P 14×13½.
1452	10 c. Ariel, Flounder and Sebastian (*horiz*)		25	25
1453	25 c. King Triton (*horiz*)		35	30
1454	45 c. Sebastian playing drums (*horiz*)		50	30
1455	60 c. Flotsam and Jetsam taunting Ariel (*horiz*)		75	55
1456	$1 Scuttle, Flounder and Ariel with pipe (*horiz*)		1·00	1·00
1457	$2 Ariel and Flounder discovering book (*horiz*)		1·75	2·00
1458	$4 Prince Eric and crew (*horiz*)		3·00	3·50
1459	$5 Ursula the Sea Witch (*horiz*)		3·50	4·00
1452/9		*Set of 8*	10·00	11·00

MS1460 Two sheets, each 127×102 mm. (a) $6 Ariel without tail (*horiz*). P 14×13½. (b) $6 Ariel and Prince Eric dancing. P 13½×14.
Set of 2 sheets 8·50 9·00

248 Empire State Building, New York

249 Japanese Aircraft leaving Carrier *Akagi*

(Des W. Wright. Litho Questa)

1991 (12 Aug). *World Landmarks. T 248 and similar multicoloured designs.* P 14.
1461	10 c. Type 248		30	30
1462	25 c. Kremlin, Moscow (*horiz*)		30	30
1463	45 c. Buckingham Palace, London (*horiz*)		50	30
1464	60 c. Eiffel Tower, Paris		75	60
1465	$1 Taj Mahal, Agra (*horiz*)		1·50	1·25
1466	$2 Opera House, Sydney (*horiz*)		2·50	2·50
1467	$4 Colosseum, Rome (*horiz*)		3·25	3·75
1468	$5 Pyramids, Giza (*horiz*)		3·75	4·25
1461/8		*Set of 8*	11·50	12·00

MS1469 Two sheets, each 100×68 mm. (a) $6 Galileo on Leaning Tower, Pisa (*horiz*). (b) $6 Emperor Shi Huang and Great Wall of China (*horiz*) .. .. *Set of 2 sheets* 9·50 11·00

(Des W. Wright. Litho Questa)

1991 (2 Sept). *50th Anniv of Japanese Attack on Pearl Harbor. T 249 and similar horiz designs. Multicoloured.* P 14.
1470	10 c. Type 249		25	25
1471	15 c. U.S.S. *Ward* (destroyer) and Consolidated PBY-5 Catalina flying boat attacking midget submarine		30	30
1472	45 c. Second wave of Mitsubishi A6M Zero-Sen aircraft leaving carriers		40	30
1473	60 c. Japanese Mitsubishi A6M Zero-Sen's attacking Kaneche naval airfield		75	60
1474	$1 U.S.S. *Breeze, Medusa* and *Curtiss* (destroyers) sinking midget submarine		1·00	1·00
1475	$2 U.S.S. *Nevada* (battleship) under attack		1·75	2·00
1476	$4 U.S.S. *Arizona* (battleship) sinking		3·00	3·50
1477	$5 Mitsubishi A6M Zero-Sen aircraft		3·75	4·25
1470/7		*Set of 8*	9·75	11·00

MS1478 Two sheets, each 118×78 mm. (a) $6 Mitsubishi A6M Zero-Sen over anchorage. (b) $6 Mitsubishi A6M Zero-Sen attacking Hickam airfield .. .. *Set of 2 sheets* 8·50 10·00

250 *Eurema venusta*

251 Symbolic Cheque

(Litho Cartor)

1991 (14 Oct)–**93**. *Butterflies. T 250 and similar vert designs. Multicoloured.* P 13½.
1479	1 c. Type 250		20	40
1480	2 c. Agraulis vanillae		20	40
1481	5 c. Danaus plexippus		30	40
1482	10 c. Biblis hyperia		30	15
1483	15 c. Dryas julia		30	15
1484	20 c. Phoebis agarithe		30	20
1485	25 c. Junonia genoveva		30	20
1486	35 c. Battus polydamas		40	30
1487	45 c. Leptotes cassius		45	30
1487a	55 c. Ascia monuste (11.1.93)		55	55
1488	60 c. Anaea dominicana		45	35
1488a	65 c. Hemiargus hanno (11.1.93)		55	55
1489	90 c. Hypolimnas misippus		60	55
1490	$1 Urbanus proteus		60	60
1490a	$1.20, Historis odius (11.1.93)		75	1·00
1491	$2 Phoebis sennae		1·25	1·50
1492	$5 Cynthia cardui ("Vanessa cardui")		2·50	3·25
1493	$10 Marpesia petreus		4·75	5·50
1494	$20 Anartia jatrophae		9·50	11·00
1479/94		*Set of 19*	22·00	25·00

(Des J. Iskowitz. Litho Questa)

1991 (1 Nov). *Birth Centenary of Charles de Gaulle (French statesman) (1990). Designs as T 283 of Antigua showing De Gaulle in uniform.* P 14.
1495	45 c. agate		75	75

MS1496 70×100 mm. $5 agate and deep ultramarine .. .. .. 3·50 4·00
No. 1495 is a vertical design.

(Litho Questa)

1991 (1 Nov). *40th Anniv of Credit Union Bank. T 251 and similar designs.* P 14.
1497	10 c. grey-black and black		20	20
1498	60 c. multicoloured		80	80
Design: *Horiz*—60 c. Credit Union symbol.

252 "18th-Century Creole Dress" (detail) (Agostino Brunias)

253 Island Beach

(Litho Questa)

1991 (1 Nov). *Creole Week. T 252 and similar multicoloured designs. P 14.*
1499	45 c. Type **252**	50	25
1500	60 c. Jing Ping band	70	60
1501	$1 Creole dancers	1·00	1·40
1499/501	*Set of 3*	2·00	2·00
MS1502	100×70 mm. $5 "18th-century Stick- fighting Match" (detail) (Agostino Brunias) (horiz)	4·00	5·00

(Litho Cartor)

1991 (18 Nov). *Year of Environment and Shelter. T 253 and similar horiz designs. Multicoloured. P 14.*
1503	15 c. Type **253**	15	15
1504	60 c. Imperial Amazon	1·75	1·10
MS1505	Two sheets. (a) 100×70 mm. $5 River estuary. (b) 70×100 mm. $5 As 60 c. *Set of 2 sheets*	8·00	9·00

(Litho Walsall)

1991 (2 Dec). *Christmas. Religious Paintings by Jan van Eyck. Vert designs as T 287 of Antigua. Multicoloured. P 12.*
1506	10 c. "Virgin Enthroned with Child" (detail)	30	20
1507	20 c. "Madonna at the Fountain"	40	30
1508	35 c. "Virgin in a Church"	45	30
1509	45 c. "Madonna with Canon van der Paele"	60	30
1510	60 c. "Madonna with Canon van der Paele" (detail)	80	60
1511	$1 "Madonna in an Interior"	1·00	1·00
1512	$3 "The Annunciation"	2·50	3·25
1513	$5 "The Annunciation" (different)	3·25	4·75
1506/13	*Set of 8*	8·50	9·50
MS1514	Two sheets, each 102×127 mm. (a) $5 "Virgin and Child with Saints and Donor". (b) $5 "Madonna with Chancellor Rolin". P 14 *Set of 2 sheets*	8·00	9·50

(Des D. Miller. Litho Questa)

1992 (13 Mar). *40th Anniv of Queen Elizabeth II's Accession. Horiz designs as T 288 of Antigua. Multicoloured. P 14.*
1515	10 c. Coastline	10	10
1516	15 c. Mountains overlooking small village	10	10
1517	$1 River estuary	45	60
1518	$5 Waterfall	2·25	3·00
1515/18	*Set of 4*	2·75	3·50
MS1519	Two sheets, each 74×97 mm. (a) $6 Roseau. (b) $6 Mountain stream *Set of 2 sheets*	5·50	7·00

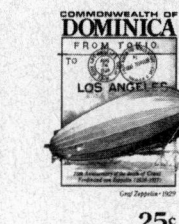

254 Cricket Match

255 Columbus and *Dynastes hercules* (beetle)

(Des Mary Walters. Litho B.D.T.)

1992 (30 Mar). *Centenary of Botanical Gardens (1991). T 254 and similar vert designs. Multicoloured. P 14.*
1520	10 c. Type **254**	20	20
1521	15 c. Scenic Entrance	20	20
1522	45 c. Traveller's Tree	30	25
1523	60 c. Bamboo House	40	30
1524	$1 The Old Pavilion	60	60
1525	$2 Ficus benjamina	1·10	1·40
1526	$4 Cricket match (different)	2·25	2·50
1527	$5 Thirty-five Steps	2·50	2·75
1520/7	*Set of 8*	6·75	7·50
MS1528	Two sheets, each 104×71 mm. (a) $6 Past and present members of national cricket team. (b) $6 The Fountain *Set of 2 sheets*	6·50	7·50

(Litho Questa)

1992 (21 Apr). *Easter. Religious Paintings. Multicoloured designs as T 291 of Antigua. P 14×13½ (horiz) or 13½×14 (vert).*
1529	10 c. "The Supper at Emmaus" (Van Honthorst)	20	20
1530	15 c. "Christ before Caiaphas" (Van Honthorst) (vert)	25	25
1531	45 c. "The Taking of Christ" (De Boulogne)	40	30
1532	60 c. "Pilate washing his Hands" (Preti) (vert)	55	45
1533	$1 "The Last Supper" (detail) (Master of the Church of S. Francisco d'Evora)	75	75
1534	$2 "The Three Marys at the Tomb" (detail) (Bouguereau) (vert)	1·50	1·75
1535	$3 "Denial of St. Peter" (Terbrugghen)	1·75	2·25
1536	$5 "Doubting Thomas" (Strozzi)	2·75	3·50
1529/36	*Set of 8*	7·50	8·50
MS1537	Two sheets, each 72×102 mm. (a) $6 "The Crucifixion" (detail) (Grünewald) (vert). (b) $6 "The Resurrection" (detail) (Caravaggio) (vert) *Set of 2 sheets*	7·00	8·50

(Litho B.D.T.)

1992 (4 May). *"Granada '92" International Stamp Exhibition, Spain. Art of Diego Rodriguez Velásquez. Multicoloured designs as T 292 of Antigua. P 13×13½.*
1538	10 c. "Pope Innocent X" (detail)	20	15
1539	15 c. "The Forge of Vulcan" (detail)	20	15

1540	45 c. "The Forge of Vulcan" (different detail)	40	25
1541	60 c. "Queen Mariana of Austria" (detail)	55	40
1542	$1 "Pablo de Valladolid"	70	70
1543	$2 "Sebastián de Morra"	1·50	2·00
1544	$3 "King Felipe IV" (detail)	1·75	2·25
1545	$4 "King Felipe IV"	2·25	2·50
1538/45	*Set of 8*	6·75	7·50
MS1546	Two sheets, each 120×95 mm. (a) $6 "The Drunkards" (110×81 mm). (b) $6 "Surrender of Breda" (110×81 mm). Imperf *Set of 2 sheets*	7·00	8·00

(Des R. Brown. Litho Questa)

1992 (18 May). *500th Anniv of Discovery of America by Columbus (5th issue). World Columbian Stamp "Expo '92", Chicago. T 255 and similar multicoloured designs. P 14.*
1547	10 c. Type **255**	15	15
1548	25 c. Columbus and Leptodactylus fallax (frog)	20	15
1549	75 c. Columbus and Red-necked Amazon (bird)	60	60
1550	$2 Columbus and Ameiva fuscata (lizard)	1·25	1·75
1551	$4 Columbus and Royal Gramma (fish)	2·25	2·75
1552	$5 Columbus and Rosa sinensis (flower)	2·50	3·00
1547/52	*Set of 6*	6·25	7·50
MS1553	Two sheets, each 100×67 mm. (a) $6 Ships of Columbus (horiz). (b) $6 Mastophyllum scabricolle (katydid) (horiz) *Set of 2 sheets*	6·50	7·50

(Des R. Brown. Litho Questa)

1992 (28 May). *"Genova '92" International Thematic Stamp Exhibition. Hummingbirds. Horiz designs as T 295 of Antigua. Multicoloured. P 14.*
1554	10 c. Female Purple-throated Carib	20	20
1555	15 c. Female Rufous-breasted Hermit	20	20
1556	45 c. Male Puerto Rican Emerald	50	30
1557	60 c. Female Antillean Mango	60	45
1558	$1 Male Green-throated Carib	95	85
1559	$2 Male Blue-headed Hummingbird	1·50	1·75
1560	$4 Female Eastern Streamertail	2·50	2·75
1561	$5 Female Antillean Crested Hummingbird	2·75	3·00
1554/61	*Set of 8*	8·25	8·50
MS1562	Two sheets, each 105×72 mm. (a) $6 Jamaican Mango ("Green Mango"). (b) $6 Vervain Hummingbird *Set of 2 sheets*	7·00	8·50

(Des D. Burkhart. Litho Questa)

1992 (23 June). *Prehistoric Animals. Multicoloured designs as T 290 of Antigua, but horiz. P 14.*
1563	10 c. Head of Camptosaurus	20	20
1564	15 c. Edmontosaurus	20	20
1565	25 c. Corythosaurus	30	20
1566	60 c. Stegosaurus	60	45
1567	$1 Torosaurus	95	85
1568	$3 Euoplocephalus	2·00	2·25
1569	$4 Tyrannosaurus	2·50	2·75
1570	$5 Parasaurolophus	2·75	3·00
1563/70	*Set of 8*	8·50	9·00
MS1571	Two sheets, each 100×70 mm. (a) $6 As 25 c. (b) $6 As $1 *Set of 2 sheets*	8·50	9·50

256 Trumpetfish and Blue Chromis

(Des I. MacLaury. Litho B.D.T.)

1992 (20 July). *Marine Life. T 256 and similar horiz designs. P 14.*
1572/1601	65 c.×30 multicoloured	12·00	13·00
MS1602	Two sheets, each 73×105 mm. (a) $6 multicoloured (Harlequin Bass). (b) $6 multicoloured (Flamefish) *Set of 2 sheets*	9·00	10·00

Nos. 1572/86 and 1587/1601 were each issued in se-tenant sheetlets of 15 (3×5) showing reef marine life by day or by night.

(Litho Questa)

1992 (10 Aug). *Olympic Games, Barcelona (2nd issue). Vert designs as T 268 of Antigua. Multicoloured. P 14.*
1603	10 c. Archery	15	15
1604	15 c. Two-man canoeing	15	15
1605	25 c. Men's 110 metres hurdles	20	15
1606	60 c. Men's high jump	40	30
1607	$1 Greco-Roman wrestling	65	65
1608	$2 Men's gymnastics – rings	1·25	1·75
1609	$4 Men's gymnastics – parallel bars	2·50	3·00
1610	$5 Equestrian dressage	3·00	3·25
1603/10	*Set of 8*	7·50	8·50
MS1611	Two sheets, each 100×70 mm. (a) $6 Women's platform diving. (b) $6 Men's hockey *Set of 2 sheets*	7·00	8·50

(Des F. Paul ($1), J. Esquino ($2). Litho Questa)

1992 (2 Sept). *500th Anniv of Discovery of America by Columbus (6th issue). Organization of East Caribbean States. Vert designs as Nos. 1670/1 of Antigua. Multicoloured. P 14½.*
1612	$1 Columbus meeting Amerindians	65	65
1613	$2 Ships approaching island	1·10	1·25

(Litho Questa)

1992 (2 Nov). *Hummel Figurines. Vert designs as T 302 of Antigua. Multicoloured. P 14.*
1614	20 c. Angel playing violin	15	15
1615	25 c. Angel playing recorder	15	15
1616	55 c. Angel playing lute	35	35
1617	65 c. Seated angel playing trumpet	45	45
1618	90 c. Angel on cloud with lantern	60	60
1619	$1 Angel with candle	65	65
1620	$1.20, Flying angel with Christmas tree	75	1·00
1621	$6 Angel on cloud with candle	4·25	5·00
1614/21	*Set of 8*	6·50	7·50
MS1622	Two sheets, each 97×127 mm. (a) Nos. 1614/17. (b) Nos. 1618/21 *Set of 2 sheets*	6·50	8·00

257 Brass *Reno* Locomotive, Japan (1963)

(Des W. Hanson. Litho B.D.T.)

1992 (11 Nov). *Toy Trains from Far Eastern Manufacturers. T 257 and similar multicoloured designs. P 14.*
1623	15 c. Type **257**	15	15
1624	25 c. Union Pacific Golden Classic locomotive, China (1992)	20	20
1625	55 c. L.M.S. third class brake coach, Hong Kong (1970s)	40	40
1626	65 c. Brass Wabash locomotive, Japan (1958)	50	50
1627	75 c. Pennsylvania "Duplex" type locomotive, Korea (1991)	60	60
1628	$1 Streamlined locomotive, Japan (post 1945)	70	70
1629	$3 Japanese National Railways Class "C62" locomotive, Japan (1960)	2·00	2·50
1630	$5 Tinplate friction driven trains, Japan (1960s)	2·75	3·25
1623/30	*Set of 8*	6·50	7·50
MS1631	Two sheets, each 119×87 mm. (a) $6 Rocket's tender, Japan (1972) (multicoloured) (51½×40 mm). (b) $6 American model steam train presented to Emperor of Japan, 1854 (black, blackish olive and flesh) (40×51½ mm). P 13 *Set of 2 sheets*	7·00	8·00

258 Goofy in *Two Weeks Vacation*, 1952

(Des Walt Disney Co. Litho Questa)

1992 (17 Nov). *60th Anniv of Goofy (Disney cartoon character). T 258 and similar multicoloured designs showing sports from cartoon films. P 14×13½.*
1632	10 c. Type **258**	25	15
1633	15 c. Aquamania, 1961	30	15
1634	25 c. Goofy Gymnastics, 1949	35	15
1635	45 c. How to Ride a Horse, 1941	50	25
1636	$1 Foul Hunting, 1947	75	65
1637	$2 For Whom the Bulls Toil, 1953	1·40	1·50
1638	$4 Tennis Racquet, 1949	2·25	2·50
1639	$5 Double Dribble, 1946	2·50	2·75
1632/9	*Set of 8*	7·50	7·25
MS1640	Two sheets, each 128×102 mm. (a) $6 The Goofy Sports Story, 1956 (vert). (b) $6 Aquamania, 1961 (different) (vert). P 13½×14 *Set of 2 sheets*	8·00	9·00

259 Airship LZ-127 *Graf Zeppelin*, 1929

260 Elvis Presley

(Des W. Wright and W. Hanson (Nos. 1641, 1655, MS1656a), W. Wright and L. Fried (Nos. 1645, 1654, MS1656b), J. Genzo (Nos. 1649, MS1656d), W. Wright (others). Litho Questa)

1992 (30 Dec). *Anniversaries and Events. T 259 and similar vert designs. Multicoloured. P 14.*
1641	25 c. Type **259**	15	15
1642	45 c. Elderly man on bike	30	25
1643	45 c. Elderly man with seedling	30	25

1644	45 c.	Elderly man and young boy fishing	30	25
1645	90 c.	Space Shuttle *Atlantis*	60	60
1646	90 c.	Konrad Adenauer (German states-man)	60	60
1647	$1.20,	Sir Thomas Lipton and *Shamrock N* (yacht)	75	75
1648	$1.20,	Snowy Egret (bird)	75	75
1649	$1.20,	Wolfgang Amadeus Mozart	75	75
1650	$2	Pulling fishing net ashore	1·25	1·25
1651	$3	Helen Keller (lecturer)	1·75	1·75
1652	$4	Eland (antelope)	2·50	2·50
1653	$4	Map of Allied Zones of Occupation, Germany, 1949	2·50	2·50
1654	$4	Earth Resources satellite	2·50	2·50
1655	$5	Count von Zeppelin	2·75	3·00
1641/55		*Set of 15*	16·00	16·00

MS1656 Five sheets. (a) 100×70 mm. $6 Airship propeller. (b) 100×70 mm. $6 M.I.R. Russian space station with "Soyuz". (c) 70×100 mm. $6 Cologne Cathedral. (d) 100×70 mm. $6 Rhinoceros Hornbill (bird). (e) 100×70 mm. $6 Monostatos from *The Magic Flute Set of 5 sheets* 15·00 16·00
Anniversaries and Events:—Nos. 1641, 1655, **MS**1656a, 75th death anniv of Count Ferdinand von Zeppelin; Nos. 1642/4, International Day of the Elderly; Nos. 1645, 1654, **MS**1656b, International Space Year; Nos. 1646, 1653, **MS**1656c, 25th death anniv of Konrad Adenauer; No. 1647, Americas Cup Yachting Championship; Nos. 1648, 1652, **MS**1656d, Earth Summit '92, Rio; Nos. 1649, **MS**1656e, Death bicent of Mozart; No. 1650, International Conference on Nutrition, Rome; No. 1651, 75th anniv of International Association of Lions Clubs.
No. **MS**1656d is inscribed "Rhinocerus Hornbill" in error.

(Litho Walsall)

1993 (24 Mar). *Bicentenary of the Louvre, Paris. Vert designs as T 305 of Antigua. Multicoloured. P 12.*

1657	$1	"Madonna and Child with St. Catherine and a Rabbit" (left detail) (Titian)	65	70
	a.	Sheetlet. Nos. 1657/64	4·75	
1658	$1	"Madonna and Child with St. Catherine and a Rabbit" (right detail) (Titian)	65	70
1659	$1	"Women at her Toilet" (Titian)	65	70
1660	$1	"The Supper at Emmaus" (left detail) (Titian)	65	70
1661	$1	"The Supper at Emmaus" (right detail) (Titian)	65	70
1662	$1	"The Pastoral Concert" (Titian)	65	70
1663	$1	"An Allegory, perhaps of Marriage" (detail) (Titian)	65	70
1664	$1	"An Allegory, perhaps of Marriage" (different detail) (Titian)	65	70
1657/64		*Set of 8*	4·75	5·00

MS1665 70×100 mm. $6 "The Ship of Fools" (Bosch) (52×85 *mm*). P 14½ 3·50 4·00
Nos. 1657/64 were printed together, *se-tenant*, in sheetlets of 8 stamps and one centre label.

(Des A. Nahigian. Litho Walsall)

1993 (24 Mar). *15th Death Anniv of Elvis Presley (singer). T 260 and similar vert designs. Multicoloured. P 14.*

1666	$1	Type 260	70	70
	a.	Strip of 3. Nos. 1666/8	1·90	
1667	$1	Elvis with guitar	70	70
1668	$1	Elvis with microphone	70	70
1666/8		*Set of 4*	1·90	1·90

Nos. 1666/8 were printed together, horizontally and vertically *se-tenant*, in sheetlets of 9 (3×3).

261 Plumbeous Warbler

262 School Crest

(Des Tracy Pedersen. Litho Questa)

1993 (30 Apr). *Birds. T 261 and similar vert designs. Multicoloured. P 14.*

1669	90 c.	Type 261	70	80
	a.	Sheetlet. Nos. 1669/80	7·50	
1670	90 c.	Black Swift	70	80
1671	90 c.	Blue-hooded Euphonia	70	80
1672	90 c.	Rufous-throated Solitaire	70	80
1673	90 c.	Ringed Kingfisher	70	80
1674	90 c.	Blue-headed Hummingbird	70	80
1675	90 c.	Bananaquit	70	80
1676	90 c.	Brown Trembler	70	80
1677	90 c.	Forest Thrush	70	80
1678	90 c.	Purple-throated Carib	70	80
1679	90 c.	Ruddy Quail Dove	70	80
1680	90 c.	Least Bittern	70	80
1669/80		*Set of 12*	7·50	8·50

MS1681 Two sheets, each 100×70 mm. (a) $6 Imperial Amazon. (b) $6 Red-necked Amazon *Set of 2 sheets* 7·00 7·50
Nos. 1669/80 were printed together, *se-tenant*, in sheetlets of 12 forming a composite design.

(Litho Questa)

1993 (17 May). *Centenary of Dominica Grammar School. T 262 and similar horiz designs. Multicoloured. P 14.*

1682	25 c.	Type 262	15	10
1683	30 c.	V. Archer (first West Indian headmaster)	20	20
1684	65 c.	Hubert Charles (first Dominican headmaster)	35	45
1685	90 c.	Present school buildings	50	65
1682/5		*Set of 4*	1·10	1·25

263 Leatherback Turtle on Beach

(Des S. Barlowe. Litho Walsall)

1993 (26 May). *Turtles. T 263 and similar horiz designs. Multicoloured. P 14.*

1686	25 c.	Type 263	35	15
1687	55 c.	Hawksbill Turtle swimming	50	40
1688	65 c.	Atlantic Ridley Turtle	60	50
1689	90 c.	Green Turtle laying eggs	75	70
1690	$1	Green Turtle swimming	75	70
1691	$2	Hawksbill Turtle swimming (*different*)	1·25	1·50
1692	$4	Loggerhead Turtle	2·25	2·50
1693	$5	Leatherback Turtle swimming	2·25	2·75
1686/93		*Set of 8*	7·75	8·25

MS1694 Two sheets, each 99×70 mm. (a) $6 Green Turtle hatchling. (b) $6 Head of Hawksbill Turtle *Set of 2 sheets* 7·00 7·50

264 Ford "Model A", 1928

(Des W. Wright. Litho Walsall)

1993 (28 May). *Centenaries of Henry Ford's First Petrol Engine (90 c.), $5, $6) and Karl Benz's First Four-wheeled Car (others). T 264 and similar horiz designs. Multicoloured. P 14.*

1695	90 c.	Type 264	70	50
1696	$1.20,	Mercedes Benz car winning Swiss Grand Prix, 1936	1·00	1·00
1697	$4	Mercedes Benz car winning German Grand Prix, 1935	2·50	2·75
1698	$5	Ford "Model T", 1915	2·50	2·75
1695/8		*Set of 4*	6·00	6·25

MS1699 Two sheets, each 99×70 mm. (a) $3 Benz "Viktoria", 1893; $3 Mercedes Benz sports coupe, 1993. (b) $6 Ford "G.T.40", Le Mans, 1966 (57½×48 *mm*) *Set of 2 sheets* 7·00 7·50

(Des Kerri Schiff. Litho Questa)

1993 (10 June). *40th Anniv of Coronation. Vert designs as T 307 of Antigua. P 13½×14.*

1700	20 c.	multicoloured	10	10
	a.	Sheetlet. Nos. 1700/3×2	5·50	
1701	25 c.	reddish brown and black	10	10
1702	65 c.	multicoloured	30	35
1703	$5	multicoloured	2·25	2·40
1700/3		*Set of 4*	2·75	3·00

MS1704 71×101 mm. $6 multicoloured. P 14 3·25 3·75
Designs:—20 c. Queen Elizabeth II at Coronation (photograph by Cecil Beaton); 25 c. Queen wearing King Edward's Crown during Coronation ceremony; 65 c. Coronation coach; $5 Queen and Queen Mother in carriage. (28½×42½ *mm*)—$6 "Queen Elizabeth II, 1969" (detail) (Norman Hutchinson).
Nos. 1700/3 were printed together in sheetlets of 8 containing two *se-tenant* blocks of 4.

265 New G.P.O. and Duke of Edinburgh

(Des Kerri Schiff (Nos. 1712, 1719, **MS**1721f). Litho Questa)

1993 (30 July). *Anniversaries and Events. T 265 and similar designs. Each reddish brown, deep brown and black (Nos. 1707, 1717, **MS**1721b) or multicoloured (others). P 14.*

1705	25 c.	Type 265	10	10
1706	25 c.	"Bather with Beach Ball" (Picasso) (*vert*)	10	10
1707	65 c.	Willy Brandt and Pres. Eisenhower, 1959	30	35
1708	90 c.	As Type 265, but portrait of Queen Elizabeth II	40	45
1709	90 c.	"Portrait of Leo Stein" (Picasso) (*vert*)	40	45
1710	90 c.	Monika Holzner (Germany) (speed skating) (*vert*)	40	45
1711	90 c.	"Self-portrait" (Marian Szczyrbula) (*vert*)	40	45
1712	90 c.	Prince Naruhito and engagement photographs	40	45
1713	$1.20,	16th-century telescope (*vert*)	55	60
1714	$3	"Bruno Jasienski" (Tytus Czyzewski) (*vert*)	1·40	1·50
1715	$3	Modern observatory (*vert*)	1·40	1·50
1716	$4	Ray Leblanc and Tim Sweeney (U.S.A.) (ice hockey) (*vert*)	1·90	2·00
1717	$5	"Wilhelm Unde" (Picasso) (*vert*)	2·25	2·40
1718	$5	Willy Brandt and N.K. Winston at World's Fair, 1964	2·25	2·40
1719	$5	Masako Owada and engagement photographs	2·25	2·40
1720	$5	Pres. Clinton and wife applauding	2·25	2·40
1705/20		*Set of 16*	16·00	18·00

MS1721 Seven sheets, each 105×75 mm (a, c and f) or 75×105 mm (others). (a) $5 Copernicus (*vert*). (b) $6 "Man with Pipe" (detail) (Picasso) (*vert*). (c) $6 Willy Brandt, 1972. (d) $6 Toni Nieminen (Finland) (120 metre ski jump) (*vert*). (e) $6 "Miser" (detail) (Tadeusz Makowski) (*vert*). (f) $6 Masako Owada (*vert*). (g) $6 Pres. W. Clinton (*vert*) *Set of 7 sheets* 19·00 20·00
Anniversaries and Events:—Nos. 1705, 1708, Opening of New General Post Office Building; Nos. 1706, 1709, 1717, **MS**1721b, 20th death anniv of Picasso (artist); Nos. 1707, 1718, **MS**1721c, 80th birth anniv of Willy Brandt (German politician); Nos. 1710, 1716, **MS**1721d, Winter Olympic Games '94, Lillehammer; Nos. 1711, 1714, **MS**1721e, "Polska '93" International Stamp Exhibition, Poznań; Nos. 1712, 1719, **MS**1721f, Marriage of Crown Prince Naruhito of Japan; Nos. 1713, 1715, **MS**1721a, 450th death anniv of Copernicus (astronomer); Nos. 1720, **MS**1721g, Inauguration of U.S. President William Clinton.
No. 1714 is inscribed "Tyrus" in error.

266 Hugo Eckener in New York Parade, 1928   267 Maradona (Argentina) and Buchwald (Germany)

(Des W. Wright. Litho Walsall)

1993 (30 July). *Aviation Anniversaries. T 266 and similar multicoloured designs. P 14.*

1722	25 c.	Type 266	30	15
1723	55 c.	English Electric Lightning F.2 (fighter)	50	40
1724	65 c.	Airship LZ-127 *Graf Zeppelin* over Egypt, 1929	60	55
1725	$1	Boeing 314A (flying boat) on trans-Atlantic mail flight	80	75
1726	$2	Astronaut carrying mail to the Moon	1·50	1·75
1727	$4	Airship LZ-11 *Viktoria Luise* over Kiel harbour, 1912	2·50	3·00
1728	$5	Supermarine Spitfire (*vert*)	2·50	3·00
1722/8		*Set of 7*	8·00	8·75

MS1729 Three sheets, each 99×70 mm. (a) $6 Hugo Eckener (42½×57 *mm*). (b) $6 Royal Air Force crest (42½×57 *mm*). (c) $6 Jean-Pierre Blanchard's hot air balloon, 1793 (*vert*) *Set of 3 sheets* 8·75 9·50
Anniversaries:—Nos. 1722, 1724, 1727, **MS**1729a, 125th birth anniv of Hugo Eckener (airship commander); Nos. 1723, 1728, **MS**1729b, 75th anniv of Royal Air Force; Nos. 1725/6, **MS**1729c, Bicentenary of First Airmail Flight.

(Des Rosemary DeFiglio. Litho Questa)

1993 (8 Sept). *World Cup Football Championship, U.S.A. (1994) (1st issue). T 267 and similar vert designs. Multicoloured. P 14.*

1730	25 c.	Type 267	30	15
1731	55 c.	Ruud Gullit (Netherlands)	50	40
1732	65 c.	Chavarria (Costa Rica) and Bliss (U.S.A.)	55	45
1733	90 c.	Diego Maradona (Argentina)	70	60
1734	90 c.	Leonel Alvares (Colombia)	70	60
1735	$1	Altobelli (Italy) and Yong-hwang (South Korea)	75	70
1736	$2	Stopyra (France)	1·25	1·50
1737	$5	Renquin (Belgium) and Yaremtchuk (Russia)	2·25	3·00
1730/7		*Set of 8*	6·25	6·75

MS1738 Two sheets. (a) 73×103 mm. $6 Nestor Fabbri (Argentina). (b) 103×73 mm. $6 Andreas Brehme (Germany) *Set of 2 sheets* 5·50 6·50
See also Nos. 1849/56.

268 Ornate Chedi, Wat Phra Boromathat Chaiya

(Des Kerri Schiff. Litho Questa)

1993 (4 Oct). *Asian International Stamp Exhibitons. T* **268** *and similar vert designs. Multicoloured. P* 13½×14.

(a) "Indopex '93", Surabaya, Indonesia

1739	25 c. Type **268**	40	15
1740	55 c. Temple ruins, Sukhothai	65	45
1741	90 c. Prasat Hin Phimai, Thailand	80	65
1742	$1.65, Arjuna and Prabu Gilling Wesi puppets	1·00	1·10
	a. Sheetlet. Nos. 1742/7	5·50	
1743	$1.65, Loro Blonyo puppet	1·00	1·10
1744	$1.65, Yogyanese puppets	1·00	1·10
1745	$1.65, Wayang gedog puppet, Ng Setro	1·00	1·10
1746	$1.65, Wayang golek puppet	1·00	1·10
1747	$1.65, Wayang gedog puppet, Raden Damar Wulan	1·00	1·10
1748	$5 Main sanctuary, Prasat Phanom Rung, Thailand	3·25	3·50
1739/48	*Set of 10*	10·00	10·00
MS1749	105×136 mm. $6 Sculpture of Majaphit noble, Pura Sada	3·50	4·00

(b) "Taipei '93", Taiwan

1750	25 c. Aw Boon Haw Gardens, Causeway Bay	40	15
1751	65 c. Observation building, Kenting Park	65	45
1752	90 c. Tzu-en pagoda on lakeshore, Taiwan	80	65
1753	$1.65, Chang E kite	1·00	1·10
	a. Sheetlet. Nos. 1753/8	5·50	
1754	$1.65, Red Phoenix and Rising Sun kite	1·00	1·10
1755	$1.65, Heavenly Judge kite	1·00	1·10
1756	$1.65, Monkey King kite	1·00	1·10
1757	$1.65, Goddess of Luo River kite	1·00	1·10
1758	$1.65, Heavenly Maiden kite	1·00	1·10
1759	$5 Villa, Lantau Island	3·25	3·50
1750/9	*Set of 10*	10·00	10·00
MS1760	105×136 mm. $6 Jade sculpture of girl, Liao Dynasty	3·50	4·00

(c) "Bangkok '93", Thailand

1761	25 c. Tugu Monument, Java	40	15
1762	55 c. Candi Cangkuang mon, West Java	65	45
1763	90 c. Merus, Pura Taman Ayun, Mengwi	80	65
1764	$1.65, Hun Lek puppets of Rama and Sita	1·00	1·10
	a. Sheetlet. Nos. 1764/9	5·50	
1765	$1.65, Burmese puppet	1·00	1·10
1766	$1.65, Burmese puppets	1·00	1·10
1767	$1.65, Demon puppet at Wat Phra Kaew	1·00	1·10
1768	$1.65, Hun Lek puppet performing Khun Chang	1·00	1·10
1769	$1.65, Hun Lek puppets performing Ramakian	1·00	1·10
1770	$5 Stone mosaic, Ceto	3·25	3·50
1761/70	*Set of 10*	10·00	10·00
MS1771	105×136 mm. $6 Thai Stone carving	3·50	4·00

Nos. 1742/7, 1753/8 and 1764/9 were each printed together, *se-tenant*, in sheetlets of 6.

No. 1753 is inscribed "Chang E Rising Up th the Moon" in error.

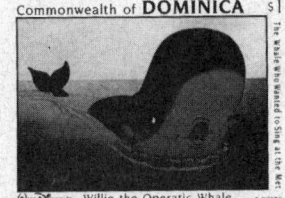

269 Willie

(Des Rosemary DeFiglio. Litho Questa)

1993 (1 Nov). *Willie the Operatic Whale. T* **269** *and similar multicoloured designs showing scenes from Walt Disney's cartoon film. P* 14×13½.

1772	$1 Type **269**	75	80
	a. Sheetlet. Nos. 1772/80	6·00	
1773	$1 Willie's pelican friend	75	80
1774	$1 Willie singing to seals	75	80
1775	$1 Willie singing *Lucia*	75	80
1776	$1 Willie in *Pagliacci*	75	80
1777	$1 Willie as Mephistopheles	75	80
1778	$1 Tetti Tatti searching for Willie	75	80
1779	$1 Whalers listening to Willie	75	80
1780	$1 Tetti Tatti with harpoon gun	75	80
1772/80	*Set of 9*	6·00	6·50
MS1781	Two sheets. (a) 130×102 mm. $6 Seals listening to Willie. P 14×13½. (b) 97×118 mm. $6 Willie in Heaven (*vert*). P 13½×14.		
	Set of 2 sheets	6·50	7·00

Nos. 1772/80 were printed together, *se-tenant*, in sheetlets of 9.

270 "Adoration of the Magi" (detail) (Dürer)

(Litho Cartor)

1993 (8 Nov). *Christmas. Religious Paintings. T* **270** *and similar designs. Black, pale lemon and red (Nos.* 1782/5, **MS**1790a) *or multicoloured (others). P* 13.

1782	25 c. Type **270**	20	10
1783	55 c. "Adoration of the Magi" (different detail) (Dürer)	35	30
1784	65 c. "Adoration of the Magi" (different detail) (Dürer)	40	35
1785	90 c. "Adoration of the Magi" (different detail) (Dürer)	60	50
1786	90 c. "Madonna of Foligno" (detail) (Raphael)	60	50
1787	$1 "Madonna of Foligno" (different detail) (Raphael)	75	60
1788	$3 "Madonna of Foligno" (different detail) (Raphael)	1·75	2·25
1789	$5 "Madonna of Foligno" (different detail) (Raphael)	2·75	3·25
1782/9	*Set of 8*	6·75	7·00
MS1790	Two sheets, each 105×130 mm. (a) $6 "Adoration of the Magi" (different detail) (Dürer) (*horiz*). (b) $6 "Madonna of Foligno" (different detail) (Raphael)		
	Set of 2 sheets	7·00	8·00

(Des W. Hanson. Litho Questa)

1994 (18 Feb). *"Hong Kong '94" International Stamp Exhibition (1st issue). Horiz designs as T* **317** *of Antigua. Multicoloured. P* 14.

1791	65 c. Hong Kong 1988 Peak Tramway 50 c. stamp and skyscrapers	30	35
	a. Horiz pair. Nos. 1791/2	60	70
1792	65 c. Dominica 1991 Cog Railways $5 stamp and Hong Kong Peak tram	30	35

Nos. 1791/2 were printed together, *se-tenant*, in horizontal pairs throughout the sheet with the centre part of each pair forming the composite design.

(Des Kerri Schiff. Litho Questa)

1994 (18 Feb). *"Hong Kong '94" International Stamp Exhibition (2nd issue). Tang Dynasty Jade. Multicoloured designs as T* **318** *of Antigua, but vert. P* 14.

1793	65 c. Horse	30	35
	a. Sheetlet. Nos. 1793/8	1·75	
1794	65 c. Cup with handle	30	35
1795	65 c. Vase with birthday peaches	30	35
1796	65 c. Vase	30	35
1797	65 c. Fu Dog with puppy	30	35
1798	65 c. Drinking cup	30	35
1793/8	*Set of 6*	1·75	2·10

Nos. 1793/8 were printed together, *se-tenant*, in sheetlets of 6.

271 Male *Dynastes hercules* (beetle) 272 *Laelio-cattleya*

(Litho Questa)

1994 (15 Mar). *Endangered Species. Birds and Insects. T* **271** *and similar horiz designs. Multicoloured. P* 14.

1799	20 c. Type **271**	10	10
1800	25 c. Male *Dynastes hercules* (different)	10	10
1801	65 c. Male *Dynastes hercules* (different)	30	35
1802	90 c. Female *Dynastes hercules*	40	45
1803	$1 Imperial Amazon ("Imperial Parrot")	45	50
1804	$2 *Marpesia petreus* (butterfly)	90	95
1805	$3 *Hypolimnus misippus* (butterfly)	1·40	1·50
1806	$5 Purple-throated Carib	2·25	2·40
1799/1806	*Set of 8*	5·75	6·25
MS1807	Two sheets, each 98×70 mm. (a) $6 Blue-headed Hummingbird. (b) $6 *Libytheana fulvescens* (butterfly)		
	Set of 2 sheets	5·50	5·75

Nos. 1803/7 do not carry the W.W.F Panda emblem.

Nos. 1799/1802 were also available in vertical *se-tenant* strips of 4 from sheetlets of 12.

(Des Mary Walters. Litho Questa)

1994 (4 Apr). *Orchids. T* **272** *and similar vert designs. Multicoloured. P* 14.

1808	20 c. Type **272**	10	10
1809	25 c. *Sophrolaelio cattleya*	10	10
1810	65 c. *Odontocidium*	30	35
1811	90 c. *Laelio-cattleya* (different)	40	45
1812	$1 *Cattleya*	45	50
1813	$2 *Odontocidium* (different)	90	95
1814	$3 *Epiphronitis*	1·40	1·50
1815	$4 *Oncidium*	1·90	2·00
1808/15	*Set of 8*	5·50	5·75
MS1816	Two sheets, each 100×70 mm. (a) $6 *Cattleya* (different). (b) $6 *Schombo cattleya*		
	Set of 2 sheets	5·50	5·75

The new-issue supplement to this Catalogue appears each month in

GIBBONS STAMP MONTHLY

—from your newsagent or by postal subscription— sample copy and details on request.

---

273 *Russula matoubensis*   274 *Appias drusilla*

(Litho Questa)

1994 (18 Apr). *Fungi. T* **273** *and similar vert designs. Multicoloured. P* 14.

1817	20 c. Type **273**	10	10
1818	25 c. *Leptonia caeruleocapitata*	10	10
1819	65 c. *Inocybe littoralis*	30	35
1820	90 c. *Russula hygrophytica*	40	45
1821	$1 *Pyrrhoglossum lilaceipes*	45	50
1822	$2 *Hygrocybe konradii*	90	95
1823	$3 *Inopilus magnificus*	1·40	1·50
1824	$5 *Boletellus cubensis*	2·25	2·40
1817/24	*Set of 8*	5·75	6·25
MS1825	Two sheets, each 110×85 mm. (a) $6 *Lentinus strigosus*. (b) $6 *Gerronema citrinum*		
	Set of 2 sheets	5·50	5·75

(Litho Questa)

1994 (3 May). *Butterflies. T* **274** *and similar horiz designs. Multicoloured. P* 14.

1826	20 c. Type **274**	10	10
1827	25 c. *Didonis biblis*	10	10
1828	55 c. *Eurema daira*	25	30
1829	65 c. *Hypolimnas misippus*	30	35
1830	$1 *Phoebis agarithe*	45	50
1831	$2 *Marpesia petreus*	90	95
1832	$3 *Libytheana fulvescens*	1·40	1·50
1833	$5 *Precis evarete*	2·25	2·40
1826/33	*Set of 8*	5·75	6·00
MS1834	Two sheets, each 100×70 mm. (a) $6 *Chlorostrymon maesites*. (b) $6 *Vanessa cardui*		
	Set of 2 sheets	5·50	5·75

275 Dachshund   (276)

ROYAL VISIT FEBRUARY 19, 1994

(Litho Questa)

1994 (17 May). *Chinese New Year ("Year of the Dog"). T* **275** *and similar vert designs. Multicoloured. P* 14.

1835	20 c. Type **275**	10	10
1836	25 c. Beagle	10	10
1837	55 c. Greyhound	25	30
1838	90 c. Jack Russell Terrier	40	45
1839	$1 Pekingese	45	50
1840	$2 Wire Fox Terrier	90	95
1841	$4 English Toy Spaniel	1·90	2·00
1842	$5 Irish Setter	2·25	2·40
1835/42	*Set of 8*	6·25	6·75
MS1843	Two sheets, each 102×72 mm. (a) $6 Welsh Corgi. (b) $6 Labrador Retriever		
	Set of 2 sheets	5·50	5·75

1994 (27 June). *Royal Visit. Nos.* 1700/4 *optd as T* **276** (*in three lines on No.* 1845 *and in silver on the sheet margin only of No.* **MS**1848).

1844	20 c. multicoloured	10	10
	a. Sheetlet. Nos. 1844/7×2	5·50	
1845	25 c. reddish brown and black	10	10
1846	65 c. multicoloured	30	35
1847	$5 multicoloured	2·25	2·40
1844/7	*Set of 4*	2·75	3·00
MS1848	71×101 mm. $6 multicoloured	2·75	3·00

277 Des Armstrong (U.S.A.)

(Litho Questa)

1994 (5 July–28 Dec). *World Cup Football Championship, U.S.A. (2nd issue). T* **277** *and similar horiz designs. Multicoloured. P* 14.

1849	25 c. Jefferey Edmund (Dominica) (28 Dec)	10	10
1850	$1 Type **277**	45	50
	a. Sheetlet. Nos. 1850/5	2·50	
1851	$1 Dennis Bergkamp (Netherlands)	45	50
1852	$1 Roberto Baggio (Italy)	45	50

1853	$1 Rai (Brazil)	45	50
1854	$1 Cafu (Brazil)	45	50
1855	$1 Marco van Basten (Netherlands)	45	50
1849/55	Set of 7	2·75	3·00

MS1856 Two sheets. (a) 70×100 mm. $6 Roberto Mancini (Italy). (b) 100×70 mm. $6 Player and Stanford Stadium, San Francisco *Set of 2 sheets* 5·50 5·75
Nos. 1850/5 were printed together, *se-tenant*, in sheetlets of 6.

278 Scout Backpacking **279** Pink Bird and Red Flowers Screen Painting

(Litho Questa)

1994 (18 July). *10th Caribbean Scout Jamboree.* T **278** *and similar multicoloured designs.* P 14.

1857	20 c. Type **278**	10	10
1858	25 c. Cooking over campfire	10	10
1859	55 c. Erecting tent	25	30
1860	65 c. Serving soup	30	35
1861	$1 Corps of drums	45	50
1862	$2 Planting tree	90	95
1863	$4 Sailing dinghy	1·90	2·00
1864	$5 Saluting	2·25	2·40
1857/64	*Set of 8*	6·25	6·50

MS1865 Two sheets, each 100×70 mm. (a) $6 Early scout troop. (b) $6 Pres. Crispin Sorhaindo (chief scout) (*vert*) .. .. *Set of 2 sheets* 5·50 5·75

(Des W. Hanson. Litho B.D.T.)

1994 (26 July). *25th Anniv of First Moon Landing. Horiz designs as* T **326** *of Antigua. Multicoloured.* P 14.

1866	$1 Crew of "Apollo 14"	45	50
	a. Sheetlet. Nos. 1866/71	2·50	
1867	$1 "Apollo 14" mission logo	45	50
1868	$1 Lunar module *Antares* on Moon	45	50
1869	$1 Crew of "Apollo 15"	45	50
1870	$1 "Apollo 15" mission logo	45	50
1871	$1 Lunar crater on Mt Hadley	45	50
1866/71	*Set of 6*	2·50	3·00

MS1872 99×106 mm. $6 "Apollo 11" logo and surface of Moon .. .. .. 2·75 3·00
Nos. 1866/71 were printed together, *se-tenant*, in sheetlets of 6.

(Des Kerri Schiff. Litho B.D.T.)

1994 (26 July). *Centenary of International Olympic Committee. Gold Medal Winners. Horiz designs as* T **327** *of Antigua. Multicoloured.* P 14.

1873	55 c. Urike Meyfarth (Germany) (high jump), 1984	25	30
1874	$1.45, Dieter Baumann (Germany) (5000 metres), 1992	65	70

MS1875 106×76 mm. $6 Ji Hoon Chae (South Korea) (500 metres speed skating), 1994 .. 2·75 3·00

(Des A. Melville-Brown. Litho B.D.T.)

1994 (26 July). *Centenary of First English Cricket Tour to the West Indies* (1995). *Multicoloured designs as* T **329** *of Antigua.* P 14.

1876	55 c. David Gower (England) (*vert*)	25	30
1877	90 c. Curtly Ambrose (West Indies) and Wisden Trophy	40	45
1878	$1 Graham Gooch (England) (*vert*)	45	50
1876/8	*Set of 3*	1·10	1·25

MS1879 76×96 mm. $3 First English touring team, 1895 .. .. 1·40 1·50

(Des J. Batchelor. Litho B.D.T.)

1994 (26 July). *50th Anniv of D-Day. Horiz designs as* T **331** *of Antigua. Multicoloured.* P 14.

1880	65 c. American Waco gliders	30	35
1881	$2 British Horsa glider	90	95
1882	$3 British glider and troops attacking Pegasus Bridge	1·40	1·50
1880/2	*Set of 3*	2·50	2·75

MS1883 107×77 mm. $6 British Hadrian glider 2·75 3·00

(Des Kerri Schiff. Litho Questa (Nos. 1884/93), B.D.T. (Nos. 1894/7))

1994 (26 July). *"Philakorea '94" International Stamp Exhibition, Seoul.* T **279** *and similar multicoloured designs.* P 13 (Nos. 1884/93) or 14 (others).

1884	55 c. Type **279**	25	30
	a. Sheetlet. Nos. 1884/93	2·50	
1885	55 c. Bird with yellow, pink and red flowers	25	30
1886	55 c. Pair of birds and yellow flowers	25	30
1887	55 c. Chickens and flowers	25	30
1888	55 c. Pair of birds and pink flowers	25	30
1889	55 c. Ducks and flowers	25	30
1890	55 c. Blue bird and red flowers	25	30
1891	55 c. Pheasant and flowers	25	30
1892	55 c. Stork and flowers	25	30
1893	55 c. Deer and flowers	25	30
1894	65 c. P'alsang-jon Hall (38×24 *mm*)	30	35

1895	90 c. Popchu-sa Temple (38×24 *mm*)	40	45
1896	$2 Uhwajong Pavilion (38×24 *mm*)	90	95
1884/96	*Set of 13*	4·00	4·75

MS1897 100×70 mm. $4 Spirit Post Guardian (38×24 *mm*). P 14 .. .. .. 1·90 2·00
Nos. 1884/93 were printed together, *se-tenant*, in sheetlets of 10 and show screen paintings.

280 Dippy Dawg **281** Marilyn Monroe

(Des Alvin White Studio. Litho Questa)

1994 (3 Oct). *65th Anniv of Mickey Mouse* (1993). T **280** *and similar multicoloured designs showing Walt Disney cartoon characters.* P 13½×14.

1898	20 c. Type **280**	10	10
1899	25 c. Clarabelle Cow	10	10
1900	55 c. Horace Horsecollar	25	30
1901	65 c. Mortimer Mouse	30	35
1902	$1 Joe Piper	45	50
1903	$3 Mr. Casey	1·40	1·50
1904	$4 Chief O'Hara	1·90	2·00
1905	$5 Mickey and The Blot	2·25	2·40
1898/1905	*Set of 8*	6·75	7·25

MS1906 Two sheets, each 127×102 mm. (a) $6 Minnie Mouse with Tanglefoot. P 13½×14. (b) $6 Minnie and Pluto (*horiz*). P 14×13½
Set of 2 sheets 5·50 5·75

(Des R. Rundo. Litho B.D.T.)

1994 (1 Dec). *Entertainers.* T **281** *and similar vert designs. Multicoloured.* P 14.

1907	20 c. Sonia Lloyd (folk singer)	10	10
1908	25 c. Ophelia Marie (singer)	10	10
1909	55 c. Edney Francis (accordion player)	25	30
1910	65 c. Norman Letang (saxophonist)	30	35
1911	90 c. Edie André (steel-band player)	40	45
1912	90 c. Type **281**	40	45
	a. Sheetlet. Nos. 1912/20	3·50	
1913	90 c. Marilyn Monroe wearing necklace	40	45
1914	90 c. In yellow frilled dress	40	45
1915	90 c. In purple dress	40	45
1916	90 c. Looking over left shoulder	40	45
1917	90 c. Laughing	40	45
1918	90 c. In red dress	40	45
1919	90 c. Wearing gold cluster earrings	40	45
1920	90 c. In yellow dress	40	45
1907/20	*Set of 14*	4·75	5·25

MS1921 Two sheets, each 106×76 mm. (a) $6 Marilyn Monroe with top hat. (b) $6 With arms above head .. .. .. *Set of 2 sheets* 5·50 5·75
Nos. 1912/20 were printed together, *se-tenant*, in sheetlets of 9.
No. 1907 is inscribed "Llyod" in error.

(Litho Questa)

1994 (2 Dec). *Christmas. Religious Paintings. Vert designs as* T **336** *of Antigua. Multicoloured.* P 13½×14.

1922	20 c. "Madonna and Child" (Luis de Morales)	10	10
1923	25 c. "Madonna and Child with Yarn Winder" (De Morales)	10	10
1924	55 c. "Our Lady of the Rosary" (detail) (Zurbaran)	25	30
1925	65 c. "Dream of the Patrician" (detail) (Murillo)	30	35
1926	90 c. "Madonna of Charity" (El Greco)	40	45
1927	$1 "The Annunciation" (Zurbaran)	45	50
1928	$2 "Mystical Marriage of St. Catherine" (Jusepe de Ribera)	90	95
1929	$3 "The Holy Family with St. Bruno and Other Saints" (detail) (De Ribera)	1·40	1·50
1922/9	*Set of 8*	3·75	4·25

MS1930 Two sheets. (a) 136×97 mm. $6 "Adoration of the Shepherds" (detail) (Murillo). (b) 99×118 mm. $6 "Vision of the Virgin to St. Bernard" (detail) (Murillo) .. *Set of 2 sheets* 5·50 5·75

(Litho Questa)

1994 (16 Dec). *First Recipients of Order of the Caribbean Community. Horiz designs as Nos.* 2046/8 *of Antigua. Multicoloured.* P 14.

1931	25 c. Sir Shridath Ramphal	10	10
1932	65 c. William Demas	30	35
1933	90 c. Derek Walcott	40	45
1931/3	*Set of 3*	80	90

18th World Scout Jamboree Mondial, Holland, May 6, 1995

(282) **283** Wood Duck

1995 (21 Mar). *18th World Scout Jamboree, Netherlands. Nos.* 1860, *and* 1863/5 *optd with* T **282** (*sideways, reading upwards on No.* MS1937b).			
1934	65 c. Serving soup	30	35
1935	$4 Sailing dinghy	1·90	2·00
1936	$5 Saluting	2·25	2·40
1934/6	*Set of 3*	4·50	4·75

MS1937 Two sheets, each 100×70 mm. (a) $6 Early scout troop. (b) $6 Pres. Crispin Sorhaindo (chief scout) (*vert*) .. .. *Set of 2 sheets* 5·50 5·75

(Des R. Rundo. Litho Questa)

1995 (15 Apr). *Water Birds.* T **283** *and similar multicoloured designs.* P 14.

1938	25 c. Type **283**	10	10
1939	55 c. Mallard	25	30
1940	65 c. Blue-winged Teal	30	35
1941	65 c. Cattle Egret (*vert*)	30	35
	a. Sheetlet. Nos. 1941/52	3·50	
1942	65 c. Snow Goose (*vert*)	30	35
1943	65 c. Peregrine Falcon (*vert*)	30	35
1944	65 c. Barn Owl (*vert*)	30	35
1945	65 c. Black-crowned Night Heron (*vert*)	30	35
1946	65 c. Common Grackle (*vert*)	30	35
1947	65 c. Brown Pelican (*vert*)	30	35
1948	65 c. Great Egret (*vert*)	30	35
1949	65 c. Ruby-throated Hummingbird (*vert*)	30	35
1950	65 c. Laughing Gull (*vert*)	30	35
1951	65 c. Greater Flamingo (*vert*)	30	35
1952	65 c. Moorhen (*vert*)	30	35
1953	$5 Red-eared Conure ("Blood Eared Parakeet")	2·25	2·40
1938/53	*Set of 16*	6·50	7·25

MS1954 Two sheets, each 105×75 mm. (a) $5 Trumpeter Swan (*vert*). (b) $6 White-eyed Vireo *Set of 2 sheets* 5·00 5·25
Nos. 1941/52 were printed together, *se-tenant*, in sheetlets of 12 with the background forming a composite design.
No. 1946 is inscribed "Common Gralkle" in error.

284 Pig's Head facing Right **285** Paul Harris (founder) and Emblem

(Des Y. Lee. Litho Questa)

1995 (21 Apr). *Chinese New Year* ("Year of the Pig"). T **284** *and similar multicoloured designs.* P 14½.

1955	25 c. Type **284**	10	10
	a. Horiz strip of 3. Nos. 1955/7	85	
1956	65 c. Pig facing to the front	30	35
1957	$1 Pig facing left	45	50
1955/7	*Set of 3*	85	95

MS1958 101×50 mm. No. 1955/7 85 90
MS1959 105×77 mm. $2 Two pigs (*horiz*) 90 95
Nos. 1955/7 were printed together, *se-tenant*, in horizontal strips of 3 throughout the sheet.

(Litho Questa)

1995 (18 May). *50th Anniv of End of Second World War in Europe. Horiz designs as* T **340** *of Antigua. Multicoloured.* P 14.

1960	$2 German Panther tank in the Ardennes	90	95
	a. Sheetlet. Nos. 1960/7	7·25	
1961	$2 American fighter-bomber	90	95
1962	$2 American mechanized column crossing the Rhine	90	95
1963	$2 Messerschmitt Me 163B Komet and Allied bombers	90	94
1964	$2 V2 rocket on launcher	90	95
1965	$2 German U-boat surrendering	90	95
1966	$2 Heavy artillery in action	90	95
1967	$2 Soviet infantry in Berlin	90	95
1960/7	*Set of 8*	7·25	7·50

MS1968 106×76 mm. $6 Statue and devastated Dresden (56½×42½ *mm*) .. .. 2·75 3·00
Nos. 1960/7 were printed together, *se-tenant*, in sheetlets of 8 with the stamps arranged in two horizontal strips of 4 separated by a gutter showing liberation of Dachau.

(Litho Questa)

1995 (21 July). *90th Anniv of Rotary International.* T **285** *and similar horiz design.* P 14.

1969	$1 lake-brown, reddish purple and black	45	50
MS1970	70×100 mm. $6 vermilion and black ..	2·75	3·00

Design:—$6 Rotary emblems.

(Des J. Batchelor. Litho Questa)

1995 (21 July). *50th Anniv of End of Second World War in the Pacific. Horiz designs as* T **340** *of Antigua. Multicoloured.* P 14.

1971	$2 Mitsubishi A6M Zero-Sen torpedo-bomber	90	95
	a. Sheetlet. Nos. 1971/6	5·25	
1972	$2 Aichi D3A "Val" dive bomber	90	95
1973	$2 Nakajima B5N "Kate" bomber	90	95
1974	$2 *Zuikaku* (Japanese aircraft carrier)	90	95
1975	$2 *Akagi* (Japanese aircraft carrier)	90	95
1976	$2 *Ryuho* (Japanese aircraft carrier)	90	95
1971/6	*Set of 6*	5·25	5·75

MS1977 108×76 mm. $6 Japanese torpedo-bomber at Pearl Harbor .. .. 2·75 3·00
Nos. 1971/6 were printed together, *se-tenant*, in sheetlets of 6 with the stamps arranged in two horizontal strips of 3 separated by a gutter showing U.S. dive-bombers attacking Japanese aircraft carrier *Soryu*.

286 Boxing 287 Market Customers

(Des A. De Lorenzo. Litho Questa)

1995 (21 July). *Olympic Games, Atlanta (1st issue) (1996). T 286 and similar multicoloured designs. P 14.*

1978	15 c. Type 286		10	10
1979	20 c. Wrestling		10	10
1980	25 c. Judo		10	10
1981	55 c. Fencing		25	30
1982	65 c. Swimming		30	35
1983	$1 Gymnastics (*vert*)		45	50
1984	$2 Cycling (*vert*)		90	95
1985	$5 Volleyball		2·25	2·40
1978/85		*Set of 8*	4·50	4·75

MS1986 Two sheets, each 104×74 mm. (a) $6 Show jumping. (b) $6 Football (*vert*)
Set of 2 sheets 5·50 5·75

See also Nos. 2122/46 and 2213/14.

(Des L. Fried. Litho Questa)

1995 (16 Aug). *50th Anniv of United Nations. Vert designs as T 341 of Antigua. Multicoloured. P 14.*

1987	65 c. Signatures and U.S. delegate		30	35
	a. Horiz strip of 3. Nos. 1987/9		1·60	
1988	$1 U.S. delegate		45	50
1989	$2 Governor Stassen (U.S. delegate)		90	95
1987/9		*Set of 3*	1·60	1·75

MS1990 100×71 mm. $6 Winston Churchill 2·75 3·00

Nos. 1987/9 were printed together in sheets of 9 (3×3) containing three *se-tenant* horizontal strips, each forming a composite design.

(Des L. Fried. Litho Questa)

1995 (16 Aug). *50th Anniv of Food and Agriculture Organization. T 287 and similar multicoloured designs. P 14.*

MS1991 110×74 mm. 90 c., $1, $2 Panorama of Dominican market 1·75 1·90
MS1992 101×71 mm. $6 Women irrigating crops (*horiz*) 2·75 3·00

(Litho Questa)

1995 (16 Aug). *95th Birthday of Queen Elizabeth the Queen Mother. Vert designs as T 344 of Antigua. P 13½×14.*

1993	$1.65, orange-brown, pale brown and black		75	80
	a. Sheetlet. Nos. 1993/6, each × 2		6·00	
1994	$1.65, multicoloured		75	80
1995	$1.65, multicoloured		75	80
1996	$1.65, multicoloured		75	80
1993/6		*Set of 4*	3·00	3·25

MS1997 103×126 mm. $6 multicoloured 2·75 3·00

Designs:—No. 1993, Queen Elizabeth the Queen Mother (pastel drawing); No. 1994, Holding bouquet of flowers; No. 1995, At desk (oil painting); No. 1996, Wearing blue dress; No. MS1997, Wearing ruby and diamond tiara and necklace.

Nos. 1993/6 were printed together in sheetlets of 8, containing two *se-tenant* horizontal strips of 4.

288 Monoclonius 289 Oscar Sánchez (1987 Peace)

(Des B. Regal. Litho Questa)

1995 (8 Sept). *"Singapore '95" International Stamp Exhibition. Prehistoric Animals. T 288 and similar multicoloured designs. P 14.*

1998	20 c. Type 288		10	10
1999	25 c. Euoplocephalus		10	10
2000	55 c. Head of Coelophysis		25	30
2001	65 c. Head of Compsognathus		30	35
2002	90 c. Dimorphodon		40	45
	a. Horiz strip of 4. Nos. 2002/5		1·60	
2003	90 c. Ramphorynchus		40	45
2004	90 c. Head of Giant Alligator		40	45
2005	90 c. Pentaceratops		40	45
2006	$1 Ceratosaurus (*vert*)		45	50
	a. Sheetlet. Nos. 2006/17		5·50	
2007	$1 Comptosaurus (*vert*)		45	50
2008	$1 Stegosaur (*vert*)		45	50
2009	$1 Camarasaurs (*vert*)		45	50
2010	$1 Baronyx (*vert*)		45	50
2011	$1 Dilophosaurus (*vert*)		45	50
2012	$1 Dromaeosaurids (*vert*)		45	50
2013	$1 Deinonychus (*vert*)		45	50
2014	$1 Dinicthys (Terror Fish) (*vert*)		45	50

2015	$1 Head of Carcharodon (Giant-toothed Shark) (*vert*)		45	50
2016	$1 Nautiloid (*vert*)		45	50
2017	$1 Trilobite (*vert*)		45	50
1998/2017		*Set of 20*	7·75	8·50

MS2018 Two sheets. (a) 95×65 mm. $5 Sauropelta. (b) 65×95 mm. $6 Triceratops (*vert*)
Set of 2 sheets 5·00 5·25

Nos. 2002/5 and 2006/17 were printed together, *se-tenant*, in horizontal strips of 4 (Nos. 2002/5) or sheetlets of 12 (Nos. 2006/17), each forming composite designs.

Nos. 2002/5 do not carry the "Singapore '95" exhibition logo.

(Des R. Rundo. Litho Questa)

1995 (27 Oct). *Centenary of Nobel Prize Trust Fund. T 289 and similar vert designs. Multicoloured. P 14.*

2019	$2 Type 289		90	95
	a. Sheetlet. Nos. 2019/24		5·50	
2020	$2 Ernst Chain (1945 Medicine)		90	95
2021	$2 Aage Bohr (1975 Physics)		90	95
2022	$2 Jaroslav Seifert (1984 Literature)		90	95
2023	$2 Joseph Murray (1990 Medicine)		90	95
2024	$2 Jaroslav Heyrovsky (1959 Chemistry)		90	95
2025	$2 Adolf von Baeyer (1905 Chemistry)		90	95
	a. Sheetlet. Nos. 2025/30		5·50	
2026	$2 Eduard Buchner (1907 Chemistry)		90	95
2027	$2 Carl Bosch (1931 Chemistry)		90	95
2028	$2 Otto Hahn (1944 Chemistry)		90	95
2029	$2 Otto Diels (1950 Chemistry)		90	95
2030	$2 Kurt Alder (1950 Chemistry)		90	95
2019/30		*Set of 12*	10·50	11·00

MS2031 76×106 mm. $2 Emil von Behring (1901 Medicine) 90 95

Nos. 2019/24 and 2025/30 were printed together, *se-tenant*, in sheetlets of 6 with the backgrounds forming designs of the Nobel Medal.

(Litho Questa)

1995 (30 Nov). *Christmas. Religious Paintings. Vert designs as T 357 of Antigua. Multicoloured. P 13½×14.*

2032	20 c. "Madonna and Child with St. John" (Pontormo)		10	10
2033	25 c. "The Immaculate Conception" (Murillo)		10	10
2034	55 c. "The Adoration of the Magi" (Filippino Lippi)		25	30
2035	65 c. "Rest on the Flight into Egypt" (Van Dyck)		30	35
2036	90 c. "The Holy Family" (Van Dyck)		40	45
2037	$5 "The Annunciation" (Van Eyck)		2·25	2·40
2032/7		*Set of 6*	3·25	3·75

MS2038 Two sheets, each 102×127 mm. (a) $5 "Madonna and Child Reading" (detail) (Van Eyck). (b) $6 "The Holy Family" (detail) (Ribera)
Set of 2 sheets 5·00 5·25

(Litho Questa)

1995 (10 Dec). *Centenary of Sierra Club (environmental protection society) (1992). Endangered Species. Multicoloured designs as T 320 of Antigua. P 14.*

2039	$1 Florida Panther		45	50
	a. Sheetlet. Nos. 2039/47		4·00	
2040	$1 Manatee		45	50
2041	$1 Sockeye Salmon		45	50
2042	$1 Key Deer facing left		45	50
2043	$1 Key Deer doe		45	50
2044	$1 Key Deer stag		45	50
2045	$1 Wallaby with young in pouch		45	50
2046	$1 Wallaby feeding young		45	50
2047	$1 Wallaby and young feeding		45	50
2048	$1 Florida Panther showing teeth (*horiz*)		45	50
	a. Sheetlet. Nos. 2048/56		4·00	
2049	$1 Head of Florida Panther (*horiz*)		45	50
2050	$1 Manatee (*horiz*)		45	50
2051	$1 Pair of Manatees (*horiz*)		45	50
2052	$1 Pair of Sockeye Salmon (*horiz*)		45	50
2053	$1 Sockeye Salmon spawning (*horiz*)		45	50
2054	$1 Pair of Southern Sea Otters (*horiz*)		45	50
2055	$1 Southern Sea Otter with front paws together (*horiz*)		45	50
2056	$1 Southern Sea Otter with front paws apart (*horiz*)		45	50
2039/56		*Set of 18*	8·00	9·00

Nos. 2039/47 and 2048/56 were printed together, *se-tenant*, in sheetlets of 9.

290 Street Scene

1995 (27 Dec). *"A City of Cathay" (Chinese scroll painting). T 290 and similar multicoloured designs. Litho. P 14½.*

2057	90 c. Type 290		40	45
	a. Horiz strip of 5. Nos. 2057/61		2·00	
2058	90 c. Street scene and city wall		40	45
2059	90 c. City gate and bridge		40	45
2060	90 c. Landing stage and junk		40	45
2061	90 c. River bridge		40	45
2062	90 c. Moored junks		40	45
	a. Horiz strip of 5. Nos. 2062/6		2·00	
2063	90 c. Two rafts on river		40	45
2064	90 c. Two junks on river		40	45
2065	90 c. Roadside tea house		40	45
2066	90 c. Wedding party on the road		40	45
2057/66		*Set of 10*	4·00	4·50

MS2067 Two sheets, each 106×77 mm. (a) $2 City street and sampan; $2 Footbridge. (b) $2 Stern of sampan (*vert*); $2 Bow of sampan (*vert*)
Set of 2 sheets 3·75 4·00

Nos. 2057/61 (showing inscriptions in black) and Nos. 2062/6 (showing inscriptions in chestnut) were each issued in sheets of 20 containing four *se-tenant* strips of 5, with each horizontal row separated by imperforate gutters incorporating inscribed labels.

291 "Bindo Altoviti" (Raphael) 292 Rat

(Litho Questa)

1995 (27 Dec). *Paintings by Raphael. T 291 and similar vert designs. Multicoloured. P 13½×14.*

2068	$2 Type 291		90	95
2069	$2 "Pope Leo with Nephews"		90	95
2070	$2 "Agony in the Garden"		90	95
2068/70		*Set of 3*	2·75	2·75

MS2071 110×80 mm. $6 "Pope Leo X with Cardinals Giulio de Medici and Luigi dei Rossi" (detail) 2·75 3·00

(Des Y. Lee. Litho Questa)

1996 (16 Jan). *Chinese New Year ("Year of the Rat"). T 292 and similar designs showing rats and Chinese symbols. Multicoloured. P 14½.*

2072	25 c. black, violet and chestnut		10	10
	a. Horiz strip of 3. Nos. 2072/4		85	
2073	65 c. black, orange-vermilion & deep green		30	35
2074	$1 black, magenta and blue		45	50
2072/4		*Set of 3*	85	95

MS2075 100×50 mm. Nos. 2072/4 85 90
MS2076 105×77 mm. $2 black, grey-green and reddish violet (two rats) 90 95

Nos. 2072/4 were printed together, *se-tenant*, in horizontal strips of 3 throughout sheets of 12.

293 Mickey and Minnie Mouse (Year of the Rat)

(Litho Questa)

1996 (16 Jan). *Chinese Lunar Calendar. T 293 and similar horiz designs showing Walt Disney cartoon characters. Multicoloured. P 14×13½.*

2077	55 c. Type 293		25	30
	a. Sheetlet. Nos. 2077/88		3·00	
2078	55 c. Casey Jones (Year of the Ox)		25	30
2079	55 c. Tigger, Pooh and Piglet (Year of the Tiger)		25	30
2080	55 c. White Rabbit (Year of the Rabbit)		25	30
2081	55 c. Dragon playing flute (Year of the Dragon)		25	30
2082	55 c. Snake looking in mirror (Year of the Snake)		25	30
2083	55 c. Horace Horsecollar and Clarabelle Cow (Year of the Horse)		25	30
2084	55 c. Black Lamb and blue birds (Year of the Ram)		25	30
2085	55 c. King Louis reading book (Year of the Monkey)		25	30
2086	55 c. Cock playing lute (Year of the Cock)		25	30
2087	55 c. Mickey and Pluto (Year of the Dog)		25	30
2088	55 c. Pig building bridge (Year of the Pig)		25	30
2077/88		*Set of 12*	3·00	3·50

MS2089 Two sheets. (a) 127×102 mm. $3 Basil the Great Mouse Detective (Year of the Rat). (b) 102×127 mm. $6 Emblems for 1996, 1997 and 2007
Set of 2 sheets 4·25 4·50

Nos. 2077/88 were printed together, *se-tenant*, in sheetlets of 12.

294 Class "Dragon" Steam Locomotive, Hawaii

(Des R. Sauber. Litho B.D.T.)

1996 (29 Jan). *Trains of the World. T 294 and similar horiz designs. Multicoloured. P 14.*

2090	$2 Type 294		90	95
	a. Sheetlet. Nos. 2090/8		8·00	
2091	$2 Class "Regina" steam locomotive, Italy		90	95
2092	$2 Calazo to Padua steam locomotive, Italy		90	95

2093	$2 Class "Mogul" steam locomotive, Philippines		90	95
2094	$2 Class "Nuremberg" steam locomotives, Germany		90	95
2095	$2 Class "Stanislas" electric train, France		90	95
2096	$2 Class "Black Five" steam locomotive, Scotland		90	95
2097	$2 Diesel-electric locomotive, France		90	95
2098	$2 *Sir Nigel Gresley* steam locomotive, England		90	95
2099	$2 Class "9600" steam locomotive, Japan		90	95
	a. Sheetlet. Nos. 2099/107		8·00	
2100	$2 "Peloponnese Express" train, Greece		90	95
2101	$2 Porter type steam locomotive, Hawaii		90	95
2102	$2 Jodemans steam locomotive, Norway–Sweden		90	95
2103	$2 Class "220" diesel locomotive, Germany		90	95
2104	$2 "2-8-4T" steam locomotive, India		90	95
2105	$2 Steam locomotive, East African Railways		90	95
2106	$2 Electric trains, Russia		90	95
2107	$2 "0-8-0" steam locomotive, Austria		90	95
2090/107		*Set of 18*	16·00	17·00

MS2108 Two sheets, each 103×73 mm. (a) $5 *Duchess of Hamilton* steam locomotive, England. (b) $6 Diesel locomotive, China .. *Set of 2 sheets* 5·00 5·25
Nos. 2090/8 and 2099/107 were printed together, *se-tenant*, in sheetlets of 9 with enlarged illustrated top margins.

295 Horse-drawn Gig, 1965

1996 (29 Jan). *Traditional Island Transport. T* **295** *and similar horiz designs. Multicoloured. P* 14.

2109	65 c. Type **295**		30	35
2110	90 c. Early automobile, 1910		40	45
2111	$2 Lorry, 1950		90	95
2112	$3 Bus, 1955		1·40	1·50
2109/12		*Set of 4*	3·00	3·25

296 Giant Panda

1996 (15 May). *"CHINA '96" 9th Asian International Stamp Exhibition, Peking. Giant Pandas. T* **296** *and similar multicoloured designs. Litho. P* 13½×14.

2113	55 c. Type **296**		25	30
	a. Sheetlet. Nos. 2113/16 × 2		2·00	
2114	55 c. Panda on rock		25	30
2115	55 c. Panda eating bamboo shoots		25	30
2116	55 c. Panda on all fours		25	30
2113/16		*Set of 4*	1·00	1·10

MS2117 Two sheets. (a) 90×125 mm. $2 Huangshan Mountain, China (50×75 *mm*). P 12. (b) 160×125 mm. $3 Panda sitting (50×37 *mm*). P 14×13½ .. .. .. *Set of 2 sheets* 2·25 2·40
Nos. 2113/16 were printed together, *se-tenant*, in sheetlets of 8 containing two of each design.

(Litho Questa)

1996 (16 May). *70th Birthday of Queen Elizabeth II. Vert designs as T* **367** *of Antigua. Multicoloured. P* 13½×14.

2118	$2 As Type **367** of Antigua		90	95
	a. Strip of 3. Nos. 2118/20		2·50	
2119	$2 Queen in robes of Order of St. Michael and St. George		90	95
2120	$2 Queen in blue dress with floral brooch		90	95
2118/20		*Set of 3*	2·50	2·75

MS2121 103×125 mm. $6 Queen at Trooping the Colour. P 13½×14 .. .. .. 2·75 3·00
Nos. 2118/20 were printed together, *se-tenant*, in horizontal and vertical strips of 3 throughout the sheet.

297 Moscow Stadium, 1980

(Litho B.D.T.)

1996 (7 June). *Olympic Games, Atlanta (2nd issue). Previous Medal Winners. T* **297** *and similar multicoloured designs. P* 14.

2122	20 c. Type **297**		10	15
2123	25 c. Hermine Joseph (running) (*vert*)		10	15
2124	55 c. Zimbabwe women's hockey team, 1980		25	30
2125	90 c. Jerome Romain (long jump) (*vert*)		40	45
2126	90 c. Sammy Lee (diving), 1948 and 1952 (*vert*)		40	45
	a. Sheetlet. Nos. 2126/34		3·50	
2127	90 c. Bruce Jenner (decathalon), 1976 (*vert*)		40	45
2128	90 c. Olga Korbut (gymnastics), 1972 (*vert*)		40	45
2129	90 c. Steffi Graff (tennis), 1988 (*vert*)		40	45
2130	90 c. Florence Griffith-Joyner (track and field), 1988 (*vert*)		40	45
2131	90 c. Mark Spitz (swimming), 1968 and 1972 (*vert*)		40	45
2132	90 c. Li Ning (gymnastics), 1984 (*vert*)		40	45
2133	90 c. Erika Salumae (cycling), 1988 (*vert*)		40	45
2134	90 c. Abebe Bikila (marathon), 1960 and 1964 (*vert*)		40	45
2135	90 c. Ulrike Meyfarth (high jump), 1972 and 1984 (*vert*)		40	45
	a. Sheetlet. Nos. 2135/43		3·50	
2136	90 c. Pat McCormick (diving), 1952 and 1956 (*vert*)		40	45
2137	90 c. Takeichi Nishi (equestrian), 1932 (*vert*)		40	45
2138	90 c. Peter Farkas (Greco-Roman wrestling), 1992 (*vert*)		40	45
2139	90 c. Carl Lewis (track and field), 1984, 1988 and 1992 (*vert*)		40	45
2140	90 c. Agnes Keleti (gymnastics), 1952 and 1956 (*vert*)		40	45
2141	90 c. Yasuhiro Yamashita (judo), 1984 (*vert*)		40	45
2142	90 c. John Kelly (single sculls), 1920 (*vert*)		40	45
2143	90 c. Naim Suleymanoglu (weightlifting), 1988 and 1992 (*vert*)		40	45
2144	$1 Polo (*vert*)		45	50
2145	$2 Greg Louganis (diving), 1976, 1984 and 1988		90	95
2122/45		*Set of 24*	9·00	10·00

MS2146 Two sheets, each 105×75 mm. (a) $5 Joan Benoit (marathon), 1984 (*vert*). (b) $5 Milt Campbell (discus) .. .. *Set of 2 sheets* 4·50 4·75
Nos. 2126/34 and 2135/43 were each printed together, *se-tenant*, in sheetlets of 9, the backgrounds forming composite designs.

(Litho Questa)

1996 (31 July). *50th Anniv of U.N.I.C.E.F. Multicoloured designs as T* **366** *of Antigua. P* 14.

2147	20 c. Child and globe (*horiz*)		10	10
2148	55 c. Child with syringe and stethoscope (*horiz*)		25	30
2149	$5 Doctor and child (*horiz*)		2·25	2·40
2147/9		*Set of 3*	2·50	2·75

MS2150 74×104 mm. $5 African child .. 2·25 2·40

(Des R. Sauber. Litho Questa)

1996 (31 July). *3000th Anniv of Jerusalem. Vert designs as T* **367** *of Antigua. Multicoloured. P* 14.
MS2151 114×95.mm. 90 c. Shrine of the Book, Israel Museum; $1 Church of All Nations; $2 The Great Synagogue .. .. .. 1·75 1·90
MS2152 104×74 mm. $5 Hebrew University, Mount Scopus .. .. 2·25 2·40

(Des J. Iskowitz. Litho Questa)

1996 (31 July). *Centenary of Radio. Entertainers. Multicoloured designs as T* **368** *of Antigua. P* 13½×14.

2153	90 c. Artie Shaw		40	45
2154	$1 Benny Goodman		45	50
2155	$2 Duke Ellington		90	95
2156	$4 Harry James		1·90	2·00
2153/6		*Set of 4*	3·50	3·75

MS2157 70×99 mm. $6 Tommy and Jimmy Dorsey. P 14×13½ (*horiz*) .. .. 2·75 3·00

298 Irene Peltier in National Dress   299 Humphrey Bogart as Sam Spade

(Litho Questa)

1996 (31 July). *Local Entertainers. T* **298** *and similar vert designs. Multicoloured. P* 13½×14.

2158	25 c. Type **298**		10	15
2159	55 c. Rupert Bartley (steel-band player)		25	30
2160	65 c. Rosemary Cools-Lartigue (pianist)		30	35
2161	90 c. Celestine 'Orion' Theophile (singer)		40	45
2162	$1 Cecil Bellot (band master)		45	50
2158/62		*Set of 5*	1·50	1·75

1996 (31 July). *Centenary of Cinema. Screen Detectives. T* **299** *and similar vert designs. Multicoloured. Litho. P* 13½×14.

2163	$1 Type **299**		45	50
	a. Sheetlet. Nos. 2163/71		4·00	
2164	$1 Sean Connery as James Bond		45	50
2165	$1 Warren Beatty as Dick Tracy		45	50
2166	$1 Basil Rathbone as Sherlock Holmes		45	50
2167	$1 William Powell as the Thin Man		45	50
2168	$1 Sidney Toler as Charlie Chan		45	50
2169	$1 Peter Sellers as Inspector Clouseau		45	50
2170	$1 Robert Mitchum as Philip Marlowe		45	50
2171	$1 Peter Ustinov as Hercule Poirot		45	50
2163/71		*Set of 9*	4·00	4·50

MS2172 105×75 mm. $6 Margaret Rutherford as Miss Marple .. .. .. 2·75 3·00
Nos. 2163/71 were printed together, *se-tenant*, in sheetlets of 9.

300 Scribbled Filefish   302 "Enthroned Madonna and Child" (S. Veneziano)

(Litho Questa)

1996 (1 Oct). *Fishes. T* **300** *and similar horiz designs. Multicoloured. P* 14½×13½.

2173	1 c. Type **300**		10	10
2174	2 c. Lionfish		10	10
2175	5 c. Porcupinefish		10	10
2176	10 c. Powder-blue Surgeonfish		10	10
2177	15 c. Red Hind		10	10
2178	20 c. Golden Butterflyfish		10	10
2179	25 c. Copper-banded Butterflyfish		10	15
2180	35 c. Pennant Coralfish		15	20
2181	45 c. Spotted Drum		20	25
2182	55 c. Blue-girdled Angelfish		25	30
2183	60 c. Scorpionfish		25	30
2184	65 c. Harlequin Sweetlips		30	35
2185	90 c. Flame Angelfish		40	45
2186	$1 Queen Triggerfish		45	50
2187	$1.20, Spotlight Parrotfish		55	60
2188	$1.45, Black Durgon		65	70
2189	$2 Glass-eyed Snapper		90	95
2190	$5 Balloonfish		2·25	2·40
2191	$10 Creole Wrasse		4·50	4·75
2192	$20 Sea Bass		9·25	9·50
2173/92		*Set of 20*	20·00	21·00

For these designs in a smaller format, 24×21 mm, see Nos. 2371/86.

(Litho Questa)

1996 (25 Nov). *Christmas. Religious Paintings. T* **302** *and similar multicoloured designs. P* 14.

2201	25 c. Type **302**		10	10
2202	55 c. "Noli Me Tangere" (Fra Angelico)		25	30
2203	65 c. "Madonna and Child Enthroned" (Angelico)		30	35
2204	90 c. "Madonna of Corneto Tarquinia" (F. Lippi)		40	45
2205	$2 "The Annunciation" and "Adoration of the Magi" (School of Angelico)		90	95
2206	$5 "Madonna and Child of the Shade" (Angelico)		2·25	2·40
2201/6		*Set of 6*	4·00	4·50

MS2207 Two sheets. (a) 76×106 mm. $6 "Coronation of the Virgin" (Angelico). (b) 106×76 mm. $6 "Holy Family with St. Barbara" (Veronese) (*horiz*) .. *Set of 2 sheets* 5·50 5·75

303 "Herdboy playing the Flute" (Li Keran)

(Des Y. Lee. Litho Questa)

1997 (10 Jan). *Lunar New Year ("Year of the Ox"). Paintings by Li Keran. T* **303** *and similar vert designs. Multicoloured. P* 14.

2208	90 c. Type **303**		40	45
	a. Sheetlet. Nos. 2208/11×2		3·00	
2209	90 c. "Playing Cricket in the Autumn"		40	45
2210	90 c. "Listening to the Summer Cicada"		40	45
2211	90 c. "Grazing in the Spring"		40	45
2208/11		*Set of 4*	1·60	1·75

MS2212 76×106 mm. $2 "Return in Wind and Rain" (34×51 *mm*). P 14½ 90 95
Nos. 2208/11 were printed together *se-tenant*, in sheetlets of 8 containing two of each design.

304 Lee Lai-shan (Gold medal – Wind Surfing, 1996)

(Des Y. Lee. Litho)

1997 (12 Feb). *Olympic Games, Atlanta (3rd issue). T **304** and similar multicoloured design. P 15×14.*
2213	$2 Type **304**	..	..	90	1·00
	a. Sheetlet. No. 2213×3		..	2·50	
MS2214	97×67 mm. $5 Lee Lai-shan wearing Gold medal (37×50 *mm*). P 14			2·25	2·40

No. 2213 was printed in sheets of 3, with an enlarged illustrated left-hand margin.

305 *Meticella metis*

1997 (1 Apr). *Butterflies. T **305** and similar multicoloured designs. Litho. P 14.*
2215	55 c. Type **305**	..	..	25	30
	a. Sheetlet. Nos. 2215/23		..	2·25	
2216	55 c. *Coeliades forestan*	..	..	25	30
2217	55 c. *Papilio dardanus*	..	..	25	30
2218	55 c. *Mylothris chloris*	..	..	25	30
2219	55 c. *Poecilmitis thysbe*	..	..	25	30
2220	55 c. *Myrina silenus*	..	..	25	30
2221	55 c. *Bematistes aganice*	..	..	25	30
2222	55 c. *Euphaedra neophron*	..	..	25	30
2223	55 c. *Precis hierta*	..	..	25	30
2224	90 c. *Coeliadas forestan* (*vert*)		..	40	45
	a. Sheetlet. Nos. 2224/31		..	3·25	
2225	90 c. *Spialia spio* (*vert*)		..	40	45
2226	90 c. *Belenous aurota* (*vert*)		..	40	45
2227	90 c. *Dingana bowkom* (*vert*)		..	40	45
2228	90 c. *Charaxes jasius* (*vert*)		..	40	45
2229	90 c. *Catacroptera cloanthe* (*vert*)		..	40	45
2230	90 c. *Colias electo* (*vert*)	..		40	45
2231	90 c. *Junonia archesia* (*vert*)		..	40	45
2215/31			*Set of 17*	5·50	6·00
MS2232	Two sheets, each 102×71 mm. $6 *Eurytela dryope*. (b) $6 *Acraea natalica*				
			Set of 2 sheets	5·50	5·75

Nos. 2215/23 and 2224/31 were printed together, *se-tenant*, in sheetlets of 8 (Nos. 2224/31) or 9 (Nos. 2215/23) with the backgrounds forming composite designs.

No. 2230 is inscribed "*Collas electo*" in error.

(Des M. Freedman and Dena Rubin. Litho Questa)

1997 (7 Apr). *50th Anniv of U.N.E.S.C.O. Multicoloured designs as T **373** of Antigua. P 14×13½ (horiz) or 13½×14 (vert).*
2233	55 c. Temple roof, China	..	..	25	30
2234	65 c. The Palace of Diocletian, Split, Croatia		..	30	35
2235	90 c. St. Mary's Cathedral, Hildesheim, Germany		..	40	45
2236	$1 The Monastery of Rossanou, Mount Athos, Greece		..	45	50
2237	$1 Carved face, Copan, Honduras (*vert*)			45	50
	a. Sheetlet. Nos. 2237/44 and centre label			3·50	
2238	$1 Cuzco Cathedral, Peru (*vert*)		..	45	50
2239	$1 Church, Olinda, Brazil (*vert*)		..	45	50
2240	$1 Canaima National Park, Venezuela (*vert*)			45	50
2241	$1 Galapagos Islands National Park, Ecuador (*vert*)			45	50
2242	$1 Church ruins, La Santisima Jesuit Missions, Paraguay (*vert*)			45	50
2243	$1 San Lorenzo Fortress, Panama (*vert*)			45	50
2244	$1 Fortress, National Park, Haiti (*vert*)			45	50
2245	$2 Scandola Nature Reserve, France	..		90	95
2246	$4 Church of San Antao, Portugal	..		1·90	2·00
2233/46			*Set of 14*	7·75	8·50
MS2247	Two sheets, each 127×102 mm. (a) $6 Chengde Lakes, China. (b) $6 Pavilion, Kyoto, Japan		*Set of 2 sheets*	5·50	5·75

Nos. 2237/44 were printed together, *se-tenant*, in sheetlets of 8 with a centre label.

No. 2234 is inscribed "DICELECIAN" in error.

306 Tanglefoot and Minnie   **307** Afghan Hound

(Litho Questa)

1997 (15 Apr). *Disney Sweethearts. T **306** and similar multi-coloured designs. P 13½×14.*
2248	25 c. Type **306**	..	..	10	15
2249	35 c. Mickey and Minnie kissing on ship's wheel			15	20
2250	55 c. Pluto and kitten	..	..	25	30
2251	65 c. Clarabelle Cow kissing Horace Horsecollar			30	35
2252	90 c. Elmer Elephant and tiger	..		40	45
2253	$1 Minnie kissing Mickey in period costume			45	50
2254	$2 Donald Duck and nephew	..		90	95
2255	$4 Dog kissing Pluto	..	..	1·90	2·00
2248/55			*Set of 8*	4·50	5·00
MS2256	Two sheets, each 133×104 mm. (a) $6 Mickey covered in lipstick and Minnie (*horiz*). P 14×13½. (b) $6 Mickey and Pluto. P 13½×14				
			Set of 2 sheets	5·50	5·75

(Litho Questa)

1997 (24 Apr). *Cats and Dogs. T **307** and similar vert designs. Multicoloured. P 14.*
2257	20 c. Type **307**	..	..	10	15
2258	25 c. Cream Burmese	..	..	10	15
2259	55 c. Cocker Spaniel	..	..	25	30
2260	65 c. Smooth Fox Terrier	..	..	30	35
2261	90 c. West Highland White Terrier	..		40	45
2262	90 c. St. Bernard puppies	..		40	45
	a. Sheetlet. Nos. 2262/7		..	2·40	
2263	90 c. Boy with Grand Basset	..		40	45
2264	90 c. Rough Collie	..	..	40	45
2265	90 c. Golden Retriever	..	..	40	45
2266	90 c. Golden Retriever, Tibetan Spaniel and Smooth Fox Terrier			40	45
2267	90 c. Smooth Fox Terrier	..		40	45
2268	$1 Snowshoe	..	..	45	50
2269	$2 Sorrell Abyssinian	..	..	90	95
2270	$2 British Bicolour Shorthair	..		90	95
	a. Sheetlet. Nos. 2270/5		..	5·40	
2271	$2 Maine Coon and Somali kittens	..		90	95
2272	$2 Maine Coon kitten	..	..	90	95
2273	$2 Lynx Point Siamese	..	..	90	95
2274	$2 Blue Burmese kitten and White Persian			90	95
2275	$2 Persian kitten	..	..	90	95
2276	$5 Torbie Persian	..	..	2·25	2·40
2257/76			*Set of 20*	12·50	13·00
MS2277	Two sheets, each 106×76 mm. (a) $6 Silver Tabby. (b) $6 Shetland Sheepdog				
			Set of 2 sheets	5·50	5·75

Nos. 2262/7 and 2270/5 were each printed together, *se-tenant*, in sheetlets of 6 with the backgrounds forming composite design.

308 *Oncidium altissimum*   **309** "Mary, Mary Quite Contrary"

(Litho Questa)

1997 (10 May). *Orchids of the Caribbean. T **308** and similar multicoloured designs. P 14.*
2278	20 c. Type **308**	..	..	10	10
2279	25 c. *Oncidium papilio*	..	..	10	15
2280	55 c. *Epidendrum fragrans*	..		25	30
2281	65 c. *Oncidium lanceanum*	..		30	35
2282	90 c. *Campylocentrum micranthum*	..		40	45
2283	$1 *Brassavola cucculata* (*horiz*)			45	50
	a. Sheetlet. Nos. 2283/8		..	2·75	
2284	$1 *Epidendrum ibaguense* (*horiz*)			45	50
2285	$1 *Ionopsis utricularioides* (*horiz*)			45	50
2286	$1 *Rodriguezia lanceolata* (*horiz*)			45	50
2287	$1 *Oncidium cebolleta* (*horiz*)	..		45	50
2288	$1 *Epidendrum ciliare* (*horiz*)			45	50
2289	$4 *Pogonia rosea*	..	..	1·90	2·00
2278/89			*Set of 12*	5·75	6·25
MS2290	Two sheets, each 106×76 mm. (a) $5 *Oncidium ampliatum* (*horiz*). (b) $5 *Starhopea grandiflora* (*horiz*)		*Set of 2 sheets*	4·50	4·75

Nos. 2283/8 were printed together, *se-tenant*, in sheetlets of 6 with the backgrounds forming a composite design.

(Des R. Rundo. Litho Questa)

1997 (29 May). *300th Anniv of Mother Goose Nursery Rhymes. Sheet 72×102 mm. P 14.*
MS2291	**309** $6 multicoloured	..	..	2·75	3·00

(Litho Questa)

1997 (29 May). *10th Anniv of Chernobyl Nuclear Disaster. Vert designs as T **375** of Antigua. Multicoloured. P 13½.*
2292	$2 As Type **375** of Antigua			90	95
2293	$2 As Type **375** of Antigua; but inscribed "CHABAD'S CHILDREN OF CHERNOBYL" at foot			90	95

(Des J. Iskowitz. Litho Questa)

1997 (29 May). *50th Death Anniv of Paul Harris (founder of Rotary International). Horiz designs as T **376** of Antigua. Multicoloured. P 14.*
2294	$2 Paul Harris and irrigation project, Honduras			90	95
MS2295	78×107 mm. $6 Paul Harris with Rotary and World Community Service emblems			2·75	3·00

(Litho Questa)

1997 (29 May). *Golden Wedding of Queen Elizabeth and Prince Philip. Horiz designs as T **377** of Antigua. Multicoloured. P 14.*
2296	$1 Queen Elizabeth II	..	..	45	50
	a. Sheetlet. Nos. 2296/301		..	2·75	
2297	$1 Royal Coat of Arms	..	..	45	50
2298	$1 Queen Elizabeth and Prince Philip in shirt sleeves			45	50
2299	$1 Queen Elizabeth and Prince Philip in naval uniform			45	50
2300	$1 Buckingham Palace	..	..	45	50
2301	$1 Prince Philip	..	..	45	50
2296/301			*Set of 6*	2·75	3·00
MS2302	100×71 mm. $6 Queen Elizabeth and Prince Philip with flower arrangement			2·75	3·00

Nos. 2296/301 were printed together, *se-tenant*, in sheetlets of 6.

(Des J. Iskowitz. Litho Questa)

1997 (29 May). *"Pacific '97" International Stamp Exhibition, San Francisco. Death Centenary of Heinrich von Stephan (founder of the U.P.U.). Horiz designs as T **378** of Antigua. P 14.*
2303	$2 violet	..	..	90	95
	a. Sheetlet. Nos. 2303/5		..	2·75	
2304	$2 chestnut	..	..	90	95
2305	$2 sepia	..	..	90	95
2303/5			*Set of 3*	2·75	3·00
MS2306	82×119 mm. $6 dull blue and grey-blue			2·75	3·00

Designs:—No. 2303, Kaiser Wilhelm II and Heinrich von Stephan; No. 2304, Heinrich von Stephan and Mercury; No. 2305, Early Japanese postal messenger; No. MS2306, Heinrich von Stephan and Russian postal dog team, 1859.

Nos. 2303/5 were printed together, *se-tenant*, in sheets of 3 with enlarged right-hand margin.

310 "Ichigaya Hachiman Shrine"   **311** Hong Kong Skyline at Dusk

1997 (29 May). *Birth Bicentenary of Hiroshige (Japanese painter). "One Hundred Famous Views of Edo". T **310** and similar vert designs. Multicoloured. Litho. P 13½×14.*
2307	$1.55, Type **310**	..	..	70	75
	a. Sheetlet. Nos. 2307/12		..	4·25	
2308	$1.55, "Blossoms on the Tama River Embankment"			70	75
2309	$1.55, "Kumano Junisha Shrine, Tsunohazu"			70	75
2310	$1.55, "Benkei Moat from Soto-Sakurada to Kojimachi"			70	75
2311	$1.55, "Kinokuni Hill and View of Akasak Tameike"			70	75
2312	$1.55, "Naito Shinjuku, Yotsuya"			70	75
2307/12			*Set of 6*	4·25	4·50
MS2313	Two sheets, each 102×127 mm. (a) $6 "Sanno Festival Procession at Kojimachi l-chome". (b) $6 "Kasumigaseki" *Set of 2 sheets*			5·50	5·75

Nos. 2307/12 were printed together, *se-tenant*, in sheetlets of 6.

(Des R. Sauber. Litho Questa)

1997 (29 May). *175th Anniv of Brothers Grimm's Third Collection of Fairy Tales. The Goose Girl. Multicoloured designs as T **379** of Antigua. P 13½×14.*
2314	$2 Goose Girl with horse	..		90	95
	a. Sheetlet. Nos. 2314/16		..	2·75	
2315	$2 Geese in front of castle	..		90	95
2316	$2 Goose Girl	..	..	90	95
2314/16			*Set of 3*	2·75	3·00
MS2317	124×96 mm. $6 Goose Girl (*horiz*). P 14×13½			2·75	3·00

Nos. 2314/16 were printed together, *se-tenant*, in sheetlets of 3 with illustrated margins.

(Des Y. Lee. Litho Questa)

1997 (1 July). *Return of Hong Kong to China. T **311** and similar vert designs showing modern Hong Kong. P 14×13½.*
2318	65 c. multicoloured	..	..	30	35
	a. Sheetlet. No. 2318×4		..	1·25	
2319	$1 multicoloured	..	..	45	50
	a. Sheetlet. No. 2319×4		..	1·75	
2320	$1.45, multicoloured	..		65	70
	a. Sheetlet. No. 2320×4		..	2·50	
2321	$2 multicoloured	..	..	90	95
	a. Sheetlet. No. 2321×4		..	3·50	
2318/21			*Set of 4*	2·25	2·50

Nos. 2318/21 were each printed, *se-tenant*, in sheetlets of 4 with an illustrated left or right-hand margin.

COVER PRICES

Cover factors are quoted at the beginning of each country for most issues to 1945. An explanation of the system can be found on page x. The factors quoted do not, however, apply to philatelic covers.

312 Yukto Kasaya (Japan) (ski jump), 1972

313 Joffre Robinson (former Credit Union President)

(Litho Questa)

1997 (15 July). *Winter Olympic Games, Nagano, Japan* (1998). *T* **312** *and similar vert designs. Multicoloured. P* 14.

2322	20 c. Type **312**		10	15
2323	25 c. Jens Weissflog (Germany) (ski jump), 1994		10	15
2324	55 c. Anton Maier (Norway) (100m men's speed skating), 1968		25	30
2325	55 c. Ljubov Egorova (Russia) (women's 5km cross-country skiing), 1994		25	30
2326	65 c. Swedish ice hockey team, 1994		30	35
2327	90 c. Bernhard Glass (Germany) (men's single luge), 1980		40	45
2328	$1 Type **312**		45	50
	a. Sheetlet. Nos. 2328/31, each × 2		3·50	
2329	$1 As No. 2323		45	50
2330	$1 As No. 2324		45	50
2331	$1 Christa Rethenburger (Germany) (women's 100m speed skating), 1988		45	50
2332	$4 Frank-Peter Roetsch (Germany) (men's biathlon), 1988		1·90	2·00
2322/32		*Set of* 11	6·75	7·75

MS2333 Two sheets each, 106×76 mm. (a) $5 Charles Jewtraw (U.S.A.) (men's 500m speed skating), 1924. (b) $5 Jacob Tullin Thams (Norway) (ski jumping), 1924 .. *Set of 2 sheets* 4·50 4·75

Nos. 2328/31 were printed together, *se-tenant*, in sheetlets of 8 containing two of each design.

(Litho Questa)

1997 (21 July). *World Cup Football Championship, France* (1998). *Designs as T* **382** *of Antigua. Multicoloured (except Nos. 2340/1, 2345, 2347, 2350/1). P* 13½×14.

2334	20 c. Klinsmann, Germany (*vert*)		10	10
2335	55 c. Bergkamp, Holland (*vert*)		25	30
2336	65 c. Ravanelli, Italy (*vert*)		30	35
2337	65 c. Wembley Stadium, England		30	35
	a. Sheetlet. Nos. 2337/44 and central label		2·40	
2338	65 c. Bernabeu Stadium, Spain		30	35
2339	65 c. Maracana Stadium, Brazil		30	35
2340	65 c. Stadio Torino, Italy (grey-black)		30	35
2341	65 c. Centenary Stadium, Uruguay (grey-black)		30	35
2342	65 c. Olympiastadion, Germany		30	35
2343	65 c. Rose Bowl, U.S.A.		30	35
2344	65 c. Azteca Stadium, Mexico		30	35
2345	65 c. Meazza, Italy (grey-black)		30	35
	a. Sheetlet. Nos. 2345/52 and label		2·40	
2346	65 c. Matthaus, Germany		30	35
2347	65 c. Walter, West Germany (grey-black)		30	35
2348	65 c. Maradona, Argentina		30	35
2349	65 c. Beckenbauer, Germany		30	35
2350	65 c. Moore, England (grey-black)		30	35
2351	65 c. Dunga, Brazil (grey-black)		30	35
2352	65 c. Zoff, Italy		30	35
2353	90 c. Klinkladze, Georgia (*vert*)		40	45
2354	$2 Shearer, England (*vert*)		90	95
2355	$4 Dani, Portugal (*vert*)		1·90	2·00
2334/55		*Set of* 22	8·50	9·75

MS2356 Two sheets. (a) 102×126 mm. $5 Mario Kempes, Argentina (*vert*). (b) 126×102 mm. $6 Ally McCoist, Scotland (*vert*) .. *Set of 2 sheets* 5·00 5·25

Nos. 2337/44 and 2345/52 were each printed together, *se-tenant*, in sheetlets of 8 stamps and 1 label.

(Litho Questa)

1997 (15 Aug). *40th Anniv of Co-operative Credit Union League. T* **313** *and similar designs. P* 14×13½.

2357	25 c. deep blue and black		10	10
2358	55 c. myrtle-green and black		25	30
2359	65 c. maroon and black		30	35
2360	90 c. multicoloured		40	45
2357/60		*Set of* 4	1·00	1·25

MS2361 94×106 mm. $5 multicoloured .. 2·25 2·40

Designs: *Horiz* (as *T* **313**)—55 c. Sister Alicia (founder); 65 c. Lorrel Bruce (first Credit Union President). *Vert* (30×60 *mm*)—$5 Sister Alicia, Joffre Robinson and Lorrel Bruce.

314 Louis Pasteur

315 Diana, Princess of Wales

(Des J. Iskowitz. Litho Questa)

1997 (1 Sept). *Medical Pioneers. T* **314** *and similar vert designs. P* 14.

2362	20 c. purple-brown		10	10
2363	25 c. bright rose and orange-vermilion		10	15
2364	55 c. deep violet		25	30
2365	65 c. orange-red and yellow-brown		30	35
2366	90 c. greenish-yellow and olive-yellow		40	45
2367	$1 bright blue and dull ultramarine		45	50
2368	$2 black		90	95
2369	$3 deep brown-red and yellow-brown		1·40	1·50
2362/9		*Set of* 8	4·00	4·25

MS2370 Two sheets, each 70×100 mm. (a) $5 multicoloured. (b) $6 multicoloured

Set of 2 *sheets* 5·00 5·25

Designs:—25 c. Christiaan Barnard (first heart transplant); 55 c. Sir Alexander Fleming (discovery of penicillin); 65 c. Camillo Golgi (neurologist); 90 c. Jonas Salk (discovery of polio vaccine); $1 Har Gobind Khorana (genetics); $2 Elizabeth Black (first woman doctor); $3 Sir Frank MacFarlane Burnet (immunologist); $5 (No. **MS**2370a) Sir Alexander Fleming (*different*); $5 (No. **MS**2370b), Louis Pasteur (*different*).

(Litho Questa)

1997 (Oct). *Fishes. As Nos. 2175/90, but smaller, 24×21 mm. P* 13×13½.

2371	5 c. Porcupinefish		10	10
2372	10 c. Powder-blue Surgeonfish		10	10
2373	15 c. Red Hind		10	10
2374	20 c. Golden Butterflyfish		10	10
2375	25 c. Copper-banded Butterflyfish		10	15
2376	35 c. Pennant Coralfish		15	20
2377	45 c. Spotted Drum		20	25
2378	55 c. Blue-girdled Angelfish		25	30
2379	60 c. Scorpionfish		25	30
2380	65 c. Harlequin Sweetlips		30	35
2381	90 c. Flame Angelfish		40	45
2382	$1 Queen Triggerfish		45	50
2383	$1.20, Spotlight Parrotfish		55	60
2384	$1.45, Black Durgon		65	70
2385	$2 Glass-eyed Snapper		90	95
2386	$5 Balloonfish		2·25	2·40
2371/86		*Set of* 16	6·75	7·50

(Des J. Iskowitz. Litho Questa)

1997 (20 Oct). *Diana, Princess of Wales Commemoration. T* **315** *and similar vert designs. Multicoloured. P* 14.

2389	$2 Type **315**		90	95
	a. Sheetlet. Nos. 2389/92		3·50	
2390	$2 Wearing diamond-drop earrings		90	95
2391	$2 Resting head on hand		90	95
2392	$2 Wearing tiara		90	95
2389/92		*Set of* 4	3·50	3·75

MS2393 76×106 mm. $5 Diana, Princess of Wales .. 2·25 2·40

Nos. 2389/92 were printed together, *se-tenant*, in sheetlets of 4 with enlarged illustrated margins.

316 "Echo et Narcisse" (Toile)

317 "Tiger" (Gao Qifeng)

(Litho Questa)

1997 (10 Nov). *Christmas. Paintings. T* **316** *and similar multicoloured designs. P* 14.

2394	20 c. Type **316**		10	10
2395	55 c. "The Archangel Raphael leaving the Family of Tobias" (Rembrandt)		25	30
2396	65 c. "Seated Nymphs with Flute" (Francois Boucher)		30	35
2397	90 c. "Angel" (Rembrandt)		40	45
2398	$2 "Dispute" (Raphael)		90	95
2399	$4 "Holy Trinity" (Raphael)		1·90	2·00
2394/9		*Set of* 6	3·75	4·25

MS2400 Two sheets, each 114×104 mm. (a) $6 "Study Muse" (Raphael) (*horiz*). (b) $6 "Christ on the Mount of Olives" (El Greco) (*horiz*)

Set of 2 *sheets* 5·50 5·75

(Des Y. Lee. Litho Questa)

1998 (5 Jan). *Chinese New Year ("Year of the Tiger"). T* **317** *and similar multicoloured designs by different painters of the Ling-Nan School. P* 14½.

2401	55 c. Type **317**		25	30
	a. Sheetlet. Nos. 2401/4		1·40	
2402	65 c. "Tiger" (Zhao Shao'ang)		30	35
2403	90 c. "Tiger" (Gao Jianfu)		40	45
2404	$1.20, "Tiger" (*different*) (Gao Jianfu)		55	60
2401/4		*Set of* 4	1·40	1·75

MS2405 95×65 mm. $3 "Spirit of Kingship" (Gao Jianfu) (48×40 *mm*) .. 1·40 1·50

Nos. 2401/4 were printed together, *se-tenant*, in sheetlets of 4 with illustrated margins.

STAMP BOOKLETS

1981 (23 June). *Royal Wedding. Multicoloured cover, 165×92 mm, showing Prince Charles and Lady Diana Spencer on front and St. Paul's Cathedral on back. Stitched.*

SB1 $11.75, booklet containing *se-tenant* pane of 6 (No. 751a) and pane of 1 (No. 753a) .. .. 8·00

POSTAL FISCALS

REVENUE	Revenue
(R 1)	(R 2)

1879–88. *Optd with Type R* **1** *by De La Rue. P* 14. (*a*) *Wmk Crown CC*

R1	1	1d. lilac		75·00	7·50
		a. Bisected vert (½d.) on cover		†	
R2		6d. green		3·00	19·00
R3		1s. magenta		9·00	16·00
R1/3			*Set of* 3	80·00	38·00

(*b*) *Wmk Crown CA*

R4	1	1d. lilac (1888)		3·25	3·00

1888. *Optd with Type R* **2** *locally. Wmk Crown CA.*

R6	1	1d. rose		£250	65·00

Appendix

The following stamps have either been issued in excess of postal needs, or have not been made available to the public in reasonable quantities at face value. Miniature sheets, imperforate stamps etc. are excluded from this section.

1978–79

History of Aviation. $16 × 30, each embossed on gold foil.

If you would like to ADVERTISE

in the next edition of this catalogue or any other catalogue published by Stanley Gibbons

Phone, write or fax

Advertising Department Stanley Gibbons Publications, 5 Parkside, Christchurch Road, Ringwood, Hants BH24 3SH

Telephone: 01425 472363 Fax: 01425 470247

East Africa (G.E.A.)
see Tanzania

East Africa and Uganda Protectorates
see Kenya, Uganda and Tanzania

Egypt

TURKISH SUZERAINTY

In 1517 Sultan Selim I added Egypt to the Ottoman Empire, and it stayed more or less under Turkish rule until 1805, when Mohammed Ali became governor. He established a dynasty of governors owing nominal allegiance to the Sultan of Turkey until 1914.

Khedive Ismail

18 January 1863–26 June 1879

He obtained the honorific title of Khedive (viceroy) from the Sultan in 1867.

The operations of British Consular Post Offices in Egypt date from August 1839 when the first office, at Alexandria, was opened. Further offices at Suez (8 January 1847) and Cairo (1856) followed.

Great Britain stamps were issued to all three offices in August 1859 and continued to be used there until they closed, Cairo on 30 July 1873 and the others on 30 March 1878. "B 01" cancellations as Type **2** were issued to both Alexandria and Cairo. Cancellations with this number as Types **8**, **12** and **15** were only used at Alexandria.

Before 1 July 1873 combination covers showing Great Britain stamps and the first issue of Egypt exist with the latter paying the internal postage to the British Post Office at Alexandria.

Stamps issued after 1877 can be found with the Egyptian cancellation "Port Said", but these are on letters posted from British ships.

For cancellations used during the 1882 and 1885 campaigns, see BRITISH FORCES IN EGYPT at the end of the listing.

For illustrations of the handstamp and postmark types see BRITISH POST OFFICES ABROAD NOTES, following GREAT BRITAIN.

ALEXANDRIA

CROWNED-CIRCLE HANDSTAMPS

CC1 CC1b ALEXANDRIA (R.) (13.5.1843)
Price on cover £1300

Stamps of GREAT BRITAIN *cancelled* "B 01" *as in Types* **2** (*also used at Cairo*), **8**, **12** *or* **15**.

1859 (Aug) *to* **1878.**

Z 1	½d. rose-red (1870–79)	..	..	*From* 18·00
	Plate Nos. 5, 6, 8, 10, 13, 14, 15, 19, 20.			
Z 2	1d. rose-red (1857)	..	..	6·50
Z 3	1d. rose-red (1861) (Alph IV)	..		
Z 4	1d. rose-red (1864–79)	..	..	*From* 9·00
	Plate Nos. 71, 72, 73, 74, 76, 78, 79, 80, 81, 82, 83, 84, 85, 86, 87, 88, 89, 90, 91, 92, 93, 94, 95, 96, 97, 98, 99, 101, 102, 103, 104, 106, 107, 108, 109, 110, 111, 112, 113, 114, 115, 117, 118, 119, 120, 121, 122, 123, 124, 125, 127, 129, 131, 133, 134, 136, 137, 138, 139, 140, 142, 143, 144, 145, 146, 147, 148, 149, 150, 152, 154, 156, 157, 158, 159, 160, 162, 163, 165, 168, 169, 170, 171, 172, 174, 175, 177, 179, 180, 181, 182, 183, 185, 188, 190, 198, 200, 203, 206, 210, 220.			
Z 5	2d. blue (1858–69)	..	..	*From* 9·00
	Plate Nos. 7, 8, 9, 13, 14, 15.			
Z 6	2½d. rosy mauve (1875) (blued *paper*)		*From* 60·00
	Plate Nos. 1, 2.			
Z 7	2½d. rosy mauve (1875–6) (Plate Nos. 1, 2, 3)	..	27·00
Z 8	2½d. rosy mauve (*Error of Lettering*)	..	£1300
Z 9	2½d. rosy mauve (1876–79)	..	*From* 21·00
	Plate Nos. 3, 4, 5, 6, 7, 8, 9.			
Z10	3d. carmine-rose (1862)	..	..	£110
Z11	3d. rose (1865) (Plate No. 4)	..	55·00
Z12	3d. rose (1867–73) (Plate Nos. 4, 5, 6, 7, 8, 9)	*From* 21·00
Z13	3d. rose (1873–76)	..	..	*From* 21·00
	Plate Nos. 11, 12, 14, 15, 16, 18, 19.			
Z15	4d. rose (1857)	..	..	40·00
Z16	4d. red (1862) (Plate Nos. 3, 4)	..	*From* 40·00
Z17	4d. vermilion (1865–73)	..	..	23·00
	Plate Nos. 7, 8, 9, 10, 11, 12, 13, 14.			

Z18	4d. vermilion (1876) (Plate No. 15)	..	£140
Z19	4d. sage-green (1877) (Plate No. 15)	..	90·00
Z20	6d. lilac (1856)	..	..	45·00
Z21	6d. lilac (1862) (Plate Nos. 3, 4)	*From* 40·00
Z22	6d. lilac (1865–67) (Plate Nos. 5, 6)	*From* 32·00
Z23	6d. lilac (1867) (Plate No. 6)	..	42·00
Z24	6d. violet (1867–70) (Plate Nos. 6, 8, 9)	*From* 30·00
	a. Imperf (Plate No. 8)	..	£1200
Z25	6d. buff (1872–73) (Plate Nos. 11, 12)	*From* 55·00
Z26	6d. chestnut (1872) (Plate No. 11)	..	27·00
Z27	6d. grey (1873) (Plate No. 12)	..	70·00
Z28	6d. grey (1874–76) (Plate Nos. 13, 14, 15)	*From* 21·00
Z29	9d. straw (1862)	..	..	£140
Z30	9d. bistre (1862)	..		
Z31	9d. straw (1865)	..		
Z32	9d. straw (1867)	..		
Z33	10d. red-brown (1867)	..	..	£120
Z34	1s. green (1856)	..	..	£100
Z35	1s. green (1862)	..	..	60·00
Z36	1s. green (1862) ("K" *variety*)		
Z37	1s. green (1865) (Plate No. 4)	..	30·00
Z38	1s. green (1867–73) (Plate Nos. 4, 5, 6, 7)	*From* 12·00
Z39	1s. green (1873–77)	..	..	*From* 27·00
	Plate Nos. 8, 9, 10, 11, 12, 13.			
Z40	2s. blue (1867)	..	..	95·00
Z41	5s. rose (1867–74) (Plate Nos. 1, 2)	*From* £250

CAIRO

CROWNED-CIRCLE HANDSTAMPS

CC2 CC 6 CAIRO (R. or Blk.) (23.3.1859) *Price on cover* £1800
Cancellation "B 01" as Type **2** (also issued at Alexandria) was used to cancel mail franked with Great Britain stamps between April 1859 and June 1873.

SUEZ

CROWNED-CIRCLE HANDSTAMPS

CC3 CC 1 SUEZ (B. *or* Black) (16.7.1847) *Price on cover* £2000

Stamps of GREAT BRITAIN *cancelled* "B 02" *as in Types* **2** *and* **8**, *or with circular date stamp as Type* **5**.

1859 (Aug) *to* **1878.**

Z42	½d. rose-red (1870–79)	..	..	27·00
	Plate Nos. 6, 10, 11, 12, 13, 14.			
Z43	1d. rose-red (1857)	..	..	8·50
Z44	1d. rose-red (1864–79)	..	*From* 10·00
	Plate Nos. 73, 74, 78, 79, 80, 81, 83, 84, 86, 87, 90, 91, 93, 94, 96, 97, 100, 101, 106, 107, 108, 110, 113, 118, 119, 120, 121, 122, 123, 124, 125, 129, 130, 131, 134, 136, 137, 138, 140, 142, 143, 144, 145, 147, 148, 149, 150, 151, 152, 153, 154, 156, 158, 159, 160, 161, 162, 163, 164, 165, 166, 167, 168, 170, 174, 176, 177, 178, 179, 180, 181, 182, 184, 185, 186, 187, 189, 190, 205.			
Z45	2d. blue (1858–69)	..	..	*From* 13·00
	Plate Nos. 8, 9, 13, 14, 15.			
Z46	2½d. rosy mauve (1875) (blued *paper*)	*From* 55·00
	Plate Nos. 1, 2, 3.			
Z47	2½d. rosy mauve (1875–76) (Plate Nos. 1, 2, 3)	*From* 30·00
Z48	2½d. rosy mauve (*Error of Lettering*)	..	£1300
Z49	2½d. rosy mauve (1876–79)	..	*From* 24·00
	Plate Nos. 3, 4, 5, 6, 7, 8, 9, 10.			
Z50	3d. carmine-rose (1862)	..	..	£120
Z51	3d. rose (1865) (Plate No. 4)	..	60·00
Z52	3d. rose (1867–73) (Plate Nos. 5, 6, 7, 8, 10)	
Z53	3d. rose (1873–76) (Plate Nos. 12, 16)	*From* 24·00
Z54	4d. rose (1857)	..	..	50·00
Z55	4d. red (1862) (Plate Nos. 3, 4)	..	*From* 42·00
Z56	4d. vermilion (1865–73)	..	*From* 27·00
	Plate Nos. 7, 8, 9, 10, 11, 12, 13, 14.			
Z57	4d. vermilion (1876) (Plate No. 15)		
Z58	4d. sage-green (1877) (Plate No. 15)	..	95·00
Z59	6d. lilac (1856)	..	..	45·00
Z60	6d. lilac (1862) (Plate Nos. 3, 4)	..	*From* 40·00
Z61	6d. lilac (1865–67) (Plate Nos. 5, 6)	*From* 32·00
Z62	6d. lilac (1867) (Plate No. 6)	..	42·00
Z63	6d. violet (1867–70) (Plate Nos. 6, 8, 9)	*From* 32·00
Z64	6d. buff (1872–73) (Plate Nos. 11, 12)	*From* 60·00
Z65	6d. pale chestnut (Plate No. 12) (1872)	£2250
Z66	6d. chestnut (1872) (Plate No. 11)	..	27·00
Z67	6d. grey (1873) (Plate No. 12)	..	75·00
Z68	6d. grey (1874–76) (Plate Nos. 13, 14, 15, 16) *From* 23·00
Z69	8d. orange (1876)	..		
Z70	9d. straw (1862)	..	..	£150
	a. Thick paper	..		
Z71	9d. bistre (1862)	..		
Z72	9d. straw (1867)	..		
Z73	10d. red-brown (1867)	..	..	£150
Z74	1s. green (1856)	..	..	£100
Z75	1s. green (1862)	..	..	65·00
Z76	1s. green (1862) ("K" *variety*)		
Z77	1s. green (1865) (Plate No. 4)	..	40·00
Z78	1s. green (1867–73) (Plate Nos. 4, 5, 6, 7)	*From* 12·00
Z79	1s. green (1873–77)	..	..	*From* 27·00
	Plate Nos. 8, 9, 10, 11, 12.			
Z80	2s. blue (1867)	..	..	£150
Z81	5s. rose (1867–74) (Plate Nos. 1, 2)	*From* £275

PRICES FOR STAMPS ON COVER

Nos. 1/41	*from* × 8
Nos. 42/3	*from* × 30
Nos. 44/83	*from* × 5
Nos. 84/97	*from* × 2
Nos. D57/70	*from* × 12
Nos. D71/86	*from* × 5
Nos. D84/103	*from* × 2
Nos. O64/87	*from* × 5
Nos. O88/101	*from* × 2

(Currency: 40 paras = 1 piastre)

1 2 (3)

(Printed by Pellas Bros, Genoa. Litho, except for 1 pi. (typo). Black inscription (T **3**) litho, except on 1 pi. and 2 pi. (typo))

1866 (1 Jan). *Various designs as T* **1** *with black inscription as T* **3**. *The lowest group of characters indicates the value.* 1 pi. no wmk, others W **2** (*usually inverted*). P 12½.

1	5 pa. grey	..	32·00	24·00
	a. Greenish grey	..	32·00	24·00
	b. Imperf (pair)	..	£180	
	c. Imperf between (pair)	..	£300	
	d. Perf 12½×13 and compound	..	48·00	45·00
	e. Perf 13	..	£250	£300
2	10 pa. brown	..	50·00	28·00
	a. Imperf (pair)	..	£160	
	b. Imperf between (pair)	..	£350	
	c. Perf 12½×13 and compound	..	80·00	48·00
	d. Perf 12½×15	..	£250	£275
	e. Perf 13	..	£170	£190
3	20 pa. pale blue	..	70·00	27·00
	a. Greenish blue	..	70·00	27·00
	b. Imperf (pair)	..	£240	
	c. Imperf between (pair)	..	£400	
	d. Perf 12½×13 and compound	..	£100	80·00
	e. Perf 13	..	£425	£250
4	1 pi. claret	..	55·00	4·25
	a. Imperf (pair)	..	£100	
	b. Imperf between (pair)	..	£400	
	c. Perf 12½×13 and compound	..	90·00	20·00
	d. Perf 13	..	£300	£190
5	2 pi. yellow	..	90·00	40·00
	a. Orange-yellow	..	90·00	40·00
	b. Imperf (pair)	..		
	c. Imperf between (pair)	..	£350	£350
	d. Bisected diag (1 pi.) (on cover)	† £2250
	e. Perf 12½×13 and compound	..	£120	45·00
	f. Perf 12½×15	..	£130	
6	5 pi. rose	..	£250	£170
	a. Imperf (pair)	..		
	b. Imperf between (pair)	..	£1000	
	c. Perf 12½×13 and compound	..	£275	
	d. Error. Inscr 10 pi., perf 12½×15	..	£900	£750
	e. Do. but imperf	..	£500	
7	10 pi. slate	..	£275	£250
	a. Imperf (pair)	..		
	b. Imperf between (pair)	..	£2000	
	c. Perf 12½×13 and compound	..	£425	£425
	d. Perf 13	..	£1600	

The 2 pi. bisected was authorised for use between 16 and 31 July 1867.

Stamps perforated 13 all round occurred only in the corner of a sheet and so are very rare; of the 10 pi. only 1 example has been recorded unused. Compound perforations occur in many combinations.

The two halves of each background differ in minor details of the ornamentation. All values can be found with either half at the top.

Proofs of all values exist on smooth paper, without watermark. Beware of forgeries.

4 5

6

(Des F. Hoff, Hirschberg, Silesia. Litho V. Penasson, Alexandria)

1867 (1 Aug)–**69.** W **6**. P 15 × 12½.

11	4	5 pa. orange-yellow	..	23·00	8·00
		a. Imperf (pair)	..		
		b. Imperf between (horiz pair)	£170	
12		10 pa. dull lilac	..	70·00	8·50
		b. Bright mauve (7.69)	..	48·00	9·00
		ba. Bisected diag (5 pa.) (on piece) (12.71)	† £750
13		20 pa. deep blue-green	..	£100	13·00
		a. Pale blue-green	..	£100	13·00
		b. Yellowish green (7.69)	..	£110	12·00
14	5	1 pi. dull rose-red *to* rose	..	10·00	90
		a. Lake	..	£120	32·00
		b. Imperf (pair)	..	£100	
		c. Imperf between (horiz pair)	£170	
		d. Bisected diag (20 pa.) (on piece)	† £750
		e. Rouletted	..	55·00	
15		2 pi. bright blue	..	£110	15·00
		a. Pale blue	..	£110	15·00
		b. Imperf (pair)	..		
		c. Imperf between (pair)	..	£425	
		d. Bisected diag (1 pi.) (on cover)	†
		e. Perf 12½	..	£225	
16		5 pi. brown	..	£300	£180

Each value was engraved four times, the resulting blocks being used to form sheets of 200. There are therefore four types showing minor variations for each value.

No. 12ba was used on newspapers.

Stamps printed both sides, both imperf and perf, come from printers' waste. The 1 pi. rose without watermark is a proof.

7 **8 (Side panels transposed and inverted)**

8a (I) **8a (II)**

WATERMARK 8a. There are two types of this watermark which, as they are not always easy to distinguish, we do not list separately. Type II is slightly wider and less deep and the crescent is flatter than in Type I. The width measurement for Type I is generally about 14 mm and for Type II about 15 mm, but there is some variation within the sheets for both types.

Nos. 26/43, 45/7a, 49/a, 50/1 and 57 come with Type I only. Nos. 44a, 48/a, 52, 54b, 73/7 and 78 exist with both types of watermark (but No. 83 and official overprints on these stamps still require research); our prices are generally for Type II. Other watermarked issues between 1888 and 1907 have Type II watermarks only.

1872 (1 Jan)–**75**. *T* 7 *(the so-called "Penasson" printing*).* Thick opaque paper. W* 8a. I. *P* 12½×13½. II. *P* 13½.

A. LITHOGRAPHED

			I	II
26	7	20 pa. blue (*shades*)	£120 50·00	£200 55·00
		a. Imperf (pair)		
		b. Imperf between (pair)	—£2000	†
27		1 pi. red (*shades*)	£225 8·00	£500 17·00

B. TYPOGRAPHED

			I	II
28	7	5 pa. brown (*shades*)	7·00 4·50	24·00 9·00
29		10 pa. mauve	6·00 3·00	6·00 3·00
30		20 pa. blue (*shades*)	48·00 3·75	75·00 20·00
31		1 pi. rose-red	45·00 1·00	75·00 3·50
		a. Bisected (20 pa.) (on piece with No. 31) (7.75)	† £600	†
32		2 pi. chrome-yellow	80·00 4·00	18·00 4·00
		a. Bisected (1 pi.) (on piece)	† £650	†
33		2½ pi. violet	75·00 12·00	£700 £190
34		5 pi. yellow-green	£180 32·00	£275 55·00
		a. Tête-bêche (pair)		

*The lithographed stamps are now believed to have been printed by Penasson, but the typographed by the Government Printing Works at Bûlâq, Cairo.

The lithographed and typographed stamps each show the characteristic differences between these two processes:—

The typographed stamps show the coloured lines of the design impressed into the paper and an accumulation of ink along the margins of the lines.

The lithographed stamps are essentially flat in appearance, without the heaping of the ink. Many of the 20 pa. show evidence of retouching, particularly of the outer frame lines.

The 2 pi. vertically bisected was used at Gallipoli.

See also the footnote below No. 41.

1874 (Oct)–**75**. *Typo from new stereos at Bûlâq, on thinner paper. W* 8a. I. *P* 12½. II. *P* 13½ × 12½.

			I	II
35	8	5 pa. brown (4.75)	7·00 3·75	8·00 3·75
		a. Tête-bêche (vert pair)	35·00 35·00	60·00 60·00
		ab. Tête-bêche (horiz pair)	£275 £300	£325 £350
		b. Imperf (pair)		†
		c. Imperf between (pair)	£100 £120	†
36	7	10 pa. grey-lilac (*shades*)	8·00 2·75	13·00 3·25
		a. Tête-bêche (pair)	£140 £160	£140 £160
		b. Imperf (pair)		†
37		20 pa. grey-blue (*shades*)	85·00 3·00	8·50 2·50
		a. Imperf between (pair)	†	£300 —
		b. Bisected diag (10 pa.) (on cover)	†	†
38		1 pi. red (*shades*)	4·75 65	55·00 1·25
		a. Tête-bêche (vert pair)	90·00 90·00	£350 £350
		ab. Tête-bêche (horiz pair)	£300 £300	— —
		b. Imperf (pair)		†
		c. Imperf between (pair)	—80·00	†
39		2 pi. yellow	70·00 3·00	5·50 5·50
		a. Tête-bêche (pair)	£400 £400	£400 £400
		aa. Bisected diag (1 pi.) (on cover)	†	† £2500
		b. Perf 12½×13½		60·00 10·00
		ba. Tête-bêche (pair)		£850
40		2½ pi. violet	8·50 5·00	†
		a. Tête-bêche (pair)	£350 —	†
		b. Perf 12½×13½		45·00 19·00
		ba. Tête-bêche (pair)	†	£1000 £900
41		5 pi. green	55·00 19·00	†
		a. Perf 12½×13½	†	£300 £275
		b. Imperf (pair)		†

The 1872 printings have a thick line of colour in the top margin of the sheet and the other margins are all plain, an exception being

---

the 5 pa., which on the majority of the sheets has the line at the righthand side of the sheet. The 1874–75 printings have a wide fancy border all round every sheet.

The 1872 printings are on thick opaque paper, with the impressions sharp and clear. The 1874–75 printings are on thinner paper, often semi-transparent and oily in appearance, and having the impressions very blurred and badly printed. These are only general distinctions and there are a number of exceptions.

The majority of the 1874–75 stamps have blind or defective perforations, while the 1872 stamps have clean-cut perfs.

The two printings of the 5 pa. to 1 pi. values can be identified by their perforation gauges, which are always different; the 5 pa. also differs in the side panels (Types 7 and 8). Only the perf 12½×13½ varieties of the three higher values may need to be distinguished. As well as the general points noted above the following features are also helpful:

2 pi. In the 1872 issue the left-hand Arabic character in the top inscription is one complete shape, resembling an inverted "V" with a horizontal line on top. In the 1874 issue the character has three separate components, a line with two dots below.

2½ pi. There is a distinct thinning of the frame line in the top right-hand corner of the 1872 issue. This sometimes takes the form of a short white line within the frame.

5 pi. In the 1872 issue the top frame line is split for its entire length; in the 1874 issue the line is solid for all or most of its length. The 1872 printing always has a white dot above the "P" of "PIASTRE"; this dot appears on only a few positions of the 1874 printing.

There seem to be many different compositions of the sheets containing the *tête-bêche* varieties, settings being known with 1, 3, 9 and 10 inverted stamps in various sheets. Sheets of the 5 pa. are known with 9 of the 20 horizontal rows inverted, giving vertical *tête-bêche* pairs; four stamps were inverted within their row giving four horizontal *tête-bêche* pairs.

(9)

1879 (1 Jan). *Stamps of 1874 surch as T* 9, *at Bûlâq.*
   I. *P* 12½. II. *P* 12½ × 13½.

			I		II	
42	7	5 pa. on 2½ pi. violet	6·00	6·00	6·50	8·00
		a. Surch inverted	70·00	70·00	£140	£140
		b. Tête-bêche (pair)	£3500	—	—	—
		c. Imperf (pair)		—		†
43		10 pa. on 2½ pi. violet	10·00	10·00	15·00	15·00
		a. Surch inverted	75·00	75·00	£110	£110
		b. Tête-bêche (pair)	£1500	—	£1500	—
		c. Imperf (pair)		—		†

10 **11** **12**

13 **14** **15**

(Typo De La Rue)

1879 (1 Apr). *Ordinary paper. W* 8a *(inverted on* 10 *pa.). P* 14.

44	10	5 pa. deep brown	1·00	30
		a. Pale brown	1·00	30
45	11	10 pa. reddish lilac	50·00	3·00
46	12	20 pa. pale blue	60·00	1·75
47	13	1 pi. rose	24·00	10
		a. Pale rose	24·00	10
48	14	2 pi. orange	25·00	50
		a. Orange-yellow	21·00	80
49	15	5 pi. green	55·00	8·00
		a. Blue-green	55·00	7·00

See also Nos. 50/6.

Khedive Tewfik

26 June 1879–7 January 1892

British troops were landed in Egypt in 1882 to secure the Suez Canal against a nationalist movement led by Arabi Pasha. Arabi was defeated at Tel-el-Kebir and British troops remained in Egypt until 1954. A British resident and consul-general advised the Khedive. Holders of this post were Sir Evelyn Baring (Lord Cromer), 1883–1907; Sir Eldon Gorst, 1907–11; and Lord Kitchener, 1911–14.

1881–1902. *Colours changed. Ordinary paper. W* 8a *(inverted on No.* 50*). P* 14.

50	11	10 pa. claret (1.81)	48·00	5·50
51		10 pa. bluish grey (25.1.82)	6·50	1·75
52		10 pa. green (15.12.84)	70	40
53	12	20 pa. rose-carmine (15.12.84)	10·00	55
		a. Bright rose	10·00	50
54	13	1 pi. blue (15.12.84)	3·50	20
		a. Deep ultramarine	5·00	20
		b. Pale ultramarine	2·75	20
		c. Chalk-surfaced paper. *Ultramarine* (1902)	2·50	10
		ca. Do. *Blue*	2·50	10
55	14	2 pi. orange-brown (1.8.93)	12·00	30
		a. Chalk-surfaced paper (1902)	12·00	10
		ab. Do. *Orange*	22·00	1·00
56	15	5 pi. pale grey (15.12.84)	13·00	50
		a. Slate	11·00	40
		b. Chalk-surfaced paper. *Slate-grey* (1902)	16·00	15

---

(17)

1884 (1 Feb). *Surch with T* 17 *at Bûlâq.*

57	15	20 pa. on 5 pi. green	7·00	1·25
		a. Surch inverted	65·00	60·00

(New Currency: 1000 milliemes = 100 piastres = £1 Egyptian)

18 **19** **20**

21 **22**

1888 (1 Jan)–**1909**. *Ordinary paper. W* 8a. *P* 14.

58	18	1 m. pale brown	75	10
		a. Deep brown	1·25	10
		b. Chalk-surfaced paper. *Pale brown* (1902)	55	10
		ba. Do. *Deep brown*	65	10
59	19	2 m. blue-green	60	10
		a. Green	60	10
		ab. Chalk-surfaced paper (1902)	50	10
60	20	3 m. maroon (1.1.92)	2·25	1·00
61		3 m. yellow (1.8.93)	2·25	15
		a. Orange-yellow	2·25	15
		ab. Chalk-surfaced paper (1902)	1·75	10
62	21	4 m. verm (*chalk-surfaced paper*) (1906)	1·00	10
		a. Bisected (2 m.) (on cover) (11.09)	†	—
63		5 m. rose-carmine	1·25	10
		a. Bright rose	1·25	10
		b. Aniline rose	2·50	10
		c. Chalk-surfaced paper. *Rose* (1902)	1·50	10
		ca. Do. *Deep aniline rose*	3·00	10
64	22	10 m. mauve (1.1.89)	15·00	80
		a. Aniline mauve	18·00	80
		b. Chalk-surfaced paper. *Mauve* (1902)	22·00	50

No. 62a was used at Giza.

Khedive Abbas Hilmi

7 January 1892–19 December 1914

A set of three values, in a common design showing Cleopatra and a Nile boat, was prepared in 1895 for the Nile Winter Fête, but not issued. Examples survive from the De La Rue archives.

29 Nile Felucca **30 Cleopatra with Head-dress of Isis** **31 Ras-el-Tin Palace, Alexandria**

35 Pylon of Karnak Temple, Luxor **37 Rock Temples of Abu Simbel**

(Typo D.L.R.)

1914 (8 Jan). *W* 8a. *P* 13½×14 (1 *m. to* 10 *m.) or* 14 (20 *m. to* 200 *m.*).

73	29	1 m. sepia	60	40
74	30	2 m. green	70	20
		w. Wmk inverted		
75	31	3 m. yellow-orange	60	35
		a. Double impression		
		w. Wmk inverted		3·00
76		4 m. vermilion	1·00	65
		w. Wmk inverted		1·75
77		5 m. lake	1·00	10
		a. Wmk sideways star to right* (booklets)	10·00	20·00
		aw. Wmk sideways star to left	10·00	20·00
		w. Wmk inverted	15·00	10·00
78		10 m. dull blue	2·25	10
		w. Wmk inverted		—15·00
79	35	20 m. olive	6·50	30
		w. Wmk inverted		6·00
80	—	50 m. purple	11·00	40
		w. Wmk inverted		—50·00

81 37 100 m. slate .. .. 12·00 60
82 – 200 m. maroon .. .. .. 26·00 3·50
73/82 .. .. Set of 10 55·00 6·00
Designs: As T 29—4 m. Pyramids at Giza; 5 m. Sphinx; 10 m. Colossi of Thebes. As T 35—50 c. Cairo Citadel; 200 m. Aswân Dam.
*The normal sideways watermark shows the star to the right of the crescent, as seen from the back of the stamp.
All the above exist imperforate, but imperforate stamps without watermark are proofs.
See also Nos. 84/95.

BRITISH PROTECTORATE

On 18 December 1914, after war with Turkey had begun, Egypt was declared to be a British protectorate. Abbas Hilmi was deposed, and his uncle, Hussein Kamil, was proclaimed Sultan of Egypt.

Sultan Hussein Kamil
19 December 1914–9 October 1917

(39)

1915 (15 Oct). No. 75 surch with T 39, at Bûlâq.
83 31 2 m. on 3 m. yellow-orange .. 55 90
  a. Surch inverted £200 £200
  b. Surch double, one albino .. £120
  w. Wmk inverted £120

Sultan Ahmed Fuad
9 October 1917–15 March 1922

40 (A) (B)

(Typo Harrison)
1921–22. W 40. (a) As Nos. 73/82. (i) P 13½×14.
84 29 1 m. sepia (A) .. .. 80 1·25
  a. Two dots omitted (B) .. 35·00 45·00
  w. Wmk inverted .. 10·00 7·50
85 30 2 m. green .. .. 3·25 3·25
  a. Imperf between (pair) ..
  w. Wmk inverted .. 15·00 10·00
86 2 m. vermilion (1922) .. 1·75 55
  w. Wmk inverted .. 15·00 10·00
87 31 3 m. yellow-orange (12.21) .. 2·50 1·10
  w. Wmk inverted .. 16·00 10·00
88 – 4 m. green (1922) .. 3·00 4·00
  w. Wmk inverted .. — 10·00
89 – 5 m. lake (1.21) .. 2·75 10
  a. Imperf between (pair) ..
  w. Wmk inverted .. 15·00 10·00
90 – 5 m. pink (11.21) .. 2·75 10
  w. Wmk inverted .. 15·00 10·00
91 – 10 m. dull blue .. .. 2·75 20
  w. Wmk inverted .. — 10·00
92 – 10 m. lake (9.22) .. 1·75 15
  w. Wmk inverted .. — 10·00

(ii) P 14
93 35 20 m. olive .. .. 7·50 30
  w. Wmk inverted .. 20·00 10·00
94 – 50 m. purple .. .. 10·00 65
  w, Wmk inverted .. 18·00 12·00
95 37 100 m. slate (1922) .. 70·00 6·50
84/95 .. .. Set of 12 95·00 16·00

41 Statue of Rameses II 42

(b) New design. P 13½×14
96 41 15 m. indigo (3.22) .. 2·50 15
  w. Wmk inverted .. — 8·00
97 42 15 m. indigo .. .. 16·00 2·75
  w. Wmk inverted .. 18·00 10·00
Type 42 was printed first; but because the inscription at right was erroneous the stamps were withheld and the corrected Type 41 printed and issued. Type 42 was released later.

STAMP BOOKLETS

1903 (1 Jan). Black on pink cover inscr "Egyptian Post Office" in English and French. Stapled.
SB1 121 m. booklet containing twenty-four 5 m. (No. 63c) in blocks of 6 ..
Price reduced to 120 m. from 1 July 1911.

1903 (1 July). Black on blue cover inscr "Egyptian Post Office" in English and French. Stapled.
SB2 73 m. booklet containing twenty-four 3 m. (No. 61ab) in blocks of 6 ..

1911. Black on pink cover inscr "Egyptian Post Office" in English and Arabic. Stapled.
SB3 120 m. Contents as No. SB1

1914 (8 Jan). Black on pink cover inscr "Egyptian Post Office" in English and Arabic. Stapled.
SB4 125 m. booklet containing twenty-four 5 m. (No. 77a) in blocks of 6 .. ..

1919 (Jan). Black on pink cover inscr "Egyptian Post Office" in English and Arabic. Stapled.
SB5 120 m. Contents as No. SB4

1921 (12 June). Deep blue on pink cover inscr "POST OFFICE" in English and Arabic. Stapled.
SB6 120 m. booklet containing twenty-four 5 m. (No. 89) in blocks of 6 .. ..
  a. Stitched

1921 (Nov). Deep blue or pink cover inscr "POST OFFICE" in English and Arabic. Stapled.
SB7 120 m. booklet containing twenty-four 5 m. (No. 90) in blocks of 6 ..

POSTAGE DUE STAMPS

D 16 D 23 D 24

(Des L. Barkhausen. Litho V. Penasson, Alexandria)
1884 (1 Jan). Impressed W 6. P 10½.
D57 D 16 10 pa. red .. .. 38·00 9·00
  a. Imperf (pair) ..
  b. Imperf between (pair) .. £110
D58 20 pa. red .. .. £100 23·00
D59 1 pi. red .. .. £120 35·00
D60 2 pi. red .. .. £200 10·00
D61 5 pi. red .. .. 14·00 32·00

1886 (1 Aug). No wmk. P 10½.
D62 D 16 10 pa. rose-red .. .. 50·00 7·50
  a. Imperf between (pair) .. 90·00
D63 20 pa. rose-red .. .. £200 30·00
  a. Imperf between (pair) ..
D64 1 pi. rose-red .. .. 25·00 5·00
  a. Imperf between (pair) .. £120 £120
D65 2 pi. rose-red .. .. 25·00 3·25
  a. Imperf between (pair) .. £120
Specialists distinguish four types of each value in both these issues.

(Litho V. Penasson, Alexandria)
1888 (1 Jan). No wmk. P 11½.
D66 D 23 2 m. green .. .. 8·50 13·00
  a. Imperf between (pair) .. £170 £170
D67 5 m. rose-carmine .. 25·00 12·00
D68 1 p. blue .. .. £120 35·00
  a. Imperf between (pair) .. £170
D69 2 p. orange .. .. £140 12·00
D70 5 p. grey £190 £180
  a. With stop after left-hand "PIASTRES" .. £250 £225
Specialists distinguish four types of each value.
Beware of forgeries of the 5 p.

(Typo De La Rue)
1889 (Apr). Ordinary or chalk-surfaced paper. W 8a (upright). P 14.
D71 D 24 2 m. green .. .. 7·00 50
  a. Bisected (1 m.) (on cover with unbisected 2 m.).. † £250
D72 4 m. maroon .. .. 2·25 50
D73 1 p. ultramarine .. .. 5·50 50
D74 2 p. orange .. .. 5·50 70
  a. Bisected diagonally (1 p.) (on cover) † —
See also Nos. D84/6 for stamps with watermark sideways.

(D 26) (D 27)

Type D 26
The Arabic figure at right is less than 2 mm from the next character, which consists of a straight stroke only.

Type D 27
The distance is 3 mm and the straight character has a comma-like character above it. There are other minor differences.

1898 (Apr)–1905. No. D74 surch at Bûlâq.
(a) With Type D 26. Ordinary paper.
D75 D 24 3 m. on 2 p. orange .. 55 2·75
  a. Surch inverted .. .. 60·00 75·00
  b. Pair, one without surch
  c. Arabic "2" for "3" ..
  d. Arabic "3" over "2" .. £100
No. D75c occurred in the first printing on positions 10, 20, 30, 40, 50 and 60 of the pane of 60 (the Arabic figure is the right-hand character of the second line—see illustration on page xvii). In the second printing the correct figure was printed on top to form No. D75d. The error was corrected in subsequent printings.

(b) With Type D 27. Ordinary or chalk-surfaced paper (1905)
D76 D 24 3 m. on 2 p. orange .. .. 3·25 10·00
  a. Surch inverted .. 50·00 60·00
  b. Surch double £200

1918. As Nos. D71/3 but wmk sideways*.
D84 D 24 2 m. bright green .. .. 8·00 3·00
  w. Wmk star to left of crescent 15·00 10·00
D85 4 m. maroon .. 8·00 9·00
  w. Wmk star to left of crescent 18·00
D86 1 p. dull ultramarine .. 15·00 8·00
  w. Wmk star to left of crescent 12·00 8·50
*The normal sideways watermark shows star to right of crescent, as seen from the back of the stamp.

D 43 D 44

(Typo Harrison)
1921 (Oct)–22. Chalk-surfaced paper. W 40 (sideways*). P 14×13½.
D 98 D 43 2 m. green .. 2·75 3·00
  w. Wmk stars below crescents .. 9·00 3·00
D 99 2 m. scarlet (1922) .. 1·00 1·50
  w. Wmk stars below crescents .. 7·50 4·00
D100 4 m. scarlet .. 5·00 11·00
D101 4 m. green .. 2·50 1·00
  w. Wmk stars below crescents .. 12·00 5·00
D102 D 44 10 m. deep slate-blue (11.21) .. 4·50 14·00
D103 10 m. lake (1922) .. 5·50 70
  w. Wmk stars below crescents .. 10·00 4·00
D98/103 .. Set of 6 19·00 28·00
*The normal sideways watermark shows the stars above the crescents.

OFFICIAL STAMPS

 O.H.H.S. أميري "O.H.H.S."

O 25 (O 28) (O 29)

(Typo De La Rue)
1893 (1 Jan). Ordinary or chalk-surfaced paper. W 8a. P 14.
O64 O 25 (–) chestnut .. .. 1·40 10
  a. Wmk sideways .. .. 9·50 7·50
This stamp, with overprint 3 P.T. and Arabic equivalent, is a fiscal.

1907. Nos. 54ca, 56b, 58b, 59ab, 61ab and 63c optd with Type O 28 by De La Rue.
O73 18 1 m. pale brown .. .. 1·75 30
O74 19 2 m. green .. .. 3·50 10
  a. Opt double
O75 20 3 m. orange-yellow .. 2·75 1·25
O76 21 5 m. rose .. .. 4·25 10
O77 13 1 p. blue .. .. 2·00 20
O78 15 5 p. slate-grey .. .. 16·00 1·25
O73/8 .. .. Set of 6 27·00 2·75

1913 (Nov). No. 63c optd at Bûlâq.
(a) With Type O 29
O79 21 5 m. rose .. .. — £300
  a. Opt inverted .. ..
(b) As Type O 29 but without inverted commas
O80 21 5 m. rose .. .. 3·75 30
  a. No stop after "S" (pos. 130) 45·00 15·00
  b. Opt inverted .. £200 75·00

O.H.H.S. أميري O.H.H.S. أميري O.H.H.S. أميري

(O 38) (O 39) (O 43)

1914 (Dec)–15. Stamps of 1902–6 and 1914 optd with Type O 38 at Bûlâq.
O83 29 1 m. sepia (1.15) .. 1·25 3·00
  a. No stop after "S" .. 12·00 25·00
O84 19 2 m. green (3.15) .. 3·00 3·50
  a. No stop after "S" .. 14·00 23·00
  b. Opt inverted .. 35·00 35·00
  c. Opt double .. £325
O85 31 3 m. yellow-orange (3.15) 2·00 3·00
  a. No stop after "S" .. 14·00 25·00
O86 21 4 m. vermilion (12.14) .. 3·50 1·60
  a. Opt inverted .. £190 £140
  b. Pair, one without opt
O87 – 5 m. lake (1.15) .. 3·50 70
  a. No stop after "S" .. 15·00 22·00
O83/7 .. .. Set of 5 12·00 10·50

1915 (Oct). Nos. 59ab, 62 and 77 optd lithographically with Type O 39 at Bûlâq.
O88 19 2 m. green .. .. 1·40 2·50
  a. Opt inverted .. 20·00 20·00
  b. Opt double .. 25·00
O89 21 4 m. vermilion .. .. 3·00 3·75
O90 – 5 m. lake .. .. 3·50 1·25
  a. Pair, one without opt .. £275

1922. *Nos. 84, etc optd lithographically with Type O 43 at Bûlâq.*

O 98	29	1 m. sepia (A) (28.6)	..	3·50	8·50
		a. Two dots omitted (B)	..	£200	
		w. Wmk inverted			
O 99	30	2 m. vermilion (16.6)	..	7·00	11·00
O100	31	3 m. yellow-orange (28.6)	..	65·00	£130
O101	–	5 m. pink (13.3)	..	17·00	4·00

Egypt was declared to be an independent kingdom on 15 March 1922, and Sultan Ahmed Fuad became king.

Later stamp issues will be found listed in Part 19 (*Middle East*) of this catalogue.

EGYPTIAN POST OFFICES ABROAD

From 1865 Egypt operated various post offices in foreign countries. No special stamps were issued for these offices and use in them of unoverprinted Egyptian stamps can only be identified by the cancellation. Stamps with such cancellations are worth more than the used prices quoted in the Egypt listings.

Such offices operated in the following countries. An * indicates that details will be found under that heading elsewhere in the catalogue.

ETHIOPIA

A   B

C   D

MASSAWA. Open Nov 1867 *to* 5 Dec 1885. *Postmark types* A (*also without* REGIE), B, C, D. *An Arabic seal type is also known on stampless covers.*

SENHIT (near Keren). Open 1878 *to* April 1885. *Only one cover, cancelled "Mouderie Senhit" in 1879, is known, together with one showing a possible hand-drawn cancellation.*

A post office is also recorded at Harar, but no postal marking has so far been reported.

SOMALILAND*

Unoverprinted stamps of Egypt used from 1876 until 1884.

SUDAN*

Unoverprinted stamps of Egypt used from 1867 until 1897.

TURKISH EMPIRE

E   F

G   H

I   J

K   L

M   N

O

The offices are listed according to the spelling on the cancellation. The present-day name (if different) and country are given in brackets.

ALESSANDRETTA (Iskenderun, Turkey). Open 14 July 1870 *to* 15 Feb 1872. *Postmark types* E, I.

BAIROUT (Beirut, Lebanon). Open 14 July 1870 *to* 30 June 1881. *Postmark types* E, J.

CAVALA (Kavala, Greece). Open 14 July 1870 *to* 15 Feb 1872. *Postmark type* E.

COSTANTINOPOLI (Istanbul, Turkey). Open 13 June 1865 *to* 30 June 1881. *Postmark types* E, F, O.

DARDANELLI (Canakkle, Turkey). Open 10 June 1868 *to* 30 June 1881. *Postmark types* H, K.

DJEDDAH, *see* GEDDA.

GALIPOLI (Gelibolu, Turkey). Open 10 June 1868 *to* 30 June 1881. *Postmark types* E, L.

GEDDA, DJEDDAH (Jeddah, Saudi Arabia). Open 8 June 1865 *to* 30 June 1881. *Postmark types* F, G (*also with year replacing solid half-circle*), O (*all spelt* GEDDA), D (*spelt* DJEDDAH).

IAFFA (Jaffa, Israel). Open 14 July 1870 *to* 15 Feb 1872. *Postmark type* E.

LAGOS (Port Lago, Greece). Open 14 July 1870 *to* 15 Feb 1872. *Postmark type* E.

LATAKIA (Syria). Open 14 July 1870 *to* 15 Feb 1872. *Postmark type* E.

LEROS (Aegean Is.). Open May *to* December 1873 *and* July *to* September 1874. *Postmark type* E.

MERSINA (Mersin, Turkey). Open 14 July 1870 *to* 15 Feb 1872. *Postmark type* E.

METELINO (Lesbos, Greece). Open 14 July 1870 *to* 30 June 1881. *Postmark types* E, M.

RODI (Rhodes, Greece). Open 13 Aug 1872 *to* 30 June 1881. *Postmark type* E.

SALONNICCHI (Thessaloniki, Greece). Open 14 July 1870 *to* 15 Feb 1872. *Postmark type* E.

SCIO (Chios, Aegean Is.). Open 14 July 1870 *to* 30 June 1881. *Postmark types* E, N.

SMIRNE (Izmir, Turkey). Open 14 Nov 1865 *to* 30 June 1881. *Postmark types* E (*also without* "V. R."), F.

TENEDOS (Bozcaada, Turkey). Open 14 July 1870 *to* 15 June 1871. *Postmark type* E.

TRIPOLI (Lebanon). Open 14 July 1870 *to* 30 June 1881. *Postmark type* E.

VOLO (Volos, Greece). Open 14 July 1870 *to* 15 Feb 1872. *Postmark type* E.

PRICES OF SETS

Set prices are given for many issues, generally those containing three stamps or more. Definitive sets include one of each value or major colour change, but do not cover different perforations, die types or minor shades. Where a choice is possible the set prices are based on the cheapest versions of the stamps included in the listings.

BRITISH FORCES IN EGYPT

Following the rise of a nationalist movement led by Arabi Pasha, and serious disturbances in Alexandria, British troops landed at Ismalia in August 1882 and defeated the nationalists at Tel-el-Kebir on 13 September. During the initial stages of the occupation a British Army Post Office, staffed by volunteers from the Post Office Rifles, operated in Cairo. It is believed that the office closed in October 1882, but a similar facility also operated during the closing stages of the Gordon Relief Expedition in 1885.

ZA 1

Stamps of GREAT BRITAIN *cancelled with Type* ZA **1.**

1882 (Aug–Oct).

ZA1	½d. rose-red (Plate No. 20)	..			
ZA2	½d. green (1880)	..		..	£300
ZA3	1d. Venetian red (1880)	..	..		
ZA4	1d. lilac (1881) ..	..	..	..	£175
ZA5	2½d. blue (1881) (Plate Nos. 21, 22, 23)		..	£100

1885.

ZA6	1d. lilac (1881) ..	..	..	..	£300
ZA7	2½d. lilac (1884) ..	..	..	..	£225
ZA8	5d. green (1884)	..	..	..	£500

From 1 November 1932, to 29 February 1936 members of the British Forces in Egypt and their families were allowed to send letters to the British Isles at reduced rates. Special seals which were on sale in booklets at N.A.A.F.I. Institutes and Canteens were used instead of Egyptian stamps, and were stuck on the back of the envelopes, letters bearing the seals being franked on the front with a hand-stamp inscribed "EGYPT POSTAGE PREPAID" in a double circle surmounted by a crown.

PRICES FOR STAMPS ON COVER	
Nos. A1/9	*from* × 5
No. A10	*from* × 2
No. A11	*from* × 5
No. A12	*from* × 100
No. A13	*from* × 20
No. A14	*from* × 200
No. A15	*from* × 20

A 1   A 2

(Des Lt.-Col. C. Fraser. Typo Hanbury, Tomsett & Co, London)

1932 (1 Nov)–**33.** P 11. (*a*) *Inscr* "POSTAL SEAL".

A1	A 1	1 p. deep blue and red	..	60·00	3·00

(*b*) *Inscr* "LETTER SEAL"

A2	A 1	1 p. deep blue and red (8.33)	..	23·00	75

(Des Sgt. W. F. Lait. Litho Walker & Co, Amalgamated Press, Cairo)

1932 (26 Nov)–**35.** *Christmas Seals.* P 11½.

A3	A 2	3 m. black/*azure*	..	48·00	70·00
A4		3 m. brown-lake (13.11.33)	..	7·50	45·00
A5		3 m. deep blue (17.11.34)	..	7·00	21·00
A6		3 m. vermilion (23.11.35)	..	1·25	24·00
		a. Pale vermilion (19.12.35)	..	6·50	14·00

A 3

(Des Miss Waugh. Photo Harrison)

1934 (1 June)–**35.** (*a*) P 14½ × 14.

A7	A 3	1 p. carmine	..	32·00	75
A8		1 p. green (5.12.34)	..	4·00	4·00

(*b*) P 13½ × 14

A9	A 3	1 p. carmine (24.4.35) ..	..	1·75	2·00

JUBILEE COMMEMORATION 1935

(A 4)

1935 (6 May). *Silver Jubilee. As No. A9, but colour changed and optd with Type A 4, in red.*
A10 A 3 1 p. ultramarine £200 £180

Xmas 1935
3 Milliemes
(A 5)

1935 (16 Dec). *Provisional Christmas Seal. No. A9 surch with Type A 5.*
A11 A 3 3 m. on 1 p. carmine .. .. 15·00 70·00

The seals and letter stamps were replaced by the following Army Post stamps issued by the Egyptian Postal Administration. No. A9 was accepted for postage until 15 March 1936.

A 6 King Fuad I   A 7 King Farouk

W 48 of Egypt

(Types A 6/A 7. Photo Survey Dept, Cairo)

1936. *W 48 of Egypt. P 13½×14.*
A12 A 6 3 m. green (9.11.36) .. .. 1·00 90
A13 10 m. carmine (1.3.36) .. .. 2·50 10
   w. Wmk inverted

1939 (12 Dec). *W 48 of Egypt. P 13×13½.*
A14 A 7 3 m. green .. .. .. 1·50 3·25
A15 10 m. carmine .. .. .. 2·00 10
   w. Wmk inverted

These stamps were withdrawn in April 1941 but the concession, without the use of special stamps, continued until October 1951 when the postal agreement was abrogated.

SUEZ CANAL COMPANY

PRICES FOR STAMPS ON COVER	
Nos. 1/4	*from* × 20

100 Centimes = 1 Franc

In 1856 a concession to construct the Suez Canal was granted to Ferdinand de Lesseps and the Compagnie Universelle du Canal Maritime de Suez was formed. Work began in 1859 and the canal was opened on 17 November 1869. In November 1875 the Khedive sold his shares in the company to the British Government, which then became the largest shareholder.

The company transported mail free of charge between Port Said and Suez from 1859 to 1867, when it was decided that payment should be made for the service and postage stamps were introduced in July 1868. Letters for destinations beyond Port Said or Suez required additional franking with Egyptian or French stamps.

The imposition of charges for the service was not welcomed by the public and in August the Egyptian Government agreed to take it over.

1

(Litho Chézaud, Ainé & Tavernier, Paris)

1868 (8 July). *Imperf.*
1 1 1 c. black £250 £1000
2   5 c. green .. .. .. 85·00 £500
3   20 c. blue .. .. .. 75·00 £500
4   40 c. pink £130 £750
   Shades of all values exist.
Stamps can be found showing parts of the papermaker's watermark "LA+-F" (La Croix Frères).
   These stamps were withdrawn from sale on 16 August 1868 and demonetised on 31 August.
   Many forgeries exist, unused and cancelled. The vast majority of these forgeries show vertical lines, instead of cross-hatching, between "POSTES" and the central oval. It is believed that other forgeries, which do show cross-hatching, originate from the plate of the 40 c. value which is missing from the company's archives. These are, however, on thin, brittle paper with smooth shiny gum.

Falkland Islands

PRICES FOR STAMPS ON COVER TO 1945	
No. 1	*from* × 60
No. 2	*from* × 40
Nos. 3/4	*from* × 10
No. 5	—
Nos. 6/10	*from* × 30
Nos. 11/12	*from* × 15
Nos. 13/17	*from* × 10
Nos. 17a/b	*from* × 100
Nos. 18/21	*from* × 10
Nos. 22/a	*from* × 30
Nos. 23/4	*from* × 100
Nos. 25/6	*from* × 30
No. 27	*from* × 20
No. 28	*from* × 40
No. 29	*from* × 5
Nos. 30/a	*from* × 50
No. 30b	*from* × 15
No. 31	*from* × 5
Nos. 32/8	*from* × 15
Nos. 41/2	—
Nos. 43/8	*from* × 10
Nos. 49/50	—
Nos. 60/5	*from* × 10
Nos. 66/9	—
Nos. 70/1	*from* × 10
No. 72/b	—
Nos. 73/9	*from* × 4
No. 80	—
No. 115	*from* × 2
Nos. 116/19	*from* × 20
Nos. 120/2	*from* × 6
Nos. 123/6	—
Nos. 127/33	*from* × 5
Nos. 134/8	—
Nos. 139/45	*from* × 50
Nos. 146/63	*from* × 5

CROWN COLONY

1   2

1869–76. *The Franks.*
FR1 1 In black, *on cover* £6500
FR2 2 In red, *on cover* (1876) £12000
   On *piece,* No. FR1 on white or coloured paper £85; No. FR2 on white £130. The use of these franks ceased when the first stamps were issued.
   The first recorded use of No. FR1 is on a cover to London datestamped 4 January 1869.

½d.
3   (4)

In the ½d., 2d., 2½d. and 9d. the figures of value in the lower corners are replaced by small rosettes and the words of value are in colour.

NOTE. Nos. 1, 2, 3, 4, 8, 10, 11 and 12 exist with one or two sides imperf from the margin of the sheets.

(Recess B.W.)

1878–79. *No wmk. P 14, 14½.*
1 3 1d. claret (19.6.78) £550 £325
2   4d. grey-black (Sept 1879) .. £1000 £150
   a. On wmkd paper £2500 £500
3   6d. blue-green (19.6.78) .. 50·00 50·00
4   1s. bistre-brown (1878) .. 50·00 50·00
   No. 2a shows portions of the papermaker's watermark—"R. TURNER, CHAFFORD MILLS"—in ornate double-lined capitals.

NOTES. The dates shown for Nos. 5/12 and 15/38 are those on which the printer delivered the various printings to the Crown Agents. Several months could elapse before the stamps went on sale in the Colony, depending on the availability of shipping.

The plates used for these stamps did not fit the paper so that the watermark appears in all sorts of positions on the stamp. Well centred examples are scarce. Examples can also be found showing parts of the marginal watermarks, either CROWN AGENTS horizontally in letters 12 mm high or "CROWN AGENTS FOR THE COLONIES" vertically in 7 mm letters. Both are in double-lined capitals.

Many stamps between Nos. 5 and 38 can be found with the watermark reversed, inverted or both, in addition to those noted above where such variations are a constant feature.

1882 (22 Nov). *Wmk Crown CA* (upright). *P 14, 14½.*
5 3 1d. dull claret £325 £110
   a. Imperf vert (horiz pair) .. £42000
6   4d. grey-black .. .. £200 60·00

1885 (23 Mar)–87. *Wmk Crown CA (sideways to left or right). P 14, 14½.*
7 3 1d. pale claret .. .. 55·00 38·00
8   1d. brownish claret (3.10.87) .. 80·00 35·00
   a. Bisected (on cover) (1891)* .. † £2000
9   4d. pale grey-black .. .. £375 38·00
10   4d. grey-black (3.10.87) .. £325 35·00
*See note below No. 14.

1889 (26 Sept)–91. *Wmk Crown CA (upright). P 14, 14½.*
11 3 1d. red-brown (21.5.91) .. £130 60·00
   a. Bisected (on cover)* .. † £2250
12   4d. olive grey-black .. £110 45·00
*See note below No. 14.

1891 (Jan). *Nos. 8 and 11 bisected diagonally and each half handstamped with T 4.*
13 3 ½d. on half of 1d. brownish claret (No. 8) £500 £300
   a. Unsevered pair £2250 £1000
   b. Unsevered pair *se-tenant* with unsurcharged whole stamp .. £11000
   c. Bisect *se-tenant* with unsurcharged whole stamp .. † £1000
14   ½d. on half 1d. red-brown (No. 11) £550 £250
   a. Unsevered pair .. £2500 £1200
   b. Bisect *se-tenant* with unsurcharged whole stamp .. .. † £1000

1891 PROVISIONALS. In 1891 the postage to the United Kingdom and Colonies was reduced from 4d. to 2½d. per half ounce. As no ½d. or 2½d. stamps were available the bisection of the 1d. was authorised from 1 January 1891. This authorisation was withdrawn on 11 January 1892, although bisects were accepted for postage until July of that year. The ½d. and 2½d. stamps were placed on sale from 10 September 1891.

Cork Cancel used in 1891

The Type 4 surcharge was not used regularly; unsurcharged bisects being employed far more frequently. Genuine bisects should be cancelled with the cork cancel illustrated above. The use of any other postmark, including a different cork cancel, requires date evidence linked to known mail ship sailings to prove authenticity. Posthumous strikes of the surcharge on "souvenir" bisects usually show a broken "2" and/or a large full stop. These are known on bisected examples of No. 18 and on varieties such as surcharge inverted, double or sideways. Forgeries exist of all these provisionals.

1891 (10 Sept*)–1902. *Wmk Crown CA (upright). P 14, 14½.*
15 3 ½d. blue-green (Aug–Nov 1891) .. 18·00 26·00
16   ½d. green (20.5.92) .. 16·00 15·00
   a. *Deep dull green* (15.4.96) .. 40·00 30·00
17   ½d. deep yellow-green (1894–95) 16·00 21·00
   a. *Yellow-green* (19.6.99) .. 2·00 2·50
   b. *Dull yellowish green* (13.1.1902) .. 4·50 2·75
18   1d. orange red-brown (14.10.91) 60·00 48·00
   a. *Brown* .. .. .. 80·00 48·00
19   1d. reddish chestnut (20.4.92) .. 40·00 42·00
20   1d. orange-brn (*Wmk reversed*) (18.1.94) 38·00 35·00
21   1d. claret (23.7.94) .. .. 50·00 48·00
22   1d. Venetian red (pale to deep) (1895–96) .. .. 9·00 10·00
   a. *Venetian claret* (1898?) .. 28·00 12·00
23   1d. pale red (19.6.99) .. .. 5·00 2·00
24   1d. orange-red (13.1.1902) .. 8·50 3·00
25   2d. purple (pale to deep) (1895–98) 6·50 12·00
26   2d. reddish purple (15.4.96) .. 5·00 11·00
27   2½d. pale chalky ultramarine (Aug 1891) £110 38·00
28   2½d. dull blue (19.11.91) .. 95·00 18·00
29   2½d. Prussian blue (18.1.94) .. £225 £160
30   2½d. ultramarine (1894–96) .. 20·00 8·50
   a. *Pale ultramarine* (10.6.98) .. 25·00 12·00
   b. *Deep ultramarine* (18.9.1901) .. 27·00 27·00
31   4d. brownish black (wmk reversed) (18.1.94) £500 £275
32   4d. olive-black (11.5.95) .. 10·00 21·00
33   6d. orange-yellow (19.11.91) .. 40·00 38·00
34   6d. yellow (15.4.96) .. .. 27·00 35·00
35   9d. pale reddish orange (15.11.95) .. 28·00 55·00
36   9d. salmon (15.4.96) .. .. 32·00 48·00
37   1s. grey-brown (15.11.95) .. 42·00 45·00
38   1s. yellow-brown (15.4.96) .. 38·00 40·00
15/38   Set of 8 £120 £150
15, 26, 28, 33, 35 Optd "Specimen" Set of 5 £650
*The ½d. and 2½d. were first placed on sale in the Falkland Islands on 10 September 1891. Such stamps came from the August 1891 printing. It is now believed that the stock of the May printings sent to the Falkland Islands was lost at sea.
   The 2½d. ultramarine printing can sometimes be found in a violet shade, but the reason for this is unknown.

MINIMUM PRICE

The minimum price quote is 10p which represents a handling charge rather than a basis for valuing common stamps. For further notes about prices see introductory pages.

BRITISH EMPIRE EXCLUSIVELY

WANTS LISTS WELCOMED FROM SERIOUS COLLECTORS OF <u>FALKLAND ISLANDS.</u> EMPHASIS ON PRE-1935. WE STOCK STAMPS, POSTAL HISTORY AND SPECIALIST MATERIAL. *REFERENCES ESSENTIAL.*

REQUEST A CATALOGUE FOR OUR NEXT PUBLIC AUCTION. PLEASE SPECIFY YOUR INTERESTS.

SELLING? ASK US ABOUT CONSIGNING TO A FUTURE SALE.

𝕍ictoria 𝕊tamp ℂompany

Established 1962

PHOEBE A. MACGILLIVARY
P.O. BOX 745, RIDGEWOOD, NJ 07451, U.S.A.
Tel: 001-201-652-7283   Fax: 001-201-612-0024

FALKLAND ISLANDS

SG 138

and the British Empire 1840-1936
- Bought & Sold -
RARE AND UNUSUAL STAMPS
FOR SERIOUS COLLECTORS.
Wants Lists filled from our comprehensive 30
volume stock of stamps, varieties and postal
history (references please).

We hold several British Empire public auctions annually. Subscriptions: £25.

George W. Holschauer

Colonial Stamp Co.

5757 Wilshire Blvd., Penthouse 8
Los Angeles, CA 90036, U.S.A.
(213) 933-9435 ● FAX (213) 939-9930

Members: IFSDA, PTS, ASDA, Int'l Soc. of Appraisers

When enquiring or placing an order please quote that you have seen me in Stanley Gibbons British Commonwealth catalogue.

5   6

(Recess B.W.)

1898 (5 Oct). *Wmk Crown CC. P* 14, 14½.
41	5	2s. 6d. deep blue	..	£200	£250
42	6	5s. red	..	£160	£200
41/2 Optd "Specimen"			*Set of* 2	£450	

7   8

(Recess D.L.R.)

1904 (16 July)–**12**. *Wmk Mult Crown CA. P* 14.
43	7	½d. yellow-green	..	4·25	1·50
		aw. Wmk inverted	..	£150	£110
		b. *Pale yell-grn* (on thick paper) (6.08)	11·00	9·00
		bw. Wmk inverted			
		c. *Deep yellow-green* (7.11)	..	8·00	3·00
44		1d. vermilion	..	8·50	1·50
		aw. Wmk inverted	..	£140	£120
		ax. Wmk reversed	..	£225	£200
		b. Wmk sideways (7.06)	..	1·00	2·25
		c. Thick paper (1908)	..	11·00	1·75
		cw. Wmk inverted	..	£225	£200
		cx. Wmk reversed	..	£275	£200
		d. *Dull coppery red* (on thick paper) (3.08)		£160	35·00
		dx. Wmk reversed	..	£425	£200
		e. *Orange-vermilion* (7.11)	..	8·00	2·25
		ex. Wmk reversed	..	£225	£225
45		2d. purple (27.12.04)	..	11·00	26·00
		ax. Wmk reversed	..	£110	£110
		b. *Reddish purple* (13.1.12)	..	£225	£275
46		2½d. ultramarine (*shades*)	..	29·00	7·50
		aw. Wmk inverted and reversed	—	£325
		b. *Deep blue* (13.1.12)	..	£225	£180
47		6d. orange (27.12.04)	..	38·00	48·00
48		1s. brown (27.12.04)	..	40·00	32·00
49	8	3s. green	..	£140	£130
		aw. Wmk inverted	..	£900	
		b. *Deep green* (4.07)	..	£120	£130
		bx. Wmk reversed	..	£900	£600
50		5s. red (27.12.04)	..	£140	£150
43/50			*Set of* 8	£325	£350
43/50 Optd "Specimen"			*Set of* 8	£450	

Examples of Nos. 41/50 and earlier issues are known with a forged Falkland Islands postmark dated "OCT 15 10".

For details of South Georgia underprint, South Georgia provisional handstamps and Port Foster handstamp see under FALKLAND ISLANDS DEPENDENCIES.

---

9   10

Des B. MacKennal. Eng J. A. C. Harrison. Recess D.L.R.

1912 (3 July)–**20**. *Wmk Mult Crown CA. P* 13¾×14 (*comb*) (½d. to 1s.) *or* 14 (*line*) (3s. to £1).
60	9	½d. yellow-green	..	2·25	3·00
		a. Perf 14 (line). *Dp yell-green* (1914)	18·00	35·00
		b. Perf 14 (line). *Deep olive* (1918)	..	24·00	75·00
		c. *Deep olive* (4.19)	..	3·50	18·00
		ca. Printed both sides	..	† £5500	
		d. *Dull yellowish green* (on thick greyish paper) (1920)	4·50	25·00
61		1d. orange-red	..	4·25	2·50
		a. Perf 14 (line). *Orange-vermilion* (1914, 1916)	20·00	2·00
		b. Perf 14 (line). *Vermilion* (1918)	..	† £550
		c. *Orange-vermilion* (4.19)	..	3·50	2·75
		d. *Orange-vermilion* (on thick greyish paper) (1920)	7·00	2·00
		dx. Wmk reversed	..	£130	
62		2d. maroon	..	17·00	23·00
		a. Perf 14 (line). *Dp reddish pur* (1914)	75·00	90·00
		b. Perf 14 (line). *Maroon* (4.18)	..	80·00	75·00
		c. *Deep reddish purple* (4.19)	..	7·00	16·00
63		2½d. deep bright blue	..	16·00	19·00
		a. Perf 14 (line). *Dp bright blue* (1914)	24·00	24·00
		b. Perf 14 (line). *Deep blue* (1916, 4.18)	24·00	24·00
		c. *Deep blue* (4.19)	..	7·00	17·00

64	9	6d. yellow-orange (6.7.12)	..	14·00	20·00
		aw. Wmk inverted	..	£250	£300
		b. *Brown-orange* (4.19)	..	10·00	32·00
65		1s. light bistre-brown (6.7.12)	..	30·00	30·00
		a. *Pale bistre-brown* (4.19)	..	48·00	85·00
		b. *Brn* (on thick greyish paper) (1920)	32·00	£130
66	10	3s. slate-green	..	65·00	80·00
67		5s. deep rose-red	..	65·00	90·00
		a. *Reddish maroon* (1914)	..	£170	£190
		b. *Maroon* (1916)	..	70·00	90·00
		bx. Wmk reversed	..	£1700	£1100
68		10s. red/*green* (11.2.14)	..	£150	£225
69		£1 black/*red* (11.2.14)	..	£300	£350
60/9 (*inc* 67b)			*Set of* 11	£600	£800
60/9 (*inc* 67a) Optd "Specimen"		*Set of* 11	£1300	

The exact measurement of the comb perforation used for Type **9** is 13.7 × 13.9. The line perforation, used for the 1914, 1916 and 1918 printings and for all the high values in Type **10**, measured 14.1 × 14.1.

It was previously believed that all examples of the 1d. in vermilion with the line perforation were overprinted to form No. 71, but it has now been established that some unoverprinted sheets of No. 61b were used during 1919.

Many of the sheets showed sheets from the left-hand side in a lighter shade than those from the right. It is believed that this was due to the weight of the impression. Such differences are particularly noticeable on the 2½d. 1916 and 1918 printings where the lighter shades, approaching milky blue in appearance, are scarce.

All 1919 printings show weak impressions of the background either side of the head caused by the poor paper quality.

Examples of all values are known with forged postmarks, including one of Falkland Islands dated "5 SP 19" and another of South Shetlands dated "20 MR 27".

2½D

WAR STAMP

(11)   (12)

1918 (22 Oct*)–**20**. Optd by Govt Printing Press, Stanley, with T **11**.
70	9	½d. deep olive (line perf) (No. 60b)	..	1·00	6·50
		a. *Yellow-green* (No. 60) (4.19)	..	12·00	
		ab. Albino opt	..	£1100	
		b. *Deep olive* (comb perf) (No. 60c) (4.19)	50	6·50
		c. *Dull yellowish green* (on thick greyish paper) (No. 60d) (5.20)	10·00	65·00
		cx. Wmk reversed	..	£150	
71		1d. vermilion (line perf) (No. 61b)	..	2·00	15·00
		a. Opt double, one albino	..	£400	
		b. *Orge-verm* (line perf) (No. 61a) (4.19)	12·00	†
		c. *Orge-verm* (comb perf) (No. 61c) (4.19)	50	3·50
		ca. Opt double	..	£1600	
		cx. Wmk reversed	..	£225	
		d. *Orange-vermilion* (on thick greyish paper) (No. 61d) (5.20)	75·00	£150
72		1s. light bistre-brown (No. 65)	..	30·00	55·00
		a. *Pale bistre-brown* (No. 65a) (4.19)	4·00	40·00
		ab. Opt double, one albino	..	£1200	
		ac. Opt omitted (in pair with normal)	..	£6000	
		b. *Brown* (on thick greyish paper) (No. 65b) (5.20)	7·00	40·00
		ba. Opt double, one albino	..	£1200	
		bw. Wmk inverted	..	£150	£200
		bx. Wmk reversed	..	£400	

*Earliest known postal use. Cancellations dated 8 October were applied much later.

There were five printings of the "WAR STAMP" overprint, but all, except that in May 1920, used the same setting. Composition of the five printings was as follows:

October 1918. Nos. 70, 71 and 72
January 1919. Nos. 70, 71 and 72
April 1919. Nos. 70/b, 71b/c and 72a
October 1919. Nos. 70b, 71c and 72a
May 1920. Nos. 70c, 71d and 72b

It is believed that the entire stock of No. 70a was sold to stamp dealers. Only a handful of used examples are known which may have subsequently been returned to the colony for cancellation. Examples of Nos. 70/2 are known with a forged Falkland Islands postmark dated "5 SP 19".

1921–28. *Wmk Mult Script CA. P* 14.
73	9	½d. yellowish green	..	3·00	4·00
		a. *Green* (1925)	..	3·00	4·00
74		1d. dull vermilion (1924)	..	5·00	1·25
		ay. Wmk inverted and reversed	..	£180	
		b. *Orange-vermilion* (*shades*) (1925)	5·50	1·25
75		2d. deep brown-purple (8.23)	..	9·00	5·50
		aw. Wmk inverted	..	—	£850
		ax. Wmk reversed	..	£900	
		b. *Purple-brown* (1927)	..	9·00	13·00
		c. *Reddish maroon* (1.28)	..	10·00	15·00
		cy. Wmk inverted and reversed			
76		2½d. deep blue	..	22·00	16·00
		a. *Indigo* (28.4.27)	..	16·00	20·00
		b. *Deep steel-blue* (1.28)	..	5·50	16·00
		c. *Prussian blue* (10.28)	..	£300	£450
77		2½d. deep purple/*pale yellow* (8.23)	..	4·50	32·00
		a. *Pale purple/pale yellow* (1925)	..	4·25	32·00
		y. Wmk inverted and reversed	..	£200	
78		6d. yellow-orange (1925)	..	8·00	32·00
		w. Wmk inverted	..	£150	
		x. Wmk reversed	..	£700	
79		1s. deep ochre	..	16·00	48·00
80	10	3s. slate-green (8.23)	..	80·00	£130
73/80			*Set of* 8	£110	£225
73/80 (*incl* 76a) Optd "Specimen"		*Set of* 9	£550	

Dates quoted above are those of despatch from Great Britain. No. 76c only occurred in part of the October 1928 printing. The remainder are in the deep steel-blue shade of the January 1928 despatch, No. 76b.

1928 (7 Feb). *No. 75a surch with T* **12**.
115	9	2½d. on 2d. purple-brown	..	£650	£750
		a. Surch double	..	£30000	

No. 115 was produced on South Georgia during a shortage of 2½d. stamps. The provisional was withdrawn on 22 February 1928.

---

13 Fin Whale and Gentoo Penguins 14

(Recess P.B.)

1929 (2 Sept)–**36**. *P* 14. (*a*) *Wmk Mult Script CA.*
116	13	½d. green	..	80	3·00
117		1d. scarlet	..	2·50	80
		a. *Deep red*	..	6·00	13·00
118		2d. grey	..	2·00	1·50
119		2½d. blue	..	2·00	2·25
120	14	4d. orange (18.2.32)	..	12·00	13·00
		a. *Deep orange*	..	26·00	48·00
121	13	6d. purple	..	11·00	12·00
		a. *Reddish purple* (1936)	..	32·00	25·00
122		1s. black/*emerald*	..	17·00	25·00
		a. *On bright emerald* (1936)	..	22·00	27·00
123		2s. 6d carmine/*blue*	..	32·00	38·00
124		5s. green/*yellow*	..	55·00	70·00
125		10s. carmine/*emerald*	..	95·00	£130

(*b*) *Wmk Mult Crown CA*
126	13	£1 black/*red*	..	£275	£375
116/126			*Set of* 11	£425	£600
116/26 Perf "Specimen"			*Set of* 11	£1000	

Two kinds of perforation exist:
A. Comb perf 13.9:—original values of 1929.
B. Line perf 13.9, 14.2 or compound:—4d. and 1936 printings of ½d., 1d., 6d. and 1s.

Examples of most values are known with forged postmarks, including one of Port Stanley dated "14 JY 31" and another of South Georgia dated "AU 30 31".

15 Romney Marsh Ram   26 King George V

(Des (except 6d.) by G. Roberts. Eng and recess B.W.)

1933 (2 Jan–Apr). *Centenary of British Administration. T* **15**, **26** *and similar designs. Wmk Mult Script CA. P* 12.
127		½d. black and green	..	1·50	5·00
128		1d. black and scarlet	..	3·50	2·00
129		1½d. black and blue	..	9·50	12·00
130		2d. black and brown	..	9·00	20·00
131		3d. black and violet	..	11·00	14·00
132		4d. black and orange	..	11·00	15·00
133		6d. black and slate	..	48·00	55·00
134		1s. black and olive-green	..	38·00	55·00
135		2s. 6d. black and violet	..	£130	£150
136		5s. black and yellow	..	£500	£650
		a. *Black and yellow-orange* (Apr)	..	£1000	£1200
137		10s. black and chestnut	..	£500	£700
138		£1 black and carmine	..	£1300	£800
127/138			*Set of* 12	£2250	£3000
127/38 Perf "Specimen"			*Set of* 12	£2250	

Designs: *Horiz*—1d. Iceberg; 1½d. Whale-catcher *Bransfield*; 2d. Port Louis; 3d. Map of Falkland Islands; 4d. South Georgia; 6d. Fin Whale; 1s. Government House, Stanley. *Vert*—2s. 6d. Battle Memorial; 5s. King Penguin; 10s. Coat of Arms.

Examples of all values are known with forged Port Stanley postmarks dated "6 JA 33". Some values have also been seen with part strikes of the forged Falkland Islands postmark mentioned below Nos. 60/9 and 70/2.

1935 (7 May). *Silver Jubilee. As Nos.* 91/4 *of Antigua, but printed by B.W. P* 11 × 12.
139		1d. deep blue and scarlet	..	2·50	40
		b. Short extra flagstaff	..	£275	£275
		d. Flagstaff on right-hand turret	..	£180	£140
		e. Double flagstaff	..	£200	£160
140		2½d. brown and deep blue	..	8·00	1·60
		b. Short extra flagstaff	..	£550	£275
		d. Flagstaff on right-hand turret	..	£225	£160
		e. Double flagstaff	..	£300	£180
		l. Re-entry on value tablet (R. 8/1)	..	£200	£100
141		4d. green and indigo	..	8·00	3·00
		b. Short extra flagstaff	..	£450	£275
		d. Flagstaff on right-hand turret	..	£275	£180
		e. Double flagstaff	..	£325	£200
142		1s. slate and purple	..	8·00	3·25
		a. Extra flagstaff	..	£2500	£2250
		b. Short extra flagstaff	..	£500	£300
		c. Lightning conductor	..	£1000	£550
		d. Flagstaff on right-hand turret	..	£400	£275
		e. Double flagstaff	..	£450	£300
139/42			*Set of* 4	24·00	7·50
139/42 Perf "Specimen"			*Set of* 4	£250	

For illustrations of plate varieties see Catalogue Introduction.

1937 (12 May). *Coronation. As Nos.* 95/7 *of Antigua. P* 11×11½.
143		½d. green	..	30	10
144		1d. carmine	..	40	45
145		2½d. blue	..	80	55
143/5			*Set of* 3	1·40	1·00
143/5 Perf "Specimen"			*Set of* 3	£160	

Aron R. Halberstam Philatelists, Ltd.

For Falkland Islands
and the Entire
British Commonwealth

Pre-1960 only

Call or write to request a free price list detailing our comprehensive stock
of individual items and sets, organised by country, Scott and
Gibbons catalogue numbers, and condition
(Mounted, Unmounted, and Used)
Or send us your wants list.

We accept payment by Sterling cheque, or

P.O.B. 150168, Van Brunt Station,
Brooklyn, NY 11215-0168, U.S.A.,
Tel: +001 718 788 3978 Fax: +001 718 965 3099

Introducing Quality Albums Featuring SG Catalogue Numbers

Stanley Gibbons 'One Country' Albums

Available for
● Great Britain ● Guernsey ● Jersey ● Isle of Man
● Australia ● New Zealand ● Canada

Ideal for the straightforward single country collection these popular albums
are available as separate volumes or in a great value set. The high quality
leaves feature illustrations, SG catalogue numbers and dates of issue with supplements produced yearly to keep your collection up-to-date.

Plus
● Padded leather finish maroon PVC binders
● Secure 4 and 22 ring locking mechanism
● High quality leaves with illustrations
● Includes self-adhesive album title sheet

Available from our London showroom, at 399 Strand and by Mail Order

STANLEY GIBBONS

Stanley Gibbons Publications
5/7 Parkside, Christchurch Road,
Ringwood, Hants BH24 3SH
Tel: +44 (0)1425 472363 Fax: +44 (0)1425 470247
e.mail: sales@stangib.demon.co.uk
internet: http://www.stangib.com/

Phone Free On 0800 611 622 For Your Complimentary Colour Brochure

27 Whales' Jaw Bones

(Des G. Roberts (Nos. 146, 148/9, 158 and 160/3), K. Lellman (No. 159). Recess B.W.)

1938 (3 Jan)–50. *Horiz designs as T 27. Wmk Mult Script CA. P 12.*

146	½d. black and green (shades)		30	75
147	1d. black and carmine		26·00	80
	a. Black and scarlet		3·00	85
148	1d. black and violet (14.7.41)		2·50	1·75
	a. Black and purple-violet (1.43)		5·50	1·75
149	2d. black and deep violet		1·00	50
150	2d. black and carmine-red (14.7.41)		75	2·25
	a. Black and red (1.43)		2·00	85
151	2½d. black and bright blue		45	30
152	2½d. black and blue (15.6.49)		4·50	5·50
153	3d. black and blue (14.7.41)		6·00	2·00
	a. Black and deep blue (1.43)		7·50	2·00
154	4d. black and purple		2·75	50
155	6d. black and brown		4·00	1·75
156	6d. black (15.6.49)		4·00	4·50
157	9d. black and grey-blue		13·00	80
158	1s. pale blue		65·00	18·00
	a. Deep blue (1941)		16·00	2·50
159	1s. 3d. black and carmine-red (11.12.46)		2·00	1·40
160	2s. 6d. slate		55·00	10·00
161	5s. bright blue and pale brown		£110	50·00
	b. Indigo and yellow-brown (1942)		£475	£130
	c. Blue and buff-brown (9.2.50)		£120	£150
162	10s. black and orange		55·00	27·00
163	£1 black and violet		£110	48·00
146/63		Set of 18	£350	£140
146/63 (ex 152, 156) Perf "Specimen"	Set of 16	£900	

Designs:—Nos. 147 and 150, Black-necked Swan; Nos. 148/9, Battle Memorial; Nos. 151 and 153, Flock of sheep; Nos. 152 and 154, Magellan Goose; Nos. 155/6, *Discovery II* (polar supply vessel); No. 157, *William Scoresby* (research ship); No. 158, Mount Sugar Top; No. 159, Turkey Vultures; No. 160 Gentoo Penguins; No. 161, Southern Sealion; No. 162, Deception Island; No. 163, Arms of Falkland Islands.

1946 (7 Oct). *Victory. As Nos. 110/11 of Antigua.*

164	1d. dull violet		30	15
165	3d. blue		45	15
164/5 Perf "Specimen"	Set of 2	£140	

1948 (1 Nov). *Royal Silver Wedding. As Nos. 112/13 of Antigua.*

166	2½d. ultramarine		2·00	70
167	£1 mauve		90·00	55·00

1949 (10 Oct). *75th Anniv of Universal Postal Union. As Nos. 114/17 of Antigua.*

168	1d. violet		1·50	75
169	3d. deep blue		5·00	2·00
170	1s. 3d. deep blue-green		4·00	2·25
171	2s. blue		4·00	7·50
168/71		Set of 4	13·00	11·00

39 Sheep 43 Arms of the Colony

(Des from sketches by V. Spencer. Recess Waterlow)

1952 (2 Jan). *T 39, 43 and similar designs. Wmk Mult Script CA. P 13×13½ (vert) or 13½×13 (horiz).*

172	½d. green		70	70
173	1d. scarlet		1·25	40
174	2d. violet		3·25	2·50
175	2½d. black and light ultramarine		95	50
176	3d. deep ultramarine		1·00	1·00
177	4d. reddish purple		7·50	2·00
178	6d. bistre-brown		12·00	1·00
179	9d. orange-yellow		8·00	2·75
180	1s. black		18·00	80
181	1s. 3d. orange		12·00	6·00
182	2s. 6d. olive-green		16·00	7·00
183	5s. purple		8·50	6·00
184	10s. grey		20·00	20·00
185	£1 black		25·00	20·00
172/185		Set of 14	£120	60·00

Designs: *Horiz*—1d. *Fitzroy* (supply ship); 2d. Magellan Goose; 2½d. Map of Falkland Islands; 4d. Auster Autocrat aircraft; 6d. *John Biscoe* (research ship); 9d. View of the Two Sisters; 1s. 3d. Kelp goose and gander; 10s. Southern Sealion and South American Fur Seal; £1 Hulk of *Great Britain*. *Vert*—1s. Gentoo Penguins; 2s. 6d. Sheep-shearing; 5s. Battle Memorial.

1953 (4 June). *Coronation. As No. 120 of Antigua.*

186	1d. black and scarlet		80	1·25

53 *John Biscoe I* (research ship) 54 Austral Thrush

(Recess Waterlow)

1955–57. *Designs previously used for King George VI issue but with portrait of Queen Elizabeth II as in T 53. Wmk Mult Script CA. P 13 × 13½ (vert) or 13½ × 13 (horiz).*

187	½d. green (2.9.57)		70	1·25
188	1d. scarlet (2.9.57)		1·25	1·00
189	2d. violet (3.9.56)		2·75	4·50
190	6d. deep yellow-brown (1.6.55)		6·50	60
191	9d. orange-yellow (2.9.57)		17·00	17·00
192	1s. black (15.7.55)		5·00	1·25
187/92		Set of 6	30·00	23·00

Designs: *Horiz*—½d. Sheep; 1d. *Fitzroy* (supply ship); 2d. Magellan Goose; 9d. View of Two Sisters. *Vert*—1s. Gentoo Penguins.

(Des from sketches by S. Scott. Recess Waterlow, then D.L.R. (from 9.1.62 onwards))

1960 (10 Feb)–66. *T 54 and similar horiz designs. W w 12 (upright). P 13½.*

193	½d. black and myrtle-green		3·50	50
	a. Black and green (DLR) (9.1.62)		12·00	4·00
	aw. Wmk inverted		£2000	£1000
194	1d. black and scarlet		1·50	60
	a. Black and carmine-red (DLR) (15.7.63)		10·00	3·50
195	2d. black and blue		3·25	80
	a. Black and deep blue (DLR) (25.10.66)		17·00	12·00
196	2½d. black and yellow-brown		1·50	20
197	3d. black and olive		80	15
198	4d. black and carmine		1·25	60
199	5½d. black and violet		1·75	1·25
200	6d. black and sepia		1·75	15
201	9d. black and orange-red		1·75	80
202	1s. black and maroon		80	15
203	1s. 3d. black and ultramarine		9·00	11·00
204	2s. black and brown-red		27·00	2·25
	a. Black and lake-brown (DLR) (25.10.66)		£110	42·00
205	5s. black and turquoise		27·00	11·00
206	10s. black and purple		48·00	13·00
207	£1 black and orange-yellow		48·00	27·00
193/207		Set of 15	£150	60·00

Designs:—1d. Southern Black-backed Gull; 2d. Gentoo Penguins; 2½d. Long-tailed Meadowlark; 3d. Magellan Geese; 4d. Falkland Islands Flightless Steamer Ducks; 5½d. Rockhopper Penguin; 6d. Black-browed Albatross; 9d. Silvery Grebe; 1s. Magellanic Oystercatchers; 1s. 3d. Chilean Teal; 2s. Kelp Geese; 5s. King Cormorants; 10s. Common Caracara; £1 Black-necked Swan.

Waterlow De La Rue

Waterlow printings were from Frame Plates 1 or 2. The De La Rue printings of the ½d., 1d., 2d. and 2s. are all from Frame Plate 2 and can be distinguished by the finer lines of shading on the Queen's face, neck and shoulders (appearing as a white face) and also the very faint cross hatching left of the face. Apart from this the shades differ in varying degrees. Frame Plate 1 was used by De La Rue to print initial supplies of the 6d. value and these stamps have little to distinguish them from the original printing. Frame Plate 2 was subsequently used for this value which, although it shows the usual plate characteristics, does not differ in shade from the Waterlow printing.

For the ½d. with watermark sideways see No. 227.

69 Morse Key 70 One-valve Receiver

(Des M. Goaman. Photo Enschedé)

1962 (5 Oct). *50th Anniv of Establishment of Radio Communications. T 69/70 and similar vert design. W w 12. P 11½ × 11.*

208	69	6d. carmine-lake and orange	1·00	30
209	70	1s. deep bluish green and yellow-olive	1·25	35
210	—	2s. deep violet and ultramarine	1·25	1·25
		w. Wmk inverted	50·00	
208/10		Set of 3	3·25	1·60

Design:—2s. Rotary Spark Transmitter.

1963 (4 June). *Freedom from Hunger. As No. 146 of Antigua.*

211	1s. ultramarine		13·00	95

1963 (2 Sept). *Red Cross Centenary. As Nos. 147/8 of Antigua.*

212	1d. red and black		5·00	50
213	1s. red and blue		20·00	5·50

1964 (23 April). *400th Birth Anniv of William Shakespeare. As No. 164 of Antigua.*

214	6d. black		1·00	30

72 H.M.S. *Glasgow*

(Recess D.L.R.)

1964 (8 Dec) *50th Anniv of the Battle of the Falkland Islands. T 72 and similar designs. W w 12. P 13 × 14 (2s.) or 13 (others).*

215	2½d. black and red		9·00	3·00
216	6d. black and light blue		75	25
	a. Centre Type 72		£17000	
217	1s. black and carmine-red		75	75
	w. Wmk inverted		£1100	
218	2s. black and blue		50	75
215/18		Set of 10	9·00	4·25

Designs: *Horiz*—6d. H.M.S. *Kent*; 1s. H.M.S. *Invincible*. *Vert*—2s. Battle Memorial.

It is believed that No. 216a came from a sheet which was first printed with the centre of the 2½d. and then accidentally included among the supply of the 6d. value and thus received the wrong frame. There have been seventeen reports of stamps showing the error, although it is believed that some of these *may* refer to the same example.

1965 (26 May). *I.T.U. Centenary. As Nos. 166/7 of Antigua.*

219	1d. light blue and deep blue		75	20
	w. Wmk inverted		£500	
220	2s. lilac and bistre-yellow		9·00	1·50

1965 (25 Oct). *International Co-operation Year. As Nos. 168/9 of Antigua.*

221	1d. reddish purple and turquoise-green		2·00	20
222	1s. deep bluish green and lavender		7·50	1·10

1966 (24 Jan). *Churchill Commemoration. As Nos. 170/3 of Antigua.*

223	½d. new blue		65	50
224	1d. deep green		2·25	15
	w. Wmk inverted		6·00	
225	1s. brown		6·50	1·75
	w. Wmk inverted		55·00	
226	2s. bluish violet		3·50	1·75
223/6		Set of 4	13·50	3·75

1966 (25 Oct). *As No. 193a, but wmk w 12 sideways.*

227	54	½d. black and green	30	40

76 Globe and Human Rights Emblem 77 Dusty Miller

(Des M. Farrar Bell. Photo Harrison)

1968 (4 July). *Human Rights Year. W w 12. P 14 × 14½.*

228	76	2d. multicoloured	60	20
		a. Yellow omitted ("1968" white)	£900	
229		6d. muticoloured	70	20
230		1s. multicoloured	70	20
231		2s. multicoloured	70	30
228/31		Set of 4	2·40	80

Two types of £1:
Type I. Pale brown shading does not extend to foot of design.
Type II. Pale brown shading to foot of design.

(Des Sylvia Goaman)

1968 (9 Oct)–71. *Flowers. Designs as T 77. Chalk-surfaced paper. W w 12 (sideways on vert designs). P 14.*

232	½d. multicoloured		15	1·40
233	1½d. multicoloured		30	15
234	2d. multicoloured		40	15
235	3d. multicoloured		4·25	50
236	3½d. multicoloured		30	15
237	4½d. multicoloured		1·00	1·50
238	5½d. olive-yellow, brown and yellow-green		1·00	1·50
239	6d. carmine, black and yellow-green		60	20
240	1s. multicoloured		60	80
	w. Wmk inverted		75·00	
241	1s. 6d. multicoloured		4·50	11·00
242	2s. multicoloured		5·50	6·50
243	3s. multicoloured		8·00	6·50
244	5s. multicoloured		25·00	13·00
245	£1 multicoloured (Type I)		13·00	2·00
	a. Type II (15.2.71)		13·00	2·00
232/45		Set of 14	55·00	40·00

Designs: *Horiz*—1½d. Pig Vine; 3½d. Sea Cabbage; 5½d. Arrowleaf Marigold; 6d. Diddle Dee; 1s. Scurvy Grass; 5s. Felton's Flower. *Vert*—2d. Pale Maiden; 3d. Dog Orchid; 4½d. Vanilla Daisy; 1s. 6d. Prickly Burr; 2s. Fachine; 3s. Lavender; £1 Yellow Orchid.

For stamps inscribed in decimal currency see Nos. 276/88, 293/5 and 315.

91 De Havilland D.H.C.2
Beaver Seaplane

(Des V. Whiteley. Litho Format)

1969 (8 Apr). *21st Anniv of Government Air Services. T* **91** *and similar horiz designs. Multicoloured. W w* **12** *(sideways). P* 14.

246	2d. Type **91**		35	30
247	6d. Noorduyn Norseman V		40	35
248	1s. Auster Autocrat		50	35
249	2s. Falkland Islands Arms		1·25	1·25
246/9		*Set of 4*	2·25	2·00

92 Holy Trinity Church, 1869

(Des G. Drummond. Litho Format)

1969 (30 Oct). *Centenary of Bishop Stirling's Consecration. T* **92** *and similar horiz designs. W w* **12** *(sideways). P* 14.

250	2d. black, grey and apple-green		50	40
251	6d. black, grey and orange-red		50	40
252	1s. black, grey and lilac		50	40
253	2s. multicoloured		70	65
250/3		*Set of 4*	2·00	1·75

Designs:—6d. Christ Church Cathedral, 1969; 1s. Bishop Stirling; 2s. Bishop's Mitre.

96 Mounted Volunteer   97 S.S. *Great Britain* (1843)

(Des R. Granger Barrett. Litho B.W.)

1970 (30 Apr). *Golden Jubilee of Defence Force. T* **96** *and similar designs. Multicoloured. W w* **12** *(sideways on 2d. and 1s.). P* 13.

254	2d. Type **96**		1·90	70
255	6d. Defence Post (*horiz*)		2·00	70
256	1s. Corporal in Number One Dress Uniform		2·00	70
257	2s. Defence Force Badge (*horiz*)		3·00	75
254/7		*Set of 4*	8·00	2·50

(Des V. Whiteley. Litho J.W.)

1970 (30 Oct). *Restoration of S.S. "Great Britain". T* **97** *and views of the ship at different dates. Multicoloured. W w* **12** *(sideways*). P* 14½×14.

258	2d. Type **97**		1·75	40
259	4d. In 1845		2·00	1·00
	w. Wmk Crown to right of CA		15·00	
260	9d. In 1876		2·00	1·00
261	1s. In 1886		2·00	1·00
	w. Wmk Crown to right of CA		£700	
262	2s. In 1970		2·75	1·00
258/62		*Set of 5*	9·50	4·00

*The normal sideways watermark shows Crown to left of CA, as seen from the back of the stamp.

(98)   99 Dusty Miller

1971 (15 Feb). *Decimal Currency. Nos. 232/44 surch as T* **98**. *W w* **12** *(sideways on vert designs). P* 14.

263	½p. on ½d. multicoloured		25	20
264	1p. on 1½d. multicoloured		30	15
	a. Error. Surch 5p.		£375	
	b. Do. but surch at right		£1000	
	c. Surch albino		£100	
	d. Surch albino in pair with normal		£2750	
265	1½p. on 2d. multicoloured		30	15
266	2p. on 3d. multicoloured		50	20
267	2½p. on 3½d. multicoloured		30	20
268	3p. on 4d. multicoloured		30	20
269	4p. on 5½d. olive-yellow, brown & yell-grn		30	20

270	5p. on 6d. carmine, black and yellow-green		30	20
271	6p. on 1s. multicoloured		6·00	3·75
272	7½p. on 1s. 6d. multicoloured		8·00	4·75
273	10p. on 2s. multicoloured		8·50	3·00
274	15p. on 3s. multicoloured		6·50	2·75
275	25p. on 5s. multicoloured		7·00	3·25
263/75		*Set of 13*	35·00	17·00

1972 (1 June). *As Nos. 232/44, but Glazed, ordinary paper and with values inscr in decimal currency as T* **99**. *W w* **12** *(sideways on ½, 1½, 2, 3, 7½, 10 and 15p.). P* 14.

276	½p. multicoloured		35	3·75
277	1p. multicoloured (as 1½d.)		30	40
278	1½p. multicoloured (as 2d.)		30	3·25
279	2p. multicoloured (as 3d.)		13·00	1·25
280	2½p. multicoloured (as 3½d.)		35	3·25
281	3p. multicoloured (as 4½d.)		35	1·25
282	4p. olive-yellow, brown & yell-grn (as 5½d.)		40	50
283	5p. carmine, black and yellow-green (as 6d.)		40	55
284	6p. multicoloured (as 1s.)		20·00	9·50
285	7½p. multicoloured (as 1s. 6d.)		1·50	4·00
286	10p. multicoloured (as 2s.)		7·50	4·50
287	15p. multicoloured (as 3s.)		4·50	5·00
288	25p. multicoloured (as 5s.)		4·50	6·00
276/88		*Set of 13*	48·00	35·00

See also Nos. 293/5 and 315.

100 Romney Marsh Sheep and Southern Sealions

(Des (from photograph by D. Groves) and photo Harrison)

1972 (20 Nov). *Royal Silver Wedding. Multicoloured; background colour given. W w* **12**. *P* 14×14½.

289	**100** 1p. grey-green		40	40
290	10p. bright blue		85	85

1973 (14 Nov). *Royal Wedding. As Nos. 165/6 of Anguilla. Centre multicoloured. W w* **12** *(sideways). P* 13½.

291	5p. bright mauve		25	10
292	15p. brown-ochre		35	20

1974 (25 Feb–18 Oct). *As Nos. 276, 279 and 284, but wmk upright on ½p. and 2p. and sideways* on 6p. P* 14.

293	½p. multicoloured (18.10.74)		12·00	28·00
	w. Wmk inverted		£180	
294	2p. multicoloured		17·00	3·25
	w. Wmk inverted		£300	
295	6p. multicoloured (28.3.74)		2·00	2·25
	w. Wmk Crown to right of CA		£400	
293/5		*Set of 3*	28·00	30·00

*The normal sideways watermark shows Crown to left of CA, as seen from the back of the stamp.

101 South American Fur Seal   102 19th-Century Mail-coach

(Des J. Cooter. Litho Walsall)

1974 (6 Mar). *Tourism. T* **101** *and similar horiz designs. Multicoloured. W w* **12**. *P* 14.

296	2p. Type **101**		2·25	1·00
297	4p. Trout-fishing		3·00	1·25
298	5p. Rockhopper penguins		9·50	2·25
299	15p. Long-tailed Meadowlark		12·00	3·75
296/9		*Set of 4*	24·00	7·50

(Des PAD Studio. Litho Questa)

1974 (31 July). *Centenary of Universal Postal Union. T* **102** *and similar vert designs. Multicoloured. W w* **12** *(sideways). P* 14.

300	2p. Type **102**		25	25
301	5p. Packet ship, 1841		35	45
302	8p. First U.K. aerial post, 1911		40	55
303	16p. Ship's catapult mail, 1920's		60	75
300/3		*Set of 4*	1·40	1·75

103 Churchill and Houses of Parliament

(Des G. Vasarhelyi. Litho Enschedé)

1974 (30 Nov). *Birth Centenary of Sir Winston Churchill. T* **103** *and similar horiz design. Multicoloured. W w* **12**. *P* 13½.

304	16p. Type **103**		1·75	1·60
305	20p. Churchill with H.M.S. *Inflexible* and H.M.S. *Invincible*, 1914		2·00	1·90
MS306	108×83 mm. Nos. 304/5		8·00	7·00
	w. Wmk inverted		£170	

104 H.M.S. *Exeter*   105 Seal and Flag Badge

(Des J.W. Litho Harrison)

1974 (13 Dec). *35th Anniv of the Battle of the River Plate. T* **104** *and similar horiz designs. Multicoloured. W w* **12** *(sideways*). P* 14.

307	2p. Type **104**		3·00	1·60
	w. Wmk Crown to right of CA		10·00	6·00
308	6p. H.M.N.Z.S. *Achilles*		4·50	3·50
	w. Wmk Crown to right of CA		7·50	3·50
309	8p. *Admiral Graf Spee*		5·00	4·50
	w. Wmk Crown to right of CA		75·00	50·00
310	16p. H.M.S. *Ajax*		8·50	15·00
	w. Wmk Crown to right of CA		24·00	17·00
307/10		*Set of 4*	19·00	22·00

*The normal sideways watermark shows Crown to left of CA, as seen from the back of the stamp.

(Des PAD Studio. Litho Walsall)

1975 (28 Oct). *50th Anniv of Heraldic Arms. T* **105** *and similar vert designs. Multicoloured. W w* **14** *(inverted). P* 14.

311	2p. Type **105**		70	35
312	7½p. Coat of arms, 1925		1·40	1·40
313	10p. Coat of arms, 1948		1·60	1·60
314	16p. Arms of the Dependencies, 1952		2·25	2·75
311/14		*Set of 4*	5·50	5·50

1975 (8 Dec). *As No. 276 but W w* **14** *(sideways). P* 14.

315	**99** ½p. multicoloured		2·25	3·50

106 ½p. Coin and Brown Trout

(Des G. Drummond. Litho Questa)

1975 (31 Dec). *New Coinage. T* **106** *and similar horiz designs each showing coin. Multicoloured. W w* **12** *(sideways*). P* 14.

316	2p. Type **106**		85	45
	w. Wmk Crown to right of CA		60·00	
317	5½p. Gentoo Penguin and 1p. coin		1·25	1·10
318	8p. Magellan Goose and 2p. coin		1·60	1·60
319	10p. Black-browed Albatross and 5p. coin		1·75	1·60
320	16p. Southern Sealion and 10p. coin		1·90	2·00
316/20		*Set of 5*	6·75	6·00

*The normal sideways watermark shows Crown to left of CA, as seen from the back of the stamp.

107 Gathering Sheep

(Des PAD Studio. Litho J.W.)

1976 (28 Apr). *Sheep Farming Industry. T* **107** *and similar horiz designs. Multicoloured. W w* **14** *(sideways). P* 13½.

321	2p. Type **107**		55	35
322	7½p. Shearing		1·25	1·25
323	10p. Dipping		1·60	1·60
324	20p. Shipping		2·25	2·75
321/4		*Set of 4*	5·00	5·50

108 The Queen awaiting Anointment

(Des M. and G. Shamir; adapted J.W. Litho Questa)

1977 (7 Feb–1 Nov). *Silver Jubilee. T* **108** *and similar horiz designs. Multicoloured. P* 13½. (a) W w **14** (*sideways*).

325	6p.	Visit of Prince Philip, 1957	2·00	1·25
326	11p.	Queen Elizabeth, ampulla and anointing spoon	30	75
		a. Booklet pane of 4 with blank margins (1.11.77)	75	
327	33p.	Type **108**	40	1·25
		a. Booklet pane of 4 with blank margins (1.11.77)	1·00	

(b) W w **12** (*sideways*) (*from booklets only*) (1.11.77)

327*b*	6p.	Visit of Prince Philip, 1957	2·75	4·00
		ba. Booklet pane of 4 with blank margins	10·00	
325/7*b*		*Set of 4*	5·00	6·50

109 Map of Falkland Islands

(Des K. Penny. Litho Questa)

1977 (24 Oct). *Telecommunications. T* **109** *and similar horiz designs. Multicoloured. W w* **14** (*sideways*). *P* 14½.

328	3p.	Type **109**	60	15
329	11p.	Ship to shore communications	1·00	40
330	40p.	Telex and telephone service	2·75	1·75
328/30		*Set of 3*	4·00	2·10

110 *A.E.S.*, 1957–74

(Des J. Smith; adapted R. Granger Barrett. Litho Questa)

1978 (25 Jan)–82. *Mail Ships. Horiz designs as T* **110**. *Multicoloured. W w* **14** (*sideways**). *P* 14. A. *Without imprint date.* B. *With imprint date* ("1982") *at foot of designs* (13.7.82†).

			A		B	
331	1p.	Type **110**	20	30	45	1·00
332	2p.	*Darwin*, 1957–73	30	30	50	1·00
333	3p.	*Merak-N.*, 1951–2	25	65	65	1·00
		w. Wmk Crown to right of CA	£150	—		†
334	4p.	*Fitzroy*, 1936–57	30	40	65	1·25
335	5p.	*Lafonia*, 1936–41	30	30	65	1·25
336	6p.	*Fleurus*, 1924–33	30	40	65	1·25
337	7p.	*Falkland*, 1914–34	30	1·50	70	1·25
338	8p.	*Oravia*, 1900–12	35	50	70	1·25
339	9p.	*Memphis*, 1890–97	35	50	70	1·25
340	10p.	*Black Hawk*, 1873–80	35	50	70	1·25
341	20p.	*Foam*, 1863–72	1·75	1·50	1·25	1·75
342	25p.	*Fairy*, 1857–61	2·00	3·00	1·25	2·50
343	50p.	*Amelia*, 1852–54	2·25	4·00	2·25	3·00
		w. Wmk Crown to right of CA	£225	—		†
344	£1	*Nautilus*, 1846–48	4·00	7·00	2·50	4·50
345	£3	*Hebe*, 1842–46	11·00	16·00	5·50	9·50
331/45		*Set of 15*	21·00	32·00	17·00	30·00

*The normal sideways watermark shows Crown to left of CA, as seen from the back of the stamp.

†Nos. 331B/45B were not available locally until 1 December 1982.

111 Short Hythe at Stanley

(Des L. McCombie. Litho Walsall)

1978 (28 Apr). *26th Anniv of First Direct Flight, Southampton–Port Stanley. T* **111** *and similar horiz design. Multicoloured. W w* **14** (*sideways*). *P* 14.

346	11p.	Type **111**	2·50	2·00
347	33p.	Route map and Short Hythe	3·00	2·50

112 Red Dragon of Wales

113 First Fox Bay P.O. and 1d. Stamp of 1878

(Des C. Abbott. Litho Questa)

1978 (2 June). *25th Anniv of Coronation. T* **112** *and similar vert designs. P* 15.

348	25p.	bistre, bright blue and silver	60	1·00
		a. Sheetlet. Nos. 348/50 × 2	3·00	
349	25p.	multicoloured	60	1·00
350	25p.	bistre, bright blue and silver	60	1·00
348/50		*Set of 3*	1·60	2·75

Designs:—No. 348, Type **112**; No. 349, Queen Elizabeth II; No. 350, Hornless Ram.

Nos. 348/50 were printed together in small sheets of 6, containing two *se-tenant* strips of 3, with horizontal gutter margin between.

(Des J. Cooter. Litho B.W.)

1978 (8 Aug). *Centenary of First Falkland Is Postage Stamps. T* **113** *and similar vert designs. Multicoloured. W w* **14**. *P* 13½ × 13.

351	3p.	Type **113**	25	20
352	11p.	Second Stanley P.O. and 4d. stamp of 1879	40	50
353	15p.	New Island P.O. and 6d. stamp of 1878	50	60
		w. Wmk inverted	£700	
354	22p.	First Stanley P.O. and 1s. stamp of 1878	80	1·00
351/4		*Set of 4*	1·75	2·10

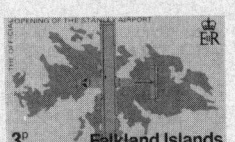

114 *Macrocystis pyrifera*

115 Britten Norman Islander over Falkland Islands

(Des I. Strange. Litho Questa)

1979 (19 Feb). *Kelp and Seaweed. T* **114** *and similar multicoloured designs. W w* **14** (*sideways on* 11 *and* 15p.). *P* 14.

355	3p.	Type **114**	30	15
356	7p.	*Durvillea* sp	50	30
357	11p.	*Lessonia* sp (*horiz*)	65	45
358	15p.	*Callophyllis* sp (*horiz*)	85	60
359	25p.	*Iradaea* sp	1·00	1·10
355/9		*Set of 5*	3·00	2·40

(Des G. Hutchins. Litho Rosenbaum Bros, Vienna)

1979 (1 May). *Opening of Stanley Airport. T* **115** *and similar horiz designs showing diagrammatic drawings. Multicoloured. W w* **14** (*sideways**). *P* 13½.

360	3p.	Type **115**	30	20
		w. Wmk Crown to right of CA	28·00	
361	11p.	Fokker F.27 Friendship over South Atlantic	70	60
		w. Wmk Crown to left of CA	50·00	
362	15p.	Fokker F.28 Fellowship over Airport	80	60
		w. Wmk Crown to left of CA	28·00	
363	25p.	Cessna 172 Skyhawk, Britten Norman Islander, Fokker F.27 Friendship and Fokker F.28 Fellowship over runway	1·50	80
		w. Wmk Crown to left of CA	3·50	
360/3		*Set of 4*	3·00	2·00

*The normal sideways watermark shows Crown to left of CA on the 3p. and Crown to right of CA on the other values, *all as seen from the back of the stamp.*

116 Sir Rowland Hill and 1953 Coronation 1d. Commemorative

(Des J.W. Litho Questa)

1979 (27 Aug). *Death Centenary of Sir Rowland Hill. T* **116** *and similar multicoloured designs showing stamps and portrait. W w* **14** (*sideways** *on* 3 *and* 25p.). *P* 14.

364	3p.	Type **116**	25	25
		w. Wmk Crown to left of CA	2·00	
365	11p.	1878 1d. stamp (*vert*)	40	70
366	25p.	Penny Black	60	85
		w. Wmk Crown to left of CA	£200	
364/6		*Set of 3*	1·10	1·60
MS367		137×98 mm. 33p. 1916 5s. stamp (*vert*)	85	1·50

*The normal sideways watermark shows Crown to right of CA, *as seen from the back of the stamp.*

PRICES OF SETS

Set prices are given for many issues, generally those containing three stamps or more. Definitive sets include one of each value or major colour change, but do not cover different perforations, die types or minor shades. Where a choice is possible the set prices are based on the cheapest versions of the stamps included in the listings.

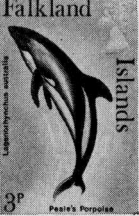

117 Mail Drop by De Havilland D.H.C.2 Beaver Aircraft

118 Peale's Dolphin

(Des A. Peake; adapted J.W. Litho Questa)

1979 (26 Nov). *Centenary of U.P.U. Membership. T* **117** *and similar horiz designs. Multicoloured. W w* **14** (*sideways**). *P* 14.

368	3p.	Type **117**	20	20
		w. Wmk Crown to right of CA	2·00	
369	11p.	Mail by horseback	45	55
370	25p.	Mail by schooner *Gwendolin*	75	1·00
368/70		*Set of 3*	1·25	1·60

*The normal sideways watermark shows Crown to left of CA, as seen from the back of the stamp.

(Des I. Strange. Litho Harrison)

1980 (25 Feb). *Dolphins and Porpoises. T* **118** *and similar designs. W w* **14** (*sideways** *on* 6, 7, 15 *and* 25p.). *P* 14.

371	3p.	black, chestnut and blue	40	30
		w. Wmk inverted	£180	
372	6p.	multicoloured	50	50
373	7p.	multicoloured	50	50
374	11p.	black, new blue and rose-red	70	70
375	15p.	black, chestnut and greyish blue	80	90
		w. Wmk Crown to right of CA	55·00	
376	25p.	multicoloured	1·00	1·60
371/6		*Set of 6*	3·50	4·00

Designs: *Horiz*—6p. Commerson's Dolphin; 7p. Hourglass Dolphin; 15p. Dusky Dolphin; 25p. Killer Whale. *Vert*—11p. Spectacled Porpoise.

*The normal sideways watermark shows Crown to left of CA, as seen from the back of the stamp.

119 1878 Falkland Islands Postmark

(Des G. Hutchins. Litho Walsall)

1980 (6 May). *"London 1980" International Stamp Exhibition. T* **119** *and similar horiz designs showing postmarks. W w* **14** (*sideways*). *P* 14.

377	11p.	black, gold and light blue	30	30
		a. Block of 6. Nos. 377/82	1·50	
378	11p.	black, gold and greenish yellow	30	30
379	11p.	black, gold and blue-green	30	30
380	11p.	black, gold and pale violet	30	30
381	11p.	black, gold and claret	30	30
382	11p.	black, gold and flesh	30	30
377/82		*Set of 6*	1·50	1·50

Designs:—No. 377, Type **119**; No. 378, 1915 New Island; No. 379, 1901 Falkland Islands; No. 380, 1935 Port Stanley; No. 381, 1952 Port Stanley first overseas airmail; No. 382, 1934 Fox Bay.

Nos. 377/82 were printed together, *se-tenant*, as a sheetlet, containing one of each design.

120 Queen Elizabeth the Queen Mother at Ascot, 1971

(Des Harrison. Litho Questa)

1980 (4 Aug). *80th Birthday of Queen Elizabeth the Queen Mother. W w* **14** (*sideways*). *P* 14.

383	**120**	11p. multicoloured	40	30

121 Forster's Caracara

(Des I. Strange. Litho Secura, Singapore)

1980 (11 Aug). *Birds of Prey. T 121 and similar horiz designs. Multicoloured.* W w 14 *(sideways**). P 13×13½.

384	3p. Type 121	..	50	25
	w. Wmk Crown to left of CA	..	3·25	
385	11p. Red-backed Buzzard	..	80	60
	w. Wmk Crown to left of CA	..	£350	
386	15p. Common Caracara	..	95	75
	w. Wmk Crown to left of CA	..	£375	
387	25p. Peregrine Falcon	..	1·25	1·00
	w. Wmk Crown to left of CA	..	1·25	
384/7		*Set of* 4	3·25	2·40

*The normal sideways watermark shows Crown to right of CA, *as seen from the back of the stamp.*

122 Stanley

(Des C. Abbott. Litho Rosenbaum Bros, Vienna)

1981 (7 Jan). *Early Settlements. T 122 and similar horiz designs. Multicoloured.* W w 14 *(sideways**). P 14.

388	3p. Type 122	..	15	15
389	11p. Port Egmont	..	30	35
390	25p. Port Louis	..	60	65
	w. Wmk Crown to left of CA	..	£300	
391	33p. Mission House, Keppel Island		70	80
	w. Wmk Crown to left of CA	..	£200	
388/91		*Set of* 4	1·60	1·75

*The normal sideways watermark shows Crown to right of CA, *as seen from the back of the stamp.*

123 Sheep

(Des P. Oxenham. Litho Questa)

1981 (9 Jan). *Farm Animals. T 123 and similar horiz designs. Multicoloured.* W w 14 *(sideways**). P 14.

392	3p. Type 123	..	20	25
393	11p. Cattle	..	35	55
	w. Wmk Crown to right of CA	..	£140	
394	25p. Horse	..	70	1·10
	w. Wmk Crown to right of CA	..	80·00	
395	33p. Dogs	..	1·00	1·40
392/5		*Set of* 4	2·00	3·00

*The normal sideways watermark shows Crown to left of CA, *as seen from the back of the stamp.*

124 Bowles and Carver, 1779   125 Wedding Bouquet from Falkland Islands

(Des I. Strange. Litho Walsall)

1981 (22 May). *Early Maps. T 124 and similar horiz designs in black, dull rose and stone (26p.) or multicoloured (others).* W w 14 *(sideways**). P 14.

396	3p. Type 124	..	25	25
397	10p. J. Hawkesworth, 1773	..	45	50
	w. Wmk Crown to right of CA	..	£170	
398	13p. Eman. Bowen, 1747	..	55	70
399	15p. T. Boutflower, 1768	..	55	80
400	25p. Philippe de Pretot, 1771	..	65	90
401	26p. Bellin *Petite Atlas Maritime,* Paris, 1764	..	65	90
396/401		*Set of* 6	2·75	3·50

*The normal sideways watermark shows Crown to left of CA, *as seen from the back of the stamp.*

(Des and litho J.W.)

1981 (22 July). *Royal Wedding. T 125 and similar vert designs. Multicoloured.* W w 14. P 13½×13.

402	10p. Type 125	..	30	40
	w. Wmk inverted	..	75·00	
403	13p. Prince Charles riding	..	40	50
	w. Wmk inverted	..	45·00	
404	52p. Prince Charles and Lady Diana Spencer	..	70	1·00
402/4		*Set of* 3	1·25	1·75

126 "Handicrafts"   127 "The Adoration of the Holy Child" (16th-century Dutch artist)

(Des BG Studio. Litho Questa)

1981 (28 Sept*). *25th Anniv of Duke of Edinburgh Award Scheme. T 126 and similar vert designs. Multicoloured.* W w 14. P 14.

405	10p. Type 126	..	20	20
406	13p. "Camping"	..	30	30
407	15p. "Canoeing"	..	40	40
408	26p. Duke of Edinburgh	..	55	60
405/8		*Set of* 4	1·25	1·40

*This is the local date of issue. The Crown Agents released the stamps in London on 14 September.

(Des BG Studio. Litho Walsall)

1981 (9 Nov*). *Christmas. Paintings. T 127 and similar vert designs. Multicoloured.* W w 14. P 14.

409	3p. Type 127	..	20	20
410	13p. "The Holy Family in an Italian Landscape" (17th-century Genoan artist)	..	35	45
411	26p. "The Holy Virgin" (Reni)	..	55	75
409/11		*Set of* 3	1·00	1·25

*This is the local date of issue. The Crown Agents released the stamps in London on 2 November.

128 Patagonian Sprat

(Des I. Strange. Litho Questa)

1981 (7 Dec). *Shelf Fishes. T 128 and similar multicoloured designs.* W w 14 *(sideways on 5, 15 and 25p.)*. P 14 × 13½ (13, 26p.) *or* 13½ × 14 *(others).*

412	5p. Type 128	..	20	20
413	13p. Gunther's Rockcod *(vert)*	..	35	35
414	15p. Argentine Hake	..	40	40
415	25p. Southern Blue Whiting	..	60	75
416	26p. Grey-tailed Skate *(vert)*	..	60	75
412/16		*Set of* 5	1·90	2·25

129 *Lady Elizabeth,* 1913

(Des J. Smith. Litho Questa)

1982 (15 Feb). *Shipwrecks. T 129 and similar horiz designs. Multicoloured.* W w 14 *(sideways).* P 14½.

417	5p. Type 129	..	30	50
418	13p. *Capricorn,* 1882	..	35	70
419	15p. *Jhelum,* 1870	..	40	85
420	25p. *Snowsquall,* 1864	..	55	1·10
421	26p. *St. Mary,* 1890	..	55	1·10
417/21		*Set of* 5	1·90	3·75

ARGENTINE OCCUPATION
2 April to 15 June 1982

Following incidents, involving the illegal presence of Argentine scrap-metal workers on the dependency of South Georgia from 18 March 1982, Argentine forces attacked Port Stanley, the capital of the Falkland Islands early in the morning of 2 April. The small garrison of Royal Marines was overwhelmed and the Governor forced to agree to a cease-fire, before being deported.

South Georgia was occupied by the Argentines on the following day.

British forces, dispatched from the United Kingdom, recaptured South Georgia on 25 April, and, after landing at various points on East Falkland, forced the surrender of the Argentine troops throughout the islands on 15 June.

The last mail to be dispatched from the Falkland Islands prior to the invasion left on 31 March. The Port Stanley Post Office was closed on 2 April, when all current issues were withdrawn. From 5 April an Argentine post office operated in the town, initially accepting mail without stamps, which was then cancelled by a postmark inscribed "ISLAS MALVINAS". Any letters tendered franked with Falkland Islands issues had these cancelled by ball-point pen. A limited range of Argentine stamps was placed on sale from 8 April. The Argentine definitive overprinted "LAS MALVINAS SON ARGENTINAS" for use throughout the country, was also available.

Following the Argentine surrender a rudimentary mail service was operating by 17 June, but the Port Stanley Post Office did not re-open until 24 June.

The last mail from South Georgia before the invasion was sent out on 16 March, although items remaining in the post office there were evacuated by the Deputy Postmaster when he was deported to the United Kingdom by the Argentines. The first mail left after recapture by the British on 2 May.

BRITISH ADMINISTRATION RESTORED

130 Charles Darwin   131 Falkland Islands Coat of Arms

(Des L. Curtis. Litho Questa)

1982 (5 July*). *150th Anniv of Charles Darwin's Voyage. T 130 and similar horiz designs. Multicoloured.* W w 14 *(sideways).* P 14.

422	5p. Type 130	..	20	25
423	17p. Darwin's microscope	..	50	60
424	25p. Falkland Islands Wolf ("Warrah")	..	65	80
425	34p. H.M.S. *Beagle*	..	85	1·10
	a. Pale brown (background to side panels) omitted	..	£700	
422/5		*Set of* 4	2·00	2·50

*It was initially intended that these stamps were to be issued on 19 April. First Day covers were prepared, postmarked with this date, but, because of the Argentine invasion, the stamps were not actually released until 5 July. A postmark showing the actual date of issue was struck alongside the stamps on the First Day covers.

(Des C. Abbott. Litho J.W.)

1982 (16 Aug). *21st Birthday of Princess of Wales. T 131 and similar vert designs. Multicoloured.* W w 14. P 13.

426	5p. Type 131	..	15	20
427	17p. Princess at Royal Opera House, Covent Garden, November 1981	..	30	40
428	37p. Bride and groom in doorway of St Paul's	..	50	70
429	50p. Formal portrait	..	65	90
426/9		*Set of* 4	1·40	2·00

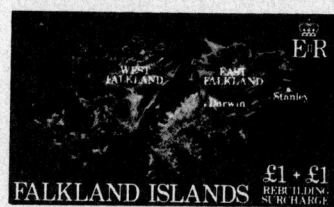

132 Map of Falkland Islands

(Des PAD Studio. Litho Format)

1982 (13 Sept). *Rebuilding Fund.* W w 14 *(sideways**). P 11.

430	132 £1 + £1 multicoloured	..	2·40	4·50
	w. Wmk Crown to right of CA	..	75·00	

*The normal sideways watermark shows Crown to left of CA, *as seen from the back of the stamp.*

1st PARTICIPATION COMMONWEALTH GAMES 1982 (133)   134 Blackish Cinclodes

1982 (7 Oct). *Commonwealth Games, Brisbane. Nos. 335B and 342B optd with T 133.*

431	5p. *Lafonia,* 1936–41	..	15	30
432	25p. *Fairy,* 1857–61	..	60	1·10

(Des I. Strange. Litho W. S. Cowells Ltd)

1982 (6 Dec). *Birds of the Passerine Family. T 134 and similar vert designs. Multicoloured.* W w 14 *(inverted on 10p.).* P 15 × 14½.

433	5p. Type 134	..	25	25
434	10p. Black-chinned Siskin	..	35	35
	w. Wmk upright	..	50·00	
435	13p. Short-billed Marsh Wren	..	40	40
436	17p. Black-throated Finch	..	45	50
437	25p. Correndera Pipit	..	55	70
438	34p. Dark-faced Ground Tyrant	..	70	85
433/8		*Set of* 6	2·40	2·75

Imperforate examples of all values, except the 34p., exist from printer's waste which escaped destruction. Some are known with thick red lines across the face of the stamps.

NEW INFORMATION

The editor is always interested to correspond with people who have new information that will improve or correct the Catalogue.

135 Raising Flag,
Port Louis, 1833

136 1933 British Administration
Centenary 3d. Commemorative

(Des I. Strange and J. Sheridan. Litho Questa)

1983 (3 Jan). *150th Anniv of British Administration. T* **135** *and similar multicoloured designs.* W w **14** *(sideways on 2, 10, 15, 25 and 50p.).* P 14 × 13½ (1, 5, 20, 40p., £1, £2) or 13½ × 14 *(others).*

439	1p. Type **135**	20	30
440	2p. Chelsea pensioners and barracks, 1849 (*horiz*)	30	40
441	5p. Development of wool trade, 1874	30	40
442	10p. Ship-repairing trade, 1850–1890 (*horiz*)	60	70
443	15p. Government House, early 20th century (*horiz*)	70	80
444	20p. Battle of Falkland Islands, 1914	90	1·25
445	25p. Whalebone Arch, 1933 (*horiz*)	90	1·25
446	40p. Contribution to War effort, 1939–45	1·40	1·60
447	50p. Duke of Edinburgh's visit, 1957 (*horiz*)	1·50	2·00
448	£1 Royal Marine uniforms	2·00	3·00
449	£2 Queen Elizabeth II	2·75	4·50
439/49	*Set of 11*	10·00	14·50

(Des L. Curtis. Litho Questa)

1983 (28 Mar*). *Commonwealth Day. T* **136** *and similar multicoloured designs.* W w **14** *(sideways on 5p., 17p.).* P 14.

450	5p. Type **136**	15	15
451	17p. 1933 British Administration Centenary ½d. commemorative	30	35
452	34p. 1933 British Administration Centenary 10s. commemorative (*vert*)	60	80
453	50p. 1983 British Administration 150th anniversary £2 commemorative (*vert*)	75	1·00
450/3	*Set of 4*	1·60	2·10

*This is the local date of issue: the Crown Agents released the stamps on 14 March.

137 British Army advancing
across East Falkland

(Des A. Theobald. Litho Questa)

1983 (14 June). *First Anniv of Liberation. T* **137** *and similar horiz designs. Multicoloured.* W w **14** *(sideways).* P 14.

454	5p. Type **137**	25	30
455	13p. S.S. *Canberra* and M.V. *Norland* at San Carlos	40	60
456	17p. R.A.F. Hawker Siddeley Harrier fighter	45	70
457	50p. H.M.S. *Hermes* (aircraft carrier)	1·00	1·40
454/7	*Set of 4*	1·90	2·75
MS458	169×130 mm. Nos. 454/7. P 12	1·75	2·75

138 Diddle Dee

(Des A. Chater. Litho Questa)

1983 (10 Oct). *Native Fruits. T* **138** *and similar horiz designs. Multicoloured.* W w **14** *(sideways).* P 14.

459	5p. Type **138**	20	20
460	17p. Tea Berry	30	50
461	25p. Mountain Berry	45	65
462	34p. Native Strawberry	65	80
459/62	*Set of 4*	1·40	1·90

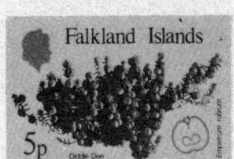

139 Britten Norman Islander

(Des Harrison. Litho Questa)

1983 (14 Nov). *Bicentenary of Manned Flight. T* **139** *and similar horiz designs. Multicoloured.* W w **14** *(sideways).* P 14.

463	5p. Type **139**	15	20
464	13p. De Havilland D.H.C.2 Beaver	35	45
465	17p. Noorduyn Norseman V	40	50
466	50p. Auster Autocrat	1·00	1·25
463/6	*Set of 4*	1·75	2·25

17 p

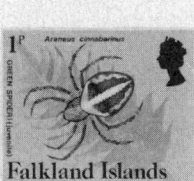

(140)	(140a)

1984 (3 Jan). *Nos. 443 and 445 surch as T* **140** *by Govt Printer, Port Stanley.*

467	17p. on 15p. Government House, early 20th century (figures as Type **140**)	60	45
	a. Surch figures as Type **140a**	90	1·00
468	22p. on 25p. Whalebone Arch, 1933	65	55

The surcharge setting used for the 17p. contained 27 examples as Type **140** and 23 as Type **140a**.

141 *Araneus
cinnabarinus* (juvenile
spider)

142 *Wavertree* (sail
merchantman)

(Des I. Strange. Litho Questa)

1984 (3 Jan)–86. *Insects and Spiders. T* **141** *and similar horiz designs. Multicoloured.* W w **14** *(sideways).* P 14×14½.

A. *Without imprint date*

469A	1p. Type **141**	20	55
470A	2p. *Alopophion occidentalis* (fly)	2·00	1·50
471A	3p. *Pareuxoina falkandica* (moth)	40	55
472A	4p. *Lissopterus quadrinotatus* (beetle)	30	55
473A	5p. *Issoria cytheris* (butterfly)	30	55
474A	6p. *Araneus cinnabarinus* (adult spider)	30	55
475A	7p. *Trachysphyrus penai* (fly)	30	55
476A	8p. *Caphornia ochricraspia* (moth)	30	55
477A	9p. *Caneorhinus biangulatus* (weevil)	30	55
478A	10p. *Syrphus octomaculatus* (fly)	30	55
479A	20p. *Malvinius compressiventris* (weevil)	2·25	75
480A	25p. *Metius blandus* (beetle)	75	90
481A	50p. *Parudenus falkandicus* (cricket)	1·00	1·50
482A	£1 *Emmenomma beauchenieus* (spider)	1·75	2·25
483A	£3 *Cynthia carye* (butterfly)	4·00	6·00
469A/83A	*Set of 15*	13·00	16·00

B. *With "1986" imprint date at foot of design*

470B	2p. *Alopophion occidentalis* (fly) (19.5.86)	2·75	2·75

(Des A. Theobald. Litho Questa)

1984 (7 May). *250th Anniv of "Lloyd's List" (newspaper). T* **142** *and similar vert designs. Multicoloured.* W w **14**. P 14½ × 14.

484	6p. Type **142**	55	30
485	17p. *Bjerk* (whale catcher) at Port Stanley	1·10	50
486	22p. *Oravia* (liner) stranded	1·10	55
487	52p. *Cunard Countess* (liner)	1·60	1·75
484/7	*Set of 4*	3·75	2·75

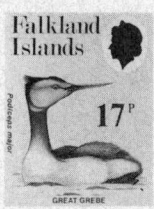

143 Ship, Lockheed C-130
Hercules Aircraft and U.P.U.
Logo

144 Great Grebe

(Des E. Nisbet, adapted L. Curtis. Litho Questa)

1984 (25 June). *Universal Postal Union Congress, Hamburg.* W w **14** *(sideways).* P 14.

488	**143** 22p. multicoloured	55	65

(Des I. Strange. Litho Questa)

1984 (6 Aug). *Grebes. T* **144** *and similar vert designs. Multicoloured.* W w **14**. P 14½.

489	17p. Type **144**	1·25	1·25
490	22p. Silvery Grebe	1·40	1·40
491	52p. White-tufted Grebe	3·00	4·75
489/91	*Set of 3*	5·00	6·75

145 Black-browed Albatross

146 Technical Drawing of
"Wren" Class Locomotive

(Des I. Strange. Litho Questa)

1984 (5 Nov). *Nature Conservation. T* **145** *and similar vert designs. Multicoloured.* W w **14**. P 14½ × 14.

492	6p. Type **145**	1·25	80
493	17p. Tussock grass	1·25	1·10
494	22p. Dusky Dolphin and Southern Sealion	1·40	1·40
495	52p. Rockcod (fish) and krill	2·00	3·00
492/5	*Set of 4*	5·50	5·50
MS496	130×90 mm. Nos. 492/5	5·50	6·00

(Des C. Abbott. Litho Questa)

1985 (18 Feb). *70th Anniv of Camber Railway. T* **146** *and similar horiz designs, each black, deep brown and pale cinnamon.* W w **14** *(sideways).* P 14.

497	7p. Type **146**	35	30
498	22p. Sail-propelled trolley	70	90
499	27p. Locomotive at work	85	1·25
500	54p. "Falkland Islands Express" passenger train (75 × 25 mm)	1·50	2·00
497/500	*Set of 4*	3·00	4·00

147 Construction
Workers' Camp

148 The Queen
Mother on 84th
Birthday

(Des N. Shewring. Litho Questa)

1985 (12 May). *Opening of Mount Pleasant Airport. T* **147** *and similar horiz designs. Multicoloured.* W w **16** *(sideways).* P 14½×14.

501	7p. Type **147**	75	40
502	22p. Building construction	1·40	90
503	27p. Completed airport	1·60	1·10
504	54p. Lockheed L-1011 TriStar 500 airliner over runway	2·00	2·50
501/4	*Set of 4*	5·25	4·50

(Des A. Theobald (£1), C. Abbott (others). Litho Questa)

1985 (7 June). *Life and Times of Queen Elizabeth the Queen Mother. T* **148** *and similar vert designs. Multicoloured.* W w **16**. P 14½×14.

505	7p. Attending reception at Lancaster House	25	20
506	22p. With Prince Charles, Mark Phillips and Princess Anne at Falklands Memorial Service	60	50
	w. Wmk inverted	14·00	
507	27p. Type **148**	70	60
508	54p. With Prince Henry at his christening (from photo by Lord Snowdon)	1·25	1·25
505/8	*Set of 4*	2·50	2·25
MS509	91×73 mm £1 With Princess Diana at Trooping the Colour. Wmk sideways	2·00	2·25

149 Captain J. McBride
and H.M.S. *Jason*, 1765

150 Painted Keyhole Limpet
(*Fissurella picta*)

(Des O. Bell. Litho Questa)

1985 (30 Sept). *Early Cartographers. T* **149** *and similar horiz designs. Multicoloured.* W w **14** *(sideways).* P 14 × 14½.

510	7p. Type **149**	1·00	40
511	22p. Commodore J. Byron and H.M.S. *Dolphin* and *Tamar*, 1765	1·40	80
512	27p. Vice-Admiral R. FitzRoy and H.M.S. *Beagle*, 1831	1·50	85
513	54p. Admiral Sir B. J. Sullivan and H.M.S. *Philomel*, 1842	2·00	1·75
510/13	*Set of 4*	5·50	3·50

(Des I. Strange. Litho Questa)

1985 (4 Nov). *Early Naturalists. Vert designs as T* **35** *of British Antarctic Territory. Multicoloured.* W w **14**. P 14½×14.

514	7p. Philibert Commerson and Commerson's Dolphin	85	40
515	22p. René Primevère Lesson and *Lessonia sp.* (kelp)	1·50	1·10

516	27p. Joseph Paul Gaimard and Common Diving Petrel	1·90	1·90
517	54p. Charles Darwin and *Calceolaria darwinii*	2·25	2·75
514/17	Set of 4	6·00	5·50

(Des I. Strange. Litho Questa)

1986 (10 Feb). *Seashells. T* **150** *and similar horiz designs. Multicoloured. W w* **16** (*sideways*). *P* 14 × 14½.

518	7p. Type **150**	65	50
519	22p. *Provocator palliata* (*Odontocymbiola magellanica*)	1·25	1·25
520	27p. Patagonian or Falkland Scallop (*Chlamys lischkei*)	1·40	2·25
521	54p. Rough Thorn Drupe (*Acanthina monodon imbricata*)	2·25	3·00
518/21	Set of 4	5·00	6·50

(Des A. Theobald. Litho Format)

1986 (21 Apr). *60th Birthday of Queen Elizabeth II. Vert designs as T* **110** *of Ascension. Multicoloured. W w* **16**. *P* 14 × 14½.

522	10p. With Princess Margaret at St Paul's, Walden Bury, Welwyn, 1932	25	25
523	24p. Queen making Christmas television broadcast, 1958	55	65
524	29p. In robes of Order of the Thistle, St. Giles Cathedral, Edinburgh, 1962	60	70
525	45p. Aboard Royal Yacht *Britannia*, U.S.A., 1976	1·25	1·50
526	58p. At Crown Agents Head Office, London, 1983	1·25	1·75
522/6	Set of 5	3·50	4·25

151 S.S. *Great Britain* crossing Atlantic, 1845

152 Head of Rockhopper Penguin

(Des O. Bell. Litho Format)

1986 (22 May). *"Ameripex '86" International Stamp Exhibition, Chicago. Centenary of Arrival of S.S. "Great Britain" in Falkland Islands. T* **151** *and similar horiz designs. Multicoloured. W w* **16** (*sideways**). *P* 14.

527	10p. Type **151**	40	40
528	24p. Beached at Sparrow Cove, 1937	50	70
529	29p. Refloated on pontoon, 1970	55	80
530	58p. Undergoing restoration, Bristol, 1986	80	1·75
	w. Wmk Crown to right of CA	55·00	
527/30	Set of 4	2·00	3·25
MS531	109×109 mm. Nos. 527/30. Wmk upright	2·00	3·25

*The normal sideways watermark shows Crown to left of CA, as seen from the back of the stamp.

(Des I. Strange. Litho Questa)

1986 (25 Aug). *Rockhopper Penguins. T* **152** *and similar vert designs. Multicoloured. W w* **16**. *P* 14½ × 14.

532	10p. Type **152**	1·00	60
533	24p. Rockhopper Penguins at sea	1·50	1·75
534	29p. Courtship display	1·75	2·00
535	58p. Adult with chick	2·25	4·00
532/5	Set of 4	6·00	7·50

153 Prince Andrew and Miss Sarah Ferguson presenting Polo Trophy, Windsor

154 Survey Party, Sapper Hill

(Des D. Miller. Litho Questa)

1986 (10 Nov). *Royal Wedding. T* **153** *and similar vert designs. Multicoloured. W w* **16**. *P* 14½ × 14.

536	17p. Type **153**	75	50
537	22p. Prince Andrew and Duchess of York on wedding day	85	65
538	29p. Prince Andrew in battledress at opening of Fox Bay Mill	1·10	90
536/8	Set of 3	2·40	1·90

(Des L. Curtis. Litho Questa)

1987 (9 Feb). *Bicentenary of Royal Engineers' Royal Warrant. T* **154** *and similar horiz designs. Multicoloured. W w* **16** (*sideways*). *P* 14 × 14½.

539	10p. Type **154**	1·25	70
540	24p. Mine clearance by robot	1·75	1·50
541	29p. Boxer Bridge, Stanley	2·00	2·25
542	58p. Unloading mail, Mount Pleasant Airport	2·75	3·75
539/42	Set of 4	7·00	7·50

155 Southern Sea Lion

156 *Suillus luteus*

(Des I. Strange. Litho Questa)

1987 (27 Apr). *Seals. T* **155** *and similar horiz designs. Multicoloured. W w* **16** (*sideways*). *P* 14½.

543	10p. Type **155**	70	40
544	24p. Falkland Fur Seal	1·50	75
545	29p. Southern Elephant Seal	1·60	1·10
546	58p. Leopard Seal	2·25	2·00
543/6	Set of 4	5·50	3·75

(Des I. Strange. Litho Questa)

1987 (14 Sept). *Fungi. T* **156** *and similar vert designs. Multicoloured. W w* **16**. *P* 14½ × 14.

547	10p. Type **156**	1·40	75
548	24p. *Mycena* sp.	2·25	1·75
549	29p. *Hygrophorous adonis* ("*Camarophyllus adonis*")	2·50	3·00
550	58p. *Gerronema schusteri*	3·50	4·50
547/50	Set of 4	8·75	9·00

157 Victoria Cottage Home, c 1912

158 Morris Truck, Fitzroy, 1940

(Des D. Hartley. Litho Questa)

1987 (8 Dec). *Local Hospitals. T* **157** *and similar horiz designs. Multicoloured. W w* **16** (*sideways*). *P* 14.

551	10p. Type **157**	40	25
552	24p. King Edward VII Memorial Hospital, c 1914	75	55
553	29p. Churchill Wing, King Edward VII Memorial Hospital, c 1953	85	60
554	58p. Prince Andrew Wing, New Hospital, 1987	1·40	1·25
551/4	Set of 4	3·00	2·40

(Des D. Hartley. Litho Questa)

1988 (11 Apr). *Early Vehicles. T* **158** *and similar horiz designs. Multicoloured. W w* **16** (*sideways*). *P* 14.

555	10p. Type **158**	40	25
556	24p. Citroen "Kegresse" half-track, San Carlos, 1929	75	55
557	29p. Ford one ton truck, Port Stanley, 1933	85	60
558	58p. Ford "Model T" car, Darwin, 1935	1·40	1·25
555/8	Set of 4	3·00	2·40

159 Kelp Goose

(Des I. Strange. Litho Walsall)

1988 (25 July). *Falkland Islands Geese. T* **159** *and similar horiz designs. Multicoloured. W w* **16** (*sideways*). *P* 13½ × 14.

559	10p. Type **159**	1·50	35
560	24p. Magellan ("Upland") Goose	2·00	70
561	29p. Ruddy-headed Goose	2·25	80
562	58p. Ashy-headed Goose	3·25	1·75
559/62	Set of 4	8·00	3·25

(Des D. Miller (10, 24p.), E. Nesbit and D. Miller (29, 58p.). Litho Format)

1988 (14 Nov). *300th Anniv of Lloyd's of London. Multicoloured designs as T* **123** *of Ascension. W w* **14** (*sideways on* 24, 29p.). *P* 14.

563	10p. Silver from Lloyd's Nelson Collection	40	30
564	24p. Falkland Islands hydroponic market garden (*horiz*)	75	65
565	29p. A.E.S. (mail ship) (*horiz*)	90	75
566	58p. *Charles Cooper* (full-rigged ship), 1866	1·25	1·25
	w. Wmk inverted	28·00	
563/6	Set of 4	3·00	2·75

COVER PRICES

Cover factors are quoted at the beginning of each country for most issues to 1945. An explanation of the system can be found on page x. The factors quoted do not, however, apply to philatelic covers.

160 *Padua* (barque)

(Des A. Theobald. Litho Questa)

1989 (28 Feb)–90. *Cape Horn Sailing Ships. T* **160** *and similar multicoloured designs. W w* **14** (*sideways on horiz designs*). *P* 14.

567	1p. Type **160**	55	55
568	2p. *Priwall* (barque) (*vert*)	90	90
569	3p. *Passat* (barque)	90	90
570	4p. *Archibald Russell* (barque) (*vert*)	70	70
571	5p. *Pamir* (barque) (*vert*)	70	70
572	6p. *Mozart* (barquentine)	1·00	1·00
573	7p. *Pommern* (barque)	80	80
574	8p. *Preussen* (full-rigged ship)	80	80
575	9p. *Fennia* (barque)	1·00	1·00
576	10p. *Cassard* (barque)	80	80
577	20p. *Lawhill* (barque)	1·50	1·60
578	25p. *Garthpool* (barque)	1·60	1·75
579	50p. *Grace Harwar* (full-rigged ship)	2·50	2·75
580	£1 *Criccieth Castle* (full-rigged ship)	6·00	7·00
581	£3 *Cutty Sark* (full-rigged ship) (*vert*)	8·00	8·00
582	£5 *Flying Cloud* (full-rigged ship) (2.1.90)	11·00	9·00
567/82	Set of 16	35·00	35·00

For 2, 3, 6, 9p. and £1 values watermarked w 16 and with imprint dates see Nos. 613/25.

161 Southern Right Whale

(Des I. Strange. Litho Questa)

1989 (15 May). *Baleen Whales. T* **161** *and similar horiz designs. Multicoloured. W w* **16** (*sideways*). *P* 13½ × 14.

583	10p. Type **161**	90	40
584	24p. Minke Whale	1·50	85
585	29p. Humpback Whale	1·75	1·25
586	58p. Blue Whale	2·50	2·50
583/6	Set of 4	6·00	4·50

162 "Gymkhana" (Sarah Gilding)

163 Vice-Admiral Sturdee and H.M.S. *Invincible* (battle cruiser)

(Adapted G. Vasarhelyi. Litho Walsall)

1989 (16 Sept). *Sports Associations' Activities. T* **162** *and similar horiz designs showing children's drawings. Multicoloured. W w* **16** (*sideways*). *P* 14.

587	5p. Type **162**	20	20
588	10p. "Steer Riding" (Karen Steen)	30	30
589	17p. "Sheep Shearing" (Colin Shepherd)	45	45
590	24p. "Sheepdog Trials" (Rebecca Edwards)	60	70
591	29p. "Horse Racing" (Dilys Blackley)	70	80
592	45p. "Sack Race" (Donna Newell)	1·00	1·10
587/92	Set of 6	3·00	3·25

(Des C. Collins. Litho B.D.T.)

1989 (8 Dec). *75th Anniv of Battle of the Falkland Islands and 50th Anniv of Battle of the River Plate. T* **163** *and similar vert designs. Multicoloured. W w* **16**. *P* 13½.

593	10p. Type **163**	30	30
594	24p. Vice-Admiral Graf von Spee and *Scharnhorst* (German cruiser)	70	75
595	29p. Commodore Harwood and H.M.S. *Ajax* (cruiser)	80	85
596	58p. Captain Langsdorff and *Admiral Graf Spee* (German pocket battleship)	1·50	2·00
593/6	Set of 4	3·00	3·50

164 Southern Sea Lions on Kidney Island

165 Supermarine Spitfire Mk 1 *Falkland Islands I*

(Des I. Strange. Litho Questa)

1990 (9 Apr). *Nature Reserves and Sanctuaries. T* **164** *and similar vert designs. Multicoloured. W w* **16**. *P* 14½.
597	12p. Type **164**		45	35
598	26p. Black-browed Albatrosses on Beauchene Island	1·00	70
599	31p. Penguin colony on Bird Island	1·10	80
600	62p. Tussock grass on Elephant Jason Island	1·40	1·40
597/600		*Set of* 4	3·50	3·00

(Des A. Theobald. Litho B.D.T.)

1990 (3 May). *"Stamp World London 90" International Stamp Exhibition, London. Presentation Spitfires. T* **165** *and similar horiz designs. Multicoloured. W w* **14** *(sideways). P* 14.
601	12p. Type **165**		50	35
602	26p. Supermarine Spitfire Mk 1 *Falkland Islands VII*	90	70
603	31p. Cockpit and wing of *Falkland Islands I*	1·00	80
604	62p. Squadron scramble, 1940	1·40	1·40
601/4		*Set of* 4	3·50	3·00
MS605	114×100 mm. £1 Supermarine Spitfire Mk 1 in action, 1940	3·00	2·50

For No. MS605 with additional inscription see No. MS628.

(Des D. Miller. Litho Questa)

1990 (4 Aug). *90th Birthday of Queen Elizabeth the Queen Mother. Vert designs as T* **134** (26p.) *or* **135** (£1) *of Ascension. W w* **16**. *P* 14×15 (26p.) *or* 14½ (£1).
606	26p. multicoloured		75	65
607	£1 brownish black and deep carmine-red	2·50	2·75

Designs:—26p. Queen Mother in Dover; £1 On bridge of liner *Queen Elizabeth,* 1946.

166 Black-browed Albatrosses   **167** *Gavilea australis*

(Des I. Strange. Litho Questa)

1990 (3 Oct). *Black-browed Albatross. T* **166** *and similar vert designs. Multicoloured. W w* **16**. *P* 13½×14.
608	12p. Type **166**		60	50
609	26p. Female with egg	1·25	1·00
610	31p. Adult and chick	1·50	1·25
611	62p. Black-browed Albatross in flight	2·50	3·00
608/11		*Set of* 4	5·25	5·25

1991 (7 Jan). *As Nos.* 568/9, 572, 575 *and* 580, *but W w* **16** *(sideways on horiz designs) and with "1991" imprint date added at foot. P* 14.
613	2p. *Priwall* (barque) (*vert*)	60	70
614	3p. *Passat* (barque)	60	70
617	6p. *Mozart* (barquentine)	70	65
620	9p. *Fennia* (barque)	80	80
625	£1 *Criccieth Castle* (full-rigged ship)	2·75	3·25
613/25		*Set of* 5	5·00	5·50

(Des A. Theobald. Litho B.D.T.)

1991 (18 Mar). *Second Visit of H.R.H. The Duke of Edinburgh. As No.* **MS**605, *but with Exhibition emblem replaced by* "SECOND VISIT OF HRH THE DUKE OF EDINBURGH". *W w* **16** *(sideways). P* 14.
MS628	114×100 mm. £1 Spitfire Mk. I in action, 1940	5·00	6·50

The margin of No. MS628 also shows the Exhibition emblem omitted and has the same commemorative inscription added.

(Des I. Strange. Litho Questa)

1991 (18 Mar). *Orchids. T* **167** *and similar vert designs. Multicoloured. W w* **14**. *P* 14×13½.
629	12p. Type **167**		60	50
630	26p. Dog Orchid	1·00	1·00
631	31p. *Chlorea gaudichaudii*	1·25	1·25
632	62p. Yellow Orchid	2·25	3·00
629/32		*Set of* 4	4·50	5·25

168 Heads of Two King Penguins   **169** ½d and 2½d Stamps of September 1891

(Des I. Strange. Litho Questa)

1991 (26 Aug). *Endangered Species. King Penguin. T* **168** *and similar vert designs. Multicoloured. W w* **16**. *P* 14.
633	2p. Type **168**		40	50
634	6p. Female incubating egg	50	55
635	12p. Female with two chicks	75	80
636	20p. Penguin underwater	1·25	1·25
637	31p. Parents feeding their chick	1·50	1·50
638	62p. Courtship dance	2·25	2·75
633/8		*Set of* 6	6·00	6·50

Nos. 637/8 do not include the W.W.F. panda emblem.

(Des D. Miller. Litho Questa)

1991 (10 Sept). *Centenary of Bisected Surcharges. T* **169** *and similar horiz designs. Multicoloured. W w* **16** *(sideways). P* 14½.
639	12p. Type **169**		60	50
640	26p. Cover of March 1891 franked with strip of five ½d bisects	1·00	1·00
641	31p. Unsevered pair of ½d. surcharge	1·25	1·40
642	62p. *Isis* (mail ship)	2·00	2·75
639/42		*Set of* 4	4·25	5·00

(Des R. Watton. Litho Walsall)

1991 (12 Dec). *500th Anniv of Discovery of America by Columbus and Re-enactment Voyages. Horiz designs as T* **144** *of Ascension. Multicoloured. W w* **14** *(sideways). P* 13½×14.
643	14p. Map of re-enactment voyages and *Eye of the Wind* (cadet brig)	60	60
644	29p. Compass rose and *Soren Larsen* (cadet brigantine)	1·25	1·25
645	34p. *Santa Maria, Pinta* and *Nina*	1·50	1·60
646	68p. Columbus and *Santa Maria*	2·50	3·50
643/6		*Set of* 4	5·25	6·25

(Des D. Miller. Litho Questa (68p.), Walsall (others))

1992 (6 Feb). *40th Anniv of Queen Elizabeth II's Accession. Horiz designs as T* **143** *of Ascension. Multicoloured. W w* **14** *(sideways). P* 14.
647	7p. "Stanley through the Narrows" (A. Asprey)	35	35
648	14p. "Hill Cove" (A. Asprey)	60	60
649	29p. "San Carlos Water" (A. Asprey)	95	95
650	34p. Three portraits of Queen Elizabeth	1·25	1·25
651	68p. Queen Elizabeth II	1·75	2·00
647/51		*Set of* 5	4·50	4·75

170 Laying Foundation Stone, 1890   **171** Captain John Davis and Backstaff

(Des N. Shewring. Litho Questa)

1992 (21 Feb). *Centenary of Christ Church Cathedral, Stanley. T* **170** *and similar multicoloured designs. W w* **16** *(sideways on 68p.). P* 14½.
652	14p. Type **170**		65	55
653	29p. Interior of Cathedral, 1920	1·25	1·00
654	34p. Bishop's chair	1·50	1·25
655	68p. Cathedral in 1900 (*horiz*)	1·90	1·90
652/5		*Set of* 4	4·75	4·25

(Des N. Shewring. Litho Questa)

1992 (14 June). *10th Anniv of Liberation. Square designs as T* **146** *of Ascension. Multicoloured. W w* **14** *(sideways). P* 14.
656	14p. + 6p. San Carlos Cemetery	75	1·00
657	29p. + 11p. War Memorial, Port Stanley	1·40	1·60
658	34p. + 16p. South Atlantic medal	1·60	1·75
659	68p. + 32p. Government House, Port Stanley	2·75	3·00
656/9		*Set of* 4	6·00	6·50
MS660	115×115 mm. Nos. 656/9	6·00	6·50

The premiums on Nos. 656/60 were for the S.S.A.F.A.

(Des R. Watton. Litho Questa)

1992 (14 Aug). *400th Anniv of First Sighting of the Falkland Islands. T* **171** *and similar horiz designs. Multicoloured. W w* **14** *(sideways). P* 14½.
661	22p. Type **171**		1·00	80
662	29p. Capt. John Davis	1·25	1·10
663	34p. Queen Elizabeth I and Queen Elizabeth II	1·50	1·50
664	68p. *Desire* sighting Falkland Islands	2·25	3·00
661/4		*Set of* 4	5·50	5·75

PRICES OF SETS

Set prices are given for many issues, generally those containing three stamps or more. Definitive sets include one of each value or major colour change, but do not cover different perforations, die types or minor shades. Where a choice is possible the set prices are based on the cheapest versions of the stamps included in the listings.

 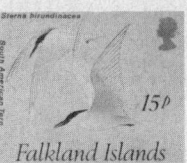

172 Private, Falkland Islands Volunteers, 1892   **173** South American Tern

(Des C. Collins. Litho Questa)

1992 (1 Oct). *Centenary of Falkland Islands Defence Force and 50th Anniv of Affiliation to West Yorkshire Regiment. T* **172** *and similar vert designs. Multicoloured. W w* **14**. *P* 14.
665	7p. Type **172**		30	30
666	14p. Officer, Falkland Islands Defence Corps, 1914	50	50
667	22p. Officer, Falkland Islands Defence Force, 1920	70	70
668	29p. Private, Falkland Islands Defence Force, 1939–45	90	90
669	34p. Officer, West Yorkshire Regiment, 1942	1·25	1·25
670	68p. Private, West Yorkshire Regiment, 1942	2·00	2·10
665/70		*Set of* 6	5·00	5·25

(Des I. Strange. Litho Questa)

1993 (2 Jan). *Gulls and Terns. T* **173** *and similar horiz designs. Multicoloured. W w* **16** *(sideways). P* 14×14½.
671	15p. Type **173**		75	65
672	31p. Brown-hooded Gull ("Pink breasted Gull")	1·25	1·25
673	36p. Magellan Gull	1·40	1·60
674	72p. Southern Black-backed Gull ("Dominican Gull")	2·50	3·50
671/4		*Set of* 4	5·50	6·25

174 *Queen Elizabeth* 2

(Des N. Shewring. Litho Questa)

1993 (22 Jan). *Visit of the* Queen Elizabeth 2 *(cruise liner). Sheet* 60×42 *mm. W w* **14** *(sideways). P* 14.
MS675	**174** £2 multicoloured	5·25	5·50

(Des A. Theobald. Litho Questa)

1993 (1 Apr). *75th Anniv of Royal Air Force. Horiz designs as T* **149** *of Ascension. Multicoloured. W w* **14** *(sideways*). *P* 14.
676	15p. Avro Vulcan B.1A	65	80
677	15p. Lockheed C-130K Hercules	65	80
678	15p. Boeing-Vertol CH-47 Chinook	65	80
679	15p. Lockheed L-1011 TriStar 500	65	80
676/9		*Set of* 4	2·40	2·75
MS680	110×77 mm. 36p. Hawker Siddeley Andover CC.2; 36p. Westland Wessex HC-2 helicopter; 36p. Panavia Tornado F Mk 3; 36p. McDonnell Douglas F-4M Phantom II w. Wmk Crown to right of CA	3·75	4·75

*The normal sideways watermark shows Crown to left of CA, as seen from the back of the stamp.

175 Short-finned Squid   **176** *Great Britain* in Drydock, Bristol

(Des O. Ball. Litho Questa)

1993 (1 July). *Fisheries. T* **175** *and similar horiz designs. Multicoloured. W w* **16** *(sideways). P* 14.
681	15p. Type **175**		60	60
682	31p. Catch of Whip-tailed Hake	1·25	1·25
683	36p. *Falklands Protector* (fisheries patrol vessel)	1·50	1·60
684	72p. Britten Norman Islander patrol aircraft and fish factory ship	2·25	3·00
681/4		*Set of* 4	5·00	5·75

(Des O. Ball. Litho Questa)

1993 (19 July). *150th Anniv of Launch of* Great Britain *(liner). T* **176** *and similar vert design. Multicoloured. W w* **16**. *P* 14×13½.
685	8p. Type **176**		50	50
686	£1 *Great Britain* at sea	2·75	4·00

177 *Explorer* (liner)　　　**178** Pony

(Des N. Shewring. Litho Questa)

1993 (1 Oct). *Tourism. T* **177** *and similar horiz designs. Multicoloured. W w* **14** (*sideways*). *P* 14.

687	16p. Type **177**	75	60
688	34p. Rockhopper Penguins	1·50	1·25
689	39p. *World Discoverer* (liner)	1·75	1·75
690	78p. *Columbus Caravelle* (liner)	2·25	2·75
687/90	*Set of* 4	5·50	5·75

(Des E. Tenney. Litho Walsall)

1993 (1 Dec). *Pets. T* **178** *and similar multicoloured designs. W w* **16** (*sideways on* 8p., 16p., 34p.; *inverted on* 39p.). *P* 14×14½ (*horiz*) *or* 14½×14 (*vert*).

691	8p. Type **178**	50	45
692	16p. Lamb	65	65
693	34p. Puppy and cat	1·50	1·50
694	39p. Kitten (*vert*)	1·60	1·90
695	78p. Collie dog (*vert*)	2·50	3·00
691/5	*Set of* 5	6·00	6·75

1994 (18 Feb). *"Hong Kong '94" International Stamp Exhibition. Nos.* 691/5 *additionally inscribed with the exhibition logo as T* **154** *of Ascension.*

696	8p. Type **178**	50	45
697	16p. Lamb	65	65
698	34p. Puppy and cat	1·50	1·50
699	39p. Kitten (*vert*)	1·60	1·90
700	78p. Collie dog (*vert*)	2·50	3·00
696/700	*Set of* 5	6·00	6·75

On the vertical designs "FALKLAND ISLANDS" ranges left instead of being centred as on Nos. 694/5.

179 Goose　　　**180** Dockyard Blacksmith's
Barnacles　　　Shop and Sir James Clark
　　　Ross (explorer)

(Des T. Chater. Litho Walsall)

1994 (4 Apr). *Inshore Marine Life. T* **179** *and similar multicoloured designs. W w* **16** (*sideways on horiz designs*). *P* 14.

701	1p. Type **179**	10	10
702	2p. Painted Shrimp (*horiz*)	10	10
703	8p. Patagonian Copper Limpet (*horiz*)	15	20
704	9p. Eleginops ("Mullet") (*horiz*)	20	25
705	10p. Sea Anemones (*horiz*)	20	25
706	20p. Flathead Eelpout (*horiz*)	40	45
707	25p. Spider Crab (*horiz*)	50	55
708	50p. Lobster Krill	1·00	1·10
709	80p. Falkland Skate (*horiz*)	1·60	1·75
710	£1 Centollón Crab (*horiz*)	2·00	2·10
711	£3 Wilton's Notothen ("Rock Cod") (*horiz*)	6·00	6·25
712	£5 Octopus	10·00	10·50
701/12	*Set of* 12	22·00	23·00

A similar 5p. value, showing a smelt and incorrectly inscribed "Austro Menidia Smithii", was withdrawn before issue.

For miniature sheet containing £1, wmk w **14** and with imprint date, see No. **MS784**.

(Des J. Peck. Litho Questa)

1994 (1 July). *150th Anniv of Founding of Stanley. T* **180** *and similar horiz designs. Multicoloured. W w* **14** (*sideways*). *P* 14.

713	9p. Type **180**	50	45
714	17p. 21 Fitzroy Road (home of Chaplain James Moody)	75	60
715	30p. Stanley Cottage (built by Dr. Henry Hamblin)	1·25	1·25
716	35p. Pioneer Row and Sgt-maj Henry Felton	1·50	1·50
717	40p. Government House (designed by Governor R. Moody)	1·60	1·60
718	65p. View of Stanley and Edward Stanley, Earl of Derby (Secretary of State for the Colonies)	2·25	2·75
713/18	*Set of* 6	7·00	7·50

181 Lockheed L-1011 TriStar
over Gypsy Cove

(Des J. Peck. Litho Walsall)

1994 (24 Oct). *Falkland Beaches. T* **181** *and similar horiz designs. Multicoloured. W w* **16** (*sideways*). *P* 14.

719	17p. Type **181**	60	55
720	35p. Cruise ship off Sea Lion Island	1·25	1·25
721	40p. Britten Norman Islander aircraft at Pebble Island	1·50	1·50
722	65p. Landrover at Volunteer Beach	2·00	2·50
719/22	*Set of* 4	4·75	5·25

182 Mission House, Keppel　　　**183** *Lupinus*
Island　　　*arboreus*

(Des G. Vasarhelyi. Litho Questa)

1994 (1 Dec). *150th Anniv of South American Missionary Society. T* **182** *and similar horiz designs. Multicoloured. W w* **16** (*sideways*). *P* 14.

723	5p. Type **182**	20	25
724	17p. Thomas Bridges (compiler of Yahgan dictionary)	50	50
725	40p. Fuegian Indians	1·10	1·25
726	65p. Capt. Allen Gardiner and *Allen Gardiner* (schooner)	1·50	2·00
723/6	*Set of* 4	3·00	3·50

(Des I. Strange. Litho Questa)

1995 (3 Jan). *Flowering Shrubs. T* **183** *and similar vert designs. Multicoloured. W w* **16**. *P* 14½×14.

727	9p. Type **183**	40	40
728	17p. *Hebe elliptica*	60	55
729	30p. *Fuschia magellanica*	85	85
730	35p. *Berberis ilicifolia*	90	90
731	40p. *Ulex europaeus*	95	95
732	65p. *Hebe x franciscana*	1·75	2·00
727/32	*Set of* 6	5·00	5·00

184 Magellanic Oystercatcher

(Des I. Strange. Litho B.D.T.)

1995 (1 Mar). *Shore Birds. T* **184** *and similar horiz designs. Multicoloured. W w* **16** (*sideways*). *P* 13½.

733	17p. Type **184**	85	50
734	35p. Rufous-chested Dotterel	1·40	1·25
735	40p. Blackish Oystercatcher	1·50	1·40
736	65p. Two-banded Plover	2·50	3·00
733/6	*Set of* 4	5·50	5·50

(Des R. Watton. Litho Questa)

1995 (8 May). *50th Anniv of End of Second World War. Multicoloured designs as T* **161** *of Ascension. W w* **14** (*sideways*). *P* 14.

737	17p. Falkland Islands contingent in Victory Parade	60	50
738	35p. Governor Sir Alan Cardinall on Bren gun-carrier	1·10	1·10
739	40p. H.M.A.S. *Esperance Bay* (troopship)	1·25	1·25
740	65p. H.M.S. *Exeter* (cruiser)	2·25	3·00
737/40	*Set of* 4	4·75	5·25
MS741	75×85 mm. £1 Reverse of 1939–45 War Medal (*vert*). Wmk upright	2·50	3·00

185 Ox and Cart　　　**186** Kelp Geese

(Des N. Shewring. Litho B.D.T.)

1995 (1 Aug). *Transporting Peat. T* **185** *and similar horiz designs. Multicoloured. W w* **16** (*sideways*). *P* 14.

742	17p. Type **185**	60	50
743	35p. Horse and cart	1·10	1·10
744	40p. Caterpillar tractor pulling sleigh	1·25	1·25
745	65p. Lorry	2·25	3·00
742/5	*Set of* 4	4·75	5·25

(Des Sonia Felton. Litho B.D.T.)

1995 (11 Sept). *Wildlife. T* **186** *and similar vert designs. Multicoloured. W w* **16**. *P* 13½.

746	35p. Type **186**	1·10	1·10
	a. Sheetlet. Nos. 746/51	5·75	
747	35p. Black-browed Albatross	1·10	1·10
748	35p. Blue-eyed Cormorants	1·10	1·10
749	35p. Magellanic Penguins	1·10	1·10
750	35p. Fur Seals	1·10	1·10
751	35p. Rockhopper Penguins	1·10	1·10
746/51	*Set of* 6	5·75	5·75

Nos. 746/51 were printed together, *se-tenant*, in sheetlets of 6, with the backgrounds forming a composite design.

187 Cottontail Rabbit

(Des A. Robinson. Litho Walsall)

1995 (6 Nov). *Introduced Wild Animals. T* **187** *and similar horiz designs. Multicoloured. W w* **14** (*sideways*). *P* 14.

752	9p. Type **187**	45	40
753	17p. Brown Hare	65	55
754	35p. Guanacos	1·10	1·10
755	40p. Fox	1·25	1·25
756	65p. Otter	1·90	2·25
752/6	*Set of* 5	4·75	5·00

188 Princess Anne and
Government House

(Des D. Miller. Litho Walsall)

1996 (30 Jan). *Royal Visit. T* **188** *and similar horiz designs. Multicoloured. W w* **14** (*sideways*). *P* 14½×14.

757	9p. Type **188**	45	40
758	19p. Falklands War Memorial, San Carlos Cemetery	75	65
759	30p. Christ Church Cathedral	1·10	1·10
760	73p. Helicopter over Goose Green	2·50	2·50
757/60	*Set of* 4	4·25	4·25

(Des D. Miller. Litho B.D.T.)

1996 (21 Apr). *70th Birthday of Queen Elizabeth II. Vert designs as T* **165** *of Ascension, each incorporating a different photograph of the Queen. W w* **14**. *P* 13½.

761	17p. Steeple Jason	60	50
762	40p. *Tamar* (container ship)	1·50	1·25
763	45p. New Island	1·50	1·40
764	65p. Falkland Islands Community School	1·60	1·60
761/4	*Set of* 4	4·75	4·25
MS765	64×66 mm. £1 Queen Elizabeth II	2·40	3·00

189 Mounted Postman, *c.* 1890

(Des A. Theobald. Litho Walsall)

1996 (8 June). *"CAPEX '96" International Stamp Exhibition, Toronto. Mail Transport. T* **189** *and similar horiz designs. Multicoloured. W w* **16** (*sideways*). *P* 14.

766	9p. Type **189**	50	45
767	40p. Noorduyn Norseman V seaplane	1·50	1·25
768	45p. *Forrest* (freighter) at San Carlos	1·50	1·40
769	76p. De Havilland D.H.C.2 Beaver seaplane	2·50	2·50
766/9	*Set of* 4	5·50	5·00
MS770	110×80 mm. £1 L.M.S. No. 5606 *Falkland Islands* locomotive (47×31 mm). *P* 13½×14	2·40	3·00

190 Southern Bottlenose Whale

(Des E. King. Litho Walsall)

1996 (2 Sept). *Beaked Whales. T **190** and similar horiz designs. Multicoloured. W w 14 (sideways). P 13½×14.*

771	9p. Type **190**	..	30	30
772	30p. Cuvier's Beaked Whale	..	80	80
773	35p. Straptoothed Beaked Whale	..	90	90
774	75p. Gray's Beaked Whale	..	1·90	1·90
771/4	.. .. ..	*Set of 4*	3·50	3·50

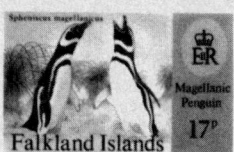

191 Pair of Magellanic Penguin

(Des I. Strange. Litho Walsall)

1997 (2 Jan). *Magellanic Penguins. T **191** and similar horiz designs. Multicoloured. W w 14 (sideways). P 14½.*

775	17p. Type **191**	.. ..	55	45
776	35p. Penguins in nest	.. ..	1·00	85
777	40p. Adult and chick	.. ..	1·10	90
778	65p. Group of Penguins swimming	..	1·60	1·60
775/8	.. .. ..	*Set of 4*	3·75	3·50

192 Black Pejerry   **193** Coral Fern

(Des T. Chater and D. Miller. Litho Questa)

1997 (3 Feb). *"HONG KONG '97" International Stamp Exhibition. Sheet 130×90 mm. W w 14 (sideways). P 14.*

MS779 **192** £1 multicoloured	.. ..	2·50	2·50

(Des I. Strange. Litho Walsall)

1997 (3 Mar). *Ferns. T **193** and similar vert designs. Multicoloured. W w 14. P 14½.*

780	17p. Type **193**	.. ..	55	45
781	35p. Adder's Tongue Fern	..	1·00	1·00
782	40p. Fuegian Tall Fern	..	1·10	1·10
783	65p. Small Fern	..	1·60	1·75
780/3	.. .. ..	*Set of 4*	3·75	3·75

(Des T. Chater. Litho Walsall)

1997 (20 June). *Return of Hong Kong to China. Sheet 130×90 mm, containing design as No. 710. With imprint date. W w 14 (sideways). P 14.*

MS784 £1 Centollón Crab	.. ..	2·50	2·50

194 Bull Point Lighthouse

(Des J. Peck. Litho Walsall)

1997 (1 July). *Lighthouses. T **194** and similar horiz designs. Multicoloured. W w 14 (sideways). P 14.*

785	9p. Type **194**	..	40	30
786	30p. Cape Pembroke Lighthouse	..	90	90
787	£1 Cape Meredith Lighthouse	..	2·40	2·75
785/7	.. ..	*Set of 3*	3·25	3·50

(Des N. Shewring (No. **MS794**), D. Miller (others). Litho Questa)

1997 (10 July). *Golden Wedding of Queen Elizabeth and Prince Philip. Multicoloured designs as T **173** of Ascension. W w 16. P 14½.*

788	9p. Queen Elizabeth holding bouquet, 1993	30	30
	a. Horiz pair. Nos. 788/9	60	60
789	9p. Prince Philip and horse, 1985	30	30
790	17p. Queen Elizabeth in phaeton at Trooping the Colour, 1996 ..	50	50
	a. Horiz pair. Nos. 790/1	1·00	1·00
791	17p. Prince Philip in R.A.F. uniform	50	50
792	40p. Queen Elizabeth wearing red coat, 1986 ..	1·00	1·00
	a. Horiz pair. Nos. 792/3	2·00	2·00
793	40p. Prince William and Princess Beatrice on horseback ..	1·00	1·00
788/93	.. .. *Set of 6*	3·25	3·25
MS794	110×71 mm. £1.50, Queen Elizabeth and Prince Philip in landau (horiz). W w 14 (sideways). P 14×14½	3·50	3·50

Nos. 788/9, 790/1 and 792/3 were each printed together, *se-tenant*, in horizontal pairs throughout the sheets with the backgrounds forming composite designs.

195 Forster's Caracara   **196** Merryweather and Son Greenwich Gem Fire Engine

(Des Sonia Felton. Litho Questa)

1997 (6 Oct). *Endangered Species. T **195** and similar horiz designs. Multicoloured. W w 16 (sideways). P 14½.*

795	17p. Type **195**	.. .. ..	50	45
796	19p. Southern Sealion	.. ..	60	55
797	40p. Felton's Flower	.. ..	1·00	1·10
798	73p. Trout ..	.. ..	1·90	2·00
795/8	.. .. ..	*Set of 4*	3·50	3·50

(Des N. Shewring. Litho Questa)

1998 (26 Feb). *Centenary of Falkland Islands Fire Service. T **196** and similar vert designs. Multicoloured. W w 16. P 14½×14.*

799	9p. Type **196**		20	25
800	17p. Merryweather's Hatfield trailer pump	35	40
801	40p. Coventry Climax Godiva trailer pump	80	85
802	65p. Carmichael Bedford "Type B" water tender	.. ..	1·25	1·40
799/802	.. ..	*Set of 4*	2·75	3·00

STAMP BOOKLETS

1977 (1 Nov). *Silver Jubilee. Multicoloured cover, 117×79 mm, showing Norroy and Ulster King of Arms. Stapled.*

SB1   £2 booklet containing 6p., 11p. and 33p., each in pane of 4 (Nos. 326a, 327a, 327ba) .. .. 10·00

1978 (27 Nov). *Mail Ships. Black and blue-green cover, 99×57 mm, showing Hebe on front and Darwin on back. Stapled.*

SB2   £1 booklet containing 1p., 3p., 5p., 6p., 10p. (Nos. 331A, 333A, 335A/6A, 340A) each in block of 4 24·00

1979 (4 June). *Mail Ships. Black and bright new blue cover, 99×57 mm, showing Nautilus on front and A.E.S. on back. Stapled.*

SB3   £1 booklet. Contents as No. SB2 .. 11·00

1980 (14 July). *Mail Ships. Black and red cover, 100×59 mm, showing Amelia on front and Merak-N on back. Stapled.*

SB4   £1 booklet. Contents as No. SB2 .. 5·50

1982 (23 Feb). *Mail Ships. Black and grey cover, 99×58 mm, showing Fairy on front and Fitzroy on back. Stapled.*

SB5   £1 booklet. Contents as No. SB2 .. 4·75

1985 (18 Feb). *Black and azure cover, 95×64 mm, with example of stamp No. 471A affixed. Stapled.*

SB6   £2.24, booklet containing eight 2p. and four each 7p., 20p., 25p. (Nos. 470A, 475A, 479A, 480A) in blocks of 4 .. .. 21·00

1988 (2 Feb). *Black and greenish grey cover, 95×64 mm, with example of stamp No. 470A affixed. Stapled.*

SB7   £2.52, booklet containing eight 4p. and four each 10p., 20p., 25p. (Nos. 472A, 478A/80A) in blocks of 4 .. .. 15·00

1988 (26 Sept). *Black and pale green cover, 95×64 mm, with example of stamp No. 471A affixed. Stapled.*

SB8   £2.52, booklet containing 1p., 4p., 6p., 8p., 9p., 10p., 25p. (Nos. 469A, 472A, 474A, 476A/8A, 480A), each in block of 4 .. .. .. 7·00

1990 (29 Oct). *Cape Horn Sailing Ships. Black and greenish yellow showing No. 575 (No. SB9) or pale blue showing No. 578 (No. SB10) covers, each 104×55 mm. Panes attached by selvedge.*

SB9   60p. booklet containing 3p., 9p. (Nos. 569, 575), each in block of 5 .. .. 6·50

SB10   £1.55, booklet containing 6p., 25p. (Nos. 572, 578), each in block of 5 .. .. 8·50

POSTAGE DUE STAMPS

D 1 King Penguin

(Des O. Bell. Litho Questa)

1991 (7 Jan). *W w 14 (sideways). P 15×14.*

D1	D 1	1p. brown-lake and cerise		10	10
D2		2p. red-orange and pale orange	..	10	10
D3		3p. brown-ochre and chrome-yellow	..	10	10
D4		4p. deep blue-green & light blue-green		10	10
D5		5p. greenish blue & light greenish blue		10	15
D6		10p. deep violet-blue and cobalt	..	20	25
D7		20p. deep reddish violet and lilac	..	40	45
D8		50p. yellowish green and apple-green	..	1·00	1·10
D1/8		.. ..	*Set of 8*	1·90	2·10

The Philatelic Register

LOOKING FOR A COMPLETE, CLASSIFIED, BUYERS GUIDE?

YOU'LL FIND OUR PHILATELIC REGISTER IN THE YELLOW SECTION AT THE BACK OF VOLUME ONE OF THIS CATALOGUE

CLASSIFIED TRADE
EASY TO USE
DIRECTORY

FALKLAND ISLANDS DEPENDENCIES

PRICES FOR STAMPS ON COVER TO 1945
Nos. A1/D8   *from* × 10

A. GRAHAM LAND

For use at Port Lockroy (established 16 February 1944) and Hope Bay (established 12 February 1945) bases.
Falkland Islands definitive stamps with face values of 1s. 3d. and above were valid for use from Graham Land in conjunction with Nos. A1/8 and subsequently Nos. G1/16.

Stamps of FALKLAND ISLANDS cancelled at Port Lockroy or Hope Bay with Graham Land circular datestamps between 16 February 1944 and 31 January 1954.

1938–50. *King George VI (Nos. 159/63).*
Z2	2s. 6d. slate		30·00
Z3	5s. indigo and yellow-brown		£130
Z4	10s. black and orange		40·00
Z5	£1 black and violet		60·00

1952. *King George VI (Nos. 181/5)*
Z 6	1s. 3d. orange		
Z 7	2s. 6d. olive-green		
Z 8	5s. purple		
Z 9	10s. grey		
Z10	£1 black		

GRAHAM LAND

DEPENDENCY OF

(A 1)

1944 (12 Feb)–45. *Falkland Islands Nos. 146, 148, 150, 153/5, 157 and 158a optd with Type A 1, in red, by B.W.*
A1	½d. black and green		30	1·50
	a. Blue-black and green		£550	£375
A2	1d. black and violet		30	1·00
A3	2d. black and carmine-red		40	1·00
A4	3d. black and blue		30	1·00
A5	4d. black and purple		3·00	1·75
A6	6d. black and brown		12·00	2·25
	a. Blue-black and brown (24.9.45)		20·00	
A7	9d. black and grey-blue		1·00	1·25
A8	1s. deep blue		1·00	1·25
A1/8		Set of 8	16·00	10·00
A1/8 Perf "Specimen"		Set of 8	£325	

B. SOUTH GEORGIA

The stamps of Falkland Islands were used at the Grytviken whaling station on South Georgia from 3 December 1909.
Mr. J. Innes Wilson, the Stipendary Magistrate whose duties included those of postmaster, was issued with a stock of stamps, values ½d. to 5s., together with an example of the current "FALKLAND ISLANDS" circular datestamp. This was used to cancel the stamps, but, as it gave no indication that mail had originated at South Georgia, a straight-line handstamp inscribed "SOUTH GEORGIA", or subsequently "South Georgia", was also supplied. It was intended that this should be struck directly on to each letter or card below the stamp, but it can sometimes be found struck across the stamp instead.
The use of the "South Georgia" handstamp continued after the introduction of the "SOUTH GEORGIA" circular datestamp in June 1910 apparently for philatelic purposes, but no example has been reported used after June 1912.

SOUTH GEORGIA.

Z 1

South Georgia.

Z 2

		On piece	On cover /card
ZU1	Example of Type Z 1 used in conjunction with "FALKLAND ISLANDS" postmark (22 Dec 1909 to 30 March 1910) *Price from*	£1000	£3750
ZU2	Example of Type Z 2 used in conjunction with "FALKLAND ISLANDS" postmark (May 1910) .. *Price from*	£750	£3000
ZU3	Example of Type Z 2 used in conjunction with "SOUTH GEORGIA" postmark (June 1910 to June 1912) .. *Price from*	£250	£900

Stamps of FALKLAND ISLANDS cancelled at Grytviken with South Georgia circular datestamps between June 1910 and 31 January 1954.

1891–1902. *Queen Victoria (Nos. 32, 36 and 38).*
Z11	4d. olive-black		£120
Z12	9d. salmon		£120
Z13	1s. yellow-brown		£130

1904–12. *King Edward VII (Nos. 43/50).*
Z14	½d. green		10·00
Z15	1d. vermilion		10·00
	d. Dull coppery red (on thick paper)		35·00
Z16	2d. purple		50·00
	b. Reddish purple		£275

Z17	2½d. ultramarine		20·00
	b. Deep blue		£180
Z18	6d. orange		£100
Z19	1s. brown		£100
Z20	3s. green		£200
Z21	5s. red		£250

SOUTH GEORGIA PROVISIONAL HANDSTAMPS.

During October 1911 the arrival of the German South Polar Expedition at Grytviken, South Georgia, resulted in the local supply of stamps becoming exhausted. The Acting Magistrate, Mr. E. B. Binnie, who was also responsible for the postal facilities, produced a handstamp reading "Paid at (or At) SOUTH GEORGIA" which, together with a manuscript indication of the postage paid and his signature, was used on mail from 18 October 1911 to January 1912. Further examples, signed by John Innes Wilson, are known from February 1912, but these may be philatelic.

PH1	"Paid 1 at SOUTH GEORGIA EBB" *Price on cover* £4250	
PH1a	"Paid 1 At SOUTH GEORGIA EBB" *Price on cover* £4500	
PH2	"Paid 2½ at SOUTH GEORGIA EBB" *Price on cover* £4750 (16 Dec)	
PH2a	"Paid 2½ At SOUTH GEORGIA EBB" *Price on cover* £5250 (16 Dec)	

1912–23. *King George V. Wmk Mult Crown CA (Nos. 60/9).*
Z22	½d. green		15·00
Z23	1d. orange-red		10·00
Z24	2d. maroon		40·00
Z25	2½d. deep bright blue		25·00
	c. Deep blue		25·00
Z26	6d. yellow-orange		50·00
	b. Brown-orange		40·00
	ba. Bisected (diag) (3d.) (on cover) (3.23)		£13000
Z27	1s. bistre-brown		£100
Z28	3s. slate-green		£150
Z29	5s. rose-red		£180
	a. Maroon		£225
Z30	10s. red/green		£275
Z31	£1 black/red		£400

1918–20. *"WAR STAMP" ovpts (Nos. 70/2).*
Z32	½d. deep olive		15·00
Z33	1d. vermilion		15·00
Z34	1s. light bistre-brown		75·00

1921–28. *King George V. Wmk Mult Script CA (Nos. 73/80).*
Z35	½d. yellowish green		5·00
Z36	1d. dull vermilion		4·00
Z37	2d. deep brown-purple		25·00
Z38	2½d. deep blue		22·00
	a. Bisected (diag) (1d.) (on cover) (3.23)		£7000
Z39	2½d. deep purple/pale yellow		45·00
Z40	6d. yellow-orange		50·00
Z41	1s. deep ochre		60·00
Z42	3s. slate-green		£150

1928 PROVISIONAL. For listing of the 2½d. on 2d. surcharge issued at Grytviken on 7 February 1928 see No. 115 of Falkland Islands.

1929–36. *King George V. Whale and Penguins design (Nos. 116/26).*
Z43	½d. green		5·00
Z44	1d. scarlet		4·00
Z45	2d. grey		10·00
Z46	2½d. blue		4·00
Z47	4d. orange		20·00
Z48	6d. purple		30·00
Z49	1s. black/emerald		35·00
Z50	2s. 6d. carmine/blue		75·00
Z51	5s. green/yellow		£110
Z52	10s. carmine/emerald		£200
Z53	£1 black/red		£500

Examples of most values are known with forged postmarks dated "Au 30" in 1928, 1930 and 1931.

1933. *Centenary of British Administration (Nos. 127/38).*
Z54	½d. black and green		7·00
Z55	1d. black and scarlet		4·00
Z56	1½d. black and blue		14·00
Z57	2d. black and brown		22·00
Z58	3d. black and violet		16·00
Z59	4d. black and orange		18·00
Z60	6d. black and slate		65·00
Z61	1s. black and olive-green		65·00
Z62	2s. 6d. black and violet		£180
Z63	5s. black and yellow		£700
	a. Black and yellow-orange		£1300
Z64	10s. black and chestnut		£750
Z65	£1 black and carmine		£2000

1935. *Silver Jubilee (Nos. 139/42).*
Z66	1d. deep blue and scarlet		3·00
Z67	2½d. brown and deep blue		4·00
Z68	4d. green and indigo		5·00
Z69	1s. slate and purple		5·00

1937. *Coronation (Nos. 143/5).*
Z70	½d. green		2·00
Z71	1d. carmine		2·00
Z72	2½d. blue		2·00

1938–50. *King George VI (Nos. 146/63).*
Z73	½d. black and green		3·00
Z74	1d. black and carmine		5·00
	a. Black and scarlet		2·00
Z75	1d. black and violet		4·00
Z76	2d. black and deep violet		6·00
Z77	2d. black and carmine-red		7·00
Z78	2½d. black and bright blue (No. 151)		2·00
Z79	3d. black and blue		6·00
Z80	4d. black and purple		6·00
Z81	6d. black and brown		8·00
Z82	9d. black and grey-blue		10·00

Z83	1s. pale blue		30·00
	a. Deep blue		30·00
Z84	1s. 3d. black and carmine-red		30·00
Z85	2s. 6d. slate		20·00
Z86	5s. bright blue and pale brown		£100
	a. Indigo and yellow-brown		£130
Z87	10s. black and orange		40·00
Z88	£1 black and violet		60·00

Falkland Islands definitive stamps with values of 1s. 3d. and above continued to be valid from South Georgia after the introduction of Nos. B1/8 and subsequently Nos. G1/16.

1952. *King George VI (Nos. 181/5).*
Z89	1s. 3d. orange		25·00
Z90	2s. 6d. olive-green		
Z91	5s. purple		
Z92	10s. grey		
Z93	£1 black		

1944 (3 Apr)–45. *Falkland Islands Nos. 146, 148, 150, 153/5, 157 and 158a optd "SOUTH GEORGIA/DEPENDENCY OF", in red, as Type A 1 of Graham Land.*
B1	½d. black and green		30	1·50
	a. Wmk sideways		£2500	
B2	1d. black and violet		30	1·00
B3	2d. black and carmine-red		40	1·00
B4	3d. black and blue		30	1·00
B5	4d. black and purple		3·00	1·75
B6	6d. black and brown		12·00	2·25
	a. Blue-black and brown (24.9.45)		20·00	
B7	9d. black and grey-blue		1·00	1·25
B8	1s. deep blue		1·00	1·25
B1/8		Set of 8	16·00	10·00
B1/8 Perf "Specimen"		Set of 8	£325	

For later issues, see after No. G44.

C. SOUTH ORKNEYS

Used from the *Fitzroy* in February 1944 and at Laurie Island (established January 1946).
Falkland Islands definitive stamps with face values of 1s. 3d. and above were valid for use from the South Orkneys in conjunction with Nos. C1/8 and subsequently Nos. G1/16.

Stamps of FALKLAND ISLANDS cancelled on the Fitzroy, at Laurie Island or at Signy Island with South Orkneys circular datestamps between 21 February 1944 and 31 January 1954.

1938–50. *King George VI (Nos. 160/3).*
Z95	2s. 6d. slate		30·00
Z96	5s. indigo and yellow-brown		£130
Z97	10s. black and orange		40·00
Z98	£1 black and violet		60·00

1952. *King George VI (Nos. 181/5).*
Z 99	1s. 3d. orange		
Z100	2s. 6d. olive-green		
Z101	5s. purple		
Z102	10s. grey		
Z103	£1 black		

1944 (21 Feb)–45. *Falkland Islands Nos. 146, 148, 150, 153/5, 157 and 158a optd "SOUTH ORKNEYS/DEPENDENCY OF", in red as Type A 1 of Graham Land.*
C1	½d. black and green		30	1·50
C2	1d. black and violet		30	1·00
	w. Wmk inverted		£3750	
C3	2d. black and carmine-red		40	1·00
C4	3d. black and blue		30	1·00
C5	4d. black and purple		3·00	1·75
C6	6d. black and brown		12·00	2·25
	a. Blue-black and brown (24.9.45)		20·00	
C7	9d. black and grey-blue		1·00	1·25
C8	1s. deep blue		1·00	1·25
C1/8		Set of 8	16·00	10·00
C1/8 Perf "Specimen"		Set of 8	£325	

D. SOUTH SHETLANDS

Postal facilities were first provided at the Port Foster whaling station on Deception Island for the 1912–13 whaling season and were available each year between November and the following April until March 1931.
No postmark was provided for the 1912–13 season and the local postmaster was instructed to cancel stamps on cover with a straight-line "PORT FOSTER" handstamp. Most letters so cancelled subsequently received a "FALKLAND ISLANDS" circular postmark dated between 19 and 28 March 1913. It is known that only low value stamps were available at Port Foster. Higher values, often with other "FALKLAND ISLANDS" postmark dates, were, it is believed, subsequently "made to order".

Stamps of FALKLAND ISLANDS cancelled at Port Foster, Deception Island with part of "PORT FOSTER" straight-line handstamp.

1904–12. *King Edward VII (Nos. 43/4).*
Z104	½d. deep yellow-green		£1200
Z105	1d. orange-vermilion		£1200

1912. *King George V. Wmk Mult Crown CA (No. 60).*
Z106	½d. yellow-green		£1200

Stamps of FALKLAND ISLANDS cancelled at Port Foster with part of oval "DECEPTION ISLAND SOUTH SHETLANDS" postmark in black or violet between 1914 and 1927.

1912–20. *King George V. Wmk Mult Crown CA (Nos. 60/9).*
Z110	½d. yellow-green		75·00
Z111	1d. orange-red		75·00
Z112	2d. maroon		£100
Z113	2½d. deep bright blue		£100

Z114	6d. yellow-orange	..	..	..	£120
Z115	1s. light bistre-brown	..			£140
Z116	3s. slate-green				£300
Z117	5s. deep rose-red				£350
Z118	10s. red/*green*				£450
Z119	£1 black/*red*	..	..	..	£550

1918–20. "WAR STAMP" *ovpts (Nos. 70/2).*

Z120	½d. deep olive				£100
Z121	1d. vermilion	..			£100
Z122	1s. light bistre-brown	..			£200

1921–28. *King George V. Wmk Mult Script CA (Nos. 73/80).*

Z123	½d. yellowish green				£100
Z126	2½d. deep blue				£130
Z129	1s. deep ochre				£150

Stamps of FALKLAND ISLANDS *cancelled at Port Foster with* "SOUTH SHETLANDS" *circular datestamp between 1923 and March 1931*

1912–20. *King George V. Wmk Mult Crown CA (Nos. 60/9).*

Z131	1d. orange-vermilion				50·00
Z132	2d. deep reddish purple				60·00
Z133	6d. brown-orange				80·00
Z134	3s. slate-green	..			£160
Z135	5s. maroon				£180
Z136	10s. red/*green*				£300
Z137	£1 black/*red*				£500

Examples of all values are known with forged postmarks dated "20 MR 27".

1918–20. "WAR STAMP" *ovpts (Nos. 70/2).*

Z139	1d. vermilion				£100
Z140	1s. light bistre brown				

1921–28. *King George V. Wmk Mult Script CA (Nos. 73/80).*

Z141	½d. yellowish green				35·00
Z142	1d. dull vermilion				35·00
Z143	2d. deep brown-purple	..			50·00
Z144	2½d. deep blue	..			40·00
Z145	2½d. deep purple/*pale yellow*			75·00
Z146	6d. yellow-orange				60·00
Z147	1s. deep ochre	..			60·00
Z148	3s. slate-green	..			£160

1929. *King George V. Whale and Penguins design (Nos. 116/26).*

Z149	½d. green	..			50·00
Z150	1d. scarlet	..			50·00
Z151	2d. grey				70·00
Z152	2½d. blue	..			60·00
Z153	6d. purple	..			80·00
Z154	1s. black/*emerald*				80·00
Z155	2s. 6d. carmine/*blue*				£110
Z156	5s. green/*yellow*				£120
Z157	10s. carmine/*emerald*	..			£250
Z158	£1 black/*red*	..	..	..	£550

The whaling station at Port Foster was abandoned at the end of the 1930–31 season.

It was reoccupied as a Falkland Islands Dependencies Survey base on 3 February 1944.

Falkland Islands definitive stamps with face values of 1s. 3d. and above were valid for use from the South Shetlands in conjunction with Nos. D1/8 and subsequently Nos. G1/16.

Stamps of FALKLAND ISLANDS *cancelled at Port Foster or Admiralty Bay with South Shetlands circular datestamps between 5 February 1944 and 31 January 1954*

1938–50. *King George VI (Nos. 160/3).*

Z159	2s. 6d. slate				30·00
Z160	5s. indigo and yellow-brown	..		£130
Z161	10s. black and orange				40·00
Z162	£1 black and violet	..			60·00

1952. *King George VI (Nos. 181/5).*

Z163	1s. 3d. orange	..			
Z164	2s. 6d. olive-green				
Z165	5s. purple				
Z166	10s. grey				
Z167	£1 black				

1944 (5 Feb)–45. *Falkland Islands Nos. 146, 148, 150, 153/5, 157 and 158a optd* "SOUTH SHETLANDS/DEPENDENCY OF", *in red, as Type A 1 of Graham Land.*

D1	½d. black and green	..		30	1·50
D2	1d. black and violet	..	..	30	1·00
D3	2d. black and carmine-red	..	..	40	1·00
D4	3d. black and blue	..	..	30	1·00
D5	4d. black and purple	..	..	3·00	1·75
D6	6d. black and brown	..	..	12·00	2·25
	a. Blue-black and brown (24.9.45)		20·00	
D7	9d. black and grey-blue	..	..	1·00	1·25
D8	1s. deep blue	..	..	1·00	1·25
D1/8		..	Set of 8	16·00	10·00
D1/8 Perf "Specimen"		Set of 8	£325	

From 12 July 1946 to 16 July 1963, Graham Land, South Georgia, South Orkneys and South Shetlands used FALKLAND ISLANDS DEPENDENCIES stamps.

The new-issue supplement to this Catalogue appears each month in

GIBBONS
STAMP MONTHLY

—from your newsagent or by postal subscription— sample copy and details on request.

E. FALKLAND ISLANDS DEPENDENCIES

For use at the following bases:

Adelaide Island (Graham Land) (*opened* 1961)
Admiralty Bay (South Shetlands) (*opened* January 1948, *closed* January 1961)
Anvers Island (Graham Land) (*opened* February 1955, *closed* 10 January 1958)
Argentine Islands (Graham Land) (*opened* 1947)
Danco Coast ("Base O") (Graham Land) (*opened* 30 March 1956, *closed* 1958)
Deception Island (South Shetlands)
Grytviken (South Georgia)
Halley Bay (Coats Land) (*opened* 1956)
Hope Bay (Graham Land) (*closed* 4 February 1949, *opened* February 1952)
Laurie Island (South Orkneys) (*closed* 1947)
Loubet Coast ("Base W") (Graham Land) (*opened* 1955, *closed* 1959)
Marguerite Bay (Graham Land) (*opened* March 1955, *closed* 1960)
Port Lockroy (Graham Land) (*closed* 16 January 1962)
Prospect Point ("Base J") (Graham Land) (*opened* 1956, *closed* 1958)
Shackleton (Coats Land) (*opened* 1956, *closed* 1957)
Signy Island (South Orkneys) (*opened* 1946)
Stonington Island (Graham Land) (*opened* 1946, *closed* 1950, *opened* 1958, *closed* 1959, *opened* 1960)

G 1

Extra island (Plate 1 R. 3/9) · "SOUTH POKE" flaw (Plate 2 R. 6/8)

Missing "I" in "S. Shetland Is." (Plate 1 R. 1/2)

Nos. G1/8

Nos. G9/16

On Nos. G9 to G16 the map is redrawn; the "o°" meridian does not pass through the "S" of "COATS", the "n" of "Alexander" is not joined to the "L" of "Land" below, and the loops of letters "s" and "t" are generally more open.

(Map litho, frame recess D.L.R.)

1946 (12 July*)–49. *Wmk Mult Script CA (sideways). P 12.*

(a) Map thick and coarse

G 1	G 1	½d. black and green		1·00	2·00
		a. Extra island	..	50·00	
		b. Missing "T"	..	50·00	
		c. "SOUTH POKE"	..	50·00	
G 2		1d. black and violet	..	1·25	1·75
		a. Extra island	..	55·00	
		b. Missing "T"	..	55·00	
G 3		2d. black and carmine	..	1·25	2·50
		a. Extra island	..	60·00	
		b. Missing "T"	..	60·00	
G 4		3d. black and blue	..	1·25	3·75
		a. Extra island	..	65·00	
		b. Missing "T"	..	65·00	
G 5		4d. black and claret	..	2·25	4·50
		c. "SOUTH POKE"	..	75·00	
G 6		6d. black and orange	..	3·25	4·50
		a. Extra island	..	95·00	
		b. Missing "T"	..	95·00	
		c. "SOUTH POKE"	..	95·00	
		d. Black and ochre	..	48·00	90·00
		da. Extra island	..	£225	
		db. Missing "T"	..	£225	
		dc. "SOUTH POKE"	..	£225	
G 7		9d. black and brown	..	2·00	2·75
		c. "SOUTH POKE"	..	85·00	
G 8		1s. black and purple	..	2·00	4·00
		c. "SOUTH POKE"	..	85·00	
G1/8			Set of 8	13·00	23·00
G1/8 Perf "Specimen"		Set of 8	£450	

(b) Map thin and clear (16.2.48)

G 9	G 1	½d. black and green		2·25	8·50
		a. Recess frame printed double, one albino and inverted	..	£850	
G10		1d. black and violet	..	1·50	12·00
G11		2d. black and carmine	..	6·50	17·00
G11a		2½d. black and deep blue (6.3.49)	9·50	7·00
G12		3d. black and blue	..	2·75	4·50
G13		4d. black and claret	..	16·00	17·00
G14		6d. black and orange	..	20·00	11·00
G15		9d. black and brown	..	20·00	10·00
G16		1s. black and purple	..	21·00	10·00
G9/16			Set of 9	90·00	90·00

*This is the date of issue for South Georgia. Nos. G1/8 were released in London on 11 February.

In Nos. G1/8 a variety with a gap in the 80th parallel occurs six times in each sheet of all values in positions R. 1/4, 1/9, 3/4, 3/9, 5/4 and 5/9 (*Price for set of 8* £40 *mint, in pairs with normal*).

A constant variety, dot on "T" of "SOUTH", occurs on R. 5/2, 5/4, 5/6, 5/8 and 5/10 of all values of the "thin map" set with the exception of the 2½d.

1946 (4 Oct*). *Victory. As Nos. 110/11 of Antigua.*

G17	1d. deep violet	..		50	15
G18	3d. blue	..		75	15
G17/18 Perf "Specimen"		Set of 2	£120	

*This is the date of issue for South Georgia. The stamps were placed on sale from the South Orkneys on 17 January 1947, from the South Shetlands on 30 January 1947 and from Graham Land on 10 February 1947.

1948 (6 Dec). *Royal Silver Wedding. As Nos. 112/13 of Antigua, but 1s. in recess.*

G19	2½d. ultramarine	..	..	1·00	75
G20	1s. violet-blue	..	..	2·50	1·75

1949 (10 Oct). *75th Anniv of U.P.U. As Nos. 114/17 of Antigua.*

G21	1d. violet	..	..	1·50	1·50
G22	2d. carmine-red	..		4·50	2·50
G23	3d. deep blue	..		4·00	1·25
G24	6d. red-orange	..		7·00	3·00
G21/4			Set of 4	15·00	7·50

1953 (4 June). *Coronation. As No. 120 of Antigua.*

G25	1d. black and violet	..		1·10	1·25

G 2 John Biscoe I, 1947–52   G 3 Trepassey, 1945–47

(Recess Waterlow, then D.L.R. (from 27.3.62))

1954 (1 Feb)–62. *Types G 2/3 and similar designs showing ships. Wmk Mult Script CA. P 12½.*

G26	½d. black and bluish green		30	1·50
	a. Black and deep green (DLR) (17.4.62)	5·50	13·00
G27	1d. black and sepia-brown		75	1·25
	a. Black and sepia (DLR) (27.3.62)	13·00	16·00
G28	1½d. black and olive		3·00	1·25
	a. Black and yellow-olive (DLR) (21.9.62)	8·50	3·00
G29	2d. black and rose-red		1·25	20
G30	2½d. black and yellow-ochre		1·25	15
G31	3d. black and deep bright blue		1·25	15
G32	4d. black and bright reddish purple		3·25	45
G33	6d. black and deep lilac		3·25	45
G34	9d. black		3·25	85
G35	1s. black and brown		3·25	75
G36	1s. 3d. black and deep blue		19·00	10·00
G37	2s. 6d. black and pale turquoise		19·00	6·00
G38	5s. black and violet		40·00	6·50

443

G39	10s. black and blue	..	..	55·00	18·00
G40	£1 black	..	..	90·00	48·00
G26/40			*Set of 15*	£200	85·00

Designs: *Horiz*—1½d. *Wyatt Earp*, 1934–36; 2d. *Eagle*, 1944–45; 2½d. *Penola*, 1934–37; 3d. *Discovery II*, 1929–37; 4d. *William Scoresby*, 1926–46; 1s. *Deutschland*, 1910–12; 2s. *Pourquoi-pas?*, 1908–10; 10s. *Antarctic*, 1901–03. *Vert*—6d. *Discovery*, 1925–27; 9d. *Endurance*, 1914–16; 2s. 6d. *Français*, 1903–05; 5s. *Scotia*, 1902–04; £1 *Belgica*, 1897–99.

TRANS-ANTARCTIC
EXPEDITION 1955-1958
(G 4)

1956 (30 Jan). *Trans-Antarctic Expedition. Nos. G27, G30/1 and G33 optd with Type* G 4.

G41	1d. black and sepia-brown	..	..	10	30
G42	2½d. black and yellow-ochre	..	..	55	50
G43	3d. black and deep bright blue	..	..	55	30
G44	6d. black and deep lilac	..	..	55	30
G41/4			*Set of 4*	1·50	1·25

The stamps of Falkland Islands Dependencies were withdrawn on 16 July 1963 after Coats Land, Graham Land, South Orkneys and South Shetlands had become a separate colony, known as British Antarctic Territory.

F. SOUTH GEORGIA

From 17 July 1963 South Georgia and South Sandwich Islands used stamps inscribed "South Georgia".

1 Reindeer　　**2** South Sandwich Islands

(Des D.L.R. (No. 16), M. Goaman (others). Recess D.L.R.)

1963 (17 July)–**69**. *T* 1/2 *and similar designs. Ordinary or glazed paper (No. 16). W w* 12. *P* 15.

1	½d. brown-red	..	..	50	75
	a. Perf 14 × 15 (13.2.67)	..	..	1·00	1·50
2	1d. violet-blue	..	..	70	50
3	2d. turquoise-blue	..	..	1·00	60
4	2½d. black	..	..	4·00	1·75
5	3d. bistre	..	..	2·25	20
6	4d. bronze-green	..	..	4·25	80
7	5½d. deep violet	..	..	2·00	20
8	6d. orange	..	..	75	20
9	9d. blue	..	..	4·50	1·00
10	1s. purple	..	..	75	20
11	2s. yellow-olive and light blue	..	..	17·00	4·50
12	2s. 6d. blue	..	..	20·00	4·00
13	5s. bronze-green	..	..	20·00	4·00
14	10s. magenta	..	..	42·00	10·00
15	£1 ultramarine	..	..	85·00	48·00
16	£1 grey-black (1.12.69)	..	..	10·00	16·00
1/16			*Set of 16*	£190	80·00

Designs: *Vert*—2d. Sperm Whale; 3d. South American Fur Seal; 6d. Light-mantled Sooty Albatross; 10s. Plankton and krill; £1 (No. 16) King Penguins. *Horiz*—2½d. Chinstrap and King Penguins; 4d. Fin Whale; 5½d. Southern Elephant-Seal; 9d. Whale-catcher; 1s. Leopard Seal; 2s. Shackleton's Cross; 2s. 6d. Wandering Albatross; 5s. Southern Elephant-Seal and South American Fur Seal; £1 (No. 15) Blue Whale.

1970 (22 Jan). *As No. 1, but wmk w* 12 *sideways and on glazed paper.*

17	½d. brown-red	..	..	2·50	2·25

(3)		(3a)
(4)		(4a)
(5)		(5a)

1971 (15 Feb)–**76**. *Decimal Currency. Nos.* 17 *and* 2/14 *surch as T* 3/4. *Nos.* 18/a *wmk sideways, glazed paper. Others wmk upright, ordinary paper.*

18	½p. on ½d. brown-red (T 3)	..	..	1·50	1·60
	a. Surch with T 3a (16.6.72)	..	..	1·00	90
	b. Do. Wmk upright (24.8.73)	..	..	3·25	5·00
19	1p. on 1d. violet-blue	..	..	1·50	50
	a. Glazed paper (1.12.72)	..	..	2·75	1·75
	b. Do. but wmk sideways (9.3.76)	..	..	1·00	4·00
20	1½p. on 5½d. deep violet (T 4)	..	..	3·00	2·25
	b. Surch with T 4a. Glazed paper (24.8.73)	..	..	7·00	4·50
21	2p. on 2d. turquoise-blue	..	..	70	50
22	2½p. on 2½d. black	..	..	1·50	40

23	3p. on 3d. bistre	..	..	1·00	50
24	4p. on 4d. bronze-green	..	..	90	50
25	6p. on 6d. orange	..	..	90	30
26	6p. on 9d. blue	..	..	1·50	70
27	7½p. on 1s. purple	..	..	2·00	70
28	10p. on 2s. yellow-olive and light blue	..	32·00	15·00
29	15p. on 2s. 6d. blue	..	..	13·00	11·00
30	25p. on 5s. orange-brown	..	..	10·00	9·00
31	50p. on 10s. magenta (Type 5)	..	35·00	16·00
	a. Surch with Type 5a. Glazed paper (1.12.72)	..	10·00	21·00
	b. Do. but wmk sideways (9.3.76)	..	15·00	32·00
18/31a			*Set of 14*	70·00	50·00

The surcharge on No. 19b shows a larger "p".
See also Nos. 53/66.

6 *Endurance* beset in Weddell Sea

(Des R. Granger Barrett. Litho A. & M.)

1972 (5 Jan). *50th Death Anniv of Sir Ernest Shackleton. T* 6 *and similar horiz designs. Multicoloured. W w* 12 *(sideways*). P* 13½.

32	1½p. Type 6	..	..	1·00	1·00
	w. Wmk Crown to right of CA	..		3·25	
33	5p. Launching the longboat *James Caird*	1·25	1·50
	w. Wmk Crown to right of CA	..		3·75	
34	10p. Route of the *James Caird*	..	1·75	1·75
	w. Wmk Crown to right of CA	..		4·00	
35	20p. Sir Ernest Shackleton and the *Quest*	2·00	2·00
	w. Wmk Crown to right of CA	..		4·25	
32/5			*Set of 4*	5·50	5·50

*The normal sideways watermark shows Crown to left of CA, as seen from the back of the stamp.

7 Southern Elephant-Seal and King Penguins

(Des (from photograph by D. Groves) and photo Harrison)

1972 (20 Nov). *Royal Silver Wedding. Multicoloured; background colour given. W w* 12. *P* 14 × 14½.

36	**7** 5p. slate-green	..	..	75	35
	w. Wmk inverted	..		42·00	
37	10p. bluish violet	..	..	75	35

1973 (1 Dec*). *Royal Wedding. As Nos.* 165/6 *of Anguilla. Centre multicoloured. W w* 12 *(sideways). P* 13½.

38	5p. brown-ochre	..	..	25	10
39	15p. chalky blue	..	..	35	20

*This is the local date of issue: the Crown Agents released the stamps on 14 November.

8 Churchill and Westminster Skyline　　**9** Captain Cook

(Des L. Curtis. Litho Questa)

1974 (14 Dec*). *Birth Centenary of Sir Winston Churchill. T* 8 *and similar horiz design. Multicoloured. W w* 12 *(sideways). P* 14½.

40	15p. Type 8	..	..	1·50	1·25
41	25p. Churchill and warship	..	1·50	1·25
MS42	122 × 98 mm. Nos. 40/1	..	6·00	6·00

*This is the local date of issue: the Crown Agents released the stamps on 30 November.

(Des J. Cooter. Litho Questa)

1975 (26 Apr). *Bicentenary of Possession by Captain Cook. T* 9 *and similar horiz designs. Multicoloured. W w* 12 *(sideways on* 8 *and* 16p.). P* 13.

43	2p. Type 9	..	..	2·00	1·25
44	8p. H.M.S. *Resolution*	..	3·25	2·00
45	16p. Possession Bay	..	..	3·50	2·25
43/5			*Set of 3*	8·00	5·00

NEW INFORMATION

The editor is always interested to correspond with people who have new information that will improve or correct the Catalogue.

---

10 *Discovery* and Biological Laboratory　　**11** Queen and Retinue after Coronation

(Des J. W. Litho Format)

1976 (21 Dec). *50th Anniv of "Discovery" Investigations. T* 10 *and similar vert designs. Multicoloured. W w* 14. *P* 14.

46	2p. Type 10	..	..	1·25	35
47	8p. *William Scoresby* and water-sampling bottles	..	1·60	50
48	11p. *Discovery II* and plankton net	..	2·00	55
49	25p. Biological Station and krill	..	2·50	85
46/9			*Set of 4*	6·50	2·00

(Des G. Drummond. Litho Questa)

1977 (7 Feb). *Silver Jubilee. T* 11 *and similar horiz designs. Multicoloured. W w* 14 *(sideways*). P* 13½.

50	6p. Visit by Prince Philip, 1957	..	50	30
51	11p. Queen Elizabeth and Westminster Abbey	..	70	35
	w. Wmk Crown to right of CA	..	80·00	
52	33p. Type 11	..	..	80	50
50/2			*Set of 3*	1·75	1·00

*The normal sideways watermark shows Crown to left of CA, as seen from the back of the stamp.

1977 (17 May)–**78**. *As Nos. 18a etc., but W w* 14 *(inverted on* 1p.; *upright on* 3p., 5p. *and* 50p.; *sideways* on *others). Glazed paper.*

53	½p. on ½d. brown-red	..	..	1·50	2·00
	w. Wmk Crown to right of CA	..	35·00	
54	1p. on 1d. violet-blue (16.8.77)	..	80	1·75
	w. Wmk upright	..	..	£250	
55	1½p. on 5½d. deep violet (16.8.77)	..	90	1·75
	w. Wmk Crown to right of CA	..	£350	
57	2½p. on 2½d. black (16.8.77)	..	10·00	3·50
58	3p. on 3d. bistre (16.8.77)	..	7·00	3·50
	w. Wmk inverted	..	..	£350	
59	4p. on 4d. bronze-green (16.8.77)	..	18·00	14·00
	w. Wmk Crown to right of CA	..	£500	
60	5p. on 6d. orange	..	..	2·50	2·75
	w. Wmk upright	..	..	2·50	2·75
62	7½p. on 1s. purple (16.8.77)	..	11·00	20·00
	w. Wmk Crown to right of CA (31.7.78)	2·50	8·00
63	10p. on 2s. yellow-olive & light blue (16.8.77)	7·50	13·00
	w. Wmk Crown to right of CA (31.7.78)	2·50	8·00
64	15p. on 2s. 6d. blue (16.8.77)	..	10·00	20·00
	w. Wmk Crown to right of CA (31.7.78)	2·50	8·00
65	25p. on 5s. orange-brown (16.8.77)	..	14·00	22·00
	w. Wmk Crown to right of CA (31.7.78)	2·50	8·00
66	50p. on 10s. pale magenta (12.78)	..	2·25	8·50
53/66			*Set of 12*	48·00	60·00

*The normal sideways watermark shows Crown to left of CA, as seen from the back of the stamp.

Surcharges on the above differ from those on Nos. 18a/30 by having straight outlines and being slightly more slender. The change in paper also results in the colours appearing brighter.

12 Fur Seal　　**13** H.M.S. *Resolution*

(Des C. Abbott. Litho Questa)

1978 (2 June). *25th Anniv of Coronation. T* 12 *and similar vert designs. P* 15.

67	25p. indigo, ultramarine and silver	..	45	1·10
	a. Sheetlet. Nos. 67/9 × 2	..	2·50	
68	25p. multicoloured	..	..	45	1·10
69	25p. indigo, ultramarine and silver	..	45	1·10
67/9			*Set of 3*	1·25	3·00

Designs:—No. 67, Panther of Henry VI; No. 68, Queen Elizabeth II; No. 69, Type 12.

Nos. 67/9 were printed together in small sheets of 6, containing two *se-tenant* strips of 3, with horizontal gutter margin between.

(Des and litho (25p. also embossed) Walsall)

1979 (14 Feb). *Bicentenary of Captain Cook's Voyages, 1768–79. T* 13 *and similar vert designs. Multicoloured. P* 11.

70	3p. Type 13	..	..	1·50	1·25
71	6p. *Resolution* and map of South Georgia and S. Sandwich Isles showing route	1·50	1·00
72	11p. King Penguin (based on drawing by George Forster)	..	2·50	2·25
73	25p. Flaxman/Wedgwood medallion of Captain Cook	..	2·75	2·75
70/3			*Set of 4*	7·50	6·50

From 5 May 1980 South Georgia and South Sandwich Islands used stamps inscribed FALKLAND ISLANDS DEPENDENCIES.

G. FALKLAND ISLANDS DEPENDENCIES

For use in South Georgia and South Sandwich Islands.

14 Map of Falkland Islands Dependencies   **15** Magellanic Clubmoss

(Des and litho J.W.)

1980 (5 May)–**84.** *Horiz designs as T* **14**. *Multicoloured.* W w 14 *(sideways).* P 13½. A. *Without imprint date.* B. *With imprint date* ("1984") at foot of design (3.5.84).

			A		B	
74	1p.	Type 14	30	30	25	70
75	2p.	Shag Rocks	30	30	25	70
76	3p.	Bird and Willis Islands	30	30	25	70
77	4p.	Gulbrandsen Lake	30	30	25	70
78	5p.	King Edward Point	30	30	35	70
79	6p.	Sir Ernest Shackleton's Memorial Cross, Hope Point	60	30	30	70
80	7p.	Sir Ernest Shackleton's Grave, Grytviken	60	40	30	70
81	8p.	Grytviken Church	50	40	30	70
82	9p.	Coaling Hulk *Louise* at Grytviken	50	45	30	70
83	10p.	Clerke Rocks	50	45	50	70
84	20p.	Candlemas Island	2·50	1·75	2·00	1·50
85	25p.	Twitcher Rock and Cook Island, Southern Thule	2·50	1·75	2·00	2·25
86	50p.	R.R.S. *John Biscoe II* in Cumberland Bay	1·00	2·00	2·00	2·50
87	£1	R.R.S. *Bransfield* in Cumberland Bay	1·50	2·75	†	
88	£3	H.M.S. *Endurance* in Cumberland Bay	3·50	6·50	†	
74/88		Set of 15	13·00	16·00		
74B/86B		Set of 13			8·00	12·00

For some of these designs watermarked W 16 (sideways) see Nos. 148/52.

(Des L. McCombie. Litho Rosenbaum Bros, Vienna)

1981 (5 Feb). *Plants. T* **15** *and similar vert designs. Multicoloured.* W w 14 *(inverted on 25p.).* P 14.

89	3p.	Type 15	20	25
		w. Wmk inverted	6·00	
90	6p.	Alpine Cat's-tail	20	30
91	7p.	Greater Burnet	20	30
		w. Wmk inverted	£275	
92	11p.	Antarctic Bedstraw	25	35
93	15p.	Brown Rush	30	45
		a. Light brown (Queen's head and territory inscr) omitted	£1800	
94	25p.	Antarctic Hair Grass	55	75
		w. Wmk upright	£275	
89/94		Set of 6	1·50	2·25

16 Wedding Bouquet from Falkland Islands Dependencies   **17** Introduced Reindeer during Calving, Spring

(Des J.W. Litho Format)

1981 (22 July). *Royal Wedding. T* **16** *and similar vert designs. Multicoloured.* W w 14. P 14.

95	10p.	Type 16	15	30
96	13p.	Prince Charles dressed for skiing	20	35
97	52p.	Prince Charles and Lady Diana Spencer	65	85
95/7		Set of 3	90	1·40

(Des A. Theobald. Litho Format)

1982 (29 Jan). *Reindeer. T* **17** *and similar horiz designs. Multicoloured.* W w 14 *(sideways).* P 14.

98	5p.	Type 17	25	65
99	13p.	Bull at rut, Autumn	30	85
100	25p.	Reindeer and mountains, Winter	40	1·40
101	26p.	Reindeer feeding on tussock grass, late Winter	40	1·40
98/101		Set of 4	1·25	3·75

STANLEY GIBBONS STAMP COLLECTING SERIES

Introductory booklets on *How to Start, How to Identify Stamps* and *Collecting by Theme.* A series of well illustrated guides at a low price. Write for details.

---

18 *Gamasellus racovitzai* (tick)   **19** Lady Diana Spencer at Tidworth, Hampshire, July 1981

(Des I. Loe. Litho Questa)

1982 (16 Mar). *Insects. T* **18** *and similar vert designs. Multicoloured.* W w 14. P 14.

102	5p.	Type 18	15	25
103	10p.	*Alaskozetes antarcticus* (mite)	25	35
104	13p.	*Cryptopygus antarcticus* (spring-tail)	25	40
105	15p.	*Notiomaso australis* (spider)	30	45
106	25p.	*Hydromedion sparsutum* (beetle)	50	70
107	26p.	*Parochlus steinenii* (midge)	50	70
102/7		Set of 6	1·75	2·50

(Des C. Abbott. Litho Format)

1982 (7 Sept). *21st Birthday of Princess of Wales. T* **19** *and similar vert designs. Multicoloured.* W w 14. P 13½ × 14.

108	5p.	Falklands Islands Dependencies coat of arms	10	15
109	17p.	Type 19	40	35
		a. Perf 13½	2·75	6·50
110	37p.	Bride and groom on steps of St Paul's	45	80
111	50p.	Formal portrait	1·00	1·10
108/11		Set of 4	1·75	2·25

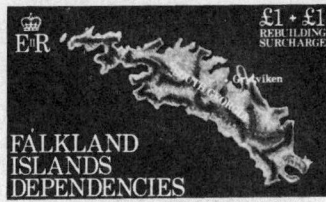

20 Map of South Georgia

(Des PAD Studio. Litho Format)

1982 (13 Sept). *Rebuilding Fund.* W w 14 *(sideways*).* P 11.

112	**20**	£1 + £1 multicoloured	2·40	4·00
		w. Wmk Crown to right of CA	80·00	

*The normal sideways watermark shows Crown to left of CA, as seen from the back of the stamp.

21 Westland Whirlwind   **22** *Euphausia superba*

(Des Harrison. Litho Questa)

1983 (23 Dec). *Bicentenary of Manned Flight. T* **21** *and similar horiz designs. Multicoloured.* W w 14 *(sideways).* P 14.

113	5p.	Type 21	30	30
114	13p.	Westland AS.1 Wasp helicopter	55	65
115	17p.	Vickers Supermarine Walrus II	60	70
116	50p.	Auster Autocrat	1·40	1·50
113/16		Set of 4	2·50	2·75

(Des N. Weaver. Litho Questa)

1984 (23 Mar). *Crustacea. T* **22** *and similar vert designs. Multicoloured.* W w 14. P 14½ × 14.

117	5p.	Type 22	40	20
118	17p.	*Glyptonotus antarcticus*	70	50
119	25p.	*Epimeria monodon*	85	60
120	34p.	*Serolis pagenstecheri*	1·10	80
117/20		Set of 4	2·75	1·90

23 Zavodovski Island

(Des. J.W. Litho Questa)

1984 (8 Nov). *Volcanoes of South Sandwich Islands. T* **23** *and similar horiz designs. Multicoloured.* W w 14 *(sideways).* P 14 × 14½.

121	6p.	Type 23	80	80
122	17p.	Mt Michael, Saunders Island	2·00	1·60
123	22p.	Bellingshausen Island	2·00	1·75
124	52p.	Bristol Island	2·50	3·25
121/4		Set of 4	6·50	6·75

---

24 Grey-headed Albatross   **25** The Queen Mother

(Des I. Loe. Litho Questa)

1985 (5 May). *Albatrosses. T* **24** *and similar horiz designs. Multicoloured.* W w 14 *(sideways).* P 14½.

125	7p.	Type 24	1·50	75
126	22p.	Black-browed Albatross	2·25	1·25
127	27p.	Wandering Albatross	2·50	1·40
128	54p.	Light-mantled Sooty Albatross	3·25	2·25
125/8		Set of 4	8·50	5·00

(Des A. Theobald (£1), C. Abbott (others). Litho Questa)

1985 (23 June). *Life and Times of Queen Elizabeth the Queen Mother. T* **25** *and similar vert designs. Multicoloured.* W w 16. P 14½ × 14.

129	7p.	At Windsor Castle on Princess Elizabeth's 14th birthday, 1940	30	30
130	22p.	With Princess Anne, Lady Sarah Armstrong-Jones and Prince Edward at Trooping the Colour	60	70
131	27p.	Type 25	70	80
		w. Wmk inverted	10·00	
132	54p.	With Prince Henry at his christening (from photo by Lord Snowdon)	1·25	1·40
129/32		Set of 4	2·50	2·75
MS133	91×73 mm. £1 Disembarking from Royal Yacht *Britannia.* Wmk sideways		2·25	2·75

(Des I. Strange. Litho Questa)

1985 (4 Nov). *Early Naturalists. Vert designs as T* **35** *of British Antarctic Territory. Multicoloured.* W w 14. P 14½ × 14.

134	7p.	Dumont d'Urville and *Durvillea antarctica* (kelp)	1·25	90
135	22p.	Johann Reinhold Forster and King Penguin	2·25	1·75
136	27p.	Johann Georg Adam Forster and Tussock Grass	2·25	2·00
137	54p.	Sir Joseph Banks and Dove Prion	3·00	3·25
134/7		Set of 4	8·00	7·00

1985 (18 Nov). *As Nos. 84/8 but* W w 16 *(sideways). With imprint date* ("1985"). P 13½.

148	20p.	Candlemas Island	2·50	4·50
149	25p.	Twitcher Rock and Cook Island, Southern Thule	2·75	4·50
150	50p.	R.R.S. *John Biscoe* in Cumberland Bay	3·00	4·50
151	£1	R.R.S. *Bransfield* in Cumberland Bay	3·00	4·50
152	£3	H.M.S. *Endurance* in Cumberland Bay	8·00	8·00
148/52		Set of 5	17·00	23·00

Under the new constitution, effective 3 October 1985, South Georgia and South Sandwich Islands ceased to be dependencies of the Falkland Islands. Issues inscribed for the separate territory are listed under SOUTH GEORGIA AND SOUTH SANDWICH ISLANDS.

Fiji

PRICES FOR STAMPS ON COVER TO 1945	
Nos. 1/9	*from* × 6
Nos. 10/34	*from* × 5
Nos. 35/59	*from* × 8
Nos. 60/3	—
Nos. 64/9	*from* × 20
Nos. 70/5	*from* × 5
Nos. 76/103	*from* × 8
Nos. 104/14	*from* × 5
Nos. 115/24	*from* × 4
Nos. 125/37	*from* × 3
Nos. 138/241	*from* × 4
Nos. 242/5	*from* × 3
Nos. 246/8	*from* × 8
Nos. 249/66b	*from* × 2
No. 267	*from* × 8
Nos. D1/5c	*from* × 4
Nos. D6/10	*from* × 15
Nos. D11/18	*from* × 20

King Cakobau 1852–Oct 1874

Christian missionaries reached Fiji in 1835 and early letters are known to and from their mission stations, sent via Sydney, Hobart or Auckland.

In 1852 Cakobau, the chief of the island of Bau, declared himself King of Fiji and converted to Christianity two years later. Internal problems and difficulties with the American government led the king to offer to cede Fiji to Great Britain. The offer was refused, but resulted in the appointment of a British Consul in 1858. A Consular Post Office operated from September 1858 until 1872 and franked mail with New South Wales stamps from 1863.

The destruction of plantations in the Confederacy during the American Civil War led to an increased demand for Fijian cotton and this upsurge in commercial activity encouraged the *Fiji Times* newspaper on Levuka to establish a postal service on 1 November 1870.

1

(Type-set and printed at the office of *The Fiji Times*, Levuka, Ovalau, Fiji)

1870 (1 Nov)–*71*. *Rouletted in the printing.* (a) *Quadrillé paper.*

1	1	1d. black/*rose*	..	..	.. £3250 £3500
2		3d. black/*rose*	..	..	.. £3000 £3000
3		6d. black/*rose*	..	..	.. £2000 £2000
4		1s. black/*rose*	..	..	.. £1500 £1800

(b) *Laid bâtonné paper* (1871)

5	1	1d. black/*rose*	..	..	£900 £1800
		a. Vert strip of 4. Nos. 5, 7/9			£35000
6		3d. black/*rose*	..	..	£1500 £2750
7		6d. black/*rose*	..	..	£1100 £2750
8		9d. black/*rose*	..	..	£1700 £2750
		a. Comma after "EXPRESS" (R.4/4)			£2250
9		1s. black/*rose*	..	..	£1000 £1400

Nos. 1/4 were printed *se-tenant* as a sheet of 24 (6 × 4) with the 6d. stamps in the first horizontal row, the 1s. in the second, the 1d. in the third and the 3d. in the fourth. Nos. 5/9 were produced from the same plate on which three of the 3d. impressions had been replaced with three 9d. values.

The issued stamps showed the vertical frame lines continuous from top to bottom of the sheet with the horizontal rules broken and not touching the verticals. Used examples are cancelled in manuscript or by the star cancellation used at Bua.

There are no reprints of these stamps, but the 1d., 3d., 6d. and 1s. are known in the correct type on *yellow wove* paper and are believed to be proofs.

There are also three different sets of imitations made by the proprietors of *The Fiji Times* to meet the demands of collectors:—

The first was produced in 1876 on *white wove* or *vertically laid* paper, rouletted on dotted lines and arranged in sheets of 40 (5 rows of 8) comprising 1d., 3d., 6d., 9d. and 1s.; the horizontal frame lines are continuous and the vertical ones broken.

The second was produced before 1888 on *thick rosy mauve wove* paper, rouletted on dotted lines and arranged in sheets of 30 (5 rows of 6) comprising 1s., 9d., 6d., 3d. and 1d.; the vertical frame lines are continuous and the horizontal ones broken.

The third only came to light in the 1960s and is rare, only one complete sheet being recorded, which has since been destroyed. The sheet arrangement is the same as Nos. 1/4, which suggests that this was the first imitation to be produced. It is on *off-white wove* paper, rouletted on closely dotted or solid lines, with vertical frame lines continuous and the horizontal ones broken, as in the originals. These differ from the proofs mentioned above in that the lettering is slightly larger and the figures also differ.

King Cakobau established a formal government in June 1871 and stamps for the royal post office were ordered from Sydney. These arrived in October 1871 and the postal service was placed on a firm basis by the First Postal Act in December of that year. Under its terms the *Fiji Times* service closed on 17 January 1872 and the British Consular Post Office followed six months later.

Two

Cents

2	3	(4)

(Eng and electrotyped by A. L. Jackson. Typo Govt Printing Office, Sydney)

1871 (Oct). *Wove paper.* Wmk "FIJI POSTAGE" *in small sans-serif capitals across the middle row of stamps in the sheet.* P 12½.

10	2	1d. blue	..	..	50·00 £180
11		3d. pale yellow-green	..	£110 £350
12	3	6d. rose	..	..	£120 £275

The 3d. differs from T **2** in having a white circle containing square dots surrounding the centre.

All three values are known *imperf*, but were not issued in that condition.

See notes after No. 33b.

1872 (13 Jan). *Surch as T* **4**, *in local currency, by Govt Ptg Office, Sydney.*

13	2	2 c. on 1d. pale blue	..	..	50·00 65·00
		a. Deep blue	..	..	28·00 48·00
14		6 c. on 3d. yellow-green	..	65·00 65·00
15	3	12 c. on 6d. carmine-rose..	..	85·00 75·00

The new-issue supplement to this Catalogue appears each month in

GIBBONS STAMP MONTHLY

—from your newsagent or by postal subscription— sample copy and details on request.

CROWN COLONY

King Cakobau renewed his offer to cede Fiji to Great Britain and this took place on 12 October 1874.

V.R.	V.R.	2d.
(5)	(6)	(7)

Varieties:—

V.R.	V.R.
(Enlarged)	
Cross pattée stop	Inverted "A"

Cross pattée stop after "R" (R. 3/6).
Round raised stop after "V" (R. 3/8).
Round raised stops after "V" and "R" (R. 3/9).
Inverted "A" for "V" (R. 3/10).
No stop after "R" (R. 2/3 on T **5**, R. 5/3 on T **6**).

(Optd at *Polynesian Gazette* Office, Levuka)

1874 (10 Oct). *Nos.* 13/15 *optd.* (a) *With T* **5**.

16	2	2 c. on 1d. blue	..	..	£800 £200
		a. No stop after "R"	..	£2250 £1000
		b. Cross pattée stop after "R"..	£2250 £1000
		c. Round raised stop after "V"	£2250 £1000
		d. Round raised stops after "V" and "R"	£2250 £1000
		e. Inverted "A" for "V"	..	£2250 £1000
17		6 c. on 3d. green.	..	..	£1200 £550
		a. No stop after "R"	..	£3250 £1500
		b. Cross pattée stop after "R"..	£3250 £1500
		c. Round raised stop after "V"	£3250 £1500
		d. Round raised stops after "V" and "R"	£3250 £1500
		e. Inverted "A" for "V"	..	£3250 £1500
18	3	12 c. on 6d. rose	..	..	£500 £170
		a. No stop after "R"	..	£2000 £1000
		b. Cross pattée stop after "R"..	£2000 £1000
		c. Round raised stop after "V"	£2000 £1000
		d. Round raised stops after "V" and "R"	£2000 £1000
		e. Inverted "A" for "V"	..	£2000 £1000
		f. Opt inverted	..	—£3750

(b) *With T* **6**

19	2	2 c. on 1d. blue	..	..	£900 £225
		a. No stop after "R"	..	£2250 £1000
20		6 c. on 3d. green	..	..	£1600 £800
		a. No stop after "R"	..	£3250 £1500
21	3	12 c. on 6d. rose	..	..	£650 £180
		a. No stop after "R"	..	£2000 £1000
		b. Opt inverted	..	£4250

Nos. 16/21 were produced in sheets of 50 (10 × 5) of which the top three rows were overprinted with Type **5** and the lower two with Type **6**.

1875. *Stamps of 1874 surch at* Polynesian Gazette Office, Levuka, *with T* **7**.

(a) *In red* (May)

22	2	2d. on 6 c. on 3d. green (No. 17)	£425 £150
		a. No stop after "R"	..	£1500 £650
		b. Cross pattée stop after "R"..	£1500 £650
		c. Round raised stop after "V"	£1500 £650
		d. Round raised stops after "V" and "R"	£1500 £650
		e. Inverted "A" for "V"	..	£1500 £650
		f. No stop after "2d" (R. 1/2)..	£1500 £650
23		2d. on 6 c. on 3d. green (No. 20)	£550 £225
		a. No stop after "R"	..	£1500 £650
		b. Stop between "2" and "d" (R. 5/7)	£1500 £650

(b) *In black* (30 Sept)

24	2	2d. on 6 c. on 3d. green (No. 17)	£1100 £400
		a. No stop after "R"	..	£2750 £1200
		b. Cross pattée stop after "R"..	£2750 £1200
		c. Round raised stop after "V"	£2750 £1200
		d. Round raised stops after "V" and "R"	£2750 £1200
		e. Inverted "A" for "V"	..	£2750 £1200
		f. No stop after "2d" (R. 1/2)..	£2750 £1200
		g. "V.R." double	..	£2750 £1200
25		2d. on 6 c. on 3d. green (No. 20)	£1500 £550
		a. No stop after "R"	..	£2750 £1200
		b. Stop between "2" and "d" (R. 5/7)	£2750 £1200
		c. "V.R." double	..	—£3250

1875 (20 Nov). *No. 15 surch at* Polynesian Gazette Office, Levuka, *with T* **7** *and* "V.R." *at one operation.* (a) "V.R." *T* **5**.

26	3	2d. on 12 c. on 6d. rose..	..	£1200 £550
		aa. Round raised stop after "R"	
		a. Inverted "A" for "V" (R. 1/3, 2/8, 4/4) £1500 £700
		b. Do. and round raised stop after "V"	
		(R. 3/3, 3/6, 3/8, 3/10)	..	£1400 £650
		c. As "a" and round raised stops after "R" and "V" (R. 3/2, 3/9)	£1600 £750
		d. Surch double	..	—£3000

(b) "V.R." *T* **6**

27	3	2d. on 12 c. on 6d. rose..	..	£1200 £550
		a. Surch double	..	—£3250

The setting used for Nos. 26/7 was similar to that of Nos. 16/21, but the fourth stamp in the fourth row had a Type **5** "V.R." instead of a Type **6**.

The position of No. 26aa is not known.

 Two Pence

(8)	(9)

(Typo Govt Printing Office, Sydney, from plates of 1871)

1876–77. *On paper previously lithographed* "VR" *as T* **8**, *the 3d. surch with T* **9**. P 12½. (a) *Wove paper* (31.1.76).

28	2	1d. grey-blue	..	..	50·00 48·00
		a. Dull blue	..	..	50·00 48·00
		b. Doubly printed	..	£550
		c. Void corner (R. 2/1)	..	£475 £275
		d. Imperf vert (horiz pair)	..	£850
29		2d. on 3d. pale green	..	40·00 50·00
		a. Deep green	..	..	38·00 50·00

30	3	6d. pale rose	..	..	60·00 60·00
		a. Dull rose	..	..	48·00 50·00
		b. Carmine-rose..	..	55·00 50·00
		c. Doubly printed	..	£2500

(b) *Laid paper* (5.1.77)

31	2	1d. blue	..	..	13·00 24·00
		a. Deep blue	..	..	14·00 24·00
		b. Void corner (R. 2/1)	..	£250 £190
		c. Imperf vert (horiz pair)	..	£650
32		2d. on 3d. yellow-green	..	55·00 60·00
		a. Deep yellow-green	..	55·00 60·00
		b. Imperf between (pair)..	£850
		c. Perf 10	..	£300
		ca. Imperf vert (horiz pair)	..	£650
		d. Perf 11	..	£300
33	3	6d. rose	..	..	48·00 27·00
		a. Carmine-rose ..	..	48·00 35·00
		b. Imperf vert (horiz pair)	..	£650

The 3d. *green* is known without the surcharge T **9** on wove paper and also without the surcharge and the monogram. In this latter condition it can only be distinguished from No. 11 by its colour, which is a fuller, deeper yellow-green.

Stamps on both wove and laid paper *imperf* are from printer's trial or waste sheets and were not issued.

All values are known on laid paper without the monogram "VR" and the 3d. stamp also without the surcharge but these are also believed to be from printer's trial sheets and were never issued. Being on laid paper they are easily distinguishable from Nos. 10/12.

1877 (12 Oct). *Optd with T* **8** *and surch as T* **9**. *Laid paper.* P 12½.

34	2	4d. on 3d. mauve	..	..	80·00 25·00
		a. Imperf vert (horiz pair)	..	£850

10	11

A **Four Pence**
B **Four Pence**

Type A: Length 12½ mm
Type B: Length 14 mm
Note also the different shape of the two "e"s.

(Typo from new plates made from original dies of 1871 with "CR" altered to "VR" at Govt Printing Office, Sydney. 2d. and 4d. made from old 3d. die.)

1878–99. *Surcharges as T* **9** *or as Types A or B for* ¼d. *value. Wove paper with paper-maker's name* "T. H. SAUNDERS" *or* "SANDERSON" *in double-lined capitals extending over seven stamps in each full sheet.* (a) P 12½ (1878–80).

35	10	1d. pale ultramarine (19.2.79)	..	6·00 6·00
		a. Ultramarine	..	9·50 7·00
36		2d. on 3d. green (17.10.78)	..	4·50 13·00
37		2d. yellow-green (1.9.79)	..	12·00 8·00
		a. Blue-green..	..	23·00 13·00
		b. Error. Ultramarine	..	£25000
38	11	6d. rose (30.7.80)	..	£100 16·00

(b) P 10 (1881–90)

39	10	1d. dull blue (11.5.82)	..	40·00 3·00
		a. Ultramarine	..	13·00 2·75
		b. Cambridge blue (12.7.83)	..	40·00 3·25
40		2d. yellow-green (20.10.81)	..	9·00 1·00
		a. Blue-green	..	18·00 4·00
41		4d. on 1d. mauve (29.1.90)	..	28·00 18·00
42		4d. on 2d. mauve (A) (23.5.83)	65·00 9·00
		a. Dull purple	..	65·00 9·00
43		4d. on 2d. dull purple (B) (7.11.88)	.. £140
44		4d. mauve (13.9.90)	..	48·00
		a. Deep purple	..	48·00 50·00
45	11	6d. pale rose (11.3.85)	..	70·00 14·00
		a. Bright rose	..	14·00 14·00

(c) P 10 × 12½ (1881–82)

46	10	1d. ultramarine (11.5.82)	..	85·00 25·00
47		2d. green (20.10.81)	..	£160 45·00
48		6d. rose (20.10.81)	..	£325 40·00

(d) P 12½ × 10 (1888–90)

49	10	1d. ultramarine (1890)..	..	— £300
49a		2d. green (1888)	..	

(e) P 10 × *nearly* 12 (3.9.86)

50	10	1d. ultramarine..	..	60·00 8·50
51		2d. yellow-green	..	60·00 7·50

(f) P *nearly* 12 × 10 (1886–88)

51a	10	1d. dull blue (7.11.88)	..	£225 35·00
51b		2d. yellow-green (3.9.86)	..	
52	11	6d. rose (1887)	..	

(g) P 11 × 10 (1892–93)

53	10	1d. ultramarine (18.8.92)	..	9·50 7·00
54		4d. pale mauve (18.8.92)	..	8·00 8·50
55	11	6d. pale rose (14.2.93)	..	6·50 14·00
		a. Rose..	..	11·00 18·00

(h) P 11 (1897–99)

56	10	4d. mauve (14.7.96)	..	9·00 6·50
57	11	6d. dull rose (14.7.96)	..	25·00 35·00
		a. Printed both sides (12.99)	..	£900 £750
		b. Bright rose	..	35·00 35·00

(i) P 11 × *nearly* 12 (1896)*

58	10	4d. deep purple (14.7.96)	..	27·00
		a. Bright purple	..	7·50 6·50
59	11	6d. rose (23.7.96)	..	30·00
		a. Bright rose ..	..	7·00 3·75

(j) Imperf (1882–90)

60	10	1d. ultramarine		
61		2d. yellow-green		
62		4d. on 2d. pale mauve		
63	11	6d. rose		

*Under this heading are included stamps from several perforating machines with a gauge varying between 11·6 and 12.

No. 37b was printed in the colour of the 1d. in error. Only four examples have been reported, one of which was subsequently destroyed.

In the absence of detailed information on dates of issue printing dates are quoted for Nos. 35/63 and 76/103.

12   13

(Typo Govt Printing Office, Sydney)

1881–99. Paper-maker's name wmkd as previous issue.

(a) P 10 (19.10.81)
64	12	1s. pale brown	..	70·00	15·00
		a. Deep brown ..	..	70·00	17·00

(b) P 11 × 10 (1894)
65	12	1s. pale brown	..	35·00	35·00

(c) P 11 (1897)
66	12	1s. pale brown	..	32·00	14·00

(d) P 11 × nearly 12 (5.99)
67	12	1s. pale brown	..	30·00	9·00
		a. Brown		30·00	9·00
		b. Deep brown		45·00	45·00

(e) P nearly 12 × 11 (3.97)
68	12	1s. brown	..	45·00	40·00

Dates given of earliest known use.

Forgeries exist.

(Centre typo, frame litho Govt Printing Office, Sydney)

1882 (23 May). Toned paper wmkd with paper-maker's name "Cowan" in old English outline type once in each sheet. P 10.
69	13	5s. dull red and black	..	55·00	35·00

In July 1900, an electrotyped plate of a 5s. stamp was made and stamps were printed from it with pale orange-red centre and grey-black frame; these are known perf 10, perf nearly 12, and imperf. These stamps were sold as remainders with a special obliteration dated "15 Dec, 00," but were not issued for postal use. The design differs in many particulars from the issued stamp.

2½d. 2½d.
(14)   (15)

T 14. Fraction bar 1 mm from "2".
T 15. Fraction bar 2 mm from "2".

(Stamps typo in Sydney and surch at Govt Printing Office, Suva)

1891 (1 Jan). T 10 surch. P 10.
70	14	2½d. on 2d. green	..	..	40·00	48·00
71	15	2½d. on 2d. green	..	..	£130	£140

½d. 5d
(16)   (17)

FIVE **FIVE**
PENCE **PENCE**
(18) 2 mm spacing (19) 3 mm spacing

1892 (1 Mar)–93. P 10. (a) Surch on T 10.
72	16	½d. on 1d. dull blue	..	45·00	65·00
		a. Ultramarine	..	38·00	60·00
73	17	5d. on 4d. deep purple (25.7.92)	..	48·00	65·00
		a. Dull purple	..	48·00	65·00

(b) Surch on T 11
74	18	5d. on 6d. brownish rose (30.11.92)	..	55·00	65·00
		a. Bright rose	..	55·00	60·00
		b. Perf 10 × 12½			
75	19	5d. on 6d. rose (4.1.93)..	..	70·00	80·00
		a. Deep rose	..	60·00	70·00
		b. Brownish rose	..	60·00	

20   21 Native Canoe   22

(Typo in Sydney)

1891–1902. Wmk in sheet, either "SANDERSON" or "NEW SOUTH WALES GOVERNMENT" in outline capitals.

(a) P 10 (1891–94)
76	20	½d. slate-grey (26.4.92)..	..	4·00	3·50
77	21	1d. black (19.9.94)	..	7·00	3·75
78		2d. pale green (19.9.94)	..	90·00	9·50
79	22	2½d. chocolate (8.6.91)	..	32·00	12·00
80	21	5d. ultramarine (14.2.93)	..	75·00	48·00

(b) P 11 × 10 (1892–93)
81	20	½d. slate-grey (20.10.93)	..	4·25	12·00
82	21	1d. black (14.2.93)	..	4·75	2·50
83		2d. green (14.2.93)	..	8·50	3·50
84	22	2½d. chocolate (17.8.92)	..	19·00	18·00
		a. Brown	..	7·00	6·50
		b. Yellowish brown			
85	21	5d. ultramarine (14.2.93)	..	8·50	7·50

(c) P 11 (1893–96)
86	20	½d. slate-grey (2.6.96)	..	3·00	5·50
		a. Greenish slate	..	2·50	6·00
87	21	1d. black (31.10.95)	..	3·00	3·00
88		1d. pale mauve (2.6.96)	..	3·75	1·00
		a. Rosy mauve..	..	4·25	1·00
89		2d. dull green (17.3.94)	..	4·75	80
		a. Emerald-green	..	6·00	2·00
90	22	2½d. brown (31.10.95)	..	16·00	7·00
		a. Yellowish brown	..	13·00	14·00
91	21	ultramarine (14.2.93)	..	£250	

(d) P 10 × nearly 12 (1893–94)
93	21	1d. black (20.7.93)	..	12·00	5·50
94		2d. dull green (19.9.94)	..	£550	£275

(e) P nearly 12 × 10 (19.9.94)
94a	20	½d. pale grey	..	..	£250

(f) Perf nearly 12 (1894–98)
95	20	½d. greenish slate (19.9.94)	..	2·75	7·50
		a. Grey..	..	26·00	
96	21	1d. black (19.9.94)	..	£180	22·00
97		1d. rosy mauve (4.5.98)	..	4·75	6·50
98		2d. dull green (19.9.94)	..	85·00	35·00

(g) P 11 × nearly 12 (1895–97)
99	20	½d. greenish slate (8.10.97)	..	1·00	2·50
100	21	1d. black (31.10.95)	..	£325	
101		1d. rosy mauve (14.7.96)	..	3·75	80
		a. Pale rosy mauve	..	3·75	2·00
102		2d. dull green (26.7.97)	..	30·00	4·00
103	22	2½d. brown (26.7.97)	..	11·00	17·00
		a. Yellow-brown	..	5·00	5·00

(h) P nearly 12 × 11 (1897–98)
103b	20	½d. greenish slate (8.10.97)	..	4·00	
103c	21	1d. rosy mauve (10.2.97)	..	10·00	
103d		2d. dull green (4.5.98)	..	£200	

The 2½d. brown is known doubly printed, but only occurs in the remainders and with the special obliteration (Price £100 cancelled-to-order). It was never issued for postal use.

23   24

(Typo D.L.R.)

1903 (1 Feb). Wmk Crown CA. P 14.
104	23	½d. green and pale green	..	2·25	1·75
105		1d. dull purple and black/red ..		11·00	55
106	24	2d. dull purple and orange	..	3·25	1·25
107	23	2½d. dull purple and blue/blue ..		14·00	10·00
108		3d. dull purple and purple	..	1·50	60
109	24	4d. dull purple and black	..	1·50	2·50
110	23	5d. dull purple and green	..	1·50	5·00
111	24	6d. dull purple and carmine	..	1·50	2·50
112	23	1s. green and carmine	..	10·00	40·00
113	24	5s. green and black	..	38·00	90·00
114	23	£1 grey-black and ultramarine	..	£300	£375
104/14			Set of 11	£350	£450
104/14 Optd "Specimen"			Set of 11	£300	

1904–9. Wmk Mult Crown CA. Chalk-surfaced paper (1s.). P 14.
115	23	½d. green and pale green	..	8·50	3·00
116		1d. purple and black/red	..	18·00	10
117		1s. green and carmine (1909)	..	26·00	40·00
115/17			Set of 3	48·00	40·00

1906–12. Colours changed. Wmk Mult Crown CA. Chalk-surfaced paper (6d. to £1). P 14.
118	23	½d. green (1908)	..	10·00	3·25
119		1d. red (1906)	..	4·50	10
120		2½d. bright blue (1910)	..	5·00	7·50
121	24	6d. dull purple (1910)	..	8·00	20·00
122	23	1s. black/green (1911)	..	4·00	10·00
123	24	5s. green and red/yellow (1911)	..	45·00	50·00
124	23	£1 purple and black/red (1912)	..	£300	£325
118/24			Set of 7	£325	£375
119/24 Optd "Specimen"			Set of 6	£300	

Nos. 112/14, 117 and 120/4 are known with a forged registered postmark of Suva dated "10 DEC 1909".

25   26   WAR STAMP (27)

(Typo D.L.R.)

1912 (Oct)–23. Die I. Wmk Mult Crown CA. Chalk-surfaced paper (5d. to £1). P 14.
125	26	¼d. brown (1.4.16)	..	1·25	30
		a. Deep brown (1917)	..	1·00	40
		y. Wmk inverted and reversed			
126	25	½d. green	..	1·25	95
		a. Yellow-green (1916)	..	8·00	8·00
		b. Blue-green (1917)	..	1·25	50
		w. Wmk inverted	..	75·00	
		y. Wmk inverted and reversed	..	75·00	

127	25	1d. carmine	..	2·00	10
		a. Bright scarlet (1916)	..	2·00	75
		b. Deep rose (1916)	..	8·00	1·60
128	26	2d. greyish slate (5.14)	..	1·50	10
		a. Wmk sideways			
129	25	2½d. bright blue (5.14)	..	3·50	3·50
130		3d. purple/yellow (5.14)	..	3·75	4·25
		a. Wmk sideways	..	£350	£425
		b. On lemon (1915)	..	2·00	8·50
		c. On pale yellow (1921)	..	1·75	13·00
		ca. "A" of "CA" missing from wmk			
		cw. Wmk inverted			
		d. Die II. On pale yellow (1922)	..	2·50	24·00
131	26	4d. black and red/yellow (5.14)	..	20·00	19·00
		a. On lemon	..	4·00	15·00
		b. On orange-buff (1920)	..	50·00	65·00
		c. On pale yellow (1921)	..	8·00	14·00
		cw. Wmk inverted			
		d. Die II. On pale yellow (1922) (Optd S. £35)	..	3·75	18·00
132	25	5d. dull purple and olive-green (5.14)	..	5·50	10·00
133	26	6d. dull and bright purple (5.14)	..	2·00	5·00
134	25	1s. black/green (10.13)	..	1·25	14·00
		a. White back (4.14)	..	1·00	8·00
		b. On blue-green, olive back (1916)	..	4·75	10·00
		c. On emerald back (1921) (Optd S. £35)	..	5·00	28·00
135	26	2s. 6d. black and red/blue (19.1.16)	..	32·00	28·00
136		5s. green and red/yellow	..	32·00	40·00
137	25	£1 purple and black/red (5.14)	..	£250	£275
		a. Die II (1923)	..	£250	£275
125/37			Set of 13	£275	£325
125/37 Optd "Specimen"			Set of 13	£425	

1915 (1 Dec). Optd with T 27 by Govt Printer, Suva.
138	25	½d. blue-green	..	50	2·25
		a. Yellow-green	..	50	3·00
		b. Opt inverted	..	£500	
		c. Opt double			
139		1d. carmine	..	21·00	23·00
		a. Bright scarlet	..	1·25	75
		ab. Horiz pair, one without opt	..	£5000	
		c. Opt inverted	..	£650	
		d. Deep rose	..	1·60	1·60
138/9 H/S "Specimen"			Set of 2	£120	

No. 139ab occurred on one pane of 120 only, the overprint being so misplaced that all the stamps of the last vertical row escaped it entirely.

Nos. 140/227 are no longer used.

1922–29. Die II. Wmk Mult Script CA. Chalk-surfaced paper (1s. to 5s.). P 14.
228	26	¼d. deep brown (1923)	..	2·25	21·00
229	25	½d. green (1923)	..	75	2·00
		w. Wmk inverted			
230		1d. carmine-red	..	2·50	2·00
231		1d. violet (6.1.27)	..	1·25	10
232	26	1½d. scarlet (6.1.27)	..	4·00	3·25
233		2d. grey	..	1·25	10
		a. Face value omitted	..	£7000	
234	25	3d. bright blue (1924)	..	2·50	1·25
235	26	4d. black and red/lemon (1924)	..	5·00	7·00
		a. On pale yellow (1929)	..	29·00	24·00
236	25	5d. dull purple and sage-green (1927)	..	1·50	2·00
237	26	6d. dull and bright purple	..	2·00	1·25
238	25	1s. black/emerald (1924)	..	4·00	6·00
		w. Wmk inverted			
239	26	2s. purple and blue/blue (6.1.27)	..	28·00	55·00
240		2s. 6d. black and red/blue (1925)	..	11·00	32·00
241		5s. green and red/pale yellow (1926)	..	28·00	60·00
228/41			Set of 14	85·00	£170
228/41 Optd "Specimen"			Set of 14	£300	

The 2d. imperforate with watermark Type 10 of Ireland came from a trial printing and was not issued.

Only one example of No. 233a is known. It was caused by an obstruction during the printing of the duty plate.

1935 (6 May). Silver Jubilee. As Nos. 91/4 of Antigua.
242	26	1½d. deep blue and carmine	..	80	4·50
		a. Deep blue and aniline red	..	4·75	14·00
		b. Frame printed double, one albino	..	£1000	
		f. Diagonal line by turret	..	45·00	
		h. Dot by flagstaff	..	75·00	
		i. Dash by turret	..	75·00	
243		2d. ultramarine and grey	..	1·50	35
		f. Diagonal line by turret	..	60·00	
		g. Dot to left of chapel	..	95·00	
244		3d. brown and deep blue	..	2·50	3·00
		f. Diagonal line by turret	..	90·00	
		h. Dot by flagstaff	..	£130	
		i. Dash by turret	..	£130	
245		1s. slate and purple	..	4·50	4·25
		a. Frame printed double, one albino	..	£1500	
		f. Diagonal line by turret	..	£140	
242/5			Set of 4	8·50	11·00
242/5 Perf "Specimen"			Set of 4	85·00	

For illustrations of plate varieties see Catalogue Introduction.

1937 (12 May). Coronation. As Nos. 95/7 of Antigua. P 11 × 11½.
246	25	1d. purple	..	70	45
247		2d. grey-black	..	80	1·00
248		3d. Prussian blue	..	80	1·00
246/8			Set of 3	2·10	2·25
246/8 Perf "Specimen"			Set of 3	55·00	

PRICES OF SETS

Set prices are given for many issues, generally those containing three stamps or more. Definitive sets include one of each value or major colour change, but do not cover different perforations, die types or minor shades. Where a choice is possible the set prices are based on the cheapest versions of the stamps included in the listings.

King George VI - Fiji

Contact us for all your **King George VI** requirements; from basic stamps, varieties, perforations, in singles, multiples or sheets to listed shades and individual printings as per SG or the latest edition (17th) of **The Commonwealth King George VI Catalogue.**

This comprehensively revised work is the result of an 18-month overhaul of the old B & K King George VI Catalogue and is now published by Murray Payne Ltd.

Request our individually-tailored lists of specialised items, or a free copy of our newsletter **'Sixth *Sense*'**

P. O. Box 1135, Axbridge, Somerset, England BS26 2EW
Telephone (01934) 732511 Fax: (01934) 733498
Email: murraypayne@compuserve.com

THE WORLD'S LEADING RANGE OF CATALOGUES, ALBUMS & ACCESSORIES

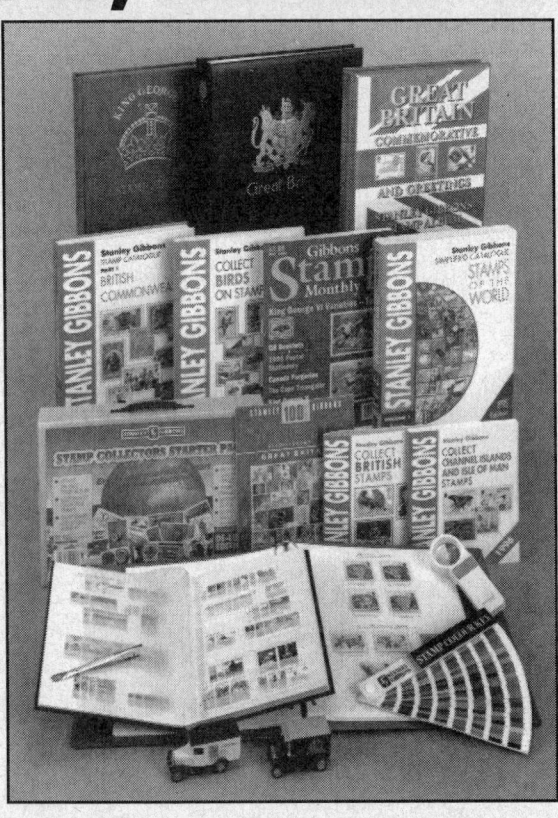

- FREE 32 PAGE COLOUR BROCHURE
- FAST AND EFFICIENT WORLD-WIDE DESPATCH
- FREE 24 HOUR TELEPHONE ORDER HOTLINE
- FREE P&P ON UK ORDERS OVER £30
- REGULAR SPECIAL OFFERS
- FREE CUSTOMER NEWSLETTER

...DELIVERED DIRECT TO YOUR DOOR

Phone **0800 611622** for your free colour brochure today

• THE COLLECTOR'S CHOICE •

Stanley Gibbons Publications
5 Parkside, Christchurch Road, Ringwood, Hampshire BH24 3SH England
Tel: +44 (0) 1425 472363
Fax: +44 (0) 1425 470247
e.mail sales@stangib.demon.co.uk

28 Native sailing Canoe　　**29** Native Village

30 Camakua (canoe)　　**31** Map of Fiji Islands

Two Dies of Type **30**:

Die I　　Die II
Empty Canoe　Native in Canoe

Two Dies of Type **31**:

Die I　　Die II
Without "180°"　With "180°"

Extra palm frond
(R. 5/8)

Extra line (R. 2/1)

Spur on arms medallion (Pl 2
R. 4/2) (ptg of 26 Nov 1945)

(Des V. E. Ousey (½d., 1s., 2s. 6d.), Miss C. D. Lovejoy (1d., 1½d.,
5d.), Miss I. Stinson (3d., 5s.) and A. V. Guy (2d. (Nos. 253/4),
2½d., 6d., 2s.). Recess De La Rue (½d., 1½d., 2d., (Nos.
253/5a), 2½d., 6d., 8d., 1s. 5d., 1s. 6d.), Waterlow (others))

1938 (5 Apr)–**1955.** *T* **28**/**31** *and similar designs. Wmk Mult Script
CA. Various perfs.*

249	28	½d. green (*p* 13½)		20	50
		a. Perf 14 (5.41)		20·00	3·50
		b. Perf 12 (8.48)		55	2·50
		ba. Extra palm frond		32·00	
250	29	1d. brown and blue (*p* 12½)		40	20
251	30	1½d. carmine (Die I) (*p* 13½)		15·00	35
252		1½d. carmine (Die II) (*p* 13½) (1.10.40)	1·40	2·75
		a. *Deep carmine* (10.42)		3·75	1·25
		b. Perf 14 (6.42)		18·00	17·00
		c. Perf 12 (21.7.49)		90	1·25

253	31	2d. brown and green (Die I) (*p* 13½)	38·00	40
		a. Extra line	..	£250	40·00
254		2d. brown & green (Die II) (*p* 13½) (1.10.40)	16·00	16·00
255	–	2d. grn & magenta (*p* 13½) (19.5.42)	40	60
		a. Perf 12 (27.5.46)		55	70
256	31	2½d. brown & grn (Die II) (*p* 14) (6.1.42)	60	75
		a. Perf 13½ (1.44)		70	70
		b. Perf 12 (19.1.48)		70	50
257	–	3d. blue (*p* 12½)		1·00	30
		a. Spur on arms medallion	£130	
258	–	5d. blue and scarlet (*p* 12½)	42·00	10·00
259	–	5d. yell-green & scar (*p* 12½) (1.10.40)	20	30
260	31	6d. black (Die I) (*p* 13×12)	60·00	12·00
261		6d. black (Die II) (*p* 13½) (1.10.40)	3·00	1·75
		a. *Violet-black* (1.44)	25·00	26·00
		b. Perf 12. *Black* (5.6.47)	1·50	1·25
261c		8d. carmine (*p* 14) (15.11.48)	1·00	1·00
		d. Perf 13 (7.6.50)		70	2·50
262	–	1s. black and yellow (*p* 12½)	75	60
263	–	1s. 5d. black & carm (*p* 14) (13.6.40)	20	10
263a		1s. 6d. ultramarine (*p* 14) (1.8.50)	4·50	2·50
		b. Perf 13 (16.2.55)	1·25	15·00
264	–	2s. violet and orange (*p* 12½)	2·50	40
265	–	2s. 6d. green and brown (*p* 12½)	2·50	1·50
266	–	5s. green and purple (*p* 12½)	2·50	1·50
266a	–	10s. orange & emer (*p* 12½) (13.3.50)	32·00	40·00
266b	–	£1 ultram & carm (*p* 12½) (13.3.50)	48·00	50·00
249/66b				*Set of* 22	£250	£120

249/66 excl 261c and 263a Perf
"Specimen" .. .. *Set of* 18　£450

Designs: *Horiz* (as *T* **30**)—2d. (Nos. 255/a) Government Offices.
(As *T* **29**)—3d. Canoe and arms of Fiji; 8d., 1s. 5d., 1s. 6d. Arms of
Fiji; 2s. Suva Harbour; 2s. 6d. River scene; 5s. Chief's hut. *Vert* (as
T **29**)—5d. Sugar cane; 1s. Spearing fish by torchlight; 10s. Paw-
paw Tree; £1 Police bugler.

2½d.

(42)

1941 (10 Feb). *No.* 254 *surch with T* **42** *by Govt Printer, Suva.*
267　31　2½d. on 2d. brown and green .. 55　20

1946 (17 Aug). *Victory. As Nos.* 110/11 *of Antigua.*
268	2½d. green		10	60
	a. Printed double, one albino	..	£250	
269	3d. blue		10	10

268/9 Perf "Specimen" .. .. *Set of* 2　60·00

1948 (17 Dec). *Royal Silver Wedding. As Nos.* 112/13 *of
Antigua.*
270	2½d. green	..	40	75
271	5s. violet-blue	..	14·00	6·50

1949 (10 Oct). *75th Anniv of U.P.U. As Nos.* 114/17 *of Antigua.*
272	2d. bright reddish purple	..	50	30
273	3d. deep blue	..	2·25	1·75
274	8d. carmine-red	..	60	1·25
275	1s. 6d. blue	..	60	1·00
272/5 ..		..	*Set of* 4	3·50	3·75

43 Children Bathing　　**44** Rugby Football

(Recess B.W.)

1951 (17 Sept). *Health Stamps. Wmk Mult Script CA. P* 13½.
276	43	1d. + 1d. brown	..	10	50
277	44	2d. + 1d. green	..	30	50

1953 (2 June). *Coronation. As No.* 120 *of Antigua.*
278　2½d. black and green .. 　50　30

45 Arms of Fiji

(Recess D.L.R.)

1953 (16 Dec). *Royal Visit. Wmk Mult Script CA. P* 13.
279　45　8d. deep carmine-red .. .. 15　15

NEW INFORMATION

The editor is always interested to correspond with
people who have new information that will
improve or correct the Catalogue.

---

46 Queen Elizabeth II　　**47** Government Offices
(after Annigoni)

48 Loading Copra　　**49** Sugar Cane Train

50 Preparing Bananas for Export　**51** Gold Industry

(Des V. E. Ousey (½d., 1s., 2s. 6d.), A. V. Guy (6d.). Recess D.L.R.
(½d., 2d., 6d., 8d.), Waterlow (1s., 2s. 6d., 10s., £1) B.W. (others))

1954 (1 Feb)–59. *T* **46**/**51** *and similar designs previously used
for King George VI issue (but with portrait of Queen Elizabeth
II as in T* **47**). *Wmk Mult Script CA. P* 12 (2d.), 13 (8d.), 12½
(6d., 1s., 2s. 6d., 10s., £1), 11½×11 (3d., 1s. 6d., 2s., 5s.) *or*
11½ (½d., 1d., 1½d., 2½d.).

280	–	½d. myrtle-green (1.7.54)	..	15	80
281	46	1d. turquoise-blue (1.6.56)	..	75	10
282	–	1½d. sepia (1.10.56)	..	50	30
283	47	2d. green and magenta	..	1·25	90
284	46	2½d. blue-violet (1.10.56)	..	85	10
285	48	3d. brown and reddish violet (1.10.56)	2·00	20
		a. *Brown & dp reddish vio* (10.11.59)	5·00	50
287	–	6d. black (1.7.54)	..	2·00	65
288	–	8d. deep carmine-red (1.7.54)	..	1·50	1·50
		a. *Carmine-lake* (6.3.58)	..	5·00	1·75
289	–	1s. black and yellow	..	2·00	10
290	49	1s. 6d. blue and myrtle-green (1.10.56)	17·00	90
291	50	2s. black and carmine (1.10.56)	..	5·50	30
292	–	2s. 6d. bluish green and brown	..	1·25	40
		a. *Bluish green & red-brown* (14.9.54)	1·25	10
293	51	5s. ochre and blue (1.10.56)	..	25·00	1·25
294	–	10s. orange and emerald (1.7.54)	..	12·00	20·00
295	–	£1 ultramarine and carmine (1.7.54)	42·00	18·00
280/95			*Set of* 15	£100	40·00

Designs: *Vert* (22½ × 36 *mm*)—½d. Fijians sailing canoe. (25
× 31 *mm*)—1s. Spearing fish by torchlight; 10s. Paw-paw tree; £1
Police bugler. *Horiz* (36 × 22½ *mm*)—6d. Map of Fiji. (31 × 25
mm)—8d. Arms of Fiji; 2s. 6d. River scene.

52 River Scene

53 Cross of Lorraine

(Recess B.W.)

1954 (1 Apr). *Health Stamps. Wmk Mult Script CA. P* 11 × 11½.
296	52	1½d. + ½d. bistre-brown and green	..	10	50
297	53	2½d. + ½d. orange and black	..	10	10

54　　　　**55** Fijian beating Lali
Queen Elizabeth II
(after Annigoni)

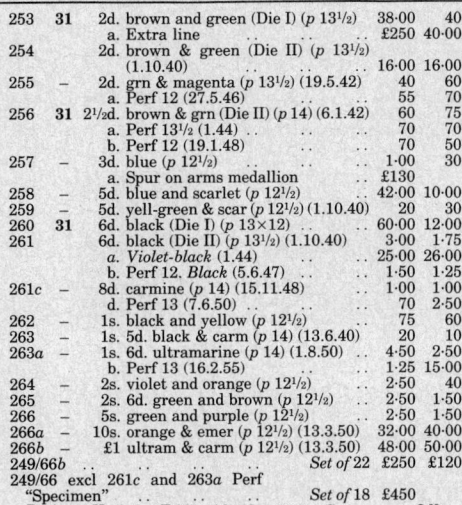

56 Hibiscus　　**60** Red Shining Parrot

(Des M. Goaman: Photo Harrison (8d., 4s.). Recess. B.W. (others))

1959–63. T **54/6, 60** *and similar designs. Wmk Mult Script CA.* P 11½ (T **46** *and* **54**), 11½ × 11 (6d., 10d., 1s., 2s. 6d., 10s., £1), 14½ × 14 (8d.) *or* 14 × 14½ (4s.).

298	46	½d. emerald-green (14.11.61)	15	60
299	54	1d. deep ultramarine (3.12.62)	1·25	80
300		1½d. sepia (3.12.62)	1·25	30
301	46	2d. rose-red (14.11.61)	50	10
302		2½d. orange-brown (3.12.62)	1·50	2·25
303	55	6d. carmine and black (14.11.61)	1·00	10
304	56	8d. scarlet, yellow, green & blk (1.8.61)	1·75	50
305	—	10d. brown and carmine (1.4.63)	1·75	50
306	—	1s. light blue and blue (14.11.61)	50	10
307	—	2s. 6d. black and purple (14.11.61)	12·00	10
308	60	4s. red, green, blue & slate-grn (13.7.59)	1·75	1·75
309	—	10s. emerald and deep sepia (14.11.61)	6·50	3·00
310	—	£1 black and orange (14.11.61)	22·00	5·50
298/310		Set of 13	45·00	13·00

Designs: *Horiz* (as T **55**)—10d. Yaqona ceremony; 1s. Location map; 2s. 6d. Nadi Airport; 10s. Cutting sugar-cane; £1 Arms of Fiji.
Nos. 299 and 311 have turtles either side of "Fiji" instead of shells.

63 Queen Elizabeth II

64 International Dateline

65 White Orchid   66 Orange Dove

(Des M. Goaman. Photo Harrison (3d., 9d. 1s. 6d., 2s., 4s., 5s.). Recess B.W. (others))

1962 (3 Dec)–**67.** W w **12** (*upright*). P 11½ (1d., 2d.), 12½ (3d.), 11½ × 11 (10d., 1s., 2s. 6d., 10s., £1), 14½ × 14 (9d., 2s.) *or* 14 × 14½ (1s. 6d., 4s., 5s.).

311	54	1d. deep ultramarine (14.1.64)	70	2·00
312	46	2d. rose-red (3.8.65)	45	10
313	63	3d. multicoloured	25	10
		w. Wmk inverted		
314	55	6d. carmine and black (9.6.64)	2·00	10
315	56	9d. scarlet, yellow, grn & ultram (1.4.64)	90	65
316	—	10d. brown and carmine (14.1.64)	60	50
317	—	1s. light blue and blue (24.1.66*)	2·50	45
318	64	1s. 6d. red, yellow, gold, black & blue	2·75	90
		a. Error. Wmk sideways	£650	
319	65	2s. yellow-green, green and copper	16·00	2·50
		a. Apple-green, grn & copper (16.5.67)	23·00	3·25
320	—	2s. 6d. black and purple (3.8.65)	2·00	60
		a. Black and deep purple (8.67)	1·75	60
321	60	4s. red, yellow-green, blue & grn (1.4.64)	5·50	2·75
322		4s. red, green, blue & slate-grn (1.3.66)	2·50	3·50
323	66	5s. red, yellow and grey	14·00	35
		w. Wmk inverted	£110	
324	—	10s. emerald and deep sepia (14.1.64)	7·00	6·00
325	—	£1 black and orange (9.6.64)	18·00	11·00
311/25		Set of 15	65·00	28·00

Designs: *Horiz* (as T **55**)—10d. Yaqona Ceremony; 1s. Location map; 2s. 6d. Nadi Airport; 10s. Cutting sugar-cane; £1 Arms of Fiji.
*This is the earliest known used date in Fiji and it was not released by the Crown Agents until 1 November.
The 3d. value exists with PVA gum as well as gum arabic.
For 4s. with watermark sideways see No. 359.

ROYAL VISIT

1963   ROYAL VISIT 1963

(67)   (68)

1963 (1 Feb). *Royal Visit.* Nos. 313 and 306 *optd with* T **67/8**.

326	67	3d. multicoloured	20	10
327	68	1s. light blue and blue	20	10

1963 (4 June). *Freedom from Hunger. As No. 146 of Antigua.*

328	2s. ultramarine	2·50	70

69 Running   (73 C.S. *Retriever*.)

(Des M. Goaman. Photo Harrison)

1963 (6 Aug). *First South Pacific Games, Suva.* T **69** *and similar designs.* W w **12.** P 14½.

329	3d. red-brown, yellow and black		25	10
330	9d. red-brown, violet and black		35	90
331	1s. red-brown, green and black		35	10
332	2s. 6d. red-brown, light blue and black		90	90
329/32		Set of 4	1·75	1·75

Designs: *Vert*—9d. Throwing the discus; 1s. Hockey. *Horiz*—2s. 6d. High-jumping.

1963 (2 Sept). *Red Cross Centenary. As Nos. 147/8 of Antigua.*

333	2d. red and black		50	10
334	2s. red and blue		2·00	2·00

1963 (3 Dec). *Opening of COMPAC (Trans-Pacific Telephone Cable). No. 317 optd with* T **73** *by B.W.*

335	1s. light blue and blue		30	10

74 Jamborette Emblem   75 Scouts of Three Races

(Des V. Whiteley assisted by Norman L. Joe, Asst. D.C., Fiji Scouts for Jamboree emblem. Photo Harrison)

1964 (4 Aug). *50th Anniv of Fijian Scout Movement.* W w **12.** P 12½.

336	74	3d. multicoloured	15	20
337	75	1s. violet and yellow-brown	15	25

76 Flying-boat *Aotearoa*   78 *Aotearoa* and Map

(Des V. Whiteley. Photo Harrison)

1964 (24 Oct). *25th Anniv of First Fiji-Tonga Airmail Service.* T **76, 78** *and similar design.* W w **12.** P 14½ × 14 (1s.) *or* 12½ (*others*).

338	3d. black and vermilion		40	10
339	6d. vermilion and bright blue		70	85
340	1s. black and turquoise-blue		70	85
338/40		Set of 3	1·60	1·60

Design: *Vert* (as T **76**)—6d. De Havilland D.H.114 Heron 2.

1965 (17 May). *I.T.U. Centenary. As Nos. 166/7 of Antigua.*

341	3d. blue and rose-carmine		35	10
342	2s. orange-yellow and bistre		80	25

1965 (25 Oct). *International Co-operation Year. As Nos. 168/9 of Antigua.*

343	2d. reddish purple and turquoise-green		20	10
344	2s. 6d. deep bluish green and lavender		60	25

1966 (24 Jan). *Churchill Commemoration. As Nos. 170/3 of Antigua.*

345	3d. new blue		70	10
346	9d. deep green		90	40
347	1s. brown		90	10
348	2s. 6d. bluish violet		1·00	50
345/8		Set of 4	3·25	1·00

1966 (1 July). *World Cup Football Championships. As Nos. 176/7 of Antigua.*

349	2d. violet, yellow-green, lake & yellow-brn		20	10
350	2s. chocolate, blue-green, lake & yellow-brn		50	20

79 H.M.S. *Pandora* approaching Split Island, Rotuma

(Des V. Whiteley. Photo Enschedé)

1966 (29 Aug). *175th Anniv of Discovery of Rotuma.* T **79** *and similar horiz designs. Multicoloured.* W w **12** (*sideways*). P 14 × 13.

351	3d. Type **79**		25	10
352	10d. Rotuma Chiefs		25	10
353	1s. 6d. Rotumans welcoming H.M.S. *Pandora*		35	20
351/3		Set of 3	75	30

1966 (20 Sept). *Inauguration of W.H.O. Headquarters, Geneva. As Nos. 178/9 of Antigua.*

354	6d. black, yellow-green and light blue		1·00	20
355	2s. 6d. black, light purple and yellow-brown		2·50	1·25

ALTERED CATALOGUE NUMBERS

Any Catalogue numbers altered from the last edition are shown as a list in the introductory pages.

---

82 Running

(Des V. Whiteley. Photo Harrison)

1966 (5 Dec*). *2nd South Pacific Games, Nouméa.* T **82** *and similar designs.* W w **12** (*sideways on* 9d.). P 14½ × 14 (9d.) *or* 14 × 14½ (*others*).

356	3d. black, chestnut and yellow-olive		10	10
357	9d. black, chestnut and greenish blue		15	15
358	1s. multicoloured		15	15
356/8		Set of 3	30	30

Designs: *Vert*—9d. Putting the shot. *Horiz*—1s. Diving.
*These were not released in London until 8.12.66.

1967 (16 Feb). *As No. 321 but wmk* w **12** *sideways.*

359	60	4s. red, yellow-green, blue and green	3·25	1·25

85 Military Forces Band

(Des G. Vasarhelyi. Photo Enschedé)

1967 (20 Oct). *International Tourist Year.* T **85** *and similar horiz designs. Multicoloured.* W w **12** (*sideways*). P 14 × 13.

360	3d. Type **85**		40	10
361	9d. Reef diving		20	10
362	1s. Beqa fire walkers		20	10
363	2s. *Oriana* (cruise liner) at Suva		55	15
360/3		Set of 4	1·25	30

89 Bligh (bust), H.M.S. *Providence* and Chart   91 Bligh's Tomb

90 "*Bounty*'s longboat being chased in Fiji waters"

(Des V. Whiteley. Photo Harrison)

1967 (11 Dec). *150th Death Anniv of Admiral Bligh.* W w **12** (*sideways on* 1s.). P 12½ × 13 (1s.) *or* 15 × 14 (*others*).

364	89	4d. multicoloured	10	10
365	90	1s. multicoloured	10	10
366	91	2s. 6d. multicoloured	15	15
364/6		Set of 3	30	30

92 Simmonds Spartan Seaplane

(Des V. Whiteley. Photo Harrison)

1968 (5 June). *40th Anniv of Kingsford Smith's Pacific Flight via Fiji.* T **92** *and similar horiz designs.* W w **12.** P 14 × 14½.

367	2d. black and green		15	10
368	6d. greenish blue, black and lake		15	10
369	1s. deep violet and turquoise-green		20	10
370	2s. orange-brown and blue		30	15
367/70		Set of 4	70	30

Designs—6d. Hawker Siddeley H.S.748 and airline insignias; 1s. Fokker F.VIIa/3M *Southern Cross* and crew; 2s. Lockheed 8D Altair *Lady Southern Cross* monoplane.

96 Bure Huts   97 Eastern Reef Heron (after Belcher)

98 Sea Snake   99 Queen Elizabeth and Arms of Fiji

(Des G. Hamori (½d., 1d., 9d.), W. O. Cernohorsky (2d., 4s.) H. S. Robinson (4d., 10d.), D. W. Blair (6d., 5s.), P. D. Clarke (1s.), G. Vasarhelyi (2s. 6d.), W. O. Cernohorsky and E. Jones (3s.), E. Jones and G. Hamori (10s.), E. Jones (£1). Adapted V. Whiteley. Photo D.L.R.)

1968 (15 July). *T 96/9 and similar designs. W w 12 (sideways on all vert designs). P 14 × 13½ (2s., 2s. 6d., 5s., £1), 13½ × 14 (3d., 1s., 1s. 6d., 4s., 10s.) or 13½ × 13 (others).*

371	½d. multicoloured		10	10
372	1d. deep greenish blue, red and yellow		10	10
373	2d. new blue, brown and ochre		10	10
374	3d. blackish green, blue and ochre		35	10
375	4d. multicoloured		80	30
376	6d. multicoloured		25	10
377	9d. multicoloured		15	30
378	10d. royal blue, orange and blackish brown		1·25	20
379	1s. Prussian blue and brown-red		20	10
380	1s. 6d. multicoloured		3·25	3·75
381	2s. turquoise, black and rosine		75	2·00
382	2s. 6d. multicoloured		75	75
383	3s. multicoloured		2·75	6·00
384	4s. yellow-ochre, black and olive		6·00	2·75
385	5s. multicoloured		3·00	2·50
386	10s. lake-brown, black and ochre		1·50	3·50
387	£1 multicoloured		1·50	6·00
371/87		*Set of 17*	14·00	26·00

Designs: *Horiz (as T 96)*—1d. Passion Flowers; 2d. Chambered or Pearly Nautilus; 4d. *Psilogramma jordana* (moth); 6d. Pennant Coralfish; 9d. Bamboo raft; 10d. *Asota woodfordi* (moth); 3s. Golden Cowrie shell. *Vert (as T 97)*—1s. Black Marlin; 1s. 6d. Orange-breasted Honeyeaters (after Belcher); 4s. Mining industry; 10s. Ceremonial whale's tooth. *Horiz (as T 98)*—2s. 6d. Outrigger canoes; 5s. Bamboo Orchids.

113 Map of Fiji, W.H.O. Emblem and Nurses

(Des V. Whiteley. Litho D.L.R.)

1968 (9 Dec). *20th Anniv of World Health Organization. T 113 and similar horiz designs. Multicoloured. W w 12 (sideways). P 14.*

388	3d. Type 113		15	10
389	9d. Transferring patient to Medical Ship *Vuniwai*		20	10
390	3s. Recreation		25	20
388/90		*Set of 3*	55	30

(New Currency. 100 cents = 1 dollar.)

116 Passion Flowers   117 Fijian Soldiers overlooking the Solomon Islands

1969 (13 Jan)–**70**. *Decimal Currency. Designs as Nos. 371/87, but with values inscr in decimal currency as T 116. W w 12 (sideways on vert designs) Chalk-surfaced paper. P 14 × 13½ (20, 25, 50 c. $2) 13½ × 14 (3, 10, 15, 40 c., $1) or 13½ × 13 (others).*

391	116	1 c. deep greenish blue, red and yellow..		10	10
392	—	2 c. new blue, brown and ochre (as 2d.)..		10	10
393	97	3 c. blackish green, blue and ochre		30	10
394	—	4 c. multicoloured (as 4d.)		1·50	
395	—	5 c. multicoloured (as 6d.)		20	10
396	96	6 c. multicoloured		10	10
397	—	8 c. multicoloured (as 9d.)		10	10
398		9 c. royal blue, orange and blackish brown (as 10d.)		1·50	1·00
399	—	10 c. Prussian blue and brown-red (as 1s.)		20	10
400	—	15 c. multicoloured (as 1s. 6d.)		9·00	3·75
401	98	20 c. turquoise, black and rosine		1·00	80
402	—	25 c. multicoloured (as 2s. 6d.)		1·00	30
403	—	30 c. multicoloured (as 3s.)		6·50	1·75
404	—	40 c. yellow-ochre, black and olive (as 4s.)		5·50	4·00
405	—	50 c. multicoloured (as 5s.)		4·50	30
		a. Glazed, ordinary paper (3.9.70)		9·00	1·50
406	—	$1 lake-brown, black and ochre (as 10s.)		2·00	60
		a. Glazed, ordinary paper (3.9.70)		5·00	3·50
407	99	$2 multicoloured		2·00	4·00
391/407			*Set of 17*	25·00	14·00

(Des G. Drummond. Photo Harrison)

1969 (23 June). *25th Anniv of Fijian Military Forces' Solomons Campaign. T 117 and similar horiz designs. W w 12. P 14.*

408	3 c. yellow-brown, black and bright emerald		20	10
409	10 c. multicoloured		25	10
410	25 c. multicoloured		35	20
408/10		*Set of 3*	70	30

Designs:—10 c. Regimental Flags and Soldiers in full dress and battledress; 25 c. Cpl. Sefanaia Sukanaivalu and Victoria Cross.

120 Javelin Thrower   123 Map of South Pacific and "Mortar-board"

(Des L. Curtis. Photo Harrison)

1969 (18 Aug). *3rd South Pacific Games. Port Moresby. T 120 and similar vert designs. W w 12 (sideways*). P 14½×14.*

411	4 c. black, brown and vermilion		10	10
	w. Wmk Crown to right of CA		3·00	
412	8 c. black, grey and new blue		10	10
413	20 c. multicoloured		20	20
411/13		*Set of 3*	30	30

Designs:—8 c. Yachting; 20 c. Games medal and winners' rostrum.

**The normal sideways watermark shows Crown to left of CA, as seen from the back of the stamp.*

(Des G. Drummond. Photo Harrison)

1969 (10 Nov). *Inauguration of University of the South Pacific. T 123 and similar horiz designs. Multicoloured. W w 12. P 14 × 15.*

414	2 c. Type 123		10	15
415	8 c. R.N.Z.A.F. badge and Short S.25 Sunderland flying boat over Laucala Bay (site of University)		15	10
416	25 c. Science students at work		25	15
	w. Wmk inverted		2·00	1·50
414/16		*Set of 3*	45	30

ROYAL VISIT 1970

(126)   127 Chaulmugra Tree, Makogai

1970 (4 Mar). *Royal Visit. Nos. 392, 399 and 402 optd with T 126.*

417	2 c. new blue, brown and ochre		10	20
418	10 c. Prussian blue and brown-red		10	10
419	25 c. multicoloured		20	10
417/19		*Set of 3*	35	30

(Des G. Drummond. Photo Harrison)

1970 (25 May). *Closing of Leprosy Hospital, Makogai. T 127 and similar designs. W w 12 (sideways* on 10 c.). P 14×14½.*

420	2 c. multicoloured		20	10
421	10 c. pale turquoise-green and black		20	10
	a. Pair. Nos. 421/2		40	20
	w. Wmk Crown to right of CA		4·00	
422	10 c. turquoise-blue, black and magenta		20	10
	w. Wmk Crown to right of CA		4·00	
423	30 c. multicoloured		35	50
420/3		*Set of 4*	70	70

Designs: *Vert*—No. 421, "Cascade" (Semisi Maya); No. 422, "Sea Urchins" (Semisi Maya). *Horiz*—No. 423, Makogai Hospital.

**The normal sideways watermark shows Crown to left of CA, as seen from the back of the stamp.*

Nos. 421/2 were printed together, *se-tenant*, throughout the sheet.

131 Abel Tasman and Log, 1643

(Des V. Whiteley. Litho D.L.R.)

1970 (18 Aug). *Explorers and Discoverers. T 131 and similar horiz designs. W w 12 (sideways*). P 13×12½.*

424	2 c. black, brown and turquoise		40	25
	w. Wmk Crown to right of CA		42·00	
425	3 c. multicoloured		1·00	25
426	8 c. multicoloured		1·00	15
427	25 c. multicoloured		1·00	15
424/7		*Set of 4*	3·00	70

Designs:—3 c. Captain Cook and H.M.S. *Endeavour*, 1774; 8 c. Captain Bligh and longboat, 1789; 25 c. Fijian and ocean-going canoe.

**The normal sideways watermark shows Crown to left of CA, as seen from the back of the stamp.*

MINIMUM PRICE

The minimum price quote is 10p which represents a handling charge rather than a basis for valuing common stamps. For further notes about prices see introductory pages.

INDEPENDENT

135 King Cakobau and Cession Stone   139 1d. and 6d. Stamps of 1870

(Des J.W. Litho Format)

1970 (10 Oct). *Independence. T 135 and similar horiz designs. Multicoloured. W w 12 (sideways). P 14.*

428	2 c. Type 135		10	10
429	3 c. Children of the World		10	10
430	10 c. Prime Minister and Fijian flag		10	10
431	25 c. Dancers in costume		20	20
428/31		*Set of 4*	30	30

The design for the 10 c. value does not incorporate the Queen's head profile.

(Des V. Whiteley. Photo Harrison)

1970 (2 Nov). *Stamp Centenary. T 139 and similar horiz designs. Multicoloured. W w 12 (sideways on 15 c.). P 14½ × 14.*

432	4 c. Type 139		15	10
433	15 c. Fijian stamps of all reigns (61×21 mm)		40	15
434	20 c. *Fiji Times* office and modern G.P.O.		40	15
	w. Wmk inverted		40·00	
432/4		*Set of 3*	85	35

140 Grey-backed White Eye   141 Masked Shining Parrot

(Des G. Drummond. Litho Questa)

1971 (6 Aug)–**72**. *Birds and Flowers. Vert designs as T 140/1. Multicoloured. W w 12 (upright).*

(a) Size as T 140. P 13½×14

435	1 c. *Cirrhopetalum umbellatum* (4.1.72)		15	30
436	2 c. Cardinal Honeyeater (22.11.71)		10	10
437	3 c. *Calanthe furcata* (23.6.72)		85	20
438	4 c. *Bulbophyllum sp nov* (23.6.72)		75	60
439	5 c. Type 140		35	10
	w. Wmk inverted		—	5·00
440	6 c. *Phaius tancarvilliae* (23.6.72)		5·50	2·75
441	8 c. Blue-headed Flycatcher (22.11.71)		35	10
442	10 c. *Acanthephippium vitiense* (4.1.72)		40	10
443	15 c. *Dendrobium tokai* (23.6.72)		5·00	1·25
444	20 c. Slaty Flycatcher		90	30

(b) Size as T 141. P 14

445	25 c. Yellow-faced Honeyeater (22.11.71)		2·25	20
446	30 c. *Dendrobium gordonii* (4.1.72)		9·00	90
447	40 c. Type 141		4·50	50
448	50 c. White-throated Pigeon		3·50	50
449	$1 Collared Lory (22.11.71)		4·00	1·25
450	$2 *Dendrobium platygastrium* (4.1.72)		5·00	11·00
435/50		*Set of 16*	38·00	17·00

See also Nos. 459/73 and 505/20.

142 Women's Basketball   143 Community Education

(Des R. Granger Barrett. Litho Questa)

1971 (6 Sept). *Fourth South Pacific Games, Tahiti. T 142 and similar vert designs. W w 12. P 14.*

451	8 c. multicoloured		10	10
452	10 c. cobalt, black and brown		10	10
453	25 c. pale turquoise-green, black and brown		30	25
451/3		*Set of 3*	45	30

Designs:—10c. Running; 25 c. Weightlifting.

(Des V. Whiteley. Litho Questa)

1972 (7 Feb). *25th Anniv of South Pacific Commission. T 143 and similar vert designs. Multicoloured. W w 12. P 14.*

454	2 c. Type 143		10	10
455	4 c. Public Health		10	10
456	50 c. Economic Growth		35	65
454/6		*Set of 3*	40	70

144 "Native Canoe" 145 Flowers, Conch and Ceremonial Whale's Tooth

(Des locally and adapted by A. B. New. Litho Questa)

1972 (10 Apr). *South Pacific Festival of Arts, Suva.* W w **12**. P 14.
457	144	10 c. black, orange and new blue			10	10

1972 (17 Nov)–74. *As Nos. 436/41, 443/5 and 447/50, but W w 12 (sideways*).*
459	2 c. Cardinal Honey-eater (12.12.73)	..	45	8·00
460	3 c. *Calanthe furcata* (8.3.73)	..	1·75	45
	w. Wmk Crown to left of CA (15.3.74)	..	1·75	80
461	4 c. *Bulbophyllum sp nov* (11.4.73)	..	6·00	45
462	5 c. Type **140** (8.3.73)	..	4·00	1·75
	w. Wmk Crown to right of CA	..	6·50	
463	6 c. *Phaius tancarvilliae* (11.4.73)	..	6·00	1·25
464	8 c. Blue-crested Broadbill (11.4.73)	..	3·75	75
466	15 c. *Dendrobium tokai* (11.4.73)	..	3·50	2·25
467	20 c. Slaty Flycatcher	..	13·00	2·00
468	25 c. Kandavu Honey-eater (11.4.73)	..	1·75	90
470	40 c. Type **141** (15.3.74)	..	3·00	4·00
471	50 c. White-throated Pigeon (15.3.74)	..	3·00	3·50
472	$1 Collared Lory	..	5·00	6·50
473	$2 *Dendrobium platygastrium*	..	7·00	7·00
459/73		*Set of 13*	50·00	35·00

*The normal sideways watermark shows Crown to right of CA on the 3 c. and Crown to left of CA on the remainder, *as seen from the back of the stamp.*

(Des (from photograph by D. Groves) and photo Harrison)

1972 (20 Nov). *Royal Silver Wedding. Multicoloured; background colour given.* W w **12**. P 14 × 14½.
474	10 c. slate-green	..	..	20	15
475	25 c. bright purple	..	..	30	15
	a. Blue printing omitted*		..	£200	

*The omission of the blue colour results in the Duke's suit appearing brown instead of deep blue.

HURRICANE RELIEF +10 c

(146) 147 Line Out

1972 (4 Dec). *Hurricane Relief. Nos. 400 and 403 surch as T 146, by the Reserve Bank of Australia.*
476	15 c. + 5 c. multicoloured	..	15	15
477	30 c. + 10 c. multicoloured	..	15	15

(Des J.W. Litho Questa)

1973 (9 Mar). *Diamond Jubilee of Fiji Rugby Union. T 147 and similar vert designs. Multicoloured.* W w **12** (sideways). P 14.
478	2 c. Type **147**	..	20	1·10
479	8 c. Body tackle	..	35	10
480	25 c. Conversion	..	80	40
478/80		*Set of 3*	1·25	1·40

148 Forestry Development 149 Christmas

(Des J.W. from local ideas. Litho Questa)

1973 (23 July). *Development Projects. T 148 and similar horiz designs. Multicoloured.* W w **12**. P 14.
481	5 c. Type **148**	..	10	10
482	8 c. Rice irrigation scheme	..	10	10
483	10 c. Low income housing	..	10	10
484	25 c. Highway construction	..	20	30
481/4		*Set of 4*	45	45

(Des L. Curtis. Litho Questa)

1973 (26 Oct). *Festivals of Joy. T 149 and similar vert designs. Multicoloured.* W w **12** (sideways). P 14.
485	3 c. Type **149**	..	10	10
486	10 c. Diwali	..	10	10
487	20 c. Id-ul-Fitar	..	15	15
488	25 c. Chinese New Year	..	15	15
485/8		*Set of 4*	35	40

150 Athletics 151 Bowler

(Des G. Drummond. Litho Questa)

1974 (7 Jan). *Commonwealth Games, Christchurch. T 150 and similar vert designs. Multicoloured.* W w **12** (sideways). P 14.
489	3 c. Type **150**	..	15	10
490	8 c. Boxing	..	15	10
491	50 c. Bowling	..	50	75
489/91		*Set of 3*	70	80

(Des Hon. P. Snow. Adapted J.W. Litho Questa)

1974 (21 Feb). *Cricket Centenary. T 151 and similar multi-coloured designs.* W w **12** (sideways* on 3 and 25 c.). P 14.
492	3 c. Type **151**	..	50	25
	w. Wmk Crown right of CA	..	3·00	
493	25 c. Batsman and wicketkeeper	..	1·25	35
	w. Wmk Crown to right of CA	..	3·00	
494	40 c. Fielder (horiz)	..	2·00	90
492/4		*Set of 3*	3·25	1·40

*The normal sideways watermark shows Crown to left of CA, *as seen from the back of the stamp.*

152 Fijian Postman

(Des L. Curtis. Litho Format)

1974 (22 May). *Centenary of the Universal Postal Union. T 152 and similar horiz designs. Multicoloured.* W w **12**. P 14.
495	3 c. Type **152**	..	10	10
496	8 c. Loading mail onto *Fijian Princess*	..	10	10
497	30 c. Fijian post office and mail bus	..	20	25
498	50 c. B.A.C. One Eleven 200/400 modern aircraft	..	35	1·40
495/8		*Set of 4*	60	1·60

153 Cubs lighting Fire 154 Cakobau Club and Flag

(Des E. W. Roberts. Litho Questa)

1974 (20 Aug). *First National Scout Jamboree, Lautoka. T 153 and similar multicoloured designs.* W w **12** (sideways* on 40 c.). P 14.
499	3 c. Type **153**	..	15	10
500	10 c. Scouts reading map	..	20	10
501	40 c. Scouts and Fijian flag (vert)	..	65	1·75
	w. Wmk Crown to right of CA	..	60·00	
499/501		*Set of 3*	90	1·75

*The normal sideways watermark shows Crown to left of CA, *as seen from the back of the stamp.*

(Des J.W. Litho Enschedé)

1974 (9 Oct). *Centenary of Deed of Cession and Fourth Anniv of Independence. T 154 and similar horiz designs. Multicoloured.* W w **12** (sideways on 8 and 50 c.). P 13½ × 13 (3 c.) or 13 × 13½ (others).
502	3 c. Type **154**	..	10	10
503	8 c. King Cakobau and Queen Victoria	..	10	10
504	50 c. Raising the Royal Standard at Nasova, Ovalau	..	30	65
502/4		*Set of 3*	40	70

1975 (9 Apr)–77. *As Nos. 435/44 and 446/50, but W w 14 (sideways on 1 and 10 c).*
505	1 c. *Cirrhopetalum umbellatum*	..	75	3·00
506	2 c. Cardinal Honey-eater	..	75	3·00
507	3 c. *Calanthe furcata*	..	40	2·75
508	4 c. *Bulbophyllum sp nov* (3.9.76)	..	3·50	10
509	5 c. Type **140**	..	1·25	3·00
	w. Wmk inverted	..	5·00	
510	6 c. *Phaius tancarvilliae* (3.9.76)	..	2·75	20
511	8 c. Blue-crested Broadbill (3.9.76)	..	35	10
512	10 c. *Acanthephippium vitiense*	..	40	90
513	15 c. *Dendrobium tokai* (3.9.76)	..	2·50	40
514	20 c. Slaty Flycatcher (15.7.77)	..	3·00	55
516	30 c. *Dendrobium gordonii* (3.9.76)	..	6·00	95
517	40 c. Type **141** (3.9.76)	..	3·50	60
	w. Wmk inverted			
518	50 c. White-throated Pigeon (3.9.76)	..	3·50	65
519	$1 Collared Lory (3.9.76)	..	3·50	2·50
520	$2 *Dendrobium platygastrium* (3.9.76)	..	3·00	2·75
505/20		*Set of 15*	30·00	19·00

155 "Diwali" (Hindu Festival) 156 Steam Locomotive No. 21

(Des Jennifer Toombs. Litho Walsall)

1975 (31 Oct). *Festivals of Joy. T 155 and similar vert designs. Multicoloured.* W w **14** (inverted). P 14.
521	3 c. Type **155**	..	10	10
522	15 c. "Id-Ul-Fitar" (Muslim Festival)	..	10	10
523	25 c. Chinese New Year	..	15	15
524	30 c. Christmas	..	20	65
521/4		*Set of 4*	40	85
MS525	121×101 mm. Nos. 521/4. W w 14 (sideways*)		1·25	6·00
	a. Imperf between (vert)		£1100	
	w. Wmk Crown to right of CA		30·00	

*The normal sideways watermark on MS525 shows Crown to left of CA, *as seen from the back of the stamp.*

(Des R. Granger Barrett. Litho Questa)

1976 (26 Jan). *Sugar Trains. T 156 and similar horiz designs. Multicoloured.* W w **14** (sideways). P 14.
526	4 c. Type **156**	..	25	10
527	15 c. Diesel locomotive No. 8	..	75	40
528	20 c. Diesel locomotive No. 1	..	85	70
529	30 c. Free passenger train	..	1·10	1·75
526/9		*Set of 4*	2·75	2·75

157 Fiji Blind Society and Rotary Symbols

(Des V. Whiteley Studio. Litho J.W.)

1976 (26 Mar). *40th Anniv of Rotary in Fiji. T 157 and similar horiz design.* W w **14** (sideways). P 13.
530	10 c. ultramarine, pale sage-green and black	..	15	10
531	25 c. multicoloured	..	40	50

Design:—25 c. Ambulance and Rotary symbol.

158 De Havilland D.H.A.3 Drover 1

(Des P. Powell. Litho Questa)

1976 (1 Sept). *25th Anniv of Air Services. T 158 and similar horiz designs. Multicoloured.* W w **14**. P 13½ × 14.
532	4 c. Type **158**	..	40	20
533	15 c. B.A.C. One Eleven 200/400	..	1·00	1·50
534	25 c. Hawker Siddeley H.S.748	..	1·25	1·25
535	30 c. Britten Norman "long nose" Trislander	1·25	3·75
532/5		*Set of 4*	3·50	6·50

The new-issue supplement to this Catalogue appears each month in

GIBBONS STAMP MONTHLY

—from your newsagent or by postal subscription— sample copy and details on request.

159 The Queen's Visit to Fiji, 1970   **160** Map of the World

(Des L. Curtis. Litho Questa)

1977 (7 Feb). *Silver Jubilee. T* **159** *and similar vert designs. Multicoloured. W* w **14**. *P* 13½.

536	10 c. Type **159**			10	10
537	25 c. King Edward's Chair			15	10
538	30 c. Queen wearing cloth-of-gold super-tunica			25	15
	w. Wmk inverted			4·75	
536/8		Set of 3		40	30

(Des J.W. Litho Walsall)

1977 (12 Apr). *E.E.C./A.C.P.* Council of Ministers Conference, Fiji. T* **160** *and similar horiz design. Multicoloured. W* w **14** *(sideways). P* 14.

539	4 c. Type **160**			10	10
540	30 c. Map of Fiji group			30	90

*A.C.P. = African, Caribbean, Pacific Group.

161 *Hibiscus rosa-sinensis*

(Des V. Whiteley Studio. Litho Walsall)

1977 (27 Aug). *21st Anniv of Fiji Hibiscus Festival. T* **161** *and similar horiz designs. W* w **14** *(sideways). P* 14.

541	**161**	4 c. multicoloured		10	10
542	–	15 c. multicoloured		15	10
543	–	30 c. multicoloured		25	15
544	–	35 c. multicoloured		40	35
541/4			Set of 4	80	60

Nos. 542/44 show different varieties of *H rosa-sinensis.*

162 Drua   **163** White Hart of Richard II

(Des P. Powell. Litho Questa)

1977 (7 Nov). *Canoes. T* **162** *and similar horiz designs. Multicoloured. W* w **14** *(sideways). P* 14.

545	4 c. Type **162**			15	10
546	15 c. Tabilai			30	20
547	25 c. Takai			35	25
548	40 c. Camakua			55	80
545/8		Set of 4		1·25	1·25

(Des C. Abbott. Litho Questa)

1978 (21 Apr). *25th Anniv of Coronation. T* **163** *and similar vert designs. P* 15.

549	25 c. bistre, blue-green and silver			15	20
	a. Sheetlet. Nos. 549/51 × 2			80	
550	25 c. multicoloured			15	20
551	25 c. bistre, blue-green and silver			15	20
549/51		Set of 3		40	55

Designs:—No. 549, Type **163**; No. 550, Queen Elizabeth II; No. 551, Banded Iguana.

Nos. 549/51 were printed together in small sheets of 6, containing two *se-tenant* strips of 3, with horizontal gutter margin between.

164 Defence Force surrounding Fokker F.VIIa/3M *Southern Cross*, Suva

(Des A. Theobald. Litho Harrison)

1978 (26 June). *Aviation Anniversaries. T* **164** *and similar horiz designs. Multicoloured. W* w **14** *(sideways). P* 14.

552	4 c. Type **164**			15	10
553	15 c. *Southern Cross* prior to leaving Naselai Beach			25	30
554	25 c. Wright Flyer 1			50	60
555	30 c. Bristol F2B "Brisfit"			50	85
552/5		Set of 4		1·25	1·60

Anniversaries—25 c. 75th of powered flight; 30 c. 60th of R.A.F.; others, 50th of first trans-Pacific flight by Kingsford-Smith.

165 Shallow Wooden Oil Dish in shape of Human Figure   **166** Advent Crown with Candles (Christmas)

(Des J. Cooter. Litho Questa)

1978 (14 Aug). *Fijian Artifacts. T* **165** *and similar multicoloured designs. W* w **14** *(sideways on 15 and 25 c.). P* 14.

556	4 c. Type **165**			10	10
557	15 c. Necklace of cachalot teeth (*horiz*)			10	10
558	25 c. Double water bottle (*horiz*)			15	10
559	30 c. Finely carved Ula or throwing club			15	15
556/9		Set of 4		35	35

(Des Jennifer Toombs. Litho Harrison)

1978 (30 Oct). *Festivals. T* **166** *and similar horiz designs. Multicoloured. W* w **14** *(sideways). P* 14.

560	4 c. Type **166**			10	10
561	15 c. Lamps (Diwali)			10	10
562	25 c. Coffee pot, cups and fruit (Id-Ul-Fitr)			10	10
563	40 c. Lion (Chinese New Year)			25	40
560/3		Set of 4		35	60

167 Banded Iguana

(Des L. Curtis and G. Drummond. Litho Questa)

1979 (19 Mar). *Endangered Wildlife. T* **167** *and similar horiz designs. Multicoloured. W* w **14** *(sideways). P* 14.

564	4 c. Type **167**			30	10
565	15 c. Tree Frog			60	10
566	25 c. Long-legged Warbler			2·50	30
567	30 c. Pink-billed Parrot Finch			2·75	1·25
564/7		Set of 4		5·50	1·50

168 Women with Dholak

(Des J.W. Litho Questa)

1979 (11 May). *Centenary of Arrival of Indians. T* **168** *and similar horiz designs. Multicoloured. W* w **14** *(sideways). P* 14.

568	4 c. Type **168**			10	10
569	15 c. Men sitting round tanoa			10	10
570	30 c. Farmer and sugar cane plantation			15	10
571	40 c. Sailing ship *Leonidas*			40	25
568/71		Set of 4		60	45

169 Soccer

(Des BG Studio. Litho Questa)

1979 (2 July). *6th South Pacific Games. T* **169** *and similar horiz designs. Multicoloured. W* w **14** *(sideways). P* 14.

572	4 c. Type **169**			15	10
573	15 c. Rugby Union			30	10
574	30 c. Lawn tennis			70	70
575	40 c. Weightlifting			70	85
572/5		Set of 4		1·60	1·50

170 Indian Child and Map of Fiji

(Des D. Bowen. Litho Walsall)

1979 (17 Sept). *International Year of the Child. T* **170** *and similar horiz designs showing children and map of Fiji. Multicoloured. W* w **14** *(sideways). P* 14½ × 14.

576	4 c. + 1 c. Type **170**			10	10
577	15 c. + 2 c. European child			15	15
578	30 c. + 3 c. Chinese child			15	15
579	40 c. + 4 c. Fijian child			15	20
576/9		Set of 4		45	50

171 Old Town Hall, Suva

(Des J.W. Litho Questa (1, 2, 3, 4, 10, 15, 20, 30 c., \$5) or Harrison (others))

1979 (11 Nov)–**94**. *Architecture. Multicoloured designs as T* **171**. *W* w **14** *(sideways* on horiz designs). P* 13½×13 (\$1), 13×13½ (\$2), 13×14 (\$5) or 14 (others).

A. *Without imprint date at foot. Chalk-surfaced paper* (1, 2, 3, 10, 15, 20, 30 c., \$5). B. *With imprint date.*

				A		B	
580	1 c. Type **171**		15	60	45	80
	a. Ordinary paper		70	1·25	†	
581	2 c. Dudley Church, Suva		45	70	40	20
	a. Ordinary paper		75	1·50	30	20
582	3 c. Fiji International Telecommunications Building, Suva		35	80	85	1·25
	a. Ordinary paper		85	1·50	†	
582c	4 c. Lautoka Mosque		†		1·25	1·75
	ca. Chalk-surfaced paper		†		1·25	1·75
583	5 c. As 4 c.		15	10	30	10
	w. Wmk Crown to right of CA		†	—	†	
584	6 c. General Post Office, Suva		15	50	15	10
585	10 c. Fiji Visitors Bureau, Suva		20	10	†	
	a. Ordinary paper		85	1·25	85	1·25
586	12 c. Public School, Levuka		20	65	55	1·25
587	15 c. Colonial War Memorial Hospital, Suva		40	30	†	
	a. Ordinary paper		75	1·25	1·25	1·25
588	18 c. Labasa Sugar Mill		20	30	†	
	w. Wmk Crown to right of CA		—	15·00	†	
589	20 c. Rewa Bridge, Nausori		55	30	1·25	1·25
	a. Ordinary paper		1·25	1·50	†	
590	30 c. Sacred Heart Cathedral, Suva (*vert*)		65	50	†	
	a. Ordinary paper		30	85	†	
591	35 c. Grand Pacific Hotel, Suva		30	1·00	†	
592	45 c. Shiva Temple, Suva		40	45	†	
593	50 c. Serua Island Village		40	40	†	
	a. Chalk-surfaced paper		†		1·50	1·50
594	\$1 Solo Rock Lighthouse (30×46 *mm*)		3·00	1·75	†	
595	\$2 Baker Memorial Hall, Nausori (46×30 *mm*)		1·40	1·90	†	
595a	\$5 Government House, Suva (46×30 *mm*)		2·50	4·00	†	
580A/95aA		Set of 17	10·00	12·50	†	
580B/93aB		Set of 11			7·75	9·50

*The normal sideways watermark shows Crown to left of CA, as seen from the back of the stamp.

Dates of issue:—11.11.79 Nos. 580A/82A. 585A, 587A, 589A/90A, 595aA; 13.6.80 Nos. 580aA, 581aA, 582aA, 585aA, 587aA, 589aA, 590aA, 22.12.80 Nos. 583A/84A, 586A, 588A, 591A/5A; 15.6.83 No. 584B; 1.84 No. 583B; 2.84 No. 581aB; 19.11.86 No. 581B; 11.91 Nos. 582cB, 585aB, 587aB; 11.93 Nos. 582B, 582caB, 586B, 589B; 22.8.94 No. 593aB; 12.94 No. 580B. Imprint dates: "1983" Nos. 581aB, 583B, 584B; "1986", No. 581B; "1991", Nos. 581aB, 582cB, 585aB, 587aB; "1993", Nos. 581B, 582B, 582caB, 586B, 589B; "1994", Nos. 580B/1B, 582caB, 586B, 589B, 593aB.

For these designs and similar 8 c. watermarked w **16** see Nos. 719/35.

172 *Southern Cross*, 1873

(Des L. Dunn. Litho Secura, Singapore)

1980 (28 Apr). *"London 1980" International Stamp Exhibition. Mail-carrying Ships. T* **172** *and similar horiz designs. Multicoloured. W* w **14** *(sideways*). P* 13½.

596	6 c. Type **172**			25	10
	w. Wmk Crown to right of CA		15·00		
597	20 c. *Levuka*, 1910			35	10
598	45 c. *Matua*, 1936			50	40
599	50 c. *Oronsay*, 1951			50	55
	w. Wmk Crown to right of CA		15·00		
596/9		Set of 4		1·40	1·00

*The normal sideways watermark shows Crown to left of CA, as seen from the back of the stamp.

173 Sovi Bay

(Des BG Studio. Litho Questa)

1980 (18 Aug.). *Tourism. T 173 and similar horiz designs. Multicoloured. W w 14 (sideways). P 13½ × 14.*

600	6 c. Type 173		10	10
601	20 c. Evening scene, Yanuca Island		15	15
602	45 c. Dravuni Beach		20	40
603	50 c. Wakaya Island		20	45
600/3		*Set of 4*	50	95

174 Official Opening of Parliament, 1979

(Des J. Cooter. Litho J.W.)

1980 (6 Oct.). *10th Anniv of Independence. T 174 and similar multicoloured designs. W w 14 (sideways on 6 and 45 c.). P 13.*

604	6 c. Type 174		10	10
605	20 c. Fiji coat of arms (vert)		15	10
606	45 c. Fiji flag		20	20
607	50 c. Queen Elizabeth II (vert). .		25	35
604/7		*Set of 4*	55	60

175 "Coastal Scene" (painting, Semisi Maya)

176 Prince Charles Sailing

(Des J.W. Litho Questa)

1981 (21 Apr.). *International Year for Disabled Persons. T 175 and similar multicoloured designs. W w 14 (sideways on 6 and 35 c.). P 14.*

608	6 c. Type 175		10	10
609	35 c. "Underwater Scene" (painting, Semisi Maya)		35	30
610	50 c. Semisi Maya (disabled artist) at work (vert)		40	40
611	60 c. "Peacock" (painting, Semisi Maya) (vert)		45	45
608/11		*Set of 4*	1·10	1·10

(Des J.W. Litho Questa)

1981 (22 July). *Royal Wedding. T 176 and similar vert designs. Multicoloured. W w 14. P 14.*

612	6 c. Wedding bouquet from Fiji		10	10
613	45 c. Type 176		30	15
614	$1 Prince Charles and Lady Diana Spencer		50	60
612/14		*Set of 3*	70	75

 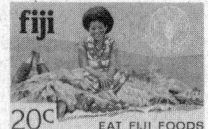

177 Operator Assistance Centre

178 "Eat Fiji Foods"

(Des A. Theobald. Litho Format)

1981 (17 Aug.). *Telecommunications. T 177 and similar horiz designs. Multicoloured. W w 14 (sideways). P 14.*

615	6 c. Type 177		10	10
616	35 c. Microwave station		45	50
617	50 c. Satellite earth station		60	75
618	60 c. Cable ship *Retriever*		80	90
615/18		*Set of 4*	1·75	2·00

(Des J.W. Litho Format)

1981 (21 Sept). *World Food Day. W w 14. P 14½ × 14.*

619	**178** 20 c. multicoloured		30	10

COVER PRICES

Cover factors are quoted at the beginning of each country for most issues to 1945. An explanation of the system can be found on page x. The factors quoted do not, however, apply to philatelic covers.

179 Ratu Sir Lala Sukuna (first Speaker, Legislative Council)

(Des A. Theobald. Litho Format)

1981 (19 Oct). *Commonwealth Parliamentary Association Conference, Suva. T 179 and similar horiz designs. W w 14 (sideways). P 14.*

620	6 c. black, buff and orange-brown		10	10
621	35 c. multicoloured		30	30
622	50 c. multicoloured		45	45
620/2		*Set of 3*	75	75
MS623	73 × 53 mm. 60 c. multicoloured		70	1·00

Designs:—35 c. Mace of the House of Representatives; 50 c. Suva Civic Centre; 60 c. Flags of C.P.A. countries.

180 Bell P-39 Airacobra

(Des A. Theobald. Litho Walsall)

1981 (7 Dec). *World War II Aircraft. T 180 and similar horiz designs. Multicoloured. W w 14 (sideways). P 14.*

624	6 c. Type 180		85	10
625	18 c. Consolidated PBY-5 Catalina		1·60	40
626	35 c. Curtiss P-40E Warhawk		1·90	85
627	60 c. Short Singapore III		2·25	4·50
624/7		*Set of 4*	6·00	5·25

181 Scouts constructing Shelter

(Des B. Melton. Litho Questa)

1982 (22 Feb). *75th Anniv of Boy Scout Movement. T 181 and similar multicoloured designs. W w 14 (sideways on 6 and 45 c.). P 14½.*

628	6 c. Type 181		15	10
629	20 c. Scouts sailing (vert)		50	30
630	45 c. Scouts by campfire		85	50
631	60 c. Lord Baden-Powell (vert)		1·00	1·00
628/31		*Set of 4*	2·25	1·75

182 Fiji Soldiers at U.N. Checkpoint

(Des J.W. Litho Format)

1982 (10 May*). *Disciplined Forces. T 182 and similar horiz designs. Multicoloured. W w 14 (sideways). P 14.*

632	12 c. Type 182		30	10
633	30 c. Soldiers engaged in rural development		60	55
634	40 c. Police patrol		1·50	1·25
635	70 c. *Kiro* (minesweeper)		1·50	2·50
632/5		*Set of 4*	3·50	3·75

*This is the local release date. The Crown Agents released the stamps in London on 3 May.

183 Footballers and Fiji Football Association Logo

184 Bride and Groom leaving St. Paul's

(Des A. Theobald. Litho Walsall)

1982 (15 June). *World Cup Football Championship, Spain. T 183 and similar horiz designs. W w 14 (sideways*). P 14.*

636	6 c. rosine, black and lemon		10	10
637	18 c. multicoloured		25	20
	w. Wmk Crown to right of CA		35·00	
638	50 c. multicoloured		70	70
639	90 c. multicoloured		1·10	2·00
	w. Wmk Crown to right of CA		3·50	
636/9		*Set of 4*	1·90	2·75

Designs:—18 c. Footballers and World Cup emblem; 50 c. Footballer and Bernabeu Stadium; 90 c. Footballers and Naranjito (mascot).

*The normal sideways watermark shows Crown to left of CA, as seen from the back of the stamp.

(Des C. Abbott. Litho Harrison)

1982 (1 July). *21st Birthday of Princess of Wales. T 184 and similar vert designs. Multicoloured. W w 14. P 14½ × 14.*

640	20 c. Fiji coat of arms		20	15
641	35 c. Lady Diana Spencer at Broadlands, May 1981		35	25
642	45 c. Type 184		40	40
643	$1 Formal portrait		1·00	2·25
640/3		*Set of 4*	1·75	2·75

185 Prince Philip

186 Baby Jesus with Mary and Joseph

(Des C. Abbott. Litho Format)

1982 (1 Nov). *Royal Visit. T 185 and similar multicoloured designs. W w 14. P 14.*

644	6 c. Type 185		20	15
645	35 c. Queen Elizabeth II		70	2·00
MS646	128 × 88 mm. Nos. 644/5 and $1 Royal Yacht *Britannia* (horiz). Wmk sideways		2·50	3·00

(Des G. Wilby. Litho Questa)

1982 (22 Nov). *Christmas. T 186 and similar horiz designs. Multicoloured. W w 14 (sideways). P 14 × 14½.*

647	6 c. Type 186		10	10
648	20 c. Three Wise Men presenting gifts		30	20
649	35 c. Carol-singing		45	45
647/9		*Set of 3*	75	55
MS650	94 × 42 mm. $1 "Faith" (from the "Three Virtues" by Raphael)		1·25	1·50

187 Red-throated Lorikeet

188 Bure in Traditional Village

(Des N. Arlott. Litho Questa)

1983 (14 Feb). *Parrots. T 187 and similar vert designs. Multicoloured. W w 14. P 14.*

651	20 c. Type 187		1·25	15
652	40 c. Blue-crowned Lory		1·60	40
653	55 c. Masked Shining Parrot		1·75	90
654	70 c. Red Shining Parrot		2·00	2·25
651/4		*Set of 4*	6·00	3·25

(Des B. Melton. Litho Questa)

1983 (14 Mar). *Commonwealth Day. T 188 and similar horiz designs. Multicoloured. W w 14 (sideways). P 14.*

655	8 c. Type 188		10	10
656	25 c. Barefoot firewalkers		20	15
657	50 c. Sugar industry		30	35
658	80 c. Kava "Yagona" ceremony		55	70
655/8		*Set of 4*	1·00	1·10

189 First Manned Balloon Flight, 1783

190 Nawanawa

(Des Harrison. Litho Questa)

1983 (18 July). *Bicentenary of Manned Flight. T 189 and similar horiz designs. Multicoloured. W w 14 (sideways). P 14.*

659	8 c. Type 189		20	10
660	20 c. Wright brothers' Flyer 1		40	30
661	25 c. Douglas Super DC-3		45	40
662	40 c. De Havilland D.H.106 Comet 1		70	60
663	50 c. Boeing 747		85	70
664	58 c. Space Shuttle		95	80
659/64		*Set of 6*	3·25	2·50

(Des Harrison. Litho Format)

1983 (3 Oct*). *Flowers (1st series). T* **190** *and similar vert designs. Multicoloured.* W w **14.** *P* 14×14½.

65	8 c. Type **190**	..	..	..	..	10	10
66	25 c. Rosawa	..	..	..	..	30	30
67	40 c. Warerega	..	..	..	..	40	50
68	$1 Saburo	..	..	..	..	80	1·40
65/8	..	..	..	..	*Set of 4*	1·40	2·00

*This is the local release date. The Crown Agents issued the stamps in London on 26 September.
See also Nos. 680/3.

191 Fijian beating Lali and 192 *Dacryopinax spathularia* Earth Satellite Station

(Des Garden Studio. Litho Questa)

1983 (7 Nov). *World Communications Year.* W w **14.** *P* 13½.

369	**191**	50 c. multicoloured	..	..	..	50	80

(Des Jennifer Toombs. Litho Enschedé)

1984 (9 Jan). *Fungi. T* **192** *and similar multicoloured designs.* W w **14** *(sideways on 50 c. and $1). P* 13½ × 13 (8 c. *to* 40 c.) *or* 13 × 13½ (*others*).

670	8 c. Type **192**	..	..	..	85	15
	w. Wmk inverted					
671	15 c. *Podoscypha involuta*	..	..	1·25	25
672	40 c. *Lentinus squarrosulus*	..	2·25	1·00
673	50 c. *Scleroderma cepa* ("*Scleroderma flavidum*") (*horiz*)	2·25	1·25
674	$1 *Phillipsia domingensis* (*horiz*)	2·75	3·50
670/4	..	..	..	..	*Set of 5*	8·50	5·50

193 Tui Lau
(freighter) on Reef

(Des L. Curtis. Litho Questa)

1984 (7 May). *250th Anniv of "Lloyd's List" (newspaper). T* **193** *and similar vert designs. Multicoloured.* W w **14.** *P* 14½ × 14.

675	8 c. Type **193**	..	..	..	40	10
676	40 c. *Tofua* (cargo liner)	..	..	1·00	80
677	55 c. *Canberra* (liner)	..	..	1·25	1·50
678	60 c. *NedLloyd Madras* (freighter) at Suva wharf	..	..	1·40	1·75
675/8	..	..	..	..	*Set of 4*	3·50	3·75

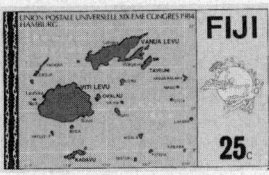

194 Map of Fijian Islands

(Des J. Cooter. Litho Questa)

1984 (14 June). *Universal Postal Union Congress, Hamburg. Sheet* 77 × 65 *mm.* W w **14** (*sideways*). *P* 14½.

MS679	**194**	25 c. multicoloured	..	..	1·50	1·00

(Des Harrison. Litho Format)

1984 (9 July). *Flowers (2nd series). Vert designs as T* **190.** W w **14.** *P* 14×14½.

680	15 c. Drividrivi	..	..	..	25	25
681	20 c. Vesida	..	..	..	35	40
682	50 c. Vuga	..	..	..	60	90
683	70 c. Qaiqi	..	..	..	80	1·40
680/3	..	..	..	..	*Set of 4*	1·75	2·75

195 Prize Bull, Yalavou Cattle Scheme

(Des D. Hartley-Marjoram. Litho Walsall)

1984 (17 Sept). *"Ausipex" International Stamp Exhibition, Melbourne. T* **195** *and similar multicoloured designs.* W w **14** (*sideways* on 8, 40 c. *and* $1). *P* 14½×14 (25 c.) *or* 14×14½ (*others*).

684	8 c. Type **195**	..	..	..	20	10
685	25 c. Wailoa Power Station (*vert*)	..	50	40
686	40 c. Air Pacific Boeing 737 airliner	..	75	90
687	$1 Container ship *Fua Kavenga*	..	1·40	2·50
	w. Wmk Crown to right of CA			1·40	
684/7	..	..	..	*Set of 4*	3·00	3·50

*The normal sideways watermark shows Crown to left of CA, as seen from the back of the stamp.

196 The Stable at Bethlehem

(Des G. Vasarhelyi. Litho Format)

1984 (5 Nov). *Christmas. Children's Paintings. T* **196** *and similar multicoloured designs.* W w **14** (*sideways on horiz designs*). *P* 14.

688	8 c. Type **196**	..	..	..	10	10
689	20 c. Outrigger canoe	..	..	30	20
690	25 c. Father Christmas and Christmas tree	..	30	25
691	40 c. Going to church	..	..	40	70
692	$1 Decorating Christmas tree (*vert*)	..	70	1·75
688/92	..	..	..	*Set of 5*	1·50	2·75

197 *Danaus plexippus*   198 Outrigger Canoe off Toberua Island

(Des Annette Robinson. Litho Questa)

1985 (4 Feb). *Butterflies. T* **197** *and similar multicoloured designs.* W w **14** (*sideways on 8 c. and 25 c.*). *P* 14.

693	8 c. Type **197**	..	..	..	1·10	15
694	25 c. *Hypolimnas bolina*	..	..	2·00	60
695	40 c. *Lampides boeticus* (*vert*)	..	2·75	1·75
696	$1 *Precis villida* (*vert*)	..	..	3·50	5·50
693/6	..	..	..	*Set of 4*	8·50	7·25

(Des D. Miller. Litho B.D.T.)

1985 (1 Apr). *"Expo '85" World Fair, Japan. T* **198** *and similar vert designs. Multicoloured.* W w **14.** *P* 14.

697	20 c. Type **198**	..	..	..	50	30
698	25 c. Wainivula Falls	..	..	85	40
699	50 c. Mana Island	..	..	95	90
700	$1 Sawa-I-Lau Caves	..	..	1·25	2·25
697/700	..	..	..	*Set of 4*	3·25	3·50

199 With Prince Charles at Garter Ceremony   200 Horned Squirrelfish

(Des A. Theobald ($1), C. Abbott (others). Litho Questa)

1985 (7 June). *Life and Times of Queen Elizabeth the Queen Mother. T* **199** *and similar vert designs. Multicoloured.* W w **16.** *P* 14½×14.

701	8 c. With Prince Andrew on her 60th Birthday	..	10	10
702	25 c. Type **199**	..	..	35	40
703	40 c. The Queen Mother at Epsom Races	..	50	80
704	50 c. With Prince Henry at his christening (from photo by Lord Snowdon)	..	65	1·25
701/4	..	..	..	*Set of 4*	1·40	2·25
MS705	91×73 mm. $1 With Prince Andrew at Royal Wedding, 1981. Wmk sideways	..	1·25	2·00

(Des M. Raj. Litho Questa)

1985 (23 Sept). *Shallow Water Marine Fishes. T* **200** *and similar horiz designs. Multicoloured.* W w **14** (*sideways*). *P* 14½.

706	40 c. Type **200**	..	..	1·50	50
707	50 c. Yellow-banded Goatfish	..	1·75	1·10
708	55 c. Yellow-edged Lyretail ("Fairy Cod")	1·75	1·40
709	$1 Peacock Hind	..	..	2·75	4·00
706/9	..	..	..	*Set of 4*	7·00	6·25

201 Collared Petrel   202 Children and "Peace for Fiji and the World" Slogan

(Des Doreen McGuinness. Litho Walsall)

1985 (4 Nov). *Seabirds. T* **201** *and similar vert designs. Multicoloured.* W w **14.** *P* 14×13½.

710	15 c. Type **201**	..	..	1·75	50
711	20 c. Lesser Frigate Bird	..	2·00	50
712	50 c. Brown Booby	..	..	3·25	3·50
713	$1 Crested Tern	..	..	5·00	7·00
710/13	..	..	..	*Set of 4*	11·00	10·50

(Des A. Theobald. Litho Format)

1986 (21 Apr). *60th Birthday of Queen Elizabeth II. Vert designs as T* **110** *of Ascension. Multicoloured.* W w **16.** *P* 14×14½.

714	20 c. With Duke of York at Royal Tournament, 1936	..	..	20	30
715	25 c. Royal Family on Palace balcony after Princess Margaret's wedding, 1960	25	35
716	40 c. Queen inspecting guard of honour, Suva, 1982	..	..	30	55
717	50 c. In Luxembourg, 1976	..	..	40	85
718	$1 At Crown Agents Head Office, London, 1983	..	..	65	1·60
714/18	..	..	..	*Set of 5*	1·60	3·25

(Litho Harrison (4 c. (1988 ptg), 8 c.) or Questa (others))

1986 (Apr)–**91.** *As Nos.* 580/2, 582c, 585, 587, 589, 591, 593/4 *and new value.* W w **16** (*sideways on* 1, 2, 3, 4, 8, 10, 15, 20, 35, 50 c.). *Chalk-surfaced paper* (2 c.). *With imprint date. P* 14×13½ ($1) *or* 14 (*others*).

719	1 c. Type **171** (11.3.91)	..	..	50	80
720	2 c. Dudley Church, Suva	..	30	30
	a. Ordinary paper (11.3.91)	..	30	30
721	3 c. Fiji International Telecommunications Building, Suva (1.6.88)	30	30
722	4 c. Lautoka Mosque (1.6.88)	..	30	30
724	8 c. Public School, Levuka (as No. 586) (1.12.86)	..	1·00	1·00
725	10 c. Fiji Visitors Bureau, Suva (1.3.90)	20	30
726	15 c. Colonial War Memorial Hospital, Suva (11.3.91)	30	20
730	20 c. Rewa Bridge, Nausori (1.6.88)	75	75
732	35 c. Grand Pacific Hotel, Suva (11.3.91)	85	1·00
734	50 c. Serua Island Village (11.3.91)	1·40	1·40
735	$1 Solo Rock Lighthouse (30×46 mm) (11.3.91)	3·50	3·75
719/35	..	..	*Set of 11*	8·50	9·00

From the 11 March 1991 printing all values were produced by Questa. The 4 c. (No. 722) was the only stamp in this issue to be printed by both Harrison and Questa.

Imprint dates: "1986", Nos. 720, 724; "1988", Nos. 720/2, 730; "1990", Nos. 725, 730; "1991", Nos. 719, 720a, 721/2, 725/6, 732, 734/5; "1992", Nos. 719, 721/2, 726, 730, 732, 734/5.

(Des G. Vasarhelyi. Litho Format)

1986 (23 June). *International Peace Year. T* **202** *and similar vert design. Multicoloured.* W w **16.** *P* 14½.

736	8 c. Type **202**	..	..	25	10
737	40 c. Peace dove and houses	..	65	1·00

203 Halley's Comet in Centaurus Constellation and Newton's Reflector   204 Ground Frog

(Des D. Hartley. Litho B.D.T.)

1986 (7 July). *Appearance of Halley's Comet. T* **203** *and similar vert designs. Multicoloured.* W w **16.** *P* 13½.

738	25 c. Type **203**	..	..	1·25	40
739	40 c. Halley's Comet over Lomaiviti	..	1·50	85
740	$1 *Giotto* spacecraft photographing Comet nucleus	..	2·50	4·25
738/40	..	..	*Set of 3*	4·75	5·00

(Litho Format)

1986 (1 Aug). *Reptiles and Amphibians. T* **204** *and similar horiz designs. Multicoloured.* W w **16** (*sideways*). *P* 14½.

741	8 c. Type **204**	..	..	55	10
742	20 c. Burrowing Snake	..	..	1·00	30
743	25 c. Spotted Gecko	..	..	1·10	35
744	40 c. Crested Iguana	..	..	1·25	80
745	50 c. Blotched Skink	..	..	1·40	2·75
746	$1 Speckled Skink	..	..	1·75	4·50
741/6	..	..	*Set of 6*	6·25	8·00

205 Gatawaka

206 Weasel Cone
(Conus mustelinus)

(Des M. Raj. Litho Walsall)

1986 (10 Nov). *Ancient War Clubs. T 205 and similar vert designs. Multicoloured.* W w **16**. P 14.
747	25 c. Type 205			80	35
748	40 c. Siriti			1·00	60
749	50 c. Bulibuli			1·25	1·40
750	$1 Culacula			2·25	2·75
747/50			Set of 4	4·75	4·50

(Des A. Riley. Litho Format)

1987 (26 Feb). *Cone Shells of Fiji. T 206 and similar vert designs. Multicoloured.* W w **16**. P 14×14½.
751	15 c. Type 206			80	25
752	20 c. Pertusus Cone (*Conus pertusus*)		90	35
753	25 c. Admiral Cone (*Conus ammiralis*)		1·00	40
754	40 c. Leaden Cone (*Conus scabriusculus*)	1·40	1·10
755	50 c. Imperial Cone (*Conus imperialis*)	1·50	2·25
	w. Wmk inverted				
756	$1 Geography Cone (*Conus geographus*)	2·00	3·75
	w. Wmk inverted				
751/6			Set of 6	7·00	7·25

207 Tagimoucia Flower   (208)

(Des M. Raj. Litho Format)

1987 (23 Apr). *Tagimoucia Flower. Sheet 72×55 mm.* W w **14** (*sideways*). P 14½.
MS757 **207** $1 multicoloured .. .. .. 2·75 2·00

1987 (13 June). *"Capex '87" International Stamp Exhibition, Toronto. No.* MS757 optd with T **208**.
MS758 72×55 mm. $1 Type **207**. .. .. 5·00 2·00
Stamps from Nos. MS757 and MS758 are identical as the overprint on MS758 appears on the margin of the sheet.

209 Traditional Fijian House

(Des National Focal Point, adapted L. Curtis. Litho Format)

1987 (20 July). *International Year of Shelter for the Homeless. T 209 and similar horiz design. Multicoloured.* W w **16** (*sideways*). P 14.
759	55 c. Type 209			45	50
760	70 c. Modern bungalows			55	60

210 *Bulbogaster ctenostomoides*
(stick insect)

(Des R. Lewington. Litho Walsall)

1987 (7 Sept). *Fijian Insects. T 210 and similar horiz designs. Multicoloured.* W w **16** (*sideways*). P 13½×14.
761	20 c. Type 210			1·10	30
762	25 c. *Paracupta flaviventris* (beetle)		1·25	35
763	40 c. *Cerambyrhynchus schoenherri* (beetle)	1·50	1·00
764	50 c. *Rhinoscapha lagopyga* (weevil)	1·60	2·00
765	$1 *Xixuthrus heros* (beetle)		2·50	4·00
761/5			Set of 5	7·00	7·00

REPUBLIC

Following a military coup on 25 September 1987 Fiji was declared a republic on 7 October. The Governor-General resigned on 15 October 1987 and Fiji's Commonwealth membership lapsed until 1 October 1997 when the country was readmitted following further constitutional changes.

211 The   212 Windsurfer
Nativity   and Beach

(Des G. Vasarhelyi. Litho Walsall)

1987 (19 Nov). *Christmas. T 211 and similar multicoloured designs.* W w **16** (*sideways on 40 c., 50 c.*). P 14×13½ (*vert*) or 13½×14 (*horiz*).
766	8 c. Type 211			35	10
767	40 c. The Shepherds (*horiz*)		1·25	40
768	50 c. The Three Kings (*horiz*)		1·40	90
769	$1 The Three Kings presenting gifts	2·00	2·50
766/9			Set of 4	4·50	3·50

(Des Ahgrafik. Litho Questa)

1988 (27 Apr). *"Expo '88" World Fair, Brisbane.* W w **16** (*sideways*). P 14.
770 **212** 30 c. multicoloured 90 50

213 Woman using Fiji   214 Pottery Bowl
"Nouna" (stove)

(Litho Questa)

1988 (14 June). *Centenary of International Council of Women.* W w **16** (*sideways*). P 14.
771 **213** 45 c. multicoloured 75 60

(Des N. Ahmed. Litho Questa)

1988 (29 Aug). *Ancient Fijian Pottery. T 214 and similar multicoloured designs.* W w **14** (*sideways*) (69 c.) or w **16** (*others, sideways on 75 c.*). P 14.
772	9 c. Type 214			15	10
773	23 c. Cooking pot			25	25
774	58 c. Priest's drinking vessel		50	80
775	63 c. Drinking vessel			55	1·00
776	69 c. Earthenware oil lamp		60	1·10
777	75 c. Cooking pot with relief pattern (*vert*)	70	1·25
772/7			Set of 6	2·50	4·00

215 Fiji Tree Frog   216 *Dendrobium mohlianum*

(Des Doreen McGuinness. Litho Walsall)

1988 (3 Oct). *Fiji Tree Frog. T 215 and similar vert designs. Multicoloured.* W w **16**. P 14×13½.
778	18 c. Type 215			1·40	50
779	23 c. Frog climbing grass stalks		1·60	95
780	30 c. On leaf			2·00	2·25
781	45 c. Moving from one leaf to another	3·00	3·50
778/81			Set of 4	7·25	6·50

(Des M. Raj. Litho Walsall)

1988 (21 Nov). *Native Flowers. T 216 and similar vert designs. Multicoloured.* W w **14**. P 14.
782	9 c. Type 216			45	15
783	30 c. *Dendrobium cattilare*		70	45
784	45 c. *Degeneria vitiensis*		70	70
785	$1 *Degeneria roseiflora*		1·25	2·00
782/5			Set of 4	2·75	3·00

217 Battle of Solferino, 1859

(Des L. Curtis. Litho Questa)

1989 (6 Feb). *125th Anniv of International Red Cross. T 217 and similar designs.* W w **16** (*sideways on 58, 69 c.*). P 13½×14 (*horiz*) or 14 × 13½ (*vert*).
786	58 c. multicoloured			90	80
787	63 c. multicoloured			1·00	1·00
788	69 c. multicoloured			1·25	1·25
789	$1 black and bright scarlet		1·40	1·50
786/9			Set of 4	4·00	4·00

Designs: Vert—63 c. Henri Dunant (founder); $1 Anniversary logo. Horiz—69 c. Fijian Red Cross worker with blood donor.

218 Plan of *Bounty's*   219 *Platygyra daedalea*
Launch

(Des Jennifer Toombs. Litho Questa)

1989 (28 Apr). *Bicentenary of Captain Bligh's Boat Voyage. T 218 and similar horiz designs. Multicoloured.* W w **16** (*sideways*). P 14×14½.
790	45 c. Type 218			1·25	50
791	58 c. Cup, bowl and Bligh's journal		1·40	1·25
792	80 c. Bligh and extract from journal		1·75	2·25
793	$1 *Bounty's* launch and map of Fiji		2·50	3·00
790/3			Set of 4	6·25	6·75

(Des M. Raj. Litho Harrison)

1989 (21 Aug). *Corals. T 219 and similar multicoloured designs.* W w **14** (*sideways on 46, 60 c.*). P 14.
794	46 c. Type 219			1·50	75
795	60 c. *Caulastrea furcata*		1·75	1·75
796	75 c. *Acropora echinata* (*vert*)		2·25	2·25
797	90 c. *Acropora humilis* (*vert*)		2·50	2·75
794/7			Set of 4	7·25	6·75

220 Goalkeeper   221 Congregation in Church

(Des S. Noon. Litho Questa)

1989 (25 Sept). *World Cup Football Championship, Italy (1990). T 220 and similar horiz designs. Multicoloured.* W w **16** (*sideways*). P 14×14½.
798	35 c. Type 220			85	40
799	63 c. Goalkeeper catching ball		1·50	1·75
800	70 c. Player with ball		1·60	1·90
801	85 c. Tackling			1·75	2·50
798/801			Set of 4	5·00	6·00

(Des L. Curtis. Litho Questa)

1989 (1 Nov). *Christmas. T 221 and similar vert designs. Multicoloured.* W w **14**. P 14½×14.
802	9 c. Type 221			25	10
803	45 c. *Delonix regia* (Christmas tree)		75	35
804	$1 The Nativity			1·50	2·00
805	$1.40, Fijian children under *Delonix regia* (tree)	1·75	3·00
802/5			Set of 4	3·75	5·00

222 River Snapper   223 1968 3d.
Eastern Reef Heron
Definitive

1990 (23 Apr). *Freshwater Fishes. T* **222** *and similar horiz designs. Multicoloured. W w* **16** *(sideways). P* 14½.
806   50 c. Type 222   ..   ..   ..   1·75   70
807   70 c. Kner's   Grunter   ("Orange-spotted
          Therapon")   ..   ..   ..   2·25   2·25
808   85 c. Spotted Scat   ..   ..   ..   2·50   2·50
809    $1 Rock Flagtail   ..   ..   ..   3·00   3·50
806/9   ..   ..   ..   *Set of 4*   8·50   8·00

(Des D. Miller. Litho Questa)

1990 (1 May). *"Stamp World London 90" International Stamp Exhibition, London. Sheet,* 120×70 *mm, containing T* **223** *and similar vert design. Multicoloured. W w* **16** *(sideways). P* 14.
MS810 $1 Type 223; $2 1968 1s. 6d. Orange-
breasted Honeyeaters definitive   ..   ..   5·50   7·00

224 Vertiver Grass Contours   **225** *Dacrydium nidulum*

(Des Ahgrafik. Litho Questa)

1990 (23 July). *Soil Conservation. T* **224** *and similar multicoloured designs. W w* **14** *(sideways on 50, 70, 90 c.). P* 14.
811   50 c. Type 224   75   50
812   70 c. Mulching   ..   ..   ..   1·00   1·25
813   90 c. Hillside contour cultivation   ..   1·25   1·75
814    $1 Land use rotation *(vert)*   ..   1·40   2·00
811/14   ..   ..   ..   *Set of 4*   4·00   5·00

(Des M. Raj. Litho Questa)

1990 (2 Oct). *Timber Trees. T* **225** *and similar vert designs. Multicoloured. W w* **14**. *P* 14.
815   25 c. Type 225   65   20
816   35 c. *Decussocarpus vitiensis*   ..   75   30
817    $1 *Agathis vitiensis*   ..   ..   2·25   2·50
818    $1.55, *Santalum yasi*   ..   ..   3·00   4·25
815/18   ..   ..   ..   *Set of 4*   6·00   6·50

226 "Hark the Herald Angels sing"   **227** Sigatoka Sand Dunes

(Des Jennifer Toombs. Litho Walsall)

1990 (26 Nov). *Christmas. Carols. T* **226** *and similar horiz designs. Multicoloured. W w* **14** *(sideways). P* 14.
819   10 c. Type 226   25   10
820   35 c. "Still the Night, Holy the Night"   ..   60   30
821   65 c. "Joy to the World!"   ..   ..   1·00   1·50
822    $1 "The Race that long in Darkness pined"   1·75   2·50
819/22   ..   ..   ..   *Set of 4*   3·25   4·00

(Des L. Curtis. Litho Leigh-Mardon Ltd, Melbourne)

1991 (25 Feb). *Environmental Protection. T* **227** *and similar square designs. Multicoloured. P* 14.
823   35 c. Type 227   90   30
824   50 c. Monu and Monuriki Islands   ..   1·25   90
825   65 c. Ravilevu Nature Reserve, Taveuni   1·40   2·00
826    $1 Colo-I-Suva Forest Park   ..   2·25   3·00
823/6   ..   ..   ..   *Set of 4*   5·25   5·50

228 H.M.S. Pandora (frigate)   **229** *Scylla serrata*

(Des D. Miller. Litho Questa)

1991 (8 Aug). *Bicentenary of Discovery of Rotuma Island. T* **228** *and similar horiz designs. Multicoloured. W w* **14** *(sideways). P* 14.
827   54 c. Type 228   ..   ..   ..   1·75   85
828   70 c. Map of Rotuma   ..   ..   2·00   2·25
829   75 c. Natives welcoming H.M.S. *Pandora*   2·00   2·25
830    $1 Mount Soloroa and Uea Island   ..   2·75   3·50
827/30   ..   ..   ..   *Set of 4*   7·75   8·00

(Des Katrina Hindle. Litho Questa)

1991 (26 Sept). *Mangrove Crabs. T* **229** *and similar horiz designs. Multicoloured. W w* **14** *(sideways). P* 14×14½.
831   38 c. Type 229   70   35
832   54 c. *Metopograpsus messor*   ..   95   85
833   96 c. *Parasesarma erythrodactyla*   ..   1·75   2·50
834    $1.65, *Cardisoma carnifex*   ..   2·50   3·75
831/4   ..   ..   ..   *Set of 4*   5·50   6·75

230 Mary and Joseph travelling to Bethlehem   **231** De Havilland D.H.89 Dragon Rapide of Fiji Airways

(Des A. Wheatcroft. Litho Leigh-Mardon Ltd, Melbourne)

1991 (31 Oct). *Christmas. T* **230** *and similar horiz designs. Multicoloured. W w* **16**. *P* 14.
835   11 c. Type 230   30   10
      a. Error. Wmk w 14   ..   ..   †   —
836   75 c. Manger scene   ..   ..   1·25   1·25
837   96 c. Presentation in the Temple   ..   1·50   2·50
838    $1 Infant Jesus with symbols   ..   1·60   2·50
835/8   ..   ..   ..   *Set of 4*   4·25   5·75

(Des D. Wood. Litho Questa)

1991 (18 Nov). *40th Anniv of Air Pacific. T* **231** *and similar horiz designs. Multicoloured. W w* **16** *(sideways). P* 14½.
839   54 c. Type 231   ..   ..   ..   1·25   80
840   75 c. Douglas DC-3   ..   ..   1·75   2·00
841   96 c. Aerospatiale/Aeritalia ATR 42   ..   2·00   2·50
842    $1.40, Boeing 767   ..   ..   2·50   3·25
839/42   ..   ..   ..   *Set of 4*   6·75   7·75

232 Ethnic Dancers

(Des. W. Addison. Litho Leigh-Mardon Ltd, Melbourne)

1992 (23 Mar). *"Expo 92" World's Fair, Seville, Spain. T* **232** *and similar horiz designs. W w* **14** *(sideways). P* 14½×14.
843   27 c. Type 232   55   30
844   75 c. Peoples of Fiji   ..   ..   1·25   1·60
845   96 c. Gold bars and sugar cane train   ..   3·00   3·25
846    $1.40, *Queen Elizabeth 2* (cruise liner) at
          Suva   ..   ..   ..   3·25   3·50
843/6   ..   ..   ..   *Set of 4*   7·25   7·75

233 *Tabusoro*   **234** Running

(Des O. Bell. Litho Walsall)

1992 (22 June). *Inter-Islands Shipping. T* **233** *and similar horiz designs. Multicoloured. W w* **14** *(sideways). P* 13½×14.
847   38 c. Type 233   ..   ..   ..   1·25   55
848   54 c. *Degei II*   ..   ..   ..   1·75   1·40
849    $1.40, *Dausoko*   ..   ..   3·00   3·50
850    $1.65, *Nivanga*   ..   ..   3·25   3·50
847/50   ..   ..   ..   *Set of 4*   8·25   8·00

(Des M. Chandler. Litho Enschedé)

1992 (30 July). *Olympic Games, Barcelona. T* **234** *and similar vert designs. Multicoloured. W w* **14**. *P* 13½.
851   20 c. Type 234   55   20
852   86 c. Yachting   ..   ..   ..   2·00   2·00
853    $1.34, Swimming   ..   ..   2·50   3·00
854    $1.50, Judo   ..   ..   ..   2·50   3·00
851/4   ..   ..   ..   *Set of 4*   6·75   7·50

235 European War Memorial, Levuka

(Des L. Curtis. Litho Leigh-Mardon Ltd, Melbourne)

1992 (21 Sept). *Historic Levuka (former capital). T* **235** *and similar multicoloured designs. W w* **14** *(sideways on horiz designs). P* 14½.
855   30 c. Type 235   30   30
856   42 c. Map of Fiji   45   55
857   59 c. Beach Street   65   1·00
858   77 c. Sacred Heart Church *(vert)*   ..   80   1·50
859    $2 Deed of Cession site *(vert)*   ..   1·75   2·75
855/9   ..   ..   ..   *Set of 5*   3·50   5·50

236 The Nativity

(Des G. Vasarhelyi. Litho Leigh-Mardon Ltd, Melbourne)

1992 (17 Nov). *Christmas. T* **236** *and similar horiz designs. Multicoloured. W w* **14** *(sideways). P* 15×14½.
860   12 c. Type 236   35   10
861   77 c. Shepherds and family giving presents   1·40   1·50
862   83 c. Shepherds at manger and giving
          presents to pensioners   ..   ..   1·50   1·60
863    $2 Wise Men and collecting Fiji produce   3·00   4·00
860/3   ..   ..   ..   *Set of 4*   5·50   6·50

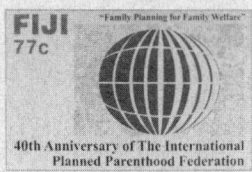

237 International Planned Parenthood Federation Logo

(Des D. Bowen. Litho Leigh-Mardon Ltd, Melbourne)

1992 (2 Dec). *40th Anniv of International Planned Parenthood Federation. T* **237** *and similar horiz design. Multicoloured. W w* **14** *(sideways). P* 15×14½.
864   77 c. Type 237   85   85
865    $2 Man weeping and pregnant mother
          with children..   ..   ..   2·50   3·25

238 Dove and Peace Corps Emblem   **239** Fijian Players performing Cibi (traditional dance)

(Des O. Bell. Litho Leigh-Mardon Ltd, Melbourne)

1993 (22 Feb). *25th Anniv of Peace Corps in Fiji. T* **238** *and similar horiz designs. Multicoloured. W w* **14**. *P* 14½.
866   59 c. Type 238   85   75
867   77 c. Handshake   ..   ..   1·10   1·40
868    $1 Educational symbols ..   ..   1·50   1·75
869    $2 Symbols of home businesses scheme   2·25   3·25
866/9   ..   ..   ..   *Set of 4*   5·00   6·50

(Des R. Larson. Litho Questa)

1993 (26 Mar). *Hong Kong Rugby Sevens Competition. T* **239** *and similar vert designs. Multicoloured. W w* **16**. *P* 14½.
870   77 c. Type 239   ..   ..   ..   1·25   1·40
871    $1.06, Players and map of Pacific   ..   1·75   2·50
872    $2 Scrum and stadium   ..   ..   2·75   3·50
870/2   ..   ..   ..   *Set of 3*   5·25   6·75

(Des A. Theobald. Litho Questa)

1993 (1 Apr). *75th Anniv of Royal Air Force. Horiz designs as T* **149** *of Ascension. Multicoloured. W w* **14** *(sideways). P* 14.
873   59 c. Gloster Gauntlet II   90   75
874   77 c. Armstrong Whitworth Whitley Mk V   1·10   1·40
875   83 c. Bristol F2b "Brisfit"   ..   1·25   1·60
876    $2 Hawker Tempest Mk V   ..   1·90   6·00
873/6   ..   ..   ..   *Set of 4*   4·75   6·00
MS877   110×77 mm. $1 Vickers Vildebeest III;
$1 Handley Page Hampden; $1 Vickers FB-27
Vimy; $1 British Aerospace Hawk T.1.   ..   4·50   5·50

240 *Chromodoris fidelis*   **241** Mango

(Des G. Drummond. Litho Leigh-Mardon Ltd, Melbourne)

1993 (27 July). *Nudibranchs. T* **240** *and similar horiz designs. Multicoloured. W w* **14.** *P* 14.

878	12 c. Type 240			40	10
879	42 c. *Halgerda carlsoni*	..	..	90	55
880	53 c. *Chromodoris lochi*	..	..	1·25	1·00
881	83 c. Blue Sea Lizard (*Glaucus atlanticus*)			1·75	2·00
882	$1 *Phyllidia bourguini*	..	..	1·90	2·25
883	$2 Spanish Dancer (*Hexabranchus sanguineus*)			3·00	3·75
878/83			Set of 6	8·25	8·75

(Des Katrina Hindle. Litho Cartor)

1993 (25 Oct). *Tropical Fruits. T* **241** *and similar vert designs. Multicoloured. W w* **14.** *P* 13½.

884	30 c. Type 241			75	45
885	42 c. Guava			95	75
886	$1 Lemon			2·00	2·00
887	$2 Soursop			3·50	4·00
884/7			Set of 4	6·50	6·50

242 *Anaphaesis java*   **243** The Last Supper

(Des I. Loe and D. Miller. Litho Enschedé (No. **MS889**))

1994 (18 Feb). *"Hong Kong '94" International Stamp Exhibition.*

(a) *No.* **MS877** *optd as T* **154** *of Ascension on each stamp*
MS888 110×77 mm. $1 Vickers Vildebeest III; $1 Handley Page Hampden; $1 Vickers FB-27 Vimy; $1 British Aerospace Hawk T.1 .. 4·50 6·00

(b) *Sheet* 122×85 mm *containing T* **242** *and similar vert designs showing butterflies. Multicoloured. W w* **14** (*sideways*). *P* 14½×13.
MS889 $1 Type 242; $1 *Euploea leucostictos*; $1 *Vagrans egista*; $1 *Acraea andromache* .. 4·50 6·00
No. **MS888** also shows "HONG KONG '94 EXHIBITION" overprinted on the bottom margin.

(Des R. Larson. Litho Enschedé)

1994 (31 Mar). *Easter. T* **243** *and similar multicoloured designs. W w* **14** (*sideways on horiz designs*). *P* 14×15 (*horiz*) *or* 15×14 (*vert*).

890	59 c. Type 243	..	..	80	60
891	77 c. The Crucifixion (*vert*)		..	1·00	1·25
892	$1 The Resurrection		..	1·60	2·00
893	$2 Examining Christ's wounds (*vert*)	..	2·75	4·00
890/3		..	Set of 4	5·50	7·00

244 Sagati   **245** White-collared Kingfisher on Branch

(Des I. Loe. Litho Walsall)

1994 (6 June). *Edible Seaweeds. T* **244** *and similar vert designs. Multicoloured. W w* **16.** *P* 14½×14.

894	42 c. Type 244			70	45
895	83 c. Nama	..		1·25	1·50
896	$1 Lumicevata	..		1·75	2·00
897	$2 Lumiwawa	..		3·00	4·00
894/7			Set of 4	6·00	7·00

(Des Doreen McGuinness. Litho Questa)

1994 (16 Aug). *White-collared Kingfisher. Sheet* 98×84 *mm, containing T* **245** *and similar vert design. Multicoloured. W w* **14.** *P* 14×13½.
MS898 $1.50, Type 245; $1.50, Kingfisher with crab in beak .. .. 6·00 6·50

STANLEY GIBBONS
STAMP COLLECTING SERIES

Introductory booklets on *How to Start, How to Identify Stamps* and *Collecting by Theme.* A series of well illustrated guides at a low price.
Write for details.

---

246 *Neoveitchia storckii*   **247** Father Ioane Batita

(Des N. Shewring. Litho Questa)

1994 (31 Aug). *"Singpex '94" International Stamp Exhibition. Endemic Palm. Sheet* 97×69 *mm, containing T* **246** *and similar vert design. Multicoloured. W w* **16.** *P* 14.
MS899 $1.50, Type 246; $1.50, Palm flowers .. 5·00 6·00

(Des S. Noon. Litho Leigh-Mardon Ltd, Melbourne)

1994 (16 Dec). *150th Anniv of Arrival of Catholic Missionaries in Fiji. T* **247** *and similar vert designs. W w* **14.** *P* 14.

900	23 c. Type 247			25	25
901	31 c. Local catechist			30	30
902	44 c. Sacred Heart Cathedral, Suva		40	60
903	63 c. Lomary Church			55	85
904	81 c. Pope Gregory XVI			90	1·25
905	$2 Pope John Paul II			2·00	2·75
900/5			Set of 6	4·00	5·50

248 Waterfall and Banded Iguana   **249** Fiji ("Red-headed") Parrot Finch

(Des B. Dare. Litho Questa)

1995 (27 Mar). *Eco-Tourism in Fiji. Sheet* 140×80 *mm containing T* **248** *and similar square designs. Multicoloured. W w* **16** (*sideways*). *P* 14.
MS906 81 c. Type 248; 81 c. Mountain trekkers and Fiji Tree Frog; 81 c. Bilibili River trip and White-collared Kingfisher; 81 c. Historic sites and Flying Fox .. .. 4·25 5·00

(Des R. Watton. Litho Cartor (Nos. 907/10) or Questa (No. **MS911**))

1995 (8 May). *50th Anniv of End of Second World War. Multicoloured designs as T* **161** *of Ascension. W w* **14** (*sideways*). *P* 13½.

907	13 c. Fijian soldiers guarding crashed Japanese Mitsubishi A6M Zero-Sen aircraft		30	15
908	63 c. American spotter plane landing on Kameli Airstrip, Solomon Islands	..	1·00	1·00
909	87 c. Corporal Sukanaivalu and Victoria Cross	..		1·40	2·00
910	$1.12, H.M.S. *Fiji* (cruiser)		1·60	2·25
907/10		Set of 4	3·75	4·75

MS911 75×85 mm. $2 Reverse of 1939–45 War Medal (*vert*). Wmk upright. P 14 .. .. 2·25 2·75

(Des A. Robinson. Litho Enschedé)

1995 (25 July–7 Nov). *Birds. T* **249** *and similar vert designs. Multicoloured. W w* **14.** *P* 13½×13.

912	1 c. Type 249 (7 Nov)	..	..	10	10
913	2 c. Golden Whistler (7 Nov)			10	10
914	3 c. Versicoloured Flycatcher ("Ogea Flycatcher") (7 Nov)	..	10	10
915	4 c. Peale's Pigeon (7 Nov)			10	10
916	6 c. Blue-headed Flycatcher ("Blue-crested Broadbill") (7 Nov)	..	10	10
917	13 c. Island Thrush	..		10	10
918	23 c. Many-coloured Fruit Dove	..	20	25
919	31 c. Green Heron ("Mangrove Heron")	..	25	30
920	44 c. Purple Swamphen	..		35	40
921	63 c. Fiji Goshawk	..		50	55
922	81 c. Kandavu Fantail	..		60	65
923	87 c. Collared Lory (7 Nov)	..		70	75
924	$1 Scarlet Robin (7 Nov)	..		80	85
925	$2 Peregrine Falcon	..		1·40	1·50
926	$3 Barn Owl	..		2·40	2·50
927	$5 Masked Shining Parrot ("Yellow-breasted Musk Parrot") (7 Nov)	4·00	4·25
912/27		Set of 16	11·50	12·50

No. 922 is inscribed "Kadavu" in error.

1995 (19 Aug). *"JAKARTA '95" Stamp Exhibition, Indonesia. No.* **MS898** *optd "JAKARTA '95" and emblem on sheet margin.*
MS928 $1.50, Type 245; $1.50, Kingfisher with crab in beak .. .. 5·00 6·00

---

250 *Arundina graminifolia*   **251** Pres. Ratu Sir Kamisese Mara, Parliament Building and National Flag

(Des I. Loe. Litho Questa)

1995 (1 Sept). *Orchids. Sheet* 100×80 *mm, containing T* **250** *and similar vert design. Multicoloured. W w* **16.** *P* 14.
MS929 $1 Type 250; $1 *Phaius tankervilliae* .. 3·25 3·75
No. **MS929** also includes "Singapore '95" and emblem on the sheet margin.

(Des S. Noon. Litho B.D.T.)

1995 (4 Oct). *25th Anniv of Independence. T* **251** *and similar horiz designs. Multicoloured. W w* **14** (*sideways*). *P* 13½.

930	81 c. Type 251			90	1·00
931	87 c. Young citizens of Fiji		95	1·10
932	$1.06, Rugby players			1·25	1·60
933	$2 Boeing 747 *Island of Viti Levu*	2·25	2·75
930/3			Set of 4	4·75	5·75

252 "Praying Madonna with the Crown of Stars" (workshop of Correggio)   **253** Trolling Lure

(Des D. Miller. Litho Cartor)

1995 (22 Nov). *Christmas. T* **252** *and similar vert designs. Multicoloured. W w* **14.** *P* 13×13½.

934	10 c. Type 252			20	10
935	63 c. "Madonna and Child with Crowns" (on porcelain)		80	80
936	87 c. "The Holy Virgin with the Holy Child and St. John" (after Titian)		1·10	1·25
937	$2 "The Holy Family and St. John" (workshop of Rubens)		2·50	3·50
934/7			Set of 4	4·25	5·00

(Des B. Dare. Litho Walsall)

1996 (24 Jan). *50th Anniv of Resettlement of Banabans (inhabitants of Ocean Island) in Fiji. T* **253** *and similar multicoloured designs. W w* **14** (*sideways on horiz designs*). *P* 14½.

938	81 c. Type 253			90	1·10
939	87 c. Banaban fishing canoes		95	1·10
940	$1.12, Banaban warrior (*vert*)		1·25	1·75
941	$2 Great Frigate Bird (*vert*)		3·25	3·75
938/41			Set of 4	5·75	7·00

254 L2B Portable Tape Recorder   **255** Winged Monster and Ring (bronze), c 450 B.C.

(Des N. Shewring. Litho Walsall)

1996 (11 Mar). *Centenary of Radio. T* **254** *and similar vert designs. Multicoloured. W w* **14.** *P* 14½×14.

942	44 c. Type 254			55	45
943	63 c. Broadcasting House, Fiji		75	70
944	81 c. Communications satellite		90	1·25
945	$3 Gugliemo Marconi			3·50	4·25
942/5			Set of 4	5·25	6·00

(Des G. Vasarhelyi. Litho B.D.T.)

1996 (25 Apr). *"CHINA '96" 9th Asian International Stamp Exhibition, Peking. T* **255** *and similar vert designs. Multicoloured.* W w **16**. *P* 13½.

946	63 c. Type **255**	..	..	75	65
947	81 c. Archer (terracotta sculpture), 210 B.C.		90	1·10
948	$1 Dragon plate, 1426–35			1·25	1·50
949	$2 Central Asian horseman (sculpture), 706			2·75	3·50
946/9			*Set of 4*	5·00	6·00
MS950	81×127 mm. 30 c. "Yan Deng Mountains" (painting) (48½×76 mm). Wmk sideways. P 13			55	75

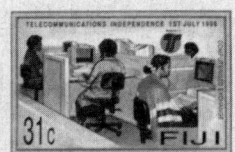

256 Hurdling   257 Computerised Telephone Exchange

(Des S. Noon. Litho Southern Colour Print, Dunedin, New Zealand)

1996 (18 June). *Centenary of Modern Olympic Games. T* **256** *and similar vert designs. Multicoloured.* W w **14**. *P* 14.

951	31 c. Type **256**	..	..	35	30
952	63 c. Judo	..		70	60
953	87 c. Sailboarding ..	..		90	1·10
954	$1.12, Swimming	..		1·25	1·60
951/4			*Set of 4*	2·75	3·25
MS955	59×99 mm. $2 Winning athlete, 1896. Wmk sideways			2·10	2·50

(Des G. Vasarhelyi. Litho Walsall)

1996 (1 July). *Inauguration of Independent Postal and Telecommunications Companies. T* **257** *and similar multicoloured designs.* W w **14** *(sideways on horiz designs). P* 14.

956	31 c. Type **257**	..	..	35	30
957	44 c. Unloading mail from aircraft	..	60	55
958	81 c. Manual telephone exchange (*vert*)	90	1·25
959	$1 Postman on motorbike (*vert*)		1·25	1·60
956/9			*Set of 4*	2·75	3·25
MS960	120×77 mm. $1.50, Fiji 1938 ½d. Sailing canoe stamp (*vert*); $1.50, Fiji 1985 20 c. "Expo '85" stamp (*vert*) .. .. *Set of 2 sheets*			3·25	4·00

258 "Our Children Our Future"

(Adapted Jennifer Toombs. Litho Questa)

1996 (13 Aug). *50th Anniv of U.N.I.C.E.F. Children's Paintings. T* **258** *and similar horiz designs. Multicoloured.* W w **16** *(sideways). P* 14½.

961	81 c. Type **258**	..	..	1·00	85
962	87 c. "Village Scene"	..		1·10	95
963	$1 "Living in Harmony the World over"	1·25	1·25
964	$2 "Their Future"	..		2·25	3·00
961/4			*Set of 4*	5·00	5·50

259 First Seaplane in Fiji, 1921

(Des N. Shewring. Litho Walsall)

1996 (1 Oct). *50th Anniv of Nadi International Airport. T* **259** *and similar horiz designs. Multicoloured.* W w **16** *(sideways). P* 14.

965	31 c. Type **259**	..	..	40	30
966	44 c. Nadi Airport in 1946	..		60	50
967	63 c. Arrival of first jet airliner, 1959	80	80
968	87 c. Airport entrance	..		1·10	1·25
969	$1 Control tower	..		1·40	1·60
970	$2 Diagram of Global Positioning System	2·25	3·00
965/70			*Set of 6*	6·00	6·75

260 The Annunciation and Fijian beating Lali (drum)

(Des M. Raj. Litho Questa)

1996 (20 Nov). *Christmas. T* **260** *and similar horiz designs. Multicoloured.* W w **14** *(sideways). P* 13½×14.

971	13 c. Type **260**	..		20	15
972	81 c. Shepherds with sheep, and canoe	..	90	85
973	$1 Wise men on camels, and people on cross		1·25	1·40
974	$3 The Nativity, and Fijian blowing conch	3·25	4·00
971/4		..	*Set of 4*	5·00	5·75

261 Brahman   262 Black-throated Shrikebill

(Des G. Vasarhelyi. Litho B.D.T.)

1997 (12 Feb). *"HONG KONG '97" International Stamp Exhibition. Cattle. Sheet* 130×92 *mm, containing T* **261** *and similar horiz designs. Multicoloured.* W w **14** *(sideways). P* 14.

MS975 $1 Type **261**; $1 Friesian (Holstein); $1 Hereford; $1 Fiji draught bullock ..   4·00   4·50

No. MS975 is inscribed "FREISIAN" in error

(Des A. Robinson and Jennifer Toombs. Litho B.D.T.)

1997 (21 Feb). *"SINGPEX '97" Stamp Exhibition, Singapore. Sheet* 92×78 *mm.* W w **14**. *P* 14×15.

MS976   **262** $2 multicoloured ..   ..   2·10   2·40

263 *Dendrobium biflorum*   264 Hawksbill Turtle laying Eggs

(Des M. Raj. Litho B.D.T.)

1997 (22 Apr). *Orchids. T* **263** *and similar vert designs. Multicoloured.* W w **16**. *P* 14.

977	81 c. Type **263**	..		90	90
978	87 c. *Dendrobium dactylodes*	..		95	95
979	$1.06, *Spathoglottis pacifica*	..		1·10	1·25
980	$2 *Dendrobium macropus*	..		2·25	2·50
977/80			*Set of 4*	4·75	5·00

(Des Sue Wickison. Litho B.D.T.)

1997 (26 May). *Life Cycle of Hawksbill Turtle. Sheet* 140×85 *mm, containing T* **264** *and similar horiz designs. Multicoloured.* W w **14** *(sideways). P* 14.

MS981   63 c. Type **264**; 81 c. Turtles hatching; $1.06, Young turtles swimming; $2 Adult turtle   4·50   4·75

265 Branching Hard Coral   266 Fijian Monkey-faced Bat

(Des M. Raj. Litho Walsall)

1997 (16 July). *Year of the Coral Reef. T* **265** *and similar horiz designs. Multicoloured.* W w **16** *(sideways). P* 14.

982	63 c. Type **265**	..	..	70	55
983	87 c. Massive Hard Coral	..		1·00	1·00
984	$1 White Soft Coral	..		1·25	1·25
985	$3 Pink Soft Coral	..		3·50	3·75
982/5			*Set of 4*	5·75	6·00

(Des Sue Wickison. Litho Enschedé)

1997 (15 Oct). *Endangered Species. Fijian Monkey-faced Bat. T* **266** *and similar vert designs showing bats. P* 13½.

986	44 c. multicoloured	..	..	50	40
987	63 c. multicoloured	..	..	70	55
988	81 c. multicoloured	..	..	95	1·00
989	$2 multicoloured	..	..	2·25	2·50
986/9			*Set of 4*	4·00	4·00
MS990	157×106 mm. Nos. 986/9, each × 2	..	8·00	8·25

267 Waisale Serevi (Captain)   268 Shepherd and Angel

(Des G. Vasarhelyi. Litho Walsall)

1997 (31 Oct). *Fiji Rugby Club's Victory in Hong Kong Rugby Sevens Competition. T* **267** *and similar multicoloured designs.* W w **16** *(sideways). P* 14.

991	50 c. Type **267**	..	..	60	70
	a. Sheetlet. Nos. 991/1001	..	6·00	
992	50 c. Taniela Qauqau	..	..	60	70
993	50 c. Jope Tuikabe	..		60	70
994	50 c. Leveni Duvuduvukula	..		60	70
995	50 c. Inoke Maraiwai	..		60	70
996	50 c. Aminiasi Naituyaga	..		60	70
997	50 c. Lemki Koroi	..		60	70
998	50 c. Marika Vunibaka	..		60	70
999	50 c. Luke Erenavula	..		60	70
1000	50 c. Manasa Bari	..		60	70
1001	$1 Fijian rugby team (56×42 mm)	..	80	85
991/1001			*Set of 11*	6·00	7·00

Nos. 991/1001 were printed together, *se-tenant*, in sheetlets of 11 with the 50 c. stamps arranged in two rows of 5 above an illustrated margin containing the $1.

(Des Jennifer Toombs. Litho Questa)

1997 (18 Nov). *Christmas. T* **268** *and similar horiz designs. Multicoloured.* W w **14** *(sideways). P* 14½.

1002	13 c. Type **268**	..	..	15	10
1003	31 c. Mary, Joseph and baby Jesus	..	35	30
1004	87 c. The Three Kings	..		90	90
1005	$3 Mary and baby Jesus	..		3·00	3·25
1002/5			*Set of 4*	4·00	4·00

269 Chief in War Dress   270 Man in Wheelchair using Computer

(Des M. Raj. Litho Questa)

1998 (20 Jan). *Traditional Chiefs' Costumes. T* **269** *and similar vert designs. Multicoloured.* W w **16**. *P* 14.

1006	81 c. Type **269**	..	..	60	65
1007	87 c. Formal dress	..	..	70	75
1008	$1.12, Presentation dress	..		90	95
1009	$2 War dress of Highland chief	..	1·40	1·50
1006/9			*Set of 4*	3·50	3·75

(Des G. Vasarhelyi. Litho Cartor)

1998 (13 Mar). *Asian and Pacific Decade of Disabled People. T* **270** *and similar horiz designs. Multicoloured.* W w **14** *(sideways). P* 13½×13.

1010	63 c. Type **270**	..	..	50	55
1011	87 c. Woman with child	..	..	70	75
1012	$1 Man at desk	..	..	80	85
1013	$2 Wheelchair race	..		1·40	1·50
1010/13			*Set of 4*	3·50	3·75

STAMP BOOKLETS

1909. *Black and red cover. Stapled.*
SB1 2s. booklet containing eleven ½d. (No. 118) in blocks of 5 and 6, and eighteen 1d. (No. 119) in blocks of 6 .. .. £2500

1914. *Black on red cover. Stapled.*
SB2 2s. booklet containing eleven ½d. (No. 126) in blocks of 5 and 6, and eighteen 1d. (No. 127) in blocks of 6 .. .. £2000

1939 (10 Mar)–**40.** *Black on green (No. SB3) or black on pink (No. SB4) covers. No advertising pages. Stapled.*
SB3 3s. booklet containing eight ½d. and eight 1d. (Nos. 249/50) in blocks of 8 and twelve 2d. (No. 253) in blocks of 6 .. .. .. £600
   a. Including four advertising pages (black on buff cover) (1940) .. ..
SB4 5s. 9d. booklet containing ten ½d. and ten 1d. (Nos. 249/50) in blocks of 10 and twenty-seven 2d. (No. 253) in blocks of 9 .. .. £1800
   a. Including four advertising pages (1940) ..
Nos. SB3/4 were produced locally and Nos. SB3a/4a by De La Rue.

1967 (23 Jan). *Black on salmon cover. Stitched.*
SB5 2s. booklet containing eight 3d. (No. 313) in blocks of four .. .. 7·50
   The first printing was not released by the Crown Agents, but a second printing was released in London on 30.6.67. The first printing had 4d. as the surface-rate for letters to the British Commonwealth on the inside back cover (*Price* £8); in the second printing this was corrected to 3d.

1969 (27 Feb). *Black on salmon cover. Stitched.*
SB6 20 c. booklet containing ten 2 c. (No. 392) in two blocks of 4 and a vert pair .. .. 4·50

1970 (27 Oct). *Black on salmon cover. Stitched.*
SB7 20 c. booklet containing four 1 c. and eight 2 c. (Nos. 391/2) in blocks of 4 .. .. 5·50

1971 (22 Nov). *Black on blue cover. Stitched.*
SB8 20 c. booklet containing 2 c. (No. 436) in block of 10 5·50

1973 (7 Sept)–**74.** *Black on blue cover. Stitched.*
SB9 20 c. booklet containing 1 c. in block of 8 and 2 c. in block of 6 (Nos. 435/6) .. .. 8·50
   a. With 2 c. watermark sideways (No. 459) (28.3.74) .. .. 7·50

POSTAGE DUE STAMPS

D 1

D 2

(Typo Govt Printer, Suva)

1917 (1 Jan). *Thick yellowish white laid paper. No gum.* P 11.
D1 D 1 ½d. black £650 £350
   a. *Se-tenant* strip of 8: 1d. (×3) + ½d. + 4d. + 3d. (×3) £12000
D2 1d. black .. .. .. £275 70·00
D3 2d. black .. .. .. £225 60·00
D4 3d. black .. .. .. £275 75·00
D5 4d. black £650 £350
   Nos. D1/2 and D4/5 were printed, *se-tenant*, in sheets of 96 (8×12) with each horizontal row containing three 1d., one ½d., one 4d. and three 3d. in that order. Only thirty-one such sheets were issued. The 2d. was printed separately in sheets of 84 (7×12). On all these sheets marginal copies were imperforate on the outer edge.

1917 (21 April)–**18.** *Narrower setting, value in ½d. as Type* D **2.**
D5a ½d. black £450 £225
D5b 1d. black £225 £110
D5c 2d. black (5.4.18) £800 £500
   1d. and 2d. stamps must have wide margins (3½ to 4 mm) on the vertical sides to be Nos. D2 or D3. Stamps with narrow margins of approximately the same width on all four sides are Nos. D5b or D5c.
   Nos. D5a/c were printed in separate sheets of 84 (7 × 12). The marginal copies are perforated on all sides.

D 3

D 4

(Typo D.L.R.)

1918 (1 June). *Wmk Mult Crown CA.* P 14.
D 6	D 3	½d. black	..	..	..	..	2·50	14·00
D 7		1d. black	..	..	..	..	3·50	4·50
D 8		2d. black	..	..	..	..	2·75	7·50
D 9		3d. black	..	..	..	..	3·25	40·00
D10		4d. black	..	..	..	..	5·50	22·00
D6/10			..	..	..	Set of 5	16·00	80·00
D6/10 Optd "Specimen"					Set of 5	£150		

No postage due stamps were in use between 31 August 1931 and 3 July 1940.

(Typo Waterlow)

1940 (3 July). *Wmk Mult Script CA.* P 12½.
D11	D 4	1d. emerald-green	..	..	..		6·00	50·00
D12		2d. emerald-green	..	..	..		8·00	50·00
D13		3d. emerald-green	..	..	..		10·00	55·00
D14		4d. emerald-green	..	..	..		13·00	60·00
D15		5d. emerald-green	..	..	..		14·00	60·00
D16		6d. emerald-green	..	..	..		16·00	65·00
D17		1s. carmine-lake	..	..	..		20·00	90·00
D18		1s. 6d. carmine-lake	..	..	..		21·00	£130
D11/18			..	..	..	Set of 8	95·00	£500
D11/18 Perf "Specimen"					Set of 8	£180		

All values are known with forged postmarks, including one of Levuka dated "8 APR 41" and others of Suva dated "12 AUG 42", "14 AU 42" or "20 MR 45".

The use of postage due stamps was discontinued on 30 April 1946.

Quality British & Commonwealth Stamps Direct to Your Door

Irresistibly simple, exceptionally quick and reassuringly reliable. Stanley Gibbons Mail Order service enables you to build your collection economically from the comfort of your own home.

We Provide:

- Free advice from our team of international specialists.
- Large stocks of guaranteed quality material.
- Fast 48 hour order despatch.
- Regular well produced, illustrated brochures and lists.
- Exclusive special offers mailed regularly.
- Wants lists service available.

Telephone 0171 836 8444 for free copies of our latest Great Britain, Channel Islands, Australia, Canada, New Zealand and Falkland Islands brochures.

Or send your wants list to:
Stanley Gibbons Mail Order
399 Strand, London
WC2R 0LX
and we'll do our best to help.

STANLEY GIBBONS
Mail Order

• **OUR NAME IS YOUR GUARANTEE OF QUALITY** •

Gambia

PRICES FOR STAMPS ON COVER TO 1945

Nos. 1/4	*from* × 20
Nos. 5/8	*from* × 15
Nos. 10/20	*from* × 20
Nos. 21/31	*from* × 40
Nos. 32/6	*from* × 20
Nos. 37/44	*from* × 10
Nos. 45/68	*from* × 8
Nos. 69/70	*from* × 20
Nos. 72/85	*from* × 8
Nos. 86/142	*from* × 5
Nos. 143/6	*from* × 6
Nos. 147/9	*from* × 8
Nos. 150/61	*from* × 3

WEST AFRICAN SETTLEMENT

British traders were active in the River Gambia area from the beginning of the 17th century, but it was not until 1808 that it was officially recognised as a Settlement. Administration passed from the merchants to the Governor of Freetown (Sierra Leone) in 1821 and in 1843 Gambia became a separate colony with a Protectorate declared over the banks of the river for 300 miles inland in 1857. A period of colonial retrenchment in 1865 saw a return to Settlement status under Sierra Leone, but Gambia once again became a Crown Colony in 1888.

There was no government postal service before 1858.

PRICES. The prices of Nos. 1 to 8 are for fine copies, with good margins and embossing. Brilliant or poor copies can be supplied at prices consistent with their condition.

DOUBLE EMBOSSING. The majority of the stamps of T 1 with so-called "double embossing" are merely specimens in which the printing and embossing do not register accurately and have no special value. We no longer list "twice embossed" or "twice embossed, once inverted" varieties as they are considered to be outside the scope of this catalogue.

1

(Typo and embossed by D.L.R.)

1869 (18 Mar)–**72.** *No wmk. Imperf.*

1	1	4d. brown		£475	£160
2		4d. pale brown (1871)		£400	£200
3		6d. deep blue		£425	£180
3a		6d. blue ..		£500	£150
4		6d. pale blue (17.2.72)		£2250	£1000

Our prices for the 6d. pale blue, No. 4, are for stamps which are pale by comparison with specimens of the "deep blue" and "blue" colour groups listed under Nos. 3 and 3a. The date given is the earliest known postmark. An exceptionally pale shade is recognized by specialists and this is rare.

1874 (Aug). *Wmk Crown CC. Imperf.*

5	1	4d. brown		£350	£180
6		4d. pale brown		£350	£180
7		6d. deep blue		£300	£200
8		6d. blue ..		£300	£180
		a. Sloping label		£500	£300
		b. Wmk sideways		†	—

SLOPING LABEL VARIETY. Traces of this flaw first occur in the 6d. imperforate on R.1/1 and R.1/5. In the perforated printings the variety on R.1/5 is much more pronounced and appears as illustrated above. Our listings give these examples from R.1/5, less noticeable varieties of this type from R.1/1, which slope from right to left, being worth less. These varieties continued to appear until the introduction of a new 6d. plate in 1893, used for No. 34.

1880–81. *Wmk Crown CC. P 14*. A. Wmk sideways. B. Wmk upright.*

				A		B	
10	1	½d. orange		£130	£110	6·00	10·00
11		½d. dull orange			†	6·00	10·00
12		1d. maroon		£225	£180	3·25	4·75
13		2d. rose		75·00	42·00	18·00	10·00
14		3d. bright ultramarine		£275	£200	50·00	25·00
14b		3d. pale dull ultramarine		†	48·00	25·00
15		4d. brown		£250	42·00	£140	14·00
16		4d. pale brown		£225	38·00	£130	15·00
17		6d. deep blue		£110	75·00	70·00	45·00
		a. Sloping label		£325	£225	£225	£150
18		6d. blue		£110	75·00	70·00	45·00
		a. Sloping label		£325	£225	£225	£150

19	1	1s. green		£350	£200	£180	£100
20		1s. deep green		£350	£200	£180	£100
10/20			*Set of* 7	£1200	£750	£400	£180

*There were three different printings of these stamps. The original supply, sent in June 1880 and covering all seven values, had watermark sideways and was perforated by a line machine. In October of the same year a further printing of the lowest five values had the watermark changed to upright, but was still with line perforation. The final printing, sent May 1881 and containing all values, also had watermark upright, but was perforated on a comb machine.

1886–93. *Wmk Crown CA, sideways. P* 14.

21	1	½d. myrtle-green (1887)		1·75	1·75
22		½d. grey-green ..		2·50	2·75
22b		1d. maroon		†	£15000
23		1d. crimson (1887)		3·75	4·75
23a		1d. aniline crimson		6·00	8·50
23b		1d. pale carmine		6·00	8·50
24		2d. orange (1887)		8·00	5·50
25		2d. deep orange..		1·40	6·50
26		2½d. ultramarine (1887)		2·00	2·00
27		2½d. deep bright blue		1·75	1·25
28		3d. slate-grey (1886)		3·50	11·00
29		3d. grey ..		2·25	12·00
30		4d. brown (1887)		2·75	2·00
31		4d. deep brown		2·75	2·00
		a. Wmk upright		†	£800
32		6d. yellowish olive-green (1886)		65·00	30·00
		a. Sloping label		£120	75·00
32b		6d. olive-green (1887) ..		55·00	48·00
		ba. Sloping label		£150	£130
33		6d. bronze-green (1889)		23·00	48·00
		a. Sloping label		55·00	80·00
33b		6d. deep bronze-green (1889) ..		23·00	48·00
		ba. Sloping label		55·00	85·00
34		6d. slate-green (1893)		10·00	40·00
35		1s. violet (1887)		3·25	14·00
36		1s. deep violet		3·75	16·00
36b		1s. aniline violet		£100	
21/36			*Set of* 8	24·00	65·00
21/24, 32 Optd "Specimen"			*Set of* 4	£400	

The above were printed in panes of 15 on paper intended for larger panes. Hence the watermark is sometimes misplaced or omitted and letters from "CROWN AGENTS FOR THE COLONIES" from the margin may appear on the stamps.

The ½d., 2d., 3d., 4d., 6d. (No. 32) are known imperforate with watermark Crown CA are known imperforate (*price from* £1100, *unused*).

Only three examples, all used, are recorded of the 1d. maroon, No. 22b.

The previously listed 3d. "pearl-grey" shade has been deleted as it is impossible to distinguish from other 3d. shades when it occurs on a single stamp. Sheets from this late printing can be identified by three coloured dots in the left sheet margin and one in the right, this being the reverse of the normal arrangement.

Only three used examples are known of the 4d. with upright watermark, No. 31a.

CROWN COLONY

2

Normal　　　Malformed "S"　　　Repaired "S"

The Malformed "S" occurs on R. 7/3 of the left pane from Key Plate 2. This was used to print the initial supply all values. Printings of the ½d., 1d. and 2½d. despatched on 24 September 1898 had the "S" repaired as shown above. Subsequent printings of the ½d., 1d. and 3d. were from Key Plate 3.

(Typo D.L.R.)

1898 (2 May)–**1902.** *Wmk Crown CA. P* 14.

37	2	½d. dull green (*shades*) ..		2·00	1·75
		a. Malformed "S"		£150	
		b. Repaired "S"		£170	£140
38		1d. carmine (*shades*)		1·25	75
		a. Malformed "S"		£150	
		b. Repaired "S"		£170	
39		2d. orange and mauve		4·25	3·50
		a. Malformed "S"		£170	
40		2½d. ultramarine..		1·40	1·50
		a. Malformed "S"		£150	
		b. Repaired "S"		£180	
41		3d. reddish purple and blue		11·00	12·00
		a. Malformed "S"		£200	
		b. *Deep purple and ultramarine* (1902)		85·00	£100
42		4d. brown and blue		7·00	24·00
		a. Malformed "S"		£180	
43		6d. olive-green and carmine		8·50	19·00
		a. Malformed "S"		£200	
44		1s. violet and green		23·00	48·00
		a. Malformed "S"		£300	
37/44			*Set of* 8	50·00	£100
37/44 Optd "Specimen"			*Set of* 8	£150	

3　　　　　4

Dented frame (R. 1/6 of left pane)

1902 (13 Mar)–**05.** *Wmk Crown CA. P* 14.

45	3	½d. green (19.4.02)		2·00	2·00
		a. Dented frame		45·00	
46		1d. carmine		1·25	70
		a. Dented frame		42·00	
47		2d. orange and mauve (14.6.02)		3·25	2·00
		a. Dented frame		75·00	
48		2½d. ultramarine (14.6.02)		24·00	16·00
		a. Dented frame		£170	
49		3d. purple and ultramarine (19.4.02)		12·00	3·50
		a. Dented frame		£140	
50		4d. brown and ultramarine (14.6.02)		3·00	22·00
		a. Dented frame		£100	
51		6d. pale sage-green & carmine (14.6.02)		3·25	10·00
		a. Dented frame		£100	
52		1s. violet and green (14.6.02)		48·00	75·00
		a. Dented frame		£250	
53	4	1s. 6d. green and carmine/*yellow* (6.4.05)		5·50	15·00
		a. Dented frame		£150	
54		2s. deep slate and orange (14.6.02)		40·00	48·00
		a. Dented frame		£225	
55		2s. 6d. purple and brown/*yellow* (6.4.05)		15·00	48·00
		a. Dented frame		£180	
56		3s. carmine and green/*yellow* (6.4.05)		19·00	48·00
		a. Dented frame		£180	
45/56			*Set of* 12	£160	£250
45/56 Optd "Specimen"			*Set of* 12	£180	

1904 (Aug)–**06.** *Wmk Mult Crown CA. P* 14.

57	3	½d. green (9.05)..		3·25	25
		a. Dented frame		55·00	
58		1d. carmine		4·00	15
		a. Dented frame		70·00	
59		2d. orange and mauve (23.2.06)		11·00	2·25
		a. Dented frame		£140	
60		2½d. bright blue (8.05)		3·50	4·00
		a. *Bright blue and ultramarine*		12·00	23·00
		b. Dented frame		75·00	
61		3d. purple and ultramarine (9.05)		5·00	2·00
		a. Dented frame		90·00	
62		4d. brown and ultramarine (23.2.06)		14·00	38·00
		a. Dented frame		£150	
63	4	5d. grey and black (6.4.05)		11·00	14·00
		a. Dented frame		£140	
64	3	6d. olive-green and carmine (23.2.06)		11·00	38·00
		a. Dented frame		£140	
65	4	7½d. green and carmine (6.4.05)		6·00	27·00
		a. Dented frame		£100	
66		10d. olive and carmine (6.4.05)		15·00	22·00
		a. Dented frame		£140	
67	3	1s. violet and green (9.05)		15·00	48·00
		a. Dented frame		£170	
68	4	2s. deep slate and orange (7.05)		55·00	65·00
		a. Dented frame		£250	
57/68			*Set of* 12	£140	£225
63, 65/6 Optd "Specimen"			*Set of* 3	70·00	

See also Nos. 72/85.

HALF PENNY

ONE PENNY

(5)　　　　　　(6)

1906 (10 Apr). *Nos. 55 and 56 surch with T* 5 *or* 6 *by Govt Printer.*

69		½d. on 2s. 6d. purple and brown/*yellow*		45·00	65·00
		a. Dented frame		£300	
70		1d. on 3s. carmine and green/*yellow*		55·00	30·00
		a. Surch double		£1800	£5000
		b. Dented frame		£350	

No. 69 was surcharged in a setting of 30 (6 × 5), the spacing between the words and the bars being 5 mm on rows 1, 2 and 5; and 4 mm on rows 3 and 4. Constant varieties occur on R.2/1 (broken "E") and R.5/1 (dropped "Y") of the setting.

No. 70 was surcharged in a setting of 60 (6 × 10) and a similar dropped "Y" variety occurs on R.6/3 and R.8/5.

Both values were withdrawn on 24 April when fresh supplies of ½d. and 1d. definitives were received from London.

1909 (1 Oct). *Colours changed. Wmk Mult Crown CA. P* 14.

72	3	½d. blue-green		2·75	2·75
		a. Dented frame		55·00	
73		1d. red		4·00	15
		a. Dented frame		70·00	
74		2d. greyish slate		1·60	7·50
		a. Dented frame		75·00	
75		3d. purple/*yellow*		3·00	1·25
		a. *Purple/lemon-yellow*		5·50	1·75
		b. Dented frame		85·00	
76		4d. black and red/*yellow*		80	65
		a. Dented frame		85·00	
77	4	5d. orange and purple		1·25	1·25
		a. Dented frame		90·00	

78	3	6d. dull and bright purple	..	1·75	2·25
		a. Dented frame	..	90·00	
79	4	7½d. brown and blue	..	1·75	2·50
		a. Dented frame	..	90·00	
80		10d. pale sage-green and carmine	..	2·25	6·50
		a. Dented frame	..	£100	
81	3	1s. black/green ..	..	2·50	14·00
		a. Dented frame	..	£100	
82	4	1s. 6d. violet and green	..	9·50	45·00
		a. Dented frame	..	£150	
83		2s. purple and bright blue/blue	..	13·00	19·00
		a. Dented frame	..	£150	
84		2s. 6d. black and red/blue	..	21·00	19·00
		a. Dented frame	..	£180	
85		3s. yellow and green	..	22·00	42·00
		a. Dented frame	..	£190	
72/85			Set of 14	75·00	£150
73/85 Optd "Specimen"			Set of 13	£225	

Most values between Nos. 45 and 85 are known with forged postmarks. These include circular types of Bathurst, dated "JA 2 97", and Macarthy Island, dated "FE 17 10", and an oval registered Gambia postmark dated "22 JU 10".

7   8   Split "A" (R. 8/3 of left pane) (ptgs to 1918)

(Typo D.L.R.)

1912 (1 Sept)–**22.** Wmk Mult Crown CA. Chalk-surfaced paper (5s.). P 14.

86	7	½d. deep green	..	80	1·00
		a. Green	..	1·75	1·00
		b. Pale green (1916)	..	2·50	2·50
		c. Split "A" ..	..	45·00	
87		1d. red	..	2·50	70
		a. Rose-red	..	1·50	30
		b. Scarlet (1916)	..	2·50	90
		c. Split "A" ..	..	55·00	
88	8	1½d. olive-green and blue-green	..	30	30
		a. Split "A" ..	..	55·00	
89	7	2d. greyish slate	..	45	2·25
		a. Split "A" ..	..	55·00	
90		2½d. deep bright blue	..	4·00	3·00
		a. Bright blue	..	4·50	2·50
		b. Split "A" ..	..	90·00	
91		3d. purple/yellow	..	30	30
		a. On lemon (1917) ..	..	13·00	18·00
		b. On orange-buff (1920)	..	10·00	8·50
		c. On pale yellow	..	80	75
		d. Split "A" ..	..	65·00	
92		4d. black and red/yellow	..	75	8·50
		a. On lemon (1917) ..	..	2·00	6·50
		b. On orange-buff (1920)	..	6·50	10·00
		c. On pale yellow	..	1·50	6·00
		d. Split "A" ..	..	75·00	
		w. Wmk inverted	..	65·00	
93	8	5d. orange and purple	..	70	1·50
		a. Split "A" ..	..	80·00	
94	7	6d. dull and bright purple	..	70	1·50
		a. Split "A" ..	..	80·00	
95	8	7½d. brown and blue	..	90	5·50
		a. Split "A" ..	..	£120	
96		10d. pale sage-green and carmine	..	2·00	17·00
		a. Deep sage-green and carmine	..	2·00	15·00
		b. Split "A" ..	..	£140	
97	7	1s. black/green	..	1·50	1·00
		a. On emerald back (1921)	..	70	14·00
		b. Split "A" ..	..	85·00	
98	8	1s. 6d. violet and green	..	7·00	10·00
		a. Split "A" ..	..	£225	
99		2s. purple and blue/blue	..	2·50	6·00
		a. Split "A" ..	..	£190	
100		2s. 6d. black and red/blue	..	2·75	13·00
		a. Split "A" ..	..	£200	
101		3s. yellow and green	..	7·50	18·00
		a. Split "A" ..	..	£300	
102		5s. green and red/pale yellow (1922)		60·00	90·00
86/102			Set of 17	80·00	£160
86/102 Optd "Specimen" ..			Set of 17	£325	

1921–22. Wmk Mult Script CA. Chalk-surfaced paper (4s.). P 14.

108	7	½d. dull green ..	..	30	12·00
		x. Wmk reversed	..	65·00	
109		1d. carmine-red	..	1·00	3·50
		x. Wmk reversed	..	60·00	10·00
110	8	1½d. olive-green and blue-green	..	1·25	9·50
111	7	2d. grey	..	1·00	1·50
		x. Wmk reversed	..	50·00	
112		2½d. bright blue	..	50	4·00
113	8	5d. orange and purple	..	1·75	13·00
		x. Wmk reversed	..	30·00	
114	7	6d. dull and bright purple	..	1·75	13·00
		x. Wmk reversed	..	20·00	
115	8	7½d. brown and blue	..	2·00	24·00
		x. Wmk reversed	..	20·00	
116		10d. pale sage-green and carmine	..	7·00	15·00
		x. Wmk reversed	..	35·00	
117		4s. black and red (1922)	..	55·00	90·00
		w. Wmk inverted	..	£100	
108/17			Set of 10	65·00	£170
108/17 Optd "Specimen" ..			Set of 10	£200	

Forged postmarks of the types mentioned below No. 85 have also been seen on various values between No. 86 and 117. Collectors should beware of partial strikes which do not show the year date.

9   10

(Recess D.L.R.)

1922 (1 Sept)–**29.** Portrait and shield in black. P 14*.

(a) Wmk Mult Crown CA

118	9	4d. red/yellow (a)	..	1·75	1·50
119		7½d. purple/yellow (a)	..	1·75	6·50
120	10	1s. purple/yellow (a)	..	4·75	18·00
		w. Wmk inverted	..	60·00	
121		5s. green/yellow (c)	..	27·00	80·00
		w. Wmk inverted			
118/21			Set of 4	32·00	95·00
118/21 Optd/H/S "Specimen"			Set of 4	£140	

(b) Wmk Mult Script CA

122	9	½d. green (abd)	..	55	40
123		½d. deep green (bd) (1925)	..	2·25	85
124		1d. brown (abd)	..	70	10
125		1½d. bright rose-scarlet (abd)	..	80	10
126		2d. grey (ab)	..	1·00	2·00
127		2½d. orange-yellow (b)	..	90	8·50
		w. Wmk inverted	..	60·00	
128		3d. bright blue (abd)	..	85	10
129		4d. red/yellow (bd) (1.3.27)	..	3·75	12·00
130		5d. sage-green (a)	..	2·00	10·00
131		6d. claret (ad)	..	1·25	30
132		7½d. purple/yellow (ab) (1927)	..	7·00	35·00
133		10d. blue (a)	..	4·50	18·00
134	10	1s. purple/yellow (aef) (9.24)	..	2·25	60
		a. Blackish purple/yell-buff (c) (1929)	32·00	42·00
135		1s. 6d. blue (af)	..	9·00	12·00
136		2s. purple/blue (ac)	..	3·50	3·25
137		2s. 6d. deep green (a)	..	4·00	9·50
138		3s. bright aniline violet (a)	..	11·00	40·00
139		3s. slate-purple (c) (1928)	..	£180	£350
140		4s. brown (ace)	..	4·00	16·00
141		5s. green/yellow (acf) (9.26)	..	12·00	32·00
142		10s. sage-green (ce)	..	70·00	95·00
122/42			Set of 19	£120	£275
122/42 Optd "Specimen" ..			Set of 19	£400	

Perforations. A number of different perforating machines were used for the various printings of these stamps and the following varieties are known: (a) the original 14 line perforation; (b) 14 × 13.8 comb perforation used for Type 9; (c) 13.8 × 13.7 comb perforation used for Type 10; (d) 13.8 × 13.7 line perforation used for Type 9; (e) 14 × 13.8 compound line perforation used for Type 10; (f) 13.8 × 14 compound line perforation used for Type 10. The occurrence of these perforations on the individual values is indicated by the letters shown after the colour descriptions above.

No. 139 has been faked, but note that this stamp is comb perf 13.8 × 13.7 whereas No. 138 is line perf 14 exactly. There are also shades of the slate-purple.

Most values of the above issue are known with a forged oval registered Gambia postmark dated "22 JU 10", often with the year date not shown. Collectors should exercise particular caution in buying used examples of No. 139.

1935 (6 May). Silver Jubilee. As T 13 of Antigua. Recess B.W. Wmk Mult Script CA. P 11 × 12.

143		1½d. deep blue and scarlet ..	..	50	30
		a. Extra flagstaff	..	£200	
		b. Short extra flagstaff	..	£110	
		c. Lightning conductor	..	£200	
		d. Flagstaff on right-hand turret	..	£150	
		e. Double flagstaff	..	£150	
144		3d. brown and deep blue	..	55	70
		a. Extra flagstaff	..	£150	
		b. Short extra flagstaff	..	£140	
		c. Lightning conductor	..	£120	
145		6d. light blue and olive-green	..	90	1·50
		a. Extra flagstaff	..	£140	
		b. Short extra flagstaff	..	£130	
		c. Lightning conductor	..	£130	
		d. Flagstaff on right-hand turret	..	£225	
146		1s. slate and purple	..	2·50	4·25
		a. Extra flagstaff	..	£200	
		b. Short extra flagstaff	..	£190	
		c. Lightning conductor	..	£170	
		d. Flagstaff on right-hand turret	..	£300	
143/6			Set of 4	4·00	6·00
143/6 Perf "Specimen"			Set of 4	90·00	

For illustrations of plate varieties see Catalogue Introduction. Examples of Nos. 145a and 146a are known with the extra flagstaff erased from the stamp with a sharp point.

1937 (12 May). Coronation. As Nos. 95/7 of Antigua. P 11×11½

147		1d. yellow-brown	..	30	15
148		1½d. carmine	..	30	30
149		3d. blue	..	80	45
147/9			Set of 3	1·25	80
147/9 Perf "Specimen"			Set of 3	60·00	

11 Elephant (from Colony Badge)

(Recess B.W.)

1938 (1 Apr)–**46.** Wmk Mult Script CA. P 12.

150	11	½d. black and emerald-green		15	50
151		1d. purple and brown	..	20	40
152		1½d. brown-lake and bright carmine	..	£140	12·00
		a. Brown-lake and scarlet	..	2·00	1·75
		b. Brown-lake and vermilion	..	30	1·50

152c	11	1½d. blue and black (2.1.45)	..	30	1·25
153		2d. blue and black	..	1·75	2·25
153a		2d. lake and scarlet (1.10.43)	..	60	1·50
154		3d. light blue and grey-blue	..	30	10
154a		5d. sage-green & purple-brn (13.3.41)	..	45	45
155		6d. olive-green and claret	..	1·50	10
156		1s. slate-blue and violet	..	2·00	10
156a		1s. 3d. chocolate & lt blue (28.11.46)	..	1·75	1·75
157		2s. carmine and blue	..	4·50	3·25
158		2s. 6d. sepia and dull green	..	12·00	2·00
159		4s. vermilion and purple	..	20·00	2·50
160		5s. blue and vermilion	..	19·00	4·00
161		10s. orange and black	..	18·00	7·00
150/61			Set of 16	75·00	26·00
150/61 Perf "Specimen"			Set of 16	£225	

1946 (6 Aug). Victory. As Nos. 110/11 of Antigua.

162		1½d. black	..	10	10
163		3d. blue	..	10	10
162/3 Perf "Specimen"			Set of 2	55·00	

1948 (24 Dec). Royal Silver Wedding. As Nos. 112/13 of Antigua.

164		1½d. black	..	25	10
165		£1 mauve	..	12·00	13·00

1949 (10 Oct). 75th Anniv of Universal Postal Union. As Nos. 114/17 of Antigua.

166		1½d. blue-black	..	40	30
167		3d. deep blue	..	1·50	60
168		6d. magenta ..	..	60	30
169		1s. violet	..	60	30
166/9			Set of 4	2·75	1·40

1953 (2 June). Coronation. As No. 120 of Antigua, but ptd by B.W.

170		1½d. black and deep bright blue	..	40	30

12 Tapping for Palm Wine   13 Cutter

(Des Mrs O. W. Meronti. Recess D.L.R.)

1953 (2 Nov)–**59.** T 12/13 and similar horiz designs. Wmk Mult Script CA. P 13½.

171	12	½d. carmine-red and bluish green	..	30	20
		a. Carmine and bluish green (7.1.59)	..	90	1·50
172	13	1d. deep ultramarine and deep brown	..	40	30
		a. Deep ultramarine & choc (22.8.56)	..	2·00	1·25
173	—	1½d. deep brown and grey-black	..	20	50
174	—	2½d. black and carmine-red	..	45	70
175	—	3d. deep blue and slate-lilac	..	35	50
176	—	4d. black and deep blue	..	60	1·75
177	12	6d. brown and reddish purple	..	35	15
178	—	1s. yellow-brown and deep blue	..	60	40
179	13	1s. 3d. ultramarine and pale blue	..	10·00	50
		a. Ultramarine and light blue (22.2.56)	..	12·00	55
180	—	2s. indigo and carmine	..	6·50	3·50
181	13	2s. 6d. deep bluish green and sepia	..	4·00	1·50
182	—	4s. grey-blue and Indian red	..	9·00	2·50
183	—	5s. chocolate and bright blue	..	2·50	1·50
184	—	10s. deep blue and myrtle-green	..	15·00	7·00
185	—	£1 green and black	..	12·00	9·00
171/85			Set of 15	55·00	26·00

Designs:—1½d., 5s. Wollof woman; 2½d., 2s. Barra canoe; 10s. S.S. Lady Wright; 4d., 4s. James Island; 1s., 2s. 6d. Woman hoeing; £1 Elephant and palm (from Colony Badge).

20 Queen Elizabeth II and Palm   21 Queen Elizabeth II and West African Map

(Des J. R. F. Ithier (T 20), A. W. Morley (T 21). Recess B.W.)

1961 (2 Dec). Royal Visit. W w 12. P 11½.

186	20	2d. green and purple	..	20	15
187	21	3d. turquoise-blue and sepia	..	55	15
188		6d. blue and cerise	..	55	50
189	20	1s. 3d. violet and myrtle-green	..	55	1·75
186/9			Set of 4	1·60	2·25

1963 (4 June). Freedom from Hunger. As No. 146 of Antigua.

190		1s. 3d. carmine	..	40	15

1963 (2 Sept). Red Cross Centenary. As Nos. 147/8 of Antigua.

191		2d. red and black	..	25	10
192		1s. 3d. red and blue	..	65	45

SELF-GOVERNMENT

22 Beautiful Sunbird   (35)

(Des V. Whiteley. Photo Harrison)

1963 (4 Nov). *Birds. Horiz designs as T* **22**. *Multicoloured. W w* **12**. *P* 12½ × 13.

193	½d. Type 22		30	60
194	1d. Yellow-mantled Whydah		30	30
195	1½d. Cattle Egret		1·75	70
196	2d. Senegal Parrot		1·75	70
197	3d. Rose-ringed Parakeet		1·75	60
198	4d. Violet Starling		1·75	80
199	6d. Village Weaver		1·75	10
200	1s. Rufous-crowned Roller		1·25	10
201	1s. 3d. Red-eyed Dove		12·00	1·40
202	2s. 6d. Double-spurred Francolin		9·00	2·50
203	5s. Palm-nut Vulture		9·00	2·75
204	10s. Orange-cheeked Waxbill		13·00	7·00
205	£1 African Emerald Cuckoo		28·00	14·00
193/205		Set of 13	70·00	28·00

1963 (7 Nov). *New Constitution. Nos.* 194, 197, 200/1 *optd with T* **35**.

206	1d. Yellow-mantled Whydah		10	20
207	3d. Rose-ringed Parakeet		25	25
208	1s. Rufous-crowned Roller		25	10
	a. Opt double		†	£4000
209	1s. 3d. Red-eyed Dove		30	35
206/9		Set of 4	75	65

1964 (23 Apr). *400th Birth Anniv of William Shakespeare. As No.* 164 *of Antigua.*

210	6d. bright blue		10	10
	w. Wmk inverted		35·00	

INDEPENDENT

36 Gambia Flag   37 Arms
and River

(Des V. Whiteley. Photo Harrison)

1965 (18 Feb). *Independence. P* 14½.

211	36	½d. multicoloured		10	15
212	37	2d. multicoloured		10	10
213	36	7½d. multicoloured		30	20
214	37	1s. 6d. multicoloured		35	20
211/14			Set of 4	70	55

(38)   39 I.T.U. Emblem and Symbols

1965 (18 Feb). *Nos.* 193/205 *optd with T* **38** *or with date centred* (1d., 2d., 3d., 4d., 1s., 5s.).

215	½d. Type 22		30	50
216	1d. Yellow-mantled Whydah		30	20
217	1½d. Cattle Egret		60	40
218	2d. Senegal Parrot		70	30
219	3d. Rose-ringed Parakeet		70	15
220	4d. Violet Starling		70	50
221	6d. Village Weaver		70	10
222	1s. Rufous-crowned Roller		70	10
223	1s. 3d. Red-eyed Dove		70	10
224	2s. 6d. Double-spurred Francolin		70	50
225	5s. Palm-nut Vulture		70	65
226	10s. Orange-cheeked Waxbill		1·60	1·50
227	£1 African Emerald Cuckoo		6·00	7·00
215/27		Set of 13	13·00	10·50

(Des V. Whiteley. Photo Harrison)

1965 (17 May). *I.T.U. Centenary. P* 14½.

228	39	1d. silver and Prussian blue	20	10
229		1s. 6d. gold and bluish violet	65	20

THE GAMBIA. From this point onwards stamps are inscribed "The Gambia".

40 Sir Winston Churchill and Houses of Parliament

(Des Jennifer Toombs. Photo Harrison)

1966 (24 Jan). *Churchill Commemoration. P* 14 × 14½.

230	40	1d. multicoloured	10	10
231		6d. multicoloured	20	10
232		1s. 6d. multicoloured	40	50
230/2		Set of 3	65	60

41 Red-cheeked   42 Pin-tailed Whydah
Cordon Bleu

(Des V. Whiteley. Photo Harrison)

1966 (18 Feb). *Birds. Horiz designs as T* **41**, *and T* **42**. *Multicoloured. P* 14 × 14½ (£1) *or* 12 × 13 (*others*).

233	½d. Type 41		60	40
234	1d. White-faced Whistling Duck		30	40
235	1½d. Red-throated Bee Eater		30	40
236	2d. Lesser Pied Kingfisher		3·75	40
237	3d. Golden Bishop		30	10
238	4d. African Fish Eagle		50	30
239	6d. Yellow-bellied Green Pigeon		40	10
240	1s. Blue-bellied Roller		40	10
241	1s. 6d. African Pygmy Kingfisher		85	30
242	2s. 6d. Spur-winged Goose		95	70
243	5s. Cardinal Woodpecker		1·00	75
244	10s. Violet Turaco		1·00	2·75
245	£1 Type 42		1·00	6·50
233/45		Set of 13	10·00	12·00

The ½d., 1d. and 2d. to 1s. values exist with PVA gum as well as gum arabic.

54 Arms, Early Settlement and Modern Buildings

(Photo, arms die-stamped Harrison)

1966 (24 June). *150th Anniv of Bathurst. P* 14½ × 14.

246	54	1d. silver, brown and yellow-orange	10	10
247		2d. silver, brown and light blue	10	10
248		6d. silver, brown and light emerald	10	10
249		1s. 6d. silver, brown and light magenta	15	15
246/9		Set of 4	30	30

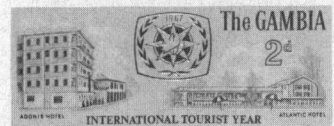

55 I.T.Y. Emblem and Hotels

(Des and photo (emblem die-stamped) Harrison)

1967 (20 Dec). *International Tourist Year. P* 14½ × 14.

250	55	2d. silver, brown and apple-green	10	10
251		1s. silver, brown and orange	10	10
252		1s. 6d. silver, brown and magenta	15	15
250/2		Set of 3	30	30

56 Handcuffs

(Des V. Whiteley. Photo Enschedé)

1968 (15 July). *Human Rights Year. T* **56** *and similar horiz designs. Multicoloured. P* 14 × 13.

253	1d. Type 56		10	10
254	1s. Fort Bullen		10	10
255	5s. Methodist Church		30	50
253/5		Set of 3	35	55

59 Queen Victoria, Queen Elizabeth II and 4d. Stamp of 1869

(Des G. Drummond. Photo and embossing (cameo head) Harrison)

1969 (20 Jan). *Gambia Stamp Centenary. P* 14½ × 13½.

256	59	4d. sepia and yellow-ochre	20	10
257		6d. Prussian blue and deep yellow-green	20	10
258	–	2s. 6d. multicoloured	70	1·00
256/8		Set of 3	1·00	1·10

Design:—2s. 6d. Queen Elizabeth II with 4d. and 6d. stamps of 1869.

In the 6d. value the stamp illustrated is the 6d. of 1869.

61 Catapult-Ship *Westfalen* launching Dornier Do-J II 10-t Wal

(Des L. Curtis. Litho Format)

1969 (15 Dec). *35th Anniv of Pioneer Air Services. T* **61** *and similar horiz designs showing various forms of transport, map of South Atlantic and Lufthansa emblem. Multicoloured. P* 13½ × 14.

259	2d. Type 61		50	20
260	1s. Dornier Do-J II 10-t Wal *Boreas* flying boat		60	20
261	1s. 6d. Airship LZ-127 *Graf Zeppelin*		70	1·40
259/61		Set of 3	1·60	1·60

REPUBLIC

63 Athlete and Gambian Flag

(Des Jennifer Toombs. Litho Format)

1970 (16 July). *Ninth British Commonwealth Games, Edinburgh. P* 14.

262	63	1d. multicoloured		10	10
263		1s. multicoloured		10	10
264		5s. multicoloured		30	30
262/4			Set of 3	35	30

64 President Sir Dawda Kairaba Jawara and State House

(Des G. Vasarhelyi. Litho Questa)

1970 (2 Nov). *Republic Day. T* **64** *and similar multicoloured designs. P* 14.

265	2d. Type 64		10	10
266	1s. President Sir Dawda Jawara		15	10
267	1s. 6d. President and flag of Gambia		30	20
265/7		Set of 3	45	30

The 1s. and 1s. 6d. are both vertical designs.

65 Methodist Church, Georgetown

(Des J. Cooter. Litho Questa)

1971 (16 Apr). *150th Anniv of Establishment of Methodist Mission. T* **65** *and similar multicoloured designs. P* 14.

268	2d. Type 65		10	10
269	1s. Map of Africa and Gambian flag (*vert*)		15	10
270	1s. 6d. John Wesley and scroll (*horiz*)		15	20
268/70		Set of 3	30	30

(New Currency. 100 bututs = 1 dalasy)

66 Yellow-finned Tunny

(Des J.W. Litho Format)

1971 (1 July). *New Currency. Fishes. Horiz designs as T* **66**. *Multicoloured. P* 14.

271	2 b. Type 66		10	40
272	4 b. Peter's Mormyrid		10	15
273	6 b. Four-winged Flyingfish		15	40
274	8 b. African Sleeper Goby		15	40
275	10 b. Yellow-tailed Snapper		20	15
276	13 b. Rock Hind		20	40
277	25 b. West African Eel Catfish		35	40
278	38 b. Tiger Shark		55	45
279	50 b. Electric Catfish		70	55
280	63 b. Black Swampeel		80	1·50
281	1 d. 25, Small-toothed Sawfish		1·40	2·50
282	d. 50, Great Barracuda		2·00	4·50
283	5 d. Brown Bullhead		2·25	7·00
271/83		Set of 13	8·00	17·00

67 Mungo Park in Scotland

(Des J.W. from ideas by P. J. Westwood. Litho Questa)

1971 (10 Sept). *Birth Bicentenary of Mungo Park (explorer). T* **67** *and similar horiz designs. Multicoloured. W w* **12** *(sideways). P* 13½ × 13.

284	4 b. Type **67**	..	..	20	10
285	25 b. Dug-out canoe		..	45	30
286	37 b. Death of Mungo Park, Busa Rapids		75	1·25
284/6 ..			*Set of 3*	1·25	1·50

68 Radio Gambia

(Des G. Drummond. Litho Questa)

1972 (1 July). *Tenth Anniv of Radio Gambia. T* **68** *and similar horiz design. P* 14.

287	**68**	4 b. orange-ochre and black		10	10
288	–	25 b. light new blue, red-orange and black	10	25
289	**68**	37 b. bright green and black	..	20	70
287/9 ..			*Set of 3*	30	90

Design:—25 b. Broadcast-area map.

69 High Jumping   70 Manding Woman

(Des and litho D.L.R.)

1972 (31 Aug). *Olympic Games, Munich. P* 13.

290	**69**	4 b. multicoloured		10	10
291		25 b. multicoloured	..	15	15
292		37 b. multicoloured	..	15	20
290/2 ..			*Set of 3*	30	30

(Des C. Abbott. Litho Questa)

1972 (16 Oct). *International Conference on Manding Studies, London. T* **70** *and similar vert designs. Multicoloured. P* 14 × 14½.

293	2 b. Type **70**	..		10	10
294	25 b. Musician playing the Kora	..	15	15
295	37 b. Map of Mali Empire	..	25	25
293/5 ..			*Set of 3*	40	40

71 Children carrying Fanal   72 Groundnuts

(Des L. Curtis. Litho Enschedé)

1972 (1 Dec). *Fanals (Model Boats). T* **71** *and similar horiz design. Multicoloured. P* 13 × 13½.

296	2 b. Type **71**	..	..	10	10
297	1 d. 25, Fanal with lanterns	..	30	45

(Des locally; adapted G. Drummond. Litho Harrison)

1973 (31 Mar). *Freedom from Hunger Campaign. P* 14½ × 14.

298	**72**	2 b. multicoloured	..	10	10
299		25 b. multicoloured	..	15	10
300		37 b. multicoloured	..	25	20
298/300 ..		..	..	*Set of 3*	40	30

73 Planting and Drying Rice   74 Oil Palm

(Des PAD Studio. Litho J.W.)

1973 (30 Apr). *Agriculture (1st series). T* **73** *and similar vert designs. Multicoloured. P* 14.

301	2 b. Type **73**	..	..	10	10
302	25 b. Guinea Corn	..	..	20	15
303	37 b. Rice	..	..	25	25
301/3 ..			*Set of 3*	45	40

(Des PAD Studio. Litho Format)

1973 (16 July). *Agriculture (2nd series). T* **74** *and similar vert designs. Multicoloured. P* 12.

304	2 b. Type **74**	..	..	10	10
305	25 b. Limes	..	..	30	30
306	37 b. Oil palm (fruits) ..	..	40	40
304/6 ..			*Set of 3*	65	65

75 Cassava

(Des PAD Studio. Litho Questa)

1973 (15 Oct). *Agriculture (3rd series). T* **75** *and similar horiz design. Multicoloured. P* 14.

307	2 b. Type **75**	..	..	10	10
308	50 b. Cotton	..	..	40	25

76 O.A.U. Emblem

(Des and litho D.L.R.)

1973 (1 Nov). *Tenth Anniv of O.A.U. P* 13½ × 13.

309	**76**	4 b. multicoloured		10	10
310		25 b. multicoloured	..	15	10
311		37 b. multicoloured	..	15	20
309/11		..	..	*Set of 3*	30	30

77 Red Cross   78 Arms of Banjul

(Des J. Cooter. Litho Questa)

1973 (30 Nov). *25th Anniv of Gambian Red Cross. P* 14 × 14½.

312	**77**	4 b. dull orange-red, and black	10	10
313		25 b. dull orange-red, black and new blue	15	15
314		37 b. dull orange-red, black & lt yell-grn	20	20
312/14		..	..	*Set of 3*	35	35

(Des and litho D.L.R.)

1973 (17 Dec). *Change of Bathurst's Name to Banjul. P* 13½ × 13.

315	**78**	4 b. multicoloured		10	10
316		25 b. multicoloured	..	15	15
317		37 b. multicoloured	..	15	20
315/17		..	..	*Set of 3*	30	30

79 U.P.U. Emblem

(Des and litho D.L.R.)

1974 (24 Aug). *Centenary of Universal Postal Union. P* 13½.

318	**79**	4 b. multicoloured		10	10
319		37 b. multicoloured	..	20	30

80 Churchill as Harrow Schoolboy   81 "Different Races"

(Des and litho J.W.)

1974 (30 Nov). *Birth Centenary of Sir Winston Churchill. T* **80** *and similar vert designs. Multicoloured. P* 13½.

320	4 b. Type **80**	..	..	10	10
321	37 b. Churchill as 4th Hussars officer..	..	25	15
322	50 b. Churchill as Prime Minister	..	40	60
320/2 ..			*Set of 3*	65	75

(Des G. Vasarhelyi. Litho Questa)

1974 (16 Dec). *World Population Year. T* **81** *and similar horiz designs. Multicoloured. P* 14.

323	4 b. Type **81**	..	..	10	10
324	37 b. "Multiplication and Division of Races"	15	15
325	50 b. "World Population"	..	..	20	25
323/5 ..			*Set of 3*	35	40

82 Dr. Schweitzer and River Scene

(Des G. Vasarhelyi. Litho Walsall)

1975 (14 Jan). *Birth Centenary of Dr. Albert Schweitzer. T* **82** *and similar horiz designs. Multicoloured. P* 14.

326	2 b. Type **82**	..	..	20	10
327	50 b. Surgery scene	..	..	55	55
328	1 d. 25, River journey..	..	1·00	55
326/8 ..			*Set of 3*	1·60	75

83 Dove of Peace   84 Development Graph

(Des and litho D.L.R.)

1975 (18 Feb). *10th Anniv of Independence. T* **83** *and similar horiz designs. Multicoloured. P* 13.

329	4 b. Type **83**	..	..	10	10
330	10 b. Gambian flag	..	..	10	10
331	50 b. Gambian arms	..	..	15	10
332	1 d. 25, Map of The Gambia ..	..	35	40
329/32		..	..	*Set of 4*	50	55

(Des PAD Studio. Litho Questa)

1975 (31 Mar). *Tenth Anniv of African Development Bank. T* **84** *and similar vert designs. Multicoloured. P* 14½.

333	10 b. Type **84**	..	..	10	10
334	50 b. Symbolic plant	..	..	20	15
335	1 d. 25, Bank emblem and symbols	..	55	60
333/5 ..			*Set of 3*	70	75

85 Statue of "David" (Michelangelo)   86 School Building

(Des C. Abbott. Litho Walsall)

1975 (14 Nov). *500th Birth Anniv of Michelangelo. T* **85** *and similar multicoloured designs. P* 14½ × 14 (1 d. 25) *or* 14 × 14½ (*others*).

336	10 b. Type **85**	..	..	15	10
337	50 b. "Madonna of the Steps"	..	45	50
338	1 d. 25, "Battle of the Centaurs" (*horiz*)	75	1·25
336/8 ..			*Set of 3*	1·25	1·40

(Des G. Vasarhelyi. Litho Format)

1975 (17 Nov). *Centenary of Gambia High School. T* **86** *and similar horiz designs. Multicoloured. P* 14½.
339	10 b. Type **86**	..	..	10	10
340	50 b. Pupil with scientific apparatus			15	10
341	1 d. 50, School crest	..	..	35	35
339/41	..	*Set of 3*		50	40

87 "Teaching"

(Des A. B. Oliver; adapted by Jennifer Toombs. Litho Questa)

1975 (15 Dec). *International Women's Year. T* **87** *and similar horiz designs. Multicoloured. P* 14½.
342	4 b. Type **87**	..	..	10	10
343	10 b. "Planting rice"	..	..	10	10
344	50 b. "Nursing"	..	..	35	15
345	1 d. 50, "Directing traffic"			85	35
342/5	..	*Set of 4*		1·25	55

88 Woman playing Golf

89 American Militiaman

(Des R. Granger Barrett. Litho J.W.)

1976 (18 Feb). *11th Anniv of Independence. T* **88** *and similar horiz designs. Multicoloured. P* 14½ × 14.
346	10 b. Type **88**	..	..	55	10
347	50 b. Man playing golf	..	..	1·50	20
348	1 d. 50, President playing golf	..		2·25	70
346/8	..	*Set of 3*		3·75	90

(Des C. Abbott. Litho Questa)

1976 (15 May). *Bicentenary of American Revolution. T* **89** *and similar vert designs. Multicoloured. P* 14 × 13½.
349	25 b. Type **89**	..	..	20	10
350	50 b. Soldier of the Continental Army	..	40	20
351	1 d. 25, Independence Declaration	..	60	60
349/51		*Set of 3*		1·10	80
MS352	110 × 80 mm. Nos. 349/51	..	1·75	4·00

90 Mother and Child

91 Serval

(Des G. Vasarhelyi. Litho Questa)

1976 (28 Oct). *Christmas. P* 14.
353	**90** 10 b. multicoloured	..	..	10	10
354	50 b. multicoloured	..	..	15	10
355	1 d. 25, multicoloured	..	..	50	45
353/5	..	*Set of 3*		60	50

(Des G. Drummond. Litho Questa)

1976 (29 Nov). *Abuko Nature Reserve (1st series). T* **91** *and similar horiz designs. Multicoloured. P* 13½.
356	10 b. Type **91**	..	..	1·75	20
357	25 b. Bushbuck	..	..	2·50	20
358	50 b. Sitatunga	..	..	3·25	40
359	1 d. 25, Leopard	..	..	8·50	2·00
356/9	..	*Set of 4*		14·50	2·50
MS360	137 × 110 mm. Nos. 356/9	..	20·00	9·00

See also Nos. 400/3, 431/5 and 460/3.

92 Festival Emblem and Gambian Weaver

(Des E. N. Sillah; adapted C. Abbott. Litho Walsall)

1977 (12 Jan). *Second World Black and African Festival of Arts and Culture, Nigeria. P* 14.
361	**92** 25 b. multicoloured	..	..	15	10
362	50 b. multicoloured	..	..	20	15
363	1 d. 25, multicoloured	..	..	50	70
361/3	..	*Set of 3*		75	85
MS364	118 × 114 mm. Nos. 361/3	..	1·75	3·75

93 The Spurs and Jewelled Sword

(Des PAD Studio. Litho Questa)

1977 (7 Feb). *Silver Jubilee. T* **93** *and similar horiz designs. Multicoloured. P* 13½.
365	25 b. Queen's visit, 1961	..	..	25	30
366	50 b. Type **93**	..	..	20	25
367	1 d. 25, Oblation of the sword	..	30	35
365/7	..	*Set of 3*		65	80

94 Stone Circles, Kuntaur

(Des J.W. Litho Questa)

1977 (18 Feb). *Tourism. T* **94** *and similar horiz designs. Multicoloured. P* 14.
368	25 b. Type **94**	..	..	10	10
369	50 b. Ruined fort, James Island	..	20	20
370	1 d. 25, Mungo Park Monument	..	70	70
368/70	..	*Set of 3*		90	90

95 Widow of Last Year

96 Endangered Animals

(Des PAD Studio. Litho Questa)

1977 (1 July)–**79**. *Flowers and Shrubs. Multicoloured designs as T* **95**. *Chalk-surfaced paper (No. 376a) or ordinary paper (others). P* 14.
371	2 b. Type **95**	..	..	10	15
	a. Chalk-surfaced paper (23.11.79)	..	40	25
372	4 b. White Water-lily	..	..	10	30
	a. Chalk-surfaced paper (23.11.79)	..	40	30
373	6 b. Fireball Lily	..	..	10	30
	a. Chalk-surfaced paper (22.6.79)	..	40	30
374	8 b. Cocks-comb	..	..	10	15
	a. Chalk-surfaced paper (23.11.79)	..	30	15
375	10 b. Broad Leaved Ground Orchid	..	2·00	30
	a. Chalk-surfaced paper (23.11.79)	..	2·00	30
376	13 b. Fibre Plant (pale yellow background)	15	40
376a	13 b. Fibre Plant (pale olive-grey background)		
	(chalk-surfaced paper) (25.7.79)	..	2·75	3·50
377	25 b. False Kapok	..	..	15	15
	a. Chalk-surfaced paper (16.3.78)	..	55	35
378	38 b. Baobab	..	..	25	55
	a. Chalk-surfaced paper (23.11.79)	..	60	35
379	50 b. Coral Tree	..	..	35	35
	a. Chalk-surfaced paper (16.3.78)	..	75	50
380	63 b. Gloriosa Lily	..	..	40	70
	a. Chalk-surfaced paper (23.11.79)	..	85	65
381	1 d. 25, Bell-flowered Mimosa	..	60	1·25
	a. Chalk-surfaced paper (23.11.79)	..	1·00	1·00
382	2 d. 50, Kindin Dolo	..	..	65	1·25
383	5 d. African Tulip Tree	..	..	85	1·25
371/83	..	*Set of 14*		7·50	9·75

The 6 to 38 b., 1 d. 25 and 2 d. 50 are vertical designs.

(Des N. Fortey (10, 50 b.), D. J. Thorp (25 b.), M. Langley (1 d. 25). Litho Questa)

1977 (15 Oct). *Banjul Declaration. T* **96** *and similar vert designs. P* 14.
384	10 b. black and light new blue	..	..	25	10
385	25 b. multicoloured	..	..	40	10
386	50 b. multicoloured	..	..	65	20
387	1 d. 25, black and light vermilion	..	1·75	75
384/7	..	*Set of 4*		2·75	1·00

Designs:—25 b. Extract from Declaration; 50 b. Declaration in full; 1 d. 25, Endangered insects and flowers.

97 "Flight into Egypt"

98 Dome of the Rock, Jerusalem

(Des BG Studio and Enschedé. Litho Enschedé)

1977 (15 Dec). *400th Birth Anniv of Rubens. T* **97** *and similar vert designs. Multicoloured. P* 13½ × 14.
388	10 b. Type **97**	..	..	15	10
389	25 b. "The Education of the Virgin"	..	25	10
390	50 b. "Clara Serena Rubens"	..	50	30
391	1 d. "Madonna with Saints"	..	90	90
388/91	..	*Set of 4*		1·60	1·25

Nos. 388/91 were each printed in small sheets of 6 including 1 se-tenant stamp-size label.

(Des J. Cooter. Litho Questa)

1978 (3 Jan). *Palestinian Welfare. P* 14½ × 14.
392	**98** 8 b. multicoloured	..	..	50	15
393	25 b. multicoloured	..	..	2·00	85

99 Walking on a Greasy Pole

100 Lion

(Des J.W. Litho Harrison)

1978 (18 Feb). *13th Anniv of Independence. T* **99** *and similar vert designs showing scenes from the Independence Regatta. Multicoloured. P* 14.
394	10 b. Type **99**	..	..	10	10
395	50 b. Pillow fighting	..	..	20	10
396	1 d. 25, Long rowing boat	..	..	45	45
394/6	..	*Set of 3*		60	55

(Des Jennifer Toombs. Litho Questa)

1978 (15 Apr). *25th Anniv of Coronation. T* **100** *and similar vert designs. P* 15.
397	1 d. black, agate and orange-yellow	..	20	45
	a. Sheetlet. Nos. 397/9 × 2	..	1·00	
398	1 d. multicoloured	..	..	20	45
399	1 d. black, agate and orange-yellow	..	20	45
397/9	..	*Set of 3*		50	1·25

Designs:—No. 397, White Greyhound of Richmond; No. 398, Queen Elizabeth II; No. 399, Type **100**.

Nos. 397/9 were printed together in small sheets of 6, containing two se-tenant strips of 3, with horizontal gutter margin between.

101 Verreaux's Eagle Owl

102 M.V. *Lady Wright* (previous vessel)

(Des M. Bryan. Litho Questa)

1978 (28 Oct). *Abuko Nature Reserve (2nd series). T* **101** *and similar vert designs. Multicoloured. P* 14 × 13½.
400	20 b. Type **101**	..	..	4·00	50
401	25 b. Lizard Buzzard	..	..	4·00	50
402	50 b. African Harrier Hawk	..	..	7·00	2·00
403	1 d. 25, Long-crested Eagle	..	12·00	8·00
400/3	..	*Set of 4*		24·00	10·00

(Des A. Theobald. Litho Questa)

1978 (1 Dec). *New River Vessel "Lady Chilel Jawara" Commemoration. T* **102** *and similar horiz designs. Multicoloured. P* 14.
404	8 b. Type **102**	..	..	15	10
405	25 b. Lady Chilel Jawara (sectional view)	40	25
406	1 d. Lady Chilel Jawara	..	..	1·25	1·10
404/6	..	*Set of 3*		1·60	1·25

25b

103 Police Service   (104)

(Des G. Vasarhelyi. Litho Questa)

1979 (18 Feb). *14th Anniv of Independence. T* **103** *and similar horiz designs. Multicoloured. P* 14.
407	10 b. Type **103** ..	60	10
408	50 b. Fire service ..	1·10	25
409	1 d. 25, Ambulance service ..	1·40	80
407/9 ..		*Set of 3* 2·75	1·00

1979 (5–26 Mar). *Nos. 376 and 380/1 surch as T* **104**.
410	25 b. on 13 b. Fibre Plant	20	35
411	25 b. on 63 b. Gloriosa Lily (26.3.79)	15	20
412	25 b. on 1 d. 25, Bell-flowered Mimosa (26.3.79)	15	20
410/12		*Set of 3* 45	65

105 "Ramsgate Sands" (detail showing Children playing on Beach)

(Des C. Abbott. Litho Questa)

1979 (25 May). *International Year of the Child. T* **105** *and similar multicoloured designs showing the painting "Ramsgate Sands" by William Powell Frith. P* 14 × 13½ (25 b.) *or* 13½ × 14 (*others*).
413	10 b. Type **105** ..	10	10
414	25 b. Detail showing child paddling (*vert*) ..	20	10
415	1 d. Complete painting (60 × 23 mm) ..	60	60
413/15 ..		*Set of 3* 80	65

106 1883 2½d. Stamp

(Des J.W. Litho Questa)

1979 (16 Aug). *Death Centenary of Sir Rowland Hill. T* **106** *and similar horiz designs showing stamps. Multicoloured. P* 14.
416	10 b. Type **106** ..	10	10
417	25 b. 1869 4d. ..	15	10
418	50 b. 1965 7½d. Independence commem-orative	20	20
419	1 d. 25, 1935 1½d. Silver Jubilee com-memorative ..	40	50
416/19		*Set of 4* 75	80
MS420	109 × 83 mm. No. 419 ..	65	1·00

107 Satellite Earth Station under Construction

108 "Apollo 11" leaving Launch Pad

(Des A. Theobald. Litho Questa)

1979 (20 Sept). *Abuko Satellite Earth Station. T* **107** *and similar horiz designs. Multicoloured. P* 14.
421	25 b. Type **107** ..	20	10
422	50 b. Satellite Earth Station (completed) ..	30	20
423	1 d. "Intelsat" satellites ..	65	60
421/3 ..		*Set of 3* 1·00	80

(Des and litho Walsall)

1979 (17 Oct). *10th Anniv of Moon Landing. T* **108** *and similar vert designs. Multicoloured.* (*a*) *Sheet stamps. P* 14.
424	25 b. Type **108** ..	20	10
425	38 b. "Apollo 11" in Moon orbit ..	25	20
426	50 b. Splashdown ..	30	40
424/6 ..		*Set of 3* 65	60

(*b*) *Booklet stamps. Roul* 5 × *imperf.* Self-adhesive*
427	25 b. Type **108** ..	25	55
	a. Booklet pane. Nos. 427/9, each × 2	1·60	
428	38 b. As No. 425 ..	30	55
429	50 b. As No. 426 ..	30	55
430	2 d. Lunar module on Moon ..	1·50	2·25
	a. Booklet pane of 1 ..	1·50	

*Nos. 427/9 are separated by various combinations of rotary-knife (giving a straight edge) and roulette. No. 430 exists only with straight edges.

109 *Acraea zetes*

(Des J. Cooter. Litho Questa)

1980 (3 Jan). *Abuko Nature Reserve* (3rd series). *Butterflies. T* **109** *and similar horiz designs. Multicoloured. P* 13½.
431	25 b. Type **109** ..	2·00	20
432	50 b. *Precis hierta* ..	2·50	50
433	1 d. *Graphium leonidas* ..	4·50	60
434	1 d. 25, *Charaxes jasius* ..	4·50	1·10
431/4		*Set of 4* 12·00	2·50
MS435	145×122 mm. Nos. 431/4	18·00	4·50

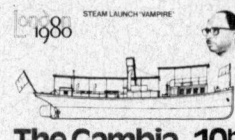

110 Steam Launch *Vampire*

(Des C. Abbott. Litho Harrison)

1980 (6 May). *"London 1980" International Stamp Exhibition. Mail Boats. T* **110** *and similar multicoloured designs. P* 14 (10, 25 b.) *or* 13 × 14 (*others*).
436	10 b. Type **110** ..	20	10
437	25 b. T.S.S. *Lady Denham* ..	30	10
438	50 b. T.S.C.M.Y. *Mansa Kila Ba* (49 × 26 mm) ..	35	20
439	1 d. 25, T.S.S. *Prince of Wales* (49 × 26 mm)..	55	60
436/9 ..		*Set of 4* 1·25	85

111 Queen Elizabeth the Queen Mother

(Des and litho Harrison)

1980 (4 Aug). *80th Birthday of Queen Elizabeth the Queen Mother. P* 14.
440	111	67 b. multicoloured ..	30	35

112 Phoenician Trading Vessel

113 "Madonna and Child" (Francesco de Mura)

(Des A. Theobald. Litho Walsall)

1980 (2 Oct). *Early Sailing Vessels. T* **112** *and similar horiz designs. Multicoloured. P* 14½ × 14.
441	8 b. Type **112** ..	10	10
442	67 b. Egyptian sea-going vessel ..	40	20
443	75 b. Portuguese caravel ..	50	30
444	1 d. Spanish galleon ..	70	50
441/4 ..		*Set of 4* 1·50	1·00

(Des BG Studio. Litho Questa)

1980 (23 Dec). *Christmas. Paintings. T* **113** *and similar vert designs. Multicoloured. P* 14.
445	8 b. Type **113** ..	10	10
446	67 b. "Praying Madonna with Crown of Stars" (workshop of Correggio) ..	25	25
447	75 b. "La Zingarella" (workshop replica of Correggio painting) ..	25	30
445/7 ..		*Set of 3* 50	60

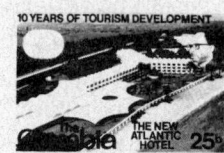

114 New Atlantic Hotel

(Des BG Studio. Litho Format)

1981 (18 Feb). *World Tourism Conference, Manila. T* **114** *and similar horiz designs. Multicoloured. P* 14.
448	25 b. Type **114** ..	15	10
449	75 b. Ancient stone circle ..	30	40
450	85 b. Conference emblem ..	40	25
448/50 ..		*Set of 3* 75	90

115 1979 Abuko Satellite Earth Station 50 b. Commemorative

116 Prince Charles in Naval Uniform

(Des BG Studio. Litho Questa)

1981 (17 May). *World Telecommunications Day. T* **115** *and similar horiz designs. P* 14.
451	50 b. multicoloured ..	40	30
452	50 b. multicoloured ..	40	30
453	85 b. black and brown-ochre ..	60	55
451/3 ..		*Set of 3* 1·25	1·00

Designs:—No. 452, 1975 Birth Centenary of Dr. Albert Schweitzer 50 b. commemorative; No. 453, I.T.U. and W.H.O. emblems.

(Des and litho J.W.)

1981 (22 July). *Royal Wedding. T* **116** *and similar vert designs. Multicoloured. P* 13½ × 13.
454	75 b. Wedding bouquet from Gambia ..	20	20
455	1 d. Type **116** ..	25	30
456	1 d. 25, Prince Charles and Lady Diana Spencer ..	30	35
454/6 ..		*Set of 3* 65	75

117 Planting-out Seedlings

(Des Jennifer Toombs. Litho Format)

1981 (4 Sept). *10th Anniv of West African Rice Development Association. T* **117** *and similar horiz designs. Multicoloured. P* 14.
457	10 b. Type **117** ..	10	10
458	50 b. Care of the crops ..	25	35
459	85 b. Winnowing and drying ..	40	40
457/9 ..		*Set of 3* 65	85

118 Bosc's Monitor

(Des J. Cooter. Litho Format)

1981 (17 Nov). *Abuko Nature Reserve* (4th series). *Reptiles. T* **118** *and similar horiz designs. Multicoloured. P* 14.
460	40 b. Type **118** ..	2·75	20
461	60 b. Dwarf Crocodile ..	3·00	60
462	80 b. Royal Python ..	4·00	1·00
463	85 b. Chameleon ..	4·25	1·00
460/3 ..		*Set of 4* 12·50	2·50

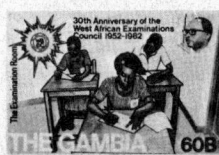

119 Examination Room   (120)

(Des PAD Studio. Litho Walsall)

1982 (16 Mar). *30th Anniv of West African Examinations Council. T* **119** *and similar horiz designs. Multicoloured. P* 14.
464	60 b. Type **119** ..	50	30
465	85 b. First High School ..	65	45
466	1 d. 10, Council's office ..	85	55
464/6 ..		*Set of 3* 1·75	1·10

1982 (19 Apr). *No. 454 surch with T* **120**.
467	60 b. on 75 b. Wedding bouquet from Gambia	1·10	2·25

121 Tree-planting ("Conservation")

(Des L. Curtis. Litho Harrison)

1982 (16 May). *75th Anniv of Boy Scout Movement. T* **121** *and similar horiz designs. Multicoloured. P* 14.
468	85 b. Type **121**	.. ..	2·00	1·25
469	1 d. 25, Woodworking	.. ..	2·25	2·50
470	1 d. 27, Lord Baden-Powell	..	2·50	3·25
468/70		*Set of 3*	6·00	6·25

122 Gambia Football Team

123 Gambia Coat of Arms

(Des A. Theobald. Litho Questa)

1982 (13 June). *World Cup Football Championship, Spain. T* **122** *and similar horiz designs. Multicoloured. P* 14.
471	10 b. Type **122**	.. ..	15	10
472	1 d. 10, Gambian team practice	.. ..	85	70
473	1 d. 25, Bernabéu Stadium, Madrid ..	90	75
474	1 d. 55, FIFA World Cup	.. ..	95	80
471/4		*Set of 4*	2·50	2·10
MS475	114 × 85 mm. Nos. 471/4		4·00	4·50

(Des C. Abbott. Litho Walsall)

1982 (1 July). *21st Birthday of Princess of Wales. T* **123** *and similar vert designs. Multicoloured. P* 14½ × 14.
476	10 b. Type **123**	.. ..	10	10
477	85 b. Princess at Cardiff City Hall, October 1981		30	20
478	1 d. 10, Bride and groom returning to Buckingham Palace		35	35
479	2 d. 50, Formal portrait	.. ..	1·25	1·00
476/9 ..		*Set of 4*	1·75	1·40

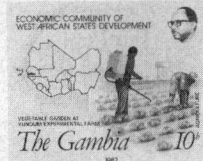

124 Vegetable Garden at Yundum Experimental Farm

(Des Harrison. Litho Questa)

1982 (5 Nov). *Economic Community of West African States Development. T* **124** *and similar horiz designs. Multicoloured. P* 14 × 14½.
480	10 b. Type **124**	.. ..	30	15
481	60 b. Banjul/Kaolack microwave tower	..	2·00	2·25
482	90 b. Soap factory, Denton Bridge, Banjul	2·00	3·00
483	1 d. 25, Control tower, Yundum Airport	3·00	3·50
480/3		*Set of 4*	6·50	8·00

125 *Kassina cassinoides*

(Des PAD Studio. Litho Questa)

1982 (2 Dec). *Frogs. T* **125** *and similar horiz designs. Multicoloured. P* 14.
484	10 b. Type **125**	.. ..	80	15
485	20 b. *Hylarana galamensis*	..	1·50	25
486	85 b. *Euphlyctis occipitalis*	..	2·50	2·00
487	2 d. *Kassina senegalensis*		4·00	6·50
484/7 ..		*Set of 4*	8·00	8·00

126 Satellite View of Gambia

127 Blessed Anne
Marie Javouhey
(foundress of the Order)

(Des Walsall. Litho Questa)

1983 (14 Mar). *Commonwealth Day. T* **126** *and similar horiz designs. Multicoloured. P* 14.
488	10 b. Type **126**	.. ..	10	10
489	60 b. Batik cloth	.. ..	20	45
490	1 d. 10, Bagging groundnuts ..		35	65
491	2 d. 10, Gambia flag	.. ..	55	1·25
488/91		*Set of 4*	1·00	2·25

(Des G. Vasarhelyi. Litho Format)

1983 (8 Apr). *Centenary of Sisters of St. Joseph of Cluny's Work in Gambia. T* **127** *and similar multicoloured design. P* 13½.
492	10 b. Type **127**	.. ..	10	10
493	85 b. Bathurst Hospital, nun and school-children (*horiz*)	.. ..	45	50

128 Canoes

(Des A. Theobald. Litho Walsall)

1983 (11 July). *River Craft. T* **128** *and similar horiz designs. Multicoloured. P* 14.
494	1 b. Type **128**	.. ..	15	40
495	2 b. Upstream ferry	.. ..	20	40
496	3 b. Dredger	.. ..	20	40
497	4 b. *Sir Dawda* (harbour launch)	..	30	40
498	5 b. Cargo liner	.. ..	30	40
499	10 b. *Lady Dale* (60 ft launch)	..	30	10
500	20 b. *Shonga* (container ship)	..	45	40
501	30 b. Large sailing canoe	..	45	40
502	40 b. *Lady Wright* (river steamer)		65	55
503	50 b. Container ship (*different*)		65	55
504	75 b. Fishing boats	.. ..	75	60
505	1 d. Tug with groundnut barges		90	80
506	1 d. 25, Groundnut canoe	..	1·00	1·25
507	2 d. 50, *Banjul* (car ferry)		1·75	2·50
508	5 d. *Bintang Bolong* (freighter)		2·50	4·00
509	10 d. *Lady Chilel Jawara* (river vessel)	4·00	6·50
494/509		*Set of 16*	13·00	18·00

Nos. 494/509 come with a pattern of blue fluorescent security markings, resembling rosettes, printed on the reverse beneath the gum.

129 Osprey in Tree

(Des N. Arlott. Litho Questa)

1983 (12 Sept). *The Osprey. T* **129** *and similar horiz designs. Multicoloured. P* 14.
510	10 b. Type **129**	.. ..	1·50	50
511	60 b. Osprey	.. ..	2·50	2·50
512	85 b. Osprey with catch	.. ..	3·00	3·00
513	1 d. 10, In flight	.. ..	3·50	4·50
510/13		*Set of 4*	9·50	9·50

130 Local Ferry

(Des L. Curtis. Litho Questa)

1983 (10 Oct). *World Communications Year. T* **130** *and similar horiz designs. Multicoloured. P* 14.
514	10 b. Type **130**	.. ..	10	10
515	85 b. Telex operator	.. ..	45	50
516	90 b. Radio Gambia	.. ..	45	50
517	1 d. 10, Loading mail onto Douglas DC-9-80 Super Eighty aircraft	.. ..	60	65
514/17	.. ..	*Set of 4*	1·40	1·60

131 "St. Paul preaching at Athens"
(detail) (Raphael)

(Des C. Abbott. Litho Questa)

1983 (1 Nov). *500th Birth Anniv of Raphael. T* **131** *and similar designs. P* 14.
518	60 b. multicoloured	.. ..	35	40
519	85 b. multicoloured	.. ..	45	50
520	1 d. multicoloured	.. ..	50	55
518/20		*Set of 3*	1·10	1·25
MS521	105 × 83 mm. 2 d. multicoloured ..		1·50	1·25

Nos. 519/21 show different details of "St. Paul preaching at Athens", the 85 b. and 1 d. being horizontal and the 2 d. vertical.

132 Montgolfier Balloon and
Siege of Paris Cover

133 Shot-putting

(Des Harrison. Litho Questa)

1983 (12 Dec). *Bicentenary of Manned Flight. T* **132** *and similar horiz designs. Multicoloured. P* 14.
522	60 b. Type **132**	.. ..	35	40
	a. Booklet pane. Nos. 522/3, each × 2	1·60	
523	85 b. Douglas DC-10 aircraft and flown cover	45	50
524	90 b. Junkers W.33 seaplane *Atlantis* and Hans Bertram cover	45	50
	a. Booklet pane. Nos. 524/5, each × 2	2·25	
525	1 d. 25, Lunar module and H. E. Sieger's space cover	65	70
526	4 d. Airship LZ-127 *Graf Zeppelin*	2·00	3·00
	a. Booklet pane of 1	2·00	
522/6		*Set of 5*	3·50	4·50

Nos. 522/6 come with a pattern of blue fluorescent security markings, resembling rosettes, printed on the reverse beneath the gum.

No. 526 only exists from booklets.

On 14 December 1983 four provisional surcharges, 1 d. 50 on 1 d. 25 (No. 439), 1 d. 50 on 1 d. 25 (No. 473), 2d. on 1 d. 25 (No. 456) and 2 d. on 1 d. 10 (No. 478), were issued in very limited quantities, there being, it is believed, no more than 600 complete sets (*Price for set of 4 £110 mint*).

(Des G. Vasarhelyi. Litho Questa)

1984 (30 Mar). *Olympic Games, Los Angeles (1st issue). T* **133** *and similar multicoloured designs. P* 11.
527	60 b. Type **133**	.. ..	25	30
528	85 b. High jumping (*horiz*)	..	35	40
529	90 b. Wrestling	.. ..	35	40
530	1 d. Gymnastics	.. ..	40	45
531	1 d. 25, Swimming (*horiz*)	..	50	55
532	2 d. Diving	.. ..	80	85
527/32		*Set of 6*	2·40	2·75
MS533	100 × 80 mm. 5 d. Yachting. P 13½ × 14	2·00	2·25

See also Nos. 555/8.

134 Goofy

(Litho Format)

1984 (27 Apr). *Easter. T* **134** *and similar vert designs showing Walt Disney cartoon characters painting eggs. P* 11.
534	1 b. Type **134**	.. ..	10	10
535	2 b. Mickey Mouse	.. ..	10	10
536	3 b. Huey, Dewey and Louie ..		10	10
537	4 b. Goofy (*different*)	..	10	10
538	5 b. Donald Duck	.. ..	10	10
539	10 b. Chip 'n Dale	.. ..	10	10
540	60 b. Pluto	.. ..	35	40
541	90 b. Scrooge McDuck	.. ..	50	60
542	5 d. Morty and Ferdie	.. ..	2·25	2·75
534/42		*Set of 9*	3·00	3·75
MS543	125 × 100 mm. 5 d. Donald Duck (*different*). P 13½ × 14	3·50	3·50

135 Young Crocodiles Hatching

136 Port Banjul

(Des Doreen McGuinness. Litho Format)

1984 (23 May). *Endangered Species. The Nile Crocodile. T* **135** *and similar horiz designs. Multicoloured. P* 14.

544	4 b. Type 135				30	30
545	6 b. Adult carrying young				30	30
546	90 b. Adult				3·75	2·50
547	1 d. 50, Crocodile at riverbank				4·50	5·50
544/7				Set of 4	8·00	7·75

MS548 126×94 mm. As Nos. 544/7, but without W.W.F. logo .. .. 4·50 7·00

Nos. 544/8 come with a pattern of blue fluorescent security markings, resembling rosettes, printed on the reverse beneath the gum.

(Des C. Collins. Litho Questa)

1984 (1 June). *250th Anniv of "Lloyd's List" (newspaper). T* **136** *and similar vert designs. Multicoloured. P* 14½ × 14.

549	60 b. Type 136				60	50
550	85 b. Bulk carrier				75	80
551	90 b. Sinking of the *Dagomba* ..			75	90
552	1 d. 25, 19th century frigate ..			1·25	1·60
549/52				Set of 4	3·00	3·50

Nos. 549/52 come with a pattern of blue fluorescent security markings, resembling rosettes, printed on the reverse beneath the gum.

19th UPU
CONGRESS HAMBURG
(137)

138 Sprinting

1984 (19 June). *Universal Postal Union Congress, Hamburg. Nos.* 507/8 *optd with T* **137**.

| 553 | 2 d. 50, *Banjul* (car ferry) | | | | 1·00 | 1·50 |
| 554 | 5 d. *Bintang Bolong* (ferry) | | | | 1·75 | 2·50 |

(Des G. Vasarhelyi. Litho Walsall)

1984 (27 July). *Olympic Games, Los Angeles (2nd issue). T* **138** *and similar horiz designs. Multicoloured. P* 14.

555	60 b. Type 138				25	30
556	85 b. Long jumping				35	40
557	90 b. Long-distance running ..			35	40
558	1 d. 25, Triple jumping				50	55
555/8				Set of 4	1·25	1·50

Nos. 555/8 come with a pattern of blue fluorescent security markings, resembling rosettes, printed on the reverse beneath the gum.

139 Airship LZ-127 *Graf Zeppelin*

(Des D. Hartley-Marjoram. Litho Questa)

1984 (1 Nov). *50th Anniv of Gambia–South America Transatlantic Flights. T* **139** *and similar horiz designs. Multicoloured. P* 14.

559	60 b. Type 139				1·10	1·00
560	85 b. Dornier Do-J II 10-t Wal on S.S. *Westfalen*				1·60	1·75
561	90 b. Dornier DO-18				1·75	2·50
562	1 d. 25, Dornier Do-J II 10-t Wal			1·75	2·75
559/62				Set of 4	5·50	7·25

Nos. 559/62 come with a pattern of blue fluorescent security markings, resembling rosettes, printed on the reverse beneath the gum.

140 Pink Shrimp

(Des Pam Johnson. Litho Questa)

1984 (27 Nov). *Marine Life. T* **140** *and similar horiz designs. Multicoloured. P* 14.

563	55 b. Type 140				35	30
564	75 b. Atlantic Loggerhead Turtle			55	40
565	1 d. 50, Portuguese Man-of-War			90	1·00
566	2 d. 35, Fiddler Crab				1·40	1·60
563/6				Set of 4	2·75	3·00

MS567 105×70 mm. 5 d. Cowrie Snail .. | 2·75 | 4·00 |

141 *Antanartia hippomene*

(Des Pam Johnson. Litho Questa)

1984 (27 Nov). *Butterflies. T* **141** *and similar horiz designs. Multicoloured. P* 14.

568	10 b. Type 141				30	20
569	85 b. *Pseudacraea eurytus*				80	90
570	90 b. *Charaxes lactitinctus*				80	90
571	3 d. *Graphium pylades*				2·00	3·75
568/71				Set of 4	3·50	5·25

MS572 105×75 mm. 5 d. *Eurema hapale* .. | 10·00 | 9·50 |

142 Oral Re-hydration Therapy

(Des L. Curtis. Litho Harrison)

1985 (27 Feb). *Campaign for Child Survival. T* **142** *and similar horiz designs. P* 14.

573	10 b. black, cobalt and deep cinnamon		10	10
574	85 b. multicoloured				35	45
575	1 d. 10, multicoloured				45	65
576	1 d. 50, multicoloured				60	80
573/6				Set of 4	1·25	1·75

Designs:—85 b. Growth monitoring; 1 d. 10, Health care worker with women and babies ("Promotion of breast feeding"); 1 d. 50, Universal immunisation.

Nos. 573/6 come with a pattern of blue fluorescent security markings, resembling rosettes, printed on the reverse beneath the gum.

143 Women at Market

144 Turkey Vulture

(Des G. Vasarhelyi. Litho Format)

1985 (11 Mar). *Women and Development. T* **143** *and similar horiz design. Multicoloured. P* 14.

577	60 b. Type 143				25	35
578	85 b. Type 143				35	50
579	1 d. Woman office worker				40	60
580	1 d. 25, As 1 d.				50	90
577/80				Set of 4	1·40	2·10

Nos. 577/80 come with a pattern of blue fluorescent security markings, resembling rosettes, printed on the reverse beneath the gum.

(Des and litho Questa)

1985 (15 July). *Birth Bicentenary of John J. Audubon (ornithologist). T* **144** *and similar multicoloured designs showing original paintings. P* 14.

581	60 b. Type 144				1·40	75
582	85 b. American Anhinga				1·60	1·50
583	1 d. 50, Green Heron				2·00	3·25
584	5 d. Wood Duck				3·25	5·50
581/4				Set of 4	7·50	10·00

MS585 100×70 mm. 10 d. Great Northern Diver (inscr "Common Loon") (*horiz*) .. .. | 3·75 | 4·00 |

145 The Queen Mother

GOLD MEDALLIST
CLAUDIA LOCH
WEST GERMANY

(146)

(Des J.W. Litho Questa)

1985 (29 July). *Life and Times of Queen Elizabeth the Queen Mother. T* **145** *and similar vert designs. Multicoloured. P* 14.

586	85 b. The Queen Mother and King George VI reviewing Home Guard		25	30
587	3 d. Type 145				80	1·00
588	5 d. The Queen Mother with posy ..		1·40	1·75
586/8				Set of 3	2·25	2·75

MS589 56×85 mm. 10 d. The Queen Mother in Garter robes .. .. | 2·50 | 3·25 |

(Des Walt Disney Studios. Litho Questa)

1985 (30 Oct). *150th Birth Anniv of Mark Twain (author). Horiz designs as T* **118** *of Anguilla showing Walt Disney cartoon characters in scenes from "Life on the Mississippi". Multicoloured. P* 14 × 13½.

| 590 | 1 d. 50, Mickey Mouse steering the *Calamity Jane* | | | 90 | 90 |
| 591 | 2 d. Mickey and Minnie Mouse at antebellum mansion | | | | 1·25 | 1·25 |

592	2 d. 50, Donald Duck and Goofy heaving the lead			1·50	1·5
593	3 d. Poker game aboard the *Gold Dust*		1·60	1·6
590/3				Set of 4	4·75	4·7

MS594 126×101 mm. 10 d. Mickey Mouse and riverboat .. .. | 4·75 | 4·2 |

(Des Walt Disney Productions. Litho Questa)

1985 (30 Oct). *Birth Bicentenaries of Grimm Brothers (folklorists). Designs as T* **119** *of Anguilla, but vert, showing Walt Disney cartoon characters in scenes from "Faithful John". Multicoloured. P* 13½ × 14.

595	60 b. The King (Mickey Mouse) and portrait of the Princess (Minnie Mouse)		40	4
596	85 b. The King showing the Princess his treasures			50	5
597	2 d. 35, Faithful John (Goofy) playing trumpet			1·10	1·4
598	5 d. Faithful John turned to stone ..		2·25	2·5
595/8				Set of 4	3·75	4·2

MS599 126×101 mm. 10 d. Faithful John after recovery .. .. | 6·00 | 5·0 |

1985 (11 Nov). *Olympic Gold Medal Winners, Los Angeles Nos.* 527/33 *optd as T* **146**.

600	60 b. Type 133 (optd with T 146)			40	4
601	85 b. High jumping (optd "GOLD MEDALLIST ULRIKE MEYFARTH WEST GERMANY")			50	5
602	90 b. Wrestling (optd "GOLD MEDALLIST PASQUALE PASSARELLI WEST GERMANY")			50	5
603	1 d. Gymnastics (optd "GOLD MEDALLIST LI NING CHINA")			55	5
604	1 d. 25, Swimming (optd "GOLD MEDALLIST MICHAEL GROSS WEST GERMANY") ..		70	7
605	2 d. Diving (optd "GOLD MEDALLIST SYLVIE BERNIER CANADA") ..		1·00	1·00
600/5				Set of 6	3·25	3·25

MS606 100×80 mm. 5 d. Yachting (opt "GOLD MEDAL STAR CLASS U.S.A.").. .. | 1·75 | 1·90 |

147 Inspecting Maize

(Des J. Farleo. Litho Questa)

1985 (15 Nov). *United Nations Anniversaries. T* **147** *and similar horiz designs. Multicoloured. P* 14.

607	60 b. Type 147				40	35
608	85 b. Football match, Independence Stadium, Banjul			50	40
609	1 d. 10, Rice fields				60	60
610	2 d. Central Bank of The Gambia ..		85	1·00
611	3 d. Cow and calf				1·50	1·75
612	4 d. Banjul harbour ..				2·00	2·25
613	5 d. Gambian fruits ..				2·25	2·50
614	6 d. Oyster Creek Bridge ..			2·50	3·00
607/14				Set of 8	9·50	10·50

Nos. 607, 609, 611 and 613 commemorate the 40th anniversary of the Food and Agriculture Organization and Nos. 608, 610, 612 and 614 the 40th anniversary of the United Nations Organization.

148 Fishermen in Fotoba, Guinea

149 "Virgin and Child" (Dieric Bouts)

(Des B. Bundock. Litho Questa)

1985 (24 Dec). *50th Anniv of Diocese of The Gambia and Guinea. T* **148** *and similar horiz designs. Multicoloured. P* 14.

615	60 b. Type 148				30	30
616	85 b. St. Mary's Primary School, Banjul		30	40
617	1 d. 10, St. Mary's Cathedral, Banjul		35	65
618	1 d. 50, Mobile dispensary at Christy Kunda			50	85
615/18				Set of 4	1·25	2·00

(Des Mary Walters. Litho Format)

1985 (24 Dec). *Christmas. Religious Paintings. T* **149** *and similar vert designs. Multicoloured. P* 15.

619	60 b. Type 149				20	25
620	85 b. "The Annunciation" (Robert Campin)..		25	30
621	1 d. 50, "Adoration of the Shepherds" (Gerard David)			45	50
622	5 d. "The Nativity" (Gerard David)		1·60	1·75
619/22				Set of 4	2·25	2·50

MS623 106×84 mm. 10 d. "Adoration of the Magi" (Hieronymus Bosch) .. .. | 3·50 | 4·00 |

No. **MS**623 exists imperforate from stock dispersed by the liquidator of Format International Security Printers Ltd.

150 Enrolment Card

(Des N. Waldman. Litho Questa)

1985 (27 Dec). *75th Anniv of Girl Guide Movement. T* **150** *and similar multicoloured designs. P* 14.
624	60 b. Type **150**	..	40	30
625	85 b. 2nd Bathurst Company centre		50	35
626	1 d. 50, Lady Baden-Powell (*vert*) ..		70	1·00
627	5 d. Miss Rosamond Fowlis (Gambian Guide Association leader) (*vert*)		2·00	3·75
624/7	.. ..	*Set of 4*	3·25	4·75
MS628	97×67 mm. 10 d. Gambian Girl Guides (*vert*)		4·50	6·00

151 Girl and Village Scene   **152 Two Players competing for Ball**

(Des B. Bundock. Litho Questa)

1985 (31 Dec). *International Youth Year. T* **151** *and similar horiz designs. Multicoloured. P* 14.
629	60 b. Type **151**	.. ..	25	30
630	85 b. Youth and wrestling bout		30	35
631	1 d. 10, Girl and Griot storyteller ..		40	85
632	1 d. 50, Youth and crocodile pool		50	1·10
629/32		*Set of 4*	1·25	2·40
MS633	106×76 mm. 5 d. Herdsman with cattle ..		2·00	3·00

(Des W. Hanson. Litho Questa)

1986 (18 Apr). *Appearance of Halley's Comet (1st issue). Horiz designs as T* **123** *of Anguilla. Multicoloured. P* 14.
634	10 b. Maria Mitchell (astronomer) and Kitt Peak National Observatory, Arizona ..		40	20
635	20 b. Neil Armstrong, first man on Moon, 1969		55	25
636	75 b. "Skylab 4" and Comet Kohoutek, 1973		85	65
637	1 d. N.A.S.A.'s infra-red astronomical satellite and Halley's Comet ..		1·00	80
638	2 d. Comet of 1577 from Turkish painting ..		1·50	1·50
639	10 d. N.A.S.A.'s International Cometary Explorer..		4·00	5·50
634/9	.. ..	*Set of 6*	7·50	8·00
MS640	102×70 mm. 10 d. Halley's Comet		5·00	6·50

See also Nos. 679/84.

(Des and litho Questa)

1986 (21 Apr). *60th Birthday of Queen Elizabeth II. Vert designs as T* **125** *of Anguilla. P* 14.
641	1 d. black and yellow	..	25	30
642	2 d. 50, multicoloured	..	65	80
643	10 d. multicoloured	..	2·50	3·50
641/3	.. .. ..	*Set of 3*	3·00	4·25
MS644	120×85 mm. 10 d. black and grey-brown		2·50	3·00

Designs:—No. 641, Duke of York and family, Royal Tournament, 1936; 642, Queen attending christening, 1983; 643, In West Germany, 1978; MS644, Duchess of York with her daughters, Balmoral, 1935.

(Des J. Birdsong. Litho Questa)

1986 (2 May). *World Cup Football Championship, Mexico. T* **152** *and similar vert designs. Multicoloured. P* 14.
645	75 b. Type **152**		75	60
646	1 d. Player kicking ball		1·00	85
647	2 d. 50, Player kicking ball (*different*)		2·00	2·25
648	10 d. Player heading ball		5·00	6·00
645/8	.. .. ..	*Set of 4*	8·00	8·75
MS649	100×70 mm. 10 d. Goalkeeper saving goal		7·50	7·00

153 Mercedes "500" (1986)

(Des P. Rhymer. Litho Format)

1986 (31 May). *"Ameripex" International Stamp Exhibition, Chicago. Centenary of First Benz Motor Car (1985). T* **153** *and similar horiz designs. Multicoloured. P* 15.
650	25 b. Type **153**		20	15
651	75 b. Cord "810" (1935)		50	40
652	1 d. Borgward "Isabella Coupe" (1957)		70	60
653	1 d. 25, Lamborghini "Countach" (1985/6)		80	70
654	2 d. Ford "Thunderbird" (1955)		90	1·25

655	2 d. 25, Citroen "DS19" (1956)		90	1·60
656	5 d. Bugatti "Atlante" (1936)		1·25	3·00
657	10 d. Horch "853" (1936)		1·75	5·00
650/7	.. .. ..	*Set of 8*	6·00	11·50
MS658	Two sheets, each 100×70 mm. (a) 12 d. Benz "8/20" (1913). (b) 12 d. Steiger "10/50" (1924)			
		Set of 2 sheets	6·00	12·00

The 25 b. value is inscribed "MECEDES" and the 10 d. "LARL BENZ".

Nos. 650/2 and 657 exist imperforate from stock dispersed by the liquidator of Format International Security Printers Ltd.

(Des J. Iskowitz. Litho Questa)

1986 (10 June). *Centenary of Statue of Liberty (1st issue). Multicoloured designs as T* **211** *of Dominica showing the Statue of Liberty and immigrants to the U.S.A. P* 14.
659	20 b. John Jacob Astor (financier) ..		10	10
660	1 d. Jacob Riis (journalist) ..		40	50
661	1 d. 25, Igor Sikorsky (aeronautics engineer)		60	65
662	5 d. Charles Boyer (actor) ..		2·50	2·50
659/62		*Set of 4*	3·25	3·25
MS663	114×80 mm. 10 d. Statue of Liberty (*vert*)		4·00	4·50

See also Nos. 705/14

(Litho Questa)

1986 (1 July). *Royal Wedding. Vert designs as T* **213** *of Antigua. Multicoloured. P* 14.
664	1 d. Prince Andrew and Miss Sarah Ferguson		40	45
665	2 d. 50, Prince Andrew		1·00	1·40
666	4 d. Prince Andrew as helicopter pilot		1·60	2·00
664/6		*Set of 3*	2·75	3·50
MS667	88×88 mm. 7 d. Prince Andrew and Miss Sarah Ferguson (*different*)..		4·25	3·50

1986 (16 Sept). *World Cup Football Championship Winners, Mexico. Nos. 645/9 optd with T* **216** *of Antigua in gold.*
668	75 b. Type **152**		30	40
669	1 d. Player kicking ball		40	55
670	2 d. 50, Player kicking ball (*different*)		1·00	1·25
671	10 d. Player heading ball		4·25	4·75
668/71		*Set of 4*	5·25	6·25
MS672	100×70 mm. 10 d. Goalkeeper saving goal		4·50	4·50

154 Minnie Mouse (Great Britain)

(Des Walt Disney Co. Litho Format)

1986 (4 Nov). *Christmas. T* **154** *and similar vert designs showing Walt Disney cartoon characters posting letters in various countries. Multicoloured. P* 11.
673	1 d. Type **154**		75	60
674	1 d. 25, Huey (U.S.A.)		80	80
675	2 d. Huey, Dewey and Louie (France)		1·25	1·40
676	2 d. 35, Kanga and Roo (Australia) ..		1·40	1·75
677	5 d. Goofy (Germany)..		2·25	3·00
673/7		*Set of 5*	5·75	6·75
MS678	127×101 mm. 10 d. Goofy (Sweden). P 13½×14		4·75	5·50

Nos. 673/8 also show the emblem of "Stockholmia '86" International Stamp Exhibition.

1986 (21 Dec). *Appearance of Halley's Comet (2nd issue). Nos. 634/40 optd with T* **218** *of Antigua in silver.*
679	10 b. Maria Mitchell (astronomer) and Kitt Peak National Observatory, Arizona ..		30	15
680	20 b. Neil Armstrong, first man on Moon, 1969		50	20
681	75 b. "Skylab 4" and Comet Kohoutek, 1973		75	50
682	1 d. N.A.S.A.'s infra-red astronomical satellite and Halley's Comet ..		85	60
683	2 d. Comet of 1577 from Turkish painting		1·40	1·75
684	10 d. N.A.S.A.'s International Cometary Explorer..		3·75	6·00
679/84		*Set of 6*	6·75	8·25
MS685	102×70 mm. 10 d. Halley's Comet		3·00	4·25

155 Bugarab and Tabala   **156 "Snowing"**

(Des B. Bundock. Litho Format)

1987 (21 Jan). *Manding Musical Instruments. T* **155** *and similar multicoloured designs. P* 15.
686	75 b. Type **155**		15	20
687	1 d. Balaphong and fiddle ..		15	25
688	1 d. 25, Bolongbato and konting (*vert*)		20	35
689	10 d. Antique and modern koras (*vert*)		1·60	3·00
686/9		*Set of 4*	1·90	3·50
MS690	100×70 mm. 12 d. Sabarr		1·90	2·50

(Litho Questa)

1987 (6 Feb). *Birth Centenary of Marc Chagall (artist). T* **156** *and similar multicoloured designs. P* 13½×14.
691	75 b. Type **156**		40	40
692	85 b. "The Boat"		50	50
693	1 d. "Maternity"		65	65
694	1 d. 25, "The Flute Player"..		75	75
695	2 d. 35, "Lovers and the Beast"		1·25	1·25
696	4 d. "Fishers at Saint Jean"		2·00	2·00
697	5 d. "Entering the Ring"		2·50	2·50
698	10 d. "Three Acrobats"		3·75	3·75
691/8		*Set of 8*	10·50	10·50
MS699	Two sheets. (a) 110×68 mm. 12 d. "The Cattle Driver" (104×61 *mm*). (b) 109×95 mm. 12 d. "The Sabbath" (104×89 *mm*). Imperf.			
		Set of 2 sheets	7·50	8·50

157 America, 1851   **158 Arm of Statue of Liberty**

(Des S. Heinmann. Litho Questa)

1987 (3 Apr). *America's Cup Yachting Championship. T* **157** *and similar horiz designs. Multicoloured. P* 14.
700	20 b. Type **157**		20	15
701	1 d. Courageous, 1974		35	35
702	2 d. 50, Volunteer, 1887		75	1·10
703	10 d. Intrepid, 1967		2·25	3·25
700/3		*Set of 4*	3·25	4·25
MS704	114×89 mm. 12 d. Australia II, 1983 ..		3·00	2·50

(Des P. Kaplan. Litho Questa)

1987 (9 Apr). *Centenary of Statue of Liberty (1986) (2nd issue). T* **158** *and similar multicoloured designs. P* 14.
705	1 b. Type **158**		10	10
706	2 b. Launch passing Statue (*horiz*)		10	10
707	3 b. Schooner passing Statue (*horiz*)		10	10
708	5 b. U.S.S. John F. Kennedy (aircraft carrier) and Queen Elizabeth 2 (liner) (*horiz*)		10	10
709	50 b. Checking Statue for damage		40	40
710	75 b. Cleaning in progress ..		55	55
711	1 d. Working on Statue		70	70
712	1 d. 25, Statue and fireworks		80	80
713	10 d. Statue illuminated		4·25	4·25
714	12 d. Statue and fireworks (*different*)		4·50	4·50
705/14	.. ..	*Set of 10*	10·50	10·50

159 Lantana camara   **160 Front of Mail Bus**

(Des Dot Barlowe. Litho Questa)

1987 (25 May). *Flowers of Abuko Nature Reserve. T* **159** *and similar vert designs. Multicoloured. P* 14.
715	75 b. Type **159**		15	15
716	1 d. Clerodendrum thomsoniae		15	20
717	1 d. 50, Haemanthus multiflorus		25	30
718	1 d. 70, Gloriosa simplex		25	35
719	1 d. 75, Combretum microphyllum..		30	40
720	2 d. 25, Eulophia quineensis		35	45
721	5 d. Erythrina senegalensis ..		80	1·25
722	15 d. Dichrostachys glomerata		2·40	3·50
715/22		*Set of 8*	4·25	6·00
MS723	Two sheets, each 100×70 mm. (a) 15 d. Costus spectabilis. (b) 15 d. Strophanthus preussii			
		Set of 2 sheets	4·75	6·50

(Des BG Studio. Litho Questa)

1987 (15 June). *"Capex '87" International Stamp Exhibition, Toronto and 10th Anniv of Gambia Public Transport Corporation. Mail Buses. T* **160** *and similar multicoloured designs. P* 14.
724	20 b. Type **160**		30	15
725	75 b. Bus in Banjul (*horiz*)		55	35
726	1 d. Passengers queuing for bus (*horiz*)		55	35
727	10 d. Two buses on rural road		3·00	4·50
724/8		*Set of 4*	4·00	4·75
MS728	77×70 mm. 12 d. Parked bus fleet (*horiz*)		2·50	3·50

161 Basketball

162 "A Partridge in a Pear Tree"

(Litho Questa)

1987 (3 July). *Olympic Games, Seoul* (1988) (1st issue). T **161** and similar vert designs. Multicoloured. P 14.
729	50 b. Type **161**		35	20
730	1 d. Volleyball		50	35
731	3 d. Hockey (horiz)		1·10	85
732	10 d. Handball (horiz)		2·50	2·25
724/32		Set of 4	4·00	3·25
MS733	101×85 mm. 15 d. Football (horiz)		2·75	2·75

See also Nos. 779/83.

(Des Dot Barlowe. Litho Questa)

1987 (2 Nov). *Christmas*. T **162** and similar multicoloured designs showing a Victorian couple in scenes from carol "The Twelve Days of Christmas". P 14.
734	20 b. Type **162**		20	25
	a. Sheetlet No. 734/45		7·00	
735	40 b. "Two turtle doves"		20	25
736	60 b. "Three French hens"		20	25
737	75 b. "Four calling birds"		30	35
738	1 d. "Five golden rings"		30	35
739	1 d. 25, "Six geese a-laying"		40	45
740	1 d. 50, "Seven swans a-swimming"		40	45
741	2 d. "Eight maids a-milking"		50	55
742	3 d. "Nine ladies dancing"		70	75
743	5 d. "Ten lords a-leaping"		1·00	1·10
744	10 d. "Eleven pipers piping"		1·60	1·75
745	12 d. "Twelve drummers drumming"		1·90	2·00
734/45		Set of 12	7·00	7·75
MS746	100×70 mm. 15 d. Exchanging presents (horiz)		2·40	3·25

Nos. 734/45 were printed together, se-tenant, in sheetlets of twelve.

163 Campfire Singsong

(Litho Questa)

1987 (9 Nov). *World Scout Jamboree, Australia*. T **163** and similar horiz designs. Multicoloured. P 14.
747	75 b. Type **163**		50	30
748	1 d. Scouts examining African Katydid		60	40
749	1 d. 25, Scouts watching Red-tailed Tropic Bird		75	75
750	2 d. Scouts helping bus passenger		2·75	3·75
747/50		Set of 4	4·25	4·75
MS751	72×98 mm. 15 d. Scouts on field trip		3·50	4·50

(Des Walt Disney Company. Litho Questa)

1987 (9 Dec). *60th Anniv of Mickey Mouse* (Walt Disney cartoon character) (1st issue). Multicoloured designs as T **220** of Dominica, but horiz. P 14×13½.
752	60 b. Morty and Ferdie examining Trevithick's locomotive, 1804		25	25
753	75 b. Clarabelle Cow in "Empire State Express", 1893		30	30
754	1 d. Donald Duck inspecting Stephenson's Rocket, 1829		40	40
755	1 d. 25, Piglet and Winnie the Pooh with Santa Fe Railway locomotive, 1920		45	45
756	2 d. Donald and Daisy Duck with Class "GG-1", Pennsylvania Railway, 1933..		70	70
757	5 d. Mickey Mouse in Stourbridge Lion, 1829		1·60	1·75
758	10 d. Goofy in Best Friend of Charleston, 1830		2·75	3·00
759	12 d. Brer Bear and Brer Rabbit with Union Pacific No. M10001, 1934		3·00	3·25
752/9		Set of 8	8·50	
MS760	Two sheets, each 127×101 mm. (a) 15 d. Chip n'Dale in The General, 1855. (b) 15 d. Donald Duck and Mickey Mouse in modern French "TGV" train		Set of 2 sheets	7·50	8·00

See also Nos. 849/58.

164 Common Duiker and Acacia

165 Wedding Portrait, 1947

(Des Mary Walters. Litho Format)

1988 (9 Feb). *Flora and Fauna*. T **164** and similar multicoloured designs. P 15.
761	50 b. Type **164**		15	10
762	75 b. Red-billed Hornbill and casuarina (vert)		20	15
763	90 b. West African Dwarf Crocodile and rice		20	20
764	1 d. Leopard and papyrus (vert)		20	20
765	1 d. 25, Crowned Crane and millet		30	30
766	2 d. Waterbuck and baobab tree (vert)		35	50
767	3 d. Oribi and Senegal palm		50	90
768	5 d. Hippopotamus and papaya (vert)		80	1·40
761/8		Set of 8	2·40	3·25
MS769	98×69 mm. (a) 12 d. Red-throated Bee Eater and acacia (vert). (b) 12 d. Eastern White Pelican		Set of 2 sheets	3·75	4·50

No. **MS769** exists imperforate from stock dispersed by the liquidator of Format International Security Printers Ltd.

(Des and litho Questa)

1988 (15 Mar). *Royal Ruby Wedding*. T **165** and similar vert designs. P 14.
770	75 b. deep brown, black and brown-orange		30	15
771	1 d. deep brown, black and bright new blue		40	20
772	3 d. multicoloured		90	1·00
773	10 d. multicoloured		2·25	3·25
770/3		Set of 4	3·50	4·25
MS774	100×75 mm. 15 d. multicoloured		2·25	3·25

Designs:— 1 d. Engagement photograph; 3 d. Wedding portrait, 1947 (different); 10 d. Queen Elizabeth II and Prince Philip (photo by Karsh), 1986; 15 d. Wedding portrait with page, 1947.

1988 (19 Apr). *Stamp Exhibitions*. Nos. 689, 703, 722 and 726 optd as T **241** of Antigua with various emblems.
775	1 d. Passengers queuing for bus (optd "Independence 40", Israel)		25	25
776	10 d. Antique and modern koras (optd "FINLANDIA 88", Helsinki)		2·00	2·50
777	10 d. Intrepid (yacht), 1967 (optd "Praga '88", Prague)		2·00	2·50
778	15 d. Dichrostachys glomerata (optd "OLYMPHILEX '88", Seoul)		2·75	3·00
775/8		Set of 4	6·25	7·50

(Des A. DiLorenzo. Litho Questa)

1988 (3 May). *Olympic Games, Seoul* (2nd issue). Multicoloured designs as T **161**. P 14.
779	1 d. Archery		15	20
780	1 d. 25, Boxing		20	25
781	5 d. Gymnastics		80	1·10
782	10 d. Start of 100 metre race (horiz)		1·60	2·25
779/82		Set of 4	2·50	3·50
MS783	74×102 mm. 15 d. Medal winners on rostrum		2·40	3·25

166 Red Cross Flag (125th anniv)

(Des W. Wright. Litho Questa)

1988 (15 May). *Anniversaries and Events*. T **166** and similar multicoloured designs. P 14.
784	50 b. Type **166**		55	55
785	75 b. "Friendship" 7 spacecraft (25th anniv of first American manned Earth orbit)		60	60
786	1 d. British Airways Concorde (10th anniv of Concorde London–New York service)		1·00	1·00
787	1 d. 25, Ryan NYP Special Spirit of St. Louis (60th anniv of first solo transatlantic flight)		1·00	1·00
788	2 d. North American X-15 (20th anniv of fastest aircraft flight)		1·40	1·40
789	3 d. Bell XS-1 rocket plane (40th anniv of first supersonic flight)		1·50	1·50
790	10 d. English and Spanish galleons (400th anniv of Spanish Armada)		3·50	3·50
791	12 d. Titanic (75th anniv of sinking)		3·75	3·75
784/91		Set of 8	12·00	12·00
MS792	Two sheets. (a) 113×85 mm. 15 d. Kaiser Wilhelm Memorial Church, Berlin (vert) (750th anniv of Berlin). (b) 121×90 mm. 15 d. Kangaroo (Bicentenary of Australian Settlement)		Set of 2 sheets	4·75	7·00

(Litho Questa)

1988 (7 July). *500th Birth Anniv of Titian* (artist). Vert designs as T **238** of Antigua. Multicoloured. P 13½×14.
793	25 b. "Emperor Charles V"		20	20
794	50 b. "St. Margaret and the Dragon"		35	35
795	60 b. "Ranuccio Farnese"		40	40
796	75 b. "Tarquin and Lucretia"		55	55
797	1 d. "The Knight of Malta"		70	70
798	5 d. "Spain succouring Faith"		2·25	2·50
799	10 d. "Doge Francesco Venier"		3·50	3·50
800	12 d. "Doge Grimani before the Faith" (detail)		3·75	3·75
793/800		Set of 8	10·50	10·50
MS801	110×95 mm. (a) 15 d. "Jealous Husband" (detail). (b) 15 d. "Venus blindfolding Cupid"		Set of 2 sheets	4·75	7·00

NEW INFORMATION

The editor is always interested to correspond with people who have new information that will improve or correct the Catalogue.

167 John Kennedy sailing

(Des G. Hinlecky. Litho Questa)

1988 (1 Sept). *25th Death Anniv of President John F. Kennedy*. T **167** and similar multicoloured designs. P 14.
802	75 b. Type **167**		15	15
803	1 d. Kennedy signing Peace Corps legislation, 1962		15	20
804	1 d. 25, Speaking at U.N., New York (vert)		20	25
805	12 d. Grave and eternal flame, Arlington National Cemetery (vert)		1·90	2·75
802/5		Set of 4	2·10	3·00
MS806	99×72 mm. 15 d. John F. Kennedy (vert)		2·40	3·50

168 Airship LZ-127 Graf Zeppelin (first regular air passenger service), 1910

169 Emmett Kelley

(Des A. Fagbohun. Litho Questa)

1988 (1 Nov). *Milestones of Transportation*. T **168** and similar multicoloured designs. P 14.
807	25 b. Type **168**		35	35
808	50 b. Stephenson's Locomotion (first permanent public railway), 1825		50	50
809	75 b. G.M. Sun Racer (first world solar challenge), 1987		65	65
810	1 d. Sprague's Premiere (first operational electric tramway), 1888		80	80
811	1 d. 25, Gold Rush Bicycle (holder of man-powered land speed record), 1986		85	85
812	2 d. 50 Robert Goddard and rocket launcher (first liquid fuel rocket), 1925		1·25	1·25
813	10 d. Orukter Amphibolos (first steam traction engine), 1805		3·25	3·25
814	12 d. Sovereign of the Seas (largest cruise liner), 1988		3·50	3·50
807/14		Set of 8	10·00	10·00
MS815	Two sheets, each 71×92 mm. (a) 15 d. U.S.S. Nautilus (first nuclear-powered submarine), 1954 (vert). (b) 15 d. Fulton's Nautilus (first fish-shaped submarine), 1800's (vert)		Set of 2 sheets	5·50	7·00

No. 807 is incorrectly inscribed "LZ-7".

(Des J. Iskowitz. Litho Questa)

1988 (9 Nov). *Entertainers*. T **169** and similar multicoloured designs. P 14.
816	20 b. Type **169**		10	10
817	1 d. Gambia National Ensemble		25	25
818	1 d. 25, Jackie Gleason		30	30
819	1 d. 50, Laurel and Hardy		40	40
820	2 d. 50, Yul Brynner		75	75
821	3 d. Cary Grant		95	95
822	10 d. Danny Kaye		3·00	3·00
823	20 d. Charlie Chaplin		5·50	5·50
816/23		Set of 8	10·00	10·00
MS824	Two sheets. (a) 110×77 mm. 15 d. Marx Brothers (horiz). (b) 70×99 mm. 15 d. Fred Astaire and Rita Hayworth (horiz)		Set of 2 sheets	9·50	9·50

170 Prince Henry the Navigator and Caravel

171 Projected Space Plane and Ernst Mach (physicist)

(Des A. Fagbohun. Litho Questa)

1988 (1 Dec). *Exploration of West Africa*. T **170** and similar multicoloured designs. P 14.
825	50 b. Type **170**		60	60
826	75 b. Jesse Ramsden's sextant, 1785		70	70
827	1 d. 15th-century hourglass		80	80
828	1 d. 25, Prince Henry the Navigator and Vasco da Gama		95	95
829	2 d. 50, Vasco da Gama and ship		1·60	1·60
830	5 d. Mungo Park and map of Gambia River (horiz)		2·50	2·50

831	10 d. Map of West Africa, 1563 (*horiz*)		3·75	3·75
832	12 d. Portuguese caravel (*horiz*)		4·00	4·00
825/32		*Set of 8*	13·50	13·50

MS833 Two sheets, each 65 × 100 mm. (a) 15 d.
Ship from Columbus's fleet off Gambia. (b) 15 d.
15th-century ship moored off Gambia
Set of 2 sheets 4·75 6·00

(Des G. Welker. Litho Questa)

1988 (12 Dec). *350th Anniv of Publication of Galileo's "Discourses". Space Achievements.* T **171** *and similar multi-coloured designs.* P 14.

834	50 b. Type **171**		30	30
835	75 b. OAO III astronomical satellite and Niels Bohr (physicist)		40	40
836	1 d. Space shuttle, projected space station and Robert Goddard (physicist) (*horiz*)		45	45
837	1 d. 25, Jupiter probe, 1979, and Edward Barnard (astronomer) (*horiz*)		60	60
838	2 d. Hubble Space Telescope and George Hale (astronomer)		75	75
839	3 d. Earth-to-Moon laser measurement and Albert Michaelson (physicist) (*horiz*) ..		85	85
840	10 d. HEAO-2 *Einstein* orbital satellite and Albert Einstein (physicist)		2·50	2·50
841	20 d. *Voyager* (first non-stop round-the-world flight), 1987, and Wright Brothers (aviation pioneers) (*horiz*)		4·50	4·50
834/41		*Set of 8*	9·25	9·25

MS842 Two sheets. (a) 99 × 75 mm. 15 d. Great
Red Spot on Jupiter (*horiz*). (b) 88 × 71 mm.
15 d. Neil Armstrong (first man on Moon), 1969
Set of 2 sheets 6·00 7·00

172 Passing Out Parade

(Des J. Genzo. Litho Questa)

1989 (10 Feb). *Army Day.* T **172** *and similar multicoloured designs.* P 14.

843	75 b. Type **172**		25	25
844	1 d. Standards of The Gambia Regiment		25	25
845	1 d. 25, Side drummer in ceremonial uniform (*vert*)		30	30
846	10 d. Marksman with Atlantic Shooting Cup (*vert*)		2·00	2·00
847	15 d. Soldiers on assault course (*vert*)		2·75	2·75
848	20 d. Gunner with 105 mm field gun		3·00	3·00
843/8		*Set of 6*	7·75	7·75

173 Mickey Mouse, 1928   174 "Le Coup de Lance" (detail)

(Des Walt Disney Company. Litho B.D.T.)

1989 (6 Apr). *60th Birthday of Mickey Mouse* (2nd issue). T **173** *and similar multicoloured designs.* P 13.

849	2 d. Type **173**		55	65
	a. Sheetlet of 9. Nos. 849/57 ..		4·50	
850	2 d. Mickey Mouse, 1931 ..		55	65
851	2 d. Mickey Mouse, 1936 ..		55	65
852	2 d. Mickey Mouse, 1955 ..		55	65
853	2 d. Mickey Mouse, 1947 ..		55	65
854	2 d. Mickey Mouse as magician, 1940		55	65
855	2 d. Mickey Mouse with palette, 1960 ..		55	65
856	2 d. Mickey Mouse as Uncle Sam, 1976 ..		55	65
857	2 d. Mickey Mouse, 1988 ..		55	65
849/57		*Set of 9*	4·50	5·25

MS858 138×109 mm. 15 d. Mickey Mouse at
60th birthday party (132×103 *mm*). Imperf 3·50 3·50
Nos. 849/57 were printed together, *se-tenant* as a composite
design, in sheetlets of nine.

(Litho Questa)

1989 (14 Apr). *Easter. Religious Paintings by Rubens.* T **174** *and similar vert designs showing details. Multicoloured.* P 13½×14.

859	2 d. Type **174**		25	25
860	75 b. "Flagellation of Christ"		35	35
861	1 d. "Lamentation for Christ"		35	35
862	1 d. 25, "Descent from the Cross"		40	40
863	2 d. "Holy Trinity"		60	70
864	5 d. "Doubting Thomas"		1·25	1·50
865	10 d. "Lamentation over Christ" ..		2·00	2·50
866	12 d. "Lamentation with Virgin and St. John"		2·25	2·75
859/66		*Set of 8*	6·75	8·00

MS867 Two sheets each 96×110 mm. (a) 15 d.
"The Last Supper". (b) 15 d. "Raising of the
Cross" .. *Set of 2 sheets* 4·50 5·50

175 African Emerald Cuckoo   176 *Druryia antimachus*

(Des W. Wright. Litho Questa)

1989 (24 Apr). *West African Birds.* T **175** *and similar horiz designs. Multicoloured.* P 14.

868	20 b. Type **175**		45	30
869	60 b. Grey-headed Bush Shrike		65	50
870	75 b. South African Crowned Crane		70	55
871	1 d. Secretary Bird		80	60
872	2 d. Red-billed Hornbill		1·25	1·00
873	5 d. Superb Sunbird		2·00	2·50
874	10 d. Pearl-spotted Owlet ("Little Owl")		2·75	3·50
875	12 d. Bateleur		2·75	3·50
868/75		*Set of 8*	10·00	11·00

MS876 Two sheets, each 115×86 mm. (a) 15 d.
Ostrich. (b) 15 d. Red-billed Fire Finch
Set of 2 sheets 7·00 8·00

(Des Mary Walters. Litho Questa)

1989 (15 May). *Butterflies of Gambia.* T **176** *and similar vert designs. Multicoloured.* P 14.

877	50 b. Type **176**		30	30
878	75 b. *Euphaedra neophron*		45	45
879	1 d. *Aterica rabena*		45	45
880	1 d. 25, *Salamis parhassus*		55	55
881	5 d. *Precis rhadama*		1·75	2·00
882	10 d. *Papilio demodocus*		2·25	2·50
883	12 d. *Charaxes etesipe*		2·50	2·75
884	15 d. *Danaus formosa*		2·50	2·75
877/84		*Set of 8*	9·75	10·50

MS885 Two sheets, each 99×68 mm. (a) 15 d.
Euptera pluto. (b) 15 d. *Euphaedra ceres*
Set of 2 sheets 7·50 8·50

177 Nigerian Steam   PHILEXFRANCE
Locomotive, 1959   '89   (178)

(Des A. Fagbohun. Litho Walsall)

1989 (15 June). *African Steam Locomotives.* T **177** *and similar multicoloured designs.* P 14.

886	50 b. Type **177**		35	35
887	75 b. Garratt Class "14A"		45	45
888	1 d. British-built locomotive, Sudan		55	55
889	1 d. 25, American-built locomotive, 1925		65	65
890	5 d. Scottish-built locomotive, 1955		1·75	1·75
891	7 d. Scottish-built locomotive, 1926		2·00	2·00
892	10 d. East African Railways British-built tank locomotive		2·25	2·25
893	12 d. American-built locomotive, Ghana		2·50	2·50
886/93		*Set of 8*	9·50	9·50

MS894 82×58 mm. (a) 15 d. British-built Class
"25" from front (*vert*). (b) 15 d. British-built Class
"25" from side (*vert*) . *Set of 2 sheets* 6·00 7·00

(Litho Questa)

1989 (23 June). *"Philexfrance '89" International Stamp Exhibition, Paris.* Nos. 686/90 optd with T **178**.

895	75 b. Type **155**		10	10
896	1 d. Balaphong and fiddle		15	20
897	1 d. 25, Bolongbato and konting (*vert*)		20	25
898	10 d. Antique and modern koras (*vert*)		1·50	2·25
895/8		*Set of 4*	1·75	2·50

MS899 100×70 mm. 12 d. Sabarr .. .. 1·40 2·00

(Litho Questa)

1989 (7 July). *Japanese Art. Multicoloured designs as* T **250** *of Antigua.* P 13½×14.

900	50 b. "Sparrow and Bamboo" (Hiroshige) (*vert*)		40	30
901	75 b. "Peonies and a Canary" (Hokusai) (*vert*)		50	40
902	1 d. "Crane and Marsh Grasses" (Hiroshige) (*vert*)		60	45
903	1 d. 25, "Crossbill and Thistle" (Hokusai) (*vert*)		70	60
904	2 d. "Cuckoo and Azalea" (Hokusai) (*vert*)		90	80
905	5 d. "Parrot on a Pine Branch" (Hiroshige) (*vert*)		1·50	1·75
906	10 d. "Mandarin Ducks in a Stream" (Hiroshige) (*vert*)		2·25	2·50
907	12 d. "Bullfinch and Drooping Cherry" (Hokusai) (*vert*)		2·25	2·50
900/7		*Set of 8*	8·25	8·50

MS908 Two sheets, each 102×77 mm. (a) 15 d.
"Tit and Peony" (Hiroshige). (b) 15 d. "Peony and
Butterfly" (Shigenobou). P 14×13½
Set of 2 sheets 4·75 5·50

Nos. 900/7 were each printed in sheets of 10 containing two
vertical strips of 5 stamps separated by printed labels
commemorating Emperor Hirohito.

179 Rialto Bridge, Venice   180 *Vitex doniana*

(Des L. Fried. Litho B.D.T.)

1989 (25 Aug). *World Cup Football Championship, Italy (1990)* (1st issue). T **179** *and similar horiz designs, each showing landmarks and players. Multicoloured.* P 14.

909	75 b. Type **179**		45	45
910	1 d. 25, The Baptistery, Pisa		60	60
911	7 d. Casino, San Remo		2·25	2·75
912	12 d. Colosseum, Rome		3·00	3·50
909/12		*Set of 4*	5·50	6·50

MS913 Two sheets, each 104×78 mm. (a) 15 d.
St. Mark's Cathedral, Venice. (b) 15 d. Piazza
Colonna, Rome . *Set of 2 sheets* 6·00 7·50
See also Nos. 1064/8.

(Des Jennifer Toombs. Litho Questa)

1989 (18 Sept). *Medicinal Plants.* T **180** *and similar vert designs. Multicoloured.* P 14.

914	20 b. Type **180**		20	20
915	50 b. *Ricinus communis*		30	30
916	75 b. *Palisota hirsuta*		45	45
917	1 d. *Smilax kraussiana*		55	55
918	1 d. 25, *Aspilia africana*		65	65
919	5 d. *Newbouldia laevis*		1·75	2·00
920	8 d. *Monodora tenuifolia*		1·90	2·50
921	10 d. *Gossypium arboreum*		2·00	2·50
914/21		*Set of 8*	7·00	8·25

MS922 Two sheets, each 87×72 mm. (a) 15 d.
Kigelia africana. (b) 15 d. *Spathodea campanulata* . *Set of 2 sheets* 6·00 7·50

181 Lookdown

(Des Mary Walters. Litho B.D.T.)

1989 (19 Oct). *Fishes.* T **181** *and similar horiz designs. Multicoloured.* P 14.

923	20 b. Type **181**		25	25
924	75 b. Boarfish		55	55
925	1 d. Grey Triggerfish		65	65
926	1 d. 25, Skipjack Tuna		75	75
927	2 d. Striped Rudderfish		95	95
928	4 d. Atlantic Manta		1·60	1·75
929	5 d. Flat-headed Grey Mullet		1·75	1·90
930	10 d. Ladyfish		2·75	3·25
923/30		*Set of 8*	8·25	9·00

MS931 Two sheets, each 104×72 mm. (a) 15 d.
Porcupinefish. (b) 15 d. Shortfin Mako
Set of 2 sheets 8·00 8·00

(Des Walt Disney Co. Litho Questa)

1989 (29 Nov). *"World Stamp Expo '89" International Stamp Exhibition, Washington* (1st issue). *Horiz designs as* T **256** *of Antigua, each showing Walt Disney cartoon characters and American carousel horses. Multicoloured.* P 14×13½.

932	20 b. Little Hiawatha on Daniel Muller Indian Pony		40	30
933	50 b. Morty on Herschell-Spillman stander		60	50
934	75 b. Goofy on Gustav Dentzel stander		75	65
935	1 d. Mickey Mouse on Daniel Muller armoured stander		80	70
936	1 d. 25, Minnie Mouse on jumper from Smithsonian Collection		90	80
937	2 d. Webby on Illion "American Beauty"		1·25	1·10
938	8 d. Donald Duck on Zalar jumper		3·00	3·50
939	10 d. Mickey Mouse on Parker bucking horse		3·00	3·50
932/9		*Set of 8*	9·50	10·00

MS940 Two sheets, each 127×102 mm. (a) 12 d.
Donald, Mickey and Goofy in carousel car. (b)
12 d. Donald's nephews on Roman chariot horses
Set of 2 sheets 8·00 9·00

(Des Design Element. Litho Questa)

1989 (29 Nov). *"World Stamp Expo '89" International Stamp Exhibition, Washington* (2nd issue). *Landmarks of Washington. Sheet* 78×61 *mm containing horiz design as* T **257** *of Antigua. Multicoloured.* P 14×13½.

MS941 10 d. White House .. .. 1·40 2·00

183 Mickey and Minnie Mouse in Pierce-Arrow, 1922

(Des Walt Disney Co. Litho Questa)

1989 (29 Nov). *Christmas. T **183** and similar horiz designs showing Walt Disney cartoon characters with cars. Multicoloured. P 14×13½.*

942	20 b. Type **183**		40	25
943	50 b. Goofy in Spyker, 1919		60	45
944	75 b. Donald and Grandma Duck with Packard, 1929		75	55
945	1 d. Mickey Mouse driving Daimler, 1920		80	65
946	1 d. 25, Mickey Mouse in Hispano "Suiza", 1924		90	75
947	2 d. Mickey and Minnie Mouse in Opel "Laubfrosch", 1924		1·25	1·10
948	10 d. Donald Duck driving Vauxhall "30/98", 1927		3·00	3·50
949	12 d. Goofy with Peerless, 1923		3·00	3·75
942/9		*Set of 8*	9·50	10·00

MS950 Two sheets, each 127×102 mm. (a) 15 d. Mickey and Minnie Mouse picnicking by Stutz "Blackhawk Speedster", 1928. (b) 15 d. Donald Duck, Mickey and Minnie Mouse in Bentley "Supercharged", 1930 .. *Set of 2 sheets* 8·50 10·00

184 Charles Nicolle (typhus transmission) and Vaccination   185 *Bulbophyllum lepidum*

(Des J. Iskowitz. Litho Walsall)

1989 (12 Dec). *Great Medical Discoveries. T **184** and similar horiz designs. Multicoloured. P 14.*

951	20 b. Type **184**		40	20
952	50 b. Paul Ehrlich (immunization pioneer) and medical examination		50	30
953	75 b. Selman Waksman (discoverer of streptomycin) and T.B. clinic		65	40
954	1 d. Edward Jenner (smallpox vaccination), and Jenner conducting experiment, 1796		75	50
955	1 d. 25, Robert Koch (developer of tuberculin test) and Gambian using vaccination gun		90	75
956	5 d. Sir Alexander Fleming (discoverer of penicillin) and doctor giving injection		2·00	2·25
957	8 d. Max Theiler (developer of yellow fever vaccine) and child clinic		2·50	2·75
958	10 d. Louis Pasteur (bacteriologist) and health survey		2·50	2·75
951/8		*Set of 8*	9·00	9·00

MS959 Two sheets, each 121×86 mm. (a) 15 d. Hughes 369 Viking medical helicopter. (b) 15 d. B.A.C. One Eleven Nightingale C.9 medical relief plane .. .. *Set of 2 sheets* 7·50 8·50
No. **MS959a** is incorrectly inscribed "Vicking".

(Des Mary Walters. Litho Walsall)

1989 (18 Dec). *Orchids. T **185** and similar vert designs. Multicoloured. P 14.*

960	20 b. Type **185**		30	30
961	75 b. *Tridactyle tridactylites*		55	55
962	1 d. *Vanilla imperialis*		70	70
963	1 d. 25, *Oeceoclades maculata*		80	90
964	2 d. *Polystachya affinis*		1·10	1·25
965	4 d. *Ancistrochilus rothschildianus*		1·90	2·25
966	5 d. *Angraecum distichum*		2·00	2·25
967	10 d. *Liparis guineensis*		3·50	4·00
960/7		*Set of 8*	9·75	11·00

MS968 Two sheets, each 99×67 mm. (a) 15 d. *Plectrelminthus caudatus*. (b) 15 d. *Eulophia guineensis* .. .. *Set of 2 sheets* 8·50 8·50

186 John Newcombe   187 Lunar Module *Eagle*

(Des D. Miller. Litho Questa)

1990 (2 Jan). *Wimbledon Tennis Champions. T **186** and similar vert designs. Multicoloured. P 14½.*

969	20 b. Type **186**		10	10
	a. Vert pair. Nos. 969/70		20	20
970	20 b. Mrs. G. W. Hillyard		10	10
971	50 b. Roy Emerson		20	20
	a. Vert pair. Nos. 971/2		40	40
972	50 b. Dorothy Chambers		20	20
973	75 b. Donald Budge		30	30
	a. Vert pair. Nos. 973/4		60	60
974	75 b. Suzanne Lenglen		30	30
975	1 d. Laurence Doherty		35	35
	a. Vert pair. Nos. 975/6		70	70
976	1 d. Helen Wills Moody		35	35
977	1 d. 25, Bjorn Borg		40	40
	a. Vert pair. Nos. 977/8		80	80
978	1 d. 25, Maureen Connolly		40	40
979	4 d. Jean Borotra		1·00	1·00
	a. Vert pair. Nos. 979/80		2·00	2·00
980	4 d. Maria Bueno		1·00	1·00
981	5 d. Anthony Wilding		1·00	1·00
	a. Vert pair. Nos. 981/2		2·00	2·00
982	5 d. Louise Brough		1·00	1·00
983	7 d. Fred Perry		1·40	1·40
	a. Vert pair. Nos. 983/4		2·75	2·75
984	7 d. Margaret Court		1·40	1·40
985	10 d. Bill Tilden		2·00	2·00
	a. Vert pair. Nos. 985/6		4·00	4·00
986	10 d. Billie Jean King		2·00	2·00
987	12 d. Rod Laver		2·25	2·25
	a. Vert pair. Nos. 987/8		4·50	4·50
988	12 d. Martina Navratilova		2·25	2·25
969/88		*Set of 20*	16·00	16·00

MS989 Two sheets, each 101×76 mm. (a) 15 d. Rod Laver (*different*). (b) 15 d. Martina Navratilova (*different*) .. *Set of 2 sheets* 8·50 9·50
The two designs for each value were printed together, *se-tenant*, in vertical pairs throughout the sheets of 20.

(Des K. Gromell. Litho B.D.T.)

1990 (16 Feb). *20th Anniv of First Manned Landing on Moon (1989). T **187** and similar multicoloured designs. P 14.*

990	20 b. Type **187**		25	20
991	50 b. Lift-off of "Apollo 11" (*vert*)		35	30
992	75 b. Neil Armstrong stepping on to Moon		45	45
993	1 d. Buzz Aldrin and American flag		55	55
994	1 d. 25, "Apollo 11" emblem (*vert*)		60	60
995	1 d. 75, Crew of "Apollo 11"		75	75
996	8 d. Lunar Module *Eagle* on Moon		2·00	2·50
997	12 d. Recovery of "Apollo 11" after splashdown		2·25	2·75
990/7		*Set of 8*	6·50	7·25

MS998 Two sheets, each 110×89 mm. (a) 15 d. Neil Armstrong (*vert*). (b) 15 d. View of Earth from Moon (*vert*) .. .. *Set of 2 sheets* 6·50 7·50

188 Bristol Type 142 Blenheim Mk 1   189 White-faced Scops Owl

(Des J. Batchelor. Litho B.D.T.)

1990 (8 May). *R.A.F. Aircraft of Second World War. T **188** and similar horiz designs. Multicoloured. P 14.*

999	10 b. Type **188**		20	20
1000	20 b. Fairey Battle		30	30
1001	50 b. Bristol Type 142 Blenheim Mk IV		40	40
1002	60 b. Vickers-Armstrong Wellington Mk 1c		40	40
1003	75 b. Armstrong Whitworth Whitley Mk V		40	40
1004	1 d. Handley Page Hampden Mk 1		45	45
1005	1 d. 25, Supermarine Spitfire Mk 1A and Hawker Hurricane Mk I		50	50
1006	2 d. Avro Manchester		60	70
1007	3 d. Short Stirling Mk I		80	90
1008	5 d. Handley Page Halifax Mk I		1·25	1·50
1009	10 d. Avro Type 683 Lancaster Mk III		2·00	2·25
1010	12 d. De Havilland D.H.98 Mosquito Mk IV		2·25	2·50
999/1010		*Set of 12*	8·50	9·50

MS1011 Two sheets, each 107×77 mm. (a) 15 d. Supermarine Spitfire Mk 1A. (b) 15 d. Avro Type 683 Lancaster Mk III (*different*) .. *Set of 2 sheets* 6·50 8·00

(Des Jennifer Toombs. Litho B.D.T.)

1990 (14 May). *African Birds. T **189** and similar horiz designs. Multicoloured. P 14.*

1012	1 d. 25, Type **189**		40	45
	a. Sheetlet. Nos. 1012/31		7·00	
1013	1 d. 25, Village Weaver		40	45
1014	1 d. 25, Red-throated Bee Eater		40	45
1015	1 d. 25, Brown Harrier Eagle		40	45
1016	1 d. 25, Red Bishop		40	45
1017	1 d. 25, Scarlet-chested Sunbird		40	45
1018	1 d. 25, Red-billed Hornbill		40	45
1019	1 d. 25, Mosque Swallow		40	45
1020	1 d. 25, White-faced Whistling Duck		40	45
1021	1 d. 25, African Fish Eagle		40	45
1022	1 d. 25, Eastern White Pelican		40	45
1023	1 d. 25, Carmine Bee Eater		40	45
1024	1 d. 25, Hadada Ibis		40	45
1025	1 d. 25, Egyptian Plover		40	45
1026	1 d. 25, Variable Sunbird		40	45
1027	1 d. 25, African Skimmer		40	45
1028	1 d. 25, Woodland Kingfisher		40	45
1029	1 d. 25, African Jacana		40	45
1030	1 d. 25, African Pygmy Goose		40	45
1031	1 d. 25, Hammerkop		40	45
1012/31		*Set of 20*	7·00	8·00

Nos. 1012/31 were printed together, *se-tenant*, in sheetlets of twenty, forming a composite design of birds at a lake.

190 Penny Black   191 Flag and National Assembly Building

(Des S. Pollard. Litho Questa)

1990 (4 June). *150th Anniv of the Penny Black. P 14.*

1032	**190** 1 d. 25, black and bright ultramarine		75	50
1033	12 d. black and scarlet		3·00	3·75

MS1034 79×73 mm. **190** 15 d. black, silver and dull orange .. .. .. 3·50 4·50
The design of No. **MS1034** is without the additional stamps behind the Penny Black as shown on Type **190**.

(Des and litho Questa)

1990 (5 June). *25th Anniv of Independence. T **191** and similar vert designs. Multicoloured.*

1035	1 d. Type **191**		40	25
1036	3 d. Pres. Sir Dawda Jawara		50	50
1037	12 d. Map of Yundum airport and Boeing 707 airliner		3·25	3·75
1035/7		*Set of 3*	3·75	4·50

MS1038 100×69 mm. 18 d. State arms 3·50 4·50

192 Baobab Tree

(Des W. Hanson Studio. Litho Questa)

1990 (14 June). *Gambian Life. T **192** and similar multicoloured designs. P 14.*

1039	5 b. Type **192**		10	20
1040	10 b. Woodcarving, Albert Market, Banjul		10	20
1041	20 b. President Jawara planting seedling (*vert*)		10	10
1042	50 b. Sailing canoe and map		30	10
1043	75 b. Batik fabric		20	10
1044	1 d. Hibiscus and Bakau beach		30	20
1045	1 d. 25, Bougainvilla and Tendaba Camp		30	20
1046	2 d. Shrimp fishing and sorting		45	35
1047	5 d. Groundnut oil mill, Denton Bridge		80	1·00
1048	10 d. Handicraft pot and kora (musical instrument)		1·50	2·00
1049	15 d. *Ansellia africana* (orchid) (*vert*)		3·25	3·50
1050	30 d. *Euriphene gambiae* (butterfly) and ancient stone ring near Georgetown		5·50	6·00
1039/50		*Set of 12*	11·50	12·50

193 Daisy Duck at 10 Downing Street   194 Lady Elizabeth Bowes-Lyon in High Chair

(Des Walt Disney Co. Litho Questa)

1990 (19 June). *"Stamp World London 90" International Stamp Exhibition. T **193** and similar multicoloured designs each showing Walt Disney cartoon characters in England. P 14.*

1051	20 b. Type **193**		30	30
1052	50 b. Goofy in Trafalgar Square		35	35
1053	75 b. Mickey Mouse on White Cliffs of Dover (*horiz*)		45	50
1054	1 d. Mickey Mouse at Tower of London		45	50
1055	5 d. Mickey Mouse and Goofy at Hampton Court Palace (*horiz*)		1·50	1·75
1056	8 d. Mickey Mouse by Magdalen Tower, Oxford		1·75	2·00
1057	10 d. Mickey Mouse on Old London Bridge (*horiz*)		2·00	2·25
1058	12 d. Scrooge McDuck and Rosetta Stone, British Museum (*horiz*)		2·10	2·25
1051/8		*Set of 8*	8·00	9·00

MS1059 Two sheets, each 125×100 mm. (a) 18 d. Mickey Mouse and Donald Duck at Piccadilly Circus (*horiz*). (b) 18 d. Mickey Mouse steering tug on River Thames (*horiz*) .. *Set of 2 sheets* 8·50 10·00

(Des Young Phillips Studio. Litho Questa)

1990 (19 July). *90th Birthday of Queen Elizabeth the Queen Mother. T **194** and similar vert portraits, 1900–09. P 14.*

1060	6 d. black, dp magenta & greenish yellow		1·25	1·60
	a. Strip of 3. Nos. 1060/2		3·25	
1061	6 d. black, dp magenta & greenish yellow		1·25	1·60
1062	6 d. black, dp magenta & greenish yellow		1·25	1·60
1060/2		*Set of 3*	3·25	4·25

MS1063 90×75 mm. 18 d. multicoloured 3·50 4·50
Designs:—Nos. 1061, **MS1063**, Lady Elizabeth Bowes-Lyon as a young girl; No. 1062, Lady Elizabeth Bowes-Lyon with wild flowers.
Nos. 1060/2 were printed together, horizontally and vertically *se-tenant*, in sheetlets of 9 (3×3).

195 Vialli, Italy   **196** Summit Logo

(Des Young Phillips Studio. Litho Questa)

1990 (24 Sept). *World Cup Football Championship, Italy (2nd issue). T* **195** *and similar vert designs. Multicoloured. P* 14.
1064	1 d.	Type 195		30	30
1065	1 d. 25, Cannegia, Argentina		35	35
1066	3 d. Marchena, Costa Rica		80	90
1067	5 d. Shaiba, United Arab Emirates		1·10	1·40
1064/7			*Set of* 4	2·25	2·75

MS1068 Two sheets, each 75×92 mm. (a) 18 d. Hagi, Rumania. (b) 18 d. Van Basten, Netherlands .. .. *Set of* 2 *sheets* 7·50 7·50

(Des B. Grout. Litho Questa)

1990 (1 Nov). *Olympic Games, Barcelona (1992) (1st issue). Multicoloured designs as T* **268** *of Antigua. P* 14.
1069	20 b.	Men's discus		25	15
1070	50 b.	Men's 100 metres		35	20
1071	75 b.	Women's 400 metres		45	30
1072	1 d.	Men's 200 metres		50	40
1073	1 d. 25,	Women's rhythmic gymnastics		55	50
1074	3 d.	Football		1·00	1·25
1075	10 d.	Men's marathon		2·25	3·00
1076	12 d.	"Tornado" class yachting		2·25	3·00
1069/76			*Set of* 8	7·00	8·00

MS1077 Two sheets, each 101×71 mm. (a) 15 d. Parade of national flags (*horiz*). (b) 15 d. Opening ceremony (*horiz*) .. .. *Set of* 2 *sheets* 7·00 8·00
See also Nos. 1289/97 and 1351/63.

(Litho Questa)

1990 (24 Dec). *Christmas. Paintings by Renaissance Masters. Multicoloured designs as T* **272** *of Antigua, but vert. P* 13½×14.
1078	20 b.	"The Annunciation, with St. Emidius" (detail) (Crivelli)		15	10
1079	50 b.	"The Annunciation" (detail) (Campin)		20	10
1080	75 b.	The Solly Madonna" (detail) (Raphael)		30	20
1081	1 d. 25,	"The Tempi Madonna" (Raphael)		30	25
1082	2 d.	"Madonna of the Linen Window" (detail) (Raphael)		40	40
1083	7 d.	"The Annunciation, with St. Emidius" (different detail) (Crivelli)		1·50	2·00
1084	10 d.	"The Orleans Madonna" (Raphael)		1·75	2·25
1085	15 d.	"Madonna and Child" (detail) (Crivelli)		2·25	3·00
1078/85			*Set of* 8	6·25	7·50

MS1086 72×101 mm. 15 d. "Niccolini-Cowper Madonna" (Raphael) .. .. 4·00 5·00

(Litho Questa)

1990 (24 Dec). *350th Death Anniv of Rubens. Multicoloured designs as T* **273** *of Antigua. P* 14×13½.
1087	20 b.	"The Lion Hunt" (sketch)		15	15
1088	75 b.	"The Lion Hunt" (detail)		25	25
1089	1 d.	"The Tiger Hunt" (detail)		30	30
1090	1 d. 25,	"The Tiger Hunt" (different detail)		35	35
1091	3 d.	"The Tiger Hunt" (different detail)		75	80
1092	5 d.	"The Boar Hunt" (detail)		1·10	1·25
1093	10 d.	"The Lion Hunt" (different detail)		1·75	2·25
1094	15 d.	"The Tiger Hunt" (different detail)		2·40	3·00
1087/94			*Set of* 8	6·25	7·50

MS1095 Four sheets. (a) 100×71 mm. 15 d. "The Boar Hunt". P 14×13½. (b) 100×71 mm. 15 d. "The Lion Hunt". P 14×13½. (c) 100×71 mm. 15 d. "The Crocodile and Hippopotamus Hunt". P 14×13½. (d) 71×100 mm. 15 d. "St. George slays the Dragon" (*vert*). P 13½×14 *Set of* 4 *sheets* 12·00 13·00

(Litho Questa)

1991 (2 Jan). *World Summit for Children, New York. P* 14.
1096 **196** 1 d. multicoloured 40 40

(Des Walt Disney Co. Litho Questa)

1991 (14 Feb). *International Literacy Year (1990). Multicoloured designs as T* **269** *of Antigua showing scenes from Disney cartoon film The Sword in the Stone. P* 14×13½.
1097	3 d.	Sir Kay and Wart searching for lost arrow (*horiz*)		90	1·00
		a. Sheetlet. Nos. 1097/105		7·00	
1098	3 d.	Merlin the Magician (*horiz*)		90	1·00
1099	3 d.	Merlin teaching Wart (*horiz*)		90	1·00
1100	3 d.	Wart writing on blackboard (*horiz*)		90	1·00
1101	3 d.	Wart transformed into bird and Madame Mim (*horiz*)		90	1·00
1102	3 d.	Merlin and Madame Mim (*horiz*)		90	1·00
1103	3 d.	Madame Mim transformed into dragon (*horiz*)		90	1·00
1104	3 d.	Wart pulling sword from stone (*horiz*)		90	1·00
1105	3 d.	King Arthur on throne (*horiz*)		90	1·00
1097/105			*Set of* 9	7·00	8·00

MS1106 Two sheets, each 131×106 mm. (a) 20 d. Sword in stone. (b) 20 d. Merlin. P 13½×14 *Set of* 2 *sheets* 13·00 14·00
Nos. 1097/105 were printed together, *se-tenant*, in sheetlets of 9.

197 *Bebearia senegalensis*   **198** *Papilio dardanus*

(Des Mary Walters. Litho Questa)

1991 (13 May). *Wildlife. T* **197** *and similar multicoloured designs. P* 14.
1107	1 d.	Type 197		30	35
		a. Sheetlet. Nos. 1107/22		4·25	
1108	1 d.	*Graphium ridleyanus* (butterfly)		30	35
1109	1 d.	*Precis antilope* (butterfly)		30	35
1110	1 d.	*Charaxes ameliae* (butterfly)		30	35
1111	1 d.	Addax		30	35
1112	1 d.	Sassaby		30	35
1113	1 d.	Civet		30	35
1114	1 d.	Green Monkey		30	35
1115	1 d.	Spur-winged Goose		30	35
1116	1 d.	Red-billed Hornbill		30	35
1117	1 d.	Osprey		30	35
1118	1 d.	Glossy Ibis		30	35
1119	1 d.	Egyptian Plover		30	35
1120	1 d.	Golden-tailed Woodpecker		30	35
1121	1 d.	Green Wood Hoopoe		30	35
1122	1 d.	Gaboon Viper		30	35
1123	1 d. 50,	Red-billed Fire Finch		40	45
		a. Sheetlet. Nos. 1123/38		5·50	
1124	1 d. 50,	Leaf-Love		40	45
1125	1 d. 50,	Piapiac		40	45
1126	1 d. 50,	African Emerald Cuckoo		40	45
1127	1 d. 50,	Red Colobus Monkey		40	45
1128	1 d. 50,	African Elephant		40	45
1129	1 d. 50,	Duiker		40	45
1130	1 d. 50,	Giant Eland		40	45
1131	1 d. 50,	Oribi		40	45
1132	1 d. 50,	Western African Dwarf Crocodile		40	45
1133	1 d. 50,	Crowned Crane		40	45
1134	1 d. 50,	Jackal		40	45
1135	1 d. 50,	Yellow-throated Longclaw		40	45
1136	1 d. 50,	Abyssinian Ground Hornbill		40	45
1137	1 d. 50,	*Papilio hesperus*		40	45
1138	1 d. 50,	*Papilio antimachus*		40	45
1139	5 d.	Martial Eagle		1·00	1·10
		a. Sheetlet. Nos. 1139/54		14·00	
1140	5 d.	Red-cheeked Cordon-bleu		1·00	1·10
1141	5 d.	Red Bishop		1·00	1·10
1142	5 d.	Eastern White Pelican		1·00	1·10
1143	5 d.	Patas Monkey		1·00	1·10
1144	5 d.	Vervet Monkey		1·00	1·10
1145	5 d.	Roan Antelope		1·00	1·10
1146	5 d.	Western Hartebeest		1·00	1·10
1147	5 d.	Waterbuck		1·00	1·10
1148	5 d.	Warthog		1·00	1·10
1149	5 d.	Spotted Hyena		1·00	1·10
1150	5 d.	Olive Baboon		1·00	1·10
1151	5 d.	*Palla decius*		1·00	1·10
1152	5 d.	*Acraea pharsalus*		1·00	1·10
1153	5 d.	*Neptidopsis ophione*		1·00	1·10
1154	5 d.	*Acraea caecilia*		1·00	1·10
1107/154			*Set of* 48	24·00	27·00

MS1155 Three sheets, each 101×69 mm. (a) 18 d. African Spoonbill (*vert*). (b) 18 d. White-billed Buffalo Weaver (*vert*). (c) 18 d. Lion (*vert*) .. .. *Set of* 3 *sheets* 10·00 11·00
Nos. 1107/22, 1123/38 and 1139/54 were printed together, *se-tenant*, in sheetlets of 16, each forming a composite design.

(Des L. Nelson. Litho Questa)

1991 (1 June). *Butterflies. T* **198** *and similar vert designs. Multicoloured. P* 14.
1156	20 b.	Type 198		35	25
1157	50 b.	*Bematistes poggei*		50	40
1158	1 d.	*Vanessa cardui*		65	55
1159	1 d. 50,	*Amphicallia tigris*		80	70
1160	3 d.	*Hypolimnas dexithea*		1·25	1·10
1161	8 d.	*Acraea egina*		2·00	2·50
1162	10 d.	*Salamis temora*		2·00	2·50
1163	15 d.	*Precis octavia*		2·75	3·50
1156/63			*Set of* 8	9·25	10·50

MS1164 Four sheets, each 100×70 mm. (a) 18 d. *Danaus chrysippus*. (b) 18 d. *Charaxes jasius* (male). (c) 18 d. *Papilio demodocus*. (d) 18 d. *Papilio nireus* .. .. *Set of* 4 *sheets* 13·00 13·00

(Des D. Miller. Litho Walsall)

1991 (12 Aug). *65th Birthday of Queen Elizabeth II. Horiz designs as T* **280** *of Antigua. Multicoloured. P* 14.
1165	50 b.	The Queen and Prince Charles at Windsor polo match		30	20
1166	1 d.	The Queen and Princess Anne at the Derby, 1988		45	35
1167	1 d. 25,	The Queen at the Royal London Hospital, 1970		55	50
1168	12 d.	The Queen and Prince Philip at Balmoral, 1976		3·00	3·50
1165/8			*Set of* 4	3·75	4·25

MS1169 68×90 mm. 18 d. Separate photographs of The Queen and Prince Philip 3·50 4·25

(Des D. Miller. Litho Walsall)

1991 (12 Aug). *10th Wedding Anniv of Prince and Princess of Wales. Horiz designs as T* **280** *of Antigua. Multicoloured. P* 14.
1170	20 b.	Prince and Princess with sons in June, 1989		25	20
1171	75 b.	Separate photographs of Prince, Princess and sons		40	40
1172	1 d. 50,	Prince Henry on first day of school, 1987, and Prince William at polo match		60	60
1173	15 d.	Separate photographs of Prince and Princess of Wales		3·25	3·75
1170/3			*Set of* 4	4·00	4·50

MS1174 68×90 mm. 18 d. The family in Italy, 1985 .. .. 3·75 4·25

(Des Walt Disney Co. Litho Questa)

1991 (22 Aug). *"Phila Nippon '91" International Stamp Exhibition, Tokyo. Multicoloured designs as T* **279** *of Antigua showing Walt Disney cartoon characters playing Japanese sports and games. P* 14×13½ (*horiz*) *or* 13½ × 14 (*vert*).
1175	50 b.	Donald Duck and Mickey Mouse playing "go" (*horiz*)		40	30
1176	75 b.	Morty, Ferdie and Pete as Sumo wrestlers (*horiz*)		55	40
1177	1 d.	Minnie Mouse, Clarabelle Cow and Daisy Duck playing battledore and shuttlecock (*horiz*)		60	45
1178	1 d. 25,	Goofy and Mickey at Okinawa bullfight		70	55
1179	5 d.	Mickey flying hawk		1·75	1·75
1180	7 d.	Mickey, Minnie and Donald playing "jan-ken-pon"		2·00	2·25
1181	10 d.	Goofy as archer (*horiz*)		2·25	2·50
1182	15 d.	Morty and Ferdie flying kites		2·75	3·00
1175/82			*Set of* 8	10·00	10·00

MS1183 Four sheets, each 127×102 mm. (a) 20 d. Mickey climbing Mt Fuji. (b) 20 d. Mickey fishing. (c) 20 d. Scrooge McDuck and Mickey playing football. (d) 20 d. Goofy playing baseball. *Set of* 4 *sheets* 14·00 15·00

(Des Walt Disney Co. Litho Questa)

1991 (28 Aug). *International Literacy Year (1990). Multicoloured designs as T* **269** *of Antigua showing Walt Disney cartoon characters in Kipling's "Just So" stories. P* 14×13½.
1184	50 b.	"How the Whale got his Throat" (*horiz*)		40	30
1185	75 b.	"How the Camel got his Hump" (*horiz*)		55	40
1186	1 d.	"How the Leopard got his Spots" (*horiz*)		60	45
1187	1 d. 25,	"The Elephant's Child" (*horiz*)		70	55
1188	1 d. 50,	"The Singsong of Old Man Kangaroo" (*horiz*)		85	70
1189	7 d.	"The Crab that played with the Sea" (*horiz*)		2·00	2·25
1190	10 d.	"The Cat that walked by Himself" (*horiz*)		2·25	2·50
1191	15 d.	"The Butterfly that Stamped" (*horiz*)		2·75	3·00
1184/91			*Set of* 8	9·00	9·00

MS1192 Four sheets, each 127×102 mm. (a) 20 d. Mickey Mouse reading story to Morte and Ferdie (*horiz*). P 14×13½. (b) 20 d. "How the Rhinoceros got his Skin" (*horiz*). P 14×13½. (c) 20 d. "How the Alphabet was made". P 13½×14. (d) 20 d. "How the first Letter was written". P 13½×14 *Set of* 4 *sheets* 14·00 15·00

199 Canadian Pacific Railway Brake-van   **200** Tiger Shark

(Litho Cartor)

1991 (12 Sept). *Railway Brake-vans. T* **199** *and similar multicoloured designs. P* 14×13½.
1193	1 d.	Type 19		25	25
		a. Sheetlet. Nos. 1193/201		2·00	
1194	1 d.	Cumberland and Pennsylvania		25	25
1195	1 d.	Ferrocarril Interoceanico, Mexico		25	25
1196	1 d.	Northern Pacific all-steel cupola van		25	25
1197	1 d.	Morristown and Erie		25	25
1198	1 d.	Burlington Northern streamlined cupola van		25	25
1199	1 d.	McCloud River brake-coach		25	25
1200	1 d.	Santa Fe wide vision van		25	25
1201	1 d.	Frisco		25	25
1202	1 d. 50,	Colorado and Southern		35	40
		a. Sheetlet. Nos. 1202/10		2·75	
1203	1 d. 50,	Santa Fe transfer Caboose		35	40
1204	1 d. 50,	Canadian National		35	40
1205	1 d. 50,	Union Pacific transfer steel van		35	40
1206	1 d. 50,	Virginia and Truckee		35	40
1207	1 d. 50,	British Rail standard van with end windows		35	40
1208	1 d. 50,	International Railways, Central America		35	40
1209	1 d. 50,	Northern Pacific steel cupola van		35	40
1210	1 d. 50,	Burlington Northern wooden van		35	40
1211	2 d.	Oahu Railway, Hawaii		40	50
		a. Sheetlet. Nos. 1211/19		3·25	
1212	2 d.	British Rail standard van		40	50
1213	2 d.	Union Pacific wide view steel van		40	50
1214	2 d.	Chicago Belt		40	50
1215	2 d.	McCloud River four-wheel caboose		40	50
1216	2 d.	Angelina County Lumber Co		40	50
1217	2 d.	Coahuila and Zacatecas, Mexico		40	50
1218	2 d.	United Yucatan Railways		40	50
1219	2 d.	Rio Grande		40	50
1193/219			*Set of* 27	8·00	9·25

MS1220 Three sheets, each 79×56 mm. (a) 20 d. Green brake-van on goods train. P 13×12. (b) 20 d. Modern brake-van (*vert*). P 12×13. (c) 20 d. Late 19th-century brake-van (*vert*). P 12×13 *Set of* 3 *sheets* 12·00 13·00
Nos. 1193/201, 1202/10 and 1211/19 were printed together, *se-tenant*, in sheetlets of 9.

(Des R. Sauber. Litho Questa)

1991 (28 Oct). *Fishes. T 200 and similar horiz designs. Multicoloured. P 14×14½.*

1221	20 b. Type 200			15	15
1222	25 b. Common Jewelfish			15	15
1223	50 b. Five-spotted Cichlid			25	25
1224	75 b. Small-toothed Sawfish			25	25
1225	1 d. Spotted Tilapia			30	30
1226	1 d. 25, Dwarf Jewelfish			35	35
1227	1 d. 50, Five-spotted Jewelfish			40	40
1228	3 d. Lion-headed Cichlid			65	65
1229	10 d. Egyptian Mouthbrooder			2·00	2·50
1230	15 d. Burton's Mouthbrooder			2·75	3·50
1221/30			*Set of 10*	6·50	7·50

MS1231 Two sheets, each 118×83 mm. (a) 18 d.
Great Barracuda. (b) 18 d. Yellow-tailed Snapper
Set of 2 sheets 8·50 9·50

(Litho Questa)

1991 (9 Nov). *Hummel Figurines. Vert designs as T 302 of Antigua. Multicoloured. P 14.*

1232	20 b. Waving children			10	10
1233	75 b. Children under umbrella			15	15
1234	1 d. Girl kissing friend			20	20
1235	1 d. 50, Children at window			30	30
1236	2 d. 50, Two girls in aprons			45	45
1237	5 d. Two boys in bow ties			85	85
1238	10 d. Two girls sitting on fence with birds			1·75	2·00
1239	15 d. Boy and girl in Swiss costume			2·50	3·00
1232/9			*Set of 8*	5·50	6·50

MS1240 Two sheets, each 98×128 mm. (a) 4 d. ×
4 As Nos. 1233/5 and 1239. (b) 5 d. × 4 As Nos.
1232 and 1236/8 *Set of 2 sheets* 7·00 8·00

(Litho Questa)

1991 (5 Dec). *Death Centenary of Vincent van Gogh (artist). Multicoloured designs as T 278 of Antigua. P 14×13½ (horiz) or 13½×14 (vert).*

1241	20 b. "The Old Cemetery Tower at Nuenen in the Snow" (*horiz*)	15	15
1242	25 b. "Head of Peasant Woman with White Cap"	15	15
1243	50 b. "The Green Parrot"	20	20
1244	75 b. "Vase with Carnations"	20	20
1245	1 d. "Vase with Red Gladioli"	25	25
1246	1 d. 25, "Beach at Scheveningen in Calm Weather" (*horiz*)	30	30
1247	1 d. 50, "Boy cutting Grass with Sickle" (*horiz*)	35	35
1248	2 d. "Coleus Plant in a Flowerpot" (detail)	40	40
1249	3 d. "Self-portrait, 1887"	60	60
1250	4 d. "Self-portrait" (*different*)	70	70
1251	5 d. "Self-portrait" (*different*)	85	85
1252	6 d. "Self-portrait, 1887" (*different*)	1·25	1·25
1253	8 d. "Still Life with Bottle, Two Glasses, Cheese and Bread" (detail)	1·75	1·75
1254	10 d. "Still Life with Cabbage, Clogs and Potatoes" (*horiz*)	2·25	2·25
1255	12 d. "Montmartre: The Street Lamps"	2·75	2·75
1256	15 d. "Head of a Peasant Woman with Brownish Cap"	3·00	3·00
1241/56		*Set of 16*	13·50	13·50

MS1257 Four sheets, each 127×102 mm. (a)
20 d. "The Potato Eaters" (*horiz*). (b) 20 d.
"Montmartre: Quarry and Mills" (*horiz*). (c) 20 d.
"Autumn Landscape" (*horiz*). (d) 20 d. "Arles:
View from the Wheat Fields" (detail) (*horiz*).
Imperf *Set of 4 sheets* 15·00 16·00

(Litho Walsall)

1991 (23 Dec). *Christmas. Religious Paintings by Fra Angelico. Vert designs as T 287 of Antigua. Multicoloured. P 12.*

1258	20 b. "The Madonna of Humility"		10	10
1259	50 b. "Madonna and Child with Angels"		20	20
1260	75 b. "Virgin and Child with Angels"		25	25
1261	1 d. "The Annunciation"		30	30
1262	1 d. 25, "Presentation in the Temple"		35	35
1263	1 d. "The Annunciation" (*different*)		1·25	1·50
1264	10 d. "Madonna della Stella"		2·00	2·50
1265	15 d. "Naming of St. John the Baptist"		2·50	3·25
1258/65		*Set of 8*	6·25	7·50

MS1266 Two sheets, each 98×128 mm. (a) 20 d.
"Coronation of the Virgin". (b) 20 d.
"Annunciation and Adoration of the Magi". P 14
Set of 2 sheets 7·00 8·00

201 Son House

202 Pope John Paul II

(Des R. Sauber. Litho Questa)

1992 (12 Feb). *Famous Blues Singers. T 201 and similar vert designs. Multicoloured. P 14.*

1267	20 b. Type 201			15	15
1268	25 b. W. C. Handy			15	15
1269	50 b. Muddy Waters			30	30
1270	75 b. Lightnin Hopkins			40	40
1271	1 d. Ma Rainey			45	45
1272	1 d. 25, Mance Lipscomb			50	50
1273	1 d. 50, Mahalia Jackson			60	60
1274	2 d. Ella Fitzgerald			70	70

1275	3 d. Howlin Wolf		85	85
1276	5 d. Bessie Smith		1·25	1·25
1277	7 d. Leadbelly		1·50	1·50
1278	10 d. Joe Willie Wilkins		2·00	2·00
1267/78		*Set of 12*	8·00	8·00

MS1279 Three sheets, each 110×78 mm. (a)
20 d. String Drum. (b) 20 d. Elvis Presley. (c)
20 d. Billie Holiday *Set of 3 sheets* 11·00 12·00

(Des G. Vasarhelyi. Litho Questa)

1992 (20 Feb). *Papal Visit. T 202 and similar horiz designs. Multicoloured. P 14.*

1280	1 d. Type 202		40	40
1281	1 d. 25, Pope John Paul II and Pres. Sir Dawda Jawara		50	50
1282	20 d. Gambian and Papal flags		4·75	5·50
1280/2		*Set of 3*	5·00	5·75

MS1283 104×70 mm. 25 d. Pope giving blessing 6·00 7·00
A 50 d. value, as Type **202**, but embossed on gold foil, exists
from a limited printing.

(Des D. Miller. Litho Questa)

1992 (2 Mar). *40th Anniv of Queen Elizabeth II's Accession. Horiz designs as T 288 of Antigua. Multicoloured. P 14.*

1284	20 b. Pottery market		10	10
1285	50 b. Ruins of early fort		20	20
1286	1 d. Fishing boat		30	30
1287	15 d. Canoes on beach		2·75	3·50
1284/7		*Set of 4*	3·00	3·75

MS1288 Two sheets, each 75×97 mm. (a) 20 d.
Lady Chilel Jawara (river vessel). (b) 20 d. River
ferry being loaded *Set of 2 sheets* 7·50 8·50

203 N. Comaneci (Rumania)
(combined gymnastic events)
and Map of Barcelona

(Litho Questa)

1992 (16 Mar). *Olympic Games, Barcelona (2nd issue). Past Medal Winners. T 203 and similar multicoloured designs. P 14.*

1289	20 b. Type 203		10	10
1290	50 b. D. Moorcroft (G.B.) (5000 metres) and map		20	20
1291	75 b. M. Nemeth (Hungary) (javelin) and decorative tiles		25	25
1292	1 d. J. Pedraza (Mexico) (20k walk) and decorative plate		30	30
1293	1 d. 25, "Soling" class yachting (Brazil), state arms and flag		40	40
1294	1 d. 50, Women's hockey (G.D.R.) and Barcelona building		45	45
1295	12 d. M. Jordan (U.S.A.) (basketball) and map		2·50	3·25
1296	15 d. V. Borzov (U.S.S.R.) (100 metres) and galleon		3·00	3·50
1289/96		*Set of 8*	6·50	7·50

MS1297 Two sheets. (a) 82×112 mm. 20 d.
Silhouette of flamenco dancer on map (*vert*). (b)
112×82 mm. 20 d. Silhouette of bull on map
Set of 2 sheets 7·25 7·50

204 Mickey Mouse as
Christopher Columbus

205 Hibiscus
rosa-sinensis

(Des Walt Disney Co. Litho Questa)

1992 (8 Apr). *International Stamp Exhibitions. T 204 and similar multicoloured designs showing Walt Disney cartoon characters. P 13½×14.*

(a) "Granada '92", Spain. Voyage of Columbus

1298	20 b. Type 204			20	15
1299	75 b. Mickey's plans derided			30	25
1300	1 d. 50, Mickey lands in America			50	50
1301	15 d. Mickey presents treasure to Minnie			3·00	3·50
1298/1301			*Set of 4*	3·50	4·00

MS1302 127×102 mm. 18 d. Mickey embarks for
America 3·25 3·75

(b) World Columbian Stamp "Expo '92". Chicago Landmarks

1303	50 b. Navy Pier			10	10
1304	1 d. Wrigley Building			20	25
1305	1 d. 25, University of Chicago			25	30
1306	12 d. Alder Planetarium			1·75	2·50
1303/6			*Set of 4*	2·00	2·75

MS1307 127×102 mm. 18 d. Goofy hanging over
Chicago (*horiz*). P 14×13½ 3·25 3·75

(Litho Questa)

1992 (16 Apr). *Easter. Religious Paintings. Multicoloured designs as T 291 of Antigua, but vert. P 13½×14.*

1308	20 b. "Christ presented to the People" (Rembrandt)	10	10
1309	50 b. "Christ carrying the Cross" (Grünewald)	20	20
1310	75 b. "The Crucifixion" (Grünewald)	25	25
1311	1 d. "The Crucifixion" (Rubens)	30	30
1312	1 d. 25, "The Road to Calvary" (detail) (Tintoretto)	35	35
1313	1 d. 50, "The Road to Calvary" (Tintoretto) (*different*)	40	40
1314	15 d. "The Crucifixion" (Masaccio)	2·75	3·25
1315	20 d. "The Descent from the Cross" (detail) (Rembrandt)	3·50	4·00
1308/15		*Set of 8*	7·00	8·00

MS1316 Two sheets, each 72×101 mm. (a) 25 d.
"The Crowning with Thorns" (detail) (Van
Dyck). (b) 25 d. "The Crowning with Thorns"
(detail) (Titian) *Set of 2 sheets* 8·50 9·50

(Des Mary Walters. Litho B.D.T.)

1992 (21 July). *Flowers. T 205 and similar vert designs. Multicoloured. P 14.*

1317	20 b. Type 205			10	10
1318	50 b. Monodora myristica			20	20
1319	75 b. Bombax costatum			25	25
1320	1 d. Oncoba spinosa			30	30
1321	1 d. 25, Combretum grandiflorum			35	35
1322	1 d. 50, Rothmannia longiflora			40	40
1323	2 d. Clerodendrum splendens			55	55
1324	5 d. Mussaenda erythrophylla			1·10	1·25
1325	10 d. Nauclea latifolia			1·75	2·00
1326	12 d. Clerodendrum capitatum			1·90	2·25
1327	15 d. Costus spectabilis			2·50	2·75
1328	18 d. Strophanthus preussii			2·75	3·00
1317/28			*Set of 12*	11·00	12·00

MS1329 Four sheets, each 102×71 mm. (a) 20 d.
Bougainvillea glabra. (b) 20 d. Nymphaea. (c)
20 d. Adansonia digitata. (d) 20 d. Clitoria
ternatea *Set of 4 sheets* 12·00 13·00

206 Joven Antonia (River
Gambia)

(Des C. Abbott. Litho Questa)

1992 (3 Aug). *River Boats of the World. T 206 and similar horiz designs. Multicoloured. P 14.*

1330	20 b. Type 206			10	10
1331	50 b. Dresden (River Elbe)			20	20
1332	75 b. Medway Queen (River Medway)			25	25
1333	1 d. Lady Wright (River Gambia)			30	30
1334	1 d. 25, Devin (River Vltava)			35	35
1335	1 d. 50, Lady Chilel Jawara (River Gambia)			40	50
1336	5 d. Robert Fulton (River Hudson)			1·10	1·25
1337	10 d. Coonawarra (River Murray)			1·75	2·00
1338	12 d. Nakusp (River Columbia)			2·00	2·25
1339	15 d. Lucy Ashton (Firth of Clyde)			2·75	2·75
1330/9			*Set of 10*	8·00	9·00

MS1340 Two sheets, each 107×69 mm. (a) 20 d.
City of Cairo (Mississippi). (b) 20 d. Rüdesheim
(Rhine) *Set of 2 sheets* 8·00 9·00

(Des W. Wright. Litho Questa)

1992 (8 Aug). *50th Anniv of Japanese Attack on Pearl Harbor. Horiz designs as T 286 of Antigua. Multicoloured. P 14½.*

1341	2 d. U.S.S. Pennsylvania (battleship) a. Sheetlet. Nos. 1341/50		60	70
				5·50
1342	2 d. Japanese Mitsubishi AGM Zero-Sen aircraft over Pearl Harbor		60	70
1343	2 d. U.S.S. Ward (destroyer) sinking midget submarine		60	70
1344	2 d. Ford Naval Station under attack		60	70
1345	2 d. Agency report of Japanese attack		60	70
1346	2 d. Newspaper headline		60	70
1347	2 d. Japanese troops on Guam		60	70
1348	2 d. U.S. forces regaining Wake Island		60	70
1349	2 d. North American B-25B Mitchell bomber raid on Japan		60	70
1350	2 d. American Douglas SBD Dauntless dive bomber attacking Japanese carrier, Midway		60	70
1341/50		*Set of 10*	5·50	6·00

Nos. 1341/50 were printed together, *se-tenant*, in sheetlets of
10 with the stamps arranged in two horizontal strips of 5
separated by a gutter showing dogfight over Pearl Harbor.

207 Women's Double Sculls

208 Pres. Jawara
playing Golf and
Map of Australia

(Litho Questa)

1992 (10 Aug). *Winter Olympic Games, Albertville, and Olympic Games, Barcelona (3rd issue).* T **207** *and similar multicoloured designs.* P 14.

1351	20 b. Type **207**		10	10
1352	50 b. Men's kayak (*vert*)		20	20
1353	75 b. Women's rapid precision pistol shooting		25	25
1354	1 d. Judo (*vert*)		30	30
1355	1 d. 25, Men's javelin (*vert*)		35	35
1356	1 d. 50, Men's vaulting horse (*vert*)		40	40
1357	2 d. Men's downhill skiing (*vert*)		55	55
1358	3 d. Windsurfing (*vert*)		70	75
1359	5 d. Men's high jump		1·10	1·25
1360	10 d. Four-man bobsled (*vert*)		1·90	2·25
1361	12 d. 90 metre ski-jump (*vert*)		2·00	2·50
1362	15 d. Men's slalom skiing (*vert*)		2·40	2·75
1351/62		*Set of 12*	9·00	10·50

MS1363 Four sheets, each 100×70 mm. (a) 18 d. Table tennis (*vert*). (b) 18 d. Men's 500 metre speed skating. (c) 18 d. Women's 200 metre backstroke. (d) 18 d. Pairs figure skating (*vert*)
Set of 4 sheets 13·00 14·00

(Litho B.D.T.)

1992 (21 Sept). *"Genova '92" International Thematic Stamp Exhibition. Dinosaurs. Vert designs as* T **290** *of Antigua. Multicoloured.* P 14.

1364	20 b. Dryosaurus		15	10
1365	25 b. Saurolophus		15	10
1366	50 b. Allosaurus		20	20
1367	75 b. Fabrosaurus		25	25
1368	1 d. Deinonychus		30	30
1369	1 d. 25, Cetiosaurus		35	35
1370	1 d. 50, Camptosaurus		35	35
1371	2 d. Ornithosuchus		45	45
1372	3 d. Spinosaurus		60	60
1373	5 d. Ornithomimus		1·00	1·00
1374	10 d. Kentrosaurus		1·75	2·00
1375	12 d. Schlermochus		1·90	2·25
1364/75		*Set of 12*	6·50	7·00

MS1376 Three sheets, each 104×75 mm. (a) 25 d. As No. 1366. (b) 25 d. As No. 1369. (c) 25 d. As No. 1371 . . *Set of 3 sheets* 14·00 15·00

(Des Kerri Schiff. Litho Questa)

1992 (28 Oct). *Postage Stamp Mega Event, New York. Sheet* 100×70 *mm containing horiz design as* T **299** *of Antigua. Multicoloured.* P 14.

MS1377 18 d. Immigration Centre, Ellis Island 3·75 4·00

(Litho Questa)

1992 (3 Nov). *Christmas. Religious Paintings. Vert designs as* T **300** *of Antigua. Multicoloured.* P 13¹⁄₂×14.

1378	50 b. "The Holy Family" (Raphael)		20	20
1379	75 b. "The Little Holy Family" (Raphael)		25	25
1380	1 d. "The Little Holy Family" (detail) (Raphael)		30	30
1381	1 d. 25, "Escape to Egypt" (Melchior Broederlam)		35	35
1382	1 d. 50, "Flight into Egypt" (Adriaen Isenbrant)		35	35
1383	2 d. "The Holy Family" (El Greco)		45	45
1384	2 d. "Flight into Egypt" (detail) (Cosimo Tura)		45	45
1385	2 d. "Flight into Egypt" (detail) (Master of Hoogstraelen)		45	45
1386	4 d. "The Holy Family" (Bernard van Orley)		80	90
1387	5 d. "Holy Family with Infant Jesus Sleeping" (detail) (Charles Le Brun)		95	1·10
1388	10 d. "Rest on The Flight to Egypt" (Orazio Gentileschi)		1·75	2·25
1389	12 d. "Rest on The Flight to Egypt" (detail) (Orazio Gentileschi)		1·90	2·50
1378/89		*Set of 12*	7·50	8·50

MS1390 Three sheets, each 102×77 mm. (a) 25 d. "The Holy Family" (detail) (Giorgione). (b) 25 d. "Flight into Egypt" (detail) (Vittore Carpaccio). (c) 25 d. "Rest on The Flight to Egypt" (detail) (Simone Cantarino)
Set of 3 sheets 11·00 12·00

(Des Walt Disney Co. Litho Questa)

1992 (16 Nov). *60th Anniv of Goofy (Disney cartoon character). Multicoloured designs as* T **258** *of Dominica.* P 14×13¹⁄₂.

1391	50 b. Goofy in *Orphan's Benefit*, 1934		30	20
1392	75 b. Goofy and Donald Duck in *Moose Hunters*, 1937		40	30
1393	1 d. Goofy in *Mickey's Amateurs*, 1937		50	40
1394	1 d. 25, Goofy, Donald and Mickey Mouse in *Lonesome Ghosts*, 1937		55	55
1395	5 d. Goofy, Donald and Mickey in *Boat Builders*, 1938		1·40	1·40
1396	7 d. Goofy, Donald and Mickey in *The Whalers*, 1938		1·75	2·00
1397	10 d. Goofy and Wilbur the grasshopper in *Goofy and Wilbur*, 1939		2·00	2·25
1398	15 d. Goofy in *Saludos Amigos*, 1941		2·50	2·75
1391/8		*Set of 8*	8·50	9·00

MS1399 Two sheets, each 127×102 mm. (a) 20 d. Goofy in *The Band Concert*, 1935 (*vert*). (b) 20 d. Goofy today (*vert*). P 13¹⁄₂×14 . *Set of 2 sheets* 7·50 8·00

(Litho B.D.T.)

1992 (8 Dec). *Open Golf Championships.* T **208** *and similar multicoloured designs.* P 14.

1400	20 b. Type **208**		15	15
1401	1 d. Pres. Jawara and Gambia Open trophy		45	45
1402	1 d. 50, Pres. Jawara (winner of Gambia Open, 1985)		55	55
1403	2 d. Pres. Jawara and map of Japan		70	70
1404	2 d. Pres. Jawara and map of U.S.A.		80	90
1405	5 d. Gambia Open trophy		1·40	1·60

1406	10 d. Pres. Jawara and map of Scotland		2·50	2·75
1407	12 d. Pres. Jawara and map of Italy		2·50	2·75
1400/7		*Set of 8*	8·00	9·00

MS1408 Two sheets. (a) 106×71 mm. 10 d. Pres. Jawara playing shot. (b) 67×99 mm. 10 d. Flag of Gambia (*horiz*) . . *Set of 2 sheets* 8·00 8·50

209 Launch of European "Ariane 4"

210 Peace Corps and Gambian Flags

(Des W. Wright and L. Fried (Nos. 1409, 1419, MS1423a), W. Wright and W. Hanson (Nos. 1411, 1422, MS1423c), W. Wright (others). Litho B.D.T.)

1993 (7 Jan). *Anniversaries and Events.* T **209** *and similar multicoloured designs.* P 14.

1409	2 d. Type **209**		50	50
1410	2 d. Konrad Adenauer and Berlin Airlift (*horiz*)		50	50
1411	2 d. Airship LZ-129 *Hindenburg*, 1928 (*horiz*)		50	50
1412	5 d. *Santa Maria* (*horiz*)		1·25	1·25
1413	6 d. Jentink's Duiker (*horiz*)		1·40	1·40
1414	7 d. World map and emblem (*horiz*)		1·40	1·40
1415	9 d. Wolfgang Amadeus Mozart		1·75	1·75
1416	10 d. Lions Club emblem		1·75	1·75
1417	10 d. *Enterprise* (yacht), 1930		1·75	1·75
1418	10 d. Imperial Amazon ("Sisserou Parrot")		1·75	1·75
1419	12 d. American space shuttle		2·00	2·00
1420	12 d. Fleet of Columbus (*horiz*)		2·00	2·00
1421	15 d. Adenauer and returning prisoners of war (*horiz*)		2·40	2·40
1422	18 d. Airship LZ-1, 1900 (*horiz*)		3·00	3·00
1409/22		*Set of 14*	20·00	20·00

MS1423 Six sheets. (a) 104×76 mm. 18 d. Nose of projected European space station "Hermes". (b) 113×87 mm. 18 d. Konrad Adenauer. (c) 85×65 mm. 18 d. Count von Zeppelin. (d) 103×75 mm. 18 d. Green-winged Macaw and bow of ship. (e) 85×65 mm. 18 d. Globe. (f) 99×69 mm. 18 d. Dancers from *The Marriage of Figaro*
Set of 6 sheets 18·00 20·00

Anniversaries and Events:—Nos. 1409, 1419, MS1423a, International Space Year; Nos. 1410, 1421, MS1423b, 25th death anniv of Konrad Adenauer (German statesman); Nos. 1411, 1422, MS1423c, 75th death anniv of Count Ferdinand von Zeppelin; Nos. 1412, 1420, MS1423d, 500th anniv of Discovery of America by Columbus; Nos. 1413, 1418, MS1423e, Earth Summit '92, Rio; No. 1414, International Conference on Nutrition, Rome; Nos. 1415, MS1423f, Death bicent of Mozart; No. 1416, 75th anniv of International Association of Lions Clubs; No. 1417, Americas Cup Yachting Championship.
No. 1411 is incorrectly inscribed "LZ-127".

(Des A. Nahigian. Litho Walsall)

1993 (7 Jan). *15th Death Anniv of Elvis Presley (singer) (1992). Vert designs as* Nos. 1666/8 *of Dominica. Multicoloured.* P 14.

1424	3 d. Elvis Presley		70	70
	a. Strip of 3. Nos. 1424/6		1·90	
1425	3 d. Elvis with guitar		70	70
1426	3 d. Elvis with microphone		70	70
1424/6		*Set of 3*	1·90	1·90

Nos. 1424/6 were printed together, horizontally and vertically *se-tenant*, in sheetlets of 9 (3×3).

(Litho Walsall)

1993 (7 Jan). *Bicentenary of the Louvre, Paris. Vert designs as* T **305** *of Antigua showing paintings. Multicoloured.* P 12.

1427	3 d. "St. John the Baptist" (Da Vinci)		55	60
	a. Sheetlet. Nos. 1427/34		4·00	
1428	3 d. "Virgin of the Rocks" (Da Vinci)		55	60
1429	3 d. "Bacchus" (Da Vinci)		55	60
1430	3 d. "Lady of the Court, Milan" (Da Vinci)		55	60
1431	3 d. "Virgin of the Rocks" (detail) (Da Vinci)		55	60
1432	3 d. "Mona Lisa" (Da Vinci)		55	60
1433	3 d. "Mona Lisa" (detail) (Da Vinci)		55	60
1434	3 d. Sketches for "Two Horsemen" (Da Vinci)		55	60
1435	3 d. "The Oath of Horatii" (left detail) (David)		55	60
	a. Sheetlet. Nos. 1435/42		4·00	
1436	3 d. "The Oath of Horatii" (right detail) (David)		55	60
1437	3 d. "The Love of Paris and Helen" (detail) (David)		55	60
1438	3 d. "The Sabine Women" (detail) (David)		55	60
1439	3 d. "Leonidas at Thermopylae" (detail) (David)		55	60
1440	3 d. "The Coronation of Napoleon" (left detail) (David)		55	60
1441	3 d. "The Coronation of Napoleon" (centre detail) (David)		55	60
1442	3 d. "The Coronation of Napoleon" (right detail) (David)		55	60
1443	3 d. "Peasant Family at Home" (detail) (L. le Nain)		55	60
	a. Sheetlet. Nos. 1443/50		4·00	
1444	3 d. "Smoking Room" (left detail) (L. le Nain)		55	60
1445	3 d. "Smoking Room" (right detail) (L. le Nain)		55	60
1446	3 d. "The Cart" (detail) (L. le Nain)		55	60
1447	3 d. "Peasants' Repast" (detail) (L. le Nain)		55	60
1448	3 d. "Portrait in an Interior" (detail) (L. le Nain)		55	60

1449	3 d. "Portrait in an Interior" (different detail) (L. le Nain)		55	60
1450	3 d. "The Forge" (L. le Nain)		55	60
1427/50		*Set of 24*	12·00	13·00

MS1451 Two sheets, each 70×100 mm. (a) 20 d. "Allegory of Victory" (M. le Nain) (52×86 mm). (b) 20 d. "Madame Vigee-Le Brun and Daughter" (Le Brun) (52×86 mm). P 14¹⁄₂ . *Set of 2 sheets* 7·50 8·50
Nos. 1427/34, 1435/42 and 1443/50 were each printed together, *se-tenant*, in sheetlets of 8 stamps and one centre label. Nos. 1432/3 are incorrectly inscribed "Monna Lisa".

(Litho Questa)

1993 (3 Mar). *25th Anniv of United States Peace Corps.* P 14.

1452	**210** 2 d. multicoloured		60	60

211 Jackie Robinson and Ruby Dee (*The Jackie Robinson Story*)

(Des P. Wolff. Litho Questa)

1993 (25 Mar). *Baseball Films.* T **211** *and similar multicoloured designs.* P 13.

1453	3 d. Type **211**		60	70
	a. Sheetlet. Nos. 1453/60		4·25	
1454	3 d. Robert DeNiro (*Bang the Drum Slowly*)		60	70
1455	3 d. James Earl Jones and Billy Dee Williams (*The Bingo Long Travelling All-Stars and Motor Kings*)		60	70
1456	3 d. Kevin Costner and Susan Sarandon (*Bull Durham*)		60	70
1457	3 d. Cast photograph (*Eight Men Out*)		60	70
1458	3 d. Ray Liotta (*Field of Dreams*)		60	70
1459	3 d. Charlie Sheen (*Major League*)		60	70
1460	3 d. Tom Selleck (*Mr. Baseball*)		60	70
1461	3 d. Wallace Beery, 1927, and Elliott Gould, 1986 (*Casey at the Bat*)		60	70
	a. Sheetlet. Nos. 1461/8		4·25	
1462	3 d. Anna Nilsson and Babe Ruth (*Babe comes Home*)		60	70
1463	3 d. Joe Brown (*Elmer the Great*)		60	70
1464	3 d. Bud Abbott and Lou Costello (*The Naughty Nineties*)		60	70
1465	3 d. Frank Sinatra, Gene Kelly and Esther Williams (*Take Me Out to the Ball Game*)		60	70
1466	3 d. Tab Hunter and Gwen Verdon (*Damn Yankees*)		60	70
1467	3 d. Dan Dailey (*The Pride of St. Louis*)		60	70
1468	3 d. John Candy and Richard Pryor (*Brewster's Millions*)		60	70
1453/68		*Set of 16*	8·75	10·00

MS1469 Four sheets, each 132×107 mm. (a) 20 d. John Goodman (*The Babe*). (b) 20 d. Ronald Reagan (*The Winning Team*). (c) 20 d. Tom Hanks and Madonna (*A League of Their Own*) (*vert*). (d) 20 d. Robert Redford (*The Natural*) (*vert*) . . *Set of 4 sheets* 15·00 17·00
Nos. 1453/60 and 1461/8 were each printed together, *se-tenant*, in sheetlets of 8.

212 Giraffe

213 Long-tailed Pangolin hanging by Tail

(Des D. Burkhart. Litho Questa)

1993 (5 Apr). *Animals of West Africa.* T **212** *and similar vert designs. Multicoloured.* P 14.

1470	2 d. Type **212**		40	45
	a. Sheetlet. Nos. 1470/81		4·25	
1471	2 d. Baboon		40	45
1472	2 d. Caracal		40	45
1473	2 d. Large-spotted Genet		40	45
1474	2 d. Bushbuck		40	45
1475	2 d. Red-fronted Gazelle		40	45
1476	2 d. Red-flanked Duiker		40	45
1477	2 d. Cape Buffalo		40	45
1478	2 d. African Civet		40	45
1479	2 d. Side-striped Jackal		40	45
1480	2 d. Ratel		40	45
1481	2 d. Striped Polecat		40	45
1482	5 d. Vervet		70	75
	a. Sheetlet. Nos. 1482/93		8·25	
1483	5 d. Blackish-green Guenon		70	75
1484	5 d. Long-tailed Pangolin		70	75
1485	5 d. Leopard		70	75
1486	5 d. Elephant		70	75

1487	5 d. Hunting Dog		70	75
1488	5 d. Spotted Hyena		70	75
1489	5 d. Lion		70	75
1490	5 d. Hippopotamus		70	75
1491	5 d. Nile Crocodile		70	75
1492	5 d. Aardvark		70	75
1493	5 d. Warthog		70	75
1470/93		Set of 24	12·50	13·00

MS1494 101×72 mm. 20 d. As No. 1483 .. 3·75 4·00
Nos. 1470/81 and 1482/93 were each printed together, se-tenant, in sheetlets of 12, with the backgrounds forming composite designs.

(Des D. Burkhart. Litho Questa)

1993 (15 Apr). *Endangered Species. Long-tailed Pangolin. T 213 and similar vert designs. Multicoloured. P 14.*

1495	1 d. 25, Type 213		35	25
1496	1 d. 50, Sitting on branch		45	30
1497	2 d. Climbing up branch		55	50
1498	5 d. Climbing down branch		1·40	1·60
1495/8		Set of 4	2·50	2·40

MS1499 72×100 mm. 20 d. As No. 1496 .. 4·00 4·50

214 Osprey

215 Rose-ringed Parakeet

(Des W. Wright. Litho Questa)

1993 (15 Apr). *Birds of Prey. T 214 and similar multicoloured designs. P 14.*

1500	1 d. 25, Type 214		60	40
1501	1 d. 50, Egyptian Vulture (horiz)		70	40
1502	2 d. Martial Eagle		80	45
1503	3 d. Ruppell's Griffon (horiz)		90	75
1504	5 d. Augur Buzzard		1·25	1·10
1505	8 d. Greater Kestrel		1·75	2·00
1506	10 d. Secretary Bird		2·00	2·25
1507	15 d. Bateleur (horiz)		2·50	3·00
1500/7		Set of 8	9·50	9·25

MS1508 Two sheets, each 108×80 mm. (a) 20 d. Owl ("Tawny Owl") (57×42½ mm). (b) 20 d. Verreaux's Eagle (57×42½ mm) Set of 2 sheets 8·00 8·50

(Des W. Wright. Litho Questa)

1993 (15 Apr). *African Birds. T 215 and similar vert designs. Multicoloured. P 14.*

1509	2 d. Type 215		60	70
	a. Sheetlet. Nos. 1509/20		6·50	
1510	2 d. Variable Sunbird		60	70
1511	2 d. Red-billed Hornbill		60	70
1512	2 d. Red-billed Fire Finch		60	70
1513	2 d. Go-away Bird		60	70
1514	2 d. Burchell's Gonolek ("Crimson-breasted Shrike")		60	70
1515	2 d. Grey-headed Bush Shrike		60	70
1516	2 d. Western Nicator		60	70
1517	2 d. Egyptian Plover		60	70
1518	2 d. Congo Peafowl		60	70
1519	2 d. Painted Snipe		60	70
1520	2 d. South African Crowned Crane		60	70
1509/20		Set of 12	6·50	7·50

Nos. 1509/20 were printed together, se-tenant, in sheetlets of 12.
No. 1509a exists imperforate from a limited printing.

(Des Kerri Schiff. Litho Questa)

1993 (2 June). *40th Anniv of Coronation. Vert designs as T 307 of Antigua. P 13½×14.*

1521	2 d. multicoloured		60	75
	a. Sheetlet. Nos. 1521/4×2		8·00	
1522	5 d. multicoloured		1·00	1·25
1523	8 d. reddish brown and black		1·25	1·50
1524	10 d. multicoloured		1·50	1·60
1521/4		Set of 4	4·00	4·50

MS1525 70×100 mm. 20 d. multicoloured. P 14 4·00 4·50
Designs: (38×47 mm)—2 d. Queen Elizabeth II at Coronation (photograph by Cecil Beaton); 5 d. Orb and Sceptre; 8 d. Sir Winston Churchill; 10 d. Queen Elizabeth II at Trooping the Colour. (28½×42½ mm)—20 d. "Queen Elizabeth II, 1972" (detail) (Joe King).
Nos. 1521/4 were printed together in sheetlets of 8 containing two se-tenant blocks of 4.

216 Hugo Eckener and LZ-127 Graf Zeppelin

(Litho Questa)

1993 (7 June). *Aviation Anniversaries. T 216 and similar multicoloured designs. P 14.*

1526	2 d. Type 216		55	50
1527	2 d. Guyot's balloon, 1785 (vert)		55	50
1528	5 d. Zeppelin LZ-3 Luftschiffe 3 and crown		1·00	1·00
1529	5 d. Sopwith Snipe (fighter)		1·00	1·00

1530	8 d. Eckener and LZ-127 Graf Zeppelin		1·60	1·75
1531	10 d. Comte D'Artois (hot air balloon), 1785 (vert)		1·90	2·00
1532	15 d. Royal Aircraft Factory S.E.5 (fighter)		2·40	2·50
1526/32		Set of 7	8·00	8·25

MS1533 Three sheets. (a) 105×84 mm. 20 d. Eckener and LZ-127 Graf Zeppelin (airship). (b) 84×105 mm. 20 d. Blanchard's balloon, 1785 (vert). (c) 84×105 mm. 20 d. Avro 504k (biplane)
Set of 3 sheets 12·00 13·00
Anniversaries:—Nos. 1526, 1528, 1530, MS1533a, 125th birth anniv of Hugo Eckener (airship pioneer); Nos. 1527, 1531, MS1533b, Bicentenary of first airmail flight; Nos. 1529, 1532, MS1533c, 75th anniv of Royal Air Force.
Nos. 1526 and MS1533a are incorrectly inscribed "Zeppelin Luftschiffe 3". All three stamps and the miniature sheet for Eckener's birth anniversary are inscribed with the wrong dates, 1870–1940 instead of 1868–1954.

217 Henry Ford and "Model T", 1910

218 Marilyn Monroe

(Des R. Sauber. Litho Questa)

1993 (7 June). *Centenaries of Henry Ford's First Petrol Engine (Nos. 1534/45) and Karl Benz's First Four-wheeled Car (Nos. 1546/57). T 217 and similar horiz designs. Multicoloured. P 14.*

1534	2 d. Type 217		45	50
	a. Sheetlet. Nos. 1534/45		4·75	
1535	2 d. Car of 1896		45	50
1536	2 d. Henry Ford with Barney Oldfield and "999", 1902		45	50
1537	2 d. Henry Ford, 1893, and car of 1896		45	50
1538	2 d. "Model A", 1903		45	50
1539	2 d. "Model T" with roof lowered, 1908		45	50
1540	2 d. "Model T" with roof raised, 1908		45	50
1541	2 d. "Model K", 1906		45	50
1542	2 d. "Model A", 1931		45	50
1543	2 d. "Model A", 1906		45	50
1544	2 d. "Model N", 1906		45	50
1545	2 d. "Model F", 1905		45	50
1546	2 d. Benz "Velo", 1894		45	50
	a. Sheetlet. Nos. 1546/57		4·75	
1547	2 d. Car of 1894		45	50
1548	2 d. Three-wheeled car of 1885 from side		45	50
1549	2 d. "Mannheim", 1905		45	50
1550	2 d. Car of 1892		45	50
1551	2 d. Car of 1900 from front		45	50
1552	2 d. Racing car of 1911 from side		45	50
1553	2 d. "Velo", 1893		45	50
1554	2 d. Black car of 1900 from side		45	50
1555	2 d. Red car of 1900 from front		45	50
1556	2 d. Racing car of 1911 from front		45	50
1557	2 d. Three-wheeled car of 1885 from back		45	50
1534/57		Set of 24	9·50	11·00

MS1558 Two sheets, each 132×115 mm. (a) 20 d. Ford car of 1896. (b) 20 d. Benz car of 1900
Set of 2 sheets 7·50 8·00
Nos. 1534/45 and 1546/57 were each printed together, se-tenant, in sheetlets of 12 with the backgrounds forming composite designs.

(Des Susan Rini. Litho B.D.T.)

1993 (26 July). *Musical Entertainers. T 218 and similar vert designs. P 14.*

1559/93 3 d.×35 multicoloured .. .. 22·00 23·00
Nos. 1559/93 were issued as four sheetlets, three of nine different designs (Nos. 1559/85) and one of eight (Nos. 1586/93), depicting Marilyn Monroe (Nos. 1559/67), Elvis Presley (Nos. 1568/76), Madonna (Nos. 1577/85) and Buddy Holly, Otis Redding, Bill Haley, Dinah Washington, musical instruments, Ritchie Valens, Clyde McPhatter, Elvis Presley (Nos. 1586/93).

219 Siamese

220 "Woman with a Comb" (Picasso)

(Des R. Sauber. Litho Questa)

1993 (13 Sept). *Oriental Cats. T 219 and similar multicoloured designs. P 14.*

1594	2 d. Type 219		70	75
	a. Sheetlet. Nos. 1594/1605		7·50	
1595	2 d. Colourpoint Longhair sitting		70	75
1596	2 d. Burmese		70	75
1597	2 d. Birman		70	75
1598	2 d. Snowshoe		70	75
1599	2 d. Tonkinese		70	75
1600	2 d. Foreign Shorthair stretching		70	75

1601	2 d. Balinese		70	75
1602	2 d. Oriental Shorthair		70	75
1603	2 d. Foreign Shorthair lying		70	75
1604	2 d. Colourpoint Longhair with black face standing		70	75
1605	2 d. Colourpoint Longhair with white face standing		70	75
1594/1605		Set of 12	7·50	8·00

MS1606 Two sheets, each 121×90 mm. (a) 20 d. Colourpoint shorthair (vert). (b) 20 d. Burmese (vert) 7·75 8·00
Nos. 1594/1605 were printed together, se-tenant, in sheetlets of 12 with the background forming a composite design.
No. MS1606 exists imperforate from a limited printing.

(Des R. Sauber. Litho Questa)

1993 (13 Sept). *Royal Dogs. Horiz designs as T 219. Multicoloured. P 14.*

1607	2 d. Shih Tzu (Emperor of China)		70	75
	a. Sheetlet. Nos. 1607/18		7·50	
1608	2 d. Skye Terrier (Queen Victoria)		70	75
1609	2 d. Berner Laufhund (King Louis XVI, France)		70	75
1610	2 d. Boxer (King Francis I, France)		70	75
1611	2 d. Welsh Corgi (Queen Elizabeth II)		70	75
1612	2 d. Dumfrieshire (Princess Anne)		70	75
1613	2 d. Lurcher (King George VI)		70	75
1614	2 d. Welsh Corgi (Princess Anne)		70	75
1615	2 d. Pekinese (Empress Ts'Eu-Hi, China)		70	75
1616	2 d. Papillon (King Louis XIII, France)		70	75
1617	2 d. Otterhound (King John)		70	75
1618	2 d. Pug (Napoleon I, France)		70	75
1607/18		Set of 12	7·50	8·00

MS1619 Two sheets, each 120×90 mm. (a) 20 d. Cairn Terrier (Mary, Queen of Scots). (b) 20 d. Long-haired Dachshund (Queen Victoria)
Set of 2 sheets 7·75 8·00
Nos. 1607/18 were printed together, se-tenant, in sheetlets of 12 with the background forming a composite design.
No. MS1619 exists imperforate from a limited printing.

(Des Kerri Schiff. Litho Questa)

1993 (27 Sept). *Asian International Stamp Exhibitions. Multicoloured designs as T 268 of Dominica. P 13½×14.*

(a) "Indopex '93", Surabaya, Indonesia

1620	20 b. National Monument and statue, Jakarta		15	15
1621	20 b. Pura Taman Ayun Temple, Bali		15	15
1622	2 d. Guardian statue, Singosari Palace, Java		50	50
1623	2 d. Candi Jawi, Java		50	50
1624	5 d. Telek Luh mask		1·00	1·00
	a. Sheetlet. Nos. 1624/9		5·50	
1625	5 d. Jero Gde mask		1·00	1·00
1626	5 d. Barong Macan mask		1·00	1·00
1627	5 d. Monkey mask		1·00	1·00
1628	5 d. Mata Gde mask		1·00	1·00
1629	5 d. Jauk Kras mask		1·00	1·00
1630	5 d. "Tree Mask" (Soedibio)		1·00	1·00
	a. Sheetlet. Nos. 1630/5		5·50	
1631	5 d. "Dry Lizard" (Hendra Gunawan)		1·00	1·00
1632	5 d. "The Corn Eater" (Sudjana Kerton)		1·00	1·00
1633	5 d. "Night Watchman" (Djoko Pekik)		1·00	1·00
1634	5 d. "Hunger" (Kerton)		1·00	1·00
1635	5 d. "Arje Player" (Soedjojono)		1·00	1·00
1636	5 d. Central Temple, Lara Djonggrang		1·00	1·00
1637	5 d. Irian Jaya Monument, Jakarta		1·00	1·00
1638	15 d. Brahma and Siva Temples, Java		2·75	3·25
1639	15 d. Date of the Year Temple, Java		2·75	3·25
1620/39		Set of 20	17·00	18·00

MS1640 Two sheets, each 135×105 mm. (a) 18 d. Tomb effigies, Torajaland (horiz). (b) 18 d. Relief from Borobudur, Java (horiz). P 14×13½.
Set of 2 sheets 7·50 8·00

(b) "Taipei '93", Taiwan

1641	20 b. Fawang Si Pagoda, Henan		15	15
1642	20 b. Wanshoubao Pagoda, Shashi		15	15
1643	2 d. Red Pavilion, Shibaozhai		50	50
1644	2 d. Songyue Si Pagoda, Henan		50	50
1645	5 d. Pottery camel (walking)		1·00	1·00
	a. Sheetlet. Nos. 1645/50		5·50	
1646	5 d. Pottery horse and rider		1·00	1·00
1647	5 d. Pottery camel (standing with mouth closed)		1·00	1·00
1648	5 d. Yellow-glazed pottery horse		1·00	1·00
1649	5 d. Pottery camel (standing with mouth open)		1·00	1·00
1650	5 d. Pottery saddled horse		1·00	1·00
1651	5 d. Qianlong vase		1·00	1·00
	a. Sheetlet. Nos. 1651/6		5·50	
1652	5 d. Small wine cup		1·00	1·00
1653	5 d. Mei-ping vase		1·00	1·00
1654	5 d. Urn vase		1·00	1·00
1655	5 d. Tureen		1·00	1·00
1656	5 d. Lidded potiche		1·00	1·00
1657	5 d. Tianning Si Pagoda, Beijing		1·00	1·00
1658	5 d. Bond Centre, Hong Kong		1·00	1·00
1659	15 d. Forbidden City pavilion, Beijing		2·75	3·25
1660	15 d. Xuanzhuang Pagoda, Shenxi		2·75	3·25
1641/60		Set of 20	17·00	18·00

MS1661 Two sheets, each 135×105 mm. (a) 18 d. Seated Buddha, Shanhua Temple, Shanxi. P 13½×14. (b) 18 d. Statues, Upper Huayan Si Temple, Datong (horiz). P 14×13½.
Set of 2 sheets 7·50 8·00

(c) "Bangkok '93", Thailand

1662	20 b. Sanctuary of Prasat Phanom Wan		15	15
1663	20 b. Lai Kham Vihan, Chiang Mai		15	15
1664	2 d. Upmarket spirit shrine, Bangkok		50	50
1665	2 d. Walking Buddha statue, Wat Phra Si Ratana Mahathat		50	50
1666	5 d. "Early Fruit Stand"		1·00	1·00
	a. Sheetlet. Nos. 1666/71		5·50	
1667	5 d. "Scene Rendered in Chinese Style"		1·00	1·00
1668	5 d. "Buddha descends from Tauatimsa"		1·00	1·00
1669	5 d. "Sang Thong Tales" (detail)		1·00	1·00
1670	5 d. "The Damned in Hell"		1·00	1·00
1671	5 d. "King Sanjaya travels on Elephant"		1·00	1·00
1672	5 d. U Thong C Buddha (bronze)		1·00	1·00
	a. Sheetlet. Nos. 1672/7		5·50	

1673	5 d.	Seated Buddha (bronze)	1·00	1·00
1674	5 d.	Phra Chai Buddha (ivory and gold)	1·00	1·00
1675	5 d.	Buddha (bronze)	1·00	1·00
1676	5 d.	U Thong A Buddha (bronze)	1·00	1·00
1677	5 d.	Crowned Buddha (bronze)	1·00	1·00
1678	5 d.	Statue of Buddha, Wat Mahathat	1·00	1·00
1679	5 d.	The Gopura of Prasat Phanom Rung	1·00	1·00
1680	15 d.	Slender Chedis, Mongkon	2·75	3·25
1681	15 d.	The Prang of Prasat Hin Phimai	2·75	3·25
1662/81		Set of 20	17·00	18·00

MS1682 Two sheets, each 135×105 mm. (a) 18 d.
Khon (Thai dance drama). P 13½×14. (b) 18 d.
Ceramics (horiz). P 14×13½ .. Set of 2 sheets 7·50 8·00
Nos. 1624/9, 1630/5, 1645/50, 1651/6, 1666/71 and 1672/7
were each printed, se-tenant, in sheetlets of 6.

(Litho Cartor (Nos. 1686, 1690, **MS**1691c) or Questa (others))

1993 (7 Oct). *Anniversaries and Events.* T **220** *and similar
multicoloured designs.* P 14 (*Nos.* 1683/5, 1687/9) *or* 13½×14
(*Nos.* 1686, 1690).

1683	2 d.	Type **220**	55	55
1684	2 d.	Niedzica Castle (horiz)	55	55
1685	5 d.	"The Mirror" (Picasso)	1·00	1·00
1686	5 d.	Early astronomical instrument	1·00	1·00
1687	7 d.	"Woman on a Pillow" (Picasso)	1·40	1·40
1688	10 d.	"Honegger's Liturgical Symphony" (Marian Bogusz) (horiz)	1·75	2·00
1689	10 d.	"Pont-Neut in Paris" (Hanna Rudzka-Cybisowa) (horiz)	1·75	2·00
1690	10 d.	Modern Telescope	1·75	2·00
1683/90		Set of 8	8·75	9·50

MS1691 Three sheets. (a) 75×105 mm. 18 d.
"The Three Dancers" (detail) (Picasso). P 14. (b)
105×75 mm. 18 d. "When You enter here,
Whisper my Name soundlessly" (detail) (Henryk
Waniek) (horiz). P 14. (c) 102×74 mm. 18 d.
Copernicus. P 12×13 .. Set of 3 sheets 10·00 11·00
Anniversaries and Events:—Nos. 1683, 1685, 1687,
MS1691a, 20th death anniv of Picasso (artist); Nos. 1684,
1688/9, **MS**1691b, "Polska '93" International Stamp Exhibition,
Poznań; Nos. 1686, 1690, **MS**1691c, 450th death anniv of
Copernicus (astronomer).
The captions printed on Nos. 1684 and 1689 are transposed in
error.
No. **MS**1691b is inscribed "WHISPERT" in error.

221 Mudville Player at the Plate

(Des Rosemary DeFiglio. Litho Questa)

1993 (25 Oct). *Casey at the Bat.* T **221** *and similar
multicoloured designs showing scenes from Walt Disney's
cartoon film.* P 14×13½.

1692	2 d.	Type **221**	60	70
		a. Sheetlet. Nos. 1692/1700	4·75	
1693	2 d.	Mudville player out	60	70
1694	2 d.	Umpire and player arguing	60	70
1695	2 d.	Fans applauding	60	70
1696	2 d.	Casey reading newspaper at plate	60	70
1697	2 d.	Casey letting second pitch go by	60	70
1698	2 d.	Over-confident Casey	60	70
1699	2 d.	Casey's striking out	60	70
1700	2 d.	Casey striking out at night	60	70
1692/1700		Set of 9	4·75	5·50

MS1701 Two sheets, each 129×103 mm. (a) 20 d.
Mudville manager. P 14×13½. (b) 20 d. Pitcher
(vert). P 13½×14 .. Set of 2 sheets 8·50 9·00
Nos. 1692/1700 were printed together, se-tenant, in sheetlets
of 9.

(Des Rosemary DeFiglio, Litho Cartor)

1993 (22 Nov). *World Cup Football Championship* 1994,
U.S.A. (1st issue). *Multicoloured designs as* T **310** *of Antigua.*
P 13½×14.

1702	1 d. 25,	Hannich (Hungary) and Stopyra (France)	40	30
1703	1 d. 50,	Labd (Morocco) and Gary Lineker (England)	55	40
1704	2 d.	Segota (Canada) and Morozov (Russia)	60	50
1705	3 d.	Roger Milla (Cameroun)	70	70
1706	5 d.	Rodax (Austria) and Weiss (Czechoslovakia)	90	1·00
1707	10 d.	Claesen (Belgium), Bossis and Amoros (France)	1·60	1·90
1708	12 d.	Candida (Brazil) and Ramirez (Costa Rica)	1·75	2·00
1709	15 d.	Silva (Brazil) and Michel Platini (France)	2·25	2·50
1702/9		Set of 8	8·00	8·50

MS1710 Two sheets, each 100×70 mm. (a) 25 d.
Muller (Brazil) and McDonald (Ireland) (horiz).
(b) 25 d. Diego Maradona (Argentina) and
Matthaeus (Germany) (horiz). P 13
Set of 2 sheets 9·75 10·00
See also Nos. 1882/90.

(Litho Questa)

1993 (1 Dec). *Christmas. Religious Paintings. Designs as*
T **270** *of Dominica. Black, pale lemon and red (Nos.* 1712/13,
1715/17 *and* **MS**1719b) *or multicoloured (others).* P 13½×14.

1711	25 b.	"The Adoration of the Magi" (detail) (Rubens)	15	10
1712	1 d.	"The Holy Family with Joachim and Anna" (Dürer)	35	20
1713	1 d. 50,	"The Annunciation" (Dürer)	50	30
1714	2 d.	"The Adoration of the Magi" (different detail) (Rubens)	55	40
1715	2 d.	"The Virgin Mary worshipped by Albrecht Bonstetten" (Dürer)	55	40
1716	7 d.	"The Holy Family with Two Angels in a Portico" (detail) (Dürer)	1·50	2·00
1717	10 d.	"Virgin on a Throne, crowned by an Angel" (Dürer)	1·90	2·25
1718	15 d.	"The Adoration of the Magi" (different detail) (Rubens)	2·25	2·75
1711/18		Set of 8	7·00	7·50

MS1719 Two sheets, each 102×127 mm. (a) 20 d.
"The Adoration of the Magi" (different detail)
(Rubens). P 13½×14. (b) 20 d. "The Holy Family
with Two Angels in a Portico" (different detail)
(Dürer) (horiz). P 14×13½ .. Set of 2 sheets 7·75 8·50

(Des Kerri Schiff. Litho Questa)

1993 (15 Dec). *Famous Paintings by Rembrandt and Matisse.*
Multicoloured designs as T **316** *of Antigua.* P 13½×14.

1720	50 b.	"A Man in a Cap" (Rembrandt)	25	15
1721	1 d. 50,	"Pierre Matisse" (Matisse)	50	35
1722	2 d.	"Man with a Gold Helmet" (Rembrandt)	55	45
1723	2 d.	"Auguste Pellerin" (Matisse)	55	45
1724	5 d.	"Andre Derain" (Matisse)	1·00	1·00
1725	7 d.	"A Franciscan Monk" (Rembrandt)	1·50	1·75
1726	12 d.	"The Young Sailor (II)" (Matisse)	2·10	2·25
1727	15 d.	"The Apostle Paul" (Rembrandt)	2·25	2·75
1720/7		Set of 8	8·00	8·25

MS1728 Two sheets, each 127×102 mm. (a) 20 d.
"Dr. Tulp demonstrating the Anatomy of the
Arm" (detail) (Rembrandt) (horiz). (b) 20 d.
"Pianist and Draughts Players" (detail) (Matisse)
(horiz). P 14×13½ .. Set of 2 sheets 7·50 8·50

222 Mickey Mouse
performing Ski Ballet

(Des Alvin White Studios. Litho Questa)

1993 (20 Dec). *Winter Sports.* T **222** *and similar vert designs
showing Walt Disney cartoon characters. Multicoloured.*
P 13½×14.

1729	50 b.	Type **222**	20	15
1730	75 b.	Clarabelle and Horace ice dancing	25	15
1731	1 d.	Donald Duck and Dale speed skating	30	20
1732	1 d. 25,	Donald in biathlon	30	20
1733	4 d.	Donald and nephews in bob-sled	90	90
1734	5 d.	Goofy on luge	1·00	1·00
1735	7 d.	Minnie Mouse figure skating	1·50	2·00
1736	10 d.	Goofy downhill skiing	2·00	2·25
1737	15 d.	Goofy playing ice hockey	2·25	2·75
1729/37		Set of 9	8·00	8·75

MS1738 Two sheets, each 128×102 mm. (a) 20 d.
Minnie mogul skiing. (b) 20 d. Goofy cross-
country skiing .. Set of 2 sheets 7·50 8·50

(Des W. Hanson. Litho Questa)

1994 (18 Feb). *"Hong Kong '94" International Stamp
Exhibition* (1st issue). *Horiz design as* T **317** *of Antigua.
Multicoloured.* P 14.

1739	1 d. 50,	Hong Kong 1979 $2 Butterflies stamp and "Spring Garden" (M. Bruce) (left detail)	20	25
		a. Horiz pair. Nos. 1739/40	40	50
1740	1 d. 50,	Gambia 1990 50 d. Gambian Life stamp and "Spring Garden" (M. Bruce) (right detail)	20	25

MS1741 82×117 mm. 20 d. Hong Kong 1970
Chinese New Year 10 c. stamp .. 2·75 3·00
Nos. 1739/40 were printed together, se-tenant, in horizontal
pairs throughout the sheet with the centre part of each pair
forming the complete painting.

(Des Kerri Schiff. Litho Questa)

1994 (18 Feb). *"Hong Kong '94" International Stamp
Exhibition* (2nd issue). *Qin Dynasty Terracotta Figures.
Multicoloured designs as* T **318** *of Antigua, but vert.* P 14.

1742	1 d. 50,	Warriors and horses	20	25
		a. Sheetlet. Nos. 1742/7	1·10	
1743	1 d. 50,	Head of warrior	20	25
1744	1 d. 50,	Kneeling warrior	20	25
1745	1 d. 50,	Chariot driver	20	25
1746	1 d. 50,	Dog	20	25
1747	1 d. 50,	Warriors as excavated	20	25
1742/7		Set of 6	1·10	1·50

Nos. 1742/7 were printed together, se-tenant, in sheetlets of 6.

223 Pluto the Racer,
1934–35

224 Ludwig von Drake
and Easter Bunny

(Des Alvin White Studios. Litho Questa)

1994 (11 Apr). *Chinese New Year ("Year of the Dog").* T **223**
*and similar multicoloured designs showing Walt Disney
cartoon dogs.* P 13½×14.

1748	25 b.	Type **223**	10	10
1749	50 b.	Fifi, 1933	10	10
1750	75 b.	Pluto Jnr, 1942	10	10
1751	1 d. 25,	Goofy and Bowser	15	20
1752	1 d. 50,	Butch, 1940	20	25
1753	2 d.	Toliver, 1936	20	25
1754	3 d.	Ronnie, 1946	35	40
1755	5 d.	Primo, 1950	60	65
1756	8 d.	Pluto's kid brother, 1946	90	95
1757	10 d.	The army mascot, 1942	1·10	1·25
1758	12 d.	Pluto and Fifi's puppies, 1937	1·40	1·50
1759	18 d.	Bent Tail Jnr, 1949	2·10	2·25
1748/59		Set of 12	6·50	8·00

MS1760 Three sheets, each 127×102 mm. (a)
20 d. Pluto and Fifi's puppies, 1950.
P 13½×14. (b) 20 d. Pluto and Dinah, 1950.
P 13½×14. (c) 20 d. Pflip (horiz). P 14×13½
Set of 3 sheets 6·75 7·00
No. 1748/59 were issued in small sheets of 10 (5×2). No. 1748
also exists as a sheetlet of 6 (3×2).
Nos. 1758 and **MS**1760a are inscribed "DINAH'S PUPPIES"
in error.

(Des Alvin White Studios. Litho Questa)

1994 (11 Apr). *Easter.* T **224** *and similar vert designs showing
Walt Disney cartoon characters. Multicoloured.* P 13½×14.

1761	25 b.	Type **224**	10	10
1762	50 b.	Minnie Mouse and Daisy Duck carrying banner	10	10
1763	3 d.	Mickey Mouse wearing top hat	35	40
1764	4 d.	Von Drake holding hatching egg	45	50
1765	5 d.	Donald Duck pushing trolley full of eggs	60	65
1766	8 d.	Bunny taking photograph of Von Drake	90	95
1767	10 d.	Goofy dressed as Easter Bunny	1·10	1·25
1768	12 d.	Von Drake holding dinosaur egg	1·40	1·50
1761/8		Set of 8	5·00	5·25

MS1769 Two sheets. (a) 102×123 mm. 20 d.
Mickey and Minnie. (b) 123×102 mm. 20 d.
Ludwig von Drake .. Set of 2 sheets 4·75 5·00

(Litho Questa)

1994 (25 Apr). *Centenary of Sierra Club (environmental
protection society)* (1992). *Endangered Environments.
Multicoloured designs as* T **320** *of Antigua.* P 14.

1770	5 d.	Briksdal Fjord	60	65
		a. Sheetlet. Nos. 1770/5	3·50	
1771	5 d.	Glacier, Briksdal Fjord	60	65
1772	5 d.	Waterfall, Briksdal Fjord	60	65
1773	5 d.	Frozen lake, Yosemite	60	65
1774	5 d.	Cliffs and river, Yosemite	60	65
1775	5 d.	Forest, Yosemite	60	65
1776	5 d.	Mother and child, Tibetan Plateau	60	65
		a. Sheetlet. Nos. 1776/83	4·75	
1777	5 d.	Yellowstone in winter	60	65
1778	5 d.	Ross Island	60	65
1779	5 d.	Mount Erebus	60	65
1780	5 d.	Tibetan Plateau	60	65
1781	5 d.	Waterfall, Yellowstone	60	65
1782	5 d.	Sunset on the Serengeti	60	65
1783	5 d.	Dead trees, Ansel Adams Wilderness	60	65
1784	5 d.	Ansel Adams Wilderness in winter (horiz)	60	65
		a. Sheetlet. Nos. 1784/91	4·75	
1785	5 d.	Ansel Adams Wilderness in summer (horiz)	60	65
1786	5 d.	Ridge on Mount Erebus (horiz)	60	65
1787	5 d.	Mount Erebus from a distance (horiz)	60	65
1788	5 d.	Prince William Sound (horiz)	60	65
1789	5 d.	Geysers, Yellowstone (horiz)	60	65
1790	5 d.	Local dwelling, Tibetan Plateau (horiz)	60	65
1791	5 d.	Sierra Club Centennial emblem (horiz)	60	65
1792	5 d.	Frozen lake, Prince William Sound (horiz)	60	65
		a. Sheetlet. Nos. 1792/7	3·50	
1793	5 d.	Forest, Prince William Sound (horiz)	60	65
1794	5 d.	Baobab Tree, Serengeti (horiz)	60	65
1795	5 d.	Plains, Serengeti (horiz)	60	65
1796	5 d.	Volcano, Ross Island (horiz)	60	65
1797	5 d.	Mountains, Ross Island (horiz)	60	65
1770/97		Set of 28	16·50	18·00

Nos. 1770/5, 1776/83, 1784/91 and 1792/7 were each printed
together, se-tenant, in two sheetlets of 6 (Nos. 1770/5 and
1792/7) or two sheetlets of 8 (Nos. 1776/91).

ALTERED CATALOGUE NUMBERS

Any Catalogue numbers altered from the last
edition are shown as a list in the introductory
pages.

225 *Oeceoclades maculata*

226 "Girl with a Kitten" (Perronneau)

(Des Wendy Smith-Griswold. Litho Questa)

1994 (1 May). *Orchids. T* **225** *and similar multicoloured designs. P* 14.
1798	1 d.	Type **225**		10	15
1799	1 d. 25, *Angraecum distichum* (*horiz*)			15	20
1800	2 d. *Plectrelminthus caudatus* (*horiz*)			20	25
1801	5 d. *Tridactyle tridactylites* (*horiz*)			60	65
1802	8 d. *Bulbophyllum lepidum* (*horiz*)			90	95
1803	10 d. *Angraecum eburneum*			1·10	1·25
1804	12 d. *Eulophia guineensis*			1·40	1·50
1805	15 d. *Angraecum eichleranum* (*horiz*)			1·75	1·90
1798/1805			*Set of* 8	6·25	6·75

MS1806 Two sheets, each 100×70 mm. (a) 25 d. *Vanilla imperialis.* (b) 25 d. *Ancistrochilus rothschildianus* (*horiz*) .. .. *Set of* 2 *sheets* 5·75 6·00

(Des Kerri Schiff. Litho Questa)

1994 (11 July). *Cats. T* **226** *and similar multicoloured designs showing paintings of cats. P* 14.
1807	5 d.	Type **226**		60	65
	a. Sheetlet. Nos. 1807/18			7·25	
1808	5 d. "Still Life with Cat and Fish" (Chardin)			60	65
1809	5 d. "Tinkle a Cat"			60	65
1810	5 d. "Naughty Puss!" (advertisement)			60	65
1811	5 d. "Cats" (T.-A. Steinlen)			60	65
1812	5 d. "Girl in Red with Cat and Dog" (Phillips)			60	65
1813	5 d. "Cat, Butterfly and Begonia" (Harunobu)			60	65
1814	5 d. "Cat and Kitten" (Pamela Higgins)			60	65
1815	5 d. "Woman with a Cat" (Renoir)			60	65
1816	5 d. "Minnie from Outskirts of the Village" (Thrall)			60	65
1817	5 d. "The Fisher" (Raphael Tuck postcard)			60	65
1818	5 d. "Artist and His Family" (detail) (Vaenius)			60	65
1819	5 d. "The Arena" (Harold Weston) (*horiz*)			60	65
	a. Sheetlet. Nos. 1819/30			7·25	
1820	5 d. "Cat killing a Bird" (Picasso) (*horiz*)			60	65
1821	5 d. "Cat and Butterfly" (Hokusai) (*horiz*)			60	65
1822	5 d. "Winter: Cat on a Cushion" (Steinlen) (*horiz*)			60	65
1823	5 d. "Rattoun Tigers" (Prang) (*horiz*)			60	65
1824	5 d. "Cat on the Floor" (Steinlen) (*horiz*)			60	65
1825	5 d. "Cat and Kittens" (*horiz*)			60	65
1826	5 d. "Cats looking over Fence" (Prang) (*horiz*)			60	65
1827	5 d. "Little White Kittens into Mischief" (Ives) (*horiz*)			60	65
1828	5 d. "Cat Bathing" (Hiroshige) (*horiz*)			60	65
1829	5 d. "Playtime" (Tuck postcard) (*horiz*)			60	65
1830	5 d. "Summer: Cat on a Balustrade" (Steinlen) (*horiz*)			60	65
1807/30			*Set of* 24	14·50	15·50

MS1831 Two sheets, each 100×70 mm. (a) 20 d. "The Graham Children" (detail) (William Hogarth). (b) 20 d. "The Morning Rising" (detail) (Michel Lepicie) (*horiz*) .. .. *Set of* 2 *sheets* 4·75 5·00
Nos. 1807/18 and 1819/30 were printed together, *se-tenant*, in sheetlets of 12.

227 Patas Monkey   **228** *Mylothris rhodope*

(Des D. Burkhart. Litho Questa)

1994 (1 Aug). *Monkeys. T* **227** *and similar vert designs. Multicoloured. P* 14.
1832	1 d.	Type **227**		10	15
1833	1 d. 50, Collared Mangabey			20	25
1834	2 d. Black and White Colobus			20	25
1835	5 d. Mona Monkey			60	65
1836	8 d. Kirk's Colobus			90	95
1837	10 d. Vervet			1·10	1·25
1838	12 d. Red Colobus			1·40	1·50
1839	15 d. Guinea Baboon			1·75	1·90
1832/9			*Set of* 8	6·25	7·00

MS1840 Two sheets, each 106×77 mm. (a) 25 d. Head of Guinea Baboon. (b) 25 d. Head of Collared Mangabey .. .. *Set of* 2 *sheets* 5·75 6·00

(Des W. Hanson. Litho B.D.T.)

1994 (16 Aug). *25th Anniv of First Moon Landing. Horiz designs as T* **326** *of Antigua. Multicoloured. P* 14.
1841	2 d. Yuri Gagarin (first cosmonaut)			20	25
	a. Sheetlet. Nos. 1841/9			1·75	
1842	2 d. Valentina Tereshkova (first woman in Space)			20	25
1843	2 d. Ham (first chimpanzee in Space)			20	25
1844	2 d. Alexei Leonov (first man to walk in Space)			20	25
1845	2 d. Neil Armstrong (first man on Moon)			20	25
1846	2 d. Svetlana Savitskaya (first woman to walk in Space)			20	25
1847	2 d. Marc Garneau (first Canadian in Space)			20	25
1848	2 d. Vladimir Komarov (first Soviet Space casualty)			20	25
1849	2 d. Ulf Merbold (first German in Space)			20	25
1841/9			*Set of* 9	1·75	2·25

MS1850 81×81 mm. 30 d. "Apollo 11" crew at news conference .. .. 3·50 3·75
Nos. 1841/9 were printed together, *se-tenant*, in sheetlets of 9.

(Des Kerri Schiff. Litho Questa)

1994 (16 Aug). *Centenary of International Olympic Committee. Gold Medal Winners. Multicoloured designs as T* **327** *of Antigua, but vert. P* 14.
1851	1 d. 50, Daley Thompson (Great Britain) (decathlon), 1980 and 1984			20	25
1852	5 d. Heide Marie Rosendohl (Germany) (long jump), 1972			60	65

MS1853 106×76 mm. 20 d. Sweden (ice hockey), 1994 .. .. 2·25 2·40

(Des J. Batchelor. Litho Questa)

1994 (16 Aug). *50th Anniv of D-Day. Horiz designs as T* **331** *of Antigua. Multicoloured. P* 14.
1854	50 b. *Soema* (Dutch sloop)			10	10
1855	75 b. H.M.S. *Belfast* (cruiser)			10	10
1856	1 d. U.S.S. *Texas* (battleship)			10	15
1857	2 d. *Georges Leygues* (French cruiser)			20	25
1854/7			*Set of* 4	40	50

MS1858 105×76 m. 20 d. H.M.S. *Ramillies* (battleship) firing broadside .. .. .. 2·25 2·40

(Des Kerri Schiff. Litho Questa (Nos. 1859, 1870/2) or B.D.T. (Nos. 1860/9))

1994 (16 Aug). *"Philakorea '94" International Stamp Exhibition, Seoul. Multicoloured designs as T* **281** *of Dominica. P* 14 (50 b., 2 d., 3 d.) *or* 13½×14 (*others*).
1859	50 b. Kungnakchon Hall (38×25 *mm*)			10	10
1860	1 d. Soldiers on horses			10	15
	a. Sheetlet. Nos. 1860/9			1·00	
1861	1 d. Soldiers defending fort			10	15
1862	1 d. Archers			10	15
1863	1 d. General on horse			10	15
1864	1 d. Three soldiers in battle			10	15
1865	1 d. Army in retreat			10	15
1866	1 d. Archers using fire arrows			10	15
1867	1 d. Horsemen attacking fort			10	15
1868	1 d. Women in summer house			10	15
1869	1 d. Old man, child and house			10	15
1870	2 d. Kettle of Popchusa (38×25 *mm*)			20	25
1871	3 d. Pomun tourist resort (38×25 *mm*)			35	40
1859/71			*Set of* 13	1·75	2·25

MS1872 98×68 mm. 20 d. Tomb guardian, Taenung (38×25 *mm*). P 14 .. .. 2·25 2·40
Nos. 1860/9 were printed together, *se-tenant*, in sheetlets of 10 showing screen paintings of the "Sanguozhi".

(Des B. Hargreaves. Litho Questa)

1994 (18 Aug). *Butterflies. T* **228** *and similar horiz designs. Multicoloured. P* 14.
1873	1 d.	Type **228**		10	15
1874	1 d. 25, *Iolaphilus menas*			15	20
1875	2 d. *Neptis nemetes*			20	25
1876	5 d. *Antanartia delius*			60	65
1877	8 d. *Acraea caecilia*			90	95
1878	10 d. *Papilio nireus*			1·10	1·25
1879	12 d. *Papilio menestheus*			1·40	1·50
1880	15 d. *Iolaphilus julus*			1·75	1·90
1873/80			*Set of* 8	6·25	6·75

MS1881 Two sheets, each 97×68 mm. (a) 25 d. *Bematistes epaea.* (b) 25 d. *Colotis evippe* .. .. *Set of* 2 *sheets* 5·75 6·00

229 Bobby Charlton (England)

230 *Suillus luteus*

(Litho Questa)

1994 (1 Sept). *World Cup Football Championships, U.S.A. (2nd issue). T* **229** *and similar vert designs. Multicoloured. P* 14.
1882	50 b.	Type **229**		10	10
1883	75 b. Ferenc Puskás (Hungary)			10	10
1884	1 d. Paolo Rossi (Italy)			10	15
1885	2 d. Biri Biri (Spain)			20	25
1886	3 d. Diego Maradona (Argentina)			35	40
1887	8 d. Johann Cruyff (Netherlands)			90	95
1888	10 d. Franz Beckenbauer (Germany)			1·10	1·25
1889	15 d. Thomas Dooley (U.S.A.)			1·75	1·90
1882/9			*Set of* 8	4·50	5·00

MS1890 Two sheets, each 70×100 mm. (a) 25 d. Pelé (Brazil). (b) 25 d. Gordon Banks (England) .. .. *Set of* 2 *sheets* 5·75 6·00

(Des Mary Walters. Litho Questa)

1994 (30 Sept). *Fungi. T* **230** *and similar vert designs. Multicoloured. P* 14.
1891	5 d.	Type **230**		60	65
	a. Sheetlet. Nos. 1891/9			5·50	
1892	5 d. *Bolbitius vitellinus*			60	65
1893	5 d. *Clitocybe nebularis*			60	65
1894	5 d. *Omphalotus olearius*			60	65
1895	5 d. *Auricularia auricula*			60	65
1896	5 d. *Macrolepiota rhacodes*			60	65
1897	5 d. *Volvariella volvacea*			60	65
1898	5 d. *Psilocybe coprophila*			60	65
1899	5 d. *Suillus granulatus*			60	65
1900	5 d. *Agaricus campestris*			60	65
	a. Sheetlet. Nos. 1900/8			5·50	
1901	5 d. *Lepista nuda*			60	65
1902	5 d. *Podaxis pistillaris*			60	65
1903	5 d. *Oudemansiella radicata*			60	65
1904	5 d. *Schizophyllum commune*			60	65
1905	5 d. *Chlorophyllum molybdites*			60	65
1906	5 d. *Hypholoma fasciculare*			60	65
1907	5 d. *Mycena pura*			60	65
1908	5 d. *Ganoderma lucidum*			60	65
1891/1908			*Set of* 18	11·00	12·00

MS1909 Two sheets, each 100×70 mm. (a) 20 d. *Leucoagaricus naucinus.* (b) 20 d. *Cyathus striatus* .. .. .. *Set of* 2 *sheets* 4·75 5·00
Nos. 1891/9 and 1900/8 were printed together, *se-tenant*, in sheetlets of 9.

(Litho Questa)

1994 (5 Dec). *Christmas. Religious Paintings. Vert designs as T* **336** *of Antigua. Multicoloured. P* 13½×14.
1910	50 b. "Expectant Madonna with St. Joseph" (French 15th-century)			10	10
1911	75 b. "Rest of the Holy Family" (Louis le Nain)			10	10
1912	1 d. "Rest on the Flight into Egypt" (Antoine Watteau)			10	15
1913	2 d. "Rest on the Flight into Egypt" (Jean-Honore Fragonard)			20	25
1914	2 d. "Rest on the Flight into Egypt" (Francois Boucher)			20	25
1915	2 d. "Noon" (Claude Lorrain)			20	25
1916	10 d. "The Holy Family" (Nicolas Poussin)			1·10	1·25
1917	12 d. "Mystical Marriage of St. Catherine" (Pierre-Francois Mignard)			1·40	1·50
1910/17			*Set of* 8	3·50	3·75

MS1918 Two sheets, each 122×87 mm. (a) 25 d. "Adoration of the Shepherds" (detail) (Mathieu le Nain). (b) 25 d. "The Nativity by Torchlight" (detail) (Louis le Nain) .. .. *Set of* 2 *sheets* 5·75 6·00

231 Marilyn Monroe   **232** Elvis as a Child

(Des R. Rundo. Litho Questa)

1995 (8 Jan). *Marilyn Monroe (American entertainer) Commemoration. T* **231** *and similar vert designs. Multicoloured. P* 14.
1919	4 d.	Type **231**		45	50
	a. Sheetlet. Nos. 1919/27			4·00	
1920	4 d. Wearing pendant necklace			45	50
1921	4 d. In blue jacket			45	50
1922	4 d. With sun-glasses on head			45	50
1923	4 d. Looking over right arm			45	50
1924	4 d. Wearing gold beret and jacket			45	50
1925	4 d. Wearing hooped earrings			45	50
1926	4 d. Smiling			45	50
1927	4 d. Laughing			45	50
1919/27			*Set of* 9	4·00	4·50

MS1928 Two sheets, each 70×100 mm. (a) 25 d. Marilyn Monroe in red dress. (b) 25 d. With pendant earrings .. .. *Set of* 2 *sheets* 5·75 6·00
Nos. 1919/27 were printed together, *se-tenant*, in sheetlets of 9.

(Des Isabelle Tanner. Litho Questa)

1995 (8 Jan). *60th Birth Anniv of Elvis Presley (singer). T* **232** *and similar vert designs. Multicoloured. P* 14.
1929	4 d.	Type **232**		45	50
	a. Sheetlet. Nos. 1929/37			4·00	
1930	4 d. Wearing white shirt			45	50
1931	4 d. With his mother Gladys			45	50
1932	4 d. With his wife Priscilla			45	50
1933	4 d. With large gold medallion			45	50
1934	4 d. In army uniform			45	50
1935	4 d. In purple shirt			45	50
1936	4 d. Wearing stetson			45	50
1937	4 d. With his daughter Lisa-Marie			45	50
1929/37			*Set of* 9	4·00	4·50

Nos. 1929/37 were printed together, *se-tenant*, in sheetlets of 9.

233 Pteranodon | 234 Pig (Chinese characters in bright green)

(Des R. Sauber. Litho Questa)

1995 (6 Feb). *Prehistoric Animals. T **233** and similar multicoloured designs. P* 14.
1938	2 d. Type **233**			20	25
	a. Sheetlet. Nos. 1938/49			2·40	
1939	2 d. Archaeopteryx			20	25
1940	2 d. Rhamphorhynchus			20	25
1941	2 d. Ornithomimus			20	25
1942	2 d. Stegosaurus			20	25
1943	2 d. Heterodontosaurus			20	25
1944	2 d. Lystrosaurus			20	25
1945	2 d. Euoplocephalus			20	25
1946	2 d. Coelophysis			20	25
1947	2 d. Staurikosaurus			20	25
1948	2 d. Giantoperis			20	25
1949	2 d. Diarthrognathus			20	25
1950	3 d. Archaeopteryx			35	40
	a. Sheetlet. Nos. 1950/61			4·25	
1951	3 d. Vangehuanosaurus			35	40
1952	3 d. Celophysis			35	40
1953	3 d. Plateosaurus			35	40
1954	3 d. Baryonyx			35	40
1955	3 d. Ornitholestes			35	40
1956	3 d. Dryosaurus			35	40
1957	3 d. Estemmenosuchus			35	40
1958	3 d. Macroplata			35	40
1959	3 d. Shonisaurus			35	40
1960	3 d. Muraeonosaurus			35	40
1961	3 d. Archelon			35	40
1938/61			*Set of* 24	6·50	7·50

MS1962 Four sheets, each 100×70 mm. (a) 20 d. Bactrosaurus. (b) 22 d. Tyrannosaurus rex (*vert*). (c) 25 d. Triceratops (*vert*). (d) 25 d. Spinosaurus
Set of 4 *sheets* 10·50 12·00

Nos. 1938/49 and 1950/61 were each printed together, *se-tenant*, in sheetlets of 12 stamps forming composite designs.

(Des Y. Lee. Litho Questa)

1995 (4 May). *Chinese New Year ("Year of the Pig"). T **234** and similar horiz designs showing symbolic pigs. P* 14½.
1963	**234**	3 d. scarlet-vermilion, black & brt grn	35	40
		a. Sheetlet. Nos. 1963/6	1·40	
1964	—	3 d. multicoloured (characters in deep ultramarine)	35	40
1965	—	3 d. reddish orange, orange-vermilion and black (characters in white)	35	40
1966	—	3 d. dull rose, scarlet-vermilion and black (characters in black)	35	40
1963/6		*Set of* 4	1·40	1·60

MS1967 76×106 mm. 10 d. deep magenta and orange-vermilion (three pigs) .. 1·10 1·25

Nos. 1963/6 were printed together, *se-tenant*, in sheetlets of 4.

235 Great White Egret | 236 Rural Road

(Litho B.D.T.)

1995 (8 May). *Water Birds. T **235** and similar horiz designs. Multicoloured. P* 14.
1968	2 d. Type **235**		20	25
1969	3 d. Pintails		35	40
	a. Sheetlet. Nos. 1969/80		4·25	
1970	3 d. Fulvous Whistling Duck		35	40
1971	3 d. Garganey		35	40
1972	3 d. White-faced Whistling Duck		35	40
1973	3 d. White-backed Duck		35	40
1974	3 d. Egyptian Goose		35	40
1975	3 d. African Pygmy Geese		35	40
1976	3 d. Little Bitterns		35	40
1977	3 d. Redshanks		35	40
1978	3 d. Ringed Plovers		35	40
1979	3 d. Black-winged Stilt		35	40
1980	3 d. Squacco Herons		35	40
1981	8 d. Hammerkop		90	95
1982	10 d. Common Shovelers		1·10	1·25
1983	12 d. Crowned Crane		1·40	1·50
1968/83		*Set of* 16	7·75	8·75

MS1984 Two sheets, each 106×76 mm. (a) 25 d. Ferruginous Ducks. (b) 25 d. Moorhen
Set of 2 *sheets* 5·75 6·00

Nos. 1969/80 were printed together, *se-tenant*, in sheetlets of 12, forming a composite design.

(Litho Questa)

1995 (30 May). *20th Anniv of Economic Community of West African States (E.C.O.W.A.S.). T **236** and similar vert design. Multicoloured. P* 14.
1985	2 d. Type **236**		20	25
1986	5 d. Pres. Yayah Jammeh		60	65

237 Leather Back Turtle | 238 First Stage of Lariat Knot

(Des J. Barbarus and G. Lott. Litho B.D.T.)

1995 (20 June). *Marine Life. T **237** and similar multicoloured designs. P* 14.
1987	3 d. Type **237**		35	40
	a. Sheetlet. Nos. 1987/98		4·25	
1988	3 d. Tiger Shark		35	40
1989	3 d. Powder-blue Surgeonfish		35	40
1990	3 d. Emperor Angelfish		35	40
1991	3 d. Blue Parrotfish		35	40
1992	3 d. Clown Triggerfish		35	40
1993	3 d. Seahorse		35	40
1994	3 d. Lionfish		35	40
1995	3 d. Moray Eel		35	40
1996	3 d. Melon Butterflyfish		35	40
1997	3 d. Octopus		35	40
1998	3 d. Common Stingray		35	40
1999	8 d. Stoplight Parrotfish ("Multicolored Parrot Fish") (*vert*)		90	95
	a. Horiz strip of 4. Nos. 1999/2002	3·50		
2000	8 d. Stoplight Parrotfish ("Sparisoma viride") (*vert*)		90	95
2001	8 d. Queen Parrotfish (*vert*)		90	95
2002	8 d. Bicoloured Parrotfish (*vert*)		90	95
1987/2002		*Set of* 16	7·75	8·50

MS2003 Two sheets, each 98×68 mm. (a) 25 d. Queen Angelfish (*Angelicthys isabelita*). (b) 25 d. Rock Beauty (*Holacanthus ciliaris*).
Set of 2 *sheets* 5·75 6·00

Nos. 1987/98 and 1999/2002 were printed together, *se-tenant*, in sheetlets of 12 (Nos. 1987/98) or horizontal strips of 4 (Nos. 1999/2002) with the backgrounds forming composite designs. No. 1991 is inscribed "BLUE PARRO FISH" in error.

(Des P. Chinelli. Litho Questa)

1995 (14 July). *18th World Scout Jamboree, Netherlands. T **238** and similar vert designs. Multicoloured. P* 14.

MS2004 Two sheets, each 101×65 mm. (a) 2 d. Type **238**; 2 d. Second stage of knot with ropes end at right; 2 d. Completed Lariat knot. (b) 5 d. Completed Bowline knot; 10 d. Second stage of knot; 12 d. First stage of knot .. *Set of* 2 *sheets* 3·75 4·00

MS2005 Two sheets, each 72×102 mm. (a) 25 d. Scout in rope using Hitch knot. (b) 25 d. Injured scout supported by Bowline knot *Set of* 2 *sheets* 5·75 6·00

(Des L. Fried. Litho B.D.T.)

1995 (1 Aug). *50th Anniv of Second World War in Europe. Film Stars. Black and scarlet (Nos. 2008 and 2010) or multicoloured designs (others) as T **340** of Antigua. P* 14.
2006	3 d. Peter Lawford	35	40
	a. Sheetlet. Nos. 2006/13	2·75	
2007	3 d. Gene Tierney and Dana Andrews	35	40
2008	3 d. Groucho and Harpo Marx	35	40
2009	3 d. James Stewart	35	40
2010	3 d. Chico and Zeppo Marx	35	40
2011	3 d. Tyrone Power	35	40
2012	3 d. Cary Grant and Ingrid Bergman	35	40
2013	3 d. Veronica Lake	35	40
2006/13		*Set of* 8	2·75 3·25

MS2014 105×75 mm. 25 d. "A Lady Fights Back" film poster (*vert*) .. 3·00 3·25

Nos. 2006/13 were printed together, *se-tenant*, in sheetlets of 8 with the stamps arranged in two horizontal strips of 4 separated by a gutter showing Laurel and Hardy, Anna Neagle and Orson Wells. No. 2012 is inscribed "BERMAN" in error.

(Des Bryna Waldman. Litho)

1995 (1 Aug). *50th Anniv of United Nations. Vert designs as T **341** of Antigua. Multicoloured. P* 14.
2015	3 d. Children in class	35	40
	a. Horiz strip of 3. Nos. 2015/17	1·00	
2016	3 d. Teacher helping child	35	40
2017	3 d. Child writing on blackboard	35	40
2015/17	*Set of* 3	1·00	1·25

MS2018 104×74 mm. 25 d. Nurse weighing baby 3·00 3·25

Nos. 2015/17 were printed together in sheets of 9 containing three *se-tenant* horizontal strips, each forming a composite design.

(Des Bryna Waldman. Litho)

1995 (1 Aug). *50th Anniv of Food and Agriculture Organization. Vert designs as T **342** of Antigua. Multicoloured. P* 14.
2019	3 d. Woman carrying sack on head	35	40
	a. Horiz strip of 3. Nos. 2019/21	1·00	
2020	3 d. Two men carrying sacks	35	40
2021	3 d. Man carrying sack	35	40
2019/21	*Set of* 3	1·00	1·25

MS2022 104×74 mm. 25 d. Fisherman with net 3·00 3·25

Nos. 2019/21 were printed together in sheets of 9 containing three *se-tenant* horizontal strips, each forming a composite design.

239 Paul Harris (founder) and Rotary Emblem | 240 Kenichi Fukui (1981 Chemistry)

(Litho Questa)

1995 (1 Aug). *90th Anniv of Rotary International. T **239** and similar horiz design. Multicoloured. Litho. P* 14.
2023	15 d. Type **239**	1·75	1·90

MS2024 75×105 mm. 20 d. National flag and Rotary emblem .. 2·25 2·40

(Litho Questa)

1995 (1 Aug). *95th Birthday of Queen Elizabeth the Queen Mother. Vert designs as T **344** of Antigua. P* 13½×14.
2025	5 d. orange-brown, pale brown and black		60	65
	a. Sheetlet. Nos. 2025/8×2	4·75		
2026	5 d. multicoloured		60	65
2027	5 d. multicoloured		60	65
2028	5 d. multicoloured		60	65
2025/8		*Set of* 4	2·40	2·50

MS2029 102×126 mm. 25 d. multicoloured .. 3·00 3·25

Designs:—No. 2025, Queen Elizabeth the Queen Mother (pastel drawing); No. 2026, Wearing blue hat and dress; No. 2027, At desk (oil painting); No. 2028, Wearing green hat and dress; No. **MS**2029, Wearing lavender hat and dress.

Nos. 2025/8 were printed together in sheetlets of 8 containing two *se-tenant* horizontal strips of 4.

(Des J. Batchelor. Litho Questa)

1995 (1 Aug). *50th Anniv of End of Second World War in the Pacific. Horiz designs as T **340** of Antigua. Multicoloured. P* 14.
2030	5 d. Fairey Firefly	60	65
	a. Sheetlet. Nos. 2030/5	3·50	
2031	5 d. Fairey Barracuda Mk III	60	65
2032	5 d. Supermarine Seafire II	60	65
2033	5 d. H.M.S. *Repulse* (battle cruiser)	60	65
2034	5 d. H.M.S. *Illustrious* (aircraft carrier)	60	65
2035	5 d. H.M.S. *Exeter* (cruiser)	60	65
2030/5		*Set of* 6	3·50 4·00

MS2036 108×76 mm. 25 d. Kamikaze aircraft heading for British cruiser .. 3·00 3·25

Nos. 2030/5 were printed together, *se-tenant*, in sheetlets of 6 with the stamps arranged in two horizontal strips of 3 separated by a gutter showing Lord Louis Mountbatten and the sinking of H.M.S. *Kelly*.

(Des Shayna Magid. Litho Questa)

1995 (1 Aug). *Centenary of Nobel Prize Trust Fund. Past Prize Winners. T **240** and similar vert designs. Multicoloured. P* 14.
2037	2 d. Type **240**	20	25
2038	3 d. Gustav Stresemann (1929 Peace)	35	40
2039	5 d. Thomas Mann (1929 Literature)	60	65
2040	5 d. Marie Curie (1911 Chemistry)	60	65
	a. Sheetlet. Nos. 2040/8	5·25	
2041	5 d. Adolf Butenandt (1939 Chemistry)	60	65
2042	5 d. Susumu Tonegwa (1987 Medicine)	60	65
2043	5 d. Nelly Sachs (1966 Literature)	60	65
2044	5 d. Yasunari Kawabata (1968 Literature)	60	65
2045	5 d. Hideki Yukawa (1949 Physics)	60	65
2046	5 d. Paul Ehrlich (1908 Medicine)	60	65
2047	5 d. Bisaku Sato (1974 Peace)	60	65
2048	5 d. Carl von Ossietsky (1935 Peace)	60	65
2049	8 d. Albert Schweitzer (1952 Peace)	90	95
2050	12 d. Leo Esaki (1973 Physics)	1·40	1·50
2051	15 d. Lech Wałęsa (1983 Peace)	1·75	1·90
2037/51		*Set of* 15	10·50 11·50

MS2052 75×105 mm. 25 d. Willy Brandt (1971 Peace) .. 3·00 3·25

Nos. 2040/8 were printed together, *se-tenant*, in sheetlets of 9, forming a composite design.

No. 2048 is dated "1974" and No. 2051 inscribed "Lech Walsea", both in error.

241 Bruce Jenner (U.S.A.) (decathlon)

(Des A. Di Lorenzo. Litho Questa)

1995 (17 Aug). *Olympic Games, Atlanta (1996) (1st issue). T **241** and similar multicoloured designs. P* 14.
2053	1 d. Type **241**	10	15
2054	1 d. 25, Greg Louganis (U.S.A.) (diving)	15	20
2055	1 d. 50, Michael Gross (Germany) (50 metre butterfly)	20	25
2056	2 d. Vasily Alexeev (Russia) (weight-lifting)	20	25
2057	3 d. Ewing (U.S.A.) and Corbalan (Spain) (basketball)	35	40
2058	3 d. Stefano Cerioni (Italy) (fencing) (*vert*)	35	40
	a. Sheetlet. Nos. 2058/65	2·75	

2059	3 d. Alberto Cova (Italy) (10000 metres) (vert)			35	40
2060	3 d. Mary Lou Retton (U.S.A.) (gymnastics) (vert)			35	40
2061	3 d. Vladimir Artemov (Russia) (gymnastics) (vert)			35	40
2062	3 d. Florence Griffith-Joyner (U.S.A.) (400 metre relay) (vert)			35	40
2063	3 d. Brazil (football) (vert)			35	40
2064	3 d. Nelson Vails (U.S.A.) (sprint cycling) (vert)			35	40
2065	3 d. Cheryl Miller (U.S.A.) (basketball) (vert)			35	40
2066	5 d. U.S.A. v Brazil (men's volleyball)			60	65
2067	10 d. Svenden (West Germany) and Fernandez (U.S.A.) (water polo)			1·10	1·25
2068	15 d. Pertii Karppinen (Finland) (single sculls)			1·75	1·90
2053/68			Set of 16	7·25	8·25

MS2069 Two sheets, each 71×101 mm. (a) 25 d. Karen Stives (U.S.A.) (equestrian) (vert). (b) 25 d. Edwin Moses (U.S.A.) (400 metre hurdles) (vert) .... *Set of 2 sheets* 5·75 6·00

Nos. 2058/65 were printed together, *se-tenant*, in sheetlets of 8.

No. 2059 is inscribed "Alberto Covo" and No. 2064 "Nelson Valis", both in error.

See also Nos. 2281/303.

242 Rotary Emblem and Rotarians supporting School for the Deaf

243 *Zantedeschia rehmannii*

(Litho Questa)

1995 (5 Sept). *Local Rotary and Boy Scout Projects.* T **242** and similar multicoloured designs. P 14.

2070	2 d. Type **242**			20	25
2071	5 d. Scout wood badge course, 1980			60	65
2072	5 d. Scout Commissioner M. J. E. Sambou (vert)			60	65
2070/2			Set of 3	1·40	1·50

(Des Mary Walters. Litho Questa)

1995 (2 Oct). *African Flowers.* T **243** and similar vert designs. Multicoloured. P 14.

2073	2 d. Type **243**			20	25
2074	3 d. Kigelia africana			35	40
	a. Sheetlet. Nos. 2074/82			3·25	
2075	3 d. Hibiscus schizopelatus			35	40
2076	3 d. Dombeya mastersii			35	40
2077	3 d. Agapanthus orientalis			35	40
2078	3 d. Strelitzia reginae			35	40
2079	3 d. Spathodea companulata			35	40
2080	3 d. Rhodolaena bakeriana			35	40
2081	3 d. Gazania rigens			35	40
2082	3 d. Ixianthes retzioides			35	40
2083	3 d. Canarina abyssinica			35	40
	a. Sheetlet. Nos. 2083/91			3·25	
2084	3 d. Nerine bowdenii			35	40
2085	3 d. Zantedeschia aethiopica			35	40
2086	3 d. Aframomum sceptrum			35	40
2087	3 d. Schotia brachypetala			35	40
2088	3 d. Catharanthus roseus			35	40
2089	3 d. Protea grandiceps			35	40
2090	3 d. Plumbago capensis			35	40
2091	3 d. Uncarina grandidieri			35	40
2092	5 d. Euadenia eminens			60	65
2093	10 d. Passiflora vitifolia			1·10	1·25
2094	15 d. Dietes grandiflora			1·75	1·90
2073/94			Set of 22	10·00	11·00

MS2095 Two sheets, each 106×75 mm. (a) 25 d. Eulophia quartiniana. (b) 25 d. Gloriosa simplex .... *Set of 2 sheets* 5·75 6·00

Nos. 2074/82 and 2083/91 were printed together, *se-tenant*, in sheetlets of 9 forming composite background designs.

244 Children outside Huts

1995 (9 Oct). *Kinderdorf International S.O.S. Children's Villages.* T **244** and similar multicoloured designs. Litho. P 14.

2096	2 d. Type **244**			20	25
2097	2 d. Charity worker with children (vert)			20	25
2098	5 d. Children at party			60	65
2096/8			Set of 3	1·00	1·10

245 Roy Orbison

1995 (1 Dec). *History of Rock n' Roll Music.* T **245** and similar vert designs. Multicoloured. Litho. P 13½×14.

2099	3 d. Type **245**			35	40
	a. Sheetlet. Nos. 2099/107			3·25	
2100	3 d. Mick Jagger			35	40
2101	3 d. Bruce Springsteen			35	40
2102	3 d. Jimi Hendrix			35	40
2103	3 d. Bill Hailey			35	40
2104	3 d. Gene Vincent			35	40
2105	3 d. Buddy Holly			35	40
2106	3 d. Jerry Lee Lewis			35	40
2107	3 d. Chuck Berry			35	40
2099/107			Set of 9	3·25	3·50

MS2108 116×86 mm. 25 d. Elvis Presley .... 3·00 3·25

Nos. 2099/2107 were printed together, *se-tenant*, in sheetlets of 9 forming a composite design.

1995 (1 Dec). *Centenary of Cinema.* Vert designs as T **245** depicting James Dean. Multicoloured. Litho. P 13½×14.

2109	3 d. As a boy			35	40
	a. Sheetlet. Nos. 2109/17			3·25	
2110	3 d. On motorbike			35	40
2111	3 d. With sports car and trophy			35	40
2112	3 d. Close-up portrait			35	40
2113	3 d. Facing left			35	40
2114	3 d. Holding girl			35	40
2115	3 d. Rebel without a Cause (film)			35	40
2116	3 d. Giant (film)			35	40
2117	3 d. East of Eden (film)			35	40
2109/17			Set of 9	3·25	3·50

MS2118 116×86 mm. 25 d. James Dean in *Rebel without a Cause* .... 3·00 3·25

Nos. 2109/17 were printed together, *se-tenant*, in sheetlets of 9 forming a composite design.

(Litho Questa)

1995 (18 Dec). *Christmas. Religious Paintings.* Vert designs as T **357** of Antigua. Multicoloured. P 13½×14.

2119	75 b. "Madonna and Child" (Maria della Vallicella)			10	10
2120	1 d. "Madonna" (Giotto)			10	10
2121	2 d. "The Flight into Egypt" (Luca Giordano)			20	25
2122	5 d. "The Epiphany" (Bondone)			60	65
2123	8 d. "Virgin and Child" (Burgkmair)			90	95
2124	12 d. "Madonna" (Bellini)			1·40	1·50
2119/24			Set of 6	3·25	3·50

MS2125 Two sheets, each 101×127 mm. (a) 25 d. "Christ" (Carpaccio). (b) 25 d. "Madonna and Child" (Rubens) .... *Set of 2 sheets* 5·75 6·00

246 Terminal Building   **247** U.P.U. Emblem

(Litho Questa)

1995 (21 Dec). *Opening of New Terminal Building, Banjul International Airport.* P 14.

2126	**246** 1 d. multicoloured			10	10
2127	2 d. multicoloured			20	25
2128	3 d. multicoloured			35	40
2129	5 d. multicoloured			60	65
2126/9			Set of 4	1·25	1·40

(Litho Questa)

1995 (21 Dec). *121st Anniv of Universal Postal Union.* P 14.

2130	**247** 1 d. black and deep bluish violet			10	10
2131	2 d. black and bright greenish blue			20	25
2132	3 d. black and bright scarlet			35	40
2133	7 d. black and bright emerald			80	85
2130/3			Set of 4	1·40	1·60

COVER PRICES

Cover factors are quoted at the beginning of each country for most issues to 1945. An explanation of the system can be found on page x. The factors quoted do not, however, apply to philatelic covers.

248 Commerson's Dolphin

(Litho Questa)

1995 (22 Dec). *Whales and Dolphins.* T **248** and similar multicoloured designs. P 14.

2134	2 d. Type **248**			20	25
2135	3 d. Bryde's Whale			35	40
	a. Sheetlet. Nos. 2135/43			3·00	
2136	3 d. Sperm Whale			35	40
2137	3 d. Humpback Whale			35	40
2138	3 d. Sei Whale			35	40
2139	3 d. Blue Whale			35	40
2140	3 d. Grey Whale			35	40
2141	3 d. Fin Whale			35	40
2142	3 d. Killer Whale			35	40
2143	3 d. Right Whale			35	40
2144	3 d. Northern Right Whale Dolphin			35	40
	a. Sheetlet. Nos. 2144/52			3·00	
2145	3 d. Spotted Dolphin			35	40
2146	3 d. Common Dolphin			35	40
2147	3 d. Pacific White-sided Dolphin			35	40
2148	3 d. Atlantic Humpbacked Dolphin			35	40
2149	3 d. Atlantic White-sided Dolphin			35	40
2150	3 d. White-beaked Dolphin			35	40
2151	3 d. Striped Dolphin			35	40
2152	3 d. Risso's Dolphin			35	40
2153	5 d. Narwhal			60	65
2154	8 d. True's Beaked Whale			90	95
2155	10 d. Rough-toothed Dolphin			1·10	1·25
2134/55			Set of 22	9·00	10·00

MS2156 Two sheets, each 110×80 mm. (a) 25 d. Beluga and Clymene Dolphin. (b) 25 d. Bowhead Whale and Blue Shark (vert) .... *Set of 2 sheets* 5·75 6·00

Nos. 2135/43 and 2144/52 were printed together, *se-tenant*, in sheetlets of 9 forming composite designs.

249 Big Pete as Seminole with Alligator

(Des Alvin White Studios. Litho Questa)

1995 (22 Dec). *Disney Cowboys and Indians.* T **249** and similar multicoloured designs showing Walt Disney cartoon characters. P 14×13½.

2157	15 b. Type **249**			10	10
2158	20 b. Donald Duck as Chinook fisherman			10	10
2159	25 b. Huey, Dewey and Louie as Blackfoot braves			10	10
2160	30 b. Minnie Mouse shooting bottles			10	10
2161	40 b. Donald riding bull			10	10
2162	50 b. Mickey Mouse branding steer			10	10
2163	2 d. Donald in Tlingit mask			20	25
2164	3 d. Mickey bronco-busting			35	40
2165	12 d. Grandma Duck with lasso			1·40	1·50
2166	15 d. Mickey in Pomo canoe			1·75	1·90
2167	15 d. Goofy as ranch hand			1·75	1·90
2168	20 d. Goofy and Minnie with Navaho weaving			2·25	2·50
2157/68			Set of 12	8·00	9·00

MS2169 Four sheets, each 127×102 mm. (a) 25 d. Minnie as Massachusetts squaw. P 14×13½. (b) 25 d. Minnie as Shoshoni squaw (vert). P 13½×14. (c) 25 d. Pluto singing to the Moon (vert). P 13½×14. (d) 25 d. Donald and steer (vert). P 13½×14 .... *Set of 4 sheets* 11·50 12·00

250 Rat   **251** "Don Tiburcio Pérez y Cuervo (detail) (Goya)

(Des Y. Lee. Litho Questa)

1996 (2 Jan). *Chinese New Year ("Year of the Rat").* T **250** and similar horiz designs showing different stylised rats. P 14½.

2170	63 b. multicoloured			10	10
	a. Horiz strip of 4. Nos. 2170/3			85	
2171	75 b. multicoloured			10	10

2172	1 d. 50, multicoloured	..	..	20	25
2173	4 d. multicoloured	..	..	45	50
2170/3			Set of 4	85	1·00

MS2174 84×68 mm. 3 d. × 4 As Nos. 2170/3 .. 1·40 1·50
MS2175 76×106 mm. 10 d. orange-vermilion, deep violet and yellow-brown .. .. 1·10 1·25
Nos. 2170/3 were printed together, se-tenant, as horizontal strips of 4 in sheets of 12.

(Litho Questa)

1996 (29 Jan). *125th Anniv of Metropolitan Museum of Art, New York.* T **251** *and similar multicoloured designs.* P 14.

2176/83 4 d. × 8 (Type **251**; "Jean Antoine Moltedo" (Ingres); "The Letter" (Corot); "General Etienne Gerard" (David); "Portrait of the Artist" (Van Gogh); "Joseph Henri Altés" (Degas); "Princess de Broglie" (Ingres); "Lady at the Table" (Cassatt))
    a. Sheetlet. Nos. 2176/83 .. 3·50

2184/91 4 d. × 8 ("Broken Eggs" (Greuze); "Johann Joachim Winckelmann" (Mengs); "Col. George Coussmaker" (Reynolds); "Self Portrait with Pupils" (Labille-Guiard); "Courtesan holding a Fan" (Utamaro); "The Woodgatherers" (Gainsborough); "Mrs Grace Elliott" (Gainsborough); "The Drummond Children" (Raeburn))
    a. Sheetlet. Nos. 2184/91 .. 3·50

2192/9 4 d. × 8 ("Sunflowers" (Monet); "Still Life with Pansies" (Fantin-Latour); "Parisians enjoying the Parc" (Monet); "La Mére Larchevêque" (Pissarro); "Rue de L'Epicerie, Rouen" (Pissarro); "The Abduction of Rebecca" (Delacroix); "Daughter, Abraham-Ben-Chimol" (Delacroix); "Christ on Lake of Gennesaret" (Delacroix))
    a. Sheetlet. Nos. 2192/9 .. 3·50

2200/7 4 d. × 8 ("Henry Prince of Wales" (Peake); "Saints Peter, Martha, Mary and Leonard" (Correggio); "Marriage Feast at Cana" (Juan de Flandes); "Portrait of One of Wedigh Family" (Holbein); "Guillaume Budé" (Clouet); "Portrait of a Cardinal" (El Greco); "St. Jerome as a Cardinal" (El Greco); "Portrait of a Man" (Titian))
    a. Sheetlet. Nos. 2200/7 .. 3·50

2176/207 .. .. Set of 32 14·00 14·50
MS2208 Four sheets, each 95×70 mm containing horiz designs, 81×53 mm. (a) 25 d. "Israelites gathering Manna in the Desert" (Rubens). (b) 25 d. "Henry IV at the Battle of Ivry" (Rubens). (c) 25 d. "The Creation of the World and the Expulsion from Paradise" (Giovanni di Paolo). (d) 25 d. "The Harvesters" (Bruegel). P 14
    Set of 4 sheets 12·00 12·50
Nos. 2176/83, 2184/91, 2192/9 and 2200/7 were each printed together, se-tenant, in sheetlets of 8 stamps and one centre label.

252 Fire-eater   253 Bruce Lee

(Litho Questa)

1996 (29 Jan). *Fire-eating in the Gambia.* T **252** *and similar designs.* P 14.

2209	1 d. multicoloured	..	..	10	10
2210	2 d. multicoloured (*horiz*)	..	..	20	25
2211	3 d. multicoloured	..	..	35	40
2212	7 d. multicoloured (*horiz*)	..	..	35	40
2209/12			Set of 4	1·40	1·60

(Des Y. Lee. Litho)

1996 (1 Apr). *Bruce Lee (film star) Commemoration.* T **253** *and similar vert designs showing different portraits. Multicoloured.* P 14.

2213	3 d. Wearing cap and mask	..	45	50
	a. Sheetlet. Nos. 2213/21	..	3·25	
2214	3 d. Type **253**	..	35	40
2215	3 d. Facing left	..	35	40
2216	3 d. Wearing blue jumper and with hand to face		35	40
2217	3 d. Wearing buff jacket	..	35	40
2218	3 d. Wearing brown jacket (Chinese characters in chestnut)		35	40
2219	3 d. Wearing black shirt (Chinese characters in lilac)		35	40
2220	3 d. Wearing white shirt	..	35	40
2221	3 d. Bare-chested	..	35	40
2213/21		Set of 9	3·25	3·50

MS2222 Two sheets. (a) 140×85 mm. 5 d. Deng Xiao Ping (Chinese leader) (78×51 *mm*). P 13. (b) 70×100 mm. 25 d. Bruce Lee. P 14
    Set of 2 sheets 6·25 6·50
Nos. 2213/21 were printed together, se-tenant, in numbered sheetlets of 9, which also included "CHINA '96 9th Asian International Philatelic Exhibition" emblem on the sheet margin.

254 Donald Duck and Big Pete giving Blood

(Litho Questa)

1996 (12 Apr). *Voluntary Activities.* T **254** *and similar horiz designs showing Walt Disney cartoon characters. Multicoloured.* P 14×13½.

2223	1 d. Type **254**		10	10
2224	4 d. Daisy Duck and Minnie Mouse adopting pets		45	50
2225	5 d. Goofy as one-man band raising money for the needy		60	65
2226	10 d. Goofy teaching outdoor skills	..	1·10	1·25
2227	15 d. Minnie teaching reading	..	1·75	1·90
2228	20 d. Donald, Mickey and Goofy as volunteer fire fighters		2·25	2·50
2223/9		Set of 6	6·25	6·75

MS2229 Two sheets, each 127×102 mm. (a) 25 d. Minnie counting whales. (b) 25 d. Mickey planting roadside sapling .. Set of 2 sheets 5·75 6·00

255 Roan Antelope

(Litho Questa)

1996 (15 Apr). *Wildlife.* T **255** *and similar multicoloured designs.* P 14.

2230	3 d. Type **255**		35	40
	a. Sheetlet. Nos. 2230/5 each × 2		4·25	
2231	3 d. Lesser Bushbaby	..	35	40
2232	3 d. Black Leopard	..	35	40
2233	3 d. Guinea Forest Red Colobus	..	35	40
2234	3 d. Kobs	..	35	40
2235	3 d. Common Eland	..	35	40
2236	4 d. African Buffalo	..	45	50
	a. Sheetlet. Nos. 2236/44		4·00	
2237	4 d. Herd of Topi	..	45	50
2238	4 d. Vervet	..	45	50
2239	4 d. Hippopotamuses	..	45	50
2240	4 d. Waterbuck	..	45	50
2241	4 d. Senegal Chameleon	..	45	50
2242	4 d. Western Green Mamba	..	45	50
2243	4 d. Slender-snouted Crocodile	..	45	50
2244	4 d. Adanson's Mud Turtle	..	45	50
2245	15 d. African Civet	..	1·75	1·90
2230/45		Set of 16	7·75	8·75

MS2246 Two sheets, each 98×68 mm. (a) 25 d. Lion (*vert*). (b) 25 d. Chimpanzee (*vert*)
    Set of 2 sheets 5·75 6·00
Nos. 2230/5 and 2236/44 were printed together, se-tenant, in sheetlets of 12 (Nos. 2230/5 × 2) or 9 (Nos. 2236/44), the latter forming a composite design.

(Litho Questa)

1996 (9 May). *70th Birthday of Queen Elizabeth II. Multicoloured designs as* T **364** *of Antigua showing different photographs.* P 13½×14.

2247	8 d. As Type **364** of Antigua	..	90	95
	a. Strip of 3. Nos. 2247/9	..	2·75	
2248	8 d. Wearing tiara facing right	..	90	95
2249	8 d. Wearing tiara facing left	..	90	95
2247/9		Set of 3	2·75	3·00

MS2250 125×104 mm. 25 d. Buckingham Palace (*horiz*). P 14×13½ .. 3·00 3·25
Nos. 2247/9 were printed together, se-tenant, in horizontal and vertical strips of 3 throughout sheets of 9.

256 Pumper Hose Cart, U.S.A. (1850)

1996 (27 May). *Classic Road Transport.* T **256** *and similar horiz designs showing fire engines (Nos. 2251/6) or cars (Nos. 2257/62). Multicoloured. Litho.* P 14.

2251	4 d. Type **256**		45	50
	a. Sheetlet. Nos. 2251/6		2·75	
2252	4 d. Steam fire engine, U.S.A. (1891)		45	50
2253	4 d. Lausitzer engine, Germany (1864)		45	50
2254	4 d. Chemical engine, Great Britain (1902)		45	50

2255	4 d. Motor fire engine, Great Britain (1904)		45	50
2256	4 d. Colonia No. 5 engine, Germany (1860)		45	50
2257	4 d. Fiat Tipo 510, Italy (1912) ..		45	50
	a. Sheetlet. Nos. 2257/62		2·75	
2258	4 d. Toyota Model 4B Phaeton, Japan (1936)		45	50
2259	4 d. Nag C4B, Germany (1924) ..		45	50
2260	4 d. Cadillac, U.S.A. (1903) ..		45	50
2261	4 d. Bentley, Great Britain (1925)		45	50
2262	4 d. Renault Model AX, France (1909)		45	50
2251/62		Set of 12	5·50	6·00

MS2263 (a) 76×58 mm. 25 d. Amoskeag Steamer (fire engine), U.S.A. (1865). (b) 81×59 mm. 25 d. Mitsubishi Model A, Japan (1917) Set of 2 sheets 5·75 6·00
Nos. 2251/6 and 2257/62 were each printed together, se-tenant, in sheetlets of 6.

257 Bulgarian Team   258 Ray Ewry (U.S.A.) (standing high jump), 1912

1996 (8 June). *European Football Championship, England.* T **257** *and similar multicoloured designs. Litho.* P 14×13½.

2264	2 d. Type **257**	..	20	25
2265	2 d. Croatian team	..	20	25
2266	2 d. Czech Republic team	..	20	25
2267	2 d. Danish team	..	20	25
2268	2 d. English team	..	20	25
2269	2 d. French team	..	20	25
2270	2 d. German team	..	20	25
2271	2 d. Dutch team	..	20	25
2272	2 d. Italian team	..	20	25
2273	2 d. Portuguese team	..	20	25
2274	2 d. Rumanian team	..	20	25
2275	2 d. Russian team	..	20	25
2276	2 d. Scottish team	..	20	25
2277	2 d. Spanish team	..	20	25
2278	2 d. Swiss team	..	20	25
2279	2 d. Turkish team	..	20	25
2264/79		Set of 16	3·25	4·00

MS2280 Sixteen sheets. (a) 115×85 mm. 25 d. Danish team celebrating (43×28 *mm*). (b) 85×115 mm. 25 d. Ruud Gullit (Netherlands) (28×43 *mm*). (c) 85×115 mm. 25 d. Gary McAllister (Scotland) (28×43 *mm*). (d) 115×85 mm. 25 d. Oleg Salenko (Russia) (28×43 *mm*). (e) 85×115 mm. 25 d. Hami Mandirali (Turkey) (28×43 *mm*). (f) 85×115 mm. 25 d. Hristo Stoitchkov (Bulgaria) (28×43 *mm*). (g) 115×85 mm. 25 d. European Championship Trophy (28×43 *mm*). (h) 85×115 mm. 25 d. Davor Suker (Croatia) (28×43 *mm*). (i) 115×85 mm. 25 d. Jurgen Klinsmann (Germany) (43×28 *mm*). (j) 85×115 mm. 25 d. Juan Goikoetxea (Spain) (28×43 *mm*). (k) 85×115 mm. 25 d. Eusebio (Portugal) (28×43 *mm*). (l) 115×85 mm. 25 d. Bryan Robson (England) (28×43 *mm*). (m) 85×115 mm. 25 d. Roberto Baggio (Italy) (28×43 *mm*) (n) 85×115 mm. 25 d. Christophe Ohrel (Switzerland) (28×43 *mm*). (o) 85×115 mm. 25 d. Pavel Hapal (Czech Republic) (43×28 *mm*). (p) 85×115 mm. 25 d. Gheorge Hagi (Rumania) (28×43 *mm*). P 14 .. Set of 16 sheets 48·00 50·00
Nos. 2264/79 were each printed in sheetlets of 8 stamps with a central label.

(Des Y. Lee. Litho Questa)

1996 (18 July). *Olympic Games, Atlanta (2nd issue). Previous Gold Medal Winners.* T **258** *and similar multicoloured designs.* P 14.

2281	1 d. Type **258**		10	10
2282	2 d. Fanny Durack (Australia) (100m freestyle swimming), 1912 ..		20	25
2283	3 d. Fu Mingxia (China) (platform diving), 1992		30	35
	a. Sheetlet. Nos. 2283/91		2·50	
2284	3 d. H. Henkel (Germany) (high jump) 1992		30	35
2285	3 d. Spanish team (soccer), 1992		30	35
2286	3 d. Jackie Joyner-Kersee (U.S.A.) (heptathlon), 1988 and 1992		30	35
2287	3 d. T. Gutsu (Russia) (gymnastics), 1992		30	35
2288	3 d. M. Johnson (U.S.A.) (400m running), 1992		30	35
2289	3 d. Lin Li (China) (200m medley swimming), 1992		30	35
2290	3 d. G. Devers (U.S.A.) (100m running), 1992		30	35
2291	3 d. Michael Powell (U.S.A.) (long jump), 1992		30	35
2292	3 d. Japanese volleyball team, 1964		30	35
	a. Sheetlet. Nos. 2292/2300		2·50	
2293	3 d. Li Neng (China) (floor exercises), 1984		30	35
2294	3 d. S. Bubka (U.S.S.R.) (pole vault), 1988		30	35
2295	3 d. Nadia Comaneci (Romania) (gymnastics), 1976		30	35
2296	3 d. Edwin Moses (U.S.A.) (400m hurdles), 1984		30	35
2297	3 d. Victor Scherbo (Russia) (gymnastics), 1992		30	35
2298	3 d. Evelyn Ashford (U.S.A.) (100m running), 1984		30	35
2299	3 d. Mohammed Ali (U.S.A.) (light heavyweight boxing), 1960 ..		30	35

2300	3 d. Carl Lewis and C. Smith (U.S.A.) (400m relay), 1984	30	35
2301	5 d. Stockholm Olympic arena, 1912	60	65
2302	10 d. Jim Thorpe (U.S.A.) (decathalon and pentathlon), 1912	1·10	1·25
2281/2302	*Set of 22*	7·00	8·50

MS2303 Two sheets each 100×70 mm. 25 d. Michael Gross (Germany) (butterfly swimming), 1984 and 1988 (*horiz*). 25 d. Ulrike Meyfarth (Germany) (high jump), 1972 and 1984

Set of 2 sheets 5·75 6·00

Nos. 2283/91 and 2292/2300 were printed together, *se-tenant*, in sheetlets of 9.

(Litho Questa)

1996 (25 July). *50th Anniv of U.N.I.C.E.F. Multicoloured designs as T 366 of Antigua. P 14.*

2304	63 b. Boy holding shoes	10	10
2305	3 d. Girl being inoculated	35	40
2306	8 d. Boy holding ladle	90	95
2307	10 d. Child with blanket	1·10	1·25
2304/7	*Set of 4*	2·40	2·75

MS2308 105×75 mm. 25 d. Boy being inoculated (*horiz*) 3·00 3·25

259 Roman Officer and Pillar of Absalom   **260** Jacqueline Kennedy Onassis in Wedding Dress

(Des J. Genzo. Litho Questa)

1996 (25 July). *3000th Anniv of Jerusalem. T 259 and similar multicoloured designs. P 14.*

2309	1 d. 50, Type **259**	20	25
2310	2 d. Turk and Gate of Mercy	20	25
2311	3 d. Ancient Greek and Church of the Holy Sepulchre	35	40
2312	10 d. Modern Hasidic Jew at Wailing Wall	1·10	1·25
2309/12	*Set of 4*	1·75	2·25

MS2313 100×70 mm. 25 d. City coat of arms (*vert*) 3·00 3·25

(Des J. Genzo. Litho Questa)

1996 (25 July). *Centenary of Radio. Entertainers. Vert designs as T 368 of Antigua. Multicoloured. P 13½×14.*

2314	1 d. Glenn Miller	10	10
2315	4 d. Louis Armstrong	45	50
2316	5 d. Nat "King" Cole	60	65
2317	10 d. The Andrew Sisters	1·10	1·25
2314/17	*Set of 4*	2·25	2·50

MS2318 105×74 mm. 25 d. President Truman 3·00 3·25
No. 2314 is inscribed "Glen Miller" in error.

(Des Zina Sanders (Nos. 2319/27 and **MS**2336), R. Sauber (Nos. 2328/35). Litho Questa)

1996 (22 Aug). *Famous People of the 20th Century. T 260 and similar vert designs. Multicoloured. P 14.*

2319	5 d. Type **260**	60	65
	a. Sheetlet. Nos. 2319/27	5·50	
2320	5 d. Jaqueline Kennedy and White House	60	65
2321	5 d. Jaqueline Kennedy wearing pink hat	60	65
2322	5 d. Jaqueline Kennedy and motor yacht	60	65
2323	5 d. Jacqueline Kennedy wearing red jumper	60	65
2324	5 d. Jacqueline Kennedy and horse	60	65
2325	5 d. Jacqueline Kennedy on book	60	65
2326	5 d. Jacqueline Kennedy in blue dress and three rows of pearls	60	65
2327	5 d. Jacqueline Kennedy and corner of fountain	60	65
2328	5 d. President John Kennedy	60	65
	a. Sheetlet. Nos. 2328/35	4·75	
2329	5 d. Jacqueline Kennedy (inscr in capitals)	60	65
2330	5 d. Willy Brandt	60	65
2331	5 d. Marilyn Monroe	60	65
2332	5 d. Mao Tse-tung	60	65
2333	5 d. Sung Ching Ling	60	65
2334	5 d. Charles De Gaulle	60	65
2335	5 d. Marlene Dietrich	60	65
2319/35	*Set of 17*	10·00	11·00

MS2336 105×74 mm. 25 d. Jacqueline Kennedy (*different*) 3·00 3·25
Nos. 2319/27 and 2328/35 were each printed together, *se-tenant*, in sheetlets of 9 or 8.
No. 2330 is inscr "WILLIE BRANDT", No. 2331 "MARYLYN MONROE" and No. 2332 "MAO TSE TONG", all in error.

PRICES OF SETS

Set prices are given for many issues, generally those containing three stamps or more. Definitive sets include one of each value or major colour change, but do not cover different perforations, die types or minor shades. Where a choice is possible the set prices are based on the cheapest versions of the stamps included in the listings.

---

261 Richard Petty's 1969 Ford   **262** Elvis Presley with Microphone

(Des W. Wright. Litho Questa)

1996 (26 Aug). *Richard Petty (stock car driver) Commemoration. T 261 and similar horiz designs. Multicoloured. P 14.*

2337	5 d. Type **261**	60	65
	a. Sheetlet. Nos. 2337/42	3·50	
2338	5 d. Richard Petty	60	65
2339	5 d. Dodge Magnum, 1978	60	65
2340	5 d. Pontiac, 1987	60	65
2341	5 d. Pontiac, 1989	60	65
2342	5 d. Dodge Daytona, 1975	60	65
2337/42	*Set of 6*	3·50	4·00

MS2343 104×74 mm. 25 d. Plymouth, 1972 (*84×27 mm*) 3·00 3·25
Nos. 2337/42 were printed together, *se-tenant*, in sheetlets of 6.

1996 (26 Aug). *Results of European Football Championship, England. As Nos. 2265/6, 2268, 2270, 2272, 2275 and* **MS**2280 *(d, h, i, l, m, o), but each additionally inscribed with date and match result. Multicoloured. Litho. P 14×13½.*

2344	2 d. Croatian team ("23/6/96 Germany 2, Croatia 1")	20	25
2345	2 d. Czech Republic team ("9/6/96 Germany 2, Czech Rep. 0")	20	25
2346	2 d. English team ("26/6/96 Germany 6, England 5")	20	25
2347	2 d. German team ("30/6/96 Germany 2, Czech Rep. 1")	20	25
2348	2 d. Italian team ("19/6/96 Germany 0, Italy 0")	20	25
2349	2 d. Russian team ("16/6/96 Germany 3, Russia 0")	20	25
2344/9	*Set of 6*	1·25	1·50

MS2350 Six sheets. (a) 114×84 mm. 25 d. Oleg Salenko (Russia) (28×43 *mm*) ("16/6/96 Germany 3, Russia 0"). (b) 84×114 mm. 25 d. Davor Suker (Croatia) (28×43 *mm*) ("23/6/96 Germany 2, Croatia 1"). (c) 114×84 mm. 25 d. Jurgen Klinsmann (Germany) (43×28 *mm*) ("Final 30/6/96 Germany 2, Czech Republic 1"). (d) 114×84 mm. 25 d. Bryan Robson (England) (28×43 *mm*) ("26/6/96 Germany 6 England 5"). (e) 84×114 mm. 25 d. Roberto Baggio (Italy) (28×43 *mm*) ("19/6/96 Germany 0 Italy 0"). (f) 84×114 mm. 25 d. Pavel Hapal (Czech Rep) (43×28 *mm*) ("9/6/96 Germany 2 Czech Republic 0") *Set of 6 sheets* 18·00 19·00
On No. **MS**2350 the dates and match results are shown on the sheet margins.

(Des Y. Lee. Litho Questa)

1996 (8 Sept). *Elvis Presley Commemoration. T 262 and similar vert designs showing different portraits. Multicoloured. P 14.*

2351	5 d. Type **262**	60	65
	a. Sheetlet. Nos. 2351/6	3·50	
2352	5 d. In dinner jacket	60	65
2353	5 d. In Mexican outfit	60	65
2354	5 d. Wearing blue jumper	60	65
2355	5 d. In leather jacket	60	65
2356	5 d. Wearing lei	60	65
2351/6	*Set of 6*	3·50	4·00

Nos. 2351/6 were printed together, *se-tenant*, in numbered sheetlets of 6 with an illustrated margin.

263 Bob Dylan   **264** Supermarine Spitfire Prototype K5054

(Des J. Iskowitz. Litho Questa)

1996 (8 Sept). *Rock and Roll Legends. Bob Dylan. P 14.*

2357	**263** 5 d. multicoloured	60	65

No. 2357 was issued in sheet of 16 with an enlarged illustrated right-hand margin.

(Des W. Wright. Litho Questa)

1996 (13 Sept). *65th Anniv of Britain's Victory in Schneider Trophy Air Race. T 264 and similar horiz designs. Multicoloured. P 13½×14.*

2358	4 d. Type **264**	45	50
	a. Sheetlet. Nos. 2358/66	4·00	
2359	4 d. First production Spitfire K9787	45	50

2360	4 d. Spitfire Mk 1A in Battle of Britain	45	50
2361	4 d. Spitfire Lfmk IXE with D-Day markings	45	50
2362	4 d. Spitfire Mk XII (first with "Griffon" engine)	45	50
2363	4 d. Spitfire Mk XIVC with jungle markings	45	50
2364	4 d. Spitfire XIX of Royal Swedish Air Force	45	50
2365	4 d. Spitfire Mk XIX	45	50
2366	4 d. Spitfire FMk 22/24 (final variant)	45	50
2367	4 d. Spitfire Mk XIX of Royal Swedish Air Force (from below)	45	50
	a. Sheetlet. Nos. 2367/75	4·00	
2368	4 d. Spitfire Mk VB of United States Army Air Corps	45	50
2369	4 d. Spitfire VC of French Air Force	45	50
2370	4 d. Spitfire VB of Soviet Air Force	45	50
2371	4 d. Spitfire Mk IXE of Netherlands East Indies Air Force	45	50
2372	4 d. Spitfire Mk IXE of Israeli Air Force	45	50
2373	4 d. Spitfire Mk VIII of Royal Australian Air Force	45	50
2374	4 d. Spitfire Mk VB of Turkish Air Force	45	50
2375	4 d. Spitfire Mk XI of Royal Danish Air Force	45	50
2358/75	*Set of 18*	8·00	9·00

MS2376 Two sheets, each 97×67 mm. (a) 25 d. Supermarine S 6B S1595 seaplane taking off (*42×29 mm*). (b) 25 d. Supermarine S 6B S1595 in flight (*42×29 mm*). P 14 *Set of 2 sheets* 5·75 6·00
Nos. 2358/66 and 2367/75 were each printed together, *se-tenant*, in sheetlets of 9.

265 Egyptian Plover   **266** Sylvester Stallone as Rocky Balboa

(Des D. Burkhart. Litho Questa)

1996 (22 Oct)–**97**. *Birds. T 265 and similar square designs. Multicoloured. P 14.*

2377	50 b. Type **265**	10	10
2378	63 b. Painted Snipe	10	10
2379	75 b. Golden-breasted Bunting	10	10
2380	1 d. Bateleur	10	10
2381	1 d. 50, Didric Cuckoo	20	25
2382	2 d. Turtle Dove	20	25
2383	3 d. Village Weaver	35	40
2384	4 d. Common Roller	45	50
2385	5 d. Cut-Throat	60	65
2386	10 d. Hoopoe	1·10	1·25
2387	15 d. White-faced Scops Owl	1·75	1·90
2388	20 d. Narina Trogon	2·25	2·40
2389	25 d. Lesser Pied Kingfisher	3·00	3·25
2390	30 d. Common Kestrel	3·50	3·75
2391	40 d. Temminck's Courser (25.3.97)	4·75	5·00
2392	50 d. European Bee-eater (25.3.97)	5·75	6·00
2377/92	*Set of 16*	23·00	24·00

No. 2388 is inscribed "TROGAN" in error

(Litho Questa)

1996 (18 Nov). *Christmas. Religious Paintings. Designs as T 369 of Antigua, showing different details of "Assumption of the Madonna" (Tiziano Vecellio) (Nos. 2393/8). P 13½×14.*

2393	1 d. multicoloured	10	10
2394	1 d. 50, multicoloured	20	25
2395	2 d. multicoloured	20	25
2396	3 d. multicoloured	35	40
2397	10 d. multicoloured	1·10	1·25
2398	15 d. multicoloured	1·75	1·90
2393/8	*Set of 6*	3·50	4·00

MS2399 Two sheets, each 76×106 mm. (a) 25 d. blackish brown, black and yellow-brown ("Adoration of the Magi" (F. Lippi) (*horiz*). P 14×13½. (b) 25 d. carmine-red, black and pale brown-rose ("Virgin and Child with Infant St. John" (Raphael)). P 13½×14 . *Set of 2 sheets* 5·75 6·00

(Des Shannon. Litho Questa)

1996 (21 Nov). *20th Anniv of Rocky (film). Sheet 143×182 mm. P 14×13½.*

MS2400 **266** 10 d.×3 multicoloured 3·50 3·75

267 Ox   **268** "Arch 22" Monument

(Des Y. Lee. Litho Questa)

1997 (16 Jan). *Chinese New Year ("Year of the Ox"). T 267 and similar horiz designs showing symbolic oxen. P 14½.*

2401	63 b. multicoloured		10	10
	a. Horiz strip of 4. Nos. 2401/4		1·00	
2402	75 b. multicoloured		10	10
2403	1 d. 50, multicoloured		20	25
2404	4 d. multicoloured		45	50
2401/4		*Set of 4*	85	95
MS2405	84×68 mm. 3 d. × 4. As Nos. 2401/4		1·40	1·50
MS2406	76×106 mm. 10 d. multicoloured (ox and sleeping peasant) (39½×24½ mm). P 14		1·10	1·25

Nos. 2401/4 were printed together, *se-tenant*, as horizontal strips of 4 in sheets of 12.

(Litho Questa)

1997 (28 Jan). *Economic Development. T 268 and similar multicoloured designs. P 14.*

2407	63 b. Type 268		10	10
2408	1 d. Tractor (horiz)		10	10
2409	1 d. 50, Man planting rice		20	25
2410	2 d. As Type 268, but with white panel at top		20	25
2411	3 d. Model of Banjul International Airport terminal building (horiz)		35	40
2412	5 d. Chamoi Bridge (horiz)		60	65
2407/12		*Set of 6*	1·25	1·75
MS2413	Two sheets. (a) 106×76 mm. 20 d. Workers in rice field (horiz). (b) 76×106 mm. 25 d. As Type 268	*Set of 2 sheets*	5·25	5·50

269 Monkey King extinguishing Fire on Flame Mountain   **270** Jackie Chan

1997 (28 Jan). *Mickey Mouse's Journey to the West. T 269 and similar multicoloured designs showing Disney cartoon characters. Litho. P 14×13½.*

2414	2 d. Type 269		20	25
	a. Sheetlet. Nos. 2414/19		1·25	
2415	2 d. Demon Ox and Monkey King fighting		20	25
2416	2 d. Mickey, Donald, Monkey King and Master San Tsang		20	25
2417	2 d. Fighting the Spider Demon		20	25
2418	2 d. Fighting the White Skeleton Demon		20	25
2419	2 d. The real and the fake Monkey King		20	25
2420	3 d. Monkey King trapped in furnace		35	40
	a. Sheetlet. Nos. 2420/5		2·10	
2421	3 d. Monkey King with magic weapon		35	40
2422	3 d. Type 269		35	40
2423	3 d. At the Gate of South Heaven		35	40
2424	3 d. Tasting the celestial peaches		35	40
2425	3 d. Monkey King rescued from Five-Finger Mountain		35	40
2414/25		*Set of 12*	3·25	4·00
MS2426	Four sheets, each 134×109 mm. (a) 5 d. Mickey and Donald with Master San Tsang (vert). P 13½×14. (b) 10 d. Monkey King, Mickey and monkeys. P 14×13½. (c) 10 d. Monkey King, Mickey and tortoise (vert). P 13½×14. (d) 15 d. Mickey and Minnie with Buddhist scriptures. P 14×13½	*Set of 4 sheets*	4·75	5·00

Nos. 2414/19 and 2420/5 were each printed together, *se-tenant*, in sheetlets of 6.

(Des Y. Lee. Litho Questa)

1997 (12 Feb). *"HONG KONG '97" International Stamp Exhibition. Jackie Chan (film star). T 270 and similar multicoloured designs. P 14.*

2427	4 d. Type 270		45	50
	a. Sheetlet. Nos. 2427/34		3·50	
2428	4 d. Wearing red jacket		45	50
2429	4 d. In open-necked shirt		45	50
2430	4 d. Bare-chested		45	50
2431	4 d. Wearing black jacket		45	50
2432	4 d. Wearing black and white spotted shirt		45	50
2433	4 d. Wearing white T-shirt and red anorak		45	50
2434	4 d. Wearing white sleeveless T-shirt		45	50
2427/34		*Set of 8*	3·50	4·00
MS2435	76×106 mm. 25 d. Jackie Chan in action (horiz)		3·00	3·25

Nos. 2427/34 were printed together, *se-tenant*, in sheetlets of 8.

271 Clouded Leopard   **272** Monkey

1997 (24 Feb). *Endangered Species. T 271 and similar horiz designs. Multicoloured. Litho. P 14.*

2436	1 d. 50, Type 271		20	25
	a. Sheetlet. Nos. 2436/55		4·00	
2437	1 d. 50, Audouin's Gull		20	25
2438	1 d. 50, Leatherback Turtle		20	25
2439	1 d. 50, White-eared Pheasant		20	25
2440	1 d. 50, Kakapo		20	25
2441	1 d. 50, Right Whale		20	25
2442	1 d. 50, Black-footed Ferret		20	25
2443	1 d. 50, Dwarf Lemur		20	25
2444	1 d. 50, Peacock Pheasant		20	25
2445	1 d. 50, Brown Hyena		20	25
2446	1 d. 50, Cougar		20	25
2447	1 d. 50, Gharial		20	25
2448	1 d. 50, Monk Seal		20	25
2449	1 d. 50, Mountain Gorilla		20	25
2450	1 d. 50, Blyth's Tragopan		20	25
2451	1 d. 50, Malayan Tapir		20	25
2452	1 d. 50, Black Rhinoceros		20	25
2453	1 d. 50, Polar Bear		20	25
2454	1 d. 50, Red Colobus		20	25
2455	1 d. 50, Tiger		20	25
2456	1 d. 50, Arabian Oryx		20	25
	a. Sheetlet. Nos. 2456/75		4·00	
2457	1 d. 50, Baiji		20	25
2458	1 d. 50, Ruffed Lemur		20	25
2459	1 d. 50, California Condor		20	25
2460	1 d. 50, Blue-headed Quail Dove		20	25
2461	1 d. 50, Numbat		20	25
2462	1 d. 50, Congo Peacock		20	25
2463	1 d. 50, White Uakari		20	25
2464	1 d. 50, Eskimo Curlew		20	25
2465	1 d. 50, Gouldian Finch		20	25
2466	1 d. 50, Coelacanth		20	25
2467	1 d. 50, Toucan Barbet		20	25
2468	1 d. 50, Snow Leopard		20	25
2469	1 d. 50, Queen Alexandra's Birdwing		20	25
2470	1 d. 50, Dalmatian Pelican		20	25
2471	1 d. 50, Chaco Tortoise		20	25
2472	1 d. 50, Giant Catfish		20	25
2473	1 d. 50, Helmeted Hornbill		20	25
2474	1 d. 50, White-eyed River Martin		20	25
2475	1 d. 50, Fluminense Swallowtail		20	25
2436/75		*Set of 40*	8·00	10·00
MS2476	Three sheets, each 103×72 mm. (a) 25 d. Giant Panda; (b) 25 d. Humpback Whale; (c) 25 d. Japanese Crane	*Set of 3 sheets*	8·75	9·00

Nos. 2436/55 and 2456/75 were each printed, *se-tenant*, in sheetlets of 20, with enlarged top margins incorporating the "HONG KONG '97" International Stamp Exhibition.

1997 (24 Feb). *The Jungle Book by Rudyard Kipling. T 272 and similar vert designs. Multicoloured. Litho. P 14.*

2477	3 d. Type 272		35	40
	a. Sheetlet. Nos. 2477/88		4·25	
2478	3 d. Baloo (bear)		35	40
2479	3 d. Elephant		35	40
2480	3 d. Monkey and temple		35	40
2481	3 d. Bagheera (panther)		35	40
2482	3 d. Buffalo		35	40
2483	3 d. Mandrill		35	40
2484	3 d. Shere Khan (tiger)		35	40
2485	3 d. Rama (wolf)		35	40
2486	3 d. Kaa (cobra)		35	40
2487	3 d. Mongoose		35	40
2488	3 d. Mowgli		35	40
2477/88		*Set of 12*	4·25	4·75

Nos. 2477/88 were printed together, *se-tenant*, in sheetlets of 12 with the background forming a composite design.

273 *Polyporus squamosus*

(Litho Questa)

1997 (10 Mar). *Fungi. T 273 and similar multicoloured designs. P 14.*

2489	1 d. Type 273		10	15
2490	3 d. Armillaria tabescens		35	40
2491	4 d. Amanita caesarea (vert)		45	50
	a. Sheetlet. Nos. 2491/9		4·00	
2492	4 d. Lepiota procera (vert)		45	50
2493	4 d. Hygrophorus psittacinus (vert)		45	50
2494	4 d. Russula xerampelina (vert)		45	50
2495	4 d. Laccaria amethystina (vert)		45	50
2496	4 d. Coprinus micaceus (vert)		45	50
2497	4 d. Boletus edulis (vert)		45	50
2498	4 d. Morchella esculenta (vert)		45	50
2499	4 d. Otidea auricula (vert)		45	50
2500	5 d. Collybia velutipes		60	65
2501	10 d. Sarcoscypha coccinea		1·10	1·25
2489/501		*Set of 13*	6·25	7·00
MS2502	76×106 mm. 25 d. Volvariella bombycina		3·00	3·25

Nos. 2491/9 were printed together, *se-tenant*, in sheetlets of 9.

(Des M. Freedman and Dena Rubin. Litho Questa)

1997 (24 Mar). *50th Anniv of U.N.E.S.C.O. Multicoloured designs as T 373 of Antigua. P 14×13½ (horiz) or 13½×14 (vert).*

2503	1 d. Cloister, Horyu-ji, Japan		10	15
2504	2 d. Great Wall, China		20	25
2505	3 d. Statues, Ayutthaya, Thailand		35	40
2506	4 d. Ascension Convent, Santa Maria, Philippines		45	50
2507	4 d. Mount Nimba Nature Reserve, Guinea (vert)		45	50
	a. Sheetlet. Nos. 2507/14 and 1 central label		3·50	

2508	4 d. Banc d'Argun National Park, Mauritania (vert)		45	50
2509	4 d. Doorway, Marrakesh, Morocco (vert)		45	50
2510	4 d. Ichkeul National Park, Tunisia (vert)		45	50
2511	4 d. Village pottery, Mali (vert)		45	50
2512	4 d. Hippopotamus, Salonga National Park, Zaire (vert)		45	50
2513	4 d. Timgad Roman Ruins, Algeria (vert)		45	50
2514	4 d. Wooden statue, Benin (vert)		45	50
2515	4 d. Temple, Magao Caves, China (vert)		45	50
	a. Sheetlet. Nos. 2515/22 and 1 central label		3·50	
2516	4 d. Statue, Magao Caves (vert)		45	50
2517	4 d. Domes, Magao Caves (vert)		45	50
2518	4 d. Great Wall from the air, China (vert)		45	50
2519	4 d. Statue, Great Wall (vert)		45	50
2520	4 d. Bronze Bird, Imperial Palace, China (vert)		45	50
2521	4 d. Temples, Imperial Palace, China (vert)		45	50
2522	4 d. Dragon statue, Imperial Palace (vert)		45	50
2523	4 d. Kyoto Gardens, Japan (vert)		45	50
	a. Sheetlet. Nos. 2523/30		3·50	
2524	4 d. Himeji Castle, Japan (vert)		45	50
2525	4 d. Horyu-ji Temple, Japan (vert)		45	50
2526	4 d. Buddha, Horyu-ji, Japan (vert)		45	50
2527	4 d. Yakushima Forest, Japan (vert)		45	50
2528	4 d. Ancient tree, Yakushima Forest, Japan (vert)		45	50
2529	4 d. Temple, Kyoto, Japan (vert)		45	50
2530	4 d. Pavilion, Kyoto, Japan (vert)		45	50
2531	5 d. Riverside houses, Inselstadt, Germany		60	65
	a. Sheetlet. Nos. 2531/5		3·00	
2532	5 d. Rosaleda Gardens, Bamberg, Germany		60	65
2533	5 d. Bamberg Cathedral, Germany		60	65
2534	5 d. Timbered house, Maulbronn, Germany		60	65
2535	5 d. Maulbronn Monastery, Germany		60	65
2536	5 d. Ruins at Delphi, Greece		60	65
	a. Sheetlet. Nos. 2536/40		3·00	
2537	5 d. Rhodes waterfront, Greece		60	65
2538	5 d. Knights' Hospital, Rhodes, Greece		60	65
2539	5 d. Temple, Delphi, Greece		60	65
2540	5 d. Delphi from air, Greece		60	65
2541	5 d. Foliage, Shirakami-Sanchi, Japan		60	65
	a. Sheetlet. Nos. 2541/5		3·00	
2542	5 d. Notice board, Shirakami-Sanchi, Japan		60	65
2543	5 d. Tower, Himeji Castle, Japan		60	65
2544	5 d. Roof tops, Himeji Castle, Japan		60	65
2545	5 d. Gateway, Himeji Castle, Japan		60	65
2546	10 d. Komodo Dragons, Indonesia		1·10	1·40
2547	15 d. Ancient hut, Timbuktu, Mali		1·75	1·90
2503/47		*Set of 44*	23·00	26·00
MS2548	Four sheets, each 127×102 mm. (a) 25 d. Plitvice Lakes National Park, Croatia; (b) 25 d. Ruins of Kilwa Kisiwani, Tanzania; (c) 25 d. Santa Maria de Alcobaca cloisters, Portugal; (d) 25 d. Watergarden, Kyoto, Japan	*Set of 4 sheets*	11·50	12·00

Nos. 2507/14, 2515/22 and 2523/30 were each printed together, *se-tenant*, in sheetlets of 8 stamps with a centre label and Nos. 2531/35, 2536/40 and 2541/45 in sheetlets of 5 stamps with a top left-hand corner label.

274 Minnie Mouse, 1928

1997 (1 May). *Minnie Mouse Through the Years. T 274 and similar vert designs showing Disney cartoon character in years stated. Multicoloured. Litho. P 13½×14.*

2549	4 d. Type 274		45	50
	a. Sheetlet. Nos. 2549/57		4·00	
2550	4 d. In 1933		45	50
2551	4 d. In 1934		45	50
2552	4 d. In 1937		45	50
2553	4 d. In 1938		45	50
2554	4 d. In 1941		45	50
2555	4 d. In 1950		45	50
2556	4 d. In 1990		45	50
2557	4 d. In 1997		45	50
2549/57		*Set of 9*	4·00	4·50
MS2558	133×108 mm. 25 d. In 1987		3·00	3·25

Nos. 2549/57 were printed together, *se-tenant*, in sheetlets of 9.

275 Dipstick

(Des Alvin White Studios. Litho Questa)

1997 (1 May). 101 Dalmatians. T **275** and similar multi-coloured designs showing Disney cartoon characters. P 13½×14 (vert) or 14×13½ (horiz).

2559	50 b. Type **275**	..	..	10	10
	a. Sheetlet. Nos. 2559/64	..	..	35	
2560	50 b. Fidget	..	..	10	10
2561	50 b. Jewel	..	..	10	10
2562	50 b. Lucky	..	..	10	10
2563	50 b. Two-Tone	..	..	10	10
2564	50 b. Wizzer	..	..	10	10
2565	2 d. Two puppies playing (horiz)			20	25
	a. Sheetlet. Nos. 2565/73	..	..	1·75	
2566	2 d. Puppy and pig (horiz)	..		20	25
2567	2 d. Two puppies with butterfly (horiz)			20	25
2568	2 d. Puppy lying on back (horiz)	..		20	25
2569	2 d. Puppy with ball (horiz)	..		20	25
2570	2 d. Puppy with bone (horiz)	..		20	25
2571	2 d. One puppy pulling another puppy's tail (horiz)	..		20	25
2572	2 d. Two puppies pulling third puppy's ears (horiz)	..		20	25
2573	2 d. Puppy with teddy bear (horiz)			20	25
2574	3 d. Puppy asleep on biscuit box (horiz)			35	40
	a. Sheetlet. Nos. 2574/82	..		3·25	
2575	3 d. Puppy with hose (horiz)	..		35	40
2576	3 d. Puppy and bottle (horiz)	..		35	40
2577	3 d. Puppy and biscuit bowl (horiz)			35	40
2578	3 d. Puppy wearing hat (horiz)	..		35	40
2579	3 d. Three puppies with lipstick (horiz)			35	40
2580	3 d. Puppy tying another up with string (horiz)	..		35	40
2581	3 d. Two puppies and lunch box (horiz)	..		35	40
2582	3 d. Three puppies and computer (horiz)			35	40
2559/82			Set of 24	5·25	6·00

MS2583 Six sheets, each 127×103 mm. (a) 25 d. Sheep and puppies (horiz). (b) 25 d. Cruella de Vil (horiz). (c) 25 d. Puppy looking at photograph (horiz). (d) 25 d. Puppies in mail sack. (e) 25 d. Two puppies covered in paint (horiz). (f) 25 d. Two puppies playing computer game (horiz).
　　　　　　　　　　Set of 6 sheets 17·00 18·00
Nos. 2559/64, 2565/73 and 2574/82 were each printed together, se-tenant, in sheetlets of 6 (Nos. 2559/64) or 9 (others).

276 Juventus Team, 1897　　**277** "Morning Glory and Cricket"

The Gambia **D4**

1997 (9 May). Centenary of Juventus Football Team. T **276** and similar horiz designs. Multicoloured. Litho. P 14×13½.

2584	5 d. Type **276**	..	..	60	65
	a. Sheetlet. Nos. 2584/9	..		3·50	
2585	5 d. Centenary emblem and player		60	65
2586	5 d. Giampiero Boniperti	..	..	60	65
2587	5 d. Roberto Bettega	..	..	60	65
2588	5 d. Juventus team, 1996	..	..	60	65
2589	5 d. Juventus '97 logo	..		60	65
2584/9			Set of 6	3·50	4·00

Nos. 2584/9 were printed together, se-tenant, in sheetlets of 6.

(Des R. Rundo. Litho Questa)

1997 (20 May). 300th Anniv of Mother Goose Nursery Rhymes. Horiz design as T **309** of Dominica. Sheet 72×102 mm. Multicoloured. P 14.
MS2590　25 d. Young girl ("I'll Tell You a Story") 3·00 3·25

(Litho Questa)

1997 (20 May). 10th Anniv of Chernobyl Nuclear Disaster. Vert designs as T **375** of Antigua. Multicoloured. P 13½.

2591	15 d. As Type **375** of Antigua	..	1·75	1·90
2592	15 d. As No. 2591 but inscribed "CHABAD'S CHILDREN OF CHERNOBYL"	..	1·75	1·90

(Des J. Iskowitz. Litho Questa)

1997 (20 May). 50th Death Anniv of Paul Harris (founder of Rotary International). Horiz designs as T **376** of Antigua. Multicoloured. P 14.

2593	10 d. Rotary President Sydney Pascall planting tree of friendship	..	1·10	1·25
MS2594　78×108 mm. 25 d. Paul Harris and Preserve Planet Earth emblem　　.. 3·00 3·25

(Litho Questa)

1997 (20 May). Golden Wedding of Queen Elizabeth and Prince Philip. Horiz designs as T **377** of Antigua. Multicoloured. P 14.

2595	4 d. Queen Elizabeth II	..	..	45	50
	a. Sheetlet. Nos. 2595/600	..	2·75	

2596	4 d. Royal coat of arms	..	..	45	50
2597	4 d. Queen Elizabeth and Prince Philip applauding	..	..	45	50
2598	4 d. Queen Elizabeth and Prince Philip taking the salute	..	..	45	50
2599	4 d. Royal Yacht Britannia	..	..	45	50
2600	4 d. Prince Philip	..	..	45	50
2595/600			Set of 6	2·75	3·00

MS2601　100×70 mm. 20 d. Princess Elizabeth, 1948 | .. | .. | 2·25 | 2·40
Nos. 2595/600 were printed together, se-tenant, in sheetlets of 6.

(Des J. Iskowitz. Litho Questa)

1997 (20 May). "Pacific '97" International Stamp Exhibition, San Francisco. Death Centenary of Henrich von Stephan (founder of U.P.U.). Horiz designs as T **378** of Antigua. P 14.

2602	5 d. deep magenta	..	..	60	65
	a. Sheetlet. Nos. 2602/4	..	1·75	
2603	5 d. chestnut	..	..	60	65
2604	5 d. turquoise-green and black	..	60	65
2602/4			Set of 3	1·75	1·90

MS2605　82×118 mm. 25 d. turquoise-green and black | .. | .. | 3·00 | 3·25
Designs:—No. 2602, Von Stephan and Otto von Bismarck; No. 2603, Von Stephan and Mercury; No. 2604, Mail wagon, Boston, 1900; No. **MS**2605, Von Stephan and Hamburg–Lubeck postilion.
Nos. 2602/4 were printed together, se-tenant, in sheetlets of 3 with enlarged illustrated right-hand margin.

1997 (20 May). Birth Bicentenary of Hiroshige (Japanese painter). T **277** and similar vert designs. Multicoloured. Litho. P 13½×14.

2606/11	4 d. × 6 (Type **277** "Dragonfly and Begonia"; "Two Ducks swimming among Reeds"; "A Black-naped Oriole perched on a Stem of Rose Mallow"; "A Pheasant on a Snow-covered Pine"; "A Cuckoo flying through the Rain")		
	a. Sheetlet. Nos. 2606/11		2·75
2612/17	4 d. × 6 ("An Egret among Rushes"; "Peacock and Peonies"; "Three Wild Geese flying across the Moon"; "A Cock in the Snow"; "A Pheasant and Bracken"; "Peonies")		
	a. Sheetlet. Nos. 2612/17		2·75
2618/23	4 d. × 6 ("Sparrow and Bamboo"; "Mandarin Ducks on an Icy Pond with Brown Leaves falling"; "Blossoming Plum Tree"; "Java Sparrow and Magnolia"; "Chinese Bellflowers and Miscanthus"; "A Small Black Bird clinging to a Tendril of Ivy")		
	a. Sheetlet. Nos. 2618/23		2·75
2624/9	5 d. × 6 ("Sparrows and Camellia in Snow"; "Parrot on a Branch of Pine"; "A Long-tailed Blue Bird on a Branch of Flowering Plum"; "Sparrow and Bamboo"; "Bird in a Tree"; "A Wild Duck swimming beneath Snow-laden reeds")		
	a. Sheetlet. Nos. 2624/9		3·50
2630/5	5 d. × 6 ("Kingfisher above a Yellow-flowered Water Plant"; "Wagtail and Roses"; "A Mandarin Duck on a Snowy Bank"; "A Japanese White-eye on a Persimmon Branch"; "Sparrows and Camellia in Snow"; "Kingfisher and Moon above a Yellow-flowered Water Plant")		
	a. Sheetlet. Nos. 2630/5		3·50
2636/41	5 d. × 6 ("Sparrow and Bamboo by Night"; "Birds Flying over Waves"; "Blossoming Plum Tree with Full Moon"; "Kingfisher and Iris"; "A Blue-and-White Flycatcher on a Hibiscus Flower"; "Mandarin Ducks in Snowfall")		
	a. Sheetlet. Nos. 2636/41		3·50
2606/41		Set of 35	15·00	16·00

MS2642　Six sheets each 95×120 mm. (a) 25 d. Hawk on perch. (b) 25 d. Two green birds on branch. (c) 25 d. Kingfisher hovering. (d) 25 d. "Three Wild Geese flying across moon". (e) 25 d. Red parrot on branch. (f) 25 d. White bird on flowering bush | .. | Set of 6 sheets 17·00 18·00
Nos. 2606/11, 2612/17, 2618/23, 2624/9, 2630/5 and 2636/41 were each printed together, se-tenant, in sheetlets of 6.

(Des R. Rundo. Litho Questa)

1997 (20 May). 175th Anniv of Brothers Grimm's Third Collection of Fairy Tales. Little Red Riding Hood. Multicoloured designs as T **379** of Antigua. P 13½×14.

2643	10 d. Grandma's cottage	..	..	1·10	1·25
	a. Sheetlet. Nos. 2643/5	..	3·25	
2644	10 d. Little Red Riding Hood	..	1·10	1·25
2645	10 d. The Wolf	..	..	1·10	1·25
2643/5			Set of 3	3·25	3·50

MS2646　124×96 mm. 10 d. Little Red Riding Hood (horiz). P 14×13½ | .. | .. | 1·25
Nos. 2643/5 were printed together, se-tenant, in sheetlets of 3 with an illustrated margin.

278 Coelophysis chasing Ornitholestes

(Des W. Wright. Litho Questa)

1997 (23 June). Dinosaurs. T **278** and similar horiz designs. Multicoloured. P 14.

2647	50 b. Type **278**	..	..	10	10
2648	63 b. Spinosaurus	..	..	10	10
2649	75 b. Kentrosaurus	..	..	10	10
2650	1 d. Ceratosaurus	..	..	10	10
2651	1 d. 50, Stygimoloch	..	..	20	25
2652	2 d. Troodon	..	..	20	25
2653	3 d. Velociraptor	..	..	35	40
2654	4 d. Triceratops	..	..	45	50
2655	4 d. Anurognathus	..	..	45	50
	a. Sheetlet. Nos. 2655/63	..	4·00	
2656	4 d. Pteranodon	..	..	45	50
2657	4 d. Pterosaurus	..	..	45	50
2658	4 d. Saltasaurus	..	..	45	50
2659	4 d. Agathaumus	..	..	45	50
2660	4 d. Stegosaurus	..	..	45	50
2661	4 d. Albertosaurus libratus	..	45	50
2662	4 d. Three Lesothosauruses running	45	50
2663	4 d. Five Lesothosauruses running	..	45	50
2664	4 d. Tarbosaurus bataar	..	45	50
	a. Sheetlet. Nos. 2664/72	..	4·00	
2665	4 d. Brachiosaurus	..	..	45	50
2666	4 d. Styracosasaurus	..	..	45	50
2667	4 d. Baryonyx	..	..	45	50
2668	4 d. Coelophysis	..	..	45	50
2669	4 d. Carnotaurus	..	..	45	50
2670	4 d. Compsognathus longipes	..	45	50
2671	4 d. Compsognathus "Elegant Jaw"	45	50
2672	4 d. Stenonychosaurus	..	45	50
2673	5 d. Protoceratops	..	..	60	65
2674	5 d. Ornithomimus	..	..	1·10	1·25
2675	15 d. Stegosaurus	..	..	1·75	1·90
2676	20 d. Ankylosaurus saichania	..	2·25	2·40
2647/76			Set of 30	15·00	17·00

MS2677　Two sheets, each 106×81 mm. (a) 25 d. Head of Deinonychus (50×37 mm). (b) 25 d. Seismosaurus (88×27 mm) | Set of 2 sheets 5·75 6·00
Nos. 2655/63 and 2664/72 were each printed together, se-tenant, in sheetlets of 9 with the backgrounds forming composite designs.

279 Margaret Thatcher and Deng Xiaoping toasting Joint Declaration, 1984

1997 (1 July). Return of Hong Kong to China. T **279** and similar horiz designs. Multicoloured. Litho. P 14.

2678	3 d. Type **279**	..	..	35	40
	a. Sheetlet. Nos. 2678/81	..	1·40	
2679	3 d. Signing Joint Declaration on Hong Kong, 1984	..	35	40
2680	3 d. Signing Joint Declaration on Macao, 1987	..	35	40
2681	3 d. Deng Xiaoping toasting Prime Minister Anibal Silva of Portugal	35	40
2682	4 d. Hong Kong in 1843 and Governor Sir Henry Pottinger	..	45	50
	a. Sheetlet. Nos. 2682/4	..	1·40	
2683	4 d. Kowloon in 1860 and Governor Sir Hercules Robinson	..	45	50
2684	4 d. Reception in New Territories, 1898, and Governor Sir Henry Blake	45	50
2685	5 d. Governor Sir Henry Pottinger and British warship	..	60	65
	a. Sheetlet. Nos. 2685/7	..	1·75	
2686	5 d. Governor Christopher Patten and Lantau Bridge	..	60	65
2687	5 d. Chief Executive C.H. Tung and Hong Kong by night	..	60	65
2688	6 d. Signing the Treaty of Nanking, 1842	70	75
	a. Sheetlet. Nos. 2688/90	..	2·10	
2689	6 d. Signing the Japanese Surrender of Hong Kong, 1945	..	70	75
2690	6 d. Signing of the Sino-British Joint Declaration, 1984	..	70	75
2678/90			Set of 13	6·50	7·25

Nos. 2678/81, 2682/4, 2685/7 and 2688/90 were each printed together, se-tenant, in sheetlets of 4 (Nos. 2678/81) or 3 (others).

STAMP BOOKLETS

1979 (17 Oct). Tenth Anniv of Moon Landing. Multicoloured cover, 165×93 mm, showing "Apollo 11" on the front and Abuko Satellite Earth Station on the back. Pane attached by selvedge.

SB1	4 d. 26, booklet containing se-tenant pane of 6 (No. 427a) and pane of 1 (No. 430a)	..	2·75

The cover of No. SB1 is folded five times "concertina fashion" and when opened out measures 165×465 mm.

1983 (12 Dec). Bicentenary of Manned Flight. Bistre-brown and bright scarlet cover, 121×81 mm, showing Bicentenary of Manned Flight logo on front and advertisement on reverse. Stitched.

SB2	11 d. 20, booklet containing se-tenant panes of 4 (Nos. 522a, 524a) and pane of 1 (No. 526a)	5·75

Ghana
(*formerly* Gold Coast)

GOLD COAST

Gold Coast originally consisted of coastal forts, owned by the Royal African Company, trading with the interior. In 1821, due to raids by the Ashanti king, the British Government took over the forts, together with some of the hinterland, and the Gold Coast was placed under the Governor of Sierra Leone.

The administration was handed back to a merchantile company in 1828, but the forts returned to British Government rule in 1843. The colony was reconstituted by Royal Charter on 24 July, 1874, and at that time also included the settlement at Lagos which became a separate colony in January, 1886.

Following the end of the final Ashanti War the whole of the territory was annexed in September 1901.

A postal service was established at Cape Coast Castle in 1853. There is no record of British stamps being officially issued in the Colony before 1875, apart from those used on board the ships of the West African Squadron, but examples do, however, exist cancelled by Gold Coast postmarks.

CROWN COLONY

PRICES FOR STAMPS ON COVER TO 1945	
Nos. 1/3	*from* × 15
Nos. 4/8	*from* × 20
Nos. 9/10	*from* × 10
Nos. 11/20	*from* × 25
Nos. 22/5	—
Nos. 26/34	*from* × 10
Nos. 35/6	*from* × 20
Nos. 38/69	*from* × 6
Nos. 70/98	*from* × 3
Nos. 100/2	—
Nos. 103/12	*from* × 5
Nos. 113/16	*from* × 3
Nos. 117/19	*from* × 4
Nos. 120/32	*from* × 3
Nos. D1/4	*from* × 8

ONE
PENNY.

1   (2)

(Typo D.L.R.)

1875 (1 July). *Wmk Crown CC. P* 12½.
1	1	1d. blue		£425	80·00
2		4d. magenta		£400	£110
3		6d. orange		£600	65·00

1876–84. *Wmk Crown CC. P* 14.
4	1	½d. olive-yellow (1879)		45·00	22·00
5		1d. blue		13·00	6·50
		a. Bisected (½d.) (on cover) (1884)		† £2750	
6		2d. green (1879)		60·00	9·00
		a. Bisected (on cover) (1884)		† £2500	
		b. Quartered (½d.) (on cover) (1884)		† £3750	
7		4d. magenta		£150	6·00
		a. Bisected (2d.) (on cover) (1884)		† £4250	
		b. Quartered (1d.) (on cover) (1884)		† £5500	
8		6d. orange		90·00	18·00
		a. Bisected (3d.) (on cover) (1884)		† £5000	
		b. Sixth (1d.) (on cover) (1884)		† £6500	

During 1884 some values were in short supply and the use of bisects and other divided stamps is known as follows:

No. 5a. Used as part of 2½d. rate from Accra and Quittah
No. 6a. Used as 1d. rate from Addah, Cape Coast Castle, Quittah, Salt Pond, Secondee and Winnebah
No. 6b. Used as part of 2½d. rate from Cape Coast Castle
No. 7a. Used as 2d. or as part of 2½d. rate from Quittah
No. 7b. Used as 1d. rate from Appam, Axim, Cape Coast Castle and Winnebah
No. 8a. Used as 3d. rate from Secondee
No. 8b. Used as 1d. rate from Cape Coast Castle and Winnebah

Examples of bisects used on piece are worth about 10% of the price quoted for those on cover.

1883 (May)? *No. 7 surch locally.*
8c	1	"1d." on 4d. magenta			

1883. *Wmk Crown CA. P* 14.
9	1	½d. olive-yellow (January)		£140	60·00
10		1d. blue (May)		£850	60·00

PENNY

Short "P" and distorted "E" (Pl 1
R. 5/6) ("P" repaired for Pl 2)

1884 (Aug)–**91.** *Wmk Crown CA. P* 14.
11	1	½d. green		1·50	55
		a. Dull green		1·25	50
12		1d. rose-carmine		2·00	50
		a. Carmine		2·00	50
		b. Bisected (½d.) on cover		† £3250	
		c. Short "P" and distorted "E"		45·00	
13		2d. grey		6·50	3·25
		b. Slate		5·00	50
		c. Bisected (1d.) (on cover)		† £3750	
		d. Quartered (½d.) (on cover)			
14		2½d. ultramarine and orange (13.3.91)		2·50	35
15		3d. olive-yellow (9.89)		6·00	4·50
		a. Olive		5·50	4·00

16	1	4d. deep mauve (3.85)		4·00	1·25
		a. Rosy mauve		6·50	3·00
17		6d. orange (1.89)		4·75	4·00
		a. Orange-brown		4·75	4·00
		b. Bisected (3d.) (on cover)			
18		1s. violet (1888)		27·00	12·00
		a. Bright mauve		3·50	1·25
19		2s. yellow-brown (1888)		80·00	35·00
		a. Deep brown		29·00	15·00
11/19a			*Set of* 9	48·00	24·00
14/15, 18/19 Optd "Specimen"			*Set of* 4	£150	

During 1884 to 1886 and in 1889 some values were in short supply and the use of bisects and other divided stamps is known as follows:

No. 12b. Used as part of 2½d. rate from Cape Coast Castle
No. 13c. Used as 1d. or as part of 2d. rate from Cape Coast Castle, Chamah, Dixcove and Elmina
No. 13d. Used as part of 2½d. rate from Cape Coast Castle
No. 17b. Used as 3d. from Appam

1889 (Mar). *No. 17 surch with T* **2.**
20	1	1d. on 6d. orange		£100	48·00
		a. Surch double		† £2500	

In some sheets examples may be found with the bar and "PENNY" spaced 8 mm, the normal spacing being 7 mm.

USED HIGH VALUES. Until the introduction of airmail in 1929 there was no postal use for values over 10s. Post Offices did, however, apply postal cancellations to high value stamps required for telegram fees.

3   4

1889 (Sept)–**94.** *Wmk Crown CA. P* 14.
22	3	5s. dull mauve and blue		60·00	12·00
23		10s. dull mauve and red		75·00	15·00
		a. Dull mauve and carmine		£425	£150
24		20s. green and red		£3250	
25		20s. dull mauve and black/red (4.94)		£150	35·00
22/5 Optd "Specimen"			*Set of* 4	£450	

No. 24 was withdrawn from sale in April 1893 when a large part of the stock was stolen. No 20s. stamps were available until the arrival of the replacement printing a year later.

1898 (May)–**1902.** *Wmk Crown CA. P* 14.
26	3	½d. dull mauve and green		1·50	60
27		1d. dull mauve and rose		1·50	40
27a	4	2d. dull mauve and orange-red (1902)		32·00	85·00
28	3	2½d. dull mauve and ultramarine		4·25	3·50
29	4	3d. dull mauve and orange		4·50	1·25
30		6d. dull mauve and violet		5·50	1·25
31	3	1s. green and black (1899)		7·50	8·00
32		2s. green and carmine		9·00	17·00
33		5s. green and mauve (1900)		48·00	26·00
34		10s. green and brown (1900)		£120	48·00
26/34			*Set of* 10	£200	£170
26/34 Optd "Specimen"			*Set of* 10	£180	

1901 (6 Oct). *Nos. 28 and 30 surch with T* **2.**
35		1d. on 2½d. dull mauve and ultramarine		1·50	3·00
		a. "ONE" omitted		£1000	
36		1d. on 6d. dull mauve and violet		1·50	3·00
		a. "ONE" omitted		£250	£550

6   7   8

1902. *Wmk Crown CA. P* 14.
38	6	½d. dull purple and green		75	40
39		1d. dull purple and carmine		1·00	15
		w. Wmk inverted		—	40·00
40	7	2d. dull purple and orange-red		11·00	7·00
41	6	2½d. dull purple and ultramarine		4·50	9·00
42	7	3d. dull purple and orange		2·75	1·50
43		6d. dull purple and violet		2·75	1·50
		w. Wmk inverted		—	50·00
44	6	1s. green and black		8·00	3·00
45		2s. green and carmine		12·00	16·00
46		5s. green and mauve		30·00	70·00
47		10s. green and brown		48·00	12·00
48		20s. purple and black/red		£120	£170
38/48			*Set of* 11	£225	£350
38/48 Optd "Specimen"			*Set of* 11	£200	

Examples of Nos. 45/8 are known showing a forged Accra postmark dated "25 MAR 1902".

1904–7. *Wmk Mult Crown CA. Ordinary paper* (½d. *to* 3d.) *or chalk-surfaced paper* (6d., 2s. 6d.).
49	6	½d. dull purple and green (3.06)		2·50	5·00
50		1d. dull purple and carmine (10.04)		3·75	20
		a. Chalk-surfaced paper (5.06)		4·75	1·50
		w. Wmk inverted			
51	7	2d. dull purple and orange-red (11.04)		3·75	50
		a. Chalk-surfaced paper (8.06)		17·00	1·25
52	6	2½d. dull purple and ultramarine (6.06)		40·00	32·00
53	7	3d. dull purple and orange (8.05)		42·00	4·00
		a. Chalk-surfaced paper (4.06)		10·00	60
54		6d. dull purple and violet (9.06)		38·00	1·50
		a. Ordinary paper (5.07)		35·00	1·25
57		2s. 6d. green & yell (3.06) (Optd S. £45)		27·00	90·00
49/57			*Set of* 7	£110	£120

1907–13. *Wmk Mult Crown CA. Ordinary paper* (½d. *to* 2½d. *and* 2s.) *or chalk-surfaced paper* (3d. *to* 1s., 2s. 6d., 5s.). *P* 14.
59	6	½d. dull green (5.07)		2·00	30
		a. Blue-green (1909)		4·25	1·25
60		1d. red (2.07)		3·75	30
61	7	2d. greyish slate (4.09)		2·00	40
62	6	2½d. blue (4.07)		3·50	1·75
63	7	3d. purple/yellow (16.4.09)		6·00	55

64	7	6d. dull and deep purple (12.08)		13·00	55
		a. Dull and bright purple (1911)		3·50	3·50
65	6	1s. black/green (10.09)		6·50	50
66		2s. purple and blue/blue (1910)		4·50	15·00
		a. Chalk-surfaced paper		12·00	15·00
67	7	2s. 6d. blue and red/blue (1911)		25·00	60·00
68	6	5s. green and red/yellow (1913)		55·00	£120
59/68			*Set of* 10	£100	£180
59/68 Optd "Specimen"			*Set of* 10	£200	

A 10s. green and red on green, and a 20s. purple and black on red, both Type **6**, were prepared for use but not issued. Both exist overprinted "Specimen" (*Price for* 10s. *in this condition* £300).

(Typo D.L.R.)

1908 (Nov). *Wmk Mult Crown CA. P* 14.
69	8	1d. red (Optd S. £45)		1·75	10

9   10   11

(Typo D.L.R.)

1913–21. *Die I. Wmk Mult Crown CA. Chalk-surfaced paper* (3d. *to* 20s.). *P* 14.
70	9	½d. green		1·25	1·00
		a. Yellow-green (1916)		1·60	1·25
72	10	1d. red		45	10
		a. Scarlet (1919)		75	50
74	11	2d. grey		1·50	2·50
		a. Slate-grey (1920)		7·50	5·50
		w. Wmk inverted		†	£100
76	9	2½d. bright blue		3·25	90
		x. Wmk reversed		†	£100
77	11	3d. purple/yellow (8.15) (Optd S. £30)		1·00	40
		aw. Wmk inverted		—	50·00
		b. White back (9.13)		30	40
		c. On orange-buff (1919)		3·25	6·50
		d. On buff (1920)			
		e. Die II. On pale yellow (1921)		24·00	5·00
78		6d. dull and bright purple		2·00	2·25
79	9	1s. black/green		1·00	1·25
		a. Wmk sideways			
		b. On blue-green, olive back (1916) (Optd S. £30)		3·00	55
		c. On emerald back (1920) (Optd S. £30)		2·00	2·00
		d. Die II. On emerald back (1921) (Optd S. £35)		1·50	50
80		2s. purple and blue/blue		7·00	1·75
		aw. Wmk inverted		—	£110
		b. Die II (1921)		£140	65·00
81	11	2s. 6d. black and red/blue		5·00	13·00
		a. Die II (1921)		22·00	32·00
82	9	5s. green & red/yell (1916) (Optd S. £40)		6·00	42·00
		a. White back (10.13)		8·50	48·00
		b. On orange-buff (1919)		60·00	65·00
		c. On buff (1920)			
		d. On pale yellow (1921)		90·00	£110
		e. Die II. On pale yellow (1921)		28·00	£120
		ew. Wmk inverted		£120	
83		10s. green and red/green		42·00	80·00
		a. On blue-green, olive back (1920)		17·00	60·00
		b. On emerald back (1921)		30·00	90·00
84		20s. purple and black/red		£120	80·00
70/84			*Set of* 12	£140	£180
70/6, 77b, 78/81, 82a/4 Optd "Specimen"			*Set of* 12	£250	

The 10s. and 20s. were withdrawn locally from September 1920 and, in common with other Gold Coast stamps, were not available to stamp dealers from the Crown Agents in London.

WAR TAX

ONE PENNY

(12)   13 King George V and Christiansborg Castle

1918 (4 June). *Surch with T* **12.**
85	10	1d. on 1d. red (Optd S. £50)		30	40

1921–24. *Die I* (15s., £2) *or Die II* (others). *Wmk Mult Script CA. Chalk-surfaced paper* (6d. *to* £2). *P* 14.
86	9	½d. green		30	30
87	10	1d. chocolate-brown (1922)		30	10
88	11	1½d. red (1922)		70	10
89		2d. grey		70	30
90	9	2½d. yellow-orange (1922)		50	8·00
91	11	3d. bright blue (1922)		70	60
94		6d. dull and bright purple		70	3·00
95	9	1s. black/emerald (1924)		1·75	2·75
96		2s. purple and blue/blue (1923)		2·50	3·25
97	11	2s. 6d. black and red/blue (1924)		4·75	14·00
98	9	5s. green and red/pale yellow (1924)		8·50	38·00
100	11	15s. dull purple and green (Die I)		£110	£275
		a. Die II (1924) (Optd S. £100)		£100	£250
102		£2 green and orange (Die I)		£350	£800
86/100a			*Set of* 12	£110	£275
86/102 Optd "Specimen"			*Set of* 13	£350	

The Duty plate for the 1½d., 15s. and £2 has the words "GOLD COAST" in distinctly larger letters.

Examples of Nos. 100/a and 102 are known showing parts of forged Accra postmarks. These are dated "3 MAY 44" and "8 MAY 44", but are invariably positioned so that the year date is not shown.

(Photo Harrison)

1928 (1 Aug). *Wmk Mult Script CA. P 13½ × 15.*
103	13	½d. green			50	40
104		1d. red-brown			50	10
105		1½d. scarlet			50	1·50
106		2d. slate			50	20
107		2½d. orange-yellow			1·25	3·50
108		3d. blue			55	40
109		6d. black and purple			65	40
110		1s. black and vermilion			1·50	75
111		2s. black and violet			13·00	3·50
112		5s. carmine and olive-green			42·00	38·00
103/12				*Set of 10*	55·00	45·00
103/12 Optd "Specimen"				*Set of 10*	£180	

1935 (6 May). *Silver Jubilee. As Nos. 91/4 of Antigua, but printed by B.W. P 11 × 12.*
113		1d. ultramarine and grey-black			60	50
	a.	Extra flagstaff			£120	
	b.	Short extra flagstaff			£110	
	c.	Lightning conductor			85·00	
	d.	Flagstaff on right-hand turret			£120	
114		3d. brown and deep blue			3·00	6·00
	a.	Extra flagstaff			£120	
	c.	Lightning conductor			95·00	
115		6d. green and indigo			3·25	8·50
	a.	Extra flagstaff			£120	
	b.	Short extra flagstaff			£180	
	c.	Lightning conductor			£100	
	d.	Flagstaff on right-hand turret			£200	
116		1s. slate and purple			3·25	8·50
	a.	Extra flagstaff			£130	
	b.	Short extra flagstaff			£150	
	c.	Lightning conductor			£120	
113/16				*Set of 4*	9·00	21·00
113/16 Perf "Specimen"				*Set of 4*	85·00	

For illustrations of plate varieties see Catalogue Introduction.

1937 (12 May). *Coronation. As Nos. 95/7 of Antigua. P 11 × 11½.*
117		1d. buff			1·25	1·00
118		2d. slate			1·40	2·75
119		3d. blue			1·40	1·25
117/19				*Set of 3*	3·50	4·50
117/19 Perf "Specimen"				*Set of 3*	50·00	

14

15 King George VI and
Christiansborg Castle, Accra

(Recess B.W.)

1938 (1 Apr)—44. *Wmk Mult Script CA. A. P 12 (line).
B. P 12×11½ (T 14) or 11½×12 (T 15) (comb)*.*
			A	B		
120	14	½d. green	1·25	70	40	50
121		1d. red-brown	1·25	30	40	10
122		1½d. scarlet	1·25	75	40	50
123		2d. slate	1·25	55	40	10
124		3d. blue	1·25	45	40	35
125		4d. magenta	1·75	1·50	70	1·25
126		6d. purple	2·00	45	70	20
127		9d. orange	2·00	65	90	55
128	15	1s. black and olive-green	4·00	1·50	1·00	50
129		1s. 3d. brn & turquoise-bl		†	2·00	40
130		2s. blue and violet	11·00	7·50	4·50	7·50
131		5s. olive-green & carmine	22·00	10·00	8·00	10·00
132		10s. black and violet		†	7·00	15·00
120A/31A			*Set of 11*	45·00	22·00	
120B/32B			*Set of 13*		24·00	35·00
120/32 Perf "Specimen"		*Set of 13*	£160			

*All values except 1s. 3d. and 10s. exist in two perforations: (a) Line-perforated 12, from early printings; (b) Comb-perforated 12×11.8 (vertical design) or 11.8×12 (horiz design) from later printings. The 1s. 3d. and 10s. only exist comb-perforated 11.8×12.

Dates of issue: 1.4.38, Nos. 120A/8A, 130A/1A; 1939; Nos. 121B, 126B; 1940; Nos. 120B, 122B/4B, 128B, 130B/1B; 7.40, No. 132B; 12.4.41, No. 129B; 1942, No. 125B; 1944, No. 127B.

1946 (14 Oct). *Victory. As Nos. 110/11 of Antigua. P 13½×14.*
133		2d. slate-violet			9·50	2·25
	a.	Perf 13½			10	10
134		4d. claret			1·50	2·50
	a.	Perf 13½			60	2·50
133/4 Perf "Specimen"				*Set of 2*	50·00	

16 Northern Territories   17 Christiansborg Castle
Mounted Constabulary

(Des B. A. Johnston (1½d.), M. Ziorkley and B. A. Abban (2d.), P.O. draughtsman (2½d.), C. Gomez (1s.), M. Ziorkley (10s.); others from photographs. Recess B.W.)

1948 (1 July). *T 16/17 and similar designs. Wmk Mult Script CA. P 12 × 11½ (vert) or 11½ × 12 (horiz).*
135		½d. emerald-green			20	30
136		1d. blue			15	15
137		1½d. scarlet			1·25	70

138		2d. purple-brown			55	10
139		2½d. yellow-brown and scarlet			2·00	2·50
140		3d. light blue			4·00	45
141		4d. magenta			3·50	1·25
142		6d. black and orange			30	30
143		1s. black and vermilion			60	10
144		2s. sage-green and magenta			3·00	2·00
145		5s. purple and black			20·00	4·50
146		10s. black and sage-green			8·00	4·50
135/46				*Set of 12*	40·00	15·00
135/46 Perf "Specimen"				*Set of 12*	£225	

Designs: *Horiz*—1½d. Emblem of Joint Provincial Council; 2½d. Map showing position of Gold Coast; 3d. Manganese mine; 4d. Lake Bosumtwi; 1s. Breaking cocoa pods; 2s. Trooping the Colour; 5s. Surfboats. *Vert*—2d. Talking drums; 6d. Cocoa farmer; 10s. Forest.

1948 (20 Dec). *Royal Silver Wedding. As Nos. 112/13 of Antigua.*
147		1½d. scarlet			30	30
148		10s. grey-olive			12·00	16·00

1949 (10 Oct). *75th Anniv of U.P.U. As Nos. 114/17 of Antigua.*
149		2d. red-brown			30	30
150		2½d. orange			2·00	1·75
151		3d. deep blue			50	70
152		1s. blue-green			50	50
149/52				*Set of 4*	3·00	3·00

28 Northern Territories Mounted Constabulary

(Recess B.W.)

1952 (19 Dec)—54. *Designs previously used for King George VI issue, but with portrait of Queen Elizabeth II, as in T 28. Portrait faces left on ½d., 4d., 6d., 1s. and 5s. Wmk Mult Script CA. P 12 × 11½ (vert) or 11½ × 12 (horiz).*
153		½d. yellow-brown and scarlet (1.4.53)			10	10
	a.	Bistre-brown and scarlet (7.4.54)			10	20
154		1d. deep blue (1.3.54)			30	10
155		1½d. emerald-green (1.4.53)			30	1·25
156		2d. chocolate (1.3.54)			30	10
157		2½d. scarlet			35	35
158		3d. magenta (1.4.53)			50	10
159		4d. blue (1.4.53)			30	30
160		6d. black and orange (1.3.54)			30	15
161		1s. black and orange-red (1.3.54)			30	15
162		2s. brown-olive and carmine (1.3.54)			11·00	85
163		5s. purple and black (1.3.54)			17·00	5·00
164		10s. black and olive-green (1.3.54)			14·00	12·00
153/64				*Set of 12*	40·00	18·00

Designs: *Horiz*—½d. Map showing position of Gold Coast; 1d. Christiansborg Castle; 1½d. Emblem of Joint Provincial Council; 3d. Manganese mine; 4d. Lake Bosumtwi; 1s. Breaking cocoa pods; 2s. Trooping the colour; 5s. Surfboats. *Vert*—2d. Talking drums; 6d. Cocoa farmer; 10s. Forest.

Nos. 153/4 exist in coils constructed from normal sheets.

1953 (2 June). *Coronation. As No. 120 of Antigua, but ptd by B.W.*
165		2d. black and sepia			60	10

Gold Coast became the Dominion of Ghana on 6 March 1957.

GHANA

DOMINION

*CANCELLED REMAINDERS. In 1961 remainders of some issues of 1957 to 1960 were put on the market cancelled-to-order in such a way as to be indistinguishable from genuine postally used copies for all practical purposes. Our used quotations which are indicated by an asterisk are the same for cancelled-to-order or post-ally used copies.

29 Dr. Kwame Nkrumah, Palm-
nut Vulture and Map of Africa

GHANA
INDEPENDENCE
6TH MARCH,
1957.
(30)

(Photo Harrison)

1957 (6 Mar). *Independence. Wmk Mult Script CA. P 14 × 14½.*
166	29	2d. scarlet			10	10*
167		2½d. green			10	15*
168		4d. brown			10	15*
169		1s. 3d. deep blue			15	15*
166/9				*Set of 4*	40	45*

1957 (6 Mar)—58. *Nos. 153a/64 of Gold Coast optd as T 30.*
170		½d. bistre-brown and scarlet			10	10*
	a.	Olive-brown and scarlet			10	10*
171		1d. deep blue (R.)			10	10*
172		1½d. emerald-green			10	10*
173		2d. chocolate (26.5.58)			30	30
174		2½d. scarlet (26.5.58)			1·00	1·25
175		3d. magenta			30	10*
176		4d. blue (26.5.58)			3·75	6·00
177		6d. black and orange (R.)			10	10*
	a.	Opt double			†	£275
178		1s. black and orange-red			10	10*

179		2s. brown-olive and carmine			60	10*
180		5s. purple and black			75	10*
181		10s. black and olive-green			75	60*
170/81				*Set of 12*	7·00	7·50*

Nos. 173/4 and 176 were officially issued on 26 May 1958 although, in error, small quantities were sold at certain post offices when the rest of the set appeared.

Nos. 170 and 171 exist in coils constructed from normal sheets.

31 Viking Ship

(Des W. Wind. Recess E. A. Wright Bank Note Co., Philadelphia)

1957 (27 Dec). *Inauguration of Black Star Shipping Line. T 31 and similar horiz designs. No wmk. P 12.*
182		2½d. emerald-green			70	20
	a.	Imperf between (vert pair)			£350	
	b.	Imperf between (horiz pair)			£350	
183		1s. 3d. deep blue			1·00	1·25
	a.	Imperf horiz (vert pair)			£400	
184		5s. bright purple			1·50	3·00
	a.	Imperf vert (horiz pair)			£475	
182/4				*Set of 3*	2·75	4·00

Designs:—1s. 3d. Galleon; 5s. M.V. *Volta River.*

PRINTERS. Nos. 185/MS568 were printed in photogravure by Harrison & Sons *except where otherwise stated.*

34 Ambassador Hotel, Accra   35 Ghana Coat of Arms

1958 (6 Mar). *First Anniv of Independence. T 34/5 and similar designs. Wmk Mult Script CA. P 14½ × 14 (2s.) or 14 × 14½ (others).*
185		½d. black, red, yellow, green and carmine			10	10
186		2½d. black, red, green and yellow			10	10
187		1s. 3d. black, red, yellow, green and blue			30	10
188		2s. red, yellow, blue, green, brown and black			45	35
185/8				*Set of 4*	75	45

Designs: *Horiz as T 34*—2½d. State Opening of Parliament; 1s. 3d. National Monument.

38 Map showing the   39 Map of Africa and
Independent   Flaming Torch
African States

(Des R. Milton)

1958 (15 Apr). *First Conference of Independent African States, Accra. Wmk Mult Script CA. P 13½ × 14½ (2½d., 3d) or 14½ × 13½ (others).*
189	38	2½d. black, bistre and bright carmine-red			10	10
190		3d. black, bistre, brown and bright green			10	10
191	39	1s. black, yellow, red and dull blue			20	10
192		2s. 6d. black, yellow, red and dull violet			40	35
189/92				*Set of 4*	60	40

40 Palm-nut Vulture   41 Bristol 175 Britannia 309
over Globe   Airliner

(Des M. Goaman (2½d., 2s. 6d.), R. Milton (1s. 3d.), W. Wind (2s.))

1958 (15 July). *Inauguration of Ghana Airways. T 40/1 and similar designs. Wmk Mult Script CA. P 15 × 14 (2s. 6d.) or 14 × 15 (others).*
193		2½d. black, yellow-bistre & rose-carmine			45	10
194		1s. 3d. multicoloured			90	20
195		2s. multicoloured			1·00	55
196		2s. 6d. black and bistre			1·00	95
193/6				*Set of 4*	3·00	1·60

Designs: *Horiz (as T 41)*—2s. Boeing 377 Stratocruiser and Yellow-nosed Albatross. (*As T 40*)—2s. 6d. Palm-nut Vulture and Vickers VC-10 aircraft.

**PRIME
MINISTER'S
VISIT,
U.S.A. AND
CANADA**

(44)   45

1958 (18 July). *Prime Minister's Visit to the United States and Canada. Nos. 166/9 optd with T 44.*

197	29	2d. scarlet	..	..	..	10	10
198		2½d. green	..	..	..	10	10
199		4d. brown	..	..	..	10	15
200		1s. 3d. deep blue	..	..	..	15	25
197/200				*Set of 4*		30	45

(Des W. Wind)

1958 (24 Oct). *United Nations Day. Wmk Mult Script CA. P 14 × 14½.*

201	45	2½d. purple-brown, green and black			10	10
202		1s. 3d. purple-brown, blue and black			20	10
203		2s. 6d. purple-brown, violet and black			25	35
201/3				*Set of 3*	40	45

46 Dr. Nkrumah and   47
Lincoln Statue, Washington

(Des M. Goaman)

1959 (12 Feb). *150th Birth Anniv of Abraham Lincoln. W 47. P 14 × 14½.*

204	46	2½d. pink and deep purple		..	10	10
205		1s. 3d. light blue and blue			15	10
206		2s. 6d. orange-yellow & dp olive-green			20	20
204/6	..			*Set of 3*	30	30
MS206a		102 × 77 mm. Nos. 204/6. Imperf	.		55	1·75

48 Kente Cloth and Traditional Symbols

(Des Mrs. T. Sutherland (½d.), M. Karoly (2½d.), K. Antubam (1s. 3d.), A. M. Medina (2s.))

1959 (6 Mar). *Second Anniv of Independence. T 48 and similar multicoloured designs. W 47. P 14½ × 14 (2s.) or 14 × 14½ (others).*

207		½d. Type 48	..	..	10	10
208		2½d. Talking drums and elephant-horn blower			10	10
209		1s. 3d."Symbol of Greeting" (*vert*)			15	10
210		2s. Map of Africa, Ghana flag and palms			30	80
207/10				*Set of 4*	50	90

52 Globe and Flags

(Des Mrs. H. Potter)

1959 (15 Apr). *Africa Freedom Day. W 47 (sideways). P 14½ × 14.*

211	52	2½d. multicoloured		15	10
212		8½d. multicoloured		15	20

53 "God's Omnipotence"   **54** Nkrumah Statue,
                                          Accra

55 Ghana Timber   56 Volta River

65a Red-fronted Gazelle

Two Types of ½d. and 3d:

I. Inscr "GOD'S OMNIPOTENCE"
II. Inscr "GYE NYAME"

(Des Mrs. T. Sutherland (½d., 3d.), Ghana Information Bureau (source of 1d. and 2d.), O. Haulkland (1½d.), A. Medina (2½d., 4d.), M. Goaman (6d., 1s. 3d., 2s. 6d.), W. Wind (11d., 1s., 2s., 5s.), W. H. Brown (10s.), M. Shamir (£1)).

1959 (5 Oct)–**61**. *T 53/6, 65a, and similar multicoloured designs. W 47 (sideways on horiz designs). P 11½ × 12 (½d.), 12 × 11½ (1d.), 14 × 14½ (1½d.), 11d., 1s., 2s. and 5s.), 14 × 15 (10s.) or 14½ × 14 (others). (a) Postage.*

213		½d. Type 53 (I)	..	..	10	10
		a. Type II (29.4.61)	..	..	30	10
214		1d. Type 54	..	..	10	10
215		1½d. Type 55	..	..	10	10
216		2d. Type 56	..	..	10	10
217		2½d. Cocoa bean	..	..	10	10
218		3d. "God's Omnipotence" (I)	..		10	10
		a. Type II (29.4.61)	..	..	30	10
219		4d. Diamond and Mine	..	..	4·50	65
220		6d. Red-crowned Bishop	..		50	10
		a. Green (flag) omitted	..		65·00	
221		11d. Golden Spider Lily	..		25	10
222		1s. Shell Ginger	..	..	25	10
223		2s. 6d. Great Blue Turaco	..		2·25	15
224		5s. Tiger Orchid	..	..	5·50	50
225		10s. Jewel Cichlid	..	..	2·00	70
225a		£1 Type 65a (29.4.61)	..		12·00	4·75

(b) Air

226		1s. 3d. Pennant-winged Nightjar		2·00	10
227		2s. Crowned Cranes	..		1·75	10
213/27				*Set of 16*	28·00	6·00

Nos. 217/224 and 226/7 are as Types 55/6, the 11d., 1s., 5s. and 2s. (air) being vertical and the remainder horizontal. No. 225 is as Type 65a.

68 Gold Cup and West African Map

(Des K. Lehmann (½d., 3d.), M. & G. Shamir (1d.), W. Wind (8d.), and K. Antubam (2s. 6d.))

1959 (15 Oct). *West African Football Competition, 1959. T 68 and similar multicoloured designs. W 47 (sideways on horiz designs). P 14 × 14½ (1d., 2s. 6d) or 14½ × 14 (others).*

228		½d. Type 68	..	..	10	10*
229		1d. Footballers (*vert*)	..		10	10*
230		3d. Goalkeeper saving ball	..		15	10*
231		8d. Forward attacking goal	..		70	15*
232		2s. 6d. "Kwame Nkrumah" Gold Cup (*vert*)		1·00	15*
228/32				*Set of 5*	1·75	40*

73 The Duke of Edinburgh
and Arms of Ghana

(Des A. S. B. New)

1959 (24 Nov). *Visit of the Duke of Edinburgh to Ghana. W 47 (sideways). P 15 × 14.*

233	73	3d. black and magenta	..	30	10*

74 Ghana Flag and Talking   **75** Ghana Flag and
           Drums   U.N. Emblem

(Des K. Antubam (2s. 6d.), A. Medina (others))

1959 (10 Dec). *United Nations Trusteeship Council. T 74/5 and similar multicoloured designs. W 47 (sideways on 3d.). P 14½ × 14 (3d.) or 14 × 14½ (others).*

234		3d. Type 74	..	..	10	10*
235		6d. Type 75	..	..	10	10*
236		1s. 3d. Ghana flag and U.N. emblem (*vert*)		30	15*
237		2s. 6d. "Totem Pole" (*vert*)		40	15*
234/7				*Set of 4*	75	45*

78 Eagles in Flight   **79** Fireworks

(Des A. Medina (½d.), M. Goaman (3d.), W. Wind (1s. 3d., 2s.))

1960 (6 Mar). *Third Anniv of Independence. T 78/9 and similar vert designs. Multicoloured. W 47. P 14 × 14½.*

238		½d. Type 78	..	..	10	10*
239		3d. Type 79	..	..	10	10*
240		1s. 3d. "Third Anniversary"	..		30	10*
241		2s. "Ship of State"	..		30	15*
238/41				*Set of 4*	70	30*

82 "A" of National Flags

(Des W. Wind)

1960 (15 Apr). *Africa Freedom Day. T 82 and similar horiz designs. Multicoloured. W 47 (sideways). P 14½ × 14.*

242		3d. Type 82	..	..	10	10*
243		6d. Letter "f"	..	..	20	10*
244		1s. Letter "d"	..	..	20	10*
242/4				*Set of 3*	40	20*

REPUBLIC

85 President Nkrumah

(Des A. Medina (3d., 10s.), W. Wind (1s. 3d., 2s.))

1960 (1 July). *Republic Day. T 85 and similar multicoloured designs. W 47. P 14½ × 14 (10s.) or 14 × 14½ (others).*

245		3d. Type 85	..	..	10	10
246		1s. 3d. Ghana flag	..		30	10
247		2s. Torch of Freedom	..		40	20
248		10s. Arms of Ghana (*horiz*)	..		90	1·25
245/8				*Set of 4*	1·50	1·50
MS248a		102 × 77 mm. Nos. 245/8. Imperf		40	1·25

89 Olympic Torch   **90** Athlete

(Des A. Medina (T 89), W. Wind (T 90))

1960 (15 Aug). *Olympic Games. W 47 (sideways on T 90). P 14 × 14½ (T 89) or 14½ × 14 (T 90).*

249	89	3d. multicoloured	..	..	10	10
250		6d. multicoloured	..		15	10
251	90	1s. 3d. multicoloured	..		25	10
252		2s. 6d. multicoloured	..		35	30
249/52				*Set of 4*	70	40

91 President Nkrumah   **94** U.N. Emblem and
                                     Ghana Flag

(Des M. Goaman (3d., 6d.), W. Wind (1s. 3d.))

1960 (21 Sept). *Founder's Day. T* **91** *and similar multicoloured designs.* W **47** *(sideways on* 3d.)*. P* 14½ × 14 (3d.) *or* 14 × 14½ *(others).*

253	3d.	Type **91**		10	10
254	6d.	President Nkrumah (*vert*)		10	10
255	1s. 3d.	Flag-draped column over map of African (*vert*)		20	20
253/5 ..			*Set of 3*	30	30

(Des M. Goaman (3d., 1s. 3d.), W. Wind (6d.))

1960 (10 Dec). *Human Rights Day. T* **94** *and similar vert designs.* W **47**. *P* 14 × 14½.

256	3d.	multicoloured		10	10
257	6d.	yellow, black and blue		20	10
258	1s. 3d.	multicoloured		40	30
256/8 ..			*Set of 3*	60	40

Designs:—6d. U.N. emblem and Torch; 1s. 3d. U.N. emblem.

97 Talking Drums   **100** Eagle on Column

(Des M. Goaman (3d.), A. S. B. New (6d.), W. Wind (2s.))

1961 (15 Apr). *Africa Freedom Day. T* **97** *and similar designs.* W **47** *(sideways on* 2s.)*. P* 14½ × 14 (2s.) *or* 14 × 14½ *(others).*

259	3d.	multicoloured		10	10
260	6d.	red, black and green		20	10
261	2s.	multicoloured		50	45
259/61 ..			*Set of 3*	70	50

Designs: *Vert.*—6d. Map of Africa. *Horiz.*—2s. Flags and map.

(Des A. S. B. New (3d.), M. Shamir (1s. 3d.), W. Wind (2s.))

1961 (1 July). *First Anniv of Republic. T* **100** *and similar vert designs. Multicoloured.* W **47**. *P* 14 × 14½.

262	3d.	Type **100**		10	10
263	1s. 3d.	"Flower"		10	10
264	2s.	Ghana flags		20	60
262/4 ..			*Set of 3*	30	70

103 Dove with Olive Branch   **106** Pres. Nkrumah and Globe

(Des V. Whiteley)

1961 (1 Sept). *Belgrade Conference. T* **103** *and similar designs.* W **47** *(sideways on* 1s. 3d., 5s.)*. P* 14 × 14½ (3d.) *or* 14½ × 14 *(others).*

265	3d.	yellow-green		10	10
266	1s. 3d.	deep blue		15	10
267	5s.	bright reddish purple		60	50
265/7 ..			*Set of 3*	70	55

Designs: *Horiz.*—1s. 3d. World map, chain and olive branch; 5s. Rostrum, conference room.

(Des A. Medina (3d.), M. Goaman (1s. 3d.), Miriam Karoly (5s.))

1961 (21 Sept). *Founder's Day. T* **106** *and similar multicoloured designs.* W **47** *(sideways on* 3d.)*. P* 14½ × 14 (3d.) *or* 14 × 14½ *(others).*

268	3d.	Type **106**		10	10
269	1s. 3d.	President and Kente Cloth (*vert*)		35	10
270	5s.	President in national costume (*vert*)		1·50	2·50
268/70 ..			*Set of 3*	1·75	2·50

MS270*a* Three sheets 106 × 86 mm (3d.) or 86 × 106 mm (1s. 3d.) each with Nos. 268/70 in block of four. Imperf   *Three sheets*   5·50   14·00

The 1s. 3d. Miniature Sheet is known with the brown colour omitted.

109 Queen Elizabeth II and African Map

(Des M. Goaman)

1961 (9 Nov). *Royal Visit.* W **47**. *P* 14½ × 14.

271	109	3d. multicoloured		15	10
272		1s. 3d. multicoloured		75	20
273		5s. multicoloured		2·50	3·50
271/3 ..			*Set of 3*	3·00	3·50

MS273*a* 106 × 84 mm. No. 273 in block of four. Imperf   4·50   8·50

110 Ships in Tema Harbour

(Des C. Bottiau. Litho Enschedé & Sons)

1962 (10 Feb). *Opening of Tema Harbour. T* **110** *and similar horiz designs. Multicoloured. No wmk. P* 14 × 13. (*a*) *Postage.*

274	3d.	Type **110**		15	10

(*b*) *Air*

275	1s. 3d.	Douglas DC-8 aircraft and ships at Tema		80	15
276	2s. 6d.	As 1s. 3d.		1·00	1·50
274/6 ..			*Set of 3*	1·75	1·50

112 Africa and Peace Dove   **113** Compass over Africa

(Des R. Hegeman. Litho Enschedé)

1962 (6 Mar). *First Anniv of Casablanca Conference. No wmk. P* 13 × 14. (*a*) *Postage.*

277	112	3d. multicoloured		10	10

(*b*) *Air*

278	112	1s. 3d. multicoloured		30	15
279		2s. 6d. multicoloured		40	85
277/9 ..			*Set of 3*	70	95

(Des R. Hegeman)

1962 (24 Apr). *Africa Freedom Day.* W **47**. *P* 14 × 14½.

280	113	3d. sepia, blue-green and reddish purple	10	10
281		6d. sepia, blue-green and orange-brown	10	15
282		1s. 3d. sepia, blue-green and red	15	15
280/2 ..			*Set of 3*	30	30

114 Ghana Star and "Five Continents"   **115** Atomic Bomb-burst "Skull"

(Des M. Goaman (3d.), M. Shamir (6d.), W. Wind (1s. 3d.))

1962 (21 June). *Accra Assembly, T* **114/15** *and similar vert design.* W **47**. *P* 14 × 14½.

283	3d.	black and lake-red		10	10
284	6d.	black and scarlet..		25	30
285	1s. 3d.	turquoise		30	35
283/5 ..			*Set of 3*	55	60

Design:—1s. 3d. Dove of Peace.

117 Patrice Lumumba   **118** Star over Two Columns

(Des A. S. B. New)

1962 (30 June). *1st Death Anniv of Lumumba.* W **47**. *P* 14½ × 14.

286	117	3d. black and orange-yellow		10	10
287		6d. black, green and lake		10	30
288		1s. 3d. black, pink and black-green		15	35
286/8 ..			*Set of 3*	30	60

(Des A. S. B. New (3d.), A. Medina (6d.), M. Goaman (1s. 3d.) Litho Enschedé)

1962 (1 July). *2nd Anniv of Republic. T* **118** *and similar multicoloured designs. P* 14 × 13½ (1s. 3d.) *or* 13½ × 14 *(others).*

289	3d.	Type **118**		10	10
290	6d.	Flaming torch		20	30
291	1s. 3d.	Eagle trailing flag (*horiz*)		40	55
289/91 ..			*Set of 3*	60	80

121 President Nkrumah   **125** Campaign Emblem

(Litho Enschedé)

1962 (21 Sept). *Founder's Day. T* **121** *and similar vert designs. P* 13 × 14½.

292	1d.	multicoloured		10	10
293	3d.	multicoloured		10	10
294	1s. 3d.	black and bright blue		30	15
295	2s.	multicoloured		30	40
292/5 ..			*Set of 4*	70	60

Designs:—3d. Nkrumah medallion; 1s. 3d. President Nkrumah and Ghana Star; 2s. Laying "Ghana" Brick.

1962 (3 Dec). *Malaria Eradication.* W **47**. *P* 14 × 14½.

296	125	1d. cerise		15	10
297		4d. yellow-green		50	90
298		6d. bistre		50	20
299		1s. 3d. bluish violet		60	80
296/9 ..			*Set of 4*	1·60	1·75
MS299*a*	90 × 115 mm. Nos. 296/9. Imperf			75	1·50

126 Campaign Emblem   **129** Map of Africa

1963 (21 Mar). *Freedom from Hunger. T* **126** *and similar designs.* W **47** *(sideways on* 4d., 1s. 3d.)*. P* 14 × 14½ (1d.) *or* 14½ × 14 *(others).*

300	1d.	multicoloured		15	10
301	4d.	sepia, yellow and orange..		75	45
302	1s. 3d.	ochre, black and green		1·60	80
300/2 ..			*Set of 3*	2·25	1·75

Designs: *Horiz*—4d. Emblem in hands; 1s. 3d. World map and emblem.

1963 (15 Apr). *Africa Freedom Day. T* **129** *and similar designs.* W **47** *(sideways on* 4d.)*. P* 14½ × 14 (4d.) *or* 14 × 14½ *(others).*

303	1d.	gold and red		10	10
304	4d.	red, black and yellow		10	10
305	1s. 3d.	multicoloured		35	10
306	2s. 6d.	multicoloured		50	1·25
303/6 ..			*Set of 4*	85	1·40

Designs: *Horiz*—4d. Carved stool. *Vert*—1s. 3d. Map and bowl of fire; 2s. 6d. Topi (antelope) and flag.

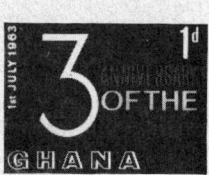

133 Red Cross   **137** "3rd Anniversary"

(Des R. Hegeman (4d.), M. Shamir (others))

1963 (28 May). *Red Cross Centenary. T* **133** *and similar multicoloured designs.* W **47** *(sideways on* 1½d., 4d.)*. P* 14½ × 14 (1d., 1s. 3d.) *or* 14 × 14½ *(others).*

307	1d.	Type **133**		60	15
308	1½d.	Centenary emblem (*horiz*)		90	1·25
309	4d.	Nurses and child (*horiz*)		2·25	20
310	1s. 3d.	Emblem, globe and laurel		3·50	2·00
307/10 ..			*Set of 4*	6·50	3·25
MS310*a*	102 × 127 mm. Nos. 307/10. Imperf			3·25	11·00

(Des M. Goaman (1d., 4d.), R. Hegeman (others))

1963 (1 July). *3rd Anniv of Republic. T* **137** *and similar multicoloured designs.* W **47** *(sideways on* 1d., 4d.)*. P* 14 × 14½ (*horiz*) *or* 14 × 14½ (*vert*).

311	1d.	Type **137**		10	10
312	4d.	Three Ghanaian flags		10	10
		a. Black (stars on flag) omitted		†	£300
313	1s. 3d.	Map, flag and star (*vert*)		35	15
314	2s. 6d.	Flag and torch (*vert*)		55	1·50
311/14 ..			*Set of 4*	1·00	1·50

141 President Nkrumah
and Ghana Flag

145 Rameses II,
Abu Simbel

(Des R. Hegeman (1d., 4d.), M. Shamir (1s. 3d.), G. Rose (5s.))

1963 (21 Sept). *Founder's Day. T* **141** *and similar designs. W* **47**
(sideways on 1s. 3d., 5s.). P 14 × 14½ *(vert) or* 14½ × 14 *(horiz).*

315	1d. multicoloured	..	10	10
316	4d. multicoloured	..	15	10
317	1s. 3d. multicoloured	..	30	10
	a. Green omitted	..	60·00	
318	5s. yellow and bright reddish purple		65	75
315/18		*Set of 4*	1·00	80

Designs: *Vert.*—4d. Nkrumah and flag. *Horiz.*—1s. 3d. Nkrumah
and fireworks; 5s. Symbol of Wisdom.

(Des M. Farrar Bell and R. Hegeman. Litho (1½d., 2d.) or photo
(others) Enschedé)

1963 (1 Nov). *Nubian Monuments Preservation. T* **145** *and
similar multicoloured designs. No wmk. P* 11½ × 11 *(vert) or*
11 × 11½ *(horiz).*

319	1d. Type **145**	..	15	10
320	1½d. Rock paintings *(horiz)*	..	20	65
321	2d. Queen Nefertari *(horiz)*	..	20	10
322	4d. Sphinx, Sebua	..	35	15
323	1s. 3d. Rock Temple, Abu Simbel *(horiz)*		80	90
319/23		*Set of 5*	1·60	1·75

150
Steam and Diesel Locomotives

151
Eleanor Roosevelt and
"Flame of Freedom"

(Des H. L. W. Stevens)

1963 (1 Dec). *60th Anniv of Ghana Railway. W* **47** *(sideways).*
P 14½ × 14.

324	**150**	1d. multicoloured	10	10
325		6d. multicoloured	60	10
326		1s. 3d. multicoloured	1·25	60
327		2s. 6d. multicoloured	2·25	2·25
324/7		*Set of 4*	3·75	2·75

(Des R. Hegeman and F. H. Savage. Photo Enschedé)

1963 (10 Dec). *15th Anniv of Declaration of Human Rights. T* **151**
and similar multicoloured designs. No wmk. P 11 × 11½ *(1s. 3d.)*
or 11½ × 11 *(others).*

328	1d. Type **151**	..	10	10
329	4d. Type **151**	..	10	10
330	6d. Eleanor Roosevelt	..	10	10
331	1s. 3d. Eleanor Roosevelt and emblems *(horiz)*		15	15
328/31		*Set of 4*	30	30

No. 329 differs from No. 328 in the arrangement of the trailing
"flame" and of the background within the circular emblem.

154 Sun and Globe
Emblem

155 Harvesting Corn on State
Farm

1964 (15 June). *International Quiet Sun Years. W* **47** *(sideways).*
Each blue, yellow, red and green; background colours given.
P 14½.

332	**154**	3d. pale brown	15	10
333		6d. pale grey	25	10
334		1s. 3d. mauve	25	15
332/4		*Set of 3*	60	30
MS334a	90 × 90 mm. No. 334 in block of four.			
	Imperf		70	2·50

Nos. 332/4 each exist in a miniature sheet of 12 in different
colours (i.e. 3d. in colours of 6d.; 6d. in colours of 1s. 3d.; 1s. 3d. in
colours of 3d.) but these were not generally available to the public.

(Des M. Shamir. Photo Govt Printer, Israel)

1964 (1 July). *4th Anniv of Republic. T* **155** *and similar horiz*
designs. P 13 × 14.

335	3d. olive, brown and yellow-olive		10	10
336	6d. bluish green, brown and turquoise-green		10	10
337	1s. 3d. brown-red, brown and salmon-red		10	10
338	5s. multicoloured		40	70
335/8		*Set of 4*	55	75
MS338a	126 × 100 mm. Nos. 335/8. Imperf		55	2·00
	ab. Olive (central design and face value of 3d.) omitted			

Designs:—6d. Oil refinery, Tema; 1s. 3d. "Communal Labour";
5s. Procession headed by flag.

159 Globe and Dove

163 Pres. Nkrumah and
Hibiscus Flowers

(Des M. Shamir. Litho Lewin-Epstein Ltd, Bat Yam, Israel)

1964 (15 July). *1st Anniv of African Unity Charter. T* **159** *and*
similar designs. P 14.

339	3d. multicoloured	..	10	10
340	6d. deep bronze-green and red	..	10	10
341	1s. 3d. multicoloured	..	15	10
342	5s. multicoloured	..	45	70
339/42		*Set of 4*	65	75

Designs: *Vert.*—6d. Map of Africa and quill pen; 5s. Planting
flower. *Horiz.*—1s. 3d. Hitched rope on map of Africa.

1964 (21 Sept). *Founder's Day. W* **47** *(sideways). P* 14 × 14½.

343	**163**	3d. sepia, red, deep green and light blue	10	10
344		6d. sepia, red, deep green and yellow	15	10
345		1s. 3d. sepia, red, deep green and grey	35	10
346		2s. 6d. sepia, red, dp grn & light emerald	50	60
343/6		*Set of 4*	1·00	70
MS346a	90 × 122 mm. No. 346 in block of four.			
	Imperf		70	2·50

IMPERFORATE STAMPS. Many issues, including miniature
sheets, from here onwards exist imperforate, but these were not
sold at post offices.

164 Hurdling

(Des A. S. B. New (No. 352))

1964 (25 Oct). *Olympic Games, Tokyo. T* **164** *and similar*
multicoloured designs. W **47** *(sideways on* 1d., 2½d., 6d., 5s.).
P 14½ × 14 *(horiz) or* 14 × 14½ *(vert).*

347	1d. Type **164**	..	10	10
348	2½d. Running	..	10	85
349	3d. Boxing *(vert)*	..	10	10
350	4d. Long-jumping *(vert)*	..	10	10
351	6d. Football *(vert)*	..	15	10
352	1s. 3d. Athlete holding Olympic Torch *(vert)*		20	10
353	5s. Olympic Rings and flags	..	85	3·25
347/53		*Set of 7*	1·40	4·00
MS353a	128 × 102 mm. Nos. 351/3. Imperf		75	2·50

171 G. Washington Carver
(botanist) and Plant

173 African Elephant

(Des M. Shamir)

1964 (7 Dec). *U.N.E.S.C.O. Week. W* **47**. *P* 14½.

354	**171**	6d. deep blue and green	15	10
355	—	1s. 3d. reddish purple & greenish blue	75	10
		w. Wmk inverted	11·00	
356	**171**	5s. sepia and orange-red	2·10	3·75
354/6		*Set of 3*	2·75	3·75
MS356a	127×77 mm. Nos. 354/6. Imperf		1·00	2·50

Design:—1s. 3d. Albert Einstein (scientist) and atomic
symbol.

(Des A. S. B. New (No. 360). Photo Enschedé)

1964 (14 Dec). *Multicoloured designs as T* **173**. *P* 11½ × 11 *(vert)*
or 11 × 11½ *(horiz).*

357	1d. Type **173**	..	50	50
358	1½d. Secretary Bird *(horiz)*		1·00	2·25
359	2½d. Purple Wreath (flower)		60	2·25
360	3d. Grey Parrot	..	1·50	10
361	4d. Blue-naped Mousebird *(horiz)*		1·50	70
362	6d. African Tulip Tree *(horiz)*		60	30
363	1s. 3d. Violet Starling *(horiz)*		1·75	1·25
364	2s. 6d. Hippopotamus *(horiz)*		1·75	5·50
357/64		*Set of 8*	8·25	12·00
MS364a	(a) 150×86 mm. Nos. 357/9. (b)			
	150×110 mm. Nos. 360/4. Imperf *Set of 2 sheets*		5·50	14·00

NEW INFORMATION

The editor is always interested to correspond with
people who have new information that will
improve or correct the Catalogue.

181 I.C.Y. Emblem

182 I.T.U. Emblem and
Symbols

(Litho Enschedé)

1965 (22 Feb). *International Co-operation Year. P* 14 × 12½.

365	**181**	1d. multicoloured	35	50
366		4d. multicoloured	1·25	85
367		6d. multicoloured	1·50	50
368		1s. 3d. multicoloured	1·75	2·50
365/8		*Set of 4*	4·25	4·00
MS368a	100 × 100 mm. No. 368 in block of four.			
	Imperf		2·50	5·00

(Litho Enschedé)

1965 (12 Apr). *I.T.U. Centenary. P* 13½.

369	**182**	1d. multicoloured	15	15
370		6d. multicoloured	55	15
371		1s. 3d. multicoloured	1·00	25
372		5s. multicoloured	2·25	2·75
369/72		*Set of 4*	3·50	3·00
MS372a	132 × 115 mm. Nos. 369/72. Imperf		4·50	8·00

183 Lincoln's Home

(Des M. Farrar Bell (6d.), A. S. B. New (1s. 3d., 5s.), R. Hegeman
(2s.))

1965 (17 May). *Death Centenary of Abraham Lincoln. T* **183** *and*
similar square-shaped designs. W **47** *(sideways). P* 12½.

373	6d. multicoloured		15	10
374	1s. 3d. black, red and blue		25	15
375	2s. black, orange-brown and greenish yellow		30	30
376	5s. black and red		70	1·50
373/6		*Set of 4*	1·25	1·75
MS376a	115 × 115 mm. Nos. 373/6. Imperf		1·25	3·50
	ab. Green (part of flag on 6d.) omitted			

Designs:—1s. 3d. Lincoln's Inaugural Address; 2s. Abraham
Lincoln; 5s. Adaptation of U.S. 90 c. Lincoln Stamp of 1869.

(New Currency. 100 pesewas = 1 cedi)

187 Obverse (Pres. Nkrumah) and Reverse
of 5 p. Coin

(Photo Enschedé)

1965 (19 July). *Introduction of Decimal Currency. T* **187** *and*
similar horiz designs. Multicoloured. P 11 × 13 (5 p., 10 p.),
13 × 12½ (25 p.) *or* 13½ × 14 (50 p.).

377	5 p. Type **187**	..	25	10
378	10 p. As Type **187**	..	30	10
379	25 p. Size 63 × 39 mm	..	1·00	1·00
380	50 p. Size 71 × 43½ mm	..	2·00	2·25
377/80		*Set of 4*	3·25	3·00

The coins in Nos. 378/80 are all circular and express the same
denominations as on the stamps.

¢2·40

*Ghana New Currency
19th July. 1965.*

(188)

1965 (19 July). *Nos.* 214, 216 *and* 218a/27 *surch as T* **188** *diagon-*
ally upwards, (D) *or horizontally,* (H), *by Govt Printer, Accra.*

(a) Postage

381	1 p. on 1d. multicoloured (R.) (D)	..	10	10
	a. Surch inverted	..	15·00	
	b. Surch double	..	45·00	
382	2 p. on 2d. multicoloured (Ultram.) (H)	..	10	10
	a. Surch inverted			
	b. Surch double	..	10·00	
	c. Surch on back only	..		
	d. Surch on front and back	..		
	e. Red surch	..	26·00	
	f. Orange surch	..	26·00	
	g. Indigo surch	..		
	ga. Surch sideways			

383	3 p. on 3d. multicoloured (II) (Br.) (H)		95	4·25	
	a. Surch inverted		18·00		
	b. Indigo surch				
384	4 p. on 4d. multicoloured (B.) (H)		3·25	45	
	a. Surch inverted		30·00		
	b. Surch double				
	c. Red surch				
385	6 p. on 6d. multicoloured (Blk.) (H)		50	10	
	a. Surch inverted		8·50		
	b. Surch double		15·00		
	c. Horiz pair, one without surch		50·00		
	d. Green (flag) omitted		60·00		
386	11 p. on 11d. multicoloured (W.) (D)		25	10	
	a. Surch inverted		11·00		
387	12 p. on 1s. multicoloured (B.) (D)		25	10	
	a. Surch double, one albino inverted				
	c. Black surch		9·00		
	ca. Surch inverted		9·00		
388	30 p. on 2s. 6d. multicoloured (B.) (H).		3·00	1·75	
389	60 p. on 5s. multicoloured (B.) (D)		4·50	70	
	a. Surch double (G. + B.)		25·00		
390	1 c. 20 on 10s. multicoloured (B.) (D)		1·00	2·25	
	a. Surch double (G. + B.)		85·00		
391	2 c. 40 on £1 multicoloured (B.) (D)		1·25	6·00	

(b) Air

392	15 p. on 1s. 3d. multicoloured (W.) (H)		2·00	50	
	a. Surch inverted				
393	24 p. on 2s. multicoloured (G.) (D)		2·50	30	
	a. Surch on front and back		25·00		
381/93		Set of 13	16·00	15·00	

On the diagonal surcharges the values are horizontal.

The 30 p. was not released in Ghana until 30 July and the 3 p. sometime later.

Numerous minor varieties exist.

189 "OAU" and Flag

190 "OAU", Heads and Flag

191 "OAU" Emblem and Flag

192 African Map and Flag

1965 (21 Oct). *O.A.U. Summit Conference, Accra. T **189/92** and similar horiz designs. Multicoloured. W 47 (sideways* except on 6p.). P 14 (T **189/91**) or 14½×14 (others).*

394	1 p. Type **189**		10	10	
	a. Red (part of flag) omitted		70·00		
395	2 p. Type **190**		10	10	
396	5 p. Type **191**		10	10	
397	6 p. Type **192**		10	10	
398	15 p. "Sunburst", map and flag		20	30	
399	24 p. "O.A.U." on map, and flag		35	60	
	w. Wmk top of G to left				
394/9		Set of 6	75	1·10	

*The 1 p. also exists with the watermark facing left or right, but positional blocks are required to show the two types. The normal sideways watermark has top of G to right, *as seen from the back of the stamp.*

195 Goalkeeper saving Ball

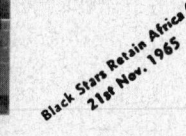

198 Pres. Kennedy and Grave Memorial

(Photo Enschedé)

1965 (15 Nov). *African Soccer Cup Competition. T **195** and similar multicoloured designs. P 13 × 14 (15 p.) or 14 × 13 (others).*

400	6 p. Type **195**		15	10	
401	15 p. Player with ball (*vert*)		25	25	
402	24 p. Players, ball and soccer cup		40	50	
400/2		Set of 3	70	75	

(Des A. S. B. New (No. 405))

1965 (15 Dec)–**66**. *2nd Anniv of President Kennedy's Death. T **198** and similar square-shaped designs. W 47 (sideways). P 12½.*

403	6 p. multicoloured		15	10	
404	15 p. violet, red and green		25	35	
405	24 p. black and reddish violet		30	60	
406	30 p. dull purple and black		40	75	
403/6		Set of 4	1·00	1·60	
MS407	114½ × 114 mm. Nos. 403/6. Imperf (21.3.66)		3·75	6·50	

Designs:—15 p. Pres. Kennedy and Eternal Flame; 24 p. Pres. Kennedy and memorial inscription; 30 p. President Kennedy.

202 Section of Dam and Generators   (206)

(Des A. S. B. New (No. 411). Photo Enschedé)

1966 (22 Jan). *Volta River Project. T **202** and similar horiz designs. P 11 × 11½.*

408	6 p. multicoloured		15	10	
409	15 p. multicoloured		20	15	
410	24 p. multicoloured		25	20	
411	30 p. black and new blue		35	50	
408/11		Set of 4	85	85	

Designs:—15 p. Dam and Lake Volta; 24 p. Word "GHANA" as dam; 30 p. "Fertility".

1966 (7 Feb). *"Black Stars" Victory in African Soccer Cup Competition. Nos. 400/2 optd with T **206**, in black.*

412	6 p. Type **195**		15	10	
	a. Green opt		20·00		
	b. Green opt double, one inverted				
	c. Stop after "Nov" omitted (R. 5/1)				
413	15 p. Player with ball		25	20	
414	24 p. Players, ball and cup		40	35	
	a. Opt inverted*		26·00		
	ab. Vert pair, one without opt, the other with opt inverted				
	b. Error. Opt for 15 p. on 24 p. inverted*				
	c. Stop after "Nov" omitted (R. 5/1)				
412/14		Set of 3	70	60	

*In No. 414a the overprint reads downwards (top right to bottom left), but in No. 414b it reads upwards (bottom right to top left).

DATES OF ISSUE of miniature sheets are approximate as they are generally released some time after the related ordinary stamps, but it is known that the G.P.O. sometimes applied first-day cancellations months after the dates shown on the cancellations.

207 W.H.O. Building and Ghana Flag

1966 (1 July). *Inauguration of W.H.O. Headquarters, Geneva. T **207** and similar horiz design. Multicoloured. W 47. P 14½ × 14.*

415	6 p. Type **207**		50	10	
416	15 p. Type **207**		1·25	65	
417	24 p. W.H.O. Building and emblem		1·40	1·10	
418	30 p. As 24 p.		1·60	2·00	
415/18		Set of 4	4·25	3·50	
MS419	120 × 101 mm. Nos. 415/18. Imperf (11.66)		17·00	18·00	

209 Atlantic Herring   214 African "Links" and Ghana Flag

(Des O. Hamann. Photo Enschedé)

1966 (10 Aug). *Freedom from Hunger. T **209** and similar horiz designs. Multicoloured. P 14 × 13.*

420	6 p. Type **209**		15	10	
421	15 p. Turbot		35	15	
422	24 p. Spadefish		65	35	
423	30 p. Red Snapper		80	90	
424	60 p. Blue-finned Tuna		2·00	3·25	
420/4		Set of 5	3·50	4·25	
MS425	126×109 mm. No. 423 in block of four. Imperf (Nov)		8·00	12·00	

(Photo Enschedé)

1966 (11 Oct). *Third Anniv of African Charter. T **214** and similar multicoloured designs. P 13½.*

426	6 p. Type **214**		15	10	
427	15 p. Flags as "Quill", and diamond (*horiz*)		35	40	
428	24 p. Ship's wheel, map and cocoa bean (*horiz*)		40	45	
426/8		Set of 3	80	80	

217 Player heading Ball, and Jules Rimet Cup

1966 (14 Nov). *World Cup Football Championships, England. T **217** and similar horiz designs. Multicoloured. W 47. P 14½ × 14.*

429	5 p. Type **217**		25	10	
430	15 p. Goalkeeper clearing ball		60	20	
	w. Wmk inverted		1·60		
431	24 p. Player and Jules Rimet Cup (replica)		75	35	
432	30 p. Players and Jules Rimet Cup (replica)		95	1·25	
433	60 p. Players with ball		1·75	4·00	
	w. Wmk inverted				
429/33		Set of 5	3·75	5·50	
MS434	120×102 mm. 60 p. (block of four). Imperf		19·00	19·00	

222 U.N.E.S.C.O. Emblem

1966 (23 Dec). *20th Anniv of U.N.E.S.C.O. W 47 (sideways). P 14½.*

435	**222** 5 p. multicoloured		25	15	
436	15 p. multicoloured		60	40	
437	24 p. multicoloured		90	85	
438	30 p. multicoloured		1·25	2·25	
439	60 p. multicoloured		2·25	4·75	
435/9		Set of 5	4·75	7·50	
MS440	140 × 115 mm. Nos. 435/9. Imperf		18·00	20·00	

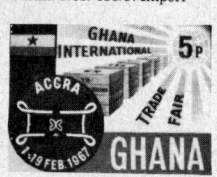

223 Fair Emblem and Crates

1967 (1 Feb). *Ghana Trade Fair, Accra. T **223** and similar multicoloured designs. W 47 (sideways on 24 p.). P 14 × 14½ (24 p.) or 14½ × 14 (others).*

441	5 p. Type **223**		10	10	
442	15 p. Fair emblem and world map		15	20	
443	24 p. Shipping and flags (*vert*)		25	30	
444	36 p. Fair emblem and hand-held hoist		40	1·60	
441/4		Set of 4	70	60	

(New Currency. 100 new pesewas = 1 new cedi (1·2 old cedi))

1½Np   N₡2.00

(227)   (228)   229 Ghana Eagle and Flag

1967 (23 Feb). *Nos. 216, 219/23, 225/6 and 393 surch as T **227/8**.*

(a) Postage

445	1½ n.p. on 2d. multicoloured (Blk.)		4·00	40	
446	3½ n.p. on 4d. multicoloured (R.)		3·50	85	
	a. Surch double, one sideways				
447	5 n.p. on 6d. multicoloured (R.)		1·25	20	

448	9 n.p. on 11d. multicoloured (W.)	..	30	20
449	10 n.p. on 1s. multicoloured (W.)	..	30	30
450	25 n.p. on 2s. 6d. multicoloured (R.)	..	3·50	4·50
451	1 n.c. on 10s. multicoloured (R.)	..	3·50	14·00
452	2 n.c. on £1 multicoloured (R.) ..	..	7·00	24·00

(b) Air

453	12½ n.p. on 1s. 3d. multicoloured (W.)		3·50	2·00
454	20 n.p. on 24 p. on 2s. multicoloured (R.)		3·50	3·00
445/54		*Set of 10*	27·00	48·00

Inverted surcharges in a different type face on the 3½, 5 and 25 n.p. are fakes.

(Des M. Shamir)

1967 (24 Feb). *First Anniv of February 24 Revolution. W 47 (sideways). P 14 × 14½.*

455	**229**	1 n.p. multicoloured	..	10	15
456		4 n.p. multicoloured	..	10	10
457		12½ n.p. multicoloured	..	40	60
458		25 n.p. multicoloured	..	85	2·25
455/8 ..			*Set of 4*	1·25	2·75
MS459	89 × 108 mm. Nos. 455/8. Perf or imperf			6·50	12·00

230 Maize

231 Forest Kingfisher

235 Rufous-crowned Roller

236 Akosombo Dam

1967 (1 June–4 Sept). *T 230/1, 235/6 and similar designs. W 47 (1½, 2, 4, 50 n.p. and 1 n.c.) or sideways (others). P 11½ × 12 (1, 8 n.p.), 12 × 11½ (4 n.p.), 14 × 14½ (1½, 2, 2½, 20 n.p., 2 n.c. 50) or 14½ × 14 (others).*

460	1 n.p. multicoloured	..	10	10
	a. Salmon omitted**	..		
461	1½ n.p. multicoloured	..	90	1·50
	a. Blue omitted*	..	75·00	
	b. Green printed double, once inverted†			
	c. Green omitted†	..		
462	2 n.p. multicoloured (4.9)	..	10	10
	a. Green (part of flag) omitted	..		
	b. Gold (frame) omitted	..		
	w. Wmk inverted	..	10·00	
463	2½ n.p. multicoloured (4.9)	..	35	10
	a. Wmk upright	..	10·00	
	ab. Face value omitted	..	£180	
464	3 n.p. multicoloured	..	20	40
	a. Green (part of flag) omitted	..		
465	4 n.p. multicoloured	..	1·50	10
	a. Green (part of flag) omitted	..	38·00	
	b. Red (part of flag) omitted	..		
	c. Black (star, bird markings and shadow) omitted	..	65·00	
466	6 n.p. multicoloured	..	15	30
467	8 n.p. multicoloured	..	15	10
468	9 n.p. multicoloured (4.9)	..	75	10
469	10 n.p. multicoloured	..	15	10
470	20 n.p. deep blue and new blue (4.9)	..	20	10
471	50 n.p. multicoloured	..	4·00	1·25
472	1 n.c. multicoloured (4.9.)	..	2·25	75
473	2 n.c. multicoloured (4.9.)	..	2·00	3·50
474	2 n.c. 50, multicoloured	..	3·50	7·50
460/74		*Set of 15*	14·50	14·00

Designs: *Vert (as T 231)*—2 n.p. The Ghana Mace; 2½ n.p. Commelina; 20 n.p. Bush Hare; 2 n.c. Frangipani; 2 n.c. 50, Seat of State. *Horiz (as T 236)*—3 n.p. West African Lungfish; 9 n.p. Chameleon; 10 n.p. Tema Harbour; 50 n.p. Black-winged Stilt; 1 n.c. Wooden Stool. *(As T 230)*—8 n.p. Adomi Bridge.

*In this stamp the blue not only affects the bird but is printed over the yellow background to give the value in green, so that its omission results in the value also being omitted.

**This affects the maize flowers, corn and foreground.

†This affects the feather-tips and the flag.

The 2 n.p. and 20 n.p. were officially issued on 4 September but small quanties of both were released in error on 1 June. The 2½ n.p. is also known to have been released in error in June.

245 Kumasi Fort

249 "Luna 10"

(Des O. Hamann)

1967 (1 July). *Castles and Forts. T 245 and similar designs. Multicoloured. W 47 (diagonal). P 14½.*

475	4 n.p. Type 245		25	10
476	12½ n.p. Christiansborg Castle and British galleon		1·00	1·00
477	20 n.p. Elmina Castle and Portuguese galleon		1·40	2·75
478	25 n.p. Cape Coast Castle and Spanish galleon		1·75	3·50
475/8 ..		*Set of 4*	4·00	6·50

(Des M. Shamir. Photo Enschedé)

1967 (16 Aug). *"Peaceful Use of Outer Space". T 249 and similar square designs. Multicoloured. P 13½ × 14.*

479	4 n.p. Type 249		10	10
480	10 n.p. "Orbiter 1"		10	30
481	12½ n.p. Man in Space		20	60
479/81		*Set of 3*	35	85
MS482	140 × 90 mm. Nos. 479/81. Imperf		1·25	2·75

252 Scouts and Camp-fire

(Photo Enschedé)

1967 (18 Sept). *50th Anniv of Ghanaian Scout Movement. T 252 and similar horiz designs. Multicoloured. P 14½ × 13.*

483	4 n.p. Type 252		20	10
484	10 n.p. Scout on march		50	40
485	12½ n.p. Lord Baden-Powell		70	1·50
483/5		*Set of 3*	1·25	1·75
MS486	167 × 95 mm. Nos. 483/5. Imperf ..		6·00	9·50

255 U.N. Headquarters Building

256 General View of U.N. H.Q., Manhattan

(Litho D.L.R.)

1967 (20 Nov). *United Nations Day (24 October). P 13½.*

487	**255**	4 n.p. multicoloured	10	10
488		10 n.p. multicoloured ..	10	15
489	**256**	50 n.p. multicoloured ..	30	70
490		2 n.c. 50, multicoloured	1·00	4·00
487/90		*Set of 4*	1·25	4·50
MS491	76 × 75 mm. No. 490. Imperf (4.12.67)		3·25	9·50

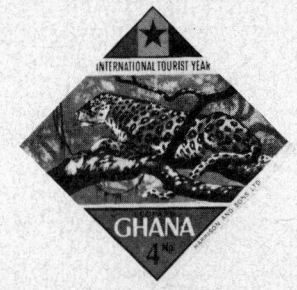

257 Leopard

1967 (28 Dec). *International Tourist Year. T 257 and similar diamond-shaped designs. Multicoloured. W 47 (diagonal). P 12½.*

492	4 n.p. Type 257 ..		80	20
493	12½ n.p. *Papilio demodocus* (butterfly)		2·00	1·50
494	20 n.p. Carmine Bee Eater		2·75	3·50
495	50 n.p. Waterbuck		3·00	6·50
492/5 ..		*Set of 4*	7·75	10·50
MS496	126 × 126 mm. Nos. 493/5. Imperf		15·00	16·00

261 Revolutionaries entering Accra

(Litho D.L.R.)

1968 (24 Feb). *2nd Anniv of February Revolution. T 261 and similar horiz designs. Multicoloured. P 14.*

497	4 n.p. Type 261		10	10
498	12½ n.p. Marching troops		20	20
499	20 n.p. Cheering people		30	40
500	40 n.p. Victory celebrations		50	1·25
497/500		*Set of 4*	1·00	1·75

265 Microscope and Cocoa Beans

1968 (18 Mar). *Cocoa Research. T 265 and similar horiz design. Multicoloured. W 47 (sideways). P 14½ × 14.*

501	2½ n.p. Type 265		10	40
502	4 n.p. Microscope and cocoa tree, beans and pods		10	10
503	10 n.p. Type 265		15	20
504	25 n.p. As 4 n.p.		60	1·10
501/4		*Set of 4*	80	1·50
MS505	102 × 102 mm. Nos. 501/4. Imperf		2·25	3·50

267 Kotoka and Flowers

271 Tobacco

(Des A. S. B. New (No. 508) and F. Mate (others) Litho D.L.R.)

1968 (17 Apr). *1st Death Anniv of Lt.-Gen. E. K. Kotoka. T 267 and similar multicoloured designs. P 14.*

506	4 n.p. Type 267		10	10
507	12½ n.p. Kotoka and wreath		20	30
508	20 n.p. Kotoka in civilian clothes		35	75
509	40 n.p. Lt.-Gen. Kotoka (*vert*)		50	1·60
506/9		*Set of 4*	1·00	2·50

(Des A. S. B. New (5 n.p.))

1968 (19 Aug). *Flora and Fauna. T 271 and similar vert designs. Multicoloured. W 47 (sideways). P 14 × 14½.*

510	4 n.p. Type 271 ..		15	10
511	5 n.p. North African Crested Porcupine		15	30
512	12½ n.p. Rubber		50	75
513	20 n.p. *Cymothoe sangaris* (butterfly)		2·25	2·75
514	40 n.p. *Charaxes ameliae* (butterfly)		2·50	4·50
510/14		*Set of 5*	5·00	7·50
MS515	88×114 mm. Nos. 510, 512/14. Imperf		3·50	8·00

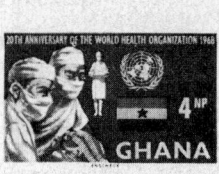

276 Surgeons, Flag and W.H.O. Emblem

277 Hurdling

(Photo Enschedé)

1968 (11 Nov). *20th Anniv of World Health Organization. P 14 × 13.*

516	**276**	4 n.p. multicoloured	..	25	10
517		12½ n.p. multicoloured	..	60	40
518		20 n.p. multicoloured	..	95	1·10
519		40 n.p. multicoloured	..	1·50	2·75
516/19			*Set of 4*	3·00	3·75
MS520	132 × 110 mm. Nos. 516/19. Imperf			3·75	6·50

1969 (10 Jan). *Olympic Games, Mexico (1968). T 277 and similar vert designs. Multicoloured. W 47 (sideways). P 14 × 14½.*

521	4 n.p. Type 277		10	10
522	12½ n.p. Boxing		20	30
523	20 n.p. Torch, Olympic Rings and flags		40	75
524	40 n.p. Football		70	2·50
521/4		*Set of 4*	1·25	3·25
MS525	89 × 114 mm. Nos. 521/4. Imperf (17.1.69)		3·50	6·00

281 U.N. Building

285 Dr. J. B. Danquah

(Litho D.L.R.)

1969 (1 Feb). *United Nations Day (1968). T 281 and similar square-shaped designs. Multicoloured. P 13½.*

526	4 n.p. Type 281		10	10
527	12½ n.p. Native stool, staff and U.N. emblem		15	25
528	20 n.p. U.N. building and emblem over Ghanaian flag		20	35
529	40 n.p. U.N. emblem encircled by flags		40	1·10
526/9		*Set of 4*	75	1·60
MS530	127 × 117 mm. No. 526/9. Imperf ..		75	3·25

1969 (7 Mar). *Human Rights Year. T 285 and similar horiz design. Multicoloured. W 47 (sideways on MS535). P 14½ × 14.*

531	4 n.p. Type 285		10	10
532	12½ n.p. Dr. Martin Luther King		20	35
533	20 n.p. As 12½ n.p.		35	75
534	40 n.p. Type 285		50	1·60
531/4		*Set of 4*	1·00	2·50
MS535	116 × 50 mm. Nos. 531/4. Imperf (17.4.69)		80	3·00

287 Constituent Assembly Building

1969 (10 Sept). *Third Anniv of the Revolution. T 287 and similar horiz design. W 47 (sideways on MS540). P 14½ × 14.*

536	4 n.p. Type 287		10	10
537	12½ n.p. Arms of Ghana		10	10
538	20 n.p. Type 287		15	15
539	40 n.p. As 12½ n.p.		20	35
536/9		*Set of 4*	40	60
MS540	114 × 89 mm. Nos. 536/9. Imperf		70	2·25

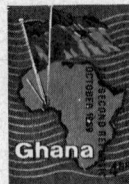

NEW CONSTITUTION
1969
(289)

290 Map of Africa and Flags

1969 (1 Oct). *New Constitution. Nos. 460/74 optd with T 289 in various positions by Government Press, Accra.*

541	1 n.p. multicoloured (Horiz)		10	1·00
542	1½ n.p. multicoloured (Vert down)		85	1·75
	a. Opt vert up		6·00	
	b. Horiz opt		25·00	
	ba. Opt omitted (in vert pair with normal)		£180	
543	2 n.p. multicoloured (Vert up)		10	1·25
	a. Opt vert down		5·00	
	b. Opt double		12·00	
544	2½ n.p. multicoloured (Vert up)		10	1·25
	a. Opt vert down		18·00	
545	3 n.p. multicoloured (Horiz)		60	1·50
	a. Opt inverted		15·00	
546	4 n.p. multicoloured (Y.) (Vert down)		2·00	30
	a. Black opt (vert down)		6·00	1·00
	b. Black opt (vert up)		10·00	
	c. Red opt (vert down)		18·00	
	d. Opt double (White vert down + yellow vert up)		27·00	
547	6 n.p. multicoloured (Horiz)		15	1·50
548	8 n.p. multicoloured (Horiz)		15	70
549	9 n.p. multicoloured (Horiz)		15	1·50
550	10 n.p. multicoloured (Horiz)		20	60
551	20 n.p. deep blue and new blue (Vert up)		35	80
	a. Opt vert down		20·00	
552	50 n.p. multicoloured (Horiz)		5·00	5·50
	a. Opt double			
553	1 n.c. multicoloured (Horiz)		1·75	7·00
554	2 n.c. multicoloured (R.) (Vert up)		2·75	8·00
	a. Opt double (vert up and down)			
555	2 n.c. 50, multicoloured (Vert down)		2·75	9·50
541/55		*Set of 15*	14·00	38·00

The 1 n.p. is known with the overprint inverted, "NEW CONSTITUTION" appearing between the stamps across the perforations.

(Litho D.L.R.)

1969 (4 Dec). *Inauguration of Second Republic. T 290 and similar vert designs. Multicoloured. P 14.*

556	4 n.p. Type 290		10	10
557	12½ n.p. Figure "2", branch and Ghanaian colours		20	10
558	20 n.p. Hands receiving egg		35	30
559	40 n.p. Type 290		60	70
556/9		*Set of 4*	1·10	1·00

293 I.L.O. Emblem and Cog-wheels

1970 (5 Jan). *50th Anniv of International Labour Organisation. W 47 (sideways). P 14½ × 14.*

560	293	4 n.p. multicoloured		10	10
561		12½ n.p. multicoloured		20	25
562		20 n.p. multicoloured		30	45
560/2			*Set of 3*	55	70
MS563	117 × 89 mm. Nos. 560/2. Imperf		70	2·50

NEW INFORMATION

The editor is always interested to correspond with people who have new information that will improve or correct the Catalogue.

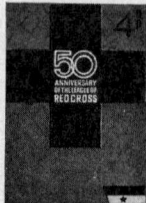

294 Red Cross and Globe

298 General Kotoka, Vickers VC-10 and Airport

1970 (2 Feb). *50th Anniv of League of Red Cross Societies. T 294 and similar multicoloured designs. W 47 (sideways on 4 n.p.). P 14 × 14½ (4 n.p.) or 14½ × 14 (others).*

564	4 n.p. Type 294		30	10
565	12½ n.p. Henri Dunant and Red Cross emblem (horiz)		50	20
	w. Wmk inverted			
566	20 n.p. Patient receiving medicine (horiz)		60	55
567	40 n.p. Patient having arm bandaged (horiz)		80	1·40
564/7		*Set of 4*	2·00	2·00
MS568	114×89 mm. Nos. 564/7. Imperf		2·50	6·00

(Des G. Vasarhelyi. Litho D.L.R.)

1970 (17 Apr). *Inauguration of Kotoka Airport. T 298 and similar horiz designs. Multicoloured. P 13 × 13½.*

569	4 n.p. Type 298		15	10
570	12½ n.p. Control tower and tail of Vickers VC-10		25	15
571	20 n.p. Aerial view of airport		40	30
572	40 n.p. Airport and flags		75	80
569/72		*Set of 4*	1·40	1·25

302 Lunar Module landing on Moon

306 Adult Education

(Des A. Medina (4 n.p., 12½ n.p.), G. Vasarhelyi (others). Litho D.L.R.)

1970 (15 June). *Moon Landing. T 302 and similar multicoloured designs. P 12½.*

573	4 n.p. Type 302		30	10
574	12½ n.p. Astronaut's first step onto the Moon		85	60
575	20 n.p. Astronaut with equipment on Moon (horiz)		1·40	1·40
576	40 n.p. Astronauts (horiz)		3·00	3·00
573/6		*Set of 4*	5·00	4·50
MS577	142 × 142 mm. Nos. 573/6. Imperf (with or without simulated perfs)		5·50	12·00

On 18 September 1970 Nos. 573/6 were issued overprinted "PHILYMPIA LONDON 1970" but it is understood that only 900 sets were made available for sale in Ghana and we do not consider that this is sufficient to constitute normal postal use. The miniature sheet was also overprinted but not issued in Ghana.

(Litho D.L.R.)

1970 (10 Aug). *International Education Year. T 306 and similar horiz designs. Multicoloured. P 13.*

578	4 n.p. Type 306		10	10
579	12½ n.p. International education		20	20
580	20 n.p. "Ntesie" and I.E.Y. symbols		35	30
581	40 n.p. Nursery schools		60	85
578/81		*Set of 4*	1·10	1·25

310 Saluting March-Past

314 *Crinum ornatum*

(Litho D.L.R.)

1970 (1 Oct). *First Anniv of the Second Republic. T 310 and similar horiz designs. Multicoloured. P 13 × 13½.*

582	4 n.p. Type 310		10	10
583	12½ n.p. Busia declaration		15	15
584	20 n.p. Doves symbol		25	30
585	40 n.p. Opening of Parliament		50	65
582/5		*Set of 4*	90	1·00

(Des G. Vasarhelyi. Photo Harrison)

1970 (2 Nov). *Flora and Fauna. T 314 and similar horiz designs. Multicoloured. W 47 (sideways). P 14½ × 14.*

586	4 n.p. Type 314		1·50	10
	w. Wmk inverted		7·00	
587	12½ n.p. Lioness		1·50	75
588	20 n.p. *Anselia africana* (flower)		1·60	1·25
589	40 n.p. African Elephant		4·75	5·00
586/9		*Set of 4*	8·50	6·50

---

315 Kuduo Brass Casket

(Des G. Vasarhelyi. Photo Harrison)

1970 (7 Dec). *Monuments and Archaeological Sites in Ghana. T 315 and similar horiz designs. Multicoloured. W 47. P 14½ × 14.*

590	4 n.p. Type 315		15	10
	w. Wmk inverted			
591	12½ n.p. Akan traditional house		40	20
592	20 n.p. Larabanga Mosque		70	50
593	40 n.p. Funerary clay head		1·00	1·10
590/3		*Set of 4*	2·00	1·75
MS594	89×71 mm. Nos. 590, 592 and 12½ n.p. Basilica of Pompeii, 40 n.p. Pistrinum of Pompeii (wmk sideways). Imperf (2.71)		5·00	7·50

316 Trade Fair Building

(Des G. Drummond (4 n.p., 50 n.p.), A. Larkins (others). Photo Harrison)

1971 (5 Feb). *International Trade Fair, Accra. T 316 and similar multicoloured designs. W 47 (sideways, except 50 n.p.). P 14 × 14½ (50 n.p.) or 14½ × 14 (others).*

595	4 n.p. Type 316		10	10
596	12½ n.p. Cosmetics and Pharmaceutical Goods		60	20
597	20 n.p. Vehicles		65	25
598	40 n.p. Construction Equipment		95	95
599	50 n.p. Transport and Packing Case (vert)		1·10	1·10
595/9		*Set of 5*	3·00	2·25

317 Christ on the Cross

318 Corn Cob

(Des from stained-glass windows. Litho D.L.R.)

1971 (19 May). *Easter. T 317 and similar square designs. Multicoloured. P 13.*

600	4 n.p. Type 317		20	10
601	12½ n.p. Christ and Disciples		45	45
602	20 n.p. Christ blessing Disciples		65	1·10
600/2		*Set of 3*	1·10	1·50

(Photo Harrison)

1971 (15 June). *Freedom from Hunger Campaign. W 47. P 14 × 14½.*

603	318	4 n.p. multicoloured		10	10
604		12½ n.p. multicoloured		35	60
605		20 n.p. multicoloured		65	1·10
603/5			*Set of 3*	1·00	1·60

Remainder stocks of the above were overprinted on the occasion of the death of Lord Boyd Orr and the 4 n.p. surcharged 60 n.p.

It is understood that 8,070 sets from the New York Agency were overprinted locally and returned to the Agency. Limited remainders of these stamps (only 330 of the 60 n.p.) were sold at the G.P.O. We do not list these as they were not freely on sale in Ghana.

319 Guides Emblem and Ghana Flag

320 Child-care Centre

(Des and litho Questa)

1971 (22 July). *Ghana Girl Guides Golden Jubilee. T 319 and similar horiz designs each with Guides Emblem. Multicoloured. P 14.*

606	4 n.p. Type 319		20	10
607	12½ n.p. Mrs. E. Ofuatey-Kodjoe (founder) and guides with flags		60	50
608	20 n.p. Guides laying stones		90	90
609	40 n.p. Camp-fire and tent		1·50	1·75
610	50 n.p. Signallers		1·75	2·00
606/10		*Set of 5*	4·50	4·75
MS611	133 × 105 mm. Nos. 606/10. Imperf		11·00	13·00

(Des and litho D.L.R.)

1971 (7 Aug). *Y.W.C.A. World Council Meeting, Accra. T* **320** *and similar horiz designs. Multicoloured. P* 13.

612	4 n.p.	Type **320**		10	10
613	12½ n.p.	Council meeting		10	15
614	20 n.p.	School typing-class		15	30
615	40 n.p.	Building Fund Day		30	60
612/15		*Set of* 4		55	1·00
MS616	84 × 83 mm. Nos. 612/15. Imperf			70	2·00

321 Firework Display

322 Weighing Baby

(Photo Harrison)

1971 (22 Nov). *Christmas. T* **321** *and similar horiz designs. Multicoloured. W* **47** *(sideways on 3 and 6 n.p.). P* 14 × 14½ *(1 n.p.) or* 14½ × 14 *(others).*

617	1 n.p.	Type **321**		10	50
618	3 n.p.	African Nativity		15	60
619	6 n.p.	The flight into Egypt		15	60
617/19		*Set of* 3		30	1·50

(Litho D.L.R.)

1971 (20 Dec). *25th Anniv of U.N.I.C.E.F. T* **322** *and similar multicoloured designs, each showing the U.N.I.C.E.F. symbol. No wmk (MS624) or W* **47** *(sideways on 5 and 30 n.p.). P* 13.

620	5 n.p.	Type **322**		10	10
621	15 n.p.	Mother and child (*horiz*)		30	30
622	40 n.p.	Nurse		40	70
623	50 n.p.	Young boy (*horiz*)		60	2·25
620/3		*Set of* 4		1·25	3·00
MS624	111 × 120 mm. Nos. 620/3. Imperf			3·75	7·00

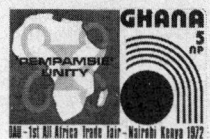

323 Unity Symbol and Trade Fair Emblem

(Litho Questa)

1972 (23 Feb). *All-Africa Trade Fair. T* **323** *and similar horiz designs. Multicoloured. W* **47**. *P* 14.

625	5 n.p.	Type **323**		10	10
626	15 n.p.	Horn of Plenty		15	30
627	30 n.p.	Fireworks on map of Africa		25	70
628	60 n.p.	"Participating Nations"		35	2·00
629	1 n.c.	As No. 628		50	2·50
625/9		*Set of* 5		1·10	5·00

All designs include the Trade Fair Emblem as in T **323**.

On 24 June 1972, on the occasion of the Belgian International Philatelic Exhibition, Nos. 625/9 were issued overprinted ' "BELGICA 72" ' in red. Only very limited supplies were sent to Ghana (we understand not more than 900 sets), and for this reason we do not list them.

(New Currency. 100 pesewas = 1 cedi = 0.8 (1967) new cedi)

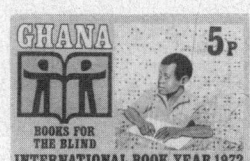

324 Books for the Blind

(Des and litho D.L.R.)

1972 (21 Apr). *International Book Year. T* **324** *and similar multicoloured designs. P* 13.

630	5 p.	Type **324**		20	10
631	15 p.	Children's books		55	50
632	30 p.	Books for recreation		1·00	1·25
633	50 p.	Books for students		1·75	2·75
634	1 c.	Book and flame of knowledge (*vert*)		2·50	3·75
630/4		*Set of* 5		5·50	7·50
MS635	99 × 106 mm. Nos. 630/4. Imperf.			8·00	11·00

325 *Hypoxis urceolata*

(Litho D.L.R.)

1972 (3 July). *Flora and Fauna. T* **325** *and similar horiz designs. Multicoloured. P* 13½.

636	5 p.	Type **325**		30	10
637	15 p.	Mona Monkey		65	65
638	30 p.	*Crinum ornatum*		5·50	4·00
639	1 c.	De Winton's Tree Squirrel		6·00	8·00
636/9		*Set of* 4		11·00	11·50

326 Football

(Litho D.L.R.)

1972 (5 Sept). *Olympic Games, Munich. T* **326** *and similar horiz designs. Multicoloured. P* 13.

640	5 p.	Type **326**		10	10
641	15 p.	Running		20	20
642	30 p.	Boxing		40	65
643	50 p.	Long-jumping		70	1·75
644	1 c.	High-jumping		1·25	3·00
640/4		*Set of* 5		2·40	5·00
MS645	86 × 43 mm. 40 p. as No. 642 *se-tenant* with 60 p. as No. 640			2·25	6·50

327 Senior Scout and Cub

(Litho Questa)

1972 (2 Oct). *65th Anniv of Boy Scouts. T* **327** *and similar diamond-shaped designs. Multicoloured. P* 13½.

646	5 p.	Type **327**		30	10
647	15 p.	Scout and tent		65	45
648	30 p.	Sea scouts		1·25	1·25
649	50 p.	Leader with cubs..		1·60	2·00
650	1 c.	Training school		3·00	3·50
646/50		*Set of* 5		6·00	6·50
MS651	110 × 110 mm. 40 p. as 30 p.; 60 p. as 1 c.			3·25	5·50

328 "The Holy Night"
(Correggio)

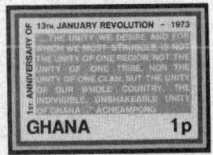

329 Extract from Speech

(Des G. Vasarhelyi and L. Apelt. Litho Questa)

1972 (1 Dec). *Christmas. T* **328** *and similar vert designs. Multicoloured. P* 13½.

652	1p.	Type **328**		10	10
653	3p.	"Adoration of the Kings" (Holbein the Elder)		10	10
654	15p.	"Madonna of the Passion" (School of Ricco)		40	30
655	30p.	"King Melchior"		70	70
656	60p.	"King Gaspar, Mary and Jesus"		1·25	2·00
657	1 c.	"King Balthasar"		2·00	3·00
652/7		*Set of* 6		4·00	5·50
MS658	139×90 mm. Nos. 655/7. Imperf			11·00	10·00

Nos. 655/7 are from a 16th-cent. Norman stained-glass window.

(Des and litho D.L.R.)

1973 (10 Apr). *First Anniv of January 13 Revolution. T* **329** *and similar multicoloured designs. P* 13 × 14 *(5, 15 p.) or* 14 × 13 *(others).*

659	1 p.	Type **329**		10	10
660	3 p.	Market scene		10	10
661	5 p.	Selling bananas (*vert*)		10	10
662	15 p.	Farmer with hoe and produce (*vert*)		20	25
663	30 p.	Market traders		30	40
664	1 c.	Farmer cutting palm-nuts		70	1·40
659/64		*Set of* 6		1·25	1·90
MS665	90 × 55 mm. 40 p. as 1 c. and 60 p. Miners			70	2·25

330 Under 5's Clinic

(Litho D.L.R.)

1973 (24 July). *25th Anniv of W.H.O. T* **330** *and similar square designs. Multicoloured. P* 13½.

666	5 p.	Type **330**		10	10
667	15 p.	Radiography		25	30
668	30 p.	Immunisation		35	50
669	50 p.	Starving child		50	1·25
670	1 c.	W.H.O. H.Q., Geneva		1·00	2·25
666/70		*Set of* 5		2·00	4·00

1st WORLD SCOUTING CONFERENCE IN AFRICA

(331)

1973 (14 Aug). *First World Scouting Conference, Nairobi/Addis Ababa. Nos.* 646/51 *optd with T* **331**.

671	5 p.	Type **327**		10	15
672	15 p.	Scout and tent		35	60
673	30 p.	Sea scouts		60	1·40
674	50 p.	Leader with cubs..		80	2·00
675	1 c.	Training school		1·50	3·00
671/5		*Set of* 5		3·00	6·50
MS676	110 × 110 mm. 40 p. as 30 p.; 60 p. as 1 c.			2·00	6·50

332 Poultry Farming

(Litho Questa)

1973 (11 Sept). *Tenth Anniv of World Food Programme. T* **332** *and similar horiz designs. Multicoloured. P* 14.

677	5 p.	Type **332**		10	10
678	15 p.	Mechanisation		15	15
679	50 p.	Cocoa harvest		40	90
680	1 c.	F.A.O. H.Q., Rome		60	1·90
677/80		*Set of* 4		1·00	2·75
MS681	92 × 104 mm. 40 p. as 15 p.; 60 p. as 1 c.			60	2·25

333 "Green Alert"

(Litho D.L.R.)

1973 (1 Oct). *50th Anniv of Interpol. T* **333** *and similar horiz designs. Multicoloured. P* 13.

682	5 p.	Type **333**		15	10
683	30 p.	"Red Alert"		75	80
684	50 p.	"Blue Alert"		1·50	1·75
685	1 c.	"Black Alert"		3·00	4·00
682/5		*Set of* 4		4·75	6·00

334 Handshake

(Litho Format)

1973 (22 Oct). *Tenth Anniv of O.A.U. T* **334** *and similar horiz designs. Multicoloured. P* 14 × 14½.

686	5 p.	Type **334**		10	10
687	30 p.	Africa Hall, Addis Ababa		15	30
688	50 p.	O.A.U. emblem		20	1·00
689	1 c.	"X" in colours of Ghana flag		35	1·50
686/9		*Set of* 4		70	2·50

MINIMUM PRICE

The minimum price quote is 10p which represents a handling charge rather than a basis for valuing common stamps. For further notes about prices see introductory pages.

335 Weather Balloon 336 Epiphany Scene

(Des G. Vasarhelyi. Litho Format)

1973 (16 Nov). *I.M.O./W.M.O. Centenary. T* **335** *and similar horiz designs. Multicoloured. P* 14 × 14½.
690	5 p. Type 335		10	10
691	15 p. Satellite "Tiros"		15	20
692	30 p. Computer weather map		30	65
693	1 c. Radar		60	2·25
690/3		*Set of* 4	1·00	2·75
MS694	120 × 95 mm. 40 p. as 15 p.; 60 p. as 30 p.		1·25	3·25

(Litho D.L.R.)

1973 (10 Dec). *Christmas. T* **336** *and similar vert designs. Multicoloured. P* 14.
695	1 p. Type 336		10	10
696	3 p. Madonna and Child		10	10
697	30 p. "Madonna and Child" (Murillo)		30	75
698	50 p. "Adoration of the Magi" (Tiepolo)		45	1·00
695/8		*Set of* 4	1·25	2·75
MS699	77 × 103 mm. Nos. 695/8. Imperf		1·25	3·00

337 "Christ carrying the Cross" (Thomas de Kolozsvar) 338 Letters

(Des M. Shamir and A. Larkins. Litho D.L.R.)

1974 (17 Apr). *Easter. T* **337** *and similar vert designs. P* 14.
700	5 p. multicoloured		10	10
701	30 p. bright blue, silver and sepia		20	35
702	50 p. light orange-vermilion, silver and sepia		30	60
703	1 c. dull yellow-green, silver and sepia		50	1·25
700/3		*Set of* 4	90	2·00
MS704	111 × 106 mm. 15 p. as No. 700, 20 p. as No. 701, 25 p. as No. 702. Imperf		80	1·75

Designs (from 15th-century English carved alabaster):—30 p. "The Betrayal"; 50 p. "The Deposition"; 1 c. "The Risen Christ and Mary Magdalene".

(Des A. Larkins. Litho Questa)

1974 (21 May). *Centenary of Universal Postal Union. T* **338** *and similar horiz designs. Multicoloured. P* 14½.
705	5 p. Type 338		10	10
706	9 p. U.P.U. Monument and H.Q.		10	15
707	50 p. Airmail letter		35	1·00
708	1 c. U.P.U. Monument and Ghana stamp		60	1·75
705/8		*Set of* 4	1·00	2·75
MS709	108 × 90 mm. 20 p. as No. 705, 30 p. as No. 706, 40 p. as No. 707, 60 p. as No. 708		75	1·60

Nos. 705/8 were issued both in sheets of 30 and in sheets of 5 stamps and 1 label.

1974 (7 June). *"Internaba 1974" Stamp Exhibition, Basle. Nos.* 705/9 *additionally inscribed* "INTERNABA 1974".
710	5 p. Type 338		10	10
711	9 p. U.P.U. Monument and H.Q.		10	15
712	50 p. Airmail letter		30	1·00
713	1 c. U.P.U. Monument and Ghana stamp		45	1·75
710/13		*Set of* 4	80	2·75
MS714	108 × 90 mm. 20 p. as No. 710; 30 p. as No. 711; 40 p. as No. 712; 60 p. as No. 713		1·50	4·00

339 Footballers

(Des G. Vasarhelyi. Litho Format)

1974 (17 June). *World Cup Football Championships, West Germany. T* **339** *and similar horiz designs showing footballers. P* 14½.
715	339	5 p. multicoloured	10	10
716	–	30 p. multicoloured	25	60
717	–	50 p. multicoloured	35	85
718	–	1 c. multicoloured	50	1·50
715/18		*Set of* 4	1·00	2·75
MS719	148 × 94 mm. 25, 40, 55 and 60 p. as Nos.			
715/18			1·00	3·25

Nos. 715/18 also exist perf 13 (*price for set of* 4 £1 *mint*, £3.25 *used*) from additional sheetlets of 5 stamps and 1 label. Stamps perforated 14½ are from normal sheets of 25.

The sheetlets, together with No. MS719, exist imperforate from stock dispersed by the liquidator of Format International Security Printers Ltd.

340 Roundabout (341)
WEST GERMANY WINNERS

(Des and litho B.W.)

1974 (16 July). *Change to Driving on the Right. T* **340** *and similar designs. P* 13½ (5 and 15 p.) *or* 14½ × 14 (*others*).
720	5 p. bright yellow-grn, rose-vermilion & blk		10	10
721	15 p. lavender, dull red and black		25	35
722	30 p. multicoloured		45	60
723	50 p. multicoloured		70	1·10
724	1 c. multicoloured		1·40	2·00
720/4		*Set of* 5	2·75	3·75

Designs: *Horiz*—15 p. Warning triangle sign. *Vert* (29 × 42 mm)—30 p. Highway arrow and slogan; 50 p. Warning hands; 1 c. Car on symbolic hands.

1974 (30 Aug). *West Germany's Victory in World Cup. Nos.* 715/19 *optd with T* **341**. *P* 14½.
725	339	5 p. multicoloured	10	10
726	–	30 p. multicoloured	35	40
727	–	50 p. multicoloured	50	55
728	–	1 c. multicoloured	90	1·25
725/8		*Set of* 4	1·75	2·10
MS729	148 × 94 mm. 25, 40, 55, 60 p. as Nos.			
725/8			1·25	2·50

This overprint also exists on the stamps perforated 13 mentioned below No. MS719 (*Price for set of* 4 £2 *mint or used*).

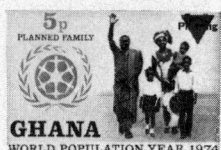

342 "Planned Family"
WORLD POPULATION YEAR 1974

(Des and litho D.L.R.)

1974 (12 Sept). *World Population Year. T* **342** *and similar horiz designs. Multicoloured. P* 12½.
730	5 p. Type 342		10	10
731	30 p. Family planning clinic		25	35
732	50 p. Immunization		35	60
733	1 c. Population census enumeration		60	1·40
730/3		*Set of* 4	1·10	2·25

APOLLO SOYUZ JULY 15, 1975

343 Angel (344)

(Des A. Medina (5 and 7 p.), A. Larkins (others). Litho D.L.R.)

1974 (19 Dec). *Christmas. T* **343** *and similar multicoloured designs. P* 13½.
734	5 p. Type 343		10	10
735	7 p. The Magi (*diamond* 47 × 47 *mm*)		10	10
736	9 p. The Nativity		10	10
737	1 c. The Annunciation		60	1·40
734/7		*Set of* 4	80	1·50
MS738	128 × 128 mm. 15 p. Type 343; 30 p. as 7 p.; 45 p. as 9 p.; 60 p. as 1 c. Imperf		80	2·50

1975 (15 Aug). *"Apollo–Soyuz" Space Link. Nos.* 715/19 *optd with T* **344**. *P* 14½.
739	5 p. multicoloured		10	10
740	30 p. multicoloured		25	25
741	50 p. multicoloured		45	55
742	1 c. multicoloured		70	80
739/42		*Set of* 4	1·25	1·50
MS743	148 × 94 mm. 25, 40, 55, 60 p. as Nos.			
739/42			1·25	2·00

This overprint also exists on the stamps perforated 13 mentioned below No. MS719 (*Price for set of* 4 £6 *mint*, £7 *used*).

345 Tractor Driver
International Womens Year 1975

(Des and litho D.L.R.)

1975 (3 Sept). *International Women's Year. T* **345** *and similar horiz designs each showing I.W.Y. emblem. Multicoloured. P* 14 × 13½.
744	7 p. Type 345		25	10
745	30 p. Motor mechanic		65	35
746	60 p. Factory workers		80	80
747	1 c. Cocoa research		1·00	1·40
744/7		*Set of* 4	2·40	2·40
MS748	136 × 110 mm. 15, 40, 65 and 80 p. as Nos.			
744/7. Imperf			2·00	6·00

346 Angel

(Litho D.L.R.)

1975 (31 Dec). *Christmas. T* **346** *and similar horiz designs. P* 14 × 13½.
749	2 p. multicoloured		10	10
750	5 p. greenish yellow and light green		10	10
751	7 p. greenish yellow and light green		10	10
752	30 p. greenish yellow and light green		20	20
753	1 c. greenish yellow and light green		50	1·00
749/53		*Set of* 5	80	1·25
MS754	98 × 87 mm. 15, 40, 65 and 80 p. as Nos.			
750/3. Imperf			90	3·00

Designs:—5 p. Angel with harp; 7 p. Angel with lute; 30 p. Angel with viol; 1 c. Angel with trumpet.

347 Map Reading

(Litho Format)

1976 (5 Jan). *14th World Scout Jamboree, Norway. T* **347** *and similar horiz designs. Multicoloured. P* 13½ × 14.
755	7 p. Type 347		20	10
756	30 p. Sailing		60	90
757	60 p. Hiking		1·00	2·25
758	1 c. Life-saving		1·50	2·50
755/8		*Set of* 4	3·00	5·25
MS759	133 × 99 mm. 15, 40, 65 and 80 p. as Nos.			
755/8			2·75	6·50

Nos. 755/9 exist imperforate from stock dispersed by the liquidator of Format International Security Printers Ltd.

348 Bottles (litre)

(Litho D.L.R.)

1976 (5 Jan). *Metrication Publicity. T* **348** *and similar horiz designs. Multicoloured. P* 14.
760	7 p. Type 348		15	10
761	30 p. Scales (kilogramme)		40	40
762	60 p. Tape measure and bale of cloth (metre)		80	1·00
763	1 c. Ice, thermometer and kettle (temperature)		1·25	1·75
760/3		*Set of* 4	2·40	2·75

349 Fair Site

(Litho Format)

1976 (6 Apr). *International Trade Fair, Accra. T* **349** *and similar horiz designs. P* 13½.
764	349	7 p. multicoloured	10	10
765	–	30 p. multicoloured	20	20
766	–	60 p. multicoloured	35	60
767	–	1 c. multicoloured	55	1·00
764/7		*Set of* 4	1·10	1·60

Nos. 765/7 are as T **349** but show different views of the Fair.

Nos. 764/7 exist imperforate from stock dispersed by the liquidator of Format International Security Printers Ltd.

'INTERPHIL' 76 BICENTENNIAL EXHIBITION

(350)

351 Shot-put

1976 (28 May). *Interphil Stamp Exhibition, Philadelphia. Nos. 755/9 optd with T 350 in blue.*

768	7 p. Type 347		15	15
769	30 p. Sailing		35	50
770	60 p. Hiking		55	75
771	1 c. Life-saving		80	1·25
768/71		*Set of 4*	1·75	2·40
MS772	133 × 99 mm. 15, 40, 65 and 80 p. as Nos.			
768/71			1·50	2·50

Nos. 768/71 exist imperforate from stock dispersed by the liquidator of Format International Security Printers Ltd.

(Des PAD Studio. Litho Format)

1976 (9 Aug). *Olympic Games, Montreal. T 351 and similar vert designs. Multicoloured. P 13½.*

773	7 p. Type 351		10	10
774	30 p. Football		20	25
775	60 p. Women's 1500 metres		35	50
776	1 c. Boxing		60	80
773/6		*Set of 4*	1·10	1·50
MS777	103 × 135 mm. 15, 40, 65 and 80 p. as Nos.			
773/6			1·50	1·50

Nos. 773/6 also exist perf 15 (*Price for set of 4 £2·25 mint or used*) from additional sheetlets of 5 stamps and 1 label. Stamps perforated 13½ are from normal sheets of 30. The sheetlets also exist imperforate from stock dispersed by the liquidator of Format International Security Printers Ltd.

352 Supreme Court

(Litho D.L.R.)

1976 (7 Sept). *Centenary of Supreme Court. T 352 and similar horiz designs. P 14.*

778	352	8 p. multicoloured	10	10
779	–	30 p. multicoloured	20	25
780	–	60 p. multicoloured	35	50
781	–	1 c. multicoloured	60	1·00
778/81		*Set of 4*	1·10	1·75

Nos. 779/81 show different views of the Court Building.

353 Examination for River Blindness

(Des and litho D.L.R.)

1976 (28 Oct). *Prevention of Blindness. T 353 and similar horiz designs. Multicoloured. P 14 × 13½.*

782	7 p. Type 353		65	10
783	30 p. Entomologist		1·75	1·40
784	60 p. Normal vision		2·75	2·75
785	1 c. Blackfly eradication		4·25	4·50
782/5		*Set of 4*	8·50	8·00

354 Fireworks Party, Christmas Eve

(Des A. Adom & A. Larkins. Litho D.L.R.)

1976 (15 Dec). *Christmas. T 354 and similar horiz designs. Multicoloured. P 13.*

786	6 p. Type 354		15	10
787	8 p. Children and gifts		15	10
788	30 p. Christmas feast		50	30
789	1 c. As 8 p.		1·10	1·75
786/9		*Set of 4*	1·75	2·00
MS790	122 × 98 mm. 15, 40, 65 and 80 p. as Nos.			
786/9. Imperf			2·00	4·00

355 "Gallows Frame" Telephone and Alexander Graham Bell

EAST GERMANY WINNERS

(356)

(Des A. Larkins. Litho Format)

1976 (17 Dec). *Telephone Centenary. T 355 and similar horiz designs showing telephones and Alexander Graham Bell. Multicoloured. P 13.*

791	8 p. Type 355		20	10
792	30 p. 1895 telephone		30	30
793	60 p. 1929 telephone		60	70
794	1 c. 1976 telephone		1·00	1·25
791/4		*Set of 4*	1·90	2·00
MS795	125 × 92 mm. 15, 40, 65 and 80 p. as Nos.			
791/4			1·50	1·75

1977 (22 Feb). *Olympic Winners. Nos. 773/7 optd with the name of the country given, as T 356. P 13½.*

796	7 p. East Germany		15	15
797	30 p. East Germany		35	40
798	60 p. U.S.S.R.		45	85
799	1 c. U.S.A.		65	1·50
796/9		*Set of 4*	1·40	2·50
MS800	103 × 135 mm. 15, 40, 65 and 80 p. as Nos.			
796/9			2·25	2·50

357 Dipo Dancers and Drum Ensemble

(Des A. Larkins. Litho Format)

1977 (24 Mar). *Second World Black and African Festival of Arts and Culture, Nigeria. T 357 and similar horiz designs. Multicoloured. P 13½.*

801	8 p. Type 357		20	15
802	30 p. Arts and Crafts		40	70
803	60 p. Acon music and dancing priests		60	1·40
804	1 c. African huts		80	2·25
801/4		*Set of 4*	1·75	4·00
MS805	164 × 120 mm. 15, 40, 65 and 80 p. as Nos.			
801/4			1·75	2·00

PRINCE CHARLES VISITS GHANA 17th TO 25th MARCH, 1977

(358)

1977 (2 June). *Prince Charles's Visit to Ghana. Nos. 791/5 optd with T 358.*

806	8 p. Type 355		50	55
807	30 p. 1895 telephone		1·25	1·00
808	60 p. 1929 telephone		1·75	2·00
809	1 c. 1976 telephone		2·25	2·50
806/9		*Set of 4*	5·25	5·50
MS810	125 × 92 mm. 15, 40, 65 and 80 p. as Nos.			
806/9			8·00	8·50

359 Olive Colobus

360 "Le Chapeau de Paille" (Rubens—400th Birth Anniv)

(Des PAD Studio. Litho Format)

1977 (22 June). *Wildlife. T 359 and similar horiz designs. Multicoloured. P 13½.*

811	8 p. Type 359		45	15
812	20 p. Temminck's Giant Squirrel		1·25	80
813	30 p. Hunting Dog		1·75	1·25
814	60 p. African Manatee		3·00	2·75
811/14		*Set of 4*	5·75	4·50
MS815	140 × 101 mm. 15, 40, 65 and 80 p. as Nos.			
811/14			5·50	5·50

No. MS815 exists imperforate from stock dispersed by the liquidator of Format International Security Printers Ltd.

(Des PAD Studio. Litho Format)

1977 (Sept). *Painters' Anniversaries. T 360 and similar vert designs. Multicoloured. P 14 × 13½.*

816	8 p. Type 360		25	10
817	30 p. "Isabella of Portugal" (Titian—500th Birth Anniv)		50	40
818	60 p. "Duke and Duchess of Cumberland" (Gainsborough—250th Birth Anniv)		65	65
819	1 c. "Rubens and Isabella Brandt"		85	1·25
816/19		*Set of 4*	2·00	2·25
MS820	99 × 149 mm. 15, 40, 65 and 80 p. as Nos.			
816/19			2·25	2·25

No. MS820 exists imperforate from stock dispersed by the liquidator of Format International Security Printers Ltd.

REFERENDUM 1978 VOTE EARLY

(362)

361 The Magi, Madonna and Child

(Litho De La Rue, Colombia)

1977 (30 Dec). *Christmas. T 361 and similar multicoloured designs. P 14 (1 p., 8 p.) or 14 × 13½ (others).*

821	1 p. Type 361		10	10
822	2 p. Choir from Abossey Okai (45 × 27 mm)		10	10
823	6 p. Methodist Church, Wesley, Accra (45 × 27 mm)		10	10
824	8 p. Madonna and Child		10	10
825	30 p. Holy Spirit Cathedral, Accra (45 × 27 mm)		40	50
826	1 c. Ebeneezer Presbyterian Church, Accra (45 × 27 mm)		1·25	1·60
821/6		*Set of 6*	1·75	2·25
MS827	122 × 97 mm. 15, 40, 65 and 80 p. as Nos. 822/3 and 825/6. Imperf			
			1·75	3·75

Nos. 822/3 and 825/6 all have as a background the score to the carol "Hark the Herald Angels Sing".

1978 (Mar). *1978 Referendum. Nos. 821/7 optd with T 362 by De La Rue, Colombia.*

828	1 p. Type 361		10	10
829	2 p. Choir from Abossey Okai		10	10
830	6 p. Methodist Church, Wesley, Accra		10	10
831	8 p. Madonna and Child		10	10
832	30 p. Holy Spirit Cathedral, Accra		40	50
833	1 c. Ebeneezer Presbyterian Church, Accra		1·25	1·60
828/33		*Set of 6*	1·75	2·10
MS834	122 × 97 mm. 15, 40, 65, 80 p. as Nos. 829/30 and 832/3			
			27·00	16·00

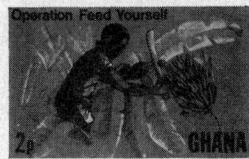

363 Cutting Bananas

(Litho De La Rue, Colombia)

1978 (15 May). *Operation "Feed Yourself". T 363 and similar horiz designs. Multicoloured. P 14.*

835	2 p. Type 363		10	10
836	8 p. Home produce		10	10
837	30 p. Market		25	35
838	60 p. Fishing		60	60
839	1 c. Mechanisation		80	1·25
835/9		*Set of 5*	1·60	2·10

364 Wright Flyer III

"CAPEX 78 JUNE 9-18 1978"

(365)

(Des J.W. Litho Format)

1978 (6 June). *75th Anniv of Powered Flight. T 364 and similar vert designs. P 14 × 13½.*

840	8 p. black, deep brown and brown-ochre		20	10
841	30 p. black, deep brown and blue-green		40	30
842	60 p. black, deep brown and rosine		60	60
843	1 c. black, deep brown and ultramarine		1·75	1·10
840/3		*Set of 4*	2·75	1·90
MS844	167 × 100 mm. 15, 40, 65, 80 p. as Nos.			
840/3			2·50	1·75

Designs:—30 p. Handley Page H.P.42; 60 p. De Havilland D.H.106 Comet 1; 1 c. Concorde.

No. 841 exists imperforate from stock dispersed by the liquidator of Format International Security Printers Ltd.

1978 (9 June). *"CAPEX 1978" International Stamp Exhibition, Toronto. Nos. 840/4 optd with T **365**.*
845	8 p. black, deep brown and brown-ochre		15	15
846	30 p. black, deep brown and blue-green		25	25
847	60 p. black, deep brown and rosine		50	50
848	1 c. black, deep brown and ultramarine		1·10	80
845/8		*Set of 4*	1·75	1·50
MS849	167 × 100 mm. 15, 40, 65, 80 p. as Nos.			
845/8			1·75	2·00

366 Players and African Cup Emblem

(Litho Format)

1978 (1 July). *Football Championships. T **366** and similar horiz designs. Multicoloured. P 13½ × 14.*
850	8 p. Type **366**		20	15
851	30 p. Players and African Cup emblem *(different)*		25	30
852	60 p. Players and World Cup emblem. .		40	60
853	1 c. Goalkeeper and World Cup emblem		55	1·00
850/3		*Set of 4*	1·25	1·90
MS854	111 × 105 mm. 15, 40, 65, 80 p. as Nos.			
850/3			1·10	1·25

The 8 and 30 p. values commemorate the African Nations Cup; the other values the World Cup Football Championship, Argentina.

Nos. 850/3 exist imperforate from stock dispersed by the liquidator of Format International Security Printers Ltd.

367 "The Betrayal"

(Litho Format)

1978 (15 July). *Easter. Details from drawings by Dürer. T **367** and similar vert designs. P 14 × 13½.*
855	11 p. black and bright reddish violet		10	10
856	39 p. black and flesh		25	30
857	60 p. black and orange-yellow. .		40	45
858	1 c. black and pale yellow-green		60	65
855/8		*Set of 4*	1·25	1·40

Designs:—39 p. "The Crucifixion"; 60 p. "The Deposition"; 1 c. "The Resurrection".

1978 (21 Aug). *Ghana—Winners of African Nations Football Cup and Argentina—Winners of World Cup Football Championship. Nos. 850/1 and MS854 optd with T **368** and Nos. 852/3 optd "ARGENTINA WINS".*
859	8 p. Type **366**		15	15
860	30 p. Players and African Cup emblem *(different)*		25	30
861	60 p. Players and World Cup emblem. .		35	45
862	1 c. Goalkeeper and World Cup emblem		55	75
859/62		*Set of 4*	1·10	1·50
MS863	111 × 105 mm. 15, 40, 65, 80 p. as Nos.			
859/62 but all optd with T **368**			1·00	1·10

Nos. 859/60 exist imperforate from stock dispersed by the liquidator of Format International Security Printers Ltd.

369 *Bauhinia purpurea*

(Litho Format)

1978 (20 Nov). *Flowers. T **369** and similar vert designs. Multicoloured. P 14 × 13½.*
864	11 p. Type **369** . .		20	10
865	39 p. *Cassia fistula*		40	55
866	60 p. *Plumeria acutifolia*		50	70
867	1 c. *Jacaranda mimosifolia*		60	1·00
864/7		*Set of 4*	1·50	2·10

No. 864 exists imperforate from stock dispersed by the liquidator of Format International Security Printers Ltd.

370 Mail Van

(Litho Format)

1978 (4 Dec). *75th Anniv of Ghana Railways. T **370** and similar horiz designs. Multicoloured. P 13½ × 14.*
868	11 p. Type **370**		25	10
869	39 p. Pay and bank car		35	65
870	60 p. Steam locomotive, 1922. .		40	1·00
871	1 c. Diesel locomotive 1960		40	1·40
868/71		*Set of 4*	1·25	2·75

Nos. 868/71 exist imperforate from stock dispersed by the liquidator of Format International Security Printers Ltd.

371 "Orbiter" Spacecraft

(Litho Format)

1979 (5 July). *"Pioneer" Venus Space Project. T **371** and similar horiz designs. Multicoloured. P 14 × 13½.*
872	11 p. Type **371** . .		15	10
873	39 p. "Multiprobe" spacecraft		30	30
874	60 p. "Orbiter" and "Multiprobe" spacecraft in Venus orbit		40	45
875	3 c. Radar chart of Venus		80	1·60
872/5		*Set of 4*	1·50	2·25
MS876	135 × 94 mm. 15, 40, 65 p., 2 c. as Nos.			
872/5. Imperf			1·10	1·25

372 "O Come All Ye Faithful"   **373** Dr. J. B. Danquah (lawyer and nationalist)

(Litho D.L.R.)

1979 (20 Dec). *Christmas. Opening Lines and Scenes from well known Carols. T **372** and similar horiz designs. Multicoloured. P 14 × 14½.*
877	8 p. Type **372**		10	10
878	10 p. "O Little Town of Bethlehem"		10	10
879	15 p. "We Three Kings of Orient Are". .		10	10
880	20 p. "I Saw Three Ships come Sailing By"		10	15
881	2 c. "Away in a Manger". .		40	80
882	4 c. "Ding Dong Merrily on High"		65	1·40
877/82		*Set of 6*	1·25	2·40
MS883	110 × 95 mm. 25, 65 p., 1, 2 c. as Nos. 877, 879 and 881/2			
			75	1·00

(Litho D.L.R.)

1980 (21 Jan). *Great Ghanaians. T **373** and similar vert designs. Multicoloured. P 14 × 13½.*
884	20 p. Type **373**		15	10
885	65 p. John Mensah Sarbah (nationalist)		25	20
886	80 p. Dr. J. E. K. Aggrey (educationalist)		30	30
887	2 c. Dr. Kwame Nkrumah (nationalist)		50	50
888	4 c. G. E. (Paa) Grant (lawyer)		1·10	1·50
884/8		*Set of 5*	2·10	2·25

374 Tribesman ringing Clack Bells   **375** Children in Classroom

(Des G. Vasarhelyi. Litho Format)

1980 (12 Mar). *Death Centenary of Sir Rowland Hill (1979). T **374** and similar horiz designs. Multicoloured. (a) P 14½.*
889	20 p. Type **374**		15	15
890	65 p. Chieftain with Golden Elephant staff . .		35	40
891	2 c. Tribesman banging drums		60	1·25
892	4 c. Chieftain with ivory and gold staff		1·10	2·25
889/92		*Set of 4*	2·00	3·50

(b) P 13½
893	25 p. Type **374**		15	20
894	50 p. As 65 p.		30	40
895	1 c. As 2 c.		50	85
896	5 c. As 4 c.		1·75	3·25
893/6		*Set of 4*	2·40	4·25
MS897	115 × 86 mm. Nos. 893/6. P 14½.		1·00	1·50

Nos. 893/6 were each printed in small sheets of 6 including one *se-tenant* stamp-size label.

(Des J.W. Litho Questa)

1980 (2 Apr). *International Year of the Child (1979). T **375** and similar vert designs. Multicoloured. P 14½.*
898	20 p. Type **375**		15	15
899	65 p. Children playing football		35	45
900	2 c. Children playing in boat. .		65	1·00
901	4 c. Mother and child. .		1·10	1·75
898/901		*Set of 4*	2·00	3·00
MS902	156 × 94 mm. 25, 50 p., 1, 3 c. as Nos.			
898/901			1·25	1·75

"LONDON 1980" 6th - 14th May 1980   **"PAPAL VISIT"** 8th - 9th May 1980
(**376**)   (**377**)

1980 (6 May). *"London 1980" International Stamp Exhibition. Nos. 889/97 optd with T **376**. (a) P 14½.*
903	20 p. Type **374**		15	15
904	65 p. Chieftain with Golden Elephant staff		30	60
905	2 c. Tribesman banging drums		60	1·40
906	4 c. Chieftain with ivory and gold staff		1·10	2·50
903/6 . .		*Set of 4*	2·00	4·25

(b) P 13½
907	25 p. Type **374**		60	1·00
908	50 p. As 65 p.		90	1·50
909	1 c. As 2 c.		1·50	2·25
910	5 c. As 4 c.		3·50	4·50
907/10		*Set of 4*	6·00	8·25
MS911	115 × 86 mm. Nos. 907/10. P 14½		1·00	2·00

1980 (8 May). *Papal Visit. Nos. 898/902 optd with T **377**.*
912	20 p. Type **375**		30	25
913	65 p. Children playing football		70	60
914	2 c. Children playing in boat. .		1·25	1·40
915	4 c. Mother and child. .		2·25	2·50
912/15		*Set of 4*	4·00	4·25
MS916	156 × 94 mm. 25, 50 p., 1, 3 c. as Nos.			
912/15			9·00	7·50

378 Parliament House   **379** Boeing 737 Airliner and Map of West Africa

(Litho Questa)

1980 (4 Aug). *Third Republic Commemoration. T **378** and similar horiz designs. Multicoloured. P 14.*
917	20 p. Type **378**		10	10
918	65 p. Supreme Court		20	25
919	2 c. The Castle		40	60
917/19		*Set of 3*	60	95
MS920	72 × 113 mm. 25 p., 1, 3 c. As Nos. 917/19		60	1·10

(Litho Questa)

1980 (5 Nov). *Fifth Anniv of E.C.O.W.A.S. (Economic Community of West African States). T **379** and similar horiz designs showing symbols named and map of West Africa. Multicoloured. P 14.*
921	20 p. Type **379**		10	10
922	65 p. Radio antenna		15	20
923	80 p. Cog-wheels		20	25
924	2 c. Corn ear . .		35	50
921/4 . .		*Set of 4*	70	90

380 "O.A.U."   **381** "The Adoration of the Magi"

(Litho Questa)

1980 (26 Nov). *Organisation of African Unity First Economic Summit, Nigeria. T **380** and similar vert designs. Multicoloured. P 14½ × 14.*
925	20 p. Type **380**		10	10
926	65 p. Banner with maps of Africa and Ghana		15	20
927	80 p. Map of Africa		15	25
928	2 c. Ghana flag, banner and map of Africa		20	65
925/8		*Set of 4*	55	1·00

(Litho Format)

1980 (10 Dec). *Christmas. Paintings by Fra Angelico. T* **381** *and similar vert designs. Multicoloured. P* 14.
929	15 p. Type **381**		10	10
930	20 p. "The Virgin and Child enthroned with four Angels"		10	10
931	2 c. "The Virgin and Child enthroned with eight Angels"		35	80
932	4 c. "The Annunciation"		60	1·60
929/32		*Set of* 4	1·00	2·25
MS933	77 × 112 mm. 25, 50 p., 1, 3 c. As Nos.			
929/32			75	1·25

382 "Health"   **383** Narina Trogon

(Litho Format)

1980 (18 Dec). *75th Anniv of Rotary International. T* **382** *and similar horiz designs. Multicoloured. P* 14.
934	20 p. Type **382**		10	10
935	65 p. Rotary emblem and motto with maps of World and Ghana		15	30
936	2 c. Rotary emblem, globe and outstretched hands		35	85
937	4 c. "Eradication of Hunger"		60	1·50
934/7		*Set of* 4	1·10	2·50
MS938	121 × 93 mm. 25, 50 p., 1, 3 c. As Nos.			
934/7			1·10	2·00

(Des G. Drummond. Litho Harrison)

1981 (12 Jan). *Birds. T* **383** *and similar vert designs. Multicoloured. P* 14.
939	20 p. Type **383**		1·25	15
940	65 p. White-crowned Robin Chat		2·25	50
941	2 c. Swallow-tailed Bee Eater		2·75	1·75
942	4 c. Rose-ringed Parakeet		4·25	3·25
939/42		*Set of* 4	9·50	5·00
MS943	89×121 mm. 25, 50 p., 1, 3 c. As Nos.			
939/42. P 14½			5·00	4·00

384 Pope John Paul II and Archbishop of Canterbury with President Limann during Papal Visit   **385** Royal Yacht *Britannia*

(Litho Format)

1981 (3 Mar). *First Anniv of Papal Visit. P* 14 × 13½.
944	**384**	20 p. multicoloured	25	15
945		65 p. multicoloured	45	55
946		80 p. multicoloured	60	70
947		2 c. multicoloured	1·10	2·00
944/7		*Set of* 4	2·25	3·00

(Des J.W. Litho Questa)

1981 (8 July–16 Sept). *Royal Wedding. T* **385** *and similar vert designs. Multicoloured.* (i) *Sheet stamps* (8 July). (a) *P* 14.
948	20 p. Prince Charles and Lady Diana Spencer		10	10
949	80 p. Prince Charles on visit to Ghana		15	20
950	4 c. Type **385**		50	80
948/50		*Set of* 3	60	1·00
MS951	95 × 85 mm. 7 c. St. Paul's Cathedral		70	1·25

(b) *P* 12
952	65 p. As 20 p.		15	25
953	1 c. As 80 p.		25	35
954	3 c. Type **385**		70	1·10
952/4		*Set of* 3	1·00	1·50

(ii) *Booklet stamps. P* 14 (16 Sept)
955	2 c. Type **385**		1·00	1·50
	a. Booklet pane. Nos. 955/6 each × 2		4·00	
956	5 c. As 20 p.		1·00	2·75

The 65 p., 1 and 3 c. values were each printed in small sheets of 6 including one *se-tenant* stamp-size label.

The above exist imperforate from a restricted printing (*price for Nos.* 948/50 *set of* 3 £5, **MS951** £6, *Nos.* 952/4 *set of* 3 £7.50 *and booklet pane No.* 955a £12, *all mint*).

STANLEY GIBBONS STAMP COLLECTING SERIES

Introductory booklets on *How to Start, How to Identify Stamps* and *Collecting by Theme*. A series of well illustrated guides at a low price.
Write for details.

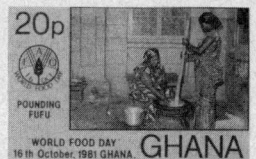

386 Earth Satellite Station   **387** Pounding Fufu

(Litho Questa)

1981 (28 Sept). *Commissioning of Earth Satellite Station. T* **386** *and similar vert designs. Multicoloured. P* 14.
957	20 p. Type **386**		10	10
958	65 p. Satellites beaming signals to Earth		15	15
959	80 p. Satellite		15	20
960	4 c. Satellite orbiting Earth		1·00	1·50
957/60		*Set of* 4	1·25	1·75
MS961	112 × 100 mm. 25 p., 50 p., 1 c., 3 c. As Nos.			
957/60			70	1·40

(Des BG Studio. Litho Format)

1981 (16 Oct). *World Food Day. T* **387** *and similar horiz designs. Multicoloured. P* 13½ × 14.
962	20 p. Type **387**		10	10
963	65 p. Plucking Cocoa		25	35
964	80 p. Preparing Banku		35	45
965	2 c. Garri processing		75	2·25
962/5		*Set of* 4	1·25	2·75
MS966	131 × 99 mm. 25 p., 50 p., 1 c., 3 c. As Nos.			
962/5			1·00	1·50

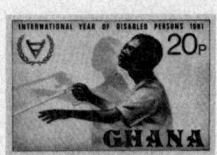

388 "The Betrothal of St. Catherine of Alexandria" (Lucas Cranach)   **389** Blind Person

(Des Clover Mill. Litho Format)

1981 (26 Nov). *Christmas. Details from Paintings. T* **388** *and similar vert designs. Multicoloured. P* 15.
967	15 p. Type **388**		15	10
968	20 p. "Angelic Musicians play for Mary and Child" (Aachener Altares)		15	10
969	65 p. "Child Jesus embracing his Mother" (Gabriel Metsu)		30	25
970	80 p. "Madonna and Child" (Fra Filippo Lippi)		30	30
971	2 c. "The Madonna with Infant Jesus" (Barnaba da Modena)		50	80
972	4 c. "The Immaculate Conception" (Murillo)		60	1·40
967/72		*Set of* 6	1·75	2·50
MS973	82 × 102 mm. 6 c. "Madonna and Child with Angels" (Hans Memling)		1·00	2·25

(Des G. Vasarhelyi. Litho Questa)

1982 (8 Feb). *International Year for Disabled Persons. T* **389** *and similar horiz designs. Multicoloured. P* 14.
974	20 p. Type **389**		10	10
975	65 p. Disabled person with crutches		35	35
976	80 p. Blind child reading braille		45	45
977	4 c. Disabled people helping one another		2·25	2·25
974/7		*Set of* 4	2·75	2·75
MS978	109 × 85 mm. 6 c. Group of disabled people		2·75	3·00

390 African Clawless Otter   **391** *Precis westermanni*

(Des G. Drummond. Litho Harrison)

1982 (22 Feb). *Flora and Fauna. T* **390** *and similar vert designs. Multicoloured. P* 14.
979	20 p. Type **390**		25	15
980	65 p. Bushbuck		60	40
981	80 p. Aardvark		70	50
982	1 c. Scarlet Bell Tree		85	60
983	2 c. Glory-Lilies		1·60	1·25
984	4 c. Blue-Pea		2·75	2·25
979/84		*Set of* 6	6·00	4·75
MS985	76 × 100 mm. 5 c. Chimpanzee		2·00	5·00

(Litho Harrison)

1982 (3 May). *Butterflies. T* **391** *and similar vert designs. Multicoloured. P* 14.
986	20 p. Type **391**		70	15
987	65 p. *Papilio menestheus*		1·50	1·00
988	2 c. *Antanartia delius*		2·50	3·50
989	4 c. *Charaxes castor*		4·00	4·75
986/9		*Set of* 4	8·00	8·50
MS990	98×123 mm. 25 p., 50 p., 1 c., 3 c. As Nos.			
986/9. P 14½			9·00	12·00

392 Scouts planting Tree

(Des M. Diamond. Litho Format)

1982 (1 June). *75th Anniv of Boy Scout Movement. T* **392** *and similar multicoloured designs. P* 14½ × 15.
991	20 p. Type **392**		35	15
992	65 p. Scouts cooking on camp-fire		90	65
993	80 p. Sea Scouts sailing		1·25	85
994	3 c. Scouts observing elephant		2·50	3·25
991/4		*Set of* 4	4·50	4·50
MS995	101 × 71 mm. 5 c. Lord Baden-Powell (*vert*).			
P 15 × 14½			2·75	6·50

393 Initial Stages of Construction

(Des C. Tetteh. Litho Questa)

1982 (28 June). *Kpong Hydro-Electric Project. T* **393** *and similar horiz designs. Multicoloured. P* 14.
996	20 p. Type **393**		65	10
997	65 p. Truck removing rubble		1·40	45
998	80 p. Hydro-electric turbines		1·60	65
999	2 c. Aerial view of completed plant		3·00	1·60
996/9		*Set of* 4	6·00	2·50

394 Footballers

(Des M. and S. Gerber Studio. Litho Format)

1982 (19 July). *World Cup Football Championship, Spain. T* **394** *and similar horiz designs showing footballers.* (a) *P* 14½.
1000	**394**	20 p. multicoloured	10	10
1001	—	65 p. multicoloured	30	35
1002	—	80 p. multicoloured	40	45
1003	—	4 c. multicoloured	1·50	2·00
1000/3		*Set of* 4	2·00	2·50
MS1004	110 × 90 mm. 6 c. multicoloured		3·75	2·75

(b) *P* 14 × 14½
1005	**394**	30 p. multicoloured	20	20
1006	—	80 p. multicoloured (as No. 1001)	35	45
1007	—	1 c. multicoloured (as No. 1002)	40	55
1008	—	3 c. multicoloured (as No. 1003)	1·00	1·60
1005/8		*Set of* 4	1·75	2·50

Nos. 1005/8 were each printed in small sheets including one *se-tenant*, stamp-size, label.

395 The Fight against Tuberculosis   **396** The Shepherds worship Jesus

(Des M. Diamond. Litho Harrison)

1982 (9 Aug). *Centenary of Robert Koch's Discovery of Tubercle Bacillus. T* **395** *and similar horiz designs. Multicoloured. P* 14.
1009	20 p. Type **395**		70	20
1010	65 p. Robert Koch		1·60	1·25
1011	80 p. Robert Koch in Africa		2·00	1·75
1012	1 c. Centenary of discovery of Tuberculosis		2·25	2·75
1013	2 c. Robert Koch and Nobel Prize, 1905		3·25	4·00
1009/13		*Set of* 5	9·00	9·00

(Des E. Mensah. Litho Format)

1982 (22 Dec). *Christmas. T* **396** *and similar vert designs. Multicoloured. P* 14½.

1014	15 p. Type **396**		10	10
1015	20 p. Mary, Joseph and baby Jesus		10	10
1016	65 p. The Three Kings sight star		25	30
1017	4 c. Winged Angel		1·00	1·75
1014/17		*Set of 4*	1·25	2·00
MS1018	90 × 110 mm. 6 c. The Three Kings with Jesus		90	1·75

Nos. 1017/18 exist imperforate from stock dispersed by the liquidator of Format International Security Printers Ltd.

WINNER ITALY
3–1
(398)

397 Ghana and Commonwealth Flags with Coat of Arms

(Des J.W. Litho Format)

1983 (14 Mar). *Commonwealth Day. T* **397** *and similar vert designs. Multicoloured. P* 14½.

1019	20 p. Type **397**		25	15
1020	55 p. Satellite view of Ghana		45	65
1021	80 p. Minerals of Ghana		1·00	1·25
1022	3 c. African Fish Eagle		2·75	4·25
1019/22		*Set of 4*	4·00	5·75

Nos. 1021/2 exist imperforate from stock dispersed by the liquidator of Format International Security Printers Ltd.

1983 (30 May). *Italy's Victory in World Cup Football Championship (1982). Nos. 1000/8 optd with T* **398**, *in gold.* (a) *P* 14½.

1023	**394**	20 p. multicoloured	10	10
1024	–	65 c. multicoloured	15	15
1025	–	80 p. multicoloured	15	20
1026	–	4 c. multicoloured	1·25	1·75
1023/6		*Set of 4*	1·40	2·00
MS1027	110 × 90 mm. 6 c. multicoloured		1·25	1·50

(b) *P* 14 × 14½

1028	**394**	30 p. multicoloured	15	30
1029	–	80 p. multicoloured	50	80
1030	–	1 c. multicoloured	60	95
1031	–	3 c. multicoloured	1·50	2·00
1028/31		*Set of 4*	2·50	3·50

No. MS1027 has an additional overprint, "FINAL: ITALY V. W. GERMANY", on the sheet margin.

INFLATION HANDSTAMPS. During 1983 the value of the Ghanaian currency fell drastically and as a result, there was a considerable rise in postal rates.

To cope with this situation supplies of past commemorative issues were made available from the post offices, many being handstamped "NOT FOR PHILATELIC USE" in one line within a frame. These handstamps were usually applied in blue, haphazardly across the sheet with examples so far reported on Nos. 656/7, 664, 670, 680, 689, 703, 708, 718, 746/7, 753, 757, 762/3, 766, 775, 780/1, 791, 793, 799, 814, 817, 846, 850/1, 853, 856/7, 860, 865, 867, 869, 875 and 882.

(398a)
399 Short-finned Pilot Whale

1983 (Oct). *No.* 470 *surch with T* **398a**.

1031a	1 c. on 20 n.p. deep blue and new blue		40	40
	ab. Surch triple			
	ac. Surch double			
	ad. Surch double, one inverted			

(Des J. Iskowitz. Litho Format)

1983 (15 Nov). *Coastal Marine Mammals. T* **399** *and similar horiz designs. Multicoloured. P* 14½.

1032	1 c. Type **399**		1·00	1·00
1033	1 c. 40, Risso's Dolphin		1·10	1·10
1034	2 c. 30, False Killer Whale		1·25	1·25
1035	3 c. Spinner Dolphin		1·60	1·60
1036	5 c. Atlantic Hump-backed Dolphin		6·25	6·25
1032/6		*Set of 5*	6·25	6·25
MS1037	117 × 76 mm. 6 c. As 5 c.		1·00	1·00

No. MS1037 exists imperforate from stock dispersed by the liquidator of Format International Security Printers Ltd.

400 Banded Jewelfish
401 Communication Devices

(Des and litho D.L.R.)

1983 (12 Dec). *T* **400** *and similar designs. P* 14.

1038	5 p. multicoloured	30	20
1039	10 p. multicoloured	30	20
1040	20 p. multicoloured	40	20
1041	50 p. deep grey-green, yellow-orange and black	40	30
1042	1 c. yellow-orange, violet-blue and black	50	20
1043	2 c. multicoloured	50	30
1044	3 c. multicoloured	60	20
1045	4 c. multicoloured	40	40
1046	5 c. multicoloured	50	40
1047	10 c. multicoloured	65	1·00
1038/47	*Set of 10*	4·00	3·25

Designs: *Horiz*—10 p. Banded Jewelfish (*different*); 2 c. Jet airliner. *Vert*—20 p. *Haemanthus rupestris*; 50 p. Mounted warrior; 1 c. Scorpion; 3 c. White-collared Mangabey; 4 c. Demidoff's Galago; 5 c. *Kaemferia nigerica*; 10 c. Grey-backed Camaroptera.

(Des PAD Studio. Litho Questa)

1983 (13 Dec). *World Communications Year. T* **401** *and similar vert designs. Multicoloured. P* 14.

1048	1 c. Type **401**	15	25
1049	1 c. 40, Satellite dish aerial	20	30
1050	2 c. 30, Cable and cable-laying ship	35	55
1051	3 c. Switchboard operators	40	65
1052	5 c. Aircraft cockpit and air traffic controllers	55	85
1048/52	*Set of 5*	1·50	2·40
MS1053	95 × 70 mm. 6 c. Space satellite	30	30

402 Children receiving Presents
403 Soldiers with Rifles

(Des Designs Images. Litho Questa)

1983 (28 Dec). *Christmas. T* **402** *and similar multicoloured designs. P* 14 × 13½ (70 p. and 3 c.) *or* 14½ × 14 (*others*).

1054	70 p. Type **402**	20	10
1055	1 c. Nativity and Star of Bethlehem (28 × 36 mm)	20	10
1056	1 c. 40, Children celebrating (28 × 36 mm)	35	55
1057	2 c. 30, Family praying (28 × 36 mm)	45	80
1058	3 c. Dancing to bongo drum	55	1·00
1054/8	*Set of 5*	1·60	2·25
MS1059	70 × 90 mm. 6 c. As 2 c. 30	30	1·00

(Des and litho B.D.T.)

1984 (26 Jan). *Namibia Day. T* **403** *and similar vert designs. P* 14.

1060	50 p. blue-green and black	10	10
1061	1 c. multicoloured	10	10
1062	1 c. 40, new blue, bright blue and black	15	15
1063	2 c. 30, multicoloured	20	25
1064	3 c. multicoloured	25	30
1060/4	*Set of 5*	65	75

Designs:—1 c. Soldiers supported by tank; 1 c. 40, Machete cutting chains; 2 c. 30, Peasant woman; 3 c. Soldiers and artillery support.

(404)
(405)

1984 (8 Feb)–85. (a) *Nos.* 948/52 *and* 954 *surch as T* **404**

1065	1 c. on 20 p. Prince Charles and Lady Diana Spencer	2·50	3·00
1066	9 c. on 65 p. Prince Charles and Lady Diana Spencer (1985)	3·00	4·00
1067	9 c. on 80 p. Prince Charles on visit to Ghana	3·00	4·00
	a. Imperf (pair) with surch inverted	£275	
1068	20 c. on 3 c. Type **385** (1985)	3·50	6·00
1069	20 c. on 4 c. Type **385**	3·50	6·00
MS1070	95 × 85 mm. 60 c. on 7 c. St. Paul's Cathedral	1·40	3·00

The above exist imperforate from a restricted printing (*Price for Nos.* 1065, 1067, 1069 *set of 3* £8, *Nos.* 1066 *and* 1068 *set of 2* £10 *and No.* MS1070 £20, *all mint*).

(b) *Nos.* 991/2 *and* 994/5 *surch as T* **405**

1071	10 c. on 20 p. Type **392**	40	45
1072	19 c. on 65 p. Scouts cooking on camp-fire	80	85
1073	30 c. on 3 c. Scouts observing elephant	1·50	1·50
MS1074	101 × 71 mm. 60 c. on 5 c. Lord Baden-Powell	1·50	3·50

(c) *Nos.* 1000/6 *and* 1008 *surch as T* **405**

1075	**394**	1 c. on 20 p. multicoloured	30	30
1076	–	9 c. on 65 p. multicoloured	70	70
1077	–	9 c. on 3 c. multicoloured	70	70
1078	**394**	10 c. on 30 p. multicoloured	70	70
1079	–	10 c. on 80 p. mult (No. 1002)	70	70
1080	–	20 c. on 4 c. mult (No. 1006)	1·50	1·50
1081	–	20 c. on 4 c. multicoloured	1·50	1·50
MS1082	110 × 90 mm. 60 c. on 6 c. multicoloured		1·50	2·25

(d) *Nos.* 1019/22 *surch as T* **405**

1083	1 c. on 20 p. Type **397**	10	10
1084	9 c. on 55 p. Satellite view of Ghana	40	45
1085	30 c. on 80 p. Minerals of Ghana	1·50	1·50
1086	50 c. on 3 c. African Fish Eagle	2·50	3·00

(e) *Nos.* 1023/9 *and* 1031 *surch as T* **405**

1087	**394**	1 c. on 20 p. multicoloured	10	10
1088	–	9 c. on 65 p. multicoloured	40	45
1089	–	9 c. on 3 c. multicoloured	40	45
1090	**394**	10 c. on 30 p. multicoloured	40	45
1091	–	10 c. on 80 p. mult (No. 1025)	40	45
1092	–	20 c. on 80 p. mult (No. 1029)	80	85
1093	–	20 c. on 4 c. multicoloured	80	85
MS1094	110 × 90 mm. 60 c. on 6 c. multicoloured		1·00	2·00
1065/9, 1071/3, 1075/81, 1083/93		*Set of 26*	30·00	35·00

c10

19ᵀᴴ U.P.U CONGRESS – HAMBURG
(406)

1984 (19 June). *Universal Postal Union Congress, Hamburg. Nos.* 1035/7 *surch as T* **406**.

1095	10 c. on 3 c. Spinner Dolphin	40	45
1096	50 c. on 5 c. Atlantic Hump-backed Dolphin	2·10	2·25
MS1097	117 × 76 mm. 60 c. on 6 c. As No. 1096	2·50	3·50

407 Cross and Crown of Thorns
408 Women's 400 Metre Race

(Litho Format)

1984 (26 June). *Easter. T* **407** *and similar vert designs. Multicoloured. P* 15.

1098	1 c. Type **407**	10	10
1099	1 c. 40, Christ praying	10	10
1100	2 c. 30, The Resurrection	10	10
1101	3 c. Palm Sunday	10	15
1102	50 c. Christ on the road to Emmaus	1·10	2·25
1098/102	*Set of 5*	1·25	2·40
MS1103	102 × 86 mm. 60 c. Type **407**	1·00	2·50

No. 1098 exists imperforate from stock dispersed by the liquidator of Format International Security Printers Ltd.

(Des P. Cox and J. Iskowitz. Litho Format)

1984 (13 Aug). *Olympic Games, Los Angeles. T* **408** *and similar vert designs. Multicoloured. P* 15.

1104	1 c. Type **408**	10	10
1105	1 c. 40, Boxing	15	10
1106	2 c. 30, Hockey	20	15
1107	3 c. Men's 400 metre hurdles race	20	15
1108	50 c. Rhythmic gymnastics	2·40	3·50
1104/8	*Set of 5*	2·75	3·50
MS1109	103 × 78 mm. 70 c. Football	2·50	3·50

No. 1108 is inscribed "RYTHMIC" in error.

Nos. 1104/8 exist imperforate from stock dispersed by the liquidator of Format International Security Printers Ltd.

409 *Amorphophallus johnsonii*
410 Young Bongo

(Litho Harrison)

1984 (24 Aug). *Flowers. T* **409** *and similar vert designs. Multicoloured. P* 14.

1110	1 c. Type **409**	10	10
1111	1 c. 40, *Pancratium trianthum*	10	10
1112	2 c. 30, *Eulophia cucullata*	15	15
1113	3 c. *Amorphophallus abyssinicus*	15	15
1114	50 c. *Chlorophytum togoense*	3·00	5·00
1110/14	*Set of 5*	3·00	5·00
MS1115	70 × 96 mm. 60 c. Type **409**	2·50	4·00

(Des Susan David. Litho B.D.T.)

1984 (7 Sept). *Endangered Antelopes. T* **410** *and similar horiz designs. Multicoloured. P* 14.

1116	1 c. Type **410**	30	20
1117	2 c. 30, Bongo bucks fighting	55	55
1118	3 c. Bongo family	70	70
1119	20 c. Bongo herd in high grass	2·50	3·50
1116/19	*Set of 4*	3·50	4·50
MS1120	Two sheets, each 100 × 71 mm. (a) 70 c. Head of Kob; (b) 70 c. Head of Bush buck		
	Set of 2 sheets	9·00	12·00

411 Dipo Girl 412 The Three Wise
Men Bringing Gifts

(Des and litho B.D.T.)

1984 (3 Oct). *Ghanaian Culture. T 411 and similar vert designs. Multicoloured. P 14.*

1121	1 c. Type 411		10	10
1122	1 c. 40, Adowa dancer		10	10
1123	2 c. 30, Agbadza dancer		10	15
1124	3 c. Damba dancer		10	15
1125	50 c. Dipo dancer		1·75	3·00
1121/5		Set of 5	1·90	3·25
MS1126	70×84 mm. 70 c. Mandolin player.			
	P 14×15		2·00	3·00

(Litho D.L.R.)

1984 (19 Nov). *Christmas. T 412 and similar vert designs. Multicoloured. P 12×12½.*

1127	70 p. Type 412		10	10
1128	1 c. Choir of angels		10	10
1129	1 c. 40, Mary and shepherds at manger		10	10
1130	2 c. The flight into Egypt		10	15
1131	3 c. Simeon blessing Jesus		10	15
1132	50 c. Holy Family and angels		1·75	3·00
1127/32		Set of 6	1·90	3·25
MS1133	70×90 mm. 70 c. Type 412		2·00	2·75

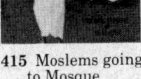

VALERIE
BRISCO-HOOKS
U.S.A.
(413)

414 The Queen Mother
attending Church Service

1984 (3 Dec). *Olympic Medal Winners, Los Angeles. Nos. 1104/9 optd as T 413 in gold.*

1134	1 c. Type 408 (optd with T 413)		10	10
1135	1 c. 40, Boxing (optd "U.S. WINNERS")		10	10
1136	2 c. 30, Field hockey (optd "PAKISTAN (FIELD HOCKEY)")		10	10
1137	3 c. Men's 400 metre hurdles race (optd "EDWIN MOSES U.S.A.")		10	10
1138	50 c. Rhythmic gymnastics (optd "LAURI FUNG CANADA")		1·50	1·60
1134/8		Set of 5	1·60	1·75
MS1139	103×78 mm. 70 c. Football (optd "FRANCE")		1·75	2·50

Nos. 1135 and MS1139 have the overprint in one line and Nos. 1136/8 in two.

(Des J.W. Litho Questa)

1985 (24 July). *Life and Times of Queen Elizabeth the Queen Mother. T 414 and similar vert designs. Multicoloured. P 14.*

1140	5 c. Type 414		10	15
1141	12 c. At Ascot Races		25	30
1142	100 c. At Clarence House on her 84th birthday		1·75	2·50
1140/2		Set of 3	1·75	2·75
MS1143	56×84 mm. 110 c. With Prince Charles at Garter ceremony		1·75	3·00

Stamps as Nos. 1140/2, but with face values of 8 c., 20 c. and 70 c., exist from additional sheetlets of 5 plus a label issued December 1985. These also have changed background colours and are perforated 12×12½ (Price for set of 3 stamps £2.25 mint).

Nos. 1140/3 and the stamps from the additional sheetlets also exist surcharged "90th Birthday 4th August 1990", but are reported not to have been available in Ghana.

415 Moslems going 416 Youths clearing
to Mosque Refuse ("Make Ghana
Clean")

(Des E. Mensah. Litho B.D.T.)

1985 (1 Aug). *Islamic Festival of Id-el-Fitr. T 415 and similar vert designs. Multicoloured. P 14.*

1144	5 c. Type 415		25	20
1145	8 c. Moslems at prayer		35	30
1146	12 c. Pilgrims visiting the Dome of the Rock		55	45
1147	18 c. Preaching the Koran		70	60
1148	50 c. Banda Nkwanta Mosque, Accra, and map of Ghana		1·75	1·60
1144/8		Set of 5	3·25	2·75

(Des E. Mensah. Litho Questa)

1985 (9 Aug). *International Youth Year. T 416 and similar vert designs. Multicoloured. P 14×13½.*

1149	5 c. Type 416		10	10
1150	8 c. Planting sapling ("Make Ghana Green")		15	15
1151	12 c. Youth carrying bananas ("Feed Ghana")		20	25
1152	100 c. Open-air class ("Educate Ghana")		1·60	2·25
1149/52		Set of 4	1·75	2·50
MS1153	103×78 mm. 110 c. As 8 c.		1·75	3·00

417 Honda "Interceptor", 1984 418 Fork-tailed
Flycatcher

(Litho Questa)

1985 (9 Sept). *Centenary of the Motorcycle. T 417 and similar multicoloured designs. P 14.*

1154	5 c. Type 417		55	55
1155	8 c. DKW, 1938		65	75
1156	12 c. BMW "R 32", 1923		1·00	1·00
1157	100 c. NSU, 1900		5·50	7·00
1154/7		Set of 4	7·00	8·50
MS1158	78×108 mm. 110 c. Zündapp, 1973 (vert)		4·50	4·75

(Litho Questa)

1985 (16 Oct). *Birth Bicentenary of John J. Audubon (ornithologist). T 418 and similar vert designs showing original paintings. Multicoloured. P 14.*

1159	5 c. Type 418		1·00	40
1160	8 c. Barred Owl		2·00	1·75
1161	12 c. Black-throated Mango		2·00	1·75
1162	100 c. White-crowned Pigeon		5·50	9·00
1159/62		Set of 4	9·50	11·50
MS1163	85×115 mm. 110 c. Downy Woodpecker		5·50	3·50

No. 1159 is inscribed "York-tailed Fly Catcher" in error.
Nos. 1159/63 also exist imperforate from a limited printing.

419 United Nations
Building, New York

(Des Mary Walters. Litho D.L.R.)

1985 (24 Oct). *40th Anniv of United Nations Organization. T 419 and similar horiz designs. Multicoloured. P 14½ (18 c.) or 14½×14 (others).*

1164	5 c. Type 419		10	10
1165	8 c. Flags of member nations and U.N. Building		15	15
1166	12 c. Dove with olive branch		15	25
1167	18 c. General Assembly		25	35
1168	100 c. Flags of Ghana and United Nations		1·25	1·75
1164/8		Set of 5	1·60	2·40
MS1169	90×70 mm. 110 c. United Nations (New York) 1955 4 cent 10th anniv stamp		1·50	2·00

Nos. 1164/9 also exist imperforate from a limited printing.

420 Coffee

(Des J. Iskowitz. Litho B.D.T.)

1985 (4 Nov). *20th Anniv of United Nations Conference on Trade and Development. T 420 and similar horiz designs showing export products. Multicoloured. P 14.*

1170	5 c. Type 420		10	10
1171	8 c. Cocoa		15	15
1172	12 c. Timber		25	25
1173	18 c. Bauxite		1·25	90
1174	100 c. Gold		6·50	8·50
1170/4		Set of 5	7·50	9·00
MS1175	104×74 mm. 110 c. Agricultural produce and plate of food. P 15×14		2·00	2·50

---

421 Growth Monitoring

(Des E. Mensah. Litho B.D.T.)

1985 (16 Dec). *U.N.I.C.E.F. Child Survival Campaign. T 421 and similar horiz designs. Multicoloured. P 14.*

1176	5 c. Type 421		30	10
1177	8 c. Oral rehydration therapy		50	30
1178	12 c. Breast feeding		70	40
1179	100 c. Immunization		3·00	4·50
		Set of 4	4·00	4·75
MS1180	99×69 mm. 110 c. Campaign logo. P 15×14		1·75	2·25

422 Airline Stewardess and Boys
with Stamp Album

(Litho Questa)

1986 (27 Oct). *"Ameripex" International Stamp Exhibition, Chicago. T 422 and similar multicoloured designs. P 14.*

1181	5 c. Type 422		15	15
1182	25 c. Globe and Douglas DC-10 aircraft		60	45
1183	100 c. Ghana Airways stewardess (vert)		2·25	3·00
1181/3		Set of 3	2·75	3·25
MS1184	90×70 mm. 150 c. Stamp collecting class		2·25	2·50

Nos. 1181/4 also exist imperforate from a limited printing.

423 Kejetia Roundabout, Kumasi 424 Tackling

(Litho B.D.T.)

1986 (10 Nov). *"Inter-Tourism '86" Conference. T 423 and similar horiz designs. Multicoloured. P 14.*

1185	5 c. Type 423		10	10
1186	15 c. Fort St. Jago, Elmina		30	30
1187	25 c. Tribal warriors		45	45
1188	100 c. Chief holding audience		1·75	3·25
1185/8		Set of 4	2·40	3·75
MS1189	110×70 mm. 150 c. African Elephants. P 15×14		3·75	5·50

(Litho D.L.R.)

1987 (16 Jan). *World Cup Football Championship, Mexico (1986). T 424 and similar vert designs. Multicoloured. P 14×14½.*

1190	5 c. Type 424		15	10
1191	15 c. Player taking control of ball		25	15
1192	25 c. Player kicking ball		40	25
1193	100 c. Player with ball		1·40	1·25
1190/3		Set of 4	2·00	1·50
MS1194	90×70 mm. 150 c. Player kicking ball (different)		1·50	2·00

Nos. 1190/4 also exist imperforate from a limited printing.

425 Fertility Doll 426 Children of Different Races,
Peace Doves and Sun

(Litho D.L.R.)

1987 (22 Jan). *Ghanaian Fertility Dolls. T 425 and similar vert designs showing different dolls. P 14×14½.*

1195	425	5 c. multicoloured	10	10
1196	–	15 c. multicoloured	20	15
1197	–	25 c. multicoloured	35	25
1198	–	100 c. multicoloured	1·25	1·50
1195/8		Set of 4	1·60	1·75
MS1199	90×70 mm. 425 150 c. multicoloured		1·50	2·00

(Litho D.L.R.)

1987 (2 Mar). *International Peace Year (1986). T 426 and similar multicoloured designs.* P 14 × 14½ (100 c.) or 14½ × 14 (others).

1200	5 c. Type 426	15	10
1201	75 c. Plough, peace dove and rising sun	75	25
1202	100 c. Peace dove, olive branch and globe (vert)	2·50	3·00
1200/2	Set of 3	3·00	3·00
MS1203	90 × 70 mm. 150 c. Dove perched on plough (vert). P 14 × 14½	1·75	2·25

427 Lumber and House under Construction   **428** Demonstrator and Arms breaking Shackles

(Des and litho B.D.T.)

1987 (10 Mar). *"Gifex '87" International Forestry Exposition, Accra. T 427 and similar horiz designs. Multicoloured.* P 14.

1204	5 c. Type 427	10	10
1205	15 c. Planks and furniture	15	15
1206	25 c. Felled trees	30	25
1207	200 c. Logs and wood carvings	1·90	2·25
1204/7	Set of 4	2·25	2·50

(Des W. Hanson. Litho D.L.R.)

1987 (8 Apr). *Appearance of Halley's Comet (1986). Horiz designs as T 123 of Anguilla. Multicoloured.* P 14½ × 14.

1208	5 c. Mikhail Lomonosov (scientist) and Chamber of Curiosities, St. Petersburg	20	10
1209	25 c. Lunar probe "Surveyor 3", 1966	70	30
1210	200 c. Wedgwood plaques for Isaac Newton, 1790, and "Apollo 11" Moon landing, 1968	3·25	2·25
1208/10	Set of 3	3·75	2·40
MS1211	100 × 70 mm. 250 c. Halley's Comet	3·50	2·75

Nos. 1208/11 also exist imperforate from a limited printing.

(Litho D.L.R.)

1987 (18 May). *Solidarity with the People of Southern Africa. T 428 and similar vert designs. Multicoloured.* P 14 × 14½.

1212	5 c. Type 428	10	10
1213	15 c. Miner and gold bars	25	15
1214	25 c. Xhosa warriors	30	25
1215	100 c. Nelson Mandela and shackles	1·25	2·00
1212/15	Set of 4	1·60	2·25
MS1216	70 × 90 mm. 150 c. Nelson Mandela	1·50	2·00

429 Aerophones

(Litho D.L.R.)

1987 (13 July). *Musical Instruments. T 429 and similar horiz designs. Multicoloured.* P 14½ × 14.

1217	5 c. Type 429	10	10
1218	15 c. Xylophone	15	15
1219	25 c. Chordophones	30	25
1220	100 c. Membranophones	1·00	1·25
1217/20	Set of 4	1·40	1·50
MS1221	90 × 70 mm. 200 c. Idiophones	1·90	2·25

430 Woman filling Water Pot at Pump   **431** Ga Women preparing Kpokpoi for Homowo Festival

(Litho B.D.T.)

1987 (21 Sept). *International Year of Shelter for the Homeless. T 430 and similar horiz designs. Multicoloured.* P 14.

1222	5 c. Type 430	10	10
1223	15 c. Building house from breeze-blocks	15	15
1224	25 c. Modern village with stream	25	25
1225	100 c. Modern houses with verandahs	1·25	1·25
1222/5	Set of 4	1·50	1·50

(Litho Format)

1988 (6 Jan). *Ghana Festivals. T 431 and similar vert designs. Multicoloured.* P 15.

1226	5 c. Type 431	10	10
1227	15 c. Efute hunters with deer, Aboakyir festival	15	15
1228	25 c. Fanti chief dancing at Odwira festival	25	25
1229	100 c. Chief in palanquin, Yam festival	1·25	1·25
1226/9	Set of 4	1·50	1·50

432 Port Installation   **433** Nurse giving Injection

(Litho National Ptg Wks, Havana)

1988 (26 Jan). *5th Anniversary of 31 December Revolution (1987). T 432 and similar horiz designs. Multicoloured.* P 13.

1230	5 c. Type 432	1·00	40
1231	15 c. Repairing railway line	7·00	2·25
1232	25 c. Planting cocoa	1·25	55
1233	100 c. Miners with ore truck	7·50	7·50
1230/3	Set of 4	15·00	9·50

(Litho Format)

1988 (1 Feb). *U.N.I.C.E.F. Global Immunization Campaign. T 433 and similar vert designs. Multicoloured.* P 15.

1234	5 c. Type 433	20	10
1235	15 c. Girl receiving injection	25	20
1236	25 c. Schoolgirl crippled by polio	35	50
1237	100 c. Nurse giving oral vaccine to baby	60	2·25
1234/7	Set of 4	1·25	2·75

434 Fishing   **435** Akwadjan Men

(Des E. Mensah. Litho National Ptg Wks, Havana)

1988 (14 Apr). *10th Anniv of International Fund for Agricultural Development. T 434 and similar horiz designs. Multicoloured.* P 13.

1238	5 c. Type 434	45	20
1239	15 c. Women harvesting crops	70	30
1240	25 c. Cattle	85	40
1241	100 c. Village granaries	2·50	4·25
1238/41	Set of 4	4·00	4·75

(Litho Questa)

1988 (9 May). *Tribal Costumes. T 435 and similar vert designs. Multicoloured.* P 14.

1242	5 c. Type 435	15	10
1243	25 c. Banaa man	35	20
1244	250 c. Agwasen woman	1·50	2·00
1242/4	Set of 3	1·75	2·00

¢20.00   ¢20.00

(436)   (436a)

¢50.00   ¢50

(437)   (437a)

¢50.00   ¢50.00

(438)   (438a)

1988 (19 July)–**90**. *Nos. 460, 464/6, 469/70, 1031a, 1038/42, 1044 and 1046 surch as T 436/8a.*

1245	–	20 c. on 50 p. dp grey-green, yell-orge & blk (No. 1041) (surch as T 436)	30	1
		a. Horiz pair, one without surch		
		b. Surch inverted	†	
1246	–	20 c. on 1 c. yell-orge, vio-blue & black (No. 1042) (surch T 436) (9.88)	30	15
		a. Surch double		
		b. Surch double, one albino		
		c. Surch double, one albino and one inverted		
		d. Surch double, one inverted (T 436 + 436a)		
		e. Pair, one without surch		
		f. Surch sideways		
		g. Surch triple		
		h. "2" omitted (R. 4/3)		
1246m	–	20 c. on 1 c. yellow-orange, violet-bl & blk (No. 1042) (surch T 436a)		
		ma. Surch double		
		mb. Surch double, one inverted		
		mc. Surch double, one sideways		
		md. Surch inverted		
		me. Pair, one without surch		
		mf. Albino surch		
		mg. Small "0"s in surch (R. 2/6)		
		mh. Space between "C 20." and "00" (R. 1/5)		
1247	–	50 c. on 10 n.p. multicoloured (No. 469) (surch T 437)	30	25
		a. Vert pair, one without surch		
		b. Surch inverted		
1248	–	50 c. on 20 n.p. deep blue & new blue (No. 470) (surch T 437a) (1990)	2·00	45
1249	–	50 c. on 20 n.p. deep blue and new blue (No. 470) (surch as T 437, reading down) (1990)	2·00	45
		a. Surch double		
1250	–	50 c. on 10 p. multicoloured (No. 1039) (surch T 438) (9.88)	30	15
		a. Pair, one without surch		
1250d	–	50 c. on 10 p. multicoloured (No. 1039) (surch T 438a)		
		da. Pair, one without surch		
		db. Surch inverted		
		dc. Surch on front and back		
		dd. Surch on front and surch inverted on back		
		de. Surch on front and double surch, one inverted, one sideways, on back		
1251	–	50 c. on 1 c. on 20 n.p. deep blue and new blue (No. 1031a) (surch T 437) (1990)	2·00	45
		a. Surch inverted		
		b. Pair, one without surch		
		c. Surch omitted, inverted on back		
		d. Albino surch (T 437a)		
1252	–	50 c. on 1 c. on 20 n.p. deep blue and new blue (No. 1031a) (surch as T 437 reading down) (1990)	2·00	45
		a. Surch double		
		b. "5C0.00" (R. 1/2)		
		c. Surch omitted, inverted on back		
		d. Albino surch		
		e. Surch as T 437 reading up		
		ea. Surch double, both reading up		
		eb. Surch double, reading up and down		
		ec. Surch triple, two reading up (one albino) and one reading down		
		ed. "5C0.00" (R. 6/4)		
		ee. Pair, one without surch		
1253	–	50 c. on 1 c. on 20 n.p. deep blue and new blue (No. 1031a) (horiz surch as T 437) (1991)	2·00	45
1254	–	50 c. on 1 c. yellow-orge, violet-blue and black (No. 1042) (surch as T 436) (1990)	2·00	45
		a. Decimal point omitted from surcharge (R. 4/6)		
1255	230	60 c. on 1 n.p. multicoloured (surch as T 437) (1990)	1·50	45
		a. Surch inverted		
		b. Surch double		
		c. Surch double, one inverted		
		d. Surch double, one sideways		
		e. Surch double, one albino		
		f. Surch triple, one albino		
		g. Surch triple, one albino		
		h. Surch on front, inverted surch on back		
		i. Pair, one without surch		
1256	235	60 c. on 4 n.p. mult (surch as T 437)	2·00	30
		a. Surch double		
		b. Surch double, one inverted		
		c. Surch double, one albino		
		d. Surch inverted		
1257	–	60 c. on 3 c. multicoloured (No. 1044) (surch as T 438) (1989)	50	30
		a. Decimal point omitted from surch (R. 4/5)		
		b. Vert pair, one without surch		
1258	400	80 c. on 5 p. mult (surch as T 437)		
		a. Pair, one without surch		
		b. Surch double		
1259	–	80 c. on 5 c. multicoloured (No. 1046) (surch as T 438) (1990)	2·75	3·00
1260	–	100 c. on 3 n.p. multicoloured (No. 464) (surch as T 437) (1990)	4·00	4·50
		a. Surch inverted		
1261	–	100 c. on 20 n.p. deep blue and new blue (No. 470) (surch as T 437)	50	55
		a. Horiz pair, one without surch		
1262	–	100 c. on 20 p. multicoloured (No. 1040) (surch as T 436) (9.88)	50	55
		a. Surch double, one sideways		
		b. Horiz pair, one without surch		
		c. Surch inverted		

▌263	– 100 c. on 3 c. multicoloured (No. 1044) (surch as T 438a) (1990)	50	55
▌264	236 200 c. on 6 n.p. mult (surch as T 437)	50	65
	a. Surch double		

Other handstamped and manuscript surcharges can be found used during 1988–89, but it is understood that only those listed above were issued by the postal authorities.

Ghana ¢20·00

Ghana ¢20.00

440 Boxing   441 Nutrition Lecture

(Litho Questa)

1988 (10 Oct). *Olympic Games, Seoul.* T **440** *and similar horiz designs. Multicoloured.* P 14.

1265	20 c. Type **440**	20	15
1266	60 c. Athletics	55	55
1267	80 c. Discus-throwing	70	80
1268	100 c. Javelin-throwing	90	1·10
1269	350 c. Weightlifting	2·25	3·00
1265/9	Set of 5	4·25	5·00
MS1270	75×105 mm. 500 c. As 80 c.	4·00	3·00

Nos. 1265/70 also exist imperforate from a limited printing.

(Litho B.D.T.)

1988 (14 Dec). *125th Anniv of International Red Cross.* T **441** *and similar vert designs. Multicoloured.* P 14.

1271	20 c. Type **441**	40	15
1272	50 c. Red Cross volunteer with blind woman	90	90
1273	60 c. Distributing flood relief supplies	1·00	1·00
1274	200 c. Giving first aid	2·50	3·25
1271/4	Set of 4	4·25	4·75

448 French Royal Standard and Field Gun   449 Storming the Bastille

(Litho B.D.T.)

1989 (7 July). *"Philexfrance 89" International Stamp Exhibition, Paris.* T **448** *and similar multicoloured designs.* P 14.

1341	20 c. Type **448**	50	25
1342	60 c. Regimental standard, 1789, and French infantryman	1·00	90
1343	80 c. Revolutionary standard, 1789, and pistol	1·25	1·00
1344	350 c. Tricolour, 1794, and musket	3·25	5·00
1341/4	Set of 4	5·50	6·50
MS1345	77×106 mm. 600 c. Street plan of Paris, 1789 (horiz)	3·00	3·50

Christmas 1988 ¢20·00

GHANA   GHANA ¢20·00

442 Tropical Forest   443 "African Solidarity"

(Litho B.D.T.)

1988 (19 Dec). *Christmas.* T **442** *and similar multicoloured designs.* P 14.

1275	20 c. Type **442**	15	10
1276	60 c. Christ Child (vert)	35	35
1277	80 c. Virgin and Child with Star (vert)	50	60
1278	100 c. Three Wise Men following Star	60	70
1279	350 c. Symbolic Crucifixion (vert)	2·00	2·50
1275/9	Set of 5	3·25	3·75
MS1280	100×70 mm. 500 c. Virgin and Child (vert)	2·50	2·75

Nos. 1275/80 also exist imperforate from a limited printing.

(Litho B.D.T.)

1989 (3 Jan). *25th Anniv of Organization of African Unity (1988).* T **443** *and similar multicoloured designs.* P 14.

1281	20 c. Type **443**	10	10
1282	50 c. O.A.U. Headquarters, Addis Ababa	15	20
1283	60 c. Emperor Haile Selassie and Ethiopian flag (horiz)	20	25
1284	200 c. Kwame Nkrumah (former Ghanaian President) and flag (horiz)	60	85
1281/4	Set of 4	90	1·25

GHANA ¢20

A. ZUELOW DDR 60 KG

444 "Amor"   (445)

(Litho B.D.T.)

1989 (16 Jan). *500th Birth Anniversary of Titian (artist).* T **444** *and similar multicoloured designs. Multicoloured.* P 14.

1285	20 c. Type **444**	40	15
1286	60 c. "The Appeal"	90	65
1287	80 c. "Bacchus and Ariadne" (detail)	1·10	85
1288	100 c. "Portrait of Musician"	1·40	1·60
1289	350 c. "Philip II seated"	3·50	4·50
1285/9	Set of 5	6·50	7·00
MS1290	77×115 mm. 500 c. "Portrait of a Gentleman"	2·50	2·75

1989 (23 Jan). *Olympic Medal Winners, Seoul.* Nos. 1265/70 optd as T **445**.

1291	20 c. Type **440** (optd with T **445**)	10	10
1292	60 c. Athletics (optd "G. BORDIN ITALY MARATHON")	20	25
1293	80 c. Discus-throwing (optd "J. SCHULT DDR")	25	30
1294	100 c. Javelin-throwing (optd "T. KORJUS FINLAND")	30	35
1295	350 c. Weightlifting (optd "B. GUIDIKOV BULGARIA 75 KG")	1·00	1·10
1291/5	Set of 5	1·60	1·90
MS1296	75×105 mm. 500 c. As 80 c. (optd "GOLD J. SCHULT DDR SILVER R. OUBARTAS USSR BRONZE R. DANNEBERG W. GERMANY" on sheet margin)	2·10	2·10

¢100   ¢100   C60

(446)   (447)

1989 (3 July–20 Nov). *Various stamps surch as T* **446/7**.

(a) On Nos. 949/50 and 952/4 (20 Nov)

1297	80 c. on 65 p. Prince Charles and Lady Diana Spencer	35	40
1298	100 c. on 80 p. Prince Charles on visit to Ghana	45	50
1299	100 c. on 1 c. Prince Charles on visit to Ghana	45	50
1300	300 c. on 3 c. Type **385**	1·25	1·60
1301	500 c. on 4 c. Type **385**	2·25	2·75
1297/1301	Set of 5	4·25	5·25

(b) On Nos. 1048/51 and **MS**1053 *(18 Sept)*

1302	60 c. on 1 c. Type **401**	50	50
1303	80 c. on 1 c. 40, Satellite dish aerial	65	65
1304	200 c. on 2 c. 30, Cable and cable-laying ship	1·75	2·00
1305	300 c. on 3 c. Switchboard operators	2·00	2·25
1302/5	Set of 4	4·50	4·75
MS1306	95×70 mm. 500 c. on 6 c. Space satellite	3·75	4·75

(c) On Nos. 1104/7 and **MS**1109

1307	60 c. on 1 c. Type **408**	30	30
1308	80 c. on 1 c. 40, Boxing	40	40
1309	200 c. on 2 c. 30, Hockey	1·25	1·60
1310	300 c. on 3 c. Men's 400 metre hurdles race	1·40	1·75
1307/10	Set of 4	3·00	3·50
MS1311	103×78 mm. 600 c. on 70 c. Football	2·75	3·75

(d) On Nos. 1134/7 and **MS**1139

1312	60 c. on 1 c. Type **408** (optd with T **413**)	85	90
1313	80 c. on 1 c. 40, Boxing (optd "U.S. WINNERS")	1·10	1·25
1314	200 c. on 2 c. 30, Field hockey (optd "PAKISTAN (FIELD HOCKEY)")	3·25	3·50
1315	300 c. on 3 c. Men's 400 metre hurdles race (optd "EDWIN MOSES U.S.A.")	3·50	3·75
1312/15	Set of 4	8·00	8·50
MS1316	103×78 mm. 600 c. on 70 c. Football (optd "FRANCE")	4·50	5·00

(e) On Nos. 1140/3 (20 Nov)

1317	80 c. on 5 c. Type **414**	35	40
1318	250 c. on 12 c. At Ascot Races	1·10	1·75
1319	300 c. on 100 c. At Clarence House on her 84th birthday	1·25	1·75
1317/19	Set of 3	2·50	3·50
MS1320	56×84 mm. 500 c. on 110 c. With Prince Charles at Garter Ceremony	3·25	4·00

(f) On Nos. 1159/61 and **MS**1163 *(20 Nov)*

1321	80 c. on 5 c. Type **418**	1·00	1·00
1322	100 c. on 8 c. Barred Owl	2·25	2·25
1323	300 c. on 12 c. Black-throated Mango	2·50	3·00
1321/3	Set of 3	5·00	5·50
MS1324	500 c. on 110 c. Downy Woodpecker	5·00	5·50

(g) On Nos. 1190/2 and **MS**1194

1325	60 c. on 5 c. Type **424**	45	45
1326	200 c. on 15 c. Player taking control of ball	1·50	2·00
1327	300 c. on 25 c. Player kicking ball	2·00	2·50
1325/7	Set of 3	3·50	4·50
MS1328	90×70 mm. 600 c. on 150 c. Player kicking ball (different)	4·00	5·00

(h) As Nos. 1190/2 and **MS**1194, *but with unissued "WINNERS" opt as T* **216** *of Antigua (18 Sept)*

1329	60 c. on 5 c. Type **424**	30	30
1330	200 c. on 15 c. Player taking control of ball	1·00	1·50
1331	300 c. on 25 c. Player kicking ball	1·40	2·00
1329/31	Set of 3	2·40	3·50
MS1332	90×70 mm. 600 c. on 150 c. Player kicking ball (different)	3·50	4·25

(i) On Nos. 1208/11

1333	60 c. on 5 c. Mikhail Lomonosov (scientist) and Chamber of Curiosities, St. Petersburg	55	55
1334	80 c. on 25 c. Lunar probe "Surveyor 3", 1966	70	70
1335	500 c. on 200 c. Wedgwood plaques for Isaac Newton, 1790, and "Apollo 11" Moon landing, 1968	3·00	4·00
1333/5	Set of 3	3·75	4·75
MS1336	100×70 mm. 750 c. on 250 c. Halley's Comet	4·00	5·00
	a. Surch double, one inverted		

(j) As Nos. 1208/11, but with unissued logo opt as T **218** *of Antigua (18 Sept)*

1337	60 c. on 5 c. Mikhail Lomonosov (scientist) and Chamber of Curiosities, St. Petersburg	35	40
1338	80 c. on 25 c. Lunar probe "Surveyor 3", 1966	45	50
1339	500 c. on 200 c. Wedgwood plaques for Isaac Newton, 1790, and "Apollo 11" Moon landing, 1968	2·50	4·00
1337/9	Set of 3	3·00	4·50
MS1340	100×70 mm. 750 c. on 250 c. Halley's Comet	5·00	6·00

The stamps, as Nos. 1140/3, from additional sheetlets also exist surcharged as 80 c. on 20 c., 200 c. on 8 c. and 250 c. on 70 c. On No. **MS**1336a the inverted surcharge occurs towards the bottom left of the miniature sheet.

(Litho Questa)

1989 (21 Aug). *Japanese Art. Portraits. Multicoloured designs as T* **250** *of Antigua.* P 13½×14.

1346	20 c. "Minamoto-no-Yoritomo" (Fujiwara-no-Takanobu) (vert)	20	20
1347	50 c. "Takami Senseki" (Watanabe Kazan) (vert)	30	30
1348	60 c. "Ikkyu Sojun" (study) (Bokusai) (vert)	35	35
1349	75 c. "Nakamura Kuranosuka" (Ogata Korin) (vert)	40	40
1350	125 c. "Portrait of a Lady" (Kyoto branch, Kano School) (vert)	65	70
1351	150 c. "Portrait of Zemmui" (anon, 12th-century) (vert)	70	75
1352	200 c. "Ono no Komachi the Poetess" (Hokusai) (vert)	90	1·00
1353	500 c. "Kobo Daisi as a Child" (anon) (vert)	2·25	3·00
1346/53	Set of 8	5·00	6·00
MS1354	Two sheets, each 102×77 mm. (a) 500 c. "Kodai-no-Kimi" (attr Fujiwara-no-Goshin). P 14×13½. (b) 500 c. "Emperor Hanazono" (Fujiwara-no-Goshin). P 14×13½ Set of 2 sheets	7·50	7·50

Nos. 1346/53 were each printed in sheetlets of 10 containing two vertical strips of 5 stamps separated by printed labels commemorating Emperor Hirohito.

(Litho B.D.T.)

1989 (22 Sept). *Bicentenary of the French Revolution.* T **449** *and similar multicoloured designs.* P 14×13½ (vert) or 13½×14 (horiz).

1355	20 c. Type **449**	35	20
1356	60 c. Declaration of Human Rights	60	50
1357	80 c. Storming the Bastille (horiz)	80	75
1358	200 c. Revolution monument (horiz)	1·75	2·00
1359	350 c. Tree of Liberty (horiz)	2·50	3·25
1355/9	Set of 5	5·50	6·00

GHANA Mushrooms   GHANA

¢20·00   "The course of true love never did run smooth. 1:"

450 Collybia fusipes   451 "The Course of True Love . . "

(Des L. Nelson. Litho B.D.T.)

1989 (2 Oct). *Fungi (1st series).* T **450** *and similar vert designs. Multicoloured.* P 14.

1360	20 c. Type **450**	25	25
1361	50 c. Coprinus comatus	40	40
1362	60 c. Xerocomus subtomentosus	40	45
1363	80 c. Lepista nuda	55	55
1364	150 c. Suillus placidus	95	95
1365	200 c. Lepista nuda (different)	1·25	1·25
1366	300 c. Marasmius oreades	1·75	1·75
1367	500 c. Agaricus campestris	3·00	3·00
1360/7	Set of 8	7·75	7·75
MS1368	Two sheets, each 110×80 mm. (a) 600 c. Boletus rhodoxanthus. (b) 600 c. Amanita rubescens	Set of 2 sheets	7·50	8·00

Nos. 1360/8 also exist imperforate from a limited printing. See also Nos. 1489/97.

(Des N. Waldman. Litho Walsall)

1989 (9 Oct). *425th Birth Anniv of Shakespeare.* T **451** *and similar vert designs showing lines and scenes from A Midsummer Night's Dream. Multicoloured.* P 13½×13.

1369	40 c. Type **451**	50	50
	a. Sheetlet. Nos. 1369/89	9·00	
1370	40 c. "Love looks not with the eye, but with the mind"	50	50
1371	40 c. "Nature here shows art"	50	50

1372	40 c.	"Things growing are not ripe till their season"		50	50
1373	40 c.	"He is defiled that draws a sword on thee"		50	50
1374	40 c.	"It is not enough to speak, but to speak true"		50	50
1375	40 c.	"Thou art as wise as thou art beautiful"		50	50
1376	40 c.	Wildcat in wood (face value at left)		50	50
1377	40 c.	Man		50	50
1378	40 c.	Woman with flower		50	50
1379	40 c.	King and queen		50	50
1380	40 c.	Bottom		50	50
1381	40 c.	Wildcat in wood (face value at right)		50	50
1382	40 c.	Woman		50	50
1383	40 c.	Leopard		50	50
1384	40 c.	Tree trunk and man		50	50
1385	40 c.	Meadow flowers		50	50
1386	40 c.	Mauve flowers		50	50
1387	40 c.	Plants		50	50
1388	40 c.	Lion		50	50
1389	40 c.	Fern and flowers		50	50
1369/89			*Set of 21*	9·00	9·00

Nos. 1369/89 were printed together, *se-tenant*, as a sheetlet of 21, forming a composite design.

(Des Mary Walters. Litho B.D.T.)

1989 (16 Oct)–90. *Birds. Multicoloured designs as T 244 of Dominica. P 14.*

1390	20 c.	Bronze Mannikin (*horiz*)		30	10
1391	50 c.	African Pied Wagtail (*horiz*)		45	30
1392	60 c.	African Pygmy Kingfisher (inscr "*Halcyon malimbicus*") (*horiz*)		1·25	1·75
1392a	60 c.	African Pygmy Kingfisher (inscr "*Ispidina picta*") (6.90) (*horiz*)		1·25	1·50
1393	80 c.	Blue-breasted Kingfisher (inscr "*Ispidina picta*") (*horiz*)		1·75	2·25
1393a	80 c.	Blue-breasted Kingfisher (inscr "*Halcyon malimbicus*") (*horiz*) (6.90)		1·50	2·00
1394	150 c.	Striped Kingfisher		1·10	1·25
1395	200 c.	Shikra		1·25	1·40
1396	300 c.	Grey Parrot		1·50	1·75
1397	500 c.	Black Kite		1·50	2·00
1390/7			*Set of 10*	11·50	14·00
MS1398		Two sheets. (a) 128×83 mm. 600 c. Cinnamon-breasted Rock Bunting and Barn Swallow (*horiz*). (b) 83×128 mm. 600 c. Senegal Puff-back Flycatcher	*Set of 2 sheets*	11·00	12·00

The original printings of Nos. 1392/3 had the Latin names of the birds transposed. Corrected versions of the two designs were supplied during 1990.
Nos. 1390/8 also exist imperforate from a limited printing.

452 Command Module *Columbia* orbiting Moon

(Des K. Gromell. Litho B.D.T.)

1989 (6 Nov). *20th Anniv of First Manned Landing on Moon. T 452 and similar horiz designs. Multicoloured. P 14.*

1399	20 c.	Type 452		30	15
1400	80 c.	Neil Armstrong's footprint on Moon		50	60
1401	200 c.	Edwin Aldrin on Moon		1·25	1·75
1402	300 c.	"Apollo 11" capsule on parachutes		1·60	2·00
1399/1402			*Set of 4*	3·25	4·00
MS1403		Two sheets, each 100×72 mm. (a) 500 c. Launch of "Apollo 11". (b) 500 c. Earth seen from Moon	*Set of 2 sheets*	5·50	7·00

453 Desertification of Pasture

(Litho B.D.T.)

1989 (15 Nov). *World Environment Day. T 453 and similar horiz designs. Multicoloured. P 14.*

1404	20 c.	Type 453		50	15
1405	60 c.	Wildlife fleeing bush fire		90	80
1406	400 c.	Industrial pollution		2·75	3·50
1407	500 c.	Erosion		3·00	3·75
1404/7			*Set of 4*	6·50	7·50

454 *Bebearia arcadius*   455 Great Ribbed Cockle (*Cardium costatum*)

(Des Mary Walters. Litho B.D.T.)

1990 (20 Feb). *Butterflies. T 454 and similar horiz designs. Multicoloured. P 14.*

1408	20 c.	Type 454		35	20
1409	60 c.	*Charaxes laodice*		50	40
1410	80 c.	*Euryphura porphyrion*		60	45
1411	100 c.	*Neptis nicomedes*		70	50
1412	150 c.	*Citrinophila erastus*		90	90
1413	200 c.	*Aethiopana honorius*		1·25	1·25
1414	300 c.	*Precis westermanni*		1·50	1·75
1415	500 c.	*Cymothoe hypatha*		2·00	2·50
1408/15			*Set of 8*	7·00	7·00
MS1416		Two sheets, each 104×72 mm. (a) 600 c. *Telipna acraea*. (b) 600 c. *Pentila abraxas*	*Set of 2 sheets*	7·50	8·00

Nos. 1408/16 also exist imperforate from a limited printing.

(Des E. Mensah. Litho D.L.R.)

1990 (23 Feb). *Seashells. T 455 and similar vert designs. Multicoloured. P 14×14¹/₂.*

1417	20 c.	Type 455		50	25
1418	60 c.	Elephant's Snout (*Cymbium glans*)		65	40
1419	80 c.	Garter Cone (*Conus genuanus*)		75	70
1420	200 c.	Tankerville's Ancilla (*Amalda tankervillii*)		1·75	2·00
1421	350 c.	Coronate Prickly-winkle (*Tectarius coronatus*)		2·50	3·25
1417/21			*Set of 5*	5·50	6·00

Nos. 1417/18 show the shell descriptions transposed in error.

456 Nehru welcoming President Nkrumah of Ghana

(Des E. Mensah. Litho D.L.R.)

1990 (27 Mar). *Birth Centenary of Jawaharlal Nehru (Indian statesman). T 456 and similar multicoloured designs. P 14¹/₂×14 (horiz) or 14×14¹/₂ (others).*

1422	20 c.	Type 456		40	25
1423	60 c.	Nehru addressing Bandung Conference, 1955		50	30
1424	80 c.	Nehru with garland and flowers (*vert*)		60	55
1425	200 c.	Nehru releasing pigeon (*vert*)		1·00	1·25
1426	350 c.	Nehru (*vert*)		1·60	2·50
1422/6			*Set of 5*	3·75	4·25

457 Wyon Medal, 1838   458 Anniversary Emblem

(Des S. Pollard. Litho B.D.T.)

1990 (23 May). *150th Anniv of Penny Black. T 457 and similar horiz designs. P 13¹/₂.*

1427	20 c.	black and reddish violet		20	20
1428	60 c.	black and deep grey-green		30	30
1429	80 c.	black and reddish violet		35	35
1430	200 c.	black and deep grey-green		90	90
1431	350 c.	black and deep grey-green		1·50	1·75
1432	400 c.	black and rosine		1·60	2·00
1427/32			*Set of 6*	4·25	5·00
MS1433		Two sheets, each 112×83 mm. (a) 600 c. red-brown and black; (b) 600 c. deep brown, buff and black	*Set of 2 sheets*	6·00	7·00

Designs:—60, 600 c. (No. **MS**1433b) Bath mail coach, 1840; 80 c. Leeds mail coach, 1840; 200 c. Proof of Queen's head engraved by Heath, 1840; 350 c. Master die, 1840; 400 c. London mail coach, 1840; 600 c. (No. **MS**1433a) Printing the Penny Black.
Nos. 1427/33 also exist imperforate from a limited printing.

(Litho D.L.R.)

1990 (5 June). *Tenth Anniv (1989) of 4 June Revolution. T 458 and similar vert designs. Multicoloured. P 14¹/₂×14.*

1434	20 c.	Type 458		15	15
1435	60 c.	Foodstuffs		20	20
1436	80 c.	Cocoa		25	30
1437	200 c.	Mining		1·50	1·75
1438	350 c.	Scales of Justice and sword		1·75	2·25
1434/8			*Set of 5*	3·50	4·25

459 Map of Africa and Satellite Network

(Litho D.L.R.)

1990 (12 July). *25th Anniv of Intelsat Satellite System. T 459 and similar horiz designs. Multicoloured. P 14×14¹/₂.*

1439	20 c.	Type 459		20	20
1440	60 c.	Map of Americas		30	30
1441	80 c.	Map of Asia and Pacific		35	35
1442	200 c.	Map of South America and Africa		90	1·00
1443	350 c.	Map of Indian Ocean and Pacific		1·50	2·00
1439/43			*Set of 5*	3·00	3·50

460 Housewife using Telephone   461 Blue Flycatcher

(Litho D.L.R.)

1990 (16 July). *Second Anniversary of Introduction of International Direct Dialling Service. T 460 and similar horiz designs. Multicoloured. P 14×14¹/₂.*

1444	20 c.	Type 460		25	20
1445	60 c.	Businessman using telephone		35	35
1446	80 c.	Man using phonecard telephone		40	40
1447	200 c.	Public telephones for internal and IDD services		90	1·00
1448	350 c.	Satellite station		1·50	2·00
1444/8			*Set of 5*	3·00	3·50

(Des W. Wright. Litho Questa)

1990 (25 Oct). *African Tropical Rain Forest. T 461 and similar multicoloured designs. P 14×14¹/₂.*

1449	40 c.	Type 461		45	50
		a. Sheetlet. Nos. 1449/68		8·00	
1450	40 c.	Boomslang (snake)		45	50
1451	40 c.	Superb Sunbird		45	50
1452	40 c.	Bateleur		45	50
1453	40 c.	Yellow-casqued Hornbill		45	50
1454	40 c.	*Salamis temora* (butterfly)		45	50
1455	40 c.	Potto		45	50
1456	40 c.	Leopard		45	50
1457	40 c.	Bongo		45	50
1458	40 c.	Grey Parrot		45	50
1459	40 c.	Okapi		45	50
1460	40 c.	Gorilla		45	50
1461	40 c.	Flap-necked Chameleon		45	50
1462	40 c.	West African Dwarf Crocodile		45	50
1463	40 c.	Python		45	50
1464	40 c.	Giant Ground Pangolin		45	50
1465	40 c.	*Pseudacraea boisduvali* (butterfly)		45	50
1466	40 c.	North African Crested Porcupine		45	50
1467	40 c.	Rosy-columned Aerangis (orchid)		45	50
1468	40 c.	*Cymothoe sangaris* (butterfly)		45	50
1449/68			*Set of 20*	8·00	9·00
MS1469		100×75 mm. 600 c. Head of Leopard (*vert*). P 14¹/₂×14		4·50	5·00

Nos. 1449/68 were printed together, *se-tenant*, as a sheetlet of 20, forming a composite design.

462 Jupiter   463 *Eulophia guineensis*

(Des K. Gromell. Litho Questa)

1990 (13 Dec). *Space Flight of "Voyager 2". T 462 and similar multicoloured designs. P 14.*

1470	100 c.	Type 462		70	70
		a. Sheetlet. Nos. 1470/8		5·75	
1471	100 c.	Neptune and Triton		70	70
1472	100 c.	Ariel, moon of Uranus		70	70
1473	100 c.	Saturn from Mimas		70	70
1474	100 c.	Saturn		70	70
1475	100 c.	Rings of Saturn		70	70
1476	100 c.	Neptune		70	70
1477	100 c.	Uranus from Miranda		70	70
1478	100 c.	Volcano on Io		70	70
1470/8			*Set of 9*	5·75	5·75
MS1479		Two sheets. (a) 111×81 mm. 600 c. "Voyager 2" spacecraft (*vert*). (b) 80×111 mm. 600 c. Lift off of "Voyager 2" (*vert*)	*Set of 2 sheets*	4·50	5·00

Nos. 1470/8 were printed together, *se-tenant*, as a sheetlet of 9.

(Litho B.D.T.)

1990 (17 Dec). *Orchids. T 463 and similar vert designs. Multicoloured. P 14.*

1480	20 c.	Type 463		45	45
1481	40 c.	*Eurychone rothschildiana*		60	60
1482	60 c.	*Bulbophyllum barbigerum*		80	80
1483	80 c.	*Polystachya galeata*		1·10	1·10
1484	200 c.	*Diaphananthe kamerunensis*		1·75	1·75
1485	300 c.	*Podangis dactyloceras*		2·00	2·00
1486	400 c.	*Ancistrochilus rothschildianus*		2·00	2·00

| 1487 | 500 c. *Rangaeris muscicola* | .. | .. | 2·00 | 2·00 |
| 1480/7 | | | *Set of 8* | 9·50 | 9·50 |

MS1488 Two sheets, each 101×70 mm. (a) 600 c. *Bolusiella imbricata.* (b) 600 c. *Diaphananthe rutila* .. .. .. *Set of 2 sheets* 7·50 8·00

464 *Coprinus atramentarius*

(Litho B.D.T.)

1990 (18 Dec). *Fungi (2nd series).* T **464** *and similar horiz designs. Multicoloured.* P 14.

1489	20 c. Type **464**	..	..	45	45
1490	50 c. *Marasmius oreades*	..	..	65	65
1491	60 c. *Oudemansiella radicata*		..	70	70
1492	80 c. *Boletus edulis* ("Cep")	..	..	90	90
1493	150 c. *Hebeloma crustuliniforme*	..	1·25	1·25
1494	200 c. *Coprinus micaceus*	..	..	1·50	1·50
1495	300 c. *Macrolepiota procera* ("*Lepiota procera*")		..	1·75	1·75
1496	500 c. *Amanita phalloides*	..	..	2·25	2·25
1489/96			*Set of 8*	8·50	8·50

MS1497 Two sheets, each 104×82 mm. (a) Nos. 1489, 1491/2 and 1496. (b) Nos. 1490 and 1493/5 .. *Set of 2 sheets* 6·00 7·00

| **465** Italian and Swedish Players chasing Ball | **466** Manganese Ore |

(Des Young Phillips Studio. Litho Questa)

1990 (18 Dec). *World Cup Football Championship, Italy.* T **465** *and similar multicoloured designs.* P 14.

1498	20 c. Type **465**	..	..	20	20
1499	50 c. Egyptian player penetrating Irish defence	..	..	30	30
1500	60 c. Cameroon players celebrating	..	30	30
1501	80 c. Rumanian player beating challenge	..	40	40
1502	100 c. Russian goalkeeper Dassayev	..	55	55
1503	150 c. Roger Milla of Cameroon (*vert*)	..	75	75
1504	400 c. South Korean player challenging opponent	..	..	1·60	1·75
1505	600 c. Klinsman of West Germany celebrating	..	..	2·25	2·75
1498/505			*Set of 8*	5·75	6·25

MS1506 Two sheets, each 88×98 mm. (a) 800 c. United Arab Emirates player watching ball. (b) 800 c. Colombian player .. *Set of 2 sheets* 4·50 5·50

(Litho Questa)

1990 (24 Dec). *350th Death Anniv of Rubens. Multicoloured designs as* T **273** *of Antigua, but vert.* P 13½×14.

1507	20 c. "Duke of Mantua"	..	..	20	20
1508	50 c. "Jan Brant"	..	..	30	30
1509	60 c. "Portrait of a Young Man"	..	30	30
1510	80 c. "Michel Ophovius"	..	..	40	40
1511	100 c. "Caspar Gevaerts"	..	..	55	55
1512	200 c. "Head of Warrior" (detail)	..	85	1·00
1513	300 c. "Study of a Bearded Man"	..	1·25	1·50
1514	400 c. "Paracelsus"	..	..	1·75	2·00
1507/14			*Set of 8*	5·00	5·50

MS1515 Two sheets, each 71×100 mm. (a) 600 c. "Warrior with two Pages" (detail). (b) 600 c. "Archduke Ferdinand" (detail) .. *Set of 2 sheets* 6·50 7·00

(Des E. Mensah. Litho D.L.R.)

1991 (2 May). *Minerals.* T **466** *and similar vert designs. Multicoloured.* P 14½×14.

1516	20 c. Type **466**	..	..	55	30
1517	60 c. Iron ore	..	..	70	60
1518	80 c. Bauxite ore	..	..	90	75
1519	200 c. Gold ore	..	..	2·00	2·00
1520	350 c. Diamond	..	..	3·00	4·00
1516/20			*Set of 5*	6·50	7·00

MS1521 70×90 mm. 600 c. Uncut and cut diamonds .. .. 5·00 6·00

| **467** Dance Drums | **468** *Amorphophallus dracontioides* |

(Des E. Mensah. Litho D.L.R.)

1991 (9 May). *Tribal Drums.* T **467** *and similar vert designs. Multicoloured.* P 14½×14.

1522	20 c. Type **467**	..	..	20	20
1523	60 c. Message drums	..	..	50	40
1524	80 c. War drums	..	..	60	50
1525	200 c. Dance drums (different)	..	1·25	1·50
1526	350 c. Ceremonial drums	..	..	1·75	2·50
1522/6			*Set of 5*	3·75	4·50

MS1527 70×90 mm. 600 c. Drum with carrying strap .. .. 3·50 5·00

(Des E. Mensah. Litho D.L.R.)

1991 (15 May). *Flowers (1st series).* T **468** *and similar vert designs. Multicoloured.* P 14½×14.

1528	20 c. Type **468**	..	..	45	25
1529	60 c. *Anchomanes difformis*	..	65	50
1530	80 c. *Kaemferia nigerica*	..	75	70
1531	200 c. *Aframomum sceptrum*	..	1·75	2·00
1532	350 c. *Amorphophallus flavovirens*		2·00	3·00
1528/32			*Set of 5*	5·00	5·75

MS1533 70×90 mm. 600 c. *Amorphophallus flavovirens* (different) .. .. .. 3·50 4·50

(Des E. Mensah. Litho D.L.R.)

1991 (17 May). *Flowers (2nd series).* Vert designs as T **468**, *but inscr* "GHANA" *in block capitals. Multicoloured.* P 14½×14.

1534	20 c. *Urginea indica*	..	..	45	25
1535	60 c. *Hymenocallis littoralis*	..	65	50
1536	80 c. *Crinum jagus*	..	..	1·00	70
1537	200 c. *Dipcadi tacazzeanum*	..	1·75	2·00
1538	350 c. *Haemanthus rupestris*	..	2·00	3·00
1534/8			*Set of 5*	5·25	5·75

MS1539 70×90 mm. 600 c. *Urginea indica* (different) .. .. 3·50 4·50

| **469** Transport and Telecommunication Symbols | **470** Drawing of Scout from First Handbook |

(Des E. Mensah. Litho Francoise-Charles Oberthur)

1991 (21 June). *40th Anniv of United Nations Development Programme.* T **469** *and similar vert designs. Multicoloured.* P 13½×14.

1540	20 c. Type **469**	..	..	30	20
1541	60 c. Agricultural research	..	50	40
1542	80 c. Literacy	..	..	60	55
1543	200 c. Advances in agricultural crop growth	1·25	1·50
1544	350 c. Industrial symbols	..	1·75	2·50
1540/4			*Set of 5*	4·00	4·75

(Des W. Hanson Studio. Litho B.D.T.)

1991 (18 July). *50th Death Anniv of Lord Baden-Powell.* T **470** *and similar designs.* P 14.

1545	20 c. black and pale buff	..	..	45	20
1546	50 c. grey, pale blue and black	..	60	40
1547	60 c. multicoloured	..	..	60	45
1548	80 c. black and pale buff	..	..	70	55
1549	100 c. multicoloured	..	..	85	75
1550	200 c. multicoloured	..	..	1·50	1·50
1551	500 c. multicoloured	..	..	2·25	2·75
1552	600 c. multicoloured	..	..	2·50	3·25
1545/52			*Set of 8*	8·50	9·00

MS1553 Two sheets. (a) 104×75 mm. 800 c. multicoloured; (b) 74×105 mm. 800 c. mult .. .. *Set of 2 sheets* 6·00 7·50

Designs: Vert—50 c. Lord Baden-Powell; 80 c. Handbook illustration by Norman Rockwell; 500 c. Scout at prayer. Horiz—60 c. Hands holding Boy Scout emblem; 100 c. Mafeking Siege 1d. Goodyear stamp and African runner; 200 c. Scouts with blitz victim, London, 1944; 600 c. Mafeking Siege 1d. Goodyear stamp; 800 c. (**MS**1553a) Scout camp; 800 c. (**MS**1553b) Envelope from Mafeking Siege.

471 Women sorting Fish

(Litho D.L.R.)

1991 (22 July). *Chorkor Smoker (fish smoking process).* T **471** *and similar horiz designs. Multicoloured.* P 14×14½.

1554	20 c. Type **471**	..	..	30	20
1555	60 c. Cleaning the ovens	..	55	40
1556	80 c. Washing fish	..	..	65	55
1557	200 c. Laying fish on pallets	..	1·25	1·50
1558	350 c. Stacking pallets over ovens	..	1·75	2·50
1554/8			*Set of 5*	4·00	4·75

472 African Hind

(Des E. Mensah. Litho B.D.T.)

1991 (29 July). *Fishes.* T **472** *and similar horiz designs. Multicoloured.* P 14.

1559	20 c. Type **472**	..	..	25	25
1560	50 c. Shrew Squeaker	..	..	40	40
1561	80 c. West African Triggerfish	..	55	55
1562	100 c. Stonehead	..	..	70	70
1563	200 c. Lesser Pipefish	..	..	1·50	1·50
1564	300 c. Aba	..	..	1·60	1·60
1565	400 c. Jewel Cichlid	..	..	1·75	1·75
1566	500 c. Smooth Hammerhead	..	1·90	1·90
1559/66			*Set of 8*	7·75	7·75

MS1567 Two sheets, each 108×81 mm. (a) 800 c. Bayad. (b) 800 c. Eastern Flying Gurnard .. *Set of 2 sheets* 6·00 7·00

(Litho B.D.T.)

1991 (12 Aug). *Death Centenary of Vincent van Gogh (artist)* (1990). *Multicoloured designs as* T **278** *of Antigua.* P 13.

1568	20 c. "Reaper with Sickle"	..	35	25
1569	50 c. "The Thresher"	..	..	55	40
1570	60 c. "The Sheaf-Binder"	..	..	60	50
1571	80 c. "The Sheep-Shearers"	..	70	65
1572	100 c. "Peasant Woman cutting Straw"	..	85	80
1573	200 c. "The Sower"	..	..	1·60	1·75
1574	500 c. "The Plough and the Harrow" (*horiz*)	2·25	2·50
1575	600 c. "The Woodcutter"	..	2·25	2·50
1568/75			*Set of 8*	8·25	8·50

MS1576 Two sheets, each 117×80 mm. (a) 800 c. "Evening: The Watch" (*horiz*). (b) 800 c. "Evening: The End of the Day" (*horiz*). Imperf .. .. *Set of 2 sheets* 7·00 8·00

| **473** Gamal Nasser (Egypt) and Conference Hall | **474** Green-winged Pytilia |

(Litho Cartor)

1991 (2 Sept). *10th Non-Aligned Ministers' Conference, Accra.* T **473** *and similar horiz designs showing statesmen. Multicoloured.* P 13½.

1577	20 c. Type **473**	..	..	40	30
1578	60 c. Josip Tito (Yugoslavia)	..	45	45
1579	80 c. Pandit Nehru (India)	..	1·50	1·00
1580	200 c. Kwame Nkrumah (Ghana)	..	1·60	2·00
1581	350 c. Achmad Sukarno (Indonesia)	..	1·90	2·75
1577/81			*Set of 5*	5·25	6·00

(Des S. Barlowe. Litho Questa)

1991 (14 Oct). *Birds.* T **474** *and similar vert designs. Multicoloured.* P 14½×14.

| 1582/1629 | 80 c. × 16, 100 c. × 32 | *Set of 48* | 22·00 | 25·00 |

MS1630 Three sheets, each 107×86 mm. (a) 800 c. Marabou Stork. (b) 800 c. African Fish Eagle. (c) 800 c. Saddle-bill Stork *Set of 3 sheets* 7·50 8·50

Nos. 1582/1629 were issued together, *se-tenant*, as three sheetlets of 16 forming composite designs. The 80 c. values show Green-winged Pytilia, Orange-cheeked Waxbill, African Paradise Flycatcher, Great Blue Turaco ("Blue Plantain-eater"), Red Bishop, Splendid Glossy Starling, Red-faced Lovebird, African Palm Swift, Narina Trogon, Tawny Eagle, Bateleur, Hoopoe, Secretary Bird, African White-backed Vulture, White-necked Bald Crow ("Bare-headed Rockfowl"), Abyssinian Ground Hornbill, and the 100 c. African Open-bill Stork, African Spoonbill, Pink-backed Pelican, Little Bittern, Purple Swamphen ("King Reed-hen"), Saddle-bill Stork, Glossy Ibis, White-faced Whistling Duck, Black-headed Heron, Hammerkop, African Darter, Woolly-necked Stork, Yellow-billed Stork, Black-winged Stilt, Goliath Heron, African Jacana ("Lily Trotter"), Shikra, Abyssinian Roller, Carmine Bee Eater, Pin-tailed Whydah, Purple Glossy Starling, Yellow-mantled Whydah, Pel's Fishing Owl, Crested Touraco, Red-cheeked Cordon-bleu, Olive-bellied Sunbird, Red-billed Hornbill, Red-billed Quelea, South African Crowned Crane, Blue Quail, Egyptian Vulture and Helmet Guineafowl.

PRICES OF SETS

Set prices are given for many issues, generally those containing three stamps or more. Definitive sets include one of each value or major colour change, but do not cover different perforations, die types or minor shades. Where a choice is possible the set prices are based on the cheapest versions of the stamps included in the listings.

475 *Nularda* (beetle)   476 Boti Falls

(Litho Cartor)

1991 (25 Oct). *Insects. T* **475** *and similar horiz designs. Multicoloured. P* 14×13½.

1631	20 c. Type 475			40	20
1632	50 c. *Zonocrus* (grasshopper)			55	30
1633	60 c. *Gryllotalpa africana* (mole cricket)		60	30
1634	80 c. Weevil			70	60
1635	100 c. *Coenagrion* (dragonfly)		80	70
1636	150 c. *Sahlbergella* (fly)			1·10	1·40
1637	200 c. *Anthia* (ant)			1·25	1·50
1638	350 c. *Megacephala* (beetle)		1·75	2·50
1631/8			*Set of 8*	6·50	6·75

MS1639 106×79 mm. 600 c. *Lacetus* (lacewing). P 13×12 .. .. .. 4·50 5·00

(Litho R. Alhelou Marfo Co Ltd, Accra)

1991 (21 Nov)–96. *T* **476** *and similar multicoloured designs. P* 13½.

1639a	20 c. Oil palm fruit (4.93)		10	10
	ab. Imperf (horiz pair) ..		†	—
1640	50 c. Type 476			15	10
	a. Imperf (pair) ..				
1641	60 c. Larabanga Mosque (*horiz*) (12.12.91)		10	10
	a. Black (inscriptions) omitted			
1642	80 c. Fort Sebastian, Shama (*horiz*) (12.12.91)		10	10
1643	100 c. Cape Coast Castle (*horiz*) (12.12.91)		20	20
	a. Black (inscriptions) omitted		†	—
	b. Perf 14 (1996)			
1644	200 c. White-toothed Cowrie (*Cyraea leucodon*) (*horiz*) (12.12.91)		40	30
	a. Black (inscriptions) omitted			
	b. Perf 14 (1996)			
1645	400 c. True Achatina (*Achatina achatina*) (*horiz*) (12.12.91)		70	55
	a. Perf 14 (1996)			
1639a/45	.. .. ..	*Set of 7*	1·50	1·40

Examples of No. 1643a have been seen used on commercial cover.
Nos. 1643b and 1645a show "GHANA" and the face value in black redrawn.

(Litho Walsall)

1991 (23 Dec). *Christmas. Religious Paintings. Vert designs as T* **287** *of Antigua. Multicoloured. P* 12.

1646	20 c. "Adoration of the Magi" (Bosch) ..	35	20
1647	50 c. "The Annunciation" (Campin) ..	50	30
1648	60 c. "Virgin and Child" (detail) (Bouts) ..	55	30
1649	80 c. "Presentation in the Temple" (Memling) ..	65	50
1650	100 c. "Virgin and Child enthroned with Angel and Donor" (Memling) ..	85	65
1651	200 c. "Virgin and Child with Saints and Donor" (Van Eyck) ..	1·50	1·75
1652	400 c. "St. Luke painting the Virgin" (Van der Weyden) ..	2·50	3·00
1653	700 c. "Virgin and Child" (Bouts) ..	3·50	4·50
1646/53		*Set of 8*	9·50	10·00

MS1654 Two sheets, each 103×128 mm. (a) 800 c. "Virgin and Child standing in a Niche" (Van der Weyden). (b) 800 c. "The Annunciation" (Memling). P 14 .. *Set of 2 sheets* 6·00 7·50

477 Women collecting   478 Mount Fuji and Flying
Water from Bore Hole   Fish

(Litho R. Alhelou Marfo Co Ltd, Accra)

1992 (2 Feb). *Decade of Revolutionary Progress. T* **477** *and similar horiz designs. Multicoloured. P* 14×13½.

1655	20 c. Type 477 ..			10	10
1656	50 c. Miners ..			10	10
1657	60 c. Wood carver			10	10
1658	80 c. Forestry ..			10	15
1659	200 c. Cacao tree			25	50
1660	350 c. Village electrification		40	70
1655/60	..		*Set of 6*	1·00	1·40

(Litho B.D.T.)

1992 (16 Feb). *"Phila Nippon '91" International Stamp Exhibition, Tokyo. T* **478** *and similar horiz designs. Multicoloured. P* 14.

1661	20 c. Type 478 ..		35	30
1662	60 c. Itsukushima Jingu Shrine ..	45	40
1663	80 c. Geisha		60	50
1664	100 c. Samurai house ..		80	70
1665	200 c. Bonsai tree ..		1·50	1·50
1666	400 c. Olympic Sports Hall	2·00	2·25
1667	500 c. Great Buddha (statue)	2·25	2·50
1668	600 c. Nagoya Castle ..	2·40	2·75
1661/8		*Set of 8*	9·25	9·75

MS1669 Two sheets, each 109×80 mm. (a) 800 c. Takamatsu Castle. (b) 800 c. Heian Shrine. *Set of 2 sheets* 7·00 8·50

479 East and West Germans   480 Steam Locomotive,
celebrating   1903

(Litho Questa)

1992 (17 Feb). *Reunification of Germany. T* **479** *and similar multicoloured designs. P* 14.

1670	20 c. Type 479 ..		30	20
1671	60 c. Signing Reunification Treaty	40	40
1672	80 c. Chariot on Brandenburg Gate and fireworks ..	45	45
1673	1000 c. Germans with unified currency	5·50	7·00
1670/3		*Set of 4*	6·00	7·25

MS1674 Three sheets. (a) 109×78 mm. 400 c. Doves and Brandenburg Gate; 400 c. Chancellor Kohl and Prime Minister De Maizière. (b) 125×87 mm. 800 c. Chancellor Kohl and members of last German Democratic Republic administration. (c) 130×92 mm. 300 c. President Gorbachev (*vert*); 300 c. Chancellor Kohl (*vert*); 300 c. Map of Western Germany (face value in black) (*vert*); 300 c. Map of Eastern Germany (face value in white) (*vert*) .. *Set of 3 sheets* 7·50 8·50

(Des W. Hanson. Litho B.D.T.)

1992 (2 Mar). *Ghanaian Railways. T* **480** *and similar horiz designs. Multicoloured. P* 14.

1675	20 c. Type 480 ..		40	30
1676	50 c. A1A-A1A diesel passenger locomotive ..	60	40
1677	60 c. First class coach, 1931	60	45
1678	80 c. Company inspection coach	70	70
1679	100 c. Steam locomotive No. 401 on Kumasi turntable	90	90
1680	200 c. Cocoa wagon, 1921	1·40	1·50
1681	500 c. Steam locomotive No. 223 *Prince of Wales*	2·25	2·50
1682	600 c. Cattle wagon	2·25	2·50
1675/82		*Set of 8*	8·00	8·25

MS1683 Two sheets. (a) 106×76 mm. 800 c. Beyer-Garratt steam locomotive No. 301, 1943. (b) 76×106 mm. 800 c. German-made steam locomotive .. .. *Set of 2 sheets* 7·50 8·50

(Litho Questa)

1992 (3 Mar). *Olympic Games, Albertville and Barcelona. Past Medal Winners. Multicoloured designs as T* **204** *of Gambia. P* 14.

1684	20 c. E. Blay (Ghana) (boxing) and windmill	30	20
1685	60 c. M. Ahey (Ghana) (athletics) and Catalan coat of arms	50	35
1686	80 c. T. Wilson (U.S.A.) (70 metres ski jump) and grapes	60	50
1687	100 c. Four-man Bob-sleighing (East Germany) and passport	75	75
1688	200 c. G. Louganis (U.S.A.) (platform diving) and decorative vase	1·25	1·25
1689	300 c. L. Visser (Netherlands) (5000 metres speed skating) and wine bottle cork	1·50	1·60
1690	350 c. J. Passler (Italy) (biathlon) and lily	1·60	1·75
1691	400 c. M. Retton (U.S.A.) (gymnastics) and silhouette of castle ..	1·75	2·00
1692	500 c. J. Hingsen (West Germany) (decathlon) and gold and silver coins	1·75	2·00
1693	600 c. R. Neubert (West Germany) (heptathlon) and leather work	1·75	2·00
1684/93		*Set of 10*	10·50	11·00

MS1694 Two sheets. (a) 112×82 mm. 800 c. Silhouette of windmill. (b) 82×112 mm. 800 c. Silhouette of folk dancer (*vert*) .. *Set of 2 sheets* 8·00 9·00

481 *Angides lugubris*   482 *Danaus
                                    chrysippus*

(Litho B.D.T.)

1992 (30 Mar). *Reptiles. T* **481** *and similar horiz designs. Multicoloured. P* 14.

1695	20 c. Type 481 ..		20	20
1696	50 c. *Kinixys erosa* (tortoise)	30	30
1697	60 c. *Agama agama* (lizard)	30	30
1698	80 c. *Chameleo gracilis* (chameleon)	40	40
1699	100 c. *Naja melanleuca* (snake)	50	50
1700	200 c. *Crocodylus niloticus* (crocodile)	90	1·10
1701	400 c. *Chelonia mydas* (turtle)	1·75	2·00
1702	500 c. *Varanus exanthematicus* (lizard)	1·90	2·25
1695/1702		*Set of 8*	5·50	6·25

MS1703 94×66 mm. 600 c. Tortoise and snake 2·75 3·50

(Litho Questa)

1992 (13 Apr). *Easter. Religious Paintings. Multicoloured designs as T* **291** *of Antigua. P* 13½×14.

1704	20 c. "The Four Apostles" (detail) (Dürer) (*vert*)	20	20
1705	50 c. "The Last Judgement" (detail) (Rubens) (*vert*)	30	30
1706	60 c. "The Four Apostles" (different detail) (Dürer) (*vert*)	30	30
1707	80 c. "The Last Judgement" (different detail) (Rubens) (*vert*)	40	40
1708	100 c. "Crucifixion" (Rubens) (*vert*)	50	50
1709	200 c. "The Last Judgement" (different detail) (Rubens) (*vert*)	90	1·10
1710	500 c. "Christum Videre" (Rubens) (*vert*)	1·75	2·00
1711	600 c. "The Last Judgement" (different detail) (Rubens) (*vert*)	1·90	2·25
1704/11		*Set of 8*	5·50	6·25

MS1712 Two sheets. (a) 69×100 mm. 800 c. "Last Communion of St. Francis of Assisi" (detail) (Rubens) (*vert*). P 13½×14. (b) 100×69 mm. 800 c. "Scourging the Money Changers from the Temple" (detail) (El Greco). P 14×13½ .. *Set of 2 sheets* 7·50 8·00

(Litho B.D.T.)

1992 (4 May). *"Granada '92" International Stamp Exhibition, Spain. Spanish Paintings. Multicoloured designs as T* **292** *of Antigua. P* 13½×13 (*horiz*) *or* 13×13½ (*vert*).

1713	20 c. "Two Men at Table" (Velázquez) (*horiz*)	20	20
1714	60 c. "Christ in the House of Mary and Martha" (detail) (Velázquez) (*horiz*)	30	30
1715	80 c. "The Supper at Emmaus" (Velázquez) (*horiz*) ..	40	40
1716	100 c. "Three Musicians" (Velázquez) (*horiz*)	50	50
1717	200 c. "Old Woman Cooking Eggs" (Velázquez)	90	90
1718	400 c. "Old Woman Cooking Eggs" (detail) (Velázquez)	1·60	1·60
1719	500 c. "The Surrender of Breda" (detail) (Velázquez)	1·75	1·75
1720	700 c. "The Surrender of Breda" (different detail) (Velázquez) ..	2·00	2·00
1713/20		*Set of 8*	7·00	7·00

MS1721 Two sheets. (a) 95×120 mm. 900 c. "The Waterseller of Seville" (Velázquez) (86×111 mm). (b) 120×95 mm. 900 c. "They still Say that Fish is Expensive" (Joaquín Sorolla y Bastida) (111×86 mm). Imperf .. *Set of 2 sheets* 7·50 8·00

(Des L. Nelson. Litho Walsall)

1992 (25 May). *"Genova '92" International Thematic Stamp Exhibition. Butterflies. T* **482** *and similar vert designs. Multicoloured. P* 14.

1722	20 c. Type 482 ..		50	30
1723	60 c. *Papilio dardanus* ..	80	45
1724	80 c. *Cynthia cardui* ..	90	60
1725	100 c. *Meneris tulbaghia* ..	1·00	75
1726	200 c. *Salamis temora* ..	1·50	1·60
1727	400 c. *Charaxes jasius* ..	2·00	2·50
1728	500 c. *Precis oenone* ..	2·25	2·50
1729	700 c. *Precis sophia* ..	2·50	2·75
1722/9		*Set of 8*	10·00	10·00

MS1730 Two sheets, each 100×70 mm. (a) 900 c. *Papilio demodocus*. (b) 900 c. *Precis octavia*. *Set of 2 sheets* 7·50 8·00

Examples of Nos. 1722/30 overprinted "40th Anniversary of the Accession of HM Queen Elizabeth II 1952–1992" in silver are reported as not having been issued in Ghana.

(Litho Walsall)

1992 (1 June). *Prehistoric Animals. Vert designs as T* **290** *of Antigua. Multicoloured. P* 14.

1731	20 c. Iguanodon ..		25	25
1732	50 c. Anchisaurus ..		35	35
1733	60 c. Heterodontosaurus ..	35	35
1734	80 c. Ouranosaurus ..	45	45
1735	100 c. Anatosaurus ..	55	55
1736	200 c. Elaphrosaurus ..	1·00	1·25
1737	500 c. Coelophysis ..	1·90	2·00
1738	600 c. Rhamphorynchus ..	2·25	2·50
1731/8		*Set of 8*	6·25	7·25

MS1739 Two sheets, each 100×70 mm. (a) 1500 c. As 200 c. (b) 1500 c. As 500 c. *Set of 2 sheets* 9·00 10·00

483 Martin Pinzon   484 Olive-grey
and *Pinta*   Ancilla (*Agaronia
                                hiatula*)

(Des J.-L. Puvilland. Litho Questa)

1992 (20 July). *World Columbian Stamp "Expo '92", Chicago. 500th Anniv of Discovery of America by Columbus. T* **483** *and similar vert designs. Multicoloured. P* 14.

1740	200 c. Type 483 ..		80	80
	a. Sheetlet. Nos. 1740/7		5·50	
1741	200 c. Vincente Pinzon and *Nina*	80	80
1742	200 c. Columbus and Father Marchena at La Rabida ..	80	80

1743	200 c. Columbus in his cabin	80	80
1744	200 c. Fleet sights land	80	80
1745	200 c. Columbus on Samana Cay	80	80
1746	200 c. Wreck of Santa Maria	80	80
1747	200 c. Amerindians at Spanish Court	80	80
1740/7	*Set of 8*	5·50	5·50

MS1748 122×86 mm. 500 c. Columbus and Santa Maria .. .. 2·75 3·50

Nos. 1740/7 were printed together, *se-tenant*, in sheetlets of 8.

(Litho Questa)

1992 (30 Sept–5 Oct). *Shells. T* **484** *and similar vert designs. Multicoloured. P* 14.

1749	20 c. Type **484**	20	20
1750	20 c. Radula Cerith (*Tympanotonus fuscatus radula*) (5 Oct)	20	20
1751	60 c. Rugose Donax (*Donax rugosus*)	30	30
1752	60 c. Horned Murex (*Murex cornutus*) (5 Oct)	30	30
1753	80 c. Concave Ear Moon (*Sinum concavum*)	40	40
1754	80 c. Triple Tivella (*Tivella tripla*) (5 Oct)	40	40
1755	200 c. Pila africana	90	90
1756	200 c. Rat Cowrie (*Cypraea stercoraria*) (5 Oct)	90	90
1757	350 c. Thais hiatula	1·60	1·60
1758	350 c. West African Helmet (*Cassis tessellata*) (5 Oct)	1·60	1·60
1749/58	*Set of 10*	6·00	6·00

MS1759 Two sheets, each 87×117 mm. (a) 600 c. Fanel Moon (*Natica fanel*). (b) 600 c. Giant Hairy Melongena (*Pugilina moria*) .. *Set of 2 sheets* 6·00 7·00

485 "Presentation in the Temple" (Master of the Braunschweiti)

486 *Calappa rubroguttata*

(Litho Questa)

1992 (16 Dec). *Christmas. Religious Paintings. T* **485** *and similar vert designs. Multicoloured. P* 13½×14.

1760	20 c. Type **485**	20	20
1761	50 c. "Presentation in the Temple" (detail) (Master of St. Severin)	30	30
1762	60 c. "The Visitation" (Sebastiano del Piombo)	30	30
1763	80 c. "The Visitation" (detail) (Giotto)	40	40
1764	100 c. "The Circumcision" (detail) (Studio of Bellini)	50	50
1765	200 c. "The Circumcision" (Studio of Garofalo)	90	90
1766	500 c. "The Visitation" (Studio of Van der Weyden)	1·60	1·60
1767	800 c. "The Visitation" (detail) (Studio of Van der Weyden)	1·90	1·90
1760/7	*Set of 8*	5·50	5·50

MS1768 Two sheets, each 77×102 mm. (a) 900 c. "Presentation in the Temple" (Bartolo di Fredi). (b) 900 c. "The Visitation" (larger detail) (Giotto) *Set of 2 sheets* 6·00 7·00

(Litho Francoise-Charles, Oberthur)

1993 (15 Feb). *Crabs. T* **486** *and similar horiz designs. Multicoloured. P* 13½×14.

1769	20 c. Type **486**	30	15
1770	60 c. Cardisoma amatum	40	25
1771	80 c. Maia squinado	55	25
1772	400 c. Ocypoda cursor	1·00	1·25
1773	800 c. Grapus grapus	1·50	2·00
1769/73	*Set of 5*	3·25	3·50

MS1774 127×97 mm. Nos. 1769/72 .. 3·00 3·25

487 *Clerodendrum thomsoniae*

488 Zeppelin LZ-3 entering Floating Hangar, Lake Constance

(Litho Questa)

1993 (1 Mar). *Flowers. T* **487** *and similar vert designs. Multicoloured. P* 14.

1775	20 c. Type **487**	20	15
1776	20 c. Lagerstroemia flos-reginae	20	15
1777	60 c. Cassia fistula	35	25
1778	60 c. Spathodea campanulata	35	25
1779	80 c. Hildegardia barteri	40	25
1780	80 c. Mellitea ferrugenea	40	25
1781	200 c. Petrea volubilis	60	75
1782	200 c. Ipomoea asarifolia	60	75
1783	350 c. Bryphyllum pinnatum	90	1·00
1784	350 c. Ritchiea reflexa	90	1·00
1775/84	*Set of 10*	4·50	4·25

MS1785 Two sheets, each 86×125 mm. (a) 50 c. As No. 1777; 100 c. As No. 1783; 150 c. As No. 1782; 300 c. As No. 1779. (b) 50 c. As No. 1778; 100 c. As No. 1776; 150 c. As No. 1780; 300 c. As No. 1784 .. .. .. *Set of 2 sheets* 4·50 5·00

(Des W. Wright and W. Hanson (Nos. 1786, 1792, **MS**1793a). W. Wright and L. Fried (Nos. 1787, 1791, **MS**1793b). J. Genzo (Nos. 1790, **MS**1793d). W. Wright (others). Litho B.D.T.)

1993 (8 Mar). *Anniversaries and Events. T* **488** *and similar multicoloured designs. P* 14.

1786	20 c. Type **488**	40	30
1787	100 c. Launch of European "Ariane 4" rocket (*vert*)	70	75
1788	200 c. Leopard	1·40	1·60
1789	300 c. Colosseum and fruit	1·60	1·75
1790	400 c. Mozart (*vert*)	1·75	2·00
1791	600 c. Launch of Japanese "H-1" rocket (*vert*)	2·25	2·50
1792	800 c. Zeppelin LZ-10 *Schwaben*	2·50	2·75
1786/92	*Set of 7*	9·50	10·50

MS1793 Four sheets. (a) 106×76 mm. 900 c. Count Ferdinand von Zeppelin (*vert*). (b) 76×106 mm. 900 c. Launch of American space shuttle (*vert*). (c) 106×76 mm. 900 c. Bongo. (d) 99×69 mm. 900 c. Cherubino from *The Marriage of Figaro* (*vert*) .. *Set of 4 sheets* 11·00 12·00

Anniversaries and Events:—Nos. 1786, 1792, **MS**1793a, 75th death anniv of Count Ferdinand von Zeppelin; Nos. 1787, 1791, **MS**1793b, International Space Year; Nos. 1788, **MS**1793c, Earth Summit '92, Rio; No. 1789, International Conference on Nutrition, Rome; Nos. 1790, **MS**1793d, Death bicent of Mozart.

(Litho Walsall)

1993 (8 Mar). *Bicentenary of the Louvre, Paris. Multicoloured designs as T* **305** *of Antigua. P* 12.

1794	200 c. "Carnival Minuet" (left detail) (Giovanni Domenico Tiepolo)	85	1·00
	a. Sheetlet. Nos. 1794/1801	6·25	
1795	200 c. "Carnival Minuet" (centre detail) (Giovanni Domenico Tiepolo)	85	1·00
1796	200 c. "Carnival Minuet" (right detail) (Giovanni Domenico Tiepolo)	85	1·00
1797	200 c. "The Tooth Puller" (left detail) (Giovanni Domenico Tiepolo)	85	1·00
1798	200 c. "The Tooth Puller" (right detail) (Giovanni Domenico Tiepolo)	85	1·00
1799	200 c. "Rebecca at the Well" (Giovanni Battista Tiepolo)	85	1·00
1800	200 c. "Presenting Christ to the People" (left detail) (Giovanni Battista Tiepolo)	85	1·00
1801	200 c. "Presenting Christ to the People" (right detail) (Giovanni Battista Tiepolo)	85	1·00
1794/1801	*Set of 8*	6·25	7·25

MS1802 100×70 mm. 700 c. "Chancellor Seguier" (Charles le Brun) (85×52 *mm*). P 14½ 2·10 2·40

Nos. 1794/1801 were printed together, *se-tenant*, in sheetlets of 8 stamps and one centre label.

489 Energy Foods

(Litho Questa)

1993 (22 Mar). *International Conference on Nutrition, Rome. T* **489** *and similar horiz designs. Multicoloured. P* 14.

1803	20 c. Type **489**	20	15
1804	60 c. Body-building foods	30	20
1805	80 c. Protective foods	35	25
1806	200 c. Disease prevention equipment	80	90
1807	400 c. Quality control and preservation of fish products	1·50	1·75
1803/7	*Set of 5*	2·75	3·00

490 Kwame Nkrumah Mausoleum

491 Resurrection Egg

(Litho Questa)

1993 (8 Apr). *Proclamation of Fourth Republic. T* **490** *and similar multicoloured designs. P* 14.

1808	50 c. Type **490**	20	15
1809	100 c. Kwame Nkrumah Conference Centre	35	25
1810	200 c. Book of Constitution (*vert*)	80	80
1811	350 c. Independence Square (*vert*)	1·60	1·75
1812	400 c. Christiansborg Castle (*vert*)	1·75	2·00
1808/12	*Set of 5*	4·25	4·50

(Des Kerri Schiff. Litho Questa)

1993 (26 Apr). *Easter. Faberge Eggs. T* **491** *and similar multicoloured designs. P* 14.

1813	50 c. Type **491**	30	15
1814	80 c. Imperial Red Cross egg with Resurrection triptych	50	25
1815	100 c. Imperial Uspensky Cathedral egg	60	25
1816	150 c. Imperial Red Cross egg with portraits	90	65
1817	200 c. Orange Tree egg	1·00	1·00
1818	250 c. Rabbit egg	1·00	1·25
1819	400 c. Imperial Coronation egg	1·75	2·00
1820	900 c. Silver-gilt enamel Easter egg	3·00	3·50
1813/20	*Set of 8*	8·25	8·25

MS1821 Two sheets, each (a) 73×100 mm. 1000 c. Renaissance egg. (b) 100×73 mm. 1000 c. Egg charms (*horiz*) .. *Set of 2 sheets* 7·75 8·25

(Des W. Wright. Litho Questa)

1993 (3 May). *Centenary of Henry Ford's First Petrol Engine* (Nos. 1823/4, **MS**1826b) *and Karl Benz's First Four-wheeled Car* (others). *Horiz designs as T* **264** *of Dominica. Multicoloured. P* 14.

1822	150 c. Mercedes Benz "300 SLR", Mille Miglia, 1955	75	50
1823	400 c. Ford "Depot Wagon", 1920	1·75	1·75
1824	600 c. Ford "Mach 1 Mustang", 1970	2·25	2·50
1825	800 c. Mercedes Benz racing car, Monaco Grand Prix, 1937	3·50	4·00
1822/5	*Set of 4*	7·50	8·00

MS1826 Two sheets, each 110×80 mm. (a) 1000 c. Mercedes Benz "Type 196" racing car, 1955 (85½×28½ *mm*). (b) 1000 c. Ford "Super T", 1910 (85½×28½ *mm*) .. *Set of 2 sheets* 7·75 8·25

(Des W. Wright. Litho Questa)

1993 (3 May). *Aviation Anniversaries. Multicoloured designs as T* **266** *of Dominica. P* 14.

1827	50 c. LZ-127 Graf Zeppelin over Alps (*vert*)	50	30
1828	150 c. Zeppelin LZ-7 Deutschland	85	55
1829	400 c. Avro Vulcan jet bomber	1·75	1·75
1830	400 c. U.S. Mail Ford 4-AT Trimotor	1·75	1·75
1831	600 c. Nieuport 27 (*vert*)	2·25	2·25
1832	600 c. Loading mail on LZ-127 Graf Zeppelin (*vert*)	2·25	2·25
1833	800 c. Zeppelin LZ-10 Schwaben	3·50	4·00
1827/33	*Set of 7*	11·50	11·50

MS1834 Three sheets, each 111×80 mm. (a) 1000 c. LZ-127 *Graf Zeppelin*. (b) 1000 c. S.E.5A, 1918. (c) 1000 c. Early airmail flight by Walter Edwards between Portland and Vancouver (57×42½ *mm*) .. .. .. *Set of 3 sheets* 11·50 12·00

Anniversaries:—Nos. 1827/8, 1833, **MS**1834a, 125th birth anniv of Hugo Eckener (airship commander); Nos. 1829, 1831, **MS**1834b, 75th anniv of Royal Air Force; Nos. 1830, 1832, **MS**1834c, Bicentenary of First Airmail Flight.

492 African Buffalo

40TH ANNIVERSARY OF CORONATION H.M. ELIZABETH II

(493)

(Des T. Muse. Litho Questa)

1993 (24 May). *Wild Animals. T* **492** *and similar horiz designs. Multicoloured. P* 14.

1835	20 c. Type **492**	25	15
1836	50 c. Giant Forest Hog	30	20
1837	60 c. Potto	40	25
1838	80 c. Bay Duiker	50	30
1839	100 c. Royal Antelope	60	35
1840	200 c. Serval	90	90
1841	500 c. Golden Cat	1·75	2·00
1842	800 c. Megaloglossus woermanni (bat)	3·00	3·50
1835/42	*Set of 8*	7·00	7·00

MS1843 Two sheets, each 68×98 mm. (a) 900 c. Dormouse. (b) 900 c. White-collared Mangabey *Set of 2 sheets* 7·00 7·50

1993 (18 June). *40th Anniv of Coronation. Nos. 1549/53 optd with T* **493**.

1844	100 c. multicoloured	50	25
1845	200 c. multicoloured	90	70
1846	500 c. multicoloured	2·50	2·75
1847	600 c. multicoloured	2·75	3·00
1844/7	*Set of 4*	6·00	6·00

MS1848 Two sheets. (a) 104×75 mm. 800 c. mult. (b) 74×105 mm. 800 c. mult *Set of 2 sheets* 6·25 6·75

The sheets of No. **MS**1848 also carry a commemorative overprint on the margin.

35 YEARS OF ROTARY INTERNATIONAL GHANA 1958

(494)

GHANA ✚ RED CROSS SOCIETY FOUNDED 1932

(495)

1993 (18 June). *35th Anniv of Rotary International and 60th Anniv of Ghana Red Cross Society (1992). Nos. 1562 and 1564/7 optd with T 494 (Nos. 1849, 1852, MS1853a) or T 495 (others).*

1849	100 c. Stonehead		50	25
1850	300 c. Aba (R.)		1·50	1·50
1851	400 c. Jewel Cichlid (R.)		1·75	1·75
1852	500 c. Smooth Hammerhead		2·00	2·25
1849/52		Set of 4	5·25	5·25

MS1853 Two sheets, each 108×81 mm. (a) 800 c. Bayad. (b) 800 c. Eastern Flying Gurnard (R.)

Set of 2 sheets 6·25 6·75

The sheets of No. **MS1853** also carry a commemorative overprint on the margin.

Ghana mushrooms

1881-Picasso-1973

The Actor, 1905

GHANA C20

496 *Cantharellus cibarius*

497 "The Actor" (Picasso)

(Des L. Nelson (Nos. 1861/2, 1866/8), E. Mensah (others). Litho Questa)

1993 (30 July). *Mushrooms. T 496 and similar vert designs. Multicoloured. P 14.*

1854	20 c. Type **496**		40	25
1855	50 c. *Russula cyanoxantha*		50	30
1856	60 c. *Clitocybe rivulosa*		55	30
1857	80 c. *Cortinarius elatior*		60	35
1858	80 c. *Mycena galericulata*		60	35
1859	200 c. *Tricholoma gambosum*		1·00	1·00
1860	200 c. *Boletus edulis*		1·00	1·00
1861	200 c. *Lepista saeva*		1·00	1·00
1862	250 c. *Gyroporus castaneus*		1·10	1·10
1863	300 c. *Boletus chrysenteron*		1·25	1·25
1864	350 c. *Nolanea sericea*		1·40	1·40
1865	350 c. *Hygrophorus puicea* ("Hygrophorus puiceus")		1·40	1·40
1866	500 c. *Gomphidius glutinosus*		1·60	1·75
1867	600 c. *Russula olivacea*		1·75	2·00
1868	1000 c. *Russula aurata*		2·25	2·75
1854/68		Set of 15	14·50	14·50

MS1869 Two sheets, each 85×130 mm. (a) 50 c. As No. 1856; 100 c. As No. 1858; 150 c. As No. 1860; 1000 c. As No. 1864. (b) 100 c. As Type **496**; 150 c. As No. 1857; 300 c. As No. 1859; 600 c. As No. 1865 .. .. Set of 2 sheets 9·50 10·00

(Litho Cartor (Nos. 1871, 1873, **MS**1877c/d), Questa (others))

1993 (19 Oct). *Anniversaries and Events. T 497 and similar multicoloured designs. P 13½×14 (Nos. 1871, 1873) or 14 (others).*

1870	20 c. Type **497**		30	20
1871	20 c. Early astronomical equipment		30	20
1872	80 c. "Portrait of Allan Stein" (Picasso)		40	25
1873	200 c. Modern telescope		80	80
1874	200 c. "Tattoo" (Lesek Sobocki)		80	80
1875	600 c. "Prison" (Sasza Blonder)		2·00	2·50
1876	800 c. "Seated Male Nude" (Picasso)		2·75	3·25
1870/6		Set of 7	6·50	7·25

MS1877 Four sheets. (a) 75×105 mm. 900 c. "Guernica" (Picasso). P 14. (b) 75×105 mm. 1000 c. "Bajika o Czlowieku Szczesliwym" (detail) (Antoni Mickalak) (*horiz*). P 14. (c) 105×75 mm. 1000 c. Copernicus (face value at top left). P 12×13. (d) 105×75 mm. 1000 c. Copernicus (face value at centre top). P 12×13

Set of 4 sheets 14·00 15·00

Anniversaries and Events:—Nos. 1870, 1872, 1876, **MS**1877a, 20th death anniv of Picasso (artist); Nos. 1871, 1873, **MS**1877c/d, 450th death anniv of Copernicus (astronomer); Nos. 1874/5, **MS**1877b, "Polska '93" International Stamp Exhibition, Poznań.

GHANA c50

Abedi Pele, GHA

C50 GHANA Domestic Animals

Meleagris gallopavo

498 Abedi Pele (Ghana)

499 Common Turkey

(Litho Questa)

1993 (1 Dec). *World Cup Football Championship, U.S.A. (1st issue). T 498 and similar vert designs. Multicoloured. P 13×14.*

1878	50 c. Type **498**		50	25
1879	80 c. Pedro Troglio (Argentina)		60	30
1880	100 c. Fernando Alvez (Uruguay)		70	40
1881	200 c. Franco Baresi (Italy)		1·25	1·00

1882	250 c. Gomez (Colombia) and Katanec (Yugoslavia)		1·25	1·25
1883	600 c. Diego Maradona (Argentina)		2·50	2·75
1884	800 c. Hasek (Czechoslovakia) and Wynalda (U.S.A.)		3·00	3·25
1885	1000 c. Lothar Matthaeus (Germany)		3·50	4·00
1878/85		Set of 8	12·00	12·00

MS1886 Two sheets, each 70×100 mm. (a) 1200 c. Rabie Yassein (Egypt) and Ruud Gullit (Netherlands). (b) 1200 c. Giuseppe Giannini (Italy). P 13 .. .. Set of 2 sheets 10·00 11·00

See also Nos. 2037/43.

(Litho Questa)

1993 (8 Dec). *Domestic Animals. T 499 and similar horiz designs. Multicoloured. P 14.*

1887	50 c. Type **499**		50	25
1888	100 c. Goats		70	40
1889	150 c. Muscovy Ducks		1·00	75
1890	200 c. Donkeys		1·25	1·00
1891	250 c. Red Junglefowl cock		1·25	1·25
1892	300 c. Pigs		1·40	1·40
1893	400 c. Helmet Guineafowl		1·75	1·75
1894	600 c. Dog		2·50	2·75
1895	800 c. Red Junglefowl hen		3·00	3·50
1896	1000 c. Sheep		3·50	4·00
1887/96		Set of 10	15·00	15·00

MS1897 Two sheets, each 133×106 mm. (a) 100 c. As No. 1888; 250 c. No. 1894; 350 c. No. 1892; 500 c. No. 1896. (b) 100 c. No. 1893; 250 c. As No. 1891; 350 c. No. 1895; 500 c. Type **499**

Set of 2 sheets 8·50 9·00

(Litho Questa)

1993 (20 Dec). *Christmas. Religious Paintings. Designs as T 270 of Dominica. Black, pale lemon and red (Nos. 1898, 1900/1, 1905 and MS1906a) or multicoloured (others). P 13½×14.*

1898	50 c. "Adoration of the Magi" (Dürer)		40	20
1899	100 c. "The Virgin and Child with St. John and an Angel" (Botticelli)		60	25
1900	150 c. "Mary as Queen of Heaven" (Dürer)		80	45
1901	200 c. "Saint Anne" (Dürer)		90	65
1902	250 c. "The Madonna of the Magnificat" (Botticelli)		1·00	75
1903	400 c. "The Madonna of the Goldfinch" (Botticelli)		1·50	1·50
1904	600 c. "The Virgin and Child with the young St. John the Baptist" (Botticelli)		2·00	2·25
1905	1000 c. "Adoration of the Shepherds" (Dürer)		2·75	3·25
1898/1905		Set of 8	9·00	8·50

MS1906 Two sheets, each 102×128 mm. (a) 1000 c. "Madonna in a Circle" (detail) (Dürer). P 13½×14. (b) 1000 c. "Mystic Nativity" (detail) (Botticelli) (*horiz*). P 14×13½ .. Set of 2 sheets 7·50 8·50

GHANA c50

art and craft C50

GHANA

500 Doll

501 Mickey Mouse in *Steamboat Willie*, 1928

(Des E. Mensah. Litho Questa)

1994 (24 Jan). *Traditional Crafts. T 500 and similar vert designs. Multicoloured. P 14.*

1907	50 c. Type **500**		25	15
1908	50 c. Pot with "head" lid		25	15
1909	200 c. Bead necklace		60	60
1910	200 c. Snake charmers (statuette)		60	60
1911	250 c. Hoe		60	60
1912	250 c. Scabbard		60	60
1913	600 c. Pipe		1·50	1·75
1914	600 c. Deer (carving)		1·50	1·75
1915	1000 c. Mask		2·25	2·50
1916	1000 c. Doll (*different*)		2·25	2·50
1907/16		Set of 10	9·25	10·00

MS1917 Two sheets, each 95×128 mm. (a) 100 c. As Type **500**; 250 c. As No. 1909; 350 c. As No. 1911; 500 c. As No. 1913. (b) 100 c. As No. 1908; 250 c. As No. 1910; 350 c. As No. 1912; 500 c. As No. 1914 .. .. Set of 2 sheets 4·50 5·50

(Des W. Hanson. Litho Questa)

1994 (18 Feb). *"Hong Kong '94" International Stamp Exhibition (1st issue). Horiz designs as T 317 of Antigua. Multicoloured. P 14.*

1918	200 c. Hong Kong 1986 50 c. "Expo '86" stamp and tram		10	15
	a. Horiz pair. Nos. 1918/19		20	30
1919	200 c. Ghana 1992 20 c. Railways stamp and tram		10	15

Nos. 1918/19 were printed together, *se-tenant*, in horizontal pairs throughout the sheet with the centre part of each pair forming the complete design.

(Des Kerri Schiff. Litho Questa)

1994 (18 Feb). *"Hong Kong '94" International Stamp Exhibition (2nd issue). Imperial Palace Clocks. Designs as T 318 of Antigua, but vert. Multicoloured. P 14.*

1920	100 c. Windmill clock		10	10
	a. Sheetlet. Nos. 1920/5		30	
1921	100 c. Horse clock		10	10
1922	100 c. Balloon clock		10	10
1923	100 c. Zodiac clock		10	10
1924	100 c. Shar-pei Dog clock		10	10
1925	100 c. Cat clock		10	10
1920/5		Set of 6	30	40

Nos. 1920/5 were printed together, *se-tenant*, in sheetlets of 6.

(Litho Questa)

1994 (1 Mar). *65th Anniv of Mickey Mouse (Walt Disney cartoon character) (1993). T 501 and similar vert designs showing scenes from various cartoon films. P 13½×14.*

1926	50 c. Type **501**		10	10
1927	100 c. *The Band Concert*, 1935		10	10
1928	150 c. *Moose Hunters*, 1937		10	10
1929	200 c. *Brave Little Tailor*, 1938		10	15
1930	250 c. *Fantasia*, 1940		15	20
1931	400 c. *The Nifty Nineties*, 1941		20	25
1932	600 c. *Canine Caddy*, 1941		30	35
1933	1000 c. *Mickey's Christmas Carol*, 1983		50	55
1926/33		Set of 8	1·40	1·75

MS1934 Two sheets, each 127×102 mm. (a) 1200 c. *Mickey's Elephant*, 1936. (b) 1200 c. *Mickey's Amateurs*, 1937. Set of 2 sheets 1·25 1·40

No. 1929 is inscribed "TAYLOR" in error. The dates on Nos. 1927 and 1932 are incorrectly shown as "1937" and "1944".

(Litho Questa)

1994 (6 Apr). *Easter. Hummel Figurines. Vert designs as T 302 of Antigua. Multicoloured. P 14.*

1935	50 c. Boy hiker		10	10
1936	100 c. Girl with basket behind back		10	10
1937	150 c. Boy with rabbits		10	10
1938	200 c. Boy holding basket		10	15
1939	250 c. Girl with chicks		15	20
1940	400 c. Girl with lamb		20	25
1941	600 c. Girl waving red handkerchief with lamb		30	35
1942	1000 c. Girl with basket and posy		50	55
1935/42		Set of 8	1·40	1·60

MS1943 Two sheets, each 93×126 mm. (a) 50 c. As No. 1935; 150 c. As No. 1942; 500 c. As No. 1936; 1200 c. As No. 1938. (b) 100 c. As No. 1940; 300 c. As No. 1939; 500 c. As No. 1941; 1000 c. As No. 1937 .. .. Set of 2 sheets 2·00 2·10

C50 GHANA WWF

GHANA c200

Norwegian Forest Cat

502 Diana Monkey with Young

503 Norwegian Forest Cat

(Des S. Barlowe. Litho Questa)

1994 (16 May). *Wildlife. T 502 and similar multicoloured designs. P 14.*

1944	50 c. Type **502**		10	10
	a. Horiz strip of 4. Nos. 1944 and 1947/9		1·25	
1945	100 c. Bushbuck (*horiz*)		10	10
1946	150 c. Spotted Hyena (*horiz*)		10	10
1947	200 c. Diana Monkey on branch facing left		10	15
1948	500 c. Diana Monkey on branch facing right		25	30
1949	800 c. Head of Diana Monkey		40	45
1950	1000 c. Aardvark (*horiz*)		50	55
1944/50		Set of 7	1·40	1·75

MS1951 Two sheets, each 106×76 mm. (a) 2000 c. Leopard. (b) 2000 c. Waterbuck

Set of 2 sheets 2·00 2·10

In addition to normal sheets of each value Nos. 1944 and 1947/9 were also available in sheets of 12 with the stamps available both vertically and horizontally *se-tenant*. Designs of Nos. 1944 and 1947/9 include the W.W.F. Panda emblem.

(Des Jennifer Toombs. Litho Questa)

1994 (6 June). *Cats. T 503 and similar horiz designs. Multicoloured. P 14.*

1952	200 c. Type **503**		10	15
	a. Sheetlet. Nos. 1952/63		1·25	
1953	200 c. Blue Longhair		10	15
1954	200 c. Red Self Longhair		10	15
1955	200 c. Black Longhair		10	15
1956	200 c. Chinchilla		10	15
1957	200 c. Dilute Calico Longhair		10	15
1958	200 c. Blue Tabby and White Longhair		10	15
1959	200 c. Ruby Somali		10	15
1960	200 c. Blue Smoke Longhair		10	15
1961	200 c. Calico Longhair		10	15

1962	200 c. Brown Tabby Longhair	.. ..	10	15
1963	200 c. Balinese	.. ..	10	15
1964	200 c. Sorrel Abyssinian ..	.. ..	10	15
	a. Sheetlet. Nos. 1964/75	.. ..	1·25	
1965	200 c. Silver Classic Tabby	.. ..	10	15
1966	200 c. Chocolate-point Siamese	..	10	15
1967	200 c. Brown Tortie Burmese	..	10	15
1968	200 c. Exotic Shorthair	.. ..	10	15
1969	200 c. Havana Brown	.. ..	10	15
1970	200 c. Devon Rex ..	.. ..	10	15
1971	200 c. Black Manx	.. ..	10	15
1972	200 c. British Blue Shorthair	..	10	15
1973	200 c. Calico American Wirehair ..		10	15
1974	200 c. Spotted Oriental Siamese	..	10	15
1975	200 c. Red Classic Tabby ..	..	10	15
1952/75		Set of 24	2·50	3·50

MS1976 Two sheets, each 102×89 mm. (a)
2000 c. Brown Mackerel Tabby Scottish Fold. (b)
2000 c. Seal-point Colourpoint .. Set of 2 sheets 2·00 2·10
Nos. 1952/63 and 1964/75 were printed together, se-tenant, in sheetlets of 12.

No. 1957 is inscribed "Dilut" in error.

504 Red-bellied Paradise
Flycatcher

(Des Mary Walters. Litho Questa)

1994 (13 June). *Birds. T 504 and similar horiz designs. Multicoloured. P 14.*

1977	200 c. Type 504	.. ..	10	15
	a. Sheetlet. Nos. 1977/88	..	1·25	
1978	200 c. Many-coloured Bush Shrike	..	10	15
1979	200 c. Broad-tailed Paradise Whydah	..	10	15
1980	200 c. White-crowned Robin Chat	..	10	15
1981	200 c. Violet Turaco ("Violet Plantain-eater")		10	15
1982	200 c. Village Weaver	.. ..	10	15
1983	200 c. Red-crowned Bishop	..	10	15
1984	200 c. Common Shoveler ..	..	10	15
1985	200 c. Spur-winged Goose	..	10	15
1986	200 c. African Crake	.. ..	10	15
1987	200 c. Purple Swamphen ("King Reed-hen")		10	15
1988	200 c. African Tiger Bittern	..	10	15
1989	200 c. Oriole Warbler ("Moho")	..	10	15
	a. Sheetlet. Nos. 1989/2000	..	1·25	
1990	200 c. Superb Sunbird	.. ..	10	15
1991	200 c. Blue-breasted Kingfisher	..	10	15
1992	200 c. African Blue Cuckoo Shrike	..	10	15
1993	200 c. Great Blue Turaco ("Blue Plantain-eater")		10	15
1994	200 c. Greater Flamingo	.. ..	10	15
1995	200 c. African Jacana ("Lily-trotter")	..	10	15
1996	200 c. Black-crowned Night Heron	..	10	15
1997	200 c. Black-winged Stilt ..	..	10	15
1998	200 c. White-spotted Crake	..	10	15
1999	200 c. African Pygmy Goose	..	10	15
2000	200 c. African Pitta	.. ..	10	15
1977/2000		Set of 24	2·50	3·50

MS2001 Two sheets, each 113×83 mm. (a)
2000 c. African Spoonbill. (b) 2000 c. Goliath
Heron .. .. .. Set of 2 sheets 2·00 2·10
Nos. 1977/88 and 1989/2000 were printed together, se-tenant, in sheetlets of 12.

505 Women at Stand-pipe

(Litho Questa)

1994 (11 July). *First Anniversary of Fourth Republic. T 505 and similar horiz designs. Multicoloured. P 14.*

2002	50 c. Type 505 ..	.. ..	10	10
2003	100 c. Presenting certificate to farmers		10	10
2004	200 c. Village electricity supply ..	..	10	15
2005	600 c. Bridge	.. ..	30	35
2006	800 c. National Theatre ..	..	40	45
2007	1000 c. Lighting Perpetual Flame	..	50	55
2002/7	..	Set of 6	1·40	1·60

(Des W. Hanson. Litho B.D.T.)

1994 (20 July). *25th Anniv of First Moon Landing. Horiz designs as T 326 of Antigua showing scientists. Multicoloured. P 14.*

2008	300 c. Sigmund Jahn	.. ..	15	20
	a. Sheetlet. Nos. 2008/16	..	1·40	
2009	300 c. Ulf Merbold	.. ..	15	20
2010	300 c. Hans Wilhelm Schegal	..	15	20
2011	300 c. Ulrich Walter	.. ..	15	20
2012	300 c. Reinhard Furrer	..	15	20
2013	300 c. Ernst Messerschmid	..	15	20
2014	300 c. Mamoru Mohri ..	..	15	20
2015	300 c. Klaus-Dietrich Flade	..	15	20
2016	300 c. Chaiki Naito-Mukai	..	15	20
2008/16		Set of 9	1·40	1·75

MS2017 130×118 mm. 2000 c. Poster for *Frau im Mond* (film) by Fritz Lang .. .. 1·00 1·10
Nos. 2008/16 were printed together, se-tenant, in sheetlets of 9.

(Des Kerri Schiff. Litho B.D.T.)

1994 (20 July). *Centenary of International Olympic Committee. Gold Medal Winners. Designs as T 327 of Antigua, but vert. Multicoloured. P 14.*

2018	300 c. Dieter Modenburg (Germany) (high jump), 1984	.. ..	15	20
2019	400 c. Ruth Fuchs (Germany) (javelin), 1972 and 1976	.. ..	20	25

MS2020 77×106 mm. 1500 c. Jans Weissflog
(Germany) (ski jump), 1994 .. .. 80 85

(Des J. Batchelor. Litho B.D.T.)

1994 (20 July). *50th Anniv of D-Day. Horiz designs as T 331 of Antigua. Multicoloured. P 14.*

2021	60 c. H.M.S. *Roberts* (monitor)	..	10	10
2022	100 c. H.M.S. *Warspite* (battleship)	..	10	10
2023	200 c. U.S.S. *Augusta* (cruiser)	..	10	15
2021/3		Set of 3	30	35

MS2024 107×76 mm. 1500 c. U.S.S. *Nevada*
(battleship) firing salvo 80 85

(Des Kerri Schiff. Litho Questa (Nos. 2027/34), B.D.T. (others))

1994 (20 July). *"Philakorea '94" International Stamp Exhibition, Seoul. Multicoloured designs as T 279 of Dominica. P 14 (Nos. 2025/6, 2035) or 13 (others).*

2025	20 c. Ch'unghak-dong village elder in traditional costume (24¹/₂×38 mm)		10	10
2026	150 c. Stone Pagoda, Punhwangsa (24¹/₂×38 mm)		10	10
2027	250 c. Character with eggs	..	15	20
	a. Sheetlet. Nos. 2027/34	..	1·10	
2028	250 c. Character with pair of birds on house		15	20
2029	250 c. Character with cock	..	15	20
2030	250 c. Character with dragon and pagoda		15	20
2031	250 c. Character with orange flowers	..	15	20
2032	250 c. Character with parrot and pagoda		15	20
2033	250 c. Character with plant	..	15	20
2034	250 c. Character with fish	..	15	20
2035	300 c. Traditional country house, Andong (24¹/₂×34 mm)		15	20
2025/35		Set of 11	1·40	1·90

MS2036 100×70 mm. 1500 c. Temple judges
deliberating (42¹/₂×28¹/₂ mm). P 14 .. 80 85
Nos. 2027/34 were printed together, se-tenant, in sheetlets of 8 and show illuminated Korean characters.

506 Dennis Bergkamp
(Netherlands)

(Litho Questa)

1994 (22 July). *World Cup Football Championship, U.S.A. (2nd issue). T 506 and similar multicoloured designs. P 14.*

2037	200 c. Type 506	.. ..	10	15
	a. Sheetlet. Nos. 2037/42	..	60	
2038	200 c. Lothar Matthaus (Germany)	..	10	15
2039	200 c. Giuseppe Signori (Italy)	..	10	15
2040	200 c. Carlos Valderama (Colombia)	..	10	15
2041	200 c. Jorge Campos (Mexico)	..	10	15
2042	200 c. Tony Meola (U.S.A.)	..	10	15
2037/42		Set of 6	60	90

MS2043 Two sheets, each 100×70 mm. (a)
1200 c. Giants' Stadium, New Jersey (vert). (b)
1200 c. Citrus Bowl, Orlando (vert)
 .. .. Set of 2 sheets 1·25 1·40
Nos. 2037/42 were printed together, se-tenant, in sheetlets of 6.

507 Common ("Crowned")
Duiker

508 Northern
Region Dancer

(Des E. Mensah. Litho Questa)

1994 (1 Sept). *Duikers (Antelopes). T 507 and similar horiz designs. Multicoloured. P 14.*

2044	50 c. Type 507	.. ..	10	10
2045	100 c. Red-flanked Duiker	..	10	10
2046	200 c. Yellow-backed Duiker	..	10	15
2047	400 c. Ogilby's Duiker	..	20	25
2048	600 c. Bay Duiker	.. ..	30	35
2049	800 c. Jentink's Duiker	..	40	45
2044/9		Set of 6	1·10	1·25

MS2050 Two sheets, each 106×76 mm. (a)
2000 c. Red Forest Duiker. (b) 2000 c. Black
Duiker .. .. .. Set of 2 sheets 2·00 2·10

(Litho Questa)

1994 (5 Dec). *Christmas. Religious Paintings. Vert designs as T 336 of Antigua. Multicoloured. P 13¹/₂×14.*

2051	100 c. "Madonna of the Annunciation" (Simone Martini) ..		10	10
2052	200 c. "Madonna and Child" (Niccolo di Pietro Gerini) ..		10	15
2053	250 c. "Virgin and Child on the Throne with Angels and Saints" (Raffaello Botticini)		15	20
2054	300 c. "Madonna and Child with Saints" (Antonio Fiorentino)		15	20
2055	400 c. "Adoration of the Magi" (Bartolo di Fredi)		20	25
2056	500 c. "The Annunciation" (Cima da Congeliano)		25	30
2057	600 c. "Virgin and Child with the Young St. John the Baptist" (workshop of Botticelli)		30	35
2058	1000 c. "The Holy Family" (Giorgione)	..	50	55
2051/8		Set of 8	1·75	1·90

MS2059 Two sheets, each 135×95 mm. (a)
2000 c. "Adoration of the Kings" (detail showing
Holy Family) (Giorgione). (b) 2000 c. "Adoration
of the Kings" (detail showing King and
attendants) (Giorgione) .. Set of 2 sheets 2·00 2·10

(Litho B.D.T.)

1994 (9 Dec). *Panafest '94 (2nd Pan-African Historical Theatre Festival). T 508 and similar vert designs. Multicoloured. P 13¹/₂×13.*

2060	50 c. Type 508	.. ..	20	15
2061	100 c. Traditional artefacts	..	35	25
2062	200 c. Chief with courtiers	..	65	60
2063	400 c. Woman in ceremonial costume	..	1·25	1·25
2064	600 c. Cape Coast Castle ..	..	1·75	2·00
2065	800 c. Clay figurines	..	2·25	2·75
2060/5	..	Set of 6	6·00	6·25

509 Red Cross Stretcher-bearers **510** Fertility Doll

(Des E. Mensah. Litho Questa)

1994 (20 Dec). *75th Anniv of Red Cross. T 509 and similar horiz designs. Multicoloured. P 14.*

2066	50 c. Type 509	.. ..	10	10
2067	200 c. Worker with children	..	10	15
2068	600 c. Workers erecting tents	..	30	35
2066/8		Set of 3	50	60

MS2069 147×99 mm. Nos. 2066/7 and 1000 c. As
600 c. 70 75

(Des E. Mensah. Litho Questa)

1994 (20 Dec). *Fertility Dolls. T 510 and similar vert designs showing different dolls. P 14.*

2070	50 c. multicoloured	.. ..	10	10
2071	100 c. multicoloured	.. ..	10	10
2072	150 c. multicoloured	.. ..	10	10
2073	200 c. multicoloured	.. ..	10	15
2074	400 c. multicoloured	.. ..	20	25
2075	600 c. multicoloured	.. ..	30	35
2076	800 c. multicoloured	.. ..	40	45
2077	1000 c. multicoloured	.. ..	50	55
2070/7		Set of 8	1·60	1·90

MS2078 147×99 mm. Nos. 2071, 2074/5 and
250 c. As 1000 c. 85 90

511 Ghanaian Family **512** Control Tower
and Emblem

(Des E. Mensah. Litho Questa)

1994 (20 Dec). *International Year of the Family. T 511 and similar vert designs. Multicoloured. P 14.*

2079	50 c. Type 511	.. ..	10	10
2080	100 c. Teaching carpentry	..	10	10
2081	200 c. Child care	..	10	15
2082	400 c. Care for the elderly	..	20	25
2083	600 c. Learning pottery	..	30	35
2084	1000 c. Adult education students	..	50	55
2079/84		Set of 6	1·25	1·40

(Des E. Mensah. Litho Questa)

1994 (24 Dec)–**95**. *50th Anniv of International Civil Aviation Organization. T 512 and similar horiz designs. Multicoloured. P 14.* (a) *Inscr* "50th Anniversary Of Ghana Civil Aviation Authority"

2085	100 c. Type **512**	10	
2086	400 c. Communications equipment	20	
2087	1000 c. Airliner taking off	50	
2085/7	*Set of 3*	80	

(b) *Inscr* "50th Anniversary Of The International Civil Aviation Organisation (I.C.A.O.)" (4.95)

2088	100 c. Type **512**	10	10
2089	400 c. Communications equipment	20	25
2090	1000 c. Airliner taking off	50	55
2088/90	*Set of 3*	80	90

Nos. 2085/7 were withdrawn from post offices in Ghana soon after issue when it was realised that the wrong organisation had been commemorated. Supplies were, however, distributed by the New York philatelic agent.

513 Pluto, Donald Duck and Chip n'Dale around Table

(Des Alvin White Studio. Litho Questa)

1995 (2 Feb). *60th Anniv of Donald Duck. T 513 and similar multicoloured designs showing Walt Disney cartoon characters at birthday party. P 14×13½.*

2091	40 c. Type **513**	10	10
2092	-50 c. Mickey Mouse and pup with banner	10	10
2093	60 c. Daisy Duck with balloons	10	10
2094	100 c. Goofy making cake	10	10
2095	150 c. Goofy on roller blades delivering cake	10	10
2096	250 c. Donald pinning donkey tail on Goofy	15	20
2097	400 c. Ludwig von Drake singing to Pluto	20	25
2098	500 c. Grandma Duck giving cake to puppies	25	30
2099	1000 c. Mickey and Minnie Mouse at piano	50	55
2100	1500 c. Pluto with bone and ball	80	85
2091/100	*Set of 10*	2·00	2·25

MS2101 Two sheets. (a) 117×95 mm. 2000 c. Donald blowing out birthday candles (*vert*). (b) 95×117 mm. 2000 c. Donald wearing party hat (*vert*). P 13½×14 .. *Set of 2 sheets* 2·00 2·10

514 Fort Appolonia, Beyin

(Des E. Mensah. Litho B.D.T.)

1995 (3 Apr). *Forts and Castles of Ghana. T 514 and similar multicoloured designs. P 14.*

2102	50 c. Type **514**	10	10
2103	200 c. Fort Patience, Apam	10	15
2104	250 c. Fort Amsterdam, Kormantin	15	20
2105	300 c. Fort St. Jago, Elmina	15	20
2106	400 c. Fort William, Anomabo	20	25
2107	600 c. Kumasi Fort	30	35
2102/7	*Set of 6*	1·00	1·25

MS2108 Two sheets, each 102×72 mm. (a) 800 c. Elmina Castle (*vert*). (b) 1000 c. Fort St. Antonio, Axim .. .. *Set of 2 sheets* 90 95

515 Cochem Castle, Germany

(Des R. Sauber. Litho B.D.T.)

1995 (3 Apr). *Castles of the World. T 515 and similar horiz designs. Multicoloured. P 14.*

2109	150 c. Type **515**	10	10
2110	500 c. Windsor Castle, England	25	30
	a. Sheetlet. Nos. 2110/18	2·25	
2111	500 c. Osaka Castle, Japan	25	30
2112	500 c. Vaj Dahunyad Castle, Hungary	25	30
2113	500 c. Karlstejn Castle, Czech Republic	25	30
2114	500 c. Kronborg Castle, Denmark	25	30
2115	500 c. Alcázar of Segovia, Spain	25	30
2116	500 c. Chambourd Castle, France	25	30
2117	500 c. Linderhof Castle, Germany	25	30
2118	500 c. Red Fort, Delhi, India	25	30
2119	600 c. Hohenzollern Castle, Germany	30	35

2120	800 c. Uwajima Castle, Japan	40	45
2121	1000 c. Hohenschwangau Castle, Germany	50	55
2109/21	*Set of 13*	3·25	3·75

MS2122 Two sheets, each 102×72 mm. (a) 2500 c. Neuschwanstein Castle, Germany (b) 2500 c. Himeji Castle, Japan .. *Set of 2 sheets* 2·50 3·00

Nos. 2110/18 were printed together, *se-tenant*, in sheetlets of 9.

516 European Pochard ("Eurasian Pochard")

517 Cycling

(Litho B.D.T.)

1995 (28 Apr). *Ducks. T 516 and similar horiz designs. Multicoloured. P 14.*

2123	200 c. Type **516**	10	15
2124	400 c. African Pygmy Goose	20	25
	a. Sheetlet. Nos. 2124/35	2·40	
2125	400 c. Southern Pochard	20	25
2126	400 c. Cape Teal	20	25
2127	400 c. Ruddy Shelduck	20	25
2128	400 c. Fulvous Whistling Duck	20	25
2129	400 c. White-faced Whistling Duck	20	25
2130	400 c. Ferruginous Duck ("Ferruginous White-eye")	20	25
2131	400 c. Hottentot Teal	20	25
2132	400 c. African Black Duck	20	25
2133	400 c. African Yellow-bill	20	25
2134	400 c. Bahama Pintail ("White-checked Pintail Duck")	20	25
2135	400 c. Hartlaub's Duck	20	25
2136	500 c. Maccoa Duck	25	30
2137	800 c. Cape Shoveler	40	45
2138	1000 c. Red-crested Pochard	50	55
2123/38	*Set of 16*	3·50	4·25

MS2139 Two sheets, each 104×74 mm. (a) 2500 c. Roseate Tern. (b) 2500 c. Common Shoveler ("Northern Shoveler").. *Set of 2 sheets* 2·50 3·00

Nos. 2124/35 were printed together, *se-tenant*, in sheetlets of 12 with the backgrounds forming a composite design.

Nos. 2128 is inscribed "Wistling" in error.

(Des J. Iskowitz. Litho Questa)

1995 (2 May). *Olympic Games, Atlanta (1996) (1st issue). T 517 and similar vert designs. Multicoloured. P 14.*

2140	300 c. Type **517**	15	20
	a. Sheetlet. Nos. 2140/51	1·75	
2141	300 c. Archery	15	20
2142	300 c. Diving	15	20
2143	300 c. Swimming	15	20
2144	300 c. Women's Gymnastics	15	20
2145	300 c. Fencing	15	20
2146	300 c. Boxing	15	20
2147	300 c. Men's Gymnastics	15	20
2148	300 c. Javelin	15	20
2149	300 c. Tennis	15	20
2150	300 c. Football	15	20
2151	300 c. Equestrian	15	20
2152	500 c. Carl Lewis (U.S.A.)	25	30
2153	800 c. Eric Liddell (Great Britain)	40	45
2154	900 c. Jesse Owens (U.S.A.)	45	50
2155	1000 c. Jim Thorpe (U.S.A.)	50	55
2140/55	*Set of 16*	3·25	4·25

MS2156 Two sheets, each 70×100 mm. (a) 1200 c. Pierre de Coubertin (founder of International Olympic Committee). (b) 1200 c. John Akii Bua (Uganda) .. *Set of 2 sheets* 1·25 1·40

Nos. 2140/51 were printed together, *se-tenant*, in sheetlets of 12 with the backgrounds forming a composite design. See Nos. 2334/55.

519 Ghanaian Scouts

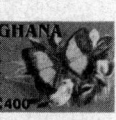

518 Cymothoe beckeri (butterfly)

(Des E. Mensah. Litho Ikam Security Ptg Ltd, Accra)

1995 (19 June). *Fauna and Flora. T 518 and similar multicoloured designs. P 14.*

2157	400 c. Type **518**	20	25
2158	500 c. Graphium policenes (butterfly)	25	30
2159	1000 c. African Long-tailed Hawk (*vert*)	50	55
2160	2000 c. Swordfish	1·00	1·10
2161	3000 c. Guinean Fingerfish	1·50	1·60
2162	5000 c. Purple Heron (*vert*)	2·50	2·75
2157/62	*Set of 6*	6·00	6·50

(Des R. Rundo. Litho Questa)

1995 (6 July). *18th World Scout Jamboree, Netherlands. T 519 and similar vert designs showing Ghanaian scouts P 14.*

2163	400 c. multicoloured	20	25
	a. Horiz strip of 3. Nos. 2163/5	1·10	
2164	800 c. multicoloured	40	45
2165	1000 c. multicoloured	50	55
2163/5	*Set of 3*	1·10	1·25

MS2166 70×100 mm. 1200 c. multicoloured 60 65

Nos. 2163/5 were printed together in sheets of 9 containing three *se-tenant* horizontal strips of 3.

(Des W. Wright. Litho B.D.T.)

1995 (6 July). *50th Anniv of End of Second World War in Europe. Multicoloured designs as T 340 of Antigua. P 14.*

2167	400 c. Winston Churchill	20	25
	a. Sheetlet. Nos. 2167/74	1·60	
2168	400 c. Gen. Dwight D. Eisenhower	20	25
2169	400 c. Air Marshal Sir Arthur Tedder	20	25
2170	400 c. Field-Marshal Sir Bernard Montgomery	20	25
2171	400 c. Gen. Omar Bradley	20	25
2172	400 c. Gen. Charles de Gaulle	20	25
2173	400 c. French resistance fighters	20	25
2174	400 c. Gen. George S. Patton	20	25
2167/74	*Set of 8*	1·60	2·00

MS2175 104×74 mm. 1200 c. "GIVE ME FIVE YEARS & YOU WILL NOT RECOGNISE GERMANY AGAIN" quote by Adolf Hitler in English and German (42×57 mm) .. 60 65

Nos. 2167/74 were printed together, *se-tenant*, in sheetlets of 8 with the stamps arranged in two horizontal strips of 4 separated by a gutter showing celebrations around the Arc de Triomphe.

520 Trygve Lie (1946–52) and United Nations Building

521 Preserving Fish

(Litho Questa)

1995 (6 July). *50th Anniv of United Nations. Secretary-Generals. T 520 and similar multicoloured designs. P 14.*

2176	200 c. Type **520**	10	15
	a. Sheetlet. Nos. 2176/81	1·40	
2177	300 c. Dag Hammarskjold (1953–61)	15	20
2178	400 c. U. Thant (1961–71)	20	25
2179	500 c. Kurt Waldheim (1972–81)	25	30
2180	600 c. Javier Perez de Cuellar (1982–91)	30	35
2181	800 c. Boutrous Boutrous-Ghali (1992)	40	45
2176/81	*Set of 6*	1·40	1·75

MS2182 104×74 mm. 1200 c. U.N. flag (*horiz*) 60 65

Nos. 2176/81 were printed together, *se-tenant*, in sheetlets of 6.

(Litho Questa)

1995 (6 July). *50th Anniv of Food and Agriculture Organization. T 521 and similar horiz designs. Multicoloured. P 14.*

2183	200 c. Type **521**	10	15
2184	300 c. Fishermen with fish traps	15	20
2185	400 c. Ox-drawn plough	20	25
2186	600 c. Harvesting bananas	30	35
2187	800 c. Planting saplings	40	45
2183/7	*Set of 5*	1·00	1·40

MS2188 100×70 mm. 2000 c. Canoe and cattle 1·00 1·10

522 National Flag and Rotary Emblem

523 Seismosaurus

(Litho Questa)

1995 (6 July). *90th Anniv of Rotary International. T 522 and similar multicoloured design. P 14.*

2189	600 c. Type **522**	30	35

MS2190 94×65 mm. 1200 c. Ghanaian Rotary banner (*vert*) .. 60 65

(Litho Questa)

1995 (6 July). *95th Birthday of Queen Elizabeth the Queen Mother. Vert designs as T 344 of Antigua. Multicoloured. P 13½×14.*

2191	600 c. orange-brown, pale brown and black	30	35
	a. Sheetlet. Nos. 2191/4×2	1·25	
2192	600 c. multicoloured	30	35
2193	600 c. multicoloured	30	35

2194 600 c. multicoloured 30 35
2191/4 .. .. *Set of 4* 1·25 1·40
MS2195 102×127 mm. 2500 c. multicoloured .. 1·25 1·40
Designs:—No. 2191, Queen Elizabeth the Queen Mother (pastel drawing); No. 2192, Wearing light blue hat and floral dress; No. 2193, At desk (oil painting); No. 2194, Wearing red hat and dress; No. **MS**2195, Wearing pale blue hat and jacket.
Nos. 2191/4 were printed together in sheetlets of 8, containing two *se-tenant* strips of 4.

(Des J. Batchelor. Litho Questa)

1995 (6 July). *50th Anniv of End of Second World War in the Pacific. Medals. Horiz designs as T 340 of Antigua. Multicoloured. P 14.*
2196 500 c. Navy Cross and Purple Heart, U.S.A. 25 30
a. Sheetlet. Nos. 2196/2201 .. 1·50
2197 500 c. Air Force Cross and Distinguished Flying Cross, Great Britain .. 25 30
2198 500 c. Navy and Marine Corps Medal and Distinguished Service Cross, U.S.A. 25 30
2199 500 c. Distinguished Service Medal and Distinguished Conduct Medal, Great Britain 25 30
2200 500 c. Military Medal and Military Cross, Great Britain 25 30
2201 500 c. Distinguished Service Cross and Distinguished Service Order, Great Britain 25 30
2196/2201 .. .. .. *Set of 6* 1·50 1·75
MS2202 108×76 mm. 1200 c. Congressional Medal of Honor, U.S.A. 60 65
Nos. 2196/2201 were printed together, *se-tenant*, in sheetlets of 6 with the stamps arranged in two horizontal strips of 3 separated by a gutter showing American troops in Japan.

(Litho Questa)

1995 (8 Aug). *"Singapore '95" International Stamp Exhibition. Prehistoric Animals. T 523 and similar multicoloured designs. P 14.*
2203 400 c. Type **523** 20 25
a. Sheetlet. Nos. 2203/11 .. 1·75
2204 400 c. Supersaurus 20 25
2205 400 c. Ultrasaurus 20 25
2206 400 c. Saurolophus 20 25
2207 400 c. Lambeosaurus 20 25
2208 400 c. Parasaurolophus 20 25
2209 400 c. Triceratops 20 25
2210 400 c. Styracosaurus 20 25
2211 400 c. Pachyrhinosaurus .. 20 25
2212 400 c. Peteinosaurus 20 25
a. Sheetlet. Nos. 2212/20 .. 1·75
2213 400 c. Quetzalcoatlus 20 25
2214 400 c. Eudimorphodon 20 25
2215 400 c. Allosaurus 20 25
2216 400 c. Daspletosaurus 20 25
2217 400 c. Tarbosaurus bataar .. 20 25
2218 400 c. Velociraptor mongoliensis .. 20 25
2219 400 c. Herrerasaurus 20 25
2220 400 c. Coelophysis 20 25
2203/20 .. .. .. *Set of 18* 3·50 4·50
MS2221 Two sheets, each 106×76 mm. (a) 2500 c. *Tyrannosaurus rex* (*horiz*). (b) 2500 c. *Albertosaur* (*horiz*) .. *Set of 2 sheets* 2·50 2·75
Nos. 2203/11 and 2212/20 were printed together, *se-tenant*, in sheetlets of 9, each forming a composite design.

524 Arms of
Otumfuo Opoku
Ware II

525 Nelson Mandela
(1993 Peace)

(Litho Ikam Security Ptg Ltd, Accra)

1995 (9 Aug). *Silver Jubilee of Otumfuo Opoku Ware II (King of Ashanti). T 524 and similar vert designs. Multicoloured. P 13½×13.*
2222 50 c. Type **524** 10 10
2223 100 c. Silver casket 10 10
2224 200 c. Golden stool 10 15
2225 400 c. Busummuru sword bearer 20 25
2226 600 c. Otumfuo Opoku Ware II .. 30 35
2227 800 c. Otumfro Opoku Ware II under umbrella 40 45
2228 1000 c. Mponponsuo sword bearer 50 55
2222/8 .. .. .. *Set of 7* 1·60 1·75

(Des R. Sauber. Litho Questa)

1995 (2 Oct). *Centenary of Nobel Prize Trust Fund. Past Prize Winners. T 525 and similar vert designs. Multicoloured. P 14.*
2229 400 c. Type **525** 20 25
a. Sheetlet. Nos. 2229/37 .. 1·75
2230 400 c. Albert Schweitzer (1952 Peace) .. 20 25
2231 400 c. Wole Soyinka (1986 Literature) .. 20 25
2232 400 c. Emil Fischer (1902 Chemistry) .. 20 25
2233 400 c. Rudolf Mossbauer (1961 Physics) .. 20 25
2234 400 c. Archbishop Desmond Tutu (1984 Peace) 20 25
2235 400 c. Max Born (1954 Physics) .. 20 25
2236 400 c. Max Planck (1918 Physics) .. 20 25
2237 400 c. Herman Hesse (1946 Literature) .. 20 25
2229/37 .. .. .. *Set of 9* 1·75 2·25
MS2238 104×75 mm. 1200 c. Paul Ehrlich (1908 Medicine) and medal 60 65
Nos. 2229/37 were printed together, *se-tenant*, in sheetlets of 9.

(Litho Questa)

1995 (1 Dec). *Christmas. Religious Paintings. Vert designs as T 357 of Antigua. Multicoloured. P 13½×14.*
2239 50 c. "The Child Jesus and the Young St. John" (Murillo) 10 10
2240 80 c. "Rest on the Flight into Egypt" (Memling) 10 10
2241 300 c. "Holy Family" (Van Dyck) .. 15 20
2242 600 c. "Enthroned Madonna and Child" (Uccello) 30 35
2243 800 c. "Madonna and Child" (Van Eyck) 40 45
2244 1000 c. "Head of Christ" (Rembrandt) .. 50 55
2239/44 .. .. .. *Set of 6* 1·40 1·60
MS2245 Two sheets, each 101×127 mm. (a) 2500 c. "The Holy Family" (Pulzone). (b) 2500 c. "Madonna and Child with Two Saints" (Montagna) .. .. *Set of 2 sheets* 2·50 2·75

526 Ernemann Camera
(1903)

527 John Lennon

(Des H. Friedman. Litho Questa)

1995 (8 Dec). *Centenary of Cinema. T 526 and similar vert designs. Multicoloured. P 13½×14.*
2246 400 c. Type **526** 20 25
a. Sheetlet. Nos. 2246/54 .. 1·75
2247 400 c. Charlie Chaplin 20 25
2248 400 c. Rudolph Valentino .. 20 25
2249 400 c. Will Rogers 20 25
2250 400 c. Greta Garbo 20 25
2251 400 c. Jackie Cooper 20 25
2252 400 c. Bette Davis 20 25
2253 400 c. John Barrymore 20 25
2254 400 c. Shirley Temple 20 25
2246/54 .. .. .. *Set of 9* 1·75 2·25
MS2255 106×76 mm. 2500 c. Laurel and Hardy 1·25 1·40
Nos. 2246/54 were printed together, *se-tenant*, in sheetlets of 9.
No. 2246 is inscribed "ERNMANN" in error.

(Litho Questa)

1995 (8 Dec). *John Lennon (musician) Commemoration. T 527 and similar vert designs. Multicoloured. P 14 (No. 2265) or 13½×14 (others).*
2256 400 c. Type **527** .. .. 1·10 1·10
a. Sheetlet. Nos. 2256/64 .. 10·00
2257 400 c. Full face portrait (green background) 1·10 1·10
2258 400 c. With guitar .. .. 1·10 1·10
2259 400 c. Wearing glasses and caftan .. 1·10 1·10
2260 400 c. Full face portrait (verm background) 1·10 1·10
2261 400 c. Wearing headphones .. 1·10 1·10
2262 400 c. Wearing purple T-shirt .. 1·10 1·10
2263 400 c. Full face portrait (blue background) 1·10 1·10
2264 400 c. Facing right .. .. 1·10 1·10
2265 400 c. As No. 2263, but smaller (24×39 mm) .. .. .. 1·10 1·10
2256/65 .. .. .. *Set of 10* 10·00 10·00
MS2266 102×73 mm. 2000 c. John Lennon playing guitar .. .. .. 6·00 6·50
Nos. 2256/64 were printed together, *se-tenant*, in sheetlets of 9.
No. 2265 was printed in sheetlets of 16 with a large illustrated margin at right.

528 Louis Pasteur in
Laboratory

529 Rat Musicians

(Des E. Mensah. Litho Questa)

1995 (13 Dec). *Death Centenary of Louis Pasteur (scientist). T 528 and similar vert designs. Multicoloured. P 14.*
2267 600 c. Type **528** 30 35
a. Sheetlet. Nos. 2267/71 .. 1·50
2268 600 c. Pasteur injecting rabid dog .. 30 35
2269 600 c. Pasteur and microscope slide .. 30 35
2270 600 c. Laboratory equipment and birds 30 35
2271 600 c. Yeast vats 30 35
2267/71 .. .. .. *Set of 5* 1·50 1·75
Nos. 2267/71 were printed together, *se-tenant*, in sheetlets of 5.

(Des Y. Lee. Litho Questa)

1996 (28 Jan). *Chinese New Year ("Year of the Rat"). T 529 and similar designs. P 14.*
2272 250 c. orange-brown, violet and rosine .. 15 20
a. Horiz strip of 4. Nos. 2272/5 .. 60
2273 250 c. orange-brown, violet and rosine .. 15 20
2274 250 c. orange-brown, violet and rosine .. 15 20
2275 250 c. orange-brown, violet and rosine .. 15 20
2272/5 .. .. .. *Set of 4* 60 80
MS2276 142×60 mm. As Nos. 2272/5, but face values and "GHANA" in rosine instead of white 60 80
MS2277 106×75 mm. 1000 c. scarlet-vermilion and yellow-orange 50 55
Designs: Vert—No. 2272, Type **529**; No. 2273, Rats carrying banners; No. 2274, Rats carrying palanquin; No. 2275, Rats with offerings. Horiz—No. **MS**2277, Four rats carrying palanquin.
Nos. 2272/5 were printed together, *se-tenant*, in horizontal strips of 4 throughout the sheets.

(Litho Questa)

1996 (12 Feb). *125th Anniv of Metropolitan Museum of Art, New York. Multicoloured designs as T 251 of Gambia. P 13½×14.*
2278 400 c. "Portrait of a Man" (Van der Goes) 20 25
a. Sheetlet. Nos. 2278/85 plus centre label .. .. 1·60
2279 400 c. "Paradise" (detail) (Di Paolo) .. 20 25
2280 400 c. "Portrait of a Young Man" (Messina) 20 25
2281 400 c. "Tommaso Portinari" (detail) (Memling) 20 25
2282 400 c. "Maria Portinari" (detail) (Memling) 20 25
2283 400 c. "Portrait of a Lady" (detail) (Ghirlandaio) 20 25
2284 400 c. "St. Christopher and the Infant Christ" (Ghirlandi) 20 25
2285 400 c. "Francesco D'Este" (detail) (Weyden) 20 25
2286 400 c. "The Interrupted Sleep" (Boucher) 20 25
a. Sheetlet. Nos. 2286/93 plus centre label .. .. 1·60
2287 400 c. "Diana and Cupid" (detail) (Batoni) 20 25
2288 400 c. "Boy blowing Bubbles" (Chardin) .. 20 25
2289 400 c. "Ancient Rome" (detail) (Pannini) .. 20 25
2290 400 c. "Modern Rome" (detail) (Pannini) .. 20 25
2291 400 c. "The Calmady Children" (Lawrence) 20 25
2292 400 c. "The Triumph of Marius" (detail) (Tiepolo) 20 25
2293 400 c. "Garden at Vaucresson" (detail) (Vuillard) 20 25
2278/93 .. .. .. *Set of 16* 3·25 4·00
MS2294 Two sheets, each 95×70 mm. (a) 2500 c. "The Epiphany" (detail) (Giotto) (80×56 mm). (b) 2500 c. "The Calling of Matthew" (detail) (Hemessen) (80×56 mm). P 14 .. *Set of 2 sheets* 2·50 2·75
Nos. 2278/85 and 2286/93 were each printed together, *se-tenant*, in sheetlets of 8 stamps and one centre label.

530 Toco Toucan

531 Pagoda of Kaiyuan
Si Temple, Fujian

(Des Y. Lee. Litho)

1996 (15 Apr). *Wildlife of the Rainforest. T 530 and similar vert designs. Multicoloured. P 14.*
2295 400 c. Type **530** 20 25
a. Sheetlet. Nos. 2295/2306 .. 2·40
2296 400 c. Two-toed Sloth 20 25
2297 400 c. Orang-utan 20 25
2298 400 c. Crested Hawk Eagle .. 20 25
2299 400 c. Tiger 20 25
2300 400 c. Yellow-billed Stork .. 20 25
2301 400 c. Green-winged Macaw .. 20 25
2302 400 c. Common Squirrel-monkey .. 20 25
2303 400 c. Crab-eating Macaque .. 20 25
2304 400 c. *Cithaerias menander* and *Ithomiidae* (butterflies) 20 25
2305 400 c. *Coryptophanes cristatus* and *Gekkonidae* (lizards) .. 20 25
2306 400 c. Boa Constrictor 20 25
2307 400 c. Hoatzin 20 25
a. Sheetlet. Nos. 2307/18 .. 2·40
2308 400 c. Western Tarsier 20 25
2309 400 c. Golden Lion Tamarin .. 20 25
2310 400 c. *Pteropus gouldii* (bat) .. 20 25
2311 400 c. Guianan Cock of the Rock .. 20 25
2312 400 c. Resplendent Quetzal .. 20 25
2313 400 c. Tree Frog and Poison-arrow Frog .. 20 25
2314 400 c. Ring-tailed Lemur 20 25
2315 400 c. Iguana 20 25
2316 400 c. *Heliconius burneyi* (butterfly) .. 20 25
2317 400 c. Vervain Hummingbird .. 20 25
2318 400 c. Verreaux's Sifaka .. 20 25
2295/2318 .. .. .. *Set of 24* 4·75 6·00
MS2319 Two sheets, each 74×104 mm. (a) 3000 c. King of Saxony Bird of Paradise. (b) 3000 c. King Vulture .. *Set of 2 sheets* 3·00 3·25
Nos. 2295/2306 and 2307/18 were each printed together, *se-tenant*, in sheetlets of 12.

1996 (13 May). *"CHINA '96" 9th Asian International Stamp Exhibition. Pagodas. T* **531** *and similar vert designs. Multicoloured. Litho.* P 14.
2320   400 c. Type **531**   20   25
    a. Sheetlet. Nos. 2320/3×2   ..   1·60
2321   400 c. Kaiyuan Si Temple, Hebei   20   25
2322   400 c. Fogong Si Temple, Shanxi   20   25
2323   400 c. Xiangshan, Beijing   ..   20   25
2320/3   *Set of 4*   80   1·00
MS2324   Two sheets. (a) 100×70 mm. 1000 c.
Baima Si Temple, Henan. (b) 143×98 mm.
1000 c. Gold statue (38×50 *mm*) *Set of 2 sheets*   1·00   1·10
Nos. 2320/3 were printed together, *se-tenant*, in sheetlets of 8 containing two of each design.

(Litho Questa)

1996 (10 June). *70th Birthday of Queen Elizabeth II. Multicoloured designs as T* **364** *of Antigua showing different photographs.* P 13½×14.
2325   1000 c. As Type **364** of Antigua   ..   50   55
    a. Strip of 3. Nos. 2325/7   ..   1·50
2326   1000 c. In blue hat and coat   ..   50   55
2327   1000 c. Wearing straw hat and carrying
    bouquet   50   55
2325/7   *Set of 3*   1·50   1·60
MS2328   125×103 mm. 2500 c. In open carriage at Trooping the Colour (*horiz*). P 14×13½   1·25   1·40
Nos. 2325/7 were printed together, *se-tenant*, in horizontal and vertical strips of 3 throughout the sheet.

532   Serafim Todorow   533   Ancient Greek Wrestlers
    (Bulgaria)

(Litho B.D.T.)

1996 (27 June). *50th Anniv of International Amateur Boxing Association. T* **532** *and similar vert designs. Multicoloured.* P 14.
2329   300 c. Type **532**   15   20
2330   400 c. Oscar de la Hoya (U.S.A.)   ..   20   25
2331   800 c. Ariel Hernandez (Cuba) ..   40   45
2332   1500 c. Arnoldo Mesa (Cuba)   ..   80   85
2329/32   *Set of 4*   1·50   1·75
MS2333   80×110 mm. 3000 c. Tadahiro Sasaki (Japan)   ..   ..   ..   1·50   1·60

(Litho B.D.T.)

1996 (27 June). *Olympic Games, Atlanta (2nd issue). Previous Medal Winners. T* **533** *and similar multicoloured designs.* P 14.
2334   300 c. Type **533**   15   20
2335   400 c. Aileen Riggin, 1920 (U.S.A.)   20   25
    a. Sheetlet. Nos. 2335/43   ..   1·75
2336   400 c. Pat McCormick, 1952 (U.S.A.)   20   25
2337   400 c. Dawn Fraser, 1956 (Australia)   20   25
2338   400 c. Chris von Saltza, 1960 (U.S.A.)   20   25
2339   400 c. Anita Lonsbrough, 1960 (Great
    Britain)   20   25
2340   400 c. Debbie Meyer, 1968 (U.S.A.)   20   25
2341   400 c. Shane Gould, 1972 (Australia)   20   25
2342   400 c. Petra Thuemer, 1976 (Germany)   20   25
2343   400 c. Marjorie Gestring, 1936 (U.S.A.)   20   25
2344   400 c. Abedi Pele (Ghana) (*vert*) ..   20   25
    a. Sheetlet. Nos. 2344/52   ..   1·75
2345   400 c. Quico Navarez (Spain) (*vert*)   20   25
2346   400 c. Heino Hanson (Denmark) (*vert*)   20   25
2347   400 c. Mostafa Ismail (Egypt) (*vert*)   20   25
2348   400 c. Anthony Yeboah (Ghana) (*vert*)   20   25
2349   400 c. Jurgen Klinsmann (Germany) (*vert*)   20   25
2350   400 c. Cobi Jones (U.S.A.) (*vert*)   ..   20   25
2351   400 c. Franco Baresi (Italy) (*vert*)   ..   20   25
2352   400 c. Igor Dobrovolski (Russia) (*vert*)   20   25
2353   500 c. Wilma Rudolph (U.S.A.) (track and
    field, 1960)   25   30
2354   600 c. Olympic Stadium, 1960, and Roman
    landmarks   30   35
2355   800 c. Ladies Kayak pairs, 1960 (Soviet
    Union)   40   45
2334/55   *Set of 22*   4·50   5·75
MS2356   Two sheets, each 110×80 mm. (a) 2000 c. Tracy Caulkins (U.S.A.) (200m freestyle, 1984). (b) 2000 c. Kornelia Ender (Germany) (200m freestyle, 1976) ..   *Set of 2 sheets*   2·00   2·10
Nos. 2335/43 (swimming and diving) and 2344/52 (football) were each printed together, *se-tenant*, in sheetlets of 9, with the backgrounds forming composite designs.

PRICES OF SETS

Set prices are given for many issues, generally those containing three stamps or more. Definitive sets include one of each value or major colour change, but do not cover different perforations, die types or minor shades. Where a choice is possible the set prices are based on the cheapest versions of the stamps included in the listings.

534   E. W. Agyare (35   535   Fiddles
    years service with
    Ghana Broadcasting)

(Litho Questa)

1996 (31 July). *Local Broadcasting.* P 14.
2357   **534**   100 c. multicoloured   10   10

(Litho Questa)

1996 (31 July). *50th Anniv of U.N.I.C.E.F. Multicoloured designs as T* **366** *of Antigua.* P 14.
2358   400 c. Ghanaian child   20   25
2359   500 c. Mother and child   ..   25   30
2360   600 c. Mother and child drinking ..   30   35
2358/60   *Set of 3*   75   90
MS2361   74×104 mm. 1000 c. Young child   50   55

(Des Jennifer Toombs. Litho Questa)

1996 (31 July). *3000th Anniv of Jerusalem. Multicoloured designs as T* **367** *of Antigua.* P 14½.
2362   400 c. St. Stephen's Gate and *Jasminum
    mesnyi*   20   25
2363   600 c. The Citadel, Tower of David and
    Nerium oleander   30   35
2364   800 c. Chapel of the Ascension and
    Romulea bulbocodium   ..   40   45
2362/4   *Set of 3*   90   1·00
MS2365   65×80 mm. 2000 c. Russian Orthodox Church of St. Mary Magdalene. P 14 (48×30 *mm*) ..   ..   1·00   1·10

(Des R. Sauber. Litho Questa)

1996 (31 July). *Centenary of Radio. Entertainers. Multicoloured designs as T* **368** *of Antigua.* P 13½×14.
2366   500 c. Frank Sinatra   25   30
2367   600 c. Judy Garland   30   35
2368   600 c. Bing Crosby   30   35
2369   800 c. Martin and Lewis   40   45
2366/9   *Set of 4*   1·25   1·40
MS2370   81×110 mm. 2000 c. Edgar Bergen and Charlie McCarthy   ..   ..   1·00   1·10

(Des M. Freedman and Dena Rubin. Litho Questa)

1996 (31 July). *50th Anniv of U.N.E.S.C.O. Multicoloured designs as T* **373** *of Antigua.* P 14×13½ (1000 c.) *or* 13½×14 (*others*).
2371   400 c. The Citadel, Haiti (*vert*)   ..   20   25
2372   800 c. Ait-Ben-Hadou (fortified village),
    Morocco (*vert*)   40   45
2373   1000 c. Spissky Hrad, Slovakia   ..   50   55
2371/3   *Set of 3*   1·10   1·25
MS2374   106×76 mm. 2000 c. Cape Coast Castle, Ghana. P 14×13½   ..   ..   1·00   1·10

1996 (5 Aug). *Musical Instruments. T* **535** *and similar vert designs. Multicoloured. Litho.* P 14.
2375   500 c. Type **535**   45   50
    a. Sheetlet. Nos. 2375/9   ..   2·25
2376   500 c. Proverbial drum   ..   45   50
2377   500 c. Double clapless bell and castanet   45   50
2378   500 c. Gourd rattle   45   50
2379   500 c. Horns   45   50
2375/9   *Set of 5*   2·25   2·50
Nos. 2375/9 were printed together, *se-tenant*, in sheetlets of 5.

536   Ariel, Flounder and Sebastian

(Des Alvin White Studios. Litho Questa)

1996 (25 Aug). *Disney Friends. T* **536** *and similar multicoloured designs showing Disney cartoon characters.* P 14×13½.
2380   60 c. Type **536**   10   10
2381   60 c. Pinocchio and Jiminy Cricket   10   10
2382   60 c. Cogsworth and Lumiere   ..   10   10
2383   60 c. Copper and Tod   10   10
2384   60 c. Pocahontas, Meeko and Flit   10   10
2385   60 c. Bambi, Flower and Thumper   10   10
2386   150 c. Type **536**   10   10
    a. Sheetlet. Nos. 2386/94 ..   1·75
2387   200 c. Type **536**   10   15
2388   200 c. As No. 2383   10   15
2389   300 c. As No. 2385   15   20
2390   350 c. As No. 2382   20   25
2391   450 c. As No. 2384   25   30
2392   600 c. Aladdin and Abu   30   35
2393   700 c. Penny and Rufus   35   40

2394   800 c. Mowgli and Baloo   ..   40   45
2380/94   *Set of 15*   1·90   2·25
MS2395   Two sheets. (a) 98×124 mm. 3000 c. Winnie the Pooh (*vert*). P 13½×14. (b) 133×108 mm. 3000 c. Simba and Timon   *Set of 2 sheets*   3·00   3·25
Nos. 2386/94 were printed together, *se-tenant*, in sheetlets of 9.

(Des Shannon. Litho Questa)

1996 (21 Nov). *20th Anniv of Rocky (film). Sheet* 143×182 *mm, containing vert design as T* **266** *of Gambia. Multicoloured.* P 13½×13½.
MS2396   2000 c.×3 Sylvester Stallone in *Rocky II*   3·00   3·25
No. MS2396 was printed with an enlarged illustrated left hand margin.

537   Herd Boy and Ox   538   The Tomb of
                          Dr. Hideyo Noguchi

(Des Y. Lee. Litho Questa)

1997 (22 Jan). *Chinese New Year ("Year of the Ox"). "The Herd Boy and Weaver". T* **537** *and similar vert designs. Each lake-brown, silver and black.* P 13½×14.
2397   500 c. Type **537**   25   30
    a. Sheetlet. Nos. 2397/405   ..   2·25
2398   500 c. Ox and weaver in lake   ..   25   30
2399   500 c. Weaver at work   25   30
2400   500 c. Herd boy with dying Ox   ..   25   30
2401   500 c. Weaver flying out of window   25   30
2402   500 c. Herd boy carrying children   ..   25   30
2403   500 c. Family separated by "river"   ..   25   30
2404   500 c. Petitioning the emperor   ..   25   30
2405   500 c. Family reunited   25   30
2397/405   *Set of 9*   2·25   2·40
Nos. 2397/405 were printed together, *se-tenant*, in sheetlets of 9 with an enlarged illustrated right-hand margin.

1997 (3 Mar). *120th Birth Anniv of Dr. Hideyo Noguchi (bacteriologist). T* **538** *and similar vert designs. Multicoloured. Litho.* P 14.
2406   1000 c. Type **538**   50   55
    a. Sheetlet. Nos. 2406/10   ..   2·50
2407   1000 c. Dr. Hideyo Noguchi   ..   50   55
2408   1000 c. Birth place of Dr. Noguchi at
    Sanjogarta   50   55
2409   1000 c. Noguchi Institute, Legon ..   50   55
2410   1000 c. Noguchi Gardens, Accra ..   50   55
2406/10   *Set of 5*   2·50   2·75
MS2411   Two sheets, each 67×97 mm. (a) 3000 c. Dr. Noguchi in his laboratory. (b) 3000 c. Statue of Dr. Noguchi ..   ..   *Set of 2 sheets*   3·00   3·25
Nos. 2406/10 were printed together, *se-tenant*, in sheetlets of 5.

539   Dipo Hairstyle   540   Independence Anniversary
                          Emblem

1997 (3 Mar). *Ghanaian Women's Hairstyles. T* **539** *and similar vert designs. Multicoloured. Litho.* P 14.
2412   1000 c. Type **539**   50   55
    a. Sheetlet. Nos. 2412/16   ..   2·50
2413   1000 c. Oduku with flowers   ..   50   55
2414   1000 c. Dansinkran   50   55
2415   1000 c. Mbobom   50   55
2416   1000 c. Oduku with hair pins   ..   50   55
2417   1000 c. African Corn Row   ..   50   55
    a. Sheetlet. Nos. 2417/21   ..   2·50
2418   1000 c. Chinese Raster   50   55
2419   1000 c. Chinese Raster with top knot   50   55
2420   1000 c. Corn Row   50   55
2421   1000 c. Mbakaa   50   55
2412/21   *Set of 10*   5·00   5·50
Nos. 2412/16 and 2417/21 were each printed together, *se-tenant*, in sheetlets of 5.

(Des J. Iskowitz (No. MS2427b), Dena Rubin (others). Litho B.D.T.)

1997 (6 Mar). *40th Anniv of Independence. T* **540** *and similar multicoloured designs.* P 14.
2422   200 c. Type **540**   10   10
2423   200 c. President J. J. Rawlings (*vert*)   1·50   1·50
2424   550 c. Dr. Kwame Nkrumah (first
    President) (*vert*)   30   35

2425	800 c. Children in class ..	..	40	45
2426	1100 c. Akosombo Dam	..	55	60
2422/6		Set of 5	2·50	2·75

MS2427 Two sheets. (a) 70×100 mm. 2000 c. Dr. Nkrumah proclaiming independence (*vert*). (b) 101×141 mm. 3000 c. United Nations Secretary-General Kofi Annan (37×50 mm) *Set of 2 sheets* 2·50 2·75
No. 2423 was withdrawn on 22 March at the request of the Office of the President.
No. 2425 is inscribed "Acheivement" in error

(Litho Questa)

1997 (8 Apr). *10th Anniv of Chernobyl Nuclear Disaster. Vert designs as T 375 of Antigua. Multicoloured. P 13½.*

2428	800 c. As Type 375 of Antigua ..	40	45
2429	1000 c. As No. 2428, but inscribed "CHABAD'S CHILDREN OF CHERNOBYL" at foot	50	55

C300 GHANA
541 Deng Xiaoping

542 Jackie Gleason

(Des Y. Lee. Litho Questa)

1997 (26 Apr). *Deng Xiaoping (Chinese statesman) Commemoration. T 541 and similar vert designs showing different portraits. Multicoloured. P 14×13½.*

2430	300 c. Type 541	..	15	20
	a. Sheetlet. Nos. 2430, 2432, 2434 and 2436	..	1·25	
2431	500 c. Looking thoughtful ..	..	25	30
	a. Sheetlet. Nos. 2431, 2433, 2435 and 2437	..	1·40	
2432	600 c. Wearing glasses ..	..	30	35
2433	600 c. Delivering speech ..	..	30	35
2434	800 c. As No. 2432 ..	..	40	45
2435	800 c. As No. 2433 ..	..	40	45
2436	1000 c. Type 541 ..	..	50	55
2437	1000 c. As No. 2431 ..	..	50	55
2430/7		Set of 8	2·75	3·25

MS2438 Two sheets, each 101×70 mm. (a) 3000 c. Deng Xiaoping making speech (47×34 mm). (b) 4000 c. Deng Xiaoping with hand raised (47×34 mm) .. .. *Set of 2 sheets* 3·75 4·00
Nos. 2430, 2432, 2434 and 2436, and 2431, 2433, 2435 and 2437 were each printed together, *se-tenant*, in sheetlets of 4 with an enlarged illustrated margin at left or right.

(Litho Questa)

1997 (29 May). *50th Death Anniv of Paul Harris (founder of Rotary International). Horiz designs as T 376 of Antigua. Multicoloured. P 14.*

2439	2000 c. Paul Harris and Egyptian patient receiving polio vaccination ..	1·00	1·10

MS2440 78×107 mm. 3000 c. Paul Harris with Rotary and PolioPlus emblems .. .. 1·50 1·60

(Litho Questa)

1997 (29 May). *Golden Wedding of Queen Elizabeth and Prince Philip. Horiz designs as T 377 of Antigua. Multicoloured. P 14.*

2441	800 c. Queen Elizabeth II ..	..	40	45
	a. Sheetlet. Nos. 2441/6 ..	..	2·40	
2442	800 c. Royal coat of arms ..	..	40	45
2443	800 c. Queen Elizabeth and Prince Philip waving	..	40	45
2444	800 c. Queen Elizabeth and Prince Philip on offical visit		40	45
2445	800 c. Queen in Irish State Coach ..	..	40	45
2446	800 c. Prince Philip in 1947 ..	..	40	45
2441/6		Set of 6	2·40	2·75

MS2447 100×71 mm. 300 c. Queen Elizabeth in 1947 .. .. 15 20
Nos. 2441/6 were printed together, *se-tenant*, in sheetlets of 6.

1997 (29 May). *"Pacific '97" International Stamp Exhibition, San Francisco. Death Centenary of Heinrich von Stephan (founder of the U.P.U.). Horiz designs as T 378 of Antigua. Litho. P 14.*

2448	1000 c. deep blue ..	..	50	55
	a. Sheetlet. Nos. 2448/50 ..	..	1·50	
2449	1000 c. orange-brown ..	..	50	55
2450	1000 c. pale Indian red ..	..	50	55
2448/50		Set of 3	1·50	1·60

MS2451 82×119 mm. 3000 c. turquoise-green .. 1·50 1·60
Designs:—No. 2448, Early motor car; No. 2449, Von Stephan and Mercury; No. 2450, Blanchard's balloon flight, 1784; No. MS2451, African messenger.
Nos. 2448/50 were printed together, *se-tenant*, in sheetlets of 3 with enlarged illustrated right-hand margin.

1997 (29 May). *Birth Bicentenary of Hiroshige (Japanese painter). "One Hundred Famous Views of Edo". Vert designs as T 310 of Antigua. Multicoloured. P 13½×14.*

2452	600 c. "Nihonbashi Bridge and Edobashi Bridge"	30	35
	a. Sheetlet. Nos. 2452/7 ..	1·75	

2453	600 c. "View of Nihonbashi Tori 1-chome"	30	35
2454	600 c. "Open Garden at Fukagawa Hachiman Shrine" ..	30	35
2455	600 c. "Inari Bridge and Minato Shrine, Teppozu" ..	30	35
2456	600 c. "Bamboo Yards, Kyobashi Bridge"	30	35
2457	600 c. "Hall of Thirty-Three Bays, Fukagawa" ..	30	35
2452/7		Set of 6	1·75	1·90

MS2458 Two sheets, each 102×127 mm. (a) 3000 c. "Sumiyoshi Festival, Tsukudajima". (b) 3000 c. "Teppozu and Tsukjji Honganji Temple" *Set of 2 sheets* 3·00 3·25
Nos. 2452/7 were printed together, *se-tenant*, in sheetlets of 6.

(Des E. Mensah (No. MS2468b), Zina Saunders (others). Litho Questa)

1997 (1 July). *Famous Comedians. T 542 and similar vert designs. Multicoloured. P 13½×14.*

2459	600 c. Type 542 ..	..	30	35
	a. Sheetlet. Nos. 2459/67 ..	..	2·75	
2460	600 c. Danny Kaye ..	..	30	35
2461	600 c. John Cleese ..	..	30	35
2462	600 c. Lucille Ball ..	..	30	35
2463	600 c. Jerry Lewis ..	..	30	35
2464	600 c. Sidney James ..	..	30	35
2465	600 c. Louis Defuenes ..	..	30	35
2466	600 c. Mae West ..	..	30	35
2467	600 c. Bob Hope ..	..	30	35
2459/67		Set of 9	2·75	3·25

MS2468 Two sheets. (a) 83×113 mm. 3000 c. Groucho Marx. P 13½×14. (b) 76×106 mm. 2000 c. Professor Ajax Bukana in front of curtain; 2000 c. Professor Ajax Bukana (*different*) (*both* 28×42 *mm*). P 14 *Set of 2 sheets* 2·50 2·75
Nos. 2459/67 were printed together, *se-tenant*, in sheetlets of 9.

543 African Pygmy Angelfish

544 *Galerina calyptrata*

(Des R. Martin. Litho Questa)

1997 (1 July). *Marine Life. T 543 and similar horiz designs. Multicoloured. P 14.*

2469	400 c. Type 543 ..	..	20	25
2470	500 c. Violet-crested Turaco	..	25	30
	a. Sheetlet. Nos. 2470/81 ..	..	3·00	
2471	500 c. Pied Avocet ..	..	25	30
2472	500 c. Bottle-nosed Dolphin ..	..	25	30
2473	500 c. Bottle-nosed Dolphin and Long-toed Lapwing	..	25	30
2474	500 c. Longfinned Spadefish ..	..	25	30
2475	500 c. Imperial Angelfish and Manta	..	25	30
2476	500 c. Raccoon Butterflyfish and African Pompano	..	25	30
2477	500 c. Silvertip Shark ..	..	25	30
2478	500 c. Longfin Banner Fish ..	..	25	30
2479	500 c. Longfin Banner Fish and Manta	..	25	30
2480	500 c. Rust Parrotfish ..	..	25	30
2481	500 c. Coral Trout ..	..	25	30
2482	600 c. Angelfish ..	..	30	35
2483	800 c. Broomtail Wrasse ..	..	40	45
2484	1000 c. Indian Butterflyfish ..	..	50	55
2469/84		Set of 16	4·50	5·25

MS2485 Two sheets, each 106×76 mm. (a) 3000 c. King Angelfish. (b) 3000 c. Crown Butterflyfish .. *Set of 2 sheets* 3·00 2·25
Nos. 2470/81 were printed together, *se-tenant*, in sheetlets of 12 with the backgrounds forming a composite design.

(Litho Questa)

1997 (9 July). *Fungi of the World. T 544 and similar vert designs. Multicoloured. P 14.*

2486	200 c. Type 544 ..	..	10	15
2487	300 c. *Lepiota ignivolvata* ..	..	15	20
2488	400 c. *Omphalotus olearius* ..	..	20	25
2489	550 c. *Amanita phalloides* ..	..	30	35
2490	600 c. *Entoloma conferendum* ..	..	30	35
2491	800 c. *Entoloma nitidum* ..	..	40	45
2492	800 c. *Coprinus picaceus* ..	..	40	45
	a. Sheetlet. Nos. 2492/7 ..	..	2·40	
2493	800 c. *Stropharia aurantiaca* ..	..	40	45
2494	800 c. *Cortinarius splendens* ..	..	40	45
2495	800 c. *Gomphidius roseus* ..	..	40	45
2496	800 c. *Russula sardonia* ..	..	40	45
2497	800 c. *Geastrum schmidelia* ..	..	40	45
2486/97		Set of 12	3·75	4·50

MS2498 Two sheets, each 73×103 mm. (a) 3000 c. *Craterellus cornucopioides*. (b) 3000 c. *Mycena crocata* .. .. *Set of 2 sheets* 3·00 3·25
Nos. 2492/7 were printed together, *se-tenant*, in sheetlets of 6.

(Litho Questa)

1997 (12 July). *World Football Championship, France (1998). Horiz designs as T 382 of Antigua. Multicoloured. P 14×13½.*

2499	200 c. Azteca Stadium, Mexico ..	10	10
2500	300 c. The Rose Bowl, U.S.A. ..	15	20
2501	400 c. Stadio Giuseppe Meazza, Italy	20	25
2502	500 c. Olympiastadion, Germany ..	25	30
2503	600 c. Patrick Kluivert, Netherlands "	30	35
	a. Sheetlet. Nos. 2503/10 and central label	2·40	

2504	600 c. Roy Keane, Republic of Ireland	..	30	35
2505	600 c. Abedi Ayew Pele, Ghana ..		30	35
2506	600 c. Peter Schmeichel, Denmark	..	30	35
2507	600 c. Roberto di Matteo, Italy ..		30	35
2508	600 c. Bebeto, Brazil ..	..	30	35
2509	600 c. Steve McManaman, England	..	30	35
2510	600 c. George Oppon Weah, Liberia	..	30	35
2511	1000 c. Maracana Stadium, Brazil ..		50	55
2512	2000 c. Bernabeu Stadium, Spain ..		1·00	1·10
2499/512		Set of 14	4·50	5·50

MS2513 Two sheets. (a) 127×102 mm. 3000 c. David Seaman, England. (b) 102×127 mm. 3000 c. Juninho, Brazil .. .. *Set of 2 sheets* 3·00 3·25
Nos. 2503/10 were printed together, *se-tenant*, in sheetlets of 8 stamps and 1 central label.

c200+50 GHANA

545 Ghanaian Players holding Trophy

GHANA c200
546 *Eurychone rothschildiana*

1997 (25 July). *J.V.C. Under-17 World Soccer Champions (1995). T 545 and similar multicoloured designs. Litho. P 13½×13 (vert) or 13×13½ (horiz).*

2514	200 c. + 50 c. Type 545	15	20
2515	550 c. + 50 c. Ghana football team (*horiz*)	30	35
2516	800 c. + 50 c. Abu Iddrisu ..	45	50
2517	1100 c. + 50 c. Emmanuel Bentil (*captain*)	60	65
2518	1500 c. + 50 c. Basiru Gambo ..	80	85
2514/18		Set of 5	2·25	2·50

(Des Jennifer Toombs. Litho Questa)

1997 (1 Aug). *Flowers of the World. T 546 and similar multicoloured designs. P 14×14½ (horiz) or 14½×14 (vert).*

2519	200 c. Type 546 ..	..	10	10
2520	550 c. *Bulbophyllum lepidum* ..		30	35
2521	800 c. *Ansellia africana* ..	..	40	45
	a. Sheetlet. Nos. 2522/30 ..		3·50	
2523	800 c. *Ancistrochilus rothschildlanus* (*vert*)	..	40	45
2524	800 c. *Mussaenda arcuata* (*vert*) ..		40	45
2525	800 c. *Microcoelia guyoniane* (*vert*)		40	45
2526	800 c. *Gloriosa simplex* (*vert*) ..		40	45
2527	800 c. *Brachycorythis kalbreyeri* (*vert*)		40	45
2528	800 c. *Aframomum sceptrum* (*vert*)		40	45
2529	800 c. *Thunbergia alata* (*vert*) ..		40	45
2530	800 c. *Clerodendrum thomsoniae* (*vert*) ..		40	45
2531	1100 c. *Combbretum grandiflorum* ..		60	65
2519/31		Set of 13	5·00	5·75

MS2532 Two sheets each 82×77 mm. (a) 3000 c. *Kigelia africana* (*vert*). (b) 3000 c. *Spathodea campanulata* (*vert*) .. .. *Set of 2 sheets* 3·00 3·75
Nos. 2522/30 were printed together, *se-tenant*, in sheetlets of 9 with the backgrounds forming a composite design.

EURASIAN GOLDFINCH *Carduelis carduelis*
GHANA c200

HAVANA
GHANA c20

547 Goldfinch

548 Havana Cat

1997 (20 Oct). *Birds. T 547 and similar vert designs. Multicoloured. Litho. P 14.*

2533	200 c. Type 547 ..	..	10	10
2534	300 c. Cape Puff-back Flycatcher ("Batis")	15	20
2535	400 c. Red-headed Barbet ..	..	20	25
2536	500 c. African White-necked Raven	..	25	30
2537	600 c. Purple Grenadier ..	..	30	35
2538	800 c. Black Bustard ..	..	40	45
	a. Sheetlet. Nos. 2538/46 ..	..	3·50	
2539	800 c. Lapwing ..	..	40	45
2540	800 c. Lichtenstein's Sandgrouse	..	40	45
2541	800 c. Red-crested Turaco ..	..	40	45
2542	800 c. White-browed Coucal ..	..	40	45
2543	800 c. Lilac-breasted Roller ..	..	40	45
2544	800 c. Golden Pipet ..	..	40	45
2545	800 c. Burchell's Gonolek ..	..	40	45
2546	800 c. Blackcap ..	..	40	45
2547	1000 c. Zebra Waxbill ..	..	50	55
2533/47		Set of 5	5·00	5·25

MS2548 Two sheets, each 106×75 mm. (a) 3000 c. Shaft-tailed Whydah. (b) 3000 c. Yellow-tufted Malachite Sunbird *Set of 2 sheets* 3·00 3·25
Nos. 2538/46 were printed together, se-tenant, in sheetlets of 9.

(Des D. Burkhart. Litho Questa)

1997 (20 Oct). *Cats and Dogs.* T **548** *and similar horiz designs. Multicoloured. P* 14.

2549	20 c. Type **548**	..	..	..	10	10
2550	50 c. Singapura cat		..	..	10	10
2551	80 c. Papillon	..	..	..	10	10
2552	100 c. Sphinx cat	..	..	..	10	10
2553	150 c. British White cat		..	..	10	10
2554	200 c. Bulldog	..	..	..	10	15
2555	300 c. Snowshoe cat		..	..	15	20
2556	400 c. Shetland Sheepdog		..	..	20	25
2557	500 c. Schnauzer	..	..	..	25	30
2558	600 c. Persian cat	..	..	..	30	35
2559	800 c. Shih Tzu	..	..	..	40	45
2560	1000 c. Russian Wolfhound		..	..	50	55
	a. Sheetlet. Nos. 2560/5		..	..	3·00	
2561	1000 c. Birman cat	..	..	..	50	55
2562	1000 c. Basset Hound		..	..	50	55
2563	1000 c. Silver Tabby cat		..	..	50	55
2564	1000 c. Afghan	..	..	..	50	55
2565	1000 c. Burmilla cat		..	..	50	55
2566	1000 c. Abyssinian cat		..	..	50	55
	a. Sheetlet. Nos. 2566/71		..	..	3·00	
2567	1000 c. Border Terrier		..	..	50	55
2568	1000 c. Scottish Fold cat		..	..	50	55
2569	1000 c. Boston Terrier		..	..	50	55
2570	1000 c. Oriental cat		..	..	50	55
2571	1000 c. Keeshond	..	..	..	50	55
2572	2000 c. Chow Chow		..	..	1·00	1·10
2549/72				*Set of* 24	8·50	9·50

MS2573 Two sheets, each 73×100 mm. (a) 3000 c. Alaskan Malamute. (b) 3000 c. Ragdoll cat .. .. *Set of 2 sheets* 3·00 3·25
Nos. 2560/5 and 2566/71 were each printed together, *se-tenant*, in sheetlets of 6.

549 "Landscape"   550 "Cupid" (Botticelli)
(Huang Binhong)

(Des Y. Lee. Litho Questa)

1997 (10 Nov). *Return of Hong Kong to China.* T **549** *and similar designs showing landscape paintings by Huang Binhong* (Nos. 2574/81 *and* **MS**2582) *or historical scenes* (No. **MS**2583). *P* 14.

2574	200 c. multicoloured	..	..	10	15
	a. Sheetlet. Nos. 2574/81		..	3·00	
2575	300 c. multicoloured	..	..	15	20
2576	400 c. multicoloured	..	..	20	25
2577	500 c. multicoloured	..	..	25	30
2578	600 c. multicoloured	..	..	30	35
2579	800 c. multicoloured	..	..	40	45
2580	1000 c. multicoloured	..	..	50	55
2581	2000 c. multicoloured	..	..	1·00	1·10
2574/81			*Set of* 8	3·00	3·25

MS2582 138×105 mm. (a) 2000 c. multicoloured (farm). (b) 2000 c. multicoloured (mountains) (each 50×37 mm). P 14×13½ .. 2·00 2·10
MS2583 150×125 mm. (a) 1000 c. × 2 multicoloured (Lin Tse-Hue). (b) 1000 c. × 2 multicoloured (Gwen Tian-Pei) (each 63×31 mm) .. 2·00 2·10
Nos. 2574/81 were printed together, *se-tenant*, in sheetlets of 8.

(Litho B.D.T.)

1997 (8 Dec). *Christmas. Paintings.* T **550** *and similar vert designs. Multicoloured. P* 14.

2584	200 c. Type **550**	..	10	15
2585	550 c. "Zephyr and Chloris" (Botticelli)		30	35
2586	800 c. "Triumphant Cupid" (Caravaggio)		40	45
2587	1100 c. "The Seven Works of Mercy" (Caravaggio)		55	60
2588	1500 c. "The Toilet of Venus" (Diego Velazquez)		80	85
2589	2000 c. "Freeing of St. Peter" (Raphael)		1·00	1·10
2584/9			3·25	3·50

MS2590 Two sheets. (a) 95×105 mm. 5000 c. "The Cavalcanti Annunciation" (Donatello). (b) 105 x 95 mm. 5000 c. Ancient Egyptian painting of Isis and Nephthys .. *Set of 2 sheets* 5·00 5·25

STAMP BOOKLETS

1961. *Red* (No. SB1), *yellow* (No. SB2) *or green* (No. SB3) *covers. Stitched.*

SB1 3s. booklet containing twelve 3d. (No. 218a) in blocks of 4 .. .. .. 6·00
SB2 6s. booklet containing eight 3d. and eight 6d. (Nos. 218a, 220) in blocks of 4 .. 7·50
SB3 10s. booklet containing four 3d., eight 6d. and four 1s. 3d. (Nos. 218a, 220 and 226) in blocks of 4 .. 9·50

1963 (Jan). *Yellow cover. Stitched.*
SB4 6s. booklet containing twelve 4d. and four 6d. (Nos. 219/20) in blocks of four

1981 (16 Sept). *Royal Wedding. Multicoloured cover,* 120×82 *mm, showing Prince Charles and Lady Diana Spencer on front and map of Ghana on back. Stapled.*
SB5 14 c. booklet containing *se-tenant* pane of 4 (No. 955a) .. .. 4·50

POSTAGE DUE STAMPS

D 1
(Typo D.L.R.)

1923. *Yellowish toned paper. Wmk Mult Script CA. P* 14.

D1	D **1**	½d. black	..	..	14·00	£100
D2		1d. black	..	..	75	1·25
D3		2d. black	..	..	13·00	9·00
D4		3d. black	..	..	22·00	6·00
D1/4				*Set of 4*	45·00	£110
D1/4	Optd "Specimen"			*Set of 4*	70·00	

A bottom marginal strip of six of No. D2 is known showing the "A" of "CA" omitted from the watermark in the margin below the third vertical column.

Normal   Lower serif at left of "3" missing (R. 9/1)

1951–52. *Chalk-surfaced paper. Wmk Mult Script CA. P* 14.

D5	D **1**	2d. black (13.12.51)	..	3·00	16·00
		a. Error. Crown missing, W 9*a*			£450
		b. Error. St. Edward's Crown, W 9*b*			£250
		c. Large "d" (R. 9/6, 10/6)			14·00
D6		3d. black (13.12.51)	..	1·50	14·00
		a. Error. Crown missing, W 9*a*			£450
		b. Error. St. Edward's Crown, W 9*b*			£250
		c. Missing serif			14·00
D7		6d. black (1.10.52)	..	1·75	8·00
		a. Error. Crown missing, W 9*a*			£600
		b. Error. St. Edward's Crown, W 9*b*			£400
D8		1s. black (1.10.52)	..	1·75	55·00
		b. Error. St. Edward's Crown, W 9*b*			£550
D5/8			*Set of 4*	7·25	85·00

For illustration of No. D5c see above Nos. D4/6 of Botswana.

GHANA
(D **2**)   D **3**

1958 (25 June). *Nos. D5/8 and similar 1d. value optd with Type* D **2** *in red.*

D9	D **1**	1d. black	..	10	20
D10		2d. black	..	10	25
D11		3d. black	..	10	30
		a. Missing serif		2·00	
D12		6d. black	..	15	65
D13		1s. black	..	20	1·25
D9/13			*Set of 5*	50	2·40

(Typo De La Rue)

1958 (1 Dec). *Chalk-surfaced paper. Wmk Mult Script CA. P* 14.

D14	D **3**	1d. carmine	..	10	30
D15		2d. green	..	10	30
D16		3d. orange	..	10	30
		a. Missing serif		2·50	
D17		6d. bright ultramarine		10	50
D18		1s. reddish violet		15	2·00
D14/18			*Set of 5*	45	3·00

3p.
Ghana New Currency 19th July, 1965.   1½Np
(D **4**)   (D **5**)

1965 (19 July). *Nos. D14/18 surch as Type* D **4** *diagonally upwards* (D) *or horiz* (H), *by Govt Printer, Accra.*

D19	D **3**	1 p. on 1d. (D)		10	60
		a. Surch inverted		7·50	
		b. Surch double		..	
D20		2 p. on 2d. (B.) (H)		10	60
		a. Surch inverted		6·00	

D21	D **3**	3 p. on 3d. (indigo) (H)	..	10	60
		a. Surch inverted		..	
		b. Surch omitted (in horiz pair with normal)		..	
		c. Ultramarine surch		..	
		ca. Surch inverted		9·00	
		cb. Surch on front and back		..	
		d. Black surch		..	
		e. Missing serif		1·50	
D22		6 p. on 6d. (R.) (H)		10	1·50
		a. Surch inverted		..	
		b. Purple-brown surch		..	
		ba. Surch double		19·00	
		c. Green surch		13·00	
D23		12 p. on 1s. (B.) (D)		15	2·00
D19/23			*Set of 5*	45	5·00

On the diagonal surcharges the figures of value are horizontal.
No. D21b occurs in the first or second vertical row of one sheet which shows the surcharges shifted progressively to the right.

1968 (Feb)–**70.** *Nos. D20/2 additionally surch as Type* D **5**, *in red* (1½ *n.p.,* 5 *n.p.*) *or black* (2½ *n.p.*).

D24	D **3**	1½ n.p. on 2 p. on 2d.	..	5·50	4·25
		a. Type D **5** double, one albino		..	
		b. Albino surch (Type D **4**)		..	
D25		2½ n.p. on 3 p. on 3d. (4.70?)	..	1·00	4·50
		a. Type D **5** double, one albino		5·50	
		b. Missing serif		3·75	
D26		5 n.p. on 6 p. on 6d. (1970)	..	1·00	
D24/6			*Set of 3*	6·00	

The above were three in a series of surcharges, the others being 1 n.p. on 1 p. and 10 n.p. on 12 p., which were prepared, but owing to confusion due to the two surcharges in similar currency it was decided by the authorities not to issue the stamps, however, Nos. D24/6 were issued in error.

(Litho D.L.R.)

1970. *Inscr in new currency. P* 14¼ × 14.

D27	D **3**	1 n.p. carmine-red	..	80	3·75
D28		1½ n.p. green	..	80	3·75
D29		2½ n.p. yellow-orange	..	1·10	4·25
D30		5 n.p. ultramarine	..	1·75	4·50
D31		10 n.p. reddish violet	..	2·50	5·50
D27/31			*Set of 5*	6·50	19·00

(Litho D.L.R.)

1980–81. *Currency described as "p". P* 14½ × 14.

D32	D **3**	2 p. reddish orange	..	90	2·75
D33		3 p. brown	..	90	2·75

— URCH HARRIS —
ALL WORLD
NEW ISSUE SERVICE

■ Over thirty year's experience.
■ 260 countries and 100 plus themes.
■ Service tailored to your requirements.
■ Regular distributions every 6 weeks.
■ Free magazine with every distribution.
■ Customer advice helpline.
■ Free gifts and regular special offers.

Telephone 0117 9349333 for a Free Welcome Pack.

UH
Urch Harris & Co
1 Denmark Avenue
Bristol BS1 5HD
A Division of Stanley Gibbons Ltd

Gibraltar

CROWN COLONY

Early details of postal arrangements in Gibraltar are hard to establish, although it is known that postal facilities were provided by the Civil Secretary's Office from the early 1750s. Gibraltar became a packet port in 1806, although the Civil Secretary's Office continued to be responsible for other mail. The two services were amalgamated on 1 January 1857 as a Branch Office of the British G.P.O., the control of the postal services not reverting to Gibraltar until 1 January 1886.

Spanish stamps could be used at Gibraltar from their introduction in 1850 and, indeed, such franking was required on letters weighing over ½ oz. sent to Spain after 1 July 1854. From 1 July 1856 until 1 July 1875 all mail to Spain required postage to be prepaid by Spanish stamps and these issues were supplied by the Gibraltar postal authorities, acting as a Spanish Postal Agent. The mail, forwarded under this system was cancelled at San Roque with a horizontal barred oval, later replaced by a cartwheel type mark showing numeral 63. From 1857 combination covers showing the ship mail fee paid in British stamps and the inland postage by Spanish issues exist.

Stamps of Great Britain were issued for use in Gibraltar from 3 September 1857 to the end of 1885.

The initial supply contained 1d., 4d. and 6d. values. No supplies of the 2d. or 1s. were sent until the consignment of October 1857. No other values were supplied until early 1862.

For illustrations of the postmark types see BRITISH POST OFFICES ABROAD notes, following GREAT BRITAIN.

Stamps of GREAT BRITAIN *cancelled* "G" *as Type* **1** (3 Sept 1857 *to* 19 Feb 1859.)

Z 1	1d. red-brown (1854) Die I, *wmk* Small Crown, *Perf* 16			£300
Z 2	1d. red-brown (1855), Die II, *wmk* Small Crown, *perf* 16			£550
Z 3	1d. red-brown (1855), Die II, *wmk* Small Crown, *perf* 14			£250
Z 4	1d. red-brown (1855), Die II, *wmk* Large Crown, *perf* 14			65·00
Z 5	1d. rose-red (1857), Die II, *wmk* Large Crown, *perf* 14			20·00
Z 6	2d. blue (1855), *wmk* Small Crown, *perf* 14			£325
Z 7	2d. blue (1855–58), *wmk* Large Crown, *perf* 16			£275
Z 8	2d. blue (1855), *wmk* Large Crown, *perf* 14		*From*	55·00
	Plate Nos. 5, 6.			
Z 9	2d. blue (1858) (Plate No. 7)			£200
Z10	4d. rose (1857)			42·00
	a. Thick glazed paper			
Z11	6d. lilac (1856)			40·00
Z12	6d. lilac (1856) (blued *paper*)			£750
Z13	1s. green (1856)			£100
	a. Thick paper			
Z14	1s. green (1856) (blued *paper*)			£1300

Stamps of GREAT BRITAIN *cancelled* "A 26" *as in Types* **2, 5, 11** *or* **14** (20 Feb 1859 *to* 31 Dec 1885).

Z15	½d. rose-red (1870–79)		*From*	22·00
	Plate Nos. 4, 5, 6, 8, 10, 11, 12, 13, 14, 15, 19, 20.			
Z16	1d. red-brown (1841), *imperf*			£1000
Z17	1d. red-brown (1855), *wmk* Large Crown, *perf* 14			£150
Z18	1d. rose-red (1857), *wmk* Large Crown, *perf* 14			12·00
Z19	1d. rose-red (1864–79)		*From*	19·00
	Plate Nos. 71, 72, 73, 74, 76, 78, 79, 80, 81, 82, 83, 84, 85, 86, 87, 88, 89, 90, 91, 92, 93, 94, 95, 96, 97, 98, 99, 100, 101, 102, 103, 104, 105, 106, 107, 108, 109, 110, 111, 112, 113, 114, 115, 116, 117, 118, 119, 120, 121, 122, 123, 124, 125, 127, 129, 130, 131, 132, 133, 134, 135, 136, 137, 138, 139, 140, 141, 142, 143, 144, 145, 146, 147, 148, 149, 150, 151, 152, 153, 154, 155, 156, 157, 158, 159, 160, 161, 162, 163, 164, 165, 166, 167, 168, 169, 170, 171, 172, 173, 174, 175, 176, 177, 178, 179, 180, 181, 182, 183, 184, 185, 186, 187, 188, 189, 190, 191, 192, 193, 194, 195, 196, 197, 198, 199, 200, 201, 202, 203, 204, 205, 206, 207, 208, 209, 210, 211, 212, 213, 214, 215, 216, 217, 218, 219, 220, 221, 222, 223, 224, 225.			
Z20	1½d. lake-red (1870) (Plate No. 3)			£350
Z21	2d. blue (1855), *wmk* Large Crown, *perf* 14			£100
	Plate No. 6.			
Z22	2d. blue (1858–69)		*From*	18·00
	Plate Nos. 7, 8, 9, 12, 13, 14, 15.			
Z23	2½d. rosy mauve (1875) (blued *paper*)		*From*	£100
	Plate Nos. 1, 2, 3.			
Z24	2½d. rosy mauve (1875–76) (Plate Nos. 1, 2, 3)		*From*	27·00
Z25	2½d. rosy mauve (*Error of Lettering*)			£1800
Z26	2½d. rosy mauve (1876–79)		*From*	20·00
	Plate Nos. 3, 4, 5, 6, 7, 8, 9, 10, 11, 12, 13, 14, 15, 16, 17.			
Z27	2½d. blue (1880–81) (Plate Nos. 17, 18, 19, 20)		*From*	12·00
Z28	2½d. blue (1881) (Plate Nos. 21, 22, 23)		*From*	10·00
Z29	3d. carmine-rose (1862)			£150
Z30	3d. rose (1865) (Plate No. 4)			45·00
Z31	3d. rose (1867–73)		*From*	19·00
	Plate Nos. 4, 5, 6, 7, 8, 9, 10.			
Z32	3d. rose (1873–76)		*From*	28·00
	Plate Nos. 11, 12, 14, 15, 16, 17, 18, 19, 20.			
Z33	3d. rose (1881) (Plate Nos. 20, 21)			
Z34	3d. lilac (1883) (3d. *on* 3d)			95·00
Z35	4d. rose (1857)			45·00
Z36	4d. red (1862) (Plate Nos. 3, 4)		*From*	45·00
Z37	4d. vermilion (1865–73)		*From*	30·00
	Plate Nos. 7, 8, 9, 10, 11, 12, 13, 14.			
Z38	4d. vermilion (1876) (Plate No. 15)			£225
Z39	4d. sage-green (1877) (Plate Nos. 15, 16)			90·00
Z40	4d. grey-brown (1880) *wmk* Large Garter			£180
	Plate No. 17.			
Z41	4d. grey-brown (1880) *wmk* Crown		*From*	30·00
	Plate Nos. 17, 18.			
Z42	6d. lilac (1856)			42·00
Z43	6d. lilac (1862) (Plate Nos. 3, 4)		*From*	38·00
Z44	6d. lilac (1865–67) (Plate Nos. 5, 6).		*From*	32·00
Z45	6d. lilac (1867) (Plate No. 6).			42·00
Z46	6d. violet (1867–70) (Plate Nos. 6, 8, 9)		*From*	32·00
Z47	6d. buff (1872–73) (Plate Nos. 11, 12)		*From*	£180
Z48	6d. chestnut (1872) (Plate No. 11)			30·00

Z49	6d. grey (1873) (Plate No. 12)			85·00
Z50	6d. grey (1874–80)		*From*	28·00
	Plate Nos. 13, 14, 15, 16, 17.			
Z51	6d. grey (1881) (Plate Nos. 17, 18)			£170
Z52	6d. lilac (1883) (6d. *on* 6d.)			80·00
Z53	8d. orange (1876)			£250
Z54	9d. bistre (1862)			£160
Z55	9d. straw (1862)			£600
Z56	9d. straw (1865)			£550
Z57	9d. straw (1867)			£120
Z58	10d. red-brown (1867)			£150
Z59	1s. green (1856)			£100
Z60	1s. green (1862)			70·00
Z61	1s. green (1862) ("K" *variety*)			£2000
Z62	1s. green (1865) (Plate No. 4)			60·00
Z63	1s. green (1867–73) (Plate Nos. 4, 5, 6, 7)		*From*	16·00
Z64	1s. green (1873–77)		*From*	38·00
	Plate Nos. 8, 9, 10, 11, 12, 13.			
Z65	1s. orange-brown (1880) (Plate No. 13)			£225
Z66	1s. orange-brown (1881) (Plate Nos. 13, 14)		*From*	55·00
Z67	2s. blue (1867)			£140
Z68	5s. rose (1867) (Plate No. 1).			£650

1880.

Z69	½d. deep green			19·00
Z70	½d. pale green			19·00
Z71	1d. Venetian red			21·00
Z72	1½d. Venetian red			£170
Z73	2d. pale rose			60·00
Z74	2d. deep rose			60·00
Z75	5d. indigo			£100

1881.

Z76	1d. lilac (14 *dots*)			21·00
Z77	1d. lilac (16 *dots*)			9·00

1884.

Z78	½d. slate-blue			18·00
Z79	2d. lilac			80·00
Z80	2½d. lilac			15·00
Z81	3d. lilac			
Z82	4d. dull green			£120
Z83	6d. dull green			

POSTAL FISCAL

Z83a	1d. purple (Die 4) (1878) *wmk* Small Anchor	£600
Z84	1d. purple (1881), *wmk* Orb	£1100

PRICES FOR STAMPS ON COVER TO 1945	
Nos. 1/2	*from* × 25
No. 3	*from* × 10
No. 4	*from* × 25
Nos. 5/6	*from* × 8
Nos. 7/33	*from* × 6
Nos. 39/45	*from* × 5
Nos. 46/109	*from* × 3
Nos. 110/13	*from* × 4
Nos. 114/17	*from* × 3
Nos. 118/20	*from* × 5
Nos. 121/31	*from* × 3

GIBRALTAR
(1)

1886 (1 Jan). *Contemporary types of Bermuda optd with T* **1** *by D.L.R. Wmk Crown CA. P* 14.

1	**9**	½d. dull green		8·50	6·00
2	**1**	1d. rose-red		48·00	4·00
3	**2**	2d. purple-brown		90·00	75·00
4	**11**	2½d. ultramarine		£120	3·00
		a. Optd in blue-black		£500	£150
5	**10**	4d. orange-brown		£110	85·00
6	**4**	6d. deep lilac		£200	£180
7	**5**	1s. yellow-brown		£400	£350
1/7			*Set of 7*	£850	£650
1/3, 4a/7 Optd "Specimen"			*Set of 7*	£2500	

PRINTER. All Gibraltar stamps to No. 109 were typographed by De La Rue & Co, Ltd.

2

3

4

5

1886 (Nov)–**87.** *Wmk Crown CA. P* 14.

8	**2**	½d. dull green (1.87)		6·50	3·50
9	**3**	1d. rose (12.86)		42·00	3·75
10	**4**	2d. brown-purple (12.86)		30·00	17·00
11	**5**	2½d. blue		70·00	2·25
12	**4**	4d. orange-brown (16.4.87)		65·00	70·00
13		6d. lilac (16.4.87)		95·00	95·00
14		1s. bistre (2.87)		£180	£180
8/14			*Set of 7*	£425	£325
8/14 Optd "Specimen"			*Set of 7*	£500	
See also Nos. 39 to 45.					

5 CENTIMOS
(6)

7

1889 (1 Aug). *Surch as T* **6.**

15	**2**	5 c. on ½d. green		6·00	14·00
16	**3**	10 c. on 1d. rose		9·50	6·50
17	**4**	25 c. on 2d. brown-purple		4·25	5·00
		a. Small "T" (R.6/2)		£100	£140
		b. Broken "N" (R.10/5)		£100	£140
18	**5**	25 c. on 2½d. bright blue		25·00	2·00
		a. Small "T" (R.6/2)		£300	£100
		b. Broken "N" (R.10/5)		£300	£100
19	**4**	40 c. on 4d. orange-brown		60·00	80·00
20		50 c. on 6d. bright lilac		60·00	80·00
21		75 c. on 1s. bistre.		65·00	75·00
15/21			*Set of 7*	£200	£225
15/21 Optd "Specimen"			*Set of 7*	£350	

10 c., 40 c. and 50 c. values from this issue and that of 1889–96 are known bisected and used for half their value from various post offices in Morocco (*price on cover from* £500). These bisects were never authorised by the Gibraltar Post Office.

Two varieties of the figure "5" of the 5 c., 25 c., 50 c. and 75 c. may be found.

Broken "M" (Pl 2 R. 4/5)

Flat top to "C" (Pl 2 R. 4/4)

1889 (8 Oct)*–96. *Issue in Spanish currency. Wmk Crown CA. P* 14.

22	**7**	5 c. green		3·25	70
		a. Broken "M"			
23		10 c. carmine		3·25	45
		b. Value omitted		£5000	
24		20 c. olive-green and brown (2.1.96)		32·00	17·00
25		20 c. olive-green (8.7.96)		8·00	45·00
		a. Flat top to "C"			
26		25 c. ultramarine		12·00	70
		a. Deep ultramarine		25·00	80
27		40 c. orange-brown		2·50	2·25
28		50 c. bright lilac (1890)		2·00	1·50
29		75 c. olive-green (1890)		32·00	32·00
30		1 p. bistre (11.89)		75·00	20·00
31		1 p. bistre and ultramarine (6.95)		3·75	3·50
32		2 p. black and carmine (2.1.96)		8·00	24·00
33		5 p. slate-grey (12.89)		42·00	95·00
22/33			*Set of 12*	£200	£225
22/33 (excluding No. 25) Optd "Specimen"			*Set of 11*	£350	

*Earliest recorded postmark date.

1898 (1 Oct). *Reissue in Sterling currency. Wmk Crown CA. P* 14.

39	**2**	½d. grey-green		3·00	1·25
40	**3**	1d. carmine		5·00	35
41	**4**	2d. brown-purple and ultramarine		16·00	1·50
42	**5**	2½d. bright ultramarine		22·00	40
43	**4**	4d. orange-brown and green		14·00	6·50
44		6d. violet and red		35·00	20·00
45		1s. bistre and carmine		30·00	16·00
39/45			*Set of 7*	£110	42·00
39/45 Optd "Specimen"			*Set of 7*	£250	

No. 39 is greyer than No. 8, No. 40 brighter and deeper than No. 9 and No. 42 much brighter than No. 11.

8

9

½ ½

Normal   Large "2"
2½d.

This occurs on R.10/1 in each pane of 60. The diagonal stroke is also longer.

1903 (1 May). *Wmk Crown CA. P* 14.

46	**8**	½d. grey-green and green		8·50	8·50
47		1d. dull purple/*red*		27·00	60
48		2d. grey-green and carmine		14·00	23·00
49		2½d. dull purple and black/*blue*		3·00	60
		a. Large "2" in "½"		£150	90·00
50		6d. dull purple and violet		12·00	18·00

51	8	1s. black and carmine	..	27·00	30·00
52	9	2s. green and blue	..	£110	£140
53		4s. dull purple and green	..	75·00	£140
54		8s. dull purple and black/*blue* ..		£100	£140
55		£1 dull purple and black/*red* ..		£425	£500
46/55			Set of 10	£700	£900
46/55 Optd "Specimen"			Set of 10	£475	

1904–8. *Wmk Mult Crown CA. Ordinary paper (½d. to 2d. and 6d. to 2s.) or chalk-surfaced paper (others). P 14.*

56	8	½d. dull and bright green (16.4.04*)		6·50	2·00
		a. Chalk-surfaced paper (10.05)		8·50	5·50
57		1d. dull purple/*red* (6.9.04*)		4·50	40
		b. Bisected (½d.) (on card)		†	£1200
		bw. Wmk inverted			
		c. Chalk-surfaced paper (16.9.05)		2·00	60
58		2d. grey-green and carmine (9.1.05)		7·00	3·25
		a. Chalk-surfaced paper (2.07)		6·00	3·50
59		2½d. purple and black/*blue* (4.5.07)		30·00	85·00
		a. Large "2" in "½"		£400	£450
60		6d. dull purple and violet (19.4.06)		20·00	15·00
		a. Chalk-surfaced paper (4.08)		17·00	8·00
61		1s. black and carmine (13.10.05)		32·00	10·00
		a. Chalk-surfaced paper (4.06)		42·00	10·00
62	9	2s. green and blue (2.2.05)		60·00	80·00
		a. Chalk-surfaced paper (10.07)		70·00	75·00
63		4s. dull purple and green		£170	£225
64		£1 deep purple and black/*red* (15.3.08)		£450	£500
56/64			Set of 9	£700	£800

*Earliest known date of use.

1906 (Oct)**–12.** *Colours changed. Wmk Mult Crown CA. Chalk-surfaced paper (6d. to 8s.). P 14.*

66	8	½d. blue-green	..	2·25	90
67		1d. carmine	..	3·75	45
		a. Wmk sideways	..	—	£3250
		w. Wmk inverted		†	£500
68		2d. greyish slate (5.10)	..	6·50	9·00
69		2½d. ultramarine (6.07)	..	4·25	1·25
		a. Large "2" in "½"	..	£170	95·00
70		6d. dull and bright purple (3.12)		£120	£375
71		1s. black/*green* (1910)	..	21·00	18·00
72	9	2s. purple and bright blue/*blue* (4.10)		45·00	45·00
73		4s. black and carmine (4.10)	..	85·00	£130
		x. Wmk reversed	..		£1000
74		8s. purple and green (1911)	..	£180	£180
66/74			Set of 9	£425	£650
67/74 Optd "Specimen"			Set of 8	£500	

Examples of many values between Nos. 46 and 74 are known showing a forged oval registered postmark dated "6 OC 10".

10   11   (12)

WAR TAX

1912 (17 July)**–24.** *Wmk Mult Crown CA. Ordinary paper (½d. to 2½d.) or chalk-surfaced paper (others). P 14.*

76	10	½d. blue-green	..	2·25	70
		a. Yellow-green (4.17)	..	2·75	1·25
		w. Wmk inverted			
		x. Wmk reversed	..		† £1000
77		1d. carmine-red	..	2·25	75
		a. Scarlet (6.16)	..	2·75	85
78		2d. greyish slate	..	5·00	1·50
79		2½d. deep bright blue	..	3·25	1·75
		a. Large "2" in "½"		£110	85·00
		b. Pale ultramarine (1917)		6·00	2·00
		ba. Large "2" in "½"		£250	£120
80		6d. dull purple and mauve		7·00	11·00
81		1s. black/*green*	..	7·00	3·25
		a. Ordinary paper (8.18)		£500	
		b. On blue-green, olive back (1919)		12·00	25·00
		c. On emerald surface (12.23)		20·00	50·00
		d. On emerald back (3.24) (Optd S. £65)	16·00	70·00
82	11	2s. dull purple and blue/*blue*		24·00	3·00
83		4s. black and carmine		29·00	55·00
84		8s. dull purple and green		65·00	95·00
85		£1 dull purple and black/*red*		£140	£190
76/85			Set of 10	£250	£300
76/85 Optd "Specimen"			Set of 10	£425	

1918 (15 Apr). *Optd with T 12 by Beanland, Malin & Co, Gibraltar.*

86	10	½d. green	..	45	1·10
		a. Opt double	..	£650	
		w. Wmk inverted	..	£350	
		y. Wmk inverted and reversed		£350	

Two printings of this overprint exist, the second being in slightly heavier type on a deeper shade of green.

3 PENCE	THREE PENCE
(I)	

1921–27. *Wmk Mult Script CA. Chalk-surfaced paper (6d. to 8s.). P 14.*

89	10	½d. green (25.4.27)	..	50	80
90		1d. carmine-red (2.21)	..	1·50	70
91		1½d. chestnut (1.12.22)	..	1·25	40
		a. Pale chestnut (7.24)	..	1·00	30
		w. Wmk inverted	..		£500
93		2d. grey (17.2.21)	..	1·25	85
94		2½d. bright blue (2.21)	..	17·00	25·00
		a. Large "2" in "½"	..	£275	£325
95		3d. bright blue (I) (1.1.22)	..	2·50	4·25
		a. Ultramarine	..	1·40	1·50

97	10	6d. dull purple and mauve (1.23)		5·50	3·75
		a. Bright purple & magenta (22.7.26)		1·60	3·50
98		1s. black/*emerald* (20.6.24)		7·50	13·00
99	11	2s. grey-purple and blue/*blue* (20.6.24)	18·00	65·00
		a. Reddish purple and blue/*blue* (1925)	5·00	35·00
100		4s. black and carmine (20.6.24)		60·00	95·00
101		8s. dull purple and green (20.6.24)		£180	£325
89/101			Set of 11	£225	£425
89/101 Optd "Specimen"			Set of 11	£500	

The ½d. exists in coils constructed from normal sheets.

1925 (15 Oct)**–32.** *New values and colours changed. Wmk Mult Script CA. Chalk-surfaced paper. P 14.*

102	10	1s. sage-green and black (8.1.29)		14·00	21·00
		a. Olive and black (1932)		14·00	12·00
103	11	2s. red-brown and black (8.1.29)		9·00	29·00
104		2s. 6d. green and black		8·50	17·00
105		5s. carmine and black		12·00	48·00
106		10s. deep ultramarine and black		32·00	65·00
107		£1 red-orange and black (16.11.27)		£140	£180
108		£5 violet and black (Optd S. £700)		£1400	£3250
102/7			Set of 6	£190	£300
102/7 Optd/Perf "Specimen"			Set of 6	£400	

Examples of Nos. 83/5, 99/101 and 102/8 are known showing forged oval registered postmarks dated "24 JA 25" or "6 MY 35".

1930 (12 Apr). *T 10 inscribed* "THREE PENCE". *Wmk Mult Script CA. P 14.*

109		3d. ultramarine (II) (Perf S. £70)		7·50	2·00

13 The Rock of Gibraltar

(Des Capt. H. St. C. Garrood. Recess D.L.R.)

1931–33. *T 13. Wmk Mult Script CA. A. P 14. B. P 13½ × 14.*

			A		B	
110		1d. scarlet (1.7.31)	..	1·75	2·25	13·00	4·50
111		1½d. red-brown (1.7.31)	..	1·75	2·25	10·00	3·50
112		2d. pale grey (1.11.32)	..	4·50	1·00	11·00	2·25
113		3d. blue (1.6.33)	..	4·50	2·75	19·00	26·00
110/13			Set of 4	11·50	7·50	48·00	32·00
110/13 Perf "Specimen"			Set of 4	£160			

Figures of value take the place of both corner ornaments at the base of the 2d. and 3d.

1935 (6 May). *Silver Jubilee. As Nos. 91/4 of Antigua but ptd by B.W. P 11 × 12.*

114		2d. ultramarine and grey-black	..	1·60	2·50
		a. Extra flagstaff	..	60·00	
		b. Short extra flagstaff	..	90·00	
		c. Lightning conductor	..	55·00	
		d. Flagstaff on right-hand turret		£130	
		e. Double flagstaff	..	£130	
115		3d. brown and deep blue	..	3·25	3·50
		a. Extra flagstaff	..	£300	
		b. Short extra flagstaff	..	£250	
		c. Lightning conductor	..	£275	
116		6d. green and indigo	..	8·50	12·00
		a. Extra flagstaff	..	£225	
		b. Short extra flagstaff	..	£300	
		c. Lightning conductor	..	£225	
117		1s. slate and purple	..	8·50	8·50
		a. Extra flagstaff	..	£200	
		b. Short extra flagstaff	..	£275	
		c. Lightning conductor	..	£250	
114/17			Set of 4	20·00	24·00
114/17 Perf "Specimen"			Set of 4	£160	

For illustrations of plate varieties see Catalogue Introduction.

1937 (12 May). *Coronation. As Nos. 95/7 of Antigua. P 11×11½.*

118		½d. green	..	25	10
119		2d. grey-black	..	80	1·75
120		3d. blue	..	2·00	1·75
118/20			Set of 3	2·75	3·25
118/20 Perf "Specimen"			Set of 3	75·00	

14 King George VI   **15** Rock of Gibraltar

16 The Rock (North Side)

Broken second "R" in "GIBRALTAR"
(Frame Pl.2 R.9/4)

(Des Captain H. St. C. Garrood. Recess D.L.R.)

1938 (25 Feb)**–51.** *Designs as T 14/16. Wmk Mult Script CA.*

121		½d. deep green (p 13½×14)		10	40
122		1d. yellow-brown (p 14)		23·00	2·25
		a. Perf 13½		26·00	2·25
		ab. Perf 13½. Wmk sideways (1940)	5·50	6·50
		b. Perf 13. Wmk sideways. Red-brown (1942)	50	55
		c. Perf 13. Wmk sideways. Deep brown (1944)	30	3·25
		d. Perf 13. Red-brown (1949)		1·50	1·50
123		1½d. carmine (p 14)		35·00	75
		a. Perf 13½		£250	35·00
123b		1½d. slate-violet (p 13) (1.1.43)		30	40
124		2d. grey (p 14)		25·00	40
		ab. Perf 13½. Wmk sideways (1939)	£600	42·00
		b. Perf 13. Wmk sideways (1943)	30	85
		ba. "A" of "CA" missing from wmk	£1200	
124c		2d. carm (p 13) (*wmk sideways*) (15.7.44)	40	60
125		3d. light blue (p 13½)		15·00	90
		a. Perf 14		£120	5·00
		b. Perf 13 (1942)		30	30
125b		ba. Greenish blue (2.51)		3·50	2·50
125c		5d. red-orange (p 13) (1.10.47)		70	1·25
126		6d. carm & grey-violet (p 13½) (16.3.38)	48·00	3·00
		a. Perf 14		£120	1·25
		b. Perf 13 (1942)		2·00	1·40
		c. Perf 13. Scarlet and grey-violet (1945)	4·25	3·00
127		1s. black and green (p 14) (16.3.38)	38·00	20·00
		a. Perf 13½		60·00	7·00
		b. Perf 13 (1942)		3·00	3·75
		ba. Broken "R"		£110	
128		2s. black and brown (p 14) (16.3.38)	65·00	25·00
		a. Perf 13½		£110	32·00
		b. Perf 13 (1942)		3·25	5·50
		ba. Broken "R"		£120	
129		5s. black and carmine (p 14) (16.3.38)	90·00	£150
		a. Perf 13½		38·00	17·00
		b. Perf 13 (1944)		12·00	17·00
		ba. Broken "R"		£180	
130		10s. black and blue (p 14) (16.3.38)	65·00	£120
		a. Perf 13 (1943)		35·00	25·00
		ab. Broken "R"		£275	
131		£1 orange (p 13½×14) (16.3.38)	38·00	45·00
121/31			Set of 14	£120	85·00
121/31 Perf "Specimen"			Set of 14	£500	

Designs:—½d., £1, Type 14. *Horiz as T* 15/16—1d., 1½d. (*both*), Type 15; 2d. (*both*), Type 16; 3d., 5d. Europa Point; 6d. Moorish Castle; 1s. Southport Gate; 2s. Eliott Memorial; 5s. Government House; 10s. Catalan Bay.

The ½d., 1d. and both colours of the 2d. exist in coils constructed from normal sheets. These were originally joined vertically, but, because of technical problems, the 1d. and 2d. grey were subsequently issued in horizontal coils. The 2d. carmine only exists in the horizontal version.

1946 (12 Oct). *Victory. As Nos. 110/11 of Antigua.*

132		½d. green	..	10	10
133		3d. ultramarine	..	30	20
132/3 Perf "Specimen"			Set of 2	60·00	

1948 (1 Dec). *Royal Silver Wedding. As Nos. 112/13 of Antigua.*

134		½d. green	..	70	70
135		£1 brown-orange	..	50·00	60·00

1949 (10 Oct). *75th Anniv of Universal Postal Union. As Nos. 114/17 of Antigua.*

136		2d. carmine	..	1·00	95
137		3d. deep blue	..	2·50	95
138		6d. purple	..	2·00	95
139		1s. blue-green	..	1·60	2·25
136/9			Set of 4	6·50	4·50

NEW CONSTITUTION
1950
(23)

1950 (1 Aug). *Inauguration of Legislative Council. Nos. 124c, 125b, 126b and 127b optd as T* 23.

140	16	2d. carmine		30	1·00
141	—	3d. light blue		40	1·00
142	—	6d. carmine and grey-violet		50	1·40
		a. Opt double		£550	£650
143	—	1s. black and green (R.)		50	1·40
		a. Broken "R"		45·00	
140/3			Set of 4	1·50	4·25

On stamps from the lower part of the sheet of No. 142a the two impressions are almost coincident.

1953 (2 June). *Coronation. As No. 120 of Antigua.*

144		½d. black and bronze-green	..	30	65

24 Cargo and Passenger Wharves

25 Tower of Homage, Moorish Castle   **26** Arms of Gibraltar

Major re-entry causing doubling of "ALTA" in "GIBRALTAR" (R. 4/6)

(Des N. Cummings. Recess (except £1, centre litho) De La Rue)

1953 (19 Oct)–59. *T* **24/26** *and similar designs. Wmk Mult Script CA. P* 13.

145	½d. indigo and grey-green	15	30
146	1d. bluish green	1·50	30
	a. *Deep bluish green* (31.12.57)	2·25	50
147	1½d. black	90	90
148	2d. deep olive-brown	1·25	40
	a. *Sepia* (18.6.58)	2·25	90
149	2½d. carmine	3·50	85
	a. *Deep carmine* (11.9.56)	2·75	70
	aw. Wmk inverted	£300	
150	3d. light blue	3·00	10
	a. *Deep greenish blue* (8.6.55)	5·00	30
	b. *Greenish blue* (18.6.58)	7·00	20
151	4d. ultramarine	2·25	1·50
	a. *Blue* (17.6.59)	8·50	5·00
152	5d. maroon	60	70
	a. *Major re-entry*	17·00	
	b. *Deep maroon* (31.12.57)	1·50	1·50
	b. *Major re-entry*	20·00	
153	6d. black and pale blue	40	50
	a. *Black and blue* (24.4.57)	3·25	1·25
	b. *Black and grey-blue* (17.6.59)	4·00	2·75
154	1s. pale blue and red-brown	30	60
	a. *Pale blue and deep red-brown* (27.3.56)	30	60
155	2s. orange and reddish violet	27·00	5·00
	a. *Orange and violet* (17.6.59)	19·00	3·50
156	5s. deep brown	24·00	12·00
157	10s. reddish brown and ultramarine	60·00	35·00
158	£1 scarlet and orange-yellow	60·00	38·00
145/58	*Set of* 14	£160	80·00

Designs: *Horiz as T* **24**—1d. South View from Straits; 1½d. Tuna Fishing Industry; 2d. Southport Gate; 2½d. Sailing in the Bay; 3d. *Saturnia* (liner); 4d. Coaling wharf; 5d. Airport; 6d. Europa Point; 1s. Straits from Buena Vista; 2s. Rosia Bay and Straits; 5s. Main Entrance, Government House.

Nos. 145/6, 148 and 150 exist in coils, constructed from normal sheets.

1954 (10 May). *Royal Visit. As No.* 150 *but inscr* "ROYAL VISIT 1954" *at top*.

159	3d. greenish blue	15	20

38 Gibraltar Candytuft

40 Rock and Badge of Gibraltar Regiment

39 Moorish Castle

(Des J. Celecia (½d., 2d., 2½d., 2s., 10s.), N. A. Langdon (1d., 3d., 6d., 7d., 9d., 1s.), M. Bonilla (4d.), L. V. Gomez (5s.), Sgt. T. A. Griffiths (£1). Recess (£1) or photo (others) D.L.R.)

1960 (29 Oct)–62. *Designs as T* **38/9**, *and T* **40**. *W w* **12** *(upright). P* 14 (£1) *or* 13 *(others)*.

160	½d. bright purple and emerald-green	15	30
161	1d. black and yellow-green	10	10
162	2d. indigo and orange-brown	15	15
163	2½d. black and blue	55	55
	a. *Black and grey-blue* (16.10.62)	20	15
164	3d. deep blue and red-orange	30	10
165	4d. deep red-brown and turquoise	2·75	55
166	6d. sepia and emerald	70	40
167	7d. indigo and carmine-red	70	75
168	9d. grey-blue and greenish blue	50	50
169	1s. sepia and bluish green	90	30
170	2s. chocolate and ultramarine	13·00	2·25
171	5s. turquoise-blue and olive-brown	8·00	5·50
172	10s. yellow and blue	14·00	9·50
173	£1 black and brown-orange	17·00	11·00
160/73	*Set of* 14	48·00	27·00

Designs: *Horiz*—2d. St. George's Hall; 3d. The Rock by moonlight; 4d. Catalan Bay; 1s. Barbary Ape; 2s. Barbary Partridge; 5s. Blue Rock Thrush. *Vert*—2½d. The Keys; 6d. Map of Gibraltar; 7d. Air terminal; 9d. American War Memorial; 10s. Rock Lily (*Narcissus niveus*).

Vignette cylinders 2A and 2B, used for printings of the 9d. from 13 March 1962 onwards, had a finer screen (250 dots per inch instead of the 200 of the original printing).

Nos. 160/2, 164 and 166 exist in coils, constructed from normal sheets.

See also No. 199.

1963 (4 June). *Freedom from Hunger. As No.* 146 *of Antigua*.

174	9d. sepia	9·00	1·50

1963 (2 Sept). *Red Cross Centenary. As Nos.* 147/8 *of Antigua*.

175	1d. red and black	1·50	1·50
176	9d. red and blue	14·00	3·00

1964 (23 Apr). *400th Birth Anniv of William Shakespeare. As No.* 164 *of Antigua*.

177	7d. bistre-brown	40	20

NEW CONSTITUTION 1964.

(**52**)

53 Red Seabream

1964 (16 Oct). *New Constitution. Nos.* 164 *and* 166 *optd with T* **52**.

178	3d. deep blue and red-orange	15	10
179	6d. sepia and emerald	15	20
	a. No stop after "1964" (R.2/5)	15·00	24·00

1965 (17 May). *I.T.U. Centenary. As Nos.* 166/7 *of Antigua*.

180	4d. light emerald and yellow	4·00	50
	w. Wmk inverted	25·00	
181	2s. apple-green and deep blue	11·00	3·00

1965 (25 Oct). *International Co-operation Year. As Nos.* 168/9 *of Antigua*.

182	½d. deep bluish green and lavender	20	1·25
183	4d. reddish purple and turquoise-green	1·00	80

The value of the ½d. stamp is shown as "1/2".

1966 (24 Jan). *Churchill Commemoration. As Nos.* 170/3 *of Antigua*.

184	½d. new blue	20	1·00
	w. Wmk inverted	27·00	
185	1d. deep green	30	10
186	4d. brown	1·25	10
187	9d. bluish violet	1·25	2·00
184/7	*Set of* 4	2·75	2·75

1966 (1 July). *World Cup Football Championships. As Nos.* 176/7 *of Antigua*.

188	2½d. violet, yellow-green, lake & yellow-brn	75	30
189	6d. chocolate, blue-green, lake & yellow-brn	1·00	50

PRINTERS. All stamps from here to No. 239 were printed in photogravure by Harrison and Sons Ltd, London.

(Des A. Ryman)

1966 (27 Aug). *European Sea Angling Championships, Gibraltar. T* **53** *and similar designs. W w* **12** *(sideways on 1s.). P* 13½ × 14 (1s.) *or* 14 × 13½ *(others)*.

190	4d. rosine, bright blue and black	20	10
191	7d. rosine, deep olive-green and black	30	30
	a. Black (value and inscr) omitted	£900	
	w. Wmk inverted	2·50	
192	1s. lake-brown, emerald and black	30	30
190/2	*Set of* 3	70	60

Designs: *Horiz*—7d. Red Scorpionfish. *Vert*—1s. Stone Bass.

1966 (20 Sept). *Inauguration of W.H.O. Headquarters, Geneva. As Nos.* 178/9 *of Antigua*.

193	6d. black, yellow-green and light blue	2·50	1·50
194	9d. black, light purple and yellow-brown	3·00	1·50

56 "Our Lady of Europa"

57 H.M.S. *Victory*

(Des A. Ryman)

1966 (15 Nov). *Centenary of Re-enthronement of "Our Lady of Europa". W w* **12**. *P* 14 × 14½.

195	**56** 2s. bright blue and black	30	70

1966 (1 Dec). *20th Anniv of U.N.E.S.C.O. As Nos.* 196/8 *of Antigua*.

196	2d. slate-violet, red, yellow and orange	25	10
197	7d. orange-yellow, violet and deep olive	60	10
198	5s. black, bright purple and orange	2·50	2·25
196/8	*Set of* 3	3·00	2·25

1966 (23 Dec). *As No.* 165 *but wmk w* **12** *sideways*.

199	4d. deep red-brown and turquoise	30	60

(Des A. Ryman)

1967 (3 Apr)–69. *Horiz designs as T* **57**. *Multicoloured. W w* **12**. *P* 14 × 14½.

200	½d. Type **57**	10	15
	a. Grey (sails, etc) omitted	£375	
201	1d. *Arab* (early steamer)	10	10
	w. Wmk inverted	2·75	2·50
202	2d. H.M.S. *Carmania* (merchant cruiser)	15	10
	a. Grey-blue (hull) omitted	£2000	
203	2½d. *Mons Calpe* (ferry)	30	30
204	3d. *Canberra* (liner)	20	10
	w. Wmk inverted	21·00	6·50
205	4d. H.M.S. *Hood* (battle cruiser)	30	10
205a	5d. *Mirror* (cable ship) (7.7.69)	3·25	55
	aw. Wmk inverted		

206	6d. *Xebec* (sailing vessel)	30	40
207	7d. *Amerigo Vespucci* (Italian cadet ship)	30	35
	w. Wmk inverted	14·00	
208	9d. *Raffaello* (liner)	30	60
209	1s. *Royal Katherine* (galleon)	30	35
210	2s. H.M.S. *Ark Royal* (aircraft carrier), 1937	3·50	2·25
211	5s. H.M.S. *Dreadnought* (nuclear submarine)	3·50	6·50
212	10s. *Neuralia* (liner)	14·00	22·00
213	£1 *Mary Celeste* (sailing vessel)	14·00	22·00
200/13	*Set of* 15	35·00	50·00

No. 202a results from the misaligning of the grey-blue cylinder. The bottom horizontal row of the sheet involved has this colour completely omitted except for the example above the cylinder numbers which shows the grey-blue "1A" towards the top of the stamp.

The ½d., 1d., 2d., 3d., 6d., 2s., 5s. and £1 exist with PVA gum as well as gum arabic, but the 5d. exists with PVA gum only.

Nos. 201/2, 204/5 and 206 exist in coils constructed from normal sheets.

58 Aerial Ropeway

(Des A. Ryman)

1967 (15 June). *International Tourist Year. T* **58** *and similar designs but horiz. Multicoloured. W w* **12** *(sideways on* 7d.). *P* 14½ × 14 (7d.) *or* 14 × 14½ *(others)*.

214	7d. Type **58**	10	10
215	9d. Shark fishing	10	10
216	1s. Skin-diving	15	15
214/16	*Set of* 3	30	30

59 Mary, Joseph and Child Jesus

60 Church Window

1967 (1 Nov). *Christmas. W w* **12** *(sideways* * *on* 6d.). *P* 14.

217	**59** 2d. multicoloured	10	10
	w. Wmk inverted	1·25	
218	**60** 6d. multicoloured	10	10
	w. Wmk Crown to right of CA	£110	

*The normal sideways watermark shows Crown to left of CA, as seen from the back of the stamp.

61 Gen. Eliott and Route Map

62 Eliott directing Rescue Operations

(Des A. Ryman)

1967 (11 Dec). *250th Birth Anniv of General Eliott. Multicoloured designs as T* **61** (4d. *to* 1s.) *or T* **62**. *W w* **12** *(sideways on horiz designs). P* 14 × 15 (1s.) *or* 15 × 14 *(others)*.

219	4d. Type **61**	10	10
220	9d. Heathfield Tower and Monument, Sussex (38 × 22 *mm*)	10	10
221	1s. General Eliott (22 × 38 *mm*)	10	10
222	2s. Type **62**	30	20
219/22	*Set of* 4	45	40

65 Lord Baden-Powell

(Des A. Ryman)

1968 (27 Mar). *60th Anniv of Gibraltar Scout Association. T* **65** *and similar horiz designs. W* w **12.** *P* 14 × 14½.

223	4d. buff and bluish violet		15	10
224	7d. ochre and blue-green		15	10
225	9d. bright blue, yellow-orange and black		20	30
226	1s. greenish yellow and emerald		20	30
223/6		*Set of* 4	65	65

Designs:—7d. Scout Flag over the Rock; 9d. Tent, scouts and salute; 1s. Scout badges.

66 Nurse and W.H.O. Emblem

68 King John signing Magna Carta

(Des A. Ryman)

1968 (1 July). *20th Anniv of World Health Organization. T* **66** *and similar horiz design. W* w **12.** *P* 14 × 14½.

227	2d. ultramarine, black and yellow		10	15
228	4d. slate, black and pink		10	15

Design:—4d. Doctor and W.H.O. emblem.

1968 (26 Aug). *Human Rights Year. T* **68** *and similar vert design. W* w **12** *(sideways). P* 13½ × 14.

229	1s. yellow-orange, brown and gold		15	10
230	2s. myrtle and gold		15	20

Design:—2s. "Freedom" and Rock of Gibraltar.

70 Shepherd, Lamb and Star

72 Parliament Houses

(Des A. Ryman)

1968 (1 Nov). *Christmas. T* **70** *and similar vert design. Multicoloured. W* w **12.** *P* 14½ × 13½.

231	4d. Type **70**		10	10
	a. Gold (star) omitted		£225	
232	9d. Mary holding Holy Child		10	10

(Des A. Ryman)

1969 (26 May). *Commonwealth Parliamentary Association Conference. T* **72** *and similar designs. W* w **12** *(sideways on 2s.). P* 14 × 14½ (2s.) *or* 14½ × 14 *(others).*

233	4d. green and gold		10	10
234	9d. bluish violet and gold		10	10
235	2s. multicoloured		15	20
233/5		*Set of* 3	30	30

Designs: *Horiz*—9d. Parliamentary emblem and outline of "The Rock". *Vert*—2s. Clock Tower, Westminster (Big Ben) and arms of Gibraltar.

75 Silhouette of Rock, and Queen Elizabeth II

77 Soldier and Cap Badge, Royal Anglian Regiment, 1969

(Des A. Ryman)

1969 (30 July). *New Constitution. W* w **12.** *P* 14 × 13½ *(in addition, the outline of the Rock is perforated).*

236	**75** ½d. gold and orange		10	10
237	5d. silver and bright green		15	10
	a. Portrait and inscr in gold and silver*			
238	7d. silver and bright purple		15	10
239	5s. gold and ultramarine		55	70
236/9		*Set of* 4	75	85

*No. 237a was first printed with the head and inscription in gold and then in silver but displaced slightly to lower left.

(Des A. Ryman. Photo D.L.R.)

1969 (6 Nov). *Military Uniforms* (1st series). *T* **77** *and similar vert designs. Multicoloured. W* w **12.** *P* 14.

240	1d. Royal Artillery officer, 1758 and modern cap badge		20	10
241	6d. Type **77**		45	20
242	9d. Royal Engineers' Artificer, 1786 and modern cap badge		55	30
243	2s. Private, Fox's Marines, 1704 and modern Royal Marines cap badge		2·00	1·25
240/3		*Set of* 4	2·75	1·60

Nos. 240/3 have a short history of the Regiment printed on the reverse side over the gum, therefore, once the gum is moistened the history disappears.

See also Nos. 248/51, 290/3, 300/3, 313/16, 331/4, 340/3 and 363/6.

80 "Madonna of the Chair" (detail, Raphael)

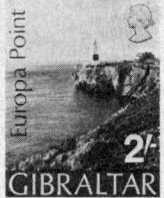

83 Europa Point

(Des A. Ryman. Photo Enschedé)

1969 (1 Dec). *Christmas. T* **80** *and similar vert designs. Multicoloured. W* w **12** *(sideways). P* 14 × *Roulette* 9.

244	5d. Type **80**		10	10
	a. Strip of 3. Nos. 244/6		35	
245	7d. "Virgin and Child" (detail, Morales)		15	15
246	1s. "The Virgin of the Rocks" (detail, Leonardo da Vinci)		15	20
244/6		*Set of* 3	35	40

Nos. 244/6 were issued together in *se-tenant* strips of three throughout the sheet.

(Des A. Ryman. Photo Enschedé)

1970 (8 June). *Europa Point. W* w **12.** *P* 13½.

247	**83** 2s. multicoloured		30	30
	w. Wmk inverted		1·90	1·90

(Des A. Ryman. Photo D.L.R.)

1970 (28 Aug). *Military Uniforms* (2nd series). *Vert designs as T* **77.** *Multicoloured. W* w **12.** *P* 14.

248	2d. Royal Scots officer, 1839 and cap badge		30	10
249	5d. South Wales Borderers private, 1763 and cap badge		60	10
250	7d. Queen's Royal Regiment private, 1742 and cap badge		60	15
251	2s. Royal Irish Rangers piper, 1969 and cap badge		2·75	1·25
248/51		*Set of* 4	3·75	1·40

Nos. 248/51 have a short history of the Regiment printed on the reverse side under the gum.

88 No. 191a and Rock of Gibraltar

(Des A. Ryman. Litho D.L.R.)

1970 (18 Sept). *"Philympia* 1970" *Stamp Exhibition, London. T* **88** *and similar horiz design. W* w **12** *(sideways). P* 13.

252	1s. vermilion and bronze-green		15	10
253	2s. bright blue and magenta		25	55

Design:—2s. Victorian stamp (No. 23b) and Moorish Castle. The stamps shown in the designs are well-known varieties with values omitted.

90 "The Virgin Mary" (stained-glass window by Gabriel Loire)

(Photo Enschedé)

1970 (1 Dec). *Christmas. W* w **12.** *P* 13 × 14.

254	**90** 2s. multicoloured		30	30

(New Currency: 100 pence = £1)

91 Saluting Battery, Rosia

---

92 Saluting Battery, Rosia, Modern View

(Des A. Ryman. Litho Questa)

1971 (15 Feb). *Decimal Currency. Designs as T* **91/2.** *W* w **12** *(sideways* on horiz designs). *P* 14.

255	½p. multicoloured		15	20
	a. Pair. Nos. 255/6		30	40
256	½p. multicoloured		15	20
257	1p. multicoloured		80	30
	a. Pair. Nos. 257/8		1·60	60
258	1p. multicoloured		80	30
259	1½p. multicoloured		20	40
	a. Pair. Nos. 259/60		40	80
260	1½p. multicoloured		20	40
261	2p. multicoloured		1·50	1·50
	a. Pair. Nos. 261/2		3·00	3·00
262	2p. multicoloured		1·50	1·50
263	2½p. multicoloured		20	40
	a. Pair. Nos. 263/4		40	80
264	2½p. multicoloured		20	40
265	3p. multicoloured		20	20
	a. Pair. Nos. 265/6		40	40
266	3p. multicoloured		20	20
267	4p. multicoloured		2·00	2·00
	a. Pair. Nos. 267/8		4·00	4·00
268	4p. multicoloured		2·00	2·00
269	5p. multicoloured		30	30
	a. Pair. Nos. 269/70		60	60
270	5p. multicoloured		30	30
271	7p. multicoloured		65	65
	aw. Wmk Crown to right of CA		40·00	
	a. Pair. Nos. 271/2		1·25	1·25
	bw. Pair. Nos. 271aw/2aw		80·00	
272	7p. multicoloured		65	65
	aw. Wmk Crown to right of CA		40·00	
273	8p. multicoloured		70	80
	a. Pair. Nos. 273/4		1·40	1·60
274	8p. multicoloured		70	80
275	9p. multicoloured		70	70
	a. Pair. Nos. 275/6		1·40	1·40
276	9p. multicoloured		70	70
277	10p. multicoloured		80	80
	aw. Wmk Crown to right of CA		70·00	
	b. Pair. Nos. 277/8		1·60	1·60
	bw. Pair. Nos. 277aw/8aw		£140	
278	10p. multicoloured		80	80
	aw. Wmk Crown to right of CA		70·00	
279	12½p. multicoloured		1·00	1·60
	a. Pair. Nos. 279/80		2·00	3·00
280	12½p. multicoloured		1·00	1·60
281	25p. multicoloured		1·10	1·60
	a. Pair. Nos. 281/2		2·10	3·00
282	25p. multicoloured		1·10	1·60
283	50p. multicoloured		1·25	2·50
	a. Pair. Nos. 283/4		2·50	5·00
284	50p. multicoloured		1·25	2·50
285	£1 multicoloured		2·00	4·00
	a. Pair. Nos. 285/6		4·00	8·00
286	£1 multicoloured		2·00	4·00
255/86		*Set of* 32	24·00	32·00

Designs (the two versions of each value show the same Gibraltar view taken from an early 19th-century print (first design) or modern photograph (second design): *Horiz*—1p. Prince George of Cambridge Quarters and Trinity Church; 1½p. The Wellington Bust, Alameda Gardens; 2p. Gibraltar from the North Bastion; 2½p. Catalan Bay; 3p. Convent Garden; 4p. The Exchange and Spanish Chapel; 5p. Commercial Square and Library; 7p. South Barracks and Rosia Magazine; 8p. Moorish Mosque and Castle; 9p. Europa Pass Road; 10p. South Barracks from Rosia Bay; 12½p. Southport Gates; 25p. Trooping the Colour, The Alameda. *Vert*—50p. Europa Pass Gorge; £1 Prince Edward's Gate.

The two designs of each value were printed together, *se-tenant*, in horizontal and vertical pairs throughout.

*The normal sideways watermark shows Crown to left of CA, as seen from the back of the stamp.

See also Nos. 317/20 and 344/5.

93

94 Regimental Arms

(Des A. Ryman. Photo Harrison)

1971 (15 Feb). *Coil Stamps. W* w **12.** *P* 14½ × 14.

287	**93** ½p. red-orange		15	30
	a. Coil strip (287 × 2, 288 × 2 and 289 *se-tenant*)		1·00	
288	1p. blue		15	30
289	2p. bright green		50	1·10
287/9		*Set of* 3	70	1·50

(Des A. Ryman. Litho Questa)

1971 (6 Sept). *Military Uniforms* (3rd series). *Multicoloured designs as T* **77,** *showing uniform and cap-badge. W* w **12.** *P* 14.

290	1p. The Black Watch (1845)		35	20
291	2p. Royal Regt of Fusiliers (1971)		65	30
	w. Wmk inverted			
292	4p. King's Own Royal Border Regt (1704)		1·25	50
293	10p. Devonshire and Dorset Regt (1801)		3·75	2·00
	w. Wmk inverted			
290/3		*Set of* 4	5·50	2·75

Nos. 290/3 have a short history of the regiment printed on the reverse side under the gum.

(Des A. Ryman. Litho Harrison)

1971 (25 Sept). *Presentation of Colours to the Gibraltar Regiment. W w **12** (sideways). P 12½ × 12.*
294 **94** 3p. black, gold and red 30 30

95 Nativity Scene   96 Soldier Artificer, 1773

(Des A. Ryman. Photo Enschedé)

1971 (1 Dec). *Christmas. T **95** and similar horiz design. Multicoloured. W w **12**. P 13 × 13½.*
295 3p. Type **95** 45 45
296 5p. Mary and Joseph going to Bethlehem 55 55

(Des A. Ryman. Litho Questa)

1972 (6 Mar). *Bicentenary of Royal Engineers in Gibraltar. T **96** and similar multicoloured designs. W w **12** (sideways on 1 and 3p.). P 13½ × 14 (5p.) or 14 × 13½ (others).*
297 1p. Type **96** 40 20
298 3p. Modern tunneller 60 50
299 5p. Old and new uniforms and badge (horiz) 75 65
297/9 .. .. Set of 3 1·60 1·25

(Des A. Ryman. Litho Questa)

1972 (19 July). *Military Uniforms (4th series). Multicoloured designs as T **77**. W w **12** (sideways). P 14.*
300 1p. Duke of Cornwall's Light Infantry, 1704 60 20
301 3p. King's Royal Rifle Corps, 1830 .. 1·75 40
302 7p. Officer, 37th North Hampshire, 1825 2·75 70
303 10p. Royal Navy, 1972 .. .. 3·25 1·50
300/3 .. .. Set of 4 7·50 2·50
Nos. 300/303 have a short history of the Regiment printed on the reverse side under the gum.

97 "Our Lady of Europa"   98 Keys of Gibraltar and *Narcissus niveus*

(Des A. Ryman. Litho Harrison)

1972 (4 Oct). *Christmas. W w **12** (sideways)*. P 14½×14.
304 **97** 3p. multicoloured 10 10
    w. Wmk Crown to right of CA .. 7·00
305 5p. multicoloured 10 30
    w. Wmk Crown to right of CA .. 1·00
*The normal sideways watermark shows Crown to left of CA, as seen from the back of the stamp.
These stamps have an inscription printed on the reverse side.

(Des (from photograph by D. Groves) and photo Harrison)

1972 (20 Nov). *Royal Silver Wedding. Multicoloured; background colour given. W w **12**. P 14 × 14½.*
306 **98** 5p. carmine-red 20 20
    w. Wmk inverted .. .. .. 35·00
307 7p. deep grey-green 20 20
    w. Wmk inverted .. .. ..

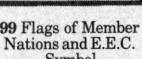

99 Flags of Member Nations and E.E.C. Symbol   100 Skull

(Des A. Ryman. Litho Questa)

1973 (22 Feb). *Britain's Entry into E.E.C. W w **12** (sideways). P 14½ × 14.*
308 **99** 5p. multicoloured 40 30
309 10p. multicoloured 60 50

(Des A. Ryman. Litho B.W.)

1973 (22 May). *125th Anniv of Gibraltar Skull Discovery. T **100** and similar horiz designs. Multicoloured. W w **12**. P 13 (10p.) or 13½ (others).*
310 4p. Type **100** .. .. .. 1·25 50
    a. Gold ("GIBRALTAR") omitted ..£1700
311 6p. Prehistoric man .. .. 1·25 70
312 10p. Prehistoric family (40×26 mm) .. 1·75 1·25
310/12 .. .. Set of 3 3·75 2·25
Four mint examples of No. 310a have been found in presentation packs.

(Des A. Ryman. Litho Questa)

1973 (22 Aug). *Military Uniforms (5th series). Multicoloured designs as T **77**. W w **12** (sideways). P 14.*
313 1p. King's Own Scottish Borderers, 1770 50 40
314 4p. Royal Welch Fusiliers, 1800 .. 1·50 1·00
315 6p. Royal Northumberland Fusiliers, 1736 . 2·25 1·75
316 10p. Grenadier Guards, 1898 .. .. 3·00 4·00
313/16 .. .. Set of 4 6·50 6·50
Nos. 313/16 have a short history of the Regiment printed on the reverse side under the gum.

1973 (12 Sept). *As Nos. 261/2 and 267/8 but W w **12** upright.*
317 2p. multicoloured .. .. .. 90 1·75
    a. Pair. Nos. 317/18 .. .. 1·75 3·50
318 2p. multicoloured .. .. .. 90 1·75
319 4p. multicoloured .. .. .. 1·00 1·75
    a. Pair. Nos. 319/20 .. .. 2·00 3·50
320 4p. multicoloured .. .. .. 1·00 1·75
317/20 .. .. Set of 4 3·50 6·25

101 "Nativity" (Danckerts)   102 Victorian Pillar-box

(Des and litho Enschedé)

1973 (17 Oct). *Christmas. W w **12**. P 12½ × 12.*
321 **101** 4p. violet and Venetian red .. 25 15
322 6p. magenta and turquoise-blue .. 35 75

1973 (14 Nov). *Royal Wedding. As Nos. 165/6 of Anguilla. Centre multicoloured. W w **12** (sideways). P 13½.*
323 6p. turquoise 10 10
324 14p. yellow-green 20 20

(Des A. Ryman. Litho Walsall)

1974 (2 May). *Centenary of Universal Postal Union. T **102** and similar vert designs. Multicoloured. (a) W w **12** (sideways). P 14½.*
325 2p. Type **102** 15 20
326 6p. Pillar-box of George VI .. 25 30
327 14p. Pillar-box of Elizabeth II .. 40 65
325/7 .. .. Set of 3 70 1·00
    (b) No wmk. Imperf × roul 5*. Self-adhesive (from booklets).
328 2p. Type **102** 25 90
    a. Booklet pane Nos. 328/30 se-tenant .. 6·00
    b. Booklet pane Nos. 328 × 3 and 329 × 3 .. 2·00
329 6p. As No. 326 .. .. .. 35 1·00
330 14p. As No. 327 .. .. .. 6·00 8·00
328/30 .. .. Set of 3 6·00 9·00
*Nos. 328/30 were separated by various combinations of rotary-knife (giving a straight edge) and roulette.

(Des A. Ryman. Litho Questa)

1974 (21 Aug). *Military Uniforms (6th series). Multicoloured designs as T **77**. W w **12** (sideways)*. P 14.*
331 4p. East Lancashire Regt, 1742 .. 50 50
332 6p. Somerset Light Infantry, 1833 .. 70 70
333 10p. Royal Sussex Regt, 1790 .. 1·00 1·40
334 16p. R.A.F. officer, 1974 .. .. 2·25 4·00
    w. Wmk Crown to right of CA .. £100
331/4 .. .. Set of 4 4·00 6·00
*The normal sideways watermark shows Crown to left of CA, as seen from the back of the stamp.
Nos. 331/4 have a short history of the regiment printed on the reverse side under the gum.

103 "Madonna with the Green Cushion" (Solario)   104 Churchill and Houses of Parliament

(Des A. Ryman and M. Infante. Litho Questa)

1974 (5 Nov). *Christmas. T **103** and similar vert design. Multicoloured. W w **14**. P 14.*
335 4p. Type **103** 40 30
336 6p. "Madonna of the Meadow" (Bellini) .. 60 95

(Des L. Curtis. Litho Harrison)

1974 (30 Nov). *Birth Centenary of Sir Winston Churchill. T **104** and similar horiz design. W w **12**. P 14 × 14½.*
337 6p. black, reddish purple and light lavender 25 15
338 20p. brownish black, lake-brown and light orange-red 50 65
MS339 114×93 mm. Nos. 337/8. W w **12** (sideways*). P 14 .. .. .. 4·50 6·00
    w. Wmk Crown to right of CA .. £225
Design:—20p. Churchill and *King George V* (battleship).
*The normal sideways watermark shows Crown to left of CA, as seen from the back of the stamp.

(Des A. Ryman. Litho Questa)

1975 (14 Mar). *Military Uniforms (7th series). Multicoloured designs as T **77**. W w **14**. P 14.*
340 4p. East Surrey Regt, 1846 .. .. 30 30
341 6p. Highland Light Infantry, 1777 .. 50 50
342 10p. Coldstream Guards, 1704 .. 70 80
343 20p. Gibraltar Regt, 1974 .. .. 1·25 2·25
340/3 .. .. Set of 4 2·40 3·50
Nos. 340/3 have a short history of each regiment printed on the reverse side under the gum.

1975 (9 July). *As Nos. 257/8 but W w **14** (sideways).*
344 1p. multicoloured .. .. .. 1·25 1·75
    a. Pair. Nos. 344/5 .. .. 2·50 3·50
345 1p. multicoloured .. .. .. 1·25 1·75

105 Girl Guides' Badge   106 Child at Prayer

(Des A. Ryman. Litho Harrison)

1975 (10 Oct). *50th Anniv of Gibraltar Girl Guides. W w **12**. P 13 × 13½.*
346 **105** 5p. gold, light blue and dull violet .. 30 45
    a. Tête-bêche (pair) .. .. 75 1·00
    w. Wmk inverted 45 60
347 7p. gold, sepia and light lake-brown 40 50
    a. Tête-bêche (pair) .. .. 1·00 1·10
    w. Wmk inverted 60 70
348 — 15p. silver, brownish black & yellow-brn 65 1·00
    a. Tête-bêche (pair) .. .. 1·50 2·00
    b. Silver omitted
    w. Wmk inverted .. .. 85 1·25
346/8 .. .. Set of 3 1·25 1·75
No. 348 is as T **105** but shows a different badge.
Nos. 346/8 were each issued in sheets of 25 (5×5) with each horizontal row containing three upright stamps and two inverted.

(Des A. Ryman. Litho Walsall)

1975 (26 Nov). *Christmas. T **106** and similar vert designs. Multicoloured. W w **14** (sideways)*. P 14.*
349 6p. Type **106** 40 60
    aw. Wmk Crown to right of CA .. 5·50
    b. Sheetlet. Nos. 349/54 .. 2·10
    bw. Sheetlet. Nos. 349aw/54aw .. 30·00
350 6p. Angel with lute 40 60
    aw. Wmk Crown to right of CA .. 5·50
351 6p. Child singing carols 40 60
    aw. Wmk Crown to right of CA .. 5·50
352 6p. Three children 40 60
    aw. Wmk Crown to right of CA .. 5·50
353 6p. Girl at prayer 40 60
    aw. Wmk Crown to right of CA .. 5·50
354 6p. Boy and lamb 40 60
    aw. Wmk Crown to right of CA .. 5·50
349/54 .. .. Set of 6 2·10 3·25
*The normal sideways watermark shows Crown to left of CA, as seen from the back of the stamp.
Nos. 349/54 were issued together se-tenant in sheetlets of 6 (3×2).

107 Bruges Madonna   108 Bicentennial Emblem and Arms of Gibraltar

(Des Jennifer Toombs. Litho Walsall)

1975 (17 Dec). *500th Birth Anniv of Michelangelo. T* **107** *and similar vert designs. Multicoloured*

(a) W w **14** (sideways*). P 14

355	6p.	Type **107**			20	25
356	9p.	Taddei Madonna			25	40
357	15p.	Pietà			35	90
	w.	Wmk Crown to right of CA		90·00		
355/7				Set of 3	70	1·40

(b) No wmk. Imperf×roul 5†. Self-adhesive (from booklets)

358	6p.	Type **107**			35	45
	a.	Booklet pane. Nos. 358/60 se-tenant			1·50	
	b.	Booklet pane. Nos. 358×2, 359×2 and 360×2			3·00	
359	9p.	As No. 356			55	75
360	15p.	As No. 357			80	1·25
358/60				Set of 3	1·50	2·25

*The normal sideways watermark shows Crown to left of CA, as seen from the back of the stamp.
†Nos. 358/60 were separated by various combinations of rotary knife (giving a straight edge) and roulette.

(Des A. Ryman. Litho Walsall)

1976 (28 May). *Bicentenary of American Revolution.* W w **14** (inverted). P 14.

361	**108**	25p. multicoloured			50	50
MS362		85 × 133 mm. No. 361 × 4.			6·00	8·50

The edges of **MS**362 are rouletted.

(Des A. Ryman. Litho Walsall)

1976 (21 July). *Military Uniforms (8th series). Multicoloured designs as T* **77**. *W w* **14** (inverted). P 14.

363	1p.	Suffolk Regt, 1795			20	15
364	6p.	Northamptonshire Regt, 1779			40	30
365	12p.	Lancashire Fusiliers, 1793			65	55
366	25p.	Ordnance Corps, 1896			1·25	1·10
363/6				Set of 4	2·25	1·90

Nos. 363/6 have a short history of each regiment printed on the reverse side under the gum.

109 The Holy Family

110 Queen Elizabeth II, Royal Arms and Gibraltar Arms

(Des A. Ryman. Litho Questa)

1976 (3 Nov). *Christmas. T* **109** *and similar vert designs showing stained-glass windows in St. Joseph's Church, Gibraltar. Multicoloured.* W w **14**. P 14.

367	6p.	Type **109**			25	15
368	9p.	Madonna and Child			30	25
369	12p.	St. Bernard			45	60
370	20p.	Archangel Michael			70	1·25
367/70				Set of 4	1·50	2·00

(Des A. Ryman. Litho J.W.)

1977 (7 Feb). *Silver Jubilee.* W w **14**. P 13½.

371	**110**	6p. multicoloured			25	20
372		£1 multicoloured			1·40	2·25
MS373		124 × 115 mm. Nos. 371/2. P 13			1·60	2·25

The outer edges of the miniature sheet are either guillotined or rouletted.

111 Toothed Orchid (*Orchis tridentata*)

(Des A. Ryman. Litho Questa)

1977 (1 Apr)–82. *Multicoloured designs as T* **111**. *W w* **14** (sideways* on horiz designs; inverted on £5). Chalk-surfaced paper (15p., £5). Imprint date at foot. P 14.

374	½p.	Type **111**			60	1·50
	a.	Chalk-surfaced paper (22.2.82)			2·75	3·00
375	1p.	Red Mullet (*Mullus surmuletus*) (horiz)			15	10
	w.	Wmk Crown to right of CA		6·00	6·50	
376	2p.	*Maculinea arion* (butterfly) (horiz)			30	50
377	2½p.	Sardinian Warbler (*Sylvia melanocephala*)			40	1·25
378	3p.	Giant Squill (*Scilla peruviana*)			20	10
379	4p.	Grey Wrasse (*Crenilabrus cinereus*) (horiz)			30	10
	b.	Chalk-surfaced paper (21.4.81)			55	55
380	5p.	*Vanessa atalanta* (butterfly) (horiz)			50	70
381	6p.	Black Kite (*Milvus migrans*)			1·00	95
	w.	Wmk inverted			75·00	
382	9p.	Shrubby Scorpion-vetch (*Coronilla valentina*)			70	70

383	10p.	John Dory (fish) (*Zeus faber*) (horiz)		40	20
	a.	Chalk-surfaced paper (21.4.81)		70	1·00
384	12p.	*Colias crocea* (butterfly) (horiz)		1·00	35
	a.	Chalk-surfaced paper (21.4.81)		4·00	4·00
384b	15p.	Winged Asparagus Pea (*Tetragonolobus purpureus*) (12.11.80)		3·25	55
	bw.	Wmk inverted		75·00	
385	20p.	Audouin's Gull (*Larus audouinii*)		1·25	2·00
386	25p.	Barbary Nut (iris) (*Iris sisyrinchium*)		1·25	2·00
	a.	Chalk-surfaced paper (21.4.81)		3·75	4·25
387	50p.	Swordfish (*Xiphias gladius*) (horiz)		2·00	95
	a.	Chalk-surfaced paper (21.4.81)		5·50	6·50
388	£1	*Papilio machaon* (butterfly) (horiz)		4·25	4·50
389	£2	Hoopoe (*Upupa epops*)		7·50	10·00
389a	£5	Arms of Gibraltar (16.5.79)		10·00	10·00
374/89a			Set of 18	30·00	32·00

The ½p. to £2 values have a descriptive text printed on the reverse, beneath the gum.
*The normal sideways watermark shows Crown to left of CA, as seen from the back of the stamp.
Imprint dates: "1977", Nos. 374/84, 385/9; "1978", No. 382; "1979", No. 389a; "1980", No. 384b; "1981", Nos. 379b, 383a, 384a, 386a, 387a; "1982", No. 374a.

112 "Our Lady of Europa" Stamp

(Des J. Cooter. Litho Questa)

1977 (27 May). "*Amphilex 77" Stamp Exhibition. Amsterdam. T* **112** *and similar vert designs. Multicoloured.* W w **14** (sideways on 6p.; inverted on 12p.). P 13½.

390	6p.	Type **112**			10	20
391	12p.	"Europa Point" stamp			20	30
	w.	Wmk upright			18·00	
392	25p.	"E.E.C. Entry" stamp			30	50
	w.	Wmk inverted			2·25	
390/2				Set of 3	55	90

113 "The Annunciation" (Rubens)

114 Aerial View of Gibraltar

(Des A. Ryman. Litho Enschedé)

1977 (2 Nov). *Christmas and Rubens' 400th Birth Anniv. T* **113** *and similar multicoloured designs.* W w **14** (sideways on 12p.). P 13½.

393	3p.	Type **113**			10	10
394	9p.	"The Adoration of the Magi"			25	20
395	12p.	"The Adoration of the Magi" (horiz)			30	30
396	15p.	"The Holy Family under the Apple Tree"			30	40
393/6				Set of 4	85	85
MS397		110 × 200 mm. Nos. 393/6 (wmk upright)			3·50	4·00

(Des A. Ryman. Litho Enschedé)

1978 (3 May). *Gibraltar from Space.* P 13½.

398	**114**	12p. multicoloured			25	40
	a.	Horiz pair imperf 3 sides			£3000	
MS399		148×108 mm. 25p. multicoloured			80	80

Design:—25p. Aerial view of Straits of Gibraltar.
No. 398a occurs on the bottom pair from two sheets of 10 (2×5) and shows the stamps perforated at top only.

115 Holyroodhouse

(Des and litho Walsall)

1978 (12 June). *25th Anniv of Coronation. T* **115** *and similar horiz designs. Multicoloured.* (a) From sheets. P 13½ × 14.

400	6p.	Type **115**			20	15
401	9p.	St. James's Palace			25	15
402	12p.	Sandringham			30	25
403	18p.	Balmoral			40	40
400/3				Set of 4	1·00	85

(b) From booklets. Imperf × roul 5*. Self-adhesive.

404	12p.	As No. 402			35	75
	a.	Booklet pane. Nos. 404/5, each × 3			2·00	
405	18p.	As No. 403			40	90
406	25p.	Windsor Castle			70	1·50
	a.	Booklet pane of 1			70	
404/6				Set of 3	1·25	2·75

*Nos. 404/5 were separated by various combinations of rotary-knife (giving a straight edge) and roulette. No. 406 exists only with straight edges.

116 Short S.25 Sunderland, 1938–58

117 "Madonna with Animals"

(Des A. Theobald. Litho Harrison)

1978 (6 Sept). *60th Anniv of Royal Air Force. T* **116** *and similar horiz designs. Multicoloured.* W w **14** (sideways). P 14.

407	3p.	Type **116**			15	10
408	9p.	Caudron G-3, 1918			35	40
409	12p.	Avro Shackleton M.R.2, 1953–66			40	55
410	16p.	Hawker Hunter F.6, 1954–77			45	80
411	18p.	Hawker Siddeley H.S.801 Nimrod M.R.1, 1969–78			50	90
407/11				Set of 5	1·75	2·50

(Des A. Ryman. Litho Questa)

1978 (1 Nov). *Christmas. Paintings by Dürer. T* **117** *and similar vert designs. Multicoloured.* W w **14**. P 14.

412	5p.	Type **117**			15	10
413	9p.	"The Nativity"			20	15
414	12p.	"Madonna of the Goldfinch"			25	30
415	15p.	"Adoration of the Magi"			35	40
412/15				Set of 4	85	85

118 Sir Rowland Hill and 1d. Stamp of 1886

(Des A. Ryman. Litho Format)

1979 (7 Feb). *Death Centenary of Sir Rowland Hill. T* **118** *and similar horiz designs.* W w **14** (sideways*). P 13½×14.

416	3p.	multicoloured			10	10
417	9p.	multicoloured			20	15
418	12p.	multicoloured			25	20
	w.	Wmk Crown to right of CA		65·00		
419	25p.	black, dull claret and yellow			35	50
416/19				Set of 4	80	80

Designs:—9p. Sir Rowland Hill and 1p. coil stamp of 1971; 12p. Sir Rowland Hill and Post Office Regulations document, 1840; 25p. Sir Rowland Hill and "G" cancellation.
*The normal sideways watermark shows Crown to left of CA, as seen from the back of the stamp.

119 Posthorn, Dish Antenna and Early Telephone

120 African Child

(Des A. Ryman. Litho Format)

1979 (16 May). *Europa. Communications.* W w **14** (sideways). P 13½.

420	**119**	3p. green and pale green			15	10
421		9p. lake-brown and ochre			30	90
422		12p. ultramarine and dull violet-blue			35	1·25
420/2				Set of 3	70	2·00

(Des G. Hutchins. Litho Walsall)

1979 (14 Nov). *Christmas. International Year of the Child. T* **120** *and similar vert designs. Multicoloured.* W w **14** (sideways). P 14.

423	12p.	Type **120**			25	30
	a.	Block of 6. Nos. 423/8			1·40	
424	12p.	Asian child			25	30
425	12p.	Polynesian child			25	30
426	12p.	American Indian child			25	30
427	12p.	Children of different races and Nativity scene			25	30
428	12p.	European child			25	30
423/8				Set of 6	1·40	1·60

Nos. 423/8 were printed together, se-tenant, in blocks of 6, with margin separating the two blocks in each sheet.

121 Early Policemen

122 Peter Amigo (Archbishop)

(Des C. Abbott. Litho Questa)

1980 (5 Feb). *150th Anniv of Gibraltar Police Force. T* **121** *and similar horiz designs. Multicoloured. W* w **14** *(sideways). P* 14.
29   3p. Type **121** 20   10
30   6p. Policemen of 1895, early 1900s and 1980   20   15
31   12p. Policeman and police ambulance .. 25   20
32   37p. Policewoman and police motor-cyclist .. 55   90
29/32 .. .. *Set of 4* 1·10 1·25

(Des A. Ryman. Litho Questa)

1980 (6 May). *Europa. Personalities. T* **122** *and similar vert designs. Multicoloured. W* w **14** *(inverted on No.* 434).
P 14½ × 14.
33   12p. Type **122** 20   25
34   12p. Gustavo Bacarisas (artist) .. 20   25
35   12p. John Mackintosh (philanthropist) .. 20   25
33/5 .. .. *Set of 3* 55   70

123 Queen Elizabeth the
Queen Mother

124 "Horatio Nelson"
(J. F. Rigaud)

(Des Harrison. Litho Questa)

1980 (4 Aug). *80th Birthday of Queen Elizabeth the Queen Mother. W* w **14** *(sideways). P* 14.
436 **123** 15p. multicoloured 30   30

(Des BG Studio. Litho Questa)

1980 (20 Aug). *175th Death Anniv of Nelson. Paintings. T* **124** *and similar multicoloured designs. W* w **14** *(sideways on 9 and 40p.).
P* 14.
437   3p. Type **124** 15   10
438   9p. "H.M.S. *Victory*" (*horiz*) .. 25   25
439   15p. "Horatio Nelson" (Sir William Beechey) 35   35
440   40p. "H.M.S. *Victory* being towed into
         Gibraltar" (Clarkson Stanfield) (*horiz*) 80   1·00
437/40 .. .. *Set of 4* 1·40 1·50
MS441 159 × 99 mm. No. 439 .. .. 75 1·75
Examples of the 3p. value showing Nelson facing left in error were prepared, but not issued by the Gibraltar Post Office.

125 Three Kings

126 Hercules creating
Mediterranean Sea

(Des A. Ryman. Litho Questa)

1980 (12 Nov). *Christmas. T* **125** *and similar horiz design, each in deep brown and orange-yellow. W* w **14** *(sideways). P* 14½.
442   15p. Type **125** 25   35
         a. Horiz pair. Nos. 442/3 .. 50   70
443   15p. Nativity scene 25   35
Nos. 442/3 were printed together, *se-tenant*, in horizontal pairs throughout the sheet.

(Des G. Vasarhelyi. Litho Enschedé)

1981 (24 Feb). *Europa. Folklore. T* **126** *and similar vert design. Multicoloured. W* w **14**. *P* 13½ × 13.
444   9p. Type **126** 20   15
445   15p. Hercules and Pillars of Hercules (Straits
         of Gibraltar) 25   35

127 Dining-room

128 Prince Charles and
Lady Diana Spencer

(Des A. Ryman. Litho Harrison)

1981 (22 May). *450th Anniv of The Convent (Governor's Residence). T* **127** *and similar square designs. Multicoloured. W* w **14** *(sideways). P* 14½ × 14.
446   4p. Type **127** 10   10
447   14p. King's Chapel 15   15
448   15p. The Convent 15   15
449   55p. Cloister 60   80
446/9 .. .. *Set of 4* 85 1·00

(Des A. Ryman. Litho Questa)

1981 (27 July). *Royal Wedding. W* w **14** *(sideways). P* 14½.
450 **128** £1 multicoloured .. .. 1·25 1·50

129

130 Paper Aeroplane

(Des A. Ryman. Litho Questa)

1981 (2 Sept). *Booklet stamps. W* w **14**. *P* 13½×14.
451 **129** 1p. black 10   10
         a. Booklet pane. Nos. 451/2 and 453 ×
            3 plus printed label 90
         b. Booklet pane. Nos. 451/2 × 2 and 453
            × 6 plus two printed labels .. 1·75
452   4p. Prussian blue 10   10
453   15p. light green 25   30
451/3 .. .. *Set of 3* 35   45

(Des A. Ryman. Litho Walsall)

1981 (29 Sept*). *50th Anniv of Gibraltar Airmail Service. T* **130** *and similar horiz designs. Multicoloured. W* w **14** *(sideways).
P* 14½ × 14.
454   14p. Type **130** 15   15
455   15p. Airmail letters, post box and aircraft
         tail fin 15   15
456   55p. Jet airliner circling globe .. 60   70
454/6 .. .. *Set of 3* 80   90
*This is the local release date. The Crown Agents released the stamps on 21 September.

131 Carol Singers

132 I.Y.D.P. Emblem and
Stylised Faces

(Des Clive Torres (15p.); Peter Parody (55p.); adapted
G. Vasarhelyi. Litho Questa)

1981 (19 Nov). *Christmas. Children's Drawings. T* **131** *and similar multicoloured design. W* w **14** *(sideways on 15p.). P* 14.
457   15p. Type **131** 30   15
458   55p. Postbox (*vert*) .. .. 1·00   85

(Des A. Ryman. Litho Questa)

1981 (19 Nov). *International Year For Disabled Persons. W* w **14** *(sideways). P* 14 × 14½.
459 **132** 14p. multicoloured 30   30

133 Douglas DC-3

134 Crest, H.M.S. *Opossum*

(Des A. Theobald. Litho J.W.)

1982 (10 Feb). *Aircraft. Horiz designs as T* **133**. *Multicoloured. W* w **14**. *Imprint date at foot. P* 14.
460   1p. Type **133** .. .. .. 25 1·00
461   2p. Vickers Viking 1B .. 30 1·00
462   3p. Airspeed A.S.57 Ambassador .. 30   90
463   4p. Vickers Viscount 800 .. 40   20
464   5p. Boeing 727-100 90   60
465   10p. Vickers 953 Vanguard .. 1·25   50
466   14p. Short S.45A Solent 2 .. 1·00 2·00
467   15p. Fokker F.27 Friendship .. 2·00 1·25
468   17p. Boeing 737 .. .. 1·00   55
469   20p. B.A.C. One Eleven .. 1·00   50
470   25p. Lockheed Constellation .. 3·50 3·00
471   50p. Hawker Siddeley Comet 4B .. 4·00 2·25
472   £1 Saro A.21 Windhover .. 5·50 2·25
473   £2 Hawker Siddeley Trident 2E .. 6·50 5·00
474   £5 De Havilland D.H.89A Dragon Rapide 9·00 14·00
460/74 .. .. *Set of 15* 32·00 32·00
Imprint dates: "1982", Nos. 460/74; "1985", No. 469.
For 2p. and 5p. values watermarked w **16** see Nos. 549 and 552.

(Des A. Ryman. Litho Questa)

1982 (14 Apr). *Naval Crests (1st series). T* **134** *and similar vert designs. Multicoloured. W* w **14**. *P* 14.
475   ½p. Type **134** 10   10
476   15½p. H.M.S. *Norfolk* 55   60
477   17p. H.M.S. *Fearless* 60   65
478   60p. H.M.S. *Rooke* .. .. 1·40 2·50
         w. Wmk inverted .. .. 35·00
475/8 .. .. *Set of 4* 2·25 3·50
See also Nos. 493/6, 510/13, 522/5, 541/4, 565/8, 592/5, 616/19, 638/41 and 651/4.

---

135 Hawker Hurricane Mk 1
and Supermarine Spitfires at
Gibraltar

136 Gibraltar Chamber
of Commerce Centenary

(Des A. Ryman. Litho Questa)

1982 (11 June). *Europa. Operation Torch. T* **135** *and similar horiz design. Multicoloured. W* w **14** *(sideways). P* 14.
479   14p. Type **135** 25   70
480   17p. General Giraud, General Eisenhower and
         Gibraltar 35   80

(Des A. Ryman. Litho Questa)

1982 (22 Sept). *Anniversaries. T* **136** *and similar vert designs. Multicoloured. W* w **14** *(sideways). P* 14½.
481   ½p. Type **136** 10   10
482   15½p. British Forces Postal Service centenary 30   25
483   60p. 75th anniv of Gibraltar Scout
         Association .. .. .. 1·10 1·25
481/3 .. .. *Set of 3* 1·25 1·40

137 Printed Circuit forming Map of World

(Des A. Ryman. Litho Harrison)

1982 (1 Oct). *International Direct Dialling. W* w **14** *(sideways).
P* 14½.
484 **137** 17p. black, pale blue and bright orange 35   35

138 Gibraltar illuminated at Night and Holly

(Des A. Ryman. Litho Questa)

1982 (18 Nov). *Christmas. T* **138** *and similar horiz design. Multicoloured. W* w **14** *(sideways). P* 14 × 14½.
485   14p. Type **138** 45   30
486   17p. Gibraltar illuminated at night and
         Mistletoe 50   35

139 Yacht Marina

(Des Olympia Reyes. Litho Questa)

1983 (14 Mar). *Commonwealth Day. T* **139** *and similar multicoloured designs. W* w **14** *(sideways on 4, 14p.). P* 14.
487   4p. Type **139** 10   10
488   14p. Scouts and Guides Commonwealth Day
         Parade 20   15
489   17p. Flag of Gibraltar (*vert*) .. 25   20
490   60p. Queen Elizabeth II (from photo by Tim
         Graham) (*vert*) .. .. 70 1·00
487/90 .. .. *Set of 4* 1·00 1·25

140 St George's Hall Gallery

(Des A. Ryman. Litho Harrison)

1983 (21 May). *Europa. T* **140** *and similar horiz design. W* w **14** *(sideways). P* 13½ × 13.
491   16p. black and brown-ochre .. 30   35
492   19p. black and pale blue .. 40   40
Design:—19p. Water catchment slope.

(Des A. Ryman. Litho Questa)

1983 (1 July). *Naval Crests (2nd series). Vert designs as T* **134.** *Multicoloured. W* w **14.** *P* 14.

493	4p. H.M.S. *Faulknor*	..	..	30	10
494	14p. H.M.S. *Renown*	..	..	70	35
495	17p. H.M.S. *Ark Royal*	..	..	75	40
496	60p. H.M.S. *Sheffield*	..	..	1·75	1·50
	w. Wmk inverted	..	..	27·00	
493/6			Set of 4	3·25	2·10

141 Landport Gate, 1729

(Des Olympia Reyes. Litho Enschedé)

1983 (13 Sept). *Fortress Gibraltar in the 18th Century. T* **141** *and similar horiz designs. Multicoloured. W* w **14** (*sideways*). *P* 13 × 13½.

497	4p. Type **141** ..	..	..	20	10
498	17p. Koehler Gun, 1782	..	..	50	45
499	77p. King's Bastion, 1779	..	..	1·50	1·75
497/9			Set of 3	2·00	2·00
MS500	97 × 145 mm. Nos. 497/9 ..	..	..	2·00	2·00

142 "Adoration of the Magi" (Raphael)

143 1932 2d. Stamp and Globe

(Des A. Ryman. Litho Questa)

1983 (17 Nov). *Christmas. 500th Birth Anniv of Raphael. T* **142** *and similar multicoloured designs. W* w **14** (*sideways on 4p.*). *P* 14.

501	4p. Type **142** ..	..	..	25	10
502	17p. "Madonna of Foligno" (*vert*)	..	..	70	35
503	60p. "Sistine Madonna" (*vert*)..	..	..	1·75	1·40
501/3			Set of 3	2·40	1·60

(Des E. Field. Litho Walsall)

1984 (6 Mar). *Europa. Posts and Telecommunications. T* **143** *and similar vert designs. Multicoloured. W* w **14.** *P* 14½ × 14.

504	17p. Type **143**	..	..	35	50
505	23p. Circuit board and globe	..	..	45	1·00
	w. Wmk inverted	..	..	95·00	

144 Hockey

145 Mississippi River Boat Float

(Des A. Ryman. Litho Walsall)

1984 (25 May). *Sports. T* **144** *and similar horiz designs. Multicoloured. W* w **14** (*sideways*). *P* 14 × 14½.

506	20p. Type **144** ..	..	..	40	60
507	21p. Basketball	..	..	40	60
508	26p. Rowing	..	..	55	90
509	29p. Football	..	..	60	95
506/9	..		Set of 4	1·75	2·75

(Des A. Ryman. Litho Walsall)

1984 (21 Sept). *Naval Crests (3rd series). Vert designs as T* **134.** *Multicoloured. W* w **14.** *P* 13½ × 13.

510	20p. H.M.S. *Active*	..	..	1·60	1·75
511	21p. H.M.S. *Foxhound*	..	..	1·60	1·75
512	26p. H.M.S. *Valiant*	..	..	1·75	2·00
513	29p. H.M.S. *Hood* ..	..	..	1·90	2·00
	w. Wmk inverted	..	..	12·00	
510/13	..		Set of 4	6·25	6·75

(Des A. Ryman. Litho Questa)

1984 (7 Nov). *Christmas. Epiphany Floats. T* **145** *and similar horiz design. Multicoloured. W* w **14** (*sideways*). *P* 14 × 14½.

514	20p. Type **145** ..	..	..	40	50
515	80p. Roman Temple float	..	..	1·60	2·00

MINIMUM PRICE

The minimum price quote is 10p which represents a handling charge rather than a basis for valuing common stamps. For further notes about prices see introductory pages.

---

146 Musical Symbols, and Score from Beethoven's 9th (Choral) Symphony

147 Globe and Stop Polio Campaign Logo

(Des Olympia Reyes. Photo Courvoisier)

1985 (26 Feb). *Europa. European Music Year. T* **146** *and similar horiz design. Multicoloured. Granite paper. P* 12½.

516	**146** 20p. multicoloured	..	..	60	50
517	— 29p. multicoloured	..	..	90	2·00

The 29p. is as T **146** but shows different symbols.

(Des E. Field. Litho J.W.)

1985 (3 May). *Stop Polio Campaign. Vert designs as T* **147.** *Multicoloured. W* w **14** (*inverted*). *P* 13 × 13½.

518	26p. multicoloured (Type **147**)	..	70	1·00
	a. Horiz strip of 4. Nos. 518/21	..	2·50	
519	26p. multicoloured ("ST" visible)	..	70	1·00
520	26p. multicoloured ("STO" visible)	..	70	1·00
521	26p. multicoloured ("STOP" visible)	..	70	1·00
518/21		Set of 4	2·50	3·50

Nos 518/21 were printed in horizontal *se-tenant* strips of four within the sheet. Each design differs in the position of the logo across the centre of the globe. On the left hand stamp in the strip only the letter "S" is visible, on the next "ST", on the next "STO" and on the last "STOP".

Other features of the design also differ, so that the word "Year" moves towards the top of the stamp and on No. 521 the upper logo is omitted.

(Des A. Ryman. Litho Questa)

1985 (3 July). *Naval Crests (4th series). Vert designs as T* **134.** *Multicoloured. W* w **16.** *P* 14.

522	4p. H.M.S. *Duncan* ..	..	..	50	10
523	9p. H.M.S. *Fury*	..	..	80	50
524	71p. H.M.S. *Firedrake*	..	..	1·75	1·75
525	80p. H.M.S. *Malaya*	..	..	3·75	5·00
522/5	..		Set of 4	6·00	6·50

148 I.Y.Y. Logo

149 St. Joseph

(Des Olympia Reyes. Litho Walsall)

1985 (6 Sept). *International Youth Year. T* **148** *and similar horiz designs. Multicoloured. W* w **14** (*sideways*). *P* 14 × 14½.

526	20p. Type **148** ..	..	..	25	10
527	20p. Hands passing diamond	..	..	95	1·10
528	80p. 75th anniv logo of Girl Guide Movement	2·50	3·25
526/8	..		Set of 3	3·25	4·00

(Des A. Ryman (4p.), Olympia Reyes (80p.). Litho Cartor)

1985 (25 Oct). *Christmas. Centenary of St. Joseph's Parish Church. T* **149** *and similar vert designs. Multicoloured. W* w **14.** *P* 13½*.

529	4p. Type **149** ..	..	..	50	70
	a. Vert pair. Nos. 529/30	..	..	1·00	1·40
530	4p. St. Joseph's Parish Church	..	..	50	70
531	80p. Nativity crib	..	..	3·00	3·25
529/31			Set of 3	3·50	4·50

*Nos. 529/30 were printed together in panes of 25; No. 529 on rows 1, 3 and 5, and No. 530 on rows 2 and 4. *Se-tenant* vertical pairs from rows 1/2 and 3/4, forming composite designs, have the stamps separated by a line of roulettes instead of perforations. Examples of No. 529 from row 5 have perforations on all four sides.

150 *Papilio machaon* (butterfly) and The Convent.

151 1887 Queen Victoria 6d. Stamp

(Des E. Field. Litho Walsall)

1986 (10 Feb). *Europa. Nature and the Environment. T* **150** *and similar horiz design. Multicoloured. W* w **16** (*sideways*). *P* 13 × 13½.

532	22p. Type **150** ..	..	..	1·25	50
533	29p. Herring Gull and Europa Point	..	1·75	4·25

(Des A. Ryman. Litho Walsall)

1986 (26 Mar). *Centenary of First Gibraltar Postage Stamps. T* **151** *and similar vert designs showing stamps. Multicoloured. W* w **16.** *P* 14 × 13½ (44p.) *or* 13½ × 13 (*others*).

534	4p. Type **151** ..	..	..	30	10
535	22p. 1903 Edward VII 2½d.	..	..	1·00	1·00
536	32p. 1912 George V 1d.	..	..	1·50	2·00
537	36p. 1938 George VI £1	..	..	1·60	2·50
538	44p. 1953 Coronation ½d. (29 × 46 *mm*)	..	2·00	3·00
534/8			Set of 5	5·75	7·75
MS539	102×73 mm. 29p. 1886 "GIBRALTAR" overprint on Bermuda 1d.		2·25	2·50
	w. Wmk inverted				

152 Queen Elizabeth II in Robes of Order of the Bath

153 Prince Andrew and Miss Sarah Ferguson

(Des A. Ryman. Litho Walsall)

1986 (22 May). *60th Birthday of Queen Elizabeth II. W* w **16.** *P* 14 × 13½.

540	**152** £1 multicoloured ..	..	..	1·60	3·00

(Des A. Ryman. Litho Questa)

1986 (28 Aug). *Naval Crests (5th series). Vert designs as T* **134.** *Multicoloured. W* w **16.** *P* 14.

541	22p. H.M.S. *Lightning*	..	..	1·75	1·00
542	29p. H.M.S. *Hermione*	..	..	2·00	1·75
543	32p. H.M.S. *Laforey* ..	..	..	2·25	3·25
544	44p. H.M.S. *Nelson* ..	..	..	2·75	4·00
541/4	..		Set of 4	8·00	9·00

(Des A. Ryman. Litho Questa)

1986 (28 Aug). *Royal Wedding. Sheet* 115×85 *mm. W* w **16.** *P* 14½.

MS545	**153** 44p. multicoloured	..	..	1·10	2·00

154 Three Kings and Cathedral of St. Mary the Crowned

155 Neptune House

(Des M. Infante. Litho Walsall)

1986 (14 Oct). *Christmas. International Peace Year. T* **154** *and similar vert design. Multicoloured. W* w **16.** *P* 14.

546	18p. Type **154** ..	..	..	1·00	50
547	32p. St. Andrew's Church	..	..	1·50	2·75

(Litho Questa)

1986 (12 Dec)–**87.** *As Nos. 461 and 464, but W* w **16** (*sideways*). *With* "1986" *imprint date. P* 14.

549	2p. Vickers Viking 1B	..	..	1·50	2·50
552	5p. Boeing 727-100 (2.1.87)	..	..	2·00	2·50

(Des M. Infante. Litho Questa)

1987 (17 Feb). *Europa. Architecture. T* **155** *and similar horiz design. Multicoloured. W* w **16.** *P* 14½.

563	22p. Type **155** ..	..	..	1·50	50
564	29p. Ocean Heights	..	..	2·50	4·00

(Des A. Ryman. Litho Walsall)

1987 (15 Apr). *Naval Crests (6th series). Vert designs as T* **134.** *Multicoloured. W* w **16.** *P* 13½ × 13.

565	18p. H.M.S. *Wishart* (destroyer)	..	1·25	75
566	22p. H.M.S. *Charybdis* (cruiser)	..	1·40	1·10
567	32p. H.M.S. *Antelope* (destroyer)	..	1·90	2·75
568	44p. H.M.S. *Eagle* (aircraft carrier)..	..	2·50	3·75
565/8	..		Set of 4	6·50	7·50

156 13-inch Mortar, 1783   **157** Victoria Stadium

(Des A. Ryman. Litho Format)

1987 (1 June). *Guns. T* **156** *and similar horiz designs. Multi-coloured. W* w **14**. *P* 12½.

569	1p.	Type **156**		20	50
570	2p.	6-inch coastal gun, 1909		30	50
571	3p.	8-inch howitzer, 1783		30	50
572	4p.	Bofors "L40/70" AA gun, 1951		40	10
573	5p.	100 ton rifled muzzle-loader, 1882		40	40
574	10p.	5.25-inch heavy AA gun, 1953		40	55
575	18p.	25-pounder gun-how, 1943		65	80
576	19p.	64-pounder rifled muzzle-loader, 1873		70	90
577	22p.	12-pounder gun, 1758		70	50
578	50p.	10-inch rifled muzzle-loader, 1870		1·40	3·00
579	£1	Russian 24-pounder gun, 1854		2·50	3·50
580	£3	9.2-inch "Mk.10" coastal gun, 1935		6·50	14·00
581	£5	24-pounder gun, 1779		10·00	16·00
569/81			*Set of* 13	22·00	38·00

(Des A. Ryman. Litho Walsall)

1987 (16 Sept). *Bicentenary of Royal Engineers' Royal Warrant. T* **157** *and similar vert designs. Multicoloured. W* w **14**. *P* 14½.

582	18p.	Type **157**		1·25	65
583	32p.	Freedom of Gibraltar scroll and casket	1·75	2·75
584	44p.	Royal Engineers' badge		2·50	3·75
582/4			*Set of* 3	5·00	6·50

158 The Three Kings

(Des Olympia Reyes. Litho Walsall)

1987 (12 Nov). *Christmas. T* **158** *and similar horiz designs. Multicoloured. W* w **16** *(sideways). P* 14½.

585	4p.	Type **158**		15	10
586	22p.	The Holy Family		90	1·00
587	44p.	The Shepherds		1·75	2·75
585/7			*Set of* 3	2·50	3·50

159 *Canberra* (liner) passing   **160** European Bee Eater
Gibraltar

(Des Olympia Reyes. Litho Format)

1988 (16 Feb). *Europa. Transport and Communications. T* **159** *and similar horiz designs. Multicoloured. W* w **14**. *P* 14½ × 14 × *roul between se-tenant pairs.*

588	22p.	Type **159**		1·50	2·25
		a. Horiz pair. Nos. 588/9		3·00	4·50
589	22p.	*Gibline I* (ferry), dish aerial and Boeing 737		1·50	2·25
590	32p.	Horse-drawn carriage and modern coach		2·00	2·75
		a. Horiz pair. Nos. 590/1		4·00	5·50
591	32p.	Car, telephone and Rock of Gibraltar	2·00	2·75
588/91			*Set of* 4	6·25	9·00

The two designs for each value were printed in sheets of ten, each containing five horizontal *se-tenant* pairs in which the stamps were rouletted between vertically.

(Des A. Ryman. Litho Walsall)

1988 (7 Apr). *Naval Crests (7th series). Vert designs as T* **134**. *W* w **16**. *P* 13½ × 13.

592	18p.	multicoloured		1·50	65
593	22p.	black, brownish black and gold	2·00	1·25
594	32p.	multicoloured		2·25	3·00
595	44p.	multicoloured		3·00	4·00
592/5			*Set of* 4	8·00	8·00

Designs:—18p. H.M.S. *Clyde;* 22p. H.M.S. *Foresight;* 32p. H.M.S. *Severn;* 44p. H.M.S. *Rodney.*

(Des Olympia Reyes. Litho B.D.T.)

1988 (15 June). *Birds. T* **160** *and similar horiz designs. Multicoloured. W* w **14** *(sideways). P* 13½.

596	4p.	Type **160**		65	20
597	22p.	Atlantic Puffin		1·50	90
598	32p.	Honey Buzzard		2·00	3·00
599	44p.	Blue Rock Thrush		2·50	4·25
596/9			*Set of* 4	6·00	7·50

161 *Zebu* (brigantine)   **162** "Snowman"
(Rebecca Falero)

(Des A. Ryman. Litho B.D.T.)

1988 (14 Sept). *Operation Raleigh. T* **161** *and similar horiz designs. Multicoloured. W* w **14**. *P* 13.

600	19p.	Type **161**		55	60
601	22p.	Miniature of Sir Walter Raleigh and logo		60	70
602	32p.	Sir Walter Raleigh (expedition ship) and world map		85	1·50
600/2			*Set of* 3	1·75	2·50

MS603 135×86 mm. 22p. As No. 601; 44p. *Sir Walter Raleigh* (expedition ship) passing Gibraltar ... 3·75 4·25

(Des A. Ryman. Litho Questa)

1988 (2 Nov). *Christmas. Children's Paintings. T* **162** *and similar multicoloured designs. W* w **16** *(sideways). P* 14½ (44p.) *or* 14 *(others).*

604	4p.	Type **162**		15	10
605	22p.	"The Nativity" (Dennis Penalver)		55	60
606	44p.	"Father Christmas" (Gavin Key) (23×31 mm)		1·00	1·50
604/6			*Set of* 3	1·50	2·00

163 Soft Toys and Toy Train   **164** Port Sergeant
with Keys

(Des Olympia Reyes. Litho Walsall)

1989 (15 Feb). *Europa. Children's Toys. T* **163** *and similar horiz design. Multicoloured. W* w **16** *(sideways). P* 13 × 13½.

607	25p.	Type **163**		1·25	75
608	32p.	Soft toys, toy boat and doll's house	1·75	2·75

(Des A. Ryman. Litho Walsall)

1989 (28 Apr). *50th Anniv of Gibraltar Regiment. T* **164** *and similar vert designs. Multicoloured. W* w **14**. *P* 13½×13.

609	4p.	Type **164**		30	10
610	22p.	Regimental badge and colours		90	95
611	32p.	Drum major		1·40	2·25
609/11			*Set of* 3	2·40	3·00

MS612 124×83 mm. 22p. As No. 610; 44p. Former Gibraltar Defence Force badge ... 3·00 3·50

165 Nurse and Baby   **166** One Penny
Coin

(Des E. Field. Litho Questa)

1989 (7 July). *125th Anniv of International Red Cross. T* **165** *and similar vert designs. Multicoloured. W* w **16**. *P* 15 × 14½.

613	25p.	black, bright scarlet and grey-brown	60	60
614	32p.	black, bright scarlet and grey-brown	75	1·40
615	44p.	black, bright scarlet and grey-brown	1·00	2·50
613/15			*Set of* 3	2·10	4·00

Designs:—32p. Famine victims; 44p. Accident victims.

(Des A. Ryman. Litho B.D.T.)

1989 (7 Sept). *Naval Crests (8th series). Vert designs as T* **134**. *W* w **16**. *P* 14×13½.

616	22p.	multicoloured		1·25	75
617	25p.	black and gold		1·25	1·50
618	32p.	gold, black and bright scarlet	1·75	2·00
619	44p.	multicoloured		2·75	3·25
616/19			*Set of* 4	6·25	6·75

Designs:—22p. H.M.S. *Blankney;* 25p. H.M.S. *Deptford;* 32p. H.M.S. *Exmoor;* 44p. H.M.S. *Stork.*

(Des A. Ryman. Litho Questa)

1989 (11 Oct). *New Coinage. T* **166** *and similar vert designs in two miniature sheets. W* w **16** *(sideways). P* 14½.
MS620 72×94 mm. 4p. bronze, black & dull verm (Type 166); 4p. bronze, blk & dp brn (two pence); 4p. silver, blk & greenish yellow (ten pence); 4p. silver, black and emerald (five pence) ... 1·00 1·50
MS621 100×95 mm. 22p. silver, black & reddish orge (fifty pence); 22p. gold, black & ultram (five pounds); 22p. gold, blk & orge-brn (two pounds); 22p. gold, blk & brt emer (one pound); 22p. gold, blk & brt reddish vio (obverse of coin series); 22p. silver, black and pale violet-blue (twenty pence) 4·00 5·00

167 Father Christmas in   **168** General Post
Sleigh   Office Entrance

(Des M. Infante. Litho Questa)

1989 (11 Oct). *Christmas. T* **167** *and similar horiz designs. Multicoloured. W* w **16** *(sideways). P* 14½.

622	4p.	Type **167**		15	10
623	22p.	Shepherds and sheep		70	70
624	32p.	The Nativity		1·10	1·75
625	44p.	The Three Wise Men		1·75	3·00
622/5			*Set of* 4	3·25	5·00

(Des Olympia Reyes. Litho Questa)

1990 (6 Mar). *Europa. Post Office Buildings. T* **168** *and similar vert designs. Multicoloured. P* 14½×*roul between se-tenant pairs.*

626	22p.	Type **168**		1·00	1·50
		a. Horiz pair. Nos. 626/7		2·00	3·00
627	22p.	Interior of General Post Office	1·00	1·50
628	32p.	Interior of South District Post Office	1·50	2·25
		a. Horiz pair. Nos. 628/9		3·00	4·50
629	32p.	South District Post Office		1·50	2·25
626/9			*Set of* 4	4·50	6·50

Nos. 626/7 and 628/9 were printed in *se-tenant* horizontal pairs within separate sheets of eight, the stamps in each pair being divided by a line of roulettes.

169 19th-century   **170** Henry Corbould
Firemen   (artist) and Penny
Black

(Des D. Gonzalez. Litho Questa)

1990 (2 Apr). *125th Anniv of Gibraltar Fire Service. T* **169** *and similar multicoloured designs. P* 14½×14 *(vert) or* 14×14½ *(horiz).*

630	4p.	Type **169**		50	15
631	20p.	Early fire engine (*horiz*)		1·25	1·50
632	42p.	Modern fire engine (*horiz*)		1·60	2·50
633	44p.	Fireman in breathing apparatus	1·90	2·50
630/3			*Set of* 4	4·75	5·50

(Des A. Ryman. Litho Questa)

1990 (3 May). *150th Anniv of the Penny Black. T* **170** *and similar vert designs. Multicoloured. P* 13½×14.

634	19p.	Type **170**		70	70
635	22p.	Bath Royal Mail coach		80	80
636	32p.	Sir Rowland Hill and Penny Black	1·50	2·75
634/6			*Set of* 3	2·75	3·75

MS637 145×95 mm. 44p. Penny Black with Maltese Cross cancellation. P 14½×14 ... 2·75 3·00

(Des A. Ryman. Litho Questa)

1990 (10 July). *Naval Crests (9th series). Vert designs as T* **134**. *Multicoloured. P* 14.

638	22p.	H.M.S. *Calpe*		1·40	70
639	25p.	H.M.S. *Gallant*		1·50	1·60
640	32p.	H.M.S. *Wrestler*		1·75	2·50
641	44p.	H.M.S. *Greyhound*		2·25	3·50
638/41			*Set of* 4	6·25	7·50

ALTERED CATALOGUE NUMBERS

Any Catalogue numbers altered from the last edition are shown as a list in the introductory pages.

171 Model of Europort Development

172 Candle and Holly

(Des A. Ryman. Litho Questa)

1990 (10 Oct). *Development Projects. T* **171** *and similar horiz designs. Multicoloured. P* 14½.

642	22p. Type **171**		75	80
643	23p. Construction of building material factory		75	1·40
644	25p. Land reclamation		95	1·40
642/4		Set of 3	2·25	3·25

(Des D. Gonzalez. Litho B.D.T.)

1990 (10 Oct). *Christmas. T* **172** *and similar vert designs. Multicoloured. P* 13½.

645	4p. Type **172**		15	10
646	22p. Father Christmas		75	65
647	42p. Christmas Tree		1·50	2·25
648	44p. Nativity crib		1·50	2·25
645/8		Set of 4	3·50	4·75

173 Space Laboratory and Spaceplane (Colombus Development Programme)

174 Shag

(Des D. Gonzalez. Litho B.D.T.)

1991 (26 Feb). *Europa. Europe in Space. T* **173** *and similar horiz design. Multicoloured. P* 13½×13.

649	25p. Type **173**		75	75
650	32p. "ERS-1" earth resources remote sensing satellite		1·00	2·00

(Des A. Ryman. Litho Walsall)

1991 (9 Apr). *Naval Crests (10th series). Vert designs as T* **134**. *P* 13½×13.

651	4p. black, new blue and gold		35	10
652	21p. multicoloured		1·25	1·25
653	22p. multicoloured		1·25	1·25
654	62p. multicoloured		3·25	4·75
651/4		Set of 4	5·50	6·50

Designs:—4p. H.M.S. *Hesperus*; 21p. H.M.S. *Forester*; 22p. H.M.S. *Furious*; 62p. H.M.S. *Scylla*.

(Des Olympia Reyes. Litho B.D.T.)

1991 (30 May). *Endangered Species. Birds. T* **174** *and similar horiz designs. Multicoloured. P* 13½.

655	13p. Type **174**		75	1·00
	a. Block of 4. Nos. 655/8		2·75	
656	13p. Barbary Partridge		75	1·00
657	13p. Egyptian Vulture		75	1·00
658	13p. Black Stork		75	1·00
655/8		Set of 4	2·75	3·50

Nos. 655/8 were printed together, *se-tenant*, in differently arranged blocks of 4 throughout the sheet of 16.

(175)   £1·05

176 "North View of Gibraltar" (Gustavo Bacarisas)

1991 (30 May). *No. 580 surch with T* **175**.

659	£1·05 on £3 9.2-inch "Mk.10" coastal gun, 1935		3·50	2·00

(Des A. Ryman. Litho B.D.T.)

1991 (10 Sept). *Local Paintings. T* **176** *and similar multicoloured designs. P* 14×15 (42p.) *or* 15×14 (*others*).

660	22p. Type **176**		85	50
661	26p. "Parson's Lodge" (Elena Mifsud)		1·00	1·00
662	32p. "Governor's Parade" (Jacobo Azagury)		1·50	2·00
663	42p. "Waterport Wharf" (Rudesindo Mannia) (*vert*)		2·25	3·00
660/3		Set of 4	5·00	6·00

NEW INFORMATION

The editor is always interested to correspond with people who have new information that will improve or correct the Catalogue.

177 "Once in Royal David's City"

178 *Danaus chrysippus*

(Des D. Gonzalez. Litho Questa)

1991 (15 Oct). *Christmas. Carols. T* **177** *and similar horiz designs. Multicoloured. P* 14×14½.

664	4p. Type **177**		20	10
665	24p. "Silent Night"		1·00	70
666	25p. "Angels We have Heard on High"		1·00	1·25
667	49p. "O Come All Ye Faithful"		1·75	3·00
664/7		Set of 4	3·50	4·50

(Des A. Ryman. Litho Questa)

1991 (15 Nov). *"Phila Nippon '91" International Stamp Exhibition, Tokyo. Sheet* 116×91 *mm. P* 14½.

MS668	**178** £1·05, multicoloured		3·50	4·25

179 Columbus and *Santa Maria*

180 Compass Rose, Sail and Atlantic Map

(Des Olympia Reyes. Litho Walsall)

1992 (6 Feb). *Europa. 500th Anniv of Discovery of America by Columbus. T* **179** *and similar horiz designs. Multicoloured. P* 14½.

669	24p. Type **179**		1·00	1·50
	a. Horiz pair. Nos. 669/70		2·00	3·00
670	24p. Map of Old World and *Nina*		1·00	1·50
671	34p. Map of New World and *Pinta*		1·25	1·75
	a. Horiz pair. Nos. 671/2		2·50	3·50
672	34p. Map of Old World and look-out		1·25	1·75
669/72		Set of 4	4·00	6·00

The two designs of each value were printed together, *se-tenant*, in sheets of eight, the background to each horizontal pair forming a composite design.

(Des D. Miller. Litho Questa (54p.), B.D.T. (others))

1992 (6 Feb). *40th Anniv of Queen Elizabeth II's Accession. Horiz designs as T* **143** *of Ascension. Multicoloured. W w* **14** (*sideways*). *P* 14.

673	4p. Gibraltar from North		15	10
674	20p. H.M.S. *Arrow* (frigate) and Gibraltar from South		60	60
675	24p. Southport Gates		75	80
676	44p. Three portraits of Queen Elizabeth		1·25	1·60
677	54p. Queen Elizabeth II		1·60	1·90
673/7		Set of 5	4·00	4·50

(Des E. Field. Litho B.D.T.)

1992 (15 Apr). *Round the World Yacht Rally. T* **180** *and similar multicoloured designs, each incorporating compass rose and sail. P* 13½.

678	21p. Type **180**		75	80
679	24p. Map of Indonesian Archipelago (*horiz*)		95	1·40
680	25p. Map of Indian Ocean (*horiz*)		95	1·75
678/80		Set of 3	2·40	3·50
MS681	108×72 mm. 21p. Type **180**; 49p. Map of Mediterranean and Red Sea		2·25	3·25

181 Holy Trinity Cathedral

182 Sacred Heart of Jesus Church

(Des M. Infante. Litho Questa)

1992 (21 Aug). *150th Anniv of Anglican Diocese of Gibraltar-in-Europe. T* **181** *and similar multicoloured designs. P* 14.

682	4p. Type **181**		20	10
683	24p. Diocesan crest and map (*horiz*)		1·00	65
684	44p. Construction of Cathedral and Sir George Don (*horiz*)		1·75	2·50
685	54p. Bishop Tomlinson		2·00	2·75
682/5		Set of 4	4·50	5·50

(Des W. Stagnetto. Litho B.D.T.)

1992 (10 Nov). *Christmas. Churches. T* **182** *and similar vert designs. Multicoloured. P* 14×13½.

686	4p. Type **182**		20	10
687	24p. Cathedral of St. Mary the Crowned		1·00	55
688	34p. St. Andrew's Church of Scotland		1·60	2·00
689	49p. St. Joseph's Church		2·25	3·50
686/9		Set of 4	4·50	5·50

183 "Drama and Music"

184 H.M.S. *Hood* (battle cruiser)

(Des E. Field. Litho Questa)

1993 (2 Mar). *Europa. Contemporary Art. T* **183** *and similar vert designs. Multicoloured. P* 14½×14.

690	24p. Type **183**		1·25	1·50
	a. Horiz pair. Nos. 690/1		2·50	3·00
691	24p. "Sculpture, Art and Pottery"		1·25	1·50
692	34p. "Architecture"		1·75	2·25
	a. Horiz pair. Nos. 692/3		3·50	4·50
693	34p. "Printing and Photography"		1·75	2·25
690/3		Set of 4	5·50	6·50

Nos. 690/1 and 692/3 were printed together, *se-tenant*, in horizontal pairs in sheetlets of 8 with decorative margins.

(Des D. Miller. Litho B.D.T.)

1993 (27 Apr). *Second World War Warships (1st series). Sheet* 120×79 *mm containing T* **184** *and similar horiz designs. Multicoloured. P* 14.

MS694	24p. Type **184**; 24p. H.M.S. *Ark Royal* (aircraft carrier, 1937); 24p. H.M.A.S. *Waterhen* (destroyer); 24p. U.S.S. *Gleaves* (destroyer)		4·50	5·50

See also Nos. **MS724**, **MS748**, **MS779** and **MS809**.

185 Landport Gate

186 £sd and Decimal British Coins (25th anniv of Decimal Currency)

(Des Olympia Reyes. Litho and thermography Cartor (£5), litho Cartor (6, 7, 8, 9, 20, 30, 40p. and £2) or B.D.T. (others))

1993 (28 June)–95. *Architectural Heritage. T* **185** *and similar multicoloured designs. P* 13.

695	1p. Type **185**		10	10
696	2p. St. Mary the Crowned Church (*horiz*)		10	10
697	3p. Parsons Lodge Battery (*horiz*)		10	10
698	4p. Moorish Castle (*horiz*)		10	10
699	5p. General Post Office		10	10
699a	6p. House of Assembly (1.9.95)		10	10
699b	7p. Bleak House (*horiz*) (1.9.95)		15	20
699c	8p. General Eliott Memorial (1.9.95)		15	20
699d	9p. Supreme Court Building (*horiz*) (1.9.95)		20	25
700	10p. South Barracks (*horiz*)		20	25
700a	20p. The Convent (*horiz*) (1.9.95)		40	45
701	21p. American War Memorial		40	45
702	24p. Garrison Library (*horiz*)		50	55
703	25p. Southport Gates		50	55
704	26p. Casemates Gate (*horiz*)		50	55
704a	30p. St. Bernard's Hospital (1.9.95)		60	65
704b	40p. City Hall (*horiz*) (1.9.95)		80	85
705	50p. Central Police Station (*horiz*)		1·00	1·10
706	£1 Prince Edward's Gate		2·00	2·25
706a	£2 Church of the Sacred Heart of Jesus (1.9.95)		4·00	4·25
707	£3 Lighthouse, Europa Point		6·00	6·25
708	£5 Coat of arms and Fortress keys (6.6.94)		10·00	10·50
695/708		Set of 22	27·00	29·00

(Des W. Stagnetto. Litho Cartor)

1993 (21 Sept). *Anniversaries. T* **186** *and similar horiz designs. Multicoloured. P* 13.

709	21p. Type **186**		75	65
710	24p. R.A.F. crest with Handley Page 0/400 biplane and Panavia Tornado F Mk 3 fighter (75th anniv)		1·00	75
711	34p. Garrison Library badge and building (Bicent)		1·40	2·00
712	49p. Sir Winston Churchill and air raid (50th anniv of visit)		2·00	3·00
709/12		Set of 4	4·75	5·75

187 Mice decorating Christmas Tree

(Des Josie Evans. Litho Cartor)

1993 (16 Nov). *Christmas. T* **187** *and similar horiz designs. Multicoloured. P* 13½.
713 5p. Type **187** 20 10
714 24p. Mice pulling cracker 90 70
715 44p. Mice singing carols .. .. 1·75 2·25
716 49p. Mice building snowman .. 1·90 2·50
713/16 .. .. *Set of 4* 4·25 5·00

188 Exploding Atom (Lord Penney)

(Des M. Braunewell. Litho Cartor)

1994 (1 Mar). *Europa. Scientific Discoveries. T* **188** *and similar horiz designs. Multicoloured. P* 13½.
717 24p. Type **188** .. .. .. 80 1·00
　a. Horiz pair. Nos. 717/18 .. 1·60 2·00
718 24p. Polonium and radium experiment
　(Marie Curie) .. .. 80 1·00
719 34p. First diesel engine (Rudolph Diesel) .. 1·00 1·50
　a. Horiz pair. Nos. 719/20 .. 2·00 3·00
720 34p. Early telescope (Galileo) .. 1·00 1·50
717/20 .. .. *Set of 4* 3·25 4·50
　Nos. 717/18 and 719/20 were printed together, *se-tenant*, in horizontal pairs in sheetlets of 8 with decorative margins.

189 World Cup and Map of U.S.A

(Des M. Braunewell. Litho Cartor)

1994 (19 Apr). *World Cup Football Championship, U.S.A. T* **189** *and similar multicoloured designs. P* 13½.
721 26p. Type **189** 80 55
722 39p. Players and pitch in shape of U.S.A. 1·25 1·75
723 49p. Player's legs (*vert*) .. .. 1·60 2·50
721/3 .. .. *Set of 3* 3·25 4·25

(Des D. Miller. Litho Cartor)

1994 (6 June). *Second World War Warships (2nd series). Sheet* 112×72 *mm containing horiz designs as T* **184**. *Multicoloured. P* 13.
MS724 5p. H.M.S. *Penelope* (cruiser); 25p. H.M.S. *Warspite* (battleship); 44p. U.S.S. *McLanahan* (destroyer); 49p. *Isaac Sweers* (Dutch destroyer) .. .. .. 4·25 5·50

190 Pekingese　**191** Golden Star Coral

(Des M. Braunewell. Litho B.D.T.)

1994 (16 Aug). *"Philakorea '94" International Stamp Exhibiton, Seoul. Sheet* 102×76 *mm. P* 13.
MS725 **190** £1.05, multicoloured .. .. 3·00 4·00

(Des M. Whyte. Litho Walsall)

1994 (27 Sept). *Marine Life. T* **191** *and similar square designs. Multicoloured. P* 14½×14.
726 21p. Type **191** 75 45
727 24p. Star Fish 90 55
728 34p. Gorgonian Sea-fan .. .. 1·50 2·00
729 49p. Peacock Wrasse ("Turkish Wrasse") 2·00 3·00
726/9 .. .. *Set of 4* 4·75 5·50

192 Throwing the Discus and　**193** Great Tit
Centenary Emblem

(Des S. Perera. Litho Walsall)

1994 (22 Nov). *Centenary of International Olympic Committee. T* **192** *and similar horiz design. Multicoloured.* P 14.
730 49p. Type **192** .. .. 1·50 2·00
731 54p. Javelin throwing and emblem .. 1·75 2·50

(Des W. Stagnetto. Litho B.D.T.)

1994 (22 Nov). *Christmas. Songbirds. T* **193** *and similar multicoloured designs. P* 14×13½ (*vert*) or 13½×14 (*horiz*).
732 5p. Type **193** 25 10
733 24p. European Robin (*horiz*) .. 90 70
734 34p. Blue Tit (*horiz*) .. .. 1·25 1·50
735 54p. Goldfinch .. .. .. 1·75 2·75
732/5 .. .. *Set of 4* 3·75 4·50

194 Austrian Flag, Hand and Star

(Des R. Ollington. Litho Questa)

1995 (3 Jan). *Expansion of European Union. T* **194** *and similar horiz designs. Multicoloured. P* 14.
736 24p. Type **194** 60 55
737 26p. Finnish flag, hand and star .. 60 60
738 34p. Swedish flag, hand and star .. 90 1·50
739 49p. Flags of new members and European
　Union emblem .. .. 1·60 2·50
736/9 .. .. *Set of 4* 3·25 4·50

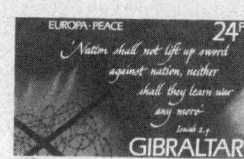

195 Barbed Wire and Quote from Isaiah Ch 2.4

(Des Jennifer Toombs. Litho B.D.T.)

1995 (28 Feb). *Europa. Peace and Freedom. T* **195** *and similar horiz designs. Multicoloured. P* 13½.
740 24p. Type **195** .. .. 70 1·00
　a. Horiz pair. Nos. 740/1 .. 1·40 2·00
741 24p. Rainbow and hands releasing peace
　dove .. .. .. 70 1·00
742 34p. Shackles on wall and quote from Isaiah
　ch 61.1 .. .. 1·00 1·40
　a. Horiz pair. Nos. 742/3 .. 2·00 2·75
743 34p. Hands and sea-birds .. .. 1·00 1·40
740/3 .. .. *Set of 4* 3·00 4·25
　Nos. 740/1 and 742/3 were each printed together, *se-tenant*, as horizontal pairs in sheetlets of 8 with decorative margins.

196 Fairey Swordfish, I Class Destroyer and Rock of Gibraltar

(Des A. Theobald. Litho B.D.T.)

1995 (8 May). *50th Anniv of End of Second World War. Sheet* 101×66 *mm. P* 13½.
MS744 **196** £1.05, multicoloured .. .. 2·75 3·50

197 Yachting　**198** Bee Orchid

(Des S. Perera. Litho B.D.T.)

1995 (8 May). *Island Games '95. T* **197** *and similar vert designs. Multicoloured. P* 14×13½.
745 24p. Type **197** 50 60
　a. Booklet pane. No. 745×3, with margins
　all round .. .. 1·40
　b. Booklet pane. Nos. 745/7, with margins
　all round .. .. 3·25

746 44p. Athlete on starting blocks .. 1·50 2·25
　a. Booklet pane. No. 746×3, with margins
　all round .. .. 4·25
747 49p. Swimmer at start of race .. 1·50 2·25
　a. Booklet pane. No. 747×3, with margins
　all round .. .. 4·25
745/7 .. .. *Set of 3* 3·25 4·50

(Des D. Miller. Litho Questa)

1995 (6 June). *Second World War Warships (3rd series). Sheet* 133×85 *mm containing horiz designs as T* **184**. *Multicoloured. P* 13½×14.
MS748 5p. H.M.S. *Calpe* (destroyer); 24p. H.M.S. *Victorious* (aircraft carrier); 44p. U.S.S. *Weehawken* (attack transport); 49p. *Savorgan de Brazza* (French sloop) .. .. 4·25 5·00

(Des R. Gorringe. Litho B.D.T.)

1995 (1 Sept). *"Singapore '95" International Stamp Exhibition. Orchids. T* **198** *and similar vert designs. Multicoloured. P* 14×14½.
749 22p. Type **198** 65 85
　a. Horiz strip of 5. Nos. 749/53 .. 3·00
750 23p. Brown Bee Orchid 65 85
751 24p. Pyramidal Orchid 65 85
752 25p. Mirror Orchid 65 85
753 26p. Sawfly Orchid 65 85
749/53 .. .. *Set of 5* 3·00 3·75
　Nos. 749/53 were printed together, *se-tenant*, in horizontal strips of 5.

199 Handshake and United Nations Emblem

(Des S. Perera. Litho B.D.T.)

1995 (24 Oct). *50th Anniv of United Nations. T* **199** *and similar horiz design. Multicoloured. P* 13½.
754 34p. Type **199** .. .. 1·10 1·10
755 49p. Peace dove and U.N. emblem .. 1·40 2·00

200 Marilyn Monroe　**201** Father Christmas

(Des M. Whyte. Litho Questa)

1995 (13 Nov). *Centenary of Cinema. T* **200** *and similar horiz designs showing film stars. Multicoloured. P* 14½×14.
MS756 Two sheets, each 116×80 mm. (a) 5p. Type **200**; 25p. Romy Schneider; 28p. Yves Montand; 38p. Audrey Hepburn. (b) 24p. Ingrid Bergman; 24p. Vittorio de Sica; 24p. Marlene Dietrich; 24p. Laurence Olivier *Set of 2 sheets* 4·50 5·50

(Des M. Whyte. Litho B.D.T.)

1995 (27 Nov). *Christmas. T* **201** *and similar square designs. Multicoloured. P* 14.
757 5p. Type **201** 15 10
758 24p. Toys in sack 65 55
759 34p. Reindeer .. .. .. 90 1·25
760 54p. Sleigh over houses .. .. 1·25 1·75
757/60 .. .. *Set of 4* 2·75 3·25

202 Shih Tzu

(Des Doreen McGuinness. Litho B.D.T.)

1996 (24 Jan). *Puppies. T* **202** *and similar horiz designs. Multicoloured. P* 14.
761 5p. Type **202** 30 40
　a. Sheetlet. Nos. 761/6 .. 3·50
762 21p. Dalmatians 60 70
763 24p. Cocker Spaniels 70 80
764 24p. West Highland White Terriers .. 70 80
765 34p. Labrador 80 85
766 35p. Boxer 80 85
761/6 .. .. *Set of 6* 3·50 4·00
　Nos. 761/6 were printed together, *se-tenant*, in sheetlets of 6. No. 762 is inscr "Dalmation" in error.

203 Princess Anne **204** West German Player, 1980

(Des R. Ollington. Litho B.D.T.)

1996 (9 Feb). *Europa. Famous Women. T* **203** *and similar horiz designs.* P 13½.

767	**203**	24p. black and yellow	75	75
768	–	24p. black and deep turquoise-green	75	75
769	–	34p. black and vermilion	1·00	1·50
770	–	34p. black and purple	1·00	1·50
767/70		*Set of* 4	3·25	4·00

Details:—No. 768, Princess Diana; No. 769, Queen Elizabeth II; No. 770, Queen Elizabeth the Queen Mother.

Nos. 767/70 were each printed in sheets of 10 with inscribed margins all round.

(Des S. Noon. Litho Walsall)

1996 (2 Apr). *European Football Championship, England. T* **204** *and similar vert designs showing players from previous winning teams. Multicoloured.* P 13.

771	21p. Type **204**	55	45
772	24p. French player, 1984	65	55
773	34p. Dutch player, 1988	95	1·10
774	£1.20, Danish player, 1992	3·00	3·75
771/4	*Set of* 4	4·75	5·25
MS775	135×91 mm. As Nos. 771/4. P 13×13½	5·50	6·00

205 Ancient Greek Athletes **206** Asian Children

(Des K. Bassford. Litho Walsall)

1996 (2 May). *Centenary of Modern Olympic Games. T* **205** *and similar horiz designs.* P 13½.

776	34p. black, deep reddish purple & brt orange	95	90
777	49p. black and grey-brown	1·40	1·75
778	£1.05, multicoloured	2·75	3·50
776/8	*Set of* 3	4·50	5·50

Designs:—49p. Start of early race; £1.05, Start of modern race.

(Des D. Miller. Litho Walsall)

1996 (8 June). *Second World War Warships* (4th series). *Sheet, 118×84 mm, containing horiz designs as T* **184**. *Multicoloured.* P 14.

MS779	5p. H.M.S. *Starling* (sloop); 25p. H.M.S. *Royalist* (cruiser); 49p. U.S.S. *Philadelphia* (cruiser); 54p. H.M.C.S. *Prescott* (corvette)	3·00	3·75

(Des S. Noon. Litho Walsall)

1996 (8 June). *50th Anniv of U.N.I.C.E.F. T* **206** *and similar horiz designs showing children from different continents.* P 13½×13.

780	21p. multicoloured	60	80
	a. Horiz strip of 4. Nos. 780/3	3·50	
781	24p. multicoloured	70	90
782	49p. multicoloured	1·25	1·40
783	54p. multicoloured	1·40	1·60
780/3	*Set of* 4	3·50	4·25

Nos. 780/3 were printed together, *se-tenant*, in horizontal strips of 4 throughout the sheet.

207 Red Kites in Flight

(Des R. Gorringe. Litho Walsall)

1996 (30 Sept). *Endangered Species. Red Kite. T* **207** *and similar horiz designs. Multicoloured.* P 14½.

784	34p. Type **207**	90	1·10
	a. Block of 4. Nos. 784/7	3·25	
785	34p. Red Kite on ground	90	1·10
786	34p. On rock	90	1·10
787	34p. Pair at nest	90	1·10
784/7	*Set of* 4	3·25	4·00

Nos. 784/7 were printed together, *se-tenant*, in blocks of four throughout the sheet.

208 Christmas Pudding **209** *Mary Celeste* passing Gibraltar

(Des K. Bassford. Litho Questa)

1996 (27 Nov). *Christmas. T* **208** *and similar horiz designs created from "Lego" blocks. Multicoloured.* P 14×14½.

788	5p. Type **208**	15	15
789	21p. Snowman face	60	45
790	24p. Present	70	55
791	34p. Father Christmas face	90	1·10
792	54p. Candle	1·25	1·60
788/92	*Set of* 5	3·25	3·50

(Des S. Tarabay. Litho Questa)

1997 (12 Feb). *Europa '97. Tales and Legends. The* Mary Celeste. *T* **209** *and similar square designs. Multicoloured.* P 14.

793	28p. Type **209**	70	75
794	28p. Boarding the *Mary Celeste*	70	75
795	30p. Crew leaving *Mary Celeste*	80	85
796	30p. *Mary Celeste* found by *Dei Gratia*	80	85
793/6	*Set of* 4	2·75	3·00

210 American Shorthair Silver Tabby **211** *Anthocharis belia euphenoides*

(Des Colleen Corlett. Litho B.D.T.)

1997 (12 Feb). *Kittens. T* **210** *and similar horiz designs. Multicoloured.* P 13½×14.

797	5p. Type **210**	30	40
	a. Booklet pane. Nos. 797, 799 and 801 with margins all round	1·50	
	b. Booklet pane. Nos. 797/8 and 801/2 with margins all round	2·25	
798	24p. Rumpy Manx Red Tabby	65	75
	a. Booklet pane. Nos. 798/800 with margins all round	1·75	
799	26p. Blue Point Birmans	65	75
	a. Booklet pane. Nos. 799/802 with margins all round	2·50	
800	28p. Red Self Longhair	70	85
801	30p. British Shorthair Tortoiseshell and White	70	85
802	35p. British Bicolour Shorthairs	80	90
797/802	*Set of* 6	3·50	4·00
MS803	132×80 mm. Nos. 797/802 with "HONG KONG '97" International Stamp Exhibition logo at bottom left	3·50	4·00
	a. Booklet pane. As No. **MS**803, but without "HONG KONG '97" logo and with additional line of roulettes at left	3·50	

Nos. 797/802 were only issued in £5 stamp booklets or miniature sheet No. **MS**803.

(Des R. Gorringe. Litho Enschedé)

1997 (7 Apr). *Butterflies. T* **211** *and similar vert designs. Multicoloured.* P 14×13½.

804	23p. Type **211**	60	50
805	26p. *Charaxes jasius*	75	60
806	30p. *Vanessa cardui*	80	80
807	£1.20, *Iphiclides podalirius*	3·00	3·25
804/7	*Set of* 4	4·75	4·75
MS808	135×90 mm. Nos. 804/7	4·75	5·00

(Des D. Miller. Litho Cartor)

1997 (9 June). *Second World War Warships* (5th series). *Sheet, 117×82 mm, containing horiz designs as T* **184**. *Multicoloured.* P 13½.

MS809	24p. H.M.S. *Enterprise* (cruiser); 26p. H.M.S. *Cleopatra* (cruiser); 38p. U.S.S. *Iowa* (battleship); 50p. *Orkan* (Polish destroyer)	3·25	3·50

212 Queen Elizabeth and Prince Philip at Carriage-driving Trials

(Des C. Abbott. Litho Questa)

1997 (10 July). *Golden Wedding Of Queen Elizabeth and Prince Philip. T* **212** *and similar horiz design. Multicoloured.* P 13½.

810		£1.20, Type **212**	3·00	3·25
		a. Horiz pair. Nos. 810/11	6·00	6·50
811		£1.40 Queen Elizabeth in Trooping the Colour uniform	3·00	3·25

Nos. 810/11 were printed together, *se-tenant*, in horizontal pairs throughout the sheet.

213 Christian Dior Evening Dress **214** "Our Lady and St. Bernard" (St. Joseph's Parish Church)

(Des M. Whyte. Litho B.D.T.)

1997 (24 Oct). *Christian Dior Spring/Summer '97 Collection designed by John Galliano. T* **213** *and similar vert designs. Multicoloured.* P 13½.

812	30p. Type **213**	80	90
	a. Horiz pair. Nos. 812 and 814	2·00	2·25
813	35p. Tunic top and skirt	1·10	1·25
	a. Horiz pair. Nos. 813 and 815	2·50	3·00
814	50p. Ballgown	1·25	1·40
815	62p. Two-piece suit	1·60	1·90
812/15	*Set of* 4	4·25	5·00
MS816	110×90 mm. £1.20, Ballgown (*different*)	2·75	3·25

Nos. 812 with 814 and 813 with 815 were each printed together, *se-tenant*, in sheets of 8 with enlarged illustrated right-hand margin.

(Des S. Perera. Litho Cartor)

1997 (18 Nov). *Christmas. Stained Glass Windows. T* **214** *and similar vert designs. Multicoloured.* P 13½.

817	5p. Type **214**	10	10
818	26p. "The Epiphany" (Our Lady of Sorrows Church)	55	60
819	38p. "St. Joseph" (Our Lady of Sorrows Church)	75	80
820	50p. "The Holy Family" (St. Joseph's Parish Church)	1·00	1·10
821	62p. "The Miraculous Medal" (St. Joseph's Parish Church)	1·25	1·40
817/21	*Set of* 5	3·75	4·00

215 Sir Joshua Hassan **216** Wales v Brazil (1958)

(Des S. Perera. Litho Cartor)

1997 (15 Dec). *Sir Joshua Hassan (former Chief Minister) Commemoration.* P 13.

822	**215**	26p. black	55	60

(Des L. Montgomery. Litho Cartor)

1998 (23 Jan). *World Football Championship, France* (1998). *T* **216** *and similar vert designs. Multicoloured.* P 13.

823	5p. Type **216**	10	10
824	26p. Northern Ireland v France (1958)	55	60
825	38p. Scotland v Holland (1958)	75	80
826	$1.20, England v West Germany (1966)	2·40	2·50
823/6	*Set of* 4	3·75	4·00
MS827	153×96 mm. Nos. 823/6	3·75	4·00

STAMP BOOKLETS

909. *Black on red cover. Stapled.*
B1 2s. ½d. booklet containing twenty-four ½d. and
    twelve 1d. (Nos. 66/7) in blocks of 6 .. ..

912 (15 May). *Black on red cover with Edwardian cypher.
Stapled.*
B2 2s. ½d. booklet containing twenty-four ½d. and
    twelve 1d. (Nos. 76/7) in blocks of 6 .. ..

921. *Black on red cover. Stapled.*
B2a 2s. booklet containing twenty-four ½d. and
    twelve 1d. (Nos. 89/90) in blocks of 6 ..

B 1
(Illustration reduced. Actual size 152×79 mm)

974 (2 May). *Centenary of Universal Postal Union.
Multicoloured cover as Type B 1. Stitched.*
B3 46p. booklet containing *se-tenant* panes of 3 (No.
    328a) and 6 (No. 328b) .. .. 7·50

975 (17 Dec). *500th Birth Anniv of Michelangelo.
Multicoloured cover as Type B 1, but 165×91 mm showing
Michelangelo. Stitched.*
B4 90p. booklet containing *se-tenant* panes of 3 (No.
    358a) and 6 (No. 358b) .. .. 4·50

978 (12 June). *25th Anniv of Coronation. Multicoloured cover
as Type B 1, but 165×92 mm showing Buckingham Palace.
Stitched.*
B5 £1.15, booklet containing *se-tenant* pane of 6 (No.
    404a) and pane of 1 (No. 406a) .. .. 2·50

GIBRALTAR POST OFFICE

B 2

1981 (2 Sept). *Black and vermilion (No. SB6) and black and
ultramarine (No. SB7) covers as Type B 2. Stamps attached by
selvedge.*
SB6 50p. booklet containing *se-tenant* pane of 5 and 1
    label (No. 451a) 90
SB7 £1 booklet containing *se-tenant* pane of 10 and 2
    labels (No. 451b) .. .. 1·75

B 3 Moorish Castle

1993 (21 Sept). *Multicoloured covers as Type B 3. Stamps
affixed by selvedge.*
SB8 20p. booklet containing 5p. (No. 699) in strip of 4 40
SB9 £1.20 booklet containing 24p. (No. 702) in strip
    of 5 .. .. 2·40

B 4 Rock of Gibraltar and Games Events
(Illustration reduced. Actual size 175×97 mm)

1995 (8 May). *Island Games '95. Multicoloured cover as Type
B 4. Stitched.*
SB10 £4.68, booklet containing four panes of 3 (Nos.
    745a/b, 746a and 747a) .. .. 12·00

B 5
(Illustration reduced. Actual size 150×80 mm)

1997 (12 Feb). *Kittens. Multicoloured cover as Type B 5.
Stitched.*
SB11 £5 booklet containing five *se-tenant* panes (Nos.
    797a/b, 798a, 799a and MS803a) .. .. 12·00

POSTAGE DUE STAMPS

   D 1   **D 2**   **D 3** Gibraltar
                             Coat of Arms

(Typo D.L.R.)

1956 (1 Dec). *Chalk-surfaced paper. Wmk Mult Script CA.
P 14.*
D1	D 1	1d. green	..	..	2·00	3·50
D2		2d. sepia	..	..	2·50	3·75
		a. Large "d" (R. 9/6, 10/6)	..	20·00	
D3		4d. blue	..	..	3·00	6·25
D1/3		..	..	*Set of 3*	6·75	12·00

For illustrations of No. D2a, see above No. D4 of Botswana.

1971 (15 Feb). *As Nos. D1/3 but inscr in decimal currency.
W w 12. P 17½ × 18.*
D4	D 1	½p. green	..	..	30	80
D5		1p. sepia	..	..	30	70
D6		2p. blue ..	..	..	30	80
D4/6	..	..	..	*Set of 3*	80	2·10

(Des A. Ryman. Litho Questa)

1976 (13 Oct). *W w 14. P 14 × 13½.*
D 7	D 2	1p. light red-orange	..	..	15	50
D 8		3p. bright blue	..	..	15	65
D 9		5p. orange-vermilion	..	..	20	75
D10		7p. reddish violet	..	..	25	75
D11		10p. greenish slate	..	..	35	75
D12		20p. green	..	..	70	1·00
D7/12	..			*Set of 6*	1·60	4·00

(Des A. Ryman. Litho B.D.T.)

1984 (2 July). *W w 14 (sideways). P 15×14.*
D13	D 3	1p. black	..	..	25	40
D14		3p. vermilion	..	..	35	40
D15		5p. ultramarine	..	..	40	40
D16		10p. new blue	..	..	50	40
D17		25p. deep mauve ..	..	..	90	1·00
D18		50p. reddish orange	..	..	1·40	1·50
D19		£1 blue-green	..	..	2·25	2·50
D13/19	..	..	..	*Set of 7*	5·50	6·00

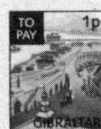

D 4 Water Port
Gates

(Des Olympia Reyes. Litho B.D.T.)

1996 (30 Sept). *Gibraltar Landmarks. Type D 4 and similar
vert designs. P 14½×14.*
D20	1p. black, emerald & bright yellow-green	10	10
D21	10p. black and bluish grey	..	20	25
D22	25p. black, red-brown and chestnut	..	50	55
D23	50p. black and reddish lilac	..	1·00	1·10
D24	£1 black, olive-brown and chestnut	..	2·00	2·10
D25	£2 black and light blue ..	..	4·00	4·25
D20/5		*Set of 6*	7·50	8·25

Designs:—10p. Naval Dockyard; 25p. Military Hospital; 50p.
Governor's Cottage; £1 Swans on the Laguna; £2 Catalan Bay.

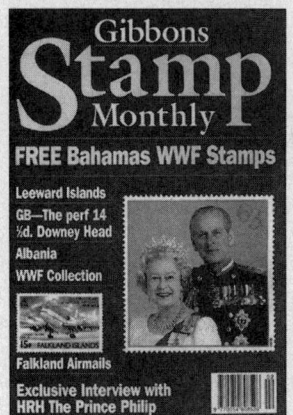

Keep This Catalogue up to Date With

Gibbons Stamp Monthly

FREE Bahamas WWF Stamps

Leeward Islands
GB—The perf 14 ½d. Downey Head
Albania
WWF Collection
Falkland Airmails
Exclusive Interview with HRH The Prince Philip

The Magazine with the Stanley Gibbons Catalogue Supplement

Plus

■ More editorial than other magazines.

■ Regular features for all collectors from beginners to specialists.

■ Authoritatively written.

■ Regular special offers, competitions and free gifts.

Get Gibbons Stamp Monthly delivered direct to your door!

*For a free sample copy and subscription details phone
01425 472363
or write to:*

**Hugh Jefferies
Gibbons Stamp Monthly
5 Parkside, Christchurch Road,
Ringwood, Hants BH24 3SH**

Gilbert and Ellice Islands

No organised postal service existed in the Gilbert and Ellice Islands before the introduction of stamp issues in January 1911. A New Zealand Postal Agency was, however, provided on Fanning Island, one of the Line Islands, primarily for the use of the staff of the Cable & Wireless Ltd cable station which was established in 1902. The agency opened on 29 November 1902 and continued to operate until replaced by a Protectorate post office on 14 February 1939. The cable station closed in 1964. Fanning Island is now known as Tabuaeran.

Z 1

The following NEW ZEALAND stamps are known postmarked on Fanning Island with Type Z 1 (in use from November 1902 until November 1936. The earliest known cover is postmarked 10 January 1903):

1882–1900 Q.V. (p 11) ¹/₂d., 1d., 2d. (Nos. 236/8)
1898 Pictorials (no wmk) 1d., 2d. (Nos. 247/8)
1900 Pictorials (W 38) ¹/₂d., 2d. (Nos. 273, 276)
1901 1d. "Universal" (W 38) (No. 278)
1902 1d. "Universal" (no wmk) (No. 295)
1902–09 Pictorials (W 43) 2¹/₂d., 6d., 9d., 1s., 2s. (Nos. 312, 315, 320, 326, 328)
1907–08 Pictorials (W 43) 4d. (No. 379)
1908 1d. "Universal" (De La Rue paper) 1d. (No. 386)
1909–12 King Edward VII (typo) ¹/₂d. (No. 387)
1909–16 King Edward VII (recess) 2d., 3d., 4d., 5d., 6d., 8d., 1s. (Nos. 388/91, 393/6, 398)
1909–26 1d. "Universal" (W 43) 1d. (Nos. 405, 410)
1915–30 King George V (recess) 1¹/₂d., 2d. bright violet, 2¹/₂d., 3d., 4d. bright violet, 6d., 7¹/₂d., 9d., 1s. (Nos. 416/17, 419/20, 422, 425/6, 429/30)
1915–34 King George V (typo) ¹/₂d., 1¹/₂d. (all 3) 2d., 3d. (Nos. 435/40, 446, 448, 449)
1915 "WAR STAMP" opt ¹/₂d. (No. 452)
1920 Victory 1d., 1¹/₂d. (Nos. 454/5)
1922 2d. on ¹/₂d. (No. 459)
1923–25 Penny Postage 1d. (No. 460)
1926–34 Admiral design 1d. (No. 468)
1935–36 Pictorials ¹/₂d., 2d., 4d., 8d., 1s. (Nos. 556, 559, 562 565, 567)
1935 Silver Jubilee ¹/₂d., 1d., 6d. (Nos. 573/5)
1936 Anzac 1d.+1d. (No. 592)

Z 2

The following NEW ZEALAND stamps are known postmarked on Fanning Island with Type Z 2 (in use from 7 December 1936 to 13 February 1939):

1935–36 Pictorials (W 43) 1d (No. 557)
1936–39 Pictorials (W 98) ¹/₂d., 1d., 1¹/₂d. (Nos. 577/9)
1936 Chambers of Commerce Congress ¹/₂d. (No. 593)
1936 Health 1d. + 1d. (No. 598)
1937 Coronation 1d., 2¹/₂d., 6d. (Nos. 599/601)
1938–39 King George VI ¹/₂d., 1d., 1¹/₂d. (Nos. 603, 605, 607)

The schooner which carried the mail from Fanning Island also called at Washington Island, another of the Line group. Problems arose, however, as the authorities insisted that mail from Washington must first pass through the Fanning Island Postal Agency before being forwarded which resulted in considerable delays. Matters were resolved by the opening of a New Zealand Postal Agency on Washington Island which operated from 1 February 1921 until the copra plantations were closed in early 1923. The postal agency was re-established on 15 May 1924, but finally closed on 30 March 1934. Manuscript markings dating from the resettlement of the island in 1937 to 1948 are unofficial. Washington Island is now known as Teraina.

NEW INFORMATION

The editor is always interested to correspond with people who have new information that will improve or correct the Catalogue.

Z 3

The following NEW ZEALAND stamps are known postmarked on Washington Island with Type Z 3:

1909–16 King Edward VII 5d., 8d. (Nos. 402, 404b)
1915–30 King George V (recess) 6d., 7¹/₂d., 8d., 9d., 1s. (Nos. 425/7, 429/30)
1915–34 King George V (typo) ¹/₂d., 1¹/₂d., 2d., 3d. (Nos. 435, 438/9, 449)
1915 "WAR STAMP" opt ¹/₂d. (No. 452)
1920 Victory 1d., 1¹/₂d., 6d. (Nos. 454/5, 457)
1922 2d. on ¹/₂d. (No. 459)
1926–34 Admiral design 1d. (No. 468)

The above information is based on a special survey undertaken by members of the Kiribati & Tuvalu Philatelic Society and the Pacific Islands Study Circle, co-ordinated by Mr. Michael Shaw.

PRICES FOR STAMPS ON COVER TO 1945	
Nos. 1/7	from × 5
Nos. 8/11	from × 10
Nos. 12/23	from × 6
No. 24	—
No. 26	from × 15
Nos. 27/30	from × 6
No. 35	—
Nos. 36/9	from × 4
Nos. 40/2	from × 12
Nos. 43/54	from × 4
Nos. D1/8	from × 5

BRITISH PROTECTORATE

GILBERT&ELLICE

PROTECTORATE

(1)   2 Pandanus Pine

1911 (1 Jan). Stamps of Fiji optd with T **1**. Wmk Mult Crown CA. Chalk-surfaced paper (5d. to 1s.).

1	23	¹/₂d. green			4·50	35·00
2		1d. red			45·00	27·00
3	24	2d. grey			7·50	12·00
4	23	2¹/₂d. ultramarine			12·00	24·00
5		5d. purple and olive-green			38·00	65·00
6	24	6d. dull and bright purple			20·00	40·00
7	23	1s. black/green (R.)			19·00	42·00
1/7				Set of 7	£130	£225
1/7 Optd "Specimen"				Set of 7	£275	

The 2d. to 6d. are on special printings which were not issued without overprint.

Examples of Nos. 1/7 are known showing a forged Ocean Island postmark dated "JY 15 11".

(Recess D.L.R.)

1911. Wmk Mult Crown CA. P 14.

8	2	¹/₂d. green			4·25	10·00
9		1d. carmine			2·00	6·00
10		2d. grey			1·50	6·00
11		2¹/₂d. blue			3·00	8·00
8/11				Set of 4	9·75	27·00
8/11 Optd "Specimen"				Set of 4	£140	

3

WAR TAX

(5)

(Typo D.L.R.)

1912 (May)–**24.** Die I (¹/₂d. to 5s.) or Die II (£1). Wmk Mult Crown CA. Chalk-surfaced paper (3d. to £1). P 14.

12	3	¹/₂d. green (7.12)			30	3·75
		a. Yellow-green (1914)			4·00	7·50
13		1d. carmine (12.12)			1·40	3·75
		a. Scarlet (1915)			3·75	9·00
14		2d. greyish slate (1.16)			12·00	18·00
15		2¹/₂d. bright blue (1.16)			1·75	11·00
16		3d. purple/yellow (1918)			2·00	7·00
17		4d. black and red/yellow (10.12)			60	4·75
18		5d. dull purple and sage-green			1·50	7·00
19		6d. dull and bright purple			1·25	7·50
20		1s. black/green			1·25	5·00
21		2s. purple and blue/blue (10.12)			14·00	27·00
22		2s. 6d. black and red/blue (10.12)			12·00	23·00
23		5s. green and red/yellow (10.12)			30·00	50·00
24		£1 purple and black/red (Die II) (3.24)			£600	£1400
12/24				Set of 13	£600	£1400
12/24 Optd "Specimen"				Set of 13	£550	

CROWN COLONY

1918 (June). Optd with T **5**.

26	3	1d. red (Optd S. £60)			30	5·50

1922–27. Die II. Wmk Mult Crown CA. Chalk-surfaced paper (10s.). P 14.

27	3	¹/₂d. green (1923)			2·00	1·60
28		1d. violet (1927)			3·25	3·50
29		1¹/₂d. scarlet (1924)			3·00	1·00
30		2d. slate-grey			5·00	18·00
35		10s. green and red/emerald (3.24)			£180	£350
27/35 Optd "Specimen"				Set of 5	£250	

Examples of most values between Nos. 12 and 35 are known showing part strikes of the forged postmark mentioned below Nos. 1/7. Collectors should exercise particular caution when buying used examples of Nos. 24 and 35.

1935 (6 May). Silver Jubilee. As Nos. 91/4 of Antigua, but ptd by B.W. P 11 × 12.

36		1d. ultramarine and grey-black			2·25	7·00
		d. Flagstaff on right-hand turret			£140	
		e. Double flagstaff			£180	
37		1¹/₂d. deep blue and scarlet			1·75	3·25
		d. Flagstaff on right-hand turret			£140	
		e. Double flagstaff			£180	
38		3d. brown and deep blue			5·00	11·00
		d. Flagstaff on right-hand turret			£200	
		e. Double flagstaff			£225	
39		1s. slate and purple			32·00	24·00
		d. Flagstaff on right-hand turret			£325	
		e. Double flagstaff			£350	
36/9				Set of 4	38·00	40·00
36/9 Perf "Specimen"				Set of 4	£110	

For illustrations of plate varieties see Catalogue Introduction.

1937 (12 May). Coronation. As Nos. 95/7 of Antigua, but ptd by D.L.R. P 14.

40	1d. violet			35	55
41	1¹/₂d. scarlet			45	55
42	3d. bright blue			60	60
40/2			Set of 3	1·25	1·50
40/2 Perf "Specimen"			Set of 3	65·00	

6 Great Frigate Bird   7 Pandanus Pine

8 Canoe crossing Reef

(Recess B.W. (¹/₂d., 2d., 2s. 6d.), Waterlow (1d., 5d., 6d., 2s., 5s.) D.L.R. (1¹/₂d., 2¹/₂d., 3d., 1s.))

1939 (14 Jan)–**55.** T **6/8** and similar horiz designs. Wmk Mult Script CA (sideways on ¹/₂d., 2d. and 2s. 6d.) P 11¹/₂×11 (¹/₂d., 2d., 2s. 6d.), 12¹/₂ (1d., 5d., 6d., 2s., 5s.) or 13¹/₂ (1¹/₂d., 2¹/₂d., 3d., 1s.).

43	¹/₂d. indigo and deep bluish green		30	75
	a. "A" of "CA" missing from wmk			
44	1d. emerald and plum		30	1·50
45	1¹/₂d. brownish black and bright carmine		30	90
46	2d. red-brown and grey-black		50	1·00
47	2¹/₂d. brownish black and deep olive		40	70
	a. Brownish black & olive-green (12.5.43)		3·00	3·25
48	3d. brownish black and ultramarine		45	1·00
	a. Perf 12. Black and bright blue (24.8.55)		50	2·25
49	5d. deep ultramarine and sepia		4·25	1·25
	a. Ultramarine and sepia (12.5.43)		4·75	5·00
	b. Ultramarine & blackish brn (20.10.44)		4·25	4·25
50	6d. olive-green and deep ivory		40	50
51	1s. brownish black and turquoise-green		7·50	1·75
	a. Brownish black & turquoise-bl (12.5.43)		4·50	2·00
	ab. Perf 12 (8.5.51)		4·50	13·00
52	2s. deep ultramarine and orange-red		16·00	9·50
53	2s. 6d. deep blue and emerald		17·00	14·00
54	5s. deep rose-red and royal blue		18·00	16·00
43/54		Set of 12	55·00	42·00
43/54 Perf "Specimen"		Set of 12	£250	

Designs: As T **6**—2d. Canoe and boat-house; 2s. 6d. Gilbert Islands canoe. As T **7**—5d. Ellice Islands canoe; 6d. Coconut palms; 2s. H.M.C.S. Nimanoa; 5s. Coat of arms. As T **8**—2¹/₂d. Native house; 3d. Seascape; 1s. Cantilever jetty, Ocean Island.

1946 (16 Dec). Victory. As Nos. 110/11 of Antigua.

55	1d. purple		15	25
56	3d. blue		15	25
55/6 Perf "Specimen"		Set of 2	55·00	

1949 (29 Aug). Royal Silver Wedding. As Nos. 112/13 of Antigua.

57	1d. violet		40	55
58	£1 scarlet		15·00	18·00

1949 (10 Oct). 75th Anniv of U.P.U. As Nos. 114/17 of Antigua.

59	1d. purple		55	95
60	2d. grey-black		2·25	2·25
61	3d. deep blue		1·25	2·00
62	1s. blue		1·50	2·00
59/62		Set of 4	5·00	6·00

1953 (2 June). Coronation. As No. 120 of Antigua.

63	2d. black and grey-black		55	2·00

18 Great Frigate Bird   19 Loading Phosphate from Cantilever

Recess B.W. (½d., 2d., 2s. 6d.), Waterlow (1d., 5d., 6d., 2s., 5s.), D.L.R. (2½d., 3d., 1s., 10s. and after 1962, 1d., 5d.))

956 (1 Aug)–62. *Designs previously used for King George VI issue; but with portrait of Queen Elizabeth II as in T 18. Wmk Mult Script CA. P 11½×11 (½d., 2d., 2s. 6d.), 12½ (1d., 5d., 6d., 2s., 5s.) or 12 (2½d., 3d., 1s., 10s.).*

4	½d. black and deep bright blue		35	90
5	1d. brown-olive and deep violet		60	40
6	2d. bluish green and deep purple	..	90	1·75
	a. *Bluish green and purple* (30.7.62)		15·00	15·00
7	2½d. black and myrtle-green		50	60
8	3d. black and carmine-red ..		50	55
9	5d. ultramarine and red-orange		8·50	2·50
	a. *Ultramarine & brn-orge* (DLR) (30.7.62)	15·00	20·00
0	6d. chestnut and black-brown	..	55	1·50
1	1s. black and bronze-green	..	1·00	50
2	2s. deep bright blue and sepia	..	8·50	5·50
3	2s. 6d. scarlet and deep blue	..	10·00	5·50
4	5s. greenish blue and bluish green	..	12·00	8·00
5	10s. black and turquoise		28·00	15·00
54/75		*Set of 12*	65·00	38·00

Designs: *Horiz* (30 × 22½ *mm*)—1d. Pandanus pine; 5d. Ellice Islands canoe; 6d. Coconut palms; 2s. H.M.C.S. *Nimanoa*; 5s. Coat of arms. (35½ × 22½ *mm*)—2d. Canoe and boat-house; 2½d. Native house; 3d. Seascape; 1s. Cantilever jetty, Ocean Island; 2s. 6d. Gilbert Islands canoe; 10s. Canoe crossing reef.
See also Nos. 85/6.

(Des R. Turrell (2d.), M. Thoma (2½d.), M. A. W. Hook and A. Larkins (1s.). Photo D.L.R.)

1960 (1 May). *Diamond Jubilee of Phosphate Discovery at Ocean Island. T 19 and similar horiz designs. W w 12. P 12.*

76	2d. green and carmine-rose..	..	1·10	85
77	2½d. black and olive-green	..	1·10	85
78	1s. black and deep turquoise	..	1·10	85
76/8		*Set of 3*	3·00	2·40

Designs:—2½d. Phosphate rock; 1s. Phosphate mining.

1963 (1 Aug). *Freedom from Hunger. As No. 146 of Antigua.*

79	10d. ultramarine ..	1·75	30

1963 (5 Oct). *Red Cross Centenary. As Nos. 147/8 of Antigua.*

80	2d. red and black	1·25	50
81	10d. red and blue	3·00	2·25

22 De Havilland   24 De Havilland
D.H.114 Heron 2   D.H.114 Heron 2
and Route Map   over Tarawa Lagoon

23 Eastern Reef Heron in Flight

(Des Margaret Barwick. Litho Enschedé)

1964 (20 July). *First Air Service. W w 12 (sideways* on 3d., 3s. 7d.). P 11×11½ (1s.) or 11½×11 (others).*

82	22	3d. blue, black and light blue ..	..	70	20
		w. Wmk Crown to right of CA		70	30
83	23	1s. light blue, black and deep blue		90	25
84	24	3s. 7d. deep green, black & light emerald	1·40	1·10
82/4			*Set of 3*	2·75	1·40

**The normal sideways watermark shows Crown to left of CA, as seen from the back of the stamp.*

(Recess B.W. (2d.), D.L.R. (6d.))

1964 (30 Oct)–65. *As Nos. 66a and 70 but wmk w 12.*

85	2d. bluish green and purple ..		75	2·00
86	6d. chestnut and black-brown (26.4.65)*	1·00	2·25

**Earliest known postmark date.*

1965 (4 June). *I.T.U. Centenary. As Nos. 166/7 of Antigua.*

87	3d. red-orange and deep bluish green	20	10
88	2s. 6d. turquoise-blue and light purple	80	20

25 Maneaba and   26 Gilbertese Women's Dance
Gilbertese Man
blowing Bu Shell

(Des V. Whiteley from drawings by Margaret Barwick. Litho B.W.)

1965 (16 Aug). *Vert designs as T 25 (½d. to 2s.) or horiz designs as T 26 (3s. 7d. to £1). Centres multicoloured. W w 12. P 12 × 11 (½d. to 2s.) or 11 × 12 (3s. 7d. to £1).*

89	½d. turquoise-green	..	10	10
90	1d. deep violet-blue	..	10	10
91	2d. bistre	..	10	10
92	3d. rose-red	..	10	10
93	4d. purple	..	15	10
94	5d. cerise	..	20	10
95	6d. turquoise-blue	..	20	10
96	7d. bistre-brown	..	25	10
97	1s. bluish violet	..	50	10
98	1s. 6d. lemon ..	..	1·00	65
99	2s. yellow-olive	..	1·00	1·25
100	3s. 7d. new blue	..	2·25	65
101	5s. light yellow-olive	..	2·25	80
102	10s. dull green	..	4·00	1·25
103	£1 light turquoise-blue	..	4·50	2·50
89/103		*Set of 15*	15·00	6·50

Designs:—1d. Ellice Islanders reef fishing by flare; 2d. Gilbertese girl weaving head garland; 3d. Gilbertese woman performing Ruoia; 4d. Gilbertese man performing Kamei; 5d. Gilbertese girl drawing water; 6d. Ellice islander performing a Fatele; 7d. Ellice youths performing spear dance; 1s. Gilbertese girl tending Ikaroa Babai plant; 1s. 6d. Ellice islanders dancing a Fatele; 2s. Ellice islanders pounding Pulaka; 5s. Gilbertese boys playing stick game; 10s. Ellice youths beating the box for the Fatele; £1 Coat of arms.

1965 (25 Oct). *International Co-operation Year. As Nos. 168/9 of Antigua.*

104	½d. reddish purple and turquoise-green	10	10
105	3s. 7d. deep bluish green and lavender	..	60	20

1966 (24 Jan). *Churchill Commemoration. As Nos. 170/3 of Antigua.*

106	½d. new blue	..	10	10
107	3d. deep green	..	20	10
108	3s. brown	..	35	35
109	3s. 7d. bluish violet ..	..	40	35
106/9		*Set of 4*	90	75

(New Currency, 100 cents = 1 Australian dollar)

≡2ᶜ

(40)   41 H.M.S. *Royalist*

1966 (14 Feb). *Decimal currency. Nos. 89/103 surch as T 40.*

110	1 c. on 1d. deep violet-blue	..	10	10
111	2 c. on 2d. bistre	..	10	10
112	3 c. on 3d. rose-red	..	10	10
113	4 c. on ½d. turquoise-green	..	10	10
114	5 c. on 6d. turquoise-blue	..	15	10
115	6 c. on 4d. purple	..	15	10
116	8 c. on 5d. cerise	..	15	10
117	10 c. on 1s. bluish violet	..	15	10
118	15 c. on 7d. bistre-brown	..	80	30
119	20 c. on 1s. 6d. lemon	..	45	25
120	25 c. on 2s. yellow-olive	..	45	20
121	35 c. on 3s. 7d. new blue	..	1·25	20
122	50 c. on 5s. light yellow-olive ..	..	75	35
123	$1 on 10s. dull green	..	75	40
124	$2 on £1 light turquoise-blue	..	1·50	2·00
110/24		*Set of 15*	6·00	3·75

1966 (1 July). *World Cup Football Championships. As Nos. 176/7 of Antigua.*

125	3 c. violet, yellow-green, lake & yellow-brn ..	15	10
126	35 c. chocolate, blue-green, lake & yell-brn ..	45	20

1966 (20 Sept). *Inauguration of W.H.O. Headquarters, Geneva. As Nos. 178/9 of Antigua.*

127	3 c. black, yellow-green and light blue	30	10
128	12 c. black, light purple and yellow-brown ..	60	40

1966 (1 Dec). *20th Anniv of U.N.E.S.C.O. As Nos. 196/8 of Antigua.*

129	5 c. slate-violet, red, yellow and orange	30	10
130	10 c. orange-yellow, violet and deep olive	50	10
131	20 c. black, bright purple and orange..	80	45
129/31		*Set of 3*	1·40	55

(Des V. Whiteley. Photo Harrison)

1967 (1 Sept). *75th Anniv of the Protectorate. T 41 and similar horiz designs. W w 12. P 14½.*

132	3 c. red, blue and myrtle-green		30	40
133	10 c. multicoloured		15	15
134	35 c. sepia, orange-yellow & dp bluish green	30	40
132/4		*Set of 3*	65	85

Designs:—10 c. Trading Post; 35 c. Island family.

44 Gilbertese Women's Dance

1968 (1 Jan). *Decimal Currency. Designs as Nos. 89/103 but with values inscr in decimal currency as T 44. W w 12 (sideways on horiz designs). P 12 × 11 (vert) or 11 × 12 (horiz).*

135	1 c. deep violet-blue (as 1d.)	..	10	10
136	2 c. bistre (as 2d.)	..	15	10
137	3 c. rose-red (as 3d.)	..	15	10
138	4 c. turquoise-green (as ½d.)	..	15	10
139	5 c. turquoise-blue (as 6d.)	..	15	10
140	6 c. purple (as 4d.)	..	20	10
141	8 c. cerise (as 5d.)	..	20	10
142	10 c. bluish violet (as 1s.)	..	20	10
143	15 c. bistre-brown (as 7d.)	..	50	20
144	20 c. lemon (as 1s. 6d.)	..	65	15
	w. Wmk inverted	..	14·00	14·00
145	25 c. yellow-olive (as 2s.)	..	1·25	20
146	35 c. new blue	..	1·50	20
147	50 c. light yellow-olive (as 5s.)	..	1·50	2·00
148	$1 dull green (as 10s.)	..	1·50	3·00
149	$2 light turquoise-blue (as £1)	..	4·00	3·00
135/49		*Set of 15*	11·00	8·00

45 Map of Tarawa Atoll

(Des V. Whiteley. Photo D.L.R.)

1968 (21 Nov). *25th Anniv of the Battle of Tarawa. T 45 and similar designs. Multicoloured. W w 12 (sideways). P 14.*

150	3 c. Type 45	..	20	20
151	10 c. Marines landing	..	20	15
152	15 c. Beach-head assault	..	30	25
153	35 c. Raising U.S. and British flags	..	40	30
150/3	..	*Set of 4*	1·00	80

CHRISTMAS 1969

46 Young Pupil against outline   47 "Virgin and Child" in
of Abemama Island   Pacific Setting

(Des J.W. (from original designs by Mrs V. J. Anderson and Miss A. Loveridge). Litho D.L.R.)

1969 (2 June). *End of Inaugural Year of South Pacific University. T 46 and similar horiz designs. W w 12 (sideways). P 12½.*

154	10 c. multicoloured	..	10	10
155	10 c. multicoloured	..	10	10
156	35 c. black, brown and grey-green	..	20	20
154/6 ..		*Set of 3*	30	30

Designs:—10 c. Boy and girl students and Tarawa atoll; 35 c. University graduate and South Pacific islands.

(Des Jennifer Toombs. Litho B.W.)

1969 (20 Oct). *Christmas. W w 12 (sideways). P 11½.*

157	– 2 c. olive-grn & multicoloured (*shades*)	15	20
158	47 10 c. olive-grn & multicoloured (*shades*)	15	10

Design:—2 c. As T 47 but foreground has grass instead of sand.

48 "The Kiss of Life"

(Des Manate Tenang Manate. Litho J.W.)

1970 (9 Mar*). *Centenary of British Red Cross.* W w **12** (sideways). P 14.

159	**48**	10 c. multicoloured	20	10
160	–	15 c. multicoloured	30	30
161	–	35 c. multicoloured	60	50
159/61		Set of 3	1·00	80

Nos. 160/1 are as T **48**, but arranged differently.
*The above were released by the Crown Agents on 2 March, but not sold locally until the 9 March.

49 Foetus and Patients

(Des Jennifer Toombs. Litho Enschedé)

1970 (26 June). *25th Anniv of United Nations.* T **49** and similar horiz designs. W w **12** (sideways). P 12½ × 13.

162	5 c. multicoloured	15	15
163	10 c. black, grey and red	15	10
164	15 c. multicoloured	20	15
165	35 c. new blue, black and turquoise-green	30	20
162/5	Set of 4	70	55

Designs:—10 c. Nurse and surgical instruments; 15 c. X-ray plate and technician; 35 c. U.N. emblem and map.

53 Map of Gilbert Islands   **57** "Child with Halo" (T. Collis)

(Des G. Vasarhelyi. Litho Harrison)

1970 (1 Sept). *Centenary of Landing in Gilbert Islands by London Missionary Society.* T **53** and similar designs. W w **12** (sideways on vert designs). P 14½ × 14 (2 c., 35 c.) or 14 × 14½ (others).

166	2 c. multicoloured	15	60
167	10 c. black and pale green	20	10
168	25 c. chestnut and cobalt	20	15
169	35 c. turquoise-blue, black and red	40	60
166/9	Set of 4	85	1·25

Designs: Vert—10 c. Sailing-ship *John Williams III*; 25 c. Rev. S. J. Whitmee. Horiz—35 c. M.V. *John Williams VII*.

(Des L. Curtis. Litho Format)

1970 (3 Oct). *Christmas. Sketches.* T **57** and similar vert designs. Multicoloured. W w **12**. P 14½.

170	2 c. Type **57**	10	15
171	10 c. "Sanctuary, Tarawa Cathedral" (Mrs. A. Burroughs)	10	10
172	35 c. "Three ships inside star" (Mrs. C. Barnett)	20	20
170/2	Set of 3	35	35

60 Casting Nets

(Des G. Drummond. Litho Walsall)

1971 (31 May). *Multicoloured designs as T* **60**. W w **12** (sideways* on 2, 3, 4, 5, 20, 25 and 35 c.). P 14.

173	1 c. Cutting toddy (vert)	10	10
174	2 c. Lagoon fishing	15	20
	w. Wmk Crown to right of CA	10·00	
175	3 c. Cleaning pandanus leaves	15	15
	w. Wmk Crown to right of CA		
176	4 c. Type **60**	20	25
	w. Wmk Crown to right of CA		
177	5 c. Gilbertese canoe	35	15
	w. Wmk Crown to right of CA		
178	6 c. De-husking coconuts (vert)	30	35
179	8 c. Weaving pandanus fronds (vert)	35	15
180	10 c. Weaving a basket (vert)	40	15
	w. Wmk inverted	1·50	1·50
181	15 c. Tiger Shark and fishermen (vert)	2·50	1·50
182	20 c. Beating a rolled pandanus leaf	1·50	90
	w. Wmk Crown to right of CA	3·75	
183	25 c. Loading copra	2·00	1·00
184	35 c. Fishing at night	2·25	50
	w. Wmk Crown to left of CA	3·50	
185	50 c. Local handicrafts (vert)	1·50	1·25
186	$1 Weaving coconut screens (vert)	2·00	2·25
187	$2 Coat of Arms (vert)	6·50	10·00
173/87	Set of 15	18·00	17·00

*The normal sideways watermark shows Crown to right of CA on 35 c., and Crown to left of CA on the others, *as seen from the back of the stamp.*
See also Nos. 203/7.

61 House of Representatives   **62** Pacific Nativity Scene

(Des V. Whiteley. Litho J.W.)

1971 (1 Aug). *New Constitution.* T **61** and similar horiz design. Multicoloured. W w **12** (sideways). P 14.

188	3 c. Type **61**	10	20
189	10 c. Maneaba Betio (Assembly hut)	20	10

(Des L. Curtis and T. Collis. Litho Questa)

1971 (1 Oct). *Christmas.* T **62** and similar vert designs. W w **12**. P 14 × 14½.

190	3 c. black, yellow and ultramarine	10	15
191	10 c. black, gold and turquoise-blue	10	10
192	35 c. black, gold and magenta	25	25
190/2	Set of 3	40	45

Designs:—10 c. Star and palm leaves; 35 c. Outrigger canoe and star.

63 Emblem and Young Boys

(Des G. Vasarhelyi. Litho Questa)

1971 (11 Dec). *25th Anniv of UNICEF.* T **63** and similar horiz designs, showing UNICEF emblem and young boys. W w **12** (sideways). P 14.

193	3 c. multicoloured	10	50
194	10 c. multicoloured	15	10
195	35 c. multicoloured	45	50
193/5	Set of 3	60	1·00

64 Flag and Map of South Pacific

(Des A. New. Litho Questa)

1972 (21 Feb). *25th Anniv of South Pacific Commission.* T **64** and similar horiz designs. Multicoloured. W w **12**. P 13½.

196	3 c. Type **64**	10	65
197	10 c. Flag and native boats	15	20
198	35 c. Flags of member nations	15	95
196/8	Set of 3	30	1·60

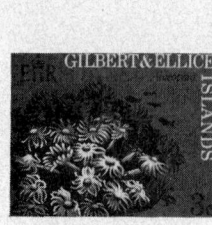

65 Alveopora   **66** Star of Peace

(Des Sylvia Goaman after original designs by H. Wickison. Litho Questa)

1972 (26 May). *Coral.* T **65** and similar horiz designs. Multicoloured. W w **12** (sideways*). P 14.

199	3 c. Type **65**	25	30
200	10 c. *Euphyllia*	30	10
201	15 c. *Melithea*	40	20
	w. Wmk Crown to left of CA	1·75	
202	35 c. *Spongodes*	80	40
199/202	Set of 4	1·60	90

*The normal sideways watermark shows Crown to right of CA, *as seen from the back of the stamp.*

1972 (7 Sept)–**73**. *As Nos. 174, 177/8 and 181/2 but W w* **12** *upright on 2, 5 and 20 c.; sideways on 6 and 15 c.*

203	2 c. Lagoon fishing (13.6.73)	11·00	14·00
204	5 c. Gilbertese canoe	4·00	4·50
205	6 c. De-husking coconuts (13.6.73)	11·00	15·00
206	15 c. Tiger Shark and fishermen	6·00	6·00
207	20 c. Beating a rolled pandanus leaf	6·00	6·00
203/7	Set of 5	35·00	40·00

(Des T. Matarena (35 c.), Father Bermond (others); adapted by Jennifer Toombs. Litho Questa)

1972 (15 Sept). *Christmas.* T **66** and similar multicoloured designs. W w **12** (sideways on 3 and 10 c.). P 13½.

208	3 c. Type **66**	10	10
209	10 c. "The Nativity"	10	10
210	35 c. Baby in "manger" (horiz)	20	10
208/10	Set of 3	30	30

67 Floral Head-dresses

(Des (from photograph by D. Groves) and photo Harrison)

1972 (20 Nov). *Royal Silver Wedding.* Multicoloured; background colour given. W w **12**. P 14 × 14½.

211	**67** 3 c. brown-olive	10	15
	w. Wmk inverted	6·00	
212	35 c. lake-brown	25	15
	w. Wmk inverted	32·00	

68 Funafuti ("The Land of Bananas")   **69** Dancer

(Des H. Wickison; adapted J. Cooter. Litho Walsall)

1973 (5 Mar). *Legends of Island Names (1st series).* T **68** and similar horiz designs. Multicoloured. W w **12**. P 14½ × 14.

213	3 c. Type **68**	10	30
214	10 c. Butaritari ("The Smell of the Sea")	20	15
215	25 c. Tarawa ("The Centre of the World")	30	15
216	35 c. Abemama ("The Land of the Moon")	35	35
	w. Wmk inverted		
213/16	Set of 4	80	1·00

See also Nos. 252/5.

(Des Sister Juliette (3 c.), R. P. Turner (10 and 35 c.), C. Potts (50 c.); adapted Jennifer Toombs. Litho Questa)

1973 (24 Sept). *Christmas.* T **69** and similar vert designs. Multicoloured. W w **12** (sideways*). P 14.

217	3 c. Type **69**	10	10
218	10 c. Canoe and lagoon	10	10
	w. Wmk Crown to right of CA	7·50	
219	35 c. Lagoon at evening	20	10
220	50 c. Map of Christmas Island	30	1·00
	w. Wmk Crown to right of CA	6·00	
217/20	Set of 4	60	1·10

*The normal sideways watermark shows Crown to left of CA, as seen from the back of the stamp.

1973 (14 Nov). *Royal Wedding. As Nos. 165/6 of Anguilla.* Centre multicoloured. W w **12** (sideways). P 13½.

221	3 c. pale green	10	15
222	35 c. Prussian blue	20	15

70 Meteorological Observation

(Des E. S. Cheek; adapted PAD Studio. Litho Questa)

1973 (26 Nov). *I.M.O./W.M.O. Centenary.* T **70** and similar horiz designs. Multicoloured. W w **12**. P 14.

223	3 c. Type **70**	60	30
224	10 c. Island observing-station	60	20
225	35 c. Wind-finding radar	90	25
226	50 c. World weather watch stations	1·40	1·25
223/6	Set of 4	3·25	1·75

71 Te Mataaua Crest

(Des J. Cooter. Litho Questa)

1974 (4 Mar). *Canoe Crests.* T **71** and similar horiz designs showing sailing craft and the canoe crests given. Multicoloured. W w **12**. P 13½.

227	3 c. Type **71**	10	10
228	10 c. Te Nimta-wawa	15	10
229	35 c. Tara-ta-venei-na	25	10
230	50 c. Te Bou-uoua	35	10
227/30	Set of 4	75	65
MS231	154 × 130 mm. Nos. 227/30	2·00	5·00

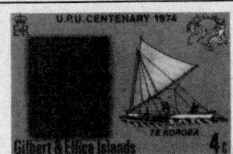

72 £1 Stamp of 1924 and Te Koroba (canoe)

(Des E. S. Cheek; adapted J. Cooter. Litho Questa)

1974 (10 June). *Centenary of Universal Postal Union. T* **72** *and similar horiz designs.* W w **12**. *P* 14.

232	4 c. multicoloured				15	10
233	10 c. multicoloured				15	10
234	25 c. multicoloured				20	20
	w. Wmk inverted				48·00	
235	35 c. light vermilion and black			20	20
232/5				*Set of 4*	60	50

Designs:—10 c. 5s. stamp of 1939 and sailing vessel *Kiakia*; 25 c. $2 stamp of 1971 and B.A.C. One Eleven airplane; 35 c. U.P.U. emblem.

73 Toy Canoe

74 North Front Entrance, Blenheim Palace

(Des H. Wickison and G. J. Hayward; adapted J. Cooter. Litho Questa)

1974 (5 Sept). *Christmas. T* **73** *and similar horiz designs. Multicoloured.* W w **12** (*sideways**). *P* 14.

236	4 c. Type **73**				10	10
237	10 c. Toy windmill				10	10
	w. Wmk Crown to right of CA			1·00	
238	25 c. Coconut "ball"				15	25
239	35 c. Canoes and constellation Pleiades		20	25
236/9				*Set of 4*	45	60

*The normal sideways watermark shows Crown to left of CA, as seen from the back of the stamp.

(Des J. Cooter. Litho Questa)

1974 (30 Nov). *Birth Centenary of Sir Winston Churchill. T* **74** *and similar vert designs. Multicoloured.* W w **14**. *P* 14.

240	4 c. Type **74**				10	20
241	10 c. Churchill painting				10	10
242	35 c. Churchill's statue, London			25	25
240/2				*Set of 3*	40	50

75 Barometer Crab

(Des J. Cooter. Litho Questa)

1975 (27 Jan). *Crabs. T* **75** *and similar horiz designs. Multicoloured.* W w **12** (*sideways**). *P* 14.

243	4 c. Type **75**				30	50
	w. Wmk Crown to right of CA			6·00	
244	10 c. *Ranina ranina*				40	20
245	25 c. Pelagic Swimming Crab			80	55
246	35 c. Ghost Crab				95	85
243/6				*Set of 4*	2·25	1·90

*The normal sideways watermark shows Crown to left of CA, as seen from the back of the stamp.

76 Eyed Cowrie (*Cypraea argus*)

77 "Christ is Born"

(Des E. S. Cheek; adapted J. Cooter. Litho Questa)

1975 (26 May). *Cowrie Shells. T* **76** *and similar vert designs. Multicoloured.* W w **14**. *P* 14.

247	4 c. Type **76**				55	45
248	10 c. Sieve Cowrie (*Cypraea cribraria*)		80	15
249	25 c. Mole Cowrie (*Cypraea talpa*)		1·75	80
250	35 c. All-red Map Cowrie (*Cypraea mappa panerythra*)		2·00	1·25
247/50				*Set of 4*	4·50	2·40
MS251	146×137 mm. Nos. 247/50			12·00	15·00

(Des J. Cooter. Litho Questa)

1975 (1 Aug). *Legends of Island Names (2nd series). Horiz designs as T* **68**. *Multicoloured.* W w **12** (*sideways**). *P* 14.

252	4 c. Beru ("The Bud")			10	15
253	10 c. Onotoa ("Six Giants")			10	10
254	25 c. Abaiang ("Land to the North")		20	20
	w. Wmk Crown to right of CA		8·50	
255	35 c. Marakei ("Fish-trap floating on eaves")		30	30
252/4			*Set of 4*	60	65

*The normal sideways watermark shows Crown to left of CA, as seen from the back of the stamp.

(Des C. J. Barnett (4 and 25 c.), Philatelic Advisory Committee (10 c.), P. T. Burangke (35 c.); adapted J. Cooter. Litho Questa)

1975 (22 Sept). *Christmas. T* **77** *and similar vert designs. Multicoloured.* W w **14**. *P* 14.

256	4 c. Type **77**			15	40
257	10 c. Protestant Chapel, Tarawa		15	30
258	25 c. Catholic Church, Ocean Island		25	80
259	35 c. Fishermen and star			30	1·25
256/9			*Set of 4*	75	2·50

POSTAGE DUE STAMPS

D 1

(Typo B.W.)

1940 (Aug). *Wmk Mult Script CA. P* 12.

D1	D **1**	1d. emerald-green			7·50	19·00
D2		2d. scarlet			8·50	19·00
D3		3d. brown			12·00	20·00
D4		4d. blue			14·00	26·00
D5		5d. grey-green			19·00	26·00
D6		6d. purple			19·00	26·00
D7		1s. violet			21·00	35·00
D8		1s. 6d. turquoise-green			40·00	70·00
D1/8				*Set of 8*	£130	£225
D1/8 Perf "Specimen"			*Set of 8*	£160	

Examples of all values are known showing a forged Post Office Ocean Island postmark dated "16 DE 46".

Stamps for the Gilbert and Ellice Islands were withdrawn on 31 December 1975 when the separate colonies of KIRIBATI (GILBERT ISLANDS) and TUVALU were created.

Gilbert Islands
see Kiribati

Gold Coast
see Ghana

Grenada

The earliest recorded postmark of the British administration of Grenada dates from 1784, and, although details of the early period are somewhat sparse, it would appear that the island's postal service was operated at a branch of the British G.P.O. In addition to a Packet Agency at St. George's, the capital, there was a further agency at Carriacou, in the Grenadines, which operated for a few years from 15 September 1847.

Stamps of Great Britain were supplied to the St. George's office from April 1858 until the colony assumed responsibility for the postal service on 1 May 1860. Following the take-over the crowned-circle handstamp, No. CC2, was again used until the Grenada adhesives were issued in 1861.

There was no internal postal service before 1861.

For illustrations of the handstamp and postmark types see BRITISH POST OFFICE ABROAD notes, following GREAT BRITAIN.

CARRIACOU

CROWNED-CIRCLE HANDSTAMPS

CC1 CC **1** CARRIACOU (13.11.1846) .. .. .. †

Although recorded in the G.P.O. proof book no example of No. CC1 has been reported used from Grenada.

ST. GEORGE'S

CROWNED-CIRCLE HANDSTAMPS

CC2 CC **1** GRENADA (R.) (24.10.1850) *Price on cover* £1100

Stamps of GREAT BRITAIN *cancelled* "A 15" *as Type* **2**

1858 *to* 1860.

Z1	1d. rose-red (1857), *perf* 14			£350
Z2	2d. blue (1858) (Plate No. 7)			£650
Z3	4d. rose (1857)			£225
Z4	6d. lilac (1856)			£120
Z5	1s. green (1856)			£650

PRICES FOR STAMPS ON COVER TO 1945

Nos. 1/19	*from* × 15
Nos. 20/3	*from* × 20
Nos. 24/6	*from* × 10
No. 27	*from* × 15
No. 28	—
No. 29	*from* × 10
Nos. 30/6	*from* × 20
Nos. 37/9	*from* × 10
No. 40	*from* × 30
Nos. 41/7	*from* × 10
Nos. 48/101	*from* × 4
Nos. 109/11	*from* × 8
Nos. 112/48	*from* × 4
Nos. 149/51	*from* × 10
Nos. 152/63	*from* × 4
Nos. D1/3	*from* × 25
Nos. D4/7	*from* × 12
Nos. D8/14	*from* × 10

CROWN COLONY

PRINTERS. Types **1** and **5** recess-printed by Perkins, Bacon and Co.

1

2 Small Star

(Eng C. Jeens)

1861 (3 June)–**62**. *No wmk. Wove paper.*

(a) Rough perf 14 to 16

1	**1**	1d. bluish green			£4500	£300
2		1d. green (5.62)			50·00	40·00
		a. Imperf between (horiz pair)				
3		6d. rose (*shades*)			£800	90·00

(b) Perf 11 to 12½

3a	**1**	6d. lake-red (6.62)			£750

No. 3a is only known unused, and may be the result of perforating machine trials undertaken by Perkins, Bacon. It has also been seen on horizontally laid paper (*Price* £1100).

SIDEWAYS WATERMARK. W **2/3** when sideways show two points of star downwards.

1863–71. W **2** (*Small Star*). *Rough perf 14 to 16.*

4	**1**	1d. green (3.64)			60·00	12·00
		a. Wmk sideways			—	20·00
5		1d. yellowish green			95·00	26·00
6		6d. rose (*shades*) (5.63)			£600	12·00
		a. Wmk sideways			—	60·00
7		6d. orange-red (*shades*) (5.66)		£650	12·00
8		6d. dull rose-red (*wmk sideways*)		£3000	£225
9		6d. vermilion (5.71)			£750	12·00
		a. Double impression			—	£1800

1873 (Jan). W **2** (*Small Star, sideways*). *Clean-cut perf* 15.

10	**1**	1d. deep green			70·00	27·00
		a. Bisected diag (on cover)			†	£6000
		b. Imperf between (pair)			—	£3750

No. 10a, and later bisected 1d. values, were authorised until 1881 to pay the island newspaper rate (½d.) or the newspaper rate to Great Britain (1½d.). Examples also exist on covers to France.

3 Large Star

4 Broad-pointed Star

1873 (Sept)–**74**. W **3** (*Large Star*). *Intermediate perf* 15.

11	**1**	1d. blue-green (*wmk sideways*) (2.74)		60·00	17·00
		a. Double impression				
		b. Bisected diag (on cover)			†	
12		6d. orange-vermilion			£600	26·00

POSTAGE

5

ONE SHILLING

(6)

NOTE. The early ½d., 2½d., 4d. and 1s. postage stamps were made by surcharging the undenominated Type **5** design.

The surcharges were from two founts of type—one about 1½ mm high, the other 2 mm high—so there are short and tall letters on the same stamp; also the spacing varies considerably, so that the length of the words varies.

Examples of Type **5** with surcharges, but without the "POSTAGE" inscription, are revenue stamps.

1875 (July). *Surch with T* **6**. *W* **3**. *P* 14.
13 **5** 1s. deep mauve (B.) .. .. £650 9·00
   a. "SHLLIING" .. .. † £700
   b. "NE SHILLING" .. .. † £2500
   c. Inverted "S" in "POSTAGE" .. £3500 £500
   d. "OSTAGE" .. .. .. † £2000

1875 (Dec). *W* **3** (*Large Star, upright*).
14 **1** 1d. green *to yellow-green* (*p* 14) .. 55·00 5·50
   a. Bisected diag (on cover) .. † £6500
15 1d. green (*p* 15) £7000 £2000
No. 14 was perforated at Somerset House. 40 sheets of No. 15 were perforated by Perkins, Bacon to replace spoilages and to complete the order.

1878 (Aug). *W* **2** (*Small Star, sideways*). *Intermediate perf* 15.
16 **1** 1d. green .. .. .. £225 26·00
   b. Bisected diag (on cover) .. †
17 6d. deep vermilion .. .. £750 26·00
   a. Double impression .. .. — £1500

1879 (Dec). *W* **2** (*Small Star, upright*). *Rough perf* 15.
18 **1** 1d. pale green (*thin paper*) .. £300 19·00
   a. Double impression .. .. †
   b. Bisected diag (on cover) .. †

1881 (Apr). *W* **2** (*Small Star, sideways*). *Rough perf* 14½.
19 **1** 1d. green .. .. .. £110 6·00
   a. Bisected diag (on cover) .. † £6500

POSTAGE   POSTAGE   POSTAGE

TWO PENCE HALF-PENNY.

HALF-PENNY   FOUR PENCE
  (7)   (8)   (9)

1881 (Apr). *Surch with T* **7/9**. *P* 14½. (*a*) *W* **3** (*Large Star, sideways on* ½d.)
20 **5** ½d. pale mauve .. .. 30·00 10·00
21 ½d. deep mauve .. .. 11·00 5·50
   a. Imperf (pair) £300
   ab. Ditto. "OSTAGE" (R.9/4) .. £3250
   b. Surch double £275
   c. "OSTAGE" (R.9/4) .. £180 £130
   d. No hyphen £180 £130
   e. "ALF-PENNY" £3000
   f. Wmk upright £300 £140
   g. Ditto. "OSTAGE" (R.9/4) .. £1700 £750
22 2½d. rose-lake .. .. 50·00 5·50
   a. Imperf (pair) £400
   b. Imperf between (horiz pair) .. £3250
   c. No stop .. .. .. £250 75·00
   d. "PENCF" (R.8/12) .. £450 £180
23 4d. blue .. .. .. 90·00 8·00
   a. Wmk sideways
   b. Inverted "S" in "POSTAGE"
   (*b*) *W* **4** (*Broad-pointed Star*)
24 **5** 2½d. rose-lake .. .. £130 48·00
   a. No stop £550 £200
   b. "PENCF" (R.8/12) .. £750 £275
25 2½d. claret £400 £120
   a. No stop £1000 £475
   b. "PENCF" (R.8/12) .. £1500 £600
25c 2½d. deep claret £600 £225
   d. No stop £2250 £900
   e. "PENCF" (R.8/12) .. £2750 £1100
26 4d. blue £225 £180
Examples of the "F" for "E" error on the 2½d. value should not be confused with a somewhat similar broken "E" variety. The latter is always without the stop and shows other damage to the "E". The authentic error always occurs with the full stop shown.
The "no stop" variety occurs on R.3/4, R.6/2, R.8/3 and R.9/7.

ONE PENNY POSTAGE.

POSTAGE   POSTAGE
  (10)   (11)   (12)

1883 (Jan). *Revenue stamps* (*T* **5** *with green surcharge as in T* **10**) *optd for postage. W* **2** (*Small Star*). *P* 14½.
   (*a*) *Optd horizontally with T* **11**.
27 **5** 1d. orange .. .. £250 48·00
   a. "POSTAGE" inverted .. £1700 £1200
   b. "POSTAGE" double .. £1200 £1100
   c. Inverted "S" in "POSTAGE" .. £800 £600
   d. Bisected diag (on cover) .. † £3000
  (*b*) *Optd diagonally with T* **11** *twice on each stamp, the stamp being cut and each half used as* ½d.
28 **5** Half of 1d. orange £650 £225
   a. Unsevered pair £3750 £1200
   b. "POSTAGE" inverted .. £1200
  (*c*) *Optd with T* **12**, *the stamps divided diagonally and each half used as* ½d.
29 **5** Half of 1d. orange £200 £110
   a. Unsevered pair £1200 £450
Nos. 27/9 exist with wmk either upright or sideways.
1d. Revenue stamps with "POSTAGE" added in black manuscript were used at Gouyave during February and March 1883 (*Price* £2250, *used*). Similar manuscript overprints, in black or red, were also used at Sauteurs in September 1886 (*Price* £3250, *used*).

---

13   (14)   15

(Typo D.L.R.)

1883. *Wmk Crown CA. P* 14.
30 **13** ½d. dull green (February) 90 70
   a. *Tête-bêche* (vert pair) .. 4·00 14·00
31 1d. carmine (February) .. .. 60·00 3·25
   a. *Tête-bêche* (vert pair) .. £225 £225
32 2½d. ultramarine (May) .. .. 6·50 70
   a. *Tête-bêche* (vert pair) .. 24·00 50·00
33 4d. greyish slate (May) .. .. 4·50 1·75
   a. *Tête-bêche* (vert pair) .. 17·00 55·00
34 6d. mauve (May) .. .. .. 3·00 3·75
   a. *Tête-bêche* (vert pair) .. 18·00 55·00
35 8d. grey-brown (February) .. 8·50 12·00
   a. *Tête-bêche* (vert pair) .. 32·00 75·00
36 1s. pale violet (April) .. .. £100 55·00
   a. *Tête-bêche* (vert pair) .. £850
30/36 .. .. .. *Set of* 7 £160 65·00
Types **13** and **15** were printed in rows *tête-bêche* in the sheets.

1886. *Revenue stamps* (*T* **5** *with green surch as T* **10**), *surch with T* **14**. *P* 14. (*a*) *Wmk Large Star, T* **3**.
37 **5** 1d. on 1½d. orange (October) .. 32·00 28·00
   a. Surch inverted £300 £300
   b. Surch double £475 £300
   c. "THRFE" £250 £225
   d. "PFNCE" £250 £225
   e. "HALH" £250 £225
   f. Bisected diag (on cover) .. † £1900
38 1d. on 1s. orange (December) .. 32·00 30·00
   a. "POSTAGE" (no stop) .. £350
   b. "SHILLNG" £425 £375
   c. Wide space (3½ mm) between "ONE" and "SHILLING" .. £300 £250
   d. Bisected diag (on cover) .. † £1900
  (*b*) *Wmk Small Star, T* **2**
39 **5** 1d. on 4d. orange (November) .. £140 90·00

1887 (Jan). *Wmk Crown CA. P* 14.
40 **15** 1d. carmine (Optd S. £50) .. 50 40
   a. *Tête-bêche* (vert pair) .. 1·75 17·00

4d.   **HALF PENNY**
POSTAGE   **POSTAGE**
  (16)   (17)

1888 (31 Mar)–**91**. *Revenue stamps* (*T* **5** *with green surch as T* **10**) *further surcharged. W* **2**. *P* 14½, *and No.* 35.
  I. *Surch with T* **16**.
  (*a*) 4 *mm between value and* "POSTAGE"
41 **5** 4d. on 2s. orange .. .. 35·00 17·00
   a. Upright "d" (R. 5/6) .. £750 £400
   b. Wide space (2¼ mm) between "TWO" and "SHILLINGS" .. £250 £150
   c. First "S" in "SHILLINGS" inverted £450 £325
   d. Imperf between (horiz pair)
  (*b*) 5 *mm between value and* "POSTAGE"
42 **5** 4d. on 2s. orange .. .. 60·00 28·00
   a. Wide space £300 £225
   b. "S" inverted £650 £550
  II. *Surch as T* **17** (December 1889)
43 **5** ½d. on 2s. orange .. .. 12·00 17·00
   a. Surch double £300 £325
   b. Wide space £110 £130
   c. "S" inverted £275 £300

POSTAGE   POSTAGE
d.   **AND**
AND   **REVENUE**
1   **2¼d.**
REVENUE   **1d.**
  (18)   (19)   (20)

  III. *Surch with T* **18** (December 1890)
44 **5** 1d. on 2s. orange .. .. 70·00 70·00
   a. Surch inverted £550
   b. Wide space £325 £325
   c. "S" inverted £650 £650
  IV. *Surch with T* **19** (January 1891)
45 **5** 1d. on 2s. orange .. .. 50·00 50·00
   a. No stop after "1d" (R.3/8) .. £325
   b. Wide space £250 £250
   c. "S" inverted £500 £500
46 **13** 1d. on 8d. grey-brown .. 9·00 11·00
   a. *Tête-bêche* (vert pair) .. 40·00 60·00
   b. Surch inverted £300 £275
   c. No stop after "1d" (R.6/5) .. £250 £250
  V. *Surch with T* **20** (December 1891)
47 **13** 2½d. on 8d. grey-brown (Optd S. £65) .. 8·00 11·00
   a. *Tête-bêche* (vert pair) .. 40·00 60·00
   b. Inverted surcharge
   c. Double surcharge £750 £800
   d. Double surcharge, one inverted £550 £500
   e. Treble surcharge, two inverted — £850
The wide space between "TWO" and "SHILLINGS" occurs on R. 1/4 and 10/3 of the original 2s. Revenue stamp which was printed in sheets of 120 (12×10).

The surcharges, Types **16/19**, were applied to half sheets as a setting of 60 (12×5).
There are two varieties of fraction in Type **20**, which each occur 30 times in the setting; in one the "1" has horizontal serif and the "2" commences in a ball; in the other the "1" has sloping serif and the "2" is without ball.
See also D4/7.

21   22   23 Flagship of Columbus (Columbus named Grenada "La Concepcion")

(Type D.L.R.)

1895 (6 Sept)–**99**. *Wmk Crown CA. P* 14.
48 **22** ½d. mauve and green (9.99) .. 2·50 90
49 **21** 1d. mauve and carmine (5.96) .. 4·25 60
50 2d. mauve and brown (9.99) .. 38·00 32·00
51 2½d. mauve and ultramarine .. 5·00 1·00
52 **22** 3d. mauve and orange .. 6·50 16·00
53 **21** 6d. mauve and green .. 9·50 16·00
54 **22** 8d. mauve and black .. 12·00 30·00
55 1s. green and orange .. 17·00 28·00
48/55 .. .. .. *Set of* 8 80·00 £110
48/55 Optd "Specimen" .. *Set of* 8 £140

(Recess D.L.R.)

1898 (15 Aug). 400*th Anniv of Discovery of Grenada by Columbus. Wmk Crown CC. P* 14
56 **23** 2½d. ultramarine (Optd S. £85) .. 13·00 5·50
   a. Bluish paper .. .. 32·00 40·00

24   25

(Typo D.L.R.)

1902. *Wmk Crown CA. P* 14.
57 **24** ½d. dull purple and green .. 3·00 30
58 **25** 1d. dull purple and carmine .. 3·00 20
59 2d. dull purple and brown .. 3·00 7·00
60 2½d. dull purple and ultramarine .. 3·50 1·75
61 **24** 3d. dull purple and orange .. 3·50 6·00
62 **25** 6d. dull purple and green .. 2·50 15·00
63 **24** 1s. green and orange .. 3·25 20·00
64 2s. green and ultramarine .. 17·00 50·00
65 **25** 5s. green and carmine .. 38·00 55·00
66 **24** 10s. green and purple .. £100 £190
57/66 .. .. .. *Set of* 10 £160 £300
57/66 Optd "Specimen" .. *Set of* 10 £200

1904–6. *Wmk Mult Crown CA. Ordinary paper. P* 14.
67 **24** ½d. purple and green (1905) .. 17·00 21·00
68 **25** 1d. purple and carmine .. 9·00 2·50
69 2d. purple and brown (1905) .. 48·00 85·00
70 2½d. purple and ultramarine (1905) .. 48·00 65·00
71 **24** 3d. purple and orange (1905) .. 2·50 6·50
   a. Chalk-surfaced paper .. 2·50 7·50
72 **25** 6d. purple and green (1906) .. 4·50 8·00
   a. Chalk-surfaced paper .. 6·50 14·00
73 **24** 1s. green and orange (1905) .. 6·00 22·00
74 2s. green and ultramarine (1906) .. 35·00 70·00
   a. Chalk-surfaced paper .. 25·00 75·00
75 **25** 5s. green and carmine (1906) .. 55·00 85·00
76 **24** 10s. green and purple (1906) .. £140 £225
67/76 .. .. .. *Set of* 10 £300 £500
Examples of most values between Nos. 57 and 76 are known showing a forged G.P.O. Grenada B.W.I. postmark dated "OC 6 09".

26   Badge of the Colony   27

(Recess D.L.R.)

1906. *Wmk Mult Crown CA. P* 14.
77 **26** ½d. green .. .. .. 2·00 30
78 1d. carmine .. .. .. 2·75 10
   y. Wmk inverted and reversed
79 2d. orange .. .. .. 1·75 3·00
80 2½d. blue .. .. .. 3·50 1·50
   a. Ultramarine .. .. 7·50 3·50

(Typo D.L.R.)

1908. *Wmk Crown CA. Chalk-surfaced paper. P* 14.
82 **27** 1s. black/*green* .. .. 19·00 38·00
83 10s. green and red/*green* .. 80·00 £150

08–11. *Wmk Mult Crown CA. Chalk-surfaced paper. P* 14.
27	3d. dull purple/*yellow*			3·00	1·75
5	6d. dull purple and purple			18·00	23·00
	1s. black/*green* (1911)			5·00	4·00
7	2s. blue and purple/*blue*			18·00	12·00
8	5s. green and red/*yellow*			50·00	65·00
7/88			*Set of* 11	£180	£250
7/80, 82/5, 87/8 Optd "Specimen"			*Set of* 10	£120	

Examples of Nos. 82/8 are known showing a forged G.P.O.
renada B.W.I. postmark dated "OC 6 09".

WAR TAX   WAR TAX
28   (29)   (30

(Typo D.L.R.)

1913 (3 Jan)–22. *Wmk Mult Crown CA. Chalk-surfaced paper*
(3d. *to* 10s.). *P* 14.
89	28	½d. yellow-green		90	1·25
90		½d. green		90	70
91		1d. red		2·25	30
92		1d. scarlet (1916)		2·75	50
		w. Wmk inverted			
93		2d. orange		1·50	30
94		2½d. bright blue		1·40	2·50
95		2½d. dull blue (1920)		4·00	4·00
96		3d. purple/*yellow*		55	85
		a. *White back* (3.14) (Optd S. £30)		45	1·50
		b. *On lemon* (1917)		3·50	8·50
		c. *On pale yellow* (1921)		6·00	24·00
97		6d. dull and bright purple		1·25	7·50
98		1s. black/*green*		1·00	7·50
		a. *White back* (3.14) (Optd S. £30)		1·00	4·50
		b. *On blue-green, olive back* (1917)		48·00	15·00
		c. *On emerald surface*		1·50	8·50
		d. *On emerald back* (6.22) (Optd S. £30)		1·00	8·50
		dw. Wmk inverted		75·00	
99		2s. purple and blue/*blue*		4·50	10·00
100		5s. green and red/*yellow*		16·00	55·00
		a. *On pale yellow* (1921) (Optd S. £45)		24·00	75·00
101		10s. green and red/*green*		48·00	80·00
		a. *On emerald back* (6.22) (Optd S. £55)		50·00	£130
89/101			*Set of* 10	70·00	£140
89/101 Optd "Specimen"			*Set of* 10	£150	
98 Optd in black instead of red				30·00	

1916 (1 June). *Optd by Govt Press, St. George's. With T* 29.
109	28	1d. red (shades) (H/S S. £50)		2·25	1·75
		a. Opt inverted		£275	
		b. "T△X"		55·00	70·00

A small "A" in "WAR", 2 mm high is found on Nos. 29, 38 and 48
of the setting of 60 and a very small "A" in "TAX", 1½ mm high, on
No. 11. Value about twice normal. The normal "A" is 2¼ mm high.
No. 109b is on No. 56 of the setting.

1916 (1 Sept)–18. *Optd with T* 30 *in London.*
111	28	1d. scarlet		30	20
		a. Carmine-red/*bluish* (5.18)		3·25	1·50
		w. Wmk inverted			
111 Optd "Specimen"				40·00	

1921–32. *Wmk Mult Script CA. Chalk-surfaced paper* (3d.
(No. 122) *to* 10s.) *P* 14.
112	28	½d. green		1·25	15
113		1d. carmine-red		80	40
114		1d. brown (1923)		1·50	20
115		1½d. rose-red (6.22)		1·50	1·50
116		2d. orange		1·25	15
117		2d. grey (1926)		2·50	2·00
117a		2½d. dull blue		3·00	2·00
118		2½d. grey (6.22)		75	7·50
119		2½d. bright blue (1926)		3·00	3·25
120		2½d. ultramarine (1931)		4·25	7·50
120a		2½d. chalky blue and blue (1932)		48·00	48·00
121		3d. bright blue (6.22)		1·25	8·00
122		3d. purple/*yellow* (1926)		3·00	4·75
123		4d. black and red/*yellow* (1926)		1·00	3·50
124		5d. dull purple & sage-green (27.12.22)		1·50	3·50
125		6d. dull and bright purple		1·25	15·00
126		6d. black and carmine (1926)		2·25	2·50
127		9d. dull purple and black (27.12.22)		2·25	7·50
128		1s. black/*emerald* (1923)		2·50	30·00
		w. Wmk inverted			
129		1s. chestnut (1926)		3·00	10·00
130		2s. purple and blue/*blue* (1922)		6·00	14·00
131		2s. 6d. black and carmine/*blue* (1929)		6·00	16·00
132		3s. green and violet (27.12.22)		6·00	27·00
133		5s. green and red/*pale yellow* (1923)		12·00	30·00
134		10s. green and red/*emerald* (1923)		50·00	£130
112/19, 121/34			*Set of* 22	£100	£275
112/34 Optd/Perf "Specimen"			*Set of* 23	£300	

31 Grand Anse Beach   32 Badge of the Colony

---

33 Grand Etang   34 St. George's

(Recess Waterlow)

1934 (23 Oct)–36. *Wmk Mult Script CA* (*sideways on T* 32).
P 12½.
135	31	½d. green		15	60
		a. Perf 12½ × 13½ (1936)		3·50	32·00
136	32	1d. black and sepia		80	2·00
		a. Perf 13½ × 12½ (1936)		65	35
137	33	1½d. black and scarlet		4·75	2·50
		a. Perf 12½ × 13½ (1936)		90	55
138	32	2d. black and orange		90	40
139	34	2½d. blue		40	30
140	32	3d. black and olive-green		55	1·75
141		6d. black and purple		1·25	1·10
142		1s. black and brown		90	2·50
143		2s. 6d. black and ultramarine		7·00	22·00
144		5s. black and violet		32·00	65·00
135/144			*Set of* 10	40·00	65·00
135/44 Perf "Specimen"			*Set of* 10	£160	

1935 (6 May). *Silver Jubilee. As Nos.* 91/4 *of Antigua but ptd
by Waterlow. P* 11×12.
145		½d. black and green		40	60
		k. Kite and vertical log		35·00	
		l. Kite and horizontal log		38·00	
146		1d. ultramarine and grey		50	1·00
		l. Kite and horizontal log		38·00	
147		1½d. deep blue and scarlet		50	1·00
		l. Kite and horizontal log		50·00	
148		1s. slate and purple		5·50	15·00
		l. Kite and horizontal log		£130	
145/8			*Set of* 4	6·25	16·00
145/8 Perf "Specimen"			*Set of* 4	70·00	

For illustrations of plate varieties see Catalogue Introduction.

1937 (12 May). *Coronation. As Nos.* 95/7 *of Antigua.
P* 11x11½.
149		1d. violet		40	20
150		1½d. carmine		40	20
151		2½d. blue		80	30
149/51			*Set of* 3	1·40	65
149/51 Perf "Specimen"			*Set of* 3	50·00	

35 King George VI

(Photo Harrison)

1937 (12 July)–50. *Wmk Mult Script CA. Chalk-surfaced
paper. P* 15×14.
152	35	¼d. brown		1·40	10
		a. Ordinary paper (11.42)		30	50
		b. Ordinary paper. *Chocolate* (1.45)		20	60
		c. Chalk-surfaced paper. *Chocolate* (8.50)		50	2·00

The ordinary paper is thick, smooth and opaque.

36 Grand Anse Beach   40 Badge of the Colony

Colon flaw
(R. 5/8. Corrected on
ptg of Nov 1950)

(Recess D.L.R. (10s.), Waterlow (others))

1938 (16 Mar)–50. *As T* 31/4 (*but portrait of King George VI as
in T* 36) *and T* 40. *Wmk Mult Script CA* (*sideways on T* 32).
P 12½ *or* 12 × 13 (10s.).
153	36	½d. yellow-green		4·50	1·00
		a. Perf 12½ × 13½ (1938)		6·00	80
		b. Perf 12½. *Blue-green*		60	1·25
		ba. Perf 12½ × 13½. *Blue-green*		5·00	4·50
154	32	1d. black and sepia		1·00	20
		a. Perf 13½ × 12½ (1938)		50	50
155	33	1½d. black and scarlet		50	50
		a. Perf 12½ × 13½ (1938)		2·25	30
156	32	2d. black and orange		30	50
		a. Perf 13½ × 12½ (1938)		2·50	40

157	34	2½d. bright blue (?March 1950)		30	30
		a. Perf 12½ × 13½ (?March 1950)		£4000	£225
158	32	3d. black and olive-green		9·00	1·40
		a. Perf 13½ × 12½ (16.3.38)		6·00	80
		ab. Perf 13½ × 12½. *Black and brown-olive* (1942)		30	80
		b. Perf 12½. *Black and brown-olive* (16.8.50)		30	1·60
		ba. Colon flaw		42·00	
159		6d. black and purple		1·25	40
		a. Perf 13½ × 12½ (1942)		2·25	50
160		1s. black and brown		2·25	30
		a. Perf 13½ × 12½ (1941)		3·50	1·25
161		2s. black and ultramarine		16·00	1·50
		a. Perf 13½ × 12½ (1941)		19·00	1·50
162		5s. black and violet		3·50	1·50
		a. Perf 13½ × 12½ (1947)		2·75	5·50
163	40	10s. steel blue and carmine (*narrow*) (p 12 × 13)		55·00	9·00
		a. Perf 14. *Steel blue and bright carmine* (*narrow*)		£180	45·00
		b. Perf 14. *Slate-blue and bright carmine* (*narrow*) (1943)		£190	£110
		c. Perf 12. *Slate-blue and bright carmine* (*narrow*) (1943)		£450	£700
		d. Perf 14. *Slate-blue and carmine-lake* (*wide*) (1944)		85·00	7·50
		e. Perf 14. *Slate-blue and carmine* (*narrow*) (1943)		27·00	8·00
		f. Perf 14. *Blue-black and carmine* (*narrow*) (1943)		25·00	25·00
		f. Perf 14. *Blue-black and bright carmine* (*wide*) (1947)		25·00	25·00
152/63e			*Set of* 12	45·00	12·00
152/63 Perf "Specimen"			*Set of* 12	£225	

In the earlier printings of the 10s. the paper was dampened
before printing and the subsequent shrinkage produced narrow
frames 23½ to 23¾ mm wide. Later printings were made on dry
paper producing wide frames 24¼ mm wide.

No. 163a is one of the earlier printings line perf 13.8 × 14.1.
No. 163b is line-perf 14.1.
Nos. 163b/c show a blurred centre caused by the use of a worn
plate.
Nos. 163a and 163b may be found with gum more or less
yellow due to local climatic conditions.
Examples of No. 163c are known showing forged St. George's
postmarks dated "21 AU 42", "21 AU 43" or "2 OC 43".

1946 (25 Sept). *Victory. As Nos.* 110/11 *of Antigua.*
164		1½d. carmine		10	10
165		3½d. blue		10	10
164/5 Perf "Specimen"			*Set of* 2	50·00	

1948 (27 Oct). *Royal Silver Wedding. As Nos.* 112/13 *of
Antigua.*
166		1½d. scarlet		15	10
167		10s. slate-green		8·00	16·00

(New Currency. 100 cents = 1 West Indian, later Eastern
Caribbean, dollar)

1949 (10 Oct). *75th Anniv of Universal Postal Union. As Nos.*
114/17 *of Antigua.*
168		5 c. ultramarine		20	10
169		6 c. olive		90	70
170		12 c. magenta		35	30
171		24 c. red-brown		35	30
168/71			*Set of* 4	1·60	1·25

41 King George VI   42 Badge of the Colony   43 Badge of the Colony

(Recess B.W. (T 41), D.L.R. (others))

1951 (8 Jan). *Wmk Mult Script CA. P* 11½ (*T* 41), 11½ × 12½
(*T* 42), *and* 11½ × 13 (*T* 43).
172	41	½ c. black and red-brown		15	1·00
173		1 c. black and emerald-green		15	25
174		2 c. black and brown		15	30
175		3 c. black and rose-carmine		15	10
176		4 c. black and orange		35	40
177		5 c. black and violet		20	10
178		6 c. black and olive		30	60
179		7 c. black and light blue		1·75	10
180		12 c. black and purple		2·25	30
181	42	25 c. black and sepia		2·25	50
182		50 c. black and blue		6·00	40
183		$1.50, black and yellow-orange		7·50	4·75
184	43	$2.50, slate-blue and carmine		5·50	5·00
172/184			*Set of* 13	24·00	12·00

1951 (16 Feb). *Inauguration of B.W.I. University College. As Nos.*
118/19 *of Antigua.*
185		3 c. black and carmine		45	20
186		6 c. black and olive		45	20

NEW CONSTITUTION

1951
(44)

King George VI - Grenada

Contact us for all your **King George VI** requirements; from basic stamps, varieties, perforations, in singles, multiples or sheets to listed shades and individual printings as per SG or the latest edition (17th) of **The Commonwealth King George VI Catalogue.**

This comprehensively revised work is the result of an 18-month overhaul of the old B & K King George VI Catalogue and is now published by Murray Payne Ltd.

Request our individually-tailored lists of specialised items, or a free copy of our newsletter
'Sixth *Sense*'

P. O. Box 1135, Axbridge, Somerset, England BS26 2EW
Telephone (01934) 732511 Fax: (01934) 733498
Email: murraypayne@compuserve.com

Classic Albums For Traditional Collectors
SG Classic Albums Re-introduced By Popular Demand

New Imperial Stamp Album (1840-1936)

Successor to the Imperial album first published in 1873, this new edition provides space for the stamps of the British Empire, Egypt and Iraq, from SG1 up until the end of King George V. Provision is made for major variations of watermark, perforation and shade as well as postage dues, officials, special delivery stamps and an illustrated catalogue is included on the facing leaf. Fastbound with glassine interleaving.

King George VI Album (1936-1953)

Loose Leaf Edition
Consists of four luxurious 22-ring binders presented in two matching slipcases. Cream cartridge leaves feature glassine interleaving whilst a special mount pack and extra blank pages are also available separately.

Fastbound Edition
Leaves have been printed both sides, interleaved with glassine and securely bound into a single attractive album. Not designed to be used with hingeless mounts.

New Age Album (1953-1962)

This New Age album first appeared in the late 1930's. In response to considerable demand we have carefully reprinted the popular 460 page section covering the early Elizabethan period. Fine cartridge leaves contain spaces for all Commonwealth stamps issued between 1953 -1962 with provision for listed shades and perforation changes. Five special title pages enable you to split your collection into individual springback binders, available separately.

**Available from our
London showroom at 399 Strand
and by mail order**

Stanley Gibbons Publications
5/7 Parkside, Christchurch Road,
Ringwood, Hants BH24 3SH
Tel:+44 (0)1425 472363 Fax: +44 (0)1425 470247
e.mail: sales@stangib.demon.co.uk internet: http://www.stangib.com/

STANLEY GIBBONS

Phone 0800 611 622 Today For Your Free Colour Brochure

1951 (21 Sept). *New Constitution. Nos. 175/7 and 180 optd with T 44 by B.W.*
187 41 3 c. black and rose-carmine . . 10 10
188 4 c. black and orange 10 10
189 5 c. black and violet (R.) 10 10
190 12 c. black and purple 10 15
187/90 . . . . *Set of 4* 30 40

1953 (3 June). *Coronation. As No. 120 of Antigua.*
191 3 c. black and carmine-red . . 20 10

45 Queen   46 Badge of the   47 Badge of the
Elizabeth II   Colony   Colony

(Recess B.W. (T 45), D.L.R. (T 46/7))

1953 (15 June)–59. *Wmk Mult Script CA. P 11½ (T 45), 11½ × 12½ (T 46), or 11½ × 13 (T 47).*
192 45 ½ c. black and brown (28.12.53) . . 10 10
193 1 c. black and deep emerald . . 10 10
194 2 c. black and sepia (15.9.53) . . 30 10
195 3 c. black and carmine-red (22.2.54) . . 10 10
196 4 c. black and brown-orange (22.2.54) . . 10 10
197 5 c. black and deep violet (22.2.54) . . 10 10
198 6 c. black and olive-green (28.12.53) . . 45 70
199 7 c. black and blue (6.6.55) . . 1·25 10
200 12 c. black and reddish purple . . 30 10
201 46 25 c. black and sepia (10.1.55) . . 1·25 20
202 50 c. black and deep blue (2.12.55) . . 5·50 40
203 $1.50, black & brown-orange (2.12.55) 11·00 11·00
204 47 $2.50, slate-blue & carmine (16.11.59) 18·00 8·50
192/204 . . *Set of 13* 35·00 19·00
On 23 December 1965, No. 203 was issued surcharged "2" but this was intended for fiscal and revenue purposes and it was not authorised to be used postally, although some are known to have passed through the mail.
For stamps in Types 45/6 watermarked w 12 see Nos. 214/20.

1958 (22 Apr). *Inauguration of British Caribbean Federation. As Nos. 135/7 of Antigua.*
205 3 c. deep green 35 10
206 6 c. blue 45 60
207 12 c. scarlet 55 10
205/7 . . . . *Set of 3* 1·25 70

48 Queen Victoria, Queen Elizabeth II,
Mail Van and Post Office, St. George's

(Photo Harrison)

1961 (1 June). *Grenada Stamp Centenary. T 48 and similar horiz designs. W w 12. P 14½ × 14.*
208 3 c. crimson and black . . 25 10
209 8 c. bright blue and orange . . 55 25
210 25 c. lake and blue . . 55 25
208/10 . . . . *Set of 3* 1·25 55
Designs:—8 c. Queen Victoria, Queen Elizabeth II and flagship of Columbus; 25 c. Queen Victoria, Queen Elizabeth II, *Solent I* (paddle-steamer) and Douglas DC-3 aircraft.

1963 (4 June). *Freedom from Hunger. As No. 146 of Antigua.*
211 8 c. bluish green 30 15

1963 (2 Sept). *Red Cross Centenary. As Nos. 147/8 of Antigua.*
212 3 c. red and black . . 10 15
213 25 c. red and blue . . 20 15

1964 (12 May)–66. *As Nos. 194/8, 201/1, but wmk w 12.*
214 45 2 c. black and sepia . . 10 10
215 3 c. black and carmine-red . . 15 10
216 4 c. black and brown-orange . . 15 40
217 5 c. black and deep violet . . 15 10
218 6 c. black and olive-green (4.1.66) . . £190 65·00
219 12 c. black and reddish purple . . 20 10
220 46 25 c. black and sepia . . 2·25 40
214/20 . . . . *Set of 7* £190 65·00

1965 (17 May). *I.T.U. Centenary. As Nos. 166/7 of Antigua.*
221 5 c. red-orange and yellow-olive . . 10 10
222 50 c. lemon and light red . . 25 20

1965 (25 Oct). *International Co-operation Year. As Nos. 168/9 of Antigua*
223 1 c. reddish purple and turquoise-green . . 10 15
224 25 c. deep bluish green and lavender . . 20 15

1966 (24 Jan). *Churchill Commemoration. As Nos. 170/3 of Antigua.*
225 1 c. new blue . . 10 15
226 3 c. deep green . . 10 15
227 25 c. brown . . 15 10
228 35 c. bluish violet . . 25 15
225/8 . . . . *Set of 4* 45 40

1966 (4 Feb). *Royal Visit. As Nos. 174/5 of Antigua.*
229 3 c. black and ultramarine . . 25 15
230 35 c. black and magenta . . 65 15

52 Hillsborough, Carriacou 53 Badge of the Colony

54 Queen Elizabeth II 55 Map of Grenada

(Des V. Whiteley. Photo Harrison)

1966 (1 Apr). *Horiz designs as T 52, and T 53/5. Multicoloured. W w 12. P 14½ ($1, $2, $3) or 14½×13½ (others).*
231 1 c. Type 52 . . 20 30
232 2 c. Bougainvillea . . 20 10
233 3 c. Flamboyant plant . . 20 20
234 5 c. Levera beach . . 40 10
235 6 c. Carenage, St. George's . . 40 10
236 8 c. Annandale Falls . . 40 10
  w. Wmk inverted
237 10 c. Cocoa pods . . 30 10
238 12 c. Inner Harbour . . 30 40
239 15 c. Nutmeg . . 30 40
240 25 c. St. George's . . 30 10
241 35 c. Grand Anse beach . . 30 10
242 50 c. Bananas . . 80 10
243 $1 Type 53 . . 6·00 2·50
244 $2 Type 54 . . 4·50 4·00
245 $3 Type 55 . . 4·50 10·00
231/45 . . *Set of 15* 17·00 17·00

1966 (1 July). *World Cup Football Championships. As Nos. 176/7 of Antigua.*
246 5 c. violet, yellow-green, lake & yellow-brn 10 10
247 50 c. chocolate, blue-green, lake & yelllow-brn 25 20

1966 (20 Sept). *Inauguration of W.H.O. Headquarters, Geneva. As Nos. 178/9 of Antigua.*
248 8 c. black, yellow-green and light blue 10 10
249 25 c. black, light purple and yellow-brown 25 20

1966 (1 Dec). *20th Anniv of U.N.E.S.C.O. As Nos. 196/8 of Antigua.*
250 2 c. slate-violet, red, yellow and orange . . 10 10
251 15 c. orange-yellow, violet and deep olive . . 15 10
252 50 c. black, bright purple and orange . . 30 50
250/2 . . . . *Set of 3* 45 55

ASSOCIATED STATEHOOD

ASSOCIATED   1c
STATEHOOD   expo67
1967   MONTREAL CANADA
(67)   (68)

1967 (3 Mar). *Statehood. Nos. 232/3, 236 and 240 optd with T 67, in silver*
253 2 c. Bougainvillea . . 10 15
254 3 c. Flamboyant plant . . 10 10
255 8 c. Annandale Falls . . 15 10
256 25 c. St. George's . . 15 15
253/6 . . . . *Set of 4* 30 30

1967 (June). *World Fair, Montreal. Nos. 232, 237, 239 and 243/4 surch as T 68 or optd with "Expo" emblem only.*
257 1 c. on 15 c. Nutmeg . . 10 20
  a. Surch and opt albino . . 14·00
258 2 c. Bougainvillea . . 10 20
259 3 c. on 10 c. Cocoa pods . . 10 20
  w. Wmk inverted . . 7·00
260 $1 Type 53 . . 30 25
261 $2 Type 54 . . 45 30
257/61 . . . . *Set of 5* 70 1·00

COVER PRICES

Cover factors are quoted at the beginning of each country for most issues to 1945. An explanation of the system can be found on page x. The factors quoted do not, however, apply to philatelic covers.

ASSOCIATED
STATEHOOD
(69)   70 Kennedy and Local Flower

1967 (Oct). *Statehood. Nos. 231/45 optd with T 69.*
262 1 c. Type 52 . . 10 10
263 2 c. Bougainvillea . . 10 10
264 3 c. Flamboyant plant . . 10 10
265 5 c. Levera beach . . 10 10
266 6 c. Carenage, St. George's . . 10 10
267 8 c. Annandale Falls . . 10 10
268 10 c. Cocoa pods . . 10 10
269 12 c. Inner Harbour . . 10 10
270 15 c. Nutmeg . . 15 10
271 25 c. St. George's . . 20 10
272 35 c. Grand Anse beach . . 55 10
273 50 c. Bananas . . 70 20
274 $1 Type 53 . . 70 60
275 $2 Type 54 . . 1·25 3·00
276 $3 Type 55 . . 2·25 3·00
262/76 . . . . *Set of 15* 5·50 7·00
See also No. 295.

(Des M. Shamir. Photo Harrison)

1968 (13 Jan). *50th Birth Anniv of President Kennedy. T 70 and similar horiz designs. Multicoloured. P 14½ × 14.*
277 1 c. Type 70 . . 10 15
278 15 c. Type 70 . . 10 10
279 25 c. Kennedy and strelitzia . . 10 10
280 35 c. Kennedy and roses . . 10 10
281 50 c. As 25 c. . . 15 20
282 $1 As 35 c. . . 25 50
277/82 . . . . *Set of 6* 55 80

73 Scout Bugler   76 "Near Antibes"

(Des K. Plowitz. Photo Govt Printer, Israel)

1968 (17 Feb). *World Scout Jamboree, Idaho. T 73 and similar vert designs. Multicoloured. P 13 × 13½.*
283 1 c. Type 73 . . 10 10
284 2 c. Scouts camping . . 10 10
285 3 c. Lord Baden-Powell . . 10 10
286 35 c. Type 73 . . 20 10
287 50 c. As 2 c. . . 25 20
288 $1 As 3 c. . . 40 40
283/8 . . . . *Set of 6* 85 65

(Des G. Vasarhelyi. Photo Harrison)

1968 (23 Mar). *Paintings by Sir Winston Churchill. T 76 and similar horiz designs. Multicoloured. P 14 × 14½.*
289 10 c. Type 76 . . 10 10
290 12 c. "The Mediterranean" . . 15 10
291 15 c. "St. Jean Cap Ferratt" . . 15 10
292 25 c. Type 76 . . 20 10
293 35 c. As 15 c. . . 25 10
294 50 c. Sir Winston painting . . 35 25
289/94 . . . . *Set of 6* 1·10 45

CHILDREN
NEED
MILK   CHILDREN
   NEED
$5   MILK

2cts. + 3cts.

   1c. + 3cts.
(80) (81) (82)

1968 (18 May). *No. 275 surch with T 80*
295 54 $5 on $2 multicoloured . . 1·50 2·25

1968 (22 July–19 Aug). *"Children Need Milk".*
  (a) Nos. 244/5 surch locally as T 81 (22 July)
296 54 2 c. + 3 c. on $2 multicoloured . . 10 10
297 55 3 c. + 3 c. on $3 multicoloured . . 10 10
  a. Surch inverted . . 50·00 15·00
  b. Surch double . . 22·00
  c. Surch double, one albino
  (b) Nos. 243/4 surch locally as T 82 (19 Aug)
298 53 1 c. + 3 c. on $1 multicoloured . . 10 40
  a. Surch on No. 274 . . 70·00 70·00
  b. Surch double . . 35·00
299 54 2 c. + 3 c. on $2 multicoloured . . 13·00 45·00
  a. Surch on No. 275 . . 80·00
296/9 . . . . *Set of 4* 13·00 45·00

83 Edith McGuire (U.S.A.)   86 Hibiscus

(Des M. Shamir. Photo Harrison)

1968 (24 Sept). *Olympic Games, Mexico. T* **83** *and similar square designs. P* 12½.

300	1 c. brown, black and blue	..	..	10	10
301	2 c. orange, brown, blue and lilac	..	10	10
	a. Orange (badge, etc.) omitted	..			
302	3 c. scarlet, brown and dull green	..	10	10
	a. Scarlet (rings, "MEXICO" etc.) omitted	£650		
303	10 c. brown, black, blue and vermilion	..	15	10
304	50 c. orange, brown, blue and turquoise	..	55	65
305	60 c. scarlet, brown and red-orange	..	60	80
300/5	..		*Set of* 6	1·25	1·50

Designs:—2, 50 c. Arthur Wint (Jamaica); 3, 60 c. Ferreira da Silva (Brazil); 10 c. Type **83**.

Nos. 300/2 and 303/5 were issued in separate composite sheets containing three strips of three, with three *se-tenant* labels showing Greek athlete (Nos. 300/2) or Discobolos (Nos. 303/5). (*Price for two sheets* £6 *mint,* £8 *used*.)

(Des G. Vasarhelyi (No. 314a), V. Whiteley (75 c.), M. Shamir (others). Litho Format (Nos. 314a and 317a). Photo Harrison (others))

1968 (Oct)–**71**. *Multicoloured designs as T* **86**. *P* 13½ (*Nos.* 314a *and* 317a), 13½ × 14½ (*vert except No.* 314a) *or* 14½ × 13½ (*horiz except No.* 317a).

306	1 c. Type **86**	..	..	..	10	10
307	2 c. Strelitzia	..	..	..	10	10
308	3 c. Bougainvillea (1.7.69)	..	..	10	10
309	5 c. Rock Hind (*horiz*) (4.2.69)	..	10	10
310	6 c. Sailfish	..	..	..	10	10
311	8 c. Red Snapper (*horiz*) (1.7.69)	..	10	30
312	10 c. Marine Toad (*horiz*) (4.2.69)	..	10	10
313	12 c. Turtle	..	..	..	15	10
314	15 c. Tree Boa (*horiz*)	..	..	90	60
314a	15 c. Thunbergia (1970)	..	..	5·50	2·50
315	25 c. Greater Trinidadian Murine Opossum (4.2.69)	..	..		30	10
316	35 c. Nine-banded Armadillo (*horiz*) (1.7.69)		35	10
317	50 c. Mona Monkey	..	..	45	25
317a	75 c. Yacht in St. George's Harbour (*horiz*) (9.10.71)	..	..	11·00	8·50
318	$1 Bananaquit	..	..	..	3·00	1·50
319	$2 Brown Pelican (4.2.69)	..	..	4·50	8·00
320	$3 Magnificent Frigate Bird	..	4·50	5·00
321	$5 Bare-eyed Thrush (1.7.69)	..	6·00	15·00
306/21	..		*Set of* 18	32·00	38·00

Nos. 314a, 317a and the dollar values are larger—29×45½, 44×28½ and 25½×48 mm respectively.

No. 317a exists imperforate from stock dispersed by the liquidator of Format International Security Printers Ltd.

102 Kidney Transplant   106 "The Adoration of the Kings" (Veronese)

(Des M. Shamir. Litho B.W.)

1968 (25 Nov). *20th Anniv of World Health Organization. T* **102** *and similar vert designs. Multicoloured. P* 13 × 13½.

322	5 c. Type **102**	..	..	..	20	10
323	25 c. Heart transplant	..	..	30	10
324	35 c. Lung transplant	..	..	30	10
325	50 c. Eye transplant	..	..	35	50
322/5	..	..	..	*Set of* 4	1·10	60

(Photo Harrison)

1968 (3 Dec). *Christmas. T* **106** *and similar square designs. P* 12½.

326	5 c. multicoloured	..	..	..	10	10
327	15 c. multicoloured	..	..	10	10
328	35 c. multicoloured	..	..	10	10
329	$1 multicoloured	..	..	..	30	40
326/9	..	..	..	*Set of* 4	40	45

Designs:—15 c. "Madonna and Child with Sts. John and Catherine" (Titian); 35 c. "Adoration of the Kings" (Botticelli); $1 "A Warrior Adoring" (Catena).

VISIT CARIFTA EXPO '69
April 5-30

(110)

1969 (Feb). *Caribbean Free Trade Area Exhibition. Nos.* 300/5 *surch in red as T* 110.

330	5 c. on 1 c. brown, black and blue	..	10	10
	a. Surch double	..	..		
331	8 c. on 2 c. orange, brown, blue and lilac	..	10	10
	a. Surch double	..	..		
332	25 c. on 3 c. scarlet, brown and dull green	..	10	10
	a. Surch double	..	..		
333	35 c. on 10 c. brown, black, blue and vermilion	10	10
334	$1 on 50 c. orange, brown, blue & turquoise	20	30
335	$2 on 60 c. scarlet, brown and red-orange	..	35	60
	a. Scarlet (rings, "MEXICO" etc) omitted	†	—
330/5	..		*Set of* 6	65	95

The centre of the composite sheets is also overprinted with a commemorative inscription publicising CARIFTA EXPO 1969 (*Price for two sheets* £11 *mint or used*).

111 Dame Hylda Bynoe (Governor) and Island Scene

(Des and litho D.L.R.)

1969 (1 May). *Carifta Expo 1969. T* **111** *and similar horiz designs. Multicoloured. P* 13 × 13½.

336	5 c. Type **111**	..	..	..	10	10
337	15 c. Premier E. M. Gairy and Island scene	..	10	10
338	50 c. Type **111**	..	..	..	10	25
339	60 c. Emblems of 1958 and 1967 World's Fairs	..	10	30
336/9	..	..	..	*Set of* 4	30	60

114 Dame Hylda Bynoe   115 "Balshazzar's Feast" (Rembrandt)

(Photo Enschedé)

1969 (8 June). *Human Rights Year. T* **114/15** *and similar multicoloured design. P* 12½ × 13 ($1) *or* 13 × 12½ (*others*).

340	5 c. Type **114**	..	..	..	10	10
341	25 c. Dr. Martin Luther King (*vert*)	..	15	10
342	35 c. Type **114**	..	..	..	15	10
343	$1 Type **115**	..	..	..	30	55
340/3	..	..	..	*Set of* 4	55	55

117 Batsman and Wicket-keeper

(Des M. Shamir and L. W. Denyer. Photo Harrison)

1969 (1 Aug). *Cricket. T* **117** *and similar horiz designs. P* 14 × 14½.

344	3 c. yellow, brown and ultramarine	..	25	70
	a. Yellow (caps and wicket) omitted	..	£400	
345	10 c. multicoloured	..	..	30	40
346	25 c. brown, ochre and myrtle-green	..	60	85
347	35 c. multicoloured	..	..	80	90
344/7	..	..	..	*Set of* 4	1·75	2·50

Designs:—10 c. Batsman playing defensive stroke; 25 c. Batsman sweeping ball; 35 c. Batsman playing on-drive.

Nos. 344/7 were each issued in small sheets of 9 (3 × 3) with decorative borders.

129 Astronaut handling Moon Rock

(Des G. Vasarhelyi. Photo)

1969 (24 Sept). *First Man on the Moon. T* **129** *and similar multicoloured designs. P* 13½ (½ c.) *or* 12½ (*others*).

348	½ c. As Type **129** but larger (56 × 35 *mm*)	..	10	10
349	1 c. Moon rocket and moon	..	..	10	10
350	2 c. Module landing	..	..	10	10
351	3 c. Declaration left on moon	..	..	10	10
352	8 c. Module leaving rocket	..	..	10	10
353	25 c. Rocket lifting-off (*vert*)	..	..	15	10
354	35 c. Spacecraft in orbit (*vert*)	..	..	15	10
355	50 c. Capsule with parachutes (*vert*)	..	20	25
356	$1 Type **129**	..	..	..	35	55
348/56	..	..		*Set of* 9	85	1·10
MS357	115 × 90 mm. Nos. 351 and 356. Imperf	90	2·25

130 Gandhi

(Des A. Robledo. Litho B.W.)

1969 (8 Oct). *Birth Centenary of Mahatma Gandhi. T* **130** *and similar designs. P* 11½.

358	**130**	6 c. multicoloured	..	..	15	10
359	–	15 c. multicoloured	..	..	20	10
360	–	25 c. multicoloured	..	..	30	10
361	–	$1 multicoloured	..	..	75	60
358/61			*Set of* 4	1·25	75
MS362	155 × 122 mm. Nos. 358/61. Imperf	2·50	3·50

Designs: *Vert*—15 c. Gandhi standing; 25 c. Gandhi walking *Horiz*—$1 Head of Gandhi.

═══1969

(134)   135 "Blackbeard" (Edward Teach)

1969 (23 Dec). *Christmas. Nos.* 326/9 *surch with T* **134** *in black (2 c.) or optd with new date only in silver (others).*

363	2 c. on 15 c. multicoloured	..	..	10	10
	a. Surch inverted	..	..	40·00	
364	5 c. multicoloured	..	..	10	10
	a. Opt double	..	..	40·00	
365	35 c. multicoloured	..	..	20	10
	a. Opt inverted	..	..	40·00	
	b. Horiz pair, one with opt omitted	£200	
	c. Opt double, one vertical	..	45·00	
366	$1 multicoloured	..	..	80	1·50
	a. Opt inverted	..	..	40·00	
363/6	..	..		*Set of* 4	1·00	1·60

(Des K. Plowitz. Recess B.W.)

1970 (2 Feb). *Pirates. T* **135** *and similar vert designs. P* 13½.

367	15 c. black	..	..	..	35	10
368	25 c. dull green	..	..	50	10
369	50 c. lilac	..	..	..	90	20
370	$1 carmine	..	..	..	1·50	70
367/70	..	..		*Set of* 4	3·00	1·00

Designs:—25 c. Anne Bonney; 50 c. Jean Lafitte; $1 Mary Read.

5c   **5c**

(139)   (140)

1970 (18 Mar). *No.* 348 *surch with T* **139.**

371	5 c. on ½ c. multicoloured	..	..	10	10
	a. Surch double	..	..	25·00	
	b. Surch with T **140**	..	..	70	70
	ba. Surch double, one inverted	..	40·00	

141 "The Last Supper" (detail, **142** Del Sarto)

(Des and litho B.W.)

1970 (13 Apr). *Easter. Paintings. T* **141/2** *and similar vert designs. Multicoloured. P* 11½.

372	5 c.	} Type **141/2**		10	15
373	5 c.			10	15
374	15 c.	"Christ crowned with Thorns" (detail,	20	25
375	15 c.	Van Dyck)		20	25
376	25 c.	"The Passion of Christ" (detail,	25	30
377	25 c.	Memling)		25	30
378	60 c.			40	55
379	60 c.	} "Christ in the Tomb" (detail, Rubens)	40	55
372/9			*Set of* 8	1·60	2·25
MS380	120 × 140 mm. Nos. 376/9.		1·00	1·25

Nos. 372/9 were issued with each design spread over two *se-tenant* stamps of the same denomination.

149 Girl with Kittens in Pram

(Des A. Robledo. Litho Questa)

1970 (27 May). *Birth Bicentenary of William Wordsworth (poet). "Children and Pets". T* **149** *and similar horiz designs. Multicoloured. P* 11.

381	5 c. Type **149**				15	15
382	15 c. Girl with puppy and kitten				20	15
383	30 c. Boy with fishing rod and cat				25	20
384	60 c. Boys and girls with cats and dogs				40	1·10
381/4				*Set of* 4	90	1·40
MS385	Two sheets each 114 × 126 mm. Nos. 381, 383 and Nos. 382, 384. Imperf				1·25	2·00

153 Parliament of India·

(Des G. Vasarhelyi. Litho Questa)

1970 (15 June). *Seventh Regional Conference of Commonwealth Parliamentary Association. T* **153** *and similar horiz designs. Multicoloured. P* 14

386	5 c. Type **153**				10	10
387	25 c. Parliament of Great Britain, Westminster				10	10
388	50 c. Parliament of Canada				15	15
389	60 c. Parliament of Grenada				15	15
386/9				*Set of* 4	40	35
MS390	126 × 90 mm. Nos. 386/9				50	90

157 Tower of the Sun

(Litho Kyodo Printing Co, Tokyo)

1970 (8 Aug). *World Fair, Osaka. T* **157** *and similar multicoloured designs. P* 13.

391	1 c. Type **157**				10	10
392	2 c. Livelihood and Industry Pavilion (*horiz*)				10	10
393	3 c. Flower painting, 1634				10	10
394	10 c. "Adam and Eve" (Tintoretto) (*horiz*)				15	10
395	25 c. O.E.C.D. (Organisation for Economic Co-operation and Development) Pavilion (*horiz*)				20	10
396	50 c. San Francisco Pavilion				45	1·25
391/6				*Set of* 6	90	1·50
MS397	121 × 91 mm. $1 Japanese Pavilion (56 × 34 *mm*)				55	1·50

164 Roosevelt and "Raising U.S. Flag on Iwo Jima"

(Litho Questa)

1970 (3 Sept). *25th Anniv of Ending of World War II. T* **164** *and similar horiz designs. Multicoloured. P* 11.

398	½ c. Type **164**				10	10
399	5 c. Zhukov and "Fall of Berlin"				70	15
400	15 c. Churchill and "Evacuation at Dunkirk"				1·25	35
401	25 c. De Gaulle and "Liberation of Paris"				1·40	45
402	50 c. Eisenhower and "D-Day Landing"				1·75	1·25
403	60 c. Montgomery and "Battle of Alamein"				1·75	2·50
398/403				*Set of* 6	6·25	4·25
MS404	163 × 113 mm. Nos. 398, 400, 402/3				3·25	7·00
	a. Brown (panel) on 60 c. value omitted					£700

PHILYMPIA
LONDON 1970
(169)

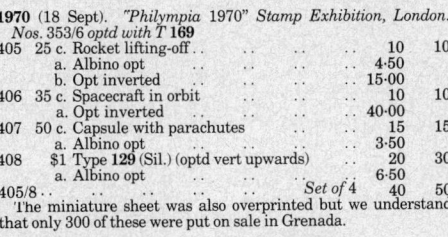

170 U.P.U. Emblem, Building and Transport

1970 (18 Sept). *"Philympia 1970" Stamp Exhibition, London. Nos. 353/6 optd with T* **169**

405	25 c. Rocket lifting-off				10	10
	a. Albino opt				4·50	
	b. Opt inverted				15·00	
406	35 c. Spacecraft in orbit				10	10
	a. Opt inverted				40·00	
407	50 c. Capsule with parachutes				15	15
	a. Albino opt				3·50	
408	$1 Type **129** (Sil.) (optd vert upwards)				20	30
	a. Albino opt				6·50	
405/8				*Set of* 4	40	50

The miniature sheet was also overprinted but we understand that only 300 of these were put on sale in Grenada.

(Litho Questa)

1970 (17 Oct). *New U.P.U. Headquarters Building. T* **170** *and similar multicoloured designs. P* 14.

409	15 c. Type **170**				35	10
410	25 c. As Type **170**, but modern transport				35	10
411	50 c. Sir Rowland Hill and U.P.U. Building				35	30
412	$1 Abraham Lincoln and U.P.U. Building				40	90
409/12				*Set of* 4	1·25	1·25
MS413	79 × 85 mm. Nos. 411/12				90	3·00

The 50 c. and $1 are both vertical designs.

171 "The Madonna of the Goldfinch" (Tiepolo)

172 19th-Century Nursing

(Des G. Vasarhelyi. Litho Questa)

1970 (5 Dec). *Christmas. T* **171** *and similar vert designs. Multicoloured. P* 13½.

414	½ c. Type **171**				10	10
415	½ c. "The Virgin and Child with St. Peter and St. Paul" (Bouts)				10	10
416	½ c. "The Virgin and Child" (Bellini)				10	10
417	2 c. "The Madonna of the Basket" (Correggio)				10	10
418	3 c. Type **171**				10	10
419	35 c. As No. 415				20	10
420	50 c. As 2 c.				30	35
421	$1 As No. 416				50	1·25
414/21				*Set of* 8	1·10	1·75
MS422	102 × 87 mm. Nos. 420/1				1·60	3·00

(Des G. Vasarhelyi. Litho Questa)

1970 (12 Dec). *Centenary of British Red Cross. T* **172** *and similar horiz designs. Multicoloured. P* 14½ × 14.

423	5 c. Type **172**				20	10
424	15 c. Military Ambulance, 1918				25	10
425	25 c. First-Aid Post, 1941				35	10
426	60 c. Red Cross Transport, 1970				90	80
423/6				*Set of* 4	1·50	95
MS427	113 × 82 mm. Nos. 423/6				2·00	1·60
	a. Error. Imperf				25·00	

173 John Dewey and Art Lesson

(Des G. Vasarhelyi. Litho Questa)

1971 (1 May). *International Education Year (1970). T* **173** *and similar horiz designs. Multicoloured. P* 13½.

428	5 c. Type **173**				10	10
429	10 c. Jean-Jacques Rousseau and "Alpha-betisation"				15	10
430	50 c. Maimonides and laboratory				50	15
431	$1 Bertrand Russell and mathematics class				95	40
428/31				*Set of* 4	1·50	55
MS432	90 × 98 mm. Nos. 430/1				1·40	2·00

NEW INFORMATION

The editor is always interested to correspond with people who have new information that will improve or correct the Catalogue.

174 Jennifer Hosten and outline of Grenada

176 "Napolean reviewing the Guard" (E. Detaille)

175 French and Canadian Scouts

(Des local artist; adapted G. Drummond. Litho Format)

1971 (1 June). *Winner of "Miss World" Competition (1970). P* 13½.

433	**174**	5 c. multicoloured			10	10
434		10 c. multicoloured			10	10
435		15 c. multicoloured			15	10
436		25 c. multicoloured			15	10
437		35 c. multicoloured			15	10
438		50 c. multicoloured			35	55
433/8				*Set of* 6	80	75
MS439	92 × 89 mm. **174** 50 c. multicoloured. Printed on silk. Imperf				75	1·75

(Litho Format)

1971 (11 Sept). *13th World Scout Jamboree, Asagiri, Japan. T* **175** *and similar horiz designs. Multicoloured. P* 11.

440	5 c. Type **175**				10	10
441	35 c. German and American scouts				30	25
442	50 c. Australian and Japanese scouts				40	50
443	75 c. Grenada and British scouts				60	75
440/3				*Set of* 4	1·10	1·40
MS444	101 × 114 mm. Nos. 442/3				1·25	2·50

(Des G. Vasarhelyi. Litho Questa)

1971 (9 Oct). *150th Death Anniversary of Napolean Bonaparte. T* **176** *and similar vert designs showing paintings. Multicoloured. P* 13½.

445	5 c. Type **176**				15	15
446	15 c. "Napoleon before Madrid" (Vernet)				25	15
447	35 c. "Napoleon crossing Mt St. Bernard" (David)				30	15
448	$2 "Napoleon in his Study" (David)				75	1·50
445/8				*Set of* 4	1·25	1·75
MS449	101 × 76 mm. No. 447. Imperf				1·75	1·60

177 1d. Stamp of 1861 and Badge of Grenada

(Des R. Granger Barrett. Litho Questa)

1971 (6 Nov). *110th Anniv of the Postal Service. T* **177** *and similar horiz designs. Multicoloured. W w* **12** *(sideways*). P* 11.

450	5 c. Type **177**				15	20
451	15 c. 6d. stamp of 1861 and Queen Elizabeth II				20	15
452	35 c. 1d. and 6d. stamps of 1861 and badge of Grenada				40	20
453	50 c. Scroll and 1d. stamp of 1861				55	1·40
450/3				*Set of* 4	1·10	1·75
MS454	96 × 114 mm. Nos. 452/3				90	1·00

* This issue is printed on thick paper and consequently the watermark is very faint.

178 Apollo Splashdown

(Des R. Granger Barrett. Litho Questa)

1971 (13 Nov). *Apollo Moon Exploration Series. T 178 and similar multicoloured designs. P 11.*

455	1 c. Type 178 ..	10	10
456	2 c. Recovery of Apollo 13	10	10
457	3 c. Separation of Lunar Module from Apollo 14 ..	10	10
458	10 c. Shepard and Mitchell taking samples of moon rock	25	10
459	25 c. Moon Buggy	75	20
460	$1 Apollo 15 blast-off (*vert*) ..	2·00	3·25
455/60	*Set of 6*	2·75	3·25
MS461	77 × 108 mm. 50 c. as $1 ..	1·40	1·50

179 67th Regiment of Foot, 1787	**180** "The Adoration of the Kings" (Memling)

(Des G. Vasarhelyi. Litho Format)

1971 (11 Dec). *Military Uniforms. T 179 and similar vert designs. Multicoloured. P 13½.*

462	½ c. Type 179 ..	10	10
463	1 c. 45th Regiment of Foot, 1792	10	10
464	2 c. 29th Regiment of Foot, 1794	10	10
465	10 c. 9th Regiment of Foot, 1801	45	10
466	25 c. 2nd Regiment of Foot, 1815	85	20
467	$1 70th Regiment of Foot, 1764	2·50	2·00
462/7	*Set of 6*	3·50	2·25
MS468	108 × 99 mm. Nos. 466/7. P 15	3·25	3·75

(Des G. Vasarhelyi. Litho Questa)

1972 (15 Jan). *Christmas (1971). T 180 and similar vert designs. Multicoloured. P 14 × 13½.*

469	15 c. Type 180..	15	10
470	25 c. "Madonna and Child" (Michelangelo)..	20	10
471	35 c. "Madonna and Child" (Murillo)	25	10
472	50 c. "The Virgin with the Apple" (Memling)	30	75
469/72	*Set of 4*	80	90
MS473	105×80 mm. $1 "The Adoration of the Kings" (Mostaert)..	75	1·25

35c   ⬭⬭⬭

WINTER OLYMPICS FEB. 3-13, 1972 SAPPORO, JAPAN	VOTE FEB. 28 1972
(181)	(182)

1972 (3 Feb). *Winter Olympic Games, Sapporo, Japan. Nos. 462/4 and MS468 surch or optd only (MS475).*

(a) Postage. As T 181

474	$2 on 2 c. multicoloured ..	50	90
MS475	108 × 99 mm. Nos. 466/7 (R.)	1·00	1·25

(b) Air. As T 181, but additionally surch "AIR MAIL"

476	35 c. on ½ c. multicoloured ..	15	25
477	50 c. on 1 c. multicoloured ..	15	35

1972 (25 Feb). *General Election. Nos. 307/8, 310 and 315 optd with T 182.*

478	2 c. multicoloured ..	10	10
	b. Stop after "1972" (R.1/2, 1/10) ..	6·00	
479	3 c. multicoloured ..	10	10
	a. Opt inverted ..	95·00	
	b. Stop after "1972" (R.1/2, 1/10)	6·00	
480	6 c. multicoloured ..	10	15
	b. Stop after "1972" (R.1/2, 1/10)	6·00	
481	25 c. multicoloured ..	15	30
	b. Stop after "1972" (R.1/2, 1/10)	7·50	
478/81	*Set of 4*	40	60

183 King Arthur

(Litho Questa)

1972 (4 Mar). *U.N.I.C.E.F. T 183 and similar multicoloured designs. P 14.*

482	½ c. Type 183 ..	10	10
483	1 c. Robin Hood ..	10	10
484	2 c. Robinson Crusoe (*vert*) ..	10	10
485	25 c. Type 183 ..	10	10
486	50 c. As No. 483 ..	25	40

487	75 c. As No. 484 ..	30	80
488	$1 Mary and her little lamb (*vert*) ..	45	1·10
482/8	*Set of 7*	1·10	2·25
MS489	65 × 98 mm. No. 488 ..	55	80

AIR MAIL

INTERPEX
1972 ══ 12¢

(184)   (185)   (186)

1972 (17 Mar). *"Interpex" Stamp Exhibition, New York. Nos. 433/9 optd with T 184.*

490 **174**	5 c. multicoloured ..	10	10
491	10 c. multicoloured ..	10	10
492	15 c. multicoloured ..	10	10
493	25 c. multicoloured ..	10	10
494	35 c. multicoloured ..	15	15
	a. Opt double		
495	50 c. multicoloured ..	25	30
	a. Vert pair, top stamp with opt omitted	£100	
490/5	*Set of 6*	60	65
MS496	92×89 mm. 174 50 c. multicoloured. Printed on silk. Imperf. ..	8·00	12·00

1972 (20 Apr). *Nos. 306/8 surch with T 185, and No. 433 surch similarly, but with obliterating bars under "12c".*

497	12 c. on 1 c. Type 88 ..	40	55
498	12 c. on 2 c. Strelitzia ..	40	55
499	12 c. on 3 c. Bougainvillea ..	40	55
	a. Horiz pair, left stamp with surch omitted		
500	12 c. on 5 c. Type 174 ..	40	55
497/500	*Set of 4*	1·40	2·00

1972. *Air. (a) Nos. 306/12, 314a/17 and 318/21 optd as T 186 or surch in addition (2 May)*

501	5 c. Rock Hind ..	10	10
	a. Opt double	28·00	
502	8 c. Snapper ..	15	10
	a. Opt double	60·00	
503	10 c. Marine Toad ..	15	10
	a. Opt double	40·00	
504	15 c. Thunbergia ..	30	10
505	25 c. Greater Trinidadian Murine Opossum	35	20
	a. Horiz pair, one without opt	£130	
506	30 c. on 1 c. Type 86 ..	40	25
507	35 c. Nine-banded Armadillo ..	40	25
508	40 c. on 2 c. Strelitzia ..	50	25
509	45 c. on 3 c. Bougainvillea ..	55	35
510	50 c. Mona Monkey ..	55	35
	a. Horiz pair, one without opt ..	90·00	
	b. Opt double	£180	
511	60 c. on 5 c. Rock Hind ..	60	40
512	70 c. on 6 c. Sailfish ..	70	50
513	$1 Bananaquit ..	4·00	60
514	$1·35 on 8 c. Snapper ..	3·25	1·50
515	$2 Brown Pelican ..	5·50	4·00
516	$3 Magnificent Frigate Bird ..	6·00	4·25
517	$5 Bare-eyed Thrush ..	7·50	8·50

(b) Nos. 440/3 optd as T 186 (5 June)

518 **175**	5 c. multicoloured ..	75	10
519	35 c. multicoloured ..	2·00	30
520	50 c. multicoloured ..	2·25	45
521	75 c. multicoloured ..	3·00	1·00
501/21	*Set of 21*	35·00	21·00

187 Yachting

(Litho Format)

1972 (8 Sept). *Olympic Games, Munich. T 187 and similar multicoloured designs. P 14. (a) Postage.*

522	½ c. Type 187 ..	10	10
523	1 c. Show-jumping ..	10	10
524	2 c. Running (*vert*) ..	10	10
525	35 c. As 2 c. ..	30	10
526	50 c. As 1 c. ..	40	40

(b) Air

527	25 c. Boxing ..	25	10
528	$1 As 25 c. ..	65	85
522/8	*Set of 7*	1·50	1·40
MS529	82 × 85 mm. 60 c. as 25 c. and 70 c. as 1 c.	1·00	1·40

188 Badge of Grenada and Nutmegs

(Des (from photographs by D. Groves) and photo Harrison)

1972 (20 Nov). *Royal Silver Wedding. Multicoloured; background colour given. W w 12. P 14 × 14½.*

530 **188**	8 c. olive-brown ..	10	10
531	$1 ultramarine ..	45	55

189 Boy Scout Saluting	**190** Madonna and Child

(Des R. Granger Barrett. Litho Questa)

1972 (2 Dec). *65th Anniv of Boy Scouts. T 189 and similar horiz designs. Multicoloured. P 14. (a) Postage.*

532	½ c. Type 189 ..	10	10
533	1 c. Scouts knotting ropes ..	10	10
534	2 c. Scouts shaking hands ..	10	10
535	3 c. Lord Baden-Powell ..	10	10
536	75 c. As 2 c. ..	1·40	2·75
537	$1 As 3 c. ..	1·60	2·75

(b) Air

538	25 c. Type 189 ..	50	30
539	35 c. As 1 c. ..	70	30
532/9	*Set of 8*	4·00	5·50
MS540	87 × 88 mm. 60 c. as 3 c., and 70 c. as 2 c.	2·00	2·00

(Des V. Whiteley. Litho Format)

1972 (9 Dec). *Christmas. T 190 and similar vert designs. Multicoloured. P 13½.*

541	1 c. Type 190 ..	10	10
542	3 c. The Three Kings..	10	10
543	5 c. The Nativity ..	10	10
544	25 c. Type 190 ..	15	10
545	35 c. As 3 c. ..	20	10
546	$1 As 5 c. ..	60	75
541/6	*Set of 6*	1·00	1·00
MS547	102 × 76 mm. 60 c. Type 190 and 70 c. as 3 c. P 15	60	80

191 Greater Flamingoes

(Des M. and G. Shamir. Litho Questa)

1973 (26 Jan). *National Zoo. T 191 and similar horiz designs. Multicoloured. P 14½.*

548	25 c. Type 191..	80	35
549	35 c. Brazilian Tapir ..	80	35
550	60 c. Blue and Yellow Macaw, and Scarlet Macaw ..	1·50	1·25
551	70 c. Ocelot ..	1·50	1·50
548/51	*Set of 4*	4·25	3·00

192 Class II Racing Yacht

(Des V. Whiteley. Litho Format)

1973 (26 Feb). *Yachting. T 192 and similar horiz designs. Multicoloured. P 13½.*

552	25 c. Type 192 ..	25	10
553	35 c. Harbour, St George's ..	30	10
554	60 c. Yacht *Bloodhound* ..	45	65
555	70 c. St. George's ..	50	75
552/5	*Set of 4*	1·40	1·40

193 Helios (Greek god) and Earth orbiting the Sun

(Des G. Vasarhelyi. Litho Format)

1973 (6 July). *I.M.O./W.M.O. Centenary. T 193 and similar horiz designs showing Greek Gods. Multicoloured. P 13½.*

556	½ c. Type 193 ..	10	10
557	1 c. Poseidon and "Normad" storm detector	10	10
558	2 c. Zeus and radarscope ..	10	10
559	3 c. Iris and weather balloon..	10	10
560	35 c. Hermes and "ATS-3" satellite ..	35	10
561	50 c. Zephyrus and diagram of pressure zones	50	30
562	75 c. Demeter and space photo ..	60	60
563	$1 Selene and rainfall diagram ..	65	1·00
556/63	*Set of 8*	2·00	2·00
MS564	123 × 92 mm. $2 Computer weather map (42 × 31 mm). P 13½.	90	1·25

194 Racing Class Yachts   195 Ignatius Semmelweis (obstetrician)

(Des G. Drummond. Litho Format)

1973 (3 Aug). *Carriacou Regatta. T* **194** *and similar horiz designs. Multicoloured. P* 13½.

565	½ c. Type **194**			10	10
566	1 c. Cruising Class Yacht			10	10
567	2 c. Open-decked sloops			10	10
568	35 c. *Mermaid* (sloop)			35	10
569	50 c. St. George's Harbour			40	35
570	75 c. Map of Carriacou			55	70
571	$1 Boat-building			75	80
565/71			*Set of* 7	1·90	1·90
MS572	109 × 88 mm. $2 End of Race			90	1·75

(Des G. Vasarhelyi. Litho Format)

1973 (17 Sept). *25th Anniv of W.H.O. T* **195** *and similar vert designs. Multicoloured. P* 14½.

573	½ c. Type **195**			10	10
574	1 c. Louis Pasteur			10	10
575	2 c. Edward Jenner			10	10
576	3 c. Sigmund Freud			10	10
577	25 c. Emil Von Behring (bacteriologist)			65	10
578	35 c. Carl Jung			75	20
579	50 c. Charles Calmette (bacteriologist)			1·10	80
580	$1 William Harvey			1·40	2·00
573/80			*Set of* 8	3·50	2·75
MS581	105 × 80 mm. $2 Marie Curie			1·60	1·60

196 Princess Anne and Capt.   197 "Virgin and Child" Mark Phillips   (Maratti)

(Des G. Drummond. Litho Format)

1973 (14 Nov). *Royal Wedding. P* 13½.

582	196	25 c. multicoloured			10	10
583		$2 multicoloured			30	45
MS584	79 × 100 mm. 75 c. and $1 as Nos. 582/3				40	30

Nos. 582/3 were each issued in small sheets of five stamps and one stamp-size label.

(Litho Format)

1973 (10 Dec). *Christmas. T* **197** *and similar vert designs. Multicoloured. P* 14½.

585	½ c. Type **197**			10	10
586	1 c. "Madonna and Child" (Crivelli)			10	10
587	2 c. "Virgin and Child with Two Angels" (Verrocchio)			10	10
588	3 c. "Adoration of the Shepherds" (Roberti)			10	10
589	25 c. "The Holy Family with the Infant Baptist" (Baroccio)			15	10
590	35 c. "The Holy Family" (Bronzino)			20	10
591	75 c. "Mystic Nativity" (Botticelli)			30	20
592	$1 "Adoration of the Kings" (Geertgen)			40	30
585/92			*Set of* 8	1·00	60
MS593	89 × 89 mm. $2 "Adoration of the Kings" (Mostaert) (30 × 45 *mm*). P 13½				85	1·10

INDEPENDENT

INDEPENDENCE 7TH FEB. 1974

(198)   199 Creative Arts Theatre, Jamaica Campus

1974 (7 Feb). *Independence. Nos.* 306/9, 311/13, 315/16 *and* 317a/21 *optd as T* **198**

594	1 c. Hibiscus			10	10
595	2 c. Strelitzia			10	10
596	3 c. Bougainvillea			10	10
597	5 c. Rock Hind			10	10
598	8 c. Snapper			15	10
599	10 c. Marine Toad			20	15
600	12 c. Turtle			20	15
601	25 c. Greater Trinidadian Murine Opossum			45	35
602	35 c. Nine-banded Armadillo			75	50
603	75 c. Yacht in St. George's Harbour			2·00	1·25
604	$1 Bananaquit			3·75	1·50
605	$2 Brown Pelican			6·00	5·00
606	$3 Magnificent Frigate Bird			8·00	6·50
607	$5 Bare-eyed Thrush			12·00	14·00
594/607			*Set of* 14	30·00	26·00

(Des G. Drummond. Litho Format)

1974 (10 Apr). *25th Anniv of University of West Indies. T* **199** *and similar multicoloured designs. P* 13½ × 14.

608	10 c. Type **199**			10	10
609	25 c. Marryshow House			10	10
610	50 c. Chapel, Jamaica Campus (*vert*)			20	10
611	$1 University arms (*vert*)			30	30
608/11			*Set of* 4	55	50
MS612	69 × 86 mm. $2 as No. 611			50	90

200 Nutmeg Pods and   201 Footballers (West Scarlet Mace   Germany v Chile)

(Des G. Drummond. Litho Format)

1974 (19 Aug). *Independence. T* **200** *and similar vert designs. Multicoloured. P* 13½.

613	3 c. Type **200**			10	10
614	8 c. Map of Grenada			10	10
615	25 c. Prime Minister Eric Gairy			15	10
616	35 c. Grand Anse Beach and flag			15	10
617	$1 Coat of arms			35	40
613/17			*Set of* 5	70	60
MS618	91 × 125 mm. $2 as $1			55	90

(Des G. Vasarhelyi. Litho Format)

1974 (3 Sept). *World Cup Football Championships, West Germany. T* **201** *and similar multicoloured designs showing footballers of the countries given. P* 14½.

619	½ c. Type **201**			10	10
620	1 c. East Germany v Australia			10	10
621	2 c. Yugoslavia v Brazil			10	10
622	10 c. Scotland v Zaire			10	10
623	25 c. Netherlands v Uruguay			15	10
624	50 c. Sweden v Bulgaria			20	10
625	75 c. Italy v Haiti			35	15
626	$1 Poland v Argentina			50	25
619/26			*Set of* 8	1·25	60
MS627	114 × 76 mm. $2 Country flags. P 13			90	1·75

202 Early U.S. Mail-trains and Concorde

(Des G. Vasarhelyi. Litho Format)

1974 (8 Oct). *Centenary of Universal Postal Union. T* **202** *and similar horiz designs. Multicoloured. P* 14½.

628	½ c. Type **202**			10	10
629	1 c. *Caesar* (snow) (1839) and Westland Wessex HU Mk 5 helicopter			10	10
630	2 c. Airmail transport			10	10
631	8 c. Pigeon post (1480) and telephone dial			15	10
632	15 c. 18th-century bellman and tracking antenna			30	10
633	25 c. Messenger (1450) and satellite			35	10
634	35 c. French pillar-box (1850) and mail-boat			50	10
635	$1 18th-century German postman and mail-train of the future			1·50	1·75
628/35			*Set of* 8	2·50	2·00
MS636	105×66 mm. $2 St. Gotthard mail-coach (1735). P 13			1·00	1·75

203 Sir Winston Churchill   204 "Madonna and Child of the Eucharist" (Botticelli)

(Des G. Vasarhelyi. Litho Format)

1974 (28 Oct). *Birth Centenary of Sir Winston Churchill. T* **203** *and similar portrait design. P* 13½.

637	203	35 c. multicoloured			15	10
638	–	$2 multicoloured			45	50
MS639	129 × 96 mm. 75 c. as 35 c. and $1 as $2				75	75

(Des. M. Shamir. Litho Format)

1974 (18 Nov). *Christmas. T* **204** *and similar vert designs, showing "The Madonna and Child" by the artists given. Multicoloured. P* 14½.

640	½ c. Type **204**			10	10
641	1 c. Niccolo di Pietro			10	10
642	2 c. Van der Weyden			10	10
643	3 c. Bastiani			10	10
644	10 c. Giovanni			10	10
645	25 c. Van der Weyden			20	10
646	50 c. Botticelli			25	20
647	$1 Mantegna			35	50
640/7			*Set of* 8	85	80
MS648	117 × 96 mm. $2 as 1 c. P 13			75	90

205 Yachts, Point Saline

(Des G. Drummond. Litho Format)

1975 (13 Jan)–78. *Multicoloured designs as T* **205**. A. *P* 14½ (½ *to* 50 *c.*) *or* 13½ (75 *c. to* \$10). B. *P* 13.

			A		B	
649	½ c. Type **205** (inscr "POINT SALINE")		10	40	†	
	a. Inscr "POINT SALINES"	50·00	—	†		
650	1 c. Yacht club race		10	10	10	50
651	2 c. Carenage taxi		10	10	10	50
652	3 c. Large working boats		10	10	10	30
653	6 c. Deep-water dock		20	10	10	15
654	6 c. Cocoa beans in drying trays		10	10	10	30
655	8 c. Nutmegs		40	10	†	
656	10 c. Rum distillery, River Antoine Estate, c 1785		10	10	15	40
657	12 c. Cocoa tree		30	10	†	
658	15 c. Fishermen at Fontenoy		10	10	15	45
659	20 c. Parliament Building, St. George's		15	15	20	55
660	25 c. Fort George cannons		20	15	25	55
661	35 c. Pearls Airport		20	15	—	
662	50 c. General Post Office		25	30	45	90
663	75 c. Carib's Leap, Sauteurs Bay (45 × 28 *mm*)		45	50	†	
664	$1 Carenage, St. George's (45 × 28 *mm*)		50	70	†	
665	$2 St. George's Harbour by night (45 × 28 *mm*)		65	1·50	†	
666	$3 Grand Anse Beach (45 × 28 *mm*)		75	2·00	†	
667	$5 Canoe Bay and Black Bay from Point Saline Lighthouse (45 × 28 *mm*)		1·10	3·00	†	
668	$10 Sugar-loaf Island from Levera Beach (45 × 28 *mm*)		2·50	6·50	†	
649/68		*Set of* 20	7·00	13·00	†	

No. 649a occurs on R. 6/1 and 7/1 from plate 1A and R. 10/5 from plate 1C. It is believed that the plate was originally produced showing the incorrect inscription ("POINT SALINES") on every stamp. Each position was then individually corrected, but those noted were missed.

Dates of issue:—13.1.75, Nos. 649A/62A; 22.1.75, 663A/7A; 26.3.75, No. 668A; 1978, Nos. 650B/4B, 656B, 658B/62B.

Nos. 649/59, 661/4 and 666/8 exist imperforate from stock dispersed by the liquidator of Format International Security Printers Ltd.

206 Sailfish

(Des V. Whiteley. Litho Format)

1975 (3 Feb). *Big Game Fishing. T* **206** *and similar horiz designs. Multicoloured. P* 14½.

669	½ c. Type **206**			10	10
670	1 c. Blue Marlin			10	10
671	2 c. White Marlin			10	10
672	10 c. Yellow-finned Tuna			10	10
673	25 c. Wahoo			25	10
674	50 c. Dolphin (fish)			40	15
675	70 c. Giant Grouper			60	20
676	$1 Great Barracuda			80	35
669/76			*Set of* 8	2·00	70
MS677	107×80 mm. $2 Short-finned Mako. P 13			1·25	1·25

207 Granadilla Barbadine   208 Dove, Grenada Flag and U.N. Emblem

(Des G. Vasarhelyi. Litho Format)

1975 (26 Feb). *Flowers. T* **207** *and similar horiz designs. Multicoloured. P* 14½.

678	½ c. Type **207**			10	10
679	1 c. Bleeding Heart (Easter Lily)			10	10
680	2 c. Poinsettia			10	10
681	3 c. Cocoa flower			10	10
682	10 c. Gladioli			10	10
683	25 c. Redhead/Yellowhead			25	10

684	50 c. Plumbago	..	..	45	15
685	$1 Orange flower	..	..	70	25
678/85			*Set of 8*	1·40	55
MS686	102 × 82 mm. $2 Barbados Gooseberry.				
	P 13	..	..	1·10	1·25

(Des G. Drummond. Litho Format)

1975 (19 Mar). *Grenada's Admission to the U.N.* (1974). *T* **208** *and similar vert designs. Multicoloured. P* 14½.

687	½ c. Type **208**	..	..	10	10
688	1 c. Grenada and U.N. flags	..	..	10	10
689	2 c. Grenada coat of arms	..	..	10	10
690	35 c. U.N. emblem over map of Grenada			15	10
691	50 c. U.N. buildings and flags.	..		20	15
692	$2 U.N. emblem and scroll	..		45	45
687/92			*Set of 6*	80	70
MS693	122 × 91 mm. 75 c. Type **208** and $1 as 2 c.				
	P 13	..	..	65	90

CANCELLED REMAINDERS*. Some of the following issues have been remaindered, cancelled-to-order, at a fraction of their face-value. For all practical purposes these are indistinguishable from genuine postally used copies. Our used quotations which are indicated by an asterisk are the same for cancelled-to-order or postally used copies.

209 Paul Revere's Midnight Ride   210 "Blood of the Redeemer" (G. Bellini)

(Des J. Cornel (½ to 10 c.), PAD Studio (40 c. to $1), J.W. (**MS**704). Litho Format)

1975 (6 May). *Bicentenary of American Revolution* (1st issue). *T* **209** *and similar multicoloured designs. P* 14½.

(a) Postage. Horiz designs

694	½ c. Type **209**	..	..	10	10*
695	1 c. Crispus Attucks ..	..	..	10	10*
696	2 c. Patrick Henry	..	..	10	10*
697	3 c. Franklin visits Washington	..		10	10*
698	5 c. Rebel troops	..	..	10	10*
699	10 c. John Paul Jones	..	..	10	10*

(b) Air. Vert designs

700	40 c. "John Hancock" (Copley)	..		35	10*
701	50 c. "Benjamin Franklin" (Roslin)	..		50	15*
702	75 c. "John Adams" (Copley)	..		70	15*
703	$1 "Lafayette" (Casanova)	..		80	20*
694/703			*Set of 10*	2·25	60*
MS704	Two sheets 131 × 102 mm: $2 Grenada arms and U.S. seal; $2 Grenada and U.S. flags.				
	P 13½	..	..	1·50	60*

Stamps from **MS**704 are horiz and larger: 47½ × 35mm.
Nos. 694/703 also exist perf 13 (*Price for set of 10 £2·25 mint or used*) from additional sheetlets of 5 stamps and 1 label. Stamps perforated 14½ are from normal sheets of 40.
See also Nos. 785/92.

(Des M. Shamir. Litho Format)

1975 (21 May). *Easter. T* **210** *and similar vert designs. Multicoloured. P* 14½.

705	½ c. Type **210**	..	..	10	10*
706	1 c. "Pietà" (Bellini)	..	..	10	10*
707	2 c. "The Entombment" (Van der Weyden)			10	10*
708	3 c. "Pietà" (Bellini)	..	..	10	10*
709	35 c. "Pietà" (Bellini)	..	..	25	10*
710	75 c. "The Dead Christ" (Bellini)	..		35	10*
711	$1 "The Dead Christ supported by Angels" (Procaccini)			50	10*
705/11			*Set of 7*	1·00	30*
MS712	117 × 100 mm. $2 "Pietà" (Botticelli).P 13			75	30*

211 Wildlife Study   212 Leafy Jewel Box (*Chama macerophylla*)

(Des J.W. Litho Format)

1975 (2 July). *14th World Scout Jamboree, Norway. T* **211** *and similar horiz designs. Multicoloured. P* 14.

713	½ c. Type **211**	..	..	10	10*
714	1 c. Sailing	..	..	10	10*
715	2 c. Map-reading	..	..	10	10*
716	35 c. First-aid	..	..	40	10*
717	40 c. Physical training	..	..	45	10*
718	75 c. Mountaineering	..	..	60	10*
719	$2 Sing-song	..	..	1·25	20*
713/19			*Set of 7*	2·50	40*
MS720	106 × 80 mm. $1 Boat-building	..		90	30*

(Des J.W. Litho Questa)

1975 (1 Aug). *Seashells. T* **212** *and similar vert designs. Multicoloured. P* 14.

721	½ c. Type **212**	..	..	10	10*
722	1 c. Emerald Nerite (*Smaragdia viridis viridemaris*)			10	10*
723	2 c. Yellow American Cockle (*Trachycardium muricatum*)			10	10*
724	25 c. Common Purple Janthina (*Janthina janthina*)			85	10*
725	50 c. Atlantic Turkey Wing (*Arca zebra*) ..			1·75	10*
726	75 c. West Indian Fighting Conch (*Strombus pugilis*)			2·25	15*
727	$1 Noble Wentletrap (*Sthenorytis pernobilis*)			2·25	15*
721/7			*Set of 7*	6·50	60*
MS728	102×76 mm. $2 Music Volute (*Voluta musica*)			2·00	80*

213 *Lycorea ceres*   214 Rowing

(Des J.W. Litho Format)

1975 (22 Sept). *Butterflies. T* **213** *and similar vert designs. Multicoloured. P* 14.

729	½ c. Type **213**	..	..	10	10*
730	1 c. Adelpha cytherea	..	..	10	10*
731	2 c. Atlides polybe	..	..	10	10*
732	35 c. Anteos maerula	..	..	80	10*
733	45 c. Parides neophilus	..	..	85	10*
734	75 c. Nymula orestes	..	..	1·25	15*
735	$2 Euptychia cephus	..	..	1·75	20*
729/35			*Set of 7*	4·25	50*
MS736	108×83 mm. $1 Papilio astyalus (sub-species lycophron)			1·25	40*

(Des J.W. Litho Questa)

1975 (13 Oct). *Pan-American Games, Mexico City. T* **214** *and similar vert designs. Multicoloured. P* 14.

737	½ c. Type **214**	..	..	10	10*
738	1 c. Swimming	..	..	10	10*
739	2 c. Show-jumping	..	..	10	10*
740	35 c. Gymnastics	..	..	15	10*
741	45 c. Football	..	..	15	10*
742	75 c. Boxing	..	..	25	15*
743	$2 Cycling	..	..	65	20*
737/43			*Set of 7*	1·10	40*
MS744	106 × 81 mm. $1 Yachting	..		1·00	40*

215 "The Boy David" (Michelangelo)   216 "Madonna and Child" (Filippino Lippi)

(Des M. and G. Shamir. Litho J.W.)

1975 (3 Nov). *500th Birth Anniv of Michelangelo. T* **215** *and similar vert designs. Multicoloured. P* 14.

745	½ c. Type **215**	..	..	10	10*
746	1 c. "Young Man" (detail)	..	..	10	10*
747	2 c. "Moses"	..	..	10	10*
748	40 c. "Prophet Zachariah"	..	..	40	10*
749	50 c. "St John the Baptist"	..	..	40	15*
750	75 c. "Judith and Holofernes" ..		..	70	20*
751	$2 "Doni Madonna" (detail from "Holy Family")			1·25	25*
745/51			*Set of 7*	2·50	65*
MS752	104 × 89 mm. $1 "Madonna" (head from Pietà)			1·00	30*

The sculpture on No. 749 though ascribed to Michelangelo, shows a work by Francesco Sangallo.

(Des M. Shamir. Litho Questa)

1975 (8 Dec). *Christmas. T* **216** *and similar vert designs showing "Virgin and Child". Multicoloured. P* 14.

753	½ c. Type **216**	..	..	10	10*
754	1 c. Mantegna	..	..	10	10*
755	2 c. Luis de Morales	..	..	10	10*
756	35 c. G. M. Morandi	..	..	20	10*
757	50 c. Antonello da Messina	..	..	25	10*
758	75 c. Dürer	..	..	30	10*
759	$1 Velasquez	..	..	40	10*
753/9			*Set of 7*	1·10	35*
MS760	125 × 98 mm. $2 Bellini	..		90	30*

217 Bananaquit   218 Carnival Time

(Des G. Drummond. Litho Questa)

1976 (20 Jan). *Flora and Fauna. T* **217** *and similar multicoloured designs. P* 14.

761	½ c. Type **217**	..	..	10	10*
762	1 c. Brazilian Agouti	..	..	10	10*
763	2 c. Hawksbill Turtle (*horiz*)	..		10	10*
764	5 c. Dwarf Poinciana	..	..	10	10*
765	35 c. Black-finned Tuna ("Albacore") (*horiz*)			90	10*
766	40 c. Cardinal's Guard	..	..	95	10*
767	$2 Nine-banded Armadillo (*horiz*)	..		3·00	30*
761/7			*Set of 7*	4·50	60*
MS768	82×89 mm. $1 Belted Kingfisher	..		7·50	90*

(Des G. Drummond. Litho Questa)

1976 (25 Feb). *Tourism. T* **218** *and similar horiz designs. Multicoloured. P* 14.

769	½ c. Type **218**	..	..	10	10*
770	1 c. Scuba diving	..	..	10	10*
771	2 c. Liner *Southward* at St. George's			10	10*
772	35 c. Game fishing	..	..	65	10*
773	50 c. St George's Golf Course	..		2·25	20*
774	75 c. Tennis	..	..	2·50	25*
775	$1 Ancient rock carvings at Mount Rich			2·75	25*
769/75			*Set of 7*	7·50	80*
MS776	100×73 mm. $2 Small boat sailing	..		1·75	60*

219 "Pietà" (Master of Okolicsno)   220 Sharpshooters

(Des M. and G. Shamir. Litho Questa)

1976 (29 Mar). *Easter. T* **219** *and similar vert designs by the artists listed. Multicoloured. P* 14.

777	½ c. Type **219**	..	..	10	10*
778	1 c. Correggio	..	..	10	10*
779	2 c. Van der Weyden ..	..	..	10	10*
780	3 c. Dürer	..	..	10	10*
781	35 c. Master of the Holy Spirit	..		20	10*
782	75 c. Raphael	..	..	45	15*
783	$1 Raphael	..	..	50	20*
777/83			*Set of 7*	1·25	50*
MS784	108 × 86 mm. $2 Crespi ..	..		85	60*

(Des J.W. Litho Questa)

1976 (15 Apr). *Bicentenary of American Revolution* (2nd issue). *T* **220** *and similar vert designs. Multicoloured. P* 14.

785	½ c. Type **220**	..	..	10	10*
786	1 c. Defending the Liberty Pole	..		10	10*
787	2 c. Loading muskets.	..	..	10	10*
788	35 c. The fight for Liberty	..	..	40	10*
789	50 c. Peace Treaty, 1783	..	..	50	10*
790	$1 Drummers	..	..	75	20*
791	$3 Gunboat ..	..	..	1·75	30*
785/91			*Set of 7*	3·00	60*
MS792	93 × 79 mm. 75 c. as 35 c. and $2 as 50 c.			1·00	80*

221 Nature Study   222 Volleyball

(Des G. Vasarhelyi. Litho Questa)

1976 (1 June). *50th Anniv of Girl Guides in Grenada. T* **221** *and similar vert designs. Multicoloured. P* 14.

793	½ c. Type **221**	..	..	10	10*
794	1 c. Campfire cooking	..	..	10	10*
795	2 c. First Aid	..	..	10	10*
796	50 c. Camping	..	..	65	10*
797	75 c. Home economics	..	..	90	15*
798	$2 First Aid	..	..	1·75	25*
793/8			*Set of 6*	3·00	55*
MS799	111 × 85 mm. $1 Painting	..		85	70*

(Des J.W. Litho Questa)

1976 (21 June). *Olympic Games, Montreal. T* **222** *and similar vert designs. Multicoloured. P* 14.

800	½ c. Type 222	..	..	..	10	10*
801	1 c. Cycling	..	..	..	10	10*
802	2 c. Rowing	..	..	..	10	10*
803	35 c. Judo	..	..	..	30	10*
804	45 c. Hockey	..	..	..	60	10*
805	75 c. Gymnastics	..	..	..	60	20*
806	$1 High jump	..	..	..	60	20*
800/6				*Set of 7*	2·00	60*
MS807	106 × 81 mm. $3 Equestrian event		..		1·25	80*

223 "Cha-U-Kao at the Moulin Rouge"   224 Piper PA-23 Apache 235

(Des M. Shamir. Litho Questa)

1976 (20 July). *75th Death Anniv of Toulouse Lautrec. T* **223** *and similar vert designs. Multicoloured. P* 14.

808	½ c. Type 223	..	..	..	10	10*
809	1 c. "Quadrille at the Moulin Rouge"			..	10	10*
810	2 c. "Profile of a Woman"	..	..	..	10	10*
811	3 c. "Salon in the Rue des Moulins"	..			10	10*
812	40 c. "The Laundryman"	..	..	..	55	10*
813	50 c. "Marcelle Lender dancing the Bolero"		..		65	10*
814	$2 "Signor Boileau at the Cafe"			..	1·75	25*
808/14				*Set of 7*	2·75	55*
MS815	152 × 125 mm. $1 "Woman with Boa"		..		2·00	70*

1976 (26 July). *West Indian Victory in World Cricket Cup. As Nos.* 559/60 *of Barbados.*

816	35 c. Map of the Caribbean	..	..	..	1·25	35
817	$1 The Prudential Cup	..	..	..	2·75	5·00

(Des J.W. Litho Questa)

1976 (18 Aug). *Airplanes. T* **224** *and similar horiz designs. Multicoloured. P* 14.

818	½ c. Type 224	..	..	..	10	10*
819	1 c. Beech 50 Twin Bonanza	..	..		10	10*
820	2 c. De Havilland D.H.C.6 Twin Otter 100				10	10*
821	40 c. Britten Norman Islander	..	..		70	10*
822	50 c. De Havilland D.H.114 Heron 2	..			75	10*
823	$2 Hawker Siddeley H.S.748			..	2·50	50*
818/23				*Set of 6*	3·50	70*
MS824	75×83 mm. $3 B.A.C. One Eleven 500			2·00	80*

225 Satellite Assembly   226 S.S. *Geestland*

(Des PAD Studio. Litho Questa)

1976 (1 Sept). *Viking and Helios Space Missions. T* **225** *and similar multicoloured designs. P* 14.

825	½ c. Type 225	..	..	..	10	10*
826	1 c. Helios satellite	..	..	..	10	10*
827	2 c. Helios encapsulation	..	..		10	10*
828	15 c. Systems test	..	..	..	10	10*
829	45 c. Viking lander (*horiz*)	..	..		20	10*
830	75 c. Lander on Mars	..	..	..	35	15*
831	$2 Viking encapsulation	..	..		90	20*
825/31				*Set of 7*	1·40	55*
MS832	110 × 85 mm. $3 Orbiter and lander	..		1·00	75*

(Des J.W. Litho Format)

1976 (3 Nov). *Ships. T* **226** *and similar horiz designs. Multicoloured. P* 14½.

833	½ c. Type 226	..	..	..	10	10*
834	1 c. M. V. *Federal Palm*	..	..		10	10*
835	2 c. H.M.S. *Blake*	..	..	..	10	10*
836	25 c. M. V. *Vistafjord*	..	..		45	10*
837	75 c. S.S. *Canberra*	..	..	..	1·10	15*
838	$1 S.S. *Regina*	..	..	..	1·40	20*
839	$5 S.S. *Arandora Star*	..	..		3·25	40*
833/39				*Set of 7*	5·50	85*
MS840	91 × 78 mm. $2 *Santa Maria*	..		2·00	4·00

227 "Altarpiece of San Barnaba" (Botticelli)

(Des PAD Studio. Litho Questa)

1976 (8 Dec). *Christmas. T* **227** *and similar horiz designs. Multi-coloured. P* 14.

841	½ c. Type 227	..	..	..	10	10*
842	1 c. "Annunciation" (Botticelli)	..		10	10*
843	2 c. "Madonna of Chancellor Rolin" (Jan van Eyck)				10	10*
844	35 c. "Annunciation" (Fra Filippo Lippi)		15	10*
845	50 c. "Madonna of the Magnificat" (Botticelli)		20	10*
846	75 c. "Madonna of the Pomegranate" (Botticelli)			35	15*
847	$3 "Madonna with St. Cosmas and Other Saints" (Botticelli)			1·00	25*
841/7				*Set of 7*	1·50	50*
MS848	71 × 57 mm. $2 "Gypsy Madonna" (Titian)	1·00	60*

228 Alexander Graham Bell and Telephones   229 Coronation Scene

(Des G. Vasarhelyi. Litho Questa)

1976 (17 Dec). *Telephone Centenary. T* **228** *and similar horiz designs. Multicoloured. P* 14.

849	½ c. Type 228	..	..	..	10	10*
850	1 c. Telephone-users within globe	..		10	10*
851	2 c. Telephone satellite	..	..		10	10*
852	18 c. Telephone viewer and console	..		20	10*
853	40 c. Satellite and tracking stations	..		35	10*
854	$1 Satellite transmitting to ships	..		60	15*
855	$2 Dish aerial and modern telephone		1·10	25*
849/55				*Set of 7*	2·00	55*
MS856	107 × 80 mm. $5 Globe encircled by flags	1·75	75*

(Des J.W. Litho Questa (Nos. 857/62), Walsall (863/6))

1977 (8 Feb). *Silver Jubilee. T* **229** *and similar vert designs. Multicoloured. (a) Sheet stamps. P* 13½ × 14.

857	½ c. Type 229	..	..	..	10	10*
858	1 c. Sceptre and orb	..	..		10	10*
859	35 c. Queen on horseback	..	..		10	10*
860	$2 Spoon and ampulla	..	..		25	15*
861	$2.50 Queen and Prince Philip	..		25	15*
857/61				*Set of 5*	60	45*
MS862	103 × 79 mm. $5 Royal Visit to Grenada ..		75	60*

Nos. 857/61 also exist perf 11½×12 (*price for set of 5* 60p. *mint or used*) from additional sheetlets of 5 stamps and 1 label. They also have different frame colours to those perforated 13½×14 which come from normal sheets of 40.

(*b*) *Booklet stamps. Roul* 5 × *imperf*. *Self-adhesive*

863	35 c. As No. 861	..	..	..	15	25
	a. Booklet pane of 6. .	..	..		70	
864	50 c. As No. 860	..	..	..	25	1·00
	a. Booklet pane. Nos. 864/6. .	..		1·90	
865	$1 As No. 858	..	..	..	50	1·40
866	$3 As No. 859	..	..	..	1·25	2·75
863/6				*Set of 4*	2·00	4·75

*No. 863/6 are separated by various combinations of rotary knife (giving a straight edge) and roulette.

230 Water Skiing

(Des G. Drummond. Litho Questa)

1977 (Apr). *Easter Water Parade. T* **230** *and similar horiz designs. Multicoloured. P* 14.

867	½ c. Type 230	..	..	..	10	10*
868	1 c. Speedboat race	..	..	..	10	10*
869	2 c. Row boat race	..	..	..	10	10*
870	22 c. Swimming	..	..	..	15	10*
871	35 c. Work boat race	..	..	..	25	10*
872	75 c. Water polo	..	..	..	50	10*
873	$2 Game fishing	..	..	..	1·40	25*
867/73				*Set of 7*	2·25	55*
MS874	115 × 85 mm. $3 Yacht race	..		1·50	75*

231 Meeting Place, Grand Anse Beach

(Litho Questa)

1977 (14 June). *Seventh Meeting of Organization of American States. P* 14.

875	231	35 c. multicoloured	..	..	10	10
876		$1 multicoloured	..	..	25	60
877		$2 multicoloured	..	..	40	1·75
875/7				*Set of 3*	65	2·25

232 Rafting

(Des G. Drummond. Litho Questa)

1977 (6 Sept). *Caribbean Scout Jamboree, Jamaica. T* **232** *and similar horiz designs. Multicoloured. P* 14.

878	½ c. Type 232	..	..	..	10	10*
879	1 c. Tug-of-war	..	..	..	10	10*
880	2 c. Sea Scouts regatta	..	..		10	10*
881	18 c. Camp fire. .	..	..	..	25	10*
882	40 c. Field kitchen	..	..	..	50	10*
883	$1 Scouts and sea scouts	..	..		1·25	15*
884	$2 Hiking and map reading. .	..		1·75	25*
878/84				*Set of 7*	3·50	60*
MS885	107 × 85 mm. $3 Semaphore	..		2·00	80*

233 Angel and Shepherd   Royal Visit W. I. 1977 (234)

(Des G. Vasarhelyi. Litho Questa)

1977 (3 Nov). *Christmas. T* **233** *and similar horiz designs showing ceiling panels from the church of St. Martin in Zillis. Multicoloured. P* 14.

886	½ c. Type 233	..	..	..	10	10*
887	1 c. St. Joseph	..	..	..	10	10*
888	2 c. Virgin and Child Fleeing to Egypt		10	10*
889	22 c. Angel	..	..	..	10	10*
890	35 c. A Magus on horseback	..	..		15	10*
891	75 c. Three horses	..	..	..	20	15*
892	$2 Virgin and Child. .	..	..		50	25*
886/92				*Set of 7*	85	50*
MS893	85 × 112 mm. $3 Magus offering gifts	1·00	70*

1977 (10 Nov). *Royal Visit. Nos.* 857/62 *optd with T* **234**. *P* 13½×14 (35 c., $2, $2.50) *or* 11½×12 (*others*).

894	½ c. Type 229	..	..	..	10	10
895	1 c. Sceptre and orb	..	..		10	10
896	35 c. Queen on horseback	..	..		10	10
897	$2 Spoon and ampulla	..	..		30	40
898	$2.50, Queen and Prince Philip	..		35	45
894/8				*Set of 5*	75	85
MS899	103 × 79 mm. $5 Royal Visit to Grenada	75	1·25

Nos. 894/5 also exist perforated 11½×12, but the remaining three values come perforated 13½×14 or 11½×12 (Nos. 896/8 perf 11½×12. Price for set of 3 75p mint or used).

235 Christjaan Eijkman (Medicine)   236 Count von Zeppelin and First Zeppelin Airship LZ-1

(Des J.W. Litho Questa)

1978 (25 Jan). *Nobel Prize Winners. T* **235** *and similar vert designs. Multicoloured. P* 14.

900	½ c. Type 235	..	..	..	10	10*
901	1 c. Sir Winston Churchill (Literature)		30	10*
902	2 c. Woodrow Wilson (Peace)	..		10	10*
903	35 c. Frederic Passy (Peace)	..		15	10*
904	$1 Albert Einstein (Physics)	..		1·00	15*
905	$3 Carl Bosch (Chemistry) . .	..		1·75	25*
900/5				*Set of 6*	3·00	55*
MS906	114 × 99 mm. $2 Alfred Nobel	..		70	60*

(Des G. Vasarhelyi. Litho Questa)

1978 (13 Feb). *75th Anniv of First Zeppelin Flight and 50th Anniv of Lindbergh's Transatlantic Flight. T* **236** *and similar horiz designs. Multicoloured. P* 14.

907	½ c. Type 236	..	..	..	10	10*
908	1 c. Lindbergh with Ryan NYP Special *Spirit of St. Louis*			10	10*
909	2 c. Airship LZ-7 *Deutschland*	..		10	10*
910	22 c. Lindbergh's arrival in France	..		25	10*
911	75 c. Lindbergh and Ryan NYP Special *Spirit of St. Louis* in flight			50	10*
912	$1 LZ-127 *Graf Zeppelin* over Alps		55	15*
913	$3 LZ-127 *Graf Zeppelin* over White House			1·25	65*
907/13				*Set of 7*	2·50	55*
MS914	103×85 mm. Lindbergh in cockpit; $2 Count von Zeppelin and airship LZ-5 ..	..	1·40	60*

NEW INFORMATION

The editor is always interested to correspond with people who have new information that will improve or correct the Catalogue.

237 Rocket Launching   238 Black-headed Gull

(Des J.W. Litho Questa)

1978 (28 Feb). *Space Shuttle. T* **237** *and similar vert designs. Multicoloured. P* 14.
915	½ c. Type **237**	10	10*
916	1 c. Booster jettison	10	10*
917	2 c. External tank jettison	10	10*
918	18 c. Space shuttle in orbit	20	10*
919	75 c. Satellite placement	45	10*
920	$2 Landing approach	1·10	20*
915/20	*Set of 6*	1·60	50*
MS921	103 × 85 mm. $3 Shuttle after landing	1·40	60*

(Des G. Drummond. Litho Questa)

1978 (9 Mar). *Wild Birds of Grenada. T* **238** *and similar vert designs. Multicoloured. P* 14.
922	½ c. Type **238**	10	10*
923	1 c. Wilson's Petrel	10	10*
924	2 c. Killdeer	10	10*
925	50 c. White-necked Jacobin	1·50	10*
926	75 c. Blue-faced Booby	2·00	15*
927	$1 Broad-winged Hawk	3·00	20*
928	$2 Red-necked Pigeon	4·00	30*
922/8	*Set of 7*	9·50	80*
MS929	103×94 mm. $3 Scarlet Ibis	6·00	1·00*

239 "The Landing of   240 Ludwig van Beethoven
Marie de Medici
at Marseilles"

(Des PAD Studio. Litho Questa)

1978 (30 Mar). *400th Birth Anniv of Rubens. T* **239** *and similar vert designs showing paintings. Multicoloured. P* 13½ × 14.
930	5 c. Type **239**	10	10*
931	15 c. "Rubens and Isabella Brandt"	10	10*
932	18 c. "Marchesa Brigida Spindola-Doria"	10	10*
933	25 c. "Ludovicus Nonninus"	10	10*
934	45 c. "Helene Fourment and her Children"	15	10*
935	75 c. "Clara Serena Rubens"	25	10*
936	$3 "Le Chapeau de Paille"	60	20*
930/6	*Set of 7*	1·10	50*
MS937	65 × 100 mm. $5 "Self Portrait"	1·50	60*

(Des PAD Studio. Litho Questa)

1978 (24 Apr). *150th Death Anniv of Beethoven. T* **240** *and similar multicoloured designs. P* 14.
938	5 c. Type **240**	10	10*
939	15 c. Woman violinist (*horiz*)	15	10*
940	18 c. Musical instruments (*horiz*)	20	10*
941	22 c. Piano (*horiz*)	20	10*
942	50 c. Violins	40	10*
943	75 c. Piano and sonata score	60	15*
944	$3 Beethoven's portrait and home (*horiz*)	2·25	25*
938/44	*Set of 7*	3·50	60*
MS945	83 × 62 mm. $2 Beethoven and score	1·10	60*

241 King Edward's   242 Queen Elizabeth II taking
Chair   Salute at Trooping the Colour

(Des J.W. Litho Questa. (Nos. 946/9). Manufactured by Walsall.
(Nos. 950/2))

1978 (2 May–14 June). *25th Anniv of Coronation. Multicoloured.*

(*a*) *Sheet stamps. Vert designs as T* **241**. *P* 14 (14 June)
946	35 c. Type **241**	10	10
947	$2 Queen with regalia	30	35
948	$2.50, St. Edward's Crown	30	40
946/8	*Set of 3*	60	75
MS949	102 × 76 mm. $5 Queen and Prince Philip	80	80

(*b*) *Booklet stamps. Vert designs as T* **242**. *Roul 5 × imperf*. Self-adhesive* (2 May)
950	25 c. Type **242**	15	15
	a. Booklet pane. Nos. 950/1, each × 3	80	
951	35 c. Queen taking part in Maundy Thursday ceremony	15	25
952	$5 Queen and Prince Philip at Opening of Parliament	1·50	2·50
	a. Booklet pane of 1	1·50	
950/2	*Set of 3*	1·60	2·50

Nos. 946/8 also exist perf 12 (*Price for set of 3 75p. mint or used*) from additional sheetlets of 3 stamps and 1 label, issued 2 June. These have different frame colours from the stamps perforated 14, which come from normal sheets of 50.

*Nos. 950/1 are separated by various combinations of rotary-knife (giving a straight edge) and roulette. No. 952 exists only with straight edges.

243 Goalkeeper   244 Aerial Phenomena, Germany,
reaching for Ball   1561 and U.S.A., 1952

(Des M. Rubin. Litho Format)

1978 (1 Aug). *World Cup Football Championship, Argentina. T* **243** *and similar vert designs showing goalkeeper reaching for ball. P* 14½.
953	40 c. multicoloured	10	10
954	60 c. multicoloured	15	20
955	90 c. multicoloured	25	30
956	$2 multicoloured	60	60
953/6	*Set of 4*	1·00	1·00
MS957	130 × 97 mm. $2.50, multicoloured	1·10	1·10

(Des G. Vasarhelyi. Litho Format)

1978 (17 Aug). *U.F.O. Research. T* **244** *and similar horiz designs. Multicoloured. P* 14½.
958	5 c. Type **244**	15	10
959	35 c. Various aerial phenomena, 1950	35	25
960	$3 U.F.O.'s, 1965	2·00	1·75
958/60	*Set of 3*	2·25	1·90
MS961	112 × 89 mm. $2 Sir Eric Gairy and U.F.O. research laboratory	1·25	1·25

245 Wright Flyer III

(Des G. Vasarhelyi. Litho Questa)

1978 (28 Aug). *75th Anniv of Powered Flight. T* **245** *and similar horiz designs. Multicoloured. P* 14.
962	5 c. Type **245**	10	10
963	15 c. Flyer I, 1903	10	10
964	18 c. Wright Type A	10	10
965	22 c. Flyer I from above	15	10
966	50 c. Orville Wright and Wright Type A	20	20
967	75 c. Wright Type A in Pau, France, 1908	25	25
968	$3 Wilbur Wright and Wright glider No. IV	80	70
962/8	*Set of 7*	1·40	1·25
MS969	114×85 mm. $2 Wright glider No. III	1·00	75

246 Cook and Hawaiian Feast   247 "Paumgartner
Altarpiece" (detail)

(Des G. Vasarhelyi. Litho Questa)

1978 (5 Dec). *Bicentenary of Discovery of Hawaii and 250th Birth Anniv of Captain Cook. T* **246** *and similar horiz designs. Multicoloured. P* 14.
970	18 c. Type **246**	60	20
971	35 c. Cook and Hawaiian warriors	80	25
972	75 c. Cook and Honolulu Harbour	1·75	1·50
973	$3 Cook (statue) and H.M.S. *Resolution*	4·00	6·00
970/3	*Set of 4*	6·50	7·00
MS974	116 × 88 mm. $4 Cook and death scene	3·75	3·00

(Des M. Rubin. Litho Questa)

1978 (20 Dec). *Christmas. Paintings by Dürer. T* **247** *and similar vert designs. Multicoloured. P* 14.
975	40 c. Type **247**	20	15
976	60 c. "The Adoration of the Magi"	25	20
977	90 c. "The Virgin and Child"	30	20
978	$2 "Virgin and Child with St. Anne" (detail)	55	55
975/8	*Set of 4*	1·10	1·10
MS979	113 × 83 mm. $4 "Madonna and Child"	1·10	1·50

---

248 National Convention and   249 *Acalypha hispida*
Cultural Centre (interior)

(Des BG Studio. Litho Questa)

1979 (8 Feb). *5th Anniv of Independence. T* **248** *and similar vert designs. Multicoloured. P* 14.
980	5 c. Type **248**	10	10
981	18 c. National Convention and Cultural Centre (exterior)	10	10
982	22 c. Easter Water Parade, 1978	10	10
983	Sir Eric M. Gairy (Prime Minister)	15	10
984	$3 The Cross, Fort Frederick	60	80
980/4	*Set of 5*	80	90

(Des J.W. Litho Questa)

1979 (26 Feb). *Flowers. T* **249** *and similar vert designs. Multicoloured. P* 14.
985	18 c. Type **249**	10	10
986	50 c. *Hibiscus rosa sinensis*	25	15
987	$1 *Thunbergia grandiflora*	40	25
988	$3 *Nerium oleander*	1·10	1·10
985/8	*Set of 4*	1·60	1·40
MS989	115 × 90 mm. $2 *Lagerstroemia speciosa*	1·00	1·40

250 Birds in Flight   251 Children playing Cricket

(Des M. Rubin. Litho Questa)

1979 (15 Mar). *30th Anniv of Declaration of Human Rights. T* **250** *and similar vert design. Multicoloured. P* 14.
990	15 c. Type **250**	10	10
991	$2 Bird in flight	55	65

(Des J.W. Litho Questa)

1979 (23 Apr). *International Year of the Child* (1st issue). *T* **251** *and similar vert designs. Multicoloured. P* 14.
992	18 c. Type **251**	40	30
993	22 c. Children playing baseball	40	30
994	$5 Children playing in tree	3·75	6·00
992/4	*Set of 3*	4·00	6·00
MS995	114×92 mm. $4 Children with model spaceship	1·75	2·25

See also Nos. 1006/7 and 1025/34.

252 "Around the World in 80 Days"

(Des G. Vasarhelyi. Litho Questa)

1979 (4 May). *150th Birth Anniv of Jules Verne* (author). *T* **252** *and similar horiz designs showing scenes from his books and modern technological developments. Multicoloured. P* 14.
996	18 c. Type **252**	25	10
997	35 c. "20,000 Leagues under the Sea"	35	15
998	75 c. "From the Earth to the Moon"	50	50
999	$3 "Master of the World"	1·40	1·60
996/9	*Set of 4*	2·25	2·00
MS1000	110×85 mm. $4 "Clipper of the Clouds"	1·25	1·25

253 Mail Runner, Africa (early   254 "The Pistol of Peace"
19th-century)   (vaccination gun), Map of
Grenada and Children

(Des J.W. Litho Questa)

1979 (23 July). *Death Centenary of Sir Rowland Hill. T* **253** *and similar horiz designs. Multicoloured. P* 14.

1001	20 c. Type 253	10	10
1002	40 c. Pony Express, America (mid 19th-century)	10	10
1003	$1 Pigeon post	20	25
1004	$3 Mail coach, Europe (18th-19th-century)	50	80
1001/4	*Set of* 4	80	1·10
MS1005	127 × 100 mm. $5 Sir Rowland Hill and 1891 1d. on 8d. *tête-bêche* block of 4	75	1·10

Nos. 1001/4 also exist perf 12 (*Price for set of* 4 80p. *mint or used*) from additional sheetlets of 5 stamps and 1 label, issued 8 August. These have different background colours from the stamps perforated 14, which come from normal sheets of 40.

(Des G. Vasarhelyi. Litho Questa)

1979 (20 Aug). *International Year of the Child* (2nd Issue). *"Grenada—First Nation 100% Immunized". P* 14.

1006	254	5 c. multicoloured	30	30
1007		$1 multicoloured	1·00	2·00

255 Reef Shark

(Des G. Drummond. Litho Questa)

1979 (22 Aug). *Marine Wildlife. T* **225** *and similar horiz designs. Multicoloured. P* 14.

1008	40 c. Type 255	40	30
1009	45 c. Spotted Eagle Ray	40	30
1010	50 c. Many-toothed Conger	45	40
1011	60 c. Golden Olive (shell)	70	75
1012	70 c. West Indian Murex (shell)	85	90
1013	75 c. Giant Tun (shell)	90	1·00
1014	90 c. Brown Booby	2·25	2·00
1015	$1 Magnificent Frigate Bird	2·25	2·00
1008/15	*Set of* 8	7·50	7·00
MS1016	109×78 mm. $2.50, Sooty Tern	2·50	2·00

256 The Flight into Egypt

(Des W. Grout. Litho Questa)

1979 (19 Oct). *Christmas. Religious Tapestries. T* **256** *and similar multicoloured designs. P* 14.

1017	6 c. Type 256	10	10
1018	25 c. The Flight into Egypt (detail)	10	10
1019	30 c. Angel (*vert*)	15	10
1020	40 c. Doge Marino Grimani (detail) (*vert*)	15	10
1021	90 c. The Annunciation to the Shepherds (*vert*)	30	20
1022	$1 The Flight into Egypt (Rome) (*vert*)	30	25
1023	$2 The Virgin in Glory (*vert*)	40	50
1017/23	*Set of* 7	1·25	1·10
MS1024	111 × 148 mm. $4 Doge Marino Grimani (*vert*)	70	1·00

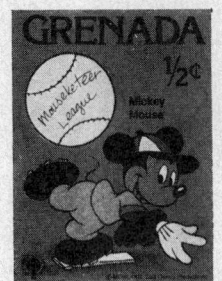

257 Mickey Mouse playing Baseball

258 Paul Harris (founder)

(Litho Format)

1979 (2 Nov). *International Year of the Child* (3rd issue). *Walt Disney Cartoon Characters. T* **257** *and similar vert designs showing characters playing sport. Multicoloured. P* 11.

1025	½ c. Type 257	10	10
1026	1 c. Donald Duck high-jumping	10	10
1027	2 c. Goofy playing basketball	10	10
1028	3 c. Goofy hurdling	10	10
1029	4 c. Donald Duck playing golf	10	10
1030	5 c. Mickey Mouse playing cricket	10	10
1031	10 c. Mickey Mouse playing football	10	10
1032	$2 Mickey Mouse playing tennis	2·75	2·75
1033	$2.50, Minnie Mouse riding horse	2·75	2·75
1025/33	*Set of* 9	5·50	5·50
MS1034	125 × 100 mm. $3 Goofy in riding gear. P 13½.	2·00	2·00

(Des J.W. Litho Questa)

1980 (25 Feb). *75th Anniv of Rotary International. T* **258** *and similar vert designs. Multicoloured. P* 14.

1035	6 c. Type 258	10	10
1036	30 c. "Health"	20	15
1037	90 c. "Hunger"	40	30
1038	$2 "Humanity"	80	80
1035/8	*Set of* 4	1·40	1·10
MS1039	104 × 89 mm. $4 Rotary International emblem	1·00	1·60

PEOPLE'S REVOLUTION
13 MARCH 1979

(259)

1980 (28 Feb–8 Apr). *1st Anniv of Revolution* (1st issue). Nos. 651A/2A, 654A/7A, 659A, 660B *and* 662A/8A *optd with T* **259**.

1040	2 c. Carenage taxi	10	10
	a. Optd on No. 651B	8·50	
1041	3 c. Large working boats	10	10
	a. Optd on No. 652B	8·50	
1042	6 c. Cocoa beans in drying trays	10	10
1043	8 c. Nutmegs	10	10
1044	10 c. River Antoine Estate Rum Distillery, c. 1785	10	10
1045	12 c. Cocoa Tree	10	10
1046	20 c. Parliament Building, St. George's	10	15
1047	25 c. Fort George cannons (8.4.80)	30	30
1048	50 c. General Post Office	30	30
1049	75 c. Caribs Leap, Sauteurs Bay	50	40
1050	$1 Carenage, St. George's	60	60
1051	$2 St. George's Harbour by night	1·25	2·00
1052	$3 Grand Anse Beach	1·50	3·25
1053	$5 Canoe Bay and Black Bay from Point Saline Lighthouse	2·50	5·00
1054	$10 Sugar Loaf Island from Levera Beach	3·75	7·50
1040/54	*Set of* 15	10·00	18·00

See also Nos. 1069/73.

260 Boxing

261 Tropical Kingbird

(Des Design Images Inc. Litho Questa)

1980 (24 Mar). *Olympic Games, Moscow. T* **260** *and similar horiz designs. Multicoloured. P* 14.

1055	25 c. Type 260	10	10
1056	40 c. Cycling	15	15
1057	90 c. Show-jumping	20	30
1058	$2 Running	40	1·00
1055/8	*Set of* 4	75	1·40
MS1059	128 × 95 mm. $4 Sailing	80	1·40

(Des G. Drummond. Litho Questa)

1980 (8 Apr). *Wild Birds. T* **261** *and similar vert designs. Multicoloured. P* 14.

1060	20 c. Type 261	85	15
1061	40 c. Rufous-breasted Hermit	1·25	25
1062	$1 Troupial	1·75	1·75
1063	$2 Ruddy Quail Dove	2·25	3·50
1060/3	*Set of* 4	5·50	5·00
MS1064	85×114 mm. $3 Prairie Warbler	3·75	2·25

263 Free Hot Lunch at Schools

1980 (6 May). *"London 1980" International Stamp Exhibition.* Nos. 1001/4 *optd with T* **262**. *P* 12.

1065	20 c. Type 253	20	20
1066	40 c. Pony Express, America (mid 19th-century)	30	30
1067	$1 Pigeon Post	60	60
1068	$3 Mail coach, Europe (18th-19th-century)	1·75	1·75
1065/8	*Set of* 4	2·50	2·50

(Des M. Diamond. Litho Questa)

1980 (19 May). *1st Anniv of Revolution* (2nd issue). *T* **263** *and similar horiz designs. Multicoloured. P* 14.

1069	10 c. Type 263	10	10
1070	40 c. "From tree to can" (agro-industry)	15	20
1071	$1 National Health care	40	45
1072	$2 New housing projects	75	90
1069/72	*Set of* 4	1·25	1·40
MS1073	110 × 85 mm. $5 Prime Minister Maurice Bishop (*vert*)	1·00	1·25

264 Jamb Statues, West Portal, Chartres Cathedral

(Des J.W. Litho Questa)

1980 (15 July). *Famous Works of Art. T* **264** *and similar horiz designs. Multicoloured. P* 13½.

1074	8 c. Type 264	10	10
1075	10 c. "Les Demoiselles D'Avignon" (painting by Picasso)	10	10
1076	40 c. Winged Victory of Samothrace (statue)	20	20
1077	50 c. "The Night Watch" (painting by Rembrandt)	20	20
1078	$1 "Portrait of Edward VI as a Child" (painting by Holbein the Younger)	35	35
1079	$3 Portrait head of Queen Nefertiti (carving)	80	80
1074/9	*Set of* 6	1·50	1·50
MS1080	101 × 101 mm. $4 "Weier Haws" (detail of painting by Dürer) (*vert*)	1·00	1·00

265 Carib Canoes

(Des G. Drummond. Litho Questa)

1980 (9 Sept)–84. *Shipping. Horiz designs as T* **265**. *Multicoloured. A. Without imprint date. P* 14.

1081A	½ c. Type 265	10	10
1082A	1 c. Boat building	10	10
1083A	2 c. Small working boat	15	10
1084A	4 c. Columbus' *Santa Maria*	40	10
1085A	5 c. West Indiaman barque, *circa* 1840	40	10
1086A	6 c. *Orinoco* (paddle-steamer), *circa* 1851	40	10
1087A	10 c. Working schooner	50	10
1088A	12 c. Trimaran at Grand Anse anchorage	50	10
1089A	15 c. Spice Island cruising yacht *Petite Amie*	50	10
1090A	20 c. Fishing pirogue	1·00	10
1091A	25 c. Harbour police launch	1·75	20
1092A	30 c. Grand Anse speed-boat	1·50	20
1093A	40 c. *Seimstrand* (freighter)	1·50	25
1094A	50 c. *Ariadne* (cadet schooner)	1·50	35
1095A	90 c. *Geestide* (freighter)	1·75	50
1096A	$1 *Cunard Countess* (liner)	2·00	70
1097A	$3 Rum-runner	3·00	4·00
1098A	$5 *Statendam* (liner) off St. George's	4·50	7·00
1099A	$10 Coastguard patrol boat	8·00	13·00
1081A/99A	*Set of* 19	26·00	24·00

B. With imprint date at foot of design. P 14 ($1) *or* 12 (*others*)

1081B	½ c. Type 265 (1982)	75	1·50
1085B	5 c. West Indiaman barque, *circa* 1840 (1982)	2·00	1·25
1087B	10 c. Working schooner (1982)	2·00	60
	a. Perf 14		†
1090B	20 c. Fishing pirogue (1982)	2·50	95
1091B	25 c. Harbour police launch (1982)	2·25	90
	a. Perf 14	3·25	3·00
1092B	30 c. Grand Anse speed-boat (1982)	2·00	1·25
	a. Perf 14	3·75	3·00
1093B	40 c. *Seimstrand* (freighter) (1982)	3·50	1·60
1094B	50 c. *Ariadne* (cadet schooner) (1.84)	50	50
	a. Perf 14 (1984)	55	50
1096B	$1 *Cunard Countess* (liner) (1982)	28·00	14·00
1097B	$3 Rum-runner (1982)	4·00	6·50
1098B	$5 *Statendam* (liner) off St. George's (1982)	6·00	9·00
1099B	$10 Coastguard patrol boat (1.84)	8·00	8·50
1081B/99B	*Set of* 12	55·00	42·00

Imprint dates: "1982", Nos. 1081B, 1085B, 1087B/aB, 1090B, 1091B/aB, 1092B/aB, 1093B, 1096B/8B; "1984", Nos. 1094B/aB, 1099B.

(Litho Walsall)

1980 (25 Sept). *Christmas. Walt Disney Cartoon Scenes from "Snow White and the Seven Dwarfs". Horiz designs as T* **257**. *Multicoloured. P* 11.

1100	½ c. Snow White at well	10	10
1101	1 c. The Wicked Queen	10	10
1102	2 c. Snow White singing to animals	10	10
1103	3 c. Snow White doing housework for Dwarfs	10	10
1104	4 c. The Seven Dwarfs	10	10
1105	5 c. Snow White with Dwarfs	10	10
1106	10 c. Witch offering Snow White apple	10	10
1107	$2.50, Snow White with Prince, and Dwarfs	3·00	1·75
1108	$3 Snow White and Prince	3·50	2·00
1100/8	*Set of* 9	6·50	3·75
MS1109	127 × 102 mm. $4 Snow White sleeping (*vert*)	4·25	2·50

(Litho Format)

1981 (19 Jan). *50th Anniv of Walt Disney's Cartoon Character, Pluto. Vert designs as T* **257**. *Multicoloured. P* 13½.

1110	$2 Pluto with birthday cake	1·25	1·50
MS1111	127 × 102 mm. $4 Pluto in scene from film *Pueblo Pluto*	2·25	2·25

No. 1110 was printed in small sheets of 8 stamps.

266 Revolution and Grenada Flags

1981 (13 Mar). *Festival of the Revolution. T* **266** *and similar triangular designs. Multicoloured. Litho. P* 12½.
1112 5 c. Type **266** 10 10
1113 10 c. Teacher, pupil, book and pencil ("education") 10 10
1114 15 c. Food processing plant ("industry") .. 10 10
1115 25 c. Selection of fruits and farm scene ("agriculture") 15 15
1116 40 c. Crawfish and boat ("fishing") .. 20 20
1117 90 c. *Cunard Countess* arriving at St. George's Harbour ("shipping") .. 50 50
1118 $1 Straw-work ("native handicrafts") .. 60 60
1119 $3 Map of Caribbean with expanded view of Grenada .. .. 1·75 1·75
1112/19 .. .. *Set of 8* 3·00 3·00

(Litho Format)

1981 (7 Apr). *Easter. Walt Disney Cartoon Characters. Vert designs as T* **257**. *Multicoloured. P* 11.
1120 35 c. Mickey Mouse and Goofy .. 40 25
1121 40 c. Donald Duck, Chip and Daisy Duck .. 40 25
1122 $2 Minnie Mouse .. .. .. 1·40 1·50
1123 $2.50, Pluto and Mickey Mouse .. 1·60 1·75
1120/3 .. .. *Set of 4* 3·50 3·25
MS1124 127×101 mm. $4 Goofy. P 13½ .. 3·00 3·50

267 "Woman-Flower"

268 Prince Charles playing Polo

(Des J.W. Litho Questa)

1981 (28 Apr). *Birth Centenary of Picasso. T* **267** *and similar vert designs. Multicoloured. P* 13½ × 14.
1125 25 c. Type **267** 15 15
1126 30 c. "Portrait of Madame" 20 15
1127 90 c. "Cavalier with Pipe" 40 45
1128 $4 "Large Heads" .. .. .. 1·50 1·75
1125/8 .. .. *Set of 4* 2·00 2·25
MS1129 128 × 103 mm. $5 "Woman on the Banks of the Seine" (after Courbet). Imperf .. 5·00 2·25

(Des J.W. Litho Format)

1981 (16 June). *Royal Wedding. T* **268** *and similar vert designs. Multicoloured.* (a) *P* 15.
1130 50 c. Prince Charles and Lady Diana Spencer 10 10
1131 $2 Holyrood House 35 50
1132 $4 Type **268** 50 75
    a. Imperf (pair) £400
1130/2 .. .. *Set of 3* 85 1·25
MS1133 98 × 84 mm. $5 Glass Coach .. 75 75

(b) *P* 15×14½
1134 30 c. As 50 c. 20 20
1135 40 c. As $2 .. .. .. 30 30
The 30 and 40 c. values were each printed in small sheets of 6 including one *se-tenant* stamp-size label.
The $4 value, with changed background colour, also exists perforated 15×14½ (*price* 90p. *mint or used*) from similar sheetlets in addition to the original version issued in sheets of 40.

269 Lady Diana Spencer   270 "The Bath" (Mary Cassatt)

(Manufactured by Walsall)

1981 (16 June). *Royal Wedding. Booklet stamps. T* **269** *and similar vert designs. Multicoloured. Roul* 5 × *imperf*. Self-adhesive.*
1136 $1 Type **269** 30 65
    a. Booklet pane. Nos. 1136/7 each × 3 .. 1·60
1137 $2 Prince Charles 30 65
1138 $5 Prince Charles and Lady Diana Spencer 1·00 1·75
    a. Booklet pane of 1 .. .. .. 1·00
1136/8 .. .. *Set of 3* 1·40 2·75
*The $1 and $2 values were each separated by various combinations of rotary knife (giving a straight edge) and roulette. The $5 value exists only with straight edges.

(Des BG Studio. Litho Questa)

1981 (Oct). *"Decade for Women". Paintings. T* **270** *and similar multicoloured designs. P* 14.
1139 15 c. Type **270** 15 10
1140 40 c. "Mademoiselle Charlotte du Val d'Ognes" (Constance Marie Charpentier) 45 20
1141 60 c. "Self-portrait" (Mary Beale) .. 65 30
1142 $3 "Woman in White Stockings" (Suzanne Valadon) .. .. .. 2·00 1·25
1139/42 .. .. *Set of 4* 3·00 1·75
MS1143 101×77 mm. $5 "The Artist hesitating between the Arts of Music and Painting" (Angelica Kauffman) (*horiz*) .. 1·75 2·00

(Litho Questa)

1981 (Nov). *Christmas. Horiz designs as T* **257** *showing scenes from Walt Disney's cartoon film "Cinderella". P* 13½.
1144 ½ c. multicoloured 10 10
1145 1 c. multicoloured 10 10
1146 2 c. multicoloured 10 10
1147 3 c. multicoloured 10 10
1148 4 c. multicoloured 10 10
1149 5 c. multicoloured 10 10
1150 10 c. multicoloured 15 10
1151 $2.50, multicoloured .. .. .. 3·50 2·25
1152 $3 multicoloured .. .. .. 3·50 2·50
1144/52 .. .. *Set of 9* 7·00 4·75
MS1153 127 × 103 mm. $5 multicoloured .. 5·50 3·25

271 Landing   272 West German Footballer and Flag

(Des M. Brodie. Litho Format)

1981 (12 Nov). *Space Shuttle Project. T* **271** *and similar vert designs. Multicoloured. P* 14½.
1154 30 c. Type **271** 20 15
1155 60 c. Working in space 40 30
1156 70 c. Lift off 45 35
1157 $3 Separation .. .. .. 1·40 1·25
1154/7 .. .. *Set of 4* 2·25 1·75
MS1158 117 × 89 mm. $5 In orbit .. 1·75 1·50

(Des Clover Mill. Litho Format)

1981 (30 Nov.) *World Cup Football Championship, Spain* (1982). *T* **272** *and similar multicoloured designs. P* 14.
1159 25 c. + 10 c. Type **272** 55 30
1160 40 c. + 20 c. Argentinian footballer and flag .. 70 40
1161 50 c. + 25 c. Brazilian footballer and flag 80 50
1162 $1 + 50 c. English footballer and flag 1·25 95
1159/62 .. .. *Set of 4* 3·00 1·90
MS1163 141 × 128 mm. $5 + 50 c. Spanish orange mascot and Jules Rimet Trophy (*vert*) .. 4·00 2·50
Nos. 1159/62 were each printed in sheetlets of 12 on an overall background design showing a football.

273 General Post Office, St. George's   274 Artist without Hands

(Des J.W. Litho Format)

1981 (10 Dec). *Centenary of U.P.U. Membership. T* **273** *and similar horiz designs. Multicoloured. P* 15.
1164 25 c. Type **273** 20 15
1165 30 c. 1861 1d. stamp 25 20
1166 90 c. 1970 New U.P.U. Headquarters Building 25 c. commemorative 65 50
1167 $4 1961 Stamp Centenary 25 c. commemorative .. .. .. 1·75 2·00
1164/7 .. .. *Set of 4* 2·50 2·50
MS1168 113×87 mm. $5 1974 Centenary of U.P.U. ½ c. commemorative .. .. 3·50 3·25

(Litho Questa)

1982 (4 Feb). *International Year for the Disabled* (1981). *T* **274** *and similar vert designs. Multicoloured. P* 14.
1169 30 c. Type **274** 45 15
1170 40 c. Computer operator without hands .. 50 15
1171 70 c. Blind schoolteacher teaching braille 75 25
1172 $3 Midget playing drums .. .. 1·75 1·10
1169/72 .. .. *Set of 4* 3·00 1·50
MS1173 101 × 72 mm. $4 Auto mechanic confined to wheelchair .. .. .. 3·00 2·25

---

275 Tending Vegetable Patch   276 *Dryas julia*

(Des Design Images. Litho Format)

1982 (19 Feb). *75th Anniv of Boy Scout Movement and 125th Birth Anniv of Lord Baden-Powell. T* **275** *and similar horiz designs. Multicoloured. P* 14½.
1174 70 c. Type **275** 50 45
1175 90 c. Map-reading 55 55
1176 $1 Bee-keeping 65 65
1177 $4 Hospital reading .. .. .. 2·25 2·75
1174/7 .. .. *Set of 4* 3·50 4·00
MS1178 100 × 71 mm. $5 Presentation of trophies 2·50 2·50

(Des G. Drummond. Litho Questa)

1982 (24 Mar). *Butterflies. T* **276** *and similar vert designs. Multicoloured. P* 14.
1179 10 c. Type **276** 75 30
1180 60 c. *Phoebis agarithe* .. .. 2·50 1·50
1181 $1 *Anartia amathea* .. .. 3·00 2·00
1182 $3 *Battus polydamas* .. .. 4·25 7·00
1179/82 .. .. *Set of 4* 9·50 9·75
MS1183 111×85 mm. $5 *Junonia evarete* .. 7·50 4·50

277 "Saying Grace"   278 Kensington Palace

(Des M.B.I. Studio. Litho Questa)

1982 (14 Apr). *Norman Rockwell (painter) Commemoration. T* **277** *and similar vert designs. Multicoloured. P* 14 × 13½.
1184 15 c. Type **277** 35 10
1185 30 c. "Nothing Up His Sleeve" (inscr "Card Tricks") 60 15
1186 60 c. "Pharmacist" 75 25
1187 70 c. "Hobo" (inscr "Pals") 80 35
1184/7 .. .. *Set of 4* 2·25 75

(Des PAD Studio. Litho Questa)

1982 (1 July). *21st Birthday of Princess of Wales. T* **278** *and similar vert designs. Multicoloured. P* 14½ × 14.
1188 50 c. Type **278** 40 45
1189 60 c. Type **278** 80 45
1190 $1 Prince and Princess of Wales .. 90 1·00
1191 $2 As $1 .. .. 1·75 1·25
1192 $3 Princess of Wales .. .. 2·00 2·25
1193 $4 As $3 .. .. 2·25 2·25
1188/93 .. .. *Set of 6* 7·25 7·00
MS1194 103 × 75 mm. $5 Princess Diana (*different*) .. .. .. 2·00 2·00
Nos. 1188, 1190 and 1192 come from sheetlets of 5 stamps and 1 label.

279 Mary McLeod Bethune appointed Director of Negro Affairs, 1942

(Des Design Images. Litho Questa)

1982 (27 July). *Birth Centenary of Franklin D. Roosevelt. T* **279** *and similar horiz designs. Multicoloured. P* 14.
1195 10 c. Type **279** 10 10
1196 60 c. Huddie Ledbetter ("Leadbelly") in concert (Works Progress administration) 35 20
1197 $1.10, Signing bill No. 8802, 1941 (Fair Employment committee) 65 40
1198 $3 Farm Security administration .. 1·00 80
1195/8 .. .. *Set of 4* 1·75 1·25
MS1199 100×70 mm. $5 William Hastie, first Negro judicial appointee .. .. 1·50 1·50

1982 (30 Aug). *Birth of Prince William of Wales. Nos.* 1188/94 *optd with T* 171 *of Antigua.*
1200 50 c. Type **278** 30 60
1201 60 c. Type **278** 35 35
1202 $1 Prince and Princess of Wales .. 55 85
1203 $2 As $1 .. .. 1·00 1·00
1204 $3 Princess of Wales .. .. 1·75 1·90
1205 $4 As $3 .. .. 1·90 1·90
1200/5 .. .. *Set of 6* 5·50 6·00
MS1206 103 × 75 mm. $5 Princess Diana (*different*) .. .. .. 2·00 2·00
Nos. 1200, 1202 and 1204 come from sheetlets of 5 stamps and 1 label.

280 Apostle and Tormentor

(Des Clover Mill. Litho Format)

1982 (2 Sept). *Easter. Details from Painting "The Way to Calvary" by Raphael. T 280 and similar multicoloured designs. P 14 × 14½ (40 c.) or 14½ × 14 (others).*
1207	40 c. Type 280	30	15
1208	70 c. Captain of the guards (vert)	40	25
1209	$1.10, Christ and apostle (vert)	60	35
1210	$4 Mourners (vert)	1·50	1·50
1207/10	Set of 4	2·50	2·00
MS1211	102 × 126 mm. $5 Christ falls beneath the cross (vert)	3·00	3·00

281 "Orient Express"

(Des Artists International. Litho Format)

1982 (4 Oct). *Famous Trains of the World. T 281 and similar horiz designs. Multicoloured. P 15 × 14½.*
1212	30 c. Type 281	50	35
1213	60 c. "Trans-Siberian Express"	60	70
1214	70 c. "Golden Arrow"	70	80
1215	90 c. "Flying Scotsman"	85	1·00
1216	$1 German Federal Railways	1·00	1·25
1217	$3 German National Railways	2·25	4·00
1212/17	Set of 6	5·50	7·25
MS1218	109 × 81 mm. $5 "20th Century Limited"	3·00	3·50

No. 1217 exists imperforate from stock dispersed by the liquidator of Format International Security Printers Ltd.

282 Footballers   283 Killer Whale

(Des D. Miller. Litho Questa)

1982 (2 Dec). *World Cup Football Championship Winners. T 282 and similar horiz designs. P 14 × 13½.*
1219	60 c. multicoloured	35	35
1220	$4 multicoloured	2·00	2·00
MS1221	93 × 119 mm. $5 multicoloured	2·50	2·75

(Litho Questa)

1982 (14 Dec). *Christmas. Horiz designs as T 257 depicting scenes from Walt Disney's cartoon film "Robin Hood". P 13½.*
1222	½ c. multicoloured	10	10
1223	1 c. multicoloured	10	10
1224	2 c. multicoloured	10	10
1225	3 c. multicoloured	10	10
1226	4 c. multicoloured	10	10
1227	5 c. multicoloured	10	10
1228	10 c. multicoloured	10	10
1229	$2.50, multicoloured	2·00	2·25
1230	$3 multicoloured	2·25	2·50
1222/30	Set of 9	4·25	4·75
MS1231	121 × 96 mm. $5 multicoloured	6·00	4·00

(Des Artists International. Litho Questa)

1983 (10 Jan). *Save the Whales. T 283 and similar vert designs. Multicoloured. P 14.*
1232	15 c. Type 283	1·00	30
1233	40 c. Sperm Whale	2·25	90
1234	70 c. Blue Whale	2·75	2·75
1235	$3 Common Dolphin	3·50	6·50
1232/5	Set of 4	8·50	9·50
MS1236	84 × 74 mm. $5 Humpback Whale	5·50	4·00

284 "Construction of Ark"

(Des Design Images. Litho Format)

1983 (15 Feb). *500th Birth Anniv of Raphael. T 284 and similar horiz designs showing painting details. Multicoloured. P 13½.*
1237	25 c. Type 284	20	15
1238	30 c. "Jacob's Vision"	20	20
1239	90 c. "Joseph interprets the Dreams to his Brothers"	40	45
1240	$4 "Joseph interprets Pharaoh's Dreams"	1·60	1·75
1237/40	Set of 4	2·25	2·25
MS1241	128 × 100 mm. $5 "Creation of the Animals"	1·25	1·75

Nos. 1237/41 exist imperforate from stock dispersed by the liquidator of Format International Security Printers Ltd.

285 Dentistry at Health Centre

(Des J.W. Litho Questa)

1983 (14 Mar). *Commonwealth Day. T 285 and similar horiz designs. Multicoloured. P 14.*
1242	10 c. Type 285	10	10
1243	70 c. Airport runway construction	35	35
1244	$1.10, Tourism	40	55
1245	$3 Boat-building	80	1·40
1242/5	Set of 4	1·50	2·10

286 Maritime Communications via Satellite

(Des G. Vasarhelyi. Litho Questa)

1983 (29 Mar). *World Communications Year. T 286 and similar horiz designs. Multicoloured. P 14.*
1246	30 c. Type 286	15	15
1247	40 c. Rural telephone installation	20	20
1248	$2.50, Satellite weather map	1·25	1·25
1249	$3 Airport control room	1·40	1·40
1246/9	Set of 4	2·75	2·75
MS1250	111 × 85 mm. $5 Communications satellite	2·50	2·50

287 Franklin Sport Sedan, 1928

(Des J. Mendola. Litho Format)

1983 (4 May). *75th Anniv of Model "T" Ford Car. T 287 and similar horiz designs showing cars of the 20th century. Multicoloured. P 14½.*
1251	6 c. Type 287	15	10
1252	10 c. Delage "D8", 1933	20	10
1253	40 c. Alvis, 1938	35	25
1254	60 c. Invicta "S-type" tourer, 1931	45	45
1255	70 c. Alfa-Romeo "1750 Gran Sport", 1930	55	55
1256	90 c. Isotta Fraschini, 1930	60	65
1257	$1 Bugatti "Royale Type 41"	70	65
1258	$2 BMW "328", 1938	1·40	1·50
1259	$3 Marmon "V16", 1931	1·60	2·25
1260	$4 Lincoln "K8" saloon, 1932	1·90	2·75
1251/60	Set of 10	7·00	8·50
MS1261	114 × 90 mm. $5 Cougar "XR 7", 1972	2·50	3·00

Nos. 1251/60 were each issued in sheets of eight stamps with a stamp-size label in the centre position.

288 N.1 Norge (airship)

(Des W. Wright. Litho Questa)

1983 (18 July). *Bicentenary of Manned Flight. T 288 and similar multicoloured designs. P 14.*
1262	30 c. Type 288	60	30
1263	60 c. Gloster VI seaplane	1·00	1·00
1264	$1.10, Curtiss NC-4 flying boat	3·50	4·50
1265	$4 Dornier Do-18 flying boat *Aeolus*	3·50	4·50
1262/5	Set of 4	6·00	6·75
MS1266	114×85 mm. $5 Modern hot-air balloon (vert)	2·75	3·00

289 Morty

(Litho Format)

1983 (7 Nov). *Christmas. T 289 and similar vert designs showing Disney cartoon characters in scenes from "It's beginning to look a lot like Christmas" (song). Multicoloured. P 11.*
1267	½ c. Type 289	10	10
1268	1 c. Ludwig von Drake	10	10
1269	2 c. Gyro Gearloose	10	10
1270	3 c. Pluto and Figaro	10	10
1271	4 c. Morty and Ferdie	10	10
1272	5 c. Mickey Mouse and Goofy	10	10
1273	10 c. Chip'n Dale	10	10
1274	$2.50, Mickey and Minnie Mouse	2·75	3·50
1275	$3 Donald and Grandma Duck	3·00	3·50
1267/75	Set of 9	5·75	7·00
MS1276	127 × 102 mm. $5 Goofy with Christmas tree. P 13½	4·50	4·50

290 Daisy Duck on Pommel Horse   291 William I

(Litho Questa)

1984 (17 Jan–May). *Olympic Games, Los Angeles. T 290 and similar horiz designs showing Disney cartoon characters in Olympic events. Multicoloured. A. Inscr. "1984 LOS ANGELES". P 14 × 13½. B. Inscr. "1984 OLYMPICS LOS ANGELES" and Olympic emblem. P 12 (May).*

		A		B	
1277	½ c. Type 290	10	10	10	10
1278	1 c. Mickey Mouse boxing	10	10	10	10
1279	2 c. Daisy Duck in archery event	10	10	10	10
1280	3 c. Clarabelle Cow on uneven bars	10	10	10	10
1281	4 c. Mickey and Minnie Mouse in hurdles race	10	10	10	10
1282	5 c. Donald Duck with Chip and Dale weightlifting	10	10	10	10
1283	$1 Little Hiawatha in single kayak	1·75	2·00	1·75	2·00
1284	$2 The Tortoise and the Hare in marathon	2·25	3·00	2·25	3·00
1285	$3 Mickey Mouse pole-vaulting	2·75	3·25	2·75	3·25
1277/85	Set of 9	6·75	8·00	6·75	8·00
MS1286	127 × 101 mm. $5 Donald Duck in medley relay (vert). P 13½ × 14	4·50	3·50	5·50	5·50

1984 (25 Jan). *British Monarchs. T 291 and similar vert designs. Multicoloured. Litho. P 14.*
1287	$4 Type 291	3·00	3·25
	a. Sheetlet. Nos. 1287/93	19·00	
1288	$4 William II	3·00	3·25
1289	$4 Henry I	3·00	3·25
1290	$4 Stephen	3·00	3·25
1291	$4 Henry II	3·00	3·25
1292	$4 Richard I	3·00	3·25
1293	$4 John	3·00	3·25
1294	$4 "Henry III"	3·00	3·25
	a. Sheetlet. Nos. 1294/1300	19·00	
1295	$4 Edward I	3·00	3·25
1296	$4 Edward II	3·00	3·25
1297	$4 Edward III	3·00	3·25
1298	$4 Richard II	3·00	3·25
1299	$4 Henry IV	3·00	3·25
1300	$4 Henry V	3·00	3·25
1301	$4 Henry VI	3·00	3·25
	a. Sheetlet. Nos. 1301/7	19·00	
1302	$4 Edward IV	3·00	3·25
1303	$4 Edward V	3·00	3·25
1304	$4 Richard III	3·00	3·25
1305	$4 Henry VII	3·00	3·25
1306	$4 Henry VIII	3·00	3·25
1307	$4 Edward VI	3·00	3·25
1308	$4 Lady Jane Grey	3·00	3·25
	a. Sheetlet. Nos. 1308/14	19·00	
1309	$4 Mary I	3·00	3·25
1310	$4 Elizabeth I	3·00	3·25
1311	$4 James I	3·00	3·25
1312	$4 Charles I	3·00	3·25
1313	$4 Charles II	3·00	3·25
1314	$4 James II	3·00	3·25
1315	$4 William III	3·00	3·25
	a. Sheetlet. Nos. 1315/21	19·00	
1316	$4 Mary II	3·00	3·25
1317	$$ Anne	3·00	3·25

1318	$4 George I		..	..	3·00	3·25
1319	$4 George II	..		..	3·00	3·25
1320	$4 George III	..	..	..	3·00	3·25
1321	$4 George IV	..	..	..	3·00	3·25
1322	$4 William IV	..	..	..	3·00	3·25
	a. Sheetlet. Nos. 1322/8		..	..	19·00	
1323	$4 Victoria	..	..	..	3·00	3·25
1324	$4 Edward VII	..	..		3·00	3·25
1325	$4 George V	..	..	..	3·00	3·25
1326	$4 Edward VIII	..	..		3·00	3·25
1327	$4 George VI	..	..	..	3·00	3·25
1328	$4 Elizabeth II	..	..	..	3·00	3·25
1287/1328			Set of 42		£110	£120

Nos. 1287/93, 1294/1300, 1301/7, 1308/14, 1315/21 and 1322/8 were printed together, in small sheets of 8 including one se-tenant stamp-size label.

Although inscribed "Henry III" the portrait on No. 1294 is actually that of Edward II.

Although announced as all being issued on 25 January 1984 the different sheetlets were distributed at monthly intervals.

292 Lantana

(Des P.U.B. Graphics. Litho Format)

1984 (9 Apr). *Flowers. T* **292** *and similar horiz designs. Multicoloured. P* 15.

1329	25 c. Type 292	..	..	..	20	15
1330	30 c. Plumbago	..	..	..	25	20
1331	90 c. Spider Lily	..	..	..	70	60
1332	$4 Giant Alocasia		..	..	2·50	3·00
1329/32			Set of 4		3·25	3·50
MS1333	108 × 90 mm. $5 Orange Trumpet Vine				1·50	2·50

Nos. 1329/32 exist imperforate from stock dispersed by the liquidator of Format International Security Printers Ltd.

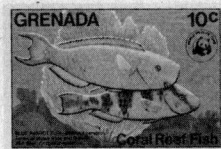

293 Blue Parrotfish (294)

(Litho Questa)

1984 (21 May). *Coral Reef Fishes. T* **293** *and similar horiz designs. Multicoloured. P* 14.

1334	10 c. Type 293	..	..	..	1·40	45
1335	30 c. Flame-backed Angelfish		..		2·75	1·10
1336	70 c. Painted Wrasse		..	..	4·00	3·25
1337	90 c. Rosy Razorfish		..	..	4·75	3·50
1334/7			Set of 4		11·50	7·50
MS1338	81 × 85 mm. $5 Spanish Hogfish			..	6·00	4·75

1984 (19 June). *Universal Postal Union Congress, Hamburg. Nos.* 1331/3 *optd with T* **294**.

1339	90 c. Spider Lily	..	..	..	60	65
1340	$4 Giant Alocasia	..	..	..	2·50	3·00
MS1341	108 × 90 mm. $5 Orange Trumpet Vine				1·75	3·00

295 Freighter 296 "The Night" (detail) (Correggio)

(Des Artists International. Litho Format)

1984 (16 July). *Ships. T* **295** *and similar horiz designs. Multicoloured. P* 15.

1342	40 c. Type 295	..	..	..	1·25	55
1343	70 c. Queen Elizabeth 2		..	..	1·50	1·50
1344	90 c. Sailing boats	..	..	..	1·90	2·00
1345	$4 Amerikanis		..	..	6·00	8·00
1342/5			Set of 4		9·50	11·00
MS1346	107 × 80 mm. $5 Spanish galleon				7·00	7·00

Nos. 1342/6 exist imperforate from stock dispersed by the liquidator of Format International Security Printers Ltd.

(Litho Questa)

1984 (22 Aug). *450th Death Anniv of Correggio (painter). T* **296** *and similar vert designs showing paintings. Multicoloured. P* 14.

1347	10 c. Type 296	..	..	..	45	15
1348	30 c. "The Virgin adoring the Child"		..		80	50
1349	90 c. "The Mystical Marriage of St. Catherine with St. Sebastian"			..	2·00	1·75
1350	$4 "The Madonna and the Fruit Basket"			..	4·50	5·50
1347/50			Set of 4		7·00	7·00
MS1351	54 × 73 mm. $5 "The Madonna at the Spring"				4·25	3·75

297 "L'Absinthe" (Degas) 298 Train on "Puffing Billy" Line, Victoria

(Litho Questa)

1984 (22 Aug). *150th Birth Anniv of Edgar Degas (painter). T* **297** *and similar multicoloured designs showing paintings. P* 14.

1352	25 c. Type 297	..	..	..	80	30
1353	70 c. "Pouting" (horiz)		..	..	1·50	1·25
1354	$1.10, "The Millinery Shop"		..	..	2·00	2·00
1355	$3 "The Bellelli Family" (horiz)			..	3·75	4·25
1352/5			Set of 4		7·25	7·00
MS1356	84 × 54 mm. $5 "The Cotton Market"			..	4·25	3·75

(Des Bonny Redecker. Litho Questa)

1984 (21 Sept). *"Ausipex" International Stamp Exhibition, Melbourne. T* **298** *and similar vert designs. Multicoloured. P* 14.

1357	90 c. Type 298	..	..	..	2·25	1·75
1358	$4 Yacht Australia II (winner of America's Cup)			..	4·75	5·25
MS1359	107 × 76 mm. $5 Melbourne tram			..	3·75	4·50

299 Locomotion (1825) OPENING OF POINT SALINE INT'L AIRPORT (300)

(Des J.W. Litho Format)

1984 (3 Oct). *Railway Locomotives. T* **299** *and similar horiz designs. Multicoloured. P* 15.

1360	30 c. Type 299	..	..	..	80	35
1361	40 c. Novelty (1829)		..	..	95	40
1362	60 c. Washington Farmer (1836)			..	1·10	75
1363	70 c. French Crampton type (1859)			..	1·25	1·00
1364	90 c. Dutch State Railways (1873)			..	1·50	1·50
1365	$1.10, Champion (1882)		..	..	1·75	2·00
1366	$2 Webb Compound type (1893)			..	2·25	3·25
1367	$4 Berlin "No. 74" (1900)		..	..	3·75	5·50
1360/7			Set of 8		12·00	13·00
MS1368	Two sheets, each 100 × 70 mm. (a) $5 Crampton Phoenix (1863); (b) $5 Mikado type (1897)				8·00	8·50

1984 (28 Oct). *Opening of Point Saline International Airport (1st issue). Nos.* 1247 *and* 1249/50 *optd as T* **300**.

1369	40 c. Rural telephone installation			..	30	30
1370	$3 Airport control room		..	..	2·00	2·00
MS1371	111 × 85 mm. $5 Communications satellite				3·50	3·25

On No. MS1371 the overprint, 54 × 8 mm., appears in two lines on the sheet margin only.

See also Nos. 1393/6.

301 Donald Duck as Father Christmas looking into Mirror

(Litho Questa)

1984 (26 Nov). *Christmas. Walt Disney Cartoon Characters. T* **301** *and similar vert designs. Multicoloured. P* 12 ($2) *or* 13½ × 14 *(others).*

1372	45 c. Type 301	..	..	..	1·25	40
1373	60 c. Donald Duck filling stocking with presents				1·50	55
1374	90 c. As Father Christmas pulling a sleigh			..	2·00	1·10
1375	$2 As Father Christmas decorating Christmas tree			..	3·50	3·50
1376	$4 Donald Duck and nephews singing carols				5·00	5·50
1372/6			Set of 5		12·00	10·00
MS1377	127 × 102 mm. $5 As Father Christmas in sleigh				7·00	8·00

No. 1375 was printed in sheetlets of 8 stamps.

(Litho Questa)

1985 (11 Feb). *Birth Bicentenary of John J. Audubon (ornithologist) (1st issue). Multicoloured designs as T* **198** *of Antigua showing original paintings. P* 14.

1378	50 c. Clapper Rail (vert)		..	..	2·00	75
1379	70 c. Hooded Warbler (vert)		..		2·25	1·40
1380	90 c. Common Flicker (vert)		..		2·75	1·75
1381	$4 Bohemian Waxwing (vert)		..		5·50	8·00
1378/81			Set of 4		11·00	11·00
MS1382	82 × 112 mm. $5 Merlin ("Pigeon Hawk")				8·50	4·50

See also Nos. 1480/4.

302 Honda "XL500R"

(Des R. Sentnor. Litho Questa)

1985 (11 Mar). *Centenary of the Motor Cycle. T* **302** *and similar horiz designs. Multicoloured. P* 14.

1383	25 c. Type 302	..	..	..	90	50
1384	50 c. Suzuki "GS1100ES"		..		1·40	1·40
1385	90 c. Kawasaki "KZ700"		..		2·00	2·00
1386	$4 BMW "K100"		..	..	5·50	6·50
1383/6			Set of 4		8·75	9·00
MS1387	109 × 81 mm. $5 Yamaha "500CC V Four"				6·00	5·00

303 "Explorer"

(Des Susan David. Litho Questa)

1985 (15 Apr). *75th Anniv of Girl Guide Movement. T* **303** *and similar horiz designs, showing work for Guide badges. Multicoloured. P* 14.

1388	25 c. Type 303	..	..	..	55	30
1389	70 c. "Cook"	..	..	..	90	65
1390	90 c. "Musician"		..	..	1·50	1·10
1391	$3 "Home nurse"		..	..	3·00	3·50
1388/91			Set of 4		5·50	5·00
MS1392	97 × 70 mm. $5 Flags of Girl Guides and Grenada				3·00	3·00

304 Hawker Siddeley H.S.748 on Inaugural Flight from Barbados

(Des Susan David. Litho Questa)

1985 (30 Apr). *Opening of Point Saline International Airport (1984) (2nd issue). T* **304** *and similar horiz designs. Multicoloured. P* 14.

1393	70 c. Type 304	..	..	..	2·50	1·00
1394	$1 Lockheed L-1011 TriStar 500 on inaugural flight from New York				3·25	1·50
1395	$4 Lockheed L-1011 TriStar 500 on inaugural flight to Miami				6·50	7·00
1393/5			Set of 3		11·00	8·50
MS1396	101 × 72 mm. $5 Point Saline Airport terminal and Hawker Siddeley H.S.748 on tarmac				4·50	3·75

305 Douglas DC-8-61

(Des BG Studio. Litho Questa)

1985 (15 May). *40th Anniv of International Civil Aviation Organization. T* **305** *and similar horiz designs. Multicoloured. P* 14.

1397	10 c. Type 305	..	..	..	40	20
1398	50 c. Lockheed L.1649A Starliner			..	1·00	75
1399	60 c. Vickers 952 Cargoliner			..	1·25	85
1400	$4 De Havilland D.H.C.6 Twin Otter 200/300				4·50	5·50
1397/400			Set of 4		6·50	6·50
MS1401	102 × 64 mm. $5 Hawker Siddeley H.S.748 turboprop				3·00	3·00

NEW INFORMATION

The editor is always interested to correspond with people who have new information that will improve or correct the Catalogue.

306 Model Boat Racing   307 Bird of Paradise (flower)

(Litho Format)

1985 (15 June). *Water Sports. T* **306** *and similar horiz designs. Multicoloured. P* 15.
1402	10 c. Type **306**		20	10
1403	50 c. Scuba diving, Carriacou		45	35
1404	$1.10, Windsurfers on Grand Anse Beach		75	1·10
1405	$4 Windsurfing		2·00	3·50
1402/5		*Set of 4*	3·00	4·50
MS1406	107×77 mm. $5 Beach scene		2·75	3·00

Nos. 1402/5 exist imperforate from stock dispersed by the liquidator of Format International Security Printers Ltd.

(Des Mary Walters. Litho Questa)

1985 (1 July)–88. *Native Flowers. T* **307** *and similar vert designs. Multicoloured. Chalk-surfaced paper. A. Without imprint date. P* 14. *B. Without imprint date. P* 12.

				A		B	
1407	½ c. Type **307**			40	40	30	40
1408	1 c. Passion Flower			50	40	40	40
1409	2 c. Oleander			50	40	40	40
1410	4 c. Bromeliad			85	40	45	40
1411	5 c. Anthurium			85	40	45	40
1412	6 c. Bougainvillea			85	50	45	50
1413	10 c. Hibiscus			1·00	40	45	30
1414	15 c. Ginger			1·75	40	65	30
1415	25 c. Poinsettia			1·75	40	65	30
1416	30 c. Mexican Creeper			1·75	70	65	30
1417	40 c. Angel's Trumpet			2·00	70	75	50
1418	50 c. Amaryllis			2·00	1·00	75	75
1419	60 c. Prickly Pear			2·00	1·75	75	90
1420	70 c. Chenille Plant			2·00	1·75	75	1·00
1420c	75 c. Cordia			1·25	1·75		†
1421	$1 Periwinkle			3·25	2·00	1·75	1·75
1422	$1.10, Ixora			3·50	2·75	1·75	2·25
1423	$3 Shrimp Plant			4·75	6·00	2·50	5·00
1424	$5 Plumbago			4·75	2·50	6·00	
1425	$10 *Lantana camara*			4·75	8·50	4·00	9·00
1425c	$20 Peregrina			8·50	16·00		†
	cd. Ordinary paper			9·00	16·00		†
1407A/25cA		*Set of 21*		42·00	45·00		†
1407B/25B		*Set of 19*			†	18·00	28·00

C. *With imprint date. P* 14.
1413C	10 c. Hibiscus		3·00	3·25
1416C	30 c. Mexican Creeper		20	50
1418C	50 c. Amaryllis		30	65
1419C	60 c. Prickly Pear		30	85
1421C	$1 Periwinkle		35	1·00
1413C/21C		*Set of 5*	3·75	5·50

Dates of issue:—1.7.85, Nos. 1407A/24A; 11.11.85, No. 1425A; 3.86, Nos. 1407B/12B, 1414B/19B, 1421B/3B; 7.86, Nos. 1413B, 1420B, 1424B; 1.8.86, No. 1425cA; 12.86, No. 1425B; 5.8.87, No. 1425cdA; 1987, Nos. 1416C, 1418C/19C, 1421C; 7.88, No. 1413C; 1.12.88, No. 1420cA.
Imprint dates: "1987", Nos. 1416C/21C; "1988", No. 1413C.

308 The Queen Mother at   309 Youth Gardening
Royal Opera House,   (Horticulture)
London

(Des J.W. Litho Questa)

1985 (3 July). *Life and Times of Queen Elizabeth the Queen Mother. T* **308** *and similar multicoloured designs. P* 14.
1426	$1 Type **308**		40	60
1427	$1.50, The Queen Mother playing snooker at London Press Club (*horiz*)		55	85
1428	$2.50, At Epsom Races, 1960		95	1·50
1426/8		*Set of 3*	1·75	2·75
MS1429	56×85 mm. $5 With Prince of Wales on 80th Birthday		1·75	3·00

Stamps as Nos. 1426/8, but with face values of 90 c., $1 and $3, exist from additional sheetlets of 5 plus a label issued December 1985. These also have changed background colours and are perforated 12½×12 ($1) or 12×12½ (others) (*Price for set of 3 stamps £1.50 mint*).

(Des Liane Fried. Litho Format)

1985 (21 Aug). *International Youth Year. T* **309** *and similar vert designs. Multicoloured. P* 15.
1430	25 c. Type **309**		25	20
1431	50 c. Young people on beach (Leisure)		45	40
1432	$1.10, Girls in classroom (Education)		90	1·10
1433	$3 Nurse and young patient (Health Care)		2·25	2·50
1430/3		*Set of 4*	3·50	3·75
MS1434	111×80 mm. $5 Children of different races		2·50	3·25

(Des Susan David. Litho Questa)

1985 (3 Sept). *300th Birth Anniv of Johann Sebastian Bach* (*composer*). *Vert designs as T* **206** *of Antigua. P* 14.
1435	25 c. multicoloured		80	20
1436	70 c. multicoloured		1·50	85
1437	$1 multicoloured		2·00	1·25
1438	$3 multicoloured		3·00	4·00
1435/8		*Set of 4*	6·50	5·75
MS1439	104×74 mm. $5 black, lavender-grey and cinnamon		3·50	3·75

Designs:—25 c. Crumhorn; 70 c. Oboe d'amore; $1 Violin; $3 Harpsichord; $5 Johann Sebastian Bach.

310 Cub Scouts Camping

(Des A. DiLorenzo. Litho Questa)

1985 (5 Sept). *4th Caribbean Cuboree. T* **310** *and similar multicoloured designs. P* 14.
1440	10 c. Type **310**		30	15
1441	50 c. Cub scouts swimming ("Physical Fitness")		65	40
1442	$1 Stamp collecting		1·50	80
1443	$4 Birdwatching		3·50	3·00
1440/3		*Set of 4*	5·50	4·00
MS1444	103×75 mm. $5 Cub scouts saluting leader (*vert*)		3·25	3·50

(Des Mary Walters. Litho Format)

1985 (4 Nov). *Royal Visit. Multicoloured designs as T* **207** *of Antigua. P* 14½.
1445	50 c. Flags of Great Britain and Grenada		75	40
1446	$1 Queen Elizabeth II (*vert*)		1·00	1·00
1447	$4 Royal Yacht *Britannia*		2·50	4·50
1445/7		*Set of 3*	3·75	5·50
MS1448	111×83 mm. $5 Map of Grenada		1·75	3·25

(Des Walt Disney Productions. Litho Questa)

1985 (4 Nov). *150th Birth Anniv of Mark Twain* (*author*). *Horiz designs as T* **118** *of Anguilla showing Walt Disney cartoon characters in scenes from "The Prince and the Pauper". Multicoloured. P* 14×13½.
1449	25 c. Mortie as Tom meeting the Prince (Ferdie)		50	2υ
1450	50 c. Tom and the Prince exchanging clothes		70	50
1451	$1.10, The Prince with John Cantry		1·60	1·60
1452	$1.50, The Prince knights Mike Hendon (Goofy)		2·00	2·50
1453	$2 Tom and the Whipping Boy		2·25	2·75
1449/53		*Set of 5*	6·25	6·75
MS1454	124×100 mm. $5 The Prince, Tom and Mike Hendon		5·00	5·00

(Des Walt Disney Productions. Litho Questa)

1985 (4 Nov). *Birth Bicentenaries of Grimm Brothers* (*folklorists*). *Horiz designs as T* **119** *of Anguilla, showing Walt Disney cartoon characters in scenes from "The Fisherman and his Wife". Multicoloured. P* 14×13½.
1455	30 c. The Fisherman (Goofy) catching enchanted fish		55	30
1456	60 c. The Fisherman scolded by his Wife (Clarabelle)		80	80
1457	70 c. The Fisherman's Wife with dream cottage		95	95
1458	$1 The Fisherman's Wife as King		1·50	1·50
1459	$3 The Fisherman and Wife in their original shack		3·00	3·00
1455/9		*Set of 5*	6·00	6·50
MS1460	126×100 mm. $5 The Fisherman in boat		5·00	5·00

311 Red-spotted Hawkfish

(Des R. Sauber. Litho Questa)

1985 (15 Nov). *Marine Life. T* **311** *and similar horiz designs. Multicoloured. P* 14.
1461	25 c. Type **311**		1·25	55
1462	50 c. Spot-finned Butterflyfish		2·00	1·10
1463	$1.10, Fire Coral and Orange Sponges		3·25	3·25
1464	$3 Pillar Coral		6·00	7·50
1461/4		*Set of 4*	11·00	11·00
MS1465	127×100 mm. $5 Bigeye		3·75	4·50

(Litho Format)

1985 (22 Nov). *40th Anniv of United Nations Organization. Multicoloured designs as T* **208** *of Antigua showing United Nations (New York) stamps. P* 14½.
1466	50 c. Mary McLeod Bethune (educationist) and 1975 International Women's Year 10 c.		50	50
1467	$2 Maimonides (physician) and 1966 W.H.O. 5 c.		3·00	3·50
1468	$2.50, Alexander Graham Bell (telephone inventor) and 1956 I.T.U. 3 c.		3·00	3·75
1466/8		*Set of 3*	6·00	7·00
MS1469	110×85 mm. $5 Dag Hammarskjold (Secretary-General) (*vert*)		1·50	2·00

VISIT OF

PRES REAGAN

20 FEB. 1986

312 "The Adoration of the   (313)
Shepherds" (Mantegna)

(Des Mary Walters. Litho Format)

1985 (23 Dec). *Christmas. Religious Paintings. T* **312** *and similar horiz designs. Multicoloured. P* 15.
1470	25 c. Type **312**		20	15
1471	60 c. "Journey of the Magi" (Sassetta)		40	40
1472	90 c. "Madonna and Child enthroned with Saints" (Raphael)		50	70
1473	$4 "Nativity" (Monaco)		1·50	3·50
1470/3		*Set of 4*	2·40	4·25
MS1474	107×81 mm. $5 "Madonna and Child enthroned with Saints" (Gaddi)		1·75	2·50

(Des J. Iskowitz. Litho Questa)

1986 (6 Jan). *Centenary of Statue of Liberty* (1st issue). *Multicoloured designs as T* **211** *of Dominica. P* 15.
1475	5 c. Columbus Monument, 1893 (*vert*)		15	20
1476	25 c. Columbus Monument, 1986 (*vert*)		40	20
1477	40 c. Mounted police, Central Park, 1895 (*vert*)		1·75	1·10
1478	$4 Mounted police, 1986		6·50	8·00
1475/8		*Set of 4*	8·00	8·50
MS1479	104×76 mm. $5 Statue of Liberty (*vert*)		2·25	2·50

See also Nos. 1644/52.

(Litho Questa)

1986 (20 Jan). *Birth Bicentenary of John J. Audubon* (*ornithologist*) (2nd issue). *Multicoloured designs as T* **198** *of Antigua. P* 12×12½.
1480	50 c. Snowy Egret		2·00	80
1481	90 c. Greater Flamingo		2·75	2·00
1482	$1.10, Canada Goose		2·75	2·50
1483	$3 Smew		4·50	6·00
1480/3		*Set of 4*	11·00	10·00
MS1484	103×72 mm. $5 Brent Goose (*horiz*). P 14		12·00	13·00

Nos. 1480/3 were each issued in sheetlets of five stamps and one stamp-size label, which appears in the centre of the bottom row.

1986 (20 Feb). *Visit of President Reagan. Nos.* 1418A *and* 1424A *optd with T* **313**.
1485	50 c. Amaryllis		50	50
1486	$5 Plumbago		3·50	5·00

314 Methodist Church,   315 Player with
St. Georges   Ball

(Litho Format)

1986 (24 Feb). *Bicentenary of Methodist Church in Grenada. T* **314** *and similar horiz design. Multicoloured. P* 15.
1487	60 c. Type **314**		70	1·00
MS1488	102×73 mm. $5 St. Georges		1·40	3·00

(Des N. Waldman. Litho Questa)

1986 (6 Mar). *World Cup Football Championship, Mexico. T* **315** *and similar vert designs. Multicoloured. P* 14.
1489	50 c. Type **315**		80	55
1490	70 c. Player heading ball		1·00	1·00
1491	90 c. Player controlling ball		1·50	1·50
1492	$4 Player controlling ball with right foot		5·50	7·00
1489/92		*Set of 4*	8·00	9·00
MS1493	101×71 mm. $5 Player tackling		4·25	5·00

(Des W. Hanson. Litho Questa)

1986 (20 Mar). *Appearance of Halley's Comet* (1st issue). *Horiz designs as T* **123** *of Anguilla. Multicoloured. P* 14.
1494	5 c. Clyde Tombaugh (astronomer) and Dudley Observatory, New York		40	40
1495	20 c. N.A.S.A. – U.S.A.F. "X-24B" Space Shuttle prototype, 1973		50	30
1496	40 c. German comet medal, 1618		70	45
1497	$4 Destruction of Sodom and Gomorrah, 1949 B.C.		3·50	4·50
1494/7		*Set of 4*	4·50	5·00
MS1498	102×70 mm. $5 Halley's Comet over Grenada		6·50	7·00

See also Nos. 1533/7 and 1980/4.

(Litho Questa)

1986 (21 Apr). *60th Birthday of Queen Elizabeth II. Vert designs as T* **125** *of Anguilla. P* 14.
1499	2 c. black and yellow		10	15
1500	$1.50, multicoloured		60	80
1501	$4 multicoloured		1·50	2·50
1499/1501		*Set of 3*	2·00	3·00
MS1502	120×85 mm. $5 black and grey-brown		2·00	3·50

Designs:—2 c. Princess Elizabeth in 1951; $1.50, Queen presenting trophy at polo match, Windsor, 1965; $4 At Epsom, Derby Day, 1977; $5 King George VI and family, 1939.

(Des Walt Disney Productions. Litho Format)

1986 (22 May). *"Ameripex" International Stamp Exhibition, Chicago. Horiz designs as T 212 of Dominica, showing Walt Disney cartoon characters playing baseball. Multicoloured. P 11.*

1503	1 c. Goofy as pitcher	10	10
1504	2 c. Goofy as catcher	10	10
1505	3 c. Mickey Mouse striking ball and Donald Duck as catcher	10	10
1506	4 c. Huey forcing out Dewey	10	10
1507	5 c. Chip n'Dale chasing flyball	10	10
1508	6 c. Mickey Mouse, Donald Duck and Clarabelle in argument	10	10
1509	$2 Minnie Mouse and Donald Duck reading baseball rules	1·75	2·50
1510	$3 Ludwig von Drake as umpire with Goofy and Pete colliding	2·25	3·00
1503/10	*Set of 8*	4·00	5·50
MS1511	Two sheets, each 126×101 mm. (a) $5 Donald Duck striking ball. (b) $5 Minnie and Mickey Mouse running between bases. P 14×13½		
	Set of 2 sheets	11·00	13·00

(Litho Questa)

1986 (1 July). *Royal Wedding. Vert designs as T 213 of Antigua. Multicoloured. P 14.*

1512	2 c. Prince Andrew and Miss Sarah Ferguson	10	15
1513	$1.10, Prince Andrew	70	80
1514	$4 Prince Andrew with H.M.S. *Brazen's* Westland WG-13 Lynx helicopter	2·50	3·25
1512/14	*Set of 3*	3·00	3·75
MS1515	88×88 mm. $5 Prince Andrew and Miss Sarah Ferguson (*different*)	4·00	5·00

316 Brown-lined Latirus   **317** *Lepiota roseolamellata*

(Des L. Birmingham. Litho Format)

1986 (15 July). *Sea Shells. T 316 and similar horiz designs. Multicoloured. P 15.*

1516	25 c. Type **316**	45	25
1517	60 c. Lamellose Wentletrap	75	90
1518	70 c. Atlantic Turkey Wing	85	1·00
1519	$4 Rooster-tail Conch	2·75	5·00
1516/19	*Set of 4*	4·25	6·50
MS1520	110×75 mm. $5 Angular Triton	3·25	5·00

(Des R. Sauber. Litho Format)

1986 (1 Aug). *Mushrooms. T 317 and similar vert designs. Multicoloured. P 15.*

1521	10 c. Type **317**	60	40
1522	60 c. *Lentinus bertieri*	1·75	1·75
1523	$1 *Lentinus retinervis*	2·50	2·50
1524	$4 *Eccilia cystiophorus*	5·75	7·50
1521/4	*Set of 4*	9·50	11·00
MS1525	127×100 mm. $5 *Cystolepiota eriophora*	10·00	12·00

No. **MS**1525 exists imperforate from stock dispersed by the liquidator of Format International Security Printers Ltd.

1986 (15 Sept). *World Cup Football Championship Winners, Mexico. Nos. 1489/93 optd with T 216 of Antigua in gold.*

1526	50 c. Type **315**	85	85
1527	70 c. Player heading ball	1·00	1·00
1528	90 c. Player controlling ball	1·40	1·60
1529	$4 Player controlling ball with right foot	4·50	5·00
1526/9	*Set of 4*	7·00	7·75
MS1530	101×71 mm. $5 Player tackling	3·50	4·50

318 Dove on Rifles and Mahatma Gandhi (Disarmament Week)   **319** Cockerel and Hen

(Des Mary Walters. Litho Format)

1986 (15 Sept). *International Events. T 318 and similar multicoloured design. P 15.*

1531	60 c. Type **318**	50	50
1532	$4 Hands passing olive branch and Martin Luther King (International Peace Year) (*horiz*)	1·50	3·00

Nos. 1531/2 exist imperforate from stock dispersed by the liquidator of Format International Security Printers Ltd.

1986 (15 Oct). *Appearance of Halley's Comet (2nd issue). Nos. 1494/8 optd with T 218 of Antigua (in silver on $5).*

1533	5 c. Clyde Tombaugh (astronomer) and Dudley Observatory, New York	60	60
1534	20 c. N.A.S.A.—U.S.A.F. "X-24B" Space Shuttle prototype, 1973	85	60
1535	40 c. German comet medal, 1618	1·25	70
1536	$4 Destruction of Sodom and Gomorrah, 1949 B.C.	5·00	7·00
1533/6	*Set of 4*	7·00	8·00
MS1537	102×70 mm. $5 Halley's Comet over Grenada	3·50	4·25

(Des Walt Disney Co. Litho Format)

1986 (3 Nov). *Christmas. Multicoloured designs as T 220 of Antigua showing Walt Disney cartoon characters. P 11.*

1538	30 c. Mickey Mouse asleep in armchair (*vert*)	35	25
1539	45 c. Young Mickey Mouse with Father Christmas (*vert*)	45	30
1540	60 c. Donald Duck with toy telephone	60	50
1541	70 c. Pluto with pushcart	70	70
1542	$1.10, Daisy Duck with doll	1·00	1·25
1543	$2 Goofy as Father Christmas (*vert*)	1·75	2·00
1544	$2.50, Goofy singing carols at piano (*vert*)	2·00	2·50
1545	$3 Mickey Mouse, Donald Duck and nephew riding toy train	2·25	3·00
1538/45	*Set of 8*	8·00	9·50
MS1546	Two sheets, each 127×101 mm. (a) $5 Donald Duck, Goofy and Mickey Mouse delivering presents (*vert*). P 13½×14. (b) $5 Father Christmas playing toy piano. P 14×13½		
	Set of 2 sheets	6·50	9·00

(Litho Questa)

1986 (17 Nov). *Fauna and Flora. T 319 and similar horiz designs. Multicoloured. P 14.*

1547	10 c. Type **319**	20	10
1548	30 c. Fish-eating Bat	35	20
1549	60 c. Goat	55	45
1550	70 c. Cow	60	50
1551	$1 Anthurium	1·50	1·25
1552	$1.10, Royal Poinciana	1·50	1·25
1553	$2 Frangipani	2·50	3·25
1554	$4 Orchid	8·50	9·50
1547/54	*Set of 8*	14·00	15·00
MS1555	Two sheets, each 104×73 mm. (a) $5 Grenada landscape. (b) $5 Horse *Set of 2 sheets*	12·00	13·00

320 Maserati "Biturbo" (1984)   **321** Pole Vaulting

(Des J. Martin. Litho Format)

1986 (20 Nov). *Centenary of Motoring. T 320 and similar horiz designs. Multicoloured. P 15.*

1556	10 c. Type **320**	25	25
1557	30 c. AC "Cobra" (1960)	40	40
1558	60 c. Corvette (1963)	60	60
1559	70 c. Dusenberg "SJ7" (1932)	70	70
1560	90 c. Porsche (1957)	85	1·00
1561	$1.10, Stoewer (1930)	1·00	1·25
1562	$2 Volkswagen "Beetle" (1957)	1·60	2·00
1563	$3 Mercedes "600 Limo" (1963)	1·90	2·50
1556/63	*Set of 8*	6·50	8·00
MS1564	Two sheets, each 106 × 77 mm. (a) $5 Stutz (1914). (b) $5 Packard (1941)		
	Set of 2 sheets	5·50	7·00

(Des BG Studio. Litho Format)

1986 (1 Dec). *Olympic Games, Seoul, South Korea (1988). T 321 and similar vert designs. Multicoloured. P 15.*

1565	10 c. + 5 c. Type **321**	10	30
1566	50 c. + 20 c. Gymnastics	35	60
1567	70 c. + 30 c. Putting the shot	50	85
1568	$2 + $1 High jumping	1·00	2·25
1565/8	*Set of 4*	1·75	3·50
MS1569	80 × 100 mm. $3 + $1 Swimming	2·00	3·25

The premiums on Nos. 1565/9 were to support the participation of the Grenada team.

Nos. 1565/8 exist imperforate from stock dispersed by the liquidator of Format International Security Printers Ltd.

(Litho Questa)

1986 (19 Dec). *Birth Centenary of Marc Chagall (artist). Designs as T 225 of Antigua, showing various paintings. P 13½×14 (vert) or 14×13½ (horiz).*

1570/1609	$1×40 multicoloured	*Set of 40*	24·00 26·00
MS1610	Ten sheets, each 110×95 mm. $5×10 multicoloured (*each 104×89 mm*). Imperf		
	Set of 10 sheets	24·00	26·00

Although announced as all being released on 19 December 1986 the issue was distributed in ten parts, each of four stamps and one miniature sheet, at monthly intervals.

(Des J. Iskowitz. Litho Format)

1987 (5 Feb). *America's Cup Yachting Championship. Vert designs as T 222 of Antigua. Multicoloured. P 15.*

1611	30 c. Columbia, 1958	25	20
1612	60 c. Resolute, 1920	55	60
1613	$1.10, Endeavor, 1934	1·00	1·25
1614	$4 Rainbow, 1934	2·25	3·50
1611/14	*Set of 4*	3·50	5·00
MS1615	113×84 mm. $5 Weatherly, 1962	2·25	4·00

---

322 Virgin Mary and Outline Map of Grenada   **323** Black Grouper

(Des G. Hamilton (10, 30, 50 c.), Mary Walters (others). Litho Format)

1987 (27 Apr). *500th Anniv of Discovery of America by Columbus (1992) (1st issue). T 322 and similar multicoloured designs. P 15.*

1616	10 c. Type **322**	20	20
1617	30 c. *Santa Maria, Pinta* and *Nina* (*horiz*)	50	35
1618	50 c. Columbus and outline map of Grenada	60	45
1619	60 c. Christopher Columbus	60	55
1620	90 c. King Ferdinand and Queen Isabella of Spain (*horiz*)	60	80
1621	$1.10, Map of Antilles by Columbus	85	1·00
1622	$2 Caribs with sailing raft (*horiz*)	1·40	2·00
1623	$3 Columbus in the New World, 1493 (contemporary drawing)	1·75	2·00
1616/23	*Set of 8*	6·00	7·00
MS1624	Two sheets, each 104×72 mm. (a) $5 Route map and Columbus' signature. (b) $5 Columbus carrying Christ Child *Set of 2 sheets*	6·00	7·50

Nos. 1616/23 exist imperforate from stock dispersed by the liquidator of Format International Security Printers Ltd. See also Nos. 2051/5, 2091/9, 2222/30, 2389/95 and 2423/4.

(Des W. Wright. Litho Questa)

1987 (18 May). *Milestones of Transportation. Horiz designs as T 226 of Antigua. Multicoloured. P 14.*

1625	10 c. Cornu's first helicopter, 1907	40	40
1626	16 c. *Monitor* and *Merrimack* (first battle between ironclad warships), 1862	50	50
1627	30 c. LZ1 (first Zeppelin), 1900	70	70
1628	50 c. *Sirius* (first transatlantic paddle-steamer crossing), 1838	75	75
1629	60 c. Steam locomotive on Trans-Siberian Railway (longest line)	90	90
1630	70 c. U.S.S. *Enterprise* (largest aircraft carrier), 1960	1·00	1·00
1631	90 c. Blanchard and Jeffries' balloon (first balloon across English Channel), 1785	1·25	1·25
1632	$1.50, U.S.S. *Holland I* (first steam-powered submarine), 1900	1·75	1·75
1633	$2 *Oceanic I* (first luxury liner), 1871	2·25	2·25
1634	$3 Lamborghini "Countach" (fastest commercial car), 1984	2·50	2·50
1625/34	*Set of 10*	11·00	11·00

(Des J. Martin. Litho Format)

1987 (15 June). *"Capex '87" International Stamp Exhibition, Toronto. Game Fishes. T 323 and similar multicoloured designs. P 15.*

1635	10 c. Type **323**	30	15
1636	30 c. Blue Marlin (*horiz*)	40	15
1637	60 c. White Marlin	60	55
1638	70 c. Bigeye Threshershark (*horiz*)	70	70
1639	$1 Bonefish (*horiz*)	90	1·00
1640	$1.10, Wahoo (*horiz*)	1·00	1·25
1641	$2 Sailfish (*horiz*)	1·75	2·25
1642	$4 Albacore (*horiz*)	2·75	3·50
1635/42	*Set of 8*	7·50	8·50
MS1643	Two sheets, each 100×70 mm. (a) $5 Yellow-finned Tuna. (b) $5 Great Barracuda (*horiz*) *Set of 2 sheets*	6·00	8·00

(Litho Questa)

1987 (5 Aug). *Centenary of Statue of Liberty (1986) (2nd issue). Multicoloured designs as T 227 of Antigua. P 14.*

1644	10 c. Computer projections of Statue and base (*horiz*)	15	15
1645	25 c. Statue and fireworks (*horiz*)	20	15
1646	50 c. Statue and fireworks (*different*) (*horiz*)	35	35
1647	60 c. Statue and boats	45	45
1648	70 c. Computer projections of top of Statue (*horiz*)	50	50
1649	$1 Rear view of Statue and fireworks	80	80
1650	$1.10, Aerial view of Statue	95	1·00
1651	$2 Statue and flotilla	2·00	2·25
1652	$4 *Queen Elizabeth 2* in New York Harbour	3·50	4·00
1644/52	*Set of 9*	8·00	9·00

324 Alice and the Rabbit Hole

(Des Walt Disney Co. Litho Questa)

1987 (9 Sept). *50th Anniv of First Full-Length Disney Cartoon Film. T* **324** *and similar designs. P* 14 × 13½.
1653/1706　30 c. × 54 multicoloured　Set of 54　15·00　16·00
MS1707　Six sheets, each 127 × 102 mm. $5 × 6 multicoloured. P 13½ × 14 (*vert*) or 14 × 13½ (*horiz*)　..　..　..　Set of 6 sheets　30·00　30·00
Nos. 1653/1706 (issued as six sheetlets each of nine different designs) depict scenes from *Alice in Wonderland, Cinderella, Peter Pan, Pinocchio, Sleeping Beauty* and *Snow White and the Seven Dwarfs.*

325 Isaac Newton holding Apple (Law of Gravity)

(Litho Questa)

1987 (9 Sept). *Great Scientific Discoveries. T* **325** *and similar horiz designs. Multicoloured. P* 14.
1708　50 c. Type **325**　..　..　..　85　85
1709　$1.10, John Jacob Berzelius and symbols of chemical elements　..　..　1·75　1·75
1710　$2 Robert Boyle (law of Pressure and Volume)　..　..　..　2·50　3·00
1711　$3 James Watt and drawing of steam engine　..　..　..　..　3·75　4·25
1708/11　..　..　..　..　Set of 4　8·00　9·00
MS1712　105 × 75 mm. $5 *Voyager* (experimental aircraft) and Wright glider No. IV　3·00　4·00
No. 1711 is inscribed "RUDOLF DIESEL" and No. **MS**1712 "Flyer I", both in error.

International Social Security Association

326 Wade Boggs (Boston Red Sox)　　(**327**)

(Des W. Storozuk. Litho Questa)

1987 (2 Nov). *All-Star Baseball Game, Oakland, California. Sheet* 114 × 82 *mm, containing T* **326** *and similar horiz design. Multicoloured. P* 14 × 13½.
MS1713　$1 Type **326**; $1 Eric Davis (Cincinnati Reds)　..　..　..　1·00　1·50

1987 (2 Nov). *60th Anniv of International Social Security Association. Nos.* 1413A, 1418A *and* 1423A *optd with T* **327**.
1714　10 c. Hibiscus　..　..　..　10　15
1715　50 c. Amaryllis　..　..　..　25　35
1716　$3 Shrimp Plant　..　..　..　1·40　2·25
1714/16　..　..　..　..　Set of 3　1·50　2·50

(Litho Questa)

1987 (2 Nov). *Bicentenary of U.S. Constitution. Multicoloured designs as T* **232** *of Antigua. P* 14.
1717　15 c. Independence Hall, Philadelphia (*vert*)　10　10
1718　50 c. Benjamin Franklin (Pennsylvania delegate) (*vert*)　..　..　25　35
1719　60 c. State Seal, Massachusetts　..　25　35
1720　$4 Robert Morris (Pennsylvania delegate) (*vert*)　..　..　1·75　2·75
1717/20　..　..　..　..　Set of 4　2·10　3·25
MS1721　105 × 75 mm. $5 James Madison (Virginia delegate) (*vert*)　..　..　2·25　3·50
Nos. 1717/20 were each issued in sheetlets of five stamps and one stamp-size label, which appears in the centre of the bottom row.

328 Goofy in "The Shadow"　**329** "The Annunciation" (Fra Angelico)

(Des Walt Disney Co. Litho Questa)

1987 (16 Nov). *"Hafnia '87" International Stamp Exhibition, Copenhagen. T* **328** *and similar vert designs showing Walt Disney cartoon characters in scenes from Hans Christian Andersen's fairy tales. Multicoloured. P* 13½ × 14.
1722　25 c. Type **328**　..　..　..　50　30
1723　30 c. Mother Stork and brood in "The Storks"　..　..　..　50　30
1724　50 c. King Richard, Robin Hood and Little John (from *Robin Hood*) in "The Emperor's New Clothes"　..　75　55
1725　60 c. Goofy and Pluto in "The Tinderbox"　..　75　55

1726　70 c. Daisy and Donald Duck in "The Shepherdess and the Chimney Sweep"　..　80　70
1727　$1.50, Mickey and Minnie Mouse in "The Little Mermaid"　..　..　1·60　1·75
1728　$3 Clarabelle and Goofy in "The Princess and the Pea"　..　..　2·50　3·50
1729　$4 Minnie Mouse and Pegleg Pete in "The Marsh King's Daughter"　..　2·50　3·50
1722/9　..　..　..　..　Set of 8　9·00　10·00
MS1730　Two sheets, each 127 × 102 mm. (a) $5 Goofy in "The Flying Trunk". (b) $5 Goofy as "The Sandman"　..　..　Set of 2 sheets　11·00　13·00

(Litho Questa)

1987 (15 Dec). *Christmas. T* **329** *and similar vert designs showing religious paintings. Multicoloured. P* 14.
1731　15 c. Type **329**　..　..　..　55　10
1732　30 c. "The Annunciation" (attr. Hubert van Eyck)　..　..　..　90　30
1733　60 c. "The Adoration of the Magi" (Januarius Zick)　..　..　1·75　1·40
1734　$4 "The Flight into Egypt" (Gerard David)　5·50　7·00
1731/4　..　..　..　..　Set of 4　8·00　8·00
MS1735　99 × 75 mm. $5 "The Circumcision" (Giovanni Bellini studio)..　..　7·00　8·00

330 T. Albert Marryshow

(Litho Questa)

1988 (22 Jan). *Birth Centenary of T. Albert Marryshow (nationalist). P* 14.
1736　**330**　25 c. reddish brown, chestnut & brt crim　30　30

(Des and litho Questa)

1988 (15 Feb). *Royal Ruby Wedding. Vert designs as T* **234** *of Antigua. Multicoloured. P* 14.
1737　15 c. deep brown, black and bright new blue　35　10
1738　50 c. multicoloured　..　..　70　50
1739　$1 deep brown and black..　..　1·25　2·00
1740　$4 multicoloured　..　..　3·00　4·00
1737/40　..　..　..　..　Set of 4　4·75　6·00
MS1741　76 × 100 mm. $5 multicoloured..　..　2·25　3·25
Designs:—15 c. Wedding photograph, 1947; 50 c. Queen Elizabeth II with Prince Charles and Princess Anne, c. 1955; $1 Queen with Princess Anne, c. 1957; $4 Queen Elizabeth (from photo by Tim Graham), 1980; $5 Princess Elizabeth in wedding dress, 1947.

331 Goofy and Daisy Duck lighting Olympic Torch, Olympia　**332** Scout fishing from Boat

(Des Walt Disney Company. Litho Questa)

1988 (13 Apr). *Olympic Games, Seoul. T* **331** *and similar vert designs showing Walt Disney cartoon characters. Multicoloured. P* 13½ × 14.
1742　1 c. Type **331**　..　..　..　10　10
1743　2 c. Donald and Daisy Duck carrying Olympic torch　..　..　10　10
1744　3 c. Donald Duck, Goofy and Mickey Mouse carrying flags of U.S., Korea and Spain　..　..　10　10
1745　4 c. Donald Duck releasing doves　..　10　10
1746　5 c. Mickey Mouse flying with rocket belt　10　10
1747　10 c. Morty and Ferdie carrying banner with Olympic motto　..　..　10　10
1748　$6 Donald Duck, Minnie Mouse and Hodori the Tiger (mascot of Seoul Games)　..　..　..　4·75　5·00
1749　$7 Pluto, Hodori and old post office, Seoul　4·75　5·00
1742/9　..　..　..　..　Set of 8　9·00　9·50
MS1750　Two sheets, each 127 × 101 mm. (a) $5 Mickey Mouse taking athlete's oath. (b) $5 Donald and Daisy Duck as athletes at Closing Ceremony　..　..　Set of 2 sheets　8·50　9·50

1988 (19 Apr). *Stamp Exhibitions. Nos.* 1631/4 *optd as T* **241** *of Antigua with various emblems.*
1751　90 c. Blanchard and Jefferies' balloon, 1785 (optd "OLYMPHILEX '88", Seoul)　75　85
1752　$1.50, U.S.S. *Holland I*, 1900 (optd "INDEPENDENCE 40", Israel)　..　1·00　1·25
1753　$2 *Oceanic I*, 1871 (optd "FINLANDIA 88", Helsinki)　..　..　1·40　1·75
1754　$3 Lamborghini "Countach", 1984 (optd "Praga 99", Prague)　..　1·90　2·25
1751/4　..　..　..　..　Set of 4　4·50　5·50

(Des J. Martin. Litho Questa)

1988 (3 May). *World Scout Jamboree, Australia. T* **332** *and similar multicoloured designs. P* 14.
1755　20 c. Type **332**　..　..　40　15
1756　70 c. Scouts hiking through forest (*horiz*)　1·00　1·00
1757　90 c. Practicing first aid (*horiz*)　..　1·40　1·40
1758　$3 Shooting rapids in inflatable canoe　3·00　3·75
1755/8　..　..　..　..　Set of 4　5·25　5·75
MS1759　114 × 80 mm. $5 Scout with Koala　..　2·10　3·00

333 Santa Maria de Guia (Columbus), 1498, and Map of Rotary District　**334** Roseate Tern

(Des W. Hanson. Litho Questa)

1988 (5 May). *Rotary District* 405 *Conference, St. George's. T* **333** *and similar multicoloured design. P* 13½ × 14.
1760　$2 Type **333**　..　..　..　1·00　1·25
MS1761　133 × 90 mm. $10 Rotary emblem (*horiz*). P 14 × 13½　..　4·25　5·50

(Des Mary Walters. Litho Questa)

1988 (31 May). *Birds. T* **334** *and similar vert designs. Multicoloured. P* 14.
1762　10 c. Type **334**　..　..　50　20
1763　25 c. Laughing Gull　..　..　65　25
1764　50 c. Osprey　..　..　..　1·00　60
1765　60 c. Rose-breasted Grosbeak　..　1·00　60
1766　90 c. Purple Gallinule　..　..　1·00　90
1767　$1.10, White-tailed Tropic Bird　..　1·00　1·00
1768　$3 Blue-faced Booby　..　..　1·75　2·50
1769　$4 Common Shoveler　..　..　1·90　2·75
1762/9　..　..　..　..　Set of 8　8·00　8·50
MS1770　Two sheets, each 100 × 71 mm. (a) $5 Belted Kingfisher. (b) $5 Grenada Flycatcher ("Rusty-tailed Flycatcher")　..　Set of 2 sheets　7·00　8·50

335 Vauxhall Type "OE 30/98", 1925　**336** LZ-127 *Graf Zeppelin* over Chicago World's Fair, 1933

(Des W. Wright. Litho B.D.T.)

1988 (1 June). *Cars. T* **335** *and similar vert designs. Multicoloured. P* 13.
1771　$2 Type **335**　..　..　..　1·00　1·25
　　　a. Sheetlet. Nos. 1771/80　..　9·00
1772　$2 Wills "Sainte Claire", 1926　..　1·00　1·25
1773　$2 Bucciali, 1928　..　..　1·00　1·25
1774　$2 Irving Napier "Golden Arrow", 1929　1·00　1·25
1775　$2 Studebaker "President", 1930　..　1·00　1·25
1776　$2 Thomas "Flyer", 1907　..　1·00　1·25
1777　$2 Isotta-Fraschini "Tipo J", 1908　..　1·00　1·25
1778　$2 Fiat 10/14HP, 1910　..　..　1·00　1·25
1779　$2 Mercer "Type 35 Raceabout", 1911　1·00　1·25
1780　$2 Marmon "Model 34 Cloverleaf", 1917　1·00　1·25
1781　$2 Tatra "Type 77", 1934　..　..　1·00　1·25
　　　a. Sheetlet. Nos. 1781/90　..　9·00
1782　$2 Rolls-Royce "Phantom III", 1938　..　1·00　1·25
1783　$2 Studebaker "Champion Starlight", 1947..　..　..　..　1·00　1·25
1784　$2 Porsche "Gmund", 1948　..　1·00　1·25
1785　$2 Tucker, 1948　..　..　1·00　1·25
1786　$2 Peerless "V-16", 1931　..　1·00　1·25
1787　$2 Minerva "AL", 1931　..　..　1·00　1·25
1788　$2 Reo "Royale", 1933　..　..　1·00　1·25
1789　$2 Pierce Arrow "Silver Arrow", 1933　..　1·00　1·25
1790　$2 Hupmobile "Aerodynamic", 1934　..　1·00　1·25
1791　$2 Peugeot "404", 1965　..　..　1·00　1·25
　　　a. Sheetlet. Nos. 1791/1800　..　9·00
1792　$2 Ford "Capri", 1969　..　..　1·00　1·25
1793　$2 Ferrari "312T", 1975　..　1·00　1·25
1794　$2 Lotus "T-79", 1978　..　..　1·00　1·25
1795　$2 Williams-Cosworth "FW07", 1979　..　1·00　1·25
1796　$2 H.R.G. "1500 Sports", 1948　..　1·00　1·25
1797　$2 Crosley "Hotshot", 1949　..　1·00　1·25
1798　$2 Volvo "PV444", 1955　..　..　1·00　1·25
1799　$2 Maserati "Tipo 61", 1960　..　1·00　1·25
1800　$2 Saab "96", 1963　..　..　1·00　1·25
1771/1800　..　..　Set of 30　27·00　30·00
Nos. 1771/80, 1781/90 and 1791/1800 were each printed together, *se-tenant*, in sheetlets of 10.

(Litho Questa)

1988 (15 June). *500th Birth Anniv of Titian (artist). Multicoloured designs as T 238 of Antigua.* P 13½×14.

1801	10 c. "Lavinia Vecellio"	10	10
1802	20 c. "Portrait of a Man"	10	10
1803	25 c. "Andrea de Franceschi"	10	15
1804	90 c. "Head of a Soldier"	40	45
1805	$1 "Man with a Flute"	45	50
1806	$2 "Lucrezia and Tarquinius"	80	1·00
1807	$3 "Duke of Mantua with Dog"	1·25	1·60
1808	$4 "La Bella di Tiziano"	1·60	2·00
1801/8	*Set of 8*	4·25	5·25

MS1809 Two sheets, each 110×95 mm. (a) $5 "Allegory of Alfonso D'Avalos (detail). P 13½×14. (b) $5 "Fall of Man" (detail) (*horiz*). P 14×13½ ... *Set of 2 sheets* 4·25 5·50

(Des W. Hanson. Litho Questa)

1988 (1 July). *Airships. T 336 and similar multicoloured designs.* P 14.

1810	10 c. Type 336	20	20
1811	15 c. LZ-1 over Lake Constance, 1901 (*horiz*)	25	25
1812	25 c. *Washington* (balloon) and *George Washington Curtis* (balloon barge), 1862	30	30
1813	45 c. LZ-129 *Hindenburg* and Maybach "Zeppelin" car (*horiz*)	40	40
1814	50 c. Goodyear Aerospace airship in Statue of Liberty Centenary Race, 1986	40	40
1815	60 c. LZ-129 *Hindenburg* over Statue of Liberty, 1937 (*horiz*)	50	50
1816	90 c. Heinkel biplane docking experiment with LZ-129 *Hindenburg*, 1936 (*horiz*)	80	80
1817	$2 LZ-129 *Hindenburg* over Olympic Stadium, Berlin, 1936	1·60	1·60
1818	$3 LZ-129 *Hindenburg* over Christ of the Andes Monument, 1937	2·00	2·00
1819	$4 LZ-129 *Hindenburg* and *Bremen* (liner), 1936 (*horiz*)	2·25	2·25
1810/19	*Set of 10*	8·00	8·00

MS1820 (a) 75×95 mm. $5 LZ-127 *Graf Zeppelin*, 1930 (*horiz*). (b) 95×75 mm. $5 LZ-129 *Hindenburg*, 1935 (*horiz*) ... *Set of 2 sheets* 4·75 5·50

337 Tasmanian Wolf, Mickey Mouse and Pluto   338 Pineapple

(Des Walt Disney Co. Litho Questa)

1988 (1 Aug). *"Sydpex '88" National Stamp Exhibition, Sydney and 60th Birthday of Mickey Mouse. T 337 and similar horiz designs. Multicoloured.* P 14×13½.

1821	1 c. Type 337	10	10
1822	2 c. Mickey Mouse feeding wallabies	10	10
1823	3 c. Mickey Mouse and Goofy with kangaroo	10	10
1824	4 c. Mickey and Minnie Mouse riding emus	10	10
1825	5 c. Mickey and Minnie Mouse with wombat	10	10
1826	10 c. Mickey Mouse and Donald Duck watching platypus	10	10
1827	$5 Mickey Mouse and Goofy photographing Blue-winged Kookaburra	4·25	4·75
1828	$6 Mickey Mouse and Koala on map of Australia	4·25	4·75
1821/8	*Set of 8*	8·00	9·00

MS1829 Two sheets, each 127×102 mm. (a) $5 Mickey Mouse with birthday cake. (b) $5 Mickey and Minnie Mouse with Rainbow Lories ... *Set of 2 sheets* 8·00 10·00

(Des J. Martin. Litho Questa)

1988 (11 Aug). *10th Anniv of International Fund for Agricultural Development. T 338 and similar multicoloured designs.* P 14.

1830	20 c. Type 338	20	15
1831	75 c. Bananas	50	60
1832	$3 Mace and nutmeg (*horiz*)	1·75	2·50
1830/2	*Set of 3*	2·25	3·00

339 Lignum Vitae

(Des W. Wright. Litho Questa)

1988 (30 Sept). *Flowering Trees and Shrubs. T 339 and similar horiz designs. Multicoloured.* P 14.

1833	15 c. Type 339	15	15
1834	20 c. Saman	20	15
1835	35 c. Red Frangipani	25	20
1836	45 c. Flowering Maple	30	25
1837	60 c. Yellow Poui	40	40
1838	$1 Wild Chestnut	60	70
1839	$3 Mountain Immortelle	1·50	2·25
1840	$4 Queen of Flowers	1·75	2·50
1833/40	*Set of 8*	4·50	6·00

MS1841 Two sheets, each 117 × 88 mm. (a) $5 Flamboyant. (b) $5 Orchid Tree ..*Set of 2 sheets* 4·25 5·50

340 Mickey Mantle (New York Yankees)

(Des Rosemary De Figlio. Litho Questa)

1988 (28 Nov). *Major League Baseball Players (1st series). T 340 and similar horiz designs showing portraits or league emblems.* P 14 × 13½.

1842/1922 30 c. × 81 multicoloured .. *Set of 81* 8·75 9·50
Nos. 1842/1922 were issued as nine sheetlets, each of nine different designs.
One sheetlet was subsequently reissued with the Pete Rose stamp replaced by a label inscribed "U.S. BASEBALL SERIES I".

(Des Walt Disney Co. Litho Questa)

1988 (1 Dec). *Christmas. "Mickey's Christmas Eve". Vert designs as T 246 of Antigua showing Walt Disney cartoon characters. Multicoloured.* P 13½ × 14.

1923	$1 Donald Duck's nephew on mantelpiece	65	65
	a. Sheetlet. Nos. 1923/30	4·75	
1924	$1 Goofy with string of popcorn	65	65
1925	$1 Chip n' Dale decorating Christmas tree	65	65
1926	$1 Father Christmas in sleigh	65	65
1927	$1 Donald's nephew with stocking	65	65
1928	$1 Donald's nephew unpacking Xmas decorations	65	65
1929	$1 Donald Duck with present	65	65
1930	$1 Mickey Mouse with present	65	65
1923/90	*Set of 8*	4·75	4·75

MS1931 Two sheets, each 127×102 mm. (a) $5 Ferdie leaving drink for Father Christmas. (b) $5 Mordie and Ferdie asleep .. *Set of 2 sheets* 7·00 8·50
Nos. 1923/30 were printed together, *se-tenant*, in a sheetlet of eight forming a composite design.

341 Tina Turner   342 Canada Atlantic Railway No. 2, 1889

(Litho Questa)

1988 (5 Dec). *Entertainers. T 341 and similar vert designs. Multicoloured.* P 14.

1932	10 c. Type 341	25	15
1933	25 c. Lionel Ritchie	25	20
1934	45 c. Whitney Houston	35	30
1935	60 c. Joan Armatrading	50	45
1936	75 c. Madonna	70	60
1937	$1 Elton John	90	80
1938	$3 Bruce Springsteen	1·90	2·50
1939	$4 Bob Marley	2·50	3·25
1932/9	*Set of 8*	6·50	7·50

MS1940 115×155 mm. 55 c.×2 Yoko Minamino; $1×2 Yoko Minamino (*different*) .. 1·90 2·75
No. 1935 is incorrectly inscribed "JOAN AMMERTRADING".

(Des T. Hadley and W. Wright. Litho B.D.T.)

1989 (23 Jan). *North American Railway Locomotives. T 342 and similar vert designs. Multicoloured.* P 13.

1941	$2 Type 342	1·25	1·25
	a. Sheetlet. Nos. 1941/50	11·00	
1942	$2 Virginia & Truckee Railroad "J. W. Bowker" type, 1875	1·25	1·25
1943	$2 Philadelphia & Reading Railway *Ariel*, 1872	1·25	1·25
1944	$2 Chicago & Rock Island Railroad "America" type, 1867	1·25	1·25
1945	$2 Lehigh Valley Railroad Consolidation No. 63, 1866	1·25	1·25
1946	$2 Great Western Railway *Scotia*, 1860	1·25	1·25
1947	$2 Grand Trunk Railway "Birkenhead" Class, 1854	1·25	1·25
1948	$2 Camden & Amboy Railroad *Monster*, 1837	1·25	1·25
1949	$2 Baltimore & Ohio Railroad "Grasshopper" Class, 1834	1·25	1·25
1950	$2 Baltimore & Ohio Railroad *Tom Thumb*, 1829	1·25	1·25
1951	$2 United Railways of Yucatan *Yucatan*, 1925	1·25	1·25
	a. Sheetlet. Nos. 1951/60	11·00	
1952	$2 Canadian National Railways Class "T2", 1924	1·25	1·25
1953	$2 St. Louis—San Francisco Railroad "Light Mikado" class, 1919	1·25	1·25
1954	$2 Atlantic Coast Line Railroad "Light Pacific" class, 1919	1·25	1·25
1955	$2 Edaville Railroad No. 7, 1913	1·25	1·25
1956	$2 Denver & Rio Grande Western Railroad Class "K27", 1903	1·25	1·25
1957	$2 Pennsylvania Railroad Class "E-2" No. 7002, 1902	1·25	1·25
1958	$2 Pennsylvania Railroad Class "H6", 1899	1·25	1·25
1959	$2 Mohawk & Hudson Railroad *De Witt Clinton*, 1831	1·25	1·25
1960	$2 St. Clair Tunnel Company No. 598, 1891	1·25	1·25
1961	$2 Chesapeake & Ohio Railroad Class "M-1" No. 500 steam turbine electric, 1947	1·25	1·25
	a. Sheetlet. Nos. 1961/70	11·00	
1962	$2 Rutland Railroad No. 93, 1946	1·25	1·25
1963	$2 Pennsylvania Railroad Class "T1", 1942	1·25	1·25
1964	$2 Chesapeake & Ohio Railroad Class "H-8", 1942	1·25	1·25
1965	$2 Atchison, Topeka & Santa Fe Railway Model "FT" diesel, 1941	1·25	1·25
1966	$2 Gulf, Mobile & Ohio Railroad Models "S-1" & "S-2" diesel, 1940	1·25	1·25
1967	$2 New York, New Haven & Hartford Railroad Class "15", 1937	1·25	1·25
1968	$2 Seaboard Air Line Railroad Class "R", 1936	1·25	1·25
1969	$2 Newfoundland Railway Class "R-2", 1930	1·25	1·25
1970	$2 Canadian National Railway diesel No. 9000, 1928	1·25	1·25
1941/70	*Set of 30*	32·00	32·00

Nos. 1941/50, 1951/60 and 1961/70 were each printed together, *se-tenant*, in sheetlets of 10.

343 Women's Long Jump (Jackie Joyner-Kersee, U.S.A.)   344 Nebulae

(Des L. Fried. Litho B.D.T.)

1989 (6 Apr). *Olympic Gold Medal Winners, Seoul (1988). T 343 and similar vert designs. Multicoloured.* P 14.

1971	10 c. Type 343	20	20
1972	25 c. Women's Singles Tennis (Steffi Graf, West Germany)	50	35
1973	45 c. Men's 1500 metres (Peter Rono, Kenya)	60	40
1974	75 c. Men's 1000 metres single kayak (Greg Barton, U.S.A.)	70	60
1975	$1 Women's team foil (Italy)	85	75
1976	$2 Women's 100 metres freestyle swimming (Kristin Otto, East Germany)	1·75	2·00
1977	$3 Men's still rings gymnastics (Holger Behrendt, East Germany)	2·10	2·25
1978	$4 Synchronized swimming pair (Japan)	2·40	2·50
1971/8	*Set of 8*	8·25	8·25

MS1979 Two sheets, each 76×100 mm. (a) $6 Olympic flame. (b) $6 Runner with Olympic torch ... *Set of 2 sheets* 8·50 9·50

(Litho Questa)

1989 (25 Apr). *Appearance of Halley's Comet (1986) (3rd issue). T 344 and similar horiz designs.* P 14.

1980	25 c. + 5 c. multicoloured	35	45
1981	75 c. + 5 c. black and turquoise-green	65	85
1982	90 c. + 5 c. multicoloured	75	95
1983	$2 + 5 c. multicoloured	1·25	1·75
1980/3	*Set of 4*	2·50	3·50

MS1984 111×78 mm. $5 + 5 c. multicoloured. Imperf .. 3·00 4·00
Designs: (As T 344)—75 c. + 5 c. Marine astronomical experiments; 90 c. + 5 c. Moon's surface; $2 + 5 c. Edmond Halley, Sir Isaac Newton and his book *Principia*. (102×69 mm)—$5 + 5 c. 17th-century warships and astrological signs.

(Litho Questa)

1989 (15 May). *Japanese Art. Paintings by Hiroshige. Horiz designs as T 250 of Antigua. Multicoloured.* P 14×13½.

1985	10 c. "Shinagawa on Edo Bay"	20	20
1986	25 c. "Pine Trees on the Road to Totsuka"	30	30
1987	60 c. "Kanagawa on Edo Bay"	50	50
1988	75 c. "Crossing Banyu River to Hiratsuka"	55	55
1989	$1 "Windy Shore at Odawara"	70	70
1990	$2 "Snow-Covered Post Station of Mishima"	1·25	1·50
1991	$3 "Full Moon at Fuchu"	1·60	1·75
1992	$4 "Crossing the Stream at Okitsu"	2·25	2·50
1985/92	*Set of 8*	6·50	7·25

MS1993 Two sheets, each 102×76 mm. (a) $5 "Mountain Pass at Nissaka". (b) $5 "Mt Uzu at Okabe" ... *Set of 2 sheets* 4·25 5·50
Nos. 1985/92 were each printed in sheetlets of 10 containing two horizontal strips of 5 stamps separated by printed labels commemorating Emperor Hirohito.

COVER PRICES

Cover factors are quoted at the beginning of each country for most issues to 1945. An explanation of the system can be found on page x. The factors quoted do not, however, apply to philatelic covers.

345 Great Blue Heron

(Des D. Bruckner. Litho Questa)

1989 (6 June)–**94**. *Birds.* T **345** *and similar multicoloured designs.* A. P 14. B. P 11½×12½ (*horiz*) or 12½×11½ (*vert*).

			A		B	
1994	5 c.	Type 345	30	30	30	30
1995	10 c.	Green Heron	30	30	30	30
1996	15 c.	Turnstone	40	30	30	30
1997	25 c.	Blue-winged Teal ..	40	20	30	20
1998	35 c.	Little Ringed Plover (*vert*)	50	20	35	20
1999	45 c.	Green-throated Carib ("Emerald-throated Hummingbird") (*vert*) ..	55	30	40	30
2000	50 c.	Rufous-breasted Hermit (*vert*)	60	45	45	35
2001	60 c.	Lesser Antillean Bullfinch (*vert*)	70	50	55	50
2002	75 c.	Brown Pelican (*vert*)	80	65	60	60
2003	$1	Black-crowned Night Heron (*vert*)	1·00	90	80	80
2004	$3	American Kestrel ("Sparrow Hawk") (*vert*)	2·25	2·75	1·75	2·25
2005	$5	Barn Swallow (*vert*)	3·00	3·50	2·50	3·00
2006	$10	Red-billed Tropic Bird (*vert*)	6·00	7·00	7·00	8·00
2007	$20	Barn Owl (*vert*)	12·00	13·00	13·00	14·00
1994/2007		*Set of 14*	26·00	27·00	26·00	28·00

Dates of issue:—6.6.89, Nos. 1994A/2005A;13.11.89, No. 2006A; 22.1.90, No. 2007A; 1993, Nos. 1994B/2006B; 1994, No. 2007B.

Nos. 1994B/2007B show a larger perforation hole on every sixth perforation, both vertically and horizontally.

(Des D. Bruckner. Litho B.D.T.)

1989 (12 June). *World Cup Football Championship, Italy (1990)* (1st issue). *Vert designs as* T **252** *of Antigua. Multicoloured.* P 14.

2008	10 c.	Scotland player	20	20
2009	25 c.	England and Brazil players ..	30	30
2010	60 c.	Paolo Rossi (Italy) ..	55	55
2011	75 c.	Jairzinho (Brazil) ..	70	70
2012	$1	Sweden striker	90	90
2013	$2	Péle (Brazil)	1·75	1·75
2014	$3	Mario Kempes (Argentina) ..	2·50	2·50
2015	$4	Pat Jennings (Northern Ireland) ..	2·75	2·75
2008/15		*Set of 8*	8·75	8·75

MS2016 Two sheets. (a) 70×93 mm. $6 Players jumping for ball. (b) 82×71 mm. $6 Goalkeeper *Set of 2 sheets* 8·50 10·00

See also Nos. 2174/8 and MS2179.

346 Xebec and Sugar Cane

(Des T. Agans. Litho B.D.T.)

1989 (7 July). *"Philexfrance 89" International Stamp Exhibition, Paris.* T **346** *and similar horiz designs showing French sailing vessels and plantation crops. Multicoloured.* P 14.

2017	25 c.	Type 346	70	30
2018	75 c.	Lugger and cotton ..	1·25	85
2019	$1	Full-rigged ship and cocoa ..	1·40	1·00
2020	$4	Ketch and coffee ..	3·50	5·00
2017/20		*Set of 4*	6·00	6·50

MS2021 114×70 mm. $6 "View of Fort and Town of St. George, 1779" (105×63 mm). Imperf 4·00 5·00

347 Alan Shepard and "Freedom 7" Spacecraft, 1961 (first American in Space)

348 *Hygrocybe occidentalis*

(Des L. Birmingham. Litho Questa)

1989 (20 July). *20th Anniv of First Manned Landing on Moon.* T **347** *and similar horiz designs. Multicoloured.* P 14.

2022	15 c.	Type 347	50	40
2023	35 c.	"Friendship 7" spacecraft, 1962 (first manned earth orbit)	65	55
2024	45 c.	"Apollo 8" orbiting Moon, 1968 (first manned lunar orbit)	75	65
2025	70 c.	"Apollo 15" lunar rover, 1972	1·00	85

2026	$1	"Apollo 11" emblem and lunar module *Eagle* on Moon, 1969	1·25	1·10
2027	$2	"Gemini 8" and "Agena" rocket, 1966 (first space docking)	2·25	2·00
2028	$3	Edward White in space, 1965 (first U.S. space walk)	3·00	2·75
2029	$4	"Apollo 7" emblem	3·50	3·25
2022/9		*Set of 8*	11·50	10·50

MS2030 Two sheets, each 101×71 mm. (a) $5 Moon and track of "Apollo 11", 1969. (b) $5 Armstrong and Aldrin raising U.S. flag on Moon, 1969 .. .. *Set of 2 sheets* 8·00 8·00

(Des J. Cooter. Litho B.D.T.)

1989 (17 Aug). *Fungi.* T **348** *and similar vert designs. Multicoloured.* P 14.

2031	15 c.	Type 348	50	40
2032	40 c.	*Marasmius haematocephalus*	65	55
2033	50 c.	*Hygrocybe hypohaemacta*	75	65
2034	70 c.	*Lepiota pseudoignicolor*	1·00	90
2035	90 c.	*Cookeina tricholoma*	1·25	1·25
2036	$1.10,	*Leucopaxillus gracillimus*	1·50	1·50
2037	$2.25,	*Hygrocybe nigrescens*	2·75	3·00
2038	$4	*Clathrus crispus*	3·75	4·00
2031/8		*Set of 8*	11·00	11·00

MS2039 Two sheets, each 57×70 mm. (a) $6 *Mycena holoporphyra*. (b) $6 *Xeromphalina tenuipes* .. .. .. *Set of 2 sheets* 12·00 13·00

349 Y.W.C.A. Logo and Grenada Scenery

350 *Historis odius*

(Litho Questa)

1989 (11 Sept). *Centenary of Young Women's Christian Association.* T **349** *and similar multicoloured design.* P 14.

2040	50 c.	Type 349	45	45
2041	75 c.	Y.W.C.A. logo and town (*horiz*)	80	80

(Des Deborah Dudley Max. Litho B.D.T.)

1989 (2 Oct). *Butterflies.* T **350** *and similar horiz designs. Multicoloured.* P 14.

2042	6 c.	Type 350	30	30
2043	30 c.	*Marpesia petreus* ..	55	55
2044	40 c.	*Danaus gilippus* ..	60	60
2045	60 c.	*Dione juno*	80	80
2046	$1.10,	*Agraulis vanillae* ..	1·25	1·25
2047	$1.25,	*Danaus plexippus* ..	1·50	1·50
2048	$4	*Papilio androgeus* (inscr "*Battus polydamas*")	3·25	3·25
2049	$5	*Dryas julia*	3·25	3·25
2042/9		*Set of 8*	10·50	10·50

MS2050 Two sheets, each 87×115 mm. (a) $6 *Anartia jatrophae*. (b) $6 *Strymon simaethis* .. .. *Set of 2 sheets* 9·50 11·00

351 Amerindian Hieroglyph

352 Amos leaving Home

(Litho Questa)

1989 (16 Oct). *500th Anniv of Discovery of America by Columbus (1992)* (2nd issue). T **351** *and similar vert designs showing different hieroglyphs.* P 14.

2051	45 c.	brownish black, black and new blue	60	50
2052	60 c.	brownish black, black & bright green	70	60
2053	$1	brownish black, black & dp reddish vio	1·00	1·00
2054	$4	brownish black, black & orange-brn	3·25	4·00
2051/4		*Set of 4*	5·00	5·50

MS2055 74×86 mm. $6 brownish black, black and vermilion .. .. .. 4·00 5·50

(Des Walt Disney Co. Litho Questa)

1989 (20 Nov). *"World Stamp Expo '89" International Stamp Exhibition, Washington.* T **352** *and similar multicoloured designs showing Walt Disney cartoon characters in scenes from Ben and Me.* P 14×13½.

2056	1 c.	Type 352	10	10
2057	2 c.	Meeting of Benjamin Franklin and Amos	10	10
2058	3 c.	The Franklin stove ..	10	10
2059	4 c.	Ben and Amos with bi-focals	10	10
2060	5 c.	Amos on page of *Pennsylvania Gazette*	10	10
2061	6 c.	Ben working printing press	10	10

2062	10 c.	Conducting experiment with electricity	10	10
2063	$5	Ben disembarking in England	5·00	5·50
2064	$6	Ben with Document of Agreement	5·50	6·00
2056/64		*Set of 9*	10·00	11·00

MS2065 Two sheets, each 127×101 mm. (a) $6 Benjamin Franklin teaching (*vert*). P 13½×14. (b) $6 Signatories of Declaration of Independence. P 14×13½ .. .. *Set of 2 sheets* 8·00 10·00

(Litho Questa)

1990 (4 Jan). *Christmas. Paintings by Rubens. Vert designs as* T **259** *of Antigua. Multicoloured.* P 14.

2066	20 c.	"Christ in the House of Mary and Martha"	30	25
2067	35 c.	"The Circumcision"	45	40
2068	60 c.	"Trinity adored by Duke of Mantua and Family"	75	65
2069	$2	"Holy Family with St. Francis"	2·25	2·50
2070	$3	"The Ildefonso Altarpiece"	2·75	3·00
2071	$4	"Madonna and Child with Garland and Putti"	3·25	3·50
2066/71		*Set of 6*	8·75	9·25

MS2072 Two sheets, each 70×95 mm. (a) $5 "Adoration of the Magi". (b) $5 "Virgin and Child adored by Angels" .. *Set of 2 sheets* 7·50 9·00

353 Alexander Graham Bell and Early Telephone System (150th anniv of invention)

354 *Odontoglossum triumphans*

(Des J. Genzo. Litho B.D.T.)

1990 (12 Feb). *Anniversaries.* T **353** *and similar horiz designs. Multicoloured.* P 14.

2073	10 c.	Type 353	15	15
2074	25 c.	George Washington and Capitol (bicent of presidential inauguration)	20	20
2075	35 c.	Shakespeare and birthplace, Stratford (425th birth anniv)	40	30
2076	75 c.	Nehru and Gandhi (birth cent of Nehru)	90	90
2077	$1	Dr. Hugo Eckener, Ferdinand von Zeppelin and LZ-127 *Graf Zeppelin* (80th anniv of first passenger Zeppelin)	90	90
2078	$2	Charlie Chaplin (birth cent)	1·75	1·75
2079	$3	Container ship in Hamburg Harbour (800th anniv)	2·25	2·50
2080	$4	Friedrich Ebert (first President) and Heidelberg gate (70th anniv of German Republic)	2·25	2·50
2073/80		*Set of 8*	8·00	8·25

MS2081 Two sheets, each 100×72 mm. (a) $6 13th-century ships in Hamburg Harbour (*vert*) (800th anniv). (b) $6 Concorde (20th anniv of first test flight) .. *Set of 2 sheets* 8·50 10·00

No. 2080 is inscribed "40th Anniversary of German Republic" in error.

(Des L. Nelson. Litho Questa)

1990 (6 Mar). *"EXPO 90" International Garden and Greenery Exhibition, Osaka. Caribbean Orchids.* T **354** *and similar vert designs. Multicoloured.* P 14.

2082	10 c.	Type 354	10	10
2083	25 c.	*Oncidium splendidum* ..	30	20
2084	60 c.	*Laelia anceps* ..	60	60
2085	75 c.	*Cattleya trianaei* ..	75	75
2086	$1	*Odontoglossum rossii* ..	1·00	1·00
2087	$2	*Brassia gireoudiana* ..	1·75	1·75
2088	$3	*Cattleya dowiana* ..	2·25	2·25
2089	$4	*Sobralia macrantha* ..	2·50	2·50
2082/9		*Set of 8*	8·25	8·25

MS2090 Two sheets, each 97×68 mm. (a) $6 *Oncidium lanceanum*. (b) $6 *Laelia rubescens* *Set of 2 sheets* 8·50 9·50

(Des Mary Walters. Litho Questa)

1990 (16 Mar). *500th Anniv of Discovery of America by Columbus (1992)* (3rd issue). *New World Natural History – Butterflies. Vert designs as* T **260** *of Antigua. Multicoloured.* P 14.

2091	15 c.	*Marpesia petreus* ..	20	20
2092	25 c.	*Junonia evarete* ..	30	25
2093	75 c.	*Siproeta stelenes* ..	70	70
2094	90 c.	*Historis odius* ..	85	85
2095	$1	*Mestra cana* ..	90	90
2096	$2	*Biblis hyperia* ..	1·75	1·75
2097	$3	*Dryas julia* ..	2·25	2·25
2098	$4	*Anartia amathea* ..	2·25	2·25
2091/8		*Set of 8*	8·25	8·25

MS2099 Two sheets, each 101×69 mm. (a) $6 *Pseudolycaena marsyas*. (b) $6 *Phoebis philea* *Set of 2 sheets* 8·50 9·50

(Des J. Barbaris. Litho B.D.T.)

1990 (3 Apr). *Local Fauna. Multicoloured designs as* T **254** *of Antigua.* P 14.

2100	10 c.	Caribbean Monk Seal ..	20	20
2101	15 c.	Little Brown Bat ..	25	25
2102	45 c.	Brown Rat	50	50
2103	60 c.	Common Rabbit ..	60	60

2104	$1 Water Opossum	..	95	95
2105	$2 White-nosed Ichneumon	..	1·75	1·75
2106	$3 Little Big-eared Bat (vert)	..	2·25	2·25
2107	$4 Mouse Opossum	..	2·25	2·25
2100/7		Set of 8	8·00	8·00

MS2108 Two sheets, each 107×80 mm. (a) $6 Common Rabbit (different). (b) $6 Water Opossum (different) .. .. Set of 2 sheets 8·50 9·50

(Des W. Wright. Litho Questa)

1990 (30 Apr). *50th Anniv of Second World War. Horiz designs as T* **274** *of Antigua. Multicoloured. P* 14.

2109	25 c. British tanks during Operation Battleaxe, 1941	30	30
2110	35 c. Allied tank in southern France, 1944	40	40
2111	45 c. U.S. forces landing on Guadalcanal, 1942 ..	45	45
2112	50 c. U.S. attack in New Guinea, 1943 ..	50	50
2113	60 c. Hoisting U.S. flag on Leyte, Phillippines, 1944	60	60
2114	75 c. U.S. tanks entering Cologne, 1945 ..	75	75
2115	$1 Anzio offensive, 1944	95	95
2116	$2 Battle of the Bismarck Sea, 1943 ..	1·75	1·75
2117	$3 U.S. battle fleet, 1944 ..	2·25	2·25
2118	$4 Focke Wulf Fw190A German fighter attacking Salerno landing, 1943 ..	2·50	2·50
2109/18	.. .. Set of 10	9·50	9·50

MS2119 111×83 mm. $6 German *U-30* submarine, 1939 .. .. .. 3·50 4·00

(Des Walt Disney Co. Litho Questa)

1990 (21 June). *"Stamp World London 90" International Stamp Exhibition (1st issue). Multicoloured designs as T* **193** *of Gambia showing Walt Disney cartoon characters and British trains. P* 14×13½.

2120	5 c. Mickey Mouse driving "King Arthur" Class locomotive, 1925 (horiz)	20	10
2121	10 c. Mickey and Minnie Mouse with *Puffing Billy*, 1813 (horiz)	25	10
2122	20 c. Mickey Mouse with Pluto pulling Durham colliery waggon, 1765 (horiz)	35	15
2123	45 c. Mickey Mouse timing locomotive No. 2509, *Silver Link*, 1935 (horiz)	65	25
2124	$1 Mickey Mouse and Donald Duck with locomotive No. 60149, *Amadis*, 1948 (horiz)	1·50	1·00
2125	$2 Goofy and Mickey Mouse with Liverpool & Manchester Railway locomotive, 1830 (horiz)	2·25	2·50
2126	$4 Goofy and Donald Duck with *Flying Scotsman*, 1870 (horiz)	3·25	3·75
2127	$5 Mickey Mouse and Gyro the Mechanic with Advanced Passenger Train, 1972 (horiz)	3·25	3·75
2120/7	.. .. Set of 8	10·50	10·50

MS2128 Two sheets, each 127×101 mm. (a) $6 Minnie Mouse, Donald and Daisy Duck in Trevithick's *Catch-Me-Who-Can*, 1808 (horiz). P 14×13½. (b) $6 Donald Duck and Stockton and Darlington Railway locomotive, 1825. P 13½×14 .. .. Set of 2 sheets 10·00 11·00
See also No. **MS**2146.

355 U.S. Paratroop Drop over Grenada

(Litho B.D.T.)

1990 (3 July). *50th Anniv of United States' Airborne Forces. T* **355** *and similar horiz designs. Multicoloured. P* 14.
2129 75 c. Type **355** 75 80
MS2130 Two sheets, each 115×87 mm. (a) $2.50, Paratrooper landing. (b) $6 Paratroop uniforms of 1940 and 1990 .. .. Set of 2 sheets 5·50 6·50

(Des Young Phillips Studio. Litho Questa)

1990 (5 July). *90th Birthday of Queen Elizabeth the Queen Mother. Vert designs as T* **194** *of Gambia showing photographs, 1960–69. Multicoloured. P* 14.

2131	$2 Queen Mother in coat and hat ..	1·40	1·75
	a. Strip of 3. Nos. 2131/3	3·75	
2132	$2 Queen Mother in evening dress ..	1·40	1·75
2133	$2 Queen Mother in Garter robes ..	1·40	1·75
2131/3	.. .. Set of 3	3·75	4·75

MS2134 90×75 mm. $6 Queen Mother (as No. 2131) .. .. 3·50 4·00
Nos. 2131/3 were printed together, horizontally and vertically *se-tenant*, in sheetlets of 9 (3×3).

(Des B. Grout. Litho Questa)

1990 (9 July). *Olympic Games, Barcelona (1992) (1st issue). Vert designs as T* **268** *of Antigua. Multicoloured. P* 14.

2135	10 c. Men's steeplechase	20	20
2136	15 c. Dressage	30	30
2137	45 c. Men's 200 m butterfly swimming ..	45	45
2138	50 c. Men's hockey	60	60
2139	65 c. Women's beam gymnastics ..	60	60
2140	75 c. "Flying Dutchman" class yachting ..	80	80
2141	$2 Freestyle wrestling ..	1·75	1·75
2142	$3 Men's springboard diving ..	2·25	2·25
2143	$4 Women's 1000 m sprint cycling ..	2·50	2·50
2144	$5 Men's basketball ..	3·00	3·00
2135/44	.. .. Set of 10	11·50	11·50

MS2145 Two sheets, each 101×70 mm. (a) $8 Equestrian three-day event. (b) $8 Men's 10000 metres .. .. Set of 2 sheets 9·50 11·00
See also Nos. 2414/22.

356 Map of North America and Logo

(Des M. Pollard. Litho Questa)

1990 (12 July). *"Stamp World London 90" International Stamp Exhibition (2nd issue). Sheet* 97×75 mm. P 14.
MS2146 **356** $6 deep mauve .. .. 4·00 5·00

357 Yellow Goatfish

(Des Mary Walters. Litho B.D.T.)

1990 (8 Aug). *Coral Reef Fishes. T* **357** *and similar horiz designs. Multicoloured. P* 14.

2147	10 c. Type **357** ..	20	20
2148	25 c. Black Margate ..	35	35
2149	65 c. Blue-headed Wrasse ..	75	75
2150	75 c. Puddingwife ..	85	85
2151	$1 Four-eyed Butterflyfish ..	95	95
2152	$2 Honey Damselfish ..	1·75	1·75
2153	$3 Queen Angelfish ..	2·25	2·25
2154	$5 Cherub Angelfish ..	3·00	3·00
2147/54	.. .. Set of 8	9·00	9·00

MS2155 Two sheets, each 103×72 mm. (a) $6 Smooth Trunkfish. (b) $6 Sergeant Major .. .. Set of 2 sheets 8·00 9·00

358 Tropical Mockingbird

(Des J. Anderton. Litho B.D.T.)

1990 (10 Sept). *Birds. T* **358** *and similar horiz designs. Multicoloured. P* 14.

2156	15 c. Type **358** ..	30	30
2157	25 c. Grey Kingbird ..	35	35
2158	65 c. Bare-eyed Thrush ..	75	75
2159	75 c. Antillean Crested Hummingbird ..	85	85
2160	$1 House Wren ..	1·00	1·00
2161	$2 Purple Martin ..	1·75	1·75
2162	$4 Hooded Tanager ..	2·50	2·50
2163	$5 Scaly-breasted Ground Dove ..	3·00	3·00
2156/63	.. .. Set of 8	9·50	9·50

MS2164 Two sheets, each 101×72 mm. (a) $6 Fork-tailed Flycatcher. (b) $6 Smooth-billed Ani .. .. Set of 2 sheets 10·00 11·00

359 Coral Crab   **360** Cameroun Player

(Des Deborah Dudley Max. Litho Questa)

1990 (17 Sept). *Crustaceans. T* **359** *and similar horiz designs. Multicoloured. P* 14.

2165	5 c. Type **359** ..	10	10
2166	10 c. Smoothtail Spiny Lobster ..	15	15
2167	15 c. Flamestreaked Box Crab ..	15	15
2168	25 c. Spotted Swimming Crab ..	25	25
2169	75 c. Sally Lightfoot Rock Crab ..	60	60
2170	$1 Spotted Spiny Lobster ..	80	80
2171	$3 Longarm Spiny Lobster ..	2·00	2·50
2172	$20 Caribbean Spiny Lobster ..	13·00	18·00
2165/72	.. .. Set of 8	15·00	20·00

MS2173 Two sheets, 106×75 mm. (a) $6 Copper Lobster. (b) $6 Spanish Lobster .. Set of 2 sheets 8·00 9·00

(Des Young Phillips Studio. Litho Questa)

1990 (24 Sept). *World Cup Football Championship, Italy (2nd issue). T* **360** *and similar vert designs. Multicoloured. P* 14.

2174	10 c. Type **360** ..	20	15
2175	25 c. Michel (Spain) ..	25	15
2176	$1 Brehme (West Germany) ..	85	85
2177	$5 Nevin (Scotland) ..	3·00	4·00
2174/7	.. .. Set of 4	3·75	4·50

MS2178 Two sheets, each 95×90 mm. (a) $6 Giannini (Italy). (b) $6 Perdomo (Uruguay) .. .. Set of 2 sheets 8·50 10·00

1990 W GERMANY 1   ARGENTINA 0

(361)

1990 (30 Nov). *World Cup Football Championship, Italy* (1990) *(3rd issue). No.* **MS**2016a *optd with T* **361**.
MS2179 70×93 mm. $6 Players jumping for ball 4·75 5·50
No. **MS**2179 shows the overprint, Type **361**, added to the list of match results in the sheet margin.

(Litho Questa)

1990 (31 Dec). *Christmas. Paintings by Raphael. Multicoloured designs as T* **272** *of Antigua, but vert. P* 13½×14.

2180	10 c. "The Ansidei Madonna" ..	15	10
2181	15 c. "The Sistine Madonna" ..	15	10
2182	$1 "The Madonna of the Baldacchino" ..	1·00	70
2183	$2 "The Large Holy Family" (detail) ..	1·75	2·00
2184	$5 "Madonna in the Meadow" ..	3·25	4·25
2180/4	.. .. Set of 5	5·75	6·25

MS2185 Two sheets, each 71×101 mm. (a) $6 "Madonna of the Diadem" (detail). (b) $6 "The Madonna of the Veil" (detail) .. Set of 2 sheets 9·00 11·00
A 50 c. value in a similar design, showing "The Canigiani Holy Family" by Raphael, was prepared, but not issued.

(Litho Questa)

1991 (31 Jan). *350th Death Anniv of Rubens. Horiz designs as T* **273** *of Antigua. Multicoloured. P* 14×13½.

2186	5 c. "The Brazen Serpent" (detail)	15	10
2187	10 c. "The Garden of Love" ..	15	10
2188	25 c. "Head of Cyrus" (detail) ..	30	20
2189	75 c. "Tournament in Front of a Castle" ..	70	60
2190	$1 "The Brazen Serpent" (different detail) ..	85	75
2191	$2 "Judgement of Paris" (detail) ..	1·75	2·00
2192	$4 "The Brazen Serpent" (detail) ..	2·50	3·00
2193	$5 "The Karmesse" (detail) ..	3·00	3·25
2186/93	.. .. Set of 8	8·50	9·00

MS2194 Two sheets, each 101×70 mm. (a) $6 "Anger of Neptune" (detail). (b) $6 "The Prodigal Son" (detail) .. .. Set of 2 sheets 8·50 10·00

362 "The Sorcerer's Apprentice"

(Des Walt Disney Co. Litho Questa)

1991 (4 Feb). *50th Anniv of Fantasia (cartoon film). T* **362** *and similar horiz designs. Multicoloured. P* 14×13½.

2195	5 c. Type **362** ..	15	10
2196	10 c. Dancing mushrooms ("The Nut-cracker Suite")	20	10
2197	20 c. Pterodactyls ("The Rite of Spring") ..	35	15
2198	45 c. Centaurs ("The Pastoral Symphony")	75	40
2199	$1 Bacchus and Jacchus ("The Pastoral Symphony") ..	1·25	1·00
2200	$2 Dancing ostrich ("Dance of the Hours") ..	2·25	2·50
2201	$4 Elephant ballet ("Dance of the Hours")	3·00	3·50
2202	$5 Diana ("The Pastoral Symphony") ..	3·25	3·50
2195/202	.. .. Set of 8	10·00	10·00

MS2203 Two sheets, each 122×102 mm. (a) $6 Mickey Mouse as the Sorcerer's Apprentice; (b) $6 Mickey Mouse with Leopold Stokowski (conductor) .. .. Set of 2 sheets 9·50 11·00
MS2204 176×213 mm. $12 Mickey Mouse as the Sorcerer's Apprentice (vert). P 13½×14 .. 9·50 11·00

363 *Adelpha iphicla*   **364** *Psilocybe cubensis*

(Des W. Wright. Litho Questa)

1991 (8 Apr). *Butterflies. T* **363** *and similar horiz designs. Multicoloured. P* 14.

2205	5 c. Type **363** ..	30	15
2206	10 c. Nymphalidae claudina ..	30	20
2207	15 c. Brassolidae polyxena ..	35	20
2208	20 c. Zebra Longwing ..	40	20
2209	25 c. Marpesia corinna ..	40	25
2210	30 c. Morpho hecuba ..	40	30
2211	45 c. Morpho rhetenor ..	55	45
2212	50 c. Dismorphia spio ..	65	55
2213	60 c. Prepona omphale ..	75	65
2214	70 c. Morpho anaxibia ..	85	75
2215	75 c. Marpesia iole ..	90	80
2216	$1 Amarynthis meneria ..	1·00	90

2217	$2 Morpho cisseis	1·75	2·25
2218	$3 Danaidae plexippus	2·25	2·75
2219	$4 Morpho achilleana	2·75	3·50
2220	$5 Calliona argenissa	3·25	4·00
2205/20	Set of 16	15·00	16·00

MS2221 Four sheets, each 118×80 mm. (a) $6 *Anteos clorinde.* (b) $6 *Haetera piera.* (c) $6 *Papilio cresphontes.* (d) $6 *Prepona pheridames.*
Set of 4 sheets 17·00 19·00

(Des T. Agans. Litho Questa)

1991 (29 Apr). *500th Anniv of Discovery of America by Columbus (1992) (4th issue). History of Exploration. Multicoloured designs as T 277 of Antigua. P 14.*

2222	5 c. Vitus Bering in Bering Sea, 1728–29	10	10
2223	10 c. De Bougainville off Pacific island, 1766–69	15	15
2224	25 c. Polynesian canoe	20	20
2225	50 c. De Mendana off Solomon Islands, 1567–69	40	40
2226	$1 Darwin's H.M.S. *Beagle*, 1831–35	80	80
2227	$2 Cook's H.M.S. *Endeavour*, 1768–71	2·00	2·00
2228	$4 Willem Schouten in LeMaire Strait, 1615–17	2·75	2·75
2229	$5 Tasman off New Zealand, 1642–44	3·00	3·00
2222/9	Set of 8	8·50	8·50

MS2230 Two sheets, each 116×77 mm. (a) $6 *Santa Maria sinking.* (b) $6 *Bow of Santa Maria (vert)* Set of 2 sheets 7·50 8·50

(Des Walt Disney Co. Litho Questa)

1991 (6 May). *"Phila Nippon '91" International Stamp Exhibition, Tokyo. Multicoloured designs as T 279 of Antigua showing Walt Disney cartoon characters at Japanese festivals. P 14×13½.*

2231	5 c. Minnie Mouse and Daisy Duck at Dolls festival (horiz)	15	10
2232	10 c. Morty and Ferdie with Boys' Day display (horiz)	20	15
2233	20 c. Mickey and Minnie Mouse at Star festival (horiz)	35	20
2234	45 c. Minnie and Daisy folk-dancing (horiz)	50	35
2235	$1 Huey, Dewey and Louie wearing Eboshi headdresses (horiz)	95	85
2236	$2 Mickey and Goofy pulling decorated cart at Gion festival (horiz)	2·25	2·50
2237	$4 Minnie and Daisy preparing rice broth, Seven Plants festival (horiz)	2·75	3·00
2238	$5 Huey and Dewey with straw boat at Lanterns festival (horiz)	3·25	3·50
2231/8	Set of 8	9·25	9·50

MS2239 Three sheets, each 127×101 mm. (a) $6 Minnie Mouse in kimono. P 13½×14. (b) $6 Mickey taking photo (horiz). P 14×13½. (c) $6 Goofy behind fair stall (horiz). P 14×13½.
Set of 3 sheets 13·00 14·00

(Litho Walsall)

1991 (13 May). *Death Centenary of Vincent van Gogh (artist) (1990). Multicoloured designs as T 278 of Antigua. P 13½.*

2240	20 c. "Blossoming Almond Branch in Glass"	15	15
2241	25 c. "La Mousmé sitting"	15	15
2242	30 c. "Still Life with Red Cabbages and Onions" (horiz)	20	20
2243	40 c. "Japonaiserie: Flowering Plum Tree"	30	30
2244	45 c. "Japonaiserie: Bridge in Rain"	30	30
2245	60 c. "Still Life with Basket of Apples" (horiz)	50	50
2246	75 c. "Italian Woman"	60	60
2247	$1 "The Painter on his Way to Work"	80	80
2248	$2 "Portrait of Pére Tanguy"	1·50	1·50
2249	$3 "Still Life with Plaster Statuette, a Rose and Two Novels"	2·25	2·25
2250	$4 "Still Life: Bottle, Lemons and Oranges" (horiz)	2·50	2·50
2251	$5 "Orchard with Blossoming Apricot Trees" (horiz)	2·75	2·75
2240/51	Set of 12	11·00	11·00

MS2252 Five sheets. (a) 76×102 mm. $6 "Roubine du Roi Canal with Washerwoman" (73×99 mm). (b) 102×76 mm. $6 "Farmhouse in a Wheatfield" (99×73 mm). (c) 102×76 mm. $6 "The Gleize Bridge over the Vigueirat Canal" (99×73 mm). (d) 102×76 mm. $6 "Rocks with Oak Tree" (99×73 mm). (e) 76×102 mm. $6 "Japonaiserie: Oiran" (73×99 mm). Imperf.
Set of 5 sheets 18·00 21·00

(Des Mary Walters. Litho Questa)

1991 (1 June). *Fungi. T 364 and similar vert designs. Multicoloured. P 14.*

2253	15 c. Type 364	40	30
2254	25 c. Leptonia caeruleocapitata	50	30
2255	65 c. Cystolepiota eriophora	90	75
2256	75 c. Chlorophyllum molybdites	1·00	85
2257	$1 Xerocomus hypoxanthus	1·25	1·10
2258	$2 Volvariella cubensis	2·00	2·25
2259	$4 Xerocomus coccolobae	3·00	3·25
2260	$5 Pluteus chrysophlebius	3·00	3·25
2253/60	Set of 8	11·00	11·00

MS2261 Two sheets, each 100×70 mm. (a) $6 *Psathyrella tuberculata.* (b) $6 *Hygrocybe miniata.* Set of 2 sheets 11·00 12·00

365 Johannes Kepler (astronomer)

(Des G. Vasarhelyi. Litho Questa)

1991 (21 June). *Exploration of Mars. T 365 and similar horiz designs showing astronomers, spacecraft and Martian landscapes. Multicoloured. P 14×13½.*

2262/97	75 c. × 9, $1.25 × 9, $2 × 9, $7 × 9		
	Set of 36	48·00	48·00

MS2298 Three sheets, each 112×92 mm. (a) $6 Projected spacecraft. (b) $6 Mars and part of spacecraft. (c) $6 Phobos satellite over Mars. P 13×12 Set of 3 sheets 11·00 12·00
Nos. 2262/97 were issued as four sheetlets, each containing nine different designs of the same face values.

(Des D. Miller. Litho Walsall)

1991 (5 July). *65th Birthday of Queen Elizabeth II. Horiz designs as T 280 of Antigua. Multicoloured. P 14.*

2299	15 c. Royal Family on balcony after Trooping the Colour, 1985	15	15
2300	40 c. Queen and Prince Philip at Peterborough, 1988	35	35
2301	$2 Queen and Queen Mother at Windsor, 1986	1·50	1·75
2302	$4 Queen and Prince Philip on visit to United Arab Emirates	2·50	2·75
2299/302	Set of 4	4·00	4·50

MS2303 68×90 mm. $5 Separate photographs of the Queen and Prince Philip 3·50 4·25

(Des D. Miller. Litho Walsall)

1991 (5 July). *10th Wedding Anniv of the Prince and Princess of Wales. Horiz designs as T 280 of Antigua. Multicoloured. P 14.*

2304	10 c. Prince and Princess in July 1985	10	10
2305	50 c. Separate photographs of Prince, Princess and sons	45	45
2306	$1 Prince Henry at Trooping the Colour and Prince William in Majorca	90	90
2307	$5 Separate photographs of Prince Charles and Princess Diana	3·00	3·50
2304/7	Set of 4	4·00	4·50

MS2308 68×90 mm. $5 Prince, Princess and sons on holiday in Majorca 3·50 4·25

366 Anglican High School Pupils

(Litho Questa)

1991 (29 July). *75th Anniv of Anglican High School (10, 25 c.) and 40th Anniv of University of the West Indies (45, 50 c.). T 366 and similar horiz designs. Multicoloured. P 14.*

2309	10 c. Type 366	15	15
2310	25 c. Artist's impression of new Anglican High School	25	20
2311	45 c. Marryshow House, Grenada	45	50
2312	50 c. University Administrative Building, Barbados	55	60
2309/12	Set of 4	1·25	1·25

367 Stephenson's Locomotive, 1814 (Great Britain)

(Des G. Vasarhelyi. Litho Walsall)

1991 (2 Dec). *Great Railways of the World. T 367 and similar horiz designs. Multicoloured. P 14.*

2313	75 c. Type 367	60	60
	a. Sheetlet. Nos. 2313/21	4·75	
2314	75 c. George Stephenson	60	60
2315	75 c. Killingworth locomotive, 1816 (Great Britain)	60	60
2316	75 c. Locomotion, 1825 (Great Britain)	60	60
2317	75 c. Locomotion in Darlington, 1825 (Great Britain)	60	60
2318	75 c. Opening of Stockton & Darlington Railway, 1825	60	60
2319	75 c. Royal George, 1827 (Great Britain)	60	60
2320	75 c. Northumbrian Rocket, 1829 (Great Britain)	60	60
2321	75 c. Planet, 1830 (Great Britain)	60	60
2322	$1 Old Ironsides, 1832 (U.S.A.)	80	80
	a. Sheetlet. Nos. 2322/30	6·50	
2323	$1 Wilberforce, 1832 (Great Britain)	80	80
2324	$1 Der Adler, 1835 (Germany)	80	80
2325	$1 North Star, 1837 (Great Britain)	80	80
2326	$1 London & Birmingham Railway No.1, 1838 (Great Britain)	80	80
2327	$1 Stephenson's 2-2-2, 1838 (Austria)	80	80
2328	$1 "Mud Digger" locomotive, 1840 (U.S.A.)	80	80
2329	$1 Standard Norris, 1840 (U.S.A.)	80	80
2330	$1 Centaur, 1840 (Great Britain)	80	80
2331	$2 Lion, 1841 (Great Britain)	1·50	1·50
	a. Sheetlet. Nos. 2331/9	12·50	
2332	$2 Beuth, 1843 (Germany)	1·50	1·50
2333	$2 Derwent, 1845 (Great Britain)	1·50	1·50
2334	$2 Bets, 1846 (Hungary)	1·50	1·50
2335	$2 Opening of Budapest to Vac railway, 1846 (Hungary)	1·50	1·50
2336	$2 Carriages, Stockton & Darlington Railway, 1846 (Great Britain)	1·50	1·50
2337	$2 Stephenson's "Long Boiler" type, 1847 (France)	1·50	1·50
2338	$2 Baldwin locomotive, 1850 (U.S.A.)	1·50	1·50
2339	$2 German 2-4-0 type, 1850	1·50	1·50
2313/39	Set of 27	23·00	23·00

MS2340 Two sheets, each 116×86 mm. (a) $6 Part of Stephenson's *Locomotion*, 1825 (Great Britain). (b) $6 Train on Liverpool & Manchester Railway, 1833 (Great Britain) Set of 2 sheets 8·50 9·50
Nos. 2313/21, 2322/30 and 2331/9 were printed together, se-tenant, in sheetlets of 9.

368 Barbu

(Des I. MacLaury. Litho Questa)

1991 (5 Dec). *Marine Life of the Sandflats. T 368 and similar horiz designs. Multicoloured. P 14.*

2341	50 c. Type 368	55	55
	a. Sheetlet. Nos. 2341/55	7·50	
2342	50 c. Beau Gregory	55	55
2343	50 c. Porcupinefish	55	55
2344	50 c. Queen or Pink Conch and Conchfish	55	55
2345	50 c. Hermit Crab	55	55
2346	50 c. Bluestripe Lizardfish	55	55
2347	50 c. Spot-finned Mojarra	55	55
2348	50 c. Southern Stingray	55	55
2349	50 c. Long-spined Sea Urchin and Slippery Dick	55	55
2350	50 c. Peacock Flounder	55	55
2351	50 c. West Indian Sea Star	55	55
2352	50 c. Spotted Goatfish	55	55
2353	50 c. Netted Olive and West Indian Sea Egg	55	55
2354	50 c. Pearly Razorfish	55	55
2355	50 c. Spotted Jawfish and Yellow-headed Jawfish	55	55
2341/55	Set of 15	7·50	7·50

MS2356 105×96 mm. $6 Short-nosed Batfish 6·50 8·00
Nos. 2341/55 were printed together, se-tenant, in sheetlets of fifteen, forming a composite design.

(Litho Walsall)

1991 (9 Dec). *Christmas. Religious Paintings by Albrecht Dürer. Vert designs as T 287 of Antigua. Multicoloured. P 12.*

2357	10 c. "Adoration of the Magi" (detail)	20	10
2358	35 c. "Madonna with the Siskin" (detail)	35	25
2359	50 c. "Feast of the Rose Garlands" (detail)	55	45
2360	75 c. "Virgin with the Pear" (detail)	80	70
2361	$1 "Virgin in Half-length" (detail)	1·10	90
2362	$2 "Madonna and Child" (detail)	2·00	2·00
2363	$4 "Virgin and Child with St. Anne" (detail)	2·50	3·00
2364	$5 "Virgin and Child" (detail)	3·00	3·25
2357/64	Set of 8	9·50	9·50

MS2365 Two sheets, each 102×127 mm. (a) $6 "Virgin with a Multitude of Animals" (detail). (b) $6 "The Nativity" (detail). P 14½×14
Set of 2 sheets 7·50 8·50

369 Goofy windsurfing

(Des Walt Disney Co. Litho Questa)

1992 (11 Feb). *Thrill Sports. T 369 and similar multicoloured designs showing Walt Disney cartoon characters. P 14×13½.*

2366	5 c. Type 369	15	10
2367	10 c. Mickey Mouse skateboarding	20	10
2368	20 c. Daisy Duck gliding	30	10
2369	45 c. Mickey's nephews stunt kite flying	55	25
2370	$1 Donald Duck mountain biking	1·00	85
2371	$2 Donald and Chipmunk parachuting	1·75	2·00
2372	$4 Mickey go-karting	3·00	3·50
2373	$5 Minnie water skiing	3·00	3·50
2366/73	Set of 8	9·00	9·00

MS2374 Four sheets, each 128×102 mm. (a) $6 Mickey bungee jumping (vert). P 13½×14. (b) $6 Mickey and Minnie river rafting. P 14×13½. (c) $6 Donald's nephews playing roller hockey. P 14×13½. (d) $6 Mickey hang-gliding. P 14×13½ Set of 4 sheets 16·00 17·00

(Des D. Miller. Litho Questa)

1992 (2 Mar). *40th Anniv of Queen Elizabeth II's Accession. Horiz designs as T 288 of Antigua. Multicoloured. P 14.*

2375	10 c. Waterfall	25	15
2376	50 c. Street in St. George's	50	40
2377	$1 Colonial-style houses, St. George's	80	80

2378	$5 St. George's from the sea	3·25	3·50
2375/8	Set of 4	4·00	4·25

MS2379 Two sheets, each 75×96 mm. (a) $6 Village on hillside. (b) $6 Yacht at anchor off village .. .. Set of 2 sheets 8·00 10·00

(Litho B.D.T.)

1992 (30 Apr). *"Granada '92" International Stamp Exhibition, Spain. Spanish Paintings. Multicoloured designs as T 292 of Antigua. P 13×13½ (vert) or 13½×13 (horiz).*

2380	10 c. "The Corpus Christi Procession in Seville" (Manuel Cabral y Aguado) (horiz)	15	15
2381	35 c. "The Mancorbo Channel" (Carlos de Haes)	25	20
2382	50 c. "Amalia de Llano y Dotres, Countess of Vilches" (Federico de Madrazo y Kuntz)	40	40
2383	75 c. "Conchita Serrano y Domínguez, Countess of Santovenia" (Eduardo Rosales Gallina)	55	55
2384	$1 "Queen María Isabel de Braganza" (Bernardo López Piquer)	70	70
2385	$2 "The Presentation of Don John of Austria to Charles V" (detail) (Gallina)	1·40	1·75
2386	$4 "The Presentation of Don John of Austria to Charles V" (different detail) (Gallina)	2·75	3·25
2387	$5 "The Testament of Isabella the Catholic" (Gallina) (horiz)	3·00	3·25
2380/7	Set of 8	8·25	9·25

MS2388 Two sheets, each 120×95 mm. (a) $6 "The Horse Corral in the Old Madrid Bullring" (Manuel Castellano) (111×85 mm). (b) $6 "Meeting of Poets in Antonio Mariá Esquivel's Studio" (Antonia Mariá Esquivel y Suárez de Urbina) (111×85 mm). Imperf .. Set of 2 sheets 8·00 9·00

370 Green-winged Macaw   371 Gracie Fields

(Des L. Fried. Litho Questa)

1992 (7 May). *500th Anniv of Discovery of America by Columbus (5th issue). World Columbian Stamp "Expo '92", Chicago. T 370 and similar vert designs. Multicoloured. P 14.*

2389	10 c. Type 370	25	15
2390	25 c. Santa Maria	35	20
2391	35 c. Christopher Columbus	40	30
2392	50 c. 15th-century sandglass	55	55
2393	75 c. Queen Isabella	70	80
2394	$4 Cantino map of 1502 (detail)	3·50	4·75
2389/94	Set of 6	5·25	6·00

MS2395 Two sheets, each 80×108 mm. (a) $6 Map of Genoa (detail). (b) $6 Detail of 15th-century map by Thomas Bly .. Set of 2 sheets 8·00 9·00

(Des R. Brickman. Litho Questa)

1992 (28 May). *"Genova '92" International Thematic Stamp Exhibition. Hummingbirds. Multicoloured designs as T 295 of Antigua, but vertical. P 14.*

2396	10 c. Ruby-throated Hummingbird	20	15
2397	25 c. Vervain Hummingbird	30	20
2398	35 c. Blue-headed Hummingbird	35	25
2399	50 c. Cuban Emerald	55	55
2400	75 c. Antillean Mango	75	75
2401	$2 Purple-throated Carib	1·50	1·75
2402	$4 Puerto Rican Emerald	2·75	3·25
2403	$5 Green-throated Carib	2·75	3·25
2396/403	Set of 8	8·25	9·25

MS2404 Two sheets, each 109×80 mm. (a) $6 Young Antillean Crested Hummingbird. (b) $6 Rufous-breasted Hermit .. Set of 2 sheets 10·00 11·00

(Des R. Jung. Litho B.D.T.)

1992 (1 June). *50th Anniv of United Service Organization (forces' entertainment programme). T 371 and similar vert designs. Multicoloured. P 14.*

2405	15 c. Type 371	15	15
2406	25 c. Jack Benny	20	20
2407	35 c. Jinx Falkenburg	25	25
2408	50 c. Francis Langford	40	40
2409	75 c. Joe E. Brown	70	70
2410	$1 Phil Silvers	80	80
2411	$2 Danny Kaye	1·50	1·75
2412	$5 Frank Sinatra	3·00	3·50
2405/12	Set of 8	6·25	7·00

MS2413 Two sheets, each 107×80 mm. (a) $6 Bob Hope. (b) $6 Anna May Wong Set of 2 sheets 8·00 9·00

STANLEY GIBBONS
STAMP COLLECTING SERIES

Introductory booklets on *How to Start, How to Identify Stamps* and *Collecting by Theme*. A series of well illustrated guides at a low price.
Write for details.

---

372 Badminton   373 Matador (yacht), Newport News Regatta

(Litho Questa)

1992 (17 June). *Olympic Games, Barcelona (2nd issue). T 372 and similar multicoloured designs. P 14.*

2414	10 c. Type 372	15	15
2415	25 c. Women's long jump	20	20
2416	35 c. Women's 100 metres	30	30
2417	50 c. 1000 metres cycling sprint	50	50
2418	75 c. Decathlon (horiz)	70	70
2419	$2 Judo (horiz)	1·60	1·75
2420	$4 Women's gymnastics – asymmetrical bars	2·75	3·25
2421	$5 Men's javelin	2·75	3·25
2414/21	Set of 8	8·00	9·00

MS2422 Two sheets, each 100×70 mm. (a) $6 Men's gymnastics – vault. (b) $6 Men's gymnastics – floor exercise .. Set of 2 sheets 8·00 9·00

(Des F. Paul ($1), J. Esquino ($2). Litho Questa)

1992 (24 Aug). *500th Anniv of Discovery of America by Columbus (6th issue). Organization of East Caribbean States. As Nos. 1670/1 of Antigua. Multicoloured. P 14½.*

2423	$1 Columbus meeting Amerindians	70	70
2424	$2 Ships approaching island	1·40	1·60

(Des W. Hanson. Litho B.D.T.)

1992 (22 Oct). *Toy Trains from American Manufacturers. Multicoloured designs as T 257 of Dominica. P 14.*

2425	10 c. The Blue Comet locomotive, Boucher (1933)	15	15
2426	35 c. No. 2220 switching locomotive, Voltamp (1906)	25	25
2427	40 c. No. 221 tunnel locomotive, Knapp (1905)	30	30
2428	75 c. Grand Canyon locomotive, American Flyer (1931)	55	55
2429	$1 Streamliner tin locomotive, Hafner (1930s)	70	70
2430	$2 No. 237 switching locomotive, Elektoy (1911)	1·40	1·75
2431	$4 Parlor car, Ives (1928)	2·75	3·25
2432	$5 The Improved President's Special locomotive, American Flyer (1927)	2·75	3·25
2425/32	Set of 8	8·00	9·00

MS2433 Two sheets, each 133×103 mm. (a) $6 No. 11132 locomotive, Ives (1921) (38½×50 mm). (b) $6 No. 3239 locomotive, Ives (1912) (50×38½ mm). P 13 .. Set of 2 sheets 8·00 9·00

(Des Kerri Schiff. Litho Questa)

1992 (28 Oct). *Postage Stamp Mega Event, New York. Sheet 100×70mm containing multicoloured design as T 299 of Antigua. P 14.*

MS2434 $6 Guggenheim Museum .. .. 3·50 4·25

(Litho Questa)

1992 (12 Nov). *World Regattas. T 373 and similar multicoloured designs. P 14.*

2435	15 c. Type 373	20	20
2436	25 c. Awesome, Antigua	25	25
2437	35 c. Mistress Quickly, Bermuda	30	30
2438	50 c. Emeraude, St. Tropez	50	50
2439	$1 Diva G, German Admirals Cup	80	80
2440	$2 Lady Be, French Admirals Cup	1·50	1·75
2441	$4 Midnight Sun, Admirals Cup	2·75	3·25
2442	$5 Carat, Sardinia Cup	2·75	3·25
2435/42	Set of 8	8·00	9·00

MS2443 Two sheets, each 113×85 mm. (a) $6 Yachts, Grenada Regatta (horiz). (b) $6 Fastnet Race, 1979 (horiz) .. Set of 2 sheets 8·00 9·00

(Litho Questa)

1992 (16 Nov). *Christmas. Religious Paintings. Vert designs as T 300 of Antigua. Multicoloured. P 13½×14.*

2444	10 c. "Adoration of the Magi" (detail) (Fra Filippo Lippi)	25	15
2445	15 c. "Madonna adoring Child in a Wood" (Lippi)	30	20
2446	25 c. "Adoration of the Magi" (detail) (Botticelli)	40	20
2447	35 c. "The Epiphany - Adoration of the Magi" (detail) (Hieronymus Bosch)	45	20
2448	50 c. "Adoration of the Magi" (detail) (Giovanni de Paolo)	70	45
2449	75 c. "Adoration of the Magi" (Gentile da Fabriano)	90	60
2450	90 c. "Adoration of the Magi" (detail) (Juan Batista Maino)	1·10	70

2451	$1 "Adoration of the Child" (Master of Liesborn)	1·25	80
2452	$2 "Adoration of the Kings" (Master of Liesborn)	2·00	2·25
2453	$3 "Adoration of the Three Wise Men" (Pedro Berruguete)	2·25	3·00
2454	$4 "Adoration of the Child" (Lippi)	3·00	3·50
2455	$5 "Adoration of the Child" (Correggio)	3·00	3·50
2444/55	Set of 12	14·00	14·00

MS2456 Three sheets, each 72×97 mm. (a) $6 "Adoration of the Magi" (detail) (Andrea Mantegna). (b) $6 "Adoration of the Magi" (detail) (Hans Memling). (c) $6 "Adoration of the Shepherds" (La Tour) .. Set of 3 sheets 12·00 14·00
No. 2447 is inscribed "Hieronymus" in error.

374 Cher   375 Grenada Dove

(Des J. Genzo. Litho Questa)

1992 (19 Nov). *Gold Record Award Winners. T 374 and similar vert designs. Multicoloured. P 14.*

2457	90 c. Type 374	1·25	1·25
	a. Sheetlet. Nos. 2457/64	8·50	
2458	90 c. Michael Jackson	1·25	1·25
2459	90 c. Elvis Presley	1·25	1·25
2460	90 c. Dolly Parton	1·25	1·25
2461	90 c. Johnny Mathis	1·25	1·25
2462	90 c. Madonna	1·25	1·25
2463	90 c. Nat King Cole	1·25	1·25
2464	90 c. Janice Joplin	1·25	1·25
2457/64	Set of 8	8·50	8·50

MS2465 Two sheets, each 100×70 mm. (a) $3 Chuck Berry; $3 James Brown. (b) $3 Frank Sinatra; $3 Perry Como .. Set of 2 sheets 9·50 11·00
Nos. 2457/64 were printed together, se-tenant, in sheetlets of 8 with a composite background design.

(Des W. Wright and W. Hanson (Nos. 2467, 2476, MS2478a), W. Wright and L. Fried (Nos. 2468, 2474, MS2478b), J. Genzo (Nos. 2473, MS2478e), W. Wright (others). Litho B.D.T)

1992 (15 Dec). *Anniversaries and Events. T 375 and similar multicoloured designs. P 14.*

2466	10 c. Type 375	50	40
2467	25 c. Airship LZ-1 on maiden flight, 1900 (horiz)	70	30
2468	50 c. ENDOSAT (robot plane) project (horiz)	75	55
2469	75 c. Konrad Adenauer (German statesman) and industrial skyline (horiz)	80	70
2470	$1.50, Golden Lion Tamarin (horiz)	2·00	2·00
2471	$2 Mountain Gorilla (horiz)	2·50	2·50
2472	$2 Outline of man and heart (horiz)	2·50	2·50
2473	$3 Wolfgang Amadeus Mozart	3·25	3·25
2474	$4 "Voyager 2" and Neptune (horiz)	3·50	3·50
2475	$4 Adenauer with flag and map of West Germany (horiz)	3·50	3·50
2476	$5 Count von Zeppelin and LZ-127 Graf Zeppelin (horiz)	3·50	3·50
2477	$6 Admiral Richard Byrd (polar explorer) (horiz)	3·50	3·50
2466/77	Set of 12	24·00	24·00

MS2478 Five sheets. (a) 110×80 mm. $6 Count von Zeppelin (horiz). (b) 110×80 mm. $6 Space shuttle recovering "Intelsat 6" satellite. (c) 110×80 mm. $6 Konrad Adenauer (horiz). (d) 95×70 mm. $6 Spotted Little Owl (horiz). (e) 100×70 mm. $6 Papageno costume from The Magic Flute .. Set of 5 sheets 18·00 20·00
Anniversaries and Events:—No. 2466, National bird; Nos. 2467, 2476, MS2478a, 75th death anniv of Count Ferdinand von Zeppelin; Nos. 2468, 2475, MS2478b, International Space Year; Nos. 2469, 2475, MS2478c, 25th death anniv of Konrad Adenauer; Nos. 2470/1, MS2478d, Earth Summit '92, Rio; No. 2472, United Nations World Health Organization Projects; No. 2473, MS2478e, Death bicent of Mozart; No. 2477, 75th anniv of International Association of Lions Clubs.

376 Care Bear on Beach

(Des T.C.F.C. Inc. Litho Questa)

1992 (15 Dec). *Ecology. T 376 and similar multicoloured design showing Care Bear cartoon characters. P 14.*

2479	75 c. Type 376	45	45

MS2480 71×101 mm. $2 Care Bear and butterfly (vert) .. .. 1·75 1·90

377 Samoyed and St. Basil's
Cathedral, Moscow

378 Baha'i Shrine,
Haifa

(Des Joan Popeio. Litho Questa)

1993 (20 Jan). *Dogs of the World. T* **377** *and similar horiz
designs. Multicoloured. P* 14.

2481	10 c. Type **377**	30	30
2482	15 c. Chow and Ling Yin Monastery, China	35	30
2483	25 c. Boxer and Tower of London	40	30
2484	90 c. Basenji and Yamma Mosque, Niger	80	65
2485	$1 Golden Labrador and Parliament Building, Ottawa	90	70
2486	$3 St. Bernard and Parsenn, Switzerland	2·00	2·50
2487	$4 Rhodesian Ridgeback and Melrose House, South Africa	2·25	2·75
2488	$5 Afghan Hound and Mazar-i-Sharif, Afghanistan	2·50	2·75
2481/8	*Set of* 8	8·50	9·00

MS2489 Two sheets, each 100×70 mm. (a) $6
Australian Cattle Dog. (b) $6 Alaskan Malamute
Set of 2 sheets 7·00 8·00
No. MS2489(a) is inscribed "Australian" in error.

(Litho Walsall)

1993 (8 Mar). *Bicentenary of the Louvre, Paris. Paintings by
Jean-Antoine Watteau. Multicoloured designs as T* **305** *of
Antigua. P* 12.

2490	$1 "The Faux-pas"	60	65
	a. Sheetlet. Nos. 2490/7	4·25	
2491	$1 "Portrait of a Gentleman"	60	65
2492	$1 "Young Lady with Archlute"	60	65
2493	$1 "Young Man Dancing"	60	65
2494	$1 "Autumn, Pamona and a Cherub"	60	65
2495	$1 "Judgement of Paris"	60	65
2496	$1 "Pierrot" (detail)	60	65
2497	$1 "Pierrot" (different detail)	60	65
2490/7	*Set of* 8	4·25	4·50

MS2498 100×70 mm. $6 "The Embarkation for
Cythére" (85×52 mm). P 14½ 3·50 4·00
Nos. 2490/7 were printed together, *se-tenant*, in sheetlets of 8
stamps and one centre label.

(Litho Cartor)

1993 (7 Apr). *Centenary of Baha'i Faith. P* 13½×14.
2499 **378** 75 c. multicoloured 45 45

379 *Citheronia magnifica*   **380** Heliconia

(Litho Questa)

1993 (13 Apr). *Moths. T* **379** *and similar multicoloured
designs. P* 14.

2500	10 c. Type **379**	25	25
2501	35 c. *Automeris metali*	40	25
2502	45 c. *Thysania zenobia*	50	30
2503	75 c. *Agrius cingulatus*	70	55
2504	$1 *Composia fidelissima*	80	65
2505	$2 *Synchlora xysteraria*	1·50	1·75
2506	$4 *Eumorpha labruscae*	2·50	2·75
2507	$5 *Ascalapha odorata*	2·50	2·75
2500/7	*Set of* 8	8·25	8·25

MS2508 Two sheets, each 100×70 mm. (a) $6
Epimecis detexta (vert). (b) $6 *Xylophanes titana*
(vert) *Set of 2 sheets* 7·00 8·00

(Des D. Delouise. Litho Questa)

1993 (17 May). *Flowers. T* **380** *and similar multicoloured
designs. P* 14.

2509	10 c. Type **380**	25	25
2510	35 c. Pansy	40	20
2511	45 c. Water Lily	50	30
2512	75 c. Bougainvillea	70	55
2513	$1 Calla Lily	80	65
2514	$2 California Poppy	1·50	1·75
2515	$4 Red Ginger	2·50	2·75
2516	$5 Anthurium	2·50	2·75
2509/16	*Set of* 8	8·25	8·25

MS2517 Two sheets, each 70×100 mm. (a) $6
Christmas Rose (horiz). (b) $6 Moth Orchid
(horiz) *Set of 2 sheets* 7·00 8·00

(Des Kerri Schiff. Litho Questa)

1993 (2 June). *40th Anniv of Coronation. Vert designs as T* **307**
of Antigua. P 13½×14.

2518	35 c. multicoloured	40	50
	a. Sheetlet. Nos. 2518/21×2	6·50	
2519	70 c. multicoloured	50	60
2520	$1 reddish brown and black	60	70
2521	$5 multicoloured	2·25	2·40
2518/21	*Set of* 4	3·25	3·75

MS2522 70×100 mm. $6 multicoloured. P 14 3·50 4·00
Designs: (38×47 mm)—35 c. Queen Elizabeth II at Coronation
(photograph by Cecil Beaton); 70 c. Sceptres; $1 Queen
Elizabeth receiving sceptre from Archbishop of Canterbury; $5
Queen and Prince Philip with their children, 1960s. (28½×42½
mm)—$6 "Queen Elizabeth II, 1965" (detail) (Peter Greenham).
Nos. 2518/21 were printed together in sheetlets of 8
containing two *se-tenant* blocks of 4.

381 "Woman with
Loaves" (Picasso)

382 Red-eyed Vireo

(Litho Questa)

1993 (1 July). *Anniversaries and Events. T* **381** *and similar
designs. Each reddish brown, deep brown and black (Nos.
2527, 2535,* MS2536d) *or multicoloured (others). P* 14.

2523	25 c. Type **381**	30	20
2524	35 c. 16th-century telescope	35	20
2525	35 c. Public Library building	35	20
2526	35 c. Gaetan Boucher (speed skating, 1984)	35	20
2527	50 c. Willy Brandt with Senator Edward Kennedy (horiz)	40	30
2528	75 c. Carnival float (horiz)	50	40
2529	90 c. "Weeping Woman" (Picasso)	65	45
2530	$1 "Marii Prohaska" (Tyrus Czyzewski)	70	50
2531	$3 "Marysia et Burek a Geylan" (S. Wirkiewicz)	2·25	2·25
2532	$4 "Woman seated in Airchair" (Picasso)	2·75	2·75
2533	$4 Astronaut on Moon	2·75	2·75
2534	$5 Norbert Schramm (figure skating, 1984)	2·75	2·75
2535	$5 Willy Brandt and Kurt Waldheim (horiz)	2·75	2·75
2523/35	*Set of* 13	15·00	14·00

MS2536 Five sheets. (a) 76×107 mm. $5
Copernicus. (b) 75×105 mm. $6 "Three Women
at the Spring" (detail) (Picasso). (c) 76×105 mm.
$6 Women's Super G skiing medal winners, 1988
(horiz). (d) 105×75 mm. $6 Newspaper headline,
1974. (e) 105×76 mm. $6 "Parting" (detail)
(Witold Wojtkiewicz) *Set of 5 sheets* 17·00 18·00
Anniversaries and Events:—Nos. 2523, 2529, 2532,
MS2536b, 20th death anniv of Picasso (artist); Nos. 2524, 2533,
MS2536a, 450th death anniv of Copernicus (astronomer); No.
2525, Centenary of Grenada Public Library (1992); Nos. 2526,
2534, MS2536c, Winter Olympic Games '94, Lillehammer; Nos.
2527, 2535, MS2536d, 80th birth anniv of Willy Brandt
(German politician) (1992); No. 2528, Grenada Carnival; Nos.
2530/1, MS2536e, "Polska '93" International Stamp Exhibition,
Poznań.

(Des R. Sauber. Litho B.D.T.)

1993 (13 July). *Songbirds. T* **382** *and similar horiz designs.
Multicoloured. P* 14.

2537	15 c. Type **382**	35	35
	a. Sheetlet. Nos. 2537/48	7·00	
2538	25 c. Fork-tailed Flycatcher ("Scissor-tailed Flycatcher")	40	40
2539	35 c. Palm Chat	45	45
2540	35 c. Chaffinch	45	45
2541	45 c. Yellow Wagtail	50	50
2542	45 c. Painted Bunting	50	50
2543	50 c. Short-tailed Pygmy Tyrant ("Short-tailed Pygmy Flycatcher")	50	50
2544	65 c. Orange-breasted Bunting ("Rainbow Bunting")	60	60
2545	75 c. Red Crossbill	60	60
2546	75 c. Akialoa	60	60
2547	$1 Yellow-throated Longclaw ("Yellow-throated Wagtail")	75	75
2548	$4 Barn Swallow	2·25	2·25
2537/48	*Set of* 12	7·00	7·00

MS2549 Two sheets, each 105×86 mm. (a) $6
Song Thrush. (b) $6 White-crested Laughing
Thrush *Set of 2 sheets* 7·00 8·00
Nos. 2537/48 were printed together, *se-tenant*, in sheetlets of
12 with the backgrounds forming a composite design.

PRICES OF SETS

Set prices are given for many issues, generally
those containing three stamps or more. Definitive
sets include one of each value or major colour
change, but do not cover different perforations,
die types or minor shades. Where a choice is
possible the set prices are based on the cheapest
versions of the stamps included in the listings.

383 Atlantic Grey Cowrie
(*Cypraea cinerea*) and Atlantic
Yellow Cowrie (*Cypraea spurca
acicularis*)

384 James K.
Spensley

(Des I. MacLaury. Litho B.D.T.)

1993 (19 July). *Sea Shells. T* **383** *and similar horiz designs.
Multicoloured. P* 14.

2550	15 c. Type **383**	35	35
	a. Sheetlet. Nos. 2550/61	7·00	
2551	15 c. Candy-stick Tellin (*Tellina similis*) and Sunrise Tellin (*Tellina radiata*)	35	35
2552	25 c. Caribbean Vase (*Vasum muricatum*)	40	40
2553	35 c. Lightning Venus (*Pitar fulminatus*) and Royal Comb Venus (*Pitar dione*)	45	45
2554	35 c. Crown Cone (*Conus regius*)	45	45
2555	45 c. Reticulated Cowrie-helmet (*Cypraecassis testiculus*)	50	50
2556	50 c. Barbados Mitre (*Mitra barbadensis*) and Variegated Turret Shell (*Turritella variegata*)	50	50
2557	50 c. Common Egg Cockle (*Laevicardium laevigatum*) and Atlantic Strawberry Cockle (*Americardia media*)	50	50
2558	75 c. Measled Cowrie (*Cypraea zebra*)	60	60
2559	75 c. Rooster-tail Conch (*Strombus gallus*)	60	60
2560	$1 Lion's-paw Scallop (*Lyropecten nodosa*) and Antillean Scallop (*Lyropecten antillarum*)	75	75
2561	$4 Dog-head Triton (*Cymatium moritinctum caribbaeum*)	2·25	2·25
2550/61	*Set of* 12	7·00	7·00

MS2562 Two sheets, each 76×106 mm. (a) $6
Dyson's Keyhole Limpet (*Diodora dysoni*). (b) $6
Virgin Nerite (*Neritina virginea*) and Emerald
Nerite (*Smaragdia viridis viridemaris*)
Set of 2 sheets 7·50 8·00
Nos. 2550/61 were printed together, *se-tenant*, in sheetlets of
12 with the backgrounds forming a composite design.

(Litho Questa)

1993 (13 Aug). *Asian International Stamp Exhibitions.
Multicoloured designs as T* **268** *of Dominica. P* 13½×14.

(a) "Indopex '93", Surabaya, Indonesia

2563	35 c. Megalithic Carving, Sumba Island	35	25
2564	45 c. Entrance to Gao Gajah, Bali	45	30
2565	$1.50, Statue of kris holder	1·00	1·00
	a. Sheetlet. Nos. 2565/70	5·50	
2566	$1.50, Hanuman protecting Sita	1·00	1·00
2567	$1.50, Sendi of Visu mounted on Garuda	1·00	1·00
2568	$1.50, Wahana (votif figure)	1·00	1·00
2569	$1.50, Hanuman (different)	1·00	1·00
2570	$1.50, Singa (symbolic lion)	1·00	1·00
2571	$2 Loving-mother Bridge, Taroko Gorge National Park	1·40	1·50
2572	$4 Head of Kala over temple gateway, Northern Bali	2·50	2·75
2563/72	*Set of* 10	9·50	9·25

MS2573 104×134 mm. $6 Slow Loris 3·75 4·25

(b) "Taipei '93", Taiwan

2574	35 c. Fire-breathing Dragon, New Year's Fair, Chongqing	35	25
2575	45 c. Stone elephant, Ming Tomb, Nanjing	45	30
2576	$1.50, "Ornamental Cock" (Han Meilin)	1·00	1·00
	a. Sheetlet. Nos. 2576/81	5·50	
2577	$1.50, "He's even afraid of Cows" (Meilin)	1·00	1·00
2578	$1.50, "On a Moonlit Night" (Meilin)	1·00	1·00
2579	$1.50, "Eyes that see in the Dark" (Meilin)	1·00	1·00
2580	$1.50, "He's well behaved" (Meilin)	1·00	1·00
2581	$1.50, "He doesn't Bite" (Meilin)	1·00	1·00
2582	$2 Marble peifang, Ming 13 Tombs, Beijing	1·40	1·50
2583	$4 Stone pillar, Nanjing	2·50	2·75
2574/83	*Set of* 10	9·50	9·75

MS2584 104×134 mm. $6 Orang-utan, Mt
Leuser National Park 3·75 4·25

(c) "Bangkok 1993", Thailand

2585	35 c. Nora Nair, Prasad Phra Thepidon, Wat Phra Kaew	35	25
2586	45 c. Stucco deities at Library of Wat Phra Singh	45	30
2587	$1.50, Wooden carved horses	1·00	1·00
	a. Sheetlet. Nos. 2587/92	5·50	
2588	$1.50, Wheel of the law	1·00	1·00
2589	$1.50, Lanna bronze elephant	1·00	1·00
2590	$1.50, Kendi in the form of elephant	1·00	1·00
2591	$1.50, Bronze duck	1·00	1·00
2592	$1.50, Horseman	1·00	1·00
2593	$2 Naga snake, Chiang Mai's Temple	1·40	1·50
2594	$4 Stucco figures, Wat Chang Lom	2·50	2·75
2585/94	*Set of* 10	9·50	9·75

MS2595 134×104 mm. $6 Elephant calf (horiz).
P 14×13½ 3·75 4·25
Nos. 2565/70, 2576/81 and 2571/92 were each printed
together, *se-tenant*, in sheetlets of 6.
No. 2590 is incorrectly inscribed "Kendi in the form of an
Elephant".

(Des Rosemary DeFiglio. Litho Questa)

1993 (7 Sept). *World Cup Football Championship, U.S.A.
(1994) (1st issue). Vert designs as T* **310** *of Antigua.
Multicoloured. P* 14.

2596	10 c. Nikolai Larionov (Russia)	20	20
2597	25 c. Andrea Carnevale (Italy)	40	25

2598	35 c. Enzo Schifo (Belgium) and Soon-Ho Choi (South Korea)	45	25
2599	45 c. Gary Lineker (England)	50	30
2600	$1 Diego Maradona (Argentina)	1·00	80
2601	$2 Lothar Mattaeus (Germany)	1·60	1·60
2602	$4 Jan Karas (Poland) and Julio César Silva (Brazil)	2·25	2·50
2603	$5 Claudio Caniggia (Argentina)	2·50	2·75
2596/603	Set of 8	8·00	7·75

MS2604 Two sheets, each 75×104 mm. (a) $6 Wlodzimierz (Poland). (b) $6 José Basualdo (Argentina) .. .. Set of 2 sheets 7·00 8·00
See also Nos. 2721/7.

(Litho Questa)

1993 (7 Sept). *Centenary of Italian Football. T* **384** *and similar designs showing past and present Genoa players. Each blue-black, bright vermilion and black (Nos. 2605/16) or multicoloured (No. MS2617). P* 14.

2605	$3 Type **384**	2·00	2·00
	a. Sheetlet. Nos. 2605/10	11·00	
2606	$3 Renzo de Vecchi	2·00	2·00
2607	$3 Giovanni de Pra'	2·00	2·00
2608	$3 Luigi Burlando	2·00	2·00
2609	$3 Felice Levratto	2·00	2·00
2610	$3 Guglielmo Stabile	2·00	2·00
2611	$3 Vittorio Sardelli	2·00	2·00
	a. Sheetlet. Nos. 2611/16	11·00	
2612	$3 Juan Carlos Verdeal	2·00	2·00
2613	$3 Fosco Becattini	2·00	2·00
2614	$3 Julio Cesar Abadie	2·00	2·00
2615	$3 Luigi Meroni	2·00	2·00
2616	$3 Roberto Pruzzo	2·00	2·00
2605/16	Set of 12	22·00	22·00

MS2617 Two sheets. (a) 100×75 mm. $15 Genoa Football Club badge (29×45 *mm*). P 14. (b) 129×106 mm. $15 Genoa team of 1991–92 (48×35 *mm*). P 14×13½ .. Set of 2 sheets 19·00 21·00
Nos. 2605/10 and 2611/16 were printed together, *se-tenant*, in sheetlets of 6.

385 *The Band Concert*, 1935

(Des Rosemary DeFiglio. Litho Questa)

1993 (11 Nov). *65th Anniv of Mickey Mouse. T* **385** *and similar multicoloured designs showing Mickey Mouse in scenes from Walt Disney cartoon films. P* 14×13½.

2618	25 c. Type **385**	30	20
2619	35 c. Mickey's Circus, 1936	40	20
2620	50 c. Magician Mickey, 1937	50	35
2621	75 c. Moose Hunters, 1937	65	60
2622	$1 Mickey's Amateurs, 1937	75	70
2623	$2 Tugboat Mickey, 1940	1·25	1·25
2624	$4 Orphan's Benefit, 1941	2·25	2·50
2625	$5 Mickey's Christmas Carol, 1983	2·25	2·50
2618/25	Set of 8	7·50	7·50

MS2626 Two sheets, each 127×102 mm. (a) $6 Mickey's Birthday Party, 1942. P 14×13½. (b) $6 Mickey's Trailer, 1938 (*vert*). P 13½×14
.. .. Set of 2 sheets 7·50 8·00
No. 2624 is inscribed "Oprhan's Benefit" in error.

(Litho Questa)

1993 (22 Nov). *Christmas. Religious Paintings. Vert designs as T* **270** *of Dominica. Black, pale lemon and red (Nos. 2627/8, 2632, 2634, MS2635a) or multicoloured (others). P* 13½×14.

2627	10 c. "The Nativity" (Dürer)	25	15
2628	25 c. "The Annunciation" (Dürer)	35	15
2629	35 c. "The Litta Madonna" (Da Vinci)	40	20
2630	60 c. "The Virgin and Child with St. John the Baptist and St. Anne" (Da Vinci)	50	40
2631	90 c. "The Madonna with the Carnation" (Da Vinci)	65	60
2632	$1 "Adoration of the Magi" (Dürer)	75	70
2633	$4 "The Benois Madonna" (Da Vinci)	2·50	2·75
2634	$5 "The Virgin Mary in the Sun" (Dürer)	2·50	2·75
2627/34	Set of 8	7·25	7·00

MS2635 Two sheets, each 102×128 mm. (a) $6 "The Holy Family with Three Hares" (detail) (Dürer). (b) $6 "Adoration of the Magi" (detail) (Da Vinci) .. Set of 2 sheets 7·00 8·00
Nos. 2629/31, 2633 and **MS**2635b are inscribed "LEONARDO DI VINCI".

386 *Blanchard's Balloon over Walnut St. Prison*

(Litho Questa)

1993 (21 Dec). *Aviation Anniversaries. T* **386** *and similar multicoloured designs. P* 14.

2636	35 c. Airship LZ-127 *Graf Zeppelin* over Vienna at night	35	20
2637	45 c. Type **386**	20	25
2638	50 c. Lysander	50	35
2639	75 c. *Graf Zeppelin* over Pyramids	75	55
2640	$2 Blanchard waving hat from balloon (*vert*)	90	95
2641	$3 Hawker Typhoon	2·00	2·50
2642	$5 *Graf Zeppelin* over Rio de Janeiro	3·25	3·75
2636/42	Set of 7	7·25	7·75

MS2643 Three sheets, each 106×77 mm. (a) $6 *Graf Zeppelin*. (b) $6 Blanchard's balloon (*vert*). (c) $6 Hawker Hurricane .. Set of 3 sheets 8·25 8·50
Anniversaries:—Nos. 2636, 2639, 2642, **MS**2643a, 125th birth anniv of Hugo Eckener (airship commander); Nos. 2637, 2640, **MS**2643b, Bicentenary of First Airmail Flight; Nos. 2638, 2641, **MS**2643c, 75th anniv of Royal Air Force.

387 *Mercedes Benz "370 S" Cabriolet, 1932*   388 *Fishermen with Blue Marlin*

(Des K. Gromell. Litho Questa)

1993 (21 Dec). *Centenaries of Henry Ford's First Petrol Engine (Nos. 2645/6, MS2648b) and Karl Benz's First Four-wheeled Car (others). T* **387** *and similar horiz designs. Multicoloured. P* 14.

2644	35 c. Type **387**	15	20
2645	45 c. Ford "Mustang", 1966	40	30
2646	$3 Ford "Model A" Phaeton, 1930	1·40	1·50
2647	$4 Mercedes Benz "300 Sl" Gullwing	3·50	3·75
2644/7	Set of 4	5·00	5·25

MS2648 Two sheets, each 76×106 mm. (a) $6 Mercedes Benz "290", 1934. (b) $6 Ford "Model A", 1903 .. .. Set of 2 sheets 7·00 8·00

(Des Kerri Schiff. Litho Questa)

1993 (31 Dec). *Famous Paintings by Rembrandt and Matisse. Multicoloured designs as T* **316** *of Antigua. P* 13½×14.

2649	15 c. "Self-portrait", 1900 (Matisse)	30	20
2650	35 c. "Self-portrait", 1629 (Rembrandt)	35	20
2651	45 c. "Self-portrait", 1918 (Matisse)	40	25
2652	50 c. "Self-portrait", 1640 (Rembrandt)	50	35
2653	75 c. "Self-portrait", 1652 (Rembrandt)	65	55
2654	$2 "Self-portrait", 1906 (Matisse)	1·40	1·50
2655	$4 "Self-portrait", 1900 (*different*) (Matisse)	2·50	3·00
2656	$5 "Self-portrait", 1625–31 (Rembrandt)	2·75	3·00
2649/56	Set of 8	8·00	8·00

MS2657 Two sheets. (a) 100×125 mm. $6 "The Painter in his Studio" (detail) (Matisse). P 13½×14. (b) 125×100 mm. $6 "The Sampling Officials of the Drapers' Guild" (detail) (Rembrandt) (*horiz*). P 14×13½ Set of 2 sheets 7·00 8·00

(Litho Questa)

1994 (21 Jan). *25th Anniv of Spice Island Billfish Tournament. T* **388** *and similar vert designs. Multicoloured. P* 14.

2658	15 c. Type **388**	25	15
2659	25 c. Sailfish and angler	30	15
2660	35 c. Yellow-finned Tuna with angler	40	20
2661	50 c. White Marlin with angler	50	40
2662	75 c. Catching a Sailfish	65	65
2658/62	Set of 5	1·90	1·40

389 *National Flag and Ketch in Bay*   390 *Hygrocybe acutoconica*

(Litho Questa)

1994 (8 Feb). *25th Anniv of Independence. T* **389** *and similar vert design. Multicoloured. P* 14.

2663	35 c. Type **389**	15	20

MS2664 76×106 mm. $6 Map of Grenada .. 2·75 3·00

(Des W. Hanson. Litho Questa)

1994 (18 Feb). *"Hong Kong '94" International Stamp Exhibition (1st issue). Horiz designs as T* **317** *of Antigua. Multicoloured. P* 14.

2665	40 c. Hong Kong 1971 Scouting 50 c. stamp and "Hong Kong Post Office, 1846" (left detail) (M. Bruce)	20	25
	a. Horiz pair. Nos. 2665/6	40	50

2666	40 c. Grenada 1988 Rotary $2 and "Hong Kong Post Office, 1846" (right detail) (M. Bruce)	20	25

Nos. 2665/6 were printed together, *se-tenant*, in horizontal pairs throughout the sheet with the centre part of each pair forming the complete painting.

(Des Kerri Schiff. Litho Questa)

1994 (18 Feb). *"Hong Kong '94" International Stamp Exhibition (2nd issue). Qing Dynasty Porcelain. Multicoloured designs as T* **318** *of Antigua, but vert. P* 14.

2667	45 c. Vase with dragon decoration	20	25
	a. Sheetlet. Nos. 2667/72	1·10	
2668	45 c. Hat stand with brown base	20	25
2669	45 c. Gourd-shaped vase	20	25
2670	45 c. Rotating vase with openwork	20	25
2671	45 c. Candlestick with dogs	20	25
2672	45 c. Hat stand with orange base	20	25
2667/72	Set of 6	1·10	1·50

Nos. 2667/72 were printed together, *se-tenant*, in sheetlets of 6.

(Des Susan Carlson. Litho Questa)

1994 (6 Apr). *Fungi. T* **390** *and similar vert designs. Multicoloured. P* 14.

2673	35 c. Type **390**	15	20
2674	45 c. Leucopaxillus gracillimus	20	25
2675	50 c. Leptonia caeruleocapitata	25	30
2676	75 c. Leucocoprinus birnbaumii	35	40
2677	$1 Marasmius atrorubens	45	50
2678	$2 Boletellus cubensis	90	95
2679	$4 Chlorophyllum molybdites	1·90	2·00
2680	$5 Psilocybe cubensis	2·25	2·40
2673/80	Set of 8	6·25	7·00

MS2681 Two sheets, each 100×70 mm. (a) $6 Mycena pura. (b) $6 Pyrrhoglossum lilaceipes
.. .. Set of 2 sheets 5·50 5·75

391 *Quetzalcoatlus*   392 *Brassavola cuculatta*

(Des V. DiFate. Litho Questa)

1994 (13 Apr). *Prehistoric Animals. T* **391** *and similar multicoloured designs. P* 14.

2682	75 c. Type **391**	35	40
	a. Sheetlet. Nos. 2682/93	4·25	
2683	75 c. Pteranodon ingens	35	40
2684	75 c. Tropeognathus	35	40
2685	75 c. Phobetor	35	40
2686	75 c. Alamosaurus	35	40
2687	75 c. Triceratops	35	40
2688	75 c. Tyrannosaurus rex	35	40
2689	75 c. Head of Tyrannosaurus rex	35	40
2690	75 c. Lambeosaurus	35	40
2691	75 c. Spinosaurus	35	40
2692	75 c. Parasaurolophus	35	40
2693	75 c. Hadrosaurus	35	40
2694	75 c. Germanodactylus	35	40
	a. Sheetlet. Nos. 2694/705	4·25	
2695	75 c. Dimorphodon	35	40
2696	75 c. Ramphorynchus	35	40
2697	75 c. Apatosaurus	35	40
2698	75 c. Pterodactylus	35	40
2699	75 c. Stegosaurus	35	40
2700	75 c. Brachiosaurus	35	40
2701	75 c. Allosaurus	35	40
2702	75 c. Plesiosaurus	35	40
2703	75 c. Ceratosaurus	35	40
2704	75 c. Compsognathus	35	40
2705	75 c. Elaphosaurus	35	40
2682/705	Set of 24	8·25	9·50

MS2706 Two sheets. (a) 100×70 mm. $6 Pteranodon ingens (*different*). (b) 70×100 mm. $6 Head of Plateosaurus (*vert*) Set of 2 sheets 5·50 5·75
Nos. 2682/93 and 2694/705 were printed together, *se-tenant*, in sheetlets of 12 forming composite designs.

(Des W. Hanson. Litho B.D.T.)

1994 (4 Aug). *25th Anniv of First Moon Landing. Space Shuttle Challenger. Horiz designs as T* **326** *of Antigua. Multicoloured. P* 14.

2707	$2 Space Shuttle Challenger	90	95
	a. Sheetlet. Nos. 2707/12	5·25	
2708	$2 Judith Resnick (astronaut)	90	25
2709	$2 Aircraft in memorial fly past	90	25
2710	$2 Dick Scobee (astronaut)	90	25
2711	$2 Mission logo	90	25
2712	$2 Michael Smith (astronaut)	90	25
2707/12	Set of 6	5·25	5·50

MS2713 107×76 mm. $6 Challenger crew .. 2·75 3·00
Nos. 2707/12 were printed together, *se-tenant*, in sheetlets of 6.

(Litho Questa)

1994 (4 Aug). *Centenary of International Olympic Committee. Gold Medal Winners. Multicoloured designs as T* **327** *of Antigua, but vert. P* 14.

2714	50 c. Heike Dreschler (Germany) (long jump), 1992	25	30
2715	$1.50, Nadia Comaneci (Rumania) (gymnastics), 1976 and 1980	70	75

MS2716 107×76 mm. $6 Dan Jansen (U.S.A.) (1000 metre speed skating), 1994 .. 2·75 3·00

(Litho Questa)

994 (4 Aug). *International Year of the Family. Horiz design as T 328 of Antigua. Multicoloured. P 14.*
717 $1 Grenadian family 45 50

(Des J. Batchelor. Litho Questa)

994 (4 Aug). *50th Anniv of D-Day. Horiz designs as T 331 of Antigua. Multicoloured. P 14.*
718 40 c. Sherman amphibious tank leaving landing craft 20 25
719 $2 Tank on Churchill "Ark" bridging vehicle 90 95
720 $3 Churchill "Bobbin" tank laying roadway .. .. .. 1·40 1·50
718/20 .. .. .. *Set of 3* 2·40 2·50
MS2721 107×76 mm. $6 Churchill AVRE with fascine .. .. 2·75 3·00

(Des Kerri Schiff. Litho Questa (Nos. 2724/31, MS2733), B.D.T. (others))

1994 (4 Aug). *"Philakorea '94" International Stamp Exhibition, Seoul. Multicoloured designs as T 279 of Dominica. P 13¹/₂×14 (Nos. 2724/31) or 14 (others).*
2722 40 c. Wonson Park (*horiz*) 20 25
2723 $1 Pusan (*horiz*) 45 50
2724 $1 "Lady in a Hooded Cloak" (left detail) (Sin Yunbok) 45 50
   a. Sheetlet. Nos. 2724/31 .. 3·50
2725 $1 "Lady in a Hooded Cloak" (right detail) 45 50
2726 $1 "Kiaseng House" (left detail) (Sin Yunbok) 45 50
2727 $1 "Kiaseng House" (right detail) (Sin Yunbok) 45 50
2728 $1 "Amorous Youth on a Picnic" (left detail) (Sin Yunbok) .. 45 50
2729 $1 "Amorous Youth on a Picnic" (right detail) 45 50
2730 $1 "Chasing a Cat" (left detail) (Sin Yunbok) 45 50
2731 $1 "Chasing a Cat" (right detail) 45 50
2732 $4 Korean orchestra, National Theatre, Seoul (*horiz*) .. 1·90 2·00
2722/32 .. .. .. *Set of 11* 6·00 6·75
MS2733 70×102 mm. $6 "Roof Tiling" (detail) (Kim Hongdo). P 14 .. 2·75 3·00
Nos. 2724/31, each 26×49 mm, were printed together, *se-tenant*, in sheetlets of 8. Paintings are shown across horizontal pairs without white vertical margins in the centre.

(Des Claudia Sergeant. Litho Questa)

1994 (7 Aug). *Orchids. T 392 and similar vert designs. Multicoloured. P 14.*
2734 15 c. Type 392 .. .. 10 10
2735 25 c. Comparettia falcata 10 10
2736 45 c. Epidendrum ciliare .. 20 25
2737 75 c. Epidendrum cochleatum .. 35 40
2738 $1 Ionopsis utricularioides .. 45 50
2739 $2 Onicidium ceboletta .. 90 95
2740 $4 Onicidium luridium .. .. 1·90 2·00
2741 $5 Rodriquezia secunda .. 2·25 2·40
2734/41 .. .. .. *Set of 8* 6·25 6·50
MS2742 Two sheets, each 100×70 mm. (a) $6 Ionopsis utricularioides (*different*). (b) $6 Onicidium luridium (*different*) .. *Set of 2 sheets* 5·50 5·75
No. MS2742(b) is inscribed "Onicium luridum" in error.

393 Tony Meola (U.S.A.)   394 Yellow-tailed Snapper

(Litho Questa)

1994 (11 Aug). *World Cup Football Championship, U.S.A. (2nd issue). T 393 and similar vert designs. Multicoloured. P 14.*
2743 75 c. Type 393 .. .. 35 40
   a. Sheetlet. Nos. 2743/8 .. 2·00
2744 75 c. Steve Mark (Grenada) .. 35 40
2745 75 c. Gianluigi Lentini (Italy) .. 35 40
2746 75 c. Belloumi (Algeria) .. 35 40
2747 75 c. Nunoz (Spain) .. 35 40
2748 75 c. Lothar Matthaus (Germany) .. 35 40
2743/8 .. .. .. *Set of 6* 2·00 2·40
MS2749 Two sheets. (a) 99×70 mm. $6 World Cup Championship poster, 1930. (b) 70×114 mm. $6 Steve Mark (Grenada) (*different*) .. .. .. *Set of 2 sheets* 5·50 5·75
Nos. 2743/8 were printed together, *se-tenant*, in sheetlets of 6.

(Litho Questa)

1994 (1 Sept). *First Recipients of Order of the Caribbean Community. Horiz designs as Nos. 2046/8 of Antigua. Multicoloured. P 14.*
2750 15 c. Sir Shridath Ramphal .. 10 10
2751 65 c. William Demas 30 35
2752 $2 Derek Walcott 90 95
2750/2 .. .. .. *Set of 3* 1·25 1·40

(Des P. Gonzalez. Litho Questa)

1994 (1 Sept). *Fishes. T 394 and similar multicoloured designs. P 14.*
2753 15 c. Type 394 .. .. 10 10
2754 20 c. Blue Tang 10 10
2755 25 c. Porkfish (*vert*) .. 10 10
2756 75 c. Four-eyed Butterflyfish .. 35 40
2757 $1 Reid's Seahorse (*vert*) .. 45 50
2758 $2 Spotted Moray (*vert*) .. 90 95
2759 $4 Royal Gramma ("Fairy Basslet") 1·90 2·00
2760 $5 Queen Triggerfish (*vert*) .. 2·25 2·40
2753/60 .. .. .. *Set of 8* 6·00 6·50
MS2761 Two sheets, each 106×76 mm. (a) $6 Queen Angelfish. (b) $6 Long-spined Squirrelfish .. .. *Set of 2 sheets* 5·50 5·75

395 Mickey Mouse bathing Pluto   396 Anartia amathea

(Des Alvin White Studios. Litho Questa)

1994 (22 Sept). *Chinese New Year ("Year of the Dog"). T 395 and similar horiz designs showing Walt Disney cartoon characters. Multicoloured. P 14×13¹/₂.*
2762 2 c. Type 395 .. .. 10 10
2763 3 c. Dog taking mouthwash .. 10 10
2764 4 c. Dog with curlers in tail .. 10 10
2765 5 c. Brushing dog's eyelashes .. 10 10
2766 10 c. Giving dog manicure .. 10 10
2767 15 c. Mickey spraying Pluto with flea powder 10 10
2768 20 c. Dogs on display 10 10
2769 $4 Judge checking Pluto's teeth .. 1·90 2·00
2770 $5 Pluto wearing "1st Prize" rosette 2·25 2·40
2762/70 .. .. .. *Set of 9* 4·50 4·75
MS2771 Three sheets, each 127×102 mm. (a) $6 King Charles Spaniel rubbing against judge's leg. (b) $6 Pluto holding rosette. (c) $6 Pluto with No. 13 on coat .. .. *Set of 3 sheets* 8·25 8·50

(Des I. MacLaury. Litho Questa)

1994 (28 Sept)-96. *Butterflies. T 396 and similar vert designs. Multicoloured. A. Without imprint date. P 14. B. With imprint date ("1996"). P 12.*

		A		B	
2772	10 c. Type 396 ..	10	10	†	
2773	15 c. Marpesia petreus ..	10	10	†	
2774	25 c. Hylephila phylaeus ..	10	10	10	10
2775	35 c. Junonia evarete ..	15	20	15	20
2776	45 c. Pseudolycaena marsyas	20	25	†	
2777	50 c. Heliconius charitonius	25	30	†	
2778	75 c. Hypolimnas misippus ..	35	40	†	
2778c	90 c. Pyrgus oilcus ..	†		40	45
2779	$1 Cepheuptychia cephus ..	45	50	†	
2779c	$1.50, Allosmaitia piplea	†		70	75
2780	$2 Historis odius ..	90	95	†	
2781	$3 Phoebis philea ..	1·40	1·50	†	
2782	$4 Urbanus proteus ..	1·90	2·00	†	
2783	$5 Battus polydamas ..	2·25	2·40	†	
2784	$10 Philaethria dido ..	4·50	4·75	†	
2785	$20 Hamadryas arethusa ..	9·25	9·50	†	
2772A/85A	*Set of 14*	21·00	23·00		
2774B/9cB	*Set of 4*			1·25	1·40

Dates of issue:—28.9.94, Nos. 2772A/85A; 7.11.96, Nos. 2774B/5B, 2778cB, 2779cB.

(Litho Questa)

1994 (5 Dec). *Christmas. Religious Paintings by Francisco de Zurbaran. Multicoloured designs as T 336 of Antigua. P 13¹/₂×14.*
2786 10 c. "The Virgin and Child with St. John" (1658) 10 10
2787 15 c. "The Circumcision" 10 10
2788 25 c. "Adoration of St. Joseph" .. 10 10
2789 35 c. "Adoration of the Magi" .. 15 20
2790 75 c. "The Portiuncula" 35 40
2791 $1 "The Virgin and Child with St. John" (1662) 45 50
2792 $2 "The Virgin and Child with St. John" (1658/64) 90 95
2793 $4 "The Flight into Egypt" .. 1·90 2·00
2786/93 .. .. .. *Set of 8* 4·00 4·25
MS2794 Two sheets. (a) 74×86 mm. $6 "Our Lady of Ransom and Two Mercedarians" (detail). P 13¹/₂×14. (b) 114×100 mm. $6 "Adoration of the Shepherds" (detail) (*horiz*). P 14×13¹/₂ .. .. .. *Set of 2 sheets* 5·50 5·75

397 Grenada Dove on Nest

(Litho Questa)

1995 (10 Jan). *Birds. T 397 and similar multicoloured designs. P 14.*
2795 25 c. Type 397 .. .. 10 10
2796 35 c. Pair of Grenada Doves at nest 15 20
2797 45 c. Cuban Tody (*vert*) .. 20 25
2798 75 c. Grenada Dove on branch (*vert*) 35 40
2799 75 c. Painted Bunting .. 35 40
2800 $1 Grenada Dove in flight (*vert*) 45 50
2801 $1 Red-legged Honeycreeper .. 45 50
2802 $5 Green Jay .. .. 2·25 2·40
2795/802 .. .. .. *Set of 8* 4·25 4·75
MS2803 Two sheets, each 101×71 mm. (a) $6 Chaffinch. (b) $6 Chestnut-sided Shrike Vireo .. .. *Set of 2 sheets* 5·50 5·75
Nos. 2795/6, 2798 and 2800 also show the W.W.F. Panda emblem.

(Des A. Melville-Brown. Litho Questa)

1995 (12 Jan). *Centenary of First English Cricket Tour to the West Indies. Multicoloured designs as T 329 of Antigua. P 14.*
2804 25 c. Junior Murray (West Indies) (*vert*) 10 10
2805 35 c. Richie Richardson (West Indies) (*vert*) 15 20
2806 $2 Alex Stewart (England) and Wisden Trophy 90 95
2804/6 .. .. .. *Set of 3* 1·10 1·25
MS2807 75×95 mm. $3 West Indian team, 1994 1·40 1·50

398 Hooded Merganser

(Litho Questa)

1995 (27 Mar). *Water Birds of the World. T 398 and similar horiz designs. Multicoloured. P 14.*
2808 25 c. Type 398 .. .. 10 10
2809 35 c. Green-winged Teal .. 15 20
2810 75 c. King Eider 35 40
   a. Sheetlet. Nos. 2810/21 4·25
2811 75 c. Common Shoveler .. 35 40
2812 75 c. Long-tailed Duck .. 35 40
2813 75 c. Chiloe Wigeon .. 35 40
2814 75 c. Red-breasted Merganser .. 35 40
2815 75 c. Falcated Teal .. 35 40
2816 75 c. Versicolor Teal .. 35 40
2817 75 c. Smew 35 40
2818 75 c. Red-crested Pochard .. 35 40
2819 75 c. Pintail 35 40
2820 75 c. Barrow's Goldeneye .. 35 40
2821 75 c. Stellar's Eider .. 35 40
2822 $1 Harlequin Duck .. 45 50
2823 $3 European Wigeon .. 1·40 1·50
2808/23 .. .. .. *Set of 16* 6·25 7·00
MS2824 Two sheets, each 74×104 mm. (a) $5 Common Shelduck ("European Wigeon"). (b) $6 Egyptian Goose .. .. *Set of 2 sheets* 5·00 5·25
Nos. 2810/21 were printed together, *se-tenant*, in sheetlets of 12 with the background forming a composite design.
No. 2811 is inscribed "Shobeler" in error.

399 Pig Priest, China   400 Yellow-tailed Damselfish

(Des R. Sauber. Litho Questa)

1995 (21 Apr). *Chinese New Year ("Year of the Pig"). T 399 and similar vert designs showing ornaments. Multicoloured. P 14.*
2825 50 c. Type 399 .. .. 25 30
   a. Horiz strip of 3. Nos. 2825/7 1·00
2826 75 c. Porcelain pig, Scotland .. 35 40
2827 $1 Seated porcelain pig, Italy .. 45 50
2825/7 .. .. .. *Set of 3* 1·00 1·25
MS2828 107×77 mm. $2 Jade pig, China 90 95
Nos. 2825/7 were printed together, *se-tenant*, in horizontal strips of 3 throughout the sheet.

(Des D. Burkhart. Litho Questa)

1995 (24 Apr). *Marine Life. T 400 and similar horiz designs. Multicoloured. P 14.*
2829 $1 Type 400 .. .. 45 40
   a. Sheetlet. Nos. 2829/34 2·75
2830 $1 Blue-headed Wrasse .. 45 50
2831 $1 Balloonfish 45 50
2832 $1 Shy Hamlet 45 50
2833 $1 Orange Tube Coral .. 45 50
2834 $1 Rock Beauty 45 50
2835 $1 Creole Wrasse .. 45 50
   a. Sheetlet. Nos. 2835/43 4·00
2836 $1 Queen Angelfish .. 45 50
2837 $1 Trumpetfish 45 50
2838 $1 Barred Hamlet .. 45 50
2839 $1 Tube Sponge 45 50
2840 $1 Porcupine Fish .. 45 50
2841 $1 Firecoral 45 50

2842	$1 Royal Gramma ("Fairy Basslet")	..	45	50
2843	$1 Sea Anemone ..	..	45	50
2829/43		*Set of 15*	6·75	7·50

MS2844 Two sheets, each 106×76 mm. (a) $5
Seahorse. (b) $6 Elkhorn Coral .. *Set of 2 sheets* 5·00 5·25
Nos. 2829/34 and 2835/43 were printed together, *se-tenant*, in sheetlets of 6 (with narrow horizontal gutter) (Nos. 2829/34) or 9 (Nos. 2835/43) forming composite designs.

401 National Flags **402** Cocker
Spaniel

(Litho Questa)

1995 (27 Apr). *Grenada–Taiwan (Republic of China) Friendship. T* **401** *and similar horiz design. Multicoloured.* P 14.

2845	75 c. Type **401**	..	35	40
2846	$1 Prime Minister Brathwaite and President Lee Teng-hui	..	45	50

MS2847 76×106 mm. Nos. 2845/6 .. 80 90

(Des D. Burkhart. Litho Questa)

1995 (3 May). *Domestic Animals. T* **402** *and similar vert designs. Multicoloured.* P 14.

2848	10 c. Type **402**	..	10	10
2849	15 c. Pinto (horse)	..	10	10
2850	25 c. Rottweiler	..	10	10
2851	35 c. German Shepherd	..	15	20
2852	45 c. Persian (cat)	..	20	25
2853	50 c. Snowshoe (cat)	..	25	30
2854	75 c. Percheron (horse)	..	35	40
2855	$1 Scottish Fold (cat)	..	45	50
2856	$2 Arabian (horse)	..	90	95
2857	$3 Andalusian (horse)	..	1·40	1·50
2858	$4 C.P. Shorthair (cat)	..	1·90	2·00
2859	$5 Chihuahua	..	2·25	2·40
2848/59		*Set of 12*	8·00	8·75

MS2860 Three sheets, each 100×71 mm. (a) $5
Manx (cat). (b) $5 Donkey. (c) $6 Shar Pei
Set of 3 sheets 7·25 7·50

(Litho Questa)

1995 (5 May). *Centenary of Sierra Club (environmental protection society) (1992). Endangered Species. Multicoloured designs as T* **320** *of Antigua.* P 14.

2861	$1 Head of Margay at night	..	45	50
	a. Sheetlet. Nos. 2861/9 ..	..	4·00	
2862	$1 Margay sitting	..	45	50
2863	$1 Head of Margay in daylight	..	45	50
2864	$1 Head of Andean Condor	..	45	50
2865	$1 Andean Condor facing right	..	45	50
2866	$1 Andean Condor facing left	..	45	50
2867	$1 White-faced Saki on branch	..	45	50
2868	$1 White-faced Saki showing mane	..	45	50
2869	$1 Patagonia landscape	..	45	50
2870	$1 Lesser Rheas feeding (*horiz*)	..	45	50
	a. Sheetlet. Nos. 2870/8 ..	..	4·00	
2871	$1 Pair of Lesser Rheas (*horiz*)	..	45	50
2872	$1 Lesser Rhea (*horiz*)	..	45	50
2873	$1 Sunset over snow-covered mountains, Patagonia (*horiz*)	..	45	50
2874	$1 Volcanic eruption, Patagonia (*horiz*)	..	45	50
2875	$1 White-faced Saki (*horiz*)	..	45	50
2876	$1 Common Caracara on branch (*horiz*)	..	45	50
2877	$1 Pair of Common Caracaras at nest (*horiz*)	..	45	50
2878	$1 Common Caracara facing left (*horiz*)	..	45	50
2861/78		*Set of 18*	8·00	9·00

Nos. 2861/9 and 2870/8 were printed together, *se-tenant*, in sheetlets of 9.

403 Grenadian Scout **404** "Swords into
Ploughshares"

(Litho Questa)

1995 (8 May). *18th World Scout Jamboree, Netherlands. T* **403** *and similar horiz designs. Multicoloured.* P 14.

2879	75 c. Type **403**	..	35	40
	a. Horiz strip of 3. Nos. 2879/81		1·75	
2880	$1 Scout abseiling	..	45	50
2881	$2 Scout saluting and national flag	..	90	95
2879/81		*Set of 3*	1·75	1·90

MS2882 107×77 mm. $6 Scouts in canoe .. 2·75 3·00
Nos. 2879/81 were printed together in sheets of 9 containing three *se-tenant* horizontal strips of 3.

(Des W. Wright. Litho Questa)

1995 (8 May). *50th Anniv of End of Second World War in Europe. Fighter Aircraft. Horiz designs as T* **340** *of Antigua. Multicoloured.* P 14.

2883	$2 Lavochkin La-7 (fighter)	..	90	95
	a. Sheetlet. Nos. 2883/90	..	7·00	
2884	$2 Hawker Hurricane	..	90	95
2885	$2 North American P-51D Mustang	..	90	95
2886	$2 Messerschmitt Bf 109	..	90	95
2887	$2 Bristol Type 152 Beaufighter	..	90	95
2888	$2 Messerschmitt Me 262	..	90	95
2889	$2 Republic P-47 Thunderbolt	..	90	95
2890	$2 Hawker Tempest	..	90	95
2883/90		*Set of 8*	7·00	7·50

MS2891 106×76 mm. $6 Nose of Republic P-47
Thunderbolt .. .. 2·75 3·00
Nos. 2883/90 were printed together, *se-tenant*, in sheetlets of 8 with the stamps arranged in two horizontal strips of 4 separated by a gutter showing a dogfight.

(Des J. Iskowitz. Litho Questa)

1995 (8 May). *50th Anniv of United Nations. T* **404** *and similar multicoloured designs.* P 14.

2892	75 c. Type **404**	..	35	40
	a. Horiz strip of 3. Nos. 2892/4		1·60	
2893	$1 Globe and dove	..	45	50
2894	$2 U.N. Building, New York	..	90	95
2892/4		*Set of 3*	1·60	1·75

MS2895 101×71 mm. $6 Anniversary logo
(*horiz*) .. .. 2·75 3·00
Nos. 2892/4 were printed together in sheets of 9 containing three *se-tenant* horizontal strips of 3.

405 Woman with **406** National Flag
Baskets and Rotary Logo

(Des J. Iskowitz. Litho Questa)

1995 (8 May). *50th Anniv of Food and Agriculture Organization. T* **405** *and similar vert designs. Multicoloured.* P 14.

2896	75 c. Type **405**	..	35	40
	a. Horiz strip of 3. Nos. 2896/8		1·60	
2897	$1 Boy with basket on head	..	45	50
2898	$2 Men harvesting bananas	..	90	95
2896/8		*Set of 3*	1·60	1·75

MS2899 72×102 mm. $6 F.A.O. logo .. 2·75 3·00
Nos. 2896/8 were printed together in sheets of 9 containing three *se-tenant* horizontal strips of 3.

(Litho Questa)

1995 (8 May). *90th Anniv of Rotary International. T* **406** *and similar vert design. Multicoloured.* P 14.

2900	$5 Type **406**	..	2·25	2·40

MS2901 76×106 mm. $6 Paul Harris (founder)
and logo .. .. 2·75 3·00

(Litho Questa)

1995 (8 May). *95th Birthday of Queen Elizabeth the Queen Mother. Vert designs as T* **344** *of Antigua.* P 13½×14.

2902	$1.50, orange-brown, pale brown and black	..	70	75
	a. Sheetlet. Nos. 2902/5×2		5·50	
2903	$1.50, multicoloured	..	70	75
2904	$1.50, multicoloured	..	70	75
2905	$1.50, multicoloured	..	70	75
2902/5		*Set of 4*	2·75	3·00

MS2906 127×102 mm. $6 multicoloured .. 2·75 3·00
Designs:—No. 2902, Queen Elizabeth the Queen Mother (pastel drawing); No. 2903, Holding rose; No. 2904, At desk (oil painting); No. 2905, In blue hat and white coat; No. **MS**2906, Wearing floral hat.
Nos. 2902/5 were printed together in sheetlets of 8, containing two *se-tenant* horizontal strips of 4.

(Des J. Batchelor. Litho Questa)

1995 (8 May). *50th Anniv of End of Second World War in the Pacific. Horiz designs as T* **340** *of Antigua. Multicoloured.* P 14.

2907	$2 Dogfight over the Marianas	..	90	95
	a. Sheetlet. Nos. 2907/12	..	5·25	
2908	$2 U.S. dive-bomber and burning aircraft carrier, Battle of Midway	..	90	95
2909	$2 U.S. aircraft attacking Japanese transport, Battle of the Bismarck Sea	..	90	95
2910	$2 *Mushashi* (Japanese battleship) on fire in Leyte Gulf	..	90	95
2911	$2 U.S. aircraft taking off from Henderson Field	..	90	95
2912	$2 Battleships at Guadalcanal	..	90	95
2907/12		*Set of 6*	5·25	5·50

MS2913 108×77 mm. $6 U.S. bomber .. 2·75 3·00
No. 2907/12 were printed together, *se-tenant*, in sheetlets of 6 with the stamp arranged in two horizontal strips of 3 separated by a gutter showing Doolittle's B-25 *Ruptured Duck* leaving U.S.S. *Hornet*.

---

407 Tian Bingyi **408** Junior Murray
(China) (badminton) (West Indies)

(Litho B.D.T.)

1995 (23 June). *Olympic Games, Atlanta (1996) (1st issue). T* **407** *and similar vert designs. Multicoloured.* P 14.

2914	75 c. Type **407**	..	35	40
	a. Horiz strip of 4. Nos. 2914/17	..	1·40	
2915	75 c. Waldemar Leigien (Poland) and Frank Wieneke (West Germany) (judo)	..	35	40
2916	75 c. Nelli Kim (U.S.S.R) (gymnastics)	..	35	40
2917	75 c. Alessandro Andri (Italy) (shot put)	..	35	40
2918	$2 Jackie Joyner (U.S.A.) (heptathlon)	..	90	95
	a. Horiz strip of 4. Nos. 2918/21	..	3·50	
2919	$2 Mitsuo Tsukahara (Japan) (gymnastics)	..	90	95
2920	$2 Flo Hyman (U.S.A.) and Zhang Rung Fang (China) (volleyball)	..	90	95
2921	$2 Steffi Graf (West Germany) (tennis)	..	90	95
2914/21		*Set of 8*	5·00	5·25

MS2922 Two sheets, each 72×102 mm. (a) $6
Wilma Rudolph (U.S.A.) (athletics). (b) $6 Soling
class yacht .. .. *Set of 2 sheets* 5·50 5·75
Nos. 2914/17 and 2918/21 were printed together in sheets of 12 containing three *se-tenant* strips of 4.
No. **MS**2922(b) is inscribed "Sailing" in error.
See also Nos. 3102/24.

(Litho Questa)

1995 (18 Aug). *Anniversaries and Events. T* **408** *and similar vert designs. Multicoloured.* P 14.

2923	25 c. Type **408** (Centenary of first English cricket tour to the West Indies)	..	10	10
2924	75 c. Nutmeg (Opening of Grenada Spice Factory)	..	35	40
2925	$1 Sendall Tunnel (Centenary (1994))	..	45	50
2926	$1 Caribbean Development Bank building (25th anniv)	..	45	50
2923/6		*Set of 4*	1·25	1·50

409 Ajamu **410** Elvis Presley
and Signature

(Litho Questa)

1995 (5 Sept). *Local Entertainers. T* **409** *and similar vert designs. Multicoloured.* P 14.

2927	35 c. Type **409**	..	15	20
2928	35 c. Mighty Sparrow	..	15	20
2929	50 c. Mighty Sparrow in evening dress	..	25	30
2930	75 c. Ajamu (*different*)	..	35	40
2927/30		*Set of 4*	90	1·10

(Des Y. Lee. Litho Questa)

1995 (5 Sept). *Entertainment Legends. T* **410** *and similar vert design. Multicoloured.* P 14.

2931	75 c. Type **410**	..	35	40
2932	75 c. Marilyn Monroe	..	35	40

Nos. 2931/2 were each issued in numbered sheets of 16 including an enlarged illustrated right-hand margin.

411 Elvis Presley

(Des Isabelle Tanner. Litho Questa)

1995 (5 Sept). *60th Birth Anniv of Elvis Presley (singer). T 411 and similar vert designs. Multicoloured. P 14.*

2933	$1 Type 411		45	50
	a. Sheetlet. Nos. 2933/41		4·00	
2934	$1 With beard		45	50
2935	$1 With long hair and microphone		45	50
2936	$1 Wearing white shirt		45	50
2937	$1 Wearing pink shirt and purple jacket		45	50
2938	$1 With short hair and microphone		45	50
2939	$1 Wearing magenta shirt		45	50
2940	$1 Wearing orange shirt		45	50
2941	$1 Wearing purple shirt		45	50
2933/41		Set of 9	4·00	4·50

Nos. 2933/41 were printed together, *se-tenant*, in sheetlets of 9.

412 Film Reel and Oscar Statuette

(Des J. Rosata. Litho Questa)

1995 (5 Sept). *Centenary of Cinema. T 412 and similar multicoloured designs. P 13½×14.*

2942	$1 Type 412		45	50
	a. Sheetlet. Nos. 2942/50		4·00	
2943	$1 "HOLLYWOOD" sign		45	50
2944	$1 Charlie Chaplin		45	50
2945	$1 Shirley Temple		45	50
2946	$1 Spencer Tracy and Katherine Hepburn		45	50
2947	$1 Marilyn Monroe		45	50
2948	$1 John Wayne		45	50
2949	$1 Marlon Brando		45	50
2950	$1 Tom Cruise		45	50
2942/50		Set of 9	4·00	4·50
MS2951	107×77 mm. $5 Orson Welles (*horiz*). P 14×13½		2·25	2·40

Nos. 2942/50 were printed together, *se-tenant*, in sheetlets of 9 forming a composite design.

413 "B1 Level Vista Dome" Electric Locomotive, Japan   414 Teresa Teng

(Des D. Miller. Litho Questa)

1995 (5 Sept). *Trains of the World (1st series). T 413 and similar horiz designs. Multicoloured. P 14.*

2952	$1 Type 413		45	50
	a. Sheetlet. Nos. 2952/60		4·00	
2953	$1 Rolios Rail steam locomotive, South Africa		45	50
2954	$1 Class "460 BO BO" electric locomotive, Switzerland		45	50
2955	$1 Central Line diesel locomotive, Peru		45	50
2956	$1 "X2000" tilt body train, Sweden		45	50
2957	$1 Toronto to Vancouver train, Canada		45	50
2958	$1 Intercity 125 diesel locomotive, Great Britain		45	50
2959	$1 The Flying Scotsman steam locomotive, Great Britain		45	50
2960	$1 Indian Pacific diesel locomotive, Australia		45	50
2961	$1 "ETR 450" electric train, Italy		45	50
	a. Sheetlet. Nos. 2961/9		4·00	
2962	$1 Isparta to Bozanonu Line steam locomotive, Turkey		45	50
2963	$1 "TGV" train, France		45	50
2964	$1 "ICE" train, Germany		45	50
2965	$1 Nishi Line electric locomotive, Japan		45	50
2966	$1 "Bullet Train", Japan		45	50
2967	$1 Central Pacific Jupiter steam locomotive, U.S.A.		45	50
2968	$1 "AMTRAK 900 BO BO" electric locomotive, U.S.A.		45	50
2969	$1 Sir Nigel Gresley steam locomotive, Great Britain		45	50
2952/69		Set of 18	8·00	9·00
MS2970	Two sheets, each 106×76 mm. (a) $5 Diesel hydraulic train, Korea. (b) $6 Trans-Mongolian train, China		5·00	5·25	Set of 2 sheets

Nos. 2952/60 and 2961/9 (which include the "Singapore '95" International Stamp Exhibition logo) were printed together, *se-tenant*, in sheetlets of 9.
See also No. 3167/83.

(Litho Questa)

1995 (29 Sept). *Teresa Teng (Chinese actress) Commemoration. T 414 and similar vert designs showing different portraits. Multicoloured unless otherwise indicated. P 14 (Nos. 2971/86) or 13½×14 (others).*

2971	35 c. Type 414		30	30
	a. Sheetlet. Nos. 2971/86		4·25	
2972	35 c. As a child (agate, ochre & orge-yellow)		30	30
2973	35 c. Wearing feather boa (black, pale grey and orange-yellow)		30	30
2974	35 c. With motor scooter		30	30
2975	35 c. Holding microphone		30	30
2976	35 c. In white sweater		30	30
2977	35 c. Playing flute		30	30
2978	35 c. With hand to hair (black, pale grey and orange-yellow)		30	30
2979	35 c. Wearing gold decorated dress		30	30
2980	35 c. With fan		30	30
2981	35 c. As South-sea islander		30	30
2982	35 c. With hands clasped		30	30
2983	35 c. In kimono		30	30
2984	35 c. Holding bow tie		30	30
2985	35 c. Wearing black blouse		30	30
2986	35 c. Resting on chair arm		30	30
2987	75 c. In army uniform		45	45
	a. Sheetlet. Nos. 2987/95		3·50	
2988	75 c. In navy uniform		45	45
2989	75 c. In air force uniform		45	45
2990	75 c. Singing with hand outstretched (black, pale grey and orange-yellow)		45	45
2991	75 c. Singing with flower in hair		45	45
2992	75 c. Singing in blue floral dress		45	45
2993	75 c. With pink scarf		45	45
2994	75 c. In fringed dress		45	45
2995	75 c. In pale green sweater		45	45
2996	75 c. With hands to face		45	45
2971/96		Set of 26	8·00	8·00

Nos. 2987/96 are larger, 34×46 mm.
Nos. 2971/86 and 2987/95 were each printed together, *se-tenant*, in sheetlets of 16 with a large illustrated margin at right (Nos. 2971/86), or 9 (Nos. 2987/95).

415 Mickey Mouse fighting Big Pete   416 Albert Michelson (1907 Physics)

(Des Walt Disney Company and Rosemary DeFiglio. Litho Questa)

1995 (2 Oct). *Mickey's Pirate Adventure. T 415 and similar vert designs showing Walt Disney cartoon characters. Multicoloured. P 13½×14.*

2997	15 c. Type 415		10	10
2998	25 c. Mickey with treasure chest		10	10
2999	35 c. Minnie Mouse trying on plunder		15	20
3000	75 c. Goofy with telescope and Mickey swimming with barrel		35	40
3001	$3 Big Pete		1·40	1·50
3002	$5 Mickey and monkey, seagull and handkerchief		2·25	2·40
2997/3002		Set of 6	4·25	4·50
MS3003	Two sheets, each 108×130 mm. (a) $6 Sea rat pirate. (b) $6 Minnie being thrown overboard by pirates		5·50	5·75	Set of 2 sheets

(Des B. DuRand. Litho Questa)

1995 (18 Oct). *Centenary of Nobel Trust Fund. T 416 and similar vert designs. Multicoloured. P 14.*

3004	$1 Type 416		45	50
	a. Sheetlet. Nos. 3004/12		4·00	
3005	$1 Ralph Bunche (1950 Peace)		45	50
3006	$1 Edwin Neher (1991 Medicine)		45	50
3007	$1 Klaus Vonklitzing (1985 Physics)		45	50
3008	$1 Johann Deisenhofer (1988 Chemistry)		45	50
3009	$1 Max Delbruck (1969 Medicine)		45	50
3010	$1 J. Georg Bednorz (1987 Physics)		45	50
3011	$1 Feodor Lynen (1964 Medicine)		45	50
3012	$1 Walther Bothe (1954 Physics)		45	50
3013	$1 James Franck (1925 Physics)		45	50
	a. Sheetlet. Nos. 3013/21		4·00	
3014	$1 Gustav Hertz (1925 Physics)		45	50
3015	$1 Friedrich Bergius (1931 Chemistry)		45	50
3016	$1 Otto Loewi (1936 Medicine)		45	50
3017	$1 Fritz Lipmann (1953 Medicine)		45	50
3018	$1 Otto Meyerhof (1922 Medicine)		45	50
3019	$1 Paul Heyse (1910 Literature)		45	50
3020	$1 Jane Addams (1931 Peace)		45	50
3021	$1 Carl Braun (1909 Physics)		45	50
3022	$1 Hans Dehmelt (1989 Physics)		45	50
	a. Sheetlet. Nos. 3022/30		4·00	
3023	$1 Heinrich Böll (1972 Literature)		45	50
3024	$1 Georges Köhler (1984 Medicine)		45	50
3025	$1 Wolfgang Pauli (1945 Physics)		45	50
3026	$1 Sir Bernard Katz (1970 Medicine)		45	50
3027	$1 Ernest Ruska (1986 Physics)		45	50
3028	$1 William Golding (1983 Literature)		45	50
3029	$1 Hartmut Michel (1988 Chemistry)		45	50
3030	$1 Hans Bethe (1967 Physics)		45	50
3004/30		Set of 27	12·00	13·50
MS3031	Three sheets, each 105×76 mm. (a) $6 Theodore Roosevelt (1906 Peace). (b) $6 Woodrow Wilson (1919 Peace). (c) $6 Sir Winston Churchill (1953 Literature)		8·25	8·50	Set of 3 sheets

Nos. 3004/12, 3013/21 and 3022/30 were each printed together, *se-tenant*, in sheetlets of 9 forming composite designs.
No. 3015 is inscribed "Freidrich" in error.

(Litho Questa)

1995 (28 Nov). *Christmas. Religious Paintings. Vert designs as T 357 of Antigua. Multicoloured. P 13½×14.*

3032	15 c. "The Madonna" (Bartolommeo Montagna)		10	10
3033	25 c. "Sacred Conversation Piece" (Bonifacio dei Pitati)		10	10
3034	35 c. "Nativity" (Van Loo)		15	20
3035	75 c. "Madonna of the Fountain" (Van Eyck)		35	40
3036	$2 "The Apparition of the Virgin to St. Philip Neri" (Giovanni Tiepolo)		90	95
3037	$5 "The Holy Family" (Ribera)		2·25	2·40
3032/7		Set of 6	3·75	4·00
MS3038	Two sheets. (a) 127×101 mm. $6 "Madonna and Child" (detail) (Van Dyck). (b) 101×127 mm. $6 "The Vision of St. Anthony" (detail) (Van Dyck)		5·50	5·75	Set of 2 sheets

417 Pres. Ronald Reagan at Fort George   418 Pres. Ronald Reagan

(Des J. Iskowitz. Litho Questa)

1995 (8 Dec). *12th Anniv of Liberation of Grenada (1st issue). T 417 and similar horiz designs. Multicoloured. P 14.*

3039	75 c. Type 417		35	40
	a. Horiz strip of 3. Nos. 3039/41		1·10	
3040	75 c. Pres. Reagan with U.S. and Grenadian flags		35	40
3041	75 c. St. George's		35	40
3039/41		Set of 3	1·10	1·25
MS3042	Two sheets, each 70×100 m. (a) $5 Pres. Reagan and beach. (b) $6 Pres Reagan and waterfall		5·00	5·25	Set of 2 sheets

Nos. 3039/41 were printed in sheets of 9 containing three *se-tenant* horizontal strips, each strip forming a composite design.

(Litho Questa)

1995 (8 Dec). *12th Anniv of Liberation of Grenada (2nd issue). T 418 and similar vert designs each showing Ronald Reagan. Multicoloured. P 13½×14.*

3043	$1 With wife		45	50
	a. Sheetlet. Nos. 3043/51		4·00	
3044	$1 Type 418		45	50
3045	$1 With microphones		45	50
3046	$1 Wearing stetson		45	50
3047	$1 In front of U.S. flag		45	50
3048	$1 In front of Brandenburg Gate, Berlin		45	50
3049	$1 Saluting by helicopter		45	50
3050	$1 On horseback		45	50
3051	$1 Addressing troops		45	50
3043/51		Set of 9	4·00	4·50

Nos. 3043/51 were printed together, *se-tenant*, in sheetlets of 9 with an enlarged illustrated right margin.

419 Pope John Paul II and Statue of Liberty   420 Rat asleep

(Des R. Rundo. Litho Questa)

1995 (13 Dec). *Papal Visit to New York. T 419 and similar vert designs. Multicoloured. P 14.*

3052	$1 Type 419		45	50
3053	$1 Pope John Paul II and cathedral		45	50
MS3054	105×76mm. $6 Pope John Paul II		2·75	3·00

Nos. 3052/3 were printed separately in sheets of 9 with enlarged illustrated margin at right.
A $30 value embossed on gold foil exists from a limited printing.

(Des Y. Lee. Litho Questa)

1996 (2 Jan). *Chinese New Year ("Year of the Rat"). T 420 and similar designs. P 14.*

3055	420	75 c. buff, brown-olive and deep brown	35	40
		a. Horiz strip of 3. Nos. 3055/7	1·10	
3056	–	75 c. salmon, deep rose-red & dp violet	35	40
3057	–	75 c. buff, dull verm & blackish green	35	40
3055/7		Set of 3	1·10	1·25
MS3058	95×58 mm. Nos. 3055/7		1·10	1·25
MS3059	76×106 mm. $1 multicoloured		45	50

Designs: *Vert*—No. 3056, Rat eating; No. 3057, Rat asleep (T 420 reversed). *Horiz*—No. MS3059, Two rats.
Nos. 3055/7 were printed together, *se-tenant*, in horizontal strips of 3 throughout the sheet.

421 "Young Woman" (Dürer)

(Litho Questa)

1996 (29 Jan). *Famous Drawings and Paintings by Dürer and Rubens. T* **421** *and similar vert designs. P* 13½×14.
3060	15 c. Type **421**	10	10
3061	25 c. "Four Horsemen of the Apocalypse" (Dürer)	10	15
3062	35 c. "Assumption and Coronation of the Virgin" (Dürer)	15	20
3063	75 c. "Mulay Ahmed" (Rubens)	35	40
3064	$1 "Anthony van Dyck aged 15" (Rubens)	45	50
3065	$2 "Head of a Young Monk" (Rubens)	90	95
3066	$3 "A Scholar inspired by Nature" (Rubens)	1·40	1·50
3067	$5 "Hanns Dürer" (Dürer)	2·25	2·40
3060/7	*Set of* 8	5·50	6·00

MS3068 Two sheets, each 102×127 mm. (a) $5 "Martyrdom of St. Ursula" (detail) (Rubens). (b) $6 "The Death of the Virgin" (detail) (Dürer) *Set of* 2 *sheets* 5·00 5·25

422 Goofy tap-dancing

(Litho Questa)

1996 (26 Feb). *Famous Dances. T* **422** *and similar multi-coloured designs showing Walt Disney cartoon characters dancing. P* 13½×14 (*vert*) *or* 14×13½ (*horiz*).
3069	35 c. Type **422**	15	20
3070	45 c. Donald Duck doing Mexican hat dance (*horiz*)	20	25
3071	75 c. Daisy Duck as hula dancer (*horiz*)	35	40
3072	90 c. Mickey and Minnie Mouse doing the tango (*horiz*)	40	45
3073	$1 Donald and Daisy doing the jitterbug	45	50
3074	$2 Mickey and Minnie performing Ukrainian folk dance (*horiz*)	90	95
3075	$3 Goofy and Pluto as ballet dancers (*horiz*)	1·40	1·50
3076	$4 Mickey and Minnie line-dancing	1·90	2·00
3069/76	*Set of* 8	5·75	6·25

MS3077 Two sheets, each 133×109 mm. (a) $5 Minnie doing the can-can (*horiz*). (b) $6 Scrooge McDuck doing Scottish sword dance *Set of* 2 *sheets* 5·00 5·25

(Litho Questa)

1996 (8 May). *70th Birthday of Queen Elizabeth II. Vert designs as T* **364** *of Antigua showing different photographs. Multicoloured. P* 13½×14.
3078	35 c. As Type **364** of Antigua	15	20
	a. Strip of 3. Nos. 3078/80	2·40	
3079	75 c. Wearing white hat	35	40
3080	$4 With bouquet	1·90	2·00
3078/80	*Set of* 3	2·40	2·50

MS3081 103×125 mm. $6 Queen and Prince Philip 2·75 3·00
Nos. 3078/80 were printed together, *se-tenant*, in horizontal and vertical strips of 3 throughout the sheet.

423 Ferrari "125 F1"   **424** Lions' Gate, Jerusalem

(Des W. Wright. Litho)

1996 (8 May). *Ferrari Racing Cars. T* **423** *and similar horiz designs. Multicoloured. P* 14.
3082	$1.50, Type **423**	70	75
	a. Sheetlet. Nos. 3082/7	4·00	
3083	$1.50, "Tipo 625"	70	75
3084	$1.50, "P4"	70	75
3085	$1.50, "312P"	70	75
3086	$1.50, "312" Formula 1	70	75
3087	$1.50, "312B"	70	75
3082/7	*Set of* 6	4·00	4·50

MS3088 100×71 mm. $6 "F333 SP" (84×28 *mm*) 2·75 3·00
Nos. 3082/7 were printed together, *se-tenant* in sheetlets of 6, which include the "CHINA '96" International Stamp Exhibition logo on the margin.

(Litho Questa)

1996 (26 June). *50th Anniv of U.N.I.C.E.F. Multicoloured designs as T* **366** *of Antigua. P* 14.
3089	35 c. Child writing in book (*horiz*)	15	20
3090	$2 Child planting seedling (*horiz*)	90	95
3091	$3 Children and U.N.I.C.E.F. emblem (*horiz*)	1·40	1·50
3089/91	*Set of* 3	2·40	2·50

MS3092 75×106 mm. $5 Young boy 2·25 2·40

(Des Rachel Deitch. Litho Questa)

1996 (26 June). *3,000th Anniv of Jerusalem. T* **424** *and similar multicoloured designs. P* 14.
3093	75 c. Type **424**	35	40
3094	$2 New Gate	90	95
3095	$3 Dung Gate	1·40	1·50
3093/5	*Set of* 3	2·50	2·75

MS3096 114×74 mm. $5 The Old City (*horiz*) 2·25 2·40

(Des J. Iskowitz. Litho Questa)

1996 (26 June). *Centenary of Radio. Entertainers. Multi-coloured designs as T* **368** *of Antigua. P* 13½.
3097	35 c. Jack Benny	15	20
3098	75 c. Gertrude Berg	35	40
3099	$1 Eddie Cantor	45	50
3100	$2 Groucho Marx	90	95
3097/100	*Set of* 4	1·75	2·00

MS3101 70×100 mm. $6 George Burns and Gracie Allen (*horiz*) 2·75 3·00

425 Olympic Stadium, Athens, 1896

(Litho B.D.T.)

1996 (8 July). *Olympic Games, Atlanta (2nd issue). Previous Medal Winners. T* **425** *and similar multicoloured designs. P* 14.
3102	35 c. Gold medal of 1896 (*vert*)	15	20
3103	75 c. Type **425**	35	40
3104	$1 Boughera el Quafi (France) (Gold, 1928)	45	50
	a. Sheetlet. Nos. 3104/12	4·00	
3105	$1 Gustav Jansson (Sweden) (Bronze, 1952)	45	50
3106	$1 Spiridon Louis (Greece) (Gold, 1896)	45	50
3107	$1 Basil Heatley (Great Britain) (Silver, 1964)	45	50
3108	$1 Emil Zatopek (Czechoslovakia) (Gold, 1952)	45	50
3109	$1 Frank Shorter (U.S.A.) (Gold, 1972)	45	50
3110	$1 Alain Minoun O'Kacha (France) (Gold, 1956)	45	50
3111	$1 Kokichi Tsu Uraya (Japan) (Bronze, 1964)	45	50
3112	$1 Delfo Cabrera (Argentina) (Gold, 1948)	45	50
3113	$1 Harald Sakata (U.S.A.) (Silver – light heavyweight, 1948)	45	50
	a. Sheetlet. Nos. 3113/21	4·00	
3114	$1 Tom Kono (U.S.A.) (Gold – middle-weight, 1952 and 1956)	45	50
3115	$1 Naim Suleymanoglu (Turkey) (Gold – featherweight, 1988)	45	50
3116	$1 Lee Hyung Kun (South Korea) (Gold – light heavyweight, 1988)	45	50
3117	$1 Vassily Alexeyev (U.S.S.R.) (Gold – super heavyweight, 1972 and 1976)	45	50
3118	$1 Chen Weiqiang (China) (Gold – featherweight, 1984)	45	50
3119	$1 Ye Huanming (China) (Gold – feather-weight, 1988)	45	50
3120	$1 Manfred Nerlinger (Germany) (Silver – super heavyweight, 1988)	45	50
3121	$1 Joseph Depietro (U.S.A.) (Gold – bantamweight, 1948)	45	50
3122	$2 Ancient Greek runners	90	95
3123	$3 Spiridon Louis (Greece) (Gold – marathon, 1896)	1·40	1·50
3102/23	*Set of* 22	10·50	12·00

MS3124 Two sheets, each 75×105 mm. (a) $5 Manfred Nerlinger (Germany) (Silver – super heavyweight weightlifting, 1988) (*vert*). (b) $6 Thomas Hicks (U.S.A.) (Gold – marathon, 1904) (*vert*) *Set of* 2 *sheets* 5·00 5·25
Nos. 3104/12 (marathon runners) and 3113/21 (weightlifters) were each printed together, *se-tenant*, in sheetlets of 9, with the backgrounds forming composite designs.

---

426 Mercedes-Benz, 1929

1996 (25 July). *Classic Cars. T* **426** *and similar horiz designs. Multicoloured. Litho. P* 14.
3125	35 c. Type **426**	15	20
	a. Sheetlet. Nos. 3125/8 and 3135/6	3·50	
3126	50 c. Bugatti Type 35, 1927	25	30
3127	75 c. J. Dusenberg, 1935	35	40
3128	$1 Mercer, 1914	45	50
3129	$1 Type 57C Atalante, 1939	45	50
	a. Sheetlet. Nos. 3129/34	2·50	
3130	$1 Cannstatt-Daimler, 1900	45	50
3131	$1 Delage, 1925	45	50
3132	$1 Coventry Daimler, 1899	45	50
3133	$1 Vauxhall, 1900	45	50
3134	$1 T-15 Hispano-Suza, 1912	45	50
3135	$2 Alfa Romeo, 1929	90	95
3136	$3 Rolls Royce, 1910	1·40	1·50
3125/36	*Set of* 12	6·00	6·75

MS3137 Two sheets, each 66×96 mm. (a) $6 L-Head Mercer, 1915 (56×42 *mm*). (b) $6 Mercedes, 1937 (56×42 *mm*) *Set of* 2 *sheets* 5·50 5·75
Nos. 3125/8 with 3135/6 and 3129/34 were each printed together, *se-tenant*, in sheetlets of 6.

427 *Gorch Fock* (cadet barque), Germany, 1916   **428** Jacqueline Kennedy

(Des R. Sauber. Litho Questa)

1996 (14 Aug). *Ships. T* **427** *and similar horiz designs. Multicoloured. P* 14.
3138	$1 Type **427**	45	50
	a. Sheetlet. Nos. 3138/46	4·00	
3139	$1 *Henry B. Hyde*, U.S.A., 1886	45	50
3140	$1 *Resolution* (galleon), Great Britain, 1652	45	50
3141	$1 U.S.S. *Constitution* (frigate), U.S.A., 1797	45	50
3142	$1 *Nippon Maru* (cadet ship), Japan, 1930	45	50
3143	$1 *Preussen* (full-rigged sailing ship), Germany, 1902	45	50
3144	$1 *Taeping* (tea clipper), Great Britain, 1852	45	50
3145	$1 *Chariot of Fame*, U.S.A., 1853	45	50
3146	$1 *Star of India* (clipper), U.S.A., 1861	45	50
3147	$1 H.M.S. *Bounty*	45	50
	a. Sheetlet. Nos. 3147/55	4·00	
3148	$1 *Bismarck* (German battleship)	45	50
3149	$1 *Chuii Apoo* and two junks	45	50
3150	$1 *Lubeck* (German frigate)	45	50
3151	$1 Dutch galleon	45	50
3152	$1 *Augsburg* (German frigate)	45	50
3153	$1 *Henri Grace a Dieu* (British galleon)	45	50
3154	$1 H.M.S. *Prince of Wales* (battleship)	45	50
3155	$1 *Santa Anna* (Spanish carrack)	45	50
3138/55	*Set of* 18	8·00	9·00

MS3156 Two sheets, each 104×74 mm. (a) $5 H.M.S. *Victory* (ship of the line), Great Britain, 1805. (b) $6 *Cutty Sark* (clipper), Great Britain, 1869 *Set of* 2 *sheets* 5·00 5·25
Nos. 3138/46 and 3147/55 were each printed together, *se-tenant*, in sheetlets of 9.
No. 3151 is inscribed "BARBARY CORSAIR" and No. 3153 is stated to be French, both in error.

1996 (26 Aug). *Jacqueline Kennedy Onassis Commemoration. T* **428** *and similar vert designs. Multicoloured. Litho. P* 14.
3157	$1 Type **428**	45	50
	a. Sheetlet. Nos. 3157/65	4·00	
3158	$1 Wearing mauve blouse	45	50
3159	$1 In evening dress (inscr at right)	45	50
3160	$1 In evening dress (inscr at left)	45	50
3161	$1 Wearing pink dress	45	50
3162	$1 Wearing blue dress with collar embroidered	45	50
3163	$1 Wearing white jacket and brooch	45	50
3164	$1 In yellow jacket and green shirt	45	50
3165	$1 Wearing black jacket	45	50
3157/65	*Set of* 9	4·00	4·50

MS3166 76×106 mm. $6 Jacqueline Kennedy Onassis (*different*) 2·75 3·00
Nos. 3157/65 were printed together, *se-tenant*, in sheetlets of 9 with an enlarged illustrated left-hand margin

---

MINIMUM PRICE

The minimum price quote is 10p which represents a handling charge rather than a basis for valuing common stamps. For further notes about prices see introductory pages.

429 Class "C51" Locomotive of Imperial Train, Japan

(Litho Questa)

1996 (28 Aug). *Trains of the World (2nd series). T* **429** *and similar horiz designs. Multicoloured. P* 14.

3167	35 c. Type **429**		15	20
3168	75 c. The Rheingold Express, Germany		35	40
3169	$1 Atlantic Coast lines, U.S.A.		45	50
	a. Sheetlet. Nos. 3169/74		2·50	
3170	$1 Smith Compound No. 1619, Great Britain		45	50
3171	$1 Trans-Siberian Soviet Railways		45	50
3172	$1 "Atlantic" Type, Palatinate Railway, Germany		45	50
3173	$1 Paris, Lyons and Mediterranean line, France		45	50
3174	$1 Diesel-electric locomotive, Italy		45	50
3175	$1 Class "C62" locomotive, Japan		45	50
	a. Sheetlet. Nos. 3175/80		2·50	
3176	$1 Shantung Railways locomotive, China		45	50
3177	$1 Class "C57 Light" locomotive, Japan		45	50
3178	$1 Diesel express train, Japan		45	50
3179	$1 Shanghai–Nanking Railway locomotive, China		45	50
3180	$1 Class "051" locomotive, Japan		45	50
3181	$2 *The Pioneer*, U.S.A.		90	95
3182	$3 *La France*, France		1·40	1·50
3167/82		*Set of* 16	7·75	9·00

MS3183 Two sheets, each 105×73 mm. (a) $5 Baden State Railways locomotive, Germany, (b) $6 Class "C11" locomotive, Japan *Set of 2 sheets* 5·00 5·25
Nos. 3169/74 and 3175/80 were each printed together, *se-tenant*, in sheetlets of 6.

430 Winter Jasmine

(Des H. Friedman. Litho Questa)

1996 (9 Sept). *Flowers. T* **430** *and similar multicoloured designs. P* 14.

3184	$1 Type **430**		45	50
	a. Sheetlet. Nos. 3184/92		4·00	
3185	$1 Chrysanthemum		45	50
3186	$1 Lilac		45	50
3187	$1 Japanese Iris		45	50
3188	$1 Hibiscus		45	50
3189	$1 Sacred Lotus		45	50
3190	$1 Apple blossom		45	50
3191	$1 Gladiolus		45	50
3192	$1 Japanese Quince		45	50
3193	$1 Canterbury Bell (*vert*)		45	50
	a. Sheetlet. Nos. 3193/201		4·00	
3194	$1 Rose (*vert*)		45	50
3195	$1 Nasturtium (*vert*)		45	50
3196	$1 Daffodil (*vert*)		45	50
3197	$1 Tulip (*vert*)		45	50
3198	$1 Snapdragon (*vert*)		45	50
3199	$1 Zinnia (*vert*)		45	50
3200	$1 Sweetpea (*vert*)		45	50
3201	$1 Pansy (*vert*)		45	50
3184/201		*Set of* 18	8·00	9·00

MS3202 Two sheets. (a) 104×74 mm. $5 Aster. (b) 74×104 mm. $6 Peony *Set of 2 sheets* 5·00 5·25
Nos. 3184/92 and 3193/201 were each printed together, *se-tenant*, in sheetlets of 9 with the backgrounds forming composite designs.

431 Zeppelin L-31 (Germany)

(Des R. Rundo. Litho Questa)

1996 (9 Sept). *Airships. T* **431** *and similar horiz designs. Multicoloured. P* 14.

3203	30 c. Type **431**		15	20
	a. Sheetlet. Nos. 3203/6 and 3213/14		3·50	
3204	30 c. Zeppelin L-35 (Germany)		15	20
3205	50 c. Zeppelin L-30 (Germany)		25	30
3206	75 c. Zeppelin L-2 10 (Germany)		35	40
3207	$1·50 Zeppelin L-21 (Germany)		70	75
	a. Sheetlet. Nos. 3207/12		4·00	
3208	$1·50, Zodiac Type 13 Spiess (France)		70	75
3209	$1·50, N1 *Norge* (Roald Amundsen)		70	75
3210	$1·50, LZ-127 *Graf Zeppelin* (Germany)		70	75
3211	$1·50, LZ-129 *Hindenburg* (Germany)		70	75

3212	$1·50, Zeppelin NT (Germany)		70	75
3213	$3 Zeppelin L-3 (Germany)		1·40	1·50
3214	$3 Beardmore No. 24 (Great Britain)		1·40	1·50
3203/14		*Set of* 12	7·50	8·50

MS3215 Two sheets, each 104×74 mm. (a) $6 Zeppelin ZT (Germany). (b) $6 Zeppelin L-13 (Germany) *Set of 2 sheets* 5·50 5·75
Nos. 3203/6 with 3213/14 and 3207/12 were each printed together, *se-tenant*, in sheetlets of 9.

432 Horned Guan

1996 (18 Sept). *West Indian Birds. T* **432** *and similar horiz designs. Multicoloured. Litho. P* 14.

3216	$1·50, Type **432**		70	75
	a. Sheetlet. Nos. 3216/21		4·00	
3217	$1·50, St. Lucia Parrot		70	75
3218	$1·50, Black Penelopina		70	75
3219	$1·50, Grenada Dove		70	75
3220	$1·50, St. Vincent Parrot		70	75
3221	$1·50, White-breasted Trembler		70	75
3216/21		*Set of* 6	4·00	4·50

MS3222 Two sheets, each 100×70 mm. (a) $5 Semper's Warbler. (b) $6 Barbados Yellow Warbler *Set of 2 sheets* 5·00 5·25
Nos. 3216/21 were printed together, *se-tenant*, in sheetlets of 6 with the backgrounds forming a composite design.
The inscriptions on Nos. MS3222a and MS3222b are transposed in error.

433 Blue Whale   **434** Killer Whale

1996 (18 Sept). *Whales and Turtles. T* **433** *and similar horiz designs. Multicoloured. Litho. P* 14.

3223	$1·50, Type **433**		70	75
	a. Sheetlet. Nos. 3223/8		4·00	
3224	$1·50, Humpback Whale		70	75
3225	$1·50, Right Whale		70	75
3226	$1·50, Hawksbill Turtle		70	75
3227	$1·50, Leatherback Turtle		70	75
3228	$1·50, Green Turtle		70	75
3223/8		*Set of* 6	4·00	4·50

Nos. 3223/8 were printed together, *se-tenant*, in sheetlets of 6.

(Des T. Wood. Litho Questa)

1996 (7 Nov). *Marine Life. T* **434** *and similar multicoloured designs. P* 14.

3229	$1 Type **434**		45	50
	a. Sheetlet. Nos. 3229/37		4·00	
3230	$1 Dolphin		45	50
3231	$1 Two dolphins		45	50
3232	$1 Sea Lion and Regal Angelfish		45	50
3233	$1 Dolphins and Hawksbill Turtle		45	50
3234	$1 Three Hawksbill Turtles		45	50
3235	$1 Regal Angelfish and Pennant Coralfish		45	50
3236	$1 Pennant Coralfish		45	50
3237	$1 Sea Lion and Squirrelfish		45	50
3238	$1 Brown Pelican		45	50
	a. Sheetlet. Nos. 3238/46		4·00	
3239	$1 Killer Whale (*different*)		45	50
3240	$1 Whale		45	50
3241	$1 Dolphins and Sea Lion		45	50
3242	$1 Shortfin Pilot Whale, Blue-ringed Octopus and Sea Lion		45	50
3243	$1 Hammerhead Sharks and Sea Lion		45	50
3244	$1 Blue-striped Grunts		45	50
3245	$1 Stingray and Van Gogh Fusilier		45	50
3246	$1 Van Gogh Fusilier, Ribbon Moray and percoid fish		45	50
3229/46		*Set of* 18	8·00	9·00

MS3247 Two sheets, each 106×76 mm. (a) $6 Pair of Sea Lions (*horiz*). (b) $6 Pair of Dolphins (*horiz*) *Set of 2 sheets* 5·50 5·75
Nos. 3229/37 and 3238/46 were each printed together, *se-tenant*, in sheetlets of 9 with the backgrounds forming composite designs.

(Litho Questa)

1996 (18 Nov). *Christmas. Religious Paintings. Vert designs as T* **369** *of Antigua. Multicoloured. P* 13½×14.

3248	25 c. "The Visitation" (Tintoretto)		10	15
3249	35 c. "Virgin with the Child" (Palma Vecchio)		15	20
3250	50 c. "The Adoration of the Magi" (Botticelli)		25	30
3251	75 c. "The Annunciation" (Titian)		35	40
3252	$1 "The Flight into Egypt" (Tintoretto)		45	50
3253	$3 "The Holy Family with the Infant Saint John" (Andrea del Sarto)		1·40	1·50
3248/53		*Set of* 6	2·50	3·00

MS3254 Two sheets, each 106×76 mm. (a) $6 "Adoration of the Magi" (Paolo Schiavo). (b) $6 "Madonna and Child with Saints" (Vincenzo Poppa) *Set of 2 sheets* 5·50 5·75
No. 3250 in inscr "Botticeli" in error.

(Des Shannon. Litho Questa)

1996 (21 Nov). *20th Anniv of Rocky (film). Sheet* 143×182 *mm, containing vert design as T* **266** *of Gambia. Multicoloured. P* 14×13½.
MS3255 $2×3, Sylvester Stallone in *Rocky V* .. 2·75 3·00

435 Ox

(Des Y. Lee. Litho Walsall)

1997 (2 Jan). *Chinese New Year ("Year of the Ox"). Sheet,* 150×75 *mm, containing T* **435** *and similar triangular designs. Multicoloured. Self-adhesive on silver foil. P* 9½.
MS3256 $2 Type **435** ("GRENADA" in black); $2 Ox ("GRENADA" in pink); $2 Ox ("GRENADA" in blue) .. .. .. 2·75 3·00
No. **MS3256** also exists on gold foil from a limited printing.

436 Mickey at Tram Stop   **437** Devon Rex

(Des Speedy Studio. Litho Questa)

1997 (12 Feb). *"HONG KONG '97" International Stamp Exhibition. Mickey in Hong Kong. T* **436** *and similar multicoloured designs showing Disney cartoon characters. P* 14×13½.

3257	35 c. Type **436**		15	20
	a. Sheetlet. Nos. 3257/60 and 3267/8		3·25	
3258	50 c. Mickey and Donald fishing at Victoria Harbour		25	30
3259	75 c. Donald and Mickey parachuting		35	40
3260	90 c. Mickey and Minnie visiting Bank of China		40	45
3261	$1 Mickey with pet parrot		45	50
	a. Sheetlet. Nos. 3261/6		2·50	
3262	$1 Mickey drinking Kung-fu Tea		45	50
3263	$1 Mickey, Minnie and Goofy shopping at Chinese Wet Market		45	50
3264	$1 Mickey, Minnie and Goofy with grass-hoppers		45	50
3265	$1 Mickey and Goofy with lanterns		45	50
3266	$1 Mickey and Minnie practising Tai-chi		45	50
3267	$2 Goofy delivering bottled gas		90	95
3268	$3 Mickey, Minnie and Donald at *Jumbo* floating restaurant		1·40	1·50
3257/68		*Set of* 12	6·00	6·50

MS3269 Four sheets, each 132×108 mm. (a) $3 Mickey and skyscrapers (*vert*). (b) $4 Mickey and Minnie dancing (*vert*). (c) $5 Mickey pulling rickshaw (*vert*). (d) $6 Mickey with noodles (*vert*).
P 13½×14 *Set of 4 sheets* 8·25 8·50
Nos. 3257/60 with 3267/8 and 3261/6 were each printed together, *se-tenant*, in sheetlets of 6.
Nos. **MS3269a** and **MS3269c** show the "HONG KONG '97" International Stamp Exhibition logo on the margins.

(Des M. Freedman and Dena Rubin. Litho Questa)

1997 (3 Apr). *50th Anniv of U.N.E.S.C.O. Multicoloured designs as T* **373** *of Antigua. P* 14×13½ (*horiz*) or 13½×14 (*vert*).

3270	35 c. Temple, Kyoto, Japan		15	20
3271	75 c. Timbered houses, Quedlinburg, Germany		35	40
3272	90 c. View from walls, Dubrovnik, Croatia		40	45
3273	$1 Ruins at Delphi, Greece		45	50
3274	$1 Bryggen Wharf, Bergen, Norway (*vert*)		45	50
	a. Sheetlet. Nos. 3274/81 and central label		3·50	
3275	$1 Old city, Berne, Switzerland (*vert*)		45	50
3276	$1 Warsaw, Poland (*vert*)		45	50
3277	$1 Fortress walls, Luxembourg (*vert*)		45	50
3278	$1 Interior of Drottningholm Palace, Sweden (*vert*)		45	50
3279	$1 Petajavesi Church, Finland (*vert*)		45	50
3280	$1 Vilnius, Lithuania (*vert*)		45	50
3281	$1 Jelling Church, Denmark (*vert*)		45	50
3282	$1 Entrance to caves, Desert of Taklamakan, China (*vert*)		45	50
	a. Sheetlet. Nos. 3282/9 and central label		3·50	
3283	$1 House, Desert of Taklamakan, China (*vert*)		45	50

3284	$1 Monument, Desert of Taklamakan, China (vert)		45	50
3285	$1 Palace of Cielos Purpuras, Wudang, China (vert)		45	50
3286	$1 House, Wudang, China (vert)		45	50
3287	$1 Stone Guardian, The Great Wall, China (vert)		45	50
3288	$1 Ming Dynasty statue, Wudang, China (vert)		45	50
3289	$1 The Great Wall, China (vert)		45	50
3290	$1.50, Segovia Cathedral, Spain		70	75
	a. Sheetlet. Nos. 3290/4 and label		3·50	
3291	$1.50, Wurtzburg, Germany		70	75
3292	$1.50, Plitvice Lakes, Croatia		70	75
3293	$1.50, Batalha Monastery, Portugal		70	75
3294	$1.50, River Seine, Paris, France		70	75
3295	$2 Tomar, Portugal		90	95
3296	$3 Palace of Chaillot, Paris, France		1·40	1·50
3270/96		Set of 27	13·50	15·00

MS3297 Three sheets, each 127×102 mm. (a) $6 Popocatepetl Monastery, Mexico. (b) $6 Woodland path, Shirakami-Sanchi, Japan. (c) $6 Interior of the Hieronymites' Monastery, Portugal .. Set of 3 sheets 8·25 8·50
Nos. 3274/81 and 3282/9 were each printed together, se-tenant, in sheetlets of 8 stamps with a centre label and Nos. 3290/4 in a sheetlet of 5 with a top left-hand corner label.

(Des D. Miller. Litho Questa)

1997 (10 Apr). *Cats and Dogs. T 437 and similar vert designs. Multicoloured. P 14.*

3298	35 c. Type 437		15	20
3299	75 c. King Charles Spaniel		35	40
3300	90 c. Japanese Bobtail		40	45
3301	$1 Afghan Hound		45	50
3302	$1 Turkish Van		45	50
	a. Sheetlet. Nos. 3302/10		4·00	
3303	$1 Ragdoll		45	50
3304	$1 Siberian		45	50
3305	$1 Egyptian Mau		45	50
3306	$1 American Shorthair		45	50
3307	$1 Bengal		45	50
3308	$1 Asian Longhair		45	50
3309	$1 Somali		45	50
3310	$1 Turkish Angora		45	50
3311	$1 Lhasa Apso		45	50
	a. Sheetlet. Nos. 3311/19		4·00	
3312	$1 Rough Collie		45	50
3313	$1 Norwich Terrier		45	50
3314	$1 American Cocker Spaniel		45	50
3315	$1 Chinese Crested Dog		45	50
3316	$1 Old English Sheepdog		45	50
3317	$1 Standard Poodle		45	50
3318	$1 German Shepherd		45	50
3319	$1 German Shorthair Pointer		45	50
3320	$2 Cornish Rex		90	95
3321	$3 Pekingese		1·40	1·50
3298/321		Set of 24	11·50	12·50

MS3322 Two sheets, each 106×76 mm. (a) $6 Singapura. (b) $6 Bernese Mountain Dog
.. Set of 2 sheets 5·50 5·75
Nos. 3302/10 (cats) and 3311/19 (dogs) were each printed together, se-tenant, in sheetlets of 9.

438 Dunkleosteus

(Litho Questa)

1997 (15 Apr). *Dinosaurs. T 438 and similar multicoloured designs. P 14.*

3323	35 c. Type 438		15	20
3324	75 c. Tyrannosaurus rex		35	40
3325	$1.50, Sordes		70	75
	a. Sheetlet. Nos. 3325/30		4·25	
3326	$1.50, Dimorphodon		70	75
3327	$1.50, Diplodocus		70	75
3328	$1.50, Allosaurus		70	75
3329	$1.50, Pentaceratops		70	75
3330	$1.50, Protoceratops		70	75
3331	$2 Askeptosaurus (vert)		90	95
3332	$3 Triceratops (vert)		1·40	1·50
3323/32		Set of 10	7·00	7·50

MS3333 Two sheets, each 103×74 mm. (a) $6 Tristychius (vert). (b) $6 Maiasaura (vert)
.. Set of 2 sheets 5·50 5·75
Nos. 3325/30 were printed together, se-tenant, in sheetlets of 6 with the backgrounds forming a composite design.

439 Porcelain Crab

(Des R. Rundo. Litho Questa)

1997 (2 May). *Marine Life. T 439 and similar multicoloured designs. P 14.*

3334	45 c. Type 439		20	25
3335	75 c. Humpback Whale		35	40
3336	90 c. Hermit Crab		40	45
3337	$1 Great White Shark		45	50

3338	$1.50, Octopus (vert)		70	75
	a. Sheetlet. Nos. 3338/43		4·25	
3339	$1.50, Lei Triggerfish (vert)		70	75
3340	$1.50, Lionfish (vert)		70	75
3341	$1.50, Harlequin Wrasse (vert)		70	75
3342	$1.50, Clown Fish (vert)		70	75
3343	$1.50, Moray Eel (vert)		70	75
3344	$3 Green Sea Turtle		1·40	1·50
3345	$4 Whale Shark		1·90	2·00
3334/45		Set of 12	9·00	9·50

MS3346 Two sheets, each 106×76 mm. (a) $6 Pacific Barracudas. (b) $6 Scalloped Hammerhead Shark .. Set of 2 sheets 5·50 5·75
Nos. 3338/43 were printed together, se-tenant, in sheetlets of 6 with the backgrounds forming a composite design.

(Des R. Rundo. Litho Questa)

1997 (28 May). *300th Anniv of Mother Goose Nursery Rhymes. Sheet 72×102 mm containing multicoloured design as T 309 of Dominica. P 14.*
MS3347 $5 Boy holding umbrella ("Rain") (vert) 2·25 2·40

(Litho Questa)

1997 (28 May). *10th Anniv of Chernobyl Nuclear Disaster. Vert designs as T 375 of Antigua. P 13½×14.*

3348	$2 As Type 375 of Antigua		90	95
3349	$2 As No. 3348, but inscribed "CHABAD'S CHILDREN OF CHERNOBYL" at foot		90	95

(Des J. Iskowitz. Litho Questa)

1997 (28 May). *50th Death Anniv of Paul Harris (founder of Rotary International). Horiz designs as T 376 of Antigua. Multicoloured. P 14.*
3350 $3 Paul Harris and vocational training programme, Philippines .. .. 1·40 1·50
MS3351 78×107 mm. $6 Hands holding globe and doves .. .. 2·75 3·00

(Litho Questa)

1997 (28 May). *Golden Wedding of Queen Elizabeth and Prince Philip. Horiz designs as T 377 of Antigua. Multicoloured. P 14.*

3352	$1 Queen Elizabeth and Prince Philip waving		45	50
	a. Sheetlet. Nos. 3352/7		2·75	
3353	$1 Royal coat of arms		45	50
3354	$1 Queen Elizabeth with Prince Philip in naval uniform		45	50
3355	$1 Queen Elizabeth and Prince Philip at Buckingham Palace		45	50
3356	$1 Windsor Castle		45	50
3357	$1 Prince Philip		45	50
3352/7		Set of 6	2·75	3·00

MS3358 100×70 mm. $6 Queen Elizabeth with Prince Philip in naval uniform (different) .. 2·75 3·00
Nos. 3352/7 were printed together, se-tenant, in sheetlets of 6.

(Des J. Iskowitz. Litho Questa)

1997 (28 May). *"Pacific '97" International Stamp Exhibition, San Francisco (1st issue). Death Centenary of Henrich von Stephan (founder of the U.P.U.) Horiz designs as T 378 of Antigua. P 14.*

3359	$2 turquoise-green and black		90	95
	a. Sheetlet. Nos. 3359/61		2·75	
3360	$2 chestnut		90	95
3361	$2 dull blue		90	95
3359/61		Set of 3	2·75	3·00

MS3362 82×119 mm. $6 violet and black 2·75 3·00
Designs:—No. 3359, Postman on motorcycle; No. 3360, Von Stephan and Mercury; No. 3361, Postman on skis, Rocky Mountains 1900's; No. MS3362, Von Stephan and Chinese letter carrier.
Nos. 3359/61 were printed together, se-tenant, in sheets of 3 with enlarged right-hand margin.
See also Nos. 3392/409.

1997 (28 May). *Birth Bicentenary of Hiroshige (Japanese painter). "One Hundred Famous Views of Edo". Vert designs as T 310 of Dominica. Multicoloured. Litho. P 13½×14.*

3363	$1.50, "Nihon Embankment, Yoshiwara"		70	75
	a. Sheetlet. Nos. 3363/8		4·25	
3364	$1.50, "Asakusa Ricefields and Torino-machi Festival"		70	75
3365	$1.50, "Senju Great Bridge"		70	75
3366	$1.50, "Dawn inside the Yoshiwara"		70	75
3367	$1.50, "Tile Kilns and Hasiba Ferry, Sumida River"		70	75
3368	$1.50, "View from Massaki of Suijin Shrine, Uchigawa Inlet and Sekiya"		70	75
3363/8		Set of 6	4·25	4·50

MS3369 Two sheets, each 102×127 mm. (a) $6 "Kinryuzan Temple, Asakusa"; (b) $6 "Night view of Saruwaka-machi" .. Set of 2 sheets 5·50 5·75
Nos. 3363/8 were printed together, se-tenant, in sheetlets of 6.

(Des R. Sauber. Litho Questa)

1997 (28 May). *175th Anniv of Brothers Grimm's Third Collection of Fairy Tales. Snow White. Vert designs as T 379 of Antigua. Multicoloured. P 14.*

3370	$2 Queen looking in mirror		90	95
	a. Sheetlet. Nos. 3370/2		2·75	
3371	$2 Snow White and the Seven Dwarfs		90	95
3372	$2 Snow White and Prince		90	95
3370/2		Set of 3	2·75	3·00

MS3373 124×96 mm. $6 Witch with apple 2·75 3·00
Nos. 3370/2 were printed together, se-tenant, in sheetlets of 3 with illustrated margins.

440 One-man Luge   **441** Bank of China

(Litho B.D.T.)

1997 (26 June). *Winter Olympic Games, Nagano, Japan. T 440 and similar multicoloured designs. P 14.*

3374	45 c. Type 440		20	25
3375	75 c. Men's speed-skating		35	40
3376	$1 One-man luge (different)		45	50
	a. Sheetlet. Nos. 3376/84		4·00	
3377	$1 Ski-jumping (blue ski suit)		45	50
3378	$1 Downhill skiing		45	50
3379	$1 Speed-skating		45	50
3380	$1 Two-man bobsleigh		45	50
3381	$1 Women's figure-skating		45	50
3382	$1 Alpine combined		45	50
3383	$1 Ice hockey		45	50
3384	$1 Ski-jumping (yellow ski suit)		45	50
3385	$2 Men's figure-skating		90	95
3386	$3 Slalom		1·40	1·50
3374/86		Set of 13	6·75	7·50

MS3387 Two sheets, each 96×69 mm. (a) $6 Four-man bobsleigh; (b) $6 Downhill skiing (vert)
.. Set of 2 sheets 5·50 5·75
Nos. 3376/84 were printed together, se-tenant, in sheetlets of 9.

(Des Y. Lee. Litho Questa)

1997 (1 July). *Return of Hong Kong to China. T 441 and similar multicoloured designs. P 14×13½ (90 c., $1) or 14 (others).*

3388	90 c. Type 441		40	45
	a. Sheetlet of 4		1·60	
3389	$1 Skyscrapers		45	50
	a. Sheetlet of 4		1·75	
3390	$1.75, "Hong Kong '97" on modern buildings (63×32 mm)		80	85
	a. Sheetlet of 3		2·40	
3391	$2 Deng Xiaoping and Hong Kong (63×32 mm)		90	95
	a. Sheetlet of 3		2·75	
3388/91		Set of 4	2·50	2·75

Nos. 3388/91 were printed in sheetlets of 3 or 4, each with enlarged illustrated margins.

442 Minnie Mouse dancing the Hula

(Des Alvin White Studios. Litho Questa)

1997 (7 Aug). *"Pacific '97" International Stamp Exhibition, San Francisco (2nd issue). Centenary of the Cinema. Minnie Mouse in Hawaiian Holiday. T 442 and similar horiz designs showing a series of cartoon frames. Multicoloured. P 14×13½.*

3392	50 c. Type 442 (Frame 1)		25	30
	a. Sheetlet. Nos. 3392/9 and 1 label		2·00	
3393	50 c. Frame 2		25	30
3394	50 c. Frame 3		25	30
3395	50 c. Frame 4		25	30
3396	50 c. Frame 5		25	30
3397	50 c. Frame 6		25	30
3398	50 c. Frame 7		25	30
3399	50 c. Frame 8		25	30
3400	50 c. Frame 9		25	30
	a. Sheetlet. Nos. 3400/8		2·25	
3401	50 c. Frame 10		25	30
3402	50 c. Frame 11		25	30
3403	50 c. Frame 12		25	30
3404	50 c. Frame 13		25	30
3405	50 c. Frame 14		25	30
3406	50 c. Frame 15		25	30
3407	50 c. Frame 16		25	30
3408	50 c. Frame 17		25	30
3392/408		Set of 17	4·25	5·00

MS3409 110×130 mm. $6 Frame 18 .. 2·75 3·00
Nos. 3392/9 and 3400/8 were printed together, se-tenant, in sheetlets of 8 or 9. It is intended that the stamps should be separated and used as a flip book to produce a moving image.

OMNIBUS ISSUES

Details, together with prices for complete sets, of the various Omnibus issues from the 1935 Silver Jubilee series to date are included in a special section following Zimbabwe at the end of Volume 2.

443 Hercules lifting Rock

(Des Alvin White Studios. Litho Questa)

1997 (7 Aug). *Hercules (film). T* **443** *and similar vert designs showing Disney cartoon characters. Multicoloured. P* 13½×14.

3410	$1 Type **443**	45	50
	a. Sheetlet. Nos. 3410/17	3·50	
3411	$1 Pegasus	45	50
3412	$1 Megara	45	50
3413	$1 Philoktetes	45	50
3414	$1 Nessus	45	50
3415	$1 Hydra	45	50
3416	$1 Pain and Panic	45	50
3417	$1 Hades	45	50
3410/17	*Set of* 8	3·50	4·00

MS3418 Two sheets. (a) 131×104 mm. $6 Hercules as a boy. (b) 104×131 mm. $6 The Muses .. .. .. *Set of 2 sheets* 5·50 5·75
Nos. 3410/17 were printed together, *se-tenant*, in sheetlets of 8.

(Litho Questa)

1997 (11 Aug). *World Cup Football Championship, France (1998). Designs as T* **382** *of Antigua. Multicoloured (except Nos.* 3422/3 *and* 3428). *P* 13½×14 (vert) *or* 14×13½ (horiz).

3419	15 c. West German and Italian players, 1982 (vert)	10	10
3420	75 c. Italian player holding World Cup, 1982 (vert)	35	40
3421	90 c. West German and Italian players wearing "20" shirts, 1982 (vert)	40	45
3422	$1 Uruguay team, 1950 (agate)	45	50
	a. Sheetlet. Nos. 3422/9 and central label	3·50	
3423	$1 Brazilian team, 1958 (agate)	45	50
3424	$1 West German team, 1974	45	50
3425	$1 Argentine team, 1986	45	50
3426	$1 Italian team, 1982	45	50
3427	$1 West German team, 1990	45	50
3428	$1 Italian team, 1934 (agate)	45	50
3429	$1 Brazilian team, 1970	45	50
3430	$1 Seaman, England	45	50
	a. Sheetlet. Nos. 3430/7 and central label	3·50	
3431	$1 Klinsmann, Germany	45	50
3432	$1 Berger, Czech Republic	45	50
3433	$1 McCoist, Scotland	45	50
3434	$1 Gascoigne, England	45	50
3435	$1 Djorkaeff, France	45	50
3436	$1 Sammer, Germany	45	50
3437	$1 Futre, Portugal	45	50
3438	$2 Italian player beating goal keeper, 1982 (vert)	90	95
3439	$3 Goal-mouth melee, 1982 (vert)	1·40	1·50
3440	$4 Two West German players tackling Italian player (vert)	1·90	2·00
3419/40	*Set of* 22	10·00	11·00

MS3441 Two sheets. (a) 102×127 mm. $6 Beckenbaur holding World Cup, Germany (vert). (b) 127×102 mm. $6 Moore, England
Set of 2 sheets 5·50 5·75
Nos. 3422/9 and 3430/7 were each printed together, *se-tenant*, in sheetlets of 8 with central label.

444 Peacock

(Des Joni Popes. Litho Questa)

1997 (12 Aug). *Butterflies and Moths. T* **444** *and similar horiz designs. Multicoloured. P* 14.

3442	45 c. Type **444**	20	25
3443	75 c. Orange Flambeau	35	40
3444	90 c. Eastern Tailed Blue	45	50
3445	$1 Brimstone	45	50
	a. Sheetlet. Nos. 3445/52	3·50	
3446	$1 Mocker Swallowtail	45	50
3447	$1 American Painted Lady	45	50
3448	$1 Tiger Swallowtail	45	50
3449	$1 Long Wing	45	50
3450	$1 Sunset Moth	45	50
3451	$1 Australian Blue Mountain Swallowtail	45	50
3452	$1 Bird Wing	45	50
3453	$2 Black and Red	90	95
3454	$3 Large White	1·40	1·50
3455	$4 Oriental Swallowtail	1·90	2·00
3442/55	*Set of* 14	8·75	9·50

MS3456 Two sheets, each 76×106 mm. (a) $5 Monarch. (b) $5 Blue Morpho. *Set of 2 sheets* 4·50 4·75
Nos. 3445/52 were printed together, *se-tenant*, in sheetlets of 8.

445 Paphiopedilum urbanianum

(Des R. Rundo. Litho B.D.T.)

1997 (4 Sept). *Orchids of the World. T* **445** *and similar multicoloured designs. P* 14.

3457	20 c. Type **445**	10	10
3458	35 c. Trichoceros parviflorus	15	20
3459	45 c. Euanthe sanderiana (vert)	20	25
3460	75 c. Oncidium macranthum (vert)	35	40
3461	90 c. Psychopsis kramerianum (vert)	40	45
3462	$1 Oncidium hastatum (vert)	45	50
3463	$2 Broughtonia sanguinea (vert)	90	95
	a. Sheetlet. Nos. 3463/8	5·50	
3464	$2 Anguloa virginalis (vert)	90	95
3465	$2 Dendrobium bigibbum (vert)	90	95
3466	$2 Lucasiana (vert)	90	95
3467	$2 Cymbidium (vert)	90	95
3468	$2 Cymbidium and vase (vert)	90	95
3469	$2 Odontoglossum crispum (vert)	90	95
	a. Sheetlet. Nos. 3469/74	5·50	
3470	$2 Cattleya brabantiae (vert)	90	95
3471	$2 Cattleya bicolor (vert)	90	95
3472	$2 Trichopilia suavia (vert)	90	95
3473	$2 Encyclia mariae (vert)	90	95
3474	$2 Angraecum leonis (vert)	90	95
3475	$3 Masdevallia saltatix (vert)	1·40	1·50
3476	$4 Cattleya luteola	1·90	2·00
3457/76	*Set of* 20	16·00	17·00

MS3477 Two sheets. (a) 76×106 mm. $6 Laelia milleri. (b) 106×76 mm. $6 Oncidium onustum
Set of 2 sheets 5·50 5·75
Nos. 3463/8 and 3469/74 were each printed together, *se-tenant*, in sheetlets of 6 with the backgrounds forming composite designs.

446 Boletus erythropus

(Litho B.D.T.)

1997 (4 Sept). *Fungi of the World. T* **446** *and similar horiz designs. Multicoloured. P* 14.

3478	35 c. Type **446**	15	20
3479	75 c. Armillariella mellea	35	40
3480	90 c. Amanita flavorubens	40	45
3481	$1 Indigo Milky	45	50
3482	$1.50, Agaricus solidipes	70	75
	a. Sheetlet. Nos. 3482/7	4·25	
3483	$1.50, Salmon Waxy Cap	70	75
3484	$1.50, Fused Maramius	70	75
3485	$1.50, Shellfish-scented Russula	70	75
3486	$1.50, Red-capped Scaber Stalk	70	75
3487	$1.50, Calocybe gambosum	70	75
3488	$1.50, Boletus parasiticus	70	75
	a. Sheetlet. Nos. 3488/93	4·25	
3489	$1.50, Frostis bolete	70	75
3490	$1.50, Amanita myscara flavilolvata	70	75
3491	$1.50, Volvariella volvacea	70	75
3492	$1.50, Stuntz's Blue Legs	70	75
3493	$1.50, Orange-latex Milky	70	75
3494	$2 Tylopilus balloui	90	95
3495	$4 Boletus parasiticus	1·90	2·00
3478/95	*Set of* 18	12·50	13·50

MS3496 Two sheets, each 97×67 mm. (a) $6 Agaricus argenteus. (b) $6 Omphalotus illudens
Set of 2 sheets 5·50 5·75
Nos. 3482/7 and 3488/93 were each printed together, *se-tenant*, in sheetlets of 6.

447 Princess Diana with Landmine Victims

448 "Angel" (Matthias Grünewald)

(Des R. Sauber. Litho Questa)

1997 (15 Oct). *Diana, Princess of Wales Commemoration. T* **447** *and similar horiz designs. Multicoloured. P* 14½.

3497	$1.50, Type **447**	70	75
	a. Sheetlet. Nos. 3497/502	4·25	
3498	$1.50, With sick child	70	75
3499	$1.50, With young boy on crutches	70	75
3500	$1.50, With leper	70	75
3501	$1.50, Holding baby	70	75
3502	$1.50, Walking through minefield	70	75
3497/502	*Set of* 6	4·25	4·50

MS3503 76×106 mm. $5 With Mother Theresa 2·25 2·40
Nos. 3497/502 were printed together, *se-tenant*, in sheetlets of 6 with enlarged illustrated right-hand margin.

(Litho Questa)

1997 (5 Dec). *Christmas. Religious Paintings. T* **448** *and similar multicoloured designs. P* 14.

3504	35 c. Type **448**	15	20
3505	50 c. "St. Demetrius" (icon)	25	30
3506	75 c. Three-panelled reliquary	35	40
3507	$1 "Angel of the Annunciation" (Jan van Eyck)	45	50
3508	$3 "The Annunciation" (Simone Martini)	1·40	1·50
3509	$4 "St. Michael" (icon)	1·90	2·00
3504/9	*Set of* 6	4·50	5·00

MS3510 Two sheets. (a) 104×114 mm. $6 "The Coronation of the Virgin" (Fra Angelico). (b) 114×104 mm. $6 "The Annunciation" (Titian) (horiz) .. .. .. *Set of 2 sheets* 4·50 5·00

1998 (5 Jan). *Chinese New Year ("Year of the Tiger"). Sheet* 150×75 *mm containing triangular designs as T* **435** *showing tigers. Multicoloured. Self-adhesive on silver foil. P* 9½.
MS3511 $1.50, "GRENADA" in pink; $1.50, "GRENADA" in gold; $1.50, "GRENADA" in bronze .. .. 2·00 2·10
No. **MS**3511 also exists on gold foil

If you would like to ADVERTISE

in the next edition of this catalogue or any other catalogue published by Stanley Gibbons

Phone, write or fax

Advertising Department
Stanley Gibbons Publications,
5 Parkside, Christchurch Road,
Ringwood, Hants BH24 3SH

Telephone: 01425 472363
Fax: 01425 470247

STAMP BOOKLETS

1977 (8 Feb). *Silver Jubilee. Multicoloured cover, 165×92 mm, showing Queen in Coronation Coach. Stitched.*
SB1 $6.60, booklet containing 35 c. in pane of 6 (No. 863a) and *se-tenant* pane of 3 (No. 864a)   ..   2·50

1978 (2 May). *25th Anniv of Coronation. Multicoloured cover, 165×92 mm, showing photograph of Queen Elizabeth II. Stitched.*
SB2 $6.80, booklet containing *se-tenant* pane of 6 (No. 950a) and pane of 1 (No. 952a)   ..   2·00

1981 (16 June). *Royal Wedding. Multicoloured cover, 95×166 mm, showing commemorative inscription on front and Queen, Prince Charles, Lady Diana Spencer and group of Privy Councillors on back. Stitched.*
SB3 $14 booklet containing *se-tenant* pane of 6 (No. 1136a) and pane of 1 (No. 1138a)   ..   2·50

POSTAGE DUE STAMPS

D 1		(D 2)

(Typo D.L.R.)

1892 (18 Apr–Oct).   (*a*) *Type* D 1. *Wmk Crown CA. P* 14.
D1   D 1   1d. blue-black   ..   ..   ..   22·00   1·50
D2   2d. blue-black   ..   ..   £130   1·50
D3   3d. blue-black   ..   ..   £130   2·50
D1/3   ..   ..   ..   *Set of 3*   £250   5·00

(*b*) *Nos. 34 and 35 surch locally as Type* D 2
D4   13   1d. on 6d. mauve (10.92)   ..   70·00   1·25
    a. *Tête-bêche* (pair)   ..   £950   £700
    b. Surch double   ..   —   £140
D5   1d. on 8d. grey-brown (8.92)   ..   £550   3·25
    a. *Tête-bêche* (pair)   ..   £2750 £1200
D6   2d. on 6d. mauve (10.92)   ..   £130   2·50
    a. *Tête-bêche* (pair)   ..   £1400   £950
D7   2d. on 8d. grey-brown (8.92)   ..   £1000   9·50
    a. *Tête-bêche* (pair)   ..   £4250 £2500

Nos. D4/7 were in use from August to November 1892. As supplies of Nos. D1/3 were available from April or May of that year it would not appear that they were intended for postage due purposes. There was a shortage of 1d. postage stamps in July and August, but this was alleviated by Nos. 44/5 which were still available. The provisionals *may* have been intended for postal purposes, but the vast majority appear to have been used philatelically.

1906 (July)–**11**. *Wmk Mult Crown CA. P* 14.
D 8   D 1   1d. blue-black (1911)   ..   2·25   6·00
D 9   2d. blue-black   ..   ..   8·00   1·75
D10   3d. blue-black (9.06)   ..   10·00   6·00
D8/10 ..   ..   ..   *Set of 3*   18·00   12·00

1921 (Dec)–**22**. *As Type* D 1, *but inscr* "POSTAGE DUE". *Wmk Mult Script CA. P* 14.
D11   1d. black   90   1·00
D12   1½d. black (15.12.22)   ..   8·50   16·00
D13   2d. black   ..   ..   2·00   1·75
D14   3d. black   ..   ..   2·00   4·25
D11/14   ..   ..   *Set of 4*   12·00   21·00
D11/14 Optd "Specimen"   ..   *Set of 4*   80·00

1952 (1 Mar). *As Type* D 1, *but inscr* "POSTAGE DUE". *Value in cents. Chalk-surfaced paper. Wmk Mult Script CA. P* 14.
D15   2 c. black   30   4·50
    a. Error. Crown missing. W 9*a*   80·00
    b. Error. St. Edward Crown. W 9*b* ..   40·00
D16   4 c. black   30   10·00
    a. Error. Crown missing. W 9*a*   80·00
    b. Error. St. Edward Crown. W 9*b* ..   40·00
D17   6 c. black   45   10·00
    a. Error. Crown missing. W 9*a*   £110
    b. Error. St. Edward Crown. W 9*b* ..   75·00
D18   8 c. black   75   10·00
    a. Error. Crown missing. W 9*a*   £190
    b. Error. St. Edward Crown. W 9*b* ..   £120
D15/18   ..   ..   ..   *Set of 4*   1·60   32·00

OFFICIAL STAMPS

P.R.G.

(O 1)

(= People's Revolutionary Government)

1982 (June). *Various stamps optd with Type* O 1.
(*a*) *Nos. 1085A/97A and 1099A*
O 1   5 c. West Indiaman barque, circa 1840   15   20
O 2   6 c. R.M.S.P. *Orinoco*, circa 1851   ..   15   20
O 3   10 c. Working Schooner   ..   15   20
O 4   12 c. Trimaran at Grand Anse anchorage   15   20
O 5   15 c. Spice Island cruising yacht *Petite Amie*   20   20
O 6   20 c. Fishing pirogue   25   20
O 7   25 c. Harbour police launch   ..   30   30
O 8   30 c. Grand Anse speedboat   ..   30   30
O 9   40 c. M.V. *Seimstrand*   35   30

O10   50 c. Three-masted schooner *Ariadne*   ..   40   40
O11   90 c. M.V. *Geestide*   70   80
O12 $1 M.V. *Cunard Countess*   70   80
O13 $3 Rum-runner   ..   ..   ..   2·00   3·75
O14 $10 Coast-guard patrol boat. ..   ..   6·00   12·00

(*b*) *Nos. 1130/2 and 1134/5*
O15   30 c. Prince Charles and Lady Diana Spencer   1·75   2·25
O16   40 c. Holyrood House ..   ..   2·25   2·75
O17   50 c. Prince Charles and Lady Diana Spencer   1·25   2·00
O18 $2 Holyrood House ..   ..   2·75   3·50
O19 $4 Type **268**   ..   ..   6·50   8·00
O1/19 .   ..   ..   *Set of 19*   23·00   35·00
The $4 from sheetlets, perforated 14½×14 and with changed background colour, also exists with the overprint (*Price £4 mint, £7 used*).

Quality British & Commonwealth Stamps Direct to Your Door

Irresistibly simple, exceptionally quick and reassuringly reliable. Stanley Gibbons Mail Order service enables you to build your collection economically from the comfort of your own home.

We Provide:

■ Free advice from our team of international specialists.

■ Large stocks of guaranteed quality material.

■ Fast 48 hour order despatch.

■ Regular well produced, illustrated brochures and lists.

■ Exclusive special offers mailed regularly.

■ Wants lists service available.

Telephone 0171 836 8444 for free copies of our latest Great Britain, Channel Islands, Australia, Canada, New Zealand and Falkland Islands brochures.

Or send your wants list to:
Stanley Gibbons Mail Order
399 Strand, London
WC2R 0LX
and we'll do our best to help.

STANLEY GIBBONS *Mail Order*

• OUR NAME IS YOUR GUARANTEE OF QUALITY •

GRENADINES OF GRENADA

Part of a group of islands north of Grenada, the most important of which is Carriacou. The Grenadine islands further north are administered by St. Vincent, and their stamps are listed after that country.

GRENADINES

	(1)				(2)

1973 (29 Dec). *Royal Wedding. Nos. 582/4 of Grenada optd with T 1.*

1	**196**	25 c. multicoloured			20	10
2		$2 multicoloured			70	50
		a. Albino opt				
MS3		79 × 100 mm. 75 c. and $1 as Nos. 1/2			1·00	50

1974 (29 May). *Nos. 306 etc of Grenada optd with T 2.*

4	1 c. multicoloured			10	10
5	2 c. multicoloured			10	10
6	3 c. multicoloured			10	10
7	5 c. multicoloured			10	10
8	8 c. multicoloured			10	10
9	10 c. multicoloured			15	10
10	12 c. multicoloured			25	10
11	25 c. multicoloured			10	10
12	$1 multicoloured			2·25	45
13	$2 multicoloured			2·75	1·00
14	$3 multicoloured			2·75	1·50
15	$5 multicoloured			3·75	1·75
4/15		*Set of 12*		11·00	4·50

1974 (17 Sept). *World Cup Football Championships. As Nos. 619/27 of Grenada but additionally inscr "GRENADINES".*

16	**201**	½ c. Type **201**			10	10
17		1 c. East Germany v Australia			10	10
18		2 c. Yugoslavia v Brazil			10	10
19		10 c. Scotland v Zaire			10	10
20		25 c. Netherlands v Uruguay			10	10
21		50 c. Sweden v Bulgaria			15	15
22		75 c. Italy v Haiti			20	20
23		$1 Poland v Argentina			25	25
16/23			*Set of 8*		70	70
MS24		114 × 76 mm. $2 Country flags			75	80

1974 (8 Oct). *Centenary of Universal Postal Union. Designs as Nos. 628 etc of Grenada, but additionally inscr "GRENADINES".*

25	8 c. Mailboat *Caesar* (1839) and helicopter		10	10
26	25 c. Messenger (1450) and satellite		15	10
27	35 c. Airmail transport		15	10
28	$1 Type **202**		70	40
25/8		*Set of 4*	1·00	60
MS29	172 × 109 mm. $1 Bellman and antenna; $2 18th-century postman and mail-train of the future. P 13		1·00	1·00

1974 (11 Nov). *Birth Centenary of Sir Winston Churchill. As Nos. 637/9 of Grenada but additionally inscr "GRENADINES".*

30	**203**	35 c. multicoloured			15	10
31	—	$2 multicoloured			40	45
MS32		129 × 96 mm. 75 c. as 35 c. and $1 as $2			35	80

1974 (27 Nov). *Christmas. As Nos. 640/8 of Grenada but additionally inscr "GRENADINES".*

33	**204**	½ c. Type **204**			10	10
34		1 c. Niccolo di Pietro			10	10
35		2 c. Van der Weyden			10	10
36		3 c. Bastiani			10	10
37		10 c. Giovanni			10	10
38		25 c. Van der Weyden			10	10
39		50 c. Botticelli			15	15
40		$1 Mantegna			30	25
33/40			*Set of 8*		65	60
MS41		117 × 96 mm. $2 as 1 c.			45	60

CANCELLED REMAINDERS*. Some of the following issues have been remaindered, cancelled-to-order, at a fraction of their face value. For all practical purposes these are indistinguishable from genuine postally used copies. Our used quotations, which are indicated by an asterisk, are the same for cancelled-to-order or postally used copies.

1975 (17 Feb). *Big Game Fishing. As Nos. 669 etc of Grenada, but additionally inscr "GRENADINES" and background colours changed.*

42	**206**	½ c. Type **206**			10	10
43		1 c. Blue Marlin			10	10
44		2 c. White Marlin			10	10
45		10 c. Yellow-finned Tuna			10	10
46		25 c. Wahoo			20	15
47		50 c. Dolphin (fish)			25	20
48		70 c. Giant Grouper			35	35
49		$1 Great Barracuda			90	85
42/9			*Set of 8*		90	85
MS50		107×80 mm. $2 Short-finned Mako			60	90

1975 (11 Mar). *Flowers. As Nos. 678 etc of Grenada, but additionally inscr. "GRENADINES".*

51	**207**	½ c. Type **207**			10	10
52		1 c. Bleeding Heart (Easter Lily)			10	10
53		2 c. Poinsettia			10	10
54		3 c. Cocoa flower			10	10
55		10 c. Gladioli			10	10
56		25 c. Redhead/Yellowhead			20	15
57		50 c. Plumbago			30	20
58		$1 Orange flower			30	20
51/8			*Set of 8*		65	50
MS59		102 × 82 mm. $2 Barbados Gooseberry			60	70

3 "Christ Crowned with Thorns" (Titian)   4 "Dawn" (detail from Medici Tomb)

(Des M. Shamir. Litho Format)

1975 (24 June). *Easter. T 3 and similar vert designs showing Crucifixion and Deposition scenes by the artists listed. Multicoloured. P 14½.*

60	½ c. Type **3**			10	10*
61	1 c. Giotto			10	10*
62	2 c. Tintoretto			10	10*
63	3 c. Cranach			10	10*
64	35 c. Caravaggio			15	10*
65	75 c. Tiepolo			20	10*
66	$2 Velasquez			40	15*
60/6		*Set of 7*		70	30*
MS67	105 × 90 mm. $1 Titian. P 13			60	30

(Des M. Shamir. Litho Format)

1975 (16 July). *500th Birth Anniv of Michelangelo. T 4 and similar vert designs. Multicoloured. P 14½.*

68	½ c. Type **4**			10	10*
69	1 c. "Delphic Sibyl"			10	10*
70	2 c. "Giuliano de Medici"			10	10*
71	40 c. "The Creation" (detail)			20	10*
72	50 c. "Lorenzo de Medici"			20	10*
73	75 c. "Persian Sibyl"			30	10*
74	$2 "Head of Christ"			40	15*
68/74		*Set of 7*		1·00	35*
MS75	118 × 96 mm. $1 "The Prophet Jeremiah". P 13			75	50

1975 (12 Aug). *Butterflies. Designs as Nos. 729 etc of Grenada, but additionally inscr "GRENADINES". P 14½.*

76	½ c. *Morpho peleides*			10	10*
77	1 c. *Danaus eresimus* ("*Danaus gilippus*")			10	10*
78	2 c. *Dismorphia amphione*			10	10*
79	35 c. *Hamadryas feronia*			35	10*
80	45 c. *Philaethria dido*			45	10*
81	75 c. *Phoebis argante*			70	15*
82	$2 *Prepona laertes*			1·40	30*
76/82		*Set of 7*		2·75	60*
MS83	104×77 mm. $1 *Siproeta stelenes*. P 13			2·75	2·25

5 Progress "Standard" Badge

(Des J.W. Litho Format)

1975 (22 Aug). *14th World Scout Jamboree, Norway. T 5 and similar horiz designs. Multicoloured. P 14½.*

84	½ c. Type **5**			10	10*
85	1 c. Boatman's badge			10	10*
86	2 c. Coxswain's badge			10	10*
87	35 c. Interpreter's badge			25	10*
88	45 c. Ambulance badge			25	10*
89	75 c. Chief Scout's award			35	10*
90	$2 Queen's Scout award			55	10*
84/90		*Set of 7*		1·25	35*
MS91	106 × 80 mm. $1 Venture award. P 13			55	30*

6 The Surrender of Lord Cornwallis

(Des J.W. Litho Questa)

1975 (30 Sept)–**76**. *Bicentenary of American Revolution (1st issue). Multicoloured. (a) Horiz designs as T 6. P 14.*

92	½ c. Type **6**			10	10*
93	1 c. Minute-men			10	10*
94	2 c. Paul Revere's ride			10	10*
95	3 c. Battle of Bunker Hill			10	10*
96	5 c. Fifer and drummers			10	10*
97	45 c. Backwoodsman			30	10*
98	75 c. Boston Tea Party			45	10*
99	$2 Naval engagement			1·25	10*

(b) Larger designs. P 11 (16.1.76)

100	$2 George Washington (35 × 60 mm)		1·25	50
101	$2 White House and flags (60 × 35 mm)		1·25	50
92/101		*Set of 10*	4·25	1·25
MS102	Two sheets 113 × 128 mm containing No. 100, and 128 × 113 mm containing No. 101. Imperf		1·75	1·75

See also Nos. 176/**MS**183

7 Fencing   8 "Madonna and Child" (Dürer)

(Des J.W. Ltd. Litho Format)

1975 (27 Oct). *Pan-American Games, Mexico City. T 7 and similar horiz designs. Multicoloured. P 14½.*

103	½ c. Type **7**			10	10*
104	1 c. Hurdling			10	10*
105	2 c. Pole-vaulting			10	10*
106	35 c. Weightlifting			15	10*
107	45 c. Throwing the javelin			15	10*
108	75 c. Throwing the discus			15	10*
109	$2 Diving			35	15*
103/109		*Set of 7*		75	35*
MS110	78 × 104 mm. $1 Sprinter. P 13			40	20*

1975 (5 Nov)–**76**. *As Nos. 649A/68A of Grenada but additionally inscribed "GRENADINES". Multicoloured.*

111	½ c. Yachts, Port Saline		10	30
112	1 c. Yacht Club race, St. George's		10	15
113	2 c. Carenage taxi		10	15
114	3 c. Large working boats		10	15
115	5 c. Deep-water dock, St. George's		10	15
116	6 c. Cocoa beans in drying trays		10	15
117	8 c. Nutmegs		10	15
118	10 c. Rum distillery, River Antoine Estate, circa 1785		10	15
119	12 c. Cocoa tree		10	15
120	15 c. Fishermen landing catch at Fontenoy		10	15
121	20 c. Parliament Building, St. George's		10	30
122	25 c. Fort George cannons		10	15
123	35 c. Pearls Airport		15	15
124	50 c. General Post Office		20	50
125	75 c. Caribs Leap, Sauteurs Bay		40	60
126	$1 Carenage, St. George's		60	85
127	$2 St. George's Harbour by night		90	2·00
128	$3 Grand Anse beach		1·10	2·50
129	$5 Canoe Bay and Black Bay from Point Saline Lighthouse		1·75	5·00
130	$10 Sugar-loaf Island from Levera Beach (1.76)		3·50	5·50
111/30		*Set of 20*	8·00	17·00

(Des M. Shamir. Litho Questa)

1975 (17 Dec). *Christmas. T 8 and similar vert designs showing "Virgin and Child". Multicoloured. P 14.*

131	½ c. Type **8**			10	10*
132	1 c. Dürer			10	10*
133	2 c. Correggio			10	10*
134	40 c. Botticelli			15	10*
135	50 c. Niccolo da Cremona			15	10*
136	75 c. Correggio			15	10*
137	$2 Correggio			30	15*
131/7		*Set of 7*		70	35*
MS138	114 × 102 mm. $1 Bellini			60	50*

9 Bleeding Tooth (*Nerita peloronta*)

(Des J.W. Litho Questa)

1976 (13 Jan). *Shells. T 9 and similar horiz designs. Multicoloured. P 14.*

139	½ c. Type **9**			10	10*
140	1 c. Toothed Donax (*Donax denticulatus*)			10	10*
141	2 c. Hawk-wing Conch (*Strombus raninus*)			10	10*
142	3 c. Atlantic Distorsio (*Distorsio clathrata*)			10	10*
143	25 c. Scotch Bonnet (*Phalium ganulatum*)			30	10*
144	50 c. King Helmet (*Cassis tuberosa*)			60	10*
145	75 c. Queen or Pink Conch (*Strombus gigas*)			85	15*
139/45		*Set of 7*		1·75	30*
MS146	79×105 mm. $2 Atlantic Trumpet Triton (*Charonia variegata*)			1·00	70*

10 Cocoa Thrush

(Des J.W. Litho Questa)

1976 (4 Feb). *Flora and Fauna. T 10 and similar horiz designs. Multicoloured. P 14.*

147	½ c. *Lignum vitae*			10	10*
148	1 c. Type **10**			10	10*
149	2 c. *Eurypelma* sp (spider)			10	10*
150	35 c. Hooded Tanager			1·25	10*
151	50 c. *Nyctaginaceae*			1·00	15*
152	75 c. Grenada Dove			2·50	25*
153	$1 Marine Toad			2·50	25*
147/53		*Set of 7*		6·50	70*
MS154	108 × 84 mm. $2 Blue-hooded Euphonia			3·75	1·00*

11 Hooked Sailfish

(Des G. Drummond. Litho Questa)

1976 (17 Feb). *Tourism. T* **11** *and similar horiz designs. Multi-coloured. P* 14.

155	½ c. Type **11**		10	10*
156	1 c. Careened schooner, Carriacou		10	10*
157	2 c. Carriacou Annual Regatta		10	10*
158	18 c. Boat building on Carriacou		20	10*
159	22 c. Workboat race, Carriacou Regatta		20	10*
160	75 c. Cruising off Petit Martinique		30	20*
161	$1 Water skiing		40	20*
155/61		Set of 7	1·00	60*
MS162	105 × 87 mm. $2 Yacht racing at Carriacou		70	75*

12 Making a Camp Fire

13 "Christ Mocked" (Bosch)

(Des G. Vasarhelyi. Litho Questa)

1976 (17 Mar). *50th Anniv of Girl Guides in Grenada. T* **12** *and similar horiz designs. Multicoloured. P* 14.

163	½ c. Type **12**		10	10*
164	1 c. First aid		10	10*
165	2 c. Nature study		10	10*
166	50 c. Cookery		65	15*
167	$1 Sketching		1·00	25*
163/7		Set of 5	1·60	50*
MS168	85 × 110 mm. $2 Guide playing guitar		1·00	75*

(Des PAD Studio. Litho Questa)

1976 (28 Apr). *Easter. T* **13** *and similar vert designs. Multi-coloured. P* 14.

169	½ c. Type **13**		10	10*
170	1 c. "Christ Crucified" (Antonello da Messina)		10	10*
171	2 c. "Adoration of the Trinity" (Dürer)		10	10*
172	3 c. "Lamentation of Christ" (Dürer)		10	10*
173	35 c. "The Entombment" (Van der Weyden)		20	10*
174	$3 "The Entombment" (Raphael)		75	30*
169/74		Set of 6	95	50*
MS175	57 × 72 mm. $2 "Blood of the Redeemer" (G. Bellini)		65	70*

14 *South Carolina* (frigate)

(Des J.W. Litho Questa)

1976 (18 May). *Bicentenary of American Revolution (2nd issue). T* **14** *and similar horiz designs. Multicoloured. P* 14.

176	½ c. Type **14**		10	10*
177	1 c. *Lee* (schooner)		10	10*
178	2 c. H.M.S. *Roebuck* (frigate)		10	10*
179	35 c. *Andrew Doria* (brig)		60	10*
180	50 c. *Providence* (sloop)		80	15*
181	$1 *Alfred* (frigate)		1·50	20*
182	$2 *Confederacy* (frigate)		2·00	30*
176/82		Set of 7	4·50	75*
MS183	72×85 mm. $3 *Revenge* (cutter)		1·50	1·00*

15 Piper PA-23 Apache

(Des J.W. Litho Format)

1976 (10 June). *Aircraft. T* **15** *and similar horiz designs. Multicoloured. P* 14.

184	½ c. Type **15**		10	10*
185	1 c. Beech 50 Twin Bonanza		10	10*
186	2 c. De Havilland D.H.C.6 Twin Otter 100		10	10*
187	40 c. Britten Norman Islander		30	10*
188	50 c. De Havilland D.H.114 Heron 2		40	10*
189	$2 Hawker Siddeley H.S.748		1·25	25*
184/9		Set of 6	1·75	55*
MS190	71×85 mm. $3 B.A.C. One Eleven 500		1·00	1·00*

16 Cycling

17 "Virgin and Child" (Cima)

(Des J.W. Litho Format)

1976 (1 July). *Olympic Games, Montreal. T* **16** *and similar horiz designs. Multicoloured. P* 14.

191	½ c. Type **16**		10	10*
192	1 c. Pommel horse		10	10*
193	2 c. Hurdling		10	10*
194	35 c. Shot putting		10	10*
195	45 c. Diving		15	10*
196	75 c. Sprinting		15	10*
197	$2 Rowing		35	25*
191/7		Set of 7	70	60*
MS198	101 × 76 mm. $3 Sailing		80	75*

(Litho Format)

1976 (19 Oct). *Christmas. T* **17** *and similar multicoloured designs. P* 13½.

199	½ c. Type **17**		10	10*
200	1 c. "The Nativity" (Romanino)		10	10*
201	2 c. "The Nativity" (Romanino) (*different*)		10	10*
202	35 c. "Adoration of the Kings" (Bruegel)		15	10*
203	50 c. "Madonna and Child" (Girolamo)		20	10*
204	75 c. "Adoration of the Magi" (Giorgione) (*horiz*)		20	15*
205	$2 "Adoration of the Kings" (School of Fra Angelico) (*horiz*)		40	25*
199/205		Set of 7	1·00	60*
MS206	120 × 100 mm. $3 "The Holy Family" (Garofalo)		60	2·25

18 Alexander Graham Bell and First Telephone

(Des G. Vasarhelyi. Litho Questa)

1977 (28 Jan). *Telephone Centenary (1976). T* **18** *and similar horiz designs showing Alexander Graham Bell and telephone. Multicoloured. P* 14.

207	½ c. Type **18**		10	10*
208	1 c. Telephone, 1895		10	10*
209	2 c. Telephone, 1900		10	10*
210	35 c. Telephone, 1915		15	10*
211	75 c. Telephone, 1920		20	10*
212	$1 Telephone, 1929		25	15*
213	$2 Telephone, 1963		35	25*
207/13		Set of 7	85	60*
MS214	107 × 78 mm. $3 Telephone, 1976		1·10	75*

19 Coronation Coach

20 Royal Visit

(Des Jennifer Toombs. Litho and embossed Walsall. (Nos. 215/18). Des and litho Walsall (Nos. 219/22))

1977 (7 Feb). *Silver Jubilee. Multicoloured.*

(a) *Sheet stamps. Horiz designs as T* **19**. *P* 13½

215	35 c. Type **19**		10	10*
216	$2 Queen entering Abbey		20	20*
217	$4 Queen crowned		35	25*
215/17		Set of 3	55	35*
MS218	100 × 70 mm. $5 The Mall on Coronation Night		60	1·25

Nos. 215/17 also exist perf 11 (*Price for set of 3 60p. mint or used*) from additional sheetlets of 3 stamps and 1 label. These have different background colours from the stamps perforated 13½, which come from normal sheets of 25.

(b) *Booklet stamps. Vert designs as T* **20**. *Roul* 5 × *imperf.**
Self-adhesive

219	35 c. Type **20**		15	20
	a. Booklet pane of 6.		70	
220	50 c. Crown of St. Edward		40	80
	a. Booklet pane. Nos. 220/2.		1·75	

221	$2 The Queen and Prince Charles		75	1·60
222	$5 Royal Standard		90	1·75
219/22		Set of 4	2·00	4·00

*Nos. 219/22 are separated by various combinations of rotary knife (giving a straight edge) and roulette.

21 "Disrobing of Christ" (Fra Angelico)

22 "The Virgin adoring the Child" (Correggio)

(Des J.W. Litho Questa)

1977 (5 July). *Easter. Vert designs as T* **21** *showing paintings by the artists given. Multicoloured. P* 14.

223	½ c. Type **21**		10	10*
224	1 c. Fra Angelico		10	10*
225	2 c. El Greco		10	10*
226	18 c. El Greco		10	10*
227	35 c. Fra Angelico		15	10*
228	50 c. Giottino		20	10*
229	$2 Antonello da Messina		50	25*
223/9		Set of 7	85	50*
MS230	121 × 94 mm. $3 Fra Angelico		85	75*

(Des J.W. Litho Questa)

1977 (17 Nov). *Christmas. T* **22** *and similar vert designs. Multicoloured. P* 14.

231	½ c. Type **22**		10	10*
232	1 c. "Virgin and Child" (Giorgione)		10	10*
233	2 c. "Virgin and Child" (Morales)		10	10*
234	18 c. "Madonna della Tenda" (Raphael)		10	10*
235	35 c. "Rest on the Flight into Egypt" (Van Dyck)		15	10*
236	50 c. "Madonna and Child" (Lippi)		20	10*
237	$2 "Virgin and Child" (Lippi) (*different*)		60	25*
231/7		Set of 7	95	50*
MS238	114 × 99 mm. $3 "Virgin and Child with Angels and Saints" (Ghirlandaio)		85	75*

ROYAL VISIT   **W.I. 1977**

(23)

1977 (23 Nov). *Royal Visit. Nos. 215/18 optd with T* **23**. *P* 13½.

239	35 c. Type **19**		10	10
240	$2 Queen entering Abbey		25	20
241	$4 Queen crowned		40	30
239/41		Set of 3	60	50
MS242	100 × 70 mm. $5 The Mall on Coronation Night		70	90

This overprint also exists on the stamps perforated 11, mentioned below No. MS218 (*price for set of 3 90p. mint or used*).

24 Life-saving

(Des G. Drummond. Litho Questa)

1977 (7 Dec). *Caribbean Scout Jamboree, Jamaica. T* **24** *and similar horiz designs. Multicoloured. P* 14.

243	½ c. Type **24**		10	10*
244	1 c. Overnight hike		10	10*
245	2 c. Cubs tying knots		10	10*
246	22 c. Erecting a tent		15	10*
247	35 c. Gang show limbo dance		25	10*
248	75 c. Campfire cooking		40	15*
249	$3 Sea Scouts' yacht race		1·25	30*
243/9		Set of 7	1·90	65*
MS250	109 × 85 mm. $2 Pioneering project —Spring bridge		1·10	90*

25 Blast-off

(Des J.W. Litho Questa)

1978 (3 Feb). *Space Shuttle. T* **25** *and similar horiz designs. Multicoloured. P* 14.

251	½ c. Type **25**		10	10*
252	1 c. Booster jettison		10	10*
253	2 c. External tank jettison		10	10*
254	22 c. Working in orbit		15	10*
255	50 c. Shuttle re-entry		25	10*
256	$3 Shuttle landing		85	30*
251/6		Set of 6	1·10	50*
MS257	85 × 103 mm. $2 Shuttle being towed		60	70*

26 Alfred Nobel and Physiology/Medicine Medal

(Des J.W. Litho Questa)

1978 (22 Feb). *Nobel Prize Awards. T **26** and similar horiz designs. Multicoloured. P 14.*

258	½ c. Type **26**		10	10*
259	1 c. Physics and Chemistry medal		10	10*
260	2 c. Peace medal		10	10*
261	22 c. Nobel Institute, Oslo		25	10*
262	75 c. Peace Prize committee		50	15*
263	$3 Literature medal		1·50	30*
258/63		Set of 6	2·00	60*
MS264	127 × 103 mm. $2 Peace medal and Nobel's will		50	60*

27 German Zeppelin Stamp of 1930

(Des J.W. Litho Questa)

1978 (15 Mar). *75th Anniv of First Zeppelin Flight and 50th Anniv of Lindbergh's Trans-atlantic Flight. T **27** and similar horiz designs. Multicoloured. P 14 × 13½.*

265	5 c. Type **27**		20	10*
266	15 c. French Concorde stamp, 1970		60	10*
267	25 c. Liechtenstein Zeppelin stamp, 1931		20	10*
268	35 c. Panama Lindbergh stamp, 1928		20	10*
269	50 c. Russian airship stamp, 1931		25	10*
270	$3 Spanish Lindbergh stamp, 1930		75	30*
265/70		Set of 6	2·00	50*
MS271	140×79 mm. 75 c. U.S.A. Lindberg stamp, 1927; $2 German LZ-129 *Hindenburg* stamp, 1936		1·10	90*

28 Coronation Ring

29 Drummer, Royal Regiment of Fusiliers.

(Des J.W. Litho Questa (Nos. 272/5). Manufactured by Walsall (Nos. 276/8))

1978 (12 Apr). *25th Anniv of Coronation. Multicoloured.*

*(a) Sheet stamps. Horiz designs as T **28**. P 14*

272	50 c. Type **28**		10	10
273	$2 Queen's Orb		25	30
274	$2.50 Imperial State Crown		30	35
272/4		Set of 3	60	65
MS275	97 × 67 mm. $5 Queen Elizabeth II		60	60

Nos. 272/4 also exist perf 12 (*Price for set of 3 90p. mint or used*) from additional sheetlets of 3 stamps and 1 label, issued 2 June. These have different background colours from the stamps perforated 14, which come from normal sheets of 50.

*(b) Booklet stamps. Vert designs as T **29**. Roul 5 × imperf.* Self-adhesive

276	18 c. Type **29**		15	35
	a. Booklet pane. Nos. 276/7 × 3		70	
277	50 c. Drummer, Royal Anglian Regiment		15	45
278	$5 Drum Major, Queen's Regiment		1·00	3·00
	a. Booklet pane of 1		1·00	
276/8		Set of 3	1·10	3·50

*Nos. 276/7 are separated by various combinations of rotary-knife (giving a straight edge) and roulette. No. 278 exists only with straight edges.

30 "Le Chapeau de Paille"

31 Wright Flyer I

(Litho Questa)

1978 (18 May). *400th Birth Anniv of Rubens. T **30** and similar vert designs. Multicoloured. P 14.*

279	5 c. Type **30**		10	10
280	15 c. "Achilles slaying Hector"		15	10

281	18 c. "Helene Fourment and her Children"		15	10
282	22 c. "Rubens and Isabella Brandt"		20	10
283	35 c. "The Ildefonso Altarpiece"		20	10
284	$3 "Heads of Negroes" (detail)		1·10	1·00
279/84		Set of 6	1·60	1·25
MS285	85 × 127 mm. $2 "Self-portrait"		70	1·00

(Des BG Studio. Litho Questa)

1978 (10 Aug). *75th Anniv of Powered Flight. T **31** and similar designs. P 14.*

286	5 c. black, chestnut and pale blue		10	10
287	15 c. black, vermilion and yellow-ochre		10	10
288	18 c. black, vermilion and yellow-ochre		10	10
289	25 c. multicoloured		10	10
290	35 c. black, purple and magenta		15	10
291	75 c. multicoloured		25	25
292	$3 black, magenta and new blue		75	75
286/92		Set of 7	1·10	1·10
MS293	126 × 83 mm. $2 black, blue and bright blue-green		75	1·00

Designs: *Vert*—15 c. Orville Wright; 18 c. Wilbur Wright. *Horiz*—25 c. Wright Flyer III; 35 c. Wright glider No. 1; 75 c. Wright Flyer I; $2 Various Wright aircraft; $3 Wright Type A.

32 Audubon's Shearwater

33 Players with Ball

(Des Jennifer Toombs. Litho Questa)

1978 (28 Sept). *Birds. T **32** and similar multicoloured designs. P 14.*

294	5 c. Type **32**		50	10
295	10 c. Semipalmated Plover		70	10
296	18 c. Purple-throated Carib (*horiz*)		1·00	15
297	22 c. Red-billed Whistling Duck (*horiz*)		1·00	20
298	40 c. Caribbean Martin (*horiz*)		1·50	35
299	$1 White-tailed Tropic Bird		2·25	75
300	$2 Long-billed Curlew		3·25	1·25
294/300		Set of 7	9·00	2·50
MS301	78 × 78 mm. $5 Snowy Egret		5·00	2·75

(Des G. Vasarhelyi. Litho Questa)

1978 (2 Nov). *World Cup Football Championship, Argentina. T **33** and similar vert designs showing football scenes. P 14.*

302	15 c. multicoloured		10	10
303	35 c. multicoloured		20	10
304	50 c. multicoloured		25	20
305	$3 multicoloured		80	80
302/5		Set of 4	1·10	90
MS306	114 × 85 mm. $2 multicoloured		80	1·25

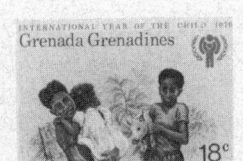

34 Captain Cook and Kalaniopu (king of Hawaii), 1778

35 "Virgin at Prayer"

(Des BG Studio. Litho Questa)

1978 (13 Dec). *250th Birth Anniv of Captain Cook and Bicentenary of Discovery of Hawaii. T **34** and similar horiz designs. Multicoloured. P 14.*

307	18 c. Type **34**		45	10
308	22 c. Captain Cook and native of Hawaii		60	15
309	50 c. Captain Cook and death scene, 14 February 1779		1·00	30
310	$3 Captain Cook and offering ceremony		2·25	1·75
307/10		Set of 4	3·75	2·00
MS311	171 × 113 mm. $4 H.M.S. *Resolution* (*vert*)		2·00	2·00

(Des M. Rubin. Litho Questa)

1978 (20 Dec). *Christmas. Paintings by Dürer. T **35** and similar vert designs. Multicoloured. P 14.*

312	40 c. Type **35**		20	10
313	60 c. "The Dresden Altarpiece"		25	15
314	90 c. "Madonna and Child with St. Anne"		30	15
315	$2 "Madonna and Child with Pear"		60	50
312/15		Set of 4	1·25	80
MS316	114 × 84 mm. $4 "Salvator Mundi"		1·00	1·40

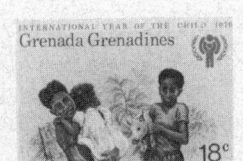

36 *Strelitzia reginae*

37 Children with Pig

(Des J.W. Litho Questa)

1979 (15 Feb). *Flowers. T **36** and similar vert designs. Multicoloured. P 14.*

317	22 c. Type **36**		15	10
318	40 c. *Euphorbia pulcherrima*		25	15
319	$1 *Heliconia humilis*		55	30
320	$3 *Thunbergia alata*		1·25	80
317/20		Set of 4	2·00	1·10
MS321	114 × 90 mm. $2 *Bougainvillea glabra*		75	1·00

(Des G. Drummond. Litho Questa)

1979 (22 Mar). *International Year of the Child. T **37** and similar horiz designs. Multicoloured. P 14.*

322	18 c. Type **37**		10	10
323	50 c. Children with donkey		20	25
324	$1 Children with goats		25	30
325	$3 Children fishing		65	80
322/5		Set of 4	1·00	1·25
MS326	104 × 86 mm. $4 Child with coconuts		1·00	1·90

38 20,000 *Leagues Under the Sea*

(Des G. Vasarhelyi. Litho Questa)

1979 (20 Apr). *150th Birth Anniv of Jules Verne (author). T **38** and similar horiz designs showing scenes from his books and modern technological developments. Multicoloured. P 14.*

327	18 c. Type **38**		20	10
328	38 c. *From the Earth to the Moon*		25	20
329	75 c. *From the Earth to the Moon* (*different*)		40	35
330	$3 *Five Weeks in a Balloon*		80	1·00
327/30		Set of 4	1·50	1·50
MS331	111 × 86 mm. $4 *Around the World in 80 days*		1·00	1·60

39 Sir Rowland Hill and Mail Van

(Des BG Studio. Litho Questa)

1979 (30 July). *Death Centenary of Sir Rowland Hill. T **39** and similar horiz designs showing Sir Rowland Hill and mail transport. Multicoloured. P 14.*

332	15 c. Type **39**		10	10
333	$1 *Britanis* (cargo liner)		20	20
334	$2 Diesel mail train		30	30
335	$3 Concorde		90	70
332/5		Set of 4	1·25	1·10
MS336	85×67 mm. $4 Sir Rowland Hill		75	1·00

Nos. 332/5 also exist perf 12 (*Price for set of 4 £1.25 mint or used*) from additional sheetlets of 5 stamps and 1 label issued 6 September. These have different background colours to the stamps perforated 14, which come from normal sheets of 40.

40 "Virgin and Child Enthroned" (11th-century Byzantine)

41 Great Hammerhead

(Des G. Vasarhelyi. Litho Questa)

1979 (23 Oct). *Christmas. Sculptures. T **40** and similar vert designs. Multicoloured. P 14.*

337	6 c. Type **40**		10	10
338	25 c. "Presentation in the Temple" (Andre Beauneveu)		10	10
339	30 c. "Flight to Egypt", Utrecht, *circa* 1510		10	10
340	40 c. "Madonna and Child" (Jacopo della Quercia)		10	10
341	90 c. "Madonna della Mela" (Luca della Robbia)		15	15
342	$1 "Madonna and Child" (Antonio Rossellino)		20	20
343	$2 "Madonna", Antwerp, 1700		35	35
337/43		Set of 7	80	80
MS344	125 × 95 mm. $4 "Virgin", Krumau		65	1·10

(Des J.W. Litho Questa)

1979 (9 Nov). *Marine Life. T **41** and similar horiz designs. Multicoloured. P 14 × 13½.*

345	40 c. Type **41**		40	30
346	45 c. Spot-finned Butterflyfish		45	30
347	50 c. Permit (fish)		45	40
348	60 c. Threaded Turban (shell)		65	55
349	70 c. Milk Conch (shell)		75	75
350	75 c. Great Blue Heron		85	90
351	90 c. Colourful Atlantic Moon (shell)		95	1·00

352	$1 Red-footed Booby	1·50	1·75
345/52	*Set of 8*	5·50	5·50
MS353	99 × 86 mm. $2.50 Collared Plover	2·00	1·10

42 Goofy as Doctor   **43** Classroom

(Litho Format)

1979 (12 Dec). *International Year of the Child. Walt Disney Cartoon Characters. T* **42** *and similar multicoloured designs showing characters at various occupations. P* 11.

354	½ c. Type **42**	10	10
355	1 c. Mickey Mouse as admiral	10	10
356	2 c. Goofy as fireman	10	10
357	3 c. Minnie Mouse as nurse	10	10
358	4 c. Mickey Mouse as drum major	10	10
359	5 c. Donald Duck as policeman	10	10
360	10 c. Donald Duck as pilot	10	10
361	$2 Goofy as postman (*horiz*)	2·25	2·25
362	$2.50, Donald Duck as train driver (*horiz*)	2·25	2·25
354/62	*Set of 9*	4·50	4·50
MS363	128 × 102 mm. $3 Mickey Mouse as fireman. P 13½	1·75	2·00

1980 (10 Mar). *1st Anniv of Revolution. Nos.* 116 *and* 119/30 *optd with T* **259** *of Grenada.*

364	6 c. Cocoa beans in drying trays	10	10
365	12 c. Cocoa Tree	10	10
366	15 c. Fishermen landing catch at Fontenoy	10	10
367	20 c. Parliament Building, St. George's	10	10
368	25 c. Fort George cannons	15	10
369	35 c. Pearls Airport	20	10
370	50 c. General Post Office	35	15
371	75 c. Caribs Leap, Sauteurs Bay	40	20
372	$1 Carenage, St. George's	55	30
373	$2 St. George's Harbour by night	85	70
374	$3 Grand Anse Beach	1·60	1·60
375	$5 Canoe Bay and Black Bay from Point Saline Lighthouse	2·25	2·50
376	$10 Sugar Loaf Island from Levera Beach	3·75	4·25
364/76	*Set of 13*	9·50	9·00

(Des BG Studio. Litho Questa)

1980 (12 Mar). *75th Anniv of Rotary International. T* **43** *and similar horiz designs. Multicoloured. P* 14.

377	6 c. Type **43**	10	10
378	30 c. Rotary International emblem encircled by people of different races	20	10
379	60 c. Rotary International executive presenting doctor with cheque	35	20
380	$3 Nurses with young patients	1·60	75
377/80	*Set of 4*	2·00	1·00
MS381	85 × 72 mm. $4 Paul P. Harris (founder)	1·00	1·60

44 Yellow-bellied Seedeater   **45** Running

(Des G. Drummond. Litho Questa)

1980 (14 Apr). *Wild Birds. T* **44** *and similar vert designs. Multicoloured. P* 14.

382	25 c. Type **44**	50	15
383	40 c. Blue-hooded Euphonia	55	20
384	90 c. Yellow Warbler	1·25	65
385	$2 Tropical Mockingbird	1·75	1·25
382/5	*Set of 4*	3·50	2·00
MS386	83 × 110 mm. $3 Barn Owl	3·50	2·00

(Des G. Vasarhelyi. Litho Questa)

1980 (21 Apr). *Olympic Games, Moscow. T* **45** *and similar horiz designs. Multicoloured. P* 14.

387	30 c. Type **45**	15	15
388	40 c. Football	15	20
389	90 c. Boxing	30	35
390	$2 Wrestling	60	75
387/90	*Set of 4*	1·00	1·25
MS391	104 × 75 mm. $4 Athletes in silhouette	75	1·10

LONDON 1980   (46)   **47** Long-jawed Squirrelfish

1980 (6 May). *"London 1980" International Stamp Exhibition. Nos.* 332/5 *optd with T* **46**. *P* 12.

392	15 c. Type **39**	15	15
393	$1 Britanis (cargo liner)	75	35
394	$2 Diesel mail train	1·50	1·00
395	$3 Concorde	2·25	2·00
392/5	*Set of 4*	4·25	3·25

(Des G. Drummond. Litho Questa)

1980 (6 Aug)–**87**. *Fishes. Horiz designs as T* **47**. *Multicoloured. P* 14. **A**. *Without imprint date.*

396A	½ c. Type **47**	10	10
397A	1 c. Blue Chromis	10	10
398A	2 c. Four-eyed Butterflyfish	10	10
399A	4 c. Sergeant Major	10	10
400A	5 c. Yellow-tailed Snapper	10	10
401A	6 c. Mutton Snapper	10	10
402A	10 c. Cocoa Damselfish	10	10
403A	12 c. Royal Gramma	10	10
404A	15 c. Cherub Angelfish	15	10
405A	20 c. Black-barred Soldierfish	15	10
406A	25 c. Mottled Grouper	15	15
407A	30 c. Caribbean Long-nosed Butterflyfish	15	20
408A	40 c. Puddingwife	20	25
409A	50 c. Midnight Parrotfish	25	35
410A	90 c. Red-spotted Hawkfish	40	55
411A	$1 Hogfish	45	60
412A	$3 Beau Gregory	1·25	1·50
413A	$5 Rock Beauty	2·00	2·50
414A	$10 Barred Hamlet	3·50	5·00
396A/414A	*Set of 19*	8·00	10·00

B. *With imprint date at foot of design.*

396B	½ c. Type **47** (p 12) (1982)	7·00	8·00
402B	10 c. Cocoa Damselfish (1984)	30	30
405B	20 c. Black-barred Soldierfish (1987)	1·00	1·00
346B/405B	*Set of 3*	7·50	8·50

Imprint dates: "1982", No. 396B; "1984", No. 402B; "1987", No. 405B.

(Litho Walsall)

1980 (7 Oct). *Christmas. Walt Disney Cartoon Scenes from "Bambi". Horiz designs as T* **42**. *Multicoloured. P* 11.

415	½ c. Bambi with Mother	10	10
416	1 c. Bambi with quails	10	10
417	2 c. Bambi meets Thumper the rabbit	10	10
418	3 c. Bambi meets Flower the skunk	10	10
419	4 c. Bambi and Faline	10	10
420	5 c. Bambi with his father	10	10
421	10 c. Bambi on ice	10	10
422	$2.50, Faline with foals	1·75	1·25
423	$3 Bambi and Faline	1·75	1·25
415/23	*Set of 9*	3·50	2·50
MS424	127 × 102 mm. $4 Bambi as Prince of the Forest (*vert*)	2·00	2·00

48 "The Unicorn in Captivity" (15th-century unknown artist)   **49** "Bust of a Woman"

(Litho Format)

1981 (25 Jan). *Paintings. T* **48** *and similar multicoloured designs. P* 13½.

425	6 c. Type **48**	10	10
426	10 c. "The Fighting *Temeraire*" (Turner) (*horiz*)	10	10
427	25 c. "Sunday Afternoon on the Ile de la Grande-Jatte" (Georges-Pierre Seurat) (*horiz*)	15	15
428	90 c. "Max Schmitt in a Single Scull" (Thomas Eakins) (*horiz*)	45	45
429	$2 "The Burial of the Count of Orgaz" (El Greco)	85	85
430	$3 "George Washington" (Gilbert Stuart)	1·10	1·10
425/30	*Set of 6*	2·40	2·40
MS431	66 × 101 mm. $5 "Kaiser Karl de Grosse" (detail, Dürer)	1·75	2·00

No. MS431 exists imperforate from stock dispersed by the liquidator of Format International Security Printers Ltd.

(Litho Format)

1981 (26 Jan). *50th Anniv of Walt Disney's Cartoon Character, Pluto. Vert designs as T* **42**. *Multicoloured. P* 13½.

432	$2 Mickey Mouse serving birthday cake to Pluto	90	80
MS433	127 × 101 mm. $4 Pluto in scene from film *Pluto's Dream House*	1·75	1·75

No. 432 was printed in small sheets of 8 stamps.

(Litho Format)

1981 (14 Apr). *Easter. Walt Disney Cartoon Characters. Vert designs as T* **42**. *Multicoloured. P* 11.

434	35 c. Chip	20	20
435	40 c. Dewey	20	20
436	$2 Huey	60	60
437	$2.50, Mickey Mouse	75	75
434/7	*Set of 4*	1·60	1·60
MS438	126 × 102 mm. $4 Jiminy Cricket. P 13½	2·00	2·00

(Des J.W. Litho Questa)

1981 (5 May). *Birth Centenary of Picasso. T* **49** *and similar vert designs. Multicoloured. P* 14.

439	6 c. Type **49**	10	10
440	40 c. Woman (study for "Les Demoiselles d'Avignon")	25	15

50 Balmoral Castle   **51** Lady Diana Spencer

441	90 c. "Nude with raised Arms (The Dancer of Avignon)"	40	30
442	$4 "The Dryad"	1·25	1·25
439/42	*Set of 4*	1·75	1·50
MS443	103 × 128 mm. $5 "Les Demoiselles d'Avignon". Imperf	2·25	2·00

(Des J.W. Litho Format)

1981 (16 June). *Royal Wedding. T* **50** *and similar vert designs. Multicoloured.* (*a*) *P* 15.

444	40 c. Prince Charles and Lady Diana Spencer	15	15
445	$2 Type **50**	35	35
446	$4 Prince Charles as parachutist	50	50
MS447	97 × 84 mm. $5 Royal Coach	90	90

(*b*) *P* 15 × 14½

448	30 c. As No. 444	20	20
449	40 c. Type **50**	20	20
444/9	*Set of 5*	1·25	1·25

The 30 and 40 c. values were each printed in small sheets of 6 including one *se-tenant* stamp-size label.

The $4 value, with changed background colour, also exists perforated 15×14½ (*price* £1.10 *mint or used*) from similar sheetlets in addition to the original version from sheets of 40.

(Manufactured by Walsall)

1981 (16 June). *Royal Wedding. Booklet stamps. T* **51** *and similar multicoloured designs. Roul* 5 × *imperf**. *Self-adhesive.*

450	$1 Type **51**	20	35
	a. Booklet pane. Nos. 450/1 each × 3	1·25	
451	$2 Prince Charles	25	50
452	Prince Charles and Lady Diana Spencer (*horiz*)	1·25	2·00
	a. Booklet pane of 1	1·25	
450/2	*Set of 3*	1·50	2·50

*The $1 and $2 values were each separated by various combinations of rotary knife (giving a straight edge) and roulette. The $5 value exists only with straight edges.

52 Amy Johnson (1st solo flight, Britain to Australia by Woman, May 1930)   **53** Boeing 747 SCA

(Des BG Studio. Litho Questa)

1981 (13 Oct). *"Decade for Women". Famous Female Aviators. T* **52** *and similar vert designs. Multicoloured. P* 14.

453	30 c. Type **52**	45	15
454	70 c. Mme la Baronne de Laroche (1st qualified woman pilot, March 1910)	70	30
455	$1.10, Ruth Nichols (solo Atlantic flight attempt, June 1931)	80	40
456	$3 Amelia Earhart (1st North Atlantic solo flight by woman, May 1932)	1·75	1·10
453/6	*Set of 4*	3·25	1·75
MS457	90 × 85 mm. $5 Valentina Nikolayeva-Tereshkova (1st woman in space, June 1963)	1·25	1·40

(Litho Questa)

1981 (2 Nov). *Christmas. Horiz designs as T* **42** *showing scenes from Walt Disney's cartoon film "Lady and the Tramp". P* 13½.

458	½ c. multicoloured	10	10
459	1 c. multicoloured	10	10
460	2 c. multicoloured	10	10
461	3 c. multicoloured	10	10
462	4 c. multicoloured	10	10
463	5 c. multicoloured	10	10
464	10 c. multicoloured	10	10
465	$2.50, multicoloured	2·50	1·25
466	$3 multicoloured	3·00	1·25
458/66	*Set of 9*	5·25	2·50
MS467	128 × 103 mm. $5 multicoloured	4·00	3·00

(Des M. Brodie. Litho Format)

1981 (2 Nov). *Space Shuttle Project. T* **53** *and similar horiz designs. Multicoloured. P* 14½.

468	10 c. Type **53**	30	10
469	40 c. Re-entry	65	10
470	$1.10, External tank separation	1·25	45
471	$3 Touchdown	1·75	1·00
468/71	*Set of 4*	3·50	1·50
MS472	117 × 89 mm. $5 Launch	2·75	2·00

54 Footballer   **55** Mail Van and Stage-Coach

(Des Clover Mill. Litho Questa)

1981 (30 Nov). *World Cup Football Championship, Spain* (1982). *T* **54** *and similar vert designs showing footballers. P* 14.

473	20 c. multicoloured			15	10
474	40 c. multicoloured			20	15
475	$1 multicoloured			35	30
476	$2 multicoloured			65	55
473/6			*Set of 4*	1·25	1·00
MS477	106 × 128 mm. $4 multicoloured			1·40	1·60

Nos. 473/6 were each printed in small sheets of 6 including one se-tenant stamp-size label.

(Des G. Vasarhelyi. Litho Format)

1982 (13 Jan). *Centenary of U.P.U. Membership. T* **55** *and similar horiz designs. Multicoloured. P* 14½.

478	30 c. Type **55**			30	15
479	40 c. U.P.U. emblem			30	15
480	$2.50, *Queen Elizabeth 2* (liner) and sailing ship			1·50	70
481	$4 Concorde and De Havilland D.H.9 biplane			2·25	1·25
478/81			*Set of 4*	4·00	2·00
MS482	117×78 mm. $5 Streamlined diesel-electric, and steam trains			3·50	2·25

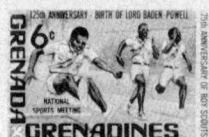

56 National Sports Meeting

(Des M. Diamond. Litho Format)

1982 (19 Feb). *75th Anniv of Boy Scout Movement and 125th Birth Anniv of Lord Baden-Powell. T* **56** *and similar horiz designs. Multicoloured. P* 14½.

483	6 c. Type **56**			15	10
484	90 c. Sea scouts sailing			50	30
485	$1.10, Handicraft			65	60
486	$3 Animal tending			1·40	1·40
483/6			*Set of 4*	2·40	2·10
MS487	100 × 71 mm. $5 Music around campfire			1·40	1·75

57 *Anartia jatrophae*   **58** Prince and Princess of Wales

(Des J.W. Litho Questa)

1982 (24 Mar). *Butterflies. T* **57** *and similar horiz designs. Multicoloured. P* 14.

488	30 c. Type **57**			75	30
489	40 c. *Chioides vintra*			80	35
490	$1.10, *Cynthia cardui*			1·75	75
491	$3 *Historis odius*			2·75	1·60
488/91			*Set of 4*	5·50	2·75
MS492	103×77 mm. $5 *Dione juno*			3·25	3·25

(Des PAD Studio. Litho Questa)

1982 (1 July). *21st Birthday of Princess of Wales. T* **58** *and similar vert designs. Multicoloured. P* 14½ × 14.

493	50 c. Blenheim Palace			50	60
494	60 c. As 50 c.			60	60
495	$1 Type **58**			70	1·25
496	$2 Type **58**			1·50	1·40
497	$3 Princess of Wales			2·00	2·00
498	$4 As $3			2·25	2·00
493/8			*Set of 6*	6·75	7·00
MS499	103 × 75 mm. $5 Princess Diana (*different*)			2·25	2·50

Nos. 493, 495 and 497 come from sheetlets of 5 stamps and 1 label.

PRICES OF SETS

Set prices are given for many issues, generally those containing three stamps or more. Definitive sets include one of each value or major colour change, but do not cover different perforations, die types or minor shades. Where a choice is possible the set prices are based on the cheapest versions of the stamps included in the listings.

---

59 "New Deal"—Soil Conservation   **60** "Presentation of Christ in the Temple"

(Des M. Diamond. Litho Questa)

1982 (27 July). *Birth Centenary of Franklin D. Roosevelt. T* **59** *and similar horiz designs. Multicoloured. P* 14.

500	30 c. Type **59**			25	15
501	40 c. Roosevelt and George Washington Carver (scientist)			25	15
502	70 c. Civilian conservation corps and reafforestation			45	30
503	$3 Roosevelt with Pres. Barclay of Liberia, Casablanca Conference, 1943			1·75	90
500/3			*Set of 4*	2·40	1·40
MS504	100 × 72 mm. $5 Roosevelt delivering address at Howard University			2·00	2·10

1982 (30 Aug). *Birth of Prince William of Wales. Nos.* 493/9 *optd with T* **171** *of Antigua.*

505	50 c. Blenheim Palace			50	50
506	60 c. As 50 c.			55	60
507	$1 Type **58**			70	75
508	$2 Type **58**			1·00	1·25
509	$3 Princess of Wales			1·25	1·75
510	$4 As $3			1·50	1·75
505/10			*Set of 6*	5·00	6·00
MS511	103 × 75 mm. $5 Princess Diana (*different*)			2·10	2·25

Nos. 505, 507 and 509 come from sheetlets of 5 stamps and 1 label.

(Des Clover Mill. Litho Format)

1982 (2 Sept). *Easter. T* **60** *and similar vert designs depicting Easter paintings by Rembrandt. Multicoloured. P* 14½.

512	30 c. Type **60**			40	15
513	60 c. "Descent from the Cross"			55	20
514	$2 "Raising of the Cross"			1·25	75
515	$4 "Resurrection of Christ"			1·75	1·50
512/15			*Set of 4*	3·50	2·40
MS516	101 × 126 mm. $5 "The Risen Christ"			3·00	2·40

61 "Santa Fe"

(Des Artists International. Litho Format)

1982 (4 Oct). *Famous Trains of the World. T* **61** *and similar vert designs. Multicoloured. P* 15.

517	10 c. Type **61**			50	15
518	40 c. "Mistral"			70	20
519	70 c. "Rheingold"			80	45
520	$1 "ET 403"			1·00	50
521	$1.10, Steam locomotive *Mallard*			1·25	60
522	$2 "Tokaido"			1·40	90
517/22			*Set of 6*	5·00	2·50
MS523	121 × 95 mm. $5 "Settebello"			2·25	2·50

62 Footballers

(Des D. Miller. Litho Questa)

1982 (2 Dec). *World Cup Football Championship Winners. T* **62** *and similar horiz designs. P* 14 × 13½.

524	60 c. multicoloured			35	35
525	$4 multicoloured			1·75	1·25
MS526	92 × 134 mm. $5 multicoloured			1·50	1·50

(Litho Questa)

1982 (14 Dec). *Christmas. Horiz designs as T* **42** *showing scenes from Walt Disney's cartoon film "The Rescuers". P* 13½.

527	½ c. multicoloured			10	10
528	1 c. multicoloured			10	10
529	2 c. multicoloured			10	10
530	3 c. multicoloured			10	10
531	4 c. multicoloured			10	10
532	5 c. multicoloured			10	10
533	10 c. multicoloured			10	10
534	$2.50, multicoloured			2·75	1·75
535	$3 multicoloured			2·75	1·75
527/35			*Set of 9*	5·50	3·50
MS536	120 × 96 mm. $5 multicoloured			4·25	2·75

---

63 Short-finned Pilot Whale

(Des Artists International. Litho Questa)

1983 (10 Jan). *Save the Whales. T* **63** *and similar horiz designs. Multicoloured. P* 14.

537	10 c. Type **63**			85	55
538	60 c. Dall's Porpoise			2·00	1·75
539	$1.10, Humpback Whale			3·50	2·75
540	$3 Bowhead Whale			6·00	7·00
537/40			*Set of 4*	11·00	11·00
MS541	113 × 84 mm. $5 Spotted Dolphin			4·50	4·00

64 "David and Goliath"

(Des Design Images. Litho Format)

1983 (15 Feb). *500th Birth Anniv of Raphael. T* **64** *and similar horiz designs showing painting details. Multicoloured. P* 13½.

542	25 c. Type **64**			15	15
543	30 c. "David sees Bathsheba"			15	15
544	90 c. "Triumph of David"			30	35
545	$4 "Anointing of Solomon"			70	90
542/5			*Set of 4*	1·10	1·40
MS546	126 × 101 mm. $5 "Anointing of David"			80	1·10

Nos. 542/5 exist imperforate from stock dispersed by the liquidator of Format International Security Printers Ltd.

65 Voice and Visual Communication

(Des Artists International. Litho Questa)

1983 (7 Apr). *World Communications Year. T* **65** *and similar horiz designs. Multicoloured. P* 14.

547	30 c. Type **65**			10	10
548	60 c. Ambulance			25	20
549	$1.10, Westland Whirlwind helicopters			45	45
550	$3 Satellite			1·00	1·00
547/50			*Set of 4*	1·60	1·60
MS551	127×85 mm. $5 Diver and Bottle-nosed Dolphin			2·25	2·50

66 Chrysler "Imperial Roadster", 1931

(Des R. Sauber. Litho Format)

1983 (4 May). *75th Anniv of Model "T" Ford Car. T* **66** *and similar horiz designs showing cars of the 20th century. Multicoloured. P* 14½.

552	10 c. Type **66**			15	15
553	30 c. Doble steam car, 1925			25	25
554	40 c. Ford "Mustang", 1965			25	30
555	60 c. Packard tourer, 1930			35	40
556	70 c. Mercer "Raceabout" 1913			35	40
557	90 c. Corvette "Stingray", 1963			35	40
558	$1.10, Auburn "851 Supercharger Speedster", 1935			40	45
559	$2.50, Pierce-Arrow "Silver Arrow", 1933			65	95
560	$3 Duesenberg dual cowl phaeton, 1929			75	1·25
561	$4 Mercedes-Benz "SSK", 1928			75	1·50
552/61			*Set of 10*	3·75	5·50
MS562	119 × 90 mm. $5 McFarlan "Knickerbocker" cabriolet, 1923			2·00	2·50

Nos. 552/61 were each issued in sheets of eight stamps with a stamp-size label in the centre position.

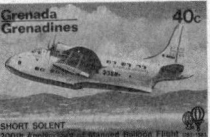

67 Short S.45A Solent 2 Flying Boat

(Des W. Wright. Litho Questa)

1983 (18 July). *Bicentenary of Manned Flight. T* **67** *and similar horiz designs. Multicoloured.* P 14.

563	40 c. Type **67**	..	75	20
564	70 c. Curtiss R3C-2 seaplane	..	90	35
565	90 c. Hawker Nimrod biplane	..	1·10	40
566	$4 Montgolfier balloon ..	..	3·25	2·75
563/6		Set of 4	5·50	3·25
MS567	112×85 mm. $5 LZ-11 *Viktoria Luise* (airship)	..	2·25	2·50

68 Goofy

69 Weightlifting

(Litho Walsall)

1983 (7 Nov). *Christmas. T* **68** *and similar vert designs showing Disney cartoon characters in scenes from "Jingle Bells" (Christmas carol). Multicoloured.* P 11.

568	½ c. Type **68**	..	10	10
569	1 c. Clarabelle Cow	..	10	10
570	2 c. Donald Duck	..	10	10
571	3 c. Pluto	..	10	10
572	4 c. Morty and Ferdie	..	10	10
573	5 c. Huey, Dewey and Louie ..	..	10	10
574	10 c. Daisy and Chip 'n Dale	..	10	10
575	$2.50, Big Bad Wolf	..	4·75	5·00
576	$3 Mickey Mouse	..	5·00	5·50
568/76		Set of 9	9·00	10·00
MS577	102 × 124 mm. $5 Donald Duck in sleigh. P 13½		8·00	8·00

(Des N. Waldman. Litho Questa)

1984 (9 Jan). *Olympic Games, Los Angeles. T* **69** *and similar vert designs. Multicoloured.* P 14.

578	30 c. Type **69**	..	20	15
579	60 c. Gymnastics	..	45	35
580	70 c. Archery	..	50	40
581	$4 Sailing	..	1·90	1·90
578/81		Set of 4	2·75	2·50
MS582	70 × 102 mm. $5 Basketball	..	2·00	2·25

70 Frangipani

71 Goofy

(Des J. Cooter. Litho Format)

1984 (9 Apr). *Flowers. T* **70** *and similar vert designs. Multicoloured.* P 15.

583	15 c. Type **70**	..	15	10
584	40 c. Dwarf Poinciana ..	..	30	25
585	70 c. Walking Iris	..	55	45
586	$4 Lady's Slipper	..	2·25	2·50
583/6		Set of 4	3·00	3·00
MS587	66 × 57 mm. $5 Brazilian Glory Vine	..	2·25	3·00

Nos. 583/6 exist imperforate from stock dispersed by the liquidator of Format International Security Printers Ltd.

(Litho Format)

1984 (1 May). *Easter. T* **71** *and similar vert designs showing Disney cartoon characters with Easter hats. Multicoloured.* P 11.

588	½ c. Type **71**	..	10	10
589	1 c. Chip and Dale	..	10	10
590	2 c. Daisy Duck and Huey	..	10	10
591	3 c. Daisy Duck	..	10	10
592	4 c. Donald Duck	..	10	10
593	5 c. Merlin and Madam Mim	..	10	10
594	10 c. Flower	..	10	10
595	$2 Minnie and Mickey Mouse	..	1·50	2·00
596	$4 Minnie Mouse	..	2·25	2·75
588/96		Set of 9	3·75	4·75
MS597	126 × 100 mm. $5 Minnie Mouse (*different*). P 13½ × 14		3·00	3·75

72 Bobolink

(73)

(Litho Questa)

1984 (21 May). *Songbirds. T* **72** *and similar horiz designs. Multicoloured.* P 14.

598	40 c. Type **72**	..	1·75	1·50
599	50 c. Eastern Kingbird	..	2·00	1·60
600	60 c. Barn Swallow	..	2·25	2·00
601	70 c. Yellow Warbler	..	2·25	2·00
602	$1 Rose-breasted Grosbeak	..	2·50	2·50
603	$1.10, Yellowthroat ..	..	2·75	2·75
604	$2 Catbird	..	3·50	4·50
598/604		Set of 7	15·00	15·00
MS605	71 × 65 mm. $5 Fork-tailed Flycatcher		6·50	5·00

1984 (19 June). *Universal Postal Union Congress, Hamburg. Nos. 585/7 optd with T* **73**.

606	70 c. Walking Iris	..	1·00	1·00
607	$4 Lady's Slipper	..	4·50	5·00
MS608	66 × 57 mm. $5 Brazilian Glory Vine		2·25	3·00

74 *Geeststar* (freighter)

(Litho Format)

1984 (16 July). *Ships. T* **74** *and similar horiz designs. Multicoloured.* P 15.

609	30 c. Type **74**	..	1·00	75
610	60 c. *Daphne* (liner)	..	1·25	1·25
611	$1.10 *Southwind* (schooner)	..	1·50	2·00
612	$4 *Oceanic* (liner)	..	2·50	2·75
609/12		Set of 4	5·50	8·50
MS613	108×80 mm. $5 Pirate ship	..	3·50	4·00

No. MS613 exists imperforate from stock dispersed by the liquidator of Format International Security Printers Ltd.

(Litho Questa)

1984 (22 Aug). *450th Death Anniv of Correggio (painter). Multicoloured designs as T* **296** *of Grenada showing paintings.* P 14.

614	10 c. "The Hunt—Blowing the Horn".	..	10	10
615	30 c. "St. John the Evangelist" (*horiz*)	..	15	15
616	90 c. "The Hunt—The Deer's Head"	..	50	50
617	$4 "The Virgin crowned by Christ" (*horiz*) ..		2·00	2·00
614/17		Set of 4	2·50	2·50
MS618	73 × 63 mm. $5 "Martyrdom of the Four Saints"	..	2·40	3·00

(Litho Questa)

1984 (22 Aug). *150th Birth Anniv of Edgar Degas (painter). Vert designs as T* **297** *of Grenada showing paintings. Multicoloured.* P 14.

619	25 c. "The Song of the Dog"	..	40	15
620	70 c. "Cafe-concert"	..	70	50
621	$1.10 "The Orchestra of the Opera"	..	1·50	1·25
622	$3 "The Dance Lesson"	..	2·75	2·75
619/22		Set of 4	4·75	4·25
MS623	53 × 73 mm. $5 "Madame Camus at the Piano"	..	2·40	3·00

(Des Bonny Redecker. Litho Questa)

1984 (21 Sept). *"Ausipex" International Stamp Exhibition, Melbourne. Horiz designs as T* **298** *of Grenada. Multicoloured.* P 14.

624	$1.10, Queen Victoria Gardens, Melbourne		50	50
625	$4 Ayers Rock	..	2·00	2·00
MS626	107 × 76 mm. $5 River Yarra, Melbourne		2·00	3·00

75 Col. Steven's Model (1825)

76 Kawasaki "750" (1972)

(Des Bonny Redecker. Litho Format)

1984 (3 Oct). *Railway Locomotives. T* **75** *and similar horiz designs. Multicoloured.* P 15.

627	20 c. Type **75**	..	65	25
628	50 c. *Royal George* (1827)	..	80	50
629	60 c. *Stourbridge Lion* (1829)	..	85	65
630	70 c. *Liverpool* (1830)	..	90	85
631	90 c. *South Carolina* (1832)	..	1·00	1·25
632	$1.10, *Monster* (1836)	..	1·10	1·50
633	$2 *Lafayette* (1837)	..	1·40	2·25
634	$4 *Lion* (1838)	..	1·75	3·75
627/34		Set of 8	7·50	10·00
MS635	Two sheets, each 100×70 mm. (a) $5 Sequin's locomotive (1829); (b) $5 *Der Adler* (1835)	Set of 2 sheets	7·00	8·00

1984 (28 Oct). *Opening of Point Saline International Airport. Nos. 547, 549 and MS551 optd as T* **300** *of Grenada.*

636	30 c. Type **65**	..	30	25
637	$1.10, Westland Whirlwind helicopters	..	95	75
MS638	127×85 mm. Diver and Bottle-nosed Dolphin	..	3·75	3·50

The overprint on No. MS638 appears on the sheet margin as for No. MS1371 of Grenada.

(Litho Questa)

1984 (26 Nov). *Christmas. Walt Disney Cartoon Characters Vert designs as T* **301** *of Grenada. Multicoloured.* P 12 ($2) or 13½ × 14 (*others*).

639	45 c. Donald Duck, and nephews knitting Christmas stockings		70	40
640	60 c. Donald Duck and nephews sitting on sofa		80	65
641	90 c. Donald Duck getting out of bed	..	1·25	1·00
642	$2 Donald Duck putting presents in wardrobe		2·00	2·50
643	$4 Nephews singing carols outside Donald Duck's window ..	..	3·25	4·25
639/43		Set of 5	7·25	8·00
MS644	126×102 mm. $5 Donald Duck filming nephews	..	4·25	4·00

No. 642 was printed in sheetlets of 8 stamps.

(Litho Questa)

1985 (11 Feb). *Birth Bicentenary of John J. Audubon (ornithologist) (1st issue). Multicoloured designs as T* **198** *of Antigua showing original paintings.* P 14.

645	50 c. Blue-winged Teal	..	2·00	60
646	90 c. White Ibis	..	2·50	1·25
647	$1.10, Swallow-tailed Kite	..	3·50	2·00
648	$3 Moorhen ("Common Gallinule")	..	4·50	4·75
645/8		Set of 4	11·00	7·75
MS649	82×111 mm. $5 Mangrove Cuckoo (*vert*)		3·25	3·75

See also Nos. 736/40.

(Des BG Studio. Litho Questa)

1985 (11 Mar). *Centenary of the Motor Cycle. T* **76** *and similar multicoloured designs.* P 14.

650	30 c. Type **76**	..	65	45
651	60 c. Honda "Goldwing GL1000" (1974) (*horiz*)		90	1·00
652	70 c. Kawasaki "Z650" (1976) (*horiz*)	..	1·00	1·10
653	$4 Honda "CBX" (1977)	..	4·00	6·50
650/3		Set of 4	6·00	8·00
MS654	113×76 mm. $5 BMW "R100RS" (1978).		3·50	4·25

77 Nursing Cadets folding Bandages (Health)

(Des Susan David. Litho Questa)

1985 (15 Apr). *International Youth Year. T* **77** *and similar horiz designs. Multicoloured.* P 14.

655	50 c. Type **77** ..	..	70	45
656	70 c. Scuba diver and turtle (Environment)..		1·00	80
657	$1.10, Yachting (Leisure) ..	..	1·60	1·50
658	$3 Boys playing chess (Education)	..	5·50	6·50
655/8		Set of 4	8·00	8·25
MS659	98×70 mm. $5 Hands touching globe ..		2·75	3·00

(Des BG Studio. Litho Questa)

1985 (30 Apr). *40th Anniv of International Civil Aviation Organization. Horiz designs as T* **305** *of Grenada. Multicoloured.* P 14.

660	5 c. Lockheed L.18 Lodestar	..	40	20
661	70 c. Hawker Siddeley H.S.748	..	1·75	55
662	$1.10, Boeing 727-200	..	2·25	90
663	$3 Boeing 707	..	3·50	2·50
660/3		Set of 4	7·00	3·75
MS664	87×68 mm. $4 Pilatus Britten Norman Islander	..	3·50	3·00

78 Lady Baden-Powell (founder) and Grenadian Guide Leaders

(Des D. Francis. Litho Questa)

1985 (30 May). *75th Anniv of Girl Guide Movement. T* **78** *and similar multicoloured designs.* P 14.

665	30 c. Type **78**	..	40	20
666	50 c. Guide leader and guides on botany field trip		70	30
667	70 c. Guide leader and guides camping (*vert*)		95	45
668	$4 Guides sailing (*vert*)	..	3·25	2·25
665/8		Set of 4	4·75	3·00
MS669	100×73 mm. $5 Lord and Lady Baden-Powell (*vert*)	..	3·75	4·25

The new-issue supplement to this Catalogue appears each month in

GIBBONS
STAMP MONTHLY

—from your newsagent or by postal subscription— sample copy and details on request.

79 *Chiomara asychis*   80 The Queen Mother before Prince William's Christening

(Des I. MacLaury. Litho Questa)

1985 (17 June)–**89.** *Butterflies. T 79 and similar horiz designs. Multicoloured. A. P 14. B. P 12.*

		A		B	
670	½ c. Type 79	10	10	10	10
671	1 c. *Anartia amathea*	10	10	10	10
672	2 c. *Pseudolycaena marsyas*	10	10	10	10
673	4 c. *Urbanus proteus*	10	10	15	10
674	5 c. *Polygonus manueli*	15	10	15	10
675	6 c. *Battus polydamas*	20	15	20	15
676	10 c. *Eurema daira*	30	15	30	15
677	12 c. *Phoebis agarithe*	45	20	45	20
678	15 c. *Aphrissa statira*	45	20	45	20
679	20 c. *Strymon simaethis*	60	20	60	20
680	25 c. *Mestra cana*	60	25	60	25
681	30 c. *Agraulis vanillae*	60	30	60	30
682	40 c. *Junonia evarete*	75	45	75	45
683	60 c. *Dryas julia*	1·00	65	1·00	65
684	70 c. *Philaethria dido*	1·10	75	1·10	75
685	$1.10, *Hamadryas feronia*	1·75	1·25	1·75	1·25
686	$2.50, *Strymon rufofusca*	3·25	3·00	3·25	3·75
687	$5 *Appias drusilla*	5·00	4·75	5·00	5·50
688	$10 *Polites dictynna*	8·00	9·00	8·00	11·00
688c	$20 *Euptychia cephus*	12·00	14·00	12·00	15·00
670/88c	Set of 20	32·00	32·00	32·00	35·00

Dates of issue: 17.6.85, Nos. 670A/87A; 11.11.85, No. 688A; 1986, Nos. 670B/85B, 687B; 1.8.86, No. 688cA; 9.86, Nos. 686B, 688B; 5.89, No. 688cB.

(Des J.W. Litho Questa)

1985 (3 July). *Life and Times of Queen Elizabeth the Queen Mother. T 80 and similar multicoloured designs. P 14.*

689	$1 Type 80	45	60
690	$1.50, In winner's enclosure at Ascot (horiz)	60	75
691	$2.50, With Prince Charles at Garter ceremony, Windsor Castle	85	1·10
689/91	Set of 3	1·75	2·10
MS692	56×85 mm. $5 At opening of Royal York Hospice, London	1·75	3·00

Stamps as Nos. 689/91, but with face values of 70 c., $1.10 and $3, exist from additional sheetlets of 5 plus a label issued 28 January 1986. These also have changed background colours and are perforated 12½×12 ($1.10) or 12×12½ (others) (*Price for set of 3 stamps £1.75 mint*).

81 Scuba Diving   82 Queen or Pink Conch

(Des Marlise Nakaja. Litho Format)

1985 (15 July). *Water Sports. T 81 and similar vert designs. Multicoloured. P 15.*

693	15 c. Type 81	30	10
694	70 c. Boys playing in waterfall	70	45
695	90 c. Water skiing	85	55
696	$4 Swimming	2·50	2·25
693/6	Set of 4	4·00	3·00
MS697	103×78 mm. $5 Scuba diver	3·25	3·25

(Des Mary Walters. Litho Questa)

1985 (1 Aug). *Marine Life. T 82 and similar horiz designs. Multicoloured. P 14.*

698	60 c. Type 82	65	40
699	90 c. Porcupinefish and Fire Coral	85	55
700	$1.10, Ghost Crab	1·00	70
701	$4 West Indies Spiny Lobster	2·50	2·25
698/701	Set of 4	4·50	3·50
MS702	299×70 mm. $5 Long-spined Urchin	4·50	4·00

(Des Susan David. Litho Questa)

1985 (3 Sept). *300th Birth Anniv of Johann Sebastian Bach (composer). Vert designs as T 206 of Antigua. Multicoloured. P 14.*

703	15 c. Natural trumpet	50	10
704	60 c. Bass viol	85	40
705	$1.10, Flute	1·50	70
706	$3 Double flageolet	2·25	1·75
703/6	Set of 4	4·50	2·75
MS707	110×75 mm. $5 Johann Sebastian Bach	3·25	3·50

(Litho Format)

1985 (4 Nov). *Royal Visit. Multicoloured designs as T 207 of Antigua. P 14½.*

708	10 c. Arms of Great Britain and Grenada	20	20
709	$1 Queen Elizabeth II (vert)	1·25	1·75
710	$4 Royal Yacht *Britannia*	3·75	4·75
708/10	Set of 3	4·75	6·00
MS711	111×83 mm. $5 Map of Grenada Grenadines	3·75	3·75

(Litho Format)

1985 (22 Nov). *40th Anniv of United Nations Organization. Multicoloured designs as T 208 of Antigua showing United Nations (New York) stamps. P 14½.*

712	$1 Neil Armstrong (first man on Moon) and 1982 Peaceful Uses of Outer Space 20 c.	1·10	1·10
713	$2 Gandhi and 1971 Racial Equality Year 13 c.	3·00	3·50
714	$2.50, Maimonides (physician) and 1956 World Health Organization 3 c.	4·25	4·75
712/14	Set of 3	7·50	8·50
MS715	110×85 mm. $5 U.N. Under-Secretary Ralph Bunche (vert)	2·75	3·00

(Des Walt Disney Productions. Litho Questa)

1985 (27 Nov). *150th Birth Anniv of Mark Twain (author). Horiz designs as T 118 of Anguilla showing Walt Disney cartoon characters illustrating scenes from "Letters from Hawaii". Multicoloured. P 14×13½.*

716	25 c. Minnie Mouse dancing the hula	60	90
717	50 c. Donald Duck surfing	90	65
718	$1.50, Donald Duck roasting marshmallow in volcano	2·25	2·25
719	$3 Mickey Mouse and Chip'n'Dale canoeing	3·75	4·00
716/19	Set of 4	6·75	6·50
MS720	127×102 mm. $5 Mickey Mouse with cat	4·75	3·75

(Des Walt Disney Productions. Litho Questa)

1985 (27 Nov). *Birth Bicentenaries of Grimm Brothers (folklorists). Designs as T 119 of Anguilla, but vert, showing Walt Disney cartoon characters in scenes from "The Elves and the Shoemaker". Multicoloured. P 13½×14.*

721	30 c. Mickey Mouse as the unsuccessful Shoemaker	70	40
722	60 c. Two elves making shoes	1·10	85
723	70 c. The Shoemaker discovering the new shoes	1·40	1·00
724	$4 The Shoemaker's wife (Minnie Mouse) making clothes for the elves	4·25	5·00
721/4	Set of 4	6·75	6·50
MS725	126×101 mm. $5 The Shoemaker and his wife waving	5·50	5·00

VISIT OF PRES. REAGAN

20 FEBRUARY 1986

83 "Madonna and Child" (Titian)   (84)

(Des Mary Walters. Litho Format)

1985 (23 Dec). *Christmas. Religious Paintings. T 83 and similar vert designs. Multicoloured. P 15.*

726	50 c. Type 83	45	35
727	70 c. "Madonna and Child with St. Mary and John the Baptist" (Bugiardini)	55	50
728	$1.10, "Adoration of the Magi" (Di Fredi)	90	1·40
729	$3 "Madonna and Child with Young St. John the Baptist" (Bartolomeo)	1·75	3·25
726/9	Set of 4	3·25	5·00
MS730	112×81 mm. $5 "The Annunciation" (Botticelli)	3·25	5·50

Nos. 726 and MS730 exist imperforate from stock dispersed by the liquidator of Format International Security Printers Ltd.

(Des J. Iskowitz. Litho Questa)

1986 (6 Jan). *Centenary of the Statue of Liberty (1st issue). Multicoloured designs as T 211 of Dominica. P 15.*

731	5 c. Croton Reservoir, New York (1875)	10	10
732	10 c. New York Public Library (1986)	10	10
733	70 c. Old Boathouse, Central Park (1894)	25	40
734	$4 Boating in Central Park (1986)	1·40	2·25
731/4	Set of 4	1·50	2·50
MS735	103×76 mm. $5 Statue of Liberty (vert)	2·50	3·50

See also Nos. 892/903.

(Litho Questa)

1986 (28 Jan). *Birth Bicentenary of John J. Audubon (ornithologist) (2nd issue). Horiz designs as T 198 of Antigua. Multicoloured. P 12½×12.*

736	50 c. Louisiana Heron	2·00	1·00
737	70 c. Black-crowned Night Heron	2·50	1·50
738	90 c. American Bittern	2·75	2·00
739	$4 Glossy Ibis	5·00	6·50
736/9	Set of 4	11·00	10·00
MS740	103×74 mm. $5 King Eider. P 14	6·50	8·50

Nos. 736/9 were each issued in sheetlets of five stamps and one stamp-size label, which appears in the centre of the bottom row.

1986 (20 Feb). *Visit of President Reagan of U.S.A. Nos. 684A and 687A optd with T 84.*

741	70 c. *Philaethria dido*	1·50	1·25
742	$5 *Appias drusilla*	6·50	8·00

ALTERED CATALOGUE NUMBERS

Any Catalogue numbers altered from the last edition are shown as a list in the introductory pages.

85 Two Footballers   86 *Hygrocybe firma*

(Des BG Studio. Litho Questa)

1986 (18 Mar). *World Cup Football Championship, Mexico. Vert designs as T 85 showing footballers. P 14.*

743	10 c. multicoloured	40	30
744	70 c. multicoloured	1·40	1·25
745	$1 multicoloured	1·75	1·75
746	$4 multicoloured	5·00	6·00
743/6	Set of 4	7·50	8·50
MS747	86×104 mm. $5 multicoloured	3·75	4·50

(Des W. Hanson. Litho Questa)

1986 (26 Mar). *Appearance of Halley's Comet (1st issue). Horiz designs as T 123 of Anguilla. Multicoloured. P 14.*

748	5 c. Nicholas Copernicus (astronomer) and Earl of Rosse's six foot reflector telescope	40	40
749	20 c. "Sputnik I" (first satellite) orbiting Earth, 1957	60	40
750	40 c. Tycho Brahe's notes and sketch of 1577 Comet	80	60
751	$4 Edmond Halley and 1682 Comet	3·75	4·50
748/51	Set of 4	5·00	5·50
MS752	101×70 mm. $5 Halley's Comet	3·00	3·00

The captions of Nos. 750/1 are transposed.

See also Nos. 790/4.

(Litho Questa)

1986 (21 Apr). *60th Birthday of Queen Elizabeth II. Vert designs as T 125 of Anguilla. P 14.*

753	2 c. black and yellow	10	15
754	$1.50, multicoloured	80	1·00
755	$4 multicoloured	2·00	2·00
753/5	Set of 3	2·50	3·50
MS756	120×85 mm. $5 black and grey-brown	2·00	3·50

Designs:—2 c. Princesses Elizabeth and Margaret, Windsor Park, 1933; $1.50, Queen Elizabeth; $4 In Sydney, Australia, 1970; $5 The Royal Family, Coronation Day, 1937.

(Des Walt Disney Productions. Litho Format)

1986 (22 May). *"Ameripex '86" International Stamp Exhibition, Chicago. Horiz designs as T 212 of Dominica showing Walt Disney cartoon characters. Multicoloured. P 11.*

757	30 c. Donald Duck riding mule in Grand Canyon	45	45
758	60 c. Daisy Duck, Timothy Mouse and Dumbo on Golden Gate Bridge, San Francisco	70	1·00
759	$1 Mickey Mouse and Goofy in fire engine and Chicago Watertower	1·25	1·75
760	$3 Mickey Mouse as airmail pilot and White House	3·00	4·00
757/60	Set of 4	5·00	6·50
MS761	126×101 mm. $5 Donald Duck and Mickey Mouse watching Halley's Comet over Statue of Liberty. P 14×13½	5·00	7·50

No. 757 exists imperforate from stock dispersed by the liquidator of Format International Security Printers Ltd.

(Litho Questa)

1986 (1 July). *Royal Wedding. Vert designs as T 213 of Antigua. Multicoloured. P 14.*

762	60 c. Prince Andrew and Miss Sarah Ferguson	55	45
763	70 c. Prince Andrew in car	65	55
764	$4 Prince Andrew with Westland WG-13 Lynx naval helicopter	2·75	3·50
762/4	Set of 4	3·50	4·00
MS765	88×88 mm. $5 Prince Andrew and Miss Sarah Ferguson (different)	4·00	5·50

(Des BG Studio. Litho Format)

1986 (15 July). *Mushrooms of the Lesser Antilles. T 86 and similar vert designs. Multicoloured. P 15.*

766	15 c. Type 86	80	40
767	50 c. *Xerocomus coccolobae*	1·75	1·25
768	$2 *Volvariella cubensis*	3·50	4·00
769	$3 *Lactarius putidus*	4·50	5·00
766/9	Set of 4	9·50	9·50
MS770	76×80 mm. $5 *Leptonia caeruleocapitata*	9·00	11·00

No. MS770 exists imperforate from stock dispersed by the liquidator of Format International Security Printers Ltd.

87 Giant Atlantic or Doldorate Pyram (*Pyramidella dolabrata*)   88 Common Opossum

(Des L. Birmingham. Litho Format)

1986 (1 Aug). *Sea Shells. T* **87** *and similar multicoloured designs.* P 15.

771	15 c. Type **87**		75	40
772	50 c. Beau's Murex (*Murex beauii*)		1·60	1·00
773	$1.10, West Indian Fighting Conch (*Strombus pugilis*)		2·25	2·50
774	$4 Alphabet Cone (*Conus spurius*)		4·75	6·50
771/4		*Set of 4*	8·50	9·50
MS775	109×75 mm. $5 Brown-lined Paper Bubble (*Hydatina vesicaria*)		6·00	8·00

1986 (15 Sept). *World Cup Football Championship Winners, Mexico. Nos.* 743/7 *optd with T* **216** *of Antigua in gold.*

776	**85** 10 c. multicoloured		30	30
777	— 70 c. multicoloured		90	1·00
778	— $1 multicoloured		1·25	1·40
779	— $4 multicoloured		3·50	4·50
776/9		*Set of 4*	5·50	6·50
MS780	86×104 mm. $5 multicoloured		8·00	9·00

(Des Dot and S. Barlowe. Litho Format)

1986 (15 Sept). *Wildlife. T* **88** *and similar multicoloured designs.* P 15.

781	10 c. Type **88**		20	20
782	30 c. Giant Toad		40	40
783	60 c. Land Tortoise (*Testudo denticulata*)		80	80
784	70 c. Murine Opossum (*vert*)		85	85
785	90 c. Burmese Mongoose (*vert*)		90	1·00
786	$1.10, Nine-banded Armadillo		1·00	1·25
787	$2 Agouti		1·75	2·25
788	$3 Humpback Whale		3·50	4·25
781/8		*Set of 8*	8·50	10·00
MS789	Two sheets, each 103×72 mm. (a) $5 Mona Monkey (*vert*) (b) $5 Iguana			
		Set of 2 sheets	11·00	14·00

Nos. 781/8 exist imperforate from stock dispersed by the liquidator of Format International Security Printers Ltd.

1986 (15 Oct). *Appearance of Halley's Comet (2nd issue). Nos.* 748/52 *optd with T* **218** *of Antigua (in silver on 20 c.,* $4 *and* $5).

790	5 c. Nicholas Copernicus (astronomer) and Earl of Rosse's six foot reflector telescope		60	60
791	20 c. "Sputnik I" (first satellite) orbiting Earth, 1957		80	50
792	40 c. Tycho Brahe's notes and sketch of 1577 Comet		1·00	60
793	$4 Edmond Halley and 1682 Comet		5·00	6·00
790/3		*Set of 4*	6·50	7·00
MS794	102×70 mm. $5 Halley's Comet		4·00	5·50

(Des Walt Disney Co. Litho Format)

1986 (3 Nov). *Christmas. Multicoloured designs as T* **220** *of Antigua showing Walt Disney cartoon characters.* P 11.

795	25 c. Chip n'Dale with hummingbird		25	15
796	30 c. Robin delivering card to Mickey Mouse (*vert*)		25	20
797	50 c. Piglet, Pooh and Jose Carioca on beach		40	30
798	60 c. Grandma Duck feeding birds (*vert*)		50	40
799	70 c. Cinderella and birds with mistletoe (*vert*)		55	50
800	$1.50, Huey, Dewey and Louie windsurfing		1·25	1·75
801	$3 Mickey Mouse and Morty on beach with turtle		1·50	2·50
802	$4 Kittens playing on piano (*vert*)		2·00	3·25
795/802		*Set of 8*	6·00	8·00
MS803	Two sheets, each 127×102 mm. (a) $5 Mickey Mouse and Willie the Whale. P 14×13½. (b) $5 Bambi, Thumper and Blossom in snow (*vert*). P 13½×14	*Set of 2 sheets*	8·00	11·50

89 Cycling   90 Aston-Martin "Volanté" (1984)

(Des BG Studio. Litho Format)

1986 (18 Nov). *Olympic Games, Seoul, South Korea (1988). T* **89** *and similar vert designs. Multicoloured.* P 15.

804	10 c. + 5 c. Type **89**		30	40
805	50 c. + 20 c. Sailing		60	90
806	70 c. + 30 c. Gymnastics		75	1·10
807	$2 + $1 Horse trials		2·25	3·00
804/7		*Set of 4*	3·50	4·75
MS808	80×100 mm. $3 + $1 Marathon		3·00	4·50

The premiums on Nos. 804/8 were to support the participation of the Grenada team.

Nos. 804/8 exist imperforate from stock dispersed by the liquidator of Format International Security Printers Ltd.

(Des W. Wright. Litho Format)

1986 (20 Nov). *Centenary of Motoring. T* **90** *and similar horiz designs. Multicoloured.* P 15.

809	10 c. Type **90**		25	25
810	30 c. Jaguar "Mk V" (1948)		45	45
811	60 c. Nash "Ambassador" (1956)		65	65
812	70 c. Toyota "Supra" (1984)		70	70
813	90 c. Ferrari "Testarossa" (1985)		80	90
814	$1 BMW "501B" (1955)		85	95
815	$2 Mercedes-Benz "280 SL" (1968)		1·40	2·00
816	$3 Austro-Daimler "ADR8" (1932)		1·90	2·50
809/16		*Set of 8*	6·25	7·50
MS817	Two sheets, each 116 × 85 mm. (a) $5 Morgan "+8" (1977). (b) $5 Checker taxi			
		Set of 2 sheets	7·00	11·00

(Litho Questa)

1986 (19 Dec). *Birth Centenary of Marc Chagall (artist). Designs as T* **225** *of Antigua, showing various paintings.* P 13½×14 (*vert*) or 14×13½ (*horiz*).

818/57	$1.10×40 multicoloured	*Set of 40*	28·00	28·00
MS858	Ten sheets, each 110×95 mm. $5×10 multicoloured (*each* 104×89 *mm*). Imperf			
		Set of 10 sheets	28·00	28·00

Although announced as all being released on 19 December 1986 the issue was distributed in ten parts, each of four stamps' and one miniature sheet, at monthly intervals.

(Des J. Iskowitz. Litho Format)

1987 (5 Feb). *America's Cup Yachting Championship. Multicoloured designs as T* **222** *of Antigua.* P 15.

859	25 c. *Defender*, 1895		50	40
860	45 c. *Galatea*, 1886		70	60
861	70 c. *Azzurra*, 1981		90	1·00
862	$4 *Australia II*, 1983		3·50	3·50
859/62		*Set of 4*	3·75	5·00
MS863	113×83 mm. $5 *Columbia* defeating *Shamrock*, 1899 (*horiz*)		5·00	6·50

(Des Mary Walters. Litho Format)

1987 (27 Apr). *500th Anniv of Discovery of America by Columbus (1992) (1st issue). Vert designs as T* **322** *of Grenada. Multicoloured.* P 15.

864	15 c. Christopher Columbus		25	25
865	30 c. Queen Isabella of Castile		30	30
866	50 c. *Santa Maria*		45	50
867	60 c. Claiming the New World for Spain		50	60
868	90 c. Early Spanish map of Lesser Antilles		65	75
869	$1 King Ferdinand of Aragon		70	80
870	$2 Fort La Navidad (drawing by Columbus)		1·40	2·00
871	$3 Galley and Caribs, Hispaniola (drawing by Columbus)		1·90	2·50
864/71		*Set of 8*	5·50	7·00
MS872	Two sheets, each 104×72 mm. (a) $5 Caribs pearl fishing. (b) $5 *Santa Maria* at anchor			
		Set of 2 sheets	8·50	11·00

See also Nos. 1191/5, 1224/32, 1366/74, 1494/1500 and 1519/20.

(Des W. Wright. Litho Questa)

1987 (18 May). *Milestones of Transportation. Horiz designs as T* **226** *of Antigua. Multicoloured.* P 14.

873	10 c. Saunders Roe "SR-N1" (first hovercraft), 1959		30	30
874	15 c. Bugatti "Royale" (largest car), 1931		35	35
875	30 c. Aleksei Leonov and "Voskhod II" (first spacewalk), 1965		55	55
876	50 c. C.S.S. *Hunley* (first submarine to sink enemy ship), 1864		75	75
877	60 c. Rolls Royce "Flying Bedstead" (first VTOL aircraft), 1954		85	85
878	70 c. *Jenny Lind* (first mass produced locomotive class), 1847		90	1·00
879	90 c. Duryea "Buggvaut" (first U.S. petrol-driven car), 1893		1·00	1·25
880	$1.50, Steam locomotive, Metropolitan Railway, London (first underground line), 1863		1·75	2·00
881	$2 S.S. *Great Britain* (first transatlantic crossing by screw-steamship), 1843		2·25	2·50
882	$3 "Budweiser Rocket" (fastest car), 1979		2·75	3·00
873/82		*Set of 10*	10·00	11·50

(Des Susan Barrasi. Litho Format)

1987 (15 June). *"Capex '87" International Stamp Exhibition, Toronto. Game Fishes. Multicoloured designs as T* **323** *of Grenada, but horiz.* P 15.

883	6 c. Yellow Chub		15	15
884	30 c. King Mackerel		40	30
885	50 c. Short-finned Mako		55	55
886	60 c. Dolphin (fish)		60	60
887	90 c. Skipjack Tuna ("Bonito")		75	75
888	$1.10, Cobia		1·00	1·25
889	$3 Tarpon		2·25	2·75
890	$4 Swordfish		2·50	3·25
883/90		*Set of 8*	7·50	8·75
MS891	Two sheets, each 100×70 mm. (a) $5 Spotted Jewfish. (b) $5 Amberjack *Set of 2 sheets*		8·00	10·00

(Litho Questa)

1987 (5 Aug). *Centenary of Statue of Liberty (1986) (2nd issue). Multicoloured designs as T* **227** *of Antigua.* P 14.

892	10 c. Cleaning face of Statue		20	20
893	15 c. Commemorative lapel badges		30	30
894	25 c. Band playing and Statue		40	40
895	30 c. Band on parade and Statue		45	45
896	45 c. Face of Statue		50	50
897	50 c. Cleaning head of Statue (*horiz*)		55	55
898	60 c. Models of Statue (*horiz*)		65	65
899	70 c. Small boat flotilla (*horiz*)		75	85
900	$1 Unveiling ceremony		85	90
901	$1.10, Statue and Manhattan skyline		90	1·00
902	$2 Parade of warships		1·75	2·00
903	$3 Making commemorative flags		1·90	2·25
892/903		*Set of 12*	8·25	9·00

(Litho Questa)

1987 (9 Sept). *Great Scientific Discoveries. Horiz designs as T* **325** *of Grenada. Multicoloured.* P 14.

904	60 c. Newton medal		85	80
905	$1 Louis Daguerre (inventor of daguerreotype)		1·25	1·00
906	$2 Antoine Lavoisier and apparatus		2·25	2·75
907	$3 Rudolf Diesel and diesel engine		4·00	4·75
904/7		*Set of 4*	7·50	8·50
MS908	105×75 mm. $5 Halley's comet		6·00	7·50

No. 907 is inscribed "JAMES WATT" in error.

(Litho Questa)

1987 (1 Nov). *Bicentenary of U.S. Constitution. Multicoloured designs as T* **232** *of Antigua.* P 14.

909	10 c. Washington addressing delegates, Constitutional Convention		25	20
910	50 c. Flag and State Seal, Georgia		85	75
911	60 c. Capitol, Washington (*vert*)		85	80
912	$4 Thomas Jefferson (statesman) (*vert*)		3·75	3·50
909/12		*Set of 4*	5·25	6·50
MS913	105×75 mm. $5 Alexander Hamilton (New York delegate) (*vert*)		3·00	4·00

Nos. 909/12 were each issued in sheetlets of five stamps and one stamp-size label, which appears in the centre of the bottom row.

(Des Walt Disney Co. Litho Questa)

1987 (16 Nov). *"Hafnia '87" International Stamp Exhibition, Copenhagen. Designs as T* **328** *of Grenada, but horiz, illustrating Hans Christian Andersen's fairy tales. Multicoloured.* P 14×13½.

914	25 c. Donald and Daisy Duck in "The Swineherd"		50	30
915	30 c. Mickey Mouse, Donald and Daisy Duck in "What the Good Man Does is Always Right"		55	55
916	50 c. Mickey and Minnie Mouse in "Little Tuk"		75	75
917	60 c. Minnie Mouse and Ferdie in "The World's Fairest Rose"		75	75
918	70 c. Mickey Mouse in "The Garden of Paradise"		80	80
919	$1.50, Goofy and Mickey Mouse in "The Naughty Boy"		2·00	2·25
920	$3 Goofy in "What the Moon Saw"		2·75	3·00
921	$4 Alice as "Thumbelina"		3·25	3·50
914/21		*Set of 8*	10·00	10·50
MS922	Two sheets, each 127×101 mm. (a) $5 Daisy Duck in "Hans Clodhopper". (b) $5 Aunt Matilda and Mickey Mouse in "Elder-Tree Mother"	*Set of 2 sheets*	11·00	12·00

91 "The Virgin and Child with Saints Martin and Agnes"   92 Scout signalling with Semaphore Flags

(Litho Questa)

1987 (15 Dec). *Christmas. Religious Paintings by El Greco. T* **91** *and similar vert designs. Multicoloured.* P 14.

923	10 c. Type **91**		40	15
924	50 c. "St. Agnes" (detail from "The Virgin and Child with Saints Martin and Agnes")		1·25	75
925	60 c. "The Annunciation"		1·25	75
926	$4 "The Holy Family with St. Anne"		4·75	7·25
923/6		*Set of 4*	7·00	8·00
MS927	75×101 mm. $5 "The Adoration of the Shepherds"		7·50	8·50

(Des and litho Questa)

1988 (15 Feb). *Royal Ruby Wedding. Vert designs as T* **234** *of Antigua. Multicoloured.* P 14.

928	20 c. deep brown, black and light green		35	15
929	30 c. deep brown and black		40	20
930	$2 multicoloured		2·00	2·50
931	$3 multicoloured		2·50	3·25
928/31		*Set of 4*	4·75	5·50
MS932	76×100 mm. $5 multicoloured		4·50	5·50

Designs:—20 c. Queen Elizabeth II with Princess Anne, c. 1957; 30 c. Wedding photograph, 1947; $2 Queen with Prince Charles and Princess Anne, c. 1955; $3 Queen Elizabeth (from photo by Tim Graham), 1980; $5 Princess Elizabeth in wedding dress, 1947.

(Des Walt Disney Company. Litho Questa)

1988 (13 Apr). *Olympic Games, Seoul. Multicoloured designs as T* **331** *of Grenada, showing Walt Disney cartoon characters as Olympic competitors.* P 14×13½.

933	1 c. Minnie Mouse as rhythmic gymnast (*horiz*)		10	10
934	2 c. Pete and Goofy as pankration wrestlers (*horiz*)		10	10
935	3 c. Huey and Dewey as synchronized swimmers (*horiz*)		10	10
936	4 c. Huey, Dewey and Louey in hoplite race (*horiz*)		10	10
937	5 c. Clarabelle and Daisy Duck playing baseball (*horiz*)		10	10
938	10 c. Goofy and Donald Duck in horse race (*horiz*)		10	10
939	$6 Donald Duck and Uncle Scrooge McDuck windsurfing (*horiz*)		4·00	5·50
940	$7 Mickey Mouse in chariot race (*horiz*)		4·50	5·50
933/40		*Set of 8*	8·00	10·00
MS941	Two sheets, each 127×101 mm. (a) $5 Mickey Mouse throwing discus in pentathlon. (b) $5 Donald Duck playing tennis. P 13½×14			
		Set of 2 sheets	7·00	8·50

(Des J. Martin. Litho Questa)

1988 (3 May). *World Scout Jamboree, Australia.* T **92** *and similar multicoloured designs.* P 14.

942	50 c. Type **92**	50	35
943	70 c. Canoeing	60	50
944	$1 Cooking over campfire (*horiz*)	70	65
945	$3 Scouts around campfire (*horiz*)	2·00	3·00
942/5	*Set of 4*	3·50	4·00
MS946	110×77 mm. $5 Erecting tent (*horiz*)	3·50	4·50

(Des Mary Walters. Litho Questa)

1988 (31 May). *Birds. Designs as* T **334** *of Grenada, but horiz. Multicoloured.* P 14.

947	20 c. Yellow-crowned Night Heron	30	25
948	25 c. Brown Pelican	30	25
949	45 c. Audubon's Shearwater	40	35
950	60 c. Red-footed Booby	50	45
951	70 c. Bridled Tern	55	50
952	90 c. Red-billed Tropic Bird	70	70
953	$3 Blue-winged Teal	1·75	2·25
954	$4 Sora	2·00	2·75
947/54	*Set of 8*	6·00	6·75
MS955	Two sheets, each 105×75 mm. (a) $5 Purple-throated Carib. (b) $5 Little Blue Heron *Set of 2 sheets*	4·75	6·50

(Litho Questa)

1988 (15 June). *500th Birth Anniv of Titian (artist). Vert designs as* T **238** *of Antigua. Multicoloured.* P 13½×14.

956	15 c. "Man with Blue Eyes"	15	15
957	30 c. "The Three Ages of Man" (detail)	20	20
958	60 c. "Don Diego Mendoza"	35	35
959	75 c. "Emperor Charles V seated"	50	50
960	$1 "A Young Man in a Fur"	60	60
961	$2 "Tobias and the Angel"	1·10	1·40
962	$3 "Pietro Bembo"	1·60	1·90
963	$4 "Pier Luigi Farnese"	1·75	2·25
956/63	*Set of 8*	5·50	6·50
MS964	110×95 mm. (a) $5 "Sacred and Profane Love" (detail). (b) $5 "Venus and Adonis" (detail) *Set of 2 sheets*	7·00	8·00

(Des W. Hanson. Litho Questa)

1988 (1 July). *Airships. Multicoloured designs as* T **336** *of Grenada.* P 14.

965	10 c. LZ-129 *Hindenburg* over Sugarloaf Mountain, Rio de Janeiro, 1937 (*horiz*)	20	20
966	20 c. LZ-129 *Hindenburg* over New York, 1937 (*horiz*)	30	30
967	30 c. U.S. Navy "K" Class airships on Atlantic escort duty, 1944 (*horiz*)	35	35
968	45 c. LZ-129 *Hindenburg* approaching Lakehurst, 1937	45	45
969	60 c. LZ-127 *Graf Zeppelin* and LZ-129 *Hindenburg* over Germany, 1936	60	60
970	70 c. LZ-129 *Hindenburg* and ZR-3 *Los Angeles* moored at Lakehurst, 1936 (*horiz*)	65	70
971	$1 LZ-130 *Graf Zeppelin II* over Dover, 1939	80	85
972	$2 LZ-8 *Ersatz Deutschland* on scheduled passenger flight, 1912 (*horiz*)	1·40	1·60
973	$3 LZ-127 *Graf Zeppelin* over Dome of the Rock, Jerusalem, 1931 (*horiz*)	1·90	2·25
974	$4 LZ-129 *Hindenburg* over Olympic stadium, Berlin, 1936 (*horiz*)	2·00	2·25
965/74	*Set of 10*	7·75	8·50
MS975	Two sheets (a) 76×95 mm. $5 LZ-127 *Graf Zeppelin*, 1933. (b) 95×76 mm. $5 LZ-127 *Graf Zeppelin*, 1931 (*horiz*) *Set of 2 sheets*	8·00	10·00

93 Bambi and his Mother

(Des Walt Disney Co. Litho Questa)

1988 (25 July). *Disney Animal Cartoon Films.* T **93** *and similar designs.* P 14×13½.

976/1029	30 c.×54 multicoloured *Set of 54*	14·00	15·00
MS1030	Six sheets, each 127×102 mm. $5×6 multicoloured. P 14×13½ (*horiz*) or 13½×14 (*vert*) *Set of 6 sheets*	28·00	30·00

Nos. 976/1029 (issued as six sheetlets each of nine different designs) and MS1030 depict scenes from *Bambi*, *Dumbo* ($5 vert), *Lady and The Tramp* ($5 vert), *The Aristocats*, *The Fox and the Hound* and *101 Dalmatians*.

(Des Walt Disney Co. Litho Questa)

1988 (1 Aug). *"Sydpex '88" National Stamp Exhibition, Sydney and 60th Birthday of Mickey Mouse. Horiz designs as* T **337** *of Grenada. Multicoloured.* P 14×13½.

1031	1 c. Mickey Mouse conducting at Sydney Opera House	10	10
1032	2 c. Mickey Mouse and Donald Duck at Ayers Rock	10	10
1033	3 c. Goofy and Mickey Mouse on sheep station	10	10
1034	4 c. Goofy and Mickey Mouse at Lone Pine Koala Sanctuary	10	10
1035	5 c. Mickey Mouse, Donald Duck and Goofy playing Australian football	10	10
1036	10 c. Mickey Mouse and Goofy camel racing	10	10
1037	$5 Donald Duck and his nephews bowling	4·50	5·00

1038	$6 Mickey Mouse with America's Cup trophy and *Australia II* (yacht)	5·50	6·00
1031/8	*Set of 8*	9·50	10·50
MS1039	Two sheets, each 127×102 mm. (a) $5 Goofy diving on Great Barrier Reef. (b) $5 Donald Duck, Mickey and Minnie Mouse at beach barbecue *Set of 2 sheets*	7·00	9·00

(Des W. Wright. Litho Questa)

1988 (30 Sept). *Flowering Trees and Shrubs. Multicoloured designs as* T **339** *of Grenada.* P 14.

1040	10 c. Potato Tree (*vert*)	15	15
1041	20 c. Wild Cotton	15	15
1042	30 c. Shower of Gold (*vert*)	20	20
1043	60 c. Napoleon's Button (*vert*)	35	30
1044	90 c. Geiger Tree	60	70
1045	$1 Fern Tree	70	80
1046	$2 French Cashew	1·25	2·00
1047	$4 Amherstia (*vert*)	2·00	3·00
1040/7	*Set of 8*	5·00	6·50
MS1048	Two sheets, each 117×88 mm. (a) $5 African Tulip Tree (*vert*). (b) $5 Swamp Immortelle *Set of 2 sheets*	4·25	5·50

(Des W. Wright. Litho B.D.T.)

1988 (7 Oct). *Cars. Vert designs as* T **335** *of Grenada. Multicoloured.* P 13.

1049	$2 Doble "Series E", 1925	1·00	1·00
	a. Sheetlet. Nos. 1049/58	9·00	
1050	$2 Alvis "12/50", 1926	1·00	1·00
1051	$2 Sunbeam 3-litre, 1927	1·00	1·00
1052	$2 Franklin "Airman", 1928	1·00	1·00
1053	$2 Delage "D8S", 1929	1·00	1·00
1054	$2 Mors, 1897	1·00	1·00
1055	$2 Peerless "Green Dragon", 1904	1·00	1·00
1056	$2 Pope-Hartford, 1909	1·00	1·00
1057	$2 Daniels "Submarine Speedster", 1920	1·00	1·00
1058	$2 McFarlan 9.3 litre, 1922	1·00	1·00
1059	$2 Frazer Nash "Lemans" replica, 1949	1·00	1·00
	a. Sheetlet. Nos. 1059/68	9·00	
1060	$2 Pegaso "Z102", 1953	1·00	1·00
1061	$2 Siata "Spyder V-8", 1953	1·00	1·00
1062	$2 Kurtis-Offenhauser, 1953	1·00	1·00
1063	$2 Kaiser-Darrin, 1954	1·00	1·00
1064	$2 Tracta, 1930	1·00	1·00
1065	$2 Maybach "Zeppelin", 1932	1·00	1·00
1066	$2 Railton "Light Sports", 1934	1·00	1·00
1067	$2 Hotchkiss, 1936	1·00	1·00
1068	$2 Mercedes-Benz "W163", 1939	1·00	1·00
1069	$2 Aston Martin "Vantage V8", 1982	1·00	1·00
	a. Sheetlet. Nos. 1069/78	9·00	
1070	$2 Porsche "956", 1982	1·00	1·00
1071	$2 Lotus "Esprit Turbo", 1983	1·00	1·00
1072	$2 McLaren "MP4/2", 1984	1·00	1·00
1073	$2 Mercedes-Benz "190E 2.3-16", 1985	1·00	1·00
1074	$2 Ferrari "250 GT Lusso", 1963	1·00	1·00
1075	$2 Porsche "904", 1964	1·00	1·00
1076	$2 Volvo "P1800", 1967	1·00	1·00
1077	$2 McLaren-Chevrolet "M8D", 1970	1·00	1·00
1078	$2 Jaguar "XJ6", 1981	1·00	1·00
1049/78	*Set of 30*	27·00	27·00

Nos. 1049/58, 1059/68 and 1069/78 were each printed together, se-tenant, in sheetlets of 10.

(Des Walt Disney Co. Litho Questa)

1988 (1 Dec). *"Mickey's Christmas Parade". Multicoloured designs as* T **246** *of Antigua showing Walt Disney cartoon characters.* P 13½×14.

1079	$1 Dumbo	55	65
	a. Sheetlet. Nos. 1079/86	4·00	
1080	$1 Goofy as Father Christmas	55	65
1081	$1 Minnie Mouse waving from window	55	65
1082	$1 Clarabelle, Mordie and Ferdie watching parade	55	65
1083	$1 Donald Duck's nephews	55	65
1084	$1 Donald Duck as drummer	55	65
1085	$1 Toy soldiers	55	65
1086	$1 Mickey Mouse on wooden horse	55	65
1079/86	*Set of 8*	4·00	4·75
MS1087	Two sheets, each 127 × 102 mm. (a) $7 Peter Pan and Captain Hook on float (*horiz*). (b) $7 Mickey Mouse as Father Christmas and Donald Duck in carnival train (*horiz*). P 14 × 13½ *Set of 2 sheets*	10·00	11·00

94 Middleweight Boxing (Gold, Henry Maske, East Germany)

95 Launch of "Apollo 11"

(Des L. Fried. Litho B.D.T.)

1989 (13 Apr). *Olympic Medal Winners, Seoul (1988).* T **94** *and similar horiz designs. Multicoloured.* P 14.

1088	15 c. Type **94**	20	20
1089	50 c. Freestyle wrestling (130 kg) (Bronze, Andreas Schroeder, East Germany)	40	40
1090	60 c. Women's team gymnastics (Bronze, East Germany)	50	50
1091	75 c. Platform diving (Gold, Greg Louganis, U.S.A.)	55	55
1092	$1 Freestyle wrestling (52 kg) (Gold, Mitsuru Sato, Japan)	70	70
1093	$2 Men's freestyle 4×200 metres relay swimming (Bronze, West Germany)	1·25	1·50
1094	$3 Men's 5000 metres (Silver, Dieter Baumann, West Germany)	1·60	1·75

1095	$4 Women's heptathlon (Gold, Jackie Joyner-Kersee, U.S.A.)	2·00	2·50
1088/95	*Set of 8*	6·50	7·25
MS1096	Two sheets, each 70×100 mm. (a) $6 Weightlifting (67.5 kg) (Gold, Joachim Kunz, East Germany). (b) $6 Team Three-Day Event (Gold, West Germany) *Set of 2 sheets*	6·00	7·50

(Litho Questa)

1989 (15 May). *Japanese Art. Paintings by Hiroshige. Horiz designs as* T **250** *of Antigua. Multicoloured.* P 14×13½.

1097	15 c. "Crossing the Oi at Shimada by Ferry"	25	25
1098	20 c. "Daimyo and Entourage at Arai"	30	30
1099	45 c. "Cargo Portage through Goyu"	50	50
1100	75 c. "Snowfall at Fujigawa"	75	75
1101	$1 "Horses for the Emperor at Chirifu"	85	85
1102	$2 "Rainfall at Tsuchiyama"	1·60	1·60
1103	$3 "An Inn at Ishibe"	2·25	2·25
1104	$4 "On the Shore of Lake Biwa at Otsu"	2·75	2·75
1097/104	*Set of 8*	8·25	8·25
MS1105	Two sheets, each 102×78 mm. (a) $5 "Fishing Village of Yokkaichi on the Mie". (b) $5 "Pilgrimage to Atsuta Shrine at Miya" *Set of 2 sheets*	4·75	6·50

Nos. 1097/104 were each printed in sheetlets of 10 containing two horizontal strips of 5 stamps separated by printed labels commemorating Emperor Hirohito.

(Des D. Bruckner. Litho B.D.T.)

1989 (12 June). *World Cup Football Championship, Italy (1990) (1st issue). Multicoloured designs as* T **252** *of Antigua.* P 14.

1106	15 c. World Cup trophy	30	20
1107	20 c. Flags of Argentina (winners 1986) and International Federation of Football Associations (F.I.F.A.) (*horiz*)	30	20
1108	45 c. Franz Beckenbauer (West Germany) with World Cup, 1974	50	35
1109	75 c. Flags of Italy (winners 1982) and F.I.F.A. (*horiz*)	65	55
1110	$1 Péle (Brazil) with Jules Rimet trophy	75	70
1111	$2 Flags of West Germany (winners 1974) and F.I.F.A. (*horiz*)	1·25	1·50
1112	$3 Flags of Brazil (winners 1970) and F.I.F.A. (*horiz*)	1·75	2·25
1113	$4 Jules Rimet trophy and Brazil players	1·90	2·50
1106/13	*Set of 8*	6·75	7·50
MS1114	(a) 100×81 mm. $5 Goalkeeper (*vert*). (b) 66×95 mm. $6 Péle with Jules Rimet trophy *Set of 2 sheets*	6·75	7·50

See also Nos. 1285/9.

(Des W. Wright. Litho B.D.T.)

1989 (28 June). *North American Railway Locomotives. Vert designs as* T **342** *of Grenada. Multicoloured.* P 13.

1115	$2 Morris & Essex Railroad *Dover*, 1841	1·50	1·50
	a. Sheetlet. Nos. 1115/24	13·00	
1116	$2 Baltimore & Ohio Railroad *Memnon* No. 57, 1848	1·50	1·50
1117	$2 Camden & Amboy Railroad *John Stevens*, 1849	1·50	1·50
1118	$2 Lawrence Machine Shop *Lawrence*, 1853	1·50	1·50
1119	$2 South Carolina Railroad *James S. Corry*, 1859	1·50	1·50
1120	$2 Mine Hill & Schuylkill Haven Railroad Flexible Beam No. 3 type, 1860	1·50	1·50
1121	$2 Delaware, Lackawanna & Western Railroad *Montrose*, 1861	1·50	1·50
1122	$2 Central Pacific Railroad *Pequop* No. 68, 1868	1·50	1·50
1123	$2 Boston & Providence Railroad *Daniel Nason*, 1863	1·50	1·50
1124	$2 Morris & Essex Railroad *Joe Scranton*, 1870	1·50	1·50
1125	$2 Central Railroad of New Jersey No. 124, 1871	1·50	1·50
	a. Sheetlet. Nos. 1125/34	13·00	
1126	$2 Baldwin tramway steam locomotive, 1876	1·50	1·50
1127	$2 Lackawanna & Bloomsburg Railroad *Luzerne*, 1878	1·50	1·50
1128	$2 Central Mexicano Railroad No. 150, 1892	1·50	1·50
1129	$2 Denver, South Park & Pacific Railroad *Breckenridge* No. 15, 1879	1·50	1·50
1130	$2 Miles Planting & Manufacturing Company plantation locomotive *Daisy*, 1894	1·50	1·50
1131	$2 Central of Georgia Railroad Baldwin "854" No. 1136, 1895	1·50	1·50
1132	$2 Savannah, Florida & Western Railroad No. 111, 1900	1·50	1·50
1133	$2 Douglas, Gilmore & Company contractors locomotive No. 3, 1902	1·50	1·50
1134	$2 Lehigh Valley Coal Company compressed air locomotive No. 900, 1903	1·50	1·50
1135	$2 Morgan's Louisiana & Texas Railroad McKeen diesel locomotive, 1908	1·50	1·50
	a. Sheetlet. Nos. 1135/44	13·00	
1136	$2 Clear Lake Lumber Company Type "B Climax" locomotive No. 6, 1910	1·50	1·50
1137	$2 Blue Jay Lumber Company Heisler locomotive No. 10, 1912	1·50	1·50
1138	$2 Stewartstown Railroad gasoline locomotive No. 6, 1920s	1·50	1·50
1139	$2 Bangor & Aroostock Railroad Class "G" No. 186, 1921	1·50	1·50
1140	$2 Hammond Lumber Company No. 6, 1923	1·50	1·50
1141	$2 Central Railroad of New Jersey diesel locomotive No. 1000, 1925	1·50	1·50
1142	$2 Atchison, Topeka & Santa Fe Railroad "Super Chief" diesel express, 1935	1·50	1·50
1143	$2 Norfolk & Western Railroad Class "Y-6", 1948	1·50	1·50

1144	$2 Boston & Maine Railroad Budd diesel railcar, 1949	1·50	1·50
1115/44	*Set of 30*	38·00	38·00

Nos. 1115/24, 1125/34 and 1135/44 were each printed together, *se-tenant*, in sheetlets of 10.

(Des Walt Disney Co. Litho Questa)

1989 (7 July). *"Philexfrance 89" International Stamp Exhibition, Paris. Multicoloured designs as T 251 of Antigua showing Walt Disney cartoon characters in Paris. P 14×13½ (horiz) or 13½×14 (vert).*

1145	1 c. Mickey Mouse and Donald Duck at Ecole Militaire inflating balloon	10	10
1146	2 c. Mickey and Minnie Mouse on river boat passing Conciergerie	10	10
1147	3 c. Mickey Mouse at Hotel de Ville (*vert*)	10	10
1148	4 c. Mickey Mouse at Genie of the Bastille monument (*vert*)	10	10
1149	5 c. Mickey and Minnie Mouse arriving at Opera House	10	10
1150	10 c. Mickey and Minnie Mouse on tandem in Luxembourg Gardens	10	10
1151	$5 Mickey Mouse in aeroplane over L'Arch de la Defense (*vert*)	5·50	6·50
1152	$6 Mickey Mouse at Place Vendome (*vert*)	5·50	6·50
1145/52	*Set of 8*	10·00	12·00

MS1153 Two sheets, each 127×102 mm. (a) $6 Mickey and Minnie Mouse on scooter in Place de la Concorde. (b) $6 Donald Duck, Mickey and Minnie Mouse in balloon over Versailles. P 14×13½ . . *Set of 2 sheets* 11·00 13·00

(Des L. Birmingham. Litho Questa)

1989 (20 July). *20th Anniv of First Manned Landing on Moon. T 95 and similar multicoloured designs. P 14.*

1154	25 c. Type 95	30	30
1155	50 c. Splashdown (*horiz*)	50	50
1156	60 c. Modules in space	60	60
1157	75 c. Aldrin setting up experiment (*horiz*)	70	70
1158	$1 "Apollo 11" leaving Earth orbit (*horiz*)	80	80
1159	$2 Moving "Apollo 11" to launch site	1·60	1·90
1160	$3 Lunar module *Eagle* leaving Moon (*horiz*)	2·00	2·50
1161	$4 *Eagle* landing on Moon	2·25	2·75
1154/61	*Set of 8*	8·00	9·00

MS1162 (a) 71×100 mm. $5 Armstrong stepping onto Moon. (b) 101×72 mm. $5 Armstrong's footprint on Moon . . *Set of 2 sheets* 6·50 8·00

(Des J. Cooter. Litho B.D.T.)

1989 (17 Aug). *Fungi. Vert designs as T 348 of Grenada. Multicoloured. P 14.*

1163	6 c. *Agaricus purpurellus* (incorrectly inscr *Collybia aurea*)	35	25
1164	10 c. *Podaxis pistillaris*	35	25
1165	20 c. *Hygrocybe firma*	55	45
1166	30 c. *Agaricus rufoaurantiacus*	65	55
1167	75 c. *Leptonia howellii*	1·40	1·40
1168	$2 *Marasmiellus purpureus*	2·50	2·75
1169	$3 *Marasmius trinitatis*	3·00	3·25
1170	$4 *Collybia aurea* (incorrectly inscr *Hygrocybe martinicensis*)	3·25	3·50
1163/70	*Set of 8*	11·00	11·00

MS1171 Two sheets, each 56×71 mm. (a) $6 *Lentinus crinitus* (incorrectly inscr *Agaricus purpurellus*). (b) $6 *Hygrocybe martinicensis* (incorrectly inscr *Lentinus crinitus*) . . *Set of 2 sheets* 12·00 13·00

(Des Deborah Dudley Max. Litho B.D.T.)

1989 (2 Oct). *Butterflies. Horiz designs as T 350 of Grenada. Multicoloured. P 14.*

1172	25 c. *Battus polydamas* (inscr "*Papilio androgeus*")	40	40
1173	35 c. *Phoebis sennae*	45	45
1174	45 c. *Hamadryas feronia*	55	55
1175	50 c. *Cynthia cardui*	55	55
1176	75 c. *Ascia monuste*	80	80
1177	90 c. *Eurema lisa*	90	90
1178	$2 *Aphrissa statira*	2·00	2·00
1179	$3 *Hypolimnas misippus*	2·50	2·50
1172/9	*Set of 8*	7·50	7·50

MS1180 Two sheets, each 87×115 mm. (a) $6 *Anartia amathea*. (b) $6 *Pseudolycaena marsyas* . . *Set of 2 sheets* 9·00 11·00

96 Ethel Barrymore 97 Buddy Holly

(Des J. Genzo. Litho B.D.T.)

1989 (9 Oct). *425th Birth Anniv of Shakespeare. Shakespearean Actors. T 96 and similar horiz designs. Multicoloured. P 14.*

1181	15 c. Type 96	25	25
1182	$1.10, Richard Burton	1·25	1·25
1183	$2 John Barrymore	2·00	2·00
1184	$3 Paul Robeson	2·25	2·25
1181/4	*Set of 4*	5·25	5·25

MS1185 103×77 mm. $6 Bando Tamasaburo and Nakamura Kanzaburo . . 4·50 5·50

(Des J. Genzo. Litho B.D.T.)

1989 (9 Oct). *Musicians. T 97 and similar vert designs. Multicoloured. P 14.*

1186	10 c. Type 97	35	25
1187	25 c. Jimmy Hendrix	55	40
1188	75 c. Mighty Sparrow	70	70
1189	$4 Katsutoji Kineya	3·00	4·00
1186/9	*Set of 4*	4·25	4·75

MS1190 103×77 mm. $6 Kurt Weill . . 4·25 4·75

(Des D. Miller. Litho Questa)

1989 (16 Oct). *500th Anniv of Discovery of America by Columbus (1992) (2nd issue). Pre-Columbian Arawak Society. Vert designs as T 247 of Antigua. Multicoloured. P 14.*

1191	15 c. Arawaks canoeing	25	25
1192	75 c. Family and campfire	75	75
1193	90 c. Using stone tools	95	95
1194	$3 Eating and drinking	2·50	3·00
1191/4	*Set of 4*	4·00	4·50

MS1195 84×87 mm. $6 Making fire . . 3·50 4·25

(Des Walt Disney Co. Litho Questa)

1989 (17 Nov). *"World Stamp Expo '89" International Stamp Exhibition, Washington. Multicoloured designs as T 352 of Grenada showing Walt Disney cartoon characters illustrating proverbs from Poor Richard's Almanack. P 14×13½.*

1196	1 c. Scrooge McDuck with gold coins in sinking boat	10	10
1197	2 c. Robin Hood shooting apple off Friar Tuck	10	10
1198	3 c. Winnie the Pooh with honey	10	10
1199	4 c. Goofy, Minnie Mouse and Donald Duck exercising	10	10
1200	5 c. Pinnochio holding Jimminy Cricket	10	10
1201	6 c. Huey and Dewey putting up wallpaper	10	10
1202	8 c. Mickey Mouse asleep in storm	15	10
1203	10 c. Mickey Mouse as Benjamin Franklin selling *Pennsylvania Gazette*	15	10
1204	$5 Mickey Mouse with chicken, recipe book and egg	4·00	5·00
1205	$6 Mickey Mouse missing carriage	4·50	5·00
1196/1205	*Set of 10*	8·50	9·50

MS1206 Two sheets, each 127×102 mm. (a) $6 Mickey Mouse bowing. P 14×13½. (b) $6 Mickey Mouse delivering basket of food (*vert*). P 13½×14 . . *Set of 2 sheets* 10·50 11·00

(Litho Questa)

1990 (4 Jan). *Christmas. Paintings by Rubens. Vert designs as T 259 of Antigua. Multicoloured. P 14.*

1207	10 c. "The Annunciation"	25	15
1208	15 c. "The Flight of the Holy Family into Egypt"	30	15
1209	25 c. "The Presentation in the Temple"	40	15
1210	45 c. "The Holy Family under the Apple Tree"	55	25
1211	$2 "Madonna and Child with Saints"	1·75	2·25
1212	$4 "The Virgin and Child enthroned with Saints"	2·75	3·75
1213	$5 "The Holy Family"	3·00	3·75
1207/13	*Set of 7*	8·00	9·50

MS1214 Two sheets, each 70×95 mm. (a) $5 "The Adoration of the Magi" (sketch). (b) $5 "The Adoration of the Magi" . . *Set of 2 sheets* 9·50 10·00

(Des L. Nelson. Litho Questa)

1990 (6 Mar). *"EXPO 90" International Garden and Greenery Exhibition, Osaka. Caribbean Orchids. Vert designs as T 354 of Grenada. Multicoloured. P 14.*

1215	15 c. *Brassocattleya* Thalie	30	30
1216	20 c. *Odontocidium* Tigersun	35	35
1217	50 c. *Odontioda* Hambuhren	55	55
1218	75 c. *Paphiopedilum* Delrosi	75	75
1219	$1 *Vuylstekeara* Yokara	95	95
1220	$2 *Paphiopedilum* Geelong	1·75	2·00
1221	$3 *Wilsonara* Tigerwood	2·00	2·25
1222	$4 *Cymbidium* Ormoulu	2·50	2·75
1215/22	*Set of 8*	8·25	9·00

MS1223 Two sheets, each 98×68 mm. (a) $6 *Odontonia* Sappho. (b) $6 *Cymbidium* Vieux Rose . . *Set of 2 sheets* 8·50 9·50

(Des Mary Walters. Litho Questa)

1990 (16 Mar). *500th Anniv of Discovery of America by Columbus (1992) (3rd issue). New World Natural History – Insects. Designs as T 260 of Antigua, but horiz. Multicoloured. P 14.*

1224	35 c. *Dynastes hercules* (beetle)	35	35
1225	40 c. *Chalcolepidius porcatus* (beetle)	35	35
1226	50 c. *Acrocinus longimanus* (beetle)	40	40
1227	60 c. *Battus polydamas* (butterfly)	75	75
1228	$1 *Orthemis ferruginea* (skimmer)	95	95
1229	$2 *Psiloptera variolosa* (beetle)	1·60	1·75
1230	$3 *Hypolimnas misippus* (butterfly)	2·50	2·75
1231	$4 Scarab Beetle	2·50	2·75
1224/31	*Set of 8*	8·50	9·00

MS1232 Two sheets, each 102×70 mm. (a) $6 *Calpodes ethlius* (butterfly). (b) $6 *Danaus plexippus* (butterfly) . . *Set of 2 sheets* 8·50 9·50

(Des J. Barbaris. Litho B.D.T.)

1990 (3 Apr). *Wildlife. Horiz designs as T 254 of Antigua. Multicoloured. P 14.*

1233	5 c. West Indies Giant Rice Rat	20	20
1234	25 c. Agouti	35	35
1235	30 c. Humpback Whale	70	65
1236	40 c. Pilot Whale	70	65
1237	$1 Spotted Dolphin	95	95
1238	$2 Egyptian Mongoose	1·75	2·00
1239	$3 Brazilian Tree Porcupine	2·25	2·75
1240	$4 American Manatee	2·50	3·00
1233/40	*Set of 8*	8·50	9·50

MS1241 Two sheets, each 107×80 mm. (a) $6 Caribbean Monk Seal. (b) $6 Egyptian Mongoose (*different*) . . *Set of 2 sheets* 8·00 9·00

(Des W. Wright. Litho Questa)

1990 (30 Apr). *50th Anniv of Second World War. Horiz designs as T 274 of Antigua. Multicoloured. P 14.*

1242	6 c. British Tanks in France, 1939	30	30
1243	10 c. Operation "Crusader", North Africa, 1941	30	30
1244	20 c. Retreat of the Afrika Corps, 1942	40	40
1245	45 c. American landing on Aleutian Islands, 1943	50	50
1246	50 c. U.S. marines landing on Tarawa, 1943	55	55
1247	60 c. U.S. army entering Rome, 1944	60	60
1248	75 c. U.S. tanks crossing River Seine, 1944	70	70
1249	$1 Battle of the Bulge, 1944	95	95
1250	$5 American infantry in Italy, 1945	3·00	3·50
1251	$6 Boeing B-29 Superfortress *Enola Gay* dropping atomic bomb on Hiroshima, 1945	3·50	3·50
1242/51	*Set of 10*	9·75	10·00

MS1252 112×84 mm. $6 St. Paul's Cathedral in London Blitz, 1940 . . 3·75 4·25

(Des Walt Disney Company. Litho Questa)

1990 (3 May). *"Stamp World London 90" International Stamp Exhibition (1st issue). Multicoloured designs as T 193 of Gambia showing Walt Disney cartoon characters at Shakespeare sites. P 14×13½ (15, 60 c., $1, $5) or 13½×14 (others).*

1253	15 c. Daisy Duck at Ann Hathaway's Cottage (*horiz*)	30	20
1254	30 c. Minnie and Bill Mouse at Shakespeare's birthplace, Stratford	45	35
1255	50 c. Minnie Mouse in front of Mary Arden's house, Wilmcote	65	55
1256	60 c. Mickey Mouse on hedge in New Place gardens, Stratford (*horiz*)	75	75
1257	$1 Mickey Mouse walking in New Place gardens, Stratford (*horiz*)	1·10	1·10
1258	$2 Mickey Mouse carrying books in Scholars Lane, Stratford	2·00	2·25
1259	$4 Mickey Mouse and Royal Shakespeare Theatre, Stratford	3·00	3·75
1260	$5 Ludwig von Drake teaching Mickey Mouse at the Stratford Grammar School (*horiz*)	3·25	3·75
1253/60	*Set of 8*	10·50	11·50

MS1261 Two sheets, each 126×101 mm. (a) $6 Mickey Mouse as Shakespeare. P 13½×14. (b) $6 Mickey and Minnie Mouse in rowing boat on River Avon, Stratford (*horiz*). P 14×13½ . . *Set of 2 sheets* 9·50 11·00

(Des Young Phillips Studio. Litho Questa)

1990 (5 July). *90th Birthday of Queen Elizabeth the Queen Mother. Vert designs as T 194 of Gambia, showing photographs, 1970–79. Multicoloured. P 14.*

1262	$2 Queen Mother in pink hat and coat	1·10	1·40
	a. Strip of 3. Nos. 1262/4	3·00	
1263	$2 Prince Charles and Queen Mother at Garter ceremony	1·10	1·40
1264	$2 Queen Mother in blue floral outfit	1·10	1·40
1262/4	*Set of 3*	3·00	3·75

MS1265 90×75 mm. $6 Queen Mother in Garter robes . . 3·75 4·75

Nos. 1262/4 were printed together, horizontally and vertically *se-tenant*, in sheetlets of 9 (3×3).

(Des M. Pollard. Litho Questa)

1990 (12 July). *"Stamp World London 90" International Stamp Exhibition (2nd issue). Sheet 97×75 mm containing horiz design as T 356 of Grenada. P 14.*

MS1266 $6 blue-green . . 5·50 6·50

Design:—$6 Map of South America and logo.

(Des J. Anderton. Litho B.D.T.)

1990 (10 Sept). *Birds. Multicoloured designs as T 358 of Grenada, but vert. P 14.*

1267	25 c. Yellow-bellied Seedeater	30	30
1268	45 c. Carib Grackle	50	50
1269	50 c. Black-whiskered Vireo	55	55
1270	75 c. Bananaquit	70	70
1271	$1 White-collared Swift	95	95
1272	$2 Yellow-billed Elaenia	1·50	1·50
1273	$3 Blue-hooded Euphonia	2·00	2·00
1274	$5 Eared Dove	3·25	3·25
1267/74	*Set of 8*	8·75	8·75

MS1275 Two sheets, each 101×72 mm. (a) $6 Mangrove Cuckoo. (b) $6 Scaly-breasted Thrasher . . *Set of 2 sheets* 8·50 10·00

(Des Deborah Dudley Max. Litho Questa)

1990 (17 Sept). *Crustaceans. Horiz designs as T 359 of Grenada. Multicoloured. P 14.*

1276	10 c. Slipper Lobster	20	20
1277	25 c. Green Reef Crab	30	30
1278	65 c. Caribbean Lobsterette	60	60
1279	75 c. Blind Deep Sea Lobster	70	70
1280	$1 Flattened Crab	95	95
1281	$2 Ridged Slipper Lobster	1·75	1·75
1282	$3 Land Crab	2·25	2·25
1283	$4 Mountain Crab	2·50	2·50
1276/83	*Set of 8*	8·25	8·25

MS1284 Two sheets, each 108×76 mm. (a) $6 Caribbean King Crab. (b) $6 Purse Crab . . *Set of 2 sheets* 8·00 9·00

98 Lineker, England

99 Angel with
Star and Lantern

(Des Young Phillips Studio. Litho Questa)

1990 (24 Sept). *World Cup Football Championship, Italy* (2nd issue). *T* **98** *and similar vert designs. Multicoloured. P* 14.

1285	15 c. Type **98**	25	25
1286	45 c. Burruchaga, Argentina	45	45
1287	$2 Hysen, Sweden	1·75	2·25
1288	$4 Sang Ho, South Korea	2·75	3·75
1285/8	*Set of* 4	4·75	6·00

MS1289 Two sheets, each 76×90 mm. (a) $6 Ramos, U.S.A. (b) $6 Stojkovic, Yugoslavia
Set of 2 *sheets* 8·50 9·50

(Des B. Grout. Litho Questa)

1990 (1 Nov). *Olympic Games, Barcelona* (1992). *Vert designs as T* **268** *of Antigua. Multicoloured. P* 14.

1290	10 c. Boxing	10	10
1291	25 c. Olympic flame	20	20
1292	50 c. Football	40	40
1293	75 c. Discus throwing	60	60
1294	$1 Pole vaulting	85	85
1295	$2 Show jumping	1·50	1·50
1296	$4 Women's basketball	2·50	2·75
1297	$5 Men's gymnastics	3·00	3·25
1290/7	*Set of* 8	8·25	8·75

MS1298 Two sheets. (a) 101×70 mm. $6 Sailboards. (b) 70×101 mm. $6 Decathlon
Set of 2 *sheets* 8·50 9·50

(Litho Questa)

1991 (31 Jan). *350th Death Anniv of Rubens. Multicoloured designs as T* **273** *of Antigua. P* 13½×14 (*vert*) *or* 14×13½ (*horiz*).

1299	5 c. "Adam and Eve" (Eve detail) (*vert*)	10	10
1300	15 c. "Esther before Ahasuerus" (detail)	15	15
1301	25 c. "Adam and Eve" (Adam detail) (*vert*)	25	25
1302	50 c. "Expulsion from Eden"	50	50
1303	$1 "Cain slaying Abel" (detail) (*vert*)	95	95
1304	$2 "Lot's Flight"	1·75	2·25
1305	$4 "Samson and Delilah" (detail)	2·75	3·50
1306	$5 "Abraham and Melchizedek"	3·25	3·50
1299/306	*Set of* 8	8·75	10·00

MS1307 Two sheets, each 101×71 mm. (a) $6 "The Meeting of David and Abigail" (detail). (b) $6 "Daniel in the Lions' Den" (detail)
Set of 2 *sheets* 7·00 8·50

(Des Mary Walters. Litho B.D.T.)

1991 (5 Feb). *Coral Reef Fishes. Horiz designs as T* **357** *of Grenada. Multicoloured. P* 14.

1308	15 c. Barred Hamlet	25	25
1309	35 c. Long-spined Squirrelfish	50	50
1310	45 c. Red-spotted Hawkfish	60	60
1311	75 c. Bigeye	85	85
1312	$1 Balloonfish ("Spiny Puffer")	1·10	1·10
1313	$2 Small-mouthed Grunt	2·00	2·00
1314	$3 Harlequin Bass	2·50	2·50
1315	$4 Creole Fish	3·00	3·00
1308/15	*Set of* 8	9·75	9·75

MS1316 Two sheets, each 103×72 mm. (a) $6 Copper Sweeper. (b) $6 Royal Gramma ("Fairy Basslet") | *Set of* 2 *sheets* 8·50 10·00

(Litho Questa)

1991 (1 Mar). *Christmas* (1990). *Hummel Figurines. T* **99** *and similar vert designs. Multicoloured. P* 14.

1317	10 c. Type **99**	10	10
1318	15 c. Christ Child and Angel playing mandolin	15	15
1319	25 c. Shepherd	25	25
1320	50 c. Angel with trumpet and lantern	50	50
1321	$1 Nativity scene	95	95
1322	$2 Christ Child and Angel holding candle	1·75	2·25
1323	$4 Angel with baskets	2·75	3·50
1324	$5 Angels singing	3·25	3·50
1317/24	*Set of* 8	8·75	10·00

MS1325 Two sheets, each 99×122 mm. (a) 5 c. As No. 1318; 40 c. As No. 1320; 60 c. As No. 1321; $3 As No. 1324. (b) 20 c. As Type **99**; 30 c. As No. 1319; 75 c. As No. 1322; $6 As No. 1323
Set of 2 *sheets* 9·00 10·00

100 *Brassia maculata*

101 Donald and Daisy Duck with Solar-powered Car

(Des S. Barlowe. Litho Walsall)

1991 (1 Apr)–92. *Orchids. T* **100** *and similar vert designs. Multicoloured. P* 14.

1326	5 c. Type **100**	30	30
1327	10 c. *Oncidium lanceanum*	30	30
1328	15 c. *Broughtonia sanguinea*	35	20
1329	25 c. *Diacrium bicornutum*	40	20
1330	35 c. *Cattleya labiata*	40	20
1331	45 c. *Epidendrum fragrans*	50	25
1332	50 c. *Oncidium papilio*	55	30
1333	75 c. *Neocogniauxia monophylla*	70	50
1334	$1 *Epidendrum polybulbon*	80	70
1335	$2 *Spiranthes speciosa*	1·40	1·40
1336	$4 *Epidendrum ciliare*	2·25	2·75
1337	$5 *Phais tankervilliae*	2·50	3·00
1338	$10 *Brassia caudata* (27.11.91)	4·50	5·50
1339	$20 *Brassavola cordata* (29.6.92)	9·25	11·00
1326/39	*Set of* 14	22·00	24·00

(Des W. Wright. Litho Questa)

1991 (8 Apr). *Butterflies. Horiz designs as T* **363** *of Grenada. Multicoloured. P* 14.

1340	5 c. Crimson-patched Longwing	40	30
1341	10 c. *Morpho helena*	40	30
1342	15 c. *Morpho sulkowskyi*	55	35
1343	20 c. *Dynastor napoleon*	60	40
1344	25 c. *Pieridae callinira*	60	45
1345	30 c. *Anartia amathea*	65	50
1346	35 c. *Heliconiidae dido*	65	50
1347	45 c. *Papilionidae columbus*	75	65
1348	50 c. *Nymphalidae praeneste*	85	70
1349	60 c. *Panacea prola*	1·00	80
1350	75 c. *Dryas julia*	1·00	90
1351	$1 *Papilionidae orthosilaus*	1·25	1·10
1352	$2 *Pyrrhopyge cometes*	1·75	2·00
1353	$3 *Papilionidae paeon*	2·00	2·50
1354	$4 *Morpho cypris*	2·50	3·00
1355	$5 *Choringa*	3·00	3·25
1340/55	*Set of* 16	16·00	16·00

MS1356 Four sheets, each 118×80 mm. (a) $6 *Danaus plexippus*. (b) $6 *Caligo idomenides*. (c) $6 *Nymphalidae amydon*. (d) $6 *Papilio childrenae* | *Set of* 4 *sheets* 15·00 15·00

(Des Walt Disney Co. Litho Questa)

1991 (22 Apr). *Ecology Conservation. T* **101** *and similar multicoloured designs showing Walt Disney cartoon characters. P* 14×13½.

1357	10 c. Type **101**	20	15
1358	15 c. Goofy saving water	30	20
1359	25 c. Donald and Daisy on nature hike	45	35
1360	45 c. Donald Duck returning chick to nest	65	55
1361	$1 Donald Duck and balloons	1·25	1·00
1362	$2 Minnie Mouse and Daisy Duck on hot day	2·00	2·25
1363	$4 Mickey's nephews cleaning beach	3·00	3·50
1364	$5 Donald Duck on pedal generator	3·25	3·75
1357/64	*Set of* 8	10·00	11·00

MS1365 Three sheets, each 127×102 mm. (a) $6 Hiawatha and felled forest. P 14×13½. (b) $6 Donald Duck recycling (*vert*). P 13½×14. (c) $6 Mickey Mouse with Arbor Day notice. P 14×13½ | *Set of* 3 *sheets* 12·00 13·00
d. Error. Imperf (sheet) (a)

(Des T. Agans. Litho Questa)

1991 (29 Apr). *500th Anniv of Discovery of America by Columbus* (1992) (4th issue). *History of Exploration. Multicoloured designs as T* **277** *of Antigua. P* 14.

1366	15 c. Magellan's *Vitoria* rounding Cape Horn, 1519–21	15	15
1367	20 c. Drake's *Golden Hind*, 1577–80	20	20
1368	50 c. Cook's H.M.S. *Resolution*, 1768–71	40	40
1369	60 c. Douglas World Cruiser seaplane, 1924	50	50
1370	$1 *Sputnik I* satellite, 1957	85	90
1371	$2 Gagarin's space flight, 1961	1·50	1·75
1372	$4 Glenn's space flight, 1962	2·50	2·75
1373	$5 Space shuttle, 1981	3·00	3·25
1366/73	*Set of* 8	8·25	9·00

MS1374 Two sheets. (a) 105×78 mm. $6 Bow of *Pinta* (*vert*). (b) 78×105 mm. $6 Fleet of Columbus | *Set of* 2 *sheets* 8·00 9·00

(Des Walt Disney Co. Litho Questa)

1991 (6 May). *"Phila Nippon '91" International Stamp Exhibition, Tokyo. Multicoloured designs as T* **279** *of Antigua showing Walt Disney cartoon characters in Japanese scenes. P* 14×13½.

1375	15 c. Minnie Mouse with silkworms (*horiz*)	30	20
1376	30 c. Minnie, Minnie, Morty and Ferdie at Torii Gate (*horiz*)	45	35
1377	50 c. Donald Duck and Mickey Mouse trying origami (*horiz*)	70	60
1378	60 c. Mickey and Minnie diving for pearls (*horiz*)	80	70
1379	$1 Minnie Mouse in kimono (*horiz*)	1·25	1·10
1380	$2 Mickey making masks (*horiz*)	2·25	2·50
1381	$4 Donald and Mickey making paper (*horiz*)	3·00	3·25
1382	$5 Minnie and Pluto making pottery (*horiz*)	3·25	3·50
1375/82	*Set of* 8	11·00	11·00

MS1383 Four sheets, each 122×102 mm. (a) $6 Mickey flower-arranging. (b) $6 Mickey carving a netsuke. (c) $6 Mickey at tea ceremony. (d) $6 Mickey making printing plate. P 13½×14 | *Set of* 4 *sheets* 16·00 16·00

(Des Mary Walters. Litho Questa)

1991 (1 June). *Fungi. Vert designs as T* **364** *of Grenada. Multicoloured. P* 14.

1384	5 c. *Pyrrhoglossum pyrrhum*	15	15
1385	45 c. *Agaricus purpurellus*	50	50
1386	50 c. *Amanita craseoderma*	55	55
1387	90 c. *Hygrocybe acutoconica*	90	90
1388	$1 *Limacella guttata*	95	95

1389	$2 *Lactarius hygrophoroides*	1·75	1·75
1390	$4 *Boletellus cubensis*	2·50	2·50
1391	$5 *Psilocybe caerulescens*	3·00	3·00
1384/91	*Set of* 8	9·25	9·25

MS1392 Two sheets, each 100×70 mm. (a) $6 *Marasmius haematocephalus*. (b) $6 *Lepiota spiculata* | *Set of* 2 *sheets* 10·00 11·00

(Des D. Miller. Litho Walsall)

1991 (5 July). *65th Birthday of Queen Elizabeth II. Horiz designs as T* **280** *of Antigua. Multicoloured. P* 14.

1393	20 c. Queen, Prince Philip, Prince Charles and Prince William at Trooping the Colour, 1990	30	20
1394	25 c. Queen and Prince Charles at polo match, 1985	30	20
1395	$2 Queen and Prince Philip at Maundy service, 1989	2·00	2·50
1396	$4 Queen with Queen Mother on her 87th birthday, 1987	3·25	3·75
1393/6	*Set of* 4	5·25	6·00

MS1397 68×90 mm. $5 The Queen at Caen Hill, 1990, and Prince Philip at R.A.F. Benson, 1989 | 3·75 4·50

(Des D. Miller. Litho Walsall)

1991 (5 July). *10th Wedding Anniv of Prince and Princess of Wales. Horiz designs as T* **280** *of Antigua. Multicoloured. P* 14.

1398	5 c. Prince and Princess of Wales kissing, 1987	15	15
1399	60 c. Portraits of Prince, Princess and sons	70	70
1400	$1 Prince Henry in 1988 and Prince William in 1987	1·10	1·10
1401	$5 Princess Diana in 1990 and Prince Charles in 1988	3·75	4·75
1398/1401	*Set of* 4	5·25	6·00

MS1402 68×90 mm. $5 Princess with Prince Henry in Majorca, and Prince and Princess with Prince Henry at polo match | 3·75 4·50

(Litho Questa)

1991 (18 Nov). *Death Centenary of Vincent van Gogh* (artist) (1990). *Multicoloured designs as T* **278** *of Antigua. P* 13½×14 (*vert*) *or* 14×13½ (*horiz*).

1403	5 c. "Two Thistles"	20	20
1404	10 c. "Baby Marcelle Roulin"	25	20
1405	15 c. "Still Life: Basket with Six Oranges" (*horiz*)	30	15
1406	25 c. "Orchard in Blossom"	35	20
1407	45 c. "Armand Roulin"	50	35
1408	50 c. "Wood Gatherers in Snow" (detail) (*horiz*)	60	40
1409	60 c. "Almond Tree in Blossom"	70	50
1410	$1 "An Old Man"	1·00	1·00
1411	$2 "The Seine Bridge at Asnières" (*horiz*)	1·75	2·00
1412	$3 "Vase with Lilacs, Daises and Anemones"	2·25	2·50
1413	$4 "Self Portrait"	2·40	2·75
1414	$5 "Patience Escalier"	2·50	2·75
1403/14	*Set of* 12	11·50	11·50

MS1415 Three sheets. (a) 127×102 mm. $6 "Quay with Men unloading Sand Barges" (*horiz*). (b) 127×102 mm. $6 "Sunset: Wheat Fields near Arles" (*horiz*). (c) 102×127 mm. "Les Alys-camps". Imperf | *Set of* 3 *sheets* 12·00 13·00

102 Sargassum Triggerfish

(Litho Questa)

1991 (5 Dec). *Reef Fishes. T* **102** *and similar horiz designs. Multicoloured. P* 14.

1416	50 c. Type **102**	60	60
	a. Sheetlet. Nos. 1416/30	8·00	
1417	50 c. Tobaccofish	60	60
1418	50 c. Caribbean Long-nosed Butterflyfish	60	60
1419	50 c. Cherub Angelfish	60	60
1420	50 c. Black Jack	60	60
1421	50 c. Masked Goby and Black Jack	60	60
1422	50 c. Spot-finned Hogfish	60	60
1423	50 c. Royal Gramma ("Fairy Basslet")	60	60
1424	50 c. Orange-backed Bass	60	60
1425	50 c. Candy Basslet	60	60
1426	50 c. Black-capped Basslet	60	60
1427	50 c. Long-jawed Squirrelfish	60	60
1428	50 c. Jacknife-fish	60	60
1429	50 c. Bigeye	60	60
1430	50 c. Short Bigeye	60	60
1416/30	*Set of* 15	8·00	8·00

MS1431 106×66 mm. $6 Caribbean Flashlight Fish | 6·00 7·00
Nos. 1416/30 were printed together, *se-tenant*, as a sheetlet of 15, forming a composite design.

(Litho Walsall)

1991 (9 Dec). *Christmas. Religious Paintings by Martin Schongauer. Vert designs as T* **287** *of Antigua. P* 12.

1432	10 c. black and cinnamon	30	15
1433	35 c. multicoloured	55	30
1434	50 c. multicoloured	75	50
1435	75 c. multicoloured	1·00	80
1436	$1 multicoloured	1·40	1·25
1437	$2 multicoloured	2·25	2·50
1438	$4 black and cinnamon	3·25	3·75

1439	$5 black, grey and vermilion	3·50	4·00
1432/9	*Set of 8*	11·50	12·00

MS1440 Two sheets, each 102×127 mm. (a) $6 multicoloured. (b) $6 multicoloured. P 14½.

	Set of 2 sheets	7·50	9·00

Designs:—10 c. "Angel of the Annunciation"; 35 c. "Madonna of the Rose Hedge" (detail); 50 c. "Madonna of the Rose Hedge" (different detail); 75 c. "Nativity" (detail); $1 "Adoration of the Shepherds" (detail); $2 "The Nativity"; $4 "Nativity" (*different*); $5 "Symbol of St. Matthew"; $6 (No. MS1442a) "Adoration of the Shepherds" (different detail); $6 (No. MS1442b) "Nativity"

(Des G. Vasarhelyi. Litho Walsall)

1992 (13 Feb). *Great Railways of the World. Horiz designs as T* **367** *of Grenada. Multicoloured.* P 14.

1441	75 c. Class "Medoc", 1857 (Switzerland)	80	80
	a. Sheetlet. Nos. 1441/9	6·50	
1442	75 c. Sterling type, 1870 (Great Britain)	80	80
1443	75 c. Locomotive No. 90, 1877 (France)	80	80
1444	75 c. Standard type, 1880 (U.S.A.)	80	80
1445	75 c. *Vittorio Emanuel II*, 1884 (Italy)	80	80
1446	75 c. Johnson "Single" type, 1887 (Great Britain)	80	80
1447	75 c. Locomotive No. 999, 1893 (U.S.A.)	80	80
1448	75 c. Class "Q1", 1896 (Great Britain)	80	80
1449	75 c. *Claud Hamilton*, 1900 (Great Britain)	80	80
1450	$1 Class "P8", 1906 (Germany)	80	80
	a. Sheetlet. Nos. 1450/8	6·50	
1451	$1 Class "P", 1910 (Denmark)	80	80
1452	$1 Class "Ps", 1926 (U.S.A.)	80	80
1453	$1 *Kestrel*, 1932 (Ireland)	80	80
1454	$1 Class "GS", 1937 (U.S.A.)	80	80
1455	$1 Class "12", 1938 (Belgium)	80	80
1456	$1 Class "J4-84", 1941 (U.S.A.)	80	80
1457	$1 PA Series "AIA-AIA", 1946 (U.S.A.)	80	80
1458	$1 Class "4E", 1954 (South Africa)	80	80
1459	$2 Trans Europe Express train, 1957	1·40	1·40
	a. Sheetlet. Nos. 1459/67	12·00	
1460	$2 FL9 "B.-AIA", 1960 (U.S.A.)	1·40	1·40
1461	$2 Shin-kansen train, 1964 (Japan)	1·40	1·40
1462	$2 Class "103.1", 1970 (Germany)	1·40	1·40
1463	$2 RTG Trainset, 1972 (France)	1·40	1·40
1464	$2 ETR "401" Pendolino train, 1976 (Italy)	1·40	1·40
1465	$2 Class "APT-P 370", 1981 (Great Britain)	1·40	1·40
1466	$2 LRC "B.-B", 1982 (Canada)	1·40	1·40
1467	$2 MAV BZMOT "601 1B1", 1983 (Hungary)	1·40	1·40
1441/67	*Set of 27*	22·00	22·00

MS1468 Two sheets, each 120×80 mm. (a) $6 Werner von Siemens's electric locomotive, 1879 (Germany). (b) $6 ETR "401" Pendolino train, 1976 (Italy) .. .. *Set of 2 sheets* 8·00 8·50

Nos. 1441/9, 1450/8 and 1459/67 were printed together, *se-tenant*, in sheetlets of 9.

(Des D. Miller. Litho Questa)

1992 (2 Mar). *40th Anniv of Queen Elizabeth II's Accession. Horiz designs as T* **288** *of Antigua. Multicoloured.* P 14.

1469	60 c. Swimming Jetty on beach	40	40
1470	75 c. View of Grenadines	45	45
1471	$2 Surf on beach	1·40	1·60
1472	$4 Secluded bay	2·50	3·00
1469/72	*Set of 4*	4·25	5·00

MS1473 Two sheets, each 74×92 mm. (a) $6 Plantation house. (b) $6 St. George's
.. .. *Set of 2 sheets* 7·50 8·50

(Litho Questa)

1992 (23 Mar). *Olympic Games, Barcelona. Vert designs as T* **268** *of Antigua. Multicoloured.* P 14.

1474	10 c. Women's backstroke swimming	15	15
1475	15 c. Women's handball	20	20
1476	25 c. Men's 4 × 100 m relay	30	30
1477	35 c. Men's hammer throw	35	35
1478	50 c. Men's 110 m hurdles	45	45
1479	65 c. Men's pole vault	65	65
1480	$1 Men's volleyball	85	85
1481	$2 Men's weightlifting	1·75	2·00
1482	$5 Men's gymnastics	2·75	3·25
1483	$6 Football	3·00	3·50
1474/83	*Set of 10*	9·50	10·50

MS1484 Two sheets, each 100×70 mm. (a) $15 Finn class single-handed dinghy sailing. (b) $15 Baseball .. .. .. *Set of 2 sheets* 16·00 17·00

(Litho B.D.T.)

1992 (30 Apr). *"Granada '92" International Stamp Exhibition, Spain. Spanish Paintings. Multicoloured designs as T* **292** *of Antigua.* P 13½×13 (50 c.) *or* 13×13½ (others).

1485	10 c. "The Surrender of Seville" (Zurbarán)	20	20
1486	35 c. "The Liberation of St. Peter by an Angel" (Antonio de Pereda)	35	35
1487	50 c. "Joseph explains the Dreams of the Pharaoh" (Antonio del Castillo Saavedra) (*horiz*)	55	55
1488	75 c. "The Flower Vase" (Juan de Arellano)	70	70
1489	$1 "The Duke of Pastrana" (Juan Carreño de Miranda)	80	80
1490	$2 "The Annunciation" (detail) (Francisco Rizi)	1·60	1·75
1491	$4 "The Annunciation" (different detail) (Francisco Rizi)	2·50	2·75
1492	$5 "Old Women Seated" (attr Antonio Puga)	2·50	2·75
1485/92	*Set of 8*	8·25	8·75

MS1493 Two sheets. (a) 95×120 mm. $6 "The Triumph of Saint Hermenegildo" (Francisco de Herrera the younger) (86×111 *mm*). (b) 120×95 mm. $6 "Relief of Genoa" (De Pereda) (110×84 *mm*). *Imperf* .. .. *Set of 2 sheets* 7·00 8·00

103 Don Isaac Abarbanel, Minister of Finance

104 *Atalanta* and *Mischief* (yachts), 1881

(Des L. Fried. Litho Questa)

1992 (7 May). *500th Anniv of Discovery of America by Columbus (5th issue). World Columbian Stamp "Expo '92", Chicago. T* **103** *and similar horiz designs.* P 14.

1494	10 c. Type **103**	15	15
1495	25 c. Columbus on voyage	25	25
1496	35 c. Look-out sighting land	30	30
1497	50 c. King Ferdinand and Queen Isabella of Spain	50	50
1498	60 c. Columbus showing map to Queen Isabella	55	55
1499	$5 *Santa Maria* and bird	4·00	5·50
1494/9	*Set of 6*	5·25	6·50

MS1500 Two sheets, each 100×71 mm. (a) $6 Christopher Columbus. (b) $6 Columbus with hand to face .. .. .. *Set of 2 sheets* 7·00 8·00

(Des Wendy Griswold-Smith. Litho Questa)

1992 (28 May). *"Genova '92" International Thematic Stamp Exhibition. Hummingbirds. Multicoloured designs as T* **295** *of Antigua, but vertical.* P 14.

1501	5 c. Male Blue-headed Hummingbird	10	10
1502	10 c. Female Rufous-breasted Hermit	10	10
1503	20 c. Female Blue-headed Hummingbird	15	15
1504	45 c. Male Green-throated Carib	30	30
1505	90 c. Male Antillean Crested Hummingbird	60	70
1506	$2 Male Purple-throated Carib	1·40	1·60
1507	$4 Male Purple-throated Carib	2·40	2·75
1508	$5 Female Antillean Crested Hummingbird	2·50	2·75
1501/8	*Set of 8*	6·50	7·50

MS1509 Two sheets, each 104×75 mm. (a) $6 Male Rufous-breasted Hermit. (b) $6 Female Green-throated Carib .. *Set of 2 sheets* 8·00 9·00

(Des R. Jung. Litho B.D.T.)

1992 (1 June). *50th Anniv of United Service Organization (forces' entertainment programme). Vert designs as T* **371** *of Grenada. Multicoloured.* P 14.

1510	10 c. James Cagney	15	15
1511	15 c. Anne Sheridan	15	15
1512	35 c. Jerry Colonna	25	25
1513	50 c. Spike Jones	40	40
1514	75 c. Edgar Bergen	55	55
1515	$1 The Andrews Sisters	70	70
1516	$2 Dinah Shore	1·40	1·75
1517	$5 Bing Crosby	3·25	3·75
1510/17	*Set of 8*	6·25	7·00

MS1518 Two sheets, each 107×80 mm. (a) $6 Fred Astaire. (b) $6 Marlene Dietrich
.. .. *Set of 2 sheets* 7·00 7·50

No. 1515 is incorrectly inscribed "THE ANDREW SISTERS".

(Des F. Paul ($1), J. Esquino ($2). Litho Questa)

1992 (24 Aug). *500th Anniv of Discovery of America by Columbus (6th issue). Organization of East Caribbean States. As Nos.* 1670/1 *of Antigua.* P 14½.

1519	$1 Columbus meeting Amerindians	65	65
1520	$2 Ships approaching island	1·25	1·50

(Des W. Hanson. Litho B.D.T.)

1992 (22 Oct). *Toy Trains from American Manufacturers. Horiz designs as T* **257** *of Dominica. Multicoloured.* P 14.

1521	15 c. No. 2220 switcher locomotive, Voltamp (1910)	15	15
1522	25 c. Clockwork locomotive of Bridge Port Line, American Miniature Railroad (1907)	20	20
1523	50 c. First electric toy locomotive, Ives (1910)	40	40
1524	75 c. J.C. Penney Special locomotive, American Flyer (1920s)	60	60
1525	$1 Clockwork cast-metal locomotive, Hafner (1916)	80	80
1526	$2 Pull toy copper-plated locomotive, probably Hubley (1900)	1·50	1·75
1527	$4 *Mayflower* locomotive, American Flyer (1928)	2·50	3·00
1528	$5 *Olympian* locomotive, Ives (1929)	2·75	3·00
1521/8	*Set of 8*	8·00	9·00

MS1529 Two sheets. (a) 128×93 mm. $6 Clockwork locomotive, Ives (1910) (50×38½ *mm*). (b) 142×95 mm. $6 Statesman locomotive, American Flyer (50×38½ *mm*). P 13
.. .. *Set of 2 sheets* 7·00 8·00

(Des Kerri Schiff. Litho Questa)

1992 (28 Oct). *Postage Stamp Mega Event, New York. Sheet* 100×70 *mm containing multicoloured design as T* **299** *of Antigua.* P 14.

MS1530	$6 Brooklyn Bridge	3·50	4·25

(Litho Questa)

1992 (19 Nov). *Christmas. Religious Paintings. Multicoloured designs as T* **300** *of Antigua, showing "The Annunciation" by various artists.* P 14×13½ ($5) *or* 13½×14 (others).

1531	5 c. Robert Campin	10	10
1532	15 c. Melchior Broederlam	15	10
1533	25 c. Fra Filippo Lippi (two-panel diptych)	20	15
1534	35 c. Simone Martini	30	20
1535	50 c. Lippi (detail from left panel)	45	45
1536	75 c. Lippi (detail from right panel)	60	60
1537	90 c. Albert Bouts	70	80
1538	$1 D. di Michelino	80	90
1539	$2 Rogier van der Weyden	1·50	1·75
1540	$3 Sandro Botticelli (detail of angel)	1·90	2·25
1541	$4 Botticelli (detail of Virgin Mary)	2·75	3·00
1542	$5 Bernardo Daddi (*horiz*)	2·75	3·00
1531/42	*Set of 12*	11·00	12·00

MS1543 Three sheets, each 72×97 mm. (a) $6 Van der Weyden (*different*). (b) $6 Botticelli (as $3). (c) $6 Hubert van Eyck .. *Set of 3 sheets* 10·50 11·00

(Des J. Genzo. Litho Questa)

1992 (19 Nov). *Gold Record Award Winners. Vert designs as T* **374** *of Grenada. Multicoloured.* P 14.

1544	90 c. Leonard Bernstein	90	90
	a. Sheetlet. Nos. 1544/51	6·50	
1545	90 c. Ray Charles	90	90
1546	90 c. Bob Dylan	90	90
1547	90 c. Barbara Streisand	90	90
1548	90 c. Frank Sinatra	90	90
1549	90 c. Harry Belafonte	90	90
1550	90 c. Aretha Franklin	90	90
1551	90 c. Garth Brooks	90	90
1544/51	*Set of 8*	6·50	6·50

MS1552 Two sheets, each 100×70 mm. (a) $3 Charlie Parker; $3 Miles Davis. (b) $3 Johnny Cash; $3 Willie Nelson. *Set of 2 sheets* 7·00 8·00

Nos. 1544/51 were printed together, *se-tenant*, in sheetlets of 8 with a composite background design.

(Des Walt Disney Co. Litho Questa)

1992 (24 Nov). *60th Anniv of Goofy (Disney cartoon character). Multicoloured designs as T* **258** *of Dominica showing Goofy in various cartoon films.* P 14×13½.

1553	5 c. Father's Day Off, 1953	20	20
1554	10 c. Cold War, 1951	25	20
1555	15 c. Home Made Home, 1951	30	20
1556	25 c. Get Rich Quick, 1951	35	25
1557	50 c. Man's Best Friend, 1952	55	40
1558	75 c. Aquamania, 1961	75	55
1559	90 c. Tomorrow We Diet, 1951	85	65
1560	$1 Teachers Are People, 1952	90	75
1561	$2 The Goofy Success Story, 1955	1·60	1·60
1562	$3 Double Dribble, 1946	2·00	2·25
1563	$4 Hello Aloha, 1952	2·25	2·50
1564	$5 Father's Lion, 1952	2·40	2·75
1553/64	*Set of 12*	11·00	11·00

MS1565 Three sheets, each 128×102 mm. (a) $6 Motor Mania, 1956. P 14×13½. (b) $6 Hold that Pose, 1950 (vert). P 13½×14. (c) $6 Father's Weekend, 1953 (vert). P 13½×14 *Set of 3 sheets* 11·00 12·00

(Des W. Wright and W. Hanson (Nos. 1566, 1575, **MS1577a**), W. Wright and L. Fried (Nos. 1567, 1574, **MS1577b**), J. Genzo (Nos. 1572, **MS1577e**), W. Wright (others). Litho B.D.T)

1992 (15 Dec). *Anniversaries and Events. Designs as T* **375** *of Grenada. Multicoloured, except No. 1571.* P 14.

1566	25 c. Zeppelin LZ-11 *Viktoria Luise* over Kiel Harbour (*horiz*)	30	20
1567	50 c. Space shuttle *Columbia* landing (*horiz*)	40	30
1568	75 c. German Federal Republic flag and arms (*horiz*)	45	40
1569	$1.50, Giant Anteater (*horiz*)	85	85
1570	$2 Scarlet Macaw	1·40	1·40
1571	$2 W.H.O. emblem (black and new blue) (*horiz*)	1·25	1·25
1572	$3 Wolfgang Amadeus Mozart	2·25	2·25
1573	$4 The Berlin Airlift (*horiz*)	2·25	2·25
1574	$4 Repairing "Intelsat VI" satellite in space (*horiz*)	2·25	2·25
1575	$5 Zeppelin LZ-129 *Hindenburg* on fire (*horiz*)	2·50	2·50
1576	$5 Admiral Richard Byrd's Ford 4-AT-B Trimotor *Floyd Bennett* aircraft (*horiz*)	2·50	2·50
1566/76	*Set of 11*	15·00	14·50

MS1577 Five sheets. (a) 110×80 mm. $6 Zeppelin LZ-4, 1913 (51½×39½ *mm*). P 13. (b) 110×80 mm. $6 First flight of space shuttle *Endeavour* (51½×39½ *mm*). P 13. (c) 110×80 mm. $6 Map of West Germany (39½×51½ *mm*). P 13. (d) 110×80 mm. $6 Jaguar (51½×39½ *mm*). P 13. (e) 98×67 mm. $6 Figaro costume from *The Marriage of Figaro*. P 14 .. .. .. *Set of 5 sheets* 18·00 19·00

Anniversaries and Events:—Nos. 1566, 1575, **MS1577a**, 75th death anniv of Count Ferdinand von Zeppelin; Nos. 1567, 1574, **MS1577b**, International Space Year; Nos. 1568, 1573, **MS1577c**, 25th death anniv of Konrad Adenauer (German statesman); Nos. 1569/70, **MS1577d**, Earth Summit '92, Rio; No. 1571, United Nations World Health Organization Projects; Nos. 1572, **MS1577e**, Death bicent of Mozart; No. 1576, 75th anniv of International Association of Lions Clubs.

(Litho Questa)

1992 (15 Dec). *History of the Americas Cup Challenge Trophy. T* **104** *and similar multicoloured designs.* P 14.

1578	15 c. Type **104**	20	20
1579	25 c. *Valkyrie III* and *Defender*, 1895	30	30
1580	35 c. *Shamrock IV* and *Resolute*, 1920	45	45
1581	75 c. *Endeavour II* and *Ranger*, 1937	70	70
1582	$1 *Sceptre* and *Columbia*, 1958	85	85
1583	$2 *Australia II* and *Liberty*, 1983	1·50	1·75
1584	$4 *Stars & Stripes* and *Kookaburra III*, 1987	2·40	3·00

585    $5 *New Zealand* and *Stars & Stripes*,
1988   ..   ..   ..   2·50   3·00
578/85   ..   ..   *Set of 8*   8·00   9·00
MS1586   Two sheets, each 114×85 mm. (a) $6
America (schooner), 1851 (57×43 *mm*). (b) $6
Americas Cup emblems (57×43 *mm*)
   Set of 2 sheets   8·50   9·00

(Des Joan Popeio. Litho Questa)

1993 (20 Jan). *Dogs of the World. Multicoloured designs as
T 377 of Grenada, but vertical.* P 14.
1587   35 c. Irish Setter and Glendalough, Ireland   40   30
1588   50 c. Boston Terrier and Boston State
House, U.S.A.   60   45
1589   75 c. Beagle and Temple to Athena, Greece   90   55
1590 $1 Weimaraner and Nesselwang,
Germany   ..   ..   1·10   75
1591 $3 Norwegian Elkhound and Urnes
Stave Church, Norway   ..   2·25   2·50
1592 $4 Mastiff and Sphinx, Egypt   ..   2·50   2·75
1593 $5 Akita and Torii Temple, Kyoto, Japan   2·50   2·75
1594 $5 Saluki and Rub'al Khali, Saudi Arabia   2·50   2·75
1587/94   ..   ..   *Set of 8*   11·50   11·50
MS1595   Two sheets, each 99×71 mm. (a) $6 Bull
Dog, Great Britain. (b) $6 Shar Pei, China
   Set of 2 sheets   7·00   8·00

(Litho Walsall)

1993 (8 Mar). *Bicentenary of the Louvre, Paris. Vert designs as
T 305 of Antigua. Multicoloured (except No. 1599). P 12.*
1596 $1 "Madonna and Child with the young
John the Baptist" (Botticelli) ..   80   80
   a. Sheetlet. Nos. 1596/1603   ..   5·50
1597 $1 "The Buffet" (Chardin)   ..   80   80
1598 $1 "Return from Market" (Chardin)   ..   80   80
1599 $1 "Erasmus" (Dürer) (black & bluish grey)   80   80
1600 $1 "Self-portrait with Eryngium" (Dürer)   80   80
1601 $1 "Jeanne of Aragon" (Raphael)   ..   80   80
1602 $1 "La Belle Jardinière" (detail) (Raphael)   80   80
1603 $1 "La Belle Jardinière" (different detail)
(Raphael)   80   80
1596/1603   ..   *Set of 8*   5·50   5·50
MS1604   70×100 mm. $6 "King Charles I
Hunting" (Van Dyck) (52×85 *mm*). P 14½   3·50   4·00
Nos. 1596/1603 were printed together, *se-tenant,* in sheetlets
of 8 stamps and one centre label.

105 *Battus
polydamus*

(Litho Questa)

1993 (13 Apr). *Butterflies. T 105 and similar vert designs.
Multicoloured.* P 14.
1605   15 c. Type **105**   40   20
1606   35 c. *Astraptes talus*   55   20
1607   45 c. *Pseudolycaena marsyas*   ..   55   25
1608   75 c. *Siproeta stelenes*   70   50
1609 $1 *Phoebis sennae*   80   60
1610 $2 *Dione juno*   ..   ..   1·40   1·40
1611 $4 *Chlorostrymon simaethis*   ..   2·25   2·75
1612 $5 *Urbanus proteus*   ..   ..   2·50   2·75
1605/12   ..   *Set of 8*   8·25   7·75
MS1613   Two sheets, each 100×70 mm. (a) $6
Historis odius ("Orion"). (b) $6 *Heliconius
charitonia* ("Zebra") ..   *Set of 2 sheets*   7·00   8·00

(Des D. Delouise. Litho Questa)

1993 (17 May). *Flowers. Multicoloured designs as T 380 of
Grenada.* P 14.
1614   35 c. Hibiscus   50   20
1615   35 c. Columbine   50   20
1616   45 c. Red Ginger   50   25
1617   75 c. Bougainvillea   70   50
1618 $1 Crown Imperial   80   60
1619 $2 Fairy Orchid   ..   ..   1·40   1·40
1620 $4 Heliconia   ..   ..   2·25   2·75
1621 $5 Tulip   ..   ..   2·50   2·75
1614/21   ..   *Set of 8*   8·25   7·75
MS1622   Two sheet, each 70×100 mm. (a) $6
Blackberry Lily (*horiz*). (b) $6 Balloonflower
(*horiz*) ..   ..   *Set of 2 sheets*   7·00   8·00

(Des Kerri Schiff. Litho Questa)

1993 (2 June). *40th Anniv of Coronation. Vert designs as T 307
of Antigua.* P 13½×14.
1623   35 c. multicoloured   15   40
   a. Sheetlet. Nos. 1623/6×2   ..   6·25
1624   50 c. multicoloured   25   50
1625 $2 bronze-green and black   ..   90   1·10
1626 $4 multicoloured   ..   ..   1·90   2·00
1623/6   ..   *Set of 4*   3·00   3·50
MS1627   70×100 mm. $6 multicoloured. P 14   4·00   4·25
Designs: (38×47 *mm*)—35 c. Queen Elizabeth II at Coronation
(photograph by Cecil Beaton); 50 c. Ampulla and spoon; $2
Queen Elizabeth II leaving for Coronation; $4 Prince Henry's
christening. (28½×42½ *mm*)—$6 "Queen Elizabeth II, 1954"
(detail) (Pietro Annigoni).
Nos. 1623/6 were printed together in sheetlets of 8 containing
two *se-tenant* blocks of 4.

(Litho Questa)

1993 (1 July). *Anniversaries and Events. Multicoloured
designs as T 381 of Grenada.* P 14.
1628   15 c. "Painter and Model" (Picasso) (*horiz*)   55   30
1629   35 c. Keith Tkachuk and Dmitri Mironov
(ice hockey, 1992) (*horiz*)   ..   80   40
1630   50 c. Early telescope   85   50
1631   75 c. "Gra w Gudziki" (Ludomir Slerdinski)
(*horiz*)   90   70
1632   75 c. Willy Brandt and Lyndon Johnson,
1961 (*horiz*)   90   70
1633 $1 "Artist and Model" (Picasso) (*horiz*)   1·00   80
1634 $2 "Pocalunek Mongolskiego Ksiecia"
(S. Wirkiewicz) (*horiz*)   ..   1·40   1·40
1635 $4 "The Drawing Lesson" (Picasso)
(*horiz*)   ..   ..   2·25   2·25
1636 $4 Radio telescope   ..   ..   2·25   2·25
1637 $5 Alberto Tomba (Giant Slalom, 1984)   2·25   2·40
1638 $5 Willy Brandt and Eleanor Hulles,
1957 (*horiz*) ..   ..   2·25   2·40
1628/38   ..   *Set of 11*   14·00   13·00
MS1639   Five sheets. (a) 105×75 mm. $5
Copernicus. (b) 105×75 mm. $6 Picasso (*horiz*).
(c) 75×105 mm. $6 Emil Zogragski (70 metre ski
jump, 1984). (d) 75×105 mm. $6 "Allegory"
(detail) (Jan Wydra). (e) 105×75 mm. $6 Willy
and Rut Brandt (brownish grey and black)
(*horiz*)   ..   *Set of 5 sheets*   17·00   18·00
Anniversaries and Events:—Nos. 1628, 1633, 1635,
MS1639b, 20th death anniv of Picasso (artist); Nos. 1629, 1637,
MS1639c, Winter Olympic Games '94, Lillehammer; Nos. 1630,
1636, **MS**1639a, 450th death anniv of Copernicus (astronomer);
Nos. 1631, 1634, **MS**1639d, "Polska '93" International Stamp
Exhibition, Poznan; Nos. 1632, 1638, **MS**1639e, 80th birth
anniv of Willy Brandt (German politician).

(Des R. Sauber. Litho B.D.T.)

1993 (13 July). *Songbirds. Multicoloured designs as T 382 of
Grenada.* P 14.
1640   15 c. Painted Bunting   ..   35   35
   a. Sheetlet. Nos. 1640/51   ..   7·00
1641   15 c. White-throated Sparrow   ..   35   35
1642   25 c. Common Grackle   40   40
1643   25 c. Amazonian Royal Flycatcher   ..   40   40
1644   35 c. Swallow Tanager   45   45
1645   35 c. Vermilion Flycatcher   ..   45   45
1646   45 c. Black-headed Bunting   ..   50   50
1647   50 c. Rose-breasted Grosbeak   ..   50   50
1648   75 c. Corn Bunting   60   60
1649   75 c. Rose-breasted Thrush Tanager   60   60
1650 $1 Buff-throated Saltator   ..   75   75
1651 $4 Plush-capped Finch ..   ..   2·25   2·25
1640/51   ..   *Set of 12*   7·00   7·00
MS1652   Two sheets, each 115×86 mm. (a) $6
Pine Grosbeak. (b) $6 Bohemian Waxwing
   Set of 2 sheets   8·00   8·50
Nos. 1640/51 were printed together, *se-tenant,* in sheetlets of
12 with the backgrounds forming a composite design.
Nos. 1645/6 show the scientific inscriptions transposed
between the designs.

(Des I. MacLaury. Litho B.D.T.)

1993 (19 July). *Shells. Multicoloured designs as T 383 of
Grenada.* P 14.
1653   15 c. Hawk-wing Conch (*Strombus
raninus*)   25   25
   a. Sheetlet. Nos. 1653/64   ..   5·75
1654   15 c. Music Volute (*Volute musica*)   25   25
1655   25 c. Globe Vase (*Vasum globulus nuttingi*)
and Deltoid Rock Shell (*Thais
deltoidea*)   30   30
1656   35 c. Spiny Caribbean Vase (*Vasum
capitellum*)   30   30
1657   35 c. American Common Sundial (*Architectonica nobilis*) and Common Purple
Janthina (*Janthina janthina*)   ..   30   30
1658   45 c. Toothed Donax (*Donax denticulatus*)
and Gaudy Asaphis (*Asaphis
deflorata*)   35   35
1659   45 c. Mouse Cone (*Conus mus*)   ..   35   35
1660   50 c. Gold-mouthed Triton (*Cymatium
nicobaricum*)   40   40
1661   75 c. Tulip Mussel (*Modiolus americanus*)
and Trigonal Tivela (*Tivela
mactroides*)   50   50
1662   75 c. Common Dove Shell (*Columbella
mercatoria*) and Chestnut Latirus
(*Leucozonia nassa*)   50   50
1663 $1 Wide-mouthed Purpura (*Purpura
patula*)   60   60
1664 $4 American Thorny Oyster (*Spondylus
americanus*) and Atlantic Wing
Oyster (*Pteria columbus*)   ..   1·90   2·00
1653/64   ..   *Set of 12*   5·75   5·75
MS1665   Two sheets, each 76×106 mm. (a) $6
Atlantic Turkey Wing (*Arca zebra*). (b) $6 Zebra
or Zigzag Periwinkle (*Littornia ziczac*)
   Set of 2 sheets   7·00   8·00
Nos. 1653/64 were printed together, *se-tenant,* in sheetlets of
12 with the backgrounds forming a composite design.

(Litho Questa)

1993 (13 Aug). *Asian International Stamp Exhibitions.
Multicoloured designs as T 268 of Dominica.* P 14×13½.

(a) "*Indopex '93*", Surabaya, Indonesia
1666   35 c. National Museum, Central Jakarta
(*horiz*)   30   20
1667   45 c. Sacred wheel and deer (*horiz*)   35   25
1668 $1 Ramayana relief, Panataran Temple
(*horiz*)   60   60
1669 $1.50, "Bullock Carts" (Batara Lubis)
(*horiz*)   ..   ..   1·00   1·00
   a. Sheetlet. Nos. 1669/74   ..   5·50
1670 $1.50, "Surat Irsa II" (A.D. Pirous) (*horiz*)   1·00   1·00
1671 $1.50, "Self-portrait with Goat" (Kartika)
(*horiz*)   ..   ..   1·00   1·00
1672 $1.50, "The Cow-est Cow" (Ivan Sagito)
(*horiz*)   ..   ..   1·00   1·00

1673 $1.50, "Rain Storm" (Sudjana Kerton)
(*horiz*)   ..   ..   1·00   1·00
1674 $1.50, "Story of Pucuk Flower" (Effendi)
(*horiz*)   ..   ..   1·00   1·00
1675 $5 Candi Tikus, Trawulan, East Java
(*horiz*)   ..   ..   2·50   2·75
1666/75   ..   *Set of 10*   8·75   8·75
MS1676   134×105 mm. $6 Banteng Cattle (*horiz*)   3·50   4·00

(b) "*Taipei '93*", Taiwan
1677   35 c. Macau Palace Casino, Hong Kong
(*horiz*)   30   20
1678   45 c. Stone lion, Ming Tomb, Nanjing
(*horiz*)   35   25
1679 $1 Stone camels, Ming Tomb, Nanjing
(*horiz*)   60   60
1680 $1.50, Nesting quail incense burner
(*horiz*)   ..   ..   1·00   1·00
   a. Sheetlet. Nos. 1680/5   ..   5·50
1681 $1.50, Standing quail incense burner
(*horiz*)   ..   ..   1·00   1·00
1682 $1.50, Seated qilin incense burner (*horiz*)   1·00   1·00
1683 $1.50, Pottery horse, Han period (*horiz*)   1·00   1·00
1684 $1.50, Seated caparisoned elephant
(*horiz*)   ..   ..   1·00   1·00
1685 $1.50, Cow in imitation of Delft faience
(*horiz*)   ..   ..   1·00   1·00
1686 $5 Stone lion and elephant, Ming Tomb,
Nanjing (*horiz*)   ..   ..   2·50   2·75
1677/86   ..   *Set of 10*   8·75   8·75
MS1687   134×105 mm. $6 Sumatran Tiger, Mt
Leuser National Park. P 13½×14   ..   3·50   4·00

(c) "*Bangkok 1993*", Thailand
1688   35 c. Three Naga snakes, Chiang Mai's
Temple (*horiz*)   30   20
1689   45 c. Sri Mariamman Temple, Singapore
(*horiz*)   35   25
1690 $1 Topiary, Hua Hin Resort (*horiz*)   60   60
1691 $1.50, "Buddha's Victory over Mara"
(*horiz*)   ..   ..   1·00   1·00
   a. Sheetlet. Nos. 1691/6   ..   5·50
1692 $1.50, "Mythological Elephant" (*horiz*)   1·00   1·00
1693 $1.50, "Battle with Mara" (Thon Buri)
(*horiz*)   ..   ..   1·00   1·00
1694 $1.50, "Untitled" (Panya Wijinthana-
sarn) (*horiz*)   ..   ..   1·00   1·00
1695 $1.50, "Temple Mural" (*horiz*)   ..   1·00   1·00
1696 $1.50, "Elephants in Pahcekha Buddha's
Heaven" (*horiz*)   ..   ..   1·00   1·00
1697 $5 Pak Tai Temple, Cheung Chau Island
(*horiz*)   ..   ..   2·50   2·75
1688/97   ..   *Set of 10*   8·75   8·75
MS1698   134×105 mm. $6 Monkey from Chiang
Kong. P 13½×14   ..   ..   3·50   4·00
Nos. 1669/74, 1680/5 and 1691/6 were each printed together,
se-tenant, in sheetlets of 6.

(Des Rosemary DeFiglio. Litho Questa)

1993 (7 Sept). *World Cup Football Championship, U.S.A.
(1994) (1st issue). Multicoloured designs as T 310 of Antigua.*
P 14.
1699   15 c. McCall (Scotland) and Verri (Brazil)
(*horiz*)   30   20
1700   25 c. Verri (Brazil) and Maradona
(Argentina) (*horiz*)   ..   40   20
1701   35 c. Schillaci (Italy) and Saldana
(Uruguay) (*horiz*)   ..   45   25
1702   45 c. Gullit (Holland) and Wright (England)
(*horiz*)   50   35
1703 $1 Verri (Brazil) and Maradona
(Argentina) (*different*) (*horiz*)   70   70
1704 $2 Zubizarreta and Fernandez (Spain)
with Albert (Belgium) (*horiz*)   1·25   1·25
1705 $4 Hagi (Rumania) and McGrath
(Ireland) (*horiz*)   ..   2·25   2·40
1706 $5 Gorriz (Spain) and Scifo (Belgium)
(*horiz*)   ..   ..   2·25   2·40
1699/1706   ..   *Set of 8*   7·25   7·00
MS1707   Two sheets, each 104×75 mm. (a) $6
Foxboro Stadium, Massachusetts (*horiz*). (b) $6
Rudi Voeller (Germany) ..   *Set of 2 sheets*   7·00   8·00
See also Nos. 1810/16.

(Des Rosemary DeFiglio. Litho Questa)

1993 (11 Nov). *65th Anniv of Mickey Mouse. Multicoloured
designs as T 385 of Grenada showing Mickey Mouse in scenes
from Walt Disney cartoon films.* P 14×13½.
1708   15 c. *Mickey's Rival*, 1936   ..   30   20
1709   35 c. *The Worm Turns*, 1937   ..   40   25
1710   50 c. *The Pointer*, 1939   ..   55   55
1711   75 c. *Society Dog Show*, 1939   ..   70   70
1712 $1 *A Gentleman's Gentleman*, 1941   80   80
1713 $2 *The Little Whirlwind*, 1941   ..   1·40   1·40
1714 $4 *Mickey Down Under*, 1948   ..   2·50   2·75
1715 $5 *R'coon Dawg*, 1951   ..   ..   2·50   2·75
1708/15   ..   *Set of 8*   8·25   8·50
MS1716   Two sheets, each 127×102 mm. (a) $6
Lonesome Ghosts, 1937. P 14×13½. (b) $6
Mickey's Garden, 1935 (vert). P 13½×14
   Set of 2 sheets   8·00   8·50

(Litho Questa)

1993 (22 Nov). *Christmas. Religious Paintings. Designs as
T 270 of Dominica. Black, pale lemon and red (Nos. 1717,
1721/3 and MS1725a) or multicoloured (others). P 13½×14.*
1717   10 c. "Adoration of the Shepherds" (detail)
(Dürer)   20   20
1718   25 c. "Adoration of the Magi" (detail)
(Raphael)   30   20
1719   35 c. "Presentation at the Temple" (detail)
(Raphael)   40   20
1720   50 c. "Adoration of the Magi" (different
detail) (Raphael)   ..   45   35
1721   75 c. "Adoration of the Shepherds"
(different detail) (Dürer)   ..   65   50
1722 $1 "Adoration of the Shepherds"
(different detail) (Dürer)   ..   75   65
1723 $4 "Adoration of the Shepherds"
(different detail) (Dürer)   ..   2·25   2·50

1724	$5 "Presentation at the Temple" (different detail) (Raphael)		2·25	2·50
1717/24		*Set of 8*	6·50	6·50

MS1725 Two sheets. (a) 102×128 mm. $6 "Adoration of the Shepherds" (different detail) (Dürer) (*horiz*). P 14×13¹⁄₂. (b) 128×102 mm. $6 "Annunciation" (detail) (Raphael). P 13¹⁄₂×14 .. .. .. *Set of 2 sheets* 7·00 8·00

(Litho Questa)

1993 (21 Dec). *Aviation Anniversaries. Multicoloured designs as T* **386** *of Grenada.* P 14.

1726	15 c. Avro Lancaster		30	20
1727	35 c. Blanchard's balloon crossing the River Delaware		15	20
1728	50 c. Airship LZ-127 *Graf Zeppelin* over Rio de Janeiro		50	35
1729	75 c. Hugo Eckener		65	50
1730	$3 Pres. Washington handing passport to Blanchard		1·40	1·50
1731	$5 Short Sunderland flying boat		2·50	2·75
1732	$5 Eckener in *Graf Zeppelin*		2·50	2·75
1726/32		*Set of 7*	7·25	7·50

MS1733 Three sheets. (a) 76×107 mm. $6 Supermarine Spitfire. (b) 107×76 mm. $6 Blanchard's balloon (*vert*). (c) 107×76 mm. $6 Eckener with Pres. Hoover .. *Set of 3 sheets* 10·50 11·50
Anniversaries:—Nos. 1726, 1731, **MS**1733a, 75th anniv of Royal Air Force; Nos. 1727, 1730, **MS**1733b, Bicentenary of First Airmail Flight; Nos. 1728/9, 1732, **MS**1733c, 125th birth anniv of Hugo Eckener (airship commander).

(Des K. Gromell. Litho Questa)

1993 (21 Dec). *Centenaries of Henry Ford's First Petrol Engine* (Nos. 1735/6, **MS**1738b) *and Karl Benz's First Four-wheeled Car* (others). *Horiz designs as T* **387** *of Grenada. Multicoloured.* P 14.

1734	25 c. Mercedes Benz "300 SLR", 1955		30	20
1735	45 c. Ford "Thunderbird", 1957		20	25
1736	$4 Ford "150-A" station wagon, 1929		1·90	2·00
1737	$5 Mercedes Benz "540 K"		2·75	3·00
1734/7		*Set of 4*	4·75	5·00

MS1738 Two sheets, 76×107 mm. (a) $6 Mercedes Benz "SSK", 1929. (b) $6 Ford "Model T", 1924 .. .. *Set of 2 sheets* 7·00 8·00

(Des Kerri Schiff. Litho Questa)

1993 (31 Dec). *Famous Paintings by Rembrandt and Matisse. Multicoloured designs as T* **316** *of Antigua.* P 13¹⁄₂×14.

1739	15 c. "Hendrickje Stoffels as Flora" (Rembrandt)		30	25
1740	35 c. "Lady and Gentleman in Black" (Rembrandt)		40	25
1741	50 c. "Aristotle with the Bust of Homer" (Rembrandt)		45	35
1742	75 c. "Interior: Flowers and Parakeets" (Matisse)		60	50
1743	$1 "Goldfish" (Matisse)		80	70
1744	$2 "The Girl with Green Eyes" (Matisse)		1·40	1·50
1745	$3 "Still Life with a Plaster Figure" (Matisse)		1·75	2·00
1746	$5 "Christ and the Woman of Samaria" (Rembrandt)		2·25	2·40
1739/46		*Set of 8*	7·00	7·00

MS1747 Two sheets. (a) 100×125 mm. $6 "Anna accused of stealing the Kid" (detail) (Rembrandt). P 13¹⁄₂×14. (b) 125×100 mm. $6 "Tea in the Garden" (detail) (Matisse) (*horiz*). P 14×13¹⁄₂ .. .. *Set of 2 sheets* 7·00 8·00

(Des W. Hanson. Litho Questa)

1994 (18 Feb). *"Hong Kong '94" International Stamp Exhibition* (1st issue). *Horiz designs as T* **317** *of Antigua. Multicoloured.* P 14.

1748	40 c. Hong Kong 1984 $5 aviation stamp and airliner at Kai Tak Airport		20	25
	a. Horiz pair. Nos. 1748/9		40	50
1749	40 c. Grenada Grenadines 1988 20 c. airships stamp and junk in Kowloon Bay		20	25

Nos. 1748/9 were printed together, *se-tenant*, in horizontal pairs throughout the sheet with the centre part of each pair forming a composite design.

(Des Kerri Schiff. Litho Questa)

1994 (18 Feb). *"Hong Kong '94" International Stamp Exhibition* (2nd issue). *Jade Sculptures. Horiz designs as T* **318** *of Antigua. Multicoloured.* P 14.

1750	45 c. White jade brush washer		20	25
	a. Sheetlet. Nos. 1750/5		1·10	
1751	45 c. Archaic jade brush washer		20	25
1752	45 c. Dark green jade brush washer		20	25
1753	45 c. Green jade almsbowl		20	25
1754	45 c. Archaic jade dog		20	25
1755	45 c. Yellow jade brush washer		20	25
1750/5		*Set of 6*	1·10	1·40

Nos. 1750/5 were printed together, *se-tenant*, in sheetlets of 6.

(Des Susan Carlson. Litho Questa)

1994 (6 Apr). *Fungi. Vert designs as T* **390** *of Grenada, but with white backgrounds. Multicoloured.* P 14.

1756	35 c. Hygrocybe hypohaemacta		15	20
1757	45 c. Cantharellus cinnabarinus		20	25
1758	50 c. Marasmius haematocephalus		25	30
1759	75 c. Mycena pura		35	40
1760	$1 Gymnopilus russipes		45	50
1761	$2 Calocybe cyanocephala		90	95
1762	$4 Pluteus chrysophlebius		1·90	2·00
1763	$5 Chlorophyllum molybdites		2·25	2·40
1756/63		*Set of 8*	6·25	7·00

MS1764 Two sheets, each 100×70 mm. (a) $6 *Xeromphalina tenuipes*. (b) $6 *Collybia fibrosipes* .. .. *Set of 2 sheets* 5·50 5·75
No. 1757 is inscribed "Cantherellus cinnabarinus" and No. 1762 "Pleuteus chrysophlebius", both in error.

(Des V. DiFate. Litho Questa)

1994 (13 Apr). *Prehistoric Animals. Multicoloured designs as T* **391** *of Grenada.* P 14.

1765	15 c. Spinosaurus		10	10
1766	35 c. Apatosaurus (Brontosaurus)		15	20
1767	45 c. Tyrannosaurus rex		20	25
1768	55 c. Triceratops		25	30
1769	$1 Pachycephalosaurus		45	50
1770	$2 Pteranodon		90	95
1771	$4 Parasaurolophus		1·90	2·00
1772	$5 Brachiosaurus		2·25	2·40
1765/72		*Set of 8*	6·00	6·50

MS1773 Two sheets, each 100×70 mm. (a) $6 Head of Brachiosaurus (*vert*). (b) $6 Spinosaurus and Tyrannosaurus rex fighting (*vert*) .. .. .. *Set of 2 sheets* 5·50 5·75

(Des W. Hanson. Litho B.D.T.)

1994 (4 Aug). *25th Anniv of First Moon Landing. Space Shuttle* Challenger. *Multicoloured designs as T* **326** *of Antigua.* P 14.

1774	$1.10, *Challenger* crew in training		50	55
	a. Sheetlet. Nos. 1774/9		3·00	
1775	$1.10, Christa McAuliffe (astronaut)		50	55
1776	$1.10, *Challenger* on launch pad		50	55
1777	$1.10, Gregory Jarvis (astronaut)		50	55
1778	$1.10, Ellison Onizuka (astronaut)		50	55
1779	$1.10, Ronald McNair (astronaut)		50	55
1774/9		*Set of 6*	3·00	3·25

MS1780 107×76 mm. $6 Judith Resnick (astronaut) (*vert*) .. .. .. 2·75 3·00
Nos. 1774/9 were printed together, *se-tenant*, in sheetlets of 6.

(Litho Questa)

1994 (4 Aug). *Centenary of International Olympic Committee. Gold Medal Winners. Horiz designs as T* **327** *of Antigua. Multicoloured.* P 14.

1781	50 c. Silke Renk (Germany) (javelin), 1992		25	30
1782	$1.50, Mark Spitz (U.S.A.) (swimming), 1972		70	75

MS1783 106×77 mm. $6 Japanese team (Nordic skiing), 1994 .. .. .. 2·75 3·00

(Litho Questa)

1994 (4 Aug). *International Year of the Family. Horiz design as T* **328** *of Antigua.* P 14.

1784	$1 Grenadines family		45	50

(Des J. Batchelor. Litho Questa)

1994 (4 Aug). *50th Anniv of D-Day. Horiz designs as T* **331** *of Antigua. Multicoloured.* P 14.

1785	40 c. Churchill bridge-laying tank		20	25
1786	$2 Sherman "Firefly" tank leaving landing craft		90	95
1787	$3 Churchill "Crocodile" flame-thrower		1·40	1·50
1785/7		*Set of 3*	2·40	2·50

MS1788 107×76 mm. $6 Sherman "Crab" flail tank .. .. 2·75 3·00

*(Des Kerri Schiff. Litho Questa (Nos. 1791/8, **MS**1800), B.D.T. (others))*

1994 (4 Aug). *"Philakorea '94" International Stamp Exhibition, Seoul* (1st issue). *Multicoloured designs as T* **281** *of Dominica.* P 13¹⁄₂×14 (Nos. 1791/8) or 14 (others).

1789	40 c. Onung Tomb (*horiz*)		20	25
1790	$1 Stone pagoda, Mt Namsam (*horiz*)		45	50
1791	$1 "Admiring Spring in the Country" (left detail) (Sin Yunbok)		45	50
	a. Sheetlet. Nos. 1791/8		3·50	
1792	$1 "Admiring Spring in the Country" (right detail)		45	50
1793	$1 "Woman on Dano Day" (left detail) (Sin Yunbok)		45	50
1794	$1 "Woman on Dano Day" (right detail)		45	50
1795	$1 "Enjoying Lotuses while Listening to Music" (left detail) (Sin Yunbok)		45	50
1796	$1 "Enjoying Lotuses while Listening to Music" (right detail)		45	50
1797	$1 "Women by a Crystal Stream" (left detail) (Sin Yunbok)		45	50
1798	$1 "Women by a Crystal Stream" (right detail)		45	50
1799	$4 Pusan (*horiz*)		1·90	2·00
1789/99		*Set of 11*	6·00	6·75

MS1800 70×102 mm. $6 "Blacksmith's Shop" (detail) (Kim Duksin). P 14 .. .. 2·75 3·00
Nos. 1791/8, each 26×49 mm, were printed together, *se-tenant*, in sheetlets of 8. Paintings are shown across horizontal pairs without white vertical margins in the centre.

(Des Claudia Sergeant. Litho Questa)

1994 (7 Aug). *Orchids. Multicoloured designs as T* **392** *of Grenada.* P 14.

1801	15 c. *Cattleya aurantiaca*		10	10
1802	25 c. *Blettia patula*		10	10
1803	45 c. *Sobralia macrantha*		20	25
1804	75 c. *Encyclia belizensis*		35	40
1805	$1 *Sophrolaeliocattleya*		45	50
1806	$2 *Encyclia fragrans*		90	95
1807	$4 *Schombocattleya*		1·90	2·00
1808	$5 *Brassolaeliocattleya*		2·25	2·40
1801/8		*Set of 8*	6·25	6·50

MS1809 Two sheets, each 100×70 mm. (a) $6 *Ornithidium coccineum* (*horiz*). (b) $6 *Brassavola nodosa* (*horiz*) .. .. *Set of 2 sheets* 5·50 5·75

(Litho Questa)

1994 (11 Aug). *World Cup Football Championship, U.S.A.* (2nd issue). *Vert designs as T* **393** *of Grenada. Multicoloured.* P 14.

1810	75 c. Steve Mark (Grenada)		35	40
	a. Sheetlet. Nos. 1810/15		2·00	

1811	75 c. Jurgen Kohler (Germany)		35	40
1812	75 c. Almir (Brazil)		35	40
1813	75 c. Michael Windiscmann (U.S.A.)		35	40
1814	75 c. Guiseppe Giannini (Italy)		35	40
1815	75 c. Rashidi Yekini (Nigeria)		35	40
1810/15		*Set of 6*	2·00	2·40

MS1816 Two sheets, each 99×70 mm. (a) $6 Kemari (ancient Japanese game). (b) $6 Hand holding trophy .. .. *Set of 2 sheets* 5·50 5·75
Nos. 1810/15 were printed together, *se-tenant*, in sheetlets of 6.

106 Mickey Mouse and Unjin Mirŭk Window from Kwanch Ok Temple

(Litho Questa)

1994 (16 Aug). *"Philakorea '94" International Stamp Exhibition, Seoul* (2nd issue). *T* **106** *and similar multicoloured designs showing Walt Disney cartoon characters.* P 14×13¹⁄₂.

1817	3 c. Type **106**		10	10
1818	4 c. Goofy imitating statue of Admiral Yi, Chŏnju		10	10
1819	5 c. Cousin Gus and Donald Duck eating dinner		10	10
1820	10 c. Mickey playing flute		10	10
1821	15 c. Goofy with Tolharubang (statue)		10	10
1822	15 c. Type **106**		10	10
1823	20 c. Mickey and Minnie at Hyang-Wonjŏng		10	10
1824	35 c. As 4 c.		15	20
1825	50 c. As 5 c.		25	30
1826	75 c. As 10 c.		35	40
1827	$1 As 15 c.		45	50
1828	$2 As 20 c.		90	95
1829	$4 Mickey as Somori-Kut shaman		1·90	2·00
1830	$5 Minnie holding ceremonial fan		2·25	2·40
1817/30		*Set of 14*	6·50	7·00

MS1831 Two sheets, each 130×103 mm. (a) $6 Minnie beating Buk drum (*vert*). (b) $6 Mickey in swimming pool at Pugok Hawaii (*vert*). P 13¹⁄₂×14 .. .. *Set of 2 sheets* 5·50 5·75

(Litho Questa)

1994 (1 Sept). *First Recipients of Order of the Caribbean Community. Horiz designs as Nos. 2046/8 of Antigua. Multicoloured.* P 14.

1832	25 c. Sir Shridath Ramphal		10	10
1833	50 c. William Demas		25	30
1834	$2 Derek Walcott		90	95
1832/34		*Set of 3*	1·25	1·40

(Des P. Gonzalez. Litho Questa)

1994 (1 Sept). *Fishes. Horiz designs as T* **394** *of Grenada. Multicoloured.* P 14.

1835	75 c. Porkfish		35	40
	a. Sheetlet. Nos. 1835/46		4·25	
1836	75 c. Blue Chromis		35	40
1837	75 c. Caribbean Reef Shark (facing left)		35	40
1838	75 c. Long-spined Squirrelfish		35	40
1839	75 c. Four-eyed Butterflyfish		35	40
1840	75 c. Blue Head		35	40
1841	75 c. Royal Gramma		35	40
1842	75 c. Sharp-nosed Puffer		35	40
1843	75 c. Reid's Seahorse		35	40
1844	75 c. Black-barred Soldierfish		35	40
1845	75 c. Red-lipped Blenny		35	40
1846	75 c. Painted Wrasse		35	40
1847	75 c. Yellow-tailed Snapper		35	40
	a. Sheetlet. Nos. 1847/58		4·25	
1848	75 c. Caribbean Reef Shark (facing right)		35	40
1849	75 c. Great Barracuda		35	40
1850	75 c. Red-tailed Parrotfish		35	40
1851	75 c. Blue Tang		35	40
1852	75 c. Queen Angelfish		35	40
1853	75 c. Red Hind		35	40
1854	75 c. Rock Beauty		35	40
1855	75 c. Queen Parrotfish		35	40
1856	75 c. Spanish Hogfish		35	40
1857	75 c. Spotted Moray		35	40
1858	75 c. Queen Triggerfish		35	40
1835/58		*Set of 24*	8·25	9·50

MS1859 Two sheets, each 102×72 mm. (a) $6 Head of Queen Angelfish. (b) $6 Head of Painted Wrasse .. .. *Set of 2 sheets* 5·50 5·75
Nos. 1835/46 and 1847/58 were printed together, *se-tenant*, in sheetlets of 12 each forming composite designs.

(Litho Questa)

1994 (5 Dec). *Christmas. Religious Paintings by Bartolome Murillo. Vert designs as T* **336** *of Antigua. Multicoloured.* P 13¹⁄₂×14.

1860	15 c. "The Annunciation"		10	10
1861	35 c. "The Adoration of the Shepherds"		15	20
1862	50 c. "Virgin and Child with St. Rose"		25	30
1863	50 c. "Flight into Egypt"		25	30
1864	75 c. "Virgin and Child"		35	40
1865	$1 "Virgin of the Rosary"		45	50
1866	$4 "The Holy Family"		1·90	2·00
1860/6		*Set of 7*	3·25	3·75

MS1867 Two sheets, each 85×95 mm. $6 "Adoration of the Shepherds" (*different*) (detail). (b) 95×125 mm. $6 "The Holy Family with a Little Bird" (detail) .. *Set of 2 sheets* 5·50 5·75

(Litho Questa)

1995 (10 Jan). *Birds. Multicoloured designs as* T **397** *of Grenada. Multicoloured. P* 14.

1868	25 c.	Scaly-breasted Ground Dove (*vert*) ..	10	10
1869	50 c.	White-winged Dove	25	30
1870	$2	Inca Dove (*vert*)	90	95
1871	$4	Mourning Dove	1·90	2·00
1868/71	..	.. .. .. *Set of* 4	3·00	3·25

(Des A. Melville-Brown. Litho Questa)

1995 (12 Jan). *Centenary of First English Cricket Tour to the West Indies. Multicoloured designs as* T **329** *of Antigua. P* 14.

1872	50 c.	Mike Atherton (England) and Wisden Trophy	25	30
1873	75 c.	Curtly Ambrose (West Indies) (*vert*)	35	40
1874	$1	Brian Lara (West Indies) (*vert*)	45	50
1872/4	..	.. .. .. *Set of* 3	1·00	1·10
MS1875	75×95 mm.	$3 West Indian team, 1994	1·40	1·50

107 Aspects of London, National Flag and Map

108 Pig

(Des S. and Dot Barlowe. Litho Questa)

1995 (10 Mar). *Capitals of the World.* T **107** *and similar vert designs showing aspects of various cities, national flags and maps. Multicoloured. P* 14.

1876	$1	Type **107**	45	50
		a. Sheetlet. Nos. 1876/85 ..	4·50	
1877	$1	Cairo	45	50
1878	$1	Vienna	45	50
1879	$1	Paris	45	50
1880	$1	Rome	45	50
1881	$1	Budapest	45	50
1882	$1	Moscow	45	50
1883	$1	Peking ("Beijing")	45	50
1884	$1	Tokyo	45	50
1885	$1	Washington	45	50
1876/85	..	.. .. .. *Set of* 10	4·50	5·00

Nos. 1876/85 were printed together, *se-tenant*, in sheetlets of 10.

(Des Y. Lee. Litho Questa)

1995 (21 Apr). *Chinese New Year ("Year of the Pig").* T **108** *and similar multicoloured designs showing "GRENADA GRENADINES" in colours indicated. P* 14½.

1886	75 c.	Type **108** (deep reddish violet) ..	35	40
		a. Block of 4. Nos. 1886/9 ..	1·40	
1887	75 c.	Pig (deep carmine) ..	35	40
1888	75 c.	Pig (lake-brown) ..	35	40
1889	75 c.	Pig (scarlet-vermilion) ..	35	40
1886/9	..	.. .. .. *Set of* 4	1·40	1·60
MS1890	Two sheets. (a) 106×77 mm. $2 Two pigs (*horiz*). (b) 67×83 mm. Nos. 1886/9			
		Set of 2 *sheets*	2·25	2·40

Nos. 1886/9 were printed together, *se-tenant*, as blocks of 4 in sheetlets of 16.

109 Bull Shark and Diver

(Des Y. Lee. Litho Questa)

1995 (3 May). *Marine Life of the Caribbean.* T **109** *and similar horiz designs. Multicoloured. P* 14.

1891	$1	Type **109**	45	50
		a. Sheetlet. Nos. 1891/9 ..	4·00	
1892	$1	Great White Shark ..	45	50
1893	$1	Octopus and shoal of fish ..	45	50
1894	$1	Great Barracuda ..	45	50
1895	$1	Green Moray	45	50
1896	$1	Spotted Eagle Ray ..	45	50
1897	$1	Sea Snake	45	50
1898	$1	Stingray	45	50
1899	$1	Grouper	45	50
1900	$1	Dolphins	45	50
		a. Sheetlet. Nos. 1900/8 ..	4·00	
1901	$1	Lionfish	45	50
1902	$1	Sea Turtle and Rock Beauty (fish) ..	45	50
1903	$1	Blue-cheeked Butterflyfish and Nurse Shark	45	50
1904	$1	Queen Angelfish ..	45	50
1905	$1	Grouper and Coney ..	45	50
1906	$1	Rainbow Eel and Spotted Moray ..	45	50
1907	$1	Sun Flower-star and Coral Crab ..	45	50
1908	$1	Octopus on sea bed ..	45	50
1891/1908	..	.. .. .. *Set of* 18	8·00	9·00
MS1909	Two sheets, each 107×77 mm. (a) $5 French Angelfish. (b) $6 Smooth Hammerhead			
		Set of 2 *sheets*	5·00	5·25

Nos. 1891/9 and 1900/8 were printed together, *se-tenant*, in sheetlets of 9.

110 Suffolk Punch

(Des Jennifer Toombs. Litho Questa)

1995 (3 May). *Domestic Animals.* T **110** *and similar horiz designs. Multicoloured. P* 14.

1910	15 c.	Type **110**	10	10
1911	25 c.	Shetland pony	10	10
1912	75 c.	Blue Persian (cat) ..	35	40
		a. Sheetlet. Nos. 1912/23 ..	4·25	
1913	75 c.	Sorrel Abyssinian (cat) ..	35	40
1914	75 c.	White Angora (cat) ..	35	40
1915	75 c.	Brown Burmese (cat) ..	35	40
1916	75 c.	Red Tabby Exotic Shorthair (cat) ..	35	40
1917	75 c.	Seal-point Birman (cat) ..	35	40
1918	75 c.	Korat (cat)	35	40
1919	75 c.	Norwegian Forest Cat ..	35	40
1920	75 c.	Lilac-point Balinese (cat) ..	35	40
1921	75 c.	British Shorthair (cat) ..	35	40
1922	75 c.	Red Self Longhair (cat) ..	35	40
1923	75 c.	Calico Manx (cat) ..	35	40
1924	75 c.	Shetland Sheepdog ..	35	40
		a. Sheetlet. Nos. 1924/35 ..	4·25	
1925	75 c.	Bull Terrier	35	40
1926	75 c.	Afghan Hound	35	40
1927	75 c.	Scottish Terrier	35	40
1928	75 c.	Labrador Retriever ..	35	40
1929	75 c.	English Springer Spaniel ..	35	40
1930	75 c.	Samoyed (dog)	35	40
1931	75 c.	Irish Setter	35	40
1932	75 c.	Border Collie	35	40
1933	75 c.	Pekingese	35	40
1934	75 c.	Dachshund	35	40
1935	75 c.	Weimaraner (dog) ..	35	40
1936	$1	Arab	45	50
1937	$3	Shire horse	1·40	1·50
1910/37	..	.. .. .. *Set of* 28	10·50	11·50
MS1938	Two sheets, each 105×75 mm. (a) $6 Seal-point Colourpoint (cat). (b) $6 English Setter .. .. .. *Set of* 2 *sheets*		5·50	5·75

Nos. 1912/23 and 1924/35 were printed together, *se-tenant*, in sheetlets of 12.

(Litho Questa)

1995 (5 May). *Centenary of Sierra Club (environmental protection society) (1992). Endangered Species. Multicoloured designs as* T **320** *of Antigua. P* 14.

1939	$1	Spotted Owl	45	50
		a. Sheetlet. Nos. 1939/47 ..	4·00	
1940	$1	Brown Pelican on perch ..	45	50
1941	$1	Head of Brown Pelican ..	45	50
1942	$1	Head of Jaguarundi ..	45	50
1943	$1	Jaguarundi looking over shoulder ..	45	50
1944	$1	Maned Wolf in undergrowth ..	45	50
1945	$1	American Wood Stork standing on two legs	45	50
1946	$1	American Wood Stork standing on one leg	45	50
1947	$1	Close-up of Maned Wolf ..	45	50
1948	$1	Brown Pelican (*horiz*) ..	45	50
		a. Sheetlet. Nos. 1948/56 ..	4·00	
1949	$1	Close-up of Spotted Owl (*horiz*) ..	45	50
1950	$1	Spotted Owl chick (*horiz*) ..	45	50
1951	$1	Jaguarundi (*horiz*) ..	45	50
1952	$1	Central American Spider Monkey sitting with young (*horiz*) ..	45	50
1953	$1	Central American Spider Monkey carrying young (*horiz*) ..	45	50
1954	$1	Central American Spider Monkey swinging from branch (*horiz*) ..	45	50
1955	$1	American Wood Stork (*horiz*) ..	45	50
1956	$1	Pair of Maned Wolves (*horiz*) ..	45	50
1939/56	..	.. .. .. *Set of* 18	8·00	9·00

Nos. 1939/47 and 1948/56 were printed together, *se-tenant*, in sheetlets of 9.

(Litho Questa)

1995 (8 May). *18th World Scout Jamboree, Netherlands. Horiz designs as* T **403** *of Grenada. Multicoloured. P* 14.

1957	75 c.	Grenadian scout on beach ..	35	40
		a. Horiz strip of 3. Nos. 1957/9 ..	1·60	
1958	$1	Scout with staff on hill ..	45	50
1959	$2	Scout saluting and national flag ..	90	95
1957/9	..	.. .. .. *Set of* 3	1·60	1·75
MS1960	107×77 mm. $6 Scout snorkelling		2·75	3·00

Nos. 1957/9 were printed together in sheets of 9 containing three *se-tenant* horizontal strips of 3.

(Des W. Wright. Litho Questa)

1995 (8 May). *50th Anniv of End of Second World War in Europe. Bombers. Horiz designs as* T **340** *of Antigua. Multicoloured. P* 14.

1961	$2	Avro Type 683 Lancaster ..	90	95
		a. Sheetlet. Nos. 1961/8 ..	7·25	
1962	$2	Junkers Ju 88	90	95
1963	$2	North American B-25 Mitchell ..	90	95
1964	$2	Boeing B-17 Flying Fortress ..	90	95
1965	$2	Petlyakov Pe-2	90	95
1966	$2	Martin B-26 Marauder ..	90	95
1967	$2	Heinkel He 111H	90	95
1968	$2	Consolidated B-24 Liberator ..	90	95
1961/8	..	.. .. .. *Set of* 8	7·25	7·50
MS1969	105×75 mm. $6 Pres. Truman and newspaper headline (57×43 *mm*)		2·75	3·00

Nos. 1961/8 were printed together, *se-tenant*, in sheetlets of 8 with the stamps arranged in two horizontal strips of 4 separated by a gutter showing a De Havilland D.H.98 Mosquito.

(Des R. Martin. Litho Questa)

1995 (8 May). *50th Anniv of United Nations. Vert designs as* T **404** *of Grenada. Multicoloured. P* 14.

1970	75 c.	U. N. Headquarters, New York, and flag	35	40
		a. Horiz strip of 3. Nos. 1970/2 ..	1·60	
1971	$1	Trygve Lie (first Secretary-General)	45	50
1972	$2	U.N. soldier	90	95
1970/2	..	.. .. .. *Set of* 3	1·60	1·75
MS1973	101×76 mm. $6 Peace dove over emblem		2·75	3·00

Nos. 1970/2 were printed together in sheets of 9 containing three *se-tenant* horizontal strips of 3, each forming a composite design.

(Des R. Martin. Litho Questa)

1995 (8 May). *50th Anniv of Food and Agriculture Organization. Vert designs as* T **405** *of Grenada. Multicoloured. P* 14.

1974	75 c.	Man hoeing	35	40
		a. Horiz strip of 3. Nos. 1974/6 ..	1·60	
1975	$1	Woman hoeing	45	50
1976	$1	Man and woman hoeing ..	90	95
1974/6	..	.. .. .. *Set of* 3	1·60	1·75
MS1977	106×76 mm. $6 Child eating with chopsticks		2·75	3·00

Nos. 1974/6 were printed together in sheets of 9 containing three *se-tenant* horizontal strips of 3, each forming a composite design.

(Litho Questa)

1995 (8 May). *90th Anniv of Rotary International. Multicoloured designs as* T **406** *of Grenada. P* 14.

1978	$5	Paul Harris (founder) and logo (*horiz*)	2·25	2·40
MS1979	106×76 mm. $6 Rotary Club and International logos (*horiz*) ..		2·75	3·00

(Litho Questa)

1995 (8 May). *95th Birthday of Queen Elizabeth the Queen Mother. Vert designs as* T **344** *of Antigua. P* 13½×14.

1980	$1.50,	orange-brown, pale brown and black	70	75
		a. Sheetlet. Nos. 1980/3×2 ..	5·50	
1981	$1.50,	multicoloured	70	75
1982	$1.50,	multicoloured	70	75
1983	$1.50,	multicoloured	70	75
1980/3	..	.. .. .. *Set of* 4	2·75	3·00
MS1984	102×127 mm. $6 multicoloured ..		2·75	3·00

Designs:—No. 1980, Queen Elizabeth the Queen Mother (pastel drawing); No. 1981, At Remembrance Day service; No. 1982, At desk (oil painting); No. 1983, Wearing green hat; No. MS1984, Unveiling memorial to Blitz victims.

Nos. 1980/3 were printed together in sheetlets of 8, containing two *se-tenant* horizontal strips of 4.

(Des J. Batchelor. Litho Questa)

1995 (8 May). *50th Anniv of End of Second World War in the Pacific. Horiz designs as* T **340** *of Antigua. Multicoloured. P* 14.

1985	$2	Mitsubishi G4M1 "Betty" (bomber) ..	90	95
		a. Sheetlet. Nos. 1985/90 ..	5·50	
1986	$2	Japanese submarine "I 14" with seaplane on catapult ..	90	95
1987	$2	Mitsubishi GM31 "Nell" (bomber) ..	90	95
1988	$2	Akizuki (Japanese destroyer) ..	90	95
1989	$2	Kirishima (Japanese battleship) ..	90	95
1990	$2	Asigari (Japanese cruiser) ..	90	95
1985/90	..	.. .. .. *Set of* 6	5·50	5·75
MS1991	108×76 mm. $6 Japanese Aichi D3A1 "Val" dive bomber ..		2·75	3·00

Nos. 1985/90 were printed together, *se-tenant*, in sheetlets of 6 with the stamps arranged in two horizontal strips of 3 separated by a gutter showing Yokosuka MXY-7 "Okha" (Kamikaze airplane) attacking ships.

(Litho B.D.T.)

1995 (23 June). *Olympic Games, Atlanta (1996). Designs as* T **407** *of Grenada. Multicoloured. P* 14.

1992	15 c.	Rosemary Ackerman (East Germany) (high jump) (*horiz*) ..	10	10
		a. Horiz strip of 3. Nos. 1992/4 ..	15	
1993	15 c.	Li Ning (China) (gymnastics) (*horiz*)	10	10
1994	15 c.	Denise Parker (U.S.A.) (archery) (*horiz*) ..	10	10
1995	$3	Terry Carlisle (U.S.A.) (skeet shooting) (*horiz*) ..	1·40	1·50
		a. Horiz strip of 3. Nos. 1995/7 ..	4·00	
1996	$3	Kathleen Nord (East Germany) (swimming) (*horiz*) ..	1·40	1·50
1997	$3	Brigit Schmidt (East Germany) (canoeing) (*horiz*) ..	1·40	1·50
1992/7	..	.. .. .. *Set of* 6	4·25	4·50
MS1998	Two sheets, each 102×72 mm. (a) $6 Dan Gable (U.S.A.) and Kikuo Wada (Japan) (wrestling). (b) $6 George Foreman (U.S.A.) (boxing).. .. *Set of* 2 *sheets*		5·50	5·75

Nos. 1992/4 and 1995/7 were printed in sheets of 12 containing four *se-tenant* horizontal strips of 3.

111 Brown Pelican

(Des T. Wood. Litho Questa)

1995 (5 Sept). *Birds of the Caribbean.* T **111** *and similar horiz designs. Multicoloured.* P 14.

1999	10 c. Type **111**		10	10
2000	15 c. Black-necked Stilt		10	10
2001	25 c. Cuban Trogon		10	10
2002	35 c. Greater Flamingo		15	20
2003	75 c. Imperial Amazon		35	40
2004	$1 Pintail		45	50
2005	$1 Great Blue Heron		45	50
	a. Sheetlet. Nos. 2005/12		3·50	
2006	$1 Jamaican Tody		45	50
2007	$1 Laughing Gull		45	50
2008	$1 Purple-throated Carib		45	50
2009	$1 Red-legged Thrush		45	50
2010	$1 Ruddy Duck		45	50
2011	$1 Common Shoveler		45	50
2012	$1 West Indian Red-bellied Woodpecker		45	50
2013	$2 Ringed Kingfisher		90	95
2014	$3 Stripe-headed Tanager		1·40	1·50
1999/2014		*Set of 16*	7·00	7·75

MS2015 Two sheets, each 104×73 mm. (a) $5 Village Weaver. (b) $5 Blue-hooded Euphonia
Set of 2 sheets 4·50 4·75

Nos. 2005/12 were printed together, *se-tenant*, in sheetlets of 8, and, together with No. MS2015, carry the "Singapore '95" exhibition logo.

No. 2001 is inscr "Cuban Trogan", No. 2008 "Purple-throated Carb" and No. 2013 "Ringed King Fisher", all in error.

(Des Walt Disney Company and Rosemary DeFiglio. Litho Questa)

1995 (2 Oct). *Mickey's Pirate Adventure. Multicoloured designs as* T **415** *of Grenada showing Walt Disney cartoon characters.* P 14×13½.

2016	10 c. Goofy and Donald Duck with treasure chests (*horiz*)		10	10
2017	35 c. Mickey and Minnie Mouse at ship's wheel (*horiz*)		15	20
2018	75 c. Mickey, Donald and Goofy opening chest (*horiz*)		35	40
2019	$1 Big Pete and rats confronting Mickey (*horiz*)		45	50
2020	$2 Mickey, Goofy and Donald in boat (*horiz*)		90	95
2021	$5 Goofy fighting rat pirate with mop (*horiz*)		2·25	2·40
2016/21		*Set of 6*	4·00	4·50

MS2022 Two sheets, each 108×130 mm. (a) $6 Goofy and cannon-balls. (b) $6 Monkey pinching Mickey's nose. P 13½×14 .. *Set of 2 sheets* 5·50 5·75

(Des R. Martin. Litho Questa)

1995 (18 Oct). *Centenary of Nobel Trust Fund. Vert designs as* T **416** *of Grenada. Multicoloured.* P 14.

2023/51	75 c. × 2, $1×27	*Set of 29*	13·50	14·00

MS2052 Three sheets, each 105×76 mm. (a) $6 Sir Winston Churchill (1953 Literature). (b) $6 Willy Brandt (1971 Peace). (c) $6 Albert Schweitzer (1952 Peace) .. *Set of 3 sheets* 8·25 8·50

Designs:—75 c. W. Arthur Lewis (1979 Economics); Derek Walcott (1992 Literature); $1 Jules Border (1919 Medicine); René Cassin (1968 Peace); Verner von Heidenstam (1916 Literature); José Echegaray (1904 Literature); Otto Wallach (1910 Chemistry); Corneille Heymans (1938 Medicine); Ivar Giaever (1973 Physics); Sir William Cremer (1903 Peace); John Strutt (1904 Physics); James Franck (1925 Physics); Tobias Asser (1911 Peace); Carl Spitteler (1919 Literature); Christiaan Eijkman (1929 Medicine); Ragnar Granit (1967 Medicine); Frederic Passy (1901 Peace); Louis Neel (1970 Physics); Sir William Ramsay (1904 Chemistry); Philip Noel-Baker (1959 Peace); Heike Önnes (1913 Physics); Fridtjof Nansen (1922 Peace); Sir Ronald Ross (1902 Medicine); Paul Müller (1948 Medicine); Allvar Gullstrand (1911 Medicine); Gerhart Hauptmann (1912 Literature); Hans Spemann (1935 Medicine); Cecil Powell (1950 Physics); Walther Bothe (1954 Physics).

Nos. 2025/33, 2034/42 and 2043/51 were each printed together, *se-tenant*, in sheetlets of 9 forming composite designs.

No. 2027 (Von Heidenstam) is inscribed "1906" and No. 2044 is inscribed "Fridtjof Nanser", both in error.

112 Nita Naldi and Rudolph Valentino

(Des J. Iskowitz. Litho Questa)

1995 (3 Nov). *Centenary of Cinema.* T **112** *and similar multicoloured designs.* P 13½.

2053	$1 Type **112**		45	50
	a. Sheetlet. Nos. 2053/61		4·00	
2054	$1 Ramon Novaro and Alice Terry		45	50
2055	$1 Frederic March and Joan Crawford		45	50
2056	$1 Clark Gable and Vivien Leigh		45	50
2057	$1 Barbara Stanwyck and Burt Lancaster		45	50
2058	$1 Warren Beatty and Natalie Wood		45	50
2059	$1 Spencer Tracy and Katharine Hepburn		45	50
2060	$1 Humphrey Bogart and Lauren Bacall		45	50
2061	$1 Omar Sharif and Julie Christie		45	50
2062	$1 Marion Davis		45	50
	a. Sheetlet. Nos. 2062/70		4·00	

2063	$1 Marlene Dietrich		45	50
2064	$1 Lillian Gish		45	50
2065	$1 Bette Davis		45	50
2066	$1 Elizabeth Taylor		45	50
2067	$1 Veronica Lake		45	50
2068	$1 Ava Gardner		45	50
2069	$1 Grace Kelly		45	50
2070	$1 Kim Novak		45	50
2053/70		*Set of 18*	8·00	9·00

MS2071 Two sheets. (a) 72×102 mm. $6 Sophia Loren. (b) 102×72 mm. $6 Greta Garbo and John Gilbert (*horiz*) .. *Set of 2 sheets* 5·50 5·75

Nos. 2053/61 and 2062/70 were each printed together, *se-tenant*, in sheetlets of 9 forming composite designs.

(Litho Questa)

1995 (7 Nov). *Racing Cars. Multicoloured designs as* T **423** *of Grenada.* P 14.

2072	10 c. Williams-Renault Formula 1, 1990s		10	10
2073	25 c. Porsche "956", Le Mans, 1980s		10	15
2074	35 c. Lotus "John Player Special", 1970s		15	20
2075	75 c. Ford "GT-40", 1960s		35	40
2076	$2 Mercedes-Benz "W196", 1950s		90	95
2077	$3 Mercedes "SSK", 1920s		1·40	1·50
2072/7		*Set of 6*	3·00	3·25

MS2078 103×73 mm. $6 Jackie Stewart in Tyrrell-Ford, 1971 (*vert*) .. .. 2·75 3·00

113 Man on Donkey   114 Symbolic Rat and Candle

(Litho Questa)

1995 (7 Nov). *Local Transport.* T **113** *and similar horiz design. Multicoloured.* P 14.

2079	35 c. Type **113**		15	20
2080	75 c. Local bus		35	40

(Des W. Wright. Litho Questa)

1995 (7 Nov). *Evolution of Sailing Ships. Horiz designs as* T **427** *of Grenada. Multicoloured.* P 14.

2081	$1 *Preussen* (full-rigged ship)		45	50
	a. Sheetlet. Nos. 2081/6		2·50	
2082	$1 Japanese junk		45	50
2083	$1 Caribbean pirate ship		45	50
2084	$1 *Mayflower* (Pilgrim Fathers)		45	50
2085	$1 Chinese junk		45	50
2086	$1 *Santa Maria* (Columbus)		45	50
2081/6		*Set of 6*	2·50	3·00

MS2087 103×73 mm. $5 Spanish galleon (56×41 mm) .. .. .. 2·25 2·40

Nos. 2081/6 were printed together, *se-tenant*, in sheetlets of 6.

(Litho Questa)

1995 (28 Nov). *Christmas. Religious Paintings. Vert designs as* T **357** *of Antigua. Multicoloured.* P 13½×14.

2088	10 c. "Immaculate Conception" (Piero di Cosimo)		10	10
2089	15 c. "St. Michael dedicating Arms to the Madonna" (Le Nain)		10	10
2090	35 c. "Annunciation" (Lorenzo di Credi)		15	20
2091	50 c. "The Holy Family" (Jacob Jordaens)		25	30
2092	$3 "Madonna and Child" (Lippi)		1·40	1·50
2093	$5 "Madonna and Child with Ten Saints" (Fiorentino)		2·25	2·40
2088/93		*Set of 6*	4·00	4·50

MS2094 102×127 mm. (a) $6 "Adoration of the Shepherds" (detail) (Van Oost). (b) $6 "Holy Family" (detail) (Del Start) .. *Set of 2 sheets* 5·50 5·75

(Des Y. Lee. Litho Questa)

1996 (2 Jan). *Chinese New Year* ("Year of the Rat"). T **114** *and similar multicoloured designs.* P 14½.

2095	75 c. Type **114** (dull blue background)		35	40
	a. Block of 4. Nos. 2095/8		1·40	
2096	75 c. Type **114** (lilac background)		35	40
2097	75 c. Type **114** (orange-brown background)		35	40
2098	75 c. Type **114** (yellow-green background)		35	40
2095/8		*Set of 4*	1·40	1·60

MS2099 69×84 mm. No. 2095/8 .. 1·40 1·60
MS2100 76×106 mm. $2 Two rats (*horiz*) .. 90 95

Nos. 2095/8 were printed together, *se-tenant*, as blocks of 4 in sheets of 16, with the four designs showing different Chinese characters.

(Litho Questa)

1996 (29 Jan). *Works of Art by Dürer and Rubens. Vert designs as* T **421** *of Grenada. Multicoloured.* P 13½×14.

2101	15 c. "The Children" (Dürer)		10	10
2102	35 c. "Oriental Ruler Seated" (Dürer)		15	20
2103	50 c. "The Entombment" (Dürer)		25	30
2104	75 c. "Man in Armour" (Rubens)		35	40
2105	$1 "Peace embracing Plenty" (Rubens)		45	50
2106	$2 "Departure of Lot" (Rubens)		90	95
2107	$3 "The Four Evangelists" (Rubens)		1·40	1·50
2108	$5 "Knight, Death and Devil" (Dürer)		2·25	2·40
2101/8		*Set of 8*	5·75	6·25

MS2109 Two sheets, each 101×127 mm. (a) $5 "The Fathers of the Church" (detail) (Rubens). (b) $6 "St. Jerome" (detail) (Dürer).
Set of 2 sheets 5·00 5·25

115 Mickey and Minnie at New Year's Day "Hopping John" Tradition

(Des Alvin White Studios. Litho Questa)

1996 (17 Apr). *Traditional Holidays.* T **115** *and similar multi-coloured designs showing Walt Disney cartoon characters.* P 14×13½.

2110	25 c. Type **115**		10	15
2111	50 c. Disney characters dancing around maypole		25	30
2112	75 c. Mickey, Minnie and Pluto watching Independence Day fireworks		35	40
2113	90 c. Gyro Gearloose and Donald's nephews in Halloween costumes		40	45
2114	$3 Donald Duck as Puritan and nephews as Indians on Thanksgiving Day		1·40	1·50
2115	$4 Huey and Dewey with Hanukkah dreidle		1·90	2·00
2110/15		*Set of 6*	4·25	4·75

MS2116 Two sheets, each 124×98 mm. (a) $6 Mickey, Minnie and Donald taking part in Caribbean carnival. P 14×13½. (b) $6 Traditional pot of gold in St. Patrick's Day parade (*vert*). P 13½×14 .. *Set of 2 sheets* 5·50 5·75

116 Gateway in Imperial Palace, Peking

1996 (8 May). "*CHINA '96*" *9th Asian International Stamp Exhibition, Peking.* T **116** *and similar multicoloured designs.* Litho. P 13.

2117	$1 Type **116**		45	50
	a. Sheetlet. Nos. 2117/20		1·75	
2118	$1 Eastern end of Great Wall at Shanhaiguan		45	50
2119	$1 Great Wall fortress, Shanhaiguan		45	50
2120	$1 Gate of Heavenly Peace, Peking		45	50
2121	$1 Sun Yat-sen's Mausoleum, Nanjing		45	50
	a. Sheetlet. Nos. 2121/4		1·75	
2122	$1 Summer Palace, Peking		45	50
2123	$1 Temple of Heaven, Peking		45	50
2124	$1 Hall of Supreme Harmony, Forbidden City, Peking		45	50
2117/24		*Set of 8*	3·50	4·00

MS2125 Three sheets. (a) 150×100 mm. $2 Traditional Chinese painting (39×50 mm). (b) 90×68 mm. $6 Great Wall of China from the air (39×50 mm). (c) 90×68 mm. $6 Marble Boat, Summer Palace, Peking (50×39 mm)
Set of 3 sheets 6·50 6·75

Nos. 2117/20 and 2121/4 were each printed together, *se-tenant*, in sheetlets of 4.

(Litho Questa)

1996 (8 May). *70th Birthday of Queen Elizabeth II. Vert designs as* T **364** *of Antigua. Multicoloured.* P 13½×14.

2126	35 c. As Type **364** of Antigua		15	20
	a. Strip of 3. Nos. 2126/8		2·75	
2127	$2 Queen wearing tiara and green dress		90	95
2128	$4 Windsor Castle		1·90	2·00
2126/8		*Set of 3*	2·75	3·00

MS2129 103×125 mm. $6 Queen Elizabeth at Windsor .. .. 2·75 3·00

Nos. 2126/8 were printed together, *se-tenant*, in horizontal and vertical strips of 3 throughout the sheet.

(Litho B.D.T.)

1996 (12 June). *Flowers. Multicoloured designs as* T **430** *of Grenada, but vert.* P 14.

2130	35 c. Camellia "Apple Blossom"		15	20
2131	75 c. *Odontoglossum*		35	40
	a. Sheetlet. Nos. 2131/4×3		4·25	
2132	75 c. *Cattleya*		35	40
2133	75 c. *Paphiopedilum* "Venus's Slipper"		35	40
2134	75 c. *Laeliocattleya* "Marysville"		35	40
2135	75 c. Fuchsia "Citation"		35	40
	a. Sheetlet. Nos. 2135/46		4·25	
2136	75 c. Fuchsia "Amy Lye"		35	40
2137	75 c. *Clysonimus* (butterfly) and temple		35	40
2138	75 c. *Digitalis purpurea* "Foxglove"		35	40
2139	75 c. *Lilium martagon* "Martagon Lily"		35	40
2140	75 c. *Tulipa* "Couleur Cardinal"		35	40
2141	75 c. *Galanthus nivalis* "Snowdrop"		35	40

2142	75 c. *Rosa* "Superstar"		35	40
2143	75 c. *Crocus* "Dutch Yellow Mammoth"		35	40
2144	75 c. *Lilium speciosum* "Japanese Lily"		35	40
2145	75 c. *Lilium* "Joan Evans"		35	40
2146	75 c. *Rosa* "Rosemary Harkness"		35	40
2147	90 c. *Camellia japonica* "Extravaganza"		40	45
2148	$1 *Chrysanthemum* "Primrose Dorothy Else"		45	50
2149	$2 *Dahlia* "Brandaris"		90	95
2130/49		*Set of 20*	10·00	11·00
MS2150	Two sheets, each 68×98 mm. (a) $5 Narcissus "Rembrandt". (b) $6 Gladiolus "Flowersong"	*Set of 2 sheets*	5·00	5·25

Nos. 2131/4 and 2135/46 were each printed together, *se-tenant*, in sheetlets of 12 containing three of each design (Nos. 2131/4) or with the backgrounds forming a composite design (Nos. 2135/46).

No. 2135 is inscribed "Fuschcia", No. 2143 "Mammouth" and No. **MS**2150b "Gladiollus", all in error.

(Litho Questa)

1996 (26 June). *50th Anniv of U.N.I.C.E.F. Horiz designs as T 366 of Antigua. Multicoloured. P 14.*

2151	75 c. Child's face			35	40
2152	$2 Child with spoon			90	95
2153	$3 Girl sewing			1·40	1·50
2151/3			*Set of 3*	2·50	2·75
MS2154	105×75 mm. $6 Mother carrying child			2·75	3·00

(Des Jennifer Toombs. Litho Questa)

1996 (26 June). *3000th Anniv of Jerusalem. Multicoloured designs as T 367 of Antigua, but horiz. P 14.*

MS2155	137×47 mm. $1 Pool of Bethesda and *Papaver rhoeas*; $2 Damascus Gate and *Chrysanthemum coronarium*; $3 Church of All Nations and *Myrtus communis*	2·75	3·00
MS2156	82×62 mm. $6 Church of the Holy Sepulchre	2·75	3·00

(Des J. Iskowitz. Litho Questa)

1996 (26 June). *Centenary of Radio. Entertainers. Multicoloured designs as T 368 of Antigua. P 13½×14.*

2157	35 c. Ed Wynn			15	20
2158	75 c. Red Skelton			35	40
2159	$1 Joe Penner			45	50
2160	$3 Jerry Colonna			1·40	1·50
2157/60			*Set of 4*	2·25	2·50
MS2161	70×99 mm. $6 Bob Elliot and Ray Goulding (*horiz*). P 14×13½			2·75	3·00

(Litho Questa)

1996 (15 July). *Olympic Games, Atlanta. Previous Medal Winners. Multicoloured designs as T 425 of Grenada. P 14.*

2162	35 c. Los Angeles Memorial Coliseum	15	20
2163	75 c. Connie Carpenter-Phinney (U.S.A.) (Cycling)	35	40
2164	$1 Josef Neckermann (Germany) (*vert*)	45	50
	a. Sheetlet. Nos. 2164/72	4·00	
2165	$1 Harry Boldt (Germany) (*vert*)	45	50
2166	$1 Elena Petouchkova (Russia) (*vert*)	45	50
2167	$1 Alwin Schockemoehle (Germany) (*vert*)	45	50
2168	$1 Hans Winkler (Germany) (*vert*)	45	50
2169	$1 Joe Fargis (U.S.A.) (*vert*)	45	50
2170	$1 David Broome (Great Britain) (*vert*)	45	50
2171	$1 Reiner Klimke (Germany) (*vert*)	45	50
2172	$1 Richard Meade (Great Britain) (*vert*)	45	50
2173	$1 Julianne McNamara (U.S.A.) (*vert*)	45	50
	a. Sheetlet. Nos. 2173/81	4·00	
2174	$1 Takuti Hayata (Japan) (*vert*)	45	50
2175	$1 Nikolai Adriana (Russia) (*vert*)	45	50
2176	$1 Mitch Gaylord (U.S.A.) (*vert*)	45	50
2177	$1 Ludmilla Touristcheva (Russia) (*vert*)	45	50
2178	$1 Karin Janz (Germany) (*vert*)	45	50
2179	$1 Peter Kormann (U.S.A.) (*vert*)	45	50
2180	$1 Sawoo Kato (Japan) (*vert*)	45	50
2181	$1 Nadia Comaneci (Rumania) (*vert*)	45	50
2182	$2 Mohamed Bouchighe (Algeria) (Boxing) (*vert*)	90	95
2183	$3 Jackie Joyner Kersee (U.S.A.) (Javelin)	1·40	1·50
2162/83	*Set of 22*	11·00	12·00
MS2184	Two sheets, each 103×74 mm. (a) $5 Child waving flag (*vert*). (b) $6 William Steinkraus (U.S.A.) (Show jumping)		
	Set of 2 sheets	5·00	5·25

Nos. 2164/72 (equestrians) and 2173/81 (gymnasts) were each printed together, *se-tenant*, in sheetlets of 9 with the backgrounds forming composite designs.

(Des J. Puvilland. Litho B.D.T.)

1996 (25 July). *Classic Cars. Multicoloured designs as T 426 of Grenada. P 14.*

2185	35 c. Chevrolet Belair convertible	15	20
	a. Sheetlet. Nos. 2185/8 and 2195/6	3·50	
2186	50 c. V.I.P. car	25	30
2187	75 c. Rolls-Royce Torpedo	35	40
2188	$1 Nissan "Cepric" type	45	50
2189	$1 Delaunay-Belleville HB6	45	50
	a. Sheetlet. Nos. 2189/94	2·75	
2190	$1 Bugatti Type-15	45	50
2191	$1 Mazda Type 800	45	50
2192	$1 Mercedes 24/100/140 Sport	45	50
2193	$1 MG K3 Rover	45	50
2194	$1 Plymouth Fury	45	50
2195	$2 Mercedes-Benz 500K	90	95
2196	$3 Bugatti Type-13	1·40	1·50
2185/96	*Set of 12*	6·25	6·75
MS2197	Two sheets, each 106×76 mm. (a) $5 Bugatti "Roadster" Type-55. (b) $6 Lincoln Type-L		
	Set of 2 sheets	5·00	5·25

Nos. 2185/8 with 2195/6 and 2189/94 were each printed together, *se-tenant*, in sheetlets of 6.

(Litho Questa)

1996 (14 Aug). *Ships. Multicoloured designs as T 427 of Grenada. P 14.*

2198	35 c. Grenada schooner	15	20
2199	75 c. Grenada schooner (*different*)	35	40
2200	$1 Athenian triremes, 1000 B.C.	45	50
	a. Sheetlet. Nos. 2200/5	2·75	
2201	$1 Egyptian Nile galley, 30 B.C.	45	50
2202	$1 Bangladesh dinghi, 310 B.C.	45	50
2203	$1 Warship of Queen Hatshepsut, 476 B.C.	45	50
2204	$1 Chinese junk, 200 B.C.	45	50
2205	$1 Polynesian ocean-going canoe, 600 B.C.	45	50
2206	$1 *Europa* (liner), 1957	45	50
	a. Sheetlet. Nos. 2206/11	2·75	
2207	$1 *Lusitania* (liner), 1906	45	50
2208	$1 *Queen Mary* (liner), 1936	45	50
2209	$1 *Bianca C* (liner)	45	50
2210	$1 *France* (liner), 1952	45	50
2211	$1 *Orion* (liner), 1915	45	50
2198/211	*Set of 14*	6·00	6·50
MS2212	Two sheets, each 104×74 mm. (a) $5 Queen Elizabeth 2 (liner), 1969 (56×42 mm). (b) $6 Viking longship, 610 (42×56 mm)		
	Set of 2 sheets	5·00	5·25

Nos. 2200/5 and 2206/11 were each printed together, *se-tenant*, in sheetlets of 6.

117 Felix Mendelssohn
118 Man Ho Temple, 1841

1996 (26 Aug). *Composers. T 117 and similar vert designs. Multicoloured. Litho. P 14.*

2213	$1 Type 117	45	50
	a. Sheetlet. Nos. 2213/21	4·00	
2214	$1 Franz Schubert	45	50
2215	$1 Franz Joseph Haydn	45	50
2216	$1 Robert Schumann	45	50
2217	$1 Ludwig van Beethoven	45	50
2218	$1 Gioacchino Rossini	45	50
2219	$1 George Frederick Handel	45	50
2220	$1 Peter Tchaikovsky	45	50
2221	$1 Frederic Chopin	45	50
2222	$1 Bela Bartok	45	50
	a. Sheetlet. Nos. 2222/30	4·00	
2223	$1 Giacomo Puccini	45	50
2224	$1 George Gershwin	45	50
2225	$1 Leonard Bernstein	45	50
2226	$1 Kurt Weill	45	50
2227	$1 John Cage	45	50
2228	$1 Aaron Copland	45	50
2229	$1 Sergei Prokofiev	45	50
2230	$1 Igor Stravinsky	45	50
2213/30	*Set of 18*	8·00	9·00
MS2231	Two sheets, each 74×104 mm. (a) $5 Richard Strauss. (b) $6 Wolfgang Amadeus Mozart		
	Set of 2 sheets	5·00	5·25

Nos. 2213/21 and 2222/30 were each printed together, *se-tenant*, in sheetlets of 9 with the backgrounds forming a composite designs.

1996 (28 Aug). *Railway Steam Locomotives. Horiz designs as T 429 of Grenada. Multicoloured. Litho. P 14.*

2232	$1.50, German Federal Railway Class 38 No. 382 locomotive	70	75
	a. Sheetlet. Nos. 2232/7	4·25	
2233	$1.50, *Duchess of Hamilton*, Great Britain	70	75
2234	$1.50, Indian State Railways Class W.P.	70	75
2235	$1.50, Class 141R 'L' Americaine	70	75
2236	$1.50, Class A4 *Mallard*, Great Britain	70	75
2237	$1.50, German Railways Class 18	70	75
2238	$1.50, Class A2 *Blue Peter*, Great Britain	70	75
	a. Sheetlet. Nos. 2238/43	4·25	
2239	$1.50, Class P36, Russia	70	75
2240	$1.50, Class QJ, China	70	75
2241	$1.50, Class 12, Belgium	70	75
2242	$1.50, "Challenger" Class, U.S.A.	70	75
2243	$1.50, Class 25, South Africa	70	75
2232/43	*Set of 12*	8·50	9·00
MS2244	Two sheets, each 100×70 mm. (a) $5 "King" Class, Great Britain. (b) $6 "Royal Scot" Class, Great Britain	5·00	5·25
	Set of 2 sheets		

Nos. 2232/7 and 2238/43 were each printed together, *se-tenant*, in sheetlets of 6.

(Litho Questa)

1996 (18 Nov). *Christmas. Religious Paintings. Vert designs as T 369 of Antigua showing different details from "Suffer Little Children to Come Unto Me" by Van Dyck. P 13½×14.*

2245	15 c. multicoloured	10	10
2246	25 c. multicoloured	10	15
2247	$1 multicoloured	45	50
2248	$1.50, multicoloured	70	75
2249	$2 multicoloured	90	95
2250	$4 multicoloured	1·90	2·00
2245/50	*Set of 6*	4·25	4·50
MS2251	Two sheets, each 106×76 mm. (a) $6 "Suffer Little Children to Come Unto Me" (detail) (Van Dyck) (*horiz*). (b) $6 "Adoration of the Magi" (Rembrandt) (*horiz*). P 14×13½		
	Set of 2 sheets	5·50	5·75

(Des Dena Rubin. Litho B.D.T.)

1997 (12 Feb). *"HONG KONG '97" International Stamp Exhibition. Hong Kong Past and Present. T 118 and similar horiz designs. Multicoloured. P 14.*

MS2252	Five sheets, each 120×96 mm. (a) $3 Type 118; $3 Man Ho Temple, 1983. (b) $3 St. John's Cathedral, Victoria 1886; $3 St. John's Cathedral, Victoria 1983. (c) $3 Victoria Harbour, 1858; $3 Victoria Harbour, 1983. (d) $3 Water front skyscraper; $3 Aerial view of central Victoria. (e) $3 Signing of Treaty of Nanking, 1852. $3 Margaret Thatcher signing The Joint Declaration, 1984		
	Set of 5 sheets	14·00	14·50

(Des M. Freedman and Dena Rubin. Litho Questa)

1997 (3 Apr). *50th Anniv of U.N.E.S.C.O. Multicoloured designs as T 373 of Antigua. Multicoloured. P 14×13½ (horiz) or 13½×14 (vert).*

2253	15 c. Temple, Kyoto, Japan	10	10
2254	25 c. Roman ruins, Trier, Germany	10	15
2255	$1 Gateway, Mount Taishan, China	45	50
2256	$1 Temple guardian, Kyoto, Japan (*vert*)	45	50
	a. Sheetlet. Nos. 2256/63 and central label	3·50	
2257	$1 Temple deity, Kyoto, Japan (*vert*)	45	50
2258	$1 Temple lamp, Kyoto, Japan (*vert*)	45	50
2259	$1 Ayutthaya, Thailand (*vert*)	45	50
2260	$1 Statue, Borobudur Temple, Indonesia (*vert*)	45	50
2261	$1 Monuments at Pattadakal, India (*vert*)	45	50
2262	$1 Sleeping buddha, Polonnaruwa, Sri Lanka (*vert*)	45	50
2263	$1 Sagarmatha National Park, Nepal (*vert*)	45	50
2264	$1 Congonhas Sanctuary, Brazil (*vert*)	45	50
	a. Sheetlet. No. 2264/71 and central label	3·50	
2265	$1 Cartagena, Colombia (*vert*)	45	50
2266	$1 Pueblo, Guatemala (*vert*)	45	50
2267	$1 Maya statue, Honduras (*vert*)	45	50
2268	$1 Popocatepetl Monastery, Mexico (*vert*)	45	50
2269	$1 Galapagos Islands, Ecuador (*vert*)	45	50
2270	$1 Waterfall, Costa Rica (*vert*)	45	50
2271	$1 Glaciares National Park, Argentina (*vert*)	45	50
2272	$1.50, Notre Dame Cathedral, Paris, France	70	75
	a. Sheetlet. Nos. 2272/6	3·50	
2273	$1.50, Timbered house, Maulbronn, Germany	70	75
2274	$1.50, Gateway, Himeji-jo, Japan	70	75
2275	$1.50, Lion statues, Delphi, Greece	70	75
2276	$1.50, Palace of Fontainebleau, France	70	75
2277	$1.50, Scandola Nature Reserve, France	70	75
2278	$2 Citadel, Dubrovnik, Croatia	90	95
2279	$4 Angra do Heroismo, Portugal	1·90	2·00
2253/79	*Set of 7*	14·00	15·00
MS2280	Three sheets, each 127×102 mm. (a) $6 Mont St. Michel, France; (b) $6 Ruins of Teotihuacau, Mexico; (c) $6 Temple, Chengde, China		
	Set of 3 sheets	8·25	8·50

Nos. 2256/63 and 2264/71 were each printed together, *se-tenant*, in sheetlets of 8 stamps with a centre label and Nos. 2272/6 in sheetlet of 5 stamps with a top left-hand corner label.

119 Springer Spaniel
120 Hong Kong

(Des R. Rundo. Litho Questa)

1997 (10 Apr). *Cats and Dogs. T 119 and similar multicoloured designs. P 14.*

2281	35 c. Type 119	15	20
2282	45 c. Abyssinian Blue	20	25
2283	50 c. Burmese Cream (*vert*)	25	30
2284	75 c. Doberman Pinscher	35	40
2285	90 c. Persian Tortoiseshell and White	40	45
2286	$1 Italian Spinone (*vert*)	45	50
2287	$1.50, Siamese Chocolate Point	70	75
	a. Sheetlet. Nos. 2287/92	4·25	
2288	$1.50, Oriental Shorthair White	70	75
2289	$1.50, Burmese Sable	70	75
2290	$1.50, Abyssinian Tabby	70	75
2291	$1.50, Persian Shaded Silver	70	75
2292	$1.50, Tonkinese Natural Mink	70	75
2293	$2 Cocker Spaniel (*vert*)	90	95
2294	$3 Oriental Shorthair Agouti (*vert*)	1·40	1·50
2281/94	*Set of 14*	8·25	9·00
MS2295	Two sheets. (a) 75×105 mm. $6 Sphynx (*vert*). (b) 105×75 mm. $6 Golden Retriever puppy		
	Set of 2 sheets	5·50	5·75

Nos. 2287/92 (cats) were printed together, *se-tenant*, in sheetlets of 6 with the backgrounds forming a composite design.

(Litho Questa)

1997 (15 Apr). *Dinosaurs. Multicoloured designs as T 438 of Grenada. P 14.*

2296	45 c. Stegosaurus	20	25
2297	90 c. Diplodocus	40	45
2298	$1 Pteranodon (*vert*)	45	50
2299	$1.50, Rhamphorhynchus and head of Brachiosaurus	70	75
	a. Sheetlet. Nos. 2299/304	4·25	

2300	$1.50, Archaeopteryx		70	75
2301	$1.50, Anurognathus and body of Brachiosaurus		70	75
2302	$1.50, Head of Albertosaurus		70	75
2303	$1.50, Herrerasaurus and legs of Brachiosaurus		70	75
2304	$1.50, Platyhystrix and body of Albertosaurus		70	75
2305	$2 Deinonychus and Ankylasaurus (*vert*)		90	95
2296/305		*Set of 10*	6·25	6·50

MS2306 Two sheets, each 103×74 mm. (a) $6 Allosaurus (*vert*); (b) $6 Hydacrosaurus
Set of 2 sheets 5·50 5·75
Nos. 2299/2304 were printed together, *se-tenant*, in sheetlets of 6 with the backgrounds forming a composite design.

(Des R. Rundo. Litho Questa)

1997 (28 May). *300th Anniv of Mother Goose Nursery Rhymes. Sheet* 72×102 *mm containing vert design as* T **309** *of Dominica. Multicoloured.* P 14.
MS2307 $6 Girl and sheep ("Baa, Baa, Black Sheep") .. .. 2·75 3·00

(Des J. Iskowitz. Litho Questa)

1997 (28 May). *50th Death Anniv of Paul Harris (founder of Rotary International). Horiz design as* T **376** *of Antigua. Multicoloured.* P 14.
2308 $3 Paul Harris and village women with water pump, Burkina Faso .. 1·40 1·50
MS2309 78×108 mm. $6 Early Rotary parade float .. .. 2·75 3·00

(Litho Questa)

1997 (28 May). *Golden Wedding of Queen Elizabeth and Prince Philip. Horiz designs as* T **377** *of Antigua. Multi-coloured (except Nos. 2312/13).* P 14.

2310	$1 Engagement photograph, 1947		45	50
	a. Sheetlet. Nos. 2310/15		2·75	
2311	$1 Royal coat of arms		45	50
2312	$1 Queen Elizabeth and Duke of Edinburgh, 1953 (blackish brown)		45	50
2313	$1 Formal portrait of Queen Elizabeth with Prince Philip in uniform (blackish brown)		45	50
2314	$1 Sandringham House		45	50
2315	$1 Queen Elizabeth and Prince Philip in carriage		45	50
2310/15		*Set of 6*	2·75	3·00

MS2316 100×70 mm. $6 Wedding photograph, 1947 .. .. 2·75 3·00
Nos. 2310/15 were printed together, *se-tenant*, in sheetlets of 6.

(Des J. Iskowitz. Litho Questa)

1997 (28 May). *"Pacific '97" International Stamp Exhibition, San Francisco. Death Centenary of Heinrich von Stephan (founder of the U.P.U.). Horiz design as* T **378** *of Antigua.* P 14.

2317	$1.50, olive-green		70	75
	a. Sheetlet. Nos. 2317/19		2·10	
2318	$1.50, chestnut		70	75
2319	$1.50, violet		70	75
2317/19		*Set of 3*	2·10	2·25

MS2320 82×118 mm. $6 deep blue and black 2·75 3·00
Designs:—No. 2317, Pony Express, 1860; No. 2318, Von Stephan and Mercury; No. 2319, American steam locomotive; No. **MS**2320, Von Stephan and camel courier, Baghdad.
Nos. 2317/19 were printed together, *se-tenant*, in sheets of 3 with enlarged right-hand margin.

1997 (28 May). *Birth Bicentenary of Hiroshige (Japanese painter). "One Hundred Famous Views of Edo". Horiz designs as* T **310** *of Dominica. Multicoloured. Litho.* P 13½×14.

2321	$1.50, "Koume Embankment"		70	75
	a. Sheetlet. Nos. 2321/6		4·25	
2322	$1.50, "Azuma Shrine and the Entwined Camphor"		70	75
2323	$1.50, "Yanagishima"		70	75
2324	$1.50, "Inside Akiba Shrine, Ukeji"		70	75
2325	$1.50, "Distant View of Kinryuzan Temple and Azuma Bridge"		70	75
2326	$1.50, "Night View of Matsuchiyama and the San'ya Canal"		70	75
2321/6		*Set of 6*	4·25	4·50

MS2327 Two sheets, each 102×127 mm. (a) $6 "Five Pines, Onagi Canal". (b) $6 "Spiral Hall, Five Hundred Rakan Temple" .. *Set of 2 sheets* 5·50 5·75
Nos. 2321/6 were printed together, *se-tenant*, in sheetlets of 6.

(Des R. Rundo. Litho Questa)

1997 (28 May). *175th Anniv of Brothers Grimm's Third Collection of Fairy Tales. The Fox and the Geese. Multi-coloured designs as* T **379** *of Antigua.* P 13½×14.

2328	$2 Fox and geese		90	95
	a. Sheetlet. Nos. 2328/30		2·75	
2329	$2 Fox with knife and fork and geese		90	95
2330	$2 Fox asleep and singing geese		90	95
2328/30		*Set of 3*	2·75	3·00

MS2331 124×96 mm. $6 Fox (*horiz*). P 14×13½ 2·75 3·00
Nos. 2328/30 were printed together, *se-tenant*, in sheetlets of 3 with an illustrated margin.

(Litho B.D.T.)

1997 (26 June). *Winter Olympic Games, Nagano, Japan. Multicoloured designs as* T **440** *of Grenada.* P 14.

2332	90 c. Slalom		40	45
2333	$1 Downhill skiing		45	50
	a. Sheetlet. Nos. 2333/41		4·00	
2334	$1 Freestyle ski-jumping (blue and green ski suit)		45	50
2335	$1 Curling		45	50
2336	$1 Ski-jumping (pink ski suit)		45	50
2337	$1 Four-man bobsleigh		45	50
2338	$1 Nordic combined		45	50

2339	$1 Speed skating		45	50
2340	$1 Ice hockey		45	50
2341	$1 Cross-country skiing		45	50
2342	$2 One-man luge		90	95
2343	$3 Men's figure-skating		1·40	1·50
2344	$5 Speed skating (*different*)		2·25	2·40
2332/44		*Set of 13*	9·00	10·00

MS2345 Two sheets, each 97×67 mm. (a) $6 Figure skating. (b) $6 One-man luge (*vert*)
Set of 2 sheets 5·50 5·75
Nos. 2333/41 were printed together, *se-tenant*, in sheetlets of 9.

1997 (1 July). *Return of Hong Kong to China.* T **120** *and similar multicoloured designs showing modern Hong Kong through inscription.* P 14×13½ (*Nos. 2346/7*) *or* 14 (*others*).

2346	$1 multicoloured		45	50
	a. Sheetlet of 4		1·75	
2347	$1.25, multicoloured		55	60
	a. Sheetlet of 4		2·25	
2348	$1.50, multicoloured (63×32 *mm*)		70	75
	a. Sheetlet of 3		2·10	
2349	$2 multicoloured (63×32 *mm*)		90	95
	a. Sheetlet of 3		2·75	
2346/9		*Set of 4*	2·50	2·75

Nos. 2346/9 were printed in sheetlets of 3 or 4, each with enlarged illustrated margins.

(Litho Questa)

1997 (22 July). *Marine Life. Horiz designs as* T **439** *of Grenada. Multicoloured.* P 14.

2350	10 c. Wimplefish		10	10
2351	15 c. Clown Triggerfish		10	10
2352	25 c. Ringed Emperor Angelfish		10	15
2353	35 c. Hooded Butterflyfish		15	20
2354	45 c. Semicircle Angelfish		20	25
2355	75 c. Scribbled Angelfish		35	40
2356	90 c. Threadfin Butterflyfish		40	45
2357	$1.10, Clown Surgeonfish		50	55
2358	$2 Bottle-nosed Dolphin		90	95
2359	$5 Triggerfish		2·25	2·40
2360	$10 Lionfish		4·50	4·75
2350/60		*Set of 11*	9·50	10·00

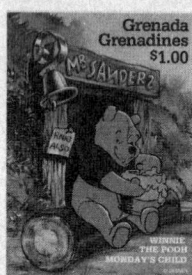

121 Winnie the Pooh as Monday's Child

(Des Alvin White Studios. Litho Questa)

1997 (7 Aug). *"Monday's Child" (poem).* T **121** *and similar vert designs showing Disney cartoon characters from Winnie the Pooh illustrating the various verses. Multicoloured.* P 13½×14.

2362	$1 Type **121**		45	50
	a. Sheetlet. Nos. 2362/7		2·75	
2363	$1 Kanga as Tuesday's child		45	50
2364	$1 Eeyore as Wednesday's child		45	50
2365	$1 Tigger as Thursday's child		45	50
2366	$1 Piglet as Friday's child		45	50
2367	$1 Rabbit as Saturday's child		45	50
2362/7		*Set of 6*	2·75	3·00

MS2368 128×107 mm. $6 Christopher Robin as Sunday's child .. .. 2·75 3·00
Nos. 2362/7 were printed together, *se-tenant*, in sheetlets of 6.

122 Snow White kissing Grumpy

(Des Alvin White Studios. Litho Questa)

1997 (7 Aug). *Disney Sweethearts.* T **122** *and similar multi-coloured designs showing Disney cartoon characters kissing.* P 14×13½.

2369	$1 Type **122**		45	50
	a. Sheetlet. Nos. 2369/77		4·00	
2370	$1 Figaro the Cat and Cleo the Fish		45	50
2371	$1 Peter Pan and Wendy		45	50
2372	$1 Cinderella and the Prince		45	50
2373	$1 Ariel and Eric		45	50
2374	$1 Beauty and the Prince		45	50
2375	$1 Aladdin and Jasmine		45	50
2376	$1 Pocahontas and Captain John Smith		45	50
2377	$1 Phoebus and Esmeralda		45	50
2369/77		*Set of 9*	4·00	4·50

MS2378 127×102 mm. $5 Georges Hautecourt kissing cat's tail (*vert*). P 13½×14 2·25 2·40
Nos. 2369/77 were printed together, *se-tenant*, in sheetlets of 9.

(Litho Questa)

1997 (11 Aug). *World Football Championship, France (1998). Designs as* T **382** *of Antigua.* P 14×13½ (*horiz*) *or* 13½×14 (*vert*).

2379	10 c. steel-blue		10	10
2380	20 c. multicoloured		10	10
2381	45 c. sepia		20	25
2382	$1 black		45	50
2383	$1 sepia		45	50
	a. Sheetlet. Nos. 2383/90 and central label		3·50	
2384	$1 black		45	50
2385	$1 sepia		45	50
2386	$1 multicoloured		45	50
2387	$1 multicoloured		45	50
2388	$1 black		45	50
2389	$1 sepia		45	50
2390	$1 multicoloured		45	50
2391	$1 black		45	50
	a. Sheetlet. Nos. 2391/8 and central label		3·50	
2392	$1 black		45	50
2393	$1 black		45	50
2394	$1 black		45	50
2395	$1 black		45	50
2396	$1 black		45	50
2397	$1 black		45	50
2398	$1 black		45	50
2399	$1.50, multicoloured		70	75
2400	$5 black		2·25	2·40
2379/400		*Set of 22*	11·00	12·00

MS2401 Two sheets. (a) 127×102 mm. $6 black. (b) 102×127 mm. $6 black .. *Set of 2 sheets* 5·50 5·75
Designs: *Horiz*—No. 2379, Italian team, 1934; No. 2380, Angolan team; No. 2381, Brazilian team, 1958; No. 2382, Uruguay team, 1950; No. 2383, Winning England team, 1966; No. 2384, West German team, 1954; No. 2385, Uruguyans officials with Jules Rimet trophy, 1930; No. 2386, West German players celebrating, 1990; No. 2387, Maradonna (Argentine player), 1986; No. 2388, Brazilian players, 1994; No. 2389, Argentine players, 1978; No. 2390, West German player holding World Cup, 1974; No. 2399, West German team, 1974; No. 2400, Italian team, 1938; No. **MS**2401b, Paulao, Angola. *Vert*—No. 2391, Ademir, Brazil; No. 2392, Kocsis, Hungary; No. 2393, Leonidas, Brazil; No. 2394, Nejedly, Czechoslovakia; No. 2395, Schiavio, Italy; No. 2396, Stabile, Uruguay; No. 2397, Pele, Brazil; No. 2398, Fritzwalter, West Germany, No. **MS**2401a, Shearer, England.
Nos. 2383/90 and 2391/8 were each printed together, *se-tenant*, in sheetlets of 8 stamps and a central label.

1997 (12 Aug). *Butterflies. Multicoloured designs as* T **444** *of Grenada. Litho.* P 14.

2402	75 c. *Polyura dehaani*		35	40
2403	90 c. *Polyura dolon*		40	45
2404	$1 *Charaxes candiope*		45	50
2405	$1.50, *Pantaporia punctata*		70	75
2406	$1.50, *Euthalia confucius*		70	75
	a. Sheetlet. Nos. 2406/11		4·25	
2407	$1.50, *Euthalia kardama*		70	75
2408	$1.50, *Limenitis albomaculata*		70	75
2409	$1.50, *Hestina assimilis*		70	75
2410	$1.50, *Kallima inachus*		70	75
2411	$1.50, *Euthalia teutoides*		70	75
2412	$1.50, *Euphaedra francina*		70	75
	a. Sheetlet. Nos. 2412/17		4·25	
2413	$1.50, *Euphaedra eleus*		70	75
2414	$1.50, *Euphaedra harpalyce*		70	75
2415	$1.50, *Euphaedra cyparissa*		70	75
2416	$1.50, *Euphaedra gausape*		70	75
2417	$1.50, *Euphaedra imperialis*		70	75
2418	$2 *Charaxes etesippe*		90	95
2419	$3 *Charaxes castor*		1·40	1·50
2402/19		*Set of 18*	13·00	13·50

MS2420 106×76 mm. (a) $5 *Charaxes nobilis* (*vert*). (b) $6 *Charaxes numenes* (*vert*)
Set of 2 sheets 5·00 5·25
Nos. 2406/11 and 2412/17 were each printed together, *se-tenant*, in sheetlets of 6 with the backgrounds forming a composite design.

123 James Dean   **124** *Symphyglossum sanguineum*

(Des Shannon. Litho Questa)

1997 (22 Aug). *James Dean (actor) Commemoration.* T **123** *and similar vert designs showing different portraits. Multicoloured.* P 13½×14.

2421	$1 Type **123**		45	50
	a. Sheetlet. Nos. 2421/9		4·00	
2422	$1 Wearing purple jumper		45	50
2423	$1 Wearing stetson and smoking		45	50
2424	$1 Wearing dinner jacket and tie		45	50
2425	$1 Full face portrait		45	50
2426	$1 Grimacing		45	50
2427	$1 Wearing stetson		45	50
2428	$1 Leaning on arms		45	50
2429	$1 Smoking		45	50
2421/9		*Set of 9*	4·00	4·50

Nos. 2421/9 were printed together, *se-tenant*, in sheetlets of 9 with enlarged illustrated right-hand margin.

(Des T. Wood. Litho B.D.T.)

1997 (4 Sept). *Orchids of the World. T 124 and similar vert designs. Multicoloured. P 14.*

2430	35 c. Type 124	15	20
2431	45 c. *Doritaenopsis* "Mythic Beauty"	20	25
2432	75 c. *Odontoglossum cervantesii*	35	40
2433	90 c. *Cattleya* "Pumpernickel"	40	45
2434	$1 *Vanda* "Patricia Low"	45	50

2435/43 $1 × 9 (*Lycaste* "Aquila"; *Brassolaeliocattleya* "Dorothy Bertsch; *Phalaenopsis* "Zuma Urchin"; *Promenaea xanthina*; *Amesiella philippinensis*; *Brassocattleya* "Angel Lace"; *Brassoepidendrum* "Peggy Ann"; *Miltonia seine*; *Sophralaeliocattleya* "Precious Stones)

	a. Sheetlet. Nos. 2435/43	4·25

2444/52 $1 × 9 (*Cymbidium* "Showgirl"; *Disa blackii*; *Phalaenopsis aphrodite*; *Iwanagaara* "Apple Blossom"; *Masdevallia* "Copper Angel"; *Paphiopedilum micranthum*; *Paphiopedilum* "Clare de Lune"; *Cattleya forbesii*; *Dendrobium* "Dawn Maree")

	a. Sheetlet. Nos. 2444/52	4·25	
2453	$1.50, *Odontonia* "Debutante"	70	75

2454/9 $1.50 × 6 (*Miltoniopsis* "Jean Sabourin"; *Cymbididium* "Red Beauty"; *Brassocattleya* "Green Dragon"; *Phalaenopsis* hybrid; *Laelio cattleya* "Mary Ellen Carter"; *Disa* hybrid)

	a. Sheetlet. Nos. 2454/9	4·25

2460/5 $1.50 × 6 (*Lycaste macrobulbon*; *Cochleanthes discolor*; *Cymbidium* "Nang Carpenter"; *Paphiopedilum* "Claire de Lune"; *Masdevallia caudata*; *Cymbidium* "Showgirl")

	a. Sheetlet. Nos. 2460/5	4·25	
2466	$2 *Laeliocattleya* "Mini Purple"	90	95
2467	$3 *Phragmipedium dominiarum*	1·40	1·50
2430/67	*Set of 38*	21·00	22·00

MS2468 Two sheets, each 76×106 mm. (a) $5 *Phalenopsis* "Medford Star". (b) $6 *Brassolaeliocattleya* "Dorothy Bertsch" .. *Set of 2 sheets* 5·00 5·25
Nos. 2435/43, 2444/52, 2454/9 and 2460/5 were each printed together, *se-tenant*, in sheetlets of 9 (Nos. 2435/43, 2444/52) or 6 some with the backgrounds forming a composite designs (Nos. 2454/9, 2460/5).

STAMP BOOKLETS

1977 (7 Feb). *Silver Jubilee. Multicoloured cover, 165×92 mm, showing the Queen enthroned. Stitched.*
SB1 $9.60, booklet containing 35 c. in pane of 6 (No. 219a) and *se-tenant* pane of 3 (No. 220a) .. 2·25

1978 (12 Apr). *25th Anniv of Coronation. Multicoloured cover, 165×92 mm, showing the Queen's Division on parade. Stitched.*
SB2 $7.04, booklet containing *se-tenant* pane of 6 (No. 276a) and pane of 1 (No. 278a) .. 1·60

1981 (16 June). *Royal Wedding. Multicoloured cover, 90×165 mm, showing Prince Charles on front and back. Panes attached by selvedge.*
SB3 $14 booklet containing *se-tenant* pane of 6 (No. 450a) and pane of 1 (No. 452a) .. 2·50
The cover of No. SB3 is folded five times "concertina fashion" and when opened up measures 550×165 mm.

OFFICIAL STAMPS

1982 (June). *Various stamps optd with Type O 1 of Grenada.*

(a) Nos. 400/12 and 414

O 1	5 c. Yellow-tailed Snapper	10	15
O 2	6 c. Mutton Snapper	10	15
O 3	10 c. Cocoa Damselfish	10	15
O 4	12 c. Royal Gramma	10	15
O 5	15 c. Cherub Angelfish	10	15
O 6	20 c. Black-barred Soldierfish	10	20
O 7	25 c. Mottled Grouper	10	20
O 8	30 c. Long-snouted Butterflyfish	15	20
O 9	40 c. Puddingwife	15	25
O10	50 c. Midnight Parrotfish	20	30
O11	90 c. Red-spotted Hawkfish	40	55
O12	$1 Hogfish	40	60
O13	$3 Beau Gregory	1·25	2·25
O14	$10 Barred Hamlet	4·25	6·00

(b) Nos. 444/6 and 448/9

O15	30 c. Prince Charles and Lady Diana Spencer	2·00	2·00
O16	40 c. Prince Charles and Lady Diana Spencer	1·60	1·60
O17	40 c. Type 50	2·00	2·75
O18	$2 Type 50	2·50	3·50
O19	$4 Prince Charles as parachutist	6·50	8·50

The Royal Wedding $4 from sheetlets, perforated 14½×14 and with changed background colour, also exists with this overprint (*Price £6 mint, £8 used*).

(c) Nos. 473/6

O20	54 20 c. multicoloured	10	20
O21	– 40 c. multicoloured	15	25
O22	– $1 multicoloured	35	70
O23	– $2 multicoloured	70	1·40
O1/23	*Set of 23*	20·00	29·00

STANLEY GIBBONS
Auctions & Acquisitions

LEADING
PHILATELIC AUCTIONEERS
SINCE 1901

A PROFESSIONAL
AUCTION SERVICE FROM
THE MOST FAMOUS
NAME IN PHILATELY

A PROVEN PROGRAMME
OF SPECIALISED
INTERNATIONAL SALES

FREE ADVICE AND EXPERT
MARKET VALUATIONS

0% VENDOR COMMISSION
(on realisations over £5000)

FAST GUARANTEED PAYMENT

CASH ADVANCES AVAILABLE

SETTLEMENT IN ANY CURRENCY

THE INDUSTRY'S LARGEST
DATABASE OF SPECIALIST BUYERS

HIGH QUALITY CATALOGUES
DISTRIBUTED WORLDWIDE

REGULAR TELESALES CONTACT
WITH MAJOR BUYERS

SPECIALIST
SUBSCRIPTION SERVICE

REFINED VENUES AND
EXTENSIVE VIEWING TIMES

*TELEPHONE TODAY FOR A FULL
INFORMATION PACK.*

STANLEY GIBBONS AUCTIONS
399 STRAND • LONDON • WC2R 0LX
TELEPHONE: 0171 836 8444
FACSIMILE: 0171 836 7342

Griqualand West
see South Africa

Guyana
(*formerly* British Guiana)

BRITISH GUIANA

The postal service from what was to become British Guiana dates from the last years of the 18th-century, being placed on a more regular basis after the final British occupation.

An inland postal system was organised in 1850, using the adhesive stamps of British Guiana, but, until 1 May 1860, overseas mails continued to be the province of the British G.P.O. The stamps of Great Britain were supplied for use on such letters from 11 May 1858 and examples of their use in combination with British Guiana issues have been recorded.

For illustration of the handstamp and postmark type see BRITISH POST OFFICES ABROAD notes, following GREAT BRITAIN.

CROWNED-CIRCLED HANDSTAMPS

The provision of a handstamp, probably as Type CC **1**, inscribed "DEMERARA", is recorded in the G.P.O. proof book under 1 March 1856. No examples have been reported. A further handstamp, as Type CC **6**, recorded in the proof book on 17 February 1866, is known used as a cancellation in at least two instances, *circa* 1868.

GEORGETOWN (DEMERARA)

Stamps of GREAT BRITAIN *cancelled* "A 03" *as Type* **2**.

1858 to 1860.
Z1	1d. rose-red (1857), *perf* 14	..	..	..	..	£200
Z2	4d. rose (1857)	..	..	..	..	£130
Z3	6d. lilac (1856)	..	..	..	..	£100
	a. Azure paper					
Z4	1s. green (1856)	..	..	..	..	£1100

NEW AMSTERDAM (BERBICE)

Stamps of GREAT BRITAIN *cancelled* "A 04" *as Type* **2**.

1858 to 1860.
Z5	1d. rose-red (1857), *perf* 14	..	..	..	£600
Z6	2d. blue (1858) (Plate Nos. 7, 8)	..	..	£600
Z7	4d. rose (1857)	..	..	..	£300
Z8	6d. lilac (1856)	..	..	..	£200
Z9	1s. green (1856)	..	..	..	£1200

PRICES FOR STAMPS ON COVER TO 1945

Nos.	
Nos. 1/21	*from* × 3
No. 23	†
Nos. 24/7	*from* × 3
Nos. 29/115	*from* × 4
Nos. 116/24	*from* × 6
Nos. 126/36	*from* × 5
Nos. 137/59	*from* × 6
Nos. 162/5	*from* × 8
Nos. 170/4	*from* × 5
Nos. 175/89	*from* × 6
No. 192	*from* × 20
Nos. 193/210	*from* × 4
Nos. 213/15	*from* × 5
Nos. 216/21	*from* × 3
Nos. 222/4	*from* × 8
Nos. 233/50	*from* × 3
No. 251	—
Nos. 252/7	*from* × 3
Nos. 259/82	*from* × 4
Nos. 283/7	*from* × 5
Nos. 288/300	*from* × 4
Nos. 301/4	*from* × 5
Nos. 305/7	*from* × 6
Nos. 308/19	*from* × 5
Nos. D1/4	*from* × 12
Nos. O1/12	*from* × 12

CROWN COLONY

(Currency. 100 cents = 1 dollar)

1

2

(Set up and printed at the office of the *Royal Gazette*, Georgetown, British Guiana)

1850 (1 July)**–51.** *Type-set. Black impression.* (*a*) *Medium wove paper. Prices are for*—I. Cut square. II. Cut round.

					I Used	II Used
1	1	2 c. *rose* (1.3.51)	..	..	..	—£70000
2		4 c. *orange*	..	..	£24000	£3750
3		4 c. *lemon-yellow* (1851)	..	£35000	£4250
4		8 c. *green*	..	..	£15000	£3000
5		12 c. *blue*	..	..	£5000	£1900
6		12 c. *indigo*	..	..	£9500	£2500
7		12 c. *pale blue* (1851)	..	£8500	£2750
		a. "2" of "12" with straight foot	..	—	£4750
		b. "1" of "12" omitted	..		†£35000

(*b*) *Pelure paper* (1851)

8	1	4 c. *pale yellow*	..	..	£45000	£4750

These stamps were initialled by the postmaster, or the Post Office clerks, before they were issued. The initials are—E. T. E. D(alton), E. D. W(ight), J. B. S(mith), H. A. K(illikelley), and W. H. L(ortimer). There are several types of each value and it has been suggested that the setting contained one horizontal row of four slightly different impressions.

Ten examples of No. 1 have been recorded, including three pairs on separate covers.

(Litho Waterlow)

1852 (1 Jan). *Surface-coloured paper. Imperf.*

						Un	Used
9	2	1 c. black/*magenta*	..	..	£8500	£4250
10		4 c. black/*deep blue*	..	..	£11000	£5500

There are two types of each value.

Reprints on thicker paper and perf 12½, were made in 1865 (*Price* £16 *either value*).

Such reprints with the perforations removed are sometimes offered as genuine originals.

CONDITION. Prices for Nos. 9 to 21 are for fine copies. Poor to medium specimens can be supplied when in stock at much lower rates.

3

4

5

(Dies eng and stamps litho Waterlow)

1853–59. *Imperf.* (*a*) *Original printing.*

11	3	1 c. vermilion	..	..	£3000	£1000

This 1 c. in *reddish brown* is probably a proof (*Price* £650).

A   B

C   D

A. "O" large and 1 mm from left corner.
B. "O" small and ¾ mm from left corner.
C. "O" small and ¾ mm from left corner. "NT" widely spaced.
D. "ONE" close together, "O" 1¼ mm from left corner.

(*b*) *Fresh lithographic transfers from the 4 c. with varying labels of value. White line above value* (1857–59).

12	3	1 c. dull red (A)	..	..	£2500	£900
13		1 c. brownish red (A)	..	..	£5500	£1200
14		1 c. dull red (B)	..	..	£3000	£950
15		1 c. brownish red (B)	..	..	£5500	£1300
16		1 c. dull red (C)	..	..	£3750	£1200
17		1 c. dull red (D)	..	..	£8500	£3750

1853–55. *Imperf.*

18	4	4 c. deep blue	..	..	£1700	£600
		a. Retouched	..	..	£2500	£850
19		4 c. blue (1854)	..	..	£1100	£425
		a. Retouched	..	..	£1700	£600
20		4 c. pale blue (1855)	..	..	£850	£325
		a. Retouched	..	..	£1500	£550

The 4 c. value was produced from transfers from the original 1 c., with the bottom inscription removed, teamed with a new face value. The join often shows as a white line or traces of it above the label of value and lower corner figures. In some stamps on the sheet this line is missing, owing to having been retouched, and in these cases a line of colour usually appears in its place.

The 1 c. and 4 c. stamps were printed in 1865 from fresh transfers of five varieties. These are on thin paper and perf 12½ (*Price* £14 *each unused*).

1860 (May). *Figures in corners framed. Imperf.*

21	5	4 c. blue	..	..	..	£2500	£450

6

(Type-set and printed at the *Official Gazette* by Baum and Dallas, Georgetown).

1856. (*a*) *Surface-coloured paper.*

23	6	1 c. black/*magenta*	..	..	†	—
24		4 c. black/*magenta* (Feb)	..	†	£6000
25		4 c. black/*rose-carmine* (Sept)	.£20000	£8500
26		4 c. black/*blue* (Oct)	..	†	£38000

(*b*) *Paper coloured through*

27	6	4 c. black/*deep blue* (Aug)	..	†	£50000

Since only one example of No. 23 is known, no market price can be given. This celebrated stamp frequently termed "the world's rarest", was last on the market in 1980.

These stamps, like those of the first issue, were initialled before being issued; the initials are—E.T.E.D(alton), E.D.W (ight), C.A. W(atson), and W.H.L (ortimer). The unique 1 c. is initialled by E.D. Wight.

The 4 c. is known in four types, differing in the position of the inscriptions.

PAPERMAKERS' WATERMARKS. Seven different papermakers' watermarks were used in the period 1860 to 1875 and stamps bearing portions of these are worth a premium.

7

A   B

C   D

E   F

(Dies eng and litho Waterlow)

1860 (July)**–63.** *Tablets of value as illustrated. Thick paper.* P 12.

29	7	1 c. pale rose	..	..	£1000	£190
30		2 c. deep orange (8.60)	..	£160	38·00
31		2 c. pale orange	..	..	£160	38·00
32		4 c. deep blue (8.60)	..	£350	60·00
33		4 c. blue	..	..	£250	50·00
34		8 c. brownish rose	..	£375	75·00
35		8 c. pink	..	..	£300	60·00
36		12 c. lilac (12.60)	..	£425	35·00
37		12 c. grey-lilac	..	£350	32·00
38		24 c. deep green (6.63)	..	£950	85·00
39		24 c. green	..	..	£800	65·00

The 1 c. was reprinted in 1865 on thin paper, P 12½–13, in a different shade. *Price* £13.

The 12 c. in both shades is frequently found surcharged with a large "5d" in *red*; this is to denote the proportion of postage repayable by the colony to Great Britain for overseas letters.

1861 (3 Aug*). *Colour changed. Thick paper.* P 12.

40	7	1 c. reddish brown	..	..	..	£300	85·00

*Earliest known postmark date.

1862–65. (*a*) *Thin paper.* P 12.

41	7	1 c. brown	..	..	£375	£170
42		1 c. black (1863)	..	90·00	48·00
43		2 c. orange	..	..	85·00	32·00
44		4 c. blue	..	..	£100	35·00
45		4 c. pale blue	..	85·00	24·00
46		8 c. pink (1863)	..	£110	50·00
47		12 c. dull purple (1863)	..	£120	22·00
48		12 c. purple	..	£140	25·00
49		12 c. lilac	..	£150	35·00
50		24 c. green	..	£700	85·00

(*b*) *Thin paper.* P 12½–13 (1863)

51	7	1 c. black	..	..	50·00	17·00
52		2 c. orange	..	..	70·00	17·00
53		4 c. blue	..	..	75·00	17·00
54		8 c. pink	..	..	£200	75·00
55		12 c. brownish lilac	..	£450	£100
56		24 c. green	..	£550	65·00

Copies are found on *pelure* paper.

(*c*) *Medium paper.* P 12½–13

57	7	1 c. black (1864)	..	45·00	27·00
58		2 c. deep orange (1864)	..	60·00	17·00
59		2 c. orange	..	65·00	15·00
60		4 c. greyish blue (1864)	..	70·00	14·00
61		4 c. blue	..	90·00	21·00
62		8 c. pink (1864)	..	£130	48·00
63		12 c. brownish lilac (1865)	..	£400	90·00
64		24 c. green (1864)	..	£150	50·00
65		24 c. deep green	..	£300	70·00

(*d*) *Medium paper.* P 10 (Nov 1865)

65*a*	7	12 c. grey-lilac	..	..	£375	65·00

8

9

G   H

I

K

New transfers for the 1 c., 2 c., 8 c., and 12 c. with the spaces between values and the word "CENTS" about 1 mm.

1863–75. *Medium paper* (a) *P* 12½–13 (1863–68).
66	8	1 c. black (1866)				30·00	19·00
67		2 c. orange-red (1865)				38·00	4·25
68		2 c. orange				32·00	4·25
69	9	6 c. blue (1865)				90·00	40·00
70		6 c. greenish blue				£100	45·00
71		6 c. deep blue				£130	50·00
72		6 c. milky blue				95·00	40·00
73	8	8 c. pink (1868)				£150	16·00
74		8 c. carmine				£170	18·00
75		12 c. grey-lilac (1867)				£400	24·00
76		12 c. brownish purple				£475	30·00
77	9	24 c. green (*perf* 12)				£200	19·00
78		24 c. yellow-green (*perf* 12)				£110	9·50
79		24 c. yellow-green (*perf* 12½–13)				£120	40·00
80		24 c. green (*perf* 12½–13) (1864)				£130	9·50
81		24 c. blue-green (*perf* 12½–13)				£160	19·00
82		48 c. pale red				£180	45·00
83		48 c. deep red				£200	48·00
84		48 c. carmine-rose				£250	48·00

The 4 c. corresponding to this issue can only be distinguished from that of the previous issue by minor plating flaws.
There is a variety of the 6 c. with stop before "VICISSIM".
Varieties of most of the values of 1863–64 and 1866 are to be found on both very thin and thick papers.

(b) *P* 10 (1866–71)
85	8	1 c. black (1869)				8·00	3·25
86		1 c. grey-black				9·00	6·00
87		2 c. orange (1868)				18·00	2·50
88		2 c. reddish orange				28·00	3·50
89		4 c. slate-blue				65·00	12·00
90		4 c. blue				75·00	7·00
		a. Bisected (on cover)				†£4000	
		b. Ditto Imperf (on cover)				†	—
91		4 c. pale blue				70·00	9·50
92	9	6 c. milky blue (1867)				£100	27·00
93		6 c. ultramarine				£110	42·00
94		6 c. dull blue				£100	32·00
95	8	8 c. pink (5.71)				£100	17·00
96		8 c. brownish pink				£110	18·00
96a		8 c. carmine				£160	23·00
97		12 c. pale lilac (1867)				£190	13·00
98		12 c. grey-lilac				£150	13·00
99		12 c. brownish grey				£140	16·00
100		12 c. lilac				£140	16·00
101	9	24 c. deep green				£180	9·00
102		24 c. bluish green				£180	8·00
103		24 c. yellow-green				£130	7·50
104		48 c. crimson (1867)				£275	28·00
105		48 c. red				£275	24·00
104		Handstamped "Specimen"				£200	
104		Perf "Specimen"				£160	

(c) *P* 15 (1875–76)
106	8	1 c. black				35·00	7·50
107		2 c. orange-red				£120	8·50
108		2 c. orange				£120	8·50
109		4 c. bright blue				£200	50·00
110	9	6 c. ultramarine				£400	70·00
111	8	8 c. deep rose (1876)				£190	75·00
112	8	8 c. deep rose				£500	48·00
113		12 c. lilac				£500	
114	9	24 c. yellow-green				£500	35·00
115		24 c. deep green				£500	

There is a variety of the 48 c. with stop after "P" in "PETIMUSQUE".
Imperforate stamps of this and of the previous issue are considered to be proofs, although examples of the 24 c. imperforate from the 1869–73 period are known commercially used.

PRICES for stamps of the 1862 issue are for good average copies. Copies with roulettes on all sides very seldom occur and do not exist in marginal positions.

10	11	12

13	14	15

(Type-set and printed at the Office of the *Royal Gazette*, Georgetown)

1862 (Sept). *Black on coloured paper. Roul* 6.
116	10	1 c. *rose*				£1800	£400
		a. Unsigned				£190	
		b. Wrong ornament (as T **13**) at left (R. 1/1)				—	£650
		c. "1" for "I" in "BRITISH" (R. 1/5)				—	£650
117	11	1 c. *rose*				£2500	£500
		a. Unsigned				£225	
		b. Narrow "T" in "CENTS" (R. 3/1)				—	£650
		c. Wrong ornament (as T **15**) at top (R. 3/3)				—	£650
		d. "1" for "I" in "BRITISH" and italic "S" in "POSTAGE" (R. 3/5)				—	£650
118	12	1 c. *rose*				£4000	£700
		a. Unsigned				£425	
		b. "1" for "I" in "GUIANA" (R. 4/4)				—	£700
		c. Wrong ornament (as T **15**) at left (R. 4/5)				—	£700
		d. "C" for "O" in "POSTAGE" (R. 4/6)				—	£700
119	10	2 c. *yellow*				£1800	£250
		a. Unsigned				£650	
		b. Wrong ornament (as T **13**) at left (R. 1/1)				—	£450
		c. "1" for "I" in "BRITISH" (R. 1/5)				—	£450

120	11	2 c. *yellow*				£2500	£325
		a. Unsigned				£700	
		b. "C" for "O" in "TWO" and narrow "T" in "CENTS" (R. 3/1)				—	£450
		c. Wrong ornament (as T **15**) at top (R. 3/3)				—	£450
		d. "1" for "I" in "BRITISH" and italic "S" in "POSTAGE" (R. 3/5)				—	£450
		e. Italic "T" in "TWO" (R. 3/6)				—	£450
121	12	2 c. *yellow*				£4000	£500
		a. Unsigned				£850	
		b. "1" for "I" in "GUIANA" (R. 4/4)				—	£500
		c. Wrong ornament (as T **15**) at left (R. 4/5)				—	£500
		d. "C" for "O" in "POSTAGE" (R. 4/6)				—	£500
122	13	4 c. *blue*				£2000	£425
		a. Unsigned				£400	
		b. Wrong ornament (as T **15**) at left (R. 1/6)				—	£700
		c. Wrong ornament (as T **15**) at top and italic "S" in "CENTS" (R. 2/2)				—	£700
		d. Ornament omitted at right (R. 2/4)				—	£700
123	14	4 c. *blue*				£2750	£550
		a. Unsigned				£425	
		b. With inner frame lines (as in T **10/13**) (R. 2/5–6)				£4000	£1300
		ba. "1" for "I" in "BRITISH" (R. 2/5)				£4000	£1300
		c. "1" for "I" in "BRITISH" and "GUIANA" (R. 4/1)				—	£700
124	15	4 c. *blue*				£2750	£550
		a. Unsigned				£450	
		b. Wrong ornament (as T **12**) at foot (R. 3/1)				—	£700
		c. Italic "S" in "CENTS" (R. 3/2)				—	£700
		d. Italic "S" in "BRITISH" (R. 3/3)				—	£700

Stamps were initialled across the centre before use by the Acting Receiver-General, Robert Mather. Black was used on the 1 c., red for the 2 c. and an ink which appears white for the 4 c.
The three values of this provisional were each printed in sheets of 24 (6 × 4). The 1 c. and 2 c. were produced from the same setting of the border ornaments which contained 12 examples as Type **10** (Rows 1 and 2), 8 as Type **11** (R. 3/1 to R. 4/2) and 4 as Type **12** (R. 4/3–6).
The setting of the 4 c. contained 10 examples as Type **13** (R. 1/1 to R. 2/4), 8 as Type **14** (R. 2/5–6 and Row 4) and 6 as Type **15** (Row 3).

16	(17)

(Typo D.L.R.)

1876 (1 July)–79. *Wmk Crown CC.* (a) *P* 14.
126	16	1 c. slate				2·75	1·40
127		2 c. orange				38·00	1·25
128		4 c. blue				£110	8·50
129		6 c. brown				75·00	6·50
130		8 c. rose				£100	75
131		12 c. pale violet				50·00	1·25
132		24 c. emerald-green				60·00	3·00
133		48 c. red-brown				£110	25·00
134		96 c. olive-bistre				£475	£250
126/134				*Set of* 9		£900	£250
126/132, 134		Handstamped/Perf "Specimen"		*Set of* 8		£600	

(b) *P* 12½ (1877)
135	16	4 c. blue				£1200	£200

(c) *Perf compound of* 14 × 12½ (1879)
136	16	1 c. slate				—	£200

1878. *Provisionals. Various stamps with old values ruled through with thick bars, in black ink, the bars varying in depth of colour.*
(a) *With two horiz bars* (17 Apr)
137	16	(1 c.) on 6 c. brown				38·00	£100

(b) *Official stamps with horiz bars across* "OFFICIAL" (end Aug)
138	8	1 c. black				£150	70·00
139	16	1 c. slate				£120	55·00
140		2 c. orange				£250	65·00

(c) *With horiz and vert bars as T* **17** (6 Nov)
141	9	(1 c.) on 6 c. ultramarine (93)				£130	75·00
142	16	(1 c.) on 6 c. brown				£225	90·00

(d) *Official stamps with bars across* "OFFICIAL" (23 Nov)
(i) *With two horiz bars and one vert*
144	16	(1 c.) on 4 c. blue				£180	85·00
145	16	(1 c.) on 6 c. brown				£225	85·00
146	8	(2 c.) on 8 c. rose				£950	£250

(ii) *With one horiz bar and one vert*
147	16	(1 c.) on 4 c. blue				†£1800	
148		(2 c.) on 8 c. rose				£250	90·00

1 2 2
(18) (19) (20)

1881 (21 Dec). *No.* 134 *with old value ruled through with bar in black ink and surch.*
149	18	1 on 96 c. olive-bistre				3·50	5·50
		a. Bar in red					
		b. Bar omitted					
150	19	2 on 96 c. olive-bistre				4·00	9·50
		a. Bar in red					
		b. Bar omitted					
151	20	2 on 96 c. olive-bistre				45·00	75·00
		a. Bar in red					

In the setting of 60 Type **19** occurs on the first five vertical rows and Type **20** on the sixth.

1 2 2
(21) (23) (24)

1881 (28 Dec). *Various stamps with old value ruled with bar and surch.* (a) *On No.* 105.
152	21	1 on 48 c. red				35·00	5·00
		a. Bar omitted				—	£475

(b) *On Official stamps (including unissued* 48 c. *optd with Type O* **2**)
153	21	1 on 12 c. brownish purple (O4)				£110	70·00
154		1 on 48 c. red-brown				£120	90·00
155	23	2 on 12 c. pale violet (O11)				60·00	24·00
		a. Pair. Nos. 155/6				£650	£700
		b. Surch double				£750	£400
		c. Surch double (T **23 + 24**)				£1900	
		d. Extra bar through "OFFICIAL"				—	
156	24	2 on 12 c. pale violet (O11)				£350	£250
157	23	2 on 24 c. emerald-green (O12)				70·00	38·00
		a. Pair. Nos. 157/8				£800	£850
		b. Surch double				£850	
158	24	2 on 24 c. emerald-green (O12)				£475	£475
159	19	2 on 24 c. green (O5)				£200	£110

On Nos. 149/59 the bar is found in various thicknesses ranging from 1 to 4 mm.
It is believed that the same composite surcharge setting of 60 (6×10) was used for Nos. 155/6 and 157/8. Type **24** occurs on R. 7/2, 4–6 and R. 8/1

26	27

(Type-set, Baldwin & Co. Georgetown)

1882 (9 Jan). *Black impression. P* 12. *Perforated with the word* "SPECIMEN" *diagonally.*
162	26	1 c. magenta				35·00	28·00
		a. Imperf between (horiz pair)				†	—
		b. Without "SPECIMEN"				£400	£275
		c. "1" with foot				70·00	60·00
163		2 c. yellow				55·00	45·00
		a. Without "SPECIMEN"				£350	£325
		b. Small "2"				55·00	45·00
164	27	1 c. magenta				35·00	28·00
		a. Without "SPECIMEN"				£400	£275
		b. "1" with foot				70·00	60·00
		c. Imperf between (horiz pair)				†£3750	
165		2 c. yellow				50·00	40·00
		a. Bisected diagonally (1 c.)					
		b. Without "SPECIMEN"				£350	£325
		c. Small "2"				85·00	75·00

These stamps were perforated "SPECIMEN" as a precaution against fraud. Stamps are known with "SPECIMEN" double.
The 1 c. and 2 c. stamps were printed in separate sheets, utilising the same clichés, these being altered according to the face value required. Two settings were used, common to both values:—
1st setting. Four rows of three, T **26** being Nos. 5, 6, 7, 8, 11 and 12, and T **27** the remainder.
From this setting there were two printings of the 2 c., but only one of the 1 c.
2nd setting. Six rows of two, T **26** being Nos. 3, 7, 8, 9, 11 and 12, and T **27** the remainder.
There were two printings of each value from this setting.
Se-tenant pairs are worth about 20% more.
The "1" with foot occurs on T **27** on No. 9 in the first setting and on T **26** on No. 7 in the first printing only of the second setting.
The small "2" appears on T **26** on No. 6 in the first setting and 12 in the first printing and on Nos. 7, 8 and 12 only in the second printing; in the second setting it comes on Nos. 3, 9 and 12 in the first printing and on Nos. 9, 11 and 12 in the second printing.
On T **27** the variety occurs in the first setting on No. 9 of the second printing only and in the second setting on No. 10 in both printings.

(Typo D.L.R.)

1882. *Wmk Crown C.A. P* 14.
170	16	1 c. slate (27 Jan)				7·50	20
171		2 c. orange (27 Jan)				20·00	15
		a. Value doubly printed				†	
172		4 c. blue				80·00	5·00
173		6 c. brown				5·00	6·50
174		8 c. rose				85·00	40
170/4				*Set of* 5		£180	11·00
170/4		Perf "Specimen"		*Set of* 5		£250	

INLAND 4 CENTS 4 CENTS
(a) (b)
Two types of "4"

2 CENTS REVENUE 6 6
(28) (c) (d)
Two types of "6"

1888–89. T **16** (*without value in lower label*) optd. "INLAND REVENUE", *and surch with value as T* **28**, *by D.L.R. Wmk Crown CA. P* 14.
175		1 c. dull purple (8.89)				1·25	20
176		2 c. dull purple (25.5.89)				1·25	30
177		3 c. dull purple				75	20
178		4 c. dull purple (a)				4·00	30
		a. Larger figure "4" (b)				20·00	6·00
179		6 c. dull purple (c)				4·00	2·75
		a. Figure 6 with straight top (d)				19·00	4·00
180		8 c. dull purple (8.89)				1·50	25
181		10 c. dull purple				6·00	2·50
182		20 c. dull purple				19·00	10·00
183		40 c. dull purple				20·00	17·00
184		72 c. dull purple (1.10.88)				35·00	40·00
185		$1 green (1.10.88)				£400	£400

186	$2 green (1.10.88) ..	.. .. ..	£180	£180
187	$3 green (1.10.88) ..	.. .. ..	£120	£120
188	$4 green (a) (1.10.88) ..	.. ..	£375	£375
	a. Larger figure "4" (b)	.. ..	£1000	£1100
189	$5 green (1.10.88) ..	.. .. ..	£225	£200
175/189		Set of 15	£1200	£1200

Nos. 175/89 were surcharged in settings of 60 (6×10). No. 178a occurs on all stamps in the third vertical row, No. 179a in the fourth and sixth vertical rows and No. 188a in the second vertical row.

INLAND

One
Cent
~~1 DOLLAR~~
REVENUE

2

(29)   30   (31)

1889 (6 June). *No. 176 surch with T **29** in red by Official Gazette.*

192	"2" on 2 c. dull purple	.. ..	1·25	15

The varieties with figure "2" *inverted* or *double* were made privately by a postal employee in Demerara.

1889 (Sept). *Wmk Crown CA. P 14.*

193	**30**	1 c. dull purple and slate-grey ..	..	2·25	1·50
194		2 c. dull purple and orange	..	1·50	10
195		4 c. dull purple and ultramarine	..	4·50	1·50
196		4 c. dull purple and cobalt	..	18·00	2·25
197		6 c. dull purple and brown	..	35·00	10·00
198		6 c. dull purple and maroon	..	7·00	9·00
199		8 c. dull purple and rose	..	12·00	60
200		12 c. dull purple and bright purple	..	18·00	1·75
200a		12 c. dull purple and mauve	..	8·50	2·00
201		24 c. dull purple and green	..	6·00	2·50
202		48 c. dull purple and orange-red..		15·00	9·00
203		72 c. dull purple and red-brown ..		28·00	35·00
204		72 c. dull purple and yellow-brown		65·00	75·00
205		96 c. dull purple and carmine	..	65·00	70·00
206		96 c. dull purple and rosine	..	75·00	80·00
193/205			Set of 10	£130	£120
193/205	Optd "Specimen"		Set of 10	£130	

1890 (15 July). *Stamps of 1888–89 surch locally "One Cent", in red, as in T* **31**.

207	1 c. on $1 (No. 185) ..	.. ..	1·00	35
	a. Surch double	.. ..	—	80·00
208	1 c. on $2 (No. 186)..	.. ..	1·00	60
	a. Surch double	.. ..	75·00	
209	1 c. on $3 (No. 187)..	.. ..	1·40	1·25
	a. Surch double	.. ..	85·00	
210	1 c. on $4 (No. 188)..	.. ..	2·00	5·50
	a. Surch double	.. ..	75·00	
	b. Larger figure "4" (b)	..	10·00	25·00
207/10		Set of 4	4·75	7·00

1890–91. *Colours changed. Wmk Crown CA. P 14*

213	**30**	1 c. sea-green (12.90)	..	40	10
214		5 c. ultramarine (1.91)	..	2·75	10
215		8 c. dull purple and greenish black (10.90)	..	2·75	1·10
213/15			Set of 3	5·50	1·10
213/215	Optd "Specimen"		Set of 3	60·00	

32 Mount Roraima   **33** Kaieteur Falls

(Recess D.L.R.)

1898 (18 July). *Queen Victoria's Jubilee. Wmk Crown CC (sideways on T* **32**). *P 14.*

216	**32**	1 c. blue-black and carmine	..	3·50	55
217	**33**	2 c. brown and indigo	..	9·00	1·25
		a. Imperf between (horiz pair)	..	£4250	
218		2 c. brown and blue	..	15·00	1·75
219	**32**	5 c. green and sepia	..	30·00	2·75
		a. Imperf between (horiz pair)			
220	**33**	10 c. blue-black and orange-red..		15·00	20·00
221	**32**	15 c. red-brown and blue..	..	26·00	16·00
216/21			Set of 5	75·00	35·00
216/21	Optd "Specimen"		Set of 5	95·00	

A second plate was later used for the 1 c. on which the lines of shading on the mountains in the background are strengthened, and those along the ridge show distinct from each other, whereas, in the original, they are more or less blurred. In the second plate the shading of the sky is less pronounced.

TWO CENTS.

(34)

Shaved "E"

35

(Surch at Printing Office of the *Daily Chronicle*, Georgetown)

1899 (24 Feb–15 June). *Surch with T* **34**.

222	**32**	2 c. on 5 c. (No. 219) (15 June)	2·25	1·60
		a. No stop after "CENTS"	70·00	55·00
		b. Comma after "CENTS" (R.7/2)		
		c. "CINTS" (R.4/1)	80·00	
		d. Shaved "E" (R.6/2)	19·00	
223	**33**	2 c. on 10 c. (No. 220)	1·50	1·75
		a. No stop after "CENTS" (R.5/5 or 2/9)	20·00	50·00
		b. "GENTS" for "CENTS" (R.5/7)	50·00	70·00
		c. Surch inverted	£350	£375
		d. Shaved "E" (R.4/2 or 3/8)	14·00	
224	**32**	2 c. on 15 c. (No. 221)	1·25	1·25
		a. No stop after "CENTS" (R.9/2)	55·00	60·00
		b. Surch double	£475	£600
		c. Surch double, one without stop		
		d. Surch inverted	£350	£400
		e. Surch inverted and stop omitted		
		f. Shaved "E" (R.6/2)	14·00	
222/4			Set of 3	4·50	4·25

No. 222c was caused by damage to the first "E" of "CENTS" which developed during surcharging. The listing is for an example with only the upright stroke of the letter visible.

There were two settings of No. 223 with the no stop and shaved "E" varieties occurring on R.5/5 and R.4/2 of the first and on R.2/9 and R.3/8 of the second.

No. 224b occurred on the first five vertical columns of one sheet, the surcharges on the right hand vertical column being normal.

Only two examples of No. 224c are known.

There is only one known example of No. 224e.

1900–7. *T* **30**. *Wmk Crown CA. P 14*

233		1 c. grey-green (1907)	3·00	3·25
234		2 c. dull purple and carmine	3·25	25
235		2 c. dull purple and black/*red* (1901)	1·00	10
236		6 c. grey-black and ultramarine (1902)	6·50	11·00
237		48 c. grey and purple-brown (1901)	50·00	35·00
		a. Brownish grey and brown (1907)	28·00	28·00
238		60 c. green and rosine (1903)	60·00	£170
233/8			Set of 6	90·00	£190
233/8	Optd "Specimen"		Set of 6	90·00	

No. 233 is a reissue of No. 213 in non-fugitive ink.

1905–7. *Wmk Multiple Crown CA. Ordinary paper (1 c. to 60 c.) or chalk-surfaced paper (72, 96 c.).*

240	**30**	1 c. grey-green	3·50	30
		a. Chalk-surfaced paper	3·75	30
241		2 c. purple and black/*red*	9·00	10
		a. Chalk-surfaced paper	3·50	10
242		4 c. dull purple and ultramarine	8·00	9·50
		a. Chalk-surfaced paper	6·00	10·00
243		5 c. dull pur & bl/*bl* (1.5.05) (Optd S. £20)	11·00	6·00
		a. Chalk-surfaced paper	3·50	6·00
244		6 c. grey-black and ultramarine	16·00	38·00
		a. Chalk-surfaced paper	15·00	38·00
245		12 c. dull and bright purple	22·00	32·00
		a. Chalk-surfaced paper	22·00	40·00
246		24 c. dull purple and green (1906)	9·50	9·50
		a. Chalk-surfaced paper	3·75	4·50
247		48 c. grey and purple-brown	24·00	28·00
		a. Chalk-surfaced paper	14·00	20·00
248		60 c. green and rosine	25·00	80·00
		a. Chalk-surfaced paper	14·00	80·00
249		72 c. purple and orange-brown (1907)	32·00	60·00
250		96 c. black & vermilion/*yellow* (20.11.05)		
		(Optd S. £30)	35·00	45·00
240/50			Set of 11	£130	£275

1905. *Optd "POSTAGE AND REVENUE". Wmk Multiple Crown CA. Chalk-surfaced paper. P 14.*

251	**35**	$2.40 green and violet (S. £75)	£160	£275

1907–10. *Colours changed. Wmk Mult Crown CA. P 14*

252	**30**	1 c. blue-green	14·00	2·75
253		2 c. rose-red	14·00	10
		a. Redrawn (1910)	8·50	10
254		4 c. brown and purple	2·25	60
255		5 c. ultramarine	7·50	80
256		6 c. grey and black	13·00	7·00
257		12 c. orange and mauve	4·00	4·00
252/7			Set of 6	45·00	13·50
253/7	Optd "Specimen"		Set of 5	75·00	

In No. 253a the flag at the main truck is close to the mast, whereas in the original type it appears to be flying loose from halyards. There are two background lines above the value "2 CENTS" instead of three and the "S" is further away from the end of the tablet.

**War
Tax**

37   (38)

(Typo D.L.R.)

1913–21. *Wmk Mult Crown CA. Chalk-surfaced paper (4 c. and 48 c. to 96 c.). P 14.*

259	**37**	1 c. yellow-green	1·50	70
		a. Blue-green (1917)	1·50	25
260		2 c. carmine	70	10
		a. Scarlet (1916)	2·00	10
		b. Wmk sideways	† £1500	
261		4 c. brown and bright purple (1914)	3·25	25
		aw. Wmk inverted		
		b. Deep brown and purple	3·00	25
262		5 c. bright blue	1·50	85
263		6 c. grey and black	1·50	85
264		12 c. orange and violet	1·00	90
265		24 c. dull purple and green (1915)	3·25	4·00
266		48 c. grey and purple-brown (1914)	15·00	15·00
267		60 c. green and rosine (1915)	15·00	48·00
268		72 c. purple and orange-brown (1915)	40·00	70·00
269		96 c. black and vermilion/*yellow* (1915)	30·00	55·00
		a. White back (1913)	15·00	38·00
		b. On lemon (1916) (Optd S. £28)	18·00	38·00
		c. On pale yellow (1921) (Optd S. £28)	19·00	55·00
259/69a			Set of 11	85·00	£160
259/69a	Optd "Specimen"		Set of 11	£130	

1918 (4 Jan). *No. 260a optd with T* **38**, *by D.L.R.*

271	**37**	2 c. scarlet	40	15

The relative position of the words "WAR" and "TAX" vary considerably in the sheet.

1921–27. *Wmk Mult Script CA. Chalk-surfaced paper (24 c. to 96 c.). P 14.*

272	**37**	1 c. green (1922)	4·00	25
273		2 c. rose-carmine	3·00	20
274		2 c. bright violet (1923)	2·00	10
275		4 c. brown and bright purple (1922)	4·50	10
276		6 c. bright blue (1922)	2·50	25
277		12 c. orange and violet (1922)	2·50	1·50
278		24 c. dull purple and green	2·00	4·50
279		48 c. black and purple (1926)	9·00	3·50
280		60 c. green and rosine (1926)	9·00	48·00
281		72 c. dull purple and orange-brown (1923)	15·00	45·00
282		96 c. black and red/*yellow* (1927)	17·00	42·00
272/82			Set of 11	60·00	£130
272/82	Optd "Specimen"		Set of 11	£150	

39 Ploughing a Rice Field   **40** Indian shooting Fish

(Recess Waterlow)

1931 (21 July). *Centenary of County Union T* **39/40** *and similar designs. Wmk Mult Script CA. P 12½.*

283		1 c. emerald-green	2·00	75
284		2 c. brown	1·50	10
285		4 c. carmine	1·75	45
286		6 c. blue	1·75	2·50
287		$1 violet	19·00	38·00
283/7			Set of 5	23·00	38·00
283/7	Perf "Specimen"		Set of 5	75·00	

Designs: *Vert*—4 c., $1 Kaieteur Falls. *Horiz*—6 c. Public buildings, Georgetown.

43 Ploughing a Rice Field   **44** Gold Mining

(Recess Waterlow)

1934 (1 Oct)–**51.** *T* **40** (*without dates at top of frame*), **43/4** *and similar designs. Wmk Mult Script CA* (*sideways on horiz designs*). *P 12½.*

288	**43**	1 c. green	60	50
289	**40**	2 c. red-brown	1·50	40
290	**44**	3 c. scarlet	30	10
		aa. Wmk error. Crown missing		
		a. Perf 12½ × 13½ (30.12.43)	40	40
		b. Perf 13 × 14 (28.4.49)	40	10
291	–	4 c. slate-violet	2·00	75
		a. Imperf between (vert pair)	† £11000	
		b. Imperf horiz (vert pair)	£6000	£6500
292	–	6 c. deep ultramarine	2·50	2·50
293	–	12 c. red-orange	10	20
		a. Perf 14 × 13 (16.4.51)	20	30
294	–	24 c. purple	2·50	3·75
295	–	48 c. black	7·00	8·50
296	–	50 c. green	10·00	16·00
297	–	60 c. red-brown	26·00	27·00
298	–	72 c. purple	1·25	1·75
299	–	96 c. black	20·00	30·00
300	–	$1 bright violet	32·00	27·00
288/300			Set of 13	95·00	£100
288/300	Perf "Specimen"		Set of 13	£140	

Designs: *Vert*—4 c., 50 c. Kaieteur Falls (as No. 285, but with dates omitted); 96 c. Sir Walter Raleigh and his son. *Horiz*—6 c. Shooting logs over falls; 12 c. Stabroek Market 24 c. Sugar cane in punts; 48 c. Forest road; 60 c. Victoria Regia Lilies; 72 c. Mount Roraima; $1 Botanical Gardens.

1935 (6 May). *Silver Jubilee. As Nos. 91/4 of Antigua.*

301		2 c. ultramarine and grey	20	10
		f. Diagonal line by turret	23·00	
		h. Dot by flagstaff	42·00	
302		6 c. brown and deep blue	1·00	75
		f. Diagonal line by turret	50·00	
		g. Dot to left of chapel	75·00	
		h. Dot by flagstaff	75·00	
303		12 c. green and indigo	2·50	6·50
		f. Diagonal line by turret	70·00	
		h. Dot by flagstaff	£100	
		i. Dash by turret	£100	
304		24 c. slate and purple	4·75	6·50
		h. Dot by flagstaff	£140	
		i. Dash by turret	£140	
301/4			Set of 4	7·50	12·50
301/4	Perf "Specimen"		Set of 4	70·00	

For illustrations of plate varieties see Catalogue Introduction.

1937 (12 May). *Coronation. As Nos. 95/7 of Antigua, but ptd by D.L.R. P 14.*

305		2 c. yellow-brown	15	10
306		4 c. grey-black	65	30
307		6 c. bright blue	85	10
305/7			Set of 3	1·50	1·25
305/7	Perf "Specimen"		Set of 3	50·00	

53 South America   **54** Victoria Regia Lilies

(Recess Waterlow)

1938 (1 Feb)–1952. *As earlier types but with portrait of King George VI as in T* 53/4. *Wmk Mult Script CA. P* 12½

308	43	1 c. yellow-green			12·00	55
		aa. *Green* (1944)			30	10
		a. Perf 14 × 13 (1949)			30	80
309	–	2 c. slate-violet			60	10
		a. Perf 13 × 14 (28.4.49)			30	10
310	53	4 c. scarlet and black			70	30
		a. Imperf horiz (vert pair)			£10000	£8000
		b. Perf 13 × 14 (1952)			45	15
311	40	6 c. deep ultramarine			40	10
		a. Perf 13 × 14 (24.10.49)			30	30
312	–	24 c. blue-green			26·00	10·00
		a. Wmk sideways			1·25	10
313	–	36 c. bright violet (7.3.38)			2·00	20
		a. Perf 13 × 14 (13.12.51)			2·50	30
314	–	48 c. orange			60	40
		a. Perf 14 × 13 (8.5.51*)			1·50	1·25
315	–	60 c. red-brown			11·00	3·50
316	–	96 c. purple			2·50	2·75
		a. Perf 12½ × 13½ (1944)			4·75	6·00
		b. Perf 13 × 14 (8.2.51)			2·75	5·00
317	–	$1 bright violet			11·00	35
		a. Perf 14 × 13(1951)			£275	£375
318	–	$2 purple (11.6.45)			4·50	14·00
		a. Perf 14 × 13 (9.8.50)			10·00	15·00
319	54	$3 red-brown (2.7.45)			27·00	25·00
		a. *Bright red-brown* (12.46)			28·00	28·00
		b. Perf 14 × 13. *Red-brown* (29.10.52)			25·00	45·00
308a/19			*Set of* 12		55·00	40·00
308/19 Perf "Specimen"			*Set of* 12		£200	

Designs: *Vert*—2 c., 36 c. Kaieteur Falls; 96 c. Sir Walter Raleigh and his son. *Horiz*—24 c. Sugar cane in punts; 48 c. Forest road; 60 c. Shooting logs over falls; $1 Botanical Gardens; $2 Mount Roraima.

* Earliest known postmark date.

1946 (1 Oct). *Victory. As Nos.* 110/11 *of Antigua.*

320		3 c. carmine			10	10
321		6 c. blue			20	20
320/1 Perf "Specimen"			*Set of* 2		48·00	

1948 (20 Dec). *Royal Silver Wedding. As Nos.* 112/13 *of Antigua, but* $3 *in recess.*

322		3 c. scarlet			10	40
323		$3 red-brown			12·00	23·00

1949 (10 Oct). *75th Anniv of Universal Postal Union. As Nos.* 114/17 *of Antigua.*

324		4 c. carmine			30	20
325		6 c. deep blue			90	65
326		12 c. orange			30	45
327		24 c. blue-green			30	60
324/7			*Set of* 4		1·60	1·75

1951 (16 Feb). *University College of B.W.I. As Nos.* 118/19 *of Antigua.*

328		3 c. black and carmine			30	15
329		6 c. black and blue			30	50

1953 (2 June). *Coronation. As No.* 120 *of Antigua.*

330		4 c. black and scarlet			20	10

55 G.P.O., Georgetown   **62** Felling Greenheart.

(Centre litho, frame recess ($1); recess (others). Waterlow (until 1961), then D.L.R.)

1954 (1 Dec)–63. *T* 55, 62 *and similar designs. Wmk Mult Script CA. P* 12½×13* (*horiz*) *or* 13 (*vert*).

331		1 c. black			10	10
332		2 c. myrtle-green			10	10
333		3 c. brown-olive and red-brown			3·00	10
		w. Wmk inverted				
334		4 c. violet			20	10
		a. D.L.R. ptg (5.12.61)			7·00	2·25
		ab. *Deep violet* (3.1.63)			8·00	1·25
335		5 c. scarlet and black			30	10
		w. Wmk inverted				
336		6 c. yellow-green			10	10
		a. D.L.R. ptg. *Green* (22.5.62)			40	1·25
337		8 c. ultramarine			10	10
		a. D.L.R. ptg. *Blue* (19.9.61)			7·50	65
338		12 c. black and reddish brown			60	40
		a. *Black and light brown* (13.6.56)			15	10
		b. D.L.R. ptg. *Black and brown* (11.7.61)			14·00	2·50
339		24 c. black and brownish orange			4·50	
		a. *Black and orange* (13.6.56)			5·50	10
340		36 c. rose-carmine and black			2·50	80
		w. Wmk inverted				
341		48 c. ultramarine and brown-lake			60	50
		a. *Brt ultram & pale brown-lake* (13.6.56)			40	40
		ab. D.L.R. ptg (19.9.61)			26·00	20·00
342		72 c. carmine and emerald			12·00	2·75
		a. D.L.R. ptg (17.7.62)			12·00	20·00

343		$1 pink, yellow, green and black			15·00	2·50
344		$2 deep mauve			15·00	5·50
		a. D.L.R. ptg. *Reddish mauve* (11.7.61)			35·00	7·00
345		$5 ultramarine and black			12·00	18·00
		a. D.L.R. ptg (19.9.61)			45·00	32·00
331/45			*Set of* 15		60·00	27·00

Designs: *Horiz*—2 c. Botanical Gardens; 3 c. *Victoria regia* water-lilies; 5 c. Map of Caribbean; 6 c. Rice combine-harvester; 8 c. Sugar cane entering factory; 24 c. Mining for bauxite; 36 c. Mount Roraima; $1 Channel-billed Toucan; $2 Dredging gold. *Vert*—4 c. Amerindian shooting fish; 48 c. Kaieteur Falls; 72 c. Arapaima (fish); $5 Arms of British Guiana.

The separately listed De La Rue printings are identifiable as singles by the single wide-tooth perfs at each side at the bottom of the stamps. In the Waterlow these wide teeth are at the top.

*All the Waterlow printing and early De La Rue printings of the horizontal designs measure 12.3×12.8, but De La Rue printings of 22 May 1962 and all later printings (including those on the Block CA watermark) measure 12.3×12.6.

The 1 c. and 2 c., printed by Waterlow, exist in coils constructed from normal sheets.

See also Nos. 354/65.

SELF-GOVERNMENT

70

(Photo Harrison)

1961 (23 Oct). *History and Culture Week. W w* 12 *P* 14½ × 14.

346	70	5 c. sepia and orange-red			15	10
347		6 c. sepia and blue-green			15	10
348		30 c. sepia and yellow-orange			35	30
346/8			*Set of* 3		60	40

1963 (14 July). *Freedom from Hunger. As No.* 146 *of Antigua.*

349		20 c. reddish violet			30	10

1963 (2 Sept). *Red Cross Centenary. As Nos.* 147/8 *of Antigua.*

350		5 c. red and black			20	20
351		20 c. red and blue			55	35

1963–65. *As Nos.* 333/44, *but wmk w* 12.

354		3 c. brown-olive and red-brown (12.65)			5·50	5·50
356		5 c. scarlet and black (28.5.64)			30	10
		w. Wmk inverted				
359		12 c. black and yellowish brown (6.10.64)			20	10
360		24 c. black and bright orange (10.12.63)			2·75	10
361		36 c. rose-carmine and black (10.12.63)			60	60
362		48 c. brt ultram & Venetian red (25.11.63)			1·25	2·25
		w. Wmk inverted				
363		72 c. carmine and emerald (25.11.63)			4·00	19·00
364		$1 pink, yellow, green & black (10.12.63)			7·00	90
365		$2 reddish mauve (10.12.63)			9·00	14·00
354/65			*Set of* 9		28·00	38·00

There was no London release of No. 354.
The 5 c. exists in coils constructed from normal sheets.
For 1 c. value, see No. 429a.

71 Weightlifting

(Photo D.L.R.)

1964 (1 Oct). *Olympic Games, Tokyo. W w* 12. *P* 13 × 13½.

367	71	5 c. orange			10	10
368		8 c. blue			10	20
369		25 c. magenta			20	35
367/9			*Set of* 3		30	55

1965 (17 May). *I.T.U. Centenary. As Nos.* 166/7 *of Antigua.*

370		5 c. emerald and yellow-olive			10	15
371		25 c. light blue and magenta			20	15

1965 (25 Oct). *International Co-operation Year. As Nos.* 168/9 *of Antigua.*

372		5 c. reddish purple and turquoise-green			10	10
373		25 c. deep bluish green and lavender			25	20

72 St. George's Cathedral, Georgetown

(Des Jennifer Toombs, Photo Harrison)

1966 (24 Jan). *Churchill Commemoration. W w* 12. *P* 14 × 14½.

374	72	5 c. black, crimson and gold			40	10
375		25 c. black, blue and gold			1·25	40

1966 (3 Feb). *Royal Visit. As Nos.* 174/5 *of Antigua.*

376		3 c. black and ultramarine			50	15
377		25 c. black and magenta			1·50	60

GUYANA

British Guiana became independent as Guyana on 25 May 1966.

GUYANA INDEPENDENCE 1966

(73)

1966 (26 May)–67. *Various stamps as Nos.* 311/45 *optd with T* 73 *by De La Rue.* (i) *Wmk Mult Script CA.*

379		2 c. myrtle-green			20	30
380		3 c. brown-olive and red-brown			2·50	5·00
381		4 c. violet			40	10
383		6 c. yellow-green			30	10
384		8 c. ultramarine			50	40
385		12 c. black and reddish brown			60	40
392		$5 ultramarine and black			24·00	38·00
379/92			*Set of* 7		25·00	40·00

(ii) *Wmk w* 12. A. *Upright.* B. *Sideways*

					A		B	
393	1 c.				10	20	10	10
395	3 c.				80	10	†	
396	4 c.				10	40	10	10
397	5 c.				20	10	†	
398	6 c.				10	20	†	
399	8 c.				40	90	10	10
400	12 c.				10	10	10	10
401	24 c.				3·25	20	2·00	40
402	36 c.				30	30	30	90
403	48 c.				3·50	8·00	30	30
404	72 c.				40	50	1·25	2·75
405	$1				1·25	35	2·50	2·75
406	$2				1·50	75	2·00	2·75
407	$5				1·00	1·75	1·50	2·75
393A/407A			*Set of* 14		11·50	12·00		
393B/407B			*Set of* 11				9·00	11·50

Dates of issue: Of the above, the 1 c., 4 c., 6 c. (W w 12 upright) and the 12 c., 36 c., 72 c., $2 and $5 (W w 12 sideways) were issued on 28.2.67; the 8 c. upright wmk and the $1 sideways wmk on 14.3.67; the rest on 26.5.66.
See also Nos. 420/40.

74 Flag and Map   **75** Arms of Guyana

(Des V. Whiteley. Photo Harrison)

1966 (26 May). *Independence. P* 14½.

408	74	5 c. multicoloured			10	10
409		15 c. multicoloured			10	10
410	75	25 c. multicoloured			15	10
411		$1 multicoloured			55	80
408/11			*Set of* 4		70	85

76 Bank Building

(Des R. Granger Barrett. Photo Enschedé)

1966 (11 Oct). *Opening of Bank of Guyana. P* 13½ × 14.

412	76	5 c. multicoloured			10	10
413		25 c. multicoloured			10	10

CANCELLED REMAINDERS.* In 1969 remainders of some issues were put on the market cancelled-to-order in such a way as to be indistinguishable from genuine postally used copies for all practical purposes. Our used quotations which are indicated by an asterisk are the same for cancelled-to-order or postally used copies.

77 British Guiana One Cent Stamp of 1856

(Des V. Whiteley. Litho D.L.R.)

1967 (23 Feb). *World's Rarest Stamp Commemoration.* P 12½.
414 **77** 5 c. black, magenta, silver & light ochre   10   10*
415   25 c. black, magenta, gold and light green   10   10*

**GUYANA
INDEPENDENCE
1966**

78   Château Margot   (82)

(Des R. Granger Barrett. Photo Harrison)

1967 (26 May). *First Anniv of Independence.* T **78** *and similar multicoloured designs.* P 14 (6 c.), 14½ × 14 (15 c.) or 14 × 14½ (*others*).
416   6 c. Type **78**   10   10*
417   15 c. Independence Arch   10   10*
418   25 c. Fort Island (*horiz*)   10   10*
419   $1 National Assembly (*horiz*)   20   15
416/19   *Set of 4*   20   15

1967–68. *Stamps as Nos. 331/45 optd with T* **82** *locally.*

(i) *Wmk Mult Script CA*
420   1 c. black (3.10.67)   10   10
    a. Opt inverted   35·00
    b. Date misplaced 5 mm   8·50
    c. Date misplaced 2 mm   8·50
421   2 c. myrtle-green (3.10.67)   10   10
    a. "1966" for "GUYANA"   18·00
    b. Date misplaced 5 mm   8·50
    c. Date misplaced 2 mm   8·50
422   3 c. brown-olive and red-brown (3.10.67)   30   10
    a. "1966" for "GUYANA"   15·00
    b. Vert pair, one without opt   £350
    c. Date misplaced 2 mm   8·50
423   4 c. violet (10.67)   10   10
    a. Deep violet   50   50
    b. Opt inverted   45·00
424   6 c. yellow-green (11.67)   10   10
    a. "1966" for "GUYANA"   23·00
    b. Opt inverted   40·00
    c. Opt double   50·00
425   8 c. ultramarine (12.67)   10   10
426   12 c. black and brown (12.67)   10   10
426*a*   24 c. black and orange (date?)   £250   85·00
427   $2 reddish mauve (12.67)   1·00   1·75
428   $5 ultramarine and black (12.67)   1·50   2·25

(ii) *Wmk* w **12** (*upright*)
429   1 c. black (2.68)   10   10
    a. Opt omitted   £120
430   2 c. myrtle-green (2.68)   30   60
431   3 c. brown-olive and red-brown (3.10.67)   30   10
    a. "1966" for "GUYANA"   75·00
    b. Opt inverted   28·00
432   4 c. violet (2.68)   10   50
433   5 c. scarlet and black (3.10.67)   2·00   1·25
    a. Deep scarlet and black   70   1·25
    aw. Wmk inverted
    c. Date misplaced 2 mm   8·50
434   6 c. yellow-green (2.68)   10   50
    a. Opt double, one diagonal   65·00
435   24 c. black and bright orange (11.12.67)   2·25   10
    a. Opt double, one diagonal (horiz pair)   £180
436   36 c. rose-carmine and black (12.67)   70   10
437   48 c. bright ultram & Venetian red (12.67)   70   40
    a. Opt inverted   55·00
438   72 c. carmine and emerald (12.67)   1·25   40
439   $1 pink, yellow, green and black (12.67)   3·00   50
440   $2 reddish mauve (12.67)   3·00   4·00
420/40 (*excl.* 426*a*)   *Set of 21*   14·00   11·50

The "1966" errors occurred on R. 7/10 and were later corrected. Nos. 425/8 and 436/40 were issued in mid-December, but some were cancelled-to-order with a November date in error.

On Nos. 420b and 421b the "1" of "1966" is below the second "D" of "INDEPENDENCE" (R. 6/3). On Nos. 420c, 421c, 422c and 433c it is below the second "E" (R. 6/1).

No. 433a is from a printing made specially for this overprint.

83 "Millie"   84 Wicket-keeping
(Blue and Yellow Macaw)

(Des V. Whiteley. Photo Harrison)

1967–68. *Christmas.* P 14½ × 14. (*a*) *First issue* (6 Nov 1967).
441 **83** 5 c. yellow, new blue, blk & bronze-grn   10   10*
442   25 c. yellow, new blue, black and violet   15   10*

(*b*) *Second issue. Colours changed* (22 Jan 1968)
443 **83** 5 c. yellow, new blue, black and red   10   10*
444   25 c. yellow, new blue, blk & apple-grn   15   10*

(Des V. Whiteley. Photo Harrison)

1968 (8 Jan). *M.C.C.'s West Indies Tour.* T **84** *and similar vert designs.* P 14.
445   5 c. Type **84**   10   10*
    a. Strip of 3. Nos. 445/7   70
446   6 c. Batting   10   10*
447   25 c. Bowling   30   10*
445/7   *Set of 3*   70   15*
Nos. 445/7 were issued in small sheets of 9 containing three *se-tenant* strips.

87   Pike Cichlid   102 "Christ of St John of the Cross" (Salvador Dali)

(Des R. Granger Barrett. Photo Harrison)

1968 (4 Mar). *Multicoloured designs as T* **87**, *showing fish* (1 *to* 6 c.), *birds* (10 *to* 40 c.) *or animals* (*others*). *No wmk.* P 14 × 14½.
448   1 c. Type **87**   10   10
449   2 c. Red Piranha ("Pirai")   10   10
450   3 c. Peacock Cichlid ("Lukunani")   10   10
451   5 c. Armoured Catfish ("Hassar")   10   10
452   6 c. Black Acara ("Patua")   55   10
453   10 c. Spix's Guan (*vert*)   55   10
454   15 c. Harpy Eagle (*vert*)   1·60   10
455   20 c. Hoatzin (*vert*)   60   10
456   25 c. Guianan Cock of the Rock (*vert*)   60   10
457   40 c. Great Kiskadee (*vert*)   75   30
458   50 c. Brazilian Agouti ("Accouri")   80   50
459   60 c. White-lipped Peccary   80   10
460   $1 Paca ("Labba")   80   10
461   $2 Nine-banded Armadillo   1·25   2·00
462   $5 Ocelot   1·50   3·00
448/62   *Set of 15*   8·50   5·50
For Nos. 448/62 with W **106** see Nos. 485/99.

(Des and photo Harrison)

1968 (25 Mar). *Easter.* P 14.
463 **102** 5 c. multicoloured   10   10*
464   25 c. multicoloured   20   10*

103 "Efficiency Year"

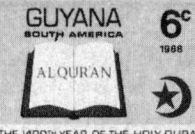

104 "Savings Bonds"

(Des W. Starzmann. Litho B.W.)

1968 (22 July). *"Savings Bonds and Efficiency".* P 14.
465 **103** 6 c. multicoloured   10   10*
466   25 c. multicoloured   10   10*
467 **104** 30 c. multicoloured   10   10*
468   40 c. multicoloured   10   10*
465/8   *Set of 4*   30   15*

GUYANA
SOUTH AMERICA   **6c**
1968
AL QURAN
THE 1400TH YEAR OF THE HOLY QURAN

105 Open Book, Star and Crescent

(Des R. Gates. Photo D.L.R.)

1968 (9 Oct). *1400th Anniv of the Holy Quran.* P 14.
469 **105** 6 c. black, gold and flesh   10   10*
470   25 c. black, gold and lilac   10   10*
471   30 c. black, gold and light apple-green   10   10*
472   40 c. black, gold and cobalt   10   10*
469/72   *Set of 4*   30   15*

ALTERED CATALOGUE NUMBERS

Any Catalogue numbers altered from the last edition are shown as a list in the introductory pages.

---

106 Lotus Blossoms   107 Broadcasting Greetings

(Des L. Pritchard; adapted G. Vasarhelyi. Litho D.L.R.)

1968 (11 Nov). *Christmas.* T **107** *and similar vert design.* W **106**. P 14.
473   6 c. brown, blue and green   10   10*
474   25 c. brown, reddish violet and green   10   10*
475   30 c. blue-green and turquoise-green   10   10*
476   40 c. red and turquoise-green   10   10*
473/6   *Set of 4*   30   15*
Designs:—25 c. Type **107**; 30, 40 c. Map showing radio link, Guyana–Trinidad.

109 Festival Ceremony

(Des J. Cooter. Litho P.B.)

1969 (26 Feb). *Hindu Festival of Phagwah.* T **109** *and similar horiz design. Multicoloured.* W **106** (*sideways*). P 13½.
477   6 c. Type **109**   10   10
478   25 c. Ladies spraying scent   10   10
479   30 c. Type **109**   10   10
480   40 c. As 25 c.   10   10
477/80   *Set of 4*   30   20

111 "Sacrament of the Last Supper"   112 Map showing
(Dali)   "CARIFTA" Countries

(Photo D.L.R.)

1969 (10 Mar). *Easter.* W **106** (*sideways*). P 13½ × 13.
481 **111** 6 c. multicoloured   10   10
482   25 c. multicoloured   10   10
483   30 c. multicoloured   10   10
484   40 c. multicoloured   10   10
481/4   *Set of 4*   30   15

1969–71. *As Nos. 448/62, but Wmk* **106** (*sideways* on* 1 *to* 6 c. *and* 50 c. *to* $5). *Chalk-surfaced paper.*
485   1 c. Type **87**   10   10
486   2 c. Red Piranha ("Pirai")   10   10
487   3 c. Peacock Cichlid ("Lukunani")   10   20
488   5 c. Armoured Catfish ("Hassar")   10   10
489   6 c. Black Acara ("Patua")   10   40
490   10 c. Spix's Guan   30   10
    a. Glazed paper (*wmk inverted*) (21.12.71)   1·00   2·75
491   15 c. Harpy Eagle   30   10
    aw. Wmk inverted
    b. Glazed paper (*wmk inverted*) (21.12.71)   1·25   3·25
492   20 c. Hoatzin   30   10
493   25 c. Guianan Cock of the Rock   30   10
    a. Glazed paper (*wmk inverted*) (21.12.71)   1·50   4·00
494   40 c. Great Kiskadee   60   50
495   50 c. Brazilian Agouti ("Accouri")   35   15
496   60 c. White-lipped Peccary   35   85
497   $1 Paca ("Labba")   70   95
    a. Glazed paper (*wmk top of blossom to right*) (21.12.71)   2·50   11·00
498   $2 Nine-banded Armadillo   1·00   3·25
499   $5 Ocelot   1·50   5·50
485/99   *Set of 15*   5·00   11·00
*The normal sideways watermark shows the top of the blossom to the left, *as seen from the back of the stamp.*

These were put on sale by the Crown Agents on 25 March 1969 but although supplies were sent to Guyana in time they were not released there until needed as ample supplies remained of the stamps without watermark. It is understood that the 3 c. and 5 c. were put on sale in early May 1969 followed by the 25 c. but there are no records of when the remainder were released.

(Des J. Cooter. Litho P.B.)

1969 (30 Apr). *First Anniv of CARIFTA (Caribbean Free Trade Area).* T **112** *and similar design.* W **106** (*sideways on* 25 c.). P 13½.
500   6 c. rose-red, ultramarine and turquoise-blue   10   10
501   25 c. lemon, brown and rose-red   10   10
Design: *Horiz*—25 c. "Strength in Unity".

114 Building *Independence*   116 Scouts raising Flag
(first aluminium ship)

(Des R. Gates. Litho B.W.)

1969 (30 Apr). *50th Anniv of International Labour Organization.*
T **114** *and similar design. W* **106** *(sideways on 40 c.). P* 12 × 11
(30 c.) *or* 11 × 12 (40 c.).
502   30 c. turquoise-blue, black and silver ..   40   15
503   40 c. multicoloured   50   15
Design: *Horiz*—40 c. Bauxite processing plant.

(Des Jennifer Toombs. Litho B.W.)

1969 (13 Aug). *Third Caribbean Scout Jamboree and Diamond*
Jubilee of Scouting in Guyana. T **116** *and similar horiz design.*
Multicoloured. W **106** *(sideways). P* 13.
504   6 c. Type **116** ..   10   10
505   8 c. Camp-fire cooking   10   10
506   25 c. Type **116** ..   10   10
507   30 c. As 8 c.   10   10
508   50 c. Type **116** ..   15   15
504/8 ..   *Set of 5*   30   30

118 Gandhi and Spinning-wheel   119 "Mother Sally Dance
                                    Troupe"

(Des G. Drummond. Litho Format)

1969 (1 Oct). *Birth Centenary of Mahatma Gandhi. W* **106** *(side-*
ways). P 14½.
509 **118**   6 c. black, brown and yellowish olive   20   50
510   15 c. black, brown and lilac ..   25   50

(Des V. Whiteley (5, 25 c.), J.W. (others). Litho B.W. (5, 25 c.),
D.L.R. (others))

1969 (17 Nov). *Christmas. T* **119** *and similar vert designs.*
Multicoloured. No wmk (5, 25 c.) *or W* **106** *(others). P* 13½ (5,
25 c.) *or* 13×13½ *(others).*
511   5 c. Type **119** ..   10   10
      a. Opt omitted ..   28·00
      b. Opt double ..   25·00
512   6 c. City Hall, Georgetown   10   10
      a. Opt omitted ..   28·00
      b. Opt inverted ..   30·00
513   25 c. Type **119** ..   10   10
      a. Opt omitted ..   28·00
514   60 c. As 6 c. ..   20   25
511/14   *Set of 4*   30   30
   Nos. 511/14 are previously unissued stamps optd as in T **119** by
Guyana Lithographic Co, Ltd.

REPUBLIC

121 Forbes Burnham   125 "The Descent from
and Map   the Cross"

(Des L. Curtis. Litho D.L.R.)

1970 (23 Feb). *Republic Day. T* **121** *and similar designs. W* **106**
(sideways on 15 and 25 c.). P 14.
515   5 c. sepia, ochre and pale blue   10   10
516   6 c. multicoloured   10   10
517   15 c. multicoloured   15   10
518   25 c. multicoloured   20   10
515/18   *Set of 4*   40   20
   Designs: *Vert*—6 c. "Rural Self-help". *Horiz*—15 c. University of
Guyana; 25 c. Guyana House.

(Des J. Cooter. Litho Questa)

1970 (24 Mar). *Easter. Paintings by Rubens. T* **125** *and similar*
vert design. Multicoloured. W **106** *(inverted). P* 14 × 14½.
519   5 c. Type **125** ..   10   10
520   6 c. "Christ on the Cross"   10   10
521   15 c. Type **125** ..   20   10
522   25 c. As 6 c. ..   20   10
519/22   *Set of 4*   45   20

127 "Peace" and U.N. Emblem   128 "Mother and Child"
                                    (Philip Moore)

(Des and litho Harrison)

1970 (26 Oct). *25th Anniv of United Nations. T* **127** *and similar*
horiz design. Multicoloured. W **106** *(inverted). P* 14.
523   5 c. Type **127** ..   10   10
524   6 c. U.N. Emblem, Gold-panning and Drilling   10   10
525   15 c. Type **127** ..   10   10
526   25 c. As 6 c. ..   10   10
523/6   *Set of 4*   20   20

(Des Harrison. Litho J.W.)

1970 (8 Dec). *Christmas. W* **106**. *P* 13½.
527 **128**   5 c. multicoloured   10   10
528   6 c. multicoloured   10   10
529   15 c. multicoloured   10   15
530   25 c. multicoloured   10   15
527/30   *Set of 4*   20   30

129 National Co-operative   130 Racial Equality
Bank   Symbol

(Des E. Samuels. Litho J.W.)

1971 (23 Feb). *Republic Day. W* **106** *(sideways). P* 14.
531 **129**   6 c. multicoloured   10   10
532   15 c. multicoloured   10   10
533   25 c. multicoloured   10   10
531/3   *Set of 3*   20   20

(Des E. Samuels. Litho Harrison)

1971 (22 Mar). *Racial Equality Year. W* **106** *(sideways). P* 14.
534 **130**   5 c. multicoloured   10   10
535   6 c. multicoloured   10   10
536   15 c. multicoloured   10   15
537   25 c. multicoloured   10   15
534/7   *Set of 4*   20   30

131 Young Volunteer felling Tree   132 Yellow Allamanda
(from painting by J. Criswick).

(Des and litho Harrison)

1971 (19 July). *First Anniv of Self-help Road Project. W* **106**. *P* 14.
538 **131**   5 c. multicoloured   10   10
539   20 c. multicoloured   25   10
540   25 c. multicoloured   30   10
541   50 c. multicoloured   45   1·60
538/41   *Set of 4*   1·00   1·60

Two types of 25 c.:

I   Flowers facing up. Value in centre.

II   Flowers facing down. Value to right. Colours changed.

(Des V. Whiteley (1 to 40 c.), PAD Studio (others). Litho D.L.R.
(1 to 6 c.), J.W. (10 c. to 40 c.), Format (50 c. to $5))

1971 (17 Sept)–76. *Flowering Plants. Vert designs as T* **132**.
Multicoloured. W **106** *(sideways on 1 c. to 40 c.). P* 13 × 13½
(1 to 6 c.) *or* 13½ (10 c. to $5).
542   1 c. Pitcher Plant of Mt Roraima (15.1.72)   10   10
543   2 c. Type **132** ..   10   10

---

544   3 c. Hanging Heliconia ..   10   10
545   5 c. Annatto tree   10   10
546   6 c. Cannon-ball tree   10   10
547   10 c. Cattleya (18.9.72)   3·25   10
      a. Perf 13 (28.1.76)   3·50   10
548   15 c. Christmas Orchid (18.9.72) ..   80   10
      a. Perf 13 (3.9.76)   65   10
549   20 c. *Paphinia cristata* (18.9.72) ..   3·00   20
      a. Perf 13 (28.1.76)   4·00   20
550   25 c. Marabunta (I) (18.9.72) ..   4·00   5·50
550a   25 c. Marabunta (II) (*wmk inverted*)
         (20.8.73)   30   85
      ab. Perf 13 (*wmk sideways*) (3.9.76)   45   10
551   40 c. Tiger Beard (18.9.72)   3·50   10
552   50 c. *Guzmania lingulata* (3.9.73)   40   85
553   60 c. Soldier's Cap (3.9.73)   30   65
554   $1 *Chelonanthus uliginoides* (3.9.73)   30   55
555   $2 *Norantea guianensis* (3.9.73) ..   35   70
556   $5 *Odontadenia grandiflora* (3.9.73)   55   80
542/56   *Set of 16*   15·00   9·00
   The watermark is often indistinct, particularly on the early
printings.

133 Child praying at Bedside   134 Obverse and Reverse
                                 of Guyana $1 Coin

(Des V. Bassoo (T **133**), M. Austin (25, 50 c.). Litho J.W.)

1971 (29 Nov). *Christmas. T* **133** *and similar vert design. Multi-*
coloured. W **106** *(sideways on 5 c. and 20 c.). P* 13½.
557   5 c. Type **133** ..   10   10
558   20 c. Type **133** ..   10   10
559   25 c. Carnival Masquerader ..   10   10
560   50 c. As 25 c. ..   20   60
557/60   *Set of 4*   35   75

(Des G. Drummond. Litho Questa)

1972 (23 Feb). *Republic Day. T* **134** *and similar vert design. W* **106**
(sideways). P 14½ × 14.
561 **134**   5 c. silver, black and orange-red   10   10
562   20 c. silver, black and magenta ..   15   10
563 **134**   25 c. silver, black and ultramarine   15   15
564   50 c. silver, black and yellow-green   25   30
561/4 ..   *Set of 4*   55   55
Design:—20, 50 c. Reverse and obverse of Guyana $1 coin.

 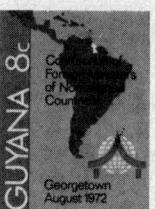

135 Hands and Irrigation Canal   136 Map and Emblem

(Des J. Criswick. Litho J.W.)

1972 (3 Apr). *Youman Nabi (Mohammed's Birthday). W* **106**.
P 14
565 **135**   5 c. multicoloured   10   10
566   25 c. multicoloured   10   10
567   30 c. multicoloured   10   10
568   60 c. multicoloured   20   20
565/8 ..   *Set of 4*   35   35

(Des J. Criswick. Litho J.W.)

1972 (20 July). *Conference of Foreign Ministers of Non-aligned*
Countries. W **106**. *P* 13½.
569 **136**   8 c. multicoloured   10   10
570   25 c. multicoloured   10   10
571   40 c. multicoloured   15   15
572   50 c. multicoloured   20   20
569/72 ..   *Set of 4*   40   40

137 Hand reaching for Sun   138 Joseph, Mary, and
                                 the Infant Jesus

(Des G. Bowen. Litho J.W.)

1972 (25 Aug). *First Caribbean Festival of Arts.* W **106** (inverted on 40, 50 c.). P 13½.

573	137	8 c. multicoloured			10	10
574		25 c. multicoloured			10	10
575		40 c. multicoloured			15	20
576		50 c. multicoloured			20	25
573/6				Set of 4	45	55

(Des Megan Anderson. Litho B.W.)

1972 (18 Oct). *Christmas.* W **106**. P 13 × 13½.

577	138	8 c. multicoloured			10	10
578		25 c. multicoloured			10	10
579		40 c. multicoloured			15	25
580		50 c. multicoloured			15	25
577/80				Set of 4	40	60

139 Umana Yana
(Meeting-house)

140 Pomegranate

(Des J. Cooter. Litho Questa)

1973 (23 Feb). *Republic Day. T* **139** *and similar vert design. Multicoloured.* W **106** (inverted on 8 c.). P 14.

581		8 c. Type 139			10	10
582		25 c. Bethel Chapel			10	10
583		40 c. As 25 c.			20	20
584		50 c. Type 139			25	20
581/4				Set of 4	55	50

(Des E. Samuels. Litho Format)

1973 (19 Apr). *Easter. T* **140** *and similar multicoloured design.* W **106** (sideways on 25 and 40 c.). P 14½ (8, 50 c.) or 13½ (others).

585		8 c. Type 140			10	10
586		25 c. Cross and map (34 × 47 mm)			10	10
587		40 c. As 25 c.			10	10
588		50 c. Type 140			15	15
585/8				Set of 4	35	35

141 Stylized Blood Cell 142 Steel-Band Players

(Des S. Greaves. Litho Harrison)

1973 (1 Oct). *25th Anniv of Guyana Red Cross.* W **106**. P 14.

589	141	8 c. vermilion and black			10	10
590		25 c. vermilion and bright purple			25	15
591		40 c. vermilion and ultramarine			35	50
592		50 c. vermilion and blackish olive			50	1·00
589/92				Set of 4	1·00	1·50

(Des E. Samuels; adapted J. Cooter. Litho Questa)

1973 (20 Nov). *Christmas. T* **142** *and similar vert design. Multicoloured.* W **106**. P 14 (8, 25 c.) or 13½ (others).

593		8 c. Type 142			10	10
594		25 c. Type 142			20	10
595		40 c. "Virgin and Child" (stained-glass window) (34 × 47 mm)			50	75
596		50 c. As 40 c.			55	75
593/6				Set of 4	1·25	1·50

143 Symbol of Progress   (144)

(Des PAD Studio. Litho Questa)

1974 (23 Feb). *Republic Day. T* **143** *and similar vert design. Multicoloured.* W **106**. P 13½.

597		8 c. Type 143			10	10
598		25 c. Wai-Wai Indian			10	10
599		40 c. Type 143			15	30
600		50 c. As 25 c.			15	40
597/600				Set of 4	40	75

1974 (18 Mar). *No. 546 surch with T* **144**.

601		8 c. on 6 c. Cannon-ball tree			10	10

See also No. 620.

145 Kite with Crucifixion Motif   146 British Guiana 24 c.
Stamp of 1874

(Des R. Savory; adapted J. Cooter. Litho Questa)

1974 (8 Apr). *Easter. T* **145** *and similar vert design.* W **106**. P 13½.

602	145	8 c. multicoloured			10	10
603	—	25 c. black and dull green			10	10
604	—	40 c. black and magenta			10	15
605	145	50 c. multicoloured			15	25
602/5				Set of 4	35	50

Design:—Nos. 603/4, "Crucifixion" in pre-Columbian style.

(Des R. Savory. Litho Harrison)

1974 (18 June). *Centenary of Universal Postal Union. T* **146** *and similar horiz design.* W **106** (sideways on 8 and 40 c.). P 13½ × 14 (8, 40 c.) or 14 (others).

606	146	8 c. multicoloured			25	10
607	—	25 c. bright yellow-green, deep slate-violet and black			35	10
608	146	40 c. multicoloured			35	20
609	—	50 c. bright yellow-green, reddish chestnut and black			45	45
606/9				Set of 4	1·25	75

Design (42 × 25 mm):—25 c., 50 c. U.P.U. emblem and Guyana postman.

147 Guides with Banner   148 Buck Toyeau

(Des M. Broodhagen; adapted J. Cooter. Litho Questa)

1974 (1 Aug). *Girl Guides' Golden Jubilee. T* **147** *and similar horiz design. Multicoloured.* W **106** (sideways). P 14½.

610		8 c. Type 147			20	10
611		25 c. Guides in camp			30	15
612		40 c. As 25 c.			45	40
613		50 c. Type 147			45	45
610/13				Set of 4	1·25	1·00
MS614		170 × 137 mm. Nos. 610/13			1·25	2·75

(Des S. Greaves and R. Granger Barrett. Litho Enschedé)

1974 (18 Nov). *Christmas. T* **148** *and similar vert designs. Multi-coloured.* W **106**. P 13½ × 13.

615		8 c. Type 148			10	10
616		25 c. Five-fingers and awaras			10	10
617		50 c. Pawpaw and tangerine			15	10
618		$1 Pineapple and sapodilla			30	60
615/18				Set of 4	55	70
MS619		127 × 94 mm. Nos. 615/18			90	2·50

1975 (20 Jan). *No. 544 surch as T* **144**.

620		8 c. on 3 c. Hanging Heliconia			10	10

149 Golden Arrow   150 Old Sluice Gate
of Courage

(Des L. Curtis. Litho D.L.R.)

1975 (23 Feb). *Republic Day. Guyana Orders and Decorations. T* **149** *and similar vert designs.* W **106**. P 13½.

621		10 c. Type 149			10	10
622		35 c. Cacique's Crown of Honour			10	15
623		50 c. Cacique's Crown of Valour			15	20
624		$1 Order of Excellence			35	60
621/4				Set of 4	60	90

(Des E. Samuels; adapted PAD Studio. Litho Questa)

1975 (2 May). *Silver Jubilee of International Commission of Irrigation and Drainage. T* **150** *and similar horiz design. Multicoloured.* W **106** (sideways on 35 c. and $1). P 14.

625		10 c. Type 150			10	10
626		35 c. Modern sluice gate			10	15
627		50 c. Type 150			15	30
628		$1 As 35 c.			35	60
625/8				Set of 4	60	1·00
MS629		162 × 121 mm. Nos. 625/8. Wmk sideways			75	2·50

151 I.W.Y. Emblem and   152 Freedom Monument
Rock Drawing

(Des C. Henriques; adapted PAD Studio. Litho Questa)

1975 (1 July). *International Women's Year. T* **151** *and similar horiz designs showing different rock drawings.* W **106** (sideways). P 14.

630	151	10 c. grey-green and yellow			10	10
631	—	35 c. reddish violet and greenish blue			20	10
632	—	50 c. royal blue and orange			25	15
633	—	$1 brown and bright blue			45	45
630/3				Set of 4	85	75
MS634		178 × 89 mm. Nos. 630/3			1·00	3·00

(Des PAD Studio. Litho Questa)

1975 (26 Aug). *Namibia Day. T* **152** *and similar vert design. Multicoloured.* W **106**. P 14.

635		10 c. Type 152			10	10
636		35 c. Unveiling of Monument			15	10
637		50 c. Type 152			25	15
638		$1 As 35 c.			35	40
635/8				Set of 4	70	60

153 G.N.S. Emblem   154 Court Building, 1875 and
Forester's Badge

(Des C. Henriques; adapted PAD Studio. Litho Questa)

1975 (1 Oct*). *First Anniv of National Service.* W **106**. P 14.

639	153	10 c. greenish yellow, light green and light reddish violet			10	10
640	—	35 c. orange, lt green & reddish violet			10	10
641	—	50 c. light violet-blue, light green and light yellow-brown			15	15
642	—	$1 light mauve, dull green & lt emerald			40	40
639/42				Set of 4	60	60
MS643		196 × 133 mm. Nos. 639/42. W **106** (inverted)			1·10	2·00

*This is the local date of issue; the Crown Agents released the stamps a day later.

Nos. 640/2 are as T **153** but have different symbols within the circle.

(Des R. Savory; adapted PAD Studio. Litho Questa)

1975 (14 Nov). *Centenary of Guyanese Ancient Order of Foresters. T* **154** *and similar horiz designs. Multicoloured.* W **106** (sideways). P 14.

644		10 c. Type 154			10	10
645		35 c. Rock drawing of hunter and quarry			10	10
646		50 c. Crossed axes and bugle-horn			15	10
647		$1 Bow and arrow			40	40
644/7				Set of 4	60	50
MS648		129 × 97 mm. Nos. 644/7			75	2·25

STANLEY GIBBONS
STAMP COLLECTING SERIES

Introductory booklets on *How to Start, How to Identify Stamps* and *Collecting by Theme.* A series of well illustrated guides at a low price.
Write for details.

35ᶜ

(155)   156 Shoulder Flash

1976 (10 Feb). No. 553 surch with T 155.
649   35 c. on 60 c. Soldier's Cap   20   15

(Des C. Henriques; adapted J.W. Litho Questa)

1976 (29 Mar). 50th Anniv of the St. John's Ambulance in Guyana. T 156 and similar vert designs. W 106. P 14.
650 156   8 c. silver, black and magenta   ..   10   10
651   –   15 c. silver, black and orange   ..   10   10
652   –   35 c. silver, black and green   ..   20   20
653   –   40 c. silver, black and new blue   ..   25   25
650/3   ..   ..   ..   Set of 4   55   50
Nos. 651/3 are as T 156 but show different shoulder flashes.

157 Triumphal Arch   158 Flame in Archway

(Des C. Henriques. Litho J.W.)

1976 (25 May). Tenth Anniv of Independence. T 157 and similar vert designs. Multicoloured. W 106. P 13½.
654   8 c. Type 157   10   10
655   15 c. Stylised Victoria Regia lily   ..   10   10
656   35 c. "Onward to Socialism"   ..   15   15
657   40 c. Worker pointing the way   ..   15   15
654/7   ..   ..   ..   Set of 4   35   50
MS658   120×100 mm. Nos. 654/7. Wmk inverted.
P 14½   50   1·50

1976 (3 Aug). West Indian Victory in World Cricket Cup. As Nos. 559/60 of Barbados.
659   15 c. Map of the Caribbean   ..   1·50   1·75
660   15 c. Prudential Cup   ..   1·50   1·75

(Des G. Vasarhelyi. Litho J.W.)

1976 (21 Oct). Deepavali Festival. T 158 and similar vert designs. Multicoloured. W 106. P 14.
661   8 c. Type 158   10   10
662   15 c. Flame in hand   ..   10   10
663   35 c. Flame in bowl   ..   15   20
664   40 c. Goddess Latchmi..   ..   15   25
661/4 ..   ..   ..   Set of 4   35   50
MS665   94 × 109 mm. Nos. 661/4   50   1·50

159 Festival Emblem and   160 1 c. and 5 c. Coins
"Musical Instrument"

(Des C. Henriques. Litho Questa)

1977 (1 Feb). Second World Black and African Festival of Arts and Culture, Nigeria. W 106. P 14.
666 159   10 c. dull red, black and gold   ..   10   10
667   35 c. deep violet, black and gold..   15   10
668   50 c. ultramarine, black and gold   ..   20   25
669   $1 blue-green, black and gold..   35   75
666/9 ..   ..   ..   Set of 4   65   1·00
MS670   90 × 157 mm. Nos. 666/9   75   3·00
The above were scheduled for release in 1975, and when finally issued had the original inscription obliterated and a new one applied by overprinting. Examples of Nos. 666/70 are known without overprint.

(Des J.W. Litho Questa)

1977 (26 May). New Coinage. T 160 and similar horiz designs. W 106. P 14.
671   8 c. multicoloured   20   10
672   15 c. yellow-brown, grey and black   ..   25   10
673   35 c. bright yellow-green, grey and black   45   30
674   40 c. carmine-red, grey and black   ..   50   35
675   $1 multicoloured   ..   ..   1·25   1·25
676   $2 multicoloured   ..   ..   1·75   2·75
671/6   ..   ..   ..   Set of 6   4·00   4·25
Designs:—15 c. 10 and 25 c. coins; 35 c. 50 c. and $1 coins; 40 c. $5 and $10 coins; $1 $50 and $100 coins; $2 Reverse of $1 coin.

161 Hand Pump, circa 1850   162 Cuffy Monument

(Des J. Porteous Wood. Litho Harrison)

1977 (15 Nov). National Fire Prevention Week. T 161 and similar horiz designs. Multicoloured. W 106. P 14 × 14½.
677   8 c. Type 161   40   10
678   15 c. Steam engine, circa 1860   ..   70   10
679   35 c. Fire engine, circa 1930   ..   1·00   60
680   40 c. Fire engine, 1977   ..   1·10   85
677/80   ..   ..   ..   Set of 4   2·75   1·50

(Des BG Studio. Litho Questa)

1977 (7 Dec). Cuffy Monument (commemorating 1763 Slave Revolt). W 106. P 14.
681 162   8 c. multicoloured   10   10
682   –   15 c. multicoloured   10   10
683 162   35 c. multicoloured   15   20
684   –   40 c. multicoloured   15   30
681/4 ..   ..   ..   Set of 4   35   55
Nos. 682 and 684 show a different view of the monument.

163 American Manatee

(Des BG Studio. Litho Questa)

1978 (15 Feb). Wildlife Conservation. T 163 and similar multicoloured designs. W 106 (sideways on 8 and 15 c.). P 14.
685   8 c. Type 163   65   10
686   15 c. Giant sea turtle   85   20
687   35 c. Harpy Eagle (vert)   ..   3·25   1·50
688   40 c. Iguana (vert)   ..   3·25   1·50
685/8 ..   ..   ..   Set of 4   7·25   3·00

164 L. F. S. Burnham (Prime Minister)   165 Dr. George Giglioli
and Parliament Buildings, Georgetown   (scientist and physician)

(Des Walsall. Litho Questa)

1978 (27 Apr). 25th Anniv of Prime Minister's Entry into Parliament. T 164 and similar horiz designs. W 106 (sideways). P 13½ × 14.
689   8 c. black, violet and bluish grey   ..   10   10
690   15 c. black, light violet-blue and bluish grey ..   10   10
691   35 c. black, red and bluish grey   ..   15   20
692   40 c. black, red-orange and bluish grey   ..   15   20
689/92   ..   ..   ..   Set of 4   40   45
MS693   176 × 118 mm. Nos. 689/92   ..   55   1·50
Designs:—15 c. Burnham, graduate and children ("Free Education"); 35 c. Burnham and industrial works (Nationalization of Bauxite industry); 40 c. Burnham and village scene ("The Co-operative Village").

(Des J.W. Litho Harrison)

1978 (4 Sept). National Science Research Council. T 165 and similar multicoloured designs. W 106 (sideways on 10 and 50 c.). P 13½ × 14 (10, 50 c.) or 14 × 13½ (others).
694   10 c. Type 165   15   10
695   30 c. Institute of Applied Science and Technology (horiz)   ..   20   15
696   50 c. Emblem of National Science Research Council   ..   25   25
697   60 c. Emblem of Commonwealth Science Council (commemorating the 10th Meeting) (horiz)   ..   25   25
694/7 ..   ..   ..   Set of 4   75   60

___

OMNIBUS ISSUES

Details, together with prices for complete sets, of the various Omnibus issues from the 1935 Silver Jubilee series to date are included in a special section following Zimbabwe at the end of Volume 2.

166 Prepona   167 Agrias claudina
pheridamas

(Des J. Cooter. Litho J.W.)

1978 (1 Oct)–80. Butterflies. Horiz designs as T 166 (5 to 60 c.) or vert as T 167 ($1 to $10). Multicoloured. W 106. P 14 × 13½ (5 to 60 c.) or 13 ($1 to $10).
698   5 c. Type 166   ..   ..   1·25   10
699   10 c. Archonias bellona   ..   1·25   10
700   15 c. Eryphanis polyxena   ..   1·25   10
701   20 c. Helicopis cupido..   ..   1·25   10
702   25 c. Nessaea batesii ..   ..   1·50   10
702a   30 c. Nymphidium mantus (25.1.80)..   1·25   1·75
703   35 c. Anaea galanthis   ..   1·50   10
704   40 c. Morpho rhetenor (male)   ..   1·50   10
705   50 c. Hamadryas amphinome   ..   1·50   20
705a   60 c. Papilio androgeus (25.1.80)   ..   1·25   1·00
706   $1 Type 167   ..   ..   3·25   20
707   $2 Morpho rhetenor (female)   ..   5·00   35
708   $5 Morpho deidamia   ..   6·50   90
708a $10 Elbella patrobas (25.1.80)   ..   7·50   4·25
698/708a   ..   ..   Set of 14   32·00   8·00

168 Amerindian Stone-chip   169 Dish Aerial by Night
Grater in Preparation

(Des L. Curtis. Litho Questa)

1978 (18 Dec). National/International Heritage Year. T 168 and similar vert designs. Multicoloured. W 106. P 14.
709   10 c. Type 168   10   10
710   30 c. Cassiri and decorated Amerindian jars ..   15   10
711   50 c. Fort Kyk-over-al..   ..   20   15
712   60 c. Fort Island   20   20
709/12   ..   ..   Set of 4   55   45

(Des L. Curtis. Litho Questa)

1979 (7 Feb). Satellite Earth Station. T 169 and similar horiz designs. Multicoloured. W 106 (sideways). P 14 × 14½.
713   10 c. Type 169   10   10
714   30 c. Dish aerial by day   ..   20   15
715   50 c. Satellite with solar veins   ..   30   15
716   $3 Cylinder satellite   ..   1·50   90
713/16   ..   ..   Set of 4   1·90   1·10

170 Sir Rowland Hill   171 "Me and my Sister"
and British Guiana 1850 12 c.
"Cottonreel" Stamp

(Des and litho J.W.)

1979 (11 June). Death Centenary of Sir Rowland Hill. T 170 and similar multicoloured designs. W 106 (sideways on 10 and 50 c.). P 14.
717   10 c. Type 170   15   10
718   30 c. British Guiana 1856 1 c. black on magenta stamp (vert)   ..   25   15
719   50 c. British Guiana 1898 1 c. stamp..   ..   35   25
720   $3 Printing press used for early British Guiana stamps (vert)   ..   70   1·10
717/20   ..   ..   Set of 4   1·25   1·40

(Des J.W. Litho Questa)

1979 (20 Aug). International Year of the Child. Paintings by local children. T 171 and similar multicoloured designs. W 106 (sideways on 30, 50 c. and $3). P 13½.
721   10 c. Type 171   10   10
722   30 c. "Fun with the Fowls" (horiz)   ..   15   15
723   50 c. "Two Boys catching Ducks" (horiz)   ..   20   20
724   $3 "Mango Season" (horiz)   ..   65   1·25
721/4 ..   ..   ..   Set of 4   90   1·50

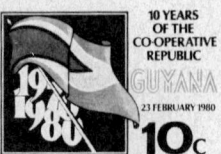

172 "An 8 Hour Day"   173 Guyana Flag

(Des C. Rodriguez. Litho Walsall)

1979 (27 Sept). *60th Anniv of Guyana Labour Union. T* **172** *and similar multicoloured designs. W* **106** *(sideways on 30 c.). P* 14 × 14½ (30 c.) *or* 14½ × 14 *(others).*
725	10 c. Type 172	10	10
726	30 c. "Abolition of Night Baking" (*horiz*)	10	10
727	50 c. "Introduction of the Workmen's Compensation Ordinance"	15	15
728	$3 H. N. Critchlow (founder)	55	90
725/8	*Set of 4*	75	1·10

(Des BG Studio. Litho Questa)

1980 (23 Feb). *10th Anniv of Republic. T* **173** *and similar horiz designs. W* **106** *(sideways). P* 14.
729	10 c. multicoloured	10	10
730	35 c. black and red-orange	30	10
731	60 c. multicoloured	50	20
732	$3 multicoloured	80	90
729/32	*Set of 4*	1·50	1·10

Designs:—35 c. View of Demerara River Bridge; 60 c. Kaieteur Falls; $3 "Makanaima the Great Ancestral Spirit of the Amerindians".

174 Common Snook   175 Children's Convalescent Home (Community Service)

(Des J.W. Litho Questa)

1980 (6 May). *"London 1980" International Stamp Exhibition. Fishes. T* **174** *and similar horiz designs. Multicoloured. W* **106** *(sideways). P* 14½.
733	35 c. Type 174	35	25
	a. Block of 12. Nos. 733/44	3·75	
734	35 c. Trahira ("Haimara")	35	25
735	35 c. Electric Eel	35	25
736	35 c. Golden Rivulus	35	25
737	35 c. Golden Pencilfish	35	25
738	35 c. Four-eyed Fish	35	25
739	35 c. Red Piranha ("Pirai")	35	25
740	35 c. Smoking Hassar	35	25
741	35 c. Manta	35	25
742	35 c. Festive Cichlid ("Flying Patwa")	35	25
743	35 c. Arapaima	35	25
744	35 c. Peacock Cichlid ("Lukanani")	35	25
733/44	*Set of 12*	3·75	2·75

Nos. 733/44 were printed together, *se-tenant*, in a block of 12 within the sheetlet containing one of each design.

(Des local artist; adapted J.W. Litho Walsall)

1980 (23 June). *75th Anniv of Rotary International. T* **175** *and similar multicoloured designs. P* 14.
745	10 c. Type 175	10	10
746	30 c. Rotary Club of Georgetown and Rotary emblems	10	10
747	50 c. District 404 emblem (*vert*)	20	20
748	$3 Rotary anniversary emblem (*vert*)	80	80
745/8	*Set of 4*	1·00	1·10

176 "C" encircling Globe, Caduceus Emblem and Sea   177 *Virola surinamensis*

(Des L. Curtis. Litho Enschedé)

1980 (23 Sept). *25th Anniv of Commonwealth Caribbean Medical Research Council. T* **176** *and similar horiz designs. Multicoloured. W* **106** *(sideways). P* 13.
749	10 c. Type 176	10	10
750	60 c. Researcher with microscope, Caduceus emblem, stethoscope and beach scene	40	20
751	$3 Caduceus emblem, "C" encircling researcher and island silhouettes	1·10	1·00
749/51	*Set of 3*	1·40	1·10

(Des L. Curtis. Litho Format)

1980 (1 Dec). *Christmas. Trees and Foliage. T* **177** *and similar horiz designs. Multicoloured. W* **106** *(sideways). P* 13½.
752	10 c. Type 177	10	10
753	30 c. *Hymenaea courbaril*	20	10
754	50 c. *Mora excelsa*	30	15
755	$3 *Peltogyne venosa*	1·25	1·10
752/5	*Set of 4*	1·75	1·25

1981 CONFERENCE

$1·05 X

178 Brazilian Tree Porcupine   (179)

(Des G. Drummond. Litho Questa)

1981 (2 Mar). *Wildlife. T* **178** *and similar horiz designs. Multicoloured. W* **106** *(sideways). P* 14.
756	30 c. Type 178	60	50
	a. Sheetlet of 12. Nos. 756/67	6·50	
757	30 c. Red Howler	60	50
758	30 c. Common Squirrel-Monkey	60	50
759	30 c. Two-toed Sloth	60	50
760	30 c. Brazilian Tapir	60	50
761	30 c. Collared Peccary	60	50
762	30 c. Six-banded Armadillo	60	50
763	30 c. Tamandua ("Ant Eater")	60	50
764	30 c. Giant Anteater	60	50
765	30 c. Murine Opossum	60	50
766	30 c. Brown Four-eyed Opossum	60	50
767	30 c. Brazilian Agouti	60	50
756/67	*Set of 12*	6·50	5·50

Nos. 756/67 were printed together, *se-tenant*, within the sheet of 12.

See also No. 852.

1981 (4 May). *Liberation of Southern Africa Conference. No.* 635 *surch with T* **179** *by Govt Printer.*
768	$1.05 on 10 c. Type 152	40	30

ROYAL WEDDING 1981

$3·60 X

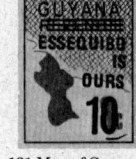

X   7·20

(180)   181 Map of Guyana   (182)

1981 (6 May). *Royal Wedding (1st issue). Nos.* 554 *and* 556 *surch as T* **180** *by Govt Printer. A. In blue. B. In black.*
		A		B	
769	$3.60 on $5 *Odontadenia grandiflora*	1·00	1·00	60	65
	a. Surch inverted	£100	—	†	
	b. Surch double	18·00	—	†	
770	$7.20 on $1 *Chelonanthus uliginoides*	80	80	1·00	1·00
	a. Surch on No. 556	†	25·00	†	
	b. Surch double	20·00	—	†	
	c. Surch triple			†	

See also Nos. 841/3 and 930/6.

(Surch by Govt Printer)

1981 (11 May). *W* **106** *(sideways). P* 13.
771	**181**	10 c. on 3 c. black, ind & Venetian red	40	10
772		30 c. on 2 c. black, ind & greenish grey	45	15
773		50 c. on 2 c. black, ind & greenish grey	55	15
774		60 c. on 2 c. black, ind & greenish grey	65	15
775		75 c. on 3 c. black, ind & Venetian red	65	20
		a. Surch double	40·00	
		b. Surch triple	60·00	
771/5		*Set of 5*	2·40	60

Nos. 771/5 are fiscal stamps surcharged for postal use.
See also Nos. 940/76, 988/9 and 1029.

1981 (11 May). *No.* 544 *surch with T* **182** *by Govt Printer.*
775c	720 c. on 3 c. Hanging Heliconia	70·00	15·00
	ca. Surch quadruple	75·00	

1981

(183)

1981 (8 June). *Optd with T* **183** *by Bovell's Printery.*
776	**105**	25 c. black, gold and lilac (R.)	10	10
777		30 c. black, gold & lt apple-green (R.)	15	10
778	—	35 c. multicoloured (No. 645) (R.)	15	10
779		$1 multicoloured (No. 554)	70	40
776/9		*Set of 4*	1·00	55

210

ESSEQUIBO IS OURS   ESSEQUIBO IS OURS

7   X   15   15

(184)   (185)   (186)   (186a)

1981 (8 June–1 July) *Nos.* 545 *and* 556 *surch with T* **184** (*No.* 780) *or as T* **185**, *all by Bovell's Printery.*
780	75 c. on 5 c. Annatto tree	50	50
781	210 c. on $5 *Odontadenia grandiflora*	80	1·00
781a	220 c. on 5 c. Annatto tree (1 July)	80·00	8·50

1981 (8 June). *Nos. D8/11 surch in black (15 c.) or red (others). A. As T* **186**. *B. As T* **186a**. *Both by Bovell's Printery.*
			A		B	
782	D 2	10 c. on 2 c. black	25	10	50	10
		c. Surch omitted (in vert pair with normal)	—		†	
		w. Wmk inverted	—		†	
783		15 c. on 12 c. bright scarlet	25	15	60	20
784		20 c. on 1 c. olive	20	20	30	20
		a. "ESSEOUIBO"	†		25·00	
		c. Surch omitted (in vert pair with normal)	†			
		w. Wmk inverted	†			
785		45 c. on 2 c. black	60	20	80	35
786		55 c. on 4 c. dull ultram	30	20	6·00	3·50
		c. Surch inverted			†	
		d. Surch double, one inverted (T **186** + T **186**)			†	
		da. Ditto, but T **186** + T **186a**			†	
		db. Ditto, but T **186a** + T **186**	†			
		e. Surch double (55 c. + 60 c.)	—		†	
		f. Vert pair, one surch inverted, one surch albino			†	
		w. Wmk inverted			50	15
787		60 c. on 4 c. dull ultram	†		50	15
		a. "ESSEOUIBO"	†		10·00	
		c. Surch omitted (in vert pair with normal)	†			
788		65 c. on 2 c. black	40	20	50	25
789		70 c. on 4 c. dull ultram	80	55	75	45
		w. Wmk inverted				
790		80 c. on 4 c. dull ultram	35	20	60	30
		c. Surch inverted			†	
		d. Surch omitted (in vert pair with inverted)			†	
782A/90A		*Set of 8*	2·75	1·60		
782B/90B		*Set of 9*			9·00	5·00

With the exception of No. 787 these stamps were surcharged with a setting of eighteen (three horizontal rows) as Type **186** and twelve as Type **186a**. The two types of surcharge can, therefore, be found as vertical *se-tenant* pairs.

No. 787 was produced from a setting of 12 containing Type **186a** only. The same setting was also used for the bottom two rows of the 20 c. on 1 c. value. The "ESSEOUIBO" error occurs on the first stamp in the second horizontal row of this setting.

Examples of 15, 45 and 60 c. surcharges are also known on stamps with watermark w **12**.

1981 **1981** **1981**
(187)   (188)   (189)

1981 (8 June–1 July). *Nos.* 491, 494 *and* 555 *optd with T* **187**, **188** *or* **189**, *all by Bovell's Printery.*
791	15 c. Harpy Eagle (R.)	8·00	10
	a. Opt omitted (in vert pair with normal)	†	
	b. Opt double	40·00	
	c. Opt inverted	40·00	
	d. Opt in black	42·00	5·00
	da. Opt double, one inverted	40·00	
792	40 c. Great Kiskadee (1.7.81)	8·50	40
	a. Opt double	30·00	
793	$2 *Norantea guianensis* (1.7.81)	3·00	55
791/3	*Set of 3*	18·00	90

X 120

50c ■   ■

(190)   (191)

150

X

(192)

(Surch by Bovell's Printery)

1981 (1 July). (*a*) *Postage.* (i) *No.* 545 *surch with T* **190**.
794	50 c. on 5 c. Annatto tree	30	20
	a. Surch inverted	6·00	2·00

(ii) *No.* 554 *surch as T* **191**
795	120 c. on $1 *Chelonanthus uliginoides*	75	40
796	140 c. on $1 *Chelonanthus uliginoides*	70	40

(iii) *Nos.* F7 *and* F9 *surch as T* **192**
797	150 c. on $2 *Norantea guianensis*	75	40
798	360 c. on $2 *Norantea guianensis*	3·00	60
799	720 c. on 60 c. Soldier's Cap	3·00	55

(iv) *Nos.* 556 *and* 716 *surch as T* **185**
800	220 c. on $3 Cylinder satellite (surch vert – reading downwards)	1·75	45
	a. Surch reading upwards	30·00	
801	250 c. on $5 *Odontadenia grandiflora*	1·25	45
802	280 c. on $5 *Odontadenia grandiflora*	1·50	50
803	375 c. on $5 *Odontadenia grandiflora*	1·75	55
	a. Surch inverted		
	b. "7" of "375" omitted		

(b) *Air. No. 843 with commemorative opt cancelled by three bars*
304 $1.10 on $2 *Norantea guianensis* .. .. 3·00 2·50
No. 803b was subsequently corrected by the insertion of a
very uneven "7".

100

15   AIR
(193)   (194)

(Surch by Bovell's Printery)

1981 (1 July). *No. 485 surch.* (a) *Postage. With T* 193.
805   15 c. on 1 c. Type 87 .. .. .. 70 20
   a. Horiz strip of 3. Nos. 805/7 .. 2·00
   b. Surch inverted .. .. .. 48·00
   c. Surch double .. .. .. 40·00

(b) *Air. As T* 194
806 100 c. on 1 c. Type 87 .. .. .. 70 40
807 110 c. on 1 c. Type 87 .. .. .. 70 40
Nos. 805/7 were printed together, *se-tenant*, within the same
sheet providing 36 examples of No. 805 and 32 each of the others.
No. 805 appears in the six vertical columns of Rows 3 to 8 with
horizontal pairs of Nos. 806/7 in vertical columns 1, 2, 9, 10 and
vertical pairs in the central six vertical columns of Rows 1, 2, 9,
10.

ESSEQUIBO   ESSEQUIBO   1981
IS OURS   IS OURS
(195)   (195a)   (196)

1981 (1 July). *No. 700 optd.* A. *With T* 195. B. *With T* 195a.
Both by Bovell's Printery.
                      A   B
808   15 c. *Eryphanis polyxena* .. 1·00   10   1·00   15
   a. "I" of "IS" omitted .. .. † —
No. 808Ba is believed to occur on either R. 5/1 or R. 5/5.

1981 (7 July–15 Sept). *Various stamps optd with T* 196 *by*
Bovell's Printery.
809   15 c. multicoloured (No. 548) .. 6·00   10
   a. Opt inverted
810   15 c. multicoloured (No. 659) (opt vert
      —reading downwards) .. 6·00   20
   a. Opt reading upwards .. 26·00
   b. Opt albino .. .. 26·00
811   15 c. multicoloured (No. 660) .. 4·50   20
   a. Opt inverted
   b. Vert pair, one with opt omitted
811c   40 c. multicoloured (No. F5) .. — £200
812   50 c. multicoloured (No. 623) .. 60   20
   a. Opt inverted .. .. 28·00
813 150 50 c. multicoloured .. .. 1·00   20
814   50 c. royal blue and orange (No. 632) 23·00 2·00
815   50 c. multicoloured (No. 646) .. 2·75   20
816 159 50 c. ultramarine, black and gold .. 13·00 2·00
817   50 c. multicoloured (No. F6) .. 4·00   20
818   60 c. multicoloured (No. 731) (15.9.81) 60   20
819   60 c. multicoloured (No. 750) (15.9.81) 60   20
820   $1 multicoloured (No. 624) .. 6·00   55
821 159 $1 blue-green, black and gold .. 6·00   30
822   $2 multicoloured (No. 555) .. 9·00   75
823   $3 multicoloured (No. 732) .. 2·50   65
824   $5 multicoloured (No. 556) .. 3·25 1·25
Overprints on Nos. 814/15 and 823 are vertical, reading
upwards.

55   55
(197)   (198)

110
(199)

440   440
(200)   (201)

550   550
(202)   (203)

240
(204)

(Surch by Bovell's Printery)

1981 (7 July–15 Sept). (a) *Various stamps surch as T* 197/203.
825 116   55 c. on 6 c. multicoloured (surch T 197)
          (15.9.81) .. .. 4·00   80
   a. Surch with T 198 .. .. 10·00 3·50
   b. Vert pair. Nos. 825/a .. 14·00 4·50

826 111   70 c. on 6 c. multicoloured (15.9.81) .. 1·00   20
827   100 c. on 6 c. multicoloured .. 1·25   20
   a. Surch inverted .. .. 3·50   75
828   – 100 c. on 8 c. multicoloured (No. 505) .. 4·50   20
829 152 100 c. on $1.05 on 10 c. mult (No. 768)
      (surch vert—reading upwards) .. 29·00 4·00
   a. Surch reading downwards .. 35·00
830 116 110 c. on 6 c. multicoloured .. 3·00   30
831 149 110 c. on 10 c. multicoloured (surch vert—
      reading downwards) .. 2·50   30
832 151 110 c. on 10 c. grey-green and yellow .. 6·00   45
833 154 110 c. on 10 c. multicoloured .. 5·00   45
834   – 125 c. on $2 multicoloured (No. 555) .. 12·00   80
835 116 180 c. on 6 c. multicoloured (15.9.81) .. 3·50   45
836   400 c. on 6 c. multicoloured .. 3·50   80
837   440 c. on 6 c. multicoloured (surch T 200) 10·00 3·50
   a. Surch with T 201 .. .. 2·00   55
   b. Vert pair. Nos. 837/a .. 12·00 6·00
838   – 550 c. on $10 multicoloured (No. O21)
      (surch T 202) (15.9.81) .. 5·50 1·00
   a. Surch with T 203 .. .. 13·00 5·50
   b. Vert pair. Nos. 838/a .. 17·00 8·00
839   – 625 c. on 40 c. multicoloured (No. F5) .. 14·00 1·75

(b) *No. 728 surch with T* 204
840   – 240 c. on $3 multicoloured (15.9.81) .. 9·50   75
Nos. 825/a, 837/a and 838/a were each printed together,
se-tenant, in vertical pairs throughout sheets containing five of
these pairs plus an additional fifteen examples of Nos. 825, 837a
and 838.

                         75

Royal Wedding

1981

X   60   X
(205)   (206)

Air Mail   **X**   Royal Wedding 1981

       1.10

(207)

(Surch by Bovell's Printery)

1981 (22 July). *Royal Wedding* (2nd issue). (a) *Postage. Nos.* 544
and 556 *surch with T* 205/6.
841   60 c. on 3 c. Hanging Heliconia .. 30   35
   a. Surch inverted .. .. 55·00
   b. "Royal Wedding" diagonal (as T 206) .. 55·00
   c. Surch double (T 205 + T 206) .. 25·00
   d. Surch T 205 double .. .. 70·00
842   75 c. on $5 *Odontadenia grandiflora* .. 30   40

(b) *Air. No.* 555 *surch with T* 207.
843   $1.10 on $2 *Norantea guianensis* .. 30   45
   a. Surch double .. .. 38·00
   b. Surch inverted .. .. 80·00
841/3 .. .. *Set of 3* 80 1·10
It is believed No. 841b comes from trial sheets which were accidentally included in supplies of the normal No. 841.

1831-1981
Espana 82   Von Stephan
330
(208)   (209)

1981 (22 July). *World Cup Football Championship, Spain* (1982)
(*1st issue*). *No.* 781a *optd with T* 208 *by Bovell's Printery.*
844 220 c. on 5 c. Annatto tree .. .. 1·25   40
See also Nos. 937/9 and 1218.

1981 (22 July). 150th Birth Anniv of Heinrich von Stephan
(*founder of U.P.U.*). *No.* 720 *surch with T* 209.
845 330 c. on $3 Printing press used for early
      British Guiana stamps.. .. 1·50   55

12   ▬
(211)

1981 (24 Aug). *No.* 452 *surch as T* 211 *by Bovell's Printery.*
847   12 c. on 12 c. on 6 c. Black Acara ("Patua") 20   25
   a. Large surch omitted .. .. 15·00
   b. Strip of 3. Nos. 847/9 .. 50
   c. Strip of 3. Nos. 847, 850/1 .. 50
848   15 c. on 10 c. on 6 c. Black Acara ("Patua") 15   10
849   15 c. on 30 c. on 6 c. Black Acara ("Patua") 15   10
   a. Small surch omitted .. .. 25·00

850   15 c. on 50 c. on 6 c. Black Acara ("Patua") 15   10
851   15 c. on 60 c. on 6 c. Black Acara ("Patua") 15   10
Nos. 847/51 are further surcharges on previously unissued
stamps.
No. 847 exists with the smaller of the two 12 c. surcharges
printed by either lithography or typography.
Nos. 847/9 and 847, 850/1 were each printed together,
se-tenant, within the sheets providing 36 examples of No. 847
and 30 each of Nos. 848/9 or 850/1. Each sheet also contained
four stamps cancelled with a black diagonal cross. In each
instance No. 847 appeared in the six central vertical columns
of Rows 3 to 8 with horizontal pairs of Nos. 848/9 or 850/1 in
vertical columns 1, 2, 9, 10 and vertical pairs in R. 1/4–8,
R. 2/4–8, R. 9/3–7 and R. 10/3–7.

1981 (1 Sept). *As No.* 762 *but perf* 12.
852   30 c. Six-banded Armadillo 60   15
No. 852 was printed in sheets of 50.

214 Coromantyn Free   215 Louis Braille
Negro Armed Ranger,
circa 1772 and Cuffy
Monument

(Des G. Drummond. Litho Rosenbaum Bros, Vienna)

1981 (1 Oct). 16th Anniv of Guyana Defence Force. T 214 and
similar vert designs. Multicoloured. W 106 (*inverted on* $1).
P 13½.
853   15 c. on 10 c. Type 214.. .. 50   10
854   50 c. Private, 27th Foot Regiment, *circa* 1825 75   50
855   $1 on 30 c. Private, Col. Fourgeoud's
      Marines, *circa* 1775 .. 80   75
856   $1.10 on $3 W.O. and N.C.O., Guyana
      Defence Force, 1966 .. 1·25 1·10
853/6 .. .. *Set of 4* 3·00 2·25
The 15 c., $1 and $1.10 values are surcharged on previously
unissued stamps.

(Des G. Vasarhelyi. Litho Questa)

1981 (2 Nov). *International Year for Disabled Persons. Famous*
Disabled People. T 215 *and similar horiz designs. Multicoloured.*
W 106 (*sideways*). *P* 13½ × 14.
857   15 c. on 10 c. Type 215.. .. 25   10
858   50 c. Helen Keller and Rajkumari Singh .. 50   40
859   $1 on 60 c. Beethoven and Sonny Thomas .. 55   50
860   $1.10 on $3 Renoir 55   55
857/60 .. .. *Set of 4* 1·60 1·40
The 15 c., $1 and $1.10 values are surcharged, by Bovell's
Printery, on previously unissued stamps. Examples of Nos. 857,
859 and 860 are known without surcharge.

12   X 50   AIR
(216)   (217)

(Surch by Bovell's Printery)

1981 (10 Nov). *Nos.* 452 *and* 489 *surch.* (a) *Postage. With*
T 216.
                    A. *On No.*   B. *On No.*
                    452   489
861   12 c. on 6 c. Black Acara
     ("Patua") .. 15   10   15   10
   a. Strip of 3. Nos. 861/3 .. 1·25 — 1·10

(b) *Air. As T* 217
862   50 c. on 6 c. Black Acara
     ("Patua") .. 25   15   20   15
863   $1 on 6 c. Black Acara
     ("Patua") .. 50   30   50   30
Nos. 861/3 were printed together, *se-tenant*, throughout the
sheet. All sheets of Nos. 861B/3B and about half of Nos. 861A/3A
contained 36 examples of the 12 c., 35 of the 50 c. and 29 of the $1.
On the remainder of the unwatermarked sheets there were the
same number of the 12 c., but 34 of the 50 c. and 30 of the $1. No.
861 appeared in the six central vertical columns of Rows 3 to 8
with horizontal pairs of Nos. 862/3 in vertical columns 1, 2, 9, 10
and vertical pairs in the six central vertical columns of Rows 1, 2,
9, 10. The additional $1 value on the second stage of the setting
occurred on R. 9/1.

1981
(218)

1981 (14 Nov). *Nos.* 548 *and* 554/5 *optd with T* 218 *in red by*
Bovell's Printery.
864   15 c. Christmas Orchid .. .. 4·00   10
   a. Optd on No. 548a .. .. 5·00
   b. Opt inverted ..
865   $1 *Chelonanthus uliginoides* .. 40   20
866   $2 *Norantea guianensis* 90   35

110   Nov 81
(219)   110   ☾   50c   ☾
          (220)   (221)

1981 (14 Nov). (a) *Nos. 601, 620, 644, and O13 surch with T 219/20 in blue by Bovell's Printery.*

867	110 c. on 10 c. Type **154** (surch T **219**)		3·00	30
868	110 c. on 110 c. on 8 c. on 3 c. Hanging Heliconia (surch T **219** + **220**)		3·00	40
	a. Type **220** albino		25·00	
869	110 c. on 110 c. on 8 c. on 6 c. Cannon-ball tree (surch T **219** + **220**)		3·00	40
869a	110 c. on 10 c. on 25 c. Marabunta (surch T **219** vert)		2·25	40

(b) *Nos. 717, 720, 728, 749, 751 and 755 surch with T **220** by Bovell's Printery.*

870	110 c. on 10 c. Type **170** (R.)		2·00	30
	a. Surch albino		15·00	
871	110 c. on 10 c. Type **176** (B.)		8·00	50
872	110 c. on $3 Printing press used for early British Guiana stamps (R.) (surch vert)		1·75	30
873	110 c. on $3 H.N. Critchlow (B.) (surch vert)		6·50	45
874	110 c. on $3 Caduceus emblem, "C" encircling researcher, and island silhouettes (B.)		2·00	30
	a. Surch in red		3·25	70
875	110 c. on $3 *Peltogyne venosa* (B.)		4·00	50
	a. Surch in red		48·00	6·50

(c) *No. 698 surch with T **221** by Herald Printing-Kitty*

876	50 c. on 5 c. Type **166**		3·25	20

222 Yellow Allamanda
(*Allamanda cathartica*)

X X
**Human Rights
Day
1981**
110 **AIR**
(223)

1981 (14 Nov)–82. *Flowers. Coil stamps. Vert designs as T **222**.
W **106**. P 15 × 14.*

877	15 c. on 2 c. grey-lilac, blue & turquoise-green		15	15
	a. Vert pair. Nos. 877/8		50	45
	b. New blue surch (12.82)		20	10
	ba. Vert pair. Nos. 877b/8b		65	50
878	15 c. on 8 c. grey-lilac, blue and mauve		15	15
	b. New blue surch (12.82)		20	10

Design:—15 c. on 8 c. Mazaruni Pride (*Sipanea prolensis*).
Nos. 877/8 are surcharges on previously unissued stamps and were printed together, *se-tenant*, in vertical pairs throughout the coil.

1981 (14 Nov). *Air. Human Rights Day. No. 748 surch with T **223** in blue by Bovell's Printery.*

879	110 c. on $3 Rotary anniversary emblem		1·75	60

U.N.I.C.E.F.
1946 - 1981
125 XX
(224)

1981 (14 Nov). *35th Anniv of U.N.I.C.E.F. No. 724 surch with T **224** by Bovell's Printery.*

880	125 c. on $3 "Mango Season"		1·00	40

Cancun 81
◗ 50c ◖
(224a)

1981 (14 Nov). *"Cancun 81" International Conference. No. 698 surch with T **224a** by Herald Printing-Kitty.*

880a	50 c. on 5 c. Type **166**		3·50	55

225 Tape Measure and
Guyana Metrication Board Van

1982
(226)

(Des local artist; adapted A. Theobald. Litho Questa)

1982 (18 Jan). *Metrication. T **225** and similar vert designs. Multi-coloured. W **106**. P 14½ × 14.*

881	15 c. Type **225**		25	25
	a. Sheetlet of 6. Nos. 881/6		1·40	
882	15 c. "Metric man"		25	25
883	15 c. "Postal service goes metric"		25	25
884	15 c. Weighing child on metric scales.		25	25
885	15 c. Canje Bridge		25	25
886	15 c. Tap filling litre bucket		25	25
881/6		*Set of 6*	1·40	1·40

Nos. 881/6 were printed together, *se-tenant*, in a sheetlet of 6.

1982 (8 Feb). *Various stamps optd with T **226** in blue by Autoprint.*

887	– 20 c. multicoloured (No. 549)		2·00	20
	a. Optd on No. 549a		4·50	1·75
888	105 25 c. black, gold and lilac		60	15
889	– 25 c. multicoloured (No. 550a)		2·50	20
	a. Optd on No. 550		5·00	3·00
	b. Optd on No. 550ab		4·75	2·50

See also Nos. 914/17, 919/21, 923/4, 977, 992/8, 1001, 1004, 1006/8, 1015, 1017, 1059, 1117 and OP3/4.

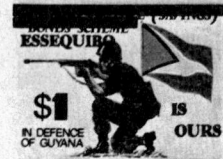

20c
(227)
20
(228)

POSTAGE
(229)

1982 (8 Feb). *Nos. 506, 546 and 601 surch or optd as T **227/9** by Bovell's Printery (No. 890) or Autoprint (others).*

890	20 c. on 6 c. Cannon-ball tree (surch T **227**) (G.)		35	10
891	20 c. on 6 c. Cannon-ball tree (surch T **228**) (B.)		35	10
892	25 c. Type **116** (optd T **229**) (B.)		1·00	10
893	125 c. on 8 c. on 6 c. Cannon-ball tree (surch T **228**)		35	20

230 Guyana Soldier and Flag

1982 (8 Feb). *Savings Campaign. W **106** (sideways). P 14 × 14½.*

894	230 $1 multicoloured		30	20

No. 894 is a fiscal stamp overprinted, by Bovell's Printery, for postal use.

110 X
BADEN POWELL
1857 - 1982
(231)

1982 (15–22 Feb). *125th Birth Anniv of Lord Baden-Powell and 75th Anniv of Boy Scout Movement. Nos. 543, 545 and 601 surch as T **231** by Bovell's Printery.*

895	15 c. on 2 c. Type **132** (surch T **231**) (22 Feb)		10	30
	a. Sheetlet of 25. Nos. 895/6, each × 8, Nos. 897/8, each × 4 and No. 899		8·00	
	ab. Surch inverted (sheetlet of 25)			
896	15 c. on 2 c. Type **132** (surch "Scout Movement 1907–1982") (22 Feb)		10	30
897	15 c. on 2 c. Type **132** (surch "1907–1982") (22 Feb).		15	40
898	15 c. on 2 c. Type **132** (surch "1857–1982") (22 Feb).		15	15
899	15 c. on 2 c. Type **132** (surch "1982") (22 Feb)		10	10
900	110 c. on 5 c. Annatto tree (surch T **231**)		1·00	20
	a. Sheetlet of 25. Nos. 900/1, each × 8, Nos. 902/3, each × 4, and No. 904 (22 Feb)		12·00	
901	110 c. on 5 c. Annatto tree (surch "Scout Movement 1907–1982")		60	20
902	110 c. on 5 c. Annatto tree (surch "1907–1982") (22 Feb).		1·25	1·00
903	110 c. on 5 c. Annatto tree (surch "1857–1982") (22 Feb).		1·25	1·00
904	110 c. on 5 c. Annatto tree (surch "1982") (22 Feb).		60	20
	a. "110" larger		95·00	
905	125 c. on 8 c. on 6 c. Cannon-ball tree (surch T **231**) (G.)		1·00	20
	a. Sheetlet of 25. Nos. 905/6, each × 8, Nos. 907/8, each × 4, and No. 909		16·00	
906	125 c. on 8 c. on 6 c. Cannon-ball tree (surch "Scout Movement 1907–1982") (G.)		1·00	20
907	125 c. on 8 c. on 6 c. Cannon-ball tree (surch "1907–1982") (G.) (22 Feb)		1·50	1·00
908	125 c. on 8 c. on 6 c. Cannon-ball tree (surch "1857–1982") (G.) (22 Feb)		1·50	1·00
909	125 c. on 8 c. on 6 c. Cannon-ball tree (surch "1982") (G.) (22 Feb)		75	20
895/909		*Set of 15*	9·00	5·50

In addition to the sheetlets of 25, Nos. 895a, 900a and 905a, Nos.

899/901, 904/6 and 909 also come from sheets containing one type of surcharge only.
No. 904a occurs in the printing of sheets containing this surcharge only. The "110" is in the same size as the surcharge on Type **241**.

Geo Washington 1732...1982	**GEORGE WASHINGTON 1732–1982**
100	
(232)	(233)

1982 (15 Feb). *250th Birth Anniv of George Washington. Nos. 708, 718 and 720 surch as T **232** by Herald Printing-Kitty or optd only with T **233** by Autoprint.*

910	100 c. on $3 Printing press used for early British Guiana stamps.		45	30
911	400 c. on 30 c. British Guiana 1856 1 c. black on magenta stamp		1·60	1·25
	a. Surch inverted		20·00	
912	$5 *Morpho deidamia* (B.)		7·50	5·50
910/12		*Set of 3*	8·50	6·25

1982 (3 Mar). *Savings Campaign. Horiz design as T **230**. Multi-coloured. W **106**. P 14 × 14½.*

913	110 c. on $5 Guyana male and female soldiers with flag		50	20

No. 913 is a fiscal stamp surcharged, by Bovell's Printery, for postal use.
See also No. 990.

45 ● **20** **210**
(234) (235) (236)

1982 (15 Mar). *Easter. Nos. 481/4 optd with T **226**, in blue, or surch as T **234**, all by Autoprint.*

914	111 25 c. multicoloured		25	15
915	30 c. multicoloured		25	15
916	45 c. on 6 c. multicoloured (B.)		30	25
917	75 c. on 40 c. multicoloured (R.)		55	25
914/17		*Set of 4*	1·25	70

No. 917 exists with the surcharge either at the right or in the centre of the design.

1982 (15 Mar). *No. 703 surch with T **235** by Herald Printing-Kitty.*

918	20 c. on 35 c. *Anaea galanthis*		3·00	10

1982 (8 Apr). *No. F5 optd with T **226** and surch as T **228** in blue, both by Autoprint.*

919	180 c. on 40 c. Tiger Beard		3·50	40

1982 (23 Apr). *Nos. 555/6 optd with T **226** in blue by Autoprint.*

920	$2 *Norantea guianensis*		80	30
921	$5 *Odontadenia grandiflora*		1·40	70

1982 (23 Apr). *No. 542 surch as T **228** in blue by Autoprint.*

922	220 c. on 1 c. Pitcher Plant of Mt Roraima		1·25	40

1982 (27 Apr). *Nos. 472 and 684 optd with T **226** in blue by Autoprint.*

923	105 40 c. black, gold and cobalt		35	15
924	– 40 c. multicoloured		50	25

1982 (27 Apr). *Nos. 469, 751, 842 and 843 surch as T **228**, verti-cally (Nos. 925/7), or as T **236** (others), all in blue by Autoprint.*

925	105 80 c. on 6 c. black, gold and flesh		30	20
926	– 85 c. on 6 c. black, gold and flesh		50	20
927	– 160 c. on $1.10 on $2 multicoloured (No 843)		60	30
928	– 210 c. on $3 multicoloured (No. 751) (surch reading up)		2·50	20
	a. Surch reading down		12·00	
929	– 235 c. on 75 c. on $5 multicoloured (No. 842)		2·50	60

The surcharge on No. 929 is as Type **236**, but horizontal.

● **85** ● ✕ **130**
(237) (238)

I 70
(239)

(Surch by Herald Printing-Kitty)

1982 (27 Apr–May). *Royal Wedding (3rd issue). Coil stamps. Nos. 841/3 surch as T **237** (No. 930), **238** (Nos. 931/2, 934/5) or **239** (others).*

930	85 c. on 60 c. on 3 c. Hanging Heliconia		1·50	50
931	130 c. on 60 c. on 3 c. Hanging Heliconia		1·50	60
	a. Surch (as T **238**) inverted		90·00	
932	160 c. on $1.10 on $2 *Norantea guianensis* (vert surch)		1·75	1·00
	a. Surch (as T **238**) double		32·00	

933 170 c. on $1.10 on $2 *Norantea guianensis* 6·00 4·50
934 210 c. on 75 c. on $5 *Odontadenia grandiflora* (B.) 1·25 40
   a. Surch (as T 238) inverted 28·00
935 235 c. on 75 c. on $5 *Odontadenia grandiflora* 1·60 1·40
   a. Surch (T 206) omitted 75·00
   b. Surch (as T 238) double
936 330 c. on $1.10 on $2 *Norantea guianensis* 1·75 40
930/6 *Set of 7* 13·50 7·50

220 AIR

ESPANA 1982
(240)

Princess of Wales 1961 - 1982
(241)

1982 (15 May). *World Cup Football Championship, Spain (2nd issue). Nos. 544, 546 and 554 optd with T 240 or surch also as T 228, both by Autoprint.*
937 $1 Chelonanthus uliginoides 75 40
938 110 c. on 3 c. Hanging Heliconia (B.) 75 25
939 250 c. on 6 c. Cannon-ball tree (B.) 1·00 60
937/9 *Set of 3* 2·25 1·10
See also No. 1218.

(Optd Govt Printer and surch by Autoprint)

1982 (17 May). *W 106 (sideways). P 13.*
940 **181** 15 c. on 2 c. black, ind & greenish grey 50 15
   a. Opt ("ESSEQUIBO etc") omitted 18·00
941 20 c. on 2 c. black, ind & greenish grey 3·50 30
942 25 c. on 2 c. black, ind & greenish grey 5·00 20
943 30 c. on 2 c. black, ind & greenish grey 50 15
944 40 c. on 2 c. black, ind & greenish grey 7·00 30
   a. Surch inverted 12·00
945 45 c. on 2 c. black, ind & greenish grey 1·75 45
946 50 c. on 2 c. black, ind & greenish grey 6·00 30
   a. Opt ("ESSEQUIBO etc") omitted 18·00
947 60 c. on 2 c. black, ind & greenish grey 7·00 20
948 75 c. on 2 c. black, ind & greenish grey 6·00 25
949 80 c. on 2 c. black, ind & greenish grey 4·50 20
950 85 c. on 2 c. black, ind & greenish grey 75 25
951 100 c. on 3 c. black, ind and Venetian red 1·00 35
952 110 c. on 3 c. black, ind and Venetian red 80 30
953 120 c. on 3 c. black, ind and Venetian red 8·00 35
954 125 c. on 3 c. black, ind and Venetian red 2·25 35
955 130 c. on 3 c. black, ind and Venetian red 1·00 35
   a. Surch inverted 17·00
   b. Error. Nos. 952 and 955 *se-tenant*
   c. Error. Nos. 955 and 956 *se-tenant*
956 150 c. on 3 c. black, ind and Venetian red 8·50 40
957 160 c. on 3 c. black, ind and Venetian red 2·00 40
958 170 c. on 3 c. black, ind and Venetian red 1·40 45
959 175 c. on 3 c. black, ind and Venetian red 6·00 45
960 180 c. on 3 c. black, ind and Venetian red 2·00 60
961 200 c. on 3 c. black, ind and Venetian red 2·25 45
962 210 c. on 3 c. black, ind and Venetian red 7·00 50
963 220 c. on 3 c. black, ind and Venetian red 8·50 50
964 235 c. on 3 c. black, ind and Venetian red 8·00 50
965 240 c. on 3 c. black, ind and Venetian red 9·00 50
966 250 c. on 3 c. black, ind and Venetian red 2·25 50
967 300 c. on 3 c. black, ind and Venetian red 12·00 55
968 330 c. on 3 c. black, ind and Venetian red 2·75 65
969 375 c. on 3 c. black, ind and Venetian red 7·00 75
970 400 c. on 3 c. black, ind and Venetian red 10·00 75
971 440 c. on 3 c. black, ind and Venetian red 4·00 75
972 500 c. on 3 c. black, ind and Venetian red 3·50 1·10
973 550 c. on 3 c. black, ind and Venetian red 1·00 1·25
974 625 c. on 3 c. black, ind and Venetian red 2·75 1·75
975 1500 c. on 2 c. black, ind & greenish grey 11·00 3·00
976 2000 c. on 2 c. black, ind & greenish grey 11·00 3·75
940/76 *Set of 37* £160 21·00

Nos. 940/76 are fiscal stamps, surcharged for postal use, as Type **181**, but with the overprinted inscription and face value redrawn. On the 15 to 85 c., the surcharged face value is in blue, on the 100 to 625 c. in black, and on the 1500 and 2000 c. in red.
Nos. 955b/c come from the first printing of the 130 c. which had one cliché of the 110 c. surcharge (R. 4/1) and three of the 150 c. (R. 2/8–10) included in error.
For 25 c. and 40 c. surcharges in black see Nos. 988/9 and for the 25 c. in red, No. 1029.

1982 (7 June). *No. 548 optd with T 226 in blue by Autoprint.*
977 15 c. Christmas Orchid 7·00 10
   a. Optd on No. 548a. 48·00 12·00

1982 (15 June). *No. O26 optd with T 229 in blue by Autoprint.*
978 110 c. on 6 c. Type **116** 4·50 35

1982 (25 June). *Air. 21st Birthday of Princess of Wales. Nos. 542, 545 and 555 surch as T 241 by Bovell's Printery.*
979 110 c. on 5 c. Annatto tree (R.) 50 30
   a. Surch in black 38·00
980 220 c. on 1 c. Pitcher Plant of Mt Roraima 80 60
   a. Surch double 65·00
981 330 c. on $2 Norantea guianensis (B.) 90 90
   a. Surch in greenish blue
   ab. Surch double 48·00
979/81 *Set of 3* 2·00 1·60

STANLEY GIBBONS STAMP COLLECTING SERIES

Introductory booklets on *How to Start, How to Identify Stamps* and *Collecting by Theme*. A series of well illustrated guides at a low price. Write for details.

GUYANA

H.R.H. Prince William 21st June 1982

 $1.10

(242)

H.R.H. Prince William 21st June 1982

$2.20

(243)

1982 (12 July). *Birth of Prince William of Wales. Surch as T 242 (50 c. and $1.10) or with T 243 (others), all in blue by Autoprint.*

(a) On stamps of British Guiana
982 50 c. on 2 c. myrtle-green (No. 332) 40 30
   a. Surch as T 243 (lines at foot) 50·00
983 $1.10 on 3 c. brown-olive and red-brown (No. 354) 80 50
   a. Surch inverted 23·00
   b. Surch double 3·25
   c. Surch on No. 333 80 50
   ca. Surch inverted 55·00
   cb. Surch double 75·00
   cc. Surch as T 243 (lines at foot) 45·00
(b) On stamps of Guyana previously optd "GUYANA INDEPENDENCE 1966"
984 50 c. on 2 c. myrtle-green (No. 430) 8·50 3·25
985 $1.10 on 3 c. brown-olive and red-brown (No. 431) 15·00 3·25
   a. Surch on No. 422 26·00 10·00
986 $1.25 on 6 c. yellow-green (No. 398A) 60 60
   a. Surch inverted 28·00
   b. Surch double 75·00
   c. Surch on No. 434 3·50 2·00
987 $2.20 on 24 c. black and brownish orange (No. 401B) 1·50 1·50
   a. Surch inverted 75·00
   b. Surch on No. 401A 10·00 9·00
   c. Surch on No. 435 23·00 22·00
982/7 *Set of 6* 24·00 8·50
Nos. 982, 983c and 985a have Mult Script CA watermark and the remainder watermark w **12** (sideways on No. 987).

1982 (13 July). *As Nos. 942 and 944 but with surcharged face values in black by Autoprint.*
988 **181** 25 c. on 2 c. black, ind & greenish grey 2·25 20
989 40 c. on 2 c. black, ind & greenish grey 1·00 15

1982 (13 July). *Savings Campaign. Coil stamp. As No. 913 but showing inverted comma before "OURS" in overprint.*
990 110 c. on $5 Guyana male and female soldiers with flag 5·50 75

ITALY

$2.35

(244)

C.A. & CARIB GAMES 1982
(245)

1982 (15 July). *Italy's Victory in World Cup Football Championship. No. F7 optd as T 240 and surch with T 244, both in blue by Autoprint.*
991 $2.35 on 180 c. on 60 c. Soldier's Cap 2·50 55

1982 (16 Aug). *Wildlife Protection. Nos. 687 and 733/8 optd with T 226 (vert on Nos. 993/8) in blue by Autoprint.*
992 35 c. Harpy Eagle 2·00 40
993 35 c. Type **174** 2·00 40
   a. Block of 6. Nos. 993/8 12·50
994 35 c. Trahira ("Haimara") 2·00 40
995 35 c. Electric Eel 2·00 40
996 35 c. Golden Rivulus 2·00 40
997 35 c. Golden Pencilfish 2·00 40
998 35 c. Four-eyed Fish 2·00 40
992/8 *Set of 7* 12·50 2·50

1982 (16 Aug). *Central American and Caribbean Games, Havana. Nos. 542/3 surch as T 245 by Autoprint.*
999 50 c. on 2 c. Type **132** 1·00 25
   a. Surch inverted.. † —
1000 60 c. on 1 c. Pitcher Plant of Mt Roraima 1·25 15

1982 (15 Sept). *No. 730 optd with T 226 vertically in blue by Autoprint.*
1001 35 c. black and red-orange 30 20

1982 (15 Sept). *Nos. 841 and 979 further surch as T 228 (No. 1003 has solid bar) in blue by Autoprint.*
1002 130 c. on 60 c. on 3 c. Hanging Heliconia 40 30
   a. Surch as T 228 inverted £150
1003 170 c. on 110 c. on 5 c. Annatto tree 70 45
   a. With six lines as in T 228 90·00

1982 (15 Sept). *No. 841 optd with T 226 and surch as T 228, both in blue by Autoprint.*
1004 440 c. on 60 c. on 3 c. Hanging Heliconia 75 45
   a. T 226 and T 228 both inverted 32·00
   b. Surch and optd on No. 841b 3·00 2·25
   c. Without opt T 226 4·00 55
No. 1004c also differs from No. 1004 by showing a "c" after the surcharge "60" on Type 205.

Commonwealth GAMES AUSTRALIA 1982 1.25
(246)

INT. FOOD DAY 1982
(247)

1982 (27 Sept). *Commonwealth Games, Brisbane, Australia. No. 546 surch with T 246 in blue by Autoprint.*
1005 $1.25 on 6 c. Cannon-ball tree 1·50 30

1982 (1 Oct). *Nos. 552, 641 and 719 optd with T 226 (vertically reading upwards on Nos. 1007/8) in blue by Autoprint.*
1006 50 c. multicoloured (No. 552) 2·00 25
1007 50 c. lt vio-bl, lt grn & lt yell-brn (No. 641) 1·50 25
1008 50 c. multicoloured (No. 719) 60 25
   a. Opt reading downwards

1982 (1 Oct). *Various Official stamps additionally optd for postal purposes as T 229, but smaller (29 mm in length), all in blue by Autoprint.*
1009 15 c. Christmas Orchid (No. O23) (vert opt) 8·00 30
1010 50 c. Guzmania lingulata (No. O14) (vert opt) 90 15
1011 100 c. on $3 Cylinder satellite (No. O19) 1·25 35

1982 (15 Oct). *International Food Day. No. 617 optd with T 247 in blue by Autoprint.*
1012 50 c. Pawpaw and tangerine 13·00 65

INT. YEAR OF THE ELDERLY
(248)

Dr. R. KOCH CENTENARY TBC BACILLUS DISCOVERY
(249)

F. D. ROOSEVELT 1882-1982
(250)

1982 (15 Oct). *International Year of the Elderly. No. 747 optd with T 248 in blue by Autoprint.*
1013 50 c. District 404 emblem 6·50 50

1982 (15 Oct). *Centenary of Robert Koch's Discovery of Tubercle Bacillus. No. 750 optd with T 249 in blue by Autoprint.*
1014 60 c. Researcher with microscope, Caduceus emblem, stethoscope and beach scene 2·50 30

1982 (15 Oct). *International Decade for Women. No. 633 optd with T 226 in blue by Autoprint.*
1015 $1 brown and bright blue 3·25 60
   a. Opt inverted 18·00

1982 (15 Oct). *Birth Centenary of F. D. Roosevelt (American statesman). No. 706 optd with T 250 in blue by Autoprint.*
1016 $1 Type **167** 3·00 50

GAC Inaug. Flight Georgetown—Boa Vista, Brasil 200
(251)

50 CARICOM Heads of Gov't Conference July 1982
(252)

1982 (15 Oct). *1st Anniv of G.A.C. Inaugural Flight Georgetown to Boa Vista, Brazil. No. 842 optd with T 226 and surch with T 251, both in blue by Autoprint.*
1017 200 c. on 75 c. on $5 Odontadenia grandiflora 8·00 1·40

1982 (18 Nov). *CARICOM Heads of Government Conference, Kingston, Jamaica. Nos. 881/6 surch with T 252 by Herald Printing-Kitty.*
1018 50 c. on 15 c. Type **225** 1·25 30
   a. Sheetlet of 6. Nos. 1018/23 6·75
1019 50 c. on 15 c. "Metric man" 1·25 30
1020 50 c. on 15 c. "Postal service goes metric" 1·25 30
1021 50 c. on 15 c. Weighing child on metric scales 1·25 30
1022 50 c. on 15 c. Canje Bridge 1·25 30
1023 50 c. on 15 c. Tap filling litre bucket 1·25 30
1018/23 *Set of 6* 6·75 1·75

CHRISTMAS 1982

15 (253) **||||** (254) **50** (255)

1982 (1 Dec). *Christmas. Nos. 895/9 optd with T 253 in red by Autoprint.*
1024	15 c. on 2 c. Type **132** (surch T **231**)		25	15
	a. Sheetlet of 25. Nos. 1024/5, each × 8, Nos. 1026/7, each × 4 and No. 1028		13·00	
1025	15 c. on 2 c. Type **132** (surch "Scout Movement 1907–1982")		25	15
1026	15 c. on 2 c. Type **132** (surch "1907–1982")		65	50
1027	15 c. on 2 c. Type **132** (surch "1857–1982")		65	50
1028	15 c. on 2 c. Type **132** (surch "1982")		5·50	6·00
1024/8		*Set of 5*	6·50	6·50

Nos. 1024/8 were only issued in the *se-tenant* sheetlets of 25.

1982 (15 Dec). *As No. 942 but with surcharged face value in red by Autoprint.*
1029	**181** 25 c. on 2 c. black, indigo and greenish grey		50	10

1982 (15 Dec). *Nos. 543 and 546 surch as T 254 by Autoprint.*
1030	15 c. on 2 c. Type **132** (B.)		15	10
1031	20 c. on 6 c. Cannon-ball tree (Blk.)		25	10

For similar surcharges in different colours see Nos. 1034/5 and 1063; and for surcharges incorporating "c" Nos. 1085/7 and 1098/9.

1982 (15 Dec). *No. 489 surch as T 255 by Autoprint.*
1032	50 c. on 6 c. Black Acara ("Patua")		20	15
1033	100 c. on 6 c. Black Acara ("Patua")		40	30

1983 (5 Jan). *As Nos. 1030/1, but with colours of surcharge changed.*
1034	15 c. on 2 c. Type **132** (Blk.)		10	10
1035	20 c. on 6 c. Cannon-ball tree (G.)		10	10

1983 (256)   **POSTAGE** (257)

258 Guyana Flag (inscr "60th BIRTHDAY ANNIVERSARY")

1983 (1 Feb). *Optd with T 256 by Autoprint.*
1036	– 15 c. multicoloured (No. 655) (opt vert)		4·50	1·00
1037	– 15 c. yellow-brown, grey and black (No. 672)		60	10
1038	– 15 c. multicoloured (No. 682) (opt vert)		40	10
1039	**214** 15 c. on 10 c. multicoloured (opt vert)		35	10
1040	**215** 15 c. on 10 c. multicoloured		15	10
1041	– 50 c. multicoloured (No. 646)		4·00	25
1042	– 50 c. multicoloured (No. 696) (opt vert)		4·00	25
1043	– 50 c. multicoloured (No. 719)		1·50	25
1036/43		*Set of 8*	14·00	1·75

See also Nos. 1060/1, 1069/70, 1072/9c, 1096, 1101 and 1110/16.

1983 (1 Feb). *No. O17 optd for postal purposes with T 257 in red by Autoprint.*
1044	15 c. Harpy Eagle		9·50	10

1983 (8 Feb). *National Heritage. Nos. 710/12 and No. 778 surch as T 234 in black (No. 1045) or blue (others) by Autoprint.*
1045	90 c. on 30 c. Cassiri and decorated Amerindian jars		1·50	50
1046	90 c. on 35 c. Rock drawing of hunter and quarry		35	50
1047	90 c. on 50 c. Fork Kyk-over-al		1·50	50
1048	90 c. on 60 c. Fort Island		2·25	20
1045/8		*Set of 4*	5·00	1·25

(Des K. Everett (25 c.). Litho Format)

1983 (19 Feb). *President Burnham's 60th Birthday and 30 Years in Parliament. T 258 and similar multicoloured designs. W 106 (sideways) (25 c., $1.30). P 13½ ($1.30) or 14 (others).*
1049	25 c. Type **258**		15	20
	a. Horiz pair. Nos. 1049/50		25	40
1050	25 c. As T **258**, but position of flag reversed and inscr "30th ANNIVERSARY IN PARLIAMENT"		15	20
1051	$1.30, Youth display (41 × 25 mm)		40	65
1052	$6 Presidential standard (43½ × 25 mm)		1·00	2·75
1049/52		*Set of 4*	1·50	3·50

Nos. 1049/50 were printed together, *se-tenant*, in horizontal pairs throughout the sheet.
No. 1052 exists imperforate from stock dispersed by the liquidator of Format International Security Printers Ltd.
For stamps as Nos. 1049/50, but without commemorative inscriptions, see Nos. 1108/9.

PRINTERS. Nos. 1053/1126 were surcharged or overprinted by Autoprint, Georgetown.

FIFTY CENTS (259)   **20 X** (260)

1983 (7 Mar). *Surch as T 259.*
1053	**170** 50 c. on 10 c. mult (No. 717) (R.)		2·00	30
1054	– 50 c. on 400 c. on 30 c. multicoloured (No. 911) (surch vert)		2·50	30
1055	**152** $1 on 10 c. multicoloured (No. 635) (surch vert)		7·00	45
1056	– $1 on $1.05 on 10 c. multicoloured (No. 768) (surch vert)		6·00	45
1056a	– $1 on $1.10 on $2 multicoloured (No. 843)		1·40	2·50
1057	– $1 on 220 c. on 5 c. mult (No. 844) (B.)		7·00	75
1058	– $1 on 330 c. on $2 mult (No. 981) (B.)		60	45
1059	– $1 on $12 on $1.10 on $2 mult (similar to No. P3) (B.)		5·00	2·00
1053/9		*Set of 8*	28·00	6·50

Nos. 1057/9 have thin bars cancelling previous surcharges, and, in addition, No. 1059 is optd with T **226** in blue.
See also Nos. 1062 and 1080/4.

1983 (7 Mar). *No. 859 optd with T 256.*
1060	$1 on 60 c. Beethoven and Sonny Thomas		6·00	45

1983 (11 Mar). *Conference of Foreign Ministers of Non-aligned Countries, New Delhi. No. 569 surch as T 259 and No. 570 optd with T 256.*
1061	**136** 25 c. multicoloured (opt vert)		1·50	25
1062	– 50 c. on 8 c. mult (surch vert) (R.)		2·50	25

1983 (14 Mar). *As No. 1030, but colour of surcharge changed.*
1063	15 c. on 2 c. Type **132** (R.)		1·50	10

1983 (14 Mar). *No. 771 further surch with T 260 in blue.*
1064	**181** 20 c. on 10 c. on 3 c. black, indigo and Venetian red		55	10

Commonwealth Day 14 March 1983

(261)   (262)   **$1.30**

1983 (14 Mar). *Commonwealth Day. Nos. 398A and 401B surch as T 261 in black (25 c., $1.30) or blue (others).*
1065	25 c.on 6 c. yellow-green		1·00	20
1066	$1.20 on 6 c. yellow-green		50	50
1067	$1.30 on 24 c. black and bright orange		1·25	55
1068	$2.40 on 24 c. black and bright orange		1·75	1·25
1065/8		*Set of 4*	4·00	2·25

1983 (17 Mar). *Easter. Nos. 482/3 optd with T 256.*
1069	**111** 25 c. multicoloured		15	10
1070	– 30 c. multicoloured		30	15

1983 (17 Mar). *25th Anniv of International Maritime Organization. British Guiana fiscal stamp optd in red as T 262. Wmk Mult Crown CA. P 14.*
1071	$4.80, bright blue and deep dull green		2·00	4·00

1983 (1 Apr). *Optd with T 256.*
1072	**152** 50 c. mult (No. 637) (opt vert)		1·50	25
1073	**159** 50 c. ultramarine, black and gold (No. 668) (opt vert)		3·50	25
1073a	– 50 c. multicoloured (No. 723)		25·00	2·00
1074	– 50 c. mult (No. 854) (opt vert)		60	25
1075	– 50 c. multicoloured (No. 858)		65	25
1076	– $1 multicoloured (No. 628)		7·50	45
1077	– $1 mult (No. 638) (opt vert)		5·50	45
1078	– $1 multicoloured (No. 675)		4·00	45
1079	– $1 on 30 c. mult (No. 855) (opt vert)		1·45	45
1079a	– $3 multicoloured (No. 720)		17·00	90
1079b	– $3 multicoloured (No. 724)		20·00	1·50
1079c	– $3 multicoloured (No. 748)		65·00	7·00

1983 (1 Apr). *Surch with T 259, vertically, in black (No. 1082) or blue (others).*
1080	**148** 50 c. on 8 c. multicoloured (No. 615)		1·75	25
1081	**162** 50 c. on 8 c. multicoloured (No. 681)		6·00	25
1082	**171** 50 c. on 10 c. multicoloured (No. 721)		3·00	25
1083	– 50 c. on 10 c. on 25 c. mult (No. O13)		5·00	25
1084	– 50 c. on 330c on $3 mult (No. 845)		4·00	25

1983 (2 May). *Surch as T 254, but with "c" after new face value.*
1085	**105** 15 c. on 6 c. black, gold and flesh (No. 469) (B.)		30	10
1086	– 20 c. on 6 c. multicoloured (No. 546)		30	10
1087	**111** 50 c. on 6 c. multicoloured (No. 481)		40	30

For No. 1085 with black overprint, see No. 1098.

|||| (263)   **ITU 1983** (264)   **25** (265)

$1   **110**

1983 (2 May). *No. 489 surch with T 263.*
1088	$1 on 6 c. Black Acara ("Patua")		1·25	30

1983 (2 May). *No. 639 surch with T 264 in blue.*
1089	**153** 110 c. on 10 c. greenish yellow, light green and light reddish violet		1·75	50
	a. Error. Surch on 35 c (No. 640)		£100	

1983 (2 May). *Nos. 551 and 556 surch as T 228 in blue.*
1090	250 c. on 40 c. Tiger Beard		7·50	55
1091	400 c. on $5 Odontadenia grandiflora		5·50	70

1983 (17 May). *World Telecommunications and Health Day. Nos. 842 and 980 further surch as T 265.*
1092	25 c. on 220 c. on 1 c. Pitcher Plant of Mt Roraima (surch T **265**) (R.)		30	30
	a. Sheetlet of 25. Nos. 1092/3 each × 8 and No. 1094 × 9		6·50	
	b. Six bars only at top			
1093	25 c. on 220 c. on 1 c. Pitcher Plant of Mt Roraima (surch "WHO 1983 25") (R.)		30	30
	b. Six bars only at top			
1094	25 c. on 220 c. on 1 c. Pitcher Plant of Mt Roraima (surch "17 MAY '83 ITU/WHO 25") (R.)		30	30
	b. Six bars only at top			
1095	$4.50 on 75 c. on $5 Odontadenia grandiflora (surch "ITU/WHO 17 MAY 1983") (B.)		13·00	1·50
	a. Surch on 235 c. on 75 c. on $5 (No. 929)		1·75	1·50
1092/5		*Set of 4*	13·00	2·25

1983 (18 May). *30th Anniv of President's Entry into Parliament. Nos. 690 and 692 surch as T 259, the former additionally optd with T 256.*
1096	$1 on 15 c. black, light violet-blue and bluish grey		6·00	50
1097	$1 on 40 c. black, red-orange and bluish grey		9·00	50

No. **MS693** was also reissued with examples of Nos. 1096/7 affixed over the 8 c. and 35 c. values, and an example of No. 1050 added to the righthand sheet margin. These miniature sheets, revalued to $6, numbered on the reverse and cancelled with First Day of Issue postmarks, were for presentation purposes and were not available for postage.

1983 (23 May). *Surch as T 254, but with "c" after new face value.*
1098	**105** 15 c. on 6 c. black, gold and flesh (No. 469) (Blk.)		10	10
1099	– 50 c. on 6 c. multicoloured (No. 489) (Blk.)		30	30

1983 (23 May). *No. 546 surch as T 228, but with "c" after new face value.*
1100	20 c. on 6 c. Cannon-ball tree		15	10

1983 (23 May). *No. 611 optd with T 256.*
1101	25 c. Guides in camp		48·00	4·00

120 **$1.30** (266)   **CANADA 1983** (267)   **XXX** (268)

$1

1983 (23 May). *No. 489 surch with T 266 in red.*
1102	$1 on 6 c. Black Acara ("Patua")		1·25	35

1983 (15 June). *15th World Scout Jamboree, Alberta. Nos. 835/6 and O25 additionally surch or optd as T 267.*
1103	– $1.30 on 100 c. on 8 c. multicoloured		3·00	1·75
1104	**116** 180 c. on 6 c. multicoloured		3·00	3·00
1105	– $3.90 on 400 c. on 6 c. multicoloured		3·50	4·50
1103/5		*Set of 3*	8·50	8·25

1983 (22 June). *Nos. 659/60 surch as T 254.*
1106	60 c. on 15 c. Map of the Caribbean		8·00	40
1107	$1.50 on 15 c. Prudential Cup		9·00	1·25

1983 (1 July). *As Nos. 1049/50, but without commemorative inscr above flag. W 106 (sideways). P 14.*
1108	25 c. As Type **258**		15	15
	a. Horiz pair. Nos. 1108/9		30	30
1109	25 c. As No. 1050		15	15

Nos. 1108/9 were printed together, *se-tenant* in horizontal pairs throughout the sheet.

1983 (1 July). *Optd with T 256.*
1110	**105** 30 c. black, gold and light apple-green (No. 471)		75	20
1111	– 30 c. multicoloured (No. 695)		9·50	30
1112	– 30 c. multicoloured (No. 718) (opt vert)		4·50	20
1113	– 30 c. multicoloured (No. 722)		8·00	20
1114	– 30 c. multicoloured (No. 746)		12·00	20
1115	– 60 c. multicoloured (No. 697)		4·50	20
1116	– 60 c. multicoloured (No. 731)		5·50	20
1110/16		*Set of 7*	40·00	1·25

1983 (1 July). *No. 553 optd with T 226 in blue.*
1117	60 c. Soldier's Cap		4·50	35

1983 (1 July). *Surch as T 264 in blue.*
1118	**157** 120 c. on 8 c. multicoloured (No. 654)		3·25	40
1119	**159** 120 c. on 10 c. dull red, black and gold (No. 666)		3·50	40
1120	– 120 c. on 35 c. multicoloured (No. 622)		3·50	40
	a. Surch reading upwards			
1121	– 120 c. on 35 c. orange, light green and reddish violet (No. 640)		3·50	40

1983 (1 July). *Nos. 716 and 729 surch as T 268.*
1122	120 c. on 10 c. Type **173** (R.)		3·25	40
1123	370 c. on $3 Cylinder satellite		5·00	40

No. 1123 also carries an otherwise unissued surcharge in red, reading "INTERNATIONAL SCIENCE YEAR 1982 375". As issued much of this is obliterated by two heavy bars.

CARICOM DAY 1983

120

GUYANA 60 XXX

(269) (270)

1983 (1 July). *British Guiana No. D1a and Guyana No. D8 surch with T 269 in blue.*
1124 D 1 120 c. on 1 c. deep green.. .. .. 3·25 45
1125 D 2 120 c. on 1 c. olive .. .. .. 3·25 45

1983 (1 July). *CARICOM Day. No. 823 additionally surch with T 270 in red.*
1126 60 c. on $3 "Makanaima the Great Ancestral Spirit of the Amerindians" .. .. 1·75 35

271 *Kurupukari*

(Litho Format)

1983 (11 July*). *Riverboats. T 271 and similar horiz designs. W 106. P 14.*
1127 30 c. black and vermilion 20 20
  a. Tête-bêche (vert pair) 75
  w. Wmk inverted 55 35
1128 60 c. black and bright reddish violet .. 35 35
  a. Tête-bêche (vert pair) .. .. 1·00
  w. Wmk inverted 65 60
1129 120 c. black and bright lemon 40 60
  a. Tête-bêche (vert pair) .. .. 1·40
  w. Wmk inverted 90 95
1130 130 c. black 40 65
  a. Tête-bêche (vert pair) .. .. 1·40
  w. Wmk inverted 90 95
1131 150 c. black and bright emerald .. 40 80
  a. Tête-bêche (vert pair) .. .. 1·40
  w. Wmk inverted .. .. .. 95 1·00
1127/31 .. .. Set of 5 1·60 2·40
Designs:—60 c. *Makouria*; 120 c. *Powis*; 130 c. *Pomeroon*; 150 c. *Lukanani.*
*Although not finally issued until 11 July First Day Covers of Nos. 1127/31 are postmarked with the intended release date of 1 July.
Nos. 1127/31 were each issued in sheets of 80 (10 × 8) with the bottom three rows inverted forming tête-bêche vertical pairs from Rows 5 and 6.

2.30

(272)

1983 (22 July). *Unissued Royal Wedding surcharge, similar to No. 843, surch as T 272 in blue by Autoprint.*
1132 $2.30 on $1.10 on $2 *Norantea guianensis* .. 80 55
1133 $3.20 on $1.10 on $2 *Norantea guianensis* .. 80 55

BW **Mont Golfier**
1783-1983

(273) (274)

1983 (5 Sept). *Bicentenary of Manned Flight and 20th Anniv of Guyana Airways. Nos. 701/2a optd as T 273/4, in red (Nos. 1134/47) or blue (Nos. 1148/68) by Autoprint.*
1134 20 c. multicoloured (optd T 273) .. 20 20
  a. Sheetlet of 25. Nos. 1134/8 each × 4 and 1139 × 5 .. .. .. 4·50
1135 20 c. multicoloured (optd "LM") .. 20 20
1136 20 c. multicoloured (optd "GY 1963 1983") .. 20 20
1137 20 c. multicoloured (optd "JW") .. 20 20
1138 20 c. multicoloured (optd "CU") .. 20 20
1139 20 c. multicoloured (optd T 274) .. 20 20
1140 25 c. multicoloured (optd "BGI") .. 50 25
  a. Sheetlet of 25. Nos. 1140 × 2, 1141 × 8, 1142/44 each × 2, 1145 × 5 and 1146/7 each × 2 .. .. .. 9·00
1141 25 c. multicoloured (optd "GEO") .. 15 10
1142 25 c. multicoloured (optd "MIA") .. 50 25
1143 25 c. multicoloured (optd "BVB") .. 50 25
1144 25 c. multicoloured (optd "PBM") .. 50 25
1145 25 c. multicoloured (optd T 274) .. 20 15
1146 25 c. multicoloured (optd "POS") .. 50 25
1147 25 c. multicoloured (optd "JFK") .. 50 25
1148 30 c. multicoloured (optd "AHL") .. 40 40
  a. Sheetlet of 25. Nos. 1148/54, 1155 × 5 and 1156/68 .. .. 8·00
1149 30 c. multicoloured (optd "BCG") .. 40 30
1150 30 c. multicoloured (optd "BMJ") .. 40 30
1151 30 c. multicoloured (optd "EKE") .. 40 30
1152 30 c. multicoloured (optd "GEO") .. 40 30
1153 30 c. multicoloured (optd "GFO") .. 40 30
1154 30 c. multicoloured (optd "IBM") .. 40 30
1155 30 c. multicoloured (optd T 274) .. 25 10
1156 30 c. multicoloured (optd "KAI") .. 40 30
1157 30 c. multicoloured (optd "KAR") .. 40 30
1158 30 c. multicoloured (optd "KPG") .. 40 30
1159 30 c. multicoloured (optd "KRG") .. 40 30
1160 30 c. multicoloured (optd "KTO") .. 40 30
1161 30 c. multicoloured (optd "LTM") .. 40 30
1162 30 c. multicoloured (optd "MHA") .. 40 30
1163 30 c. multicoloured (optd "MWJ") .. 40 30

1164 30 c. multicoloured (optd "MYM") .. 40 30
1165 30 c. multicoloured (optd "NAI") .. 40 30
1166 30 c. multicoloured (optd "ORJ") .. 40 30
1167 30 c. multicoloured (optd "USI") .. 40 30
1168 30 c. multicoloured (optd "VEG") .. 40 30
1134/68 .. .. Set of 35 11·50 8·00
The overprints on the 20 c. value represent airlines, on the 25 c. international airports and on the 30 c. internal airports. Those on Nos. 1150 and 1154 were incorrect and examples of the former exist with the manuscript correction "PMT".

240 240

(275) (275a)

1983 (14 Sept). *No. 649 surch with T 275 in blue by Autoprint.*
1169 240 c. on 35 c. on 60 c. Soldier's Cap .. 1·25 1·00
  a. Surch with T 275a .. .. 1·25 1·00
  b. Pair. Nos. 1169/a .. .. 2·50
Types 275 and 275a occur *se-tenant* within the sheet.

FAO 1983

30

(276)

25c

. GUYANA

277 G.B. 1857 1d. with
Georgetown "AO3" Postmark

1983 (15 Sept). *F.A.O. Fisheries Project. Nos. 485 and 487 surch as T 276 in red by Autoprint.*
1170 30 c. on 1 c. Type 87 .. .. 15 15
1171 $2.60 on 3 c. Peacock Cichlid ("Lukunani") .. .. 1·50 2·25

(Des K. Everett. Litho Format)

1983 (1 Oct). *125th Anniv of Use of Great Britain Stamps in Guyana. T 277 and similar square designs. P 14½.*

(a) Inscriptions in black. W 106
1172 277 25 c. lake-brown and black .. 15 10
  a. Tête-bêche (pair) 75
  w. Wmk inverted 60
1173 — 30 c. rose-red and black .. 15 15
  a. Tête-bêche (pair) 75
  w. Wmk inverted 60
1174 — 60 c. bright violet and black .. 35 30
  a. Tête-bêche (pair) .. .. 1·75
  w. Wmk inverted .. .. 1·40
1175 — 120 c. dull green and black .. 75 55
  a. Tête-bêche (pair) .. .. 3·50
  w. Wmk inverted .. .. 2·75

(b) Inscriptions in bright blue. W 106 (inverted).
1176 277 25 c. lake-brown and black .. 15 10
  a. Block of 4. Nos. 1176/9 .. 55
1177 — 25 c. rose-red and black .. 15 10
1178 — 25 c. bright violet and black .. 15 10
1179 — 25 c. dull green and black .. 15 10
1180 277 30 c. lake-brown and black .. 15 15
  a. Block of 4. Nos. 1180/3 .. 55
1181 — 30 c. rose-red and black .. 15 15
1182 — 30 c. bright violet and black .. 15 15
1183 — 30 c. dull green and black .. 15 15
1184 277 45 c. lake-brown and black .. 30 25
  a. Block of 4. Nos. 1184/7 .. 1·10
1185 — 45 c. rose-red and black .. 30 25
1186 — 45 c. bright violet and black .. 30 25
1187 — 45 c. dull green and black .. 30 25
1188 277 120 c. lake-brown and black .. 40 55
  a. Block of 4. Nos. 1188/91 .. 1·40
1189 — 130 c. rose-red and black .. 40 60
1190 — 150 c. bright violet and black .. 40 70
1191 — 200 c. dull green and black .. 40 95
1172/91 .. .. Set of 20 4·50 5·00
Designs:—Nos. 1173, 1177, 1181, 1185, 1189, G.B. 1857 4d. rose; Nos. 1174, 1178, 1182, 1186, 1190, G.B. 1856 6d. lilac; Nos. 1175, 1179, 1183, 1187, 1191, G.B. 1856 1s. green.
Each design incorporates the "AO3" postmark except Nos. 1189/91 which show mythical postmarks of the Crowned-circle type inscribed "DEMERARA", "BERBICE" or "ESSEQUIBO".
Nos. 1172/5 were each printed in sheets with the bottom row inverted, forming vertical *tête-bêche* pairs. Nos. 1176/87 were issued in sheets of 60, one for each value, with the four designs *se-tenant*. Nos. 1188/91 were issued in sheets of 20, containing five *se-tenant* blocks.

75

**INT.
COMMUNICATIONS
YEAR 50**

(278) (279)

1983 (15 Oct). *International Communications Year. No. 716 surch with T 278 by Autoprint.*
1192 50 c. on 375 c. on $3 Cylinder satellite 4·50 30
No. 1192 also carries an otherwise unissued "375" surcharge. As issued much of this surcharge is obliterated by two groups of six thin horizontal lines.

1983 (15 Oct). *St. John's Ambulance Commemoration. Nos. 650 and 653 surch as T 279, vertically on No. 1194 by Autoprint.*
1193 156 75 c. on 8 c. silver, black and magenta .. 4·50 50
1194 — $1.20 on 40 c. silver, black and new blue 6·50 50

$1.20

**Int. Food Day 1918-1983
1983**

I.L.O.

(280) (281)

1983 (15 Oct). *International Food Day. No. 616 surch with T 280 by Autoprint.*
1195 $1.20 on 35 c. Five-fingers and awaras .. 1·00 50

1983 (15 Oct). *65th Anniv of I.L.O. and 25th Death Anniv. of H. N. Critchlow (founder of Guyana Labour Union). No. 840 further optd with T 281 by Autoprint.*
1196 240 c. on $3 H. N. Critchlow .. 1·50 1·50

25c. Human Rights Day

(282) (283)

1983 (1 Nov). *Deepavali Festival. Nos. 661 and 663/4 surch as T 282 by Autoprint.*
1197 25 c. on 8 c. Type 158 .. .. 20 10
1198 $1.50 on 35 c. Flame in bowl .. 1·25 60
1199 $1.50 on 40 c. Goddess Latchmi .. 80 60
1197/9 .. .. Set of 3 2·00 1·25
On Nos. 1198/9 the original face values are obliterated by "XX" and the surcharges are horizontal.

1983 (3 Nov). *No. 732 optd with T 226 and No. 798 further optd with T 256, both vertically reading upwards by Autoprint.*
1200 $3 "Makanaima the Great Ancestral Spirit of the Amerindians" (B.) .. 1·50 70
  a. Opt reading downwards .. 14·00
1201 360 c. on $2 *Norantea guianensis* .. 1·75 80

1983 (15 Nov). *Wildlife Protection. Nos. 686 and 688 surch as T 234, and No. 852 optd with T 256 by Autoprint.*
1202 30 c. Six-banded Armadillo .. 50 15
1203 60 c. on 15 c. Giant sea turtle .. 75 30
1204 $1.20 on 40 c. Iguana .. .. 1·25 50
1202/4 .. .. Set of 3 2·25 85

1983 (1 Dec). *Human Rights Day. No. 1079c optd with T 283 by Autoprint.*
1205 $3 Rotary anniversary emblem .. 2·00 1·25

**LOS ANGELES
1984**

125 ●●●

(284)

●●● 55

(284a)

1983 (6 Dec). *Olympic Games, Los Angeles (1984) (1st issue). Nos. 733/44 surch with T 284 by Herald Printing-Kitty or further surch with T 284a by Autoprint.*
1206 55 c. on 125 c. on 35 c. Type 174 .. 25 25
  a. Block of 12. Nos. 1206/17 3·50
1207 55 c. on 125 c. on 35 c. Trahira ("Haimara") .. 25 25
1208 55 c. on 125 c. on 35 c. Electric Eel .. 25 25
1209 55 c. on 125 c. on 35 c. Golden Rivulus .. 25 25
1210 55 c. on 125 c. on 35 c. Golden Pencilfish .. 25 25
1211 55 c. on 125 c. on 35 c. Four-eyed Fish .. 25 25
1212 55 c. on 125 c. on 35 c. Red Piranha ("Pirai") .. 25 25
1213 55 c. on 125 c. on 35 c. Smoking Hassar 25 25
1214 55 c. on 125 c. on 35 c. Manta .. 25 25
1215 55 c. on 125 c. on 35 c. Festive Cichlid ("Flying Patwa") .. 25 25
1216 55 c. on 125 c. on 35 c. Arapaima .. 25 25
1217 55 c. on 125 c. on 35 c. Peacock Cichlid ("Lukanani") .. 25 25
1217a 125 c. on 35 c. Type 174 .. 4·50
  ab. Block of 12. Nos. 1217a/l .. 48·00
1217b 125 c. on 35 c. Trahira ("Haimara") .. 4·50
1217c 125 c. on 35 c. Electric Eel .. 4·50
1217d 125 c. on 35 c. Golden Rivulus .. 4·50
1217e 125 c. on 35 c. Golden Pencilfish .. 4·50
1217f 125 c. on 35 c. Four-eyed Fish .. 4·50
1217g 125 c. on 35 c. Red Piranha ("Pirai") .. 4·50
1217h 125 c. on 35 c. Smoking Hassar .. 4·50
1217i 125 c. on 35 c. Manta .. 4·50
1217j 125 c. on 35 c. Festive Cichlid ("Flying Patwa") .. 4·50
1217k 125 c. on 35 c. Arapaima .. 4·50
1217l 125 c. on 35 c. Peacock Cichlid ("Lukanani") .. 4·50
See also Nos. 1308/17 and 1420.

1983 (14 Dec). *No. F7 with unissued "ESPANA 1982" surch, as Nos. 938/9 in blue, further optd with T 256 vertically by Autoprint.*
1218 180 c. on 60 c. Soldier's Cap .. .. 2·00 65
    a. Opt (T 256) omitted .. .. .. 15·00

(285) COMMONWEALTH HEADS OF GOV'T MEETING—INDIA 1983 150

(286) CHRISTMAS 1983 20c

1983 (14 Dec). *Commonwealth Heads of Government Meeting, New Delhi. No. 542 surch with T 285 by Autoprint.*
1219 150 c. on 1 c. Pitcher Plant of Mt Roraima .. 2·25 60

1983 (14 Dec). *Christmas. Nos. 861A/B further surch with T 286 by Autoprint.*
                  A. No wmk B. Wmk 106
1220 20 c. on 12 c. on 6 c. Black
    Acara ("Patua") .. 1·00 10 1·00 10

1984 (8 Jan). *Nos. 838 and F9 optd as T 229, but smaller 24 × 6 mm, vertically in blue by Autoprint.*
1221 $2 Norantea guianensis .. .. 3·00 70
1221a 550 c. on $10 Elbella patrobas .. .. 11·00 7·50

17¢
(287)

1984 (Jan). *Flowers. Unissued coil stamps as T 222 handstamped with T 287 in blue.*
1222 17 c. on 2 c. grey-lilac, blue & turquoise-green 1·00 75
    a. Vert pair. Nos. 1222/3 .. .. 2·00 1·50
1223 17 c. on 8 c. grey-lilac, blue and mauve .. 1·00 75
Nos. 1222/3 were intended for use on 8 c. postal stationery envelopes to uprate them to the new price of 25 c.

ALL OUR HERITAGE
1984
(288) ● 25 (289) ● 25
1984
(290) ● 25 (291) ● 25

1984 (24 Feb). *Republic Day. No. 703 surch as T 288/91 in black and No. 705a optd as T 288/9 in blue by Autoprint.*
1224 25 c. on 35 c. multicoloured (surch T 288) 35 20
    a. Sheetlet of 25. No. 1224 × 6, Nos. 1225/7 each × 4, Nos. 1228/30 each × 2 and No. 1231 .. .. 18·00
1225 25 c. on 35 c. multicoloured (surch T 289) 40 20
1226 25 c. on 35 c. multi (surch "REPUBLIC DAY") 40 20
1227 25 c. on 35 c. multicoloured (surch T 290) 40 20
1228 25 c. on 35 c. multi (surch "BERBICE") 1·50 1·25
1229 25 c. on 35 c. multi (surch "DEMERARA") 1·50 1·25
1230 25 c. on 35 c. multi (surch "ESSEQUIBO") 1·50 1·25
1231 25 c. on 35 c. multicoloured (surch T 291) 5·50 6·00
1232 60 c. multicoloured (opt T 288) .. 50 30
    a. Sheetlet of 25. Nos. 1232/3 each × 8 and No. 1234 × 9 .. .. .. 11·00
1233 60 c. multicoloured (opt "REPUBLIC DAY") 50 30
1234 60 c. multicoloured (opt T 289) .. 50 30
1224/34 .. .. Set of 11 11·50 10·50

(292) **25** ($+2·25) SURTAX POSTAGE OLYMPIC GAMES 84 ○○○ ○○○

1984 (1 Mar). *Guyana Olympic Committee Appeal. Nos. 841/3 handstamped with T 292 in blue.*
1235 25 c. + $2.25 on 60 c. on 3 c. Hanging Heliconia .. .. .. 2·00 4·50
1236 25 c. + $2.25 on 75 c. on $5 Odontadenia grandiflora .. .. 2·00 4·50
1237 25 c. + $2.25 on £1.10 on $2 Norantea guianensis .. .. 2·00 4·50
1235/7 .. .. .. Set of 3 5·50 12·00
Nos. 1235/7 come from stamp booklets, the $2.25 charity premium on each stamp being donated to the local Olympic Committee Appeal Fund. All examples of these handstamps are inverted.

PRINTERS. Nos. 1238/97 and 1302/27 were overprinted or surcharged by Autoprint, Georgetown.

(293) **[XXXX** Protecting Our Heritage

(294) **90**

1984 (5 Mar). *Nature Protection. Various stamps optd with T 293 in black (except for No. 1239 in blue) with some additionally surch as T 272 (Nos. 1238/40, 1250/1 and 1254/5) or as T 294 (Nos. 1242, 1247 and 1252/3) all in blue.*
1238 20 c. on 15 c. multicoloured (No. 491) (opt + surch vert) .. .. 7·50 10
    a. Opt T 293 in blue .. .. 15·00 50
1239 20 c. on 15 c. multicoloured (No. 791) (opt + surch vert) .. .. 7·50 10
    a. Surch on No. 791a (pair)
1240 20 c. on 15 c. multicoloured (No. 1044) (opt + surch vert) .. .. 35·00 1·75
    a. Opt T 293 in blue .. .. 15·00 1·25
1241 25 c. multicoloured (No. 550a) .. 9·50 10
    a. On No. 550ab .. .. 45·00 3·50
1242 30 c. on 15 c. multicoloured (No. 548) 18·00 30
1243 40 c. multicoloured (No. 494) (opt vert) 11·00 20
1244 50 c. multicoloured (No. 552) .. 1·25 25
1245 50 c. multicoloured (No. F6).. .. 1·25 25
    a. Opt Type F 1 double .. 25·00
1246 60 c. multicoloured (No. 459) .. 9·00 30
    a. On No. 496 .. .. 55·00 4·00
1247 90 c. on 40 c. multicoloured (No. 551) 15·00 50
    a. On No. F5 .. .. £100 7·50
1248 180 c. on 40 c. multicoloured (No. 919) 15·00 90
1249 $2 multicoloured (No. 461) .. 50·00 1·50
1250 225 c. on 10 c. multicoloured (No. 490a) (opt + surch vert) .. .. 22·00 1·00
1251 260 c. on $1 multicoloured (No. 497a) 10·00 1·00
1252 320 c. on 40 c. multicoloured (No. 551) 11·00 2·25
1253 350 c. on 40 c. multicoloured (No. 551) 18·00 2·50
1254 390 c. on 50 c. multicoloured (No. 495) 4·50 2·50
    a. On No. 458 .. .. 80·00 20·00
1255 450 c. on $5 multicoloured (No. 499).. 6·00 2·50
1238/55 .. .. .. Set of 18 £200 15·00

(295) **1984**

(296) **ITU DAY 1984** **25**

1984 (17 Mar). *Easter. Nos. 483 and 916/17 optd with T 295, and No. 481 surch as T 272, but without decimal point, all in blue.*
1256 111 30 c. multicoloured 20 20
1257 45 c. on 6 c. multicoloured .. 25 25
1258 75 c. on 40 c. multicoloured .. 35 35
1259 130 c. on 6 c. multicoloured .. 65 60
1256/9 .. .. .. Set of 4 1·40 1·25
No. 1258 exists with the previous surcharge either at the right or in the centre of the design.

1984 (2 Apr). *Nos. 937/9 and 991 surch as T 294.*
1260 75 c. on $1 Chelonanthus uliginoides .. 9·50 35
1261 75 c. on 110 c. on 3 c. Hanging Heliconia 9·50 35
1262 225 c. on 250 c. on 6 c. Cannon-ball tree 3·00 1·25
1263 230 c. on $2.35 on 180 c. on 60 c. Soldier's Cap 3·00 1·00

1984 (2 May). *Nos. 899/901, 904/6 and 909 surch as T 294.*
1264 20 c. on 15 c. on 2 c. Type 132 (No. 899) 1·50 30
1265 75 c. on 110 c. on 5 c. Annatto tree (No. 904) 9·00 70
1266 90 c. on 110 c. on 5 c. Annatto tree (No. 900) (B.) .. .. 5·50 85
1267 90 c. on 110 c. on 5 c. Annatto tree (No. 901) (B.) .. .. 7·00 85
1268 120 c. on 125 c. on 8 c. on 6 c. Cannon-ball tree (No. 905) .. .. 7·00 1·00
1269 120 c. on 125 c. on 8 c. on 6 c. Cannon-ball tree (No. 906) .. .. 7·00 1·00
1270 120 c. on 125 c. on 8 c. on 6 c. Cannon-ball tree (No. 909) .. .. 2·75 1·00
1264/70 .. .. .. Set of 7 35·00 5·25
Nos. 1264/70 were surcharged on the sheets which contained one type of the previous surcharge only.

1984 (17 May). *World Telecommunications and Health Day. Nos. 802 and 980 surch as T 296 in blue.*
1271 25 c. on 220 c. on 1 c. Pitcher Plant of Mt Roraima (surch T 296) 20 20
    a. Sheetlet of 25. Nos. 1271/2 each × 8 and No. 1273 × 9 .. .. 4·50
1272 25 c. on 220 c. on 1 c. Pitcher Plant of Mt Roraima (surch "WHO DAY 1984") .. 20 20
1273 25 c. on 220 c. on 1 c. Pitcher Plant of Mt Roraima (surch "ITU/WHO DAY 1984") 20 20
1274 $4.50 on 280 c. on $5 Odontadenia grandiflora (surch "ITU/WHO DAY 1984") .. .. 1·75 1·25
1271/4 .. .. .. Set of 4 2·10 1·75
The surcharge is horizontal on No. 1274 and vartical on the others.

1984 (11 June). *No. 1005 surch vertically as T 272, but without decimal point.*
1275 120 c. on $1.25 on 6 c. Cannon-ball tree .. 7·00 55

1984 (15 June). *World Forestry Conference. Nos. 752/5 surch as T 272, but without decimal point, or optd with T 295 ($3), and No. 875 surch as T 294.*
1276 55 c. on 30 c. Hymenaea courbaril .. 2·75 30
1277 75 c. on 110 c. on $3 Peltogyne venosa (B.) 40 35
1278 160 c. on 50 c. Mora excelsa (B.) .. 75 70
1279 260 c. on 10 c. Type 177 (B.) .. .. 1·25 1·25
1280 $3 Peltogyne venosa (B.) .. .. 1·40 1·40
1276/80 .. .. .. Set of 5 6·00 3·50

1984 (18 June). *No. 625 surch vertically as T 294.*
1281 55 c. on 110 c. on 10 c. Type 150 .. 75 30
1282 90 c. on 110 c. on 10 c. Type 150 (B.) .. 1·00 45
Nos. 1281/2 also carry an otherwise unissued 110 c. surcharge in blue as Type 264.

(297) **UPU Congress 1984 Hamburg**

(298) **60**

1984 (19 June). *U.P.U. Congress, Hamburg. Nos. 1188/91 optd with T 297.*
1283 120 c. lake-brown and black 50 60
    a. Block of 4. Nos. 1283/6.. .. 2·25
1284 130 c. rose-red and black 55 70
1285 150 c. bright violet and black.. .. 60 75
1286 200 c. dull green and black 80 90
1283/6 .. .. .. Set of 4 2·25 2·75

1984 (21 June). *Nos. 982/3 and 986/7 surch with T 298 (60 c.) or as T 272, but without the decimal point (others).*
1287 45 c. on 50 c. on 2 c. myrtle-green .. 60 25
1288 60 c. on $1.10 on 3 c. brown-olive and red-brown (B.) .. .. .. 2·25 40
    a. Surch on No. 983c .. .. 2·50 40
1289 120 c. on $1.25 on 6 c. yellow-green .. 75 55
1290 200 c. on $2.20 on 24 c. black and brownish orange (B.) .. .. 5·00 1·10

1984 (30 June). *Nos. 979/80 and 1003 surch as T 294, and No. 981 optd vertically with T 295.*
1291 75 c. on 110 c. on 5 c. Annatto tree .. 60 35
1292 120 c. on 170 c. on 110 c. on 5 c. Annatto tree 80 55
1293 200 c. on 220 c. on 1 c. Pitcher Plant of Mt Roraima (B.) .. .. 11·00 85
1294 330 c. on $2 Norantea guianensis (B.) .. 1·75 1·75

CARICOM DAY 1984

(299) **60** **XX**

1984 (30 June). *CARICOM Day. No. 1200 additionally surch with T 299.*
1295 60 c. on $3 "Makanaima the Great Ancestral Spirit of the Amerindians" 40 30

1984 (30 June). *No. 544 surch as T 275 in blue.*
1296 150 c. on 3 c. Hanging Heliconia .. .. 1·25 65

60 CARICOM HEADS OF GOV'T CONFERENCE JULY 1984 **X**
(300)

301 Children and Thatched School

1984 (2 July). *CARICOM Heads of Government Conference. No. 544 surch with T 300 in blue.*
1297 60 c. on 3 c. Hanging Heliconia 40 30

(Litho Format)

1984 (16 July). *Centenary of Guyana Teachers' Association. T 301 and similar horiz designs. Multicoloured. W 106 (sideways). P 14.*
298 25 c. Type 301 .. .. .. 10 15
    a. Block of 4. Nos. 1298/301 .. 35
299 25 c. Torch and graduates 10 15
300 25 c. Torch and target emblem .. 10 15
301 25 c. Teachers of 1884 and 1984 in front of school 10 15
1298/301 .. .. .. Set of 4 35 55
Nos. 1298/301 were printed together, se-tenant, in blocks of 4 throughout the sheet.

INT. CHESS FED. 1924-1984 **25** TRACK AND FIELD
25 XX
(302)   (303)

1984 (20 July). *60th Anniv of International Chess Federation.* No. 1048 *optd or surch as T 295 or optd with T 295, all in blue.*
1302	25 c. on 90 c. on 60 c. Fort Island (surch T 302)	1·00	25
	a. Sheetlet of 25. No. 1302 × 16 and No.		
	1303 × 9..	27·00	
1303	25 c. on 90 c. on 60 c. Fort Island (opt T 295)	1·75	45
1304	75 c. on 90 c. on 60 c. Fort Island (surch T 302)	1·10	40
	a. Sheetlet of 25. No. 1304 × 16 and No.		
	1305 × 9..	32·00	
1305	75 c. on 90 c. on 60 c. Fort Island (opt T 295)	2·00	70
1306	90 c. on 60 c. Fort Island (opt T 302)	1·25	50
	a. Sheetlet of 25. No. 1306 × 16 and No.		
	1307 × 9..	35·00	
1307	90 c. on 60 c. Fort Island (opt T 295)	2·25	90
1302/7		*Set of 6*	8·50	2·75

Overprints as Type **295** occur in the central horizontal and vertical rows of each sheet.

1984 (28 July). *Olympic Games, Los Angeles (2nd issue).* No. 1051 *surch as T 303 in blue.*
1308	25 c. on $1.30, multicoloured (surch T 303) ..	20	25
	a. Booklet pane of 10. No. 1308 × 4 and Nos.		
	1309/10, each × 3	2·50	
	b. Coil strip of 5. Nos. 1308 × 2, 1311 × 2		
	and 1312	4·25	
1309	25 c. on $1.30, mult (surch "BOXING")	20	30
1310	25 c. on $1.30, mult (surch "OLYMPIC		
	GAMES 1984 LOS ANGELES")	20	30
1311	25 c. on $1.30, mult (surch "CYCLING")	1·00	50
1312	25 c. on $1.30, mult (surch "OLYMPIC		
	GAMES 1984") ..	3·00	1·25
1313	$1.20 on $1.30, multicoloured (surch T 303)	1·00	1·10
	a. Booklet pane of 10. No. 1313 × 4 and Nos.		
	1314/15 each × 3	10·00	
	b. Coil strip of 5. Nos. 1313 × 2, 1316 × 2		
	and 1317	7·00	
1314	$1.20 on $1.30, mult (surch "BOXING")	1·00	1·10
1315	$1.20 on $1.30, mult (surch "OLYMPIC		
	GAMES 1984 LOS ANGELES")	1·00	1·25
1316	$1.20 on $1.30, mult (surch "CYCLING") ..	1·75	1·50
1317	$1.20 on $1.30, multicoloured (surch		
	"OLYMPIC GAMES 1984")	3·50	3·00
1308/17		*Set of 10*	11·50	9·50

Nos. 1308 and 1313 come from booklets and coils, Nos. 1309/10 and 1314/15 from booklets only, and Nos. 1311/12 and 1316/17 from coils only.

The coils were constructed from normal sheets with coil joins on every fifth stamp.

(304)

1984 (15 Aug). *60th Anniv of Girl Guide Movement in Guyana.* Nos. 900/9 *surch with T 304 in blue.*
1318	25 c. on 110 c. on 5 c. Annatto tree (No. 900)	15	15
	a. Sheetlet of 25. Nos. 1318/19, each × 8,		
	Nos. 1320/1, each × 4 and No. 1322	8·50	
1319	25 c. on 110 c. on 5 c. Annatto tree (No. 901) ..	15	15
1320	25 c. on 110 c. on 5 c. Annatto tree (No. 902) ..	50	35
1321	25 c. on 110 c. on 5 c. Annatto tree (No. 903) ..	50	35
1322	25 c. on 110 c. on 5 c. Annatto tree (No. 904) ..	3·00	3·25
1323	25 c. on 125 c. on 8 c. on 6 c. Cannon-ball tree		
	(No. 905)..	15	15
	a. Sheetlet of 25. Nos. 1323/4, each × 8, Nos.		
	1325/6, each × 4 and No. 1327	8·50	
1324	25 c. on 125 c. on 8 c. on 6 c. Cannon-ball tree		
	(No. 906)..	15	15
1325	25 c. on 125 c. on 8 c. on 6 c. Cannon-ball tree		
	(No. 907)..	50	35
1326	25 c. on 125 c. on 8 c. on 6 c. Cannon-ball tree		
	(No. 908)..	50	35
1327	25 c. on 125 c. on 8 c. on 6 c. Cannon-ball tree		
	(No. 909)..	3·00	3·25
1318/27		*Set of 10*	7·75	7·75

25   130   1984

(305)   (306)   (307)

1984

1984

(308)   (309)

1984 (Sept–Nov). *Various stamps surch or optd.*

(a) As T 294 or as T 298 (60 c.)
1328	20 c. on 15 c. on 2 c. Type 132 (No. 1030)	30	10
1329	20 c. on 15 c. on 2 c. Type 132 (No. 1034) ..	65	10
1330	20 c. on 15 c. on 2 c. Type 132 (No. 1063) ..	90	10
1331	60 c. on 110 c. on 8 c. on 3 c. Hanging Heli-		
	conia (as No. 868, but without T 219)		
	(two vert obliterating panels)	29·00	
	a. One vert obliterating panel*	90·00	
1332	120 c. on 125 c. on 8 c. on 6 c. Cannon-ball tree		
	(No. 893)	5·00	50
1333	120 c. on 125 c. on $2 *Norantea guianensis*		
	(No. 834)	35·00	

1334	120 c. on 125 c. on $2 *Norantea guianensis*		
	(No. O20)	2·00	50
1335	120 c. on 140 c. on $1 *Chelonanthus uligino-*		
	ides (No. 796)	5·50	50
1336	200 c. on 220 c. on 1 c. Pitcher Plant of Mt		
	Roraima (No. 922) (B.)..	6·50	75
1337	320 c. on $1.10 on $2 *Norantea guianensis*		
	(No. 804) (B.)..	1·75	75
1338	350 c. on 375 c. on $5 *Odontadenia grandiflora*		
	(No. 803) (B.)..	3·25	80
1339	390 c. on 400 c. on $5 *Odontadenia grandiflora*		
	(No. 1091) (B.)..	4·00	90
1340	450 c. on $5' *Odontadenia grandiflora* (No.		
	O16) (B.)..	5·50	2·50

*The small original printing of the 60 c. surcharge has the "8 c" and "110" values obliterated by a single vertical block of six lines. On the vast majority of the supply these features were covered by two vertical blocks of six lines each.

(b) As T 305 (figures surch, bar in ballpoint pen)
1341	25 c. on 10 c. Cattleya (No. 547) .. ..28·00	2·00
	a. Surch on No. 547a	50·00	3·25
1342	25 c. on 15 c. Christmas Orchid (No. 864a)..	13·00	15
1342a	25 c. on 35 c. on 60 c. Soldier's Cap (No. 649)	90·00	4·50

(c) As T 306 (on Nos. 1343/8 the original face value is obliterated by a fleur-de-lys
1343	25 c. on 15 c. Christmas Orchid (No. 548) ..	£120	5·00
1344	25 c. on 15 c. Christmas Orchid (No. 809) ..	60·00	3·00
1345	25 c. on 15 c. Christmas Orchid (No. 864) ..	23·00	2·25
1346	25 c. on 15 c. Christmas Orchid (No. 977) ..	12·00	10
	a. Surch on No. 977a	£120	6·00
1347	25 c. on 15 c. Christmas Orchid (No. 1009)..	12·00	10
1348	25 c. on 15 c. Christmas Orchid (No. O23)..	12·00	10
1349	130 c. on 110 c. on $2 *Norantea guianensis* (No		
	804)	70·00	4·00
1350	130 c. on 110 c. on $2 *Norantea guianensis* (No		
	O22)	3·00	1·50
1351	600 c. on $7.20 on 1 c. *Chelonanthus uligino-*		
	ides (No. 770A)..	3·00	1·00
	a. With two fleur-de-lys over original op	75	80
	b. Surch on No. 770B	3·00	2·00
	ba. With two fleur-de-lys over original op	75	75

(d) With T 307 (Nov)
1352	20 c. *Paphinia cristata* (No. 549) .. ..17·00	10
	a. Optd on No. 549a	£120	5·00
1353	$3.60 on $5 *Odontadenia grandiflora* (No.		
	769A)	1·50	1·50
	a. Optd on No. 769B	3·50	1·25

(e) With T 308 vertically in blue (Nov)
1354	50 c. on 8 c. Type 136 (No. 1062)	10·00	25
1355	60 c. on 1 c. Pitcher Plant of Mt Roraima (No.		
	1000)	65	25
1356	$2 *Norantea guianensis* (No. O33) ..	1·50	60

(f) With T 309
1357	20 c. *Paphinia cristata* (No. 549) ..	55·00	3·25
	a. Optd on No. 549a	£120	6·00
1357b	20 c. *Paphina cristata* (No. 887a) ("1984"		
	omitted)	55·00	3·25
1358	25 c. Marabunta (No. 550) ..	85·00	4·50
1358a	25 c. Marabunta (No. 889) ("1984" omitted)	85·00	4·50
1358b	25 c. Marabunta (No. 889b) ("1984" omit-		
	ted)	35·00	2·50
1359	25 c. Marabunta (No. F4) ..	3·75	50
	a. Optd on No. F4a	2·00	30
1360	$3.60 on $5 *Odontadenia grandiflora* (No.		
	769A)	85	1·10
	a. Optd on No. 769B	85	1·40

ICAO

(310)   (311)

1984 (6 Sept). *40th Anniv of International Civil Aviation Organization.* Nos. 981 (*with previously unissued surcharge*), 1017 *and* 1148/68 *optd as T 310 (30 c.) or T 311 (200 c.), all in blue by Autoprint.*
1361	30 c. multicoloured (No. 1148)	50	50
	a. Sheetlet of 25. Nos. 1361/71, 1372 × 2		
	and 1373/84	11·00	
1362	30 c. multicoloured (No. 1149)	50	50
1363	30 c. multicoloured (No. 1150)	50	50
1364	30 c. multicoloured (No. 1151)	50	50
1365	30 c. multicoloured (No. 1152)	50	50
1366	30 c. multicoloured (No. 1153)	50	50
1367	30 c. mult (No. 1154) (optd "IMB/ICAO")	50	50
1368	30 c. mult (No. 1155) (optd "KCV/ICAO")	50	50
1369	30 c. mult (No. 1156) (optd "KAI/ICAO")	50	50
1370	30 c. multicoloured (No. 1157) ..	50	50
1371	30 c. multicoloured (No. 1158) ..	50	50
1372	30 c. mult (No. 1155) (optd "1984")	50	50
1373	30 c. mult (No. 1155) (optd "KPM/ICAO")	50	50
1374	30 c. multicoloured (No. 1159) ..	50	50
1375	30 c. multicoloured (No. 1160) ..	50	50
1376	30 c. multicoloured (No. 1161) ..	50	50
1377	30 c. mult (No. 1155) (optd "PMT/ICAO")	50	50
1378	30 c. multicoloured (No. 1162) ..	50	50
1379	30 c. multicoloured (No. 1163) ..	50	50
1380	30 c. multicoloured (No. 1164) ..	50	50
1381	30 c. multicoloured (No. 1165) ..	50	50
1382	30 c. multicoloured (No. 1166) ..	50	50
1383	30 c. multicoloured (No. 1167) ..	50	50
1384	30 c. multicoloured (No. 1168) ..	50	50
1385	200 c. on 330 c. on $2 mult (No. 981) ..	65	70
	a. Opt T 311 omitted	35·00	
1386	200 c. on 75 c. on $5 mult (No. 1017) ..	2·00	1·50
1361/86		*Set of 26*	13·50	13·00

No. 1385 also carries an otherwise unissued surcharge "G.A.C. Inaug. Flight Georgetown—Toronto 200" in black.

$1.50

(312)   (313)   (314)

1984 (15 Sept). *Wildlife Protection.* Nos. 756/67 *optd with T 312 by Autoprint.*
1387	30 c. Type 178	30	25
	a. Sheetlet of 12. Nos. 1387/98 ..	3·25	
1388	30 c. Red Howler	30	25
1389	30 c. Common Squirrel-Monkey	30	25
1390	30 c. Two-toed Sloth..	30	25
1391	30 c. Brazilian Tapir	30	25
1392	30 c. Collared Peccary	30	25
1393	30 c. Six-banded Armadillo..	30	25
1394	30 c. Tamandua ("Ant Eater")	30	25
1395	30 c. Giant Anteater	30	25
1396	30 c. Murine Opossum	30	25
1397	30 c. Brown Four-eyed Opossum	30	25
1398	30 c. Brazilian Agouti	30	25
1387/98		*Set of 12*	3·25	2·75

1984 (1 Oct). Nos. D6/7 *and* D10/11 *surch with T 269 in blue by Autoprint.*
1399	D 2	120 c. on 4 c. dp ultramarine (No. D6)	3·75	45
1400		120 c. on 4 c. dull ultram (No. D10)	19·00	1·50
1401		120 c. on 12 c. reddish scarlet (No. D7)	3·75	45
1402		120 c. on 12 c. bright scarlet (No. D11)	3·75	45
1399/402			*Set of 4*	27·00	2·40

1984 (15 Oct). *175th Birth Anniv of Louis Braille (inventor of alphabet for the blind).* No. 1040 *surch with T 313 in blue by Autoprint.*
1403	$1.50 on 15 c. on 10 c. Type 215	6·50	55

1984 (15 Oct). *International Food Day.* No. 1012 *surch with T 314 by Tip Torres.*
1404	150 c. on 50 c. Pawpaw and tangerine ..	1·50	55

Type **314** places a "1" alongside the original face value and obliterates the "1982" date on the previous overprint.

1984 (15 Oct). *Birth Centenary of H. N. Critchlow (founder of Guyana Labour Union).* No. 873, *surch horizontally as T 236, and No.* 1196, *both optd with T 312 by Autoprint.*
1405	240 c. on 110 c. on $3 H. N. Critchlow (No.		
	873)	1·00	65
1406	240 c. on $3 H. N. Critchlow (No. 1196) ..	6·50	70

1984 (22 Oct). Nos. 910/12 *surch as T 272, but vertically and without the decimal point, and Nos.* 1184/7 *surch as T 234 by Autoprint.*
1407	277	25 c. on 45 c. lake-brown and black ..	15	15
		a. Block of 4. Nos. 1407/10	55	
1408	–	25 c. on 45 c. rose-red and black (No.		
		1185)	15	15
1409	–	25 c. on 45 c. bright violet and black		
		(No. 1186)	15	15
1410	–	25 c. on 45 c. dull green and black		
		(No. 1187)	15	15
1411	–	120 c. on 100 c. on $3 multicoloured		
		(No. 910)	7·50	45
1412	–	120 c. on 400 c. on 30 c. multicoloured		
		(No. 911)	85	45
1413	–	320 c. on $5 mult (No. 912) (B.) ..	15·00	1·75
1407/13			*Set of 7*	22·00	3·00

25   X

MAHA SABHA
1934-1984   Philatelic Exhibition
    New York 1984

(315)   (316)

1984 (1 Nov). *Deepavali Festival.* Nos. 544/5 *surch as T 315 in blue by Autoprint.*
1414	25 c. on 5 c. Annatto tree	20	10
1415	$1.50 on 3 c. Hanging Heliconia.. ..	1·40	55

1984 (15 Nov). *A.S.D.A. Philatelic Exhibition, New York.* Nos. 1188/91 *optd with T 316 in red by Autoprint.*
1416	277	120 c. lake-brown and black..	40	45
		a. Block of 4. Nos. 1416/19	1·90	
1417	–	130 c. rose-red and black	45	50
1418	–	150 c. bright violet and black	50	55
1419	–	200 c. dull green and black ..	70	75
1416/19			*Set of 4*	1·90	2·00

(Litho Format)

1984 (16 Nov). *Olympic Games, Los Angeles (3rd issue).* Design as No. 1051, *but with Olympic rings and inscr "OLYMPIC GAMES 1984 LOS ANGELES". P 13½.*
1420	$1.20, Youth display (41 × 25 mm). ..	1·50	45

No. 1420 also exists from coils of 500 or 1,000 with numbers on the reverse of each stamp.

X 20

(317)

318 Pair of Swallow-tailed Kites on Tree

1984 (24 Nov). *Nos. 847, 861B, 1099 and 1102 surch as T 317.*

1421	20 c. on 12 c. on 12 c. on 6 c. multicoloured (No. 847)	60	10
1422	20 c. on 12 c. on 6 c. mult (No. 861B)	65·00	
1423	25 c. on 50 c. on 6 c. mult (No. 1099)	30	10
1424	60 c. on $1 on 6 c. mult (No. 1102)	45	25

No. 1423 shows the previous surcharge obliterated by horizontal parallel lines.

(Litho Questa)

1984 (3 Dec). *Christmas. Swallow-tailed Kites. T 318 and similar horiz designs. Multicoloured. W 106 (sideways). P 14 × 14½.*

1425	60 c. Type 318	2·75	1·75
	a. Horiz strip of 5. Nos. 1425/9	12·50	
1426	60 c. Swallow-tailed Kite on branch	2·75	1·75
1427	60 c. Kite in flight with wings raised	2·75	1·75
1428	60 c. Kite in flight with wings lowered	2·75	1·75
1429	60 c. Kite gliding	2·75	1·75
1425/9	*Set of 5*	12·50	8·00

Nos. 1425/9 were printed together, *se-tenant*, in horizontal strips of 5 throughout the sheet with the backgrounds forming a composite design. Each stamp is inscribed "CHRISTMAS 1982".

319 St. George's Cathedral, Georgetown

(Litho Format)

1985 (8 Feb–Oct). *Georgetown Buildings. T 319 and similar horiz designs, each black and stone. W 106 (sideways). P 14.*

1430	25 c. Type 319	10	10
1431	60 c. Demerara Mutual Life Assurance Building	15	25
1432	120 c. As No. 1431	20	45
	a. Horiz strip of 3. Nos. 1432/4	55	
	b. No wmk (10.85)	20	45
	ba. Horiz strip of 3. Nos. 1432b/4b	1·10	
1433	120 c. Town Hall	20	45
	b. No wmk (10.85)	40	45
1434	120 c. Victoria Law Courts	20	45
	b. No wmk (10.85)	40	45
1435	200 c. As No. 1433	20	75
1436	300 c. As No. 1434	20	1·10
1430/6	*Set of 7*	1·10	3·25

Nos. 1432/4 were printed together, *se-tenant*, in horizontal strips of 3 within the sheet, forming a composite design.

International Youth Year 1985	Republic Day 1970-1985
(320)	(321)

1985 (15 Feb). *International Youth Year. As No. 1420, but W 106 (sideways), optd with T 320 by Tip Torres.*

1437	$1.20, Youth display	2·00	45

Examples used for this overprint all show the second line of the original inscription as "LOS ANGELLES".

1985 (22 Feb). *Republic Day. Nos 1049/50 and 1052 optd or surch as T 321 in red by Autoprint.*

1438	25 c. Type 238	20	20
	a. Horiz pair. Nos. 1438/9	40	40
1439	25 c. Flag (inscr "30th ANNIVERSARY IN PARLIAMENT")	20	20
1440	120 c. on $6 Presidential standard	65	65
1441	130 c. on $6 Presidential standard	70	70
1438/41	*Set of 4*	1·60	1·60

Examples of Nos. 1438/9 overprinted "1980–1985" in error come from stock dispersed by the liquidator of Format International Security Printers Ltd.

322 Young Ocelot on Branch	(323)

(Des K. Everett. Litho Format)

1985 (11 Mar)–87. *Wildlife Protection. T 322 and similar multicoloured designs. W 106 inverted. A. P 14½ (320 c., 330 c.) or 12½ (others). Without imprint. B. P 14. With imprint date at foot (18.2.87).*

		A	B	
1442	25 c. Type 322 (grey-olive background)	1·50	10	†
1443	60 c. Young Ocelot (*different*) (yell-brn background)	30	25	†
1444	120 c. As No. 1443	50	55	15 20
	a. Vert strip of 3. Nos. 1444/6	1·50	40	
1445	120 c. Type 322	50	55	15 20
1446	120 c. Young Ocelot (*diff*) (red-brown background)	50	55	15 20
1447	130 c. As No. 1446	45	60	†
1448	320 c. Scarlet Macaw (28 × 46 mm)	3·00	1·50	†
1449	330 c. Young Ocelot reaching for branch (28 × 46 mm)	90	1·50	†
1442/9	*Set of 8*	7·00	5·00	†

Nos. 1444/6 were printed together, *se-tenant*, in vertical strips of 3 throughout the sheet.

Examples of the 25 c. with imprint date and perforated 14 come from stock dispersed by the liquidator of Format International Security Printers Ltd.

1985 (11 Mar–11 Apr). *No. 940 and Revenue stamp, as T 181, surch as T 305 with fleur-de-lys over existing value, by Tip Torres, and Nos. 912, 1016 and O 24 surch as T 272, but without the decimal point, by Autoprint.*

1450	30 c. on 50 c. multicoloured (No. O24) (B.)	50	10
1451	55 c. on 2 c. black, indigo & greenish grey	65	20
	a. Opt "ESSEQUIBO etc" omitted	10·00	
1452	55 c. on 15 c. on 2 c. black, indigo and greenish grey (No. 940)	65	20
1453	90 c. on $1 multicoloured (No. 1016) (B.)	4·50	30
1454	225 c. on $5 multicoloured (No. 912) (11.4)	6·50	90
1455	230 c. on $5 multicoloured (No. 912) (B.)	6·50	95
1456	260 c. on $5 multicoloured (No. 912) (B.)	6·50	1·00
1450/6	*Set of 7*	23·00	3·25

On Nos. 1454/6 the surcharges are sideways.

1985 (15 Apr). *International Youth Year Save the Children Fund Campaign. Nos. 880, 1073a, 1079b and 1082 optd or surch as T 323 in blue by Autoprint.*

1457	50 c. "Two Boys catching Ducks" (No. 1073a)	2·00	20
1458	50 c. on 10 c. Type 171 (No. 1082)	5·00	20
1459	120 c. on 125 c. on $3 "Mango Season" (No. 880)	2·00	45
1460	$3 "Mango Season" (No. 1079b)	2·00	1·10
	a. Opt Type 256 ("1983") omitted	12·00	
1457/60	*Set of 4*	10·00	1·75

On Nos. 1457 and 1459/60 the overprints and surcharge as Type 323 are sideways.

Airy Hall

25	1985
(324)	(325)

1985 (2 May). *125th Anniv of British Guiana Post Office (1st issue). No. 699 surch as T 324 in blue by Autoprint.*

1461	25 c. on 10 c. multicoloured (surch T 324)	40	40
	a. Sheetlet of 25. Nos. 1461/85	9·00	
1462	25 c. on 10 c. multicoloured (surch "Belfield Arab. Coast")	40	40
1463	25 c. on 10 c. multicoloured (surch "Belfield E. C. Dem.")	40	40
1464	25 c. on 10 c. mult (surch "Belladrum")	40	40
1465	25 c. on 10 c. multicoloured (surch "Beterver-wagting")	40	40
1466	25 c. on 10 c. multicoloured (surch "Blair-mont Ferry")	40	40
1467	25 c. on 10 c. mult (surch "Boeraserie")	40	40
1468	25 c. on 10 c. mult (surch "Brahm")	40	40
1469	25 c. on 10 c. mult (surch "Bushlot")	40	40
1470	25 c. on 10 c. mult (surch "De Kinderen")	40	40
1471	25 c. on 10 c. multicoloured (surch "Fort Wellington")	40	40
1472	25 c. on 10 c. mult (surch "Georgetown")	40	40
1473	25 c. on 10 c. mult (surch "Hague")	40	40
1474	25 c. on 10 c. mult (surch "Leguan")	40	40
1475	25 c. on 10 c. mult (surch "Mahaica")	40	40
1476	25 c. on 10 c. mult (surch "Mahaicony")	40	40
1477	25 c. on 10 c. multicoloured (surch "New Amsterdam")	40	40
1478	25 c. on 10 c. mult (surch "Plaisance")	40	40
1479	25 c. on 10 c. multicoloured (surch "No. 6 Police Station")	40	40
1480	25 c. on 10 c. mult (surch "Queenstown")	40	40
1481	25 c. on 10 c. mult (surch "Vergenoegen")	40	40
1482	25 c. on 10 c. mult (surch "Vigilance")	40	40
1483	25 c. on 10 c. mult (surch "Vreed-en-Hoop")	40	40
1484	25 c. on 10 c. mult (surch "Wakenaam")	40	40
1485	25 c. on 10 c. mult (surch "Windsor Castle")	40	40
1461/85	*Set of 25*	9·00	9·00

The surcharged names are those of the post offices and postal agencies open in 1860.

See also Nos. 1694/1717, 2140/64 and 2278/301.

1985 (17 May). *I.T.U./W.H.O. Day. Nos. 1148/68 optd with T 325, or with single capital letter, in red by Autoprint.*

1486	30 c. multicoloured (No. 1148)	40	40
	a. Sheetlet of 25. Nos. 1486/510	9·00	
1487	30 c. multicoloured (No. 1149)	40	40
1488	30 c. multicoloured (No. 1150)	40	40
1489	30 c. multicoloured (No. 1151)	40	40
1490	30 c. multicoloured (No. 1152)	40	40
1491	30 c. multicoloured (No. 1153)	40	40
1492	30 c. multicoloured (No. 1154) (optd "I")	40	40
1493	30 c. multicoloured (No. 1155) (optd "T")	40	40
1494	30 c. multicoloured (No. 1156) (optd "U")	40	40
1495	30 c. multicoloured (No. 1157)	40	40
1496	30 c. multicoloured (No. 1158)	40	40

1497	30 c. multicoloured (No. 1155) (optd "W")	40	40
1498	30 c. multicoloured (No. 1155) (optd "H")	40	40
1499	30 c. multicoloured (No. 1155) (optd "O")	40	40
1500	30 c. multicoloured (No. 1159)	40	40
1501	30 c. multicoloured (No. 1160)	40	40
1502	30 c. multicoloured (No. 1161) (optd "D")	40	40
1503	30 c. multicoloured (No. 1155) (optd "A")	40	40
1504	30 c. multicoloured (No. 1162) (optd "Y")	40	40
1505	30 c. multicoloured (No. 1163)	40	40
1506	30 c. multicoloured (No. 1164)	40	40
1507	30 c. multicoloured (No. 1165)	40	40
1508	30 c. multicoloured (No. 1166)	40	40
1509	30 c. multicoloured (No. 1167)	40	40
1510	30 c. multicoloured (No. 1168)	40	40
1486/1510	*Set of 25*	9·00	9·00

60	
20	CARDI 1975-1985
(326)	(327)

1985 (21 May). *No. 861B surch with T 326 by Autoprint.*

1511	20 c. on 12 c. on 6 c. Black Acara ("Patua")	2·00	10
	a. Surch on No. 861A (no wmk)	6·00	1·50

For a similar surcharge, but with new face value at right see Nos. 1655/6.

1985 (29 May). *10th Anniv of Caribbean Agricultural Research Development Institute. No. 544 surch with T 327 in blue by Autoprint.*

1512	60 c. on 3 c. Hanging Heliconia	90	25

1985 (3 June). *No. 839 surch as Type O 10 by Autoprint, but with two blocks of obliterating bars over the previous surch.*

1513	600 c. on 625 c. on 40 c. Tiger Beard	17·00	2·50

	300
ROTARY INTERNATIONAL 1905-1985	
(328)	

1985 (21 June). *80th Anniv of Rotary International. Nos. 707 and 879 surch as T 328 in red by Autoprint.*

1514	120 c. on 110 c. on $3 Rotary anniversary emblem	9·00	45
1515	300 c. on $2 *Morpho rhetenor*	5·50	2·25

No. 1205 exists with a similar 120 c. horizontal surcharge. A limited quantity was available mint, but examples are mainly found on First Day Covers (*Price £8 on First Day Cover*).

CARICOM DAY 1985

60	XX
	(329)

1985 (28 June). *CARICOM Day. No. 1200 surch with T 329 in red.*

1516	60 c. on $3 "Makanaima the Great Ancestral Spirit of the Amerindians"	60	30

135th Anniversary Cotton Reel 1850-1985

120	
(330)	

1985 (28 June). *135th Anniv of First British Guiana Stamps. No. 870 surch with T 330 in red.*

1517	120 c. on 110 c. on 10 c. Type 170	65	55

"REICHENBACHIA" ISSUES. Due to the proliferation of these designs the catalogue uses the book plate numbers as description for each design. The following index gives the species on each plate and the stamp numbers on which they occur.

Series 1
Plate No. 1 – *Odontoglossum crispum* – 1578, 2112
Plate No. 2 – *Cattleya percivaliana* – 1519, 2026, 2394, 3293, 4321
Plate No. 3 – *Cypripedium sanderianum* – 1525, 2084
Plate No. 4 – *Odontoglossum rossi* – 1533, **MS**1539, 2095, **MS**2105
Plate No. 5 – *Cattleya dowiana aurea* – 1667, 1779, 1942/3, 2030, 2464
Plate No. 6 – *Coelogyne cristata maxima* – 1526, **MS**1685, 1759, 2085, 2093, 2119, **MS**2234, 2519, 2751
Plate No. 7 – *Odontoglossum insleayi splendens* – 1520, 1967
Plate No. 8 – *Laelia euspatha* – 1571, 1933, 1950
Plate No. 9 – *Dendrobium wardianum* – 1552, 1763, 1979/80, 1981a, 1996, 2002, 2005, 2017, 2022, 2138/9, 2387, 2748
Plate No. 10 – *Laelia autumnalis xanthotropis* – 1521, 1968, 2027, 3290, 4319
Plate No. 11 – *Phalaenopsis grandiflora aurea* – 1579, 2113
Plate No. 12 – *Cattleya lawrenceana* – 1518, 1935
Plate No. 13 – *Masdevallia shuttleworthii* and *M. xanthocorys* – 1527, 1684, 1760, 2092, 2107, 2110, 2120, 2233, 2448, 2520, 3839
Plate No. 14 – *Aeranthus sesquipedalis* – 1584, 2096, 2472
Plate No. 15 – *Cattleya mendelii* Duke of Marlborough – 1752, 1804, 2009, 2050, 2259, 2532
Plate No. 16 – *Zygopetalum intermedium* – 1559, 2090
Plate No. 17 – *Phaius humblotii* – 1732, 1792, 1885, 1965, 1977a, 2062, 2393
Plate No. 18 – *Chysis bractescens* – 1528, 1536, 2087, 2133
Plate No. 19 – *Masdevallia backhousiana* – 1522, 1969, 2028, 3292, 4320
Plate No. 20 – *Cattleya citrina* – 1529, **MS**1570, 1761, 2086, 2094, **MS**2106, 2121, 2449, 2521
Plate No. 21 – *Oncidium jonesianum* and *Oncidium jonesianum phaeanthum* – 1585, 2097, 2129
Plate No. 22 – *Saccolabium giganteum* – 1553, **MS**1619, 1764, 1940/1, 1989, 1997, 2006, 2018, 2023, **MS**2232, 2388, **MS**2531
Plate No. 23 – *Cypripedium io* – 1572, 1936
Plate No. 24 – *Odontoglossum blandum* – 1635, 1774, 1864/5, 1931, 1961, 2019, 2047, 2344, 2527, 2529
Plate No. 25 – *Maxillaria sanderiana* – 1530, 1762, 2108, 2111, 2122, 2522, 2752/3
Plate No. 26 – *Odontoglossum* Edward II – 1633, 2137, 2258, 2450
Plate No. 27 – *Vanda teres* – 1524, 2438
Plate No. 28 – *Odontoglossum hallii xanthoglossum* – 1580, 2114
Plate No. 29 – *Odontoglossum crispum hrubyanum* – 1531, 1537, 2088, 2134
Plate No. 30 – *Oncidium concolor* – 1532, 1538, 2089, 2135
Plate No. 31 – *Trichopilia suavis alba* – 1523, 1970, 2029, 3291, 4322
Plate No. 32 – *Cattleya superba splendens* – 1561, 2512
Plate No. 33 – *Odontoglossum luteo-purpureum* – 1634, 2098, 2342, 2479, 3827
Plate No. 34 – *Cypripedium niveum* – 1562
Plate No. 35 – *Stanhopea shuttleworthii* – 1563
Plate No. 36 – *Laelia anceps percivaliana* – 1558, 2439
Plate No. 37 – *Odontoglossum hebraicum* – 1627, 2115, 2440
Plate No. 38 – *Cypripedium oenanthum superbum* – 1560, 2445
Plate No. 39 – *Dendrobium superbiens* – 1737, 1797, 1985, 2063, 2104, 2414, 2515
Plate No. 40 – *Laelia harpophylla* – 1581, 1767, 2123, 2126, 2523, 3350
Plate No. 41 – *Lycaste skinneri* and *alba* – 1564
Plate No. 42 – *Phalaenopsis stuartiana* – 1582, 1657, 1768, 1993, 2125, 2127, 2524, 3349
Plate No. 43 – *Cattleya trianaei ernesti* – 1586, 1658, 1770, 2099, 2130/1, 2525, 3351/2
Plate No. 44 – *Sobralia xantholeuca* – 1556, 1971
Plate No. 45 – *Odontoglossum crispum kinlesideanum* – 1583, 1769, 2124, 2128, 2526, 3348
Plate No. 46 – *Cattleya trianaei schroederiana* – 1628, 2116, 2476
Plate No. 47 – *Epidendrum vitellinum* – 1557, 1972
Plate No. 48 – *Laelia anceps stella* and *barkeriana* – 1565
Plate No. 49 – *Odontoglossum harryanum* – 1554, 1765, 1912, 1964, 1966, 1994, 2003, 2007, 2015, 2024, 2749
Plate No. 50 – *Dendrobium leechianum* – 1672, 1784, 2031, 2403, 2496, 2558
Plate No. 51 – *Phalaenopsis speciosa* – 1573, 1934
Plate No. 52 – *Laelia elegans schilleriana* – 1551, 1949
Plate No. 53 – *Zygopetalum wendlandi* – 1621, 1771, 1930, 1954, 1962, 1983, 1986, 2020, 2048, 2361, 2364, E4
Plate No. 54 – *Cypripedium selligerum majus* – 1664, 1776, 2032, 2381, 2404
Plate No. 55 – *Angraecum articulatum* – 1597, 1625, 1772, 1927, 1990, 2046, 2265, 2463, 2465
Plate No. 56 – *Laelia anceps sanderiana* – 1629, 2117, 2441, 3841
Plate No. 57 – *Vanda coerulea* – 1622, 1973, 2395/6, 3828
Plate No. 58 – *Dendrobium nobile sanderianum* – 1630, 2118, 2442, 3840
Plate No. 59 – *Laelia gouldiana* – 1620, 2243, 2359
Plate No. 60 – *Odontoglossum grande* – 1682, 1789, 1944, 2038, 2514, 2528
Plate No. 61 – *Cypripedium rothschildianum* – 1574, 2356
Plate No. 62 – *Vanda sanderiana* – 1566, 2513
Plate No. 63 – *Dendrobium aureum* – 1575, 2357
Plate No. 64 – *Oncidium macranthum* – 1555, 1766, 1913, 1981/2, 1995, 2004, 2008, 2016, 2025, 2750
Plate No. 65 – *Cypripedium tautzianum* – 1598, 1626, 1773, 1963, 2021, 2049, 2221, 2434, 2437, 2530, E1
Plate No. 66 – *Cymbidium mastersi* – 1632, 2091, 2136, 2257, 2446
Plate No. 67 – *Angraecum caudatum* – 1631, 2132, 2256, 2443
Plate No. 68 – *Laelia albida* – 1734, 1794, 1884, 1937, 2056, 2378/9, 2435
Plate No. 69 – *Odontoglossum roezlii* – 1680, 1787, 2033, 2405, 2444
Plate No. 70 – *Oncidium ampliatum majus* – 1576, 2358

Plate No. 71 – *Renanthera lowii* – 1679, 1786, 1952, 1976, 2034, 2360
Plate No. 72 – *Cattleya warscewiczii* – 1577, 1951, 2429
Plate No. 73 – *Oncidium lanceanum* – 1623, 1974, 2397, 3826
Plate No. 74 – *Vanda hookeriana* – 1736, 1796, 1984, 2064, 2103, 2415, 2454
Plate No. 75 – *Cattleya labiata gaskelliana* – 1624, 1975, 2398/9, 3829
Plate No. 76 – *Epidendrum prismatocarpum* – 1751, 1803, 2058, 2453
Plate No. 77 – *Cattleya guttata leopoldi* – 1663, 1775, 1955, 1958, 2042, 2372/3
Plate No. 78 – *Oncidium splendidum* – 1669, 1781, 1959, 2043, 2451
Plate No. 79 – *Odontoglossum hebraicum aspersum* – 1670, 1782, 2035, 2100, 2343, 2406, 2473
Plate No. 80 – *Cattleya dowiana var chrysotoxa* – 1754, 1806, 2059, 2517
Plate No. 81 – *Cattleya trianae alba* – 1748, 1800, 1957, 2010, 2051, 2382
Plate No. 82 – *Odontoglossum humeanum* – 1753, 1805, 2011, 2052, 2260, 2516
Plate No. 83 – *Cypripedium argus* – 1671, 1783, 2039, 2466, 2480
Plate No. 84 – *Odontoglossum luteo-purpureum prionopetalum* – 1668, 1780, 2044, 2421
Plate No. 85 – *Cattleya rochellensis* – 1673, 1785, 1960, 2045, 2497, 2518
Plate No. 86 – *Odontoglossum triumphans* – 1731, 1791, 1847, 1868, 1953, 1956, 1956a, 2055, 2055a, 2264, 2362, 2377, E2, E2a, E11, (Nos. 1847, 1956a, 2055a, 2264, E2 and E11 are inscr "ONTOGLOSSUM" in error)
Plate No. 87 – *Phalaenopsis casta* – 1681, 1788, 1977, 2036, 2452, 2474, 2478
Plate No. 88 – *Oncidium tigrinum* – 1750, 1802, 2060, 2436
Plate No. 89 – *Cypripedium lemoinierianum* – 1749, 1801, 1978, 2012, 2053, 2422
Plate No. 90 – *Catasetum bungerothii* – 1738, 1798, 1938, 1947/8, 1988, 2014, 2057, 2380, 2433
Plate No. 91 – *Cattleya ballantiniana* – 1735, 1795, 1987, 2013, 2054, 2109, 2375/6, 2447
Plate No. 92 – *Dendrobium brymerianum* – 1665, 1777, 1945, 1988a, 2040, 2384
Plate No. 93 – *Cattleya eldorado crocata* – 1733, 1793, 1991/2, 2065, 2401, 2416
Plate No. 94 – *Odontoglossum sanderianum* – 1683, 1790, 2037, 2345, 2407, 2484
Plate No. 95 – *Cattleya labiata warneri* – 1666, 1778, 1990a, 2041, 2400, 2467
Plate No. 96 – *Odontoglossum schroderianum* – 1747, 1799, 2061, 2374

Series 2
Plate No. 1 – *Cypripedium morganiae burfordiense* – 2178, 2556
Plate No. 2 – *Cattleya bowringiana* – 1886, 1929, 2102, 2426
Plate No. 3 – *Dendrobium formosum* – 1919, 1998, 2389
Plate No. 4 – *Phaius tuberculosus* – 1813, 2428, 2500
Plate No. 5 – *Odontoglossum crispum mundyanum* – 1815, 2475
Plate No. 6 – *Laelia praestans* – 1881, 1999, 2390, 2624/6
Plate No. 7 – *Dendrobium phalaenopsis var statterianum* – 1917, 2365
Plate No. 8 – *Cypripedium boxalli atratum* – 1811, 2408
Plate No. 9 – *Odontoglossum wattianum* – 1816, 2101, 2409/10
Plate No. 10 – *Cypripedium lathamianum inversum* – 1869, 1880, 2423, 2482
Plate No. 11 – *Paphinia rugosa* and *Zygopetalum xanthinum* – 2503, E6
Plate No. 12 – *Dendrobium melanodiscus* – 1817, 2411/12, **MS**2590
Plate No. 13 – *Laelia anceps schroderiana* – 1877, 1907, 2385, 2424
Plate No. 14 – *Phaius hybridus cooksonii* – 1920, 2366/7
Plate No. 15 – *Disa grandiflora* – 1918, 1926, 2386, 2419
Plate No. 16 – *Selenipedium hybridum grande* – 2314, 2331
Plate No. 17 – *Cattleya schroederae alba* – 1872, 2413, 2610/11
Plate No. 18 – *Lycaste skinnerii armeniaca* – 1923, 1928, 1946, 2420, 2557
Plate No. 19 – *Odontoglossum excellens* – 2175
Plate No. 20 – *Laelio-cattleya elegans var blenheimensis* – 1916, 2000, 2391
Plate No. 21 – *Odontoglossum coradinei* – 1810, 2383
Plate No. 22 – *Odontoglossum wilckeanum var rothschildianum* – 1922, 2368
Plate No. 23 – *Cypripedium lawrenceanum hyeanum* – 2504, 2601, O65
Plate No. 24 – *Cattleya intermedia punctatissima* – 1887, 1914, 2418
Plate No. 25 – *Laelia purpurata* – 2067, 2576
Plate No. 26 – *Masdevallia harryana splendens* – 2505, 2596, O59
Plate No. 27 – *Selenipedium hybridum nitidissimum* – 1874, 1915, 2402, 2425
Plate No. 28 – *Cattleya mendelii var measuresiana* – 1924, 2369/70
Plate No. 29 – *Odontoglossum vexillarium (miltonia vexillaria)* – 1818, 2485
Plate No. 30 – *Saccolabium coeleste* – 1809, 2363, 2430
Plate No. 31 – *Cypripedium hybridum youngianum* – 2324, 2594, O57
Plate No. 32 – *Miltonia (hybrida) bleuana* – 1921, 2001, 2392
Plate No. 33 – *Laelia grandis* – 1873, 2616/19
Plate No. 34 – *Cattleya labiata var lueddemanniana* – 1819, 2431, 2481
Plate No. 35 – *Odontoglossum coronarium* – 2511, E9
Plate No. 36 – *Cattleya granulosa var schofieldiana* – 2316, 2592, O55
Plate No. 37 – *Odontoglossum (hybridum) leroyanum* – 2174
Plate No. 38 – *Cypripedium (hybridum) laucheanum* and *eyermanianum* – 1814, 2477, 2580
Plate No. 39 – *Cychnoches chlorochilon* – 2172
Plate No. 40 – *Cattleya O'Brieniana* – 2276
Plate No. 41 – *Odontoglossum ramosissimum* – 2066, 2581
Plate No. 42 – *Dendrobium phalaenopsis var* – 1812, 2427, 2499
Plate No. 43 – *Cypripedium (hybridum) pollettianum* and *maynardii* – 2216, 2593, O56

Plate No. 44 – *Odontoglossum naevium* – 1878, 2498, 2656
Plate No. 45 – *Cypripedium (hybridum) castleanum* – 1876, 1925, 2371, 2417
Plate No. 46 – *Odontoglossum cervantesii decorum* – **MS**2275, **MS**2332
Plate No. 47 – *Cattleya amethystoglossa* – 2171
Plate No. 48 – *Cattleya (hybrida) arnoldiana* – 2217, O53
Plate No. 49 – *Cattleya labiata* – 2239, 2605, 2614/15, 2646/7
Plate No. 50 – *Dendrobium (hybridum) venus* and *cassiope* – 1879, 2501, 2620/1
Plate No. 51 – *Selenipedium (hybridum) weidlichianum* – 2177, 2502
Plate No. 52 – *Cattleya mossiae var. reineckiana* – 2072, 2577
Plate No. 53 – *Cymbidium lowianum* – 2236, 2585, 2606
Plate No. 54 – *Oncidium loxense* – 2176, 2579
Plate No. 55 – *Cattleya (hybrida) hardyana* – **MS**2275, **MS**2332
Plate No. 56 – *Coelogyne sanderae* – 1875, 2612/13, 2627
Plate No. 57 – *Cypripedium leeanum var giganteum* – **MS**2275, **MS**2332
Plate No. 58 – *Coelogyne pandurata* – 2173, 2582
Plate No. 59 – *Schomburgkia sanderiana* – 2323, 2595, O61
Plate No. 60 – *Oncidium superbiens* – 2227, 2607
Plate No. 61 – *Dendrobium johnsoniae* – 2235, O58
Plate No. 62 – *Laelia hybrida behrensiana* – 2322, 2509, 2622/3
Plate No. 63 – Hybrid *Calanthes Victoria Regina, Bella* and *Burfordiense* – 2510, E8
Plate No. 64 – *Cattleya mendelii* Quorndon House var – 2238, 2608
Plate No. 65 – *Arachnanthe clarkei* – 2073, 2578
Plate No. 66 – *Zygopetalum burtii* – 2240, 2583
Plate No. 67 – *Cattleya (hybrida) parthenia* – 2318, 2584
Plate No. 68 – *Phalaenopsis sanderiana* and *intermedia portei* – 2225, 2597, O60
Plate No. 69 – *Phaius blumei var assamicus* – 2317, 2598, O62
Plate No. 70 – *Angraecum humblotii* – 2470, 2602, O67
Plate No. 71 – *Odontoglossum pescatorei* – 2471, 2603, O68
Plate No. 72 – *Cattleya rex* – 2193
Plate No. 73 – *Zygopetalum crinitum* – 2315, 2329
Plate No. 74 – *Cattleya lueddemanniana alba* – 2219/20, 2222/3, 2328
Plate No. 75 – *Cymbidium (hybridum) winnianum* – 2506, O64
Plate No. 76 – Hybrid *Masdevallias courtauldiana, geleniana* and *measuresiana* – 2242
Plate No. 77 – *Cypripedium (hybridum) calypso* – 2191
Plate No. 78 – *Masdevallia chimaera var mooreana* – 2325
Plate No. 79 – *Miltonia phalaenopsis* – 2241, 2508
Plate No. 80 – *Lissochilus giganteus* – 2190
Plate No. 81 – *Aerides savageanum* – **MS**2275, **MS**2332
Plate No. 82 – *Thunia brymeriana* – 2069, 2483
Plate No. 83 – *Miltonia moreliana* – 2182
Plate No. 84 – *Oncidium kramerianum* – 2469, 2604, O69
Plate No. 85 – *Cattleya Victoria Regina* – 2068
Plate No. 86 – *Zygopetalum klabochorum* – 2180
Plate No. 87 – *Laelia autumnalis alba* – 2070, 2432
Plate No. 88 – *Spathoglottis kimballiana* – 2071
Plate No. 89 – *Laelio-cattleya* ("The Hon. Mrs. Astor") – 2181
Plate No. 90 – *Phaius hybridus amabilis* and *marthiae* – 2468, 2599, O63
Plate No. 91 – *Zygopetalum rostratum* – 2277
Plate No. 92 – *Coelogyne swaniana* – 2218, 2591, O54
Plate No. 93 – *Laelio-cattleya (hybrida) phoebe* – 2507, E7
Plate No. 94 – *Epidendrum atro-purpureum var randianum* – 2192
Plate No. 95 – *Dendrobium imperatrix* – 2226, 2600, O66
Plate No. 96 – *Vanda parishii var marriottiana* – 2237, 2330

25
Guyana

331 *Cattleya lawrenceana*
(Plate No. 12 (Series 1))

332 Arms of Guyana

(Litho Format)

1985 (9 July). *Centenary of Publication of Sanders'* Reichenbachia (1st issue). *T* **331** *and similar vert designs showing orchids. Multicoloured. No wmk. P* 13½ × 14.

1518	25 c. Type **331**	..	..	40	30
1519	60 c. Plate No. 2 (Series 1)	..	..	50	35
1520	60 c. Plate No. 7 (Series 1)	..	..	50	35
1521	60 c. Plate No. 10 (Series 1)	..	..	50	35
1522	60 c. Plate No. 19 (Series 1)	..	..	50	35
1523	60 c. Plate No. 31 (Series 1)	..	..	50	35
1524	120 c. Plate No. 27 (Series 1)	..	..	75	55
1525	130 c. Plate No. 3 (Series 1)	..	..	75	55
1526	130 c. Plate No. 6 (Series 1)	..	..	1·10	55
1527	130 c. Plate No. 13 (Series 1)	..	..	75	55
1528	130 c. Plate No. 18 (Series 1)	..	..	1·50	55
1529	130 c. Plate No. 20 (Series 1)	..	..	1·00	55
1530	130 c. Plate No. 25 (Series 1)	..	..	75	55
1531	130 c. Plate No. 29 (Series 1)	..	..	1·25	55
1532	130 c. Plate No. 30 (Series 1)	..	..	1·25	55
1533	200 c. Plate No. 4 (Series 1)	..	..	1·25	85
1518/33			*Set of* 16	12·00	7·00

Nos. 1518/33 were printed in four sheets each of 16 orchid stamps, arranged as blocks of four of each design, and 9 examples of Type **332** which appear on the vertical and horizontal gutters between the blocks.

For 130 c. stamps as Nos. 1526/7 and 1529/30, but with watermark **106** see Nos. 1759/62.

(Litho Format)

1985 (9 July–16 Sept). *Booklet and Coil Stamps. No wmk.*

1534	**332** 25 c. multicoloured (*imperf* × p 14)		20	25
1534a	25 c. multicoloured (*imperf* × p 13½)			
	(16 Sept)			20	25
1534b	25 c. multicoloured (*p* 13½ × 14)		20	25
1535	25 c. multicoloured (*p* 13½ × *imperf*)		20	25
1535a	25 c. mult (*p* 14 × *imperf*) (16 Sept)		20	25
1535b	25 c. mult (*p* 14 × 13½) (16 Sept)		15	20
1534/5b			*Set of* 6	1·00	1·25

See note below No. 1533. Examples of Nos. 1534/5b were cut from the gutters of the orchid sheets and the white area surrounding the design varies considerably in size. Nos. 1534, 1534b and 1535 occur from sheets with vertical orchid designs and Nos. 1534a and 1535a/b from those with horizontal designs.

See also Nos. 1807/8b (watermarked **106**), 1820/1a (additionally inscribed "1966–1986") and 2183/4c (within frame).

333 QUEEN MOTHER 1900 - 1923

334 International Youth Year 1985

1985 (9 July). *85th Birthday of Queen Elizabeth the Queen Mother* (1st issue). *Nos.* 1528 and 1531/3 optd with T **333** (*in two lines on No.* 1538) *or with similar opts* (*No.* **MS**1539), *all in blue by Format.*

1536	130 c. Plate No. 18 (Series 1)	..	..	45	50
1537	130 c. Plate No. 29 (Series 1)	..	..	45	50
1538	130 c. Plate No. 30 (Series 1)	..	..	45	50
1536/8			*Set of* 3	1·25	1·40
MS1539	100 × 126 mm. 200 c. × 4 Plate No. 4 (Series 1)	..		3·75	5·00

The four stamps in No. **MS**1539 are overprinted "LADY BOWES-LYON 1900–1923", "DUCHESS OF YORK 1923–1937", "QUEEN ELIZABETH 1937–1952" or "QUEEN MOTHER 1952–1985", all reading upwards.

See also No. **MS**1570.

1985 (18 July). *International Youth Year. Nos.* 900/4 *surch with T* **334** *in red by Autoprint.*

1540	25 c. on 110 c. on 5 c. mult (No. 900)	..	10	10
	a. Sheetlet of 25. Nos. 1540/1, each × 8,			
	Nos. 1542/3, each × 4 and No. 1544	5·25		
1541	25 c. on 110 c. on 5 c. mult (No. 901)	..	15	15
1542	25 c. on 110 c. on 5 c. mult (No. 902)	..	35	25
1543	25 c. on 110 c. on 5 c. mult (No. 903)	..	35	25
1544	25 c. on 110 c. on 5 c. mult (No. 904)	..	2·50	25
1540/4			*Set of* 5	3·00	2·75

In addition to the sheetlet containing the five different original surcharges, Type **334** can also be found on the sheets of No. 900.

240

225

1910 - 1985

(335)

(336)

1985 (26 July). *75th Anniv of Girl Guide Movement. No.* 612 *surch with T* **335** *by Tip Torres.*

1545	225 c. on 350 c. on 225 c. on 40 c. Guides in camp	..	..	25·00	1·75
	a. Inverted "L"'s for 1's in surcharged dates	..			

No. 1545a occurs on all stamps in the bottom row.

In addition to Type **335** No. 1545 also carries two otherwise unissued surcharges at top right.

Nos. 610 and 613 also exist surcharged with Type **335**. A limited quantity was available mint, but examples were mainly found on First Day Covers (*Price £25 per pair on First Day Cover*).

1985 (26 July). *Birth Bicentenary of John J. Audubon* (*ornithologist*). *No.* 992 *surch with T* **336** *by Tip Torres.*

1546	240 c. on 35 c. Harpy Eagle	..	..	18·00	2·00

Guyana/Libya Friendship 1985 150

1763 Revolution
GUYANA 25c

337 Leaders of the 1763 Rebellion

(338)

(Des K. Everett (150 c.). Litho Format)

1985 (29 July). *150th Anniv of Abolition of Slavery* (1984) (1st issue). *T* **337** *and similar horiz designs. P* 14.

1547	25 c. black and bluish grey	..	..	25	10
1548	60 c. black and mauve	..	..	20	25
1549	130 c. black and light greenish blue	..		25	50
1550	150 c. black and rose-lilac	..		60	55
1547/50			*Set of* 4	1·10	1·25

Designs:—60 c. Damon and Parliament Buildings, Georgetown; 130 c. Quamina and Demerara, 1823; 150 c. Den Arendt (slave ship), 1627.

Nos. 1549/50 exist imperforate from stock dispersed by the liquidator of Format International Security Printers Ltd.

For these designs in changed colours see Nos. 2552/5.

(Litho Format)

1985 (1 Aug). *Centenary of Publication of Sanders'* Reichenbachia (2nd issue). *Vert designs as T* **331** *showing orchids. Multicoloured. No wmk. P* 13½ × 14.

1551	25 c. Plate No. 52 (Series 1)	..	..	50	25
1552	55 c. Plate No. 9 (Series 1)	..	..	60	35
1553	55 c. Plate No. 22 (Series 1)	..	..	60	35
1554	55 c. Plate No. 49 (Series 1)	..	..	60	25
1555	55 c. Plate No. 64 (Series 1)	..	..	60	35
1556	60 c. Plate No. 44 (Series 1)	..	..	60	35
1557	60 c. Plate No. 47 (Series 1)	..	..	60	35
1558	120 c. Plate No. 36 (Series 1)	..	..	85	55
1559	130 c. Plate No. 16 (Series 1)	..	..	85	55
1560	130 c. Plate No. 38 (Series 1)	..	..	85	55
1561	150 c. Plate No. 32 (Series 1)	..	..	85	55
1562	150 c. Plate No. 34 (Series 1)	..	..	85	55
1563	150 c. Plate No. 35 (Series 1)	..	..	85	55
1564	150 c. Plate No. 41 (Series 1)	..	..	85	55
1565	150 c. Plate No. 48 (Series 1)	..	..	85	55
1566	150 c. Plate No. 62 (Series 1)	..	..	85	55
1551/66			*Set of* 16	10·00	6·50

Nos. 1551/66 were printed in a similar sheet format to Nos. 1518/33.

For 55 c. stamps as Nos. 1552/5, but with watermark **106** see Nos. 1763/6.

For 50 c. stamps in designs of Nos. 1554/5 see Nos. 1912/13.

(Litho Format)

1985 (16 Aug). *Signing of Guyana—Libya Friendship Treaty. No.* 621 *surch with T* **338** *by Autoprint.*

1567	150 c. on 10 c. Type 149	..	..	8·00	2·75

ALTERED CATALOGUE NUMBERS

Any Catalogue numbers altered from the last edition are shown as a list in the introductory pages.

Mexico 1986 275

150

X

(339)

(340)

(341)

1985 (16 Aug). *Namibia Day. No.* 636 *surch with T* **339** *in deep carmine by Tip Torres.*

1568	150 c. on 35 c. Unveiling of Monument	..	2·50	55

1985 (16 Aug). *World Cup Football Championship. Mexico* (1986) (1st issue). *No.* F2 *surch with T* **340** *by Autoprint.*

1569	275 c. on 3 c. Hanging Heliconia	..	..	4·50	1·10

See also No. 1727.

1985 (12 Sept). *85th Birthday of Queen Elizabeth the Queen Mother* (2nd issue). *Sheet* 120 × 129 mm *containing No.* 1529 × 4 *optd as No.* **MS**1539, *each stamp surch with T* **341** *by Tip Torres.*

MS1570	200 c. on 130 c. × 4 Plate No. 20 (Series 1)	11·00	6·00

(Litho Format)

1985 (16 Sept). *Centenary of Publication of Sanders'* Reichenbachia (3rd issue). *Multicoloured designs as T* **331** *showing orchids. No wmk. P* 13½ × 14 (*Nos.* 1571/7 and 1584) *or* 14 × 13½ (*others*).

1571	25 c. Plate No. 8 (Series 1)	..	..	70	20
1572	25 c. Plate No. 23 (Series 1)	..	..	70	20
1573	25 c. Plate No. 51 (Series 1)	..	..	70	20
1574	25 c. Plate No. 61 (Series 1)	..	..	70	20
1575	25 c. Plate No. 63 (Series 1)	..	..	70	20
1576	25 c. Plate No. 70 (Series 1)	..	..	70	20
1577	25 c. Plate No. 72 (Series 1)	..	..	70	20
1578	120 c. Plate No. 1 (Series 1) (*horiz*)	..	1·00	55
1579	120 c. Plate No. 11 (Series 1) (*horiz*)	..	1·00	55
1580	120 c. Plate No. 28 (Series 1) (*horiz*)	..	1·00	55
1581	150 c. Plate No. 40 (Series 1) (*horiz*)	..	1·00	65
1582	150 c. Plate No. 42 (Series 1) (*horiz*)	..	1·00	65
1583	150 c. Plate No. 45 (Series 1) (*horiz*)	..	1·00	65
1584	200 c. Plate No. 14 (Series 1)	..	1·50	80
1585	200 c. Plate No. 21 (Series 1) (*horiz*)	..	1·50	80
1586	200 c. Plate No. 43 (Series 1) (*horiz*)	..	1·50	80
1571/86			*Set of* 16	14·00	6·75

Nos. 1571/86 were printed in a similar sheet format to Nos. 1518/33.

For 150 c. and 200 c. stamps as Nos. 1581/3 and 1586, but with watermark **106** see Nos. 1767/70.

120

1955-1985

1965-1985 25

(342)

(343)

1985 (23 Sept). *30th Anniv of Commonwealth Caribbean Medical Research Council. Nos.* 819, 871, 874/a, 928a *and* 1014 *surch or optd* (*vertically reading upwards on Nos.* 1587/8) *as T* **342** *by Autoprint.*

1587	— 60 c. multicoloured (No. 819)	..	20	25
1588	— 60 c. multicoloured (No. 1014)	..	20	25
1589	176 120 c. on 110 c. on 10 c. multicoloured (No. 871)	..	40	45
1590	— 120 c. on 110 c. on $3 mult (No. 874) ..	40	45
1591	— 120 c. on 110 c. on $3 mult (No. 874a)..	40	45
1592	— 120 c. on 210 c. on $3 mult (No. 928a)..	40	45
1587/92			*Set of* 6	1·75	2·10

1985 (30 Sept). *20th Anniv of Guyana Defence Force. No.* 856 *surch as T* **343** *by Autoprint.*

1593	25 c. on $1.10 on $3 W.O. and N.C.O., Guyana Defence Force, 1966	..	1·00	10
1594	225 c. on $1.10 on $3 W.O. and N.C.O., Guyana Defence Force, 1966	..	2·50	1·25

1985 (5 Oct). *Fire Prevention. Nos.* 678 and 680 *optd with T* **325** *and surch as T* **255** *by Autoprint.*

1595	25 c. on 40 c. Fire engine, 1977	..	8·00	20
1596	320 c. on 15 c. Steam engine, *circa* 1860	..	14·00	3·75

(Litho Format)

1985 (7 Oct). *Centenary of Publication of Sanders'* Reichenbachia (4th issue). *Vert design as T* **331**. *Multicoloured. No wmk. P* 13½ × 14.

1597	60 c. Plate No. 55 (Series 1)	..	..	75	30

CRISTOBAL COLON
1492-1992

SIR WINSTON CHURCHILL
1965-1985

350

(344)　　　　　　　(345)

1985 (12 Oct). *Columbus Day. Unissued value as T **331** surch with T **344** in red. Multicoloured. P 13½×14.*
1598　350 c. on 120 c. Plate No. 65 (Series 1)　.. 4·25　2·25

1985 (15 Oct). *20th Death Anniv of Sir Winston Churchill. No. 707 optd with T **345** by Autoprint.*
1599　$2 *Morpho rhetenor* (female)　　.. .. 6·50　1·60

XX
1950-1985

200

United
Nations
1945-1985

POSTAGE

(346)　　　　(347)　　　　(348)

1985 (15 Oct). *35th Anniv of International Commission on Irrigation and Drainage. No. 625 with unissued surcharge as T **264** in blue further surch as T **346** by Autoprint.*
1600　**150**　25 c. on 110 c. on 10 c. multicoloured　　15　10
1601　　　200 c. on 110 c. on 10 c. multicoloured ..　85　85

1985 (24 Oct). *40th Anniv of United Nations Organization. Nos. 714/16, 800 and O19 optd with T **347** by Autoprint.*
1602　30 c. multicoloured (No. 714)　.. ..　1·50　10
1603　50 c. multicoloured (No. 715)　.. ..　1·50　20
1604　100 c. on $3 multicoloured (No. O19)　..　1·50　40
1605　225 c. on 220 c. on $3 multicoloured (No. 800)　7·00　75
1606　$3 multicoloured (No. 716)　.. ..　3·00　1·40
1602/6　　　　　　　　*Set of 5*　13·00　2·50

1985 (29 Oct). *Nos. 551/3, O14/15, O18, O21, OP1/2 and F7 optd as T **348** (horizontally 22×4 on Nos. 1607 and 1615/16) by Autoprint.*
1607　30 c. on $2 *Norantea guianensis* (No. O18)..　40　10
1608　40 c. Tiger Beard (No. 551)..　.. ..　32·00　40
1609　50 c. *Guzmania lingulata* (No. 552)　..　40　20
1610　50 c. *Guzmania lingulata* (No. O14)　..　40　20
1611　60 c. Soldier's Cap (No. 553)　.. ..　3·00　25
1612　60 c. Soldier's Cap (No. O15)　.. ..　2·75　25
1613　60 c. Soldier's Cap (No. F7)..　.. ..　1·50　25
1614　$10 *Elbella patrobas* (No. O21)　.. ..　16·00　5·50
1615　$15 on $1 *Chelonanthus uliginoides* (No. OP1)　.. .. ..　8·00　9·00
1616　$20 on $1 *Chelonanthus uliginoides* (No. OP2)　.. .. ..　9·00　11·00
1607/16　　　　　　　*Set of 10*　65·00　24·00

150　　　**X**

**Deepavali
1985**
(349)

Christmas 1985
(350)

1985 (1 Nov). *Deepavali Festival. Nos. 542/3 surch as T **349** by Autoprint.*
1617　25 c. on 2 c. Type **132**　.. ..　20　10
1618　150 c. on 1 c. Pitcher Plant of Mt Roraima..　1·40　55

1985 (3 Nov). *Christmas. Sheet 120×129 mm containing No. 1553×4 optd as T **350** in red by Format.*
MS1619　55 c. × 4 Plate No. 22 (Series 1), each with a different overprint (Type **350**, "Happy New Year", "Merry Christmas" or "Happy Holidays")　.. .. ..　6·00　4·00

(Litho Format)

1985 (4 Nov). *Centenary of Publication of Sanders' Reichenbachia (5th issue). Multicoloured designs as T **331** showing orchids. No wmk. P 14×13½ (60, 200 c.) or 13½×14 (others).*
1620　25 c. Plate No. 59 (Series 1)　..　55　20
1621　30 c. Plate No. 53 (Series 1)　..　60　20
1622　60 c. Plate No. 57 (Series 1) (*horiz*)　70　35
1623　60 c. Plate No. 73 (Series 1)　..　70　35
1624　60 c. Plate No. 75 (Series 1) (*horiz*)　70　35
1625　75 c. Plate No. 55 (Series 1)　..　90　40
1626　100 c. Plate No. 65 (Series 1)　..　1·00　50

1627　120 c. Plate No. 37 (Series 1)　.. ..　1·00　55
1628　120 c. Plate No. 46 (Series 1)　.. ..　1·00　55
1629　120 c. Plate No. 56 (Series 1)　.. ..　1·00　55
1630　120 c. Plate No. 58 (Series 1)　.. ..　1·00　55
1631　120 c. Plate No. 67 (Series 1)　.. ..　1·00　55
1632　130 c. Plate No. 66 (Series 1)　.. ..　1·10　65
1633　150 c. Plate No. 26 (Series 1)　.. ..　1·25　75
1634　200 c. Plate No. 33 (Series 1) (*horiz*)　1·50　85
1635　225 c. Plate No. 24 (Series 1)　.. ..　2·00　95
1620/35　　　　　　*Set of 16*　14·50　7·50
Nos. 1620/35 were printed in a similar format to Nos. 1518/33.
The 30, 75, 100 and 225 c. values show face values and "Guyana" in blue. Examples of these four stamps with face values and "Guyana" in black were prepared, but not issued.
For stamps as Nos. 1621, 1625/6 and 1635, but with watermark **106** see Nos. 1771/4.
For 50 c. in design of No. 1625 see No. 1927.

CLIVE
LLOYD'S　TESTIMONIAL
YEAR 1985

GUYANA

25 c

REICHENBACHIA 1886-1986

351 Clive Lloyd　　　　　(352)
(cricketer)

(Litho Format)

1985 (7 Nov). *Clive Lloyd's Testimonial Year. T **351** and similar vert designs. Multicoloured. W **106** (sideways on $3.50). P 14½×14 (25 c.), 12½ ($3.50) or 14 (others).*
1636　25 c. Type **351**　.. .. ..　50　60
　　a. Horiz strip of 3. Nos. 1636/8 ..　1·40
1637　25 c. Clive Lloyd, bat and wicket ..　50　60
1638　25 c. Cricket equipment　.. ..　50　60
1639　60 c. As No. 1638 (25×33 mm)　..　60　40
1640　$1.30, As No. 1637 (25×33 mm)　..　70　85
1641　2.25, Type **351** (25×33 mm)　..　80　1·25
1642　$3.50, Clive Lloyd with the Prudential Cup (36×56 mm)　.. ..　90　1·75
1636/42　　　　　　*Set of 7*　4·00　5·50
Nos. 1636/8 were printed together, *se-tenant*, in horizontal strips of 3 throughout the sheet.

1985 (15 Nov). *Wildlife Protection. Nos. 756/67 optd with T **325** vertically in red by Autoprint.*
1643　30 c. Type **178**　.. ..　75　75
　　a. Sheetlet of 12. Nos. 1643/54 ..　8·00
1644　30 c. Red Howler　.. ..　75　75
1645　30 c. Common Squirrel Monkey ..　75　75
1646　30 c. Two-toed Sloth..　.. ..　75　75
1647　30 c. Brazilian Tapir　.. ..　75　75
1648　30 c. Collared Peccary　.. ..　75　75
1649　30 c. Six-banded Armadillo..　..　75　75
1650　30 c. Tamandua ("Ant Eater")　..　75　75
1651　30 c. Giant Anteater　.. ..　75　75
1652　30 c. Murine Opossum　.. ..　75　75
1653　30 c. Brown Four-eyed Opossum　..　75　75
1654　30 c. Brazilian Agouti　.. ..　75　75
1643/54　　　　　　*Set of 12*　8·00　8·00

1985 (23 Dec). *Nos. 847 and 861B surch as T **326**, but with face value of surch at right.*
1655　20 c. on 12 c. on 6 c. Black Acara ("Patua") (No. 847)　.. .. ..　1·00　15
1656　20 c. on 12 c. on 6 c. Black Acara ("Patua") (No. 861B)　.. ..　1·00　15

1986 (13 Jan). *Centenary of the Appearance of Reichenbachia Volume I. Nos. 1582 and 1586 optd with T **352** in reddish violet.*
1657　150 c. Plate No. 42 (Series 1)　.. ..　1·50　60
1658　200 c. Plate No. 43 (Series 1)　.. ..　1·75　75

Republic Day

1986　　　**1986**
(353)　　　　(354)

1986 (22 Feb). *Republic Day. Nos. 1108/9 and 1052 optd or surch as T **353** by Autoprint.*
1659　25 c. As Type **258**　.. ..　10　10
　　a. Horiz pair. Nos. 1659/60　.. ..　15　20
1660　25 c. As No. 1050..　.. ..　10　10
1661　120 c. on $6 Presidential standard (surch vert)　.. .. ..　40　45
1662　225 c. on $6 Presidential standard (surch vert)　.. .. ..　70　75
1659/62　　　　　　*Set of 4*　1·10　1·25

(Litho Format)

1986 (26 Feb). *Centenary of Publication of Sanders' Reichenbachia (6th issue). Vert designs as T **331**. Multicoloured. No wmk. P 13½×14.*
1663　40 c. Plate No. 77 (Series 1)　.. ..　55　20
1664　45 c. Plate No. 54 (Series 1)　.. ..　55　25
1665　50 c. Plate No. 92 (Series 1)　.. ..　55　25
1666　60 c. Plate No. 95 (Series 1)　.. ..　60　30
1667　75 c. Plate No. 5 (Series 1)　.. ..　65　35
1668　90 c. Plate No. 84 (Series 1)　.. ..　75　40
1669　150 c. Plate No. 78 (Series 1)　.. ..　95　60
1670　200 c. Plate No. 79 (Series 1)　.. ..　1·25　80
1671　300 c. Plate No. 83 (Series 1)　.. ..　1·75　1·25
1672　320 c. Plate No. 50 (Series 1)　.. ..　1·75　1·40
1673　360 c. Plate No. 85 (Series 1)　.. ..　1·90　1·50
1663/73　　　　　　*Set of 11*　10·00　6·50
Nos. 1663/73 were printed in a similar sheet format to Nos. 1518/33.
For stamps as Nos. 1663/73, but with watermark **106** see Nos. 1775/85.

1926　　　1986

1926

X　150

1986
QUEEN ELIZABETH
(355)　　　　(356)

1986 (24 Mar). *Easter. No. 481 optd with T **354** and surch as T **317**, but without the "X", both by Autoprint.*
1674　111　25 c. on 6 c. multicoloured　..　25　10
1675　　50 c. on 6 c. multicoloured　..　40　20
1676　　100 c. on 6 c. multicoloured　..　65　40
1677　　200 c. on 6 c. multicoloured　..　1·25　70
1674/7　.. .. ..　*Set of 4*　2·25　1·25

1986 (27 Mar). *60th Anniv of St. John's Ambulance in Guyana. No. 652 surch with T **355** by Autoprint.*
1678　150 c. on 35 c. silver, black and green　..　3·00　55

(Litho Format)

1986 (4 Apr). *Centenary of Publication of Sanders' Reichenbachia (7th issue). Multicoloured designs as T **331**. No wmk. P 13½×14 (225 c.) or 14×13½ (others).*
1679　25 c. Plate No. 71 (Series 1) (*horiz*)　..　50　20
1680　120 c. Plate No. 69 (Series 1) (*horiz*)　..　1·25　55
1681　150 c. Plate No. 87 (Series 1) (*horiz*)　..　1·50　65
1682　225 c. Plate No. 60 (Series 1)　.. ..　1·50　90
1683　350 c. Plate No. 94 (Series 1) (*horiz*)　..　2·00　1·50
1679/83　.. ..　*Set of 5*　6·00　3·50
Nos. 1679/83 were printed in a similar sheet format to Nos. 1518/33.
For stamps as Nos. 1679/83, but with watermark **106** see Nos. 1786/90.

1986 (21 Apr). *60th Birthday of Queen Elizabeth II. Nos. 1526/7 optd or surch as T **356** by Tip Torres.*
1684　150 c. Plate No. 13 (Series 1)　.. ..　1·00　50
MS1685　100×126 mm. 130 c. on 130 c., 200 c. on 130 c., 260 c. on 130 c., 330 c. on 130 c., Plate No. 6 (Series 1)　.. .. ..　4·00　4·25
The original face values on No. MS 1685 are obliterated by a floral pattern.

Protect the

GUYANA
INDEPENDENCE
1966-1986

60
25

(357)　　　　(358)

1986 (3 May). *Wildlife Protection. Nos. 685, 739/44 and 993/8 surch as T **357** by Tip Torres.*
1686　60 c. on 35 c. Type **174**　.. ..　35　35
　　a. Block of 6. Nos. 1686/91　..　1·90
1687　60 c. on 35 c. Trahira ("Haimara")　..　35　35
1688　60 c. on 35 c. Electric Eel　.. ..　35　35
1689　60 c. on 35 c. Golden Rivulus　..　35　35
1690　60 c. on 35 c. Golden Pencilfish　..　35　35
1691　60 c. on 35 c. Four-eyed Fish　..　35　35
1691a　60 c. on 35 c. Red Piranha ("Pirai")　..　4·00　2·00
　　ab. Block of 6. Nos. 1691a/f　..　22·00
1691b　60 c. on 35 c. Smoking Hassar　..　4·00　2·00
1691c　60 c. on 35 c. Manta　.. ..　4·00　2·00
1691d　60 c. on 35 c. Festive Cichlid ("Flying Patwa")　.. ..　4·00　2·00
1691e　60 c. on 35 c. Arapaima　.. ..　4·00　2·00
1691f　60 c. on 35 c. Peacock Cichlid ("Lukanani")　4·00　2·00
1692　$6 on 8 c. Type **163**　.. ..　3·00　2·50
1686/92　.. ..　*Set of 13*　26·00　15·00
Nos. 1686/91 were previously overprinted with Type **226**.
On No. 1692 the previous value is covered by a fleur-de-lys.

1986 (5 May). *No. 799 surch as T **326** by Autoprint.*
1693　600 c. on 720 c. on 60 c. Soldier's Cap ..　8·00　75

1986 (15 May). *125th Anniv of British Guiana Post Office (2nd issue). No. 702a surch as T **324** by Autoprint.*
1694　25 c. on 30 c. multicoloured (surch "Abary")　40　40
　　a. Sheetlet of 25. Nos. 1694/1704, 1705×2, 1706/17　.. ..　9·00
1695　25 c. on 30 c. mult (surch "Anna Regina")　40　40
1696　25 c. on 30 c. mult (surch "Aurora")　40　40
1697　25 c. on 30 c. mult (surch "Bartica Grove")　40　40
1698　25 c. on 30 c. mult (surch "Bel Air")　40　40
1699　25 c. on 30 c. mult (surch "Belle Plaine")..　40　40
1700　25 c. on 30 c. multicoloured (surch "Clonbrook")　.. ..　40　40
1701　25 c. on 30 c. multicoloured (surch "T.P.O. Dem. Railway")　.. ..　40　40
1702　25 c. on 30 c. mult (surch "Enmore")　40　40
1703　25 c. on 30 c. multicoloured (surch "Fredericksburg")　.. ..　40　40
1704　25 c. on 30 c. mult (surch "Good Success")　40　40
1705　25 c. on 30 c. mult (surch "1986")　40　40
1706　25 c. on 30 c. mult (surch "Mariabba")　40　40
1707　25 c. on 30 c. multicoloured (surch "Massaruni")　.. ..　40　40
1708　25 c. on 30 c. multicoloured (surch "Nigg")　40　40
1709　25 c. on 30 c. multicoloured (surch "No. 50")　40　40

1710	25 c. on 30 c. mult (surch "No. 63 Benab")	40	40
1711	25 c. on 30 c. multicoloured (surch "Philadelphia")	40	40
1712	25 c. on 30 c. mult (surch "Sisters")	40	40
1713	25 c. on 30 c. mult (surch "Skeldon")	40	40
1714	25 c. on 30 c. mult (surch "Suddie")	40	40
1715	25 c. on 30 c. multicoloured (surch "Taymouth Manor")	40	40
1716	25 c. on 30 c. multicoloured (surch "Wales")	40	40
1717	25 c. on 30 c. multicoloured (surch "Whim")	40	40
1694/717	Set of 24	9·00	9·00

The surcharged names are those of postal agencies opened between 1860 and 1880.

1986 (26 May). *20th Anniv of Independence. (a) No. 332 surch as T 358 by Autoprint, Nos. 398A, 401B surch with "1986", bars and new value by Autoprint and No. 656 surch as T 339 by Tip Torres.*

1718	25 c. on 2 c. myrtle-green (No. 332)	15	10
1719	25 c. on 35 c. multicoloured (No. 656)	15	10
1720	60 c. on 2 c. myrtle-green (No. 332)	25	10
1721	120 c. on 6 c. yellow-green (No. 398A)	40	20
1722	130 c. on 24 c. black & brt orange (No. 401B)	3·50	30

(b) Nos. 1188/91 surch as T 358, but without "GUYANA", by Autoprint.

1723	**277**	25 c. on 120 c. lake-brown, black and bright blue (No. 1188)	25	20
	a.	Block of 4. Nos. 1723/6	1·25	
1724	–	25 c. on 130 c. rose-red, black and bright blue (No. 1189)	25	20
1725	–	25 c. on 150 c. bright violet, black and bright blue (No. 1190)	25	20
1726	–	225 c. on 200 c. dull green, black and bright blue (No. 1191)	65	60
1718/26		Set of 9	5·00	1·75

On Nos. 1721/2 "1986" has been added below the existing overprint.

Nos. 1718 and 1720 have Mult Script CA watermark, No. 1721 watermark w **12** upright and No. 1722 watermark w **12** sideways.

MEXICO
1986

225	CARICOM DAY 1986
(359)	(360)

1986 (31 May). *World Cup Football Championship, Mexico (2nd issue). No. 544 surch with T 359 in blue by Autoprint.*

1727	225 c. on 3 c. Hanging Heliconia	6·50	70

1986 (28 June). *CARICOM Day. No. 705a optd with T 360 in blue by Autoprint.*

1728	60 c. Papilio androgeus	4·50	30

CARICOM HEADS OF GOV'T CONFERENCE JULY 1986	INT. YEAR OF PEACE
60	25
(361)	(362)

1986 (1 July). *CARICOM Heads of Government Conference, Georgetown. Nos. 544 and 601 surch as T 361 in blue by Autoprint.*

1729	25 c. on 8 c. on 6 c. Cannon-ball Tree	75	10
1730	60 c. on 3 c. Hanging Heliconia	1·25	25

(Litho Format)

1986 (10 July). *Centenary of Publication of Sanders' Reichenbachia (8th issue). Vert designs as T 331. Multicoloured. No wmk. P 13½×14.*

1731	30 c. Plate No. 86 (Series 1)	50	15
1732	55 c. Plate No. 17 (Series 1)	50	15
1733	60 c. Plate No. 93 (Series 1)	50	20
1734	100 c. Plate No. 68 (Series 1)	85	20
1735	130 c. Plate No. 91 (Series 1)	90	30
1736	250 c. Plate No. 74 (Series 1)	1·00	60
1737	260 c. Plate No. 39 (Series 1)	1·00	60
1738	375 c. Plate No. 90 (Series 1)	1·50	85
1731/8	Set of 8	6·00	2·75

Nos. 1731/8 were printed in a similar sheet format to Nos. 1518/33.

For stamps as Nos. 1731/8, but with watermark **106** see Nos. 1791/8.

For these designs with different face values see Nos. 1822, 1868 and 1884/5.

1986 (14 July). *International Peace Year. Nos. 542 and 546 surch as T 362 in blue (No. 1739) or black (others).*

1739	25 c. on 1 c. Pitcher Plant of Mt Roraima	15	15
	a. Sheetlet of 25. No. 1739×24 and one label	3·25	
1740	60 c. on 6 c. Cannon-ball Tree	40	40
	a. Sheetlet of 25. Nos. 1740/3, each×4, and nine labels	5·50	
1741	120 c. on 6 c. Cannon-ball Tree	40	40
1742	130 c. on 6 c. Cannon-ball Tree	40	40
1743	150 c. on 6 c. Cannon-ball Tree	40	40
1739/43	Set of 5	1·60	1·60

As surcharged the sheet of No. 1739 contained a stamp

---

without face value, overprinted "1986", in the centre position. Nos. 1740/3 were each surcharged in blocks of four from the corner positions of the same sheet. Stamps in the central horizontal and vertical rows were without value and were overprinted with one letter of "PEACE".

363 Halley's Comet and British Guiana 1907 2 c. Stamp

(Litho Format)

1986 (19 July). *Appearance of Halley's Comet. T 363 and similar vert design. P 13½×14.*

1744	**363**	320 c. rosine, black & deep reddish lilac	30	50
	a.	Horiz pair. Nos. 1744/5	60	1·00
	ab.	Imperf between (horiz pair)		
1745	–	320 c. multicoloured	30	50
MS1746		76×50 mm. Nos. 1744/5. Imperf	1·50	1·25

Design:—No. 1745, Guyana 1985 320 c. Scarlet Macaw stamp.

(Litho Format)

1986 (24 July). *Centenary of Publication of Sanders' Reichenbachia (9th issue). Vert designs as T 331. Multicoloured. No wmk. P 13½×14.*

1747	40 c. Plate No. 96 (Series 1)	45	15
1748	45 c. Plate No. 81 (Series 1)	45	15
1749	90 c. Plate No. 89 (Series 1)	65	20
1750	100 c. Plate No. 88 (Series 1)	65	20
1751	150 c. Plate No. 76 (Series 1)	75	35
1752	180 c. Plate No. 15 (Series 1)	75	40
1753	320 c. Plate No. 82 (Series 1)	90	55
1754	330 c. Plate No. 80 (Series 1)	95	70
1747/54	Set of 8	5·00	2·40

Nos. 1747/54 were printed in a similar sheet format to Nos. 1518/33.

For stamps as Nos. 1747/54, but with watermark **106** see Nos. 1799/1806.

1986 (28 July). *No. 489 surch as T 317, but without the "X".*

1755	20 c. on 6 c. Patua	2·50	15

	REGIONAL PHARMACY CONFERENCE 1986	
GUSIA	1936-1986	130
(364)		(365)

1986 (15 Aug). *50th Anniv of Guyana United Sadr Islamic Association. Nos. 469/70 optd or surch as T 364 by Autoprint.*

1756	**105** 25 c. black, gold and lilac	1·00	10
1757	$1.50 on 6 c. black, gold and flesh	2·00	80

1986 (19 Aug). *Regional Pharmacy Conference. No. 545 surch with T 365 in blue.*

1758	130 c. on 5 c. Annatto Tree	3·75	30

1986 (21 Aug)–87. *As previous Reichenbachia issues, but W 106 (sideways on horiz designs). P 13½×14 (vert) or 14×13½ (horiz).*

(a) As Nos. 1526/7 and 1529/30

1759	130 c. Plate No. 6 (Series 1)	55	20
1760	130 c. Plate No. 13 (Series 1)	55	20
1761	130 c. Plate No. 20 (Series 1)	55	20
1762	130 c. Plate No. 25 (Series 1)	55	20
1759/62	Set of 4	2·00	70

(b) As Nos. 1552/5

1763	55 c. Plate No. 9 (Series 1)	55	10
1764	55 c. Plate No. 22 (Series 1)	55	10
1765	55 c. Plate No. 49 (Series 1)	55	10
1766	55 c. Plate No. 64 (Series 1)	55	10
1763/6	Set of 4	2·00	30

(c) As Nos. 1581/3 and 1586

1767	150 c. Plate No. 40 (Series 1) (horiz)	45	20
1768	150 c. Plate No. 42 (Series 1) (horiz)	45	20
1769	150 c. Plate No. 45 (Series 1) (horiz)	45	20
1770	200 c. Plate No. 43 (Series 1) (horiz)	55	30
1767/70	Set of 4	1·75	80

(d) As Nos. 1621, 1625/6 and 1635

1771	30 c. Plate No. 53 (Series 1) (10.86)	30	10
1772	75 c. Plate No. 55 (Series 1) (1.87)	35	15
1773	100 c. Plate No. 65 (Series 1) (1.87)	35	15
1774	225 c. Plate No. 24 (Series 1) (10.86)	45	35
1771/4	Set of 4	1·25	60

(e) As Nos. 1663/73 (1987)

1775	40 c. Plate No. 77 (Series 1)	1·50	1·50
1776	45 c. Plate No. 54 (Series 1)	1·50	1·50
1777	50 c. Plate No. 92 (Series 1)	1·50	1·50
1778	60 c. Plate No. 95 (Series 1)	2·00	2·00
1779	75 c. Plate No. 5 (Series 1)	2·50	2·50

1780	90 c. Plate No. 84 (Series 1)	3·00	3·00
1781	150 c. Plate No. 78 (Series 1)	5·00	5·00
1782	200 c. Plate No. 79 (Series 1)	6·50	6·50
1783	300 c. Plate No. 83 (Series 1)	10·00	10·00
1784	320 c. Plate No. 50 (Series 1)	11·00	11·00
1785	360 c. Plate No. 85 (Series 1)	12·50	12·50
1775/85	Set of 11	50·00	50·00

(f) As Nos. 1679/83 (1987)

1786	25 c. Plate No. 71 (Series 1)	1·50	1·50
1787	120 c. Plate No. 69 (Series 1)	6·00	6·00
1788	150 c. Plate No. 87 (Series 1)	7·00	7·00
1789	225 c. Plate No. 60 (Series 1)	8·50	8·50
1790	350 c. Plate No. 94 (Series 1)	15·00	15·00
1786/90	Set of 5	32·00	32·00

(g) As Nos. 1731/8 (1987)

1791	30 c. Plate No. 86 (Series 1)	1·00	1·00
1792	55 c. Plate No. 17 (Series 1)	1·50	1·50
1793	60 c. Plate No. 93 (Series 1)	1·50	1·50
1794	100 c. Plate No. 68 (Series 1)	2·00	2·00
1795	130 c. Plate No. 91 (Series 1)	2·50	2·50
1796	250 c. Plate No. 74 (Series 1)	5·00	5·00
1797	260 c. Plate No. 39 (Series 1)	5·00	5·00
1798	375 c. Plate No. 90 (Series 1)	7·00	7·00
1791/8	Set of 8	20·00	20·00

(h) As Nos. 1747/54 (1987)

1799	40 c. Plate No. 96 (Series 1)	1·00	1·00
1800	45 c. Plate No. 81 (Series 1)	1·00	1·00
1801	90 c. Plate No. 89 (Series 1)	2·00	2·00
1802	100 c. Plate No. 88 (Series 1)	2·00	2·00
1803	150 c. Plate No. 76 (Series 1)	3·00	3·00
1804	180 c. Plate No. 15 (Series 1)	4·00	4·00
1805	320 c. Plate No. 82 (Series 1)	5·50	5·50
1806	330 c. Plate No. 80 (Series 1)	6·50	6·50
1799/1806	Set of 8	22·00	22·00

Nos. 1759/1806 were printed in a similar sheet format to Nos. 1518/33.

These stamps, together with other unwatermarked values from the 1st to the 9th issues, also exist made up into two small books which reproduce the order of the plates in the original volumes.

Some designs in these booklets show changed face values, as detailed below, but there is no evidence that such printings were available for postal purposes without surcharge:

Plate No.	5	= 60 c.	Plate No. 76	=	65 c.
Plate No.	6	= 100 c.	Plate No. 77	=	45 c.
Plate No.	9	= 50 c.	Plate No. 78	=	45 c.
Plate No.	13	= 100 c.	Plate No. 79	=	60 c.
Plate No.	15	= 55 c.	Plate No. 80	=	65 c.
Plate No.	22	= 50 c.	Plate No. 81	=	55 c.
Plate No.	24	= 50 c.	Plate No. 82	=	55 c.
Plate No.	25	= 50 c.	Plate No. 83	=	75 c.
Plate No.	39	= 80 c.	Plate No. 84	=	45 c.
Plate No.	40	= 100 c.	Plate No. 85	=	45 c.
Plate No.	43	= 100 c.	Plate No. 87	=	60 c.
Plate No.	45	= 100 c.	Plate No. 88	=	65 c.
Plate No.	50	= 60 c.	Plate No. 89	=	55 c.
Plate No.	53	= 50 c.	Plate No. 90	=	40 c.
Plate No.	54	= 60 c.	Plate No. 92	=	75 c.
Plate No.	60	= 75 c.	Plate No. 93	=	80 c.
Plate No.	65	= 50 c.	Plate No. 94	=	60 c.
Plate No.	69	= 60 c.	Plate No. 95	=	75 c.
Plate No.	71	= 60 c.	Plate No. 96	=	65 c.
Plate No.	74	= 80 c.			

See also after No. 2471.

1986 (21 Aug). *Booklet and Coil Stamps. As Nos. 1534/5b, but W 106 (sideways on Nos. 1807a, 1808a/b).*

1807	**332** 25 c. multicoloured (imperf × p 14)	20	25
1807a	25 c. multicoloured (imperf × p 13½)	20	25
1807b	25 c. multicoloured (p 13½×14)	20	25
1808	25 c. multicoloured (p 13½×imperf)	20	25
1808a	25 c. multicoloured (p 14×imperf)	20	25
1808b	25 c. multicoloured (p 14×13½)	20	25
1807/8b	Set of 6	1·10	1·40

The note below Nos. 1534/5b also applies to Nos. 1807/8b.

(Litho Format)

1986 (23 Sept). *Centenary of Publication of Sanders' Reichenbachia (10th issue). Multicoloured designs as T 331. No wmk. P 14×13½ (Nos. 1810, 1812, 1815, 1818) or 13½×14 (others).*

1809	30 c. Plate No. 30 (Series 2)	35	15
1810	45 c. Plate No. 21 (Series 2) (horiz)	40	15
1811	75 c. Plate No. 8 (Series 2)	65	15
1812	80 c. Plate No. 42 (Series 2) (horiz)	65	15
1813	90 c. Plate No. 4 (Series 2)	75	25
1814	130 c. Plate No. 38 (Series 2)	80	35
1815	160 c. Plate No. 5 (Series 2) (horiz)	95	40
1816	200 c. Plate No. 9 (Series 2)	1·25	50
1817	320 c. Plate No. 12 (Series 2)	2·00	70
1818	350 c. Plate No. 29 (Series 2) (horiz)	2·25	70
1819	360 c. Plate No. 34 (Series 2)	2·25	70
1809/19	Set of 11	11·00	3·75

Nos. 1809/19, together with Nos. 1820/1a, were printed in a similar sheet format to Nos. 1518/33.

(Litho Format)

1986 (23 Sept). *20th Anniv of Independence (2nd issue). Booklet and Coil Stamps. T 332 additionally inscr "1966–1986" at foot. No wmk.*

1820	25 c. multicoloured (imperf×p 14)	20	25
1821	25 c. multicoloured (p 13½×imperf)	20	25
1821a	25 c. multicoloured (p 13½×14)	20	25
1820/1a	Set of 3	55	65

Nos. 1820/1a together with Nos. 1809/19, were printed in the sheet format described beneath No. 1533.

(Litho Format)

1986 (26 Sept). *Centenary of Publication of Sanders' Reichenbachia (11th issue). Design as No. 1735, but with different face value. Multicoloured. No wmk. P 13½×14.*

1822	40 c. Plate No. 91 (Series 1)	75	15

650 *(symbol)*

(vertical text) 12th World Orchid Conference

(vertical text) TOKYO JAPAN MARCH 1987

120

(366)   (367)

1986 (3 Oct). *Nos. 1361/84 surch with T **366** by Autoprint.*

1823	120 c. on 30 c. multicoloured (No. 1361)	..	60	60
	a. Sheetlet of 25. Nos. 1823/33, 1834×2			
	and 1835/46	..	13·00	
1824	120 c. on 30 c. multicoloured (No. 1362)	..	60	60
1825	120 c. on 30 c. multicoloured (No. 1363)	..	60	60
1826	120 c. on 30 c. multicoloured (No. 1364)	..	60	60
1827	120 c. on 30 c. multicoloured (No. 1365)	..	60	60
1828	120 c. on 30 c. multicoloured (No. 1366)	..	60	60
1829	120 c. on 30 c. multicoloured (No. 1367)	..	60	60
1830	120 c. on 30 c. multicoloured (No. 1368)	..	60	60
1831	120 c. on 30 c. multicoloured (No. 1369)	..	60	60
1832	120 c. on 30 c. multicoloured (No. 1370)	..	60	60
1833	120 c. on 30 c. multicoloured (No. 1371)	..	60	60
1834	120 c. on 30 c. multicoloured (No. 1372)	..	60	60
1835	120 c. on 30 c. multicoloured (No. 1373)	..	60	60
1836	120 c. on 30 c. multicoloured (No. 1374)	..	60	60
1837	120 c. on 30 c. multicoloured (No. 1375)	..	60	60
1838	120 c. on 30 c. multicoloured (No. 1376)	..	60	60
1839	120 c. on 30 c. multicoloured (No. 1377)	..	60	60
1840	120 c. on 30 c. multicoloured (No. 1378)	..	60	60
1841	120 c. on 30 c. multicoloured (No. 1379)	..	60	60
1842	120 c. on 30 c. multicoloured (No. 1380)	..	60	60
1843	120 c. on 30 c. multicoloured (No. 1381)	..	60	60
1844	120 c. on 30 c. multicoloured (No. 1382)	..	60	60
1845	120 c. on 30 c. multicoloured (No. 1383)	..	60	60
1846	120 c. on 30 c. multicoloured (No. 1384)	..	60	60
1823/46	.. ..	*Set of 24*	13·00	13·00

1986 (6 Oct). *12th World Orchid Conference, Tokyo (1st issue). Unissued design as No. 1731, but with different face value, surch with T **367** by Tip Torres.*

1847	650 c. on 40 c. Plate No. 86 (Series 1)	..	6·50	3·50

No. 1847 is inscribed "ONTOGLOSSUM TRIUMPHANS" in error.

See also Nos. 2138/9.

(vertical text) 1492-1992

(vertical text) CHRISTOPHER COLUMBUS

320

(368)

1986 (10–30 Oct). *Columbus Day. Unissued design as No. 1635, but with different face value, surch with T **368** by Tip Torres.*

1864	320 c. on 150 c. Plate No. 24 (Series 1) (surch in black (figures and obliterating device) and red)	..	2·00	80
1865	320 c. on 150 c. Plate No. 24 (Series 1) (entire surch in red) (30 Oct)	..	2·00	80

AIR

(vertical text) UNICEF 1946-1986

1986

50 *(symbol)* **120**

(369)   (370)

1986 (15 Oct). *International Food Day. Nos. 1170/1 further surch as T **369** by Autoprint.*

1866	50 c. on 30 c. on 1 c. Type **87**	..	1·00	15
1867	225 c. on $2·60 on 3 c. Peacock Cichlid ("Lukunani")	..	3·50	60

(Litho Format)

1986 (23 Oct). *Centenary of Publication of Sanders' Reichenbachia (12th issue). Vert designs as T **331**, one as No. 1731 with different face value. Multicoloured. No wmk. P 13½×14.*

1868	40 c. Plate No. 86 (Series 1)	..	50	15
1869	90 c. Plate No. 10 (Series 2)	..	75	30

1986 (24 Oct). *Air. 40th Anniv of U.N.I.C.E.F. and U.N.E.S.C.O. No. 706 surch as T **370** by Autoprint.*

1870	120 c. on $1 Type **167** (surch T **370**)	..	2·75	3·75
	a. Pair. Nos. 1870/1		5·50	5·50
1871	120 c. on $1 Type **167** (surch "UNESCO 1946–1986")	..	2·75	2·75

Nos. 1870/1 were surcharged together, *se-tenant*, in horizontal and vertical pairs throughout the sheet.

(Litho Format)

1986 (30 Oct). *Centenary of Publication of Sanders' Reichenbachia (13th issue). Vert designs as T **331**. Multicoloured. No wmk. P 13½×14.*

1872	45 c. Plate No. 17 (Series 2)	..	30	15
1873	50 c. Plate No. 33 (Series 2)	..	30	15
1874	60 c. Plate No. 27 (Series 2)	..	45	15
1875	75 c. Plate No. 56 (Series 2)	..	55	20
1876	85 c. Plate No. 45 (Series 2)	..	55	20
1877	90 c. Plate No. 13 (Series 2)	..	70	20
1878	200 c. Plate No. 44 (Series 2)	..	1·00	45
1879	300 c. Plate No. 50 (Series 2)	..	1·60	60
1880	320 c. Plate No. 10 (Series 2)	..	1·75	70
1881	390 c. Plate No. 6 (Series 2)	..	2·00	95
1872/81	.. ..	*Set of 10*	8·25	3·25

Nos. 1872/81 were printed in a similar sheet format to Nos. 1518/33.

For these designs with different face values see Nos. 1907, 1915 and 1925.

25 X   **CHRISTMAS 1986**

Deepavali 1986   **20**

(371)   (372)

1986 (3 Nov). *Deepavali Festival. Nos. 543 and 601 surch as T **371** by Autoprint.*

1882	25 c. on 2 c. Type **132**	..	40	10
1883	200 c. on 8 c. on 6 c. Cannon-ball Tree	..	1·00	40

(Litho Format)

1986 (25 Nov). *Centenary of Publication of Sanders' Reichenbachia (14th issue). Vert designs as T **331**, two as Nos. 1732 and 1734 with different face values. Multicoloured. No wmk. P 13½×14.*

1884	40 c. Plate No. 68 (Series 1)	..	75	15
1885	80 c. Plate No. 17 (Series 1)	..	1·25	25
1886	200 c. Plate No. 2 (Series 2)	..	1·60	60
1887	225 c. Plate No. 24 (Series 2)	..	1·90	70
1884/7	.. ..	*Set of 4*	5·00	1·50

Nos. 1884/7 were printed in a similar sheet format to Nos. 1518/33.

For these designs with different face values see Nos. 1914 and 1929.

1986 (26 Nov). *Christmas. No. 452 surch with T **372** and previously unissued miniature sheet containing Nos. 1425/9, each surch as T **342**, but without dates, all in red by Autoprint.*

1888	20 c. on 6 c. Black Acara ("Patua")	..	55	10
MS1889	215×75 mm. 120 c. on 60 c. × 5 Nos.			
1425/9	..		6·00	6·00

(vertical text) 1986

$15

(373)   (374)

1986 (26 Nov). *Wildlife Protection. Nos. 756/67 optd with T **373** in blue by Autoprint.*

1894	30 c. Type **178**	..	70	70
	a. Sheetlet of 12. Nos. 1894/905.		7·50	
1895	30 c. Red Howler	..	70	70
1896	30 c. Common Squirrel-Monkey	..	70	70
1897	30 c. Two-toed Sloth	..	70	70
1898	30 c. Brazilian Tapir	..	70	70
1899	30 c. Collared Peccary	..	70	70
1900	30 c. Six-banded Armadillo	..	70	70
1901	30 c. Tamandua ("Ant Eater")	..	70	70
1902	30 c. Giant Anteater	..	70	70
1903	30 c. Murine Opossum	..	70	70
1904	30 c. Brown Four-eyed Opossum	..	70	70
1905	30 c. Brazilian Agouti	..	70	70
1894/905	.. ..	*Set of 12*	7·50	7·50

1986 (1 Dec). *No. 1642 surch with T **374** in red by Autoprint.*

1906	$15 on $3.50, Clive Lloyd with the Prudential Cup	..	17·00	11·00

(Litho Format)

1986 (3 Dec). *Centenary of Publication of Sanders' Reichenbachia (15th issue). Design as No. 1877, but with different face value. Multicoloured. No wmk. P 13½×14.*

1907	50 c. Plate No. 13 (Series 2)	..	65	15

G P O C

$10   1977 - 1987

375 Memorial   (376)

(Litho Format)

1986 (13 Dec). *President Burnham Commemoration. T **375** and similar multicoloured designs. P 12½.*

1908	25 c. Type **375**	..	10	10
1909	120 c. Map of Guyana and flags	..	20	20
1910	130 c. Parliament Buildings and mace	..	20	20
1911	$6 L. F. Burnham and Georgetown mayoral chain (*vert*)	..	60	1·25
1908/11	.. ..	*Set of 4*	90	1·60

(Litho Format)

1986 (15–22 Dec). *Centenary of Publication of Sanders' Reichenbachia (16th issue). Multicoloured designs as Nos. 1554/5, 1874 and 1887 with different face values. W **106** (Nos. 1912/13) or no wmk (others).*

1912	50 c. Plate No. 49 (Series 1) (22.12)	..	75	15
1913	50 c. Plate No. 64 (Series 1)	..	75	15
1914	85 c. Plate No. 24 (Series 2)	..	90	25
1915	90 c. Plate No. 27 (Series 2)	..	90	25
1912/15	.. ..	*Set of 4*	3·00	70

(Litho Format)

1986 (27 Dec). *Centenary of Publication of Sanders' Reichenbachia (17th issue). Vert designs as T **331**. Multicoloured. No wmk. P 13½×14.*

1916	25 c. Plate No. 20 (Series 2)	..	35	15
1917	40 c. Plate No. 7 (Series 2)	..	35	15
1918	85 c. Plate No. 15 (Series 2)	..	50	20
1919	90 c. Plate No. 3 (Series 2)	..	50	20
1920	120 c. Plate No. 14 (Series 2)	..	65	30
1921	130 c. Plate No. 32 (Series 2)	..	65	30
1922	150 c. Plate No. 22 (Series 2)	..	80	35
1923	320 c. Plate No. 18 (Series 2)	..	1·25	55
1924	330 c. Plate No. 28 (Series 2)	..	1·25	70
1916/24	..	*Set of 9*	5·50	2·75

Nos. 1916/24 were printed in a similar sheet format to Nos. 1518/33.

For these designs with different face values see Nos. 1926 and 1928.

(Litho Format)

1987 (5–16 Jan). *Centenary of Publication of Sanders' Reichenbachia (18th issue). Multicoloured designs as Nos. 1625, 1876, 1886, 1918 and 1923 with different face values. W **106** (No. 1927) or no wmk (others). P 13½×14.*

1925	35 c. Plate No. 45 (Series 2)	..	40	15
1926	50 c. Plate No. 15 (Series 2)	..	40	15
1927	50 c. Plate No. 55 (Series 1) (16.1)	..	40	15
1928	85 c. Plate No. 18 (Series 2)	..	65	25
1929	90 c. Plate No. 2 (Series 2)	..	65	25
1925/9	.. ..	*Set of 5*	2·25	85

Nos. 1925/9 were printed in a similar sheet format to Nos. 1518/33.

1987 (19 Jan). *10th Anniv of Guyana Post Office Corporation (1st issue). Unissued designs as Nos. 1621 and 1635, but with different face values, surch or optd as T **376** by Tip Torres.*

1930	$2.25, Plate No. 53 (Series 1)	..	1·00	35
1931	$10 on 150 c. Plate No. 24 (Series 1)	..	3·00	3·50

See also Nos. 2074/80.

200

200   *(symbol)*

(377)   (378)

200

TWO DOLLARS

(379)   (380)

1987

15.oo
(381)

225
(382)

120
(383)

120
(384)

1987 (9 Feb–Sept). *Various Reichenbachia issues surch as* T 377/84.

(a) As T 377 in red by Tip Torres (9 Feb)
1932	200 c. on 40 c. Plate No. 90 (Series 1)	60	50

(b) As T 378 by Tip Torres (6 Mar)
1933	200 c. on 25 c. Plate No. 8 (Series 1) (No. 1571)	60	50
1934	200 c. on 25 c. Plate No. 51 (Series 1) (No. 1573)	60	50

(c) As T 379 by Tip Torres (No. 1935 without ornament) (6 Mar)
1935	$2 on 25 c. Plate No. 12 (Series 1) (No. 1518)	60	50
1936	$2 on 25 c. Plate No. 23 (Series 1) (No. 1572)	60	50

(d) As T 380 by Tip Torres (17 Mar)
1937	200 c. on 40 c. Plate No. 68 (Series 1) (No. 1884) (ornament inverted)	60	50
	a. Ornament upright	60	50
1938	200 c. on 40 c. Plate No. 90 (Series 1)	60	50
1939	200 c. on 50 c. Plate No. 92 (Series 1) (No. 1665)	60	50
1940	200 c. on 50 c. Plate No. 22 (Series 1) (wmkd)	60	50
1941	200 c. on 55 c. Plate No. 22 (Series 1) (No. 1764) (wmkd)	60	50
1942	200 c. on 60 c. Plate No. 5 (Series 1) (ornament inverted)	60	50
1943	200 c. on 75 c. Plate No. 5 (Series 1) (No. 1667) (ornament inverted)	60	50
1944	200 c. on 75 c. Plate No. 60 (Series 1)	60	50
1945	200 c. on 75 c. Plate No. 92 (Series 1)	60	50
1946	200 c. on 85 c. Plate No. 18 (Series 2) (No. 1928)	60	50
1947	200 c. on 375 c. Plate No. 90 (Series 1) (No. 1738)	60	50
1948	200 c. on 375 c. Plate No. 90 (Series 1) (No. 1798) (wmkd)	60	50
1937/48	*Set of 12*	6·50	5·50

(e) As T 377 by Tip Torres (March)
1949	200 c. on 25 c. Plate No. 52 (Series 1) (No. 1551)	60	50
1950	200 c. on 25 c. Plate No 8 (Series 1) (No. 1571)	60	50
1951	200 c. on 25 c. Plate No. 72 (Series 1) (No. 1577)	60	50
1952	200 c. on 25 c. Plate No. 71 (Series 1) (No. 1679) (surch vert–reading downwards)	60	50
1953	200 c. on 30 c. Plate No. 86 (Series 1) (No. 1731)	60	50

1954	200 c. on 30 c. Plate No. 53 (Series 1) (No. 1771) (wmkd)	60	50
1955	200 c. on 40 c. Plate No. 77 (Series 1) (No. 1663)	60	50
1956	200 c. on 40 c. Plate No. 86 (Series 1) (No. 1868)	60	50
	a. Inscr "ONTOGLOSSUM TRIUM-PHANS" in error		
1957	220 c. on 45 c. Plate No. 81 (Series 1) (No. 1748)	60	50
1958	200 c. on 45 c. Plate No. 77 (Series 1)	60	50
1959	200 c. on 45 c. Plate No. 78 (Series 1)	60	50
1960	200 c. on 45 c. Plate No. 85 (Series 1)	60	50
1961	200 c. on 50 c. Plate No. 24 (Series 1) (wmkd)	60	50
1962	200 c. on 50 c. Plate No. 53 (Series 1) (wmkd)	60	50
1963	200 c. on 50 c. Plate No. 65 (Series 1) (wmkd)	60	50
1964	200 c. on 55 c. Plate No. 49 (Series 1) (No. 1554)	60	50
1965	200 c. on 55 c. Plate No. 17 (Series 1) (No. 1732)	60	50
1966	200 c. on 55 c. Plate No. 49 (Series 1) (No. 1765) (wmkd)	60	50
1967	200 c. on 60 c. Plate No. 7 (Series 1) (No. 1520)	60	50
1968	200 c. on 60 c. Plate No. 10 (Series 1) (No. 1521)	60	50
1969	200 c. on 60 c. Plate No. 19 (Series 1) (No. 1522)	60	50
1970	200 c. on 60 c. Plate No. 31 (Series 1) (No. 1523)	60	50
1971	200 c. on 60 c. Plate No. 44 (Series 1) (No. 1556)	60	50
1972	200 c. on 60 c. Plate No. 47 (Series 1) (No. 1557)	60	50
1973	200 c. on 60 c. Plate No. 57 (Series 1) (No. 1622) (surch vert – reading down)	60	50
1974	200 c. on 60 c. Plate No. 73 (Series 1) (No. 1623) (surch vert – reading up)	60	50
1975	200 c. on 60 c. Plate No. 75 (Series 1) (No. 1624) (surch vert – reading down)	60	50
1976	200 c. on 60 c. Plate No. 71 (Series 1) (surch vert – reading down)	60	50
1977	200 c. on 60 c. Plate No. 87 (Series 1) (surch vert–reading down)	60	50
1977a	200 c. on 80 c. Plate No. 17 (Series 1) (No. 1885)	1·50	1·25
1978	225 c. on 90 c. Plate No. 89 (Series 1) (No. 1749)	65	55
1949/78	*Set of 31*	17·00	14·00

(f) As T 381 by Gardy Ptg (March)
1979	120 c. on 50 c. Plate No. 9 (Series 1) (wmkd)	50	30
1980	120 c. on 55 c. Plate No. 9 (Series 1) (No. 1552)	50	30
1981	120 c. on 55 c. Plate No. 64 (Series 1) (No. 1555)	50	30
1981a	120 c. on 55 c. Plate No. 9 (Series 1) (No. 1763) (wmkd)	1·50	1·00
1982	120 c. on 55 c. Plate No. 64 (Series 1) (No. 1766) (wmkd)	50	30
1983	$10 on 25 c. Plate No. 53 (Series 1)	2·00	2·25
1984	$12 on 80 c. Plate No. 74 (Series 1)	2·25	2·50
1985	$15 on 80 c. Plate No. 39 (Series 1)	2·75	3·00
1986	$25 on 25 c. Plate No. 53 (Series 1)	4·50	5·00
1979/86	*Set of 9*	13·50	13·50

Nos. 1979/82 do not show a date as part of the surcharge. On No. 1986 the surcharge is achieved by a dollar sign in front of the original face value.

(g) With T 382 by Gardy Ptg (June)
1987	225 c. on 40 c. Plate No. 91 (Series 1) (No. 1822)	70	60
1988	225 c. on 40 c. Plate No. 90 (Series 1)	70	60
1988a	225 c. on 50 c. Plate No. 92 (Series 1) No. 1665)	10·00	3·00
1989	225 c. on 50 c. Plate No. 22 (Series 1) (wmkd)	70	60
1990	225 c. on 60 c. Plate No. 55 (Series 1) (No. 1597)	70	60
1990a	225 c. on 60 c. Plate No. 95 (Series 1) (No. 1666)	10·00	3·00
1991	225 c. on 60 c. Plate No. 93 (Series 1) (No. 1733)	70	60
1992	225 c. on 80 c. Plate No. 93 (Series 1)	70	60
1993	225 c. on 150 c. Plate No. 42 (Series 1) (No. 1657) (surch vert–reading down)	70	60
1987/93	*Set of 9*	22·00	9·00

(h) As T 383 (July)
1994	120 c. on 50 c. Plate No. 49 (Series 1) (No. 1912) (wmkd)	50	40
1995	120 c. on 50 c. Plate No. 64 (Series 1) (No. 1913) (wmkd)	50	40
1996	120 c. on 50 c. Plate No. 9 (Series 1) (wmkd)	50	40
1997	120 c. on 50 c. Plate No. 22 (Series 1) (wmkd)	50	40
1998	120 c. on 50 c. Plate No. 3 (Series 2)	50	40
1999	120 c. on 50 c. Plate No. 6 (Series 2)	50	40
2000	120 c. on 50 c. Plate No. 20 (Series 2)	50	40
2001	120 c. on 50 c. Plate No. 32 (Series 2)	50	40
2002	120 c. on 55 c. Plate No. 9 (Series 1) (No. 1552)	50	40
2003	120 c. on 55 c. Plate No. 49 (Series 1) (No. 1554)	50	40
2004	120 c. on 55 c. Plate No. 64 (Series 1) (No. 1555)	50	40
2005	120 c. on 55 c. Plate No. 9 (Series 1) (No. 1763) (wmkd)	50	40
2006	120 c. on 55 c. Plate No. 22 (Series 1) (No. 1764) (wmkd)	50	40
2007	120 c. on 55 c. Plate No. 49 (Series 1) (No. 1765) (wmkd)	50	40
2008	120 c. on 55 c. Plate No. 64 (Series 1) (No. 1766) (wmkd)	50	40
2009	120 c. on 55 c. Plate No. 15 (Series 1)	50	40
2010	120 c. on 55 c. Plate No. 81 (Series 1)	50	40
2011	120 c. on 55 c. Plate No. 82 (Series 1)	50	40
2012	120 c. on 55 c. Plate No. 89 (Series 1)	50	40
1994/2012	*Set of 19*	8·50	7·00

(i) As T 384 by Gardy Ptg (Sept)
2013	120 c. on 40 c. Plate No. 91 (Series 1) (No. 1822)	50	40
2014	120 c. on 40 c. Plate No. 90 (Series 1)	50	40
2015	120 c. on 50 c. Plate No. 49 (Series 1) (No. 1912) (wmkd)	50	40
2016	120 c. on 50 c. Plate No. 64 (Series 1) (No. 1913) (wmkd)	50	40
2017	120 c. on 50 c. Plate No. 9 (Series 1) (wmkd)	50	40
2018	120 c. on 50 c. Plate No. 22 (Series 1) (wmkd)	50	40
2019	120 c. on 50 c. Plate No. 24 (Series 1) (wmkd)	50	40
2020	120 c. on 50 c. Plate No. 53 (Series 1) (wmkd)	50	40
2021	120 c. on 50 c. Plate No. 65 (Series 1) (wmkd)	50	40
2022	120 c. on 55 c. Plate No. 9 (Series 1) (No. 1763) (wmkd)	50	40
2023	120 c. on 55 c. Plate No. 22 (Series 1) (No. 1764) (wmkd)	50	40
2024	120 c. on 55 c. Plate No. 49 (Series 1) (No. 1765) (wmkd)	50	40
2025	120 c. on 55 c. Plate No. 64 (Series 1) (No. 1766) (wmkd)	50	40
2026	120 c. on 60 c. Plate No. 2 (Series 1) (No. 1519)	50	40
2027	120 c. on 60 c. Plate No. 10 (Series 1) (No. 1521)	50	40
2028	120 c. on 60 c. Plate No. 19 (Series 1) (No. 1522)	50	40
2029	120 c. on 60 c. Plate No. 31 (Series 1) (No. 1523)	50	40
2030	120 c. on 60 c. Plate No. 5 (Series 1)	50	40
2031	120 c. on 60 c. Plate No. 50 (Series 1)	50	40
2032	120 c. on 60 c. Plate No. 54 (Series 1)	50	40
2033	120 c. on 60 c. Plate No. 69 (Series 1) (surch vert – reading down)	50	40
2034	120 c. on 60 c. Plate No. 71 (Series 1) (surch vert – reading up)	50	40
	a. Surch reading down	50	40
2035	120 c. on 60 c. Plate No. 79 (Series 1)	50	40
2036	120 c. on 60 c. Plate No. 87 (Series 1) (surch vert – reading up)	50	40
	a. Surch reading down	50	40
2037	120 c. on 60 c. Plate No. 94 (Series 1) (surch vert – reading down)	50	40
2038	120 c. on 75 c. Plate No. 60 (Series 1)	50	40
2039	120 c. on 75 c. Plate No. 83 (Series 1)	50	40
2040	120 c. on 75 c. Plate No. 92 (Series 1)	50	40
2041	120 c. on 75 c. Plate No. 95 (Series 1)	50	40
2042	200 c. on 45 c. Plate No. 77 (Series 1)	50	40
2043	200 c. on 45 c. Plate No. 78 (Series 1)	50	40
2044	200 c. on 45 c. Plate No. 84 (Series 1)	50	40
2045	200 c. on 45 c. Plate No. 85 (Series 1)	50	40
2046	200 c. on 50 c. Plate No. 55 (Series 1) (No. 1927) (wmkd)	90	50
2047	200 c. on 50 c. Plate No. 24 (Series 1) (wmkd)	90	50
2048	200 c. on 50 c. Plate No. 53 (Series 1) (wmkd)	90	50
2049	200 c. on 50 c. Plate No. 65 (Series 1) (wmkd)	90	50
2050	200 c. on 55 c. Plate No. 15 (Series 1)	2·00	50
2051	200 c. on 55 c. Plate No. 81 (Series 1)	2·00	50
2052	200 c. on 55 c. Plate No. 82 (Series 1)	5·00	50
2053	200 c. on 55 c. Plate No. 89 (Series 1)	2·00	50
2054	225 c. on 40 c. Plate No. 91 (Series 1) (No. 1822)	1·25	60
2055	225 c. on 40 c. Plate No. 86 (Series 1) (No. 1868)	1·25	60
	a. Inscr "ONTOGLOSSUM TRIUM-PHANS" in error	1·00	60
2056	225 c. on 40 c. Plate No. 68 (Series 1) (No. 1884)	90	60
2057	225 c. on 40 c. Plate No. 90 (Series 1)	90	60
2058	225 c. on 65 c. Plate No. 76 (Series 1)	90	60
2059	225 c. on 65 c. Plate No. 80 (Series 1)	90	60
2060	225 c. on 65 c. Plate No. 88 (Series 1)	90	60
2061	225 c. on 65 c. Plate No. 96 (Series 1)	90	60
2062	600 c. on 80 c. Plate No. 17 (Series 1) (No. 1885)	1·50	1·50
2063	600 c. on 80 c. Plate No. 39 (Series 1)	1·50	1·50
2064	600 c. on 80 c. Plate No. 74 (Series 1)	1·50	1·50
2065	600 c. on 80 c. Plate No. 93 (Series 1)	1·50	1·50
2013/65	*Set of 53*	40·00	24·00

Initially some values were surcharged in sheets of sixteen orchid stamps together with nine examples of No. 2081. Subsequently, however, the surcharges appeared in the individual blocks of 4 with the arms design issued separately as Nos. 2082/3.

For 600 c. on 900 c. with surcharge as T 384 see No. 2219.

(Litho Format)

1987 (16 Feb). *Centenary of Publication of Sanders' Reichenbachia (19th issue). Vert designs as* T 331. *Multicoloured. No wmk.* P 13½×14.
2066	180 c. Plate 41 (Series 2)	1·00	40
2067	230 c. Plate 25 (Series 2)	1·10	40
2068	300 c. Plate 85 (Series 2)	1·75	65
2069	330 c. Plate 82 (Series 2)	2·00	70
2070	425 c. Plate 87 (Series 2)	2·25	85
2071	440 c. Plate 88 (Series 2)	2·25	85
2072	590 c. Plate 52 (Series 2)	2·25	1·25
2073	650 c. Plate 65 (Series 2)	3·00	1·50
2066/73	*Set of 8*	14·00	6·00

Nos. 2066/73 were printed in a similar sheet format to Nos. 1518/33.

PRICES OF SETS

Set prices are given for many issues, generally those containing three stamps or more. Definitive sets include one of each value or major colour change, but do not cover different perforations, die types or minor shades. Where a choice is possible the set prices are based on the cheapest versions of the stamps included in the listings.

1987

Post Office Corp. 1977-1987

25c (385)   200 (386)

1987 (17 Feb). *10th Anniv of Guyana Post Office Corporation (2nd issue). Nos. 543, 545, 548a and 601 surch as T 385 in blue by Autoprint.*

2074	25 c. on 2 c. Type **132**	15	10
2075	25 c. on 5 c. Annatto tree	15	10
2076	25 c. on 8 c. on 6 c. Cannon-ball tree	15	10
2077	25 c. on 15 c. Christmas Orchid	1·00	10
2078	60 c. on 15 c. Christmas Orchid	2·00	15
2079	$1.20 on 2 c. Type **132**	75	65
2080	$1.30 on 15 c. Christmas Orchid	2·50	85
2074/80	*Set of 7*	6·00	1·75

1987 (6 Mar). *Nos. 1534/5 surch with T 386 by Tip Torres.*

2081	**332** 200 c. on 25 c. mult (p 13½ × 14)	70	70
2082	200 c. on 25 c. mult (imperf × p 14)	70	70
2083	200 c. on 25 c. mult (p 13½ × imperf)	70	70
2081/3	*Set of 3*	1·90	1·90

See note below No. 2065.

1987 1987 **1987** 1987
(387)   (388)   (389)   (390)

1987 (6 Mar–Dec). *Various Reichenbachia issues optd as T 387/90.*

(a) With T 387 by Tip Torres (March)

2084	130 c. Plate No. 3 (Series 1) (No. 1525)	50	40
2085	130 c. Plate No. 6 (Series 1) (No. 1526)	50	40
2086	130 c. Plate No. 20 (Series 1) (No. 1529)	50	40
2087	130 c. Plate No. 18 (Series 1) (No. 1536)	50	40
2088	130 c. Plate No. 29 (Series 1) (No. 1537)	50	40
2089	130 c. Plate No. 30 (Series 1) (No. 1538)	50	40
2090	130 c. Plate No. 16 (Series 1) (No. 1559)	50	40
2091	130 c. Plate No. 66 (Series 1) (No. 1632)	50	40
2092	130 c. Plate No. 13 (Series 1) (No. 1684)	50	40
2093	130 c. Plate No. 6 (Series 1) (No. 1759) (wmkd)	50	40
2094	130 c. Plate No. 20 (Series 1) (No. 1761) (wmkd)	50	40
2095	200 c. Plate No. 4 (Series 1) (No. 1533)	60	50
2096	200 c. Plate No. 14 (Series 1) (No. 1584)	60	50
2097	200 c. Plate No. 21 (Series 1) (No. 1585) (opt vert – reading down)	60	50
2098	200 c. Plate No. 33 (Series 1) (No. 1634) (opt vert – reading down)	60	50
2099	200 c. Plate No. 43 (Series 1) (No. 1658) (opt vert – reading down)	60	50
2100	200 c. Plate No. 79 (Series 1) (No. 1670)	60	50
2101	200 c. Plate No. 9 (Series 2) (No. 1816)	60	50
2102	200 c. Plate No. 2 (Series 2) (No. 1886)	60	50
2103	250 c. Plate No. 74 (Series 1) (No. 1736)	70	60
2104	200 c. Plate No. 39 (Series 1) (No. 1737)	70	60
2084/2104	*Set of 21*	10·50	8·50
MS2105	100×129 mm. 200 c.×4 Plate 4 (Series 1) (No. MS1539)	2·00	1·75
MS2106	100×129 mm. 200 c. on 130 c.×4 Plate 20 (Series 1) (No. MS1570)	2·00	1·75

(b) With T 388 by Gardy Ptg (March)

2107	130 c. Plate No. 13 (Series 1) (No. 1527)	50	40
2108	130 c. Plate No. 25 (Series 1) (No. 1530)	50	40
2109	130 c. Plate No. 91 (Series 1) (No. 1735)	50	40
2110	130 c. Plate No. 13 (Series 1) (No. 1760) (wmkd)	50	40
2111	130 c. Plate No. 25 (Series 1) (No. 1762) (wmkd)	50	40
2107/11	*Set of 5*	2·25	1·75

(c) With T 389 by Gardy Ptg (July)

2112	120 c. Plate No. 1 (Series 1) (No. 1578) (opt vert – reading down)	2·00	60
2113	120 c. Plate No. 11 (Series 1) (No. 1579) (opt vert – reading down)	1·50	60
2114	120 c. Plate No. 28 (Series 1) (No. 1580) (opt vert – reading down)	2·00	60
2115	120 c. Plate No. 37 (Series 1) (No. 1627)	1·00	60
2116	120 c. Plate No. 46 (Series 1) (No. 1628)	4·50	60
2117	120 c. Plate No. 56 (Series 1) (No. 1629)	1·50	60
2118	120 c. Plate No. 58 (Series 1) (No. 1630)	1·50	60
2119	130 c. Plate No. 6 (Series 1) (No. 1759) (wmkd)	1·50	60
2120	130 c. Plate No. 13 (Series 1) (No. 1760) (wmkd)	1·50	60
2121	130 c. Plate No. 20 (Series 1) (No. 1761) (wmkd)	1·00	60
2122	130 c. Plate No. 25 (Series 1) (No. 1762) (wmkd)	1·25	60
2123	150 c. Plate No. 40 (Series 1) (No. 1581) (opt vert–reading down)	1·25	70
2124	150 c. Plate No. 45 (Series 1) (No. 1583) (opt vert–reading down)	1·00	70
2125	150 c. Plate No. 42 (Series 1) (No. 1657) (opt vert–reading down)	3·00	70
2126	150 c. Plate No. 40 (Series 1) (No. 1767) (wmkd) (opt vert–reading up)	1·00	70
2127	150 c. Plate No. 42 (Series 1) (No. 1768) (wmkd) (opt vert–reading up)	1·50	70
2128	150 c. Plate No. 45 (Series 1) (No. 1769) (wmkd) (opt vert–reading up)	1·25	70
2129	200 c. Plate No. 21 (Series 1) (No. 1585) (opt vert–reading down)	1·00	75
2130	200 c. Plate No. 43 (Series 1) (No. 1658) (opt vert–reading down)	3·00	75

2131	200 c. Plate No. 43 (Series 1) (No. 1770) (wmkd) (opt vert–reading up)	3·00	75
2112/31	*Set of 20*	32·00	11·50

(d) With T 390 by Gardy Ptg (Dec)

2132	120 c. Plate No. 67 (Series 1) (No. 1631)	50	40
2133	130 c. Plate No. 18 (Series 1) (No. 1536)	50	40
2134	130 c. Plate No. 29 (Series 1) (No. 1537)	50	40
2135	130 c. Plate No. 30 (Series 1) (No. 1538)	50	40
2136	130 c. Plate No. 66 (Series 1) (No. 1632)	50	40
2137	150 c. Plate No. 26 (Series 1) (No. 1633)	50	40
2132/7	*Set of 6*	2·75	2·25

650

12th World Orchid Conference

TOKYO JAPAN (391)

28 MARCH 1927 PAA GEO-POS (392)

1987 (12 Mar). *12th World Orchid Conference, Tokyo (2nd issue). Nos. 1552 and 1763 surch with T 391 by Tip Torres.*

2138	650 c. on 55 c. Plate No. 9 (Series 1) (No. 1552)	3·50	2·50
2139	650 c. on 55 c. Plate No. 9 (Series 1) (No. 1763)	3·50	2·50

1987 (17 Mar). *125th Anniv of British Guiana Post Office (3rd issue). No. 699 surch as T 324 by Autoprint.*

2140	25 c. on 10 c. mult (surch "AGRICOLA")	50	30
	a. Sheetlet of 25. Nos. 2140/64	11·00	
2141	25 c. on 10 c. mult (surch "BAGOTVILLE")	50	30
2142	25 c. on 10 c. mult (surch "BOURDA")	50	30
2143	25 c. on 10 c. mult (surch "BUXTON")	50	30
2144	25 c. on 10 c. mult (surch "CABACABURI")	50	30
2145	25 c. on 10 c. multicoloured (surch "CARMICHAEL STREET")	50	30
2146	25 c. on 10 c. multicoloured (surch "COTTON TREE")	50	30
2147	25 c. on 10 c. mult (surch "DUNOON")	50	30
2148	25 c. on 10 c. mult (surch "FELLOWSHIP")	50	30
2149	25 c. on 10 c. mult (surch "GROVE")	50	30
2150	25 c. on 10 c. mult (surch "HACKNEY")	50	30
2151	25 c. on 10 c. mult (surch "LEONORA")	50	30
2152	25 c. on 10 c. multicoloured (surch "1987")	50	30
2153	25 c. on 10 c. mult (surch "MALLALI")	50	30
2154	25 c. on 10 c. mult (surch "PROVIDENCE")	50	30
2155	25 c. on 10 c. mult (surch "RELIANCE")	50	30
2156	25 c. on 10 c. mult (surch "SPARTA")	50	30
2157	25 c. on 10 c. multicoloured (surch "STEWARTVILLE")	50	30
2158	25 c. on 10 c. mult (surch "TARLOGY")	50	30
2159	25 c. on 10 c. multicoloured (surch "T.P.O. BERBICE RIV.")	50	30
2160	25 c. on 10 c. multicoloured (surch "T.P.O. DEM. RIV.")	50	30
2161	25 c. on 10 c. multicoloured (surch "T.P.O. ESSEO. RIV.")	50	30
2162	25 c. on 10 c. multicoloured (surch "T.P.O. MASSARUNI RIV.")	50	30
2163	25 c. on 10 c. multicoloured (surch "TUSCHEN (De VRIENDEN)")	50	30
2164	25 c. on 10 c. multicoloured (surch "ZORG")	50	30
2140/64	*Set of 25*	11·00	6·50

The surcharged names are those of postal agencies opened by 1885.

1987 (28 Mar). *50th Anniv of First Georgetown to Port-of-Spain Flight by P.A.A. No. 708a optd with T 392 by Autoprint.*

2165	$10 *Elbella patrobas*	7·00	4·00

1987 (6 Apr). *No. 704 surch with figures only as T 324 by Autoprint.*

2166	25 c. on 40 c. *Morpho rhetenor* (male)	3·00	10

1987

120 1987   CAPEX '87
(393)   (394)   (395)

1987 (21 Apr). *Easter. Nos. 481/2 and 484 optd or surch as T 393 by Autoprint.*

2167	**111** 25 c. multicoloured	20	10
2168	120 c. on 6 c. multicoloured	30	20
2169	320 c. on 6 c. multicoloured	65	65
2170	500 c. on 40 c. multicoloured	95	90
2167/70	*Set of 4*	1·90	1·50

(Litho Format)

1987 (24 Apr). *Centenary of Publication of Sanders' Reichenbachia (20th issue). Multicoloured designs as T 331. No wmk. P 13½×14 (240, 260, 500, 560 c.) or 13½×14 (others).*

2171	240 c. Plate No. 47 (Series 2)	80	45
2172	260 c. Plate No. 39 (Series 2)	90	55

2173	275 c. Plate No. 58 (Series 2) (horiz)	90	55
2174	390 c. Plate No. 37 (Series 2) (horiz)	1·10	70
2175	450 c. Plate No. 19 (Series 2) (horiz)	1·50	90
2176	460 c. Plate No. 54 (Series 2) (horiz)	1·50	90
2177	500 c. Plate No. 51 (Series 2)	1·75	1·10
2178	560 c. Plate No. 1 (Series 2)	2·00	1·50
2171/8	*Set of 8*	9·50	6·00

Nos. 2171/8 were printed in a similar sheet format to Nos. 1518/33.

1987 (Apr). *No. 706 optd with T 394 by Autoprint.*

2179	**167** $1 multicoloured	2·25	15

(Litho Format)

1987 (2 June). *Centenary of Publication of Sanders' Reichenbachia (21st issue). Vert designs as T 331. Multicoloured. No wmk. P 13½×14.*

2180	500 c. Plate No. 86 (Series 2)	1·75	1·10
2181	520 c. Plate No. 89 (Series 2)	1·90	1·25
2182	$20 Plate No. 83 (Series 2)	6·00	7·00
2180/2	*Set of 3*	8·75	8·50

Nos. 2180/2 were printed in a similar sheet format to Nos. 1518/33, but included Nos. 2183/4 instead of Nos. 1534/5.

Two types of bird in coat of arms:

A   B

(Litho Format)

1987 (2 June–29 Sept). *Booklet and Coil Stamps. As T 332, but within frame. No wmk. A. Bird with short tail. B. Bird with crest and long tail (29 Sept).*

		A		B	
2183	25 c. mult (imperf×p 14)	30	30	30	30
2183c	25 c. mult (p 13½×14)	30	30	30	30
2184	25 c. mult (p 13½×imperf)	30	30	30	30
2184c	25 c. mult (p 14×13½)	†		30	30

Nos. 2183/4c were cut from the gutters of the orchid stamps as detailed in the note below No. 1533.

1987 (10 June). *"Capex '87" International Stamp Exhibition, Toronto. Nos. 1744/5 optd with T 395.*

2185	**363** 320 c. rosine, black and dp reddish lilac	65	80
	a. Horiz pair. Nos. 2185/6	1·25	1·60
	ab. Imperf between (horiz pair)		
2186	– 320 c. multicoloured	65	80

1987 (15 July). *Commonwealth Heads of Government Meeting, Vancouver. Nos. 1066/8 further optd with T 394.*

2187	$1.20 on 6 c. yellow-green	30	20
2188	$1.30 on 24 c. black and bright orange	2·50	30
2189	$2.40 on 24 c. black and bright orange	3·25	90
2187/9	*Set of 3*	5·50	1·25

(Litho Format)

1987 (22 July). *Centenary of Publication of Sanders' Reichenbachia (22nd issue). Vert designs as T 331. Multicoloured. No wmk. P 13½×14.*

2190	400 c. Plate No. 80 (Series 2)	1·25	80
2191	480 c. Plate No. 77 (Series 2)	1·50	1·00
2192	600 c. Plate No. 94 (Series 2)	2·00	1·50
2193	$25 Plate No. 72 (Series 2)	6·50	8·00
2190/3	*Set of 4*	10·00	10·00

Nos. 2190/3 were printed in a similar sheet format to Nos. 1518/33.

G $1·20 GUYANA

396 Steam Locomotive *Alexandra*

FAIREY NICHOLL 8 AUG 1927 GEO-MAZ (397)

(Litho Format)

1987 (3 Aug–4 Dec). *Guyana Railways. T 396 and similar horiz designs. No wmk. P 12½×13 ($10, $12) or 15 (others).*

2194	**396** $1.20, bronze-green	25	30
	a. Block of 4. Nos. 2194/7	90	
2195	– $1.20, bronze-green	25	30
2196	– $1.20, bronze-green	25	30
2197	– $1.20, bronze-green	25	30
2198	**396** $1.20, maroon (4 Dec)	25	30
	a. Block of 4. Nos. 2198/201	90	
2199	– $1.20, maroon (4 Dec)	25	30
2200	– $1.20, maroon (4 Dec)	25	30
2201	– $1.20, maroon (4 Dec)	25	30
2202	**396** $3.20, deep dull blue	80	90
	a. Block of 5. Nos. 2202/6	3·50	
2203	– $3.20, deep dull blue	80	90
2204	– $3.20, deep dull blue	80	90
2205	– $3.20, deep dull blue	80	90
2206	– $3.20, deep dull blue	80	90
2207	– $3.30, brownish black (4 Dec)	80	90
	a. Block of 5. Nos. 2207/11	3·50	

2208	396	$3.30, brownish black (4 Dec)	..	80	90
2209	–	$3.30, brownish black (4 Dec)		80	90
2210	–	$3.30, brownish black (4 Dec)		80	90
2211	–	$3.30, brownish black (4 Dec)		80	90
2212	–	$10 multicoloured (4 Dec)		1·00	1·50
2213	–	$12 multicoloured		1·25	1·75
2194/213	..		*Set of 20*	10·00	13·00

Designs: (As T **396**)—Nos. 2195, 2199, 2203, 2207, Front view of diesel locomotive; Nos. 2196, 2200, 2204, 2210, Steam locomotive with searchlight; Nos. 2197, 2201, 2205, 2209, Side view of diesel locomotive. (82×55 *mm*)—Nos. 2206, Molasses warehouses and early locomotive; No. 2211, Diesel locomotive and passenger train. (88×39 *mm*)—No. 2212, Cattle train; No. 2213, Molasses train.

Nos. 2194/7 and 2198/201 were each printed together, *se-tenant*, in blocks of 4, within the sheets of 40.

Nos. 2202/6 and 2207/11 were each printed together, *se-tenant*, in blocks of 5 within the sheets of 25. The order of the stamps as Type **396** differs in the $3.30 block.

1987 (7 Aug). *50th Anniv of First Flights from Georgetown to Massaruni and Mabaruma. No. 706 optd as T* **397** *by Autoprint.*

2214	167	$1 multicoloured (optd T **397**)		3·50	3·50
		a. Pair. Nos. 2214/15	..	7·00	7·00
2215		$1 mult (optd "FAIREY NICHOLL 15 AUG 1927 GEO-MAB")		3·50	3·50

Nos. 2214/15 were overprinted together, *se-tenant*, in vertical or horizontal pairs within the sheet.

(Litho Format)

1987 (29 Sept). *Centenary of Publication of Sanders' Reichenbachia (23rd issue). Vert designs as T* **331**. *Multicoloured. No wmk. P* 13½×14.

2216	200 c. Plate No. 43 (Series 2)		..	1·50	55
2217	200 c. Plate No. 48 (Series 2)			1·50	55
2218	200 c. Plate No. 92 (Series 2)			1·50	55
2216/18	..	..	*Set of 3*	4·00	1·50

Nos. 2216/18 were printed in a similar sheet format to Nos. 1518/33.

(Litho Format)

1987 (9 Oct). *Centenary of Publication of Sanders' Reichenbachia (24th issue). Vert design as T* **331**, *optd as T* **384** *by Gardy Ptg* (600 c.). *Multicoloured. No wmk. P* 13½ × 14.

2219	600 c. on 900 c. Plate No. 74 (Series 2)		..	2·25	2·50
	a. Pair. Nos. 2219/20			7·00	7·00
2220	900 c. Plate No. 74 (Series 2)			2·25	2·50

Nos. 2219/20 were printed in a similar sheet format to Nos. 1518/33 with the surcharge on the first and last stamp of each block of four.

950

CRISTOVÃO COLOMBO 1492 — 1992

(398)

THE PASSING OF HALLEY'S COMET: PROPHESY OF THE ARRIVAL OF HERNAN CORTES 1519.

V CENTENARY OF THE LANDING OF CHRISTOPHER COLUMBUS IN THE AMERICAS

$ 20.00

(399)

1987 (9 Oct). *Columbus Day. No.* 1598 *further surch with T* **382**, *No.* 2220 *surch as T* **398** *and No.* MS1746 *surch with T* **399**.

2221	225 c. on 350 c. on 120 c. Plate No. 65 (Series 1)		..	75	35
2222	950 c. on 900 c. Plate No. 74 (Series 2) (surch with T **398**)	..	..	1·75	1·75
	a. Horiz pair. Nos. 2222/3			3·50	3·50
2223	950 c. on 900 c. Plate No. 74 (Series 2) (surch "950 CHRISTOPHE COLOMB 1492 — 1992")			1·75	1·75
2221/3	..	..	*Set of 3*	3·75	3·50
MS2224	76 × 50 mm. $20 on 320 c. × 2 Nos. 1744/5	..	..	6·00	7·00

Nos. 2222/3 were surcharged together, *se-tenant*, in horizontal pairs in the sheetlet of 4.

(Litho Format)

1987 (26 Oct). *Centenary of Publication of Sanders' Reichenbachia (25th issue). Multicoloured designs as T* **331**. *No wmk. P* 13½ × 14 (575 c.) *or* 14 × 13½ (*others*).

2225	325 c. Plate No. 68 (Series 2) (*horiz*)		1·75	80
2226	420 c. Plate No. 95 (Series 2) (*horiz*)		2·00	1·00
2227	575 c. Plate No. 60 (Series 2)		2·50	1·75
2225/7	..	..	*Set of 3*	5·50	3·25

Nos. 2225/7, together with No. E7, were printed in a similar sheet format to Nos. 1518/33.

DEEPAVALI
1987
25

(400)

1987 (2 Nov). *Deepavali Festival. Nos.* 544/5 *surch as T* **400**.

2228	25 c. on 3 c. Hanging Heliconia	..	20	10
2229	$3 on 5 c. Annatto tree		80	60

120

CHRISTMAS
1987
20 1987

(401)   (402)

1987 (9 Nov). *Christmas. No.* 452 *surch with T* **401** *in red, previously unissued miniature sheet containing Nos.* 1425/9 *each surch with T* **402** *in blue and No.* MS1619 *with each stamp surch with T* **382**.

2230	20 c. on 6 c. Black Acara ("Patua")	..	45	10
MS2231	215×75 mm. 120 c. on 60 c. × 5 Nos. 1425/9		6·00	3·25
MS2232	120×129 mm. 225 c. on 55 c. × 4 Plate No. 22 (Series 1), each with a different overprint (Type **350**, "Happy New Year", "Merry Christmas" or "Happy Holidays")	..	1·10	1·25

1987 (20 Nov). *Royal Ruby Wedding. Nos.* 1684/5 *optd with T* **390** (130 c.) *or surch as T* **384** *by Gardy Ptg.*

2233	130 c. Plate No. 13 (Series 1)		1·00	30
MS2234	600 c. on 130 c. on 130 c., 600 c. on 200 c. on 130 c., 600 c. on 260 c. on 130 c., 600 c. on 330 c. on 130 c., Plate No. 6 (Series 1)	..	8·00	9·00

(Litho Format)

1987 (23 Nov). *Centenary of Publication of Sanders' Reichenbachia (26th issue). Vert designs as T* **331**. *Multicoloured. No wmk. P* 13½ × 14.

2235	255 c. Plate No. 61 (Series 2)		1·75	1·00
2236	290 c. Plate No. 53 (Series 2)	..	2·00	1·25
2237	375 c. Plate No. 96 (Series 2)		2·50	1·40
2238	680 c. Plate No. 64 (Series 2)		3·50	2·25
2239	720 c. Plate No. 49 (Series 2)	•	4·00	3·50
2240	750 c. Plate No. 66 (Series 2)		4·00	3·50
2241	800 c. Plate No. 79 (Series 2)		4·50	4·00
	a. Face value omitted			
2242	850 c. Plate No. 76 (Series 2)		4·50	4·00
	a. Face value omitted			
2235/42	..	..	*Set of 8*	24·00	19·00

Nos. 2235/42 were printed in a similar sheet format to Nos. 1518/33.

Nos. 2241a and 2242a occurred in the same sheet as Nos. 2276a and 2277a.

AIR

75

(403)

1987 (Nov). *Air. No.* 1620 *surch with T* **403** *by Gardy Ptg.*

2243	75 c. on 25 c. Plate No. 59 (Series 1)	..	2·50	40

ALTERED CATALOGUE NUMBERS

Any Catalogue numbers altered from the last edition are shown as a list in the introductory pages.

Protect our Heritage '87

320

PROTECT OUR HERITAGE '87

(404)   (405)

1987 (9 Dec). *Wildlife Protection. Nos.* 756/67 *optd vertically with T* **394**, *Nos.* 1432b/4b *surch with T* **404** *in red and Nos.* 1631/3, 1752/3 *and* 1847 *optd with T* **405**.

2244	30 c. Type **178**	..	..	20	15
	a. Sheetlet of 12. Nos. 2244/55			2·25	
2245	30 c. Red Howler	..	..	20	15
2246	30 c. Common Squirrel-Monkey	..		20	15
2247	30 c. Two-toed Sloth	..	..	20	15
2248	30 c. Brazilian Tapir	..	..	20	15
2249	30 c. Collared Peccary	..	..	20	15
2250	30 c. Six-banded Armadillo	..	..	20	15
2251	30 c. Tamandua ("Ant Eater")	..		20	15
2252	30 c. Giant Anteater	..	..	20	15
2253	30 c. Murine Opossum	..	..	20	15
2254	30 c. Brown Four-eyed Opossum	..		20	15
2255	30 c. Brazilian Agouti	..	..	20	15
2256	120 c. Plate No. 67 (Series 1)	..	..	50	30
2257	130 c. Plate No. 66 (Series 1)	..	..	50	30
2258	150 c. Plate No. 26 (Series 1)	..	..	55	35
2259	180 c. Plate No. 15 (Series 1)	..	..	60	40
2260	320 c. Plate No. 82 (Series 1)	..	..	80	60
2261	320 c. on 120 c. Demerara Mutual Life Assurance Building	..		80	80
	a. Horiz strip of 3. Nos. 2261/3	..		2·25	
	b. Surch on No. 1432				
	ba. Horiz strip of 3. Nos. 2261b/3b				
2262	320 c. on 120 c. Town Hall	..		80	80
	b. Surch on No. 1433				
2263	320 c. on 120 c. Victoria Law Courts	..		80	80
	b. Surch on No. 1434				
2264	650 c. on 40 c. Plate No. 86 (Series 1)	..		2·00	2·00
2244/64	..	..	*Set of 21*	8·75	7·00

AIR

(406)

1987 (Dec). *Air. No.* 1597 *optd with T* **406**.

2265	60 c. Plate No. 55 (Series 1)	..	3·50	4·00

No. 2265 was only issued in $15 stamp booklets.

★ AUSTRALIA ★
1987 JAMBOREE 1988

* AUSTRALIA *
$10
1987 Jamboree 1988

(407)   (408)

1988 (7 Jan). *World Scout Jamboree, Australia. Nos.* 830, 837/a *and* 1104 *handstamped with T* **407** (No. 2266) *or surch with T* **408** *by Tip Torres (others), all in red.*

2266	116	440 c. on 6 c. multicoloured (No. 837a) (surch T **201**)	..	3·75	30
		a. On 837 (surch T **200**)		8·50	
2267		$10 on 110 c. on 6 c. mult (No. 830)		75	70
2268		$10 on 180 c. on 6 c. mult (No. 1104)		75	70
2269		$10 on 440 c. on 6 c. mult (No. 837)		2·50	2·00
		a. On No. 837a	..	75	70
2266/9a			*Set of 4*	5·50	2·25

IFAD
For a World
Without Hunger
25

Republic
Day
1988
25

(409)   (410)

1988 (26 Jan). *10th Anniv of International Fund for Agricultural Development. Nos.* 485 *and* 487 *surch as T* **409** *by Autoprint.*

2270	25 c. on 1 c. Type **87**	..	..	20	10
2271	$5 on 3 c. Lukunani	..	..	80	70

1988 (23 Feb). *Republic Day. Nos.* 545, 548a *and* 555 *surch as T* **410** *in blue.*

2272	25 c. on 5 c. Annatto tree	..		10	10
2273	120 c. on 15 c. Christmas Orchid	..		1·50	40
2274	$10 on $2 *Noranthea guianensis*	..		1·75	1·25
2272/4	..		*Set of 3*	3·00	1·50

(Litho Format)

1988 (26 Feb). *Centenary of Publication of Sanders' Reichenbachia (27th issue). Four sheets, each 102×127 mm, containing vert designs as T* **331**. *Multicoloured. No wmk. P* 13½×14.

MS2275 (a) 320 c. Plate No. 46 (Series 2); 330 c. Plate No. 55 (Series 2); 350 c. Plate No. 57 (Series 2); 500 c. Plate No. 81 (Series 2). (b) 320 c. Plate No. 55 (Series 2); 330 c. Plate No. 46 (Series 2); 350 c. Plate No. 81 (Series 2); 500 c. Plate No. 57 (Series 2). (c) 320 c. Plate No. 57 (Series 2); 330 c. Plate No. 81 (Series 2); 350 c. Plate No. 46 (Series 2); 500 c. Plate No. 55 (Series 2). (d) 320 c. Plate No. 81 (Series 2); 330 c. Plate No. 57 (Series 2); 350 c. Plate No. 55 (Series 2); 500 c. Plate No. 46 (Series 2)
    Set of 4 sheets 15·00 12·00

(Litho Format)

1988 (24 Mar). *Centenary of Publication of Sanders' Reichenbachia (28th issue). Vert designs as T* **331**. *Multicoloured. No wmk. P* 13½×14.
2276 $10 Plate No. 40 (Series 2) 1·75 2·00
 a. Face value omitted
2277 $12 Plate No. 91 (Series 2) 1·75 2·00
 a. Face value omitted
Nos. 2276/7 were printed in a similar sheet format to Nos. 1518/33.
Nos. 2276a/7a occurred in the same sheet as Nos. 2241a and 2242a.

1988 (5 Apr). *125th Anniv of British Guiana Post Office (4th issue). No. 702a surch as T* **324** *by Autoprint.*
2278 25 c. on 30 c. mult (surch "Albouystown") 50 40
 a. Sheetlet of 25. Nos. 2278/88, 2289×2, 2290/301 11·00
2279 25 c. on 30 c. mult (surch "Anns Grove") 50 40
2280 25 c. on 30 c. mult (surch "Amacura") 50 40
2281 25 c. on 30 c. mult (surch "Arakaka") 50 40
2282 25 c. on 30 c. mult (surch "Baramanni") 50 40
2283 25 c. on 30 c. mult (surch "Cuyuni") 50 40
2284 25 c. on 30 c. mult (surch "Hope Placer") 50 40
2285 25 c. on 30 c. mult (surch "H M P S") 50 40
2286 25 c. on 30 c. multicoloured (surch "Kitty") 50 40
2287 25 c. on 30 c. mult (surch "M'M'Zorg") 50 40
2288 25 c. on 30 c. mult (surch "Maccaseema") 50 40
2289 25 c. on 30 c. multicoloured (surch "1988") 50 40
2290 25 c. on 30 c. mult (surch "Morawhanna") 50 40
2291 25 c. on 30 c. mult (surch "Naamryck") 50 40
2292 25 c. on 30 c. multicoloured (surch "Purini") 50 40
2293 25 c. on 30 c. mult (surch "Potaro Landing") 50 40
2294 25 c. on 30 c. mult (surch "Rockstone") 50 40
2295 25 c. on 30 c. mult (surch "Rosignol") 50 40
2296 25 c. on 30 c. mult (surch "Stanleytown") 50 40
2297 25 c. on 30 c. mult (surch "Santa Rosa") 50 40
2298 25 c. on 30 c. mult (surch "Tumatumari") 50 40
2299 25 c. on 30 c. mult (surch "Weldaad") 50 40
2300 25 c. on 30 c. mult (surch "Wismar") 50 40
2301 25 c. on 30 c. multicoloured (surch "TPO Berbice Railway") 50 40
2278/301   *Set of 24* 11·00 8·50
The surcharged names are those of postal agencies opened between 1886 and 1900.

120

Olympic Games 1988
(411)

Caricom Day 1988

25
(412)

1988 (3 May). *Olympic Games, Seoul (1st issue). Nos.* 1206/17 *further surch with T* **411**.
2302 120 c. on 55 c. on 125 c. on 35 c. Type 174 50 50
 a. Block of 12. Nos. 2302/13 5·50
2303 120 c. on 55 c. on 125 c. on 35 c. Trahira ("Haimara") 50 50
2304 120 c. on 55 c. on 125 c. on 35 c. Electric Eel 50 50
2305 120 c. on 55 c. on 125 c. on 35 c. Golden Rivulus 50 50
2306 120 c. on 55 c. on 125 c. on 35 c. Golden Pencilfish 50 50
2307 120 c. on 55 c. on 125 c. on 35 c. Four-eyed Fish 50 50
2308 120 c. on 55 c. on 125 c. on 35 c. Red Piranha ("Pirai") 50 50
2309 120 c. on 55 c. on 125 c. on 35 c. Smoking Hassar 50 50
2310 120 c. on 55 c. on 125 c. on 35 c. Manta 50 50
2311 120 c. on 55 c. on 125 c. on 35 c. Festive Cichlid ("Flying Patwa") 50 50
2312 120 c. on 55 c. on 125 c. on 35 c. Arapaima 50 50
2313 120 c. on 55 c. on 125 c. on 35 c. Peacock Cichlid ("Lukanani") 50 50
2302/13   *Set of 12* 5·50 5·50
See also Nos. 2476/95

(Litho Format)

1988 (1 June). *Centenary of Publication of Sanders' Reichenbachia (29th issue). Vert designs as T* **331**. *Multicoloured. No wmk. P* 13½×14.
2314 320 c. Plate No. 16 (Series 2) 70 40
2315 475 c. Plate No. 73 (Series 2) 90 60
2316 525 c. Plate No. 36 (Series 2) 1·25 75
2317 530 c. Plate No. 69 (Series 2) 1·25 75
2318 $15 Plate No. 67 (Series 2) 2·75 3·50
2314/18   *Set of 5* 6·25 5·50
Nos. 2314/18 were printed in a similar sheet format to Nos. 1518/33.

1988 (15 June). *CARICOM Day. Nos.* 545/6 *and* 555 *surch as T* **412**.
2319 25 c. on 5 c. Annatto tree 15 10
2320 $1.20 on 6 c. Cannon-ball tree 30 10
2321 $10 on $2 *Norantea guianensis* 1·75 1·75
2319/21   *Set of 3* 2·00 1·75

(Litho Format)

1988 (15 June). *Centenary of Publication of Sanders' Reichenbachia (30th issue). Vert designs as T* **331**. *Multicoloured. No wmk. P* 13½×14.
2322 700 c. Plate No. 62 (Series 2) 1·25 90
2323 775 c. Plate No. 59 (Series 2) 1·50 1·10
2324 875 c. Plate No. 31 (Series 2) 1·75 1·25
2325 950 c. Plate No. 78 (Series 2) 2·00 1·40
2322/5   *Set of 4* 6·00 4·25
Nos. 2322/5 were printed in a similar sheet format to Nos. 1518/33.

WHO 1948-1988
(413)

1988
(414)

1988 (17 June). *40th Anniv of World Health Day. No.* 705a *optd with T* **413** *or T* **414** *by Autoprint.*
2326 60 c. *Papilio androgeus* (T 413) 6·50 7·50
 a. Sheetlet of 25. Nos. 2326 and 2327×24 8·00
2327 60 c. *Papilio androgeus* (T 414) 15 10
Nos. 2326 and 2327 were overprinted together, *se-tenant*, in a sheetlet of 25 showing a single example of No. 2326 in the central position.

(Litho Format)

1988 (22 June). *Centenary of Publication of Sanders' Reichenbachia (31st issue). Vert design as T* **331**. *No wmk. P* 13½×14.
2328 350 c. Plate No. 74 (Series 2) 65 40
No. 2328 was printed in a similar sheet format to Nos. 1518/33.

(Litho Format)

1988 (9 July). *Centenary of Publication of Sanders' Reichenbachia (32nd issue). Vert designs as T* **331**, *with Nos.* 2329/31 *additional inscr* "1985 – 1988". *No wmk. P* 13½×14.
2329 130 c. Plate No. 73 (Series 2) 70 25
2330 200 c. Plate No. 96 (Series 2) 80 30
2331 260 c. Plate No. 16 (Series 2) 1·25 45
2329/31   *Set of 3* 2·50 90
MS2332 Four sheets, each 102×127 mm. (a) 120 c. Plate No. 81 (Series 2); 120 c. Plate No. 57 (Series 2); 120 c. Plate No. 55 (Series 2); 120 c. Plate No. 46 (Series 2). (b) 150 c. Plate No. 57 (Series 2); 150 c. Plate No. 81 (Series 2); 150 c. Plate No. 46 (Series 2); 150 c. Plate No. 55 (Series 2). (c) 225 c. Plate No. 46 (Series 2); 225 c. Plate No. 55 (Series 2); 225 c. Plate No. 57 (Series 2); 225 c. Plate No. 81 (Series 2). (d) 305 c. Plate No. 55 (Series 2); 305 c. Plate No. 46 (Series 2); 305 c. Plate No. 81 (Series 2); 305 c. Plate No. 57 (Series 2) *Set of 4 sheets* 7·50 5·00

CONSERVE TREES
(415)

CONSERVE WATER
(416)

1988 (15 July). *Conservation of Resources.*
(a) *Nos.* 1444B/6B *optd as T* **415** *by Gardy Ptg.*
2333 120 c. Young Ocelot (No. 1444B) (opt T 415) 50 40
 a. Block of 9. Nos. 2333/41 4·00
2334 120 c. Young Ocelot (No. 1444B) (opt "CONSERVE ELECTRICITY") 50 40
2335 120 c. Young Ocelot (No. 1444B) (opt "CONSERVE WATER") 50 40
2336 120 c. Type 322 (opt "CONSERVE ELECTRICITY") 50 40
2337 120 c. Type 322 (opt "CONSERVE WATER") 50 40
2338 120 c. Type 322 (opt T 415) 50 40
2339 120 c. Young Ocelot (No. 1446B) (opt "CONSERVE WATER") 50 40
2340 120 c. Young Ocelot (No. 1446B) (opt T 415) 50 40
2341 120 c. Young Ocelot (No. 1446B) (optd "CONSERVE ELECTRICITY") 50 40
(b) *Nos.* 1634, 1670, 1683 *and* 1774 *optd with T* **416** (*opt vert– reading upwards on Nos.* 2342, 2345) *by Tip Torres.*
2342 200 c. Plate No. 33 (Series 1) 50 40
2343 200 c. Plate No. 79 (Series 1) 50 40
2344 225 c. Plate No. 24 (Series 1) 50 40
2345 350 c. Plate No. 94 (Series 1) 60 60
2333/45   *Set of 13* 6·00 4·75
The three different overprints as T **415** were applied, *se-tenant*, in strips of three, both horizontally and vertically, on blocks of nine.

120

BEWARE OF ANIMALS
(417)

(418)

1988 (15 July). *Road Safety Campaign. Nos.* 2194/2201 *optd as T* **417** *by Gardy Ptg.*
2346 396 $1.20, bronze-green (opt T 417) 85 85
 a. Block of four. Nos. 2346/9 3·00
2347 — $1.20, bronze-green (No. 2195) (opt "BEWARE OF CHILDREN") 85 85
2348 — $1.20, bronze-green (No. 2196) (opt "DRIVE SAFELY") 85 85
2349 — $1.20, bronze-green (No. 2197) (opt "DO NOT DRINK AND DRIVE") 85 85

2350 396 $1.20, maroon (opt T 417) 85 85
 a. Block of four. Nos. 2350/3 3·00
2351 — $1.20, maroon (No. 2199) (opt "BEWARE OF CHILDREN") 85 85
2352 — $1.20, maroon (No. 2200) (opt "DRIVE SAFELY") 85 85
2353 — $1.20, maroon (No. 2201) (opt "DO NOT DRINK AND DRIVE") 85 85
2346/53   *Set of 8* 6·00 6·00

1988 (July). *No.* 706 *optd with T* **414** *or surch with T* **418**, *both by Autoprint.*
2354 $1 Type 167 2·00 40
2355 120 c. on $1 Type 167 2·00 40

120

(419)

(420)

120

240

(420) (421)

1988 (July–Oct). *Various Reichenbachia issues surch by Gardy Ptg.*

(a) *As T* **419**
2356 120 c. on 25 c. Plate No. 61 (Series 1) (No. 1574) 60 40
2357 120 c. on 25 c. Plate No. 63 (Series 1) (No. 1575) 60 40
2358 120 c. on 25 c. Plate No. 70 (Series 1) (No. 1576) 60 40
2359 120 c. on 25 c. Plate No. 59 (Series 1) (No. 1620) 60 40
2360 120 c. on 25 c. Plate No. 71 (Series 1) (No. 1679) (surch vert - reading down) 60 40
2361 120 c. on 30 c. Plate No. 53 (Series 1) (No. 1621) 60 40
2362 120 c. on 30 c. Plate No. 86 (Series 1) (No. 1731) 60 40
2363 120 c. on 30 c. Plate No. 30 (Series 2) (No. 1809) 60 40
 a. Horiz pair, one without surch 2·50
2364 120 c. on 30 c. Plate No. 53 (Series 1) (No. 1771) (*wmkd*) 60 40
2365 120 c. on 30 c. Plate No. 7 (Series 2) 60 40
2366 120 c. on 30 c. Plate No. 14 (Series 2) ("120" at foot) 60 40
2367 120 c. on 30 c. Plate No. 14 (Series 2) ("120" at top below bars) 60 40
2368 120 c. on 30 c. Plate No. 22 (Series 2) 60 40
2369 120 c. on 30 c. Plate No. 28 (Series 2) ("120" at bottom right) 60 40
2370 120 c. on 30 c. Plate No. 28 (Series 2) ("120" at top left) 60 40
2371 120 c. on 35 c. Plate No. 45 (Series 2) (No. 1925) 60 40
 a. Horiz pair, one without surch 2·50
2372 120 c. on 40 c. Plate No. 77 (Series 1) (No. 1663) ("120" at bottom right) 60 40
2373 120 c. on 40 c. Plate No. 77 (Series 1) (No. 1663) ("120" at top left) 60 40
2374 120 c. on 40 c. Plate No. 96 (Series 1) (No. 1747) 60 40
2375 120 c. on 40 c. Plate No. 91 (Series 1) (No. 1822) ("120" at bottom right) 60 40
2376 120 c. on 40 c. Plate No. 91 (Series 1) (No. 1822) ("120" at top left) 60 40
2377 120 c. on 40 c. Plate No. 86 (Series 1) (No. 1868) 60 40
2378 120 c. on 40 c. Plate No. 68 (Series 1) (No. 1884) ("120" at top left) 60 40
2379 120 c. on 40 c. Plate No. 68 (Series 1) (No. 1884) ("120" at bottom left) 60 40
2380 120 c. on 40 c. Plate No. 90 (Series 1) 60 40
2381 120 c. on 45 c. Plate No. 54 (Series 1) (No. 1664) 60 40
2382 120 c. on 45 c. Plate No. 81 (Series 1) (No. 1748) 60 40
2383 120 c. on 45 c. Plate No. 21 (Series 2) (No. 1810) 60 40
 a. Vert pair, one without surch 2·50
2384 120 c. on 50 c. Plate No. 92 (Series 1) (No. 1665) 60 40
2385 120 c. on 50 c. Plate No. 13 (Series 2) (No. 1907) 60 40
 a. Horiz pair, one without surch 2·50

2386	120 c. on 50 c. Plate No. 15 (Series 2) (No. 1926)		60	40
	a. Horiz pair, one without surch		2·50	
2387	120 c. on 50 c. Plate No. 9 (Series 1) (wmkd)		60	40
2388	120 c. on 50 c. Plate No. 22 (Series 1) (wmkd)		60	40
2389	120 c. on 50 c. Plate No. 3 (Series 2)		60	40
2390	120 c. on 50 c. Plate No. 6 (Series 2)		60	40
2391	120 c. on 50 c. Plate No. 20 (Series 2)		60	40
2392	120 c. on 50 c. Plate No. 32 (Series 2)		60	40
2393	120 c. on 55 c. Plate No. 17 (Series 1) (No. 1732)		60	40
2394	120 c. on 60 c. Plate No. 2 (Series 1) (No. 1519)		60	40
2395	120 c. on 60 c. Plate No. 57 (Series 1) (No. 1622) (surch vert at top - reading down)		60	40
2396	120 c. on 60 c. Plate No. 57 (Series 1) (No. 1622) (surch vert at foot - reading down)		60	40
2397	120 c. on 60 c. Plate No. 73 (Series 1) (No. 1623) (surch vert - reading up)		60	40
2398	120 c. on 60 c. Plate No. 75 (Series 1) (No. 1624) (surch vert at top - reading down)		60	40
2399	120 c. on 60 c. Plate No. 75 (Series 1) (No. 1624) (surch vert at foot - reading down)		60	40
2400	120 c. on 60 c. Plate No. 95 (Series 1) (No. 1666)		60	40
2401	120 c. on 60 c. Plate No. 93 (Series 1) (No. 1733)		60	40
2402	120 c. on 60 c. Plate No. 27 (Series 2) (No. 1874)		60	40
	a. Horiz pair, one without surch		2·50	
2403	120 c. on 60 c. Plate No. 50 (Series 1)		60	40
2404	120 c. on 60 c. Plate No. 54 (Series 1)		60	40
2405	120 c. on 60 c. Plate No. 69 (Series 1) (surch vert–reading up)		60	40
2406	120 c. on 60 c. Plate No. 79 (Series 1)		60	40
2407	120 c. on 60 c. Plate No. 94 (Series 1) (surch vert - reading down)		60	40
2408	120 c. on 70 c. Plate No. 8 (Series 2)		60	40
2409	120 c. on 70 c. Plate No. 9 (Series 2) ("120" at foot above bars)		60	40
2410	120 c. on 70 c. Plate No. 9 (Series 2) ("120" at top right)		60	40
2411	120 c. on 70 c. Plate No. 12 (Series 1) ("120" at foot above bars)		60	40
2412	120 c. on 70 c. Plate No. 12 (Series 2) "120" at top left)		60	40
2413	120 c. on 70 c. Plate No. 17 (Series 2)		60	40
2414	120 c. on 80 c. Plate No. 39 (Series 1)		60	40
2415	120 c. on 80 c. Plate No. 74 (Series 1)		60	40
2416	120 c. on 80 c. Plate No. 93 (Series 1)		60	40
2417	120 c. on 85 c. Plate No. 45 (Series 2) (No. 1876)		60	40
2418	120 c. on 85 c. Plate No. 24 (Series 2) (No. 1914)		60	40
	a. Horiz pair, one without surch		2·50	
2419	120 c. on 85 c. Plate No. 15 (Series 2) (No. 1918)		60	40
2420	120 c. on 85 c. Plate No. 18 (Series 2) (No. 1928)		60	40
	a. Horiz pair, one without surch		2·50	
2421	120 c. on 90 c. Plate No. 84 (Series 1) (No. 1668)		60	40
2422	120 c. on 90 c. Plate No. 89 (Series 1) (No. 1749)		60	40
2423	120 c. on 90 c. Plate No. 10 (Series 2) (No. 1869)		60	40
	a. Horiz pair, one without surch		2·50	
2424	120 c. on 90 c. Plate No. 13 (Series 2) (No. 1877)		60	40
2425	120 c. on 90 c. Plate No. 27 (Series 2) (No. 1915)		60	40
2426	120 c. on 90 c. Plate No. 2 (Series 2) (No. 1929)		60	40
	a. Horiz pair, one without surch		2·50	
2427	200 c. on 80 c. Plate No. 42 (Series 2) (No. 1812) (surch vert–reading down)		60	40
2428	200 c. on 90 c. Plate No. 4 (Series 2) (No. 1813)		60	40

(b) As T 420 (Sept)

2429	120 c. on 25 c. Plate No. 72 (Series 1) (No. 1577)		60	40

(c) As T 421 (Oct)

2430	240 c. on 140 c. Plate No. 30 (Series 2)		60	40
2431	240 c. on 140 c. Plate No. 34 (Series 2)		60	40
2432	240 c. on 425 c. Plate No. 87 (Series 2) (No. 2070)		60	40
2433	260 c. on 375 c. Plate No. 90 (Series 1) (No. 1738)		60	40
2356/433		Set of 78	40·00	27·00

Nos. 2363, 2371, 2383, 2385/6, 2402, 2418, 2420, 2423 and 2426 come from sheetlets of four on which the surcharge was applied to two of the stamps only.

On No. 2433 there are no bars and the surcharge is placed over the original face value.

CONSERVE
OUR RESOURCES ＋ AIR
(422)   (423)   (424)

1988 (July). *Conservation of Resources. Various Reichenbachia issues optd with T* **422** *by Gardy Ptg.*

2434	100 c. Plate No. 65 (Series 1) (No. 1626)		60	40
2435	100 c. Plate No. 68 (Series 1) (No. 1734)		60	40
2436	100 c. Plate No. 88 (Series 1) (No. 1750)		60	40
2437	100 c. Plate No. 65 (Series 1) (No. 1773) (wmkd)		60	40
2438	120 c. Plate No. 27 (Series 1) (No. 1524)		60	40
2439	120 c. Plate No. 36 (Series 1) (No. 1558)		60	40
2440	120 c. Plate No. 37 (Series 1) (No. 1627)		60	40
2441	120 c. Plate No. 56 (Series 1) (No. 1629)		60	40
2442	120 c. Plate No. 58 (Series 1) (No. 1630)		60	40
2443	120 c. Plate No. 67 (Series 1) (No. 1631)		60	40
2444	120 c. Plate No. 69 (Series 1) (No. 1680) (opt vert - reading down)		60	40
2445	130 c. Plate No. 38 (Series 1) (No. 1560)		60	40

2446	130 c. Plate No. 66 (Series 1) (No. 1632)		60	40
2447	130 c. Plate No. 91 (Series 1) (No. 1735)		60	40
2448	130 c. Plate No. 13 (Series 1) (No. 1760) (wmkd)		60	40
	a. Opt inverted		60	40
2449	130 c. Plate No. 20 (Series 1) (No. 1761) (wmkd)		60	40
2450	150 c. Plate No. 26 (Series 1) (No. 1633)		60	40
2451	150 c. Plate No. 78 (Series 1) (No. 1669)		60	40
2452	150 c. Plate No. 87 (Series 1) (No. 1681) (opt vert - reading down)		60	40
2453	150 c. Plate No. 76 (Series 1) (No. 1751)		60	40
2454	250 c. Plate No. 74 (Series 1) (No. 1736)		70	60
2434/54		Set of 21	11·50	7·50

The 130 c., No. 2448, exists in equal quantities with the overprint either upright or inverted.

1988 (3 Aug). *125th Anniv of International Red Cross. Nos.* 2202/5 *and* 2207/10 *optd with T* **423** *in red by Gardy Ptg.*

2455	**396**	$3.20, deep dull blue	65	65
		a. Vert pair. Nos. 2455 and 2457	1·25	1·25
2456	–	$3.20, deep dull blue (No. 2203)	65	65
		a. Vert pair. Nos. 2456 and 2458	1·25	1·25
2457	–	$3.20, deep dull blue (No. 2204)	65	65
2458	–	$3.20, deep dull blue (No. 2205)	65	65
2459	–	$3.30, brownish black (No. 2207)	65	65
		a. Vert pair. Nos. 2459 and 2461	1·25	1·25
2460	**396**	$3.30, brownish black	65	65
		a. Vert pair. Nos. 2460 and 2462	1·25	1·25
2461	–	$3.30, brownish black (No. 2209)	65	65
2462	–	$3.30, brownish black (No. 2210)	65	65
2455/62		Set of 8	4·75	4·75

Nos. 2455/62 were issued in vertical strips of ten, each strip containing two designs se-tenant.

1988 (Aug). *Air. Various Reichenbachia issues optd with T* **424** *by Gardy Ptg.*

2463	75 c. Plate No. 55 (Series 1) (No. 1625)		60	40
2464	75 c. Plate No. 5 (Series 1) (No. 1667)		60	40
2465	75 c. Plate No. 55 (Series 1) (No. 1772) (wmkd)		60	40
2466	75 c. Plate No. 83 (Series 1)		60	40
2467	75 c. Plate No. 95 (Series 1)		60	40
2463/7		Set of 5	2·75	1·75

(Litho Format)

1988 (15 Aug). *Centenary of Publication of Sanders'* Reichenbachia (33rd issue). *Multicoloured designs as T* **331**. *P* 13½×14 (270 c., 360 c.) *or* 14×13½ (others).

2468	270 c. Plate No. 90 (Series 2)		85	60
2469	360 c. Plate No. 84 (Series 2)		1·25	75
2470	550 c. Plate No. 70 (Series 2) (horiz)		2·00	1·40
2471	670 c. Plate No. 71 (Series 2) (horiz)		2·50	1·75
2468/71		Set of 4	6·00	4·00

Nos. 2468/71 were printed in a similar sheet format to Nos. 1518/33.

A further small book similar to those described under Nos. 1767/1806, containing stamps showing plate numbers 1 to 48 of the second series, was issued on 23 August 1988.

Some designs in this booklet show changed face values, as detailed below, but there is no evidence that such printings were available for postal purposes without surcharge.

Plate No. 1	= 175 c.	Plate No. 25	= 140 c.
Plate No. 3	= 50 c.	Plate No. 28	= 30 c.
Plate No. 5	= 130 c.	Plate No. 29	= 130 c.
Plate No. 6	= 50 c.	Plate No. 32	= 50 c.
Plate No. 7	= 30 c.	Plate No. 33	= 100 c.
Plate No. 8	= 70 c.	Plate No. 34	= 140 c.
Plate No. 9	= 70 c.	Plate No. 37	= 175 c.
Plate No. 12	= 70 c.	Plate No. 38	= 140 c.
Plate No. 14	= 30 c.	Plate No. 39	= 175 c.
Plate No. 17	= 70 c.	Plate No. 40	= 250 c.
Plate No. 19	= 175 c.	Plate No. 41	= 140 c.
Plate No. 20	= 50 c.	Plate No. 46	= 150 c.
Plate No. 22	= 30 c.	Plate No. 47	= 175 c.

1928 – 1988

CRICKET

JUBILEE

(425)

1988 (5 Sept). *60th Anniv of Cricket in Guyana. Nos.* 1584, 1670, 1681 *and* 1815 *optd as T* **425** *or surch also by Gardy Ptg.*

2472	200 c. Plate No. 14 (Series 1)		9·00	10·00
2473	200 c. Plate No. 79 (Series 1)		1·00	40
2474	800 c. on 150 c. Plate No. 87 (Series 1)		6·00	7·00
2475	800 c. on 160 c. Plate No. 5 (Series 2)		3·25	3·25
2472/5		Set of 4	17·00	19·00

Nos. 2472 and 2474 were only issued in $20 stamp booklets.

OLYMPIC GAMES
1988
(426)

KOREA 1988

150
≡≡≡≡
(427)

1988 (16 Sept). *Olympic Games, Seoul (2nd issue).* (a) *Nos.* 1628, 1634, 1671, 1681, 1683, 1814, 1818/19, 1880 *and* 2069 *optd as T* **426** *or surch also by Gardy Ptg.*

2476	120 c. Plate No. 46 (Series 1)		20	20
2477	130 c. Plate No. 38 (Series 1)		20	20
2478	150 c. Plate No. 87 (Series 1)		20	20
2479	200 c. Plate No. 33 (Series 1)		20	20
2480	300 c. Plate No. 83 (Series 1)		30	30
2481	300 c. on 360 c. Plate No. 34 (Series 2)		30	30
2482	320 c. Plate No. 10 (Series 2)		30	30
2483	330 c. Plate No. 82 (Series 2)		30	30
2484	350 c. Plate No. 94 (Series 1) (opt vert - reading up)		30	30
2485	350 c. Plate No. 29 (Series 2)		30	30

(b) *Design as No. 1420, but incorrectly inscr "LOS ANGELLES", optd or surch as T* **427**, *inscr "OLYMPICS 1988" (A) or "KOREA 1988" (B), by Gardy Ptg.*

2486	$1.20, multicoloured (A)		20	20
	a. Horiz strip of 5. Nos. 2486, 2488, 2490, 2492 and 2494		1·10	
	b. Booklet pane of 10. Nos. 2486/95		12·00	
2487	$1.20, multicoloured (B)		20	20
2488	130 c. on $1.20, multicoloured (A)		20	20
2489	130 c. on $1.20, multicoloured (B)		20	20
2490	150 c. on $1.20, multicoloured (A)		20	20
2491	150 c. on $1.20, multicoloured (B)		20	20
2492	200 c. on $1.20, multicoloured (A)		25	25
2493	200 c. on $1.20, multicoloured (B)		25	25
2494	350 c. on $1.20, multicoloured (A)		35	35
2495	350 c. on $1.20, multicoloured (B)		35	35
2476/95		Set of 20	4·50	4·50

Nos. 2486/95 were issued in $20 stamp booklets which included pane No. 2486b. Nos. 2486, 2488, 2490, 2492 and 2494 were also available from sheets containing horizontal se-tenant strips of 5. All values later appeared in coils of 500 or 1,000.

V CENTENARY OF
THE LANDING OF
CHRISTOPHER COLUMBUS
IN THE AMERICAS

(428)

1988 (12 Oct). *Columbus Day. Nos.* 1672/3 *optd or surch as T* **428** *by Gardy Ptg.*

2496	320 c. Plate No. 50 (Series 1)		75	30
2497	$15 on 360 c. Plate No. 85 (Series 1)		2·25	2·25

(Litho Format)

1988 (3 Nov). *Centenary of Publication of Sanders'* Reichenbachia (34th issue). *Multicoloured designs as T* **331**. *P* 14×13½ (130 c.) *or* 13¼×14 (others).

2498	100 c. Plate No. 44 (Series 2)		85	55
2499	130 c. Plate No. 42 (Series 2) (horiz)		85	55
2500	140 c. Plate No. 4 (Series 2)		1·00	65
2501	160 c. Plate No. 50 (Series 2)		1·00	65
2502	175 c. Plate No. 51 (Series 2)		1·25	75
2503	200 c. Plate No. 11 (Series 2)		1·25	75
2504	200 c. Plate No. 23 (Series 2)		1·25	75
2505	200 c. Plate No. 26 (Series 2)		1·25	75
2506	200 c. Plate No. 75 (Series 2)		1·25	75
2507	200 c. Plate No. 93 (Series 2)		1·25	75
2508	250 c. Plate No. 79 (Series 2)		1·60	90
2509	280 c. Plate No. 62 (Series 2)		1·60	1·00
2510	285 c. Plate No. 63 (Series 2)		1·75	1·00
2511	380 c. Plate No. 35 (Series 2)		2·00	1·25
2498/511		Set of 14	16·00	12·50

Nos. 2498/511 were printed in a similar sheet format to Nos. 1518/33.

SEASON'S
GREETINGS

120

SEASON'S
GREETINGS   ▨▨▨
(429)   (430)

SEASON'S
GREETINGS

SEASON'S   240
GREETINGS
1988   ▨▨▨
(431)   (432)

988 (10 Nov). *Christmas (1st issue). Various Reichenbachia issues optd or surch by Gardy Ptg*

(a) With T 429

512	150 c. Plate No. 32 (Series 1) (No. 1561)		50	50
513	150 c. Plate No. 62 (Series 1) (No. 1566)		50	50
514	225 c. Plate No. 60 (Series 1) (No. 1682)		50	50
515	260 c. Plate No. 39 (Series 1) (No. 1737)		50	50
516	320 c. Plate No. 82 (Series 1) (No. 1753)		50	50
517	330 c. Plate No. 80 (Series 1) (No. 1754)		50	50
518	360 c. Plate No. 85 (Series 1) (No. 1673)		50	50

(b) As T 430 in blue

519	120 c. on 100 c. Plate No. 6 (Series 1) (wmkd)		50	50
520	120 c. on 100 c. Plate No. 13 (Series 1) (wmkd)		50	50
521	120 c. on 100 c. Plate No. 20 (Series 1) (wmkd)		50	50
522	120 c. on 100 c. Plate No. 25 (Series 1) (wmkd)		50	50
523	120 c. on 100 c. Plate No. 40 (Series 1) (horiz) (wmkd)		50	50
524	120 c. on 100 c. Plate No. 42 (Series 1) (horiz) (wmkd)		50	50
525	120 c. on 100 c. Plate No. 43 (Series 1) (horiz) (wmkd)		50	50
526	120 c. on 100 c. Plate No. 45 (Series 1) (horiz) (wmkd)		50	50

(c) With T 431 in blue

527	225 c. Plate No. 24 (Series 1) (No. 1635)		75	75
528	225 c. Plate No. 60 (Series 1) (No. 1682)		75	75
529	225 c. Plate No. 24 (Series 1) (No. 1774) (wmkd)		75	75
530	225 c. on 350 c. on 120 c. Plate No. 65 (Series 1) (No. 2221)		75	75

MS2531 120×129 mm. 225 c. on 55 c.×4 Plate No. 22 (Series 1) each with a different overprint (Type **350**, "Happy New Year", "Merry Christmas" or "Happy Holidays") (No. MS2232) ... 2·00 2·00

(d) With T 432

2532	240 c. on 180 c. Plate No. 15 (Series 1) (No. 1752)		60	60
2512/30 and 2532		Set of 20	10·00	10·00

CHRISTMAS
1988
20

(433)

Protect yourself from AIDS.
Better safe than sorry.

(434)

1988 (16 Nov). *Christmas (2nd issue). Nos. 489, 1188/91 and 1449 surch or optd as T 433 by Autoprint.*

2533	–	20 c. on 6 c. mult (No. 489) (R.)	10	10
2534	277	120 c. lake-brown, black & bright blue	20	25
		a. Block of 4. Nos. 2534/7	75	
2535	–	120 c. on 130 c. rose-red, black and bright blue (No. 1189)	20	25
2536	–	120 c. on 150 c. bright violet, black and bright blue (No. 1190)	20	25
2537	–	120 c. on 200 c. dull green, black and bright blue (No. 1191)	20	25
2538	–	500 c. on 330 c. mult (No. 1449) (R.)	1·00	1·10
2533/8		Set of 6	1·60	2·00

No. 2538 shows "CHRISTMAS 1988" vertical, reading up.

1988 (1 Dec). *AIDS Information Campaign. Nos. 707/8a optd as T 434 or surch also.*

2539	120 c. on $5 *Morpho deidamia* (A)		1·40	1·40
	a. Strip of 5. Nos. 2539/43		6·00	
2540	120 c. on $5 *Morpho deidamia* (B)		1·40	1·40
2541	120 c. on $5 *Morpho deidamia* (C)		1·40	1·40
2542	120 c. on $5 *Morpho deidamia* (D)		1·40	1·40
2543	120 c. on $5 *Morpho deidamia* (Type **434**)		1·40	1·40
2544	120 c. on $10 *Elbella patrobas* (A)		1·40	1·40
	a. Strip of 5. Nos. 2544/8		6·00	
2545	120 c. on $10 *Elbella patrobas* (B)		1·40	1·40
2546	120 c. on $10 *Elbella patrobas* (C)		1·40	1·40
2547	120 c. on $10 *Elbella patrobas* (D)		1·40	1·40
2548	120 c. on $10 *Elbella patrobas* (Type **434**)		1·40	1·40
2549	$2 *Morpho rhetenor* (female) (Type **434**)		3·75	1·75
2550	$5 *Morpho deidamia* (Type **434**)		6·00	3·75
2551	$10 *Elbella patrobas* (Type **434**)		7·50	5·00
2539/51		Set of 13	27·00	20·00

Nos. 2539/43 and 2544/8 were surcharged horizontally and vertically *se-tenant* with Type **434** and four other slogans: (A) "Be compassionate towards AIDS victims."; (B) "Get information on AIDS. it may save your life."; (C) "Get the facts. Education helps to prevent AIDS."; (D) "Say no to Drugs and limit the spread of AIDS.".

(Des K. Everett (150 c.). Litho Format)

1988 (16 Dec). *150th Anniv of Abolition of Slavery (1984) (2nd issue). Designs as Nos. 1547/50, but colours changed. P 14.*

2552	337	25 c. black and bistre-brown	10	10
2553	–	60 c. black and brown-lilac	15	10
2554	–	130 c. black and blue-green	20	30
2555	–	150 c. black and dull blue	25	40
2552/5		Set of 4	55	75

Nos. 2552/5 exist imperforate from stock dispersed by the liquidator of Format International Security Printers Ltd.

The new-issue supplement to this Catalogue appears each month in

GIBBONS
STAMP MONTHLY

—from your newsagent or by postal subscription— sample copy and details on request.

1050

SALUTING WINNERS
OLYMPIC GAMES
1988

(435)

1989 (3 Jan). *Olympic Medal Winners, Seoul. Nos. 1672, 1923 and 2178 surch as T 435 by Gardy Ptg.*

2556	550 c. on 560 c. Plate No. 1 (Series 2)		80	85
2557	900 c. on 320 c. Plate No. 18 (Series 2)		1·25	1·40
2558	1050 c. on 320 c. Plate No. 50 (Series 1)		1·60	1·75
2556/8		Set of 3	3·25	3·50

A further small book, similar to these described under Nos. 1767/1806, containing stamps showing plate numbers 49 to 96 of the second series, was issued on 3 January 1989.

REPUBLIC DAY 1989

(436)

$5.00

(437)

1989 (22 Feb). *Republic Day. Nos. 2194/201 and 2212 optd with T 436 by Gardy Ptg.*

2559	396	$1.20, bronze-green	15	20
		a. Block of 4. Nos. 2559/62	60	
2560	–	$1.20, bronze-green (No. 2195)	15	20
2561	–	$1.20, bronze-green (No. 2196)	15	20
2562	–	$1.20, bronze-green (No. 2197)	15	20
2563	396	$1.20, maroon	15	20
		a. Block of 4. Nos. 2563/6	60	
2564	–	$1.20, maroon (No. 2199)	15	20
2565	–	$1.20, maroon (No. 2200)	15	20
2566	–	$1.20, maroon (No. 2201)	15	20
2567	–	$10 multicoloured	1·25	1·75
2559/67		Set of 9	2·25	3·00

1989 (22 Feb). *Nos. 2202/5 and 2207/10 surch with T 437 in red.*

2568	396	$5 on $3.20, deep dull blue	80	1·00
		a. Vert pair. Nos. 2568 and 2570	1·60	2·00
2569	–	$5 on $3.20, deep dull blue (No. 2203)	80	1·00
		a. Vert pair. Nos. 2569 and 2571	1·60	2·00
2570	–	$5 on $3.20, deep dull blue (No. 2204)	80	1·00
2571	–	$5 on $3.20, deep dull blue (No. 2205)	80	1·00
2572	–	$5 on $3.30, brownish blk (No. 2207)	80	1·00
		a. Vert pair. Nos. 2572 and 2574	1·60	2·00
2573	396	$5 on $3.30, brownish black	80	1·00
		a. Vert pair. Nos. 2573 and 2575	1·60	2·00
2574	–	$5 on $3.30, brownish blk (No. 2209)	80	1·00
2575	–	$5 on $3.30, brownish blk (No. 2210)	80	1·00
2568/75		Set of 8	5·50	7·00

Nos. 2568/75 were issued in vertical strips of ten, each strip containing two designs *se-tenant*.

1989 (22 Feb–Mar). *Various Reichenbachia issues surch by Gardy Ptg.*

(a) As T 420 in red

2576	120 c. on 140 c. Plate No. 25 (Series 2)		60	60
2577	120 c. on 140 c. Plate No. 52 (Series 2)		60	60
2578	120 c. on 140 c. Plate No. 65 (Series 2)		60	60
2579	120 c. on 175 c. Plate No. 54 (Series 2) (surch vert–reading down)		60	60

(b) As T 421, but with two bars only

2580	120 c. on 140 c. Plate No. 38 (Series 2)		60	60
2581	120 c. on 140 c. Plate No. 41 (Series 2)		60	60
2582	170 c. on 175 c. Plate No. 58 (Series 2) (Mar)		70	70
2583	250 c. on 280 c. Plate No. 66 (Series 2) (Mar)		1·00	1·00
2584	250 c. on 280 c. Plate No. 67 (Series 2) (Mar)		1·00	1·00
2585	300 c. on 290 c. Plate No. 53 (Series 2) (No. 2236) (Mar)		1·10	1·10
2576/85		Set of 10	6·50	6·50

TEN DOLLARS

$10.00

(438)

TEN DOLLARS

(439)

1989 (22 Feb). *Nos. 1744/5 and 2185/6 surch with T 438 (Nos. 2586, 2588) or T 439 (Nos. 2587, 2589), both in red.*

2586	363	$10 on 320 c. rosine, black and deep reddish violet (No. 1744)	1·25	1·40
		a. Horiz pair. Nos. 2586/7	2·50	
2587	–	$10 on 320 c. multicoloured (No. 1745)	1·25	1·40
2588	363	$10 on 320 c. rosine, black and deep reddish violet (No. 2185)	1·25	1·40
		a. Horiz pair. Nos. 2588/9	2·50	
2589	–	$10 on 320 c. multicoloured (No. 2186)	1·25	1·40
2586/9		Set of 4	4·50	5·00

EASTER
125

(440)

POSTAGE

(441)

1989 (22 Mar). *Easter. No. 1817 in block of four surch as T 440.*
MS2590 97×124 mm. 125 c. on 320 c., 250 c. on 320 c., 300 c. on 320 c., 350 c. on 320 c., Plate No. 12 (Series 2) ... 1·50 1·60

1989 (Mar). *Nos. O54/7, O59/63 and O65/9 optd with T 441 or surch additionally as T 421 with two bars only by Gardy Ptg.*

2591	125 c. on 130 c. Plate No. 92 (Series 2)		50	50
2592	125 c. on 140 c. Plate No. 36 (Series 2)		50	50
2593	150 c. Plate No. 43 (Series 2)		50	50
2594	150 c. on 175 c. Plate No. 31 (Series 2)		50	50
2595	250 c. Plate No. 59 (Series 2)		60	60
2596	250 c. on 225 c. Plate No. 26 (Series 2) (surch at top)		60	60
	a. Surch at foot		60	60
2597	250 c. on 230 c. Plate No. 68 (Series 2)		60	60
2598	250 c. on 260 c. Plate No. 69 (Series 2) (surch at top)		60	60
	a. Surch in centre		60	60
2599	300 c. on 275 c. Plate No. 90 (Series 2)		60	60
2600	350 c. Plate No. 95 (Series 2) (opt vert – reading up)		60	60
	a. Opt vert – reading down		60	60
2601	350 c. on 330 c. Plate No. 23 (Series 2)		60	60
2602	600 c. Plate No. 70 (Series 2) (opt vert – reading up)		80	80
2603	$12 Plate No. 71 (Series 2) (opt vert – reading up)		1·50	1·50
2604	$15 Plate No. 84 (Series 2)		1·75	1·75
2591/604		Set of 14	9·00	9·00

1989 (Mar). *Centenary of Publication of Sanders' Reichenbachia (35th issue). Vert designs as T 331. Multicoloured. P 13½×14.*

2605	200 c. Plate No. 49 (Series 2)		30	30
2606	200 c. Plate No. 53 (Series 2)		30	30
2607	200 c. Plate No. 60 (Series 2)		30	30
2608	200 c. Plate No. 64 (Series 2)		30	30
2605/8		Set of 4	1·10	1·10

Nos. 2605/8 were printed in a similar sheet format to Nos. 1518/33.

250

(442)

1989 (Mar). *As No. 1442, but with imprint date, surch with T 442. P 14.*
2609 322 250 c. on 25 c. multicoloured ... 70 10

375

RED CROSS

1948
1988

(443)

1989 (Apr). *40th Anniv of Guyana Red Cross. No. 1872 surch as T 443.*

2610	375 c. on 45 c. Plate No. 17 (Series 2)		90	50
2611	425 c. on 45 c. Plate No. 17 (Series 2)		90	50

HEALTH FOR ALL

250

(444)

1989 (3 Apr). *World Health Day. Nos. 1875 and 2239 surch as T* **444**.

2612	250 c. on 75 c. Plate No. 56 (Series 2) (surch T **444**)		50	50
	a. Pair. Nos. 2612/13		1·00	1·00
2613	250 c. on 75 c. Plate No. 56 (Series 2) (surch "ALL FOR HEALTH")		50	50
2614	675 c. on 720 c. Plate No. 49 (Series 2) (surch "ALL FOR HEALTH")		90	90
	a. Pair. Nos. 2614/15		1·75	1·75
2615	675 c. on 720 c. Plate No. 49 (Series 2) (surch as T **444**)		90	90
2612/15		*Set of* 4	2·50	2·50

Nos. 2612/13 and 2614/15 were each issued, *se-tenant*, in horizontal and vertical pairs, within the sheets of four.

PHOTOGRAPHY 1839 - 1989

BOY SCOUTS

1909   1989

(445)

550

(446)

1989 (11 Apr). *Scouting Anniversaries. Nos. 1873, 1879, 2322, 2509 and unissued value as No. 1873 optd or surch as T* **445**.

2616	250 c. on 50 c. Plate No. 33 (Series 2) (surch T **445**)		60	60
	a. Pair. Nos. 2616/17		1·10	1·10
2617	250 c. on 50 c. Plate No. 33 (Series 2) (surch "GIRL GUIDES 1924 1989")		60	60
2618	250 c. on 100 c. Plate No. 33 (Series 2) (surch as T **445**)		60	60
	a. Pair. Nos. 2618/19		1·10	1·10
2619	250 c. on 100 c. Plate No. 33 (Series 2) (surch "GIRL GUIDES 1924 1989")		60	60
2620	300 c. Plate No. 50 (Series 2) (optd as T **445**)		75	75
	a. Pair. Nos. 2620/1		1·50	1·50
2621	300 c. Plate No. 50 (Series 2) (optd "GIRL GUIDES 1924 1989")		75	75
2622	$25 on 280 c. Plate No. 62 (Series 2) (surch "LADY BADEN POWELL 1889 – 1989")		3·50	4·00
2623	$25 on 700 c. Plate No. 62 (Series 2) (surch "LADY BADEN POWELL 1889 – 1989")		3·50	4·00
2616/23		*Set of* 8	9·50	10·50

The events commemorated are the 80th anniversary of Boy Scout Movement in Guyana, 65th anniversary of Girl Guide Movement in Guyana and birth centenary of Lady Baden-Powell.

On Nos. 2616/17 the surcharge is a "2" applied in front of the original face value to form "250".

Nos. 2616/17, 2618/19 and 2620/1 were each issued, *se-tenant*, in horizontal and vertical pairs within the sheets of four.

1989 (15 Apr). *150 Years of Photography. No. 1881 surch as T* **446**.

2624	550 c. on 390 c. Plate No. 6 (Series 2)		50	50
	a. Pair. Nos. 2624/5		1·00	1·00
2625	650 c. on 390 c. Plate No. 6 (Series 2) (original value cancelled by two bars)		50	50
2626	650 c. on 390 c. Plate No. 6 (Series 2) (original value cancelled by six bars)		50	50
2624/6		*Set of* 3	1·40	1·40

No. 2624 exists either as complete sheets of four or horizontally and vertically *se-tenant* with No. 2625. No. 2626 only comes as sheets of four all showing the same surcharge.

PRICES OF SETS

Set prices are given for many issues, generally those containing three stamps or more. Definitive sets include one of each value or major colour change, but do not cover different perforations, die types or minor shades. Where a choice is possible the set prices are based on the cheapest versions of the stamps included in the listings.

I.L.O. 1919-1989

300

(447)

1989 (2 May). *70th Anniv of International Labour Organization. No. 1875 surch with T* **447**.

2627	300 c. on 75 c. Plate No. 56 (Series 2)		2·50	40

80ᶜ

(448)

$6·40

(449)

$5

$2·55   **X**   **$6·40**

(450)   (451)   (452)

1989 (8 May)–92?. *Various stamps surch*

(a) As T **448** *with short obliterating bars over original value*

2628	80 c. on 6 c. Patua (No. 452)		40	20
2629	$1 on 2 c. Type **132** (15.6.89)		40	20
2630	$2.05 on 3 c. Hanging Heliconia (No. 544) (15.6.89)		40	25
2631	$2.55 on 5 c. Annatto tree (No. 545) (15.6.89)		40	30
2632	$3.25 on 6 c. Cannon-ball tree (No. 546) (15.6.89)		40	30
2633	$5 on 6 c. Type **111** (16.8.89)		40	30
2634	$6.40 on 10 c. *Archonias bellona* (No. 699) (18.5.89)		2·25	75
2635	$8.90 on 60 c. *Papilio androgeus* (No. 705a) (26.5.89)		3·25	85

(b) As T **449** *(larger figures on 80 c.) without any obliterating bars*

2636	80 c. on 6 c. Patua (No. 452)		40	20
2637	$6.40 on 10 c. *Archonias bellona* (No. 699) (18.5.89)		2·25	75
2637a	$7.65 on 35 c. *Anaea galanthus* (No. 703) (1992?)		2·75	80
2638	$7.65 on 40 c. *Morpho rhetenor* (male) (No. 704) (18.5.89)		2·75	80
2639	$8.90 on 60 c. *Papilio androgeus* (No. 705a) (26.5.89)		3·25	85

(c) As T **450** *(larger figures on $1) with "X" over original value*

2640	$1 on 2 c. Type **132** (15.6.89)		40	20
2641	$2.55 on 5 c. Annatto tree (No. 545) (15.6.89)		40	25
2642	$3.25 on 6 c. Cannon-ball tree (No. 546) (15.6.89)		40	25
2643	$50 on $2 *Morpho rhetenor* (female) (No. 707 (B). (5.6.89)		10·00	3·50
2644	$100 on $2 *Morpho rhetenor* (female) (No. 707) (5.6.89)		15·00	8·50

(d) As T **451**

2645	$5 on 6 c. Type **111** (with T **451**) (16.8.89)		40	20
2645a	$5 on 6 c. Type **111** (as T **451**, but with "X" instead of bars at foot) (1992)		40	20

(e) As T **421**, *but two obliterating bars only*

2646	640 c. on 675 on 720 c. Plate No. 49 (Series 2) (surch "ALL FOR HEALTH") (No. 2614)		1·25	1·25
	a. Pair. Nos. 2646/7		2·50	2·50
2647	640 c. on 675 c. on 720 c. Plate No. 49 (Series 2) (surch "HEALTH FOR ALL") (No. 2615)		1·25	1·25

(f) As T **452**

2648	–	$6.40 on $3.30, brownish black (No. 2207)	2·50	1·50
	a. Vert pair. Nos. 2648 and 2650		5·00	3·00
2649	396	$6.40 on $3.30, brownish black	2·50	1·50
	a. Vert pair. Nos. 2649 and 2651		5·00	3·00
2650	–	$6.40 on $3.30, brownish black (No. 2209)	2·50	1·50
2651	–	$6.40 on $3.30, brownish black (No. 2210)	2·50	1·50
2652	396	$7.65 on $3.20, deep dull blue	2·50	1·50
	a. Vert pair. Nos. 2652 and 2654		5·00	3·00
2653	–	$7.65 on $3.20, dp dull blue (No. 2203)	2·50	1·50
	a. Vert pair. Nos. 2653 and 2655		5·00	3·00
2654	–	$7.65 on $3.20, dp dull blue (No. 2204)	2·50	1·50
2655	–	$7.65 on $3.20, dp dull blue (No. 2205)	2·50	1·50
2628/55		*Set of* 30	60·00	30·00

CARICOM DAY

125

(453)

454 *Stalachtis calliope*

1989 (26 June). *CARICOM Day. No. 1878 surch with T* **453**.

2656	125 c. on 200 c. Plate No. 44 (Series 2)		1·50	30
	a. Original face value cancelled by 6 thin lines		1·75	50

(Des Mary Walters. Litho Questa)

1989 (7 Sept). *Butterflies* (1st series). T **454** *and similar vert designs. Multicoloured. P* 14.

2657	80 c. Type **454**		30	10
2658	$2.25, *Morpho rhetenor*		40	10
2659	$5 *Agrias claudia*		45	10
2660	$6.40, *Marpesia marcella*		50	15
2661	$7.65, *Papilio zagreus*		55	15
2662	$8.90, *Chorinea faunus*		70	20
2663	$25 *Euptychia cephus*		2·00	2·00
2664	$100 *Nessaea regina*		5·50	6·50
2657/64		*Set of* 8	9·25	8·25

For miniature sheets accompanying this issue see Nos. EMS18/19.

See also Nos. 2789/861.

AHMADIYYA CENTENARY 1889-1989

$8·90

455 Kathryn Sullivan   (456)
(first U.S woman to walk in space)

(Des M. Dorfman. Litho Questa)

1989 (8 Nov). *25 Years of Women in Space. T* **455** *and similar vert designs. Multicoloured. P* 14.

2665	$6.40, Type **455**		30	10
2666	$12.80, Svetlana Savitskaya (first Soviet woman to walk in space)		55	30
2667	$15.30, Judy Resnik and Christa McAuliffe with *Challenger* logo		55	30
2668	$100 Sally Ride (first U.S woman astronaut)		3·75	4·50
2665/8		*Set of* 4	4·75	4·75

For miniature sheet accompanying this issue see No. EMS20.

1989 (22 Nov). *Centenary of Ahmadiyya (Moslem organization). Nos. 543/5 surch as T* **456**.

2669	80 c. on 2 c. Type **132**		1·00	30
2670	$6.40 on 3 c. Hanging Heliconia		4·00	2·00
2671	$8.90 on 5 c. Annatto tree		5·00	3·00
2669/71		*Set of* 3	9·00	5·25

457 Head of   **458** Channel-billed
Harpy Eagle   Toucan

(Des J. Barbaris. Litho Questa)

1990 (23 Jan). *Endangered Species. Harpy Eagle. T* **457** *and similar vert designs. Multicoloured. P* 14.

2672	$2.25, Type **457**		50	25
2673	$5 Harpy Eagle with monkey prey		75	30
2674	$8.90, Eagle on branch (facing right)		1·10	50
2675	$30 Eagle on branch (facing left)		3·00	3·50
2672/5		*Set of* 4	4·75	4·00

(Des J. Barbaris. Litho Questa)

1990 (23 Jan). *Birds of Guyana. T* **458** *and similar multicoloured designs. P* 14.

2676	$15 Type **458**		90	40
2677	$25 Blue and Yellow Macaw		1·40	70
2678	$50 Wattled Jacana (*horiz*)		2·75	2·25
2679	$60 Hoatzin (*horiz*)		3·00	2·50
2676/9		*Set of* 4	7·25	5·25
MS2680	Two sheets, each 110×80 mm. (a) $100 Great Kiskadee. (b) $100 Amazon Kingfisher			
		Set of 2 *sheets*	9·00	9·00

Rotary International 1905-1990

(459)   460 Indian Post Runner, 1837

1990 (15 Mar). *85th Anniv of Rotary International. Optd as T 459 in silver.* (a) On Nos. 2657/64

2681	80 c. Type 454	..	..	..	50	20
2682	$2.25, *Morpho rhetenor*	..			80	30
2683	$5 *Agrias claudia*	..	..		1·00	30
2684	$6.40, *Marpesia marcella*	..			1·10	35
2685	$7.65, *Papilio zagreus*	..			1·25	50
2686	$8.90, *Chorinea faunus*	..			1·40	55
2687	$25 *Euptychia cephus*	..			2·50	3·00
2688	$100 *Nessaea regina*	..			7·00	8·00
2681/8				*Set of 8*	14·00	12·00

(b) On Nos. 2665/8

2689	$6.40, Type 455	..	..		75	35
2690	$12.80, *Svetlana Savitskaya* (first Soviet woman to walk in space)				1·25	80
2691	$15.30, *Judy Resnik* and *Christa McAuliffe* with *Challenger* logo				1·40	90
2692	$100 *Sally Ride* (first U.S. woman astronaut)				5·00	6·00
2689/92				*Set of 4*	7·75	7·25

(Des G. Vasarhelyi. Litho Questa)

1990 (3 May). *150th Anniv of Penny Black and 500th Anniv of Thurn and Taxis Postal Service. T 460 and similar horiz designs. Multicoloured. P 14.*

2693/2746	$15.30×27, $17.80×9, $20×18			
			Set of 54	23·00 26·00

MS2747 Three sheets, each 116×86 mm. (a) $150 Post boy; (b) $150 Thurn and Taxis (Northern District) 3 sgr. of 1852; (c) $150 Thurn and Taxis (Southern District) 6 k. of 1852
Set of 3 sheets 9·50 11·00

Nos. 2693/746 (issued as six sheetlets each of nine different designs) depict various forms of mail transport.

80

ROTARY
DISTRICT 405
9th CONFERENCE
MAY 1990
GEORGETOWN

90th Birthday
H.M. The Queen Mother

(461)   (462)

1990 (8 May). *9th Conference of Rotary District 405, Georgetown. Nos. 1526, 1530, 1552 and 1554/5 surch as T 461.*

2748	80 c. on 55 c. Plate No. 9 (Series 1)	
2749	80 c. on 55 c. Plate No. 49 (Series 1)	..
2750	80 c. on 55 c. Plate No. 64 (Series 1)	..
2751	$6.40, on 130 c. Plate No. 6 (Series 1)	..
2752	$6.40, on 130 c. Plate No. 25 (Series 1)	
2753	$7.65, on 130 c. Plate No. 25 (Series 1)	

1990 (8 June). *90th Birthday of Queen Elizabeth the Queen Mother. Nos. 2657/64 surch with T 462.*

2754	80 c. Type 454	..	..	30	20
2755	$2.25, *Morpho rhetenor*	..		55	30
2756	$5 *Agrias claudia*	..	..	70	30
2757	$6.40, *Marpesia marcella*	..		80	35
2758	$7.65, *Papilio zagreus*	..		85	40
2759	$8.90, *Chorinea faunus*	..		90	45
2760	$25 *Euptychia cephus*	..		2·00	2·25
2761	$100 *Nessaea regina*	..		6·00	7·00
2754/61			*Set of 8*	11·00	10·00

For miniature sheets accompanying this issue see Nos. EMS31/3.

GUYANA   Guyana 80¢

463 Collared Trogon   464 *Melinaea idae*

(Litho Format)

1990 (12 Sept). *Birds. T 463 and similar multicoloured designs. P 13½×14 (80 c.) or 14×13½ (others).*

2762	80 c. Guiana Partridge (*horiz*)	..		10	10
2763	$2.55, Type 463	..	..	10	10
2764	$3.25, Derby Aracari	..	..	10	10
2765	$5 Black-necked Aracari	..	..	10	10

2766	$5.10, Green Aracari	..	..	10	10
2767	$5.80, Ivory-billed Aracari	..	..	10	10
2768	$6.40, Guiana Toucanet	..	..	10	10
2769	$6.50, Sulphur-breasted Toucan	..		10	10
2770	$7.55, Red-billed Toucan	..		10	10
2771	$7.65, Toco Toucan	..	..	10	10
2772	$8.25, Natterers Toucanet	..		10	10
2773	$8.90, Welcome Trogon	..		10	10
2774	$9.75, Doubtful Trogon	..		10	10
2775	$11.40, Banded Aracari	..		10	10
2776	$12.65, Golden-headed Train Bearer		15	20
2777	$12.80, Rufous-breasted Hermit		15	20
2778	$13.90, Band Tail Barbthroat			15	20
2779	$15.30, White-tipped Sickle Bill		15	20
2780	$17.80, Black Jacobin	..		20	25
2781	$19.20, Fiery Topaz	..	..	20	25
2782	$22.95, Tufted Coquette	..		25	30
2783	$26.70, Ecuadorian Pied-tail	..		25	30
2784	$30 Quetzal	..	..	30	35
2785	$50 Green-crowned Brilliant	..		50	55
2786	$100 Emerald-chinned Hummingbird		1·00	1·10
2787	$190 Lazuline Sabre-wing	..		1·90	2·00
2788	$225 Beryline Hummingbird	..		2·25	2·40
2762/88			*Set of 27*	8·25	9·25

(Litho Questa)

1990 (26 Sept). *Butterflies (2nd series). T 464 and similar multicoloured designs. P 14.*

2789/2860	80 c., $2.55, $5, $6.40, $7.65, $8.90, $10×64, $50 and $100		*Set of 72*	8·00 9·00

MS2861 Four sheets, each 102×71 mm. (a) $150 *Heliconius aoede.* (b) $150 *Phyciodes clio* (*horiz*).
(c) $150 *Thecla hemon.* (d) $190 *Nymphidium caricae* .. .. .. *Set of 4 sheets* 9·00 10·00

Designs: *Vert*—$2.55, *Rhetus dysonii;* $5 *Actinote anteas;* $6.40, *Heliconius tales;* $7.65, *Thecla telemus;* $8.90, *Theope eudocia;* $10 (No. 2795), *Heliconius vetustus;* No. 2796, *Mesosemia eumene;* No. 2797, *Parides phosphorus;* No. 2798, *Polystichtis emylius;* No. 2799, *Xanthocleis aedesia;* No. 2800, *Doxocopa agathina;* No. 2801, *Adelpha plesaure;* No. 2802, *Heliconius wallacei;* No. 2803, *Notheme eumeus;* No. 2804, *Melinaea mediatrix;* No. 2805, *Theritas coronata;* No. 2806, *Dismorphia orise;* No. 2807, *Phyciodes ianthe;* No. 2808, *Morpho aega;* No. 2809, *Zaretis isidora;* No. 2810, *Pierella lena;* No. 2811, *Heliconius silvana;* No. 2812, *Eunica alcmena;* No. 2813, *Mechanitis polymnia;* No. 2814, *Mesosemia ephyne;* No. 2815, *Thecla erema;* No. 2816, *Callizona acesta;* No. 2817, *Stalachtis phaedusa;* No. 2818, *Battus belus;* No. 2819, *Nymula phliasus;* No. 2820, *Parides childrenae;* No. 2821, *Stalachtis euterpe;* No. 2822, *Dysmathia portia;* No. 2823, *Tithorea hermias;* No. 2824, *Prepona pheridamas;* No. 2825, *Dismorphia fortunata;* No. 2826, *Hamadryas amphinome;* $50 *Heliconius vicini;* $100 *Amarynthis meneria. Horiz*—$10 (No. 2827), *Thecla falerina;* No. 2828, *Pheles heliconides;* No. 2829, *Echenias leucocyana;* No. 2830, *Heliconius xanthocles;* No. 2831, *Mesopthalma idotea;* No. 2832, *Parides aeneas;* No. 2833, *Heliconius numata;* No. 2834, *Thecla critola;* No. 2835, *Themone pais;* No. 2836, *Nymula agle;* No. 2837, *Adelpha cocala;* No. 2838, *Anaea eribotes;* No. 2839, *Prepona demophon;* No. 2840, *Selenophanes cassiope;* No. 2841, *Consul hippona;* No. 2842, *Antirrhaea avernus;* No. 2843, *Thecla telemus;* No. 2844, *Thyridia confusa;* No. 2845, *Heliconius burneyi;* No. 2846, *Parides lysander;* No. 2847, *Eunica orphise;* No. 2848, *Adelpha melona;* No. 2849, *Morpho menelaus;* No. 2850, *Nymula phylleus;* No. 2851, *Stalachtis phlegia;* No. 2852, *Theope barea;* No. 2853, *Morpho perseus;* No. 2854, *Lycorea ceres;* No. 2855, *Archonias bellona;* No. 2856; *Caeronis chorinaeus;* No. 2857, *Vila azeca;* No. 2858, *Nessaea batesii.*

Nos. 2795/2810, 2811/26, 2827/42 and 2843/58 were printed together, *se-tenant,* in sheetlets of 16 with the backgrounds forming composite designs.

GUYANA $7.65 Vanilla inodora

465 *Vanilla inodora*   466 Ivory-billed Woodpecker

(Litho B.D.T.)

1990 (16 Oct). *Flowers. T 465 and similar multicoloured designs. P 14.*

2862/2965	$7.65, $8.90, $10×32, $12.80×65, $15.30, $17.80, $20, $25 and $100 *Set of 104*			11·00 12·00

MS2966 Five sheets. (a) 65×95 mm. $150 *Delonix regia* (*horiz*). (b) 86×65 mm. $150 *Hexisea bidentata* (*horiz*). (c) 70×105 mm. $150 *Galeandra devoniana* (*horiz*). (d) 68×110 mm. $150 *Lecythis ollaria.* (e) 74×104 mm. $190 *Ionopsis utricularioides* .. *Set of 5 sheets* 9·00 10·00

Designs: *Vert*—$8.90, *Epidendrum ibaguense;* $10 (No. 2864), *Dichea muricata;* No. 2865, *Octomeria erosilabia;* No. 2866, *Spiranthes orchioides;* No. 2867, *Brassavola nodosa;* No. 2868, *Epidendrum rigidum;* No. 2869, *Brassia caudata;* No. 2870, *Pleurothallis diffusa;* No. 2871, *Aspasia variegata;* No. 2872, *Stenia pallida;* No. 2873, *Cyrtopodium punctatum;* No. 2874, *Cattleya deckeri;* No. 2875, *Cryptarrhena lunata;* No. 2876, *Cattleya violacea;* No. 2877, *Caularthron bicornutum;* No. 2878, *Oncidium carthagenense;* No. 2879, *Galeandra devoniana;* No. 2880, *Bifrenaria aurantiaca;* No. 2881, *Epidendrum ciliare;* No. 2882, *Dichaea picta;* No. 2883, *Scaphyglottis violacea;* No. 2884, *Cattleya percivaliana;* No. 2885, Map and national flag; No. 2886, *Epidendrum difforme;* No. 2887, *Eulophia maculata;* No. 2888, *Spiranthes tenuis;* No. 2889, *Peristoria guttata;* No. 2890, *Pleurothallis cardium;* No. 2891, *Cleistes rosea;* No. 2892, *Maxillaria variabilis;* No. 2893, *Brassavola cucullata;* No. 2894, *Epidendrum moyobambae;* No. 2895, *Oncidium orthostate;* $12.80, *Maxillaria parkeri;* $12.80 (No. 2897), *Brassavola martiana;* No. 2898, *Paphinia cristata;* No. 2899, *Aganisia pulchella;* No. 2900, *Oncidium lanceanum;* No. 2901, *Lockhartia*

---

imbricata; No. 2902, *Caularthron bilamellatum;* No. 2903, *Oncidium nanum;* No. 2904, *Pleurothallis ovalifolia;* No. 2905, *Galeandra dives;* No. 2906, *Cycnoches loddigesii;* No. 2907, *Ada aurantiaca;* No. 2908, *Catasetum barbatum;* No. 2909, *Palmorchis pubescens;* No. 2910, *Epidendrum anceps;* No. 2911, *Huntleya meleagris;* No. 2912, *Sobralia sessilis;* $15.30, *Epidendrum nocturnum;* $17.80, *Catasetum discolor;* $20 *Scuticaria hadwenii;* $25 *Epidendrum fragrans;* $100 *Epistephium parviflorum. Horiz*—$12.80 (No. 2913), *Cochlospermum vitifolium;* No. 2914, *Eugenia malaccensis;* No. 2915, *Plumiera rubra;* No. 2916, *Erythrina glauca;* No. 2917, *Spathodea campanulata;* No. 2918, *Jacaranda filicifolia;* No. 2919, *Samanea saman;* No. 2920, *Cassia fistula;* No. 2921, *Abutilon integerrimum;* No. 2922, *Lagerstroemia speciosa;* No. 2923, *Tabebuia serratifolia;* No. 2924, *Guaiacum officinale;* No. 2925, *Solanum macranthum;* No. 2926, *Peltophorum roxburghii;* No. 2927, *Bauhinia variegata;* No. 2928, *Plumiera alba;* No. 2929, *Maxillaria camaridii;* No. 2930, *Vanilla pompona;* No. 2931, *Stanhopea grandiflora;* No. 2932, *Oncidium pusillum;* No. 2933, *Polycycnis vittata;* No. 2934, *Cattleya lawrenceana;* No. 2935, *Menadenium labiosum;* No. 2936, *Rodriguezia secunda;* No. 2937, *Mormodes buccinator;* No. 2938, *Otostylis brachystalix;* No. 2939, *Maxillaria discolor;* No. 2940, *Liparis elata;* No. 2941, *Gongora maculata;* No. 2942, *Koellensteinia graminea;* No. 2943, *Rudolfiella aurantiaca;* No. 2944, *Scuticaria steelei;* No. 2945, *Gloriosa rothschildiana;* No. 2946, *Pseudocalymma alliaceum;* No. 2947, *Callichlamys latifolia;* No. 2948, *Distictis riversii;* No. 2949, *Maurandya barclaiana;* No. 2950, *Beaumontia fragrans;* No. 2951, *Phaseolus caracalla;* No. 2952, *Mandevilla splendens;* No. 2953, *Solandra longiflora;* No. 2954, *Passiflora coccinea;* No. 2955, *Allamanda cathartica;* No. 2956, *Bauhinia galpini;* No. 2957, *Verbena maritima;* No. 2958, *Mandevilla sauveolens;* No. 2959, *Phryganocydia corymbosa;* No. 2960, *Jasminum sambac.*

Nos. 2864/79, 2880/95, 2897/2912, 2913/28, 2929/44 and 2945/60 were each printed together, *se-tenant,* in sheetlets of 16 with the backgrounds forming composite designs.

Nos. MS2966b/c and MS2966e show the "EXPO '90" logo on the sheet margin.

1990 (16 Nov). *Fauna. T 466 and similar multicoloured designs. Litho. P 14×13½ (vert) or 13½×14 (horiz).*

2967/86	$12.80×20 (*vert* designs showing endangered birds)		
2987/3006	$12.80×20 (*vert* designs showing tropical birds)		
3007/26	$12.80×20 (*vert* designs showing prehistoric animals)		
3027/46	$12.80×20 (*horiz* designs showing endangered wildlife)		
2967/3046		*Set of 80*	30·00 30·00

Designs: *Vert*—No. 2968, Cauca Guan; No. 2969, Sun Conure; No. 2970, Quetzal; No. 2971, Long-wattled Umbrellabird; No. 2972, Banded Cotinga; No. 2973, Blue-chested Parakeet; No. 2974, Rufous-bellied Chachalaca; No. 2975, Yellow-faced Amazon; No. 2976, Toucan Barbet; No. 2977, Red Siskin; No. 2978, Cock-of-the-Rock; No. 2979; Hyacinth Macaw; No. 2980, Yellow Cardinal; No. 2981, Bare-necked Umbrellabird; No. 2982, Saffron Toucanet; No. 2983, Red-billed Curassow; No. 2984, Spectacled Parrotlet; No. 2985, Lovely Cotinga; No. 2986, Black-breasted Gnateater; No. 2987, Swallow-tailed Kite; No. 2988, Hoatzin; No. 2989, Ruby-Topaz Hummingbird; No. 2990, American Black Vulture; No. 2991, Rufous-tailed Jacamar; No. 2992, Scarlet Macaw; No. 2993, Rose-breasted Thrush Tanager; No. 2994, Toco Toucan; No. 2995, Bearded Bellbird; No. 2996, Blue-crowned Motmot; No. 2997, Green Oropendola; No. 2998, Pompadour Cotinga; No. 2999; Vermilion Flycatcher; No. 3000, Blue and Yellow Macaw; No. 3001, White-barred Piculet; No. 3002, Great Razor-billed Curassow; No. 3003, Ruddy Quail Dove; No. 3004, Paradise Tanager; No. 3005, American Darter ("Anhinga"; No. 3006, Greater Flamingo; No. 3007, Palaelodus; No. 3008, Archaeotrogon; No. 3009, Vulture; No. 3010, Bradypus tridactylus; No. 3011, Natalus stramineus bat; No. 3012, Cebidae; No. 3013, Cuvieronius; No. 3014, Phororhacos; 3015, Smilodectes; No. 3016, Megatherium; No. 3017, Titanotylopus; No. 3018, Teleoceras; No. 3019, Macrauchenia; No. 3020, Mylodon; No. 3021, Smilodon; No. 3022, Glyptodon; No. 3023, Protohydrocherus; No. 3024, Archaeohyrax; No. 3025, Pyrotherium; No. 3026, Platypittamys. *Horiz*—$12.80 (No. 3027), Harpy Eagle and Hyacinth Macaw; No. 3028, Andean Condor; No. 3029, Amazonian Umbrellabird; No. 3030, Spider Monkeys; No. 3031, Hyacinth Macaws; No. 3032, Red Siskin; No. 3033, Toucan Barbet; No. 3034, Three-toed Sloth; No. 3035, Guanacos; No. 3036, Spectacled Bear; No. 3037, White-lipped Peccary; No. 3038, Maned Wolf; No. 3039, Jaguar; No. 3040, Spectacled Cayman; No. 3041, Giant Armadillo; No. 3042, Giant Anteater; No. 3043, South American River Otter; No. 3044, Yapok; No. 3045, Central American River Turtle; No. 3046, Cauca Guan.

Nos. 2967/86, 2987/3006, 3007/26 and 3027/46 were printed together, *se-tenant,* in sheetlets of 20 forming composite designs.

No. 2982 is inscribed "Toucanette" and No. 2995 inscribed "Belllbird" both in error.

For miniature sheets accompanying this issue see Nos. EMS34/5.

GUYANA $225

467 National Flag

1991 (26 May). *25th Anniv of Independence. Sheet 100×70 mm. Litho. Imperf.*

MS3047	467 $225 multicoloured	.. ..	5·50 6·00

NEW INFORMATION

The editor is always interested to correspond with people who have new information that will improve or correct the Catalogue.

468 Ramon Folist (Cuba)   **(469)**
(fencing, 1900)

(Litho Cartor)

1991 (12 Aug). *Winter Olympic Games, Albertville (1st issue) and Olympic Games, Barcelona, Previous Gold Medal Winners. T **468** and similar multicoloured designs. P 14×13½.*

3048/3119 $15.30×9, $17.80×9, $20×18, $25
  ×18 and $30×18   ..   ..   *Set of* 72   30·00   32·00

MS3120 Three sheets, each 98×70 mm. (a) $150 Johannes Kolehmainen (Finland) (10,000 metres, 1912) (*vert*). (b) $150 Paavo Nurmi (Finland) (5000 metres, 1924) (*vert*). (c) $190 Nedo Nadi (Italy) (fencing, 1920) (*vert*).
P 13×13½   ..   ..   *Set of* 3 *sheets*   10·50   11·00

Designs:—$15.30 (No. 3049), Lucien Gaudin (France) (fencing, 1924); No. 3050, Ole Lilloe-Olsen (Norway) (shooting, 1924); No. 3051, Morris Fisher (U.S.A.) (rifle shooting, 1924); No. 3052, Ray Ewry (U.S.A.) (long jump, 1900); No. 3053, Hubert van Innes (Belgium) (archery, 1900); No. 3054, Alvin Kraenzlein (U.S.A.) (hurdles, 1900); No. 3055, Johnny Weissmuller (U.S.A.) (swimming, 1924); No. 3056, Hans Winkler (West Germany) (show jumping, 1956); $17.80 (No. 3057, Viktor Chukarin (Russia) (gymnastics, 1952); No. 3058, Agnes Keleti (Hungary) (gymnastics, 1952); No. 3059, Barbel Wochel (East Germany) (200 metres, 1980); No. 3060, Eric Heiden (U.S.A.) (speed skating, 1980); No. 3061, Alvodár Gerevich (Hungary) (fencing, 1932); No. 3062, Giuseppe Delfino (Italy) (fencing, 1952); No. 3063, Alexander Tikhonov (Russia) (skiing, 1980); No. 3064, Pahud de Mortanges (Netherlands) (equestrian, 1932); No. 3065 Patricia McCormick (U.S.A.) (diving, 1952); $20 (No. 3066), Olga Korbut (Russia) (gymnastics, 1972); No. 3067, Lyudmila Turischeva (Russia) (gymnastics, 1972); No. 3068, Lasse Viren (Finland) (10,000 metres, 1972); No. 3069, George Miez (Switzerland) (gymnastics, 1936); No. 3070, Roland Matthes (East Germany) (swimming, 1972); No. 3071 Pal Kovaks (Hungary) (fencing, 1936); No. 3072, Jesse Owens (U.S.A.) (200 metres, 1936); No. 3073, Mark Spitz (U.S.A.) (swimming, 1972); No. 3074, Eduardo Mangiarotti (Italy) (fencing, 1936); No. 3075, Nelli Kim (Russia) (gymnastics, 1976); No. 3076, Viktor Krovopuskov (Russia) (fencing, 1976); No. 3077, Viktor Sidiak (Russia) (fencing, 1976); No. 3078, Nikolai Andrianov (Russia) (gymnastics, 1976); No. 3079, Nadia Comaneci (Rumania) (gymnastics, 1976); No. 3080, Mitsuo Tsukahara (Japan) (gymnastics, 1976); No. 3081, Yelena Novikova-Belova (Russia) (fencing, 1976); No. 3082, John Naber (U.S.A.) (swimming, 1976); No. 3083, Kornelia Ender (Rumania) (swimming, 1976); $25 (No. 3084), Lydia Skoblikova (Russia) (speed skating, 1964); No. 3085, Ivar Ballangrud (Norway) (speed skating, 1928); No. 3086, Clas Thunberg (Finland) (speed skating, 1928); No. 3087, Anton Heida (U.S.A.) (gymnastics, 1904); No. 3088, Akinori Nakayama (Japan) (gymnastics, 1968); No. 3089, Sixten Jernberg (Sweden) (skiing, 1964); No. 3090, Yevgeniy Grischin (Russia) (speed skating, 1956); No. 3091, Paul Radmilovic (East Germany) (waterpolo, 1920); No. 3092, Charles Daniels (U.S.A.) (swimming, 1904); No. 3093, Sawao Kato (Japan) (gymnastics, 1968); No. 3094, Rudolf Karpáti (Hungary) (fencing, 1948); No. 3095, Jenö Fuchs (Hungary) (fencing, 1908); No. 3096, Emil Zátopek (Czechoslovakia) (10,000 metres, 1948); No. 3097, Fanny Blankers-Koen (Netherlands) (hurdles, 1948); No. 3098, Melvin Sheppard (U.S.A.) (4 x 400 metres relay, 1908); No. 3099, Gert Fredriksson (Sweden) (kayak, 1948); No. 3100, Paul Elvstrom (Denmark) (yachting, 1948); No. 3101, Harrison Dillard (U.S.A.) (100 metres, 1948); $30 (No. 3102), Al Oerter (U.S.A.) (discus, 1956); No. 3103, Polina Atsakhova (Russia) (gymnastics, 1956); No. 3104, Takashi Ono (Japan) (gymnastics, 1956); No. 3105, Valentin Muratov (Russia) (gymnastics, 1956); No. 3106, Henri St. Cyr (Sweden) (equestrian, 1956); No. 3107, Iain Murray Rose (Australia) (swimming, 1956); No. 3108, Larisa Latynina (Russia) (gymnastics, 1956); No. 3109, Carlo Pavesi (Italy) (fencing, 1956); No. 3110, Dawn Fraser (Australia) (swimming, 1956); No. 3111, Betty Cuthbert (Australia) (400 metres, 1964); No. 3112, Vera Cáslavská (Czechoslovakia) (gymnastics, 1964); No. 3113, Galin Kulakova (Russia) (skiing, 1972); No. 3114, Yukio Endo (Japan) (gymnastics, 1972); No. 3115, Vladimir Morozov (Russia) (kayak, 1972); No. 3116, Boris Shaklin (Russia) (gymnastics, 1964); No. 3117, Don Schollander (U.S.A.) (swimming, 1964); No. 3118, Gyözö Kulscár (Hungary) (fencing, 1964); No. 3119, Christian D'Oriloa (France) (fencing, 1956).

Nos. 3048/56, 3057/65, 3066/74, 3075/83, 3084/92, 3093/3101, 3102/10 and 3111/19 were printed together, *se-tenant*, in sheetlets of 9 forming composite designs.

Sheetlets containing Nos. 3057/65, 3084/92 and 3111/19 were subsequently re-issued with No. 3063, 3086 and 3113 overprinted "ALBERTVILLE '92". No. **MS3120** also exists with the 1992 venues printed on the sheet margins.

See also Nos. 3186/94 and 3246/54

1991 (29 Oct). *85th Anniv of Rotary International (1990).*

(a) *Nos. 2789/94 and 2859/60 optd or surch as T **469** (A) or with Rotary emblem and "1905–1990" (B)*

3121	80 c. Type **464** (B)	..	10	10
3122	$2.55, *Rhetus dysonii* (B)	..	10	10
3123	$5 *Actinote anteas* (A)	..	10	10
3124	$6.40, *Heliconius tales* (A)	..	10	10
3125	$7.65, *Thecla telemus* (A)	..	10	10
3126	$100 on $8.90, *Theope eudocia* (A)	..	1·25	1·40
3127	$190 on $50 *Heliconius vicini* (B)	..	2·25	2·50
3128	$225 on $100 *Amarynthis meneria* (B)	..	2·50	2·75

(b) *Nos. 2795/2810 and **MS2861**a/b optd or surch as Nos. 3121/8, but some with emblems and inscriptions of other international organizations.*

3129	$10 *Heliconius vetustus* (B)	..	15	15
	a. Sheetlet. Nos. 3129/44	..	6·00	
3130	$10 *Mesosemia eumene* (optd Boy Scout emblem and "1907–1992")		15	15
3131	$10 *Parides phosphorus* (optd Lions Club emblem and "1917–1992")		15	15
3132	$10 *Polystichtis emylius* (a)	..	15	15
3133	$10 *Xanthocleis aedesia* (optd "125 Years Red Cross" and cross)		15	15
3134	$10 *Doxocopa agathina* (optd with part Rotary emblem)		15	15
3135	$10 *Adelpha plesaure* (optd with part Rotary emblem)		15	15
3136	$10 *Heliconius wallacei* (optd "125 Years Red Cross" and cross)		15	15
3137	$10 *Notheme eumeus* (optd Lions Club emblem and "1917–1992")		15	15
3138	$10 *Melinaea mediatrix* (optd with part Rotary emblem)		15	15
3139	$10 *Theritas coronata* (optd with part Rotary emblem)		15	15
3140	$10 *Dismorphia orise* (optd Boy Scout emblem and "1907–1992")		15	15
3141	$50 on $10 *Phyciodes ianthe* (A)	..	65	65
3142	$75 on $10 *Morpho aega* (surch Boy Scout emblem and "1907–1992")		1·00	1·10
3143	$100 on $10 *Zaretis isidora* (surch Lions Club emblem and "1917–1992")		1·25	1·40
3144	$190 on $10 *Pierella lena* (B)	..	2·25	2·50
3121/44			*Set of* 24	12·00 13·00

MS3145 Two sheets, each 102×71 mm. (a) $400 on $150 *Heliconius aoede*. (b) $400 on $150 *Phyciodes clio*   ..   *Set of* 2 *sheets*   9·00   9·25

Nos. 3134/5 and 3138/9 show the Rotary International emblem overprinted at the centre of the block of four.

Nos. **MS3145**a/b only show the new face values on the stamps and have international organization emblems overprinted on the sheet margins.

(Des D. Miller. Litho B.D.T.)

1991 (25 Nov). *65th Birthday of Queen Elizabeth II and 70th Birthday of Prince Philip. Horiz designs as T **280** of Antigua. Multicoloured. P 14.*

3146	$12.80, Queen and Prince Philip in evening dress		15	20
3147	$15.30, Queen Elizabeth II	..	15	20
3148	$100 Queen and Prince Philip	..	1·00	1·10
3149	$130 Prince Philip	..	1·25	1·40
3150	$150 Prince Philip in R.A.F. uniform	..	1·50	1·60
3151	$200 The Queen with Queen Elizabeth the Queen Mother		2·25	2·40
3146/51			*Set of* 6	5·75 6·25

MS3152 68×90 mm. $225 Queen Elizabeth II   3·00   3·25

(Des D. Miller. Litho B.D.T.)

1991 (25 Nov). *10th Wedding Anniv of Prince and Princess of Wales. Horiz designs as T **280** of Antigua. Multicoloured. P 14.*

3153	$8.90, Prince and Princess of Wales	..	15	15
3154	$50 Separate portraits of Princess and sons		65	65
3155	$75 Prince Charles with Prince William		1·00	1·10
3156	$190 Princess Diana with Prince Henry	..	2·25	2·40
3153/6			*Set of* 4	3·50 3·75

MS3157 68×90 mm. $225 Separate portraits of Prince Charles, Prince William and Princess Diana with Prince Henry   ..   3·00   3·25

$100

Melvin Jones
Founder   1880-1961
(470)

1991 (26 Nov). *75th Anniv of Lions International (1992). (a) Nos. 2789/94 and 2859/60 optd or surch as T **470** (A) or with Lions Club emblem and "Lions International 1917–1992" (B)*

3158	80 c. Type **464** (B)	..	15	10
3159	$2.55, *Rhetus dysonii* (B)	..	20	15
3160	$5 *Actinote anteas* (A)	..	30	20
3161	$6.40, *Heliconius tales* (A)	..	30	25
3162	$7.65, *Thecla telemus* (A)	..	35	25
3163	$100 on $8.90, *Theope eudocia* (A)	..	1·50	1·50
3164	$190 on $50 *Heliconius vicini* (B)	..	2·50	2·75
3165	$225 on $100 *Amarynthis meneria* (B)	..	2·50	2·75

(b) *Nos. 2843/58 and **MS2861**c/d optd or surch as Nos. 3158/65, but some with emblems and inscriptions of other international organizations*

3166	$10 *Thecla telemus* (optd Lions Club emblem and "1917–1992")		15	15
	a. Sheetlet. Nos. 3166/81	..	6·00	
3167	$10 *Thyridia confusa* (optd Rotary emblem and "1905–1990")		15	15
3168	$10 *Heliconius burneyi* (optd Boy Scout emblem and "1907–1992")		15	15
3169	$10 *Parides lysander* (a)	..	15	15
3170	$10 *Eunica orphise* (optd "125 Years Red Cross" and cross)		15	15
3171	$10 *Adelpha melona* (optd with part Lions Club emblem)		15	15
3172	$10 *Morpho menelaus* (optd with part Lions Club emblem)		15	15
3173	$10 *Nymula phylleus* (optd "125 Years Red Cross" and cross)		15	15
3174	$10 *Stalachtis phlegia* (optd Rotary emblem and "1905–1990")		15	15
3175	$10 *Theope barea* (optd with part Lions Club emblem)		15	15
3176	$10 *Morpho perseus* (optd with part Lions Club emblem)		15	15
3177	$10 *Lycorea ceres* (optd Boy Scout emblem and "1907–1992")		15	15
3178	$50 on $10 *Archonias bellona* (A)	..	65	65
3179	$75 on $10 *Caerois chorinaeus* (surch Boy Scout emblem and "1907–1992")		1·00	1·10
3180	$100 on $10 *Vila azeca* (surch Rotary emblem and "1905–1990")		1·25	1·40
3181	$190 on $10 *Nessaea batesii* (surch Lions Club emblem and "1917–1992")		2·25	2·50
3158/81			*Set of* 24	12·00 13·00

MS3182 Two sheets, each 102×71 mm. (a) $400 on $190 *Nymphidium caricae*. (b) $500 on $190 *Thecla hemon*   ..   *Set of* 2 *sheets*   9·00   9·25

Nos. 3171/2 and 3175/6 show the Lions Club International emblem overprinted at the centre of the block of four.

Nos. **MS3182**a/b only show new face values on the stamps and have international organization emblems overprinted on the sheet margins.

(471)

1991 (29 Nov). *"Phila Nippon '91" International Stamp Exhibition, Tokyo. Sheetlets containing Nos. 2880/95 and 2897/2912, now sold as miniature sheets, and **MS2966**d with some stamps surch as T **471** and inscriptions and exhibition logo on the sheet margins, all in red.*

MS3183 135×203 mm. $10×12; $25 on $10; $50 on $10; $75 on $10; $130 on $10   ..   5·00   5·50

MS3184 135×203 mm. $12.80×12; $25 on $12.80; $50 on $12.80; $75 on $12.80; $100 on $12.80   ..   5·00   5·50

MS3185 68×110 mm. $250 on $150 *Lecythis ollaria*   ..   3·75   4·00

(472)   **(473)**

1991 (3 Dec). *Winter Olympic Games, Albertville (1992) (2nd issue). Nos. 2738/46 optd or surch with T **472** or "XVIth Olympic Winter Games in Albertville" (No. 3190), in black or red.*

3186/94 $20×6, $70 on $20, £100 on $20, $190 on $20   ..   ..   ..   *Set of* 9   7·00   7·00

1991 (19 Dec). *John F. Kennedy and Sir Winston Churchill Commemorations. Nos. **MS2966**c and **MS2966**e surch with T **473** in black or red.*

MS3195 70×105 mm. $600 on $150 *Galeandra devoniana* (*horiz*)

MS3196 74×104 mm. $600 on $190 *Ionopsis utricularioides*

No. **MS3195** is additionally overprinted with "IN MEMORIAM John F. Kennedy 1917–1963", "First Man on Moon July 20, 1969" and "Apollo 11" emblem, and No. **MS3196** "IN MEMORIAM Sir Winston S. Churchill 1874–1965" and "50th Anniversary World War II" on sheet margins.

474 Akagi (Japanese aircraft
carrier)

(Des J. Batchelor. Litho Questa)

1991 (23 Dec). *50th Anniv of Japanese Attack on Pearl Harbor. T **474** and similar horiz designs, each deep ultramarine, bright scarlet and black. P 14½.*

3197	$50 Type **474**	..	80	80
	a. Sheetlet. Nos. 3197/206	..	7·00	
3198	$50 Beached Japanese midget submarine		80	80
3199	$50 Mitsubishi A6M Zero-Sen fighter	..	80	80
3200	$50 U.S.S. *Arizona* (battleship) under attack		80	80
3201	$50 Aichi D3A1 "Val" dive bomber	..	80	80
3202	$50 U.S.S. *California* (battleship) sinking		80	80
3203	$50 Curtiss P-40 fighters taking off	..	80	80
3204	$50 U.S.S. *Cassin* and U.S.S. *Downes* damaged in dry dock		80	80
3205	$50 Boeing B-17 Flying Fortress crash landing at Bellows Field		80	80
3206	$50 U.S.S. *Nevada* (battleship) on fire	..	80	80
3197/206			*Set of* 10	7·00 7·00

Nos. 3197/206 were printed together, *se-tenant*, in sheetlets of 10 with the stamps arranged in two horizontal rows of 5 separated by an illustrated gutter showing American battleships after the attack.

475 Brandenburg Gate and
Location Plan

Des L. Fried (Nos. 3207/8, 3220, **MS3225c**), W. Hanson (Nos. 3209/11, 3221, **MS3225d**), J. Iskowitz (Nos. 3212/14, 3217/18, 3222/3, **MS3225a/b**, **MS3225e**), W. Wright (Nos. 3215/16, 3219, 3224, **MS3225f**). Litho Questa)

1991 (23 Dec). *Anniversaries and Events.* T **475** *and similar multicoloured designs.* P 14.

3207	$10 Type **475**		20	20
3208	$25 President Bush, President Lech Walesa of Poland and Brandenburg Gate		50	50
3209	$25 Scout handshake		50	50
3210	$30 Scouts hiking at Philmont Scout Ranch		60	60
3211	$40 Jamboree and Scout Movement emblems		70	70
3212	$60 General de Gaulle at Venice, 1944		90	90
3213	$75 De Gaulle with Khrushchev, 1960		1·25	1·25
3214	$75 Mozart and Castle of Laxenburg		1·25	1·25
3215	$75 Caroline Herschel (astronomer) and Old Town Hall, Hanover		1·25	1·25
3216	$75 Map of Switzerland and woman in Valais costume		1·25	1·25
3217	$80 De Gaulle at Algiers, 1958		1·40	1·40
3218	$80 Mozart and death of Leopold II		1·40	1·40
3219	$80 Otto Lilienthal and *Flugzeug Nr. 3*		1·40	1·40
3220	$100 Chancellor Kohl, Foreign Minister Genscher and Brandenburg Gate		1·50	1·50
3221	$100 Lord Baden-Powell (*vert*)		1·50	1·50
3222	$100 De Gaulle with Pope Paul VI, 1967		1·50	1·50
3223	$100 Mozart and birthplace, Salzburg		1·50	1·50
3224	$100 Steam locomotive		1·50	1·50
3207/24		*Set of 18*	18·00	18·00

MS3225 Six sheets. (a) 67×99 mm. $150 General De Gaulle (*vert*). (b) 75×104 mm. $190 General De Gaulle (*different*) (*vert*). (c) 101×71 mm. $190 Ceremonial helmet and statues from Brandenburg Gate. (d) 114×83 mm. $190 Rocket-flown commemorative cover, 1960. (e) 73×104 mm. $190 Mozart cameo (*vert*). (f) 103×74 mm. $190 Arms of Berne and Solothurn .. *Set of 6 sheets* 15·00 16·00
Anniversaries and Events:—Nos. 3207/8, 3220, **MS3225c**, Bicentenary of Brandenburg Gate, Berlin; Nos. 3209/11, 3221, **MS3225d**, 17th World Scout Jamboree, Korea; Nos. 3212/13, 3217, 3222, **MS3225a/b**, Birth centenary of Charles de Gaulle (French statesman) (1990); Nos. 3214, 3218, 3223, **MS3225e**, Death bicentenary of Mozart; No. 3215, 750th anniv of Hanover; No. 3216, **MS3225f**, 700th anniv of Swiss Confederation; No. 3219, Centenary of Otto Lilienthal's first gliding experiments; No. 3224, Centenary of Trans-Siberian Railway.
No. 3222 is inscribed "Pope John VI" in error.

476 Disney Characters Carol Singing, 1989

(Des Walt Disney Co. Litho Questa)

1991 (30 Dec). *Christmas. Walt Disney Christmas Cards.* T **476** *and similar multicoloured designs.* P 14×13½ (*horiz*) or 13½×14 (*vert*).

3226	80 c. Type **476**		10	10
3227	$2.55, Disney characters and carol singers in tram, 1962		10	10
3228	$5 Donald Duck and Pluto with parcel, 1971		10	10
3229	$6.40, "SEASON'S GREETINGS" and Mickey Mouse with candle, 1948		10	10
3230	$7.65, Mickey Mouse as Father Christmas, 1947		10	10
3231	$8.90, Shadow of Pinocchio with candle, 1939		10	10
3232	$50 Three Little Pigs dancing on wolf rug, 1933		50	55
3233	$50 Conductor and Donald Duck, 1940 (*vert*)		50	55
	a. Horiz strip of 5. Nos. 3233/7		2·50	
3234	$50 Elephant and ostrich carol singing, 1940 (*vert*)		50	55
3235	$50 Hippo, centaurs, Pinocchio and Goofy, 1940 (*vert*)		50	55
3236	$50 Snow White, Dopey, Mickey and Minnie, 1940 (*vert*)		50	55
3237	$50 Dino, Pluto and Walt Disney, 1940 (*vert*)		50	55
3238	$50 Mickey Mouse in sleigh, 1974 (*vert*)		50	55
	a. Horizontal strip of 6. Nos. 3238/43		3·00	
3239	$50 Three Little Pigs, Winnie the Pooh, Bambi and Thumper, 1974 (*vert*)		50	55
3240	$50 Baloo, King Louis, Lady and the Tramp, 1974 (*vert*)		50	55
3241	$50 Alice, Robin Hood, the Cheshire Cat and Goofy, 1974 (*vert*)		50	55
3242	$50 Dumbo, Pinocchio, Peter Pan, Tinkerbelle, Seven Dwarfs and Donald Duck, 1974 (*vert*)		50	55
3243	$50 Pluto pulling sleigh, 1974 (*vert*)		50	55
3244	$200 Mickey and mice carol singing, 1949		2·00	2·10
3226/44		*Set of 19*	8·25	9·00

MS3245 Eight sheets. (a) 127×101 mm. $260 Mickey, Minnie, Clarabelle and Pluto in mail coach, 1932 (*vert*). (b) 127×101 mm. $260 Mickey's House, 1935 (*vert*). (c) 101×127 mm. $260 Jose Carioca, Rooster and Donald Duck on flying carpet, 1944 (*vert*). (d) 101×127 mm. $260 Casey at the Bat and dancers, 1945. (e) 127×101 mm. $260 Mickey, Donald and Goofy on musical score, 1946. (f) 127×101 mm. $260 Picture of Winnie the Pooh, 1969. (g) 127×101 mm. $260

Father Christmas in chimney, 1969 (*vert*). (h) 101×127 mm. $260 Letters of film titles forming Mickey Mouse, 1978 (*vert*) .. *Set of 8 sheets* 20·00 21·00
Nos. 3233/7 and 3238/43 were each printed together, *se-tenant*, in horizontal strips of 5 or 6 throughout the sheets, each strip showing the design of the complete card.

477 Gus Gander playing Ice Hockey

(Des Walt Disney Co. Litho B.D.T.)

1991 (30 Dec). *Winter Olympic Games, Albertville (1992) (3rd issue).* T **477** *and similar horiz designs showing Walt Disney cartoon characters. Multicoloured.* P 13.

3246	$6.40, Type **477**		20	10
3247	$7.65, Mickey and Minnie Mouse in bobsleigh		20	10
3248	$8.90, Donald's Nephews on luge and skis		25	10
3249	$12.80, Goofy freestyle skiing		40	20
3250	$50 Goofy ski jumping		80	80
3251	$100 Donald and Daisy Duck speed skating		1·25	1·25
3252	$130 Pluto cross-country skiing		1·40	1·50
3253	$190 Mickey and Minnie Mouse ice dancing		2·25	2·25
3246/53		*Set of 8*	6·00	6·00

MS3254 Two sheets, each 125×100 mm. (a) $225 Donald's nephew curling; (b) $225 Donald Duck slalom skiing .. .. *Set of 2 sheets* 6·00 6·50

478 Columbus landing on Trinidad   479 Tom Mix in *The Great K&A Train Robbery*, 1926

(Des J. Genzo. Litho Questa)

1992 (2 Jan). *500th Anniv of Discovery of America by Columbus.* T **478** *and similar multicoloured designs.* P 14.

3255	$6.40, Type **478**		40	40
3256	$7.65, Columbus the map-maker		45	45
3257	$8.90, Fleet blown off course		45	45
3258	$12.80, Map of Third Voyage and Columbus in chains		55	55
3259	$15.30, Sighting land		55	55
3260	$50 Nina and Pinta		90	90
3261	$75 Santa Maria		1·25	1·25
3262	$100 Columbus trading with Amerindians		1·75	1·75
3263	$125 Crew and sea monster		2·00	2·00
3264	$130 Columbus landing on San Salvador and map of First Voyage		2·00	2·00
3265	$140 Priest and Amerindians		2·00	2·00
3266	$150 Columbus before King Ferdinand and Queen Isabella of Spain		2·00	2·00
3255/66		*Set of 12*	13·00	13·00

MS3267 Three sheets, each 126×91 mm. (a) $280 *Nina* (*vert*). (b) $280 Columbus (*vert*). (c) $280 Early map of Caribbean .. *Set of 3 sheets* 13·00 14·00

(Litho B.D.T.)

1992 (11 Mar). *Classic Movie Posters.* T **479** *and similar multicoloured designs.* P 14.

3268	$8.90, Type **479**		30	30
3269	$12.80, Richard Dix and Irene Dunne in *Cimarron*, 1931		40	40
3270	$15.30, Fatty Arbuckle in *Buzzin' Around*, 1934		40	40
3271	$25 Tom Tyler in *The Adventures of Captain Marvel*, 1941		55	55
3272	$30 Boris Karloff in *The Mummy*, 1932		70	70
3273	$50 Rudolph Valentino in *A Sainted Devil*, 1924		90	90
3274	$75 Seven posters for *A Tale of Two Cities*, 1935		1·25	1·25
3275	$100 Chester Conklin in *A Tugboat Romeo*, 1916		1·75	1·75
3276	$130 Douglas Fairbanks in *The Thief of Bagdad*, 1924		2·00	2·00
3277	$150 Laurel and Hardy in *Bacon Grabbers*, 1929		2·50	2·50
3278	$190 Marx Brothers in *A Night at the Opera*, 1935		3·00	3·00
3279	$200 Orson Welles in *Citizen Kane*, 1941		3·00	3·00
3268/79		*Set of 12*	15·00	15·00

MS3280 Four sheets (a) 70×99 mm. $225 Babe Ruth in *Babe Comes Home*, 1927. (b) 70×99 mm. $225 Mae West in *She Done Him Wrong*, 1933. (c) 70×99 mm. $225 Charlie Chaplin in *The Circus*, 1928. (d) 99×70 mm. $225 Poster for never-made film *Zeppelin*, 1933. Imperf
         Set of 4 sheets 15·00 16·00

(Litho Questa)

1992 (11 May). *Easter. Paintings by Dürer. Multicoloured designs as* T **291** *of Antigua, but vert.* P 13½×14.

3281	$6.40, "The Martyrdom of Ten Thousand" (detail)		20	10
3282	$7.65, "Adoration of the Trinity" (detail of Virgin Mary)		20	10
3283	$12.80, "The Martyrdom of Ten Thousand" (execution detail)		35	20
3284	$15.30, "Adoration of the Trinity" (different detail)		40	25
3285	$50 "The Martyrdom of Ten Thousand" (detail of bishop)		80	65
3286	$100 "Adoration of the Trinity" (different detail)		1·25	1·25
3287	$130 "The Martyrdom of Ten Thousand" (different detail)		1·50	1·60
3288	$190 "Adoration of the Trinity" (different detail)		3·00	3·25
3281/8		*Set of 8*	7·00	6·75

MS3289 Two sheets, each 71×101 mm. (a) $225 "The Martyrdom of Ten Thousand". (b) $225 "Adoration of the Trinity" (detail of Christ on cross) .. .. .. *Set of 2 sheets* 7·00 7·50

$6.40   X

BAHA'I HOLY YEAR 1992

(480)

1992 (29 May). *Baha'i Holy Year. Nos.* 1519 *and* 1521/3 *surch as* T **480**.

3290	$6.40 on 60 c. Plate No. 10 (Series 1) (No. 1521)		
3291	$7.65 on 60 c. Plate No. 31 (Series 1) (No. 1523)		
3292	$8.90 on 60 c. Plate No. 19 (Series 1) (No. 1522)		
3293	$50 on 60 c. Plate No. 2 (Series 1) (No. 1519)		

481 Queen Elizabeth II and Duke of Edinburgh

(Litho Questa)

1992 (1 June). *40th Anniv of Queen Elizabeth II's Accession.* T **481** *and similar horiz designs. Multicoloured.* P 14.

3294	$8.90, Type **481**		15	15
3295	$12.80, Queen at Trooping the Colour		20	20
3296	$100 Queen at Coronation		1·50	1·75
3297	$130 Queen in Garter robes		1·75	1·90
3294/7		*Set of 4*	3·25	3·50

MS3298 Two sheets, each 119×79 mm. (a) $225 Queen in Coronation robes. (b) $225 Queen in blue dress .. .. .. *Set of 2 sheets* 7·00 7·50

482 Holy Cross Church, Annai Rupununi   483 Burmese

(Litho B.D.T.)

1992 (10 Aug). *150th Anniv of Diocese of Guyana.* T **482** *and similar multicoloured designs.* P 14.

3299	$6.40, Type **482**		15	10
3300	$50 St. Peter's Church		80	65
3301	$100 Interior of St. George's Cathedral (*vert*)		1·50	1·60
3302	$190 Map of Guyana (*vert*)		2·75	3·25
3299/302		*Set of 4*	4·75	5·00

MS3303 104×70 mm. $225 Religious symbols 3·75 4·25

(Des S. Barlowe. Litho Questa)

1992 (10 Aug). *Cats.* T **483** *and similar multicoloured designs.* P 14 (Nos. 3309/16) or 14½×13½ (*others*).

3304	$5 Type **483**		10	10
3305	$6.40, Turkish Van		10	10
3306	$12.80, American Shorthair		15	20
3307	$15.30, Sphynx		15	20
3308	$50 Egyptian Mau		50	55
3309	$50 Russian Blue		50	55
	a. Sheetlet. Nos. 3309/16		4·00	
3310	$50 Havana Brown		50	55
3311	$50 Himalayan		50	55
3312	$50 Manx		50	55

3313	$50 Cornish Rex	..	..	50	55
3314	$50 Black Persian	..	..	50	55
3315	$50 Scottish Fold	..	..	50	55
3316	$50 Siamese	..	..	50	55
3317	$100 Japanese Bobtail	..	..	1·00	1·10
3318	$130 Abyssinian	..	..	1·25	1·40
3319	$225 Oriental Shorthair	..		2·25	2·40
3304/19			Set of 16	9·25	10·25

MS3320 Four sheets, each 99×69 mm. (a) $250 Chartreuse (*vert*). (b) $250 Turkish Angora (*vert*). (c) $250 Maine Coon (*vert*). (d) $250 Chinchilla (*vert*). P 13½×14½ .. *Set of 4 sheets* 10·00 10·50
Nos. 3309/16 were printed together, *se-tenant*, in sheetlets of 8.

484 Red Howler

(Des L. Nelson. Litho Questa)

1992 (10 Aug). *Animals of Guyana. T 484 and similar multicoloured designs.* P 14.

3321	$8.90, Type 484	..	..	20	10
3322	$12.80, Ring-tailed Coati	..		25	20
3323	$15.30, Jaguar	..	..	30	20
3324	$25 Two-toed Sloth	..		40	30
3325	$50 Giant Armadillo	..		80	65
3326	$75 Giant Anteater	..		1·25	1·40
3327	$100 Capybara	..	..	1·40	1·60
3328	$130 Ocelot	..	..	1·75	1·90
3321/8			Set of 8	5·50	5·50

MS3329 Two sheets, each 70×100 mm. (a) $225 Woolly Opossum (*vert*). (b) $225 Night Monkey (*vert*) .. .. .. *Set of 2 sheets* 7·00 7·50
No. MS3329a is inscribed "WOLLY OPOSSUM" in error.

 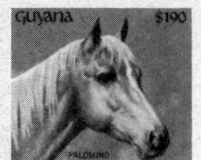

485 Oligocene Mammoth   486 Palomino

(Des J.-L. Puvilland. Litho Questa)

1992 (10 Aug). *Elephants. T 485 and similar horiz designs. Multicoloured.* P 14.

3330	$50 Type 485	..	..	1·00	1·00
	a. Sheetlet. Nos. 3330/7	..		7·00	
3331	$50 Mid-Miocene Stegodon	..		1·00	1·00
3332	$50 Pliocene Mammoth	..		1·00	1·00
3333	$50 Carthaginian elephant crossing Alps, 219 B.C.			1·00	1·00
3334	$50 Ceremonial elephant of Maharaja of Mysore, India			1·00	1·00
3335	$50 Elephant pulling teak trunks, Burma			1·00	1·00
3336	$50 Tiger-hunting by elephant, India			1·00	1·00
3337	$50 Elephant towing raft on River Kwai, Thailand			1·00	1·00
3330/7			Set of 8	7·00	7·00

MS3338 110×80 mm. $225 African Elephants 4·25 4·25
Nos. 3330/7 were printed together, *se-tenant*, in sheetlets of 8.

(Des S. Barlowe. Litho Questa)

1992 (10 Aug). *Horses. T 486 and similar horiz designs. Multicoloured.* P 14.

3339	$190 Type 486	..	..	2·75	2·75
	a. Sheetlet. Nos. 3339/46	..		20·00	
3340	$190 Appaloosa	..	..	2·75	2·75
3341	$190 Clydesdale	..	..	2·75	2·75
3342	$190 Arab	..	..	2·75	2·75
3343	$190 Morgan	..	..	2·75	2·75
3344	$190 Friesian	..	..	2·75	2·75
3345	$190 Pinto	..	..	2·75	2·75
3346	$190 Thoroughbred	..	..	2·75	2·75
3339/40			Set of 8	20·00	20·00

MS3347 109×80 mm. $190 Lipizzaner (47×29 mm) .. .. 3·50 3·75
Nos. 3339/46 were printed together, *se-tenant*, in sheetlets of 8.
No. 3340 is inscribed "APALOOSA" in error.

X

**INT.
CONFERENCE
ON NUTRITION
1992**

$6.40

(487)

1992 (2 Nov). *International Conference on Nutrition, Rome. Nos. 1658 and 1767/9 surch as T 487.*

3348	$6.40 on 150 c. Plate No. 45 (Series 1) (No. 1769)	
3349	$7.65 on 150 c. Plate No. 42 (Series 1) (No. 1768)	
3350	$8.90 on 150 c. Plate No. 40 (Series 1) (No. 1767)	
3351	$10 on 200 c. Plate No. 43 (Series 1) (No. 1658)	
3352	$50 on 200 c. Plate No. 43 (Series 1) (No. 1658)	

488 Marklin "Crocodile" Locomotive, 1933

(Des W. Hanson. Litho B.D.T.)

1992 (25 Nov). *"Genova '92" International Thematic Stamp Exhibition. Toy Trains from German Manufacturers. T 488 and similar horiz designs. Multicoloured.* P 14.

3353/61 $45 × 9 (Made by Marklin: Type 488; French prototype streetcar, 1902; British prototype "Flatiron" tank engine, 1913; German National Railways switching engine, 1970; Third Class carriage, 1909; American style locomotive, 1904; Swiss prototype streetcar, 1928; Central London Railway locomotive in Paris–Orleans livery, 1904; *The Great Bear* "Pacific" locomotive, 1909
  a. Sheetlet. Nos. 3353/61 .. .. 5·00

3362/70 $45 × 9 (Made by Marklin: L.M.S. "Precursor" tank engine, 1923; American "Congressional Limited" passenger car, 1908; Swiss prototype "Ae 3/6" locomotive, 1934; German National Railways Class 80, 1975; British Southern Railways third class coach, 1926; "Bowen-Cooke" tank engine, 1913; "Two Penny Tube" prototype, London, 1901; "Paris–Orsay" steeplecab, 1920; Passenger engine, 1895
  a. Sheetlet. Nos. 3362/70 .. 5·00

3371/9 $45 × 9 (Made by Marklin: American style locomotive, 1907; German passenger car, 1908; British Great Eastern Railway locomotive, 1908; English prototype steeplecab, 1904; Santa Fe General Electric diesel locomotive, 1962; British Great Northern locomotive, 1903; Caledonian Railway *Cardean*, 1904; British L.N.W.R. passenger car, 1903; Swiss St. Gottard Railway locomotive, 1920 ..
  a. Sheetlet. Nos. 3371/9 .. 5·00

3380/8 $45 × 9 (Made by Marklin: British L.B. & S.C.R. tank engine, 1920; Central London Railway tunnel locomotive, 1904; "Borsig" streamliner, 1935; French P.L.M. first class car, 1929; American style locomotive #1021, 1904; French "Paris–Orsay" long-nose steeplecab, 1920; British *Cock o' the North*, 1936; Prussian State Railways P8, 1975; German "Schnell-Triebwagen", 1937
  a. Sheetlet. Nos. 3380/8 .. 5·00

3389/97 $45 × 9 (Marklin North British Railway "Atlantic", 1913; Bing British London & Western Railway "Precursor", 1916; Marklin British G.W.R. *King George V*, 1937; Marklin "Kaiser Train" passenger car, 1901; Bing side tank engine, 1904; Marklin short-nose steeplecab, 1912; Marklin *Der Adler*, 1935; Bing British G.W.R. *County of Northampton*, 1909; Bing British Midland Railway *Black Prince*, 1908
  a. Sheetlet. Nos. 3389/97 .. 5·00

3398/406 $45 × 9 (Made by Bing: Midland Railway "Deeley Type", 1909; British Midland Railway #2631, 1903; German "Pacific", 1927; British G.W.R. third class coach, 1926; British London & South Western "M7", 1909; Side tank engine *Pilot*, 1901; British London & North Western Railway Webb "Cauliflower", 1912; Side tank locomotive, No. 112, 1910; British Great Northern Railway "Stirling single", 1904
  a. Sheetlet. Nos. 3398/406 .. 5·00

3407/15 $45 × 9 (Carette tin "Penny Bazaar" train, 1904; Winteringham locomotive, 1917; Carette British Northeastern Railway "Smith Compound", 1905; Carette S.E. & C.R. steam railcar, 1908; Carette British Great Northern Railway Stirling "single" No. 776, 1903; Carette British Midland Railways locomotive, 1911; Carette London

---

Metropolitan Railway Co. "Westinghouse" locomotive, 1908; Carette Clestory coach, 1907; Carette steam railcar No. 1, 1906
  a. Sheetlet. Nos. 3407/15 .. 5·00

3416/24 $45 × 9 (Made by Bing: Engine and tender, 1895; British Midland Railway "Single", 1913; #524/510 reversible express passenger locomotive, 1916; "Kaiser Train" passenger car, 1902; British rural station, 1915; British L.S.W.R. "M7" tank locomotive, 1909; "Windcutter", 1912; British Great Central Railway *Sir Sam Fay*, 1914; Scottish Caledonian Railway *Dunalastair* locomotive, 1910)
  a. Sheetlet. Nos. 3416/24 .. 5·00

3353/424 .. .. .. *Set of 72* 35·00 40·00

MS3425 Eight sheets, each 116×83 mm. (a) $350 Bing contractor's locomotive, 1904 (51×39 *mm*); (b) $350 Marklin rack railway "steeplecab" locomotive, 1908 (51×39 *mm*); (c) $350 Bing British G.W.R. *County of Northampton* locomotive, 1909 (51×39 *mm*); (d) $350 Marklin French prototype PLM "Pacific" locomotive, 1912 (51×39 *mm*); (e) $350 Bing Pabst Blue Ribbon beer refrigerator car, 1925 (51×39 *mm*); (f) $350 Marklin "Mountain Etat" locomotive, second series, 1933 (51×39 *mm*); (g) $350 Marklin German National Railroad Class 0-1 "Pacific" locomotive, 1937 (51×39 *mm*); (g) $350 Marklin American *Commodore Vanderbilt* locomotive, 1937 (51×39 *mm*). P 13.. .. *Set of 8 sheets* 30·00 32·00

(Des Kerri Schiff. Litho Questa)

1992 (29 Dec). *Postage Stamp Mega Event, New York. Sheet 100×70 mm containing multicoloured design as T 299 of Antigua, but vert.* P 14.
MS3426 $325 Statue of Liberty .. .. 5·00 6·00

 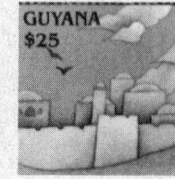

489 Aquarius   490 City Walls and Two Birds

1992 (29 Dec). *Signs of the Zodiac. T 489 and similar horiz designs. Multicoloured. Litho.* P 14×13½.

3427	$30 Type 489	..	..	60	60
	a. Sheetlet. Nos. 3427/38	..		6·50	
3428	$30 Pisces	..	..	60	60
3429	$30 Aries	..	..	60	60
3430	$30 Taurus	..	..	60	60
3431	$30 Gemini	..	..	60	60
3432	$30 Cancer	..	..	60	60
3433	$30 Leo	..	..	60	60
3434	$30 Virgo	..	..	60	60
3435	$30 Libra	..	..	60	60
3436	$30 Scorpio	..	..	60	60
3437	$30 Sagittarius	..	..	60	60
3438	$30 Capricorn	..	..	60	60
3427/38			Set of 12	6·50	6·50

Nos. 3427/38 were printed together, *se-tenant*, in sheetlets of 12.

(Des N. Waldman. Litho B.D.T.)

1992 (29 Dec). *Bible Stories (1st series). David and Goliath. T 490 and similar square designs. Multicoloured.* P 14.

3439	$25 Type 490	..	50	50
	a. Sheetlet. Nos. 3439/63	..	11·00	
3440	$25 City walls and one bird at right	..	50	50
3441	$25 Sun over city gateway	..	50	50
3442	$25 City walls and one bird at left	..	50	50
3443	$25 City walls and no birds	..	50	50
3444	$25 Philistine army and edge of shield	..	50	50
3445	$25 Goliath's head and torso	..	50	50
3446	$25 Goliath's arm and spear	..	50	50
3447	$25 Philistine army and spearhead	..	50	50
3448	$25 Philistine infantry	..	50	50
3449	$25 Philistine cavalry and infantry	..	50	50
3450	$25 Goliath's shield	..	50	50
3451	$25 Goliath's waist and thigh	..	50	50
3452	$25 David with sling	..	50	50
3453	$25 Israelite soldier with spear	..	50	50
3454	$25 Two Israelite soldiers with spears and shields	..	50	50
3455	$25 Goliath's right leg	..	50	50
3456	$25 Goliath's left leg (face value at foot)	..	50	50
3457	$25 David's legs and Israelite standard	..	50	50
3458	$25 Three Israelite soldiers	..	50	50
3459	$25 Israelite soldier and parts of two shields	..	50	50
3460	$25 Israelite soldier with sword	..	50	50
3461	$25 Back of Israelite soldier	..	50	50
3462	$25 Israelite soldier leaning on rock	..	50	50
3463	$25 Israelite soldier looking left	..	50	50
3439/63		Set of 25	11·00	11·00

Nos. 3439/63 were printed together, *se-tenant*, forming a composite design.
See also Nos. 4020/116.

COVER PRICES

Cover factors are quoted at the beginning of each country for most issues to 1945. An explanation of the system can be found on page x. The factors quoted do not, however, apply to philatelic covers.

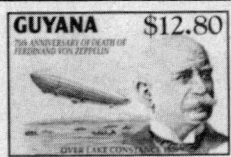

491 Count Ferdinand von Zeppelin and Airship over Lake Constance, 1909

(Des W. Hanson and W. Wright (Nos. 3464, 3474, **MS**3475a), W. Wright and L. Fried (Nos. 3465, 3472, **MS**3475b), W. Wright (others). Litho B.D.T.)

1992 (29 Dec). *Anniversaries and Events.* T **491** *and similar multicoloured designs.* P 14.

3464	$12.80, Type **491**		50	35
3465	$50 *Voyager I* and Jupiter		1·50	1·00
3466	$50 Chancellor Adenauer with President Kennedy, 1961		1·00	1·00
3467	$100 Aeromedical airlift		2·00	2·00
3468	$100 Boutu ("Amazon Dolphin")		2·00	2·00
3469	$130 Baby gorilla		2·50	2·50
3470	$130 Mobile eye screening unit and doctor with child		2·50	2·50
3471	$130 *Stars and Stripes* (winning yacht, 1987)		2·50	2·50
3472	$130 Lift-off of *Voyager I,* 1977		2·50	2·50
3473	$190 Adenauer with President De Gaulle of France, 1962		3·25	3·25
3474	$225 Von Zeppelin and airship preparing for take-off, 1905		3·50	3·50
3464/74		*Set of 11*	21·00	21·00

MS3475 Four sheets. (a) 76×105 mm. $225 Ferdinand von Zeppelin (*vert*). (b) 116×80 mm. $225 Earth from Space (*vert*). (c) 84×111 mm. $225 Konrad Adenauer (*vert*). (d) 87×111 mm. $225 *Hyperohus marmoratus* (tree frog) (*vert*)

	Set of 4 sheets	15·00 16·00

Anniversaries and Events:—Nos. 3464, 3474, **MS**3475a, 75th death anniv of Count Ferdinand von Zeppelin; Nos. 3465, 3472, **MS**3475b, International Space Year; Nos. 3466, 3473, **MS**3475c, 75th death anniv of Konrad Adenauer (German statesman); No. 3467, United Nations World Health Organization projects; Nos. 3468/9, **MS**3475d, Earth Summit 92, Rio; No. 3470, 75th anniv of International Association of Lions Clubs; No. 3471, Americas Cup Yachting Championship.

492 Hyacinth Macaw   493 Crimson Topaz

(Des R. Duburke. Litho B.D.T.)

1993 (10 Mar). *South American Parrots.* T **492** *and similar multicoloured designs.* P 14.

3476	80 c. Type **492**		30	15
3477	$6.40, Scarlet Macaw (preening)		50	25
3478	$7.65, Buffon's Macaw ("Green Macaw") (*vert*)		50	25
3479	$15.30, Orange-chinned Parakeet ("Tovi Parakeet")		70	50
3480	$50 Blue and Yellow Macaw		1·00	80
3481	$100 Military Macaw (*vert*)		1·50	1·25
3482	$130 Green-winged Macaw ("Red and Green Macaw") (*vert*)		1·75	1·75
3483	$190 Chestnut-fronted Macaw ("Severa Macaw")		2·50	3·00
3476/83		*Set of 8*	8·00	7·00

MS3484 Two sheets, each 108×74 mm. (a) $225 Scarlet Macaw. (b) $225 Green Conure ("Green Parakeet") (*vert*) .. *Set of 2 sheets* 7·00 7·50

(Des P. Chenelli. Litho Questa)

1993 (10 Mar). *Birds of Guyana.* T **493** *and similar multicoloured designs.* P 14.

3485	$50 Type **493**		75	75
	a. Sheetlet. Nos. 3485/96		8·00	
3486	$50 Bearded Bellbird		75	75
3487	$50 Amazonian Umbrellabird		75	75
3488	$50 Paradise Jacamar		75	75
3489	$50 Paradise Tanager		75	75
3490	$50 White-tailed Trogon		75	75
3491	$50 Scarlet Macaw		75	75
3492	$50 Hawk-headed Parrot ("Red-fan Parrot")		75	75
3493	$50 Cuvier's Toucan ("Red-billed Toucan")		75	75
3494	$50 White-faced Antcatcher ("White-plumed Antbird")		75	75
3495	$50 Crimson-hooded Manakin		75	75
3496	$50 Guianan Cock of the Rock		75	75
3485/96		*Set of 12*	8·00	8·00

MS3497 70×100 mm. $325 Tufted Coquette (*horiz*) .. .. 5·00 5·00

Nos. 3485/96 were printed together, *se-tenant*, in sheetlets of 12, with the backgrounds forming a composite design.

494 Manatee surfacing   495 Tamandua

(Des P. Chenelli. Litho Questa)

1993 (10 Mar). *Endangered Species. American Manatee* ("*Caribbean Manatee*"). T **494** *and similar horiz designs. Multicoloured.* P 14½.

3498	$6.40, Type **494**		40	20
3499	$7.65, Cow and calf feeding		40	20
3500	$8.90, Manatee underwater		40	20
3501	$50 Two Manatees		2·00	1·50
3498/501		*Set of 4*	2·75	1·90

(Des P. Chenelli. Litho Questa)

1993 (10 Mar). *Animals of Guyana.* T **495** *and similar vert designs. Multicoloured.* P 14.

3502	$50 Type **495**		75	75
	a. Sheetlet. Nos. 3502/13		8·00	
3503	$50 Pale-throated Sloth ("Three-toed Sloth")		75	75
3504	$50 Red Howler		75	75
3505	$50 Four-eyed Opossum		75	75
3506	$50 Black Spider Monkey		75	75
3507	$50 Giant Otter		75	75
3508	$50 Red Brocket		75	75
3509	$50 Brazilian Tree Porcupine		75	75
3510	$50 Tayra		75	75
3511	$50 Brazilian Tapir		75	75
3512	$50 Ocelot		75	75
3513	$50 Giant Armadillo		75	75
3502/13		*Set of 12*	8·00	8·00

MS3514 100×70 mm. $325 Paca .. .. 4·50 5·00

Nos. 3502/13 were printed together, *se-tenant*, in sheetlets of 12, the backgrounds forming a composite design.

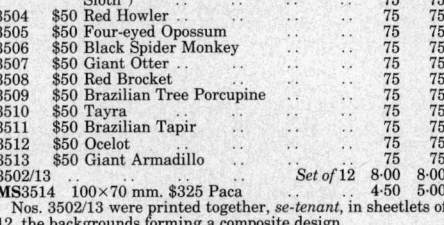

496 Pteranodon

(Des R. Sauber. Litho B.D.T.)

1993 (10 Mar). *Prehistoric Animals.* T **496** *and similar horiz designs. Multicoloured.* P 14.

3515/26 $30 × 12 (Type **496**; Cearadactylus; Eudimorphodon; Pterodactylus; Stauirkosaurus; Euoplocephalus; Tuojiangosaurus; Oviraptor; Protoceratops; Panaoplosaurus; Psittacosaurus; Corythosaurus)
a. Sheetlet. Nos. 3515/26 .. .. 4·25

3527/38 $30 × 12 (Sordes; Quetzalcoatlus; Archaeopteryx in flight; Rhamphorynchus; Spinosaurus; Anchisaurus; Stegosaurus; Leaellynosaurus; Minmi; Heterdontosaurus; Lesothosaurus; Deninonychus)
a. Sheetlet. Nos. 3527/38 .. .. 4·25

3539/50 $30 × 12 (Archaeopteryx on branch; Pteranodon (*different*); Quetzalcoatlus (three); Protoavis; Dicraeosaurus; Moschops; Lystrosaurus; Dimetrondon; Staurikosaurus; Cacops; Diarthrognathus; Estemmenosuchus)
a. Sheetlet. Nos. 3539/50 .. .. 4·25

3515/50 .. .. .. *Set of 36* 11·50 13·00

Nos. 3515/26, 3527/38 and 3539/50 were each printed together, *se-tenant*, in sheetlets of 12, with the backgrounds forming composite designs.

(Des Kerri Schiff. Litho Questa)

1993 (2 June). *40th Anniv of Coronation. Vert designs as* T **307** *of Antigua. Multicoloured.* P 13½×14.

3551	$25 Queen Elizabeth II in Coronation robes (photograph by Cecil Beaton)		75	75
	a. Sheetlet. Nos. 3551/4×2		7·00	
3552	$50 Royal gems		1·00	1·00
3553	$75 Queen Elizabeth and Prince Philip		1·25	1·40
3554	$130 Queen opening Parliament		1·50	1·75
3551/4		*Set of 4*	4·00	4·50

MS3555 69×100 mm. $325 "Queen in Coronation Robes" (Sir James Gunn) (28½×42½ mm). P 14 .. .. 4·25 4·50

Nos. 3551/4 were printed together, *se-tenant*, in sheetlets of 8, containing two *se-tenant* blocks of 4.

NEW INFORMATION

The editor is always interested to correspond with people who have new information that will improve or correct the Catalogue.

497 Gabriel Marquez (author)   498 "Bather, Paris" (Picasso)

(Des J. Genzo. Litho Questa)

1993 (26 July). *Famous People of the Twentieth Century.* T **497** *and similar horiz designs. Multicoloured.* P 14.

(a) Arts and Literature

3556	$50 Type **497**		50	55
	a. Sheetlet. Nos. 3556/64		4·50	
3557	$50 Pablo Picasso (artist)		50	55
3558	$50 Cecil De Mille (film director)		50	55
3559	$50 Martha Graham (dancer)		50	55
3560	$50 Peace dove (inscr "20th Century Arts and Literature")		50	55
3561	$50 Charlie Chaplin (actor)		50	55
3562	$50 Paul Robeson (actor)		50	55
3563	$50 Rudolph Dunbar (musician)		50	55
3564	$50 Louis Armstrong (musician)		50	55
3556/64		*Set of 9*	4·00	4·75

MS3565 100×70 mm. $250 Elvis Presley (singer) (*vert*) .. .. .. 3·50 3·50

(b) Science and Medicine

3566	$50 Louis Leakey (archaeologist and anthropologist)		50	55
	a. Sheetlet. Nos. 3566/74		4·50	
3567	$50 Jonas Salk (discoverer of polio vaccine)		50	55
3568	$50 Hideyo Noguchi (bacteriologist)		50	55
3569	$50 Karl Landsteiner (pathologist)		50	55
3570	$50 As No. 3550, but inscr "20th Century Science and Medicine"		50	55
3571	$50 Sigmund Freud (founder of psychoanalysis)		50	55
3572	$50 Louis Pasteur (chemist)		50	55
3573	$50 Madame Curie (physicist)		50	55
3574	$50 Jean Baptiste Perrin (physicist)		50	55
3566/74		*Set of 9*	4·50	4·75

MS3575 100×70 mm. $250 Einstein's Theory of Relativity equation (*vert*) .. .. 3·50 3·50

(c) Sports Personalities

3576	$50 O. J. Simpson (American football)		50	55
	a. Sheetlet. Nos. 3576/84		4·50	
3577	$50 Rohan Kanhai (cricket)		50	55
3578	$50 Gabriela Sabatini (tennis)		50	55
3579	$50 Severiano Ballesteros (golf)		50	55
3580	$50 As No. 3550, but inscr "20th Century Sports"		50	55
3581	$50 Franz Beckenbauer (football)		50	55
3582	$50 Pele (football)		50	55
3583	$50 Wilt Chamberlain (basketball)		50	55
3584	$50 Nadia Comaneci (gymnastics)		50	55
3576/84		*Set of 9*	4·50	4·75

MS3585 100×70 mm. $250 Jackie Robinson (baseball) (*vert*) .. .. 3·50 3·50

(d) Peace and Humanity

3586	$100 Mahatma Gandhi (India)		1·00	1·10
	a. Sheetlet. Nos. 3586/94		9·00	
3587	$100 Dalai Lama (Tibet)		1·00	1·10
3588	$100 Michael Manley (Jamaica)		1·00	1·10
3589	$100 Pérez de Cuéllar (U.N. Secretary-General)		1·00	1·10
3590	$100 Peace dove and globe		1·00	1·10
3591	$100 Mother Teresa (India)		1·00	1·10
3592	$100 Martin Luther King (U.S.A.)		1·00	1·10
3593	$100 Pres. Nelson Mandela (South Africa)		1·00	1·10
3594	$100 Raoul Wallenberg (Sweden)		1·00	1·10
3586/94		*Set of 9*	9·00	9·75

MS3595 100×70 mm. $250 Nobel Peace Prize scroll (*vert*) .. .. 3·50 3·50

(e) Politics

3596	$100 Nehru (India)		1·00	1·10
	a. Sheetlet. Nos. 3596/604		9·00	
3597	$100 Dr. Eric Williams (Trinidad and Tobago)		1·00	1·10
3598	$100 Pres. John F. Kennedy (U.S.A.)		1·00	1·10
3599	$100 Pres. Hugh Desmond Hoyte (Guyana)		1·00	1·10
3600	$100 Peace dove and map of the Americas		1·00	1·10
3601	$100 Friedrich Ebert (Germany)		1·00	1·10
3602	$100 Pres. F. D. Roosevelt (U.S.A.)		1·00	1·10
3603	$100 Mikhail Gorbachev (Russia)		1·00	1·10
3604	$100 Sir Winston Churchill (Great Britain)		1·00	1·10
3596/604		*Set of 9*	9·00	9·75

MS3605 100×70 mm. $250 Flags of United Nations and member countries (*vert*) .. 3·50 3·50

(f) Transportation and Technology

3606	$100 Douglas DC-3 cargo plane		1·00	1·10
	a. Sheetlet. Nos. 3606/14		9·00	
3607	$100 Space Shuttle		1·00	1·10
3608	$100 Concord		1·00	1·10
3609	$100 Count Ferdinand von Zeppelin and *Graf Zeppelin*		1·00	1·10
3610	$100 Peace dove and rocket trails		1·00	1·10
3611	$100 Marconi and aerial tower		1·00	1·10
3612	$100 Adrian Thompson (mountaineer) and Mt. Roraima		1·00	1·10
3613	$100 Japan's "Bullet Train"		1·00	1·10
3614	$100 Johann von Neumann and computer		1·00	1·10
3606/14		*Set of 6*	9·00	9·75

MS3615 100×70 mm. $250 Lunar module *Eagle* on Moon .. .. .. 3·50 3·50

Nos. 3556/64, 3566/74, 3576/84, 3586/94, 3596/604 and 3606/14 were each printed together, *se-tenant*, in sheetlets of 9 with composite background designs on Nos. 3586/94, 3596/604 and 3606/14.

No. 3562 is inscribed "Paul Roebeson" in error.

(Des Kerri Schiff (Nos. 3619, 3624, **MS**3628e). Litho Questa)

1993 (16 Aug). *Anniversaries and Events.* T **498** *and similar multicoloured designs (except No.* **MS**3628c). P 14.

3616	$15.30, Type **498**		15	20
3617	$25 Willy Brandt with Prime Minister of Israel Golda Meir, 1969 (*horiz*)		40	40
3618	$50 "Pantaloons" (left half) (Tadeusz Brzozowski)		50	55
	a. Horiz pair. Nos. 3618 and 3623		1·75	
3619	$50 Georg Hackl (men's single luge, 1992)		70	70
3620	$50 Astrolabe		70	70
3621	$75 Miedzyrecz Castle		75	80
3622	$100 "Two Nudes" (Picasso)		1·00	1·10
3623	$130 "Pantaloons" (right half) (Tadeusz Brzozowski)		1·25	1·40
3624	$130 Karen Magnussen (women's figure skating, 1972)		1·50	1·50
3625	$190 "Nude seated on a Rock" (Picasso)		1·90	2·00
3626	$190 Willy Brandt at Georgsmarienhutten Steel Mill, 1969 (*horiz*)		2·25	2·25
3627	$190 Dish aerial		2·25	2·25
3616/27		*Set of 12*	12·00	13·00

MS3628 Five sheets. (a) 104×75 mm. $300 Copernicus. (b) 75×104 mm. $325 "The Rescue" (detail) (Picasso). (c) 104×75 mm. $325 Willy Brandt giving interview, 1969 (lake-brown and black). (d) 99×70 mm. $325 "Children in the Garden" (Wladyslaw Podkowinski) (*horiz*). (e) 75×104 mm. $325 German four-man bobsleigh team, 1992 .. .. .. *Set of 5 sheets* 20·00 22·00
Anniversaries and Events:—Nos. 3616, 3622, 3625, **MS**3628b, 20th death anniv of Picasso (artist); Nos. 3617, 3626, **MS**3628c, 80th birth anniv of Willy Brandt (German politician) (1992); Nos. 3618, 3621, 3623, **MS**3628d, "Polska '93" International Stamp Exhibition, Poznań; Nos. 3619, 3624, **MS**3628e, Winter Olympic Games '94, Lillehammer; Nos. 3620, 3627, **MS**3628a, 450th death anniv of Copernicus (astronomer).

Nos. 3618 and 3623 were printed together, *se-tenant*, in horizontal pairs throughout the sheet, each pair forming a composite design showing the complete painting.

499 Audie Murphy (most decorated U.S. serviceman)

(Des K. Gromoll. Litho Questa)

1993 (27 Sept). *50th Anniv of Second World War* (1st issue). T **499** *and similar horiz designs. Multicoloured.* P 14.

3629	$6.40, Type **499**		30	20
3630	$7.65, Allied troops in Normandy (8 June 1944)		30	25
3631	$8.90, American howitzer crew, Battle of Monte Cassino (18 May 1944)		35	30
3632	$12.80, American aircraft attacking *Yamato* (Japanese battleship), Battle of East China Sea (7 April 1945)		50	40
3633	$15.30, St. Basil's Cathedral, Moscow (Foreign Ministers' Conference, 19 October 1943)		50	40
3634	$50 American troops crossing Rhine at Remagen (7 March 1945)		80	65
3635	$100 Boeing B-29 Superfortresses raiding Japan from China (15 June 1944)		1·50	1·50
3636	$130 General Patton and map of Sicily (17 August 1943)		1·60	1·60
3637	$190 Destruction of *Tirpitz* (German battleship) (12 November 1944)		2·40	2·50
3638	$200 American forces in Brittany (1 August 1944)		2·50	2·75
3639	$225 American half-track (ceasefire in Italy, 2 May 1945)		2·75	3·00
3629/39		*Set of 11*	12·00	12·00

MS3640 100×69 mm. $325 Meeting of American and Russian troops on the Elbe (25 April 1945) 5·00 5·50
No. 3631 is inscribed "Monte Casino" in error.
See also Nos. 3641/60 and 3942/61.

500 R.A.A.F. Bristol Type 156 Beaufighter, Battle of the Bismarck Sea (2–4 March 1943)

501 Stuart Pearce (England)

1993 (27 Sept). *50th Anniv of Second World War* (2nd issue). T **500** *and similar horiz designs. Multicoloured.* P 14½.

3641	$50 Type **500**		75	75
	a. Sheetlet. Nos. 3641/50		6·50	
3642	$50 Lockheed P-38 Lightning attacking Admiral Yamamoto's plane, Bougainville (7 April 1943) ..		75	75
3643	$50 Consolidated B-24 Liberator bombers, Tarawa (17–19 September 1943)		75	75
3644	$50 North American B-25 Mitchell bomber, Rabaul (12 October 1943) ..		75	75
3645	$50 U.S. Navy aircraft attacking Makin (19 November 1943)		75	75
3646	$50 U.S.A.A.F. bombers on first daylight raid over Germany (27 January 1943)		75	75

3647	$50 R.A.F. De Havilland D.H.98 Mosquito bombers on first daylight raid over Berlin (30 January 1943)		75	75
3648	$50 Allied aircraft over Hamburg (24–30 July 1943)		75	75
3649	$50 Consolidated B-24 Liberators bombing Ploesti oil refineries, Rumania (1 August 1943)		75	75
3650	$50 German nightfighter attacking Allied bombers over Berlin (18 November 1943)		75	75
3651	$50 Japanese aircraft carriers during Operation 1 (7 April 1943)		75	75
	a. Sheetlet. Nos. 3651/60		6·50	
3652	$50 Lt. John F. Kennedy's motor torpedo boat U.S.S. *PT109* in Blackett Strait (1 August 1943)		75	75
3653	$50 U.S.S. *Enterprise* (aircraft carrier) ..		75	75
3654	$50 American battleships bombarding Rabaul (12 October 1943)		75	75
3655	$50 American landing craft at Cape Gloucester (26 December 1943)		75	75
3656	$50 Commissioning of U.S.S. *Bogue* (first anti-submarine escort carrier) (February 1943)		75	75
3657	$50 Grumman FM-2 Wildcat fighters from U.S.S. *Bogue* sinking *U-118*		75	75
3658	$50 U-boat launching torpedo during peak of Battle of the Atlantic (March 1943)		75	75
3659	$50 Surrender of Italian fleet at Malta (10 September 1943)		75	75
3660	$50 H.M.S. *Duke of York* (battleship) sinking *Scharnhorst* (26 December 1943)		75	75
3641/60		*Set of 20*	13·00	13·00

Nos. 3641/50 and 3651/60 were each printed together, *se-tenant*, in sheetlets of 10 with the stamps arranged in two horizontal strips of 5 separated by gutters showing the Dambusters Raid (Nos. 3641/50) or the sinking of *Chuyo* (Japanese aircraft carrier) by U.S.S. *Sailfish* (Nos. 3651/60).

(Des Rosemary DeFiglio. Litho Questa)

1993 (27 Sept). *World Cup Football Championship, U.S.A.* (1994) (1st issue). T **501** *and similar multicoloured designs.* P 14.

3661	$5 Type **501**		15	10
3662	$6.40, Ronald Koeman (Netherlands) ..		15	10
3663	$7.65, Gianluca Vialli (Italy)		20	10
3664	$12.80, McStay (Scotland) and Alemao (Brazil)		30	20
3665	$15.30, Ceulemans (Belgium) and Butcher (England)		30	20
3666	$50 Dragan Stojkovic (Yugoslavia) ..		75	65
3667	$100 Ruud Gullit (Netherlands)		1·25	1·25
3668	$130 Miloslav Kadlec (Czechoslovakia) ..		1·40	1·50
3669	$150 Ramos (Uruguay) and Berthold (Germany)		1·75	2·00
3670	$190 Baggio (Italy) and Wright (England)		2·25	2·50
3671	$200 Yarentchuck (Russia) and Renquin (Belgium)		2·40	2·75
3672	$225 Timofte (Rumania) and Aleinikov (Russia)		2·50	3·00
3661/72		*Set of 12*	12·00	12·50

MS3673 Two sheets. (a) 101×73 mm. $325 Salvatore Schillaci (Italy) and José Pintos (Uruguay) (*horiz*). (b) 73×101 mm. $325 Rene Higuita (Colombia) .. .. *Set of 2 sheets* 8·00 8·50
See also Nos. 4142/58.

502 Sir Shridath Ramphal

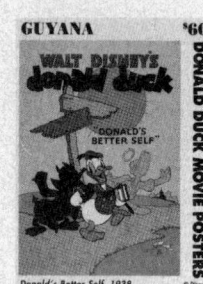

503 Donald's Better Self, 1938

(Litho Questa)

1993 (29 Nov). *First Recipients of Order of the Caribbean Community.* T **502** *and similar vert designs. Multicoloured.* P 14.

3674	$7.65, Type **502**		50	30
3675	$7.65, William Demas		50	30
3676	$7.65, Derek Walcott ..		50	30
3674/6		*Set of 3*	1·40	80

(Adapted Pauline Cianciolo. Litho Questa)

1993 (1 Dec). *Christmas. Paintings by Rubens and Dürer. Vert designs as T 270 of Dominica. Black, pale lemon and red (Nos. 3678, 3680/1, 3684, **MS**3685b) or multicoloured (others).* P 13½×14.

3677	$6.40, "The Holy Family under the Apple Tree" (detail) (Rubens)		10	10
3678	$7.65, "The Virgin in Glory" (detail) (Dürer)		10	10
3679	$12.80, "The Holy Family under the Apple Tree" (different detail) (Rubens) ..		10	15
3680	$15.30, "The Virgin in Glory" (different detail) (Dürer) ..		15	20
3681	$50 "The Virgin in Glory" (different detail) (Dürer)		50	55
3682	$130 "The Holy Family under the Apple Tree" (different detail) (Rubens) ..		1·25	1·40

3683	$190 "The Holy Family under the Apple Tree" (different detail) (Rubens) ..		1·90	2·00
3684	$250 "The Virgin in Glory" (different detail) (Dürer)		2·50	2·75
3677/84		*Set of 8*	6·50	7·25

MS3685. Two sheets. (a) 126×101 mm. $325 "The Holy Family under the Apple Tree" (Rubens). (b) 101×126 mm. $325 "The Virgin in Glory" (woodcut by Dürer from *The Life of the Virgin*) .. .. .. *Set of 2 sheets* 6·50 7·75

(Litho Questa)

1993 (6 Dec). *Bicentenary of the Louvre, Paris. Vert designs as T 305 of Antigua. Multicoloured.* P 13½×14.

3686	$50 "Mona Lisa" (Leonardo da Vinci)		
	a. Sheetlet. Nos. 3686×8		4·00
3687/94	$50 × 8 "Self-portrait with Spectacles" (Chardin); "Infanta Maria Theresa" (Velázquez); "Spring" (Arcimboldo); "The Virgin of Sorrows" (Bouts); "The Student" (Fragonard); "François I" (Clouet); "Le Condottière" (Antonello da Messina); "La Bohémienne" (Hals)		
	a. Sheetlet. Nos. 3687/94		4·00
3695/702	$50 × 8 "The Village Bride" (left detail) (Greuze); "The Village Bride" (centre detail); "The Village Bride" (right detail); "Self-portrait" (Melendez); "The Knight, the Girl and the Mountain" (Baldung-Grien); "The Young Beggar" (Murillo); "The Pilgrims of Emmaus" (left detail) (Le Nain); "The Pilgrims of Emmaus" (right detail)		
	a. Sheetlet. Nos. 3695/3702		4·00
3703/10	$50 × 8 "Woman with a Flea" (detail) (Crespi); "The Woman with Dropsy" (detail) (Dou); "Portrait of a Couple" (Ittenbach); "Cleopatra" (Moreau); "Riches" (Vouet); "Old Man and Young Boy" (Ghirlandaio); "Louis XIV" (Rigaud); "The Drinker" (Pieter de Hooch)		
	a. Sheetlet. Nos. 3703/10		4·00
3711/18	$50 × 8 "Woman with a Flea" (Crespi); "Self-portrait at Easel" (Rembrandt); "Algerian Women" (detail) (Delacroix); "Head of a Young Man" (Raphael); "Venus and The Graces" (detail) (Botticelli); "Still Life with Chessboard" (detail) (Lubin Baugin); "Lady Macbeth" (Füssli); "The Smoke-filled Room" (detail) (Chardin)		
	a. Sheetlet. Nos. 3711/18		4·00
3719/26	$50 × 8 "The Virgin with the Rabbit" (Titian); "The Virgin with the Rabbit" (detail of head) (Titian); "The Beautiful Gardener" (detail) (Raphael); "The Lace-maker" (Vermeer); "Jeanne d'Aragon" (detail) (Raphael); "The Astronomer" (Vermeer); "The Rialto Bridge" (detail) (Canaletto); "Sigismond Malatesta" (Piero della Francesca)		
	a. Sheetlet. Nos. 3719/26		4·00
3686/726		*Set of 48*	24·00 25·00

MS3727 Six sheets, each 95×70 mm. (a) $325 "Mona Lisa" and details (Leonardo da Vinci) (84×56 *mm*); (b) $325 "The Coronation of Napoleon I" (David) (84×56 *mm*); (c) $325 "Farmyard" (Jan Brueghel the Younger) (84×56 *mm*); (d) $325 "The Marriage Feast at Cana" (Veronese) (84×56 *mm*); (e) $325 "The Fortuneteller" (Caravaggio) (84×56 *mm*); (f) $325 "The Rialto Bridge" (Canaletto) (84×56 *mm*). P 12 .. .. *Set of 6 sheets* 3·25 3·50
Nos. 3686×8, 3687/94, 3695/702, 3703/10, 3711/18 and 3719/26 were each printed together, *se-tenant*, in sheetlets of 8 stamps and one centre label.

(Litho Questa)

1993 (6 Dec). *Donald Duck Film Posters.* T **503** *and similar multicoloured designs.* P 13½×14 (*vert*) or 14×13½ (*horiz*).

3728/35	$60 × 8 Type **503**; *Donald's Golf Game, 1938; Sea Scouts, 1939; Donald's Penguin, 1939; A Good Time for a Dime, 1941; Truant Officer Donald; Orphan's Benefit, 1941; Chef Donald, 1941*		
	a. Sheetlet. Nos. 3728/35		4·75
3736/43	$60 × 8 *The Village Smithy; Donald's Snow Fight; Donald's Garden; Donald's Gold Mine; The Vanishing Private; Sky Trooper; Bellboy Donald; The New Spirit,* all 1942		
	a. Sheetlet. Nos. 3736/43		4·75
3744/51	$60 × 8 *Saludos Amigos, 1943; The Eyes Have It, 1945; Donald's Crime, 1945; Straight Shooters, 1947; Donald's Dilemma, 1947; Bootle Beetle, 1947; Daddy Duck, 1948; Soup's On, 1948*		
	a. Sheetlet. Nos. 3744/51		4·75
3752/9	$80 × 8 *Donald's Happy Birthday, 1949; Sea Salts, 1949; Honey Harvester, 1949; All in a Nutshell, 1949; The Greener Yard, 1949; Slide, Donald, Slide, 1949; Lion Around, 1950; Trailer Horn, 1950*		
	a. Sheetlet. Nos. 3752/9		6·50
3760/7	$80 × 8 *Bee at the Beach, 1950; Out on a Limb, 1950; Corn Chips, 1951; Test Pilot Donald, 1951; Lucky Number, 1951; Out of Scale, 1951; Bee on Guard, 1951; Let's Stick Together, 1952*		
	a. Sheetlet. Nos. 3760/7		6·50

3768/75 $80 × 8 Trick or Treat, 1952; Don's
Fountain of Youth, 1953; Rugged
Bear, 1953; Canvas Back Duck, 1953;
Dragon Around, 1954; Grin and Bear
It, 1954; The Flying Squirrel, 1954;
Up a Tree, 1955
a. Sheetlet. Nos. 3768/75 .. .. 6·50
3776/81 $80 × 6 Scenes from Pirate Gold: In the
crow's nest; Aracuan Bird carrying
treasure chest; Donald with treasure
map; Donald at souvenir stall;
Aracuan Bird with Donald; Donald
on jetty (all horiz)
a. Sheetlet. Nos. 3776/81 .. .. 4·75
3728/81 .. .. Set of 56 38·00 40·00
MS3782 Five sheets, each 129×103 mm. (a) $500
Book cover of The Wise Little Hen, 1934 (horiz).
P 14×13½; (b) $500 Sketch for Timber, 1941.
P 13½×14; (c) $500 Fan-card for The Three
Caballeros, 1945 (horiz). P 14×13½; (c) $500
Fan-card for Melody Time, 1948. Imperf; (d)
$500 Donald Duck. P 14×13½ .. Set of 5 sheets 25·00 26·00
Nos. 3728/35, 3736/43, 3744/51, 3752/9, 3760/7, 3768/75 and
3776/81 were each printed together, se-tenant, in sheetlets of 8
or 6 (Nos. 3776/81).

504 Aladdin   505 President Dr.
Cheddi Jagan

(Des Walt Disney Co. Litho Questa)
1993 (6 Dec). Aladdin (film). T 504 and similar multicoloured
designs showing Disney cartoon characters. P 13½×14 (vert)
or 14×13½ (horiz).
3783/90 $7·65 × 8 Type 504; Abu the monkey;
Jasmine; Rajah the tiger; Jafar; Iago
the parrot; The Sultan; The Genie
a. Sheetlet. Nos. 3783/90 60
3791/9 $50 × 9 Jafar and magic scarab; Tiger
Head entrance, Cave of Wonders;
Jafar; Aladdin and Abu at breakfast;
Aladdin rescuing Jasmine; Aladdin,
Jasmine and Abu; Rajah comforts
Jasmine; Jafar disguised as an old
man; Aladdin and Abu in treasure
chamber (all horiz)
a. Sheetlet. Nos. 3791/9 .. .. 4·50
3800/8 $65 × 9 Aladdin with lamp and magic
carpet; The Genie measuring
Aladdin; Abu turned into an
elephant; Aladdin in disguise at
palace; Aladdin and Jasmine on
magic carpet; Aladdin in disguise,
Jasmine and Sultan; Aladdin fighting
Jafar; Aladdin and Jasmine; The
Genie with suitcase and golf clubs (all
horiz)
a. Sheetlet. Nos. 3800/8 .. .. 5·50
3783/808 .. .. Set of 26 10·50 11·00
MS3809 Four sheets, each 127×102 mm. (a)
$325 Aladdin, The Genie, Abu and magic carpet
in Cave of Wonders (horiz); (b) $325 Aladdin in
disguise on elephant; (c) $325 Aladdin and
Jasmine on magic carpet (horiz); (d) $325 The
Genie, The Sultan, Jasmine, Aladdin and Abu
(horiz) .. .. .. Set of 4 sheets 13·00 13·50
Nos. 3783/90, 3791/9 and 3800/8 were printed together,
se-tenant, in sheetlets of 8 (Nos. 3783/90) or 9 (others).

1993 (17 Dec). 1st Anniv of Election of President Jagan. T 505
and similar multicoloured design. Litho. P 13½×14.
3810 $6·40, Type 505 .. .. .. 10 10
MS3811 97×69 mm. $325 "REBIRTH OF
DEMOCRACY" emblem. P 13 .. .. 3·25 3·50

(Des W. Hanson. Litho Questa)
1994 (18 Feb). "Hong Kong '94" International Stamp
Exhibition (1st issue). Horiz designs as T 317 of Antigua.
Multicoloured. P 14.
3812 $50 Hong Kong 1984 Royal Hong Kong
Jockey Club $1·30 stamp and Happy
Valley Racecourse 50 55
a. Horiz pair. Nos. 3812/13 .. .. 1·00
3813 $50 Guyana 1992 Movie Posters $190
stamp and Happy Valley Racecourse 50 55
Nos. 3812/13 were printed together, se-tenant, in horizontal
pairs throughout the sheet with the centre part of each pair
forming a composite design.

(Des Kerri Schiff. Litho Questa)
1994 (18 Feb). "Hong Kong '94" International Stamp
Exhibition (2nd issue). Ch'ing Dynasty Snuff Boxes (Nos.
3814/19) or Porcelain (Nos. 3820/5). Multicoloured designs as
T 318 of Antigua, but vert. P 14.
3814 $20 Painted enamel in shape of bamboo 20 25
a. Sheetlet. Nos. 3814/19 .. .. 1·25
3815 $20 Painted enamel showing woman .. 20 25
3816 $20 Amber with lions playing ball .. 20 25
3817 $20 Agate in shape of two gourds .. 20 25
3818 $20 Glass overlay with dog design .. 20 25

3819 $20 Glass with foliage design 20 25
3820 $20 Covered jar with dragon design .. 20 25
a. Sheetlet. Nos. 3820/5 .. .. 1·25
3821 $20 Rotating brush-holder 20 25
3822 $20 Covered jar with horses design .. 20 25
3823 $20 Amphora vase with bats and peaches 20 25
3824 $20 Tea caddy with Fo dogs 20 25
3825 $20 Vase with camellias and peaches
design 20 25
3814/25 .. .. Set of 12 2·50 3·00
Nos. 3814/19 and 3820/5 were each printed together,
se-tenant, in sheetlets of 6.

$20.00

CENTENARY
Sign For The
MAHDI
1894-1994

(506)

1994 (21 Mar). Centenary of the Sign for the Mahdi. Nos.
1622/4 and 1634 surch as T 506 in blue.
3826 $6 on 60 c. Plate No. 73 (Series 1) (horiz)
3827 $20 on 200 c. Plate No. 33 (Series 1) (horiz)
3828 $30 on 60 c. Plate No. 57 (Series 1) (horiz)
3829 $35 on 60 c. Plate No. 75 (Series 1) (horiz)
The surcharges on Nos. 3826 and 3828 show the third line as
"MADHI".

(Litho Questa)
1994 (5 May). Hummel Figurines. Vert designs as T 302 of
Antigua. Multicoloured. P 14.
3830 $20 Girl holding inscribed heart .. 20 25
3831 $25 Boy with heart under arm 25 30
3832 $35 Baker 35 40
3833 $50 Girl with pot of flowers 50 55
3834 $60 Girl with trumpet, pot plant and bird 60 65
3835 $130 Four girls .. .. .. 1·25 1·40
3836 $190 Boy and two girls with dog .. 1·90 2·00
3837 $250 Boy with cake and dog .. .. 2·50 2·75
3830/7 .. .. Set of 8 7·50 8·50
MS3838 Two sheets, each 92×124 mm. (a) $6 As
No. 3835; $25 No. 3831; $30 As No. 3830; $190
No. 3836. (b) $20 As No. 3832; $35 As No. 3837;
$60 No. 3834; $130 As No. 3833 Set of 2 sheets 5·00 5·25

I L O
75th Anniversary
1919-1994

$6.00

(507)

1994 (16 May). 75th Anniv of International Labour Organization. Nos. 1527 and 1629/30 surch as T 507.
3839 $6 on 130 c. Plate No. 13 (Series 1) ..
3840 $30 on 120 c. Plate No. 58 (Series 1) ..
3841 $35 on 120 c. Plate No. 56 (Series 1) ..

1994 (20 May). Centenary of Sierra Club (environmental
protection society) (1992). Endangered Species. Multicoloured
designs as T 320 of Antigua. P 14.
3842 $70 Red Kangaroo with young .. 70 75
a. Sheetlet. Nos. 3842/9 .. .. 5·50
3843 $70 Head of American Alligator .. 70 75
3844 $70 Head of Bald Eagle 70 75
3845 $70 Giant Panda eating bamboo .. 70 75
3846 $70 Head of Red Kangaroo 70 75
3847 $70 Alaskan Brown Bear sitting .. 70 75
3848 $70 Bald Eagle 70 75
3849 $70 Head of Giant Panda 70 75
3850 $70 Red Kangaroo (horiz) 70 75
a. Sheetlet. Nos. 3850/7 .. .. 5·50
3851 $70 Whooping Crane facing left (horiz) 70 75
3852 $70 Male Whooping Crane in courtship
display (horiz) 70 75
3853 $70 Whooping Crane looking right (horiz) 70 75
3854 $70 Alaskan Brown Bear and cub (horiz) 70 75
3855 $70 Alaskan Brown Bear fishing (horiz) 70 75
3856 $70 Bald Eagle on branch (horiz) .. 70 75
3857 $70 Giant Panda (horiz) 70 75
3858 $70 American Alligator (logo at left)
(horiz) 70 75
a. Sheetlet. Nos. 3858/63 .. .. 4·25
3859 $70 American Alligator (logo at right)
(horiz) 70 75
3860 $70 Italian Alps at sunrise (horiz) .. 70 75
3861 $70 Italian Alps and meadow (horiz) .. 70 75
3862 $70 Mono Lake at sunset (horiz) .. 70 75
3863 $70 Rock pinnacles, Mono Lake (horiz) 70 75
3864 $70 Sea Lion 70 75
a. Sheetlet. Nos. 3864/72 .. .. 6·25
3865 $70 Head of Sea Lion 70 75
3866 $70 Sea Lions on rocks 70 75
3867 $70 Rock pinnacles, Mono Lake .. 70 75
3868 $70 Sierra Club Centennial emblem
(black, buff and deep blue-green) .. 70 75

3869 $70 Lake, Italian Alps 70 75
3870 $70 Summit of Matterhorn 70 75
3871 $70 Matterhorn and village 70 75
3872 $70 Clouds over Matterhorn 70 75
3842/72 .. .. Set of 31 21·00 23·00
Nos. 3842/9, 3850/7, 3858/63 and 3864/72 were printed
together se-tenant in sheetlets of 8 (Nos. 3842/9 and 3850/7), 6
(Nos. 3858/63) or 9 (Nos. 3864/72).

ROYAL VISIT FEB 19-22, 1994

(508)

1994 (26 May). Royal Visit. Nos. 3551/5 optd as T 508 (in three
lines on $75 or two lines on $130).
3873 $25 Queen Elizabeth II in Coronation
robes (photograph by Cecil Beaton) 25 30
a. Sheetlet. Nos. 3873/6×2 .. 5·50
3874 $50 Royal gems 50 55
3875 $75 Queen Elizabeth and Prince Philip .. 75 80
3876 $130 Queen opening Parliament .. 1·25 1·40
3873/6 .. .. Set of 4 2·75 3·00
MS3877 69×100 mm. $325 "Queen in Coronation
Robes" (Sir James Gunn) (28½×42½ mm) .. 3·25 3·50
No. MS3877 shows the overprint in three lines on the sheet
margin.

509 Cestrum parqui

1994 (20 June). Flowers. T 509 and similar horiz designs.
Multicoloured. Litho. P 14×13½.
3878 $6·40, Type 509 .. .. .. 10 10
3879 $7·65, Brunfelsia calycina 10 10
3880 $12·80, Datura rosei 10 15
3881 $15·30, Ruellia macrantha 15 20
3882 $50 Portlandia albiflora 50 55
3883 $50 Clusia grandiflora 50 55
a. Sheetlet. Nos. 3883/94 .. 6·00
3884 $50 Begonia haageana 50 55
3885 $50 Fuchsia simplicicaulis 50 55
3886 $50 Guaiacum officinale 50 55
3887 $50 Pithecoctenium cynanchoides .. 50 55
3888 $50 Sphaeralcea umbellata 50 55
3889 $50 Erythrina poeppigiana 50 55
3890 $50 Steriphoma paradoxa 50 55
3891 $50 Allemanda violacea 50 55
3892 $50 Centropogon cornutus 50 55
3893 $50 Passiflora quadrangularis 50 55
3894 $50 Victoria amazonica 50 55
3895 $50 Cobaea scandens 50 55
a. Sheetlet. Nos. 3895/906 .. 6·00
3896 $50 Pyrostegia venusta 50 55
3897 $50 Petrea kohautiana 50 55
3898 $50 Hippobroma longiflora 50 55
3899 $50 Cleome hassleriana 50 55
3900 $50 Verbena peruviana 50 55
3901 $50 Tropaeolum peregrinum 50 55
3902 $50 Plumeria rubra 50 55
3903 $50 Selenicereus grandiflorus 50 55
3904 $50 Mandevilla splendens 50 55
3905 $50 Pereskia aculeata 50 55
3906 $50 Ipomoea learii 50 55
3907 $130 Pachystachys coccinea .. .. 1·25 1·40
3908 $190 Beloperone guttata .. .. 1·90 2·00
3909 $250 Ferdinandusa speciosa .. .. 2·50 2·75
3878/909 .. .. Set of 32 19·00 20·00
MS3910 Two sheets, each 99×70 mm. (a) $325
Lophospermum erubescens. (b) $325 Columnea
fendleri. P 13 .. .. Set of 2 sheets 6·50 6·75
Nos. 3883/94 and 3895/906 were printed together, se-tenant,
in sheetlets of 12, forming composite background designs.

(Des W. Hanson. Litho)
1994 (20 June). 25th Anniv of First Moon Landing (1st issue).
Horiz designs as T 326 of Antigua. Multicoloured. P 14.
3911 $60 Walter Dornberger and launch of first
A-4 rocket 60 65
a. Sheetlet. Nos. 3911/16 .. 3·50
3912 $60 Rudolph Nebel and "Surveyor 1" .. 60 65
3913 $60 Robert H. Goddard and "Apollo 7" .. 60 65
3914 $60 Kurt Debus and view of Earth from
Moon ("Apollo 8") 60 65
3915 $60 James T. Webb and "Apollo 9" .. 60 65
3916 $60 George E. Mueller and "Apollo 10"
lunar module 60 65
3917 $60 Wernher von Braun and launch of
"Apollo 11" 60 65
a. Sheetlet. Nos. 3917/22 .. 3·50
3918 $60 Rocco A. Petrone and "Apollo 11"
astronaut on Moon 60 65
3919 $60 Eberhard Rees and "Apollo 12"
astronaut on Moon 60 65
3920 $60 Charles A. Berry and damaged
"Apollo 13" 60 65
3921 $60 Thomas O. Paine and "Apollo 14"
before splashdown 60 65
3922 $60 A. F. Staats and "Apollo 15" on Moon 60 65
3923 $60 Robert R. Gilruth and "Apollo 16"
astronaut on Moon 60 65
a. Sheetlet. Nos. 3923/8 .. 3·50
3924 $60 Ernst Stuhlinger and "Apollo 17" crew
on Moon 60 65
3925 $60 Christopher C. Kraft and X-30
National Aero-Space Plane .. 60 65
3926 $60 Rudolf Opitz and Messerschmitt Me
163B Komet (rocket engine), 1943 .. 60 65
3927 $60 Clyde W. Tombaugh and "face" on
Mars 60 65

3928	$60 Hermann Oberth and scene from *The Girl in the Moon*		60	65
3911/28		*Set of 18*	10·50	11·50

MS3929 125×112 mm. $325 Frank J. Everest Jr and "Apollo 11" anniversary logo .. .. 3·25 3·50
Nos. 3911/16, 3917/22 and 3923/8 were each printed together, *se-tenant*, in sheetlets of 6.
See also Nos. 4169/87

(Des Kerri Schiff. Litho B.D.T.)

1994 (20 June). *Centenary of International Olympic Committee. Medal Winners. Multicoloured designs as T* **327** *of Antigua, but vert. P* 14.

3930	$20 Nancy Kerrigan (U.S.A.) (1994 figure skating silver)		20	25
3931	$35 Sawao Kato (Japan) (1976 gymnastics gold)		35	40
3932	$130 Florence Griffith Joyner (U.S.A.) (1988 100 and 200 metres gold)		1·25	1·40
3930/2		*Set of 3*	1·90	2·00

MS3933 110×80 mm. $325 Mark Wasmeier (Germany) (1994 super giant slalom and giant slalom gold) .. .. .. 3·25 3·50

(Des A. Melville-Brown. Litho B.D.T.)

1994 (20 June). *Centenary of First English Cricket Tour to the West Indies* (1995). *Multicoloured designs as T* **329** *of Antigua. P* 14.

3934	$20 Clive Lloyd (Guyana and West Indies) (*vert*)		20	25
3935	$35 Carl Hooper (Guyana and West Indies) and Wisden Trophy		35	40
3936	$60 Graham Hick (England) and Wisden Trophy		60	65
3934/6		*Set of 3*	1·10	1·25

MS3937 79×100 mm. $200 English team of 1895 (black and grey-brown) .. .. 2·00 2·10

(Des J. Batchelor. Litho B.D.T.)

1994 (20 June). *50th Anniv of D-Day. Aircraft. Horiz designs as T* **331** *of Antigua. Multicoloured. P* 14.

3938	$6 Supermarine Spitfire Mk XI fighter on photo reconnaissance		10	10
3939	$35 North American B-25 Mitchell bomber		35	40
3940	$190 Republic P-47 Thunderbolt fighters		1·90	2·00
3938/40		*Set of 3*	2·40	2·50

MS3941 109×79 mm. $325 Avro Type 683 Lancaster bomber of 419 Squadron .. 3·25 3·50

(Des J. Batchelor (Nos. 3942/51), W. Wright (Nos. 3952/60). Litho B.D.T.)

1994 (20 June). *50th Anniv of Second World War* (3rd issue). *Horiz designs as T* **500**. *Multicoloured. P* 13.

3942	$60 Paratroops drop, D-Day		60	65
	a. Sheetlet. Nos. 3942/51		6·00	
3943	$60 Glider assault, D-Day		60	65
3944	$60 U.S.S. *Arkansas* (battleship) bombarding Omaha Beach, D-Day		60	65
3945	$60 U.S. fighters attacking train		60	65
3946	$60 Allied landing craft approaching beaches		60	65
3947	$60 Troops in beach obstacles		60	65
3948	$60 Commandos leaving landing craft		60	65
3949	$60 U.S. flail tank destroying mines		60	65
3950	$60 U.S. tank breaking through sea wall		60	65
3951	$60 Tanks and infantry advancing		60	65
3952	$60 Landings at Anzio (22 January 1944)		60	65
	a. Sheetlet. Nos. 3952/61		6·00	
3953	$60 R.A.F. attacking Amiens Prison (18 February 1944)		60	65
3954	$60 Soviet Army tank in Sevastopol (9 May 1944)		60	65
3955	$60 British bren-gun carriers at the Gustav Line (19 May 1944)		60	65
3956	$60 D-Day landings (6 June 1944)		60	65
3957	$60 "V-1" over London (13 June 1944)		60	65
3958	$60 Allies entering Paris (19 August 1944)		60	65
3959	$60 German "V-2" rocket ready for launch (8 September 1944)		60	65
3960	$60 Sinking of *Tirpitz* (German battleship) (12 November 1944)		60	65
3961	$60 U.S. tanks at Bastogne (29 December 1944)		60	65
3942/61		*Set of 20*	12·00	13·00

Nos. 3942/51 and 3952/61 were each printed together, *se-tenant*, in sheetlets of 10 with the stamps arranged in two horizontal strips of 5 separated by gutters showing a D-Day Mulberry Harbour (Nos. 3942/51) or map of Europe and North Africa (Nos. 3952/61).

(Des Kerri Schiff. Litho Questa (Nos. 3964/83) or B.D.T. (others))

1994 (20 June). *"Philakorea '94" International Stamp Exhibition, Seoul* (1st issue). *Multicoloured designs as T* **330** *of Antigua. P* 13 (*Nos.* 3964/83) *or* 14 (*others*).

3962	$6 Socialist ideals statue, Pyongyang (*vert*)		10	10
3963	$25 Statue of Admiral Yi Sun-sin (*vert*)		25	30
3964	$60 Fruits and mountain peaks		60	65
	a. Sheetlet. Nos. 3964/73		6·00	
3965	$60 Manchurian crane, bamboo and peaks		60	65
3966	$60 Rising sun and two cranes on pine		60	65
3967	$60 Five cranes on pine and peak		60	65
3968	$60 Three cranes in flight		60	65
3969	$60 Sea, rocky shore and fungi		60	65
3970	$60 Sea, rocky shore and fruit		60	65
3971	$60 Hind at seashore and fruit		60	65
3972	$60 Stag in pine forest		60	65
3973	$60 Deer and fungi by waterfall		60	65
3974	$60 Tops of pines and mountain peaks		60	65
	a. Sheetlet. Nos. 3974/83		6·00	
3975	$60 Manchurian crane in flight		60	65
3976	$60 Three cranes on pine tree		60	65
3977	$60 Crane on pine tree		60	65
3978	$60 Top of fruit tree		60	65

3979	$60 Stag and two hinds on mountainside		60	65
3980	$60 Deer and fungi		60	65
3981	$60 Stag by waterfall and hind drinking		60	65
3982	$60 Pine tree, fruit and fungi		60	65
3983	$60 Fungi on mountainside		60	65
3984	$120 Sŏkkat'ap Pagoda, Pulguksa		1·25	1·40
3985	$130 Village Guardian (statue), Chejudo Island		1·25	1·40
3962/85		*Set of 24*	15·00	16·00

MS3986 Two sheets. (a) 104×73 mm. $325 Europeans at the Korean Court (early lithograph). (b) 73×104 mm. $325 Pagoda by Ch'urae-am Rock. P 14 .. *Set of 2 sheets* 6·50 6·75
Nos. 3964/73 and 3974/83, all 23×49 mm, were printed together, *se-tenant*, in sheetlets of 10, each sheetlet forming a composite design showing panels from a screen painting of longevity symbols from the late Chosun dynasty.
See also Nos. 4117/41

510 *Miki Maya*

1994 (20 June). *80th Anniv of Takarazuka Revue of Japan. T* **510** *and similar multicoloured designs. Litho. P* 14½×15.

3987	$20 Type **510**		20	25
	a. Sheetlet. Nos. 3987/94		3·25	
3988	$20 Fubuki Takane		20	25
3989	$20 Seika Kuze		20	25
3990	$20 Saki Asaji		20	25
3991	$60 Mira Anju (34×47 *mm*)		60	65
3992	$60 Yuki Amami (34×47 *mm*)		60	65
3993	$60 Maki Ichiro (34×47 *mm*)		60	65
3994	$60 Yu Shion (34×47 *mm*)		60	65
3987/94		*Set of 8*	3·25	3·50

Nos. 3987/94 were printed together, *se-tenant*, in sheetlets of 8 stamps and 4 34×21½ mm labels.

511 *Heliconius melpomene* **512** *Jacob*

(Litho Questa)

1994 (5 July). *Butterflies. T* **511** *and similar horiz designs. Multicoloured. P* 14½ (*Nos.* 4000/15) *or* 14 (*others*).

3995	$6 Type **511**		10	10
3996	$20 *Helicopis cupido*		20	25
3997	$25 *Agrias claudina*		25	30
3998	$30 *Parides coelus*		30	35
3999	$50 *Heliconius hecale*		50	55
4000	$50 *Anaea marthesia*		50	55
	a. Sheetlet. Nos. 4000/15		8·00	
4001	$50 *Brassolis astyra*		50	55
4002	$50 *Heliconius melpomene*		50	55
4003	$50 *Haetera piera*		50	55
4004	$50 *Morpho diana*		50	55
4005	$50 *Parides coelus*		50	55
4006	$50 *Catagramma pitheas*		50	55
4007	$50 *Nessaea obrinus*		50	55
4008	$50 *Automeris janus*		50	55
4009	$50 *Papilio torquatus*		50	55
4010	$50 *Eunica sophonisba*		50	55
4011	$50 *Ceratinia nise*		50	55
4012	$50 *Panacea procilla*		50	55
4013	$50 *Pyrrhogyra neaerea*		50	55
4014	$50 *Morpho deidamia*		50	55
4015	$50 *Dismorphia orise*		50	55
4016	$60 *Morpho diana*		60	65
4017	$190 *Dismorphia orise*		1·90	2·00
4018	$250 *Morpho deidamia*		2·50	2·75
3995/4018		*Set of 24*	14·50	15·50

MS4019 Four sheets. (a) 104×76 mm. $325 *Anaea eribotes*. P 14. (b) 104×76 mm. $325 *Eunica sophonisba*. P 14. (c) 110×80 mm. $325 *Hamadryas velutina* (39×30 mm). P 14½. (d) 110×80 mm. $325 *Agrias claudina* (39×30 mm). P 14½ .. .. *Set of 4 sheets* 13·00 13·50
Nos. 4000/15, which measure 39×30 mm, were printed together, *se-tenant*, in sheetlets of 16.

(Des Bryna Waldman (Nos. 4020/43), K. Tanner (Nos. 4044/91), Marilyn Abramowitz (Nos. 4092/116). Litho Questa)

1994 (4 Aug). *Bible Stories* (2nd series). *T* **512** *and similar square designs. Multicoloured. P* 14.

(a) *Joseph*

4020/43 $20 × 24 arranged as blocks of 4 depicting Jacob giving Joseph a coat of many colours (Type **512** at top left); Joseph thrown into a pit; Joseph sold as a slave; Joseph accused by Potiphar's wife; Joseph interprets Pharoah's dreams; Joseph reunited with his brothers
  a. Sheetlet. Nos. 4020/43 .. 4·75

(b) *The Parting of the Red Sea*

4044/67 $20 × 24 Palm trees on shore; Pyramids; Palm trees on shore and black cloud; Three palm trees; Blue and white dove; Red and white bird; Egyptian army engulfed by sea; Yellow and white dove; Red and green fishes; Egyptian chariot with wall of water at left; Chariots between walls of water; Two doves; Israelites and water to left; Israelites and water to right; Turquoise and purple fishes; Israelites with tree at left; Iraelites with goats; Moses; Israelites with tree at right; Israelites with woman on horse; Israelites with old man and woman carrying pack; Israelites with woman carrying young child; Israelites with cart
  a. Sheetlet. Nos. 4044/67 .. 4·75

(c) *Ruth*

4068/91 $20 × 24 arranged as blocks of 6 depicting Ruth and Naomi: Ruth gleaning in cornfield; Boaz establishing kinsman's rights; Naomi with Ruth, Boaz and Obed
  a. Sheetlet. Nos. 4068/91 .. 4·75

(d) *Daniel in the Lions' Den*

4092/116 $20 × 25 Palm fronds and hibiscus flower; Frigate bird and palm fronds; Frigate birds and tops of stone pillars; Frigate bird, pillars and sail at bottom right; Hibiscus, sails of ship and top of pillar; Yellow arum lilies and palm trees; Heads of adult and immature frigate birds and palm trees; Palm trees, butterfly and stone pillars; Two butterflies and stone pillars; Stone pillar and sailing ship; Standing heron; Purple irises and palm trees; Daniel; Angel; Donkey foal; Orchids; Lioness and two cubs; Daniel's legs and lions; Lion; Three crowns; Goat and kid; Kid; Cub and head of lion; Lioness; Heron in flight
  a. Sheetlet. Nos. 4092/116 .. 5·00
4020/116 .. .. *Set of 97* 19·00 20·00
Nos. 4020/43, 4044/67, 4068/91 and 4092/116 were each printed together, *se-tenant*, in sheetlets of 25 (Nos. 4092/116) or 24 (others), forming composite designs.

513 *Peregrine Falcon* **514** *Paulo Futre (Portugal)*

(Des G. Bibby. Litho Questa)

1994 (16 Aug). *"Philakorea '94" International Stamp Exhibition, Seoul* (2nd issue). *Birds of the World. T* **513** *and similar vert designs. Multicoloured. P* 14.

4117	$35 Type **513**		35	40
	a. Sheetlet. Nos. 4117/28		4·25	
4118	$35 Great Spotted Woodpecker		35	40
4119	$35 White-throated Kingfisher		35	40
4120	$35 Peruvian Cock of the Rock		35	40
4121	$35 Yellow-headed Amazon		35	40
4122	$35 Victoria Crowned Pigeon		35	40
4123	$35 Little Owl		35	40
4124	$35 Ring-necked Pheasant		35	40
4125	$35 Goldfinch		35	40
4126	$35 Jay		35	40
4127	$35 Sulphur-breasted Toucan		35	40
4128	$35 Japanese Blue Flycatcher		35	40
4129	$35 Northern Goshawk		35	40
	a. Sheetlet. Nos. 4129/40		4·25	
4130	$35 Lapwing		35	40
4131	$35 Ornate Umbrellabird		35	40
4132	$35 Slaty-headed Parakeet		35	40
4133	$35 Regent Bowerbird		35	40
4134	$35 Egyptian Goose		35	40
4135	$35 White-winged Crossbill		35	40
4136	$35 Waxwing		35	40
4137	$35 Ruff		35	40
4138	$35 Hoopoe		35	40
4139	$35 Superb Starling		35	40
4140	$35 Great Jacamar		35	40
4117/40		*Set of 24*	8·50	9·50

MS4141 Two sheets, each 70×100 mm. (a) $325 American Bald Eagle; (b) $325 Gould's Violet-ear .. .. *Set of 2 sheets* 6·50 6·75
Nos. 4117/28 and 4129/40 were each printed together, *se-tenant*, in sheetlets of 12.

(Litho B.D.T.)

1994 (1 Sept). *World Cup Football Championship, U.S.A.* (2nd issue). *T* **514** *and similar vert designs. Multicoloured. P* 14.

4142	$6 Type **514**		10	10
4143	$35 Lyndon Hooper (Canada)		35	40
4144	$60 Enzo Francescoli (Uruguay)		60	65
4145	$60 Paolo Maldini (Italy)		60	65
	a. Sheetlet. Nos. 4145/50		3·50	
4146	$60 Guyana player		60	65
4147	$60 Bwalya Kalusha (Zambia)		60	65

148	$60 Diego Maradona (Argentina)	60	65
149	$60 Andreas Brehme (Germany)	60	65
150	$60 Eric Wynalda (U.S.A.) (pursuing ball)	60	65
151	$60 John Doyle (U.S.A.)	60	65
	a. Sheetlet. Nos. 4151/6	3·50	
152	$60 Eric Wynalda (U.S.A.) (kicking ball)	60	65
153	$60 Thomas Dooley (U.S.A.)	60	65
154	$60 Ernie Stewart (U.S.A.)	60	65
155	$60 Marcelo Balboa (U.S.A.)	60	65
156	$60 Bora Milutinovic (U.S.A. coach)	60	65
157	$190 Freddy Rincón (Colombia)	1·90	2·00
142/57	Set of 16	10·00	11·00

MS4158 Two sheets. (a) 105×75 mm. $325 "94" symbol and player. (b) 75×105 mm. $325 Oiler Watson (U.S.A.) . . Set of 2 sheets 6·50 6·75
Nos. 4145/50 and 4151/6 were each printed together, se-tenant, in sheetlets of 6, forming composite background designs.

515 Anja Fichtel (individual foil, 1988)

(Des Kerri Schiff. Litho Questa)

1994 (28 Sept). Olympic Games, Atlanta (1996) (1st issue). Previous German Gold Medal Winners. T 515 and similar multicoloured designs. P 14.

4159	$6 Type 515	10	10
4160	$25 Annegret Richter (100 metres, 1976) (vert)	25	30
4161	$30 Heike Henkel (high jump, 1992) (vert)	30	35
4162	$35 Armin Hary (100 metres, 1960) (vert)	35	40
4163	$50 Heide Rosendahl (long jump, 1972) (vert)	50	55
4164	$60 Josef Neckermann (dressage, 1968) (vert)	60	65
4165	$130 Heike Drechsler (long jump, 1988) (vert)	1·25	1·40
4166	$190 Ulrike Mayfarth (high jump, 1984) (vert)	1·90	2·00
4167	$250 Michael Gross (200 metres freestyle and 100 metres butterfly, 1984) (vert)	2·50	2·75
4159/67	Set of 9	7·75	8·50

MS4168 Three sheets. (a) 105×75 mm. $135 Markus Wasmeier (skiing, 1994) (vert); $190 Katja Seizinger (skiing, 1994) (vert). (b) 105×75 mm. $325 Franziska van Almsick (swimming, 1992) (vert). (c) 75×105 mm. $325 Steffi Graf (tennis, 1988, 1992) (vert) . . Set of 3 sheets 6·50 7·00
See also Nos. 4492/508.

516 Dog Laika and Rocket, 1957

(Des J.-L. Puviland. Litho Questa)

1994 (10 Nov). 25th Anniv of First Moon Landing (2nd issue). T 516 and similar vert designs. Multicoloured. P 13½×14.

4169	$60 Type 516	60	65
	a. Sheetlet. Nos. 4169/77	5·50	
4170	$60 Yuri Gagarin (first man in space), 1961	60	65
4171	$60 John Glenn (first American to orbit Earth), 1962	60	65
4172	$60 Edward White walking in space, 1965	60	65
4173	$60 Neil Armstrong, walking on Moon and "Apollo 11" logo	60	65
4174	$60 "Luna 16" leaving Moon, 1970	60	65
4175	$60 Lunar Module 1 on Moon, 1970	60	65
4176	$60 Skylab 1, 1973	60	65
4177	$60 Astronauts and Apollo–Soyuz link-up, 1975	60	65
4178	$60 "Mars 3"	60	65
	a. Sheetlet. Nos. 4178/86	5·50	
4179	$60 "Mariner 10"	60	65
4180	$60 "Voyager"	60	65
4181	$60 "Pioneer"	60	65
4182	$60 "Giotto"	60	65
4183	$60 "Magellan"	60	65
4184	$60 "Galileo"	60	65
4185	$60 "Ulysses"	60	65
4186	$60 "Cassini"	60	65
4169/86	Set of 18	11·00	12·00

MS4187 Two sheets, each 142×104 mm. (a) $325 "Apollo 11" astronauts. (b) $325 "Galileo" . . Set of 2 sheets 6·50 6·75
Nos. 4169/77 and 4178/86 were each printed together, se-tenant, in sheetlets of 9, with the backgrounds of Nos. 4178/86 forming a composite design of Space.

517 West Point Foundry Locomotive, 1830

(Des R. Sauber. Litho Questa)

1994 (15 Nov). History of Trains. Steam Locomotives. T 517 and similar horiz designs. Multicoloured. P 14.

4188	$25 Type 517	25	30
4189	$25 South Eastern Railway "285", 1882	25	30
4190	$30 John Bull, 1831	30	35
	a. Sheetlet. Nos. 4190/7	2·40	
4191	$30 Stephenson locomotive, 1837	30	35
4192	$30 Atlantic, 1832	30	35
4193	$30 Stourbridge Lion, 1829	30	35
4194	$30 Polonceau locomotive, 1854	30	35
4195	$30 Rogers locomotive, 1856	30	35
4196	$30 Vulcan, 1858	30	35
4197	$30 Namur, 1846	30	35
4198	$30 West Point Foundry locomotive, 1832	30	35
	a. Sheetlet. Nos. 4198/205	2·40	
4199	$30 Sequin locomotive, 1830	30	35
4200	$30 Stephenson's Planet, 1830	30	35
4201	$30 Norris locomotive, 1840	30	35
4202	$30 Union Iron Works of San Francisco Sampson, 1867	30	35
4203	$30 Andrew Jackson, 1832	30	35
4204	$30 Herald, 1831	30	35
4205	$30 Cumberland, 1845	30	35
4206	$30 Pennsylvania Class K, 1880	30	35
	a. Sheetlet. Nos. 4206/13	2·40	
4207	$30 Cooke locomotive, 1885	30	35
4208	$30 John B. Turner, 1867	30	35
4209	$30 Baldwin locomotive, 1871	30	35
4210	$30 Richard Trevithick's locomotive, 1804	30	35
4211	$30 John Stephens' locomotive, 1825	30	35
4212	$30 John Blenkinsop's locomotive, 1814	30	35
4213	$30 Pennsylvania, 1803	30	35
4214	$300 Mount Washington Cog Railway locomotive, 1886	30	35
4215	$300 Stroudley locomotive, 1872	30	35
4188/215	Set of 28	13·50	15·50

MS4216 Two sheets, 100×70 mm. (a) $250 Est Railway locomotive, 1878; (b) $300 Claud Hamilton, 1840 . . Set of 2 sheets 5·50 5·75
Nos. 4190/7, 4198/205 and 4206/13 were each printed together, se-tenant, in sheetlets of 8, with the stamps arranged in two horizontal strips of 4 separated by a large illustrated gutter.
No. 4202 is inscr "Union Iron Works os San Francisco" in error.

(Litho Questa)

1994 (1 Dec). Christmas. Religious Paintings. Vert designs as T 336 of Antigua. Multicoloured. P 13½×14.

4217	$6 "Joseph with the Christ Child" (Guido Reni)	10	10
4218	$20 "Adoration of the Christ Child" (Girolamo Romanino)	20	25
4219	$25 "Adoration of the Christ Child with St. Barbara and St. Martin" (Raffaello Botticini)	25	30
4220	$30 "Holy Family" (Pompeo Batoni)	30	35
4221	$35 "Flight into Egypt" (Bartolommeo Carducci)	35	40
4222	$60 "Holy Family and the Baptist" (Andrea del Sarto)	60	65
4223	$120 "Sacred Conversation" (Cesare de Sesto)	1·25	1·40
4224	$190 "Madonna and Child with Saints Joseph and John the Baptist" (Pontormo)	1·90	2·00
4217/24	Set of 8	5·00	5·50

MS4225 (a) 112×93 mm. $325 "Presentation of Christ in the Temple" (Fra Bartolommeo). (b) 85×95 mm. $325 "Holy Family and St. Elizabeth and St. John the Baptist" (Francisco Primaticcio) Set of 2 sheets 6·50 6·75

518 Riker and Dr. Crusher

519 Cross and Map of Guyana

(Des J. Gordon. Litho Questa)

1994 (7 Dec). Star Trek Generations (film). T 518 and similar multicoloured designs showing Enterprise crew in 19th-century naval uniforms (Nos. 4226/34) or in 23rd-century (Nos. 4235/43). P 13½×14.

4226	$100 Type 518	1·00	1·10
	a. Sheetlet. Nos. 4226/34	9·00	
4227	$100 Geordi, Dr. Crusher with Lt. Worf in chains	1·00	1·10
4228	$100 Captain Picard	1·00	1·10
4229	$100 Data and Geordi	1·00	1·10
4230	$100 "U.S.S. Enterprise" (sailing ship)	1·00	1·10
4231	$100 Captain Picard and Riker on quarterdeck	1·00	1·10
4232	$100 Data	1·00	1·10
4233	$100 Lt. Worf	1·00	1·10
4234	$100 Dr. Crusher	1·00	1·10
4235	$100 Captain Picard	1·00	1·10
	a. Sheetlet. Nos. 4235/43	9·00	
4236	$100 Riker	1·00	1·10
4237	$100 Captain Kirk	1·00	1·10
4238	$100 Soron with phaser	1·00	1·10
4239	$100 Captains Kirk and Picard on horseback	1·00	1·10
4240	$100 Klingon women	1·00	1·10
4241	$100 Captains Kirk and Picard	1·00	1·10
4242	$100 Troi	1·00	1·10
4243	$100 Captain Picard and Data	1·00	1·10
4244	$100 "BOLDLY GO" film poster	1·00	1·10
4226/44	Set of 18	18·00	20·00

MS4245 86×103 mm. $500 U.S.S. Enterprise from film poster (horiz). P 14×13½ 5·00 5·25
Nos. 4226/34 and 4235/43 were each printed together, se-tenant, in sheetlets of 9. No. 4244 was printed in sheets of 9 of the one design.
Two $1000 values with designs as Nos. 4235 with 4237 and 4239 embossed on gold foil also exist from limited printings.

(Litho Questa)

1994 (12 Dec). Centenary of Sisters of Mercy in Guyana. P 14.
4246 519 $60 multicoloured . . 60 65

(Litho Questa)

1994 (12 Dec). First Recipients of Order of the Caribbean Community. Horiz designs as Nos. 2046/8 of Antigua. Multicoloured. P 14.

4247	$60 Sir Shridath Ramphal	60	65
4248	$60 William Demas	60	65
4249	$60 Derek Walcott	60	65
4247/9	Set of 3	1·75	2·00

520 Garfield Sobers congratulating Brian Lara

521 Babe Ruth

(Litho Questa)

1995 (3 Feb). Brian Lara's Achievements in Cricket. T 520 and similar multicoloured designs. P 14.

4250	$20 Type 520	20	25
4251	$30 Brian Lara setting world record for highest Test Match score (vert)	30	35
4252	$375 Lara and Chanderpaul	3·75	4·00

MS4253 70×100 mm. $300 Brian Lara (vert) 3·00 3·25

(Des J. Gordon. Litho Questa)

1995 (6 Feb). Birth Centenary of Babe Ruth (baseball player). T 521 and similar designs, all reddish brown and black. P 13½×14.

4254	$65 Type 521	65	70
	a. Sheetlet. Nos. 4254/65	7·75	
4255	$65 Preparing to bat (full-length photo)	65	70
4256	$65 Head and shoulders portrait (cap with limp brim)	65	70
4257	$65 In retirement (bare-headed)	65	70
4258	$65 Running (in plain shirt)	65	70
4259	$65 Head and shoulders portrait (cap with emblem and stiff brim)	65	70
4260	$65 Wearing "NEW YORK" shirt	65	70
4261	$65 Preparing to hit (in "NEW YORK" shirt)	65	70
4262	$65 Wearing "YANKEES" shirt	65	70
4263	$65 At base with bat on shoulder (in striped shirt)	65	70
4264	$65 Watching the ball (in striped shirt)	65	70
4265	$65 In cap and coat at Old Timer's Day, Yankee Stadium, 1948	65	70
4254/65	Set of 12	7·75	8·50

MS4266 89×118 mm. $500 Babe Ruth (horiz). P 14×13½ 5·00 5·25
Nos. 4254/65 were printed together, se-tenant, in sheetlets of 12.
A $1000 value, showing a similar portrait, embossed on gold foil exists from a limited printing.

522 Mickey Mouse as Family Doctor

(Des Alvin White Studio. Litho Questa)

1995 (24 Feb). *Disney Characters at Work.* T **522** *and similar multicoloured designs.* P 14×13½ (*horiz*) or 13½×14 (*vert*).

4267/75 $30 × 9 Type **522**; Goofy and optometrist; Daisy Duck as nurse; Scrooge McDuck as psychiatrist; Daisy Duck as physiotherapist; Horace Horsecollar and dentist; Goofy and radiologist; Goofy as pharmacist; Big Pete as chiropractor
 a. Sheetlet. Nos. 4267/75   2·75

4276/84 $30 × 9 Mickey Mouse as vet; Donald Duck training seals; Ludwig von Duck as animal psychiatrist; Goofy as ornithologist; Daisy Duck grooming Old English Sheepdog; Minnie Mouse as herpetologist; Mickey Mouse as pet shop keeper with Pluto; J. Audubon Woodlore as park ranger; Donald Duck as aquarist
 a. Sheetlet. Nos. 4276/84   2·75

4285/93 $30 × 9 Mickey Mouse as animator with Pluto; Goofy the tailor with Mickey Mouse; Pete the glassblower with Morty; Minnie Mouse painting Clarabelle; Daisy Duck sculpting Donald; Donald Duck as potter; Chip and Dale the watchmakers; Donald Duck the locksmith; Grandma Duck making quilt;
 a. Sheetlet. Nos. 4285/93   2·75

4294/301 $35 × 8 Mickey Mouse as policeman; Donald Duck as fireman; Uncle Scrooge as ambulance driver; Grandma Duck as crossing patrol; Daisy Duck as museum attendant and Donald as visitor; Goofy as census taker and family of rabbits; Horace Horsecollar and Big Pete as street maintenance workers; Donald Duck as sanitation worker at recyling bin (*all vert*)
 a. Sheetlet. Nos. 4294/301   2·75

4302/9 $35 × 8 Mickey Mouse with Pluto driving lorry; Mickey Mouse as carpenter sawing; Goofy riding road drill; Minnie Mouse with electric drill; Donald Duck driving forklift; Minnie Mouse and Goofy as construction contractors; Mickey Mouse with Pluto as carpenter making table; Pluto driving bulldozer (*all vert*)
 a. Sheetlet. Nos. 4302/9   2·75

4310/17 $35 × 8 Mickey Mouse as plumber; Mickey Mouse the paperboy; Huey, Dewey and Louie moving furniture; Big Pete as handyman; Donald Duck and nephews house painting; Goofy as washing machine repairman; Minnie Mouse as babysitter; Daisy Duck as carer (*all vert*)
 a. Sheetlet. Nos. 4310/17   2·75
4267/317   *Set of 51* 16·50 17·00
MS4318 Six sheets. (a) 132×107 mm. $200 Goofy as surgeon. (b) 107×129 mm. $200 Goofy the zookeeper. (c) 132×107 mm. $200 Ferdie riding Pluto for photographer (*vert*). (d) 107×129 mm. $200 Horace Horsecollar campaigning for mayor. (e) 132×107 mm. $200 Minnie Mouse as carpenter and puppies. (f) 107×129 mm. $200 Minnie Mouse as maid   *Set of 6 sheets* 12·00 12·50
Nos. 4267/75, 4276/84, 4285/93, 4294/301, 4302/9 and 4310/17 were printed together, *se-tenant*, in sheetlets of 9 (Nos. 4267/75, 4276/84 and 4285/93) or 8 (others).
No. 4271 is inscribed "PHYSICAL THEREPIST" in error.

(523)   524 Pig

1995 (24 Apr). *Centenary of Salvation Army. Nos. 1519 and 1521/3 surch as T* **523** *in red.*
4319 $6 on 60 c. Plate No. 10 (Series 1) ..
4320 $20 on 60 c. Plate No. 19 (Series 1) ..
4321 $30 on 60 c. Plate No. 2 (Series 1) ..
4322 $35 on 60 c. Plate No. 31 (Series 1) ..

1995 (4 May). *Chinese New Year ("Year of the Pig").* T **524** *and similar vert designs showing symbolic pigs. Multicoloured.* P 14½.
4323 $20 Type **524**   20   25
 a. Block of 4. Nos. 4323/6   2·00
4324 $30 Pig facing left   30   35
4325 $50 Pig facing front (face value bottom right)   50   55
4326 $100 Pig facing front (face value bottom left)   1·00   1·10
4323/6   *Set of 4* 2·00 2·25
MS4327 67×89 mm. $50×4 As Nos. 4323/6   2·00 2·10
MS4328 104×76 mm. $150 Pig's head   1·50 1·60
Nos. 4323/6 were printed together, *se-tenant*, in blocks of 4 throughout the sheet.

525 Goshawk   526 Norwegian Forest Cat

(Litho Questa)

1995 (8 May). *Birds.* T **525** *and similar vert designs. Multicoloured.* P 14½×14.
4329 $5 Type **525**   10   10
4330 $6 Lapwing   10   10
4331 $8 Ornate Umbrellabird   10   10
4332 $15 Slaty-headed Parakeet   10   10
4333 $19 Regent Bowerbird   20   25
4334 $20 Egyptian Goose   20   25
4335 $25 White-winged Crossbill   25   30
4336 $30 Waxwing   30   35
4337 $35 Ruff   35   40
4338 $60 Hoopoe   60   65
4339 $100 Superb Starling   1·00   1·10
4340 $500 Great Jacamar   5·00   5·25
4329/40   *Set of 12* 8·25 9·00

(Des T. Wood. Litho Questa)

1995 (11 June). *"Singapore '95" International Stamp Exhibition.* T **526** *and similar vert designs. Multicoloured.* P 14.
4341/52 $35 × 12 Cats (Type **526**; Scottish Fold; Red Burmese; British Blue-hair; Abyssinian; Siamese; Exotic Shorthair; Turkish Van Cat; Black Persian; Black-tipped Burmilla; Singapura; Calico Shorthair)
 a. Sheetlet. Nos. 4341/52   4·25
4353/64 $35 × 12 Dogs (Gordon Setter; Long-haired Chihuahua; Dalmatian; Afghan Hound; Old English Bulldog; Miniature Schnauzer; Clumber Spaniel; Pekingese; St. Bernard; English Cocker Spaniel; Alaskan Malamute; Rottweiler)
 a. Sheetlet. Nos. 4353/64   4·25
4365/76 $35 × 12 Horses (chestnut Thoroughbred colt; liver chestnut Quarter horse; black Friesian; chestnut Belgian; Appaloosa; Lippizaner; chestnut hunter; British Shire; Palomino; Pinto ("Seal Brown Point"); Arab; Afghanistan Kabardin)
 a. Sheetlet. Nos. 4365/76   4·25
4341/76   *Set of 36* 13·00 15·00
MS4377 Three sheets, each 87×71 mm. (a) $300 Maine Coon. (b) $300 Golden Retriever. (c) $300 American Anglo-Arab   *Set of 3 sheets* 9·00 9·25
Nos. 4341/52, 4353/64 and 4365/76 were printed together, *se-tenant*, in sheetlets of 12.
No. 4355 is inscribed "Dalmation", No. 4367 "Freisian" and No. 4370 "Lipizzanas", all in error.

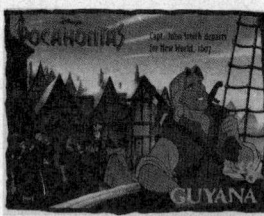

527 Captain John Smith leaving for New World, 1607

(Des Walt Disney Co. Litho Questa)

1995 (28 June–9 Oct). *Pocahontas.* T **527** *and similar multicoloured designs showing characters and scenes from Disney cartoon film.*

(a) *Vert designs showing characters.* P 13½×14
4378/85 $50 × 8 Pocahontas and Meeko; John Smith; Chief Powhatan; Kocoum; Ratcliffe; Wiggins; Nakoma; Thomas
 a. Sheetlet. Nos. 4378/85   4·00

(b) *Horiz designs showing film scenes.* P 14×13½ (9 Oct)
4386/94 $8 × 9 Type **527**; Ratcliffe; Chief Powhatan greeted by his people; Pocahontas standing on cliff; Pocahontas, Nakoma and Meeko in canoe; Powhatan asking Pocahontas to marry Kocoum; Pocahontas receiving her mother's necklace; Pocahontas seeking guidance from Grandmother Willow; Pocahontas watching arrival of *Susan Constant*
 a. Sheetlet. Nos. 4386/94   90

4395/403 $30 × 9 Ratcliffe claiming land for English Crown; Kekata having vision; Meeting of John Smith and Pocahontas; Namantack watching settlers; Powhatan and wounded Namantack; Pocahontas showing John Smith the colours of the wind; Nakoma finds Pocahontas with John Smith; Pocahontas offering John "Indian gold" (corn); Pocahontas, John Smith and Grandmother Willow
 a. Sheetlet. Nos. 4395/403   2·75
4404/12 $35 × 9 Kocoum telling Pocahontas about the war council; Nakoma telling Kocoum to find Pocahontas; John Smith and Kocoum wrestling over knife; Powhatan sentencing John to death; Pocahontas and Grandmother Willow; Pocahontas saving John Smith; Ratcliffe under arrest; Powhatan draping his cloak over wounded John Smith; Pocahontas and John Smith saying goodbye
 a. Sheetlet. Nos. 4404/12   3·25
4378/412   *Set of 35* 17·00 18·00
MS4413 Four sheets. (a) 98×120 mm. $300 Meeko (9 Oct). P 14×13½. (b) 132×107 mm. $325 Pocahontas hiding. P 14×13½. (c) 132×107 mm. $325 Powhatan and Pocahontas. P 14×13½. (d) 132×107 mm. $325 Pocahontas kneeling (*vert*). P 13½×14   *Set of 4 sheets* 13·00 13·50
Nos. 4378/85, 4386/94, 4395/403 and 4404/12 were printed together, *se-tenant*, in sheetlets of 8 (Nos. 4378/85) or 9 (others).

(Litho Questa)

1995 (6 July). *95th Birthday of Queen Elizabeth the Queen Mother. Vert designs as T* **344** *of Antigua.* P 13½×14.
4414 $100 orange-brown, pale brown and black   1·00   1·10
 a. Sheetlet. Nos. 4414/17×2   ..   8·00
4415 $100 multicoloured   1·00   1·10
4416 $100 multicoloured   1·00   1·10
4417 $100 multicoloured   1·00   1·10
4414/17   *Set of 4* 4·00 4·50
MS4418 121×126 mm. $325 multicoloured   3·25 3·50
Designs:—No. 4414, Queen Elizabeth the Queen Mother (pastel drawing); No. 4415, Wearing purple hat; No. 4416, Wearing turquoise hat; No. 4417, At desk (oil painting); No. **MS**4418, Wearing blue dress and mink stole
Nos. 4414/17 were printed together in sheetlets of 8, containing two *se-tenant* horizontal strips of 4.

528 Paul Harris (founder) and Rotary Emblem   529 Girl carrying Sack on Head

(Litho Questa)

1995 (6 July). *90th Anniv of Rotary International.* T **528** *and similar horiz design. Multicoloured.* P 14.
4419 $200 Type **528**   2·00   2·10
MS4420 104×74 mm. $300 Rotary emblems   3·00 3·25

(Des R. Martin. Litho)

1995 (6 July). *50th Anniv of Food and Agriculture Organization.* T **529** *and similar vert designs. Multicoloured.* P 14.
4421 $35 Type **529**   35   40
 a. Horiz strip of 3. Nos. 4421/3   3·00
4422 $60 Man and woman carrying sacks of food aid   60   65
4423 $200 Woman holding sack   2·00   2·10
4421/3   *Set of 3* 3·00 3·25
MS4424 104×74 mm. $300 Bowl of food and F.A.O. emblem   3·00 3·25
Nos. 4421/3 were printed together in sheets of 9 (3×3) containing three *se-tenant* horizontal strips, each forming a composite design.

530 Scouts around Campfire

(Litho Questa)

1995 (6 July). *18th World Scout Jamboree, Netherlands.* T **530** *and similar horiz designs. Multicoloured.* P 14.
4425 $20 Type **530**   20   25
4426 $25 Scout on beach   25   30
4427 $30 Scouts hiking   30   35
4428 $35 Scout snorkelling   35   40
4429 $60 Scout saluting and flag of Guyana   60   65
4430 $200 Scout fishing from boat   2·00   2·10
4425/30   *Set of 6* 3·75 4·00
MS4431 Two sheets, each 100×70 mm. (a) $300 Scouts putting up tent. (b) $300 Scouts canoeing   *Set of 2 sheets* 6·00 6·25

(Des W. Wright. Litho Questa)

1995 (6 July). *50th Anniv of End of World War II in Europe. Horiz designs as* T **340** *of Antigua. Multicoloured.* P 14.

4432	$60 American tank during Battle of the Bulge		60	65
	a. Sheetlet. Nos. 4432/9		4·75	
4433	$60 Allied tanks crossing Siegfried Line		60	65
4434	$60 Liberated concentration camp prisoners		60	65
4435	$60 Allied plane dropping food to Dutch		60	65
4436	$60 U.S. infantry patrol, North Italy		60	65
4437	$60 *Daily Mail* headline announcing Hitler's death		60	65
4438	$60 Soviet tanks entering Berlin		60	65
4439	$60 Surrender of *U858* in U.S. waters		60	65
4432/9		*Set of* 8	4·75	5·25
MS4440	105×74 mm. $300 Soviet troops raising flag on Brandenburg Gate (56×42 *mm*)		3·00	3·25

Nos. 4432/9 were printed together, *se-tenant*, in sheetlets of 8 with the stamps arranged in two horizontal strips of 4 separated by a gutter showing sounding of ceasefire on the Western Front. No. 4433 was incorrectly inscribed "SIGFRIED LINE".

(Des J. Batchelor. Litho Questa)

1995 (6 July). *50th Anniv of End of Second World War in the Pacific. U.S. Ships and Aircraft. Horiz designs as* T **340** *of Antigua. Multicoloured.* P 14.

4441	$60 P61 Black Widow		60	65
	a. Sheetlet. Nos. 4441/6		3·50	
4442	$60 PT boat		60	65
4443	$60 Martin B-26 Marauder bomber		60	65
4444	$60 U.S.S. *San Juan* (cruiser)		60	65
4445	$60 Gato class submarine		60	65
4446	$60 Destroyer		60	65
4441/6		*Set of* 6	3·50	4·00
MS4447	107×77 mm. $300 Cruiser and aircraft carrier		3·00	3·25

Nos. 4441/6 were printed together, *se-tenant*, in sheetlets of 6 with the stamps arranged in two horizontal strips of 3 separated by a gutter showing Curtiss P-40B Tomahawk II Flying Tiger aircraft.

531 Thanksgiving (U.S.A.)

532 Map of the Americas and U.N. Soldier

(Des R. Sauber. Litho Questa)

1995 (8 Aug). *Holidays of the World.* T **531** *and similar horiz designs. Multicoloured.* P 14.

4448	$60 Type **531**		60	65
	a. Sheetlet. Nos. 4448/55		4·75	
4449	$60 Christmas (Germany)		60	65
4450	$60 Hanukkah (Israel)		60	65
4451	$60 Easter (Spain)		60	65
4452	$60 Carnivale (Brazil)		60	65
4453	$60 Bastille Day (France)		60	65
4454	$60 Independence Day (India)		60	65
4455	$60 St. Patrick's Day (Ireland)		60	65
4448/55		*Set of* 8	4·75	5·25
MS4456	105×76 mm. $300 Chinese New Year (China)		3·00	3·25

Nos. 4448/55 were printed together, *se-tenant*, in sheetlets of 8, with the designs extending onto the sheetlet margin.

(Des R. Martin. Litho)

1995 (1 Sept). *50th Anniv of United Nations.* T **532** *and similar vert designs. Multicoloured.* P 14.

4457	$35 Type **532**		35	40
	a. Horiz strip of 3. Nos. 4457/9		3·00	
4458	$60 Map of Africa and Western Asia		60	65
4459	$200 Map of Eastern Asia and Australasia with refugees		2·00	2·10
4457/9		*Set of* 3	3·00	3·25
MS4460	74×104 mm. $300 Secretary-General Boutros Boutros Ghali		3·00	3·25

Nos. 4457/9 were printed together in sheets of 9 (3×3) containing three *se-tenant* horizontal strips, each forming a composite design.

533 Four-eyed Butterflyfish

534 Pole Vaulting

(Des D. Burkhart. Litho Questa)

1995 (5 Sept). *Marine Life.* T **533** *and similar multicoloured designs.* P 14.

4461	$30 Type **533**		30	35
	a. Sheetlet. Nos. 4461, 4463, 4465 and 4489		3·25	
4462	$30 Lemon Shark		30	35
	a. Sheetlet. Nos. 4462, 4464, 4466 and 4490		3·25	
4463	$35 Blue-headed Wrasse		35	40
4464	$35 Green Turtle		35	40
4465	$60 Three-spotted Damselfish		60	65
4466	$60 Sawfish		60	65
4467	$60 Sei Whales		60	65
	a. Sheetlet. Nos. 4467/75		5·50	
4468	$60 Great Barracuda		60	65
4469	$60 Mutton Snapper		60	65
4470	$60 Hawksbill Turtle		60	65
4471	$60 Spanish Hogfish		60	65
4472	$60 Queen Angelfish		60	65
4473	$60 Porkfish		60	65
4474	$60 Trumpetfish		60	65
4475	$60 Lesser Electric Ray		60	65
4476	$60 Tiger Shark		60	65
	a. Sheetlet. Nos. 4476/84		5·50	
4477	$60 Needlefish		60	65
4478	$60 Horse-eyed Jack		60	65
4479	$60 Princess Parrotfish		60	65
4480	$60 Yellow-tailed Snapper		60	65
4481	$60 Spotted Snake Eel		60	65
4482	$60 Buffalo Trunkfish		60	65
4483	$60 Cherubfish Angelfish		60	65
4484	$60 French Angelfish		60	65
4485	$80 Cocoa Damselfish (*vert*)		80	85
	a. Horiz strip of 4. Nos. 4485/8		3·25	
4486	$80 Sergeant Major (*vert*)		80	85
4487	$80 Beaugregory (*vert*)		80	85
4488	$80 Yellow-tailed Damselfish (*vert*)		80	85
4489	$200 Fin-spot Wrasse		2·00	2·10
4490	$200 Stingray		2·00	2·10
4461/90		*Set of* 30	21·00	22·00
MS4491	Two sheets, each 100×70 mm. (a) $300 Great White Shark. (b) $300 Leatherback Turtle			
		Set of 2 *sheets*	6·00	6·25

Nos. 4461, 4463, 4465 and 4489, Nos. 4462, 4464, 4466 and 4490, Nos. 4467/75 and Nos. 4476/84 were each printed together, *se-tenant*, in sheetlets of 4 or 9, the backgrounds forming composite designs.
Nos. 4485/8 were printed together, *se-tenant*, in horizontal strips of 4, each strip forming a composite background design.

(Litho B.D.T.)

1995 (9 Oct). *Olympic Games, Atlanta* (1996) (*2nd issue*). T **534** *and similar vert designs. Multicoloured.* P 14.

4492	$60 Type **534**		60	65
	a. Sheetlet. Nos. 4492/9		4·75	
4493	$60 Long jumping		60	65
4494	$60 Woman with relay baton		60	65
4495	$60 Wrestling		60	65
4496	$60 Discus (side view)		60	65
4497	$60 Basketball		60	65
4498	$60 Boxing		60	65
4499	$60 Weightlifting		60	65
4500	$60 Shot put		60	65
	a. Sheetlet. Nos. 4500/7		4·75	
4501	$60 Man in relay race		60	65
4502	$60 Female gymnast on beam		60	65
4503	$60 Cycling		60	65
4504	$60 Synchronized swimming		60	65
4505	$60 Hurdling		60	65
4506	$60 Male gymnast on pommel horse		60	65
4507	$60 Discus (front view)		60	65
4492/507		*Set of* 18	9·50	10·50
MS4508	Two sheets (a) 105×75 mm. $300 Athletes at start of race. (b) 75×105 mm. $300 Long jumping			
		Set of 2 *sheets*	6·00	6·25

Nos. 4492/9 and 4500/7 were each printed together, *se-tenant*, in sheetlets of 8, the backgrounds forming composite designs.

535 Sand Martin

536 Queenstown Jama Masjid

(Des Mary Walters. Litho Questa)

1995 (18 Oct). *Wildlife.* T **535** *and similar vert designs. Multicoloured.* P 14.

4509	$20 Type **535**		20	25
	a. Block of 4. Nos. 4509/11 and 4521		3·25	
4510	$35 House Martin		35	40
4511	$60 Hobby		60	65
4512	$60 Olive Colobus		60	65
	a. Sheetlet. Nos. 4512/20		5·50	
4513	$60 Violet-backed Starling		60	65
4514	$60 Diana Monkey		60	65
4515	$60 African Palm Civet		60	65
4516	$60 Giraffe and zebras		60	65
4517	$60 African Linsang		60	65
4518	$60 Royal Antelope		60	65
4519	$60 Duikers		60	65
4520	$60 Palm Squirrel		60	65
4521	$200 Long-tailed Skua		2·00	2·10
4509/21		*Set of* 13	8·75	9·25
MS4522	Two sheets, each 110×80 mm. (a) $300 Brush Pig and Giant Forest Hog. (b) $300 Chimpanzee			
		Set of 2 *sheets*	6·00	6·25

Nos. 4509/11 and 4521 were printed together, *se-tenant*, in blocks of 4, each block forming a composite background design.
Nos. 4512/20 were printed together, *se-tenant*, in sheetlets of 9, forming a composite background design.

(Des R. Sauber. Litho Questa)

1995 (1 Dec). *Centenary of Queenstown Jama Masjid* (*mosque*), *Georgetown.* P 14.

4523 **536**	$60 multicoloured	60	65

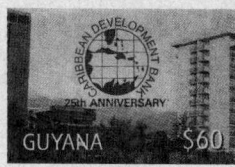

537 Woman Soldier with Sub-machine Gun

538 Bank Logo and Headquarters

(Des Rina Lamphe. Litho Questa)

1995 (1 Dec). *30th Anniv of Guyana Defence Force.* T **537** *and similar vert design. Multicoloured.* P 14.

4524	$6 Type **537**		10	10
4525	$60 Soldier with rifle		60	65

(Des M. Friedman. Litho Questa)

1995 (1 Dec). *25th Anniv of Caribbean Development Bank.* P 14.

4526 **538**	$60 multicoloured	60	65

(Litho Questa)

1995 (4 Dec). *Christmas. Religious Paintings. Vert designs as* T **357** *of Antigua. Multicoloured.* P 13½×14.

4527	$25 "Angel of the Annunciation" (Carracci)		25	30
4528	$30 "Virgin of the Annunciation" (Carracci)		30	35
4529	$35 "Assumption of the Madonna" (Carracci)		35	40
4530	$60 "Baptism of Christ" (Carracci)		60	65
4531	$100 "Madonna and Child with Saints" (detail) (Carracci)		1·00	1·10
4532	$300 "Birth of the Virgin" (Carracci)		3·00	3·25
4527/32		*Set of* 6	5·50	6·00
MS4533	Two sheets, each 101×127 mm. (a) $325 "Madonna and Child enthroned with Ten Saints" (Rosso Fiorentino). (b) $325 "Mystic Marriage of St. Catherine" (Carracci)	*Set of* 2 *sheets*	6·50	6·75

STAMP BOOKLETS

1909 (14 June). *Black on pink cover without face value. Stapled.*
SB1 49 c. booklet containing twelve 1 c. and eighteen
2 c. (Nos. 252/3) in blocks of 6 .. ..

1923. *Black on pink cover without face value. Stapled.*
SB2 30 c. booklet containing six 1 c. and twelve 2 c.
(Nos. 272, 274) in blocks of 6 .. ..

1923. *Black on pink without face value. Stapled.*
SB3 48 c. booklet containing twelve 1 c. and eighteen
2 c. (Nos. 272, 274) in blocks of 6 .. .. £950
a. With face value on front cover .. ..

1923. *Black on red cover without face value. Stapled.*
SB4 72 c. booklet containing twelve 1 c., six 2 c. and
twelve 4 c. (Nos. 272, 274/5) in blocks of 6 .. £1300

1934. *Black on orange cover. Stitched.*
SB5 24 c. booklet containing eight 1 c. and eight 2 c.
(Nos. 288/9) in blocks of 4 ..

1934. *Black on orange cover. Stitched.*
SB6 36 c. booklet containing four 1 c., eight 2 c. and
four 4 c. (Nos. 288/9, 291) in blocks of 4 ..

1938. *Black on orange cover. Stitched.*
SB7 36 c. booklet containing four 1 c., eight 2 c. and
four 4 c. (Nos. 308/10) in blocks of 4 .. .. £180

1944. *Black on orange cover. Stitched.*
SB8 24 c. booklet containing eight 1 c. and eight 2 c.
(Nos. 308/9) in blocks of 4 .. .. .. £140

1945–49. *Black on red cover. Stitched.*
SB9 24 c. booklet containing 1 c., 2 c. and 3 c. (Nos. 290,
308, 309), each in block of 4 .. .. 65·00
a. Containing Nos. 290, 308aa, 309 .. .. 65·00
b. Containing Nos. 290, 308aa, 309a .. .. 65·00
c. Containing Nos. 290a, 308aa, 309 .. .. 65·00
d. Containing Nos. 290b, 308aa, 309 .. .. 65·00
e. Containing Nos. 290b, 308aa, 309a .. .. 65·00
f. Containing Nos. 290b, 308a, 309a .. .. 65·00

B 1

1981 (1 July). *Blue cover as Type B 1, printed in black. Stapled.*
SB10 $6 booklet containing two 15 c. (No. 808A or B),
three 50 c. on 5 c. (No. 794), two 100 c. on 1 c.
(No. 806) and two 110 c. on 1 c. (No. 807) .. 4·25

1981 (22 July). *Royal Wedding. Red, yellow and blue cover as Type B 2. Stitched.*
SB11 $5 booklet containing two 60 c. on 3 c., two 75 c.
on $5 and two $1.10 on $2 (Nos. 841/3) in pairs
and pane of four air mail labels .. .. 3·25

1981 (1 Aug). *Green cover as Type B 1, printed in black. Stapled.*
SB12 $3 booklet containing ten 15 c. on 10 c. on 6 c. and
ten 15 c. on 30 c. on 6 c. (Nos. 848/9) .. 4·25
SB13 $3 booklet containing ten 15 c. on 50 c. on 6 c. and
ten 15 c. on 60 c. on 6 c. (Nos. 850/1) .. 4·75

1981 (10 Nov). *Cover as Nos. SB12/13 surcharged "$5". Stapled.*
SB14 $5 on $3 booklet containing six 50 c. on 6 c. (No.
862A or B) and two $1 on 6 c. (No. 863A or B) 4·00

1981 (10 Nov). *Blue cover as Type B 1, printed in black. Stapled.*
SB15 $6 booklet containing four 50 c. on 6 c. (No. 862A
or B) and four $1 on 6 c. (No. 863A or B) .. 4·00

1982 (Apr). *Cover as Nos. SB12/13 surcharged "$5". Stapled.*
SB16 $5 on $3 booklet containing ten 20 c. on 35 c. (No.
918), two 50 c. on 6 c. (No. 862A or B) and two
$1 on 6 c. (No. 863A or B) .. .. 11·00

1982 (15 June). *75th Anniv of Boy Scout Movement. Cover as No. SB16 further overprinted "SCOUT MOVEMENT 1907–1982". Stapled.*
SB17 $5 on $3 booklet containing two 125 c. on 8 c. on
6 c. and two 125 c. on 8 c. on 6 c. (Nos. 905/6) 5·00

1982 (15 June). *75th Anniv of Boy Scout Movement. Cover as No. SB15 overprinted "SCOUT MOVEMENT 1907–1982" in red. Stapled.*
SB18 $6 booklet containing two 25 c. and five 110 c. on
6 c. (Nos. 892, 978) .. .. 20·00

1982 (15 July). *75th Anniv of Boy Scout Movement. Cover as No. SB16 further overprinted "SCOUT MOVEMENT 1907–1982". Stapled.*
SB19 $5 on $3 booklet containing two 15 c. on 2 c., two
15 c. on 2 c. and four 110 c. on 6 c. (Nos. 895/6,
978) .. .. 14·00
SB20 $5 on $3 booklet containing 15 c. on 2 c., 15 c. on
2 c., 110 c. on 5 c., 110 c. on 5 c., 125 c. on 8 c.
on 6 c. and 125 c. on 8 c. on 6 c. (Nos. 895/6,
900/1, 905/6) .. .. 4·00

1982 (15 July). *75th Anniv of Boy Scout Movement. Covers as No. SB15 overprinted "SCOUT MOVEMENT 1907–1982" in red. Stapled.*
SB21 $6 booklet containing four 15 c. on 2 c., four 15 c.
on 2 c., four 15 c. on 2 c., three 25 c., 110 c. on
5 c., 110 c. on 5 c. and 125 c. on 8 c. on 6 c. (Nos.
895/7, 892, 900/1, 905) .. .. 9·00
SB22 $6 booklet containing four 15 c. on 2 c., four 15 c.
on 2 c., four 15 c. on 2 c., three 25 c., 110 c. on
5 c., 110 c. on 5 c. and 125 c. on 8 c. on 6 c. (No.
895/6, 898, 892, 900/1, 906) .. .. 9·00

1983 (July). *Covers as Type B 1, printed in black on green ($3), surcharged as No. SB16 ($5) or on blue ($6). Stapled.*
SB23 $3 booklet containing ten 30 c. (No. 1127) .. 2·50
SB24 $5 on $3 booklet containing twenty 25 c. (No.
1108a) .. .. 3·75
SB25 $6 booklet containing ten 60 c. (No. 1128) .. 5·50
SB26 $6 booklet containing five 120 c. (No. 1129) .. 5·50
SB27 $6 booklet containing four 150 c. (No. 1131) .. 5·50

1983 (Oct). *Covers as Type B 1, printed in black on green ($3), surcharged as No. SB16 ($5) or on blue ($6). Stamps attached by selvedge.*
SB28 $3 booklet containing ten 30 c. (No. 1173) .. 1·90
SB29 $5 on $3 booklet containing twenty 25 c. (No.
1172) .. .. 3·00
SB30 $6 booklet containing ten 30 c. and five 60 c. (Nos.
1173/4) .. .. 2·75
SB31 $6 booklet containing ten 60 c. (No. 1174) .. 2·75
SB32 $6 booklet containing five 120 c. (No. 1175) .. 2·75

1984 (1 Mar). *Guyana Olympic Committee Appeal. Booklet No. SB11 with cover surcharged "HELP SEND OUR ATHLETES TO THE 1984 OLYMPICS BOOKLET $15.00" in blue.*
SB33 $15 on $5 booklet containing two 25 c.+2.25 c. on
60 c. on 3 c., two 25 c.+2.25 c. on 75 c. on $5
and two 25 c.+2.25 c. on $1.10 on $2 (Nos.
1235/7) and pane of four air mail labels .. 10·00

1984 (28 July). *Olympic Games, Los Angeles. Covers as Nos. SB10 and SB12 surcharged "OLYMPIC GAMES 1984" and "$5.00" on $3 black on green or "$12.00" on $6 black on blue.*
SB34 $5 on $3 booklet containing two panes of 10 (No.
1308a) .. .. 5·00
SB35 $12 on $6 booklet containing two panes of 10 (No.
1313a) .. .. 18·00

1985 (9 July). *Green cover as Type B 1, printed in black. Stapled.*
SB36 $3 booklet containing twelve 25 c. (No. 1534) in
pairs .. .. 2·00

1986 (26 May). *20th Anniv of Independence (1st issue). Green cover as Type B 1, printed in black. Stamps attached by selvedge.*
SB37 $3 booklet containing 25 c. on 120 c., 25 c. on
130 c., 25 c. on 150 c. and 225 c. on 200 c. (No.
1723a) .. .. 3·00

1986 (14 July). *International Peace Year. Blue cover as Type B 1, printed in black. Stamps attached by selvedge.*
SB38 $6 booklet containing twenty-four 25 c. on 1 c.
(No. 1739) and label as block of 25 .. .. 3·00

1986 (21 Aug). *Green cover as Type B 1, printed in black. Stapled.*
SB39 $3 booklet containing twelve 25 c. (No. 1807) in
pairs .. .. 3·50

1986 (23 Sept). *20th Anniv of Independence (2nd issue). Green cover as Type B 1, printed in black. Stapled.*
SB40 $3 booklet containing twelve 25 c. (No. 1820) in
pairs .. .. 3·50

Post Office
Corp.

1977 - 1987

B 3

1987 (17 Feb). *10th Anniv of Guyana Post Office Corporation. Covers as Type B 3, printed in black with face value handstamped in blue. Stapled.*
SB41 $5 booklet containing twenty 25 c. (Nos. 2074/7)
in strips of 5 .. .. .. 7·00
SB42 $20 booklet containing five 60 c., five $1.20 and
five $1.30 (Nos. 2078/80), each in strips of 5,
and two $2.25 (No. 1930) in pair .. 17·00

1987 (2 June). *Green cover as Type B 1, printed in black. Stamps attached by selvedge.*
SB43 $3 booklet containing twelve 25 c. (No. 2183A) in
pairs .. .. 2·25

1987 (29 Sept). *Green cover as Type B 1, printed in black. Stamps attached by selvedge.*
SB44 $3 booklet containing twelve 25 c. (No. 2183B) in
pairs .. .. 2·25

1987 (Dec). *Covers as Nos. SB10 and SB12 handstamped with new face value in blue. Stamps attached by selvedge.*
SB45 $15 on $3 booklet containing twelve $1.20 (No.
2194a) in blocks of 4 and one 60 c. (No. 2265) 8·00
SB46 $15 on $3 booklet containing twelve $1.20 (No.
2198a) in blocks of 4 and one 60 c. (No. 2265) 8·00
SB47 $24 on $6 booklet containing twenty $1.20 (No.
2194a) in blocks of 4 or 8 .. .. 9·00
SB48 $24 on $6 booklet containing twenty $1.20 (No.
2198a) in blocks of 4 or 8 .. .. 9·00
Blocks of Nos. 2194a and 2198a in booklet Nos. SB45/8 have
the perforations at top and bottom removed by guillotine.

1988 (3 Sept). *60th Anniv of Cricket in Guyana. Cream covers with black inscr. Stamps attached by selvedge.*
SB49 $20 booklet containing two 200 c. and two 800 c.
on 150 c. (Nos. 2472, 2474), each in pair .. 26·00
SB50 $20 booklet containing two 200 c. and two 800 c.
on 150 c. (Nos. 2473/4), each in pair .. 12·00

1988 (16 Sept). *Olympic Games, Seoul. Greenish yellow covers with black inscr. Stamps attached by selvedge.*
SB51 $20 booklet containing four 25 c. (No. 1534) in
pairs and se-tenant pane of 10 (No. 2486b) 15·00
SB52 $20 booklet containing four 25 c. (No. 1535a) in
pairs and se-tenant pane of 10 (No. 2486b) 15·00

EXPRESS LETTER STAMPS

$12.oo

EXPRESS
(E 1)

1986 (10 Nov). *Various stamps surch as Type* E 1 *by Tip Torres.*
E1	$12 on 350 c. on 120 c. mult (No. 1598)	..	5·50	5·50
E2	$15 on 40 c. multicoloured (as No. 1868, but inscr "ONTOGLOSSUM")	..	7·00	7·00
	a. Surch on No. 1868 (inscr "ODONTO-GLOSSUM")	..	7·00	7·00
E3	$20 on $6.40, multicoloured (No. **MS**1746)		5·50	5·50
E4	$25 on 25 c. multicoloured (as No. 1621, but value changed)	..	9·50	9·50
E1/4		*Set of 4*	25·00	25·00

The surcharges on Nos. E2/3 include a pattern of leaves over the original value. On No. E4 a dollar sign has been added in front of the original value and a small maltese cross overprinted above "EXPRESS" at bottom right.

1987 (3 Mar). *No.* E3 *additionally optd with small Maltese cross above surch.*
E5	$20 on $6.40, multicoloured	..	5·50	5·50
	a. With additional "2" optd at bottom left		5·50	5·50

(Litho Format)

1987 (1 Sept)–88. *Centenary of Publication of Sanders' Reichenbachia. Vert designs as* T **331** *additionally inscr* "EXPRESS". *Multicoloured. No wmk. P* 13½×14.
E6	$15 Plate No. 11 (Series 2) (29.9.87)		3·50	3·75
E7	$20 Plate No. 93 (Series 2) (17.5.88)		3·50	4·00
E8	$25 Plate No. 63 (Series 2) (26.10.87)		3·75	4·25
E9	$45 Plate No. 35 (Series 2)		7·00	8·00
E6/9		*Set of 4*	16·00	18·00

Nos. E6/9, in conjunction with postage issues, were printed in a similar sheet format to Nos. 1518/33.

EXPRESS

FORTY DOLLARS
(E 2) *(Illustration reduced. Actual size of surcharge 64 × 36 mm)*

1987 (Nov). *No.* 1744ab *surch with Type* E 2 *by Gardy Ptg.*
E10	$40 on $6.40, multicoloured	..	11·00	11·00

1987 (Dec). *No.* E 2 *additionally optd with* T **390** *by Gardy Ptg.*
E11	$15 on 40 c. multicoloured (inscr "ONTO-GLOSSUM")	..	8·00	5·00

SPECIAL DELIVERY

$40-00
(E 3)
(Illustration reduced. Actual size of surcharge 80×45 mm)

1988 (10 Aug). *Nos.* 2206 *and* 2211 *surch as Type* E 3 *in red by Gardy Ptg.*
E12	$40 on $3.20, deep dull blue	..	7·50	8·50
E13	$45 on $3.30, brownish black	..	8·00	9·50

Nos. E12/13 were only issued in vertical strips of five, being the remainders of the sheets utilised to produce Nos. 2455/62.

EXPRESS

FORTY DOLLARS
(E 4)

1989 (Mar). *Nos.* 1744ab *and* 2185ab *surch with Type* E 4 *in red.*
E14	$40 on $6.40, multicoloured (No. 1744ab)	4·00	4·50
E15	$40 on $6.40, multicoloured (No. 2185ab)	4·00	4·50

1989 (May). *Nos.* 2206 *and* 2211 *surch as Type* E 3.
E16	$190 on $3.30, brownish black	..	12·00	14·00
E17	$225 on $3.20, deep dull blue	..	13·00	15·00

Nos. E16/17 were surcharged on the remains of the sheets utilized for Nos. 2648/55.

EXPRESS
(E 5)   (E 6)

(Des Mary Walters. Litho Questa)

1989 (7 Sept). *Butterflies. Two sheets, each* 97×67 *mm, containing vert designs as* T **454** *optd with Type* E 5. *Multicoloured. P* 14.
EMS18	$130 *Phareas coeleste*	..	3·75	3·75
EMS19	$190 *Papilio torquatus* ..		4·75	4·75

(Des M. Dorfman. Litho Questa)

1989 (8 Nov). *Women in Space. Sheet,* 92×67 *mm, containing vert design as* T **455** *optd with Type* E 5. *Multicoloured. P* 14.
EMS20	$190 Valentina Tereshkova (first woman cosmonaut)		3·50	3·75

1989 (17 Nov). *"World Stamp Expo '89" International Stamp Exhibition, Washington. Nos.* EMS18/19 *optd with Type* E 6.
EMS21	$130 *Phareas coeleste*	..	3·00	3·00
EMS22	$190 *Papilio torquatus* ..		4·00	4·00

Nos. EMS21/22 show additional overprints on sheet margins.

1990 (15 Mar). *85th Anniv of Rotary International. Nos.* EMS18/20 *optd* "ROTARY INTERNATIONAL 1905–1990" *and emblem on sheet margins only.*
EMS23	$130 *Phareas coeleste*	..	3·00	3·00
EMS24	$190 *Papilio torquatus*	..	4·00	4·00
EMS25	$190 Valentina Tereshkova (first woman cosmonaut)	..	3·50	4·00
EMS23/5	..	*Set of 3*	9·50	10·00

1990 (3 May). *"Stamp World London '90" International Stamp Exhibition. Nos.* EMS18/20 *optd* "Stamp World London '90" *and emblem on sheet margins only.*
EMS26	$130 *Phareas coeleste* (R.)	..	3·00	3·00
	a. Opt in black			
EMS27	$190 *Papilio torquatus* ..		4·00	4·00
EMS28	$190 Valentina Tereshkova (first woman cosmonaut)	..	3·50	4·00
EMS26/8	..	*Set of 3*	9·50	10·00

1990 (2 June). *"Belgica '90" International Stamp Exhibition, Brussels. Nos.* EMS18 *and* EMS20 *additionally optd* "BELGICA PHILATELIC EXPOSITION 1990" *and emblem on sheet margins only.*
EMS29	$130 *Phareas coeleste* ..	..	2·50	2·50
EMS30	$190 Valentina Tereshkova (first woman cosmonaut)	..	2·75	3·00

1990 (8 June). *90th Birthday of Queen Elizabeth the Queen Mother. Nos.* EMS18/20 *optd* "90TH BIRTHDAY H.M. THE QUEEN MOTHER" *on sheet margins only.*
EMS31	$130 *Phareas coeleste*	..	2·25	2·25
EMS32	$190 *Papilio torquatus* ..		3·00	3·00
EMS33	$190 Valentina Tereshkova (first woman cosmonaut)	..	3·00	3·00
EMS31/3	..	*Set of 3*	7·50	7·50

(Des W. Wright. Litho)

1990 (16 Nov). *Fauna. Two sheets, each* 110×80 *mm, containing vert designs as* T **466**, *but larger* (40×55 *mm*) *inscr* "EXPRESS". *Multicoloured. P* 14.
EMS34	$130 Harpy Eagle	..	2·50	2·50
EMS35	$150 Ocelot	..	2·50	2·50

STANLEY GIBBONS
STAMP COLLECTING SERIES

Introductory booklets on *How to Start, How to Identify Stamps* and *Collecting by Theme.* A series of well illustrated guides at a low price.
Write for details.

PARCEL POST

X   X   PARCEL POST
$15.00 $15.00 $12.00
(P 1)   (P 2)

1981 (8 June). *No.* 554 *surch as Type* P 1 *by Bovell's Printery.*
P1	$15 on $1 *Chelonanthus uliginoides* ..		10·00	3·00
P2	$20 on $1 *Chelonanthus uliginoides* ..		10·00	6·00

1983 (15 Jan). *No.* 843 *surch with Type* P 2 *in blue by Autoprint.*
P3	$12 on $1.10 on $2 *Norantea guianensis*	..	4·50	2·50

Parcel Post
$12.00
(P 3)

1983 (14 Sept). *Unissued Royal Wedding surch, similar to No.* 843, *further surch with Type* P 3 *in blue by Autoprint.*
P4	$12 on $1.10 on $2 *Norantea guianensis*	..	1·00	1·75

TWENTY FIVE DOLLARS
PARCEL POST 25.00
(P 4)

1985 (25 Apr). *No.* 673 *surch with Type* P 4 *in red by Tip. Torres.*
P5	$25 on 35 c. bright yellow-green, grey & black	20·00	18·00

POSTAGE DUE STAMPS

D 1   D 2

(Typo D.L.R.)

1940 (Mar)–**55**. *Wmk Mult Script CA. Chalk-surfaced paper* (4 c.). *P* 14.
D1	D 1	1 c. green	..	3·25	6·50
		a. Chalk-surfaced paper. *Deep green,* (30.4.52)	..	1·50	7·50
		ab. W9*a* (Crown missing)		£180	
		ac. W9*b* (St. Edward's Crown)		80·00	
D2		2 c. black	..	12·00	2·50
		a. Chalk-surfaced paper (30.4.52)	..	1·50	3·50
		ab. W9*a* (Crown missing)		£150	
		ac. W9*b* (St. Edward's Crown)		70·00	
D3		4 c. bright blue (1.5.52)	..	30	8·00
		a. W9*a* (Crown missing)		£130	
		b. W9*b* (St. Edward's Crown)		70·00	
D4		12 c. scarlet	..	25·00	5·00
		a. Chalk-surfaced paper (19.7.55)	..	10·00	20·00
D1a/4a			*Set of 4*	12·00	35·00
D1, D2 and D4 Perf "Specimen"			*Set of 3*	50·00	

(Typo D.L.R.)

1967–8. *Chalk-surfaced paper. W w* 12. *P* 14.
D5	D 2	2 c. black (11.12.68)	..	70	14·00
D6		4 c. deep ultramarine	..	30	3·75
D7		12 c. reddish scarlet	..	30	4·50
D5/7	..		*Set of 3*	1·10	20·00

1973 (24 May). *Glazed, ordinary paper. W* 106. *P* 14.
D 8	D 2	1 c. olive	..	20	2·75
D 9		2 c. black	..	20	2·75
D10		4 c. dull ultramarine	..	20	2·75
D11		12 c. bright scarlet	..	30	2·75
D8/11	..	..	*Set of 4*	80	10·00

OFFICIAL STAMPS

OFFICIAL   OFFICIAL   OFFICIAL
(O 1)   (O 1a)   (O 2)

1875. *Optd with Type* O 1 (1 c.) *or* O 1a *(others) by litho. P* 10.
O1	8	1 c. black (R.)	..	40·00	14·00
		a. Imperf between (horiz pair)		—	£4250
O2		2 c. orange	..	£150	14·00
O3		8 c. rose	..	£300	£120
O4	7	12 c. brownish purple	..	£1500	£475
O5	9	24 c. green	..	£850	£225

Two types of the word "OFFICIAL" are found on each value. On the 1 c., the word is either 16 or 17 mm long. On the other values the chief difference is in the shape and position of the letter "o" in "OFFICIAL". In one case the "o" is upright, in the other it slants to the left.

1877. *Optd with Type O 2 by typo. Wmk Crown CC. P 14.*

O 6	**16**	1 c. slate	..	£200	55·00
		a. Imperf between (vert pair)..		—	£6500
O 7		2 c. orange	..	90·00	15·00
O 8		4 c. blue ..	..	80·00	20·00
O 9		6 c. brown	..	£2500	£600
O10		8 c. rose ..	..	£1700	£450

Prepared for use, but not issued

O11	**16**	12 c. pale violet	..	£900
O12		24 c. green	..	£1000

The "OFFICIAL" overprints have been extensively forged.

The use of Official stamps was discontinued in June 1878, but was resumed in June 1981.

(O 3)   (O 4)

OPS
(O 5)

1981 (8 June). *Nos. 556, F4a and F6/7 surch or optd with Types O 3/5 by Bovell's Printery.*

O13	10 c. on 25 c. Marabunta (Blk. + R.)	..	1·50	2·00
O14	50 c. *Guzmania lingulata* (R.)	..	1·60	30
O15	60 c. Soldier's Cap (R.)	..	1·25	20
O16	$5 *Odontadenia grandiflora* (opt Type O 5) (R.)..	..	4·50	1·75
O13/16		*Set of* 4	8·00	3·75

OPS 100
OPS

(O 6)   (O 7)

1981 (1 July). *(a) Postage. Nos. 491, 708a, 716, 834 and F9 optd or surch as Types O 5/7 or additionally surch as T 227.*

O17	15 c. Harpy Eagle (opt Type O 6)	..	8·50	65
O18	30 c. on $2 *Norantea guianensis* (No. F9) (opt Type O 5) (Blk. + R.)		45	30
O19	100 c. on $3 Cylinder satellite (surch Type O 7) (Blk. + R.)	..	3·00	40
O20	125 c. on $2 *Norantea guianensis* (opt Type O 5) (R.)	..	2·25	60
O21	$10 *Elbella patrobas* (opt Type O 5)	..	7·00	8·00

(b) Air. No. 804 optd with Type O 5 in red

O22	$1.10 on $2 *Norantea guianensis*	..	1·00	2·50
	a. Opt Type O 5 double	..	£110	
O17/22		*Set of* 6	20·00	11·00

1981 (7 July). *Nos. 548, 719, 828 and 830 optd with Type O 5.*

O23	15 c. Christmas Orchid	..	8·00	1·50
O24	50 c. British Guiana 1898 1 c. stamp	..	1·25	35
O25	100 c. on 8 c. Camp-fire cooking	..	2·00	50
O26	110 c. on 6 c. Type **116**	..	3·50	1·25

OPS

OPS 250

(O 8)   (O 9)

(Surch or optd by Autoprint)

1982 (17 May). *(a) Postage. (i) Various stamps optd with Type O 8 in blue*

O27	–	20 c. multicoloured (No. 701)..	..	2·75	60
O28	**136**	40 c. multicoloured	..	75	15
O29	–	40 c. carmine-red, grey & blk (No. 674)	1·00	15	
O30	–	$2 multicoloured (No. 676)..	..	7·00	75
O27/30			*Set of* 4	10·50	1·50

(ii) No. 911 additionally surch with Type O 9 in blue

O31	–	250 c. on 400 c. on 30 c. multicoloured ..	80	60

(b) Air. No. 980 additionally optd with Type O 8 in blue

O32	–	220 c. on 1 c. multicoloured	1·50	60

1982 (12 July). *No. F9 optd with Type O 5 in red by Bovell's Printery.*

O33	$2 *Norantea guianensis*	..	10·00	2·00

1982 (15 Sept). *Air. No. 979 optd with Type O 8 by Autoprint.*

O34	110 c. on 5 c. Annatto tree	..	1·75	60

1984 (2 Apr). *No. 912 surch as Type O 9 vertically, in blue (except for No. O37 which has "OPS" in blue and "225" in black) by Autoprint.*

O35	150 c. on $5 multicoloured	..	4·00	2·50
O36	200 c. on $5 multicoloured	..	4·25	2·75
O37	225 c. on $5 multicoloured	..	4·50	3·00
O38	230 c. on $5 multicoloured	..	4·50	3·00
O39	260 c. on $5 multicoloured	..	4·75	3·25
O40	320 c. on $5 multicoloured	..	5·50	3·50
O41	350 c. on $5 multicoloured	..	6·00	3·75
O42	600 c. on $5 multicoloured	..	7·50	4·25
O35/42		*Set of* 8	35·00	23·00

25

(O 10)

(Surch or optd by Autoprint)

1984 (25 June). *Nos. O32 and O34 surch as Type O 10 (25 c., 60 c.) or as T 294 (others), and No. 981 optd vertically with Type O 8.*

O43	25 c. on 110 c. on 5 c. Annatto tree	..	50	30
O44	30 c. on 110 c. on 5 c. Annatto tree (B.)	..	60	35
O45	45 c. on 220 c. on 1 c. Pitcher Plant of Mt Roraima		70	40
O46	55 c. on 110 c. on 5 c. Annatto tree ..	..	80	50
O47	60 c. on 220 c. on 1 c. Pitcher Plant of Mt Roraima		80	50
O48	75 c. on 220 c. on 1 c. Pitcher Plant of Mt Roraima		85	60
O49	90 c. on 220 c. on 1 c. Pitcher Plant of Mt Roraima (B.)		95	70
O50	120 c. on 220 c. on 1 c. Pitcher Plant of Mt Roraima		1·10	85
O51	130 c. on 220 c. on 1 c. Pitcher Plant of Mt Roraima (B.)		1·25	90
O52	330 c. on $2 *Norantea guianensis* (B.)	..	2·75	2·25
O43/52		*Set of* 10	9·25	6·50

(Litho Format)

1987 (5 Oct)–**88.** *Centenary of Publication of Sanders' Reichenbachia. Multicoloured designs as T 331 additionally inscr "OFFICIAL". No wmk. P 14×13¹/₂ (230, 350, 600 c., $12) or 13¹/₂×14 (others).*

O53	120 c. Plate No. 48 (Series 2)	..	50	25
O54	130 c. Plate No. 92 (Series 2)	..	50	25
O55	140 c. Plate No. 36 (Series 2) (5.10.88)	..	50	25
O56	150 c. Plate No. 43 (Series 2)	..	50	25
O57	175 c. Plate No. 31 (Series 2) (5.10.88)	..	55	30
O58	200 c. Plate No. 61 (Series 2)	..	60	35
O59	225 c. Plate No. 26 (Series 2)	..	60	35
O60	230 c. Plate No. 68 (Series 2) (*horiz*)	..	60	35
O61	250 c. Plate No. 59 (Series 2) (5.10.88)	..	60	40
O62	260 c. Plate No. 69 (Series 2) (5.10.88)	..	60	40
O63	275 c. Plate No. 90 (Series 2)	..	60	40
O64	320 c. Plate No. 75 (Series 2)	..	60	50
O65	330 c. Plate No. 23 (Series 2)	..	70	60
O66	350 c. Plate No. 95 (Series 2) (*horiz*)	..	70	60
O67	600 c. Plate No. 70 (Series 2) (*horiz*)	..	95	95
O68	$12 Plate No. 71 (Series 2) (*horiz*)	..	1·75	1·75
O69	$15 Plate No. 84 (Series 2)	..	2·00	2·00
O53/69		*Set of* 17	11·00	9·00

Nos. O53/69 were printed in a similar sheet format to Nos. 1518/33.

OFFICIAL PARCEL POST STAMPS

1981 (8 June). *Nos. P1/2 optd with Type O 5 in red by Bovell's Printery.*

OP1	$15 on $1 *Chelonanthus uliginoides*..		9·00	2·25
	a. Opt in black	..	65·00	8·00
OP2	$20 on $1 *Chelonanthus uliginoides*..		11·00	2·75

OPS

Parcel Post
$12.00

(OP 1)

1983 (15 Jan). *No. 843 surch with Type OP 1, and optd with T 226, both in blue by Autoprint.*

OP3	$12 on $1.10 on $2 *Norantea guianensis*	65·00	17·00
	a. Surch Type OP 1 omitted	..	90·00	

1983 (22 Aug). *As No. OP3, but additionally optd with Type O 8 by Autoprint.*

OP4	$12 on $1.10 on $2 *Norantea guianensis*	29·00	5·00

1983 (3 Nov). *No. P4 additionally optd with Type O 8 in blue by Autoprint.*

OP5	$12 on $1.10 on $2 *Norantea guianensis*	9·00	5·00

POSTAL FISCAL STAMPS

REVENUE ONLY

✱

(F 1)

1975 (1 Nov). *Nos. 543/5 and 550a/56 optd with Type F 1.*

F 1	2 c. Type **132**	..	..	40	40
F 2	3 c. Hanging Heliconia	..	..	40	40
F 3	5 c. Annatto tree	..	..	65	30
F 4	25 c. Marabunta (Type II)	..	..	2·50	30
	a. Optd on No. 550 (Type I).	..	15·00	13·00	
F 5	40 c. Tiger Beard	..	..	5·00	30
F 6	50 c. *Guzmania lingulata*	..	..	60	40
F 7	60 c. Soldier's Cap	..	..	75	50
F 8	$1 *Chelonanthus uliginoides*	..	75	1·25	
F 9	$2 *Norantea guianensis*	..	..	1·00	2·75
F10	$5 *Odontadenia grandiflora*	..	1·75	9·00	
F1/F10		*Set of* 10	12·00	14·00	

Although intended for fiscal use Nos. F1/10 were allowed, by the postal authorities, as "an act of grace" to do duty as postage stamps until 30 June 1976.

FREE COLOUR BROCHURE

The World's Best Value
STAMP CATALOGUES, HANDBOOKS, ALBUMS & ACCESSORIES

1997-1998 Price List

32 pages of Albums, Catalogues, Handbooks and Accessories.

Available Post Free from:

Stanley Gibbons Publications
5 Parkside, Christchurch Road,
Ringwood, Hants BH24 3SH
Tel: 01425 472363

Heligoland

Stamps of HAMBURG (see Part 7 (*Germany*) of this catalogue) were used in Heligoland until 16 April 1867. The Free City of Hamburg ran the Heligoland postal service between 1796 and 1 June 1866. Its stamps continued in use on the island until replaced by Heligoland issues.

PRICES FOR STAMPS ON COVER

Nos. 1/19   *from × 3*

PRINTERS. All the stamps of Heligoland were typographed at the Imperial Printing Works, Berlin.

REPRINTS. Many of the stamps of Heligoland were subsequently reprinted at Berlin (between 1875 and 1885), Leipzig (1888) and Hamburg (1892 and 1895). Of these only the Berlin productions are difficult to distinguish from the originals so separate notes are provided for the individual values. Leipzig reprints can be identified by their highly surfaced paper and those from Hamburg by their 14 perforation. All of these reprints are worth much less than the original stamps priced below.

There was, in addition, a small reprinting of Nos. 13/19, made by the German government in 1890 for exchange purposes, but examples of this printing are far scarcer than the original stamps.

Forgeries, printed by lithography instead of typography, also exist for Nos. 1/4, 6 and 8 perforated 12½ or 13. Forged cancellations can also be found on originals and, on occasion, genuine postmarks on reprints.

1

(Currency. 16 schillings = 1 mark)

Three Dies of Embossed Head for Types 1 and 2:

Die I   Die II

Die III

Die I. Blob instead of curl beneath the chignon. Outline of two jewels at top of diadem.
Die II. Curl under chignon. One jewel at top of diadem.
Die III. Shorter curl under chignon. Two jewels at top of diadem.

(Des Wedding. Die eng E. Schilling)

1867 (Mar)–**68.** *Head Die I embossed in colourless relief. Roul.*
1	1	½ sch. blue-green and rose	£300	£800
		a. Head Die II (7.68)	£700	£1100
2	1	2 sch. rose and blue-green (21.3.67)	£160	£180
3		2 sch. rose and grass-green (21.3.67)	10·00	55·00
4		6 sch. green and rose	12·00	£250

For Nos. 1/4 the second colour given is that of the spandrels on the ½ and 1 sch., and of the spandrels and central background for the 2 and 6 sch.

All four values exist from the Berlin, Leipzig and Hamburg reprintings. The following points are helpful in identifying originals from Berlin reprints; for Leipzig and Hamburg reprints see general note above:

½ sch. – Reprints are all in yellowish green and show Head Die II
1 sch. – All reprints are Head Die III
2 sch. – Berlin reprints are in dull rose with a deeper blue-green
6 sch. – Originals show white specks in green. Berlin reprints have a more solid bluish green

---

1869 (Apr)–**73.** *Head embossed in colourless relief.* P 13½×14½.
5	1	¼ sch. rose and green (background) (I) (*quadrillé paper*) (8.73)	26·00	£1500
		a. Error. Green and rose (background) (9.73)		£110 £3000
		b. *Deep rose and pale green* (background) (11.73)	85·00	£1500
6		½ sch. blue-green and rose (II)	£190	£200
		a. *Yellow-green and rose* (7.71)	£140	£190
		b. Quadrillé paper (6.73)	95·00	£150
7		¾ sch. green and rose (I) (*quadrillé paper*) (12.73)	29·00	£1100
8		1 sch. rose and yellow-green (III) (7.71)	£140	£180
		a. Quadrillé paper. *Rose and pale blue-green* (6.73)	£120	£180
9		1½ sch. grn & rose (I) (*quadrillé paper*) (9.73) 65·00	£250

For Nos. 5/9 the second colour given is that of the spandrels on the ½ and 1 sch., of the central background on the ¼ and 1½ sch., and of the central background, side labels and side marginal lines of the ¾ sch.

No. 5a was a printing of the ¼ sch. made in the colour combination of the 1½ sch. by mistake.

A further printing of the ¼ sch. (head die I) in deep rose-red and yellowish green (background), on non-*quadrillé* paper, was made in December 1874, but not issued (*Price £15, unused*).

All five values exist from the Berlin, Leipzig and Hamburg reprintings. The following points are helpful in identifying originals from Berlin reprints; for Leipzig and Hamburg reprints see general note above:

¼ sch. – All Berlin and some Hamburg reprints are Head Die I
½ sch. – Berlin reprints on thinner paper with solid colour in the spandrels.
¾ sch. – Berlin reprints on thinner, non-quadrillé paper
1 sch. – Berlin reprints are on thinner paper or show many breaks in the rose line beneath "SCHILLING" at the top of the design or in the line above it at the foot.
1½ sch. – All Berlin and some Hamburg reprints are Head Die II

Berlin, Leipzig and Hamburg reprints also exist of the 2 and 6 sch., but these values do not come as perforated originals.

(New Currency. 100 pfennig = 1 mark)

2   3   4

5

(Des H. Gätke. Die eng E. Schilling (T 2), A. Schiffner (others)

1875 (Feb)–**90.** *Head Die II on* T **2** *embossed in colourless relief.* P 13½×14½.
10	2	1 pf. (¼d.) deep green and rose	10·00	£500
11		2 pf. (½d.) deep rose and deep green	10·00	£600
12	3	3 pf. (⅝d.) pale green, red and yellow (6.76)	£225	£1100
		a. *Green, red and orange* (6.77)	£160	£850
13	2	5 pf. (¾d.) deep yellow-green and rose	10·00	18·00
		a. *Deep green and rose* (6.90)	12·00	40·00
14		10 pf. (1½d.) deep rose and deep green	30·00	20·00
		a. *Scarlet and pale blue-green* (5.87)	12·00	20·00
15	3	20 pf. (2½d.) rose, green and yellow (6.76)	£200	£120
		a. *Rose-carmine, dp green & orge* (4.80)	£150	50·00
		b. *Dull red, pale green and lemon* (7.88)	12·00	28·00
		c. *Aniline verm, brt grn & lemon* (6.90)	12·00	50·00
16	2	25 pf. (3d.) deep green and rose	12·00	26·00
17		50 pf. (6d.) rose and green	18·00	32·00
18	4	1 m. (1s.) deep green, scarlet & black (8.79)	£140	£200
		a. Perf 11½		£1000
		b. *Deep green, aniline rose & black* (5.89)	£140	£200
19	5	5 m. (5s.) deep green, aniline rose, black and yellow (8.79)	£150	£950
		a. Perf 11½		£1000
		ab. Imperf between (horiz pair)		£3500

For stamps as Type **2** the first colour is that of the central background and the second that of the frame. On the 3 pf. the first colour is of the frame and the top band of the shield, the second is the centre band and the third the shield border. The 20 pf. is similar, but has the centre band in the same colour as the frame and the upper band on the shield in the second colour.

The 1, 2 and 3 pf. exist from the Berlin, Leipzig and Hamburg reprintings. There were no such reprints for the other values. The following points are helpful in identifying originals from Berlin reprints; for Leipzig and Hamburg reprints see general note above:

1 pf. – Berlin printings show a peculiar shade of pink
2 pf. – All reprints are much lighter in shade than the deep rose and deep green of the originals
3 pf. – Berlin reprints either show the band around the shield in brownish orange, or have this feature in deep yellow with the other two colours lighter.

Heligoland was ceded to Germany on 9 August 1890.

MINIMUM PRICE

The minimum price quote is 10p which represents a handling charge rather than a basis for valuing common stamps. For further notes about prices see introductory pages.

Hong Kong

CROWN COLONY

Hong Kong island was formally ceded to Great Britain on 26 January 1841. The Hong Kong Post Office was established in October 1841, when much of the business previously transacted through the Macao postal agency was transferred to the island. The first cancellation is known from April 1842, but local control of the posts was shortlived as the Hong Kong Office became a branch of the British G.P.O. on 15 April 1843.

The colonial authorities resumed control of the postal service on 1 May 1860 although the previously established postal agencies in the Chinese Treaty Ports remained part of the British G.P.O. system until 1 May 1868.

For illustrations of the handstamp types see BRITISH POST OFFICES ABROAD notes, following GREAT BRITAIN.

CROWNED-CIRCLE HANDSTAMPS

CC1 CC1b	HONG KONG (R.) (17.10.1843)	*Price on cover*	£475
CC2 CC1	HONG KONG (R.) (21.8.1844)	*Price on cover*	£700
CC3 CC3	HONG KONG (R.) (16.6.1852)	*Price on cover*	£300

We no longer list the Great Britain stamps with obliteration "B 62" within oval. The Government notification dated 29 November 1862 stated that only the Hong Kong stamps to be issued on 8 December would be available for postage and the stamps formerly listed were all issued in Great Britain later than the date of the notice.

(Currency. 100 cents = 1 Hong Kong dollar)

PRICES FOR STAMPS ON COVER TO 1945
Nos. 1/27	*from × 6*
Nos. 28/36	*from × 4*
Nos. 37/9	*from × 5*
Nos. 40/4	*from × 4*
Nos. 45/8	*from × 10*
Nos. 49/50	*from × 4*
No. 51	*from × 15*
Nos. 52/61	*from × 5*
Nos. 62/99	*from × 4*
Nos. 100/32	*from × 3*
Nos. 133/6	*from × 2*
Nos. 137/9	*from × 4*
Nos. 140/68	*from × 2*
Nos. D1/12	*from × 8*
Nos. F1/11	*from × 4*
No. F12	*from × 3*
Nos. P1/3	*from × 2*

PRINTERS. All definitive issues up to 1962 were typographed by De La Rue and Co., *except for some printings between 1941 and 1945.*

1   2   3

1862 (8 Dec)–**63.** *No wmk.* P 14.
1	1	2 c. brown		£375	85·00
		a. *Deep brown* (1863)		£500	£100
2		8 c. yellow-buff		£600	60·00
3		12 c. pale greenish blue		£475	48·00
4	3	18 c. lilac		£500	45·00
5		24 c. green		£900	90·00
6		48 c. rose		£2500	£325
7		96 c. brownish grey		£3500	£375

1863 (Aug)–**71.** *Wmk Crown CC.* P 14.
8	1	2 c. deep brown (11.64)		£250	27·00
		a. *Brown*		£110	7·00
		b. *Pale yellowish brown*		£130	11·00
9	2	6 c. grey		£120	13·00
		a. *Slate*		95·00	5·50
		b. *Deep slate*		£140	10·00
		c. *Greenish grey*		£275	45·00
		d. *Bluish slate*		£450	21·00
		e. Perf 12½. *Slate* (12.70)		£8000	£275
10		6 c. lilac		£300	9·50
		a. *Mauve*		£400	10·00
11	1	8 c. pale dull orange (10.64)		£450	9·50
		a. *Brownish orange*		£400	11·00
		b. *Bright orange*		£350	10·00
12		12 c. pale greenish blue (4.65)		£900	28·00
		a. *Pale blue*		24·00	5·50
		b. *Deep blue*		£180	12·00
13	3	18 c. lilac (1866)		£5000	£300
14		24 c. green (10.64)		£450	8·50
		a. *Pale green*		£550	15·00
		b. *Deep green*		£750	28·00
15	2	30 c. vermilion		£750	14·00
		a. *Orange-vermilion*		£650	15·00
16		30 c. mauve (14.8.71)		£180	5·50
17		48 c. pale rose (1.65)		£950	38·00
		a. *Rose-carmine*		£800	22·00

18	**2**	96 c. olive-bistre (1.65)	..	.. .. ..£25000	£550
19		96 c. brownish grey (1865)	..	£1000	42·00
		a. Brownish black		£1100	32·00

There is a wide range of shades in this issue, of which we can only indicate the main groups.

No. 12 is the same shade as No. 3 without wmk, the impression having a waxy appearance.

A single used example of the 48 c. in a bright claret shade is known. No other stamps in this shade, either mint or used, have been discovered.

See also Nos. 22 and 28/31.

16 *cents.* (4) **28** *cents.* (5) **5** *cents.* (6) **10** *cents.* (7)

ts .
No. 20b

1876 (Aug)–77. *Nos. 13 and 16 surch with T* **4** *or* **5** *by Noronha and Sons, Hong Kong.*

20	**3**	16 c. on 18 c. lilac (1.4.77)	..	.. £1900	£150
		a. Space between "n" and "t"	..	£6000	£800
		b. Space between "s" and stop	..	£6000	£800
21	**2**	28 c. on 30 c. mauve	..	£950	48·00

1877 (Aug). *New value. Wmk Crown CC. P* 14.

22	**3**	16 c. yellow	..	.. £1200	65·00

1880 (1 Mar–Sept). *Surch with T* **6** *or* **7** *by Noronha and Sons.*

23	**1**	5 c. on 8 c. brt orange (No. 11b) (Sept)	£600	85·00
		a. Surch inverted	..	† £10000	
		b. Surch double	..	† £15000	
24	**3**	5 c. on 18 c. lilac (No. 13)	..	£600	55·00
25	**1**	10 c. on 12 c. pale blue (No. 12a)	..	£700	55·00
		a. Blue	..	£900	70·00
26	**3**	10 c. on 16 c. yellow (No. 22) (May)	£3500	£140
		a. Surch inverted	..	† £40000	
		b. Surch double	..	† £50000	
27		10 c. on 24 c. green (No. 14) (June)	..	£1200	80·00

Two examples of No. 26b are known, both used in Shanghai.

1880 (Mar–Dec). *Colours changed and new values. Wmk Crown CC. P* 14.

28	**1**	2 c. dull rose	..	.. £110	17·00
		a. Rose	..	.. £120	18·00
29	**2**	5 c. blue (Dec)	..	.. £275	30·00
30		10 c. mauve (Nov)	..	.. £425	13·00
31	**3**	48 c. brown	..	.. £950	80·00

1882 (May)–96. *Wmk Crown CA. P* 14.

32	**1**	2 c. rose-lake (7.82)	..	£120	24·00
		a. Rose-pink	..	£170	32·00
		ab. Perf 12	..	..£70000	£70000
33		2 c. carmine (1884)	..	25·00	85
		a. Aniline carmine	..	27·00	85
34	**2**	4 c. slate-grey (1.4.96)	..	9·00	85
35		5 c. pale blue	..	20·00	85
		a. Blue	..	21·00	85
36		10 c. dull mauve (8.82)	..	£500	8·50
37		10 c. deep blue-green (1884)	..	£1600	35·00
37a		10 c. green (2.84)	..	£110	1·00
38		10 c. purple/red (1.1.91)	..	18·00	85
39		10 c. yellowish green (1.1.91)	..	£120	38·00
		a. Grey-green	..	60·00	16·00

38, 39a Optd "Specimen" .. *Set of* 2 £375

Examples of No. 39 should not be confused with washed or faded stamps from the grey-green shade which tend to turn to a very yellow-green when dampened.

For other stamps with this watermark, but in colours changed to the U.P.U. scheme see Nos. 56/61.

20 CENTS (8) **50 CENTS** (9) **1 DOLLAR** (10)

1885 (Sept). *As Nos. 15, 19 and 31, but wmkd Crown CA, surch with T* **8** *to* **10** *by De La Rue.*

40	**2**	20 c. on 30 c. orange-red	..	85·00	5·00
		a. Surch double			
41	**3**	50 c. on 48 c. yellowish brown	..	£300	25·00
42		$1 on 96 c. grey-olive	..	£550	45·00

40/2 Optd "Specimen" .. *Set of* 3 £750

7 cents. (11) **14 cents.** (12)

五 (13) (20 c.) 十 (14) (50 c.) 壹圓 (15) ($1)

1891 (1 Jan–Mar). *(a) Nos.* **16** *and* **37** *surch with T* **11** *or* **12** *by Noronha and Sons, Hong Kong*

43	**2**	7 c. on 10 c. green	..	60·00	7·50
		a. Antique "t" in "cents" (R.1/1)	..	£550	£150
		b. Surch double	..	£6000	£1300
44		14 c. on 30 c. mauve (Feb)	..	£120	50·00
		a. Antique "t" in "cents" (R.1/1)	..	£2250	£900

(b) As Nos. 40/2 *(surch with T* **8** *to* **10** *by De La Rue), but colours changed*

45	**2**	20 c. on 30 c. yellowish green (No. 39)	..	£160	£150
		a. Grey-green (No. 39a)	..	95·00	£130
46	**3**	50 c. on 48 c. dull purple	..	£225	£250
47		$1 on 96 c. purple/red	..	£600	£325

45a/7 Optd "Specimen" .. *Set of* 3 £600

(c) Nos. 45/7 *with further surch, T* **13/15**, *in Chinese characters, handstamped locally* (Mar)

48	**2**	20 c. on 30 c. yellowish green	..	55·00	6·50
		a. Grey-green	..	25·00	4·00
49	**3**	50 c. on 48 c. dull purple	..	65·00	5·50
50		$1 on 96 c. purple/red	..	£375	£200

The true antique "t" variety (Nos. 43a and 44a) should not be confused with a small "t" showing a short foot. In the antique "t" the crossbar is accurately bisected by the vertical stroke, which is thicker at the top. The lower curve bends towards the right and does not turn upwards to the same extent as on the normal.

The handstamped surcharges on Nos. 48/50 were applied over the original Chinese face values. The single character for "2" was intended to convert "30 c." to "20 c.". There were six slightly different versions of the "2" handstamp and three for the "50 c.".

A used example of No. 48 in the Royal Philatelic Collection shows surcharge Type **8** double.

The errors of the Chinese surcharges previously listed on the above issue and also on Nos. 52 and 55 are now omitted as being outside the scope of the catalogue. While some without doubt possess philatelic merit, it is impossible to distinguish between the genuine errors and the clandestine copies made to order with the original chops. No. 55c is retained as this represents a distinctly different chop which was used for the last part of the printing.

1841
Hong Kong
JUBILEE
1891 **10 CENTS** 拾 拾
(16) (17) (18) (19)

1891 (22 Jan). *50th Anniversary of Colony. Optd with T* **16** *by Noronha and Sons, Hong Kong.*

51	**1**	2 c. carmine (No. 33)	..	£375	95·00
		a. Short "J" in "JUBILEE" (R. 1/6)	£550	£140
		b. Short "U" or "JUBILEE" (R. 1/1)	£550	£140
		c. Broken "1" in "1891" (R. 2/1)	£700	£200
		d. Tall narrow "K" in "Kong" (R. 1/3)	£1100	£425
		e. Opt double	..	£16000	£12000
		f. Space between "O" and "N" of "Hong" (R. 1/5)	£1500	£650

Most of the supply of No. 51, which was only on sale for three days, was overprinted from a setting of 12 (6×2) applied five times to complete each sheet. There were six printings from this setting, but a second setting, possibly of 30 or 60, was used for the seventh. Positions quoted are from the setting of twelve. Most varieties only occur in some printings and many less marked overprint flaws also exist.

SG7

HONG KONG

and the British Empire 1840-1936

- Bought & Sold -

RARE AND UNUSUAL STAMPS
FOR SERIOUS COLLECTORS.

Wants Lists filled from our comprehensive
30 volume stock of stamps, varieties and
postal history (references please).

We hold several British Empire public auctions annually. Subscriptions: £25.

George W. Holschauer

Colonial Stamp Co.

5757 Wilshire Blvd., Penthouse 8
Los Angeles, CA 90036, U.S.A.
(213) 933-9435 ● FAX (213) 939-9930

Members: IFSDA, PTS, ASDA, Int'l Soc. of Appraisers

When enquiring or placing an order please quote that you have seen me in Stanley Gibbons British Commonwealth catalogue.

The prices quoted for No. 51e are for examples on which the two impressions are distinctly separated. Examples on which the two impressions are almost coincidental are worth considerably less.

1898 (1 Apr). *Wmk Crown CA. P* 14. (*a*) *Surch with T* **10** *by D.L.R. and handstamped Chinese characters as T* **15**

52	3	$1 on 96 c. black		£130	25·00
		a. Grey-black		£130	25·00

(*b*) *Surch with T* **10** *only*

53	3	$1 on 96 c. black		£3000	£3750
		a. Grey-black (Optd S. £600)		£2750	£3500

1898 (1 Apr). (*a*) *Surch with T* **17** *by Noronha and Sons, Hong Kong*

54	2	10 c. on 30 c. grey-green (No. 39a)		£450	£750
		a. Figures "10" widely spaced (1½ mm) £3500			
		b. Surch double			

Type **17** was applied in a horizontal setting of 12, No. 54a appearing on position 12 for the first printing only.

(*b*) *As No.* 54, *but with Chinese character, T* **18**, *in addition*

55	2	10 c. on 30 c. grey-green (No. 39a) (H/S S.			
		£120		38·00	70·00
		a. Yellowish green (Optd S. £150)		80·00	£110
		b. Figures "10" widely spaced (1½ mm)		£700	£800
		c. Chinese character large (Type **19**)		£850	£950
		ca. Ditto. Figures "10" widely spaced		£6500	
		d. Surch Type **17** double			

1900 (Aug)–**01**. *Wmk Crown CA. P* 14.

56	1	2 c. dull green		25·00	85
57	2	4 c. carmine (1901)		14·00	85
58		5 c. yellow		17·00	6·00
59		10 c. ultramarine		45·00	1·75
60	1	12 c. blue (1901)		30·00	40·00
61	2	30 c. brown (1901)		30·00	20·00
56/61			*Set of 6*	£140	60·00
56/9, 61 Optd "Specimen"			*Set of 5*	£425	

20

21

22

23

1903 (Jan–July). *Wmk Crown CA. P* 14.

62	20	1 c. dull purple and brown		2·00	50
63		2 c. dull green (July)		5·00	1·50
		w. Wmk inverted			
64	21	4 c. purple/red (July)		8·00	40
65		5 c. dull green and brown-orange (July)	8·50	8·50
66		8 c. slate and violet (12 Feb)		7·00	1·25
67	20	10 c. purple and blue/blue (July)	28·00	1·25
68	23	12 c. green and purple/yellow (18 Feb)	7·00	4·25
69		20 c. slate and chestnut (June)	30·00	2·50
70	22	30 c. dull green and black (21 May)	30·00	13·00
71	23	50 c. dull green and magenta (June)	26·00	26·00
72	20	$1 purple and sage-green (June)	65·00	17·00
73	23	$2 slate and scarlet (July)	£160	£190
74	22	$3 slate and dull blue (July)	£170	£275
75	23	$5 purple and blue-green (June)	£325	£375
76	22	$10 slate and orange/blue (July)	£800	£375
62/76			*Set of 15*	£1500	£1100
62/76 Optd "Specimen"			*Set of 15*	£1000	

1904 (4 Oct)–**06**. *Wmk Mult Crown CA. Chalk-surfaced paper* (8, 12 c., $3, $5) *or ordinary paper* (others). *P* 14.

77	20	2 c. dull green		4·00	1·25
		a. Chalk-surfaced paper (1906)		6·00	2·50
78	21	4 c. purple/red		8·00	40
		a. Chalk-surfaced paper (1906)		4·75	40
79		5 c. dull green and brown-orange	15·00	6·00
		a. Chalk-surfaced paper (1906)		8·00	5·00
		aw. Wmk inverted			
80		8 c. slate and violet (1906)		7·50	2·00
81	20	10 c. purple and blue/blue (3.05)	11·00	60
82	23	12 c. green and purple/yellow (1906)	8·00	5·50
83		20 c. slate and chestnut		22·00	2·25
		a. Chalk-surfaced paper (1906)		18·00	2·25
		w. Wmk inverted			
84	22	30 c. dull green and black		22·00	11·00
		a. Chalk-surfaced paper (1906)		29·00	14·00
85	23	50 c. green and magenta		40·00	5·50
		a. Chalk-surfaced paper (1906)		40·00	8·50
86	20	$1 purple and sage-green		85·00	16·00
		a. Chalk-surfaced paper (1906)		80·00	16·00
87	23	$2 slate and scarlet		£150	85·00
		a. Chalk-surfaced paper (1905)		£140	75·00
88	22	$3 slate and dull blue (1905)		£150	£180
89	23	$5 purple and blue-green (1905)		£325	£300
90	22	$10 slate and orange/blue (5.05)		£1300	£850
		a. Chalk-surfaced paper (1906)		£1200	£650
77/90			*Set of 14*	£1800	£1100

1907–11. *Colours changed and new value. Wmk Mult Crown CA. Chalk-surfaced paper* (6 c. *and* 20 c. *to* $2). *P* 14.

91	20	1 c. brown (9.10)		3·00	90
92		2 c. deep green		17·00	1·75
		a. Green		17·00	1·50
93	21	4 c. carmine-red		4·25	40
94	22	6 c. orange-vermilion and purple (10.07)	14·00	2·75

95	20	10 c. bright ultramarine		14·00	40
96	23	20 c. purple and sage-green (3.11)	32·00	35·00
97	22	30 c. purple and orange-yellow (3.11)	45·00	18·00
98	23	50 c. black/green (3.11)		32·00	13·00
99		$2 carmine-red and black (1910)	£250	£225
91/9			*Set of 9*	£375	£275
91, 93/9 Optd "Specimen"			*Set of 8*	£600	

24 25 26

  (A) (B)

27 28

In Type A of the 25 c. the upper Chinese character in the left-hand label has a short vertical stroke crossing it at the foot. In Type B this stroke is absent.

1912 (9 Nov)–**21**. *Wmk Mult Crown CA. Chalk-surfaced paper* (12 c. *to* $10). *P* 14.

100	24	1 c. brown		2·00	55
		a. Black-brown		3·50	2·00
		b. Crown broken at right (R. 9/2)	£190	£140
101		2 c. deep green		5·00	30
		a. Green		5·00	30
102	25	4 c. carmine-red		3·75	30
		a. Scarlet (1914)		15·00	1·75
103	26	6 c. yellow-orange		3·75	85
		a. Brown-orange		3·75	1·25
		w. Wmk inverted			
104	25	8 c. grey		22·00	4·50
		a. Slate (1914)		30·00	4·50
105	24	10 c. ultramarine		28·00	30
		a. Deep bright ultramarine		22·00	30
106	27	12 c. purple/yellow		3·50	5·50
		a. White back (Optd S. £80) (1914)	6·50	11·00
107		20 c. purple and sage-green		4·25	90
108	25	25 c. purple & magenta (Type A) (1.14)	12·00	16·00
109		25 c. purple & magenta (Type B) (8.19)	£110	50·00
110	26	30 c. purple and orange-yellow	25·00	5·00
		a. Purple and orange		12·00	4·50
		w. Wmk inverted			
111	27	50 c. black/blue-green		10·00	1·50
		a. White back (Optd S. £120) (5.14)	10·00	4·25
		b. On blue-green, olive back (1917)	£800	24·00
		c. On emerald surface (9.19)	19·00	9·00
		d. On emerald back (Optd S. £120) (7.12.21)	20·00	6·50
112	24	$1 purple and blue/blue		32·00	2·25
		w. Wmk inverted		90·00	70·00
113	27	$2 carmine-red and grey-black	£100	35·00
114	26	$3 green and purple		£160	55·00
115	27	$5 green and red/green		£450	£275
		a. White back (Optd S. £225) (5.14)	£450	£225
		b. On blue-green, olive back (Optd S. £250) (1917)	£800	£200
		bw. Wmk inverted			
116	26	$10 purple and black/red		£450	70·00
100/16			*Set of 17*	£1300	£375
100/16 Optd "Specimen"			*Set of 17*	£1300	

No. 100b occurs on R. 9/2 of the lower right pane.

Broken flower at top right
(Upper left pane R. 1/3)

1921 (Jan)–**37**. *Wmk Mult Script CA. Chalk-surfaced paper* (12 c. *to* $5). *P* 14.

117	24	1 c. brown		1·00	40
		b. Crown broken to right (R. 9/2)			
118		2 c. blue-green		2·25	30
		a. Yellow-green (1932)		6·50	30
		bw. Wmk inverted		50·00	
118c		3 c. grey (14.4.37)		13·00	5·00
119	25	3 c. grey (8.10.31)		4·00	90
120		4 c. carmine-rose		3·25	70
		a. Carmine-red (1932)		2·25	30
		b. Top of lower Chinese characters at right broken off (R. 9/4)	75·00	60·00
121		5 c. violet (16.10.31)		4·25	30
122		6 c. grey		8·00	32·00
123		8 c. orange (7.12.21)		2·50	90
124	24	10 c. bright ultramarine		2·25	30
		aw. Wmk inverted		75·00	
124b	27	12 c. purple/yellow (3.4.33)		11·00	95
125		20 c. purple and sage-green (7.12.21)	3·50	30
126	28	25 c. purple and magenta (B) (7.12.21)	2·50	40
		a. Broken flower		30·00	35·00
		w. Wmk inverted		†	£100
127	26	30 c. purple & chrome-yellow (7.12.21)	10·00	1·50
		a. Purple and orange-yellow		22·00	7·00
		w. Wmk inverted		75·00	
128	27	50 c. black/emerald (1924)		8·50	30

129	24	$1 purple and blue/blue (7.12.21)	22·00	50
130	27	$2 carmine-red & grey-black (7.12.21)	80·00	5·50
131	26	$3 green and dull purple (1926)	£140	42·00
132	27	$5 green and red/emerald (1925)	£375	55·00
117/32			*Set of 18*	£600	£130
117/32 Optd/Perf "Specimen"			*Set of 18*	£1100	

No. 120b occurs on R. 9/4 of the lower left pane.

1935 (6 May). *Silver Jubilee. As Nos.* 91/4 *of Antigua, but ptd by B.W. P* 11×12.

133		3 c. ultramarine and grey-black		4·00	3·00
		c. Lightning conductor		£275	
134		5 c. green and indigo		10·00	3·00
		a. Extra flagstaff		£275	£250
		b. Short extra flagstaff		£300	
		c. Lightning conductor		£250	
		d. Flagstaff on right-hand turret		£300	
135		10 c. brown and deep blue		20·00	1·50
136		20 c. slate and purple		45·00	7·00
		a. Short extra flagstaff		£550	£200
		d. Flagstaff on right-hand turret		£500	£200
		e. Double flagstaff		£500	£200
133/6			*Set of 4*	70·00	13·00
133/6 Perf "Specimen"			*Set of 4*	£300	

For illustrations of plate varieties see Catalogue Introduction.

1937 (12 May). *Coronation. As Nos.* 95/7 *of Antigua. P* 11×11½.

137		4 c. green		6·00	2·50
138		15 c. carmine		12·00	3·25
139		25 c. blue		15·00	2·50
137/9			*Set of 3*	30·00	7·50
137/9 Perf "Specimen"			*Set of 3*	£180	

29 King George VI   Short right leg to "R" (Right pane R. 8/3, left pane R. 3/1)

1938–52. *Wmk Mult Script CA. Chalk-surfaced paper* (80 c., $1 (*No.* 155), $2 (*No.* 157), $5 (*No.* 159), $10 (*No.* 161)). *P* 14.

140	29	1 c. brown (24.5.38)		1·75	80
		a. Pale brown (4.2.52)		2·00	4·50
141		2 c. grey (5.4.38)		2·00	30
		a. Perf 14½×14 (28.9.45)		1·75	4·50
142		4 c. orange (5.4.38)		2·75	1·25
		a. Perf 14½×14 (28.9.45)		4·50	3·25
143		5 c. green (24.5.38)		1·25	20
		a. Perf 14½×14 (28.9.45)		2·50	5·00
144		8 c. red-brown (1.11.41)		1·75	2·25
		a. Imperf (pair)		£22000	
145		10 c. bright violet (13.4.38)		45·00	75
		a. Perf 14½×14. Dull violet (28.9.45)	6·50	20
		b. Dull reddish violet (9.4.46)	5·50	70
		c. Reddish lilac (9.4.47)		15·00	20
146		15 c. scarlet (13.4.38)		1·25	30
147		20 c. black (1.2.46)		1·25	30
148		20 c. scarlet-vermilion (1.4.48)	7·00	40
		a. Rose-red (25.4.51)		15·00	5·50
149		25 c. bright blue (5.4.38)		23·00	80
150		25 c. pale yellow-olive (9.4.46)	4·75	1·25
151		30 c. yellow-olive (13.4.48)		£150	1·40
		a. Perf 14½×14. Yellowish olive (28.9.45)	17·00	8·00
152		30 c. blue (9.4.46)		7·00	20
153		50 c. reddish purple (13.4.38)		40·00	70
		a. Perf 14½×14. Deep magenta (28.9.45)	27·00	1·10
		b. Chalk-surfaced paper. Brt purple (9.4.47)	9·00	20
154		80 c. carmine (2.2.48)		5·00	95
155		$1 dull lilac and blue (chalk-surfaced paper) (27.4.38)	8·00	2·50
		a. Short right leg to "R"		£100	
		b. Ordinary paper. Pale reddish lilac and blue (28.9.45)	10·00	5·00
156		$1 red-orange and green (9.4.46)	14·00	30
		a. Chalk-surfaced paper (21.6.48)	45·00	3·50
		b. Chalk-surfaced paper. Yellow-orge and green (6.11.52)	65·00	14·00
157		$2 red-orange and green (24.5.38)	70·00	14·00
158		$2 reddish violet and scarlet (9.4.46)	23·00	1·25
		a. Chalk-surfaced paper (9.4.47)	32·00	75
159		$5 dull lilac and scarlet (2.6.38)	55·00	48·00
160		$5 green and violet (9.4.46)		80·00	5·00
		a. Yellowish green and violet (9.4.46)	£150	16·00
		ab. Chalk-surfaced paper (9.4.47)	95·00	2·75
161		$10 green and violet (2.6.38)		£375	75·00
162		$10 bright lilac and blue (9.4.46)	£140	22·00
		a. Chalk-surfaced paper. Reddish violet and blue (9.4.47)	£170	18·00
140/62			*Set of 23*	£750	£150
140/62 Perf "Specimen"			*Set of 23*	£2000	

Following bomb damage to the De La Rue works on the night of 29 December 1940 various emergency arrangements were made to complete current requisitions for Hong Kong stamps:

Nos. 141a, 143a, 145a, 151a and 153a (all printings perforated 14½×14 except the 4 c.) were printed and perforated by Bradbury, Wilkinson & Co. Ltd. using De La Rue plates. These stamps are on rough-surfaced paper.

Nos. 142a and 144 were printed by Harrison & Sons in sheets of 120 (12×10) instead of the normal 120 two panes (6×10).

Printings of the $1 and $2 values were made by Williams, Lea & Co. using De La Rue plates.

With the exception of the 8 c. it is believed that none of these printings were issued in Hong Kong before its occupation by the Japanese on 25 December 1941, although examples could be obtained in London from late 1941. The issue dates quoted are those on which the stamps were eventually released in Hong Kong following liberation in 1945.

Nos. 160/a were separate printings released in Hong Kong on the same day.

No. 144a. One imperforate sheet was found and most of the stamps were sold singly to the public at a branch P.O. and used for postage.

30 Street Scene   **31** *Empress of Japan (liner) and Junk*

(Des W. E. Jones. Recess B.W.)

1941 (26 Feb). *Centenary of British Occupation. T 30/1 and similar designs. Wmk Mult Script CA (sideways on horiz designs). P* 13½ × 13 (*2 c. and* 25 *c.*) *or* 13 × 13½ (*others*).

163	2 c. orange and chocolate	4·00	1·75
164	4 c. bright purple and carmine	4·50	1·75
165	5 c. black and green	2·50	50
166	15 c. black and scarlet	5·50	1·00
167	25 c. chocolate and blue	14·00	3·25
168	$1 blue and orange	55·00	7·00
163/168	Set of 6	75·00	14·00
163/8	Perf "Specimen"	Set of 6 £325	

Designs: *Horiz*—5 c. The University; 15 c. The Harbour; $1 Falcon (clipper) and Short S.23 Empire "C" Class flying boat. *Vert*—25 c. The Hong Kong Bank.

Hong Kong was under Japanese occupation from 25 December 1941 until 30 August 1945. The Japanese post offices in the colony were closed from 31 August and mail was carried free, marked with cachets reading "HONG KONG/1945/POSTAGE PAID". Military administration lasted until 1 May 1946. Hong Kong stamps were re-introduced on 28 September 1945.

36 King George VI and Phoenix   **37** Queen Elizabeth II

Extra stroke (R. 1/2)

(Des W. E. Jones. Recess D.L.R.)

1946 (29 Aug). *Victory. Wmk Mult Script CA. P* 13.

169	**36** 30 c. blue and red (*shades*)	1·75	1·00
	a. Extra stroke	42·00	
170	$1 brown and red	3·50	75
	a. Extra stroke	75·00	
169/70	Perf "Specimen"	Set of 2 £160	

Spur on "N" of "KONG" (R. 2/9)

1948 (22 Dec). *Royal Silver Wedding. As Nos. 112/13 of Antigua.*

171	10 c. violet	2·50	80
	a. Spur on "N"	50·00	
172	$10 carmine	£325	70·00

1949 (10 Oct). *75th Anniv of Universal Postal Union. As Nos. 114/17 of Antigua.*

173	10 c. violet	3·75	50
174	20 c. carmine-red	15·00	3·00
175	30 c. deep blue	12·00	1·75
176	80 c. bright reddish purple	35·00	9·50
173/6	Set of 4	60·00	13·00

1953 (2 June). *Coronation. As No. 120 of Antigua.*

177	10 c. black and slate-lilac	5·00	30

1954 (5 Jan)–*62. Chalk-surfaced paper* (20 *c. to* $10). *Wmk Mult Script CA. P* 14.

178	**37** 5 c. orange	1·25	20
	a. Imperf (pair)	£1100	
179	10 c. lilac	2·25	10
	aw. Wmk inverted	£130	
	b. Reddish violet (18.7.61)	6·50	10
180	15 c. green	4·00	45
	a. Pale green (6.12.55)	3·75	45
181	20 c. brown	5·00	30
182	25 c. scarlet	3·25	1·00
	a. Rose-red (26.5.58)	3·00	70
183	30 c. grey	4·00	20
	a. Pale grey (26.2.58)	6·00	20
184	40 c. bright blue	3·50	40
	a. Dull blue (10.1.61)	9·50	70

185	**37** 50 c. reddish purple	4·75	20
186	65 c. grey (20.6.60)	19·00	7·50
187	$1 orange and green	7·50	20
188	$1.30, blue and red (20.6.60)	23·00	1·00
	a. Bright blue and red (23.1.62)	40·00	2·75
189	$2 reddish violet and scarlet	12·00	40
	a. Lt reddish violet & scarlet (26.2.58)	13·00	60
190	$5 green and purple	75·00	1·50
	a. Yellowish green and purple (7.3.61)	90·00	2·25
191	$10 reddish violet and bright blue	60·00	8·50
	a. Lt reddish violet & brt blue (26.2.58)	65·00	8·50
178/91	Set of 14	£200	19·00

No. 178a exists from two sheets, each of which had 90 stamps imperforate and 10 perforated on three sides only.

The 10 c. exists in coils constructed from normal sheets.

38 University Arms   **39** Statue of Queen Victoria

(Des and photo Harrison)

1961 (11 Sept). *Golden Jubilee of Hong Kong University. W w* 12. *P* 11½ × 12.

192	**38** $1 multicoloured	9·00	2·00
	a. Gold ptg omitted	£1300	

(Des Cheung Yat-man. Photo Harrison)

1962 (4 May). *Stamp Centenary. W w* 12. *P* 14½.

193	**39** 10 c. black and magenta	60	10
194	20 c. black and light blue	1·75	1·75
195	50 c. black and bistre	4·00	40
193/5	Set of 3	5·75	2·00

40 Queen Elizabeth II (after Annigoni) **41**

(Photo Harrison)

1962 (4 Oct)–*73. W w* 12 (*upright*). *Chalk-surfaced paper. P* 15 × 14 (5 *c. to* $1) *or* 14 × 14½ (*others*).

196	**40** 5 c. red-orange	40	40
197	10 c. bright reddish violet	1·00	10
	a. Reddish violet (19.11.71)	3·50	10
	ab. Glazed paper (14.4.72)	8·50	1·75
198	15 c. emerald	2·25	60
199	20 c. red-brown	1·50	60
	a. Brown (13.12.71)	7·00	2·00
	ab. Glazed paper (27.9.72)	12·00	8·50
200	25 c. cerise	2·25	1·25
201	30 c. deep grey-blue	2·25	10
	a. Chalky blue (19.11.71)	6·50	1·50
	ab. Glazed paper (27.9.72)	14·00	3·50
202	40 c. deep bluish green	1·75	30
203	50 c. scarlet	1·50	30
	a. Vermilion (13.12.71)	10·00	1·50
	ab. Glazed paper (27.9.72)	14·00	1·75
204	65 c. ultramarine	17·00	2·00
205	$1 sepia	17·00	30
206	**41** $1.30, multicoloured	5·00	20
	a. Pale yellow omitted	32·00	
	b. Pale yellow inverted (horiz pair)	£2750	
	c. Ochre (sash) omitted	25·00	
	d. Glazed paper (3.2.71)	12·00	2·25
	da. Ochre (sash) omitted	30·00	
	dw. Wmk inverted	15·00	
207	$2 multicoloured	6·50	30
	a. Pale yellow omitted†	32·00	
	b. Ochre (sash) omitted	30·00	
	c. Pale yellow† and ochre (sash) omitted	£140	
	dw. Wmk inverted	10·00	
	e. Glazed paper (1973)*	£130	6·00
208	$5 multicoloured	17·00	1·25
	a. Ochre (sash) omitted	32·00	
	bw. Wmk inverted	25·00	
	c. Glazed paper (3.2.71)	25·00	9·50
	cw. Wmk inverted	40·00	
209	$10 multicoloured	30·00	2·00
	a. Ochre (sash) omitted	95·00	
	b. Pale yellow† and ochre (sash) omitted	£160	
	cw. Wmk inverted	60·00	
	d. Glazed paper (1973)*	£1800	£110
210	$20 multicoloured	£140	20·00
	w. Wmk inverted	£550	
196/210	Set of 15	£225	26·00

*These are from printings which were sent to Hong Kong in March 1973 but not released in London.

†This results in the Queen's face appearing pinkish.

It is believed that No. 206b comes from the last two vertical rows of a sheet, the remainder of which had the pale yellow omitted.

The $1.30 to $20 exist with PVA gum as well as gum arabic. The glazed paper printings are with PVA gum only.

See also Nos. 222, etc.

1963 (4 June). *Freedom from Hunger. As No. 146 of Antigua, but additionally inscr in Chinese characters.*

211	$1.30, bluish green	55·00	8·00

1963 (2 Sept). *Red Cross Centenary. As Nos. 147/8 of Antigua, but additionally inscr in Chinese characters at right.*

212	10 c. red and black	5·00	30
213	$1.30, red and blue	35·00	8·00

1965 (17 May). *I.T.U. Centenary. As Nos. 166/7 of Antigua.*

214	10 c. light purple and orange-yellow	4·00	25
	w. Wmk inverted	4·00	
215	$1.30, olive-yellow and deep bluish green	25·00	5·50

1965 (25 Oct). *International Co-operation Year. As Nos. 168/9 of Antigua.*

216	10 c. reddish purple and turquoise-green	3·00	25
	w. Wmk inverted	4·00	
217	$1.30, dp bluish green & lavender (*shades*)	20·00	5·50

1966 (24 Jan). *Churchill Commemoration. As Nos. 170/3 of Antigua but additionally inscr in Chinese characters.*

218	10 c. new blue	3·00	15
	w. Wmk inverted	12·00	
219	50 c. deep green	3·50	30
	w. Wmk inverted	3·50	
220	$1.30, brown	24·00	3·00
221	$2 bluish violet	38·00	10·00
	w. Wmk inverted	£130	
218/21	Set of 4	60·00	12·00

1966 (Aug)–*72. As Nos. 196/208 and 210 but wmk W w* 12 (*sideways**). *Chalk-surfaced paper* (5 *c. to* $1) *or glazed, ordinary paper* ($1.30 *to* $20).

222	**40** 5 c. red-orange (5.12.66)	50	70
223	10 c. reddish violet (31.3.67)†	70	30
	a. Imperf (horiz pair)	£500	
	w. Wmk Crown to right of CA		
224	15 c. emerald (31.3.67)†	2·00	1·25
225	20 c. red-brown	1·75	1·25
	a. Glazed, ordinary paper (14.4.72)	8·00	7·00
226	25 c. cerise (31.3.67)†	3·00	3·00
	aw. Wmk Crown to right of CA	8·50	
	b. Glazed, ordinary paper (14.4.72)	14·00	14·00
227	30 c. deep grey-blue (31.3.70)	10·00	1·50
	a. Glazed, ordinary paper (14.4.72)	13·00	7·00
228	40 c. deep bluish green (1967)	3·00	1·50
	a. Glazed, ordinary paper (14.4.72)	13·00	12·00
229	50 c. scarlet (31.3.67)†	2·50	80
	w. Wmk Crown to right of CA (13.5.69)	3·50	1·25
230	65 c. ultramarine (29.3.67)†	5·50	6·50
	a. Bright blue (16.7.68)	5·00	6·50
231	$1 sepia (29.3.67)†	12·00	1·50
	w. Wmk Crown to right of CA	35·00	
232	**41** $1.30, multicoloured (14.4.72)	10·00	2·00
	w. Wmk Crown to right of CA (17.11.72)	12·00	2·25
233	$2 multicoloured (13.12.71)	11·00	2·50
	a. Ochre (sash) omitted	38·00	
	w. Wmk Crown to right of CA (17.11.72)	12·00	3·25
234	$5 multicoloured (13.12.71)	65·00	12·00
236	$20 multicoloured (14.4.72)	£150	60·00
222/36	Set of 14	£250	85·00

*The normal sideways watermark shows Crown to left of CA, as seen from the back of the stamp.

†Earliest known postmark dates.

The 5 c. to 25 c., 40 c. and 50 c. exist with PVA gum as well as gum arabic, but the 30 c., and all stamps on glazed paper exist with PVA gum only.

1966 (20 Sept). *Inauguration of W.H.O. Headquarters, Geneva. As Nos. 178/9 of Antigua, but additionally inscr in Chinese characters.*

237	10 c. black, yellow-green and light blue	3·00	30
238	50 c. black, light purple and yellow-brown	10·00	1·75

1966 (1 Dec). *20th Anniv of U.N.E.S.C.O. As Nos. 196/8 of Antigua, but additionally inscr in Chinese characters.*

239	10 c. slate-violet, red, yellow and orange	3·50	20
240	50 c. orange-yellow, violet and deep olive	13·00	90
241	$2 black, light purple and orange	55·00	17·00
239/41	Set of 3	65·00	17·00

42 Rams' Heads on Chinese Lanterns

(Des V. Whiteley. Photo Harrison)

1967 (17 Jan). *Chinese New Year ("Year of the Ram"). T 42 and similar horiz design. W w* 12 (*sideways*). *P* 14½.

242	10 c. rosine, olive-green and light yellow-olive	4·00	50
243	$1.30, emerald, rosine and light yellow-olive	32·00	11·00

Design:—$1.30, Three rams.

44 Cable Route Map

(Des V. Whiteley. Photo Harrison)

1967 (30 Mar). *Completion of Malaysia–Hong Kong Link of SEACOM Telephone Cable. W w* 12. *P* 12½.

244	**44** $1.30, new blue and red	17·00	4·50

45 Rhesus Macaques in Tree ("Year of the Monkey")

(Des R. Granger Barrett. Photo Harrison)

1968 (23 Jan). *Chinese New Year ("Year of the Monkey").* T **45** *and similar horiz design.* W w **12** (*sideways*). P 14½.
245   10 c. gold, black and scarlet   ..   ..   4·50   50
246   $1.30, gold, black and scarlet   ..   30·00   9·50
Design:—$1.30, Family of Rhesus Macaques.

47 *Iberia* (liner) at Ocean Terminal

(Des and litho D.L.R.)

1968 (24 Apr). *Sea Craft.* T **47** *and similar horiz designs.* P 13.
247   10 c. multicoloured   ..   ..   ..   2·00   15
   a. Dull orange and new blue omitted   ..   £850
248   20 c. cobalt-blue, black and brown   ..   3·25   1·00
249   40 c. orange, black and mauve   ..   13·00   9·00
250   50 c. orange-red, black and green   ..   8·50   75
   a. Green omitted £700
251   $1 greenish yellow, black and red   ..   20·00   4·50
252   $1.30, Prussian blue, black and pink   ..   48·00   4·25
247/52   ..   ..   *Set of* 6   85·00   18·00
Designs:—20 c. Pleasure launch; 40 c. Car ferry; 50 c. Passenger ferry; $1, Sampan; $1.30, Junk.

53 *Bauhinia blakeana*   **54** Arms of Hong Kong

(Des V. Whiteley. Photo Harrison)

1968 (25 Sept)–**73**.   W w **12**. P 14 × 14½.
   (*a*) *Upright wmk. Chalk-surfaced paper*
253   **53**   65 c. multicoloured ..   ..   9·00   50
   aw. Wmk inverted   ..   ..   17·00
   b. Glazed, ordinary paper (3.73)   50·00   12·00
254   **54** $1 multicoloured ..   ..   9·00   40
   (*b*) *Sideways wmk. Glazed, ordinary paper*
254a   **53**   65 c. multicoloured (27.9.72)   ..   35·00   14·00
254b   **54** $1 multicoloured (13.12.71)   ..   7·50   2·00
Nos. 253/4 exist with PVA gum as well as gum arabic; Nos. 254a/b with PVA gum only.

55 "Aladdin's Lamp" and Human Rights Emblem

(Des R. Granger Barrett. Litho B.W.)

1968 (20 Nov). *Human Rights Year.* W w **12** (*sideways*). P 13½.
255   **55**   10 c. orange, black and myrtle-green   1·50   75
256   50 c. yellow, black & dp reddish purple ..   4·50   2·25

56 Cockerel

(Des R. Granger Barrett. Photo Enschedé)

1969 (11 Feb). *Chinese New Year ("Year of the Cock").* T **56** *and similar multicoloured design.* P 13½.
257   10 c. Type **56** ..   ..   ..   5·00   1·00
   a. Red omitted £160
258   $1.30, Cockerel (*vert*)   ..   ..   65·00   14·00

58 Arms of Chinese University   **59** Earth Station and Satellite

(Des V. Whiteley. Photo Govt Ptg Bureau, Tokyo)

1969 (26 Aug). *Establishment of Chinese University of Hong Kong.* P 13½.
259   **58**   40 c. violet, gold and pale turquoise-blue   7·00   2·75

(Des V. Whiteley. Photo Harrison)

1969 (24 Sept). *Opening of Communications Satellite Tracking Station.* W w **12**. P 14½.
260   **59** $1 multicoloured   ..   ..   24·00   4·00

60 Chow's Head   **62** "Expo 70" Emblem

(Des R. Granger Barrett. Photo D.L.R.)

1970 (28 Jan). *Chinese New Year ("Year of the Dog").* T **60** *and similar design.* W w **12** (*sideways on* $1.30). P 14½×14 (10 c.) *or* 14×14½ ($1.30).
261   10 c. lemon-yellow, orange-brown and black ..   5·50   1·25
262   $1.30, multicoloured   ..   ..   65·00   14·00
Design: Horiz—$1.30, Chow standing.

(Des and litho B.W.)

1970 (14 Mar). *World Fair, Osaka.* T **62** *and similar multicoloured design.* W w **12** (*sideways on* 25 c.). P 13½ × 13 (15 c.) *or* 13 × 13½ (25 c.).
263   15 c. Type **62**   65   85
264   25 c. "Expo '70" emblem and junks (*horiz*)   1·40   1·50

64 Plaque in Tung Wah Hospital   **65** Symbol

(Des M. F. Griffith. Photo Harrison)

1970 (9 Apr). *Centenary of Tung Wah Hospital.* W w **12** (*sideways*). P 14½.
265   **64**   10 c. multicoloured   75   25
266   50 c. multicoloured   ..   ..   3·25   1·50
   w. Wmk Crown to right of CA   ..   4·00
*The normal sideways watermark shows Crown to left of CA, as seen from the back of the stamp.

(Des J. Cooter. Litho B.W.)

1970 (5 Aug). *Asian Productivity Year.* W w **12**. P 14 × 13½.
267   **65**   10 c. multicoloured   80   60

66 Pig

(Des Kan Tai-keung. Photo Govt Ptg Bureau, Tokyo)

1971 (20 Jan). *Chinese New Year ("Year of the Pig").* P 13½.
268   **66**   10 c. multicoloured   ..   ..   5·00   90
269   $1.30, multicoloured   ..   ..   30·00   11·00

67 "60" and Scout Badge   **68** Festival Emblem

(Des Kan Tai-keung. Litho Harrison)

1971 (23 July). *Diamond Jubilee of Scouting in Hong Kong.* W w **12** (*sideways*). P 14×15.
270   **67**   10 c. black, scarlet and yellow   ..   65   10
271   50 c. black, green and blue   ..   3·25   1·00
272   $2 black, magenta and bluish violet ..   18·00   9·50
270/2 ..   ..   *Set of* 3   20·00   9·50

(Des Kan Tai-keung. Litho J.W.)

1971 (2 Nov). *Hong Kong Festival.* T **68** *and similar designs.* W w **12** (*sideways on* 10 c. *and* 50 c.). P 14 (10 c.) *or* 14½ (*others*).
273   **68**   10 c. orange and purple   ..   ..   1·25   20
274   —   50 c. multicoloured   ..   ..   2·50   90
275   — $1 multicoloured   ..   ..   7·50   6·00
273/5 ..   ..   *Set of* 3   10·00   6·50
Designs: Horiz (39 × 23 *mm*)—50 c. Coloured streamers. Vert (23 × 39 *mm*)—$1 "Orchid".

69 Stylised Rats

(Des Kan Tai-keung. Photo D.L.R.)

1972 (8 Feb). *Chinese New Year ("Year of the Rat").* W w **12**. P 13½.
276   **69**   10 c. red, gold and black   ..   3·50   50
277   $1.30, gold, red and black   ..   32·00   10·00
   w. Wmk inverted   ..   ..   40·00

70 Tunnel Entrance

(Des G. Drummond from painting by G. Baxter. Litho Harrison)

1972 (20 Oct). *Opening of Cross-Harbour Tunnel.* W w **12**. P 14×15.
278   **70** $1 multicoloured   ..   ..   5·00   2·25
   w. Wmk inverted   ..   ..   55·00

71 Phoenix and Dragon   **72** Ox

(Des (from photograph by D. Groves) and photo Harrison)

1972 (20 Nov). *Royal Silver Wedding.* W w **12**. P 14×15.
279   **71**   10 c. multicoloured   30   15
   a. Gold omitted £650
280   50 c. multicoloured   ..   ..   1·10   1·40
   a. Dull purple ("50 c", "HONG KONG" and background) double   ..   £600
   w. Wmk inverted   ..   ..   35·00

(Des R. Granger Barrett. Photo Harrison)

1973 (25 Jan). *Chinese New Year ("Year of the Ox").* W w **12** (*sideways on* 10 c.). P 14½.
281   **72**   10 c. reddish orange, brown and black   2·00   40
282   — $1.30, lt yellow, yellow-orange & black   6·50   6·00
   w. Wmk inverted   ..   ..   8·00
Design:—$1.30, similar to 10 c., but horiz.

73   Queen Elizabeth II   **74**

(Des from coinage. Photo ($10 and $20 also embossed) Harrison)

1973 (12 June)–**74**. W w **12** (*sideways* on 15, 30, 40 c. $1.30, 2, 5, 10, $20). P 14½×14 (*Nos.* 283/91) *or* 14×14½ (292/6).
283   **73**   10 c. bright orange   ..   80   50
   a. Wmk sideways (from coils)   ..   1·75   2·00
284   15 c. yellow-green   ..   7·00   6·00
   w. Wmk Crown to left of CA (21.1.74)   9·00   6·50
285   20 c. reddish violet   ..   50   30
   w. Wmk inverted   ..   3·00
286   25 c. lake-brown   ..   9·00   6·50
287   30 c. ultramarine   ..   1·00   50
   w. Wmk Crown to left of CA (21.1.74)   4·50   1·10
288   40 c. turquoise-blue   ..   2·50   2·00
289   50 c. light orange-vermilion   ..   1·25   50
290   65 c. greenish bistre   ..   11·00   11·00
291   $1 bottle-green   ..   2·25   70
292   **74** $1.30, pale yellow and reddish violet   7·00   75
293   $2 pale green and reddish brown   ..   8·00   1·00
294   $5 pink and royal blue   ..   11·00   3·25
   a. Imperf (horiz pair)   ..   £400
295   $10 pink and deep blackish olive   ..   15·00   8·50
296   $20 pink and brownish black   ..   25·00   27·00
   w. Wmk Crown to right of CA
283/96   ..   ..   *Set of* 14   90·00   60·00
*The normal sideways watermark shows Crown to right of CA on the 15 and 30 c., and to left of CA on 40 c. and T **74**, as seen from the back of the stamp.
Nos. 295/6 are known with embossing omitted, but it has been reported that such errors can be faked.
See also Nos. 311/24c and 340/53.

1973 (14 Nov). *Royal Wedding. As Nos.* 165/6 *of Anguilla, but additionally inscr in Chinese characters.*
297   50 c. ochre   50   15
   w. Wmk Crown to right of CA   ..   20·00
298   $2 bright mauve   ..   ..   2·25   1·50
The normal sideways watermark shows Crown to left of CA, as seen from the back of the stamp.

75 Festival Symbols forming Chinese Character

(Des Kan Tai-keung. Litho B.W.)

1973 (23 Nov). *Hong Kong Festival. T* **75** *and similar horiz designs. W w* **12**. *P* 14½.

299	**75**	10 c. brownish red and bright green	40	10
		w. Wmk inverted	3·50	
300	—	50 c. deep magenta and reddish orange	2·00	90
		w. Wmk inverted	6·50	
301	—	$1 bright green and deep mauve	4·75	3·75
299/301		*Set of* 3	6·50	4·25

Each value has the festival symbols arranged to form a Chinese character. "Hong" on the 10 c.; "Kong" on the 50 c.; "Festival" on the $1.

76 Tiger　　　　**77** Chinese Mask

(Des R. Granger Barrett. Litho Harrison)

1974 (8 Jan). *Chinese New Year* ("*Year of the Tiger*"). *W w* **12** (*sideways* on* $1.30). *P* 14½.

302	**76**	10 c. multicoloured	3·50	50
		w. Wmk inverted	9·50	
303	—	$1.30, multicoloured	11·00	12·00
		w. Wmk Crown to left of CA	14·00	

Design:—$1.30, Similar to T **76**, but vert.
*The normal sideways watermark shows Crown to right of CA, *as seen from the back of the stamp.*

(Des R. Hookham. Litho Enschedé)

1974 (1 Feb). *Arts Festival. Vert designs as T* **77** *showing Chinese opera masks. W w* **12** (*sideways*). *P* 12 × 12½.

304	**77**	10 c. multicoloured	75	10
305	—	$1 multicoloured	6·00	4·25
306	—	$2 multicoloured	9·00	8·50
304/6		*Set of* 3	14·00	11·50
MS307		159×94 mm. Nos. 304/6. Wmk upright.		
		P 14×13	60·00	48·00

78 Pigeons with Letters

(Des Kan Tai-keung. Litho Harrison)

1974 (9 Oct). *Centenary of Universal Postal Union. T* **78** *and similar horiz designs. W w* **12** (*sideways* on* 10 *and* 50 *c.*). *P* 14½.

308	10 c. lt greenish blue, lt yell-grn & slate-blk	40	10
	aw. Wmk Crown to right of CA	3·00	
	b. No wmk	35·00	
309	50 c. deep mauve, orange and slate-black	1·00	40
	w. Wmk Crown to right of CA	30·00	
310	$2 multicoloured	5·25	3·75
	w. Wmk inverted	8·00	
308/10	*Set of* 3	6·00	3·75

Designs:—50 c. Globe within letter; $2 Hands holding letters.
*The normal sideways watermark shows Crown to left of CA, *as seen from the back of the stamp.*

1975 (21 Jan)–**82**. *New values* (60, 70, 80 *and* 90 *c.*) *or as Nos.* 283/96 *but W w* **14** (*sideways* on* 10, 20, 25, 50, 65 *c. and* $1).

311	**73**	10 c. bright orange (21.2.75)	55	30
		a. Wmk upright (from coils) (10.78)	4·00	4·50
312		15 c. yellow-green (21.1.75)	15·00	9·00
313		20 c. reddish violet (19.3.75)	50	10
		a. Deep reddish mauve (21.6.77)	1·25	10
		b. Deep reddish purple (22.6.79)	1·25	10
		bw. Wmk Crown to right of CA	1·00	20
314		25 c. lake-brown (19.3.75)	14·00	10·00
315		30 c. ultramarine (9.4.75)	70	30
		a. Deep ultramarine (20.4.78)	1·50	55
		w. Wmk inverted	4·00	
316		40 c. turquoise-blue (19.3.75)	1·25	1·25
		w. Wmk inverted	4·00	
317		50 c. light orange-vermilion (19.3.75)	1·75	50
318		60 c. lavender (4.5.77)	1·75	1·75
		w. Wmk inverted	6·00	
319		65 c. greenish bistre (19.3.75)	18·00	13·00
320		70 c. yellow (4.5.77)	1·75	30
		a. Chrome-yellow (24.1.80)	2·75	90
		w. Wmk inverted	5·00	
321		80 c. bright magenta (4.5.77)	2·25	2·50
		a. Magenta (24.1.80)	2·75	2·75
		bw. Wmk inverted	5·50	

321c	**73**	90 c. sepia (1.10.81)	7·50	1·40
322		$1 bottle-green (19.3.75)	3·00	60
		a. Blackish olive (24.1.80)	3·00	70
		w. Wmk Crown to right of CA	3·75	
323	**74**	$1.30, pale yell & reddish vio (19.3.75)	2·50	30
		w. Wmk inverted	3·75	
324		$2 pale green & reddish brn (19.3.75)	3·00	1·25
		a. Pale green and brown (10.5.82)	7·50	3·00
		bw. Wmk inverted	5·50	
324c		$5 pink and royal blue (20.4.78)	4·75	1·75
		ca. Pink & deep ultramarine (10.5.82)	12·00	4·50
		cw. Wmk inverted (10.5.82)	9·00	4·50
324d		$10 pink and deep blackish olive (20.4.78)	8·00	5·50
		dw. Wmk inverted	9·00	
324e		$20 pink and brownish black (20.4.78)	13·00	11·00
		ea. Imperf (horiz pair)	£500	
		ew. Wmk inverted	17·00	
311/24e		*Set of* 18	90·00	55·00

*The normal sideways watermark shows Crown to left of CA, *as seen from the back of the stamp.*
Nos. 324d/e are known with the embossing omitted. See note after No. 296.

79 Stylized Hare

(Des Kan Tai-keung. Litho Harrison)

1975 (5 Feb). *Chinese New Year* ("*Year of the Hare*"). *T* **79** *and similar horiz design. P* 14½. (*a*) *No wmk.*

325	**79**	10 c. silver and light red	1·00	75
326	—	$1.30, gold and light green	8·50	11·00

(*b*) *W w* **12**

327	**79**	10 c. silver and light red	1·00	60
		w. Wmk inverted	35·00	
328	—	$1.30, gold and light green	8·00	8·00
		w. Wmk inverted	45·00	

Design:—$1.30, Pair of hares.

80 Queen Elizabeth II, the Duke of　　**81** Mid-Autumn
Edinburgh and Hong Kong Arms　　　　Festival

(Des PAD Studio. Litho Questa)

1975 (30 Apr). *Royal Visit. W w* **14** (*sideways*). *P* 13½×14.

329	**80**	$1.30, multicoloured	2·75	2·00
330	—	$2 multicoloured	3·75	4·00

(Des Tao Ho. Litho De La Rue, Bogotá)

1975 (31 July). *Hong Kong Festivals of 1975. T* **81** *and similar vert designs. Multicoloured. No wmk. P* 14.

331	50 c. Type **81**	2·00	50
332	$1 Dragon-boat Festival	8·00	2·50
	a. Black (oars, etc) omitted	£500	
	b. Printed on the gummed side		
333	$2 Tin Hau Festival	28·00	7·50
331/3	*Set of* 3	35·00	9·50
MS334	102×83 mm. Nos. 331/3	£110	45·00

82 Hwamei　　　　**83** Dragon

(Des C. Kuan. Litho Harrison)

1975 (29 Oct). *Birds. T* **82** *and similar vert designs. Multicoloured. W w* **14**. *P* 14½.

335	50 c. Type **82**	2·00	50
	w. Wmk inverted	5·00	
336	$1.30, Chinese Bulbul	8·00	5·00
337	$2 Black-capped Kingfisher	14·00	12·00
	w. Wmk inverted	17·00	
335/7	*Set of* 3	22·00	16·00

(Des Kan Tai-keung. Litho Questa)

1976 (21 Jan). *Chinese New Year* ("*Year of the Dragon*"). *T* **83** *and similar horiz design. W w* **14** (*sideways**). *P* 14½.

338	**83**	20 c. mauve, dull lake and gold	75	10
		w. Wmk Crown to right of CA		
339	—	$1.30, light yellow-green, lt red & gold	6·50	3·25

No. 339 is as T **83** but has the design reversed.
*The normal sideways watermark shows Crown to left of CA, *as seen from the back of the stamp.*

1976 (20 Feb–19 Mar). *As Nos.* 283, 285, 287 *and* 293/6 *but without wmk.*

340	**73**	10 c. bright orange (coil stamp) (19.3.76)	24·00	8·50
342		20 c. reddish violet	3·50	1·25
		a. Imperf (pair)	£500	
344		30 c. ultramarine	7·00	2·25
350	**74**	$2 pale green and reddish brown	9·00	3·75
351		$5 pink and royal blue	9·00	7·00
352		$10 pink and deep blackish olive (19.3.76)	75·00	42·00
353		$20 pink and brownish black (19.3.76)	£160	60·00
340/53		*Set of* 7	£250	£110

No. 353 is known with the embossing omitted. See note after No. 296.

84 "60" and Girl Guides Badge　　**85** "Postal Services" in
　　　　　　　　　　　　　　　　Chinese Characters

(Des P. Ma. Photo Harrison)

1976 (23 Apr). *Girl Guides Diamond Jubilee. T* **84** *and similar horiz design. Multicoloured. W w* **12**. *P* 14½.

354	20 c. Type **84**	50	10
	w. Wmk inverted	3·00	
355	$1.30, Badge, stylised diamond and "60"	5·00	3·50
	w. Wmk inverted	9·00	

(Des Tao Ho. Litho Harrison)

1976 (11 Aug). *Opening of new G.P.O. T* **85** *and similar vert designs. W w* **14**. *P* 14½.

356	20 c. yellow-green, lt greenish grey & black	75	10
	w. Wmk inverted		
357	$1.30, reddish orge, lt greenish grey & blk	3·75	2·00
358	$2 yellow, light greenish grey and black	6·50	4·50
356/8	*Set of* 3	10·00	6·00

Designs:—$1.30, Old G.P.O.; $2 New G.P.O.

86 Tree Snake on Branch

(Des Jennifer Wong. Litho J.W.)

1977 (6 Jan). *Chinese New Year* ("*Year of the Snake*"). *T* **86** *and similar horiz design. W w* **14** (*sideways**). *P* 13½.

359	**86**	20 c. multicoloured	50	15
360	—	$1.30, multicoloured	4·00	4·75
		w. Wmk Crown to left of CA	8·50	

The $1.30 shows a snake facing left.
*The normal sideways watermark shows Crown to right of CA, *as seen from the back of the stamp.*

87 Presentation of the Orb　　**88** Tram Cars

(Des Hong Kong Govt Services Dept; adapted J.W. Litho Harrison)

1977 (7 Feb). *Silver Jubilee. T* **87** *and similar multicoloured designs. W w* **14** (*sideways on* $2). *P* 14½ × 14 ($2) *or* 14 × 14½ (*others*).

361	20 c. Type **87**	40	10
	w. Wmk inverted	30·00	
362	$1.30, Queen's visit, 1975	1·25	1·25
363	$2 The Orb (*vert*)	1·50	1·50
361/3	*Set of* 3	2·75	2·50

(Des Tao Ho. Litho J.W.)

1977 (30 June). *Tourism. T* **88** *and similar vert designs. Multicoloured. W w* **14**. *P* 13½.

364	20 c. Type **88**	55	10
	w. Wmk inverted	†	—
365	60 c. Star Ferryboat	1·50	2·25
	w. Wmk inverted	2·75	
366	$1.30, The Peak Railway	2·50	2·25
	w. Wmk inverted	12·00	
367	$2 Junk and sampan	3·25	3·75
	w. Wmk inverted	6·00	
364/7	*Set of* 4	7·00	7·50

89 Buttercup Orchid

90 Horse

(Des Beryl Walden. Litho Questa)

1977 (12 Oct). *Orchids. T* **89** *and similar vert designs. Multicoloured.* W w **14.** *P* 14½.

68	20 c. Type 89	1·25	15
69	$1.30, Lady's Slipper Orchid	4·00	2·25
70	$2 Susan Orchid	6·00	4·25
68/70	*Set of* 3	10·00	6·00

(Des Graphic Atelier Ltd, Hong Kong. Litho Harrison)

1978 (26 Jan). *Chinese New Year ("Year of the Horse").* W w **14** *(sideways*).* P 14½.

71	90	20 c. magenta, yellow-olive & brn-olive	50	10
		w. Wmk Crown to left of CA	2·75	
72		$1.30, orange, yell-brn & reddish brn	3·50	4·00

*The normal sideways watermark shows Crown to right of CA, *as seen from the back of the stamp.*

91 Queen Elizabeth II

92 Girl and Boy holding Hands

(Des G. Vasarhelyi. Litho Harrison)

1978 (2 June). *25th Anniv of Coronation.* W w **14.** *P* 14×14½.

373	91	20 c. magenta and ultramarine	40	10
374		$1.30, ultramarine and magenta	1·50	2·25
		w. Wmk inverted	25·00	

(Des Annette Walker. Litho Harrison)

1978 (8 Nov). *Centenary of Po Leung Kuk (child care organisation). T* **92** *and similar horiz design. Multicoloured.* W w **14** *(sideways*).* P 14½.

375		20 c. Type 92	30	15
		w. Wmk Crown to left of CA	30	15
376		$1.30, Ring of children	1·75	2·00
		w. Wmk Crown to left of CA	1·75	2·00

*The normal sideways watermark shows the Crown to the right of CA *as seen from the back of the stamp.*

93 Electronics Industry

94 *Precis orithya*

(Litho Harrison)

1979 (9 Jan). *Industries. T* **93** *and similar horiz designs.* W w **14** *(sideways).* P 14½.

377		20 c. orange-yellow, olive-yellow & yell-olive	30	10
378		$1.30 multicoloured	1·10	1·75
379		$2 multicoloured	1·10	2·25
377/9		*Set of* 3	2·25	3·75

Designs:—$1.30, Toy industry; $2, Garment industry.

(Des Jane Thatcher. Photo Harrison)

1979 (20 June). *Butterflies. T* **94** *and similar vert designs. Multicoloured. No wmk.* P 14½.

380		20 c. Type 94	1·00	10
381		$1 *Graphium sarpedon*	1·75	80
382		$1.30, *Heliophorus epicles*	2·50	1·60
383		$2 *Danus genutia*	2·75	3·50
380/3		*Set of* 4	7·00	5·50

STANLEY GIBBONS STAMP COLLECTING SERIES

Introductory booklets on *How to Start, How to Identify Stamps* and *Collecting by Theme.* A series of well illustrated guides at a low price.
Write for details.

95 Diagrammatic view of Railway Station

96 Tsui Shing Lau Pagoda

(Des Tao Ho. Litho J.W.)

1979 (1 Oct). *Mass Transit Railway. T* **95** *and similar horiz designs. Multicoloured.* W w **14** *(sideways*).* P 13½.

384		20 c. Type 95	80	10
		w. Wmk Crown to left of CA	3·50	
385		$1.30, Diagrammatic view of car	2·25	80
		w. Wmk Crown to left of CA	13·00	
386		$2 Plan showing route of railway	2·50	1·75
		w. Wmk Crown to left of CA	40·00	
384/6		*Set of* 3	5·00	2·40

*The normal sideways watermark shows Crown to right of CA, *as seen from the back of the stamp.*

(Des D. Leonard. Litho J.W.)

1980 (14 May). *Rural Architecture. T* **96** *and similar designs.* W w **14** *(sideways on* $1.30 *and* $2).* P 13 × 13½ (20 c.) *or* 13½ × 13 *(others).*

387		20 c. black, magenta and yellow	40	20
		w. Wmk inverted	22·00	
388		$1.30, multicoloured	1·10	1·25
389		$2 multicoloured	1·60	2·50
387/9		*Set of* 3	2·75	3·50

Designs: *Horiz*—$1.30, Village House, Sai O; $2, Ching Chung Koon Temple.

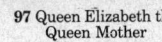

97 Queen Elizabeth the Queen Mother

98 Botanical Gardens

(Des Harrison. Litho Questa)

1980 (4 Aug). *80th Birthday of Queen Elizabeth the Queen Mother.* W w **14** *(sideways).* P 14.

390	97	$1.30, multicoloured	1·00	1·25

(Des D. Chan. Litho J.W.)

1980 (12 Nov). *Parks. T* **98** *and similar vert designs. Multicoloured.* W w **14.** *P* 13½.

391		20 c. Type 98	40	15
392		$1 Ocean Park	75	60
393		$1.30, Kowloon Park	80	85
394		$2 Country Parks	1·75	2·50
391/4		*Set of* 4	3·25	3·75

99 Red-spotted Grouper

100 Wedding Bouquet from Hong Kong

(Des Jane Thatcher. Litho J.W.)

1981 (28 Jan). *Fishes. T* **99** *and similar horiz designs. Multicoloured.* W w **14** *(sideways*).* P 13½.

395		20 c. Type 99	30	15
		w. Wmk Crown to left of CA	4·00	
396		$1 Golden Thread-finned Bream	1·00	70
397		$1.30, Scar-breasted Tuskfish	1·10	95
398		$2 Blue-barred Orange Parrotfish	2·00	3·25
395/8		*Set of* 4	4·00	4·50

*The normal sideways watermark shows Crown to right of CA, *as seen from the back of the stamp.*

(Des J.W. Photo Harrison)

1981 (29 July). *Royal Wedding. T* **100** *and similar vert designs. Multicoloured.* W w **14** *(sideways).* P 14.

399		20 c. Type 100	30	10
400		$1.30, Prince Charles in Hong Kong	70	50
401		$5 Prince Charles and Lady Diana Spencer	2·25	2·75
399/401		*Set of* 3	3·00	3·00

101 Suburban Development

102 "Victoria from the Harbour, c 1855"

(Des Tao Ho. Litho J.W.)

1981 (14 Oct). *Public Housing. T* **101** *and similar vert designs showing suburban development.* W w **14.** *P* 13½.

402		20 c. multicoloured	20	10
		a. Red (jacket and trousers) omitted	£120	
		w. Wmk inverted (pair)		
403		$1 multicoloured	80	60
404		$1.30, multicoloured	1·10	80
405		$2 multicoloured	1·25	1·75
402/5		*Set of* 4	3·00	2·75
MS406		148×105 mm. Nos. 402/5. Wmk inverted	4·25	5·50
		w. Wmk upright	25·00	25·00

(Des R. Solley. Litho Questa)

1982 (5 Jan). *Port of Hong Kong, Past and Present. T* **102** *and similar horiz designs. Multicoloured.* W w **14.** *P* 14½.

407		20 c. Type 102	60	15
408		$1 "West Point, Hong Kong, 1847"	1·75	90
409		$1.30, Fleet of Junks	2·25	1·10
410		$2 Liner *Queen Elizabeth 2* at Hong Kong	3·00	2·75
407/10		*Set of* 4	7·00	4·50

103 Large Indian Civet

(Des Karen Phillipps. Litho Harrison)

1982 (4 May). *Wild Animals. T* **103** *and similar horiz designs.* W w **14** *(sideways*).* P 14½.

411		20 c. black, salmon-pink and olive-bistre	60	15
		w. Wmk Crown to right of CA	13·00	
412		$1 multicoloured	1·25	90
413		$1.30, black, emerald and yellow-orange	1·50	1·10
		w. Wmk Crown to right of CA	16·00	
414		$5 black, orange-brown & greenish yellow	3·00	4·50
411/14		*Set of* 4	5·50	6·00

Designs:—$1 Chinese Pangolin; $1.30, Chinese Porcupine; $5 Indian Muntjac ("Barking Deer").

*The normal sideways watermark shows Crown to left of CA, *as seen from the back of the stamp.*

104 Queen Elizabeth II **105**

(Des and photo ($5 to $50 also embossed) Harrison)

1982 (30 Aug). W w **14** *(sideways* on Nos.* 427/30).* P 14½×14 *(Nos.* 415/26) *or* 14×14½ *(others).*

415	104	10 c. bright carmine, carmine and lemon	70	60
416		20 c. bluish violet, violet and lavender	90	60
417		30 c. bluish violet, violet and salmon	90	30
418		40 c. vermilion and pale blue	90	30
419		50 c. chestnut, orange-brn & sage-green	90	30
420		60 c. bright purple and brownish grey	2·50	1·40
421		70 c. dp grey-grn, myrtle-grn & orge-yell	2·50	40
		a. Imperf (pair)	£450	
422		80 c. bistre-brown, lt brown & sage-grn	2·50	1·50
423		90 c. bottle-green, deep grey-green and pale turquoise-green	4·00	30
424		$1 reddish orge, red-orge & pale rose	2·50	30
425		$1.30, turquoise-blue and mauve	4·00	30
426		$2 ultramarine and flesh	6·50	1·00
427	105	$5 dp magenta, brt purple & olive-yell	7·00	2·50
		w. Wmk Crown to right of CA	8·00	
428		$10 sepia and grey-brown	8·00	5·00
		w. Wmk Crown to right of CA	9·00	
429		$20 deep claret and pale blue	14·00	15·00
		w. Wmk Crown to right of CA	15·00	
430		$50 deep claret and brownish grey	35·00	30·00
		w. Wmk Crown to right of CA	40·00	
415/30		*Set of* 16	80·00	55·00

*The normal sideways watermark shows Crown to left of CA, *as seen from the back of the stamp.*

Nos. 415/30 come with a fluorescent security marking, "Hong Kong" in Chinese characters encircled by the same in English, printed over the central oval of the design.

Nos. 415 and 424 also exist from coils.

No. 428 is known with the embossing omitted. See note after No. 296.

For similar stamps without watermark see Nos. 471/87.

106 Table Tennis   **107** Dancing

(Des A. Wong. Litho J.W.)

1982 (20 Oct). *Sport for the Disabled. T* **106** *and similar horiz designs. Multicoloured.* W w 14. P 14 × 14½.

431	30 c. Type 106 ..	..	50	10
432	$1 Racing	..	75	80
433	$1.30, Basketball	..	2·75	1·50
434	$5 Archery	..	5·00	6·50
431/4		*Set of 4*	8·00	8·00

(Des Tao Ho. Litho J.W.)

1983 (26 Jan). *Performing Arts. T* **107** *and similar vert designs.* W w 14 (*sideways*). P 14½×14.

435	30 c. cobalt and deep grey-blue	..	50	10
436	$1.30, rose and brown-purple	..	2·00	1·25
437	$5 bright green and deep green	..	6·50	5·00
435/7		*Set of 3*	8·00	5·50

Designs:—$1.30. "Theatre"; $5 "Music".

108 Aerial View of Hong Kong

(Des local artist. Litho Enschedé)

1983 (14 Mar). *Commonwealth Day. T* **108** *and similar horiz designs. Multicoloured.* W w 14 (*sideways**). P 14½×13.

438	30 c. Type 108 ..	..	70	10
	w. Wmk Crown to right of CA ..	..	2·50	
439	$1 *Liverpool Bay* (container ship)	..	1·75	1·25
	w. Wmk Crown to right of CA	..	5·50	
440	$1.30, Hong Kong flag	..	1·75	1·25
	w. Wmk Crown to right of CA	..	5·00	
441	$5 Queen Elizabeth II and Hong Kong ..		3·50	4·50
438/41		*Set of 4*	7·00	6·25

*The normal sideways watermark shows Crown to left of CA, as seen from the back of the stamp.

109 Victoria Harbour

(Des Tao Ho. Litho Harrison)

1983 (17 Aug). *Hong Kong by Night. T* **109** *and similar horiz designs. Multicoloured.* W w 14 (*sideways**). P 14½.

442	30 c. Type 109	..	1·25	15
	w. Wmk Crown to right of CA	..	4·75	
443	$1 Space Museum, Tsim Sha Tsui Cultural Centre	..	3·75	1·50
444	$1.30, Fireworks display	..	4·75	2·00
	a. Silver (value and inscr) omitted	..	£850	
445	$5 *Jumbo*, floating restaurant	..	15·00	8·50
	a. Silver (value and inscr) omitted	..	£950	
442/5		*Set of 4*	22·00	11·00

*The normal sideways watermark shows Crown to left of CA, as seen from the back of the stamp.

110 Old and New Observatory Buildings

(Des C. Shun Wah. Litho Harrison)

1983 (23 Nov). *Centenary of Hong Kong Observatory. T* **110** *and similar horiz designs.* W w 14 (*sideways*). P 14½.

446	40 c. yellow-orange, bistre-brown and black		75	10
447	$1 reddish mauve, deep mauve and black ..		2·00	1·75
448	$1.30, new blue, steel-blue and black	..	2·75	1·75
449	$5 olive-yellow, brown-olive and black	..	9·00	9·00
446/9		*Set of 4*	12·00	11·00

Designs:—$1 Wind-measuring equipment; $1.30, Thermometer; $5 Ancient and modern seismometers.

---

111 De Havilland D.H.86 Dragon Express *Dorado* (Hong Kong–Penang Service, 1936)

(Des M. Harris. Litho J.W.)

1984 (7 Mar). *Aviation in Hong Kong. T* **111** *and similar multicoloured designs.* W w 14 (*sideways** on 40 c. to $1.30, *inverted on* $5). P 13½.

450	40 c. Type 111	..	1·00	15
	w. Wmk Crown to left of CA		4·75	
451	$1 Sikorsky S-42B flying boat (San Francisco–Hong Kong Service, 1937)		2·25	1·75
452	$1.30, Cathay-Pacific Boeing 747 jet leaving Kai Tak Airport		3·25	1·75
453	$5 Baldwin brothers' balloon, 1891 (*vert*)		9·00	10·00
450/3		*Set of 4*	14·00	12·00

*The normal sideways watermark shows Crown to right of CA, as seen from the back of the stamp.

112 Map by Capt E. Belcher, 1836

(Des R. Solley. Litho B.D.T.)

1984 (21 June). *Maps of Hong Kong. T* **112** *and similar horiz designs. Multicoloured.* W w 14 (*sideways*). P 14.

454	40 c. Type 112	..	1·00	20
455	$1 Bartholomew map of 1929	..	1·75	1·25
456	$1.30, Early map of Hong Kong waters		3·00	1·75
457	$5 Chinese-style map of 1819		11·00	10·00
454/7 ..		*Set of 4*	15·00	12·00

113 Cockerel

(Des J. Yim. Litho Cartor)

1984 (6 Sept). *Chinese Lanterns. T* **113** *and similar horiz designs showing stylised animals as lanterns. Multicoloured.* W w 14 (*sideways**). P 13½×13.

458	40 c. Type 113	..	80	15
	w. Wmk Crown to right of CA	..	9·00	
459	$1 Dog	..	1·75	1·25
460	$1.30, Butterfly ..	..	3·00	1·75
461	$5 Fish	..	9·00	8·50
458/61		*Set of 4*	13·00	10·50

*The normal sideways watermark shows Crown to left of CA, as seen from the back of the stamp.

114 Jockey on Horse and Nurse with Baby ("Health Care")

(Des M. Harris. Litho Walsall)

1984 (21 Nov). *Centenary of Royal Hong Kong Jockey Club. T* **114** *and similar horiz designs showing aspects of Club's charity work. Multicoloured.* W w 14 (*sideways**). P 14½.

462	40 c. Type 114	..	1·25	20
463	$1 Disabled man playing handball ("Support for Disabled")	..	2·00	1·75
464	$1.30, Ballerina ("The Arts")	..	3·00	2·00
	w. Wmk Crown to right of CA	..	3·00	
465	$5 Humboldt Penguins ("Ocean Park")	..	9·00	11·00
462/5		*Set of 4*	14·00	13·50
MS466	178×98 mm. Nos. 462/5	..	22·00	23·00

*The normal sideways watermark shows Crown to left of CA, as seen from the back of the stamp.

115 Hung Sing Temple

(Des M. Harris. Litho J.W.)

1985 (14 Mar). *Historic Buildings. T* **115** *and similar horiz designs. Multicoloured.* P 13½.

467	40 c. Type 115 ..	..	60	20
468	$1 St. John's Cathedral	..	1·75	1·60
469	$1.30, The Old Supreme Court Building		2·25	1·75
470	$5 Wan Chai Post Office	..	9·50	8·50
467/70		*Set of 4*	12·50	11·00

1985 (13 June)–**87**. *As Nos.* 415/16, 418/30 *and new value* ($1.70). *No wmk.* P 14½×14 (10 c. to $2) *or* 14×14½ (*others*).

471	104	10 c. brt carm, carm & lemon	70	60
472		20 c. bluish violet, vio & lavender (6.87)	17·00	15·00
474		40 c. vermilion and pale blue (23.10.85)	90	80
475		50 c. chestnut, orange-brown and sage-green (23.10.85)	90	40
476		60 c. brt purple & brnish grey (23.10.85)	1·50	1·10
477		70 c. deep grey-green, myrtle-green and orange-yellow (23.10.85) ..	1·50	40
478		80 c. bistre-brown, light brown and sage-green (23.10.85)	1·75	1·75
479		90 c. bottle-green, deep grey-green and pale turquoise-green (23.10.85) ..	1·75	50
480		$1 reddish orange, red-orange and pale rose (23.10.85)	1·75	40
		a. Imperf (horiz pair)		
481		$1.30, turquoise-blue and mauve	2·25	45
482		$1.70, dull ultramarine, bright blue and bright green (2.9.85)	3·00	1·50
483		$2 ultramarine and flesh (23.10.85) ..	3·75	1·50
484	105	$5 deep magenta, bright purple and olive-yellow (23.10.85)	6·00	3·00
485		$10 sepia and grey-brown (23.10.85) ..	7·00	4·00
486		$20 deep claret and pale blue (23.10.85)	10·00	7·50
487		$50 dp claret & brownish grey (23.10.85)	30·00	25·00
471/87		*Set of 16*	80·00	55·00

116 Prow of Dragon Boat   **117** The Queen Mother with Prince Charles and Prince William, 1984

(Des R. Hookham. Litho Cartor)

1985 (19 June). *10th International Dragon Boat Festival. T* **116** *and similar horiz designs showing different parts of dragon boat. Multicoloured.* P 13½×13.

488	40 c. Type 116..	..	50	15
489	$1 Drummer and rowers	..	1·75	1·25
490	$1.30, Rowers	..	3·00	1·60
491	$5 Stern of boat	..	9·25	7·00
488/91		*Set of 4*	13·00	9·00
MS492	190×100 mm. Nos. 488/91. P 13×12 ..		22·00	22·00

(Des C. Abbott. Litho Questa)

1985 (7 Aug). *Life and Times of Queen Elizabeth the Queen Mother. T* **117** *and similar vert designs. Multicoloured.* P 14½×14.

493	40 c. At Glamis Castle, aged 7	..	60	10
494	$1 Type 117	..	1·75	1·25
495	$1.30, The Queen Mother, 1970 (from photo by Cecil Beaton) ..	..	2·00	1·40
496	$5 With Prince Henry at his christening (from photo by Lord Snowdon)..		3·25	4·00
493/6 ..		*Set of 4*	7·00	6·00

118 Melastoma

(Des N. Jesse. Litho B.D.T.)

1985 (25 Sept). *Native Flowers. T* **118** *and similar horiz designs. Multicoloured.* P 13½.

497	40 c. Type 118..	..	1·50	20
498	50 c. Chinese Lily	..	1·75	40
499	60 c. Grantham's Camellia	..	2·00	70
500	$1.30, Narcissus	..	3·25	1·25
501	$1.70, Bauhinia	..	3·75	1·50
502	$5 Chinese New Year Flower	..	7·00	8·50
497/502		*Set of 6*	17·00	11·00

119 Hong Kong Academy for Performing Arts

(Des N. Jesse. Litho Format)

1985 (27 Nov). *New Buildings.* T **119** *and similar multi-coloured designs.* P 15.

503	50 c. Type **119**.	..	..	..	80	15
504	$1.30, Exchange Square (*vert*)				1·75	1·50
505	$1.70, Hong Kong Bank Headquarters (*vert*)			..	2·50	1·75
506	$5 Hong Kong Coliseum	..	..	..	8·00	10·00
503/6	..	..	..	Set of 4	11·50	12·00

120 Halley's Comet in the Solar System

(Des A. Chan. Litho Cartor)

1986 (26 Feb). *Appearance of Halley's Comet.* T **120** *and similar designs. Multicoloured.* P 13½×13.

507	50 c. Type **120**.		..	..	1·25	20
508	$1.30, Edmond Halley and Comet		..	2·00	1·40
509	$1.70, Comet over Hong Kong		..	2·75	1·50
510	$5 Comet passing the Earth		..	11·00	8·00
507/10				Set of 4	15·00	10·00
MS511	135×80 mm. Nos. 507/10		..	22·00	18·00

(Des A. Theobald. Litho Harrison)

1986 (21 Apr). *60th Birthday of Queen Elizabeth II. Vert designs as* T **110** *of Ascension. Multicoloured.* P 14½×14.

512	50 c. At wedding of Miss Celia Bowes-Lyon, 1931		40	10
513	$1 Queen in Garter procession, Windsor Castle, 1977		75	60
514	$1.30, In Hong Kong, 1975	..	1·00	70
515	$1.70, At Royal Lodge, Windsor, 1980 (from photo by Norman Parkinson)	..	1·10	75
516	$5 At Crown Agents Head Office, London, 1983		3·25	4·00
512/16	..	..	..	Set of 5	6·00	5·50

121 Train, Boeing 747 Airliner and Map of World

(Des Agay Ng Kee Chuen. Litho B.D.T.)

1986 (18 July). *"Expo '86" World Fair, Vancouver.* T **121** *and similar horiz designs. Multicoloured.* P 13½.

517	50 c. Type **121**.	..	..	80	30
518	$1.30, Hong Kong Bank Headquarters and map of world		1·50	1·00
519	$1.70, Container ship and map of world	..	2·25	1·40
520	$5 Dish aerial and map of world	..	6·50	7·00
517/20	..	..	..	Set of 4	10·00	8·75

122 Hand-liner Sampan	123 "The Second Puan Khequa" (attr Spoilum)

(Des Graphic Communications Ltd. Litho B.D.T.)

1986 (24 Sept). *Fishing Vessels.* T **122** *and similar horiz designs, each showing fishing boat and outline of fish. Multicoloured.* P 13½.

521	50 c. Type **122**.	..	..	80	15
522	$1.30, Stern trawler	..	..	1·50	1·10
523	$1.70, Long liner junk	..	..	2·25	1·40
524	$5 Junk trawler	..	..	7·00	7·50
521/4	..	..	..	Set of 4	10·50	9·00

(Des R. Solley. Litho B.D.T.)

1986 (9 Dec). *19th-century Hong Kong Portraits.* T **123** *and similar vert designs. Multicoloured.* P 14×13½.

525	50 c. Type **123**.	..	..	55	15
526	$1.30, "Chinese Lady" (19th-century copy)	1·50	1·10
527	$1.70, "Lamqua" (self-portrait)	..	1·75	1·40
528	$5 "Wife of Wo Hing Qua" (attr G. Chinnery)		5·50	5·50
525/8	..	..	..	Set of 4	8·50	7·50

OMNIBUS ISSUES

Details, together with prices for complete sets, of the various Omnibus issues from the 1935 Silver Jubilee series to date are included in a special section following Zimbabwe at the end of Volume 2.

MACHINE LABELS. A single machine operated at the G.P.O. from 30 December 1986 issuing 10 c., 50 c., $1.30 and $1.70 labels showing a carp. These are inscribed "O1". A second machine was installed at Tsim Sha Tsui post office from 18 August 1987 which issued labels coded "O2".

From 1987 a new design was introduced each year to reflect the Chinese calendar. Details of the various issues are as follows:

Year of the Rabbit	18 August 1987	10 c., 50 c., $1.30, $1.70
Year of the Dragon	23 March 1988	10 c., 50 c., $1.30, $1.70
	1 September 1988	10 c., 60 c., $1.40, $1.80
Year of the Snake	24 February 1989	10 c., 60 c., $1.40, $1.80
Year of the Horse	21 February 1990	10 c., 60 c., $1.40, $1.80
Year of the Ram	21 February 1991	10 c., 60 c., $1.40, $1.80
	2 April 1991	10 c., 80 c., $1.80, $2.30
Year of the Monkey	12 March 1992	10 c., 80 c., 90 c., $1.70, $1.80, $2.30, $5
Year of the Cock	10 February 1993	10 c., 80 c., 90 c., $1.70, $1.80, $2.30, $5
	1 November 1993	10 c., $1, $1.90, $2.40
Year of the Dog	1 March 1994	10 c., 80 c., $1, $1.20, $1.30, $1.90, $2, $2.40, $5
Year of the Pig	15 February 1995	10 c., 80 c., $1, $1.20, $1.30, $1.90, $2, $2.40, $5
Year of the Rat	28 February 1996	10 c., $1.20, $1.50, $2.10, $2.30, $2.60, $5
Year of the Ox	12 March 1997	10 c., $1.30, $1.60, $2.50, $2.60, $3.10, $5

From 8 November 1991 the "O1" machine, in addition to the fixed face values, could be used to produce labels of any value in 10 c. steps between 10 c. and $5.

124 Rabbit

(Des Kan Tai-keung. Litho B.D.T.)

1987 (21 Jan). *Chinese New Year ("Year of the Rabbit").* T **124** *and similar horiz designs showing stylized rabbits.* P 13½.

529	50 c. multicoloured	..	..	..	65	15
530	$1.30, multicoloured	..	..	..	1·50	1·25
531	$1.70, multicoloured	..	..	..	1·75	1·40
532	$5 multicoloured	..	..	..	6·50	6·00
529/32				Set of 4	9·50	8·00
MS533	133×84 mm. Nos. 529/32	..	..	32·00	25·00

Nos. 530/1 have the "0" omitted from their face values.

125 "Village Square, Hong Kong Island, 1838" (Auguste Borget)	126 Queen Elizabeth II and Central Victoria

(Des J. Yim. Litho B.D.T.)

1987 (23 Apr). *19th-century Hong Kong Scenes.* T **125** *and similar horiz designs. Multicoloured.* P 14.

534	50 c. Type **125**.	..	..	60	15
535	$1.30, "Boat Dwellers, Kowloon Bay, 1838" (Auguste Borget)	1·75	1·10
536	$1.70, "Flagstaff House, 1846" (Murdoch Bruce)	2·25	1·40
537	$5 "Wellington Street, late 19th-century" (C. Andrasi)	7·00	6·50
534/7	..	..	Set of 4	10·50	8·00

Two types of Nos. 538/52.

I. Heavy shading under mouth and cheek	II. Lighter shading

(Des W. Hookham. Litho Leigh-Mardon Ltd, Melbourne)

1987 (13 July)–**88**. T **126** *and similar vert designs, each showing Queen Elizabeth II and Hong Kong skyline.* P 14½×14 (10 c. to $2) or 14 ($5 to $50). A. *Shading as Type* I. B. *Shading as Type* II (1.9.88).

				A		B	
538	**126**	10 c. multicoloured	..	80	90	75	65
539		40 c. multicoloured	..	1·50	1·40	1·50	1·40
540		50 c. multicoloured	..	1·50	40	1·50	30
541		60 c. multicoloured	..	1·75	75	1·75	60
542		70 c. multicoloured	..	2·00	80	2·00	80
543		80 c. multicoloured	..	2·00	1·50	2·00	1·50
544		90 c. multicoloured	..	2·25	70	2·25	70
545		$1 multicoloured	..	2·25	70	8·00	1·25
546		$1.30, multicoloured	..	3·00	80	3·00	90
546c		$1.40, multicoloured	..		†	3·00	1·75
547		$1.70, multicoloured	..	3·00	80	8·00	1·40
547c		$1.80, multicoloured	..		†	3·00	1·75
548		$2 multicoloured	..	3·00	1·50	3·25	90
549	—	$5 multicoloured	..	7·50	2·50	4·75	2·25
550	—	$10 multicoloured	..	8·50	4·75	8·50	4·25
551	—	$20 multicoloured	..	13·00	13·00	15·00	9·50
552	—	$50 multicoloured	..	25·00	27·00	35·00	16·00
538A/52A	..	..	Set of 15	70·00	50·00		
538B/52B	..	..	Set of 17			90·00	40·00

Designs (25×31 mm): $5 Kowloon; $10 Victoria Harbour; $20 Legislative Council Building; $50 Government House.

Nos. 538/52 carry the fluorescent security markings as described beneath Nos. 415/30 with the $5 to $50 values showing an additional vertical fluorescent bar at right.

For these stamps as Type II, but with imprint dates, see Nos. 600/15.

127 Hong Kong Flag	128 Alice Ho Miu Ling Nethersole Hospital, 1887

(Des R. Hookham. Photo Enschedé)

1987 (13 July)–**92**. *Coil Stamps.* T **127** *and similar vert design.* P 14½×14. A. *Without imprint date.* B. *With imprint date.*

				A	B		
553		10 c. multicoloured	..	1·00	1·50	50	50
554		50 c. bistre, lake and black	..	2·00	3·00	1·25	1·50
554c		80 c. bright mauve, deep blue-green and black		†	60	80
554d		90 c. bright blue, reddish brown and black		†	60	80
554e		$1.80, bright emerald, royal blue and black		†	1·10	1·50
554f		$2.30, orange-brown, deep violet and black		†	1·40	2·00
553/4f			Set of 6		†	5·00	6·50

Design:—50 c. to $2.30, Map of Hong Kong.

Dates of issue: 13.7.87, Nos. 553A/4A; 1.8.89, Nos. 553B/4B; 26.3.92, Nos. 554cB/fB.

Nos. 553/4f carry the fluorescent security marking as described beneath Nos. 415/30.

The printings with imprint date have every fifth stamp in the rolls of 1,000 numbered on the reverse.

Imprint dates: "1989", Nos. 553B/4B; "1990", No. 553B; "1991", Nos. 553B/4/B.

(Des A. Fung. Litho Walsall)

1987 (8 Sept). *Hong Kong Medical Centenaries.* T **128** *and similar horiz designs. Multicoloured.* P 14½.

555	50 c. Type **128**.			1·00	20
556	$1.30, Matron and nurses, Nethersole Hospital, 1891		2·25	1·40
557	$1.70, Scanning equipment, Faculty of Medicine.		2·75	1·40
558	$5 Nurse and patient, Faculty of Medicine	8·50	8·00
555/8	..	..	Set of 4	13·00	10·00

129 Casual Dress with Fringed Hem, 220–589

(Des Sumiko Davies. Litho CPE Australia Ltd, Melbourne)

1987 (18 Nov). *Historical Chinese Costumes.* T **129** *and similar horiz designs. Multicoloured.* P 13½.

559	50 c. Type **129**.			55	10
560	$1.30, Two-piece dress and wrap, 581–960	1·40	1·25
561	$1.70, Formal dress, Song Dynasty, 960–1279	1·75	1·50
562	$5 Manchu empress costume, 1644–1911.	5·75	6·50
559/62			Set of 4	8·50	8·50

130 Dragon	131 White-breasted Kingfisher

(Des Kan Tai-keung. Litho CPE Australia Ltd, Melbourne)

1988 (27 Jan). *Chinese New Year ("Year of the Dragon"). T 130 and similar horiz designs showing dragons. P 13½.*

563	50 c. multicoloured	..	75	15
564	$1.30, multicoloured	..	1·75	1·25
565	$1.70, multicoloured	..	2·00	1·40
566	$5 multicoloured	..	4·00	5·00
563/6		*Set of 4*	7·50	7·00
MS567	134×88 mm. Nos. 563/6	..	10·00	11·00

(Des Karen Phillipps. Litho CPE Australia Ltd, Melbourne)

1988 (20 Apr). *Hong Kong Birds. T 131 and similar vert designs. P 13½.*

568	50 c. Type 131	..	1·10	30
569	$1.30, Fukien Niltava	..	2·25	1·40
570	$1.70, Black Kite	..	2·75	1·50
571	$5 Lesser Pied Kingfisher	..	5·00	6·00
568/71	..	*Set of 4*	10·00	8·50

132 Chinese Banyan

133 Lower Terminal, Peak Tramway

(Des A. Chan. Litho B.D.T.)

1988 (16 June). *Trees of Hong Kong. T 132 and similar vert designs. Multicoloured. P 13½.*

572	50 c. Type 132	..	35	10
573	$1.30, Hong Kong Orchid Tree	..	75	65
574	$1.70, Cotton Tree	..	1·10	85
575	$5 Schima	..	3·50	4·00
572/5		*Set of 4*	5·00	5·00
MS576	135×85 mm. Nos. 572/5	..	10·00	7·50

(Des Lilian Tang. Litho Leigh-Mardon Ltd, Melbourne)

1988 (4 Aug). *Centenary of The Peak Tramway. T 133 and similar vert designs. Multicoloured. P 14½×15.*

577	50 c. Type 133	..	60	10
578	$1.30, Tram on incline	..	1·00	90
579	$1.70, Peak Tower Upper Terminal	..	1·10	90
580	$5 Tram	..	3·50	4·00
577/80		*Set of 4*	5·50	5·50
MS581	160×90 mm. Nos. 577/80	..	8·00	8·00

134 Hong Kong Catholic Cathedral

135 Deaf Girl

(Des C. Buendia. Litho CPE Australia Ltd, Melbourne)

1988 (30 Sept). *Centenary of Hong Kong Catholic Cathedral. P 14.*

582	**134** 60 c. multicoloured	..	1·25	75

(Des M. Tucker. Litho Harrison)

1988 (30 Nov). *Community Chest Charity. T 135 and similar vert designs. P 14½.*

583	60 c. + 10 c. brownish black, vermilion and greenish blue	..	60	75
584	$1.40 + 20 c. brownish black, vermilion and bright green	..	80	1·00
585	$1.80 + 30 c. brownish black, vermilion and bright orange	..	1·50	1·60
586	$5 + $1 brownish blk, verm and yell-brn	..	4·25	5·00
583/6		*Set of 4*	6·50	8·00

Designs:—$1.40, Elderly woman; $1.80, Blind boy using braille typewriter; $5 Mother and baby.

136 Snake

137 Girl and Doll

(Des Kan Tai-keung. Litho Enschedé)

1989 (18 Jan). *Chinese New Year. ("Year of the Snake"). T 136 and similar horiz designs. Multicoloured. P 13½×14.*

587	60 c. Type 136	..	30	15
	a. Booklet pane. Nos. 587 and 589, each ×5	..	5·50	
588	$1.40, Snake and fish	..	1·25	60
589	$1.80, Snake on branch	..	1·75	75
590	$5 Coiled snake	..	5·00	5·00
587/90		*Set of 4*	7·50	6·00
MS591	135×85 mm. Nos. 587/90	..	12·00	7·50

(Des M. Tucker. Litho B.D.T.)

1989 (4 May). *Cheung Chau Bun Festival. T 137 and similar vert designs. Multicoloured. P 13½.*

592	60 c. Type 137	..	45	15
593	$1.40, Girl in festival costume	..	1·10	60
594	$1.80, Paper effigy of god Taai Si Wong	..	1·25	70
595	$5 Floral gateway	..	3·25	3·75
592/5		*Set of 4*	5·50	4·75

138 "Twins" (wood carving, Cheung Yee)

139 Lunar New Year Festivities

(Des Kan Tai-keung. Litho Enschedé)

1989 (19 July). *Modern Art. T 138 and similar vert designs. Multicoloured. P 12×12½.*

596	60 c. Type 138	..	40	15
597	$1.40, "Figures" (acrylic on paper, Chan Luis)	..	1·00	60
598	$1.80, "Lotus" (copper sculpture, Van Lau)	..	1·25	70
599	$5 "Zen Painting" (ink and colour on paper, Lui Shou-kwan)	..	3·00	3·75
596/9		*Set of 4*	5·00	4·75

1989 (1 Aug)–91. *As Nos. 538B/52B, and new values, with imprint date added to designs. P 14½×14 (10 c. to $2.30) or 14 ($5 to $50).*

600	**126** 10 c. multicoloured	..	40	40
601	40 c. multicoloured	..	1·00	1·25
602	50 c. multicoloured	..	60	30
603	60 c. multicoloured	..	60	30
604	70 c. multicoloured	..	60	50
605	80 c. multicoloured	..	60	40
606	90 c. multicoloured	..	70	40
607	$1 multicoloured	..	70	30
607a	$1.20, multicoloured (2.4.91)	..	2·50	2·00
608	$1.30, multicoloured	..	1·25	50
609	$1.40, multicoloured	..	1·25	70
609a	$1.70, multicoloured (2.4.91)	..	2·50	2·00
610	$1.80, multicoloured	..	80	60
611	$2 multicoloured	..	1·00	50
611a	$2.30, multicoloured (2.4.91)	..	2·50	2·00
612	$5 multicoloured	..	3·00	1·25
613	$10 multicoloured	..	4·00	3·00
614	$20 multicoloured	..	7·00	6·00
615	$50 multicoloured	..	18·00	13·00
600/15		*Set of 19*	42·00	32·00

Imprint dates: "1989", Nos. 600/7, 608/9, 610/11, 612/15; "1990", Nos. 600/7, 608/9, 610/11, 612/15; "1991", Nos. 600, 602/7a, 609a/15.

For miniature sheets containing No. 613 see Nos. **MS646**, **MS684/5** and **MS701**.

(Des Sumiko Davies. Litho Enschedé)

1989 (6 Sept). *Hong Kong People. T 139 and similar vert designs. Multicoloured. P 13×14½.*

616	60 c. Type 139	..	40	10
617	$1.40, Shadow boxing and horse racing	..	1·00	60
618	$1.80, Foreign-exchange dealer and traditional builder	..	1·40	70
619	$5 Multi-racial society	..	3·75	4·50
616/19		*Set of 4*	6·00	5·50

For miniature sheet containing design as $5, but smaller (75×35 mm), see No. **MS847**.

140 University of Science and Technology

(Des I. Leung. Litho CPE Australia Ltd, Melbourne)

1989 (5 Oct). *Building for the Future. T 140 and similar square designs. P 13.*

620	60 c. blue-black, orange-yellow & yellow-brn	..	35	15
621	70 c. black, pale rose and rose	..	40	20
622	$1.30, black, brt yellow-green & blue-grn	..	80	55
623	$1.40, black, azure and bright blue	..	80	55
624	$1.80, brownish black, pale turquoise-green and turquoise-blue	..	95	80

625	$5 agate, pale red-orange and orange-red		3·25	3·50
620/5		*Set of 6*	6·00	5·25

Designs:—70 c. Cultural Centre; $1.30, Eastern Harbour motorway interchange; $1.40, New Bank of China Building; $1.80, Convention and Exhibition Centre; $5 Light Rail Transit train.

141 Prince and Princess of Wales and Hong Kong Skyline

142

(Des Ng Kee-chuen. Litho Leigh-Mardon Ltd, Melbourne)

1989 (8 Nov). *Royal Visit. T 141 and similar vert designs, each showing portrait and different view. Multicoloured. W 142 (sideways). P 14½.*

626	60 c. Type 141	..	60	15
627	$1.40, Princess of Wales	..	1·00	60
628	$1.80, Prince of Wales	..	1·25	95
629	$5 Prince and Princess of Wales in evening dress	..	5·00	5·50
626/9		*Set of 4*	7·00	6·50
MS630	128×75 mm. No. 629	..	8·50	8·00

143 Horse

144 Chinese Lobster Dish

(Des Kan Tai-keung. Litho Enschedé)

1990 (23 Jan). *Chinese New Year. ("Year of the Horse"). T 143 and similar horiz designs. P 13½×12½.*

631	60 c. multicoloured	..	60	20
	a. Booklet pane. Nos. 631 and 633, each×3	..	3·50	
632	$1.40, multicoloured	..	1·25	1·00
633	$1.80, multicoloured	..	1·50	1·25
634	$5 multicoloured	..	4·25	4·75
631/4		*Set of 4*	7·00	6·50
MS635	135×85 mm. Nos. 631/4	..	13·00	10·00

(Des N. Yung and Sumiko Davies. Litho Enschedé)

1990 (26 Apr). *International Cuisine. T 144 and similar vert designs showing various dishes. Multicoloured. P 12½×13.*

636	60 c. Type 144	..	50	15
637	70 c. Indian	..	50	15
638	$1.30, Chinese vegetables	..	80	40
639	$1.40, Thai	..	80	50
640	$1.80, Japanese	..	1·25	70
641	$5 French	..	4·00	4·50
636/41		*Set of 6*	7·00	5·75

145 Air Pollution and Clean Air

146 Street Lamp and Des Voeux Road, 1890

(Litho Leigh-Mardon Ltd, Melbourne)

1990 (5 June). *United Nations World Environment Day. T 145 and similar vert designs. Multicoloured. P 14½.*

642	60 c. Type 145	..	40	15
643	$1.40, Noise pollution and music	..	75	40
644	$1.80, Polluted and clean water	..	90	50
645	$5 Litter on ground and in bin	..	2·40	2·50
642/5		*Set of 4*	4·00	3·25

(Des R. Hookham and I. Leung. Litho Leigh-Mardon Ltd, Melbourne)

1990 (24 Aug). *"New Zealand 1990" International Stamp Exhibition, Auckland. Sheet 130×75 mm containing No. 613. P 14.*

MS646	$10 multicoloured	..	95·00	85·00

The stamp in No. **MS646** shows the imprint date as "1990".

(Des M. Tucker. Litho Leigh-Mardon Ltd, Melbourne)

1990 (2 Oct). *Centenary of Electricity Supply.* T **146** *and similar horiz designs.* P 14½.
647	60 c. black, olive-bistre & pale orange-brown		40	10
648	$1.40, multicoloured		1·00	80
649	$1.80, black, olive-bistre and deep cobalt		1·10	90
650	$5 multicoloured		2·50	3·50
647/50		Set of 4	4·50	4·75
MS651	155×85 mm. Nos. 648 and 650		5·50	7·00

Designs:—$1.40, Street lamp and *Jumbo* (floating restaurant), 1940; $1.80, Street lamp and pylon, 1960; $5 Street lamp and Hong Kong from harbour, 1980.

147 Christmas Tree and Skyscrapers

(Litho Leigh-Mardon Ltd, Melbourne)

1990 (8 Nov). *Christmas.* T **147** *and similar horiz designs. Multicoloured.* P 14½.
652	50 c. Type **147**		20	10
653	60 c. Dove with holly		20	15
654	$1.40, Firework display		70	40
655	$1.80, Father Christmas hat on skyscraper		90	50
656	$2 Children with Father Christmas		1·25	1·10
657	$5 Candy stick with bow and Hong Kong skyline		2·75	3·50
652/7		Set of 6	5·50	5·25

148 Ram **149** Letter "A", Clock, Teddy Bear and Building Bricks (Kindergarten)

(Des Kan Tai-keung. Litho Enschedé)

1991 (24 Jan). *Chinese New Year.* ("*Year of the Ram*"). T **148** *and similar horiz designs.* P 13½×12½.
658	60 c. multicoloured		25	15
	a. Booklet pane. Nos. 658 and 660, each × 3, with margins all round		3·75	
659	$1.40, multicoloured		55	45
660	$1.80, multicoloured		75	60
661	$5 multicoloured		2·25	3·00
658/61		Set of 4	3·50	3·75
MS662	135×85 mm. Nos. 658/61		6·50	7·50

(Litho Enschedé)

1991 (18 Apr). *Education.* T **149** *and similar vert designs. Multicoloured.* P 13½×13.
663	80 c. Type **149**		40	20
664	$1.80, Globe, laboratory flask and mathematical symbols (Primary and Secondary)		90	70
665	$2.30, Machinery (Vocational)		1·10	1·10
666	$5 Mortar board, computer and books (Tertiary)		2·50	3·50
663/6		Set of 4	4·50	5·00

150 Rickshaw **151** Victorian Pillar Box and Cover of 1888

(Des C. Tillyer. Litho B.D.T.)

1991 (6 June). *100 Years of Public Transport.* T **150** *and similar square designs. Multicoloured.* P 14.
667	80 c. Type **150**		30	15
668	90 c. Double-decker bus		45	30
669	$1.70, Harbour ferry		75	60
670	$1.80, Tram		1·00	60
671	$2.30, Mass Transit Railway train		1·40	1·50
672	$5 Jetfoil		3·25	4·00
667/72		Set of 6	6·50	6·50

(Des H. Choi. Litho B.D.T.)

1991 (25 Aug). *150th Anniv of Hong Kong Post Office (1st issue).* T **151** *and similar vert designs. Multicoloured.* P 14.
673	80 c. Type **151**		40	15
674	$1.70, Edwardian pillar box and cover		80	65
675	$1.80, King George V pillar box and cover of 1935		90	65
676	$2.30, King George VI pillar box and cover of 1938		1·25	1·50
677	$5 Queen Elizabeth II pillar box and cover of 1989		3·50	4·25
673/7		Set of 5	6·00	6·50
MS678	130×75 mm. $10 As No. 677		11·00	13·00

See also Nos. **MS745** and **MS899**.

152 Bronze Buddha, Lantau Island **153** Monkey

(Litho Questa)

1991 (24 Oct). *Landmarks.* T **152** *and similar vert designs.* P 14.
679	80 c. rosine and black		40	15
680	$1.70, bright emerald and black		90	70
681	$1.80, reddish violet and black		1·00	70
682	$2.30, new blue and black		1·25	1·50
683	$5 bright yellow-orange and black		3·50	4·25
679/83		Set of 5	6·25	6·50

Designs:—$1.70, Peak Pavilion; $1.80, Clock Tower; $2.30, Catholic Cathedral; $5 Wong Tai Sin Temple.

(Des Kan Tai-keung. Litho Leigh-Mardon Ltd, Melbourne)

1991 (16 Nov). *"Phila Nippon '91" International Stamp Exhibition, Tokyo. Sheet* 130×75 *mm containing No.* 613. P 14.
MS684	$10 multicoloured		35·00	25·00

The stamp in No. **MS684** shows the imprint date as "1991".

(Des Li Shik-kwong. Litho Leigh-Mardon Ltd, Melbourne)

1991 (4 Dec). *Olympic Games, Barcelona (1992) (1st issue). Sheet* 130×75 *mm. containing No.* 613. P 14.
MS685	$10 multicoloured		15·00	13·00

The stamp in No. **MS685** shows the imprint date as "1991".
See also Nos. **696/700** and **MS722**.

(Des Kan Tai-keung. Litho Leigh-Mardon Ltd, Melbourne)

1992 (22 Jan). *Chinese New Year.* ("*Year of the Monkey*"). T **153** *and similar horiz designs.* P 14½.
686	80 c. multicoloured		40	15
	a. Booklet pane. Nos. 686 and 688, each × 3, with margins all round		4·50	
687	$1.80, multicoloured		70	55
688	$2.30, multicoloured		1·25	1·10
689	$5 multicoloured		2·75	3·50
686/9		Set of 4	4·50	4·75
MS690	135×85 mm. Nos. 686/9		8·50	9·00

(Des D. Miller. Litho Leigh-Mardon Ltd, Melbourne)

1992 (11 Feb). *40th Anniv of Queen Elizabeth II's Accession. Horiz designs as T* **143** *of Ascension. Multicoloured.* P 14½.
691	80 c. Royal barge in Hong Kong harbour		25	15
692	$1.70, Queen watching dancing display		50	35
693	$1.80, Fireworks display		50	35
694	$2.30, Three portraits of Queen Elizabeth		80	75
695	$5 Queen Elizabeth II		2·00	2·25
691/5		Set of 5	3·50	3·50

154 Running **155** Queen Elizabeth II

(Des Li Shik-kwong. Litho Leigh-Mardon Ltd, Melbourne)

1992 (2 Apr). *Olympic Games, Barcelona (2nd issue).* T **154** *and similar horiz designs.* P 14½.
696	80 c. Type **154**		40	20
697	$1.80, Swimming and javelin		80	80
698	$2.30, Cycling		1·60	1·50
699	$5 High jump		2·25	3·00
696/9		Set of 4	4·50	5·00
MS700	130×75 mm. As Nos. 696/9*		5·50	6·50

* The stamps from No. **MS700** show the inscriptions in different colours, instead of the black on Nos. 696/9. The designs of the $1.80 and $5 values from the miniature sheet have also been rearranged so that "HONG KONG" and the Royal Cypher occur at the right of the inscription.
For No. **MS700** additionally inscribed for the opening of the Games see No. **MS722**.

(Des Kan Tai-keung. Litho Leigh-Mardon Ltd, Melbourne)

1992 (22 May). *"World Columbian Stamp Expo '92" Exhibition, Chicago. Sheet* 130×75 *mm containing No.* 613, *but colours changed.* P 14.
MS701	$10 multicoloured		5·50	7·00

The stamp in No. **MS701** shows the imprint date as "1992".

(Des I. Leung. Photo Enschedé)

1992 (16 June)–**96.** P 14½×14 (10 c. to $5) *or* 14 ($10, $20, $50).
702	**155** 10 c. magenta, black and pale cerise		20	20
	ap. Two phosphor bands (24.4.96)		40	40
702b	20 c. black, blue-blk & pale bl (1.11.93)		30	30
	bp. Two phosphor bands (24.4.96)		40	40
703	50 c. orange-red, black and yellow		30	20
	p. Two phosphor bands (24.4.96)		40	40
704	60 c. greenish blue, black and light blue		35	35
705	70 c. bright mauve, black and rose-lilac		40	40
706	80 c. cerise, black and rose		30	20
707	90 c. bronze-green, blk & greenish grey		30	20
708	$1 red-brown, black & orange-yellow		35	20
	ap. Two phosphor bands (24.4.96)		50	30
708b	$1.10, deep carmine, black and pale salmon (1.6.95)		35	35
	bp. Two phosphor bands (24.4.96)		60	60
709	$1.20, bright violet, black and lilac		35	25
	ap. Two phosphor bands (24.4.96)		60	60
709b	$1.30, blue, brownish black and salmon (1.11.93)		70	30
	bp. Two phosphor bands (24.4.96)		60	60
709c	$1.40, brt yellow-grn, blk & greenish yell (two phosphor bands) (2.9.96)		35	30
709d	$1.50 reddish brn, blk & lt bl (1.6.95)		60	45
	dp. Two phosphor bands (24.4.96)		65	65
709e	$1.60, light green, black and rose-lilac (two phosphor bands) (2.9.96)		45	40
710	$1.70, dull ultramarine, blk & pale bl		55	55
711	$1.80, deep magenta, black and grey		85	45
711a	$1.90, deep blue-green, brownish black and yellow-ochre (1.11.93)		55	50
	ap. Two phosphor bands (24.4.96)		75	75
712	$2 turq-blue, black & brt turq-green		85	60
	ap. Two phosphor bands (24.4.96)		85	75
712b	$2.10, bright crimson, black & pale turquoise-green (1.6.95)		65	60
	bp. One centre phosphor band (24.4.96)		75	60
	bq. Two phosphor bands (2.9.96)		2·50	2·50
713	$2.30, blackish brn, blk & rose-pink		50	60
713a	$2.40, dull ultramarine, black and brownish grey (1.11.93)		1·25	75
713b	$2.50, brown-olive, black and lemon (one centre phosphor band) (2.9.96)		55	60
713c	$2.60, choc, blk & yellow-brn (1.6.95)		75	70
	cp. One centre phosphor band (24.4.96)		90	90
713d	$3.10, orange-brown, black & pale bl (one centre phosphor band) (2.9.96)		65	70
714	$5 blue-green, black & lt green (24.4.96)		1·75	1·25
	p. One centre phosphor band		1·75	1·75
715	— $10 red-brown, black and cinnamon		2·75	2·50
716	— $20 rosine, black and bright salmon		4·00	4·00
717	— $50 grey-black, black and grey		8·50	10·00
702/17		Set of 27	27·00	25·00

Nos. 715/17 are as Type **155**, but larger, 26×30 mm, and show a large perforation hole at each corner of the stamp.
Nos. 702/17 show "HONG KONG" printed in yellow fluorescence as a security marking. Nos. 715/17 additionally show a horizontal line at foot in green fluorescence.
Nos. 702, 703, 706/7, 709bp, 709e, 711, 713, 713b and 713d also exist from coils with every fifth stamp numbered on the reverse.
For stamps in this design from stamp booklets, printed in lithography without watermark or with watermark w **14**, see Nos. 757/65.
For miniature sheets containing designs as Nos. 714 and 715 see Nos. **MS723**, **MS745/6**, **MS751**, **MS771**, **MS782**, **MS810/11**, **MS821**, **MS827** and **MS841/2**.

156 Stamps and Perforation Gauge **157** Principal Male Character

(Des Kan Tai-keung. Litho Leigh-Mardon Ltd, Melbourne)

1992 (15 July). *Stamp Collecting.* T **156** *and similar horiz designs. Multicoloured.* P 14½.
718	80 c. Type **156**		30	20
719	$1.80, Handstamp of 1841, 1891 Jubilee overprint and tweezers		60	55
720	$2.30, Stamps of 1946 and 1949 under magnifying glass		85	90
721	$5 2 c. of 1862 and watermark detector		2·00	3·00
718/21		Set of 4	3·25	4·25

(Des Li Shik-kwong. Litho Leigh-Mardon Ltd, Melbourne)

1992 (25 July). *Olympic Games, Barcelona (3rd issue). As No.* **MS700**, *but additionally inscribed "To Commemorate the Opening of the* 1992 *Summer Olympic Games* 25 *July* 1992", *in English and Chinese, at foot of sheet.*
MS722	130×75 mm. As Nos. 696/9		3·50	4·50

(Des C. Tillyer. Litho Enschedé)

1992 (1 Sept). *"Kuala Lumpur '92" International Stamp Exhibition. Sheet 130×75 mm containing design as No. 715, but litho and colours changed. P 14.*
MS723 $10 dull ultramarine, black and pale blue 4·75 6·00
No. MS723 shows "HONG KONG" printed in yellow fluorescence with a horizontal green fluorescent line beneath as a security marking. There is a larger perforation hole at each corner of the stamp.

(Des I. Leung. Litho Enschedé)

1992 (24 Sept). *Chinese Opera. T 157 and similar vert designs. Multicoloured. P 13½.*

724	80 c. Type 157			40	25
725	$1.80, Martial character			90	80
	a. Grey (face value and inscr) omitted			£750	
726	$2.30, Principal female character			1·10	1·25
	a. Grey (face value and inscr) omitted			£750	
727	$5 Comic character			2·25	3·50
724/7			*Set of 4*	4·25	5·25

Nos. 725a and 726a each occur on the bottom row of a sheet and were caused by the upward displacement of the grey colour. One example of each also exists showing the plate number from the bottom margin printed in the design.

158 Hearts

(Des C. Tillyer. Litho Leigh-Mardon Ltd, Melbourne)

1992 (19 Nov). *Greetings Stamps. T 158 and similar horiz designs. Multicoloured. P 14½.*

728	80 c. Type 158			30	20
	a. Booklet pane. Nos. 728×3 and 729/31 with margins all round			3·50	
729	$1.80, Stars			55	60
730	$2.30, Presents			75	85
731	$5 Balloons			1·60	2·25
728/31			*Set of 4*	2·75	3·50

159 Cockerel   **160** Pipa

(Des Kan Tai-keung. Litho Enschedé)

1993 (7 Jan). *Chinese New Year. ("Year of the Cock"). T 159 and similar horiz designs. P 13½.*

732	80 c. multicoloured			30	20
	a. Booklet pane. Nos. 732 and 734, each ×3, with margins all round			3·50	
733	$1.80, multicoloured			70	70
734	$2.30, multicoloured			95	95
735	$5 multicoloured			2·25	2·75
732/5			*Set of 4*	3·75	4·25
MS736	133×84 mm. Nos. 732/5			4·75	5·50

(Des Sumiko Davies. Litho Leigh-Mardon Ltd, Melbourne)

1993 (14 Apr). *Chinese String Musical Instruments. T 160 and similar vert designs. Multicoloured. Fluorescent paper. P 14½.*

737	80 c. Type 160			40	20
738	$1.80, Erhu			70	60
739	$2.30, Ruan			95	1·00
740	$5 Gehu			2·00	2·75
737/40			*Set of 4*	3·50	4·00

161 Central Waterfront, Hong Kong in 1954

(Des C. Tillyer. Litho Leigh-Mardon Ltd, Melbourne)

1993 (2 June). *40th Anniv of Coronation. T 161 and similar horiz designs. Multicoloured. Fluorescent paper. P 14.*

741	80 c. Type 161			40	20
742	$1.80, Hong Kong in 1963			70	50
743	$2.30, Hong Kong in 1975			90	90
744	$5 Hong Kong in 1992			2·25	2·50
741/4			*Set of 4*	3·75	3·75

(Des Julia Brown and G. Smith. Litho Enschedé)

1993 (6 July). *150th Anniv of Hong Kong Post Office (2nd issue). Sheet 130×75 mm containing design as No. 715, but litho. P 14.*
MS745 $10 red-brown, black and cinnamon 4·50 5·50
No. MS745 shows "HONG KONG" printed in yellow fluorescence with a horizontal green fluorescent line beneath as a security marking. There is a larger perforation hole at each corner of the stamp.

(Des Lam Bing-pui. Litho Enschedé)

1993 (12 Aug). *"Hong Kong '94" International Stamp Exhibition. Sheet 115×78 mm containing design as No. 715, but litho and colours changed. P 14.*
MS746 $10 deep purple, black, bistre-yellow and greenish blue 4·50 5·00
No. MS746 shows "HONG KONG" printed in yellow fluorescence with a horizontal green fluorescent line beneath as a security marking. There is a larger perforation hole at each corner of the stamp.

162 University of Science and Technology Building and Student

(Des Lam Bing-pui. Litho Leigh-Mardon Ltd, Melbourne)

1993 (8 Sept). *Hong Kong's Contribution to Science and Technology. T 162 and similar horiz designs. Multicoloured. P 14½.*

747	80 c. Type 162			30	20
748	$1.80, Science Museum building and energy machine exhibit			50	40
749	$2.30, Governor's Award and circuit board			70	80
750	$5 Dish aerials and world map			1·75	2·50
747/50			*Set of 4*	2·75	3·50

(Des Lam Bing-pui. Litho Enschedé)

1993 (5 Oct). *"Bangkok '93" International Stamp Exhibition. Sheet 131×75 mm containing design as No. 715, but litho and colours changed. P 14.*
MS751 $10 bright emerald, blackish green and bright blue-green 2·75 3·50
No. MS751 shows "HONG KONG" printed in yellow fluorescence with a horizontal green fluorescent line beneath as a security marking. There is a larger perforation hole at each corner of the stamp.

163 Red Calico Egg-fish

(Des N. Young. Litho Leigh-Mardon Ltd, Melbourne)

1993 (17 Nov). *Goldfish. T 163 and similar horiz designs. Multicoloured. P 14½.*

752	$1 Type 163			35	20
753	$1.90, Red Cap Oranda			60	50
754	$2.40, Red and White Fringetail			90	90
755	$5 Black and Gold Dragon-eye			2·25	3·00
752/5			*Set of 4*	3·75	4·25
MS756	130×75 mm. Nos. 752/5			6·50	7·50

1993 (14 Dec)–97. *Booklet Stamps. As Nos. 702, 708, 709, 709bp, 709e, 710/12, 712b, 713a and 714, but printed in lithography by Leigh-Mardon Ltd (Nos. 757, 758, 759 and 760/5) or Enschedé (others). P 14½/×14.*

(a) No wmk

757	155	$1 red-brown, black & orange-yellow	50	50
		a. Booklet pane. No. 757×10 with margins all round	5·00	
757b		$1.20, brt violet, black & lilac (1.6.95)	50	50
		ba. Booklet pane. No. 757b×10 with margins all round	5·00	
757c		$1.30, blue, deep brown and salmon (two phosphor bands) (2.9.96)	45	50
		ca. Booklet pane. No. 757c×10 with margins all round	4·50	
		cb. Sheetlet Nos. 757c×4 and 759e×2 with margins all round (14.2.97)	4·00	
		cc. Booklet pane. As No. 757cb, but with enlarged margins at left and foot (14.2.97)	7·00	
757d		$1.60, light green, black and rose-lilac (two phosphor bands) (14.2.97)	85	1·00
		da. Sheetlet Nos. 757d×2 and 759d×4 with margins all round	4·00	
		db. Booklet pane. As No. 759da, but with enlarged margins at left and foot	7·00	
758		$1.90, dp blue-green, brownish black and yellow-ochre (28.12.93)	75	85
		a. Booklet pane. No. 758×10 with margins all round	7·50	
758b		$2.10, deep claret, black & turquoise-green (1.6.95)	70	80
		ba. Booklet pane. No. 758b×10 with margins all round	7·00	
		bb. Two phosphor bands (14.2.97)	1·00	1·25
		bc. Sheetlet Nos. 758bb×2 and 759b×4 with margins all round	4·00	
		bd. Booklet pane. As No. 758bc, but with enlarged margins at left and foot	7·00	
759		$2.40, dull ultramarine, black and brownish grey (28.12.93)	85	1·00
		a. Booklet pane. No. 759×10 with margins all round	8·50	

759b	155	$2.50, bistre, black and lemon (one centre phosphor band) (2.9.96)	60	75
		ba. Booklet pane. No. 759b×10 with margins all round	6·00	
759c		$2.60, dp choc, black & brown (1.6.95)	80	95
		ca. Booklet pane. No. 759c×10 with margins all round	8·00	
759d		$3.10, orge-brown, blk & pale bl (one centre phosphor band) (2.9.96)	70	85
		da. Booklet pane. No. 759d×10 with margins all round	7·00	
759e		$5 bright blue-green, black and light green (one centre phosphor band) (14.2.97)	1·00	1·25
757/9e		*Set of 11*	7·00	8·00

(b) W w 14 (12.1.94)

760	155	10 c. magenta, black and pale cerise	2·50	3·00
		a. Booklet pane. Nos. 760 and 764×5 with margins all round	5·50	
761		$1 red-brown, black & orange-yellow	60	75
		a. Booklet pane. Nos. 761×5 and 765 with margins all round	5·50	
762		$1.70 dull ultram, black & pale blue	2·50	3·00
		a. Booklet pane. Nos. 762 and 763×5 with margins all round	5·50	
763		$1.80, deep magenta, black and grey	60	75
764		$2 turquoise-blue, blk & brt turq-grn	60	75
765		$5 brt blue-green, black & lt green	2·50	3·00
760/5		*Set of 6*	8·50	9·00

Nos. 757/65 show "HONG KONG" printed in yellow fluorescence as a security marking.
Nos. 757/9d come from definitive booklets and Nos. 760/5 from the Prestige booklet issued to commemorate the 130th anniversary of Hong Kong stamps.

164 Dog

(Des Kan Tai-keung. Litho Leigh-Mardon Ltd, Melbourne)

1994 (27 Jan). *Chinese New Year. ("Year of the Dog"). T 164 and similar horiz designs. P 14½.*

766	$1 multicoloured		30	20
	a. Booklet pane. Nos. 766 and 768, each × 3, with margins all round		3·75	
767	$1.90, multicoloured		50	45
768	$2.40, multicoloured		70	80
769	$5 multicoloured		1·75	2·50
766/9		*Set of 4*	3·00	3·50
MS770	133×84 mm. Nos. 766/9		8·00	6·00

(Des Lam Bing-pui. Litho Leigh-Mardon Ltd, Melbourne)

1994 (18 Feb). *"Hong Kong '94" International Stamp Exhibition. Sheet 130×75 mm containing design as No. 714, but litho. P 14½/×14.*
MS771 155 $5 bright blue-green, black & lt green 5·00 6·00
No. MS771 shows "HONG KONG" printed in yellow fluorescence as a security marking.

165 Modern Police Constables on Traffic Duty   **166** Dragon Boat Festival

(Des Li Shik-kwong. Litho Enschedé)

1994 (4 May). *150th Anniv of Royal Hong Kong Police Force. T 165 and similar horiz designs. Multicoloured. P 13½.*

772	$1 Type 165		30	20
773	$1.20, Marine policeman with binoculars		40	25
774	$1.90, Police uniforms of 1950		55	35
775	$2 Tactical firearms unit officer with sub-machine gun		75	45
776	$2.40, Early 20th-century police uniforms		90	75
777	$5 Sikh and Chinese constables of 1900		2·75	3·25
772/7		*Set of 6*	5·00	4·75

(Des Li Shik-kwong. Litho Questa)

1994 (8 June). *Traditional Chinese Festivals. T 166 and similar vert designs. Multicoloured. P 14½.*

778	$1 Type 166		35	20
779	$1.90, Lunar New Year		60	50
780	$2.40, Seven Sisters Festival		85	95
781	$5 Mid-Autumn Festival		1·75	2·50
778/81		*Set of 4*	3·25	3·75

(Des C. Tillyer. Litho Enschedé)

1994 (16 Aug). *Conference of Commonwealth Postal Administrations, Hong Kong. Sheet 134×83 mm, containing design as No. 715, but litho. P 14.*
MS782 $10 red-brown, black and cinnamon 5·00 6·00
No. MS782 shows "HONG KONG" printed in yellow fluorescence with a horizontal green fluorescent line beneath as a security marking. There is a larger perforation hole at each corner of the stamp.

167 Swimming

(Des C. Tillyer. Litho Walsall)

1994 (25 Aug). *15th Commonwealth Games, Victoria, Canada. T* **167** *and similar horiz designs. Multicoloured. P* 14½.

783	$1 Type **167**	..	..	25	20
784	$1.90, Bowls	..	..	50	50
785	$2.40, Gymnastics	..	..	70	75
786	$5 Weightlifting	..	..	1·60	2·25
783/6			*Set of 4*	2·75	3·25

168 Dr. James Legge and
Students

169 Alcyonium Coral

(Des Lai Wai-kwan. Litho Leigh-Mardon Ltd, Melbourne)

1994 (5 Oct). *Dr. James Legge (Chinese scholar) Commemoration. P* 14½.

787	**168** $1 multicoloured	..	..	55	50

(Des Brushstroke Design. Litho Questa)

1994 (17 Nov). *Corals. T* **169** *and similar square designs. Multicoloured. P* 14.

788	$1 Type **169**	..	..	35	20
789	$1.90, Zoanthus	..		60	55
790	$2.40, Tubastrea	..		75	90
791	$5 Platygyra	..		1·75	2·25
788/91			*Set of 4*	3·00	3·50
MS792	130×75 mm. Nos. 788/91		..	4·50	5·00

170 Pig

(Des Kan Tai-keung. Litho Leigh-Mardon Ltd, Melbourne)

1995 (17 Jan). *Chinese New Year ("Year of the Pig"). T* **170** *and similar horiz designs. P* 14½.

793	$1 multicoloured	..	..	30	30
	a. Booklet pane. Nos. 793 and 795, each				
	× 3, with margins all round	..		3·00	
794	$1.90, multicoloured	..		60	70
795	$2.40, multicoloured	..		70	85
796	$5 multicoloured	..		1·25	1·75
793/6			*Set of 4*	2·50	3·25
MS797	130×84 mm. Nos. 793/6			4·25	4·50

171 Hong Kong Rugby Sevens

(Des Kan Tai-keung and Roxy Lou Sze-wan. Litho
Leigh-Mardon Ltd, Melbourne)

1995 (22 Mar). *International Sporting Events in Hong Kong. T* **171** *and similar horiz designs. Multicoloured. P* 14½.

798	$1 Type **171**	..	..	35	20
799	$1.90, The China Sea Yacht Race	..		55	55
800	$2.40, International Dragon Boat Races	..		75	90
801	$5 Hong Kong International Horse Races		1·50	2·25
798/801			*Set of 4*	2·75	3·50

172 Tsui Shing Lau Pagoda

173 Regimental Badge

(Des I. Leung. Recess and litho Enschedé)

1995 (24 May). *Hong Kong Traditional Rural Buildings. T* **172** *and similar horiz designs. Multicoloured. P* 13½.

802	$1 Type **172**	..		30	20
803	$1.90, Sam Tung Uk Village	..		55	55
804	$2.40, Lo Wai Village	..		75	90
805	$5 Man Shek Tong house	..		1·50	2·25
802/5			*Set of 4*	2·75	3·50

(Des Lam Bing-pui. Litho Leigh-Mardon Ltd, Melbourne)

1995 (16 Aug). *Disbandment of the Royal Hong Kong Regiment. T* **173** *and similar multicoloured designs. P* 14½.

806	$1.20, Type **173**	..		30	25
807	$2.10, Regimental guidon (*horiz*)	..		50	55
808	$2.60, Colour of Hong Kong Volunteer				
	Defence Corps, 1928 (*horiz*)		65	75
809	$5 Cap badge of Royal Hong Kong Defence				
	Force, 1951	..	..	1·10	1·50
806/9			*Set of 4*	2·25	2·75

(Des C. Tillyer and Valerie Carter. Litho Enschedé)

1995 (1 Sept). *"Singapore '95" International Stamp Exhibition. Sheet 130×75 mm, containing design as No. 715, but litho and colours changed. P* 14.

MS810	$10 dp mag, yellow-olive, yell & brn-lilac		4·00	5·00

No. **MS810** shows "HONG KONG" printed in yellow
fluorescence with a horizontal green fluorescent line beneath as
a security marking. There is a larger perforation hole at each
corner of the stamp.

(Des D. Lai. Litho Enschedé)

1995 (9 Oct). *50th Anniv of End of Second World War. Sheet 130×75 mm, containing design as No. 715, but litho. P* 14.

MS811	$10 red-brown, black and cinnamon		4·00	5·00

No. **MS811** shows "HONG KONG" printed in yellow
fluorescence with a horizontal green fluorescent line beneath as
a security marking. There is a larger perforation hole at each
corner of the stamp.

174 Bruce Lee

(Des Lau Siu-hong and Wong Kum. Litho Enschedé)

1995 (15 Nov). *Hong Kong Film Stars. T* **174** *and similar horiz designs. Multicoloured. P* 13½.

812	$1.20, Type **174**	..		1·50	45
813	$2.10, Leung Sing-por	..		1·75	1·25
814	$2.60, Yam Kim-fai	..		2·75	1·40
815	$5 Lin Dai	..		2·75	3·00
812/15			*Set of 4*	8·00	5·50

175 Rat

176 Rhythmic
Gymnastics

(Des Kan Tai-keung. Litho Enschedé)

1996 (31 Jan). *Chinese New Year ("Year of the Rat"). T* **175** *and similar horiz designs. P* 13½.

816	$1.20, multicoloured	..		25	30
	a. Booklet pane. Nos. 816 and 818, each				
	× 3, with margins all round	..		2·50	
817	$2.10, multicoloured	..		45	55
818	$2.60, multicoloured	..		50	65
819	$5 multicoloured	..		1·25	1·75
816/19			*Set of 4*	2·25	3·00
MS820	133×83 mm. Nos. 816/19		..	2·50	3·50

(Des Lam Bing-pui. Litho Enschedé)

1996 (23 Feb). *Visit "HONG KONG '97" Stamp Exhibition (1st issue). Sheet 130×80 mm, containing designs as No. 715, but litho and colours changed. P* 14.

MS821	$10 yellow-orange, black & bright green		4·50	5·50

No. **MS821** shows "HONG KONG" printed in yellow fluorescence with a horizontal green fluorescent line beneath as a
security marking. There is a large perforation hole at each
corner of the stamp.
See also Nos. **MS827**, **MS841** and **MS872/3**.

(Des B. Kwan. Litho Ashton-Potter America Inc, New York)

1996 (20 Mar). *Olympic Games, Atlanta. T* **176** *and similar vert designs. Multicoloured with Royal Cypher and face values in black and Olympic Rings multicoloured (Nos. 822/5/5). Two phosphor bands ($1.20) or one side phosphor band (others). P* 13½.

822	$1.20, Type **176**	..		25	25
823	$2.10, Diving	..	..	45	50

(Des A. Lam. Litho Enschedé)

824	$2.60, Athletics	..	..	55	65
825	$5 Basketball	..	..	1·25	1·75
822/5			*Set of 4*	2·25	2·75
MS826	130×75 mm. As Nos. 822/5, but Royal				

Cypher and Olympic Rings in gold and face
values in black (medal in bottom sheet margin) 2·50 3·50
For these designs with Royal Cypher and Olympic Rings in
gold see Nos. 832/6.

(Des A. Lam. Litho Enschedé)

1996 (18 May). *Visit "HONG KONG '97" Stamp Exhibition (2nd issue). Sheet 130×80 mm, containing design as No. 715, but litho and colours changed. P* 14.

MS827	$10 brt emer, greenish blk & bluish vio		2·50	3·00

No. **MS827** shows "HONG KONG" printed in yellow fluorescence with a horizontal green fluorescent line beneath as a
security marking. There is a large perforation hole at each
corner of the stamp.

177 Painted Pottery Basin,
c. 4500–3700 B.C.

(Des I. Leung. Litho Enschedé)

1996 (26 June). *Archaeological Discoveries. T* **177** *and similar horiz designs. Two phosphor bands ($1.20) or one side band (others). P* 13½.

828	$1.20, Type **177**	..		40	25
829	$2.10, Stone "yue" (ceremonial axe),				
	c. 2900–2200 B.C.	..		60	60
830	$2.60, Stone "ge" (halberd), *c.* 2200–1500				
	B.C.	..		70	90
831	$5 Pottery tripod, *c.* 25–220 A.D.	..		1·40	2·25
828/31			*Set of 4*	2·75	3·50

(Des B. Kwan, Litho Ashton-Potter America Inc, New York)

1996 (19 July). *Opening of Centennial Olympic Games, Atlanta. Designs as Nos. 822/5, but with Royal Cypher and Olympic Rings in gold and face values in colours quoted. Two phosphor bands ($1.20) or one side band (others). P* 14½.

832	$1.20, Type **176** (bright magenta)	..		40	25
833	$2.10, As No. 823 (deep ultramarine)		60	60
834	$2.60, As No. 824 (light green)	..		70	90
835	$5 As No. 825 (orange-vermilion)		1·40	2·25
832/5			*Set of 4*	2·75	3·50
MS836	130×75 mm. As No. **MS826**, but with				
	medal in top margin. P 13½			2·50	3·50

The stamps in Nos. **MS826** and **MS836** are similar. The
miniature sheets differ in the marginal inscriptions and
illustrations. No. **MS826** is inscribed "1996 OLYMPIC GAMES"
and has a Gold Medal in the bottom margin. No. **MS836** is
inscribed "TO COMMEMORATE THE OPENING OF THE
CENTENNIAL OLYMPIC GAMES 19 JULY 1996" and has the
medal in the top margin.

178 Pat Sin Leng Mountain

(Des Lam Bing-pui. Litho Harrison)

1996 (24 Sept). *Mountains. T* **178** *and similar multicoloured designs. Two phosphor bands ($1.30) or one side phosphor band (others). P* 13½×14½ ($1.30), 14×14½ ($2.50), 14½×14 ($3.10) or 14½×13½ ($5).

837	$1.30, Type **178**	..		50	35
838	$2.50, Ma On Shan (40×35 mm)	..		70	1·00
839	$3.10, Lion Rock (35×40 mm)	..		90	1·40
840	$5 Lantau Peak (25×46½ mm)	..		1·25	2·25
837/40			*Set of 4*	3·00	4·50

(Des A. Lam. Litho Enschedé)

1996 (16 Oct). *Visit "HONG KONG '97" Stamp Exhibition (3rd issue). Sheet 130×80 mm, containing design as No. 715 but litho and colours changed. P* 14½×14.

MS841	$10 apple-green, black and rose-carmine		2·50	3·50

No. **MS841** shows "HONG KONG" printed in yellow fluorescence with a horizontal green fluorescent line beneath as a
security marking. There is a larger perforation hole at each
corner of the stamp.

(Des B. Kwan. Litho Enschedé)

1996 (29 Oct). *Hong Kong Team's Achievements in Atlanta Olympic Games. Sheet 130×75 mm, containing design as No. 715 but litho. P* 14½×14.

MS842	$10 red-brown, black and cinnamon		2·50	3·25

No. **MS842** shows "HONG KONG" printed in yellow fluorescence with a horizontal green fluorescent line beneath as a
security marking. There is a larger perforation hole at each
corner of the stamp.

179 Main Building, University of Hong Kong, 1912

180 Part of Hong Kong Skyline

(Des T. Li. Recess and litho Ashton-Potter America Inc, New York)

1996 (20 Nov). *Urban Heritage.* T **179** *and similar horiz designs. Multicoloured. Two phosphor bands* ($1.30) *or one phosphor band* (*others*). P 13¹/₂.

843	$1.30, Type **179**	..	..	40	30
844	$2.50, Western Market, 1906		..	70	85
845	$3.10, Old Pathological Institute, 1905	..	75	1·00
846	$5 Flagstaff House, 1846		..	1·00	1·75
843/6			*Set of* 4	2·50	3·50

(Des A. Lam. Litho Walsall)

1996 (4 Dec). *Serving the Community. Sheet* 130×75 mm, *containing design as No. 619, but smaller,* 25×35 mm. *Multicoloured. One phosphor band.* P 13×13¹/₂.
MS847 $5 Multi-racial society .. .. .. 1·00 1·25

(Des Kan Tai-keung)

1997 (26 Jan). T **180** *and similar vert designs showing different sections of Hong Kong skyline. Two phosphor bands* (10 c. to $2.10), *one centre phosphor band* ($2.50 to $5) *or phosphorised paper* ($10).

(*a*) *Sheet stamps. Litho Ashton-Potter America Inc, New York.* P 13¹/₂×13 (10 c. to $5) or 14×13¹/₂ ($10, $20, $50)

848	10 c. purple and rose-pink	..	..	10	10
849	20 c. purple-brown and orange-red	..	10	10
850	50 c. deep green and bright orange	..	10	10
851	$1 greenish blue and orange-yellow	..	15	20
852	$1.20, deep dull green and olive-yellow	..	20	25
853	$1.30, deep violet and apple green	..	20	25
	a. Booklet pane. No. 853×10 with margins all round			2·00	
854	$1.40, maroon and bright green	..	20	25
855	$1.60, deep purple and bright blue-green		25	30
856	$2 deep olive and greenish blue	..	30	35
857	$2.10, deep turquoise-blue and bright blue		30	35
858	$2.50, violet and bright mauve	..	40	45
	a. Booklet pane. No. 858×10 with margins all round			4·00	
859	$3.10, purple and cerise		..	50	55
	a. Booklet pane. No. 859×10 with margins all round			5·00	
860	$5 deep magenta and bright orange	..	80	85
861	$10 multicoloured (28×32 mm)	..	1·60	1·75
862	$20 multicoloured (28×32 mm)	..	3·25	3·25
863	$50 multicoloured (28×32 mm)	..	8·00	8·25
848/63			*Set of* 16	16·50	17·50

MS864 273×53 mm. Nos. 848/56, and as Nos. 857/60 each with one side phosphor band 3·50 4·00
MS865 95×72 mm. Nos. 861/3 .. .. 13·00 13·50

(*b*) *Coil stamps. Designs as Nos. 849, 851, 853, 856 and 859/60, but photo Enschedé.* P 14¹/₂×14.

866	10 c. purple and rose-pink	..	..	10	10
867	50 c. deep green and bright orange	..	10	10
868	$1.30, deep violet and apple-green	..	20	25
869	$1.60, deep purple and bright blue-green		25	30
870	$2.50, violet and bright mauve	..	40	45
871	$3.10, purple and cerise	..	..	50	55
866/71			*Set of* 6	1·50	1·75

Nos. 848/71 show "HONG KONG" printed in yellow fluorescence. The perforations on Nos. 848/65 showing alternate small and large holes.

Nos. 866/71 were printed in coils with every fifth stamp numbered on the reverse.

For miniature sheets containing No. 861 see Nos. MS872/3 and MS892.

(Des Kan Tai-keung. Litho Ashton-Potter America Inc, New York)

1997 (12 Feb). *Visit* "HONG KONG '97" *Stamp Exhibition* (4th issue). *Sheet* 130×75 mm *containing design as No. 861, but ordinary paper, and with marginal illustration in bluish violet.* P 14×13.
MS872 $10 multicoloured .. .. 2·25 3·00
No. MS872 shows "HONG KONG" in yellow fluorescence. The perforations show alternate small and large holes.

(Des Kan Tai-keung. Litho Ashton-Potter America Inc, New York)

1997 (16 Feb). *Visit* "HONG KONG '97" *Stamp Exhibition* (5th issue). *Sheet* 130×80 mm *containing design as No. 861, but ordinary paper, and with marginal illustration in chestnut.* P 14×13.
MS873 $10 multicoloured .. .. 2·25 3·00
No. MS873 shows "HONG KONG" in yellow fluorescence. The perforations show alternate small and large holes.

181 Ox

(Des Kan Tai-keung)

1997 (27 Feb). *Chinese New Year* ("Year of the Ox"). T **181** *and similar horiz designs. Two phosphor bands* ($1.30) *or one phosphor band* (*others*).

(*a*) *Litho Ashton-Potter America Inc, New York.* P 14¹/₂.

874	$1.30, multicoloured	..	..	25	25
875	$2.50, multicoloured	..	..	50	55
876	$3.10, multicoloured	..	..	75	80
877	$5 multicoloured	..		1·25	1·75
874/7			*Set of* 4	2·50	3·00

MS878 133×84 mm. Nos. 874/7 .. 2·50 3·00

(*b*) *Litho Enschedé.* P 13¹/₂.

879	$1.30, multicoloured	..	..	25	25
	a. Booklet pane. Nos. 879 and 881 each × 3		5·00	
880	$2.50, multicoloured	..	..	50	55
881	$3.10, multicoloured	..	..	75	80
882	$5 multicoloured	..		1·25	1·75
879/82			*Set of* 4	2·50	3·00

MS883 133×84 mm. Nos. 879/82 .. 2·50 3·00

182 Yellow-breasted Bunting

(Des Shek Tak-sheun. Litho Enschedé)

1997 (27 Apr). *Migratory Birds.* T **182** *and similar horiz designs. Multicoloured. Two phosphor bands* ($1.30) *or one phosphor band* (*others*). P 13¹/₂.

884	$1.30, Type **182**	..	..	30	35
885	$2.50, Great Knot	..	..	50	55
886	$3.10, Falcated Teal	..	..	75	80
887	$5 Black-faced Spoonbill	..		1·25	1·75
884/7			*Set of* 4	2·50	3·00

183 Hong Kong Stadium

(Des M. Chan)

1997 (18 May). *Modern Landmarks.* T **183** *and similar horiz designs. Multicoloured. Two phosphor bands* ($1.30) *or one phosphor band* (*others*). (*a*) *Litho Enschedé.* P 13¹/₂.

888	$1.30, Type **183**	..	..	25	25
889	$2.50, Peak Tower	..	..	50	55
890	$3.10, Hong Kong Convention and Exhibition Centre		75	85
891	$5 Lantau Bridge	..	..	1·10	1·40
888/91			*Set of* 4	2·40	2·75

MS892 130×76 mm. No. 891 .. .. 1·25 1·75

(*b*) *Photo Walsall.* P 14×14¹/₂.

893	$1.30, Type **183**	..	..	25	25
894	$2.50, Peak Tower	..	..	50	55
895	$3.10, Hong Kong Convention and Exhibition Centre		75	85
896	$5 Lantau Bridge	..	..	1·10	1·40
893/6			*Set of* 4	2·40	2·75

MS897 130×76 mm. No. 896 .. .. 1·25 1·75

(Des G. Lai and Leung Ka-shun. Litho Ashton-Potter America Inc, New York)

1997 (1 June). *Paralympic Games, Atlanta* (1996). *Sheet* 130×75 mm *containing design as No. 861 but on ordinary paper.* P 14×13.
MS898 $10 multicoloured .. .. 2·00 2·75
No. MS898 shows "HONG KONG" printed in yellow fluorescence. The perforations show alternate small and large holes.

(Des A. Lam. Litho Courvoisier)

1997 (30 June). *History of the Hong Kong Post Office. Sheet* 130×75 mm *containing design as No. 677, but redrawn smaller,* 22×38 mm. *One phosphor band.* P 11¹/₂.
MS899 $5 multicoloured .. .. 1·40 2·00
Details of the Post Office buildings depicted on the miniature sheet are printed on the reverse.

Hong Kong became a Special Administrative Region of the People's Republic of China on 1 July 1997 when all previous stamp issues, with exception of Nos. 848/71, were withdrawn and invalidated. Later issues are included in the *Part 17 (China)* catalogue.

PRICES OF SETS

Set prices are given for many issues, generally those containing three stamps or more. Definitive sets include one of each value or major colour change, but do not cover different perforations, die types or minor shades. Where a choice is possible the set prices are based on the cheapest versions of the stamps included in the listings.

1903 (Mar). *Black on white cover. Postage rates on front. Stapled.*
SB1 $1 booklet containing twelve 1 c. (No. 62), twelve 2 c. (No. 56), each in blocks of 6, and sixteen 4 c. (No. 57) in blocks of 8

1904 (1 Jan). *Black on white cover. Postage rates on front. Stapled.*
SB2 $1 booklet containing twelve 1 c. (No. 62), twelve 2 c. (No. 56), each in blocks of 6, and sixteen 4 c. (No. 64) in blocks of 8 .. .. .. £4250

1904. *Black on white cover. Postage rates on front. Stapled.*
SB3 $1 booklet containing twelve 1 c., twelve 2 c. (Nos. 62/3), each in blocks of 6, and sixteen 4 c. (No. 64) in blocks of 8 .. .. .. £3250

1907–08. *Black on white cover. Stapled.*
SB4 $1 booklet containing twelve 1 c., twelve 2 c. (Nos. 62, 92), each in blocks of 6, and sixteen 4 c. (No. 93) in blocks of 8 .. .. .. £2750
a. 4 c. in two blocks of 6 and block of 4 (1908) .. £2750

1910. *Black on white cover. Contents on front. Stapled.*
SB5 $1 booklet containing twelve 1 c., twelve 2 c. (Nos. 91/2), each in blocks of 6, and sixteen 4 c. (No. 93) in two blocks of 6 and block of 4 .. £2750

1912. *Black on white cover. Stapled.*
SB6 $1 booklet containing twelve 1 c., twelve 2 c. (Nos 100/1), each in block of 12, and sixteen 4 c. (No. 102) in block of 12 and block of 4 .. £2500

1929. *Black on white cover. Stapled.*
SB7 $1 booklet containing twelve 1 c., twelve 2 c. (Nos. 117/18), each in block of 12, and sixteen 4 c. (No. 120) in blocks of 8 .. .. .. £2250

1965 (10 May). *Orange-brown* (*No. SB8*) *or yellow-green* (*No. SB9*) *covers. Stitched.*
SB8 $2 booklet containing eight 5 c. and sixteen 10 c. (Nos. 196/7) in blocks of 4 .. .. 32·00
SB9 $5 booklet containing twelve 5 c., eight 10 c., eight 20 c. and four 50 c. (Nos. 196/7, 199, 203) in blocks of 4 .. .. £110

1973 (12 June). *Buff* (*No. SB10*) *or green* (*No. SB11*) *covers. Stitched.*
SB10 $2 booklet containing twenty 10 c. (No. 283) in blocks of 4 .. .. .. 30·00
SB11 $5 booklet containing eight 10 c., four 15 c., eight 20 c. and four 50 c. (Nos. 283, 284/5, 289) each in blocks of 4 .. .. .. 65·00

1975 (27 Jan). *Covers as Nos. SB10/11. Stitched.*
SB12 $2 booklet containing twenty 10 c. (No. 311) in blocks of 4 .. .. .. 28·00
SB13 $5 booklet containing eight 10 c., four 15 c., eight 20 c. and four 50 c. (Nos. 311/13, 317) in blocks of 4 .. .. .. 60·00

1976 (1 July). *Orange* (*No. SB14*) *or green* (*No. SB15*) *covers. Stitched.*
SB14 $2 booklet containing four 10 c. and eight 20 c. (Nos. 311, 313) in blocks of 4 .. 25·00
SB15 $5 booklet containing eight 10 c., four 15 c., eight 20 c. and four 50 c. (Nos. 311, 284, 313, 289) in blocks of 4 .. .. .. 50·00

B 1 *World Map*

1985 (1 Apr–Nov). *Multicoloured cover as Type B* **1**. *Stamps attached by selvedge.*
SB16 $13 booklet containing $1.30 (No. 464) in block of 10 .. .. .. 24·00
a. Containing No. 469 in block of 10 .. 20·00
b. Containing No. 490 in block of 10 (June) 22·00
c. Containing No. 500 in block of 10 (Sept) 24·00
d. Containing No. 504 in block of 10 (Nov) 20·00
Supplies of a similar $13 booklet, but containing ten examples of No. 495, were produced for sale by the Crown Agents Stamp Bureau. Such booklets are reported not to have been available from post offices in Hong Kong.

1985 (2 Sept)–87. *Multicoloured cover as Type B* **1**. *Stamps attached by selvedge.*
SB18 $17 booklet containing $1.70 (No. 482) in block of 10 .. .. .. 35·00
a. Containing No. 547 in block of 10 (1987) 28·00

1985 (28 Oct)–87. *Multicoloured cover as Type B* **1**, *showing map of Hong Kong. Stamps attached by selvedge.*
SB19 $5 booklet containing 50 c. (No. 475) in block of 10 .. .. .. 7·00
a. Containing No. 540 in block of 10 (1987) .. 5·50

B 2 Hong Kong Bank Headquarters and Lion's Head
(Illustration further reduced. Actual size 159×86 mm)

1986 (7 Apr). *New Hong Kong Bank Headquarters. Multicoloured cover as Type B 2. Booklet contains text and illustrations on interleaving pages. Stitched.*
SB20 $29 booklet containing 50 c. in block of 24 and
$1.70 in block of 10 (Nos. 475, 505) .. 35·00

B 3 Early and Modern Views of the Peak Tramway
(Illustration further reduced. Actual size 161×91 mm)

1988 (26 Aug). *Centenary of The Peak Tramway. Multicoloured cover as Type B 3. Booklet contains text and illustrations on interleaving pages. Stitched.*
SB21 $26 booklet containing No. **MS**581×3 .. .. 22·00

B 4 *(Illustration further reduced. Actual size 145×55 mm)*

1989 (18 Jan). *Year of the Snake. Multicoloured cover as Type B 4. Pane attached by selvedge.*
SB22 $12 booklet containing *se-tenant* pane of 10 (No.
587a) .. .. 5·50

B 5 *(Illustration further reduced. Actual size 140×65 mm)*

1990 (23 Jan). *Year of the Horse. Multicoloured cover as Type B 5. Pane attached by selvedge.*
SB23 $14.50, booklet containing two *se-tenant* panes of
6 (No. 631a) .. .. .. 7·00

1990 (3 May). *"Stamp World London 90" International Stamp Exhibition. As No. SB23, but "Stamp World London 90" emblem printed on cover and top selvedge of each pane.*
SB24 $14.50, booklet. Contents as No. SB23 .. .. 11·00
No. SB24 additionally includes an imperforate black print on gummed paper of the 60 c. and $1.80 values of the New Year issue.

B 6 Hong Kong Skyline at Night
(Illustration further reduced. Actual size 168×86 mm)

1990 (29 Nov). *Centenary of Electricity Supply. Multicoloured cover as Type B 6. Booklet contains text and illustrations on interleaving pages. Stitched.*
SB25 $26 booklet containing No. **MS**651×4 .. 25·00

1991 (24 Jan). *Year of the Ram. Multicoloured cover as Type B 5. Pane attached by selvedge.*
SB26 $14.40, booklet containing two *se-tenant* panes of
6 (No. 658a) .. .. .. 7·50

1992 (22 Jan). *Year of the Monkey. Multicoloured cover as Type B 5. Panes attached by selvedge.*
SB27 $18.60, booklet containing two *se-tenant* panes of
6 (No. 686a) .. .. .. 9·00

B 7 "Greetings"
(Illustration further reduced. Actual size 153×67 mm)

1992 (19 Nov). *Greetings Stamps. Multicoloured cover as Type B 7. Panes attached by selvedge.*
SB28 $24 booklet containing two *se-tenant* panes of 6
(No. 728a) and 24 half stamp-size labels .. 7·00

1993 (7 Jan). *Year of the Cock. Multicoloured cover as Type B 5. Panes attached by selvedge.*
SB29 $18.60, booklet containing two *se-tenant* panes of
6 (No. 732a) .. .. .. 7·00

B 8 Skyscrapers

1993 (14–28 Dec). *Multicoloured cover as Type B 8. Panes attached by selvedge.*
SB30 $10 booklet containing pane of ten $1 (No. 757a) 5·00
SB31 $19 booklet containing pane of ten $1.90 (No.
758a) (cover showing Exhibition Centre)
(28 Dec) .. .. .. 7·50
SB32 $24 booklet containing pane of ten $2.40 (No.
759a) (cover showing historical buildings)
(28 Dec) .. .. .. 8·50

B 9 *(Illustration further reduced. Actual size 160×85 mm)*

1994 (12 Jan). *"A History of Hong Kong Definitive Stamps 1862–1992". Multicoloured cover Type B 9. Booklet contains text and illustrations on panes and on interleaving pages. Stapled.*
SB33 $38 booklet containing three different *se-tenant*
panes of 6 (Nos. 760a/2a) .. .. 16·00

1994 (27 Jan). *Year of the Dog. Multicoloured cover as Type B 5. Panes attached by selvedge.*
SB34 $20.40, booklet containing two *se-tenant* panes of
6 (No. 766a) .. .. .. 7·50

1995 (17 Jan). *Year of the Pig. Multicoloured cover as Type B 5. Panes attached by selvedge.*
SB35 $20.40, booklet containing two *se-tenant* panes
of 6 (No. 793a) .. .. 6·00

1995 (1 June). *Multicoloured covers as Nos. SB30/2. Panes attached by selvedge.*
SB36 $12 booklet containing pane of ten $1.20 (No.
757ba) (Type B 8 cover) .. 5·00
SB37 $21 booklet containing pane of ten $2.10 (No.
758ba) (cover as No. SB31) .. 7·00
SB38 $26 booklet containing pane of ten $2.60 (No.
759ca) (cover as No. SB32) .. 8·00
On the initial supply of No. SB36 the inside of the card covers were matt. A printing later in 1995 showed both sides of the cover card glossy.

1996 (31 Jan). *Year of the Rat. Multicoloured cover as Type B 5. Panes attached by selvedge.*
SB39 $22.80, booklet containing two *se-tenant* panes
of 6 (No. 816a) .. .. 5·00

1996 (2 Sept). *Multicoloured covers as Nos. SB30/2. Panes attached by selvedge.*
SB40 $13 booklet containing pane of ten $1.30 (No.
757ca) (Type B 8 cover) .. 4·50
SB41 $25 booklet containing pane of ten $2.50 (No.
759ba) (cover as No. SB31) .. 6·00
SB42 $31 booklet containing pane of ten $3.10 (No.
759da) (cover as No. SB32) .. 7·00

B 10 Water Front

1997 (26 Jan). *Multicoloured covers as Type B 10, each incorporating the design from the stamps included. Panes attached by selvedge.*
SB43 $13 booklet containing pane of ten $1.30 (No.
853a) .. .. .. 2·00
SB44 $25 booklet containing pane of ten $2.50 (No.
858a) .. .. .. 4·00
SB45 $31 booklet containing pane of ten $3.10 (No.
859a) .. .. .. 7·00

B 11 Hong Kong Waterfront
(Illustration further reduced. Actual size 183×130 mm)

1997 (14 Feb). *Hong Kong Past and Present. Multicoloured cover as Type B 11. Booklet containing text and illustrations on interleaving pages. Stitched.*
SB46 $55 booklet containing three different *se-tenant*
panes of 6 (Nos. 757cc, 757db and 758bd) .. 20·00

1997 (27 Feb). *Year of the Ox. Multicoloured cover as Type B 5. Panes attached by selvedge.*
SB47 $26.40, booklet containing two panes of 6 (No.
879a) .. .. .. 5·00

POSTAGE DUE STAMPS

PRINTERS. Nos. D1/23 were typographed by De La Rue & Co.

D 1 Post-office Scales D 2

1923 (Dec)–**56.** *Wmk Mult Script CA. Ordinary paper. P 14.*
D1	D 1	1 c. brown	2·00	65
		a. Wmk sideways (1931)	1·25	2·75
		ab. Chalk-surfaced paper (21.3.56)	30	1·00
D2		2 c. green	17·00	5·00
		a. Wmk sideways (1928)	10·00	5·00
D3		4 c. scarlet	29·00	7·00
		a. Wmk sideways (1928)	27·00	7·00
D4		6 c. yellow	26·00	13·00
		a. Wmk sideways (1931)	45·00	28·00
D5		10 c. bright ultramarine	23·00	8·00
		a. Wmk sideways (1934)	80·00	16·00
D1/5		*Set of 5*	85·00	30·00
D1a/5a		*Set of 5*	£150	50·00
D1/5 Optd "Specimen"		*Set of 5*	£225	

1938 (Feb)–**63.** *Wmk Mult Script CA (sideways). Ordinary paper. P 14.*
D 6	D 1	2 c. grey	13·00	9·00
		a. Chalk-surfaced paper (21.3.56)	1·10	10·00
D 7		4 c. orange	14·00	6·50
		a. Chalk-surfaced paper. *Orange-yellow* (23.5.61)	2·50	8·50
D 8		6 c. scarlet	9·50	5·50
D 9		8 c. chestnut (26.2.46)	5·50	32·00
D10		10 c. violet	26·00	45
		a. Chalk-surfaced paper (17.9.63)	14·00	6·50
D11		20 c. black (26.2.46)	9·50	3·00
D12		50 c. blue (7.47)	35·00	15·00
D6a/12		*Set of 7*	70·00	65·00
D6/12 Perf "Specimen"		*Set of 7*	£300	

1965 (15 Apr)–**72.** *Chalk-surfaced paper. P 14.*
(a) Wmk w 12 (sideways)
D13	D 1	4 c. yellow-orange	5·50	24·00
D14		5 c. red (13.5.69)	3·00	4·75
		a. Glazed paper (17.11.72)	11·00	29·00
D15		10 c. violet (27.6.67)	3·00	3·75
D16		20 c. black (1965)	4·50	3·75
D17		50 c. deep blue (1965)	20·00	9·00
		a. Blue (13.5.69)	19·00	9·00
D13/17		*Set of 5*	32·00	40·00

639

(b) Wmk w **12** *(upright)*

D18	D 1	5 c. red (20.7.67)	2·00	4·50
D19		50 c. deep blue (26.8.70) ..	35·00	10·00

The 5 c. is smaller, 21 × 18 mm.

1972 (17 Nov)–74. *Glazed, ordinary paper.* W w **12** *(sideways).*

(a) P 14 × 14½

D20	D 1	10 c. bright reddish violet	6·00	3·75
D21		20 c. grey-black	7·00	5·50
D22		50 c. deep dull blue	4·00	9·50

(b) P 13½ × 14

D23	D 1	5 c. brown-red (1.5.74) ..	2·25	5·00
D20/3 ..		.. .. ..	*Set of 4* 17·00	21·00

(Typo Walsall)

1976 (19 Mar*)–78. *Smaller design (21 × 17 mm) with redrawn value-tablet. Glazed, ordinary paper.* W w **14**. *P* 14.

D25	D 1	10 c. bright reddish violet	50	3·50
		a. Chalk-surfaced paper (15.12.78)	60	1·75
D26		20 c. grey-black	85	4·00
		a. Chalk-surfaced paper (15.12.78)	60	2·00
D27		50 c. deep dull blue	75	4·50
		a. Chalk-surfaced paper (15.12.78)	60	2·50
D28		$1 yellow (1.4.76)	11·00	11·00
		a. Chalk-surfaced paper (15.12.78)	90	3·25
D25/8 ..		.. .. ..	*Set of 4* 12·00	21·00
D25a/8a		.. .. ..	*Set of 4* 2·40	8·50

*This is the London release date. It is believed that the stamps were not released locally until 14 April.

(Typo Walsall)

1986 (11 Jan). *As Nos.* D27a/8a, *but without watermark. P* 14.

D29	D 1	50 c. slate-blue ..	1·75	4·00
D30		$1 lemon	2·25	4·50

(Des A. Chan. Litho B.D.T.)

1987 (25 Mar). *P* 14×15.

D31	D 2	10 c. light green ..	10	10
D32		20 c. red-brown	10	10
D33		50 c. bright violet	10	10
D34		$1 yellow-orange	15	20
D35		$5 dull ultramarine	80	85
D36		$10 bright rose-red	1·60	1·75
D31/6 ..		.. .. ..	*Set of 6* 2·75	3·00

POSTCARD STAMPS

Stamps specially surcharged for use on Postcards.

PRICES. Those in the left-hand column are for unused examples on complete postcards; those on the right for used examples off card. Examples used on postcards are worth more.

3
CENTS
(P **1**)

THREE
(P **2**)

1879 (1 Apr). *Nos.* 22 *and* 13 *surch as Type* P **1** *by D.L.R.*

P1	3	3 c. on 16 c. yellow (No. 22)	..	£300 £325
P2		5 c. on 18 c. lilac (No. 13)	..	£275 £325

1879 (Nov). *No.* P2 *handstamped with Type* P **2**.

P3	3	3 c. on 5 c. on 18 c. lilac	.. £5000 £6500

POSTAL FISCAL STAMPS

I. Stamps inscribed "STAMP DUTY"

NOTE. The dated circular "HONG KONG" cancellation with "PAID ALL" in lower segment was used for fiscal purposes, in black, from 1877. Previously it appears in red on mail to the U.S.A., but is usually not used as a cancellation.

F 1

F 2

F 3

1874–1902. *Wmk Crown CC.* (a) *P* 15½×15

F1	F 1	$2 olive-green ..	..	£300 45·00
F2	F 2	$3 dull violet ..	..	£275 32·00
		b. Bluish paper		£1500
F3	F 3	$10 rose-carmine ..	..	£7000 £650

(b) P 14

F4	F 1	$2 dull bluish green (10.97) ..	..	£350 £225
F5	F 2	$3 dull mauve (3.02) ..	..	£400 £350
		a. Bluish paper		£1500
F6	F 3	$10 grey-green (1892) ..	..	£9500 £10000
F4/5		Optd "Specimen" ..	*Set of 2* £400	

Nos. F1/3 and F7 exist on various papers, ranging from thin to thick.

All three of the values perforated 15½×15 were authorised for postal use in 1874. The $10 was withdrawn from such use in 1880, the $2 in September 1897 and the $3 in 1902.

The $2 and $3 perforated 14 were available for postal purposes until July 1903. The $10 in grey-green was issued for fiscal purposes in 1892 and is known with postal cancellations.

12
CENTS.
(F **4**)

F 5

1880. *No.* F3 *surch with Type* F **4** *by Noronha and Sons, Hong Kong.*

F7	F 5	12 c. on $10 rose-carmine	£700 £250

1890 (24 Dec). *Wmk Crown CA. P* 14.

F8	F 5	2 c. dull purple ..	..	55·00 14·00

No. F8 was authorised for postal use between 24 and 31 December 1890.

5
DOLLARS
(F **6**)

ONE
DOLLAR
(F **7**)

F 8

1891 (1 Jan). *Surch with Type* F **6** *by D.L.R. Wmk Crown CA. P* 14.

F9	F 3	$5 on $10 purple/*red* (Optd S. £160)	£275 95·00

No. F9 was in use for postal purposes until June 1903.

1897 (Sept). *Surch with Type* F **7** *by Noronha and Sons, Hong Kong, and with the value in Chinese characters subsequently applied twice by handstamp as T* **15**.

F10	F **1**	$1 on $2 olive-green (No. F1)		£180 95·00
		a. Both Chinese handstamps omitted		£2500 £1800
F11		$1 on $2 dull bluish green (No. F4)		
		(H/S S, £140)		£200 £120
		a. Both Chinese handstamps omitted		£1500 £1100
		b. Diagonal Chinese handstamp omitted ..		£9000
		c. Vertical Chinese handstamp omitted ..		

1938 (11 Jan). *Wmk Mult Script CA. P* 14.

F12	F **8**	5 c. green ..	..	50·00 9·50

No. F12 was authorised for postal use between 11 and 20 January 1938 due to a shortage of the 5 c., No. 121.

Forged cancellations are known on this stamp inscribed "VICTORIA 9.AM 11 JA 38 HONG KONG" without side bars between the rings.

II. Stamps overprinted "S.O." (Stamp Office), or "S.D." (Stamp Duty)

S. O.
(S **1**)

S. D.
(S **2**)

1891 (1 Jan). *Optd with Types* S **1** *or* S **2**.

S1	S **1**	2 c. carmine (No. 33) ..	..	£750 £275
S2	S **2**	2 c. carmine (No. 33) ..	..	£350 £150
		a. Opt inverted ..	..	† £3750
S3	S **2**	10 c. purple/*red* (No. 38) ..	..	£1000 £350

Examples of No. S1 exist with the "O" amended to "D" in manuscript.

Other fiscal stamps are found apparently postally used, but there is no evidence that this use was authorised.

The new-issue supplement to this Catalogue appears each month in

GIBBONS STAMP MONTHLY

—from your newsagent or by postal subscription— sample copy and details on request.

JAPANESE OCCUPATION OF HONG KONG

Hong Kong surrendered to the Japanese on 25 December 1941. The postal service was not resumed until 22 January 1942 when the G.P.O. and Kowloon Central Office re-opened.

Japanese postmarks used in Hong Kong can be identified by the unique combination of horizontal lines in the central circle and three stars in the lower segment of the outer circle. Dates shown on such postmarks are in the sequence Year/Month/Day with the first shown as a Japanese regnal year number so that Showa 17 = 1942 and so on.

Initially six current Japanese definitives, 1, 2, 3, 4, 10 and 30 s. (Nos. 297, 315/17, 322 and 327). were on sale, but the range gradually expanded to cover all values between ½ s. and 10 y. with Nos. 313/14, 318, 325, 328/31, 391, 395/6, 398/9 and 405 of Japan also available from Hong Kong post offices during the occupation. Philatelic covers exist showing other Japanese stamps, but these were not available from the local post offices. Supply of these Japanese stamps was often interrupted and, during the period between 28 July 1942 and 21 April 1943, circular "Postage Paid" handstamps were sometimes used. A substantial increase in postage rates on 16 April 1945 led to the issue of the local surcharges, Nos. J1/3.

PRICES FOR STAMPS ON COVER
Nos. J1/3 *from* × 7

(1)   (2)

1945 (16 Apr). *Stamps of Japan surch with T* **1** *(No.* J1*) or as T* **2**.

J1		1.50 yen on 1 s. brown	..	25·00 21·00
J2		3 yen on 2 s. scarlet	..	12·00 17·00
J3		5 yen on 5 s. claret ..	..	£850 £130

Designs (18½ × 22 mm):—1 s. Girl Worker; 2 s. Gen. Nogi; 5 s. Admiral Togo.

No. J3 has four characters of value similarly arranged but differing from T **2**.

BRITISH POST OFFICES IN CHINA

Under the terms of the 1842 Treaty of Nanking China granted Great Britain and its citizens commercial privileges in five Treaty Ports, Amoy, Canton, Foochow, Ningpo and Shanghai. British Consuls were appointed to each Port and their offices, as was usual during this period, collected and distributed mail for the British community. This system was formally recognised by a Hong Kong Government notice published on 16 April 1844. Mail from the consular offices was postmarked when it passed through Hong Kong.

The number of Chinese Treaty Ports was increased to sixteen by the ratification of the Treaty of Peking in 1860 with British postal facilities being eventually extended to the Ports of Chefoo, Hankow, Kiungchow (Hoihow), Swatow, Tainan (Anping) and Tientsin.

As postal business expanded the consular agencies were converted into packet agencies or post offices which passed under the direct control of the Hong Kong postal authorities on 1 May 1868.

In May 1898 the British Government leased the territory of Wei Hai Wei from China for use as a naval station to counter the Russian presence at Port Arthur.

The opening of the Trans-Siberia Railway and the extension of Imperial Penny Postage to the Treaty Port agencies resulted in them becoming a financial burden on the colonial post office. Control of the agencies reverted to the G.P.O., London, on 1 January 1911.

The pre-adhesive postal markings of the various agencies are a fascinating, but complex, subject. Full details can be found in *Hong Kong & the Treaty Ports of China & Japan* by F.W. Webb (reprinted edition J. Bendon, Limassol, 1992) and in various publications of the Hong Kong Study Circle.

From 15 October 1864 the use of Hong Kong stamps on mail from the Treaty Ports became compulsory, although such stamps were, initially, not cancelled (with the exception of Amoy) until they reached Hong Kong where the "B62" killer was applied. Cancellation of mail at the actual Ports commenced during 1866 at Shanghai and Ningpo, spreading to all the agencies during the next ten years. Shanghai had previously used a c.d.s. on adhesives during 1863 and again in 1865–66.

The main types of cancellation used between 1866 and 1930 are illustrated below. The illustrations show the style of each postmark and no attempt has been made to cover differences in type letters or figures, arrangement, diameter or colour.

Until 1885 the vertical and horizontal killers were used to obliterate the actual stamps with an impression of one of the circular date stamps shown elsewhere on the cover. Many of the early postmarks were also used as backstamps or transit marks and, in the notes which follow, references to use are for the first appearance of the mark, not necessarily its first use as an obliterator.

Illustrations in this section are taken from *Hong Kong & the Treaty Ports of China & Japan* by F. W. Webb and are reproduced with the permission of the Royal Philatelic Society, London.

Details of the stamps known used from each post office are taken, with permission, from *British Post Offices in the Far East* by Edward B. Proud, published by Proud-Bailey Co. Ltd.

Postmark Types

Type A
Vertical killer

Type B
Horizontal killer

Type C
Name horizontal

Type D
Name curved

Type E
Double circle Name at top

Type F
Double circle Name at foot

Type G
Single circle Name at top

PRICES. The prices quoted in this section are for fine used stamps which show a clear impression of a substantial part of the cancellation.

AMOY

One of the five original Treaty Ports, opened to British trade by the Treaty of Nanking in 1842. A consular postal agency was established in 1844 which expanded in 1876 into two separate offices, one on the off-shore island of Ku Lang Seu and the other in Amoy itself.

Amoy "PAID" (*supplied* 1858) *used* 1859–67
Type A ("A1") (*supplied* 1866) *used at Ku Lang Seu* 1869–82
Type D (*supplied* 1866) *used* 1867–1922
Type B ("D27") (*supplied* 1876) *used at Amoy* 1876–84
Type C *used* 1876–94
Type F (*supplied* 1913) *used* 1916–22

Stamps of HONG KONG *cancelled at Amoy between* 1864 *and* 1916 *with postmarks detailed above.*

1862. *No wmk* (*Nos.* 1/7).
Z1	2 c. brown	..	..	..	£120
Z2	8 c. yellow-buff	..	..	..	£110
Z3	12 c. pale greenish blue	..	..		95·00
Z4	18 c. lilac	..	..	..	60·00
Z5	24 c. green	..	..	..	£120
Z6	48 c. rose	..			
Z7	96 c. brownish grey	..	..		£425

1863–71. *Wmk Crown CC* (*Nos.* 8/19).
Z 8	2 c. brown	..	..	..	26·00
Z 9	4 c. grey	..	..	..	24·00
	a. Perf 12½				
Z10	6 c. lilac	..	..	..	35·00
Z11	8 c. orange	..	..	..	29·00
Z12	12 c. blue	..	..	..	13·00
Z13	18 c. lilac	..	..	..	£425
Z14	24 c. green	..	..	..	35·00
Z15	30 c. vermilion	..	..	..	55·00
Z16	30 c. mauve	..	..	..	9·00

Z17	48 c. rose	..	..	..	32·00
Z18	96 c. olive-bistre	..	..		£1000
Z19	96 c. brownish grey	..	..	..	£140

1876–77. (*Nos.* 20/1).
Z20	16 c. on 18 c. lilac	..	..	..	£250
Z21	28 c. on 30 c. mauve	..	..	..	£110

1877. *Wmk Crown CC* (*No.* 22).
Z22	16 c. yellow	..	..	..	85·00

1880. (*Nos.* 23/7).
Z23	5 c. on 8 c. orange	..	..	..	£100
Z24	5 c. on 18 c. lilac	..	..	..	90·00
Z25	10 c. on 12 c. blue	..	..	..	90·00
Z26	10 c. on 16 c. yellow	..	..	..	£150
Z27	10 c. on 24 c. green	..	..	..	£100

1880. *Wmk Crown CC* (*Nos.* 28/31).
Z28	2 c. rose	..	..	..	32·00
Z29	5 c. blue	..	..	..	45·00
Z30	10 c. mauve	..	..	..	38·00
Z31	48 c. brown	..	..	..	£100

1882–96. *Wmk Crown CA* (*Nos.* 32/9).
Z31a	2 c. rose-lake	..			
Z32	2 c. carmine	..	..	..	2·50
Z33	4 c. slate-grey	..	..	..	5·00
Z34	5 c. blue	..	..	..	2·50
Z35	10 c. dull mauve	..	..		19·00
Z36	10 c. green	..	..	..	3·00
Z37	10 c. purple/*red*	..	..	..	3·00
Z38	30 c. green	..	..	..	20·00

1885. (*Nos.* 40/2).
Z39	20 c. on 30 c. orange-red	..	..		8·00
Z40	50 c. on 48 c. yellowish brown	..		35·00
Z41	$1 on 96 c. grey-olive	..	..		60·00

1891. (*Nos.* 43/4, 48/50).
Z42	7 c. on 10 c. green	..	..		15·00
Z43	14 c. on 30 c. mauve	..	..		65·00
Z44	20 c. on 30 c. green	..	..		8·50
Z45	50 c. on 48 c. dull purple	..		11·00
Z46	$1 on 96 c. purple/*red*	..	..		28·00

1891. 50*th Anniv of Colony* (*No.* 51).
Z47	2 c. carmine	..	..	..	£750

1898. (*No.* 52).
Z48	$1 on 96 c. black	..	..	..	35·00

1898. (*No.* 55).
Z49	10 c. on 30 c. green	..	..	..	£160

1900–01. *Wmk Crown CA* (*Nos.* 56/61).
Z50	2 c. dull green	..	..	..	2·50
Z51	4 c. carmine	..	..	..	1·75
Z52	5 c. yellow	..	..	..	10·00
Z53	10 c. ultramarine	..	..	..	3·00
Z54	12 c. blue	..	..	..	80·00
Z55	30 c. brown	..	..	..	42·00

1903. *Wmk Crown CA* (*Nos.* 62/76).
Z56	1 c. dull purple and brown	..		3·00
Z57	2 c. dull green	..	..		2·50
Z58	4 c. purple/*red*	..	..		1·60
Z59	5 c. dull green and brown-orange		11·00
Z60	8 c. slate and violet	..	..		4·25
Z61	10 c. purple and blue/*blue*	..		2·50
Z62	12 c. green and purple/*yellow*		8·00
Z63	20 c. slate and chestnut	..		6·50
Z64	30 c. dull green and black	..		25·00
Z65	50 c. dull green and magenta	..		42·00
Z67	$2 slate and scarlet	..			£225
Z68	$3 slate and dull blue	..			

1904–06. *Wmk Mult Crown CA* (*Nos.* 77/90).
Z71	2 c. dull green	..	..		2·50
Z72	4 c. purple/*red*	..	..		1·60
Z73	5 c. dull green and brown-orange		8·50
Z74	8 c. slate and violet	..	..		6·50
Z75	10 c. purple and blue/*blue*	..		2·25
Z76	12 c. green and purple/*yellow*		10·00
Z77	20 c. slate and chestnut	..		5·50
Z78	30 c. dull green and black	..		17·00
Z79	50 c. green and magenta	..		15·00
Z83	$5 purple and blue-green	..		£375

1907–11. *Wmk Mult Crown CA* (*Nos.* 91/9).
Z85	1 c. brown	..	..	..	3·00
Z86	2 c. green	..	..	..	2·50
Z87	4 c. carmine-red	..	..		1·60
Z88	6 c. orange-vermilion and purple		9·00
Z89	10 c. bright ultramarine	..		2·25
Z90	20 c. purple and sage-green	..		40·00
Z91	30 c. purple and orange-yellow		35·00

1912–15. *Wmk Mult Crown CA* (*Nos.* 100/16).
Z 93	1 c. brown	..	..	..	3·75
Z 94	2 c. green	..	..	..	3·50
Z 95	4 c. red	..	..	..	1·60
Z 96	6 c. orange	..	..	..	2·75
Z 97	8 c. grey	..	..	..	15·00
Z 98	10 c. ultramarine	..	..		2·75
Z 99	12 c. purple/*yellow*	..	..		13·00
Z100	20 c. purple and sage-green	..		4·75
Z102	30 c. purple and orange-yellow		10·00
Z103	50 c. black/*green*	..	..		7·00
Z104	$1 purple and blue/*blue*	..		15·00
Z105	$3 green and purple	..	..		85·00

POSTCARD STAMPS

1879. (*Nos.* P1/2).
ZP106	3 c. on 16 c. yellow	..	..	..	£400
ZP107	5 c. on 18 c. lilac	..	..	..	£450

POSTAL FISCAL STAMPS

1874–1902. *Wmk Crown CC.* (a) P 15½×15 (*Nos.* F1/3).
ZF109	$2 olive-green	..	..	..	90·00
ZF110	$3 dull violet	..	..	..	80·00

1891. (*No.* F9).
ZF116	$5 on $10 purple/*red*	..	..	..	£170

1897. (*No.* F10).
ZF118	$1 on $2 olive-green	..	..		

ANPING

Anping is the port for Tainan, on the island of Formosa, opened to British trade in 1860. A British Vice-consulate operated in the port and mail is known postmarked there between 1889 and 1895. Formosa passed under Japanese control in 1895 and British Treaty Port rights then lapsed.

Type D *used* 1889–95

Stamps of HONG KONG *cancelled at Anping between* 1889 *and* 1895 *with postmark detailed above.*

1882–91. *Wmk Crown CA* (*Nos.* 32/9).
Z120	2 c. carmine	..	..	..	£550
Z121	5 c. blue	..	..	..	£400
Z123	10 c. green	..	..	..	£550
Z124	10 c. purple/*red*	..	..	..	£700

1885. (*Nos.* 40/2).
Z126	20 c. on 30 c. orange-red	..		£550
Z127	50 c. on 48 c. yellowish brown	..		£750

CANTON

A British postal service was organised in Cantom from 1834, but was closed when the foreign communities were evacuated in August 1839. The city was one of the original Treaty Ports and a consular agency was opened there in 1844. The consulate closed during the riots of 1857, being replaced by a temporary postal agency at Whampoa, further down the river. When British forces reached Canton a further temporary agency was set up in 1859, but both closed in July 1863 when the consulate was re-established.

Type A ("C1") (*supplied* 1866) *used* 1875–84
Type C (*supplied* 1866) *used* 1870–1901
Type D *used* 1890–1922

Stamps of HONG KONG *cancelled at Canton between* 1870 *and* 1916 *with postmarks detailed above.*

1862. *No wmk* (*Nos.* 1/7).
Z135	18 c. lilac	..	..	..	80·00

1863–71. *Wmk Crown CC* (*Nos.* 8/19).
Z136	2 c. brown	..	..	..	25·00
Z137	4 c. grey	..	..	..	28·00
Z138	6 c. lilac	..	..	..	32·00
Z139	8 c. orange	..	..	..	28·00
Z140	12 c. blue	..	..	..	14·00
Z142	24 c. green	..	..	..	38·00
Z143	30 c. vermilion	..	..	..	
Z144	30 c. mauve	..	..	..	12·00
Z145	48 c. rose	..	..	..	48·00
Z147	96 c. brownish grey	..	..	..	55·00

1876–77. (*Nos.* 20/1).
Z148	16 c. on 18 c. lilac	..	..	..	£200
Z149	28 c. on 30 c. mauve	..	..	..	85·00

1877. *Wmk Crown CC* (*No.* 22).
Z150	16 c. yellow	..	..	..	£100

1880. (*Nos.* 23/7).
Z151	5 c. on 8 c. orange	..	..	..	£110
Z152	5 c. on 18 c. lilac	..	..	..	95·00
Z153	10 c. on 12 c. blue	..	..	..	90·00
Z154	10 c. on 16 c. yellow	..	..	..	£170
Z155	10 c. on 24 c. green	..	..	..	£110

1880. *Wmk Crown CC* (*Nos.* 28/31).
Z156	2 c. rose	..	..	..	28·00
Z157	5 c. blue	..	..	..	38·00
Z158	10 c. mauve	..	..	..	32·00

1882–96. *Wmk Crown CA* (*Nos.* 32/9).
Z159	2 c. rose-lake	..	..	..	
Z160	2 c. carmine	..	..	..	1·50
Z161	4 c. slate-grey	..	..	..	6·00
Z162	5 c. blue	..	..	..	3·00
Z163	10 c. dull mauve	..	..	..	16·00
Z164	10 c. green	..	..	..	5·00
Z165	10 c. purple/*red*	..	..	..	3·00
Z166	30 c. green	..	..	..	21·00

1885. (Nos. 40/2).
Z167	20 c. on 30 c. orange-red	..	..	..	7·50
Z168	50 c. on 48 c. yellowish brown	..	..	..	35·00
Z169	$1 on 96 c. grey-olive	..	..	..	60·00

1891. (Nos. 43/5, 48/50).
Z170	7 c. on 10 c. green	..	..	..	14·00
Z171	14 c. on 30 c. mauve	..	..	..	70·00
Z171a	20 c. on 30 c. green (No. 45)	..	..	..	£150
Z172	20 c. on 30 c. green (No. 48)	..	..	..	10·00
Z173	50 c. on 48 c. dull purple	..	..	..	12·00
Z174	$1 on 96 c. purple/*red*	..	..	..	32·00

1891. *50th Anniv of Colony* (No. 51).
Z175	2 c. carmine	..	..	..	£700

1898. (No. 52).
Z176	$1 on 96 c. black	..	..	..	35·00

1898. (No. 55)
Z177	10 c. on 30 c. grey-green	..	..	

1900–01. *Wmk Crown CA* (Nos. 56/61).
Z178	2 c. dull green	..	..	..	2·50
Z179	4 c. carmine	..	..	..	2·50
Z180	5 c. yellow	..	..	..	19·00
Z181	10 c. ultramarine	..	..	..	2·50
Z182	12 c. blue	..	..	..	50·00
Z183	30 c. brown	..	..	..	38·00

1903. *Wmk Crown CA* (Nos. 62/76).
Z184	1 c. dull purple and brown	..	..	..	2·50
Z185	2 c. dull green	..	..	..	2·50
Z186	4 c. purple/*red*	..	..	..	1·60
Z187	5 c. dull green and brown-orange	..	..	11·00
Z188	8 c. slate and violet	..	..	..	5·00
Z189	10 c. purple and blue/*blue*	..	..	..	2·50
Z190	12 c. green and purple/*yellow*	..	..	8·50
Z191	20 c. slate and chestnut	..	..	..	4·25
Z192	30 c. dull green and black	..	..	..	20·00

1904–06. *Wmk Mult Crown CA* (Nos. 77/90).
Z199	2 c. dull green	..	..	..	2·50
Z200	4 c. purple/*red*	..	..	..	1·60
Z201	5 c. dull green and brown-orange	..	..	9·00
Z202	8 c. slate and violet	..	..	..	8·00
Z203	10 c. purple and blue/*blue*	..	..	..	2·25
Z204	12 c. green and purple/*yellow*	..	..	11·00
Z205	20 c. slate and chestnut	..	..	..	7·00
Z206	30 c. dull green and black	..	..	..	14·00
Z207	50 c. green and magenta	..	..	..	17·00
Z208	$1 purple and sage-green	..	..	..	30·00
Z212	$10 slate and orange/*blue*	..	..	£1000

1907–11. *Wmk Mult Crown CA* (Nos. 91/9).
Z213	1 c. brown	..	..	..	2·50
Z214	2 c. green	..	..	..	2·50
Z215	4 c. carmine-red	..	..	..	1·60
Z216	6 c. orange-vermilion and purple	..	..	9·00
Z217	10 c. bright ultramarine	..	..	..	2·25
Z218	20 c. purple and sage-green	..	..	40·00
Z219	30 c. purple and orange-yellow	..	..	30·00
Z220	50 c. black/*green*	..	..	..	26·00

1912–15. *Wmk Mult Crown CA* (Nos. 100/16).
Z222	1 c. brown	..	..	..	3·00
Z223	2 c. green	..	..	..	2·25
Z224	4 c. red	..	..	..	1·40
Z225	6 c. orange	..	..	..	2·50
Z226	8 c. grey	..	..	..	12·00
Z227	10 c. ultramarine	..	..	..	2·50
Z228	12 c. purple/*yellow*	..	..	..	9·50
Z229	20 c. purple and sage-green	..	..	3·75
Z231	30 c. purple and orange-yellow	..	..	9·50
Z232	50 c. black/*green*	..	..	..	3·25
Z235	$3 green and purple	..	..	..	85·00

POSTCARD STAMPS

1879. (Nos. P1/2).
ZP236	3 c. on 16 c. yellow	..	..	..	£375
ZP237	5 c. on 18 c. lilac	..	..	..	£475

POSTAL FISCAL STAMPS

1874–1902. *Wmk Crown CC.* (a) *P* 15½×15 (Nos. F1/3)
ZF238	$2 olive-green	..	..	..	£110

1891. (No. F9).
ZF246	$5 on $10 purple/*red*	..	..	£225

1897. (No. F10).
ZF247	$1 on $2 olive-green	..	..	..	

CHEFOO

Chefoo was opened to British trade in 1860. Although a consulate was established in 1863 no organised postal agency was provided until 1 January 1903 when one was opened at the premises of Curtis Brothers, a commercial firm.

Type **E** (*supplied* 1902) *used* 1903–20
Type **D** (*supplied* 1907) *used* 1907–13
Type **F** *used* 1916–22

Stamps of HONG KONG *cancelled at Chefoo between* 1903 *and* 1916 *with postmarks detailed above.*

1882–96. *Wmk Crown CA* (Nos. 32/9).
Z249	5 c. blue	..	..	..	18·00

1891. (Nos. 43/50)
Z250	20 c. on 30 c. grey-green (No. 48a)	..	26·00

1898. (No. 52).
Z251	$1 on 96 c. black	..	..	..	55·00

1900–01. *Wmk Crown CA* (Nos. 56/61).
Z252	2 c. dull green	..		..	16·00
Z253	4 c. carmine	..	..	..	15·00
Z254	5 c. yellow	..	..	..	30·00
Z255	10 c. ultramarine	..	..	..	16·00
Z257	30 c. brown	..	..	..	70·00

1903. *Wmk Crown CA* (Nos. 62/76).
Z258	1 c. dull purple and brown	..	..	6·00
Z259	2 c. dull green	..	..	..	5·50
Z260	4 c. purple/*red*	..	..	..	5·00
Z261	5 c. dull green and brown-orange	..	..	12·00
Z262	8 c. slate and violet	..	..	..	10·00
Z263	10 c. purple and blue/*blue*	..	..	6·50
Z264	12 c. green and purple/*yellow*	..	..	15·00

1904–06. *Wmk Mult Crown CA* (Nos. 77/90).
Z273	2 c. dull green	..	..	..	5·00
Z274	4 c. purple/*red*	..	..	..	4·50
Z275	5 c. dull green and brown-orange	..	..	10·00
Z276	8 c. slate and violet	..	..	..	10·00
Z277	10 c. purple and blue/*blue*	..	..	5·00
Z278	12 c. green and purple/*yellow*	..	..	14·00
Z279	20 c. slate and chestnut	..	..	..	12·00
Z280	30 c. dull green and black	..	..	24·00
Z281	50 c. green and magenta	..	..	..	29·00
Z283	$2 slate and scarlet	..	..	..	£140
Z284	$3 slate and dull blue	..	..	..	£250
Z285	$5 purple and blue-green	..	..		

1907–11. *Wmk Mult Crown CA* (Nos. 91/9).
Z287	1 c. brown	..	..	..	6·00
Z288	2 c. green	..	..	..	5·50
Z289	4 c. carmine-red	..	..	..	5·00
Z290	6 c. orange-vermilion and purple	..	..	15·00
Z291	10 c. bright ultramarine	..	..	..	5·00
Z292	20 c. purple and sage-green	..	..	42·00
Z293	30 c. purple and orange-yellow	..	..	29·00
Z295	$2 carmine-red and black	..	..	..	

1912–15. *Wmk Mult Crown CA* (Nos. 100/16).
Z296	1 c. brown	..	..	..	4·25
Z297	2 c. green	..	..	..	4·75
Z298	4 c. red	..	..	..	3·75
Z299	6 c. orange	..	..	..	7·50
Z301	10 c. ultramarine	..	..	..	4·25
Z302	12 c. purple/*yellow*	..	..	..	15·00
Z303	20 c. purple and sage-green	..	..	7·00
Z305	30 c. purple and orange-yellow	..	..	9·00
Z306	50 c. black/*green*	..	..	..	5·50
Z307	$1 purple and blue/*blue*	..	..	..	7·50
Z308	$2 carmine-red and grey-black	..	..	48·00
Z309	$3 green and purple	..	..	..	75·00
Z310	$5 green and red/*green*	..	..	£300
Z311	$10 purple and black/*red*	..	..	£180

FOOCHOW

Foochow, originally known as Foochowfoo, was one of the original Treaty Ports opened to British trade in 1842. A British consulate and postal agency was established in June 1844.

Type **A** ("F1") (*supplied* 1866) *used* 1873–84
Type **D** (inscr "FOOCHOWFOO") (*supplied* 1866) *used* 1867–1905
Type **D** (inscr "FOOCHOW") (*supplied* 1894) *used* 1894–1917
Type **E** (inscr "B.P.O.") *used* 1906–10
Type **F** *used* 1915–22

Stamps of HONG KONG *cancelled at Foochow between* 1867 *and* 1916 *with postmarks detailed above.*

1862. *No wmk* (Nos. 1/7).
Z312	18 c. lilac	..	..	..	90·00

1863–71. *Wmk Crown CC* (Nos. 8/19).
Z313	2 c. brown	..	..	..	28·00
Z314	4 c. grey	..	..	..	28·00
Z315	6 c. lilac	..	..	..	38·00
Z316	8 c. orange	..	..	..	30·00
Z317	12 c. blue	..	..	..	12·00
Z318	18 c. lilac	..	..	..	£450
Z319	24 c. green	..	..	..	50·00
Z320	30 c. vermilion	..	..	..	
Z321	30 c. mauve	..	..	..	9·50
Z322	48 c. rose	..	..	..	50·00
Z324	96 c. brownish grey	..	..	..	60·00

1876–77. (Nos. 20/1).
Z325	16 c. on 18 c. lilac	..	..	£300
Z326	28 c. on 30 c. mauve	..	..	£140

1877. *Wmk Crown CC* (No. 22).
Z327	16 c. yellow	..	..	..	£100

1880. (Nos. 23/7).
Z328	5 c. on 8 c. orange	..	..	..	£325
Z329	5 c. on 18 c. lilac	..	..	..	£120
Z330	10 c. on 12 c. blue	..	..	..	£120
Z331	10 c. on 16 c. yellow	..	..	..	£160
Z332	10 c. on 24 c. green	..	..	..	

1880. *Wmk Crown CC* (Nos. 28/31).
Z333	2 c. rose	..	..	..	26·00
Z334	5 c. blue	..	..	..	45·00
Z335	10 c. mauve	..	..	..	32·00
Z336	48 c. brown	..	..	..	£120

1882–96. *Wmk Crown CA* (Nos. 32/9).
Z336a	2 c. rose-lake	..	..	..	
Z337	2 c. carmine	..	..	..	1·50
Z338	4 c. slate-grey	..	..	..	4·00
Z339	5 c. blue	..	..	..	2·50
Z340	10 c. dull mauve	..	..	..	19·00
Z341	10 c. green	..	..	..	7·00
Z342	10 c. purple/*red*	..	..	..	3·00
Z343	30 c. green	..	..	..	26·00

1885. (Nos. 40/2).
Z344	20 c. on 30 c. orange-red	..	..	8·50
Z345	50 c. on 48 c. yellowish brown	..	..	35·00
Z346	$1 on 96 c. grey-olive	..	..	..	60·00

1891. (Nos. 43/4, 48/50).
Z348	14 c. on 30 c. mauve	..	..	..	75·00
Z349	20 c. on 30 c. green	..	..	..	13·00
Z350	50 c. on 48 c. dull purple	..	..	14·00
Z351	$1 on 96 c. purple/*red*	..	..	35·00

1898. (No. 52).
Z353	$1 on 96 c. black	..	..	..	45·00

1900–01. *Wmk Crown CA* (Nos. 56/61).
Z355	2 c. dull green	..	..	..	2·50
Z356	4 c. carmine	..	..	..	3·00
Z357	5 c. yellow	..	..	..	9·50
Z358	10 c. ultramarine	..	..	..	2·50

1903. *Wmk Crown CA* (Nos. 62/76).
Z361	1 c. dull purple and brown	..	..	3·00
Z362	2 c. dull green	..	..	..	2·50
Z363	4 c. purple/*red*	..	..	..	1·60
Z364	5 c. dull green and brown-orange	..	..	11·00
Z365	8 c. slate and violet	..	..	..	6·50
Z366	10 c. purple and blue/*blue*	..	..	2·75
Z367	12 c. green and purple/*yellow*	..	..	8·50
Z368	20 c. slate and chestnut	..	..	..	5·50
Z369	30 c. dull green and black	..	..	20·00
Z370	50 c. dull green and magenta	..	..	30·00

1904–06. *Wmk Mult Crown CA* (Nos. 77/90).
Z376	2 c. dull green	..	..	..	2·50
Z377	4 c. purple/*red*	..	..	..	1·60
Z378	5 c. dull green and brown-orange	..	..	7·50
Z379	8 c. slate and violet	..	..	..	6·00
Z380	10 c. purple and blue/*blue*	..	..	2·75
Z381	12 c. green and purple/*yellow*	..	..	11·00
Z382	20 c. slate and chestnut	..	..	..	5·50
Z383	30 c. dull green and black	..	..	14·00
Z384	50 c. green and magenta	..	..	..	15·00
Z385	$1 purple and sage-green	..	..	..	28·00

1907–11. *Wmk Mult Crown CA* (Nos. 91/9).
Z390	1 c. brown	..	..	..	2·50
Z391	2 c. green	..	..	..	2·50
Z392	4 c. carmine-red	..	..	..	1·60
Z393	6 c. orange-vermilion and purple	..	..	9·50
Z394	10 c. bright ultramarine	..	..	..	2·25
Z395	20 c. purple and sage-green	..	..	40·00
Z396	30 c. purple and orange-yellow	..	..	30·00
Z397	50 c. black/*green*	..	..	..	24·00

1912–15. *Wmk Mult Crown CA* (Nos. 100/16).
Z399	1 c. brown	..	..	..	2·75
Z400	2 c. green	..	..	..	2·75
Z401	4 c. red	..	..	..	1·60
Z402	6 c. orange	..	..	..	6·00
Z403	8 c. grey	..	..	..	13·00
Z404	10 c. ultramarine	..	..	..	2·50
Z406	20 c. purple and sage-green	..	..	4·00
Z407	25 c. purple and magenta (Type A)	..		
Z408	30 c. purple and orange-yellow	..	..	5·50

POSTCARD STAMPS

1879. (Nos. P1/2).
ZP413	3 c. on 16 c. yellow	..	..	..	£450

POSTAL FISCAL STAMPS

1874–1902. *Wmk Crown CC.* (a) *P* 15½×15 (Nos. F1/3)
ZF415	$2 olive-green	..	..	..	90·00
ZF416	$3 dull violet	..	..	..	80·00

HANKOW

Hankow, on the Yangtse River 600 miles from the sea, became a Treaty Port in 1860. A British consulate opened the following year, but no organised British postal agency was established until 1872.

Type **D** (*supplied* 1874) *used* 1874–1916
Type **B** ("D29") (*supplied* 1876) *used* 1878–83
Type **F** *used* 1916–22

Stamps of HONG KONG *cancelled at Hankow between* 1874 *and* 1916 *with postmarks detailed above.*

1862. *No wmk* (Nos. 1/7).
Z426	18 c. lilac	..	..	..	£120

1863–71. *Wmk Crown CC (Nos. 8/19).*

Z427	2 c. brown	..	55·00
Z428	4 c. grey	..	55·00
Z429	6 c. lilac	..	70·00
Z430	8 c. orange	..	55·00
Z431	12 c. blue	..	20·00
Z432	18 c. lilac	..	£475
Z433	24 c. green	..	70·00
Z435	30 c. mauve	..	80·00
Z436	48 c. rose	..	90·00
Z438	96 c. brownish grey	..	

1876–77. *(Nos. 20/1).*

Z439	16 c. on 18 c. lilac	..	£250
Z440	28 c. on 30 c. mauve	..	£140

1877. *Wmk Crown CC (No. 22).*

Z441	16 c. yellow	..	£120

1880. *(Nos. 23/7).*

Z442	5 c. on 8 c. orange	..	£130
Z443	5 c. on 18 c. lilac	..	£110
Z444	10 c. on 12 c. blue	..	£120
Z445	10 c. on 16 c. yellow	..	£200
Z446	10 c. on 24 c. green	..	£140

1880. *Wmk Crown CC (Nos. 28/31).*

Z447	2 c. rose	..	45·00
Z448	5 c. blue	..	50·00
Z449	10 c. mauve	..	50·00
Z450	48 c. brown	..	£150

1882–96. *Wmk Crown CA (Nos. 32/9).*

Z451	2 c. carmine	..	4·00
Z452	4 c. slate-grey	..	9·00
Z453	5 c. blue	..	4·50
Z454	10 c. dull mauve	..	35·00
Z455	10 c. green	..	6·00
Z456	10 c. purple/red	..	5·00
Z457	30 c. green	..	28·00

1885. *(Nos. 40/2).*

Z458	20 c. on 30 c. orange-red	..	15·00
Z459	50 c. on 48 c. yellowish brown	..	40·00
Z460	$1 on 96 c. grey-olive	..	75·00

1891. *(Nos. 43/4, 48/50).*

Z461	7 c. on 10 c. green	..	18·00
Z462	14 c. on 30 c. mauve	..	75·00
Z463	20 c. on 30 c. green	..	12·00
Z464	50 c. on 48 c. dull purple	..	12·00
Z465	$1 on 96 c. purple/red	..	35·00

1898. *(No. 52).*

Z467	$1 on 96 c. black	..	45·00

1898. *(No. 55).*

Z468	10 c. on 30 c. green	..	£160

1900–01. *Wmk Crown CA (Nos. 56/61).*

Z469	2 c. dull green	..	3·00
Z470	4 c. carmine	..	3·00
Z471	5 c. yellow	..	12·00
Z472	10 c. ultramarine	..	4·00
Z473	12 c. blue	..	70·00
Z474	30 c. brown	..	40·00

1903. *Wmk Crown CA (Nos. 62/76).*

Z475	1 c. dull purple and brown	..	3·00
Z476	2 c. dull green	..	3·00
Z477	4 c. purple/red	..	2·50
Z478	5 c. dull green and brown-orange	..	8·50
Z479	8 c. slate and violet	..	8·50
Z480	10 c. purple and blue/blue	..	3·00
Z481	12 c. green and purple/yellow	..	9·50
Z482	20 c. slate and chestnut	..	6·50
Z483	30 c. dull green and black	..	16·00
Z484	50 c. dull green and magenta	..	35·00
Z485	$1 purple and sage-green	..	25·00

1904–06. *Wmk Mult Crown CA (Nos. 77/90).*

Z490	2 c. dull green	..	3·00
Z491	4 c. purple/red	..	2·50
Z492	5 c. dull green and brown-orange	..	9·50
Z493	8 c. slate and violet	..	6·00
Z494	10 c. purple and blue/blue	..	3·00
Z495	12 c. green and purple/yellow	..	12·00
Z496	20 c. slate and chestnut	..	10·00
Z497	30 c. dull green and black	..	14·00
Z498	50 c. green and magenta	..	13·00
Z499	$1 purple and sage-green	..	27·00

1907–11. *Wmk Mult Crown CA (Nos. 91/9).*

Z504	1 c. brown	..	3·00
Z505	2 c. green	..	3·00
Z506	4 c. carmine-red	..	1·75
Z507	6 c. orange-vermilion and purple	..	12·00
Z508	10 c. bright ultramarine	..	3·00
Z509	20 c. purple and sage-green	..	48·00
Z510	30 c. purple and orange-yellow	..	35·00

1912–15. *Wmk Mult Crown CA (Nos. 100/16).*

Z513	1 c. brown	..	3·50
Z514	2 c. green	..	3·50
Z515	4 c. red	..	2·50
Z516	6 c. orange	..	6·00
Z518	10 c. ultramarine	..	3·00
Z520	20 c. purple and sage-green	..	7·50
Z522	30 c. purple and orange-yellow	..	9·50
Z523	50 c. black/green	..	6·50
Z527	$5 green and red/green	..	£275

POSTCARD STAMPS

1879. *(Nos. P1/2).*

ZP528	3 c. on 16 c. yellow	..	£650

POSTAL FISCAL STAMPS

1874–1902. *Wmk Crown CC. (a) P 15½×15 (Nos. F1/3).*

ZF529	$2 olive-green	..	£120

(b) P 14 (Nos. F4/6)

ZF532	$2 dull bluish green	..	

KIUNGCHOW (HOIHOW)

Kiungchow, a city on the island of Hainan, and its port of Hoihow was added to the Treaty Port system in 1860. A consular postal agency was opened at Kiungchow in 1876, being transferred to Hoihow in 1878. A second agency was opened at Kiungchow in 1879.

Type **B** ("D28") *(supplied 1876) used* 1879–83
Type **D** (inscr "KIUNG-CHOW") *(supplied 1876) used* 1879–81

"REGISTERED KIUNG-CHOW" with "REGISTERED" removed *(originally supplied 1876) used* 1883–85
Type **D** (inscr "HOIHOW") *used* 1885–1922

Stamps of HONG KONG *cancelled at Kiungchow (Hoihow) between 1879 and 1916 with postmarks detailed above.*

1863–71. *Wmk Crown CC (Nos. 8/19).*

Z540	2 c. brown	..	£600
Z541	4 c. grey	..	£400
Z542	6 c. lilac	..	£700
Z543	8 c. orange	..	£450
Z544	12 c. blue	..	£425
Z546	24 c. green	..	£600
Z547	30 c. vermilion	..	
Z548	30 c. mauve	..	£550
Z549	48 c. rose	..	£600
Z551	96 c. brownish grey	..	£700

1876–77. *(Nos. 20/1).*

Z552	16 c. on 18 c. lilac	..	£600
Z553	28 c. on 30 c. mauve	..	£475

1877. *(No. 22)*

Z554	16 c. yellow	..	£800

1880. *(Nos. 23/7).*

Z555	5 c. on 8 c. orange	..	£450
Z556	5 c. on 18 c. lilac	..	£450
Z557	10 c. on 12 c. blue	..	£450
Z558	10 c. on 16 c. yellow	..	£850
Z559	10 c. on 24 c. green	..	

1880. *Wmk Crown CC (Nos. 28/31).*

Z561	5 c. blue	..	£400
Z562	10 c. mauve	..	£500

1882–96. *Wmk Crown CA (Nos. 32/9).*

Z564	2 c. carmine	..	30·00
Z565	4 c. slate-grey	..	40·00
Z566	5 c. blue	..	30·00
Z567	10 c. dull mauve	..	£300
Z568	10 c. green	..	38·00
Z569	10 c. purple/red	..	30·00
Z570	30 c. green	..	60·00

1885. *(Nos. 40/2).*

Z571	20 c. on 30 c. orange-red	..	65·00
Z572	50 c. on 48 c. yellowish brown	..	70·00
Z573	$1 on 96 c. grey-olive	..	£100

1891. *(Nos. 43/4, 48/50).*

Z574	7 c. on 10 c. green	..	£120
Z576	20 c. on 30 c. green	..	30·00
Z577	50 c. on 48 c. dull purple	..	38·00
Z578	$1 on 96 c. purple/red	..	80·00

1891. *50th Anniv of Colony (No. 51).*

Z579	2 c. carmine	..	

1898. *(No. 52).*

Z580	$1 on 96 c. black	..	£140

1900–01. *Wmk Crown CA (Nos. 56/61).*

Z583	4 c. carmine	..	21·00
Z584	5 c. yellow	..	45·00
Z585	10 c. ultramarine	..	23·00
Z587	30 c. brown	..	95·00

1903. *Wmk Crown CA (Nos. 62/76).*

Z588	1 c. dull purple and brown	..	16·00
Z589	2 c. dull green	..	16·00
Z590	4 c. purple/red	..	11·00
Z591	5 c. dull green and brown-orange	..	24·00
Z592	8 c. slate and violet	..	22·00
Z593	10 c. purple and blue/blue	..	13·00
Z594	12 c. green and purple/yellow	..	28·00
Z598	$1 purple and sage-green	..	65·00

1904–06. *Wmk Mult Crown CA (Nos. 77/90).*

Z603	2 c. dull green	..	14·00
Z604	4 c. purple/red	..	11·00
Z605	5 c. dull green and brown-orange	..	24·00
Z606	8 c. slate and violet	..	17·00
Z607	10 c. purple and blue/blue	..	12·00
Z608	12 c. green and purple/yellow	..	27·00
Z609	20 c. slate and chestnut	..	32·00
Z610	30 c. dull green and black	..	42·00

1907–11. *Wmk Mult Crown CA (Nos. 91/9).*

Z617	1 c. brown	..	14·00
Z618	2 c. green	..	13·00
Z619	4 c. carmine-red	..	11·00
Z620	6 c. orange-vermilion and purple	..	27·00
Z621	10 c. bright ultramarine	..	12·00
Z622	20 c. purple and sage-green	..	50·00

1912–15. *Wmk Mult Crown CA (Nos. 100/16).*

Z625	1 c. brown	..	12·00
Z626	2 c. green	..	12·00
Z627	4 c. red	..	11·00
Z628	6 c. orange	..	16·00
Z629	8 c. grey	..	
Z630	10 c. ultramarine	..	11·00
Z631	12 c. purple/yellow	..	28·00
Z632	20 c. purple and sage-green	..	22·00
Z633	25 c. purple and magenta (Type A)	..	45·00
Z635	50 c. black/green	..	32·00
Z636	$1 purple and blue/blue	..	38·00

POSTAL FISCAL STAMPS

1874–1902. *Wmk Crown CC. (a) P 15½×15 (Nos. F1/3).*

ZF641	$2 olive-green	..	£130

(b) P 14 (Nos. F4/6)

ZF644	$2 dull bluish green	..	£250

1897. *(Nos. F10/11).*

ZF650	$1 on $2 olive-green	..	£225

NINGPO

Ningpo was one of the 1842 Treaty Ports and a consular postal agency was established there in 1844.

Type **A** ("N1") *(supplied 1866) used* 1870–82
Type **C** *(supplied 1866) used* 1870–99
Type **D** *used* 1899–1922

Stamps of HONG KONG *cancelled at Ningpo between 1866 and 1916 with postmarks detailed above.*

1862. *No wmk (Nos. 1/7).*

Z652	18 c. lilac	..	£200

1863–71. *Wmk Crown CC (Nos. 8/19).*

Z653	2 c. brown	..	£110
Z654	4 c. grey	..	£110
	a. Perf 12½	..	
Z655	6 c. lilac	..	£130
Z656	8 c. orange	..	£100
Z657	12 c. blue	..	80·00
Z658	18 c. lilac	..	
Z659	24 c. green	..	£130
Z660	30 c. vermilion	..	£140
Z661	30 c. mauve	..	70·00
Z662	48 c. rose	..	£150
Z663	96 c. olive-bistre	..	
Z664	96 c. brownish grey	..	£190

1876–77. *(Nos. 20/1).*

Z665	16 c. on 18 c. lilac	..	£300
Z666	28 c. on 30 c. mauve	..	£150

1877. *Wmk Crown CC (No. 22).*

Z667	16 c. yellow	..	£150

1880. *(Nos. 23/7).*

Z668	5 c. on 8 c. orange	..	£170
Z669	5 c. on 18 c. lilac	..	£160
Z670	10 c. on 12 c. blue	..	£170
Z672	10 c. on 24 c. green	..	£170

1880. *Wmk Crown CC (Nos. 28/31).*
Z674	5 c. blue	..	..	90·00
Z675	10 c. mauve	..	..	90·00
Z676	48 c. brown	..	..	£300

1882–96. *Wmk Crown CA (Nos. 32/9).*
Z677	2 c. carmine	..	..	20·00
Z678	4 c. slate-grey ..	..	..	30·00
Z679	5 c. blue	..	..	20·00
Z680	10 c. dull mauve	..	..	80·00
Z681	10 c. green	..	..	22·00
Z682	10 c. purple/red ..	..	..	22·00
Z683	30 c. green	..	..	45·00

1885. *(Nos. 40/2).*
Z685	50 c. on 48 c. yellowish brown	..	..	50·00

1891. *(Nos. 43/4, 48/50).*
Z687	7 c. on 10 c. green	..	..	25·00
Z688	20 c. on 30 c. green	..	..	17·00
Z689	50 c. on 48 c. dull purple	..	..	29·00
Z690	$1 on 96 c. purple/red	..	..	50·00

1898. *(No. 52).*
Z692	$1 on 96 c. black	..	..	60·00

1898. *(No. 55).*
Z693	10 c. on 30 c. green	..	..	£160

1900–01. *Wmk Crown CA (Nos. 56/61).*
Z694	2 c. dull green ..	..	..	12·00
Z695	4 c. carmine	..	..	11·00
Z697	10 c. ultramarine	..	..	12·00

1903. *Wmk Crown CA (Nos. 62/76).*
Z700	1 c. dull purple and brown	..	..	11·00
Z701	2 c. dull green ..	..	..	12·00
Z702	4 c. purple/red ..	..	..	9·00
Z703	5 c. dull green and brown-orange	..	..	20·00
Z704	8 c. slate and violet	..	..	13·00
Z705	10 c. purple and blue/blue	..	..	9·50
Z706	12 c. green and purple/yellow	..	..	26·00
Z709	50 c. dull green and magenta	..	..	40·00

1904–06. *Wmk Mult Crown CA (Nos. 77/90).*
Z715	2 c. dull green ..	..	..	12·00
Z716	4 c. purple/red ..	..	..	10·00
Z718	8 c. slate and violet	..	..	18·00
Z720	12 c. green and purple/yellow	..	..	28·00
Z721	20 c. slate and chestnut	..	..	28·00
Z722	30 c. dull green and black	..	..	35·00
Z724	$1 purple and sage-green	..	..	42·00

1907–11. *Wmk Mult Crown CA (Nos. 91/9).*
Z729	1 c. brown	..	..	9·00
Z730	2 c. green	..	..	9·00
Z731	4 c. carmine-red	..	..	8·00
Z733	10 c. bright ultramarine	..	..	9·00
Z734	20 c. purple and sage-green	..	..	50·00
Z735	30 c. purple and orange-yellow	..	..	40·00

1912–15. *Wmk Mult Crown CA (Nos. 100/16).*
Z738	1 c. brown	..	..	9·50
Z739	2 c. green	..	..	9·00
Z740	4 c. red	..	..	8·00
Z742	8 c. grey	..	..	26·00
Z743	10 c. ultramarine	..	..	9·00
Z745	20 c. purple and sage-green	..	..	
Z749	$1 purple and blue/blue	..	..	28·00

POSTCARD STAMPS

1879. *(Nos. P1/2).*
ZP751	3 c. on 16 c. yellow	..	..	£550

POSTAL FISCAL STAMPS

1874–1902. *Wmk Crown CC. (a) P 15½×15 (Nos. F1/3).*
ZF754	$2 olive-green ..	..	..	£140

1881. *(No. F7).*
ZF760	12 c. on $10 rose-carmine	..	..	

1897. *(No. F10).*
ZF763	$1 on $2 olive-green	..	..	

SHANGHAI

Shanghai was one of the original Treaty Ports of 1842 and a packet agency was opened at the British consulate in April 1844. It moved to a separate premises in 1861 and was upgraded to a Post Office in September 1867.

British military post offices operated in Shanghai from 1927 until 1940.

Type D (inscr "SHANGHAE" (supplied 1861) used 1861–99

Sunburst *used 1864–65*
Type A ("S1") *(supplied 1866) used 1866–85*
Type D (inscr "SHANGHAI") *(supplied 1885) used 1886–1906*
Type G (inscr "B.P.O." at foot) *(supplied 1904) used 1904–21*
Type G (inscr "Br.P.O." at foot) *(supplied 1907) used 1907–22*
Type E (figures "I" to "VIII" at foot) *used 1912–22*

Stamps of HONG KONG cancelled at Shanghai between 1863 and 1916 with postmarks detailed above.

1862. *No wmk (Nos. 1/7).*
Z765	2 c. brown	..	..	90·00
Z766	8 c. yellow-buff	..	..	75·00
Z767	12 c. pale greenish blue	..	..	60·00
Z768	18 c. lilac	..	..	48·00
Z769	24 c. green	..	..	£100
Z770	48 c. rose	..	..	£350
Z771	96 c. brownish grey	..	..	£400

1863–71. *Wmk Crown CC (Nos. 8/19).*
Z772	2 c. brown	..	..	7·00
Z773	4 c. grey	..	..	5·50
	a. Perf 12½	..	..	£275
Z774	6 c. lilac	..	..	9·50
Z775	8 c. orange	..	..	9·50
Z776	12 c. blue	..	..	5·50
Z777	18 c. lilac	..	..	£325
Z778	24 c. green	..	..	8·50
Z779	30 c. vermilion	..	..	14·00
Z780	30 c. green	..	..	5·50
Z781	48 c. rose	..	..	22·00
Z782	96 c. olive-bistre	..	..	£650
Z783	96 c. brownish grey	..	..	35·00

1876–77. *(Nos. 20/1).*
Z784	16 c. on 18 c. lilac	..	..	£150
Z785	28 c. on 30 c. mauve	..	..	48·00

1877. *Wmk Crown CC (No. 22).*
Z786	16 c. yellow	..	..	65·00

1880. *(Nos. 23/7).*
Z787	5 c. on 8 c. orange	..	..	85·00
Z788	5 c. on 18 c. lilac	..	..	55·00
Z789	10 c. on 12 c. blue	..	..	55·00
Z790	10 c. on 16 c. yellow	..	..	£140
Z791	10 c. on 24 c. green	..	..	80·00

1880. *Wmk Crown CC (Nos. 28/31).*
Z792	2 c. rose	..	..	17·00
Z793	5 c. blue	..	..	30·00
Z794	10 c. mauve	..	..	13·00
Z795	48 c. brown	..	..	80·00

1882–96. *Wmk Crown CA (Nos. 32/9).*
Z795a	2 c. rose-lake	..	..	
Z796	2 c. carmine	..	..	90
Z797	4 c. slate-grey ..	..	..	90
Z798	5 c. blue	..	..	1·00
Z799	10 c. dull mauve	..	..	8·50
Z800	10 c. green	..	..	1·40
Z801	10 c. purple/red ..	..	..	1·25
Z802	30 c. green	..	..	17·00

1885. *(Nos. 40/2).*
Z803	20 c. on 30 c. orange-red	..	..	5·00
Z804	50 c. on 48 c. yellowish brown	..	..	25·00
Z805	$1 on 96 c. grey-olive	..	..	45·00

1891. *(Nos. 43/44, 46, 48/50).*
Z806	7 c. on 10 c. green	..	..	8·50
Z807	14 c. on 30 c. mauve	..	..	50·00
Z807a	50 c. on 48 c. dull purple (No. 46)	..	..	£275
Z808	20 c. on 30 c. green	..	..	4·00
Z809	50 c. on 48 c. dull purple (No. 49)	..	..	5·50
Z810	$1 on 96 c. purple/red	..	..	22·00

1898. *(No. 52).*
Z812	$1 on 96 c. black	..	..	25·00

1898. *(No. 55).*
Z813	10 c. on 30 c. green	..	..	75·00

1900–01. *Wmk Crown CA (Nos. 56/61).*
Z814	2 c. dull green ..	..	..	85
Z815	4 c. carmine	..	..	90
Z816	5 c. yellow	..	..	6·00
Z817	10 c. ultramarine	..	..	1·75
Z818	12 c. blue	..	..	45·00
Z819	30 c. brown	..	..	20·00

1903. *Wmk Crown CA (Nos. 62/76).*
Z820	1 c. dull purple and brown	..	..	60
Z821	2 c. dull green	..	..	1·60
Z822	4 c. purple/red	..	..	45
Z823	5 c. dull green and brown-orange	..	..	8·50
Z824	8 c. slate and violet	..	..	1·25
Z825	10 c. purple and blue/blue	..	..	1·25
Z826	12 c. green and purple/yellow	..	..	4·50
Z827	20 c. slate and chestnut	..	..	2·50
Z828	30 c. dull green and black	..	..	13·00
Z829	50 c. dull green and magenta	..	..	26·00
Z830	$1 purple and sage-green	..	..	18·00
Z832	$3 slate and dull blue	..	..	£300
Z833	$5 purple and blue-green	..	..	£400
Z834	$10 slate and orange/blue	..	..	£450

1904–06. *Wmk Mult Crown CA (Nos. 77/90).*
Z835	2 c. dull green ..	..	..	1·25
Z836	4 c. purple/red ..	..	..	40
Z837	5 c. dull green and brown-orange	..	..	5·50
Z838	8 c. slate and violet	..	..	2·00
Z839	10 c. purple and blue/blue	..	..	60
Z840	12 c. green and purple/yellow	..	..	6·00
Z841	20 c. slate and chestnut	..	..	2·25
Z842	30 c. dull green and black	..	..	11·00
Z843	50 c. green and magenta	..	..	5·50
Z844	$1 purple and sage-green	..	..	16·00
Z845	$2 slate and scarlet ..	..	..	85·00
Z846	$3 slate and dull blue	..	..	£200
Z847	$5 purple and blue-green	..	..	£300
Z848	$10 slate and orange/blue	..	..	£650

1907–11. *Wmk Mult Crown CA (Nos. 91/9).*
Z849	1 c. brown	..	..	90
Z850	2 c. green	..	..	1·50
Z851	4 c. carmine-red	..	..	40
Z852	6 c. orange-vermilion and purple	..	..	2·75
Z853	10 c. bright ultramarine	..	..	40
Z854	20 c. purple and sage-green	..	..	35·00
Z855	30 c. purple and orange-yellow ..	..	..	18·00
Z856	50 c. black/green	..	..	13·00
Z857	$2 carmine-red and black	..	..	£250

1912–15. *Wmk Mult Crown CA (Nos. 100/16).*
Z858	1 c. brown	..	..	55
Z859	2 c. green	..	..	30
Z860	4 c. red	..	..	30
Z861	6 c. orange	..	..	85
Z862	8 c. grey	..	..	6·50
Z863	10 c. ultramarine	..	..	30
Z864	12 c. purple/yellow	..	..	5·50
Z865	20 c. purple and sage-green	..	..	90
Z867	30 c. purple and orange-yellow	..	..	4·75
Z868	50 c. black/green	..	..	1·75
Z869	$1 purple and blue/blue	..	..	2·50

POSTCARD STAMPS

1879. *(Nos. P1/2).*
ZP871	3 c. on 16 c. yellow	..	..	£325
ZP872	5 c. on 18 c. lilac	..	..	£325

POSTAL FISCAL STAMPS

1874–1902. *Wmk Crown CC. (a) P 15½×15 (Nos. F1/5).*
ZF874	$2 olive-green ..	..	..	50·00
ZF875	$3 dull violet	..	..	35·00
ZF876	$10 rose-carmine	..	..	£600

(b) P 14
ZF877	$2 dull bluish green	..	..	£200
ZF878	$3 dull mauve ..	..	..	£350

1881. *(No. F7).*
ZF880	12 c. on $10 rose-carmine	..	..	£250

1891. *(No. F9).*
ZF882	$5 on $10 purple/red	..	..	£100

1897. *(No. F10/11).*
ZF883	$1 on $2 olive-green	..	..	£150
ZF884	$1 on $2 dull bluish green	..	..	£200

SWATOW

Swatow became a Treaty Port in 1860 and a consular packet agency was opened in the area made available for foreign firms during the following year. In 1867 the original agency was transferred to the Chinese city on the other side of the Han river, but a second agency was subsequently opened in the foreign concession during 1883.

Type A ("S2") *(supplied 1866) used 1875–85*
Type C *(supplied 1866) used 1866–90*
Type D *(supplied 1883) used 1884–1922*
Type F *used 1916–22*

Stamps of HONG KONG cancelled at Swatow between 1866 and 1916 with postmarks detailed above.

1862. *No wmk (Nos. 1/7).*
Z885	18 c. lilac	..	..	£130

1863–71. *Wmk Crown CC (Nos. 8/19).*
Z886	2 c. brown	..	..	70·00
Z887	4 c. grey	..	..	70·00
	a. Perf 12½ ..	..	..	
Z888	6 c. lilac	..	..	£300
Z889	8 c. orange	..	..	75·00
Z890	12 c. blue	..	..	30·00
Z891	18 c. lilac	..	..	£475
Z892	24 c. green	..	..	75·00
Z893	30 c. vermilion	..	..	
Z894	30 c. mauve	..	..	30·00
Z895	48 c. rose	..	..	85·00
Z897	96 c. brownish grey	..	..	£450

1876–77. *(Nos. 20/1).*
Z898 16 c. on 18 c. lilac £300
Z899 28 c. on 30 c. mauve £130

1877. *Wmk Crown CC (No. 22).*
Z900 16 c. yellow £275

1880. *(Nos. 23/7).*
Z901 5 c. on 8 c. orange £130
Z902 5 c. on 18 c. lilac £120
Z903 10 c. on 12 c. blue £130
Z904 10 c. on 16 c. yellow £225
Z905 10 c. on 24 c. green £170

1880. *Wmk Crown CC (Nos. 28/31).*
Z906 2 c. rose .. .. .. 55·00
Z907 5 c. blue .. .. .. 55·00
Z908 10 c. mauve .. .. .. 70·00

1882–96. *Wmk Crown CA (Nos. 32/9).*
Z910 2 c. carmine .. .. .. 3·50
Z911 4 c. slate-grey .. .. 10·00
Z912 5 c. blue .. .. .. 4·00
Z913 10 c. dull mauve .. .. 45·00
Z914 10 c. green .. .. .. 5·00
Z915 10 c. purple/red .. .. 3·50
Z916 30 c. green .. .. .. 27·00

1885. *(Nos. 40/2).*
Z917 20 c. on 30 c. orange-red .. 7·50

1891. *(No. 43/4, 48/50).*
Z920 7 c. on 10 c. green .. .. 14·00
Z921 14 c. on 30 c. mauve .. 65·00
Z922 20 c. on 30 c. green .. .. 12·00
Z923 50 c. on 48 c. dull purple .. 13·00
Z924 $1 on 96 c. purple/red .. 28·00

1891. *50th Anniv of Colony (No. 51).*
Z925 2 c. carmine £750

1898. *(No. 52).*
Z926 $1 on 96 c. black .. .. 40·00

1898. *(No. 55).*
Z927 10 c. on 30 c. green .. £130

1900–01. *Wmk Crown CA (Nos. 56/61).*
Z928 2 c. dull green .. .. .. 4·00
Z929 4 c. carmine .. .. .. 3·50
Z930 5 c. yellow .. .. .. 12·00
Z931 10 c. ultramarine .. .. 4·00
Z933 30 c. brown .. .. .. 30·00

1903. *Wmk Crown CA (Nos. 62/76).*
Z934 1 c. dull purple and brown .. 3·50
Z935 2 c. dull green .. .. 3·50
Z936 4 c. purple/red .. .. 2·75
Z937 5 c. dull green and brown-orange .. 9·00
Z938 8 c. slate and violet .. .. 6·00
Z939 10 c. purple and blue/blue .. 3·75
Z940 12 c. green and purple/yellow .. 8·00
Z941 20 c. slate and chestnut .. 4·50
Z942 30 c. dull green and black .. 17·00

1904–06. *Wmk Mult Crown CA (Nos. 77/90).*
Z949 2 c. dull green .. .. 3·50
Z950 4 c. purple/red .. .. 2·75
Z951 5 c. dull green and brown-orange .. 9·00
Z952 8 c. slate and violet .. .. 6·00
Z953 10 c. purple and blue/blue .. 3·50
Z954 12 c. green and purple/yellow .. 8·00
Z955 20 c. slate and chestnut .. 6·00
Z956 30 c. dull green and black .. 15·00
Z957 50 c. green and magenta .. 12·00
Z958 $1 purple and sage-green .. 30·00
Z959 $2 slate and scarlet .. £110
Z962 $10 slate and orange/blue .. £750

1907–11. *Wmk Mult Crown CA (Nos. 91/9).*
Z963 1 c. brown .. .. .. 4·00
Z964 2 c. green .. .. .. 4·00
Z965 4 c. carmine-red .. .. 3·00
Z966 6 c. orange-vermilion and purple .. 7·50
Z967 10 c. bright ultramarine .. 3·50
Z969 30 c. purple and orange-yellow .. 28·00
Z970 50 c. black/green .. .. 19·00

1912–15. *Wmk Mult Crown CA (Nos. 100/16).*
Z972 1 c. brown .. .. .. 3·00
Z973 2 c. green .. .. .. 3·00
Z974 4 c. red .. .. .. 2·50
Z975 6 c. orange .. .. .. 4·00
Z976 8 c. grey .. .. .. 12·00
Z977 10 c. ultramarine .. .. 2·25
Z978 12 c. purple/yellow .. .. 7·50
Z979 20 c. purple and sage-green .. 3·50
Z980 25 c. purple and magenta (Type A) .. 25·00
Z981 30 c. purple and orange-yellow .. 10·00
Z982 50 c. black/green .. .. 5·00
Z983 $1 purple and blue/blue .. 9·00

POSTCARD STAMPS

1879. *(Nos. P1/2).*
ZP986 3 c. on 16 c. yellow .. £600

POSTAL FISCAL STAMPS

1874–1902. *Wmk Crown CC. (a) P 15½×15 (Nos. F1/3).*
ZF988 $2 olive-green .. .. 75·00
ZF989 $3 dull violet .. .. 65·00

(b) P 14
ZF991 $2 dull bluish green .. £225

TIENTSIN

Tientsin became a Treaty Port in 1860. A British consulate was established in 1861, but no formal postal agency was organised there until 1882. It was not, however, very successful and was closed during 1890. The British Post Office reopened on 1 October 1906 under the management of the Chinese Engineering and Mining Company.

British military post offices operated in Tientsin from 1927 until 1940.

Type **E** used 1906–13
Type **G** (supplied 1907) used 1907–22

Stamps of HONG KONG cancelled at Tientsin between 1906 and 1916 with postmarks detailed above.

1903. *Wmk Crown CA (Nos. 62/76).*
Z 998 1 c. dull purple and brown .. .. 6·00
Z 999 5 c. dull green and brown-orange .. 15·00
Z1000 8 c. slate and violet .. .. 5·00

1904–06. *Wmk Mult Crown CA (Nos. 77/90).*
Z1001 2 c. dull green .. .. 3·00
Z1002 4 c. purple/red .. .. 2·25
Z1003 5 c. dull green and brown-orange .. 8·00
Z1004 8 c. slate and violet .. .. 6·00
Z1005 10 c. purple and blue/blue .. 2·75
Z1006 12 c. green and purple/yellow .. 9·00
Z1007 20 c. slate and chestnut .. 6·00
Z1008 30 c. dull green and black .. 15·00
Z1009 50 c. green and magenta .. 12·00
Z1010 $1 purple and sage-green .. 25·00
Z1011 $2 slate and scarlet .. £110
Z1013 $5 purple and blue-green .. £350
Z1014 $10 slate and orange/blue .. £750

1907–11. *Wmk Mult Crown CA (Nos. 91/9).*
Z1015 1 c. brown .. .. .. 3·00
Z1016 2 c. green .. .. .. 2·50
Z1017 4 c. carmine-red .. .. 1·90
Z1018 6 c. orange-vermilion and purple .. 9·00
Z1019 10 c. bright ultramarine .. 2·25
Z1020 20 c. purple and sage-green .. 40·00
Z1021 30 c. purple and orange-yellow .. 29·00
Z1022 50 c. black/green .. .. 22·00

1912–15. *Wmk Mult Crown CA (Nos. 100/16).*
Z1024 1 c. brown .. .. .. 2·50
Z1025 2 c. green .. .. .. 2·50
Z1026 4 c. red .. .. .. 1·60
Z1027 6 c. orange .. .. .. 3·50
Z1028 8 c. grey .. .. .. 15·00
Z1029 10 c. ultramarine .. .. 3·00
Z1030 20 c. purple and sage-green .. 5·00
Z1033 30 c. purple and orange-yellow .. 6·50
Z1034 50 c. black/green .. .. 4·00
Z1035 $1 purple and blue/blue .. 5·50
Z1037 $3 green and purple .. 80·00

WEI HAI WEI

The territory of Wei Hai Wei was leased from the Chinese by the British Government from 24 May 1898. At that time there were no organised postal services from the area, although a private local post did operate between the port and Chefoo from 8 December 1898 until 15 March 1899. A Chinese Imperial post office opened in March 1899 to be followed by a British postal agency on the offshore island of Liu Kung Tau on 1 September 1899. A second British agency opened at Port Edward on 1 April 1904.

Liu Kung Tau oval used 1899–1901
Type **D** (inscr "LIU KUNG TAU") (supplied 1899) used 1901–30

Stamps of HONG KONG cancelled at Liu Kung Tau between 1899 and 1916 with postmarks detailed above.

1882–96. *Wmk Crown CA (Nos. 32/9).*
Z1040 2 c. carmine .. .. 25·00
Z1041 4 c. slate-grey .. .. 35·00
Z1042 5 c. blue .. .. .. 25·00
Z1043 10 c. purple/red .. .. 15·00
Z1044 30 c. green .. .. 30·00

1891. *(Nos. 48/50).*
Z1045 20 c. on 30 c. green .. .. 20·00
Z1046 50 c. on 48 c. dull purple .. 20·00

1898. *(No. 52).*
Z1047 $1 on 96 c. black .. .. 42·00

1900–01. *Wmk Crown CA (Nos. 56/61).*
Z1049 2 c. dull green .. .. 3·50
Z1050 4 c. carmine .. .. 3·50
Z1051 5 c. yellow .. .. 12·00
Z1052 10 c. ultramarine .. .. 3·50
Z1053 12 c. blue .. .. .. 60·00
Z1054 30 c. brown .. .. .. 35·00

1903. *Wmk Crown CA (Nos. 62/76).*
Z1055 1 c. dull purple and brown .. 3·50
Z1056 2 c. dull green .. .. 3·00
Z1057 4 c. purple/red .. .. 3·00
Z1058 5 c. dull green and brown-orange .. 9·00
Z1059 8 c. slate and violet .. .. 6·00
Z1060 10 c. purple and blue/blue .. 4·50
Z1061 12 c. green and purple/yellow .. 13·00
Z1062 20 c. slate and chestnut .. 6·00
Z1063 30 c. dull green and black .. 16·00
Z1064 50 c. dull green and magenta .. 35·00
Z1065 $1 purple and sage-green .. 30·00

1904–06. *Wmk Mult Crown CA (Nos. 77/90).*
Z1070 2 c. dull green .. .. 3·50
Z1071 4 c. purple/red .. .. 3·00
Z1073 8 c. slate and violet .. 5·00
Z1076 20 c. slate and chestnut .. 6·00
Z1078 50 c. green and magenta .. 25·00

1907–11. *Wmk Mult Crown CA (Nos. 91/9).*
Z1084 1 c. brown .. .. .. 3·50
Z1085 2 c. green .. .. .. 3·50
Z1086 4 c. carmine-red .. .. 2·75
Z1088 10 c. bright ultramarine .. 3·00
Z1089 20 c. purple and sage-green .. 42·00
Z1090 30 c. purple and orange-yellow .. 32·00
Z1091 50 c. black/green .. .. 27·00

1912–15. *Wmk Mult Crown CA (Nos. 100/16).*
Z1093 1 c. brown .. .. .. 3·50
Z1094 2 c. green .. .. .. 2·75
Z1095 4 c. red .. .. .. 2·50
Z1096 6 c. orange .. .. .. 5·00
Z1097 8 c. grey .. .. .. 15·00
Z1098 10 c. ultramarine .. .. 3·00
Z1104 $1 purple and blue/blue .. 13·00

POSTAL FISCAL STAMPS

1874–1902. *Wmk Crown CC. (b) P 14 (Nos. F4/6).*
Z1106 $2 dull bluish green £550

Port Edward rectangle used 1904–08
Type **D** (inscr "WEI-HAI-WEI" at top and "PORT EDWARD" at foot) (supplied 1907) used 1907–30

Stamps of HONG KONG cancelled at Port Edward between 1904 and 1916 with postmarks detailed above.

1900–01. *Wmk Crown CA (Nos. 56/61).*
Z1109 2 c. dull green .. .. 35·00
Z1110 10 c. ultramarine .. .. 38·00

1903. *Wmk Crown CA (Nos. 62/76).*
Z1111 1 c. dull purple and brown .. .. 12·00
Z1112 2 c. dull green .. .. 12·00
Z1113 4 c. purple/red .. .. 10·00
Z1114 5 c. dull green and brown-orange .. 14·00
Z1115 8 c. slate and violet .. .. 15·00
Z1116 10 c. purple and blue/blue .. 13·00
Z1117 12 c. green and purple/yellow .. 20·00
Z1118 20 c. slate and chestnut .. 32·00
Z1119 30 c. dull green and black .. 25·00
Z1120 50 c. dull green and magenta .. 30·00
Z1121 $1 purple and sage-green .. 32·00

1904–06. *Wmk Mult Crown CA (Nos. 77/90).*
Z1126 2 c. dull green .. .. 6·50
Z1127 4 c. purple/red .. .. 6·00
Z1128 5 c. dull green and brown-orange .. 10·00
Z1129 8 c. slate and violet .. .. 7·00
Z1132 20 c. slate and chestnut .. 35·00
Z1133 30 c. dull green and black .. 22·00
Z1134 50 c. green and magenta .. 30·00

1907–11. *Wmk Mult Crown CA (Nos. 91/9).*
Z1140 1 c. brown .. .. .. 7·00
Z1141 2 c. green .. .. .. 7·00
Z1142 4 c. carmine-red .. .. 4·75
Z1143 6 c. orange-vermilion and purple ..
Z1144 10 c. bright ultramarine .. 5·50

1912–15. *Wmk Mult Crown CA (Nos. 100/16).*
Z1151 1 c. brown .. .. .. 6·00
Z1152 2 c. green .. .. .. 4·75
Z1153 4 c. red .. .. .. 3·00
Z1155 8 c. grey .. .. .. 13·00
Z1156 10 c. ultramarine .. .. 3·00
Z1158 20 c. purple and sage-green .. 8·50
Z1161 50 c. black/green .. .. 8·00
Z1162 $1 purple and blue/blue .. 8·50

<table>
<tr><td colspan="2">PRICES FOR STAMPS ON COVER</td></tr>
<tr><td>Nos. 1/14</td><td>from × 50</td></tr>
<tr><td>Nos. 15/17</td><td>—</td></tr>
<tr><td>Nos. 18/28</td><td>from × 30</td></tr>
</table>

The overprinted stamps Nos. 1/17 were introduced on 1 January 1917 to prevent currency speculation in the Treaty Ports. They were used in the then-existing agencies of Amoy, Canton, Chefoo, Foochow, Hankow, Hoihow, Ningpo,. Shanghai, Swatow, Tientsin and were also supplied to the British naval base of Wei Hai Wei.

CHINA

(1)

1917 (1 Jan)–**21.** *Stamps of Hong Kong, 1912–21 (wmk Mult Crown CA), optd with T 1, at Somerset House.*

1	1 c. brown		2·50	1·50
	a. Black-brown		2·00	2·50
	b. Crown broken at right	£225	£275
	c. Wmk sideways		†	£2500
2	2 c. green		2·25	30
3	4 c. carmine-red		3·25	30
4	6 c. orange		3·00	60
5	8 c. slate		7·00	1·25
6	10 c. ultramarine		7·00	30
	y. Wmk inverted and reversed		†	£250
7	12 c. purple/*yellow*		4·50	2·50
8	20 c. purple and sage-green		9·50	60
9	25 c. purple and magenta (A)		7·50	15·00
11	30 c. purple and orange-yellow		20·00	5·00
12	50 c. black/*blue-green* (*olive back*)		40·00	1·50
	a. Emerald surface (1917?)		25·00	8·50
	b. On emerald back (1919)		17·00	5·50
	c. On white back (1920)		£160	42·00
13	$1 reddish purple and bright blue/*blue*		55·00	2·25
	a. Grey-purple and blue/*blue* (1921)		55·00	6·00
14	$2 carmine-red and grey-black		£160	45·00
15	$3 green and purple		£275	£140
16	$5 green and red/*blue-green* (*olive back*)		£275	£180
17	$10 purple and black/*red*		£700	£350
1/17		Set of 16	£1400	£650
12/17	H/S "Specimen"	Set of 6	£1400	

1922 (Mar)–**27.** *As last, but wmk Mult Script CA.*

18	1 c. brown		1·75	3·50
19	2 c. green		2·50	2·25
	w. Wmk inverted		85·00	
20	4 c. carmine-rose		3·25	2·00
	a. Lower Chinese character at right broken at top	£120	£100
21	6 c. orange-yellow		3·00	4·25
22	8 c. grey		3·75	13·00
23	10 c. bright ultramarine		4·75	2·00
	w. Wmk inverted		85·00	
24	20 c. purple and sage-green		7·00	5·00
25	25 c. purple and magenta (B)		13·00	60·00
	a. Broken flower		£275	
26	50 c. black/*emerald* (1927) (H/S S. £225)		48·00	£150
27	$1 purple and blue/*blue*		60·00	35·00
28	$2 carmine-red and grey-black		£190	£250
18/28		Set of 11	£300	£475

STAMP BOOKLETS

1917. *Black on red cover inscribed* "BRITISH POST OFFICE AGENCIES IN CHINA". *Stapled.*
SB1 $1 booklet containing eight 2 c., six 4 c. and six 10 c. (Nos. 2/3, 6)

1922. *Cover as No. SB1. Stapled.*
SB2 $1 booklet containing eight 2 c., six 4 c., and six 10 c. (Nos. 19/20, 23) .. £3750

The British P.O.'s in the Treaty Ports closed by agreement with the Chinese on 30 November 1922, but the above overprinted issues continued in use at the Wei Hai Wei offices until they in turn closed on 30 September 1930. Under the terms of the Convention signed with China the Royal Navy continued to use the base at Wei Hai Wei until the mid-1930s.

BRITISH POST OFFICES IN JAPAN

Under the terms of the Anglo-Japanese Treaty of Yedo, signed on 26 August 1858, five Japanese ports were opened to British trade. British consulates were established at Decima (Nagasaki), Kanagawa (Yokohama), Hiogo (Kobe) and Hakodadi (Hakodate). The postage stamps of Hong Kong became available at the Yokohama and Nagasaki consulates during October 1864 and at Hiogo in 1869, although cancellation of mail did not commence until 1866 at Yokohama and Nagasaki or 1876 at Hiogo. Japan became a member of the U.P.U. on 1 June 1877 and all of the British Postal Agencies were closed by the end of 1879.

For illustrations of postmark types see BRITISH POST OFFICES IN CHINA.

HAKODATE

A British consular office existed at Hakodate, but it was never issued with a c.d.s., obliterator or Hong Kong stamps. No British covers are recorded from this consulate prior to opening of the Japanese Post Office.

HIOGO

The Port of Hiogo (Kobe) was first opened to foreigners on 1 January 1868. The British Consular mail service at Hiogo commenced during 1869 to serve the foreigners at Hiogo, Kobe and Osaka. The cities of Hiogo and Kobe later merged to become the single city of Kobe. The consular office at Hiogo closed on 30 November 1879.

Type B ("D30") *(supplied* 1876) *used* 1876–79
Type D *(supplied* 1876) *used* 1876–79

Stamps of HONG KONG *cancelled at Hiogo between* 1876 *and* 1879 *with postmarks detailed above.*

1863–71. *Wmk Crown CC (Nos. 8/19).*

Z 1	2 c. brown		£3250
Z 2	4 c. grey		£2250
Z 3	6 c. lilac		£2750
Z 4	8 c. orange		£2500
Z 5	12 c. blue		£3250
Z 6	18 c. lilac		
Z 7	24 c. green		£2250
Z 8	30 c. vermilion		
Z 9	30 c. mauve		£3250
Z10	48 c. rose		£3750
Z12	96 c. brownish grey		£3750

1877. *(Nos. 20/1).*
Z13 16 c. on 18 c. lilac

1877. *Wmk Crown CC (No. 22).*
Z15 16 c. yellow .. £3000

NAGASAKI

The British Consulate opened in Nagasaki on 14 June 1859, but, with few British residents at the port, the consular staff found it inconvenient to carry out postal duties so that few Nagasaki c.d.s. or "N2" cancellations exist. The postal service was terminated on 30 September 1879.

Type A ("N2") *(supplied* 1866) *used* 1876–79
Type D *(supplied* 1866) *used* 1876–79

Stamps of HONG KONG *cancelled at Nagasaki between* 1876 *and* 1879 *with postmarks detailed above.*

1863–71. *Wmk Crown CC (Nos. 8/19).*

Z16	2 c. brown		£850
Z17	4 c. grey		£650
Z18	6 c. lilac		£750
Z19	8 c. orange		£650
Z20	12 c. blue		£750
Z21	18 c. lilac		£1300
Z22	24 c. green		£1000
Z24	30 c. mauve		£950
Z25	48 c. rose		£1400
Z27	96 c. brownish grey		

1876–77. *(Nos. 20/1).*
Z28 16 c. on 18 c. lilac .. £1000
Z29 28 c. on 30 c. mauve .. £750

1877. *Wmk Crown CC (No. 22).*
Z30 16 c. yellow .. £800

YOKOHAMA

The British Consulate opened in Kanagawa on 21 July 1859, but was relocated to Yokohama where it provided postal services from 1 July 1860 until a separate Post Office was established in July 1867. The British Post Office in Yokohama closed on 31 December 1879.

Type A ("Y1") *(supplied* 1866) *used* 1867–79
Type D *(supplied* 1866) *used* 1876–79

Stamps of HONG KONG *cancelled at Yokohama between* 1866 *and* 1879 *with postmarks detailed above.*

1862. *No wmk (Nos. 1/8).*
Z30a 8 c. yellow-buff .. £120
Z31 18 c. lilac .. 60·00

1863–71. *Wmk Crown CC (Nos. 8/19).*

Z32	2 c. brown		14·00
Z33	4 c. grey		14·00
	a. Perf 12½		£450
Z34	6 c. lilac		19·00
Z35	8 c. orange		20·00
Z36	12 c. blue		14·00
Z37	18 c. lilac		£400
Z38	24 c. green		16·00
Z39	30 c. vermilion		25·00
Z40	30 c. mauve		14·00
Z41	48 c. rose		30·00
Z43	96 c. brownish grey		38·00

1876–77. *(Nos. 20/1).*
Z44 16 c. on 18 c. lilac .. £200
Z45 28 c. on 30 c. mauve .. 60·00

1877. *Wmk Crown CC (No. 22).*
Z46 16 c. yellow .. 85·00

POSTAL FISCAL STAMPS

1874. *Wmk Crown CC. P 15½×15 (Nos. F1/3).*

ZF47	$2 olive-green		65·00
ZF48	$3 dull violet		60·00
ZF49	$10 rose-carmine		£1100

India

<table>
<tr><td colspan="2">PRICES FOR STAMPS ON COVER TO 1945</td></tr>
<tr><td>Nos. S1/3</td><td>from × 2</td></tr>
<tr><td>No. 1</td><td>†</td></tr>
<tr><td>Nos. 2/26</td><td>from × 3</td></tr>
<tr><td>Nos. 27/30</td><td>—</td></tr>
<tr><td>Nos. 31/4</td><td>from × 8</td></tr>
<tr><td>Nos. 35/49</td><td>from × 3</td></tr>
<tr><td>Nos. 50</td><td>†</td></tr>
<tr><td>Nos. 51/3</td><td>from × 4</td></tr>
<tr><td>Nos. 54/65</td><td>from × 2</td></tr>
<tr><td>Nos. 66/8</td><td>from × 5</td></tr>
<tr><td>Nos. 69/74</td><td>from × 3</td></tr>
<tr><td>Nos. 73/277</td><td>from × 2</td></tr>
<tr><td>Nos. O1/14</td><td>from × 6</td></tr>
<tr><td>Nos. O15/18</td><td>from × 5</td></tr>
<tr><td>No. O19</td><td>from × 5</td></tr>
<tr><td>Nos. O20/30a</td><td>from × 10</td></tr>
<tr><td>No. O30b</td><td>†</td></tr>
<tr><td>Nos. O31/133</td><td>from × 6</td></tr>
<tr><td>Nos. O135/150</td><td>from × 2</td></tr>
</table>

(Currency. 12 pies = 1 anna; 16 annas = 1 rupee)

ISSUE FOR SIND PROVINCE

1

1852 (1 July). "Scinde Dawk." *Embossed.*

S1	1	½ a. white	£4500	£80●
S2		½ a. blue	£12000	£3500
S3		½ a. scarlet	£65000	£8000

These stamps were issued under the authority of Sir Bartle Frere, Commissioner in Sind. They were suppressed in October 1854.

No. S3 is on sealing wax (usually cracked). Perfect copies are very rare.

EAST INDIA COMPANY ADMINISTRATION

2 *(Much reduced)*

3

The ½ a., 1 a. and 4 a. were lithographed in Calcutta at the office of the Surveyor-General. The die was engraved by Mr Maniruddin (spelling uncertain). *Ungummed* paper watermarked as T 2 (the "No. 4" paper) with the Arms of the East India Co in the sheet. The watermark is sideways on the ½ a. and 1 a., and upright on the 4 a. where the paper was trimmed so that only the central portion showing the oval and the arms was used. Imperforate.

1854 (April).
1 3 ½ a. vermilion .. £800
     a. Deep vermilion .. £1200

This stamp, with 9½ arches in the side border, was prepared for use and a supply was sent to Bombay, but was not officially issued.

The vermilion shade is normally found on toned paper and the deep vermilion on white.

The new-issue supplement to this Catalogue appears each month in

GIBBONS
STAMP MONTHLY

—from your newsagent or by postal subscription— sample copy and details on request.

ILLUSTRATIONS. Types 4/8 are shown twice actual size.

4

1854 (1 Oct).   *Die I.*

2	4	½ a. blue	..	..	55·00	13·00
		a. Printed on both sides	..		† £8000	
		b. Printed double	..	..	† £6000	
3		½ a. pale blue	..	..	85·00	18·00
4		½ a. deep blue	..	..	70·00	18·00
5		½ a. indigo	..	..	£250	65·00

We give the official date of issue, but copies are known which were put on sale as much as a fortnight earlier.

These stamps were printed between 5 May and 29 July 1854 (Printing 30 millions).

4a

Die II

6	4a	½ a. blue	..	..	50·00	75·00
7		½ a. indigo	..	..	60·00	85·00

The bulk were printed between 1 and 12 August 1854, with some extra sheets on or before 2 November (Printing about 2 millions).

5

Die III

8	5	½ a. pale blue	..	..	£750	38·00
8a		½ a. blue	..	..	£700	35·00
9		½ a. greenish blue	..	..	£1500	£160
10		½ a. deep blue	..	..	£950	70·00

These stamps were printed between 3 July and 25 August 1855 (Printing about 4¾ millions).

THE THREE DIES OF THE ½ ANNA

DIE I. *Chignon shading* mostly solid blobs of colour. *Corner ornaments,* solid blue stars with long points, always conspicuous. *Band below diadem* always heavily shaded. *Diadem and jewels.* The middle and right-hand jewels usually show a clearly defined cross. *Outer frame lines.* Stamps with white or faintly shaded chignons and weak frame lines are usually Die I (worn state).

DIE II. *Chignon* normally shows much less shading. A strong line of colour separates hair and chignon. *Corner ornaments.* The right blue star is characteristic (see illustration) but tends to disappear. It never obliterates the white cross. *Band below diadem.* As Die I but heavier, sometimes solid. *Diadem and jewels.* As Die I but usually fainter. *Outer frame lines.* Always strong and conspicuous.

DIE III. *Chignon shading* shows numerous fine lines, often blurred. *Corner ornaments* have a small hollow blue star with short points, which tends to disappear as in Die II. *Band below diadem,* shows light shading or hardly any shading. *Diadem and jewels.* Jewels usually marked with a solid squat star. The ornaments between the stars appear in the shape of a characteristic white "w". *Frame lines* variable.

The above notes give the general characteristics of the three Dies, but there are a few exceptions due to retouching, etc.

6   (*See note below No. 14*)

Die I

11	6	1 a. deep red	..	..	£375	45·00
12		1 a. red	..	..	£225	32·00

Printing of these stamps commenced on 26 July 1854, and continued into August (Printing, see note below No. 14).

7

Die II: With more lines in the chignon than in Die I, and with white curved line where chignon joins head*

13	7	1 a. deep red	..	..	£150	48·00
14		1 a. dull red	..	..	42·00	35·00

*Very worn printings of Die II may be found with chignon nearly as white as in Die I.

In stamps of Die I, however, the small blob of red projecting from the hair into the chignon is always visible.

These stamps were printed in August and September 1854 (Total printing, Dies I and II together, about 7¾ millions).

8

Die III. With pointed bust

15	8	1 a. red	..	..	£900	£130
16		1 a. dull red	..	..	£1400	£180

These stamps were printed between 7 July and 25 August 1855 (Printing, about 1½ millions).

9

NOTE. Our catalogue prices for Four Annas stamps are for cut-square specimens, with clear margins and in good condition. Cut-to-shape copies are worth from 3% to 20% of these prices according to condition.

Four Dies of the Head:—

I   II

DIE I. Band of diadem and chignon strongly shaded.

DIE II. Lines in band of diadem worn. Few lines in the upper part of the chignon, which, however, shows a strong drawn comma-like mark.

IIIA   III

DIE IIIA. Upper part of chignon partly redrawn, showing two short, curved vertical lines in the NE corner. "Comma" has disappeared.

DIE III. Upper part of chignon completely redrawn, but band of diadem shows only a few short lines.

Two Dies of the Frame:—

Die I. Outer frame lines weak. Very small dots of colour, or none at all, in the "R" and "A's". The white lines to the right of "INDIA" are separated, by a line of colour, from the inner white circle.

Die II. Outer frame lines strengthened. Dots in the "R" and "A's" strong. White lines to right of "INDIA" break into inner white circle.

(Des Capt. H. Thuillier)

1854 (15 Oct).   *W 2 upright, central portion only. Imperf.*
1st Printing. Head Die I. Frame Die I. Stamps widely spaced and separated by blue wavy line.

					Un	*Used*	*Us pr*
17	9	4 a. indigo and red	..	..	£4250	£500	£1800
18		4 a. blue and pale red	..	..	£4250	£425	£1600
		a. Head inverted	..		† £25000/ £80000		†

This printing was made between 13 and 28 Oct 1854 (Printing, 206,040).

Twenty-seven confirmed examples of No. 18a are now known, only three of which are cut-square. The range of prices quoted reflects the difference in value between a sound cut-to-shape stamp and the finest example known.

2nd Printing. Head Die II. Frame Die I. Stamps widely spaced and separated by blue wavy line.

19	**9**	4 a. blue and red		£4000	£275 £1000
		a. Blue (head) printed double		† £6000	†
20		4 a. indigo and deep red		£4000	£325 £1200

This printing was made between 1 and 13 Dec 1854 (Printing, 393,960).

No. 19a is only known used cut-to-shape.

3rd Printing. Head Dies II, IIIA and III. Frame Dies I and II. Stamps, often in bright shades, widely spaced and separated by wavy line.

21	**9**	4 a. blue and red (*shades*) (Head			
		III, Frame I		£9000	£1100 £3500
		a. Head II, Frame I		—	£1600 £5000
		b. Head IIIA, Frame I		—	£1600 £4750
		c. Head III, Frame II		—	— £9500

This printing was made between 10 March and 2 April 1855 (Printing, 138,960).

4th Printing. Head Die III. Frame Die II. Stamps closely spaced 2 to 2½ mm without separating line.

22	**9**	4 a. deep blue and red		£2750	£275 £850
23		4 a. blue and red		£2500	£225 £750
		a. Blue (head) printed double		† £4500	†
24		4 a. pale blue and pale red		£2750	£300 £900

This printing was made between 3 April and 9 May 1855 (Printing, 540,960).

No. 23a is only known used cut-to-shape.

5th Printing. Head Die III. Frame Die II. Stamps spaced 4 to 6 mm without separating line.

25	**9**	4 a. blue and rose-red		£4500	£400 £1600
26		4 a. deep blue and red		£4500	£400 £1600

This printing was made between 4 Oct and 3 Nov 1855 (Printing, 380,064).

Serrated perf about 18, or pin-perf

27	½ a. blue (Die I)		† £4000	—
28	1 a. red (Die I)		† £2250	—
29	1 a. red (Die II)		† £2000	—
30	4 a. blue and red (Die II)		† £9000	—

This is believed to be an unofficial perforation. Most of the known specimens bear Madras circle postmarks (C122 to C126), but some are known with Bombay postmarks. Beware of fakes.

BISECTS. The bisected stamps for issues between 1854 and 1860 were used exclusively in the Straits Settlements during shortages of certain values. Prices quoted are for those with Singapore "B 172" cancellations. Penang marks are considerably rarer.

10	11

(Plate made at Mint, Calcutta. Typo Stamp Office)

1854 (4 Oct). *Sheet wmk sideways, as W 2 but with "No. 3" at top left. Imperf.*

31	**10**	2 a. green (*shades*)		85·00 22·00
		a. Bisected (1 a.) (1857) (on cover)		† £95000
34		2 a. emerald-green		£1000

The 2 a. was also printed on paper with sheet watermark incorporating the words "STAMP OFFICE. One Anna", etc. (*Price* £450 *unused*, £375 *used*).

Apart from the rare emerald-green shade, there is a range of shades of No. 31 varying from bluish to yellowish green.

Many stamps show traces of lines external to the design shown in our illustration. Stamps with this frame on all four sides are scarce.

Many reprints of the ½, 1, 2, and 4 a. exist.

PRINTERS. All Indian stamps from No. 35 to 200 were typographed by De La Rue & Co.

1855 (Oct). *Blue glazed paper. No wmk. P 14.*

35	**11**	4 a. black		£400 13·00
		a. Imperf (pair)		£2500 £2500
		b. Bisected (2 a.) (1859) (on cover)		† £7500
36		8 a. carmine (Die I)		£375 11·00
		a. Imperf (pair)		£1800
		b. Bisected (4 a.) (1859) (on cover)		† £35000

The first supply of the 4 a. was on white paper, but it is difficult to distinguish it from No. 45.

In the 8 a. the paper varies from deep blue to almost white.

For difference between Die I and Die II in the 8 a., see illustrations above No. 73.

1856–64. *No wmk. Paper yellowish to white. P 14.*

37	**11**	½ a. blue (Die I)		45·00 2·75
		a. Imperf (pair)		£325 £950
38		½ a. pale blue (Die I)		38·00 1·25
39		1 a. brown		35·00 1·75
		a. Imperf between (vert pair)		
		b. Imperf (pair)		£750 £1300
		c. Bisected (½ a.) (1859) (on cover)		† £50000
40		1 a. deep brown		48·00 3·00
41		2 a. dull pink		£375 20·00
		a. Imperf (pair)		£1700
42		2 a. yellow-buff		£160 20·00
		a. Imperf (pair)		£1000 £1800
43		2 a. yellow		£190 21·00
44		2 a. orange		£200 21·00
		a. Imperf (pair)		
45		4 a. black		£170 6·50
		a. Bisected diagonally (2 a.) (1859) (on cover)		† £16000
		b. Imperf (pair)		£1800 £1800
46		4 a. grey-black		£160 4·75
47		4 a. green (1864)		£800 32·00
48		8 a. carmine (Die I)		£160 13·00
49		8 a. pale carmine (Die I)		£180 13·00
		a. Bisected (4 a.) (1859) (on cover)		† £38000

Prepared for use, but not officially issued

50	**11**	2 a. yellow-green		£700 £800
		a. Imperf (pair)		£1700

This stamp is known with trial obliterations, and a few are known postally used. It also exists *imperf*, but is not known used thus.

For difference between Die I and Die II in the ½ a., see illustrations above No. 73.

CROWN COLONY

On the 1 November 1858, Her Majesty Queen Victoria assumed the government of the territories in India "heretofore administered in trust by the Honourable East India Company".

12	13

1860 (9 May). *No wmk. P 14.*

51	**12**	8 p. purple/*bluish*		£190 85·00
52		8 p. purple/*white*		32·00 4·50
		a. Bisected diagonally (4 p.) (1862) (on cover)		† £50000
		b. Imperf (pair)		£2000 £3000
53		8 p. mauve		38·00 6·00

1865. *Paper yellowish to white. W 13. P 14.*

54	**11**	½ a. blue (Die I)		6·00 50
		a. Imperf		† £800
55		½ a. pale blue (Die I)		6·00 50
56	**12**	8 p. purple		8·50 7·50
57		8 p. mauve		9·00 7·50
58	**11**	1 a. pale brown		3·25 50
59		1 a. deep brown		2·75 40
60		1 a. chocolate		8·50 60
61		2 a. yellow		50·00 3·00
62		2 a. orange		38·00 1·25
		a. Imperf (pair)		† £3000
63		2 a. brown-orange		20·00 2·00
64		4 a. green		£325 18·00
65		8 a. carmine (Die I)		£1000 75·00

The 8 p. mauve, No. 57, is found variously surcharged "NINE" or "NINE PIE" by local postmasters, to indicate that it was being sold for 9 pies, as was the case during 1874. Such surcharges were made without Government sanction.

The stamps of India, wmk Elephant's Head, surcharged with a crown and value in "cents", were used in the Straits Settlements.

14	(15)	(16)

1866 (28 June). *Fiscal stamps as T 14 optd. Wmk Crown over "INDIA". P 14 (at sides only). (a) As T 15.*

66		6 a. purple (G.)		£600 £110
		a. Overprint inverted		† £8500

There are 20 different types of this overprint.

(b) With T 16

68		6 a. purple (G.)		£1100 £140

17	18

Die I	Die II

Two Dies of 4 a:—

Die I.—Mouth closed, line from corner of mouth downwards only. Pointed chin.

Die II.—Mouth slightly open; lips, chin, and throat defined by line of colour. Rounded chin.

1866 (Sept)**–1878.** *W 13. P 14.*

69	**17**	4 a. green (Die I)		45·00 1·75
70		4 a. deep green (Die I)		48·00 1·75
71		4 a. blue-green (Die II) (1878)		15·00 1·25
72	**18**	6 a. 8 p. slate (5.67)		28·00 18·00
		a. Imperf (pair)		£1700

Die I (8 a.)	(Die I (½ a.)

Die II (8 a.)	Die II (½ a.)

1868 (1 Jan). *Die II. Profile redrawn and different diadem. W 13. P 14.*

73	**11**	8 a. rose (Die II)		22·00 4·50
74		8 a. pale rose (Die II)		22·00 4·50

1873. *Die II. Features, especially the mouth, more firmly drawn. W 13. P 14.*

75	**11**	½ a. deep blue (Die II)		3·00 40
76		½ a. blue (Die II)		3·00 50

19	20

1874 (18 July–1 Sept). *W 13. P 14.*

77	**19**	9 p. bright mauve (18.7.74)		10·00 10·00
78		9 p. pale mauve		10·00 10·00
79	**20**	1 r. slate (1.9.74)		30·00 18·00

21	22

1876 (19 Aug). *W 13. P 14.*

80	**21**	6 a. olive-bistre		4·75 2·00
81		6 a. pale brown		5·00 1·50
82	**22**	12 a. Venetian red		6·50 17·00

EMPIRE

Queen Victoria assumed the title of Empress of India in 1877, and the inscription on the stamps was altered from "EAST INDIA" to "INDIA".

23	24	25

26	27	28

29	30	31

32	33	34

1882 (1 Jan)–88. W 34. P 14.

84	23	½ a. deep blue-green (1883)	.. ..	3·00	10
85		½ a. blue-green	.. ..	3·00	10
		a. Double impression	..	£400	£475
86	24	9 p. rose (1883)	.. ..	50	1·50
87		9 p. aniline carmine	.. ..	80	1·75
88	25	1 a. brown-purple (1883)	..	3·00	20
89		1 a. plum	.. ..	3·00	20
90	26	1 a. 6 p. sepia	..	50	80
91	27	2 a. pale blue (1883)	..	3·00	20
92		2 a. blue	.. ..	3·00	20
		a. Double impression		£750	£1000
93	28	3 a. orange	.. ..	12·00	5·00
94		3 a. brown-orange	..	5·00	40
95	29	4 a. olive-green (6.85)	..	11·00	40
96		4 a. slate-green	..	11·00	40
97	30	4 a. 6 p. yellow-green (1.5.86)		14·00	4·00
98	31	8 a. dull mauve (1883)	..	18·00	2·00
99		8 a. magenta	..	18·00	2·00
100	32	12 a. purple/red (1.4.88)	..	6·50	2·50
101	33	1 r. slate (1883)	.. ..	12·00	5·00
84/101		.. .. ..	Set of 11	70·00	15·00
97, 100		Handstamped "Specimen"	Set of 2	75·00	

No. 92a is from a sheet of 2 a. stamps with a very marked double impression issued in Karachi in early 1898.

2½ As.
(35)   36   37

1891 (1 Jan). No. 97 surch with T 35 by Govt Press, Calcutta.
102	30	2½ a. on 4½ a. yellow-green	..	1·90	60

There are several varieties in this surcharge due to variations in the relative positions of the letters and figures.

1892 (Jan)–97. W 34. P 14.
103	36	2 a. 6 p. yellow-green	..	1·00	40
104		2 a. 6 p. pale blue-green (1897)		2·50	80
105	37	1 r. green and rose	..	19·00	5·00
106		1 r. green and aniline carmine		7·00	2·00

38   (39)   40

USED HIGH VALUES. It is necessary to emphasise that used prices quoted for the following and all later high value stamps are for postally used copies.

(Head of Queen from portrait by von Angeli)

1895 (1 Sept). W 34. P 14.
107	38	2 r. carmine and yellow-brown..		35·00	11·00
107a		2 r. carmine and brown..		40·00	13·00
108		3 r. brown and green	..	25·00	10·00
109		5 r. ultramarine and violet	..	35·00	23·00
107/9		.. ..	Set of 3	85·00	40·00

1898 (1 Oct). No. 85 surch with T 39 by Govt Press, Calcutta.
110	23	¼ on ½ a. blue-green..	..	10	40
		a. Surch double	..	£150	
		b. Double impression of stamp		£225	

1899. W 34. P 14.
111	40	3 p. aniline carmine	..	10	10

1900 (1 Oct)–02. W 34. P 14.
112	40	3 p. grey	.. ..	45	70
113	23	½ a. pale yellow-green	..	1·00	45
114		½ a. yellow-green	..	1·10	45
115	25	1 a. carmine	..	75	15
116	27	2 a. pale violet	..	3·25	85
117		2 a. mauve (1902)	..	6·50	2·25
118	36	2 a. 6 p. ultramarine	..	3·25	3·75
112/18		.. ..	Set of 5	8·00	5·25

41   42   43

44   45   46

47   48   49

50   51   52

1902 (9 Aug)–11. W 34. P 14.
119	41	3 p. grey	..	80	10
120		3 p. slate-grey (1904)	..	80	10
121	42	½ a. yellow-green	..	65	20
122		½ a. green	..	65	20
123	43	1 a. carmine	..	75	10
124	44	2 a. violet (13.5.03)	..	2·75	40
125		2 a. mauve	..	2·00	10
126	45	2 a. 6 p. ultramarine (1902)		3·75	25
		w. Wmk inverted	..	†	£100
127	46	3 a. orange-brown (1902)	..	3·25	30
128	47	4 a. olive (20.4.03)	..	3·00	30
129		4 a. pale olive	..	3·00	30
130		4 a. olive-brown	..	9·00	3·00
131	48	6 a. olive-bistre (6.8.03)	..	11·00	4·75
132		6 a. maize	..	10·00	4·50
133	49	8 a. purple (shades) (8.5.03)		7·50	1·00
134		8 a. claret (1910)	..	9·50	1·00
135	50	12 a. purple/red (1903)	..	7·50	2·00
136	51	1 r. green and carmine (1903)		6·50	70
137		1 r. green and scarlet (1911)		29·00	1·75
138	52	2 r. rose-red and yellow-brown (1903)		35·00	4·00
139		2 r. carmine and yellow-brown		35·00	4·00
140		3 r. brown and green (1904)		24·00	19·00
141		3 r. red-brown and green (1911)		35·00	22·00
142		5 r. ultramarine and violet (1904)		50·00	35·00
143		5 r. ultramarine and deep lilac (1911)		90·00	42·00
144		10 r. green and carmine (1909)		£100	24·00
146		15 r. blue and olive-brown (1909)		£130	42·00
147		25 r. brownish orange and blue (1909)		£750	£800
119/47		..	Set of 17	£1000	£850

No. 147 can often be found with telegraph cancellation; these can be supplied at one third of the price given above.

1905 (2 Feb). No. 122 surch with T 39.
148	42	¼ on ½ a. green	..	55	10
		a. Surch inverted	..	—	£800

It is doubtful if No. 148a exists unused with genuine surcharge.

53   54

1906 (6 Dec)–07. W 34. P 14.
149	53	½ a. green	.. ..	1·90	10
150	54	1 a. carmine (7.1.07)	..	1·00	10

55   56   57

58*   59   60

61   62   63

64   65   66

67   "Rs" flaw in right value tablet (R.1/4)

*T 58. Two types of the 1½ a.; (A) As illustrated. (B) Inscribed "1½ As". "ONE AND A HALF ANNAS".

1911 (Dec)–22. W 34. P 14.
151	55	3 p. pale grey (1912)	..	50	20
152		3 p. grey	..	50	20
153		3 p. slate-grey	..	50	20
		a. "Rs" flaw	..	12·00	
154		3 p. blue-slate (1922)	..	1·75	50
		w. Wmk inverted	..	10·00	
155	56	½ a. yellow-green (1912)	..	65	15
156		½ a. pale blue-green	..	65	15
159	57	1 a. rose-carmine	..	1·75	20
160		1 a. carmine	..	1·75	20
161		1 a. aniline carmine	..	1·60	15
162		1 a. pale rose-carmine (chalk-surfaced paper) (1918)		2·25	40
163	58	1½ a. chocolate (Type A) (1919)		2·00	30
164		1½ a. grey-brown (Type A)		7·50	2·50
165		1½ a. chocolate (Type B) (1921)		2·25	3·25
		w. Wmk inverted	..	8·00	
166	59	2 a. dull purple	..	2·25	20
167		2 a. mauve	..	2·25	20
		w. Wmk inverted	..	15·00	
168		2 a. violet	..	4·25	35
169		2 a. bright purple (1.19)	..	4·50	60
170	60	2 a. 6 p. ultramarine (1912)		1·75	3·00
171	61	2 a. 6 p. ultramarine (1913)		1·50	20
172	62	3 a. dull orange	..	4·50	45
173		3 a. orange-brown	..	2·50	20
174	63	4 a. deep olive (1912)	..	4·50	35
175		4 a. olive-green	..	4·25	30
		w. Wmk inverted	..	15·00	
176	64	6 a. bistre (1912)	..	3·75	90
177		6 a. yellow-bistre	..	3·75	1·00
178		6 a. deep bistre-brown	..	16·00	3·50
179	65	8 a. purple (1912)	..	6·00	70
180		8 a. mauve	..	11·00	85
181		8 a. deep lilac	..	14·00	1·25
182		8 a. bright aniline mauve	..	25·00	4·50
183	66	12 a. dull claret (1912)	..	10·00	2·50
184		12 a. claret	..	7·00	2·25
185	67	1 r. brown and green (1913)		16·00	2·00
186		1 r. red-brown and blue-green (1913)		11·00	1·50
		w. Wmk inverted	..	30·00	
187		2 r. carmine and brown (1913)		15·00	1·50
		w. Wmk inverted	..	40·00	
188		5 r. ultramarine and violet (1913)		42·00	6·50
189		10 r. green and scarlet (1913)		65·00	12·00
190		15 r. blue and olive (1913)		90·00	23·00
191		25 r. orange and blue (1913)		£160	30·00
151/91		..	Set of 19	£350	70·00

Examples of the ½ a. printed double are now believed to be forgeries.

FORGERIES.—Collectors are warned against forgeries of all the later surcharges of India, and particularly the errors.

NINE

PIES

(68)

1921. T 57 surch with T 68.
192		9 p. on 1 a. rose-carmine	..	60	30
		a. Error. "NINE NINE"..	..	70·00	£120
		b. Error. "PIES PIES"	..	70·00	£120
		c. Surch double	..	£140	£170
193		9 p. on 1 a. carmine-pink	..	1·75	60
194		9 p. on 1 a. aniline carmine		6·00	2·25

In the initial setting of the surcharge No. 192a occurred on R. 2/13–16 of the fourth pane and No. 192b on R. 4/13–16 of the third. For the second setting No. 192a was corrected. Examples of No. 192b still occur but on R. 2/13–16 of the third pane. Later printings showed this corrected also.

1922. T 56 surch with T 39.
195		¼ a. on ½ a. yellow-green	..	30	35
		a. Surch inverted	..	9·00	
		b. Surch omitted (in horiz pair with normal)	..	£180	
196		¼ a. on ½ a. blue-green	..	1·75	65

1922–26. W 34. P 14.
197	57	1 a. chocolate	..	50	10
198	58	1½ a. rose-carmine (Type B) (1926)		1·75	30
199	61	2 a. 6 p. orange (1926)	..	4·50	4·25
200	62	3 a. ultramarine (1923)	..	12·00	60
197/200		..	Set of 4	16·00	4·75

NEW INFORMATION

The editor is always interested to correspond with people who have new information that will improve or correct the Catalogue.

69	70	71

PRINTERS. The following issues of postage and contemporary official stamps were all printed by the Security Printing Press, Nasik, *unless otherwise stated.*

1926–33. *Typo.* **W 69.** *P* 14.

201	55	3 p. slate				30	10
		w. Wmk inverted	..	..	..	1·00	30
202	56	½ a. green				50	10
		w. Wmk inverted	..	..	..	—	30
203	57	1 a. chocolate				50	10
		a. Tête-bêche (pair) (1932)	..			1·25	10·00
		w. Wmk inverted	..	..	..	50	10
204	58	1½ a. rose-carmine (Type B) (1929)				1·25	10
		w. Wmk inverted	..	..	..	1·50	30
205	59	2 a. bright purple	..	..	..	4·25	5·50
		a. Stop under "s" in right value tablet (R. 4/16)	..			65·00	
206	70	2 a. purple	..			1·00	10
		a. Tête-bêche (pair) (1933)	..			8·00	38·00
		w. Wmk inverted	..	..	..	1·25	30
207	61	2 a. 6 p. orange (1929)	..			1·25	10
		w. Wmk inverted	..	..	..	1·50	40
208	62	3 a. ultramarine	..	..	..	5·50	1·00
209		3 a. blue (1928)	..	..	..	5·50	10
		w. Wmk inverted	..	..	..	6·00	50
210	63	4 a. pale sage-green	..			1·50	10
211	71	4 a. sage-green	..	..	..	6·00	10
		w. Wmk inverted	..	..	..	—	40
212	65	8 a. reddish purple	..	..	..	4·00	10
		w. Wmk inverted	..	..	..	6·00	40
213	66	12 a. claret	..	..	..	5·00	30
		w. Wmk inverted	..	..	..	7·00	60
214	67	1 r. chocolate and green	..			5·00	45
		a. Chocolate (head) omitted	..			£3000	
		w. Wmk inverted	..	..	..	8·00	75
215		2 r. carmine and orange	..			9·00	70
		w. Wmk inverted	..	..	..	11·00	1·25
216		5 r. ultramarine and purple	..			22·00	1·25
		w. Wmk inverted	..	..	..	—	2·00
217		10 r. green and scarlet (1927)	..			38·00	2·50
		w. Wmk inverted	..	..	..	—	3·50
218		15 r. blue and olive (1928)	..			35·00	30·00
		w. Wmk inverted	..	..	..	24·00	24·00
219		25 r. orange and blue (1928)	..			90·00	27·00
		w. Wmk inverted	..	..	..	£100	30·00
201/19		..	..		*Set of* 18	£190	55·00

Examples of the ½ a. printed double are believed to be forgeries.

72 De Havilland D.H.66 Hercules

Missing tree-top (R. 11/6 of 8 a.)	Reversed serif on second "I" of "INDIA"

(Des R. Grant. Litho)

1929 (22 Oct). *Air.* **W 69** (*sideways**). *P* 14.

220	72	2 a. deep blue-green	..	..		1·75	50
		w. Wmk stars pointing left	..			1·50	60
221		3 a. blue	..	..		1·00	1·40
		w. Wmk stars pointing left	..			1·25	1·40
222		4 a. olive-green	..	..		2·25	85
		w. Wmk stars pointing left	..			2·75	1·00
223		6 a. bistre	..	..		2·25	90
		w. Wmk stars pointing left	..			2·50	1·00
224		8 a. purple	..	..		2·50	1·00
		a. Missing tree-top	..			80·00	50·00
		b. Reversed serif	..			£140	75·00
		w. Wmk stars pointing left	..			3·00	1·00
225		12 a. rose-red	..	..		9·00	4·50
		w. Wmk stars pointing left	..			11·00	4·50
220/5		..	..		*Set of* 6	17·00	8·25

*The normal sideways watermark shows the stars pointing right, *as seen from the back of the stamp.*

73 Purana Qila

(Des H. W. Barr. Litho)

1931 (9 Feb). *Inauguration of New Delhi.* T **73** *and similar horiz designs.* **W 69** (*sideways**). *P* 13½×14.

226		¼ a. olive-green and orange-brown			1·25	2·00
		a. "F" for "P" in "PURANA"	..	..	70·00	
		w. Wmk stars pointing left	..	..	1·25	2·00
227		½ a. violet and green	..	..	1·25	40
		w. Wmk stars pointing left	..	..	1·75	40
228		1 a. mauve and chocolate	..	..	1·25	20
		w. Wmk stars pointing left	..	..	1·75	25
229		2 a. green and blue	..	..	1·50	1·50
		w. Wmk stars pointing left	..	..	1·75	1·25
230		3 a. chocolate and carmine	..	..	2·50	2·50
		w. Wmk stars pointing left	..	..	2·50	2·50
231		1 r. violet and green	..	..	7·50	18·00
		w. Wmk stars pointing left	..	..	7·50	18·00
226/31				*Set of* 6	14·00	22·00

Designs:—½ a. War Memorial Arch; 1 a. Council House; 2 a. The Viceroy's House; 3 a. Government of India Secretariat; 1 r. Dominion Columns and the Secretariat.

*The normal sideways watermark shows the stars pointing to the right, *as seen from the back of the stamp.*

79	80	81

82	83

(T **82/3** des T. I. Archer. 9 p. litho and typo; 1¼ a., 3½ a. litho; others typo)

1932–36. **W 69.** *P* 14.

232	79	½ a. green (1934)	..	..		75	10
		w. Wmk inverted	..	..		—	50
233	80	9 p. deep green (22.4.32)	..	..		30	10
234	81	1 a. chocolate (1934)	..	..		2·50	10
235	82	1 a. 3 p. mauve (22.4.32)	..	..		30	10
		w. Wmk inverted	..	..		30	30
236	70	2 a. vermilion	..	..		9·00	3·75
		aw. Wmk inverted	..	..		9·00	5·00
236b	59	2 a. vermilion (1934)	..	..		3·75	50
236c		2 a. vermilion (*small die*) (1936)	..			4·50	30
237	62	3 a. carmine	..	..		2·75	10
238	83	3 a. 6 p. ultramarine (22.4.32)	..			2·00	10
		w. Wmk inverted	..	..		2·00	20
239	64	6 a. bistre (1935)	..	..		7·00	1·50
232/9				*Set of* 9	26·00	5·00

No. 236b measures 19×22.6 mm and No. 236c 18.4×21.8 mm.

84 Gateway of India, Bombay   "Bird" flaw (R.9/3)

1935 (6 May). *Silver Jubilee.* T **84** *and similar horiz designs.* *Litho.* **W 69** (*sideways**). *P* 13½×14.

240		½ a. black and yellow-green	..	..		60	10
		w. Wmk stars pointing left	..			60	10
241		9 p. black and grey-green	..	..		45	20
		w. Wmk stars pointing left	..			45	30
242		1 a. black and brown	..	..		45	15
		w. Wmk stars pointing left	..			45	10
243		1¼ a. black and bright violet	..	..		45	15
		w. Wmk stars pointing left	..			65	15
244		2½ a. black and orange	..	..		2·00	1·25
		w. Wmk stars pointing left	..			1·50	95
245		3½ a. black and dull ultramarine	..	..		3·25	2·50
		a. "Bird" flaw	..	..		80·00	55·00
		w. Wmk stars pointing left	..			3·75	2·50
246		8 a. black and purple	..	..		3·25	3·00
		w. Wmk stars pointing left	..			4·50	3·50
240/6				*Set of* 7	9·00	6·00

Designs:—9 p. Victoria Memorial Calcutta; 1 a. Rameswaram Temple, Madras; 1¼ a. Jain Temple, Calcutta; 2½ a. Taj Mahal, Agra; 3½ a. Golden Temple, Amritsar; 8 a. Pagoda in Mandalay.

*The normal sideways watermark shows the stars pointing to the right, *as seen from the back of the stamp.*

ALTERED CATALOGUE NUMBERS

Any Catalogue numbers altered from the last edition are shown as a list in the introductory pages.

---

91 King George VI	92 Dak Runner

93 King George VI

1937 (23 Aug–15 Dec). *Typo.* **W 69.** *P* 13½×14 *or* 14×13½ (T **93**).

247	91	3 p. slate	..	..		50	10
248		½ a. red-brown	..	..		1·25	10
249		9 p. green (23.8.37)	..	..		3·75	20
250		1 a. carmine (23.8.37)	..	..		40	10
		a. Tête-bêche (vert pair)	..			80	1·75
		w. Wmk inverted (from booklets)	..			40	40
251	92	2 a. vermilion	..	..		2·50	10
252	—	2 a. 6 p. bright violet	..	..		75	20
253	—	3 a. yellow-green	..	..		4·50	30
254	—	3 a. 6 p. bright blue	..	..		3·25	50
255	—	4 a. brown	..	..		13·00	20
256	—	6 a. turquoise-green	..	..		14·00	80
257	—	8 a. slate-violet	..	..		7·50	50
258	—	12 a. lake	..	..		18·00	1·10
259	93	1 r. grey and red-brown	..	..		1·00	15
260		2 r. purple and brown	..	..		3·75	30
261		5 r. green and blue	..	..		15·00	50
		w. Wmk inverted	..	..		32·00	
262		10 r. purple and claret	..			15·00	70
263		15 r. brown and green	..			70·00	55·00
		w. Wmk inverted	..	..		70·00	55·00
264		25 r. slate-violet and purple	..			90·00	17·00
247/64				*Set of* 18	£225	70·00

Designs: *Horiz as* T **92**—2 a. 6 p. Dak bullock cart; 3 a. Dak tonga; 3 a. 6 p. Dak camel; 4 a. Mail train; 6 a. *Strathnaver* (liner); 8 a. Mail lorry; 12 a. Armstrong Whitworth A.W.27 Ensign 1 mail plane (small head).

100a King George VI	101 King George VI	102

103 Armstrong Whitworth A.W.27 Ensign I Mail Plane (large head)

(T **100a/102** des T. I. Archer. Typo)

1940–43. **W 69.** *P* 13½ × 14.

265	100a	3 p. slate	..	..		25	10
266		½ a. purple (1.10.42)	..	..		40	10
267		9 p. green	..	..		40	10
268		1 a. carmine (1.4.43)	..	..		40	10
269	101	1 a. 3 p. yellow-brown	..	..		90	10
269a		1½ a. dull violet (9.42)	..	..		50	10
270		2 a. vermilion	..	..		1·00	10
271		3 a. bright violet (1942)	..	..		2·00	10
272		3½ a. bright blue	..	..		70	10
273	102	4 a. brown	..	..		45	10
274		6 a. turquoise-green	..	..		2·50	10
275		8 a. slate-violet	..	..		1·50	30
276		12 a. lake	..	..		2·75	10
277	103	14 a. purple (15.10.40)	..	..		18·00	1·50
265/277				*Set of* 14	28·00	2·25

The 1½ a. and 3 a. were at first printed by lithography and were of finer execution and without Jubilee lines in the sheet margins.

= =

3 PIES

105 "Victory" and King George VI	(106)

1946 (2 Jan). *Victory. Litho.* **W 69.** *P* 13.

278	105	9 p. yellow-green (8.2.46)	..	..		30	30
279		1½ a. dull violet	..	..		30	30
280		3½ a. bright blue	..	..		75	60
281		12 a. claret (8.2.46)	..	..		1·50	55
278/81				*Set of* 4	2·50	1·60

1946 (8 Aug). *Surch with* T **106**.

282	101	3 p. on 1 a. 3 p. yellow-brown	..	..	10	15

DOMINION

301 Asokan Capital
(Inscr reads
"Long Live India")

302 Indian National Flag

303 Douglas DC-4

(Des T. I. Archer. Litho)

1947 (21 Nov–15 Dec). *Independence.* W **69**. *P* 14 × 13½ (1½ a.)
or 13½ × 14 (*others*).

301	301	1½ a. grey-green (15 Dec)	..	15	10
302	302	3½ a. orange-red, blue and green	..	30	70
		w. Wmk inverted ..	..	5·00	5·00
303	303	12 a. ultramarine (15 Dec)	..	1·50	1·50
301/3	..	.. .. ..	*Set of* 3	1·75	2·00

304 Lockheed Constellation

(Des T. I. Archer. Litho)

1948 (29 May). *Air. Inauguration of India-U.K. Air Service.* W **69**.
P 13½ × 14.

304	304	12 a. black and ultramarine	..	1·00	2·00

305 Mahatma Gandhi **306**

(Photo Courvoisier)

1948 (15 Aug). *First Anniv of Independence. P* 11½.

305	305	1½ a. brown	..	1·75	30
306		3½ a. violet	..	4·25	1·50
307		12 a. grey-green	..	6·00	60
308	306	10 r. purple-brown and lake	..	55·00	40·00
305/8	..	.. .. ..	*Set of* 4	60·00	40·00

307 Ajanta
Panel

308 Konarak Horse

309 Trimurti

310 Bodhisattva

311 Nataraja

312 Sanchi Stupa,
East Gate

313 Bodh Gaya
Temple

314 Bhuvanesvara

315 Gol Gumbad,
Bijapur

316 Kandarya Mahadeva
Temple

317 Golden Temple,
Amritsar

318 Victory Tower,
Chittorgarh

319 Red Fort, Delhi

320 Taj Mahal, Agra

321 Qutb Minar,
Delhi

322 Satrunjaya Temple, Palitana

(Des T. I. Archer and I. M. Das. Typo (low values), litho (rupee
values))

1949 (15 Aug). W **69** (*sideways** *on* 6 *p.,* 1 *r. and* 10 *r.*). *P* 14
(3 *p. to* 2 *a.*), 13½ (3 *a. to* 12 *a.*), 14×13½ (1 *r. and* 10 *r.*),
13½×14 (2 *r. and* 5 *r.*), 13 (15 *r.*)).

309	307	3 p. slate-violet	..	15	10
		w. Wmk inverted ..	..		
310	308	6 p. purple-brown	..	25	10
		w. Wmk star pointing right	..	2·75	90
311	309	9 p. yellow-green	..	40	10
312	310	1 a. turquoise	..	60	10
313	311	2 a. carmine	..	80	10
		w. Wmk inverted ..	..	8·00	90
314	312	3 a. brown-orange	..	1·50	10
315	313	3½ a. bright blue	..	1·50	2·75
316	314	4 a. lake	..	4·00	10
		w. Wmk inverted ..	..	11·00	1·00
317	315	6 a. violet	..	1·50	10
		w. Wmk inverted ..	..	3·00	45
318	316	8 a. turquoise-green	..	1·50	10
		w. Wmk inverted ..	..		
319	317	12 a. dull blue	..	1·50	10
		w. Wmk inverted ..	..	4·00	60
320	318	1 r. dull violet and green	..	9·00	10
		w. Wmk star pointing left	..	17·00	60
321	319	2 r. claret and violet	..	10·00	15
		w. Wmk inverted ..	..	20·00	80
322	320	5 r. blue-green and red-brown	..	28·00	80
		w. Wmk inverted ..	..	40·00	1·25
323	321	10 r. purple-brown and deep blue	..	45·00	4·50
		a. *Purple-brown and blue*	..	90·00	3·75
		aw. Wmk star pointing left			
324	322	15 r. brown and claret	..	14·00	17·00
309/24	..	.. .. ..	*Set of* 16	£110	22·00

*The normal sideways watermark has the star pointing to the
left on the 6 p. value and to the right on the 1 r. and 10 r. (323*a*)
when seen from the back of the stamp.
For T **310** with statue reversed see No. 333.

323 Globe and Asokan Capital

1949 (10 Oct). *75th Anniv of U.P.U. Litho.* W **69**. *P* 13.

325	323	9 p. green	..	1·00	1·75
326		2 a. rose	..	1·25	1·75
327		3½ a. bright blue	..	2·00	2·25
328		12 a. brown-purple	..	3·50	2·50
325/8	..	.. .. ..	*Set of* 4	7·00	7·50

REPUBLIC

324 Rejoicing Crowds

328 As T **310**, but
statue reversed

(Des D. J. Keymer & Co. Litho)

1950 (26 Jan). *Inauguration of Republic.* T **324** *and similar
designs.* W **69** (*sideways on* 3½ a.). *P* 13.

329		2 a. scarlet	..	1·00	40
		w. Wmk inverted	..	10·00	1·60
330		3½ a. ultramarine ..	..	1·75	2·75
331		4 a. violet	..	1·75	65
332		12 a. maroon	..	3·75	2·25
		w. Wmk inverted	..	12·00	4·00
329/32	..	.. ..	*Set of* 4	7·50	5·50

Designs: *Vert*—3½ a. Quill, ink-well and verse. *Horiz*—4 a. Ear
of corn and plough; 12 a. Spinning-wheel and cloth.

1950 (15 July)–**51**. *Typo.* W **69**. *P* 14 (1 a.), 13½ (*others*).

333	328	1 a. turquoise	..	2·50	10
		aw. Wmk inverted	..		
333b	313	2½ a. lake (30.4.51)	..	2·50	2·50
333c	314	4 a. bright blue (30.4.51)	..	6·00	10
333/c	..	.. ..	*Set of* 3	10·00	2·50

329 *Stegodon ganesa*

330 Torch

1951 (13 Jan). *Centenary of Geological Survey of India. Litho.*
W **69**. *P* 13.

334	329	2 a. black and claret	..	2·00	30

1951 (4 Mar). *First Asian Games, New Delhi. Litho.* W **69** (*sideways*). *P* 14.

335	330	2 a. reddish purple and brown-orange	..	1·00	30
336		12 a. chocolate and light blue	..	4·00	90

PROCESS. All the following issues were printed in photogravure,
except where otherwise stated.

331 Kabir **332** Locomotives in 1853 and 1953

1952 (1 Oct). *Indian Saints and Poets.* T **331** *and similar vert
designs.* W **69**. *P* 14.

337		9 p. bright emerald-green	..	30	40
338		1 a. carmine	..	30	15
339		2 a. orange-red	..	1·00	20
340		4 a. bright blue	..	1·25	40
341		4½ a. bright mauve	..	30	80
342		12 a. brown	..	2·00	80
337/42		.. ..	*Set of* 6	4·50	2·50

Designs:—1 a. Tulsidas; 2 a. Meera; 4 a. Surdas; 4½ a. Ghalib;
12 a. Tagore.

1953 (16 Apr). *Railway Centenary.* W **69**. *P* 14½ × 14.

343	332	2 a. black	..	75	10

333 Mount Everest

1953 (2 Oct). *Conquest of Mount Everest.* W **69**. *P* 14½ × 14.

344	333	2 a. bright violet	..	50	10
345		14 a. brown	..	3·00	25

334 Telegraph Poles of 1851 and 1951

1953 (1 Nov). *Centenary of Indian Telegraphs.* W **69**. *P* 14½ × 14.
346 **334** 2 a. blue-green 30 10
347 12 a. blue .. .. 3·00 40

335 Postal Transport, 1854

1954 (1 Oct). *Stamp Centenary. T* **335** *and similar horiz designs.*
W **69**. *P* 14½ × 14.
348 1 a. reddish purple 30 20
349 2 a. cerise 30 10
350 4 a. orange-brown .. .. .. 2·75 40
351 14 a. blue .. .. 1·50 40
348/51 .. .. .. *Set of* 4 4·25 1·00
Designs:—2, 14 a. "Airmail"; 4 a. Postal transport, 1954.

338 U.N. Emblem and Lotus

1954 (24 Oct). *United Nations Day.* W **69** (*sideways*). *P* 13.
352 **338** 2 a. turquoise-green 40 30

339 Forest Research Institute

1954 (11 Dec). *Fourth World Forestry Congress, Dehra Dun.* W **69**.
P 14½ × 14.
353 **339** 2 a. ultramarine 20 10

340 Tractor   344 Woman
                     Spinning

347 "Malaria Control" (Mosquito
and Staff of Aesculapius)

1955 (26 Jan). *Five Year Plan. T* **340**, **344**, **347** *and similar
designs.* W **69** (*sideways on small horiz designs*). *P* 14×14½
(*small horiz*) *or* 14½×14 (*others*).
354 3 p. bright purple 30 10
355 6 p. violet 30 10
356 9 p. orange-brown 40 10
357 1 a. blue-green 45 10
358 2 a. light blue 30 10
359 3 a. pale blue-green 50 10
360 4 a. rose-carmine 50 10
361 6 a. yellow-brown .. .. .. 1·50 10
362 8 a. blue .. .. 6·00 10
363 10 a. turquoise-green .. .. 2·00 1·50
364 12 a. bright blue .. .. .. 1·50 10
365 14 a. bright green .. .. .. 3·00 20
366 1 r. deep dull green .. .. .. 4·00 10
367 1 r. 2 a. grey .. .. 2·00 2·75
368 1 r. 8 a. reddish purple .. .. 7·00 4·00
369 2 r. cerise .. .. 4·25 10
370 5 r. brown .. .. 14·00 30
371 10 r. orange .. .. 14·00 4·00
354/71 .. .. .. *Set of* 18 50·00 11·50
Designs: *Horiz* (*as T* **340**)—6 p. Power loom; 9 p. Bullock-driven
well; 1 a. Damodar Valley Dam; 4 a. Bullocks; 8 a. Chittaranjan
Locomotive Works; 12 a. Hindustan Aircraft Factory, Bangalore;
1 r. Telephone engineer; 2 r. Rare Earth Factory, Alwaye; 5 r.
Sindri Fertiliser Factory; 10 r. Steel plant. (*As T* **347**)—10 a.
Marine Drive, Bombay; 14 a. Kashmir landscape; 1 r. 2 a. Cape
Comorin; 1 r. 8 a. Mt Kangchenjunga. *Vert* (*as T* **344**)—3 a. Woman
weaving with hand loom.
For stamps as Nos. 366, 369/71 but W **374** see Nos. 413/16.

358 Bodhi Tree   359 Round Parasol and Bodhi Tree

(Des C. Pakrashi (2 a.), R. D'Silva (14 a.))

1956 (24 May). *Buddha Jayanti.* W **69** (*sideways on* 14 *a.*).
P 13 × 13½ (2 *a.*) *or* 13½ × 13 (14 *a.*).
372 **358** 2 a. sepia 75 10
373 **359** 14 a. vermilion .. .. .. 4·00 3·50

360 Lokmanya Bal   361 Map of India
Gangadhar Tilak

1956 (23 July). *Birth Centenary of Tilak* (*journalist*). W **69**.
P 13 × 13½.
374 **360** 2 a. chestnut 10 10

(New Currency. 100 naye paise = 1 rupee)

1957 (1 Apr)–58. W **69** (*sideways*). *P* 14 × 14½.
375 **361** 1 n.p. blue-green 10 10
376 2 n.p. light brown 10 10
377 3 n.p. deep brown 10 10
378 5 n.p. bright green .. .. 4·25 10
379 6 n.p. grey 10 10
379a 8 n.p. light blue-green (7.5.58) .. 5·50 1·25
380 10 n.p. deep dull green .. .. 4·25 10
381 13 n.p. bright carmine-red 30 10
381a 15 n.p. violet (16.1.58) .. .. 2·50 10
382 20 n.p. blue 30 10
383 25 n.p. ultramarine 30 10
384 50 n.p. orange .. .. .. 2·25 10
385 75 n.p. reddish purple .. .. 1·25 10
385a 90 n.p. bright purple (16.1.58) .. 2·50 1·50
375/85a .. .. .. *Set of* 14 21·00 2·75
The 8, 15 and 90 n.p. have their value expressed as "nP".
For similar stamps but W **374** see Nos. 399/412.

362 The Rani of Jhansi   363 Shrine

1957 (15 Aug). *Indian Mutiny Centenary.* W **69**. *P* 14½ × 14
(15 *n.p.*) *or* 13 × 13½ (90 *n.p.*).
386 **362** 15 n.p. brown 15 10
387 **363** 90 n.p. reddish purple .. .. 1·50 50

364 Henri Dunant and Conference   365 "Nutrition"
Emblem

1957 (28 Oct). *19th International Red Cross Conference, New
Delhi.* W **69** (*sideways*). *P* 13½ × 13.
388 **364** 15 n.p. deep grey and carmine .. 10 10

1957 (14 Nov). *Children's Day. T* **365** *and similar designs.*
W **69** (*sideways on* 90 *n.p.*). *P* 14×13½ (90 *n.p.*) *or* 13½×14
(*others*).
389 8 n.p. reddish purple 10 15
390 15 n.p. turquoise-green 10 10
391 90 n.p. orange-brown 25 15
389/91 .. .. .. *Set of* 3 30 30
Designs: *Horiz*—15 n.p. "Education". *Vert*—90 n.p. "Recreation".

OMNIBUS ISSUES

Details, together with prices for complete sets,
of the various Omnibus issues from the 1935
Silver Jubilee series to date are included in a
special section following Zimbabwe at the end of
Volume 2.

368 Bombay University   369 Calcutta University

1957 (31 Dec). *Centenary of Indian Universities. T* **368/9** *and
similar design.* W **69** (*sideways on T* **368**). *P* 14 × 14½ (*No.* 392)
or 13½ × 14 (*others*).
392 10 n.p. violet 15 20
393 10 n.p. grey 15 20
394 10 n.p. light brown 30 20
392/4 .. .. .. *Set of* 3 55 55
Design: *Horiz as T* **369**—No. 394, Madras University.

371 J. N. Tata (founder) and   372 Dr. D. K. Karve
Steel Plant

1958 (1 Mar). *50th Anniv of Steel Industry.* W **69**. *P* 14½ × 14.
395 **371** 15 n.p. orange-red 10 10

1958 (18 Apr). *Birth Centenary of Karve* (*educationalist*). W **69**
(*sideways*). *P* 14.
396 **372** 15 n.p. orange-brown 10 10

373 Westland Wapiti   374 Asokan Capital
Biplane and Hawker Hunter

1958 (30 Apr). *Silver Jubilee of Indian Air Force.* W **69**.
P 14½ × 14.
397 **373** 15 n.p. blue .. .. .. 1·00 10
398 90 n.p. ultramarine .. .. 1·25 1·25

ASOKAN CAPITAL WATERMARK. When the watermark
was originally introduced in 1958 the base of each individual
capital was 10 mm wide. During 1985 a modified version, with
the capital base measurement reduced to 8 mm, was introduced.
Examples have been seen on Nos. 921a, 922a, 923a and 928a.

1958–63. *As Nos.* 366, 369/71 *and* 375/85a *but* W **374**.
399 **361** 1 n.p. blue-green (1960) .. 90 10
a. Imperf (pair) £170
400 2 n.p. light brown (27.10.58) .. 10 10
401 3 n.p. deep brown (1958) .. 10 10
402 5 n.p. bright green (27.10.58) .. 10 10
403 6 n.p. grey (1963) .. .. 15 3·25
404 8 n.p. light blue-green (1958) .. 90 10
405 10 n.p. deep dull green (27.10.58) .. 15 10
a. Imperf (pair) .. .. †
406 13 n.p. bright carmine-red (1963) .. 60 3·50
407 15 n.p. violet (10.60) 60 10
408 20 n.p. blue (27.10.58) 30 10
409 25 n.p. ultramarine (27.10.58) .. 30 10
410 50 n.p. orange (1959) 30 10
411 75 n.p. reddish purple (1959) .. 40 10
412 90 n.p. bright purple (1960) .. 5·50 10
413 — 1 r. deep dull green (1959) .. 3·75 10
414 — 2 r. cerise (1959) .. .. 5·50 10
415 — 5 r. brown (1959) .. .. 9·00 30
416 — 10 r. orange (1959) .. .. 20·00 4·25
399/416 .. .. *Set of* 18 42·00 10·50
The 5, 10, 15, 20, 25 and 50 n.p. with serial numbers on the back
are coil stamps prepared from sheets for experimenting with coil
machines. In the event the machines were not purchased and the
stamps were sold over the counter.

375 Bipin Chandra Pal   376 Nurse with
                          Child Patient

1958 (7 Nov). *Birth Centenary of Pal* (*patriot*). W **374**. *P* 14 × 13½.
418 **375** 15 n.p. deep dull green 10 10

1958 (14 Nov). *Children's Day.* W **374**. *P* 14×13½.
419 **376** 15 n.p. violet 10 10

377 Jagadish Chandra Bose   **378** Exhibition Gate

1958 (30 Nov). *Birth Centenary of Bose (botanist). W* **374**. *P* 14 × 13½.
20   377   15 n.p. deep turquoise-green   20   10

1958 (30 Dec). *India 1958 Exhibition, New Delhi. W* **374** *(sideways). P* 14½ × 14.
21   378   15 n.p. reddish purple   10   10

379 Sir Jamsetjee Jejeebhoy   **380** "The Triumph of Labour" (after Chowdhury)

1959 (15 Apr). *Death Centenary of Jejeebhoy (philanthropist). W* **374**. *P* 14 × 13½.
422   379   15 n.p. brown   10   10

1959 (15 June). *40th Anniv of International Labour Organization. W* **374** *(sideways). P* 14½ × 14.
423   380   15 n.p. dull green   10   10

381 Boys awaiting admission to Children's Home   **382** "Agriculture"

1959 (14 Nov). *Children's Day. W* **374**. *P* 14 × 14½.
424   381   15 n.p. deep dull green   10   10
       a. Imperf (pair)   £650

1959 (30 Dec). *First World Agricultural Fair, New Delhi. W* **374**. *P* 13½ × 13.
425   382   15 n.p. grey   20   10

383 Thiruvalluvar (philosopher)

1960 (15 Feb). *Thiruvalluvar Commemoration. W* **374**. *P* 14 × 13½.
426   383   15 n.p. reddish purple   10   10

384 Yaksha pleading with the Cloud (from the "Meghaduta")   **385** Shakuntala writing a letter to Dushyanta (from the "Shakuntala")

1960 (22 June). *Kalidasa (poet) Commemoration. W* **374**. *P* 13.
427   384   15 n.p. grey   30   10
428   385   1 r. 3 n.p. pale yellow and brown   1·40   60

NEW INFORMATION

The editor is always interested to correspond with people who have new information that will improve or correct the Catalogue.

386 S. Bharati (poet)   **387** Dr. M. Visvesvaraya

1960 (11 Sept). *Subramania Bharati Commemoration. W* **374**. *P* 14 × 13½.
429   386   15 n.p. blue   10   10

1960 (15 Sept). *Birth Centenary of Dr. M. Visvesvaraya (engineer). W* **374**. *P* 13 × 13½.
430   387   15 n.p. brown and bright carmine   10   10

388 "Children's Health"

1960 (14 Nov). *Children's Day. W* **374**. *P* 13½ × 13.
431   388   15 n.p. deep dull green   10   10

389 Children greeting U.N. Emblem   **390** Tyagaraja

1960 (11 Dec). *U.N.I.C.E.F. Day. W* **374**. *P* 13½ × 13.
432   389   15 n.p. orange-brown and olive-brown   10   10

1961 (6 Jan). *114th Death Anniv of Tyagaraja (musician). W* **374**. *P* 14×13½.
433   390   15 n.p. greenish blue   10   10

391 "First Aerial Post" cancellation

392 Air India Boeing 707 Airliner and Humber Sommer Biplane

1961 (18 Feb). *50th Anniv of First Official Airmail Flight, Allahabad-Naini. T* **391**/2 *and similar design. W* **374**. *P* 14 (5 *n.p.) or* 13 × 13½ (*others*).
434   5 n.p. olive-drab   1·10   30
435   15 n.p. deep green and grey   1·10   30
436   1 r. purple and grey   3·75   1·60
434/6   *Set of 3*   5·50   2·00
    Design: *Horiz as T* **392**—1 r. H. Pecquet flying Humber Sommer plane and "Aerial Post" cancellation.

394 Shivaji on horseback   **395** Motilal Nehru (politician)

1961 (17 Apr). *Chatrapati Shivaji (Maratha ruler) Commemoration. W* **374**. *P* 13×13½.
437   394   15 n.p. brown and green   70   30

1961 (6 May). *Birth Centenary of Pandit Motilal Nehru. W* **374**. *P* 14.
438   395   15 n.p. olive-brown and brown-orange   10   10

396 Tagore (poet)   **397** All India Radio Emblem and Transmitting Aerials

1961 (7 May). *Birth Centenary of Rabindranath Tagore. W* **374**. *P* 13 × 13½.
439   396   15 n.p. yellow-orange and blue-green   70   30

1961 (8 June). *Silver Jubilee of All India Radio. W* **374**. *P* 13½ × 13.
440   397   15 n.p. ultramarine   10   10

398 Prafulla Chandra Ray   **399** V. N. Bhatkande

1961 (2 Aug). *Birth Centenary of Ray (social reformer). W* **374**. *P* 14×13½.
441   398   15 n.p. grey   10   20

1961 (1 Sept). *Birth Centenary of Bhatkande (composer)* (1960). *W* **374**. *P* 13×13½.
442   399   15 n.p. olive-brown   10   10

400 Child at Lathe   **401** Fair Emblem and Main Gate

1961 (14 Nov). *Children's Day. W* **374**. *P* 14 × 13½.
443   400   15 n.p. brown   10   20

1961 (14 Nov). *Indian Industries Fair, New Delhi. W* **374**. *P* 14 × 14½.
444   401   15 n.p. blue and carmine   10   10

402 Indian Forest

1961 (21 Nov). *Centenary of Scientific Forestry. W* **374**. *P* 13 × 13½.
445   402   15 n.p. green and brown   30   20

403 Pitalkhora: Yaksha   **404** Kalibangan Seal

1961 (14 Dec). *Centenary of Indian Archaeological Survey. W* **374**. *P* 14 × 13½ (15 *n.p.) or* 13½ × 14 (90 *n.p.*).
446   403   15 n.p. orange-brown   20   10
447   404   90 n.p. yellow-olive and light brown   40   20

405 M. M. Malaviya   406 Gauhati Refinery

1961 (24 Dec). *Birth Centenary of Malaviya (educationist).* W **374**. *P* 14×13½.
448   405   15 n.p. deep slate   10   20

1962 (1 Jan). *Inauguration of Gauhati Oil Refinery.* W **374**. *P* 13×13½.
449   406   15 n.p. blue   30   20

407 Bhikaiji Cama   408 Village Panchayati and Parliament Building

1962 (26 Jan). *Birth Centenary of Bhikaiji Cama (patriot).* W **374**. *P* 14.
450   407   15 n.p. reddish purple   10   10

1962 (26 Jan). *Inauguration of Panchayati System of Local Government.* W **374**. *P* 13×13½.
451   408   15 n.p. bright purple   10   10

409 D. Saraswati (religious reformer)   410 G. S. Vidhyarthi (journalist)

1962 (4 Mar). *Dayanard Saraswati Commemoration.* W **374**. *P* 14.
452   409   15 n.p. orange-brown   10   10

1962 (25 Mar). *Ganesh Shankar Vidhyarthi Commemoration.* W **374**. *P* 14×13½.
453   410   15 n.p. red-brown   10   10

411 Malaria Eradication Emblem   412 Dr. R. Prasad

1962 (7 Apr). *Malaria Eradication.* W **374**. *P* 13 × 13½.
454   411   15 n.p. yellow and claret   10   10

1962 (13 May). *Retirement of President Dr. Rajendra Prasad.* W **374**. *P* 13.
455   412   15 n.p. bright purple (*shades*)   ..   20   10

The new-issue supplement to this Catalogue appears each month in

GIBBONS STAMP MONTHLY

—from your newsagent or by postal subscription— sample copy and details on request.

413 Calcutta High Court   416 Ramabai Ranade

1962. *Centenary of Indian High Courts.* T **413** *and similar horiz designs.* W **374**. *P* 14.
456   15 n.p. dull green (1 July)   ..   50   20
457   15 n.p. red-brown (6 August) ..   50   20
458   15 n.p. slate (14 August)   ..   50   20
456/8   *Set of 3*   1·40   55
Designs:—No. 457, Madras High Court; No. 458, Bombay High Court.

1962 (15 Aug). *Birth Centenary of Ramabai Ranade (social reformer).* W **374**. *P* 14 × 13½.
459   416   15 n.p. orange-brown   ..   10   20

417 Indian Rhinoceros   418 "Passing the Flag to Youth"

1962 (1 Oct). *Wild Life Week.* W **374**. *P* 13½ × 14.
460   417   15 n.p. red-brown and deep turquoise ..   40   15

INSCRIPTIONS. From No. 461 onwards all designs are inscribed "BHARAT" in Devanagari in addition to "INDIA" in English.

1962 (14 Nov). *Children's Day.* W **374**. *P* 13½ × 13.
461   418   15 n.p. orange-red and turquoise-green   15   20

419 Human Eye within Lotus Blossom   420 S. Ramanujan

1962 (3 Dec). *19th International Ophthalmology Congress, New Delhi.* W **374**. *P* 13½ × 13.
462   419   15 n.p. deep olive-brown   ..   20   10

1962 (22 Dec). *75th Birth Anniv of Srinivasa Ramanujan (mathematician).* W **374**. *P* 13½×14.
463   420   15 n.p. deep olive-brown   ..   50   30

Re.1

421 S. Vivekananda   (422)

1963 (17 Jan). *Birth Centenary of Vivekananda (philosopher).* W **374**. *P* 14 × 14½.
464   421   15 n.p. orange-brown and yellow-olive ..   15   20

1963 (2 Feb). *No. 428 surch with T* **422**.
465   385   1 r. on 1 r. 3 n.p. pale yellow & brn   ..   30   10

423 Hands reaching for F.A.O. Emblem   424 Henri Dunant (founder) and Centenary Emblem

1963 (21 Mar). *Freedom from Hunger.* W **374**. *P* 13.
466   423   15 n.p. grey-blue   ..   ..   1·00   30

1963 (8 May). *Red Cross Centenary.* W **374**. *P* 13.
467   424   15 n.p. red and grey   ..   ..   2·50   30
     a. Red (cross) omitted   ..   £2500

425 Artillery and Helicopter

1963 (15 Aug). *Defence Campaign.* T **425** *and similar horiz design.* W **374**. *P* 14.
468   15 n.p. grey-green   40   10
469   1 r. red-brown   70   65
Design:—1 r. Sentry and parachutists.

427 D. Naoroji (parliamentarian)   428 Annie Besant (patriot and theosophist)

1963 (4 Sept). *Dadabhai Naoroji Commemoration.* W **374**. *P* 13.
470   427   15 n.p. grey   10   10

1963 (1 Oct). *Annie Besant Commemoration.* W **374**. *P* 13½×14.
471   428   15 n.p. turquoise-green   15   10
No 471 is incorrectly dated "1837". Mrs. Besant was born in 1847.

429 Gaur   430 Lesser Panda

1963 (7 Oct). *Wild Life Preservation.* T **429/30** *and similar designs.* W **374**. *P* 13½ × 14 (10 *n.p.*) *or* 13 (*others*).
472   10 n.p. black and yellow-orange   ..   75   1·50
473   15 n.p. orange-brown and green   ..   1·50   60
474   30 n.p. slate and yellow-ochre   ..   3·75   1·50
475   50 n.p. orange and deep grey-green ..   3·50   80
476   1 r. light brown and blue   ..   2·50   50
472/6   *Set of 5*   11·00   4·50
Designs: Vert—30 n.p. Indian elephant. *Horiz (as T* **430**)— 50 n.p. Tiger; 1 r. Lion.

434 "School Meals"   435 Eleanor Roosevelt at Spinning-wheel

1963 (14 Nov). *Children's Day.* W **374**. *P* 14 × 13½.
477   434   15 n.p. bistre-brown   10   10

1963 (10 Dec). *15th Anniv of Declaration of Human Rights.* W **374**. *P* 13½ × 13.
478   435   15 n.p. reddish purple   10   15

436 Dipalakshmi (bronze)   437 Gopabandhu Das (social reformer)

1964 (4 Jan). *26th International Orientalists Congress, New Delhi.* W 374. P 13 × 13½.
479 436 15 n.p. deep ultramarine 15 15

1964 (4 Jan). *Gopabandhu Das Commemoration.* W 374. P 13 × 13½.
480 437 15 n.p. deep dull purple 10 10

438 Purandaradasa

1964 (14 Jan). *400th Death Anniv of Purandaradasa (composer).* W 374. P 13 × 13½.
481 438 15 n.p. light brown 15 10

439 S. C. Bose and I. N. A. Badge   **440** Bose and Indian National Army

1964 (23 Jan). *67th Birth Anniv of Subhas Chandra Bose (nationalist).* W 374. P 13.
482 439 15 n.p. yellow-bistre 40 20
483 440 55 n.p. black, orange and orange-red .. 40 45

441 Sarojini Naidu   **442** Kasturba Gandhi

1964 (13 Feb). *85th Birth Anniv of Sarojini Naidu (poetess).* W 374. P 14.
484 441 15 n.p. deep grey-green and purple .. 10 10

1964 (22 Feb). *20th Death Anniv of Kasturba Gandhi.* W 374. P 14 × 13½.
485 442 15 n.p. orange-brown 10 10

443 Dr. W. M. Haffkine (immunologist)   **444** Jawaharlal Nehru (statesman)

1964 (16 Mar). *Haffkine Commemoration.* W 374. P 13.
486 443 15 n.p. deep purple-brown/*buff* 10 10

(Value expressed as paisa instead of naye paise.)

1964 (12 June). *Nehru Mourning Issue. No wmk.* P 13½ × 13.
487 444 15 p. deep slate 10 10

445 Sir Asutosh Mookerjee   **446** Sri Aurobindo

1964 (29 June). *Birth Centenary of Sir Asutosh Mookerjee (education reformer).* W 374. P 13½ × 13.
488 445 15 p. bistre-brown and yellow-olive .. 10 10

1964 (15 Aug). *92nd Birth Anniv of Sri Aurobindo (religious teacher).* W 374. P 13×13½.
489 446 15 p. dull purple 15 10

447 Raja R. Roy (social reformer)   **448** I.S.O. Emblem and Globe

1964 (27 Sept). *Raja Rammohun Roy Commemoration.* W 374. P 13 × 13½.
490 447 15 n.p. brown 10 10

1964 (9 Nov). *Sixth International Organization for Standardization General Assembly, Bombay. No wmk.* P 13 × 13½.
491 448 15 p. carmine 15 20

449 Jawaharlal Nehru (from 1 r. commemorative coin)   **450** St. Thomas (after statue, Ortona Cathedral, Italy)

1964 (14 Nov). *Children's Day. No wmk.* P 14 × 13½.
492 449 15 p. slate 10 10

1964 (2 Dec). *St. Thomas Commemoration. No wmk.* P 14 × 13½.
493 450 15 p. reddish purple 10 30
No. 493 was issued on the occasion of Pope Paul's visit to India.

451 Globe   **452** J. Tata (industrialist)

1964 (14 Dec). *22nd International Geological Congress.* W 374. P 14 × 13½.
494 451 15 p. blue-green 30 30

1965 (7 Jan). *Jamsetji Tata Commemoration. No wmk.* P 13½ × 13.
495 452 15 p. dull purple and orange 30 20

453 Lala Lajpat Rai   **454** Globe and Congress Emblem

1965 (28 Jan). *Birth Centenary of Lala Lajpat Rai (social reformer). No wmk.* P 13×13½.
496 453 15 p. light brown 10 10

1965 (8 Feb). *20th International Chamber of Commerce Congress, New Delhi. No wmk.* P 13½ × 13.
497 454 15 p. grey-green and carmine 15 15

STANLEY GIBBONS
STAMP COLLECTING SERIES

Introductory booklets on *How to Start, How to Identify Stamps* and *Collecting by Theme.* A series of well illustrated guides at a low price.
Write for details.

---

455 Freighter *Jalausha* and Visakhapatnam   **456** Abraham Lincoln

1965 (5 Apr). *National Maritime Day.* W 374 *(sideways).* P 14½ × 14.
498 455 15 p. blue 30 30

1965 (15 Apr). *Death Centenary of Abraham Lincoln.* W 374. P 13.
499 456 15 p. brown and yellow-ochre 15 10

457 I.T.U. Emblem and Symbols   **458** "Everlasting Flame"

1965 (17 May). *I.T.U. Centenary.* W 374 *(sideways).* P 14½ × 14.
500 457 15 p. reddish purple 90 30

1965 (27 May). *First Anniv of Nehru's Death.* W 374. P 13.
501 458 15 p. carmine and blue 15 10

459 I.C.Y. Emblem   **460** Climbers on Summit

1965 (26 June). *International Co-operation Year.* P 13½ × 13.
502 459 15 p. deep olive and yellow-brown .. 90 60

1965 (15 Aug). *Indian Mount Everest Expedition.* P 13.
503 460 15 p. deep reddish purple 20 10

461 Bidri Vase   **462** Brass Lamp   **466** Electric Locomotive

474 Medieval Sculpture   **475** Dal Lake, Kashmir

1965–75. T 461/2, 466, 474/5 *and similar designs.*

(a) W 374 *(sideways on* 2, 3, 5, 6, 8, 30, 50, 60 p., 2, 5, 10 r.).
P 14 × 14½ (4, 10, 15, 20, 40, 70 p., 1 r.) or 14½ × 14 (others)
504 2 p. red-brown (16.10.67) 10 50
505 3 p. brown-olive (16.10.67) .. 10 2·00
505a 4 p. lake-brown (15.5.68) .. 10 2·00
506 5 p. cerise (16.10.67) 10 10
  a. Imperf (pair) £180
507 6 p. grey-black (1.7.66) .. .. 10 2·25
508 8 p. red-brown (15.3.67) .. 30 3·50
509 10 p. new blue (1.7.66) .. 40 10
510 15 p. bronze-green (15.8.65) .. 1·25 10
511 20 p. purple (16.10.67) .. 4·50 10
512 30 p. sepia (15.3.67) 15 10
513 40 p. maroon (2.10.68) .. 15 10
514 50 p. blue-green (15.3.67) .. 20 10
515 60 p. deep grey (16.10.67) .. 35 10
516 70 p. chalky blue (15.3.67) .. 60 10

517	1 r. red-brown and plum (1.7.66)	..	60	10
518	2 r. new blue & deep slate-violet (15.3.67)		2·00	10
519	5 r. deep slate-violet and brown (15.3.67)		2·50	60
520	10 r. black and bronze-green (14.11.65)	..	13·00	80
504/20	.. .. *Set of 18*		23·00	10·00

(b) No wmk. P 14½×14

520a	5 p. cerise (12.5.74)	..	30	10

(c) Wmk Large Star and "INDIA GOVT"† in sheet. P 14½×14

521	2 p. red-brown (1.3.75)	..	50	1·25
	aw. Wmk reversed		4·00	
521b	5 p. cerise (1.3.75)	..	65	10

Designs: *Horiz* (as T **466**)—4 p. Coffee berries; 15 p. Plucking tea; 20 p. Hindustan Aircraft Industries Ajeet jet fighter; 40 p. Calcutta G.P.O.; 70 p. Hampi Chariot (sculpture). (As T **475**)—5 r. Bhakra Dam, Punjab; 10 r. Atomic reactor, Trombay. *Vert* (as T **461/2**)—5 p. "Family Planning"; 6 p. Konarak Elephant; 8 p. Spotted Deer ("Chital"); 30 p. Indian dolls; 50 p. Mangoes; 60 p. Somnath Temple.

†The arrangement of this watermark in the sheet results in the words and the star appearing upright, inverted or sideways.

Two different postal forgeries exist of No. 511, both printed in lithography and without watermark. The cruder version is roughly perforated 15, but the more sophisticated is perforated 14×14½.

See also Nos. 721/38.

479 G. B. Pant (statesman)   480 V. Patel

1965 (10 Sept). *Govind Ballabh Pant Commemoration. P* 13.
522 479 15 p. brown and deep green .. 10 20

1965 (31 Oct). *90th Birth Anniv of Vallabhbhai Patel (statesman). P* 14×13½.
523 480 15 p. blackish brown 10 30

481 C. Das   482 Vidyapati (poet)

1965 (5 Nov). *95th Birth Anniv of Chittaranjan Das (lawyer and patriot). P* 13.
524 481 15 p. yellow-brown 10 10

1965 (17 Nov). *Vidyapati Commemoration. P* 14×14½.
525 482 15 p. yellow-brown 10 10

483 Sikandra, Agra   484 Soldier, Hindustan Aircraft Industries Ajeet jet fighters and Cruiser Mysore

1966 (24 Jan). *Pacific Area Travel Association Conference. New Delhi. P* 13½×14.
526 483 15 p. slate 10 10

1966 (26 Jan). *Indian Armed Forces. P* 14
527 484 15 p. violet 70 30

485 Lal Bahadur Shastri (statesman)   486 Kambar (poet)

1966 (26 Jan). *Shastri Mourning Issue. P* 13×13½.
528 485 15 p. black 40 10

1966 (5 Apr). *Kambar Commemoration. P* 14×14½.
529 486 15 p. grey-green 10 10

487 B. R. Ambedkar   488 Kunwar Singh (patriot)

1966 (14 Apr). *75th Birth Anniv of Dr. Bhim Rao Ambedkar (lawyer). P* 14×13½.
530 487 15 p. purple-brown 10 10

1966 (23 Apr). *Kunwar Singh Commemoration. P* 14×13½.
531 488 15 p. chestnut 10 10

489 G. K. Gokhale   490 Acharya Dvivedi (poet)

1966 (9 May). *Birth Centenary of Gopal Krishna Gokhale (patriot). P* 13½×13.
532 489 15 p. brown-purple and pale yellow .. 10 10

1966 (15 May). *Dvivedi Commemoration. P* 13½×14.
533 490 15 p. drab.. .. .. 10 10

491 Maharaja Ranjit Singh (warrior)   492 Homi Bhabha (scientist) and Nuclear Reactor

1966 (28 June). *Maharaja Ranjit Singh Commemoration. P* 14×13½.
534 491 15 p. purple 30 15

1966 (4 Aug). *Dr. Homi Bhabha Commemoration. P* 14½×14.
535 492 15 p. dull purple 15 30

493 A. K. Azad (scholar)   494 Swami Tirtha

1966 (11 Nov). *Abul Kalam Azad Commemoration. P* 13½×14.
536 493 15 p. chalky blue 15 15

1966 (11 Nov). *60th Death Anniv of Swami Rama Tirtha (social reformer). P* 13×13½.
537 494 15 p. turquoise-blue 15 30

495 Infant and Dove Emblem   496 Allahabad High Court

(Des C. Pakrashi)

1966 (14 Nov). *Children's Day. P* 13×13½.
538 495 15 p. bright purple 30 20

1966 (25 Nov). *Centenary of Allahabad High Court. P* 14½×14.
539 496 15 p. dull purple 20 30

497 Indian Family   498 Hockey Game

1966 (12 Dec). *Family Planning. P* 13.
540 497 15 p. brown 15 15

1966 (31 Dec). *India's Hockey Victory in Fifth Asian Games. P* 13
541 498 15 p. new blue .. .. 1·00 50

499 "Jai Kisan"   500 Voter and Polling Booth

1967 (11 Jan). *First Anniv of Shastri's Death. P* 13½×14.
542 499 15 p. yellow-green 15 30

1967 (13 Jan). *Indian General Election. P* 13½×14.
543 500 15 p. red-brown 15 15

501 Gurudwara Shrine, Patna   502 Taj Mahal, Agra

1967 (17 Jan). *300th Birth Anniv (1966) of Guru Gobind Singh (Sikh religious leader). P* 14×13½.
544 501 15 p. bluish violet 15 15

1967 (19 Mar). *International Tourist Year. P* 14½×14.
545 502 15 p. bistre-brown and orange .. 15 15

503 Nandalal Bose and "Garuda"   504 Survey Emblem and Activities

1967 (16 Apr). *First Death Anniv of Nandalal Bose (painter). P* 14×13½.
546 503 15 p. bistre-brown 15 15

1967 (1 May). *Survey of India Bicentenary. P* 13½×13.
547 504 15 p. reddish lilac 30 30

505 Basaveswara   506 Narsinha Mehta (poet)

1967 (11 May). *800th Death Anniv of Basaveswara (reformer and statesman). P* 13½×14.
548 505 15 p. orange-red 15 15

1967 (30 May). *Narsinha Mehta Commemoration. P* 14×13½.
549 506 15 p. blackish brown 15 15

507 Maharana Pratap   508 Narayana Guru

1967 (11 June). *Maharana Pratap (Rajput leader) Commemoration. P* 14×14½.
550 **507** 15 p. red-brown 15 15

1967 (21 Aug). *Narayana Guru (philosopher) Commemoration. P* 14.
551 **508** 15 p. brown 15 20

509 President
Radhakrishnan

510 Martyrs' Memorial, Patna

1967 (5 Sept). *75th Birth Anniv of Sarvepalli Radhakrishnan (former President). P* 13.
552 **509** 15 p. claret 40 15

1967 (1 Oct). *25th Anniv of "Quit India" Movement. P* 14½ × 14.
553 **510** 15 p. lake 15 15

511 Route Map

512 Wrestling

1967 (9 Nov). *Centenary of Indo-European Telegraph Service. P* 13½ × 14.
554 **511** 15 p. black and light blue 15 20

1967 (12 Nov). *World Wrestling Championships, New Delhi. P* 13½×14.
555 **512** 15 p. purple and light orange-brown . . 30 20

513 Nehru leading
Naga Tribesmen

514 Rashbehari
Basu (nationalist)

1967 (1 Dec). *4th Anniv of Nagaland as a State of India. P* 13×13½.
556 **513** 15 p. ultramarine 15 15

1967 (26 Dec). *Rashbehari Basu Commemoration. P* 14.
557 **514** 15 p. maroon 15 20

515 Bugle, Badge and Scout Salute

1967 (27 Dec). *60th Anniv of Scout Movement in India. P* 14½×14.
558 **515** 15 p. chestnut 60 30

516 Men embracing Universe

517 Globe and Book
of Tamil

1968 (1 Jan). *Human Rights Year. P* 13.
559 **516** 15 p. bronze-green 30 30

1968 (3 Jan). *International Conference-Seminar of Tamil Studies, Madras. P* 13.
560 **517** 15 p. reddish lilac 30 15

518 U.N. Emblem and
Transport

519 Quill and Bow
Symbol

1968 (1 Feb). *United Nations Conference on Trade and Development, New Delhi. P* 14½×14.
561 **518** 15 p. turquoise-blue 40 15

1968 (20 Feb). *Centenary of Amrita Bazar Patrika (newspaper). P* 13½×14.
562 **519** 15 p. sepia and orange-yellow . . 15 15

520 Maxim Gorky

521 Emblem and
Medal

1968 (28 Mar). *Birth Centenary of Maxim Gorky. P* 13½.
563 **520** 15 p. plum 15 20

1968 (31 Mar). *First Triennale Art Exhibition, New Delhi. P* 13.
564 **521** 15 p. orange, royal blue and light blue 30 20
  a. Orange omitted £600

522 Letter-box and
"100,000"

523 Stalks of Wheat, Agricultural
Institute and Production Graph

(Des C. Pakrashi)

1968 (1 July). *Opening of 100,000th Indian Post Office. P* 13.
565 **522** 20 p. red, blue and black 30 15

1968 (17 July). *Wheat Revolution. P* 13.
566 **523** 20 p. bluish green and orange-brown . . 30 15

524 "Self-portrait"

525 Lakshminath
Bezbaruah

(Des from self-portrait)

1968 (17 Sept). *30th Death Anniv of Gaganendranath Tagore (painter). P* 13.
567 **524** 20 p. brown-purple and ochre 30 15

1968 (5 Oct). *Birth Centenary of Lakshminath Bezbaruah (writer). P* 13½ × 14.
568 **525** 20 p. blackish brown 15 15

526 Athlete's Legs and Olympic Rings

1968 (12 Oct). *Olympic Games, Mexico. P* 14½ × 14.
569 **526** 20 p. brown and grey 15 15
570   1 r. sepia and brown-olive 40 15

527 Bhagat Singh and Followers

528 Azad Hind Flag,
Swords and Chandra
Bose (founder)

1968 (19 Oct). *61st Birth Anniv of Bhagat Singh (patriot). P* 13.
571 **527** 20 p. yellow-brown 20 20

1968 (21 Oct). *25th Anniv of Azad Hind Government. P* 14 × 14½.
572 **528** 20 p. deep blue 20 15

529 Sister
Nivedita

530 Marie Curie and Radium
Treatment

1968 (27 Oct). *Birth Centenary of Sister Nivedita (social reformer). P* 14×14½.
573 **529** 20p. deep bluish green 30 30

1968 (6 Nov). *Birth Centenary of Marie Curie. P* 14½ × 14.
574 **530** 20 p. slate-lilac . . . . . . 1·40 50

531 Map of the World

532 Cochin Synagogue

1968 (1 Dec). *21st International Geographical Congress, New Delhi. P* 13.
575 **531** 20 p. new blue 15 15

1968 (15 Dec). *400th Anniv of Cochin Synagogue. P* 13.
576 **532** 20 p. blue and carmine 55 40

533 I.N.S. *Nilgiri* (frigate)

534 Red-billed Blue Magpie

1968 (15 Dec). *Navy Day. P* 13.
577 **533** 20 p. grey-blue . . . . . . 1·50 40

1968 (31 Dec). *Birds. T* **534** *and similar designs. P* 14 × 14½ (1 r.) or 14½ × 14 (others).
578 20 p. multicoloured 55 40
579 50 p. scarlet, black and turquoise-green . . 1·10 1·50
580 1 r. deep blue, yellow-brown and pale blue . . 1·75 1·00
581 2 r. multicoloured . . . . . . 1·75 1·50
578/81 . . . . . . *Set of* 4 4·50 4·00
Designs: *Horiz*—50 p. Brown-fronted Pied Woodpecker; 2 r. Yellow-backed Sunbird. *Vert*—1 r. Slaty-headed Scimitar Babbler.

538 Bankim Chandra
Chatterjee

539 Dr. Bhagavan
Das

1969 (1 Jan). *130th Birth Anniv of Bankim Chandra Chatterjee (writer). P* 13½.
582 538 20 p. ultramarine 15 20

1969 (12 Jan). *Birth Centenary of Dr. Bhagavan Das (philosopher). P* 13½.
583 539 20 p. pale chocolate 15 15

540 Dr. Martin Luther King   **541** Mirza Ghalib and Letter Seal

1969 (25 Jan). *Martin Luther King Commemoration. P* 13½.
584 540 20 p. deep olive-brown 40 20

1969 (17 Feb). *Death Centenary of Mirza Ghalib (poet). P* 14½ × 14.
585 541 20 p. sepia, brown-red and flesh 15 15

542 Osmania University

1969 (15 Mar). *50th Anniv of Osmania University. P* 14½ × 14.
586 542 20 p. olive-green 15 20

543 Rafi Ahmed Kidwai and Lockheed Constellation Mail Plane

1969 (1 Apr). *20th Anniv of "ALL-UP" Air Mail Scheme. P* 13.
587 543 20 p. deep blue 60 30

544 I.L.O. Badge and Emblem   **545** Memorial, and Hands dropping Flowers

1969 (11 Apr). *50th Anniv of International Labour Organisation. P* 14½ × 14.
588 544 20 p. chestnut 15 20

1969 (13 Apr). *50th Anniv of Jallianwala Bagh Massacre, Amritsar. P* 14×13½.
589 545 20 p. rose-carmine 15 20

546 K. Nageswara Rao Pantulu (journalist)   **547** Ardaseer Cursetjee Wadia, and Ships

1969 (1 May). *Kasinadhuni Nageswara Rao Pantulu Commemoration. P* 13½ × 14.
590 546 20 p. brown 15 20

1969 (27 May). *Ardaseer Cursetjee Wadia (ship-builder) Commemoration. P* 14½×14.
591 547 20 p. turquoise-green 40 30

ALTERED CATALOGUE NUMBERS

Any Catalogue numbers altered from the last edition are shown as a list in the introductory pages.

548 Serampore College   **549** Dr. Zakir Husain

1969 (7 June). *150th Anniv of Serampore College. P* 13½.
592 548 20 p. plum 15 20

1969 (11 June). *President Dr. Zakir Husain Commemoration. P* 13.
593 549 20 p. sepia 15 20

550 Laxmanrao Kirloskar

1969 (20 June). *Birth Centenary of Laxmanrao Kirloskar (agriculturalist). P* 13.
594 550 20 p. grey-black 15 15

551 Gandhi and his Wife   **552** Gandhi's Head and Shoulders

553 Gandhi walking (woodcut)   **554** Gandhi with Charkha

(Des Suraj Sadan (20 p.), P. Chitnis (75 p.), Indian Security Press (1 r.) and C. Pakrashi (5 r.))

1969 (2 Oct). *Birth Centenary of Mahatma Gandhi. P* 13½ × 14 (20 p.), 14 × 14½ (1 r.) or 13 (others).
595 551 20 p. blackish brown 60 30
596 552 75 p. cinnamon and drab .. .. 1·25 90
597 553 1 r. blue .. .. .. 1·25 65
598 554 5 r. greyish brown and red-orange .. 4·50 6·50
595/8 .. .. *Set of* 4 7·00 7·50

555 *Ajanta* (bulk carrier) and I.M.C.O. Emblem

1969 (14 Oct). *10th Anniv of Inter-Governmental Maritime Consultative Organization. P* 13.
599 555 20 p. violet-blue .. .. .. 1·50 40

556 Outline of Parliament Building and Globe   **557** Astronaut walking beside Space Module on Moon

1969 (30 Oct). *57th Inter-Parliamentary Conference, New Delhi. P* 14½ × 14.
600 556 20 p. new blue 15 20

1969 (19 Nov). *First Man on the Moon. P* 14 × 14½.
601 557 20 p. olive-brown 30 40

558 Gurudwara Nankana Sahib (birthplace)   **559** Tiger's Head and Hands holding Globe

1969 (23 Nov). *500th Birth Anniv of Guru Nanak Dev (Sikh religious leader). P* 13½.
602 558 20 p. slate-violet 15 20

1969 (24 Nov). *International Union for the Conservation of Nature and Natural Resources Conference, New Delhi. P* 14½ × 14.
603 559 20 p. orange-brown and bronze-green .. 30 30

560 Sadhu Vaswani   **561** Thakkar Bapa

1969 (25 Nov). *90th Birth Anniv of Sadhu Vaswani (educationist). P* 14 × 14½.
604 560 20 p. grey 15 15

1969 (29 Nov). *Birth Centenary of Thakkar Bapa (humanitarian). P* 13½.
605 561 20 p. chocolate 15 20

562 Satellite, Television, Telephone and Globe   **563** C. N. Annadurai

1970 (21 Jan). *12th Plenary Assembly of International Radio Consultative Committee. P* 13.
606 562 20 p. Prussian blue 30 20

1970 (3 Feb). *First Death Anniv of Conjeevaram Natrajan Annadurai (statesman). P* 13.
607 563 20 p. reddish purple and royal blue .. 15 15

564 M. N. Kishore and Printing Press   **565** Nalanda College

1970 (19 Feb). *75th Death Anniv of Munshi Newal Kishore (publisher). P* 13.
608 564 20 p. lake 15 20

1970 (27 Mar). *Centenary of Nalanda College. P* 14½ × 14.
609 565 20 p. brown 60 40

566 Swami Shraddhanand (social reformer)   **567** Lenin

1970 (30 Mar). *Swami Shraddhanand Commemoration.*
P 14 × 13½.
10 **566** 20 p. yellow-brown 60 40

1970 (22 Apr). *Birth Centenary of Lenin. P* 13.
11 **567** 20 p. orange-brown and sepia .. 30 20

568 New U.P.U. H.Q. Building

569 Sher Shah Suri
(15th-century ruler)

1970 (20 May). *New U.P.U. Headquarters Building, Berne.*
P 13.
612 **568** 20 p. emerald, grey and black .. 15 20

1970 (22 May). *Sher Shah Suri Commemoration. P* 13.
613 **569** 20 p. deep bluish green 15 20

570 V. D. Savarkar (patriot)
and Cellular Jail, Andaman
Islands

571 "UN" and Globe

1970 (28 May). *Vinayak Damodar Savarkar Commemoration.*
P 13.
614 **570** 20 p. orange-brown 15 20

1970 (26 June). *25th Anniv of United Nations. P* 13.
615 **571** 20 p. light new blue 30 20

572 Symbol and Workers

1970 (18 Aug). *Asian Productivity Year. P* 14½ × 14.
616 **572** 20 p. violet 20 20

573 Dr. Montessori and I.E.Y. Emblem

1970 (31 Aug). *Birth Centenary of Dr. Maria Montessori*
(educationist). P 13.
617 **573** 20 p. dull purple 30 30

574 J. N. Mukherjee
(revolutionary) and Horse

575 V. S. Srinivasa Sastri

1970 (9 Sept). *Jatindra Nath Mukherjee Commemoration.*
P 14½ × 14.
618 **574** 20 p. chocolate 75 30

1970 (22 Sept). *Srinivasa Sastri (educationist) Commem-*
oration. P 13×13½.
619 **575** 20 p. yellow and brown-purple .. 30 30

NEW INFORMATION

The editor is always interested to correspond with
people who have new information that will
improve or correct the Catalogue.

576 I. C. Vidyasagar

577 Maharishi Valmiki

1970 (26 Sept). *150th Birth Anniv of Iswar Chandra*
Vidyasagar (educationist). P 13.
620 **576** 20 p. brown and purple 30 30

1970 (14 Oct). *Maharishi Valmiki (ancient author) Commem-*
oration. P 13.
621 **577** 20 p. purple 20 30

578 Calcutta Port

1970 (17 Oct). *Centenary of Calcutta Port Trust. P* 13½ × 13.
622 **578** 20 p. greenish blue 75 50

579 University Building

1970 (29 Oct). *50th Anniv of Jamia Millia Islamia University.*
P 14½ × 14.
623 **579** 20 p. yellow-green 40 40

580 Jamnalal Bajaj

581 Nurse and Patient

1970 (4 Nov). *Jamnalal Bajaj (industrialist) Commemoration.*
W 374. *P* 13½×13.
624 **580** 20 p. olive-grey 15 30

1970 (5 Nov). *50th Anniv of Indian Red Cross. W* 374 *(sideways).*
P 13 × 13½.
625 **581** 20 p. red and greenish blue .. 40 40

582 Sant Namdeo

583 Beethoven

1970 (9 Nov). *700th Birth Anniv of Sant Namdeo (mystic).*
W 374. *P* 13.
626 **582** 20 p. orange 15 30

1970 (16 Dec). *Birth Bicentenary of Beethoven. P* 13.
627 **583** 20 p. orange and greyish black .. 1·50 60

584 Children examining Stamps

585 Girl Guide

1970 (23 Dec). *Indian National Philatelic Exhibition, New*
Dehli. T 584 *and similar horiz design. P* 13.
628 **584** 20 p. orange and myrtle-green .. 30 10
629 1 r. orange-brown and pale yellow-brown .. 2·25 80
Design:—1 r. Gandhi commemorative through magnifier.

1970 (27 Dec). *Diamond Jubilee of Girl Guide Movement in*
India. P 13.
630 **585** 20 p. maroon 60 30

586 Hands and Lamp
(Emblem)

587 Vidyapith Building

1971 (11 Jan). *Centenary of Indian Life Insurance. P* 13.
631 **586** 20 p. sepia and crimson 20 30

1971 (10 Feb). *50th Anniv of Kashi Vidyapith University.*
P 14½×14.
632 **587** 20 p. blackish brown 20 30

588 Sant Ravidas

589 C. F. Andrews

1971 (10 Feb). *Sant Ravidas (15th-cent mystic) Commem-*
oration. P 13.
633 **588** 20 p. lake 30 30

1971 (12 Feb). *Birth Centenary of Charles Freer Andrews*
(missionary). P 13×13½.
634 **589** 20 p. chestnut 35 30

590 Acharya
Narendra Deo
(scholar)

591 Crowd and "100"

1971 (19 Feb). *15th Death Anniv of Acharya Narendra Deo. P* 13.
635 **590** 20 p. dull green 15 30

1971 (10 Mar). *Centenary of Decennial Census. P* 13.
636 **591** 20 p. brown and blue 30 30

592 Sri Ramana Maharishi
(mystic)

593 Raja Ravi Varma
and "Damayanti and
the Swan"

1971 (14 Apr). *21st Death Anniv of Ramana Maharishi. P* 13½.
637 **592** 20 p. orange and sepia 20 30

1971 (29 Apr). *65th Death Anniv of Ravi Varma (artist). P* 13.
638 **593** 20 p. green 40 40

594 Dadasaheb Phalke and
Camera

595 "Abhisarika"
(Tagore)

1971 (30 Apr). *Birth Centenary of Dadasaheb Phalke*
(cinematographer). P 13½×13.
639 **594** 20 p. deep maroon 70 40

1971 (7 Aug). *Birth Centenary of Abanindranath Tagore*
(painter). P 14×14½.
640 **595** 20 p. grey, buff-yellow & blackish brown 30 30

596 Swami Virjanand
(Vedic scholar)

597 Cyrus the Great and
Procession

1971 (14 Sept). *Swami Virjanand Commemoration. P* 13½.
641 **596** 20 p. chestnut 30 40

1971 (12 Oct). *2500th Anniv of Charter of Cyrus the Great. P* 13.
642 **597** 20 p. blackish brown 75 55

598 Globe and Money Box

1971 (31 Oct). *World Thrift Day. P* 14½ × 14.
643 **598** 20 p. blue-grey 20 30

599 Ajanta Caves
Painting

600 "Women at
Work" (Geeta
Gupta)

1971 (4 Nov). *25th Anniv of U.N.E.S.C.O. P* 13.
644 **599** 20 p. red-brown .. .. .. 1·25 40

(Des from painting by Geeta Gupta)

1971 (14 Nov). *Children's Day. P* 14 × 14½.
645 **600** 20 p. scarlet 20 40

शरणार्थी
सहायता
REFUGEE RELIEF
(601)

Refugee
Relief
(602)

शरणार्थी
सहायता
REFUGEE
RELIEF
(603)

REFUGEE
RELIEF
(604)

REFUGEE
RELIEF
(605)

Refugee Relief
(606)

Refugee
relief
(606a)

शरणार्थी
सहायता
Refugee
Relief
(606b)

607 Refugees

1971. *Obligatory Tax. Refugee Relief.*

(a) *Provisional issues.* No. 506 *variously optd*

(i) *For all India, optd at Nasik*
646 **601** 5 p. cerise (15 Nov) 40 10
  a. Opt double .. .. .. 2·50

(ii) *For various areas*
647 **602** 5 p. Bangalore .. .. 2·25 90
  a. Opt double, one inverted ..
648 **603** 5 p. Jaipur .. .. 5·50 1·25
649 **604** 5 p. Rajasthan .. .. 3·00 1·25
  a. Error. "RELIEF REFUGEE" .. 12·00
  b. Opt inverted ..
650 **605** 5 p. New Delhi .. .. 13·00 3·00
  a. Opt inverted .. .. 13·00
650*b* **606** 5 p. Goa .. .. 13·00 3·50
650*c* **606a** 5 p. Jabalpur .. .. 10·00 3·00
650*d* **606b** 5 p. Alwar ..

(b) *Definitive issue.* W **374.** *P* 14 × 14½
651 **607** 5 p. carmine (1 Dec) .. 30 10
  From 15 November 1971 until 31 March 1973, the Indian
Government levied a 5 p. surcharge on all mail, except postcards
and newspapers, for the relief of refugees from the former East
Pakistan.
  As supplies of the provisional overprint could not be sent to all
Indian post offices in time, local postmasters were authorised to
make their own overprints. Most of these were applied by rubber
stamps and so we do not list them. Those listed have typographed
overprints and No. 649 also has a rubber handstamp in native
language. Some of the above overprints were also used in areas
other than those where they were produced.

608 C. V. Raman (scientist)
and Light Graph

1971 (12 Nov). *First Death Anniv of Chandrasekhara Venkata
Raman. P* 13.
652 **608** 20 p. orange and deep brown .. 50 30

609 Visva Bharati
Building and
Rabindranath Tagore
(founder)

1971 (24 Dec). *50th Anniv of Visva Bharati University.
P* 14½×14.
653 **609** 20 p. sepia and yellow-brown .. 20 30

610 Cricketers

611 Map and Satellite

1971 (30 Dec). *Indian Cricket Victories. P* 14½ × 14.
654 **610** 20 p. green, myrtle-green and sage-green 2·00 65

1972 (26 Feb). *First Anniv of Arvi Satellite Earth Station.
P* 13½.
655 **611** 20 p. plum 15 30

612 Elemental Symbols
and Plumb-line

613 Signal-box Panel

1972 (29 May). *25th Anniv of Indian Standards Institution.
P* 13.
656 **612** 20 p. turquoise-grey and black .. 15 40

1972 (30 June). *50th Anniv of International Railways Union.
P* 13.
657 **613** 20 p. multicoloured 40 40
  a. Blue omitted .. .. .. 60·00

614 Hockey-player

615 Symbol of Sri
Aurobindo

1972 (10 Aug). *Olympic Games, Munich.* T **614** *and similar horiz
design. P* 13.
658 20 p. deep bluish violet .. 1·50 25
659 1 r. 45, light turquoise-green & brown-lake 2·00 2·00
  Design:—1 r. 45, Various sports.

1972 (15 Aug). *Birth Centenary of Sri Aurobindo (religious
teacher). P* 13½.
660 **615** 20 p. yellow and new blue .. 20 30

616 Celebrating Independence
Day in front of Parliament

617 Inter-Services Crest

1972 (15 Aug). *25th Anniversary of Independence (1st issue). P* 13.
661 **616** 20 p. multicoloured .. 15 30
See also Nos. 673/4.

1972 (15 Aug). *Defence Services Commemoration. P* 13.
662 **617** 20 p. multicoloured 30 40

618 V. O. Chidambaram
Pillai (trade union leader)
and Ship

619 Bhai Vir Singh

1972 (5 Sept). *Birth Centenary of V. O. Chidambaram Pillai. P* 13.
663 **618** 20 p. new blue and purple-brown .. 75 40

1972 (16 Oct). *Birth Centenary of Bhai Vir Singh (poet). P* 13.
664 **619** 20 p. plum 30 40

620 T. Prakasam

621 Vemana

1972 (16 Oct). *Birth Centenary of Tanguturi Prakasam
(lawyer). P* 13.
665 **620** 20 p. brown 20 40

1972 (16 Oct). *300th Birth Anniv of Vemana (poet).* W **374.**
P 13½ × 14.
666 **621** 20 p. black 20 40

622 Bertrand Russell

623 Symbol of "Asia 72"

1972 (16 Oct). *Birth Centenary of Bertrand Russell (philosopher).
P* 13½ × 14.
667 **622** 1 r. 45, black .. .. 3·25 2·75

1972 (3 Nov). *"Asia '72" (Third Asian International Trade
Fair), New Delhi.* T **623** *and similar vert design.* W **374.** *P* 13.
668 20 p. black and orange 10 20
669 1 r. 45, orange and slate-black .. 60 1·75
  Design:—1 r. 45, Hand of Buddha.

624 V. A. Sarabhai and
Rocket

625 Flag of U.S.S.R. and
Kremlin Tower

1972 (30 Dec). *First Death Anniv of Vikram A. Sarabhai (scientist). P* 13.
670 **624** 20 p. brown and myrtle-green .. 20 40

1972 (30 Dec). *50th Anniv of U.S.S.R. P* 13.
671 **625** 20 p. light yellow and red .. 20 40

626 Exhibition Symbol

627 "Democracy"

1973 (8 Jan). *"Indipex '73" Stamp Exhibition (1st issue). P* 13.
672 **626** 1 r. 45, light mauve, gold and black .. 45 1·25
See also Nos. 701/**MS704.**

1973 (26 Jan). *25th Anniv of Independence (2nd issue). T* **627** *and similar multicoloured design. P* 13 (20 p.) *or* 14½ × 14 (1 *r*. 45).
673 20 p. Type 627 .. .. .. 15 15
674 1 r. 45, Hindustan Aircraft Industries Gnat
  jet fighters over India Gate (38×20
  mm) .. .. 1·10 1·60

628 Sri Ramakrishna   629 Postal Corps
Paramahamsa   Emblem
(religious leader)

1973 (18 Feb). *Sri Ramakrishna Paramahamsa Commemoration. P* 13.
675 628 20 p. light brown 20 40

1973 (1 Mar). *First Anniv of Army Postal Service Corps. P* 13.
676 629 20 p. deep ultramarine and vermilion .. 40 50

630 Flag and Map of   631 Kumaran Asan
Bangladesh

(*Des C. Pakrashi*)

1973 (10 Apr). *"Jai Bangla" (Inauguration of First Bangladesh Parliament). P* 13.
677 630 20 p. multicoloured 15 40

1973 (12 Apr). *Birth Centenary of Kumaran Asan (writer and poet). P* 13.
678 631 20 p. sepia 20 45

632 Flag and Flames   633 Dr. B. R. Ambedkar
              (lawyer)

(*Des C. Pakrashi*)

1973 (13 Apr). *Homage to Martyrs for Independence. P* 13.
679 632 20 p. multicoloured 15 40

(*Des Charanjit Lal*)

1973 (14 Apr). *Bhim Rao Ambedkar Commemoration. P* 13.
680 633 20 p. bronze-green and deep purple .. 20 75

634 "Radha-Kishangarh"   635 Mount Everest
(Nihal Chand)

1973 (5 May). *Indian Miniature Paintings. T* **634** *and similar vert designs. Multicoloured. P* 13.
681 20 p. Type 634 .. .. .. 30 35
682 50 p. "Dance Duet" (Aurangzeb's period) .. 60 1·50
683 1 r. "Lovers on a Camel" (Nasir-ud-din) .. 1·50 2·75
684 2 r. "Chained Elephant" (Zain-al-Abidin) .. 2·00 3·25
681/4 .. .. *Set of 4* 4·00 7·00

1973 (15 May). *15th Anniv of Indian Mountaineering Foundation. P* 13.
685 635 20 p. blue 40 50

---

636 Tail of Boeing 747   637 Cross, Church of St.
              Thomas' Mount, Madras

(*Des Air-India Art Studies from photograph by Jehangir Gazdar*)

1973 (8 June). *25th Anniv of Air-India's International Services. P* 13.
686 636 1 r. 45, indigo and carmine-red .. 4·00 4·00

1973 (3 July). *19th Death Centenary of St. Thomas. P* 13.
687 637 20 p. blue-grey and agate .. 20 50

638 Michael Madhusudan   639 A. O. Hume
Dutt (poet—Death Centenary)

1973 (21 July). *Centenaries. T* **638** *and similar horiz designs. P* 13.
688 20 p. sage-green and orange-brown .. .. 1·00 65
  a. Orange-brown omitted £450
689 30 p. red-brown .. .. .. 1·25 2·50
690 50 p. deep brown .. .. .. 1·50 2·50
691 1 r. dull violet and orange-vermilion .. 1·50 1·50
688/91 .. .. .. *Set of 4* 4·75 6·50
  Designs:—30 p. Vishnu Digambar Paluskar (musician—birth centenary); 50 p. Dr G. A. Hansen (centenary of discovery of leprosy bacillus); 1 r. Nicolaus Copernicus (astronomer—5th birth centenary).

1973 (31 July). *Allan Octavian Hume (founder of Indian National Congress) Commemoration. P* 13.
692 639 20 p. grey 20 40

640 Gandhi and Nehru   641 R. C. Dutt

(*Des C. Pakrashi from photograph*)

1973 (15 Aug). *Gandhi and Nehru Commemoration. P* 13.
693 640 20 p. multicoloured 20 40

1973 (27 Sept). *Romesh Chandra Dutt (writer) Commemoration. P* 13.
694 641 20 p. brown 20 40

642 K. S. Ranjitsinhji   643 Vithalbhai
              Patel

1973 (27 Sept). *K. S. Ranjitsinhji (cricketer) Commemoration. P* 13.
695 642 30p. myrtle-green .. .. 3·50 3·25

1973 (27 Sept). *Vithalbhai Patel (lawyer) Commemoration. P* 13.
696 643 50 p. light red-brown 20 65

ALTERED CATALOGUE NUMBERS

Any Catalogue numbers altered from the last edition are shown as a list in the introductory pages.

---

644 Sowar of   645 Interpol Emblem
President's Bodyguard

1973 (30 Sept). *Bicentenary of President's Bodyguard. P* 13.
697 644 20 p. multicoloured 35 40

1973 (9 Oct). *50th Anniv of Interpol. P* 13.
698 645 20 p. brown 30 40

646 Syed Ahmad Khan   647 "Children at Play" (Bela
(social reformer)   Raval)

1973 (17 Oct). *Syed Ahmad Khan Commemoration. P* 13.
699 646 20 p. sepia 20 60

1973 (14 Nov). *Children's Day. P* 13.
700 647 20 p. multicoloured 20 30

648 Indipex Emblem

1973 (14 Nov). *"Indipex '73" Philatelic Exhibition, New Delhi (2nd issue). T* **648** *and similar multicoloured designs. P* 13½ × 13 (2 *r*.) *or* 13 × 13½ (*others*).
701 20 p. Type 648 .. .. .. 20 30
702 1 r. Ceremonial elephant and 1½ a. stamp of
  1947 (*vert*) .. .. .. 1·25 2·00
703 2 r. Common Peafowl (*vert*) .. .. 1·50 2·75
701/3 .. .. .. *Set of 3* 2·75 4·50
MS704 127 × 127 mm. Nos. 672 and 701/3. Imperf 5·00 8·00

649 Emblem of National   650 C. Rajagopalachari
Cadet Corps   (statesman)

1973 (25 Nov). *25th Anniv of National Cadet Corps. P* 13.
705 649 20 p. multicoloured 20 30

1973 (25 Dec). *Chakravarti Rajagopalachari Commemoration. P* 13.
706 650 20 p. olive-brown 20 50

651 "Sun" Mask   652 Chhatrapati

1974 (15 Apr). *Indian Masks. T* **651** *and similar multicoloured designs. P* 13.
707 20 p. Type 651 .. .. .. 15 15
708 50 p. "Moon" mask 30 55
709 1 r. "Narasimha" .. .. .. 70 1·25
710 2 r. "Ravana" (*horiz*) .. .. 1·00 2·00
707/10 .. .. .. *Set of 4* 1·90 3·50
MS711 109 × 135 mm. Nos. 707/10 .. 2·75 6·50

1974 (2 June). *300th Anniv of Coronation of Chhatrapati Shri Shivaji Maharaj. P* 13.
712 **652** 25 p. multicoloured 30 30

653 Maithili Sharan Gupta (poet)   **654** Kandukuri Veeresalingam (social reformer)

1974 (3 July). *Indian Personalities (1st series). T* **653** *and similar vert designs. P* 13.
713 25 p. chestnut 15 45
714 25 p. deep brown 15 45
715 25 p. sepia 15 45
713/15 .. .. .. *Set of 3* 40 1·25
Portraits:—No. 714, Jainarain Vyas (politician and journalist); No. 715, Utkal Gourab Madhusudan Das (social reformer).

1974 (15 July). *Indian Personalities (2nd series). T* **654** *and similar vert designs. P* 13.
716 25 p. lake-brown 25 50
717 50 p. dull purple .. .. .. 55 1·75
718 1 r. chestnut-brown .. .. .. 70 1·75
716/18 .. .. .. *Set of 3* 1·40 3·50
Portraits:—50 p. Tipu Sultan; 1 r. Max Mueller (Sanskrit scholar).

655 Kamala Nehru

(Des Charanjit Lal)

1974 (1 Aug). *Kamala Nehru Commemoration. P* 14½ × 14.
719 **655** 25 p. multicoloured 50 50

656 W. P. Y. Emblem

1974 (14 Aug). *World Population Year. P* 13½.
720 **656** 25 p. maroon and buff 20 30

LARGE STAR AND INDIA GOVT WATERMARK. Two types exist of this sheet watermark. The initial arrangement resulted in the stars appearing upright, inverted and sideways, in either direction, within the same sheet.

Printings issued from the beginning of 1980 shows a second type on which the stars in each sheet all point in the same direction. All commemoratives with this watermark used the second type.

657 Spotted Deer   **657b** Bidri Vase

657a Vina

Two types of No. 732:

I   II

Type I. Left shoulder cut square.
Top of Hindi inscription aligns with edge of shoulder.

Type II. Shoulder ends in point.
Top of English inscription aligns with edge of shoulder. Portrait redrawn slightly smaller.

Two types of No. 736:

I   II

Type I. "INDIA" inscription falls below foot of main design. Distance between "2" in face value and top of Hindi inscription 11 mm.

Type II. "INDIA" above foot of design. Distance between "2" and inscription 10½ mm. Inscription redrawn slightly smaller.

1974 (20 Aug)–**83**. *P* 14 × 14½ (10, 20, 50 p.) or 14½ × 14 (others).

  (a) Various designs with values expressed with "p" or "Re" as T **657a**. *W* **374** *(sideways)*
721 — 15 p. blackish brown (deep background) (1.10.74) .. .. 3·25 70
722 **657** 25 p. sepia (20.8.74) 75 85
  a. Imperf (pair) £170
723 **657a** 1 r. red-brown and black (1.10.74) .. 2·50 30
  a. Black (face value and inscr) omitted £100

  (b) Various designs with values expressed in numerals only as in T **657b**
  (i) *Wmk Large Star and "INDIA GOVT" in sheet**
724 **657b** 2 p. red-brown (photo) (1.11.76) .. 70 2·00
724a 2 p. pale reddish brn (litho) (15.3.79) 70 2·00
725 — 5 p. cerise (as No. 506) (1.11.76) .. 30 10
727 **466** 10 p. new blue (5.7.79) .. 3·00 40
  w. Wmk reversed
  (ii) *W* **374** *(sideways† on 15, 25, 30, 60 p., 1, 2, 5, 10 r.)*
729 **466** 10 p. new blue (1.11.76) .. 30 15
  a. Imperf (pair) £100
  w. Wmk inverted
730 — 15 p. blackish brn (light background) (15.7.75) .. .. 1·50 10
731 — 20 p. deep dull green (15.7.75) .. 15 10
  a. Imperf (horiz pair) .. £250
732 — 25 p. reddish brown (I) (25.10.78) .. 4·50 1·50
  a. Type II (31.5.79) .. 4·50 1·50
732b — 30 p. sepia (as No. 512) (1.5.79) 2·50 55
733 — 50 p. deep violet (15.7.75) .. 3·25 10
734 — 60 p. deep grey (as No. 515) (1.11.76) 75 80
735 **657a** 1 r. red-brown & grey-blk (15.7.75) 3·25 10
736 — 2 r. violet & blackish brn (I) (15.7.75) 11·00 40
  a. Type II (1977) .. .. 11·00 40
737 — 5 r. deep slate-violet and brown (as No. 519) (1.11.76) .. 1·25 1·00
738 — 10 r. slate and bronze-green (as No. 520) (1.11.76) .. 1·25 1·25
  aw. Wmk capital heads to right 2·00 1·25
  b. Printed on the gummed side .. 35·00
  c. Wmk upright .. .. 1·25 1·25
  cw. Wmk inverted .. 4·25 1·25
  d. Perf 13 (22.10.83) .. 1·10 1·10
  da. Wmk upright .. .. 1·10 1·10
  dw. Wmk inverted .. 20·00
721/38 .. .. *Set of 18* 35·00 10·00
Designs: *Vert as T* **657**, **657b**:—15 p. Tiger; 25 p. Gandhi. *Horiz (20×17 mm)*—20 p. Handicrafts toy; 50 p. Great Egret in flight. *Horiz as T* **657a**:—2 r. Himalayas.
*See note below No. 720. Nos. 724a and 727 exist on both types of watermark, Nos. 724 and 725 on the first type only.
†The normal sideways watermark shows the capital heads to left, *as seen from the back of the stamp.*
No. 724a can be easily identified by the background of horizontal lines.
From early in 1976 Nos. 730, 731 and 735 were printed from new cylinders, which produced stamps with a slightly smaller design area than that of the original issue.
The 2 r. value with the blackish brown omitted is a chemically produced fake.
For stamps as No. 732, but with face value changed to 30 p., 35 p., 50 p., 60 p. or 1 r. see Nos. 968, 979, 1073, 1320 and 1436.

658 President V. Giri   **659** U.P.U. Emblem

(Des Charanjit Lal)

1974 (24 Aug). *Retirement of Pres. Giri. P* 13.
739 **658** 25 p. multicoloured 15 30

(Des C. Pakrashi (25 p.), A. Ramachandran (1 r.), Jyoti Bhatt (2 r.))

1974 (3 Oct). *Centenary of Universal Postal Union. T* **659** *and similar designs. P* 13.
740 25 p. violet-blue, royal blue and black .. 40 10
741 1 r. multicoloured .. .. 1·50 1·75
742 2 r. multicoloured .. .. 1·75 2·50
  a. Red (inscr etc) omitted .. £300
740/2 .. .. .. *Set of 3* 3·25 3·75
MS743 108 × 108 mm. Nos. 740/2 .. 4·50 9·50
Designs: *Horiz*—1 r. Birds and nest, "Madhubani" style. *Vert*—2 r. Arrows around globe.

660 Woman Flute-player (sculpture)   **661** Nicholas Roerich (medallion by H. Dropsy)

(Des Benoy Sarkar)

1974 (9 Oct). *Centenary of Mathura Museum. T* **660** *and similar vert design. P* 13½.
744 25 p. chestnut and blackish brown .. 50 45
  a. Horiz pair. Nos. 744/5 .. 1·00 1·60
745 25 p. chestnut and blackish brown .. 50 45
Design:—No. 745, Vidyadhara with garland.
Nos. 744/5 were printed together within the sheet, horizontally se-tenant.

1974 (9 Oct). *Birth Centenary of Professor Roerich (humanitarian). P* 13.
746 **661** 1 r. deep blue-green and greenish yellow 50 55

662 Pavapuri Temple   **663** "Cat" (Rajesh Bhatia)

(Des Benoy Sarkar)

1974 (13 Nov). *2,500th Anniv of Bhagwan Mahavira's attainment of Nirvana. P* 13.
747 **662** 25 p. indigo 40 20

1974 (14 Nov). *Children's Day. P* 13.
748 **663** 25 p. multicoloured 50 40

664 "Indian Dancers" (Amita Shah)   **665** Territorial Army Badge

(Des Benoy Sarkar)

1974 (14 Nov). *25th Anniv of UNICEF in India. P* 14½ × 14.
749 **664** 25 p. multicoloured 55 45
  a. Black (name and value) omitted £300
On No. 749a the background is in greenish black instead of the intense black of the normal.

(Des Benoy Sarkar)

1974 (16 Nov). *25th Anniv of Indian Territorial Army. P* 13.
750 **665** 25 p. black, bright yellow and emerald .. 60 40

666 Krishna as Gopal Bal with Cows (Rajasthan painting on cloth)　**667** Symbols and Child's Face

1974 (2 Dec). *19th International Dairy Congress, New Delhi.* P 13½.
751 666　25 p. brown-purple and brown-ochre　.. 　40　30

(Des Benoy Sarkar)

1974 (8 Dec). *Help for Retarded Children.* P 13.
752 667　25 p. red-orange and black　..　40　50

668 Marconi　**669** St. Francis Xavier's Shrine, Goa

1974 (12 Dec). *Birth Centenary of Guglielmo Marconi (radio pioneer).* P 13.
753 668　2 r. deep slate　..　2·00　1·25

1974 (24 Dec). *St Francis Xavier Celebration.* P 13.
754 669　25 p. multicoloured　..　15　30

670 Saraswati (Deity of Language and Learning)　**671** Parliament House, New Delhi

1975 (10 Jan). *World Hindi Convention, Nagpur.* P 14 × 14½.
755 670　25 p. slate and carmine-red　..　30　30
For similar stamp see No. 761.

1975 (26 Jan). *25th Anniv of Republic.* P 13.
756 671　25 p. grey-black, silver and azure　..　30　30

672 Table-tennis Bat

1975 (6 Feb). *World Table-tennis Championships, Calcutta.* P 13.
757 672　25 p. black, vermilion and yellow-olive　55　30

673 "Equality, Development and Peace"　**674** Stylised Cannon

(Des Shyama Sarabhai)

1975 (16 Feb). *International Women's Year.* P 13.
758 673　25 p. multicoloured　..　85　45

(Des Benoy Sarkar)

1975 (8 Apr). *Bicentenary of Indian Army Ordnance Corps.* P 13.
759 674　25 p. multicoloured　..　55　45

675 Arya Samaj Emblem　**676** Saraswati

1975 (11 Apr). *Centenary of Arya Samaj Movement.* P 13.
760 675　25 p. light red-orange & brownish black　30　30

1975 (12 Apr). *World Telugu Language Conference, Hyderabad.* P 14 × 14½.
761 676　25 p. black and deep bluish green　45　30

677 Satellite "Aryabhata"

1975 (20 Apr). *Launch of First Indian Satellite.* P 13.
762 677　25 p. lt blue, deep indigo & dull purple　..　50　40

678 Blue-winged Pitta　**679** Page from "Ramcharitmanas" Manuscript

(Des J. P. Irani)

1975 (28 Apr). *Indian Birds.* T 678 and similar multicoloured designs. P 13.
763　25 p. Type 678　..　55　25
764　50 p. Asian Black-headed Oriole　..　1·25　1·75
765　1 r. Western Tragopan (vert)..　2·25　2·75
766　2 r. Himalayan Monal Pheasant (vert)　2·75　4·50
763/6　..　Set of 4　6·00　8·25

(Des R. K. Joshi)

1975 (24 May). *4th Centenary of Ramcharitmanas (epic poem by Goswami Tulsidas).* P 13.
767 679　25 p. black, orange-yellow and vermilion　40　20

680 Young Women within Y.W.C.A. Badge　**681** "The Creation"

(Des Benoy Sarkar)

1975 (20 June). *Centenary of Indian Y.W.C.A.* P 13.
768 680　25 p. multicoloured　..　30　30

1975 (28 June). *500th Birth Anniv of Michelangelo.* T 681 and similar designs showing "Creation" frescoes from Sistine Chapel. P 14 × 13½.
769　50 p. multicoloured　..　80　80
　a. Block of 4. Nos 769/72　..　2·75
　ab. Black (inscr & face value) omitted　£450
770　50 p. multicoloured　..　80　80
771　50 p. multicoloured　..　80　80
772　50 p. multicoloured　..　80　80
769/72　..　Set of 4　2·75　2·75
　T 681 illustrates No. 769. Nos. 770 and 772 are horizontal designs, size 49 × 34 mm.
　Nos. 769/72 were printed in *se-tenant* blocks of four within the sheet, forming two composite designs in horizontal pairs.

682 Commission Emblem　**683** Stylised Ground Antenna

1975 (28 July). *25th Anniv of International Commission on Irrigation and Drainage.* P 13½.
773 682　25 p. multicoloured　..　40　20

(Des Benoy Sarkar)

1975 (1 Aug). *Inauguration of Satellite Instructional Television Experiment.* P 13.
774 683　25 p. multicoloured　..　40　20

684 St. Arunagirinathar　**685** Commemorative Text

1975 (14 Aug). *600th Birth Anniv of St. Arunagirinathar.* P 13½.
775 684　50 p. dull purple and slate-black　1·00　1·00

1975 (26 Aug). *Namibia Day.* P 13½.
776 685　25 p. grey-black and rose-red　40　40

686 Mir Anees (poet)　**687** Memorial Temple to Ahilyabai Holkar (ruler)

1975 (4 Sept). *Indian Celebrities.* P 13½ (No. 777) or 13 (No. 778).
777 686　25 p. blackish green　..　25　65
778 687　25 p. chestnut　..　25　65

688 Bharata Natyam　**689** Ameer Khusrau

1975 (20 Oct). *Indian Dances.* T 688 and similar vert designs. Multicoloured. P 13.
779　25 p. Type 668　..　65　20
780　50 p. Orissi　..　1·00　1·25
　a. Turquoise-green (dress) omitted　60·00
781　75 p. Kathak　..　1·25　1·50
782　1 r. Kathakali　..　1·50　1·25
783　1 r. 50, Kuchipudi　..　2·25　3·00
784　2 r. Manipuri　..　2·25　3·75
779/84　..　Set of 6　8·00　10·00

1975 (24 Oct). *650th Death Anniv of Ameer Khusrau (poet).* P 13.
785 689　50 p. reddish brown and buff　..　80　1·50

690 V. K. Krishna Menon　**691** Text of Poem

1975 (24 Oct). *First Death Anniv of V. K. Krishna Menon (statesman).* P 13 × 13½.
786 690　25 p. olive　..　50　60

(Des R. K. Joshi)

1975 (24 Oct). *Birth Bicentenary of Emperor Bahadur Shah Zafar.* P 13½×13.
787 691　1 r. black, stone and yellow-brown　65　90

692 Sansadiya Soudha, New Delhi　**693** V. Patel

1975 (28 Oct). *21st Commonwealth Parliamentary Conference, New Delhi.* P 14½ × 14.
788 692 2 r. olive .. .. .. 2·00 2·50

1975 (31 Oct). *Birth Centenary of Vallabhbhai Patel (statesman).* P 13 × 13½.
789 693 25 p. slate-green 15 40

694 N. C. Bardoloi **695** "Cow" (Sanjay Nathubhai Patel)

1975 (3 Nov). *Birth Centenary of Nabin Chandra Bardoloi (politician).* P 13 × 13½.
790 694 25 p. reddish brown 30 50

1975 (14 Nov). *Children's Day.* P 13½ × 13.
791 695 25 p. multicoloured 60 60

696 Original Printing Works, Nasik Road **697** Gurdwara Sisganj (site of martyrdom)

1975 (13 Dec). *50th Anniv of India Security Press.* P 13.
792 696 25 p. multicoloured 40 40

1975 (16 Dec). *Tercentenary of the Martyrdom of Guru Tegh Bahadur (Sikh leader).* P 13.
793 697 25 p. multicoloured 40 40

698 Theosophical Society Emblem **699** Weather Cock

1975 (20 Dec). *Centenary of the Theosophical Society.* P 13.
794 698 25 p. multicoloured 40 40

(Des Benoy Sarkar)

1975 (24 Dec). *Centenary of the Indian Meteorological Department.* P 13 × 13½.
795 699 25 p. multicoloured 50 50

700 Early Mail Cart **701** L. N. Mishra (politician)

(Des Benoy Sarkar)

1975 (25 Dec). *"Inpex 75" National Philatelic Exhibition, Calcutta.* T **700** and similar vert design. P 13.
796 700 25 p. black and lake-brown .. 50 30
797 — 2 r. grey-brown, brown-purple & black 2·25 3·25
Design:—2 r. Indian Bishop Mark, 1775.

1976 (3 Jan). *First Death Anniv of Lalit Narayan Mishra.* P 13.
798 701 25 p. olive-sepia 40 40

702 Tiger **703** Painted Storks

1976 (24 Jan). *Birth Centenary of Jim Corbett (naturalist).* P 13.
799 702 25 p. multicoloured .. .. 1·00 70

(Des Charanjit Lal)

1976 (10 Feb). *Keoladeo Ghana Bird Sanctuary, Bharatpur.* P 13.
800 703 25 p. multicoloured 80 50

704 Vijayanta Tank **705** Alexander Graham Bell

1976 (4 Mar). *Bicentenary of 16th Light Cavalry Regt.* P 13.
801 704 25 p. multicoloured .. .. 1·40 30

1976 (10 Mar). *Alexander Graham Bell Commemoration.* P 13.
802 705 25 p. grey-black and yellow-ochre .. 70 40

706 Muthuswami Dikshitar **707** Eye and Red Cross

1976 (18 Mar). *Birth Bicentenary of Dikshitar (composer).* P 13½.
803 706 25 p. purple 70 40

(Des Benoy Sarkar)

1976 (7 Apr). *World Health Day. Prevention of Blindness.* P 13.
804 707 25 p. reddish brown and dull vermilion .. 80 50

708 "Industries" **709** Diesel Locomotive, 1963

(Des Benoy Sarkar)

1976 (30 Apr). *Industrial Development.* P 13.
805 708 25 p. multicoloured 30 30

1976 (15 May). *Locomotives.* T **709** and similar horiz designs. Multicoloured. P 14½ × 14.
806 25 p. Type **709** 55 10
807 50 p. Steam locomotive, 1895 .. 1·50 55
808 1 r. Steam locomotive, 1963 .. 2·75 1·25
809 2 r. Steam locomotive, 1853 .. 3·50 2·50
806/9 .. .. .. *Set of 4* 7·50 4·00

710 Nehru **711**

712

Three types of Nehru portrait (*illustrated actual size*)
Type 710. Portrait measures 24 mm at base. First character above "NEHRU" has two prongs.
Type 711. Whole portrait is larger, measuring 25½ mm at base. Character above "NEHRU" has three prongs.
Type 712. Small portrait, 23 mm at base, with smaller inscription. Character above "NEHRU" has three prongs.

1976. T **710/12** and similar vert design. W **374**. P 13½.
810 710 25 p. dull violet (27.5.76) .. .. 7·00 80
810a 711 25 p. dull violet (9.76) .. 5·00 80
810b 712 25 p. dull violet (14.11.76) .. 4·00 80
811 — 25 p. red-brown (2.10.76) .. 1·00 30
    a. Imperf (pair)
Design:—No. 811, Gandhi.
For these designs in a smaller size see Nos. 732, 968/9, 979/80 and 1073/4 and 1320.

713 "Spirit of 76" (Willard) **714** K. Kamaraj (politician)

1976 (29 May). *Bicentenary of American Revolution.* P 13.
812 713 2 r. 80, multicoloured .. .. 1·25 1·25

1976 (15 July). *Kumaraswamy Kamaraj Commemoration.* P 13.
813 714 25 p. sepia 15 15

715 "Shooting" **716** Subhadra Kumari Chauhan (poetess)

(Des Gopi Gajwani (25 p., 1 r.), Sukumar Shankar (1 r. 50), India Security Press (2 r. 80))

1976 (17 July). *Olympic Games, Montreal.* T **715** and similar vert designs. P 13.
814 25 p. deep violet and vermilion .. 30 10
815 1 r. multicoloured .. 1·00 90
816 1 r. 50, deep mauve and grey-black .. 1·75 2·50
817 2 r. 80, multicoloured .. 1·75 3·75
814/17 .. .. *Set of 4* 4·25 6·50
    Designs:—1 r. Shot-put; 1 r. 50, Hockey; 2 r. 80, Sprinting.

1976 (6 Aug). *S. K. Chauhan Commemoration.* P 13.
818 716 25 p. grey-blue 15 40

717 Param Vir Chakra Medal **718** University Building, Bombay

(Des Benoy Sarkar)

1976 (15 Aug). *Param Vir Chakra Commemoration.* P 13.
819 717 25 p. multicoloured .. 15 50
Examples of No. 819 are found pre-released at Jodhpur on 28 July 1976.

1976 (3 Sept). *60th Anniv of Shreemati Nathibai Damodar Thackersey Women's University.* P 13½.
820 718 25 p. bluish violet 30 30

719 Bharatendu Harischandra (writer) **720** S. C. Chatterji

1976 (9 Sept). *Harischandra Commemoration.* P 13.
821 719 25 p. agate 15 30

1976 (15 Sept). *Birth Centenary of Sarat Chandra Chatterji (writer).* P 13.
822 720 25 p. grey-black 15 30

721 Planned Family   722 Maharaja Agrasen and Coins

(Des A. K. Nagar)

1976 (22 Sept). *Family Planning.* P 14 × 14½.
823   721   25 p. multicoloured   15   30

1976 (24 Sept). *Maharaja Agrasen Commemoration.* P 13.
824   722   25 p. red-brown . .   15   30

723 Swamp Deer   724 Hands holding Hearts

(Des from photos by Rajesh Bedi)

1976 (1 Oct). *Wildlife.* T 723 *and similar multicoloured designs.*
P 14 × 14½ (25, 50 p.) or 14½ × 14 (others).
825   25 p. Type 723   45   40
    a. Black (name and year date) omitted . . £400
826   50 p. Lion   1·25   2·25
827   1 r. Leopard (*horiz*) . .   1·75   2·25
828   2 r. Caracal (*horiz*) . .   2·00   3·50
825/8 . .   Set of 4   5·00   7·50

(Des B. G. Varma)

1976 (1 Oct). *Voluntary Blood Donation.* P 13.
829   724   25 p. yellow-ochre, scarlet and black   40   40

725 Suryakant Tripathi ("Nirala")   726 "Loyal Mongoose" (H. D. Bhatia)

1976 (15 Oct). *80th Birth Anniv of "Nirala" (poet).* P 13.
830   725   25 p. deep blue . .   15   30

1976 (14 Nov). *Children's Day.* P 13½ × 14.
831   726   25 p. multicoloured   40   40

727 Hiralal Shastri (social reformer)   728 Dr. Hari Singh Gour (lawyer)

1976 (24 Nov). *Shastri Commemoration.* P 13.
832   727   25 p. sepia   20   30

1976 (26 Nov). *Dr. Gour Commemoration.* P 13.
833   728   25 p. deep reddish purple   20   30

729 Airbus Industrie A300B4   730 Hybrid Coconut Palm

1976 (1 Dec). *Inauguration of Indian Airlines' Airbus Service.*
P 14½ × 14.
834   729   2 r. multicoloured   2·25   2·25

1976 (27 Dec). *Diamond Jubilee of Coconut Research.* P 13.
835   730   25 p. multicoloured   20   30

731 First Stanza of *Vande Mataram*

1976 (30 Dec). *Centenary of "Vande Mataram" (patriotic song by B. C. Chatterjee).* P 13.
836   731   25 p. multicoloured   20   30

732 Globe and Film Strip   733 Seismograph and Crack in Earth's Crust

1977 (3 Jan). *Sixth International Film Festival of India, New Delhi.* P 13.
837   732   2 r. multicoloured   1·50   2·25

1977 (10 Jan). *Sixth World Conference on Earthquake Engineering, New Delhi.* P 13.
838   733   2 r. deep plum   1·40   2·25

734 Tarun Ram Phookun   735 Paramahansa Yogananda (religious leader)

1977 (22 Jan). *Birth Centenary of Tarun Ram Phookun (politician).* P 13.
839   734   25 p. blackish brown   15   30

1977 (7 Mar). *Yogananda Commemoration.* P 13.
840   735   25 p. reddish orange   40   30

736 Asian Regional Red Cross Emblem   737 Fakhruddin Ali Ahmed

1977 (9 Mar). *First Asian Regional Red Cross Conference, New Delhi.* P 13.
841   736   2 r. pink, deep blue and scarlet. .   2·00   2·50

1977 (22 Mar). *Death of President Ahmed.* P 13.
842   737   25 p. multicoloured   35   35

738 Emblem of Asian-Oceanic Postal Union

1977 (1 Apr). *15th Anniv of Asian-Oceanic Postal Union.* P 13.
843   738   2 r. multicoloured   1·10   1·75

739 Narottam Morarjee and Loyalty (liner)   740 Makhanlal Chaturvedi (writer and poet)

1977 (2 Apr). *Birth Centenary of Morarjee (ship owner).* P 13.
844   739   25 p. greenish blue   75   70

1977 (4 Apr). *Chaturvedi Commemoration.* P 13.
845   740   25 p. lake-brown . .   15   30

741 Mahaprabhu Vallabhacharya (philosopher)   742 Federation Emblem

1977 (14 Apr). *Vallabhacharya Commemoration.* P 13.
846   741   1 r. sepia   30   40

1977 (23 Apr). *50th Anniv of Federation of Indian Chambers of Commerce and Industry.* P 13.
847   742   25 p. dull purple, brown-ochre and buff . .   15   40

744 "Environment Protection"   745 Rajya Sabha Chamber

1977 (5 June). *World Environment Day.* P 13.
848   744   2 r. multicoloured   60   1·25

1977 (21 June). *25th Anniv of Rajya Sabha (Upper House of Parliament).* P 13.
849   745   25 p. multicoloured   15   30

746 Lotus

(Des from paintings by J. P. Irani)

1977 (1 July). *Indian Flowers.* T 746 *and similar multicoloured designs.* P 14½ × 14 (25 p., 2 r.) or 14 × 14½ (others).
850   25 p. Type 746   25   15
    a. Black (inscription) omitted   £300
851   50 p. Rhododendron (*vert*)   45   90
852   1 r. Kadamba (*vert*)   60   1·00
853   2 r. Gloriosa Lily   90   2·25
850/3 . .   Set of 4   2·00   3·75

747 Berliner Gramophone   748 Coomaraswamy and Siva

(Des Benoy Sarkar)

1977 (20 July). *Centenary of Sound Recording.* P 13.
854   747   2 r. yellow-brown and black   1·00   2·00

1977 (22 Aug). *Birth Centenary of Ananda Kentish Coomaraswamy (art historian).* P 13.
855   748   25 p. multicoloured   40   40

749 Ganga Ram and Hospital   **750** Dr. Samuel Hahnemann
(founder of homeopathy)

1977 (4 Sept). *50th Death Anniv of Sir Ganga Ram (social reformer).* P 14½×14.
856 749 25 p. maroon   30   30

1977 (6 Oct). *32nd International Homeopathic Congress, New Delhi.* P 13.
857 750 2 r. black and green   ..   ..   3·50   2·75

751 Ram Manohar Lohia   **752** Early Punjabi
(politician)   Postman

1977 (12 Oct). *R. M. Lohia Commemoration.* P 13.
858 751 25 p. red-brown   30   30

1977 (12 Oct). *"Inpex-77" Philatelic Exhibition. Bangalore.* T **752** and similar horiz design. P 13 (25 p.) or 13½ × 14 (2 r.).
859   25 p. multicoloured   50   30
860   2 r. olive-grey/flesh   ..   ..   2·00   2·75
Design:—2 r. "Lion and Palm" essay, 1853.

753 Scarlet "Scinde Dawks"   **754** "Mother and Child"
of 1852   (Khajuraho sculpture)

1977 (19 Oct). *"Asiana 77" Philatelic Exhibition, Bangalore.* T **753** and similar horiz design. P 13.
861   1 r. orange, black and yellow   ..   1·50   1·00
862   3 r. orange, black and light blue   ..   2·50   3·00
Design:—3 r. Foreign mail arriving at Ballard Pier, Bombay, 1927.

1977 (23 Oct). *15th International Congress of Pediatrics, New Delhi.* P 13.
863 754 2 r. reddish brown and grey   ..   2·25   2·75

755 Statue of Kittur Rani   **756** Symbolic Sun
Channamma, Belgaum

1977 (23 Oct). *Kittur Rani Channamma (ruler) Commemoration.* P 13.
864 755 25 p. grey-green   80   40

1977 (8 Nov). *Union Public Service Commission Commemoration.* P 13.
865 756 25 p. multicoloured   35   30

757 Ear of Corn   **758** "Cats" (Nikur Dilipbhai
Mody)

(Des Benoy Sarkar)

1977 (13 Nov). *"Agriexpo 77" Agricultural Exhibition, New Delhi.* W 374 (sideways). P 13.
866 757 25 p. blue-green   40   40

1977 (14 Nov). *Children's Day.* T **758** and similar horiz design. Multicoloured. P 13.
867   25 p. Type **758**   50   30
868   1 r. "Friends" (Bhavsar Ashish Ramanlal)   ..   2·75   3·00

759 Jotirao Phooley   **760** Diagram of Population
(social reformer)   Growth

1977 (28 Nov). *Indian Personalities.* T **759** and similar vert design. W 374 (sideways). P 13.
869   25 p. brown-olive   .'   30   45
870   25 p. chestnut   30   45
Portrait:—No. 870, Senapti Bapat (patriot).

1977 (13 Dec). *41st Session of International Statistical Institute, New Delhi.* P 13.
871 760 2 r. blue-green and red   85   1·40

761 Kamta Prasad Guru and   **762** Kremlin Tower and
Vyakarna (Hindi Grammar)   Soviet Flag

1977 (25 Dec). *Kamta Prasad Guru (writer) Commemoration.* W 374 (sideways). P 13½×14.
872 761 25 p. deep brown   20   30

1977 (30 Dec). *60th Anniv of October Revolution.* P 13.
873 762 1 r. multicoloured   45   75

763 Climber crossing a   **764** "Shikara" on Lake
Crevice   Dal, Kashmir

1978 (15 Jan). *Conquest of Kanchenjunga (1977).* T **763** and similar horiz design. Multicoloured. P 13
874   25 p. Type **763**   10   10
875   1 r. Indian flag near summit..   ..   45   80

1978 (23 Jan). *27th Pacific Area Travel Association Conference, New Delhi.* P 13.
876 764 1 r. multicoloured   ..   2·00   1·50

765 Children in Library   **766** Mother-
Pondicherry

1978 (11 Feb). *Third World Book Fair, New Delhi.* P 13.
877 765 1 r. chestnut and slate   45   80

1978 (21 Feb). *Birth Centenary of Mother-Pondicherry (philosopher).* P 13.
878 766 25 p. brown and light grey   ..   20   30

---

767 Wheat and Globe   **768** Nanalal Dalpatram
Kavi (poet)

1978 (23 Feb). *Fifth International Wheat Genetics Symposium, New Delhi.* P 13.
879 767 25 p. yellow and blue-green   ..   20   30

1978 (16 Mar). *Nanalal Kavi Commemoration.* W 374 (sideways). P 13.
880 768 25 p. red-brown   20   30

769 Surjya Sen   **770** "Two Vaishnavas"
(revolutionary)   (Jamini Roy)

1978 (22 Mar). *Surjya Sen Commemoration.* W 374 (sideways). P 13.
881 769 25 p. sepia and orange-red   ..   20   30

1978 (23 Mar). *Modern Indian Paintings.* T **770** and similar vert designs. Multicoloured. P 14.
882   25 p. Type **770**   20   30
    a. Black (face value and inscr) omitted   £250
883   50 p. "The Mosque" (Sailoz Mookherjea)   ..   40   1·25
884   1 r. "Head" (Rabindranath Tagore)   ..   70   1·50
885   2 r. "Hill Women" (Amrita Sher Gil)   ..   90   2·00
882/5 ..   ..   Set of 4   2·00   4·50

771 "Self-portrait" (Rubens)   **772** Charlie Chaplin

1978 (4 Apr). *400th Birth Anniv of Rubens.* P 13.
886 771 2 r. multicoloured   ..   ..   2·00   3·00

1978 (16 Apr). *Charlie Chaplin Commemoration.* P 13.
887 772 25 p. Prussian blue and gold   ..   90   45

773 Deendayal   **774** Syama Prasad
Upadhyaya   Mookerjee
(politician)

1978 (5 May). *Deendayal Upadhyaya Commemoration.* P 13.
888 773 25 p. olive-brown and pale orange   ..   20   40

1978 (6 July). *Syama Prasad Mookerjee (politician) Commemoration.* P 13×13½.
889 774 25 p. brown-olive   30   50

STANLEY GIBBONS STAMP COLLECTING SERIES

Introductory booklets on *How to Start, How to Identify Stamps* and *Collecting by Theme.* A series of well illustrated guides at a low price.
Write for details.

775 Airavat (mythological) elephant), Jain Temple, Gujerat (Kachchh Museum)   **776** Krishna and Arjuna in Battle Chariot

1978 (27 July). *Treasures from Indian Museums. T* **775** *and similar multicoloured designs. P* 13 × 13½ (25, 50 p.) *or* 13½ × 13 (*others*).
890 25 p. Type **775**   30   30
891 50 p. Kalpadruma (magical tree), Besnagar (Indian Museum)   50   1·25
892 1 r. Obverse and reverse of Kushan gold coin (National Museum) (*horiz*)   70   1·50
893 2 r. Dagger and knife of Emperor Jehangir, Mughal (Salar Jung Museum) (*horiz*) ..   1·00   2·00
890/3   ..   ..   ..   *Set of* 4   2·25   4·50

1978 (25 Aug). *Bhagawadgeeta (Divine Song of India) Commemoration. P* 13.
894 **776** 25 p. gold and vermilion   ..   20   30

777 Bethune College   **778** E. V. Ramasami

1978 (4 Sept). *Centenary of Bethune College, Calcutta. P* 13.
895 **777** 25 p. deep brown and deep green   20   30

1978 (17 Sept). *E. V. Ramasami (social reformer) Commemoration. P* 13.
896 **778** 25 p. black   20   20

779 Uday Shankar   **780** Leo Tolstoy

1978 (26 Sept). *Uday Shankar (dancer) Commemoration. P* 13.
897 **779** 25 p. reddish brown and stone   ..   20   30

1978 (2 Oct). *150th Birth Anniv of Leo Tolstoy (writer). P* 13.
898 **780** 1 r. multicoloured   30   30

781 Vallathol Narayana Menon   **782** "Two Friends" (Dinesh Sharma)

1978 (15 Oct). *Birth Centenary of Vallathol Narayana Menon (poet). P* 13.
899 **781** 25 p. bright purple and brown   15   40

1978 (14 Nov). *Children's Day. P* 13.
900 **782** 25 p. multicoloured   20   40

783 Machine Operator   **784** Sowars of Skinner's Horse

1978 (17 Nov). *National Small Industries Fair, New Delhi. P* 13½.
901 **783** 25 p. bronze-green   20   30

1978 (25 Nov). *175th Anniv of Skinner's Horse (cavalry regiment). P* 13.
902 **784** 25 p. multicoloured   60   60

785 Mohammad Ali Jauhar   **786** Chakravarti Rajagopalachari

1978 (10 Dec). *Birth Centenary of Mohammad Ali Jauhar (patriot). P* 13.
903 **785** 25 p. olive-green   20   30

1978 (10 Dec). *Birth Centenary of Chakravarti Rajagopalachari (first post-independence Governor-General). P* 13.
904 **786** 25 p. lake-brown   20   30

787 Wright Brothers and Flyer 1   **788** Ravenshaw College

1978 (23 Dec). *75th Anniv of Powered Flight. W* 374 (*sideways*). *P* 13 × 13½.
905 **787** 1 r. purple and yellow-ochre   ..   65   30

1978 (24 Dec). *Centenary of Ravenshaw College, Cuttack. P* 14.
906 **788** 25 p. lake and deep green   ..   20   30

789 Schubert   **790** Uniforms of 1799, 1901 and 1979 with Badge

1978 (25 Dec). *150th Death Anniv of Franz Schubert (composer). P* 13.
907 **789** 1 r. multicoloured   ..   70   55
   a. Black (face value) omitted   ..   £600
Two black cylinders were used for the design of No. 907. No. 907a shows the black still present on the portrait.

(Des Charanjit Lal)

1979 (20 Feb). *Fourth Reunion of Punjab Regiment. P* 13.
908 **790** 25 p. multicoloured   90   70

791 Bhai Parmanand   **792** Gandhi with Young Boy

1979 (24 Feb). *Bhai Parmanand (scholar) Commemoration. P* 13.
909 **791** 25 p. deep violet-blue   20   30

1979 (5 Mar). *International Year of the Child. T* 792 *and similar vert design. P* 13.
910 25 p. reddish brown and scarlet-vermilion   40   30
911 1 r. reddish brown and yellow-orange   60   1·50
   Design:—1 r. Indian I.Y.C. emblem.

During October 1979 two stamps inscribed "HAPPY CHILD NATION'S PRIDE" with face values of 50 p. and 1 r. were issued to post offices. These were intended for sale as charity labels, without postal validity, the proceeds going to a Child Welfare fund. It would seem that the instructions issued were unclear, however, as some post offices sold these labels as postage stamps and accepted mail franked with them.

---

793 Albert Einstein   **794** Rajarshi Shahu Chhatrapati

1979 (14 Mar). *Birth Centenary of Albert Einstein (physicist). P* 13.
912 **793** 1 r. blue-black   30   50

1979 (1 May). *Rajarshi Shahu Chhatrapati (ruler of Kolhapur State, 1874–1922, and precursor of social reform in India) Commemoration. P* 13.
913 **794** 25 p. deep dull purple   ..   20   30

795 Exhibition Logo   **796** Postcards under Magnifying Glass

1979 (2 July). *"India 80" International Stamp Exhibition (1st issue). P* 13.
914 **795** 30 p. deep green and orange   ..   20   30
   See also Nos. 942/5 and 955/8.

1979 (2 July). *Centenary of Indian Postcards. P* 13.
915 **796** 50 p. multicoloured   20   40

797 Raja Mahendra Pratap   **798** Hilsa, Pomfret and Prawn   **799** Rubber Tapping

1979 (15 Aug). *Raja Mahendra Pratap (patriot) Commemoration. P* 13.
916 **797** 30 p. brown-olive   20   40

1979 (3 Sept)–**88**. *Designs as T* **798/9**.

   (*a*) *Photo. Wmk Large Star and "INDIA GOVT" in sheet*. P* 14½×14 (15 p.) *or* 14×14½ (*others*)
917 2 p. slate-violet (31.3.80)   ..   75   2·00
918 5 p. new blue (26.11.79)   ..   1·50   30
919 15 p. deep bluish green (10.3.80)   ..   2·25   30

   (*b*) *Photo. W* 374† (*sideways** on* 15, 20, 35 p., 1, 2 r., 2 r. 25, 2 r. 80, 3 r. 25 *and* 10 r.). *P* 14½×14 (15, 20, 35 p., 1, 2 r.), 13 (25 p. (*No*. 925b), 3 r. 25, 10 r.) *or* 14×14½ (*others*).
920 2 p. slate-violet (25.3.81)   ..   10   10
921 5 p. new blue (25.3.81)   10   10
   a. Perf 13 (5.7.82)   10   10
   ab. Wmk sideways (1988)   ..   10   10
   aw. Wmk inverted   60   10
922 10 p. deep green (25.1.82)   ..   60   10
   a. Perf 13 (5.7.82)   10   10
   ab. Printed double
   ac. Wmk sideways (1988)   ..   10   10
923 15 p. deep bluish green (25.3.81)   15   10
   a. Perf 13 (5.7.82)   10   10
   ab. Wmk upright   50   10
924 20 p. Indian red (25.3.81)   60   10
   a. Perf 13 (5.7.82)   10   10
   ab. Wmk upright (1988)   ..   10   10
   aw. Wmk capital heads to right   ..   60   10
925 25 p. red-brown (26.11.79)   ..   60   10
   a. Perf 13 (5.7.82)   30   10
925b 25 p. deep blue-green (5.9.85)   ..   70   10
   ba. Printed double
   bb. Wmk sideways (1988)   ..   10   10
926 30 p. yellowish green   80   10
   a. Perf 13 (6.9.82)   45   10
   ab. Wmk sideways (1987)   ..   10   10
   aw. Wmk inverted   60   10
927 35 p. cerise (15.9.80)   40   10
   a. Perf 13 (5.7.82)   50   20
   ab. Wmk upright   70   20
   aw. Wmk capital heads to right   ..   60   20
928 50 p. deep violet (25.1.82)   ..   1·50   10
   a. Imperf (pair)   ..   ..   30·00
   b. Perf 13 (5.7.82)   40   10
   bb. Imperf between (vert pair)   ..   †
   bw. Wmk inverted   ..   ..   5·00
   c. Wmk sideways (*p* 13) (1988)   ..   10   10
929 1 r. bistre-brown (17.6.80)   ..   40   10
   a. Imperf (pair)   ..   ..   75·00
   b. Perf 13 (10.11.83)   10   10
   ba. Wmk upright (1987)   ..   20   10
932 2 r. deep rose-lilac (7.12.80)   ..   70   10
   a. Perf 13 (10.11.83)   20   10
   ab. Wmk upright (1987)   ..   10   10

933	2 r. 25, red and blue-green (25.3.81)	..		70	30
	aw. Wmk capital heads to right		..	1·50	45
	b. Wmk upright		..	70	30
	bw. Wmk inverted				
	c. Perf 13 (wmk upright) (1983)		..	30	30
	ca. Wmk sideways* (1987)		..	75	30
	cw. Wmk capital heads to right				
934	2 r. 80, red and blue-green (25.3.81)		..	40	30
	aw. Wmk capital heads to right	..			
	b. Wmk upright		..	65	30
934b	3 r. 25, reddish orange & bl-grn (28.12.82)			30	30
	ba. Wmk upright		..	30	30
	bw. Wmk inverted				
935	5 r. red and emerald (23.11.80)	..		4·50	30
	aw. Wmk inverted	..	..	16·00	60
	b. Wmk sideways*	..	..	4·50	30
	bw. Wmk capital heads to right	..			
	c. Perf 13×12½ (wmk upright) (11.8.83)			60	40
	ca. Wmk sideways	..		90	40
	cw. Wmk inverted	..		5·50	50
936	10 r. maroon and bright green (24.2.84)	..		50	45
	a. Imperf (pair)		..		
	b. Wmk upright (1988)	..		40	45
920/36			Set of 17	3·00	2·25

(c) *Litho. Wmk Large Star and "INDIA GOVT" in sheet** (2 p.) *or W* **374** (5 p.). *P* 14×14½ (2 p.) *or* 13 (5 p.)

937	2 p. slate-violet (2.2.81)		..	10	60
938	5 p. new blue (29.11.82)		..	10	10

Designs: *Horiz as T* **798**—2 p. Adult education class; 10 p. Irrigation canal; 25 p. (No. 925) Chick hatching from egg; 25 p. (No. 925b) Village, wheat and tractor; 30 p. Harvesting maize; 50 p. Woman dairy farmer, cows and milk bottles. (36 × 19 *mm*)—10 r. Forest and hillside. *Vert as T* **798**—15 p. Farmer and agriculture symbols; 20 p. Mother feeding child; 35 p. "Family". (17 × 28 *mm*)—1 r. Cotton plant; 2 r. Weaving. *Vert as T* **799**—2 r. 25, Cashew; 2 r. 80, Apples; 3 r. 25, Oranges.

*See note concerning this watermark below No. 720. The 2 p. and 5 p. exist on both types of this watermark, the others on the second type only.

†For notes on the amended version of W **374** see above No. 399. The changes in watermark position from 1987 onwards show the reduced size base.

**The normal sideways watermark shows the capital heads to left, *as seen from the back of the stamp.*

Nos. 920/1 and 923/4 were originally intended for issue on 9 March 1981 and First Day Covers showing this date are known from at least one post office.

At least one sheet of No. 924a exists without an impression from the ink cylinder on the first horizontal row.

No. 937 can be easily identified by the background of horizontal lines.

For 75 p. in same design as No. 927 see No. 1214.

800 Jatindra Nath Das   801 De Havilland D.H.80A Puss Moth

1979 (13 Sept). *50th Death Anniv of Jatindra Nath Das (revolutionary). P* 13.

941	**800**	30 p. blackish brown	..	20	30

1979 (15 Oct). *Air. "India 80" International Stamp Exhibition (2nd issue). Mail-carrying Aircraft. T* **801** *and similar horiz designs. Multicoloured. P* 14½ × 14.

942		30 p. Type **801**		30	25
943		50 p. Indian Air Force Hindustan Aircraft Industries Chetak helicopter		50	45
944		1 r. Indian Airlines Boeing 737 airliner	..	65	75
945		2 r. Air India Boeing 747 airliner	..	75	95
942/5			Set of 4	2·00	2·25

802 Early and Modern Lightbulbs   803 Gilgit Record

1979 (21 Oct). *Centenary of Electric Lightbulb. P* 13.

946	**802**	1 r. brown-purple	..	20	30

1979 (23 Oct). *International Archives Week. P* 14½×14.

947	**803**	30 p. yellow-ochre and sepia	..	20	50

804 Hirakud Dam, Orissa   805 Fair Emblem

1979 (29 Oct). *50th Anniv, and 13th Congress, of International Commission on Large Dams. P* 13.

948	**804**	30 p. lake-brown and deep blue-green	..	20	30

1979 (10 Nov). *India International Trade Fair, New Delhi. P* 13.

949	**805**	1 r. grey-black and salmon	..	20	30

806 Child learning to Read

1979 (10 Nov). *International Children's Book Fair, New Delhi. P* 14½ × 14.

950	**806**	30 p. multicoloured	..	20	30

807 Dove with Olive Branch and I.A.E.A. Emblem

1979 (4 Dec). *23rd I.A.E.A. (International Atomic Energy Agency) Conference, New Delhi. P* 13.

951	**807**	1 r. multicoloured	..	20	45

808 Hindustan Aircraft Industries HAL-26 Pushpak Light Plane and Rohini-1 Glider   809 Gurdwara Baoli Sahib Temple, Goindwal, Amritsar District

(Des R. N. Pasricha)

1979 (10 Dec). *Flying and Gliding. P* 13.

952	**808**	30 p. black, orange-brown and blue	..	1·00	80

1979 (21 Dec). *500th Birth Anniv of Guru Amar Das (Sikh leader). P* 13.

953	**809**	30 p. multicoloured	..	20	30

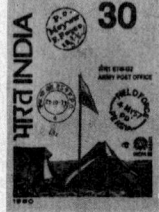

810 Ring of People encircling U.N. Emblem and Cogwheel   811 Army Post Office and Postmarks

1980 (21 Jan). *3rd U.N.I.D.O. (United Nations Industrial Development Organisation) General Conference, New Delhi. P* 13.

954	**810**	1 r. multicoloured	..	20	30

(Des Benoy Sarkar (30, 50 p.), India Security Press (others))

1980 (25 Jan). *"India 80" International Stamp Exhibition (3rd issue).* T **811** *and similar vert designs. No wmk* (1 r.) *or Large Star and "INDIA GOVT" in sheet** (others). *P* 13.

955		30 p. grey-olive	..	40	30
956		50 p. bistre-brown and dull olive-bistre		70	1·00
957		1 r. Venetian red	..	80	1·00
958		2 r. olive-brown	..	80	2·00
955/8			Set of 4	2·40	3·75

Designs:—50 p. Money order transfer document, 1879; 1 r. Copper prepayment ticket, 1774; 2 r. Sir Rowland Hill and birthplace at Kidderminster.

*See note below No. 720.

812 Energy Symbols   813 Uniforms of 1780 and 1980, Crest and Ribbon

(Des C. Pakrashi)

1980 (17 Feb). *Institution of Engineers (India) Commemoration. Wmk Large Star and "INDIA GOVT" in sheet. P* 13.

959	**812**	30 p. gold and blue	..	20	30

1980 (26 Feb). *Bicentenary of Madras Sappers. P* 13.

960	**813**	30 p. multicoloured	..	60	50

814 Books   815 Bees and Honey-comb

(Des J. Gupta)

1980 (29 Feb). *4th World Book Fair, New Delhi. Wmk Large Star and "INDIA GOVT" in sheet. P* 13.

961	**814**	30 p. new blue	..	30	30

(Des M. Bardhan)

1980 (29 Feb). *2nd International Apiculture Conference, New Delhi. P* 13.

962	**815**	1 r. deep brown and olive-bistre	..	30	45

816 Welthy Fisher and Saksharta Nicketan (Literacy House), Lucknow   817 Darul-Uloom, Deoband

(Des M. Choudhury)

1980 (18 Mar). *Welthy Fisher (teacher) Commemoration. Wmk Large Star and "INDIA GOVT" in sheet. P* 13.

963	**816**	30 p. chalky blue	..	30	30

(Des Charanjit Lal)

1980 (21 Mar). *Darul-Uloom (college), Deoband Commemoration. Wmk Large Star and "INDIA GOVT" in sheet. P* 13.

964	**817**	30 p. deep grey-green	..	20	30

818 Keshub Chunder Sen   819 Chhatrapati Shivaji Maharaj

1980 (15 Apr). *Keshub Chunder Sen (religious and social reformer) Commemoration. Wmk. Large Star and "INDIA GOVT" in sheet. P* 13.

965	**818**	30 p. bistre-brown	..	20	30

1980 (21 Apr). *300th Death Anniv of Chhatrapati Shivaji Maharaj (warrior). P* 13.

966	**819**	30 p. multicoloured	..	20	30

820 Table Tennis   821 N. M. Joshi

1980 (9 May). *5th Asian Table Tennis Championships, Calcutta. Wmk Large Star and "INDIA GOVT" in sheet. P* 13.

967	**820**	30 p. deep reddish purple	..	30	30

1980 (27 May). *Designs as Nos.* 732 *and* 810b. *Size* 17 × 20 *mm. W* **374** (sideways). *P* 14½ × 14.

968		30 p. red-brown (Gandhi)	..	3·50	80
969		30 p. dull violet (Nehru)	..	75	40

1980 (5 June). *Narayan Malhar Joshi (trade-unionist) Commemoration. Wmk Large Star and "INDIA GOVT" in sheet. P 13.*
970 821 30 p. magenta 60 40

822 Ulloor S.
Parameswara Iyer

823 S. M. Zamin Ali

1980 (6 June). *Ulloor S. Parameswara Iyer (poet) Commemoration. Wmk Large Star and "INDIA GOVT" in sheet. P 13.*
971 822 30 p. maroon 60 40

1980 (25 June). *Syed Mohammed Zamin Ali (educationist and poet) Commemoration. Wmk Large Star and "INDIA GOVT" in sheet. P 13.*
972 823 30 p. bronze-green 20 40

824 Helen Keller   825 High-jumping

1980 (27 June). *Birth Centenary of Helen Keller (campaigner for the handicapped). P 13.*
973 824 30 p. black and dull orange 50 40

1980 (19 July). *Olympic Games, Moscow. T 825 and similar vert design. Multicoloured. P 13½ × 14.*
974 1 r. Type 825 .. .. 40 40
975 2 r. 80, Horse-riding .. .. .. 1·10 2·25

826 Prem Chand   827 Mother Teresa and Nobel
Peace Prize Medallion

1980 (31 July). *Birth Centenary of Prem Chand (novelist). Wmk Large Star and "INDIA GOVT" in sheet. P 13.*
976 826 30 p. red-brown 20 40

1980 (27 Aug). *Award of 1979 Nobel Peace Prize to Mother Teresa. Wmk Large Star and "INDIA GOVT" in sheet. P 13.*
977 827 30 p. bluish violet 40 30

828 Lord Mountbatten   829 Scottish Church College,
Calcutta

1980 (28 Aug). *Lord Mountbatten Commemoration. P 13.*
978 828 2 r. 80, multicoloured .. .. 1·75 2·50

1980 (1 Sept)–82. *As Nos. 968/9, but new face value. W 374 (sideways). P 14½×14.*
979 35 p. red-brown (Gandhi) (16.9.80) .. 75 30
a. Perf 13 (5.7.82) 75 30
980 35 p. dull violet (Nehru) 30 20
a. Perf 13 (5.7.82) 30 20

(Des C. Pakrashi)
1980 (27 Sept). *150th Anniv of Scottish Church College, Calcutta. Wmk Large Star and "INDIA GOVT" in sheet. P 13.*
981 829 35 p. deep rose-lilac 20 30

830 Rajah Annamalai
Chettiar

831 Gandhi marching
to Dandi

1980 (30 Sept). *Rajah Annamalai Chettiar (banker and educationist) Commemoration. P 14×14½.*
982 830 35 p. deep lilac 20 30

(Des S. Ramachandran)
1980 (2 Oct). *50th Anniv of "Dandi March" (Gandhi's defiance of Salt Tax Law). T 831 and similar vert design. P 14½×14.*
983 35 p. black, turquoise-blue and gold .. 15 65
a. Horiz pair. Nos. 983/4 .. .. 30 1·25
984 35 p. black, deep mauve and gold .. 15 65
Design:—No. 983, Type 831; No. 984, Gandhi picking up handful of salt at Dandi.
No. 984 with the deep mauve omitted is a chemically produced fake.
Nos. 983/4 were printed together, *se-tenant*, in horizontal pairs throughout the sheet.

832 Jayaprakash Narayan   833 Great Indian Bustard

(Des Directorate of Advertising and Visual Publicity, New Delhi)
1980 (8 Oct). *Jayaprakash Narayan (socialist) Commemoration. Wmk Large Star and "INDIA GOVT" in sheet. P 14×14½.*
985 832 35 p. chocolate 40 40

(Des J. Irani)
1980 (1 Nov). *International Symposium on Bustards, Jaipur. P 13.*
986 833 2 r. 30, multicoloured .. .. 1·00 2·00

834 Arabic Commemorative Inscription

(Des B. Makhmoor)
1980 (3 Nov). *Moslem Year 1400 A.H. Commemoration. P 13.*
987 834 35 p. multicoloured 15 30

835 "Girls Dancing" (Pampa
Paul)   836 Dhyan Chand

1980 (14 Nov). *Children's Day. P 13½ × 13.*
988 835 35 p. multicoloured 40 40

1980 (3 Dec). *Dhyan Chand (hockey player) Commemoration. P 14 × 14½.*
989 836 35 p. red-brown 80 75

MINIMUM PRICE

The minimum price quote is 10p which represents a handling charge rather than a basis for valuing common stamps. For further notes about prices see introductory pages.

837 Gold Mining   838 M. A. Ansari

1980 (20 Dec). *Centenary of Kolar Gold Fields, Karnataka. P 13.*
990 837 1 r. multicoloured .. .. .. 1·10 30

1980 (25 Dec). *Mukhtayar Ahmad Ansari (medical practitioner and politician) Commemoration. Wmk Large Star and "INDIA GOVT" in sheet. P 14×14½.*
991 838 35 p. dull olive 40 40

839 India Government Mint,
Bombay   840 Bride from
Tamil Nadu

1980 (27 Dec). *150th Anniv of India Government Mint. Bombay. P 13.*
992 839 35 p. black, silver and dull blue .. 20 30

1980 (30 Dec). *Brides in Traditional Costume. T 840 and similar vert designs. Multicoloured. P 13.*
993 1 r. Type 840 .. .. .. 40 75
994 1 r. Bride from Rajasthan 40 75
995 1 r. Bride from Kashmir 40 75
996 1 r. Bride from Bengal 40 75
993/6 .. .. .. Set of 4 1·40 2·75

841 Mazharul Haque   842 St. Stephen's College

1981 (2 Jan). *Mazharul Haque (journalist) Commemoration. Wmk Large Star and "INDIA GOVT" in sheet. P 14×14½.*
997 841 35 p. chalky blue 20 40

1981 (1 Feb). *Centenary of St. Stephen's College, Delhi. Wmk Large Star and "INDIA GOVT" in sheet. P 14 × 14½.*
998 842 35 p. dull scarlet 20 40

843 Gommateshwara   844 G. V. Mavalankar

1981 (9 Feb). *Millenium of Gommateshwara (statue at Shravanabelgola). P 14×14½.*
999 843 1 r. multicoloured 20 30

1981 (27 Feb). *25th Death Anniv of Ganesh Vasudeo Mavalankar (parliamentarian). P 14×14½.*
1000 844 35 p. Venetian red 20 40

845 Flame of Martyrdom   846 Heinrich von Stephan
and U.P.U. Emblem

(Des D. Dey)

1981 (23 Mar). *"Homage to Martyrs".* P 14 × 14½.
1001 845 35 p. multicoloured 20 30

1981 (8 Apr). *150th Birth Anniv of Heinrich von Stephan (founder of U.P.U.).* P 14½ × 14.
1002 846 1 r. red-brown and new blue .. 20 50

847 Disabled Child being helped by Able-bodied Child
848 Bhil

(Des K. Raha)

1981 (20 Apr). *International Year for Disabled Persons.* P 14½ × 14.
1003 847 1 r. black and blue 20 30

(Des from photographs by A. Pareek (No. 1004), S. Dutta (No. 1005), S. Theodore Baskaran (No. 1006), Kikrumielie Angami (No. 1007))

1981 (30 May). *Tribes of India.* T 848 and similar vert designs. Multicoloured. P 14.
1004 848 1 r. Type 848 .. .. .. 40 35
1005 1 r. Dandami Maria 40 35
1006 1 r. Toda 40 35
1007 1 r. Khlamngam Naga 40 35
1004/7 .. .. .. Set of 4 1·40 1·25

849 Stylised Trees
850 Nilmoni Phukan

(Des M. Bardhan)

1981 (15 June). *Conservation of Forests.* P 14 × 14½.
1008 849 1 r. multicoloured 20 30

1981 (22 June). *Nilmoni Phukan (poet) Commemoration.* P 14 × 14½.
1009 850 35 p. red-brown 20 40

851 Sanjay Gandhi
852 Launch of "SLV 3" and Diagram of "Rohini"

(Des C. Pakrashi)

1981 (23 June). *First Death Anniv of Sanjay Gandhi (politician).* P 13.
1010 851 35 p. multicoloured 40 55

1981 (18 July). *Launch of "SLV 3" Rocket with "Rohini" Satellite.* P 14 × 14½.
1011 852 1 r. black, pink and pale blue .. 30 30

853 Games Logo
854 Flame of the Forest

(Des M. Chaudhury (No. 1013))

1981 (28 July). *Asian Games, New Delhi (1st issue).* T 853 and similar horiz design. Multicoloured. P 13½ × 13.
1012 1 r. Type 853 .. .. 1·25 65
1013 1 r. Games emblem and stylised hockey players .. 1·25 65
See also Nos. 1026, 1033, 1057, 1059 and 1061/6.

(Des from photographs by K. Vaid (35 p., 2 r.), R. Bedi (others))

1981 (1 Sept). *Flowering Trees.* T 854 and similar vert designs. Multicoloured. P 13 × 13½.
1014 35 p. Type 854 .. .. 40 15
1015 50 p. Crateva 75 75
1016 1 r. Golden Shower .. .. 1·00 50
1017 2 r. Bauhinia .. .. 1·40 2·00
1014/17 .. .. Set of 4 3·25 3·00

855 W.F.D. Emblem and Wheat
856 Stichophthalma camadeva

(Des M. Bardhan)

1981 (16 Oct). *World Food Day.* P 14 × 14½.
1018 855 1 r. greenish yellow and Prussian blue 20 20

(Des from paintings by M. Mandal)

1981 (20 Oct). *Butterflies.* T 856 and similar multicoloured designs. P 13.
1019 35 p. Type 856 .. .. 90 15
1020 50 p. Cethosia biblis .. 1·75 1·25
1021 1 r. Cyrestis achates (vert) .. 2·25 70
1022 2 r. Teinopalpus imperialis (vert) 2·75 4·50
1019/22 .. .. Set of 4 7·00 6·00

857 Bellary Raghava
858 Regimental Colour

1981 (31 Oct). *Bellary Raghava (actor) Commemoration.* P 14½ × 14.
1023 857 35 p. brown-olive 70 30

1981 (9 Nov). *40th Anniv of Mahar Regiment.* P 13 × 13½.
1024 858 35 p. multicoloured .. 90 30

859 "Toyseller" (Kumari Ruchita Sharma)
860 Rajghat Stadium

1981 (14 Nov). *Children's Day.* P 14 × 14½.
1025 859 35 p. multicoloured .. 75 30

1981 (19 Nov). *Asian Games, New Delhi (2nd issue).* P 13½ × 13.
1026 860 1 r. multicoloured .. 1·50 30

861 Kashi Prasad Jayasawal and Yaudheya Coin
862 India and P.L.O. Flags, and People

1981 (27 Nov). *Birth Centenary of Kashi Prasad Jayasawal (lawyer and historian).* P 14 × 14½.
1027 861 35 p. chalky blue .. 50 30

(Des B. Makhmoor)

1981 (29 Nov). *Palestinian Solidarity.* P 14½ × 14.
1028 862 1 r. multicoloured .. .. 2·00 40

863 I.N.S. *Taragiri* (frigate)
864 Henry Heras and Indus Valley Seal

1981 (4 Dec). *Indian Navy Day.* P 14½ × 14.
1029 863 35 p. multicoloured .. .. 2·25 1·25

1981 (14 Dec). *Henry Heras (historian) Commemoration.* P 14½ × 14.
1030 864 35 p. deep rose-lilac 45 30

865 Map of South-East Asia showing Cable Route
866 Stylised Hockey-players and Championship Emblem

1981 (24 Dec). *Inauguration of I.O.C.O.M. (Indian Ocean Commonwealth Cable) Submarine Telephone Cable.* P 13½ × 13.
1031 865 1 r. multicoloured .. 2·00 35

(Des C. Lal)

1981 (29 Dec). *World Cup Hockey Championship, Bombay.* P 13½ × 13.
1032 866 1 r. multicoloured 95 30

867 Jawaharlal Nehru Stadium
868 Early and Modern Telephones

1981 (30 Dec). *Asian Games, New Delhi (3rd issue).* P 13½ × 13.
1033 867 1 r. multicoloured .. 30 20

(Des C. Pakrashi)

1982 (28 Jan). *Centenary of Telephone Services.* P 13.
1034 868 2 r. black, new blue and olive-grey 30 30

869 Map of World
870 Sir J. J. School of Art

1982 (8 Feb). *International Soil Science Congress, New Delhi.* P 13.
1035 869 1 r. multicoloured .. 30 20

(Des M. Patel)

1982 (2 Mar). *125th Anniv of Sir J. J. School of Art, Bombay.* P 14 × 14½.
1036 870 35 p. multicoloured .. 20 20

871 "Three Musicians"
872 Deer (stone carving), 5th-century A.D.

1982 (15 Mar). *Birth Centenary of Picasso* (1981). *P* 14.
1037 **871** 2 r. 85, multicoloured 90 50

1982 (23 Mar). *Festival of India. Ancient Sculpture. T* **872** *and similar vert design. Multicoloured. P* 14 × 14½.
1038 2 r. Type **872** 20 40
1039 3 r. 05, Kaliya Mardana (bronze statue), 9th-century A.D. 35 60

873 Radio Telescope, Ooty

874 Robert Koch and Symbol of Disease

1982 (23 Mar). *Festival of India. Science and Technology. P* 13½ × 13.
1040 **873** 3 r. 05, multicoloured 35 40

(Des A. Ramachandran)

1982 (24 Mar). *Centenary of Robert Koch's Discovery of Tubercle Bacillus. P* 13½ × 13.
1041 **874** 35 p. deep rose-lilac .. .. .. 1·40 75

875 Durgabai Deshmukh

876 Blue Poppy

1982 (9 May). *First Death Anniv of Durgabai Deshmukh* (*social reformer*). *P* 14½ × 14.
1042 **875** 35 p. blue 60 70

1982 (29 May). *Himalayan Flowers. T* **876** *and similar vert designs. Multicoloured. P* 14.
1043 35 p. Type **876** 65 20
1044 1 r. Showy Inula .. .. 1·50 30
1045 2 r. Cobra Lily .. .. 2·00 2·50
1046 2 r. 85, Brahma Kamal .. .. .. 2·50 3·25
1043/6 .. .. *Set of* 4 6·00 5·75

877 "Apple" Satellite

878 Bidhan Chandra Roy

1982 (19 June). *1st Anniv of "Apple" Satellite Launch. P* 13½ × 13.
1047 **877** 2 r. multicoloured 50 80

1982 (1 July). *Birth Centenary of Bidhan Chandra Roy* (*doctor and politician*). *P* 15 × 14.
1048 **878** 50 p. chestnut .. .. 80 1·10

879 Oil Rig *Sagar Samrat*

880 "Bindu" (S. H. Raza)

1982 (14 Aug). *25th Anniv of Oil and Natural Gas Commission. P* 13½ × 13.
1049 **879** 1 r. multicoloured .. .. .. 1·00 60

1982 (17 Sept). *Festival of India. Contemporary Paintings. T* **880** *and similar vert design. Multicoloured. P* 14×14½.
1050 2 r. Type **880** 40 50
1051 3 r. 05, "Between the Spider and the Lamp" (M. F. Hussain) .. .. 60 1·25

881 Red Deer Stag, Kashmir

882 Westland Wapiti Biplane and Mikoyan Gurevich MiG-25

1982 (1 Oct). *Wildlife Conservation. P* 13 × 13½.
1052 **881** 2 r. 85, multicoloured .. .. .. 1·50 1·25

1982 (8 Oct). *50th Anniv of Indian Air Force. P* 13½ × 13.
1053 **882** 1 r. multicoloured .. .. .. 3·50 1·25

883 J. Tata with De Havilland D.H.80A Puss Moth

884 Police Patrol

1982 (15 Oct). *50th Anniv of Civil Aviation in India. P* 13½ × 13.
1054 **883** 3 r. 25, multicoloured .. .. .. 3·50 1·60

(Des B. Prakash)

1982 (21 Oct). *Police Commemoration Day. P* 13.
1055 **884** 50 p. bronze-green 50 30

885 Coins and Economic Symbols

886 Wrestling Bout

(Des S. Jha)

1982 (23 Oct). *Centenary of Post Office Savings Bank. P* 13.
1056 **885** 50 p. brown and cinnamon 20 20

(Des A. Ramachandran)

1982 (30 Oct). *Asian Games, New Delhi* (*4th issue*). *P* 13½ × 14.
1057 **886** 1 r. multicoloured 30 30

887 Troposcatter Communication Link

888 Arjuna shooting Arrow at Fish

1982 (2 Nov). *1st Anniv of Troposcatter Communication Link between India and U.S.S.R. P* 13.
1058 **887** 3 r. 05, multicoloured 30 40

(Des A. Ramachandran)

1982 (6 Nov). *Asian Games, New Delhi* (*5th issue*). *P* 13½ × 14.
1059 **888** 1 r. multicoloured .. .. .. 1·75 30

PRICES OF SETS

Set prices are given for many issues, generally those containing three stamps or more. Definitive sets include one of each value or major colour change, but do not cover different perforations, die types or minor shades. Where a choice is possible the set prices are based on the cheapest versions of the stamps included in the listings.

889 "Mother and Child" (Deepak Sharma)

890 Stylised Cyclists

1982 (14 Nov). *Children's Day. P* 14 × 14½.
1060 **889** 50 p. multicoloured 30 30

(Des C. Pakrashi (50 p.), B. Prakash (3 r. 25))

1982 (19 Nov). *Asian Games, New Delhi* (*6th issue*). *T* **890** *and similar horiz designs. Multicoloured. P* 13.
1061 50 p. Type **890** 10 10
1062 2 r. Javelin-throwing 25 30
1063 2 r. 85, Discus-throwing 30 45
1064 3 r. 25, Football 40 55
1061/4 .. .. *Set of* 4 90 1·25

891 Yachting

892 Chetwode Building

(Des C. Pakrashi)

1982 (25 Nov). *Asian Games, New Delhi* (*7th issue*). *T* **891** *and similar horiz design. Multicoloured. P* 13.
1065 2 r. Type **891** 90 30
1066 2 r. 85, Rowing .. .. 1·10 55

1982 (10 Dec). *50th Anniv of Indian Military Academy, Dehradun. P* 13.
1067 **892** 50 p. multicoloured 30 50

893 Purushottamdas Tandon

894 Darjeeling Himalayan Railway

1982 (15 Dec). *Birth Centenary of Purushottamdas Tandon* (*politician*). *P* 12½×13.
1068 **893** 50 p. yellow-brown 30 70

1982 (18 Dec). *Centenary of Darjeeling Himalayan Railway. P* 13
1069 **894** 2 r. 85, multicoloured .. .. .. 4·00 4·00

895 Vintage Rail Coach and Silhouette of Steam Engine

896 Antarctic Camp

(Des C. Pakrashi)

1982 (30 Dec). *"Inpex 82" Stamp Exhibition. T* **895** *and similar multicoloured design. P* 13 (50 *p.*) *or* 13½ × 14 (2 *r.*).
1070 50 p. Type **895** 65 85
1071 2 r. 1854 ½ a. stamp and 1947 3½ a. Independence commemorative (33 × 44 *mm*) 1·90 2·25

1983 (9 Jan). *First Indian Antarctic Expedition. P* 13.
1072 **896** 1 r. multicoloured .. .. .. 3·25 2·25

1983 (25 Jan). *As Nos.* 968/9, *but new face value. W* **374** (*sideways**). *P* 12½×13.
1073 50 p. red-brown (Gandhi) .. .. .. 3·00 1·50
a. Wmk upright .. .. .. 3·00 1·50
1074 50 p. deep ultramarine (Nehru) .. .. 3·00 1·50
a. Wmk upright .. .. .. 1·50 55
w. Wmk capital heads to right .. .. 4·00 55

*The normal sideways watermark shows the capital heads to left, *as seen from the back of the stamp.*

897 Roosevelt with Stamp Collection

898 "Siberian (Great White) Cranes at Bharatpur" (Diane Pierce)

1983 (30 Jan). *Birth Centenary of Franklin D. Roosevelt (American statesman) (1982). P* 12½ × 13.
1075 897 3 r. 25, bistre-brown .. .. .. 55 1·25

1983 (7 Feb). *International Crane Workshop, Bharatpur. P* 13.
1076 898 2 r. 85, multicoloured .. .. .. 2·00 2·50

899 Jat Regiment Uniforms Past and Present   900 Non-aligned Summit Logo

(Des C. Lal)

1983 (16 Feb). *Presentation of Colours to Battalions of the Jat Regiment. P* 13.
1077 899 50 p. multicoloured .. .. .. 1·50 1·00

(Des N. Srivastava)

1983 (7 Mar). *7th Non-aligned Summit Conference, New Delhi. T* **900** *and similar horiz design. P* 13.
1078 1 r. bistre, orange-brown and black 20 30
1079 2 r. multicoloured 30 95
Design:–2 r. Nehru.

901 Shore Temple, Mahabalipuram   902 Acropolis and Olympic Emblems

(Des R. Pasricha)

1983 (14 Mar). *Commonwealth Day. T* **901** *and similar horiz design. Multicoloured. P* 13.
1080 1 r. Type **901** 15 30
1081 2 r. Gomukh, Gangotri Glacier .. .. 30 1·25

(Des B. Makhmoor)

1983 (25 Mar). *International Olympic Committee Session, New Delhi. P* 13.
1082 902 1 r. multicoloured 30 50

903 "St. Francis and Brother Falcon" (statue by Giovanni Collina)   904 Karl Marx and *Das Kapital*

1983 (4 Apr). *800th Birth Anniv of St. Francis of Assisi. P* 13.
1083 903 1 r. bistre-brown 30 30

1983 (5 May). *Death Centenary of Karl Marx. P* 13.
1084 904 1 r. brown 20 30

905 Darwin and Map of Voyage

(Des M. Mandal)

1983 (18 May). *Death Centenary (1982) of Charles Darwin (naturalist). P* 13.
1085 905 2 r. multicoloured .. .. .. 2·25 2·75

ALTERED CATALOGUE NUMBERS

Any Catalogue numbers altered from the last edition are shown as a list in the introductory pages.

906 Swamp Deer   907 Globe and Satellite

1983 (30 May). *50th Anniv of Kanha National Park. P* 13.
1086 906 1 r. multicoloured .. .. .. 1·50 75

(Des M. Mandal)

1983 (18 July). *World Communications Year. P* 13 × 12½.
1087 907 1 r. multicoloured 40 40

908 Simon Bolivar

1983 (24 July). *Birth Bicentenary of Simon Bolivar (South American statesman). P* 12½ × 13.
1088 908 2 r. multicoloured .. .. .. 1·75 2·00

909 Meera Behn   910 Ram Nath Chopra

(Des C. Pakrashi (No. 1091))

1983 (9 Aug–28 Dec). *India's Struggle for Freedom (1st series). T* **909** *and similar designs. P* 14×13½ *(No.* 1091) *or* 13 (*others*).
1089 50 p. dull vermilion and dull green 90 1·75
       a. Horiz pair. Nos. 1089/90 .. 1·75 3·50
1090 50 p. lt brown, dull green & dull vermilion 90 1·75
1091 50 p. multicoloured .. .. 90 1·25
1092 50 p. reddish brn, yell-grn & red-orge (18.10) 15 30
1093 50 p. olive-sepia, green and orange (18.10).. 15 30
1094 50 p. olive-green, yellow-grn & orge (28.12) 15 30
1089/94 Set of 6 2·75 5·00
Designs: *Vert*—No. 1089, Type **909**; No. 1090, Mahadev Desai; No. 1092, Hemu Kalani (revolutionary); No. 1093, Acharya Vinoba Bhave (social reformer); No. 1094, Surendranath Banerjee (political reformer). *Horiz* (43×31 *mm*)—No. 1091, Quit India Resolution.
Nos. 1089/90 were printed together, *se-tenant*, in horizontal pairs throughout the sheet.
See also Nos. 1119/24, 1144/9, 1191/4, 1230/5, 1287/96 and 1345/9.

1983 (17 Aug). *Ram Nath Chopra (pharmacologist) Commemoration. P* 12½ × 13.
1095 910 50 p. Venetian red 40 80

911 Nanda Devi Mountain   912 Great Indian Hornbill

1983 (27 Aug). *25th Anniv of Indian Mountaineering Federation. P* 13.
1096 911 2 r. multicoloured .. .. .. 1·10 90

(Des J. Irani)

1983 (15 Sept). *Centenary of Natural History Society, Bombay. P* 13.
1097 912 1 r. multicoloured .. .. .. 2·50 90

913 View of Garden   914 Golden Langur

1983 (23 Sept). *Rock Garden, Chandigarh. P* 13.
1098 913 1 r. multicoloured .. .. .. 1·25 85

1983 (1 Oct). *Indian Wildlife. Monkeys. T* **914** *and similar horiz design. Multicoloured. P* 13.
1099 1 r. Type **914**.. .. .. .. 1·10 50
1100 2 r. Liontail Macaque .. .. .. 2·25 2·75

915 Ghats of Varanasi   916 Krishna Kanta Handique

1983 (3 Oct). *Fifth General Assembly of World Tourism Organization. P* 14 × 13½.
1101 915 2 r. multicoloured 40 40

1983 (7 Oct). *Krishna Kanta Handique (scholar) Commemoration. P* 13 × 12½.
1102 916 50 p. deep blue 30 70

918 Woman and Child (from "Festival" by Kashyap Premsawala)   920 *Udan Khatola*, First Indian Hot Air Balloon

1983 (14 Nov). *Children's Day. P* 13 × 13½.
1103 918 50 p. multicoloured 30 50

1983 (21 Nov). *Bicentenary of Manned Flight. T* **920** *and similar vert design. Multicoloured. P* 13.
1104 1 r. Type **920**.. .. .. .. 75 20
1105 2 r. Montgolfier balloon .. .. 1·00 80

921 Tiger   922 Commonwealth Logo

1983 (22 Nov). *Ten Years of "Project Tiger". P* 13 × 13½.
1106 921 2 r. multicoloured .. .. .. 2·50 3·00

(Des K. Raha (1 r.))

1983 (23 Nov). *Commonwealth Heads of Government Meeting, New Delhi. T* **922** *and similar vert design. Multicoloured. P* 13 × 12½.
1107 1 r. Type **922**.. .. .. .. 10 15
1108 2 r. Early 19th-century Goanese couple .. 25 30

923 "Pratiksha"   925 Lancer in Ceremonial Uniform

1983 (5 Dec). *Birth Cent of Nanda Lal Bose (artist). P* 13 × 12½.
1109 923 1 r. multicoloured 30 30

1984 (7 Jan). *Bicentenary of 7th Light Cavalry Regiment. P* 13 × 12½.
1110 925 1 r. multicoloured .. .. .. 3·25 1·40

926 Troopers in Ceremonial Uniform, and Tank   **927** Society Building and William Jones (founder)

1984 (9 Jan). *Presentation of Regimental Guidon to the Deccan Horse.* P 13 × 13½.
1111 **926** 1 r. multicoloured .. .. .. 3·25 1·40

1984 (15 Jan). *Bicentenary of Asiatic Society.* P 13.
1112 **927** 1 r. emerald and bright purple.. .. 30 50

928 Insurance Logo   **929** Hawker Siddeley Sea Harrier

(Des S. Jha)

1984 (1 Feb). *Centenary of Postal Life Insurance.* P 13 × 13½.
1113 **928** 1 r. multicoloured 30 30

(Des Capt. A. Dhir and S. Dheer)

1984 (12 Feb). *President's Review of the Fleet.* T **929** *and similar horiz designs. Multicoloured.* P 13½ × 13.
1114 1 r. Type **929** .. .. .. 1·25 1·40
    a. Block of 4. Nos. 1114/17 .. 4·50
1115 1 r. *Vikrant* (aircraft carrier) .. 1·25 1·40
1116 1 r. *Vela* (submarine) .. .. 1·25 1·40
1117 1 r. *Kashin* (destroyer) .. .. 1·25 1·40
1114/17 .. .. .. Set of 4 4·50 5·00
Nos. 1114/17 were printed in *se-tenant* blocks of four within the sheet, forming a composite design.

930 I.L.A. Logo and Hemispheres

(Des J. Irani)

1984 (20 Feb). *12th International Leprosy Congress.* P 13.
1118 **930** 1 r. multicoloured 30 30

(Des C. Pakrashi (Nos. 1119, 1121/4))

1984 (21 Feb–10 May). *India's Struggle for Freedom* (2nd series). *Vert portraits as* T **909**. P 13.
1119 50 p. dp brownish olive, yell-grn & brt orge 30 40
1120 50 p. bistre-brown, emerald & brt orge (23.4) 30 40
1121 50 p. multicoloured (10.5) .. 50 60
1122 50 p. multicoloured (10.5) 50 60
1123 50 p. multicoloured (10.5) 50 60
1124 50 p. multicoloured (10.5) 50 60
1119/24 .. .. .. Set of 6 2·40 2·75
Designs:—No. 1119, Vasudeo Balvant Phadke (revolutionary); No. 1120, Baba Kanshi Ram (revolutionary); No. 1121, Tatya Tope; No. 1122, Nana Sahib; No. 1123, Begum Hazrat Mahal; No. 1124, Mangal Pandey.

932 "Salyut 7"

(Des R. Pasricha)

1984 (3 Apr). *Indo-Soviet Manned Space Flight.* P 14.
1125 **932** 3 r. multicoloured 55 55

COVER PRICES

Cover factors are quoted at the beginning of each country for most issues to 1945. An explanation of the system can be found on page x. The factors quoted do not, however, apply to philatelic covers.

935 G. D. Birla   **936** Basketball

1984 (11 June). *90th Birth Anniv of G. D. Birla* (*industrialist*). P 13.
1126 **935** 50 p. chocolate 30 70

(Des K. Reha and S. Jha)

1984 (28 July). *Olympic Games, Los Angeles.* T **936** *and similar multicoloured designs.* P 13.
1127 50 p. Type **936** 90 55
1128 1 r. High jumping 75 30
1129 2 r. Gymnastics (*horiz*) .. .. 1·00 1·50
1130 2 r. 50, Weightlifting (*horiz*) .. 1·25 2·25
1127/30 .. .. Set of 4 3·50 4·25

937 Gwalior   **938** B.V. Paradkar and Newspaper

1984 (3 Aug). *Forts.* T **937** *and similar multicoloured designs.* P 13½ × 13 (50 p., 2 r.) or 13 × 13½ (others).
1131 50 p. Type **937** 70 55
1132 1 r. Vellore (*vert*) 95 30
1133 1 r. 50, Simhagad (*vert*) .. .. 1·75 2·50
1134 2 r. Jodhpur .. .. .. 2·00 2·75
1131/4 .. .. Set of 4 4·75 5·50

1984 (14 Sept). *B. V. Paradkar* (*journalist*) *Commemoration.* P 13 × 13½.
1135 **938** 50 p. reddish brown 30 60

939 Dr. D. N. Wadia and Institute of Himalayan Geology, Dehradun   **940** "Herdsman and Cattle in Forest" (H. Kassam)

1984 (23 Oct). *Birth Centenary* (1983) *of Dr. D. N. Wadia* (*geologist*). P 13.
1136 **939** 1 r. multicoloured .. .. 1·25 30

1984 (14 Nov). *Children's Day.* P 13 × 13½.
1137 **940** 50 p. multicoloured 75 95

941 Indira Gandhi

(Des C. Lal)

1984 (19 Nov). *Prime Minister Indira Gandhi Commemoration* (*1st issue*). P 15 × 14.
1138 **941** 50 p. black, lavender and bright orange 1·75 1·75
See also Nos. 1151, 1167 and 1170.

942 Congress Emblem   **943** Dr. Rajendra Prasad at Desk

1984 (20 Nov). *12th World Mining Congress, New Delhi.* P 13 × 13½.
1139 **942** 1 r. black and orange-yellow .. 1·25 30

1984 (3 Dec). *Birth Centenary of Dr. Rajendra Prasad* (*former President*). P 13.
1140 **943** 50 p. multicoloured .. .. .. 1·00 85

944 Mrinalini (rose)   **945** "Fergusson College" (Gopal Deuskar)

1984 (23 Dec). *Roses.* T **944** *and similar vert design. Multicoloured.* P 13.
1141 1 r. 50, Type **944** .. .. .. 2·00 2·00
1142 2 r. Sugandha .. .. .. 2·25 2·25

1985 (2 Jan). *Centenary of Fergusson College, Pune.* P 13.
1143 **945** 1 r. multicoloured 55 55

1985 (10 Jan–24 Dec). *India's Struggle for Freedom* (3rd series). *Portraits as* T **909**. P 13.
1144 50 p. chestnut, deep green & bright orange 50 60
1145 50 p. chocolate, emerald & brt orange (21.7) 50 60
1146 50 p. reddish brown, emer & red-orge (22.7) 50 60
1147 50 p. olive-sepia, emer & reddish orge (2.12) 50 60
1148 50 p. royal blue, emerald & brt orge (23.12) 50 60
1149 50 p. grey-black, emerald & brt orge (24.12) 50 60
1144/9 .. .. .. Set of 6 2·75 3·25
Designs: Vert—No. 1144, Narhar Vishnu Gadgil (politician); No. 1145, Jairamdas Doulatram (journalist); No. 1147, Kakasaheb Kalelkar (author); No. 1148, Master Tara Singh (politician); No. 1149, Ravishankar Maharaj (politician). Horiz—No. 1146, Jatindra and Nellie Sengupta (politicians).

947 Gunner and Howitzer from Mountain Battery

1985 (15 Jan). *50th Anniv of Regiment of Artillery.* P 13½ × 13.
1150 **947** 1 r. multicoloured .. .. 3·50 1·50

948 Indira Gandhi making speech

(Des R. Chopra)

1985 (31 Jan). *Indira Gandhi Commemoration* (2nd issue). P 14.
1151 **948** 2 r. multicoloured .. .. .. 2·50 2·75

949 Minicoy Lighthouse   **950** Medical College Hospital

1985 (2 Feb). *Centenary of Minicoy Lighthouse.* P 13.
1152 **949** 1 r. multicoloured .. .. .. 3·50 85

1985 (20 Feb). *150th Anniv of Medical College, Calcutta.* P 13½ × 13.
1153 **950** 1 r. yellow, reddish brown and deep reddish purple .. .. .. 2·50 70

951 Medical College, Madras   952 Riflemen of 1835 and 1985, and Map of North-East India

1985 (6 Mar). *150th Anniv of Medical College, Madras.* P 13½ × 13.
1154 **951** 1 r. yellow-brown and reddish brown .. 2·50 70

(Des A. Sharma)

1985 (29 Mar). *150th Anniv of Assam Rifles.* P 13½ × 13.
1155 **952** 1 r. multicoloured .. .. .. 3·25 1·25

953 Potato Plant   954 Baba Jassa Singh Ahluwalia

(Des Indian Council of Agricultural Research)

1985 (1 Apr). *50th Anniv of Potato Research in India.* P 13.
1156 **953** 50 p. deep brown and grey-brown .. 1·50 1·60

1985 (4 Apr). *Death Bicentenary (1983) of Baba Jassa Singh Ahluwalia (Sikh leader).* P 13.
1157 **954** 50 p. deep reddish purple .. .. 1·50 1·60

955 St. Xavier's College   956 White-winged Wood Duck

1985 (12 Apr). *125th Anniv of St. Xavier's College, Calcutta.* P 13.
1158 **955** 1 r. multicoloured 90 50

1985 (18 May). *Wildlife Conservation. White-winged Wood Duck.* P 14.
1159 **956** 2 r. multicoloured .. .. .. 4·25 4·25

957 "Mahara"   958 Yaudheya Copper Coin, c 200 B.C.

1985 (5 June). *Bougainvillea. T 957 and similar vert design. Multicoloured.* P 13.
1160 50 p. Type **957** .. .. .. 1·25 1·75
1161 1 r. "H. B. Singh" .. .. .. 1·50 1·50

1985 (7 June). *Festival of India (1st issue).* P 13.
1162 **958** 2 r. multicoloured .. .. .. 2·00 2·00

MINIMUM PRICE

The minimum price quote is 10p which represents a handling charge rather than a basis for valuing common stamps. For further notes about prices see introductory pages.

959 Statue of Didarganj Yakshi (deity)   962 Swami Haridas

1985 (13 June). *Festival of India (2nd issue).* P 13.
1163 **959** 1 r. multicoloured .. .. .. 1·00 40

1985 (19 Sept). *Swami Haridas (philosopher) Commemoration.* P 13.
1164 **962** 1 r. multicoloured .. .. .. 1·75 1·50
Although not officially issued until 19 September 1985 examples of No. 1164 are known to have circulated from 27 November 1984, the date on which it was originally scheduled for release.

963 Stylised Mountain Road

1985 (10 Oct). *25th Anniv of Border Roads Organization.* P 13.
1165 **963** 2 r. brt carmine, bluish violet & black 2·00 2·00

964 Nehru addressing General Assembly

1985 (24 Oct). *40th Anniv of United Nations Organization.* P 13.
1166 **964** 2 r. multicoloured 90 90

965 Indira Gandhi with Crowd

1985 (31 Oct). *Indira Gandhi Commemoration (3rd issue).* P 14.
1167 **965** 2 r. brownish black and black .. 2·25 2·50

966 Girl using Home Computer   967 Halley's Comet

1985 (14 Nov). *Children's Day.* P 13½ × 13.
1168 **966** 50 p. multicoloured 90 90

1985 (19 Nov). *19th General Assembly of International Astronomical Union, New Delhi.* P 13 × 13½.
1169 **967** 1 r. multicoloured .. .. .. 1·75 1·25

968 Indira Gandhi   969 St. Stephen's Hospital

1985 (19 Nov). *Indira Gandhi Commemoration (4th issue).* P 14.
1170 **968** 3 r. multicoloured .. .. .. 2·50 2·75

1985 (25 Nov). *Centenary of St. Stephen's Hospital, Delhi.* P 13.
1171 **969** 1 r. black and buff 80 40

971 Map showing Member States   972 Shyama Shastri

1985 (8 Dec). *1st Summit Meeting of South Asian Association for Regional Co-operation, Dhaka, Bangladesh.* T 971 and similar multicoloured design. P 13½ × 13 (1 r.) or 14 (3 r.).
1172 1 r. Type **971** .. .. 1·50 35
1173 3 r. Flags of member nations (44 × 32 mm).. 2·50 3·25

1985 (21 Dec). *Shyama Shastri (composer) Commemoration.* P 13.
1174 **972** 1 r. multicoloured .. .. .. 2·25 1·50

975 Young Runners and Emblem

(Des J. Irani)

1985 (24 Dec). *International Youth Year.* P 13½ × 13.
1175 **975** 2 r. multicoloured .. .. .. 1·25 75

976 Handel and Bach

1985 (27 Dec). *300th Birth Anniv of George Frederick Handel and Johann Sebastian Bach (composers).* P 13 × 13½.
1176 **976** 5 r. multicoloured .. .. .. 3·25 3·50

977 A. O. Hume (founder) and Early Congress Presidents   978 Bombay and Duncan Dry Docks, Bombay

(Des C. Pakrashi)

1985 (28 Dec). *Centenary of Indian National Congress.* T 977 and similar vert designs showing miniature portraits of Congress Presidents. P 14.
1177 **977** 1 r. black, bright orange, lt green & grey 1·50 1·60
a. Block of 4. Nos. 1177/80 .. 5·50
1178 — 1 r. black, bright orange and light green 1·50 1·60
1179 — 1 r. black, bright orange and light green 1·50 1·60
1180 — 1 r. black, bright orange, lt green & grey 1·50 1·60
1177/80 .. .. Set of 4 5·50 5·75
Nos. 1178/80 each show sixteen miniature portraits. The individual stamps can be distinguished by the position of the face value and inscription which are at the top on Nos. 1177/8 and at the foot on Nos. 1179/80. No. 1180 shows a portrait of Prime Minister Rajiv Gandhi in a grey frame at bottom right.

(Des Capt. A. Dhir)

1986 (11 Jan). *250th Anniv of Naval Dockyard, Bombay.* P 13½ × 13.
1181 **978** 2 r. 50, multicoloured .. .. .. 3·25 3·25

979 Hawa Mahal and Jaipur 1904 2 a. Stamp

980 I.N.S. *Vikrant* (aircraft carrier)

(Des C. Pakrashi (2 r.))

1986 (14 Feb). *"INPEX '86" Philatelic Exhibition, Jaipur.* T **979** *and similar horiz design. Multicoloured.* P 13½×13.

1182	50 p. Type **979**			1·00	1·00
1183	2 r. Mobile camel post office, Thar Desert			2·25	2·75

(Des A. Sharma)

1986 (16 Feb). *Completion of 25 Years Service by I.N.S. Vikrant.* P 13×13½.

1184	**980** 2 r. multicoloured			4·00	4·00

981 Humber Sommer Biplane and Later Mail Planes

982 Triennale Emblem

(Des R. Pasricha)

1986 (18 Feb). *75th Anniversary of First Official Airmail Flight, Allahabad – Naini.* T **981** *and similar horiz design. Multicoloured.* P 13½×13 (50 p.) or 13 (3 r.).

1185	50 p. Type **981**			2·25	1·75
1186	3 r. Modern Air India Airbus Industrie A300 mail plane and Humber Sommer biplane (37×24 *mm*)			4·75	6·00

1986 (22 Feb). *6th Triennale Art Exhibition, New Delhi.* P 13½×13½.

1187	**982** 1 r. black, brt purple & orange-yellow			1·50	95

983 Chaitanya Mahaprabhu

984 Main Building, Mayo College

1986 (13 Mar). *500th Birth Anniv of Chaitanya Mahaprabhu (religious leader).* P 13.

1188	**983** 2 r. multicoloured			2·75	3·50

1986 (12 Apr). *Mayo College (public school), Ajmer, Commem.* P 13½×13.

1189	**984** 1 r. multicoloured			1·50	1·00

985 Two Footballers

987 Swami Sivananda

(Des Vandana Joshi)

1986 (31 May). *World Cup Football Championship, Mexico.* P 13.

1190	**985** 5 r. multicoloured			4·00	4·00

1986 (14 Aug–30 Dec). *India's Struggle for Freedom (4th series). Vert portraits as* T **909**. P 13.

1191	50 p. sepia, emerald and orange-red			1·25	1·50
1192	50 p. olive-sepia, emerald & orge-red (26.12)			1·25	1·50
1193	50 p. slate-blk, emer & reddish orge (29.12)			1·25	1·50
1194	50 p. red-brown, emerald & orge-red (30.12)			1·25	1·50
1191/4			*Set of 4*	4·50	5·50

Designs:—No. 1191, Bhim Sen Sachar; No. 1192, Alluri Seeta Rama Raju; No. 1193, Sagarmal Gopa; No. 1194, Veer Surendra Sai.

1986 (8 Sept). *Birth Centenary of Swami Sivananda (spiritual leader).* P 13.

1195	**987** 2 r. multicoloured			3·00	3·25

988 Volleyball

989 Madras G.P.O.

(Des Mohinder Dhadwal)

1986 (16 Sept). *Asian Games, Seoul, South Korea.* T **988** *and similar vert design. Multicoloured.* P 13×13½.

1196	1 r. 50, Type **988**			2·50	2·75
1197	3 r. Hurdling			3·00	3·75

1986 (9 Oct). *Bicentenary of Madras G.P.O.* P 13.

1198	**989** 5 r. black and Indian red			4·50	5·00

990 Parachutist

991 Early and Modern Policemen

(Des Nenu Bagga)

1986 (17 Oct). *225th Anniv of 8th Battalion of Coast Sepoys (now 1st Battalion Parachute Regiment).* P 13×13½.

1199	**990** 3 r. multicoloured			5·00	5·00

(Des A. Ali)

1986 (21 Oct). *125th Anniv of Indian Police.* T **991** *and similar vert design showing early and modern police.* P 13×13½.

1200	1 r. 50, multicoloured			3·25	3·50
	a. Horiz pair. Nos. 1200/1			6·50	7·00
1201	2 r. multicoloured			3·25	3·50

Nos. 1200/1 were printed together, *se-tenant*, in horizontal pairs with the 2 r. at left, each pair forming a composite design.

992 Hand holding Flower and World Map

993 "Girl Rock Climber" (Sujasha Dasgupta)

(Des B. Raj)

1986 (24 Oct). *International Peace Year.* P 13½×13.

1202	**992** 5 r. multicoloured			2·25	1·25

1986 (14 Nov). *Children's Day.* P 13×13½.

1203	**993** 50 p. multicoloured			2·25	2·25

994 Windmill

1986 (15 Nov)–**95**. *Science and Technology.* T **994** *and similar designs.* W **374** *(sideways on 75 p., 1, 5, 50 r.).* P 13. (a) *Photo.*

1211	35 p. vermilion (27.2.87)			10	10
	a. Wmk sideways			10	10
1212	40 p. rose-red (15.10.88)			10	10
	a. Wmk sideways				
	w. Wmk inverted			90	10
1213	60 p. emerald and scarlet (27.2.87)			20	10
	a. Wmk sideways			20	10
1214	75 p. orange-vermilion (20.11.90)			50	30
	a. Wmk upright			30	20
1215	1 r. black and Indian red (18.2.95)			30	10
1217	5 r. deep brown & reddish orange (1.1.88)			40	25
	a. Wmk upright			40	25
1218	20 r. bistre-brown and blue (30.11.88)			80	85
	a. Wmk sideways				
1219	50 r. black, turquoise-blue and cerise			2·00	2·10
	a. Wmk upright			2·00	2·10
	w. Wmk inverted				

(b) *Litho*

1220	40 p. rose-red (1991)			10	10
	w. Wmk inverted				
1211/20			*Set of 9*	3·50	3·50

Designs: *Horiz* (20×17 *mm*)—35 p. Family planning. (37×20 *mm*)—60 p. Indian family; 20 r. Bio gas production. *Vert* (17×20 *mm*)—40 p. Television set, dish aerial and transmitter; 75 p. "Family" (as No. 927). (20×37 *mm*)—1 r. Petrol pump nozzle (Oil conservation); 5 r. Solar energy.

Numbers have been left for further values in this new definitive series.

Postal forgeries of the 5 r., No. 1217, were discovered in the village of Nehru Nagar (Hyderabad) in February 1992. A number of these forgeries, which are on unwatermarked paper and perforated 10½ line, have been found commercially used.

995 Growth Monitoring

996 Tansen

1986 (11 Dec). *40th Anniv of United Nations Children's Fund.* T **995** *and similar horiz design. Multicoloured.* P 13½×13.

1221	50 p. Type **995**			1·75	1·75
1222	5 r. Immunization			4·00	5·50

1986 (12 Dec). *Tansen (musician and composer) Commem.* P 13.

1223	**996** 1 r. multicoloured			2·00	60

997 Indian Elephant

998 St. Martha's Hospital

(Des Pratibha Pandey)

1986 (15 Dec). *50th Anniv of Corbett National Park.* T **997** *and similar horiz design. Multicoloured.* P 13½×13.

1224	1 r. Type **997**			3·25	1·00
1225	2 r. Gharial			3·75	5·50

1986 (30 Dec). *Centenary of St. Martha's Hospital, Bangalore.* P 13½×13.

1226	**998** 1 r. Prussian blue, vermilion and black			2·00	1·40

999 Yacht *Trishna* and Route Map

1000 Map of Southern Africa and Logo

1987 (10 Jan). *Indian Army Round the World Yacht Voyage, 1985–7.* P 13½×13.

1227	**999** 6 r. 50, multicoloured			4·25	4·00

1987 (25 Jan). *Inauguration of AFRICA Fund.* P 14.

1228	**1000** 6 r. 50, black			4·25	4·50

1001 Emblem

1002 Blast Furnace

1987 (11 Feb). *29th Congress of International Chamber of Commerce, New Delhi.* P 13×13½.

1229	**1001** 5 r. bluish violet, new blue and rosine		3·00	1·75

1987 (13 Feb–12 Dec). *India's Struggle for Freedom (5th series). Vert portraits as* T **909**. P 13.

1230	60 p. bistre-brown, emerald & reddish orge			2·00	30
1231	60 p. deep violet, emerald & orge-red (18.3)			30	30
1232	60 p. red-brown, dp green & orge-red (21.3)			30	30
1233	60 p. bl, yellowish grn & reddish orge (25.4)			30	30
1234	60 p. yellowish brn, emer & orge-red (17.6)			30	30
1235	60 p. brown, emerald and orange-red (22.8)			30	30
1236	60 p. brown-red, emerald and reddish orange (31.12)			30	30
1230/6			*Set of 7*	3·50	1·90

Designs:—No. 1230, Hakim Ajmal Khan; No. 1231, Lala Har Dayal; No. 1232, M. N. Roy; No. 1233, Tripuraneni Ramaswamy Chowdary; No. 1234, Dr. Kailas Nath Katju; No. 1235, S. Satyamurti; No. 1236, Pandit Hriday Nath Kunzru.

(Des P. Biswas)

1987 (28 Mar). *Centenary of South Eastern Railway.* T **1002** *and similar multicoloured designs.* P 13 × 13½ (*vert*) or 13½ × 13 (*horiz*).

1237	1 r. Type **1002**	..	..	..	40	15
1238	1 r. 50, Metre-gauge tank locomotive, No. 691, 1887 (*horiz*)	..	..		45	35
1239	2 r. Electric train on viaduct, 1987	..		55	60
1240	4 r. Steam locomotive, c 1900 (*horiz*)		80	1·25
1237/40				Set of 4	2·00	2·10

1003 Kalia Bhomora Bridge, Tezpur, Assam **1004** Madras Christian College

1987 (14 Apr). *Inauguration of Brahmaputra Bridge.* P 13½ × 13.

1241	**1003**	2 r. multicoloured	..	..	30	30

1987 (16 Apr). *150th Anniv of Madras Christian College.* P 13.

1242	**1004**	1 r. 50, black and brown-lake..	..	20	20

1005 Shree Shree Ma Anandamayee **1006** "Rabindranath Tagore" (self-portrait)

1987 (1 May). *Shree Shree Ma Anandamayee* (*Hindu spiritual leader*) *Commem.* P 13 × 13½.

1243	**1005**	1 r. bistre-brown	..	..	..	30	20

1987 (8 May). *Rabindranath Tagore* (*poet*) *Commem.* P 14.

1244	**1006**	2 r. multicoloured	..	..	..	40	30

1007 Garwhal Rifles Uniforms of 1887 **1008** J. Krishnamurti

1987 (10 May). *Centenary of Garwhal Rifles Regiment.* P 13 × 13½.

1245	**1007**	1 r. multicoloured	..	..	..	50	20

1987 (11 May). *J. Krishnamurti* (*philosopher*) *Commem.* P 13 × 13½.

1246	**1008**	60 p. sepia	..	..	..	60	90

1009 Regimental Uniforms of 1887 **1010** Hall of Nations, Pragati Maidan, New Delhi

1987 (3 June). *Centenary of 37th Dogra Regt* (*now 7th Battalion* (*1 Dogra*)), *Mechanised Infantry Regt.* P 13½ × 13.

1247	**1009**	1 r. multicoloured	..	..	..	40	20

(Des P. Biswas (Nos. 1248/9), Nenu Bagga (No. MS1250)

1987 (15 June)–89. *"India–89" International Stamp Exhibition, New Delhi* (1st issue). T **1010** *and similar horiz design. Multicoloured.* P 13½ × 13.

1248	50 p. Exhibition logo	..	..	..	10	15
	a. Booklet pane. No. 1248×4 (20.1.89)		15	
1249	5 r. Type **1010**	..	..	45	50
	a. Booklet pane. No. 1249×4 (20.1.89)	1·50	
MS1250	156×58 mm. Nos. 1248/9 (*sold at 8 r.*)	70	1·00

Booklet panes Nos. 1248a and 1249a have margins all round.
See also Nos. 1264/8, 1333/4, 1341/2 and 1358/61.

1011 "Sadyah-Snata" Sculpture, Sanghol **1012** Flag and Stylized Birds with "40" in English and Hindi

1987 (3 July). *Festival of India, U.S.S.R.* P 13.

1251	**1011**	6 r. 50, multicoloured ..	..	..	1·00	75

1987 (15 Aug). *40th Anniv of Independence.* P 13 × 13½.

1252	**1012**	60 p. reddish orange, dp green & new bl	20	20

1013 Sant Harchand Singh Longowal **1014** Guru Ghasidas

1987 (20 Aug). *Sant Harchand Singh Longowal* (*Sikh leader*) *Commemoration.* P 13 × 13½.

1253	**1013**	1 r. multicoloured	..	..	..	40	20

1987 (1 Sept). *Guru Ghasidas* (*Hindu leader*) *Commemoration.* P 13.

1254	**1014**	60 p. deep Indian red ..	..	20	20

1015 Thakur Anukul Chandra **1016** University of Allahabad

1987 (2 Sept). *Thakur Anukul Chandra* (*spiritual leader*) *Commemoration.* P 13 × 13½.

1255	**1015**	1 r. multicoloured	..	..	40	20

1987 (23 Sept). *Centenary of Allahabad University.* P 13.

1256	**1016**	2 r. multicoloured	..	..	30	40

1017 Pankha Offering **1018** Chhatrasal on Horseback

1987 (1 Oct). *Phoolwalon Ki Sair Festival, Delhi.* P 13 × 13½.

1257	**1017**	2 r. multicoloured	..	..	30	40

1987 (2 Oct). *Chhatrasal* (*Bundela ruler*) *Commemoration.* P 14.

1258	**1018**	60 p. chestnut ..	..	..	30	20

1019 Family and Stylized Houses **1020** Map of Asia and Logo

1987 (5 Oct). *International Year of Shelter for the Homeless.* P 13½ × 13.

1259	**1019**	5 r. multicoloured	..	..	45	60

1987 (14 Oct). *Asia Regional Conference of Rotary International.* T **1020** *and similar horiz design.* P 13½ × 13.

1260	60 p. chestnut and emerald..	..	..	15	15
1261	6 r. 50, multicoloured	..	..	60	80

Design:—6 r. 50, Oral Polio vaccination.

1021 Blind Boy, Braille Books and Computer **1022** Iron Pillar, Delhi

1987 (15 Oct). *Centenary of Service to Blind.* T **1021** *and similar horiz design.* P 13½ × 13.

1262	1 r. multicoloured	..	..	..	15	15
1263	2 r. deep blue and new blue	..	35	30

Design:—2 r. Eye donation.

1987 (17 Oct)–89. *"India–89" International Stamp Exhibition, New Delhi* (2nd issue). *Delhi Landmarks.* T **1022** *and similar horiz designs. Multicoloured.* P 13½ × 13.

1264	60 p. Type **1022**	..	..	..	10	15
	a. Booklet pane. No. 1264×4 (20.1.89)	20	
1265	1 r. 50, India Gate	..	..	15	20
	a. Booklet pane. No. 1265×4 (20.1.89)	45	
1266	5 r. Dewan-e-Khas, Red Fort	..	45	50
	a. Booklet pane. No. 1266×4 (20.1.89)	1·50	
1267	6 r. 50, Old Fort	..	..	60	65
	a. Booklet pane. No. 1267×4 (20.1.89)	2·00	
1264/7			Set of 4	1·10	1·40
MS1268	100×86 mm. Nos. 1264/7 (*sold at 15 r.*)	1·40	2·00

Booklet panes Nos. 1264a, 1265a, 1266a and 1267a have margins all round.

1023 Tyagmurti Goswami Ganeshdutt **1024** "My Home" (Siddharth Deshprabha)

1987 (2 Nov). *Tyagmurti Goswami Ganeshdutt* (*spiritual leader and social reformer*) *Commemoration.* P 13 × 13½.

1269	**1023**	60 p. brown-red	..	..	..	20	20

1987 (14 Nov). *Children's Day.* P 13½ × 13.

1270	**1024**	60 p. multicoloured	..	..	30	20

1025 Chinar **1026** Logo (from sculpture "Worker and Woman Peasant" by V. Mukhina)

(Des O. Ravindran, A. Mehta, T. D. Singh, Sudha Chowdhary)

1987 (19 Nov). *Indian Trees.* T **1025** *and similar multicoloured designs.* P 13 × 13½ (*vert*) or 13½ × 13 (*horiz*).

1271	60 p. multicoloured ..	..	..	15	15
1272	1 r. 50, multicoloured	..	..	20	20
1273	5 r. black, dull yellow-green and chestnut	55	65
1274	6 r. 50, brown, carmine-red & yellow-green	80	80
1271/4			Set of 4	1·40	1·60

Designs: *Horiz*—1 r. 50, Pipal; 6 r. 50, Banyan. *Vert*—5 r. Sal.

1987 (21 Nov). *Festival of U.S.S.R., India.* P 14.

1275	**1026**	5 r. multicoloured	..	..	50	50

1027 White Tiger **1028** Execution of Veer Narayan Singh

1987 (29 Nov). *Wildlife.* T **1027** *and similar multicoloured design.* P 13 × 13½ (1 r.) or 13½ × 13 (5 r.).

1276	1 r. Type **1027**	..	..	..	50	15
1277	5 r. Snow Leopard (*horiz*)	..	1·25	85

(Des S. Samanta)

1987 (10 Dec). *Veer Narayan Singh* (*patriot*) *Commemoration.* P 13½ × 13.

1278	**1028**	60 p. deep brown	..	..	20	20

1029 Rameshwari Nehru

1030 Father Kuriakose Elias Chavara

1987 (10 Dec). *Rameshwari Nehru (women's rights campaigner) Commemoration.* P 13×13½.
1279 **1029** 60 p. red-brown 20 20

1987 (20 Dec). *Father Kuriakose Elias Chavara (founder of Carmelites of Mary Immaculate) Commemoration.* P 13×13½.
1280 |**1030** 60 p. bistre-brown 20 20

1031 Dr. Rajah Sir Muthiah Chettiar
1032 Golden Temple, Amritsar

1987 (21 Dec). *Dr. Rajah Sir Muthiah Chettiar (politician) Commemoration.* P 13.
1281 **1031** 60 p. slate 20 20

1987 (26 Dec). *400th Anniv of Golden Temple, Amritsar.* P 13×13½.
1282 **1032** 60 p. multicoloured 30 20

1033 Rukmini Devi and Dancer
1034 Dr. Hiralal

1987 (27 Dec). *Rukmini Devi (Bharatanatyam dance pioneer) Commemoration.* P 13½×13.
1283 **1033** 60 p. deep rose-red 30 20

1987 (31 Dec). *Dr. Hiralal (historian) Commemoration.* P 13×13½.
1284 **1034** 60 p. deep violet-blue 20 20

1035 Light Frequency Experiment and Bodhi Tree
1036 Rural Patient

1988 (7 Jan). *75th Session of Indian Science Congress Association.* P 13.
1285 **1035** 4 r. multicoloured 50 60

(Des M. Sharma)

1988 (28 Jan). *13th Asian Pacific Dental Congress.* P 13×13½.
1286 **1036** 4 r. multicoloured 50 50

1988 (2 Feb–6 Oct). *India's Struggle for Freedom (6th series).* Vert portraits as T 909. P 13.
1287 60 p. black, emerald and reddish orange .. 20 40
1288 60 p. chestnut, emerald & brt orange (4.2) 20 40
1289 60 p. brt carmine, emer & orge-red (27.2) .. 20 40
1290 60 p. blackish purple, emer & brt orge (7.3) 20 40
1291 60 p. plum, dp green & reddish orge (18.6) 20 40
1292 60 p. slate-blk, dp grn & reddish orge (19.6) 20 40
1293 60 p. deep lilac, dp green & orge-red (28.6) 20 40
1294 60 p. dp bluish green, grn & orge-red (6.9) 20 30
1295 60 p. red-brown, emerald & orge-red (6.10) 20 30
1296 60 p. magenta, dp green & brt orange (5.12) 20 30
1287/96 .. .. .. Set of 10 1·75 3·25
Designs:—No. 1287, Mohan Lal Sukhadia; No. 1288, Dr. S. K. Sinha; No. 1289, Chandra Shekhar Azad; No. 1290, G. B. Pant; No. 1291, Dr. Anugrah Narain Singh; No. 1292, Kuladhor Chaliha; No. 1293, Shivprasad Gupta; No. 1294, Sarat Chandra Bose; No. 1295, Baba Kharak Singh; No. 1296, Sheikh Mohammad Abdullah.

1037 U Tirot Singh
1038 Early and Modern Regimental Uniforms

1988 (3 Feb). *U Tirot Singh (Khasis leader) Commemoration.* P 13×13½.
1297 **1037** 60 p. bistre-brown 20 20

1988 (19 Feb). *Bicentenary of 4th Battalion of the Kumaon Regiment.* P 14.
1298 **1038** 1 r. multicoloured 30 20

1039 Balgandharva
1040 Soldiers and Infantry Combat Vehicle

1988 (22 Feb). *Birth Centenary of Balgandharva (actor).* P 13×13½.
1299 **1039** 60 p. bistre-brown 20 20

1988 (24 Feb). *Presentation of Colours to Mechanised Infantry Regiment.* P 13½×13.
1300 **1040** 1 r. multicoloured 35 20

1041 B. N. Rau
1042 Mohindra Government College

1988 (26 Feb). *B. N. Rau (constitutional lawyer) Commemoration.* P 13.
1301 **1041** 60 p. grey-black 20 20

1988 (14 Mar). *Mohindra Government College, Patiala.* P 13×13½.
1302 **1042** 1 r. cerise 20 20

1043 Dr. D. V. Gundappa
1044 Rani Avantibai

1988 (17 Mar). *Dr. D. V. Gundappa (scholar) Commemoration.* P 13½×13.
1303 **1043** 60 p. slate 20 20

1988 (20 Mar). *Rani Avantibai of Ramgarh Commemoration.* P 13×13½.
1304 **1044** 60 p. cerise 20 20

1045 Malayalam Manorama Office, Kottayam
1046 Maharshi Dadhichi

1988 (23 Mar). *Centenary of Malayala Manorama (newspaper).* P 13.
1305 **1045** 1 r. black and new blue 20 20

1988 (26 Mar). *Maharshi Dadhichi (Hindu saint) Commemoration.* P 13×13½.
1306 **1046** 60 p. Indian red 20 20

1047 Mohammad Iqbal
1048 Samarth Ramdas

(Des Alka Sharma)

1988 (21 Apr). *50th Death Anniv of Mohammad Iqbal (poet).* P 13.
1307 **1047** 60 p. gold and rosine 20 20

1988 (1 May). *Samarth Ramdas (Hindu spiritual leader) Commem.* P 13.
1308 **1048** 60 p. deep yellow-green 20 20

1049 Swati Tirunal Rama Varma
1050 Bhaurao Patil and Class

1988 (2 May). *175th Birth Anniv of Swati Tirunal Rama Varma (composer).* P 13×13½.
1309 **1049** 60 p. deep mauve 20 20

1988 (9 May). *Bhaurao Patil (educationist) Commemoration.* P 13½×13.
1310 **1050** 60 p. reddish brown 20 20

1051 "Rani Lakshmi Bai" (M. F. Husain)

1988 (9 May). *Martyrs from First War of Independence.* P 13×13½.
1311 **1051** 60 p. multicoloured 20 20
 a. Myrtle-green (lowest stripe of flag, date, etc) omitted

1052 Broad Peak
1053 Child with Grandparents

(Des R. Pasricha (1 r. 50, 4 r.), N. Roerich (5 r.))

1988 (19 May). *Himalayan Peaks.* T **1052** *and similar horiz designs.* P 13½×13.
1312 1 r. 50, reddish lilac, deep violet and blue 35 30
1313 4 r. multicoloured 70 60
1314 5 r. multicoloured 80 70
1315 6 r. 50, multicoloured 95 85
1312/15 .. .. Set of 4 2·50 2·25
Designs:—4 r. K 2 (Godwin Austen); 5 r. Kanchenjunga; 6 r.50, Nanda Devi.

(Des Neeta Verma)

1988 (24 May). *"Love and Care for Elders".* P 13×13½.
1316 **1053** 60 p. multicoloured 20 20

1054 Victoria Terminus, Bombay   1055 Lawrence School, Lovedale

1988 (30 May). *Centenary of Victoria Terminus Station, Bombay.* P 13½×13.
1317 1054 1 r. multicoloured 40 20

1988 (31 May). *130th Anniv of Lawrence School, Lovedale.* P 13.
1318 1055 1 r. red-brown and deep green .. 30 20

1056 Khejri Tree

1988 (5 June). *World Environment Day.* P 14.
1319 1056 60 p. multicoloured 20 15

1988 (15 June). *As No. 732, but new face value.* W 374. P 12½ × 13.
1320 60 p. grey-black (Gandhi).. .. 55 15
    a. Wmk sideways 55 15

1057 Rani Durgawati   1058 Acharya Shanti Dev

1988 (24 June). *Rani Durgawati (Gondwana ruler) Commemoration.* P 13.
1322 1057 60 p. deep rose-red 20 20

1988 (28 July). *Acharya Shanti Dev (Buddhist scholar) Commemoration.* P 13×13½.
1323 1058 60 p. red-brown 20 20

1059 Y. S. Parmar

1988 (4 Aug). *Dr. Yashwant Singh Parmar (former Chief Minister of Himachal Pradesh) Commemoration.* P 13×13½.
1324 1059 60 p. slate-violet 20 20

1060 Arm pointing at Proclamation in Marathi

(Des Contract Advertising (India) Ltd)

1988 (16 Aug). *40th Anniv of Independence. Bal Gangadhar Tilak (patriot) Commemoration.* T 1060 *and similar horiz design. Multicoloured.* P 13×13½.
1325 60 p. Type 1060 .. .. 20 20
    a. Vert pair. Nos. 1325/6 .. 40 40
1326 60 p. Battle scene 20 20
Nos. 1325/6 were printed together, *se-tenant*, in vertical pairs throughout the sheet, each pair forming a composite design showing a painting by M. F. Husain.

1061 Durgadas Rathore   1062 Gopinath Kaviraj

1988 (26 Aug). *150th Birth Anniv of Durgadas Rathore (Regent of Marwar). Litho.* P 13×13½.
1327 1061 60 p. reddish brown 20 20

1988 (7 Sept). *Gopinath Kaviraj (scholar) Commemoration.* P 13×13½.
1328 1062 60 p. bistre-brown 20 20

1063 Lotus and Outline Map of India   1064 Indian Olympic Association Logo

1988 (14 Sept). *Hindi Day.* P 13×13½.
1329 1063 60 p. orange-verm, grn & reddish brn 20 20

(Des C. Parameswaran (5 p.))

1988 (17 Sept). *"Sports–1988" and Olympic Games, Seoul.* T 1064 *and similar design.* P 13.
1330 60 p. brown-purple 30 15
1331 5 r. multicoloured .. .. 1·60 60
Design: *Horiz*—5 r. Various sports.

1065 Jerdon's Courser   1066 *Times of India* Front Page

1988 (7 Oct). *Wildlife Conservation. Jerdon's Courser.* P 13×13½.
1332 1065 1 r. multicoloured 75 20

(Des C. Meena (4 r.), C. Pakrashi (5 r.))

1988 (9 Oct)–89. *"India–89" International Stamp Exhibition, New Delhi (3rd issue). General Post Offices. Horiz designs as* T 1022. *Multicoloured.* P 13½×13.
1333 4 r. Bangalore G.P.O. 40 35
    a. Booklet pane. No. 1333×6 (20.1.89) 2·25
1334 5 r. Bombay G.P.O. 50 45
    a. Booklet pane. No. 1334×6 (20.1.89) 2·75
Booklet panes Nos. 1333a and 1334a have margins all round.

(Des A. Nath)

1988 (3 Nov). *150th Anniv of The Times of India.* P 14.
1335 1066 1 r. 50, black, gold and lemon .. 20 20

1067 "Maulana Abul Kalam Azad" (K. Hebbar)

1988 (11 Nov). *Birth Centenary of Maulana Abul Kalam Azad (politician).* P 13½×13.
1336 1067 60 p. multicoloured 20 20

1068 Nehru

1988 (14 Nov). *Birth Centenary of Jawaharlal Nehru (1989) (1st issue).* T 1068 *and similar design.* P 13×13½ (60 p.) or 13½×13 (1 r.).
1337 60 p. grey-black, red-orange & deep green 30 15
1338 1 r. multicoloured 35 15
Design: *Vert*—1 r. "Jawaharlal Nehru" (Svetoslav Roerich). See also No. 1393.

1069 Birsa Munda

(Des S. Samantha)

1988 (15 Nov). *Birsa Munda (Munda leader) Commemoration.* P 13½ × 13.
1339 1069 60 p. reddish brown 20 20

1070 Bhakra Dam

1988 (15 Dec). *25th Anniv of Dedication of Bhakra Dam.* P 14.
1340 1070 60 p. bright carmine 35 60

1071 Dead Letter Office Cancellations of 1886   1072 K. M. Munshi

1988 (20 Dec)–89. *"India–89" International Stamp Exhibition, New Delhi (4th issue). Postal Cancellations.* T 1071 *and similar horiz design.* P 13½×13.
1341 60 p. dp cinnamon, black & carm-vermilion 25 15
    a. Booklet pane. No. 1341×6 (20.1.89) 1·40
1342 6 r. 50, orange-brown and black .. 1·00 1·00
    a. Booklet pane. No. 1342×6 (20.1.89) 5·50
Design:—6 r. 50, Travelling post office handstamp of 1864. Booklet panes Nos. 1341a and 1342a have margins all round.

1988 (30 Dec). *Birth Centenary of K. M. Munshi (author and politician) (1987).* P 13½ × 13.
1343 1072 60 p. deep olive 20 20

1073 Mannathu Padmanabhan   1074 Lok Sabha Secretariat

1989 (2 Jan). *Mannathu Padmanabhan (social reformer) Commemoration.* P 13 × 13½.
1344 1073 60 p. olive-brown 20 20

1989 (2 Jan–11 May). *India's Struggle for Freedom (7th series). Vert portraits as* T 909. P 13.
1345 60 p. blk, dull yellowish grn & reddish orge 20 20
1346 60 p. red-orange, dp grn & dp lilac (8.3.89) 20 50
1347 60 p. grey-black, bottle-green and bright orange (13.4.89) 20 50
1348 60 p. bistre-brown, emerald and reddish orange (13.4.89) 20 50
1349 60 p. brown, dp green & orge-red (11.5.89) 20 30
1345/9   Set of 5 90 1·90
Designs:—No. 1345, Hare Krishna Mahtab; No. 1346, Balasaheb Gangadhar Kher; No. 1347, Raj Kumari Amrit Kaur; No. 1348, Saifuddin Kitchlew; No. 1349, Asaf Ali.

1989 (10 Jan). *60th Anniv of Lok Sabha Secretariat (formerly Legislative Assembly Department). P* 13½ × 13.
1355 **1074** 60 p. brown-olive 20 20

1075 Goddess Durga seated on Lion (5th-cent terracotta plaque)
1076 Baldev Ramji Mirdha

1989 (11 Jan). *125th Anniv of Lucknow Museum. P* 14.
1356 **1075** 60 p. deep blue and new blue .. 20 20

1989 (17 Jan). *Birth Centenary of Baldev Ramji Mirdha (nationalist). P* 13 × 13½.
1357 **1076** 60 p. slate-green 20 20

1077 Girl with Stamp Collection
1078 St. John Bosco and Boy

(Des K. Radhakrishnan (60 p.), M. Jain (1 r. 50))

1989 (20 Jan). *"India–89" International Stamp Exhibition, New Delhi (5th issue). Philately.* T **1077** *and similar horiz designs. P* 13½×13.
1358 **60** p. orge-yellow, rose-red & dp violet-blue 15 10
  a. Booklet pane. No. 1358×6 .. 80
1359 **1** r. 50, brownish grey, orge-yellow & blk 20 15
  a. Booklet pane. No. 1359×6 .. 1·10
1360 **5** r. dull vermilion and blue .. 60 50
  a. Booklet pane. No. 1360×6 .. 3·25
1361 **6** r. 50, black, red-brown & turquoise-blue 70 60
  a. Booklet pane. No. 1361×6 .. 3·75
1358/61 .. *Set of 4* 1·50 1·25
Designs:—1 r. 50, Dawk gharry, c. 1842; 5 r. Travancore 1888 2 ch. conch shell stamp; 6 r. 50, Early Indian philatelic magazines.
Booklet panes Nos. 1358a, 1359a, 1360a and 1361a have margins all round.

1989 (31 Jan). *St. John Bosco (founder of Salesian Brothers) Commemoration. P* 13.
1362 **1078** 60 p. carmine 20 20

1079 Modern Tank and 19th-century Sowar
1080 Dargah Sharif, Ajmer

(Des P. Biswas)

1989 (8 Feb). *Third Cavalry Regiment. P* 13½ × 13.
1363 **1079** 60 p. multicoloured 30 20

1989 (13 Feb). *Dargah Sharif (Sufi shrine), Ajmer. P* 13½ × 13.
1364 **1080** 1 r. multicoloured 20 20

1081 Task Force and Indian Naval Ensign

1989 (15 Feb). *President's Review of the Fleet. P* 14.
1365 **1081** 6 r. 50, multicoloured .. .. 1·25 1·00

COVER PRICES
Cover factors are quoted at the beginning of each country for most issues to 1945. An explanation of the system can be found on page x. The factors quoted do not, however, apply to philatelic covers.

1082 Shaheed Laxman Nayak and Barbed Wire Fence
1083 Rao Gopal Singh

1989 (29 Mar). *Shaheed Laxman Nayak Commemoration. P* 13½×13.
1366 **1082** 60 p. dp brown, dp green & red-orange 20 20

1989 (30 Mar). *Rao Gopal Singh Commemoration. P* 13×13½.
1367 **1083** 60 p. olive-brown 20 20

1084 Sydenham College
1085 Bishnu Ram Medhi

1989 (19 Apr). *75th Anniv of Sydenham College, Bombay (1988). P* 13½×13.
1368 **1084** 60 p. grey-black 30 20

1989 (24 Apr). *Birth Centenary of Bishnu Ram Medhi (politician) (1988). P* 13.
1369 **1085** 60 p. yellowish green, deep blue-green and orange-red 30 20

1086 Dr. N. S. Hardikar
1087 "Advaita" in Devanagari Script

1989 (13 May). *Birth Centenary of Dr. Narayana Subbarao Hardikar (nationalist). P* 13×13½.
1370 **1086** 60 p. orange-brown 20 20

1989 (17 May). *Sankaracharya (philosopher) Commemoration. P* 14.
1371 **1087** 60 p. multicoloured 20 20

1088 Gandhi Bhavan, Punjab University
1089 Scene from Film *Raja Harischandra*

1989 (19 May). *Punjab University, Chandigarh. P* 13½×13.
1372 **1088** 1 r. light brown and turquoise-blue .. 20 20

1989 (30 May). *75 Years of Indian Cinema. P* 14.
1373 **1089** 60 p. black and yellow 20 20

1090 Cactus and Cogwheels
1091 Early Class and Modern University Students

1989 (20 June). *Centenary of Kirloskar Brothers Ltd (engineering group). P* 13½×13.
1374 **1090** 1 r. multicoloured 20 20

1989 (27 June). *Centenary of First D.A.V. College. P* 13½×13.
1375 **1091** 1 r. multicoloured 20 20

1092 Post Office, Dakshin Gangotri Base, Antarctica
1093 First Allahabad Bank Building

(Des S. Samantha)

1989 (11 July). *Opening of Post Office, Dakshin Gangotri Research Station, Antarctica. P* 14.
1376 **1092** 1 r. multicoloured 80 20

1989 (19 July). *125th Anniv of Allahabad Bank (1990). P* 14.
1377 **1093** 60 p. maroon and new blue .. 20 20

1094 Nehru inspecting Central Reserve Police, Neemuch, 1954
1095 Dairy Cow

1989 (27 July). *50th Anniv of Central Reserve Police Force (formerly Crown Representative's Police). P* 13½×13.
1378 **1094** 60 p. brown 60 20

1989 (18 Aug). *Centenary of Military Farms. P* 13½×13.
1379 **1095** 1 r. multicoloured 50 20

1096 Mustafa Kemal Atatürk
1097 Dr. S. Radhakrishnan

1989 (30 Aug). *50th Death Anniv of Mustafa Kemal Atatürk (Turkish statesman) (1988). P* 13×13½.
1380 **1096** 5 r. multicoloured .. .. 1·25 45

1989 (11 Sept). *Birth Centenary of Dr. Sarvepalli Radhakrishnan (former President) (1988). P* 13½×13.
1381 **1097** 60 p. grey-black 20 20

1098 Football Match
1099 Dr. P. Subbarayan

1989 (23 Sept). *Centenary of Mohun Bagan Athletic Club. P* 13½×13.
1382 **1098** 1 r. multicoloured 40 20

1989 (30 Sept). *Birth Centenary of Dr. P. Subbarayan (politician). P* 13×13½.
1383 **1099** 60 p. orange-brown 20 20

1100 Shyamji Krishna Varma
1101 Sayajirao Gaekwad III

1989 (4 Oct). *Shyamji Krishna Varma (nationalist) Commemoration. P* 13.
1384 1100 60 p. purple-brown, dp grn & orge-red 20 20

1989 (6 Oct). *50th Death Anniv of Maharaja Sayajirao Gaekwad III of Baroda. P* 13×13½.
1385 1101 60 p. brownish grey .. 20 20

1102 Symbolic Bird with Letter   1103 Namakkal Kavignar

1989 (14 Oct). *"Use Pincode" Campaign. P* 14.
1386 1102 60 p. multicoloured .. 20 20

1989 (19 Oct). *Namakkal Kavignar (writer) Commemoration. P* 13×13½.
1387 1103 60 p. brownish black .. 20 20

1104 Diagram of Human Brain   1105 Pandita Ramabai and Original Sharada Sadan Building

1989 (21 Oct). *18th International Epilepsy Congress and 14th World Congress on Neurology, New Delhi. P* 13½×13.
1388 1104 6 r. 50, multicoloured .. 2·25 75

1989 (26 Oct). *Pandita Ramabai (women's education pioneer) Commemoration. P* 13½×13.
1389 1105 60 p. light brown .. 30 20

1106 Releasing Homing Pigeons   1107 Acharya Narendra Deo

1989 (3 Nov). *Orissa Police Pigeon Post. P* 13½×13.
1390 1106 1 r. Indian red .. 50 20

1989 (6 Nov). *Birth Centenary of Acharya Narendra Deo (scholar). P* 13.
1391 1107 60 p. brown, emerald and red-orange 20 20

1108 Acharya Kripalani

1989 (11 Nov). *Acharya Kripalani (politician) Commemoration. P* 13½×13.
1392 1108 60 p. grey-blk, myrtle-grn & orge-red 20 20

STANLEY GIBBONS STAMP COLLECTING SERIES

Introductory booklets on *How to Start, How to Identify Stamps* and *Collecting by Theme*. A series of well illustrated guides at a low price.
Write for details.

1109 Nehru

(Des S. Debnath)

1989 (14 Nov). *Birth Centenary of Jawaharlal Nehru (2nd issue). P* 14×15.
1393 1109 1 r. dull brown, purple-brown and buff 65 20

1110 Meeting Logo   1111 Sir Gurunath Bewoor

1989 (19 Nov). *8th Asian Track and Field Meeting, New Delhi. P* 14.
1394 1110 1 r. black, reddish orge & yellowish grn 30 20

1989 (20 Nov). *Sir Gurunath Bewoor (former Director-General, Posts and Telegraphs) Commemoration. P* 13×13½.
1395 1111 60 p. light brown .. 20 20

1112 Balkrishna Sharma Navin   1113 Abstract Painting of Houses

1989 (8 Dec). *Balkrishna Sharma Navin (politician and poet) Commemoration. P* 13×13½.
1396 1112 60 p. black .. 20 20

1989 (15 Dec). *Centenary of Bombay Art Society (1988). P* 13½×13.
1397 1113 1 r. multicoloured .. 20 20

1114 Lesser Florican   1115 Centenary Logo

1989 (20 Dec). *Wildlife Conservation. Lesser Florican. P* 13×13½.
1398 1114 2 r. multicoloured .. 1·50 55

1989 (29 Dec). *Centenary of Indian Oil Production. P* 14.
1399 1115 60 p. red-brown .. 30 20

1116 Dr. M. G. Ramachandran   1117 Volunteers working at Sukhna Lake, Chandigarh

---

1990 (17 Jan). *Dr. M. G. Ramachandran (former Chief Minister of Tamil Nadu) Commemoration. P* 13×13½.
1400 1116 60 p. reddish brown .. 40 20

(Des T. Bedi and S. Singh)
1990 (29 Jan). *Save Sukhna Lake Campaign. P* 13½×13.
1401 1117 1 r. multicoloured .. 20 20

1118 Gallantry Medals

1990 (21 Feb). *Presentation of New Colours to Bombay Sappers. P* 15×14*.
1402 1118 60 p. multicoloured .. 80 80
*On No. 1402 the left hand side of the triangle is perforated 15 and the remaining two sides 14.

1119 Indian Chank Shell and Logo   1120 Penny Black and Envelope

1990 (2 May). *23rd Annual General Meeting of Asian Development Bank, New Delhi. P* 14.
1403 1119 2 r. black, brt orange & greenish yell 75 30

(Des M. Deogawanka)
1990 (6 May). *150th Anniv of the Penny Black. P* 13×13½.
1404 1120 6 r. multicoloured .. 1·25 40

1121 Ho Chi-Minh and Vietnamese House   1122 Chaudhary Charan Singh

1990 (17 May). *Birth Centenary of Ho Chi-Minh (Vietnamese leader). P* 13½×13.
1405 1121 2 r. reddish brown and yellowish green 30 30

1990 (29 May). *3rd Death Anniv of Chaudhary Charan Singh (former Prime Minister). P* 13.
1406 1122 1 r. orange-brown .. 20 20

1123 Armed Forces' Badge and Map of Sri Lanka   1124 Wheat

1990 (30 July). *Indian Peace-keeping Operations in Sri Lanka. P* 13.
1407 1123 2 r. multicoloured .. 30 30

1990 (31 July). *60th Anniv of Indian Council of Agricultural Research* (1989). *P* 14.
'408 1124 2 r. blk, brt yellow-grn & dp bluish grn 30 30

1125 Khudiram   1126 "Life in India" (Tanya
Bose   Vorontsova)

1990 (11 Aug). *Khudiram Bose (patriot) Commemoration.*
P 13×13½.
1409 1125 1 r. dull vermilion, dull grn & brn-red   20   20

1990 (16 Aug). *Indo-Soviet Friendship. Children's Paintings.*
T 1126 *and similar horiz design. Multicoloured. P* 14.
1410   1 r. Type 1126   1·50 2·00
       a. Horiz pair. Nos. 1410/11   3·00 4·00
1411   6 r. 50, "St. Basil's Cathedral and
          Kremlin, Moscow" (Sanjay Adhikari) 1·50 2·00
    Nos. 1410/11 were printed together, *se-tenant*, in horizontal
pairs throughout the sheet.
Stamps in similar designs were also issued by U.S.S.R.

1127 K. Kelappan   1128 Girl in
                            Garden

1990 (24 Aug). *K. Kelappan (social reformer) Commemoration.*
P 13×13½
1412 1127 1 r. reddish brown   ..   20   20

1990 (5 Sept). *Year of the Girl Child. P* 13×13½
1413 1128 1 r. multicoloured   50   30

1129 Hand guiding Child's   1130 Woman
      Writing   using Water Pump

1990 (8 Sept). *International Literacy Year. P* 13½×13.
1414 1129 1 r. multicoloured   50   30

1990 (10 Sept). *Safe Drinking Water Campaign. P* 13×13½.
1415 1130 4 r. black, scarlet-verm & dp bluish grn 1·25 1·50

1131 Sunder Lal   1132 Kabbadi
     Sharma

1990 (28 Sept). *50th Death Anniv of Sunder Lal Sharma*
(patriot). P 13×13½.
1416 1131 60 p. lake   50   40

  (Des C. Pakrashi (Nos. 1418/19), R. Pasricha (No. 1420))
1990 (29 Sept). *11th Asian Games, Peking. T* 1132 *and similar*
vert designs. Multicoloured. P 13×13½.
1417   1 r. Type 1132   ..   40   20
1418   4 r. Athletics   1·50 1·75
1419   4 r. Cycling   1·50 1·75
1420   6 r. 50, Archery   1·75 2·25
1417/20   ..   ..   *Set of* 4 4·75 5·25

1133 A. K.   1134 Gurkha
  Gopalan   Soldier

1990 (1 Oct). *Ayillyath Kuttiari Gopalan (social reformer)*
Commemoration. P 13×13½.
1421 1133 1 r. red-brown   50   30

           (Des R. Pasricha)
1990 (1 Oct). *50th Anniv of 3rd and 5th Battalions, 5th Gurkha*
Rifles. P 13.
1422 1134 2 r. black and ochre   ..   1·40 1·40

1135 Suryamall   1136 "Doll and Cat"
  Mishran   (Subhash Kumar
                   Nagarajan)

1990 (19 Oct). *75th Birth Anniv of Suryamall Mishran (poet).*
P 13 × 13½.
1423 1135 2 r. brown and pale orange   .. 50   50

1990 (14 Nov). *Children's Day. P* 13½×13.
1424 1136 1 r. multicoloured   60   30

1137 Security Post and   1138 Hearts and
Border Guard on Camel   Flowers

1990 (30 Nov). *25th Anniv of Border Security Force.*
P 13½×13.
1425 1137 5 r. greenish blue, yellow-brown & blk 1·50 1·50

        (Des R. Pasricha (1 r.))
1990 (17 Dec). *Greetings Stamps. T* 1138 *and similar*
multicoloured design. P 13×13½ (1 r.) *or* 13½×13 (4 r.).
1426   1 r. Type 1138   .. 20   15
1427   4 r. Ceremonial elephants (*horiz*)   50   65

1139 Bikaner   1140 Bhakta
                 Kanakadas and
                 Udipi Temple

  (Des R. Pasricha (4, 5 r.), P. Biswas (6 r. 50))
1990 (24 Dec). *Cities of India. T* 1139 *and similar horiz*
designs. Multicoloured. P 13½×13.
1428   4 r. Type 1139   55   60
1429   5 r. Hyderabad   65   75
1430   6 r. 50, Cuttack   90 1·25
1428/30   ..   ..   *Set of* 3 1·90 2·40

1990 (26 Dec). *Bhakta Kanakadas (mystic and poet)*
Commemoration. P 14.
1431 1140 1 r. orange-red   ..   55   30

NEW INFORMATION

The editor is always interested to correspond with
people who have new information that will
improve or correct the Catalogue.

1141 Shaheed   1142 Dnyaneshwari
  Minar   (poet) and
  Monument   Manuscript

1990 (28 Dec). *300th Anniv of Calcutta. T* 1141 *and similar*
design. P 14.
1432   1 r. multicoloured   30   20
1433   6 r. black, ochre and rosine   .. 1·25 1·50
    Design: *Horiz* (44×36 *mm*)—6 r. Eighteenth-century shipping
on the Ganges.

1990 (31 Dec). *700th Anniv of Dnyaneshwari (spiritual epic).*
P 13×13½.
1434 1142 2 r. multicoloured   ..   30   40

1143 Madan Mohan   1144 Road Users
Malaviya (founder) and
    University

1991 (20 Jan). *75th Anniv of Banaras Hindu University.*
P 13½×13.
1435 1143 1 r. brown-lake   ..   30   20

1991 (30 Jan). *As No. 732, but new face value. W* 374. *P* 13.
1436   1 r. orange-brown (Gandhi)   .. 10   10
       a. Wmk sideways   ..   ..
      ab. Imperf (pair)   ..   30·00

           (Des J. Das)
1991 (30 Jan). *International Traffic Safety Conference, New*
Delhi. P 13½×13.
1437 1144 6 r. 50, black, dp blue & orge-vermilion 75 85

1145 Exhibition   1146 Jagannath
  Emblem   Sunkersett and
                  Central Railways
                  Headquarters

1991 (12 Feb). *7th Triennale Art Exhibition, New Delhi.*
P 13×13½.
1438 1145 6 r. 50, multicoloured   .. 60   75

1991 (15 Feb). *125th Death Anniv (1990) of Jagannath*
Sunkersett (educationist and railway pioneer). P 13×13½.
1439 1146 2 r. royal blue and Indian red   .. 50   40

1147 Tata Memorial Centre   1148 River Dolphin

1991 (28 Feb). *50th Anniv of Tata Memorial Medical Centre.*
P 13½×13.
1440 1147 2 r. light brown and stone   .. 30   30

1991 (4 Mar). *Endangered Marine Mammals. T* 1148 *and*
similar horiz design. P 13½×13.
1441   4 r. red-brown, turquoise-blue & brt green 1·50 1·50
1442   6 r. 50, multicoloured   2·00 2·00
    Design:—6 r. 50, Sea Cow.

1149 Drugs

1150 Hand, Bomb Explosion and Dove

(Des J. Irani)

1991 (5 Mar). *International Conference on Drug Abuse, Calcutta.* P 13×13½.
1443 1149 5 r. bluish violet and bright scarlet ... 1·60 1·60

(Des J. Das)

1991 (7 Mar). *World Peace.* P 13×13½.
1444 1150 6 r. 50, black, cinnamon & orge-brown 75 1·00

1151 Remote Sensing Satellite "1A"

1152 Babu Jagjivan Ram

1991 (18 Mar). *Launch of Indian Remote Sensing Satellite "1A".* P 14.
1445 1151 6 r. 50, chestnut and deep violet-blue 60 75

1991 (5 Apr). *Babu Jagjivan Ram (politician) Commemoration.* P 13×13½.
1446 1152 1 r. yellow-brown ... 20 20

1153 Dr. B. R. Ambedkar and Demonstration

1154 Valar Dance

1991 (14 Apr). *Birth Centenary of Dr. Bhimrao Ramji Ambedkar (social reformer).* P 13½×13.
1447 1153 1 r. reddish brown and deep dull blue 30 20

1991 (30 Apr). *Tribal Dances.* T 1154 *and similar horiz designs. Multicoloured.* P 13½×13.
1448 2 r. 50, Type 1154 ... 50 40
1449 4 r. Kayang ... 70 80
1450 5 r. Hozagiri ... 80 90
1451 6 r. 50, Velakali ... 1·00 1·40
1448/51 ... Set of 4 2·75 3·25

1155 Ariyakudi Ramanuja Iyengar and Temples

1156 Karpoori Thakur

(Des J. Sharma)

1991 (18 May). *Ariyakudi Ramanuja Iyengar (singer and composer) Commemoration.* P 13½×13.
1452 1155 2 r. red-brown and deep bluish green 50 50

(Des L. Sahu)

1991 (30 May). *Jan Nayak Karpoori Thakur (politician and social reformer) Commemoration.* P 13×13½.
1453 1156 1 r. reddish brown ... 20 20

MINIMUM PRICE

The minimum price quote is 10p which represents a handling charge rather than a basis for valuing common stamps. For further notes about prices see introductory pages.

1157 Emperor Penguins

1158 Rashtrapati Bhavan Building, New Delhi

1991 (23 June). *30th Anniv of Antarctic Treaty.* T 1157 *and similar horiz design. Multicoloured.* P 13½×13.
1454 5 r. Type 1157 ... 1·75 2·00
  a. Horiz pair. Nos. 1454/5 ... 3·50 4·00
1455 6 r. 50, Antarctic map and pair of Adelie Penguins ... 1·75 2·00
Nos. 1454/5 were printed together, *se-tenant*, in horizontal pairs throughout the sheet, each pair forming a composite design.

(Des P. Biswas)

1991 (25 June). *60th Anniv of New Delhi.* T 1158 *and similar horiz designs. Multicoloured.* P 13½×13.
1456 5 r. Type 1158 ... 1·00 1·40
  a. Horiz pair. Nos. 1456/7 ... 2·00 2·75
1457 6 r. 50, New Delhi monuments ... 1·00 1·40
Nos. 1456/7 were printed together, *se-tenant*, in horizontal pairs throughout the sheet, each pair forming a composite design.

1159 Sri Ram Sharma Acharya

1160 "Shankar awarded Padma Vibhushan" (cartoon)

1991 (27 June). *Sri Ram Sharma Acharya (social reformer) Commemoration.* P 13½×13.
1458 1159 1 r. turquoise-green and rosine ... 20 20

1991 (31 July). *Keshav Shankar Pillai (cartoonist) Commemoration.* T 1160 *and similar design.* P 13½×13 (4 r.) or 13×13½ (6 r. 50).
1459 4 r. light brown ... 1·00 1·40
1460 6 r. 50, deep rose-lilac ... 1·40 1·75
Design: *Vert*—6 r. 50, "The Big Show".

1161 Sriprakash and Kashi Vidyapith University

1162 Gopinath Bardoloi

1991 (3 Aug). *20th Death Anniv of Sriprakash (politician).* P 13½×13.
1461 1161 2 r. red-brown and light brown ... 30 30

1991 (5 Aug). *Birth Centenary of Gopinath Bardoloi (Assamese politician) (1990).* P 13×13½.
1462 1162 1 r. deep reddish lilac ... 20 20

1163 Rajiv Gandhi

(Des R. Chopra)

1991 (20 Aug). *Rajiv Gandhi (Congress Party leader) Commemoration.* P 13.
1463 1163 1 r. multicoloured ... 40 40

1164 Muni Mishrimalji and Memorial

1165 Mahadevi Verma (poetess) and "Varsha"

1991 (24 Aug). *Birth Centenary of Muni Mishrimalji (Jain religious leader).* P 13½×13.
1464 1164 1 r. yellow-brown ... 30 20

(Des S. Samant)

1991 (16 Sept). *Hindu Writers.* T 1165 *and similar horiz design.* P 13½×13.
1465 1165 2 r. black and light blue ... 15 25
  a. Horiz pair. Nos. 1465/6 ... 30 50
1466 – 2 r. black and light blue ... 15 25
Design:—No. 1466, Jayshankar Prasad (poet and dramatist) and scene from "Kamayani".
Nos. 1465/6 were printed together, *se-tenant*, in horizontal pairs throughout the sheet.

1166 Parliament House and C.P.A. Emblem

1167 Frog

(Des P. Biswas)

1991 (27 Sept). *37th Commonwealth Parliamentary Association Conference, New Delhi.* P 13½×13.
1467 1166 6 r. 50, blue and reddish brown ... 40 60

1991 (30 Sept). *Greetings Stamps.* T 1167 *and similar vert design.* P 13×13½.
1468 1 r. emerald and deep rose-red ... 20 40
  a. Horiz pair. Nos. 1468/9 ... 55 95
1469 6 r. 50, deep rose-red and emerald ... 35 55
Design:—6 r. 50, Symbolic bird carrying flower.
Nos. 1468/9 were printed together, *se-tenant*, in horizontal pairs throughout the sheet.

1168 *Cymbidium aloifolium*

1169 Gurkha Soldier in Battle Dress

(Des O. Ravindran)

1991 (12 Oct). *Orchids.* T 1168 *and similar vert designs. Multicoloured.* P 13×13½.
1470 1 r. Type 1168 ... 30 15
1471 2 r. 50, *Paphiopedilum venustum* ... 35 35
1472 3 r. *Aerides crispum* ... 40 40
1473 4 r. *Cymbidium bicolour* ... 50 65
1474 5 r. *Vanda spathulata* ... 55 70
1475 6 r. 50, *Cymbidium devonianum* ... 70 1·00
1470/5 ... Set of 6 2·50 3·00

(Des R. Pasricha)

1991 (18 Oct). *90th Anniv of 2nd Battalion, Third Gurkha Rifles.* P 13½×13.
1476 1169 4 r. multicoloured ... 1·50 1·50

1170 Couple on Horse (embroidery)

1171 Chithira Tirunal and Temple Sculpture

1991 (29 Oct). *3rd Death Anniv of Kamaladevi Chattopadhyaya, (founder of All India Handicrafts Board).* T 1170 *and similar vert design.* P 13×13½.
1477 1 r. carmine-lake, crimson and yellow ... 40 20
1478 6 r. 50, multicoloured ... 1·50 1·75
Design:—6 r. 50, Traditional puppet.

1991 (7 Nov). *Chithira Tirunal Bala Rama Varma (former Maharaja of Travancore) Commemoration.* P 13½×13.
1479 1171 2 r. slate-violet 65 75

1172 "Children in Traditional Costume" (Arpi Snehalbhai Shah)

1173 Mounted Sowar and Tanks

1991 (14 Nov). *Children's Day.* P 13×13½.
1480 1172 1 r. multicoloured 70 30

(Des R. Pasricha)
1991 (14 Nov). *70th Anniv of the 18th Cavalry Regiment* (1992). P 13½×13.
1481 1173 6 r. 50, multicoloured .. .. 2·00 2·25

1174 Kites

1175 Sports on Bricks

1991 (15 Nov). *India Tourism Year.* P 13½×13.
1482 1174 6 r. 50, multicoloured 60 85
It was originally intended to release No. 1482 on 28 January 1991, but the issue was postponed until 15 November. Examples are known used from Jaipur on the original date.

1991 (18 Nov). *International Conference on Youth Tourism, New Delhi.* P 13×13½.
1483 1175 6 r. 50, multicoloured .. .. 1·00 1·40

1176 "Mozart at Piano" (unfinished painting, J. Lange)

1177 Homeless Family

1991 (5 Dec). *Death Bicentenary of Mozart.* P 13×13½.
1484 1176 6 r. 50, multicoloured .. .. 1·50 1·75

(Des N. Srivastav)
1991 (7 Dec). *South Asian Association for Regional Co-operation Year of Shelter.* P 13×13½.
1485 1177 4 r. lake-brown and ochre 55 70

1178 People running on Heart

1179 "Sidhartha with an Injured Bird" (Asit Kumar Haldar)

1991 (11 Dec). *"Run for Your Heart" Marathon, New Delhi.* P 13½×13.
1486 1178 1 r. black, slate and bright scarlet .. 20 20

1991 (28 Dec). *Birth Centenary of Asit Kumar Haldar (artist)* (1990). P 13×13½.
1487 1179 2 r. yellow, Indian red and black .. 30 50

1180 Bhujangasana

1181 Y.M.C.A. Logo

1991 (30 Dec). *Yoga Exercises.* T 1180 and similar horiz designs. Multicoloured. P 13½×13.
1488 2 r. Type 1180 .. .. 20 25
1489 5 r. Dhanurasana 40 55
1490 6 r. 50, Ustrasana 50 70
1491 10 r. Utthita trikonasana .. .. 85 1·25
1488/91 .. .. Set of 4 1·75 2·50

1992 (21 Feb). *Centenary of National Council of Y.M.C.As.* (1991). P 13×13½.
1492 1181 1 r. vermilion and deep dull blue .. 20 20

1182 Madurai Temple Tower and Hooghly River Bridge

1183 Goat Seal from Harappa Culture, 2500 to 1500 B.C.

1992 (1 Mar). *14th Congress of International Association for Bridge and Structural Engineering, New Delhi.* T 1182 and similar horiz design. P 13½×13.
1493 1182 2 r. bistre-brown, dull vermilion & bl 40 50
a. Horiz pair. Nos. 1493/4 80 1·00
1494 2 r. bistre-brown, dull vermilion & bl 40 50
Design:—No. 1494, Gate, Sanchi Stupa and Hall of Nations, New Delhi.
Nos. 1493/4 were printed together, se-tenant, in horizontal pairs throughout the sheet.

1992 (2 Mar). *5th International Goat Conference, New Delhi.* P 13½×13.
1495 1183 6 r. royal blue and bistre-brown .. 1·50 1·75

1184 Early 19th-century Letter with Mail Pouch and National Archives Building, New Delhi

1185 Krushna Chandra Gajapathi

(Des C. Pakrashi)
1992 (20 Apr). *Centenary of National Archives* (1991). P 13½×13.
1496 1184 6 r. multicoloured 50 65

1992 (25 Apr). *Krushna Chandra Gajapathi (former Chief Minister of Orissa) Commemoration.* P 13×13½.
1497 1185 1 r. deep lilac.. .. .. .. 15 15

1186 Vijay Singh Pathik

1187 Hang-gliding

1992 (29 Apr). *Vijay Singh Pathik (writer) Commemoration.* P 13×13½.
1498 1186 1 r. reddish brown 15 15

(Des R. Pasricha)
1992 (29 Apr). *Adventure Sports.* T 1187 and similar horiz designs. Multicoloured. P 13½×13.
1499 2 r. Type 1187 .. .. .. 20 20
1500 4 r. Windsurfing 40 50
1501 5 r. River rafting 45 55
1502 11 r. Skiing .. .. .. 1·00 1·75
1499/1502 .. .. Set of 4 1·75 2·75

1188 Henry Gidney and Anglo-Indians

1189 Telecommunications Training Centre, Jabalpur

(Des S. Kitson and A. Ali)
1992 (9 May). *50th Death Anniv of Sir Henry Gidney (ophthalmologist).* P 13½×13.
1503 1188 1 r. black and light blue .. 30 15

1992 (30 May). *50th Anniv of Telecommunications Training Centre, Jabalpur.* P 13½×13.
1504 1189 1 r. bistre 20 15

1190 Sardar Udham Singh

1191 Men's Discus

(Des S. Samanta)
1992 (31 July). *Sardar Udham Singh (patriot) Commemoration.* P 13×13½.
1505 1190 1 r. black and light brown .. 20 15

(Des P. Biswas)
1992 (8 Aug). *Olympic Games, Barcelona.* T 1191 and similar vert designs. Multicoloured. P 13×13½.
1506 1 r. Type 1191 .. .. 30 10
1507 6 r. Women's gymnastics .. 80 90
1508 8 r. Men's hockey .. 1·75 1·75
1509 11 r. Boxing .. 1·75 2·00
1506/9 .. .. Set of 4 4·25 4·25

1192 Spinning Wheel Emblem

1193 Treating Casualty

(Des C. Pakrashi)
1992 (9 Aug). *50th Anniv of "Quit India" Movement.* T 1192 and similar horiz design. P 13½×13.
1510 1 r. black and brown-rose .. 50 20
1511 2 r. black, lake-brown and grey .. 1·10 1·25
Design:—2 r. Mahatma Gandhi and mantra

1992 (10 Aug). *50th Anniv of 60th Parachute Field Ambulance.* P 13½×13.
1512 1193 1 r. multicoloured .. .. 1·00 40

1194 Dr. S. R. Ranganathan and Madras University

1195 "Dev Narayan"

1992 (30 Aug). *Birth Centenary of Shiyali Ramamrita Ranganathan (librarian).* P 13½×13.
1513 1194 1 r. deep turquoise-blue 55 30

1992 (2 Sept). *Phad Scroll Paintings from Rajasthan.* P 14.
1514 1195 5 r. multicoloured 55 70

1196 Hanuman Prasad Poddar

1197 Mikoyan Gurevich MiG-29 Fighter and Ilyushin Il-76 Transport

1992 (19 Sept). *Hanuman Prasad Poddar (editor) Commemoration. P* 13×13½.
1515 **1196** 1 r. deep green 15 15

(Des S. Surve)

1992 (8 Oct). *60th Anniv of Indian Air Force.* T **1197** *and similar horiz design. Multicoloured. P* 13½×13.
1516   1 r. Type **1197** 40 50
    a. Horiz pair. Nos. 1516/17 .. 1·25 1·50
1517 10 r. MiG-27 fighter and Westland Wapiti
    biplane .. .. 85 1·00
Nos. 1516/17 were printed together, *se-tenant,* in horizontal pairs throughout the sheet.

1198 Lighting Candle

1199 "Sun" (Harshit Prashant Patel)

(Des S. Samanta)

1992 (13 Nov). *150th Anniv of Sisters of Jesus and Mary's Arrival in India. P* 13×13½.
1518 **1198** 1 r. royal blue and light grey .. 15 15

1992 (14 Nov). *Childrens Day. P* 13½×13.
1519 **1199** 1 r. multicoloured 20 15

1200 Yogiji Maharaj

1201 Army Service Corps Transport

1992 (2 Dec). *Birth Centenary of Yogiji Maharaj (Hindu reformer). P* 13×13½.
1520 **1200** 1 r. deep ultramarine .. 15 15

1992 (8 Dec). *Army Service Corps Commemoration. P* 13½×13.
1521 **1201** 1 r. multicoloured .. .. 1·00 40

1202 Stephen Smith and Early Rocket Post Covers

1203 Electricity Pylons, Farmers and Crops

1992 (19 Dec). *Birth Centenary of Stephen Smith (rocket mail pioneer) (1991). P* 13½×13.
1522 **1202** 11 r. multicoloured .. .. 90 1·25

1992 (20 Dec). *25th Anniv of Haryana State. P* 13½×13.
1523 **1203** 2 r. orange-verm, dp grn & yellow-grn 15 15

MINIMUM PRICE

The minimum price quote is 10p which represents a handling charge rather than a basis for valuing common stamps. For further notes about prices see introductory pages.

1204 Madanlal Dhingra

1205 Osprey

1992 (28 Dec). *Madanlal Dhingra (revolutionary) Commemoration. P* 13×13½.
1524 **1204** 1 r. deep brown, orange-red & dp green 30 15

1992 (30 Dec). *Birds of Prey.* T **1205** *and similar vert designs. Multicoloured. P* 13×13½.
1525   2 r. Type **1205** 75 50
1526   6 r. Peregrine Falcon .. .. 1·00 1·00
1527   8 r. Lammergeier .. .. 1·25 1·40
1528 11 r. Golden Eagle .. .. 1·50 1·75
1525/8 .. .. .. *Set of* 4 4·00 4·25

1206 Pandit Ravishankar Shukla

1207 William Carey

1992 (31 Dec). *Pandit Ravishankar Shukla (social reformer) Commemoration. P* 13×13½.
1529 **1206** 1 r. deep purple 15 15

1993 (9 Jan). *Bicentenary of William Carey's Appointment as Baptist Missionary to India. P* 13½×13.
1530 **1207** 6 r. multicoloured 80 90

1208 Fakirmohan Senapati

1209 Workers and C.S.I.R. Emblem

1993 (14 Jan). *Fakirmohan Senapati Commemoration. P* 13×13½.
1531 **1208** 1 r. Indian red 30 15

1993 (28 Feb). *50th Anniv of Council of Scientific and Industrial Research. P* 13½×13.
1532 **1209** 1 r. maroon 30 15

1210 Parachute Drop and Field Gun

1211 Westland Wapiti Biplane

1993 (1 Apr). *50th Anniv of 9th Parachute Field Artillery Regiment. P* 13½.
1533 **1210** 1 r. multicoloured 75 30

1993 (1 Apr). *60th Anniv of No. 1 Squadron, Indian Air Force. P* 13½.
1534 **1211** 1 r. multicoloured 75 30

1212 Rahul Sankrityayan

1213 Parliament Building and Emblem

1993 (9 Apr). *Birth Centenary of Rahul Sankrityayan (politician). P* 13½×13.
1535 **1212** 1 r. blue-black, cinnamon & yellow-brn 15 15

1993 (11 Apr). *89th Inter-Parliamentary Union Conference, New Delhi. P* 13½×13.
1536 **1213** 1 r. blue-black 15 15

1214 Neral Metheran Locomotive, 1905

1215 Students and College Building

1993 (16 Apr). *Mountain Locomotives.* T **1214** *and similar horiz designs. Multicoloured. P* 13½×13.
1537   1 r. Type **1214** 55 20
1538   6 r. Darjeeling, 1889 .. .. 1·00 1·00
1539   8 r. Nilgiri, 1914 .. .. 1·25 1·40
1540 11 r. Kalka–Simla, 1934 .. .. 1·75 2·00
1537/40 .. .. .. *Set of* 4 4·00 4·25

1993 (25 Apr). *Centenary of Meerut College. P* 14.
1541 **1215** 1 r. blue-black and orange-brown .. 15 15

1216 Mahalanobis and Office Block

1217 Bombay Town Hall

1993 (29 June). *Prasanta Chandra Mahalanobis Commemoration. P* 13.
1542 **1216** 1 r. yellow-brown 15 15

1993 (31 July). *Centenary of Bombay Municipal Corporation. P* 13×13½.
1543 **1217** 2 r. multicoloured 20 30

1218 Abdul Ghaffar Khan and Mountainside

1219 National Integration Emblem

1993 (9 Aug). *Abdul Ghaffar Khan Commemoration. P* 13½×13.
1544 **1218** 1 r. multicoloured 15 15

(Des C. Pakrashi)

1993 (19 Aug). *National Integration Campaign. P* 13½×13.
1545 **1219** 1 r. bright orange and deep green .. 15 15

1220 Dadabhai Naoroji and Houses of Parliament, London

1221 Swami Vivekananda and Art Institute, Chicago

1993 (26 Aug). *Centenary of Dadabhai Naoroji's Election to the House of Commons.* P 14.
1546 **1220** 6 r. multicoloured 45 60

(Des C. Pakrashi)
1993 (11 Sept). *Centenary of Swami Vivekananda's Chicago Address.* P 13×13½.
1547 **1221** 2 r. reddish orange and grey .. 40 40

1222 *Lagerstroemia speciosa*
1223 College Building and Emblem

(Des O. Ravindran)
1993 (9 Oct). *Flowering Trees. T* **1222** *and similar vert designs.* P 13×13½.
1548 1 r. rose-carmine, yellow-grn & chocolate 20 15
1549 6 r. multicoloured 40 55
1550 8 r. multicoloured 55 70
1551 11 r. multicoloured .. .. .. 75 1·00
1548/51 Set of 4 1·75 2·25
Designs:—6 r. *Cochlospermum religiosum*; 8 r. *Erythrina variegata*; 11 r. *Thespesia populnea.*

1993 (8 Nov). *50th Anniv of College of Military Engineering, Pune.* P 13×13½.
1552 **1223** 2 r. multicoloured 20 30

1224 Dr. Dwaram Venkataswamy Naidu playing Violin
1225 Children on Elephant

(Des Alka Sharma)
1993 (8 Nov). *Birth Centenary of Dwaram Venkataswamy Naidu (violinist).* P 13×13½.
1553 **1224** 1 r. Indian red 20 20

1993 (14 Nov). *Children's Day.* P 14.
1554 **1225** 1 r. multicoloured 20 20

1226 People with Stress
1227 Dr. Kotnis performing Operation

1993 (9 Dec). *Heart Care Festival.* P 13½×13.
1555 **1226** 6 r. 50, multicoloured 60 70

1993 (9 Dec). *Dr. Dwarkananth Kotnis (surgeon) Commemoration.* P 13½×13.
1556 **1227** 1 r. blue-black 20 20
a. Printed on the gummed side

1228 Tea Symbol
1229 Papal Seminary Arms and Building

1993 (11 Dec). *Indian Tea Production.* P 13.
1557 **1228** 6 r. deep dull green and bright carmine 50 65

1993 (16 Dec). *Centenary of Papal Seminary, Pune.* P 13½×13.
1558 **1229** 6 r. multicoloured 50 65

1230 Meghnad Saha and Eclipse of the Sun
1231 Speedpost Letter and Arrows circling Globe

1993 (23 Dec). *Meghnad Saha (astronomer) Commemoration.* P 13×13½.
1559 **1230** 1 r. deep violet-blue 30 20

(Des C. Pakrashi (1 r.))
1993 (25–27 Dec). *"Inpex '93" National Philatelic Exhibition, Calcutta. T* **1231** *and similar horiz design. Multicoloured.* P 13½×13.
1560 1 r. Type **1231** .. 15 15
1561 2 r. "Custom-house Wharf, Calcutta" (Sir Charles D'Oyly) (27 Dec) .. 25 35

1232 Dinanath Mangeshkar
1233 Nargis Dutt

(Des C. Pakrashi)
1993 (29 Dec). *Dinanath Mangeshkar Commemoration.* P 13½×13.
1562 **1232** 1 r. orange-red .. 15 15

1993 (30 Dec). *Nargis Dutt Commemoration.* P 13.
1563 **1233** 1 r. Indian red 15 15

1234 S.C. Bose inspecting Troops
1235 Satyendra Nath Bose and Equation

1993 (31 Dec). *50th Anniv of Indian National Army.* P 13½×13.
1564 **1234** 1 r. slate-green, dp green & orange-red 30 20

1994 (1 Jan). *Birth Centenary of Satyendra Nath Bose (scientist).* P 13½×13.
1565 **1235** 1 r. purple-brown 30 15

1236 Dr. Sampurnanand

1994 (10 Jan). *Dr. Sampurnanand (politician) Commemoration.* P 13½×13.
1566 **1236** 1 r. reddish brn, slate-grn & orge-red 15 10

The new-issue supplement to this Catalogue appears each month in

GIBBONS STAMP MONTHLY

—from your newsagent or by postal subscription— sample copy and details on request.

1237 Scene from *Pather Panchali*

1994 (11 Jan). *Satyajit Ray (film director) Commemoration. T* **1237** *and similar multicoloured design.* P 13.
1567 6 r. Type **1237** .. .. 1·00 1·25
a. Horiz pair. Nos. 1567/8 .. 2·25 2·75
1568 11 r. Satyajit Ray and Oscar (35×35 mm) 1·25 1·50
Nos. 1567/8 were printed together, *se-tenant,* in horizontal pairs throughout the sheet.

1238 Dr. Bhatnagar and University Building
1239 Prajapita Brahma and Memorial

1994 (21 Feb). *Dr. Shanti Swarup Bhatnagar (scientist) Commemoration.* P 13½×13.
1569 **1238** 1 r. deep violet-blue 15 10

1994 (7 Mar). *25th Death Anniv of Prajapita Brahma (social reformer).* P 13½×13.
1570 **1239** 1 r. deep rose-lilac & deep ultramarine 15 10

1240 "Window" (K. Subramanyan)
1241 Agricultural Products and Tea Garden

1994 (14 Mar). *8th Triennale Art Exhibition, New Delhi.* P 13½×13.
1571 **1240** 6 r. salmon, carmine-verm & ultram 40 60

(Des S. Samanta)
1994 (26 Mar). *Centenary of United Planters' Association of Southern India.* P 13×13½.
1572 **1241** 2 r. multicoloured 20 20

1242 Indian Family
1242a Sanchi Stupa

1994 (4 Apr)–97. *W* **374** *(sideways on 5 r.).* P 13.
1573 **1242** 75 p. brown and vermilion (11.7.94) 10 10
1574 — 1 r. cerise & dp bluish grn (11.7.94) 10 10
a. Wmk sideways (1997) 10 10
1575 **1242a** 5 r. reddish brown & turquoise-grn 20 25
a. Wmk upright
Design: Horiz (as *T* **1242**)—1 r. Family outside home.

1243 Rani Rashmoni on River Bank
1244 Indians releasing Peace Doves

1994 (9 Apr). *Birth Bicentenary of Rani Rashmoni.* P 13½×13.
1589 **1243** 1 r. reddish brown 15 10

(Des S. Kumar)
1994 (13 Apr). *75th Anniv of Jallianwala Bagh Massacre, Amritsar.* P 13½×13.
1590 **1244** 1 r. black and rosine 15 10

1245 Chandra Singh
Garhwali

1246 Emblems and
National Flag

1994 (23 Apr). *15th Death Anniv of Chandra Singh Garhwali (nationalist).* P 13½×13.
1591 1245 1 r. deep olive-green and red-orange 15 10

1994 (1 May). *75th Anniv of International Labour Organization.* P 13½×13.
1592 1246 6 r. multicoloured .. 40 60

1247 Silhouette of
Drummer and Logo

1248 Statue of
Sepoy

(Des A. Sharma)

1994 (25 May). *50th Anniv of Indian People's Theatre Association.* P 13.
1593 1247 2 r. black, yellowish green and gold 15 15

1994 (12 Aug). *Bicentenary of 4th Battalion, The Madras Regiment.* P 13.
1594 1248 6 r. 50, multicoloured 55 65

1249 Institute Building
and Emblem

1250 Mahatma Gandhi
and Indian Flag

(Des C. Pakrashi)

1994 (23 Sept). *Bicentenary of Institute of Mental Health, Madras.* P 13½×13.
1595 1249 2 r. deep rose-red and deep blue .. 15 15

(Des S. Samanta and S. Kumar)

1994 (2 Oct). *125th Birth Anniv of Mahatma Gandhi.* T 1250 and similar multicoloured design. P 13.
1596   6 r. Type 1250 .. .. 1·00 1·25
   a. Horiz pair. Nos. 1596/7 .. 2·25 2·75
1597   11 r. Aspects of Gandhi's life on flag (69×34 mm) .. .. 1·25 1·50
Nos. 1596/7 were printed together, *se-tenant*, in horizontal pairs throughout the sheet, with the backgrounds forming a composite design.

1251 Symbols of
Cancer

1252 Human Resources
Emblem

(Des A. Sharma)

1995 (30 Oct). *16th International Cancer Congress, New Delhi.* P 13×13½.
1598 1251 6 r. multicoloured 55 65

1994 (8 Nov). *Human Resource Development World Conference, New Delhi.* P 13½×13.
1599 1252 6 r. blue, vermilion and azure .. 55 65

COVER PRICES

Cover factors are quoted at the beginning of each country for most issues to 1945. An explanation of the system can be found on page x. The factors quoted do not, however, apply to philatelic covers.

1253 "Me and My Pals"
(Namarata Amit Shah)

1254 Family and
Emblem

1994 (14 Nov). *Children's Day.* P 13½×13.
1600 1253 1 r. multicoloured 10 10

(Des S. Kumar)

1994 (20 Nov). *International Year of the Family.* P 13.
1601 1254 2 r. multicoloured 20 15

1255 "Taj Mahal"
(illustration from
Badsha Nama)

1256 Andaman Teal

1994 (21 Nov). *Khuda Bakhsh Oriental Public Library, Patna, Commemoration.* P 14.
1602 1255 6 r. multicoloured .. .. 4·00 1·00

(Des J. Irani. Litho Madras Security Printers)

1994 (23 Nov). *Endangered Water Birds.* T 1256 and similar horiz designs. Multicoloured. P 13½×13.
1603   1 r. Type 1256 .. .. 5·00 2·00
   a. Block of 4. Nos. 1603/6 .. 30·00
1604   6 r. Eastern White Stork .. 8·00 4·00
1605   8 r. Black-necked Crane .. 9·00 4·50
1606   11 r. Pink-headed Duck .. .. 11·00 6·00
1603/6   *Set of 4* 30·00 15·00
Nos. 1603/6 were printed together, *se-tenant*, in blocks of 4 throughout the sheet.
It is reported that Nos. 1603/6 were withdrawn shortly after issue due to technical difficulties.

1257 J. R. D. Tata and Aspects
of Industrial Symbols

(Des C. Pakrashi)

1994 (29 Nov). *J. R. D. Tata (industrialist) Commemoration.* P 14.
1607 1257 2 r. multicoloured 30 30

1258 School Building and
Computer Class

1259 Begum
Akhtar

1994 (30 Nov). *Centenary of Calcutta Blind School.* P 13½×13.
1608 1258 2 r. rosine, chocolate and cinnamon 20 15

(Litho Madras Security Printers)

1994 (2 Dec). *80th Birth Anniv of Begum Akhtar (singer).* P 13×13½.
1609 1259 2 r. multicoloured .. .. 3·75 3·75
It is reported that No. 1609 was withdrawn shortly after issue due to technical difficulties

1260 College Building

1261 Cavalryman,
Infantryman and
Dog Handler

1994 (4 Dec). *125th Anniv of St. Xavier's College, Bombay.* P 13½×13.
1610 1260 2 r. purple-brown and azure .. 15 15

1994 (14 Dec). *215th Anniv of Remount Veterinary Corps.* P 13×13½.
1611 1261 6 r. multicoloured 75 60

1262 College Building

1263 Righthand
Ornament of
Bronze Stand

1994 (19 Dec). *Bicentenary of College of Engineering, Guindy, Madras.* P 14.
1612 1262 2 r. dull vermilion, red-brown & black 15 10

1994 (20 Dec). *Centenary of Baroda Museum.* T 1263 and similar vert design. P 14.
1613   6 r. bistre-yellow and agate .. .. 3·00 75
   a. Horiz pair. Nos. 1613/14 .. 6·00 1·50
1614   11 r. bistre-yellow and agate .. .. 3·00 75
Design:—11 r. Bronze Rishabhanatha statue of Buddha on stand.
Nos. 1613/14 were printed together, *se-tenant*, in horizontal pairs throughout the sheet.

1264 "200" and Aspects of Postal Service

(Des M. Rajadhyaksha. Litho Calcutta Security Printers, Kanpur)

1994 (28 Dec). *Bicentenary of Bombay General Post Office.* P 13½×13.
1615 1264 6 r. multicoloured .. .. 6·00 1·50

1265 Statue of King
Rajaraja Chola

1266 Globe and
Emblem

(Litho Madras Security Printers)

1995 (5 Jan). *8th International Conference-Seminar of Tamil Studies, Thanjavur.* P 13×13½.
1616 1265 2 r. light blue, ultramarine and black 3·50 75

(Des C. Pakrashi)

1995 (7 Jan). *60th Anniv of National Science Academy.* P 13×13½.
1617 1266 6 r. multicoloured 50 60

1267 Chhotu Ram   1268 Film Reel and Globe

1995 (9 Jan). *Chhotu Ram (social reformer) Commemoration.*
P 13×13½.
618 **1267** 1 r. yellow-brown .. .. .. 1·00   25

(Des S. Kumar. Litho Calcutta Security Printers, Kanpur)

1995 (11 Jan). *Centenary of Cinema.* T **1268** *and similar horiz design. Multicoloured.* P 13½×13.
619   6 r. Type **1268** 60   70
    a. Horiz pair. Nos. 1619/20 .. .. 1·40   1·60
620   11 r. Film reel and early equipment .. 80   90
Nos. 1619/20 were printed together, *se-tenant,* in horizontal pairs throughout the sheet.

1269 Symbolic Hands   1270 Prithviraj
and Children   Kapoor and Mask

1995 (12 Jan). *South Asian Association for Regional Cooperation Youth Year.* P 13×13½.
1621 **1269** 2 r. multicoloured 20   20

(Des S. Pawar)

1995 (15 Jan). *50th Anniv of Prithvi Theatre.* P 13×13½.
1622 **1270** 2 r. multicoloured .. .. .. 3·75   75

1271 Field-Marshal   1272 Textile
Cariappa   Pattern

1995 (15 Jan). *Field-Marshal K. Cariappa Commemoration.*
P 13×13½.
1623 **1271** 2 r. multicoloured 30   20

1995 (18 Jan). *"TEX-STYLES INDIA '95" Fair, Bombay.*
P 13×13½.
1624 **1272** 2 r. chestnut, pale buff & brt scarlet 20   20

1273 Rafi Ahmed   1274 K. L. Saigal,
Kidwai   Film Reel and
                Gramophone

1995 (18 Feb). *Birth Centenary of Rafi Ahmed Kidwai (politician) (1994).* P 13×13½.
1625 **1273** 1 r. chestnut 10   10

1995 (4 Apr). *90th Birth Anniv of K. L. Saigal (singer).*
P 13½×13.
1626 **1274** 5 r. chestnut, grey and black .. 75   80

1275 R. S. Ruikar   1276 Radio Tower, Globe
                  and Dish Aerial

1995 (1 May). *Birth Centenary of R. S. Ruikar (trade unionist).*
P 13×13½.
1627 **1275** 1 r. purple-brown 10   10

(Des S. Kumar. Litho Calcutta Security Printers Ltd, Kanpur)

1995 (17 May). *Centenary of Telecommunications.* P 13½×13.
1628 **1276** 5 r. multicoloured 60   70

1277 Leaves and Symbolic   1278 Handshake
Houses

(Des D. Banduni. Litho Calcutta Security Printers Ltd, Kanpur)

1995 (23 May). *Delhi Development Authority.* P 13½×13.
1629 **1277** 2 r. multicoloured 20   20

(Des C. Pakrashi. Litho Calcutta Security Printers Ltd, Kanpur)

1995 (26 June). *50th Anniv of United Nations.* T **1278** *and similar vert design. Multicoloured.* P 13×13½.
1630   1 r. Type **1278** 10   10
1631   6 r. Work of U.N. Agencies 45   55

1279 Colonnade   1280 Globe showing
on Book Cover   South-east Asia

(Des D. Banduni)

1995 (30 Aug). *Centenary of Bharti Bhawan Library, Allahabad.* P 14.
1632 **1279** 6 r. black, chestnut & bright rose-red 55   65

(Des S. Kumar. Litho Calcutta Security Printers Ltd, Kanpur)

1995 (4 Sept). *25th Anniv of Asian-Pacific Postal Training Centre, Bangkok.* P 13½×13.
1633 **1280** 10 r. multicoloured 80   90

1281 "75" and Taurus   1282 Louis Pasteur in
Formation Sign   Laboratory (from
                painting by Edelfelt)

1995 (26 Sept). *75th Anniv of Area Army Headquarters, Delhi.*
P 13×13½.
1634 **1281** 2 r. multicoloured 30   20

(Des S. Samantha)

1995 (28 Sept). *Death Centenary of Louis Pasteur (chemist).*
P 13×13½.
1635 **1282** 5 r. black and stone 60   70

1283 La Martiniere   1284 Gandhi in
College, Lucknow   South Africa

1995 (1 Oct). *150th Anniv of La Martiniere College, Lucknow.*
P 13½×13.
1636 **1283** 2 r. multicoloured 20   20

(Des A. Ainslie)

1995 (2 Oct). *India–South Africa Co-operation. 125th Birth Anniv of Mahatma Gandhi (1994).* T **1284** *and similar vert design.* P 13.
1637   1 r. scarlet 25   25
    a. Horiz pair. Nos. 1637/8 55   55
1638   2 r. scarlet 30   30
MS1639   68×80 mm. Nos. 1637/8 (*sold at 8 r.*) 55   65
    a. Printed double
Design:—2 r. Gandhi wearing dhoti.
Nos. 1637/8 were issued together, *se-tenant,* in horizontal pairs throughout the sheet.
Stamps in similar designs were issued by South Africa.

1285 Ears of Grain, "50"   1286 P. M. Thevar
and Emblem on Globe

(Des and litho Calcutta Security Printers Ltd, Kanpur)

1995 (16 Oct). *50th Anniv of Food and Agriculture Organization.* P 13½×13.
1640 **1285** 5 r. multicoloured 60   70

1995 (30 Oct). *Pasumpon Muthuramalingam Thevar (social reformer) Commemoration.* P 13.
1641 **1286** 1 r. deep rose-red 10   10

1287 W. C. Rontgen   1288 Children in
                    Circle

1995 (8 Nov). *150th Birth Anniv of W. C. Rontgen (discoverer of X-rays).* P 13×13½.
1642 **1287** 6 r. multicoloured 65   75

1995 (14 Nov). *Children's Day.* P 13×13½.
1643 **1288** 1 r. multicoloured 20   10

1289 Sitar   1290 Jat War Memorial,
              Bareilly

1995 (19 Nov). *Communal Harmony Campaign.* P 13.
1644 **1289** 2 r. multicoloured 30   20

1995 (20 Nov). *Bicentenary of Jat Regiments.* P 13.
1645 **1290** 5 r. multicoloured 65   75

1291 Men of Rajputana Rifles

1292 Sant Tukdoji Maharaj and Rural Meeting

1995 (28 Nov). *175th Anniv of 5th (Napier's) Battalion, Rajputana Rifles. P* 13½×13.
1646 **1291** 5 r. multicoloured 70 70

1995 (10 Dec). *Sant Tukdoji Maharaj Commemoration. P* 13½×13.
1647 **1292** 1 r. yellow-brown 10 10
Although dated "1993" No. 1647 was not issued until the date quoted above.

1293 Dr. Yellapragada Subbarow

1294 Pres. Giani Zail Singh

1995 (19 Dec). *Dr. Yellapragada Subbarow (pharmaceutical scientist) Commemoration. P* 13.
1648 **1293** 1 r. orange-brown 30 10

1995 (25 Dec). *First Death Anniv of Pres. Giani Zail Singh. P* 13.
1649 **1294** 1 r. multicoloured 10 10

1295 Dargah of Ala Hazrat Barelvi

1296 Tata Institute Building

(Litho Calcutta Security Printers Ltd, Kanpur)

1995 (31 Dec). *75th Death Anniv of Ala Hazrat Barelvi (Moslem scholar). P* 13×13½.
1650 **1295** 1 r. multicoloured 10 10
    a. "1995" omitted from bottom right (R. 2/2)

1996 (9 Feb). *50th Anniv of Tata Institute of Fundamental Research* (1995). *P* 13½×13.
1651 **1296** 2 r. multicoloured 20 20

1297 Kasturba Gandhi

1298 Sectioned Heart

(Des S. Samantha)

1996 (22 Feb). *50th Anniv of the Kasturba Trust. P* 13.
1652 **1297** 1 r. slate, brt green & bright scarlet 10 10

(Litho Calcutta Security Printers Ltd, Kanpur)

1996 (25 Feb). *100 Years of Cardiac Surgery. P* 13×13½.
1653 **1298** 5 r. multicoloured 60 70

NEW INFORMATION

The editor is always interested to correspond with people who have new information that will improve or correct the Catalogue.

1299 C. K. Nayudu

1300 "Vasant" (Spring) (Ragini Basanti)

1996 (13 Mar). *Cricketers. T* **1299** *and similar vert designs. Multicoloured. P* 14.
1654 2 r. Type **1299** 20 20
1655 2 r. Vinoo Mankad 20 20
1656 2 r. Deodhar 20 20
1657 2 r. Vijay Merchant 20 20
1654/7 .. .. Set of 4 70 70

(Litho Calcutta Security Printers Ltd, Kanpur)

1996 (13 Mar). *Miniature Paintings of the Seasons. T* **1300** *and similar vert designs. Multicoloured. P* 13½.
1658 5 r. Type **1300** 50 60
1659 5 r. "Greeshma" (Summer) (Jyestha) 50 60
1660 5 r. "Varsha" (Monsoon) (Rag Megh Malbar) 50 60
1661 5 r. "Hemant" (Winter) (Pausha) 50 60
1658/61 .. .. Set of 4 1·75 2·25

1301 Kunjilal Dubey

1302 Morarji Desai

1996 (18 Mar). *Kunjilal Dubey Commemoration. P* 13.
1662 **1301** 1 r. olive-sepia and chocolate 10 10

1996 (10 Apr). *Birth Centenary of Morarji Desai (former Prime Minister)* (1st issue). *P* 13×13½.
1663 **1302** 1 r. deep rose-red .. 20 20
See also Nos. 1702

1303 Blood Pheasant

1304 S.K.C.G. College Building

(Des R. Sukumar (Nos. 1663/4), V. Kumar (Nos. 1665/6). Litho Calcutta Security Printers Ltd, Kanpur)

1996 (10 May). *Himalayan Ecology. T* **1303** *and similar horiz designs. Multicoloured. P* 13½×13.
1664 5 r. Type **1303** 50 60
1665 5 r. Markhor (goat) 50 60
1666 5 r. *Meconopis horridula* (Tsher Gnoin) (plant) 50 60
1667 5 r. *Saussurea simpsoniana* (Sunflower) 50 60
1664/7 .. Set of 4 1·75 2·25
MS1668 175×105 mm. Nos. 1664/7 (*sold at 30 r.*) 2·10 2·10
No. **MS**1668 exists with either blue or white gum.

(Litho Calcutta Security Printers, Kanpur)

1996 (25 May). *Centenary of S.K.C.G. College, Gajapati. P* 13½×13.
1669 **1304** 1 r. brown and cream .. 10 10

1305 Muhammad Ismail Sahib

1306 Modern Stadium and Ancient Athens

1996 (5 June). *Birth Centenary of Muhammad Ismail Sahib (Moslem politician). P* 13×13½.
1670 **1305** 1 r. deep reddish purple .. 10 10

(Des S. Kumar. Litho Calcutta Security Printers Ltd, Kanpur)
1996 (25 June). *Olympic Games, Atlanta. T* **1306** *and similar vert designs. Multicoloured. P* 13×13½.
1671 5 r. Type **1306** 35 40
1672 5 r. Hand holding Olympic torch .. 35 40

1307 Sister Alphonsa

1308 "Communications"

(Des S. Samanta)

1996 (19 July). *50th Death Anniv of Sister Alphonsa. P* 13×13½.
1673 **1307** 1 r. black and dull blue .. 10 10

(Des S. Gujral)

1996 (2 Aug). *125th Anniv of Videsh Sanchar Nigam Limited (telecommunications company). P* 14.
1674 **1308** 5 r. multicoloured 35 40

1309 Sir Pherozeshah Mehta

1310 Ahilyabai

1996 (4 Aug). *150th Birth Anniv of Sir Pherozeshah Mehta (politician). P* 13.
1675 **1309** 1 r. deep slate-blue 10 10

(Des S. Samanta)

1996 (25 Aug). *Death Bicentenary* (1995) *of Ahilyabai (ruler of Holkar). P* 13×13½.
1676 **1310** 2 r. yellow-brown and purple-brown 15 15

1311 Chembai Vaidyanatha Bhagavathar

1312 Red Junglefowl Cockerel

(Des S. Samanta)

1996 (28 Aug). *Birth Centenary of Chembai Vaidanatha Bhagavathar (musician). P* 13×13½.
1677 **1311** 1 r. chestnut and deep turquoise-green 10 10

(Des R. Sukumar. Litho Calcutta Security Printers Ltd, Kanpur)

1996 (2 Sept). *20th World Poultry Congress, New Delhi. P* 13½×13.
1678 **1312** 5 r. multicoloured 35 40

1313 Rani Gaidinliu

1314 Nath Pai

1996 (12 Sept). *Rani Gaidinliu (Naga leader) Commem-oration. P* 13.
1679 **1313** 1 r. deep turquoise-blue 10 10

1996 (25 Sept). *25th Death Anniv of Nath Pai (politician). P* 13×13½.
1680 **1314** 1 r. dull blue 10 10

1315 Exhibition Logo   1316 Historic Steam Locomotives

(Des S. Samanta. Litho Calcutta Security Printers Ltd, Kanpur)
1996 (5 Oct). *"INDEPEX '97" International Stamp Exhibition, New Delhi (1st issue). P* 13×13½.
1681 **1315** 2 r. gold and brown-purple 15 15
See also Nos. 1713/16 and 1722/5.

(Des S. Samanta. Litho Calcutta Security Printers Ltd, Kanpur)
1996 (7 Oct). *25th Anniv of National Rail Museum. P* 13½.
1682 **1316** 5 r. multicoloured 35 40

1317 Jananayak Debeswar Sarmah   1318 Monument and Sikh Sentry

(Des S. Samanta. Litho Calcutta Security Printers Ltd, Kanpur)
1996 (10 Oct). *Birth Centenary of Jananayak Debeswar Sarmah (politician). P* 13×13½.
1683 **1317** 2 r. orange-brown and red-brown .. 15 15

1996 (19 Oct). *150th Anniv of Sikh Regiment. P* 13.
1684 **1318** 5 r. multicoloured 35 40

1319 Dr. Salim Ali   1320 "Indian Village" (child's painting)

1996 (12 Nov). *Birth Centenary of Salim Ali (ornithologist). T* 1319 *and similar square design. Multicoloured. P* 13.
1685 8 r. Type 1319 .. .. 50 60
 a. Horiz pair. Nos. 1685/6 .. 1·25 1·50
1686 **11** r. Storks at nest 75 90
Nos. 1685/6 were printed together, *se-tenant*, in horizontal pairs with the backgrounds forming a composite design.

1996 (14 Nov). *Children's Day. P* 13½×13.
1687 **1320** 8 r. multicoloured 50 55

1321 Seeds in a Test-tube   1322 Regimental Shrine

1996 (17 Nov). *2nd International Crop Science Congress, New Delhi. P* 13×13½.
1688 **1321** 2 r. multicoloured 15 15

1996 (4 Dec). *Bicentenary of 2nd Battalion, Grenadiers. P* 14.
1689 **1322** 5 r. multicoloured 35 40

1323 Woman writing   1324 Abai Konunbaev

(Des V. Mehra)
1996 (8 Dec). *10th Anniv of South Asian Association for Regional Co-operation (S.A.A.R.C.). P* 13.
1690 **1323** 11 r. multicoloured 65 70

1996 (9 Dec). *150th Birth Anniv of Abai Konunbaev (Kazakh poet) (1995). P* 13×13½.
1691 **1324** 5 r. chestnut, purple-brn & slate-lilac 35 40

1325 Buglers in front of Memorial

1996 (16 Dec). *25th Anniv of the Liberation of Bangladesh. P* 14.
1692 **1325** 2 r. multicoloured 15 15

1326 Vivekananda Rock Memorial

(Des S. Samanta. Litho Calcutta Security Printers Ltd, Kanpur)
1996 (26 Dec). *25th Anniv of Vivekananda Rock Memorial, Kanyakumari. P* 13½×13.
1693 **1326** 5 r. multicoloured 35 40
 It was originally intended to release No. 1693 on 12 January 1996, but the issue was postponed until 26 December. Examples are known used from Bangalore or Jodhpur on the original date

1327 Victorian Doctors performing Operation   1328 Roorkee University Buildings

(Des S. Samanta)
1996 (27 Dec). *150th Anniv of Anaesthetics. P* 13×13½.
1694 **1327** 5 r. multicoloured 35 40

(Des H. Sinvhal)
1997 (1 Jan). *150th Anniv of Roorkee University. P* 13.
1695 **1328** 8 r. multicoloured 50 55

STANLEY GIBBONS STAMP COLLECTING SERIES

Introductory booklets on *How to Start, How to Identify Stamps* and *Collecting by Theme.* A series of well illustrated guides at a low price.
Write for details.

1329 Dr. Vrindavanlal Verma   1330 Field Post Office

(Des S. Samiti)
1997 (9 Jan). *Dr. Vrindavanlal Verma (writer) Commem-oration. P* 13.
1696 **1329** 2 r. dull scarlet 15 15

(Des S. Samanta)
1997 (22 Jan). *25th Anniv of Army Postal Service Corps. P* 13½×13.
1697 **1330** 5 r. multicoloured 35 40

1331 Subhas Chandra Bose   1332 Jose Marti

1997 (23 Jan). *Birth Centenary of Subhas Chandra Bose (nationalist). P* 13.
1698 **1331** 1 r. reddish brown 10 10

1997 (28 Jan). *Jose Marti (Cuban writer) Commemoration. P* 13×13½.
1699 **1332** 11 r. black and flesh 65 70

1333 Conference Logo   1334 St. Andrew's Church

1996 (15 Feb). *"Towards Partnership between Men and Women in Politics" Inter-Parliamentary Conference, New Delhi. P* 13.
1700 **1333** 5 r. multicoloured 35 40

1997 (25 Feb). *St. Andrew's Church, Egmore, Madras Commemoration. P* 13×13½.
1701 **1334** 8 r. multicoloured 50 55

1335 Morarji Desai   1336 Shyam Lal Gupt

(Litho Calcutta Security Printers Ltd, Kanpur)
1997 (28 Feb). *Birth Centenary of Moraji Desai (former Prime Minister) (2nd issue). P* 13×13½.
1702 **1335** 1 r. brown and reddish brown .. 10 10

(Des P. Sansthan. Litho Calcutta Security Printers Ltd, Kanpur)
1997 (4 Mar). *Birth Centenary (1996) of Shyam Lal Gupt (social reformer). P* 13×13½.
1703 **1336** 1 r. cinnamon and lake-brown .. 10 10

1337 Saint
Dnyaneshwar

1338 Parijati Tree

1997 (5 Mar). *700th Death Anniv of Saint Dnyaneshwar (1996).* P 13×13¹/₂.
1704 1337 5 r. multicoloured 20 25

(Des R. Pasricha. Litho Calcutta Security Printers Ltd, Kanpur)

1997 (8 Mar). *Parijati Tree.* T 1338 *and similar vert design. Multicoloured.* P 13×13¹/₂.
1705 5 r. Type 1338 .. .. .. 20 25
    a. Horiz pair. Nos. 1705/6 .. .. 40 50
1706 5 r. Parijati flower 20 25
    Nos. 1705/6 were printed together, *se-tenant,* in horizontal pairs throughout the sheet.

1339 Monument, Rashtriya
Military College

1340 Ram Manohar
Lohia

(Litho Calcutta Security Printers Ltd, Kanpur)

1997 (13 Mar). *75th Anniv of Rashtriya Military College, Dehra Dun.* P 13¹/₂.
1707 1339 2 r. multicoloured 10 15

(Litho Calcutta Security Printers Ltd, Kanpur)

1997 (23 Mar). *Ram Manohar Lohia Commemoration.* P 13×13¹/₂.
1708 1340 1 r. multicoloured 10 10

1341 Society
Centenary
Emblem

1342 Gyandith
Award Winners

(Des J. Irani. Litho Calcutta Security Printers Ltd, Kanpur)

1997 (27 Mar). *Centenary of the Philatelic Society of India.* T 1341 *and similar vert design. Multicoloured.* P 13¹/₂.
1709 2 r. Type 1341 .. .. 10 15
    a. Horiz pair. Nos. 1709/10 .. 20 30
1710 2 r. Cover of first *Philatelic Journal of India, 1897* 10 15
    Nos. 1709/10 were printed together, *se-tenant,* in horizontal pairs throughout the sheet.

1997 (28 Mar). *Gyandith Award Scheme.* P 13.
1711 1342 2 r. multicoloured 10 10

1343 Madhu Limaye

1344 Nalanda Monastic
University

1997 (1 May). *Madhu Limaye Commemoration.* P 13×13¹/₂.
1712 1343 2 r. deep dull green 10 10

(Litho Calcutta Security Printers Ltd, Kanpur)

1997 (6 June). *"INDEPEX '97" International Stamp Exhibition, New Delhi (2nd issue). Buddhist Cultural Sites.* T 1344 *and similar horiz designs. Multicoloured.* P 13¹/₂×13.
1713 2 r. Type 1344 .. .. .. 10 10
    a. Block of 4. Nos. 1713/16 .. 1·10
1714 6 r. The Bodhi Tree, Bodhgaya .. 25 30
1715 10 r. Stupa and Pillar, Vaishali .. 40 45
1716 11 r. Stupa, Kushinagar 40 45
1713/16 .. .. .. Set of 4 1·10 1·25
    Nos. 1713/16 were printed together, *se-tenant,* in blocks of 4 throughout the sheet.

1345 Pandit
Omkarnath Thakur

1346 Ram Sewak
Yadav

(Des S. Samanta)

1997 (24 June). *Birth Centenary of Pandit Omkarnath Thakur (musician).* P 13×13¹/₂.
1717 1345 2 r. black and deep dull blue .. 10 10

(Litho Calcutta Security Printers Ltd, Kanpur)

1997 (2 July). *Ram Sewak Yadav (politician) Commemoration.* P 13×13¹/₂.
1718 1346 2 r. brown 10 10

1347 Sibnath
Banerjee

1348 Rukmini
Lakshmipathi

(Litho Calcutta Security Printers Ltd, Kanpur)

1997 (11 July). *Birth Centenary of Sibnath Banerjee (trade unionist).* P 13×13¹/₂.
1719 1347 2 r. brown-lake and purple .. 10 10

1997 (6 Aug). *Rukmini Lakshmipathi (social reformer) Commemoration.* P 13×13¹/₂.
1720 1348 2 r. reddish brown 10 10

1349 Sri Basaveswara

1350 Gopalpur-on-Sea
Beach

1997 (8 Aug). *Sri Basaveswara (reformer and statesman) Commemoration.* P 13×13¹/₂.
1721 1349 2 r. claret 10 10

1997 (11 Aug). *"INDEPEX '97" International Stamp Exhibition, New Delhi (3rd issue). Beaches.* T 1350 *and similar horiz designs. Multicoloured.* P 13¹/₂.
1722 2 r. Type 1350 .. .. .. 10 10
1723 6 r. Kovalam 25 30
1724 10 r. Anjuna 40 45
1725 11 r. Bogmalo 40 45
1722/5 .. .. .. Set of 4 1·10 1·25

1351 Newspaper Masthead

1352 Shah Nawaz Khan,
P. K. Sahgal and G. S.
Dhillon

1997 (15 Aug). *50th Anniv of Swatantra Bharat (Hindi daily newspaper).* P 13¹/₂×13.
1726 1351 2 r. multicoloured 10 10

1997 (15 Aug). *I.A.N. Trials Commemoration.* P 13¹/₂×13.
1727 1352 2 r. multicoloured 10 10

1353 Sir Ronald Ross
(bacteriologist)

1354 Firaq
Gorakhpuri

1997 (20 Aug). *Centenary of the Discovery of the Malaria Parasite by Sir Ronald Ross.* P 13×13¹/₂.
1728 1353 2 r. slate 10 10

1997 (28 Aug). *Birth Centenary (1996) of Firaq Gorakhpuri (poet).* P 13×13¹/₂.
1729 1354 2 r. light brown 10 10

1355 Bhaktivedanta
Swami

1997 (6 Sept). *Birth Centenary (1996) of Bhaktivedanta Swami (philosopher).* P 13×13¹/₂.
1730 1355 5 r. chestnut 20 25

— URCH HARRIS —

ALL WORLD
NEW ISSUE SERVICE

- Over thirty year's experience.
- 260 countries and 100 plus themes.
- Service tailored to your requirements.
- Regular distributions every 6 weeks.
- Free magazine with every distribution.
- Customer advice helpline.
- Free gifts and regular special offers.

Telephone 0117 9349333 for a Free Welcome Pack.

Urch Harris & Co
1 Denmark Avenue
Bristol BS1 5HD

A Division of Stanley Gibbons Ltd

Index to Indian Stamp Designs from 1947

The following index is intended to facilitate the identification of all Indian stamps from 1947 onwards. Portrait stamps are usually listed under surnames only, views under the name of the town or city and other issues under the main subject or a prominent word and date chosen from the inscription. Simple abbreviations have occasionally been resorted to and when the same design or subject appears on more than one stamp, only the first of each series is indicated.

STAMP BOOKLETS

1904. *Black on green (No. SB1) or black on pink (No. SB2) covers. Stapled.*

SB1   12¼ a. booklet containing twenty-four ½ a. (No. 121) in blocks of 6 .. .. £750

SB2   12¼ a. booklet containing twelve 1 a. (No. 123) in blocks of 6 .. .. £750

1906–11. *Black on green (No. SB3), black on pink (No. SB4) or black on green and pink (No. SB5) match book type covers inscr "Post Office of India" and royal cypher of King Edward VII. Stapled.*

SB3   1 r. booklet containing thirty-two ½ a. (No. 149) in blocks of 4 .. .. £425
    a. Without "Post Office of India" inscr .. £375
    b. Ditto and showing royal cypher of King George V (1911) £350

SB4   1 r. booklet containing sixteen 1 a. (No. 150) in blocks of 4 (1907) £375
    a. Without "Post Office of India" inscr .. £325
    b. Ditto and showing royal cypher of King George V (1911) £350

SB5   1 r. booklet containing sixteen ½ a. and eight 1 a. (Nos. 149/50) in blocks of 4 (1907) .. £850
    a. Without "Post Office of India" inscr .. £750
    b. Ditto and showing royal cypher of King George V (1911) £700

1912–22. *Black on green (Nos. SB6/7, SB12), black on pink (No. SB8), black on green and pink (No. SB9), black on purple (Nos. SB10) or black on blue (No. SB11) match book type covers with foreign postage rates on back. Stapled.*

SB 6   1 r. booklet containing sixty-four 3 p. (No. 152) in blocks of 4 (blank back cover) .. £450

SB 7   1 r. booklet containing thirty-two ½ a. (No. 155) in blocks of 4 .. .. .. £180
    a. Blank back cover £180
    b. Advertisement contractor's notice on back cover £275
    c. Advertisement on back (1922) .. £275

SB 8   1 r. booklet containing sixteen 1 a. (No. 159) in blocks of 4 .. .. .. £140
    a. Blank back cover £140
    b. Advertisements on front flap and back cover (1922) £180

SB 9   1 r. booklet containing sixteen ½ a. and eight 1 a. (Nos. 155, 159) in blocks of 4 (blank back cover) £130

SB10   1 r. 8 a. booklet containing sixteen 1½ a. (No. 163) in blocks of 4 (1919) £300
    a. Blank back cover (1921) £300

SB11   2 r. booklet containing sixteen 2 a. (No. 169) in blocks of 4 (blank back cover) (1921) .. £375
    a. Black on purple cover with postage rates on back (1922) £375

SB12   2 r. booklet containing sixteen 2 a. (No. 166) in blocks of 4 (1922) £375
    a. Black on purple cover £375

1921. *Black on buff match book type cover. Stapled.*

SB13   1 r. 2 a. booklet containing twenty-four 9 p. on 1 a. (No. 192) in blocks of 4 .. .. £100

1922. *Black on brown (No. SB14) or black on green and pink (No. SB15) match book type covers with foreign postage rates on back. Stapled.*

SB14   1 r. booklet containing sixteen 1 a. (No. 197) in blocks of 4 .. .. £200
    a. Advertisement on back £200
    b. Advertisements on front flap and back cover
    c. Black on lilac cover with blank back .. £200
    ca. Advertisements on front flap and back cover £275
    d. Black on pink cover with blank back .. £250

SB15   1 r. booklet containing sixteen ½ a. and eight 1 a. (Nos. 155, 197) in blocks of 4 (blank back cover) £400

1926–28. *Black on brown (No. SB16) or black on purple (No. SB17) match book type covers with foreign postage rates on back. Stapled.*

SB16   1 r. booklet containing sixteen 1 a. (No. 203) in blocks of 4 .. .. 80·00

SB17   2 r. booklet containing sixteen 2 a. (No. 205) in blocks of 4 .. .. £250
    a. Containing No. 206 (1928) £300

1929. *Black on brown (No. SB18) or black on purple (No. SB19) separate leaf covers. Stitched.*

SB18   1 r. booklet containing sixteen 1 a. (No. 203) in blocks of 4 (blank back cover) .. .. 80·00
    a. Advertisement contractor's notice on back cover .. .. 80·00
    b. Advertisements on front flap and back cover £100
    c. Advertisement on back cover £100

SB19   2 r. booklet containing sixteen 2 a. (No. 205) in blocks of 4 (foreign postage rates on back cover) £275
    a. Advertisement contractor's notice on back cover £275
    b. Containing No. 206 (foreign postage rates on back cover) £325
    ba. Advertisement contractor's notice on back cover £325

1932. *Black on brown cover. Stitched.*

SB20   1 r. 4 a. booklet containing sixteen 1¼ a. (No. 235) in blocks of 4 .. .. .. £250

1934. *Black on buff cover. Stitched.*

SB21   1 r. booklet containing sixteen 1 a. (No. 234) in blocks of 4 .. .. £140

1937. *Black on red cover. Stamps with wmk upright or inverted. Stitched.*

SB22   1 r. booklet containing sixteen 1 a. (No. 250) in blocks of 4 .. .. £140

1980 (Jan) *"India 80" International Stamp Exhibition. Green, orange and blue cover, 80×100 mm. showing stamps. Stapled.*

SB23   33 r. 60, booklet containing twelve 30 p., twelve 50 p., eight 1 r. and eight 2 r. (Nos. 914/15, 942/5, 955/8) in blocks of four .. .. 6·50

1989 (20 Jan). *"India-89" International Stamp Exhibition, New Delhi. Multicoloured cover, showing stamp No. 1248, boatman and Taj Mahal. Stapled.*

SB24   270 r. booklet containing four 50 p., sixteen 60 p., ten 1 r. 50, six 4 r., twenty 5 r. and sixteen 6 r. 50 in panes of four or six each with margins all round (Nos. 1248a, 1249a, 1264a, 1265a, 1266a, 1267a, 1333a, 1334a, 1341a, 1342a, 1358a, 1359a, 1360a, 1361a) 26·00

OFFICIAL STAMPS

Stamps overprinted "POSTAL SERVICE" or "I.P.N." were not used as postage stamps, and are therefore omitted.

Service.
(O 1)

(Optd by the Military Orphanage Press, Calcutta)

1866 (1 Aug)–**72.** *Optd with Type O 1. P 14. (a) No wmk.*

O 1	11	½ a. blue	—	£200
O 2		½ a. pale blue	£850	£100
		a. Optd inverted		
O 3		1 a. brown	—	£140
O 4		1 a. deep brown	—	£100
O 5		8 a. carmine	14·00	35·00

(b) Wmk Elephant's Head, T 13

O 6	11	½ a. blue	£180	22·00
O 7		½ a. pale blue	£180	12·00
		a. Opt inverted		
		b. No dot on "i" (No. 50 on pane)	—	£250
		c. No stop (No. 77 on pane)	—	£200
O 8	12	8 p. purple (1.72)	18·00	42·00
		a. No dot on "i"	£225	
		b. No stop	£225	
O 9	11	1 a. brown	£180	15·00
O10		1 a. deep brown	£180	38·00
		a. No dot on "i"	—	£425
		b. No stop	—	£350
O11		2 a. orange	£170	75·00
O12		2 a. yellow	£170	75·00
		a. Opt inverted		
		b. Imperf		
O13		4 a. green	£160	70·00
		a. Opt inverted		
O14	17	4 a. green (Die I)	£950	£250

A variety with wide and more open capital "S" occurs six times in sheets of all values except No. O8. Price four times the normal.

Reprints exist of Nos. O6, O9 and O14; the latter is Die II instead of Die I.

Reprints of the overprint have also been made, in different setting, on the 8 pies, purple, no watermark.

O 2

O 6

O 3   O 4

(No. O15 surch at Calcutta, others optd at Madras)

1866 (Oct). *Fiscal stamps, Nos. O15/18 with top and bottom inscrs removed, surch or optd. Wmk Crown over "INDIA".*

(a) Surch as in Type O 2. Thick blue glazed paper. Imperf × perf 14

O15	O 2	2 a. purple	£275	£225

(b) Optd "SERVICE POSTAGE" in two lines as in Types O 3/4 and similar type. Imperf × perf 14

O16	O 3	2 a. purple (G.)	£800	£400
O17	O 4	4 a. purple (G.)	£3000	£1100
O18	—	8 a. purple (G.)	£3750	£3250
		a. Optd on complete stamp (inscr "FOREIGN BILL")	† £9000	

(c) Optd "SERVICE POSTAGE" in semi-circle. Wmk Large Crown. P 15½ × 15

O19	O 6	½ a. mauve/lilac (G.)	£350	80·00
		a. Opt double	£2250	

So-called reprints of Nos. O15 to O18 are known, but in these the surcharge differs entirely in the spacing, etc., of the words; they are more properly described as Government imitations. The imitations of No. O15 have surcharge in *black* or in *green*. No. O19 exists with reprinted overprint which has a full stop after "POSTAGE".

PRINTERS. The following stamps up to No. O108 were overprinted by De La Rue and thereafter Official stamps were printed or overprinted by the Security Printing Press at Nasik.

On	On
Service. **H. S.**	**H. S.**
M.	**M.**
(O 7) (O 8)	(O 9)

867–73. Optd with Type O 7. Wmk Elephant's Head. T 13. P 14.

O20	11	½a. blue (Die I)	23·00	40
O21		½a. pale blue (Die I)	29·00	1·75
O22		½a. blue (Die II) (1873)	£140	55·00
O23		1a. brown	28·00	45
O24		1a. deep brown	30·00	1·75
O25		1a. chocolate	38·00	1·75
O26		2a. yellow	13·00	2·50
O27		2a. orange	4·75	2·25
O28	17	4a. pale green (Die I)	12·00	2·00
O29		4a. green (Die I)	3·00	1·50
O30	11	8a. rose (Die II) (1868)	3·25	1·50
O30a		8a. pale rose (Die II)	3·25	1·50

Prepared for use, but not issued

O30b	18	6a. 8p. slate	£250

1874–82. Optd with Type O 8. (a) In black.

O31	11	½a. blue (Die II)	6·00	20
O32		1a. brown	9·50	20
O33		2a. yellow	42·00	17·00
O33a		2a. orange	30·00	9·50
O34	17	4a. green (Die I)	9·50	2·75
O35	11	8a. rose (Die II)	4·25	3·25

(b) Optd in blue-black

O36	11	½a. blue (Die II) (1879)	£300	35·00
O37		1a. brown (1882)	£500	£110

1883–99. Wmk Star, T 34. P 14. Optd with Type O 9.

O37a	40	3p. aniline carmine (1899)	20	10
O38	23	½a. deep blue-green	70	10
		a. Opt double..	†	£1100
O39		½a. blue-green	50	10
O40	25	1a. brown-purple	1·50	20
		a. Opt inverted	†£350	£450
		b. Opt double..	†	£1100
		c. Opt omitted (in horiz pair with normal)		£1200
O41		1a. plum	30	10
O42	27	2a. pale blue	3·75	60
O43		2a. blue	4·75	60
O44	29	4a. olive-green	9·50	35
O44a		4a. slate-green	9·50	35
O45	31	8a. dull mauve	13·00	1·00
O46		8a. magenta	7·00	50
O47	37	1r. green and rose (1892)	38·00	3·50
O48		1r. green and carmine (1892)	7·50	40
O37a/48		Set of 7	26·00	1·75

1900. Colours changed. Optd with Type O 9.

O49	23	½a. pale yellow-green	1·75	70
O49a		½a. yellow-green	2·25	50
		ab. Opt double		£900
O50	25	1a. carmine	2·25	10
		a. Opt inverted	†	£1100
		b. Opt double	†	£1200
O51	27	2a. pale violet	26·00	80
O52		2a. mauve	27·00	50
O49/52		Set of 3	27·00	1·00

1902–9. Stamps of King Edward VII optd with Type O 9.

O54	41	3p. grey (1903)	1·50	30
O55		3p. slate-grey (1905)	1·50	40
		a. No stop after 'M'	£120	80·00
O56	42	½a. green	1·25	30
O57	43	1a. carmine	90	10
O58	44	2a. violet	4·25	20
O59		2a. mauve	2·75	10
O60	47	4a. olive	6·00	30
O61		4a. pale olive	5·50	30
O62	48	6a. olive-bistre (1909)	1·50	15
O63	49	8a. purple (*shades*)	6·00	85
O64		8a. claret	8·00	75
O65	51	1r. green and carmine (1905)	4·00	70
O54/65		Set of 8	21·00	2·50

1906. New types. Optd with Type O 9.

O66	53	½a. green	50	10
		a. No stop after 'M'	75·00	45·00
O67	54	1a. carmine	1·25	10
		a. No stop after 'M'	£120	75·00

On

H.   S.

M.

(O 9a)

1909. Optd with Type O 9a.

O68	52	2r. carmine and yellow-brown..	8·00	85
O68a		2r. rose-red and yellow-brown..	8·00	95
O69		5r. ultramarine and violet	14·00	1·50
O70		10r. green and carmine	23·00	9·00
O70a		10r. green and scarlet	60·00	7·00
O71		15r. blue and olive-brown	60·00	32·00
O72		25r. brownish orange and blue	£140	60·00
O68/72		Set of 5	£225	90·00

NINE

SERVICE   SERVICE   PIES
(O 10)(14 mm)   (O 11) (21½ mm)   (O 12)

1912–13. Stamps of King George V (wmk Single Star, T 34) optd with Type O 10 or O 11 (rupee values).

O73	55	3p. grey..	20	10
O74		3p. slate-grey	20	10
O75		3p. blue-slate	2·25	10
		a. Opt omitted (in pair with normal)		

O76	56	½a. yellow-green	20	10
		a. Overprint double		£100
O77		½a. pale blue-green	30	10
O80	57	1a. rose-carmine	1·00	10
O81		1a. carmine	1·25	10
O82		1a. aniline carmine	1·25	10
		a. Overprint double	†	£850
O83	59	2a. mauve	55	10
O84		2a. purple	75	10
O85	63	4a. deep olive	1·00	10
O86		4a. olive-green	1·00	10
O87	64	6a. yellow-bistre	1·50	2·00
O88		6a. deep bistre-brown	3·25	3·50
O89	65	8a. purple	2·25	50
O89a		8a. mauve	2·25	50
O90		8a. bright aniline mauve	25·00	2·25
O91	67	1r. red-brown and blue-green (1913)	2·50	85
O92		2r. rose-carmine and brown (1913)	3·25	3·50
O93		5r. ultramarine and violet (1913)	12·00	15·00
O94		10r. green and scarlet (1913)	38·00	38·00
O95		15r. blue and olive (1913)	90·00	£100
O96		25r. orange and blue (1913)	£200	£160
O73/96		Set of 13	£300	£275

1921. No. O80 surch with Type O 12.

O97	57	9p. on 1a. rose-carmine	75	65

1922. No. 197 optd with Type O 10.

O98	57	1a. chocolate	75	10

ONE
RUPEE

ONE RUPEE

(O 13)   (O 14)

1925. Official stamps surcharged.

(a) Issue of 1909, as Type O 13

O99	52	1r. on 15r. blue and olive	4·25	3·00
O100		1r. on 25r chestnut and blue	20·00	60·00
O101		2r. on 10r green and scarlet	3·75	3·25
O101a		2r. on 10r. green and carmine..	£200	48·00

(b) Issue of 1912, with Type O 14

O102	67	1r. on 15r. blue and olive	19·00	70·00
O103		1r. on 25r. orange and blue	5·50	8·50
		a. Surch inverted		£500

(c) Issue of 1912, as Type O 13

O104	67	2r. on 10r. green and scarlet	£750

Examples of the above showing other surcharge errors are believed to be of clandestine origin.

SERVICE

ONE ANNA   ONE ANNA

(O 15)   (O 16)

1926. No. O62 surch with Type O 15.

O105	48	1a. on 6a. olive-bistre	30	30

1926. Postage stamps of 1911–22 (wmk Single Star), surch as Type O 16.

O106	58	1a. on 1½a. chocolate (A)	20	10
O107		1a. on 1½a. chocolate (B)	1·25	3·50
		a. Error. On 1a. chocolate (197)		£160
O108	61	1a. on 2a. 6p. ultramarine	60	1·00

The surcharge on No. O108 has no bars at top.
Examples of Nos. O106/7 with inverted or double surcharges are believed to be of clandestine origin.

SERVICE   SERVICE
(O 17)(13½ mm)   (O 18) (19½ mm)

1926–31. Stamps of King George V (wmk Multiple Star, T 69) optd with Types O 17 or O 18 (rupee values).

O109	55	3p. slate (1.10.29)	15	10
		w. Wmk inverted	75	40
O110	56	½a. green (1931)	4·00	20
		w. Wmk inverted	—	1·00
O111	57	1a. chocolate	15	10
		w. Wmk inverted	1·00	40
O112	70	2a. purple	20	10
		w. Wmk inverted	50	30
O113	71	4a. sage-green	30	10
		w. Wmk inverted	1·50	50
O115	65	8a. reddish purple	60	10
		w. Wmk inverted	60	30
O116	66	12a. claret (1927)	60	1·25
		w. Wmk inverted	—	2·50
O117	67	1r. chocolate and green (1930)	1·75	1·00
		w. Wmk inverted	1·75	1·25
O118		2r. carmine and orange (1930)	6·50	6·50
O120		10r. green and scarlet (1931)	70·00	48·00
O109/20		Set of 10	75·00	50·00

1930. As No. O111, but optd as Type O 10 (14 mm).

O125	57	1a. chocolate	—	4·00
		w. Wmk inverted	85·00	5·00

1932–36. Stamps of King George V (wmk Mult Star, T 69) optd with Type O 17.

O126	79	½a. green (1935)	60	10
O127	80	9p. deep green	20	10
O127a	81	1a. chocolate (1936)	2·25	10
		aw. Wmk inverted	2·75	40
O128	82	1a. 3p. mauve	30	10
		w. Wmk inverted	40	40
O129	70	2a. vermilion	1·00	1·75
O130	59	2a. vermilion (1935)	1·25	1·25
O130a		2a. vermilion (*small die*) (1936)	1·00	10
O131	61	2a. 6p. orange (22.4.32)	30	10
		w. Wmk inverted	1·25	50
O132	63	4a. sage-green (1935)	1·00	10
O133	64	6a. bistre (1936)	20·00	9·50
O126/33		Set of 9	24·00	10·00

1937–39. Stamps of King George VI optd as Types O 17 or O 18 (rupee values).

O135	91	½a. red-brown (1938)	16·00	15
O136		9p. green (1937)	16·00	20
O137		1a. carmine (1937)	2·25	10
O138	93	1r. grey and red-brown (5.38)	50	50
O139		2r. purple and brown (5.38)	1·50	2·50
O140		5r. green and blue (10.38)	2·50	4·75
O141		10r. purple and claret (1939)	4·00	4·75
O135/41		Set of 7	48·00	11·50

SERVICE 1A / SERVICE
(O 19)   O 20

1939 (May). Stamp of King George V, surch with Type O 19.

O142	82	1a. on 1¼a. mauve	9·50	20

(Des T. I. Archer)

1939 (1 June)–42. Typo. W 69. P 14.

O143	O 20	3p. slate	40	10
O144		½a. red-brown	3·50	10
O144a		½a. purple (1942)	30	10
O145		9p. green	30	10
O146		1a. carmine	30	10
O146a		1a. 3p. yellow-brown (1941)	3·00	70
O146b		1½a. dull violet (1942)	65	10
O147		2a. vermilion	60	10
O148		2½a. bright violet	60	40
O149		4a. brown	60	10
O150		8a. slate-violet	90	30
O143/50		Set of 11	10·00	1·50

1948 (15 Aug). First Anniv of Independence. Nos. 305/8 optd as Type O 17.

O150a	305	1½a. brown	42·00	30·00
O150b		3½a. violet	£750	£450
O150c		12a. grey-green	£2000	£1600
O150d	306	10r. purple-brown and lake	£10000	

Nos. O150a/d were only issued to the Governor-General's Secretariat.

O 21   Asokan Capital   O 22

(Des T. I. Archer)

1950 (2 Jan)–51. Typo (O 21) or litho (O 22). W 69. P 14.

O151	O 21	3p. slate-violet (1.7.50)	10	10
O152		6p. purple-brown (1.7.50)	10	10
O153		9p. green (1.7.50)	30	10
O154		1a. turquoise (1.7.50)	70	10
O155		2a. carmine (1.7.50)	1·00	10
		w. Wmk inverted		
O156		3a. red-orange (1.7.50)	3·00	1·75
O157		4a. lake (1.7.50)	5·00	20
O158		4a. ultramarine (1.10.51)	50	10
O159		6a. bright violet (1.7.50)	3·00	40
O160		8a. red-brown (1.7.50)	1·50	10
		w. Wmk inverted	8·00	
O161	O 22	1r. violet	2·75	10
		w. Wmk inverted		
O162		2r. rose-carmine	1·00	60
O163		5r. bluish green	2·00	1·50
O164		10r. reddish brown	3·00	16·00
O151/64		Set of 14	21·00	19·00

1957 (1 Apr)–58. Values in naye paise. Typo (t) or litho (l). W 69. P 14.

O165	O 21	1 n.p. slate (*l*)	30	10
		a. Slate-black (*l*)	30	10
		b. Greenish slate (*t*)	10	10
		w. Wmk inverted	3·50	1·25
O166		2 n.p. blackish violet (*t*)	10	10
		w. Wmk inverted		
O167		3 n.p. chocolate (*t*)	10	10
O168		5 n.p. green (*l*)	10	10
		a. Deep emerald (*t*)	30	10

O169	O 21	6 n.p. turquoise-blue (t)	10	10
O170		13 n.p. scarlet (t)	10	10
O171		15 n.p. reddish violet (l) (6.58)	1·50	1·40
		a. *Reddish violet* (t)	90	1·40
O172		20 n.p. red (l)	15	40
		a. *Vermilion* (t)	50	10
		aw. Wmk inverted		
O173		25 n.p. violet-blue (l)	20	10
		a. *Ultramarine* (t)	1·75	10
O174		50 n.p. red-brown (l)	30	10
		a. *Reddish brown* (t)	1·50	80
O165/74		.. .. *Set of* 10	1·90	1·75

1958–71. As Nos. O165/74a and O161/4 but W 374 (upright). Litho (l) or typo (t). P 14.

O175	O 21	1 n.p. slate-black (t) (1.59)	10	10
O176		2 n.p. blackish violet (t) (1.59)	10	10
O177		3 n.p. chocolate (t) (11.58)	10	10
		w. Wmk inverted	3·50	
O178		5 n.p. deep emerald (t) (11.58)	10	10
O179		6 n.p. turquoise-blue (t) (5.59)	10	10
O180		10 n.p. deep grey-green (l) (1963)	1·00	1·00
		a. *Deep grey-green* (t) (1966?)	2·50	2·50
O181		13 n.p. scarlet (t) (1963)	45	2·50
O182		15 n.p. deep violet (t) (11.58)	10	10
		a. *Light reddish violet* (t) (1961)	1·75	10
O183		20 n.p. vermilion (t) (5.59)	10	10
		a. *Red* (t) (1966?)	3·50	80
O184		25 n.p. ultramarine (t) (7.59)	10	10
O185		50 n.p. reddish brown (t) (6.59)	15	10
		a. *Chestnut* (l) (1966?)	3·50	1·25
O186	O 22	1 r. reddish violet (l) (2.59)	15	10
O187		2 r. rose-carmine (l) (1960)	25	10
		a. Wmk sideways.* *Pale rose-carmine* (l) (1969?)	45	75
O188		5 r. slate-green (l) (7.59)	50	60
		a. Wmk sideways*. *Deep grey-green* (l) (1969?)	80	90
O189		10 r. brown-lake (l) (7.59)	1·25	80
		a. Wmk sideways* (l) (1971)	2·75	3·00
		ab. Printed on the gummed side	38·00	
		aw. Wmk capitals to right	2·75	
O175/89		.. .. *Set of* 15	3·75	4·75

*The normal sideways watermark shows the head of the capitals pointing left, *as seen from the back of the stamp.*

शरणार्थी
सहायता
**REFUGEE
RELIEF**

O 23 (see also   (O 24)   O 25
Type O 26)

1967 (20 Mar)–73? Photo. W 374 (sideways). P 15×14.

O190	O 23	2 p. violet (1973?)	60	70
O191		5 p. green (1973?)	60	10
O192		10 p. myrtle-green (2.7.73)	1·00	15
O193		15 p. plum (2.7.73)	1·75	40
O194		20 p. red (2.7.73)	6·00	5·50
O195		30 p. ultramarine (1973)	3·50	90
O196		50 p. chestnut (2.7.73)	3·25	2·75
O197		1 r. dull purple (20.3.67)	40	10
		a. *Deep slate-purple* (1969)	90	10
O190/7		.. *Set of* 8	15·00	9·50

1967 (15 Nov)–74(?). Wmk Large Star and "INDIA GOVT" in sheet*. Photo. P 15 × 14. No gum.

O200	O 23	2 p. violet	10	80
O201		3 p. chocolate	10	90
O202		5 p. green	10	10
		a. *Yellowish green* (1969)	10	10
		w. Wmk reversed	4·00	
O203		6 p. turquoise-blue	65	85
O204		10 p. myrtle-green	10	30
		a. *Bronze-green* (1969)	90	90
		w. Wmk reversed	4·00	
O205		15 p. plum	10	30
		w. Wmk reversed		
O206		20 p. red	10	30
		w. Wmk reversed	4·00	
O207		25 p. carmine-red (1974?)	7·50	3·75
		w. Wmk reversed	8·00	
O208		30 p. ultramarine	10	50
O209		50 p. chestnut	10	10
		w. Wmk reversed	4·50	
O200/9		.. *Set of* 10	8·00	7·50

*The arrangement of this watermark in the sheet results in the words and the star appearing upright, inverted or sideways.

1971. Obligatory Tax. Refugee Relief.

(a) Provisional issue. No. O202 optd with Type O 24.

O210	O 23	5 p. yellowish green (15.11)	30	30
		a. *Green*	30	30
		w. Wmk reversed	6·00	

(b) Issue for Bangalore. No. O202 optd with T 602

O211	O 23	5 p. yellowish green	1·25	40
		a. Opt inverted	3·25	
		w. Wmk reversed	8·00	

(c) Issue for Goa. No. O202 optd with T 606

O212	O 23	5 p. yellowish green	3·25	90
		w. Wmk reversed	15·00	

(d) Definitive issue. Wmk Large Star and "INDIA GOVT" in sheet*. Litho. P 15×14. No gum.

O213	O 25	5 p. yellowish green (1.12)	15	15
		a. *Yellow-green*	15	15
		w. Wmk reversed	6·00	

*See note below No. O209.

The surcharge on mail for the relief of refugees from the former East Pakistan referred to in the note after No. 651 also applied to official mail. The cost of the stamps used by each Government Department was charged against its budget and the additional charge for refugee stamps meant that each Department had to spend less to keep within its budget.

O 26   O 27   O 28

1976 (1 Apr)–80. Redrawn, showing face-value in figures only and smaller Capital with Hindi motto beneath. P 14 (2, 5, 10 r.) or 15×14 (others). (a) Wmk Large Star and "INDIA GOVT" in sheet.* No gum.

O214	O 26	2 p. deep violet-blue	20	85
O215		5 p. yellowish green	10	30
O216		10 p. myrtle-green	15	70
		a. *Deep dull green* (1978)	10	70
O217		15 p. deep purple	10	30
O218		20 p. Indian red	15	70
O219		25 p. rose-carmine	55	1·25
		a. *Bright crimson* (1978)	90	1·25
O220		30 p. chalky blue (1.5.79)	2·00	2·00
O221		35 p. violet (6.12.80)	45	10
O222		50 p. chestnut	2·25	1·25
O223		1 r. deep brownish purple (13.8.80)	3·50	75

(b) W 374 (sideways)†

O224	O 26	1 r. deep brownish purple	85	95
O225	–	2 r. rose-red (date?)	2·75	2·75
		aw. Wmk capitals to right	3·00	
		b. Wmk upright	40	1·50
		bw. Wmk inverted	2·00	
O226	–	5 r. deep green (date?)	3·25	3·75
		aw. Wmk capitals to right	3·50	
		b. Wmk upright (1978)	60	2·25
		bw. Wmk inverted	3·50	
O227	–	10 r. brown-lake (date?)	1·25	3·50
		a. Wmk upright	3·25	4·50
		aw. Wmk inverted	3·50	
O214/27		.. *Set of* 14	11·00	14·50

The 2, 5 and 10 r. are larger, size as Type O 22.
*See note below No. 720. The 2 p. value is only known on the first type of watermark, the 35, 50 p. and 1 r. values on the second and the remaining values on both.
†The normal sideways watermark shows the top of the capitals pointing left, *as seen from the back of the stamp.*

1981 (14 Feb). Redrawn showing revised border design and inscriptions, with face value figures now in bottom corners. Litho. Wmk Large Star and "INDIA GOVT" in sheet. P 15×14.

O228	O 27	2 r. rose-red	1·00	50
O229		5 r. deep green	1·25	75
O230		10 r. brown-lake	2·00	1·50
O228/30		.. .. *Set of* 3	3·75	2·50

1981 (10 Dec). As Nos. O215/19, O221/3 and O228/30 but printed on cream paper with simulated perforations as Type O 28. Unwatermarked. Imperf.

O231	O 28	5 p. dull yellowish green	50	60
O232		10 p. deep green	55	65
O233		15 p. deep reddish violet	55	65
O234		20 p. dull vermilion	60	70
O235		25 p. bright rose	1·25	1·50
O236		35 p. violet	70	45
O237		50 p. orange-brown	1·25	1·00
O238		1 r. deep dull purple	1·50	1·00
O239		2 r. orange-vermilion	1·75	3·50
O240		5 r. deep dull green	2·00	4·25
O241		10 r. lake-brown	2·50	6·00
O231/41		.. *Set of* 11	12·00	18·00

Some values have been unofficially pin-perforated.

1982 (22 Nov). As Nos. 215/23 and 228/30. Photo. Wmk Large Star and "INDIA GOVT" in sheet. P 12½×13.

O242	O 26	5 p. light green	30	50
O243		10 p. deep dull green	35	70
O244		15 p. blackish purple	35	70
O245		20 p. Indian red	40	70
O246		25 p. cerise	50	1·00
O247		30 p. deep ultramarine	50	1·00
O248		35 p. bluish violet	50	40
O249		50 p. reddish brown	75	1·00
O250		1 r. deep purple-brown	80	1·00
O251	O 27	2 r. rose-red	1·10	2·00
		a. *Vermilion* (litho)	1·00	2·00
O252		5 r. grey-green	1·50	3·50
O253		10 r. chocolate	2·25	5·00
O242/53		.. *Set of* 12	8·25	15·00

1984 (16 Apr)–88. As Nos. O215/23, O228/30 and new values. Litho (40 p.) or photo (others). W 374 (sideways*). P 13.

O254	O 26	5 p. yellowish green	10	10
		aw. Wmk capitals to right	10	10
		b. Wmk upright	10	10
O255		10 p. deep dull green	10	10
		a. Wmk upright	10	10
O256		15 p. blackish purple	10	10
		a. Wmk upright	10	10
O257		20 p. Indian red	10	10
		a. Wmk upright	10	10
O258		25 p. rose-carmine (1986)	10	10
O259		30 p. deep ultramarine	10	10
O260		35 p. bluish violet	10	10
		aw. Wmk capitals to left	10	10
		b. Wmk upright	10	10
O261		40 p. bright violet (15.10.88)	10	10
		a. Wmk upright	10	10
		w. Wmk inverted	10	10
O262		50 p. reddish brown	10	10
		aw. Wmk capitals to right	10	10
		b. Wmk upright	10	10
O263		60 p. deep brown (15.4.88)	10	10
		a. Wmk upright	10	10
O264	O 26	1 r. deep purple-brown	10	10
		aw. Wmk capitals to right	10	10
		b. Wmk upright	10	10
O265	O 27	2 r. rose-red	10	10
		a. Wmk upright	10	10
O266		5 r. grey-green	20	25
		a. Wmk upright	20	25
O267		10 r. chocolate	40	45
		w. Wmk capitals to right		
O254/67		.. *Set of* 14	1·25	1·40

*The normal sideways watermark shows the top of the capitals pointing right on the 35 p. and to left on the other values, *all as seen from the back of the stamp.*

INDIA USED ABROAD

In the years following 1858 the influence of the Indian Empire, political, military and economic, extended beyond its borders into neighbouring states, the Arabian Gulf, East Africa and the Far East. Such influence often led to the establishment of Indian civil post offices in the countries concerned where unoverprinted stamps of India were used.

Such offices operated in the following countries. An * indicates that details will be found under that heading elsewhere in the catalogue.

ADEN (SOUTH ARABIAN FEDERATION)*

Unoverprinted stamps of India used from 1854 until 1937.

BAHRAIN*

Unoverprinted stamps of India used from 1884 until 1933.

BRITISH EAST AFRICA (KENYA, UGANDA AND TANGANYIKA)*

Unoverprinted stamps of India used during August and September 1890.

FRENCH INDIAN SETTLEMENTS

The first Indian post office, at Chandernagore, was open by 1784 to be followed by offices in the other four Settlements. By an agreement with the French, dating from 1814, these offices handled mail destined for British India, Great Britain, the British Empire and most other foreign destinations except France and the French colonies. In later years the system was expanded by a number of sub-offices and it continued to operate until the French territories were absorbed into India on 2 May 1950 (Chandernagore) or 1 November 1954.

Chandernagore. Open by 1784. Used numeral cancellations "B86" or "86".
  Sub-offices:
    Gondalpara (opened 1906)
    Lakhiganj (opened 1909)
    Temata (opened 1909)
Karikal. Open by 1794. Used numeral cancellations "C147", "147" or "6/M–21".
  Sub-offices:
    Ambagarattur (opened 1904)
    Kottuchari (opened 1901)
    Nedungaon (opened 1903)
    Puraiyar Road (opened 1901)
    Settur (opened 1905)
    Tirumalrayapatnam (opened 1875 – used numeral cancellation "6/M–21/1")
    Tiramilur (opened 1898)
Mahe. Open by 1795. Used numeral cancellations "C192" or "9/M–14".
Pondicherry. Opened 1787. Used numeral cancellations "C111", "111" (also used elsewhere), "6/M-19" (also used elsewhere) or "6/M-20".
  Sub-offices:
    Ariyankuppam (opened 1904)
    Bahoor (opened 1885)
    Mudaliarpet (opened 1897)
    Muthialpet (opened 1885)
    Pondicherry Bazaar (opened 1902)
    Pondicherry Railway Station (opened 1895)
    Olugarai (opened 1907)
    Vallinur (opened 1875) – used numeral cancellation "M-19/1"
Yanam. Opened 1876. Used numeral cancellation "5/M-4".

IRAN

The British East India Company was active in the Arabian Gulf from the early years of the 17th century with their first factory (trading centre) being established at Jask in 1619. After 1853 this commercial presence was converted into a political arm of the Indian Government culminating in the appointment of a Political Resident to Bushire in 1862.

The first Indian post office in Iran (Persia) opened at Bushire on 1 May 1864 with monthly mail services operating to the Resident there and to the British Legation at Tehran. Further offices in the other Gulf ports followed, but, unless otherwise stated below, all were closed on 1 April 1923.

Abadan. Opened during First World War.
Ahwaz. Opened March 1915.
Bandar Abbas. Opened 1 April 1867. Used numeral cancellations "22" or "1/K-5".
Bushire. Opened 1 May 1864. Used numeral cancellations "308", "26" (also used elsewhere) or "K-5".
Chabbar. Opened 20 August 1913.
Duzdab. Opened 1922. Closed 1927?
Henjam. Opened 21 June 1913
Jask. Opened 1 September 1880
Kuh-Malik-Siah-Ziarat. Opened January 1906. Closed 1924
Linga. Opened 1 April 1867. Used numeral cancellations "21" or "2/K-5".
Maidan-i-Naphtun. Opened during First World War. Closed 1920.
Mirjawa. Opened January 1921. Closed 1930.
Mohammera. Opened 19 July 1892.

IRAQ*

Unoverprinted stamps of India used from 1868 until 1918.

KUWAIT*

Unoverprinted stamps of India used from 1904 until 1923.

MALAYSIA (STRAITS SETTLEMENTS)*

Unoverprinted stamps of India used from 1854 until 1867.

MUSCAT*

Unoverprinted stamps of India used from 1864 until 1947.

NEPAL

A post office was opened in the British Residency at Kathmandu in 1816 following the end of the Gurkha War. Stamps of India were used from 1854, initially with "B137", "137" or "C-37" numeral cancellations. The Residency Post Office continued to provide the overseas mail service after Nepal introduced its own issues in 1881.

In 1920 the Residency Post Office became the British Legation Post Office. On the independence of India in 1947 the service was transferred to the Indian Embassy and continued to function until 1965.

PORTUGUESE INDIA

A British post office was open in Damaun by 1823 and Indian stamps were used there until November 1883, some with "13" and "3/B-19" numeral cancellations.

No other British post offices were opened in the Portuguese territories, but from 1854 Indian stamps were sold by the local post offices. Between 1871 and 1877 mail intended for, or passing through, British India required combined franking of India and Portuguese India issues. After 1877 the two postal administrations accepted the validity of each other's stamps.

SOMALILAND PROTECTORATE*

Unoverprinted stamps of India used from 1887 until 1903.

TIBET

The first Indian post office in Tibet accompanied the Tibetan Frontier Commission in 1903. The Younghusband Military Expedition to Lhasa in the following year operated a number of Field Post Offices which were replaced by civil post offices at Gartok (opened 23 September 1906), Gyantse (opened March 1905), Pharijong (opened 1905) and Yatung (opened 1905). All Indian post offices in Tibet closed on 1 April 1955 except Gartok which, it is believed, did not operate after 1943.

TRUCIAL STATES (DUBAI)*

Unoverprinted stamps of India used from 1909 until 1947.

ZANZIBAR (TANZANIA)*

Unoverprinted stamps of India used from 1875 until 1895.

CHINA EXPEDITIONARY FORCE

Following the outbreak of the Boxer Rising in North China the Peking Legations were besieged by the rebels in June 1900. An international force, including an Indian Army division, was assembled for their relief. The Legations were relieved on 14 August 1900, but operations against the Boxers continued in North China with Allied garrisons at key cities and along the Peking–Tientsin–Shanhaikwan railway. The last Indian Army battalion, and accompanying Field Post Offices, did not leave North China until 1 November 1923.

Field Post Offices accompanied the Indian troops and commenced operations on 23 July 1900 using unoverprinted Indian postage and official stamps. The unoverprinted postage issues were replaced in mid-August by stamps overprinted "C.E.F." to prevent currency speculation. The use of unoverprinted official stamps continued as they were not valid for public postage.

PRICES FOR STAMPS ON COVER	
Nos. C1/10	*from* × 15
No. C10a	†
Nos. C11/22	*from* × 8
Nos. C23/34	*from* × 20

C. E. F.
(C 1)

Stamps of India overprinted with Type C 1, in black

1900 (16 Aug). *Stamps of Queen Victoria.*

C 1	40	3 p. carmine	..	40	1·25
		a. No stop after "C" (R. 1/2)			
		b. No stop after "F" ..	..	£130	
C 2	23	½ a. green	..	75	30
		a. Opt double			
		b. No stop after "F" ..	..	£130	
C 3	25	1 a. plum	..	4·00	1·50
		a. No stop after "F" ..	..	£180	
C 4	27	2 a. ultramarine	..	3·00	9·00
		a. No stop after "F" ..	..	£180	
C 5	36	2 a. 6 p. green	..	2·75	13·00
		a. No stop after "F" ..	..	£250	
C 6	28	3 a. orange	..	2·75	16·00
		a. Opt double, one albino	..	£120	
		b. No stop after "F" ..	..	£250	
C 7	29	4 a. olive-green	..	2·75	7·50
		a. Opt double, one albino	..	£120	
		b. No stop after "F" ..	..	£250	
C 8	31	8 a. magenta ..	..	2·75	13·00
		a. No stop after "F" ..	..	£300	
		b. Opt double, one albino	..	£120	
C 9	32	12 a. purple/red	..	14·00	15·00
		a. Opt double, one albino	..	£160	
		b. No stop after "F" ..	..	£375	

C10	37	1 r. green and carmine	..	14·00	15·00
		a. No stop after "F" ..		£375	
C1/10			*Set of 10*	42·00	80·00

Prepared, but not issued

C10b	26	1 a. 6 p. sepia	..	£200

The missing stop after "F" variety occurs in the ninth row of the upper pane.

1904 (27 Feb).

C11	25	1 a. carmine	..	26·00	8·00

1905 (16 Sept)–**11**. *Stamps of King Edward VII.*

C12	41	3 p. grey (4.11)	..	3·75	6·50
		a. Opt double, one albino	..	£120	
		b. Opt triple, one albino	..	£350	
		c. *Slate-grey*	..	3·00	6·50
C13	43	1 a. carmine	..	5·50	70
		a. Opt double, one albino	..	£100	
C14	44	2 a. mauve (11.3.11)	..	14·00	2·00
		a. Opt double, one albino	..	£120	
C15	45	2 a. 6 p. ultramarine (11.3.11)	..	3·25	5·00
C16	46	3 a. orange-brown (11.3.11)	..	3·75	4·00
C17	47	4 a. olive-green (11.3.11)	..	8·50	11·00
C18	49	8 a. claret (11.3.11)	..	8·00	7·50
		a. *Purple*	..	55·00	
C19	50	12 a. purple/*red* (1909)	..	11·00	19·00
		a. No stop after "E"	..	£425	
C20	51	1 r. green and carmine (11.3.11)	..	13·00	28·00
C12/20			*Set of 9*	65·00	75·00

1908 (Dec)–**09**. "POSTAGE & REVENUE".

C21	53	½ a. green (No. 149) (29.9.09)	..	1·50	1·25
		a. Opt double, one albino	..	£110	
C22	54	1 a. carmine (No. 150)	..	1·50	30
		a. Opt double, one albino	..	£150	

1914 (5 May)–**22**. *Stamps of King George V. Wmk Star.*

C23	55	3 p. slate-grey (7.10.14)	..	3·00	18·00
C24	56	½ a. green	..	2·25	4·00
C25	57	1 a. aniline carmine	..	2·75	2·75
C26	58	1½ a. chocolate (Type A) (9.3.21)	..	21·00	60·00
		a. Opt double, one albino	..	£130	
C27	59	2 a. mauve (11.19)	..	9·50	45·00
		a. Opt triple	..	£400	
		b. *Dull purple*	..	9·50	45·00
C28	61	2 a. 6 p. bright blue (2.19)	..	8·00	20·00
C29	62	3 a. orange-brown (5.22)	..	22·00	£170
C30	63	4 a. olive-green (5.22)	..	18·00	£150
C32	65	8 a. mauve (12.21)	..	18·00	£325
C33	66	12 a. claret (1.20)	..	18·00	£110
C34	67	1 r. red-brown and blue-green (10.21)	..	55·00	£250
C23/34			*Set of 11*	£160	£1000

Most dates quoted for Nos. C23/34 are those of the earliest recorded postmarks.

On No. C27a two of the overprints are only lightly inked.

BRITISH RAILWAY ADMINISTRATION

As a vital communications link the North China Railway (Peking – Tientsin – Shanhaikwan) was captured by Russian forces during operations against the Boxers. Control of the line was subsequently, in February 1901, assigned to the China Expeditionary Force and a British Railway Administration was set up to run it. By international agreement the line was to provide postal services for the other national contingents and also, to a lesser extent, for the civilian population. Travelling post offices were introduced and, on 20 April 1901, a late letter service for which an additional fee of 5 c. was charged.

B.R.A.
5
Five Cents

Type 32 of China   (BR 35)

1901 (20 Apr). *No. 108 of China surch with Type* BR **35**.

BR133	32	5 c. on ½ c. brown (Bk.)	..	£325	£100
		a. Surch inverted	..	£8000	£2500
		b. Surch in green	..	£275	£140
		ba. Imperf between (horiz pair)		†	£16000

No. BR133 was used for the collection of the 5 c. late letter fee and was affixed to correspondence by a postal official at the railway station. It was cancelled with a violet circular postmark showing "RAILWAY POST OFFICE" at top and the name of the station (PEKING, TIENTSIN, TONGKU, TONGSHAN or SHANHAIKWAN) at foot. With the exception of official mail it could only be used in combination with Indian stamps overprinted "C.E.F.", stamps from the other allied contingents or of the Chinese Imperial Post (*Price used on cover:* No. BR133 *from* £250. No. BR133b *from* £300).

It is suggested that stamps overprinted in black were used at Tientsin and Tongku with those in green being available at Peking, Tongshan and Shanhaikwan.

The late fee charge was abolished on 20 May 1901 and No. BR133 was then withdrawn. The British Railway Administration continued to run the line, and its travelling post offices, until it was returned to its private owners in September 1902.

INDIAN EXPEDITIONARY FORCES 1914–21

Nos. E1/13 were for use of Indian forces sent overseas during the First World War and its aftermath. Examples were first used in France during September 1914. Other areas where the stamps were used included East Africa, Mesopotamia and Turkey. "I.E.F." overprints ceased to be valid for postage on 15 October 1921.

PRICES FOR STAMPS ON COVER	
Nos. E1/13	*from* × 10

I. E. F.
(E 1)

1914 (Sept). *Stamps of India (King George V) optd with Type E 1.*

E 1	55	3 p. slate-grey	..	15	25
		a. No stop after "F" ..	..	23·00	26·00
		b. No stop after "E" ..	..	£100	£100
		c. Opt double	..	42·00	30·00
E 2	56	½ a. yellow-green	..	20	20
		a. No stop after "F" ..	..	70·00	70·00
		b. Opt double	..	£140	£250
E 3	57	1 a. aniline carmine	..	50	20
		a. No stop after "F" ..	..	32·00	35·00
E 4		1 a. carmine	..	3·00	3·00
E 5	59	2 a. mauve	..	70	30
		a. No stop after "F" ..	..	50·00	65·00
		b. No stop after "E" ..	..	£225	£250
E 6	61	2 a. 6 p. ultramarine	..	1·25	2·50
		a. No stop after "F" ..	..	£160	£170
E 7	62	3 a. orange-brown	..	80	60
		a. No stop after "F" ..	..	£150	£160
E 8	63	4 a. olive-green	..	70	60
		a. No stop after "F" ..	..	£225	£250
E 9	65	8 a. purple	..	1·00	1·50
		a. No stop after "F" ..	..	£225	£250
E10		8 a. mauve	..	8·50	12·00
E11	66	12 a. dull claret	..	9·00	13·00
		a. No stop after "F" ..	..	£275	£275
		b. Opt double, one albino	..	55·00	
E12		12 a. claret	..	2·25	5·50
E13	67	1 r. red-brown and blue-green	..	2·50	4·00
		a. Opt double, one albino	..	£100	
E1/13			*Set of 10*	9·00	14·00

The "no stop after F" variety occurred on R. 4/12 of the upper pane, in one printing.

INDIAN CUSTODIAN FORCES IN KOREA

भारतीय
संरक्षा कटक
कोरिया

(K 1)

1953 (17 Oct). *Stamps of India optd with Type* K 1.

K 1	307	3 p. slate-violet	..	1·50	4·25
K 2	308	6 p. purple-brown	..	1·50	4·25
K 3	309	9 p. yellow-green	..	1·75	4·25
K 4	328	1 a. turquoise ..	..	1·50	4·25
K 5	311	2 a. carmine	..	1·50	4·25
K 6	313	2½ a. lake	..	1·50	4·75
K 7	312	3 a. brown-orange	..	1·50	4·75
K 8	314	4 a. bright blue	..	2·00	4·75
K 9	315	6 a. violet	..	8·50	9·00
K10	316	8 a. turquoise-green	..	3·25	9·00
K11	317	12 a. dull blue	..	4·50	17·00
K12	318	1 r. dull violet and green	..	6·00	17·00
K1/12			*Set of 12*	30·00	75·00

INDIAN U.N. FORCE IN CONGO

U.N. FORCE
(INDIA)
CONGO

(U 1)

1962 (15 Jan). *Stamps of India optd with Type* U 1. W 69 (*sideways*) (13 n.p.) *or* W 374 (*others*).

U1	361	1 n.p. blue-green ..	..	80	2·00
U2		2 n.p. light brown	..	80	80
U3		5 n.p. bright green	..	80	55
U4		8 n.p. light blue-green	..	80	30
U5		13 n.p. bright carmine-red	..	80	40
U6		50 n.p. orange	..	80	70
U1/6			*Set of 6*	4·25	4·25

INDIAN U.N. FORCE IN GAZA (PALESTINE) UNEF

UNEF
(G 1)

1965 (15 Jan). *No. 492 of India optd with Type* G 1.

G1	449	15 p. slate (C.)	..	1·25	5·50

INTERNATIONAL COMMISSION IN INDO-CHINA

The International Control Commissions for Indo-China were established in August 1954 as part of the Geneva Declaration which partitioned Vietnam and sought to achieve stable settlements in Cambodia and Laos. The three supervisory commissions were chaired by India with Canada and Poland as the other members. Joint inspection teams of servicemen from the three countries were also provided.

The Indian contingent included a postal unit which handled mail for the three commissions and the inspection teams. The unit arrived in Indo-China on 3 September 1954 and opened field post offices at Saigon (F.P.O. 742), Hanoi (F.P.O. 743), Vientiane (F.P.O. 744) and Phnom Penh (F.P.O. 745).

अन्तर्राष्ट्रीय आयोग	अन्तर्राष्ट्रीय आयोग	अन्तर्राष्ट्रीय आयोग
कम्बोज	लाओस	वियत नाम
(N 1)	(N 2)	(N 3)

1954 (1 Dec). *Stamps of India.* W 69.

(a) Optd as Type N 1, for use in Cambodia

N 1	307	3 p. slate-violet	..	..	75	6·50
N 2	328	1 a. turquoise	..	..	90	75
N 3	311	2 a. carmine	..	..	90	80
N 4	316	8 a. turquoise-green	..	..	2·00	3·50
N 5	317	12 a. dull blue	..	..	2·25	4·00

(b) Optd as Type N 2, for use in Laos

N 6	307	3 p. slate-violet	..	..	75	6·50
N 7	328	1 a. turquoise	..	..	90	75
N 8	311	2 a. carmine	..	..	90	80
N 9	316	8 a. turquoise-green	..	..	2·00	3·50
N10	317	12 a. dull blue	..	..	2·25	4·00

(c) Optd as Type N 3, for use in Vietnam

N11	307	3 p. slate-violet	..	..	75	6·50
N12	328	1 a. turquoise	..	..	90	75
N13	311	2 a. carmine	..	..	90	80
N14	316	8 a. turquoise-green	..	..	2·00	3·50
N15	317	12 a. dull blue	..	..	2·25	4·00
N1/15	..	..	Set of 15		17·00	42·00

1957 (1 Apr). *Stamps of India.* W 69 (sideways).

(a) Optd as Type N 1, for use in Cambodia

N16	361	2 n.p. light brown	..	..	75	30
N17		6 n.p. grey	..	..	50	30
N18		13 n.p. bright carmine-red	..	..	70	40
N19		50 n.p. orange	..	..	2·25	1·25
N20		75 n.p. reddish purple	..	..	2·25	1·25

(b) Optd as Type N 2, for use in Laos

N21	361	2 n.p. light brown	..	..	75	30
N22		6 n.p. grey	..	..	50	30
N23		13 n.p. bright carmine-red	..	..	70	40
N24		50 n.p. orange	..	..	2·25	1·25
N25		75 n.p. reddish purple	..	..	2·25	1·25

(c) Optd as Type N 3, for use in Vietnam

N26	361	2 n.p. light brown	..	..	75	30
N27		6 n.p. grey	..	..	50	30
N28		13 n.p. bright carmine-red	..	..	70	40
N29		50 n.p. orange	..	..	2·25	1·25
N30		75 n.p. reddish purple	..	..	2·25	1·25
N16/30			Set of 15		17·00	9·50

F.P.O. 744 (Vientiane) was closed on 25 July 1958 and F.P.O. 745 (Phnom Penh) on 26 June 1958.

1960 (Sept)–**65.** *Stamps of India.* W 374.

(a) Optd as Type N 2, for use in Laos

N38	361	2 n.p. light brown (15.1.62)	..	15	2·50
N39		3 n.p. deep brown (1.8.63)	..	10	20
N40		4 n.p. bright green (1.8.63)	..	10	15
N41		50 n.p. orange (1965)	..	3·75	3·25
N42		75 n.p. reddish purple (1965)	..	3·75	3·50

(b) Optd as Type N 3, for use in Vietnam

N43	361	1 n.p. blue-green	..	10	20
N44		2 n.p. light brown (15.1.62)	..	15	2·50
N45		3 n.p. deep brown (1.8.63)	..	10	20
N46		5 n.p. bright green (1.8.63)	..	10	15
N47		50 n.p. orange (1965)	..	3·75	3·25
N48		75 n.p. reddish purple (1965)	..	3·75	3·50
N38/48	..	..	Set of 11	14·00	17·00

F.P.O. 744 (Vientiane) re-opened on 22 May 1961.

Examples of the 2 n.p. value overprinted as Type N 1 for use in Cambodia exist, but were never placed on sale there as the Phnom Penh F.P.O. 745 was closed on 26 June 1958. Used examples appear to originate from unauthorised use of the F.P.O. 745 postmark which was in store at Saigon (*Price* 15p, *unused*).

ICC   ICC

(N 4)   (N 5)

1965 (15 Jan). *No. 492 of India optd with Type N 4, for use in Laos and Vietnam.*

N49	449	15 p. slate (C.)	..	60	3·25

F.P.O. 743 (Hanoi) was closed on 13 July 1966.

1968 (2 Oct). *Nos. 504/5, 506, 509/10, 515 and 517/18 etc of India optd as Type N 5, in red, for use in Laos and Vietnam.*

N50	2 p. red-brown	..	10	2·25
N51	3 p. brown-olive	..	10	2·25
N52	5 p. cerise	..	10	75
N53	10 p. new blue	..	1·75	1·75
N54	15 p. bronze-green	..	60	1·75
N55	60 p. deep grey	..	35	1·25
N56	1 r. red-brown and plum	..	50	1·75
N57	2 r. new blue and deep slate-violet	..	1·25	7·50
N50/7	..	Set of 8	4·00	17·00

INDIAN NATIONAL ARMY

The following are stated to have been used in the Japanese occupied areas of India during the drive on Imphal. Issued by the Indian National Army.

Genuine examples are inscribed "PROVISIONAL GOVERNMENT OF FREE INDIA". Forgeries also exist inscribed "PROVISIONAL GOVT. OF FREE INDIA".

Typo in Rangoon. No gum. Perf 11½ or imperf. 1 p. violet, 1 p. maroon, 1 a. green   *Price from £50 each unused*

JAPANESE OCCUPATION OF THE ANDAMAN AND NICOBAR ISLANDS

The Andaman Islands in the Bay of Bengal were occupied on the 23 March 1942 and the Nicobar Islands in July 1942. Civil administration was resumed in October 1945.

The following Indian stamps were surcharged with large figures preceded by a decimal point:—

Postage stamps—.3 on ½ a. (No. 248), .5 on 1 a. (No. 250), .10 on 2 a. (No. 236*b*), .30 on 6 a. (No. 274).

Official stamps—.10 on 1 a. 3 p. (No. O146*a*), .20 on 3 p. (No. O143), .20 in red on 3 p. (No. O143).

Prices from £350 each unused

1st CLASS STAMPS & SERVICE

Stanley Gibbons are pleased to offer a dedicated and completely free of charge service to today's discerning British Commonwealth collectors.

■ Specialist database of clients' interests.

■ Large stocks of specialised British Commonwealth material.

■ Free advice from our team of experts.

■ Regular advance lists and illustrated colour brochures.

■ Private viewing facilities and postal approvals service.

■ Specialist 'Wants List' service.

■ We are always interested in buying quality collections and single items.

To take advantage of our free and highly specialised service contact us today on 0171 836 8444.

STANLEY GIBBONS

—FIRST CLASS—
STAMPS & SERVICE

Stanley Gibbons Limited
399 Strand, London WC2R 0LX

INDIAN CONVENTION STATES

The following issues resulted from a series of postal conventions agreed between the Imperial Government and the state administrations of Patiala (1 October 1884), Gwalior, Jind and Nabha (1 July 1885), and Chamba and Faridkot (1 January 1887).

Under the terms of these conventions the British Indian Post Office supplied overprinted British India issues to the state administrations which, in turn, had to conform to a number of conditions covering the issue of stamps, rates of postage and the exchange of mail.

Such overprinted issues were valid for postage within the state of issue, to other "Convention States" and to destinations in British India.

Stamps of Chamba, Gwalior, Jind, Nabha and Patiala ceased to be valid for postage on 1 January 1951, when they were replaced by those of the Republic of India, valid from 1 April 1950.

RULERS OF INDIAN CONVENTION AND FEUDATORY STATES.

Details of the rulers of the various states during the period when stamps were issued are now provided in a somewhat simplified form which omits reference to minor titles. Dates quoted are of the various reigns, extended to 1971 when the titles of the surviving rulers of the former princely states were abolished by the Indian Government.

During the absorption of the Convention and Feudatory States there was often an interim period during which the administration was handed over. In some instances it is only possible to quote the end of this interim period as the point of transfer.

Stamps of India overprinted

In the Queen Victoria issues we omit varieties due to broken type, including the numerous small "A" varieties which may have come about through damaged type. We do, however, list the small "G", small "R" and tall "R" in "GWALIOR" as these were definitely the result of the use of type of the wrong size.

Variations in the length of the words due to unequal spacing when setting are also omitted.

CHAMBA

PRICES FOR STAMPS ON COVER	
Nos. 1/27	*from* × 20
Nos. 28/120	*from* × 12
Nos. O1/86	*from* × 25

Raja Sham Singh, 1873–1904

CHAMBA STATE (1)   CHAMBA (2)

1887 (1 Jan)–**95.** *Queen Victoria. Optd with T* **1.**

1	23	½ a. blue-green			10	30
		a. "CHMABA"			£275	£350
		b. "8TATE"			£550	
		c. Opt double			£600	
2	25	1 a. brown-purple			50	80
		a. "CHMABA"			£425	£500
		b. "8TATE"			£900	
3		1 a. plum			1·00	80
4	26	1 a. 6 p. sepia (1895)			60	7·50
5	27	2 a. dull blue			85	1·00
		b. "CHMABA"			£1700	£1800
		c. "8TATE"			£1700	
6		2 a. ultramarine			75	1·00
7	36	2 a. 6 p. green (1895)			22·00	60·00
8	28	3 a. orange (1887)			4·25	13·00
9		3 a. brown-orange (1891)			60	3·25
		a. "CHMABA"			£4000	£4000
		b. Opt inverted				
10	29	4 a. olive-green			2·25	4·50
		a. "CHMABA"			£1200	£1400
		b. "8TATE"			£2250	
11		4 a. slate-green			2·75	4·00
		a. Opt double, one albino			50·00	
12	21	6 a. olive-bistre (1890)			1·75	8·50
		a. Opt treble, two albino			75·00	
13		6 a. bistre-brown			7·50	9·50
14	31	8 a. dull mauve (1887)			4·25	6·50
		a. "CHMABA"			£3500	£3500
15		8 a. magenta (1895)			3·25	9·50
16	32	12 a. purple/*red* (1890)			3·25	7·50
		a. "CHMABA"			£5000	
		b. First "T" in "STATE" inverted			£5000	
		c. Opt double, one albino			30·00	
17	33	1 r. slate (1887)			24·00	85·00
		a. "CHMABA"			£7500	
18	37	1 r. green and carmine (1895)			3·75	8·50
		a. Opt double, one albino			40·00	
19	38	2 r. carmine and yellow-brown (1895)		65·00	£180
20		3 r. brown and green (1895)			65·00	£160
21		5 r. ultramarine and violet (1895)		75·00	£300
		a. Opt double, one albino			£140	
1/21				*Set of* 15	£225	£750

1900–4. *Colours changed.*

22	40	3 p. carmine			10	30
		a. Opt double, one albino			30·00	
23		3 p. grey (1904)			15	1·40
		a. Opt inverted			70·00	
24	23	½ a. pale yellow-green (1902)			70	1·50
25		½ a. yellow-green (1903)			10	50
26	25	1 a. carmine (1902)			10	30
27	27	2 a. pale violet (1903)			5·00	18·00
22/7				*Set of* 5	5·00	18·00

Raja Bhuri Singh, 1904–1919

1903–5. *King Edward VII. Optd with T* **1.**

28	41	3 p. pale grey			10	85
29		3 p. slate-grey (1905)			10	85

30	42	½ a. green			10	20
31	43	1 a. carmine			40	20
32	44	2 a. pale violet (1904)			60	1·60
33		2 a. mauve			50	1·50
34	46	3 a. orange-brown (1905)			1·75	2·75
		a. Opt double, one albino			30·00	
35	47	4 a. olive (1904)			2·25	9·00
36	48	6 a. olive-bistre (1905)			1·90	12·00
		a. Opt double, one albino			30·00	
37	49	8 a. purple (*shades*) (1904)			2·00	11·00
38		8 a. claret			5·00	16·00
39	50	12 a. purple/*red* (1905)			3·00	15·00
		a. Opt double, one albino			30·00	
40	51	1 r. green and carmine (1904)			3·75	14·00
		a. Opt double, one albino			40·00	
28/40				*Set of* 10	14·00	60·00

1907. *Nos.* 149/50 *of India optd with T* **1.**

41	53	½ a. green			25	2·00
		a. Opt double, one albino			30·00	
42	54	1 a. carmine			35	1·90

1913. *King George V optd with T* **1.**

43	55	3 p. slate-grey			10	35
44	56	½ a. green			20	40
		w. Wmk inverted				
45	57	1 a. rose-carmine			2·50	4·00
46		1 a. aniline carmine			30	1·40
		a. Opt double, one albino			30·00	
47	59	2 a. mauve			1·00	5·00
48	62	3 a. orange-brown			1·25	4·25
49	63	4 a. olive			90	2·75
50	64	6 a. olive-bistre			80	2·50
51	65	8 a. purple			1·60	6·00
52	66	12 a. dull claret			1·60	9·00
53	67	1 r. brown and green			8·00	14·00
		a. Opt double, one albino			28·00	
43/53				*Set of* 10	14·00	40·00

Raja Ram Singh, 1919–1935

1921. *No.* 192 *of India optd with T* **2.**

54	57	9 p. on 1 a. rose-carmine			80	13·00

1923–27. *Optd with T* **1.** *New values, etc.*

55	57	1 a. chocolate			70	2·25
56	58	1½ a. chocolate (Type A)			16·00	75·00
57		1½ a. chocolate (Type B) (1924)			50	3·25
58		1½ a. rose-carmine (Type B) (1927)			60	11·00
59	61	2 a. 6 p. ultramarine			50	2·75
60		2 a. 6 p. orange (1927)			80	9·00
61	62	3 a. ultramarine (1924)			1·40	10·00
55/61				*Set of* 7	18·00	£100

Nos. 58 and 60 with inverted overprint are of clandestine origin.

CHAMBA STATE (3)   CHAMBA STATE (4)

1927–37. *King George V (Nasik printing, wmk Mult Star). Optd with T* **3** *or* **4** (1 *r.*).

62	55	3 p. slate (1928)			10	60
		w. Wmk inverted			2·00	
63	56	½ a. green (1928)			20	90
		w. Wmk inverted			50	
64	80	9 p. deep green (1932)			1·10	6·50
65	57	1 a. chocolate			1·25	20
		w. Wmk inverted			2·00	30
66	82	1 a. 3 p. mauve (1932)			75	3·25
		w. Wmk inverted			2·00	3·25
67	58	1½ a. rose-carmine (B) (1932)			3·00	3·00
		w. Wmk inverted			3·00	3·00
68	70	2 a. purple (1928)			70	90
69	61	2 a. 6 p. orange (1932)			90	
		w. Wmk inverted			90	11·00
70	62	3 a. bright blue (1928)			80	10·00
71	71	4 a. sage-green (1928)			50	2·50
72	64	6 a. bistre (*wmk inverted*) (1937)		25·00	£120
73	65	8 a. reddish purple (1928)			1·00	6·50
		w. Wmk inverted			1·00	6·50
74	66	12 a. claret (1928)			1·10	7·00
75	67	1 r. chocolate and green (1928)			3·50	15·00
		w. Wmk inverted			6·00	15·00
62/75				*Set of* 14	35·00	£160

The 9 p. exists printed by lithography or typography.

Raja Lakshman Singh, 1935–1971

1935–36. *New types and colours. Optd with T* **3.**

76	79	½ a. green			50	4·75
77	81	1 a. chocolate			55	45
78	59	2 a. vermilion (No. 236a)			45	15·00
79		2 a. vermilion (*small die*, No. 236b)		90·00	£100
80	62	3 a. carmine			1·25	5·50
81	63	4 a. sage-green (1936)			1·10	6·50
76/81				*Set of* 6	90·00	£120

CHAMBA STATE (5)   CHAMBA (6)   CHAMBA (7)

1938. *King George VI. Nos.* 247/64 *optd with T* **3** (3 *p. to* 1 *a.*), **T 5** (2 *a. to* 12 *a.*) *or* **T 4** (*rupee values*).

82	91	3 p. slate			3·00	7·00
83		3 p. red-brown			90	4·00
84		9 p. green			3·75	19·00
85		1 a. carmine			90	1·10
86	92	2 a. vermilion			2·50	6·00
87		2 a. 6 p. bright violet			3·00	13·00
88		3 a. yellow-green			4·00	14·00
89		3 a. 6 p. bright blue			3·75	16·00
90		4 a. brown			12·00	9·00
91		6 a. turquoise-green			11·00	32·00
92		8 a. slate-violet			12·00	28·00
93		12 a. lake			6·00	32·00

94	93	1 r. grey and red-brown			25·00	40·00
95		2 r. purple and brown			40·00	£170
96		5 r. green and blue			65·00	£275
97		10 r. purple and claret			£110	£425
98		15 r. brown and green			£200	£600
99		25 r. slate-violet and purple			£225	£700
82/99				*Set of* 18	£650	£2000

1942–47. *Optd with T* **6** (*to* 12 *a*), "CHAMBA" *only, as in T* **5** (14 *a.*) *or T* **7** (*rupee values*). (*a*) *Stamps of* 1937. *W* **69** (*inverted on* 15 *r.*).

100	91	½ a. red-brown			20·00	14·00
101		1 a. carmine			24·00	14·00
102	93	1 r. grey and red-brown			21·00	40·00
103		2 r. purple and brown			28·00	£150
104		5 r. green and blue			60·00	£160
105		10 r. purple and claret			85·00	£325
106		15 r. brown and green			£180	£500
107		25 r. slate-violet and purple			£200	£550
100/107				*Set of* 8	£550	£1600

(*b*) *Stamps of* 1940–43.

108	100a	3 p. slate			60	2·75
109		½ a. purple (1943)			70	1·75
110		9 p. green			70	7·50
111		1 a. carmine (1943)			90	1·75
112	101	1½ a. dull violet (1943)			90	5·00
113		2 a. vermilion (1943)			1·75	5·50
114		3 a. bright violet			6·00	14·00
115		3½ a. bright blue			3·50	22·00
116	102	4 a. brown			4·50	6·50
117		6 a. turquoise-green			13·00	32·00
118		8 a. slate-violet			13·00	38·00
119		12 a. lake			26·00	48·00
120	103	14 a. purple (1947)			6·00	3·00
108/120				*Set of* 13	70·00	£160

The 3 a. exists printed by lithography or typography.

OFFICIAL STAMPS

SERVICE

CHAMBA STATE (O 1)

1887 (1 Jan)–**98.** *Queen Victoria. Optd with Type* O **1.**

O 1	23	½ a. blue-green			10	10
		a. "CHMABA"			£180	£180
		b. "SERV CE"				
		c. "8TATE"			£550	
		d. Thin serifed "I" in "SERVICE"		90·00	
O 2	25	1 a. brown-purple			65	50
		a. "CHMABA"			£325	£325
		b. "SERV CE"			£1700	
		c. "8TATE"			£1000	
		d. "SERVICE" double			£900	£900
		e. "SERVICE" double, one albino		40·00	
O 3		1 a. plum			50	10
		a. Thin serifed "I" in "SERVICE"		£100	
O 4	27	2 a. dull blue			90	75
		a. "CHMABA"			£900	£1100
O 5		2 a. ultramarine (1887)			70	95
		a. Thin serifed "I" in "SERVICE"		£160	
O 6	28	3 a. orange (1890)			1·60	7·50
O 7		3 a. brown-orange (1891)			2·00	£250
		a. "CHMABA"			£2000	£2250
		b. Thin serifed "I" in "SERVICE"			
		c. Opt double, one albino				
O 8	29	4 a. olive-green			1·10	2·75
		a. "CHMABA"			£900	£1100
		b. "SERV CE"			£2250	
		c. "8TATE"			£2250	
O 9		4 a. slate-green			1·10	4·00
		a. Thin serifed "I" in "SERVICE"			
O10	21	6 a. olive-bistre (1890)			2·75	7·00
		a. "SERVICE" double, one albino		40·00	
O11		6 a. bistre-brown				
O12	31	8 a. dull mauve (1887)			2·25	3·50
		a. "CHMABA"			£4000	£4000
O13		8 a. magenta (1895)			90	1·60
		a. Thin serifed "I" in "SERVICE"		£350	
O14	32	12 a. purple/*red* (1890)			7·00	26·00
		a. "CHMABA"			£4500	
		b. First "T" in "STATE" inverted		£4750	
		c. Thin serifed "I" in "SERVICE"			
		d. "SERVICE" double, one albino		40·00	
		e. "CHAMBA STATE" double, one albino			
O15	33	1 r. slate (1890)			12·00	80·00
		a. "CHMABA"			£4000	
O16	37	1 r. green and carmine (1898)			5·50	20·00
		a. Thin serifed "I" in "SERVICE"			
O1/16				*Set of* 10	29·00	£130

Printings up to and including that of December 1895 had the "SERVICE" overprint applied to sheets of stamps already overprinted with Type 1. From the printing of September 1898 onwards both "SERVICE" and "CHAMBA STATE" were overprinted at the same time. Nos. O6, O8 and O12 only exist using the first method, and No. O16 was only printed using the second.

The thin serifed "I" in "SERVICE" variety occured on R. 19/12 of the September 1898 printing only.

1902–4. *Colours changed. Optd as Type* O **1.**

O17	40	3 p. grey (1904)			15	45
O18	23	½ a. pale yellow-green			20	2·25
O19		½ a. yellow-green			2·00	85
O20	25	1 a. carmine			40	40
O21	27	2 a. pale violet (1903)			7·50	20·00
O17/21				*Set of* 4	7·50	20·00

1903–5. *King Edward VII. Stamps of India optd as Type* O **1.**

O22	41	3 p. pale grey			15	15
		a. Opt double, one albino			25·00	
O23		3 p. slate-grey (1905)			10	65
O24	42	½ a. yellow-green			15	10
O25	43	1 a. carmine			30	25

O26	44	2 a. pale violet (1904)	..	..	2·00	70
O27		2 a. mauve		..	50	50
O28	47	4 a. olive (1905)	..	..	2·25	10·00
O29	49	8 a. purple (1905)	..	..	2·50	10·00
O30		8 a. claret	..	..	5·50	15·00
		a. Opt double, one albino	..	30·00		
O31	51	1 r. green and carmine (1905)	..	1·40	6·00
O22/31				*Set of 7*	6·50	24·00

The 2 a. mauve King Edward VII, overprinted "On H.M.S.", was discovered in Calcutta, but was not sent to Chamba, and is an unissued variety (*Price un.* £35).

1907. *Nos. 149/50 of India, optd with Type* O 1.
O32	53	½ a. green	..	..	25	75
		a. Opt inverted	..	£3750	£3750
		b. Opt double, one albino	..	25·00	
O33	54	1 a. carmine	..	..	1·25	90

The inverted overprint, No. O32a, was due to an inverted cliché on R. 20/1 which was corrected after a few sheets had been printed.

1913–14. *King George V Official stamps* (*wmk Single Star*) *optd with T* 1.
O34	55	3 p. slate-grey	..	..	25	65
O35		3 p. grey	..	..	20	35
O36	56	½ a. yellow-green	..	..	10	10
O37		½ a. pale blue-green	..	..	75	30
O38	57	1 a. aniline carmine	..	..	10	10
O39		1 a. rose-carmine	..	..	3·00	40
O40	59	2 a. mauve (1914)	..	..	1·00	8·00
O41	63	4 a. olive	..	..	1·10	9·00
O42	65	8 a. purple	..	..	1·50	10·00
O43	67	1 r. brown and green (1914)	..	3·25	18·00
		a. Opt double, one albino	..	27·00	
O34/43				*Set of 7*	6·50	40·00

No. O36 with inverted overprint and No. O39 with double or inverted overprint (on gummed side) are of clandestine origin.

1914 *King George V. Optd with Type* O 1.
| O44 | 59 | 2 a. mauve | .. | .. | 9·50 | |
| O45 | 63 | 4 a. olive | .. | .. | 9·00 | |

1921 *No.* O97 *of India optd with T* 2 *at top.*
| O46 | 57 | 9 p. on 1 a. rose-carmine | .. | 15 | 4·25 |

1925 *As* 1913–14. *New colour.*
| O47 | 57 | 1 a. chocolate | .. | .. | 1·25 | 50 |

CHAMBA STATE
SERVICE
(O 2)

CHAMBA STATE
SERVICE
(O 3)

1927–39. *King George V* (*Nasik printing, wmk Mult Star*), *optd at Nasik with Type* O 2 *or* O 3 (*rupee values*).
O48	55	3 p. slate (1928)	..	..	40	30
		w. Wmk inverted	..	—	50
O49	56	½ a. green (1928)	..	..	30	15
O50	80	9 p. deep green (1932)	..	1·00	5·50
O51	57	1 a. chocolate	..	..	20	10
		w. Wmk inverted	..	—	20
O52	82	1 a. 3 p. mauve (1932)	..	4·25	50
		w. Wmk inverted	..		
O53	70	2 a. purple (1928)	..	..	65	55
O54	71	4 a. sage-green (1928)	..	65	80
O55	65	8 a. reddish purple (1930)	..	2·75	6·50
		w. Wmk inverted	..	4·00	
O56	66	12 a. claret (1928)	..	..	1·60	14·00
		w. Wmk inverted	..	6·00	
O57	67	1 r. chocolate and green (1930)	..	9·00	26·00
O58		2 r. carmine and orange (1939)	..	17·00	£150
O59		5 r. ultramarine and purple (1939)	..	40·00	£200
O60		10 r. green and scarlet (1939)	..	50·00	£190
O48/60				*Set of 13*	£110	£550

1935–39. *New types and colours. Optd with Type* O 2.
O61	79	½ a. green	..	..	90	35
O62	81	1 a. chocolate	..	..	1·50	45
O63	59	2 a. vermilion	..	..	2·50	85
O64		2 a. vermilion (*small die*) (1939)	..	1·25	8·50
O65	63	4 a. sage-green (1936)	..	2·75	2·50
O61/5				*Set of 5*	8·00	11·50

1938—40. *King George VI. Optd with Type* O 2 *or* O 3 (*rupee values*).
O66	91	9 p. green	..	..	6·50	30·00
O67		1 a. carmine	..	..	5·00	1·50
O68	93	1 r. grey and red-brown (1940?)	..	£500	£750
O69		2 r. purple and brown (1939)	..	50·00	£250
O70		5 r. green and blue (1939)	..	80·00	£325
O71		10 r. purple and claret (1939)	..	£120	£500
O66/71				*Set of 6*	£700	£1700

CHAMBA
SERVICE
(O 4)

1940–43. (*a*) *Official stamps optd with T* 6.
O72	O 20	3 p. slate	..	..	60	50
O73		½ a. red-brown	..	..	11·00	1·25
O74		½ a. purple (1943)	..	..	60	1·25
O75		9 p. green	..	..	2·75	4·50
		w. Wmk inverted	..	10·00	8·00
O76		1 a. carmine (1941)	..	..	60	1·00
O77		1 a. 3 p. yellow-brown (1941)	..	35·00	12·00
O78		1½ a. dull violet (1943)	..	3·75	3·75
O79		2 a. vermilion	..	..	2·75	3·00
O80		2½ a. bright violet (1941)	..	1·75	14·00
O81		4 a. brown	..	..	3·25	6·00
O82		8 a. slate-violet (1941)	..	8·50	35·00
		w. Wmk inverted	..	7·50	35·00

(*b*) *Postage stamps optd with Type* O 4.
O83	93	1 r. grey and red-brown (1942)	..	32·00	£130
O84		2 r. purple and brown (1942)	..	50·00	£190
O85		5 r. green and blue (1942)	..	80·00	£300
O86		10 r. purple and claret (1942)	..	£120	£500
O72/86				*Set of 15*	£325	£1100

Chamba became part of Himachal Pradesh on 15 April 1948.

FARIDKOT

For earlier issues, see under INDIAN FEUDATORY STATES

PRICES FOR STAMPS ON COVER

| Nos. 1/17 | *from* × 30 |
| Nos. O1/15 | *from* × 40 |

Raja Bikram Singh, 1874–1898

FARIDKOT
STATE
(1)

1887 (1 Jan)**–1900.** *Queen Victoria. Optd with T* 1.
1	23	½ a. deep green	..	..	75	75
		a. "ARIDKOT"	..	..		
		b. "FAR DKOT"	..	..	—	£1000
		c. Opt double, one albino	..	35·00	
2	25	1 a. brown-purple	..	..	85	1·50
3		1 a. plum	..	..	80	80
4	27	2 a. blue	..	..	2·25	3·00
5		2 a. deep blue	..	..	2·25	4·00
6	28	3 a. orange	..	..	4·00	6·50
7		3 a. brown-orange (1893)	..	1·25	2·25
8	29	4 a. olive-green	..	..	4·00	11·00
		a. "ARIDKOT"	..	..	£1000	
9		4 a. slate-green	..	..	4·50	13·00
10	21	6 a. olive-bistre	..	..	17·00	32·00
		a. "ARIDKOT"	..	..	£1600	
		b. Opt double, one albino	..	35·00	
11		6 a. bistre-brown	..	..	1·75	9·00
12	31	8 a. dull mauve	..	..	7·50	23·00
		a. "ARIDKOT"	..	..	£2000	
13		8 a. magenta	..	..	9·50	70·00
		a. Opt double, one albino	..	30·00	
14	32	12 a. purple/*red* (1900)	..	28·00	£300
15	33	1 r. slate	..	..	26·00	£275
		a. "ARIDKOT"	..	..	£2000	
16	37	1 r. green and carmine (1893)	..	28·00	55·00
		a. Opt double, one albino	..	50·00	
1/16				*Set of 10*	90·00	£600

The ½ a., 1 a., 2 a., 3 a., 4 a., 8 a. and 1 r. (No. 16) are known with broken "O" (looking like a "C") in "FARIDKOT".

Raja Balbir Singh, 1898–1906

1900. *Optd with T* 1.
| 17 | 40 | 3 p. carmine | .. | .. | 50 | 29·00 |

OFFICIAL STAMPS

SERVICE

FARIDKOT
STATE
(O 1)

1887 (1 Jan)**–98.** *Queen Victoria. Optd with Type* O 1.
O 1	23	½ a. deep green	..	..	15	45
		a. "SERV CE"	..	..	£1300	
		b. "FAR DKOT"	..	..		
		c. Thin seriffed "I" in "SERVICE"	..	£120	
		d. "FARIDKOT STATE" double, one albino	..	30·00	
O 2	25	1 a. brown-purple	..	..	55	90
		a. Thin seriffed "I" in "SERVICE"	..	£130	
		b. Opt double, one albino	..	40·00	
O 3		1 a. plum	..	..	55	90
		a. "SERV CE"	..	..	£1700	
O 4	27	2 a. dull blue	..	..	1·25	5·50
		a. "SERV CE"	..	..	£1700	
O 5		2 a. deep blue	..	..	75	8·00
O 6	28	3 a. orange	..	..	3·50	4·75
		a. "SERVICE" double, one albino	..	50·00	
O 7		3 a. brown-orange (12.98)	..	1·00	23·00
		a. Thin seriffed "I" in "SERVICE"	..	£325	
O 8	29	4 a. olive-green	..	..	2·25	12·00
		a. "SERV CE"	..	..	£1700	
		b. "ARIDKOT"	..	..		
		c. "SERVICE" treble, two albino	..	60·00	
O 9		4 a. slate-green	..	..	6·50	25·00
		a. "SERVICE" double, one albino	..	30·00	
O10	21	6 a. olive-bistre	..	..	23·00	60·00
		a. "ARIDKOT"	..	..	£1000	
		b. "SERVIC"	..	..	£1600	
		c. "SERVICE" double, one albino	..	40·00	
		d. "FARIDKOT STATE" double, one albino	..	40·00	
O11		6 a. bistre-brown	..	..	12·00	14·00
O12	31	8 a. dull mauve	..	..	3·50	14·00
		a. "SERV CE"	..	..	£1800	
O13		8 a. magenta	..	..	9·00	70·00
O14	33	1 r. slate	..	..	35·00	£120
		a. "SERVICE" double, one albino	..	55·00	
O15	37	1 r. green and carmine (12.98)	..	65·00	£350
		a. Thin seriffed "I" in "SERVICE"			
O1/15				*Set of 9*	£110	£475

The ½ a., 1 a., 2 a., 3 a., 4 a., 8 a. and 1 r. (No. O15) are known with the broken "O".

Printings up to and including that of November 1895 had the "SERVICE" overprint applied to sheets already overprinted with Type 1. From December 1898 onwards "SERVICE" and "FARIDKOT STATE" were overprinted at one operation to provide fresh supplies of Nos. O1/3, O7 and O15.

The thin seriffed "I" variety occurs on the December 1898 overprinting only.

This State ceased to use overprinted stamps after 31 March 1901.

GWALIOR

PRICES FOR STAMPS ON COVER

Nos. 1/3	*from* × 10
Nos. 4/11	
Nos. 12/66	*from* × 5
Nos. 67/128	*from* × 4
Nos. 129/37	*from* × 5
Nos. O1/94	*from* × 12

OVERPRINTS. From 1885 to 1926 these were applied by the Government of India Central Printing Press, Calcutta, and from 1927 at the Security Press, Nasik, *unless otherwise stated.*

Maharaja Jayaji Rao Sindhia, 1843–1886

ग्वालियर

GWALIOR
(1)

GWALIOR
ग्वालियर
(2)

GWALIOR
Small "G"

GWALIOR
Small "R"

GWALIOR
Tall "R"
(original state)

GWALIOR
Tall "R"
(damaged state)

OVERPRINT VARIETIES OF TYPE 2.

Small "G"—Occurs on R.7/11 from June 1900 printing of ½, 1, 2, 3, 4 a. and 3 p. (No. 38), and on an unknown position from May 1901 printing of 2, 3 and 5 r.

Small "R"—Occurs on R. 9/3 from June 1900 printing of 3 p. to 4 a. and on R.2/3 from May 1901 printing of 2, 3 and 5 r.

Tall "R"—Occurs on R.20/2 from printings between June 1900 and May 1907. The top of the letter is damaged on printings from February 1903 onwards.

1885 (1 July)**–97.** *Queen Victoria.* I. *Optd with T* 1.

(*a*) *Space between two lines of overprint* 13 *mm. Hindi inscription* 13 *to* 14 *mm long* (May 1885)
1	23	½ a. blue-green	..	..	80·00	15·00
2	25	1 a. brown-purple	..	..	60·00	21·00
3	27	2 a. dull blue	..	..	48·00	11·00
1/3				*Set of 3*	£170	42·00

A variety exists of the ½ a. in which the space between the two lines of overprint is only 9½ mm but this is probably from a proof sheet.

(*b*) *Space between two lines of overprint* 15 *mm on* 4 a. *and* 6 a. *and* 16 *to* 17 *mm on other values* (June 1885)

A. *Hindi inscription* 13 *to* 14 *mm long*
B. *Hindi inscription* 15 *to* 15½ *mm long*

				A	B
4	23	½ a. blue-green	..	32·00	— 80·00 —
		c. Pair. Types A and B	..	£350	
		d. Opt double, one albino	50·00	— £120 —
5	25	1 a. brown-purple	..	40·00	— 80·00 —
		c. Pair. Types A and B	..	£350	
		d. Opt double, one albino	45·00	— 90·00 —
6	26	1 a. 6 p. sepia	..	50·00	— £130 —
		c. Pair. Types A and B	..	£400	
7	27	2 a. dull blue	..	40·00	— 90·00 —
		c. Pair. Types A and B	..	£275	
8	17	4 a. green	..	60·00	— £140 —
		c. Pair. Types A and B	..	£475	
9	21	6 a. olive-bistre	..	60·00	— £140 —
		c. Pair. Types A and B	..	£475	
		d. Opt double, one albino	70·00	— £160 —
10	31	8 a. dull mauve	..	55·00	— £130 —
		c. Pair. Types A and B	..	£450	
11	33	1 r. slate	..	55·00	— £130 —
		c. Pair. Types A and B	..	£450	
4/11			*Set of 8*	£350	— £850 —

The two types of overprint on these stamps occur in the same settings, with about a quarter of the stamps in each sheet showing the long inscription (B). Nos. 4/7 and 10/11 were overprinted in sheets of 240 and Nos. 8/9 in half-sheets of 160.

II. *Optd with T* 2.

A. *Hindi inscription* 13 *to* 14 *mm long*
B. *Hindi inscription* 15 *to* 15½ *mm long*

(*a*) *In red* (Sept 1885)

				A	B		
12	23	½ a. blue-green	..	25	20	45	55
		c. Pair. Types A and B	..	7·00	9·00		
13	27	2 a. dull blue	..	8·50	9·00	22·00	24·00
		c. Pair. Types A and B	..	£225			
14	17	4 a. green	..	16·00	9·00	£140	75·00
		c. Pair. Types A and B	..	£350			
15	33	1 r. slate	..	7·50	15·00	25·00	55·00
		c. Pair. Types A and B	..	42·00	80·00		
12/15			*Set of 4*	29·00	30·00	£170	£140

No. 14 was overprinted in half-sheets of 160, about 40 stamps being Type B. The remaining three values were from a setting of 240 containing 166 as Type A and 74 as Type B.

Reprints have been made of Nos. 12 to 15, but the majority of the specimens have the word "REPRINT" overprinted upon them.

(b) *In black (1885–97)*

			A	B	A	B
16	23	½ a. blue-green (1889)	70	1·00	20	10
		a. Opt double		†		
		b. "GWALICR"		†	85·00	95·00
		c. Small "G"		†	55·00	45·00
		d. Small "R"		†	60·00	
		e. Tall "R"		†	60·00	60·00
		f. Pair. Types A and B	40·00			
17	24	9 p. carmine (1891)	27·00	50·00	45·00	65·00
		f. Pair. Types A and B	£170	—		
		g. Opt double, one albino	50·00	—	80·00	
18	25	1 a. brown-purple		30	15	1·25	30
		f. Pair. Types A and B	9·00	10·00		
19		1 a. plum			1·25	10
		a. Small "G"		†	65·00	48·00
		d. Small "R"		†	75·00	
		e. Tall "R"		†	80·00	
20	26	1 a. 6 p. sepia		30	75	55	40
		f. Pair. Types A and B	9·00	12·00		
21	27	2 a. dull blue		3·50	75	50	10
		a. "R" omitted		†	£450	£450
		f. Pair. Types A and B	90·00			
22		2 a. deep blue		4·00	1·60	1·25	30
		a. Small "G"		†	£120	£120
		d. Small "R"		†	£150	—
		e. Tall "R"		†	£160	£160
		f. Pair. Types A and B	£100	—		
23	36	2 a. 6 p. yellow-green (1896)		†	4·25	12·00
		a. "GWALICR"		†	£450	
24	28	3 a. orange		3·75	7·00	38·00	26·00
		f. Pair. Types A and B	£160	—		
		g. Opt double, one albino	40·00	—		
25		3 a. brown-orange	14·00	2·50	50	15
		a. Small "G"		†	£180	£180
		d. Small "R"		†	£325	—
		e. Tall "R"		†	£150	£150
		f. Pair. Types A and B	£140	—		
		g. Opt double, one albino		†	30·00	—
26	29	4 a. olive-green (1889)	2·50	80	6·00	2·25
		f. Pair. Types A and B	90·00			
27		4 a. slate-green	3·50	1·10	1·50	45
		a. Small "G"		†	£350	£200
		d. Small "R"		†	£350	—
		e. Tall "R"		†	£225	£225
		f. Pair. Types A and B	28·00	—		
		g. Opt double, one albino		†	50·00	—
28	21	6 a. olive-bistre	4·00	7·50	1·75	8·00
		f. Pair. Types A and B	35·00	—		
29		6 a. bistre-brown	1·00	4·25	2·75	5·00
		f. Pair. Types A and B	17·00	—		
30	31	8 a. dull mauve	7·00	29·00	1·50	60
		f. Pair. Types A and B	£180	—		
31		8 a. magenta (1897)			5·00	6·00
32	32	12 a. purple/red (1891)	3·00	8·00	2·50	65
		a. Pair, with and without opt		†		
		e. Tall "R"		†	£550	£450
		f. Pair. Types A and B	50·00	—		
33	33	1 r. slate (1889)	£100	£275	1·10	75
		f. Pair. Types A and B	£300	—		
34	37	1 r. green & carmine (1896)		†	2·25	2·75
		a. "GWALICR"		†	£650	£800
		b. Opt double, one albino	60·00	—		
35	38	2 r. carm & yell-brn (1896)		†	5·00	3·00
		a. Small "G"		†	£225	£170
		d. Small "R"		†	£225	£180
36		3 r. brown and green (1896)		†	7·00	3·50
		a. Small "G"		†	£250	£180
		d. Small "R"		†	£275	£190
37		5 r. ultram & violet (1896)		†	12·00	6·50
		a. Small "G"		†	£300	£200
		d. Small "R"		†	£325	£225
16/37		Set of 16			60·00	75·00

Printings to 1891 continued to use the setting showing both types, but subsequently a new setting containing Type B overprints only was used.

The ½ a., 1 a., 2 a. and 3 a. exist with space between "I" and "O" of "GWALIOR".

The "GWALICR" error occurs on R.1/5 in the May 1896 printing only.

Maharaja Madhav Rao Sindhia, 1886–1925

1899–1911. (a) *Optd with T 2 (B).*

			A	B
38	40	3 p. carmine	10	20
		a. Opt inverted	£600	£400
		b. Small "G"	48·00	50·00
		d. Small "R"	55·00	
		e. Tall "R"	38·00	
		f. Opt double, one albino	30·00	
39		3 p. grey (1904)	6·00	60·00
		e. Tall "R"	£200	
		f. Opt double, one albino	50·00	
40	23	½ a. pale yellow-green (1901)	20	90
		e. Tall "R"	75·00	
		f. Opt double, one albino	20·00	
40g		½ a. yellow-green (1903)	1·75	1·50
		ge. Tall "R"	£100	
41	25	1 a. carmine (1901)	30	35
		e. Tall "R"	85·00	
		f. Opt double, one albino	35·00	
42	27	2 a. pale violet (1903)	55	3·00
		e. Tall "R"	£130	
43	36	2 a. 6 p. ultramarine (1903)	85	3·50
		e. Tall "R"	£160	
38/43		Set of 6	7·00	65·00

(b) *Optd as T 2, but "GWALIOR" 13 mm long. Opt spaced 2¾ mm*

			A	B
44	38	3 r. brown and green (1911)	£140	£150
45		5 r. ultramarine and violet (1910)	55·00	55·00
		a. Opt double, one albino	80·00	

1903–11. *King Edward VII. Optd as T 2.*
A. "GWALIOR" 14 *mm long. Overprint spaced 1¾ mm*
B. "GWALIOR" 13 *mm long. Overprint spaced 2¾ mm (1908–11)*

			A	B
46	41	3 p. pale grey	40	20	1·00	10
		e. Tall "R"	26·00	28·00
		f. Slate-grey (1905)	50	20	1·40	35
		fe. Tall "R"	30·00	32·00

			A	B
48	42	½ a. green	10	10
		e. Tall "R"	25·00	27·00	†
49	43	1 a. carmine	10	10	1·50	75
		e. Tall "R"	29·00	32·00	†
		f. Opt double, one albino	30·00		†
50	44	2 a. pale violet (1904)	60	60	†
		e. Tall "R"	65·00		†
		f. Mauve	80	15	1·25	15
		fe. Tall "R"	75·00	75·00	†
52	45	2 a. 6 p. ultramarine (1904)	14·00	50·00	50	4·75
		e. Tall "R"	£600		†
53	46	3 a. orange-brown (1904)	85	30	1·40	20
		e. Tall "R"	£120		†
54	47	4 a. olive	1·10	40	†
		e. Tall "R"	£140	£120	†
		f. Pale olive	4·75	1·40	2·75	50
		fe. Tall "R"	£180		†
56	48	6 a. olive-bistre (1904)	2·25	2·75	3·00	80
		e. Tall "R"	£650		†
57	49	8 a. purple (*shades*) (1905)	2·50	1·25	4·00	1·40
		e. Tall "R"	£275	£180	†
		f. Claret			10·00	2·25
		fa. Opt double, one albino			40·00	—
59	50	12 a. purple/red (1905)	2·50	11·00	2·50	3·25
		e. Tall "R"	£700		†
		f. Opt double, one albino			50·00	—
60	51	1 r. green & carmine (1905)	1·50	1·75	2·50	1·00
		e. Tall "R"	£600		†
61	52	2 r. carm & yell-brn (1906)	30·00	42·00	7·50	11·00
		a. Opt double, one albino	50·00	—	40·00	—
62		3 r. brown and green (1910)		†	24·00	40·00
		a. Red-brown and green		†	60·00	70·00
63		5 r. ultram & violet (1911)		†	17·00	24·00
46/63		Set of 14			55·00	80·00

1907–08. *Nos. 149 and 150 of India optd as T 2.*
(a) "GWALIOR" 14 *mm long. Overprint spaced 1¾ mm*

64	53	½ a. green	10	70
		e. Tall "R"	38·00	

(b) "GWALIOR" 13 *mm long. Overprint spaced 2¾ mm (1908)*

65	53	½ a. green	35	15
66	54	1 a. carmine	60	10

1912–14. *King George V. Optd as T 2.*

67	55	3 p. slate-grey	10	10
		a. Opt double	†	£700
		b. "Rs" flaw	22·00	26·00
68	56	½ a. green	20	10
		a. Opt inverted	†	£375
69	57	1 a. aniline carmine	20	10
		a. Opt double	25·00	
70	59	2 a. mauve	40	10
		w. Wmk inverted	†	50·00
71	62	3 a. orange-brown	40	15
72	63	4 a. olive (1913)	50	60
73	64	4 a. olive-bistre	70	75
74	65	8 a. purple (1913)	70	30
75	66	12 a. dull claret (1914)	90	1·75
76	67	1 r. brown and green (1913)	2·00	40
		a. Opt double, one albino	20·00	
		b. Opt double	£600	
77		2 r. carmine-rose and brown (1913)	4·50	4·00
		a. Opt double, one albino	50·00	
78		5 r. ultramarine and violet (1913)	18·00	6·50
		a. Opt double, one albino	70·00	
67/78		Set of 12	25·00	13·00

GWALIOR
(3)

1921. *No. 192 of India optd with T 3.*

79	57	9 p. on 1 a. rose-carmine	10	40

No. 79 with inverted overprint is of clandestine origin.

1923–7. *Optd as T 2. New colours and values.*

80	57	1 a. chocolate	20	10
		a. Opt double, one albino	30·00	
81	58	1½ a. chocolate (B) (1925)	65	50
82		1½ a. rose-carmine (B) (1927)	15	20
83	61	2 a. 6 p. ultramarine (1925)	90	1·75
84		2 a. 6 p. orange (1927)	20	40
85	62	3 a. ultramarine (1924)	40	60
80/5		Set of 6	2·25	3·25

No. 82 with inverted overprint is of clandestine origin.

Maharaja George Jivaji Rao Sindhia, 1925–1961

GWALIOR
गवालियर
(4)

GWALIOR
गवालियर
(5)

1928–36. *King George V (Nasik printing, wmk Mult Star), optd at Nasik with T 4 or 5 (rupee values).*

86	55	3 p. slate (1932)	45	10
		w. Wmk inverted	1·00	1·00
87	56	½ a. green (1930)	85	10
		w. Wmk inverted		
88	80	9 p. deep green (1932)	1·25	20
		w. Wmk inverted	2·00	50
89	57	1 a. chocolate	35	10
		w. Wmk inverted		50
90	82	1 a. 3 p. mauve (1936)	30	10
91	70	2 a. purple	45	20
		w. Wmk inverted	45	20
92	63	3 a. bright blue	60	40
93	71	4 a. sage-green	80	90
		w. Wmk inverted	1·25	1·50
94	65	8 a. reddish purple (*wmk inverted*)	1·00	1·10
95	66	12 a. claret	1·00	1·75
96	67	1 r. chocolate and green	1·25	2·50
		w. Wmk inverted	2·25	2·50

97	67	2 r. carmine and orange	2·50	2·50
		w. Wmk inverted	5·00	3·50
98		5 r. ultramarine and purple (*wmk inverted*) (1929)	12·00	20·00
99		10 r. green and scarlet (1930)	40·00	30·00
100		15 r. blue & olive (*wmk inverted*) (1930)	65·00	48·00
101		25 r. orange and blue (1930)	£120	95·00
86/101		Set of 16	£225	£180

The 9 p. exists printed by lithography or typography.

1935–36. *New types and colours. Optd with T 4.*

102	79	½ a. green (1936)	20	10
		w. Wmk inverted	2·00	1·50
103	81	1 a. chocolate	10	10
104	59	2 a. vermilion (1936)	30	1·25
102/4		Set of 3	50	1·40

1938–48. *King George VI. Nos. 247/50, 253, 255/6, and 259/64 optd with T 4 or 5 (rupee values).*

105	91	3 p. slate	3·25	10
106		½ a. red-brown	3·50	10
107		9 p. green (1939)	32·00	2·50
108		1 a. carmine	3·25	15
109	—	3 a. yellow-green (1939)	8·00	2·50
110	—	4 a. brown	38·00	1·50
111	—	6 a. turquoise-green (1939)	2·50	5·50
112	93	1 r. grey and red-brown (1942)	4·00	1·50
113		2 r. purple and brown (1948)	24·00	6·00
114		5 r. green and blue (1948)	38·00	27·00
115		10 r. purple and claret (1948)	38·00	35·00
116		15 r. brown and green (1948)	£120	£150
117		25 r. slate-violet and purple (1948)	£110	£120
105/117		Set of 13	£375	£300

1942–5. *King George VI. Optd with T 4.*

118	100a	3 p. slate	45	10
		w. Wmk inverted	—	11·00
119		½ a. purple (1943)	45	10
120		9 p. green	45	10
121		1 a. carmine (1943)	40	10
		a. Optd double	—	£120
122	101	1½ a. dull violet	3·25	20
123		2 a. vermilion	55	20
124		3 a. bright violet	5·00	30
		a. Opt double	—	£120
125	102	4 a. brown	1·25	20
126		6 a. turquoise-green (1945)	20·00	15·00
127		8 a. slate-violet (1944)	2·75	2·75
128		12 a. lake (1943)	4·50	14·00
118/28		Set of 11	35·00	30·00

The 1½ a. and 3 a. exist printed by lithography or typography.

GWALIOR
गवालियर
(6)

1949 (Apr). *King George VI. Optd with T 6 at the Alizah Printing Press, Gwalior.*

129	100a	3 p. slate	60	50
130		½ a. purple	60	50
131		1 a. carmine	75	60
132	101	2 a. vermilion	13·00	1·50
133		3 a. bright violet	32·00	19·00
134	102	4 a. brown	2·25	2·50
135		6 a. turquoise-green	32·00	42·00
136		8 a. slate-violet	75·00	42·00
137		12 a. lake	£275	£120
129/137		Set of 9	£375	£200

OFFICIAL STAMPS

गवालियर
(O 1)

गवालियर
(O 2)

सरविस
(O 1)

सरविस
(O 2)

1895–96. *Queen Victoria. Optd with Type O 1.*

O 1	23	½ a. blue-green	10	10
		a. Hindi characters transposed	24·00	27·00
		b. 4th Hindi character omitted	£325	40·00
		c. Opt double	†	£800
O 2	25	1 a. brown-purple	5·50	50
O 3		1 a. plum	65	10
		a. Hindi characters transposed	38·00	42·00
		b. 4th Hindi character omitted	—	65·00
O 4	27	2 a. dull blue	90	35
O 5		2 a. deep blue	1·00	35
		a. Hindi characters transposed	60·00	75·00
		b. 4th Hindi character omitted	£100	£100
O 6	29	4 a. olive-green	1·50	75
		a. Hindi characters transposed	£400	£400
		b. 4th Hindi character omitted	£1600	£1100
O 7		4 a. slate-green	1·10	75
		a. Hindi characters transposed	£275	
O 8	31	8 a. dull mauve	1·40	1·40
		a. Opt double, one albino	30·00	
O 9		8 a. magenta	1·10	70
		a. Hindi characters transposed	£1000	£1100
O10	37	1 r. green and carmine (1896)	3·50	3·00
		a. Hindi characters transposed	£2000	
O1/10		Set of 6	6·50	4·25

In the errors listed above it is the last two Hindi characters that are transposed, so that the word reads "Sersiv". The error occurs on R.19/1 in the sheet from the early printings up to May 1896.

1901–04. *Colours changed.*

O23	40	3 p. carmine (1902)	..	30	20
O24		3 p. grey (1904)	..	85	1·50
O25	23	½ a. pale yellow-green	..	2·50	15
O26		½ a. yellow-green	..	20	10
O27	25	1 a. carmine	..	2·75	10
O28	27	2 a. pale violet (1903)	..	55	1·50
O23/8	..		*Set of 5*	4·25	3·00

1903–08. *King Edward VII. Optd as Type O 1.*

(a) Overprint spaced 10 mm (1903–5)

O29	41	3 p. pale grey	..	30	10
		a. Slate-grey (1905)	..	30	10
O31	42	½ a. green	..	1·40	10
O32	43	1 a. carmine	..	40	10
O33	44	2 a. pale violet (1905)	..	1·40	45
		a. Mauve	..	90	20
O35	47	4 a. olive (1905)	..	9·00	90
		a. Opt double, one albino	..	40·00	
O36	49	8 a. purple (1905)	..	3·00	70
		a. Claret	..	8·50	3·00
		ab. Opt double, one albino	..	30·00	
O38	51	1 r. green and carmine (1905)	..	2·75	1·40
O29/38			*Set of 7*	16·00	3·00

(b) Overprint spaced 8 mm (1907–8)

O39	41	3 p. pale grey	..	2·50	15
		a. Slate-grey	..	3·75	70
O41	42	½ a. green	..	1·50	15
O42	43	1 a. carmine	..	50	10
O43	44	1 a. mauve	..	8·50	65
O44	47	4 a. olive	..	2·50	75
O45	49	8 a. purple	..	3·00	3·75
O46	51	1 r. green and carmine (1908)	..	23·00	8·50
O39/46			*Set of 7*	38·00	12·50

1907–08. *Nos. 149 and 150 of India optd as Type O 1.*

(a) Overprint spaced 10 mm (1908)

O47	53	½ a. green	..	4·00	10
O48	54	1 a. carmine	..	3·50	15
		a. Opt double, one albino	..	30·00	

(b) Overprint spaced 8 mm (1907)

O49	53	½ a. green	..	65	15
O50	54	1 a. carmine	..	40·00	3·00

1913–23. *King George V. Optd with Type O 1.*

O51	55	3 p. slate-grey	..	20	10
		a. "Rs" flaw	..	40·00	
O52	56	½ a. green	..	20	10
		a. Opt double	..	90·00	£130
O53	57	1 a. rose-carmine	..	6·00	40
		a. Aniline carmine	..	20	10
		ab. Opt double	..	65·00	
O54		1 a. chocolate (1923)	..	2·00	15
O55	59	2 a. mauve	..	45	20
O56	63	4 a. olive	..	55	75
O57	65	8 a. purple	..	75	80
O58	67	1 r. brown and green	..	13·00	13·00
		a. Opt double, one albino	..	50·00	
O51/8			*Set of 8*	15·00	14·00

1921. *No. O97 of India optd with T 3.*

O59	57	9 p. on 1 a. rose-carmine	..	10	30

1927–35. *King George V (Nasik printing, wmk Mult Star), optd at Nasik as Type O 1 (but top line measures 13 mm instead of 14 mm) or with Type O 2 (rupee values).*

O61	55	3 p. slate	..	30	10
		w. Wmk inverted	..	10	50
O62	56	½ a. green	..	10	15
		w. Wmk inverted	..	1·50	
O63	80	9 p. deep green (1932)	..	10	15
O64	57	1 a. chocolate	..	10	10
		w. Wmk inverted	..	50	20
O65	82	1 a. 3 p. mauve (1933)	..	50	15
		w. Wmk inverted	..	2·00	
O66	70	2 a. purple	..	20	15
		w. Wmk inverted	..	1·50	
O67	71	4 a. sage-green	..	50	30
		w. Wmk inverted	..	—	60
O68	65	8 a. reddish purple (1928)	..	50	70
		w. Wmk inverted	..	1·25	70
O69	67	1 r. chocolate and green	..	80	1·60
		w. Wmk inverted	..	1·50	2·00
O70		2 r. carmine and orange (1935)	..	5·50	7·50
O71		5 r. ultramarine and purple (1932)	..	11·00	£110
		w. Wmk inverted	..	11·00	
O72		10 r. green and scarlet (1932)	..	80·00	£225
O61/72			*Set of 12*	90·00	£300

1936–37. *New types. Optd as Type O 1 (13 mm).*

O73	79	½ a. green	..	15	15
		w. Wmk inverted	..	—	2·00
O74	81	1 a. chocolate	..	15	15
O75	59	2 a. vermilion	..	20	35
O76		2 a. vermilion (small die)	..	2·00	1·10
O77	63	4 a. sage-green (1937)	..	50	60
O73/7			*Set of 5*	2·50	2·10

1938. *King George VI. Optd as Type O 1 (13 mm).*

O78	91	½ a. red-brown	..	6·50	30
O79		1 a. carmine	..	1·10	20

गवालियर

1ᴬ ___ 1ᴬ

(O 3)   (O 4)

1940–42. *Official stamps optd with Type O 3.*

O80	O 20	3 p. slate	..	50	10
O81		½ a. red-brown	..	3·00	25
O82		½ a. purple (1942)	..	50	10
O83		9 p. slate (1942)	..	70	50
O84		1 a. carmine	..	2·25	10

O85	O 20	1 a. 3 p. yellow-brown (1942)	..	26·00	1·60
		w. Wmk inverted	..	—	11·00
O86		1½ a. dull violet (1942)	..	1·00	30
O87		2 a. vermilion	..	1·00	30
O88		4 a. brown (1942)	..	1·25	1·40
O89		8 a. slate-violet (1942)	..	2·50	5·50
O80/9			*Set of 10*	35·00	9·00

1941. *Stamp of 1932 (King George V) optd with Type O 1 and surch with Type O 4.*

O90	82	1 a. on 1 a. 3 p. mauve	..	16·00	2·50
		w. Wmk inverted	..	20·00	4·00

1942–47. *King George VI. Optd with Type O 2.*

O91	93	1 r. grey and red-brown	..	8·00	12·00
O92		2 r. purple and brown	..	20·00	60·00
O93		5 r. green and blue (1943)	..	38·00	£325
O94		10 r. purple and claret (1947)	..	£110	£650
O91/4			*Set of 4*	£160	£950

Gwalior became part of Madhya Bharat by 1 July 1948.

JIND

For earlier issues, see under INDIAN FEUDATORY STATES

PRICES FOR STAMPS ON COVER	
Nos. 1/4	*from × 20*
Nos. 5/16	—
Nos. 17/40	*from × 15*
Nos. 41/149	*from × 8*
Nos. O1/86	*from × 15*

Raja Raghubir Singh, 1864–1887

		JHIND STATE (1)	STATE (2)	JEEND STATE (2)	JHIND STATE (3)

1885 (1 July). *Queen Victoria. Optd with T 1.*

1	23	½ a. blue-green	..	..	1·25	2·25
		a. Opt inverted	..	..	85·00	90·00
2	25	1 a. brown-purple	..	..	18·00	26·00
		a. Opt inverted	..	..	£600	£650
3	27	2 a. dull blue	..	..	6·00	10·00
		a. Opt inverted	..	..	£500	£550
4	17	4 a. green	..	..	38·00	50·00
5	31	8 a. dull mauve	..	..	£375	
		a. Opt inverted	..	..	£7500	
6	33	1 r. slate	..	..	£400	
		a. Opt inverted	..	..	£8500	
1/6				*Set of 6*	£750	

The overprint inverted errors occurred on R.10/8 in the setting of 120, although it is believed that one pane of the ½ a. had the overprint inverted on the entire pane. Examples of inverted overprints on the ½ a., 1 a. and 2 a. with the lines much less curved are thought to come from a trial printing.

All six values exist with reprinted overprint. This has the words "JHIND" and "STATE" 8 and 9 mm in length respectively, whereas in the originals the words are 9 and 9½ mm.

1885. *Optd with T 2.*

7	23	½ a. blue-green (R.)	..	70·00	
8	25	1 a. brown-purple	..	75·00	
9	27	2 a. dull blue (R.)	..	80·00	
10	17	4 a. green (R.)	..	£110	
		a. Opt double, one albino	..	£140	
11	31	8 a. dull mauve	..	£110	
12	33	1 r. slate (R.)	..	£120	
7/12			*Set of 6*	£500	

1886. *Optd with T 3, in red.*

13	23	½ a. blue-green	..	18·00	
		a. "JEIND" for "JHIND"	..	£900	
14	27	2 a. dull blue	..	18·00	
		a. "JEIND" for "JHIND"	..	£1000	
		b. Opt double, one albino	..	50·00	
15	17	4 a. green	..	35·00	
		a. Opt double, one albino	..	40·00	
		b. Opt treble, two albino	..	60·00	
16	33	1 r. slate	..	38·00	
		a. "JEIND" for "JHIND"	..	£1600	
13/16			*Set of 4*	95·00	

1886–99. *Optd with T 3.*

17	23	½ a. blue-green	..	10	10
		a. Opt inverted	..	£190	
18	25	1 a. brown-purple	..	45	20
		a. "JEIND" for "JHIND"	..	£375	
		b. Opt double, one albino	..	30·00	
19		1 a. plum (1899)	..	1·50	75
20	26	1 a. 6 p. sepia (1896)	..	75	2·00
		a. Opt double, one albino	..	35·00	
21	27	2 a. dull blue	..	85	40
22		2 a. ultramarine	..	90	50
		a. Opt double, one albino	..	35·00	
23	28	3 a. brown-orange (1891)	..	75	50
24	29	4 a. olive-green	..	1·90	1·50
25		4 a. slate-green	..	2·00	2·25
26	21	6 a. olive-bistre (1891)	..	4·75	11·00
		a. Opt double, one albino	..	30·00	
27		6 a. bistre-brown	..	80	6·00
28	31	8 a. dull mauve	..	3·00	9·50
		a. "JEIND" for "JHIND"	..	£1400	
29		8 a. magenta (1897)	..	4·50	14·00
		a. Opt double, one albino	..	30·00	
30	32	12 a. purple/red (1896)	..	3·00	14·00
		a. Opt double, one albino	..	30·00	
31	33	1 r. slate	..	6·00	29·00

32	37	1 r. green and carmine (1897)	..	6·00	32·00
33	38	2 r. carmine and yellow-brown (1896)	..	£200	£550
34		3 r. brown and green (1896)	..	£350	£550
35		5 r. ultramarine and violet (1896)	..	£400	£600
17/35			*Set of 14*	£850	£1600

Varieties exist in which the word "JHIND" measures 10½ mm and 9¾ mm instead of 10 mm. Such varieties are to be found on Nos. 17, 18, 21, 24, 28 and 31.

Raja (Maharaja from 1911) Ranbir Singh, 1887–1959

1900–4. *Colours changed.*

36	40	3 p. carmine	..	60	1·00
37		3 p. grey (1904)	..	15	2·00
38	23	½ a. pale yellow-green (1902)	..	2·25	3·50
39		½ a. yellow-green (1903)	..	4·75	3·00
40	25	1 a. carmine (1902)	..	20	3·75
		a. Opt double, one albino	..	25·00	
36/40			*Set of 4*	2·75	9·25

1903–9. *King Edward VII. Optd with T 3.*

41	41	3 p. pale grey	..	10	10
		a. Opt double, one albino	..	15·00	
42		3 p. slate-grey (1905)	..	20	50
43	42	½ a. green	..	30	1·10
44	43	1 a. carmine	..	1·60	1·00
45	44	1 a. pale violet	..	1·60	1·75
46		2 a. mauve (1906)	..	1·00	55
		a. Opt double, one albino	..	25·00	
47	35	2 a. 6 p. ultramarine (1909)	..	30	4·25
		a. Opt double, one albino	..	20·00	
48	46	3 a. orange-brown	..	35	35
		a. Opt double	..	£110	£200
49	47	4 a. olive	..	4·50	7·00
		a. Opt double, one albino	..	40·00	
50		4 a. pale olive	..	4·00	6·00
51	48	6 a. bistre (1905)	..	4·00	12·00
		a. Opt double, one albino	..	30·00	
52	49	8 a. purple (shades)	..	1·90	14·00
53		8 a. claret	..	7·50	18·00
54	50	12 a. purple/red (1905)	..	1·60	9·00
55	51	1 r. green and carmine (1905)	..	2·00	10·00
		a. Opt double, one albino	..	40·00	
41/55			*Set of 11*	15·00	50·00

1907–9. *Nos. 149/50 of India optd with T 3.*

56	53	½ a. green	..	10	20
57	54	1 a. carmine (1909)	..	10	55

1913. *King George V. Optd with T 3.*

58	55	3 p. slate-grey	..	10	1·60
59	56	½ a. green	..	10	60
60	57	1 a. aniline carmine	..	10	35
61	59	2 a. mauve	..	15	3·25
62	62	3 a. orange-brown	..	1·50	8·00
63	64	6 a. olive-bistre	..	3·75	20·00
58/63			*Set of 6*	5·25	30·00

		JIND STATE (4)	JIND STATE (5)	JIND STATE (6)

1914–27. *King George V. Optd with T 4.*

64	55	3 p. slate-grey	..	35	20
65	56	½ a. green	..	1·10	15
66	57	1 a. aniline carmine	..	45	15
67	58	1½ a. chocolate (Type A) (1922)	..	55	2·75
68		1½ a. chocolate (Type B) (1924)	..	35	1·50
69	59	2 a. mauve	..	85	45
70	61	2 a. 6 p. ultramarine (1922)	..	35	3·75
71	62	3 a. orange-brown	..	40	2·00
72	63	4 a. olive	..	85	4·00
73	64	6 a. olive-bistre	..	1·00	8·50
74	65	8 a. purple	..	2·75	4·50
75	66	12 a. dull claret	..	1·10	8·50
76	67	1 r. brown and green	..	4·75	10·00
		a. Opt double, one albino	..	25·00	
77		2 r. carmine and yellow-brown (1927)	..	4·00	80·00
78		5 r. ultramarine and violet (1927)	..	26·00	£160
64/78			*Set of 15*	40·00	£250

No. 71 with inverted overprint is of clandestine origin.

1922. *No. 192 of India optd "JIND" in block capitals.*

79	57	9 p. on 1 a. rose-carmine	..	1·25	13·00

1924–27. *Optd with T 4. New colours.*

80	57	1 a. chocolate	..	2·50	90
81	58	1½ a. rose-carmine (Type B) (1927)	..	20	1·50
82	61	2 a. 6 p. orange (1927)	..	30	4·75
83	62	3 a. bright blue (1925)	..	80	3·25
80/3			*Set of 4*	3·50	9·25

Nos. 81/2 with inverted overprint are of clandestine origin.

1927–37. *King George V (Nasik printing, wmk Mult Star), optd at Nasik with T 5 or 6 (rupee values).*

84	55	3 p. slate	..	10	10
		w. Wmk inverted	..	1·50	
85	56	½ a. green (1929)	..	10	30
86	80	9 p. deep green (1932)	..	30	40
87	57	1 a. chocolate (1928)	..	15	10
		w. Wmk inverted	..	—	1·00
88	82	1 a. 3 p. mauve (1932)	..	20	30
89	58	1½ a. rose-carmine (Type B) (1930)	..	30	1·25
		w. Wmk inverted	..	75	1·25
90	70	2 a. purple (1928)	..	75	30
		w. Wmk inverted	..	75	30
91	61	2 a. 6 p. orange (1930)	..	70	
		w. Wmk inverted	..	70	6·00
92	62	3 a. bright blue (1930)	..	1·50	6·00
		w. Wmk inverted	..	5·00	
93	83	3 a. 6 p. ultramarine (1937)	..	1·50	
		w. Wmk inverted	..	50	11·00
94	71	4 a. sage-green (1928)	..	2·50	1·25
		w. Wmk inverted	..	75	1·25

95	64	6 a. bistre (1937)	.. ..	55	11·00
		w. Wmk inverted	..		3·00
96	65	8 a. reddish purple (1930)	..	1·50	1·90
		w. Wmk inverted	..		1·50
97	66	12 a. claret (1930)	..		2·25 12·00
		w. Wmk inverted	..		2·25 12·00
98	67	1 r. chocolate and green (1930)		2·25	3·00
		w. Wmk inverted	..		10·00
99		2 r. carmine and orange (1930)	..	20·00	85·00
		w. Wmk inverted	..		10·00
100		5 r. ultramarine and purple (1928) ..		8·00	24·00
		w. Wmk inverted	..		30·00
101		10 r. green and carmine (1928)	..	10·00	18·00
102		15 r. blue & olive (*wmk inverted*) (1929)	60·00	£350
103		25 r. orange and blue (1929) ..		90·00	£425
84/103		.. .. *Set of 20*		£160	£850

1934. *New types and colours. Optd with T 5.*

104	79	½ a. green	..	30	15
105	81	1 a. chocolate	..	60	20
		w. Wmk inverted	..	—	2·00
106	59	2 a. vermilion ..	..	60	50
107	62	3 a. carmine	..	80	40
108	63	4 a. sage-green	..	1·25	75
104/8		.. .. *Set of 5*		3·25	1·75

1937–38. *King George VI. Nos. 247/64 optd with T 5 or T 6 (rupee values).*

109	91	3 p. slate	..	4·75	1·00
110		½ a. red-brown	..	60	2·25
111		9 p. green (1937)	..	60	1·75
112		1 a. carmine (1937)	..	60	35
113	92	2 a. vermilion	..	1·50	10·00
114	—	2 a. 6 p. bright violet	..	1·00	10·00
115	—	3 a. yellow-green	..	4·00	9·00
116	—	3 a. 6 p. bright blue	..	1·25	10·00
117	—	4 a. brown	..	5·00	10·00
118	—	6 a. turquoise-green	..	2·50	13·00
119	—	8 a. slate-violet	..	2·00	14·00
120	—	12 a. lake	..	1·75	15·00
121	93	1 r. grey and red-brown	..	14·00	25·00
122		2 r. purple and brown	..	16·00	70·00
123		5 r. green and blue	..	30·00	55·00
124		10 r. purple and claret ..	..	55·00	60·00
125		15 r. brown and green	..	£150	£550
126		25 r. slate-violet and purple	..	£325	£550
109/26		.. *Set of 18*		£550	£1200

JIND
(7)

1941–43. *King George VI. Optd with T 7. (a) Stamps of 1937. W 69 (inverted on 15 r.).*

127	91	3 p. slate	..	9·00	12·00
128		½ a. red-brown ..	..	1·00	30
129		9 p. green	..	8·00	9·50
130		1 a. carmine	..	1·00	2·75
131	93	1 r. grey and red-brown	..	8·00	18·00
132		2 r. purple and brown..	..	16·00	22·00
133		5 r. green and blue	..	38·00	60·00
134		10 r. purple and claret ..		55·00	60·00
135		15 r. brown and green	..	£120	£130
136		25 r. slate-violet and purple	..	£100	£325
127/136		*Set of 10*		£325	£550

(b) Stamps of 1940–43

137	100a	3 p. slate (1942)	..	50	50
138		½ a. purple (1943)	..	50	75
139		9 p. green (1942)	..	60	2·25
140		1 a. carmine (1942)	..	65	75
141	101	1 a. 3 p. yellow-brown	..	1·00	2·50
142		1½ a. dull violet (1942) ..		5·00	3·50
143		2 a. vermilion	..	1·75	2·25
144		3 a. bright violet (1942)	..	10·00	2·25
145		3½ a. bright blue	..	5·00	5·00
146	102	4 a. brown	..	3·00	2·25
147		6 a. turquoise-green	..	3·50	8·00
148		8 a. slate-violet	..	2·50	8·00
149		12 a. lake	..	9·50	8·00
137/149		.. *Set of 13*		40·00	42·00

The 1½ a. and 3 a. exist printed by lithography or typography.

OFFICIAL STAMPS

SERVICE

SERVICE	SERVICE	JHIND STATE
(O 14)	(O 15)	(O 16)

1885 (1 July). *Queen Victoria. Nos. 1/3 of Jind optd with Type O 14.*

O1	23	½ a. blue-green	..	30	30
		a. Opt Type 1 inverted	..	85·00	50·00
O2	25	1 a. brown-purple	..	30	10
		a. Opt Type 1 inverted	..	9·00	7·00
O3	27	2 a. dull blue	..	24·00	32·00
		a. Opt Type 1 inverted	..		£750

The three values have had the overprint reprinted in the same way as the ordinary stamps of 1885. See note after No. 6.

1885. *Nos. 7/9 of Jind optd with Type O 15.*

O7	23	½ a. blue-green (R.)	..		75·00
		a. "JEEND STATE" double, one albino		£100
O8	25	1 a. brown-purple	..		65·00
O9	27	2 a. dull blue (R.)	..		70·00
O7/9		*Set of 3*			£190

1886. *Optd with Type O 16, in red.*

O10	23	½ a. blue-green	..		12·00
		a. "ERVICE"	..		£2750
		b. "JEIND"	..		£500
		c. "JHIND STATE" double, one albino		50·00

O11	27	2 a. dull blue ..	..		15·00
		a. "ERVICE"	..		£1700
		b. "JEIND"	..		£750
		c. "SERVICE" double, one albino ..		30·00
		d. "JHIND STATE" double, one albino		30·00

1886–1902. *Optd with Type O 16.*

O12	23	½ a. blue-green	..	45	10
		a. "JHIND STATE" double, one albino	30·00	
O13	25	1 a. brown-purple	..		15·00
		a. "ERVICE"	..		£375
		b. "JEIND" ..	..		£375
		c. "SERVICE" double, one albino		20·00
O14		1 a. plum (1902)	..	6·50	15
O15	27	2 a. dull blue	..	1·40	50
		a. "SERVICE" double, one albino		30·00
		b. "SERVICE" treble, two albino		35·00
O16		2 a. ultramarine	..	45	30
		a. "JHIND STATE" double, one albino	35·00	
O17	29	4 a. olive-green (1892)	..	75	40
		a. "JHIND STATE" double, one albino	30·00	
O18		4 a. slate-green	..	1·40	1·10
O19	31	8 a. dull mauve (1892)	..	2·50	2·00
O20		8 a. magenta (1897)	..	2·00	4·25
		a. "JHIND STATE" double, one albino	30·00	
O21	37	1 r. green and carmine (1896)	..	6·00	26·00
		a. "SERVICE" double, one albino ..		40·00
		b. "JHIND STATE" treble, two albino		50·00
O12/21		*Set of 6*		14·50	27·00

Varieties mentioned in note after No. 35 exist on Nos. O12, O15, O17 and O20.

Printings up to and including that of October 1897 had the "SERVICE" overprint. Type O 15, applied to sheets already overprinted with Type 3. From the printing of December 1899 onwards "SERVICE" and "JHIND STATE" were overprinted at one operation, as Type O 16, to provide fresh supplies of Nos. O12, O14 and O21.

1902. *Colour changed. Optd with Type O 16.*

O22	23	½ a. yellow-green	..	75	20
		a. "V" of "SERVICE" omitted ..	65·00	35·00

No. O22a normally shows a tiny trace of the "V" remaining. Examples showing the letter completely missing are worth much more.

1903–6. *King Edward VII stamps of India optd with Type O 16.*

O23	41	3 p. pale grey ..	..	10	10
O24		3 p. slate-grey (1906)	..	10	10
O25	42	½ a. green	..	1·75	10
		a. "HIND"	..	£2000	£250
		b. Opt double, one albino	..	25·00	
O26	43	1 a. carmine	..	70	10
		a. "HIND"	..	†	£190
		b. Opt double, one albino ..		25·00
O27	44	2 a. pale violet	..	1·25	60
O28		2 a. mauve	..	20	10
O29	47	4 a. olive	..	40	45
		a. Opt double, one albino ..		35·00
O30	49	8 a. purple (*shades*)	..	7·00	5·00
O31		8 a. claret	..	2·50	1·50
O32	51	1 r. green and carmine (1906)	..	2·50	2·25
O23/32		*Set of 7*		7·25	4·00

1907. *Nos. 149/50 of India optd with Type O 16.*

O33	53	½ a. green	..	15	10
O34	54	1 a. carmine	..	25	10

1914–27. *King George V. Official stamps of India optd with T 4.*

O35	55	3 p. slate-grey	..	10	10
		a. "JIND STATE" double, one albino	30·00	
O36	56	½ a. green	..	10	10
O37	57	1 a. aniline carmine	..	15	10
O38		1 a. pale rose-carmine	..	35	10
O39	59	2 a. mauve	..	15	15
O40	63	4 a. olive	..	35	15
O41	64	6 a. yellow-bistre (1927)	..	45	2·25
O42	65	8 a. purple	..	30	1·00
O43	67	1 r. brown and green ..	..	90	1·60
		a. "JIND STATE" double, one albino	30·00	
O44		2 r. carmine and yellow-brown (1927)	9·00	50·00
O45		5 r. ultramarine and violet (1927)	..	16·00	£130
O35/45		*Set of 10*	25·00	£170

No. O40 with double overprint is of clandestine origin.

1924. *As 1914-27. New colour.*

O46	57	1 a. chocolate	.. ..	30	10

JIND STATE SERVICE	JIND STATE SERVICE	JIND SERVICE
(O 17)	(O 18)	(O 19)

1927–37. *King George V (Nasik printing, wmk Mult Star), optd with Types O 17 or O 18 (rupee values).*

O47	55	3 p. slate (1928)	..	10	20
O48	56	½ a. green (1929)	..	10	85
O49	80	9 p. deep green (1932)	..	40	15
O50	57	1 a. chocolate	..	10	10
		w. Wmk inverted	..		50
O51	82	1 a. 3 p. mauve (1932)	..	40	15
		w. Wmk inverted	..		50 30
O52	70	2 a. purple (1929)	..	25	15
O53	61	2 a. 6 p. orange (1937)	..	45	13·00
O54	71	4 a. sage-green (1929)	..	35	25
		w. Wmk inverted	..	1·00	50
O55	64	6 a. bistre (1937)	..	60	
		w. Wmk inverted	..	1·50	11·00
O56	65	8 a. reddish purple (1929)	..	—	1·50
		w. Wmk inverted	..	35	1·25
O57	66	12 a. claret (1937)	..	80	9·00
O58	67	1 r. chocolate and green (1928)	..	1·50	2·50
O59		2 r. carmine and orange (1930)	..	25·00	20·00
		w. Wmk inverted	..		20·00

O60	67	5 r. ultramarine and purple (1929)	..	12·00	£140
O61		10 r. green and carmine (1928)	..	23·00	80·00
		w. Wmk inverted	..		30·00
O47/61		*Set of 15*	55·00	£250

The 9 p. exists printed by lithography or typography.

1934. *Optd with Type O 17.*

O62	79	½ a. green ..	..	20	15
O63	81	1 a. chocolate ..	..	20	15
O64	59	2 a. vermilion..	..	30	15
		w. Wmk inverted	..	30	75
O65	63	4 a. sage-green	..	3·00	30
O62/5		*Set of 4*	3·25	65

1937–40. *King George VI. Optd with Types O 17 or O 18 (rupee values).*

O66	91	½ a. red-brown (1938)	..	48·00	30
O67		9 p. green	..	85	6·00
O68		1 a. carmine	..	55	30
O69	93	1 r. grey and red-brown (1940)..		23·00	42·00
O70		2 r. purple and brown (1940) ..		40·00	£170
O71		5 r. green and blue (1940)	..	85·00	£300
O72		10 r. purple and claret (1940)	..	£160	£650
O66/72		*Set of 7*	£325	£1000

1939–43. *(a) Official stamps optd with T 7.*

O73	O 20	3 p. slate	..	50	55
O74		½ a. red-brown	..	1·50	50
O75		½ a. purple (1943)	..	60	30
O76		9 p. green	..	1·50	6·50
O77		1 a. carmine	..	1·50	15
O78		1½ a. dull violet (1942)	..	4·50	1·00
O79		2 a. vermilion	..	2·00	30
		w. Wmk inverted ..	..	—	2·00
O80		2½ a. bright violet	..	1·25	5·00
O81		4 a. brown	..	2·75	1·00
O82		8 a. slate-violet	..	2·75	2·50

(b) Postage stamps optd with Type O 19

O83	93	1 r. grey and red-brown (1942)..		18·00	40·00
O84		2 r. purple and brown (1942)	..	40·00	£120
O85		5 r. green and blue (1942)	..	90·00	£275
O86		10 r. purple and claret (1942)	..	£160	£350
O73/86		*Set of 14*	£300	£700

Jind was absorbed into the Patiala and East Punjab States Union by 20 August 1948.

NABHA

PRICES FOR STAMPS ON COVER	
Nos. 1/3	*from* × 15
Nos. 4/6	—
Nos. 10/36	*from* × 12
Nos. 37/117	*from* × 7
Nos. O1/68	*from* × 15

Raja Hira Singh, 1871–1911.

NABHA STATE	NABHA STATE
(1)	(2)

1885 (1 July). *Queen Victoria. Optd with T 1.*

1	23	½ a. blue-green	..	1·10	2·75
2	25	1 a. brown-purple	..	26·00	95·00
3	27	2 a. dull blue	..	9·00	30·00
4	17	4 a. green	..	55·00	£140
5	31	8 a. dull mauve	..		£300
6	33	1 r. slate	..		£250
1/6		*Set of 6*			£550

All six values have had the overprint reprinted. On the reprints the words "NABHA" and "STATE" both measure 9¼ mm in length, whereas on the originals these words measure 11 and 10 mm respectively. The varieties with overprint double come from the reprints.

1885 (Nov)–1900. *Optd with T 2. (a) In red.*

10	23	½ a. blue-green ..	..	20	40
11	27	2 a. dull blue	..	1·40	1·40
		a. Opt double, one albino	..	40·00	
12	17	4 a. green	..	23·00	£120
13	33	1 r. slate	..	85·00	£160
		a. Opt double, one albino	..	£110	
10/13		*Set of 4*	£100	£250

(b) In black (Nov 1885–97)

14	23	½ a. blue-green (1888)	..	10	10
15	24	9 p. carmine (1892)	..	40	2·00
16	25	1 a. brown-purple	..	85	45
17		1 a. plum	..	70	35
18	26	1 a. 6 p. sepia (1891)	..	55	1·75
		a. "ABHA" for "NABHA"	..		£275
19	27	2 a. dull blue (1888)	..	1·10	75
20		2 a. ultramarine	..	90	65
21	28	3 a. orange (1889)	..	4·00	12·00
		a. Opt double, one albino	..	25·00	
22		3 a. brown-orange	..	1·60	1·00
23	29	4 a. olive-green (1888)	..	3·00	1·40
24		4 a. slate-green	..	3·00	1·40
25	21	6 a. olive-bistre (1889)	..	3·50	8·00
26		6 a. bistre-brown	..	1·10	2·00
27	31	8 a. dull mauve	..	1·10	1·60
		a. Opt double, one albino	..	30·00	
28	32	12 a. purple/*red* (1889)	..	2·25	3·00
		a. Opt double, one albino	..	27·00	
29	33	1 r. slate (1888)	..	5·50	30·00
30	37	1 r. green and carmine (1893)	..	6·00	3·75
		a. "N BHA" for "NABHA"	..		£550
		b. Opt double, one albino	..	40·00	

31	38	2 r. carmine and yellow-brown (1897)		85·00	£170
		a. Opt double, one albino			£150
32		3 r. brown and green (1897)		85·00	£190
33		5 r. ultramarine and violet (1897)		85·00	£275
14/33			*Set of 15*	£250	£600

(c) New value. In black (Nov 1900)

36	40	3 p. carmine		10	15

1903–09. *King Edward VII. Optd with T 2.*

37	41	3 p. pale grey		20	15
		a. "NAB STA" for "NABHA STATE"		£800	
		b. Opt double, one albino		20·00	
37c		3 p. slate-grey (1906)		20	15
38	42	½ a. green		30	30
		a. "NABH" for "NABHA"		£950	
39	43	1 a. carmine		50	60
40	44	2 a. pale violet		45	1·50
40a		2 a. mauve		1·40	30
40b	45	2 a. 6 p. ultramarine (1909)		17·00	75·00
		ba. Opt double, one albino		30·00	
41	46	3 a. orange-brown		40	30
		a. Opt double, one albino		35·00	
42	47	4 a. olive		1·00	1·75
43	48	6 a. olive-bistre		80	8·50
		a. Opt double, one albino		20·00	
44	49	8 a. purple		5·00	12·00
44a		8 a. claret		7·00	14·00
45	50	12 a. purple/red		2·25	14·00
46	51	1 r. green and carmine		4·75	7·50
37/46			*Set of 11*	29·00	£110

1907. *Nos. 149/50 of India optd with T 2.*

47	53	½ a. green		40	1·10
48	54	1 a. carmine		35	70

Maharaja Ripudaman (Gurcharan) Singh, 1911–1928.

1913. *King George V. Optd with T 2.*

49	55	3 p. slate-grey		20	15
50	56	½ a. green		20	10
51	57	1 a. aniline carmine		40	10
52	59	2 a. mauve		40	30
53	62	3 a. orange-brown		50	35
54	63	4 a. olive		55	80
55	64	6 a. olive-bistre		55	3·75
56	65	8 a. purple		1·10	2·75
57	66	12 a. dull claret		1·00	15·00
58	67	1 r. brown and green		5·00	2·75
		a. Opt double, one albino		32·00	
49/58			*Set of 10*	9·00	23·00

1924. *As 1913. New colour.*

59	57	1 a. chocolate		2·00	1·00

No. 59 with inverted or double overprint is of clandestine origin.

NABHA STATE	NABHA STATE
(3)	(4)

1927–36. *King George V (Nasik printing, wmk Mult Star), optd as T 3 or 4 (rupee values).*

60	55	3 p. slate (1932)		50	15
		w. Wmk inverted		1·50	1·00
61	56	½ a. green (1928)		30	20
61a	80	9 p. deep green (1934)		1·00	1·10
62	57	1 a. chocolate		45	15
		w. Wmk inverted			
63	82	1 a. 3 p. mauve (1936)		55	3·25
		w. Wmk inverted		55	
64	70	2 a. purple (1932)		1·25	35
65	61	2 a. 6 p. orange (1932)		40	5·00
66	62	3 a. bright blue (1930)		1·00	1·00
67	71	4 a. sage-green (1932)		1·25	1·40
71	67	2 r. carmine and orange (1932)		21·00	65·00
72		5 r. ultramarine and purple (*wmk inverted*) (1932)		70·00	£180
60/72			*Set of 11*	85·00	£225

The 9 p. exists printed by lithography or typography.

Maharaja Partab Singh, 1928–1971.

1936–37. *New types and colours. Optd as T 3.*

73	79	½ a. green		30	30
74	81	1 a. chocolate		30	30
75	62	3 a. carmine (1937)		2·75	7·50
76	63	4 a. slate-green (1937)		2·00	2·25
73/6			*Set of 4*	4·25	8·00

NABHA STATE	NABHA
(5)	(6)

1938. *King George VI. Nos. 247/64 optd as T 3 (3 p. to 1 a.), T 5 (2 a. to 12 a.) or T 4 (rupee values). W 69 (inverted on 15 r.).*

77	91	3 p. slate		4·75	30
78		½ a. red-brown		2·50	45
79		9 p. green		15·00	3·00
80		1 a. carmine		1·10	30
81	92	2 a. vermilion		1·00	3·75
82	–	2 a. 6 p. bright violet		1·00	6·00
83	–	3 a. yellow-green		1·10	3·25
84	–	3 a. 6 p. bright blue		1·10	12·00
85	–	4 a. brown		4·00	4·75
86	–	6 a. turquoise-green		1·75	12·00
87	–	8 a. slate-violet		1·90	12·00
88	–	12 a. lake		2·25	14·00
89	93	1 r. grey and red-brown		10·00	19·00
90		2 r. purple and brown		19·00	70·00
91		5 r. green and blue		45·00	£140
92		10 r. purple and claret		70·00	£275
93		15 r. brown and green		£180	£500
94		25 r. slate-violet and purple		£180	£500
		w. Wmk inverted		£300	£600
77/94			*Set of 18*	£500	£1400

95	91	3 p. slate (1942)		27·00	2·25
96		½ a. red-brown (1942)		65·00	3·50
97		9 p. green (1942)		10·00	9·50
98		1 a. carmine (1942)		10·00	2·00
95/8			*Set of 4*	£100	15·00

(b) Stamps of 1940-43

105	100a	3 p. slate (1942)		80	45
106		½ a. purple (1943)		3·50	45
107		9 p. green (1942)		2·75	45
108		1 a. carmine (1945)		80	2·00
109	101	1 a. 3 p. yellow-brown		80	1·25
110		1½ a. dull violet (1942)		1·00	85
111		2 a. vermilion (1943)		80	2·50
112		3 a. bright violet (1943)		1·75	2·50
113		3½ a. bright blue (1944)		8·50	30·00
114	102	4 a. brown		1·60	75
115		6 a. turquoise-green (1943)		6·50	32·00
116		8 a. slate-violet (1943)		4·75	25·00
117		12 a. lake (1943)		4·25	32·00
105/117			*Set of 13*	32·00	£110

The 1½ a. exists printed by lithography or typography.

OFFICIAL STAMPS

SERVICE

SERVICE	NABHA STATE
(O 8)	(O 9)

1885 (1 July). *Nos. 1/3 of Nabha optd with Type O 8.*

O1	23	½ a. blue-green		1·25	45
O2	25	1 a. brown-purple		30	15
		a. Opt Type O 8 double		† £1000	
O3	27	2 a. dull blue		45·00	90·00
O1/3			*Set of 3*	45·00	90·00

The three values have had the overprint reprinted in the same way as the ordinary stamps of 1885.

1885 (Nov)–97. *Optd with Type O 9. (a) In red.*

O 4	23	½ a. blue-green		4·00	3·25
O 5	27	2 a. deep blue		50	55

(b) In black (Nov 1885–97)

O 6	23	½ a. blue-green (1888)		10	10
		a. "SERVICE." with stop		£110	2·25
		b. "S ATE" for "STATE"		£110	
		c. "SERVICE" double, one albino		25·00	
O 7	25	1 a. brown-purple		65	35
O 8		1 a. plum		75	20
		a. "SERVICE." with stop		4·75	75
		ab. "SERVICE." with stop, and "NABHA STATE" double		† £250	
O 9	27	2 a. dull blue (1888)		1·25	45
O10		2 a. ultramarine		1·60	75
O11	28	3 a. orange (1889)		14·00	45·00
O12		3 a. brown-orange		14·00	45·00
		a. "NABHA STATE" double, one albino		40·00	
O13	29	4 a. olive-green (1888)		1·40	45
O14		4 a. slate-green		1·50	50
O15	21	6 a. olive-bistre (1889)		10·00	16·00
		a. "SERVICE" double, one albino		30·00	
O16		6 a. bistre-brown		£550	
O17	31	8 a. dull mauve (1889)		90	70
O18	32	12 a. purple/red (1889)		4·00	12·00
		a. "SERVICE" double, one albino		30·00	
		b. "NABHA STATE" double, one albino		30·00	
O19	33	1 r. slate (1889)		24·00	£160
O20	37	1 r. green and carmine (1.97)		20·00	50·00
O6/20			*Set of 10*	65·00	£250

Printings up to and including that of August 1895 had the "SERVICE" overprint applied to sheets of stamps already overprinted with Type 2. From the printing of January 1897 onwards the two parts of the overprint were applied at one operation. This method was only used for printings of the ½ a., 1 a. and 1 r. (O20).

1903–06. *King Edward VII stamps of India optd with Type O 9.*

O24	41	3 p. pale grey (1906)		3·25	13·00
O25		3 p. slate-grey (1906)		65	8·00
		a. Opt double, one albino		25·00	
O26	42	½ a. green		30	10
O27	43	1 a. carmine		15	10
O28	44	2 a. pale violet		1·00	60
O29		2 a. mauve		90	40
		a. Opt double, one albino		30·00	
O30	47	4 a. olive		1·10	50
O32	49	8 a. purple (*shades*)		1·10	1·00
		a. Opt double, one albino		25·00	
O33		8 a. claret		6·00	3·25
O34	51	1 r. green and carmine		1·50	2·25
O24/34			*Set of 7*	5·00	11·50

1907. *Nos. 149/50 of India optd with Type O 9.*

O35	53	½ a. green		20	30
		a. Opt double, one albino		15·00	
O36	54	1 a. carmine		25	25
		a. Opt double, one albino		25·00	

1913. *King George V. Optd with Type O 9.*

O37	63	4 a. olive		10·00	40·00
O38	67	1 r. brown and green		55·00	£250
		a. Opt double, one albino		95·00	

1913. *Official stamps of India optd with T 2.*

O39	55	3 p. slate-grey		25	5·50
O39a		3 p. bluish slate		25	5·50
O40	56	½ a. green		15	10
O41	57	1 a. aniline carmine		15	10
O42	59	2 a. mauve		30	15
O43	63	4 a. olive		40	45
O44	65	8 a. dull mauve		65	75
O46	67	1 r. brown and green		2·25	2·00
O39/46			*Set of 7*	3·75	7·50

NABHA STATE SERVICE	NABHA SERVICE
(O 10)	(O 11)

1932–42?. *King George V (Nasik printing, wmk Mult Star), optd at Nasik with Type O 10.*

O47	55	3 p. slate		10	15
O48	81	1 a. chocolate (1935)		15	15
O49	63	4 a. sage-green (1942?)		17·00	2·25
O50	65	8 a. reddish purple (1937)		1·00	1·90
O47/50			*Set of 4*	17·00	4·00

1938. *King George VI. Optd as Type O 10.*

O53	91	9 p. green		1·25	2·25
O54		1 a. carmine		7·50	35

1940–43. *(a) Official stamps optd with T 6.*

O55	O 20	3 p. slate (1942)		55	60
O56		½ a. red-brown (1942)		70	30
O57		½ a. purple (1943)		2·25	45
O58		9 p. green (1942)		1·25	90
O59		1 a. carmine (1942)		50	20
O61		1½ a. dull violet (1942)		60	40
O62		2 a. vermilion (1942)		1·00	50
		w. Wmk inverted		2·00	1·00
O64		4 a. brown (1942)		3·50	1·75
O65		8 a. slate-violet (1942)		5·50	11·00

(b) Postage stamps optd with Type O 11.

O66	93	1 r. grey and red-brown (1942)		8·50	26·00
O67		2 r. purple and brown (1942)		23·00	£130
O68		5 r. green and blue (1942)		£200	£425
O55/68			*Set of 12*	£225	£550

Nabha was absorbed into the Patiala and East Punjab States Union by 20 August 1948.

PATIALA

PRICES FOR STAMPS ON COVER	
Nos. 1/6	*from* × 10
Nos. 7/34	*from* × 6
Nos. 35/45	*from* × 8
Nos. 46/115	*from* × 4
Nos. O1/84	*from* × 15

Maharaja Rajindra Singh, 1876–1900

PUTTIALLA STATE	PUTTIALLA STATE	PATIALA STATE
(1)	(2)	(3)

1884 (1 Oct). *Queen Victoria. Optd with T 1, in red.*

1	23	½ a. blue-green		1·60	1·75
		a. Opt double, one sideways		£1700	£600
		b. Opt double, one albino		50·00	
2	25	1 a. brown-purple		35·00	35·00
		a. Opt double			
		b. Optd in red and in black		£600	
3	27	2 a. dull blue		8·00	8·00
4	17	4 a. green		45·00	45·00
5	31	8 a. dull mauve		£225	£550
		a. Opt inverted		£4750	
		b. Optd in red and in black		65·00	£200
		ba. Ditto. Opts inverted		£3250	
		c. Opt double, one albino		£275	
6	33	1 r. slate		£100	£325
1/6			*Set of 6*	£375	£850

Nos. 5a and 5ba each occur once in the setting of 120. The 8 a. value also exists with a trial overprint (showing the words more curved) reading downwards (*Price* £350 *unused*), which should not be confused with No. 5a.

1885. *Optd with T 2. (a) In red.*

7	23	½ a. blue-green		1·00	20
		a. "AUTTIALLA"		12·00	17·00
		b. "STATE" only			
		c. Wide spacing between lines		3·00	3·25
8	27	2 a. dull blue		2·50	1·00
		a. "AUTTIALLA"		24·00	
		b. Wide spacing between lines		11·00	11·00
		ba. Ditto "AUTTIALLA"		£275	
9	17	4 a. green		2·00	1·60
		a. Optd in red and in black		£180	
		b. Wide spacing between lines		£200	
		c. Opt double, one albino		30·00	
10	33	1 r. slate		5·00	45·00
		a. "AUTTIALLA"		£350	
		b. Wide spacing between lines		£200	

(b) In black

11	25	1 a. brown-purple		15	15
		a. Optd in red and in black		4·50	42·00
		b. "AUTTIALLA"		48·00	
		ba. Ditto. Optd in red and in black		£1200	
		c. Opt double		£200	£225
		d. Wide spacing between lines		£120	
12	31	8 a. dull mauve		10·00	22·00
		a. "AUTTIALLA"		£300	
		b. Opt double, one albino		50·00	
		c. Wide spacing between lines		£200	
7/12			*Set of 6*	18·00	65·00

The ½, 2 and 4 a. (T 29), and 1 r. (all overprinted in black), are proofs.

All six values exist with reprinted overprints, and the error "AUTTIALLA STATE" has been reprinted in complete sheets on all values and in addition in black on the ½, 2, 4 a. and 1 r. Nearly all these however, are found with the word "REPRINT" overprinted upon them. On these genuine "AUTTIALLA" errors, which occur on R. 9/12 in the setting of 120, the word "STATE" is 8½ mm long; on the reprints only 7¾ mm. Nos. 7c, 8b, 9b, 10b, 11d and 12c show 1¼ mm spacing etween the two lines of overprint. The normal spacing is ¾ m.

Nos. 7/8 and 10/12 exist with error "PUTTILLA", but their tatus is uncertain.

1891–96. *Optd with T 3.*

3	23	½ a. blue-green (1892)	..	10	10
4	24	9 p. carmine	..	30	70
5	25	1 a. brown-purple	..	65	20
6		1 a. plum	..	85	50
		a. "PATIALA" omitted	..	£170	£325
		b. "PA" omitted	..		
		c. "PATIA" omitted	..		
		d. "PATIAL" omitted ..			
7	26	1 a. 6 p. sepia	..	45	45
8	27	2 a. dull blue (1896)	..	65	20
9		2 a. ultramarine	..	90	55
0	28	3 a. brown-orange	..	90	35
1	29	4 a. olive-green (1896) ..		1·25	40
		a. "PATIALA" omitted	..	£350	£180
2		4 a. slate-green	..	1·25	40
3	21	6 a. bistre-brown	..	1·10	6·00
4		6 a. olive-bistre	..	1·50	11·00
		a. Opt double, one albino	..	40·00	
5	31	8 a. dull mauve	..		
6		8 a. magenta (1896)	..	90	6·00
7	32	12 a. purple/red	..	90	7·50
8	37	1 r. green and carmine (1896) ..		3·50	27·00
9	38	2 r. carmine and yellow-brown (1895) ..		90·00	£450
0		3 r. brown and green (1895) ..		£120	£475
		a. Opt double, one albino	..		
		b. Opt treble, two albino	..	£150	
1		5 r. ultramarine and violet (1895) ..		£150	£500
3/31			*Set of 14*	£325	£1300

The errors on the 1 a. plum and 4 a. olive-green occur on R.19/1 in the December 1898 printing. Nos. 16b/d are early stages of the error before the entire word was omitted.

1899–1902. *Colours changed and new value. Optd with T 3.*

32	40	3 p. carmine (1899)	..	10	10
		a. Pair, one without opt	..	£2500	
		b. Opt double, one albino	..	30·00	
33	23	½ a. pale yellow-green	..	50	25
34	25	1 a. carmine	..	1·40	45
32/4			*Set of 3*	1·75	70

Maharaja Bhupindra Singh, 1900–1938

1903–06. *King Edward VII. Optd with T 3.*

35	41	3 p. pale grey	..	10	10
		a. Additional albino opt of Jind Type 3		£180	
		b. "S" in "STATE" sideways (R.20/1)		£800	£800
36		3 p. slate-grey (1906)	..	10	10
37	42	½ a. green	..	85	10
38	43	1 a. carmine	..	10	10
		a. Horiz pair, one without opt	..	£850	
39	44	2 a. pale violet	..	70	65
		a. Mauve	..	5·00	65
40	46	3 a. orange-brown	..	45	30
41	47	4 a. olive (1905)	..	1·90	60
42	48	6 a. olive-bistre (1905)	..	1·90	4·50
43	49	8 a. purple (1906)	..	2·00	1·10
44	50	12 a. purple/red (1906)	..	3·50	14·00
45	51	1 r. green and carmine (1905)	..	1·50	3·00
35/45			*Set of 10*	11·50	22·00

1912. *Nos. 149/50 of India optd with T 3.*

46	53	½ a. green	..	10	10
47	54	1 a. carmine	..	50	35

1912–26. *King George V. Optd with T 3.*

48	55	3 p. slate-grey	..	15	10
		a. "Rs" flaw	..	19·00	
49	56	½ a. green	..	40	10
50	57	1 a. aniline carmine	..	60	10
51	58	1½ a. chocolate (Type A) (1922)	..	30	55
52	59	2 a. mauve	..	45	30
53	62	3 a. orange-brown	..	80	60
54	63	4 a. olive	..	1·40	1·25
55	64	6 a. yellow-brown	..	2·25	3·00
		a. Yellow-bistre	..	75	2·25
56	65	8 a. purple	..	1·25	90
57	66	12 a. dull claret	..	1·40	4·50
58	67	1 r. brown and green	..	2·75	8·00
		a. Opt double, one albino	..	30·00	
59		2 r. carmine and yellow-brown (1926)	..	9·00	95·00
60		5 r. ultramarine and violet (1926)	..	21·00	95·00

1923–6. *As 1912–26. New colours.*

61	57	1 a. chocolate	..	1·50	20
62	62	3 a. ultramarine (1926) ..		1·10	4·00
48/62 ..			*Set of 15*	38·00	£190

PATIALA STATE **PATIALA STATE**

(4) (5)

1928–34. *King George V (Nasik printing, wmk Mult Star) optd at Nasik with T 4 or 5 (rupee values).*

63	55	3 p. slate (1932)	..	90	10
		w. Wmk inverted	..	2·00	1·00
64	56	½ a. green	..	25	10
		w. Wmk inverted	..	1·50	1·00
65	80	9 p. deep green (1934)	..	60	20
66	57	1 a. chocolate	..	60	20
		w. Wmk inverted	..	2·00	75
67	82	1 a. 3 p. mauve (1932)	..	2·00	15
		w. Wmk inverted	..	2·25	1·00
68	70	2 a. purple	..	70	25
		w. Wmk inverted	..	2·00	
69	61	2 a. 6 p. orange (1934)	..	2·50	1·25
		w. Wmk inverted	..	2·00	
70	62	3 a. bright blue (1929)	..	1·50	75

71	71	4 a. sage-green ..	.. ..	2·00	65
		w. Wmk inverted	..	4·00	
72	65	8 a. reddish purple (1933)	..	3·25	1·50
73	67	1 r. chocolate and green (1929)	..	4·50	4·50
74		2 r. carmine and orange	..	15·00	
		w. Wmk inverted	..	7·50	35·00
63/74			*Set of 12*	23·00	40·00

The 9 p. exists printed by lithography or typography.

1935–7. *Optd with T 4.*

75	79	½ a. blue-green (1937)	..	30	15
76	81	1 a. chocolate (1936)	..	30	15
77	59	2 a. vermilion (No. 236a) (1936)	..	30	50
78	62	3 a. carmine	..	3·00	3·00
		w. Wmk inverted	..	3·75	3·75
79	63	4 a. sage-green	..	75	1·25
75/9			*Set of 5*	4·25	4·50

PATIALA STATE **PATIALA** **PATIALA**

(6) (7) (8)

1937–8. *King George VI. Nos. 247/64 optd with T 4 (3 p. to 1 a.), T 6 (2 a. to 12 a.), or T 5 (rupee values).*

80	91	3 p. slate	..	24·00	30
81		½ a. red-brown	..	6·00	20
82		9 p. green (1937)	..	1·90	45
83		1 a. carmine (1937)	..	1·25	20
84	92	2 a. vermilion	..	1·50	4·75
85	–	2 a. 6 p. bright violet	..	2·25	10·00
86	–	3 a. yellow-green	..	2·00	4·25
87	–	3 a. 6 p. bright blue	..	2·50	14·00
88	–	4 a. brown	..	14·00	8·50
89	–	6 a. turquoise-green	..	16·00	27·00
90	–	8 a. slate-violet	..	16·00	21·00
91	–	12 a. lake	..	16·00	30·00
92	93	1 r. grey and red-brown	..	17·00	32·00
93		2 r. purple and brown	..	26·00	75·00
94		5 r. green and blue	..	38·00	£140
95		10 r. purple and claret	..	55·00	£225
96		15 r. brown and green	..	£100	£375
97		25 r. slate-violet and purple	..	£130	£450
80/97 ..			*Set of 18*	£425	£1300

Maharaja Yadavindra Singh, 1938–1971

1941–6. *King George VI. Optd with T 7 or 8 (rupee value).*

(a) Stamps of 1937

98	91	3 p. slate	..	7·50	50
99		½ a. red-brown	..	6·50	20
100		9 p. green	..	£130	2·50
		w. Wmk inverted	..		
101		1 a. carmine	..	17·00	60
102	93	1 r. grey and red-brown (1946)	..	75·00	60
98/102			*Set of 5*	£150	55·00

(b) Stamps of 1940–43

103	100a	3 p. slate (1942)	..	1·25	15
104		½ a. purple (1943)	..	1·50	15
		a. Pair, one without opt	..	£3750	
105		9 p. green (1942)	..	1·00	15
		a. Vert pair, one without opt	..	£2500	
106		1 a. carmine (1944)	..	80	10
107	101	1 a. 3 p. yellow-brown	..	1·60	1·60
108		1½ a. violet (1942)	..	6·00	1·60
109		2 a. vermilion (1944)	..	5·50	25
110		3 a. bright violet (1944)	..	3·50	75
111		3½ a. bright blue (1944)	..	13·00	20·00
112	102	4 a. brown (1944)	..	4·00	1·00
113		6 a. turquoise-green (1944)	..	2·50	13·00
114		8 a. slate-violet (1944)	..	3·00	6·50
115		12 a. lake (1945)	..	8·00	42·00
103/15			*Set of 13*	45·00	75·00

The 1½ a. exists printed by lithography or typography.

OFFICIAL STAMPS

SERVICE **SERVICE**

(O 2) (O 3)

1884 (1 Oct). *Nos. 1/3 of Patiala optd with Type O 2, in black.*

O1	23	½ a. blue-green	..	8·00	15
O2	25	1 a. brown-purple	..	30	10
		a. Opt Type 1 inverted	..	£1100	£225
		b. Opt Type 1 double	..	†	90·00
		c. "SERVICE" double	..	£1100	£450
		d. "SERVICE" inverted	..	†	£1100
O3	27	2 a. dull blue	..	£4000	90·00

Essays of No. O3 exist on which "STATE" measures 10 mm long (normal 9 mm) and the words of the Type 1 overprint are more curved. These are rare (Price £750 unused).

1885–90. *(a) No. 7 of Patiala optd with Type O 2, in black.*

O4	23	½ a. blue-green	..	30	10
		a. "SERVICE" double	..	†	£600
		b. "AUTTIALLA"	..	55·00	16·00
		ba. "AUTTIALLA", and "SERVICE" double	..	†	£2250
O5	25	1 a. brown-purple	..	30	10
		a. "SERVICE" double..	..	£1100	
		b. "SERVICE" double, one inverted	..	†	£475
		c. "AUTTIALLA"	..	£475	42·00
		d. "PUTTIALLA STATE" double	..	†	£800

(c) As No. 7 of Patiala, but optd in black, and No. 8, optd with Type O 3

O6	23	½ a. blue-green (Bk.) (1890)	..	80	10
O7	27	2 a. dull blue (R.)	..	30	10
		a. "SERVICE" double, one inverted	..	30·00	£150

There are reprints of Nos. O4, O5 and O7. The first has the word "SERVICE" in the large type in red instead of the small type in black, and the second has the word in the large type in black in place of the small type. The 2 a. with Type O 3, in black, is a proof. The ½ a. "AUTTIALLA" has also been reprinted, but nearly all the above have been overprinted "REPRINT".

No. O7 exists with error "PUTTILLA", but its status is uncertain.

SERVICE

PATIALA **PATIALA STATE** **PATIALA STATE**
STATE **SERVICE** **SERVICE**
(O 4) (O 5) (O 6)

1891 (Nov)–**1900.** *Optd with Type O 4, in black.*

O 8	23	½ a. blue-green (9.95)	..	10	10
		a. "SERVICE" inverted	..	55·00	
		b. "I" of "SERVICE" omitted	..	£750	
		c. Second "T" of "STATE" omitted	..	£350	£325
O 9	25	1 a. plum (10.1900)	..	3·25	10
		a. "SERVICE" inverted	..	60·00	
O10	27	2 a. dull blue (12.98)	..	3·25	1·00
		a. Deep blue	..	2·75	1·40
		b. "SERVICE" inverted	..	60·00	£140
		c. Thin seriffed "I" in "SERVICE"	..	£120	
O12	28	3 a. brown-orange	..	45	1·40
		a. "I" of "SERVICE" omitted	..		
O13	29	4 a. olive-green	..	40	70
		a. Slate-green (9.95) ..		40	20
		b. "I" of "SERVICE" omitted			
O15	21	6 a. bistre-brown	..	75	35
		a. Olive-bistre	..	£900	
O16	31	8 a. dull mauve	..	1·25	70
		a. Magenta (12.98)	..	70	70
		b. "I" of "SERVICE" omitted	..	£2000	
		c. Thin seriffed "I" in "SERVICE"	..	£225	
O18	32	12 a. purple/red	..	50	50
		a. "I" of "SERVICE" omitted	..	£3750	
O19	33	1 r. slate	..	55	55
		a. "I" of "SERVICE" omitted			
O8/19			*Set of 9*	8·50	4·25

Stamps from the first printing of November 1891 (Nos. O12/13, O15/16, O18/19) had the "SERVICE" overprint, as Type O 3, applied to sheets already overprinted with Type 3. Subsequent printings of O8/10a, O13a and O16a had both overprints applied at one operation as shown on Type O 4.

The errors with "SERVICE" inverted occur from a trial printing, in two operations, during 1894, which was probably not issued. Some of the "I" omitted varieties may also come from the same trial printing.

1902 (Jan)–**03.** *Optd with Type O 4.*

O20	25	1 a. carmine	..	15	10
O21	37	1 r. green and carmine (5.03) ..		5·00	9·00

1903–10. *King Edward VII stamps of India optd with Type O 4.*

O22	41	3 p. pale grey ..		10	10
		a. Slate-grey (1909)	..	15	15
O24	42	½ a. green	..	10	10
O25	43	1 a. carmine	..	10	10
O26	44	2 a. pale violet (1905)	..	30	20
		a. Mauve	..	20	10
O28	46	3 a. orange-brown	..	1·40	1·60
O29	47	4 a. olive (1905)	..	30	20
		a. Opt double, one albino	..	40·00	
O30	49	8 a. purple (shades)	..	45	55
		a. Claret (1910)	..	2·75	1·25
O32	51	1 r. green and carmine (1906)	..	70	70
O22/32			*Set of 8*	3·00	3·00

1907. *Nos. 149/50 of India optd with Type O 4.*

O33	53	½ a. green	..	10	10
O34	54	1 a. carmine	..	10	10

1913–26. *King George V. Official stamps of India optd with T 3.*

O35	55	3 p. slate-grey	..	10	10
		a. Bluish slate (1926)	..	30	30
O36	56	½ a. green	..	10	10
O37	57	1 a. carmine	..	10	10
O38		1 a. brown (1925)	..	4·50	90
O39	59	2 a. mauve	..	45	20
O40	63	4 a. olive	..	40	30
O41	64	6 a. yellow-bistre (1926)	..	70	1·75
O42	65	8 a. purple	..	55	45
O43	67	1 r. brown and green	..	1·25	1·40
O44		2 r. carmine and yellow-brown (1926) ..		10·00	30·00
O45		5 r. ultramarine and violet (1926)	..	9·00	19·00
O35/45			*Set of 11*	24·00	48·00

1927–36. *King George V (Nasik printing, wmk Mult Star), optd at Nasik with Type O 5 or Type O 6 (rupee values).*

O47	55	3 p. slate	..	10	10
		a. Blue opt	..	1·00	1·00
		w. Wmk inverted	..	1·50	1·00
O48	56	½ a. green (1932)	..	30	50
		w. Wmk inverted	..	—	2·00
O49	57	1 a. chocolate	..	15	10
		w. Wmk inverted	..	1·00	50
O50	82	1 a. 3 p. mauve (1932)	..	30	10
		w. Wmk inverted	..	2·00	20
O51	70	2 a. purple	..	20	30
O52		2 a. vermilion (1933)	..	30	35
O53	61	2 a. 6 p. orange (1933)	..	1·50	35
		w. Wmk inverted	..	50	75
O54	71	4 a. sage-green (1935)	..	40	30
		w. Wmk inverted	..	1·50	1·00
O55	65	8 a. reddish purple (1929)	..	75	60
		w. Wmk inverted	..	75	75
O56	67	1 r. chocolate and green (1929)	..	2·50	1·40
		w. Wmk inverted	..	2·00	1·75
O57		2 r. carmine and orange (1936)	..	5·50	25·00
O47/57			*Set of 11*	9·50	26·00

1935–9. *New types. Optd with Type O 5.*

O58	79	½ a. green (1936)	..	10	10
O59	81	1 a. chocolate (1936)	..	10	30
O60	59	2 a. vermilion	..	15	10
O61		2 a. vermilion (small die) (1939)	..	8·00	1·90
O62	63	4 a. sage-green (1936)	..	85	35
O58/62			*Set of 5*	8·50	2·50

1937–39. *King George VI. Optd with Types O 5 or O 6 (rupee values).*

O63	91	½ a. red-brown (1938)	.. .. ..	75	20
O64		9 p. green (1938)	.. .. ..	13·00	50·00
O65		1 a. carmine	.. .. ..	75	20
O66	93	1 r. grey and red-brown (1939)..	..	1·00	3·50
O67		2 r. purple and brown (1939)	..	6·00	5·00
O68		5 r. green and blue (1939)	..	15·00	50·00
O63/8 ..		.. .. ..	*Set of* 6	32·00	£100

1^A _____ 1^A 1^A SERVICE 1^A PATIALA SERVICE

(O 7)   (O 8)   (O 9)

1939–40. *Stamp of 1932 (King George V).*

(a) Optd with Types O 5 *and* O 7

O69	82	1 a. on 1 a. 3 p. mauve	.. ..	6·00	1·40
		w. Wmk inverted	.. ..	6·00	1·75

(b) Optd with T 4 *and* O 8

O70	82	1 a. on 1 a. 3 p. mauve (1940)	..	4·50	1·60
		w. Wmk inverted	.. ..	4·50	2·00

"SERVICE" measures 9¼ mm on No. O69 but only 8¾ mm on O70.

1939–44. *(a) Official stamps optd with* T 7.

O71	O 20	3 p. slate (1940)	.. .. ..	45	10
O72		½ a. red-brown	.. .. ..	3·00	10
O73		½ a. purple (1942)	.. ..	45	10
O74		9 p. green	.. .. ..	45	20
		w. Wmk inverted	.. ..		
O75		1 a. carmine	.. ..	75	10
O76		1 a. 3 p. yellow-brown (1941)	..	85	25
O77		1½ a. dull violet (1944)	..	3·00	30
O78		2 a. vermilion (1940)	..	4·50	15
		w. Wmk inverted	.. ..		
O79		2½ a. bright violet (1940)	..	85	65
O80		4 a. brown (1943)	.. ..	85	1·10
O81		8 a. slate-violet (1944)	..	1·40	3·75

(b) Postage stamps optd with Type O 9.

O82	93	1 r. grey and red-brown (1943)	..	8·50	5·50
O83		2 r. purple and brown (1944)	..	15·00	40·00
O84		5 r. green and blue (1944)	..	21·00	60·00
O71/84 ..		.. ..	*Set of* 14	55·00	£100

Patiala became part of the Patiala and East Punjab States Union by 20 August 1948.

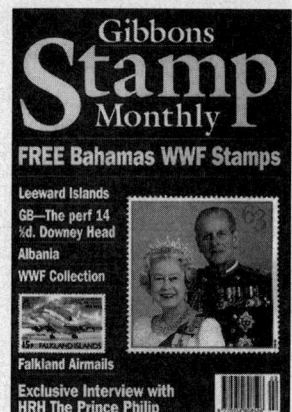

Keep This Catalogue up to Date With

Gibbons Stamp Monthly

FREE Bahamas WWF Stamps

Leeward Islands
GB—The perf 14 ½d. Downey Head
Albania
WWF Collection

Falkland Airmails

Exclusive Interview with HRH The Prince Philip

The Magazine with the Stanley Gibbons Catalogue Supplement

Plus

- ■ More editorial than other magazines.
- ■ Regular features for all collectors from beginners to specialists.
- ■ Authoritatively written.
- ■ Regular special offers, competitions and free gifts.

Get Gibbons Stamp Monthly delivered direct to your door!

For a free sample copy and subscription details phone 01425 472363 or write to:

**Hugh Jefferies
Gibbons Stamp Monthly
5 Parkside, Christchurch Road,
Ringwood, Hants BH24 3SH**

INDIAN FEUDATORY STATES

These stamps were only valid for use within their respective states, *unless otherwise indicated*.

Postage stamps of the Indian States, current at that date, were replaced by those of the Republic of India on 1 April 1950.

Unless otherwise stated, all became obsolete on 1 May 1950 (with the exception of the "Anchal" stamps of Travancore-Cochin, which remained current until 1 July 1951 or Sept 1951 for the Official issues).

ALWAR

PRICES FOR STAMPS ON COVER

Nos. 1/2	*from* × 25
No. 3	*from* × 50
No. 4	—
No. 5	*from* × 50

Maharao Raja (Maharaja from 1889) Mangal Singh, 1874–1892

1 (1 a.).

1877. *Litho. Rouletted.*

1	1	¼ a. steel blue	..	..	13·00	7·00
		a. *Bright greenish blue*	..	..	7·00	7·00
		b. *Ultramarine*	..		3·00	70
		c. *Grey-blue (shades)*	..		2·50	60
2		1 a. pale yellowish brown	..	..	6·00	4·00
		a. *Brown (shades)*	..		2·50	1·10
		b. *Chocolate*	..		9·00	8·00
		c. *Pale reddish brown*	..		1·90	75

Maharaja Jai Singh, 1892–1937

1899–1901. *Redrawn. P 12. (a) Wide margins between stamps.*

3	1	¼ a. slate-blue	..	5·00	2·25
		a. Imperf between (horiz pair)		£300	£350
		b. Imperf between (vert pair)..		£475	
4		¼ a. emerald-green	..	£550	

(b) Narrower margins (1901)

5	1	¼ a. emerald-green	..	2·50	2·00
		a. Imperf between (horiz pair)		£190	£225
		b. Imperf between (vert pair)..		£200	£225
		c. Imperf horiz (vert pair)		£200	
		d. Imperf (pair)		£275	
		e. *Pale yellow-green*		5·00	2·00
		ea. Imperf (pair)		£400	
		eb. Imperf between (horiz pair)		† £450	

In the redrawn type only the bottom outer frameline is thick, whereas in the original 1877 issue the left-hand frameline is also thick, as shown in Type 1.

The stamps of Alwar became obsolete on 1 July 1902.

BAHAWALPUR

See after PAKISTAN

BAMRA

PRICES FOR STAMPS ON COVER

Nos. 1/6	—
Nos. 8/40	*from* × 25

Raja Sudhal Deo, 1869–1903

GUM. The stamps of Bamra were issued without gum.

BAMRA postage ଯାଜ୍ଞ୍ୟ ଚ

1 (¼ a.).

BAMRA postage ଯ'ଞ୍ଜ୍ଞ:ୀ

1a

BAMRA postage ଯ'ଞ୍ଜ:ୀ୨

2 (½ a.).

BAMRA postage ଯ'ଞ୍ଜ:ୀ/

3 (1 a.).

BAMRA postage ଯ'ଞ୍ଜ:'/

4 (2 a.).

BAMRA postage ଯ'ଞ୍ଜ:·ୀ

5 (4 a.).

BAMRA postage ଯ'ଞ୍ଜ:ୀ୨

6 (8 a.).

(illustrations actual size)

(Typo Jagannata Ballabh Press, Deogarh)

1888. *Imperf.*

1	1	¼ a. black/*yellow*	..		£190
		a. "g" inverted (R.5/1)..			£2500
		b. Last native character inverted			£2750
		c. Last native character as Type 1a			£2750
2	2	½ a. black/*rose*	..		70·00
		a. "g" inverted (R.5/1)..			£1500
3	3	Postage black/*blue*	..		42·00
		a. "g" inverted (R.5/1)..			£1300
		b. Scroll inverted (R.8/4)			£1100

4	4	2 a. black/*green*	..	..	65·00	£190
		a. "a" omitted (R.8/3)		..	£1500	
		b. Scroll inverted (R.8/4)			£1300	
5	5	4 a. black/*yellow*		..	48·00	£180
		a. "a" omitted (R.8/3)			£1400	
		b. Scroll inverted (R.8/4)			£1200	
6	6	8 a. black/*rose*		..	38·00	
		a. "a" omitted (R.8/3)			£1200	
		b. Horiz pair, one printed on back			£500	
		c. Scroll inverted (R.8/4)			£1000	

These stamps were all printed from the same plate of 96 stamps, 12 × 8, but for some values only part of the plate was used. There are 96 varieties of the ½, 4 and 8 a., 72 of the 1 a., 80 of the 2 a. and not less than 88 of the ¼ a.

The scroll ornament can be found pointing to either the right or the left.

There are two forms of the third native character. In the first five horizontal rows it is as in T 1 and in the last three rows as in T 4.

These stamps have been reprinted: the ¼ a. and ½ a. in blocks of 8 varieties (all showing scroll pointing to right), and all the values in blocks of 20 varieties (all showing scroll pointing to left). On the reprints the fourth character is of a quite different shape.

8

1890 (July)**–93.** *Black on coloured paper. Nos. 24/5 and 39/40 show face value as "One Rupee". (a) "Postage" with capital "P".*

8	8	¼ a. on rose-lilac	..	..	2·50	3·50
		a. "Eeudatory" (R. 2/4)		..	11·00	19·00
		b. "Quatrer" (R. 1/3)		..	11·00	19·00
		c. Inverted "e" in "Postage" (R. 2/3)			11·00	19·00
9		¼ a. on *bright rose*		..	1·00	1·60
10		¼ a. on *reddish purple*			1·10	1·50
		a. First "a" in "anna" inverted (R. 3/3)			28·00	32·00
		b. "AMRA" inverted (R. 4/4)			42·00	42·00
		c. "M" and second "A" in "BAMRA" inverted (R. 4/4)			50·00	50·00
11		½ a. on *dull green*			1·50	1·75
		a. "Eeudatory" (R. 2/4)			32·00	40·00
12		½ a. on *blue-green*			2·75	2·50
13		1 a. on *bistre-yellow*			2·00	1·50
		a. "Eeudatory" (R. 2/4)			70·00	75·00
14		1 a. on *orange-yellow*			32·00	32·00
		a. "annas" for "anna"			£100	£100
15		2 a. on *rose-lilac*			10·00	18·00
		a. "Eeudatory" (R. 2/4)			£110	£150
16		2 a. on *bright rose*			2·50	3·00
17		2 a. on *dull rose*			7·00	4·50
18		4 a. on *rose-lilac*			£550	£700
		a. "Eeudatory" (R. 2/4)			£3500	
19		4 a. on *dull rose* ..			5·50	3·50
		a. "Eeudatory" (R. 2/4)			£650	£650
		b. "BAMBA" (R. 2/1)			£650	£650
20		4 a. on *bright rose*			3·75	5·00
20a		4 a. on *deep pink*			12·00	10·00
21		8 a. on *rose-lilac*			16·00	38·00
		a. "Foudatory" and "Postage" (R. 1/2)			£150	£190
		b. "BAMBA" (R. 2/1)			£150	£190
22		8 a. on *bright rose*			9·00	11·00
23		8 a. on *dull rose* ..			15·00	12·00
24		1 r. on *rose-lilac*			35·00	60·00
		a. "Eeudatory" (R. 2/4)			£350	£400
		b. "BAMBA" (R. 2/1)			£225	£275
		c. "Postage" (R. 1/2)			£225	£275
25		1 r. on *bright rose*			15·00	18·00
		a. Small "r" in "rupee"..			£180	£180

(b) "postage" with small "p" (1891–93)

26	8	¼ a. on *bright rose*		..	1·00	1·60
27		¼ a. on *reddish purple*			1·10	1·50
28		½ a. on *dull rose*			1·90	2·00
		a. First "a" in "anna" inverted (R. 3/3)			22·00	22·00
29		½ a. on *blue-green*			2·75	2·50
		a. First "a" in "anna" inverted (R. 3/3)			24·00	24·00
30		1 a. on *bistre-yellow*			2·00	1·50
31		1 a. on *orange-yellow*			32·00	32·00
32		2 a. on *bright rose*			2·50	3·00
33		2 a. on *dull rose* ..			7·00	4·50
34		4 a. on *dull rose* ..			7·00	4·00
35		4 a. on *bright rose*			4·00	5·50
35a		4 a. on *deep pink*			15·00	12·00
36		8 a. on *rose-lilac*			32·00	55·00
37		8 a. on *bright rose*			10·00	12·00
38		8 a. on *dull rose* ..			15·00	12·00
39		1 r. on *rose-lilac*			48·00	85·00
40		1 r. on *bright rose*			20·00	22·00
		a. Small "r" in "rupee"			£225	£225
		b. Small "r" in "rupee" and native characters in the order 2, 3, 1, 4, 5 (R. 4/4)			£1400	£1400

There are 10 settings of Type 8. The first setting (of 20 (4×5)) has capital "P" throughout. The remaining settings (of 16 (4×4)) have capital "P" and small "p" mixed.

For the first setting the 8 a. and 1 r. values were printed within the same block, the ten lefthand stamps being 8 a. values and the ten righthand stamps 1 r.

The various stamps were distributed between the settings as follows:

Setting I—Nos. 8/c, 11/a, 13/a, 15/a, 18/19a, 21, 24/a.
Setting II—Nos. 19, 19b, 21/b, 24, 24b/c, 34, 36, 39
Setting III—Nos. 9, 11, 13, 16, 26, 28, 30, 32
Setting IV—Nos. 20, 22, 25, 35, 37, 40
Setting V—Nos. 10, 10b/c, 20a, 27, 35a
Setting VI—Nos. 11, 12, 28, 28a, 29/a
Setting VII—Nos. 10/a, 12, 17, 19, 23, 25a, 27, 29, 33/4, 38, 40a/b
Setting VIII—Nos. 17, 33
Setting IX—Nos. 10/a, 12, 14/a, 17, 19, 23, 27, 29, 31, 33/4, 38
Setting X—Nos. 19, 34

There are 4 sizes of the central ornament, which represents an elephant's trunk holding a stick:—(a) 4 mm long; (b) 5 mm; (c) 6½ mm; (d) 11 mm. These ornaments are found pointing to right or left, either upright or inverted.

Ornaments (a) are found in all settings; (b) in all settings from Settings III to X; (c) in Settings I and II; and (d) only in Setting I.

The stamps of Bamra have been obsolete since 1 January 1895.

BARWANI

PRICES FOR STAMPS ON COVER

Nos. 1/2	*from* × 3
Nos. 3/43	*from* × 5

PROCESS. All Barwani stamps are typographed from clichés, and are in sheets of 4, *unless otherwise indicated*.

Issues to about 1930 were printed by the Barwani State Printing Press, and subsequently by the *Times of India* Press, Bombay.

GUM. Nos. 1/31 were issued without gum.

BOOKLET PANES. Those stamps which were printed in sheets of 4 were issued in stamp booklets, binding holes appearing in the side margin.

Rana Ranjit Singh, 1894–1930

1   2   3

1921 (Mar?). *Clear impression. Medium wove paper. P 7 all round.*

1	1	¼ a. blue-green (dull *to* deep)		..	75·00	£200
2		½ a. dull blue		..	£190	£350
		a. Imperf (pair)			—	£950

No. 1 also exists perforated on two sides only.

1921 (June?). *Blurred impression. Soft wove paper. P 7 on two or three sides.*

3	1	¼ a. green (*shades*)		..	16·00	70·00
4		½ a. ultramarine (dull *to* pale)			17·00	95·00

NOTE. As the small sheets of Barwani stamps were often not perforated all round, many of the earlier stamps are perforated on two or three sides only. Owing to the elementary method of printing, the colours vary greatly in depth, even within a single sheet.

1921. *Clear impression. Vertically laid bâtonné paper. Imperf.*

5	1	¼ a. green (*shades*)		..	13·00	42·00
6		½ a. green (*shades*)		..	3·75	
		a. Perf 11 at top or bottom only			3·00	

It is suggested that No. 5 may be an error due to printing from the wrong plate.

1922 (?). *Clear impression. Thickish glazed wove paper. P 7 on two or three sides.*

7	1	¼ a. dull blue	..	..	70·00

1922. *Smooth, soft medium wove paper. P 7 on two or three sides.*

(a) Clear impression

8	1	¼ a. deep grey-blue		..	25·00

(b) Poor impression

9	1	¼ a. steel blue		..	14·00

Examples of No. 9 exist with perforations on all four sides.

1922. *P 11 on two or three sides.*

(a) Thick, glazed white wove paper

10	2	1 a. vermilion (*shades*)		..	1·60	15·00
		a. Imperf between (vert pair)			£190	
		b. Doubly printed			£600	
11		2 a. purple (*to* violet)			1·90	16·00
		a. Doubly printed			£200	
		b. Imperf between (horiz pair)			£150	£200
		c. Imperf between (vert pair)			£150	

(b) Thick, toned wove paper

12	2	2 a. purple	..	..	10·00	35·00

1922. *Poor impression. Thin, poor wove paper. Pin-perf 8½ on two or three sides.*

13	1	¼ a. grey (*to* grey-blue)		..	1·50	30·00
		a. Imperf (pair)			£190	
		b. Imperf between (vert pair)..			£110	

1923. *Thin, smooth, unglazed wove paper. P 11 on two or three sides.*

14	1	½ a. green (pale *to* deep)		..	1·25	14·00
		a. Imperf between (vert pair)			£350	
15	2	1 a. brown-red	..	..	£2250	£2250

1923. *Poor impression. Thick, soft wove paper. P 7.*

16	1	½ a. green (pale *to* deep)		..	22·00

No. 16 also exists perforated on two or three sides.

1923 (Mar?). *Poor quality wove paper. P 7 on two or three sides.*

17	1	¼ a. black	..	..	50·00	£170
		a. Imperf between (horiz pair)			£1300	

1923 (May?). *Horizontally laid bâtonné paper. P 12.*

18	1	¼ a. rose (*shades*)		..	90	8·50
		a. Imperf between (vert pair)			£300	
		ab. Imperf between (horiz pair)			£450	
		b. Pin perf 6			90·00	45·00
		c. Perf compound of 12 and 6			38·00	48·00
		d. Perf 7			£350	
		da. On wove paper			£1200	

No. 18 was issued in sheets of 12 (3 panes of 4) and was printed on paper showing a sheet watermark of Britannia and a double-lined inscription. No. 18d was only issued in booklet panes of 4.

1925. *Vertically laid bâtonné paper. P 11.*

19	1	¼ a. blue (pale *to* deep)		..	90	8·50
		a. Tête-bêche (horiz pair)				

No. 19 was issued in sheets of 8 and was printed on paper with a sheet watermark of a shell and an inscription "SHELL" in double-lined capitals.

1927. *Very poor impression. Thin, brittle wove paper.* P 7.
20	1	¼ a. milky blue (*shades*)..		9·00 25·00
21		½ a. yellow-green (*shades*)		10·00 42·00
		a. Imperf between (horiz pair)		£600
22	3	4 a. orange-brown		55·00 £225
		a. Imperf between (horiz pair)		£900
20/2			*Set of 3*	70·00 £250

On Nos. 20/1 the portrait is nearly invisible.

1927. *Thick wove paper. Sewing machine perf* 6–10.
23	3	4 a. yellow-brown		75·00
		a. Imperf between (horiz pair)		£1300
		b. Perf 7		20·00 £160
		c. Orange-brown		90·00 £250

1928–32 (?). *Thick glazed paper.* (a) P 7.
24	1	¼ a. deep bright blue		11·00
25		½ a. bright yellow-green		21·00

(b) P 10½ (*rough*) (Nov 1928)
26	1	¼ a. ultramarine		3·75
		a. *Tête-bêche* (horiz pair)		9·00
		b. Horiz pair, one stamp printed on reverse		
27		½ a. apple-green		4·50
		a. *Tête-bêche* (vert pair)		9·00

(c) P 11 (*clean-cut*) (1929–32?)
28	1	¼ a. bright blue		2·25 8·50
		a. *Indigo*		1·75 8·50
		ab. Imperf between (horiz pair)		50·00
		b. *Deep dull blue*		1·50 8·50
		ba. Imperf between (vert pair) ..		£160
		c. *Ultramarine*		2·00 10·00
29		½ a. myrtle-green		2·75 9·00
		a. Imperf between (horiz pair)		£140
		b. *Turquoise-green*		3·50 10·00
		ba. Imperf between (vert pair) ..		£300
30	2	1 a. rose-carmine (1931)		11·00 26·00
		a. Imperf between (vert pair) ..		† £800
31	3	4 a. salmon (*to* orange) (1931)		50·00 £110
		a. Imperf between (horiz pair)		£1200
28/31 ..			*Set of 4*	55·00 £140

No. 26 was printed in sheets of 8 (4 × 2) with the two centre pairs *tête-bêche* while No. 27 in similar sheets, had the two horizontal rows *tête-bêche*. Both sheets are always found with one long side imperforate.

Nos. 28/31 were printed in sheets of 8 the two lower values existing either 4 × 2 or 2 × 4 and the two higher values 4 × 2 only. No *tête-bêche* pairs were included in these printings. It is believed that a small printing of No. 31 was produced in sheets of 4, but details are uncertain.

Rana Devi Singh, 1930–1971

4 Rana Devi Singh **5**

1932 (Oct)–47. *Medium to thick wove paper.*

A. *Close setting* (2½–4½ mm). P 11, 12 or compound (1932–41)
B. *Wide setting* (6–7 mm). P 11 (1945–47)
			A	B
32	4	¼ a. slate	1·25 13·00	3·00 18·00
33		½ a. blue-green	1·75 13·00	2·75 13·00
34		1 a. brown	1·75 12·00	7·00 13·00
		a. Imperf between (horiz pair) ..	£1100 —	†
		b. *Chocolate.* Perf 8½ (1947)	†	12·50 32·00
35		2 a. purple (*shades*)	3·25 20·00	†
		a. *Rose-carmine* (1945)	†	£150 £275
36		4 a. olive-green	6·00 24·00	20·00 28·00
32A/6A			*Set of 5*	12·50 75·00

The measurements given in the heading indicate the vertical spacing between impressions. There are eight settings of this interesting issue: four "Close" where the over-all stamp dimensions from centre to centre of perfs vary in width from 21½ to 23 mm and in height from 25 to 27½ mm; three "Wide", width 23–23½ mm and height 29–30 mm and one "Medium" (26½ × 31 mm) (No. 34b only).

1933–47. P 11.

A. *Close setting* (3–4½ mm). *Thick, cream-surfaced wove paper* (1933 *and* 1941 (No. 38aA)
B *Wide setting* (7–10 mm). *Medium to thick wove paper* (1939–47)
			A	B
37	1	¼ a. black	2·50 38·00	2·75 22·00
38		½ a. blue-green	10·00 21·00	†
		a. *Yellowish green* (1941)	7·00 18·00	3·75 24·00
39	2	1 a. brown (*shades*)	13·00 19·00	10·00 18·00
		a. Perf 8½ (5 mm) (1947)	†	10·00 30·00
40		2 a. bright purple (1939)	†	60·00 £150
41		2 a. rose-carmine (1945)	†	22·00 80·00
42	3	4 a. sage-green	24·00 50·00	20·00 40·00
		a. *Pale sage-green* (1939)	†	10·00 28·00

There were two "Close" settings (over-all stamp size 25×29 mm) and five "Wide" settings with over-all sizes 26½–31½ × 31–36½ mm. There was also one "Medium" setting (26½×31 mm) but this was confined to the 1 a. perf 8½, No. 39a.

1938. P 11.
43	5	1 a. brown		24·00 48·00

Stamps printed in red with designs similar to Types **3** and **5** were intended for fiscal use.

NEW INFORMATION

The editor is always interested to correspond with people who have new information that will improve or correct the Catalogue.

STAMP BOOKLETS

Nos. 1/17, 18d/da and 20/5 are believed to have been issued in sewn or stapled booklet, usually containing thirty-two examples of one value in blocks of 4. All these early booklets had plain covers, often in shades of brown. Few complete booklets have survived from this period.

Nos. 32/47, produced by the *Times of India* Press in a series of nine printings between 1932 and 1947, were only issued in booklet form. Booklets from the 1932, 1933, 1937 and 1939 printings had plain card or paper covers in various colours, usually containing eight blocks of 4, except for the 1933 printing, which contained twenty blocks of 4. Booklets from the 1945 printing had plain white tissue covers from the same stock as the interleaving. All these booklets were stapled at left.

The following booklets, from a printing in 1941 and a series of three printings in 1947, had printed covers, produced by a handstamp in the case of Nos. SB14/15.

1941. *Buff, green (No. SB3) or blue (No. SB7) card covers inscribed* "BARWANI STATE POSTAGE STAMPS", *booklet value in brackets and number and value of stamps thus* "(Rs 4) 32 2 Annas". *Panes of 4 with margin at left only. Stapled.*

(a) *Booklets* 59×55 mm
SB1	8 a. booklet containing thirty-two ¼ a. (No. 32A)	£225
SB2	1 r. booklet containing thirty-two ½ a. (No. 33A)	£375
SB3	2 r. booklet containing thirty-two 1 a. (No. 34A)	£425
SB4	4 r. booklet containing thirty-two 2 a. (No. 35A)	£250
SB5	8 r. booklet containing thirty-two 4 a. (No. 36A)	£375

(b) *Booklets* 63×60 mm (*No. SB6) or* 73×72 mm (*No. SB7)*
SB6	1 r. booklet containing thirty-two ½ a. (No. 38aA)	£475
SB7	8 r. booklet containing thirty-two 4 a. (No. 42B)	£700

1947. *Grey tissue covers inscribed* "32 STAMPS VALUE....' *Panes of 4 with margins all round. Stapled at left.*

(a) *Booklets* 70×95 mm.
SB 8	1 r. booklet containing thirty-two ½ a. (No. 33B)	£450
SB 9	2 r. booklet containing thirty-two 1 a. (No. 34B)	£650
SB10	8 r. booklet containing thirty-two 4 a. (No. 36B)	£750

(b) *Booklets* 76×95 mm
SB11	8 a. booklet containing thirty-two ¼ a. (No. 37B)	£550
SB12	4 r. booklet containing thirty-two 2 a. (No. 41B)	£600
SB13	8 r. booklet containing thirty-two 4 a. (No. 42aB)	£350

1947. *Buff paper covers with violet handstamp inscribed* "32 STAMPS VALUE Rs 2/-". *Panes of 4 with margins all round, Sewn with twine at left.*
SB14	2 r. booklets (71×69 mm) containing thirty-two 1 a. (No. 34bB)	£450
SB15	2 r. booklet (71×73 mm) containing thirty-two 1 a. (No. 39aB)	£350

1947. *Grey tissue covers inscribed* "32 STAMPS VALUE As 8". *Panes of 4 with margins all round. Stapled at left.*
SB16	8 a. booklet (70×75 mm) containing thirty-two ¼ a. (No. 32B)	£130
SB17	8 a. booklet (85×75 mm) containing thirty-two ¼ a. (No. 37B)	£150

Barwani became part of Madhya Bharat by 1 July 1948

BHOPAL

PRICES FOR STAMPS ON COVER	
Nos. 1/100	*from* × 10
Nos. O301/57	*from* × 15

The correct English inscription on these stamps is "H.H. NAWAB SHAH JAHAN BEGAM". In the case of Nos. 22 and 23 the normal stamps are spelt "BEGAN" and specimens with "BEGAM" are "errors".

As the stamps were printed from lithographic stones on which each unit was drawn separately by hand, numerous errors of spelling occurred. These are constant on all sheets and are listed. Some of our illustrations inadvertently include errors of spelling.

ILLUSTRATIONS. Types 1/3a and 6/12a are shown actual size.

EMBOSSING. Nos. 1/99 were only valid for postage when embossed with the device, in Urdu, of the ruling Begam. On T 1/3 and 6 to 12a. this was intended to fill the central part of the design. Almost all varieties can be found with the embossing inverted or sideways, as well as upright.

Shah Jahan   Sultan Jahan

(*actual size*)

The various basic types were often in concurrent use but for greater convenience the following list is arranged according to types instead of being in strict chronological order.

GUM. Nos. 1/99 were issued without gum.

Nawab Shah Jahan Begam, 16 November 1868–15 June 190

1 (¼ a.)

1872. *Litho.* (a) *Double frame. Sheets of* 20 (5 × 4)
1	1	¼ a. black		£275 £25•
		a. "BFGAM" (R.3/1)		£1000 £100•
		b. "BEGAN" (R.2/2, R.4/4)		£600 £60•
		c. "EGAM" (R.4/5)		£1000 £100•
2		½ a. red		12·00 25·0•
		a. "BFGAM" (R.3/1)		60·00 90·0•
		b. "BEGAN" (R.2/2, R.4/4)		40·00 65·0•
		c. "EGAM" (R.4/5)		60·00 90·0•

2 (½ a.)

(b) *Single frame. Sheets of* 20 (4 × 5)
3	2	¼ a. black		† £3750
4		½ a. red		17·00 30·00
		a. "NWAB" (R.2/2)		80·00 £130

3 (¼ a.)   **3a** (¼ a.)

1878 (Jan). *All lettered* "EEGAM" *for* "BEGAM". *Sheets of* 20 (4 × 5).

(a) *Plate 1. Frame lines extend horiz and vert between stamps throughout sheet*
5	3	¼ a. black		4·00 7·00

(b) *Plate 2. Frame lines normal.*
5a	3a	¼ a. black		4·00 8·50

Apart from the frame line difference between Types **3** and **3a** the stamps can also be distinguished by the differences in the value tablets, notably the thin vertical line in the centre in Type **3a** compared with the slightly diagonal and heavier line in Type **3**.

4 (¼ a.)   **5** (½ a.)

1878 (June?)–79. *Value in parenthesis (Nos. 6/7). Sheets of* 32 (4 × 8). *Imperf.*
6	4	¼ a. green (1879)		8·50 14·00
7		¼ a. green (*perf*) (1879) ..		7·00 10·00
8	5	½ a. red		4·25 8·50
		a. "JAHN" (R.5/2)		25·00
		b. "NWAB" (R.3/2, R.4/2)		15·00
		c. "EEGAM" (R.1/3)		25·00
9		½ a. brown		20·00 30·00
		a. "JAHN" (R.5/2)		£130
		b. "NWAB" (R.3/2, R.4/2)		80·00
		c. "EEGAM" (R.1/3)		£130

The ¼ a. shows the "N" of "NAWAB" reversed on R.6/4 and the "N" of "JAHAN" reversed on R.1/2–4 and R.2/2–4.

1880. *T* **5** *redrawn; value not in parenthesis. Sheets of* 32 (4 × 8).

(a) *Imperf*
10		¼ a. blue-green		4·50
		a. "NAWA" (R.2/2–4)		22·00
		b. "CHAH" (R.8/3) ..		60·00
11		½ a. brown-red		10·00 13·00

(b) *Perf*
12		¼ a. blue-green		7·00
		a. "NAWA" (R.2/2–4)		32·00
		b. "CHAH" (R.8/3) ..		85·00
13		½ a. brown-red		8·00

The ¼ a. shows the "N" of "NAWAB" reversed on R.8/4.
Nos. 12/13 sometimes come with gum.

1884. *T* **5** *again redrawn. Sheets of 32 (4 × 8), some with value in parenthesis, others not. Perf.*
14   ¼ a. greenish blue   2·50   8·00
     a. "ANAWAB" (R.8/1–4)   12·00
In this plate there is a slanting dash under and to left of the letters "JA" of "JAHAN," instead of a character like a large comma, as on all previous varieties of this design. With the exception of R.1/1 all stamps in the sheet show "N" of "JAHAN" reversed.

1895. *T* **5** *again redrawn. Sheets of 8 (2 × 4). Laid paper.*
15   ¼ a. red (*imperf*)   2·75   1·00
16   ¼ a. red (*perf*)   —   £450
In these cases where the same design has been redrawn several times, and each time in a number of varieties of type, it is not easy to distinguish the various issues. Nos. 6 and 7 may be distinguished from Nos. 10 and 12 by the presence or absence of the parenthesis marks (); 8, 9 and 11 differ principally in colour; 8 and 15 are very much alike, but differ in the value as well as in the paper.

6 (1 a.)

1881. *Sheets of 24 (4 × 6). Imperf.*
17 **6** ¼ a. black   3·00 9·50
     a. "NWAB" (R.6/2–4)   8·00
18   ½ a. red   3·00 8·00
     a. "NWAB" (R.6/2–4)   8·00
19   1 a. brown   2·75 8·50
     a. "NWAB" (R.6/2–4)   6·50
20   2 a. blue   1·10 8·50
     a. "NWAB" (R.6/2–4)   4·50
21   4 a. buff   9·00 30·00
     a. "NWAB" (R.6/2–4)   26·00
17/21   Set of 5 17·00 55·00
In this issue all values were produced from the same drawing, and therefore show exactly the same varieties of type. The value at foot in this and all the following issues is given in only one form.

7 (½ a.)

1886. *Similar to T* **6** *but normally lettered (incorrectly)* "BEGAN"; *larger lettering. Sheets of 32 (4 × 8). (a) Imperf.*
22 **7** ½ a. pale red   1·25 5·50
     a. "BEGAM" (R.2/1)   8·50
     b. "NWAB" (R.3/4)   8·50
(b) Perf
23 **7** ½ a. pale red   £200
     a. "BEGAM" (R.2/1)   £475
     b. "NWAB" (R.3/4)   £475

8 (4 a.)

1886. *T* **8**. *T* **6** *redrawn. Sheets of 24 (4 × 6). The* "M" *of* "BEGAM" *is an inverted* "W". *The width of the stamps is rather greater than the height. (a) Wove paper. Imperf.*
24 **8** 4 a. yellow   £550
     a. "EEGAM" (R.2/3–4, R.3/3–4, R.4/2, R.4/4, R.6/1)   £650
(b) Laid paper
25 **8** 4 a. yellow (*imperf*)   6·00
     a. "EEGAM" (R.2/3–4, R.3/3–4, R.4/2, R.4/4, R.6/1)   10·00
26   4 a. yellow (*perf*)   2·50 11·00
     a. "EEGAM" (R.2/3–4, R.3/3–4, R.4/2, R.4/4, R.6/1)   5·00 16·00

1889. *T* **6** *again redrawn. Sheets of 32 (4×8) lettered* "BEGAN."
27   ¼ a. black (*perf*)   90 3·00
     a. "EEGAM" (R.7/3)   9·00 18·00
     b. Imperf between (horiz pair)   £190
28   ¼ a. black (*imperf*)   1·10 2·75
     a. "EEGAN" (R.7/3)   12·00 19·00

---

9 (¼ a.)

1889–90. *T* **9**. *T* **6** *again redrawn. Sheets of 24 (4 × 6), all with* "M" *like an inverted* "W". *Wove paper. (a) Imperf.*
29 **9** ¼ a. black   90   70
30   1 a. brown   1·00 3·00
     a. "EEGAM" (R.2/3)   10·00 17·00
     b. "BBGAM" (R.3/1)   10·00 17·00
31   2 a. blue   75 1·10
     a. "BBEGAM" (R.1/2)   6·50 9·50
     b. "NAWAH" (R.4/2)   6·50 9·50
32   4 a. orange-yellow   1·25 2·00
29/32   Set of 4 3·50 6·00

(b) Perf
33 **9** ¼ a. black   90 1·75
34   1 a. brown   2·25 3·50
     a. "EEGAM" (R.2/3)   16·00 22·00
     b. "BBGAM" (R.3/1)   16·00 22·00
35   2 a. blue   75 1·50
     a. "BBEGAM" (R.1/2)   6·50 13·00
     b. "NAWAH" (R.4/2)   6·50 13·00
36   4 a. orange-yellow   1·50 4·00
33/6   Set of 4 4·75 9·75
Nos. 32 and 36 are nearly square, in many cases rather larger in height than in width.

1891. *As last, but sheets of 32 (4 × 8).*
37 **9** ½ a. red (*imperf*)   1·00 1·75
38   ½ a. red (*perf*)   75 2·75

1894–98. *T* **6** *again redrawn; (a) Sheets of 24 (4 × 6), almost all showing a character inside the octagon below, as in T* **9**. *Wove paper.*
39   1 a. deep brown (*imperf*)   4·25 1·40
     a. Red-brown   24·00
     b. Printed both sides   — £375
41   1 a. deep brown (*perf*)   3·75 1·75

10 (1 a.)

(b) As Nos. 39/41, but printed from a new stone showing the lines blurred and shaky. Wove paper. Imperf (1898)
42 **10** 1 a. purple-brown   2·00 2·75
     a. "NAWAH" (R.4/1)   13·00 16·00
43   1 a. purple-brown/buff   2·00 2·75
     a. "NAWAH" (R.4/1)   13·00 16·00
     b. Printed on both sides
The above are known without embossing.

11 (¼ a.)

1895. *Sheets of 8 (2 × 4), lettered* "EEGAM". *White laid paper.*
44 **11** ¼ a. black (*imperf*)   1·90 1·10
     a. "A" inserted (R.4/2)   6·50 5·00
45   ¼ a. black (*perf*)   55·00 25·00
     a. "NAW B" (R.4/2)   £225 £150
On the perf stamp the second "A" in "NAWAB" was missing on R.4/2 in the setting. This letter was later inserted for the imperf printing varying progressively from small to large.

12 (½ a.)

1895. *Narrow label at bottom. Sheets of 8 (2 × 4), lettered* "W W" *for* "H H". *Laid paper.*
46 **12** ½ a. black (*imperf*)   80 1·40

12a

1895. *Sheets of 8 (2 × 4). Laid paper.*
47 **12a** ½ a. red (*imperf*)   1·00 1·00
No. 47 is a combination of Types **1** and **6**, having the double outer frame to the octagon and the value in one form only.

13 (¼ a.)   **(14** (¼ a.)

1884. *Sheets of 32 (4 × 8). Perf.*
48 **13** ¼ a. blue-green   £120 £150
     a. "JAN" (R.2/1–2, R.3/1, R.3/3–4, R.4/1–3, R.5/1–3)   £120 £150
     b. "BEGM" (R.2/3–4)   £350
     c. "NWAB" and "JAN" (R.3/2)   £600
     ca. "NWAB" and "JN" (R.5/4)   £600
     d. "SHAHAN" (R.4/4)   £600
     e. "JAHA" (R.6/2–4)   £275

1895. *T* **14**, *double-lined frame round each stamp. Sheets of 6 (2 × 3), lettered* "JAN". *Laid paper.*
49 **14** ¼ a. bright green (*imperf*)   2·25 7·50

15 (½ a.)   **16** (¼ a.)

1884. *Sheets of 32 (4 × 8). Laid paper.*
50 **15** ¼ a. blue-green (*imperf*) 80·00 90·00
     a. "NWAB" (R.1/1)   £275
     b. "SAH" (R.1/4)   £275
     c. "NAWA" and "JANAN" (R.3/2) £275
51   ¼ a. blue-green (*perf*)   35 2·00
     a. "NWAB" (R.1/1)   3·00
     b. "SAH" (R.1/4)   3·00
     c. "NAWA" and "JANAN" (R.3/2) 3·00
     d. Imperf between (vert pair)   £200
52   ½ a. black (*imperf*)   1·25   75
     a. "NWAB" (R.1/1)   6·50
     b. "SAH" (R.1/4)   6·50
     c. "NAWA" and "JANAN" (R.3/2) 6·50
53   ½ a. black (*perf*)   35 1·50
     a. "NWAB" (R.1/1)   3·00
     b. "SAH" (R.1/4)   3·00
     c. "NAWA" and "JANAN" (R.3/2) 3·00
The ¼ a. of this issue is in *blue-green*, or *greenish blue*. Both values were printed from the same stone, the value alone being altered. There are therefore the same varieties of each. These are the only stamps of this design on laid paper.
Both values show the "N" of "NAWAB" reversed on R.1/1–4, R.2/1–4, R.3/1–4 and the "N" of "JAHAN" reversed on R.1/1–4, R.2/1–4, R.3/4.

1886. *T* **15** *redrawn. Sheets of 32 (4 × 8). Wove paper.*
54   ¼ a. green (*imperf*)   30 1·90
     a. "NAWA" (R.6/3–4)   1·50
     b. "NWAB" (R.1/1)   2·50
     c. "NWABA" (R.7/4)   2·50
     d. "NAWAA" (R.6/2)   2·50
     e. "BEGAAM" and "NWABA" (R.7/3) 2·50
55   ¼ a. green (*perf*)   1·10 2·50
     a. "NAWA" (R.6/3–4)   6·00
     b. "NWAB" (R.1/1)   9·00
     c. "NWABA" (R.7/4)   9·00
     d. "NAWAA" (R.6/2)   9·00
     e. "BEGAAM" and "NWABA" (R.7/3) 9·00
     f. Imperf between (horiz pair)   £120
56   ½ a. red (*imperf*)   40   65
     a. "SAH" (R.1/4)   3·50
     b. "NAWABA" (R.6/3–4)   2·75
The ¼ a. varies from *yellow-green* to *deep green*.
All examples of the ¼ a. value show the "N" of "NAWAB" reversed. On the same value the "N" of "JAHAN" is reversed on all positions except R.3/2, R.4/1, R.4/3. On the ½ a. both "N"s are always reversed.

1888. *T* **15** *again redrawn. Sheets of 32 (4 × 8), letters in upper angles smaller. "N" of "NAWAB" correct. Wove paper.*
57	¼ a. deep green (*imperf*)	..	..	35	65
	a. "SAH" (R.6/2)	..	..	3·50	
	b. "NAWA" (R.4/4)	..	..	3·50	
58	¼ a. deep green (*perf*)	..	..	60	1·25
	a. "SAH" (R.6/2)	..	..	4·00	
	b. "NAWA" (R.4/4)	..	..	4·00	
	c. Imperf between (vert pair)	..	..	£170	

Nos. 50 to 58 have the dash under the letter "JA" as in No. 14.

1891. *T* **15** *again redrawn. Sheets of 32 (4 × 8), lettered "NWAB." Wove paper. (a) Imperf.*
59	½ a. red	..	..	65	55
	a. "SAH" (R.2/4)	..	..	3·00	

(b) P 3 to 4½, or about 7
60	½ a. red	..	..	60	75
	a. "SAH" (R.2/4)	..	..	4·50	

Nos. 59 and 60 have the comma under "JA". The "N" of "JAHAN" is reversed on R.1/1–3, R.2/1–2.

1894. *T* **15** *again redrawn; letters in corners larger than in 1888, value in very small characters. Sheets of 32 (4 × 8), all with "G" in left-hand lower corner. Wove paper.*
61	¼ a. green (*imperf*)	..	..	55	60
	a. "NAWAH" (R.4/4)	..	..	5·50	6·00
	b. Value in brackets (R.1/1)	..	5·50	6·00
62	¼ a. green (*perf*)	..	..	1·40	1·40
	a. "NAWAH" (R.4/4)	..	..	9·00	
	b. Value in brackets (R.1/1)	..	9·00	

Nos. 61 and 62 have neither the dash nor the comma under "JA".

1896. *T* **16**; *oval narrower, stops after "H.H.", space after "NAWAB". The line down the centre is under the first "H" of "SHAH" or between "HA" instead of being under the second "H" or between "AH". Sheets of 32 (4 × 8). Wove paper. Imperf.*
63	**16**	¼ a. bright green	..	30	30
		a. "SHAN" (R.1/1)	..	3·00	
64		¼ a. pale green	..	30	30
		a. "SHAN" (R.1/1)	..	3·00	
65		¼ a. black	..	30	30
		a. "SHAN" (R.1/1)	..	3·00	

1899. *T* **15** *redrawn. Sheets of 32 (4 × 8), the first "A" of "NAWAB" always absent. Numerous defective and malformed letters. Wove paper. Imperf.*
66	½ a. black	..	..	2·25	3·25
	a. "NWASBAHJANNI" (R.2/4)	..	14·00	17·00
	b. "SBAH" (R.3/3, R.4/3–4, R.5/1–2, R.6/4)	6·00	8·00
	c. "SBAN" (R.8/2)	..	..	14·00	17·00
	d. "NWIB" (R.3/2)	..	..	14·00	17·00
	e. "BEIAM" (R.4/4)	..	..	14·00	17·00
	f. "SHH" (R.6/3)	..	..	14·00	17·00
	g. "SBAH" and "BBGAM" (R.3/4)	14·00	17·00
	h. "BBGAM" (R.1/3)	..	14·00	17·00

17 (8 a.)

18 (¼ a.)

1890. *T* **17.** *Sheets of 10 (2 × 5). Single-line frame to each stamp.*

(a) Wove paper
67	**17**	8 a. slate-green	..	30·00	55·00
		a. "HAH" (R.3/1, R.4/1, R.5/1)	..	42·00	
		b. "JABAN" (R.2/2)	..	42·00	
68		8 a. slate-green (*perf*)	..	30·00	55·00
		a. "HAH" (R.3/1, R.4/1, R.5/1)	..	42·00	
		b. "JABAN" (R.2/2)	..	42·00	

(b) Thin laid paper
69	**17**	8 a. green-black (*imperf*)	..	40·00	75·00
		a. "HAH" (R.3/1, R.4/1, R.5/1)	..	55·00	
		b. "JABAN" (R.2/2)	..	55·00	
70		8 a. green-black (*perf*)	..	40·00	75·00
		a. "HAH" (R.3/1, R.4/1, R.5/1)	..	55·00	
		b. "JABAN" (R.2/2)	..	55·00	

The "N" of "NAWAB" is reversed on R.5/2 and the "N" of "JAHAN" on R.1/1–2, R.2/2, R.3/2, R.4/2 and R.5/2.

1893. *T* **17** *redrawn. No frame to each stamp, but a frame to the sheet. Sheets of 10 (2 × 5). (a) Wove paper.*
71	8 a. green-black (*imperf*)	..	15·00	15·00
72	8 a. green-black (*perf*)	..	19·00	25·00

(b) Thin laid paper. Imperf
73	8 a. green-black	..	..	£110	£130

1898. *Printed from a new stone. Lettering irregular. Sheets of 10 (2×5). Wove paper. Imperf.*
74	8 a. green-black	..	..	25·00	32·00
	a. Reversed "E" in "BEGAM" (R.1/2, R.3/2)	60·00	
75	8 a. black	..	..	25·00	32·00
	a. Reversed "E" in "BEGAM" (R.1/2, R.3/2)	60·00	

1896–1901. *Sheets of 32 (4×8). (a) Wove paper. Imperf.*
76	**18**	¼ a. black	..	60	70

(b) Printed from a new stone, lines shaky (1899)
77	**18**	¼ a. black	..	1·40	1·40

(c) The same, on thick wove paper (1901)
78	**18**	¼ a. black	..	£450	£450

Nawab Sultan Jahan Begam, 16 June 1901–17 May 1926

19 (¼ a.) **20**

1902. *T* **19.** *With the octagonal embossed device of the previous issues. Sheets of 16 (4 × 4) ¼ a. or 8 (2 × 4) others. Thin, yellowish wove paper. Imperf.*
79	**19**	¼ a. rose	..	3·50	5·50
80		¼ a. rose-red	..	1·50	3·25
81		½ a. black	..	2·00	4·25
		a. Printed both sides	..	£425	
82		1 a. brown	..	2·75	9·00
83		1 a. red-brown	..	2·50	8·50
84		2 a. blue	..	5·50	8·00
85		4 a. orange	..	45·00	75·00
86		4 a. yellow	..	28·00	55·00
87		8 a. lilac	..	55·00	£110
88		1 r. rose	..	£150	£190
79/88	..		Set of 7	£225	£325

1903. *With a circular embossed device. Sheets of 16 (4 × 4) ¼ a. (two plates) or 8 (2 × 4) (others).*

A. Wove paper. B. Laid paper
			A	B
89	**19**	¼ a. rose-red	80 2·75	50 4·50
90		¼ a. red	65 2·25	30 3·50
91		½ a. black	55 3·00	65 4·50
92		1 a. brown	1·00 4·00	55·00 —
93		1 a. red-brown	3·00 —	—
94		2 a. blue	2·50 16·00	95·00 —
95		4 a. orange	†	£160 £160
96		4 a. yellow	14·00 40·00	80·00 75·00
97		8 a. lilac	35·00 90·00	£850 —
98		1 r. rose	48·00 £110	£750 —
89A/98A		Set of 7	85·00 £225	

1903. *No. 71 optd with initial of the new Begam, either 6 or 11 mm long, in red.*
99	8 a. green-black	..	..	65·00	65·00
	a. Opt inverted	..	£150	£150

Some of the previous stamps remained on sale (and probably in use) after the issue of the series of 1902, and some of these were afterwards put on sale with the new form of embossing; fresh plates were made of some of the old designs, in imitation of the earlier issues, and impressions from these were also sold with the new embossed device. We no longer list these doubtful items.

(Recess Perkins, Bacon & Co)

1908. *P* 13½.
100	**20**	1 a. green	..	2·25	2·25
		a. Printed both sides	..	£100	
		b. Imperf (pair)	..		

The ordinary postage stamps of Bhopal became obsolete on 1 July 1908.

OFFICIAL STAMPS

SERVICE **SERVICE**

(O 1) (O 2)

(Recess and optd Perkins, Bacon)

1908–11. *As T* **20**, *but inscribed "H.H. BEGUM'S SERVICE" at left. No wmk. P 13 to 14. Overprinted. (a) With Type O 1.*
O301	½ a. yellow-green	..	1·75	10
	a. Imperf (pair)	..	95·00	
	b. Pair, one without overprint	..	£350	
	c. Opt double, one inverted	..	£100	
	ca. Ditto. Imperf (pair)	..	£120	
	d. Opt inverted	..	£110	£110
	e. Imperf between (horiz pair)	..	£400	
O302	1 a. carmine-red	..	2·75	35
	a. Opt inverted	..	70·00	70·00
	b. Imperf (pair)	..	85·00	
	c. Red	..	3·50	10
O303	2 a. ultramarine	..	18·00	10
	a. Imperf (pair)	..	50·00	
O304	4 a. brown (1911)	..	8·00	15
O301/4	..	Set of 4	28·00	40

(b) With Type O 2
O305	½ a. yellow-green	..	4·00	30
O306	1 a. carmine-red	..	7·00	90
O307	2 a. ultramarine	..	3·00	40
	a. Opt inverted	..	25·00	
O308	4 a. brown (1911)	..	70·00	35
	a. Opt inverted	..	20·00	65·00
	b. Opt double	..	85·00	
	c. Imperf (pair)	..	75·00	
	d. Imperf (pair) and opt inverted	..	75·00	
O305/8	..	Set of 4	75·00	1·75

The two overprints differ in the shape of the letters, noticeably in the "R".

PRICES OF SETS

Set prices are given for many issues, generally those containing three stamps or more. Definitive sets include one of each value or major colour change, but do not cover different perforations, die types or minor shades. Where a choice is possible the set prices are based on the cheapest versions of the stamps included in the listings.

Nawab Mohammad Hamidullah. Khan 17 May 1926 to transfer of administration to India, 1 June 1949

SERVICE

(O 3) (O 4)

(Des T. I. Archer. Litho Indian Govt Ptg Wks, Nasik)

1930 (1 July)–**31.** *Type O* **4** (25½ × 30½ *mm*) *optd with Type O* **3.** *P 14.*
O309	O 4	½ a. sage-green (1931)	..	5·50	65
O310		1 a. carmine-red	..	7·00	15
O311		2 a. ultramarine	..	6·00	40
O312		4 a. chocolate	..	5·50	40
O309/12			Set of 4	22·00	1·40

The ½ a., 2 a. and 4 a. are inscribed "POSTAGE" at left.

(Litho Perkins, Bacon)

1932–34. *As Type O* **4** (21 × 25 *mm*), *but inscr "POSTAGE" at left. Optd with Type O* **1.** *(a) "BHOPAL STATE" at right. P 13.*
O313	¼ a. orange	..	2·25	40
	a. Perf 11½ (1933)	..	4·25	
	b. Perf 14 (1934)	..	10·00	30
	c. Perf 13½ (1934)	..	12·00	30
	ca. Vert pair, one without opt	..	£110	

(b) "BHOPAL GOVT" at right. P 13½
O314	½ a. yellow-green	..	3·00	10
O315	1 a. carmine-red	..	6·00	10
	a. Vert pair, one without opt	..	£200	
O316	2 a. ultramarine	..	6·00	45
O317	4 a. chocolate	..	4·75	65
	a. Perf 14 (1934)	..	11·00	40
O313/17		Set of 5	20·00	1·10

No. O317 is comb-perforated and No. O317a line-perforated.

¼A	THREE PIES	ONE ANNA
(O 5)	(O 6)	(O 7)

1935–36. *Nos. O314, O316 and O317 surch as Types O 5 to O 7.*
O318	O 5	¼ a. on ½ a. yellow-green (R.)	17·00	9·50
		a. Surch inverted	£100	70·00
		b. Vert pair. Nos. O318/19	27·00	17·00
		ba. Ditto. Surch inverted	£200	£130
O319	O 6	3 p. on ½ a. yellow-green (R.)	2·50	2·50
		a. "THEEE PIES" (R. 7/10)	50·00	42·00
		b. "THRFE for "THREE" (R. 10/6)	50·00	42·00
		c. Surch inverted	50·00	38·00
O320	O 5	¼ a. on 2 a. ultramarine (R.)	17·00	11·00
		a. Surch inverted	£100	60·00
		b. Vert pair. Nos. O320/1	27·00	18·00
		ba. Ditto. Surch inverted	£200	£130
O321	O 6	3 p. on 2 a. ultramarine (R.)	2·75	2·75
		a. Surch inverted	48·00	35·00
		b. "THEEE PIES" (R. 7/10)	50·00	40·00
		ba. Ditto. Surch inverted	£350	£350
		c. "THRFE" for "THREE" (R. 10/6)	50·00	40·00
		ca. Ditto. Surch inverted	£350	£350
O322	O 5	¼ a. on 4 a. chocolate (R.)	£550	£160
		a. Vert pair. Nos O322 and O324	£800	£300
O323		¼ a. on 4 a. chocolate (No. O317a, Blk.) (25.5.36)	45·00	17·00
		a. Vert pair. Nos. O323 and O325	60·00	28·00
O324	O 6	3 p. on 4 a. chocolate (R.)	65·00	35·00
		a. "THEEE PIES" (R. 7/10)	£325	£275
		c. "THRFE" for "THREE" (R. 10/6)	£325	£275
O325		3 p. on 4 a. chocolate (No. O317a, Blk.) (25.5.36)	2·50	2·25
		a. "THRER" for "THREE" (R. 8/2)	£180	£130
		b. "FHREE" for "THREE" (R.3/10, 10/1)	£200	£160
		c. "PISE" for "PIES" (R. 10/10)	£325	£250
		d. "PIFS" for "PIES" (R. 7/9)	£190	£150
O326	O 7	1 a. on ½ a. yellow-green (V.)	2·25	1·50
		a. Surch inverted	50·00	40·00
		b. First "N" in "ANNA" inverted (R. 4/5)	55·00	48·00
		ba. Ditto. Surch inverted	£350	£325
O327		1 a. on 2 a. ultramarine (R.)	2·25	1·40
		a. Surch inverted	55·00	35·00
		b. First "N" in "ANNA" inverted (R. 4/5)	55·00	45·00
		ba. Ditto. Surch inverted	£350	£325
O327d		1 a. on 2 a. ultramarine (V.)	42·00	42·00
		da. Surch inverted	85·00	85·00
		db. First "N" in "ANNA" inverted (R. 4/5)	£350	£350
		dc. Ditto. Surch inverted	£550	£525
O328		1 a. on 2 a. ultram (Blk.) (25.5.36)	70	90
		a. "ANNO"	£850	
O329		1 a. on 4 a. chocolate (B.)	3·00	3·25
		a. First "N" in "ANNA" inverted (R. 4/5)	60·00	48·00
		b. Perf 14	6·00	3·25
		ba. Ditto. First "N" in "ANNA" inverted (R. 4/5)	£130	70·00

Nos. O318 to O325 are arranged in composite sheets of 100 (10 × 10). The two upper horizontal rows of each value are surcharged as Type O 5 and the next five rows as Type O 6. The remaining three rows are also surcharged as Type O 6 but in a slightly narrower setting.

The surcharge on No. O323 differs from Type O 5 in the shape of the figures and letter.

O 8

(Des T. I. Archer. Litho Indian Govt Ptg Wks, Nasik (No. O330).
Typo Bhopal Govt Ptg Wks (others))

1935–39. *As Type O 8.*

(a) Litho. Inscr "BHOPAL GOVT POSTAGE". Optd "SERVICE"
(13½ mm). P 13½

O330	1 a. 3 p. blue and claret		2·00	30

(b) Typo. Inscr "BHOPAL STATE POSTAGE". Optd "SERVICE"
(11 mm). P 12

O331	1 a. 6 p. blue and claret (1937)		1·25	30
	a. Imperf between (pair)		95·00	£100
	b. Opt omitted		90·00	70·00
	c. Opt double, one inverted		£225	£225
	d. Imperf (pair)		†	90·00
	e. Blue printing double		†	85·00
O332	1 a. 6 p. claret (1939)		3·25	60
	a. Imperf between (pair)		95·00	£100
	b. Opt omitted		—	£190
	c. Opt double, one inverted		—	£190
	d. Opt double		—	£200

PRINTERS. From No. O333 all issues were printed by the Bhopal
Govt Ptg Wks in typography.

O 9   O 10 The Moti Mahal

1936 (July)–38. *Optd "SERVICE". P 12.*

O333	O 9	¼ a. orange (Br.)	90	20
	a. Imperf between (vert pair)	£110	
	ab. Imperf between (horiz pair)	†	£160
	b. Opt inverted	£180	£150
	c. Black opt	7·00	75
	ca. Opt inverted	†	£180
	cb. Opt double	†	£180
O334	¼ a. yellow (Br.) (1938)	1·75	50
O335	1 a. scarlet	1·25	10
	a. Imperf between (horiz pair)	75·00	75·00
	b. Imperf between (vert pair)	†	£130
	c. Imperf between (block of four)	£190	£190
	d. Imperf vert (horiz pair)	†	80·00

1936–49. *As Type O 10 (various palaces). P 12.*

(a) Optd "SERVICE" (13½ mm)

O336	½ a. purple-brown and yellow-green	70	50
	a. Imperf between (vert pair)	†	£110
	ab. Imperf between (horiz pair)	†	£110
	b. Opt double	£170	£110
	c. Frame double	85·00	15·00
	d. Purple-brown and green (1938)	70	25

(b) Optd "SERVICE" (11 mm)

O337	2 a. brown and blue (1937)	1·25	25
	a. Imperf between (vert pair)	†	£160
	ab. Imperf between (horiz pair)	†	£120
	b. Opt inverted	£160	£160
	c. Pair, one without opt	£325	
	d. As c. but opt inverted	£475	
O338	2 a. green and violet (1938)	5·50	25
	a. Imperf between (vert pair)	†	£120
	b. Imperf between (vert strip of 3)	85·00	90·00
	c. Frame double	†	£120
	d. Centre double	†	£120
O339	4 a. blue and brown (1937)	2·50	50
	a. Imperf between (horiz pair)	†	£325
	b. Opt omitted	†	£170
	c. Opt double	†	£170
	d. Centre double	†	£170
	e. Blue and reddish brown (1938)	2·50	15
	ea. Frame double	†	£130
O340	8 a. bright purple and blue (1938)	3·25	65
	a. Imperf between (vert pair)	†	£190
	b. Opt omitted	†	90·00
	c. Opt double	†	£120
	d. Imperf vert (horiz pair) and opt omitted	†	£160
	e. Imperf (pair) and opt omitted	†	£160
O341	1 r. blue and reddish purple (Br.) (1938)	9·50	4·50
	a. Imperf horiz (vert pair)	†	£700
	b. Opt in black (1942)	11·00	4·00
	ba. Light blue and bright purple	32·00	27·00
	bb. Laid paper	£375	£400
O336/41		Set of 6	20·00	5·25

(c) Optd "SERVICE" (11½ mm) with serifs

O342	1 r. dull blue and bright purple (Blk.) (1949)	40·00	65·00
	a. "SREVICE" for "SERVICE" (R. 6/6)	£130	£170
	b. "SERVICE" omitted	£450	

(d) Optd "SERVICE" (13½ mm) with serifs

O343	8 a. bright purple and blue (1949)	50·00	75·00
	a. "SERAICE" for "SERVICE" (R. 6/5)	£200	£300
	b. Fig "1" for "I" in "SERVICE" (R. 7/1)	£200	£300

The ½ a. is inscr "BHOPAL GOVT" below the arms, other values
have "BHOPAL STATE".

Designs:—(37½ × 22½ *mm*) 2 a. The Moti Masjid; 4 a. Taj
Mahal and Be-Nazir Palaces. (39 × 24 *mm*)—8 a. Ahmadabad
Palace. (45½ × 27½ *mm*)—1 r. Rait Ghat.

O 11 Tiger   O 13 The Moti Mahal

1940. *As Type O 11 (animals). P 12.*

O344	¼ a. bright blue		2·25	60
O345	1 a. bright purple (Spotted Deer)		13·00	70

1941. *As Type O 8 but coloured centre inscr "SERVICE"; bottom*
frame inscr "BHOPAL STATE POSTAGE". P 12.

O346	1 a. 3 p. emerald-green		70	70
	a. Imperf between (pair)		£275	£275

1944–47. *As Type O 13 (various palaces). P 12.*

O347	½ a. green		85	35
	a. Imperf (pair)		†	55·00
	b. Imperf between (vert pair)		†	£100
	c. Doubly printed		†	90·00
O348	2 a. violet		5·00	2·00
	a. Imperf (pair)		†	55·00
	c. Bright purple (1945)		1·60	2·00
	d. Mauve (1947)		11·00	10·00
	e. Error. Chocolate (imperf)		£100	£100
O349	4 a. chocolate		3·25	1·00
	a. Imperf (pair)		†	70·00
	b. Imperf vert (horiz pair)		†	£130
	c. Doubly printed		†	£100
O347/9		Set of 3	5·25	3·00

Design inscr "BHOPAL STATE":—2 a. The Moti Masjid; 4 a. Be-
Nazir Palaces.

O 14 Arms of Bhopal   2 As.   2 As.
                           (O 15)   (O 16)

1944–49. *P 12.*

O350	O 14	3 p. bright blue	65	20
	a. Imperf between (vert pair)	70·00	75·00
	b. Imperf between (horiz pair)	†	£130
	c. Stamp doubly printed	38·00	
O351	9 p. chestnut (shades) (1945)	6·00	1·60
	a. Imperf (pair)	†	£120
	b. Orange-brown	2·00	2·25
O352	1 a. purple (1945)	3·25	70
	a. Imperf horiz (vert pair)	†	£190
	b. Violet (1946)	5·50	1·60
O353	1½ a. claret (1945)	1·25	35
	a. Imperf between (horiz pair)	†	£180
	b. Imperf between (vert pair)	†	—
O354	3 a. yellow	6·50	6·50
	a. Imperf (pair)	†	£120
	b. Imperf horiz (vert pair)	†	£150
	c. Imperf vert (horiz pair)		—
	d. Orange-brown (1949)	60·00	55·00
O355	6 a. carmine (1945)	10·00	27·00
	a. Imperf (pair)	†	£130
	b. Imperf horiz (vert pair)	†	£150
	c. Imperf vert (horiz pair)	†	£150
O350/5		Set of 6	21·00	32·00

1949 (July). *Surch with Type O 15. P 12.*

O356	O 14	2 a. on 1½ a. claret	2·25	4·75
	a. Stop omitted	11·00	19·00
	b. Imperf (pair)	£150	£160
	ba. Stop omitted (pair)	£400	£425

The "stop omitted" variety occurs on positions 60 and 69 in the
sheet of 81.

1949. *Surch with Type O 16. Imperf.*

O357	O 14	2 a. on 1½ a. claret	£450	£475
	a. Perf 12	£475	£475

Three different types of "2" occur in the setting of Type O 16.

BHOR

PRICES FOR STAMPS ON COVER

Nos. 1/2	*from* × 40
No. 3	*from* × 6

GUM. The stamps of Bhor were issued without gum.

Pandit Shankar Rao, 1871–1922

1   2

1879. *Handstamped. Very thick to thin native paper. Imperf.*

1	1	½ a. carmine (shades)	1·75	3·25
	a. Tête-bêche (pair)	£550	
2	2	1 a. carmine (shades)	2·75	4·75

3

1901. *Typo. Wove paper. Imperf.*

3	3	½ a. red		7·00	28·00

BIJAWAR

PRICES FOR STAMPS ON COVER

The stamps of Bijawar are very rare used on cover.

Maharaja Sarwant Singh, 1899–1941

1   2

(Typo Lakshmi Art Ptg Works, Bombay)

1935 (1 July)–36. *(a) P 11.*

1	1	3 p. brown		3·75	2·75
	a. Imperf (pair)		5·50	
	b. Imperf between (vert pair)		80·00	
	c. Imperf horiz (vert pair)		50·00	
2	6 p. carmine		3·75	2·75
	a. Imperf (pair)		85·00	
	b. Imperf between (vert pair)		80·00	
	c. Imperf between (horiz pair)		80·00	
	d. Imperf horiz (vert pair)		80·00	
3	9 p. violet		4·00	3·25
	a. Imperf (pair)		£140	
	b. Imperf between (vert pair)		80·00	
	c. Imperf between (horiz pair)		80·00	
	d. Imperf horiz (vert pair)		80·00	
4	1 a. blue		4·50	3·75
	a. Imperf (pair)		85·00	
	b. Imperf between (vert pair)		£110	
	c. Imperf between (horiz pair)		85·00	
	d. Imperf horiz (vert pair)		85·00	
	e. Imperf vert (horiz strip of 3)		£130	
5	2 a. deep green		4·75	4·75
	a. Imperf (pair)		£100	
	b. Imperf horiz (vert pair)		11·00	
	c. Imperf between (vert pair)		35·00	
	d. Imperf between (horiz pair)		50·00	80·00
1/5		Set of 5	18·00	15·00

(b) Roul 7 (1936)

6	1	3 p. brown		2·25	2·50
	a. Printed on gummed side		£400	
7	6 p. carmine		3·75	13·00
8	9 p. violet		5·50	65·00
9	1 a. blue		6·00	70·00
10	2 a. deep green		6·50	75·00
6/10		Set of 5	22·00	£200

1937 (May). *Typo. P 9.*

11	2	4 a. orange		7·50	55·00
	a. Imperf between (vert pair)		£140	
	b. Imperf (pair)		£200	
12	6 a. lemon		7·50	55·00
	a. Imperf between (vert pair)		£140	
	b. Imperf (pair)		£200	
13	8 a. emerald-green		7·50	70·00
	a. Imperf (pair)		£225	
14	12 a. greenish blue		7·50	70·00
	a. Imperf (pair)		£250	
15	1 r. bright violet		28·00	£110
	a. "1 Rs" for "1 R" (R. 1/2)		48·00	£300
	b. Imperf (pair)		£300	
	ba. "1 Rs" for "1 R" (R. 1/2)		£850	
11/15		Set of 5	50·00	£325

The stamps of Bijawar were withdrawn in 1941.

BUNDI

PRICES FOR STAMPS ON COVER

No. 1	*from* × 2
No. 2	*from* × 4
Nos. 3/53	*from* × 10
Nos. 54/63	*from* × 5
Nos. 64/78	*from* × 2
Nos. 79/92	*from* × 10
Nos. O1/52	*from* × 15
Nos. O53/9	*from* × 20

GUM. Nos. 1/17 were issued without gum.

ILLUSTRATIONS. Types 1/10 and 12/19 are shown actual size.

In Nos. 1 to 17 characters denoting the value are below the
dagger, except in Nos. 2a, 11 and 17.
All Bundi stamps until 1914 are imperforate.

Maharao Raja Raghubir Singh, 1889–1927

1

1894 (May). *Each stamp with a distinct frame and the stamps not connected by the framing lines. Three vertical lines on dagger. Laid or wove paper.*

1	1	½ a. slate-grey		£4000 £1500
		a. Last two letters of value below the rest		† £3000

2 (Block of four stamps)

1894 (Dec). *Stamps joined together, with no space between them. Two vertical lines on dagger. Thin wove paper.*

2	2	½ a. slate-grey		28·00 29·00
		a. Value at top, name below		£170 £180
		b. Right upper ornament omitted		£1200 £1200
		c. Last two letters of value below the rest		£900 £900
		d. Left lower ornament omitted		£1200 £1200

3

1896 (Nov). *Dagger shorter, lines thicker. Stamps separate. Laid paper.*

3	3	½ a. slate-grey		3·50 7·50
		a. Last two letters of value below the rest		£300 £375

4 (1 anna)   5 (2 annas)

6 (2 annas)

1897–98. *No shading in centre of blade of dagger. The stamps have spaces between them, but are connected by the framing lines, both vertically and horizontally. Laid paper.*

I. *Blade of dagger comparatively narrow, and either triangular, as in T 4 and 6, or with the left-hand corner not touching the bar behind it, as in T 5 (1897-98)*

4	4	1 a. Indian red		7·50	16·00
5	5	1 a. red		7·50	13·00
6		2 a. green		9·00	18·00
7	6	2 a. yellow-green		9·00	18·00
8	5	4 a. green		35·00	48·00
9		8 a. Indian red		65·00	£130
10		1 r. yellow/*blue*		£140	£250
4/10			Set of 5	£225	£400

7

II. *Blade varying in shape, but as a rule not touching the bar; value above and name below the dagger, instead of the reverse (Jan 1898)*

11	7	4 a. emerald-green		22·00
		a. Yellow-green		15·00 35·00

8 (½ anna)   9 (8 annas)

III. *Blade wider and (except on the ½ a.) almost diamond shaped; it nearly always touches the bar (1898–1900)*

12	8	½ a. slate-grey (5.2.98)		2·00	2·50
13	9	1 a. Indian red (7.98)		1·40	1·60
14		2 a. pale green (9.11.98)		6·50	10·00
		a. First two characters of value (= two) omitted		£950	£950
15		8 a. Indian red (7.98)		5·50	11·00
16		1 r. yellow/*blue* (7.98)		18·00	28·00
		a. On wove paper		8·00	18·00
12/16a			Set of 5	21·00	38·00

10

IV. *Inscriptions as on No. 11; point of dagger to left (9.11.98)*

17	10	4 a. green		16·00 20·00
		a. Yellow-green		7·50 12·00

All the above stamps are lithographed in large sheets, containing as many varieties of type as there are stamps in the sheets.

11 Raja protecting Sacred Cows

Type 11 was produced from separate clichés printed as a block of four. The same clichés were used for all values, but not necessarily in the same order within the block. The Devanagri inscriptions, "RAJ BUNDI" at top and the face value at bottom, were inserted into the basic clichés as required so that various differences exist within the 58 settings which have been identified.

The denominations may be identified from the following illustrations. The ½ a., 3 a. and rupee values can be easily distinguished by their colours.

Bottom tablets:—

पाव आना	एक आना
¼ a.	1 a.
दो आना	ढाई आना
2 a.	2½ a.
चार आना	छै आना
4 a.	6 a.
आठ आना	दस आना
8 a.	10 a.
बारह आना	एक रुपया
12 a.	1 r.

The nine versions of the inscriptions are as follows:

राज बुँदी	राज बुंदी
A	B

Top tablet

Type A. Top tablet has inscription in two separate words with a curved line over the first character in the second. The second word has three characters. Bottom tablet has short line above the first character in the second word.

Type B. Top tablet as Type A, but without the curved line over the first character in the second word. Bottom tablet as Type A.

C

Type C. Top tablet as Type B, but with large loop beneath the first character in the second word. This loop is usually joined to the main character, but is sometimes detached as in the illustration. Bottom tablet as Type A.

D   E
Top tablet   Bottom tablet

Type D. Top tablet in thinner lettering with the inscription shown as one word of six characters. The fourth character has a curved line above it, as in Type A, and a loop beneath, as in Type C. Bottom tablet as Type A, but thinner letters.

Type E. Top tablet as Type C. Bottom tablet shows a redrawn first character to the second word. This has the line at top extending over the entire character.

F
Bottom tablet

Type F. Top tablet as Type B. Bottom tablet as Type E, but first character in second word differs.

राज बुन्दी	राज बुन्दी
G	H

Type G. Top tablet as Type C, but without dot over first character in second word. There are now four characters in the second word. Bottom tablet as Type E.

Type H. Top tablet as Type G, but with characters larger and bolder. Bottom tablet as Type E, but with characters larger and bolder.

I

Type I. Top tablet as Type H. Bottom tablet as Type E.

Some settings contained more than one inscription type within the block of four so that se-tenant examples are known of Type B with Type C (¼, 1, 2, 4, 8, 10 and 12 a.), Type C with Type E (¼, ½ and 4 a.) and Type E with Type F (½ and 4 a.). Type F only exists from this mixed setting.

1914 (Oct)–**41.** *T 11. Typo. Ungummed paper except for Nos. 73/8.*

I. *Rouletted in colour*
(a) *Inscriptions as Type A. Thin wove paper* (1916–23)

18		½ a. black		2·25 10·00
19		1 a. vermilion		3·00 15·00

20	2 a. emerald ..	..	2·75
	a. Deep green (coarse ptg on medium wove paper) (1923)		1·60 9·00
21	2½ a. chrome-yellow (*shades*) (1917)..		5·00 24·00
22	3 a. chestnut (1917)		12·00 26·00
23	4 a. yellow-green		16·00
24	6 a. cobalt (1917)		16·00 55·00
25	1 r. reddish violet (1917)		15·00 75·00

A special printing of the 1 a. took place in late 1917 in connection with the "OUR DAY" Red Cross Society Fund. This had the "RAJ BUNDI" inscription in the bottom tablet with the face value below it. The top tablet carried four Devanagri characters for "OUR DAY". No evidence has been found to suggest that this 1 a. stamp was used for postal purposes (*Price, £160 unused*).

(b) Inscriptions as Type B. Thin wove or pelure paper (1914–23)

25a	¼ a. cobalt (1916)	..	3·00 14·00
26	¼ a. ultramarine (*shades*) (1917)		1·75 4·25
	a. Indigo (1923)		2·50 5·50
	b. Error. Black (1923)		
27	½ a. black	..	2·75 6·00
28	1 a. vermilion (1915)		2·75 8·50
	a. Carmine (1923) ..		6·00 8·50
	b. Red (*shades*) (1923)		4·50
29	2 a. emerald (*shades*) (1915)		4·50 14·00
30	2½ a. olive-yellow (1917)		5·00 19·00
31	3 a. chestnut (1917)		4·50 24·00
32	4 a. apple-green (1915)		3·50 26·00
32a	4 a. olive-yellow (1917)		£100 £120
33	6 a. pale ultramarine (*shades*) (1917)		8·00 55·00
	a. Deep ultramarine (1917)		7·00
34	8 a. orange (1915)		7·50 60·00
35	10 a. olive-sepia (1917)		£225 £450
36	12 a. sage-green (1917)		£550
36a	1 r. lilac (*shades*) (1915)		24·00

(c) Inscriptions as Type C. Thin to medium wove paper (1917–41)

37	¼ a. ultramarine (*shades*) (1923)		4·00 5·50
	a. Indigo (1923)		4·50 6·50
	b. Error. Black (1923)		
	c. Cobalt (medium wove paper) (1937)		14·00 14·00
38	½ a. black		1·40 4·25
39	1 a. orange-red		11·00 16·00
	a. Carmine (1923) ..		9·00 14·00
	b. Deep red (medium wove paper) (1936)		13·00 13·00
40	2 a. emerald		7·00 17·00
	a. Sage-green		6·50
41	4 a. yellow-green (*shades*)		30·00 65·00
	a. Olive-yellow		85·00 £120
	b. Bright apple-green (medium wove paper) (1936)		£250 £150
42	8 a. reddish orange		9·00 45·00
43	10 a. brown-olive		16·00 60·00
	a. Olive-sepia		35·00
	b. Yellow-brown		50·00
44	12 a. sage-green		7·00 55·00
45	1 r. lilac		22·00 80·00
46	2 r. red-brown and black		48·00 £120
	a. Chocolate and black (medium wove paper) (1936)		60·00 £150
47	3 r. blue and red-brown		75·00 £160
	a. Grey-blue and chocolate (medium wove paper) (1941)		£100
	ab. Chocolate (inscriptions) inverted		£4750
48	4 r. emerald and scarlet		£170 £275
49	5 r. scarlet and emerald		£180 £300

(d) Inscriptions as Type D. Thin wove paper (1918?)

50	2½ a. buff (*shades*)		11·00 32·00
51	3 a. red-brown		17·00 21·00
	a. Semi-circle and dot omitted from 4th character		38·00 40·00
52	10 a. bistre		24·00 75·00
	a. 4th character turned to left instead of downwards		45·00
53	12 a. grey-olive..		32·00 80·00
	a. 4th character turned to left instead of downwards		60·00

(e) Inscriptions as Type E. (i) Medium wove paper (1930–37)

54	¼ a. deep slate		14·00 18·00
54a	¼ a. indigo (*thin wove paper*) (1935)		13·00 18·00
	b. Cobalt (1937)		14·00 14·00
55	½ a. black		9·00 11·00
56	1 a. carmine-red		17·00 22·00
57	3 a. chocolate (*shades*) (1936)		11·00 25·00
58	4 a. yellow-olive (1935)		£350 £150
	a. Bright apple-green (1936)		£350 £150

(ii) Very thick wove paper (1930–32)

59	¼ a. indigo (1932)		14·00 18·00
60	½ a. black		60·00
61	1 a. bright scarlet (1931)		13·00 17·00
	a. Carmine-red		50·00

(iii) Thin horizontally laid paper (1935)

62	¼ a. indigo		4·00 13·00
63	1 a. scarlet-vermilion		7·00 19·00

Nos. 62 and 63 exist in *tête-bêche* blocks of four on the same or opposite sides of the paper.

(f) Inscriptions as Type F. Medium wove paper (1935)

63a	½ a. black		65·00
63b	4 a. yellow-olive		£600 £375

(g) Inscriptions as Type G. (i) Horizontally laid paper (1935)

64	½ a. black		80·00 80·00
	a. Vert laid paper ..		75·00 75·00
65	1 a. scarlet		70·00 50·00
66	4 a. bright green		20·00 35·00

(ii) Medium wove paper (1936)

66a	½ a. black		4·00 22·00
66b	4 a. yellow-green		£950 £475

(h) Inscriptions as Type H. Medium wove paper (1935–41)

67	¼ a. ultramarine		1·40 7·00
68	½ a. black (1938)		75·00 75·00
69	1 a. deep red		5·50 26·00
	a. Rosine (1938)		12·00 28·00
70	4 a. emerald (1938)		18·00 27·00
71	4 r. yellow–green and vermilion (1941)		£180
72	5 r. vermilion and yellow-green (1941)		£250

No. 70 shows the currency spelt as "ANE" with the last letter missing and an accent over the Devanagri "N".

II. *P* 11.

(a) Inscriptions as Type H. Medium wove paper with gum (1939–41)

73	¼ a. ultramarine		25·00 38·00
	a. Greenish blue (1941)		1·75 45·00
74	½ a. black		27·00 27·00
75	1 a. scarlet-vermilion (1940)		£120 60·00
	a. Rose (1940)		12·00 45·00
76	2 a. yellow-green (1941)		15·00 75·00

(b) Inscriptions as Type I. Medium wove paper with gum (1940)

77	½ a. black		£120 95·00
78	2 a. bright apple-green		48·00 48·00

FISCAL USE. Collectors are warned that the low values of the later settings of Type **11** were extensively used for fiscal purposes. Stamps which have been fraudulently cleaned of pen-cancels, regummed or provided with forged postmarks are frequently met with. Particular care should be exercised with examples of Nos. 58/a, 64/5, 68/70, 74/5a and 77.

Maharao Raja Ishwari Singh, 1927–1945

20

1941–44. *Typo. P* 11.

79	20	3 p. bright blue	75	3·00
80		6 p. deep blue	2·50	4·00
81		1 a. orange-red	2·50	4·75
82		2 a. chestnut	4·00	10·00
		a. Deep brown (no gum) (1944)	13·00	14·00
83		4 a. bright green	7·50	32·00
84		8 a. dull green	10·00	£100
85		1 r. deep blue	27·00	£150
79/85		*Set of* 7	48·00	£275

The first printing only of Nos. 79/85 is usual with gum; all further printings, including No. 82a, are without gum.

Maharao Raja Bahadur Singh, 1945–1971

21 Maharao Raja Bahadur Singh   **22** Bundi

(Typo *Times of India* Press, Bombay)

1947. *P* 11.

86	21	¼ a. blue-green	1·00	22·00
87		½ a. violet	1·00	22·00
88		1 a. yellow-green	1·00	22·00
89	—	2 a. vermilion	1·10	40·00
90		4 a. orange	1·25	55·00
91	22	8 a. ultramarine	2·25	
92		1 r. chocolate	12·00	
86/92		*Set of* 7	18·00	

On the 2 and 4 a. the Maharao is in Indian dress.

OFFICIAL STAMPS

PRICES. Prices for Nos. O1/52 are for unused examples. Used stamps are generally worth a small premium over the prices quoted.

बून्दी	**BUNDI**
(O 1)	
सरविस	**SERVICE**
(O 1)	(O 2)
BUNDI	
SERVICE	
(O 3)	

1915–41. *T* 11 *handstamped as Types* O 1/3. *Ungummed paper except Nos.* O47/52.

A. *Optd with Type* O 1. B. *Optd with Type* O 2. C. *Optd with Type* O 3.

I. Rouletted in colour

(a) Inscriptions as Type A. Thin wove paper.

		A	B	C
O 1	½ a. black	£200	†	†
	a. Red opt	£180	†	†
O 1b	2 a. emerald	1·75	†	†
	ba. Deep green (coarse ptg on medium wove paper)	6·50	13·00	£160
	bb. Red opt	12·00	11·00	†
O 2	2½ a. chrome-yellow (*shades*)	2·25	9·00	£150
	a. Red opt	£110	£130	†

			A	B	C
O 3	3 a. chestnut		2·50	15·00	†
	a. Green opt		£100	†	†
	b. Red opt		£140	£140	†
O 4	6 a. cobalt		24·00	24·00	£170
	a. Red opt		£160	£170	£180
O 5	1 r. reddish violet		35·00	35·00	†
	a. Red opt		£190	£190	†

(b) Inscriptions as Type B. Thin wove or pelure paper

			A	B	C
O 6	¼ a. ultramarine (*shades*)		1·60	1·75	7·50
	a. Red opt		1·25	4·00	£110
O 7	½ a. black		5·50	4·50	23·00
	a. Red opt		4·00	11·00	£120
O 8	1 a. vermilion		4·00	†	†
	b. Carmine		18·00	12·00	48·00
	c. Red (*shades*)		—	6·00	—
O 9	2 a. emerald (*shades*)		20·00	28·00	†
O 9b	3 a. chestnut (R.)		—	80·00	†
O10	4 a. apple-green		12·00	55·00	£160
	a. Red opt		£160	†	†
O10b	4 a. olive-yellow		£160	£170	†
	ba. Red opt		—	£325	†
O11	6 a. pale ultramarine (*shades*)		11·00	£120	†
	a. Red opt		£160	£160	†
	b. Deep ultramarine		50·00	70·00	†
	ba. Red opt		£160	£140	†
O12	8 a. orange		38·00	50·00	£180
	a. Red opt		£180	†	†
O13	10 a. olive-sepia		£150	£200	£350
	a. Red opt		£400	£425	£450
O14	12 a. sage-green		£140	£300	£375
O14b	1 r. lilac		£200	†	£450

(c) Inscriptions as Type C. Thin to medium wove paper.

			A	B	C
O15	¼ a. ultramarine (*shades*)		1·90	1·60	13·00
	a. Red opt		80	5·00	†
	b. Green opt		2·50	35·00	†
	c. Cobalt (medium wove paper)		48·00	42·00	£180
	ca. Red opt		32·00	16·00	90·00
O16	½ a. black		5·50	3·00	9·00
	a. Red opt		75	8·00	£110
	b. Green opt		3·00	†	†
O17	1 a. orange-red		1·25	†	†
	a. Carmine		18·00	8·00	16·00
	b. Deep red (medium wove paper)		32·00	38·00	65·00
O18	2 a. emerald		4·50	12·00	55·00
	a. Red opt		†	6·00	†
	b. Sage-green		8·00	13·00	75·00
O19	4 a. yellow-green (*shades*)		8·00	55·00	†
	b. Red opt		†	†	†
	c. Olive-yellow		90·00	95·00	†
	ca. Red opt		£190	£190	†
O20	8 a. reddish orange		14·00	24·00	£170
	a. Red opt		£160	†	†
O21	10 a. brown-olive		38·00	60·00	£225
	a. Red opt		£225	£225	£275
O22	12 a. sage-green		32·00	70·00	£225
	a. Red opt		†	†	£325
O23	1 r. lilac		£110	†	†
	a. Red opt		£200	†	†
O24	2 r. red-brown and black		£275	£170	†
	a. Red opt		†	£600	†
	b. Chocolate and black (medium wove paper)		£425	£425	†
O25	3 r. blue and red-brown		£275	£190	†
	a. Red opt		£600	†	†
	b. Grey-blue and chocolate (medium wove paper)		£600	£600	†
	ba. Red opt		£650	†	†
O26	4 r. emerald and scarlet		£275	£300	†
O27	5 r. scarlet and emerald		£275	£300	†

(d) Inscriptions as Type D. Thin wove paper

			A	B	C
O28	2½ a. buff (*shades*)		15·00	18·00	†
	b. Red opt		£140	†	†
O29	3 a. red-brown		27·00	24·00	†
	a. Variety as No. 51a		48·00	45·00	†
	b. Red opt		†	£200	†
O30	10 a. bistre		32·00	55·00	£300
	a. Variety as No. 52a		60·00	£120	£425
	b. Red opt		£250	†	†
O31	12 a. grey-olive		45·00	65·00	£300
	a. Variety as No. 53a		75·00	£130	£375
	b. Red opt		£250	£325	†

(e) Inscriptions as Type E. (i) Medium wove paper

			A	B	C
O32	¼ a. deep slate ..		30·00	15·00	†
	a. Red opt		27·00	32·00	†
O32b	¼ a. indigo (*thin wove paper*)		25·00	30·00	†
	ba. Red opt		25·00	28·00	†
	bb. Green opt ..		55·00	60·00	†
	c. Cobalt		48·00	48·00	£180
	ca. Red opt		35·00	30·00	85·00
O33	½ a. black		28·00	12·00	†
	a. Red opt		22·00	10·00	†
	b. Green opt ..		†	£140	†
O34	1 a. carmine-red		28·00	28·00	£170
O35	3 a. chocolate (*shades*)		£150	£110	£180
	a. Red opt		£300	£300	†
O35b	4 a. yellow-olive		†	£325	†

(ii) Very thick wove paper

			A	B	C
O36	¼ a. indigo ..		9·00	12·00	†
	a. Red opt		16·00	32·00	†
	b. Green opt ..		70·00	†	†
O37	½ a. black		70·00	80·00	†
O38	1 a. bright scarlet		13·00	11·00	£160
	a. Carmine-red		†	55·00	†

(iii) Thin horizontally laid paper

			A	B	C
O39	¼ a. indigo		60·00	70·00	†
	a. Red opt		5·00	8·00	£140
O40	1 a. scarlet-vermilion		32·00	20·00	†
	a. Red opt		£180	£190	†

Nos. O39/40a exist in *tête-bêche* blocks of four on the same or opposite sides of the paper.

(f) Inscriptions as Type F. Medium wove paper

			A	B	C
O40b	½ a. black		—	—	†
	ba. Red opt		£180	†	†
O40c	4 a. yellow-olive		†	£450	†

			A	B	C

(g) Inscriptions as Type G. (i) Horizontally laid paper

O41	½ a. black (red opt)	..	..	£110	£110	†
	a. Vert laid paper	..	..	£120	£120	†
	ab. Red opt	..	..	£130	60·00	£225
O42	4 a. bright green	..	..	£150	£150	†
	a. Red opt	..	..	£170	£200	†

(ii) Medium wove paper

| O42b | ½ a. black | .. | .. | £150 | £160 | † |
| | ba. Red opt | .. | .. | £190 | £190 | † |

(h) Inscriptions as Type H. Medium wove paper

O43	¼ a. ultramarine	..	..	25·00	75·00	†
	a. Red opt	..	..	£150	£200	†
O44	½ a. black	..	..	90·00	£130	†
	a. Red opt	..	..	75·00	†	£300
O45	1 a. rosine	..	..	£130	£120	£275
O46	4 a. emerald	..	..	£130	£160	£275
	a. Red opt	..	..	£275	†	£300

II. *P* 11. *(a) Inscriptions as Type H. Medium wove paper with gum*

O47	¼ a. ultramarine	..	..	45·00	75·00	£110
	a. Red opt	..	..	60·00	90·00	†
	b. Greenish blue	..	..	70·00	70·00	£150
	c. Ditto. Red opt	..	..	£150	†	†
O48	½ a. black	..	..	45·00	55·00	£225
	a. Red opt	..	..	75·00	£180	£150
O49	1 a. scarlet-vermilion	..	..	£200	£250	£375
	a. Stamp doubly printed	..	†	†	£850
	b. Rose	..	..	£120	95·00	£275
O50	2 a. yellow-green	..	..	£275	£150	£180

(b) Inscriptions as Type I. Medium wove paper with gum

O51	½ a. black	..	..	£110	£190	£275
	a. Red opt	..	..	£200	£250	†
O52	2 a. bright apple-green	..	..	£250	£275	£450

Until 1941 it was the general practice to carry official mail free but some of the above undoubtedly exist postally used.

1941. *Nos. 79 to 85 optd* "SERVICE".

O53	20	3 p. bright blue (R.)	..	..	3·00	7·50
O54		6 p. deep blue (R.)	..	..	10·00	7·50
O55		1 a. orange-red	..	..	9·00	7·00
O56		2 a. brown	..	..	7·00	8·50
O57		4 a. bright green	..	..	24·00	70·00
O58		8 a. dull green	..	..	90·00	£275
O59		1 r. deep blue (R.)	..	..	£110	£300
O53/9				*Set of 7*	£225	£600

Two different types of "R" occur in the "SERVICE" overprint. On five positions in the sheet of 12 the "R" shows a larger loop and a pointed diagonal leg.

Bundi became part of the Rajasthan Union by 15 April 1948.

BUSSAHIR (BASHAHR)

PRICES FOR STAMPS ON COVER

Nos. 1/21	*from × 8*
Nos. 22/23	*from × 2*
Nos. 24/43	*from × 8*

Raja Shamsher Singh, 1850–1914

1   2   3

4   5   6

 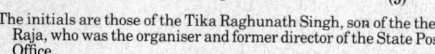

7   8   (9)

The initials are those of the Tika Raghunath Singh, son of the then Raja, who was the organiser and former director of the State Post Office.

(Litho at the Bussahir Press by Maulvi Karam Bakhsh, Rampur)

1895 (20 June). *Laid paper. Optd with T 9 in pale greenish blue (B.), rose (R.), mauve (M.) or lake (L.). With or without gum.*

(a) Imperf.

1	1	¼ a. pink (M.) (1.9.95)	..	..	£850
		a. Monogram in rose	..	..	£1200
2	2	½ a. grey (R.)	..	..	£250
		a. Monogram in mauve	..	..	
3	3	1 a. vermilion (M.)	..	..	£100
4	4	2 a. orange-yellow (M.)	..	30·00	£120
		a. Monogram in rose	..	..	65·00
		b. Monogram in lake	..	..	45·00
		c. Monogram in blue	..	..	£100
5	5	4 a. slate-violet (M.)	..	..	55·00
		a. Monogram in rose	..	..	75·00
		b. Monogram in lake	..	..	65·00
		c. Without monogram	..	..	£170

6	6	8 a. red-brown (M.)	..	..	55·00	£120
		a. Monogram in blue	..	..	80·00	
		b. Monogram in lake	..	..	£160	
		c. Without monogram	..	..	£160	
		d. Thick paper	..	..	75·00	
7	7	12 a. green (L.)	..	..	£180	
		a. Monogram in mauve	..	..		
8	8	1 r. ultramarine (R.)	..	..	55·00	
		a. Monogram in mauve	..	..	£100	
		b. Monogram in lake	..	..	85·00	
		c. Without monogram	..	..	£170	

(b) Perf with a sewing machine; gauge and size of holes varying between 7 and 11½

9	1	¼ a. pink (B.)	..	..	32·00	75·00
		a. Monogram in mauve	..	—	£100
		b. Without monogram	..	£170	95·00
10	2	½ a. grey (R.)	..	..	15·00	80·00
		a. Without monogram	..	£325	
11	3	1 a. vermilion (M.)	..	15·00	75·00
		a. Without monogram	..		
12	4	2 a. orange-yellow (B.)	..	24·00	75·00
		a. Monogram in rose	..		
		b. Monogram in mauve	..	60·00	
		c. Without monogram	..	—	£170
13	5	4 a. slate-violet (B.)	..	16·00	80·00
		a. Monogram in rose	..	23·00	90·00
		b. Monogram in mauve	..	30·00	
		c. Without monogram	..	40·00	
14	6	8 a. red-brown (M.)	..	17·00	85·00
		a. Monogram in blue	..	40·00	£120
		b. Monogram in rose	..	55·00	
		c. Without monogram	..	90·00	
15	7	12 a. green (R.)	..	50·00	95·00
		a. Monogram in mauve	..	80·00	
		b. Monogram in lake	..	75·00	
		c. Without monogram	..	£130	
16	8	1 r. ultramarine (R.)	..	28·00	85·00
		a. Monogram in mauve	..	70·00	
		b. Without monogram	..	£160	£225
9/16			*Set of 8*	£180	£600

1899. *As 1895, but pin-perf or rouletted.*

17	3	1 a. vermilion (M.)	..	£130	£150
18	4	2 a. orange-yellow (M.)	..	38·00	95·00
		a. Monogram in lake	..	40·00	
		b. Monogram in rose	..	55·00	
		c. Monogram in blue	..	80·00	
		d. Without monogram	..	£190	
19	5	4 a. slate-violet (L.)	..	£180	
		a. Monogram in blue	..		
		b. Monogram in rose	..	£200	
		c. Monogram in mauve	..	£225	
20	7	12 a. green (R.)	..	£350	£400
21	8	1 r. ultramarine (R.)	..	£350	

Nos. 1 to 21 were in sheets of 24. They seem to have been overprinted and perforated as required. Those first issued for use were perforated, but they were subsequently supplied imperf, both to collectors and for use. Nos. 17 to 21 were some of the last supplies. No rule seems to have been observed as to the colour of the overprinted monogram; pale blue, rose and mauve were used from the first. The pale blue varies to greenish blue or blue-green, and appears quite green on the yellow stamps. The lake is possibly a mixture of the mauve and the rose—it is a quite distinct colour and apparently later than the others. Specimens without overprint are either remainders left in the Treasury or copies that have escaped accidentally; they have been found sticking to the backs of others that bore the overprint.

Varieties may also be found doubly overprinted, in two different colours.

10   11   12

T 11. Lines of shading above and at bottom left and right of shield.
T 12. White dots above shield and ornaments in bottom corners.

13   14

15   16

(Printed at the Bussahir Press by Maulvi Karam Bakhsh)

1896–97. *Wove paper. Optd with monogram* "R.S.", *T* 9, *in rose. Recess singly from line-engraved dies. With or without gum. Various perfs.*

22	10	¼ a. deep violet (1897)	..	—	£600
23	11	½ a. grey-blue	..	£425	£150
23a		½ a. deep blue (1897)	..	—	£200

No. 23 exists sewing-machine perf about 10 and also perf 14½–16. Nos. 22 and 23a are pin-perf.

1896–1900. *As Nos. 22/3, but lithographed in sheets of various sizes. No gum.*

(a) Imperf

24	10	¼ a. slate-violet (R.)	..	3·50
		a. Monogram in mauve	..	5·00
		b. Monogram in blue	..	7·00
		c. Monogram in lake	..	9·50

25	11	½ a. blue (*shades*) (R.)	..	4·00	11·00
		a. Monogram in mauve	..	4·75	11·00
		b. Monogram in lake	..	5·00	
		c. Without monogram	..		
		d. Laid paper (B.)	..	65·00	
		da. Monogram in lake	..		
26	13	1 a. olive (*shades*) (R.)	..	9·50	23·00
		a. Monogram in mauve	..	21·00	
		b. Monogram in lake	..	24·00	

(b) Pin-perf or rouletted

27	10	¼ a. slate-violet (R.)	..	11·00	10·00
		a. Monogram in lake	..	14·00	13·00
		b. Monogram in mauve	..	—	19·00
28	11	½ a. blue (*shades*) (R.)	..	7·00	20·00
		a. Monogram in lake	..	10·00	21·00
		b. Monogram in blue	..	18·00	26·00
		c. Monogram in mauve	..		
		d. Laid paper (M.)	..		
29	13	1 a. olive (*shades*) (R.)	..	14·00	
		a. Monogram in mauve	..	28·00	28·00
		b. Monogram in lake	..	30·00	30·00
30	14	2 a. orange-yellow (B.)	..	£325	£350

The ¼ a. and ½ a. are in sheets of 24, the 1 a. and 2 a. in blocks of 4.

1900–01. *¼ a., 1 a, colours changed; ½ a. redrawn type; 2 a. with dash before* "STATE" *and characters in lower left label; 4 a. new value. No gum.*

(a) Imperf

31	10	¼ a. vermilion (R.)	..	2·75	5·50
		a. Monogram in blue	..	3·00	5·00
		b. Without monogram	..		
31c	12	½ a. blue (M.)	..	6·00	15·00
		ca. Monogram in rose	..	19·00	
		cb. Without monogram	..	30·00	
32	13	1 a. vermilion (M.)	..	2·50	8·00
		a. Monogram in blue	..	4·50	5·50
		b. Monogram in lake	..		
		c. Without monogram	..	26·00	
33	15	2 a. ochre (M.) (9.00)	..	26·00	55·00
34		2 a. yellow (M.) (11.00)	..	26·00	
		a. Monogram in blue	..	28·00	60·00
		b. Without monogram	..	48·00	
35		2 a. orange (B.) (1.01)	..	32·00	55·00
		a. Monogram in mauve	..	35·00	55·00
		b. Without monogram	..	42·00	
36	16	4 a. claret (R.)	..	27·00	75·00
		a. Monogram in mauve	..	38·00	
		b. Monogram in blue	..	48·00	90·00
		c. Without monogram	..	28·00	

(b) Pin-perf or rouletted

37	10	¼ a. vermilion (M.)	..	2·50	5·50
		a. Monogram in blue	..	2·75	
		b. Without monogram	..		
37c	12	½ a. blue (M.)	..	28·00	38·00
38	13	1 a. vermilion (M.)	..	3·75	8·00
		a. Monogram in blue	..	6·00	6·50
39		1 a. brown-red (M.) (3.01)	..	—	£170
40	15	2 a. ochre (M.) (9.00)	..	35·00	
		a. Monogram in blue	..		
41		2 a. yellow (M.) (11.00)	..	26·00	48·00
		a. Monogram in rose	..	40·00	60·00
		b. Monogram in blue	..	45·00	70·00
42		2 a. orange (M.) (1.01)	..	35·00	45·00
		a. Monogram in blue	..	50·00	50·00
		b. Without monogram	..	—	£110
43	16	4 a. claret (R.)	..	38·00	
		a. Monogram in blue	..	42·00	90·00
		b. Monogram in mauve	..	60·00	

The ¼ a., ½ a. and 1 a. are in sheets of 24; the 2 a. in sheets of 50 differing throughout in the dash and the characters added at lower left; the 4 a. in sheets of 28.

(17)

The stamps formerly catalogued with large overprint "R.N.S." (T 17) are now believed never to have been issued for use.

Remainders are also found with overprint "P.S.", the initials of Padam Singh who succeeded Raghunath Singh in the direction of the Post Office, and with the original monogram "R.S." in a damaged state, giving it the appearance of a double-lined "R."

The stamps of Bussahir have been obsolete since 1 April 1901. Numerous remainders were sold after this date, and all values were later reprinted in the colours of the originals, or in fancy colours, from the original stones, or from new ones. Printings were also made from new types, similar to those of the second issue of the 8 a., 12 a., and 1 r. values, in sheets of 8.

Reprints are frequently found on laid paper.

Collectors are warned against obliterated copies bearing the Rampur postmark with date "19 MA 1900." Many thousand remainders and reprints were thus obliterated for export after the closing of the State Post Office.

CHARKHARI

PRICES FOR STAMPS ON COVER

Nos. 1/4	*from × 2*
Nos. 5/26	*from × 20*
Nos. 27/44	*from × 3*
Nos. 45/53	*from × 100*
Nos. 54/5	*from × 5*
No. 56	*from × 2*

Maharaja Malkhan Singh, 1880–1908

1

The top row shows the figures of value used in the stamps of 1894-7, and the bottom row those for the 1904 issue. In the 4 a. the figure slopes slightly to the right in the first issue, and to the left in the second.

1894. *Typo from a single die. No gum. Imperf.*

1	¼ anna, rose	..	..	£900	£700
	1 annas, dull green	..	..	£1600	£2250
	2 annas, dull green	..	..	£1800	
	4 annas, dull green	..	..	£1200	

Nos. 1/2 are known pin-perforated.

1897. *Inscr "ANNA". No gum. Imperf.*

1	¼ a. magenta	..	..	30·00	38·00
	a. Purple	..	..	2·00	2·75
	b. Violet	..	..	2·00	2·75
	½ a. purple	..	..	2·25	3·50
	a. Violet	..	..	2·50	3·00
1	1 a. blue-green	..	..	4·00	6·00
	a. Turquoise-blue	..	..	4·00	4·50
	b. Indigo	..	..	10·00	16·00
	2 a. blue-green	..	..	7·00	12·00
	a. Turquoise-blue	..	..	7·00	8·00
	b. Indigo	..	..	10·00	18·00
	4 a. blue-green	..	..	6·50	13·00
	a. Turquoise-blue	..	..	6·00	9·00
	b. Indigo	..	..	19·00	30·00
	ba. Figure of value sideways				
/9		*Set of 5*		19·00	25·00

Minor varieties may be found with the first "A" in "ANNA" not printed.

All values are known on various coloured papers, but these are proofs or trial impressions.

1904. *Numerals changed as illustrated above. No gum.*

.0	1	¼ a. violet	..	1·75	3·00
.1		½ a. violet	..	2·75	4·00
.2		1 a. green	..	5·00	12·00
.3		2 a. green	..	20·00	20·00
.4		4 a. green	..	13·00	23·00
.0/14		..	*Set of 5*	38·00	55·00

Stamps of this issue can be found showing part of the paper-maker's watermark. "Mercantile Script Extra Strong John Haddon & Co.".

Maharaja Jujhar Singh, 1908–1914

2 (Right-hand sword over left)

Type I

Type II

Type I. "P" of "POSTAGE" in same size as other letters. "E" small with long upper and lower arms. White dot often appears on one or both of the sword hilts.
Type II. "P" larger than the other letters. "E" large with short upper and lower arms. No dots occur on the hilts.

1909–19. *Litho in Calcutta. Wove paper. P 11.* (a) *Type* I.

15	2	1 p. chestnut	..	32·00	40·00
		a. Pale chestnut	..	2·25	38·00
		b. Orange-brown	..	3·00	38·00
16		1 p. turquoise-blue	..	30	45
		a. Imperf between (horiz pair)	..	£140	
		b. Greenish blue (1911)	..	60	80
		c. Pale turquoise-green	..	80	70
17		½ a. vermilion	..	1·40	90
		a. Deep rose-red	..	75	1·10
18		1 a. sage-green	..	1·75	1·90
		a. Yellow-olive	..	1·50	1·25
19		2 a. grey-blue	..	2·25	3·25
		a. Dull violet-blue	..	3·00	3·00
20		4 a. deep green	..	3·00	4·00
21		8 a. brown-red	..	6·00	13·00
22		1 r. pale chestnut	..	9·50	26·00
15a/22		..	*Set of 8*	23·00	75·00

(b) *Type* II

24	2	1 p. turquoise-blue	..	1·75	2·00
25		½ a. vermilion	..	70	1·00
		a. Imperf (pair)	..	£400	
		b. Deep rose-red	..	2·75	3·25
26		1 a. yellow-olive (1919)	..	2·00	2·25
		a. Sage-green	..	1·40	1·50
24/6		..	*Set of 3*	3·50	4·00

No. 15, from the original printing, shows an upstroke to the "1", not present on other brown printings of this value.
See also Nos. 31/44.

MINIMUM PRICE

The minimum price quote is 10p which represents a handling charge rather than a basis for valuing common stamps. For further notes about prices see introductory pages.

3

4

"⌐I" below Swords
Right sword overlaps
left. Double frame
lines.

"JI" below Swords.
Left sword overlaps
right. Single frame
line.

1912–17. *Handstamped. Wove paper. No gum. Imperf.*

27	3	1 p. violet	..	£350	70·00
		a. Dull purple	..	—	80·00
28	4	1 p. violet (1917)	..	7·00	5·00
		a. Dull purple	..	11·00	5·00
		b. Tête-bêche (pair)	..	60·00	60·00
		c. Laid paper	..	—	£180

Maharaja Ganga Singh, 1914–1920
Maharaja Arimardan Singh, 1920–1942

5 (*actual size* 63 × 25 *mm*)   6 (Left-hand sword over right)

1922. *Handstamped. No gum.* (a) *Wove paper. Imperf.*

29	5	1 a. violet	..	60·00	75·00
		a. Dull purple	..	75·00	85·00

(b) *Laid paper. P 11*

30	5	1 a. violet	..	65·00	95·00
		a. Imperf	..	£130	£140

(Typo State Ptg Press, Charkhari)

1930–45. *Wove paper. No gum. Imperf.*

31	6	1 p. deep blue	..	35	10·00
		a. Vert pair, top ptd inverted on back, bottom normal upright	..	13·00	
		b. Tête-bêche (vert pair)	..	£170	
		c. Bluish slate	..	19·00	
		d. Laid paper (1944)	..	—	£250
32		1 p. dull *to* light green (*pelure*) (1943)		38·00	£130
33		1 p. violet (1943)	..	13·00	95·00
		a. Tête-bêche (vert pair)	..	50·00	
34		½ a. deep olive	..	50	10·00
35		½ a. red-brown (1940)	..	2·75	22·00
		a. Tête-bêche (vert pair)	..	£300	
36		½ a. black (*pelure*) (1943)	..	42·00	£110
37		½ a. red (*shades*) (1943)	..	16·00	32·00
		a. Tête-bêche (vert pair)	..	35·00	
		b. Laid paper (1944)	..	—	£275
38		½ a. grey-brown	..	60·00	75·00
39		1 a. green	..	50	10·00
		a. Emerald	..	24·00	40·00
40		1 a. chocolate (1940)	..	5·00	22·00
		a. Tête-bêche (vert pair)	..	75·00	
		b. Lake-brown	..	—	35·00
41		1 a. red (1940)	..	70·00	55·00
		a. Carmine	..	—	55·00
		b. Laid paper (1944)	..	—	£300
42		2 a. light blue	..	1·25	14·00
		a. Tête-bêche (vert pair)	..	9·50	
43		2 a. greenish grey (1941?)	..	32·00	45·00
		a. Tête-bêche (vert pair)	..	65·00	
		b. Laid paper (1944)	..	—	£325
		c. Greyish green	..	50·00	
43d		2 a. yellow-green (1945)	..	—	£375
44		4 a. carmine	..	4·00	17·00
		a. Tête-bêche (vert pair)	..	14·00	

There are two different versions of No. 37a, one with the stamps *tête-bêche* base to base and the other showing them top to top.

½ 2 As.

7 Imlia Palace   (8)

(Typo Batliboi Litho Works, Bombay)

1931 (25 June). *T 7 and similar designs. P 11, 11½, 12 or compound.*

45		½ a. blue-green	..	70	10
		a. Imperf between (horiz pair)	..	32·00	11·00
		b. Imperf between (vert pair)	..	32·00	
		c. Imperf horiz (vert pair)	..	32·00	
46		1 a. blackish brown	..	90	10
		a. Imperf between (horiz pair)	..	11·00	8·00
		b. Imperf between (vert pair)	..	11·00	8·00
		c. Imperf horiz (vert pair)	..	11·00	
47		2 a. violet	..	50	10
		a. Imperf between (horiz pair)	..	28·00	25·00
		b. Imperf between (vert pair)	..	28·00	25·00
		c. Imperf horiz (vert pair)	..	22·00	
		d. Doubly printed	..	8·50	
48		4 a. olive-green	..	70	10
		a. Imperf between (vert pair)	..	55·00	55·00
49		8 a. magenta	..	90	10
		a. Imperf between (horiz pair)	..	35·00	25·00
		b. Imperf between (vert pair)	..	35·00	
		c. Imperf horiz (vert pair)	..	35·00	12·00
50		1 r. green and rose	..	1·40	15
		a. Imperf between (horiz pair)	..	£100	£100
		b. Green (centre) omitted	..	—	£100

51		2 r. red and brown	..	2·25	20
		a. Imperf horiz (vert pair)	..	70·00	15·00
52		3 r. chocolate and blue-green	..	6·00	30
		a. Imperf between (horiz pair)	..	—	£150
		b. Tête-bêche (pair)	..	£140	20·00
		c. Chocolate (centre) omitted	..	19·00	
53		5 r. turquoise and purple	..	7·00	45
		a. Imperf between (horiz pair)	..	£150	
		b. Centre inverted	..	40·00	23·00
		c. Centre doubly printed	..	—	50·00
45/53		..	*Set of 9*	18·00	1·40

Designs:—½ a. The Lake; 2 a. Industrial School; 4 a. Bird's-eye view of City; 8 a. The Fort; 1 r. Guest House. 2 r. Palace Gate; 3 r. Temples at Rainpur; 5 r. Goverdhan Temple.

This issue was the subject of speculative manipulation, large stocks being thrown on the market cancelled-to-order at very low prices and unused at less than face value. The issue was an authorized one but was eventually withdrawn by the State authorities.

1939 (Dec)–**40.** *Nos. 21/2 surch as T 8.*

54	2	½ a. on 8 a. brown-red (1940)	..	26·00	£100
		a. No space between "½" and "As"	..	32·00	£100
		b. Surch inverted	..	£225	
		c. "1" of "½" inverted	..	£200	
55		1 a. on 1 r. chestnut (1940)	..	70·00	£250
		a. Surch inverted	..	£250	
56		"1 ANNA" on 1 r. chestnut	..	£500	£550

Maharaja Jaiendra Singh, 1942–1971

Charkhari became part of Vindhya Pradesh by 1 May 1948

COCHIN
(6 puttans = 5 annas. 12 pies = 1 anna; 16 annas = 1 rupee)

Stamps of Cochin were also valid on mail posted to Travancore.

PRICES FOR STAMPS ON COVER	
Nos. 1/3	*from* × 30
Nos. 4/5	*from* × 10
Nos. 6/6b	*from* × 3
Nos. 7/9	*from* × 20
Nos. 11/22	*from* × 15
Nos. 26/128	*from* × 8
Nos. O1/105	*from* × 15

Raja Kerala Varma I, 1888–1895

1   2

(Dies eng P. Orr & Sons, Madras; typo Cochin Govt, Ernakulam)

1892 (13 Apr). *No wmk, or wmk large Umbrella in the sheet. P 12.*

1	1	½ put. buff	..	1·50	1·75
		a. Orange-buff	..	1·50	1·60
		b. Yellow	..	1·75	2·25
		c. Imperf (pair)			
2		1 put. purple	..	1·75	1·25
		a. Imperf between (vert pair)	..	†	£1700
3	2	2 put. deep violet	..	1·25	1·50
1/3		..	*Set of 3*	4·00	4·00

Raja Rama Varma I, 1895–1914

1896 (End). *Similar to T 1, but 28×33 mm. P 12.*

(a) *Wmk Arms and inscription in sheet*

4		1 put. violet	..	55·00	55·00

(b) *Wmk Conch Shell to each stamp*

5		1 put. deep violet	..	16·00	26·00

Nos. 4/5 were intended for fiscal use, but are also known used for postal purposes.

1896. *Laid paper. P 12.*

6	1	½ put. orange-buff	..	£450	£120
		a. Orange	..	—	£120
		b. Yellow	..	—	£120

WATERMARKS. Prior to the 1911–23 issue, printed by Perkins, Bacon & Co, little attention was paid to the position of the watermark. Inverted and sideways watermarks are frequently found in the 1898 and 1903 issues.

1897. *Wmk a small Umbrella on each stamp. P 12.*

7	1	½ put. buff	..	3·50	2·25
		a. Orange	..	1·50	1·00
		ab. Orange. Imperf (pair)			
		b. Yellow	..	2·75	1·00
8		1 put. purple	..	4·75	3·50
9	2	2 put. deep violet	..	2·75	3·25
		a. Imperf (pair)			
		b. Doubly printed	..	†	
		c. Printed both sides			
		d. Tête-bêche (pair)	..	£2250	
7/9		..	*Set of 3*	8·00	7·00

The paper watermarked with a small umbrella is more transparent than that of the previous issue. The wmk is not easy to distinguish.

The 1 put. in deep violet was a special printing for fiscal use only.

3

4

5

6

1898. *Thin yellowish paper. Wmk small Umbrella on each stamp. With or without gum. P 12.*

11	3	3 pies, blue	1·00	70
		a. Imperf between (horiz pair)	£425	
		b. Imperf between (vert pair)	£500	
		c. Doubly printed		
12	4	½ put. green	1·50	50
		a. Imperf between (horiz pair)		
		b. Stamp sideways (in pair)		
13	5	1 put. pink	2·50	1·25
		a. *Tête-bêche* (pair)	£2000	£2000
		b. Laid paper	† £1600	
		ba. Laid paper. *Tête-bêche* (pair)	† £6000	
		c. *Red*	1·75	1·00
		d. *Carmine-red*	3·00	1·25
14	6	2 put. deep violet	3·00	1·25
		a. Imperf between (vert pair)	£400	
11/14		*Set of 4*	6·50	3·00

1903. *Thick white paper. Wmk small Umbrella on each stamp. With or without gum. P 12.*

16	3	3 pies, blue	30	10
		a. Doubly printed	— £275	
		b. Imperf between (horiz pair)	† £475	
17	4	½ put. green	75	10
		a. Stamp sideways (in pair)	£650 £650	
		b. Doubly printed	— £275	
18	5	1 put. pink	1·25	10
		a. *Tête-bêche* (pair)	† £2500	
19	6	2 put. deep violet	1·50	20
		a. Doubly printed	£700 £300	
16/19		*Set of 4*	3·50	40

(7)   (7a)

1909. *T 3 (paper and perf of 1903), surch with T 7. Wmk is always sideways. No gum.*

22	3	2 on 3 pies, rosy mauve	15	20
		a. Surch T 7 inverted	75·00 75·00	
		b. Surch T 7a	£500 £300	
		c. Stamps *tête-bêche*	£110 £120	
		d. Stamps and surchs *tête-bêche*	£150 £160	

Varieties a, c and d were caused by the inversion of one stamp (No. 7) in the plate and the consequent inversion of the corresponding surcharge to correct the error.

Type 7a was applied by a handstamp to correct the omission of the surcharge on R.3/2 in one setting only.

8 Raja Rama Varma I   8a

(Recess Perkins, Bacon & Co)

1911–13. *Currency in pies and annas. W 8a. P 14.*

26	8	2 p. brown	30	10
		a. Imperf (pair)		
27		3 p. blue	30	10
		a. Perf 14 × 12½	27·00	2·50
28		4 p. green	90	10
28a		4 p. apple-green	2·50	40
29		9 p. carmine	1·10	10
		a. Wmk sideways		
30		1 a. brown-orange	1·60	10
31		1½ a. purple	4·25	40
32		2 a. grey (1913)	7·50	40
33		3 a. vermilion (1913)	28·00	32·00
26/33		*Set of 8*	38·00	32·00

COVER PRICES

Cover factors are quoted at the beginning of each country for most issues to 1945. An explanation of the system can be found on page x. The factors quoted do not, however, apply to philatelic covers.

Raja (Maharaja from 1921) Rama Varma II, 1914–1932

9 Raja Rama Varma II 10

I   (2 p.)   II

I   (1 a.)   II

(Recess Perkins, Bacon & Co)

1916–30. *W 8a. P 13½ to 14.*

35	10	2 p. brown (Die I) (a) (b) (c)	3·75	10
		a. Imperf (pair)	£450	
		b. Die II (b) (c) (1930)	80	10
36		4 p. green (a) (b)	95	10
37		6 p. red-brown (a) (b) (c) (1922)	1·40	10
38		8 p. sepia (b) (1923)	1·40	10
39		9 p. carmine (a)	12·00	15
40		10 p. blue (b) (1923)	1·75	10
41	9	1 a. orange (Die I) (a)	9·50	65
		a. Die II (a) (b) (1922)	8·50	30
42	10	1½ a. purple (b) (1923)	2·25	15
43		2 a. grey (a) (b) (d)	4·00	10
44		2¼ a. yellow-green (a) (d) (1922)	3·75	15
45		3 a. vermilion (a) (b)	11·00	35
35/45		*Set of 11*	42·00	2·75

Four different perforating heads were used for this issue: (a) comb 13.9; (b) comb 13.6; (c) line 13.8; (d) line 14.2. Values on which each perforation occur are shown above. Stamps with perforation (a) are on hand-made paper, while the other perforations are on softer machine-made paper with a horizontal mesh.

2   2   2

Two pies	Two pies	Two pies
(11)	(12)	(13)

2   2

Two Pies	Two Pies
(14)	(15)

1922–29. *T 8 (P 14), surch with T 11/15.*

46	11	2 p. on 3 p. blue	40	30
		a. Surch double	£300 £300	
47	12	2 p. on 3 p. blue	1·75	65
		a. Surch double	£450	
		b. "Pies" for "pies" (R. 4/8)	32·00	17·00
		ba. Surch double		
48	13	2 p. on 3 p. blue (6.24)	2·75	35
		a. "Pies" for "pies" (R. 4/8)	42·00	16·00
		b. Perf 14×12½	14·00	16·00
		ba. Ditto. "Pies" for "pies" (R. 4/8)	£190	£200
49	14	2 p. on 3 p. blue (1929)	4·25	4·75
		a. Surch double	£275	
		b. Surch with Type 15	65·00	95·00
		ba. Ditto. Surch double	£1200	

There are four settings of these overprints. The first (July 1922) consisted of 39 stamps with Type 11, and 9 with Type 12, and in Type 11 the centre of the "2" is above the "o" of "Two". In the second setting (May 1924) there were 36 of Type 11 and 12 of Type 12, and the centre of the figure is above the space between "Two" and "Pies". The third setting (June 1924) consists of stamps with Type 13 only.

The fourth setting (1929) was also in sheets of 48, No. 49b being the first stamp in the fourth row.

Three Pies

ONE ANNA
ഒരു അണ

3

**ANCHAL &
REVENUE**
(16)

മൂന്നു പൈ
(17)

1928. *Surch with T 16.*

50	10	1 a. on 2¼ a. yellow-green (a)	5·00	12·00
		a. "REVENUF" for "REVENUE"	48·00	75·00
		b. Surch double		

1932–33. *Surch as T 17. W 8a. P 13½.*

51	10	3 p. on 4 p. green (b)	1·00	80
		a. "r" in "Three" inverted	† £200	
52		3 p. on 8 p. sepia (b)	1·00	1·90
53		9 p. on 10 p. blue (b)	1·50	2·25
51/3		*Set of 3*	3·00	4·50

Maharaja Rama Varma III, 1932–1941

18 Maharaja Rama Varma III

(Recess Perkins, Bacon & Co)

1933–38. *T 18 (but frame and inscription of 1 a. as T 9). W 8a. P 13 × 13½.*

54	18	2 p. brown (1936)	60	20
55		4 p. green	60	10
56		6 p. red-brown	70	10
57	—	1 a. brown-orange	70	10
58	18	1 a. 8 p. carmine	3·00	3·50
59		2 a. grey (1938)	3·25	35
60		2¼ a. yellow-green	1·50	10
61		3 a. vermilion (1938)	3·50	1·25
62		3 a. 4 p. violet	1·50	1·40
63		6 a. 8 p. sepia	1·75	8·50
64		10 a. blue	3·00	10·00
54/64		*Set of 11*	18·00	23·00

For stamps in this design, but lithographed, see Nos. 67/71.

1934. *Surcharged as T 14. W 8a. P 13½.*

65	10	6 p. on 8 p. sepia (R.) (b)	75	50
66		6 p. on 10 p. blue (R.) (b)	1·75	1·40

"DOUBLE PRINTS". The errors previously listed under this description are now identified as blanket offsets, a type of variety outside the scope of this catalogue. Examples occur on issues from 1938 onwards.

SPACING OF OVERPRINTS AND SURCHARGES. The typeset overprints and surcharges issued from 1939 onwards show considerable differences in spacing. Except for specialists, however, these differences have little significance as they occur within the same settings and do not represent separate printings.

(Litho The Associated Printers, Madras)

1938. *W 8a (A) P 11 or (B) P 13 × 13½.*

				A	B
67	18	2 p. brown	1·00	30	5·50	80
68		4 p. green	85	10	8·00	11·00
69		6 p. red-brown	2·25	10	† £2000	
70		1 a. brown-orange	55·00	65·00	65·00	70·00
71		2¼ a. sage-green	6·00	15	12·00	3·00
67/71		*Set of 5*	55·00	60·00	†	

Most examples of Nos. 70A/B were used fiscally. Collectors are warned against examples which have been cleaned and regummed or provided with forged postmarks.

ANCHAL   **ANCHAL**   **THREE PIES**
(19)   (19a)   (20)

SURCHARGED   **ANCHAL**

**ONE ANNA
THREE PIES**   **NINE PIES**
(21)   (22)

ANCHAL   **ANCHAL**

NINE PIES   **SURCHARGED
NINE PIES**
(23)   (24)

1939 (Jan). *Nos. 57 and 70 optd with T 19/a. A. P 11. B. P 13×13½.*

				A	B
72	18	1 a. brn-orge (recess) (T 19)	†	1·50	40
73		1 a. brn-orge (litho) (T 19)	£250	50	— £225
74		1 a. brn-orge (litho) (T 19a)	75	1·60	10·00 50

In 1939 it was decided that there would be separate 1 a. stamps for revenue and postal purposes. The "ANCHAL" overprints were applied to stamps intended for postal purposes.

43–44. *T* **18** *variously optd or surch.*

I. Recess-printed stamp. No. 58

3 p. on 1 a. 8 p. carmine (T **20**)	..	£160	70·00
3 p. on 1 a. 8 p. carmine (T **21**)	..	2·00	6·00
6 p. on 1 a. 8 p. carmine (T **20**)	..	2·50	16·00
1 a. 3 p. on 1 a. 8 p. carmine (T **21**)	..	1·00	30

II. Lithographed stamps. Nos. 68 *and* 70.
A. *P* 11. B. *P* 13×13½.

		A	B
3 p. on 4 p. (T **21**)	..	5·00 2·75	13·00 2·25
6 p. on 1 a. (T **22**)	..	£250 £170	†
a. "SIX PIES" double	..	† £600	
6 p. on 1 a. (T **23**)	..	£225 £150	85·00 40·00
9 p. on 1 a. (T **22**)	..	95·00 £100	†
9 p. on 1 a. (T **23**)	..		£160 27·00
9 p. on 1 a. (T **24**)	..	†	13·00 3·75

Maharaja Kerala Varma II, 1941–1943

26 Maharaja Kerala Varma II

27 (*The actual measurement of this wmk is* 6¼ × 3⅝ *in.*)

(Litho The Associated Printers, Madras)

1943. *Frame of* 1 *a. inscr* "ANCHAL & REVENUE". A. *P* 11.
B. *P* 13 × 13½. (*a*) *W* 8*a*.

			A	B
85	26	2 p. grey-brown	..	† £1500	1·00 1·40
85a		4 p. green	..	† £425	£225
85b		1 a. brown-orange	..	70·00	85·00
85/b		*Set of* 3	..	† £450	£275

(*b*) *W* **27**

86	26	2 p. grey-brown	..	† £1800 25·00 1·40
87		4 p. green	..	3·00 2·75 7·00 14·00
88		6 p. red-brown	..	8·00 1·25 1·25 10
89		9 p. ultramarine	..	21·00 1·00 †
		a. Imperf between (horiz pair)	..	£1200 — †
90		1 a. brown-orange	..	21·00 38·00 £200 £150
91		2¼ a. yellow-green	..	24·00 6·00 16·00 1·25

Part of W **27** appears on many stamps in each sheet, while others are entirely without wmk.

Although inscribed "ANCHAL (=Postage) & REVENUE" most examples of Nos. 85*b* and 90A/B were used fiscally. Collectors are warned against examples which have been cleaned and regummed or provided with forged postmarks.

Maharaja Ravi Varma 1943–1946

1943. *T* **26** *variously opt or surch.* A. *P* 11. B. *P* 13×13½.

(*a*) *W* 8*a*.

				A	B
92		3 p. on 4 p. (T **21**)	..	†	50·00 14·00
92a		9 p. on 1 a. (T **23**)	..	†	4·25 1·25
92b		9 p. on 1 a. (T **24**)	..	†	2·75 1·75
92c		1 a. 3 p. on 1 a. (T **21**)	..	†	— £2750

(*b*) *W* **27**

93		2 p. on 6 p. (T **20**)	..	85 2·00	75 2·00
94		3 p. on 4 p. (T **20**)	..	1·90 10	†
95		3 p. on 4 p. (T **21**)	..	†	2·75 10
96		3 p. on 6 p. (T **20**)	..	85 30	85 20
97		4 p. on 6 p. (T **20**)	..	†	2·50 7·50

No. 92*c* is believed to be an error; a sheet of No. 85*b* having been included in a stock of No. O52 intended to become No. O66.

28 Maharaja Ravi Varma 29

I II

(Litho The Associated Printers, Madras)

1944–48. *W* **27**. *No gum.* (*a*) *Type* I. *P* 11.

98	28	9 p. ultramarine (1944)	..	8·50 1·40

(*b*) *Type* II. *P* 13

98a	28	9 p. ultramarine (1946)	..	5·00 10·00
		ab. Perf 13 × 13½	..	26·00 2·00
99		1 a. 3 p. magenta (1948)	..	5·00 7·00
		a. Perf 13 × 13½	..	£140 28·00
100		1 a. 9 p. ultramarine (*shades*) (1948)	..	8·00 9·00
98a/100		*Set of* 3		16·00 16·00

Nos. 98*a*/100 are line-perforated, Nos. 98*ab* and 99*a* comb-perforated.

Maharaja Kerala Varma III, 1946–48

(Litho The Associated Printers, Madras)

1946–48. *Frame of* 1 *a. inscr* "ANCHAL & REVENUE". *W* **27**.
No gum (*except for stamps perf* 11). *P* 13.

101	29	2 p. chocolate	..	1·00 10
		a. Imperf horiz (vert pair)	..	£1100 £1100
		c. Perf 11	..	8·00 60
		d. Perf 11×13	..	£350 £140
102		3 p. carmine	..	50 10
103		4 p. grey-green	..	£1500 80·00
104		6 p. red-brown (1947)	..	20·00 3·00
		a. Perf 11	..	£140 2·25
105		9 p. ultramarine	..	50 10
		a. Imperf between (horiz pair)	..	† £1200
106		1 a. orange (1948)	..	5·50 25·00
		a. Perf 11	..	£500
107		2 a. black	..	80·00 6·00
		a. Perf 11	..	£110 3·00
108		3 a. vermilion	..	50·00 50
101/8		*Set of* 8		£1500 £100

Although inscribed "ANCHAL (=Postage) & REVENUE" most examples of No. 106 were used fiscally.

The 1 a. 3 p. magenta, 1 a. 9 p. ultramarine and 2¼ a. yellow-green in Type **29** subsequently appeared surcharged or overprinted for official use. Examples of the 1 a. 3 p. magenta exist without overprint, but may have not been issued in this state (*Price £275 unused*).

30 Maharaja Kerala Varma III

Tail to turban flaw (R. 1/7)

(Litho The Associated Printers, Madras)

1948–50. *W* **27**. *P* 11.

109	30	2 p. grey-brown	..	90 15
		a. Imperf vert (horiz pair)	..	† £1100
110		3 p. carmine	..	75 15
		a. Imperf between (vert pair)	..	† £1100
111		4 p. green	..	8·00 90
		a. Imperf vert (horiz pair)	..	£275 £300
112		6 p. chestnut	..	10·00 20
		a. Imperf vert (horiz pair)	..	£700
113		9 p. ultramarine	..	1·75 15
114		2 a. black	..	38·00 40
115		3 a. orange-red	..	48·00 50
		a. Imperf vert (horiz pair)	..	£1400
116		3 a. 4 p. violet (1950)	..	90·00 £350
		a. Tail to turban flaw	..	£250
109/16		*Set of* 8		£180 £350

Maharaja Rama Varma IV, 1948–1964

31 Chinese Nets 32 Dutch Palace

(Litho The Associated Printers, Madras)

1949. *W* **27**. *P* 11.

117	31	2 a. black	..	2·75 4·50
		a. Imperf vert (horiz pair)	..	£425
118	32	2¼ a. green	..	2·00 4·00
		a. Imperf vert (horiz pair)	..	£425

SIX PIES

ആറു പൈ
(33)

പൈ Normal

പൈ Error

Due to similarities between two Malayalam characters some values of the 1948 provisional issue exist with an error in the second word of the Malayalam surcharge. On Nos. 119, 122 and O103 this occurs twice in the setting of 48. No. 125 shows four examples and No. O104*b* one. Most instances are as illustrated above, but in two instances on the setting for No. 125 the error occurs on the second character.

1949. *Surch as T* **33**. (i) *On* 1944–48 *issue. P* 13.

119	28	6 p. on 1 a. 3 p. magenta	..	2·50 2·75
		a. Incorrect character	..	21·00 21·00
120		1 a. on 1 a. 9 p. ultramarine (R.)	..	75 85

(ii) *On* 1946–48 *issue*

121	29	3 p. on 9 p. ultramarine	..	7·00 14·00
122		6 p. on 1 a. 3 p. magenta	..	9·00 10·00
		a. Surch double	..	† £400
		b. Incorrect character	..	60·00 60·00
123		1 a. on 1 a. 9 p. ultramarine (R.)	..	3·00 1·25
		a. Surch in black	..	† £1800
		b. Black surch with smaller native characters 7½ mm instead of 10 mm long	..	† £2250

(iii) *On* 1948–50 *issue*

124	30	3 p. on 9 p. ultramarine	..	1·75 1·75
		a. Larger native characters 20 mm instead of 16½ mm long	..	2·00 50
		ab. Imperf between (vert pair)	..	† £1000
		b. Surch double	..	£375
		c. Surch both sides	..	£300
125		3 p. on 9 p. ultramarine (R.)	..	2·75 2·00
		a. Incorrect character	..	15·00 11·00
126		6 p. on 9 p. ultramarine (R.)	..	75 40
119/26		*Set of* 8		25·00 28·00

1949. *Surch as T* **20**. *W* **27**. *P* 13.

127	29	6 p. on 1 a. orange	..	55·00 £110
128		9 p. on 1 a. orange	..	60·00 £110

OFFICIAL STAMPS

On ON ON

C G C G C G

S S S

(O 1) (O 2 Small "ON") (O 3 "G" without serif)

1913. *Optd with Type* O 1 (3 *p.*) *or* O 2 (*others*).

O1	8	3 p. blue (R.)	..	£120 10
		a. Black opt	..	† £950
		b. Inverted "S"	..	— 45·00
		c. Opt double	..	† £475
O2		4 p. green (*wmk sideways*)	..	8·00 10
		a. Opt inverted	..	— £250
O3		9 p. carmine	..	80·00 10
		a. Wmk sideways	..	14·00 10
O4		1½ a. purple	..	30·00 10
		a. Opt double	..	£400
O5		2 a. grey	..	13·00 10
O6		3 a. vermilion	..	42·00 20
O7		6 a. violet	..	35·00 2·00
O8		12 a. ultramarine	..	32·00 5·50
O9		1½ r. deep green	..	23·00 42·00
O1/9		*Set of* 9		£275 48·00

1919–33. *Optd as Type* O 3.

O10	10	4 p. green (*a*) (*b*)	..	3·25 10
		a. Opt double	..	— £350
O11		6 p. red-brown (*a*) (*b*) (1922)	..	5·00 10
		a. Opt double	..	— £350
O12		8 p. sepia (*b*) (1923)	..	11·00 10
O13		9 p. carmine (*b*) (1923)	..	42·00 10
O14		10 p. blue (*b*) (1923)	..	12·00 10
O15		1½ a. purple (*a*) (*b*) (1921)	..	5·50 10
O16		2 a. grey (*b*) (1923)	..	38·00 10
O17		2¼ a. yellow-green (*a*) (*b*) (1922)	..	10·00 10
		a. Opt double	..	† £350
O18		3 a. vermilion (*a*) (*b*) (*c*)	..	14·00 25
		a. Opt inverted	..	† £350
O19		6 a. violet (*a*) (*b*) (1924)	..	28·00 50
O19a		12 a. ultramarine (*a*) (*b*) (1929)	..	15·00 2·75
O19b		1½ r. deep green (*a*) (*b*) (1933)	..	22·00 75·00
O10/19b		*Set of* 12		£180 75·00

All values exist showing a straight-backed "C" variety on R. 4/1.

8

ON · ON

C · G · C · G

S · S

Eight pies

(O 4 27½ mm high) · (O 5 Straight back to "C") · (O 6 Circular "O"; "N" without serifs)

1923 (Jan)–24. *T 8 and* 10 *surch with Type* O 4.

O20		8 p. on 9 p. carmine (No. O3)	.. ..	£325	1·10
	a.	"Pies" for "pies" (R. 4/8)		£800	55·00
	b.	Wmk sideways		£130	20
	ba.	"Pies" for "pies" (R. 4/8)		£350	18·00
	c.	Surch double		†	£325
O21		8 p. on 9 p. carm (a) (b) (No. O13) (11.24)		70·00	10
	a.	"Pies" for "pies" (R. 4/8)		£180	12·00
	b.	Surch double		†	£275
	c.	Opt Type O 3 double	.. ..	†	£275

Varieties with smaller "i" or "t" in "Eight" and small "i" in "Pies" are also known from a number of positions in the setting.

1925 (Apr). *T* 10 *surch as Type* O 4.

O22		10 p. on 9 p. carmine (b) (No. O13)	..	65·00	50
	b.	Surch double		†	£275
	c.	Surch 25 mm high (a)	..	£160	80
	ca.	Surch double	..	†	£300

1929. *T 8 surch as Type* O 4.

O23		10 p. on 9 p. carmine (No. O3a)	..	£700	7·50
	a.	Surch double		†	£325
	b.	Wmk upright	..	—	38·00

1929–31. *Optd with Type* O 5.

O24	10	4 p. green (b) (1931)		..	22·00	1·10
		a. Inverted "S"			£120	10·00
O25		6 p. red-brown (b) (c) (d) (1930)			13·00	10
		a. Inverted "S"			80·00	3·50
O26		8 p. sepia (b) (1930)			6·00	10
		a. Inverted "S"			45·00	3·50
O27		10 p. blue (b)			6·00	10
		a. Inverted "S"			45·00	4·25
O28		2 a. grey (b) (1930)			22·00	15
		a. Inverted "S"			95·00	6·00
O29		3 a. vermilion (b) (1930)			8·00	15
		a. Inverted "S"			70·00	6·50
O30		6 a. violet (b) (d) (1930)			65·00	30
		a. Inverted "S"			£375	75·00
O24/30		..		*Set of* 7	£130	4·25

Pie3

No. O32b

1933. *Nos.* O26/7 *surch as T* 14, *in red.*

O32	10	6 p. on 8 p. sepia (b)	..	..	2·00	10
		a. Inverted "S"			16·00	3·75
		b. "3" for "S" in "Pies"			†	
O33		6 p. on 10 p. blue (b)			4·00	10
		a. Inverted "S"			32·00	3·75

The inverted "S" varieties occur on R.2/1 of one setting of this overprint only.

1933–38. *Recess-printed stamps of* 1933–38 *optd.*

(a) With Type O 5

O34	18	4 p. green	..	..	2·00	10
O35		6 p. red-brown (1934)	..	..	2·00	10
O36		1 a. brown-orange	..	..	9·00	10
O37		1 a. 8 p. carmine	..	..	1·50	20
O38		2 a. grey	..	..	9·00	10
O39		2¼ a. yellow-green	..	..	4·00	10
O40		3 a. vermilion	..	..	30·00	10
O41		3 a. 4 p. violet	..	..	1·50	15
O42		6 a. 8 p. sepia	..	..	1·50	20
O43		10 a. blue	..	..	1·50	30
O34/43				*Set of* 10	50·00	1·25

(b) With Type O 6 (*typo*)

O44	18	1 a. brown-orange (1937)	..		35·00	35
O45		2 a. grey-black (1938)	..		19·00	75
O46		3 a. vermilion (1938)	..		10·00	75
O44/6		..		*Set of* 3	55·00	1·60

ON · ON

C · G · C · G

S · S

(O 7 Curved back to "c") · (O 8)

ON · ON · ON

C · G · C · G · C · G

S · S · S

(O 9 Circular "O"; N with serifs) · (O 10 Oval "O") · (O 11)

1938–44. *Lithographed stamps of* 1938. W 8a, *optd.*

(a) With Type O 7 *or* O 8 (1 a). A. P 11. B. P 13×13½.

				A		B	
O47	18	4 p. green	..	18·00	1·25	17·00	1·50
		a. Inverted "S"	..	22·00	1·25	†	
O48		6 p. red-brown	..	16·00	30	†	
		a. Inverted "S"	..	19·00	40	†	
O49		1 a. brown-orange	..	£250	2·50	†	
O50		2 a. grey-black	..	12·00	60	†	
		a. Inverted "S"	..	13·00	60	†	

(b) With Type O 9 (*litho*) *or* O 10 (6 p.).

						A	B
O51	18	6 p. red-brown				6·00	1·75
O52		1 a. brown-orange			1·00	10	†
O53		3 a. vermilion			2·75	50	†

(c) With Type O 11

O53a	18	6 p. red-brown	..	£700 £300	†

The inverted "S" varieties, Nos. O47a, O48a and O50a, occur 21 times in the setting of 48.

1942–43. *Unissued stamps optd with Type* O 10. *Litho.* W 27. A. P 11. B. P 13×13½.

				A		B	
O54	18	4 p. green	..	60·00	11·00	1·25	60
O55		6 p. red-brown	..	90·00	11·00	17·00	90
		a. Optd both sides		†		†	90·00
O56		1 a. brown-orange	..	16·00	5·00	1·25	3·50
		a. Optd both sides		†		—	
O56b		2 a. grey-black (1943)	..	48·00	60	†	
		ba. Opt omitted		† £1000		†	
O56c		2¼ a. sage-green (1943)	..	£850	3·50	†	
O56d		3 a. vermilion (1943)	..	10·00	3·50	†	

1943. *Official stamps variously surch with T* 20 *or* 21.

(i) On 1½ a. purple, of 1919–33

O57	10	9 p. on 1½ a. (b) (T 21)	..	..	£350	18·00

(ii) On recess-printed 1 a. 8 p. carmine of 1933–44 (*Type* O 5 opt)

O58		3 p. on 1 a. 8 p. (T 21)	..	..	3·50	40
O59		9 p. on 1 a. 8 p. (T 20)	..	..	£100	26·00
O60		1 a. 9 p. on 1 a. 8 p. (T 20)	..		1·25	1·60
O61		1 a. 9 p. on 1 a. 8 p. (T 21)	..		80	30

(iii) On lithographed stamps of 1938–44. *T* 18. A. P 11. B. P 13×13½

(a) W 8a

				A	B
O62	3 p. on 4 p. (Types O 7 and 20)		†	17·00	3·75
	a. Surch double		†	£250	£140
O63	3 p. on 4 p. (Types O 7 and 21)		†	75·00	40·00
O64	3 p. on 1 a. (Types O 9 and 20)		1·75	1·75	†
O65	9 p. on 1 a. (Types O 9 and 20)		£180	45·00	†
O66	1 a. 3 p. on 1 a. (Types O 9 and 21)		£225	90·00	†

(b) W 27

			A	B
O67	3 p. on 4 p. (Types O 10 and 20)		†	70·00	42·00
O67a	3 p. on 4 p. (Types O 10 and 21)		£400		†
O67b	3 p. on 1 a. (Types O 10 and 20)	£110	60·00	80·00	60·00

1944. *Optd with Type* O 10. W 27. P 13 × 13½.

O68	26	4 p. green	..		14·00	1·75
		a. Perf 11	..		95·00	3·75
		b. Perf 13	..		£200	60·00
O69		6 p. red-brown	..		90	15
		a. Opt double	..		—	55·00
		b. Perf 11	..		70	10
		c. Perf 13	..		7·00	2·00
O70		1 a. brown-orange	..		£1400	45·00
O71		2 a. black	..		2·50	35
O72		2¼ a. yellow-green	..		1·60	35
		a. Optd both sides			†	£100
O73		3 a. vermilion	..		4·25	40
		a. Perf 11	..		3·75	40

Stamps perforated 13 × 13½ are from a comb machine; those perforated 13 from a line perforator.

1944. *Optd with Type* O 10 *and variously surch as Types* 20 *and* 21. W 27.

				A		B	
O74	26	3 p. on 4 p. (T 20)	..	5·00	45	1·00	10
		b. Optd Type O 10 on both sides		† £100		†	
O75		3 p. on 4 p. (T 21)	..	£375	£160	3·00	30
O76		3 p. on 1 a. (T 20)			†	12·00	2·50
O77		9 p. on 6 p. (T 20)			†	5·00	1·00
		a. Stamp printed both sides ..			†	†	
O78		9 p. on 6 p. (T 21)			†	2·25	20
O79		1 a. 3 p. on 1 a. (T 20)			†	4·00	20
O80		1 a. 3 p. on 1 a. (T 21)			†	2·50	10
O74/80		..	..			27·00	4·25
				Set of 7			

1946–47. *Stamps of* 1944–48 (*Head Type* II) *optd with Type* O 10. P 13.

O81	28	9 p. ultramarine	..		1·75	10
		a. Stamp printed both sides	..		†	£300
		b. Perf 13 × 13½	..		2·75	10
O82		1 a. 3 p. magenta (1947)	..		75	20
		a. Opt double	..		17·00	12·00
		b. Optd both sides, opt double on reverse	..		40·00	
O83		1 a. 9 p. ultramarine (1947)			40	45
		a. Opt double			†	
O81b/83		..	..		*Set of* 3	2·50	65

1948. *Stamps of* 1946–48 *and unissued values optd with Type* O 2. P 13.

O84	29	3 p. carmine			35	10
		a. Stamp printed both sides			†	
O85		4 p. grey-green	..		21·00	4·50
O86		6 p. red-brown	..		4·00	40
O87		9 p. ultramarine	..		75	10
O88		1 a. 3 p. magenta	..		1·50	25
O89		1 a. 9 p. ultramarine	..		1·40	40
O90		2 a. black	..		12·00	1·75
O91		2¼ a. yellow-green	..		13·00	1·75
O84/91				*Set of* 8	50·00	8·25

1949. *Stamps of* 1948–50 *and unissued values optd with Type* O 7.

O92	30	3 p. carmine			50	10
		a. "C" for "G" in opt	..		6·50	2·75
O93		4 p. green			75	10
		a. Imperf between (pair)	..		†	£95
		b. Optd on reverse	..		55·00	55·00
		c. "C" for "G" in opt			9·50	3·50
O94		6 p. chestnut	..		1·75	10
		a. Imperf between (vert pair)			†	£100
		b. "C" for "G" in opt			14·00	2·75
O95		9 p. ultramarine	..		1·50	10
		a. "C" for "G" in opt			11·00	3·25
O96		2 a. black	..		75	10
		a. "C" for "G" in opt			11·00	3·25
O97		2¼ a. yellow-green			1·90	3·75
		a. "C" for "G" in opt			18·00	28·00
O98		3 a. orange-red			1·10	10
		a. "C" for "G" in opt			14·00	65
O99		3 a. 4 p. violet			24·00	22·00
		a. "C" for "G" in opt			£200	£200
		b. Tail to turban flaw			£150	
O92/9				*Set of* 8	29·00	24·00

The "C" for "G" variety occurs on R. 1/4. Nos. O92/9, O103/ and O104b also exist with a flat back to "G" which occurs twic in each sheet on R. 1/5 and R. 2/8.

1949. *Official stamps surch as T* 33. (i) *On* 1944 *issue.*

O100	28	1 a. on 1 a. 9 p. ultramarine (R.)			60	30

(ii) On 1948 *issue*

O101	29	1 a. on 1 a. 9 p. ultramarine (R.)	..	14·00	10·00

(iii) On 1949 *issue*

O103	30	6 p. on 3 p. carmine		35	40
		a. Imperf between (vert pair)		†	£75
		b. Surch double		†	£27
		c. "C" for "G" in opt		7·00	7·50
		d. Incorrect character		7·00	7·50
O104		9 p. on 4 p. green (18 mm long)		55	1·25
		a. Imperf between (horiz pair)		£650	
		b. Larger native characters, 22 mm long		80	10
		ba. Ditto. Imperf between (horiz pair)	£650	£65	
		bb. Incorrect character		13·00	10·00
		c. "C" for "G" in opt		10·00	13·00
		ca. Ditto. Larger native characters, 22 mm long		13·00	10·00
O100/4		..	*Set of* 4	14·00	10·50

1949. *No.* 124a, *but with lines of surch* 17½ *mm apart, optd* "SERVICE".

O105	30	3 p. on 9 p. ultramarine	..	60	65

From 1 July 1949 Cochin formed part of the new state o Travancore-Cochin. Existing stocks of Cochin issues continued to be used in conjunction with stamps of Travancore surcharged in Indian currency.

DHAR

PRICES FOR STAMPS ON COVER

The stamps of Dhar are rare used on cover.

Raja (Maharaja from 1877) Anand Rao Puar III, 1857–1898

1 · 2

अर्धा बलड. · अघॊ लबड. · आधी डबल.

No. 1c · No. 1d · No. 2

1897–1900. *Type-set. Colour-fugitive paper. With oval handstamp in black. No gum. Imperf.*

1	1	½ p. black/*red* (three characters at bottom left)	..		1·60	2·00
		a. Handstamp omitted			£250	
		b. Line below upper inscription (R. 2/2)		55·00	55·00	
		c. Character transposed (R. 2/3)		19·00	22·00	
		d. Character transposed (R. 2/5)		55·00		
2		½ p. black/*red* (four characters at bottom left)	..		1·75	2·25
		a. Handstamp omitted			£180	
3		¼ a. black/*orange*			1·40	2·50
		a. Handstamp omitted			£225	
4		½ a. black/*magenta*	..		2·50	3·00
		a. Handstamp omitted			£225	£190
		b. Line below upper inscription (R. 2/2)		£100	£110	
5		1 a. black/*green*	..		4·75	8·50
		a. Handstamp omitted			£400	
		b. Printed both sides				
		c. Line below upper inscription (R. 2/2)		£180	£190	
6		2 a. black/*yellow*			19·00	30·00
		e. Top right corner ornament transposed with one from top of frame (R. 2/5)		£100	£130	
1/6				*Set of* 6	28·00	42·00

Nos. 1/6 were each issued in sheets of 10 (5 × 2), but may, on the evidence of a single sheet of the ½ pice value, have been printed in sheets of 20 containing two of the issued sheets *tête-bêche*.

Research has identified individual characteristics for stamps printed from each position in the sheet.

The same research suggests that the type remained assembled during the entire period of production, being amended as necessary to provide the different values. Seven main settings have been identified with changes sometimes occurring during their use which form sub-settings.

The distribution of stamps between the main settings was as follows:

Setting I—½ p.
Setting II—½ a., 1 a.
Setting III—1 a.
Setting IV—½ p., ½ a., 1 a.
Setting V—½ p.
Setting VI—½ p. (No. 2), ¼ a.
Setting VII—2 a.

The listed constant errors all occurred during Setting IV.

In No. 1c the three characters forming the second word in the lower inscription are transposed to the order (2) (3) (1) and in No. d to the order (3) (2) (1).

On Nos. 1b, 4b and 5c the line which normally appears above the upper inscription is transposed so that it appears below the characters.

All values show many other constant varieties including mistakes in the corner and border ornaments, and also both constant and non-constant missing lines, dots and characters.

Examples of complete forgeries and faked varieties on genuine stamps exist.

Raja (Maharaja from 1918) Udaji Rao Puar II, 1898–1926

(Typo at Bombay)

1898–1900. *P 11 to 12.*

7	2	2½ a. carmine	..	2·50	4·50
		a. Imperf (pair) ..	..	35·00	
		b. Deep rose	..	2·00	4·25
8		1 a. claret	..	2·25	4·50
9		1 a. reddish violet	..	2·50	9·00
		a. Imperf between (horiz pair)	..	£400	
		b. Imperf (pair) ..	..	£100	
10		2 a. deep green	..	4·00	16·00
7/10			Set of 4	9·50	30·00

The stamps of Dhar have been obsolete since 31 March 1901.

DUNGARPUR

PRICES FOR STAMPS ON COVER
Nos. 1/15 *from* × 2

Maharawal Lakshman Singh, 1918–1971

1 State Arms

(Litho Shri Lakshman Bijaya Printing Press, Dungarpur)

1933–47. *P 11.*

1	1	¼ a. bistre-yellow	..	..	— £100
2		¼ a. rose (1935)	..	..	— £300
3		¼ a. red-brown (1937) ..	..	..	— £190
4		1 a. pale turquoise-blue	..	..	— 90·00
5		1 a. rose (1938)	..	..	— £950
6		1 a. 3 p. deep reddish violet (1935)	..	— £140
7		2 a. deep dull green (1947)	..	..	— £170
8		4 a. rose-red (1934)	..	..	— £325

Nos. 2 and 5 are known in a *se-tenant* strip of 3, the centre stamp being the 1 a. value.

2 3 4

Maharawal Lakshman Singh

Three dies of ½ a. (*shown actual size*):

Die I. Size 21×25½ mm. Large portrait (head 5 mm and turban 7½ mm wide), correctly aligned (sheets of 12 and left-hand stamps in subsequent blocks of four *se-tenant* horizontally with Die II)

Die II. Size 20×24½ mm. Large portrait (head 4¾ mm and turban 7 mm wide), but with less detail at foot and with distinct tilt to left (right-hand stamps in sheets of four horizontally *se-tenant* with Die I)

Die III. Size 21×25½ mm. Small portrait (head 4½ mm and turban 6½ mm wide) (sheets of 4)

(Typo L.V. Indap & Co, Bombay)

1939–46. *T 2* (*various frames*) *and 3/4. Various perfs.*

9	2	¼ a. orange (p 12, 11, 10½ or 10)	..	£325	45·00
10		½ a. verm (Die I) (p 12, 11 or 10½) (1940)	£160	35·00
		a. Die II (p 10½) (1944)	..	£160	45·00
		ab. Horiz pair. Die I and Die II	..	£350	£110
		b. Die III (p 10) (1945)	..	£225	35·00
		c. Imperf between (vert pair)	..	† £1500	
11		1 a. deep blue (p 12, 11, 10½ or 10)	..	£150	25·00
12	3	1 a. 3 p. brt mauve (p 10½ or 10) (1944)	£375	£130
13	4	1½ a. deep violet (p 10) (1946)	..	£400	£130
14	2	2 a. brt green (p 12, pin perf 11½) (1943)	£450	£225
15		4 a. brown (p 12, 10½ or 10) (1940)	..	£375	£100

Stamps perforated 12, 11 and 10½ were printed in sheets of 12 (4×3) which were imperforate along the top, bottom and, sometimes, at right so that examples exist with one or two adjacent sides imperforate. Stamps perforated 10 were printed in sheets of 4 either imperforate at top, bottom and right-hand side or fully perforated.

Dungarpur became part of Rajasthan by 15 April 1948.

DUTTIA (DATIA)

PRICES FOR STAMPS ON COVER
Nos. 1/15 —
Nos. 16/40 *from* × 20

All the stamps of Duttia were impressed with a circular hand-stamp (as a rule in *blue*) before issue.

This handstamp shows the figure of Ganesh in the centre, surrounded by an inscription in Devanagari reading "DATIYA STET POSTAJ 1893". Stamps could not be used for postage without this control mark.

PROCESS. Nos. 1/15 were type-set and printed singly. Nos. 16/40 were typo from plates comprising 8 or more clichés.

GUM. The stamps of Duttia (*except No. 25c*) were issued without gum.

Maharaja Bhawani Singh, 1857–1907

Rectangular labels each showing a double hand-drawn frame (in black for the 1 a. and in red for the others), face value in black and the Ganesh handstamp are known on thin cream (½ a.), rose (1 a.), orange (2 a.) or pale yellow (4 a.) paper. These are considered by some specialists to be the first stamps of Duttia, possibly issued during 1893, but the evidence for this is inconclusive.

1 (2 a.) 2 (½ a.) 3 (4 a.)
        Ganesh

1894?. *Rosettes in lower corners. Control handstamp in blue. Imperf.*

1	1	1½ a. black/*green*	..	£5000
2		2 a. grey-blue/*yellow*	..	£2500
		a. Handstamp in black	..	£2250

Only two examples of No. 1 have been reported. In both instances the Devanagari inscription was originally 8 a., but was amended in manuscript to ½ a.

1896. *Control handstamp in blue. Imperf.*

3	2	1 a. red	..	..	£1900 £2000
		a. Handstamp in black	..	£1900 £2000

1896. *Control handstamp in blue. Imperf.*

4	3	¼ a. black/*orange* ..	..	.. £2750
		a. Without handstamp	..	.. £1900
5		½ a. black/*blue-green*	..	£3250
		a. Without handstamp	..	.. £1900
6		2 a. black/*yellow*	..	.. £1800
		a. Without handstamp	..	.. £4000
7		4 a. black/*rose*	..	.. £1300

Two types of centre:

I II

Type I. Small Ganesh. Height 13 mm. Width of statue 11 mm. Width of pedestal 8 mm.
Type II. Large Ganesh. Height 13½ mm. Width of statue 11½ mm. Width of pedestal 11½ mm. "Flag" in god's right hand; "angle" above left. All stamps also show dot at top right corner.

1897–98. *Imperf.*

8	2	½ a. black/*green* (I) (value in one group)	38·00	
		a. Tête-bêche (horiz pair)	..	£800	
		b. Value in two groups	..	14·00	£140
		ba. Tête-bêche (vert pair)	..	£900	
		bb. Type II (1898)	..	15·00	
9		1 a. black/*white* (I)	..	60·00	£160
		a. Tête-bêche (horiz pair)	..	£850	
		b. Laid paper ..	..	13·00	
		ba. Tête-bêche (vert pair)	..	£850	
		c. Type II (1898)	..	60·00	
		ca. Laid paper	..	15·00	
10		2 a. black/*yellow* (I)	..	19·00	£150
		a. On lemon	..	25·00	
		b. Type II (1898)	..	22·00	
11		4 a. black/*rose* (I)	..	16·00	£120
		a. Tête-bêche (horiz pair)	..	£225	
		b. Tête-bêche (vert pair)	..	£150	
		c. Doubly printed	..	£1200	
		d. Type II (1898)	..	18·00	

A used example of the 4 a. is known showing black roulettes at foot.

4 (½ a.) 5 (¼ a.)

1897. *Name spelt "DATIA." Imperf.*

12	4	½ a. black/*green* ..	..	55·00	£300
13		1 a. black/*white* ..	..	£120	
14		2 a. black/*yellow*	..	65·00	
		a. Tête-bêche (vert pair)	..	£3000	
15		4 a. black/*rose*	..	60·00	
		a. Tête-bêche (vert pair)	..	£3000	
12/15 ..		..	..	Set of 4 £275

1899–1906.

(a) Rouletted in colour or in black, horizontally and at end of rows

16	5	¼ a. vermilion	..	..	2·25
		a. Rose-red	..	..	1·75
		b. Pale rose	..	..	1·50
		c. Lake	..	..	2·75 10·00
		d. Carmine	..	..	2·50
		e. Brownish red	..	..	6·00
		ea. Tête-bêche (pair)	..	£3000	
17		½ a. black/*blue-green*	..	1·50	10·00
		a. On deep green	..	4·00	
		b. On yellow-green (pelure)	..	3·75 11·00
		c. On dull green (1906)	..	2·25	
18		1 a. black/*white* ..	..	1·75 10·00
19		2 a. black/*lemon-yellow*	..	6·00	
		a. On orange-yellow	..	8·00	
		b. On buff-yellow	..	2·00 12·00
		ba. Handstamp in black	..	7·00	
		bb. Without handstamp	..	£120	
		c. On pale yellow (1906)	..	2·50 12·00
20		4 a. black/*deep rose*	..	2·00 11·00
		a. Tête-bêche (pair)	..	..	
		b. Handstamp in black	..	9·00	
		c. Without handstamp	..	£120	

(b) Rouletted in colour between horizontal rows, but imperf at top and bottom and at ends of rows

20c	5	¼ a. brownish red	..	..	28·00
21		1 a. black/*white*	..	..	11·00

One setting of 16 (8×2) of the ¼ a. value (No. 16e) showed an inverted cliché at R. 1/2.

1904–5. *Without rouletting.*
22 5 ¼ a. red .. .. 1·90 19·00
23 ½ a. black/green .. 11·00
24 1 a. black (1905) .. .. .. 8·00 23·00

Maharaja Govind Singh, 1907–1955
1911. *P 13½. Stamps very wide apart.*
25 5 ¼ a. carmine .. .. 3·75 28·00
  a. Imperf horiz (vert pair) £190
  b. Imperf between (horiz pair) .. £225
  c. Stamps closer together (with gum) .. 6·50 21·00
  d. As c. Imperf vert (horiz pair) .. £110
25e 1 a. black .. £750
No. 25e was mainly used for fiscal purposes (*Price on piece*, £75), but one example has been seen used on a registered postcard.

1912? *Printed close together. (a) Coloured roulette×imperf*
26 5 ½ a. black/green .. 6·00
  (b) *Printed wide apart. P 13½×coloured roulette (¼ a.) or 13½×imperf (½ a.)*
27 5 ¼ a. carmine .. .. 4·00 22·00
28 ½ a. black/dull green .. .. 9·50 26·00

1916. *Colours changed. Control handstamp in blue (Nos. 29/33) or black (No. 34). Imperf.*
29 5 ¼ a. deep blue .. .. 5·50 14·00
30 ½ a. green .. .. 3·50 16·00
31 1 a. purple .. .. 3·50 17·00
  a. Tête-bêche (vert pair) .. 22·00
32 2 a. brown .. .. 9·00 20·00
33 2 a. lilac .. .. 5·00 22·00
  a. Handstamp in black .. 19·00
  b. Without handstamp .. £120
34 4 a. Venetian red (date?) .. 65·00

1918. *Colours changed. (a) Imperf.*
35 5 ½ a. blue .. .. 2·50 10·00
36 1 a. pink .. .. 1·90 12·00
  a. Handstamp in black .. 4·50
  (b) *P 11½*
37 5 ¼ a. black .. .. 3·50 14·00

1920. *Rouletted.*
38 5 ¼ a. blue .. .. 1·50 7·50
  a. Roul × perf 7 .. 35·00 35·00
  b. Imperf between (vert pair) .. £475
  c. Without handstamp .. £110
39 ½ a. pink .. .. 1·50 11·00
  a. Roul × perf 7 .. £150

1920? *Rough perf about 7.*
40 5 ½ a. dull red .. .. 8·50 23·00

The stamps of Duttia have been obsolete since 1 April 1921.

FARIDKOT

PRICES FOR STAMPS ON COVER
Nos. N1/4   from × 10
Nos. N5/8   from × 30

GUM. The stamps of Faridkot (Nos. N1/8) were issued without gum.

Raja Bikram Singh, 1874-1898

N 1 (1 folus)   N 2 (1 paisa)   N 3

1879–86. *Rough, handstamped impression. Imperf.*
  (a) *Native thick laid paper*
N1 N 1 1 f. ultramarine .. .. 30·00 35·00
N2 N 2 1 p. ultramarine .. 85·00 90·00
  (b) *Ordinary laid paper*
N3 N 1 1 f. ultramarine .. .. 14·00 16·00
N4 N 2 1 p. ultramarine .. 55·00 75·00
  (c) *Wove paper, thick to thinnish*
N5 N 1 1 f. ultramarine .. .. 1·25 2·50
  a. Tête-bêche (pair) .. £225
N6 N 2 1 p. ultramarine .. 2·00 6·00
  a. Pair, one stamp sideways .. £750
  (d) *Thin wove whity brown paper*
N7 N 2 1 p. ultramarine .. 25·00 27·00
  (e) *Wove paper*
N8 N 3 1 p. ultramarine .. 1·25
  a. Tête-bêche (pair) .. £200
It is doubtful whether stamps of Type N 3 were ever used for postage.
Impressions of these types in various colours, the ½ a. labels, and the later printings from re-engraved dies, were never in circulation at all.

Faridkot became a convention state and from 1887 used the Indian stamps overprinted which are listed under the Convention States.

HYDERABAD

PRICES FOR STAMPS ON COVER
Nos. 1/3   from × 10
Nos. 4/12   —
Nos. 13/60   from × 5
Nos. O1/53   from × 10

The official title of the State in English was The Dominions of the Nizam and in Urdu "Sarkar-i-Asafia" (State of the successors of Asaf). This Urdu inscription appears in many of the designs.

Nawab Mir Mahbub Ali Khan Asaf Jah VI, 1869–1911

1   2

(Eng Mr. Rapkin. Plates by Nissen & Parker, London. Recess Mint, Hyderabad)
1869 (8 Sept). *P 11½.*
1 1 1 a. olive-green .. .. .. 11·00 6·00
  a. Imperf between (horiz pair) .. £110
  b. Imperf horiz (vert pair) .. £325 £100
  c. Imperf (pair) .. £275 £275
Reprints in the colour of the issue, and also in fancy colours, were made in 1880 on white wove paper, perforated 12½. Fakes of No. 1c are known created by the removal of the outer perforations from examples of Nos. 1a/b.

1870 (16 May). *Locally engraved; 240 varieties of each value; wove paper. Recess. P 11½.*
2 2 ½ a. brown .. .. .. 4·00 4·00
3 2 a. sage-green .. .. .. 40·00 35·00
Stamps exist showing traces of lines in the paper, but they do not appear to be printed on true laid paper.
Reprints of both values were made in 1880 on white wove paper, perforated 12½: the ½ a. in grey-brown, yellow-brown, sea-green, dull blue and carmine and the 2 a. in bright green and in blue-green.

3

A   2 a.   B
Normal   Variety

In A the coloured lines surrounding each of the four labels join a coloured circle round their inner edge, in B this circle is missing.

C   3a.   D
C. Normal
D. Character ٨ omitted

Left side of central inscription omitted (Pl 4 R. 2/11)

Dot at top of central inscription omitted

Second dot in bottom label omitted

Centre dot in bottom label omitted

(Plates by Bradbury, Wilkinson & Co. Recess Mint, Hyderabad)
1871–1909. (a) *No wmk.* (i) *Rough perf 11½*
4 3 ½ a. red-brown .. .. 17·00 18·00
5 1 a. purple-brown .. .. 95·00 £100
6 2 a. green (A) £650
7 3 a. ochre-brown .. .. 30·00 38·00
8 4 a. slate £120 £130
9 8 a. deep brown .. ..
10 12 a. dull blue £225
  (ii) *Pin perf 8–9*
11 3 ½ a. red-brown .. .. — £325
12 1 a. drab £275 £140
  (iii) *P 12½*
13 3 ½ a. orange-brown .. .. 1·00 10
  a. Imperf vert (horiz pair) .. † 75·00
  ab. Imperf horiz (vert pair) .. † £275
  b. *Orange* .. .. 2·00 10
  c. *Red-brown* .. .. 1·00 10
  d. *Brick-red* 85 10
  da. Imperf vert (horiz pair) .. † 75·00
  db Doubly printed .. † £150
  e. *Rose-red* .. .. 1·25 10
  ea. Doubly printed .. † £180
  f. Error. Magenta .. .. 45·00 8·00
  g. Left side of central inscription omitted £150 55·00
  h. Dot at top of central inscription omitted .. .. 35·00 2·00
14 1 a. purple-brown .. .. 3·50 3·50
  a. Doubly printed .. £300
  b. *Drab* 50 15
  ba. Imperf (pair) .. — £190
  bb. Doubly printed .. £140
  c. *Grey-black* 90 10
  d. *Black* (1909) .. .. 1·00 10
  da. Doubly printed .. £300
  db. Imperf vert (horiz pair) .. † £425
  dc. Imperf horiz (vert pair) .. † £425
  e. Dot at top of central inscription omitted .. — 85·00
  f. Second dot in bottom label omitted 55·00 24·00
15 2 a. green (A) .. .. 1·75 15
  a. *Deep green* (A) .. .. 2·00 40
  b. *Blue-green* (A) .. .. 1·75 40
  ba. *Blue-green* (B) .. .. £160 65·00
  c. *Pale green* (A) .. .. 1·90 15
  ca. *Pale green* (B) .. .. £160 75·00
  d. *Sage-green* (A) (1909) .. 1·50 35
  da. *Sage-green* (B) .. .. £110 45·00
  e. Dot at top of central inscription omitted .. £150 75·00
  f. Centre dot in bottom panel omitted 75·00 28·00
16 3 a. ochre-brown (C) .. .. 1·60 1·10
  a. Character omitted (D) .. £170 70·00
  b. *Chestnut* (C) 75 85
  ba. Character omitted (D) .. £120 55·00
17 4 a. slate .. .. 4·00 1·75
  a. Imperf horiz (vert pair) .. £550 £550
  b. *Greenish grey* .. .. 2·75 1·75
  ba. Imperf vert (horiz pair) .. £600
  c. *Olive-green* .. .. 2·75 85
18 8 a. deep brown .. .. 1·25 1·75
  a. Imperf vert (horiz pair) .. £600
19 12 a. pale ultramarine .. .. 3·00 4·00
  a. *Grey-green* .. .. 2·25 2·75
13/19 .. .. Set of 7 9·00 6·00
  (b) *W 7. P 12½*
19b 3 1 a. black (1909) .. .. 80·00 8·50
19c 2 a. sage-green (A) (1909) .. — 65·00
19d 12 a. bluish grey (1909?) £700

(4)   5

8 Symbols   9

15 Unani General Hospital   16 Family Reunion

1898. *Surch with T 4. P 12½.*

0	3	¼ a. on ½ a. orange-brown	..	50	85
		a. Surch inverted	..	25·00	20·00
		b. Pair, one without surcharge	..	£275	
		c. Left side of central inscription omitted	95·00		

(Des Khusrat Ullah. Recess Mint, Hyderabad)

1900 (20 Sept.) *P 12½.*

21	5	¼ a. deep blue	..	3·50	2·25
		a. Pale blue	..	3·50	2·25

6   7

(Plates by Allan G. Wyon, London. Recess Mint, Hyderabad.)

1905 (7 Aug.) *Wmk T 7. P 12½.*

22	6	¼ a. dull blue	..	1·25	45
		a. Imperf (pair)	..	28·00	75·00
		b. Dull ultramarine	..	5·00	80
		ba. Perf 11 × 12½	..	22·00	22·00
		c. Pale blue-green	..	16·00	2·00
23		½ a. orange	..	3·50	35
		a. Perf 11			
		b. Vermilion	..	1·50	25
		ba. Imperf (pair)	..	26·00	75·00
		c. Yellow	..	60·00	16·00

1908–11. *W 7. Various perfs, also compound.*

A. Perf 12½. B. Perf 11½, 12

				A	B	
24	6	¼ a. grey	45	10	2·00	
		a. Imperf between (horiz pair)	..	£170	£170	†
		b. Imperf between (vert pair)	..	†	£170	†
25		½ a. green	1·25	10	3·00	10
		a. Pale green	1·25	20	3·00	10
		b. Blue-green	5·00	90	†	
		c. Imperf between (vert pair)	..	£170	—	†
26		1 a. carmine	1·00	10	3·50	40
		a. Double impression, Perf 12½×11	..	†		†
27		2 a. lilac	1·00	20	3·25	1·10
28		3 a. brown-orange (1909)	1·10	35	6·50	2·00
29		4 a. olive-green (1909)	1·10	45	6·50	4·00
30		8 a. purple (1911)	3·00	4·00	—	
31		12 a. blue-green (1911)	..	65·00	40·00	7·50	10·00

C. Perf 11. D. Perf 13½

			C	D
24	6	¼ a. grey	42·00	19·00
25		½ a. green ..	†	70·00	35·00
26		1 a. carmine	22·00	8·50	†
27		2 a. lilac	2·50	55	1·40	15
		a. Imperf between (horiz pair)	†	†	£250
		b. Rose-lilac	†	1·10	10
28		3 a. brown-orange (1909)	90	60	1·50	30
29		4 a. olive-green (1909)	26·00	8·00	90	30
		a. Imperf between (pair) £350 £350	†
30		8 a. purple (1911)	1·75	2·25	1·10	35
31		12 a. blue-green (1911)	†	—	3·00	1·25

Nawab Mir Osman Ali Khan Asaf Jah VII, 1911–1967

1912. *New plates eng by Bradbury, Wilkinson & Co. Perfs as before, or compound.*

			A	B	
32	6	¼ a. grey-black	1·40	10	60	35
		a. Imperf horiz (vert pair)	†	£160	†
34		½ a. deep green	40	10	4·50	55
		a. Imperf between (pair)	†	£170	†
		b. Laid paper. Imperf (pair)	80·00	60·00	†

			C	D	
32	6	¼ a. grey-black	80	15	30	10
		b. Imperf between (horiz pair)	†	£160	†
		c. Imperf between (vert pair)	†	£160	†
33		¼ a. brown-purple (shades)	†	50	10
		a. Imperf horiz (vert pair)	†	£160
34		½ a. deep green	8·00	10	—	
		a. Imperf between (pair)			

In Wyon's ¼ a. stamp the fraction of value is closer to the end of the label than in the B.W. issue. In the Wyon ¼ a. and ½ a. the value in English and the label below are further apart than in the B.W.

Wyon's ¼ a. measures 19½ × 20 mm and the ½ a. 19½ × 20½ mm; both stamps from the Bradbury plates measure 19¾ × 21½ mm.

1915. *Inscr "Post & Receipt". Various perfs as above, and compound.*

				A	C	
35	8	½ a. green	..	5·50	35	60	10
		a. Imperf between (pair)	..		†	£150
		b. Imperf (pair)	£100	70·00	†
36		1 a. carmine	..	9·00	85	75	20
		a. Imperf between (pair)	..		†	†
		b. Imperf (pair)	£140	£120	†
		c. Perf 12½×11	..	6·00	3·50	†
		d. Scarlet	..		—	15·00

				D	
35	8	½ a. green	..	60	10
		a. Imperf between (pair)	..	55·00	60·00
		c. Emerald-green	..	3·00	10
36		1 a. carmine	..	80	10
		a. Imperf between (pair)	£140	
		d. Scarlet	..	1·00	10
		da. Imperf between (horiz pair)	..	†	£150
		db. Imperf horiz (vert pair)	..	†	£150

For ½ a. claret, see No. 58.

1927 (1 Feb.) *As W 7, but larger and sideways. P 13½.*

37	9	1 r. yellow	..	9·00	11·00

10 (4 pies)   11 (8 pies)

1930 (6 May). *Surch as T 10 and 11. W 7. P 13½.*

38	6	4 p. on ¼ a. grey-black (R.)	..	48·00	15·00
		a. Perf 11	..	†	£200
		b. Perf 12½	..	†	75·00
39		4 p. on ¼ a. brown-purple (R.)	25	10
		a. Imperf between (pair)	£350	£350
		b. Surch double	..	†	£160
		c. Perf 11	..	†	£400
		d. Black surch	..	£425	£425
40	8	8 p. on ½ a. green (R.)	..	25	10
		a. Imperf between (horiz pair)	..	†	£170
		b. Perf 11	..	£275	£160
		c. Perf 12½	..	†	£275

12 Symbols   13 The Char Minar

14 Bidar College

(Plates by De La Rue. Recess Stamps Office, Hyderabad)

1931 (12 Nov)–47. *T 12 to 14 (and similar types). W 7. Wove paper. P 13½.*

41	12	4 p. black	..	30	10
		a. Laid paper (1947)	..	2·25	4·25
		b. Imperf (pair)	..	48·00	70·00
42		8 p. green	..	30	10
		a. Imperf between (vert pair)	..	†	£550
		b. Imperf (pair)	..	60·00	85·00
		c. Laid paper (1947)	..	3·00	4·00
43	13	1 a. brown (shades)	..	30	10
		a. Imperf between (horiz pair)	..	—	£550
44	—	2 a. violet (shades)	..	1·60	10
		a. Imperf between (pair)	..	£130	£180
45	—	4 a. ultramarine	..	1·25	20
		a. Imperf (pair)	..	£140	£225
46	—	8 a. orange	..	3·00	2·00
		a. Yellow-orange (1944)	..	60·00	30·00
47	14	12 a. scarlet	..	3·75	7·50
48	—	1 r. yellow	..	3·25	2·75
41/8		Set of 8	12·50	11·50

Designs (as T 14): Horiz—2 a. High Court of Justice; 4 a. Osman Sagar Reservoir. Vert—8 a. Entrance to Ajanta Caves; 1 r. Victory Tower, Daulatabad.

Nos. 41a and 42c have a large sheet watermark "THE NIZAM's GOVERNMENT HYDERABAD DECCAN" and arms within a circle, but this does not appear on all stamps.

NEW INFORMATION

The editor is always interested to correspond with people who have new information that will improve or correct the Catalogue.

(Litho Indian Security Printing Press, Nasik)

1937 (13 Feb). *Various horiz designs as T 15, inscr "H.E.H. THE NIZAM'S SILVER JUBILEE". P 14.*

49		4 p. slate and violet	..	30	65
50		8 p. slate and brown	..	50	80
51		1 a. slate and orange-yellow	..	60	45
52		2 a. slate and green	..	80	2·50
49/52		..	Set of 4	1·90	3·75

Designs:—8 p. Osmania General Hospital; 1 a. Osmania University; 2 a. Osmania Jubilee Hall.

(Des T. I. Archer. Typo)

1945 (6 Dec). *Victory. W 7 (very faint). Wove paper. P 13½.*

53	16	1 a. blue	..	10	10
		a. Imperf between (vert pair)	..	£500	
		b. Laid paper	..	45	55

No. 53b shows the sheet watermark described beneath Nos. 41/8.

17 Town Hall   18 Power House, Hyderabad

(Des T. I. Archer. Litho Government Press)

1947 (17 Feb). *Reformed Legislature. P 13½.*

54	17	1 a. black	..	55	85
		a. Imperf between (pair)	..	—	£700

(Des T. I. Archer. Typo)

1947–49. *As T 18 (inscr "H. E. H. THE NIZAM'S GOVT. POSTAGE"). W 7. P 13½.*

55		1 a. 4 p. green	55	1·25
56		3 a. greenish blue	65	1·75
		a. Bluish green	1·40	2·00
57		6 a. sepia	3·00	9·00
		a. Red-brown (1949)	18·00	24·00
		ab. Imperf (pair)	95·00	
55/7		Set of 3	3·75	11·00

Designs:—3 a. Kaktyai Arch, Warangal Fort; 6 a. Golkunda Fort.

1947. *As 1915 issue but colour changed. P 13½.*

58	8	½ a. claret	..	80	50
		a. Imperf between (horizontal pair)	..	—	£275
		b. Imperf between (vert pair)	..	—	£375

An Independence commemorative set of four, 4 p., 8 p., 1 a. and 2 a., was prepared in 1948, but not issued.

1948. *As T 12 ("POSTAGE" at foot). Recess. W 7. P 13½.*

59		6 p. claret	..	5·00	4·00

Following intervention by the forces of the Dominion of India during September 1948 the Hyderabad postal system was taken over by the Dominion authorities, operating as an agency of the India Post Office.

1949. *T 12 ("POSTAGE" at top). Litho. W 7. P 13½.*

60	12	2 p. bistre-brown	..	1·00	1·50
		a. Imperf between (horizontal pair)	..	†	£550
		b. Imperf (pair)	..	£425	£475

No. 60 was produced from a transfer taken from a plate of the 4 p., No. 41, with each impression amended individually.

OFFICIAL STAMPS

Official stamps became valid for postage within India from 1910.

(O1)   (O1a)   (O2)

1873. I. *Handstamped as Type O 1. A. In red. B. In black.*

				A	B
O1	1	1 a. olive-green	..	50·00	18·00
O2	2	½ a. brown	..	—	£350	—	£375
O3		2 a. sage-green	..	—	£400	—	£120

At least ten different handstamps as Type O 1 were used to produce Nos. O1/17. These differ in the size, shape and spacing of the characters. The prices quoted are for the cheapest versions where more than one is known to exist on a particular stamp.

Imitations of these overprints on genuine stamps and on reprints are found horizontally or vertically in various shades of red, in magenta and in black.

II. *T* **3** *handstamped as Type* O **1.** A. *In red.* B. *In black.*
(a) *Rough perf* 11½.

			A	B
O 4	½ a. red-brown	..	—	£500
O 5	1 a. purple-brown	..	— £650	£110 £140
O 6	2 a. green (A)	..	—	£650
O 7	4 a. slate	..	£750	—
O 8	8 a. deep brown	..	£750	£750
O 8a	12 a. dull blue	..	£750	†

(b) *Pin perf* 8–9

O 8b	1 a. drab	†	6·50 85·00

(c) *P* 12½

O 9	½ a. red-brown	..	8·00 3·00	4·75 2·00
	a. Left side of central inscription omitted	..	†	— £100
	b. Dot at top of central inscription omitted	..	†	— 28·00
O11	1 a. purple-brown	..	60·00 42·00	— 17·00
O12	1 a. drab	..	11·00 12·00	1·25 1·40
	a. Second dot in bottom label omitted	..	†	70·00 70·00
O13	2 a. green (*to deep*) (A)	..	22·00 17·00	2·50 3·50
	b. Inner circle missing (B)	..	†	£150 —
	c. Centre dot in bottom label omitted	..	†	85·00 85·00
O14	3 a. ochre-brown	..	80·00 80·00	20·00 15·00
O15	4 a. slate	..	35·00 23·00	9·00 9·00
O16	8 a. deep brown	..	38·00 70·00	26·00 20·00
	a. Imperf vert (horiz pair)	..	£550 —	†
O17	12 a. blue	..	55·00 80·00	30·00 45·00

The use of Official Stamps (Sarkari) was discontinued in 1878, but was resumed in 1909, when the current stamps were overprinted from a new die.

1909–11. *Optd with Type* O **1***a.* (a) *On Type* **3.** *P* 12½.

O18	½ a. orange-brown	..	— 80·00	4·00
	a. Opt inverted	..	†	£300
O19	1 a. black	..	— 55·00	10
	a. Second dot in bottom label omitted	..	—	6·00
O20	2 a. sage-green (A)	..	— 55·00	20
	a. Optd on No. 15da (B)	..	—	10·00
	b. Stamp doubly printed	..	†	£120
	c. Centre dot in bottom label omitted	..	—	6·00
O20d	3 a. ochre-brown	..	2·75	90
	da. Character omitted (D)	..	—	£200
O20e	4 a. olive-green	..	£250	3·25
	ea. Perf 11½, 12	..	—	£250
O20f	8 a. deep brown	..	—	27·00
O20g	12 a. grey-green	..	—	55·00

(b) *On Type* **6.** A. *Perf* 12½. B. *Perf* 11½, 12. C. *Perf* 11

			A	B
O21	½ a. orange	..	—	1·75 †
	a. Vermilion	..	90·00	15 †
	b. Opt inverted	..	†	£200 †
	c. Imperf between (vert pair)	..	†	£200 †
O22	½ a. green (W.)	..	11·00 10	10·00 30
	a. Pale green (W.)	..	11·00 10	10·00 30
	b. Opt inverted	..	† 55·00	† 55·00
	c. Imperf between (vert pair)	..	† £160	†
	d. Imperf between (horiz pair)	..	† £150	†
	e. Stamp doubly printed	..	† £110	†
	f. Perf 13½	..	— 50·00	†
O23	1 a. carmine	..	30·00 15	42·00 30
	a. Opt double	..	£150	— †
	b. Perf 12½×11	..	— 3·00	†
	c. Stamp doubly printed	..	†	— £110
O24	2 a. lilac	..	35·00 30	65·00 3·50
O25	3 a. brown-orange	..	80·00 9·00	£140 18·00
	a. Opt inverted	..	† £130	†
	b. Perf 13½	..	— 55·00	†
O26	4 a. olive-green (1911)	..	26·00 30	65·00 3·25
O27	8 a. purple (1911)	..	13·00 1·00	70·00 4·50
O28	12 a. blue-green (1911)	..	9·00 80	22·00 2·00
	a. Perf 12×12½	..	†	— †
	b. Imperf between (horiz pair)	..	— £550	†

			C
O22	½ a. green (W.)	..	
	a. Pale green (W.)	..	
O22g	½ a. deep green (B.W.)	..	£275
O23	1 a. carmine	..	— 5·50
O24	2 a. lilac	..	£325
O25	3 a. brown-orange	..	£325 30·00
O26	4 a. olive-green (1911)	..	— 14·00
O27	8 a. purple	..	£325
O28	12 a. blue-green (1911)	..	—

The Wyon and Bradbury, Wilkinson stamps are distinguished above and below by the use of the letters (W.) and (B.W.) respectively.

1911–12. *T* **6** *optd with Type* O **2.** *Various perfs, also compound.*
A. *Perf* 12½. B. *Perf* 11½, 12

			A	B
O29	¼ a. grey (W.)	..	35·00 90	18·00 30
	a. Imperf between (vert pair)	..	† £180	†
O30	¼ a. grey-black (B.W.)	..	1·90 25	4·00 45
	a. Opt inverted	..	† 55·00	† 55·00
	b. Pair, one without opt	..	†	†
	c. Imperf between (vert pair)	..	† £150	†
O32	½ a. pale green (W.)	..	26·00 75	— 25
O33	½ a. deep green (B.W.)	..	1·75 15	5·50 60
	a. Opt inverted	..	— 22·00	†
	c. Perf 11×12½	..	25·00 25·00	†
	e. Pair, one without opt	..	†	£120
O34	1 a. carmine	..	85 15	5·50 15
	a. Opt inverted	..	— 38·00	†
	b. Perf 11×12½	..	25·00 25·00	†
	c. Imperf horiz (vert pair)	..	† £180	†
O35	2 a. lilac	..	4·00 40	14·00 1·60
O36	3 a. brown-orange	..	13·00 1·50	7·50 1·75
	a. Opt inverted	..	† 70·00	† 75·00
O37	4 a. olive-green	..	9·00 1·10	4·50 1·50
	a. Opt inverted	..	— 70·00	— 75·00
O38	8 a. purple	..	£275	—
O39	12 a. blue-green	..	—	—

C. *Perf* 11. D. *Perf* 13½

			C	D
O29	¼ a. grey (W.)	..	60·00 28·00	
O30	¼ a. grey-black (B.W.)	..	60 30	1·75 10
	a. Opt inverted	..	†	† 60·00
	b. Pair, one without opt	..	†	† £110
	d. Imperf between (horiz pair)	..	†	† £150
	e. Opt sideways	..	† 55·00	†
O31	¼ a. brown-purple (*shades*) (B.W.)	..	—	1·25 10
	a. Imperf horiz (vert pair)	..	†	† £150
	b. Imperf between (horiz pair)	..	†	† £160
O32	½ a. pale green (W.)	..	†	
O33	½ a. deep green (B.W.)	..	1·75 10	1·00 10
	a. Opt inverted	..	— 25·00	†
	d. Imperf between (horiz pair)	..	†	† £130
	d. Imperf horiz (vert pair)	..	† £160	†
	f. Yellow-green	..	—	50
O34	1 a. carmine	..	75 15	†
O35	2 a. lilac	..	85 20	4·75 10
	a. Imperf between (horiz pair)	..	†	£250
	b. Rose-lilac	..	†	1·75 10
O36	3 a. brown-orange	..	20·00 1·25	13·00 25
	a. Opt inverted	..	† 70·00	† 60·00
O37	4 a. olive-green	..	2·00 1·00	2·00 10
	a. Opt inverted	..	†	† 70·00
O38	8 a. purple	..	£225 30·00	2·75 20
O39	12 a. blue-green	..	—	9·00 35

1917–20. *T* **8** *optd with Type* O **2.** *Various perfs as above, also compound.*

			A	B
O40	½ a. green	..	— 3·50	4·75 30
	a. Opt inverted	..	†	† 22·00
	b. Pair, one without opt	..	†	†
O41	1 a. carmine	..	— 3·50	7·50 15
	a. Opt inverted	..	†	† 16·00
	e. Scarlet (1920)	..	†	— 20·00

			D
O40	½ a. green	..	1·40 10
	a. Opt inverted	..	† 20·00
	b. Pair, one without opt	..	† 85·00
	c. Imperf between (horiz pair)	..	† £100
	d. Imperf between (vert pair)	..	† £130
	e. Perf 11×13½ or 13½×11	..	25·00 25·00
	f. Emerald-green	..	2·75 40
O41	1 a. carmine	..	2·25 10
	a. Opt inverted	..	† 25·00
	b. Opt double	..	† 65·00
	c. Imperf horiz (vert pair)	..	† £150
	d. Stamp printed double	..	† £100
	e. Scarlet (1920)	..	75 10
	ea. Stamp printed double	..	† £110
	eb. Imperf between (horiz pair)	..	† £130
	ec. Imperf between (vert pair)	..	† £130

1930–34. *T* **6** *and* **8** *optd as Type* O **2** *and surch at top of stamp, in red, as Type* **10** *or* **11.**

O42	4 p. on ¼ a. grey-black (O30) (1934)	..	£170 17·00
O43	4 p. on ¼ a. brown-purple (O31)	..	65 10
	b. Imperf between (horiz pair)	..	† £150
	c. Imperf between (vert pair)	..	† £150
	d. Imperf horiz (vert pair)	..	† £150
	e. Red surch double	..	† 75·00
	f. Black opt double	..	† £160
O44	8 p. on ½ a. green (O40)	..	60 10
	c. Imperf between (horiz pair)	..	† £150
	ca. Imperf between (vert pair)	..	† £150
	d. Red surch double	..	† 75·00
	e. Stamp doubly printed	..	† £150
	f. Black opt double	..	† £160
O45	8 p. on ½ a. yellow-green (O33f)	..	35·00 45·00

For Nos. O42/5 the red surcharge was intended to appear on the upper part of the stamp, above the official overprint, Type O **2**, but surcharge and overprint are not infrequently found superimposed on one another.

1934–44. *Nos.* 41/8 *optd with Type* O **2.**

O46	4 p. black	..	85 10
	a. Imperf (pair)	..	60·00
	b. Imperf between (vert pair)	..	£500 £500
	c. Imperf between (horiz pair)	..	— £500
O47	8 p. green	..	35 10
	a. Opt inverted	..	† £150
	b. Imperf between (horiz pair)	..	† £500
	c. Opt double	..	† £120
	d. Imperf (pair)	..	£110 £140
O48	1 a. brown	..	50 10
	a. Imperf between (vert pair)	..	£400 £400
	b. Imperf between (horiz pair)	..	— £400
	c. Imperf (pair)	..	£140 £180
	d. Opt double	..	— £160
O49	2 a. violet	..	3·25 10
	a. Imperf between (horiz pair)	..	† £800
O50	4 a. ultramarine	..	1·60 20
	a. Opt double	..	† £375
	b. Imperf between (vert pair)	..	† £850
O51	8 a. orange (1935)	..	7·50 50
	a. Yellow-orange (1944)	..	— 38·00
O52	12 a. scarlet (1935)	..	5·50 1·25
O53	1 r. yellow (1935)	..	11·00 2·00
O46/53		Set of 8	27·00 3·75

1947. *No.* 58 *optd with Type* O **2.**

O54	8 ½ a. claret	..	9·00 5·00
	a. Pair, one without opt	..	

1949. *No.* 60 *optd with Type* O **2.**

O55	12 2 p. bistre-brown	..	7·00 5·50

1950. *No.* 59 *optd with Type* O **2.**

O56	6 p. claret	..	8·50 16·00

IDAR

PRICES FOR STAMPS ON COVER

Nos. 1/2b	from × 2
Nos. 3/6	from × 3
Nos. F1/4	from × 2

Maharaja Himmat Singh, 1931–1960

1 Maharaja Himmat Singh 2

(Typo M. N. Kothari & Sons, Bombay)

1932 (1 Oct)–**39.** *P* 11. (a) *White panels.*

1 1	½ a. emerald	..	10·00 15·00
	a. Imperf between (pair)	..	£850
	b. Yellow-green	..	9·00 15·00
	ba. Imperf between (horiz pair)	..	£800
	c. Pale yellow-green (thick paper)	..	11·00 17·00

(b) *Coloured panels*

2 1	½ a. emerald (1939)	..	13·00 17·00
	a. Yellow-green	..	8·00 17·00
	b. Pale yellow-green (thick paper)	..	19·00 19·00

In No. 2 the whole design is composed of half-tone dots. In No. 1 the dots are confined to the oval portrait.

(Typo P. G. Mehta & Co, Hitmatnagar)

1944 (21 Oct). *P* 12.

3 2	½ a. blue-green	..	1·75 45·00
	a. Imperf between (vert pair)	..	£225
	b. Yellow-green	..	1·25 45·00
	ba. Imperf between (vert pair)	..	12·00
4	1 a. violet	..	1·75 42·00
	a. Imperf (pair)	..	£200
	b. Imperf vert (horiz pair)	..	£225
5	2 a. blue	..	2·25 65·00
	a. Imperf between (vert pair)	..	75·00
	b. Imperf between (horiz pair)	..	£170
6	4 a. vermilion	..	2·50 70·00
	a. Doubly printed	..	£475
3/6		Set of 4	7·00 £200

Nos. 1 to 6 are from booklet panes of 4 stamps, producing single stamps with one or two adjacent sides imperf.
The 4 a. violet is believed to be a colour trial.

POSTAL FISCAL STAMPS

F 1

1940 (?)–**45.** *Typo. P* 11 (*No.* F1) *or* 12 *on two or three sides.*

F1	—	1 a. violet	..	55·00 90·00
F2	F 1	1 a. violet (1943)	..	— 90·00
F3		1¼ a. on 1 a. violet	..	85·00 £180
F4		1¼ a. yellow-green (1945)	..	12·00
		a. Imperf between (vert pair)	..	29·00
		b. Blue-green (1945)	..	40·00 90·00

No. F1 shows the portrait as Type **1.** Used prices are for examples with postal cancellations. No. F3 shows a handstamped surcharge in Gujerati.

Idar became part of Bombay Province on 10 June 1948.

INDORE

(HOLKAR STATE)

PRICES FOR STAMPS ON COVER

Nos. 1/15	from × 20
Nos. 16/43	from × 6
Nos. S1/7	from × 40

Maharaja Tukoji Rao Holkar II, 1843–1886

1 Maharaja Tukoji Rao Holkar II

(Litho Waterlow & Sons)

1886 (6 Jan). *P* 15. (a) *Thick white paper.*

1 1	½ a. bright mauve	..	6·50 7·00

(b) *Thin white or yellowish paper*

2 1	½ a. pale mauve	..	1·50 1·10
	a. Dull mauve	..	1·60 1·75

Maharaja Shivaji Rao Holkar, 1886–1903

2 Type I   2a Type II

TYPES 2 AND 2a. In addition to the difference in the topline character (marked by arrow), the two Types can be distinguished by the difference in the angles of the 6-pointed stars and the appearance of the lettering. In Type I the top characters are smaller and more cramped than the bottom; in Type II both are in the same style and similarly spaced.

1889 (Sept). *Handstamped. No gum. Imperf.*

3	2	½ a. black/*pink*	..	24·00	24·00
4	2a	½ a. black/*pink*	..	1·75	2·25
		a. *Tête-bêche* (pair)	..	£190	

3 Maharaja Shivaji   4 Maharaja Tukoji Holkar III 5
Rao Holkar

(Recess Waterlow)

1889–92. *Medium wove paper. P 14 to 15.*

5	3	¼ a. orange (9.2.92)	..	60	30
		a. Imperf between (horiz pair)	..	†	£550
		b. Very thick wove paper	..	1·25	55
		c. *Yellow*	..	80	50
6		½ a. dull violet	..	1·50	60
		a. *Brown-purple*	..	60	15
		b. Imperf between (vert pair)	..	£500	
7		1 a. green (7.2.92)	..	70	50
		a. Imperf between (vert pair)	..	£700	
		b. Very thick wove paper	..		
8		2 a. vermilion (7.2.92)	..	2·50	1·00
		a. Very thick wove paper	..	5·00	3·00
5/8			*Set of 4*	4·00	1·60

Maharaja Tukoji Rao Holkar III, 1903–1926

(Recess Perkins, Bacon & Co)

1904–20. *P 13½, 14.*

9	4	¼ a. orange	..	30	10
10	5	½ a. lake (1909)	..	8·50	10
		a. *Brown-lake* (shades)	..	8·50	15
		b. Imperf (pair)	..	16·00	
11		1 a. green	..	1·60	10
		a. Imperf (pair)	..	£120	
		b. Perf 12½ (1920)	..	†	70·00
12		2 a. brown	..	6·50	30
		a. Imperf (pair)	..	75·00	
13		3 a. violet	..	11·00	4·00
14		4 a. ultramarine	..	8·50	1·75
		a. *Dull blue*	..	5·00	1·10
9/14			*Set of 6*	30·00	5·00

घाव श्राना.

(6)   7 Maharaja Yeshwant
Rao Holkar II

1905 (June). *No. 6a surch* "QUARTER ANNA" *in Devanagari, as T 6.*

15	3	¼ a. on ½ a. brown-purple	..	2·50	15·00

NOTE. From 1 March 1908 the use of Indore stamps was restricted to official mail. Nos. S1/7 were withdrawn and replaced by Nos. 9/14.

Maharaja Yeshwant Rao Holkar II, 1926–1961

(Recess Perkins, Bacon & Co)

1927–37. *P 13 to 14.*

16	7	¼ a. orange (a) (d) (e)	..	30	10
17		½ a. claret (a) (d) (e)	..	30	10
18		1 a. green (a) (d) (e)	..	60	10
19		1¼ a. green (c) (d) (1933)	..	1·10	15
20		2 a. sepia (a)	..	3·00	80
21		2 a. bluish green (d) (1936)	..	8·50	60
		a. Imperf (pair)	..	25·00	£100
22		3 a. deep violet (a)	..	1·50	8·00
23		3 a. Prussian blue (d) (1935?)	..	15·00	
		a. Imperf (pair)	..	30·00	£225
24		3½ a. violet (d) (1934)	..	4·25	8·50
		a. Imperf (pair)	..	50·00	£225
25		4 a. ultramarine (a)	..	3·25	2·75
26		4 a. yellow-brown (1937)	..	21·00	1·50
		a. Imperf (pair)	..	30·00	£180
27		8 a. slate-grey (a)	..	5·50	4·50
28		8 a. red-orange (d) (1937)	..	15·00	18·00
29		12 a. carmine (d) (1934)	..	5·00	10·00
30		1 r. black and light blue (b)	..	8·00	14·00

31	–	2 r. black and carmine (b)	..	35·00	35·00
32	–	5 r. black & brown-orange (b)	..	55·00	60·00

Nos. 30/32 are as Type 7, but larger, size 23 × 28 mm.
Five different perforating heads were used for this issue: (a) comb 13·6; (b) comb 13·9; (c) line 13·2; (d) line 13·8; (e) line 14·2. Values on which each perforation occur are indicated above.
Nos. 21a, 23a, 24a and 26a were specifically ordered by the state government in 1933 and are known used for postage *circa* 1938–42. A plate proof of the 1 r. in green and carmine is also known postally used (*Price of pair £30 unused, £250 used*).

(8)   9

1940 (1 Aug). *Surch in words as T 8 by* Times of India *Press, Bombay.*

33	7	¼ a. on 5 r. black and brown-orange (b)	5·50	60
		a. Surch double (Blk. + G.)	..	†	£400
34		½ a. on 2 r. black and carmine (b)	9·50	1·50
35		1 a. on 1¼ a. green (c) (d) (e)	9·50	40
		b. Surch inverted (d)	..	90·00	
		c. Surch double (c)	..	£325	
33/5			*Set of 3*	22·00	2·25

(Typo "*Times of India*" Press, Bombay)

1941–46. *P 11.*

36	9	¼ a. red-orange	..	2·00	10
37		½ a. claret	..	1·10	10
38		1 a. green	..	8·00	10
39		1¼ a. yellow-green	..	13·00	30
		a. Imperf (pair)	..	£190	
40		2 a. turquoise-blue	..	11·00	1·00
41		4 a. yellow-brown (1946)	..	12·00	9·00

Larger size (23 × 28 mm)

42		2 r. black and carmine (1943)	..	9·00	90·00
43		5 r. black and yellow-orange (1943)	..	9·00	£120
36/43		..	*Set of 8*	60·00	£200

OFFICIAL STAMPS

SERVICE   SERVICE

(S 1)   (S 2)

1904–6. (a) *Optd with Type* S 1.

S1	4	¼ a. orange (1906)	..	10	40
S2	5	½ a. lake	..	10	10
		a. Opt inverted	..	17·00	26·00
		b. Opt double	..	17·00	
		c. Imperf (pair)	..	48·00	
		d. *Brown-lake*	..	10	10
		da. Opt inverted	..	16·00	
		e. Pair, one without opt	..	£425	
S3		1 a. green	..	10	15
S4		2 a. brown (1905)	..	30	20
		a. Pair, one without opt	..	£650	
S5		3 a. violet (1906)	..	1·75	1·40
		a. Imperf (pair)	..	£325	
S6		4 a. ultramarine (1905)	..	2·50	1·40

(b) *Optd with Type* S 2

S7	5	½ a. lake	..	10	40
		a. Opt double	..	£275	
S1/7			*Set of 6*	4·25	3·25

Types S 1 and S 2 differ chiefly in the shape of the letter "R".

Indore became part of Madhya Bharat by 1 July 1948

JAIPUR

PRICES FOR STAMPS ON COVER

No. 1	*from* × 3
No. 2	*from* × 2
Nos. 3/5	*from* × 10
Nos. 6/70	*from* × 4
Nos. 71/80	*from* × 6
Nos. O1/34	*from* × 8

Maharaja Sawai Madho Singh II, 1880–1922

1   1a   2
Chariot of the Sun God, Surya

Type 1 – Value at sides in small letters and characters. "HALF ANNA", shown as one word except for R. 1/1 and 1/3, measuring between 13½ and 15 mm. Sheets of 12 (4×3) with stamps 2 to 2½ mm apart.

Type 1a – Value in large letters and characters. "HALF ANNA", always with a gap between the two words, measuring between 14½ and 15½ mm. Sheets of 24 (4×6) with stamps 3 to 4 mm apart.

Type 2 – Value in large letters and characters. "HALF ANNA" measuring 16 to 17 mm. Both side inscriptions start below the inner frame line. Sheets of 24 (4×6) with stamps 1½ to 2 mm apart.

(Litho Jaipur State Press)

1904 (14 July). *Roughly perf* 14.

1	1	½ a. pale blue	..	80·00	£120
		a. *Ultramarine*	..	£120	£150
		b. *Imperf, ultramarine*	..	£350	
2	1a	½ a. grey-blue	..	£1000	£200
		a. Imperf	..	£350	£350
		b. *Ultramarine*	..	—	£300
3	2	½ a. blue	..	2·75	4·00
		a. *Deep blue*	..	3·00	4·25
		b. *Ultramarine*	..	3·25	4·25
		c. Imperf	..	£300	£300
4	1	1 a. dull red	..	3·75	10·00
		a. *Scarlet*	..	3·75	10·00
5		2 a. pale green	..	2·75	10·00
		a. *Emerald-green*	..	3·50	

Nos. 1b, 2a and 3c are on gummed paper. Imperforate plate proofs also exist for Nos. 1/5, but these are ungummed.

3 Chariot of the Sun God, Surya

(Recess Perkins, Bacon & Co)

1904. *P* 12.

6	3	½ a. blue	..	3·00	5·50
		a. Perf 12½	..	18·00	12·00
		b. Perf comp of 12 and 12½	..	15·00	15·00
7		1 a. brown-red	..	42·00	42·00
		a. Perf 12½	..	£110	£110
		b. Perf comp of 12 and 12½	..	£120	£120
		c. *Carmine*	..	2·25	3·25
		ca. Imperf between (vert pair)	..	£375	£550
		cb. Perf comp of 12 and 12½	..	10·00	12·00
8		2 a. deep green	..	5·50	9·00
		a. Perf 12½	..	£100	75·00
		b. Perf comp of 12 and 12½	..	25·00	27·00

Nos. 6b, 7b, 7cb and 8b occur on the bottom two rows of sheets otherwise perforated 12.

1905–8. *Wmk* "JAs WRIGLEY & SON Ld. 219" "SPECIAL POSTAGE PAPER LONDON" *or* "PERKINS BACON & Co Ld LONDON" *in sheet. P* 13½.

9	3	¼ a. olive-yellow (1906)	..	45	30
10		½ a. blue (1906)	..	1·60	1·50
		a. *Indigo*	..	50	40
11		1 a. brown-red (1906)	..	4·25	4·25
		a. *Bright red* (1908)	..	1·50	40
12		2 a. deep green (1906)	..	1·00	75
13		4 a. chestnut	..	4·25	2·00
14		8 a. bright violet	..	3·00	2·75
15		1 r. yellow	..	14·00	15·00
		a. *Orange-yellow*	..	13·00	15·00
		b. *Yellow-ochre*	..	16·00	20·00
9/15			*Set of 7*	21·00	20·00

4 Chariot of the Sun God,   (5)
Surya

३ त्राना

(Typo Jaipur State Press)

1911. *Thin wove paper. No gum. Imperf.*

16	4	¼ a. green	..	1·50	2·00
		a. Printed double	..	5·50	
		ab. Ditto, one inverted	..		
		b. "¼" inverted in right upper corner (R. 1/2)	..	5·00	
		c. No stop after "STATE" (R. 3/1)	..	5·00	
17		¼ a. greenish yellow	..	30	50
		a. Printed double	..	2·00	
		b. "¼" inverted in right upper corner (R. 1/2)	..	1·50	
		c. No stop after "STATE" (R. 3/1)	..	1·50	
18		½ a. ultramarine	..	30	50
		a. Printed double	..	2·00	
		b. No stop after "STATE" (R. 3/1)	..	75	
		c. Large "J" in "JAIPUR" (R. 1/2)	..	75	
		d. "¹/³" for "¹/²" at lower left (R. 3/1)	..	1·50	
		e. "1½ a." at lower right (R. 3/2)	..	1·50	
19		½ a. grey-blue	..	1·25	1·25
		a. No stop after "STATE" (R. 3/1)	..	2·25	
		b. Large "J" in "JAIPUR" (R. 1/2)	..	3·25	
		c. "¹/³" for "¹/²" at lower left (R. 3/1)	..	3·25	
		d. "1½ a." at lower right (R. 3/2)	..	3·25	
20		1 a. rose-red	..	30	50
		a. Printed double	..	£180	
21		2 a. greyish green	..	2·00	5·50
		a. *Deep green*	..	2·00	5·50
		ab. Printed double	..	£180	

Issued in sheets of 6 (2×3). There are three recognised settings. Nos. 18d/e and 19c/d come from Setting B, and Nos. 16b/c, 17b/c, 18b/c and 19a/b from Setting C.
One sheet of the ¼ a. is known in blue.

(Typo Jaipur State Press)

1912–22. *Paper-maker's wmk "DORLING & CO. LONDON" in sheet. P 11.*

22	3	¼ a. pale olive-yellow		30	50
		a. Imperf horiz (vert pair)	£200	£200
		b. Imperf vert (horiz pair)	—	£180
23		¼ a. olive		30	75
		a. Imperf between (horiz pair)		£190
		b. Imperf vert (horiz pair)		£200
		c. Imperf horiz (vert pair)		£200
24		¼ a. bistre		30	65
		a. Imperf between (horiz pair)		£190
		b. Imperf between (vert pair)	†	£275
		c. Imperf horiz (vert pair)	†	£275
		d. Doubly printed	†	
25		½ a. pale ultramarine		75	40
		a. Imperf vert (horiz pair)	†	£375
		b. Blue		80	40
		ba. Imperf between (horiz pair)		£325
26		1 a. carmine (1918)		2·75	2·75
		a. Imperf between (vert pair)	†	£425
		b. Imperf horiz (vert pair)	†	£425
27		1 a. rose-red		1·60	5·50
		a. Imperf between (vert pair)		£450
28		1 a. scarlet (1922)		1·10	1·25
		a. Imperf between (vert pair)	£450	£450
29		2 a. green (1918)		2·75	2·25
30		4 a. chocolate		2·75	4·50
31		4 a. pale brown		3·25	5·50
		a. Imperf vert (horiz pair)		£350
22/31			Set of 5	7·00	8·00

Maharaja Sawai Man Singh II 1922–1970

1926. *Surch with T 5.*

32	3	3 a. on 8 a. bright violet (R.)		90	1·75
		a. Surch inverted	£170	£140
33		3 a. on 1 r. yellow (R.)		1·50	3·00
		a. Surch inverted	£325	£170
		c. Yellow-ochre		5·00	7·00

1928. *As 1913–18 issue. Wmk "DORLING & CO. LONDON" (½ a., 1 a., 2 a.) or "OVERLAND BANK" (all values) in sheet. No gum. P 12.*

34	3	½ a. ultramarine		3·00	4·00
		a. Perf comp of 12 and 11	13·00	7·50
35		1 a. rose-red		20·00	16·00
		a. Imperf between (vert pair)		£375
36		1 a. scarlet		30·00	12·00
		a. Perf comp of 12 and 11	45·00	22·00
37		2 a. green		65·00	25·00
		a. Perf comp of 12 and 11	£140	55·00
38		8 a. bright violet			
39		1 r. orange-vermilion		£250	£350

The "OVERLAND BANK" paper has a coarser texture. The ½ a. and 2 a. values also exist on this paper perforated 11, but such stamps are difficult to distinguish from examples of Nos. 25 and 29.

6 Chariot of the Sun God, Surya

7 Maharaja Sawai Man Singh II   **8** Sowar in Armour

(Des T. I. Archer. Litho Indian Security Printing Press, Nasik)

1931 (14 Mar). *Investiture of Maharaja. T 6/8 and similar designs. No wmk. P 14.*

40		¼ a. black and deep lake		65	1·00
41		½ a. black and violet		30	10
42		1 a. black and blue		4·75	5·00
43		2 a. black and buff		3·25	5·00
44		2½ a. black and carmine		28·00	42·00
45		3 a. black and myrtle		10·00	35·00
46		4 a. black and olive-green		12·00	38·00
47		6 a. black and deep blue		6·00	35·00
48		8 a. black and chocolate		10·00	50·00
49		1 r. black and pale olive		23·00	£140
50		2 r. black and yellow-green		20·00	£150
51		5 r. black and purple		30·00	£160
40/51			Set of 12	£130	£600

Designs: *Vert*—1 a. Elephant and state banner; 2½ a. Common Peafowl; 8 a. Sireh-Deorhi Gate. *Horiz*—3 a. Bullock carriage; 4 a. Elephant carriage; 6 a. Albert Museum; 1 r. Chandra Mahal; 2 r. Amber Palace; 5 r. Maharajas Jai Singh and Man Singh.

Eighteen of these sets were issued for presentation purposes with a special overprint "INVESTITURE–MARCH 14, 1931" in red (*Price for set of 12 £2750, unused*).

MINIMUM PRICE

The minimum price quote is 10p which represents a handling charge rather than a basis for valuing common stamps. For further notes about prices see introductory pages.

---

10 Maharaja Sawai   **One Rupee**   (11)
Man Singh II

(Des T. I. Archer. Litho Indian Security Printing Press, Nasik)

1932–46. *P 14. (a) Inscr "POSTAGE & REVENUE".*

52	10	1 a. black and blue		35	45
53		2 a. black and buff		1·00	90
54		4 a. black and grey-green		3·00	4·50
55		8 a. black and chocolate		4·50	7·50
56		1 r. black and yellow-bistre		14·00	70·00
57		2 r. black and yellow-green		70·00	£275
52/7			Set of 6	85·00	£325

(b) Inscr "POSTAGE"

58	7	¼ a. black and brown-lake		30	15
59		¾ a. black and brown-red (1943?)	4·00	2·25
60		1 a. black and blue (1943)		4·75	1·75
61		2 a. black and buff (1943?)		4·75	2·25
62		2½ a. black and carmine		1·50	1·25
63		3 a. black and green		90	40
64		4 a. black and grey-green (1943?)	14·00	70·00
65		6 a. black and deep blue		1·90	16·00
		a. Black and pale blue (1946)	6·00	42·00
66		8 a. black and chocolate (1946)	12·00	65·00
67		1 r. black and yellow-bistre (1946)	19·00	90·00
58/67			Set of 10	55·00	£225

1936. *Nos. 57 and 51 surch with T 11.*

68	10	1 r. on 2 r. black and yellow-green (R.)	4·75	55·00
69	—	1 r. on 5 r. black and purple	4·75	45·00

पाव आना

(12)   **13** Maharaja and Amber Palace

1938 (Dec). *No. 41 surch "QUARTER ANNA" in Devanagari, T 12.*

70	7	¼ a. on ½ a. black and violet (R.)	8·00	11·00

(Recess D.L.R.)

1947 (Dec)–**48.** *Silver Jubilee of Maharaja's Accession to Throne. Various designs as T 13. P 13½ × 14.*

71		¼ a. red-brown and green (5.48)	60	2·25
72		½ a. green and violet		20	2·00
73		¾ a. black and lake (5.48)		60	2·75
74		1 a. red-brown and ultramarine	35	2·00
75		2 a. violet and scarlet		25	2·25
76		3 a. green and black (5.48)		70	3·25
77		4 a. ultramarine and brown		45	2·00
78		8 a. vermilion and brown		60	3·00
79		1 r. purple and green (5.48)		1·10	15·00
71/9			Set of 9	4·25	30·00

Designs:—¼ a. Palace Gate; ¾ a. Map of Jaipur; 1 a. Observatory; 2 a. Wind Palace; 3 a. Coat of Arms; 4 a. Amber Fort Gate; 8 a. Chariot of the Sun; 1 r. Maharaja's portrait between State flags.

3 PIES

(14)

1947 (Dec). *No. 41 surch with T 14.*

80	7	3 p. on ½ a. black and violet (R.)	14·00	22·00
		a. "PIE" for "PIES"		40·00	70·00
		b. Bars at left vertical.		48·00	80·00
		c. Surch inverted		35·00	32·00
		d. Surch inverted and "PIE" for "PIES"	£150	£140
		e. Surch double, one inverted	48·00	45·00
		f. As variety e, but inverted surch showing "PIE" for "PIES"	£300	£275

There were three settings of Type **14**, each applied to quarter sheets of 30 (6×5). No. 80a occurs in two of these settings on R.5/5 and one of these settings also shows No. 80b on R.6/1.

OFFICIAL STAMPS

SERVICE   SERVICE

(O 1)   (O 2)

1928 (13 Nov)–**31.** *T 3 typographed. No gum (except for Nos. O6/a). P 11, 12, or compound. Wmk "DORLING & CO. LONDON" (4 a.) or "OVERLAND BANK" (others). (a) Optd with Type O 1.*

O 1		¼ a. olive		90	1·50
		a. Bistre		1·00	1·00
O 2		½ a. pale ultramarine (Blk.)		65	15
		a. Imperf between (horiz pair)	£250	£250
		b. Imperf between (vert pair)	†	£425
		c. Opt inverted		†	£300
		d. Opt double (R. and Blk.)		†	£400
O 3		½ a. pale ultramarine (R.) (13.10.30)	2·50	15
		a. Imperf horiz (vert pair)		
		b. Stamp doubly printed		

O 3c		1 a. rose-red		70	20
		d. Imperf between (horiz pair)	†	£425
O 4		1 a. scarlet		90	50
		a. Opt inverted		£450	£450
		b. Imperf between (horiz pair)	†	£450
O 5		2 a. green		65	40
		a. Imperf between (vert pair)	†	£475
		b. Imperf between (horiz pair)	£475	£475
O 6		4 a. pale brown (with gum)		3·00	1·75
		a. Chocolate (with gum)		2·00	1·75
O 7		8 a. bright violet (R.) (13.10.30)	16·00	48·00
O 8		1 r. orange-vermilion		32·00	£180

(b) Optd with Type O 2

O 9		½ a. ultramarine (Blk.) (11.2.31)	£170	15
		a. Imperf vert (horiz pair)	†	£500
O10		½ a. ultramarine (R.) (15.10.30)	£160	15
		a. Imperf between (vert pair)	†	£500
O11		8 a. bright violet (11.2.31)		£325	£170
O12		1 r. orange-vermilion (11.2.31)	£275	£225

SERVICE   आध आना

(O 3)   (O 4)

1931–7. *Nos. 41/3 and 46 optd at Nasik with Type O 3, in red.*

O13	7	½ a. black and violet		30	10
O14		1 a. black and blue		£190	1·60
O15	8	2 a. black and buff (1936)		2·00	3·75
O16		4 a. black and olive-green (1937)	21·00	20·00
O13/16			Set of 4	£200	23·00

1932. *No. O5 surch with Type O 4.*

O17	3	½ a. on 2 a. green		£110	75

1932–7. *Nos. 52/6 optd at Nasik with Type O 3, in red.*

O18	10	1 a. black and blue		1·00	10
O19		2 a. black and buff		1·40	10
O20		4 a. black and grey-green (1937)	£225	5·00
O21		8 a. black and chocolate		4·00	1·10
O22		1 r. black and yellow-bistre		12·00	13·00
O18/22			Set of 5	£225	17·00

1936–46. *Stamps of 1932–46, inscr "POSTAGE".*

(a) Optd at Nasik with Type O 3, in red

O23	7	¼ a. black and brown-lake (1936)	40	10
O24		¾ a. black and brown-red (1944)	1·50	35
O25		1 a. black and blue (1941?)		7·50	30
O26		2 a. black and buff (date?)		6·50	1·00
O27		2½ a. black and carmine (1946)	9·00	60·00
O28		4 a. black and grey-green (1942)	5·00	2·25
O29		8 a. black and chocolate (1943)	5·00	3·75
O30		1 r. black and yellow-bistre (date?)	£120	
O23/9			Set of 7	32·00	60·00

(b) Optd locally as Type O 2 (16 mm long), in black

O31	7	¼ a. black and red-brown (1936)	65·00	55·00

9 PIES

(O 5)

1947. *No. O25 surch with Type O 5, in red.*

O32	7	9 p. on 1 a. black and blue		2·00	2·25

1947 (Dec). *No. O13 surch as T 14, but "3 PIES" placed higher.*

O33	7	3 p. on ½ a. black and violet (R.)	3·00	9·00
		a. Surch double, one inverted	35·00	38·00
		ab. "PIE" for "PIES" in inverted surcharge	£190	£200
		c. Surch inverted		£950	£950

1949. *No. O13 surch "THREE-QUARTER ANNA" in Devanagari, as T 12, but with two bars on each side.*

O34	7	¾ a. on ½ a. black and violet (R.)	11·00	12·00
		a. Surch double		£950	£950

There are three different types of surcharge in the setting of 30, which vary in one or other of the Devanagari characters.

Jaipur became part of Rajasthan by 7 April 1949.

JAMMU AND KASHMIR

PRICES FOR STAMPS ON COVER

Nos. 1/73	*from* × 3
Nos. 74/84	*from* × 2
No. 85	—
Nos. 86/9	*from* × 2
Nos. 90/101	*from* × 10
Nos. 101b/23	*from* × 5
Nos. 124/36	*from* × 10
Nos. 138/9	*from* × 100
Nos. 140/61a	*from* × 15
Nos. 162/8	*from* × 5
No. O1	*from* × 2
Nos. O2/4	*from* × 4
No. O5	—
Nos. O6/14	*from* × 30
Nos. O15/18	

ILLUSTRATIONS. Designs of Jammu and Kashmir are illustrated actual size.

Maharaja Ranbir Singh, 1857–1885

1 (½ a.)   2 (1 a.)

3 (4 a.)

Characters denoting the value (on the circular stamps only) are approximately as shown in the central circles of the stamps illustrated above.

These characters were taken from Punjabi merchants' notation and were not familiar to most of the inhabitants of the state. Type 1 was certainly the ½ anna value, but there has long been controversy over the correct face values of Types 2 and 3.

The study of surviving material suggests that, to some extent, this confusion involved contemporary post office officials. Although covers posted at Jammu, where the stamps were in use for twelve years, show Type 2 used as the 1 a. value and Type 3 as the 4 a., those originating from Srinagar (Kashmir) during 1866–68 show both Types 2 and 3 used as 1 a. stamps.

In the following listing we have followed contemporary usage at Jammu and this reflects the prevailing opinion amongst modern authorities.

GUM. The stamps of Jammu and Kashmir were issued without gum.

PRICES. Prices for the circular stamps, Nos. 1/49, are for cut-square examples. Cut-to-shape examples are worth from 10% to 20% of these prices, according to condition.

A. Handstamped in watercolours

1866 (23 Mar)–67. *Native paper, thick to thin, usually having the appearance of laid paper and tinted grey or brown. For Jammu and Kashmir.*

1	1	½ a. grey-black	..	..	£160 75·00
2	1	1 a. grey-black	..	..	£700 £650
3	3	4 a. grey-black	..		£750
4	2	1 a. royal blue	..	..	£550 £375
4a	1	½ a. ultramarine	..	..	£2250 £2250
5	2	1 a. ultramarine	..		£275 70·00
6	3	4 a. ultramarine	..	..	£600 £300
7		4 a. indigo (1867) ..	..		£1500 £850

1869–72. *Reissued for use in Jammu only.*

8	1	½ a. red	..		60·00 £275
9	2	1 a. red ..		..	£130 £200
10	3	4 a. red ..			50·00 90·00
11	1	½ a. orange-red ..	..		£425 £450
12	2	1 a. orange-red ..	..	..	£140 £225
13	3	4 a. orange-red ..	..	..	£110 £160
13a		4 a. carmine-red	..		£700
13b	2	1 a. orange (1872)	..		£500
13c	3	4 a. orange (1872)			

1874–76. *Special Printings.*

14	1	½ a. deep black ..	..		17·00 £150
		a. *Tête-bêche* (pair)	..		£325
15	2	1 a. deep black ..	..		£200
16	3	4 a. deep black ..	..		£200
17	1	½ a. bright blue (1876)	..		£225 £300
18	2	1 a. bright blue (1876)	..		85·00 £275
19	3	4 a. bright blue (1876)	..		£130
20	1	½ a. emerald-green	..		65·00 £180
21	2	1 a. emerald-green	..		75·00 £180
22	3	4 a. emerald-green	..		£150 £300
23a	1	½ a. yellow	..	..	£450 £550
24	2	1 a. yellow	..	..	£500
25	3	4 a. yellow	..	..	£350
25a		½ a. deep blue-black (1876)	..		£800 £475

These special printings were available for use, but little used.

B. Handstamped in oil colours. Heavy blurred prints

1877 (June)–78. (a) *Native paper.*

26	1	½ a. red	..	..	24·00 42·00
27	2	1 a. red ..	..	..	27·00 £150
28	3	4 a. red	..	..	£180 £400
29	1	½ a. black	..	..	22·00 42·00
32		½ a. slate-blue	..		£100 £170
34	2	1 a. slate-blue	..	..	20·00 £200
35	1	½ a. sage-green	..		£100
36	2	1 a. sage-green	..		£110
37	3	4 a. sage-green	..		£110

(b) *European laid paper, medium to thick*

38	1	½ a. red	..	..	— £600
39	3	4 a. red	..	..	£325 £350
41	1	½ a. black	..		19·00 42·00
		a. Printed both sides	..		
		b. *Tête-bêche* (pair)	..		£225
44		½ a. slate-blue	..	..	28·00 £200
45	2	1 a. slate-blue	..	..	42·00 £300
46	3	4 a. slate-blue	..	..	£500 £500
47		4 a. sage-green	..		£1000
48	1	½ a. yellow	..		£100

(c) *Thick yellowish wove paper*

49	1	½ a. red (1878)		..	— £800

Forgeries exist of the ½ a. and 1 a. in types which were at one time supposed to be authentic.

Reprints and imitations (of which some of each were found in the official remainder stock) exist in a great variety of fancy colours, both on native paper, usually thinner and smoother than that of the originals, and on various thin European *wove* papers, on which the originals were never printed.

The imitations, which do not agree in type with the above illustrations, are also to be found on *laid* paper.

All the reprints, etc. are in oil colours or printer's ink. The originals in oil colour are usually blurred, particularly when on native paper. The reprints, etc. are usually clear.

FOR USE IN JAMMU

½ a.   ½ a.

1 a.   4   ½ a.

T **4** to **11** have a star at the top of the oval band; the characters denoting the value are in the upper part of the inner oval. All are dated 1923, corresponding with A.D. 1866.

T **4.** *Printed in blocks of four, three varieties of ½ anna and one of 1 anna.*

1867. *In watercolour on native paper.*

52		½ a. grey-black	..		£500 £170
53		1 a. grey-black	..	..	£1700 £700
54		½ a. indigo	..	..	£225 £200
55		1 a. indigo	..	..	£500 £275
56		½ a. deep ultramarine	..		£190 £130
57		1 a. deep ultramarine	..		£425 £275
58		½ a. deep violet-blue	..		£120 65·00
59		1 a. deep violet-blue	..		£450 £275

1868 (May)–76. *In watercolour on native paper.*

60		½ a. red (*shades*) (1876)	..		4·25 2·50
61		1 a. red (*shades*) (1876)	..		9·50 8·00
62		½ a. orange-red	..		£170 55·00
63		1 a. orange-red	..		£450 £180
64		½ a. orange (1872)	..		85·00 90·00
65		1 a. orange (1872)	..		£1300 £850

1874–6. *Special printings; in watercolour on native paper.*

66		½ a. bright blue (1876)	..		£850 £200
67		1 a. bright blue (1876)	..		£250 £275
68		½ a. emerald-green	..		£1300 £800
69		1 a. emerald-green	..		£2250 £1400
69a		½ a. jet-black	..		95·00 £130
69b		1 a. jet-black	..		£1000 £900

1877 (June)–78. *In oil colour. (a) Native paper.*

70		½ a. red	..	..	8·50 5·50
71		1 a. red	..	..	23·00 17·00
72		½ a. brown-red (1878)	..		— 30·00
73		1 a. brown-red (1878)	..		— 85·00
74		½ a. black	..		† £700
75		1 a. black	..		† £1600
76		½ a. deep blue-black	..		† £1100
77		1 a. deep blue-black	..		† £3000

(b) *Laid paper (medium or thick)*

78		½ a. red	..		— £750

(c) *Thick wove paper*

79		½ a. red	..		† £375
80		1 a. red			

(d) *Thin laid, bâtonné paper*

84		½ a. red	..		† £1000
85		1 a. red	..		£2750

The circular and rectangular stamps listed under the heading 'Special Printings' did not supersede those in *red*, which was the normal colour for Jammu down to 1878. It is not known for what reason other colours were used during that period, but these stamps were printed in 1874 or 1875 and were certainly put into use. The rectangular stamps were again printed in *black* (jet-black, as against the greyish black of the 1867 printings) at that time, and impressions of the two periods can also be distinguished by the obliterations, which until 1868 were in *magenta* and after that in *black*.

There are reprints of these, in *oil colour*, *brown-red* and *bright blue*, on native paper; they are very clearly printed, which is not the case with the originals in *oil colour*.

OMNIBUS ISSUES

Details, together with prices for complete sets, of the various Omnibus issues from the 1935 Silver Jubilee series to date are included in a special section following Zimbabwe at the end of Volume 2.

4a

1877 (Sept). *Provisional. Seal obliterator of Jammu handstamped in red watercolour on pieces of native paper, and used as a ½ anna stamp.*

86	4a	(½ a.) rose-red	..	..	— £900

FOR USE IN KASHMIR

5

1866 (Sept(?). *Printed from a single die. Native laid paper.*

87	5	½ a. black	..	..	£1700 £275

Forgeries of this stamp are commonly found, copied from an illustration in *Le Timbre-Poste.*

6 (½ a.)   7 (1 a.)

1867. *Native laid paper.*

88	6	½ a. black	..	..	£950 £130
89	7	1 a. black	..	..	£1700 £350

Printed in sheets of 25 (5×5), the four top rows being ½ a. and the bottom row 1 a.

8 (¼ a.)   9 (2 a.)

10 (4 a.)   11 (8 a.)

1867–76. *Native laid paper.*

90	8	¼ a. black	..	..	1·50 1·75
91	6	½ a. ultramarine	..		1·50 80
92		½ a. violet-blue (1870) ..	..		3·00 1·75
93	7	1 a. ultramarine	..		£2750 £1200
94		1 a. orange (7.67)	..		6·50 7·00
95		1 a. brown-orange (1868)	..		8·50 6·50
96		1 a. orange-vermilion (1876)	..		9·50 7·00
97	9	2 a. yellow	..		8·50 10·00
98		2 a. buff	..		13·00 11·00
99	10	4 a. emerald-green	..		22·00 22·00
		a. *Tête-bêche* (pair)	..		£850
100		4 a. sage-green	..		£225 £110
100a		4 a. myrtle-green	..		£550 £550
101	11	8 a. red (1868)	..		24·00 22·00
		a. *Tête-bêche* (pair)	..		£850

Of the above, the ½ a. and 1 a. were printed from the same plate of 25 as Nos. 87/8, the ¼ a. and 2 a. from a new plate of 10 (5 × 2), the top row being ¼ a. and the lower 2 a., and the 4 a. and 8 a. from single dies. Varieties at one time catalogued upon European papers were apparently never put into circulation, though some of them were printed while these stamps were still in use.

Nos. 86 to 101 are in watercolour.

FOR USE IN JAMMU AND KASHMIR

In the following issues there are 15 varieties on the sheets of the ⅛ a., ¼ a. and ½ a.; 20 varieties of the 1 a. and 2 a. and 8 varieties of the 4 a. and 8 a. The value is in the lower part of the central oval.

12 (¼ a.)   13 (½ a.)

14 (1 a.)   15 (2 a.)

16 (4 a.)   17 (8 a.)

1878 (May)–**79.** *Provisional printings.*

I. Ordinary white laid paper, of varying thickness

(a) Rough perf 10 to 12 (i) or 13 to 16 (ii)

101b	12	¼ a. red (i)			
102	13	½ a. red (i)	..	..	12·00 13·00
103	14	1 a. red (i)	..	..	£950
104	13	½ a. slate-violet (i)	..	70·00 50·00
104a	14	1 a. violet (ii)	..	..	
104b	15	2 a. violet (ii)	..	..	£1300

(b) Imperf

105	13	½ a. slate-violet (*shades*)	..	13·00 12·00
106	14	1 a. slate-purple	..	..	18·00 19·00
107		1 a. mauve	..	..	27·00 27·00
108	15	2 a. violet	..	..	19·00 19·00
109		2 a. bright mauve	..	23·00 23·00
110		2 a. slate-blue	..	32·00 32·00
111		2 a. dull blue	..	70·00 75·00
112	12	¼ a. red	..	..	15·00 13·00
113	13	½ a. red	..	..	6·50 6·50
114	14	1 a. red	..	..	6·50 6·50
115	15	2 a. red	..	..	48·00 50·00
116	16	4 a. red	..	..	£120 £100

II. Medium wove paper. (a) Rough perf 10 to 12

117	13	½ a. red	..	..	— £150

(b) Imperf

117b	12	¼ a. red	..	..	
118	13	½ a. red	..	..	10·00 5·00
119	14	1 a. red	..	..	10·00 7·00
120	15	2 a. red	..	..	60·00

III. Thick wove paper. Imperf

121	13	½ a. red	..	..	22·00 45·00
122	14	1 a. red	..	..	40·00 17·00
123	15	2 a. red	..	..	15·00 18·00

Of the above stamps those in red were intended for use in Jammu and those in shades of violet and blue for use in Kashmir.

1879. *Definitive issue. Thin wove paper, fine to coarse.*

(a) Rough perf 10 to 12

124	13	½ a. red	..	..	£170 £120

(b) Imperf

125	12	¼ a. red	..	..	2·00 2·25
126	13	½ a. red	..	..	50 55
		a. Bisected (¼ a.) on postcard		† £3000
127	14	1 a. red	..	..	1·60 2·00
128	15	2 a. red	..	..	2·25 3·00
129	16	4 a. red	..	..	5·50 5·50
130	17	8 a. red	..	..	5·50 6·50

The plates were transferred from Jammu to Srinagar in early 1881 when further printings in red and all orange stamps were produced.

1880 (Mar). *Provisional printing in watercolour on thin bâtonné paper. Imperf.*

130a	12	¼ a. ultramarine	..	£750 £450

1881–83. *As Nos. 124 to 130. Colour changed.*

(a) Rough perf 10 to 12

130b	13	½ a. orange	..	..	

(b) Imperf

131	12	¼ a. orange	..	..	8·00 8·50
132	13	½ a. orange	..	..	18·00 12·00
133	14	1 a. orange	..	..	15·00 7·50
		a. Bisected (½ a.) (on cover)	..	† £3250

134	15	2 a. orange	..	..	14·00 8·00
135	16	4 a. orange	..	..	24·00 38·00
136	17	8 a. orange	..	..	45·00 55·00

Nos. 126a and 133a were used at Leh between April and July 1883.

Nos. 125/30 and 132/6 were re-issued between 1890 and 1894 and used concurrently with the stamps which follow. Such re-issues can be identified by the "three circle" cancellations, introduced in December 1890.

18 (⅛ a.)

1883–94. *New colours. Thin wove papers, toned, coarse to fine, or fine white (1889). Imperf.*

138	18	⅛ a. yellow-brown	..	50 80
139		⅛ a. yellow	..	..	50 80
140	12	¼ a. sepia	..	..	50 35
141		¼ a. brown	..	..	45 35
		a. Double impression	..	£1100
142		¼ a. pale brown	..	..	45 35
		a. Error. Green	..	50·00
143	13	½ a. dull blue	..	..	4·00
144		½ a. bright blue	..	40·00
145		½ a. vermillion	..	..	80 35
146		½ a. rose	..	..	80 55
147		½ a. orange-red	..	..	75 35
148	14	1 a. greenish grey	..	50 50
149		1 a. bright green	..	60 70
		a. Double impression	..	
150		1 a. dull green	..	..	50 50
151		1 a. blue-green	..	80
152	15	2 a. red/*yellow*	..	90 70
153		2 a. red/*yellow-green*	..	1·60 2·00
154		2 a. red/*deep green*	..	8·00 8·00
155	16	4 a. deep green	..	2·00 3·00
156		4 a. green	..	..	2·25 3·00
157		4 a. pale green	..	2·50 3·25
158		4 a. sage-green	..	2·50
159	17	8 a. pale blue	..	4·50 6·00
159a		8 a. deep blue	..	7·00 8·00
160		8 a. bright blue	..	6·00 7·50
161		8 a. indigo-blue	..	7·50 9·00
161a		8 a. slate-lilac	..	10·00 14·00

Well-executed forgeries of the ¼ a. to 8 a. have come from India, mostly postmarked; they may be detected by the type, which does not agree with any variety on the genuine sheets, and also, in the low values, by the margins being filled in with colour, all but a thin white frame round the stamp. The forgeries of the 8 a. are in sheets of eight like the originals.

Other forgeries of nearly all values also exist, showing all varieties of type. All values are on thin, coarse wove paper.

In February 1890, a forgery, in watercolour, of the ½ a. orange on thin wove or on thin laid paper appeared, and many have been found genuinely used during 1890 and 1891 (*Price £3*).

Nos. 143 and 144 were never issued.

Examples of the ¼ a. brown, ½ a. orange-red and 1 a. green on wove paper exist with clean-cut perf 12.

There is a reference in the Jammu and Kashmir State Administration Report covering 1890–91 to the re-introduction of perforating and the machine-gumming of paper at the Jammu printing works.

The few known examples, the ¼ a. being only recorded used, the others unused or used, would appear to date from this period, but there is, as yet, no direct confirmation as to their status.

Maharaja Partap Singh, 1885–1925

1887–94. *Thin creamy laid paper. Imperf.*

162	18	⅛ a. yellow	..	..	32·00 40·00
163	12	¼ a. brown	..	..	9·00 6·00
164	13	½ a. brown-red (March 1887)	..	— 60·00
165		½ a. orange-red	..	..	6·50 4·75
166	14	1 a. grey-green	..	£110 £100
168	17	8 a. blue (*Printed in watercolour*)	£150 £150
		a. On wove paper	..	£100 £100

19

T **19** represents a ¼ a. stamp, which exists in sheets of twelve varieties, in *red* and *black*, on thin wove and laid papers, also in *red* on native paper, but which does not appear ever to have been issued for use. It was first seen in 1886.

The ¼ a. *brown*, and the 4 a. *green*, exist on ordinary white laid paper; the ½ a. *red* on native paper; the ¼ a. in *bright green*, on thin white wove (this may be an error in the colour of the 4 a.); and the 8 a. in *lilac* on thin white wove. None of these are known to have been in use.

OFFICIAL STAMPS

1878. I. *White laid paper. (a) Rough perf 10 to 12.*

O1	13	½ a. black	..	..	—£1200

(b) Imperf

O2	13	½ a. black	..	..	90·00 85·00
O3	14	1 a. black	..	..	50·00 55·00
O4	15	2 a. black	..	..	50·00 45·00

II. Medium wove paper. Imperf

O5	14	1 a. black	..	..	£200

1880–94. *Thin wove papers, toned, coarse to fine, or fine white (1889). Imperf.*

O 6	12	¼ a. black	..	..	55 60
		a. Double print	..	£180
O 7	13	½ a. black	..	..	15 30
O 8	14	1 a. black	..	..	20 35
O 9	15	2 a. black	..	..	30 40
O10	16	4 a. black	..	..	35 60
O11	17	8 a. black	..	..	80 1·00

1887–94. *Thin creamy laid paper. Imperf.*

O12	12	¼ a. black	..	..	4·25 4·25
O13	13	½ a. black	..	..	2·50 2·75
O14	14	1 a. black	..	..	1·50 2·25
O15	15	2 a. black	..	..	12·00
O16	16	4 a. black	..	..	45·00 50·00
O17	17	8 a. black	..	..	28·00 45·00

1889. *Stout white wove paper. Imperf.*

O18	12	¼ a. black	..	..	£180 £110

The stamps of Jammu and Kashmir have been obsolete since 1 November 1894.

JASDAN

PRICES FOR STAMPS ON COVER	
Nos. 1/2	*from* × 2
No. 3	*from* × 3
Nos. 4/6	*from* × 5

Darbar Ala Khachar, 1919–1971

1 Sun

(Typo L. V. Indap & Co, Bombay)

1942 (15 Mar)–**47.** *Stamps from booklet panes. Various perfs.*

1	1 a. deep myrtle-green (*p* 10½×*imperf*)	..	£550 £400
2	1 a. light green (*p* 12×*imperf*)	..	£350 £375
3	1 a. light green (*p* 10½×*imperf*) (1943)	..	90·00 £120
4	1 a. pale yellow-green (*p* 8½×*imperf*)	..	10·00 85·00
5	1 a. dull yellow-green (*p* 10) (1946)	..	15·00 95·00
6	1 a. bluish green (*p* 9) (1947)	..	11·00 85·00

Nos. 1/4 were issued in panes of four with the stamps imperforate on one or two sides; Nos. 5/6 were in panes of eight perforated all round.

A 1 a. rose with the arms of Jasdan in the centre is a fiscal stamp.

Jasdan was merged with the United State of Kathiawar (later Saurashtra) by 15 April 1948.

JHALAWAR

PRICES FOR STAMPS ON COVER	
Nos. 1/2	*from* × 25

Maharaj Rana Zalim Singh, 1875–1896

(Figure of an Apsara, "RHEMBA", a dancing nymph of the Hindu Paradise)

1 (1 paisa)   2 (¼ anna)

1886–90. *Typo in horizontal strips of 12. Laid paper. No gum.*

1	1	1 p. yellow-green	..	..	2·50 7·00
		a. Blue-green	..	..	65·00 27·00
2	2	¼ a. green (*shades*)	..	60 1·40

The stamps formerly listed as on wove paper are from sheets on laid paper, with the laid paper lines almost invisible.

The Maharaj Rana was deposed in 1896 and much of the state's territory transferred to Kotah on 1 January 1899.

Raj (Maharaj from 1918) Rana Bhawani Singh, 1899–1929

The stamps of Jhalawar have been obsolete since 1 November 1900.

JIND

> **PRICES FOR STAMPS ON COVER**
> Nos. J1/34   *from* × 50

ILLUSTRATIONS. Designs of Jind are illustrated actual size.

Raja Raghubir Singh, 1864–1887

J 1 (½ a.)   J 2 (1 a.)

J 3 (2 a.)   J 4 (4 a.)

J 5 (8 a.)

(Litho Jind State Rajah's Press, Sungroor)

1874. *Thin yellowish paper. Imperf.*

J1	J 1	½ a. blue ..	..	5·50	2·50
		a. No frame to value. (Retouched all over)		£225	£140
J2	J 2	1 a. rosy mauve ..	..	7·00	6·00
J3	J 3	2 a. yellow ..	..	1·00	3·00
J4		2 a. brown-buff ..	..	£120	70·00
J5	J 4	4 a. green ..	..	18·00	5·00
J6	J 5	8 a. dull purple ..	..	£450	£120
J6a		8 a. bluish violet ..	..	£160	70·00
J7		8 a. slate-blue ..	..	£130	60·00

Nos. J1/7 were produced from two stones. Those from the first stone had rather blurred impressions, but those from the second are clearer with a conspicuous white frame around the value. Nos. J4 and J8/13 were only printed from the second stone.

1876. *Bluish laid card-paper. No gum. Imperf.*

J 8	J 1	½ a. blue ..	..	50	2·75
J 9	J 2	1 a. purple ..	..	1·40	6·50
J10	J 3	2 a. brown ..	..	1·75	8·50
J11	J 4	4 a. green ..	..	1·00	8·50
J11a	J 5	8 a. bluish violet ..	..	8·00	20·00
J12		8 a. slate-blue ..	..	7·00	10·00
J13		8 a. steel-blue ..	..	9·00	15·00

Stocks of the ½ a. (No. J8) and 2 a. (No. J4) were perforated 12 in 1885 for use as fiscal stamps.

J 6 (¼ a.)   J 7 (½ a.)

J 8 (1 a.)   J 9 (2 a.)

J 10 (4 a.)   J 11 (8 a.)

(Litho Jind State Rajah's Press, Sungroor)

1882–85. *Types J 6 to J 11. 25 varieties of each value. No gum.* A. *Imperf* (1882–4). B. P 12 (1885). (a) *Thin yellowish wove paper.*

				A		B	
J15	¼ a. buff (*shades*)	..		30	1·50	60	2·25
J16	¼ a. red-brown	..		30	1·25	3·00	
	a. Doubly printed			42·00	—		†
J17	½ a. lemon ..	..		70	1·40	90·00	90·00
J18	½ a. buff ..			1·40	1·40	45	3·00
J19	½ a. brown-buff	..		70	60	3·00	4·00
J20	1 a. brown (*shades*)	..		1·60	3·25	2·50	4·25
J21	2 a. blue	..		1·50	6·00	3·00	7·50
J22	2 a. deep blue	..		1·75	1·00	2·75	4·75
J23	4 a. sage-green	..		90	90	5·00	9·00
J24	4 a. blue-green	..		1·60	2·50	2·00	9·00
	a. Imperf vert (horiz pair)			†		£500	
J25	8 a. red	..		4·50	4·25	9·00	—

(b) *Various thick laid papers*

J26	¼ a. brown-buff	..			1·25		6·00
J27	½ a. lemon ..	..			1·25	—	80·00 22·00
J27a	½ a. brown-buff			—		†	
J28	1 a. brown	..		1·25	2·50	1·50	
J29	2 a. blue	..		18·00	21·00	20·00	23·00
J30	8 a. red	..		2·50	8·50	2·50	7·00

(c) *Thick white wove paper*

J31	¼ a. brown-buff	..		12·00	—	†
J32	½ a. brown-buff	..		27·00	—	†
J33	1 a. brown	..		3·75	—	—
J34	8 a. red	..		4·50	9·00	9·50

The perforated stamps ceased to be used for postal purposes in July 1885, but were used as fiscals to at least the mid-1920s. Other varieties exist, but they must either be fiscals or reprints, and it is not quite certain that all those listed above were issued as early as 1885.

Jind became a Convention State and from 1 July 1885 used overprinted Indian stamps.

KISHANGARH

> **PRICES FOR STAMPS ON COVER**
> Nos. 1/3   —
> Nos. 4/91   *from* × 8
> Nos. O1/32   *from* × 30

GUM. The stamps of Kishangarh were issued without gum, *except for Nos. 42/50 and O 17/24.*

Maharaja Sardul Singh, 1879–1900

1

1899. *Medium wove paper. Typo from a plate of eight impressions.*

1	1	1 a. green (*imperf*)	..	..	20·00 50·00
2		1 a. green (*pin-perf*)			60·00

1900. *Thin white wove paper. Printed from a single die. Imperf.*

3	1	1 a. blue ..	..	..	£400

ILLUSTRATIONS. Types **2** to **10a** are shown actual size.

2 (¼ a.)   3 (½ a.)

4 (1 a.)   5 (2 a.)
        Maharaja Sardul Singh

6 (4 a.)   7 (1 r.)

8 (2 r.)   9 (5 r.)

1899–1901. *Thin white wove paper. (a) Imperf.*

4	2	¼ a. green	..	..	..	£500
5		¼ a. carmine	..	..	..	6·00
		a. Rose-pink	..	..	60	1·50
6		¼ a. magenta	..	..	5·00	5·00
		a. Doubly printed	..	..	80·00	
7	3	½ a. lilac	..	..	90·00	£160
8		½ a. red	..	..	£1600	£1100
9		½ a. green	..	..	25·00	30·00
10		½ a. pale yellow-olive	..	..	38·00	38·00
11		½ a. slate-blue	..	..	25·00	25·00
		a. Pair, one stamp sideways			£1000	
		b. Deep blue	..	..	5·00	6·00
		c. Light blue	..	..	1·00	1·25
12	4	1 a. slate	..	..	3·50	4·50
		a. Laid paper	..	..	38·00	
12b		1 a. pink ..	..	..	50·00	£140
13		1 a. mauve	..	..	4·50	4·00
		a. Laid paper	..	..	32·00	
14		1 a. brown-lilac	..	..	1·10	90
		a. Laid paper	..	..	28·00	
15	5	2 a. dull orange	..	..	4·00	4·50
		a. Laid paper	..	..	£400	£375
16	6	4 a. chocolate	..	..	5·00	
		a. Lake-brown ..	..	..	5·00	9·00
		b. Chestnut	..	..	5·00	9·00
		c. Laid paper (*shades*)	..	..	55·00	55·00
17	7	1 r. brown-lilac	..	..	20·00	25·00
18		1 r. dull green	..	..	18·00	
19	8	2 r. brown-red	..	..	65·00	
		a. Laid paper	..	..	55·00	
20	9	5 r. mauve	..	..	55·00	65·00
		a. Laid paper	..	..	60·00	

(b) *Pin-perf 12½ or 14*

21	2	¼ a. green	..	..	£200	£350
		a. Imperf between (pair)			£1000	
22		¼ a. carmine	..	..	3·50	4·50
		a. Rose-pink	..	..	25	40
		ab. Tête-bêche (horiz pair)	..	..	£600	
		b. Rose..	..			
23		¼ a. magenta	..	..	5·00	7·00
		a. Bright purple	..	..		
		ab. Doubly printed	..	..		
24	3	½ a. green	..	..	17·00	22·00
		a. Imperf between (pair)	..	..	£160	
25		½ a. pale yellow-olive ..	..	..	13·00	16·00
		a. Imperf vert (horiz pair)	..	..	£160	
26		½ a. deep blue	..	..	1·60	2·75
		a. Light blue	..	..	50	40
		ab. Doubly printed	..	..	£100	£100
27	4	1 a. slate	..	..	4·00	2·50
		a. Laid paper	..	..	35·00	18·00
27b		1 a. pink ..	..	..	60·00	£160
28		1 a. mauve	..	..	85	1·40
		a. Laid paper	..	..	35·00	13·00
29		1 a. brown-lilac	..	..	75	75
		a. Laid paper	..	..	32·00	13·00
30	5	2 a. dull orange	..	..	4·00	5·00
31	6	4 a. chocolate	..	..	2·00	4·75
		a. Lake-brown ..	..	..	2·50	4·75
		b. Chestnut	..	..	3·50	5·00
		c. Laid paper (*shades*)	..	..	45·00	42·00
32	7	1 r. dull green	..	..	10·00	15·00
		a. Laid paper	..	..	70·00	
33		1 r. pale olive-yellow	..	..	£600	
34	8	2 r. brown-red	..	..	38·00	45·00
		a. Laid paper	..	..	40·00	
35	9	5 r. mauve	..	..	32·00	45·00
		a. Laid paper	..	..	60·00	

All the above, both imperf and pin-perf, were printed singly, sometimes on paper with spaces marked in pencil. They exist in vertical *tête-bêche* pairs imperf between from the centre of the sheet. *Prices from* 3 × *normal, unused.* No. 22ab is an error.

FISCAL STAMPS. Many of the following issues were produced in different colours for fiscal purposes. Such usage is indicated by the initials "M.C.", punched hole or violet Stamp Office handstamp.

Maharaja Madan Singh, 1900–1926

10 (¼ a.)   10a (1 r.)

1901. *Toned wove paper. Pin-perf.*

36	10	¼ a. dull pink	..	..	8·00	6·00
37	4	1 a. violet	..	..	40·00	27·00
38	10a	1 r. dull green	..	..	14·00	16·00
36/8		..	..	*Set of 3*	55·00	45·00

Nos. 36/8 were printed in sheets of 24. Sheets of the 1 r. were always torn to remove R. 5/4 where the cliché is believed to have been defective.

The 1 a. (No. 37) differs from T 4 in having an inscription in native characters below the words "ONE ANNA".

11 (½ a.)

12 Maharaja Sardul Singh

1903. *Litho. Thick white wove glazed paper. Imperf.*
39	11	½ a. pink		7·00	3·00
		a. Printed both sides		†	£950
40	12	2 a. dull yellow		3·00	4·25

12a (8 a.)

1904. *Printed singly. Thin paper. Pin-perf.*
41	12a	8 a. grey		5·00	7·50
		a. *Tête-bêche* (vert pair)		26·00	
		b. Doubly printed		£110	

13 Maharaja Madan Singh **14**

(Recess Perkins Bacon & Co)

1904–10. *With gum. P 12½.*
42	13	¼ a. carmine		45	35
		a. Perf 13½ (1910)		45	35
43		½ a. chestnut		1·25	75
		a. Perf 13½ (1906)		40	30
44		1 a. blue		3·00	1·75
		a. Perf 13½ (1906)		1·00	1·10
45		2 a. orange-yellow		10·00	7·00
		a. Perf 13½ (1907)		17·00	14·00
46		4 a. brown		17·00	14·00
		a. Perf 13½ (1907)		9·00	12·00
		b. Perf 12		40·00	32·00
47		8 a. violet (1905)		6·00	15·00
48		1 r. green		19·00	25·00
49		2 r. olive-yellow		20·00	90·00
50		5 r. purple-brown		21·00	£110
42/50				Set of 9 75·00	£225

Stamps in other colours, all perforated 13½, are colour trials.

1912. *Printed from half-tone blocks. No ornaments to left and right of value in English; large ornaments on either side of value in Hindi. Small stop after "STATE". (a) Thin wove paper. Rouletted.*
51	14	2 a. deep violet ("TWO ANNA")		3·00	7·00
		a. *Tête-bêche* (vert pair)		8·00	
		b. Imperf (pair)		£275	

No. 51 is printed in four rows, each inverted in respect to that above and below it.

(b) Thick white chalk-surfaced paper. Imperf.
52	14	2 a. lilac ("TWO ANNA")		£1000	£550

(c) Thick white chalk-surfaced paper. Rouletted in colour (Medallion only in half-tone)
53	14	¼ a. ultramarine		12·00	12·00

1913. *No ornaments on either side of value in English. Small ornaments in bottom label. With stop after "STATE". Thick white chalk-surfaced paper. Rouletted.*
54	14	2 a. purple ("TWO ANNAS")		2·50	5·00

15

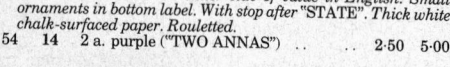

पाव अना

No. 59e. This occurs on R. 3/3 on one setting only

2 TWO ANNAS 2

No. 60. Small figures

2 TWO ANNAS 2

No. 60b. Large figures

(Typo Diamond Soap Works, Kishangarh)

1913 (Aug). *Thick surfaced paper. Half-tone centre. Type-set inscriptions. Rouletted. Inscr "KISHANGARH".*
59	15	¼ a. pale blue		20	70
		a. Imperf (pair)		7·00	
		b. Roul × imperf (horiz pair)		25·00	
		ba. Imperf between (horiz pair)		42·00	
		c. "OUARTER"		5·00	6·50
		ca. As last, imperf (pair)		28·00	
		cb. As last, roul × imperf		55·00	
		d. "KISHANGAHR"		5·00	6·50
		da. As last, imperf (pair)		28·00	
		db. As last, roul × imperf		55·00	
		dc. As last, imperf between (horiz pair)		85·00	
		e. Character omitted		7·00	7·00
		ea. As last, imperf (pair)		32·00	
60		2 a. purple		7·00	18·00
		a. "KISHANGAHR"		50·00	90·00
		b. Large figures "2"		32·00	55·00

1913–16. *Stamps printed far apart, horizontally and vertically, otherwise as No. 54, except as noted below.*
63	14	¼ a. blue		20	45
64		½ a. green (1915)		20	70
		a. Printed both sides		£200	
		b. Imperf (pair)		£150	£150
		c. Emerald-green (1916)		1·75	3·50
65		1 a. red		1·00	2·50
		a. Without stop*		1·25	4·00
		ab. Imperf (pair)		£180	
66		2 a. purple ("TWO ANNAS") (1915)		6·00	7·00
67		4 a. bright blue		6·00	8·00
68		8 a. brown		7·00	38·00
69		1 r. mauve		15·00	95·00
		a. Imperf (pair)		£250	
70		2 r. deep green		65·00	£170
71		5 r. brown		90·00	£350
63/71				Set of 9 £170	£600

*For this issue, ornaments were added on either side of the English value (except in the ¼ a.) and the inscription in the right label was without stop, except in the case of No. 65.

In Nos. 70 and 71 the value is expressed as "RUPIES" instead of "RUPEES".

Initial printings of the ¼ a., 1 a. and 4 a. values were in sheets of 20 containing two panes of 10 separated by a central gutter margin. Stamps from these sheets measure 20×25½ mm and have heavier screening dots on the perforation margins than on the designs. Subsequent printings of these stamps, and of other values in the set, were from single pane sheets of 20 on which the designs measured 19½×23¾ mm and with the screening dots uniform across the sheet.

Maharaja Yagyanarayan Singh, 1926–1939

16 Maharaja Yagyanarayan Singh **17**

1928–36. *Thick surfaced paper. Typo. Pin-perf.*
72	16	¼ a. light blue		50	1·90
73		½ a. yellow-green		1·75	1·00
		a. Deep green		2·25	2·25
		ab. Imperf (pair)		65·00	65·00
		ac. Imperf between (vert or horiz pair)	80·00	80·00
74	17	1 a. carmine		60	1·50
		a. Imperf (pair)		£120	95·00
75		2 a. purple		3·00	7·50
75a		2 a. magenta (1936)		5·50	11·00
		ab. Imperf (pair)		£180	
76	16	4 a. chestnut		1·25	1·75
		a. Imperf (pair)			
77		8 a. violet		3·50	20·00
78		1 r. light green		10·00	40·00
79		2 r. lemon-yellow (1929)		26·00	£120
80		5 r. claret (1929)		30·00	£140
		a. Imperf (pair)		£100	
72/80				Set of 9 65·00	£300

The 4 a. to 5 r. are slightly larger than, but otherwise similar to, the ¼ a. and ½ a. The 8 a. has a dotted background covering the whole design.

Maharaja Sumar Singh, 1939–1971

1943–47. *As last, but thick, soft, unsurfaced paper. Poor impression. Typo. Pin-perf.*
81	16	¼ a. pale dull blue (1945)		3·25	7·50
		a. Imperf (pair)		32·00	
82		¼ a. greenish blue (1947)		1·60	6·00
		a. Imperf (pair)		28·00	
83		½ a. deep green (1944)		90	1·50
		a. Imperf (pair)		25·00	25·00
		b. Imperf between (vert or horiz pair)	42·00	
84		½ a. yellow-green (1946)		4·50	6·50
		a. Imperf (pair)		25·00	25·00
		b. Imperf between (vert or horiz pair)	42·00	
85	17	1 a. carmine-red (1944)		5·50	2·50
		a. Double print		£300	
		b. Imperf (pair)		25·00	25·00
		c. Imperf between (vert or horiz pair)	42·00	
		d. Red-orange (1947)		50·00	22·00
		da. Imperf (pair)		85·00	65·00
86		2 a. bright magenta		6·00	12·00
		a. Imperf (pair)		50·00	55·00
87		2 a. maroon (1947)		65·00	16·00
		a. Imperf (pair)		42·00	42·00
		b. Imperf between (vert or horiz pair)	75·00	
88	16	4 a. brown (1944)		21·00	16·00
		a. Imperf (pair)			
89		8 a. violet (1945)		42·00	£100
90		1 r. green (1945)		48·00	£120
		a. Imperf (pair)		£150	£250
90b		2 r. yellow (date?)			
		ba. Imperf (pair)		£325	
91		5 r. claret (1945)		£375	£400
		a. Imperf (pair)		£275	

OFFICIAL STAMPS

ON K S D

(O 1)

1918. *Handstamped with Type O 1.*

(a) Stamps of 1899–1901. (i) Imperf
O 1	2	¼ a. green		—	£16
O 2		¼ a. rose-pink		—	6·0
O 3	4	1 a. mauve		—	50·0
O 3a		1 a. brown-lilac		35·00	5·5
O 4	6	4 a. chocolate		—	75·0

(ii) Pin-perf
O 5	2	¼ a. green		—	£120
O 6		¼ a. rose-pink		2·25	60
		a. Pair, one without opt		—	32·00
O 7	3	½ a. light blue		£120	35·00
O 8	4	1 a. mauve		28·00	1·50
O 9		1 a. brown-lilac		26·00	1·50
O10	5	2 a. dull orange		—	£120
O11	6	4 a. chocolate		38·00	16·00
		a. Pair, one without opt		—	65·00
O12	7	1 r. dull green		£110	85·00
O13	8	2 r. brown-red		—	£750
O14	9	5 r. mauve		—	£1300

(b) Stamps of 1903 and 1904
O15	12	2 a. dull yellow		48·00	5·00
		a. Stamp printed both sides		†	£750
		b. Red opt		£275	24·00
O16	12a	8 a. grey		48·00	22·00
		a. Red opt		—	£140

(c) Stamps of 1904–5. P 13½ (¼ a. to 4 a.) or 12½ (others)
O17	13	¼ a. carmine		—	£170
O18		½ a. chestnut		75	3
		a. Pair, one without opt		—	40·00
O19		1 a. blue		7·00	4·00
		a. Red opt		18·00	7·00
O20		2 a. orange-yellow		—	£700
O21		4 a. brown		40·00	18·00
		a. Red opt		48·00	26·00
O22		8 a. violet		£225	£140
		a. Red opt		—	£150
O23		1 r. green		£450	£400
		a. Red opt		—	£375
O24		5 r. purple-brown			

(d) Stamps of 1913
O25	15	¼ a. pale blue		6·00	
		a. "OUARTER"		22·00	
		b. "KISHANGAHR"		22·00	
		c. Character omitted		22·00	
		d. Imperf (pair)		85·00	
		e. Roul × imperf (horiz pair)		£140	
O26	14	2 a. purple (No. 54)		—	75·00
		a. Red opt		£100	20·00
O27	15	2 a. purple		£325	£350
		a. "KISHANGAHR"		£600	
		b. Large figures "2"		£450	£475

(e) Stamps of 1913–16
O28	14	¼ a. blue		50	50
		a. Red opt		2·00	1·75
O29		½ a. green		75	75
		a. Red opt		3·25	1·60
O30		1 a. red		7·00	4·50
		a. Without stop		1·00	1·00
		ab. Red opt		—	75·00
O31		2 a. purple		5·50	4·00
		a. Red opt		£100	55·00
		b. Pair, one without opt		—	50·00
O32		4 a. bright blue		20·00	15·00
		a. Red opt		—	30·00
O33		8 a. brown		90·00	40·00
		a. Red opt		—	80·00
O34		1 r. lilac		£275	£275
O35		2 r. deep green			
O36		5 r. brown		—	£1200

This overprint is found inverted as often as it is upright; and many other "errors" exist.

Kishangarh became part of Rajasthan by 15 April 1948.

LAS BELA

PRICES FOR STAMPS ON COVER
Nos. 1/12 *from* × 8

Mir Kamal Khan, 1896–1926

1 **2**

(Litho Thacker & Co, Bombay)

1897–98. *Thick paper. P 11½.*
1	1	½ a. black on *white*		18·00	11·00

1898–1900. *P* 11½.
2	1	½ a. black on *greyish blue* (1898)	..	11·00	7·00
3		½ a. black on *greenish grey* (1899)	..	9·00	6·00
		a. "BFLA" for "BELA"	..	£120	
		b. Imperf between (horiz strip of 3)			
4		½ a. black on *thin white surfaced paper* (1899)	..	21·00	
5		½ a. black on *slate* (1900)	..	23·00	
		a. Imperf between (horiz pair)	..	£750	

1901–2. *P* 11½.
6	1	½ a. black on *pale grey*	..	9·00	7·00
		a. "BFLA" for "BELA"	..	90·00	£120
7		½ a. black on *pale green* (1902)	..	16·00	17·00
8	2	1 a. black on *orange*	..	13·00	15·00

There are at least 14 settings of the above ½ a. stamps, the sheets varying from 16 to 30 stamps.

No. 6a occurred on R.3/2 of the July 1901 printing in sheets of 16 (4×4).

1904 (Feb–Nov). *Stamps printed wider apart. P* 11½.
11	1	½ a. black on *pale blue*	..	9·00	6·50
		a. Imperf between (pair)	..	£650	
		b. Imperf between (horiz strip of 3)	£850	
		c. Perf 12½ (Nov)	..	11·00	7·00
12		½ a. black on *pale green*	..	9·00	6·50
		c. Perf 12½ (Nov)	..	11·00	7·00

There are five plates of the above two stamps, each consisting of 18 (3×6) varieties.

All the coloured papers of the ½ a. show coloured fibres, similar to those in granite paper.

The stamps of Las Bela have been obsolete since 1 April 1907.

MORVI

PRICES FOR STAMPS ON COVER

Nos. 1/19 *from* × 6

Thakur (Maharaja from 1926) Lakhdirji, 1922–48

1   2   3

Maharaja Lakhdirji

1931 (1 April). *Typo. P* 12.

(a) *Printed in blocks of four. Stamps 10 mm apart (Nos. 1/2) or 6½ mm apart (No. 3). Perf on two or three sides*
1	1	3 p. deep red	..	3·00	14·00
2		½ a. blue	..	19·00	27·00
3		2 a. yellow-brown	..	80·00	
1/3			*Set of 3*	90·00	

(b) *Printed in two blocks of four. Stamps 5½ mm apart. Perf on four sides*
4	1	3 p. bright scarlet	..	4·00	14·00
		a. Error. Dull blue	..	4·00	14·00
		b. Ditto. Double print	£600	
		c. Ditto. Printed on gummed side	£600	
5		½ a. dull blue	..	2·25	8·50
		a. Chalk-surfaced paper	1·90	8·50
6		1 a. brown-red	..	3·25	17·00
7		2 a. yellow-brown	..	2·50	14·00
4/7			*Set of 4*	12·00	55·00

Nos. 1/3 were supplied to post offices in panes of four sewn into bundles with interleaving.

1932–33. *Horizontal background lines wider apart and portrait smaller than in T* 1. *Typo. P* 11.
8	2	3 p. carmine-rose (*shades*)	..	1·75	6·00
9		6 p. green	..	3·75	8·00
		a. Imperf between (horiz pair)	..	£1700	
		b. Emerald-green	..	2·50	6·00
10		1 a. ultramarine (*to deep*)	..	1·75	7·00
		a. Imperf between (vert pair)	..	£1300	
11		2 a. bright violet (1933)	..	10·00	26·00
		a. Imperf between (vert pair)	..	£1300	
8/11			*Set of 4*	14·50	40·00

1934. *Typo. London ptg. P* 14.
12	3	3 p. carmine	..	1·25	1·50
13		6 p. emerald-green	..	80	3·75
14		1 a. purple-brown	..	1·10	7·50
		a. Imperf between (horiz pair)	†	£1200	
15		2 a. bright violet	..	2·50	14·00
12/15			*Set of 4*	5·00	24·00

1935–48. *Typo. Morvi Press ptg. Rough perf* 11.
16	3	3 p. scarlet (*shades*)	..	60	2·00
		a. Imperf between (horiz pair)	..	£1200	
17		6 p. grey-green	..	75	2·00
		a. Emerald-green	..	4·75	21·00
18		1 a. brown	..	12·00	14·00
		a. Pale yellow-brown	..	16·00	24·00
		b. Chocolate	..	22·00	30·00
19		2 a. dull violet (*to deep*)	..	2·50	15·00
16/19			*Set of 4*	14·00	30·00

Nos. 17a, 18a and 18b were issued between 1944 and 1948.

Maharaja Mahendra Singh, 1948–1957

Morvi was merged with the United State of Kathiawar (later Saurashtra) by 15 April 1948.

NANDGAON

PRICES FOR STAMPS ON COVER

The stamps of Nandgaon are very rare used on cover.

GUM. The stamps of Nandgaon were issued without gum.

Raja Mahant Balram Das, 1883–1897

1   2 (½ a.)

(Litho at Poona)

1891. *Imperf.*
1	1	½ a. blue	..	3·50	£110
		a. Dull blue	..	3·75	
2		2 a. rose	..	16·00	£275

The few covers in existence franked with Nos. 1/2 have undated manuscript cancellations, but other forms are known on loose examples.

The state was under Imperial administration from January 1888 to November 1891 and it is possible that Nos. 1/2 may have appeared in late 1887.

Last character in top line omitted

(Typo Balram Press, Raj-Nandgaon)

1893 (1 Jan)–**94.** *Printed in sheets of* 16 (4×4). *Imperf.*

(a) *Stamps printed wide apart (8 to 10 mm) without wavy lines between them. Thin, toned wove paper*
3	2	½ a. dull *to* deep green	..	7·50	50·00
4		2 a. red	..	6·00	50·00
		a. Thick paper			
		b. Dull rose	..	6·00	50·00

(b) *Stamps printed closer together (4 to 7 mm) with wavy lines between them. Thin, white wove paper* (1894)
5	2	½ a. green	..	18·00	40·00
		a. Last character in top line omitted (R.4/3)	..	75·00	
		b. Thick paper			
		ba. Last character in top line omitted			
6		1 a. rose	..	32·00	80·00
		a. Thick paper			
		b. Thick laid paper			
		ba. Thin laid paper	..	£200	

There were three settings of Type **2** with a number of separate printings made from the third:

Setting I – Nos. 3, 4, 4a, 4b, O2
Setting II – Nos. 5, 5b, 6, 6a, 6b
Setting III – Nos. 5, 6ba, O3, O3a, O4, O4a, O5 and subsequent reprints

The same clichés were used for all values with the face value inscriptions changed. These exist in two different sizes with both occurring on the ½ a., the small on the 1 a. and the large on the 2 a. except for No. O5 which has the small type.

The ordinary postage stamps of Nandgaon became obsolete on 1 July 1894.

OFFICIAL STAMPS

(O 1)
("M.B.D." = Mahant Balram Das)

1893. *No.* 1 *handstamped with ruler's initials in oval. Type* O 1, *in purple.*
O1		½ a. blue	..	£350	

No. 2 may also exist with this overprint, but no example has been reported for many years.

1894. *Handstamped with Type* O 1 *in purple.*

(a) *Stamps printed wide apart (8 to 10 mm) without wavy lines between them. Thin, toned wove paper*
O2	2	2 a. red	..	18·00	80·00

(b) *Stamps printed closer together (4 to 7 mm) with wavy lines between them. Thin, white wove paper*
O3	2	½ a. yellow-green	..	4·00	7·00
		a. Sage-green	..	5·50	
O4		1 a. rose (*shades*)	..	6·50	24·00
		a. Thin laid paper	..	10·00	60·00
O5		2 a. rose (*shades*)	..	5·50	16·00

Further printings took place in 1895 after the Official stamps were withdrawn from postal use on 31 December 1894. These were all on thin, white wove paper with the ½ a. and 2 a. in slightly different shades and the 1 a. in brown or ultramarine.

There is a forgery of the handstamp, Type O 1, which shows 8 mm between the two ornaments below the initials instead of the normal 4 mm.

NAWANAGAR

PRICES FOR STAMPS ON COVER

No.	1	*from* ×20
No.	2	*from* ×8
Nos.	2b/c	*from* ×3
No.	2d	—
Nos.	3/10	
Nos.	11/13	*from* × 100
Nos.	14/16	—

GUM. The stamps of Nawanagar were issued without gum.

Jam Vibhaji 1882–1895

1 (1 docra)   2 (2 docra)   3 (3 docra)

1877. *Typo in sheets of* 32 (4×8 *or* 8×4). *Laid paper.* (a) *Imperf*
1	1	1 doc. blue (*shades*)	..	40	20·00
		a. Tête-bêche (pair)	..	£1000	
		b. Doubly printed	..	80·00	

(b) *Perf* 12½ (*line*) *or* 11 (*harrow*)
2	1	1 doc. slate-blue	..	60·00	£100
		a. Tête-bêche (pair) (p 11)	..	£1300	

The inverted clichés which cause the tête-bêche pairs come from different settings and occur on R. 3/2 (No. 1a) or R. 4/4 (No. 2a) of sheets of 32 (4×8).

1877. *T* 2 *and* 3. *Type-set in black. Wove paper. Thick horizontal and vertical frame lines.*
A. *Stamp* 14½–15 *mm wide.* B. *Stamp* 16 *mm wide.* C. *Stamp* 19 *mm wide.*

				A	B	C
2b		1 doc. deep mauve	..	£225	£180	£2750	£140
2c		2 doc. green	..	†	†	£2750	£1500
2d		3 doc. yellow	..	†	†	£2750	£1500

Prices for Nos. 2bA/B are for used, no unused examples being known.

1880. *As last, but thin frame lines, as illustrated.*
D. *Stamp* 15 *to* 18 *mm wide.* E. *Stamp* 14 *mm wide.*

				D		E	
3		1 doc. deep mauve	..	1·75	6·00	†	
		a. On rose	..	1·75		1·75	4·00
4		1 doc. magenta	..	†		1·75	
5		2 doc. yellow-green	..	2·25	8·00	2·25	6·50
		a. On blue-green	..	4·50		6·00	
		b. Error. Yellow	..	£325	—	†	
6		3 doc. orange-yellow	..	7·00	—	†	
		a. On yellow	..	3·50	11·00	3·50	7·50
		ab. On yellow. Laid paper	80·00	—	40·00	—	

There are several different settings of each value of this series. No. 5b occurs in the sheet of the 3 doc. value from one setting only.

4 (1 docra)

1893. *Typo in sheets of* 36. *P* 12. (a) *Thick paper.*
8	4	1 doc. black	..	1·40	
		a. Imperf (pair)	..	£475	
9		3 doc. orange	..	2·25	

(b) *Thick laid paper*
10	4	1 doc. black	..	£450	

(c) *Thin wove paper*
11	4	1 doc. black *to* grey	..	65	3·00
		a. Imperf between (pair)	..	£400	
		b. Imperf (pair)	..	£375	
12		2 doc. green	..	60	3·50
		a. Imperf (pair)	..	£400	
		b. Imperf between (vert pair)	..	£425	
13		3 doc. orange-yellow	..	1·00	6·50
		a. Imperf between (pair)	..	£425	
		b. Orange	..	70	6·00
		ba. Imperf (pair)	..	£400	
		bb. Imperf vert (horiz pair)	..	£425	

(d) *Thin, soft wove paper*
14	4	1 doc. black	..		
15		2 doc. deep green	..	2·50	
16		3 doc. brown-orange	..	3·50	

Cancellations for postal purposes were intaglio seals, applied in black. Other forms of cancellation were only used on remainders.

The stamps of Nawanagar became obsolete on 1 January 1895.

NEPAL

Nepal being an independent state, its stamps will be found listed in Part 21 (*South-East Asia*) of this catalogue.

ORCHHA

PRICES FOR STAMPS ON COVER

Nos. 1/2	—
Nos. 3/7	*from* × 8
Nos. 8/30	*from* × 50
Nos. 31/45	*from* × 4

A set of four stamps, ½ a. red, 1 a. violet, 2 a. yellow and 4 a. deep blue-green, in a design similar to T **2**, was prepared in 1897 with State authority but not put into use. These exist both imperforate and pin-perforated. (*Price for set of* 4, £16 *unused or c.t.o.*)

Maharaja Partab Singh, 1874–1930

1   **2**

(T **1/2** litho Shri Pratap Prabhakar)

1913. *Background to arms unshaded. Very blurred impression. Wove paper. No gum. Imperf.*
1	**1**	½ a. green	..	27·00	70·00
2		1 a. red	..	19·00	

1914–35. *Background shaded with short horizontal lines. Clearer impression. Wove paper. No gum. Imperf.*
3	**2**	¼ a. bright ultramarine	..	85	3·00
		a. Grey-blue	..	35	2·75
		b. Deep blue	..	1·60	3·00
		ba. Laid paper	..	£475	
4		½ a. green (shades)	..	40	3·25
		a. Dull green	..	1·50	3·50
		b. Apple-green	..	2·25	3·25
5		1 a. scarlet	..	2·00	5·00
		a. Laid paper	..	—	£300
		b. Indian red	..	1·75	8·00
		c. Carmine	..	2·50	3·75
		ca. Laid paper (1935)	..	£180	£250
6		2 a. red-brown (1916)	..	4·50	17·00
		a. Light brown	..	10·00	17·00
		b. Chestnut	..	18·00	20·00
7		4 a. ochre (1917)	..	8·50	25·00
		a. Yellow-orange	..	8·00	25·00
		b. Yellow	..	8·00	20·00
3/7			*Set of* 5	13·50	42·00

There are two sizes of T **2** in the setting of 8 (4 × 2). In each value stamps from the upper row are slightly taller than those from the lower.

Maharaja Vir Singh II, 1930–1956

3 Maharaja Vir Singh II **4**

(Typo Lakshmi Art Ptg Wks, Bombay)

1935 (1 Apr). *Thick, chalk-surfaced wove paper.* P 9½, 10, 10 × 9½, 11, 11 × 9½, 11½, 11½ × 11, 11½ × 12, 12 *or* 12 × 11.
8	**3**	¼ a. purple and slate	..	1·00	1·75
		a. Imperf between (vert pair)			
		b. Ordinary paper	..	30	1·10
		ba. Imperf between (vert pair)	..	11·00	
		bb. Imperf vert (horiz pair)	..	65·00	
9		½ a. olive-grey and emerald	..	45	60
		a. Imperf (pair)	..	75·00	
10		¾ a. magenta and deep myrtle-green	..	50	75
		a. Imperf (pair)	..	75·00	
11		1 a. myrtle-green and purple-brown	..	50	60
		a. Imperf (pair)	..	65·00	65·00
		b. Imperf horiz (vert pair)			
		c. Imperf vert (horiz pair)			
12		1¼ a. slate and mauve	..	45	60
		a. Imperf (pair)	..	75·00	£200
		b. Imperf between (horiz pair)	..	75·00	
		c. Frame doubly printed	..	75·00	
13		1½ a. brown and scarlet	..	45	60
		a. Imperf between (vert pair)	..	75·00	
		b. Imperf between (horiz pair)	..	75·00	
14		2 a. blue and red-orange	..	45	60
		a. Imperf (pair)	..	12·00	
		b. Imperf between (horiz pair)	..	75·00	
15		2½ a. olive-brown and dull orange	..	65	70
		a. Imperf (pair)	..	12·00	
		b. Imperf between (horiz pair)	..	75·00	
16		3 a. bright blue and magenta	..	65	70
		a. Imperf between (horiz pair)	..	75·00	£100
		b. Imperf (pair)	..	75·00	
17		4 a. deep reddish purple and sage-green		65	2·25
		a. Imperf (pair)	..	8·50	
		b. Imperf between (vert pair)	..	75·00	
		c. Imperf vert (horiz pair)	..	75·00	

18	**3**	6 a. black and pale ochre	..	65	2·25
		a. Imperf (pair)	..	8·50	
19		8 a. brown and purple	..	1·25	2·25
		a. Imperf (pair)	..	8·50	
		b. Imperf between (vert pair)	..	85·00	
20		12 a. bright emerald and bright purple	..	1·00	2·50
		a. Imperf (pair)	..	8·50	
		b. Imperf between (vert pair)	..	85·00	
21		12 a. pale greenish blue and bright purple	23·00	42·00	
22		1 r. chocolate and myrtle-green	..	80	3·25
		a. Imperf (pair)	..	9·00	
		b. Imperf between (horiz pair)	..	75·00	
23	**4**	1 r. chocolate and myrtle-green	..	3·50	8·00
		a. Imperf (pair)	..	85·00	
		b. Imperf between (horiz pair)	..	£100	
24	**3**	2 r. purple-brown and bistre-yellow	..	2·75	8·00
		a. Imperf (pair)	..	9·00	
25		3 r. black and greenish blue	..	1·50	8·00
		a. Imperf (pair)	..	9·00	
26		4 r. black and brown	..	2·25	9·00
		a. Imperf (pair)	..	9·00	
27		5 r. bright blue and plum	..	3·00	10·00
		a. Imperf (pair)	..	9·00	
28		10 r. bronze-green and cerise	..	7·00	15·00
		a. Imperf (pair)	..	12·00	
		b. Imperf between (horiz pair)	..	95·00	
29		15 r. black and bronze-green	..	12·00	35·00
		a. Imperf (pair)	..	12·00	
30		25 r. red-orange and blue	..	16·00	40·00
		a. Imperf (pair)	..	15·00	
8/20, 22/30			*Set of* 22	50·00	£130

Values to 5 r. except the 1 a., are inscribed "POSTAGE", and the remaining values "POSTAGE & REVENUE".

The central portrait of Type **3** is taken from a half-tone block and consists of large square dots. The portrait of Type **4** has a background of lines.

Owing to a lack of proper State control considerable quantities of these stamps circulated at below face value and the issue was subsequently withdrawn, supplies being exchanged for the 1939–42 issue. We are, however, now satisfied that the lower values at least did genuine postal duty until 1939.

Used prices are for stamps cancelled-to-order, postally used examples being worth considerably more.

5 Maharaja Vir Singh II **6**

(Litho Indian Security Printing Press, Nasik)

1939–42? P 13½ × 14 (T **5**) *or* 14 × 13½ (T **6**).
31	**5**	¼ a. chocolate	..	2·00	42·00
32		½ a. yellow-green	..	2·25	35·00
33		¾ a. bright blue	..	2·25	55·00
34		1 a. scarlet	..	2·25	11·00
35		1¼ a. blue	..	2·25	55·00
36		1½ a. mauve	..	2·50	70·00
37		2 a. vermilion	..	2·25	42·00
38		2½ a. turquoise-green	..	£120	
39		3 a. slate-violet	..	3·50	65·00
40		4 a. slate	..	4·50	18·00
41		8 a. magenta	..	7·50	£120
42	**6**	1 r. grey-green	..	13·00	
43		2 r. bright violet	..	28·00	£325
44		5 r. yellow-orange	..	80·00	
45		10 r. turquoise-green (1942)	..	£300	
46		15 r. slate-lilac (date ?)	..	£2000	
47		25 r. claret (date ?)	..	£2000	

Orchha became part of Vindhya Pradesh by 1 May 1948.

POONCH

PRICES FOR STAMPS ON COVER

Nos. 1/2	*from* × 3
Nos. 3/63	*from* × 10
Nos. O1/10	*from* × 30

GUM. The stamps of Poonch were issued without gum, except for some examples of Nos. 7/10.

The stamps of Poonch are all imperforate, and handstamped in watercolours.

ILLUSTRATIONS. Designs of Poonch are illustrated actual size.

Raja Moti Singh, 1852–1892

1   **2**

1876. T **1** (22 × 21 *mm*). *Yellowish white, wove paper.*
1		6 p. red	..	£2750	95·00

1877. *As* T **1** (19 × 17 *mm*). *Same paper.*
1*a*		½ a. red	..	£4750	£1900

1879. T **2** (21 × 19 *mm*). *Same paper.*
2		½ a. red	..	—	£1700

3 (½ a.)   **4** (1 a.)

5 (2 a.)   **6** (4 a.)

1880. *Yellowish white, wove paper.*
3	**3**	½ a. red	..	32·00	14·00
4	**4**	1 a. red	..	50·00	32·00
5	**5**	2 a. red	..	85·00	65·00
6	**6**	4 a. red	..	90·00	70·00

1884. *Toned wove bâtonné paper.*
7	**3**	½ a. red	..	4·00	4·00
8	**4**	1 a. red	..	12·00	
9	**5**	2 a. red	..	10·00	13·00
10	**6**	4 a. red	..	22·00	22·00

These are sometimes found gummed.

7 (1 pice)

1884–87. *Various papers.* (*a*) *White laid bâtonné or ribbed bâtonné.*
11	**7**	1 p. red	..	12·00	14·00
		a. Pair, one stamp sideways	..	£130	
12	**3**	½ a. red	..	1·50	2·25
13	**4**	1 a. red	..	1·75	
14	**5**	2 a. red	..	5·00	6·50
15	**6**	4 a. red	..	7·00	
		(*b*) *Thick white laid paper*			
22	**7**	1 p. red	..	29·00	
23	**3**	½ a. red	..	48·00	
24	**4**	1 a. red	..	48·00	
25	**5**	2 a. red	..	48·00	
26	**6**	4 a. red	..	55·00	
		(*c*) *Yellow wove bâtonné*			
27	**7**	1 p. red	..	2·25	2·00
		a. Pair, one stamp sideways	..	26·00	
28	**3**	½ a. red	..	2·75	3·50
29	**4**	1 a. red	..	22·00	
30	**5**	2 a. red	..	4·50	6·50
31	**6**	4 a. red	..	2·25	2·50
		(*d*) *Orange-buff wove bâtonné*			
32	**7**	1 p. red	..	1·25	1·75
		a. Pair, one stamp sideways	..	18·00	
		b. Tête-bêche (pair)	..	28·00	
33	**3**	½ a. red	..	15·00	
34	**5**	2 a. red	..	50·00	
35	**6**	4 a. red	..	12·00	
		(*e*) *Yellow laid paper*			
36	**7**	1 p. red	..	1·00	2·25
		a. Pair, one stamp sideways	..	16·00	
		b. Tête-bêche (pair)	..	22·00	
37	**3**	½ a. red	..	2·00	
38	**4**	1 a. red	..	23·00	
39	**5**	2 a. red	..	32·00	32·00
40	**6**	4 a. red	..	26·00	
		(*f*) *Yellow laid bâtonné*			
41	**7**	1 p. red	..	7·50	5·50
		(*g*) *Buff laid or ribbed bâtonné paper thicker than* (*d*)			
42	**4**	1 a. red	..	40·00	
43	**6**	4 a. red	..	42·00	
		(*h*) *Blue-green laid paper* (1887)			
44	**3**	½ a. red	..	24·00	
45	**4**	1 a. red	..	2·00	3·00
46	**5**	2 a. red	..	20·00	
47	**6**	4 a. red	..	38·00	
		(*i*) *Yellow-green laid paper*			
48	**3**	½ a. red	..	28·00	
		(*j*) *Blue-green wove bâtonné*			
49	**7**	1 p. red	..	26·00	23·00
49*a*	**3**	½ a. red	..	£600	
50	**4**	1 a. red	..	1·00	1·75
		(*k*) *Lavender wove bâtonné*			
51	**4**	1 a. red	..	50·00	
52	**5**	2 a. red	..	1·10	1·75
		(*l*) *Blue wove bâtonné*			
53	**7**	1 p. red	..	1·90	1·25
		a. Pair, one stamp sideways	..	18·00	
		b. Tête-bêche (pair)	..	26·00	
54	**4**	1 a. red	..	£250	

(m) Various coloured papers

55	7	1 p. red/grey-blue laid		5·50	3·50
56		1 p. red/lilac laid		45·00	48·00
		a. Pair, one stamp sideways	..	£250	£250
		b. *Tête-bêche* (pair) ..	..	£225	

1888. *Printed in aniline rose on various papers*

57	7	1 p. on *blue wove bâtonné* ..	..	2·75	
58		1 p. on *buff laid*	..	9·00	
59	3	½ a. on *white laid*	..	14·00	
60	4	1 a. on *green laid* ..	..	10·00	11·00
61		1 a. on *green wove bâtonné*	..	5·00	5·00
62	5	2 a. on *lavender wove bâtonné*	..	4·50	4·50
63	6	4 a. on *yellow laid* ..	..	10·00	10·00

OFFICIAL STAMPS

Raja Baldeo Singh, 1892–1918

1888. *(a) White laid bâtonné paper.*

O 1	7	1 p. black	..	1·50	1·60
		a. Pair, one stamp sideways	..	12·00	14·00
		b. *Tête-bêche* (pair)	..	15·00	
O 2	3	½ a. black	..	1·50	2·25
O 3	4	1 a. black	..	1·25	1·40
O 4	5	2 a. black	..	2·25	2·25
O 5	6	4 a. black	..	4·00	6·50

(b) White toned wove bâtonné paper

O 6	7	1 p. black	..	1·60	
O 7	3	½ a. black	..	2·25	2·00
		a. Pair, one stamp sideways	..	£750	
O 8	4	1 a. black ..	..	12·00	11·00
O 9	5	2 a. black	..	5·00	5·00
O10	6	4 a. black	..	8·50	

RAJASTHAN

Rajasthan was formed in 1948–49 from a number of States in Rajputana; these included Bundi, Jaipur and Kishangarh, whose posts continued to function more or less separately until ordered by the Indian Government to close on 1 April 1950.

PRICES FOR STAMPS ON COVER	
Nos. 1/7	*from* × 15
Nos. 8/10	—
Nos. 11/12	*from* × 5
Nos. 13/14	—
Nos. 15/25	*from* × 4
Nos. 26/42	*from* × 3
No. 43	*from* × 5
Nos. 44/60	*from* × 3
No. 61	*from* × 5
Nos. 62/5	*from* × 5

BUNDI

(1)

1949. *Nos. 86/92 of Bundi. (a) Handstamped with T 1.*

A. *In black.* B. *In violet.* C. *In blue*

			A	B	C
1	¼ a. blue-green		4·00	3·75	22·00
	a. Pair, one without opt	..	£140	†	†
2	½ a. violet		2·50	2·50	23·00
	a. Pair, one without opt	..	†	£150	†
3	1 a. yellow-green ..		3·50	9·50	26·00
	a. Pair, one without opt	..	†	£150	†
4	2 a. vermilion		6·50	20·00	
5	4 a. orange ..		27·00	20·00	60·00
6	8 a. ultramarine ..		3·50	5·00	38·00
7	1 r. chocolate		—	£140	60·00

The above prices are for unused, used stamps being worth about six times the unused prices. Most of these handstamps are known, sideways, inverted or double.

(b) Machine-printed as T 1 in black

8	¼ a. blue-green	..		
9	½ a. violet	..		
10	1 a. yellow-green	..		
11	2 a. vermilion		3·25	48·00
	a. Opt inverted		£250	
12	4 a. orange		2·00	48·00
	a. Opt double		£200	
13	8 a. ultramarine		30·00	
	a. Opt inverted		£400	
	b. Opt double		£375	
14	1 r. chocolate		7·50	

JAIPUR

राजस्थान

RAJASTHAN

(2)

1950 (26 Jan). *T 7 of Jaipur optd with T 2.*

15	¼ a. black and brown-lake (No. 58) (B.)		3·25	12·00
16	½ a. black and violet (No. 41) (R.)		3·25	13·00
17	¾ a. black and brown-red (No. 59) (Blue-blk.)	5·00	15·00
	a. Opt in pale blue	13·00	30·00
18	1 a. black and blue (No. 60) (R.) ..	4·00	25·00
19	2 a. black and buff (No. 61) (R.) ..	5·00	32·00
20	2½ a. black and carmine (No. 62) (B.)	6·50	16·00
21	3 a. black and green (No. 63) (R.) ..	7·00	40·00
22	4 a. black and grey-green (No. 64) (R.)	7·00	45·00
23	6 a. black and pale blue (No. 65a) (R.)	8·00	70·00
24	8 a. black and chocolate (No. 66) (R.)	11·00	90·00
25	1 r. black and yellow-bistre (No. 67) (R.)	12·00	£130
15/25	.. .. *Set of 11*	65·00	£425

KISHANGARH

1948–49. *Various stamps of Kishangarh handstamped with T 1 in red.*

(a) On stamps of 1899–1901

26	¼ a. rose-pink (No. 5a) (B.)		£130
26a	¼ a. rose-pink (No. 22a) ..	..	—	£120
27	½ a. deep blue (No. 26) ..	..	£200
29	1 a. brown-lilac (No. 29) ..	..	14·00	35·00
	b. Imperf (pair) ..	..	40·00	75·00
	c. Violet handstamp ..	..	—	£180
	d. Black handstamp ..		—	£225
30	4 a. chocolate (No. 31) ..	..	48·00	65·00
	a. Violet handstamp ..		—	£275
31	1 r. dull green (No. 32) ..		£150	£160
31a	2 r. brown-red (No. 34) ..		£180
32	5 r. mauve (No. 35) ..		£170	£170

(b) On stamps of 1904–10

33	13	½ a. chestnut	—	85·00
33a		1 a. blue	—	£110
34		4 a. brown	13·00
		a. Blue handstamp	£140
35	12a	8 a. grey	65·00	£100
36	13	8 a. violet	11·00
37		1 r. green	11·00
38		2 r. olive-yellow	18·00
39		5 r. purple-brown	22·00
		a. Blue handstamp	£225

(c) On stamps of 1912–16

40	14	½ a. green (No. 64)	—	£100
41		1 a. red	—	£100
42		2 a. deep violet (No. 51)	£200
43		2 a. purple (No. 66)	2·00	5·00
44		4 a. bright blue	—	£275
45		8 a. brown	5·00
		a. Pair, one without handstamp ..	£225
46		1 r. mauve	10·00
47		2 r. deep green	10·00
48		5 r. brown	£190

(d) On stamps of 1928–36

49	16	½ a. yellow-green	80·00
49a		2 a. magenta	—	£180
50		4 a. chestnut	£120
51		8 a. violet	6·00	50·00
		a. Pair, one without handstamp ..	£200
52		1 r. light green	20·00
53		2 r. lemon-yellow	14·00
54		5 r. claret	15·00

(e) On stamps of 1943–47

55	16	¼ a. pale dull blue	55·00	55·00
56		¼ a. greenish blue	38·00	35·00
		a. Imperf (pair)	£130
57		½ a. deep green	22·00	24·00
		a. Violet handstamp	—	£120
57b		½ a. yellow-green	30·00	32·00
		ba. Imperf (pair)	£130
		bb. Blue handstamp	—	£120
58	17	1 a. carmine-red	32·00	32·00
		a. Violet handstamp	—	£130
58b		1 a. orange-red (*imperf*)	85·00
		ba. Blue handstamp	95·00
59		2 a. bright magenta	90·00	90·00
60		2 a. maroon (*imperf*)	£100
61	16	4 a. brown	1·75	5·50
62		8 a. violet	15·00	42·00
63		1 r. green	6·00
64		2 r. yellow	£120
65		5 r. claret	50·00

A 1 a. value in deep violet-blue was issued for revenue purposes, but is known postally used (*Price £60 used*).

RAJPIPLA

PRICES FOR STAMPS ON COVER	
No. 1	*from* × 25
Nos. 2/3	—

Maharana Ganbhir Singh, 1860–1897

1 (1 pice)   2 (2 a.)   3 (4 a.)

1880. *Litho. With or without gum (1 p.) or no gum (others).* P 11 (1 p.) or 12½.

1	1	1 p. blue		1·50	20·00
2	2	2 a. green		19·00	55·00
		a. Imperf between (pair) ..		£550	£550
3	3	4 a. red		9·00	35·00
1/3		.. .. *Set of 3*		27·00	£100

These stamps became obsolete in 1886.

SHAHPURA

PRICES FOR STAMPS ON COVER	
Nos. 1/4	*from* × 2
No. F1	*from* × 2

DATES. Those quoted are of first known use.

Rajadhiraj Nahar Singh, 1870–1932

RAJ SHAHPURA Postage 1 pice	**RAJ SHAHPURA** 1 pice
1	2

1914–17. *Typo.*

1	1	1 p. carmine/*bluish grey* (p 11)		—	£225
2		1 p. carmine/*drab* (*imperf*) (1917) ..		—	£350

Some examples of No. 1 are imperforate on one side or on two adjacent sides.

1920–28. *Typo. Imperf.*

3	2	1 p. carmine/*drab* (1928)		—	£400
4		1 a. black/*pink*		—	£400

POSTAL FISCAL

Rajadhiraj Umaid Singh, 1932–1947

Rajadhiraj Sudarshan Deo, 1947–1971

F 1

1932–47. *Typo.* P 11, 11½ or 12.

F1	F 1	1 a. red (*shades*)		35·00	£110
		a. Pin-perf 7 (1947)			

Nos. F1/a were used for both fiscal and postal purposes. Manuscript cancellations must be assumed to be fiscal, unless on cover showing other evidence of postal use. The design was first issued for fiscal purposes in 1898.

Shahpura became part of Rajasthan by 15 April 1948.

SIRMOOR

PRICES FOR STAMPS ON COVER
The stamps of Sirmoor are very rare used on cover.

Raja Shamsher Parkash, 1886–1898

1 (1 pice)   2   3 Raja Shamsher Parkash

1878 (June)–80. *Litho.* P 11½.

1	1	1 p. pale green		7·00	£170
2		1 p. blue (on *laid* paper) (1880) ..		4·00	£120
		a. Imperf between (pair) ..		£250	
		b. Imperf (pair) ..		£250	

(*Litho at Calcutta*)

1892. *Thick wove paper.* P 11½.

3	2	1 p. yellow-green		50	55
		a. Imperf between (vert pair) ..		70·00	
		b. *Deep green*		40	45
		ba. Imperf between (vert pair) ..		70·00	70·00
4		1 p. blue		50	50
		a. Imperf between (vert pair) ..		60·00	60·00
		b. Imperf between (horiz pair) ..		60·00	60·00
		c. Imperf vert (horiz pair) ..		60·00	
		d. Imperf (pair)		75·00	

These were originally made as reprints, about 1891, to supply collectors, but there being very little demand for them they were put into use. The design was copied (including the perforations) from an illustration in a dealer's catalogue.

STANLEY GIBBONS STAMP COLLECTING SERIES

Introductory booklets on *How to Start, How to Identify Stamps* and *Collecting by Theme.* A series of well illustrated guides at a low price. Write for details.

A   B

C   D

There were seven printings of stamps as Type 3, all in sheets of 70 (10×7) and made up from groups of transfers which can be traced through minor varieties.

Printings I to V and VII of the 3 p. and 6 p. are as Types A and C (both with large white dots evenly spaced between the ends of the upper and lower inscriptions).

Printing VI is as Type B (small white dots and less space) and Type D (large white dots unevenly positioned between the inscriptions).

(Litho Waterlow)

1885–96. *P 14 to 15.*

5	3	3 p. chocolate (A)			55	30
		a. Brown (B) (1896)			30	35
6		3 p. orange (A) (1888)			1·50	20
		a. Type B (1896)			30	20
		ab. Imperf (pair)			£550	
7		6 p. blue-green (C)			3·50	2·00
		a. Green (C) (1888)			95	50
		b. Bright green (C) (1891)			50·00	50·00
		c. Deep green (C) (1894)			40	25
		d. Yellowish green (D) (1896)			40	1·50
8		1 a. bright blue			1·50	1·75
		a. Dull blue (1891)			5·50	4·50
		b. Steel-blue (1891)			75·00	75·00
		c. Grey-blue (1894)			2·25	1·00
		d. Slate-blue (1896)			50	1·75
9		2 a. pink			4·25	9·50
		a. Carmine (1894)			3·50	3·00
		b. Rose-red (1896)			3·25	4·00

Composition of the various printings was as follows:
Printing I – Nos. 5, 7, 8 and 9
Printing II – Nos. 6 and 7*a*
Printing III – Nos. 6, 7*b* and 8*a*
Printing IV – Nos. 5, 6, 7*a*, and 8*b*
Printing V – Nos. 6, 7*c*, 8*c* and 9*a*
Printing VI – Nos. 5*a*, 6*a*, 7*d*, 8*d* and 9*b*
Printing VII – Only exists overprinted "On S. S. S." (Nos. 78/81).

4 Indian Elephant   5 Raja Shamsher Parkash

(Recess Waterlow & Sons)

1894–99. *P 12 to 15 and compounds.*

22	4	3 p. orange-brown			1·25	30
23		6 p. green			65	30
		a. Imperf between (vert pair)			£1200	
24		1 a. blue			2·25	60
25		2 a. rose			1·10	1·00
26		3 a. yellow-green			13·00	25·00
27		4 a. deep green			6·00	12·00
28		8 a. deep blue			9·00	17·00
29		1 r. vermilion			22·00	40·00
22/9				*Set of 8*	50·00	85·00

Raja Surindra Bikram Parkash, 1898–1911

(Recess Waterlow & Sons)

1899. *P 13 to 15.*

30	5	3 a. yellow-green			1·50	17·00
31		4 a. deep green			2·00	11·00
32		8 a. deep blue			4·00	11·00
33		1 r. vermilion			7·50	28·00
30/3				*Set of 4*	13·50	60·00

OFFICIAL STAMPS

NOTE. The varieties occurring in the machine-printed "On S.S.S." overprints may, of course, also be found in the inverted and double overprints, and many of them are known thus.

Roman figures denote printings of the basic stamps (Nos. 7/21). Where more than one printing was overprinted the prices quoted are for the commonest.

I. MACHINE-PRINTED

On

S.   S.

S.

(11)

1890. *Optd with T 11.* (a) In black.

50	3	6 p. green (C)			£800	£800
		a. Stop before first "S"				
51		2 a. pink			50·00	£130
		a. Stop before first "S"			£130	

(b) In red

52	3	6 p. green (C)			14·00	2·50
		a. Stop before first "S"			50·00	25·00
53		1 a. bright blue			35·00	10·00
		a. Stop before first "S"			90·00	60·00
		b. Opt inverted			†	£550

(c) Doubly optd in red and in black

53c	3	6 p. green (C)			£900	£900
		ca. Stop before first "S"			£2000	£2000

Nos. 50, 52 and 53c are from Printing II and the remainder from Printing I.

On   On

S.   S.   S.

S.   S.

(12)   (13)

1891. *Optd with T 12.* (a) In black.

54	3	3 p. orange (A)			2·25	30·00
		a. Opt inverted			£375	
55		6 p. green (C)			1·50	1·50
		a. Opt inverted			£150	
		b. No stop after lower "S"			22·00	22·00
		c. Raised stop before lower "S"			£140	£100
56		1 a. bright blue			£275	£325
57		2 a. pink			13·00	42·00

(b) In red

58	3	6 p. green (C)			23·00	3·00
		a. Opt inverted			£180	£150
		b. Opt double			£180	£160
59		1 a. bright blue			16·00	23·00
		a. Opt inverted			†	£375
		b. Opt double			†	£375
		c. No stop after lower "S"			£140	£150

(c) In black and red

59d	3	6 p. green (C)			£800	

Nos. 54/5, 58 and 59d are from Printing II and the others from Printing I.

1892–97. *Optd with T 13.* (a) In black.

60	3	3 p. orange (A)			50	40
		a. Type B			2·75	60
		b. Opt inverted			£200	
		c. First "S" inverted and stop raised			5·00	5·00
		d. No stop after lower "S"			5·00	5·00
		e. Raised stop after second "S"			30·00	14·00
		f. Vertical pair, Types 12 and 13			80·00	
61		6 p. green (C)			5·00	1·00
		a. Deep green (C)			1·60	50
		b. First "S" inverted and stop raised			28·00	12·00
		c. Raised stop after second "S"			28·00	12·00
		d. No stop after lower "S"			38·00	17·00
		e. Opt double			£425	
62		1 a. steel-blue			8·00	1·00
		a. Grey-blue			8·00	
		b. Opt double			£300	
		c. First "S" inverted and stop raised			28·00	10·00
		d. No stop after lower "S"			£110	42·00
		e. Raised stop after second "S"			48·00	12·00
63		2 a. pink			9·00	14·00
		a. Carmine			7·00	7·00
		b. Opt inverted			£500	£500
		c. First "S" inverted and stop raised			35·00	35·00
		d. No stop after lower "S"			35·00	35·00
		e. Raised stop after second "S"			£140	£140

(b) In red

64	3	6 p. green (C)			3·50	50
		a. Bright green (C)			6·00	1·00
		b. Opt inverted			95·00	85·00
		c. First "S" inverted and stop raised			18·00	50·00
		d. Vertical pair, Types 12 and 13			80·00	80·00
65		1 a. bright blue			13·00	2·50
		a. Steel-blue			11·00	1·00
		b. Opt inverted			£170	£130
		c. Opt double			£200	
		d. First "S" inverted and stop raised			27·00	8·00
		e. No stop after lower "S"			27·00	8·00

(c) Doubly overprinted in black and red

65f	3	6 p. bright green (C)			—	£750
		fa. Green (C). Red opt inverted			†	£950

The printings used for this issue were as follows:
Printing I – Nos. 63 and 65
Printing II – Nos. 60, 64 and 65fa
Printing III – Nos. 60, 64a and 65f
Printing IV – Nos. 61, 62, 64 and 65a
Printing V – Nos. 60, 61a, 62a and 63a
Printing VI – No. 60a

There are seven settings of this overprint, the first of which was a composite setting of 20 (10×2), with examples of Type 12 in the upper row. The inverted "S" and the missing stop occur in the 3rd and 6th settings with the latter also including the raised stop after second "S".

On   On

S. S. S. S.

S.   S.

(14)   (15)

1896–97. *Optd as T 14.*

66	3	3 p. orange (B) (1897)			7·00	1·25
		a. Comma after first "S"			40·00	30·00
		b. Opt inverted				
		c. Opt double			†	£425
67		6 p. deep green (C)			5·50	60
		a. Yellowish green (D)			—	1·75
		b. Comma after first "S"			40·00	18·00
		c. Comma after lower "S"			£120	18·00
		d. "S" at right inverted			£120	38·00
68		1 a. grey-blue			7·00	1·25
		a. Comma after first "S"			60·00	22·00
		b. Comma after lower "S"			£140	22·00
		c. "S" at right inverted			—	40·00
69		2 a. carmine (1897)			17·00	14·00
		a. Comma after first "S"			£110	£110

Nos. 66 and 67a are from Printing VI and the remainder from Printing V.

There are four settings of this overprint, (1) 23 mm high, includes the comma after lower "S"; (2) and (3) 25 mm high, with variety, comma after first "S"; (4) 25 mm high, with variety, "S" at right inverted.

1898 (Nov). *Optd with T 15.*

70	3	6 p. deep green (C)			£140	7·00
		a. Yellowish green (D)			£130	5·50
		b. Small "S" at right			£225	25·00
		c. Comma after lower "S"			—	50·00
		d. Lower "S" inverted and stop raised			—	50·00
71		1 a. grey-blue			£150	10·00
		a. Small "S" at right			£250	40·00
		b. Small "S" without stop			—	£160

No. 70a is from Printing VI and the others Printing V. There are two settings of this overprint. Nos. 70a and 71a/b occur in the first setting, and Nos. 70b/c in the second setting.

On   On

S. S. S. S.

S.   S.

(16)   (17)

1899 (July). *Optd with T 16.*

72	3	3 p. orange (B)			£170	6·50
73		6 p. deep green (C)			—	15·00

No. 72 is from Printing VI and No. 73 from Printing V.

1899 (Dec)–1900. *Optd as T 17.*

74	3	3 p. orange (B)			—	4·50
		a. Raised stop after lower "S"			†	50·00
		b. Comma after first "S"			†	£140
		c. No stop after first "S"			—	85·00
75		6 p. deep green (C)			—	4·00
		a. Yellowish green (D)			†	7·00
		b. Raised stop after lower "S"			†	50·00
		c. Comma after first "S"			†	£130
76		1 a. bright blue			†	£120
		a. Grey-blue			†	6·00
		b. Slate-blue			—	7·50
		c. Raised stop after lower "S"			†	75·00
		d. Comma after first "S"			†	£150
		e. No stop after first "S"			†	85·00
77		2 a. carmine			—	£100
		a. Raised stop after lower "S"			†	£375

There are two settings of this overprint: (1) 22 mm high, with raised stop variety; (2) 23 mm high, with "comma" and "no stop" varieties.

The printings used for this issue were as follows:
Printing I – No. 76
Printing V – Nos. 75, 76a and 77
Printing VI – Nos. 74, 75a and 76b

On   On

S. S. S S

S.   S

(18)   (19)

(Optd by Waterlow & Sons)

1900. *Optd with T 18.*

78	3	3 p. orange			1·75	4·50
79		6 p. green			40	45
80		1 a. blue			35	50
81		2 a. carmine			3·25	50·00

Nos. 78/81 were from Printing VII which was not issued without the overprint.

II. HANDSTAMPED

The words "On" and each letter "S" struck separately (except for Type 22 which was applied at one operation).

1894. *Handstamped with T 19.* (a) In black.

82	3	3 p. orange (A)			3·00	3·75
		a. "On" only			65·00	
83		6 p. green (C)			5·00	6·00
		a. Deep green (C)			7·50	9·50
		b. "On" only			65·00	65·00
84		1 a. bright blue			32·00	24·00
		a. Dull blue			10·00	12·00
		b. Steel-blue				
		c. Grey-blue			10·00	9·00
		d. "On" only			—	85·00
85		2 a. carmine			15·00	16·00
		a. "On" only			90·00	

(b) In red

86	3	6 p. green (C)	.. ..	85·00	90·00
86a		1 a. grey-blue	.. .. ..	£225	£225

The printings used for this issue were as follows:
Printing I – No. 84
Printing III – No. 84a
Printing IV – Nos. 83, 84b and 86
Printing V – Nos. 82, 83a, 84c, 85 and 86a

1896. *Handstamped with letters similar to those of T* **13,** *with stops, but irregular.*

87	3	3 p. orange (A)	.. ..	75·00	60·00
		a. Type B			
88		6 p. green (C)	..		
		a. Deep green (C)	..	65·00	55·00
		b. "On" omitted	..	£120	
88c		1 a. grey-blue	..	80·00	80·00
89		2 a. carmine	..	£130	

Printings used for this issue were as follows:
Printing II – No. 88
Printing III – No. 87
Printing IV – No. 88
Printing V – Nos. 87, 88a, 88c and 89
Printing VI – No. 87a

1897. *Handstamped with letters similar to those of T* **14,** *with stops, but irregular.*

90	3	3 p. orange (B)	.. .. ..	8·00	15·00
91		6 p. deep green (C)	.. ..	40·00	45·00
		a. "On" only	..	—	90·00
92		1 a. grey-blue	..	£170	£170
		a. "On" only	..	—	90·00
93		2 a. carmine	..	80·00	80·00

No. 90 was from Printing VI and the remainder from Printing V.

1897. *Handstamped with letters similar to those of T* **16,** *with stops, but irregular.*

93a	3	6 p. deep green (C)	.. ..	95·00	80·00

No. 93a is from Printing V.

ON
on
S S
S S
'S
S
(20) (21)

1896. *(a) Handstamped with T* **20.**

94	3	3 p. orange (A)	.. .. ..	50·00	55·00
95		2 a. carmine	.. .. ..	55·00	60·00

(b) Handstamped with T **21**

96	3	3 p. orange (A)	.. .. ..	£130	£140
97		6 p. bright green (C)	.. ..	£160	
98		1 a. bright blue	.. ..	£160	
		a. Dull blue			
98b		2 a. carmine	..	£170	

No. 98 comes from Printing I, No. 98a from Printing III, No. 97 possibly from Printing IV and the remainder from Printing V.

On On
S S
S S
(22) (23)

(c) Handstamped with T **22**

99	3	3 p. orange (B)	..	£120
100		6 p. deep green	..	£160
101		1 a. grey-blue	..	£225
101a		2 a. carmine	..	£300

No. 99 is from Printing VI and the others from Printing V.

1899. *Handstamped with T* **23.**

102	3	3 p. orange (A)	.. ..	—	£110
		a. Type B	.. ..	17·00	7·00
103		6 p. green (C)	..		
		a. Deep green (C)	..	20·00	14·00
		b. Yellowish green (D)	..	15·00	16·00
104		1 a. bright blue	.. ..	—	75·00
		a. Grey-blue	..	35·00	30·00
105		2 a. pink	..		
		a. Carmine	..	35·00	21·00
		b. Rose-red	..	42·00	28·00
		c. "On" only	..	—	£100

Printings used for this issue were as follows:
Printing I – Nos. 104 and 105
Printing IV – Nos. 102 and 103
Printing V – Nos. 102, 103a, 104a and 105a
Printing VI – Nos. 102a, 103b and 105b

PRICES OF SETS

Set prices are given for many issues, generally those containing three stamps or more. Definitive sets include one of each value or major colour change, but do not cover different perforations, die types or minor shades. Where a choice is possible the set prices are based on the cheapest versions of the stamps included in the listings.

On
S S
S
(24)

1901 (?). *Handstamped with T* **24.**

105d	3	6 p. yellowish green (D)		—	£250

From Printing VI

III. MIXED MACHINE-PRINTED AND HANDSTAMPED

1896. *(i) Handstamped "On" as in T* **19,** *and machine-printed opt T* **13** *complete.*

106	3	6 p. green (C)	.. .. ..	—	£350

(ii) Handstamped opt as T **14,** *and machine-printed opt T* **13** *complete*

107	3	6 p. deep green (C)	

No. 106 is from Printing IV and No. 107 from Printing V.
Various other types of these handstamps are known to exist, but in the absence of evidence of their authenticity we do not list them. It is stated that stamps of T **4** were never officially overprinted.

The stamps of Sirmoor have been obsolete since 1 April 1902.

SORUTH

PRICES FOR STAMPS ON COVER	
Nos. 1/15	*from* × 5
Nos. 16/57	*from* × 10
Nos. O1/13	*from* × 20
Nos. 58/61	*from* × 10
Nos. O14/22	*from* × 10

The name "Saurashtra" corrupted to "Sorath" or "Soruth", was originally used for all the territory later known as Kathiawar. Strictly speaking the name should have been applied only to a portion of Kathiawar including the state of Junagadh. As collectors have known these issues under the heading of "Soruth" for so long, we retain the name.
The currency was 40 docras = 1 koree but early stamps are inscribed in "annas of a koree", one "anna" being a sixteenth of a koree.
GUM. Nos. 1/47 of Soruth were issued without gum.

JUNAGADH
Nawab Mahabat Khan II, 1857–1882

1

(="Saurashtra Post 1864–65")

1864 (Nov). *Handstamped in water-colour. Imperf.*

1	1	(1 a.) black/azure (laid)	.. ..	£650	55·00
2		(1 a.) black/grey (laid)	.. ..	£650	50·00
3		(1 a.) black/azure (wove)	.. ..	—	£150
4		(1 a.) black/cream (wove)	.. ..	—	£700
4a		(1 a.) black/cream (laid)	.. ..	†	£1000

ILLUSTRATIONS. Types 2 to 11 are shown actual size.

2 (1 a.)   3 (1 a.)

4 (4 a.)   5 (4 a.)

क   ऊ

No. 8   No. 8a

(Type-set at Junagadh Sarkari Saurashtra Nitiprakash Ptg Press)

1868 (June)–75. *T* **2** *to* **5** *(two characters, Devanagri and Gujerati respectively for "1" and "4" as shown in the illustrations). Imperf.*

A. Inscriptions in Gujerati characters

5		1 a. black/yellowish (wove)	.. ..	†	£5000

B. Inscriptions in Devanagri characters (as in the illustrations)

I. Accents over first letters in top and bottom lines. Wove paper.

6		1 a. red/green		†	£1900
7		1 a. red/blue	..	†	£1900
8		1 a. black/pink		£600	90·00
		a. Incorrect character at bottom left (R. 1/4)		†	£700
9		2 a. black/yellow (1869)		†	£2750

II. Accents over second letters in top and bottom lines (1869–75).

(a) Wove paper

10	2	1 a. black/pink		£325	48·00
		a. Printed both sides		†	—
		b. First two characters in last word of bottom line omitted (R. 4/1)	..	—	£425

(b) Laid paper

10c	3	1 a. black/white	..	†	£2750
11	2	1 a. black/azure (1870)	..	70·00	8·00
		a. Final character in both top and bottom lines omitted (R. 1/1)			
		b. First two characters in last word of bottom line omitted (R. 4/1)	..	—	85·00
		c. Doubly printed	.. ..	†	£600
12	3	1 a. black/azure	..	£160	17·00
		a. Printed both sides	..	†	£700
		b. Final character in bottom line omitted (R. 1/1)	..	—	85·00
		c. Accent omitted from last word in bottom line (R. 5/2, 5/4)	..	—	65·00
		d. Large numeral (R. 4/1)	..	£400	£120
		e. First character in middle line omitted (R. 2/4)	..	—	£190
		f. Central two characters in middle line omitted (R. 2/4)	..	—	£350
13		1 a. red/white (1875)	..	14·00	16·00
		a. First two characters in bottom line omitted (R. 5/1)	..	70·00	90·00
14	4	4 a. black/white	..	£110	£180
		a. Final character in bottom line omitted (R. 1/1)		£375	
15	4	4 a. black/white	..	£190	£350
		a. First two characters in last word of bottom line omitted (R. 4/1)		£750	
		b. Final character in bottom line omitted (R. 5/2)	..	—	£1200

Nos. 10/15 were printed in sheets of 20 (4×5). The same type was used throughout, but changes made to produce the different values resulted in five different settings:

Setting I   Nos. 10, 11, 15
Setting II   Nos. 11/12, 14
Setting III   Nos. 11/12, 14
Setting IV   Nos. 11/12, 15
Setting V   No. 13

The Devanagari (Type 2) and Gujerati (Type 3) numerals were mixed in settings II to IV of the 1 a. value, so that *se-tenant* pairs of Nos. 11/12 exist. Horizontally laid paper was used for setting II; vertically laid for settings I and III to V.
Official imitations, consisting of 1 a. carmine-red on white wove and white laid, 1 a. black on blue wove, 4 a. black on white wove, 4 a. black on blue wove, 4 a. red on white laid—all imperforate; 1 a. carmine-red on white laid, 1 a. black on blue wove, 4 a. black on white laid and blue wove—all perforated 12, were made in 1890. Entire sheets of originals have 20 stamps (4×5), the imitations only 4 or 16.

6   7

(Dies eng John Dickinson & Co Ltd, London. Typo Junagadh Sarkari Saurashtra Nitiprakash Ptg Press)

1877. *Imperf.*

(a) Medium laid paper, lines wide apart
(b) Thick laid paper, lines wide apart
(c) Thick laid paper, lines close together

16	6	1 a. green (a)	..	40	30
17		1 a. green (b)	..	40	30
18		1 a. green (c)	..	40	30
		a. Printed both sides	..	£425	
19	7	4 a. vermilion (a)	..	1·40	1·00
20		4 a. vermilion/toned (b)	..	1·40	1·00
		a. Printed both sides		£450	
21		4 a. scarlet/bluish (b)	..	2·00	1·50

Nawab Bahadur Khan III, 1882–1892

1886. *P* 12. *(a) Wove paper.*

22	6	1 a. green	..	1·25	65
		a. Imperf (pair)	..	48·00	65·00
		b. Error. Blue	..	—	£600
		c. Imperf horiz (vert pair)	..	95·00	
23	7	4 a. red	..	3·50	6·50
		a. Imperf (pair)	..	£120	£150

(b) Toned laid paper

24	6	1 a. green	..	15	15
		a. Imperf vert (horiz pair)	..	85·00	
		b. Doubly printed	..	†	£325
25		1 a. emerald-green	..	2·00	1·25
		a. Error. Blue	..	£600	£600
26	7	4 a. red	..	1·25	60
27		4 a. carmine	..	2·00	1·60

(c) *Bluish white laid paper*

28	6	1 a. green	..	2·00	3·00
		a. Imperf between (pair)	..	£130	
29		4 a. scarlet	..	6·50	10·00

There is a very wide range of colours in both values. The laid paper is found both vertical and horizontal.

The 1 a. was originally issued in sheets of 15 (5×3), but later appeared in sheets of 20 (5×4) with marginal inscriptions. No. 22a is known as a double sheet showing two impressions of the plate printed *tête-bêche* on opposite sides of the paper.

The 4 a. was in horizontal strips of 5. No. 19 exists as a sheet of 10 (5×2), with two impressions of the plate printed *tête-bêche*, and No. 23 in a similar sized sheet but with both impressions upright.

**Nawab Rasul Khan 1892–1911
Nawab Mahabat Khan III, 1911–1959**

(Indian currency)

Three pies.
ત્રણ પાઇ.

One anna.
એક આનો.

(8)   (9)

1913. *Surch in Indian currency with* T **8** *or* **9.** P 12.

(a) On yellowish wove paper

34	6	3 p. on 1 a. emerald	..	15	20
		a. Imperf (pair)	..	£275	
		b. Imperf between (horiz pair)	..	£225	

(b) On white wove paper

35	6	3 p. on 1 a. emerald	..	15	20
		a. Imperf between (pair)	..	£225	£225
		b. Surch inverted	..	35·00	20·00
		c. Surch double	..	†	
36	7	1 a. on 4 a. carmine	..	1·50	3·75
		a. Imperf (pair)	..		
		b. Surch both sides	..	£650	
		c. Capital "A" in "Anna"	..	12·00	

(c) On white laid paper

37	6	3 p. on 1 a. emerald	..	75·00	30·00
		a. Imperf (pair)	..	£275	
		b. Larger surch (21 mm long with capital "p" in "Pies") inverted	..	† £1100	
38	7	1 a. on 4 a. red	..	7·00	35·00
		a. Capital "A" in "Anna"	..	£160	
		b. Surch inverted	..	£600	
		c. Surch double	..	£600	
		d. Surch double, one inverted	..	£600	

(d) On toned wove paper

39	7	1 a. on 4 a. red	..	1·25	3·50
		a. Imperf (pair)	..	£550	
		b. Capital "A" in "Anna"	..	6·00	
		c. Surch inverted	..	£600	
		d. Imperf between (horiz pair)	..		

10   11

(Dies eng Thacker & Co, Bombay. Typo Junagadh State Press)

1914 (1 Sept). *New plates.* T **6/7** *redrawn as* T **10/11.** *Wove paper.* P 12.

40	10	3 p. bright green	..	35	35
		a. Imperf (pair)	..	3·75	11·00
		b. Imperf vert (horiz pair)	..	60·00	
		c. Laid paper	..	2·50	1·50
		ca. Imperf (pair)	..	10·00	17·00
41	11	1 a. red	..	60	85
		a. Imperf (pair)	..	16·00	50·00
		b. Imperf between (pair)	..	£325	
		c. Laid paper	..	£225	80·00

12 Nawab Mahabat Khan III 13

(Dies eng Popatlal Bhimji Pandya. Typo Junagadh State Press)

1923 (1 Sept). *Blurred impression. Laid paper. Pin-perf* 12.

42	12	1 a. red	..	3·00	7·00

Sheets of 16 stamps (8 × 2).

ત્રણ પાઇ   ત્રણ પાઈ

(14)   (14a)

1923 (1 Sept). *Surch with* T **14.**

43	12	3 p. on 1 a. red	..	3·00	7·00
		a. Surch with T **14a**	..	3·50	9·00

Four stamps in the setting have surch. T **14a**, i.e. with top of last character curved to right.

1923 (Oct). *Blurred impression. Wove paper. Pin-perf* 12, *small holes.*

44	13	3 p. mauve	..	35	40

1924. *Clear impression.* P 12, *large holes. Wove paper.*

45	13	3 p. mauve (1.24)	..	60	35
46	12	1 a. red (4.24)	..	4·00	4·75
		a. Imperf (pair)	..	38·00	
		b. Pin perf	..	2·00	2·75

The first plate of the 3 p., which printed No. 44, produced unsatisfactory impressions, so it was replaced by a second plate, from which No. 45 comes. Sheets printed from the first plate had very large margins.

The 1 a. is also from a new plate, giving a clearer impression. Sheets of 16 stamps (4 × 4).

1929. *Clear impression.* P 12, *large holes. Laid paper.*

47	13	3 p. mauve	..	3·00	2·25
		a. Imperf (pair)	..	3·00	18·00
		b. Perf 11	..	4·00	3·50
		ba. Imperf between (horiz pair).	..	3·00	15·00

The laid paper shows a sheet watermark of the State Arms within a circular inscription.

15 Junagadh City

16 Lion   17 Nawab
Mahabat Khan III

18 Kathi Horse

(Litho Indian Security Printing Press, Nasik)

1929 (1 Oct). P 14. *Inscr* "POSTAGE".

49	15	3 p. black and blackish green	..	50	10
50	16	½ a. black and deep blue	..	4·50	10
51	17	1 a. black and carmine	..	3·00	85
52	18	2 a. black and dull orange	..	8·00	1·75
		a. Grey and dull yellow	..	25·00	1·75
53	15	3 a. black and carmine	..	2·50	5·00
54	16	4 a. black and purple	..	11·00	16·00
55	18	8 a. black and yellow-green	..	10·00	17·00
56	17	1 r. black and pale blue. .	..	3·25	17·00
49/56	..	..	*Set of* 8	38·00	50·00

1936. *As* T **17,** *but inscr* "POSTAGE AND REVENUE". P 14.

57	17	1 a. black and carmine	..	3·75	90

OFFICIAL STAMPS

SARKARI

(O 1)

1929 (1 Oct). *Optd with Type* O 1, *in vermilion, at Nasik.*

O1	15	3 p. black and blackish green	..	80	10
		a. Red opt	..	60	10
O2	16	½ a. black and deep blue	..	1·40	10
		a. Red opt	..	2·25	30
O3	17	1 a. black and carmine (No. 51).	..	1·90	30
		a. Red opt	..	1·25	15
O4	18	2 a. black and dull orange	..	2·25	50
		a. Grey and dull yellow	..	15·00	60
		b. Red opt	..	20·00	2·00
O5	15	3 a. black and carmine	..	60	30
		a. Red opt	..	13·00	1·50
O6	16	4 a. black and purple	..	1·75	40
		a. Red opt	..	16·00	1·75
O7	18	8 a. black and yellow-green	..	1·75	1·25
O8	17	1 r. black and pale blue. .	..	2·25	12·00
O1/8	..	..	*Set of* 8	10·50	13·00

SARKARI   SARKARI
(O 2)   (O 3)

1932. *Optd with Types* O 2 (3 a., 1 r.) *or* O 3 (*others*), *all in red, at Junagadh State Press.*

O 9	15	3 a. black and carmine	..	65·00	7·00
		a. Optd with Type O 3	..	15·00	12·00
O10	16	4 a. black and purple	..	22·00	15·00
O11	18	8 a. black and yellow-green	..	24·00	17·00
O12	17	1 r. black and pale blue. .	..	85·00	85·00
		a. Optd with Type O 3	..	20·00	50·00

1938. *No. 57 optd with Type* O 1, *in vermilion.*

O13	17	1 a. black and carmine	..	9·50	1·50
		a. Brown-red opt	..	7·50	1·25

The state was occupied by Indian troops on 9 November 1947 following the flight of the Nawab to Pakistan.

UNITED STATE OF SAURASHTRA

The administration of Junagadh state was assumed by the Government of India on 7 November 1947. An Executive Council took office on 1 June 1948.

Under the new Constitution of India the United State of Saurashtra was formed on 15 February 1948, comprising 221 former states and estates of Kathiawar, including Jasdan, Morvi, Nawanagar and Wadhwan, but excluding Junagadh. A referendum was held by the Executive Council of Junagadh which then joined the United State on 20 January 1949. It is believed that the following issues were only used in Junagadh.

The following issues were surcharged at the Junagadh State Press.

POSTAGE & REVENUE

ONE ANNA

(19)

Postage & Revenue

ONE ANNA

(20)

1949. *Stamps of* 1929 *surch.* (a) *With* T **19** *in red.*

58	16	1 a. on ½ a. black and deep blue (6.49)		7·50	4·00
		a. Surch double	..	†	£375
		b. "AFNA" for "ANNA" and inverted "N" in "REVENUE"	..	£1400	
		c. Larger first "A" in "ANNA"	..	80·00	60·00

(b) With T **20** *in green*

59	18	1 a. on 2 a. grey and dull yellow (2.49)		8·50	18·00
		a. "evenue" omitted	..	—	£375

No. 58c occurs on position 10.

A number of other varieties occur on No. 58, including: small "V" in "REVENUE" (No. 8); small "N" in "REVENUE" (Nos. 9, 13 and 14); small "E" in "POSTAGE" (No. 12); thick "A" in "POSTAGE" (No. 19); inverted "N" in "REVENUE" and small second "A" in "ANNA" (No. 25); small "O" in "ONE" (No. 26); small "V" and "U" in "REVENUE" (No. 28); small "N" in "ONE" (No. 37).

In No. 59 no stop after "ANNA" is known on Nos. 4, 17, 25, 34 and 38 and small "N" in "ONE" on Nos. 9, 11, 26 and 31.

21

(Typo Waterlow)

1949 (Sept). *Court Fee stamps of Bhavnagar state optd* "SAURASHTRA" *and further optd* "U.S.S. REVENUE & POSTAGE" *as in* T **21,** *in black. Typo.* P 11.

60	21	1 a. purple	..	7·00	7·50
		a. "POSTAGE" omitted	..	£200	£180
		b. Opt double	..	£250	£300

Minor varieties include small "S" in "POSTAGE" (Nos. 9 and 49); small "N" in "REVENUE" (Nos. 15 and 55); small "U" in "REVENUE" (Nos. 18 and 58); small "V" in "REVENUE" (Nos. 24, 37, 64 and 77); and small "O" in "POSTAGE" (Nos. 31 and 71). Various missing stop varieties also occur.

POSTAGE & REVENUE
ONE ANNA

(22)

1950 (Mar). *Stamp of* 1929 *surch with* T **22.**

61	15	1 a. on 3 p. black and blackish green	..	45·00	48·00
		a. "P" of "POSTAGE" omitted	..	£425	£425
		b. "O" of "ONE" omitted	..	£500	

Other minor varieties include small "S" in "POSTAGE" with small "V" in "REVENUE" (Nos. 14 and 26) and small "V" in "REVENUE" (No. 11).

OFFICIAL STAMPS

1948 (July–Dec). *Nos.* O4/O7 *surch* "ONE ANNA" (2¼ *mm high*) *by Junagadh State Press.*

O14	18	1 a. on 2 a. grey & dull yellow (B.)	..	£3750	19·00
O15	15	1 a. on 3 a. black and carmine (Aug)	..	£1700	42·00
		a. Surch double	..	†	£1400
O16	16	1 a. on 4 a. black and purple (Dec)	..	£275	35·00
		a. "ANNE" for "ANNA" (R. 5/4)	..	£2000	£350
		b. "ANNN" for "ANNA" (R. 7/5)	..	£2000	£350
O17	18	1 a. on 8 a. black & yellow-green (Dec)	..	£250	28·00
		a. "ANNE" for "ANNA" (R. 5/4)	..	£2000	£275
		b. "ANNN" for "ANNA" (R. 7/5)	..	£2000	£275

Numerous minor varieties of fount occur in this surcharge.

1948 (Nov). *Handstamped "ONE ANNA"* (*4 mm high*).
O18	17	1 a. on 1 r. (No. O8)	£800	27·00
O19		1 a. on 1 r. (No. O12a)	£300	32·00
		a. Optd on No. O12	—	50·00

A used copy of No. O12a is known surcharged in black as on Nos. O14/17. This may have come from a proof sheet.

1949 (Jan). *Postage stamps optd with Type O 3, in red*.
O20	15	3 p. black and blackish green ..	£225	9·50
O21	16	½ a. black and deep blue	£500	9·00
O22	18	1 a. on 2 a. grey and dull yellow (No. 59)	55·00	18·00

Various wrong fount letters occur in the above surcharges.

MANUSCRIPT OVERPRINTS. Nos. 49, 50, 57, 58, 59 and 60 are known with manuscript overprints reading "Service" or 'SARKARI" (in English or Gujerati script), usually in red. Such provisionals were used at Gadhda and Una between June and December 1949 (*Price from* £80 *each, used on piece*).

The United State of Saurashtra postal service was incorporated into that of India on 31 March 1950. The use of Soruth stamps was permitted until the end of April.

TRAVANCORE

PRICES FOR STAMPS ON COVER	
Nos. 1/77	*from* × 10
Nos. O1/108	*from* × 15

(16 cash = 1 chuckram; 28 chuckrams = 1 rupee)

"Anchel" or "Anchal" = Post Office Department.

The stamps of Travancore were valid on mail posted to Cochin.

PRINTERS. All stamps of Travancore were printed by the Stamp Manufactory, Trivandrum, *unless otherwise stated*.

PRINTING METHODS. The dies were engraved on brass from which electrotypes were made and locked together in a forme for printing the stamps. As individual electrotypes became worn they were replaced by new ones and their positions in the forme were sometimes changed. This makes it difficult to plate the early issues. From 1901 plates were made which are characterised by a frame (or "Jubilee" line) round the margins of the sheets.

Up to the 6 cash of 1910 the dies were engraved by Dharmalingham Asari.

SHADES. We list only the main groups of shades but there are many others in view of the large number of printings and the use of fugitive inks. Sometimes shade variation is noticeable within the same sheet.

Maharaja Rama Varma X, 1885–1924

1 Conch or Chank Shell

1888 (16 Oct). *As T 1, but each value differs slightly. Laid paper. P* 12.
1	1	1 ch. ultramarine (*shades*) ..	2·75	2·00
2		2 ch. red	3·00	7·50
3		4 ch. green	12·00	10·00
1/3		Set of 3	16·00	18·00

The paper bears a large sheet watermark showing a large conch shell surmounted by "GOVERNMENT" in large outline letters, in an arch with "OF TRAVANCORE" at foot in a straight line. Many stamps on laid paper are without watermark.

These stamps on laid paper in abnormal colours are proofs.

2

A   B   C

Three forms of watermark Type 2.
(*as seen from the back of the stamp*)

WATERMARKS AND PAPERS.
Type A appeared upright on early printings of the 1, 2 and 4 ch. values on odd-sized sheets which did not fit the number of shells. Later it was always sideways with 15 mm between the shells on standard-sized sheets of 84 (14 × 6) containing 60 shells (10 × 6). It therefore never appears centred on the stamps and it occurs on hand-made papers only.

Type B is similar in shape but can easily be distinguished as it is invariably upright, with 11 mm between the shells, and is well centred on the stamps. It also occurs only on handmade papers. It was introduced in 1904 and from 1914, when Type A was brought back into use, it was employed concurrently until 1924.

Type C is quite different in shape and occurs on machine-made papers. There are two versions. The first, in use from 1924 to 1939, has 84 shells 11 mm apart and is always upright and well centred. The second, introduced in 1929 and believed not to have been used after 1930, has 60 shells (12 × 5) 15 mm apart and is invariably badly centred so that some stamps in the sheet are without watermark. This second version is normally found upright, but a few sideways watermark varieties are known and listed as Nos. 35g, 37c, O31j and O32i. We do not distinguish between the two versions of Type C in the lists, but stamps known to exist in the second version are indicated in footnotes. The machine-made paper is generally smoother and of more even texture.

NO WATERMARK VARIETIES. Some of these were formerly listed but we have now decided to omit them as they do not occur in full sheets. They arise in the following circumstances: (*a*) on sheets with wmk A; (*b*) on sheets with the wide-spaced form of wmk C; and (*c*) on late printings of the pictorial issues of 1939–46. They are best collected in pairs, with and without watermark.

DATES OF ISSUE. In the absence of more definite information the dates quoted usually refer to the first reported date of new printings on different watermarks but many were not noted at the time and the dates of these are indicated by a query. Dated postmarks on single stamps are difficult to find.

3   4   5

6   7   8

1889–1904. *Wove paper. Wmk A* (*upright or sideways*). *P* 12 (*sometimes rough*).
4	1	½ ch. slate-lilac (1894)	1·75	40
		a. Doubly printed	†	£170
		b. Reddish lilac	50	15
		ba. Imperf between (vert pair)	£170	£170
		bb. Doubly printed	†	£170
		c. Purple (1899)	90	15
		ca. Doubly printed	†	£170
		d. Dull purple (1904)	1·10	15
5	5	¾ ch. black (14.3.01)	2·00	60
6	1	1 ch. ultramarine	1·10	15
		a. Tête-bêche (pair)	£2000	£2000
		b. Doubly printed	†	£275
		c. Imperf vert (horiz pair) ..	†	£300
		d. Pale ultramarine (1892) ..	2·00	15
		e. Violet-blue (1901)	2·50	35
7		2 ch. salmon (1890)	3·50	75
		a. Rose (1891)	2·75	30
		ab. Imperf (pair)	†	£300
		b. Pale pink (1899)	2·25	35
		ba. Imperf between (vert pair)	£120	
		bb. Doubly printed	£190	
		c. Red (1904)	2·25	15
		ca. Imperf between (horiz pair)	†	£200
8		4 ch. green	2·50	60
		a. Yellow-green (1901)	1·75	40
		b. Dull green (1904)	5·00	85
		ba. Doubly printed	†	£275

Nos. 6, 6*d*, 7 and 8 occur with the watermark upright and sideways. No. 7*a* is known only with the watermark upright. The remainder exist only with the watermark sideways.
The sheet sizes were as follows:
½ ch. 56 (14 × 4) except for No. 4*d* which was 84 (14 × 6), initially without border, later with border.
¾ ch. 84 (14 × 6) with border.
1 ch. No. 6, 80 (10 × 8) and later 84 (14 × 6) without border and then with border; No. 6*d*, 96 (16 × 6); No. 6*e*, 84 (14 × 6) with border.
2 ch. No. 7, 80 (10 × 8); No. 7*a*, 70 (10 × 7); Nos. 7*b*, 7*c*, 60 (10 × 6).
4 ch. No. 8, 60 (10 × 6); Nos. 8*a/b*, 84 (14 × 6) with border.
After 1904 all stamps in Types 3 to 8 were in standard-sized sheets of 84 (14 × 6) with border.
For later printings watermarked Type A, see Nos. 23/30.

1904–20. *Wmk B, upright* (*centred*). *P* 12, *sometimes rough*.
9	3	4 ca. pink (11.08)	15	10
		a. Imperf between (vert pair)	£160	£160
10	1	6 ca. chestnut (2.10)	30	10
		a. Imperf between (horiz pair)	†	£160
11		½ ch. reddish lilac	80	10
		a. Reddish violet (6.10) ..	55	10
		b. Lilac	90	30
		c. "CHUCRRAM" (R. 5/6) ..	4·50	3·25
		d. Imperf horiz (vert pair) ..	†	£110

12	4	10 ca. pink (1920)	22·00	5·00
13	5	¾ ch. black	90	20
14	1	1 ch. bright blue		
		a. Blue	2·50	30
		b. Deep blue	2·50	30
		c. Indigo (8.10)	55	10
		d. Chalky blue (1912)	3·50	60
15		1¼ ch. claret (*shades*) (10.14)	40	40
		a. Imperf between (horiz pair)	£170	£170
16		2 ch. salmon	17·00	6·00
		a. Red (8.10)	45	10
17	6	3 ch. violet (11.3.11)	2·00	20
		a. Imperf between (vert pair)	£160	£160
		b. Imperf between (vert strip of 3)	†	£225
18	1	4 ch. dull green	8·50	3·25
		a. Slate-green	1·10	35
19	7	7 ch. claret (1916)	1·60	40
		a. Error. Carmine-red	—	50·00
20	8	14 ch. orange-yellow (1916) ..	2·40	1·25
		a. Imperf vert (horiz strip of 3)	£350	

¼

(9)

1 C

(10)

1906. *Surch as T 9. Wmk B.*
21	1	¼ on ½ ch. reddish lilac	30	30
		a. Reddish violet	20	20
		b. Lilac	50	30
		c. "CHUCRRAM" (R.5/6) ..	3·25	3·25
		d. Surch inverted	38·00	26·00
22		⅜ on ½ ch. reddish lilac	20	35
		a. Reddish violet	20	35
		b. Lilac	20	35
		c. "CHUCRRAM" (R.5/6) ..	3·25	3·50
		d. Surch inverted	—	38·00
		e. Surch double	—	40·00
		f. "8" omitted	—	40·00

1914–22. *Reversion to wmk A* (*sideways*). *P* 12 (*sometimes rough*).
23	3	4 ca. pink (1915)	6·50	60
24	4	5 ca. olive-bistre (30.10.21) ..	40	10
		a. Imperf between (horiz pair)	40·00	45·00
		b. Imperf between (horiz strip of 3)	85·00	90·00
		c. "TRAVANCOPE"	—	8·00
25	1	6 ca. orange-brown (2.15) ..	4·50	35
26		½ ch. reddish violet (12.14)	1·90	20
		a. "CHUCRRAM" (R.5/6) ..	8·00	3·25
		b. Imperf between (horiz pair)	£120	
27	4	10 ca. pink (26.10.21)	35	10
28	1	1 ch. grey-blue (5.22)	7·00	1·25
		a. Deep blue	7·00	1·25
29		1¼ ch. claret (12.19)	8·50	30
30	6	3 ch. reddish lilac (8.22) ..	8·50	1·25

1921 (Mar). *Surch as T 10. Wmk A.*
31	3	1 c. on 4 ca. pink	15	15
		a. Surch inverted	17·00	8·50
32	1	5 c. on 1 ch. grey-blue (R.) ..	70	10
		a. Deep blue	70	10
		b. Stamp printed both sides ..	†	£160
		c. Imperf between (vert pair) ..	†	£160
		d. Surch inverted	13·00	7·00
		e. Surch double	35·00	26·00
		f. On wmk B. Deep blue ..	18·00	18·00

ALBINO OVERPRINT VARIETIES. Stamps with overprint double, one albino are frequently found in the provisional and official issues of Travancore, and are only worth a small premium over the normal prices.

Maharaja Bala Rama Varma XI, 1924–1971

1924–39. *Wmk C. Machine-made paper. P* 12.
33	4	5 ca. olive-bistre (18.6.25) ..	9·00	2·00
		a. Imperf between (horiz pair)	£100	
		b. "TRAVANCOPE"	—	8·00
34		5 ca. chocolate (1930)	2·00	20
		a. Imperf between (horiz pair)	32·00	
		b. Imperf between (vert pair)	†	95·00
35	1	6 ca. brown-red (3.24)	4·25	10
		a. Imperf between (horiz pair)	21·00	21·00
		b. Imperf between (vert pair)	75·00	75·00
		c. Printed both sides	50·00	
		d. Perf 12½	4·25	50
		e. Perf comp of 12 and 12½ ..	8·00	4·00
		f. Perf 12½×11	—	65·00
		g. Wmk sideways	—	12·00
36		½ ch. reddish violet (date?) ..	4·25	4·25
		a. "CHUCRRAM" (R. 5/6) ..	30·00	
37	4	10 ca. pink (8.24)	1·50	10
		a. Imperf between (horiz pair)	70·00	70·00
		b. Imperf between (vert pair)	19·00	21·00
		c. Wmk sideways (16.9.28) ..	—	4·50
38	5	¾ ch. black (4.10.32)	8·00	45
39		¾ ch. mauve (16.11.32) ..	35	10
		a. Imperf between (horiz pair)	†	£100
		b. Perf 12½ (8.37)	7·50	70
		ba. Imperf between (horiz pair)	95·00	
		c. Perf comp of 12 and 12½ ..	11·00	4·75
40		¾ ch. reddish violet (1939) ..	2·50	60
		a. Perf 12½	4·50	50
		b. Perf comp of 12 and 12½ ..	7·00	2·00
		c. Perf 11	—	65·00
		d. Perf comp of 12 and 11 ..	—	65·00
41	1	1 ch. slate-blue (8.26)	2·75	20
		a. Indigo	3·75	20
		b. Imperf between (horiz pair)	†	£140
		c. Imperf between (vert pair)	†	£140
		d. Perf 12½	11·00	1·00

42	1	1½ ch. rose (1932)	1·90	10
		a. Imperf between (horiz strip of 3)	£140	
		b. Perf 12½	19·00	2·75
		c. Perf comp of 12 and 12½ ..	—	25·00
43		2 ch. carmine-red (4.6.29) ..	4·50	30
44	6	3 ch. violet (4.25)	5·50	15
		a. Imperf between (vert pair)	80·00	80·00
		b. Perf 12½	—	10·00
		c. Perf comp of 12 and 12½ ..	—	21·00
45	1	4 ch. grey-green (5.4.34) ..	5·50	45
46	7	7 ch. claret (1925)	8·00	1·75
		a. Doubly printed	†	£250
		b. Carmine-red (date?) ..	65·00	55·00
		c. Brown-purple (1932) ..	12·00	3·75
		ca. Perf 12½	8·50	13·00
		cb. Perf comb of 12 and 12½	8·50	13·00
46d	8	14 ch. orange-yellow (date?) ..	50·00	
		da. Perf 12½	£160	

It is believed that the 12½ perforation and the perf 12 and 12½ compound were introduced in 1937 and that the 11 perforation came later, probably in 1939.

The 5 ca. chocolate, 6 ca., 10 ca. and 3 ch. also exist on the wide-spaced watermark (60 shells to the sheet of 84).

11 Sri Padmanabha Shrine

12 State Chariot   13 Maharaja Bala Rama Varma XI

(Des M. R. Madhawan Unnithan. Plates by Calcutta Chromotype Co. Typo Stamp Manufactory, Trivandrum)

1931 (6 Nov). *Coronation. Cream or white paper. Wmk C. P 11½, 12.*

47	11	6 ca. black and green ..	70	70
		a. Imperf between (horiz pair) ..	£180	£200
48	12	10 ca. black and ultramarine	65	30
		a. Imperf between (vert pair) ..	†	£300
49	13	3 ch. black and purple ..	1·50	1·50
47/9		.. .. Set of 3	2·50	2·25

1 c 1 C

(14)   (15)   16 Maharaja Bala Rama Varma XI and Subramania Shrine

1932 (14 Jan). (i) *Surch as T 14. (a) Wmk A (sideways).*

50	1	1 c. on 1¼ ch. claret ..	15	45
		a. Imperf between (horiz pair)	75·00	
		b. Surch inverted ..	4·25	6·00
		c. Surch double ..	25·00	25·00
		d. Pair, one without surch ..	75·00	85·00
		e. "c" omitted ..	45·00	45·00
51		2 c. on 1¼ ch. claret ..	15	15
		a. Surch inverted ..	4·25	6·50
		b. Surch double ..	25·00	
		c. Surch double, one inverted ..	55·00	
		d. Surch treble ..	60·00	
		e. Surch treble, one inverted ..	70·00	70·00
		f. Pair, one without surch ..	80·00	80·00
		g. "2" omitted ..	45·00	45·00
		h. "c" omitted ..	45·00	45·00
		i. Imperf between (horiz pair)	75·00	
		j. Imperf between (vert pair)	80·00	

(b) Wmk B (upright)

52	1	1 c. on 1¼ ch. claret ..	75	75
		a. Surch inverted ..	18·00	
		b. Surch double ..	32·00	
53		2 c. on 1¼ ch. claret ..	5·00	5·00
		a. Imperf between (horiz pair)	95·00	

(c) Wmk C

54	1	1 c. on 1¼ ch. claret ..	11·00	12·00
		a. Surch inverted ..	42·00	42·00
55		2 c. on 1¼ ch. claret ..	16·00	12·00

(ii) Surch as T 10. Wmk B

56	1	2 c. on 1¼ ch. claret ..	3·75	12·00

1932 (5 Mar). *Surch as T 15. Wmk C.*

57	4	1 c. on 5 ca. chocolate ..	15	15
		a. Imperf between (horiz pair)	90·00	
		b. Surch inverted ..	7·50	10·00
		c. Surch inverted on back only	45·00	
		d. Pair, one without surch ..	75·00	
		e. "1" omitted ..	38·00	
		f. "C" omitted ..	—	38·00
		g. "TRAVANCOPE" ..	8·50	
58		1 c. on 6 ca. slate-purple ..	80	15
		a. Surch inverted ..	†	£140
		b. "1" inverted ..	60·00	60·00
59		2 c. on 10 ca. pink ..	15	15
		a. Imperf between (horiz pair)	80·00	
		b. Surch inverted ..	5·00	7·00
		c. Surch double ..	17·00	19·00
		d. Surch double, one inverted ..	45·00	45·00
		e. Surch double, both inverted	32·00	

No. 58 was not issued without the surcharge.

(Plates by Indian Security Printing Press, Nasik. Typo Stamp Manufactory, Trivandrum)

1937 (29 Mar). *Temple Entry Proclamation. T 16 and similar horiz designs. Wmk C. P 12.*

60		6 ca. carmine	40	60
		a. Imperf between (horiz strip of 3)	£350	
		b. Perf 12½	1·10	1·50
		c. Compound perf ..	22·00	22·00
61		12 ca. bright blue	1·10	20
		a. Perf 12½	1·50	60
		ab. Imperf between (vert pair)	£325	
		b. Compound perf ..	32·00	
62		1½ ch. yellow-green ..	75	50
		a. Imperf between (vert pair)	£250	
		b. Perf 12½	18·00	4·50
		c. Compound perf		
63		3 ch. violet	2·25	1·10
		a. Perf 12½	3·00	1·75
60/3		.. .. Set of 4	4·00	2·10

Designs:—Maharaja's portrait and temples—12 ca. Sri Padmanabha; 1½ ch. Mahadeva; 3 ch. Kanyakumari.

COMPOUND PERFS. This term covers stamps perf compound of 12½ and 11, 12 and 11 or 12 and 12½, and where two or more combinations exist the prices are for the commonest. Such compounds can occur on values which do not exist perf 12 all round.

17 Lake Ashtamudi   18 Maharaja Bala Rama Varma XI

(Des Nilakantha Pellai. Plates by Indian Security Printing Press, Nasik. Typo Stamp Manufactory, Trivandrum)

1939 (9 Nov). *Maharaja's 27th Birthday. T 17/18 and similar designs. Wmk C. P 12½.*

64		1 ch. yellow-green	2·75	10
		a. Imperf between (horiz pair) ..	20·00	
		b. Perf 11	6·50	10
		ba. Imperf between (vert pair)	21·00	28·00
		bb. Imperf between (vert strip of 3)	20·00	30·00
		c. Perf 12	11·00	75
		ca. Imperf between (horiz pair)	20·00	
		cb. Imperf between (vert pair)	22·00	
		d. Compound perf ..	14·00	1·50
		da. Imperf between (vert pair)	75·00	
65		1½ ch. scarlet	1·10	1·40
		a. Doubly printed ..	£160	
		b. Imperf between (horiz pair)	25·00	
		c. Imperf between (vert pair)	20·00	
		d. Perf 11	3·00	15·00
		da. Imperf horiz (vert pair)	8·00	
		e. Perf 12	20·00	2·50
		f. Perf 13½	12·00	42·00
		g. Compound perf ..	27·00	3·75
		h. Imperf (pair) ..	30·00	
66		2 ch. orange	3·25	50
		a. Perf 11	12·00	30
		b. Perf 12	55·00	3·75
		c. Compound perf ..	55·00	4·00
67		3 ch. brown	4·25	10
		a. Doubly printed ..	—	85·00
		b. Imperf between (horiz pair)	32·00	40·00
		c. Perf 11	13·00	30
		ca. Doubly printed ..	38·00	42·00
		d. Perf 12	27·00	2·00
		da. Imperf between (vert pair)	90·00	90·00
		e. Compound perf ..	18·00	1·00
68		4 ch. red	3·25	40
		a. Perf 11	20·00	50
		b. Perf 12	18·00	4·25
		c. Compound perf ..	85·00	70·00
69		7 ch. pale blue	5·00	10·00
		a. Perf 11	45·00	19·00
		ab. Blue	45·00	16·00
		b. Compound perf ..	55·00	22·00
70		14 ch. turquoise-green ..	5·00	32·00
		a. Perf 11	6·00	55·00
64/70		.. .. Set of 7	22·00	40·00

Designs: *Vert as T 18*—1½ ch., 3 ch. Portraits of Maharaja in different frames. *Horiz as T 17*—4 ch. Sri Padmanabha Shrine; 7 ch. Cape Comorin; 14 ch. Pachipari Reservoir.

19 Maharaja and Aruvikara Falls   2 CASH (20)

(Des Nilakantha Pellai. Plates by Indian Security Printing Press, Nasik. Typo Stamp Manufactory, Trivandrum)

1941 (20 Oct). *Maharaja's 29th Birthday. T 19 and similar horiz design. Wmk C. P 12½.*

71		6 ca. blackish violet	3·75	10
		a. Perf 11	4·00	10
		ab. Imperf between (vert pair)	20·00	
		ac. Imperf horiz (vert pair) ..	28·00	40·00
		b. Perf 12	13·00	1·00
		ba. Imperf between (horiz pair)	21·00	
		bb. Imperf between (vert pair)	29·00	
		bc. Imperf between (vert strip of 3) ..	21·00	
		c. Compound perf ..	4·00	80

72		¾ ch. brown	3·75	15
		a. Perf 11	5·50	15
		ab. Imperf between (horiz pair)	85·00	
		ac. Imperf between (vert pair)	22·00	30·00
		ad. Imperf between (vert strip of 3)	21·00	
		ae. Block of four imperf between (horiz and vert)	£110	
		b. Perf 12	30·00	5·50
		c. Compound perf ..	7·50	1·10

Design:—¾ ch. Maharaja and Marthanda Varma Bridge, Alwaye.

1943 (17 Sept). *Nos. 65, 71 (colour changed) and 72 surch as T 20. P 12½.*

73		2 ca. on 1½ ch. scarlet..	85	30
		a. Imperf between (vert pair)	30·00	
		b. "2" omitted	£160	£160
		c. "CA" omitted ..	£225	
		d. "ASH" omitted ..	£225	
		e. Perf 11	30	20
		ea. "CA" omitted ..	£225	
		f. Compound perf ..	55	85
		fa. Imperf between (vert pair)	85·00	
		fb. "2" omitted ..	£160	
74		4 ca. on ¾ ch. brown ..	2·25	80
		a. Perf 11	2·50	20
		b. Perf 12	—	80·00
		c. Compound perf ..	3·25	1·00
75		8 ca. on 6 ca. scarlet ..	3·00	10
		a. Perf 11	1·75	10
		ab. Imperf between (horiz pair)	28·00	
		b. Perf 12	—	55·00
		c. Compound perf ..	9·00	4·50
73/5		.. .. Set of 3	3·75	45

21 Maharaja Bala Rama Varma XI   SPECIAL (22)

(Des Nilakantha Pellai. Plates by Indian Security Printing Press, Nasik. Typo Stamp Manufactory, Trivandrum)

1946 (24 Oct). *Maharaja's 34th Birthday. Wmk C. P 12½.*

76	21	8 ca. carmine	15·00	2·50
		a. Perf 11	65	75
		b. Perf 12	24·00	2·50
		ba. Imperf between (horiz pair)	30·00	40·00
		bb. Imperf between (horiz strip of 3)	45·00	
		c. Compound perf ..		

1946. *No. O103 revalidated for ordinary postage with opt T 22, in orange. P 12½.*

77	19	6 ca. blackish violet ..	6·00	1·75
		a. Perf 11	25·00	4·50
		b. Compound perf ..	6·00	4·50

OFFICIAL STAMPS

GUM. Soon after 1911 the Official stamps were issued without gum. Thus only the initial printings of the 1, 2 and 4 ch. values were gummed. As Nos. O38/9, O41/2 and O95 were overprinted on stamps intended for normal postage these, also, have gum.

PRINTINGS. Sometimes special printings of postage stamps were made specifically for overprinting for Official use, thus accounting for Official stamps appearing with watermarks or in shades not listed in the postage issues.

SETTINGS. These are based on the study of complete sheets of 84, and the measurements given are those of the majority of stamps on the sheet. Examples are known showing different measurements as each overprint was set individually in loose type, but these are not included in the listings.

On   On

S S S S

(O 1)   (O 2)

Rounded "O"

1911 (16 Aug)–26. *Contemporary stamps optd with Type O 1 (13 mm wide). P 12, sometimes rough. (a) Wmk B (upright) (16.8.11–21).*

O 1	3	4 ca. pink (1916) ..	20	10
		a. Opt inverted ..	†	55·00
		b. Opt double ..	85·00	65·00
		c. "S S" inverted ..	22·00	12·00
		d. Imperf (pair) ..	£160	£160
		e. Stamp doubly printed..	†	£160
O 2	1	6 ca. chestnut (date ?) ..	28·00	28·00
O 3		½ ch. reddish lilac (R.) (1919)	70	35
		a. "CHUCRRAM" (R.5/6) ..	7·50	4·50
O 4	4	10 ca. pink (1921) ..	11·00	2·50
		a. "O" inverted ..	28·00	8·00
		b. Left "S" inverted ..	28·00	8·00
		c. Right "S" inverted ..	28·00	8·00
		d. Opt inverted ..	†	80·00
O 5	1	1 ch. chalky blue (R.) ..	50	10
		a. Imperf between (vert pair)	†	£140
		b. Opt inverted ..	7·00	4·25
		c. Opt double ..	60·00	50·00
		d. "nO" for "On" ..	75·00	75·00
		e. "O" inverted ..	6·00	1·90
		f. Left "S" inverted ..	6·00	1·90
		g. Right "S" inverted ..	6·00	1·90
		h. "S S" inverted ..	—	32·00

O 6 1 2 ch. red 35 10
   a. Opt inverted .. .. .. 8·00 8·00
   b. "O" inverted .. .. .. 7·00 1·25
   c. Left "S" inverted .. .. 5·50 1·10
   d. Right "S" inverted .. .. 7·50 1·40
O 7   2 ch. red (B.) (date ?) .. .. — 70·00
O 8 6 3 ch. violet 30 10
   a. Imperf between (vert pair) £120 £120
   b. Imperf vert (horiz pair) .. £100
   c. Opt inverted .. .. 10·00 10·00
   d. Opt double .. .. 60·00 60·00
   e. Right "S" inverted .. 4·50 1·00
   f. Right "S" omitted .. 75·00 75·00
   g. Left "S" omitted .. 75·00 75·00
O 9   3 ch. violet (B.) (date ?) .. 90·00 48·00
O10 1 4 ch. slate-green 55 10
   a. Imperf between (pair) .. £140 £140
   b. Opt inverted .. .. 32·00 11·00
   c. Opt double .. .. 80·00 80·00
   d. "O" inverted .. .. 8·00 2·40
   e. Left "S" inverted .. .. 7·00 2·40
   f. Right "S" inverted .. .. 8·00 2·75
   g. Left "S" omitted .. 75·00 75·00
O11   4 ch. slate-green (B.) (1921) — 38·00
   a. "O" inverted .. .. — 85·00
   b. Left "S" inverted .. .. — 85·00
   c. Right "S" inverted .. .. — 85·00

(b) Wmk A (sideways) (1919–25)

O12 3 4 ca. pink .. .. .. 3·50 15
   a. Imperf (pair) £180 £180
   b. Opt inverted .. .. 42·00 15·00
   c. "O" inverted .. .. 24·00 7·00
   d. Left "S" inverted .. .. 24·00 7·00
   e. Right "S" inverted .. 24·00 7·00
O13   4 ca. pink (B.) (1921) .. 28·00 75
   a. "O" inverted .. .. — 17·00
O14 4 5 ca. olive-bistre (1921) .. 40 10
   a. Opt inverted .. .. 11·00 8·50
   b. "O" inverted .. .. 3·75 1·25
   c. Left "S" inverted .. .. 3·75 1·25
   d. Right "S" inverted .. 3·75 1·25
O15 1 6 ca. orange-brown (1921) .. 30 10
   a. Imperf between (vert pair) † £130
   b. Opt inverted .. .. 10·00 8·00
   c. Opt double .. .. 50·00 50·00
   d. "O" inverted .. .. 4·75 1·00
   e. Left "S" inverted .. .. 4·75 1·00
   f. Right "S" inverted .. 4·75 1·25
O16   6 ca. orange-brown (B.) (1921) 8·00 1·25
   a. Opt inverted .. .. 85·00 85·00
   b. "O" inverted .. .. 38·00 13·00
   c. Left "S" inverted .. .. 38·00 13·00
   d. Right "S" inverted .. 38·00 13·00
O17   ½ ch. reddish violet (R.) (date?) 75 10
   a. Reddish lilac (date?) .. 75 10
   b. Imperf between (horiz pair) 90·00 90·00
   c. Imperf between (vert pair) 45·00 45·00
   d. Stamp doubly printed .. 48·00
   e. Opt inverted .. .. 9·00 3·00
   f. Opt double, both inverted 90·00
   g. "CHUCRRAM" (R. 5/6) .. 5·00 2·75
   h. "On" omitted .. .. — 85·00
   i. Right "S" inverted .. — 19·00
   j. Right "S" omitted .. — 85·00
O18 4 10 ca. pink (3.21) 45 10
   a. Scarlet (1925?) .. .. — 9·50
   b. Opt inverted .. .. — 15·00
   c. Opt double .. .. 70·00 55·00
   d. "O" inverted .. .. 6·00 2·00
   e. Left "S" inverted .. .. 5·50 1·50
   f. Right "S" inverted .. 6·00 2·00
   g. Imperf between (horiz pair) — 95·00
O19   10 ca. pink (B.) (date?) .. 45·00 10·00
   a. Opt inverted .. .. — 60·00
   b. "O" inverted .. .. — 32·00
O20 1 1 ch. grey-blue (R.) (date?) .. 3·25 60
   a. Deep blue .. .. 3·50 80
   b. "O" inverted .. .. 24·00 7·00
   c. Left "S" inverted .. .. 24·00 7·50
   d. "On" omitted .. .. † 38·00
O21 1 1¼ ch. claret (12.19) .. 40 10
   ca. Stamp doubly printed .. — £170
   b. Opt inverted .. .. 9·00 8·00
   c. Opt double .. .. 45·00
   d. "O" inverted .. .. 9·00 2·00
   e. Left "S" inverted .. .. 10·00 2·50
   f. Right "S" inverted .. 10·00 2·50
   g. Error. Carmine .. .. 50·00
O22   1¼ ch. claret (B.) (1921) .. — 48·00
   a. "O" inverted .. .. — £100
   b. Left "S" inverted .. .. — £100
   c. Right "S" inverted .. — £100

(c) Wmk C (1925–30)

O23 4 5 ca. olive-bistre (1926) .. 40 30
   a. Imperf between (horiz pair) £130 £130
   b. Opt inverted .. .. 13·00 11·00
   c. "O" inverted .. .. 4·00 2·00
   d. Left "S" inverted .. .. 4·00 2·00
   e. Right "S" inverted .. 4·00 2·00
O23f   5 ca. chocolate (1930) .. 45·00
   fa. Opt inverted .. .. — £100
O24   10 ca. pink (1926) .. .. 3·00 15
   a. Imperf between (vert pair) — £120
   b. Opt inverted .. .. 48·00 48·00
   c. "O" inverted .. .. 17·00 2·00
   d. Left "S" inverted .. .. 17·00 2·25
   e. Right "S" inverted .. 17·00 2·25
   f. Stamp doubly printed ..
   g. Opt double .. .. † 75·00
O25 1 1¼ ch. claret (1926) .. 9·50 40
   a. "O" inverted .. .. 30·00 3·00
   b. Left "S" inverted .. .. 35·00 4·50
   c. Right "S" inverted .. 35·00 4·50
   d. Opt double .. .. † 75·00
O26 7 7 ch. claret .. .. 1·50 30
   a. "O" inverted .. .. 13·00 3·00
   b. Left "S" inverted .. .. 13·00 3·00
   c. Right "S" inverted .. 13·00 3·00
   d. Error. Carmine-red .. 60·00

O27 8 14 ch. orange-yellow .. .. 1·90 40
   a. "O" inverted .. .. 13·00 3·00
   b. Left "S" inverted .. .. 13·00 3·00
   c. Right "S" inverted .. 13·00 3·50

1926–30. *Contemporary stamps optd with Type O 2 (16½ mm wide). Wmk C. P 12.*

O28 4 5 ca. olive-bistre .. .. 2·00 30
   a. Right "S" inverted .. 11·00 3·50
   b. Left "S" inverted .. .. 13·00 4·00
O29   5 ca. chocolate (1930) .. 25 35
   a. Imperf between (vert pair) † £160
   b. Opt inverted .. .. 16·00
   c. "O" inverted .. .. 3·00 3·00
   d. Left "S" inverted .. .. 3·00 3·00
O30 1 6 ca. brown-red (date?) .. 4·00 90
   a. "O" inverted .. .. 18·00 5·00
   b. Left "S" inverted .. .. 18·00 5·00
   c. Opt double .. .. † £100
O31 4 10 ca. pink 30 10
   a. Imperf between (horiz pair) 50·00 50·00
   b. Imperf between (vert pair) 40·00 40·00
   c. Imperf vert (horiz strip of 3) † 95·00
   d. Opt inverted .. .. 9·00 9·00
   e. "Ou" for "On" .. .. 38·00 38·00
   f. "O" inverted .. .. 4·00 1·50
   g. Left "S" inverted .. .. 3·50 1·40
   h. Right "S" inverted .. 3·50 1·25
   i. Left "S" omitted .. .. 32·00 32·00
   j. Wmk sideways .. .. 17·00 6·50
O32 1 1¼ ch. claret (shades) .. 1·60 30
   a. Imperf between (horiz pair) 75·00 80·00
   b. Imperf between (vert pair) 75·00 80·00
   c. Opt inverted .. .. 19·00 19·00
   d. "O" inverted .. .. 15·00 3·25
   e. Left "S" inverted .. .. 15·00 3·25
   f. Right "S" inverted .. 15·00 3·25
   g. Left "S" omitted .. .. 85·00 85·00
   h. Right "S" omitted .. 85·00 85·00
   i. Wmk sideways .. .. — 7·00
O33 6 3 ch. violet .. .. .. 8·00 70
   a. Opt inverted .. .. † 95·00
   b. "O" inverted .. .. 35·00 16·00
   c. "O" omitted .. .. 75·00 75·00
   d. "Ou" for "On" £100 £100
   e. Left "S" inverted .. .. — 27·00
O34 7 7 ch. claret (date?) .. .. 90·00 2·00
O35 8 14 ch. orange-yellow .. .. 38·00 85
   a. Imperf between (vert pair) £325
   b. "O" inverted .. .. 85·00 8·00

The 5 ca. olive-bistre, 3 ch. and 7 ch. exist only with the normal watermark spaced 11 mm; the 5 ca. chocolate and 14 ch. exist only with the wide 15 mm spacing; the 6 ca., 10 ca. and 1¼ ch. exist in both forms.

On   **On**   **On**

S   **S**   **S**   **S**   **S**   **S**

(O 3)   (O 4)   (O 5)
        Italic "S S"

1930. *Wmk C. P 12. (a) Optd with Type O 3.*

O36 4 10 ca. pink £140 £100
O37 1 1¼ ch. carmine-rose .. .. 3·25 3·25

(b) Optd with Type O 4

O38 5 ¾ ch. black (R.) 35 30
   a. Left "S" omitted .. .. 65·00
   b. Right "S" omitted .. 65·00
   c. Large roman "S" at left .. — 65·00

(c) Optd with Type O 5

O39 5 ¾ ch. black (R.) 35 15
   a. Opt inverted .. .. † £140
   b. "n" omitted .. .. 70·00 70·00
O40 1 4 ch. slate-green (R.) .. 28·00 12·00

On   **On**   **On**

S   **S**   **S**   **S**   **S**   **S**

(O 6)   (O 7)   (O 8)
        Oval "O"

1930–39 (?). *Contemporary stamps overprinted. P 12.*

(a) With Type O 6 (16 mm high) (i) Wmk A

O41 3 4 ca. pink .. .. .. 15·00 30·00
   a. Large right "S" as Type O 2 75·00 £120

(ii) Wmk B

O42 3 4 ca. pink .. .. .. 18·00 38·00
   a. Large right "S" as Type O 2 85·00 £140

(iii) Wmk C

O43 1 6 ca. brown-red (1932) .. 35 10
   a. Opt inverted .. .. 17·00
   b. Opt double .. .. 42·00 42·00
   c. "O" inverted .. .. 8·00 5·00
O44 4 10 ca. pink .. .. .. 1·60 1·25
O45 5 ¾ ch. mauve (1933) .. 2·75 10
   a. Imperf between (horiz pair) 70·00 48·00
   b. Imperf between (horiz strip of 3) † 90·00
   c. Imperf between (vert pair) † 75·00
   d. Stamp doubly printed .. † £120
   e. Perf 12½ .. .. 5·50 40
   f. Perf comp of 12 and 12½ 11·00 1·25
   g. Right "S" inverted .. — 18·00
O46 1 1¼ ch. carmine-rose .. .. 10·00 1·75
   a. Opt double .. .. 85·00 65·00
   b. Large right "S" as Type O 2 80·00 42·00

O47 1 4 ch. grey-green .. .. 1·60 3·50
O48   4 ch. grey-green (R.) (27.10.30) 70 20
   a. Imperf between (horiz pair) 85·00 85·00
   b. Opt double .. .. 25·00 25·00
   c. "O" inverted .. .. 25·00 15·00
   d. Large right "S" as Type O 2 38·00 25·00
   e. Imperf between (vert pair) 85·00
O49 8 14 ch. orange-yellow (1931) .. 5·50 1·50
   a. Imperf between (vert pair) † £100
For the 1½ ch. and 3 ch., and for Nos. O43 and O48/9 but perf 12½, see Nos. O66/70 (new setting combining Types O 6 and O 8).

(b) With Type O 7 (14 mm high). Wmk C

O50 3 4 ca. pink .. .. .. 9·50 24·00
   a. "O" inverted .. .. 35·00 70·00
O51 4 5 ca. chocolate (1932) .. 17·00 9·00
O52 1 6 ca. brown-red 20 10
   a. Imperf between (vert pair) 45·00 45·00
   b. Opt inverted .. .. 26·00
   c. Opt double .. .. † 50·00
   d. "nO" for "On" .. .. 90·00 90·00
   e. Right "S" inverted .. 15·00 11·00
   f. Left "S" omitted .. .. — 70·00
   g. Large "n" as Type O 5 .. 18·00 12·00
   h. Large italic left "S" as Type O 5 18·00 12·00
   i. Perf 12½ .. .. — 5·50
   j. Perf compound of 12 and 12½ — 12·00
O53   ½ ch. reddish violet (1932) .. 30 15
   a. "CHUCRRAM" (R.5/6) .. 7·50 5·50
   b. "Ou" for "On" .. .. 45·00 45·00
   c. Left "S" omitted .. .. — 80·00
   d. "O" of "On" omitted .. £110
O54   ½ ch. reddish violet (R.) (1935) 20 10
   a. Imperf between (vert pair) 85·00 85·00
   b. "CHUCRRAM" (R.5/6) .. 3·00 3·00
   c. Left "S" inverted .. .. 17·00 15·00
O55 4 10 ca. pink (date?) .. .. 2·75 1·40
   a. Imperf between (horiz pair) 11·00 15·00
   b. Imperf between (vert pair) 10·00 15·00
   c. "O" inverted .. .. 22·00 16·00
   d. Right "S" inverted .. 22·00 16·00
O56 5 ¾ ch. mauve (1933?) .. 30 15
   a. Imperf between (vert pair) † 90·00
   b. "Ou" for "On" .. .. 48·00 48·00
   c. "O" inverted .. .. 17·00 15·00
   d. Right "S" inverted .. — 15·00
   e. Opt double .. .. † 85·00
   f. Perf comp of 12 and 12½ .. 19·00 11·00
O57 1 1 ch. deep blue (R.) (1935) .. 1·40 25
   a. Slate-blue 90 20
   b. Imperf between (horiz pair) 80·00 80·00
   c. Imperf between (vert pair) 25·00 30·00
   d. Perf 12½ .. .. 7·50 2·75
   e. Perf comp of 12 and 12½ 14·00 4·75
O58   1¼ ch. claret .. .. 1·25 1·10
O59   1½ ch. rose (1933) 40 10
   a. Imperf between (vert pair) † 95·00
   b. Opt double .. .. 65·00 65·00
   c. "O" inverted .. .. 3·75 2·50
   e. Large "n" as type O 5 .. 40·00 20·00
   f. Large italic left "S" as type O 5 40·00 20·00
   g. Left "S" inverted .. .. — 18·00
   h. Perf 12½ .. .. — 8·00
   i. Perf comp of 12 and 12½ .. — 14·00
   ia. Stamp doubly printed .. † £130
O60 6 3 ch. reddish violet (1933) .. 1·10 60
   a. "O" inverted .. .. 14·00 7·00
   b. Opt double .. .. † 75·00
O61   3 ch. violet (R.) (1934) .. 70 10
   a. Imperf between (horiz pair) 60·00 38·00
   b. Imperf between (vert pair) 50·00 35·00
   c. Opt inverted .. .. † 38·00
   d. "O" inverted .. .. 14·00 10·00
   e. Perf 12½ .. .. — 1·90
   ea. Imperf between (vert pair) † £120
   f. Perf comp of 12 and 12½ .. — 8·50
   fa. Imperf between (horiz pair) † £120
   g. "Ou" for "On" .. .. — 60·00
O62 1 4 ch. grey-green (1934) .. — £225
O63   4 ch. grey-green (R.) (1935?) .. 80 20
   a. "Ou" for "On" .. .. 50·00 40·00
O64 7 7 ch. claret (shades) .. 1·10 30
   a. Imperf between (vert pair) 25·00 30·00
   b. "O" inverted .. .. 35·00 17·00
   c. Left "S" inverted .. .. 35·00 17·00
   d. Perf 12½ .. .. — 6·50
   e. Perf comp of 12 and 12½ .. — 6·50
   ea. Imperf between (vert pair) † 75·00
   eb. Imperf between (vert strip of 3) 90·00 90·00
O65 8 14 ch. orange (1933) .. .. 1·60 40
   a. Imperf between (horiz pair) 27·00 35·00
   b. Imperf between (vert pair) 95·00
   c. Opt inverted .. .. † £225

(c) New setting combining Type O 8 (18 mm high) in top row with Type O 6 (16 mm high) for remainder. Wmk C (dates?)

     A. Type O 8. B. Type O 6

			A		B	
O66	1	6 ca. brown-red	6·00	2·75	†	
		a. Perf 12½ ..	6·00	2·75	2·50	70
		ab. Imperf between (vert pair) ..	†	80·00	80·00	
		ac. "O" inverted ..	†	15·00	8·00	
		g. Perf comp of 12 and 12½ ..			—	13·00
O67		1½ ch. rose ..	26·00	4·25	6·50	35
		a. Perf 12½ ..	32·00	7·00	10·00	50
		ab. "O" inverted ..	†	38·00	14·00	
		c. Perf comp of 12 and 12½ ..	†	—	16·00	
O68	6	3 ch. violet (R.) ..	40·00	7·50	7·00	65
		a. Perf 12½ ..	48·00	14·00	12·00	75
		b. Perf comp of 12 and 12½ ..	—	70·00	17·00	4·50
O69	1	4 ch. grey-green (R.) ..	45·00	22·00	†	
		a. Perf 12½ ..	38·00	14·00	6·50	2·00
		ab. Imperf between (horiz pair) ..	†	†	£130	
			†	70·00	30·00	
O70	8	14 ch. orange-yellow ..	38·00	10·00	†	
		a. Perf 12½ ..	40·00	11·00	9·00	75

Nos. O66B and O69/70B naturally exist but are not distinguishable from Nos. O43 and O48/9.

Nos. O66/70A/B in vertical *se-tenant* pairs are very scarce.
As with the postage issues it is believed that the 12½ and compound perforations were issued between 1937 and 1939.

1 ch

8 c	**1 ch**
(O 9)	Wrong fount "1 c" (R.6/7)

1932. *Official stamps surch as T* **14** *or with Type* O **9.** *P* 12.

(a) With opt Type O **1** (i) *Wmk* A

O71	4	6 c. on 5 ca. olive-bistre	..	30·00	15·00
		a. "O" inverted	..	90·00	40·00
		b. Left "S" inverted	..	90·00	40·00
		c. Right "S" inverted	..	90·00	40·00

(ii) Wmk C

O72	4	6 c. on 5 ca. olive-bistre	..	16·00	5·50
		a. "O" inverted	..	40·00	14·00
		b. Left "S" inverted	..	40·00	14·00
		c. Right "S" inverted	..	40·00	14·00
O73		12 c. on 10 ca. pink	..	90·00	

(b) With opt Type O **2.** *Wmk* C

O74	4	6 c. on 5 ca. olive-bistre	..	1·40	85
		a. Opt and surch inverted	..	35·00	
		b. Surch inverted	..	45·00	
		c. Left "S" inverted	..	11·00	4·50
		d. Right "S" inverted	..	11·00	4·50
		e. "6" omitted	..	—	65·00
O75		6 c. on 5 ca. chocolate	..	20	25
		a. Surch inverted	..	9·00	9·00
		b. Surch double	..	80·00	
		c. Surch double, one inverted	..	80·00	
		d. "O" inverted	..	3·50	3·50
		e. Left "S" inverted	..	3·50	3·50
O76		12 c. on 10 ca. pink	..	90	30
		a. Opt inverted	..	9·00	9·00
		b. Surch inverted	..	7·00	7·00
		c. Opt and surch inverted	..	24·00	24·00
		d. Pair, one without surch	..	£200	
		e. "O" inverted	..	5·00	2·75
		f. Left "S" inverted	..	4·00	2·00
		g. "Ou" for "On"	..	60·00	60·00
		h. Right "S" inverted	..	4·00	2·00
		i. "c" omitted (R. 6/1)	..	42·00	42·00
O77	1	1 ch. 8 c. on 1¼ ch. claret	..	1·75	70
		a. Surch inverted	..	†	60·00
		b. "O" inverted	..	7·50	3·00
		c. Left "S" inverted	..	7·50	3·00
		d. Right "S" inverted	..	7·50	3·00
		e. Wrong fount "1 c"	..	21·00	15·00

(c) With opt Type O **3.** *Wmk* C

O78	4	12 c. on 10 ca. pink	..	†	£250
O79	1	1 ch. 8 c. on 1¼ ch. carmine-rose	..	42·00	28·00
		a. "n" omitted	..	£160	
		b. Wrong fount "1 c"	..	£150	£100

(d) With opt Type O **6.** *Wmk* C

O80	4	12 c. on 10 ca. pink	..	65·00	14·00
O81	1	1 ch. 8 c. on 1¼ ch. carmine-rose	..	80·00	14·00
		a. Wrong fount "1 c"	..	£190	60·00
		b. "h" omitted	..		
		c. Brown-red	..	—	14·00

(e) With opt Type O **7.** *Wmk* C

O82	4	6 c. on 5 ca. chocolate	..	20	25
		a. Opt inverted	..	55·00	55·00
		b. Surch inverted	..	11·00	12·00
		c. Right "S" omitted	..	80·00	80·00
		d. Two quads for right "S"	..	£450	
		e. Right "S" inverted	..	20·00	
O83		12 c. on 10 ca. pink	..	20	15
		a. Opt inverted	..	7·00	7·00
		b. Surch inverted	..	6·00	6·00
		c. Opt and surch inverted	..	30·00	30·00
		d. Opt double	..	†	75·00
		e. "O" inverted	..	13·00	13·00
		f. Right "S" inverted	..	13·00	13·00
		g. "On" omitted	..	—	75·00
		h. "n" omitted	..	—	75·00
		i. "c" omitted (R. 6/1)	..	27·00	27·00
		j. Surch double	..	†	70·00
O84	1	1 ch. 8 c. on 1¼ ch. claret	..	35	25
		a. Imperf between (vert pair)	..	†	£180
		b. Opt inverted	..	†	£325
		c. Surch inverted	..	14·00	14·00
		d. Surch double	..	50·00	
		e. "O" inverted	..	4·50	2·75
		f. Wrong fount "1 c"	..	16·00	13·00

SERVICE	**SERVICE**	**SERVICE 8 CASH**
(O 10) 13 mm	(O 11) 13½ mm	(O 12)

1939–41. *Nos.* 35 *and* 40 *with type-set opt, Type* O **10.** *P* 12½.

O85	1	6 ca. brown-red (1941)	..	70	20
		a. Perf 11	..	1·10	65
		b. Perf 12	..	70	30
		c. Compound perf	..	70	1·10
O86	5	¾ ch. reddish violet	..	80·00	45·00
		a. Perf 12	..	19·00	1·25
		b. Compound perf	..	75·00	45·00

1939 (9 Nov). *Maharaja's 27th Birthday. Nos.* 64/70 *with type-set opt, Type* O **10.** *P* 12½.

O87		1 ch. yellow-green	..	3·25	25
O88		1½ ch. scarlet	..	3·25	75
		a. "SESVICE"	..	70·00	26·00
		b. Perf 12	..	24·00	4·50
		ba. "SESVICE"	..	—	85·00
		bb. Imperf between (horiz pair)	..	†	£110
		c. Compound perf	..	8·00	1·75

O89		2 ch. orange	..	3·00	3·50
		a. "SESVICE"	..	95·00	£110
		b. Compound perf	..	60·00	60·00
O90		3 ch. brown	..	2·50	20
		a. "SESVICE"	..	50·00	21·00
		b. Perf 12	..	13·00	45
		ba. "SESVICE"	..	£120	40·00
		c. Compound perf	..	6·00	2·75
O91		4 ch. red	..	6·00	2·50
O92		7 ch. pale blue	..	7·50	1·75
O93		14 ch. turquoise-green	..	9·00	2·50
O87/93			*Set of* 7	30·00	10·00

1940 (?)–45. *Nos.* 40a *and* 42b *optd with Type* O **11.** *P* 12½.

O94	5	¾ ch. reddish violet	..	8·50	20
		a. Imperf between (horiz pair)	..	90·00	
		b. Perf 11	..	45·00	1·10
		c. Perf 12	..	12·00	20
		d. Compound perf	..	38·00	75
O95	1	1½ ch. rose (1945)	..	13·00	8·00
		a. Perf 12	..	4·00	1·00
		b. Compound perf	..	16·00	11·00

1942 (?). *Nos.* 64/70 *optd with Type* O **11.** *P* 12½.

O 96		1 ch. yellow-green	..	60	10
		a. Imperf between (vert pair)	..	42·00	42·00
		b. Opt inverted	..	†	32·00
		c. Opt double	..	20·00	
		d. Perf 11	..	60	10
		da. Imperf between (vert pair)	..	24·00	
		db. Opt double	..	75·00	75·00
		e. Perf 12	..	2·50	50
		ea. Imperf between (vert pair)	..	70·00	70·00
		eb. Stamp doubly printed	..	95·00	
		ec. Opt inverted	..	†	75·00
		ed. Opt double	..	20·00	
		f. Compound perf	..	4·50	1·00
		fa. Imperf between (vert pair)	..	†	95·00
		g. "S" inverted	..	—	28·00
O 97		1½ ch. scarlet	..	2·25	10
		a. Imperf between (horiz pair)	..	48·00	
		b. Perf 11	..	1·00	15
		ba. Imperf between (vert pair)	..	75·00	75·00
		bb. Imperf between (vert strip of 3)	..	55·00	
		bc. Imperf between (horiz pair)	..	†	80·00
		c. Perf 12	..	3·75	50
		ca. Imperf between (vert strip of 3)	..	95·00	
		d. Compound perf	..	1·75	30
		e. Imperf (pair)	..	25·00	
O 98		2 ch. orange	..	1·00	30
		a. Perf 11	..	5·00	80
		ab. Imperf between (vert pair)	..		
		b. Perf 12	..	60·00	60·00
		ba. Imperf between (vert pair)	..	£225	£225
		c. Compound perf	..	60·00	60·00
O 99		3 ch. brown	..	60	10
		a. Imperf between (vert pair)	..		
		b. Perf 11	..	1·50	10
		c. Perf 12	..	3·50	1·60
		ca. Imperf between (vert pair)	..	£180	£180
		d. Compound perf	..	12·00	75
O100		4 ch. red	..	1·25	55
		a. Perf 11	..	2·25	45
		b. Perf 12	..	11·00	3·00
		c. Compound perf	..	45·00	19·00
O101		7 ch. pale blue	..	4·50	35
		a. Perf 11	..	4·00	3·00
		b. Perf 12	..	14·00	5·50
		c. Compound perf	..	13·00	4·00
		d. Blue (p 11)	..	7·00	3·50
		da. Perf 12	..	5·50	3·50
		db. Compound perf	..	18·00	12·00
O102		14 ch. turquoise-green	..	8·00	70
		a. Perf 11	..	8·00	1·50
		b. Perf 12	..	7·00	2·40
		c. Compound perf	..	42·00	5·50
O96/102			*Set of* 7	14·00	1·90

1942. *Maharaja's 29th Birthday. Nos.* 71/2 *optd with Type* O **11.** *P* 12½.

O103		6 ca. blackish violet	..	40	30
		a. Perf 11	..	70	70
		b. Perf 12	..	38·00	4·00
		c. Compound perf	..	1·50	1·00
O104		¾ ch. brown	..	2·50	10
		a. Imperf between (vert pair)	..	†	£200
		b. Perf 11	..	5·00	10
		c. Perf 12	..	38·00	1·50
		d. Compound perf	..	5·50	85

1943. *Surch with Type* O **12.** *P* 12½.

O105	19	8 ca. on 6 ca. scarlet	..	1·60	20
		a. Perf 11	..	1·25	10
		ab. Surch inverted	..	†	£600
		b. Compound perf	..	4·75	1·25

1945. *Nos.* 73/4 *optd with Type* O **11.** *P* 12½.

O106		2 ca. on 1½ ch. scarlet	..	45	50
		a. Perf 11	..	45	15
		ab. Pair, one without surch	..	£190	
		b. Compound perf	..	70	1·00
		ba. "2" omitted	..	£170	£170
		c. Perf 12	..		
O107		4 ca. on ¾ ch. brown	..	1·75	30
		a. Perf 11	..	1·00	20
		b. Compound perf	..	1·25	1·00

1947. *Maharaja's 34th Birthday. Optd with Type* O **11.** *P* 11.

O108	21	8 ca. carmine	..	1·50	70
		a. Imperf between (horiz pair)	..	35·00	
		ab. Imperf between (vert pair)	..	†	£100
		b. Opt double	..	†	£150
		c. Perf 12½	..	3·50	1·10
		ca. Stamp doubly printed	..	30·00	
		d. Perf 12	..	3·50	1·40
		da. Stamp doubly printed	..	32·00	

From 1 July 1949 Travancore formed part of the new State of Travancore-Cochin and stamps of Travancore surcharged in Indian currency were used.

TRAVANCORE-COCHIN

On 1 July 1949 the United State of Travancore and Cochin was formed ("U.S.T.C.") and the name was changed to State of Travancore-Cochin ("T.C.") by the new constitution of India on 26 January 1950.

PRICES FOR STAMPS ON COVER	
Nos. 1/13	*from* × 8
Nos. O1/17	*from* × 15

NO WATERMARK VARIETIES. These were formerly listed but we have now decided to omit them as they do not occur in full sheets. They are best collected in pairs, with and without watermarks.

COMPOUND PERFS. The notes above Type **17** of Travancore also apply here.

VALIDITY OF STAMPS. From 6 June 1950 the stamps of Travancore-Cochin were valid on mail from both Indian and state post offices to destinations in India and abroad.

ONE ANNA
ഒരണ
(1)

2 p. on 6 ca.

രണ്ട പൈസ	രണ്ട രപൈസ
Normal	1st character of 2nd group as 1st character of 1st group (Rt pane R.14/2)

1949 (1 July). *Stamps of Travancore surch in "PIES" or "ANNAS" as T* **1.** *P* 12½.

1	19	2 p. on 6 ca. blackish violet (R.)	..	1·60	85
		a. Surch inverted	..	28·00	
		b. Character error	..	90·00	60·00
		c. "O" inverted	..	22·00	13·00
		d. Perf 11	..	1·00	20
		da. Imperf between (vert pair)	..	95·00	95·00
		db. Pair, one without surch	..	80·00	
		dc. Character error	..	85·00	60·00
		dd. "O" inverted	..	23·00	13·00
		e. Perf 12	..	40	20
		ea. Imperf between (horiz pair)	..	40·00	
		eb. Imperf between (vert pair)	..	5·00	11·00
		ec. Surch inverted	..	65·00	
		ed. Character error	..	90·00	60·00
		ee. Imperf between (vert strip of 3)	..	29·00	
		ef. Block of four imperf between (horiz and vert)	..	38·00	
		eg. "O" inverted	..	23·00	13·00
		f. Perf 14	..	†	£350
		g. Imperf (pair)	..	8·50	
		h. Compound perf	..	—	27·00
2	21	4 p. on 8 ca. carmine	..	1·10	30
		a. Surch inverted	..	32·00	
		b. "S" inverted	..	70·00	38·00
		c. Perf 11	..	1·40	30
		ca. Imperf between (vert pair)	..	£100	£100
		cb. Surch inverted	..	65·00	
		cc. Pair, one without surch	..	80·00	
		cd. "FOUP" for "FOUR"	..	£100	75·00
		ce. "S" inverted	..	65·00	38·00
		d. Perf 12	..	45	30
		da. Imperf between (vert pair)	..	17·00	
		db. Pair, one without surch	..	75·00	
		dc. "FOUP" for "FOUR"	..	90·00	70·00
		dd. "S" inverted	..	75·00	42·00
		de. Surch inverted	..	85·00	
		e. Imperf (pair)	..	60·00	
		f. Compound perf	..	—	27·00
		g. Perf 13½	..	†	£375
3	17	½ a. on 1 ch. yellow-green	..	2·00	30
		a. "NANA" for "ANNA" (Lt pane R.3/3)	..	£100	75·00
		b. Inverted "H" in "HALF"	..	—	65·00
		c. Imperf between (vert pair)	..	†	90·00
		d. Perf 11	..	1·40	20
		da. Imperf between (vert pair)	..	24·00	
		db. Surch inverted	..	†	£120
		dc. "NANA" for "ANNA" (Lt pane R.3/3)	..	£120	85·00
		dd. Inverted "H" in "HALF"	..	—	70·00
		e. Perf 12	..	65	40
		ea. Imperf between (horiz pair)	..	30·00	35·00
		eb. Imperf between (vert pair)	..	4·50	10·00
		ec. Surch inverted	..	5·00	
		ed. "NANA" for "ANNA" (Lt pane R.3/3)	..	£140	90·00
		ee. Block of four imperf between (horiz and vert)	..	38·00	
		f. Perf 14	..	†	£325
		g. Imperf (pair)	..	8·50	17·00
		h. Compound perf	..	—	26·00
4	18	1 a. on 2 ch. orange	..	2·25	30
		a. Perf 11	..	55	20
		ab. Surch double	..	48·00	
		b. Perf 12	..	2·50	50
		ba. Imperf between (horiz pair)	..	5·50	
		bb. Imperf between (vert pair)	..	4·25	10·00
		bc. Block of four imperf between (horiz and vert)	..	38·00	
		c. Perf 13½	..	£120	2·00
		d. Imperf (pair)	..	8·50	
		e. Compound perf	..	28·00	20·00
5	—	2 a. on 4 ch. red (68)	..	1·90	60
		a. Surch inverted	..	†	£180
		b. "O" inverted	..	26·00	15·00
		c. Perf 11	..	1·90	60
		ca. "O" inverted	..	—	17·00
		d. Perf 12	..	1·60	55
		da. "O" inverted	..	30·00	18·00
		e. Compound perf	..	30·00	25·00

6 18 3 a. on 7 ch. pale blue (69) .. .. 8·00 3·50
  a. Perf 11 .. .. 4·50 2·00
  ab. Blue .. .. 42·00 4·50
  ac. "3" omitted .. .. .. † £300
  b. Perf 12 .. .. .. 7·00 2·75
  c. Compound perf .. .. — 42·00
  ca. Blue .. .. .. — 55·00
7 — 6 a. on 14 ch. turquoise-green (70) .. 9·50 15·00
  a. Accent omitted from native surch (Rt
    pane R.13/4) £160 £170
  b. Perf 11 .. .. .. 7·00 13·00
  ba. Accent omitted from native surch (Rt
    pane R.13/4) £160 £170
  c. Perf 12 .. .. .. 9·00 15·00
  ca. Accent omitted from native surch (Rt
    pane R. 13/4) £170 £180
  d. Compound perf .. .. 21·00 23·00
  da. Accent omitted from native surch (Rt
    pane R.13/4) £225
  e. Imperf (pair) .. .. ..
1/7 .. .. Set of 7 13·50 15·00

There are two settings of the ½ a. surcharge. In one the first native character is under the second downstroke of the "H" and in the other it is under the first downstroke of the "A" of "HALF". They occur on stamps perf 12½, 11 and 12 equally commonly and also on the Official stamps.

U. S. T. C.   **T.-C.**   **SIX PIES**
  (2)   (3)   (4)

1949. No. 106 of Cochin optd with T 2.
8 29 1 a. orange .. .. .. 4·50 50·00
  a. No stop after "S" (R. 1/6) .. 60·00
  b. Raised stop after "T" (R. 4/1) .. 60·00

1950 (1 Apr). No. 106 of Cochin optd with T 3.
9 29 1 a. orange .. .. .. 5·50 48·00
  a. No stop after "T" .. .. 45·00
  b. Opt inverted £170
  ba. No stop after "T" £1500

The no stop variety occurs on No. 5 in the sheet and again on No. 8 in conjunction with a short hyphen.

1950 (1 Apr). No. 9 surch as T 4.
10 29 6 p. on 1 a. orange .. .. 2·00 27·00
  a. No stop after "T" (R. 1/5) .. 17·00
  b. Error. Surch on No. 8 .. 25·00
  ba. No stop after "S" £200
  bb. Raised stop after "I" £200
11 9 p. on 1 a. orange .. .. 1·40 27·00
  a. No stop after "T" (R. 1/5) .. 17·00
  b. Error. Surch on No. 8 .. £160
  ba. No stop after "S" £550
  bb. Raised stop after "T" £550

5 Conch or Chank Shell   6 Palm Trees

(Litho Indian Security Printing Press, Nasik)

1950 (24 Oct). W 69 of India. P 14.
12 5 2 p. rose-carmine .. .. .. 1·10 1·10
13 6 4 p. ultramarine .. .. .. 1·75 9·50

The ordinary issues of Travancore-Cochin became obsolete on 1 July 1951.

OFFICIAL STAMPS

VALIDITY. Travancore-Cochin official stamps were valid for use throughout India from 30 September 1950.

SERVICE   **SERVICE**
  (O 1)   (O 2)

1949–51. Stamps of Travancore surch with value as T 1 and optd "SERVICE". No gum. P 12½. (a) With Type O 1.
  (i) Wmk C of Travancore
O 1 19 2 p. on 6 ca. blackish violet (R.) .. 80 20
  a. Imperf between (vert pair) .. £100 £100
  b. Character error (Rt pane R. 14/2) 32·00 24·00
  c. "O" inverted .. .. 19·00 10·00
  d. Pair, one without surch .. 95·00
  e. Perf 11 .. .. .. 70 20
  ea. Imperf between (vert pair) .. £100 £100
  eb. Character error (Rt pane R. 14/2) 42·00 32·00
  ec. "O" inverted .. .. 19·00 11·00
  f. Perf 12 .. .. .. 35 20
  fa. Imperf between (horiz pair) .. 7·00 15·00
  fb. Imperf between (vert pair) .. 6·00
  fc. Character error (Rt pane R.14/2) 35·00 28·00
  fd. "O" inverted .. .. 19·00
  fe. Block of four imperf between (horiz
    and vert) .. .. .. 24·00
  g. Imperf (pair) .. .. 8·00 16·00
  ga. Character error (Rt pane R. 14/2)· £150

O 2 21 4 p. on 8 ca. carmine .. .. 1·75 55
  a. "FOUR" for "FOUR" (Lt pane R.2/3) £130 85·00
  b. Perf 11 .. .. .. 1·60 30
  ba. "FOUR" for "FOUR" (Lt pane R.2/3) 75·00 32·00
  c. Perf 12 .. .. .. 1·75 55
  ca. "FOUR" for "FOUR" (Lt pane R.2/3) 80·00 50·00
  d. Compound perf .. .. 16·00 16·00
O 3 17 ½ a. on 1 ch. yellow-green 50 25
  a. Pair, one without surch .. 60·00
  b. Surch inverted .. .. 22·00
  c. "NANA" for "ANNA" (Lt pane
    R.3/3) .. .. .. £150 50·00
  d. Perf 11 .. .. .. 1·00 25
  da. Pair, one without surch .. 90·00
  db. Surch inverted .. .. 55·00
  dc. "NANA" for "ANNA" (Lt pane
    R.3/3) .. .. .. £140 60·00
  e. Perf 12 .. .. .. 7·00 1·90
  ea. "NANA" for "ANNA" (Lt pane
    R.3/3) £250 £120
  eb. Pair, one without surch .. 80·00
  ec. Surch inverted on back only .. £150
  f. Compound perf .. .. — 19·00
O 4 18 1 a. on 2 ch. orange .. .. 15·00 5·00
  a. Surch inverted .. .. 75·00
  b. Pair, one without surch .. £425
  c. Perf 11 .. .. .. 13·00 7·50
O 5 — 2 a. on 4 ch. red (68) 90 60
  b. Perf 11 .. .. .. 3·75 60
  ba. Surch inverted £400
  c. Perf 12 .. .. .. 4·25 3·50
  ca. O inverted .. .. — 48·00
  cb. Pair, one without surch .. £170
  d. Compound perf .. .. — 26·00
  e. Imperf (pair) .. .. 12·00
O 6 — 3 a. on 7 ch. pale blue (69) .. 3·75 1·40
  a. Imperf between (vert pair) .. 17·00
  b. Blue .. .. .. 25·00 5·00
  c. Perf 11 .. .. .. 2·40 90
  ca. Blue .. .. .. 25·00 5·00
  d. Perf 12 .. .. .. 2·25 3·00
  da. Imperf between (horiz pair) .. 13·00
  db. Imperf between (vert pair) .. 8·00
  dc. Block of four imperf between (horiz
    and vert) .. .. .. 30·00
  dd. Blue .. .. .. 25·00 5·00
  e. Imperf (pair) .. .. 11·00
O 7 — 6 a. on 14 ch. turquoise-green (70) .. 9·00 4·75
  a. Imperf between (vert pair) .. 27·00
  b. Perf 11 .. .. .. 7·50 4·00
  c. Perf 12 .. .. .. 35·00 6·00
  ca. Imperf between (horiz pair) .. 23·00
  cb. Imperf between (vert pair) .. 28·00
  cc. Block of four imperf between (horiz
    and vert) .. .. .. 55·00
  d. Imperf (pair) .. .. 14·00
O1/7 .. .. .. Set of 7 23·00 10·00

  (ii) W 27 of Cochin
O 8 19 2 p. on 6 ca. blackish violet (R.) .. 30 1·10
  a. Type O 1 double .. .. 18·00
  b. Perf 11 .. .. .. 65 1·25
  c. Perf 12 .. .. .. 45 1·10
O 9 — 2 a. on 4 ch. red (68) .. .. 1·00 75
  a. Perf 11 .. .. .. 60 65
  ab. Imperf between (vert pair) .. £170 £170
  b. Compound perf .. .. — 30·00

(b) With Type O 2

  (i) Wmk C of Travancore
O10 21 4 p. on 8 ca. carmine 30 20
  a. "FOUR" for "FOUR" (Lt pane R.2/3) 85·00 35·00
  b. 2nd "E" of "SERVICE" in wrong
    fount .. .. .. — 48·00
  c. "S" in "PIES" inverted .. — 50·00
  d. Imperf between (vert pair) .. † 90·00
  e. Perf 11 .. .. .. 30 20
  ea. Imperf between (horiz pair) .. 4·50
  eb. Imperf between (vert pair) .. 24·00
  ec. "FOUR" for "FOUR" (Lt pane R.2/3) 85·00 32·00
  ed. 2nd "E" of "SERVICE" in wrong
    fount .. .. .. 90·00 48·00
  ee. "S" in "PIES" inverted .. — 50·00
  ef. Block of four imperf between (horiz
    and vert) .. .. .. 30·00
  f. Perf 12 .. .. .. 30 20
  fa. Imperf between (horiz pair) .. 3·25
  fb. Imperf between (vert pair) .. 2·00
  fc. Block of four imperf between (horiz
    and vert) .. .. .. 10·00 19·00
  fd. "FOUR" for "FOUR" (Lt pane R.2/3) 95·00 35·00
  ff. 2nd "E" of "SERVICE" in wrong
    fount .. .. .. 85·00 48·00
  fg. "FOUK" for "FOUR" .. † £325
  g. Perf 13½ .. .. .. 3·00 1·25
  h. Compound perf .. .. 8·00 8·00
  i. Imperf (pair) .. .. 6·00
  ia. 2nd "E" of "SERVICE" in wrong
    fount £110
O11 17 ½ a. on 1 ch. yellow-green 50 20
  a. "AANA" for "ANNA" (Rt pane
    R.13/1) .. .. .. £120 60·00
  b. Perf 11 .. .. .. 30 20
  ba. Imperf between (horiz pair) .. 48·00 48·00
  bb. Imperf between (vert pair) .. 6·50
  bc. Block of four imperf between (horiz
    and vert) .. .. .. 42·00
  bd. "AANA" for "ANNA" (Rt pane
    R.13/1) .. .. .. 65·00 40·00
  c. Perf 12 .. .. .. 50 15
  ca. Imperf between (horiz pair) .. 3·50
  cb. Imperf between (vert pair) .. 3·50 7·50
  cc. "AANA" for "ANNA" (Rt pane
    R.13/1) .. .. .. 80·00 48·00
  cd. Block of four imperf between (horiz
    and vert) .. .. .. 21·00
  d. Compound perf .. .. 18·00 13·00
  da. "AANA" for "ANNA" (Rt pane
    R.13/1) .. .. .. — £140
  e. Imperf (pair) .. .. 6·00 13·00

O12 18 1 a. on 2 ch. orange 40 30
  a. Imperf between (vert pair) .. † 95·00
  ab. Imperf between (horiz pair) .. † 95·00
  b. Perf 11 .. .. .. 1·90 50
  ba. Imperf between (horiz pair) .. 6·00 13·00
  bb. Imperf between (vert pair) .. 55·00 55·00
  c. Perf 12 .. .. .. 40 20
  ca. Imperf between (horiz pair) .. 5·00
  cb. Imperf between (vert pair) .. 3·50 8·00
  cc. Block of four imperf between (horiz
    and vert) .. .. .. 19·00
  d. Compound perf .. .. 22·00 15·00
  e. Imperf (pair) .. .. 14·00
O13 — 2 a. on 4 ch. red (68) .. .. 2·25 80
  a. "O" inverted (Lt pane R. 14/3) .. 50·00 35·00
  b. Perf 11 .. .. .. 1·50 1·10
  ba. "O" inverted (Lt pane R. 14/3) .. 45·00 35·00
  c. Perf 12 .. .. .. 7·00 1·10
  ca. Imperf between (vert pair) .. £110 £130
  cb. "O" inverted (Lt pane R. 14/3) .. 85·00 35·00
  d. Compound perf .. .. 23·00 13·00
O14 — 3 a. on 7 ch. pale blue (69) .. 5·00 1·10
  a. "S" inverted in "SERVICE" (Lt pane
    R.6/3) .. .. .. 65·00 32·00
  b. First "E" inverted (Lt pane R.7/4) £150 £110
  c. "C" inverted (Lt pane R.4/1 and 5/1) 90·00 75·00
  d. Second "E" inverted (Lt pane R.3/2) £140 £100
  e. Perf 11 .. .. .. 1·50 1·10
  ea. "S" inverted in "SERVICE" (Lt pane
    R.6/3) .. .. .. 50·00 32·00
  f. Perf 12 .. .. .. 3·75 1·60
  fa. "S" inverted in "SERVICE" (Lt pane
    R.6/3) .. .. .. £110 70·00
  g. Compound perf .. .. — 35·00
  h. Imperf (pair) .. .. 35·00
O15 — 6 a. on 14 ch. turquoise-green (70) .. 1·50 3·25
  a. Accent omitted from native surch 16·00 13·00
  b. "S" inverted in "SERVICE" (Lt pane
    R.6/3) .. .. .. 65·00 42·00
  c. Perf 11 .. .. .. 11·00 3·25
  ca. Accent omitted from native surch 55·00 22·00
  cb. "S" inverted in "SERVICE" (Lt pane
    R.6/3) .. .. .. £120 50·00
  d. Perf 12 .. .. .. 38·00 4·50
  da. Accent omitted from native surch £120 30·00
  db. "S" inverted in "SERVICE" (Lt pane
    R.6/3) .. .. .. £225 65·00
  e. Compound perf .. .. 55·00 55·00
O10/15 .. .. .. Set of 6 5·00 5·00

  (ii) W 27 of Cochin
O16 17 ½ a. on 1 ch. yellow-green .. .. 1·00 65
  a. Perf 11 .. .. .. 40 35
  b. Perf 12 .. .. .. 17·00 8·50
  c. Compound perf. .. .. 10·00 3·00
O17 18 1 a. on 2 ch. orange 50 65
  a. Perf 11 .. .. .. 50 40
  b. Perf 12 .. .. .. 11·00 4·00
  c. Perf 13½ .. .. .. 2·00 1·00
  d. Compound perf .. .. 4·50 3·00

Nos. O2, O10, O12 and O17 have the value at top in English and at bottom in native characters with "SERVICE" in between. All others have "SERVICE" below the surcharge.

Type O 2 was overprinted at one operation with the surcharges.

Nos. O10b, O10ed, O10ff and O10ia, show the second "E" of "SERVICE" with serifs matching those on the surcharge.

The "accent omitted" varieties on No. O15 occur on Left pane R. 5/1, 11/4 and Right pane R. 1/4, 12/4, 14/1 and 13/4.

The Official stamps became obsolete in September 1951.

WADHWAN

PRICES FOR STAMPS ON COVER

  No. 1   from × 50
  No. 2   —
  Nos. 3/6   from × 50

Thakur Bal Singh, 1885–1910

1

1888–94. Litho. (a) Thin toned wove paper
1 1 ½ pice, black (I, III) (p 12½ large holes) .. 12·00 42·00
  a. Imperf between (vert pair) (I) ..
  b. Pin-perf 6½ irregular (I) .. .. 80·00
  c. Compound of 12½ and pin-perf 6½ (I)
2 ½ pice, black (II) (p 12½ irregular small
  holes) .. .. 28·00
    (b) Medium toned wove paper
3 1 ½ pice, black (III) (p 12½) .. .. 7·50 32·00
4 ½ pice, black (V) (p 12) .. .. 6·50 7·50
    (c) Thick off-white or toned wove paper
5 1 ½ pice, black (IV, VI) (p 12) (7.92) .. 5·00 6·00
  a. Perf compound of 12 and 11 (IV) .. 13·00 32·00
6 ½ pice, black (VII) (fine impression) (p 12)
  (1894) .. .. 5·50 18·00

Sheets from the Stone IV printing had at least one horizontal line of perforations gauging 11, normally between the bottom two rows of the sheet.

These stamps were lithographed from seven different stones taken from a single die. Brief details of the individual stones are as follows:

Stone I – No. 1. Sheet size not known, but possibly 28
           (4×7). Sheet margins imperforate
Stone II – No. 2. Sheets of 42 (7×6) with imperforate
           margins
Stone III – Nos. 1 (thin paper) and 3 (medium paper).
           Sheets of 40 (4×10) with imperforate margins

Stone IV – Nos. 5/a. Sheets of 32 (4×8) with imperforate
    margins at top and right
Stone V – No. 4. Sheets of 20 (4×5) with imperforate
    margins at top, right and bottom
Stone VI – No. 5. Sheets of 30 (5×6) with all margins
    perforated
Stone VII – No. 6. Sheets of 32 (4×8) with all margins
    perforated. Much finer impression than the
    other stones
    Stamps from stones I and II come with or without the dot
before "STATE". Those from the later stones always show the
dot. The shading on the pennant above the shield can also be
used in stone identification. Stamps from stones I to III show
heavy shading on the pennant, but this is less evident on stone
IV and reduced further to a short line or dot on stones V to VII.
There is a ")" hairline after "HALF" on the majority of stamps
from Stone III.

    The stamps of Wadhwan became obsolete on 1 January 1895.

— URCH HARRIS —

ALL WORLD

NEW ISSUE SERVICE

Your 'First Choice' New Issue Supplier

Developed over the last 30 years
Urch Harris 'All World' combines the
widest choice of countries, themes
and formats with a reliable individual
service that helps develop and
manage your collection.

■ 260 countries and 100 plus
themes.

■ Choice of mint issues, reprints,
yearpacks, used stamps, maxi
cards, booklets, presentation packs,
specimens and first day covers.

■ Regular distributions every 6
weeks.

■ Free magazine with every
distribution.

■ Fully computerised invoices with
descriptions.

■ Customer advice helpline.

■ Free gifts and regular special offers.

■ Supported by Stanley Gibbons,
world leaders in philately.

FREE WELCOME PACK

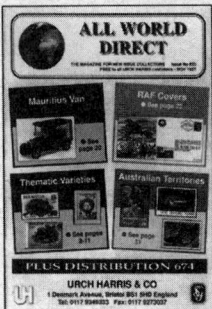

Containing full
details of our
unique service,
a full list of
countries and
themes and a
copy of 'All
World Direct'
magazine.

Telephone 0117 9349333 for a free pack.

**Urch Harris & Co
1 Denmark Avenue
Bristol BS1 5HD**

A Division of Stanley Gibbons Ltd

Ionian Islands

The British occupation of the Ionian Islands was completed in 1814 and the archipelago was placed under the protection of Great Britain by the Treaty of Paris in 1815. The United States of the Ionian Islands were given local self-government, which included responsibility for the postal services. Crowned-circle handstamps were, however, supplied in 1844, although it is believed these were intended for use on prepaid mail to foreign destinations.

Examples of the Great Britain 1855 1d. red-brown stamp are known used at Corfu, cancelled as No. CC2, and it is believed that these originate from mail sent by the British garrison.

For illustrations of the handstamp types see BRITISH POST OFFICES ABROAD notes, following GREAT BRITAIN.

CEPHALONIA

CROWNED-CIRCLE HANDSTAMPS

CC1 CC 1 CEPHALONIA (19.4.1844) *Price on cover* £1000

CORFU

CROWNED-CIRCLE HANDSTAMPS

CC2 CC 1 CORFU (19.4.1844) .. *Price on cover* £500
CC3 CC 1 CORFU (G. or B.) (1844) *Price on cover* —

ZANTE

CROWNED-CIRCLE HANDSTAMPS

CC4 CC 1 ZANTE (G. or B.) (19.4.1844) .. *Price on cover* £1000

Nos. CC1/2 were later, *circa* 1860/1, struck in green (Cephalonia) or red (Corfu).

It is believed that examples of No. CC4 in black are from an unauthorised use of this handstamp which is now on display in the local museum. A similar handstamp, but without "PAID AT" was introduced in 1861.

PRICES FOR STAMPS ON COVER
Nos. 1/3 *from* × 10

1

(Recess Perkins, Bacon & Co)

1859 (15 June). *Imperf.*
1	1	(½d.) orange (no wmk)	..	70·00	£500
2		(1d.) blue (wmk "2")	..	20·00	£180
3		(2d.) carmine (wmk "1") ..	..	15·00	£180

On 30 May 1864, the islands were ceded to Greece, and these stamps became obsolete.

Great care should be exercised in buying used stamps, on or off cover, as forged postmarks are plentiful.

Iraq

Indian post offices were opened at Baghdad and Basra, then part of the Turkish Empire, on 1 January 1868. Unoverprinted stamps of India were used, Baghdad being allocated numeral cancellations "356", "18" and "K-6", and Basra (also spelt Bussorah, Busreh, Busrah, Busra) "357", "19" and "1/K-6".

Both offices closed on 30 September 1914, but Basra re-opened the following month when Indian stamps overprinted "I.E.F." were used.

(Currency. 16 annas = 1 rupee)

I. ISSUES FOR BAGHDAD

PRICES FOR STAMPS ON COVER
Nos 1/25 *from* × 6

BRITISH OCCUPATION

British and Indian troops occupied the port of Basra on 22 November 1914 to protect the oil pipeline. They then advanced up the rivers, and after a hard campaign took Baghdad from the Turks on 11 March 1917.

IN BRITISH **BAGHDAD** OCCUPATION

2 Ans

(1)

1917 (1 Sept). *Stamps of Turkey, surch as T* **1** *in three operations.*

(a) *Pictorial designs of 1914. T* **32**, *etc., and* **31**
1	32	¼ a. on 2 pa. claret (Obelisk)	..	85·00	95·00
		a. "IN BRITISH" omitted			£4500
2	34	¼ a. on 5 pa. dull purple (Leander's Tower)	60·00	65·00
		a. Value omitted			£4250
3	36	½ a. on 10 pa. green (Lighthouse garden)	£550	£600
4	31	½ a. on 10 pa. green (Mosque of Selim)	..	£850	£1000
5	37	1 a. on 20 pa. red (Castle)	..	£325	£325
		a. "BAGHDAD" double			£1300
6	38	2 a. on 1 pi. bright blue (Mosque)	..	£100	£130

(b) *As* (a), *but overprinted with small five-pointed Star*
7	37	1 a. on 20 pa. red (B.)	..	£170	£180
		a. "OCCUPATION" omitted	..		£3750
		b. "BAGHDAD" double			£1300
8	38	2 a. on 1 pi. bright blue (R.)	..	£2250	£3000

(c) *Postal Jubilee stamps (Old G.P.O.). P* 12½
9	60	½ a. on 10 pa. carmine	..	£300	£325
		a. Perf 13½		£600	£650
10		1 a. on 20 pa. blue	..	£2500	
		a. Value omitted		£5000	
		b. Perf 13½	..	£700	£800
11		2 a. on 1 pi. black and violet	..	£120	£130
		a. "BAGHDAD" omitted		£3750	
		b. Perf 13½	..	60·00	70·00

(d) *T* **30** *(G.P.O., Constantinople) with opt T* **26**
12	30	2 a. on 1 pi. ultramarine	..	£275	£400
		a. "IN BRITISH" omitted		£4750	

(e) *Stamps optd with six-pointed Star and Arabic date* "1331" *within Crescent. T* **53** *(except No. 16, which has five-pointed Star and Arabic* "1332", *T* **57**)
13	30	½ a. on 10 pa. green (R.)	..	60·00	65·00
14		1 a. on 20 pa. rose	..	£300	£325
		a. Value omitted	..	£3750	£3750
		b. Optd with T **26** (Arabic letter "B") also	..	£4250	£4250
15	23	1 a. on 20 pa. rose (No. 554a)	..	£325	£350
		a. Value omitted		£4750	
16	21	1 a. on 20 pa. carmine (No. 732)	..	£2750	£3500
17	30	2 a. on 1 pi. ultramarine (R.)	..	70·00	85·00
		a. "BAGHDAD" omitted	..	†	
18	21	2 a. on 1 pi. dull blue (No. 543) (R.)	..	£120	£130
		a. "OCCUPATION" omitted	..	£4750	

(f) *Stamps with similar opt, but date between Star and Crescent (Nos. 19 and 22, T* **54**; *others T* **55**, *five-pointed Star)*
19	23	½ a. on 10 pa. grey-green (No. 609a) (R.)	75·00	80·00
		a. "OCCUPATION" omitted	..	£4000	
20	60	½ a. on 10 pa. carmine (p 12½) (B.)	..	£110	£120
		a. Perf 13½	..	£250	£275
21	30	1 a. on 20 pa. rose	..	70·00	90·00
22	28	1 a. on 20 pa. rose (Plate II) (No. 617)	..	£300	£325
23	15	1 a. on 10 pa. on 20 pa. claret (No. 630)	£150	£150
		a. "OCCUPATION" omitted	..	£4250	£4250
24	30	2 a. on 1 pi. ultramarine (R.)	..	£130	£140
		a. "OCCUPATION" omitted	..	£4250	
		b. "BAGHDAD" omitted	..	£4250	
25	28	2 a. on 1 pi. ultramarine (Pl. II) (No. 645	£1000	£1200

The last group (f) have the Crescent obliterated by hand in violet-black ink, as this included the inscription, "Tax for the relief of children of martyrs".

II. ISSUES FOR MOSUL

PRICES FOR STAMPS ON COVER
Nos. 1/8 *from* × 40

BRITISH OCCUPATION

A British and Indian force occupied Mosul on 1 November 1918.

As the status of the vilayet was disputed stocks of "IRAQ IN BRITISH OCCUPATION" surcharges were withdrawn in early 1919 and replaced by Nos. 1/8.

POSTAGE

I.E.F. 'D'

1 Anna   **4**   **4**
(1)   I   II

Two types of tougra in central design:
(a) Large "tougra" or sign-manual of El Ghazi 7 mm high.
(b) Smaller "tougra" of Sultan Rechad 5½ mm high.

Two types of 4 a. surcharge:
I. Normal "4". Apostrophes on D 3½ mm apart.
II. Small "4" Apostrophes on D 4½ mm apart.

1919 (28 Jan). *Turkish Fiscal stamps surch as T* **1** *by Govt Press, Baghdad. P* 11½ (½ a.), 12 (1 a.), *or* 12½ (*others*).
1		½ a. on 1 pi. green and red	..	1·40	1·40
2		1 a. on 20 pa. black/red (a)	..	1·40	1·75
		a. Imperf between (horiz pair)	..	£600	
		b. Surch double	..	£500	
		c. "A" of "Anna" omitted	..	£200	
3		1 a. on 20 pa. black/red (b)	..	4·00	3·00
		b. Surch double	..	£600	
4		2½ a. on 1 pi. mauve and yellow (b)	..	1·50	1·50
		a. No bar to fraction (R. 2/4)	..	27·00	38·00
		b. Surch double	..	£650	
5		3 a. on 20 pa. green (a)	..	1·60	2·75
6		3 a. on 20 pa. green and orange (b)	..	30·00	50·00
7		4 a. on 1 pi. deep violet (a) (I)	..	3·00	3·50
		a. "4" omitted	..	£1400	
		c. Surch double	..	£800	
7d		4 a. on 1 pi. deep violet (a) (II)	..	6·50	8·50
		da. Surch double, one with "4" omitted	..	£2250	

8		8 a. on 10 pa. lake (a)	..	4·00	5·00
		a. Surch inverted	..	£600	£700
		b. Surch double	..	£500	£600
		c. No apostrophe after "D" (R. 1/5)	..	23·00	32·00
		d. Surch inverted. No apostrophe after "D"			
		e. "na" of "Anna" omitted	..	£250	
		f. Error. 8 a. on 1 pi. deep violet	..	£1700	

No. 4a occurs on some sheets only. No. 8c comes from the first setting only.

Nos. 1/8 were replaced by "IRAQ IN BRITISH OCCUPATION" surcharges during 1921.

In December 1925 the League of Nations awarded the vilayet of Mosul to Iraq.

III. ISSUES FOR IRAQ

PRICES FOR STAMPS ON COVER	
Nos. 1/18	*from* × 4
Nos. 41/154	*from* × 2
Nos. O19/171	*from* × 2

BRITISH OCCUPATION

IRAQ IN BRITISH   OCCUPATION

1An.

(1)   A   B

1918 (1 Sept)–**21**. *Turkish pictorial issue of 1914, surch as T* **1** *by Bradbury Wilkinson. P* 12.

(a) *No wmk. Tougra as* A (1 Sept 1918–20)
1	34	¼ a. on 5 pa. dull purple	..	30	80
2	36	½ a. on 10 pa. green	..	30	15
3	37	1 a. on 20 pa. red	..	30	10
4	34	1½ a. on 5 pa. dull purple (1920) ..	2·75	50
5	38	2½ a. on 1 pi. bright blue ..	..	80	1·25
		a. Surch inverted	..	£3250	
6	39	3 a. on 1½ pi. grey and rose	..	70	25
		a. Surch double (Bk. + R.)	..	£1500	£2250
7	40	4 a. on 1¾ pi. red-brown and grey	..	70	25
		a. Centre inverted	..	†	£12000
8	41	6 a. on 2 pi. black and green	..	1·60	1·25
9	42	8 a. on 2½ pi. green and orange	..	90	60
		a. Surch inverted	..	†	£7000
10	43	12 a. on 5 pi. deep lilac	..	1·75	2·50
11	44	1 r. on 10 pi. red-brown	..	2·25	1·40
12	45	2 r. on 25 pi. yellow-green	..	7·50	2·50
13	46	5 r. on 50 pi. rose	..	20·00	19·00
14	47	10 r. on 100 pi. indigo	..	42·00	17·00
1/14			*Set of 14*	70·00	42·00
1/3, 5/14 Perf "Specimen" ..			*Set of 13*	£250	

(b) *No wmk. Tougra as* B (*one device instead of two*) (1921)
15	44	1 r. on 10 pi. red-brown..	..	£100	24·00

(c) *Wmk Mult Script CA* (*sideways on* ½ a., 1½ a.) (1921)
16	36	½ a. on 10 pa. green	..	70	1·25
17	34	1½ a. on 5 pa. dull purple..	..	95	95
18	45	2 r. on 25 pi. yellow-green	..	13·00	11·00
16/18			*Set of 3*	13·00	11·50
16/18 Optd "Specimen" ..			*Set of 3*	50·00	

Designs: *Horiz*—5 pa. Leander's Tower; 10 pa. Lighthouse-garden, Stamboul; 20 pa. Castle of Europe; 1 pi. Mosque of Sultan Ahmed; 1½ pi. Martyrs of Liberty Monument; 1¾ pi. Fountains of Suleiman; 2 pi. Cruiser *Hamidiye*; 2½ pi. Candilli, Bosphorus; 5 pi. Former Ministry of War; 10 pi. Sweet Waters of Europe; 25 pi. Suleiman Mosque; 50 pi. Bosphorus at Rumeli Hisar; 100 pi. Sultan Ahmed's Fountain.

The original settings of Nos. 1/18 showed the surcharge 27 mm wide, except for the 2½ a. (24 mm), 4 a. (26½ mm), 6 a. (32 mm), 8 a. (30½ mm), 12 a. (33 mm), 1 r. (31½ mm), 2 r. (30 mm) and 5 r. (32 mm). The 6 a., 8 a. and 5 r. also exist from a subsequent setting on which the surcharge was 27½ mm wide.

Nos. 2, 3, 5, 6 and 7/9 are known bisected and used on philatelic covers. All such covers have Makinah or F.P.O. 339 cancellations.

During January 1923 an outbreak of cholera in Baghdad led to the temporary use for postal purposes of the above issue overprinted "REVENUE".

LEAGUE OF NATIONS MANDATE

On 25 April 1920 the Supreme Council of the Allies assigned to the United Kingdom a mandate under the League of Nations to administer Iraq.

The Emir Faisal, King of Syria in 1920, was proclaimed King of Iraq on 23 August 1921.

King Faisal I

23 August 1921–8 September 1933

2 Sunni Mosque,   3 Winged Cherub
Muadhdham

4 Allegory of Date Palm

(Des Miss Edith Cheesman (½ a., 1 a., 4 a., 6 a., 8 a., 2 r., 5 r., 10 r.), Mrs. C. Garbett (Miss M. Maynard) (others). Typo (1 r.) or recess (others) Bradbury, Wilkinson)

1923 (1 June)**–25.** *T 2/4 and similar designs. Wmk Mult Script CA (sideways on 2 a., 3 a., 4 a., 8 a., 5 r.). P 12.*

41	2	½ a. olive-green			50	10
42		1 a. brown			75	10
43	3	1½ a. lake			40	10
44		2 a. orange-buff			40	15
45		3 a. grey-blue (1923)			85	15
46		4 a. violet			1·50	30
47		6 a. greenish blue			1·00	30
48		8 a. olive-bistre			1·75	30
49	4	1 r. brown and blue-green			2·75	90
50	2	2 r. black			12·00	7·00
51		2 r. olive-bistre (1925)			30·00	3·25
52		5 r. orange			26·00	13·00
53		10 r. lake			32·00	20·00
41/53				*Set of 13*	95·00	40·00
41/53	Optd "Specimen"			*Set of 13*	£225	

Designs: *Horiz (as T 2)*—1 a. Gufas on the Tigris. (30×24 mm) —2 a. Bull from Babylonian wall-sculpture, 6 a., 10 r. Shiah Mosque, Kadhimain. (34×24 mm)—3 a. Arch of Ctesiphon. *Vert (as T 3)*—4 a., 8 a., 5 r. Tribal Standard, Dulaim Camel Corps. With the exception of Nos. 49 and 50, later printings of these stamps and of No. 78 are on a thinner paper.

10	11	12

King Faisal I

(Recess Bradbury, Wilkinson)

1927 (1 Apr). *Wmk Mult Script CA. P 12.*

78	10	1 r. red-brown (Optd S. £30)			6·00	50

See note below No. 53.

(Recess Bradbury Wilkinson)

1931 (17 Feb). *Wmk Mult Script CA (sideways on 1 r. to 25 r.). P 12.*

80	11	½ a. green			50	10
81		1 a. red-brown			65	10
82		1½ a. scarlet			60	30
83		2 a. orange			65	10
84		3 a. blue			60	10
85		4 a. slate-purple			1·25	95
86		6 a. greenish blue			1·25	60
87		8 a. deep green			1·25	1·50
88	12	1 r. chocolate			3·00	1·25
89		2 r. yellow-brown			5·50	3·75
90		5 r. orange			18·00	30·00
91		10 r. scarlet			50·00	70·00
92	10	25 r. violet			£500	£650
80/91				*Set of 12*	75·00	95·00
80/92	Perf "Specimen"			*Set of 13*	£500	

(New Currency. 1000 fils = 1 dinar)

(13)   (14)

Fils   Fils

Normal "SIN"   Error "SAD" (R. 8/16 of second setting)

(Surcharged at Govt Ptg Wks, Baghdad)

1932 (1 Apr). *Nos. 80/92 and 46 surch in "Fils" or "Dinar" as T 13 or 14.*

106	11	2 f. on ½ a. green (R.)			15	10
107		3 f. on ½ a. green			15	10
		a. Surch double			£140	
		b. Surch inverted			£140	
		c. Arabic letter "SAD" instead of "SIN"			20·00	20·00
108		4 f. on 1 a. red-brown (G.)			1·25	25
109		5 f. on 1 a. red-brown			30	10
		a. Inverted Arabic "5" (R. 8/11)			27·00	32·00
		b. Surch inverted			£250	
110		8 f. on 1½ a. scarlet			35	30
		a. Surch inverted			£140	
111		10 f. on 2 a. orange			35	10
		a. Inverted Arabic "1" (R. 8/13)			18·00	18·00
		b. No space between "10" and "Fils"			35	10
112		15 f. on 3 a. blue			75	1·00
113		20 f. on 4 a. slate-purple			1·00	1·00
		a. Surch inverted			£250	

114	–	25 f. on 4 a. violet (No. 46)			1·50	2·75
		a. "Flis" for "Fils" (R. 2/1, 10/8, 10/15)			£300	£350
		b. Inverted Arabic "5" (R. 10/7, 10/14)			£350	£450
		c. Vars a and b in *se-tenant* pair			£700	
		d. Error. 20 f. on 4 a. violet (R. 10/1, 10/9)			£1200	
115	11	30 f. on 6 a. greenish blue			1·50	60
		a. Error. 80 f. on 6 a. greenish blue			£1000	
116		40 f. on 8 a. deep green			2·25	2·25
117	12	75 f. on 1 r. chocolate			1·75	2·25
		a. Inverted Arabic "5"			30·00	38·00
118		100 f. on 2 r. yellow-brown			5·50	3·75
119		200 f. on 5 r. orange			11·00	15·00
120		½ d. on 10 r. scarlet			45·00	60·00
		a. No bar in English "½"			£600	£650
		b. Scarlet-vermilion			45·00	70·00
121	10	1 d. on 25 r. violet			80·00	£130
106/121				*Set of 16*	£130	£190

Nos. 106/13 and 115/16 were in sheets of 160 (16×10), No. 114 sheets of 150 (15×10) and Nos. 117/21 sheets of 100 (10×10). There were three settings of the surcharge for the 3 f. and two settings for the 5, 10, 25, 40, 100 and 200 t. Nos. 109a and 111a come from the first setting and Nos. 107c, 111b and 114a/b come from the second.

No. 109a can be easily identified as it shows the point of the Arabic numeral at the foot of the surcharge.

All 10 f. stamps from the second setting are as No. 111b except for R. 4/7–8 and 15–16 where the spacing is the same as for the first setting (Type 13).

No. 114d shows "20" instead of "25". Many examples of this error were removed from the sheets before issue. The Arabic value "25" was unaltered.

No. 115a shows the error in the English face value only.

No. 117a occurs on R. 1/2, 1/7 and a third position in the first vertical row not yet identified.

No. 120a occurs on R. 10/1, one position in the first horizontal row and another in the second.

No. 120b was a special printing of No. 91 which does not exist unsurcharged.

15

1932 (9 May). *T 10 to 12, but with values altered to "FILS" or "DINAR" as in T 15. Wmk Mult Script CA (sideways on 50 f. to 1 d.). P 12.*

138	11	2 f. ultramarine			40	10
139		3 f. green			40	10
140		4 f. brown-purple			40	10
141		5 f. grey-green			50	10
142		8 f. scarlet			80	10
143		10 f. yellow			80	10
144		15 f. blue			80	10
145		20 f. orange			80	40
146		25 f. mauve			80	30
147		30 f. bronze-green			1·25	85
148		40 f. violet			90	70
149	12	50 f. brown			90	20
150		75 f. dull ultramarine			1·75	1·75
151		100 f. deep green			3·00	70
152		200 f. scarlet			10·00	3·25
153	10	½ d. deep blue			30·00	30·00
154		1 d. claret			65·00	65·00
138/154				*Set of 17*	£100	90·00
138/54	Perf "Specimen"			*Set of 17*	£180	

OFFICIAL STAMPS

ON STATE SERVICE

(O 2)

1920 (1 May)**–23.** *As Nos. 1/18, but surch includes additional wording "ON STATE SERVICE" as Type O 2 in black.*

(a) *No wmk. Tougra as A (1920)*

O19	36	½ a. on 10 pa. blue-green			2·75	80
O20	37	1 a. on 20 pa. red			1·50	60
O21	34	1½ a. on 5 pa. purple-brown			6·50	1·50
O22	38	2½ a. on 1 pi. blue.			1·40	2·25
O23	39	3 a. on 1½ pi. black and rose			6·50	80
O24	40	4 a. on 1¾ pi. red-brown and grey-blue			7·50	1·75
O25	41	6 a. on 2 pi. black and green			10·00	4·75
O26	42	8 a. on 2½ pi. yellow-green & orge-brn			9·00	2·75
O27	43	12 a. on 5 pi. purple			6·50	4·50
O28	44	1 r. on 10 pi. red-brown.			7·00	4·25
O29	45	2 r. on 25 pi. olive-green			15·00	10·00
O30	46	5 r. on 50 pi. rose-carmine			30·00	23·00
O31	47	10 r. on 100 pi. slate-blue			50·00	55·00
O19/31				*Set of 13*	£140	£100

(b) *No wmk. Tougra as B (No. 15) (1922)*

O32	44	1 r. on 10 pi. red-brown.			18·00	7·00

(c) *Wmk Mult Script CA (sideways on ½ a. to 8 a.) (1921–23)*

O33	36	½ a. on 10 pa. green			60	60
O34	37	1 a. on 20 pa. red			1·50	60
O35	34	1½ a. on 5 pa. purple-brown			1·50	45
O36	40	4 a. on 1¾ pi. red-brown and grey-blue			2·00	90
O37	41	6 a. on 2 pi. black and green (10.3.23)			11·00	60·00
O38	42	8 a. on 2½ pi. yellow-green & orge-brn			3·00	2·00
O39	43	12 a. on 5 pi. purple (10.3.23)			12·00	50·00
O40	45	2 r. on 25 pi. olive-green (10.3.23)			38·00	70·00
O33/40				*Set of 8*	65·00	£160
O33/40	Optd "Specimen"			*Set of 8*	£120	

Nos. O25/6, O30 and O37/8 only exist from the setting with the surcharge 27½ mm wide.

ON STATE SERVICE   ON STATE SERVICE

(O 6)   (O 7)

1923. *Optd with Types O 6 (horiz designs) or O 7 (vert designs).*

O54	2	½ a. olive-green			70	30
O55	–	1 a. brown			70	10

O56	3	1½ a. lake			1·75	45
O57		2 a. orange-buff			1·50	20
O58		3 a. grey-blue			2·50	85
O59		4 a. violet			2·50	40
O60		6 a. greenish blue			3·50	1·25
O61		8 a. olive-bistre			4·00	1·25
O62	4	1 r. brown and blue-green			5·00	1·25
O63	2	2 r. black (R.)			18·00	8·00
O64		5 r. orange			48·00	24·00
O65		10 r. lake			70·00	48·00
O54/65				*Set of 12*	£140	75·00
O54/65	Optd "Specimen"			*Set of 12*	£200	

ON STATE SERVICE   ON STATE SERVICE

(O 8)   (O 9)

1924–25. *Optd with Types O 8 (horiz designs) or O 9 (vert designs).*

O66	2	½ a. olive-green			60	10
O67		1 a. brown			40	10
O68	3	1½ a. lake			70	10
O69		2 a. orange-buff			90	10
O70		3 a. grey-blue			1·00	10
O71		4 a. violet			2·50	30
O72		6 a. greenish blue			1·75	70
O73		8 a. olive-bistre			1·75	35
O74	4	1 r. brown and blue-green			9·50	1·00
O75	2	2 r. olive-bistre (1925)			25·00	3·75
O76		5 r. orange			45·00	42·00
O77		10 r. lake			65·00	42·00
O66/77				*Set of 12*	£140	80·00
O66/77	Optd "Specimen"			*Set of 12*	£200	

1927 (1 Apr). *Optd with Type O 9.*

O79	10	1 r. red-brown (Optd S. £30)			5·50	1·75

ON STATE SERVICE

ON STATE SERVICE   ON STATE SERVICE

(O 12)   (O 13)

1931. *Optd. (a) As Type O 12.*

O 93	11	½ a. green			30	2·75
O 94		1 a. red-brown			50	10
O 95		1½ a. scarlet			4·50	15·00
O 96		2 a. orange			50	10
O 97		3 a. blue			85	70
O 98		4 a. slate-purple			95	90
O 99		6 a. greenish blue			3·50	13·00
O100		8 a. deep green			3·50	13·00

(b) *As Type O 13, horizontally*

O101	12	1 r. chocolate			11·00	12·00
O102		2 r. yellow-brown			17·00	45·00
O103		5 r. orange			35·00	80·00
O104		10 r. scarlet			70·00	£130

(c) *As Type O 13, vertically upwards*

O105	10	25 r. violet			£550	£700
O93/104				*Set of 12*	£130	£275
O93/105	Perf "Specimen"			*Set of 13*	£500	

1932 (1 Apr). *Official issues of 1924–25 and 1931 surch in "FILS" or "DINAR", as T 13 or 14.*

O122	11	3 f. on ½ a. green			3·00	3·00
		a. Pair, one without surch			£250	
O123		4 f. on 1 a. red-brown (G.)			2·25	10
O124		5 f. on 1 a. red-brown			2·00	10
		a. Inverted Arabic "5" (R. 8/11)			38·00	28·00
O125	3	8 f. on 1½ a. lake (No. O68)			3·00	50
O126	11	10 f. on 2 a. orange			2·50	10
		a. Inverted Arabic "1" (R. 8/13)			32·00	25·00
		b. "10" omitted			†£1500	
		c. No space between "10" and "Fils"			2·25	10
O127		15 f. on 3 a. blue			3·00	85
O128		20 f. on 4 a. slate-purple			3·00	1·10
O129		25 f. on 4 a. slate-purple			3·50	1·25
O130	–	30 f. on 6 a. greenish blue (No. O72)			3·50	1·75
O131	11	40 f. on 8 a. deep green			3·50	3·50
		a. "Flis" for "Fils" (R. 7/5, 7/13)			£200	£275
O132	12	50 f. on 1 r. chocolate			3·50	3·50
		a. Inverted Arabic "5" (R. 1/2)			65·00	75·00
O133		75 f. on 1 r. chocolate			5·00	6·00
		a. Inverted Arabic "5"			45·00	55·00
O134	2	100 f. on 2 r. olive-bistre (surch at top)			9·00	3·50
		a. Surch at foot			10·00	9·00
O135	–	200 f. on 5 r. orange (No. O76)			18·00	18·00
O136	–	½ d. on 10 r. lake (No. O77)			50·00	70·00
		a. No bar in English "½" (R. 2/10)			£600	3700
O137	10	1 d. on 25 r. violet			85·00	£140
O122/37				*Set of 16*	£170	£225

Nos. O122/4, O126/9 and O131 were in sheets of 160 (16×10), Nos. O130, O134 and O136 150 (10×15), No. O135 150 (15×10) and Nos. O125, O132/3 and O137 in sheets of 100 (10×10). There was a second setting of the surcharge for the 3 f. (equivalent to the third postage setting), 10 f. to 25 f., 40 f. and 100 f. to 1 d. Nos. O126c, O131a and O134a come from the second setting.

All 100 f. stamps from the second setting are as No. O134a.

For notes on other varieties see below No. 121.

1932 (9 May). *Optd. (a) As Type O 12.*

O155	11	2 f. ultramarine			1·00	10
O156		3 f. green			1·00	10
O157		4 f. brown-purple			1·00	10
O158		5 f. grey-green			1·00	10
O159		8 f. scarlet			1·00	10
O160		10 f. yellow			1·75	10
O161		15 f. blue			2·25	10
O162		20 f. orange			2·25	15
O163		25 f. mauve			2·00	15
O164		30 f. bronze-green			3·25	20
O165		40 f. violet			4·25	20

(b) As Type O 13, horizontally

O166	12	50 f. brown			3·00	20
O167		75 f. dull ultramarine			2·25	90
O168		100 f. deep green			9·00	1·00
O169		200 f. scarlet			17·00	6·50

(c) As Type O 13, vertically upwards

O170	10	½ d. deep blue			12·00	21·00
O171		1 d. claret			50·00	70·00
O155/71				*Set of 17*	£100	90·00
O155/71 Perf "Specimen"				*Set of 17*	£300	

The British Mandate was given up on 3 October 1932 and Iraq became an independent kingdom. Later issues will be found listed in Part 19 (*Middle East*) of this catalogue.

Ireland (Republic)

All the issues of Ireland are listed together here, in this section of the Gibbons Catalogue, purely as a matter of convenience to collectors.

PRICES FOR STAMPS ON COVER TO 1945	
Nos. 1/15	*from* × 5
Nos. 17/21	*from* × 3
Nos. 26/9a	*from* × 5
Nos. 30/43	*from* × 4
Nos. 44/6	—
Nos. 47/63	*from* × 5
Nos. 64/6	*from* × 3
Nos. 67/70	*from* × 6
Nos. 71/82	*from* × 2
Nos. 83/8	*from* × 3
Nos. 89/98	*from* × 2
Nos. 99/104	*from* × 3
Nos. 105/37	*from* × 2
Nos. D1/4	*from* × 7
Nos. D5/14	*from* × 6

PROVISIONAL GOVERNMENT
16 January—6 December 1922

Stamps of Great Britain overprinted. T 104/8, W 100; T 109, W 110

Rıaltaſ
Sealaɓac
na
hẽıρeann
1922
(1)

Rıaltaſ
Sealaɓac
na
hẽıρeann
1922.
(2)

Rıaltaſ
Sealaɓac
na hẽıρeann
1922
(3)

("Provisional Government of Ireland, 1922")

1922 (17 Feb–July). *T 104 to 108 (W 100) and 109 of Great Britain overprinted in black.*

(a) With T 1, by Dollard Printing House Ltd. Optd in black

1	105	½ d. green			70	40
		a. Opt inverted			£400	£550
2	104	1 d. scarlet			1·00	35
		a. Opt inverted			£250	£300
		b. Opt double, both inverted, one albino		£350		
		c. Opt double			†	
		w. Wmk inverted			—	£150
3		1 d. carmine-red			1·75	50
4		2½ d. bright blue			1·25	4·50
		a. Red opt (1 Apr)			85	3·25
5	106	3 d. bluish violet			3·75	3·75
6		4 d. grey-green			3·00	9·00
		a. Red opt (1 Apr)			7·50	15·00
		b. Carmine opt (July)			40·00	65·00
7	107	5 d. yellow-brown			3·50	8·50
		x. Wmk reversed			—	£200
8	108	9 d. agate			9·50	18·00
		a. Red opt (1 Apr)			12·00	17·00
		b. Carmine opt (July)			80·00	85·00
9		10 d. turquoise-blue			7·50	30·00
1/9				*Set of 8*	26·00	65·00

*All values except 2½ d. and 4 d. are known with greyish black overprint, but these are difficult to distinguish.
The carmine overprints on the 4 d. and 9 d. may have been produced by Alex Thom & Co. Ltd. There was a further

---

overprinting of the 2½ d. at the same time, but this is difficult to distinguish.
The ½ d. with red overprint is a trial or proof printing (*Price £150*).
Bogus inverted T 1 overprints exist on the 2 d., 4 d., 9 d and 1 s. values.

(b) With T 2, by Alex Thom & Co Ltd.

10	105	1½ d. red-brown			1·25	85
		a. Error. "PENCF"			£350	£275
		w. Wmk inverted			—	£120
		x. Wmk reversed			—	£120
12	106	2 d. orange (Die I)			2·00	50
		a. Opt inverted			£180	£250
		w. Wmk inverted			—	£100
		x. Wmk reversed			—	£120
13		2 d. orange (Die II)			1·75	50
		a. Opt inverted			£300	£400
		w. Wmk inverted			—	£120
14	107	6 d. reddish pur (*chalk-surfaced paper*)	10·00	11·00	
15	108	1 s. bistre-brown			11·00	9·00
10/15				*Set of 5*	23·00	19·00

Varieties occur throughout the T 2 overprint in the relative positions of the lines of the overprint, the "R" of "Rialtas" being over either the "Se" or "S" of "Sealadac" or intermediately.

(c) With T 3 by Dollard Printing House Ltd

17	109	2 s. 6 d. chocolate-brown		35·00	65·00
18		2 s. 6 d. reddish brown		50·00	75·00
19		5 s. rose-red		60·00	£120
21		10 s. dull grey-blue		£120	£250
17/21			*Set of 3*	£190	£400

1922 (19 June–Aug). *Optd as T 2, in black, by Harrison & Sons, for use in horiz and vert coils.*

26	105	½ d. green			2·25	10·00
27	104	1 d. scarlet			2·25	6·00
28	105	1½ d. red-brown (21.6)			4·00	32·00
29	106	2 d. bright orange (Die I)			18·00	28·00
29a		2 d. bright orange (Die II) (August)		19·00	25·00
		ay. Wmk inverted and reversed		—	£200
26/9a				*Set of 5*	40·00	90·00

The Harrison overprint measures 15×17 mm (maximum) against the 14½×16 mm of T 2 (Thom printing) and is a much bolder black than the latter, while the individual letters are taller, the "i" of "Rialtas" being specially outstanding as it extends below the foot of the "R".
The "R" of "Rialtas" is always over the "Se" of "Sealadac".

1922. *Optd by Thom.*

(a) As T 2 but bolder, in dull to shiny blue-black or red (June–Nov)

30	105	½ d. green			1·60	80
31	104	1 d. scarlet			80	50
		a. "Q" for "O" (No. 357ab)		£1200	£1100
		b. Reversed "Q" for "O" (No. 357ac)	£350	£250
32	105	1½ d. red-brown			3·00	3·25
33	106	2 d. orange (Die I)			17·00	2·00
34		2 d. orange (Die II)			2·50	50
		y. Wmk inverted and reversed		£120	£120
35	104	2½ d. blue (R.)			6·00	18·00
36	106	3 d. violet			2·25	2·00
		y. Wmk inverted and reversed		75·00	75·00
37		4 d. grey-green (R.)			2·75	4·25
38	107	5 d. yellow-brown			3·75	8·00
39		6 d. reddish pur (*chalk-surfaced paper*)	7·50	2·75	
		w. Wmk inverted			75·00	50·00
40	108	9 d. agate (R.)			12·00	15·00
41		9 d. olive-green (R.)			4·75	28·00
42		10 d. turquoise-blue			25·00	48·00
43		1 s. bistre-brown			8·50	10·00
30/43				*Set of 14*	80·00	£130

Both 2 d. stamps exist with the overprint inverted but there remains some doubt as to whether they were issued.
These Thom printings are distinguishable from the Harrison printings by the size of the overprint, and from the previous Thom printings by the intensity and colour of the overprint, the latter being best seen when the stamp is looked through with a strong light behind it.

(b) As with T 3, but bolder, in shiny blue-black (Oct–Dec)

44	109	2 s. 6 d. chocolate-brown		£180	£250
45		5 s. rose-red		£170	£275
46		10 s. dull grey-blue		£850	£1000
44/6			*Set of 3*	£1100	£1400

The above differ from Nos. 17/21 not only in the bolder impression and colour of the ink but also in the "h" and "é" of "héireann" which are closer together and horizontally aligned.

Rıaltaſ
Sealaɓac
na
hẽıρeann
1922.
(4)

Saorſcác
Éıρeann
1922
(5 Wide date)
("Irish Free State 1922")

1922 (21 Nov–Dec). *Optd by Thom with T 4 (wider setting) in shiny blue-black.*

47	105	½ d. green			1·00	1·75
		a. Opt in jet-black			£100	90·00
48	104	1 d. scarlet			3·50	2·50
49	105	1½ d. red-brown (4 December)		3·00	9·00
50	106	2 d. orange (Die II)			9·00	6·50
51	108	1 s. olive-bistre (4 December)		45·00	48·00
47/51				*Set of 5*	55·00	60·00

The overprint T 4 measures 15¾ × 16 mm (maximum).

OMNIBUS ISSUES

Details, together with prices for complete sets, of the various Omnibus issues from the 1935 Silver Jubilee series to date are included in a special section following Zimbabwe at the end of Volume 2.

---

6 December 1922—29 December 1937

1922 (Dec)–23.

(a) Optd by Thom with T 5, in dull to shiny blue-black or red

52	105	½ d. green			75	30
		a. No accent in "Saorstat"		£1000	£900
		b. Accent inserted by hand		85·00	95·00
53	104	1 d. scarlet			60	40
		aa. No accent in "Saorstat"		£7000	£5000
		a. No accent and final "t" missing	£6000	£4500
		b. Accent inserted by hand		£130	£150
		c. Accent and "t" inserted		£250	£250
		d. Reversed "Q" for "O" (No. 357ac)	£300	£250
54	105	1½ d. red-brown			3·00	8·50
55	106	2 d. orange (Die II)			1·00	1·50
56	104	2½ d. bright blue (R.) (6.1.23)		5·50	6·50
		a. No accent			£140	£170
57	106	3 d. bluish violet (6.1.23)		3·50	11·00
		a. No accent			£250	£275
58		4 d. grey-green (R.) (16.1.23)		2·50	5·50
		a. No accent			£150	£170
59	107	5 d. yellow-brown			3·25	4·75
60		6 d. reddish pur (*chalk-surfaced paper*)	2·00	2·00	
		a. Accent inserted by hand		£700	£700
		y. Wmk inverted and reversed		50·00	30·00
61	108	9 d. olive-green (R.)			3·00	5·50
		a. No accent			£250	£275
62		10 d. turquoise-blue			16·00	48·00
63		1 s. bistre-brown			7·00	9·50
		a. No accent			£5500	£6500
		b. Accent inserted by hand		£600	£650
64	109	2 s. 6 d. chocolate-brown		35·00	55·00
		a. Major Re-entry			£850	£950
		b. No accent			£350	£400
		c. Accent reversed			£425	£475
65		5 s. rose-red			65·00	£120
		a. No accent			£450	£500
		b. Accent reversed			£550	£600
66		10 s. dull grey-blue			£140	£275
		a. No accent			£2000	£2500
		b. Accent reversed			£2750	£3500
52/66				*Set of 15*	£180	£500

The accents inserted by hand are in dull black. The reversed accents are grave (thus "à") instead of acute ("á"). A variety with "S" of "Saorstat" directly over "é" of "éireann", instead of to left, may be found in all values except the 2½ d. and 4 d. In the 2 s. 6 d., 5 s. and 10 s. it is very slightly to the left in the "S" over "é" variety, bringing the "á" of "Saorstat" directly above the last "n" of "éireann".

(b) Optd with T 5, in dull or shiny blue-black, by Harrison, for use in horiz or vert coils (7.3.23)

67		½ d. green			1·75	9·50
		a. Long "1" in "1922"			20·00	48·00
		y. Wmk inverted and reversed			
68		1 d. scarlet			4·00	9·50
		a. Long "1" in "1922"			75·00	£140
69		1½ d. red-brown			6·00	40·00
		a. Long "1" in "1922"			85·00	£225
70		2 d. orange (Die II)			6·00	8·50
		a. Long "1" in "1922"			26·00	45·00
		w. Wmk inverted			—	£150
67/70				*Set of 4*	16·00	60·00

In the Harrison overprint the characters are rather bolder than those of the Thom overprint, and the foot of the "1" of "1922" is usually rounded instead of square. The long "1" in "1922" has a serif at foot. The second "e" of "éireann" appears to be slightly raised.

PRINTERS. The following and all subsequent issues to No. 148 were printed at the Government Printing Works, Dublin, *unless otherwise stated*.

6 "Sword of Light"   7 Map of Ireland   8 Arms of Ireland

9 Celtic Cross   10

(Des J. J. O'Reilly, T 6; J. Ingram, T 7; Miss M. Girling, T 8; and Miss L. Williams, T 9. Typo. Plates made by Royal Mint, London)

1922 (6 Dec)–34. *W 10. P 15×14.*

71	6	½ d. bright green (20.4.23)		85	65
		a. Imperf × perf 14, wmk sideways (11.34)	24·00	45·00
		w. Wmk inverted		30·00	15·00
72	7	1 d. carmine (23.2.23)		80	10
		a. Perf 15 × imperf (single perf) (1933)	85·00	£160
		c. Perf 15 × imperf (7.34)		18·00	40·00
		cw. Wmk inverted			
		d. Booklet pane. Three stamps plus three printed labels (21.8.31)	£225	
		dw. Wmk inverted			
73		1½ d. claret (2.2.23)		1·40	1·75
		w. Wmk inverted			
74		2 d. grey-green (6.12.22)		1·00	10
		a. Imperf × perf 14, wmk sideways (11.34)	42·00	70·00
		b. Perf 15 × imperf (1934)		£8500	£1500
		w. Wmk inverted		20·00	5·00
		y. Wmk inverted and reversed		30·00	70·00

Ireland

If you collect Ireland you should be on our mailing list because we offer
Extensive stocks of specialised and general Irish stamps.

The most detailed Retail List of Irish stamps and covers.

Four postal auctions every year.

Up to 6 Offers Lists of Ireland annually.

Free colour photocopies of items of interest to you.

The extensive range of Lindner products.

Prompt and reliable mail order service with all credit cards accepted.

Two shops packed with stamps, covers and collections.

Raven Stamps

12C Washington St. West,
Cork, Ireland.
Tel: +353 21 271750
Fax: +353 21 271779

E Mail raven1@indigo.ie

Cathedral Stamps

78 Marlborough St.,
Dublin 1, Ireland.
Tel: +353 1 8786384
Fax: +353 1 8786384

Quality Stamps
DIRECT TO YOUR DOOR

*Irresistibly simple, exceptionally quick and reassuringly reliable
Stanley Gibbons Mail Order Service enables you to economically
build your collection from the comfort of your own home.*

We Provide:

- The world's largest stocks of guaranteed quality Great Britain, Commonwealth, Foreign and Thematic material.
- Regular illustrated listings for many popular countries and themes.
- Fast 48 hour order despatch.
- A detailed register of your collecting interests.
- Exclusive special offers mailed regularly.
- Specialist 'wants list' service available.
- Free telephone advice.
- Over 140 years philatelic experience.

STANLEY GIBBONS
Mail Order

Stanley Gibbons Mail Order
399 Strand, London, WC2R 0LX England.
Tel: +44 (0)171 836 8444 Fax: +44 (0)171 836 7342
e.mail mailorder@stangiblondon.demon.co.uk
internet: http://www.stangib.com/

Free 1998 Great Britain Stamps Listing

- A comprehensive checklist of Great Britain stamps.
- Packed full of popular material, complete with colour illustrations, accurate descriptions and SG catalogue numbers throughout.
- Contains a useful checklist and a pull out order form in the centre pages.
- Many rare and specialised items are now included.
- Makes collecting easy, from the comfort of your own home.

75	8	2½d. red-brown (7.9.23)		3·50	3·50
		w. Wmk inverted	.. ..	50·00	8·00
76	9	3d. ultramarine (16.3.23)	..	1·50	75
		w. Wmk inverted	..	65·00	12·00
77	8	4d. slate-blue (28.9.23)	..	2·00	3·25
		w. Wmk inverted	..	75·00	25·00
78	6	5d. deep violet (11.5.23)	..	8·00	9·50
		w. Wmk inverted			
79		6d. claret (21.12.23)	..	3·75	50
		w. Wmk inverted		£110	25·00
80	8	9d. deep violet (26.10.23)	..	13·00	9·00
		w. Wmk inverted			
81	9	10d. brown (11.5.23)	..	9·00	18·00
		w. Wmk inverted			
82	6	1s. light blue (15.6.23)	..	17·00	5·50
		w. Wmk inverted			
71/82			Set of 12	55·00	50·00

No. 72a is imperf vertically except for a single perf at each top corner. It was issued for use in automatic machines.
See also Nos. 111/22 and 227/8.

SAORSTÁT ÉIREANN 1922

(11 Narrow Date)   12 Daniel O'Connell

1925 (Aug)–**28.** *T* **109** *of Great Britain (Bradbury, Wilkinson printing) optd at the Government Printing Works, Dublin or by Harrison and Sons. (a) With T* **11** *in black or grey-black (25.8.25).*
83		2s. 6d. chocolate-brown	..	38·00	80·00
		a. Wide and narrow date (pair) (1927)		£250	
84		5s. rose-red	..	50·00	£120
		a. Wide and narrow date (pair) (1927)		£400	
85		10s. dull grey-blue	..	£110	£275
		a. Wide and narrow date (pair) (1927)		£1000	
83/5			Set of 3	£180	£425

The varieties with wide and narrow date *se-tenant* are from what is known as the "composite setting," in which some stamps showed the wide date, as T 5, while in others the figures were close together, as in T 11.
Single specimens of this printing with wide date may be distinguished from Nos. 64 to 66 by the colour of the ink, which is black or grey-black in the composite setting and blue-black in the Thom printing.
The type of the "composite" overprint usually shows distinct signs of wear.

(b) As T **5** *(wide date) in black (1927–28)*
86		2s. 6d. chocolate-brown (9.12.27)	..	42·00	42·00
		a. Circumflex accent over "a"		£200	£250
		b. No accent over "a"		£350	£375
		c. Flat accent on "a"		£300	£350
87		5s. rose-red (2.28)	..	60·00	80·00
		a. Circumflex accent over "a"		£325	£375
		b. No accent over "a"		£400	£450
		c. Flat accent on "a"		£900	£1000
88		10s. dull grey-blue (15.2.28)	..	£150	£170
		a. Circumflex accent over "a"		£800	£900
		c. Flat accent on "a"		£900	£1000
86/8			Set of 3	£225	£250

This printing can be distinguished from the Thom overprints in dull black, by the clear, heavy impression (in deep black) which often shows in relief on the back of the stamp.
The variety showing a circumflex accent over the "a" occurred on R.9/2. The overprint in this position finally deteriorated to such an extent that some examples of the 2s. 6d. were without accent (No. 86b). A new cliché was then introduced with the accent virtually flat and which also showed damage to the "a" and the crossbar of the "t".

(Des L. Whelan. Typo)
1929 (22 June). *Catholic Emancipation Centenary. W* **10.** *P* 15 × 14.
89	12	2d. grey-green	..	50	45
90		3d. blue	..	4·00	8·50
91		9d. bright violet	..	4·00	4·00
89/91			Set of 3	7·50	11·50

13 Shannon Barrage   14 Reaper

(Des E. L. Lawrenson. Typo)
1930 (15 Oct). *Completion of Shannon Hydro-Electric Scheme. W* **10.** *P* 15 × 14.
92	13	2d. agate	..	80	55

(T **14** and **15** des G. Atkinson. Typo)
1931 (12 June). *Bicentenary of the Royal Dublin Society. W* **10.** *P* 15 × 14.
93	14	2d. blue	..	65	30

15 The Cross of Cong   16 Adoration of the Cross   17 Hurler

1932 (12 May). *International Eucharistic Congress. W* **10.** *P* 15×14.
94	15	2d. grey-green	..	80	30
		w. Wmk inverted			
95		3d. blue	..	2·25	5·00

(T **16** to **19** des R. J. King. Typo)
1933 (18 Sept). *"Holy Year". W* **10.** *P* 15 × 14.
96	16	2d. grey-green	..	1·00	15
97		3d. blue	..	2·50	2·00

1934 (27 July). *Golden Jubilee of the Gaelic Athletic Association. W* **10.** *P* 15 × 14.
98	17	2d. green	..	75	45

1935 (Mar–July). *T* **109** *of Great Britain (Waterlow printings) optd as T* **5** *(wide date), at the Government Printing Works, Dublin.*
99	109	2s. 6d. chocolate (No. 450)	..	45·00	48·00
		a. Flat accent on "a" (R. 9/2)	..	£225	£200
100		5s. bright rose-red (No. 451)	..	80·00	80·00
		a. Flat accent on "a" (R. 9/2)	..	£300	£250
101		10s. indigo (No. 452)	..	£350	£350
		a. Flat accent on "a" (R. 9/2)	..	£900	£750
99/101			Set of 3	£425	£425

18 St. Patrick   19 Ireland and New Constitution

1937 (8 Sept). *W* **10.** *P* 14×15.
102	18	2s. 6d. emerald-green	..	£140	65·00
		w. Wmk inverted		£600	£225
103		5s. maroon	..	£180	£110
		w. Wmk inverted		£500	£225
104		10s. deep blue	..	£140	50·00
		w. Wmk inverted			
102/4			Set of 3	£425	£200

See also Nos. 123/5.

EIRE
29 December 1937—17 April 1949
1937 (29 Dec). *Constitution Day. W* **10.** *P* 15×14.
105	19	2d. claret	..	1·00	20
		w. Wmk inverted		—	£180
106		3d. blue	..	4·00	3·50

For similar stamps see Nos. 176/7.

20 Father Mathew

(Des S. Keating. Typo)
1938 (1 July). *Centenary of Temperance Crusade. W* **10.** *P* 15×14.
107	20	2d. black	..	1·50	30
		w. Wmk inverted			
108		3d. blue	..	8·50	6·00

21 George Washington, American Eagle and Irish Harp   22

(Des G. Atkinson. Typo)
1939 (1 Mar). *150th Anniv of U.S. Constitution and Installation of First U.S. President. W* **10.** *P* 15 × 14.
109	21	2d. scarlet	..	1·75	60
110		3d. blue	..	3·25	4·00

SIZE OF WATERMARK. T **22** can be found in various sizes from about 8 to 10 mm high. This is due to the use of two different dandy rolls supplied by different firms and to the effects of paper shrinkage and other factors such as pressure and machine speed.

COVER PRICES

Cover factors are quoted at the beginning of each country for most issues to 1945. An explanation of the system can be found on page x. The factors quoted do not, however, apply to philatelic covers.

White line above left value tablet joining horizontal line to ornament (R. 3/7)

1940–68. *Typo. W* **22.** *P* 15×14 or 14×15 *(2s. 6d. to 10s.).*
111	6	½d. bright green (24.11.40)	..	2·00	40
		w. Wmk inverted	..	50·00	6·50
112	7	1d. carmine (26.10.40)	..	30	10
		aw. Wmk inverted	..	1·40	25
		b. From coils. Perf 14×imperf (9.40)		65·00	65·00
		c. From coils. Perf 15×imperf (20.3.46)	..	40·00	15·00
		cw. Wmk inverted	..	40·00	15·00
		d. Booklet pane. Three stamps plus three printed labels	..	£1500	
		dw. Wmk inverted			
113		1½d. claret (1.40)	..	13·00	30
		w. Wmk inverted	..	27·00	7·50
114		2d. grey-green (1.40)	..	30	10
		w. Wmk inverted	..	2·25	75
115	8	2½d. red-brown (3.41)	..	9·00	15
		w. Wmk inverted	..	18·00	4·00
116	9	3d. blue (12.40)	..	60	10
		w. Wmk inverted	..	3·50	50
117	8	4d. slate-blue (12.40)	..	55	10
		w. Wmk inverted	..	13·00	2·75
118	6	5d. deep violet (7.40)	..	65	10
		w. Wmk inverted	..	26·00	1·50
119		6d. claret (3.42)	..	2·00	50
		aw. Wmk inverted	..	17·00	3·00
		b. Chalk-surfaced paper (1967)		1·25	20
		cw. Wmk inverted	..	13·00	2·50
119c		8d. scarlet (12.9.49)	..	80	65
		cw. Wmk inverted	..	32·00	10·00
120	8	9d. deep violet (7.40)	..	1·50	60
		w. Wmk inverted	..	9·00	2·00
121	9	10d. brown (7.40)	..	60	60
		aw. Wmk inverted	..	10·00	3·50
121b		11d. rose (12.9.49)	..	1·50	2·25
122	6	1s. light blue (6.40)	..	80·00	17·00
		w. Wmk inverted	..	£600	£150
123	18	2s. 6d. emerald-green (10.2.43)	..	40·00	1·25
		aw. Wmk inverted	..	80·00	20·00
		b. Chalk-surfaced paper (1968?)		1·50	2·25
		bw. Wmk inverted	..	28·00	4·00
124		5s. maroon (15.12.42)	..	40·00	2·75
		a. Line flaw			
		bw. Wmk inverted	..	£150	30·00
		c. Chalk-surfaced paper (1968?)		13·00	3·50
		ca. Purple	..	6·00	6·50
		cb. Line flaw	..	80·00	
		cw. Wmk inverted	..	35·00	8·00
125		10s. deep blue (7.45)	..	60·00	6·00
		aw. Wmk inverted	..	£170	65·00
		b. Chalk-surfaced paper (1968)		19·00	9·50
		ba. Blue	..	12·00	16·00
		bw. Wmk inverted	..	£120	55·00
111/25			Set of 17	£110	130·00

There is a wide range of shades and also variation in paper used in this issue.
See also Nos. 227/8.

1941 I gCuimhne Aiséirge 1916
(23 *Trans* "In memory of the rising of 1916")   24 Volunteer and G.P.O., Dublin

1941 (12 Apr). *25th Anniv of Easter Rising (1916). Provisional issue. T* **7** *and* **9** *(2d. in new colour), optd with T* **23.**
126	7	2d. orange (G.)	..	2·00	50
127	9	3d. blue (V.)	..	32·00	9·50

(Des V. Brown. Typo)
1941 (27 Oct). *25th Anniv of Easter Rising (1916). Definitive issue. W* **22.** *P* 15 × 14.
128	24	2½d. blue-black	..	70	50

25 Dr. Douglas Hyde   26 Sir William Rowan Hamilton   27 Bro. Michael O'Clery

(Des S. O'Sullivan. Typo)
1943 (31 July). *50th Anniv of Founding of Gaelic League. W* **22.** *P* 15 × 14.
129	25	½d. green	..	40	30
130		2½d. claret	..	1·25	10

(Des S. O'Sullivan from a bust by Hogan. Typo)
1943 (13 Nov). *Centenary of Announcement of Discovery of Quaternions. W* **22.** *P* 15 × 14.
131	26	½d. green	..	40	40
		w. Wmk inverted			
132		2½d. brown	..	1·75	10

(Des R. J. King. Typo)

1944 (30 June). *Tercentenary of Death of Michael O'Clery. (Commemorating the "Annals of the Four Masters").* W **22** *(sideways*).* P 14×15.

133	27	½d. emerald-green				10	10
		w. Wmk facing right				55	20
134		1s. red-brown				70	10
		w. Wmk facing right				2·00	50

*The normal sideways watermark shows the top of the e facing left, *as seen from the back of the stamp.*

Although issued as commemoratives these two stamps were kept in use as part of the current issue, replacing Nos. 111 and 122.

28 Edmund Ignatius Rice   29 "Youth Sowing Seeds of Freedom"

(Des S. O'Sullivan. Typo)

1944 (29 Aug). *Death Centenary of Edmund Rice (founder of Irish Christian Brothers).* W **22**. P 15 × 14.

| 135 | 28 | 2½d. slate | | | | 60 | 45 |
| | | w. Wmk inverted | | | | | |

(Des R. J. King. Typo)

1945 (15 Sept). *Centenary of Death of Thomas Davis (founder of Young Ireland Movement).* W **22**. P 15 × 14.

136	29	2½d. blue				1·00	25
		w. Wmk inverted				—	£130
137		6d. claret				7·00	3·75

30 "Country and Homestead"

(Des R. J. King. Typo)

1946 (16 Sept). *Birth Centenaries of Davitt and Parnell (land reformers).* W **22**. P 15 × 14.

| 138 | 30 | 2½d. scarlet | | | | 1·50 | 15 |
| 139 | | 3d. blue | | | | 3·50 | 3·25 |

31 Angel Victor over Rock of Cashel

(Des R. J. King. Recess Waterlow (1d. to 1s. 3d. until 1961), D.L.R. (8d., 1s. 3d. from 1961 and 1s. 5d.))

1948 (7 Apr)–**65**. *Air. T 31 and similar horiz designs.* W **22**. P 15 (1s. 5d.) or 15 × 14 (others).

140	31	1d. chocolate (4.4.49)			2·00	3·50
141	—	3d. blue			4·00	2·25
142	—	6d. magenta			1·00	1·50
		aw. Wmk inverted				
142b	—	8d. lake-brown (13.12.54)			7·00	6·00
143	—	1s. green (4.4.49)			1·75	1·50
143a	31	1s. 3d. red-orange (13.12.54)			7·00	1·25
		aw. Wmk inverted			£550	£250
143b	—	1s. 5d. deep ultramarine (1.4.65)			3·50	1·00
140/3b				Set of 7	24·00	15·00

Designs:—3d., 8d. Lough Derg; 6d. Croagh Patrick; 1s. Glendalough.

35 Theobald Wolfe Tone

(Des K. Uhlemann. Typo)

1948 (19 Nov). *150th Anniv of Insurrection.* W **22**. P 15×14.

144	35	2½d. reddish purple			1·00	10
		w. Wmk inverted				
145		3d. violet			3·25	3·25

REPUBLIC OF IRELAND
18 April 1949

36 Leinster House and Arms of Provinces   37 J. C. Mangan

(Des Muriel Brandt. Typo)

1949 (21 Nov). *International Recognition of Republic.* W **22**. P 15 × 14.

| 146 | 36 | 2½d. reddish brown | | | 1·50 | 10 |
| 147 | | 3d. bright blue | | | 5·50 | 3·75 |

(Des R. J. King. Typo)

1949 (5 Dec). *Death Centenary of James Clarence Mangan (poet).* W **22**. P 15 × 14.

| 148 | 37 | 1d. green | | | 1·50 | 20 |
| | | w. Wmk inverted | | | | |

38 Statue of St. Peter, Rome   39 Thomas Moore   40 Irish Harp

(Recess Waterlow & Sons)

1950 (11 Sept). *Holy Year.* W **22**. P 12½.

149	38	2½d. violet				1·00	40
150		3d. blue				8·00	8·50
151		9d. brown				8·00	10·00
149/51					Set of 3	15·00	17·00

PRINTERS. Nos. 152 to 200 were recess-printed by De La Rue & Co, Dublin, *unless otherwise stated.*

(Eng W. Vacek)

1952 (10 Nov). *Death Centenary of Thomas Moore (poet).* W **22**. P 13.

| 152 | 39 | 2½d. reddish purple | | | 50 | 10 |
| 153 | | 3½d. deep olive-green | | | 1·75 | 2·75 |

(Des F. O'Ryan. Typo Government Printing Works, Dublin)

1953 (9 Feb). *"An Tostal" (Ireland at Home) Festival.* W **22** (sideways). P 14 × 15.

| 154 | 40 | 2½d. emerald-green | | | 1·25 | 35 |
| 155 | | 1s. 4d. blue | | | 15·00 | 24·00 |

41 Robert Emmet   42 Madonna and Child (Della Robbia)   43 Cardinal Newman (first Rector)

1953 (21 Sept). *150th Death Anniv of Emmet (patriot).* W **22**. P 13.

| 156 | 41 | 3d. deep bluish green | | | 3·75 | 15 |
| 157 | | 1s. 3d. carmine | | | 42·00 | 9·50 |

(Eng A. R. Lane)

1954 (24 May). *Marian Year.* W **22**. P 15.

| 158 | 42 | 3d. blue | | | 2·00 | 10 |
| 159 | | 5d. myrtle-green | | | 3·50 | 5·50 |

(Des L. Whelan. Typo Govt Printing Works, Dublin)

1954 (19 July). *Centenary of Founding of Catholic University of Ireland.* W **22**. P 15 × 14.

160	43	2d. bright purple			1·50	10
		w. Wmk inverted			—	£180
161		1s. 3d. blue			16·00	6·00

44 Statue of Commodore Barry   45 John Redmond   46 Thomas O'Crohan

(Des and eng H. Woyty-Wimmer)

1956 (16 Sept). *Barry Commemoration.* W **22**. P 15.

| 162 | 44 | 3d. slate-lilac | | | 2·00 | 10 |
| 163 | | 1s. 3d. deep blue | | | 7·00 | 8·50 |

1957 (11 June). *Birth Centenary of John Redmond (politician).* W **22**. P 14 × 15.

| 164 | 45 | 3d. deep blue | | | 1·25 | 10 |
| 165 | | 1s. 3d. brown-purple | | | 10·00 | 15·00 |

1957 (1 July). *Birth Centenary of Thomas O'Crohan (author).* W **22**. P 14 × 15.

166	46	2d. maroon			1·50	15
		a. Wmk sideways			†	
167		5d. violet			1·50	5·50

47 Admiral Brown   48 "Father Wadding" (Ribera)   49 Tom Clarke

(Des S. O'Sullivan. Typo Govt Printing Works, Dublin)

1957 (23 Sept). *Death Centenary of Admiral William Brown.* W **22**. P 15 × 14.

| 168 | 47 | 3d. blue | | | 2·25 | 10 |
| 169 | | 1s. 3d. carmine | | | 30·00 | 16·00 |

1957 (25 Nov). *300th Death Anniv of Father Luke Wadding (theologian).* W **22**. P 15.

| 170 | 48 | 3d. deep blue | | | 2·00 | 10 |
| 171 | | 1s. 3d. lake | | | 17·00 | 8·50 |

1958 (28 July). *Birth Centenary of Thomas J. ("Tom") Clarke (patriot).* W **22**. P 15.

| 172 | 49 | 3d. deep green | | | 2·50 | 10 |
| 173 | | 1s. 3d. red-brown | | | 6·50 | 13·00 |

50 Mother Mary Aikenhead   51 Arthur Guinness

(Eng Waterlow. Recess Imprimerie Belge de Securité, Brussels subsidiary of Waterlow & Sons)

1958 (20 Oct). *Death Centenary of Mother Mary Aikenhead (foundress of Irish Sisters of Charity).* W **22**. P 15 × 14.

| 174 | 50 | 3d. Prussian blue | | | 1·50 | 10 |
| 175 | | 1s. 3d. rose-carmine | | | 15·00 | 10·00 |

(Typo Govt Printing Works, Dublin)

1958 (29 Dec). *21st Anniv of the Irish Constitution.* W **22**. P 15 × 14.

| 176 | 19 | 3d. brown | | | 1·25 | 10 |
| 177 | | 5d. emerald-green | | | 2·25 | 4·50 |

1959 (20 July). *Bicentenary of Guinness Brewery.* W **22**. P 15.

| 178 | 51 | 3d. brown-purple | | | 4·00 | 10 |
| 179 | | 1s. 3d. blue | | | 14·00 | 11·00 |

52 "The Flight of the Holy Family"

(Des K. Uhlemann)

1960 (20 June). *World Refugee Year.* W **22**. P 15.

| 180 | 52 | 3d. purple | | | 50 | 10 |
| 181 | | 1s. 3d. sepia | | | 75 | 3·25 |

53 Conference Emblem

(Des P. Rahikainen)

1960 (19 Sept). *Europa.* W **22**. P 15.

| 182 | 53 | 6d. light brown | | | 4·00 | 3·00 |
| 183 | | 1s. 3d. violet | | | 10·00 | 20·00 |

The ink of No. 183 is fugitive.

NEW INFORMATION

The editor is always interested to correspond with people who have new information that will improve or correct the Catalogue.

54 Dublin Airport, De
Havilland D.H.84 Dragon
Mk 2 *Iolar* and Boeing 720

55 St. Patrick

(Des J. Flanagan and D. R. Lowther)

961 (26 June). *25th Anniv of Aer Lingus.* W **22**. P 15.

| 84 | 54 | 6d. blue | | | 1·25 | 3·25 |
| | | w. Wmk inverted | .. | .. | 1·75 | 4·75 |

(Recess B.W.)

961 (25 Sept). *Fifteenth Death Centenary of St. Patrick.* W **22**.
P 14½.

86	55	3d. blue			1·25	10
87		8d. purple			2·25	5·50
88		1s. 3d. green			2·50	1·60
86/8				Set of 3	5·50	6·50

56 John O'Donovan and
Eugene O'Curry

(Recess B.W.)

1962 (26 Mar). *Death Centenaries of O'Donovan and O'Curry*
(scholars). W **22**. P 15.

| 189 | 56 | 3d. carmine | .. | | 40 | 10 |
| 190 | | 1s. 3d. purple | .. | .. | 1·50 | 2·50 |

57 Europa "Tree"

(Des L. Weyer)

1962 (17 Sept). *Europa.* W **22**. P 15.

| 191 | 57 | 6d. carmine-red | | | 50 | 1·00 |
| 192 | | 1s. 3d. turquoise | .. | .. | 90 | 1·50 |

58 Campaign Emblem

(Des K. Uhlemann)

1963 (21 Mar). *Freedom from Hunger.* W **22**. P 15.

| 193 | 58 | 4d. deep violet | | | 50 | 10 |
| 194 | | 1s. 3d. scarlet | .. | .. | 1·75 | 2·75 |

59 "Co-operation"

(Des A. Holm)

1963 (16 Sept). *Europa.* W **22**. P 15.

| 195 | 59 | 6d. carmine | .. | | 75 | 75 |
| 196 | | 1s. 3d. blue | .. | .. | 2·50 | 3·75 |

60 Centenary Emblem

(Des P. Wildbur. Photo Harrison & Sons)

1963 (2 Dec). *Centenary of Red Cross.* W **22**. P 14½ × 14.

| 197 | 60 | 4d. red and grey | .. | | 50 | 10 |
| 198 | | 1s. 3d. red, grey and light emerald | | | 1·25 | 2·25 |

61 Wolfe Tone

(Des P. Wildbur)

1964 (13 Apr). *Birth Bicentenary of Wolfe Tone (revolutionary).*
W **22**. P 15.

| 199 | 61 | 4d. black | | | 75 | 10 |
| 200 | | 1s. 3d. ultramarine | .. | .. | 2·25 | 2·00 |

62 Irish Pavilion at Fair

(Des A. Devane. Photo Harrison & Sons)

1964 (20 July). *New York World's Fair.* W **22**. P 14½ × 14.

201	62	5d. blue-grey, brown, violet & yellow-ol	50	10
		a. Brown omitted*		£1200
202		1s. 5d. blue-grey, brown, turquoise-blue		
		and light yellow-green	..	2·25	3·75

*No. 201a comes from the top row of a sheet and shows part of the
brown cross which would appear in the sheet margin. As the second
horizontal row was normal it would appear that the brown cylinder
was incorrectly registered.

63 Europa "Flower"

64 "Waves of Communication"

(Des G. Bétemps. Photo Harrison)

1964 (14 Sept). *Europa.* W **22** *(sideways).* P 14 × 14½.

| 203 | 63 | 8d. olive-green and blue | .. | | 1·00 | 1·25 |
| 204 | | 1s. 5d. red-brown and orange | .. | 3·00 | 2·75 |

(Des P. Wildbur. Photo Harrison)

1965 (17 May). *I.T.U. Centenary.* W **22**. P 14½ × 14.

| 205 | 64 | 3d. blue and green | .. | | 40 | 10 |
| 206 | | 8d. black and green | .. | .. | 1·10 | 2·00 |

PRINTERS. Nos. 207 onwards were photogravure-printed by
the Stamping Branch of the Revenue Commissioners, Dublin
unless otherwise stated.

65 W. B. Yeats (poet)

66 I.C.Y. Emblem

(Des R. Kyne, from drawing by S. O'Sullivan)

1965 (14 June). *Yeats' Birth Centenary.* W **22** *(sideways).* P 15.

| 207 | 65 | 5d. black, orange-brown and deep green | 30 | 10 |
| 208 | | 1s. 5d. black, grey-green and brown | .. | 2·25 | 1·75 |

1965 (16 Aug). *International Co-operation Year.* W **22**. P 15.

| 209 | 66 | 3d. ultramarine and new blue | .. | | 60 | 10 |
| 210 | | 10d. deep brown and brown | .. | .. | 1·00 | 3·00 |

67 Europa "Sprig"

(Des H. Karlsson)

1965 (27 Sept). *Europa.* W **22**. P 15.

| 211 | 67 | 8d. black and brown-red | .. | | 1·00 | 1·00 |
| 212 | | 1s. 5d. purple and light turquoise-blue | | 3·00 | 3·00 |

68 James Connolly

69 "Marching to Freedom"

(Des E. Delaney (No. 216), R. Kyne, after portraits by S. O'Sullivan
(others))

1966 (12 Apr). *50th Anniv of Easter Rising.* T **68/9** *and similar*
horiz portraits. W **22**. P 15.

213		3d. black and greenish blue	..	..	50	10
		a. Horiz pair. Nos. 213/14	..	..	1·00	2·50
214		3d. black and bronze-green		..	50	10
215		3d. black and yellow-olive		..	50	10
		a. Horiz pair. Nos. 215/16	..	..	1·00	2·50
216		3d. black, orange and blue-green	..	50	10
217		7d. black and light orange-brown	..	60	2·25
		a. Horiz pair. Nos. 217/18	..	..	1·00	8·50
218		7d. black and blue-green	..	..	60	2·25
219		1s. 5d. black and turquoise	..		60	1·50
		a. Horiz pair. Nos. 219/20	..	..	1·00	11·00
220		1s. 5d. black and bright green	..	..	60	1·50
213/20				Set of 8	3·50	7·00

Designs:—No. 213, Type **68**; No. 214, Thomas J. Clarke; No. 215,
P. H. Pearse; No. 216, Type **69**; No. 217, Eamonn Ceannt; No. 218,
Sean MacDiarmada; No. 219, Thomas MacDonagh; No. 220,
Joseph Plunkett.
Nos. 213/14, 215/16, 217/18 and 219/20 were each printed
together, *se-tenant*, in horizontal pairs throughout the sheet.

76 R. Casement

77 Europa "Ship"

(Des R. Kyne)

1966 (3 Aug). *50th Death Anniv of Roger Casement (patriot).* W **22**
(sideways). P 15.

| 221 | 76 | 5d. black | .. | .. | 15 | 10 |
| 222 | | 1s. red-brown | .. | .. | 30 | 50 |

(Des R. Kyne, after G. and J. Bender)

1966 (26 Sept). *Europa.* W **22** *(sideways).* P 15.

| 223 | 77 | 7d. emerald and orange | .. | .. | 35 | 40 |
| 224 | | 1s. 5d. emerald and light grey | .. | | 90 | 1·00 |

78 Interior of Abbey (from lithograph)

79 Cogwheels

1966 (8 Nov). *750th Anniv of Ballintubber Abbey.* W **22**. P 15.

| 225 | 78 | 5d. red-brown | .. | .. | 10 | 10 |
| 226 | | 1s. black | .. | .. | 20 | 25 |

1966–67. As Nos. 116, 118 *but photo. Smaller design* (17×21
mm). Chalk-surfaced paper. W **22**. P 15.

227	9	3d. blue (1.8.67)	..		60	15
228	6	5d. bright violet (1.12.66)	..		30	15
		w. Wmk inverted (from booklets)	..	1·75	1·25

No. 228 was only issued in booklets at first but was released in
sheets on 1.4.68 in a slightly brighter shade. In the sheet stamps
the lines of shading are more regular.

(Des O. Bonnevalle)

1967 (2 May). *Europa.* W **22** *(sideways).* P 15.

| 229 | 79 | 7d. light emerald, gold and pale cream | 30 | 40 |
| 230 | | 1s. 5d. carmine-red, gold and pale cream | 70 | 1·00 |

COVER PRICES

Cover factors are quoted at the beginning of each
country for most issues to 1945. An explanation of
the system can be found on page x. The factors
quoted do not, however, apply to philatelic covers.

80 Maple Leaves

(Des P. Hickey)

1967 (28 Aug). *Canadian Centennial.* W **22**. P 15.
231	80	5d. multicoloured	..	10	10
232		1s. 5d. multicoloured	..	20	60

81 Rock of Cashel (from photo by Edwin Smith)

1967 (25 Sept). *International Tourist Year.* W **22** (*inverted*). P 15.
233	81	7d. sepia	..	15	20
234		10d. slate-blue	..	15	40

82 1 c. Fenian Stamp Essay
83 24 c. Fenian Stamp Essay

1967 (23 Oct). *Centenary of Fenian Rising.* W **22** (*sideways*). P 15.
235	82	5d. black and light green	..	10	10
236	83	1s. black and light pink	..	20	30

84 Jonathan Swift
85 Gulliver and Lilliputians

(Des M. Byrne)

1967 (30 Nov). *300th Birth Anniv of Jonathan Swift.* W **22** (*sideways*). P 15.
237	84	3d. black and olive-grey	..	10	10
238	85	1s. 5d. blackish brown and pale blue	..	20	20

86 Europa "Key"

(Des H. Schwarzenbach and M. Biggs)

1968 (29 Apr). *Europa.* W **22**. P 15.
239	86	7d. brown-red, gold and brown	..	25	50
240		1s. 5d. new blue, gold and brown	..	40	1·00

87 St Mary's Cathedral, Limerick

(Des from photo by J. J. Bambury. Recess B.W.)

1968 (26 Aug). *800th Anniv of St. Mary's Cathedral, Limerick.* W **22**. P 15.
241	87	5d. Prussian blue	..	10	10
242		10d. yellow-green	..	20	60

NEW INFORMATION

The editor is always interested to correspond with people who have new information that will improve or correct the Catalogue.

---

88 Countess Markievicz
89 James Connolly

1968 (23 Sept). *Birth Centenary of Countess Markievicz* (*patriot*). W **22**. P 15.
243	88	3d. black	..	10	10
244		1s. 5d. deep blue and blue	..	20	20

1968 (23 Sept). *Birth Centenary of James Connolly* (*patriot*). W **22** (*sideways*). P 15.
245	89	6d. deep brown and chocolate	..	15	50
246		1s. blksh grn, apple-grn & myrtle-grn		15	10

90 Stylised Dog (brooch)
91 Stag

92 Winged Ox (Symbol of St. Luke)

93 Eagle (Symbol of St. John The Evangelist)

(Des H. Gerl)

1968–70. *Pence values expressed with "p".* W **22** (*sideways* on* ½d. to 1s. 9d.). P 15.
247	90	½d. red-orange (7.6.69)	..	10	30
248		1d. pale yellow-green (7.6.69)		15	10
		a. Coil stamp. Perf 14×15 (8.70?)	..	90	3·00
249		2d. light ochre (14.10.68)		50	10
		a. Coil stamp. Perf 14×15 (8.70?)		90	3·75
250		3d. blue (7.6.69)	..	35	10
		a. Coil stamp. Perf 14×15 (8.70?)		90	3·75
251		4d. deep brown-red (31.3.69)	..	30	10
252		5d. myrtle-green (31.3.69)	..	40	35
253		6d. bistre-brown (24.2.69)	..	30	10
		w. Wmk e facing right	..	5·50	1·50
254	91	7d. brown and yellow (7.6.69)	..	45	3·50
255		8d. chocolate & orge-brown (14.10.68)		45	1·00
256		9d. slate-blue and olive-green (24.2.69)		50	10
257		10d. chocolate and bluish violet (31.3.69)		1·50	1·25
258		1s. chocolate and red-brown (31.3.69)		40	10
259		1s. 9d. black & lt turquoise-bl (24.2.69)		4·00	1·25
260	92	2s. 6d. multicoloured (14.10.68)	..	1·75	30
261		5s. multicoloured (24.2.69)	..	3·00	1·50
262	93	10s. multicoloured (14.10.68)	..	4·50	3·75
247/62			Set of 16	16·00	12·00

*The normal sideways watermark shows the top of the e facing left, *as seen from the back of the stamp.*

The 1d., 2d., 3d., 5d., 6d., 9d., 1s. and 2s. 6d. exist with PVA gum as well as gum arabic. The coil stamps exist on PVA only, and the rest on gum arabic only.

See also Nos. 287/301, 339/59 and 478/83.

94 Human Rights Emblem
95 Dail Eireann Assembly

(Des M. Byrne)

1968 (4 Nov). *Human Rights Year.* W **22** (*sideways*). P 15.
263	94	5d. yellow, gold and black		15	10
264		7d. yellow, gold and red		15	40

1969 (21 Jan). *50th Anniv of Dail Eireann (First National Parliament).* W **22** (*sideways*). P 15 × 14½.
265	95	6d. myrtle-green		15	10
266		9d. Prussian blue		15	30

---

96 Colonnade
97 Quadruple I.L.O. Emblems

(Des L. Gasbarra and G. Belli; adapted Myra Maguire)

1969 (28 Apr). *Europa.* W **22**. P 15.
267	96	9d. grey, ochre and ultramarine		40	1·10
268		1s. 9d. grey, gold and scarlet	..	70	1·40

(Des K. C. Däbczewski)

1969 (14 July). *50th Anniv of International Labour Organization.* W **22** (*sideways*). P 15.
269	97	6d. black and grey	..	20	10
270		9d. black and yellow	..	20	25

98 "The Last Supper and Crucifixion" (Evie Hone Window, Eton Chapel)

(Des R. Kyne)

1969 (1 Sept). *Contemporary Irish Art* (1st issue). W **22** (*sideways*). P 15 × 14½.
271	98	1s. multicoloured		30	1·50

See also Nos. 280, 306, 317, 329, 362, 375, 398, 408, 452, 470 and 498.

99 Mahatma Gandhi

1969 (2 Oct). *Birth Centenary of Mahatma Gandhi.* W **22**. P 15.
272	99	6d. black and green	..	20	10
273		1s. 9d. black and yellow	..	30	90

100 Symbolic Bird in Tree

(Des D. Harrington)

1970 (23 Feb). *European Conservation Year.* W **22**. P 15.
274	100	6d. bistre and black	..	35	10
275		9d. slate-violet and black	..	35	80

101 "Flaming Sun"

(Des L. le Brocquy)

1970 (4 May). *Europa.* W **22**. P 15.
276	101	6d. bright violet and silver	..	30	10
277		9d. brown and silver	..	60	1·25
278		1s. 9d. deep olive-grey and silver	..	80	2·00
276/8			Set of 3	1·50	3·00

102 "Sailing Boats"
(Peter Monamy)

103 "Madonna of
Eire" (Mainie Jellett)

(Des P. Wildbur and P. Scott)

1970 (13 July). *250th Anniv of Royal Cork Yacht Club.* **W 22.**
P 15.
279 **102** 4d. multicoloured 15 10

1970 (1 Sept). *Contemporary Irish Art (2nd issue).* **W 22** (side-ways). P 15.
280 **103** 1s. multicoloured 15 20

104 Thomas
MacCurtain

106 Kevin Barry

(Des P. Wildbur)

1970 (26 Oct). *50th Death Anniversaries of Irish Patriots.* T **104**
and similar vert design. **W 22** (sideways). P 15.
281 9d. black, bluish violet and greyish black .. 50 25
 a. Pair. Nos. 281/2 .. .. 1·00 2·50
282 9d. black, bluish violet and greyish black .. 50 25
283 2s. 9d. black, new blue and greyish black .. 1·75 1·50
 a. Pair. Nos. 283/4 .. .. 3·75 11·00
284 2s. 9d. black, new blue and greyish black .. 1·75 1·50
281/4 .. .. .. *Set of 4* 4·50 3·25
Designs:—Nos. 281 and 283, Type **104**; others, Terence
MacSwiney.
Nos. 281/2 and 283/4 were each printed together, *se-tenant,* in
horizontal and vertical pairs throughout the sheet.

(Des P. Wildbur)

1970 (2 Nov). *50th Death Anniv of Kevin Barry (patriot).* **W 22**
(*inverted*). P 15.
285 **106** 6d. olive-green 40 10
286 1s. 2d. royal blue .. .. .. 55 1·40

106a Stylized Dog
(Brooch)

107 "Europa Chain"

Two types of 10 p.:
I. Outline and markings of the ox in lilac.
II. Outline and markings in brown.

1971 (15 Feb)–**75**. *Decimal Currency. Designs as Nos. 247/62
but with "p" omitted as in* T **106a**. **W 22** (sideways* on 10, 12,
20 and 50p.). P 15.
287 **106a** ½p. bright green 10 10
 a. Wmk sideways .. .. 6·00 10·00
 ab. Booklet pane of 6 .. 30·00
 aw. Wmk e facing right .. 6·00 10·00
 awb. Booklet pane of 6 .. 30·00
288 1p. blue 40 10
 a. Coil stamp. Perf 14×14½ .. 90 60
 b. Coil strip. Nos. 288a, 289a and 291a se-tenant .. 1·50
 c. Wmk sideways .. 35 40
 ca. Booklet pane of 6 .. 2·00
 cb. Booklet pane. No. 288c×5 plus one se-tenant label (11.3.74) .. 2·00
 cw. Wmk e facing right .. 35 40
 cwa. Booklet pane of 6 .. 2·00
 cwb. Booklet pane. No. 288cw×5 plus one se-tenant label (11.3.74) .. 2·00
289 1½p. lake-brown 15 15
 a. Coil stamp. Perf 14×14½ .. 30 50
 b. Coil strip. Nos. 289a, 291a, 294a and 290a se-tenant (24.2.72) .. 1·50
 c. Coil strip. Nos. 289a×2, 290a and 295ab se-tenant (29.1.74) .. 1·50
290 2p. myrtle-green 15 10
 a. Coil stamp. Perf 14×14½ (24.2.72) .. 30 40
 b. Wmk sideways (27.1.75) .. 50 50
 ba. Booklet pane. No. 290b×5 plus one se-tenant label .. 2·00
 bw. Wmk e facing right .. 50 50
 bwa. Booklet pane. No. 290bw×5 plus one se-tenant label .. 2·00

291 **106a** 2½p. sepia .. 15 10
 a. Coil stamp. Perf 14×14½ (20.2.71) .. 50 75
 b. Wmk sideways .. 1·00 1·25
 ba. Booklet pane of 6 .. 5·50
 bw. Wmk e facing right .. 1·00 1·25
 bwa. Booklet pane of 6 .. 5·50
292 3p. cinnamon .. 15 10
293 3½p. orange-brown .. 15 10
294 4p. pale bluish violet .. 15 10
 a. Coil stamp. Perf 14×14½ (24.2.72) .. 90 60
295 **91** 5p. brown and yellow-olive .. 70 20
295a **106a** 5p. bright yellow-green (29.1.74) 3·25 45
 ab. Coil stamp. Perf 14×14½ (29.1.74) .. 1·25 90
 ac. Wmk sideways (11.3.74) 60 80
 ad. Booklet pane. No. 295ac×5 plus one se-tenant label .. 2·75
 ae. Booklet pane. No. 295ac×6 .. 8·00
 awc. Wmk e facing right .. 60 80
 awd. Booklet pane. No. 295awc×5 plus one se-tenant label .. 2·75
 awe. Booklet pane. No. 295awc×6 .. 8·00
296 **91** 6p. blackish brown and slate .. 3·50 30
296a 7p. indigo and olive-green (29.1.74) 4·00 1·00
297 7½p. chocolate and reddish lilac .. 50 85
298 9p. black and turquoise-green .. 1·00 35
299 **92** 10p. multicoloured (I) .. 18·00 10·00
299a 10p. multicoloured (II) .. 18·00 70
299b 12p. multicoloured (29.1.74) .. 75 80
300 20p. multicoloured .. 1·00 10
301 **93** 50p. multicoloured .. 2·25 65
287/301 .. *Set of 18* 30·00 5·25
Nos. 287a/awb, 288c/cwb, 290b/bwa, 291b/bwa and 295ac/awe
come from Booklet Nos. SB20/4. The sideways watermark has
the top of the e pointing left, and the sideways inverted has it
pointing right, *when seen from the back of the stamp.* Stamps
with one, or two adjoining, sides imperf come from these
booklets.
See also Nos. 339/59 and 478/83.

(Des H. Haflidason; adapted P. Wildbur)

1971 (3 May). *Europa.* **W 22** (sideways). P 15.
302 **107** 4p. sepia and olive-yellow .. 50 10
303 6p. black and new blue.. .. 1·75 2·25

108 J. M. Synge

109 "An Island Man"
(Jack B. Yeats)

(Des R. Kyne from a portrait by Jack B. Yeats)

1971 (19 July). *Birth Centenary of J. M. Synge (playwright).* **W 22.**
P 15.
304 **108** 4p. multicoloured 15 10
305 10p. multicoloured 60 80

(Des P. Wildbur)

1971 (30 Aug). *Contemporary Irish Art (3rd issue). Birth
Centenary of J. B. Yeats (artist).* **W 22.** P 15.
306 **109** 6p. multicoloured 55 55

110 Racial Harmony
Symbol

111 "Madonna and
Child" (statue by
J. Hughes)

(Des P. Wildbur. Litho Harrison)

1971 (18 Oct). *Racial Equality Year. No wmk.* P 14 × 14½.
307 **110** 4p. red 20 10
308 10p. black 50 75

(Des R. Kyne)

1971 (15 Nov). *Christmas.* **W 22.** P 15.
309 **111** 2½p. black, gold and deep bluish green 10 10
310 6p. black, gold and ultramarine .. 55 65

112 Heart

(Des L. le Brocquy)

1972 (7 Apr). *World Health Day.* **W 22** (sideways). P 15.
311 **112** 2½p. gold and brown 30 15
312 12p. silver and grey .. .. 1·10 1·75

113 "Communications"

(Des P. Huovinen and P. Wildbur)

1972 (1 May). *Europa.* **W 22** (sideways). P 15.
313 **113** 4p. orange, black and silver .. 1·25 25
314 6p. blue, black and silver .. 3·25 4·75

114 Dove and Moon

115 "Black Lake"
(Gerard Dillon)

(Des P. Scott)

1972 (1 June). *The Patriot Dead, 1922–23.* **W 22.** P 15.
315 **114** 4p. grey-blue, light orange & deep blue 15 10
316 6p. dp yellow-grn, lemon & dp dull grn 60 40

(Des P. Wildbur)

1972 (10 July). *Contemporary Irish Art (4th issue).* **W 22** (side-ways). P 15.
317 **115** 3p. multicoloured 50 35

116 "Horseman"
(Carved Slab)

117 Madonna and Child
(from Book of Kells)

(Des P. Scott)

1972 (28 Aug). *50th Anniv of Olympic Council of Ireland.* **W 22.**
P 15.
318 **116** 3p. bright yellow, black and gold .. 15 10
319 6p. salmon, black and gold 55 60

WATERMARK. All issues from here onwards are on unwater-marked paper.

(Des P. Scott)

1972 (16 Oct). *Christmas.* P 15.
320 **117** 2½p. multicoloured (*shades*) .. 15 10
321 4p. multicoloured 30 10
322 12p. multicoloured 75 65
320/2 .. .. .. *Set of 3* 1·10 70

118 2d. Stamp of
1922

119 Celtic Head Motif

(Des Stamping Branch of the Revenue Commissioners, Dublin)

1972 (6 Dec). *50th Anniv of the First Irish Postage Stamp.* P 15.
323 **118** 6p. light grey and grey-green .. 30 60
MS324 72 × 104 mm. No. 323 × 4 .. 6·50 11·00

(Des L. le Brocquy)

1973 (1 Jan). *Entry into European Communities.* P 15.
325 119 6p. multicoloured 40 90
326 12p. multicoloured .. .. 60 1·10

120 Europa "Posthorn"

(Des L. Anisdahl; adapted R. Kyne)

1973 (30 Apr). *Europa.* P 15.
327 120 4p. bright blue 50 10
328 6p. black .. .. 1·75 2·25

121 "Berlin Blues II" (W. Scott)   122 Weather Map

(Adapted by R. Scott)

1973 (9 Aug). *Contemporary Irish Art (5th issue).* P 15 × 14½.
329 121 5p. ultramarine and grey-black .. 40 30

(Des R. Ballagh)

1973 (4 Sept). *I.M.O./W.M.O. Centenary.* P 14½ × 15.
330 122 3½p. multicoloured 40 10
331 12p. multicoloured .. .. .. 1·10 2·25

123 Tractor ploughing   124 "Flight into Egypt" (Jan de Cock)

(Des P. Scott)

1973 (5 Oct). *World Ploughing Championships, Wellington Bridge.* P 15 × 14½.
332 123 5p. multicoloured 15 10
333 7p. multicoloured 75 50

(Des D. Kiely. Litho ("EIRE" and face value) and photo (3½p.) or photo (12p.))

1973 (1 Nov). *Christmas.* P 15.
334 124 3½p. multicoloured 15 10
335 12p. multicoloured .. .. 1·10 1·50

125 Daunt Island Lightship and   126 "Edmund Burke"
Ballycotton Lifeboat, 1936   (statue by J. H. Foley)

(Des M. Byrne from painting by B. Gribble)

1974 (28 Mar). *150th Anniv of Royal National Lifeboat Institution.* P 15 × 14½.
336 125 5p. multicoloured 30 30

(Des P. Wildbur)

1974 (29 Apr). *Europa.* P 14½ × 15.
337 126 5p. black and pale violet-blue .. 75 10
338 7p. black and light emerald .. 2·50 2·50

NEW INFORMATION

The editor is always interested to correspond with people who have new information that will improve or correct the Catalogue.

Two types of 50p.:

Type I. Fine screen (Cyls 1)

Type II. Coarse screen (Cyls 2)

1974–83. *Designs as Nos. 287 etc. No wmk.* P 15.
339 106a ½p. bright green (5.6.78) 30 10
340 1p. blue (14.2.75) 10 10
  a. Coil stamp. Perf 14×14½ (21.3.77) .. 60 70
  b. Coil strip. Nos. 340a, 341a×2 and 344a *se-tenant* (21.3.77) 1·90
341 2p. myrtle-green (7.4.76) .. 10 10
  a. Coil stamp. Perf 14×14½ (21.3.77) .. 40 50
342 3p. cinnamon (14.2.75) .. 10 10
343 3½p. orange-brown (9.10.74) .. 3·25 4·50
344 5p. bright yellow-green (16.8.74) 60 10
  a. Coil stamp. Perf 14 × 14½ (21.3.77) .. 85 1·40
345 91 6p. blackish brn & slate (16.10.74) 1·50 1·75
346 106a 6p. slate (17.6.75) 20 10
347 91 7p. indigo and olive-green (27.9.74) 1·25 35
348 106a 7p. deep yellow-green (17.6.75) 35 10
  a. Booklet pane. No. 348 × 5 plus *se-tenant* label (21.3.77) 11·00
349 91 8p. dp brown & dp orge-brn (17.6.75) 75 50
350 106a 8p. chestnut (14.7.76) .. 30 10
351 91 9p. black & turquoise-green (12.74) 1·25 30
352 106a 9p. greenish slate (14.7.76) 30 10
352a 9½p. vermilion (3.12.79) .. 35 20
353 92 10p. multicoloured (II) (12.74) 2·75 30
354 91 10p. black and violet-blue (14.7.76) 1·25 10
354a 106a 10p. deep mauve (8.6.77) 70 10
355 91 11p. black and rose-carmine (14.7.76) 45 30
355a 12p. black and bright green (8.6.77) 75 10
355b 106a 12p. yellowish green (26.3.80) 30 10
355c 91 13p. reddish brn & red-brn (26.3.80) 40 1·25
356 92 15p. multicoloured (17.6.74) 75 40
356a 106a 15p. ultramarine (10.7.80) .. 40 10
356b 91 16p. black & dull yellow-grn (10.7.80) 40 80
356c 92 17p. multicoloured (8.6.77) .. 70 40
357 20p. multicoloured (13.6.74) 70 15
358 93 50p. multicoloured (I) (12.74) 90 30
  a. Type II (1983) .. .. 1·75 2·50
359 £1 multicoloured (17.6.75) 1·50 30
339/59 *Set of 29* 20·00 10·50
For 18p., 19p., 22p., 24p., 26p. and 29p. values printed by lithography, see Nos. 478/83.
Stamps with one or two sides imperf come from the booklet pane.

127 "Oliver Goldsmith"   128 "Kitchen Table"
(statue by J. H. Foley)   (Norah McGuiness)

(Des P. Wildbur)

1974 (24 June). *Death Bicentenary of Oliver Goldsmith (writer).* P 14½ × 15.
360 127 3½p. black and olive-yellow .. 20 10
361 12p. black and bright yellowish green .. 90 1·00

(Design adapted by Norah McGuiness. Photo Harrison)

1974 (19 Aug). *Contemporary Irish Art (6th issue).* P 14 × 14½.
362 128 5p. multicoloured 35 3

129 Rugby Players   130 U.P.U. "Postmark"

(Design adapted from Irish Press photograph. Eng C. Slani. Recess (3½p.) or recess and photo (12p.) Harrison)

1974 (9 Sept). *Centenary of Irish Rugby Football Union.* P 14½ × 14.
363 129 3½p. greenish black 30 1
  a. Deep greenish blue .. 7·50 3·5
364 12p. multicoloured .. 2·25 2·7
No. 363a is from a second printing using a recut plate on which the engraving was deeper.

(Des R. Ballagh)

1974 (9 Oct). *Centenary of Universal Postal Union.* P 14½ × 15.
365 130 5p. light yellowish green and black 25 10
366 7p. light ultramarine and black .. 35 80

131 "Madonna and Child"   132 "Peace"
(Bellini)

(Des P. Wildbur)

1974 (14 Nov). *Christmas.* P 14½ × 15.
367 131 5p. multicoloured 15 10
368 15p. multicoloured 60 90

(Des Alexandra Wejchert)

1975 (24 Mar). *International Women's Year.* P 14½ × 15.
369 132 8p. brt reddish purple & ultramarine .. 25 75
370 15p. ultramarine and bright green .. 50 1·25

133 "Castletown Hunt" (R. Healy)

(Des R. Kyne)

1975 (28 Apr). *Europa.* P 15 × 14½.
371 133 7p. grey-black 75 15
372 9p. dull blue-green .. .. 1·25 2·50

134 Putting

(Des from photographs by J. McManus. Litho ("EIRE" and face value) and photo).

1975 (26 June). *Ninth European Amateur Golf Team Championship, Killarney.* P 15×14½.
373 134 6p. multicoloured (*shades*) .. 75 45
374 9p. multicoloured (*shades*) .. 1·50 1·50
The 9p. is similar to T 134 but shows a different view of the putting green.

135 "Bird of Prey" (sculpture by   136 Nano Nagle (founder)
Oisin Kelly)   and Waifs

(Design adapted by the artist)

75 (28 July). *Contemporary Irish Art (7th issue). P 15×14½.*
5 135 15p. yellow-brown 55 75

(Des Kilkenny Design Workshops)

975 (1 Sept). *Bicentenary of Presentation Order of Nuns.*
P 14½ × 15.
76 136 5p. black and pale blue.. .. .. 20 10
77 7p. black and light stone 30 30

137 Tower of St. Anne's   **138** St. Oliver Plunkett
Church, Shandon   (commemorative medal
by Imogen Stuart)

(Des P. Scott)

975 (6 Oct). *European Architectural Heritage Year. T 137 and*
similar vert design. P 12½.
78 137 5p. blackish brown 20 10
79 6p. multicoloured 40 85
380 7p. steel-blue 40 10
381 9p. multicoloured 45 80
378/81 .. .. *Set of 4* 1·25 1·75
Design:—Nos. 380/1, Interior of Holycross Abbey, Co. Tipperary.

(Design adapted by the artist. Recess Harrison)

1975 (13 Oct). *Canonisation of Oliver Plunkett. P 14 × 14½.*
382 138 7p. black 15 10
383 15p. chestnut 55 45

139 "Madonna and   **140** James Larkin (from a
Child" (Fra Filippo   drawing by Sean O'Sullivan)
Lippi)

(Des P. Wildbur)

1975 (13 Nov). *Christmas. P 15.*
384 139 5p. multicoloured 15 10
385 7p. multicoloured 15 10
386 10p. multicoloured 45 30
384/6 .. .. *Set of 3* 65 40

(Des P. Wildbur. Litho)

1976 (21 Jan). *Birth Centenary of James Larkin (Trade Union*
leader). P 14½×15.
387 140 7p. deep bluish green and pale grey .. 20 10
388 11p. sepia and yellow-ochre 40 55

141 Alexander Graham   **142** 1847 Benjamin Franklin
Bell   Essay

(Des R. Ballagh)

1976 (10 Mar). *Telephone Centenary. P 14½ × 15.*
389 141 9p. multicoloured 20 10
390 15p. multicoloured 45 50

(Des L. le Brocquy; graphics by P. Wildbur. Litho Irish Security
Stamp Printing Ltd)

1976 (17 May). *Bicentenary of American Revolution. T 142 and*
similar horiz designs. P 14½ × 14.
391 7p. ultramarine, light red and silver .. 20 10
a. Silver (inscr) omitted .. .. † £225
392 8p. ultramarine, light red and silver .. 30 1·10
393 9p. violet-blue, orange and silver .. 30 10
394 15p. light rose-red, grey-blue and silver .. 50 75
a. Silver (face-value and inscr) omitted .. £550 £650
391/4 .. .. *Set of 4* 1·10 1·75
MS395 95 × 75 mm. Nos. 391/4 .. .. 4·50 8·00
a. Silver omitted £1600
Designs:—7p. Thirteen stars; 8p. Fifty stars; 9, 15p. Type 142.
No. MS395 exists with the sheet margins overprinted in blue to
commemorate "Stampa 76", the Irish National Stamp Exhibition.

143 Spirit Barrel

(Des P. Hickey)

1976 (1 July). *Europa. Irish Delft. T 143 and similar horiz design.*
Multicoloured. P 15 × 14.
396 9p. Type 143 .. .. 40 20
397 11p. Dish .. .. 70 1·60

144 "The Lobster Pots, West of Ireland" (Paul Henry)

(Des R. McGrath)

1976 (30 Aug). *Contemporary Irish Art (8th issue). P 15.*
398 144 15p. multicoloured 60 60

145 Radio Waves

(Des G. Shepherd and A. O'Donnell. Litho De La Rue Smurfit Ltd,
Dublin)

1976 (5 Oct). *50th Anniv of Irish Broadcasting Service. T 145*
and similar vert design. Chalk-surfaced paper. P 14½×14
(9p.) or 14×14½ (11p.).
399 9p. light new blue and bottle-green.. 20 10
400 11p. agate, orange-red and light new blue .. 60 1·00
Design:—11p. Transmitter, radio waves and globe.

146 "The Nativity" (Lorenzo Monaco)

(Des R. McGrath)

1976 (11 Nov). *Christmas. P 15×14½.*
401 146 7p. multicoloured 15 10
402 9p. multicoloured 15 10
403 15p. multicoloured 55 55
401/3 .. .. *Set of 3* 75 65

147 16th Century Manuscript   **148** Ballynahinch, Galway

(Des P. Hickey)

1977 (9 May). *Centenaries of National Library (8p.) and National*
Museum (10p.). T 147 and similar horiz design. Multicoloured.
P 15 × 14½.
404 8p. Type 147 .. .. 30 30
405 10p. Prehistoric stone 40 35

(Des E. van der Grijn. Litho Irish Security Stamp Printing Ltd)

1977 (27 June). *Europa. T 148 and similar vert design. Multi-*
coloured. P 14 × 15.
406 10p. Type 148 .. .. 30 25
407 12p. Lough Tay, Wicklow .. .. 95 1·50

ALTERED CATALOGUE NUMBERS

Any Catalogue numbers altered from the last
edition are shown as a list in the introductory
pages.

149 "Head" (Louis le   **150** Guide and Tents
Brocquy)

(Design adapted by the artist. Litho Irish Security Stamp Ptg Ltd)

1977 (8 Aug). *Contemporary Irish Art (9th issue). P 14 × 14½.*
408 149 17p. multicoloured 55 75

(Des R. Ballagh)

1977 (22 Aug). *Scouting and Guiding. T 150 and similar horiz*
design. Multicoloured. P 15 × 14½.
409 8p. Type 150 .. .. 35 10
410 17p. Tent and Scout saluting .. .. 75 1·75

151 "The Shanachie"   **152** "Electricity" (Golden Jubilee
(drawing by Jack B. Yeats)   of Electricity Supply Board)

(Des L. Miller (10p.), R. Ballagh (12p.). Litho Irish Security Stamp
Printing Ltd)

1977 (12 Sept). *Anniversaries. T 151 and similar horiz design.*
P 14 × 14½ (10p.) or 14½ × 14 (12p.).
411 10p. black 25 15
412 12p. black .. .. 35 1·00
Designs and events:—10p. Type 151 (Golden jubilee of Irish
Folklore Society; 12p. The philosopher Eriugena (1100th death
anniv)

(Des R. Ballagh (10p.), P. Hickey (12p.), B. Blackshaw (17p.). Photo
Stamping Branch of the Revenue Commissioners (12p.); Litho
Irish Security Stamp Ptg Ltd (others))

1977 (10 Oct). *Golden Jubilees. T 152 and similar horiz designs.*
P 15 × 14½ (12p.) or 15 × 14 (others).
413 10p. multicoloured 15 10
414 12p. multicoloured .. .. .. 30 1·40
415 17p. grey-black and grey-brown .. 40 85
413/15 .. .. *Set of 3* 75 2·10
Designs:—12p. Bulls (from contemporary coinage) (Jubilee of
Agricultural Credit Corporation); 17p. Greyhound (Jubilee of
greyhound track racing).

153 "The Holy Family"   **154** Junkers W.33
(Giorgione)   *Bremen* in Flight

(Des R. McGrath)

1977 (3 Nov). *Christmas. P 14½ × 15.*
416 153 8p. multicoloured 15 10
417 10p. multicoloured 15 10
418 17p. multicoloured .. .. .. 55 1·25
416/18 .. .. *Set of 3* 75 1·25

(Des R. Ballagh. Litho Irish Security Stamp Ptg Ltd)

1978 (13 Apr). *50th Anniv of First East–West Transatlantic*
Flight. P 14 × 14½.
419 154 10p. bright blue and black .. 20 15
420 17p. olive-brown and black .. .. 35 1·10
The 17p. is as T 154, but shows a different sky and sea.

155 Spring Gentian   **156** Catherine McAuley

(Des Wendy Walsh. Litho Irish Security Stamp Ptg Ltd)

1978 (12 June). *Wild Flowers. T* **155** *and similar vert designs. Multicoloured. P* 14 × 15.

421	8p. Type **155**		30	50
422	10p. Strawberry tree		35	15
423	11p. Large-flowered Butterwort		45	70
424	17p. St. Dabeoc's Heath		70	2·00
421/4		Set of 4	1·60	3·00

(Des R. Ballagh (10p.), R. Kyne (11p.), E. van der Grijn (17p.). Litho Irish Security Stamp Ptg Ltd)

1978 (18 Sept). *Anniversaries and Events. T* **156** *and similar multicoloured designs.* P 14½ × 14 (11p.) or 14 × 14½ (others).

425	10p. Type **156**		20	10
426	11p. Doctor performing vaccination (horiz)		30	80
427	17p. "Self Portrait"		40	1·10
425/7		Set of 3	80	1·75

Events:—10p. Birth bicentenary of Catherine McAuley (founder of Sisters of Mercy); 11p. Global eradication of Smallpox; 17p. Birth centenary of Sir William Orpen (painter).

157 Diagram of Drilling Rig   **158** Farthing

(Des R. Ballagh. Litho Irish Security Stamp Ptg Ltd)

1978 (18 Oct). *Arrival Onshore of Natural Gas. P* 14 × 14½.

428	**157** 10p. maroon, turquoise-green and bistre		30	30

(Des P. Wildbur and R. Mercer)

1978 (26 Oct). *50th Anniv of Irish Currency. T* **158** *and similar horiz designs. P* 15 × 14½.

429	8p. black, copper and deep bluish green		20	20
430	10p. black, silver and blue-green		25	10
431	11p. black, copper and chocolate		25	50
432	17p. black, silver and deep blue		40	1·00
429/32		Set of 4	1·00	1·60

Designs:—10p. Florin; 11p. Penny; 17p. Half-crown.

159 "The Virgin and Child" (Guercino)   **160** Conolly Folly, Castletown

(Des P. Wildbur)

1978 (16 Nov). *Christmas. P* 14½ × 15.

433	**159** 8p. purple-brown, gold and pale turquoise-green		15	10
434	10p. purple-brown, chocolate and pale turquoise-green		15	10
435	17p. purple-brown, deep blue-green and pale turquoise-green		45	1·40
433/5		Set of 3	65	1·40

(Des R. McGrath)

1978 (6 Dec). *Europa. Architecture. T* **160** *and similar horiz design. P* 15 × 14½.

436	10p. lake-brown and red-brown		30	15
437	11p. green and deep green		30	1·00

Design:—11p. Dromoland Belvedere.

161 Athletes in Cross-country Race   **162** "European Communities" (in languages of member nations)

(Des R. Mercer. Litho Irish Security Stamp Ptg Ltd)

1979 (20 Aug). *7th World Cross-country Championships, Limerick. P* 14½ × 14.

438	**161** 8p. multicoloured		20	30

(Des P. Wildbur)

1979 (20 Aug). *First Direct Elections to European Assembly. P* 14½ × 15.

439	**162** 10p. dull turquoise-green		15	15
440	11p. reddish violet		15	35

163 Sir Rowland Hill   **164** Winter Wren (*Troglodytes troglodytes*)

(Des C. Harrison. Litho Irish Security Stamp Ptg Ltd)

1979 (20 Aug). *Death Centenary of Sir Rowland Hill. P* 14 × 14½.

441	**163** 17p. black, brownish grey and red		30	60

(Des Wendy Walsh. Litho Irish Security Stamp Ptg Ltd)

1979 (30 Aug). *Birds. T* **164** *and similar horiz designs. Multicoloured. P* 14½ × 14.

442	8p. Type **164**		40	70
443	10p. Great Crested Grebe (*Podiceps cristatus*)		40	15
444	11p. White-fronted Goose (*Anser albifrons flavirostris*)		45	70
445	17p. Peregrine Falcon (*Falco peregrinus*)		70	2·00
442/5		Set of 4	1·75	3·25

165 "A Happy Flower" (David Gallagher)

(Des P. Wildbur. Litho Irish Security Stamp Ptg Ltd)

1979 (13 Sept). *International Year of the Child. Paintings by Children. T* **165** *and similar multicoloured designs.* P 14 × 14½ (11p.) or 14½ × 14 (others).

446	10p. Type **165**		20	10
447	11p. "Myself and My Skipping Rope" (Lucy Norman) (vert)		25	60
448	17p. "Swans on a Lake" (Nicola O'Dwyer)		35	85
446/8		Set of 3	70	1·40

166 Pope John Paul II

(Des P. Byrne. Litho Irish Security Stamp Ptg Ltd)

1979 (29 Sept). *Visit of Pope John Paul II. P* 14½ × 14.

449	**166** 12p. multicoloured		30	20

167 Brother and Child

(Des R. Kyne (9½p.), P. Scott (11p.), R. Mercer (20p.). Photo Stamping Branch of the Revenue Commissioners, Dublin (11p.), Litho Irish Security Stamp Ptg Ltd (others))

1979 (4 Oct). *Commemorations. T* **167** *and similar designs.* P 14½ × 14 (9½p.), 14½ × 15 (11p.) or 14 × 14½ (others).

450	9½p. black and pale claret		20	10
451	11p. black, reddish orange and bright blue		20	70
452	20p. multicoloured		40	1·40
450/2		Set of 3	70	2·00

Designs and commemorations: Horiz—9½p. Type **167** (Centenary of Hospitaller Order of St. John of God in Ireland); 20p. "Seated Figure" (sculpture by F. E. McWilliam) (Contemporary Irish Art (10th issue)). Vert—11p. Windmill and Sun (International Energy Conservation Month).

PRICES OF SETS

Set prices are given for many issues, generally those containing three stamps or more. Definitive sets include one of each value or major colour change, but do not cover different perforations, die types or minor shades. Where a choice is possible the set prices are based on the cheapest versions of the stamps included in the listings.

168 Patrick Pearse, "Liberty" and General Post Office, Dublin   **169** Madonna and Child (panel painting from Domnach Airgid Shrine)

(Des R. Ballagh)

1979 (10 Nov). *Birth Centenary of Patrick Pearse (patriot)* P 15 × 14½.

453	**168** 12p. multicoloured		30	15

(Des Ewa Gargulinska)

1979 (15 Nov). *Christmas. P* 14½ × 15.

454	**169** 9½p. multicoloured		15	10
455	20p. multicoloured		30	50

170 Bianconi Long Car, 1836   **171** John Baptist de la Salle (founder)

(Des P. Wildbur. Litho Irish Security Stamp Ptg Ltd)

1979 (6 Dec). *Europa. Communications. T* **170** *and similar horiz design. Multicoloured. P* 14½ × 14.

456	12p. Type **170**		20	30
457	13p. Transatlantic cable, Valentia, 1866		30	1·40

(Des P. Wildbur. Litho Irish Security Stamp Ptg Ltd)

1980 (19 Mar). *Centenary of arrival of De La Salle Order.* P 14 × 14½.

458	**171** 12p. multicoloured		30	30

172 George Bernard Shaw   **173** Stoat

(Des P. Byrne. Litho Irish Security Stamp Ptg Ltd)

1980 (7 May). *Europa. Personalities. T* **172** *and similar multicoloured design. P* 14 × 14½.

459	12p. Type **172**		40	50
460	13p. Oscar Wilde (28 × 38 mm)		40	1·00

(Des Wendy Walsh. Litho Irish Security Stamp Ptg Ltd)

1980 (30 July). *Wildlife. T* **173** *and similar vert designs. Multicoloured. P* 14 × 14½.

461	12p. Type **173**		25	40
462	15p. Arctic Hare		30	15
463	16p. Red Fox		35	60
464	25p. Red Deer		50	1·60
461/4		Set of 4	1·25	2·50
MS465	73 × 97 mm. Nos. 461/4		1·75	3·50

No. **MS465** exists with the sheet margins overprinted to commemorate "STAMPA 80", the Irish National Stamp Exhibition, in black or red, and for the Dublin Stamp Show, 1992, in red.

174 Playing Bodhran and Whistle   **175** Sean O'Casey

(Des J. Dixon and P. Wildbur. Litho Irish Security Stamp Ptg Ltd)

1980 (25 Sept).   *Traditional Music and Dance.* T **174** *and similar vert designs. Multicoloured.* P 14 × 14½.

466	12p. Type **174**			15	10
467	15p. Playing Uilleann pipes			20	15
468	25p. Dancing	..	..	35	1·10
466/8			Set of 3	65	1·25

(Des P. Wildbur (12p.), P. Scott (25p.). Litho Irish Security Stamp Ptg Ltd)

1980 (23 Oct).   *Commemorations.* T **175** *and similar vert design.* P 14 × 14½.

469	12p. multicoloured	..	..	15	10
470	25p. black, buff and drab	..	..	30	55

Designs and commemorations:—12p. Type **175** (Birth centenary of Sean O'Casey (playwright)); 25p. "Gold Painting No. 57" (Patrick Scott) (Contemporary Irish Art (11th issue)).

176 Nativity Scene (painting by Geraldine McNulty)   177 Boyle Air-pump, 1659

(Des P. Wildbur)

1980 (13 Nov).   *Christmas.* P 14½ × 15.

471	**176**	12p. multicoloured		15	10
472		15p. multicoloured		20	10
473		25p. multicoloured	..	40	1·25
471/3		..	Set of 3	65	1·25

(Des P. Wildbur. Litho Irish Security Stamp Ptg Ltd)

1981 (12 Mar).   *Irish Science and Technology.* T **177** *and similar vert designs. Multicoloured.* P 14 × 14½.

474	12p. Type **177**		..	20	10
475	15p. Ferguson tractor, 1936	..		25	10
476	16p. Parsons turbine, 1884	..	..	25	90
477	25p. Holland submarine, 1878		..	30	1·25
474/7	..	..	Set of 4	90	2·10

(Litho Irish Security Stamp Ptg Ltd)

1981 (27 Apr)–**82**.   *No wmk.* P 14 × 14½.

478	**106**a	18p. dull claret	..	45	50
479		19p. light blue	..	55	1·75
480		22p. dull turquoise-blue (1.9.81)		65	10
481		24p. drab (29.10.81)	..	75	95
482		26p. blue-green (1.4.82)	..	1·50	40
483		29p. purple (1.4.82)	..	1·75	2·00
478/83		..	Set of 6	5·00	5·00

178 "The Legend of the Cock and the Pot"   179 Cycling

(Des P. Byrne. Litho Irish Security Stamp Ptg Ltd)

1981 (4 May).   *Europa. Folklore. Paintings by Maria Simonds-Gooding.* T **178** *and similar vert design.* P 14 × 14½.

491	18p. black, orange-yellow and carmine	..	25	10
492	19p. black, yellow-orange and yellow	..	35	70

Design:—19p. "The Angel with the Scales of Judgement".

(Des R. Ballagh. Litho Irish Security Stamp Ptg Ltd)

1981 (24 June).   *50th Anniv of "An Óige" (Irish Youth Hostel Association).* T **179** *and similar multicoloured designs.* P 14 × 14½ (15, 30p.) or 14½ × 14 (others).

493	15p. Type **179**		..	30	40
494	18p. Hill-walking (horiz)		..	30	10
495	19p. Mountaineering (horiz)	..		30	95
496	30p. Rock-climbing	..	..	50	95
493/6	..	..	Set of 4	1·25	2·25

180 Jeremiah O'Donovan Rossa   181 "Railway Embankment" (W. J. Leech)

(Des C. Harrison. Litho Irish Security Stamp Ptg Ltd)

1981 (31 Aug).   *150th Birth Anniv of Jeremiah O'Donovan Rossa (politician).* P 14 × 14½.

497	**180**	15p. multicoloured		30	30

(Des P. Wildbur. Litho Irish Security Stamp Ptg Ltd)

1981 (31 Aug).   *Contemporary Irish Art (12th issue).* P 14½ × 14.

498	**181**	30p. multicoloured	..	60	60

182 James Hoban and White House   183 "Arkle" (steeplechaser)

(Des B. Thompson. Litho Irish Security Stamp Ptg Ltd)

1981 (29 Sept).   *150th Death Anniv of James Hoban (White House architect).* P 14½ × 14.

499	**182**	18p. multicoloured	..	30	30

(Des Wendy Walsh and P. Wildbur. Litho Irish Security Stamp Ptg Ltd)

1981 (23 Oct).   *Famous Irish Horses.* T **183** *and similar horiz designs. Multicoloured. Ordinary paper (18p.) or chalk-surfaced paper (others).* P 14½ × 14.

500	18p. Type **183**		..	50	1·00
	a. Pair. Nos. 500/1	..		1·00	2·00
501	18p. "Boomerang" (showjumper)	..	50	1·00
502	22p. "King of Diamonds" (Draught horse)	60	30
503	24p. "Ballymoss" (flatracer)	..	60	70
504	36p. "Coosheen Finn" (Connemara pony)	75	1·00
500/4	..	..	Set of 5	2·75	3·50

The 18p values were printed together, *se-tenant*, in horizontal and vertical pairs throughout the sheet.

184 "Nativity" (F. Barocci)   185 Eviction Scene

(Des P. Wildbur. Litho Irish Security Stamp Ptg Ltd)

1981 (19 Nov).   *Christmas. Chalk-surfaced paper.* P 14 × 14½.

505	**184**	18p. multicoloured	..	25	10
506		22p. multicoloured	..	30	10
507		36p. multicoloured	..	70	2·00
505/7	..		Set of 3	1·10	2·00

(Des R. Mercer (18p.), P. Wildbur (22p.). Litho Irish Security Stamp Ptg Ltd)

1981 (10 Dec).   *Anniversaries.* T **185** *and similar multicoloured design. Chalk-surfaced paper.* P 14 × 14½ (18p.) or 14½ × 14 (22p.).

508	18p. Type **185**	..		35	25
509	22p. Royal Dublin Society emblem (horiz)	40	30

Anniversaries—18p. Centenary of Land Law (Ireland) Act; 22p. 250th of Royal Dublin Society (organization for the advancement of agriculture, industry, art and science).

186 Upper Lake, Killarney National Park   187 "The Stigmatization of St Francis" (Sassetta)

(Des P. Wildbur. Litho Irish Security Stamp Ptg Ltd)

1982 (26 Feb).   *50th Anniv of Killarney National Park.* T **186** *and similar horiz design. Multicoloured.* P 14½ × 14.

510	18p. Type **186**	..	..	35	20
511	36p. Eagle's Nest	..	..	65	1·60

(Des P. Wildbur (22p.), M. Craig (24p.). Litho Irish Security Stamp Ptg Ltd)

1982 (2 Apr).   *Religious Anniversaries.* T **187** *and similar horiz design. Chalk-surfaced paper.* P 14 × 14½ (22p.) or 14½ × 14 (24p.).

512	22p. multicoloured	..	..	35	15
513	24p. olive-brown	..	..	40	80

Designs and anniversaries:—22p. Type **187** (800th birth anniv of St Francis of Assisi (founder of Franciscan Order)); 24p. Francis Makemie (founder of American Presbyterianism) and old Presbyterian Church, Ramelton, Co Donegal (300th anniv of ordination).

---

188 The Great Famine, 1845–50   189 Pádraic Ó Conaire (writer) (Birth Centenary)

(Des P. Wildbur. Litho Irish Security Stamp Ptg Ltd)

1982 (4 May).   *Europa. Historic Events.* T **188** *and similar design. Chalk-surfaced paper.* P 14 × 14½ (26p.) or 14½ × 14 (29p.).

514	26p. black and stone	..	..	80	50
515	29p. multicoloured	..	..	80	2·00

Design: *Horiz*—29p. The coming of Christianity to Ireland.

(Des P. Wildbur. Litho Irish Security Stamp Ptg Ltd)

1982 (16 June).   *Anniversaries of Cultural Figures.* T **189** *and similar vert designs. Chalk-surfaced paper.* P 14 × 14½.

516	22p. black and light blue	..		25	30
517	26p. black and sepia	..	..	35	30
518	29p. black and blue	..	..	55	1·25
519	44p. black and greenish grey	..		65	1·75
516/19			Set of 4	1·60	3·25

Designs and anniversaries—26p. James Joyce (writer) (Birth centenary); 29p. John Field (musician) (Birth bicentenary); 44p. Charles Kickham (writer) (Death centenary).

190 Porbeagle Shark (*Lamna nasus*)   191 St. Patrick (Galway hooker)

(Des Wendy Walsh and P. Wildbur. Litho Irish Security Stamp Ptg Ltd)

1982 (29 July).   *Marine Life.* T **190** *and similar horiz designs. Multicoloured. Chalk-surfaced paper.* P 14½ × 14.

520	22p. Type **190**		..	55	1·25
521	22p. Common European Oyster (*Ostrea edulis*)	..	55	1·25
522	26p. Atlantic Salmon (*Salmo salar*)	..	70	30
523	29p. Dublin Bay Prawn (*Nephrops norvegicus*)	..	70	2·25
520/3			Set of 4	2·25	4·50

(Des P. Wildbur. Litho Irish Security Stamp Ptg Ltd)

1982 (21 Sept).   *Irish Boats.* T **191** *and similar multicoloured designs. Ordinary paper (26p.) or chalk-surfaced paper (others).* P 14 × 14½ (Nos. 524 and 527) or 14½ × 14 (others).

524	22p. Type **191**		..	60	1·25
525	22p. Currach (horiz)		..	60	1·25
526	26p. Asgard II (cadet brigantine) (horiz)	60	30
527	29p. Howth 17 foot yacht	..	60	2·25
524/7	..		Set of 4	2·25	4·50

192 "Irish House of Commons" (painting by Francis Wheatley)   193 "Madonna and Child" (sculpture)

(Des P. Wildbur (22p.) or R. Ballagh (26p.). Litho Irish Security Stamp Ptg Ltd)

1982 (14 Oct).   *Bicentenary of Grattan's Parliament (22p.) and Birth Centenary of Eamon de Valera (26p.).* T **192** *and similar multicoloured design.* P 14½ × 14 (22p.) or 14 × 14½ (26p.).

528	22p. Type **192**	..	..	35	1·25
529	26p. Eamon de Valera (vert)	..		40	40

(Des P. Wildbur. Litho Irish Security Stamp Ptg Ltd)

1982 (11 Nov).   *Christmas.* P 14 × 14½.

530	**193**	22p. multicoloured	..	30	90
531		26p. multicoloured	..	30	35

NEW INFORMATION

The editor is always interested to correspond with people who have new information that will improve or correct the Catalogue.

194 Aughnanure Castle   195 Ouzel Galley Goblet

(Des M. Craig and P. Wildbur. Litho Irish Security Stamp Ptg Ltd)

1982 (15 Dec)–**90**. *Irish Architecture. T* **194** *and similar designs. Chalk-surfaced paper* (24, 28, 32, 37, 39, 46p., £1 (*No.* 550b), £2) *or ordinary paper* (*others*). *P* 15×14 (15, 20, 22, 23, 24, 26, 39, 46, 50p., £1 (*No.* 550), £2, £5) *or* 14×15 (*others*).

532	1p. dull violet-blue (6.7.83)	10	10
	a. Chalk-surfaced paper (9.87)	30	30
533	2p. deep yellow-green (6.7.83)	20	10
	a. Chalk-surfaced paper (27.6.85)	50	40
	ab. Booklet pane. Nos. 533a, 543a and 545a, each × 2	5·50	
	ac. Booklet pane. Nos. 533a, 543a and 545a, each × 4	9·00	
	ad. Booklet pane. Nos. 533a×2, 535b×3, 544a×3 and 545c×4 (8.9.86)	9·00	
	ae. Booklet pane. Nos. 533a×4, 535b, 544a×2 and 545c×5 (24.11.88)	10·00	
534	3p. black (6.7.83)	20	10
	a. Chalk-surfaced paper (2.88)	80	80
535	4p. maroon (16.3.83)	20	10
	a. Booklet pane. Nos. 535×3, 543×4 and 1 label (15.8.83)	2·50	
	b. Chalk-surfaced paper (9.7.84)	30	30
	ba. Booklet pane. Nos. 535b×3, 543a×5 and 545a×4	6·50	
	c. Perf 13½ (3.5.90)	1·50	2·50
	ca. Booklet pane. Nos. 535c×3, 545b, 752ab×2 and 754ab×2	9·00	
536	5p. olive-sepia (6.7.83)	30	10
	a. Chalk-surfaced paper (8.87)	60	30
537	6p. deep grey-blue (16.3.83)	30	15
	a. Chalk-surfaced paper (11.85)	1·40	1·40
538	7p. dull yellow-green (16.3.83)	30	15
	a. Chalk-surfaced paper (3.88)	2·00	2·00
539	10p. black (6.7.83)	30	10
	a. Chalk-surfaced paper (3.87)	70	30
540	12p. purple-brown (6.7.83)	30	30
	a. Chalk-surfaced paper (5.87)	3·25	3·25
541	15p. deep yellow-green (6.7.83)	45	35
542	20p. deep brown-purple (16.3.83)	50	45
	a. Chalk-surfaced paper (12.84)	1·75	1·75
543	22p. chalky blue	50	10
	a. Chalk-surfaced paper (9.7.84)	1·75	50
544	23p. yellow-green (16.3.83)	85	80
544a	24p. bistre-brown (27.6.85)	1·25	35
	ab. Ordinary paper (9.87)	3·00	2·00
545	26p. blackish brown	75	10
	a. Chalk-surfaced paper (9.7.84)	1·25	30
	b. Perf 13½ (3.5.90)	2·50	3·00
545c	28p. maroon (27.6.85)	75	45
	ca. Ordinary paper (10.87)	3·25	3·25
546	29p. deep yellow-green	90	65
547	30p. black (16.3.83)	70	10
	a. Chalk-surfaced paper (3.87)	70	90
	b. Perf 13½ (3.5.90)	2·00	2·75
	ba. Booklet pane. Nos. 547b, 754ab and 774a/5a	6·75	
	bb. Booklet pane. Nos. 547b×2, 754ab×2 and 774a	6·75	
547c	32p. bistre-brown (1.5.86)	1·75	2·25
	ca. Ordinary paper (9.90)	5·00	7·00
547d	37p. chalky blue (27.6.85)	90	1·40
547e	39p. maroon (1.5.86)	1·50	2·00
548	44p. black and grey	90	90
	a. Chalk-surfaced paper (4.85)	2·75	2·75
548b	46p. olive-green and brownish grey (1.5.86)	3·50	2·00
	ba. Ordinary paper (9.87)	4·50	4·00
549	50p. dull ultramarine and grey (16.3.83)	1·00	65
	a. Chalk-surfaced paper (12.84)	2·50	90
550	£1 bistre-brown and grey	4·50	3·00
	a. Chalk-surfaced paper (9.84)	10·00	7·50
550b	£1 chalky blue & brownish grey (27.6.85)	3·25	1·25
	ba. Ordinary paper (1.88)	7·00	3·00
550c	£2 grey-olive and black (26.7.88)	4·00	4·50
551	£5 crimson and grey	10·00	5·00
	a. Chalk-surfaced paper (8.87)	17·00	11·00
532/51	*Set of 28*	35·00	24·00

Designs: *Horiz* (as *T* 194)—1p. to 5p. Central Pavilion, Dublin Botanic Gardens; 6p. to 12p. Dr. Steevens' Hospital, Dublin; 28p. to 37p. St. MacDara's Church. (37×21 *mm*)—46p., £1 (No. 550) Cahir Castle: 50p., £2 Casino, Marino; £5 Central Bus Station, Dublin. *Vert* (as *T* 194)— 15p. to 22p. Type 195; 26p., 39p. Cormac's Chapel. (21×37 *mm*)—44p., £1 (No. 550b) Killarney Cathedral.

The following stamps first appeared in booklet panes, but were later issued in sheets: Nos. 533a (7.86), 535b (7.85), 543a (10.84) and 545a (1.85).

Nos. 533ab/ae and 535a/ba show the horizontal edges of the panes imperforate so that 2, 22 and 26p. values from them exist imperforate at top, bottom, left or right, the 4p. at top or bottom the 24p. at right and the 28p. at top.

No. 535ba comes from a £2 Discount booklet and shows "Booklet Stamp" printed over the gum on the reverse of each stamp.

Nos. 535c, 545b and 547b are on ordinary paper and come from the 1990 150th Anniversary of the Penny Black £6 booklet. Examples of Nos. 535c, 545b and 752ab from the right-hand column of booklet pane No. 535ca are imperforate at right (4p.) or top (others). In booklet pane No. 547bb Nos. 547b and 754ab are imperforate at right.

Booklet pane No. 547ba exists with the margins overprinted to commemorate "New Zealand 1990" International Stamp Exhibition Auckland, and No. 547bb with the margins overprinted in blue for "STAMPA 90", the Irish National Stamp Exhibition.

Nos. 550/a were withdrawn without warning on 14 November 1984 after the authorities had discovered forged examples of the

---

£1 stamp used in P.O. savings books. Such forgeries, which it is believed were not used for postal purposes, are line perforated 14.75 or 12 instead of the 14.75×14 comb perforation of the genuine and also show the foot of the "1" rounded instead of square.

(Des P. Wildbur (22p.), C. Harrison (26p.). Litho Irish Security Stamp Ptg Ltd)

1983 (23 Feb). *Bicentenaries of Dublin Chamber of Commerce* (22p.) *and Bank of Ireland* (26p.). *T* **195** *and similar multicoloured design. P* 14 × 14½ (22p.) *or* 14½ × 14 (26p.).

552	22p. Type 195	30	55
553	26p. Bank of Ireland building (*horiz*).	35	35

196 Pádraig O Siochfhradha (writer and teacher) (Birth cent)   197 Neolithic Carved Pattern, Newgrange Tomb

(Des C. Harrison (26p.), R. Ballagh (29p.). Litho Irish Security Stamp Ptg Ltd)

1983 (7 Apr). *Anniversaries. T* **196** *and similar vert design. Multicoloured. P* 14 × 14½.

554	26p. Type 196	60	75
555	29p. Young Boys' Brigade member (Centenary)	80	1·50

(Des L. le Brocquy (26p.), P. Wildbur (29p.). Litho Irish Security Stamp Ptg Ltd)

1983 (4 May). *Europa. T* **197** *and similar horiz design. P* 14½ × 14.

556	26p. grey-black and gold	1·75	50
557	29p. black, blackish brown and gold	4·00	5·00

Design:—29p. Sir William Rowan Hamilton's formulae for the multiplication of quaternions.

198 Kerry Blue Terrier

(Des Wendy Walsh and L. Miller. Litho Irish Security Stamp Ptg Ltd)

1983 (23 June). *Irish Dogs. T* **198** *and similar horiz designs. Multicoloured. P* 14½ × 14.

558	22p. Type 198	65	35
559	26p. Irish Wolfhound	75	45
560	26p. Irish Water Spaniel	75	45
561	29p. Irish Terrier	95	2·25
562	44p. Irish Setters	1·40	2·50
558/62	*Set of 5*	4·00	5·50
MS563	142 × 80 mm. Nos. 558/62	6·00	8·00

No. MS563 exists with the sheet margins overprinted in blue to commemorate "STAMPA 83", the Irish National Stamp Exhibition.

199 Animals (Irish Society for the Prevention of Cruelty to Animals)   200 Postman with Bicycle

(Des Wendy Walsh (No. 564), B. Murphy (No. 566), K. Uhlemann (No. 567), R. Ballagh (others). Litho Irish Security Stamp Ptg Ltd)

1983 (11 Aug). *Anniversaries and Commemorations. T* **199** *and similar designs. P* 14½ × 14 (*Nos.* 564, 566) *or* 14 × 14½ (*others*).

564	199 22p. multicoloured	60	1·00
565	– 22p. multicoloured	60	1·00
566	– 26p. multicoloured	60	60
567	– 26p. multicoloured	60	60
568	– 44p. grey-blue and black	1·00	2·00
564/8	*Set of 5*	3·00	4·75

Designs: *Vert*—No. 565, Sean Mac Diarmada (patriot) (Birth cent); No. 567, "St. Vincent de Paul in the Streets of Paris" (150th anniv of Society of St. Vincent de Paul); No. 568, "Andrew Jackson" (Frank McKelvey) (President of the United States). *Horiz*—No. 566, "100" (Centenary of Industrial Credit Company).

(Des R. Ballagh. Litho Irish Security Stamp Ptg Ltd)

1983 (15 Sept). *World Communications Year. T* **200** *and simila vert design. Multicoloured. P* 14 × 14½.

569	22p. Type 200	75	7
570	29p. Dish antenna	1·00	2·0

201 Weaving   202 "La Natividad" (R. van der Weyden)

(Des R. Mercer. Litho Irish Security Stamp Ptg Ltd)

1983 (13 Oct). *Irish Handicrafts. T* **201** *and similar vert designs. Multicoloured. P* 14 × 14½.

571	22p. Type 201	50	60
572	26p. Basketmaking	50	45
573	29p. Irish crochet	60	1·50
574	44p. Harpmaking	90	2·25
571/4	*Set of 4*	2·25	4·25

(Des and litho Irish Security Stamp Ptg Ltd)

1983 (30 Nov). *Christmas. P* 14 × 14½.

575	202 22p. multicoloured	50	30
576	26p. multicoloured	60	30

203 *Princess* (Dublin and Kingstown Railway)

(Des C. Rycroft. Litho Irish Security Stamp Ptg Ltd)

1984 (30 Jan). *150th Anniv of Irish Railways. T* **203** *and similar horiz designs. Multicoloured. Ordinary paper* (23p., 26p. *and miniature sheet*) *or chalk-surfaced paper* (*others*). *P* 15×14.

577	23p. Type 203	85	1·25
578	26p. *Macha* (Great Southern Railway)	85	35
579	29p. *Kestrel* (Great Northern Railway)	1·00	1·75
580	44p. Two-car electric unit (Coras Iompair Eireann)	1·40	2·25
577/80	*Set of 4*	3·75	5·00
MS581	129 × 77 mm. Nos. 577/80	5·50	7·00

No. MS581 exists with the sheet margins overprinted in black to commemorate "STAMPA 84", the Irish National Stamp Exhibition.

204 *Sorbus hibernica*

(Des Wendy Walsh and P. Wildbur. Litho Irish Security Stamp Ptg Ltd)

1984 (1 Mar). *Irish Trees. T* **204** *and similar horiz designs. Multicoloured. P* 15 × 14.

582	22p. Type 204	75	70
583	26p. *Taxus baccata fastigiata*	80	40
584	29p. *Salix hibernica*	1·00	2·00
585	44p. *Betula pubescens*	1·40	2·75
582/5	*Set of 4*	3·50	5·00

205 St. Vincent's Hospital, Dublin

(Des B. Donegan, adapted by C. Vis (26p.), B. Murphy (44p.). Litho Irish Security Stamp Ptg Ltd)

1984 (12 Apr). *150th Anniv of St. Vincent's Hospital and Bicentenary of Royal College of Surgeons. T* **205** *and similar horiz design. Multicoloured. P* 15 × 14.

586	26p. Type 205	50	30
587	44p. Royal College and logo	90	1·50

206 C.E.P.T. 25th Anniversary Logo

(Des J. Larrivière. Litho Irish Security Stamp Ptg Ltd)

1984 (10 May). *Europa.* P 15 × 14.
588	206	26p. blue, deep dull blue and black			1·75	50
589		29p. light green, blue-green and black			2·25	2·75

207 Flags on Ballot Box   208 John McCormack

(Des R. Ballagh. Litho Irish Security Stamp Ptg Ltd)

1984 (10 May). *Second Direct Elections to European Assembly.* P 15 × 14.
590	207	26p. multicoloured			50	70

(Des R. Mercer and J. Sharpe. Litho Irish Security Stamp Ptg Ltd)

1984 (6 June). *Birth Centenary of John McCormack (tenor).* P 14 × 15.
591	208	22p. multicoloured			50	70

209 Hammer-throwing

(Des L. le Brocquy and P. Wildbur. Litho Irish Security Stamp Ptg Ltd)

1984 (21 June). *Olympic Games, Los Angeles. T* 209 *and similar horiz designs.* P 15 × 14.
592	22p. deep mauve, black and gold		45	80
593	26p. violet, black and gold		60	65
594	29p. bright blue, black and gold		75	1·25
592/4		Set of 3	1·60	2·50

Designs:—26p. Hurdling; 29p. Running.

210 Hurling   211 Galway Mayoral Chain (500th Anniv of Mayoral Charter)

(Des C. Harrison. Litho Irish Security Stamp Ptg Ltd)

1984 (23 Aug). *Centenary of Gaelic Athletic Association. T* 210 *and similar multicoloured design.* P 15 × 14 (22p.) *or* 14 × 15 (26p.).
595	22p. Type 210		50	90
596	26p. Irish football (vert)		60	90

(Des P. Wildbur. Litho Irish Security Stamp Ptg Ltd)

1984 (18 Sept). *Anniversaries. T* 211 *and similar multicoloured design.* P 14 × 15 (26p.) *or* 15 × 14 (44p.).
597	26p. Type 211		50	50
598	44p. St. Brendan (from 15th-cent Bodleian manuscript) (1500th birth anniv) (horiz)	1·00	1·50

212 Hands passing Letter   213 "Virgin and Child" (Sassoferrato)

(Litho Irish Security Stamp Ptg Ltd)

1984 (19 Oct). *Bicentenary of the Irish Post Office.* P 15 × 14.
599	212	26p. multicoloured		60	70

(Des O'Connor O'Sullivan Advertising (17p.), P. Wildbur (others). Litho Irish Security Stamp Ptg Ltd)

1984 (26 Nov). *Christmas. T* 213 *and similar multicoloured design. Chalk-surfaced paper.* P 15 × 14 (17p.) *or* 14 × 15 (others).
600	17p. Christmas star (horiz)			60	80
601	22p. Type 213			60	1·25
602	26p. Type 213			80	40
600/2			Set of 3	1·75	2·25

No. 600 represented a special concession rate for Christmas card postings to addresses within Ireland and Great Britain between 26 November and 8 December 1984.

214 "Love" and Heart-shaped Balloon   215 Dunsink Observatory (Bicentenary)

(Des Susan Dubsky (22p.), Patricia Jorgensen (26p.). Litho Irish Security Stamp Ptg Ltd)

1985 (31 Jan). *Greetings Stamps. T* 214 *and similar multicoloured design. Chalk-surfaced paper.* P 15 × 14 (22p.) *or* 14 × 15 (26p.).
603	22p. Type 214			50	75
604	26p. Bouquet of hearts and flowers (vert)		60	75

(Des R. Ballagh (22, 44p.), K. Thomson (26p.), M. Lunt (37p.). Litho Irish Security Stamp Ptg Ltd)

1985 (14 Mar). *Anniversaries. T* 215 *and similar designs. Multicoloured. Chalk-surfaced paper.* P 15 × 14 (26p.) *or* 14 × 15 (others).
605	22p. Type 215			50	50
606	26p. "A Landscape at Tivoli, Cork, with Boats" (Nathaniel Grogan) (800th anniv of City of Cork) (horiz)	60	30
607	37p. Royal Irish Academy (Bicentenary)		90	1·75
608	44p. Richard Crosbie's balloon flight (Bicentenary of first aeronautic flight by an Irishman)		1·10	1·75
605/8			Set of 4	2·75	3·75

216 *Polyommatus icarus*   217 Charles Villiers Stanford (composer)

(Des I. Loe. Litho Irish Security Stamp Ptg Ltd)

1985 (11 Apr). *Butterflies. T* 216 *and similar vert designs. Multicoloured. Chalk-surfaced paper.* P 14 × 15.
609	22p. Type 216			1·25	1·00
610	26p. Vanessa atalanta			1·25	70
611	28p. Gonepteryx rhamni			1·50	2·75
612	44p. Eurodryas aurinia			2·00	3·00
609/12			Set of 4	5·50	6·75

(Des P. Hickey and J. Farrar. Litho Irish Security Stamp Ptg Ltd)

1985 (16 May). *Europa. Irish Composers. T* 217 *and similar horiz design. Multicoloured. Chalk-surfaced paper.* P 15 × 14.
613	26p. Type 217			2·00	50
614	37p. Turlough Carolan (composer and lyricist)		4·00	5·50

218 George Frederick Handel   219 U.N. Patrol of Irish Soldiers, Congo, 1960 (25th Anniv. of Irish Participation in U.N. Peace-keeping Force)

(Des K. Uhlemann and J. Farrar. Litho Irish Security Stamp Ptg Ltd)

1985 (16 May). *European Music Year. Composers. T* 218 *and similar vert designs. Multicoloured. Chalk-surfaced paper.* P 14 × 15.
615	22p. Type 218			1·25	2·50
	a. Pair. Nos. 615/16			2·50	5·00
616	22p. Guiseppe Domenico Scarlatti		1·25	2·50
617	26p. Johann Sebastian Bach		1·50	5·00
615/17			Set of 3	3·50	5·00

Nos. 615/16 were printed together, *se-tenant*, in horizontal and vertical pairs throughout the sheet.

(Des B. Donegan and J. Farrar (22p.), R. Ballagh (26p.), B. Donegan (44p.). Litho Irish Security Stamp Ptg Ltd)

1985 (20 June). *Anniversaries. T* 219 *and similar multicoloured designs. Chalk-surfaced paper.* P 15 × 14 (22p.) *or* 14 × 15 (others).
618	22p. Type 219			75	80
619	26p. Thomas Ashe (patriot) (Birth cent) (vert)		80	60
620	44p. "Bishop George Berkeley" (James Lathan) (philosopher) (300th birth anniv) (vert)		1·25	3·00
618/20			Set of 3	2·50	4·00

220 Group of Young People

(Des J. Farrar and N. Mooney. Litho Irish Security Stamp Ptg Ltd)

1985 (1 Aug). *International Youth Year. T* 220 *and similar multicoloured design. Chalk-surfaced paper.* P 15 × 14 (22p.) *or* 14 × 15 (26p.).
621	22p. Type 220			55	50
622	26p. Students and young workers (vert)		55	50

221 Visual Display Unit

(Des B. Donegan (44p.), C. Rycraft (others). Litho Irish Security Stamp Ptg Ltd)

1985 (3 Oct). *Industrial Innovation. T* 221 *and similar horiz designs. Multicoloured. Chalk-surfaced paper.* P 15 × 14.
623	22p. Type 221			65	75
624	26p. Turf cutting with hand tool and with modern machinery		70	55
625	44p. "The Key Man" (Sean Keating) (150th anniv of Institution of Engineers of Ireland)		1·25	2·25
623/5			Set of 3	2·40	3·25

222 Lighted Candle and Holly   223 "Virgin and Child in a Landscape" (Adrian van Ijsenbrandt)

(Des R. Mahon (No. 626). Litho Irish Security Stamp Ptg Ltd)

1985 (26 Nov). *Christmas. T* 222 *and designs as T* 223 *showing paintings. Multicoloured. Chalk-surfaced paper.* P 15 × 14 (26p.) *or* 14 × 15 (others).
626	22p. Type 222			75	65
	a. Sheetlet. No. 626 × 16			11·00	
627	22p. Type 223			90	2·50
	a. Pair. Nos. 627/8			1·75	5·00
628	22p. "The Holy Family" (Murillo)		90	2·50
629	26p. "The Adoration of the Shepherds" (Louis le Nain) (horiz)		90	25
626/9			Set of 4	3·00	5·50

No. 626 was only issued in sheetlets of 16 sold at £3, providing a discount of 52p. off the face value of the stamps.

Nos. 627/8 were printed together, *se-tenant*, in horizontal and vertical pairs throughout the sheet.

224 Stylised Love Bird with Letter   225 Hart's Tongue Fern

(Des R. Hoek (22p.), T. Monaghan (26p.). Litho Irish Security Stamp Ptg Ltd)

1986 (30 Jan). *Greetings Stamps. T* 224 *and similar vert design. Multicoloured. Chalk-surfaced paper.* P 14 × 15.
630	22p. Type 224			70	1·00
631	26p. Heart-shaped pillar-box			70	1·00

(Des I. Loe. Litho Irish Security Stamp Ptg Ltd)

1986 (20 Mar). *Ferns.* T **255** *and similar vert designs. Multicoloured. Chalk-surfaced paper.* P 14 × 15.

632	24p. Type **225**		80	70
633	28p. Rusty-back Fern		90	70
634	46p. Killarney Fern		1·60	2·10
632/4		Set of 3	3·00	3·25

226 "Harmony between Industry and Nature"

227 Boeing 747-200 over Globe showing Aer Lingus Routes

(Des G. van Gelderen. Litho Irish Security Stamp Ptg Ltd)

1986 (1 May). *Europa. Protection of the Environment.* T **226** *and similar multicoloured design. Chalk-surfaced paper.* P 14 × 15 (28p.) *or* 15 × 14 (39p.).

635	28p. Type **226**		1·75	50
636	39p. *Vanessa atalanta* (butterfly) and tractor in field ("Preserve hedgerows") (*horiz*)		3·25	5·00

(Des R. Ballagh. Litho Irish Security Stamp Ptg Ltd)

1986 (27 May). *50th Anniv of Aer Lingus (airline).* T **227** *and similar multicoloured design. Chalk-surfaced paper.* P 15 × 14.

637	28p. Type **227**		1·40	75
638	46p. De Havilland D.H.84 Dragon Mk 2 *Iolar* (first aircraft)		1·90	3·00

228 Grand Canal at Robertstown

229 *Severn* (19th-century paddle-steamer)

(Des B. Matthews. Litho Irish Security Stamp Ptg Ltd)

1986 (27 May). *Irish Waterways.* T **228** *and similar multicoloured designs. Chalk-surfaced paper.* P 14 × 15 (28p.) *or* 15 × 14 (*others*).

639	24p. Type **228**		1·00	1·00
640	28p. Fishing in County Mayo (*vert*)		1·25	1·00
641	30p. Motor cruiser on Lough Derg		1·50	2·50
639/41		Set of 3	3·25	4·00

(Des C. Rycraft. Litho Irish Security Stamp Ptg Ltd)

1986 (10 July). *150th Anniv of British and Irish Steam Packet Company.* T **229** *and similar horiz design. Multicoloured.* P 15 × 14.

642	24p. Type **229**		75	1·00
643	28p. M.V. *Leinster* (modern ferry)		85	60

230 Kish Lighthouse and Bell 206B Jet Ranger III Helicopter

231 J. P. Nannetti (first president) and Linotype Operator (Dublin Council of Trade Unions Centenary)

(Des R. Ballagh. Litho Irish Security Stamp Printing Ltd)

1986 (10 July). *Irish Lighthouses.* T **230** *and similar vert design. Multicoloured.* P 14 × 15.

644	24p. Type **230**		75	75
645	30p. Fastnet Lighthouse		1·50	2·50

(Des R. Ballagh (Nos. 646/7), M. Cameron (No. 648), A. Mazer (Nos. 649/50). Litho Irish Security Stamp Ptg Ltd)

1986 (21 Aug). *Anniversaries and Commemorations.* T **231** *and similar designs. Ordinary paper* (24p.) *or chalk-surfaced paper* (*others*). P 14 × 15 (Nos. 646/7, 649) *or* 15 × 14 (*others*).

646	24p. multicoloured		60	90
647	28p. black and brownish grey		70	80
648	28p. multicoloured		70	80
649	30p. multicoloured		75	1·00
650	46p. multicoloured		90	1·75
646/50		Set of 5	3·25	4·75

Designs: *Vert*—No. 647, Arthur Griffith (statesman); No. 649, Clasped hands (International Peace Year). *Horiz*—No. 648, Woman surveyor (Women in Society); No. 650, Peace dove (International Peace Year).

232 William Mulready and his Design for 1840 Envelope

233 "The Adoration of the Shepherds" (Francesco Pascucci)

(Des C. Harrison (24p.), A. Mazer from aquatints by M. A. Hayes (others). Litho Irish Security Stamp Ptg Ltd)

1986 (2 Oct). *Birth Bicentenaries of William Mulready (artist)* (24p.) *and Charles Bianconi (originator of Irish mail coach service)* (*others*). T **232** *and similar multicoloured designs. Chalk-surfaced paper.* P 14 × 15 (28p.) *or* 15 × 14 (*others*).

651	24p. Type **232**		65	70
652	28p. Bianconi car outside Hearns Hotel, Clonmel (*vert*)		75	55
653	39p. Bianconi car on the road		1·25	1·75
651/3		Set of 3	2·40	2·75

(Des C. O'Neill (21p.). Litho Irish Security Stamp Ptg Ltd)

1986 (20 Nov). *Christmas.* T **233** *and similar multicoloured design. Chalk-surfaced paper.* P 15 × 14 (21p.) *or* 14 × 15 (28p.).

654	21p. Type **233**		1·10	1·40
	a. Sheetlet. No. 654 × 12		12·00	
655	28p. "The Adoration of the Magi" (Frans Francken III) (*vert*)		65	60

No. 654 was only issued in sheetlets of 12 sold at £2.50, providing a discount of 2p. off the face value of the stamps.

234 "Butterfly and Flowers" (Tara Collins)

235 Cork Electric Tram

(Litho Irish Security Stamp Ptg Ltd)

1987 (27 Jan). *Greetings Stamps. Children's Paintings.* T **234** *and similar multicoloured design. Chalk-surfaced paper.* P 15 × 14 (24p.) *or* 14 × 15 (28p.).

656	24p. Type **234**		80	1·25
657	28p. "Postman on Bicycle delivering Hearts" (Brigid Teehan) (*vert*)		95	1·25

(Des C. Rycraft. Litho Irish Security Stamp Ptg Ltd)

1987 (4 Mar). *Irish Trams.* T **235** *and similar horiz designs. Multicoloured. Chalk-surfaced paper.* P 15 × 14.

658	24p. Type **235**		65	65
659	28p. Dublin Standard tram		70	85
660	30p. Howth (G.N.R.) tram		80	2·00
661	46p. Galway horse tram		1·25	2·25
658/61		Set of 4	3·00	5·00
MS662	131 × 85 mm. Nos. 658/61		4·25	6·50

No. MS662 exists with the sheet margins overprinted in red for "HAFNIA 87" and in black for "STAMPA 87".

236 Ships from Crest (Bicentenary of Waterford Chamber of Commerce)

237 Bord na Mona Headquarters and "The Turf Cutter" sculpture (John Behan), Dublin

(Des K. Uhlemann (24p.), J Farrer (28p.), A. Mazer and Wendy Walsh (30p.), M. Cameron (39p.). Litho Irish Security Stamp Ptg Ltd)

1987 (9 Apr). *Anniversaries.* T **236** *and similar designs. Chalk-surfaced paper.* P 14 × 15 (30p.) *or* 15 × 14 (*others*).

663	24p. black, ultramarine and deep grey-green		80	60
664	28p. multicoloured		80	60
665	30p. multicoloured		85	1·75
666	39p. multicoloured		90	2·00
663/6		Set of 4	3·00	4·50

Designs: *Horiz*—28p. Canon John Hayes and symbols of agriculture and development (Birth centenary and 50th anniv of Muintir na Tire Programme); 39p. Mother Mary Martin and International Missionary Training Hospital, Drogheda (50th anniv of Medical Missionaries of Mary). *Vert*—30p. *Calceolaria burbidgei* and College crest (300th anniv of Trinity College Botanic Gardens, Dublin).

(Des M. Lunt. Litho Harrison.)

1987 (14 May). *Europa. Modern Architecture.* T **237** *and similar horiz design. Multicoloured.* P 15 × 14.

667	28p. Type **237**		1·50	60
668	39p. St. Mary's Church, Cong		3·50	5·00

NEW INFORMATION

The editor is always interested to correspond with people who have new information that will improve or correct the Catalogue.

238 Kerry Cow

239 Fleadh Nua, Ennis

(Des B. Driscoll. Litho Irish Security Stamp Ptg Ltd)

1987 (2 July). *Irish Cattle.* T **238** *and similar horiz designs. Multicoloured. Chalk-surfaced paper.* P 15 × 14.

669	24p. Type **238**		80	75
670	28p. Friesian cow and calf		1·00	60
671	30p. Hereford bullock		1·10	2·25
672	39p. Shorthorn bull		1·25	2·25
669/72		Set of 4	3·75	5·25

(Des R. Ballagh. Litho Irish Security Stamp Ptg Ltd)

1987 (27 Aug). *Festivals.* T **239** *and similar multicoloured designs. Chalk-surfaced paper.* P 14 × 15 (*vert*) *or* 15 × 14 (*horiz*).

673	24p. Type **239**		75	70
674	28p. Rose of Tralee International Festival		85	60
675	30p. Wexford Opera Festival (*horiz*)		1·00	2·00
676	46p. Ballinasloe Horse Fair (*horiz*)		1·40	2·00
673/6		Set of 4	3·50	4·75

240 Flagon (1637), Arms and Anniversary Ornament (1987) (350th Anniv of Dublin Goldsmiths' Company)

241 Scenes from "The Twelve Days of Christmas" (carol)

(Des B. Donegan (No. 677), R. Ballagh (No. 678), A. Mazer and Breda Mathews (No. 679), Libby Carton (No. 680). Litho Harrison (46p.) or Irish Security Stamp Ptg Ltd (others))

1987 (1 Oct). *Anniversaries and Commemorations.* T **240** *and similar designs. Ordinary paper* (46p.) *or chalk-surfaced paper* (*others*). P 15 × 14 (*horiz*) *or* 14 × 15 (*vert*).

677	**240** 24p. multicoloured		55	80
678	— 24p. grey and black		55	80
679	— 28p. multicoloured		65	60
680	— 46p. multicoloured		1·00	1·10
677/80		Set of 4	2·50	3·00

Designs: *Vert*—24p. (No. 678) Cathal Brugha (statesman); 46p. Woman chairing board meeting (Women in Society). *Horiz*—28p. Arms of Ireland and inscription (50th anniv of Constitution).

(Des M. Cameron (21p.), A. Mazer (others). Litho Irish Security Stamp Ptg Ltd)

1987 (17 Nov). *Christmas.* T **241** *and similar multicoloured designs. Chalk-surfaced paper.* P 15 × 14 (21p.) *or* 14 × 15 (*others*).

681	21p. Type **241**		60	1·00
	a. Sheetlet. No. 681 × 14		7·50	
682	24p. The Nativity (detail, late 15th-cent Waterford Vestments) (*vert*)		75	1·00
683	28p. Figures from Neapolitan crib, c 1850 (*vert*)		75	80
681/3		Set of 3	1·90	2·50

No. 681 represents a special rate for greetings cards within Ireland and to all E.E.C. countries. It was only issued in sheetlets of 14 stamps and 1 label sold at £2.90, providing an additional discount of 4p. off the face value of the stamps.

242 Acrobatic Clowns spelling "LOVE"

243 "Robert Burke" (Sidney Nolan) and Map of Burke and Wills Expedition Route

(Des M. Cameron (24p.), Aislinn Adams (28p.). Litho Irish Security Stamp Ptg Ltd)

1988 (27 Jan). *Greetings Stamps.* T **242** *and similar multicoloured design. Chalk-surfaced paper.* P 15 × 14 (24p.) *or* 14 × 15 (28p.).

684	24p. Type **242**		60	60
685	28p. Pillar box and hearts (*vert*)		65	65

(Des A. Mazer. Litho Irish Security Stamp Ptg Ltd)

1988 (1 Mar). *Bicentenary of Australian Settlement.* T **243** *and similar horiz design. Multicoloured. Chalk-surfaced paper.* P 15 × 14.

686	24p. Type **243**		50	60
687	46p. "Eureka Stockade" (mural detail, Sidney Nolan)		1·10	1·75

244 Past and Present Buildings of Dublin   **245** Showjumping

(Des S. Conlin. Litho Irish Security Stamp Ptg Ltd)

1988 (1 Mar). *Dublin Millennium. Chalk-surfaced paper. P 15×14.*
688 244 28p. multicoloured 60 55
    a. Booklet pane. No. 688 × 4 .. .. 1·75
No. 688a was printed with either Irish or English inscriptions in the centre of the pane and came from £2.24 stamp booklets. Loose panes could also be purchased from the Philatelic Bureau, Dublin, and its agents. They exist overprinted for "STAMPA 88" (in blue on Irish version and red on English) and "Sydpex 88" (both green on gold).

(Des Ann Flynn Litho Irish Security Stamp Ptg Ltd)

1988 (7 Apr). *Olympic Games, Seoul. T 245 and similar horiz design. Multicoloured. Chalk-surfaced paper. P 15×14.*
689 28p. Type 245 .. .. 1·00 1·40
    a. Sheetlet. Nos. 689/90, each × 5 9·00
690 28p. Cycling .. .. .. 1·00 1·40
Nos. 689/90 were printed together, se-tenant, in a sheetlet containing five of each design and two stamp-size labels.

246 William T. Cosgrave (statesman)   **247** Air Traffic Controllers and Airbus Industrie A320

(Des R. Ballagh (24p.), J. Farrer (30p.), K. Uhlemann (50p.). Litho Irish Security Stamp Ptg Ltd)

1988 (7 Apr). *Anniversaries and Events. T 246 and similar designs. Chalk-surfaced paper. P 14×15 (vert) or 15×14 (horiz).*
691 24p. brownish grey and black 60 45
692 30p. multicoloured .. .. 1·00 1·00
693 50p. multicoloured .. .. 1·25 1·50
691/3 .. .. Set of 3 2·50 2·75
Designs: Horiz—30p. Members with casualty and ambulance (50th anniv of Order of Malta Ambulance Corps). Vert—50p. Barry Fitzgerald (actor) (Birth centenary).

(Des C. Rycraft (28p.), M. Cameron (39p.). Litho Irish Security Stamp Ptg Ltd)

1988 (12 May). *Europa. Transport and Communications. T 247 and similar horiz design. Multicoloured. Chalk-surfaced paper. P 15×14.*
694 28p. Type 247 .. .. 1·25 55
695 39p. Globe with stream of letters from Ireland to Europe .. .. 1·75 2·25

248 *Sirius* (paddle-steamer) (150th anniv of regular transatlantic steamship services)   **249** Cottonweed

(Des C. Rycraft. Litho Irish Security Stamp Ptg Ltd)

1988 (12 May). *Transatlantic Transport Anniversaries. T 248 and similar horiz design. Multicoloured. Chalk-surfaced paper. P 15×14.*
696 28p. Type 248 .. .. 75 50
697 46p. Short S.20 seaplane *Mercury* and Short S.21 flying boat *Maia* (Short-Mayo composite aircraft) in Foynes Harbour (50th anniv of first commercial transatlantic flight) .. 1·25 2·50

(Des Frances Poskitt. Litho Irish Security Stamp Ptg Ltd)

1988 (21 June). *Endangered Flora of Ireland. T 249 and similar vert designs. Multicoloured. Chalk-surfaced paper. P 14×15.*
698 24p. Type 249 .. .. 65 65
699 28p. Hart's Saxifrage 75 55
700 46p. Purple Milk-Vetch .. .. 1·10 2·00
698/700 .. .. Set of 3 2·25 2·75

250 Garda on Duty   **251** Computer and Abacus (Institute of Chartered Accountants in Ireland Centenary)

(Des D. Teskey. Litho Irish Security Stamp Ptg Ltd)

1988 (23 Aug). *Irish Security Forces. T 250 and similar horiz designs. Multicoloured. Chalk-surfaced paper. P 15×14.*
701 28p. Type 250 .. .. 60 1·00
    a. Strip of 4. Nos. 701/4 .. 2·25
702 28p. Army unit with personnel carrier 60 1·00
703 28p. Navy and Air Corps members with *Eithne* (helicopter patrol vessel) 60 1·00
704 28p. Army and navy reservists .. 60 1·00
701/4 .. .. Set of 4 2·25 3·50
Nos. 701/4 were printed together, both horizontally and vertically se-tenant, throughout the sheet of 20 (4×5).

(Des C. Rycraft (24p.), K. King and A. Mazer (46p.). Litho Irish Security Stamp Ptg Ltd)

1988 (6 Oct). *Anniversaries. T 251 and similar multicoloured design. Chalk-surfaced paper. P 14×15 (24p.) or 15×14 (46p.).*
705 24p. Type 251 .. .. 50 50
706 46p. *Duquesa Santa Ana* off Donegal (horiz) (400th anniv of Spanish Armada) .. 1·50 1·50

252 "President Kennedy" (James Wyeth)   **253** St. Kevin's Church, Glendalough

(Des A. Mazer. Litho Irish Security Stamp Ptg Ltd)

1988 (24 Nov). *25th Death Anniv of John F. Kennedy (American statesman). Chalk-surfaced paper. P 15×14.*
707 252 28p. multicoloured 70 80

(Des Ann Flynn (21p.), B. Donegan (others). Litho Irish Security Stamp Ptg Ltd)

1988 (24 Nov). *Christmas. T 253 and similar vert designs. Multicoloured. Chalk-surfaced paper. P 14×15.*
708 21p. Type 253 .. .. 70 70
    a. Sheetlet. No. 708 × 14 .. 9·00
709 24p. The Adoration of the Magi .. 60 60
710 28p. The Flight into Egypt .. 70 55
711 46p. The Holy Family .. .. 1·10 2·00
708/11 .. .. Set of 4 2·75 3·50
No. 708 represents a special rate for greetings cards within Ireland and to all E.E.C. countries. It was only issued in sheetlets of 14 stamps and 1 label sold at £2.90, providing an additional discount of 4p. off the face value of the stamps.
The designs of Nos. 709/11 are from a 15th-century French Book of Hours.

254 Spring Flowers spelling "Love" in Gaelic   **255** Italian Garden, Garinish Island

(Des Susan Dubsky (24p.), A. Mazer (28p.). Litho Irish Security Stamp Ptg Ltd)

1989 (24 Jan). *Greetings Stamps. T 254 and similar multicoloured design. Chalk-surfaced paper. P 15×14 (24p.) or 14×15 (28p.).*
712 24p. Type 254 .. .. 60 55
713 28p. "The Sonnet" (William Mulready) (vert) 65 55

(Des Frances Poskitt. Litho Irish Security Stamp Ptg Ltd)

1989 (11 Apr). *National Parks and Gardens. T 255 and similar horiz designs. Multicoloured. Chalk-surfaced paper. P 15×14.*
714 24p. Type 255 .. .. 80 55
715 28p. Lough Veagh, Glenveagh National Park 95 55
716 32p. Barnaderg Bay, Connemara National Park .. .. 1·00 1·25
717 50p. St. Stephen's Green, Dublin .. 1·50 1·75
714/17 .. .. Set of 4 3·75 3·75

256 "Silver Stream", 1908   **257** Ring-a-ring-a-roses

(Des C. Rycraft. Litho Irish Security Stamp Ptg Ltd)

1989 (11 Apr). *Classic Irish Cars. T 256 and similar horiz designs. Multicoloured. Chalk-surfaced paper. P 15×14.*
718 24p. Type 256 .. .. 50 55
    a. Booklet pane. Nos. 718/19, each ×2 3·00
    b. Booklet pane. Nos. 718/21 3·50
719 28p. Benz "Comfortable", 1898 .. 50 55
720 39p. "Thomond", 1929 .. .. 1·25 1·50
721 46p. Chambers' 8 h.p. model, 1905 1·50 1·60
718/21 .. .. Set of 4 3·25 3·75
Booklet panes Nos. 718a/b come from £2.41 stamp booklets and stamps from them have one or two adjacent sides imperforate. Such panes were also available loose from the Philatelic Bureau, Dublin, and its agents

(Des C. Harrison. Litho Irish Security Stamp Ptg Ltd)

1989 (11 May). *Europa. Children's Games. T 257 and similar horiz design. Multicoloured. Chalk-surfaced paper. P 15×14.*
722 28p. Type 257 .. .. 1·00 75
723 39p. Hopscotch .. .. 1·40 2·25
Nos. 722/3 were each issued in sheets of 10 showing additional illustrations in the left-hand sheet margin.

258 Irish Red Cross Flag (50th anniv)   **259** Saints Kilian, Totnan and Colman (from 12th-century German manuscript)

(Des Q Design (24p.), R. Hoek (28p.). Litho Irish Security Stamp Ptg Ltd)

1989 (11 May). *Anniversaries and Events. T 258 and similar vert design. Chalk-surfaced paper. P 14×15.*
724 24p. vermilion and black 55 60
725 28p. new blue, black and lemon .. 1·10 1·10
Design:—28p. Circle of twelve stars (Third direct elections to European Parliament).

(Des P. Effert. Litho Irish Security Stamp Ptg Ltd)

1989 (15 June). *1300th Death Anniv of Saints Kilian, Totnan and Colman. Chalk-surfaced paper. P 13½.*
726 259 28p. multicoloured .. .. 80 1·10
    a. Booklet pane. No. 726×4 with margins all round 3·00
A stamp in a similar design was issued by West Germany. No. 726a exists with text in Irish, English, German or Latin on the pane margin.

260 19th-century Mail Coach passing Cashel   **261** Crest and 19th-century Dividers (150th anniv of Royal Institute of Architects of Ireland)

(Des Katie O'Sullivan and B. Donegan. Litho Irish Security Stamp Ptg Ltd)

1989 (27 July). *Bicentenary of Irish Mail Coach Service. Chalk-surfaced paper. P 15×14.*
727 260 28p. multicoloured .. .. 1·00 75

(Des R. Ballagh (24p.), A. Mazer (28p.), K. Uhlemann (30p.), Carey Clarke (46p.). Litho Irish Security Stamp Ptg Ltd)

1989 (27 July). *Anniversaries and Commemorations. T 261 and similar designs. Chalk-surfaced paper. P 15×14 (30p.) or 14×15 (others).*
728 24p. grey and black 60 55
729 28p. multicoloured 65 55
730 30p. multicoloured .. .. 1·40 1·75
731 46p. orange-brown .. .. 1·60 1·75
728/31 .. .. Set of 4 3·75 4·25
Designs: Vert—24p. Sean T. O'Kelly (statesman) (drawing by Sean O'Sullivan); 46p. Jawaharlal Nehru (Birth centenary). Horiz—30p. Margaret Burke-Sheridan (soprano) (portrait by De Gennaro) and scene from *La Bohème* (Birth centenary).

262 "NCB Ireland rounding Cape Horn" (Des Fallon)

263 Willow/Red Grouse

(Des I. Caulder. Litho Irish Security Stamp Ptg Ltd)

1989 (31 Aug). *First Irish Entry in Whitbread Round the World Yacht Race. Chalk-surfaced paper. P 15×14.*

732	262	28p. multicoloured	1·25	1·25

(Des R. Ward. Litho Irish Security Stamp Ptg Ltd)

1989 (5 Oct). *Game Birds. T 263 and similar square designs. Multicoloured. Chalk-surfaced paper. P 13½.*

733	24p. Type 263		1·00	55
734	28p. Lapwing		1·10	55
735	39p. Woodcock		1·40	2·00
736	46p. Ring-necked Pheasant		1·50	2·00
733/6		Set of 4	4·50	4·50
MS737	128×92 mm. Nos. 733/6		4·50	4·50

No. MS737 exists overprinted on the margins to commemorate "STAMPA 89", the Irish National Stamp Exhibition.

264 "The Annunciation"

265 Logo (Ireland's Presidency of the European Communities)

(Des Jacinta Fitzgerald (21p.), J. McEvoy from 13th-century Flemish Psalter (others). Litho Irish Security Stamp Ptg Ltd)

1989 (14 Nov). *Christmas. T 264 and similar vert designs. Multicoloured. Chalk-surfaced paper. P 14×15.*

738	21p. Children decorating crib		75	75
	a. Sheetlet. No. 738×14		9·50	
739	24p. Type 264		85	60
740	28p. "The Nativity"		90	55
741	46p. "The Adoration of the Magi"		1·75	2·50
738/41		Set of 4	3·75	4·50

No. 738 represents a special rate for greetings cards within Ireland and to all E.E.C. countries. It was only issued in sheetlets of 14 stamps and 1 label sold at £2.90, providing an additional discount of 4p. off the face value of the stamps.

(Des B. Donegan (30p.), Q Design (50p.). Litho Irish Security Stamp Ptg Ltd)

1990 (9 Jan). *European Events. T 265 and similar horiz design. Multicoloured. Chalk-surfaced paper. P 15×14.*

742	30p. Type 265		75	60
743	50p. Logo and outline map of Ireland (European Tourism Year)		2·00	2·75

266 Dropping Messages from Balloon

267 Silver Kite Brooch

(Des Aislinn Adams (26p.), Patricia Sleeman and R. Vogel (30p.). Litho Irish Security Stamp Ptg Ltd)

1990 (30 Jan). *Greetings Stamps. T 266 and similar vert design. Chalk-surfaced paper. P 14×15.*

744	26p. multicoloured	1·25	1·25
745	30p. rosine, pale buff and reddish brown	1·25	1·25

Design:—30p. Heart and "Love" drawn in lipstick.

PRICES OF SETS

Set prices are given for many issues, generally those containing three stamps or more. Definitive sets include one of each value or major colour change, but do not cover different perforations, die types or minor shades. Where a choice is possible the set prices are based on the cheapest versions of the stamps included in the listings.

Two Types of 20, 28, 52p.:

A. Irish Security Stamp Ptg Ltd printing (coarse background screen. Less distinct centre detail)

B. Enschedé printing (fine background screen. Clear centre detail)

Two Types of £1, £2, £3:

C. Irish Security Stamp Ptg Ltd printing

D. Enschedé printing

(Des M. Craig and Q Design. Litho Walsall (Nos. 748c, 755b), Enschedé (Nos. 751b, 753b, 762b, 763b, 764b, 765b) or Irish Security Stamp Ptg Ltd (others))

1990 (8 Mar)–**97**. *Irish Heritage and Treasures. T 267 and similar designs. Chalk-surfaced paper (5, 20, 26, 28, 30, 32, 37, 38, 41, 44, 50, 52p., £1, £5) or ordinary paper (others). P 14×15 (10, 20, 30, 32p, £5) or 15×14 (others).*

746	1p. black and new blue (26.7.90)		10	10
	a. Chalk-surfaced paper (10.91)		10	10
747	2p. black and bright red-orange (26.7.90)		10	10
	a. Chalk-surfaced paper (15.11.90)		10	10
	ab. Booklet pane. Nos. 747a, 748b×3, 752 and 754×2 plus label		3·00	
	ac. Booklet pane. Nos. 747a×2, 755×2 and 820 (17.10.91)		5·50	
748	4p. black and bluish violet (26.7.90)		10	10
	a. Booklet pane. Nos. 748 and 755a×3 (16.11.95)		2·00	
	b. Chalk-surfaced paper (15.11.90)		10	10
	ba. Booklet pane. Nos. 748b×3, 753×4 plus label (17.10.91)		5·50	
	bb. Booklet pane. Nos. 748b and 1048×3 (6.3.97)		1·60	
	c. Perf 13×13½. Chalk-surfaced paper (24.9.93)		10	10
	ca. Booklet pane. Nos. 748c and 755b×3 (4p. at bottom right)		2·00	
	cb. Ditto, but 4p. at top left (2.3.94)		2·00	
749	5p. black and bright green (29.1.91)		10	10
	a. Ordinary paper (5.92)		50	50
750	10p. black and bright red-orange (26.7.90)		50	25
	a. Chalk-surfaced paper (9.93)		50	25
751	20p. black and lemon (A) (29.1.91)		35	40
	a. Ordinary paper (3.92)		1·00	80
	b. Type B (Enschedé ptg) (16.11.95)		35	40
752	26p. black and bluish violet		45	50
	a. Ordinary paper (5.90)		2·50	1·50
	ab. Perf 13½ (3.5.90)		3·00	3·50
753	28p. black & bright red-orange (A) (3.4.91)		50	55
	a. Ordinary paper (5.91)		1·50	1·50
	b. Type B (Enschedé ptg) (16.11.95)		50	55
754	30p. black and new blue		50	55
	a. Ordinary paper (5.90)		1·50	1·50
	ab. Perf 13½ (3.5.90)		2·50	3·00
755	32p. black and bright green		55	60
	a. Ordinary paper (5.90)		55	60
	b. Perf 13½×13. Chalk-surfaced paper (24.9.93)			
756	34p. black and lemon (26.7.90)		90	90
757	37p. brownish black & brt green (3.4.91)		60	65
	a. Ordinary paper (11.91)		65	70
758	38p. black and bluish violet (3.4.91)		2·00	1·75
	a. Ordinary paper (5.95)		65	70
758b	40p. black and new blue (14.5.92)		1·25	1·25
	ba. Chalk-surfaced paper (9.93)		70	75
759	41p. black and bright red-orange		70	75
	a. Ordinary paper (10.90)		70	75
760	44p. agate and lemon (3.4.91)		2·75	2·75
760a	45p. black and bluish violet (14.5.92)		75	80
761	50p. black and lemon		75	80
	a. Ordinary paper (5.90)		90	95
762	52p. black and new blue (A) (3.4.91)		3·00	3·25
	a. Ordinary paper (2.96)		90	95
	b. Type B (Enschedé ptg) (16.11.95)		3·50	3·00
763	£1 black and lemon (A)		90	95
	a. Ordinary paper (5.90)		1·75	1·90
	b. Type D (Enschedé ptg) (16.11.95)		15·00	4·00
764	£2 black and bright green (C) (26.7.90)		1·75	1·90
	a. Chalk-surfaced paper (9.93)		3·50	3·75
	b. Type D (Enschedé ptg) (chalk-surfaced paper) (16.11.95)		3·50	3·75
765	£5 black and new blue (C) (29.1.91)		3·50	3·75
	a. Ordinary paper (10.97)		8·75	9·00
	b. Type D (Enschedé ptg) (16.11.95)		30·00	35·00
746/65		Set of 22	23·00	24·00

Designs: *Vert (as T 267)*—1p., 2p. Type 267; 4p., 5p. Dunamase Food Vessel; 26p., 28p. Lismore Crozier; 34p., 37p., 38p., 40p. Gleninsheen Collar; 41p., 44p., 45p. Silver thistle brooch; 50p., 52p. Broighter Boat. (22×38 mm)—£5 St. Patrick's Bell Shrine. *Horiz (as T 267)*—10p. Derrinboy Armlets; 20p. Gold dress fastener; 30p. Enamelled latchet brooch; 32p.

Broighter Collar. (38×22 mm)—£1 Ardagh Chalice; £2 Tara Brooch.

Nos. 747a and 748b were initially only available from booklet pane No. 747ab, but were subsequently issued in sheet form during March (4p.) and October (2p.) 1991. Nos. 748c and 755 only occur from booklet panes Nos. 748ca/cb.

With the exception of Nos. 747ac and 748ba each of the listed booklet panes shows either the upper and lower edges (Nos. 748a, 748bb) or the three outer edges of the pane imperforate. Booklet panes Nos. 535ca and 547bb, which include Nos. 752a and 754ab, and also Nos. 747ac and 748ba each show stamp from the right-hand vertical row imperforate at top, right or at foot depending on the format of the design. The following variations exist:

2p. Imperf at left (booklet pane No. 747ab)
Imperf at foot (booklet pane No. 747ac)
4p. Imperf at left or right (booklet pane No. 747ab)
Imperf at left (booklet panes Nos. 748a, 748bb)
Imperf at foot (booklet pane No. 748a)
Imperf at foot and left (p 13×13½) (booklet pane No. 748ca)
Imperf at right (p 13×13½) (booklet pane No. 748cb)
26p. Imperf at top (p 13×13½) (booklet pane No. 535ca)
Imperf at foot and left (booklet pane No. 747ab)
28p. Imperf at foot (booklet pane No. 748ba)
30p. Imperf at right (p 13½) (booklet pane No. 547bb)
Imperf at top or top and right (booklet pane No. 747ab)
32p. Imperf at right (booklet pane No. 747ac)
Imperf at top or foot (booklet pane No. 748a)
Imperf at top, top and right or foot (p 13½×13) (booklet pane No. 748ca)
Imperf at top and right, foot and right or foot (p 13½×x 13) (booklet pane No. 748cb)

For 4, 28 and 32p. stamps in same designs as Nos. 748, 753 and 755, but printed in photogravure, see Nos. 808/10.

For 32p. value as No. 755, but 27×20 mm and self-adhesive see No. 823.

268 Posy of Flowers

269 Player heading Ball

(Des M. Cameron. Litho Irish Security Stamp Ptg Ltd)

1990 (22 Mar). *Greetings Stamps. T 268 and similar vert designs. Multicoloured. P 14×15.*

766	26p. Type 268		2·00	2·50
	a. Booklet pane. Nos. 766/9		7·50	
767	26p. Birthday presents		2·00	2·50
768	30p. Flowers, ribbon and horseshoe		2·00	2·50
769	30p. Balloons		2·00	2·50
766/9		Set of 4	7·50	9·00

Nos. 766/9 come from £1.98 discount stamp booklets.

Booklet pane No. 766a exists with the 26p. values at left or right and the right-hand stamp (either No. 767 or 769) imperforate at right. The booklet pane also contains 8 small greetings labels.

(Des C. Harrison. Litho Irish Security Stamp Ptg Ltd)

1990 (5 Apr). *World Cup Football Championship, Italy. T 269 and similar vert design. Multicoloured. Chalk-surfaced paper. P 14×15.*

770	30p. Type 269		1·50	2·00
	a. Sheetlet. Nos. 770/1, each × 4		11·00	
771	30p. Tackling		1·50	2·00

Nos. 770/1 were printed together, *se-tenant*, in a sheetlet of 8 stamps and 1 central stamp-size label.

270 Battle of the Boyne, 1690

(Des S. Conlin. Litho Irish Security Stamp Ptg Ltd)

1990 (5 Apr). *300th Anniv of the Williamite Wars (1st issue). T 270 and similar horiz designs. Multicoloured. Chalk-surfaced paper. P 13½.*

772	30p. Type 270		1·00	1·50
	a. Pair. Nos. 772/3		2·00	3·00
773	30p. Siege of Limerick, 1690		1·00	1·50

Nos. 772/3 were printed together, *se-tenant*, in horizontal and vertical pairs throughout the sheet.

See also Nos. 806/7.

271 1990 Irish Heritage 30p. Stamp and 1840 Postmark

272 General Post Office, Dublin

(Des Q Design. Litho Irish Security Stamp Ptg Ltd)

1990 (3 May). *150th Anniv of the Penny Black. T* **271** *and similar horiz design. Multicoloured. Chalk-surfaced paper.* P 15×14.

774	30p. Type **271**	90	90
	a. Ordinary paper	1·75	2·50
	ab. Booklet pane. Nos. 774a/5a, each × 2	8·50	
775	50p. Definitive stamps of 1922, 1969, 1982 and 1990	1·50	2·00
	a. Ordinary paper	2·50	3·00

Nos. 774a and 775a were only issued in booklets.
In booklet pane No. 774ab one example of each value is imperforate at right.
Booklet pane No. 774ab exists with the margins overprinted in red in connection with "STAMPA 90", the Irish National Stamp Exhibition.
For other booklet panes containing Nos. 774a/5a see Nos. 547ba/bb.

(Des P. Keogh. Litho Irish Security Stamp Ptg Ltd)

1990 (3 May). *Europa. Post Office Buildings. T* **272** *and similar vert design. Multicoloured.* P 14 × 15.

776	30p. Type **272**	1·00	60
777	41p. Westport Post Office, County Mayo	1·40	2·50

Nos. 776/7 were each printed in sheets of 10 stamps and 2 stamp-size labels.

273 Medical Missionary giving Injection

274 Narcissus "Foundling" and Japanese Gardens, Tully

(Des I. Calder (26, 50p.), R. Ballagh (30p.). Litho Irish Security Stamp Ptg Ltd)

1990 (21 June). *Anniversaries and Events. T* **273** *and similar designs.* P 15×14 *(horiz)* or 14×15 *(vert).*

778	26p. multicoloured	90	55
779	30p. black	1·00	2·00
780	50p. multicoloured	1·50	1·50
778/80	Set of 3	3·00	3·75

Designs: *Vert*—30p. Michael Collins (statesman) (Birth centenary). *Horiz*—50p. Missionaries working at water pump (Irish missionary service).

(Des I. Loe. Litho Irish Security Stamp Ptg Ltd)

1990 (30 Aug). *Garden Flowers. T* **274** *and similar vert designs. Multicoloured.* P 14×15.

781	26p. Type **274**	70	55
	a. Booklet pane. Nos. 781/2, each × 2	4·50	
	b. Booklet pane. No. 781/4	4·50	
782	30p. *Rosa x hibernica* and Malahide Castle gardens	85	80
783	41p. *Primula* "Rowallane Rose" and Rowallane garden	1·75	1·75
784	50p. *Erica erigena* "Irish Dusk" and Palm House, National Botanical Gardens	2·00	2·00
781/4	Set of 4	4·75	4·50

Both booklet panes show the stamps as horizontal rows of four imperforate at top and at right. Stamps from the right of the pane, 30p. on No. 781a, 50p. on No. 781b, are imperforate at top and right with the other values imperforate at top only.
No. 781a exists overprinted in blue for Collectors' Road Shows at Waterford and Galway.

Frama label   Klussendorf label

Amiel Pitney/Bowes label

MACHINE LABELS. For a trial period of three months from 8 October 1990 labels in the above designs, ranging in value from 1p. to £99.99, were available from the head post offices at Dublin (Frama), Limerick (Klussendorf) and Cork (Amiel Pitney/Bowes. The Amiel Pitney/Bowes machine (Cork) was taken out of service on 31 January 1991. The other two machines were withdrawn on 31 May 1991.

NEW INFORMATION

The editor is always interested to correspond with people who have new information that will improve or correct the Catalogue.

275 *Playboy of the Western World* (John Synge)

276 Nativity

(Des R. Ballagh. Litho Irish Security Stamp Ptg Ltd)

1990 (18 Oct). *Irish Theatre. T* **275** *and similar horiz designs. Multicoloured.* P 13½.

785	30p. Type **275**	1·25	1·50
	a. Horiz strip of 4. Nos. 785/8	4·50	
786	30p. *Juno and the Paycock* (Sean O'Casey)	1·25	1·50
787	30p. *The Field* (John Keane)	1·25	1·50
788	30p. *Waiting for Godot* (Samuel Beckett)	1·25	1·50
785/8	Set of 4	4·50	5·50

Nos. 785/8 were printed together in sheets of 20 (4×5), producing horizontal *se-tenant* strips of 4 and vertical *se-tenant* pairs of Nos. 785 and 788 or 786/7.

(Des Pamela Leonard (No. 789), B. Cronin (others). Litho Irish Security Stamp Ptg Ltd)

1990 (15 Nov). *Christmas. T* **276** *and similar vert designs. Multicoloured. Chalk-surfaced paper (50p.) or ordinary paper (others).* P 14×15.

789	26p. Child praying by bed	70	80
	a. Sheetlet. No. 789×12	7·50	
790	26p. Type **276**	70	60
791	30p. Madonna and Child	90	90
792	50p. Adoration of the Magi	1·60	2·25
789/92	Set of 4	3·50	4·00

No. 789 was only issued in sheetlets of 12 sold at £2.86, providing a discount of 26p. off the face value of the stamps.

277 Hearts in Mail Sack and Postman's Cap

278 Starley "Rover" Bicycle, 1886

(Des Liz Manning (26p.), Louise Mullally (30p.). Litho Irish Security Stamp Ptg Ltd)

1991 (29 Jan). *Greetings Stamps. T* **277** *and similar vert design. Multicoloured. Chalk-surfaced paper.* P 14×15.

793	26p. Type **277**	85	1·00
794	30p. Boy and girl kissing	90	1·00

(Des E. Patton. Litho Irish Security Stamp Ptg Ltd)

1991 (5 Mar). *Early Bicycles. T* **278** *and similar vert designs. Multicoloured. Chalk-surfaced paper.* P 14×15.

795	26p. Type **278**	80	60
796	30p. Child's horse tricycle, 1875	90	95
797	50p. "Penny Farthing", 1871	1·60	1·75
795/7	Set of 3	3·00	3·00
MS798	113×72 mm. Nos. 795/7	3·00	3·00

No. **MS**798 exists with privately-applied marginal overprints for the "Collectorex 91" Exhibition, Dublin, the I.P.T.A. Collectors' Road Show, Birr (both in black) and "STAMPA 91" Exhibition, Dublin (in red or blue).

279 Cuchulainn (statue by Oliver Sheppard) and Proclamation

280 Scene from *La Traviata* (50th anniv of Dublin Grand Opera Society)

(Des I. Calder. Litho Irish Security Stamp Ptg Ltd)

1991 (3 Apr). *75th Anniv of Easter Rising. Chalk-surfaced paper.* P 15×14.

799	279 32p. multicoloured	1·25	1·40

(Des K. Uhlemann (28p.), M. Craig and I. Calder (32p.), M. Craig (44p.), M. Craig and Q Design (52p.). Litho Irish Security Stamp Ptg Ltd)

1991 (11 Apr). *"Dublin 1991 European City of Culture". T* **280** *and similar horiz designs. Multicoloured. Chalk-surfaced paper.* P 13½ (52p.) or 15×14 (others).

800	28p. Type **280**	65	80
	a. Booklet pane. Nos. 800/2	3·75	
	b. Booklet pane. Nos. 800/3	3·75	

801	32p. City Hall and European Community emblem	85	1·50
802	44p. St. Patrick's Cathedral (800th anniv)	1·25	1·60
803	52p. Custom House (bicent) (41×24 mm)	1·40	1·60
800/3	Set of 4	3·75	5·00

281 *Giotto* Spacecraft approaching Halley's Comet

(Des C. Rycraft. Litho Irish Security Stamp Ptg Ltd)

1991 (14 May). *Europa. Europe in Space. T* **281** *and similar horiz design. Multicoloured.* P 15×14.

804	32p. Type **281**	1·25	1·00
805	44p. Hubble Telescope orbiting Earth	1·75	2·75

Nos. 804/5 were each issued in sheetlets of 10 (2×5) with illustrations of space launches on enlarged left hand margins.

282 Siege of Athlone

283 John A. Costello (statesman)

(Des S. Conlin. Litho Irish Security Stamp Ptg Ltd)

1991 (14 May). *300th Anniv of the Williamite Wars (2nd issue). T* **282** *and similar horiz design. Multicoloured. Chalk-surfaced paper.* P 15×14.

806	28p. Type **282**	90	1·40
	a. Pair. Nos. 806/7	1·75	2·75
807	28p. Generals Ginkel and Sarsfield (signatories of Treaty of Limerick)	90	1·40

Nos. 806/7 were printed together, *se-tenant*, in horizontal and vertical pairs throughout the sheet.

1991 (14 May). *Booklet stamps. As Nos. 748, 753 and 755, but printed in photogravure by Enschedé. Chalk-surfaced paper.* P 14×15 (32p.) or 15×14 (others).

808	4p. black and bluish violet	10	10
	a. Booklet pane. Nos. 808×2, 809 and 810×2 plus label	2·00	
809	28p. black and reddish orange	55	60
810	32p. black and bright green	65	70
808/10	Set of 3	1·25	1·40

Booklet pane No. 808a has imperforate outer edges giving stamps imperforate at left or right (4p.), at left and foot (28p.) and at top or top and right (32p.).

(Des R. Ballagh (28p.), Q Design (others). Litho Irish Security Stamp Ptg, Ltd)

1991 (2 July). *Anniversaries. T* **283** *and similar designs. Chalk-surfaced paper (28p.).* P 15×14 (52p.) or 14×15 (others).

811	28p. black	70	70
812	32p. multicoloured	85	85
813	52p. multicoloured	1·40	2·25
811/13	Set of 3	2·75	3·50

Designs: *Vert*—28p. Type **283** (Birth centenary) (drawing by Sean O'Sullivan); 32p. "Charles Stewart Parnell" (Sydney Hall) (Death centenary). *Horiz*—52p. Meeting of United Irishmen (Bicentary).

284 Player on 15th Green, Portmarnock (Walker Cup)

285 Wicklow Cheviot

(Des E. Patton. Litho Irish Security Stamp Ptg Ltd)

1991 (3 Sept). *Golf Commemorations. T* **284** *and similar multicoloured design. Chalk-surfaced paper (32p.).* P 15×14 (28p.) or 14×15 (32p.).

814	28p. Type **284**	1·00	75
815	32p. Logo and golfer of 1900 (Centenary of Golfing Union of Ireland) (vert)	1·25	1·00

(Des Pamela Leonard. Litho Irish Security Stamp Ptg Ltd)

1991 (3 Sept). *Irish Sheep. T* **285** *and similar multicoloured designs. Chalk-surfaced paper.* P 15×14 (52p.) or 14×15 (others).

816	32p. Type **285**	1·00	80
817	38p. Donegal Blackface	1·40	1·50
818	52p. Galway (horiz)	2·00	3·25
816/18	Set of 3	4·00	5·00

286 Boatyard   **287 The Annunciation**

(Des C. Rycraft. Litho Irish Security Stamp Ptg Ltd)

1991 (17 Oct). *Fishing Fleet. T 286 and similar horiz designs. Multicoloured. Chalk-surfaced paper. P 15×14.*

819	28p. Type 286		60	65
	a. Booklet pane. Nos. 819/22		5·50	
	b. Booklet pane. Nos. 819/20 each × 2		5·50	
820	32p. Traditional inshore trawlers ..		70	80
821	44p. Inshore lobster pot boat		1·60	2·25
822	52p. *Veronica* (fish factory ship)		2·00	2·50
819/22		*Set of 4*	4·50	5·50

In booklet pane No. 819a the 32p. and 52p. values are imperforate at right.

Booklet pane No. 819a exists with the gutter margin overprinted in connection with the "Phila Nippon '91" International Stamp Exhibition, Tokyo.

For a further booklet pane including No. 820 see No. 747ac.

(Litho Printset-Cambec Pty Ltd, Australia (No. 823) or Irish Security Stamp Ptg Ltd (No. 823a))

1991 (31 Oct)–95. *As No. 755, but larger, 27×21 mm, and self-adhesive. P 11½.*

823	32p. black and bright green	..	65	70
	a. Perf 10×9 (8.6.95)		65	70

Examples of No. 823 have rounded perforations at each corner of the stamp and pointed die-cut "teeth". No. 823a shows a perforation at each corner and has rounded teeth. Initially both printers showed the stamps separate on the backing paper, but from September 1996 printings of No. 823a retained the surplus self-adhesive paper around each stamp. Printings from July 1992 contained "reminder" labels inserted 20 stamps and 10 stamps from the end of the coil.

Nos. 823/a were only available in coils of 100, or as strips of 3 from the Philatelic Bureau.

(Des Q. Design (No. 827), T. Gayer (others). Litho Irish Security Stamp Ptg Ltd)

1991 (14 Nov). *Christmas. T 287 and similar vert designs. Chalk-surfaced paper. P 14×15.*

827	28p. multicoloured		80	85
	a. Sheetlet. No. 827×13 ..		10·00	
828	28p. dull ultramarine, sage-green and black		75	65
829	32p. scarlet and black		85	75
830	52p. multicoloured		1·60	2·50
827/30		*Set of 4*	3·50	4·25

Designs:—No. 827, Three Kings; No. 828, Type 287; No. 829, The Nativity; No. 830, Adoration of the Kings.

No. 827 was only issued in sheetlets of 13 stamps and two labels (at the centre of rows 1 and 2) sold at £3.36 providing a discount of 28p. off the face value of the stamps.

288 Multicoloured Heart   **289 Healthy Family on Apple**

(Des T. Monaghan (28p.), R. Ballagh (32p.). Litho Irish Security Stamp Ptg Ltd)

1992 (28 Jan). *Greetings Stamps. T 288 and similar multicoloured design. P 15×14 (28p.) or 14×15 (32p.).*

831	28p. Type 288		85	95
832	32p. "LOVE" at end of rainbow (*vert*)	..	95	1·10

(Des Pamela Leonard. Litho Irish Security Stamp Ptg Ltd)

1992 (25 Feb). *"Healthy Living" Campaign. P 14×15.*

833	289	28p. multicoloured	..	85	85

290 Boxing

(Des C. Harrison. Litho Irish Security Stamp Ptg Ltd)

1992 (25 Feb). *Olympic Games, Barcelona. T 290 and similar horiz design. P 15×14.*

834	32p. Type 290 ..		90	90
835	44p. Sailing		1·40	1·90
MS836	130×85 mm. Nos. 834/5×2		4·25	4·75
	a. On chalk-surfaced paper		£170	

No. **MS**836 exists overprinted in black on the margin in connection with the "World Columbian Stamp Expo '92", Chicago. The chalk-surfaced paper variety is only known with this marginal overprint.

---

291 *Mari* (cog) and 14th-century Map

(Des C. Rycraft. Litho Irish Security Stamp Ptg Ltd)

1992 (2 Apr). *Irish Maritime Heritage. T 291 and similar multicoloured design. Chalk-surfaced paper. P 15×14 (32p) or 14×15 (52p).*

837	32p. Type 291	..	1·00	90
838	52p. *Ovoca* (trawler) and chart (*vert*)	..	1·50	2·40

292 Chamber Logo and Commercial Symbols   **293 Cliffs and Cove**

(Des E. Patton. Litho Irish Security Stamp Ptg Ltd)

1992 (2 Apr). *Bicentenary of Galway Chamber of Commerce and Industry. Chalk-surfaced paper. P 15×14.*

839	292	28p. multicoloured		70	85

(Des Pamela Leonard. Litho Irish Security Stamp Ptg Ltd)

1992 (2 Apr). *Greetings Stamps. T 293 and similar vert designs. Multicoloured. Chalk-surfaced paper. P 14×15.*

840	28p. Type 293		75	1·00
	a. Booklet pane. Nos. 840/3		2·75	
841	28p. Meadow		75	1·00
842	32p. Fuchsia and Honeysuckle		75	1·00
843	32p. Lily pond and dragonfly		75	1·00
840/3		*Set of 4*	2·75	3·50

Nos. 840/3 come from £2.40 stamp booklets.

Booklet pane No. 840a exists with the 28p. values at left or right and has the right-hand stamp (either No. 841 or 843) imperforate at right. The booklet pane also contains 8 small greetings labels.

Booklet pane No. 840a exists overprinted on the margin for Regional Stamp Shows at Sligo and Waterford.

MACHINE LABELS. Frama labels in the above design, providing values from 1p. to £99.99, were introduced at head post offices in Dublin (001), Cork (003), Limerick (004) and Galway (005) on 6 April 1992. The system was extended to Bray (008), Killarney (009) and Sligo (007) on 20 July 1992, and to Kilkenny (010) and Waterford (006) on 7 September when a second machine (002) was also provided at Dublin. Both the Dublin machines were relocated to Dublin Airport in August 1994.

294 Fleet of Columbus

(Des S. Conlin. Litho Irish Security Stamp Ptg Ltd)

1992 (14 May). *Europa. 500th Anniv of Discovery of America by Columbus. T 294 and similar horiz design. Multicoloured. P 15×14.*

844	32p. Type 294		1·25	90
845	44p. Columbus landing in the New World		1·75	2·25

Nos. 844/5 were each issued in sheetlets of 10 (2×5) with illustrated left or right margins.

295 Irish Immigrants

(Des Pamela Leonard. Litho Irish Security Stamp Ptg Ltd)

1992 (14 May). *Irish Immigrants in the Americas. T 295 and similar horiz design. Multicoloured. P 13½.*

846	52p. Type 295		1·60	1·60
	a. Pair. Nos. 846/7		3·00	3·00
847	52p. Irish soldiers, entertainers and politicians		1·60	1·60

Nos. 846/7 were printed together, *se-tenant*, in horizontal and vertical pairs throughout the sheet.

296 Pair of Pine Martens

(Des R. Ward. Litho Irish Security Stamp Ptg Ltd)

1992 (9 July). *Endangered Species. Pine Marten. T 296 and similar horiz designs. Multicoloured. P 15×14.*

848	28p. Type 296		1·00	70
849	32p. Marten on branch		1·00	70
850	44p. Female with kittens ..		1·60	1·50
851	52p. Marten catching Great Tit		2·00	1·75
848/51		*Set of 4*	5·00	4·25

297 "The Rotunda and New Rooms" (James Malton)

(Des J. McEvoy (28, 44p.), E. Patton (32, 52p.). Litho Irish Security Stamp Ptg Ltd)

1992 (2 Sept). *Dublin Anniversaries. T 297 and similar multicoloured designs. Chalk-surfaced paper (32p.). P 15×14 (28, 44p.) or 13½ (32, 52p.).*

852	28p. Type 297		80	65
853	32p. Trinity College Library (28×45 *mm*)		1·25	1·00
854	44p. "Charlemont House" ..		1·25	1·00
855	52p. Trinity College main gate (28×45 *mm*)		1·75	2·25
852/5		*Set of 4*	4·50	5·50

Anniversaries:—28, 44p. Bicentenary of publication of Malton's "Views of Dublin"; 32, 52p. 400th anniv of founding of Trinity College.

298 European Star and Megalithic Dolmen   **299 Farm Produce**

(Des R. Ballagh. Litho Irish Security Stamp Ptg Ltd)

1992 (15 Oct). *Single European Market. P 15×14.*

856	298	32p. multicoloured	..	70	80
	a. Booklet pane. No. 856×4		3·00	
	b. Booklet pane. No. 856×3		3·00	

Three versions of booklet pane No. 856a exist showing the stamps arranged as a block of 4, as singles or in two vertical pairs. The first two versions exist overprinted for "STAMPA '92" (in blue on the block of four pane and in red on the other).

The booklet panes also exist overprinted for Regional Stamp Shows at Galway, Dundalk, Kilkenny and Limerick.

(Des. Frances Poskitt. Litho Irish Security Stamp Ptg Ltd)

1992 (15 Oct). *Irish Agriculture. T 299 and similar vert designs. Multicoloured. P 14×15.*

857	32p. Type 299		1·00	1·25
	a. Horiz strip of 4. Nos. 857/60 ..		3·50	
858	32p. Dairy and beef herds		1·00	1·25
859	32p. Harvesting cereals		1·00	1·25
860	32p. Market gardening		1·00	1·25
857/60		*Set of 4*	3·50	4·50

Nos. 857/60 were printed together, *se-tenant*, in horizontal strips of 4 throughout the sheet with each strip forming a composite design.

ALTERED CATALOGUE NUMBERS

Any Catalogue numbers altered from the last edition are shown as a list in the introductory pages.

300 "The Annunciation"
(from illuminated
manuscript)

301 Queen of Hearts

(Des Frances Poskitt (No. 861), J. McEvoy (others). Litho Irish
Security Stamp Ptg Ltd)

1992 (19 Nov). *Christmas. T 300 and similar vert designs.
Multicoloured. Chalk-surfaced paper. P 14×15.*

861	28p. Congregation entering church	80	65
	a. Sheetlet. No. 861×13	9·00	
862	28p. Type **300**	80	65
863	32p. "Adoration of the Shepherds" (Da Empoli)	1·10	1·00
864	52p. "Adoration of the Magi" (Rottenhammer)	1·40	1·50
861/4	Set of 4	3·75	3·50

No. 861 was only issued in sheetlets of 13 stamps and two
labels (at the centre of rows 1 and 2) sold at £3.36 providing a
discount of 28p. off the face value of the stamps.

(Des C. Harrison (28p.), Q Design (32p.). Litho Irish Security
Ptg Ltd)

1993 (26 Jan). *Greetings Stamps. T 301 and similar
multicoloured design. Chalk-surfaced paper. P 14×15 (28p.)
or 15×14 (32p.).*

865	28p. Type **301**	75	75
866	32p. Hot air balloon trailing hearts (*horiz*)	85	85

302 "Evening at Tangier" (Sir John
Lavery)

(Des. E. Patton. Litho Irish Security Stamp Ptg Ltd)

1993 (4 Mar). *Irish Impressionist Painters. T 302 and similar
multicoloured designs. Chalk-surfaced paper. P 13.*

867	28p. Type **302**	75	60
	a. Booklet pane. Nos. 867/70 with margins all round	5·00	
	b. Booklet pane. Nos. 867/8 with margins all round	2·75	
868	32p. "The Goose Girl" (William Leech)	80	65
869	44p. "La Jeune Bretonne" (Roderic O'Conor) (*vert*)	1·25	1·60
	a. Booklet pane. Nos. 869/70 with margins all round	2·75	
870	52p. "Lustre Jug" (Walter Osborne) (*vert*)	1·75	2·25
867/70	Set of 4	4·00	4·50

Booklet pane No. 867a exists in two slightly different
versions, one containing two *se-tenant* pairs and the other the
stamps perforated individually.

The booklet panes exist overprinted in the margin in
connection with Regional Stamp Shows at Mullingar, Tralee
(overprint reads "Summer Regional Show"), Cork and
Letterkenny. No. 867b also comes with a blue marginal
overprint for "STAMPA 93".

303 Bee Orchid

304 "Pears in a Copper
Pan" (Hilda van Stockum)

(Des I. Loe. Litho Irish Security Stamp Ptg Ltd)

1993 (20 Apr). *Irish Orchids. T 303 and similar vert designs.
Multicoloured. P 14×15.*

871	28p. Type **303**	90	60
872	32p. O'Kelly's Orchid	1·00	70
873	38p. Dark Red Helleborine	1·60	2·00
874	52p. Irish Lady's Tresses	1·90	2·50
871/4	Set of 4	4·75	5·25
MS875	130×71 mm. No. 871/4	4·75	6·00

No. **MS**875 exists overprinted in red on the margin in
connection with "STAMPA 93". This miniature sheet was also
re-issued with a wider upper margin, showing the Irish and Thai
flags, for the "Bangkok '93" International Stamp Exhibition.
Such sheets were only available from the Philatelic Bureau and
the An Post stand at the exhibition.

(Des E. Patton. Litho Irish Security Stamp Ptg Ltd)

1993 (18 May). *Europa. Contemporary Art. T 304 and similar
vert design. Multicoloured. Chalk-surfaced paper. P 13.*

876	32p. Type **304**	75	75
877	44p. "Arrieta Orzola" (Tony O'Malley)	1·10	1·10

Nos. 876/7 were each issued in sheetlets of 10 stamps and two
labels (in positions 1 and 4 of the top row).

305 Cultural Activities

(Des K. Uhlemann and B. Donegan. Litho Irish Security Stamp
Ptg Ltd)

1993 (8 July). *Centenary of Conradh Na Gaelige (cultural
organization). T 305 and similar multicoloured design.
Chalk-surfaced paper. P 15×14 (32p.) or 14×15 (52p.).*

878	32p. Type **305**	85	75
879	52p. Illuminated manuscript cover (*vert*)	1·50	1·50

306 Diving

(Des C. Harrison. Litho Irish Security Stamp Ptg Ltd)

1993 (8 July). *Centenary of Irish Amateur Swimming
Association. T 306 and similar horiz design. Multicoloured.
Chalk-surfaced paper. P 15×14.*

880	32p. Type **306**	1·00	1·25
	a. Horiz pair. Nos. 880/1	2·00	2·50
881	32p. Swimming	1·00	1·25

Nos. 880/1 were printed together, *se-tenant,* in horizontal
pairs throughout the sheet.

307 Nurse with Patient and
Hospital Buildings (250th
anniv of Royal Hospital,
Donnybrook)

(Des K. Uhlemann (28p.), Q Design (32p.), C. Rycraft (44p.),
P. Monahan (52p.). Litho Irish Security Stamp Ptg Ltd)

1993 (2 Sept). *Anniversaries and Events. T 307 and similar
multicoloured designs. Chalk-surfaced paper. P 15×14 (28p.,
44p.), 14×15 (32p.) or 13½ (52p.).*

882	28p. Type **307**	80	60
883	32p. College building and crest (Bicent of St. Patrick's College, Carlow) (*vert*)	80	65
884	44p. Map of Neolithic field system, Céide (Opening of interpretative centre)	1·25	1·40
885	52p. Edward Bunting (musicologist) (150th death anniv) (25×42 mm)	1·40	1·60
882/5	Set of 4	3·75	3·75

308 Great Northern Railways
Gardner at Drogheda

309 The
Annunciation

(Des C. Rycraft. Litho Irish Security Stamp Ptg Ltd)

1993 (12 Oct). *Irish Buses. T 308 and similar horiz designs.
Multicoloured. Chalk-surfaced paper. P 15×14.*

886	28p. Type **308**	60	65
	a. Booklet pane. Nos. 886/7, each × 2	3·25	
	b. Booklet pane. Nos. 886/9	3·25	
887	32p. C.I.E. Leyland Titan at College Green, Dublin	65	70
888	52p. Horse-drawn omnibus at Old Baal's Bridge, Limerick	1·25	1·75
	a. Horiz pair. Nos. 888/9	2·50	3·50
889	52p. Char-a-banc at Lady's View, Killarney	1·25	1·75
886/9	Set of 4	3·25	4·25

Nos. 888/9 were printed together, *se-tenant,* in horizontal
pairs throughout the sheet.

Booklet panes Nos. 886a/b come from £2.84 stamp booklets
and have the outer edges of the pane imperforate.

(Des Pamela Leonard (No. 890), C. Harrison (others). Litho Irish
Security Stamp Ptg Ltd)

1993 (16 Nov). *Christmas. T 309 and similar multicoloured
designs. Chalk-surfaced paper. P 14×15 (No. 890) or 15×14
(others).*

890	28p. The Flight into Egypt (*vert*)	60	65
	a. Sheetlet. No. 890×13	5·75	
891	28p. Type **309**	60	55
892	32p. Holy Family	70	70
893	52p. Adoration of the shepherds	1·60	1·90
890/3	Set of 4	3·25	3·50

No. 890 was only issued in sheetlets of 13 stamps and two
labels (at the centre of rows 1 and 2) sold at £3.36 providing a
discount of 28p. off the face value of the stamps.

310 Airplane skywriting
"Love"

311 Smiling Sun

(Des Jean Colton (28p.), E. Rainsberry (32p.) Litho Questa)

1994 (27 Jan). *Greetings Stamps. T 310 and similar
multicoloured design. Chalk-surfaced paper. P 15×14 (28p.)
or 14×15 (32p.).*

894	28p. Type **310**	75	75
895	32p. Couple within heart (*vert*)	85	85

(Des S. Young. Litho Irish Security Stamp Ptg)

1994 (27 Jan). *Greetings Booklet Stamps. T 311 and similar
vert designs. Multicoloured. P 14×15.*

896	32p. Type **311**	70	75
	a. Booklet pane. No. 896/9	2·50	
897	32p. Smiling daisy	70	75
898	32p. Smiling heart	70	75
899	32p. Smiling rose	70	75
896/9	Set of 4	2·50	2·75

Nos. 896/9 come from £2.56 stamp booklets.

Booklet pane No. 896a exists with the right-hand stamp
(either No. 897 or 899) imperforate at right. Each booklet pane
also contains 8 small greeting labels.

The booklet pane also exists overprinted for Regional Stamp
Shows at Cork and Letterkenny and from the Dublin
International Stamp and Card Show.

(Des S. Young. Litho Irish Security Stamp Ptg Ltd)

1994 (18 Feb). *"Hong Kong '94" International Stamp
Exhibition. Chinese New Year ("Year of the Dog"). P 14×15.*
MS900 137×34 mm. Nos. 896/8 .. .. 4·25 4·75

The example of No. 898 in the above miniature sheet is
imperforate at right.

312 Stylised Logo of Macra
na Feirme (50th anniv)

(Des K. and R. Uhlemann (28p.), Creative Inputs (32p.),
E. Patton (38, 52p.). Litho Irish Security Stamp Ptg Ltd)

1994 (2 Mar). *Anniversaries and Events. T 312 and similar
horiz designs. Chalk-surfaced paper. P 15×14.*

901	28p. gold and deep ultramarine	75	65
902	32p. multicoloured	1·25	75
903	38p. multicoloured	1·25	1·50
904	52p. black, cobalt and bright blue	1·40	1·75
901/4	Set of 4	4·25	4·25

Designs: (38×35 mm)—32p. "The Taking of Christ"
(Caravaggio) (Loan of painting to National Gallery). (37½×27
mm)—38p. Sir Horace Plunkett with 19th-century milk carts
and modern tankers (Centenary of Irish Co-operative
Organisation Society); 52p. Congress emblem (Centenary of
Irish Congress of Trade Unions).

313 St. Brendan visiting
Iceland

(Des C. Harrison. Litho Irish Security Stamp Ptg, Ltd)

1994 (18 Apr). *Europa. St. Brendan's Voyages. T 313 and
similar horiz design. Multicoloured. Chalk-surfaced paper.
P 15×14.*

905	32p. Type **313**	75	70
906	44p. St. Brendan discovering Faroe Islands	1·50	1·75
MS907	82×76 mm. Nos. 905/6	2·25	2·75

Nos. 905/6 were each issued in sheetlets of 10 (2×5) with
enlarged illustrated left margins.

No. **MS**907 also exists overprinted in blue on the margins in
connection with "Stampa '94".

314 First Meeting of Dail, 1919
315 Irish and Argentine Footballers

(Des R. Hoek. Litho Irish Security Stamp Ptg Ltd)

1994 (27 Apr). *Parliamentary Anniversaries. T* **314** *and similar horiz design. Multicoloured. Chalk-surfaced paper. P* 15×14.
908	32p. Type **314** (75th anniv)		90 75
	a. Booklet pane. Nos. 908/9, each × 2		3·00
	b. Booklet pane. Nos. 908/9		1·50
909	32p. European Parliament (4th direct elections)		90 75

Booklet panes Nos. 908a/b come from £1·92 stamp booklets and have the outer edges of the panes imperforate. Booklet pane No. 908a contains examples of No. 908 either imperforate at top or at right and foot, and No. 909 imperforate at foot or at top and right. In booklet pane No. 908b No. 908 is imperforate at right and No. 909 fully perforated.

(Des J. Donohoe (Nos. 910/11), E. Patton (others). Litho Irish Security Stamp Ptg, Ltd (Nos. 910/11) or Enschedé (others))

1994 (31 May). *Sporting Anniversaries and Events. T* **315** *and similar multicoloured designs. Chalk-surfaced paper (Nos.* 910/11). P 14×15 *(Nos.* 910/11) *or* 13×13¹⁄₂ *(others).*
910	32p. Type **315**		80 90
	a. Sheetlet. Nos. 910/11, each × 4		6·00
911	32p. Irish and German footballers		80 90
912	32p. Irish and Dutch women's hockey match *(horiz)*		1·25 90
913	52p. Irish and English women's hockey match *(horiz)*		1·50 1·75
910/13		*Set of* 4	4·00 4·00

Anniversaries and Events:—Nos. 910/11, World Cup Football Championship, U.S.A.; No. 912, Women's Hockey World Cup, Dublin; No. 913, Centenary of Irish Ladies' Hockey Union.
Nos. 910/11 were printed together, *se-tenant*, in sheetlets of 8 stamps and one central label.

316 *Arctia caja*
317 Statue of Edmund Rice and Class

(Des I. Loe)

1994 (12 July). *Moths. T* **316** *and similar horiz designs. Multicoloured.* (a) *Litho Irish Security Stamp Ptg Ltd. Chalk-surfaced paper. P* 15×14.
914	28p. Type **316**		65 60
915	32p. *Calamia tridens*		75 70
916	38p. *Saturnia pavonia*		90 90
917	52p. *Deilephila elpenor*		1·50 1·75
914/17		*Set of* 4	3·50 3·50
MS918	120×71 mm. Nos. 914/17		3·50 4·00

(b) *Litho Printset-Cambec Pty Ltd, Australia. Self-adhesive. Chalk-surfaced paper. P* 11¹⁄₂.
919	32p. *Calamia tridens*		85 95
920	32p. Type **316**		85 95
921	32p. *Deilephila elpenor*		85 95
922	32p. *Saturnia pavonia*		85 95
919/22		*Set of* 4	3·00 3·50

No. **MS**918 also exists with the "Philakorea '94" International Stamp Exhibition, Seoul, logo added at bottom right and also comes overprinted in black for Collectors' Road Show, Sligo, or in red for "Stampa '94".
Nos. 919/22 are smaller, 34×22 mm, and occur, *se-tenant*, in strips of 4 or rolls of 100 with the surplus self-adhesive paper around each stamp removed.

(Des S. Conlin (No. 923), Design Factory (Nos. 925, 927), E. Patton (Nos. 924, 926). Litho Walsall (Nos. 925, 927), Irish Security Stamp Ptg Ltd (others))

1994 (6 Sept). *Anniversaries and Events. T* **317** *and similar multicoloured designs. Chalk-surfaced paper. P* 13¹⁄₂ *(No.* 923), 14 *(Nos.* 925, 927), 14×15 *(Nos.* 924) *or* 15×14 *(No.* 926).
923	28p. St. Laurence Gate, Drogheda (41¹⁄₂×25 mm)		70 70
924	32p. Type **317**		75 1·00
925	32p. Edmund Burke (politician)		75 1·00
926	52p. Vickers FB-27 Vimy and map *(horiz)*		1·25 1·40
927	52p. Eamonn Andrews (broadcaster)		1·25 1·40
923/7		*Set of* 5	4·25 5·00

Anniversaries and Events:—No. 923, 800th anniv of Drogheda; No. 924, 150th death anniv of Edmund Rice (founder of Irish Christian Brothers); Nos. 925, 927, The Irish abroad; No. 926, 75th anniv of Alcock and Brown's first Transatlantic flight.

318 George Bernard Shaw (author) and *Pygmalion* Poster
319 The Annunciation (ivory plaque)

(Des R. Ballagh. Litho Irish Security Stamp Ptg Ltd)

1994 (18 Oct). *Irish Nobel Prizewinners. T* **318** *and similar horiz designs. Multicoloured. Chalk-surfaced paper. P* 15×14.
928	28p. Type **318**		60 60
	a. Pair. Nos. 928/9		1·10 1·25
	b. Booklet pane. Nos. 928/9 and 930×2 with margins all round		3·00
	c. Booklet pane. Nos. 928/31 with margins all round		3·00
	d. Booklet pane. Nos. 928/30 with margins all round		3·00
929	28p. Samuel Beckett (author) and pair of boots		60 60
930	32p. Sean MacBride (human rights campaigner) and peace doves		70 75
	a. Booklet pane. Nos. 930 and 931×2 with margins all round		3·00
931	52p. William Butler Yeats (poet) and poem		1·10 1·60
928/31		*Set of* 4	2·75 3·25

Nos. 928/9 were printed together, *se-tenant*, in horizontal and vertical pairs throughout the sheet.
The booklet panes also exist overprinted for Regional Stamp Shows at Waterford, Galway, Athlone and Kilkenny.

(Des Pamela Leonard (No. 932), Q Design (others). Litho Irish Security Stamp Ptg Ltd)

1994 (17 Nov). *Christmas. T* **319** *and similar vert designs. Chalk-surfaced paper. P* 14×15.
932	28p. Nativity		70 60
	a. Sheetlet. No. 932×13		8·00
933	28p. Type **319**		70 60
934	32p. Flight into Egypt (wood carving)		80 70
935	52p. Nativity (ivory plaque)		1·10 2·00
932/5		*Set of* 4	3·00 3·50

No. 932 was only issued in sheetlets of 13 stamps and two labels (at the centre of rows 1 and 2) sold at £3·36 providing a discount of 28p. off the face value of the stamps.

320 Tree of Hearts
321 West Clare Railway Locomotive No. 1 *Kilkee* at Kilrush Station

(Des Bridget Flinn. Litho Irish Security Stamp Ptg Ltd)

1995 (24 Jan). *Greetings Stamps. T* **320** *and similar vert designs. Multicoloured. Chalk-surfaced paper. P* 14×15.
936	32p. Type **320**		80 80
	a. Booklet pane. Nos. 936/7		3·00
937	32p. Teddy bear holding balloon		80 80
938	32p. Clown juggling hearts		80 80
939	32p. Bouquet of flowers		80 80
936/9		*Set of* 4	3·00 3·00

Nos. 937/9 were only available from £2·56 stamp booklets containing two examples of No. 936a. This pane, which also includes 8 small greetings labels, exists in two different forms with either No. 936 at left and No. 938 at right or No. 937 at left and No. 939 at right. In each instance the right-hand stamp is imperforate at right.

(Des Bridget Flynn. Litho Irish Security Stamp Ptg Ltd)

1995 (24 Jan). *Chinese New Year ("Year of the Pig"). P* 14×15.
MS940	137×74 mm. Nos. 936, 938/9		2·25 2·25

The example of No. 939 in the above miniature sheet is imperforate at right.

(Des C. Rycraft. Litho Irish Security Stamp Ptg Ltd)

1995 (28 Feb). *Transport. Narrow Gauge Railways. T* **321** *and similar horiz designs. Multicoloured. Chalk-surfaced paper. P* 15×14.
941	28p. Type **321**		75 60
942	32p. Co. Donegal Railway locomotive No. 2 *Blanche* at Donegal Station		90 90
943	38p. Cork and Muskerry Railway locomotive No. 1 *City of Cork* on Western Road, Cork		1·25 1·60
944	52p. Cavan and Leitrim Railway locomotive No. 3 *Lady Edith* on Arigna Tramway		1·75 2·25
941/4		*Set of* 4	4·25 4·75
MS945	127×83 mm. No. 941/4		4·25 4·75

No. **MS**945 also exists with the "Singapore '95" International Stamp Exhibition logo added.

322 English and Irish Rugby Players

(Des C. Harrison. Litho Walsall)

1995 (6 Apr). *World Cup Rugby Championship, South Africa. T* **322** *and similar horiz design. Multicoloured. Chalk-surfaced paper. P* 14.
946	32p. Type **322**		75 70
947	52p. Australian and Irish players		1·25 1·40
MS948	108×77 mm. £1 Type **322**		2·50 2·75

No. **MS**948 also exists overprinted for Regional Stamp Shows at Limerick and Letterkenny.

323 Peace Dove and Skyscrapers
324 Soldiers of the Irish Brigade and Memorial Cross

(Des R. Ballagh)

1995 (6 Apr). *Europa. Peace and Freedom. T* **323** *and similar horiz design. Multicoloured. Chalk-surfaced paper.* (a) *Litho Irish Security Stamp Ptg Ltd. P* 15×14.
949	32p. Type **323**		80 70
950	44p. Peace dove and map of Europe and North Africa		1·10 1·60

(b) *Litho Printset Cambec Pty Ltd, Melbourne. Self-adhesive. P* 11¹⁄₂.
951	32p. Type **323**		80 80
952	32p. As No. 950		80 80

Nos. 949/50 were issued in sheetlets of 10 (2×5) with illustrated left margins.
Nos. 951/2 are smaller, 34¹⁄₂×23 mm, and occur, *se-tenant*, in pairs or rolls of 100 with the surplus self-adhesive paper around each stamps removed.

(Des E. Daniels. Photo Belgian Post Office Ptg Wks, Malines)

1995 (15 May). *250th Anniv of Battle of Fontenoy. Chalk-surfaced paper. P* 11¹⁄₂.
953	**324** 32p. multicoloured		80 80

325 Irish Brigade, French Army, 1745
326 Guglielmo Marconi and Original Radio Transmitter

(Des D. McAllister. Litho Irish Security Stamp Ptg Ltd)

1995 (15 May). *Military Uniforms. T* **325** *and similar vert designs. Multicoloured. Chalk-surfaced paper. P* 14×15.
954	28p. Type **325**		70 60
	a. Booklet pane. Nos. 954/5, each × 2		3·00
	b. Booklet pane. Nos. 954 and 957/8		3·00
	c. Booklet pane. Nos. 954/5 and 957		3·00
	d. Booklet pane. Nos. 954/5 and 958		3·00
955	32p. Tercio Irlanda, Spanish army in Flanders, 1605		80 75
956	32p. Royal Dublin Fusiliers, 1914		80 75
957	38p. St. Patrick's Battalion, Papal Army, 1860		1·10 1·25
958	52p. 69th Regiment, New York State Militia, 1861		1·60 1·75
954/8		*Set of* 5	4·50 4·50

Booklet panes Nos. 954a/b come with the two right-hand stamps (Nos. 954/5 or 955 and 958) imperforate at right.
The booklet panes also exist overprinted for Regional Stamp Shows at Sligo, Waterford and Galway and for "Stampa '95" (two panes).

(Des E. Jünger (No. 959), S. Young (No. 960). Litho Irish Security Stamp Ptg Ltd)

1995 (8 June). *Centenary of Radio. T* **326** *and similar horiz design. Multicoloured. Chalk-surfaced paper. P* 13¹⁄₂.
959	32p. Type **326**		80 1·00
	a. Pair. Nos. 959/60		1·60 2·00
960	32p. Traditional radio dial		80 1·00

Nos. 959/60 were printed together, *se-tenant*, in horizontal and vertical pairs throughout the sheet.

327 Bartholomew Mosse
(founder) and Hospital
Building

(Des A. May (No. 961), S. Woulfe Flanagan (No. 962), Q Design
(No. 963), Creative Inputs (No. 964). Litho Questa (Nos.
961/2) or Irish Security Stamp Ptg Ltd (others))

1995 (27 July). *Anniversaries.* T **327** *and similar
multicoloured designs. Chalk-surfaced paper.* P 15×14 (*Nos.
961), 14½ (No. 962), 14½×14 (No. 963) or 13½ (No. 964).*
961 28p. Type **327** (250th anniv of Rotunda
       Hospital) 70 70
962 32p. St. Patrick's House, Maynooth College
       (Bicent) (25×41 *mm*) 80 80
963 32p. Laurel wreath and map of Europe
       (50th anniv of end of Second World
       War) 80 80
964 52p. Geological map of Ireland (150th anniv
       of Geological Survey of Ireland)
       (32½×32½ *mm*) .. .. 1·25 1·50
961/4 .. .. *Set of 4* 3·25 3·50

328 Natterjack Toad   **329** *Crinum moorei*

(Des I. Loe. Litho Irish Security Stamp Ptg Ltd)

1995 (1 Sept). *Reptiles and Amphibians.* T **328** *and similar
horiz designs. Chalk-surfaced paper.* (a) P 15×14.
965 32p. Type **328** .. .. .. 90 1·10
       a. Horiz strip. Nos. 965/8 .. 3·25
966 32p. Common Lizards .. .. 90 1·10
967 32p. Smooth Newts .. .. 90 1·10
968 32p. Common Frog .. .. 90 1·10
965/8 .. .. .. *Set of 4* 3·25 4·00
       (b) *Self-adhesive.* P 9½.
969 32p. Type **328** .. .. .. 85 1·00
970 32p. Common Lizard .. .. 85 1·00
971 32p. Smooth Newt .. .. 85 1·00
972 32p. Common Frog .. .. 85 1·00
969/72 .. .. .. *Set of 4* 3·00 3·50
Nos. 965/8 were printed together, *se-tenant*, in horizontal
strips of 4 with the backgrounds forming a composite design.
Nos. 969/72 are smaller, 34×23 mm, and occur, *se-tenant*, in
strips of 4 or rolls of 100 with the surplus self-adhesive paper
around each stamp removed.

(Des Frances Poskitt. Litho Irish Security Stamp Ptg Ltd)

1995 (9 Oct). *Bicentenary of National Botanic Gardens,
Glasnevin. Flowers.* T **329** *and similar vert designs.
Multicoloured. Chalk-surfaced paper.* P 14×15.
973 32p. Type **329** 85 70
       a. Booklet pane. Nos. 973×2 and 974/5 3·75
       b. Booklet pane. Nos. 973/5 .. 3·75
974 38p. *Sarracenia × moorei* .. .. 1·10 95
975 44p. *Solanum crispum* "Glasnevin" .. 1·50 2·00
973/5 .. .. .. *Set of 3* 3·00 3·25
Booklet panes Nos. 973a/b come from £2.60 stamp booklets
and have the outer edges of the pane imperforate so that
examples of each value exist imperforate on one or two sides.

330 Anniversary Logo and
Irish United Nations Soldier

(Des Jarlath Hayes. Litho Enschedé)

1995 (19 Oct). *50th Anniv of United Nations.* T **330** *and
similar horiz design. Multicoloured. Chalk-surfaced paper.*
P 13×13½.
976 28p. 80 70
977 52p. Emblem and "UN" .. .. 1·25 1·40
Nos. 976/7 were each issued in sheets of 10 (2×5) with
enlarged illustrated left margins.

COVER PRICES

Cover factors are quoted at the beginning of each
country for most issues to 1945. An explanation of
the system can be found on page x. The factors
quoted do not, however, apply to philatelic covers.

---

331 "Adoration of the Shepherds"   **332** Zig and Zag on
(illuminated manuscript)   Heart
(Benedetto Bardone)

(Des Q Design. Litho Irish Security Stamp Ptg Ltd)

1995 (16 Nov). *Christmas.* T **331** *and similar horiz designs.
Multicoloured. Chalk-surfaced paper.* P 15×14.
978 28p. Adoration of the Magi 70 65
       a. Sheetlet. No. 978×13 .. 8·25
979 28p. Type **331** 70 65
980 32p. "Adoration of the Magi" (illuminated
       manuscript) (Bardone) 80 70
981 52p. "The Holy Family" (illuminated
       manuscript) (Bardone) .. .. 1·40 1·60
978/81 .. .. .. *Set of 4* 3·25 3·25
No. 978 was only issued in sheetlets of 13 stamps and two
labels (at centre of rows 1 and 2) sold at £3.36 providing a
discount of 28p. off the face value of the stamps.

(Des Double Z Enterprises. Litho Irish Security Stamp Ptg Ltd)

1996 (23 Jan). *Greetings Stamps.* T **332** *and similar vert
designs. Multicoloured. Chalk-surfaced paper.* P 14×15.
982 32p. Type **332** 80 80
       a. Booklet pane. Nos. 982/5 .. 3·00
983 32p. Zig and Zag waving 80 80
984 32p. Zig and Zag in space suits .. 80 80
985 32p. Zig and Zag wearing hats .. 80 80
982/5 .. .. .. *Set of 4* 3·00 3·00
Nos. 983/5 were only issued in £2.56 stamp booklets. No. 982
was available from sheets and booklets.
Booklet pane No. 982a, which also includes eight small
greetings labels, exists in two different forms with either No.
982 or 984 at right. In each instance the right-hand stamp is
imperforate at right.

(Des Double Z Enterprises. Litho Irish Security Stamp Ptg Ltd)

1996 (23 Jan). *Chinese New Year ("Year of the Rat"). Chalk-
surfaced paper.* P 14×15.
MS986 130×74 mm. Nos. 982, 984/5 .. 3·00 3·00
The example of No. 982 in No. MS986 is imperforate at right.
No. MS986 also exists overprinted for the Collectors' Road
Show at Kilkenny.

333 Wheelchair   **334** Before the Start,
Athlete   Fairyhouse Race Course

(Des C. Harrison. Litho Irish Security Stamp Ptg Ltd)

1996 (1 Feb). *Olympic and Paralympic Games, Atlanta.* T **333**
*and similar vert designs. Multicoloured. Chalk-surfaced
paper.* P 14×15.
987 28p. Type **333** 70 65
988 32p. Running 80 80
       a. Strip of 3. Nos. 988/90 .. 2·25
989 32p. Throwing the discus 80 80
990 32p. Single kayak 80 80
987/90 .. .. .. *Set of 4* 2·75 2·75
Nos. 988/90 were printed together, *se-tenant*, as horizontal
and vertical strips of 3 in sheets of 9.

(Des P. Curling and Q Design. Litho Irish Security Stamp Ptg
Ltd)

1996 (12 Mar). *Irish Horse Racing.* T **334** *and similar horiz
designs. Multicoloured. Chalk-surfaced paper.* P 15×14.
991 28p. Type **334** 70 65
       a. Booklet pane. Nos. 991×2 and 992/3 3·50
992 32p. Steeplechase, Punchestown .. 80 80
       a. Pair. Nos. 992/3 .. .. 1·60 1·60
       b. Booklet pane. Nos. 992/5 .. 3·50
       c. Booklet pane. Nos. 992×2 and 994 .. 3·50
993 32p. On the Flat, The Curragh .. 80 80
       a. Booklet pane. Nos. 993×2 and 995 .. 3·50
994 38p. Steeplechase, Galway .. .. 1·00 1·25
995 52p. After the race, Leopardstown .. 1·40 1·50
991/5 .. .. .. *Set of 4* 4·25 4·50
Nos. 992/3 were printed together, *se-tenant*, in horizontal and
vertical pairs throughout the sheet.
Booklet pane Nos. 991a, 992b/c and 993a come from £4.92
stamp booklets with the right-hand edge of the panes
imperforate. The complete booklet contains two examples of No.
992 and one each of Nos. 991, 993 and 995 imperforate at right.
The booklet panes also exist overprinted for Collectors' Road
Shows at Cork (No. 992c), Limerick (No. 991a) or Sligo (No.
993a) and for "Stampa '96" (No. 992c).
For designs as Nos. 992/3 in miniature sheet see No. MS1003.

---

335 Irish and French Coloured   **336** Louie Bennett
Ribbons merging   (suffragette)

(Des R. Ballagh. Litho Irish Security Stamp Ptg Ltd)

1996 (12 Mar). *"L'Imaginaire Irlandais" Festival of
Contemporary Irish Arts, France. Chalk-surfaced paper.*
P 15×14.
996 **335** 32p. multicoloured 80 80

(Des S. Young)

1996 (2 Apr). *Europa. Famous Women.* T **336** *and similar
horiz design. Chalk-surfaced paper.*
       (a) *Litho Questa.* P 15×14
997 **336** 32p. deep reddish violet .. 80 70
998 – 44p. myrtle-green .. .. 1·10 1·25
       (b) *Litho Irish Security Stamp Ptg Ltd. Self-adhesive.* P 9½
999 **336** 32p. deep reddish violet .. 80 1·00
1000 – 32p. dull green .. .. 80 1·00
Design:—Nos. 998, 1000, Lady Augusta Gregory (playwright).
Nos. 997/8 were each issued in sheetlets of 10 (2×5) with
enlarged illustrated left margins.
Nos. 999/1000 are smaller, 34×23 mm, and occur, *se-tenant*,
in rolls of 100 with the surplus self-adhesive paper around each
stamp removed.

337 Newgrange Passage Tomb
(Boyne Valley World
Heritage Site)

(Des L. Belton (28p.), Q Design (32p.). Litho Walsall)

1996 (2 Apr). *Anniversaries and Events.* T **337** *and similar
horiz design. Chalk-surfaced paper.* P 14.
1001 28p. grey-brown and black 70 60
1002 32p. multicoloured 80 90
Designs:—32p. Children playing (50th anniv of U.N.I.C.E.F.).

(Litho Irish Security Stamp Printing Ltd)

1996 (18 May). *"CHINA '96" 9th Asian International Stamp
Exhibition, Peking. Sheet 120×95 mm containing Nos. 992/3.
Chalk-surfaced paper.* P 15×14.
MS1003 32p. Steeplechase, Punchestown; 32p.
On the Flat, The Curragh .. .. 2·00 2·25

338 Stanley Woods   **339** Michael Davitt
(founder of The
Land League)

(Des J. Dunne. Litho Questa)

1996 (30 May). *Isle of Man Tourist Trophy Motorcycle Races.
Irish Winners.* T **338** *and similar horiz designs. Multicoloured. Chalk-surfaced paper.* P 14.
1004 32p. Type **338** 80 70
1005 44p. Artie Bell .. .. .. 1·25 1·40
1006 50p. Alec Bennett .. .. .. 1·50 1·60
1007 52p. Joey and Robert Dunlop .. 1·50 1·60
1004/7 .. .. .. *Set of 4* 4·50 4·75
MS1008 100×70 mm. 50p. As 52p. .. 1·25 1·50
No. MS1008 also exists overprinted for "Stampa '96" and for
the Collectors' Road Show at Dundalk.

(Des R. Ballagh (28p.), J. Tobin (32p.), C. Harrison (38p.),
L. Belton (52p.). Litho Enschedé)

1996 (4 July). *Anniversaries and Events.* T **339** *and similar
multicoloured designs. Chalk-surfaced paper.* P 13½×13
(28p.) *or* 13×13½ (*others*).
1009 28p. Type **339** (150th birth anniv) .. 70 60
1010 32p. Presidency logo (Ireland's Presidency
       of European Union) (*horiz*) .. 80 70
1011 38p. Thomas McLaughlin (hydro-electric
       engineer) and Ardnacrusha Power
       Station (Birth centenary) (*horiz*) 1·00 1·10
1012 52p. Mechanical peat harvester (50th
       anniv of Bord na Móna) (*horiz*) 1·60 1·75
1009/12 .. .. .. *Set of 4* 3·75 3·75

340 Coastal Patrol Vessel

341 Blind Woman with Child

(Des G. Fallon. Litho Irish Security Stamp Ptg Ltd)

1996 (18 July). *50th Anniv of Irish Naval Service. T* **340** *and similar multicoloured designs. Chalk-surfaced paper. P* 14×15 (52p.) *or* 15×14 (*others*).

1013	32p. Type **340**	..	80	70
	a. Booklet pane. No. 1013×3	..	2·75	
	b. Booklet pane. Nos. 1013/15	..	2·75	
1014	44p. Corvette	..	1·40	1·50
1015	52p. Motor torpedo boat (*vert*)	..	1·50	1·60
1013/15		*Set of 3*	3·25	3·50

Booklet panes Nos. 1013a/b come from £2·24 stamp booklets. Stamps from No. 1013a have either one or two adjacent sides imperforate and those from No. 1013b are imperforate at foot (32, 44p.) or at right and foot (52p.).

The booklet panes also exist overprinted for "Stampa '96" (No. 1013b) or for the Collectors' Road Shows at Galway (No. 1013b) and Waterford (No. 1013a).

(Des E. Patton. Litho Irish Security Stamp Ptg Ltd)

1996 (3 Sept). *People with Disabilities. T* **341** *and similar vert design. Multicoloured. Chalk-surfaced paper. P* 14×15.

1016	28p. Type **341**	..	55	60
	a. Pair. Nos. 1016/7	..	1·10	
1017	28p. Man in wheelchair playing bowls	..	55	60

Nos. 1016/17 were printed together, *se-tenant*, in horizontal and vertical pairs throughout the sheet.

342 Green-winged Teal

(Des R. Ward. Litho Irish Security Stamp Ptg Ltd)

1996 (24 Sept). *Freshwater Ducks. T* **342** *and similar horiz designs. Multicoloured. Chalk-surfaced paper. P* 15×14.

1018	32p. Type **342**	..	75	70
1019	38p. Common Shoveler	..	85	1·00
1020	44p. European Wigeon	..	1·00	1·25
1021	52p. Mallard	..	1·25	1·50
1018/21		*Set of 4*	3·50	4·00
MS1022	127×85 mm. Nos. 1018/21	..	4·00	4·00

343 Scene from *Man of Aran*

344 Visit of the Magi

(Des J. Reddy. Litho Irish Security Stamp Ptg Ltd)

1996 (17 Oct). *Centenary of Irish Cinema. T* **343** *and similar horiz designs. Multicoloured. Chalk-surfaced paper. P* 13½.

1023	32p. Type **343**	..	85	90
	a. Strip of 4. Nos. 1023/6	..	3·00	
1024	32p. *My Left Foot*	..	85	90
1025	32p. *The Commitments*	..	85	90
1026	32p. *The Field*	..	85	90
1023/6		*Set of 4*	3·00	3·25

Nos. 1023/6 were printed together, *se-tenant*, in vertical and horizontal strips of 4 throughout the sheet.

(Des T. Monaghan (No. 1027), E. Patton (others). Litho Irish Security Stamp Ptg Ltd)

1996 (19 Nov). *Christmas. T* **344** *and similar vert designs from 16th-century Book of Hours (Nos.* 1028/30). *Multicoloured. Chalk-surfaced paper. P* 14×15.

1027	28p. The Holy Family	..	75	60
	a. Sheetlet. No. 1027×15	..	10·00	
1028	28p. Type **344**	..	60	60
1029	32p. The Annunciation	..	80	75
1030	52p. The Shepherds receiving news of Christ's birth	..	1·40	1·60
1027/30		*Set of 4*	3·25	3·25

No. 1027 was only issued in sheetlets of 15 stamps sold at £3·92 providing a discount of 28p. off the face value of the stamps.

345 Blue Tit

346 Pair of Doves

(Des K. Mullarney. Litho Irish Security Stamp Ptg Ltd)

1997 (16 Jan–6 Dec). *Birds. T* **345** *and similar multicoloured designs. Chalk-surfaced paper* (1p., 2p., 4p., 10p., 20p., £5) *or ordinary paper* (*others*). *P* 15×14 (28p., £1, £5) *or* 14×15 (*others*).

(a) *Designs* 24×21 *mm* (28p), 24×45 *mm* (£1), 26×48 *mm* (£5) *or* 21×24 *mm* (*others*).

1031	1p. Magpie (*vert*) (27.8.97)	..	10	10
1032	2p. Gannet (*vert*) (27.8.97)	..	10	10
1033	4p. Corncrake (*vert*) (27.8.97)	..	10	10
1034	10p. Kingfisher (*vert*) (27.8.97)	..	15	20
1035	20p. Lapwing (*vert*) (27.8.97)	..	35	40
1036	28p. Type **345**	..	50	55
	a. Chalk-surfaced paper (Oct)	..	50	55
1037	32p. Robin (*vert*)	..	55	60
	a. Chalk-surfaced paper (Oct)	..	55	60
1038	44p. Puffin (*vert*)	..	75	80
1039	52p. Barn Owl (*vert*)	..	90	95
1040	£1 Greenland White-fronted Goose (24×45 *mm*)	..	1·75	1·90
1041	£5 Shelduck (26×48 *mm*) (27.8.97)	..	8·75	9·00
1031/41		*Set of 11*	13·50	14·50

(b) *Booklet stamps size* 17×21 *mm. Chalk-surfaced paper. P* 15×14

1047	4p. Corncrake (6.12.97)	..	10	10
	a. Booklet pane. Nos. 1047 and 1049×3	..	1·75	
1048	32p. Robin (6.3.97)	..	55	60
1049	32p. Peregrine Falcon (6.12.97)	..	55	60

Nos. 748bb (containing No. 1048) and 1047a show the upper and lower edges of the pane imperforate.

(c) *Self-adhesive size* 25×30 *mm.* (i) *Litho Irish State Security Ptg Ltd. P* 9×10

1050	32p. Peregrine Falcon (6.3.97)	..	55	60
	a. Vert pair. Nos. 1050/1	..	1·10	1·25
1051	32p. Robin (6.3.97)	..	55	60

(ii) *Litho Printset Cambec Pty Ltd, Melbourne. P* 11½

1052	32p. Peregrine Falcon (Apr)	..	55	1·25
	a. Vert pair. Nos. 1052/3	..	1·10	2·50
1053	32p. Robin (Apr)	..	55	1·25

Nos. 1050/1 and 1052/3 were produced in rolls of 100. Nos. 1050/1 retain the surplus self-adhesive paper, but this was removed for Nos. 1052/3.

(Des Double Z Enterprises. Litho Irish Security Stamp Ptg Ltd)

1997 (28 Jan). *Greetings Stamps. T* **346** *and similar vert designs. Multicoloured. Chalk-surfaced paper. P* 14×15.

1055	32p. Type **346**	..	85	90
	a. Booklet pane. Nos. 1055/8	..	3·00	
1056	32p. Cow jumping over moon	..	85	90
1057	32p. Pig going to market	..	85	90
1058	32p. Cockerel	..	85	90
1055/8		*Set of 4*	3·00	3·25

Nos. 1056/8 were only issued in £2·56 stamp booklets. No. 1055 was available from sheets and booklets.

Booklet pane No. 1055a, which also includes eight small greetings labels, exists in two forms with No. 1056 either at left or right. In each instance the right-hand stamp, No. 1056 or No. 1058, is imperforate at right.

(Des Double Z Enterprises. Litho Irish Security Stamp Ptg Ltd)

1997 (28 Jan). *"HONG KONG '97" International Stamp Exhibition. Chinese New Year ("Year of the Ox"). Chalk-surfaced paper. P* 14×15.

MS1059	124×74 mm. Nos. 1056/8	..	2·40	2·40

The example of No. 1058 in No. **MS**1059 is imperforate at right.

No. **MS**1059 also exists overprinted for the Collectors' Road Show at Limerick.

347 Troops on Parade

348 Grey Seals

(Des Q Design. Litho Irish Security Stamp Ptg Ltd)

1997 (18 Feb–6 Dec). *75th Anniv of Irish Free State. T* **347** *and similar horiz designs. Multicoloured. Chalk-surfaced paper. P* 15×14.

1060	28p. Page from the "Annals of the Four Masters", quill and 1944 1½d. O' Clery stamp (27 Aug)	..	50	55
1061	32p. Type **347**	..	55	60
	a. Pair. Nos. 1061/2	..	1·10	1·25
1062	32p. The Dáil, national flag and Constitution	..	55	60

1063	32p. Athlete, footballer and hurling players (3 Apr)	..	55	60
	a. Pair. Nos. 1063/4	..	1·10	1·25
1064	32p. Singer, violinist and bodhran player (3 Apr)	..	55	60
1065	32p. Stained glass window and 1929 9d. O'Connell stamp (27 Aug)	..	55	60
1066	32p. G.P.O., Dublin, and 1923 2d. map stamp (6 Dec)	..	55	60
1067	52p. Police personnel and Garda badge	..	90	95
	a. Pair. Nos. 1067/8	..	1·75	1·90
1068	52p. The Four Courts and Scales of Justice	..	90	95
1069	52p. Currency, blueprint and food-processing plant (3 Apr)	..	90	95
	a. Pair. Nos. 1069/70	..	1·75	1·90
1070	52p. Books, palette and Seamus Heaney manuscript (3 Apr)	..	90	95
1071	52p. Air Lingus airliner and 1965 1s. 5d air stamp (27 Aug)	..	90	95
1060/71		*Set of 12*	8·25	9·00
MS1072	174×209 mm. As Nos. 1060/71, but each with face value of 32p (6 Dec)	..	6·50	6·75

Nos. 1061/2, 1063/4, 1067/8 and 1069/70 were each printed together, *se-tenant*, in horiz or vert pairs throughout the sheets.

(Des Rosemary Davis. Litho Irish Security Stamp Ptg Ltd)

1997 (6 Mar). *Marine Mammals. T* **348** *and similar multicoloured designs. Chalk-surfaced paper. P* 14×15 (28p., 32p.) *or* 15×14 (*others*).

1073	28p. Type **348**	..	75	60
1074	32p. Bottle-nosed Dolphins	..	85	80
1075	44p. Harbour Porpoises (*horiz*)	..	1·25	1·40
1076	52p. Killer Whale (*horiz*)	..	1·40	1·50
1073/7		*Set of 4*	3·75	3·75
MS1077	150×68 mm. As Nos. 1073/6. P 15	..	3·75	3·75

No. **MS**1077 also exists overprinted for the Collectors' Road Show at Dublin.

349 Dublin Silver Penny of 997

(Des Creative Inputs. Litho Irish Security Stamp Ptg Ltd)

1997 (3 Apr). *Millenary of Irish Coinage. Chalk-surfaced paper. P* 15×14.

1078	**349** 32p. multicoloured	..	65	65

350 "The Children of Lir"

(Des P. Lynch)

1997 (14 May). *Europa. Tales and Legends. T* **350** *and similar horiz design. Multicoloured.* (a) *Litho Walsall. Chalk-surfaced paper. P* 14.

1079	32p. Type **350**	..	70	60
1080	44p. Oisin and Niamh	..	1·00	1·10

(b) *Litho Irish Security Ptg Ltd. Self-adhesive. P* 9½.

1081	32p. Type **350**	..	70	70
	a. Horiz pair. Nos. 1081/2	..	1·40	1·40
1082	32p. Oisin and Niamh	..	70	70
1079/82		*Set of 4*	2·75	2·75

Nos. 1081/2, which are smaller 36×25 mm, occur in rolls of 100.

351 Emigrants waiting to board Ship

(Des Q Design. Litho Irish Security Stamp Ptg Ltd)

1997 (14 May). *150th Anniv of The Great Famine. T* **351** *and similar horiz designs. Chalk-surfaced paper. P* 15×14.

1083	28p. deep dull blue, vermilion and pale yellow-ochre	..	60	60
1084	32p. reddish orange, deep dull blue and pale yellow-ochre	..	70	70
1085	52p. brown, dp dull blue & pale yell-ochre	..	1·25	1·40
1083/5		*Set of 3*	2·25	2·40

Designs—32p. Family and dying child; 52p. Irish Society of Friends soup kitchen.

(Des K. Mullarney. Litho Irish Security Stamp Ptg Ltd)

1997 (29 May). *"Pacific '97" International Stamp Exhibition, San Francisco. Sheet* 100×70 *mm containing horiz design as T* **345**. *Multicoloured. Chalk-surfaced paper. P* 14.

MS1086	£2 Pintail (48×26 *mm*)	..	4·50	4·50

352 Kate O'Brien (novelist) (birth centenary)   353 The Baily Lighthouse

(Des Creative Inputs. Litho Irish Security Ptg Ltd (No. 1088) or Walsall (others))

1997 (1 July). *Anniversaries. T 352 and similar vert designs. Multicoloured. Chalk-surfaced paper. P 14×15 (No. 1088), 14½ (No. 1089) or 14 (others).*
1087 28p. Type **352** 60 60
1088 28p. St. Columba crossing to Iona (stained glass window) (1400th death anniv) 60 60
1089 32p. "Daniel O'Connell" (J. Haverty) (politician) (150th death anniv) (27×49 mm) 70 70
1090 52p. "John Wesley" (N. Hone) (founder of Methodism) (250th anniv of first visit to Ireland) .. .. 1·25 1·40
1087/90 .. .. .. *Set of 4* 2·75 3·00

(Des Design Image. Litho Irish Security Ptg Ltd)

1997 (1 July). *Lighthouses. T 353 and similar multicoloured designs. Chalk-surfaced paper. P 15×14 (32p.) or 14×15 (others).*
1091 32p. Type **353** 55 60
  a. Pair. Nos. 1091/2 .. .. 1·10
  b. Booklet pane. Nos. 1091×2 and 1092 1·60
  c. Booklet pane. Nos. 1091/2, each × 2 2·00
  d. Perf 15 .. .. 1·10 1·40
  da. Booklet pane. Nos. 1091d/4d .. 4·00
1092 32p. Tarbert 55 60
  d. Perf 15 .. .. 1·10 1·40
1093 38p. Hookhead (*vert*) 65 70
  d. Perf 15 .. .. 1·10 1·40
  da. Booklet pane. Nos. 1093d/4d .. 2·00
1094 50p. The Fastnet (*vert*) .. 90 95
  d. Perf 15 .. .. 1·10 1·40
1091/4 .. .. .. *Set of 4* 2·75 2·90
  Nos. 1091/2 were printed together, *se-tenant*, in horizontal or vertical pairs throughout the sheet.
  Nos. 1091d/4d only exist from booklet panes Nos. 1091da and 1093da.
  The booklet panes also exist overprinted for Collectors' Road Shows at Sligo (No. 1091b), Tralee (No. 1093da) and Galway (No. 1091da) and also for "Stampa '97" (Nos. 1091b/c, 1091da and 1093da).

354 Commemorative Cross   355 Dracula and Bat

(Des L. Rafael. Litho Irish Security Ptg Ltd)

1997 (12 Sept). *Ireland–Mexico Joint Issue. 150th Anniv of Mexican St. Patrick's Battalion. Ordinary paper. P 13½.*
1095 **354** 32p. multicoloured 55 60

(Des Passmore Design. Litho Irish Security Ptg Ltd)

1997 (1 Oct). *Centenary of Publication of Bram Stoker's Dracula. T 355 and similar multicoloured designs. Chalk-surfaced paper. P 14×15 (vert) or 15×14 (horiz).*
1096 28p. Type **355** 50 55
1097 32p. Dracula and female victim 55 60
1098 38p. Dracula emerging from coffin (*horiz*) 65 70
1099 52p. Dracula and wolf (*horiz*) .. 90 95
1096/9 .. .. .. *Set of 4* 2·50 2·75
MS1100 150×90 mm. As Nos. 1096/9. P 15 .. 2·50 2·75
  A second miniature sheet, 75×55 mm, containing No. 1097, was only available as a promotional item connected with the purchase of funsize bars of various Mars products or at face value from the Philatelic Bureau.

356 "The Nativity" (Kevin Kelly)   357 Christmas Tree

(Des Creative Inputs (Nos. 1101/3), Q Design (No. 1104). Litho Irish Security Ptg Ltd)

1997 (18 Nov). *Christmas. (a) Stained Glass Windows. T 356 and similar vert designs. Multicoloured. Chalk-surfaced paper. P 14×15.*
1101 28p. Type **356** 50 55
1102 32p. "The Nativity" (Sarah Purser and A. E. Child) 55 60
1103 52p. "The Nativity" (A. E. Child) .. 90 95
1101/3 .. .. .. *Set of 3* 1·90 2·10
  (b) Self-adhesive booklet stamp. P 9×10
1104 28p. Type **357** 50 55
  a. Booklet pane. No. 1104×20 .. 10·00
  No. 1104 was only available from £5.32 stamp booklets.

358 Holding Heart   359 Lady Mary Heath and Avro Avian over Pyramids

(Des B. Asprey. Litho Irish Security Stamp Ptg Ltd)

1998 (26 Jan). *Greetings Stamps. T 358 and similar vert designs based on the "love is..." cartoon characters of Kim Casali. Multicoloured. Chalk-surfaced paper. P 14×15.*
1105 32p. Type **358** 55 60
  a. Booklet pane. Nos. 1105/8 .. 2·25
1106 32p. Receiving letter 55 60
1107 32p. Sitting on log 55 60
1108 32p. With birthday presents .. 55 60
1105/8 .. .. .. *Set of 4* 2·25 2·40
  Nos. 1106/8 were only available from £2.56 stamp booklets containing two examples of No. 1105a. This pane exists in two different forms with either No. 1105 at right and No. 1108 at left or No. 1107 at right and No. 1106 at left. In each instance the right-hand stamp is imperforate at right. No. 1105 is available from both sheets and booklets.

(Des B. Asprey. Litho Irish Security Stamp Ptg Ltd)

1998 (26 Jan). *Chinese New Year ("Year of the Tiger"). Chalk-surfaced paper. P 14×15.*
MS1109 124×73 mm. Nos. 1106/8 .. .. 1·60 1·75
  The example of No. 1107 in MS1109 is imperforate at right.

(Des V. Killowry. Litho Irish Security Ptg Ltd)

1998 (24 Feb). *Pioneers of Irish Aviation. T 359 and similar horiz designs. Multicoloured. Chalk-surfaced paper. P 15×14.*
1110 28p. Type **359** 50 55
  a. Booklet pane. Nos. 1110/13 .. 2·75
  b. Booklet pane. Nos. 1110/11 each × 2 2·10
1111 32p. Col. James Fitzmaurice and Junkers W. 33 *Bremen* over Labrador 55 60
  a. Booklet pane. Nos. 1111×2 and 1112 1·75
  b. Booklet pane. Nos. 1111 and 1113×2 2·25
1112 44p. Captain J. P. Saul and Fokker FVIIa/3m *Southern Cross* .. 75 80
1113 52p. Captain Charles Blair and Sikorsky V-s 44 (flying boat) 90 95
1110/13 .. .. .. *Set of 4* 2·75 3·00
  Booklet panes Nos. 1110b and 1111a/b have margins all round. On No. 1110a there are margins on three sides, but the two right-hand stamps (Nos. 1111 and 1113) are each imperforate at right.

— URCH HARRIS —
ALL WORLD
NEW ISSUE SERVICE

Your 'First Choice' New Issue Supplier

Developed over the last 30 years Urch Harris 'All World' combines the widest choice of countries, themes and formats with a reliable individual service that helps develop and manage your collection.

■ 260 countries and 100 plus themes.
■ Choice of mint issues, reprints, yearpacks, used stamps, maxi cards, booklets, presentation packs, specimens and first day covers.
■ Regular distributions every 6 weeks.
■ Free magazine with every distribution.
■ Fully computerised invoices with descriptions.
■ Customer advice helpline.
■ Free gifts and regular special offers.
■ Supported by Stanley Gibbons, world leaders in philately.

FREE WELCOME PACK

Containing full details of our unique service, a full list of countries and themes and a copy of 'All World Direct' magazine.

Telephone 0117 9349333 for a free pack.

Urch Harris & Co
1 Denmark Avenue
Bristol BS1 5HD
A Division of Stanley Gibbons Ltd

IRELAND

STAMP BOOKLETS

Nos. SB1 to SB24 are stitched. Subsequent booklets have their panes attached by the selvedge, *unless otherwise stated.*

B 1   Harp and Monogram

B 2   Harp and "EIRE"

1931 (21 Aug)–**40.** *Black on red cover as Type* B **1.**
SB1   2s. booklet containing six ½d., six 2d. (Nos. 71, 74), each in block of 6, and nine 1d. (No. 72) in block of 6 and pane of 3 stamps and 3 labels (No. 72d or 72dw) .. .. .. *From* £1900
   Edition Nos.:—31–1, 31–2, 32–3, 33–4, 33–5, 34–6, 34–7, 35–8, 35–9, 36–10, 36–11, 37–12, 37–13, 37–14, 15–38, 16–38, 17–38,
   a. Cover as Type B **2**
   Edition Nos.:—18–39, 19–39, 20–39, 21–40

1940. *Black on red cover as Type* B **2.**
SB2   2s. booklet containing six ½d., six 2d. (Nos. 71, 74), each in block of 6, and nine 1d. (No. 72) in block of 6 and pane of 3 stamps and 3 labels (No. 112d or 112dw) £6500
   Edition No.:—22–40

1940. *Black on red cover as Type* B **2.**
SB3   2s. booklet containing six ½d., six 2d. (Nos. 111, 114), each in block of 6, and nine 1d. (No. 112) in block of 6 and pane of 3 stamps and 3 labels (No. 112d or 112dw) £6500
   Edition No.:—23–40

1941–44. *Black on red cover as Type* B **2.**
SB4   2s. booklet containing twelve ½d., six 1d. and six 2d. (Nos. 111/12, 114) in blocks of 6 .. .. £750
   Edition Nos.:—24–41, 25–42, 26–44

B 3

1945. *Black on red cover as Type* B **3.**
SB5   2s. booklet containing twelve ½d., six 1d. and six 2d. (Nos. 111/12, 114) in blocks of 6 .. .. £650
   Edition No.:—27–45

1946. *Black on buff cover as Type* B **2.**
SB6   2s. booklet containing twelve ½d., six 1d. and six 2d. (Nos. 111/12, 114) in blocks of 6 .. .. £475
   Edition No.:—28–46

1946–47. *Black on buff cover as Type* B **2.**
SB7   2s. booklet containing twelve ½d., six 1d. and six 2d. (Nos. 133, 112, 114) in blocks of 6 .. *From* £225
   Edition Nos.:—29–46, 30–47

B 4   Harp only

1948–50. *Black on red cover as Type* B **4.**
SB8   2s. 6d. booklet containing six ½d., twelve 1d. and six 2½d. (Nos. 133, 112, 115) in blocks of 6 .. £120
   Edition Nos.:—31–48, 32–49, 33–50

1951–53. *Black on buff cover as Type* B **4.**
SB9   2s. 6d. booklet containing six ½d., twelve 1d. and six 2½d. (Nos. 133, 112, 115) in blocks of 6 .. 55·00
   Edition Nos.:—34–51, 35–52, 36–53

1954 (24 Nov). *Black on buff cover as Type* B **4.**
SB10   4s. booklet containing six ½d., six 1½d. and twelve 3d. (Nos. 133, 113, 116) in blocks of 6   £110
   Edition No.:—37–54

1956 (17 Dec). *Black on buff cover as Type* B **4.**
SB11   4s. booklet containing twelve 1d. and twelve 3d. (Nos. 112, 116) in blocks of 6 .. .. .. 60·00
   Edition No.:—38–56

B 5

1958–61. *Black on buff cover as Type* B **5.**
SB12   4s. booklet containing twelve 1d. and twelve 3d. (Nos. 112, 116) in blocks of 6 .. .. .. 60·00
   Edition Nos.:—39–58, 40–59, 41–60, 42–61

1962 (23 Oct)–**63.** *Black on buff cover as Type* B **5.**
SB13   3s. booklet containing six 2d. and six 4d. (Nos. 114, 117) in blocks of 6 .. .. *From* 55·00
   Edition Nos.:—43–62, 44–63 (June)

B 6

1964 (Sept). *Red on yellow cover as Type* B **6.**
SB14   3s. booklet containing twelve 1d. and six 4d. (Nos. 112, 117) in blocks of 6 .. .. 45·00

B 7

1966 (1–9 Dec). *Covers as Type* B **7** *in red* (No. SB15), *blue* (No. SB16) *or green* (No SB17).
SB15   2s. 6d. booklet containing six 2d. and six 3d. (Nos. 114, 116) in blocks of 6 (9 Dec) .. 17·00
SB16   2s. 6d. booklet containing six 5d. (No. 228) in block of 6 (9 Dec) .. .. 15·00
SB17   5s. booklet containing twelve 5d. (No. 228) in blocks of 6 .. .. 30·00

B 8

1969 (12 Sept). *Plain blue-green cover as Type* B **8.**
SB18   6s. booklet containing twelve 6d. (No. 253) in blocks of six .. .. 40·00

1971 (15 Feb). *Plain slate-green cover as Type* B **8.**
SB19   30p. booklet containing six ½p., twelve 1p. and six 2½p. in panes of 6 (Nos. 287ab or 287awb, 288ca or 288cwa, 291ba or 291bwa) 32·00

1974 (11 Mar). *Green cover as Type* B **8.**
SB20   50p. booklet containing ten 5p. in panes of 5 stamps and 1 label (No. 295ad or 295adw) 24·00

1974 (11 Mar). *Blue cover as Type* B **8.**
SB21   50p. booklet containing five 1p. in pane of 5 stamps and 1 label (No. 288cb or 288cwb), six 2½p. and six 5p. in panes of 6 (Nos. 291ba or 291bwa, 295ae or 295awe) .. 14·00

1975 (27 Jan). *Covers as Type* B **8,** *in rose* (No. SB22) *or light grey* (No. SB23).
SB22   40p. booklet containing five 1p., 2p. and 5p. each in panes of 5 stamps and 1 label (Nos. 288cb or 288cwb, 290ba or 290bwa, 295ad or 295awd) .. .. 4·00
SB23   70p. booklet containing ten 2p. and 5p. each in panes of 5 stamps and 1 label (Nos. 290ba or 290bwa, 295ad or 295awd) .. 5·50

1977 (21 Mar). *Yellow-olive cover similar to Type* B **8.**
SB24   50p. booklet containing five 1p., 2p. and 7p. each in panes of 5 stamps and 1 label (Nos. 288cb or 288cwb, 290ba or 290bwa, 348a) .. 12·00

B 9   Four Courts

1983 (15 Aug). *Yellow-green cover as Type* B **9.**
SB25   £1 booklet containing *se-tenant* pane of 7 stamps and 1 label (No. 535a) .. .. .. 2·50
   No. SB25 was an experimental issue available from two machines, accepting two 50p. coins, at the G.P.O. Dublin, and from the Philatelic Bureau.

B 10

1984 (9 July). *Dull green, greenish yellow and black cover as Type* B **10.**
SB26   £2 booklet containing *se-tenant* pane of 12 (No. 535ba) .. .. 6·50
   No. SB26 actually contains £2.26 worth of stamps, but was sold at a discount of 26p. by the Irish Post Office from 9 July until 10 August.

B 11   Custom House, Dublin, in 19th Century

1985 (27 June). *Yellowish green cover as Type* B **11.**
SB27   £1 booklet containing *se-tenant* pane of 6 (No. 533ab) .. .. 5·50

B 12

1985 (27 June). *Bright green cover as Type* B **12.**
SB28   £2 booklet containing *se-tenant* pane of 12 (No. 533ac) .. .. 9·00

B 13

1986 (8 Sept). *Black, light green and pale yellow cover as Type* B **13.**
SB29   £2 booklet containing *se-tenant* pane of 12 (No. 533ad) .. .. 9·00

B 14 Custom House, Dublin
(*Illustration further reduced. Actual size 137×70 mm*)

1988 (1 Mar). *Dublin Millenium. Multicoloured cover as Type B 14.*
SB30 £2.24, booklet containing eight 24p. in panes of 4 (No. 688a) (one inscr in Irish, one in English) .. 3·75
No. SB30 also exists with the booklet cover overprinted for 'SPRING STAMPEX 1988", INTERNATIONAL BRIEF-MARKEN-MESSEN" (Essen), "FINLANDIA 88" and "SYDPEX 88" exhibitions.

1988 (24 Nov). *Maroon and black cover as Type B 11, but showing Courthouse, Cork.*
SB31 £2 booklet containing *se-tenant* pane of 12 (No. 533ae) .. .. 10·00

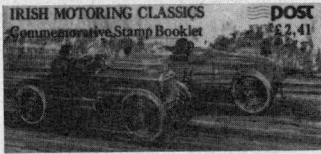

B 15 Gordon Bennett Race, 1903
(*Illustration further reduced. Actual size 132×60 mm*)

1989 (11 Apr). *Irish Motoring Classics. Multicoloured cover as Type B 15.*
SB32 £2.41, booklet containing two different *se-tenant* panes of 4 (Nos. 718a/b) .. .. 6·50

B 16 8th-century Gilt-silver Brooch
(*Illustration further reduced. Actual size 160×100 mm*)

1989 (15 June). *1300th Death Anniv of Saints Kilian, Totnan and Colman. Multicoloured cover as Type B 16. Stitched.*
SB33 £4.48, booklet containing sixteen 28p. in panes of 4 (No. 726a) .. .. .. 12·00
No. SB33 exists overprinted with either the "Philexfrance 89" or the "WORLD STAMP EXPO" logos.

B 17 (*Illustration further reduced. Actual size 136×74 mm*)

1990 (22 Mar). *Greetings Booklet. Multicoloured cover as Type B 17. Stitched.*
SB34 £1.98, booklet containing two *se-tenant* panes of 4 (No. 766a) and eight greetings labels .. 15·00
No. SB34 was sold at £1.98, providing a discount of 26p. off the face value of the stamps.

B 18 (*Illustration further reduced. Actual size 161×99 mm*)

1990 (3 May). *150th Anniv of the Penny Black. Multicoloured cover as Type B 18. Stitched.*
SB35 £6 booklet containing *se-tenant* panes of 8, 4 and 5 (Nos. 535ca, 547ba/bb and pane of 4 (No. 774a) 20·00
No. SB25 exists overprinted for "STAMP WORLD 90" exhibition.

B 19 Garden at Powerscourt, Co. Wicklow
(*Illustration further reduced. Actual size 150×75 mm*)

1990 (30 Aug). *Garden Flowers. Multicoloured cover as Type B 19. Stitched.*
SB36 £2.59, booklet containing two different *se-tenant* panes of 4 (Nos. 781a/b) .. .. .. 9·00

B 20 7th-century Tara Brooch

1990 (15 Nov). *Irish Heritage. Black and bright blue cover as Type B 20.*
SB37 £1 booklet containing *se-tenant* pane of 7 stamps and 1 label (No. 747ab) .. .. .. 3·00

B 21 View of Dublin
(*Illustration further reduced. Actual size 140×85 mm*)

1991 (11 Apr). *"Dublin 1991 European City of Culture". Multicoloured cover as Type B 21.*
SB38 £2.60, booklet containing two different *se-tenant* panes of 3 (Nos. 800a/b) .. .. 7·50

B 22 Ardagh Chalice

1991 (14 May)–92. *Covers as Type B 22.*
SB39 £1 booklet containing *se-tenant* pane of 5 stamps and 1 label (No. 808a) (black and green cover as Type B 22) .. .. 2·00
SB40 £1 booklet containing *se-tenant* pane of 5 stamps and 1 label (No. 808a) (black and orange-yellow cover showing St. Patrick's Bell Shrine) (25.2.92) .. .. .. 2·00

B 23 (*Illustration further reduced. Actual size 161×99 mm*)

1991 (17 Oct). *Fishing Fleet. Multicoloured cover as Type B 23. Stitched.*
SB41 £5 booklet containing *se-tenant* panes of 5 and 7 and 1 label (Nos. 747ac, 748ba) and two different *se-tenant* panes of 4 (Nos. 819a/b) 20·00

B 24 (*Illustration further reduced. Actual size 138×75 mm*)

1992 (2 Apr). *Greetings Booklet. Multicoloured cover as Type B 24. Stitched.*
SB42 £2.40, booklet containing two *se-tenant* panes of 4 (No. 840a) and eight greetings labels .. 5·50

B 25 (*Illustration further reduced. Actual size 161×100 mm*)

1992 (15 Oct). *Single European Market. Deep bluish violet and greenish yellow cover as Type B 25. Stitched.*
SB43 £4.80, booklet containing fifteen 32p. in three panes of 4 (No. 856a) and one pane of 3 (No. 856b) .. .. 11·00

B 26 "Banks of the Seine, near Paris" (N. Hone)
(*Illustration further reduced. Actual size 161×100 mm*)

1993 (4 Mar). *Irish Impressionist Painters. Multicoloured cover as Type B 26. Stitched.*
SB44 £4.68, booklet containing four *se-tenant* panes (Nos. 867a×2, 867b and 869a) .. .. 11·50

B 27 Lismore Crozier

1993 (24 Sept)–**95.** *Covers as Type B 27.*
SB45 £1 booklet containing *se-tenant* pane of 4 (No. 748ca) (bright greenish blue cover as Type B 27) .. 1·75
SB46 £1 booklet containing *se-tenant* pane of 4 (No. 748cb) (black and bright vermilion cover showing enamelled latchet brooch) (2.3.94) 1·75
SB46*a* £1 booklet containing *se-tenant* pane of 4 (No. 748cb) (black and bright orange-red cover showing Gleninsheen Collar) (28.2.95) 1·75
SB46*b* £1 booklet containing *se-tenant* pane of 4 (No. 748a) (black and bright reddish violet cover showing Broighter Collar) (16.11.95) .. 1·75

B 28 Front and Side View of Dublin Bus Leyland Olympian
(*Illustration further reduced. Actual size 131×61 mm*)

1993 (12 Oct). *Irish Buses. Multicoloured cover as Type B 28. Stitched.*
SB47 £2.84, booklet containing two different *se-tenant* panes (Nos. 886a/b) .. .. 6·50

B 29 (*Illustration further reduced. Actual size 138×75 mm*)

1994 (27 Jan). *Greetings Booklet. Multicoloured cover as Type B 29. Stitched.*
SB48 £2.56, booklet containing two *se-tenant* panes of four 32p. (No. 896a) .. .. 5·50

IRELAND

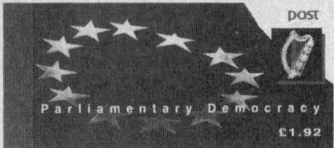

B 30 (*Illustration further reduced. Actual size 137×60 mm*)

1994 (27 Apr). *Parliamentary Anniversaries. Multicoloured cover as Type* B **30**. *Stitched.*
SB49 £1·92, booklet containing two different *se-tenant* panes (Nos. 908a/b) .. .. 4·50

B 31 (*Illustration further reduced. Actual size 161×101 mm*)

1994 (18 Oct). *Irish Nobel Prizewinners. Multicoloured cover as Type* B **31**. *Stitched.*
SB50 £4·84, booklet containing four different *se-tenant* panes (Nos. 928b/d and 930a) .. 11·50

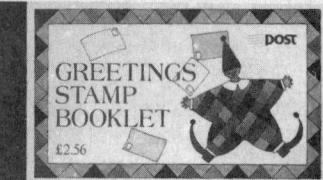

B 32 (*Illustration further reduced. Actual size 138×75 mm*)

1995 (24 Jan). *Greetings Booklet. Multicoloured cover as Type* B **32**. *Stitched.*
SB51 £2·56, booklet containing two *se-tenant* panes of four 32p. (No. 936a) .. .. .. 6·00

B 33 Blessing before Battle
(*Illustration reduced. Actual size 161×100 mm*)

1995 (15 May). *Military Uniforms. Multicoloured cover as Type* B **33**. *Stitched.*
SB52 £4·80, booklet containing four different *se-tenant* panes (Nos. 954a/d) .. .. .. 11·50

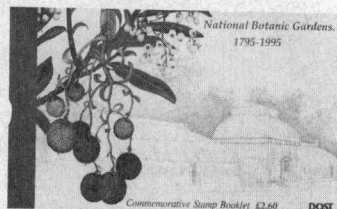

B 34 (*Illustration reduced. Actual size 140×82 mm*)

1995 (9 Oct). *Bicentenary of National Botanic Gardens, Glasnevin. Multicoloured cover as Type* B **34**. *Stitched.*
SB53 £2·60, booklet containing two different *se-tenant* panes (Nos. 973a/b) .. .. .. 7·50

MINIMUM PRICE

The minimum price quote is 10p which represents a handling charge rather than a basis for valuing common stamps. For further notes about prices see introductory pages.

768

B 35 (*Illustration reduced. Actual size 137 x 74 mm*)

1996 (23 Jan). *Greetings Booklet. Multicoloured cover as Type* B **35**. *Stitched.*
SB54 £2·56, booklet containing two *se-tenant* panes of four 32p. (No. 982a) .. .. .. 6·25

B 36 Steeplechasing
(*Illustration reduced. Actual size 161×100 mm*)

1996 (12 Mar). *Irish Horse Racing. Multicoloured cover as Type* B **36**. *Stitched.*
SB55 £4·92, booklet containing four different *se-tenant* panes (Nos. 991a, 992b/c and 993a) .. 13·00

B 37 Coastal Patrol Vessel and Sailor
(*Illustration reduced. Actual size 150×90 mm*)

(Des Design Image)

1996 (18 July). *50th Anniv of Irish Naval Service. Multicoloured cover as Type* B **37**. *Stitched.*
SB56 £2·24, booklet containing pane of three 32p. and pane of three values *se-tenant* (Nos. 1013a/b) 5·50

B 38 Farmyard Animals
(*Illustration reduced. Actual size 137×73 mm*)

1997 (28 Jan). *Greetings Booklet. Multicoloured cover as Type* B **38**. *Stitched.*
SB57 £2·56, booklet containing two *se-tenant* panes of four 32p. (No. 1055a) .. .. 6·00

B 39 Robin

1997 (6 Mar). *Birds. Multicoloured cover as Type* B **39**. *Stamps attached by selvedge.*
SB58 £1 booklet containing pane of 4 (2×2) (No. 748bb) .. .. 1·75

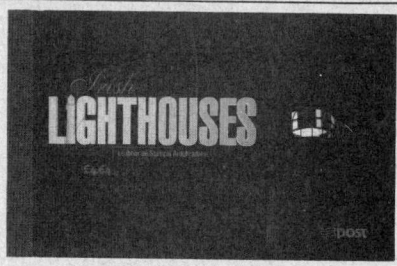

B 40 The Baily Lighthouse
(*Illustration reduced. Actual size 160×100 mm*)

1997 (1 July). *Lighthouses. Multicoloured cover as Type* B **40**. *Stitched.*
SB59 £4·64, booklet containing four different, *se-tenant*, panes (Nos. 1091b/c, 1091da and 1093da) .. .. 9·00

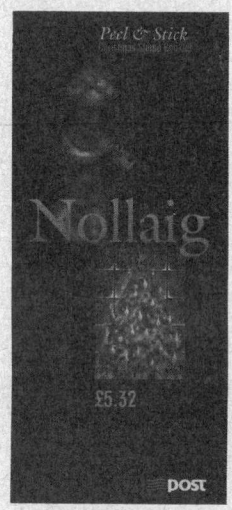

B 41 Christmas Tree

1997 (18 Nov). *Christmas. Multicoloured cover as Type* B **41**. *Self-adhesive.*
SB60 £5·32, booklet containing pane of twenty 28p. (2×10) (No. 1104a) .. .. 9·25
No. SB60 was sold at £5·32 providing a discount of 28p. off the face value of the stamps

1997 (6 Dec). *Multicoloured cover as Type* B **39** *showing Peregrine Falcon. Stamps attached by selvedge.*
SB61 £1 booklet containing pane of 4 (2×2) (No. 1047a) .. .. .. 1·75

B 42 On Swing
(*Illustration further reduced. Actual size 138×74 mm*)

1998 (26 Jan). *Greetings Booklet. Multicoloured cover as Type* B **42**. *Stitched.*
SB62 £2·56, booklet containing two different *se-tenant* panes of four 32p. (No. 1105a) .. 4·50

B 43 Early Aeroplane and Map
(*Illustration further reduced. Actual size 160×100 mm*)

1998 (24 Feb). *Pioneers of Irish Aviation. Multicoloured cover as Type* B **43**. *Stitched.*
SB63 $5·20, booklet containing four different, *se-tenant*, panes (Nos. 1110a/b and 1111a/b) .. 9·00

POSTAGE DUE STAMPS

From 1922 to 1925 Great Britain postage due stamps in both script and block watermarks were used without overprint.

D 1   D 2   D 3

(Des Ruby McConnell. Typo Govt Printing Works, Dublin)

1925 (20 Feb). *W 10. P 14×15.*

D1	D 1	½d. emerald-green		12·00	16·00
D2		1d. carmine		15·00	3·00
		a. Wmk sideways		£500	£200
		w. Wmk inverted		£200	30·00
D3		2d. deep green		28·00	5·50
		a. Wmk sideways		45·00	15·00
		w. Wmk inverted		70·00	23·00
D4		6d. plum		6·00	6·50
D1/4			*Set of 4*	55·00	28·00

1940–70. *W 22. P 14×15.*

D 5	D 1	½d. emerald-green (1942)		35·00	22·00
		w. Wmk inverted		£225	£120
D 6		1d. carmine (1941)		1·25	70
		w. Wmk inverted		55·00	6·50
D 7		1½d. vermilion (1953)		1·75	6·50
		w. Wmk inverted		15·00	21·00
D 8		2d. deep green (1940)		2·75	70
		w. Wmk inverted		20·00	6·50
D 9		3d. blue (10.11.52)		2·25	2·50
		w. Wmk inverted		6·00	4·50
D10		5d. blue-violet (3.3.43)		4·50	3·00
		w. Wmk inverted		6·50	7·00
D11		6d. plum (21.3.60)		3·00	2·00
		a. Wmk sideways (1968)		70	85
D12		8d. orange (30.10.62)		8·50	8·00
		w. Wmk inverted		17·00	18·00
D13		10d. bright purple (27.1.65)		8·50	7·50
D14		1s. apple-green (10.2.69)		6·00	9·00
		a. Wmk sideways (1970)		60·00	8·50
D5/14			*Set of 10*	65·00	55·00

1971 (15 Feb). *As Nos. D5/14, but with values in decimal currency and colours changed. W 22. P 14 × 15.*

D15	D 1	1p. sepia		30	60
		a. Wmk sideways		1·75	1·50
		w. Wmk inverted		1·00	1·50
D16		1½p. light emerald		50	1·50
D17		3p. stone		90	1·50
		w. Wmk inverted		1·25	1·75
D18		4p. orange		90	1·25
D19		5p. greenish blue		95	2·50
		w. Wmk inverted		2·00	3·00
D20		7p. bright yellow		40	3·50
		w. Wmk inverted		1·50	3·50
D21		8p. scarlet		40	2·50
D15/21			*Set of 7*	3·75	12·00

1978 (20 Mar). *As Nos. D17/19, but no wmk. Chalk-surfaced paper. P 14×15.*

D22	D 1	3p. stone		1·50	5·00
D23		4p. orange		6·00	8·00
D24		5p. greenish blue		1·50	4·00
D22/4			*Set of 3*	8·00	15·00

1980 (11 June)**–85.** *Photo. Chalk-surfaced paper. P 15.*

D25	D 2	1p. apple green		30	55
D26		2p. dull blue		30	55
D27		4p. myrtle-green		40	55
D28		6p. flesh		40	70
D29		8p. chalky blue		40	75
D30		18p. green		75	1·25
D31		20p. Indian red (22.8.85)		2·25	4·00
D32		24p. bright yellowish green		75	1·75
D33		30p. deep violet blue (22.8.85)		3·00	5·00
D34		50p. cerise (22.8.85)		3·75	6·00
D25/34			*Set of 10*	11·00	19·00

The 1p. to 18p. are on white paper and the 20p., 30p. and 50p. on cream. The 24p. value exists on both types of paper.

(Des Q Design. Litho Irish Security Stamp Ptg Ltd)

1988 (6 Oct). *Chalk-surfaced paper. P 14 × 15.*

D35	D 3	1p. black, orange-vermilion & lemon	10	10
D36		2p. black, orange-verm & purple-brn	10	10
D37		3p. black, orange-vermilion and plum	10	10
D38		4p. black, orange-vermilion & brt vio	10	10
D39		5p. black, orge-vermilion & royal blue	10	10
D40		17p. black, orange-verm & dp yell-grn	30	35
D41		20p. black, orange-vermilion & slate-bl	35	40
D42		24p. black, orange-verm & dp turq-grn	40	45
D43		30p. black, orange-vermilion & dp grey	50	55
D44		50p. black, orge-verm & brownish grey	90	95
D45		£1 black, orge-vermilion & bistre-brn	1·75	1·90
D35/45			*Set of 11*	4·50	5·00

From 20 September 1993 labels in the above style were used to indicate postage due charges in the Dublin 2 delivery area. They are dispensed by a Pitney/Bowes machine, in much the same way as a meter mark, and can show any face value between 1p. and I£99.99. Such labels are not normally postmarked. Labels with face values of 32p. and 50p. were sold to collectors by the Philatelic Bureau.

THOMOND AND LONG ISLAND

Labels inscribed "Principality of Thomond" appeared on the philatelic market in the early 1960s. Thomond is the name of a district in western Ireland. The area does not have its own administration or postal service and the labels were not recognised by the Department of Posts & Telegraphs, Dublin.

Local carriage labels were issued for Long Island, County Cork in April 1973; they were intended to cover the cost of taking mail from the island to the nearest mainland post office. A local service operated for a few weeks before it was suppressed by the Irish Post Office. As the stamps were not accepted for national or international mail they are not listed here.

1st CLASS STAMPS & SERVICE

Stanley Gibbons are pleased to offer a dedicated and completely free of charge service to today's discerning British Commonwealth collectors.

- Specialist database of clients' interests.
- Large stocks of specialised British Commonwealth material.
- Free advice from our team of experts.
- Regular advance lists and illustrated colour brochures.
- Private viewing facilities and postal approvals service.
- Specialist 'Wants List' service.
- We are always interested in buying quality collections and single items.

To take advantage of our free and highly specialised service contact us today on 0171 836 8444.

STANLEY GIBBONS

—FIRST CLASS—
STAMPS & SERVICE

Stanley Gibbons Limited
399 Strand, London WC2R 0LX

Addenda

GREAT BRITAIN

Jersey

CORRECTION: Re-number Nos. 838/47, T **191** to 848/57, T **193**

191 J.M.T. Bristol 4 Tonner, 1923   **192** Creative Arts Festival

(Des A. Copp. Litho B.D.T.)

1998 (2 Apr). *75th Anniv of Jersey Motor Transport Company. Buses. T* **191** *and similar horiz designs. Multicoloured. P* 14.

838	20p. Type **191**	.. ..	40	45
	a. Booklet pane. Nos. 838/9, each × 3 with margins all round		2·75	
	b. Booklet pane. Nos. 838/43 with margins all round		4·25	
839	24p. Safety Coach Service Regent double decker, 1934	..	50	55
840	31p. Slade's Dennis Lancet, *c.* 1936 ..	..	60	65
	a. Booklet pane. Nos. 840/1, each × 3 with margins all round		4·00	
841	37p. Tantivy Leyland PLSC Lion, 1947	..	75	80
842	43p. J.B.S. Morris, *c.* 1958 ..	..	85	90
	a. Booklet pane. Nos. 842/3, each × 3 with margins all round		6·25	
843	63p. J.M.T. Titan TD4 double decker, *c.* 1961		1·25	1·40
838/43	.. ..	*Set of* 6	4·25	4·75

(Des A. Copp. Litho Enschedé)

1998 (2 Apr). *Europa. National Festivals. T* **192** *and similar vert designs. Multicoloured. P* 14×13½.

844	20p. Type **192**	.. ..	40	45
845	24p. Jazz Festival	.. ..	50	55
846	31p. Good Food Festival	..	60	65
847	63p. Floral Festival ..	..	1·25	1·40
844/7	.. .. ..	*Set of* 4	2·75	3·00

Nos. 845/6 include the "EUROPA" emblem.

ANTIGUA

386 Diana, Princess of Wales

1998 (19 Jan). *Diana, Princess of Wales Commemoration. T* **386** *and similar vert designs. Multicoloured (except Nos. 2564, 2571/2 and* **MS**2575b). *P* 14.

2563	$1.65, Type **386**	.. ..	75	80
	a. Sheetlet. Nos. 2563/8 ..		4·50	
2564	$1.65, Wearing hoop earrings (rose-carm and black)		75	80
2565	$1.65, Carrying bouquet	..	75	80
2566	$1.65, Wearing floral hat	..	75	80
2567	$1.65, With Prince Harry	..	75	80
2568	$1.65, Wearing white jacket	..	75	80
2569	$1.65, In kitchen	..	75	80
	a. Sheetlet. Nos. 2569/74		4·50	
2570	$1.65, Wearing black and white dress		75	80
2571	$1.65, Wearing hat (orge-brown & black)		75	80
2572	$1.65, Wearing floral print dress (lakebrown and black)		75	80
2573	$1.65, Dancing with John Travolta		75	80
2574	$1.65, Wearing white hat and jacket		75	80
2563/74	.. ..	*Set of* 12	9·00	9·50

MS2575 Two sheets, each 70×100 mm. (a) $6 Wearing red jumper. (b) $6 Wearing black dress for Papal audience (lake-brown and black)

	Set of 2 *sheets*	5·50	5·75

Nos. 2563/8 and 2569/74 were each printed together, *se-tenant,* in sheetlets of 6.

ASCENSION

177 Diana, Princess of Wales, 1985   **178** Fairey Fawn

(Des D. Miller. Litho Questa)

1998 (31 Mar). *Diana, Princess of Wales Commemoration. Sheet,* 145×70 *mm, containing T* **177** *and similar vert designs. Multicoloured. W w* **14** *(sideways). P* 14½×14.
MS741 35p. Type **177**; 35p. Wearing yellow blouse, 1992; 35p. Wearing grey jacket, 1984; 35p. Carrying bouquets *(sold at* £1.40 + 20p. *charity premium)* .. .. .. 3·25 3·50

(Des A. Theobald. Litho Questa)

1998 (1 Apr). *80th Anniv of Royal Air Force. T* **178** *and similar horiz designs. Multicoloured. W w* **16** *(sideways). P* 14.

742	15p. Type **178**	.. ..	30	35
743	35p. Vickers Vernon	.. ..	70	75
744	40p. Supermarine Spitfire F.22	..	80	85
745	50p. Bristol Britannia C.2	..	1·00	1·10
742/5		*Set of* 4	2·75	3·00

MS746 110×77 mm. 50p. Blackburn Kangaroo; 50p. S.E.5a; 50p. Curtiss Kittyhawk III; 50p. Boeing Fortress II .. .. 4·00 4·25

AUSTRALIA

584 Champagne Rose

(Des Cathleen Bryant. Litho SNP Cambec)

1998 (12 Feb). *Greetings Stamp.* (a) *P* 14½×14.

1755	**584**	45 c. multicoloured ..	40	45

(b) *Self-adhesive. Phosphor band. P* 11½

1756	**584**	45 c. multicoloured ..	40	45
		a. Booklet pane. No. 1756×10 ..	4·00	

No. 1756 was only issued in $4.50 booklets on which the surplus self-adhesive paper was retained.
The phosphor, which shows pink under U.V. light, covers most of the row of roses to the left of the design.

STAMP BOOKLETS

B 52 Champagne Rose   **B 53** Brolga

1998 (12 Feb). *Greetings Stamp. Multicoloured cover as Type* B **52**. *Self-adhesive.*
SB120 $4.50, booklet containing pane of 10 45 c. (No. 1756a) and 12 self-adhesive greetings stickers affixed to the inner cover .. .. 4·00

1998 (12 Feb). *Wetland Birds. Multicoloured cover as Type* B **53**. *Self-adhesive. Stamps loose within cover.*
SB121 $9 booklet containing 20 × 45 c. (Nos. 1634c/7c) 7·75
No. SB121 was introduced as a trial product and was available at a number of Post Offices in Victoria and from Philatelic counters.

Australian Antarctic Territory

30 *Aurora Australis* (research ship)

(Des Sandra Harman. Litho McPherson's Ptg Group, Mulgrave)

1998 (5 Mar). *Antarctic Transport. T* **30** *and similar multicoloured designs. P* 14×14½ (45 c.) *or* 14½×14 (*others*).

122	45 c. Type **30**	.. ..	40	45
	a. Pair. Nos. 122/3	..	80	
123	45 c. Skidoo	..	40	45
124	$1 Helicopter lifting quad-bike (*vert*)		90	95
125	$2 Hagglunds tractor and trailer (*vert*)		1·75	1·90
122/5		*Set of* 4	3·50	3·75

Nos. 122/5 were printed together, *se-tenant,* in horizontal and vertical pairs throughout the sheet.

Norfolk Island

192 Tiger Mask   **193** "Pepper"

(Des Ren Yu. Litho Southern Colour Print, Dunedin)

1998 (12 Feb). *Chinese New Year ("Year of the Tiger"). Sheet* 75×95 *mm. P* 12.
MS657 **192** 45 c. multicoloured 40 45

(Des Mary Butterfield. Litho Southern Colour Print, Dunedin)

1998 (26 Feb). *Cats. T* **193** *and similar vert designs. Multicoloured. P* 14½.

658	45 c. Type **193**	.. ..	40	45
659	45 c. "Tabitha" at window ..	..	40	45
660	75 c. "Midnight"	.. ..	65	70
661	$1.20, "Rainbow" with flower pot	..	1·00	1·10
658/61		*Set of* 4	2·40	2·75

BAHAMAS

(Des D. Miller. Litho Questa)

1998 (31 Mar). *Diana, Princess of Wales Commemoration. Vert designs as T* **177** *of Ascension. W w* **16** (*No.* 1130). *P* 14½×14.
1130	15 c. Wearing grey jacket, 1988 ..	..	20	25

MS1131 145×70 mm. 15 c. As No. 1130; 55 c. Wearing striped jacket, 1983; 60 c. In evening dress, 1983; 70 c. Meeting crowds, 1993. W w **14** (sideways) .. .. 2·50 2·75

(Des A. Theobald. Litho Enschedé)

1998 (1 Apr). *80th Anniv of the Royal Air Force. Horiz designs as T* **178** *of Ascension. Multicoloured. W w* **14** (*sideways*). *P* 13½×14.
1132	15 c. Handley Page Hyderabad	..	20	25
1133	55 c. Hawker Demon	..	65	70
1134	60 c. Gloster Meteor F.8 ..	..	75	80
1135	70 c. Lockheed Neptune MR.1	..	85	90
1132/5		*Set of* 4	2·40	2·75

MS1136 110×76 mm. 50 c. Sopwith Camel; 50 c. Short 184 (seaplane); 50 c. Supermarine Spitfire PR.19; 50 c. North American Mitchell III .. 2·50 2·75

BELIZE

(Des D. Miller. Litho Questa)

1998 (31 Mar). *Diana, Princess of Wales Commemoration. Sheet,* 145×70 *mm, containing vert designs as T* **177** *of Ascension. Multicoloured. W w* **14** (*sideways*). *P* 14½×14.
MS1226 $1 Wearing floral dress, 1988; $1 In evening dress, 1981; $1 Wearing pearl drop earrings, 1988; $1 Carrying bouquet, 1983 .. 2·40 2·50

BERMUDA

(Des D. Miller. Litho Questa)

1998 (31 Mar). *Diana, Princess of Wales Commemoration. Sheet,* 145×70 *mm, containing vert designs as T* **177** *of Ascension. Multicoloured. W w* **14** (*sideways*). *P* 14½×14.
MS787 30 c. Wearing floral dress; 65 c. Wearing blue evening dress, 1996; 80 c. Carrying bouquets, 1993 (*sold at* $2.15 + 25 c. *charity premium*) .. .. 1·50 1·60

BRITISH ANTARCTIC TERRITORY

(Des D. Miller. Litho Questa)

998 (17 Mar). *Diana, Princess of Wales Commemoration. Sheet, 145×70 mm, containing vert designs as T* **177** *of Ascension. Multicoloured. W w* **14** *(sideways). P* 14½×14.
1S280   35p. Wearing sunglasses; 35p. Wearing round-necked white blouse, 1993; 35p. Wearing white blouse and jacket, 1990; 35p. Wearing green jacket, 1992 *(sold at £1.40 + 20p. charity premium)* .. .. .. 3·25 3·50

58 Chart of South Shetland Islands (Swedish South Polar Expedition, 1902–03)

(Des N. Shewring. Litho Walsall)

1998 (19 Mar). *History of Mapping in Antarctica. T* **58** *and similar vert designs. Multicoloured. W w* **14**. *P* 14.
281   16p. Type **58** 30 35
282   30p. Map of Antarctic Peninsula (1949) .. 60 65
283   35p. Map of Antarctic Peninsula (1964) .. 70 75
284   40p. Map of Antarctic Peninsula from Landsat (1981) 80 85
285   65p. Map of Antarctic Peninsula from satellite (1995) .. .. .. 1·25 1·40
281/5 .. .. *Set of* 5 3·75 4·00

BRITISH INDIAN OCEAN TERRITORY

(Des D. Miller. Litho Questa)

1998 (31 Mar). *Diana, Princess of Wales Commemoration. Sheet, 145×70 mm, containing vert designs as T* **177** *of Ascension. Multicoloured. W w* **14** *(sideways). P* 14½×14.
MS214   26p. Wearing patterned jacket, 1993; 26p. Wearing heart-shaped earrings, 1988; 34p. Wearing cream jacket, 1993; 60p. Wearing blue blouse, 1982 *(sold at £1.46 + 20p. charity premium)* .. .. .. 3·25 3·50

(Des A. Theobald. Litho Questa)

1998 (1 Apr). *80th Anniv of the Royal Air Force. Horiz designs as T* **178** *of Ascension. Multicoloured. W w* **16** *(sideways). P* 14.
215   26p. Blackburn Iris 50 55
216   34p. Gloster Gamecock 70 75
217   60p. North American Sabre F.4 .. 1·25 1·40
218   80p. Avro Lincoln .. .. 1·60 1·75
215/18 .. .. *Set of* 4 4·00 4·50
MS219   110×77 mm. 34p. Sopwith Baby (seaplane); 34p. Martinsyde Elephant; 34p. De Havilland Tiger Moth; 34p. North American Mustang III .. .. .. 2·75 3·00

BRUNEI

124 Children and Sign Language

(Des Padzil bin Haj Ahmed. Litho Cartor)

1998 (31 Mar). *Asian and Pacific Decade of Disabled Persons, 1993–2002. T* **124** *and similar horiz designs. Multicoloured. P* 13×13½.
585   20 c. Type **124** 15 20
586   50 c. Woman typing and firework display 40 45
587   $1 Disabled athletes 75 80
585/7 .. .. *Set of* 3 1·25 1·40

ALTERED CATALOGUE NUMBERS

Any Catalogue numbers altered from the last edition are shown as a list in the introductory pages.

CANADA

Add to Nos. 1354/8

(Litho C.B.N. (Nos. 1358d/da) or Ashton-Potter (No. 1358db))

(1358 – 45 c. multicoloured)
   d. Perf 13×13½ (2.2.98) 35 40
   da. Booklet pane. No. 1358d×10 .. 3·50
   db. Booklet pane. No. 1358d×30 (two blocks of 15 (5×3) separated by vertical gutter) .. .. 10·50
No. 1358d is smaller, 19×23 mm, instead of 21×25 mm.
Nos. 1358da/db have the vertical edges of the panes imperforate and show a margin at either end.

680 John Robarts (Ontario, 1961–71)

(Des R. Bellemare. Litho C.B.N.)

1998 (18 Feb). *Canadian Provincial Premiers. T* **680** *and similar horiz designs. Multicoloured. Fluorescent frame. P* 13½.
1769   45 c. Type **680** 35 40
   a. Sheetlet. Nos.1769/78 .. 3·50
1770   45 c. Jean Lesage (Quebec, 1960–66) .. 35 40
1771   45 c. John McNair (New Brunswick, 1940–52) 35 40
1772   45 c. Tommy Douglas (Saskatchewan, 1944–61) 35 40
1773   45 c. Joseph Smallwood (Newfoundland, 1949–72) 35 40
1774   45 c. Angus MacDonald (Nova Scotia, 1933–40, 1945–54) 35 40
1775   45 c. W. A. C. Bennett (British Columbia, 1960–66) 35 40
1776   45 c. Ernest Manning (Alberta, 1943–68) 35 40
1777   45 c. John Bracken (Manitoba, 1922–43) 35 40
1778   45 c. J. Walter Jones (Prince Edward Island, 1943–53) 35 40
1769/78 .. .. *Set of* 10 3·50 4·00
Nos. 1769/78 were printed together, *se-tenant*, in sheetlets of 10 with illustrated margins.

(Des R. Bellemare and P. Leduc. Litho C.B.N.)

1998 (13 Mar). *Birds (3rd series). Horiz designs as T* **643**. *Multicoloured. Fluorescent frame. P* 13×13½.
1779   45 c. Hairy Woodpecker 35 40
   a. Horiz strip of 4. Nos. 1779/82 .. 1·40
1780   45 c. Great Crested Flycatcher .. 35 40
1781   45 c. Eastern Screech Owl .. 35 40
1782   45 c. Gray-crowned Rosy-finch .. 35 40
1779/82 .. .. *Set of* 4 1·40 1·60
Nos. 1779/82 were printed together, *se-tenant*, in sheets of 20 (4×5) containing five examples of No. 1779a.

STAMP BOOKLETS

1998 (2 Feb). *Covers as Type B* **37**, *each showing multicoloured stamps in a continuous pattern on scarlet background.*
SB218 $4.50, booklet containing pane of 10 45 c. (5×2) (No. 1358da) .. .. 3·50
SB219 $13.50, booklet containing pane of 30 45 c. (two blocks of 15 (5×3) separated by vertical margin (No. 1358db) .. .. 10·50

CAYMAN ISLANDS

(Des D. Miller. Litho Questa)

1998 (31 Mar). *Diana, Princess of Wales Commemoration. Vert designs as T* **177** *of Ascension. Multicoloured. W w* **16** *(Nos. 856/7). P* 14½×14.
856   10 c. Wearing gold earrings, 1997 .. 15 20
857   20 c. Wearing black hat 30 35
MS858   145×70 mm. 10 c. As No. 856; 20 c. As No. 857; 40 c. With bouquet, 1995; $1 Wearing black and white blouse, 1983. W w **14** (sideways) *(sold at $1.70 + 30 c. charity premium)* .. 2·75 3·00

(Des A. Theobald. Litho B.D.T.)

1998 (1 Apr). *80th Anniv of the Royal Air Force. Horiz designs as T* **178** *of Ascension. Multicoloured. W w* **14** *(sideways). P* 14.
859   10 c. Hawker Horsley 15 20
860   20 c. Fairey Hendon 30 35
861   25 c. Hawker Siddeley Gnat .. 35 40
862   30 c. Hawker Siddeley Dominie .. 40 45
859/62 .. .. *Set of* 4 1·25 1·40
MS863   110×77 mm. 40 c. Airco D.H.9; 60 c. Spad 13 Scout; 80 c. Airspeed Oxford; $1 Martin Baltimore .. .. .. 4·00 4·25

COOK ISLANDS

CORRECTION: Re-number Nos. 1412/13 to 1419/20

Add to Nos. 1402/11
1412 $1.50, *Parthenos sylvia* (11.3.98) .. 1·10 1·25
1413 $2 *Lampides boeticus* (female) (11.3.98) 1·50 1·60
1414 $3 *Precis villida* (11.3.98) .. 2·25 2·50

274 Diana, Princess of Wales

1998 (18 Mar). *Diana, Princess of Wales Commemoration. Litho. P* 14.
1421 $1.15, Type **274** 85 90
   a. Sheetlet. No. 1421×5 and label 4·25
MS1422   70×100 mm. $3.50, Princess Diana and guard of honour .. .. 2·50 2·75
No. 1421 was printed in sheetlets of 5 stamps with a label at top left.

CYPRUS

No. 892 was reissued on 9 March 1998 with the imprint date changed to 1998.

315 Green Jasper

(Des A. Ladommatos. Litho Oriental Press, Bahrain)

1998 (9 Mar). *Minerals. T* **315** *and similar horiz designs. Multicoloured. P* 13.
934   10 c. Type **315** 20 25
935   15 c. Iron Pyrite 35 40
936   25 c. Gypsum 60 65
937   30 c. Chalcedony 70 75
934/7 .. .. *Set of* 4 1·75 2·00

Turkish Cypriot Posts

153 Open Book and Emblem

(Des H. Billur. Litho State Ptg Works, Lefkosa)

1997 (22 Dec). *Anniversaries. T* **153** *and similar designs. W* **51** *(sideways on horiz designs). P* 13½×14 *(horiz)* or 14×13½ *(vert)*.
455   25000 l. multicoloured 15 20
456   40000 l. multicoloured 25 30
457   100000 l. black, brt scarlet & yellow ochre 60 65
458   150000 l. multicoloured .. .. 95 1·00
455/8 .. .. *Set of* 4 1·90 2·10
Designs: *Horiz*:—25000 l. Type **153** (Centenary of Turkish Cypriot Scouts); 40000 l. Guides working in field (90th Anniv of Turkish Cypriot Guides); 150000 l., Rudolph Diesel and diesel motor (Centenary of the diesel engine). *Vert*:—100000 l., Couple and symbols (AIDS prevention campaign).

DOMINICA

301 Anthony Trollope and Postal Scenes

(Litho Questa)

1996 (1 Oct). *World Post Day. T* **301** *and similar vert designs. Multicoloured. P* 14.
2193   10 c. Type **301** 10 10
2194   25 c. Anthony Trollope and Dominican Postmen 10 15
2195   55 c. *Yare* (mail steamer) 25 30

2196	65 c. Rural Post Office	30	35
2197	90 c. Postmen carrying mail	40	45
2198	$1 Grumman Goose (seaplane) and 1958 Caribbean Federation 12 c. stamp	45	50
2199	$2 Old and new Post Offices and 1978 Independence 10 c. stamp	90	95
2193/9	*Set of 7*	2·50	2·75
MS2200	74×104 mm. $5 18th-centenary naval officer	2·25	2·50

FALKLAND ISLANDS

(Des D. Miller. Litho Questa)

1998 (31 Mar). *Diana, Princess of Wales Commemoration. Vert designs as T 177 of Ascension.* W w 14 (*sideways*). P 14½×14.
MS803 145×70 mm. 30p. Wearing black jacket, 1990; 30p. Wearing red dress, 1988; 30p. Resting head on hand, 1991; 30p. Wearing landmine protection clothing, Angola (*sold at £1.20 + 20p. charity premium*) .. .. .. 2·40 2·50

GAMBIA

280 Great Mosque, Samarra, Iran

281 Downhill Skiing

(Des W. Wright. Litho Questa)

1997 (15 July). *Natural and Man-made Wonders of the World. T 280 and similar multicoloured designs.* P 14 (*Nos. 2691/6*) or 13½×14 (*others*).

2691	63 b. Type 280	10	10
2692	75 b. Moai statues, Easter Island (*horiz*)	10	10
2693	1 d. Golden Gate Bridge, San Francisco (*horiz*)	10	10
2694	1 d. 50, The Statue of Liberty, New York	20	25
2695	2 d. The Parthenon, Athens (*horiz*)	20	25
2696	3 d. Pyramid of the Sun, Mexico (*horiz*)	35	40
2697	5 d. The Rock of Gibraltar (*horiz*)	60	65
	a. Sheetlet. Nos. 2697/702	3·50	
2698	5 d. St. Peter's Basilica, Rome (*horiz*)	60	65
2699	5 d. Santa Sophia, Istanbul (*horiz*)	60	65
2700	5 d. "Gateway to the West" monument, St. Louis (*horiz*)	60	65
2701	5 d. Great Wall of China (*horiz*)	60	65
2702	5 d. City of Carcassonne, France (*horiz*)	60	65
2703	5 d. Stonehenge, England (*horiz*)	60	65
	a. Sheetlet. Nos. 2703/8	3·50	
2704	5 d. Hughes HK-1 *Spruce Goose* flying boat (World's largest aircraft) (*horiz*)	60	65
2705	5 d. Hoverspeed "Seacat" catamaran (fastest Atlantic crossing by a commercial catamaran) (*horiz*)	60	65
2706	5 d. "Thrust 2" car (official land speed record) (*horiz*)	60	65
2707	5 d. Stepped Pyramid, Egypt (*horiz*)	60	65
2708	5 d. *Mallard* (fastest steam locomotive) (*horiz*)	60	65
2691/708	*Set of 18*	8·00	9·00

MS2709 Three sheets, each 98×68 mm. (a) 25 d. Mount Everest (42×28 *mm*). P 14. (b) 25 d. The Grand Canyon, Colorado (42×28 *mm*). P 14. (c) 25 d. Washington Monument (33×51 *mm*). P 15
Set of 3 sheets 9·00 9·25
Nos. 2697/702 and 2703/8 were each printed together, *se-tenant*, in sheetlets of 6.
No. 2702 is inscribed "CARCASSONNNE" in error.

(Litho B.D.T.)

1997 (21 July). *Winter Olympic Games, Nagano (1998). T 281 and similar multicoloured designs.* P 14.

2710	5 d. Type 281	60	65
2711	5 d. Two-man bob-sleigh (*vert*)	60	65
	a. Sheetlet. Nos. 2711/19	5·50	
2712	5 d. Freestyle skiing (*vert*)	60	65
2713	5 d. Speed skating (*vert*)	60	65
2714	5 d. Downhill skiing (No. 8 on bib) (*vert*)	60	65
2715	5 d. Womens figure skating (*vert*)	60	65
2716	5 d. Downhill skiing (No. 4 on bib) (*vert*)	60	65
2717	5 d. Pairs figure skating (*vert*)	60	65
2718	5 d. Cross-country (*vert*)	60	65
2719	5 d. Ski jumping (*vert*)	60	65
2720	5 d. One-man luge (*vert*)	60	65
	a. Sheetlet. Nos. 2720/8	5·50	
2721	5 d. Ice hockey (*vert*)	60	65
2722	5 d. Four-man bob-sleigh	60	65
2723	5 d. Ski-jumping	60	65
2724	5 d. Curling	60	65
2725	5 d. Figure skating	60	65
2726	5 d. Speed skating	60	65
2727	5 d. Biathlon	60	65
2728	5 d. Downhill skiing (*different*)	60	65
2729	10 d. One-man luge	1·10	1·25
2730	15 d. Speed skating	1·75	1·90
2731	20 d. Ice hockey	2·25	2·40
2710/31	*Set of 22*	17·00	18·00

MS2732 Two sheets. (a) 97×67 mm. 25 d. Bob-sleigh. (b) 67×97 mm. 25 d. Pairs figure skating (*vert*) .. .. *Set of 2 sheets* 5·75 6·00
Nos. 2711/19 and 2720/8 were each printed togther, *se-tenant*, in sheetlets of 9.

---

282 Brown Pelican

(Des J. Ruff. Litho Questa)

1997 (4 Aug). *Sea Birds. T 282 and similar multicoloured designs.* P 14.

2733	3 d. Type 282	35	40
	a. Sheetlet. Nos. 2733/44	4·25	
2734	3 d. Galapagos Penguin	35	40
2735	3 d. Red-billed Tropic Bird	35	40
2736	3 d. Little Tern	35	40
2737	3 d. Dunlin	35	40
2738	3 d. Kittiwake	35	40
2739	3 d. Atlantic Puffin	35	40
2740	3 d. Wandering Albatross	35	40
2741	3 d. Masked Booby	35	40
2742	3 d. Glaucous Winged Gull	35	40
2743	3 d. Arctic Tern	35	40
2744	3 d. Piping Plover	35	40
2745	5 d. Red-legged Cormorant	60	65
2746	10 d. Roseate Tern	1·10	1·25
2747	15 d. Blue-footed Booby	1·75	1·90
2748	20 d. Sanderling	2·25	2·40
2733/48	*Set of 16*	10·00	11·00

MS2749 Two sheets, each 106×76 mm. (a) 23 d. Long-tailed Skua (*vert*). (b) 23 d. Osprey (*vert*) *Set of 2 sheets* 2·50 2·75
Nos. 2733/44 were printed together, *se-tenant*, in sheetlets of 12.

283 Scottish Fold Cat

284 Diana, Princess of Wales

(Des D. Burkhart. Litho Questa)

1997 (12 Aug). *Cats and Dogs. T 283 and similar horiz designs. Multicoloured.* P 14.

2750	63 b. Type 283	10	10
2751	75 b. Dalmatian	10	10
2752	1 d. Rottweiler	10	15
2753	1 d. 50, American Curl cat	20	25
2754	2 d. British Bi-colour cat	20	25
2755	3 d. Newfoundland	35	40
2756	3 d. Devon Rex cat	35	40
2757	4 d. Great Dane	45	50
2758	5 d. Burmilla cat	60	65
	a. Sheetlet. Nos. 2758/63	3·50	
2759	5 d. Blue Burmese cat	60	65
2760	5 d. Korat cat	60	65
2761	5 d. British Tabby cat	60	65
2762	5 d. Foreign White cat	60	65
2763	5 d. Somali cat	60	65
2764	5 d. Akita	60	65
	a. Sheetlet. Nos. 2764/9	3·50	
2765	5 d. Welsh Corgi	60	65
2766	5 d. German Shepherd	60	65
2767	5 d. Saint Bernard	60	65
2768	5 d. Bullmastiff	60	65
2769	5 d. Malamute	60	65
2770	6 d. Silver Tabby cat	70	75
2771	10 d. Old English Sheepdog	1·10	1·25
2772	15 d. Queensland Heeler cat	1·75	1·90
2773	20 d. Abyssinian cat	2·25	2·40
2750/73	*Set of 24*	14·50	16·50

MS2774 Four sheets, each 107×78 mm. (a) 25 d. Cornish Rex cat. (b) 25 d. Siamese cat. (c) 25 d. Boxer. (d) 25 d. Doberman Pinscher
Set of 4 sheets 12·00 12·50
Nos. 2758/63 and 2764/9 were each printed together, *se-tenant*, in sheetlets of 6.

(Litho Questa)

1997 (4 Sept). *World Cup Football Championship, France (1998). Designs as T 382 of Antigua.* P 14×13½ (*horiz*) or 13½×14 (*vert*).

2775	1 d. black	10	10
2776	1 d. 50, black	20	25
2777	2 d. black	20	25
2778	3 d. black	35	40
2779/86	4 d. × 8 mult or agate (Nos. 2782/3)		
	a. Sheetlet. Nos. 2779/86 and central label	3·50	
2787/94	4 d. × 8 multicoloured or blk (No. 2788)		
	a. Sheetlet. Nos. 2787/94 and central label	3·50	
2795/802	4 d. × 8 blackish brown (Nos. 2795/6, 2800 and 2802) or multicoloured		
	a. Sheetlet. Nos. 2795/802 and central label	3·50	
2803/10	4 d. × 8 multicoloured		
	a. Sheetlet. Nos. 2803/10 and central label	3·50	
2811	5 d. black	60	65
2812	10 d. black	1·10	1·25
2775/812	*Set of 37*	16·50	18·00

MS2813 Four sheets, each 102×127 mm. (a) 25 d. multicoloured. (b) 25 d. multicoloured. (c) 25 d. black. (d) 25 d. blackish brown
Set of 4 sheets 12·00 12·50
Designs: *Horiz*—No. 2775, Uruguay team, 1950; No. 2776, West German team, 1954; No 2777, Brazilian team, 1970; No. 2778, Brazilian team, 1962; No. 2779, Brazilian team, 1994; No. 2780, Argentine team, 1986; No. 2781, Brazilian team, 1970; No. 2782, Italian team, 1934; No. 2783, Uruguay team, 1958; No. 2784, English team, 1966; No. 2785, Brazilian team, 1962; No. 2786, West German team, 1990; No. 2787, Mario Kempes, Argentina (1978); No. 2788, Ademir, Brazil (1950); No. 2789, Muller, West Germany (1970); No. 2790, Lineker, England (1986); No. 2791, Eusebio, Portugal (1966); No. 2792, Schillaci, Italy (1990); No. 2793, Lato, Poland (1974); No. 2794, Rossi, Italy (1982); No. 2811, Italian team, 1938; No. 2812, Uruguay team, 1930; No. MS2813a, Philippe Albert, Belgium; No. MS2813b, Juninho, Brazil; No. MS2813c, Eusebio, Portugal; No. MS2813d, Pele, Brazil. *Vert*—No. 2795, Moore, England (1996); No. 2796, Fritzwalter, West Germany (1954); No. 2797, Beckenbauer, West Germany (1974); No. 2798, Zoff, Italy (1982); No. 2799, Maradona, Argentina (1986); No. 2800, Passarella, Argentina (1978); No. 2801, Mattahus, West Germany (1990); No. 2802, Dunga, Brazil (1994); No. 2803, Kinkladze, Georgia; No. 2804, Shearer, England; No. 2805, Dani, Portugal; No. 2806, Weah, Portugal; No. 2807, Ravanelli, Italy; No. 2808, Raducioiu, Rumania; No. 2809, Schmeichel, Denmark; No. 2810, Bergkarnp, Holland;
Nos. 2779/86, 2787/94, 2795/802 and 2803/10 were each printed together, *se-tenant*, in sheetlets of 8 stamps and 1 central label.

(Des J. Iskowitz. Litho Questa)

1997 (26 Nov). *Diana, Princess of Wales Commemoration. T 284 and similar vert designs each red-brown and black* (*Nos. 2814/17*). P 14.

2814	10 d. Type 284	1·10	1·25
	a. Sheetlet. Nos. 2814/17	4·50	
2815	10 d. Wearing open-necked shirt	1·10	1·25
2816	10 d. Wearing polo-neck jumper	1·10	1·25
2817	10 d. Wearing diamond-drop earrings	1·10	1·25
2814/17	*Set of 4*	4·50	5·00

MS2818 76×106 mm. 25 d. Diana, Princess of Wales (multicoloured) .. .. 3·00 3·25
Nos. 2814/17 were printed together, *se-tenant*, in sheetlets of 4 with enlarged illustrated margins.

285 "Angel" (Rembrandt)

286 Tiger

(Litho B.D.T.)

1997 (8 Dec). *Christmas. Paintings. T 285 and similar vert designs. Multicoloured.* P 14.

2819	1 d. Type 285	10	15
2820	1 d. 50, "Initiation into the Rites of Dionysus", Villa dei Misteri	20	25
2821	2 d. "Pair of Erotes with Purple Cloaks"	20	25
2822	3 d. "The Ecstasy of Saint Theresa" (Gianlorenzo Bernini)	35	40
2823	5 d. "Virgin and Child with Angels" (Matthias Grunewald)	60	65
2824	10 d. "Angel playing the Organ" (Stefan Lochner)	1·10	1·25
2819/24	*Set of 6*	2·50	3·00

MS2825 Two sheets, each 105×95 mm. (a) 25 d. "The Rest on the Flight into Egypt" (Caravaggio). (b) 25 d. "The Education of Cupid" (Titian) .. .. *Set of 2 sheets* 5·75 6·00
No. MS2825b is inscribed "TITAN" in error.

(Des Y. Lee. Litho Questa)

1998 (5 Jan). *Chinese New Year ("Year of the Tiger"). T 286 and similar horiz designs. Multicoloured.* P 14½.

2826	3 d. Type 286 ("GAMBIA" in emerald)	35	40
	a. Sheetlet. Nos. 2826/9	1·40	
2827	3 d. Tiger ("GAMBIA" in magenta)	35	40
2828	3 d. Tiger ("GAMBIA" in lilac)	35	40
2829	3 d. Tiger ("GAMBIA" in deep violet-blue)	35	40
2826/9	*Set of 4*	1·40	1·60

MS2830 73×103 mm. 10 d. Tiger (42×28 *mm*) 1·10 1·25
Nos. 2826/9 were printed together, *se-tenant*, in sheetlets of 4.

GHANA

551 Diana, Princess of Wales

1997 (22 Dec). *Diana, Princess of Wales Commemoration.*
T **551** *and similar vert designs. Multicoloured (except Nos.*
2591, 2596, 2602 *and* MS2603b). *Litho. P* 14.
2591	1200 c. Type 551 (brown-red)		60	65
	a. Sheetlet. Nos. 2591/6		3·50	
2592	1200 c. Wearing blue suit and holding			
	flowers		60	65
2593	1200 c. Looking right		60	65
2594	1200 c. Sitting crossed-legged		60	65
2595	1200 c. With Prince William		60	65
2596	1200 c. Wearing spotted scarf (blue & blk)		60	65
2597	1200 c. Wearing pink shirt		60	65
	a. Sheetlet. Nos. 2597/602		3·50	
2598	1200 c. Wearing red dress		60	65
2599	1200 c. Carrying bouquet		60	65
2600	1200 c. Wearing sunglasses		60	65
2601	1200 c. With children		60	65
2602	1200 c. Wearing hat (light brown & black)		60	65
2591/602		*Set of 12*	7·00	7·75

MS2603 Two sheets. (a) 100×70 mm. 3000 c.
Diana, Princess of Wales. (b) 70×100 mm.
3000 c. Diana, Princess of Wales (dull vio & blk)
Set of 2 sheets 3·00 3·25
Nos. 2591/6 and 2597/602 were each printed together,
se-tenant, in sheetlets of 6.

GRENADA

449 Black-tailed Damselfish

(Litho B.D.T.)

1998 (10 Jan). *Fishes. T* **449** *and similar horiz designs.*
Multicoloured. P 14.
3512	65 c. Type 449		30	35
3513	90 c. Yellow Sweetlips		40	45
3514	$1 Common Squirrelfish		45	50
3515	$1.50, Blue Tang		70	75
	a. Sheetlet. Nos. 3515/20		4·25	
3516	$1.50, Porkfish		70	75
3517	$1.50, Banded Butterflyfish		70	75
3518	$1.50, Thread-finned Butterflyfish		70	75
3519	$1.50, Hooded Butterflyfish ("Red-headed")		70	75
3520	$1.50, Emperor Angelfish		70	75
3521	$1.50, Duboulay's Angelfish ("Scribbled Anglefish")		70	75
	a. Sheetlet. Nos. 3521/6		4·25	
3522	$1.50, Lemon-peel Angelfish		70	75
3523	$1.50, Bandit Angelfish		70	75
3524	$1.50, Bicoloured Angelfish ("Biclor Cherub")		70	75
3525	$1.50, Palette Surgeonfish ("Regal Tang")		70	75
3526	$1.50, Yellow Tang		70	75
3527	$2 Powder-blue Surgeonfish		90	95
3512/27		*Set of 16*	10·50	11·50

MS3528 Two sheets, each 110×80 mm. (a) $6
Two-banded Anemonefish. (b) $6 Forceps
Butterflyfish ("Long-nosed Butterflyfish")
Set of 2 sheets 5·50 5·75
Nos. 3515/20 and 3521/6 were each printed together,
se-tenant, in sheetlets of 6 with the backgrounds forming
composite designs.

Grenada Grenadines

Add to Nos. 2281/95:
2292a	$1.50, Leonberger		70	75
	a. Sheetlet. Nos. 2292a/f		4·25	
2292b	$1.50, Newfoundland		70	75
2292c	$1.50, Boxer		70	75
2292d	$1.50, St. Bernard		70	75
2292e	$1.50, Silky Terrier		70	75
2292f	$1.50, Miniature Schnauzer		70	75

Nos. 2292a/f were printed together, *se-tenant*, in sheetlets of 6
with the backgrounds forming a composite design.

Add to Nos. 2350/60:
2361	$20 Jackknife-fish		9·25	9·50

125 *Clitocybe metachroa* **126** Ludwig van
Beethoven

(Litho Questa)

1997 (4 Sept). *Fungi. T* **125** *and similar horiz designs.*
Multicoloured. P 14.
2469	75 c. Type 125		35	40
2470	90 c. *Clavulinopsis helvola*		40	45
2471	$1 *Lycoperdon pyriforme*		45	50
2472	$1.50, *Auricularia auricula-judae*		70	75
2473	$1.50, *Entoloma incanum*		70	75
	a. Sheetlet. Nos. 2473/8		4·25	
2474	$1.50, *Coprinus atramentarius*		70	75
2475	$1.50, *Mycena polygramma*		70	75
2476	$1.50, *Lepista nuda*		70	75
2477	$1.50, *Pleurotis cornucopiae*		70	75
2478	$1.50, *Laccaria amethystina*		70	75
2479	$2 *Clathrus archeri*		90	95
2480	$3 *Lactarius trivialis*		1·40	1·50
2469/80		*Set of 12*	8·50	9·00

MS2481 Two sheets, each 106×76 mm. (a) $6
Morchella esculenta. (b) $6 *Amanita muscaria*
Set of 2 sheets 5·50 5·75
Nos. 2473/8 were printed together, *se-tenant*, in sheetlets of 6.

(Des Christina de Musée. Litho Questa)

1997 (10 Oct). *Classical Composers. T* **126** *and similar vert*
designs. Multicoloured. P 14½.
2482	$1 Type 126		45	50
	a. Sheetlet. Nos. 2482/9 and label		3·50	
2483	$1 Piotra Tchaikovsky		45	50
2484	$1 Johann Christian Bach		45	50
2485	$1 Frédéric Chopin		45	50
2486	$1 Igor Stravinsky		45	50
2487	$1 Franz Joseph Haydn		45	50
2488	$1 Gustav Mahler		45	50
2489	$1 Gioacchino Antonio Rossini		45	50
2482/9		*Set of 8*	3·50	4·00

MS2490 Two sheets, each 106×76 mm. (a) $6
Wolfgang Amadeus Mozart. (b) $6 Franz
Schubert *Set of 2 sheets* 5·50 5·75
Nos. 2482/9 were printed together, *se-tenant*, in sheetlets of 8
stamps and one central label.

127 Diana, Princess of Wales
and Buckingham Palace

(Des Y. Lee. Litho Questa)

1997 (10 Nov). *Diana, Princess of Wales Commemoration.*
T **127** *and similar horiz designs. Multicoloured. P* 14.
2491	$1.50, Type 127		70	75
	a. Sheetlet. Nos. 2491/6		4·25	
2492	$1.50, Princess Diana and lake at Althorp		70	75
2493	$1.50, Princess Diana and Westminster Abbey		70	75
2494	$1.50, Princess Diana and gates to Althorp		70	75
2495	$1.50, Princess Diana in pink hat and gates to Kensington Palace		70	75
2496	$1.50, Princess Diana and Althorp House		70	75
2491/6		*Set of 6*	4·25	4·50

MS2497 115×80 mm. $6 Holding bouquet
(60×40 mm). P 14×14½ 2·75 3·00
Nos. 2491/6 were printed together, *se-tenant*, in sheetlets of 6
with enlarged illustrated right-hand margin.

GUYANA

539 John Lennon **540** Albrecht Kossel
(1910 Medicine)

(Litho Questa)

1995 (8 Dec). *15th Death Anniv of John Lennon (musician).*
P 14.
4534	539 $35 multicoloured		35	40

No. 4534 was printed in numbered sheets of 16 with enlarged
illustrated left-hand margin.

(Des R. Cassilla (Nos. 4580/8) or R. Martin (others). Litho
Questa)

1995 (20 Dec). *Centenary of Nobel Trust Fund. T* **540** *and*
similar vert designs. Multicoloured. P 14.
4535/43 $35 × 9 Type 540; Arthur H. Compton
(1927 Physics); N. M. Butler (1931
Peace); Charles Laveran (1907
Medicine); George R. Minot (1934
Medicine); Henry H. Dale (1936
Medicine); Jacques Monod (1965
Medicine); Alfred Hershey (1969
Medicine); Pär Lagerkvist (1951
Literature)
a. Sheetlet. Nos. 4535/43 .. 3·25

4544/52 $35 × 9 Norman F. Ramsey (1989
Physics); Chen Ning Yang (1957
Physics); Earl W. Sutherland Jr.
(1971 Medicine); Paul Karrer (1937
Chemistry); Harmut Michel (1988
Chemistry); Richard Kuhn (1938
Chemistry); P. A. M. Dirac (1933
Physics); Victor Grignard (1912
Chemistry); Richard Willstätter
(1915 Chemistry)
a. Sheetlet. Nos. 4544/52 .. 3·25
4553/61 $35 × 9 Adolf von Baeyer (1905
Chemistry); Hideki Yukawa (1949
Physics); George W. Beadle (1958
Medicine); Edwin M. McMillan (1951
Chemistry); Samuel C. C. Ting (1976
Physics); Saint-John Perse (1960
Literature); John F. Enders (1954
Medicine); Felix Bloch (1952
Physics); P. B. Medawar (1960
Medicine)
a. Sheetlet. Nos. 4553/61 .. 3·25
4562/70 $35 × 9 Nikolai Basov (1964 Physics);
Klas Arnoldson (1908 Peace); René
Sully-Prudhomme (1901 Literature);
Robert W. Wilson (1978 Physics);
Hugo Theorell (1955 Medicine);
Nelly Sachs (1966 Literature); Hans
von Euler-Chelpin (1929 Chemistry);
Mairead Corrigan (1976 Peace);
Willis E. Lamb Jr (1955 Physics)
a. Sheetlet. Nos. 4562/70 .. 3·25
4571/9 $35 × 9 Francis Crick (1962 Medicine);
Manne Siegbahn 1924 Physics);
Eisaku Sato (1974 Peace); Robert
Koch (1905 Medicine); Edgar D.
Adrian (1932 Medicine); Erwin
Neher (1991 Medicine); Henry
Taube (1983 Chemistry); Norman
Angell (1933 Peace); Robert
Robinson (1947 Chemistry)
a. Sheetlet. Nos. 4571/9 .. 3·25
4580/8 $35 × 9 Henri Becquerel (1903 Physics);
Igor Tamm (1958 Physics); Georges
Köhler (1984 Medicine); Gerhard
Domagk (1939 Medicine); Yasunari
Kawabata (1968 Literature);
Maurice Allais (1988 Economic
Sciences); Aristide Briand (1926
Peace); Pavel Cherenkov (1958
Physics); Feodor Lynen (1964
Medicine)
a. Sheetlet. Nos. 4580/8 .. 3·25
4535/88 *Set of 54* 20·00 21·00
MS4589 Six sheets, each 106×76 mm. (a) $300
Lech Walesa (1983 Peace). (b) $300 Heinrich
Böll (1972 Literature). (c) $300 Henry A.
Kissinger (1973 Peace). (d) $300 Kenichi Fukui
(1981 Chemistry). (e) $300 Yasunari Kawabata
(1968 Literature). (f) $300 Le Duc Tho (1973
Peace) *Set of 6 sheets* 18·00 19·00
Nos. 4535/43, 4544/52, 4553/61, 4562/70, 4571/9 and 4580/8
were each printed together, *se-tenant*, in sheetlets of 9, with the
backgrounds forming composite designs.

541 David Copperfield

(Des R. Sauber. Litho Questa)

1995 (29 Dec). *David Copperfield (magician). T* **541** *and*
similar vert designs. Multicoloured. P 13½×14.
4590	$60 Type 541		60	65
	a. Sheetlet. Nos. 4590/8		5·50	
4591	$60 David Copperfield in cloak and top hat		60	65
4592	$60 With flaming torch		60	65
4593	$60 David Copperfield in close up		60	65
4594	$60 Head of Statue of Liberty		60	65
4595	$60 David Copperfield climbing rope		60	65
4596	$60 With handcuffs		60	65
4597	$60 With woman dancer		60	65
4598	$60 David Copperfield wearing white shirt		60	65
4590/8		*Set of 9*	5·50	5·75

MS4599 76×106 mm. $300 David Copperfield
with rose 3·00 3·25
Nos. 4590/8 were printed together, *se-tenant*, in sheetlets of 9,
with the backgrounds forming a composite design.

The new-issue supplement to this Catalogue
appears each month in

GIBBONS
STAMP MONTHLY

—from your newsagent or by postal subscription—
sample copy and details on request.

542 Marilyn Monroe   543 Rat

(Des M. Staples. Litho Questa)

1995 (29 Dec). *70th Birth Anniv of Marilyn Monroe (entertainer). T* **542** *and similar multicoloured designs.* P 13½×14.
4600 $60 Type 542   60   65
    a. Sheetlet. Nos. 4600/8 .. ..   5·50
4601 $60 Marilyn Monroe with circular
     earrings   60   65
4602 $60 Marilyn Monroe (deep red top right
     corner)   60   65
4603 $60 Marilyn Monroe (signature at bottom
     right)   60   65
4604 $60 With hair over left eye   60   65
4605 $60 With pink satin at left   60   65
4606 $60 With arm raised   60   65
4607 $60 With pink satin at bottom right ..   60   65
4608 $60 With square earring   60   65
4600/8   *Set of 9*   5·50   5·75
MS4609   76×105 mm. $300 Marilyn Monroe in
pink satin dress (*horiz*). P 14×13½ ..   3·00   3·25
Nos. 4600/8 were printed together, *se-tenant*, in sheetlets of 9, with the background forming a composite design.

1995 (29 Dec). *Chinese New Year ("Year of the Rat"). T* **543** *and similar vert designs showing symbolic rats.* Litho. P 14½.
4610 $20 multicoloured   20   25
    a. Block of 4. Nos. 4610/13 .. ..   2·00
4611 $30 multicoloured (face value bottom left)   30   35
4612 $50 multicoloured (face value top right)   50   55
4613 $100 multicoloured (face value top left)   1·00   1·10
4610/13   *Set of 4*   2·00   2·25
MS4614   68×92 mm. $50×4 As Nos. 4610/13 ..   2·00   2·10
MS4615   106 x 76 mm. $150 multicoloured ..   1·50   1·60
Nos. 4610/13 were printed together, *se-tenant*, in blocks of 4 throughout sheets of 16.

INDIA

1356 Parachute Regiment   1357 Fossil of *Birbalsahnia*
Emblem   *divyadarshanii*

1997 (7 Sept). *Bicentenary of 2nd (Maratha) Battalion, Parachute Regiment.* P 13½×13.
1731 **1356** 2 r. multicoloured   10   10

1997 (11 Sept). *50th Anniv of Birbal Sahni Institute of Paleobotany, Lucknow. Plant Fossils. T* **1357** *and similar vert designs.* Multicoloured. P 13×13½.
1732   2 r. Type **1357**   10   10
1733   2 r. *Glossopteris*   10   10
1734   6 r. *Pentoxylon* (reconstruction) ..   25   30
1735   10 r. *Williamsonia sewardiana* (model) ..   40   45
1732/5   *Set of 4*   80   85

1358 Swami   1359 "Sir William
Brahmanand   Jones"

(Litho Calcutta Security Printers, Kanpur)

1997 (14 Sept). *Swami Brahmanand (social reformer) Commemoration.* P 13×13½.
1736 **1358** 2 r. brownish grey and greenish stone   10   10

1997 (28 Sept). *250th Birth Anniv (1996) of Sir William Jones (Sanskrit scholar).* P 13×13½.
1737 **1359** 4 r. multicoloured   15   20

1360 Lawrence School   1361 V. K. Krishna
Building and Crest   Menon

1997 (4 Oct). *150th Anniv of Lawrence School, Sanawar.* P 13½×13.
1738 **1360** 2 r. multicoloured   10   10

Litho Calcutta Security Printers, Kanpur)

1997 (6 Oct). *Birth Centenary (1996) of V. K. Krishna Menon (politician).* P 13×13½.
1739 **1361** 2 r. brown-red   10   10

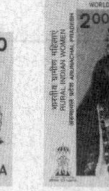

1362 Policemen and Globe   1363 Woman from
                        Arunachal Pradesh

1997 (15 Oct). *66th General Assembly Session of ICPO Interpol.* P 13½×13.
1740 **1362** 4 r. multicoloured   15   20

1997 (15 Oct). *"INDEPEX '97" International Stamp Exhibition, New Delhi (4th issue). Women's Costumes. T* **1363** *and similar vert designs.* Multicoloured. P 13×13½.
1741   2 r. Type **1363**   10   10
    a. Block of 4. Nos. 1741/4 .. ..   1·25
1742   6 r. Gujarat costume   25   30
1743   10 r. Ladakh costume   40   45
1744   11 r. Kerala costume   45   50
1741/4   *Set of 4*   1·25   1·40
Nos. 1741/4 were printed together, *se-tenant*, in blocks of 4 throughout the sheet.

1364 Children watching   1365 *Ocimum sanctum*
Performance

1997 (20 Oct). *Centenary of Scindia School. T* **1364** *and similar horiz design.* Multicoloured. P 14.
1745   5 r. Type **1364**   20   25
    a. Horiz pair. Nos. 1745/6   40
1746   5 r. School buildings   20   25
Nos. 1745/6 were printed together, *se-tenant*, in horizontal pairs throughout the sheet.

1997 (28 Oct). *Medicinal Plants. T* **1365** *and similar vert designs.* Multicoloured. P 14.
1747   2 r. Type **1365**   10   10
    a. Block of 4. Nos. 1747/50 .. ..   1·25
1748   5 r. *Curcuma longa*   20   25
1749   10 r. *Rauvolfia serpentina*   40   45
1750   11 r. *Aloe barbadensis*   45   50
1747/50   *Set of 4*   1·25   1·40
Nos. 1747/50 were printed together, *se-tenant*, in blocks of 4 throughout the sheet.

1366 Sant Kavi   1367 K. Rama Rao
Sunderdas

1997 (8 Nov). *400th Birth Anniv (1996) of Sant Kavi Sunderdas.* P 13×13½.
1751 **1366** 2 r. chestnut   10   10

1997 (9 Nov). *K. Rama Rao Commemoration.* P 13×13½.
1752 **1367** 2 r. olive bistre and bistre brown   10   10

1368 Jawaharlal Nehru   1369 Animals on
and Child   Globe

1997 (14 Nov). *Children's Day.* P 13½×13.
1753 **1368** 2 r. multicoloured   10   10

1997 (23 Nov). *World Convention on Reverence for All Life.* P 13×13½.
1754 **1369** 4 r. multicoloured   15   20

1370 Hazari Prasad   1371 Mother Teresa
Dwivedi

(Litho Calcutta Security Printers, Kanpur)

1997 (13 Dec). *90th Birth Anniv Hazari Prasad Dwivedi (scholar).* P 13×13½.
1755 **1370** 2 r. brownish grey   10   10

(Litho Calcutta Security Printers, Kanpur)

1997 (15 Dec). *"INDEPEX '97" International Stamp Exhibition, New Delhi (5th issue). Mother Teresa Commemoration.* Sheet 81×68 mm. P 13×13½.
1756 **1371** 45 r. multicoloured   90   95

1372 Vallabhbhai   1373 Post Office Heritage
Patel and Marchers   Building

(Des S. Samanta)

1997 (15 Dec). *Vallabhbhai Patel (politician) Commemoration.* P 13×13½.
1757 **1372** 2 r. purple-brown   10   10

1997 (15 Dec). *"INDEPEX '97" International Stamp Exhibition, New Delhi (6th issue). Post Office Heritage. T* **1373** *and similar horiz designs.* Multicoloured. P 13½×13.
1758   2 r. Type **1373**   10   10
    a. Block of 4. Nos. 1758/61 .. ..   1·25
1759   6 r. River mail barge   25   30
1760   10 r. Jal Cooper (philatelist) and
     cancellations   40   45
1761   11 r. *Hindoostan* (paddle-steamer) ..   45   50
1758/61   *Set of 4*   1·25   1·40
Nos. 1758/61 were printed together, *se-tenant*, in blocks of 4 throughout the sheet.

1374 50th Anniversary   1375 Dr. Pattabhi
Emblem   Sitaramayya

1997 (16 Dec). *50th Anniv of Indian Armed Forces.* P 13½×13.
1762 1374 2 r. multicoloured 10 10

1997 (17 Dec). *Dr. Pattabhi Sitaramayya Commemoration.* P 13×13½.
1763 1375 2 r. yellow-brown 10 10

1376 Jerome d'Souza and Cathedral

1377 Ram Prasad Bismil and Ashfaqullah Khan

1997 (18 Dec). *Birth Centenary of Jerome d'Souza (academic).* P 13½×13.
1764 1376 2 r. red-brown 10 10

(Des Alka Sharma)
1997 (19 Dec). *70th Death Anniv of Ram Prasad Bismail and Ashfaqullah Khan (revolutionaries).* P 13.
1765 1377 2 r. red-brown 10 10

1378 Jail Buildings

1379 Sword and Kukri

1997 (30 Dec). *Cellular Jail, Port Blair.* P 13.
1766 1378 2 r. multicoloured 10 10

1998 (2 Jan). *50th Anniv of 11th Gorkha Rifles.* P 13.
1767 1379 4 r. multicoloured 15 20

1380 Nahar Singh

1381 Nanak Singh

(Litho Calcutta Security Printers, Kanpur)
1998 (9 Jan). *Nahar Singh Commemoration.* P 13.
1768 1380 2 r. reddish purple 10 10

1998 (10 Jan). *Nanak Singh Commemoration.* P 13.
1769 1381 2 r. indian red 10 10

1382 Rotary International Emblem

1383 Maharana Pratap

1998 (12 Jan). *Rotary International Council on Legistation.* P 13½×13.
1770 1382 8 r. lemon and blue 30 35

1998 (19 Jan). *400th Death Anniv of Maharana Pratap (Rajput leader).* P 13×13½.
1771 1383 2 r. dull purple 10 10

1384 V. S. Khandekar

1385 Elephant and Dancers

1998 (19 Jan). *Birth Centenary of V. S. Khandekar (writer).* P 13×13½.
1772 1384 2 r. scarlet 10 10

1998 (25 Jan). *India Tourism Day.* P 13×13½.
1773 1385 10 r. multicoloured 40 45

1386 Jagdish Chandra Jain

1387 Gandhi as a Young Man and Peasants in Fields

1998 (28 Jan). *Jagdish Chandra Jain Commemoration.* P 13.
1774 1386 2 r. chestnut 10 10

(Des S. Samanta)
1998 (30 Jan). *50th Death Anniv of Mahatma Gandhi.* T 1387 *and similar vert designs.* P 14.
1775 2 r. Type 1387 .. .. 10 10
  a. Block of 4. Nos. 1775/8 .. 1·25
1776 6 r. Woman weaving and Gandhi distributing food .. 25 30
1777 10 r. Gandhi collecting salt .. 40 45
1778 11 r. Gandhi carrying flag .. 45 50
1775/8 *Set of* 4 1·25 1·40
Nos. 1775/8 were printed together, *se-tenant*, in blocks of 4 throughout the sheet with the backgrounds forming a composite design.

1388 A. Vedaratnam

1998 (25 Feb). *Birth Centenary (1997) of A. Vedaratnam (social reformer).* P 13×13½.
1779 1388 2 r. slate-purple 10 10

Note: The first Supplement recording new stamps not in this catalogue or the Addenda appeared in the September 1998 number of *Gibbons Stamp Monthly*.

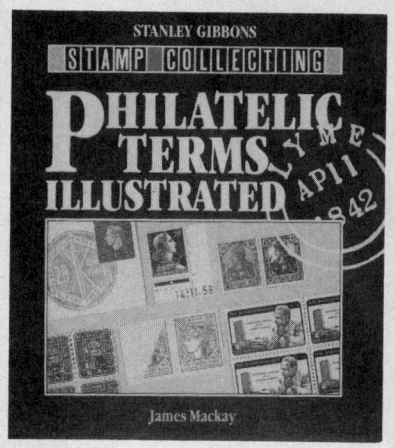

HELP!

Even the most knowledgeable collector can be faced by philatelic terms of which he does not know the meaning – if this has ever been your problem then you need:

PHILATELIC TERMS ILLUSTRATED

Now completely revised and updated in a bright new format as part of the popular Stanley Gibbons 'Stamp Collecting' series.

The new edition of this useful book not only includes all the terms which have come into use since publication of the second edition in 1978 but also provides much new information on postal markings and services.

Noted philatelic author and journalist, James Mackay, has carefully updated and augmented the original text of Russell Bennett and James Watson to produce a work of great assistance to the postal historian and an indispensable aid to stamp identification.

Fully illustrated in colour or black and white, its encyclopedic style and helpful system of cross-referencing makes Philatelic Terms Illustrated extremely easy to use and provides a helpful work of reference for all collectors from the youngest beginner to the most advanced specialist.

Available direct from:

Stanley Gibbons Publications, Parkside, Christchurch Road, Ringwood, Hampshire BH24 3SH Telephone: 01425 472363

Index

BY APPOINTMENT TO
HER MAJESTY THE QUEEN
STANLEY GIBBONS LTD
LONDON,
PHILATELISTS

First Class Stamp & Service

...from the world leaders in Philately

● Extensive stocks of specialised Great Britain and Commonwealth material
● Thousands of high quality items always available ● Detailed register of clients interests
● Specialist 'want list' service ● Regular lists and illustrated colour brochures
● Private viewing facilities and postal approval service ● Free advice from our knowledgeable team
● 0% interest free credit available on purchases over £1000

Free Membership Of Our Specialist Register

All discerning collectors are able to benefit from joining our specialist register and want list service.
We maintain an up to date record of your specific collecting requirements and furnish you with regular lists
containing only material that will interest you. We also provide a postal approval service for established clients.

New Luxury Colour Brochure

Published twice yearly our superbly illustrated brochure contains hundreds of carefully selected items
recently added to our extensive GB and Commonwealth stocks. Copies can be obtained for a yearly
subscription of just £10 and include a discount voucher for your next purchase.

Free Mail Order Stamp Listings

Choose from:
● **Great Britain** ● **Australia & New Zealand**
● **Canada** ● **Falkland Islands** ● **Channel Islands & I.O.M.**

Used by thousands of collectors worldwide our mail order service provides fast 48 hour order despatch,
a 14 day money back guarantee and free telephone advice.
Packed full of popular material each of our comprehensive listings features colour illustrations, accurate
descriptions, a useful checklist and pull out order form.

PRESTIGE
PAYMENT PLAN
0% INTEREST
FREE
CREDIT
ON PURCHASES
OVER £1000
All loans are subject to status. A written quotation is available on request.
TELEPHONE TODAY FOR AN
APPLICATION FORM

For membership of our specialist register and copies of our
specialised and mail order listings.
Please contact our Commonwealth Department today.

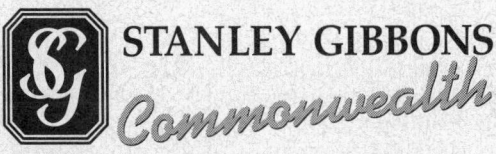

STANLEY GIBBONS
Commonwealth

Stanley Gibbons Limited
399 Strand, London WC2R 0LX England. Tel: +44 (0)171 836 8444 Fax: +44 (0)171 836 7342
e.mail: stamps@stangiblondon.demon.co.uk

Your Quick Reference Guide to Philatelic Suppliers Around the World

⬢ **Postal Administration Worldwide**

⬢ **International Stamp and Postal History Dealers**

⬢ **Auctions Houses**

⬢ **Albums and Accessory Suppliers**

⬢ **Philatelic Publishers**

⬢ **Stamp Shows and Shops**

⬢ **Clubs and Societies**

PLUS leading suppliers of Approvals, Covers, Kiloware, Literature, New Issues, Postcards, Stationery, Varieties and MUCH MORE

THE Philatelic Register 1999

STANLEY GIBBONS
CATALOGUES·

Gibbons Stamp Monthly

THE 1999 PHILATELIC REGISTER

Your quick reference guide to all types of philatelic suppliers around the world including...

- Postal Administrations Worldwide
- Auctions Houses
- Philatelic Publishers
- Clubs and Societies
- International Stamp and Postal History Dealers
- Albums and Accessory Suppliers
- Stamp Shows and Shops

Plus leading suppliers of Approvals, Covers, Kiloware, Literature, New Issues, Postcards, Stationery, Varieties and much more

FIND IT FAST IN THE PHILATELIC REGISTER

Use the quick reference classifications on the page alongside to locate your collecting interests. Turn to the pages indicated and you will find a wealth of suppliers details at your fingertips. From Fair Organisers to Philatelic Societies, Approvals to Accessories - *the Philatelic Register has it all*.

ABOUT THE PHILATELIC REGISTER

Compiled by Stanley Gibbons Publications, The Philatelic Register is distributed free in the back of the British Commonwealth 'Part 1' catalogue (Volume 1) and the August issue of Gibbons Stamp Monthly magazine.

ALL PHILATELIC SUPPLIERS SHOULD BE INCLUDED

All dealers, postal administrations, stamp shops, auctioneers and other philatelic suppliers should be included within any one of the easy to find sections in the register, under the heading of their choice. Single and additional entries can be purchased and a wide range of advertising options are available to help make your business really stand out.

To make sure your business is included phone our advertising department on +44 1425 472363.

Stanley Gibbons Publications,
5 Parkside, Christchurch Road,
Ringwood, Hants BH24 3SH England
Tel: +44 1425 472363 Fax: +44 1425 470247
e.mail: sales@stangib.demon.co.uk
http://www.stangib.com/

© **Stanley Gibbons Publications 1998**

No reproduction of this directory, in whole or in part is allowed without the express permission of Stanley Gibbons Publications. The directory must not be stored in a retrieval system of any type without the written consent of Stanley Gibbons Publications.

Classification Headings

Classic Albums For Traditional Collectors
SG Classic Albums Re-introduced By Popular Demand

New Imperial Stamp Album (1840-1936)

Successor to the Imperial album first published in 1873, this new edition provides space for the stamps of the British Empire, Egypt and Iraq, from SG1 up until the end of King George V. Provision is made for major variations of watermark, perforation and shade as well as postage dues, officials, special delivery stamps and an illustrated catalogue is included on the facing leaf. Fastbound with glassine interleaving.

King George VI Album (1936-1953)

Loose Leaf Edition

Consists of four luxurious 22-ring binders presented in two matching slipcases. Cream cartridge leaves feature glassine interleaving whilst a special mount pack and extra blank pages are also available separately.

Fastbound Edition

Leaves have been printed both sides, interleaved with glassine and securely bound into a single attractive album. Not designed to be used with hingeless mounts.

New Age Album (1953-1962)

This New Age album first appeared in the late 1930's. In response to considerable demand we have carefully reprinted the popular 460 page section covering the early Elizabethan period. Fine cartridge leaves contain spaces for all Commonwealth stamps issued between 1953 -1962 with provision for listed shades and perforation changes. Five special title pages enable you to split your collection into individual springback binders, available separately.

Available from our London showroom at 399 Strand and by mail order

Stanley Gibbons Publications
5/7 Parkside, Christchurch Road,
Ringwood, Hants BH24 3SH
Tel:+44 (0)1425 472363 Fax: +44 (0)1425 470247
e.mail: sales@stangib.demon.co.uk internet: http://www.stangib.com/

STANLEY GIBBONS

Phone 0800 611 622 Today For Your Free Colour Brochure

FREE SAMPLE

No Stamp Magazine Offers More For The GB & Commonwealth Collector

- Varied GB and Commonwealth articles written by acknowledged experts in their fields.
- GB articles on stamps, postal history, Machins and much, much more.
- Regular features include King George VI varieties, Postal Stationary, Queen Elizabeth II and much more.
- Notable GB and Commonwealth auction results and a monthly 'Tipster' column.
- Read by thousands of subscribers in over 80 countries world-wide.
- Exceptional value for money with 50% more editorial than other magazines.

But don't just take our word for it - write to the Editor requesting a sample copy and subscription details.

Gibbons Stamp Monthly
5/7 Parkside, Christchurch Road,
Ringwood, Hants BH24 3SH
Tel: +44 (0)1425 472363
Fax: +44 (0)1425 470247

e.mail: sales@stangib.demon.co.uk
internet: http://www.stangib.com/

GREAT BRITAIN

◆ Booklets Errors/Varieties

Candlish McCleery
  PO Box 1 Kempsey Worcester WR5 3YH UK
                         Tel: 01905 821152

Holt, Mike
  PO Box 177 Stourbridge West Midlands DY8 3DE
  UK ....Tel: 01384 443317
                        Fax: 01384 440877

Robertson Stamp Co.
  P O Box 3527 Durban 4000 South Africa
  ....Tel: 27 31 254 762
                      Fax: 27 31 258 906

Urch Harris & Co.
  1 Denmark Avenue Bristol BS1 5HD UK
  ....Tel: 0117 934 933
          Fax: 0117 927 3037 e.mail:
        urch@stangib.demon.co.uk

Stanley Gibbons Limited
  399 Strand London WC2R 0LX UK
  ....Tel: 0171 836 8444
                  Fax: 0171 836 7342

◆ Channel Islands

Aurigny Auctions
  PO Box 210 Coventry Warwickshire CV6 6HU UK
  ....Tel: 01203 686613
                 Fax: 01203 667428

Collectors Centre
  1 Sausmarez Street St Peter Port Guernsey
  GY1 2PT Channel Islands .... Tel: 01481 725209

Hudson, Roger
  PO Box 172 Coventry Warwickshire CV6 6NF UK
  ....Tel: 01203 686613
                 Fax: 01203 667428

Isle of Man Sales Ltd.
  19b Arlington Drive Nottingham NG3 5EN UK
  ....Tel: 0115 9856736

Robbe, R
  P O Box 585. York Chambers York Street St Helier
  Jersey JE4 8XZ Channel Islands.....Tel: 01534 23084
                  Fax: 01534 67680

Stanley Gibbons Limited
  399 Strand London WC2R 0LX UK
  ....Tel: 0171 836 8444
         Fax: 0171 836 7342 e.mail:
      stamps@stangiblondon.demon.co.uk

◆ Edward VII - George VI

McKenzie, James
  27 Tristan Crescent Willowdale Ontario M2H 1X2
  Canada...............................Tel: 416 492 7453

Mollett, Peter
  PO Box 1934 Ringwood Hampshire BH24 2YZ UK
  ....Tel: 01425 476666

Niblett, JR
  11 The Drive M Dardley Hill Welwyn Hertfordshire
  AL6 0TW UK ....Tel: 01438 714000
                 Fax: 01438 712922

Royan Ass., Doreen
  P O Box 310 Sunninghill Johannesburg 2157 South
  Africa...Tel: 011 803 3237
                 Fax: 011 803 3237

Stanley Gibbons Limited
  399 Strand London WC2R 0LX UK
  ....Tel: 0171 836 8444
                  Fax: 0171 836 7342
      e.mail: stamps@stangiblondon.demon.co.uk

◆ General

Afinsa
  C/Lagasca 18 Madrid E-28001 Spain
  ....Tel: 00341 5781405
                 Fax: 00341 5750832

Bath Stamp & Coin
  12-13 Pulteney Bridge Bath Avon BA2 4AY UK
  ....Tel: 01225 463073

SERIOUS BUYER...

Every year I travel hundreds of miles throughout the UK, Europe and Scandinavia, buying stocks, collections and accumulations. And I've been doing this since 1970.

WHAT DO I BUY?

I buy virtually anything in stamps and covers, from specialised one country collections to general lots and accumulations, from better quality single items to complete dealers' stocks. If it's philatelic, I'm interested.

WHY SELL TO ME?

For **FOUR** very good reason:

ACCURATE VALUATIONS - I have over thirty years full time experience as a major buyer in the stamp trade, and I buy from all the main UK & Continental auction houses. I make accurate efficient valuations based on the very latest market values.

FAIR VALUATIONS - I work on a high turnover with low profit margins which means I % must % buy - and I pay the top market price to make sure I do. I cannot afford to waste my time and yours by making unrealistic offers which will not stand comparison.

IMMEDIATE PAYMENT - All my offers are backed by immediate payment. We agree a price and you get paid there and then. It's that simple.

HOME VISITS - I travel extensively, which means that I can easily arrange to view bulky, valuable collections in your own home - at no extra cost to you.
And finally.... I buy most of my material from auction, usually at well below my "top price". If those people had sold directly to me they would have been paid more, paid immediately and would % not % have paid any commission or gone to any other expense.

Think about it - and then give me a ring.

Member of Philatelic Trader' Society

JOHN CURTIN LIMITED
(International Stamp Dealer)

PO Box 31, Sunbury-on-Thames
Middlesex TW16 6HS
APHV Tel: 01932 785635 Fax: 01932 770523 (24hours) ASDA

RARE AND UNUSUAL STAMPS FOR SERIOUS COLLECTORS.

Wants Lists filled from our comprehensive 30 volume stock of stamps, varieties and postal history (**references please**). We hold several British Empire public auctions annually.

Subscriptions: £25.

George W. Holschauer
Colonial Stamp Co.

5757 Wilshire Blvd., Penthouse 8, Los Angeles, CA 90036, U.S.A.

Tel: (213) 933-9435 ● Fax: (213) 939-9930

Members: IFSDA, PTS, ASDA, Int'l Soc. of Appraisers

When enquiring or placing an order please quote that you have seen me in Stanley Gibbons Philatelic Register

---

Bellew, Tony
  PO Box 4 Axminster Devon EX13 UK
  ....Tel: 01297 35280

Bloxham, Mark
  88 Dacre Street South Shields Tyne & Wear NE33
  5QB UK................................Tel: 01670 511180
  SEMI(SEE MAIN)

Bradford Stamp Centre
  390 Dudley Hill Road Undercliffe Bradford BD2
  3AA UK ....Tel: 01274 630331

British Commonwealth
  PO Box 10218 Wilmington Bristol NC 28405-0218
  USA ....Tel: 001910 2566207

Buchanan St.Stamps
  205 Buchanan Street Glasgow Scotland G1 2JZ
  ....Tel: 0141 333 9724
                 Fax: 0141 333 9714

Candlish McCleery
  PO Box 1 Kempsey Worcester WR5 3YH UK
  ....Tel: 01905 821152

Cecil Court Stamp
  6 Cecil Court London WC2N 4HE UK
  ....Tel: 0171 240 105

Chesterfield Stamp Cor
  1st Floor 2 Coronation Street Chesterfield
  Derbyshire S41 7DP UK ....Tel: 01246 211002

Coles, John (PERFINS)
  9 Woodland Freeland Oxon OX8 8HD UK
  ....Tel: 01993 881109

Curtin, John
  PO Box 31 Sunbury on Thames Middlesex TW16
  6SH UK ....Tel: 01932 785635
                 Fax: 01932 770523

Eric Paul Stamps

See our main catalogue advert under Great Britain

31 King Street
West Manchester   Tel: 0161 427 2101
M3 2PJ   Fax: 0161 427 6386

Franke Philatelics Ltd., Michael
  The Stamp Studio 200 Watford Road Croxley
  Green, Rickmansworth Hertfordshire WD3 3DD UK
  ....Tel: 01923 237710

Jones, AC
  47 Marylands Avenue Hockley Essex SS5 5AH UK
  ....Tel: 01702 206526
                 Fax: 01702 206526

M & C Stamps
  Unit 30 Antique Centre Severn Road Gloucester
  GL1 2LE UK...............................Tel: 01452 506361
                 Fax: 01452 307161

MG Stamps
  P O Box 11602 London E11 2XE UK
  ....Tel: 0181 989 1628

McKenzie, James
  27 Tristan Crescent Willowdale Ontario M2H 1X2
  Canada ....Tel: 416 492 7453

Milton, David
  PO Box 139 Ruislip Middlesex HA4 8UX UK
  ....Tel: 01895 637283

Myer, Adrian
  PO Box 137 Leatherhead Surrey KT22 0RG UK
  ....Tel: 01372 843085
                 Fax: 01372 843930

North Staffs Stamps

*Free lists available for GB + Commonwealth
Stamp Value £5.00 - £100.00*

490 Chell Heath Rd
Stoke-on-Trent
ST6 6QD.   Tel: 01782 818560

Numismery
  68 Pillar Avenue Brixham Devon TQ5 8LB UK
  ....Tel: 01803 854765
                 Fax: 01803 854765

Peter's Stamps
6 Chapel Place Lane Ramsgate Kent CT11 9SE
UK ....Tel: 01843 590972
Fax: 01843 590972

Philatelic Software Ltd

Valley View, Colemans Lane,
Nazeling, Essex   Tel: 01992 893086
EN9 2EA England   Fax: 01992 892729

Raflet Stamp Club
Swiss Cottage Huttoft Alford Lincs LN13 9RG UK
....Tel: 01507 490567

Rowan S Baker
28 Bedfordbury London WC2N 4RB UK
....Tel: 0171 3791448

Sanders, J
5 Commercial Road Southampton Hampshire
SO15 1DB UK...............................Tel: 01703 229515
Fax: 01703 231860

Spragg, David & Lori
P O Box 70 Marlow Bucks SL7 1EU UK
....Tel: 01628 476041

GREAT BRITAIN
STAMPS and POSTAL HISTORY

PRICE LIST
Available free upon request, this list includes selected fine stamps from Queen Victoria to George V, together with Postal History.

PTS

BUYING
Collections and single items of Fine Stamps and Postal History

YOUR WANTS LIST IS WELCOME –
SEND IT NOW!

Martin Townsend
*Established over 25 years –
clients may rely on our reputation and expertise.*

PO Box 10, Hitchin, Herts., SG4 9PE, U.K.
Telephone/Fax: (01462) 420678

Stamp Corner
37 Netherhall Road Doncaster Yorkshire DN1 2PG
UK ....Tel: 01302 323623

Stanley Gibbons Limited
399 Strand London WC2R 0LX UK
....Tel: 0171 836 8444
Fax: 0171 836 7342
e.mail: stamps@stangiblondon.demon.co.uk

Swan Stamps
11 Torwood Street Torquay Devon TQ1 1UD UK
....Tel: 01803 290619

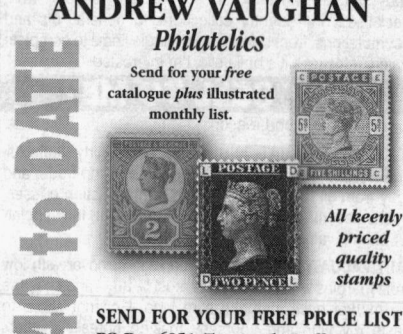

ANDREW VAUGHAN
Philatelics

Send for your *free*
catalogue *plus* illustrated
monthly list.

All keenly priced quality stamps

SEND FOR YOUR FREE PRICE LIST
PO Box 6051, Tamworth, Staffs B78 3JB
Tel: 01827 250175
Great Britain

Townsend, Martin
P O Box 10 Hitchin Hertfordshire RG4 9PE UK
....Tel: 01462 420678
Fax: 01462 42065

Tony Lester

*See our main catalogue advert
under Great Britain*

29 Momus Boulevard,
Binley Road, Stoke,   Tel: 01203 454908
Coventry CV2 5NA   Tel: 01203 650109

Vaughan, Andrew
8 Aldin Close Bonehill Tamworth Staffs. B78 3HT
UK ....Tel: 01827 250175

Warminster Stamp Centre
....Tel: 01985 216557

Wessex Philatelic Auctions

*See our main advert
under the Auction Section*

P.O. Box 3061   Phone/Fax: 01202 528495
Bournemouth   Phone: 0421 460440
BH8 9YL   E-mail: wessexauct@aol.com

Welwyn Stamps
4 Mardleywood Welwyn Hertfordshire RL6 0UX UK
....Tel: 01438 716601

◆ Postal History

Acorn Philatelics
PO Box 152 Salford Manchester M17 1BP UK
....Tel: 0161 877 8818
Fax: 0161 8778819

Berman, Alan K
1 Crabtree Lane London SW6 6LP UK
....Tel: 0171 3854496

Bodily, Gerald
72 Fitzjohn's Avenue London NW3 5LS UK
....Tel: 0171 4358425

Carlisle Stamp Centre
The Manor House Head Nook Hall Carlisle CA4
9AA UK ....Tel: 01228 560217

Forest Philatelic
PO Box 60 Carmarthen Carmarthenshire SA32
7YB Wales ....Tel: 0267 202 422

Franke Philatelics Ltd., Michael
The Stamp Studio 200 Watford Road Croxley
Green, Rickmansworth Hertfordshire WD3 3DD UK
....Tel: 01923 237710

Handstamps
7 Sandfield Terrace Guildford Surrey GU1 4LN UK
....Tel: 01483 505841
Fax: 01483 458958

Hudson, Roger
PO Box 172 Coventry Warwickshire CV6 6NF UK
....Tel: 01203 686613
Fax: 01203 667428

MacDonnell Whyte
102 Leinster Road Dublin 6 Ireland
....Tel: 00541 4977449
Fax: 003531 4977440

Do you collect G.B. Edward VII and George V?

If you do, you should contact us.
We specialise in fine mint GB stamps from 1902-1935

DAVID & LORI SPRAGG

P.O.Box 70, Marlow, Buckinghamshire SL7 1EU

Phone: 01628 476041 Fax: 01628 476027

The following lists are available free on request:
Comprehensive 28 page retail price list for all specialised shades, controls
and plating pieces of Edward VII and George V.
Monthly selected items list containing 100-200 items specially selected
to suit our regular customers interests.
(These lists are automatically sent to all our regular customers)

Our extensive and varied stock includes:
KEVII and KGV specialised shades in fine unmounted and mounted mint
Unlisted shades, Listed and unlisted varieties, blocks, booklet panes and larger multiples
Colour trials, proofs, overprints, watermark varieties and types
Control singles, strips and blocks, date cut, positional and other plating pieces

We welcome wants lists and are happy to provide items on approval to known clients
We are always interested in buying material - please contact us if you have anything for sale

SIMON ANDREWS

6 CECIL COURT
LONDON WC2N 4HE

TEL: +44 171 240 1051   FAX: +44 171 379 1477

E-mail: 106417.2574@compuserve.com

MOBILE: +44 0411009081

MOBILE FAX: +44 0411029562

SPECIALISTS IN GREAT BRITAIN & FAR EAST
STAMPS AND POSTAL HISTORY

McKenzie, James
27 Tristan Crescent Willowdale Ontario M2H 1X2
Canada ....Tel: 416 492 7453

Mollett, Peter
PO Box 1934 Ringwood Hampshire BH24 2YZ UK
....Tel: 01425 476666

Schmitt
P O Box 67 Woodbury NY 11797 USA
....Tel: 1516 367 4030
Fax: 1516 425 0460

Siegel, A
P O Box 6603 Long Island City New York NY
11106 USA ....Tel: 001 718 3924855

Song Philatelic, James
317 Outram Road 2-22 Concorde Hotel Shopping
Centre Singapore ....Tel: 00657 333992
Fax: 00657 334177

Vale Stamps
21 Tranquil Vale Blackheath London SE3 0BU UK
....Tel: 0181 852 9817

Wishart, Alan
19 Strath Nairn Lane Lanarkshire ML8 5LL
Scotland ....Tel: 01698 356337

◆ Postal Stationery

Whitworth, AA
1 Prizet House Helsington Kendall Cumbria LA8
8AB UK...Tel: 015395 60848

◆ Queen Elizabeth II

Stevens, Denis
12 Compton Court Sutton Surrey SM1 4MP UK
....Tel: 0181 661 0367

Stanley Gibbons Limited
399 Strand London WC2R 0LX UK
....Tel: 0171 836 8444
Fax: 0171 836 7342
e.mail: stamps@stangiblondon.demon.co.uk

Queen Victoria

Castle Stamps
2A Warwick Lane Worthing West Sussex BN11
3DP UK ....Tel: 01903 230064

McKenzie, James
27 Tristan Crescent Willowdale Ontario M2H 1X2
Canada...Tel: 416 492 7453

Mollett, Peter
PO Box 1934 Ringwood Hampshire BH24 2YZ UK
....Tel: 01425 476666

Royan Ass., Doreen
P O Box 310 Sunninghill Johannesburg 2157
South Africa ....Tel: 011 803 3237
Fax: 011 803 3237

Stanley Gibbons Limited
399 Strand London WC2R 0LX UK
....Tel: 0171 836 8444
Fax: 0171 836 7342

MAIL ORDER STAMP LISTINGS

● Australia ● Channel Islands & IOM ● Falklands ● Fungi
● Great Britain ● New Zealand ● Birds ● Sport ● British Europe

- Used by thousands of collectors worldwide.
- Packed full of popular material from one of the largest stocks.
- Contain illustrations (many in colour), accurate descriptions, SG catalogue numbers, a checklist and a pull out mail order form.
- Fast 48 hour order despatch and free telephone advice

SEND FOR YOUR FREE COPIES TODAY

STANLEY GIBBONS
Mail Order

Stanley Gibbons Mail Order
399 Strand, London WC2R 0LX England.
Tel: +44 (0) 171 836 8444 Fax: +44 (0) 171 836 7342
e.mail: mailorder@stangiblondon.demon.co.uk

BRITISH COMMONWEALTH

◆ Africa

British Commonwealth Stamp Co.
PO Box 10212 Wilmington Bristol NC 28405-0218
USA ....Tel: 001910 2566207

Camel Stamps
PO Box 6081 Basingstoke Hampshire RG25 2YP
UK ....Tel: 01256 465499
Fax: 01256 333587

Drummond Sharpe
22 Sandelswood End Beaconsfield
Buckinghamshire HP9 2AE UK ....Tel: 01494 674765

Loffstadt, David
Craigwell Barnet Wood Road Bromley BR2 8HJ UK
....Tel: 0181 462 7185

Phil-Index
80 Willingdon Road Eastbourne Sussex BN21
1TW UK ....Tel: 01323 721444

Allan Raw Philatelics
CATALOGUE EVERY THREE MONTHS.
APPLY NOW COST £10 P.A.
P.O. Box 194, Sarnia, Natal 3615, R.S. Africa . Tel: 00 2731 7084523
Internet: http://wwp.topgear.co.za/allenraw e-mail: arphil@iafrica.com
---

Robertson Stamp Co.
P O Box 3527 Durban 4000 South Africa
....Tel: 27 31 254 762
Fax: 27 31 258 906

Seaman, Robert
Copt Hall Stock Essex CM4 9BA UK
....Tel: 01277 840777
Fax: 01277 840777

Stanley Gibbons Limited
399 Strand London WC2R 0LX UK
....Tel: 0171 836 8444
Fax: 0171 836 7342
e.mail: shop@stangiblondon.demon.co.uk

◆ Australia

Amblyn Enterprises
PO Box 415 Unanderra NSW 2526 Australia
....Tel: 006142 713346

At Philatelic
Mantra House South Keighley W Yorkshire BD21
1SX UK....................................Tel: 01535 603372

Bob Tyne Used Stamps
PO Box 677 Nerang Queensland 4211 Australia
....Tel: 00617 5574 8107

British Commonwealth Stamp Co.
PO Box 10218 Wilmington Bristol NC 28405-0218
USA ....Tel: 001910 2566207

Chalice Stamps
22 Palmers Road Palmers Green Glastonbury
Somerset BA6 9PB UK ....Tel: 01458 835331

Farnfield, Graham
15 Sky Peals Road Woodford Green Essex IG8
9NF UK.....................................Tel: 0181 527 2735

Hyams Stamps
PO Box 12 Downham Market Norfolk PE38 9TQ UK
....Tel: 01366 384591

Irwin Philatelics
159 Ballards Way Croydon Surrey CR0 5RJ UK
....Tel: 0181 657 4851

Loffstadt, David
Craigwell Barnet Wood Road Bromley BR2 8HJ UK
....Tel: 0181 462 7185

Max Stern & Co.

See our main catalogue advert
under Australia

Port Phillip Arcade
234 Finders Street, Melbourne **Tel: 613 96546751**
Victoria 3000, Australia   **Fax: 613 96507192**

Pittwater Phil, Serv
PO Box 478 Avalon Beach NSW 2107 Australia
....Tel: 00612 9974 5707
Fax: 00612 99741177

PITTWATER PHILATELIC SERVICE
Write, 'phone or fax your choice of one of our
FREE PRICE LISTS
1. Australia & Territories
2. Australian States
3. New Zealand
4. South Pacific Islands

Member APS, ASDA, SCDAA

PO Box 478, Avalon Beach, NSW. 2107.AUSTRALIA
Ph: +61-2-9974-5707
Fax: +61-2-9974-1177

Stanley Gibbons Limited
399 Strand London WC2R 0LX UK
....Tel: 0171 836 8444
Fax: 0171 836 7342

SYDNEY PHILATELICS PTY LTD

Grahame & Elizabeth Fudge,BUYING & SELLING
Specialising in Australia Mint and Used, Pacific Is,
Booklets, Stationery, Br.C'Wealth, Asia, Accessories.

P.O. Box 382   **Tel: +61-2-9319-1533**
Strawberry Hills   **Fax: +61-2-9319-1531**
N.S.W. 2012   **Email: sydphil@msn.com**

◆ Bermuda

Empire Philatelics

See our main catalogue advert
under Great Britain

PO Box 9031, Ogden
Utah 84409   **Tel: 801 479 3764**
USA   **Fax: 801 479 3764**

Victoria Stamp Co.

See our main catalogue advert under
Bermuda

P.O. Box 745
Ridgewood, NJ 07451,   **Tel: 201-652-7283**
USA   **Fax: 201-612-0024**

◆ Canada

British Commonwealth Stamp Co.
PO Box 10218 Wilmington Bristol NC 28405-0218
USA ....Tel: 001910 2566207

Charles Firby

See our main catalogue advert
under British Commonwealth

1 Finnybank Road
Sale, Cheshire
M33 6LR   **Tel: 0161 283 2583**

Eastern Auctions Ltd

See our main catalogue advert
under Canada

P.O. Box 250, Bathurst
New Brunswick   **Tel: 506 548 8986**
E2A 3Z2, Canada   **Fax: 506 546 6627**

Loffstadt, David
Craigwell Barnet Wood Road Bromely BR2 8HJ UK
....Tel: 0181 462 7185

Millman, Robert
105-6655 Lynas Lane Richmond British Colombia
V7C 3K8 Canada ....Tel: 604 594 4155

Stanley Gibbons Limited
399 Strand London WC2R 0LX UK
....Tel: 0171 836 8444
Fax: 0171 836 7342 e.mail:
shop@stangiblondon.demon.co.uk

◆ Cyprus/Gibraltar/Malta

Fryent Stamps
MALTA, WHOLESALERS, STAMPS,
KILOWARE, BUNDLES.
17 St. Anne's Junction, Mosta, MALTA
....Fax: (356) 431 907
email: jgauci@orbit.net.mt

Garfield, AL
39 Malford Grove London E18 2DY UK
....Tel: 0181 989 6417

Loffstadt, David
Craigwell Barnet Wood Road, Bromley BR2 8HJ
UK..Tel: 0181 462 7185

Property Stamps

See our main catalogue advert
under British Commonwealth

39 Mehmet Akif Avenue
Lefkosa, Mersin 10
Turkey   **Tel: 0090 392 2288321**

Sliema Stamp Shop
93 Dymech Street Sliema Malta
....Tel: 00356 342189
Fax: 00356 346069

Stanley Gibbons Limited
399 Strand London WC2R 0LX UK
....Tel: 0171 836 8444
Fax: 0171 836 7342
e.mail: shop@stangiblondon.demon.co.uk

◆ Edward VII – George VI

Bayley, Mr K
PO Box 61 Bridgetown Barbados
....Tel: 246 429 2686
Fax: 246 435 2013

British Commonwealth
PO Box 10218 Wilmington Bristol NC 28405-0218
USA ....Tel: 001910 2566207

Burman, Richard
PO Box 5753 Southend on Sea Essex SS1 2GF UK
....Tel: 01702 616898
Fax: 01702 616898
e.mail: rburman@globalnet.co.uk

Crown Colony Stamps
PO Box 1198 Bellaire Texas 77401 USA
....Tel :001713 781 6563

Loffstadt, David
Craigwell Barnet Wood, Bromley BR2 8HJ UK
....Tel: 0181 462 7185

Penrith Coin & Stamp Centre

Commonwealth Pre 1953 & World Pre 1915 is what we
Sell/Buy. Specialists in Indian States of George VI. Buying
Commonwealth Collections of George VI and earlier.

37 King Street
Penrith, Cumbria,
CA11 7AY.   **Fax or Tel: 01768 864185**

◆ Errors/Varieties

Goldcast
43 London Street Southport Merseyside PR 9 0TH
UK ....Tel: 01704 543985

Urch Harris & Co.
1 Denmark Avenue Bristol BS1 5HD UK
....Tel: 0117 934 933
Fax: 0117 927 3037
e.mail: urch@stangib.demon.co.uk

GOLDCAST PHILATELICS

Fine British Commonwealth Pre 1960
1935 Silver Jubilees
Superb King George VI varieties
Plate blocks proofs etc.
Occasional lists issued
We are also serious buyers of all the above

43 London Street
Southport, Merseyside
PR9 0TH

TEL: 01704 543985

◆ **Falklands/Antarctica**

Aron R. Halberstam Philatelists

*See our main advert
in Volume 1*

P.O. Box 150168
Van Brunt Station, Brooklyn　　Tel: 001 718 788 3978
New York 11215-0168, USA　　Fax: 001 718 965 3099

Bil & Co
The Old Rectory Caythorpe Nottingham NG32
3DU UK ....Tel: 01400 273460

Farnfield, Graham
15 Sky Peals Road Woodford Green Essex
IG8 9NF UK ....Tel: 0181 527 2735

Loffstadt, David
Craigwell Barnet Wood Road Bromley BR2 8HJ UK
....Tel: 0181 462 7185

Murchie. Robin
69 Baring Road Bournemouth Hampshire
BH6 4DT UK..................................Tel: 01202 423758

Owen, DR (Rapid Exchange Club)
Delamere 12 Wolverley Avenue Wollaston,
Stourbridge West Midlands DY8 3PJ UK

Stanley Gibbons Limited
399 Strand London WC2R 0LX UK
....Tel: 0171 836 8444
Fax: 0171 836 7342
e.mail: shop@stangiblondon.demon.co.uk

Victoria Stamps
P O Box 745 Ridgewood New Jersey 07 451 USA

Victoria Stamp Co.

*See our main catalogue advert under
Bermuda*

P.O. Box 745
Ridgewood, NJ 07451,　　Tel: 201-652-7283
USA　　　　　　　　　　Fax: 201-612-0024

◆ **General**

Afinsa
C/Lagasca 18 Madrid E-28001 Spain
....Tel: 00341 5781405
Fax: 00341 5750832

Archer, D L
2 Litchfield Way Broxbourne Hertfordshire EN10
6PT UK ....Tel: 01992 462548

Aron R. Halberstam Philatelists

*See our main advert
in Volume 1*

P.O. Box 150168
Van Brunt Station, Brooklyn　　Tel: 001 718 788 3978
New York 11215-0168, USA　　Fax: 001 718 965 3099

B & S Stamps
Byron House 21-23 Rectory Road West Bridgford
Nottingham NG2 6BE UK ....Tel: 0115 981 6214
Fax: 0115 945 5499

Beb Ltd
Casa Ivy Trig San Guzepp Malta
....Tel: 356 373 993

Bil & Co
The Old Rectory Caythorpe Nottingham NG32 3DU
UK ....Tel: 01400 273460

Bradford Stamp Centre
390 Dudley Hill Road Undercliffe Bradford BD2 UK
....Tel: 01274 630331

Bridger & Kay
PO Box 1600 Wrington Bristol BS40 5BD UK
....Tel: 01934 863656

British Commonwealth
PO Box 10218 Wilmington Bristol NC 28405-0218
USA ....Tel: 001910 2566207

Carshalton Postal Bid
Aysgarth Radclife Gardens Carshalton Surrey SM5
4PQ UK ....Tel: 0181 408 3228

Chrysalis Stamps (UDPA, ADPS)

*Dealers in Fine British Commonwealth, Good general stock of Mint Q.V to KGVI maintained.
Monthly list of better stock items available on request. Wants lists for general material welcome. Fast friendly service. No quibble refund guarantee. Mastercard and Visa accepted.*

Ballymary, Milltown,　　Tel/Fax:
Tuam, County Galway,　　+353 (0) 93 51625
Ireland　　　　　　　　e-mail: dmmcoy@iol.ie

Collectors Forum
237 South Street Romford Essex RM1 2BE UK
....Tel: 01708 723357

Colonnial Stamp Co
Museum Square 5757 Wilshire Blvd Penthouse 8 LA
USA ....Tel: 213 93 9435
Fax: 213 939 9930

Crocker, David
PO Box 294 Montzagn 6720 South Africa
....Tel: 00 27234 41424

Crown Colony Stamps
PO Box 1198 Bellaire Texas 77401 USA
....Tel: 001713 781 6563

Dean, WHB
The Poplars New Brighton Mold Cwlyd CH7 6QQ
....Tel: 01352 754782

David Feldman S.A.

Philatelists - Auctioneers
*International All World Auctions
Specialised Private Treaty.*

C.P. 81　　　　　　　Tel: (+41 22) 727.07.77
175 rte de Chancy　　Fax: (+41 22) 727.07.78
Switzerland　　　　　e-mail: admin@davidfeldman.com
http://www.davidfeldman.com

THE BRITISH COMMONWEALTH
O·F N·A·T·I·O·N·S

We are active buyers and sellers of all areas of pre-1960 Commonwealth, including individual items, collections or estates.

Crown Colony Stamps
L.W. MARTIN, Jr.
P.O. Box 1198
BELLAIRE, TEXAS 77401, U.S.A.
Tel. (from UK): 001-713-781-6563
Fax: 001-713-789-9998

VISIT US ...
AT STAMPEX LONDON
AND
MOST MAJOR SHOWS IN THE U.S.

British Commonwealth Stamp Co.

B C

LARGEST STOCK OF QUALITY MINT/USED STAMPS

- Orders Filled bu your Own Professional Specialist
- Our Extensive Stock to 1952 Including Advanced Material
- Satisfaction Guaranteed   • Next Day Service

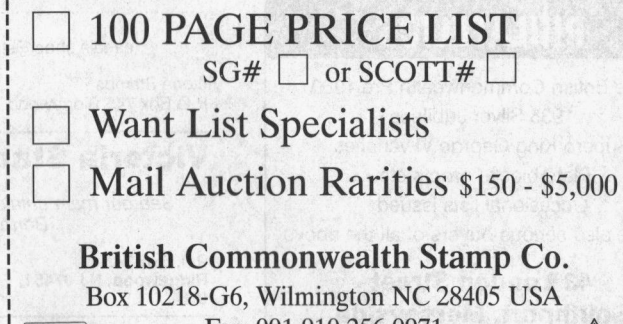

☐ 100 PAGE PRICE LIST
SG# ☐ or SCOTT# ☐

☐ Want List Specialists

☐ Mail Auction Rarities $150 - $5,000

British Commonwealth Stamp Co.
Box 10218-G6, Wilmington NC 28405 USA
Fax: 001 910 256 0971
E-mail: bcstamp@stamp-mail.com
http://www.stamp-mail.com

Faber, Ian
PO Box 217 Erindale Centre ALT 2903 Australia
....Tel: 00616 291 5573

A H Francis
BRITISH COMMONWEALTH 1840-1952 DETAILED LISTS AVAILABLE. PLEASE STATE INTERESTS
Second Floor, 19 Temple Street, Birmingham
B2 5BG United Kingdom ....Tel: 01902 745521

Franke Philatelics Ltd., Michael
The Stamp Studio 200 Watford Road Croxley Green, Rickmansworth Hertfordshire WD3 3DD UK
....Tel: 01923 237710

Gardiner, Lawrence
6 The Birches Benfleet Essex SS7 4NT UK
....Tel: 01268 750365

Gulliver Stamps
85 Hampstead Hall Avenue Handsworth Wood Birmingham B20 1HB UK............Tel: 0121 357 6253

Hale, Michael
44 North Raod Midsomer Norton Nr Bath Avon BA3 2QQ UK ....Tel: 01761 414304

Harmsworth, BJ
7 Maes Yr Orsaf Aberllefenni Street Machynlleth Powys SY20 9RR UK....................Tel: 01654 761706

Irons, Geoff
37 Tiverton Road Potter's Bar Hertfordshire EN6 5HX UK ....Tel: 01707 850707

Jones, AC
47 Marylands Avenue Hockley Essex SS5 5AH UK
....Tel: 01702 206526
                                        Fax: 01702 206526

Jones, Derek L
14 Bentley Road Castle Bromwich Birmingham B36 0ES UK ....Tel: 0121 748 6478

Loffstadt, David
Craigwell Barnet Wood Road Bromley BR2 8HJ UK
....Tel: 0181 462 7185

M & C Stamps
Unit 30, Antique Centre Severn Road Gloucester GL1 2LE UK ....Tel: 01452 506361
                                        Fax: 01452 307161

M & N Haworth
See our main advert in Volume 2
P.O. Box 20
Clitheroe,
Lancs BB7 2JQ   **Tel: 01200 423576**

Map Collectables
69 Fulbeck Road Netherfields Middlesborough TS3 0RE UK..............................Tel: 440 1642 318888

Robert Millman
FREE PRICE LISTS FEATURING CANADA, USA, GREAT BRITAIN, AUSTRALIA. WANT LISTS ACCEPTED
105-6655 Lynas Lane, Richmond, B.C. CANADA V7C 3K8
....Tel: (604) 241-1948
                                        Fax: (604) 594-4155
hotmail:rmillman@hotmail.com

Milton, David
PO Box 139 Ruislip Middlesex HA4 8UX UK
....Tel: 01895 637283

Myer, Adrian
PO Box 137 Leatherhead Surrey KT22 0RG UK
....Tel: 01372 843085
                                        Fax: 01372 843930

North Staff Stamp
490 Cheall Heath Road Chell Heath Stoke on Trent ST6 6QD UK ....Tel: 01782 818560

Philacollect
Suite 8533 16/18 Circus Road London NW8 6PG UK ....Tel: 0171 722 8112

Parkstone Philatelics
See our main advert in Prelims
P.O.Box 72,   Phone/Fax: 01642 470714
Redcar, Cleveland   E-mail: 106556.3576
TS11 8YY   @compuserve.com

Prior PE
Mandalay Bishopstrow Road Bishopstrow Wiltshire BA12 9HQ UK ....Tel: 01985 847479

Purcell Ltd., Brian
1 Ashton Way Keynsham Bristol BS31 2UF UK
....Tel: 0117 9868889

Allan Raw Philatelics
CATALOGUE EVERY THREE MONTHS.
APPLY NOW COST £10 p.a.
P.O. Box 194, Sarnia, Natal 3615, R.S. Africa.
Tel: 00 2731 7084523
Internet: http//wwp.topgear.co.za/allenraw
E-mail: arphil@iafrica.com

Raw, Allan
Box 194 Sarnia 3615 Natal R.S. Africa
....Tel: 002731 784523

Ross Shiells
4 Eldon Street London EC2M 7LS UK
....Tel: 0171 247 8011
                                        Fax: 0171 247 1563

Royan Ass., Doreen
P O Box 310 Sunninghill Johannesburg 2157 South Africa ....Tel: 011 803 3237
                                        Fax: 011 803 3237

Sandafayre/ICI
See our main catalogue advert under British Commonwealth
Marlborough Close
Parkgate, Knutsford   Tel: 01565 651637
Cheshire WA6 6DW   Fax: 01565 651637

Sandton Stamps & Coins
P O Box 78130 Sandton WA6 6DW South Africa
....Tel: 0027 117 88309
                                        Fax: 0027 11835177

RARE AND UNUSUAL STAMPS FOR SERIOUS COLLECTORS.
Wants Lists filled from our comprehensive 30 volume stock of stamps, varieties and postal history (**references please**).
We hold several British Empire public auctions annually.
Subscriptions: £25.

George W. Holschauer
Colonial Stamp Co.
5757 Wilshire Blvd., Penthouse 8, Los Angeles, CA 90036, U.S.A.
Tel: (213) 933-9435 ● Fax: (213) 939-9930
Members: IFSDA, PTS, ASDA, Int'l Soc. of Appraisers

When enquiring or placing an order please quote that you have seen me in Stanley Gibbons Philatelic Register

Scannell, Desmond
32 Nutley Park Dublin 4 Ireland
....Tel: 00353 12692865

Stamp World
124 Mint Road Cama House Opp Fort Market Bombay 400 001 India ....Tel: 9122 2614492
                                        Fax: 9122 2679429
e.mail: Asiatic@bom3.vsnl.net.in

British Commonwealth & Ireland
Send for free lists stating areas of interest.

DESMOND SCANNELL
32 Nutley Park
Dublin 4
Ireland
Tel: 353 1269 2865

THE PHILACOLLECT LIST
Philacollect Lists

If you are seeking a fast, friendly and efficient service then our postal only service is the best way of reviewing our stock.

Our MAIN LIST of 76 pages has wide ranges of Br. Commonwealth with strong sections of Australia, Br. West Indies, Canada, Great Britain, Hong Kong, New Zealand, South and S.W. Africa etc. Large range of World including stronger sections of Austria, Belgium, France, Germany generally, Hungary, Italy, Liechtenstein, Monaco, Netherlands, Rumania, Russia, Scandinavia, Spain, Switzerland, USA, Vatican plus many others. Prices are in the £5 to £500 or so range, and most are pre-1965.

Our COLLECTIONS AND LOTS LIST with over 400 items world wide priced from £15 to £500 is just for you - the collector
STRICTLY POSTAL - NO CALLERS, PLEASE.

PHILACOLLECT
Suite 8533, 16/18 Circus Road, London NW8 6PG
Tel/Fax: 0171 722 8112   e-mail: philacollect@dial.pipex.com.

Stamp Corner
37 Netherhall Road Doncaster Yorkshire DN1 2PG UK
....Tel: 01302 323623

Stewart, DK
Cairnbaan Lochgilphead Argyll PA31 8SX UK
....Tel: 01546 602099

Storie, IT
10F Millhill Lane Mussleburgh East Lothian EH21 7RD UK   Tel: 01875 841747

Westerham Stamps
18 Rysted Lane Westerham Kent TN16 1EP UK
....Tel: 01959 562 297
                                                 Fax: 01959 565 855

Winstone Stamp Co.
Bartlett Antique Centre Bath Somerset BA1 2QZ UK
....Tel: 01225 445520
                                                 Fax: 01225 444146

Wessex Philatelic Auctions
See our main advert
under the Auction Section

P.O. Box 3061   Phone/Fax: 01202 528495
Bournemouth   Phone: 0421 460440
BH8 9YL   E-mail: wessexauct@aol.com

Wrigley, PJ
7 Kendal Avenue Tynemouth Tyne & Wear NE30 3AQ UK......................................Tel: 0191 252 7440

◆ India/Pakistan

British Commonwealth
PO Box 10218 Wilmington Bristol NC 28405-0218 USA ....Tel: 001910 2566207

Choudhary, M I
20 First Floor Singhar Centre 16 Macalagan Road Lahore Pakistan ....Tel: 92 042 7237126

Dhawan & Sons
Church Road Ajit Nagar Patiala 147001 India

Dhawan, Sohan Lal
7-L Green View Rajbaha Road Patiala 147001 India
....Tel: 0091 175 219509
                                                 Fax: 0091 175 221462

A H Francis
BRITISH COMMONWEALTH 1840-1952 DETAILED LISTS AVAILABLE. PLEASE STATE INTERESTS
Second Floor, 19 Temple Street, Birmingham B2 5BG United Kingdom ....Tel: 01902 745521

Loffstadt, David
Craigwell Barnet Wood Road Bromley BR2 8HJ UK
....Tel: 0181 462 7185

AFGHANISTAN & PAKISTAN

OLD/NEW THEMATIC SETS/F.D.C's, POSTAL STATIONERY, BANK NOTES, PHONE CARDS, REVENUE, & CATALOGUE PUBLISHERS.

POPULAR ENTERPRISES
G.P.O. Box 517, Lahore, Pakistan
Tel/Fax: +92 42 7463529
E-mail: stamps@brainnet.pk

Popular Enterpise
GPO Box 517 Lahore Pakistan
....Tel: 0092 42 7463529

Popular Stamp Dealer
51a New Shalamar Road Lahore Pakistan

Stanley Gibbons Limited
399 Strand London WC2R 0LX UK
....Tel: 0171 836 8444
                                       Fax: 0171 836 7342
e.mail: shop@stangiblondon.demon.co.uk

M.Tariq   BUY - SELL - EXCHANGE
Worldwide, mint, thematic sets, packets, compositions, Pakistan new issue at face + error & varieties, ask for our lists & send your offers.
H-Railway Road, Khanpur-64100, Pakistan Fax: +92-707-72646

◆ Ireland

Raven Stamp Auctions Ltd
See our main catalogue advert
under Ireland

12c Washington Street	**Tel: 353 212 71750**
Cork	**Fax: 353 212 71779**
Ireland	

Garfield, AL
39 Malford Grove London E18 2DY UK
....Tel: 0181 989 6417

M. P. Giffney Stamps & Phonecards
P.O. Box 1096 Dublin 1 IRELAND
....Tel: 00 353 87 252 7517

Loffstadt, David
Craigwell Barnet Wood Road Bromley BR2 8HJ UK
....Tel: 0181 462 7185

MacDonnell Whyte
102 Leinster Road Dublin 6 Ireland
....Tel: 00541 4977449
                                       Fax: 003531 4977440

Rathgar Stamps
165 Rathgar Road Dublin 6 Ireland
....Tel: 00353 1497 2520

Stanley Gibbons Limited
399 Strand London WC2R 0LX UK
....Tel: 0171 836 8444
                                       Fax: 0171 836 7342
e.mail: shop@stangiblondon.demon.co.uk

Whyte's
30 Marlborough Street Dublin 1 IRELAND
....Tel: 3531 874 6161
                                       Fax: 3531 874 6020

◆ Malaya/Hong Kong

British Commonwealth
PO Box 10218 Wilmington Bristol NC 28405-0218 USA ....Tel: 001910 2566207

Peter Singer
See our main advert under
Malaysia Straits (vol 2)

P.O. Box 25249
Portland, Oregon
97298, USA   Tel: 001503 2931038

Harmsworth, BJ
7 Maes Yr Orsaf Aberllefenni Street Machynlleth Powys SY20 9RR UK ....Tel: 01654 761706

Loffstadt, David
Craigwell Barnet Wood Road Bromely BR2 8HJ UK
....Tel: 0181 462 7185

Rowland Hill Stamps
193 Comberton Hill Kidderminster Worcs DY10 1QG UK ....Tel: 01562 851101
                                       Fax: 01562 851824

Stanley Gibbons Limited
399 Strand London WC2R 0LX UK
....Tel: 0171 836 8444
                                       Fax: 0171 836 7342
e.mail: shop@stangiblondon.demon.co.uk

Topical World Stamp Co
Buying and selling Thematics, New Issues, P.R. China, Hong Kong, Macau.

7th Floor,	Tele: +86-551-2883820
279 Chaohu Road,	Fax: +86-551-2883814
Hefei City, 230001,	e-mail: twscl@public.hf.ah.cn
P. R. China	http://www.topicalworld.com

Wang, Chaomo
1 Finnybank Road Sale Cheshire M33 6LR UK
....Tel: 0161 283 2583

TOP PRICES PAID
For Good Commonwealth Collections

We also sell all reigns at competitive prices

For a prompt, courteous, fair deal.

In particular we need to purchase
Malaya, Hong Kong

Rowland Hill Stamps
Hill House, Cookley, Kidderminster, Worcestershire DY10 3UW
Telephone: (01562) 851101 • Fax: (01562) 851824

◆ New Zealand

Aron R. Halberstam Philatelists

See our main advert
in Volume 1

P.O. Box 150168
Van Brunt Station, Brooklyn   Tel: 001 718 788 3978
New York 11215-0168, USA   Fax: 001 718 965 3099

Auckland City Stamps Ltd. (New Zealand),
PUBLISHES (ANNUAL) CATALOGUE OF
NEW ZEALAND STAMPS - £5.00.
PO Box 3496, Auckland, NEW ZEALAND.
......................Tel: 649 3735489   Fax: 649 3735014

Australian Phil
10A Atherton Road Oakley Victoria Australia
....Tel: 0061 39569 6441
....Fax: 0061 39568 5169

Chalon Stamps
129 Gloucester Street Gloucester Arcade
Christchurch New Zealand..........Tel: 0064 365 7780

Dunedin Stamp Centre
P O Box 776 32 Hanover Street Dunedin
New Zealand...............................Tel: 00643 4776128
....Fax: 00643 479 2718

Farnfield, Graham
15 Sky Peals Road Woodford Green Essex
IG8 9NF UK.................................Tel: 0181 527 2735

Gary Tavendale
PO Box 74 Belfast Christchurch New Zealand
....Tel: 0064 3323 7132
....Fax: 0064 3323 7142

Irwin Philatelics
159 Ballards Way Croydon Surrey CR0 5RJ UK
....Tel: 0181 657 4851

Jury Ltd

See our main catalogue advert
under British Commonwealth

PO Box 4400
Auckland
New Zealand   Tel: 0064 9377 6806

Kadine Stamps
PO Box 3382 New Plymouth New Zealand
....Tel: 0064 675 52188

Loffstadt, David
Craigwell Barnet Wood Road Bromley BR2 8HJ UK
....Tel: 0181 462 7185

Pittwater Phil, Serv
PO Box 478 Avalon Beach NSW 2107 Australia
....Tel: 00612 9974 5707
....Fax: 00612 99741177

Skilling, Jim
P O Box 626 New Plymouth New Zealand
....Tel: 00646 758 6453

Stanley Gibbons Limited
399 Strand London WC2R 0LX UK
....Tel: 0171 836 8444
....Fax: 0171 836 7342
e.mail: shop@stangiblondon.demon.co.uk

Stanley Gibbons NZ
P O Box 80 Wellington New Zealand
....Tel: 06 364 8270
....Fax: 06 364 8252

◆ Pacific Islands

Chalon Stamps
129 Gloucester Street Gloucester Arcade
Christchurch New Zealand..........Tel: 0064 365 7780

Gammon, Roger
162 King Street Ramsgate Kent CT11 8PJ UK
....Tel: 01304 616715

International Stamp Service
GPO Box 302 Suva Fiji Islands
....Tel: 001 679 320597
....Fax: 001 679 320517

Jury Ltd. Len
PO Box 4400 Auckland New Zealand
....Tel: 0064 9377 6806

PITCAIRNS
Wants lists welcomed. U/M.
used, early covers, F.D.C's, maxi
cards, booklets, errors.
New Issues Service Available.
Collections, FDC's, Covers etc,
Purchased
For all your requirements of
Pitcairns write to the World
specialist H. Alderman.
12 Park Avenue, Shelley,
Nr. Huddersfield
HD8 8JG
Telephone: 01484 603179

Loffstadt, David
Craigwell Barnet Wood Road Bromley BR2 8HJ UK
....Tel: 0181 462 7185

Murray Payne

See our main advert under
Mauritius (vol 2)

P.O. Box 1135
Axbridge, Somerset
England BS26 2EW   Tel: 01934 732511

OVPT Philatelics

See our main catalogue advert
under Penrhyn Isles

P.O. Box 36217,
Los Angeles
CA 90036 U.S.A   Tel: 818 893 4603

Pittwater Phil, Serv
PO Box 478 Avalon Beach NSW 2107 Australia
....Tel: 00612 9974 5707
....Fax: 00612 99741177

Stanley Gibbons Limited
399 Strand London WC2R 0LX UK
....Tel: 0171 836 8444
....Fax: 0171 836 7342
e.mail: shop@stangiblondon.demon.co.uk

Alderman, H
12 Park Avenue Shelley Nr Huddersfield HD8 8JE
UK ....Tel: 01484 603179

◆ Postal History

Acorn Philatelics
PO Box 152 Salford Manchester M17 1BP UK
....Tel: 0161 877 8818

Afinsa
C/Lagasca 18 Madrid E-28001 Spain
....Tel: 00341 5781405
....Fax: 00341 5750832

Art Communications
524 Senapati Bapat Marg Dadar Bombay 400028
India ....Tel: 009122 6044359

Dean, WHB
The Poplars New Brighton Mold Cwlyd CH7 6QQ
....Tel: 01352 754782

Handstamps
7 Stanfield Terrace Guildford Surrey GU1 4LN UK
....Tel: 01483 505841
....Fax: 01483 458958

Lacey, Malcolm
PO Box 9 Winchester Hampshire SO22 5RF UK
....Tel: 01962 856060
....Fax: 01962 842563

Schmitt
P O Box 67 Woodbury NY 11797 USA
....Tel: 1516 367 4030
....Fax: 1516 425 0460

Yorkshire Cover Auctions
10 Lombard Street Halton Leeds LS15 0LT
....Tel: 0113 2641845
....Fax: 0113 2946388

◆ Queen Victoria

British Commonwealth
PO Box 10218 Wilmington Bristol NC 28405-0218
USA ....Tel: 001910 2566207

Loffstadt, David
Craigwell Barnet Wood Road Bromley BR2 8HJ UK
....Tel: 0181 462 7185

◆ Southern Africa

Aron R. Halberstam Philatelists

See our main advert
in Volume 1

P.O. Box 150168
Van Brunt Station, Brooklyn   Tel: 001 718 788 3978
New York 11215-0168, USA   Fax: 001 718 965 3099

Berman, Arnold
1 Woodhurst Lane Oxted Surrey RH8 9HN UK
....Tel: 018832 714065

Garfield, AL
39 Malford Grove London E18 2DY UK
....Tel: 0181 989 6417

Loffstadt, David
Craigwell Barnet Wood Road Bromley BR2 8HJ UK
....Tel: 0181 462 7185

Murray Payne

See our main advert under
Mauritius (vol 2)

P.O. Box 1135
Axbridge, Somerset
England BS26 2EW   Tel: 01934 732511

Ormskirk Stamps

See our main advert under
Zimbabwe (vol 2)

Rectory Road, Roos,
Nr Hull, E. Yorkshire
England HU12 0LD   Tel: 01964 670239

Ormskirk Stamps

See our main advert under
Zimbabwe (vol 2)

Rectory Road, Roos,
Nr Hull, E. Yorkshire
England HU12 0LD   Tel: 01964 670239

Phila of S. Africa
PO Box 5519 Johannesburg 2000 S Africa
....Tel: 0027 11 640 6303
....Fax: 0017 11 836 8777

Philaclassica
Gerbergasse 24 Postfach 563 Basle CH-4001
Switzerland...Tel: 61 2617379
....Fax: 61 261 7377

Robertson Stamp Co.
P O Box 3527 Durban 4000 South Africa
....Tel: 27 31 254 762
....Fax: 27 31 258 906

Stanley Gibbons Limited
399 Strand London WC2R 0LX UK
....Tel: 0171 836 8444
....Fax: 0171 836 7342
e.mail: shop@stangiblondon.demon.co.uk

Stephen Welz & Co

See our main catalogue advert
under South Africa (in volume two)

PO Box 52431
Saxonwold 2132   Tel: 2711 880 3125
South Africa   Fax: 2711 880 2656

J. P. CONSULTANTS

Offers a wide range of stamps of Southern Africa.

Postal History, Proofs, Essays, Revenues.

Emphasis on "The Unusual"

Wants Lists Welcomed

PO BOX 815
FOURWAYS 2055, SOUTH AFRICA
Tel: (-2711) 4782457 Fax: (-2711) 4782458

Wharton-Hood JP
P O Box 815 Fourways 2055 S. Africa
...................................Tel: 002711 478457

◆ **West Indies**

British Commonwealth
PO Box 10218 Wilmington Bristol NC 28405-0218
USA ....Tel: 001910 2566207

Caribbean Phil Auc
PO Box 17 Thirsk North Yorkshire YO7 1TT UK
......................................Tel: 01845 523942

Crown Colony Stamps
PO Box 1198 Bellaire Texas 77401 USA
......................................Tel: 0017 781 6563

Loffstadt, David
Craigwell Barnet Wood Road Bromley BR2 8HJ UK
......................................Tel: 0181 462 7185

Pennymead Auctions
1 Brewerton Street Knaresborough North Yorkshire
HG5 8AZ UK ....Tel: 01423 865962
      e.mail: Penny,mead@aol.com

Muscotts

See our main catalogue advert under Bermuda

Meadrow
Godalming,   **Tel: 01483 417884**
Surrey, GU7 3HK   **Fax: 01483 860572**

Nevis Philatelic Bureau
Head Post Office Charlestown Nevis WEST INDIES
....Tel: 869 469 5535
              Fax: 869 469 0617

Murray Payne

See our main advert under Mauritius (vol 2)

P.O. Box 1135
Axbridge, Somerset
England BS26 2EW   **Tel: 01934 732511**

Murray Payne

See our main advert under Mauritius (vol 2)

P.O. Box 1135
Axbridge, Somerset
England BS26 2EW   **Tel: 01934 732511**

Stanley Gibbons Limited
399 Strand London WC2R 0LX UK
....Tel: 0171 836 8444
           Fax: 0171 836 7342
e.mail: shop@stangiblondon.demon.co.uk

ALL WORLD
NEW ISSUES SERVICE

WELCOME TO THE WORLD'S No.1 NEW ISSUES SERVICE

Choose from over 260 countries, 100 plus themes and more than 10 philatelic formats...

For your Free 'Welcome Pack' and complimentary copy of our exclusive new issues magazine contact us today.

 URCH HARRIS & CO
A DIVISION OF STANLEY GIBBONS

1 Denmark Avenue, Bristol BS1 5HD England.
Tel: +44 (0) 117 934 9333
Fax: +44 (0) 117 927 3037
e-mail: urch@stangib.demon.co.uk

 The Collectors **BOOKSHELF**
From Stanley Gibbons

Reading List

For those who want to discover more about their collection this 4th Edition Stanley Gibbons reading list comprises over 1000 titles never previously listed.

Including:

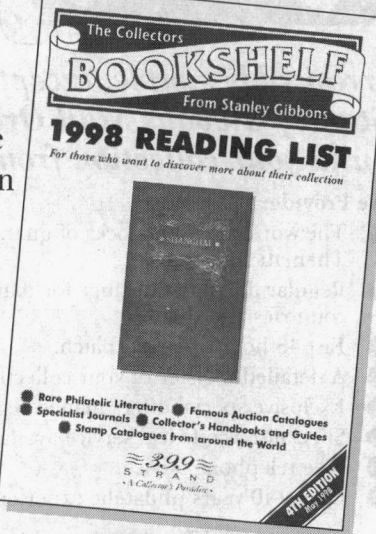

- ⬢ Rare Philatelic Literature
- ⬢ Famous Auction Catalogues
- ⬢ Specialist Journals
- ⬢ Collector's Handbook and Guides
- ⬢ Stamp Catalogues from Around the World

Ask for your FREE copy of our latest list by phoning +44 (0)171 836 8444 today.

 STANLEY GIBBONS

Stanley Gibbons Limited
399 Strand, London,
WC2R 0LX England.
Tel: +44 (0)171 836 8444
Fax: +44 (0)171 836 7342
e.mail stamps@stangiblondon.demon.co.uk
internet: http://www.stangib.com/

THE WORLD'S LEADING RANGE OF CATALOGUES, ALBUMS & ACCESSORIES

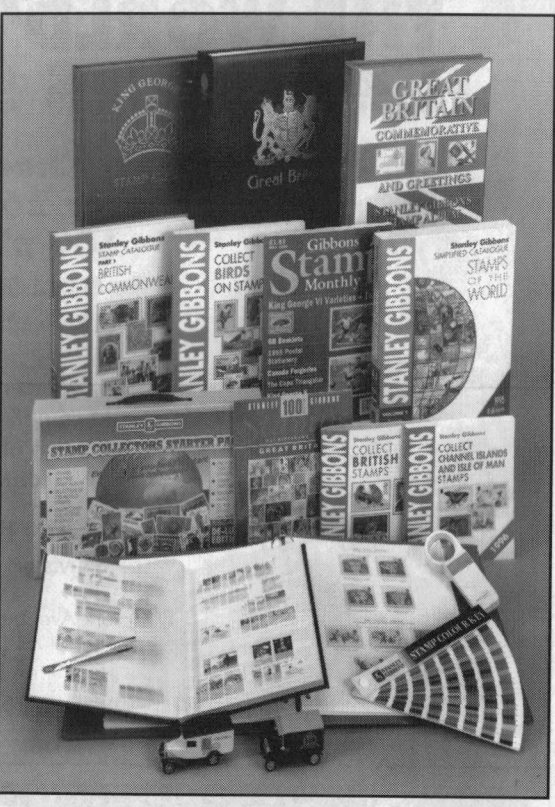

FREE 32 PAGE COLOUR BROCHURE

FAST AND EFFICIENT WORLD-WIDE DESPATCH

FREE 24 HOUR TELEPHONE ORDER HOTLINE

FREE P&P ON UK ORDERS OVER £30

REGULAR SPECIAL OFFERS

FREE CUSTOMER NEWSLETTER

...DELIVERED DIRECT TO YOUR DOOR

Phone **0800 611622** for your free colour brochure today

 STANLEY GIBBONS

• THE COLLECTOR'S CHOICE •

Stanley Gibbons Publications
5 Parkside, Christchurch Road, Ringwood,
Hampshire BH24 3SH England
Tel: +44 (0) 1425 472363
Fax: +44 (0) 1425 470247
e.mail sales@stangib.demon.co.uk

Quality Stamps
DIRECT TO YOUR DOOR

Irresistibly simple, exceptionally quick and reassuringly reliable Stanley Gibbons Mail Order Service enables you to economically build your collection from the comfort of your own home.

We Provide:
- The world's largest stocks of guaranteed quality Great Britain, Commonwealth, Foreign and Thematic material.
- Regular illustrated listings for many popular countries and themes.
- Fast 48 hour order despatch.
- A detailed register of your collecting interests.
- Exclusive special offers mailed regularly.
- Specialist 'wants list' service available.
- Free telephone advice.
- Over 140 years philatelic experience.

 STANLEY GIBBONS *Mail Order*

Stanley Gibbons Mail Order
399 Strand, London, WC2R 0LX England.
Tel: +44 (0)171 836 8444 Fax: +44 (0)171 836 7342
e.mail mailorder@stangiblondon.demon.co.uk
internet: http://www.stangib.com/

Free 1998 Great Britain Stamps Listing

- A comprehensive checklist of Great Britain stamps.
- Packed full of popular material, complete with colour illustrations, accurate descriptions and SG catalogue numbers throughout.
- Contains a useful checklist and a pull out order form in the centre pages.
- Many rare and specialised items are now included.
- Makes collecting easy, from the comfort of your own home.

FOREIGN

◆ Balkans

Euro-Yu
138 New Bond Street London W1Y 9FB UK
....Tel: 0171 495 0242
Fax: 0171 495 0244

Popov, Dimiter
PO Box 285 Plovdiv   4000 Bulgaria
....Tel: 359 32 270025

Stanley Gibbons Limited
399 Strand London WC2R 0LX UK
....Tel: 0171 836 8444
Fax: 0171 836 7342
e.mail: shop@stangiblondon.demon.co.uk

◆ Benelux

Smits Philately
*BUYING NETHERLANDS & COLONIES,
PLEASE SEND FOR IMMEDIATE CASH OFFER*
Socratesstraat 192, 7323 PI Apeldoorn, THE NETHERLANDS
...................Tel: 00 31-55-3665543 Fax: 00 31-55-3665543
email: smitphil@worldonline.nl

Stanley Gibbons Limited
399 Strand London WC2R 0LX UK
....Tel: 0171 836 8444
Fax: 0171 836 7342
e.mail: shop@stangiblondon.demon.co.uk

◆ China/Far East

Clark, Kenneth G
Brook House Collinswood Road Farnham Common
Bucks. SL2 3LH UK ....Tel: 01753 648370
Fax: 01753 648371

Cons China Stamp
PO Box 491 Brighton Le Sands New South Wales
2216 Australia ....Tel: 0061 2 9579 3750

Harmsworth. BJ
7 Maes Yr Orsaf Aberllefenni Street Machynlleth
Powys SY20 9RR UK ....Tel: 01654 761706

Phil-Index
80 Willingdon Road Eastbourne Sussex BN21
1TW UK ....Tel: 01323 721444

Stanley Gibbons Limited
399 Strand London .WC2R 0LX UK
......................................Tel: 0171 836 8444
Fax: 0171 836 7342
e.mail: shop@stangiblondon.demon.co.uk

Stoddart. LK
Box 38 Alaminos Pangasinian 2404 Philippines
....Tel: 0063 551 3513

Wang, Chaomo
1 Finnybank Road Sale Cheshire M33 6LR UK
......................................Tel: 0161 283 2583

◆ Eastern Europe/Russia

Baptiste, H E
13 Friars Way Swaythling Southampton Hampshire
SO18 3LT UK ....Tel: 01703 584803

Euro-Yu
138 New Bond Street London W1Y 9FB UK
....Tel: 0171 495 0242

Garni Stamps
PO Box 1204 London W4 2ZY UK
....Tel: 0181 994 9788

Kerr, DJM
2 Thorn Street Earlston Berwickshire TD4 6DR
Scotland ....Tel: 01896 848928

Stanley Gibbons Limited
399 Strand London WC2R 0LX UK
....Tel: 0171 836 8444
Fax: 0171 836 7342
e.mail: shop@stangiblondon.demon.co.uk

◆ France

Berman, Arnold
1 Woodhurst Lane Oxted Surrey RH8 9HN UK
....Tel: 018832 714065

Hyams Stamps

P.O. Box 12
Downham Market,
Norfolk PE38 9TQ   Tel/Fax: 01366 384591

Philacollect
Suite8533 16/18 Circus Road London NW8 6PG UK
....Tel: 0171 722 8112

THE
PHILACOLLECT LIST
Philacollect Lists
If you are seeking a fast, friendly and efficient service then our postal only service is the best way of reviewing our stock.

Our MAIN LIST of 76 pages has wide ranges of Br. Commonwealth with strong sections of Australia, Br. West Indies, Canada, Great Britain, Hong Kong, New Zealand, South and S.W. Africa etc. Large range of World including stronger sections of Austria, Belgium, France, Germany generally, Hungary, Italy, Liechtenstein, Monaco, Netherlands, Rumania, Russia, Scandinavia, Spain, Switzerland, USA, Vatican plus many others. Prices are in the £5 to £500 or so range, and most are pre-1965.

Our COLLECTIONS AND LOTS LIST with over 400 items world wide priced from £15 to £500 is just for you - the collector
STRICTLY POSTAL - NO CALLERS, PLEASE.

PHILACOLLECT
Suite 8533, 16/18 Circus Road, London NW8 6PG
Tel/Fax: 0171 722 8112 e-mail: philacollect@dial.pipex.com.

FRANCE

*Quality material at competitive prices.
Free price list available on request.
Wants lists also invited*

KEVIN P RIGLER
44 Shrewsbury Fields   **Tel: 01952 460862**
Shifnal, Shropshire TF11 8AN

Stanley Gibbons Limited
399 Strand London WC2R 0LX UK
....Tel: 0171 836 8444
Fax: 0171 836 7342
e.mail: shop@stangiblondon.demon.co.uk

White, Rex
Brookside Farm, Nobbs Crook Colden Common
Hampshire SO21 1TH UK ....Tel: 01703 693626

STAMPS
TO SELL?

We require stamps, covers, collections, old correspondence or anything philatelic - either to buy or offer for sale in one of our prestigious auctions.

You can rely on the world's oldest and largest stamp dealers for an accurate and fair appraisal of your stamps - free and without obligation.

For confidential, no obligation advice contact our buying department today

STANLEY GIBBONS

Stanley Gibbons Limited
399 Strand, London WC2R 0LX, England
Tel: +44 (0)171 836 8444
Fax: +44(0) 171 836 7342
e.mail: buying@stangiblondon.demon,co.uk

GARCIA'S FRENCH COLONIES
(1850-1980)

Telephone today for 48 page price index and 40 page monthly Buy or Bid Sale including COMPLETE STOCK LISTS from which it is simple & easy to order.

EXTENSIVE STOCKS priced from 12p to £100's covering French Colonies.

Efficient, friendly and personal service

GARCIA'S FRENCH COLONIES
80 WILLINGDON ROAD
EASTBOURNE, EAST SUSSEX, BN21 1TW
TELEPHONE: (01323) 721444

◆ French Colonies

Phil-Index
80 Willingdon Road Eastbourne Sussex BN21 1TW
UK ....Tel: 01323 721444

◆ General

Harmers Auctions

*See our main advert on the
outside back cover*

**Via Pocobelli 16
CH-6815 Melide
Switzerland**   **Tel: 00 4191 6494285**

RARE AND UNUSUAL STAMPS
FOR SERIOUS COLLECTORS.

Wants Lists filled from our
comprehensive 30 volume stock of
stamps, varieties and postal
history (**references please**).
We hold several British Empire
public auctions annually.
Subscriptions: £25.

George W. Holschauer

Colonial Stamp Co.

5757 Wilshire Blvd., Penthouse 8,
Los Angeles, CA 90036, U.S.A.

Tel: (213) 933-9435 ● Fax: (213) 939-9930

Members: IFSDA, PTS, ASDA, Int'l Soc. of Appraisers

When enquiring or placing an order please quote
that you have seen me in Stanley Gibbons
Philatelic Register

Harmsworth, BJ
7 Maes Yr Orsaf Aberllefenni Street Machynlleth
Powys SY20 9RR UK ....Tel: 01654 761706

Wishart, Alan
19 Strath Nairn Lane Lanarkshire ML8 5LL
Scotland..Tel: 01698 356337

◆ Germany/Austria

Euro-Yu
138 New Bond Street London W1Y 9FB UK
....Tel: 0171495 0242
                        Fax: 0171 495 0244

Hyams Stamps
PO Box 12 Downham Market Nofolk PE38 9TQ UK
....Tel: 01366 384591

Philaclassica
Gerbergasse 24 Postfach 563 Basle CH-4001
Switzerland ....Tel: 61 2617379
                        Fax: 61 261 7377

Stanley Gibbons Limited
399 Strand London WC2R 0LX UK
....Tel: 0171 836 8444
                        Fax: 0171 836 7342

Tokoglu, NECIP
Kakettstr. 16-18 PF 51 Aachen D52001 Germany
....Tel: 0049241 878363

◆ Italy/Switzerland

🖉 HPT
Croatian Post & Telecom

*Invites you to buy postage stamps, FDCs, first day sheets,
annual collections, blocks, maxicards, special albums,
postcards and catalogue.*

Jurišićeva 13   **Fax 00 385 1 423 495**
HR-1000 Zagreb, Croatia   **www.tel.hr**

Filatelia Riva-Reno
Via Galliera 23 Bologna 1-40121 Italy
....Tel: 0039 51237480
                        Fax: 003951 232180

Hyams Stamps
PO Box 12 Downham Market Norfolk PE38 9TQ UK
....Tel: 01366 384591

Laurent Fauquex
19 Rue Du Rhone Geneva 1204 Switzerland
....Tel: 0041 22311 6795

Philaclassica
Gerbergasse 24 Postfach 563 Basle CH-4001
Switzerland..Tel: 61 2617379
                        Fax: 61 261 7377

Stanley Gibbons Limited
399 Strand London WC2R 0LX UK
....Tel: 0171 836 8444
                        Fax: 0171 836 7342

Summit Stamps
51 Hawthorn Way Storrington West Sussex
RH26 4NY UK................................Tel: 01903 743654

ROLF & MAX WEGGLER

*Specialised in Swiss proofs, essays, varieties,
postal history and classic stamps.
Selected stock of GB & Commonwealth
and covers of the world.*

LIMMATQUAI 3, 8024   **Tel: 004 11252 1396**
ZURICH, SWITZ.,CH-8024   **Fax: 004 11252 1706**

zumstein 🏅

Since 1905 leading Stamp Dealer for
Europe, Overseas and especially Switzerland. Classic stamps of Europe and Switzerland. Editor of the Zumstein Specialised
Catalogue. Expertising department. "Ber-
ner Briefmarken Zeitung", a monthly with
interesting news and advertisements about
Switzerland and Europe. **Call us...**

ZUMSTEIN + CIE
Propr. Hertsch + Co.   Tel: 0041 3131200 55
P.O.Box   Fax: 0041 3131 223 26
CH-3000 Bern 7   www.stamp.ch
Switzerland   E-mail: post_zumstein@briefmarken.ch

◆ Latin America

Gash, Richard
240 Peppard Road Reading Berkshire RE4 8UA UK
....Tel: 0118 947 5744

Stanley Gibbons Limited
399 Strand London WC2R 0LX UK
....Tel: 0171 836 8444
                        Fax: 0171 836 7342

◆ Middle East

Agopian Norayn
PO Box 4182 Limasol Cyprus
....Tel: 003575 733357

Hyams Stamps
PO Box 12 Downham Market Norfolk PE38 9TQ UK
....Tel: 01366 384591

I R Iran Post Co.
Philatelic Bureau P O Box 16315-174 Tehran Iran
....Tel: 0098 21 8114227

Romano Stamps
P O Box 23274 Dizengoff Centre Tel Aviv 612 Israel
....Tel: 972 3528 2790

Shalaby, Kamal
3 Aly Basha Fahmy Street Gleem Alexandria 21411
Egypt..Tel: 203 5880254

Stamp World
124 Mint Road Cama House Opp Fort Market
Bombay 400 001 India
....Tel: 9122 2614492
                Fax: 9122 2679429 e.mail:
                Asiatic@bom3.vsnl.net.in

Stanley Gibbons Limited
399 Strand London WC2R 0LX UK
....Tel: 0171 836 8444
                        Fax: 0171 836 7342

Mohamad Adib Tinawi

*Selling Syria and Lebanon Stamps, Covers, Errors, New
Issues, FDC and Bank Notes, Syrian Different 100-1700,
Syrian Telecards. Want lists welcome*

**P.O. Box 3434,
Damascus -Syria**

◆ Monaco

Offices de Emissions de Timbres-Poste
23 Avenue Prince Hereditaire Albert MC 98050
Monaco Cedex..........................Tel: 00377 93154141
                        Fax: 00377 93154142

◆ Portugal/Spain

Afinsa
C/Lagasca 18 Madrid E-28001 Spain
....Tel: 00341 5781405
                        Fax: 00341 5750832

Filatelia Llach SL
Diagonal 489 Barcelona 8002 Spain
....Tel: 343 410 5000
                        Fax: 343 419 4728

Filatelia Numismatica
Aurelanio Monge Plana Calle Boters No. 2
Barcelona 8002 Spain ....Tel: 343 3179435

Minguella & Gili
Aribau 114 Barcelona 8036 Spain
....Tel: 343 4548998

Stanley Gibbons Limited
399 Strand London WC2R 0LX UK
....Tel: 0171 836 8444
                        Fax: 0171 836 7342

◆ Postal History

Network Philatelics
P O Box 440 Tasmania Australia
....Tel: 00613 9223 4724
                        Fax: 0061 3 9331 7461

Premier Postmark
PO Box 355 Victoria 3160 Australia
....Tel: 613 975 44731
                        Fax: 613 9754 8352

Sheth, Mafatal M.
Manish Nagar Buildings No 15, 15/B/56 Four
Bungalows Anhem West 400 053 India
....Tel: 009122 624 8321
                        Fax: 009122 623 8001

Tokoglu, NECIP
Kakettstr. 16-18 PF 51 Aachen D52001 Germany
....Tel: 0049241 878363

Townsend, Martin
P O Box 10 Hitchin Hertfordshire RG4 9PE UK
....Tel: 01462 420678
                        Fax: 01462 42065

Yorkshire Cover Auctions
10 Lombard Street Halton Leeds LS15 0LT UK
....Tel: 0113 2641845
                        Fax: 0113 294 6388

◆ Rest of the Wold

Afinsa
C/Lagasca 18 Madrid E-28001 Spain
....Tel: 00341 5781405
                        Fax: 00341 5750832

American Stamp Club
42 Owen Gardens Malden Essex IG8 8DJ UK
....Tel: 0181 505 7360

Filatco
PO Box 1461 Appleton Wisconsin 54911 USA
....Tel: 00414 735 0702
Fax: 001 414 735 9453

M & N Haworth

*See our main advert
in Volume 2*

P.O. Box 20
Clitheroe,
Lancs BB7 2JQ   **Tel: 01200 423576**

Nigerian Phil Co
PO Box 1791 Lagos Nigeria
......................................Fax: 234 1264 1166

P & P Harris Stamps
5 Wickerwood Drive Kirby in Ashfield Nottingham
NG17 8ER UK...............................Tel: 01623 723338

Robin Hood Stamp Company
23 Rectory Road West Bridgford Nottingham NG2
6BE UK ....Tel: 0115 981 6214
Fax: 0115 945 5499
e.mail: chris@robinhood-stamp.co.uk

Shorten, Mike
59 Greengate Swanton Morley Dereham Norfolk
NR20 4LX ....Tel: 01362 637516

Stamp World
124 Mint Road Cama House Opp Fort Market
Bombay 400 001 India ....Tel: 9122 2614492
Fax: 9122 2679429
e.mail: Asiatic@bom3.vsnl.net.in

Stanley Gibbons Limited
399 Strand London WC2R 0LX UK
....Tel: 0171 836 8444
Fax: 0171 836 7342

Tierney Co.
1360 York Avenue Suite 2B New York NY 10021-
402 USA ....Tel: 001212 5350261
e.mail: gtierney@ix.netcom.com

◆ **Scandinavia**

NORWAY QUALITY KILOWARE

Net.	450g	900g
NM1 Mission Mix	£9.50	£18.50
NM2 Commems Low Val	£19.50	£38.50
NM3 Commems High Val	£44.50	£88.00
NM4 Defins. Small/Large	£8.50	£23.00

OFF PAPER

Net. 200g	
NU1 Mission Mix	£28.00
NU2 Definitives Small	£19.50
NU3 Definitives Small & Large	£29.00
NU4 Commems w/hv. & Pairs	£49.00

200g off paper equals more than 1kg on paper.

NORWAY PACKETS

500 diff	**£12.50**
600 diff	**£19.50**
700 diff	**£42.00**

Air mail postage included in above prices.
CWO or Visa payment (no charge) or use
Post Giro (Norway) 0532 5623251

PHILCO STAMPS

P.O. Box 5, N-5560 Nedstrand, Norway
Tel: (47) 52 77 882 98 - Fax: (47) 52 77 84 78
E-mail: Shardela@online.no

Acorn Philatelics
PO Box 152 Salford Manchester M17 1BP UK
....Tel: 0161 877 8818

Amagerbro Frimaerkehus
Holmbladsgade 5 Copenhagen DK-2300 Denmark
....Tel: 45 3295 3912

Engers Frimerker
PO Box 15 Redalen N2284 Norway
....**Tel: 0047 61181737**
Fax: 0047 611 81737

Frimarks-Netto
Bruksgatan 30 SE-252 23 Helsingborg Sweden
....Tel: 46 421 44982

Hardeland, A
PO Box 5 Hinderaavaag N 5562 Norway
....Tel: 004752 778298

Stanley Gibbons Limited
399 Strand London WC2R 0LX UK
....Tel: 0171 836 8444
Fax: 0171 836 7342

◆ **Switzerland**

Baresch, Leo
PO Box 791 Hassocks W Sussex BN6 8PZ UK
....Tel: 01273 845501

Kerr, DJM
2 Thorn Street Earlston Berwickshire TD4 6DR
Scotland...Tel: 01896 848928

Kuhn, Raymond
Rumelinsplate 14 PO Box 1662 CH-4001 Basle
Switzerland ....Tel: 0041 61261 7040

Schwarzenbach, HR
Oberdorfstrasse 8 Postfach 174 Zurich CH 8024
Switzerland ....Tel: 0041 1251 4612
Fax: 0041 1261 3060

◆ **Turkey**

Tokoglu, NECIP
Kakettstr. 16-18 PF 51 Aachen D52001 Germany
....Tel: 0049241 878363

◆ **USA**

Cohen, Hy
PO Box 6701 Delray Beach Florida 33482 USA
....Tel: 561 347 0613

Duck Stamps
PO Box 222 Waltham Cross Hertfordshire EN8 8Gs
UK ....Tel: 01992 628976

Harmer-Schau Auction Galleries
617a Second Street Petaluma CA 94952   USA
....Tel: 707 778 6454
Fax: 707 763 6772

Hyams Stamps
PO Box 12 Downham Market Norfolk PE38 9TQ UK
....Tel: 01366 384591

Intercontinental Stamps & Coins
7379 Coral Way Miami Florida FL 33429-1583 USA
....Tel: 1 305 264 4983
Fax: 1 305 262 2919

McHenry, Gordon
P O Box 117 Osprey Florida USA
....Tel: 001941 9665563
Fax: 001941 9664568

Rowan S. Baker
*United States - Probably the best stock of stamps
etc. this side of the Atlantic*
28 Bedfordbury, Covent Garden, London WC2N 4RB, England
.... Tel: +44 1713791448 Fax: +44 171836 3100

Stanley Gibbons Limited
399 Strand London WC2R 0LX UK
....Tel: 0171 836 8444
Fax: 0171 836 7342

STANLEY GIBBONS

Auctions & Acquisitions

Leading Philatelic Auctioneers Since 1901

A Professional Auction Service From The Most Famous Name In Philately

A proven programme of specialised international sales

Free advice and expert market valuations

0% vendor commission
(on realisations over £5000)

Fast guaranteed payment

Cash advances available

Settlement in any currency

The industry's largest database of specialist buyers

High quality catalogues distributed worldwide

Regular telesales contact with major buyers

Specialist subscription service

Refined venues and extensive viewing times

Stanley Gibbons Auctions
399 Strand ● London ● WC2R 0LX
Telephone: +44 (0)171 836 8444
Facsimile: +44 (0)171 836 7342
e.mail: stangiblondon.demon.co.uk

Wessex
PHILATELIC AUCTIONS

ORDER YOUR
FREE COLOUR
CATALOGUE NOW!

- We hold quarterly public auctions at the Round House Hotel, Bournemouth, Dorset, England.

- We also hold specialised Postal Auctions throughout the year.

- We specialise in GB, British Commonwealth, Postal History and flaws & varieties.

- Remember no **buyer premium**
  Vendors charges by negotiation, with prompt payment.*

  * A world-wide customer Database
  * A quality private Treaty waiting list

SELLING A COLLECTION?
THEN PUT OUR NAME AT THE
BOTTOM OF YOUR LIST!

WHY?

IF THE COLLECTION MEETS OUR REQUIREMENTS WE WILL BEAT
ANY OTHER WRITTEN QUOTE

Wessex are active buyers of philatelic material from large accumulations
to specialised studies.

So, if you are selling your collection-
no matter how large or small, get as many valuations as you can.

BUT PUT OUR NAME AT THE <u>BOTTOM</u> OF YOUR LIST!

To order your catalogue
Phone 0421 460440 or
Phone or Fax 01202 528495
or write to
Wessex Philatelic Auctions,
PO Box 3061,
Bournemouth BH8 9YL.

email:
wessexauct@aol.com

MasterCard

VISA

GENERAL

◆ Accessories

Afinsa
 C/Lagasca 18 Madrid E-28001 Spain
....Tel: 00341 5781405
Fax: 00341 5750832

Prinz Publications
 13 Fore Street Hayle Cornwall TR27 4DX UK
....Tel: 01736 756742
Fax: 01736 76555

Stamp Corner
 37 Netherhall Road Doncaster Yorkshire DN1 2PG
UK ....Tel: 01302 323623

Stanley Gibbons Publications
 5 Parkside Christchurch Road Ringwood Hampshire
BH24 3SH UK ....Tel: 01425 472363
Fax: 01425 470247
e.mail: sales@stangib.demon.co.uk

Trinder, Vera
 38 Bedford Street Strand London WC3E 9EU UK
....Tel: 0171 836 2365

West Cornwall Stamp Centre
 13 Fore Street Hayle Cornwall TR27 4DX UK
....Tel: 01736 754604
Fax: 01736 765555

◆ Albums

Afinsa
 C/Lagasca 18 Madrid E-28001 Spain
....Tel: 00341 5781405
Fax: 00341 5750832

Godden, Frank Ltd.
 The Barn, Heaton Royds Shay Lane Bradford West
Yorkshire BD9 6SH UK ....Tel: 01274 544446
Fax: 01274 545634

Japan Philatelic Co. Ltd.
 PO Box 2 Suginami-Minami Tokyo 168 8081 Japan
....Tel: 0081 3 3304 1 641
Fax: 0081 3 3304 5318
e.mail: yusya@mb.infoweb.ne.jf

M & C Stamps
 Unit 30, Antique Centre Severn Road Gloucester
GL1 2LE UK ....Tel: 01452 506361
Fax: 01452 307161

Prinz Publications
 13 Fore Street Hayle Cornwall TR27 4DX UK
....Tel: 01736 756742
Fax: 01736 76555

Safe Albums
 16 Falcon Industrial Est. Ivanhose Road
Finchampstead Berkshire UK .....Tel: 01189 328976

Stamp Corner
 37 Netherhall Road Doncaster Yorkshire DN1 2PG
UK ....Tel: 01302 323623

Stanley Gibbons Publications
 5 Parkside Christchurch Road Ringwood
Hampshire BH24 3SH UK ....Tel: 01425 472363
Fax: 01425 470247
e.mail: sales@stangib.demon.co.uk

Trinder, Vera
 38 Bedford Street Strand London WC3E 9EU UK
....Tel: 0171 836 2365
Fax: 0171 836 0873

◆ Auctions

Acorn Philatelics
 PO Box 152 Salford Manchester M17 1BP UK
....Tel: 0161 877 8818

Afinsa
 C/Lagasca 18 Madrid E-28001 Spain
....Tel: 00341 5781405
Fax: 00341 5750832

Cambridgeshire Phil
 27 Fore Hill Ely Cambridgeshire CB7 1AA UK
....Tel: 01353 663919
Fax: 01353 664127

Camel Stamps
 PO Box 6081 Basingstoke Hampshire RG25 2YP
UK ....Tel: 01256 465499
Fax: 01256 333587

Corbitt Stamps
 5 Moseley Street Newcastle Upon Tyne Tyne &
Wear NE1 1YE UK ....Tel: 0191 232 7268
Fax: 0191 261 4130

Dean, WHB
 The Poplars New Brighton Mold Cwlyd CH7 6QQ
....Tel: 01352 754782

David Feldman S.A.
Philatelists - Auctioneers
International All World Auctions
Specialised Private Treaty.

C.P. 81   **Tel: (+41 22) 727.07.77**
175 rte de Chancy   **Fax: (+41 22) 727.07.78**
Switzerland   **e-mail: admin@davidfeldman.com**
          http://www.davidfeldman.com

Filatelia Llach SL
 Diagonal 489 Barcelona 8002 Spain
....Tel: 343 410 5000
Fax: 343 419 4728

Grosvenor Philatelic
 402 Strand London WC2R0NE UK
....Tel: 0171 836 7373

Harmers Auctions

*See our main advert on the
outside back cover*

**Via Pocobelli 16
CH-6815 Melide
Switzerland**   **Tel: 00 4191 6494285**

Harmer-Schau Auction Galleries
 617a Second Street Petaluma CA 94952 USA
....Tel: 707 778 6454
Fax: 707 763 6772

Horsham Stamp Auction
 23 Trafalgar Road Horsham West Sussex
RH12 2AD UK ....Tel: 01403 265255

Jury Ltd. Len
 PO Box 4400 Auckland New Zealand
....Tel: 0064 9377 6806

Lancaster Auctions, Jean
 20 Milner Road Kingston Surrey KT1 2AU UK
....Tel: 0181 547 1220
Fax: 0181 547 3739

Lars Tore
 Box 250 Kalmar S39123 Sweden
....Tel: 46 480 15090
Fax: 46 480 15006

MacDonnell Whyte
 102 Leinster Road   Dublin 6 Ireland
....Tel: 00541 4977449
Fax: 003531 4977440

Melstamps
 Old Hall House, 4 Little Lane Melbourn Royston
Hertfordshire SG8 6BU UK ....Tel: 0163 260010

Murray, Robert
 5 & 6 Inverleith Gardens Ferry Road Edinburgh
EH3 5PU Scotland ....Tel: 0131 552 1220

Myer, Adrian
 PO Box 137 Leatherhead Surrey KT22 0RG UK
....Tel: 01372 843085
Fax: 01372 843930

Network Philatelics
 P O Box 440 Tasmania Australia
....Tel: 00613 9223 4724
Fax: 0061 3 9331 7461

New Raynes Stamp Co.
 1st Floor 2a Corporation Street Chesterfield S41
7TP UK ....Tel: 01246 211002

Palmerston Auctions
 Loreburn Chambers Great King Street Dumfries
DG1 1BA UK ....Tel: 01387 255508

Philips & Son
 101 New Bond Street London W1Y 0AS UK
....Tel: 0171 468 8345
Fax: 0171 468 3466

Postiljonen
 Box 4118 Malmo S-203 12 Sweden
....Tel: 0046 4072290

Pottergate Stamps
 5-7 Bagleys Court Pottergate Norwich NR2 1TW UK
....Tel: 01603 762916

Provincial Phil
 90 Park Road Didcot Oxon OX11 8QR UK
....Tel: 01235 511083

Reeve Stamp Auctions
 Suite 155, Southbank House Black Prince Road
London SE1 7SJ UK ....Tel: 0171 587 0175

Spink
 5-7 King Street St James London SW1Y 6QS UK
....Tel: 0171 389 2275
Fax: 0171 389 2688

Stanley Gibbons Auctions
 399 Strand London WC2R 0LX UK
....Tel: 0171 836 8444
Fax: 0171 836 7342
e.mail: stamps@stangiblondon.demon.co.uk

REGULAR £100,000 POSTBID SALES

★ NO BUYERS' PREMIUM
★ FREE FULL-COLOUR CATALOGUES
★ INTEREST-FREE EXTENDED PAYMENT
★ NO CREDIT CARD SURCHARGES
★ 1000 - 2000 ALL WORLD LOTS
    FROM £5 - £1000'S

**No-one offers you more
and asks you for less.**

Request sample catalogue today

**Box 434
Kingston
Surrey KT1 3YW
Tel/Fax: 0181 5410288
or   01342 833413/833892**

Warren, R (Apex)
Oaklands Crowhurst Lane Crowhurst Nr Surrey RH7
2ZA UK ....Tel: 01985 216557

Warwick & Warwick Ltd

*See our main catalogue advert
under Great Britain*

**Pageant House
2 Jury Street, Warwick**   **Tel: 01926 499031
CV34 4EW**   **Fax: 01926 491906**

Wessex Phil Auctions
 P O Box 3061 Bournemouth Dorset BH8 9YL UK
....Tel: 01202 528495

Whyte's
 30 Marlborough Street Dublin 1 IRELAND
....Tel: 3531 874 6161
Fax: 3531 874 6020

◆ Book Publishers

Afinsa
 C/Lagasca 18 Madrid E-28001 Spain
....Tel: 00341 5781405
Fax: 00341 5750832

Japan Philatelic Co. Ltd
 PO Box 2 Suginami-Minami Tokyo 168 8081 Japan
....Tel: 0081 3 3304 1 641
Fax: 0081 3 3304 5318

Stanley Gibbons Publications
5 Parkside Christchurch Road Ringwood Hampshire
BH24 3SH UK ....Tel: 01425 472363
Fax: 01425 470247
e.mail: sales@stangib.demon.co.uk

◆ Catalogue Publishers

Afinsa
C/Lagasca 18 Madrid E-28001 Spain
......................................Tel: 00341 5781405
Fax: 00341 5750832

Filatelia Llach SL
Diagonal 489 Barcelona 8002 Spain
......................................Tel: 343 410 5000
Fax: 343 419 4728

Japan Philatelic Co. Ltd.
PO Box 2 Suginami-Minami Tokyo 168 8081 Japan
..............................Tel: 0081 3 3304 1 641
Fax: 01702 206526

Jury Ltd., Len
PO Box 4400 Auckland New Zealand
......................................Tel: 0064 9377 6806

Stanley Gibbons Publications
5 Parkside Christchurch Road Ringwood Hampshire
BH24 3SH UK ....Tel: 01425 472363
Fax: 01425 470247
e.mail: sales@stangib.demon.co.uk

◆ Clubs & Societies

American Philatelic Society

*Membership includes subscription to The American Philatelist,
100 pages monthly, expedited delivery via Royal Mail, readable
articles by the world's leading Philatelists. Free sample from*

P.O. Box 8000	**Tel: 001 814 237 3803**
State College	**Fax: 001 814 237 6128**
PA, 16803, U.S.A	**email: flsente@stamps.org**

RAFLET STAMP CLUB

B. Comm. Foreign & GB Packet Circuits.
2p & 5p Packets. Swap Shop. Auctions.
Cover Services & Library. Six Magazines annually.
Run by some 30 members on a honorary basis on
behalf of 1,200 members in the U.K.

Membership £8 per annum

Write for further details and sample magazine to:

**RAFLET STAMP CLUB
P.O. BOX 3484
COLCHESTER, CO4 4XX**

Faroe Islands Study Circle
28 Enfield Road Ellesmere Port South Wirral
L65 8BY UK..........................Tel: 0151 355 1132
Fax: 0151 356 6620

Stoddart. LK
Box 38 Alaminos Pangasinian 2404 Philippines
......................................Tel: 0063 551 3513

◆ Fairs/Exhibitions

IPM Promotions
18 Bell Lane Hendon London NW4 2AD UK
......................................Tel: 0181 2031500
Fax: 0181 2037031

Milton, David
PO Box 139 Ruislip Middlesex HA4 8UX UK
......................................Tel: 01895 637283

Stanley Gibbons Publications
5 Parkside Christchurch Road Ringwood Hampshire
BH24 3SH UK ....Tel: 01425 472363
Fax: 01425 470247
e.mail: sales@stangib.demon.co.uk

◆ Insurance

Stamp Insurance SVS
29 Bowhay Lane Exeter Devon EX4 1PE UK
......................................Tel: 01392 433949

◆ Literature

Bendon, James
PO Box 6484 Limassol 3077   Cyprus
......................................Tel: 357 5 311 235
Fax: 357 5 311 28
e.mail: jbendon@ibm.net.

Godden, Frank Ltd.
The Barn, Heaton Royds Shay Lane Bradford West
Yorkshire BD9 6SH UK ....Tel: 01274 544446

Graham, Dr Conrad
23 Rotherwick Road London NW11 7DG UK
......................................Tel: 0181 455 5080

Harmer-Schau Auction Galleries
617a Second Street Petaluma CA 94952   USA
......................................Tel: 707 778 6454
Fax: 707 763 6772

HH Sales Ltd
The Barn, Heaton Royds Shay Lane Bradford West
Yorkshire BD9 6SH UK ....Tel: 01274 544446
Fax: 01274 545634

Selwyn Stamps "Of course you can do it"
200 page illustrated book.
Interesting & helpful, esp. aspiring authors.
12 Rydal St., Christchurch, New Zealand
.....................Tel: 0064 338 8407 Fax: 0064 336 56111

Stanley Gibbons Limited
399 Strand London WC2R 0LX UK
......................................Tel: 0171 836 8444
Fax: 0171 836 7342 e.mail:
stamps@stangiblondon.demon.co.uk

Stoddart. LK
Box 38 Alaminos Pangasinian 2404 Philippines
......................................Tel: 0063 551 3513

Trinder, Vera
38 Bedford Street Strand London WC3E 9EU UK
......................................Tel: 0171 836 2365

Magazines

Afinsa
C/Lagasca 18 Madrid E-28001 Spain
......................................Tel: 00341 5781405
Fax: 00341 5750832

American Philatelic Society

*Membership includes subscription to The American Philatelist,
100 pages monthly, expedited delivery via Royal Mail, readable
articles by the world's leading Philatelists. Free sample from*

P.O. Box 8000	**Tel: 001 814 237 3803**
State College	**Fax: 001 814 237 6128**
PA, 16803, U.S.A	**email: flsente@stamps.org**

Stanley Gibbons Publications
5 Parkside Christchurch Road Ringwood Hampshire
BH24 3SH UK ....Tel: 01425 472363
Fax: 01425 470247

e.mail: sales@stangib.demon.co.uk

◆ Mail Order

Esmat A
13C Weld Road Birkdale Southport PR8 2AZ UK
......................................Tel: 01704 567070

Stanley Gibbons Limited
399 Strand London WC2R 0LX UK
......................................Tel: 0171 836 8444
Fax: 0171 836 7342

e.mail: stamps@stangiblondon.demon.co.uk

◆ Philatelic Bureaux

Afinsa
C/Lagasca 18 Madrid E-28001 Spain
......................................Tel: 00341 5781405
Fax: 00341 5750832

Nevis Philatelic Bureau
Head Post Office Charlestown Nevis WEST INDIES
......................................Tel: 869 469 5535
Fax: 869 469 0617

PTT Post Filatelic Netherlands
P.O. Box 30051 Grouingen 9700 RN
NETHERLANDS ....Tel: 31 50 586 1234
Fax: 31 50 586 3111

◆ Postal Auctions

Afinsa
C/Lagasca 18 Madrid E-28001 Spain
......................................Tel: 00341 5781405
Fax: 00341 5750832

Balasse, Willy
Rue De Hidi 45-45a Brussels 1000 Belgium
......................................Tel: 322 513 2952
Fax: 322 513 5061

British Commonwealth
PO Box 10218 Wilmington Bristol NC 28405-0218
USA..........................Tel: 001910 2566207

For collectors and dealers:

INTERNATIONAL STAMP DEALERS' DIRECTORY

1996 - 11th edition
Much acclaimed and indispensable guide to the world of international
commercial philately. Listings of dealers, postal administrations, auctioneers,
event organisers, trade organisations, publications, plus six-language glossary,
currency guide, advertisements, and much other useful information.

Was £9.95 - Now £6 post Free

For dealers only: £2.95

If you're really serious about your business you must get

THE PHILATELIC EXPORTER

every month.
Packed with trade advertisements, the latest UK and world-wide news,
controversial comment and contributors,
and new issue, auction, and event listings.
Annual subscription rates: **£24.00** UK;
£31.80 Europe airmail; **£45.80** Australasia/Far East airmail;
£42.00 rest of world airmail; **£28.00** world surface mail.
or apply for a free sample copy today!
**The world's leading stamp trade magazine
for over 50 years!**

PHILATELIC EXPORTER, PO Box 137, Hatfield AL10 9DB, UK
Telephone: 01707 266331 or 07000 STAMPS; **Fax:** 01707 274782.
(International: +44 1707 266331 or 274782)
E-mail: PhilEx@desiderata.com   Internet: http://www.desiderata.com/PhilEx/

Please mention this publication when responding

Insurance for Stamps   **H W Wood Limited**

With over 20 years experience in providing specialist insurance for Stamp Collectors, Dealers and Auctioneers, and with offices or affiliates throughout the world, we can offer a unique level of service and experience.
For further information, and details of your nearest office, please contact:

H W Wood Ltd
The Baltic Exchange
38 St. Mary Axe
London EC3A 8BH
UNITED KINGDOM

London - New York - Philadelphia - Toronto - Melbourne - Paris - Cologne - Rotterdam - Madrid

Telephone +44 (0) 171 398 9000   Fax +44 (0) 171 398 9001

Carshalton Postal Bid
Aysgarth Radcliffe Gardens Carshalton Beeches
Surrey SM5 4PQ UK ....Tel: 0181 408 3228

Filatelia Llach SL
Diagonal 489 Barcelona 8002 Spain
....Tel: 343 410 5000
Fax: 343 419 4728

Ford, R
Henllan Llandysul Ceredigion Wales SA44 5TE UK
....Tel: 01559 371

Stanley Gibbons Limited
399 Strand London WC2R 0LX UK
....Tel: 0171 836 8444
Fax: 0171 836 7342
e.mail: stamps@stangiblondon.demon.co.uk

Select Stamps
P O Box 20 Northampton NN1 1EH UK
....Tel: 01327 340619
Fax: 01604 647111

Yorkshire Cover Auctions
10 Lombard Street Halton Leeds LS15 0LT UK
....Tel: 0113 2641845
Fax: 0113 294 6388

◆ Stamp Shops

Acorn Philatelics
PO Box 152 Salford Manchester M17 1BP UK
....Tel: 0161 877 8818

Admiral Stamps, ADPS
Cordreys Collectors Centre East Grinstead Road
Lingfield Surrey RH7 6EP UK .....Tel: 018832 714065

Afinsa
C/Lagasca 18 Madrid E-28001 Spain
....Tel: 00341 5781405
Fax: 00341 5750832

Avalon Stamp Shop
1 City Walls, Rufus Court Northgate Street Chester
Cheshire CH1 2JG UK ....Tel: 01244 318406
Fax: 01244 311567

Bailey, Malcolm
Unit 6, Coliseum Exchange 20-22 Church Street
Manchester M4 1PN UK

Bradford Stamp Centre
390 Dudley Hill Road Undercliffe Bradford BD2 UK
....Tel: 01274 630331

Caerel Stamps
4 Old Post Office Court Carlisle CA3 7LE UK
....Tel: 01228 531391

Cambridge Stamp Centre
9 Sussex Street Cambridge CB1 1PA UK
....Tel: 01223 363980

Cornucopia Collectors
15 King Street Dundee Angus Scotland DD1 2JD
....Tel: 01382 224946

Curtis Rawson
54 London Road Leicestershire UK
....Tel: 01159 474747

Curtis Rawson
Nottingham Stamp Centre, Theatre Square 3
Wollaton Street Nottingham NG1 5FW UK
....Tel: 01159 474747

Dumfries Stamp Shop
Loreburn Chambers 11 Great King Street Dumfries
Scotland DG1 1BA UK..................Tel: 01387 255508

Filan Stamps & Models
Unit K5 The Cresset Bretton Peterborough PE3 8DX
....Tel: 01733 332555

Filatelia Roig
Calle Malats 21-23 Tienda Primera Barcelona 8030
Spain ....Tel: 34 3 346 3151

Folkestone Stamp Shop
8A Old High Street Folkestone Kent CT20 1RL UK
....Tel: 01303 850672

Horley Stamp Shop
28 Station Road, Horley Surrey RH6 7PB UK
....Tel: 01293 784326

Horsham Stamp Auctions
23 Trafalgar Road Horsham, West Sussex
RH12 2AD UK ....Tel: 01403 266255

Jackson, AF Hodgson
15 Clarence Street Southend on Sea Essex
SS1 1BH UK ....Tel: 01702 341268

M & C Stamps
Unit 30, Antique Centre Severn Road Gloucester
GL1 2LE UK ....Tel: 01452 506361
Fax: 01452 307161

Maidstone Stamp Emprium
34 Melville Road Maidstone Kent ME15 7UY UK
....Tel: 01622 757599
Fax: 01622 757599

Masons Hill Stamp Shop
127 Masons Hill Bromley Kent BR2 9HT UK
....Tel: 0181 464 7862

Murray, Robert
5 & 6 Inverleith Gardens Ferry Road Edinburgh
EH3 5PU Scotland ....Tel: 0131 552 1220

Oxted Stamp Shop
Caxton House 4 Station Road Oxted Surrey
RH8 9EP UK ....Tel: 01883 714082
Fax: 01883 716854

Penny Black
16 High Street Reigate RH2 9AY UK
....Tel: 01737 226122
Fax: 01737 225530

Portsmouth Stamp Shop
184 Chichester Road North End Portsmouth
PO2 0AX UK ....Tel: 01705 663450
Fax: 01705 664884

Rice, James
The Old Surgery 1 Atkinson Buildings Trimdon Street
Sunderland SR4 6AH UK ....Tel: 0191 565 8114

Richardson & Copp
4 Station Road West Oxted Surrey RH8 9EP UK
....Tel: 01883 714082
Fax: 01883 716854

Rotherham Stamps
11 The Crofts Moorgate Rotherham S60 2DJ UK
....Tel: 01709 367222

Rowan S Baker
28 Bedfordbury London WC2N 4RB UK
....Tel: 0171 3791448

Ryde Stamp Shop
14 Anglesea Street Ryde Ise of Wight PO33 2JJ UK
....Tel: 01983 566623

Smith, J
47 Shambles York 2LX UK
....Tel: 01904 654769

Stamp Centre
St Stephens House Catherine Street Exeter Devon
EX1 1EU UK ....Tel: 01392 434282
Fax: 01392 434282

Stamp Corner
37 Netherhall Road Doncaster Yorkshire DN1 2PG
UK ....Tel: 01302 323623

Stanley Gibbons Limited
399 Strand London WC2R 0LX UK
....Tel: 0171 836 8444
Fax: 0171 836 7342

Taunton Stamp Shop
66 Bridge Street Taunton Somerset TA1 1UD UK
....Tel: 01823 283 327
Fax: 01823 325 882

West Cornwall Stamp Centre
13 Fore Street Hayle Cornwall TR27 4DX UK
....Tel: 01736 754604
Fax: 01736 765555

◆ Valuations

Pantrek (John Cowell)
MacDonalds Cottage Strathcarron Rosshire
IV54 8XB UK ....Tel: 01520 733380
Fax: 01520 733381

Stanley Gibbons Auctions & Acquisitions
399 Strand London WC2R 0LX UK
....Tel: 0171 836 8444
Fax: 0171 836 7342
e.mail: stamps@stangiblondon.demon.co.uk

STAMPS TO SELL?

We require stamps, covers, collections, old correspondence or anything philatelic - either to buy or offer for sale in one of our prestigious auctions.

You can rely on the world's oldest and largest stamp dealers for an accurate and fair appraisal of your stamps - free and without obligation.

For confidential, no obligation advice contact our buying department today

STANLEY GIBBONS

Stanley Gibbons Limited
399 Strand, London WC2R 0LX, England
Tel: +44 (0)171 836 8444
Fax: +44(0) 171 836 7342
e.mail: buying@stangiblondon.demon.co.uk

OCA

◆ Aerophilately

DM Aerogrammes
94 Hilton Road Lanesfield Wolverhampton West
Midlands WV4 6DR UK ....Tel: 01902 496633

◆ Approvals

Archer, D L
2 Litchfield Way Broxbourne Hertfordshire
EN10 6PT UK.................................Tel: 01992 462548

Brookvale Stamps
196 Ivyfield Road Birmingham West Midlands B23
7HS UK ....Tel: 0121 382 5937

Gibbs, Alan
57 Normandy Way Bletchley Milton Keynes MK3
7UW UK...Tel: 01908 274496
                                                            Fax: 01908 274496

Jones, Derek L
14 Bentley Road Castle Bromwich Birmingham
B36 0ES UK ....Tel: 0121 748 6478

Tudor Philatelics
Woodlands Bryn Gardens Newtown Powys
SY16 2DR UK..................................Tel: 01686 628897

◆ Booklets

M & C Stamps
Unit 30, Antique Centre Severn Road Gloucester
GL1 2LE UK ....Tel: 01452 506361
                                                            Fax: 01452 307161

Stanley Gibbons Limited
399 Strand London WC2R 0LX UK
....Tel: 0171 836 8444
                                                            Fax: 0171 836 7342

◆ Cinderellas

Hudson, Roger
PO Box 172 Coventry Warwickshire CV6 6NF UK
....Tel: 01203 686613
                                                            Fax: 01203 667428

◆ Covers

Acorn Philatelics
PO Box 152 Salford Manchester M17 1BP UK
....Tel: 0161 877 8818

Afinsa
C/Lagasca 18 Madrid E-28001 Spain
....Tel: 00341 5781405
                                                            Fax: 00341 5750832

Art Communications
524 Senapati Bapat Marg Dadar Bombay 400028
India ....Tel: 009122 6044359

Bil & Co
The Old Rectory Caythorpe Nottingham NG32 3DU
UK ....Tel: 01400 273460

Bradbury, AG
3 Link Road Stoneygate Leicester LE2 3RA UK
....Tel: 01162 705367

Nevis Philatelic Bureau
Head Post Office Charlestown Nevis WEST INDIES
....Tel: 869 469 5535
                                                            Fax: 869 469 0617

Schmitt
P O Box 67 Woodbury NY 11797 USA
....Tel: 1516 367 4030

Yorkshire Cover Auctions
10 Lombard Street Halton Leeds LS15 0LT UK
....Tel: 0113 2641845
                                                            Fax: 0113 294 6388

◆ Kiloware

Amagerbro Frimaerkehus
Holmbladsgade 5 Copenhagen DK-2300 Denmark
....Tel: 45 3295 3912

De La Rue Stamps
Bragehurts Brage Road Vale Guernsey GY3 5PG
Channel Islands ....Tel: 01481 46354
                                                            Fax: 01481 723 177

Gibson, WJ
55 Town Lane Southport Lancashire PR9 0TH UK
....Tel: 01704 543985

International Stamp Service
GPO Box 302 Suva Fiji Islands
....Tel: 001 679 320597
                                                            Fax: 001 679 320517

◆ Lots & Collections

Healey & Wise
            Inga-Britt & Michael Berry
            Stamp dealers since 1885
P.O. Box 3, Tunbridge Wells, Kent TN2 4ZE, England
.........Tel: +44 1892 533 270   Fax: +44 1892 512 777

◆ New Issues

Afinsa
C/Lagasca 18 Madrid E-28001 Spain
....Tel: 00341 5781405
                                                            Fax: 00341 5750832

Allen, Harry
PO Box 5 Watford Hertfordshire WD2 5SW UK
....Tel: 01923 475555

Crown Agents
Old Inn House 2 Carshalton Road Sutton Surrey
UK ....Tel: 0181 770 0707

M & C Stamps
Unit 30, Antique Centre Severn Road Gloucester
GL1 2LE UK ....Tel: 01452 506361
                                                            Fax: 01452 307161

M & N Haworth

See our main advert
in Volume 2

P.O. Box 20
Clitheroe,
Lancs BB7 2JQ   Tel: 01200 423576

Nevis Philatelic Bureau
Head Post Office Charlestown Nevis WEST INDIES
....Tel: 869 469 5535
                                                            Fax: 869 469 0617

Popov, Dimiter
PO Box 285 Plovdiv 4000 Bulgaria
....Tel: 359 32 270025

Shalaby, Kamal
3 Aly Basha Fahmy Street Gleem Alexandria 21411
Egypt ....Tel: 203 5880254

Somerset Stamp Service

BRITISH COMMONWEALTH NEW ISSUES. We offer
a reliable and efficient low cost service. Full details
and latest listings free on request.

SOUTH PETHERTON,
SOMERSET,
ENGLAND TA13 5EN   Tel/Fax: (01460) 241172

Sovereign Stamps
Old Inn House 2 Carshalton Road Sutton Surrey
SM1 4RN UK.................................Tel: 0181 770 0707

Stanley Gibbons Limited
399 Strand London WC2R 0LX UK
....Tel: 0171 836 8444
                                                            Fax: 0171 836 7342

Urch Harris & Co.
1 Denmark Avenue Bristol BS1 5HD UK
....Tel: 0117 934 933

◆ Postal Stationery

DM Aerogrammes
94 Hilton Road Lanesfield Wolverhampton West
Midlands WV4 6DR UK.................Tel: 01902 496633

Faber, Ian
PO Box 217 Erindale Centre ALT 2903 Australia
....Tel: 00616 291 5573

Loffstadt, David
Craigwell Barnet Wood Road, Bromley BR2 8HJ UK
....Tel: 0181 462 7185

◆ Postcards

IPM Promotions
18 Bell Lane Hendon London NW4 2AD UK
....Tel: 0181 2031500
                                                            Fax: 0181 2037031

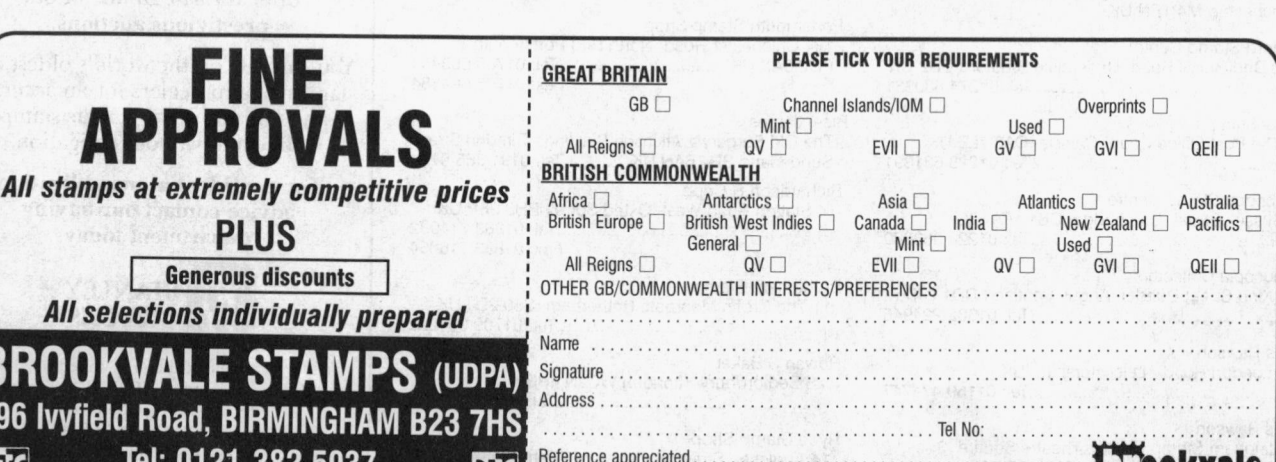

FINE APPROVALS

All stamps at extremely competitive prices

PLUS

Generous discounts

All selections individually prepared

BROOKVALE STAMPS (UDPA)

196 Ivyfield Road, BIRMINGHAM B23 7HS

Tel: 0121-382 5937

(Postal only, as stocks kept at the Bank)

PTS   PTS

PLEASE TICK YOUR REQUIREMENTS

GREAT BRITAIN

GB ☐   Channel Islands/IOM ☐   Overprints ☐
                        Mint ☐   Used ☐
All Reigns ☐   QV ☐   EVII ☐   GV ☐   GVI ☐   QEII ☐

BRITISH COMMONWEALTH

Africa ☐   Antarctics ☐   Asia ☐   Atlantics ☐   Australia ☐
British Europe ☐   British West Indies ☐   Canada ☐   India ☐   New Zealand ☐   Pacifics ☐
                        General ☐   Mint ☐   Used ☐
All Reigns ☐   QV ☐   EVII ☐   QV ☐   GVI ☐   QEII ☐

OTHER GB/COMMONWEALTH INTERESTS/PREFERENCES ....

....

Name ....
Signature ....
Address ....

                                    Tel No: ....

Reference appreciated ....

Overseas enquires welcome - UK Trade reference, Please

Brookvale stamps

M & C Stamps
Unit 30, Antique Centre Severn Road Gloucester
GL1 2LE UK ....Tel: 01452 506361
Fax: 01452 307161

Thematics

Acorn Philatelics
PO Box 152 Salford Manchester M17 1BP UK
....Tel: 0161 877 8818

Afinsa
C/Lagasca 18 Madrid E-28001 Spain
....Tel: 00341 5781405
Fax: 00341 5750832

Art Communications
524 Senapati Bapat Marg Dadar Bombay 400028
Inda ....Tel: 009122 6044359

Avion Thematics
PO Box 99 Eastwood Nottingham NG16 5QN UK
....Tel: 01773 608899
Fax: 01773 609821

Chalon Stamps
129 Gloucester Street Gloucester Arcade
Christchurch New Zealand ....Tel: 0064 365 7780

COU-GAR STAMPS

WHOLESALE DEALER

PO Box 30006
PTE CLAIRE, Quebec,   **Tel: 001 514626 28501**
H9R 5P6, Canada   **Fax: 001 514626 7555**
e-mail: cougarqc@total.net.

Dawn Cover Productions
OFFICIAL FOOTBALL AND TRANSPORT COVER
AND POSTCARD PRODUCERS

27 Ashfield Road, Davenport, Stockport SK3 8UD
England ....Tel: 0161 483 1297
Fax: 0161 483 1297

DM Aerogrammes
94 Hilton Road Lanesfield Wolverhampton West
Midlands WV4 6DR UK.................Tel: 01902 496633

Downham, BA
70 Metcalfe Road Cambridge CB4 2DD UK
....Tel: 01223 355004

Fire 999-119 Thematics
20 Queens Approach Uckfield East Sussex
TN22 1RU UK...............................Tel: 01825 762679

Gibbs, Alan
57 Normandy Way Bletchley Milton Keynes
MK3 7UW UK...............................Tel: 01908 274496
Fax: 01908 274496

Grainger, Anthony
42 Lee Lane East Horsforth Leeds LS18 5RE UK
....Tel: 0113 1583790

Jones, Derek L
14 Bentley Road Castle Bromwich Birmingham
B36 0ES UK ....Tel: 0121 748 6478

M & N Haworth

*See our main advert
in Volume 2*

P.O. Box 20
Clitheroe,
Lancs BB7 2JQ   **Tel: 01200 423576**

Nevis Philatelic Bureau
Head Post Office Charlestown Nevis WEST INDIES
....Tel: 869 469 5535
Fax: 869 469 0617

Robertson Stamp Co.
P O Box 3527 Durban 4000 South Africa
....Tel: 27 31 254 762
Fax: 27 31 258 906

Stanley Gibbons Limited
399 Strand London WC2R 0LX UK
....Tel: 0171 836 8444
Fax: 0171 836 7342

Mohamad Adib Tinawi

*Selling Syria and Lebanon Stamps, Covers, Errors, New
Issues, FDC and Bank Notes, Syrian Different 100-1700,
Syrian Telecards. Want lists welcome*

P.O. Box 3434,
Damascus -Syria

Superb Quality Great Britain Stamps from Stanley Gibbons

● The world's largest stocks of Great Britain material from 1840 to date

● Over 3,000 specialised and rare items always available

● Receive regular bi-monthly mail order lists and a luxury colour brochure

For further information and copies of our latest lists, please telephone our Great Britain Department on 0171 836 8444 or visit our showroom, open 6 days a week

STANLEY GIBBONS *Great Britain*

Stanley Gibbons Ltd
399 Strand, London WC2R 0LX
Tel: +44 (0)171 836 8444
Fax: +44 (0)171 836 7342
e.mail: mailorder@stangiblondon.demon.co.uk

THE ESSENTIAL CATALOGUE FOR ADVANCED GB COLLECTORS

GREAT BRITAIN CONCISE

Stanley Gibbons
GREAT BRITAIN
CONCISE
STAMP CATALOGUE
1998 Edition

If you are looking to discover more about your Great Britain collection the Stanley Gibbons Concise catalogue provides a more detailed, yet quick reference guide to every GB stamps from 1840 to the present day in a single, inexpensive volume.

Features:

● Pages packed full of illustrations, detailed descriptions and up-to-date prices.

● Regional, postage due, official and postal fiscal stamps plus first day covers, presentation, collector and gift packs, PHQ cards, stamp booklets, gutter pairs, yearbooks, postage labels, Channel Islands wartime issues and much more.

● Additional information on perforation and watermark varieties, plus errors of missing colour, embossing or phosphor.

● All prices carefully revised in line with the current market.

Available from all good stamp shops, our London showroom at 399 Strand or by mail order - phone 0800 611 622 for our FREE colour brochure.

Stanley Gibbons Publications
5 Parkside, Christchurch Road, Ringwood, Hampshire BH24 3SH England
Tel: +44 (0) 1425 472363
Fax: +44 (0) 1425 470247
e.mail sales@stangib.demon.co.uk

STANLEY GIBBONS *Catalogues*

Stanley Gibbons, 399 Strand, London

Visit The World's Biggest Stamp Shop

Located in London's Strand, our showroom has been serving visitors to the world's stamp capital for over 100 years. Within the prestigious air conditioned surroundings lies a team of dedicated staff, probably the finest selection of stamps, postal history and literature ever assembled and the world's most comprehensive range of stamp catalogues, albums and accessories - all under one roof.

Over 1000 Giant Stockbooks of Stamps

Take a seat at our stamp counter and our staff will guide you through over 1000 giant stockbooks packed full of some of the latest and greatest GB, European, Commonwealth, Foreign and Thematic stamps.

Plus Stamp Pages, Packets, Kiloware & Specialised Stock

We've also a great selection of stamp pages, packets and kiloware always available plus over 5,000 rare and specialised items which can be examined in one of our private viewing rooms.

Valuations & Advice

Advice on the sale of collections is available free of charge from our team of expert valuers. We are always interested in buying and will pay top prices for quality collections and individual items.

The Collector's Bookshelf

We have on our shelves one of the largest selections of philatelic literature ever seen, including numerous rare and unusual titles - many collectibles in their own right, plus the latest handbooks, magazines and catalogues from publishers all over the world.

Albums, Accessories and Much More

We stock not just Stanley Gibbons albums and accessories but also those from a number of other manufacturers including Davo, Lighthouse, Prinz, Safe, Uvitec, Showguard and Kabe plus a wide choice of giftware and souvenirs for visitors of all ages.

 STANLEY GIBBONS

399 Strand, London WC2R 0LX
Tel: +44 (0)171 836 8444
Fax: +44 (0)171 836 7342
e.mail: shop@stangiblondon.demon.co.uk
(Nearest tubes Charing Cross or Covent Garden)

 ≋ *399* ≋
S T R A N D
• *A Collector's Paradise* •

Open 6 days a week • Mon-Fri 8.30 'til 6.00 Sat 9.30 'til 5.30